The College Blue Book®

41st Edition

Narrative Descriptions

The College Blue Book®

41st Edition

Narrative Descriptions

MACMILLAN REFERENCE USA
A part of Gale, Cengage Learning

GALE
CENGAGE Learning®

Detroit • New York • San Francisco • New Haven, Conn • Waterville, Maine • London

GALE
CENGAGE Learning®

The College Blue Book, 41st Edition
Volume 1

Project Editor: Bohdan Romaniuk

Editorial Support Services: Wayne Fong

Composition and Electronic Prepress: Gary Leach

Manufacturing: Rita Wimberley

Product Management: Michele P. LaMeau

For product information and technology assistance, contact us at
Gale Customer Support, 1-800-877-4253.
For permission to use material from this text or product,
submit all requests online at **www.cengage.com/permissions.**
Further permissions questions can be emailed to
permissionrequest@cengage.com

While every effort has been made to ensure the reliability of the information presented in this publication, Gale, a part of Cengage Learning, does not guarantee the accuracy of the data contained herein. Gale accepts no payment for listing; and inclusion in the publication of any organization, agency, institution, publication, service, or individual does not imply endorsement of the editors or publisher. Errors brought to the attention of the publisher, and verified to the satisfaction of the publisher, will be corrected in future editions.

EDITORIAL DATA PRIVACY POLICY: Does this product contain information about you as an individual? If so, for more information about our editorial data privacy policies, please see our Privacy Statement at www.gale.cengage.com.

Gale
27500 Drake Rd.
Farmington Hills, MI, 48331-3535

ISBN-13: 978-0-02-866186-5 (6 vol. set)
ISBN-10: 0-02-866186-9 (6 vol. set)
ISBN-13: 978-0-02-866187-2 (vol. 1)
ISBN-10: 0-02-866187-7 (vol. 1)

ISSN 1082-7064

This title is also available as an e-book.
ISBN-13: 978-0-02-866194-0 (set)
ISBN-10: 0-02-866194-X (set)
Contact your Gale sales representative for ordering information.

Printed in the United States of America
1 2 3 4 5 6 7 18 17 16 15 14

Contents

The College Blue Book® has been a standard, professional reference on higher education since it was first published in 1923. New features have been added during the intervening years to keep pace with the changing needs for information about our educational facilities. The information, especially in the areas of tuition, room and board, enrollment figures, library holdings, is constantly changing. It is difficult to maintain up-to-date figures in these areas, as many schools change tuition and related costs on an ongoing basis. We therefore urge our readers to check directly with the schools for the most current cost information.

CONTENTS OF EACH VOLUME

Volume 1: Narrative Descriptions

More than 4,400 colleges in the United States and Canada are fully described. Entrance requirements are detailed and campus facilities and costs are described. A map of each U.S. state and Canadian province is included and each college has a grid index fore easy location. Web sites are also listed.

Volume 2: Tabular Data

Colleges are listed alphabetically by state or province. Information about costs, accreditation, enrollment figures, faculty, and names of the chief administrative officers are given for each school.

Volume 3: Degrees Offered by College and Subject

In Part I, the name of each college is listed alphabetically by state or province, with a list of the subject areas for which degrees are offered. Part II includes an alphabetical listing of subject areas for which degrees are granted by one or more institutions of higher education.

Volume 4: Occupational Education

More than 6,400 schools in the United States that provide occupational or technical training are fully described,

offering such information as tuition costs, enrollment figures, and entrance requirements. Two indexes are provided: an alphabetical listing of schools in the "Index of Occupational Education Schools," in addition to the "Curricula and Areas of Instruction" index.

Volume 5: Scholarships, Fellowships, Grants, and Loans

This volume provides a listing of more than 5,200 different sources of financial aid for students wishing to further their education. Split alphabetically into eight broad subject areas (each containing several more specialized concentrations of study), as well as a general section, each listing provides basic information about a specific award, including eligibility requirements, amount of award, and application deadlines.

Volume 6: Distance Learning Programs

Responding to this rapidly growing trend in post-secondary education, this volume features comprehensive profiles of nearly 1,000 institutions offering distance learning programs within the United States and Canada.

FOR MORE INFORMATION

We are always open to suggestions and recommendations for improvement of The College Blue Book® from our readers and from the educational professions. Please write or call: Editor, The College Blue Book

Macmillan Reference USA

27500 Drake Rd.

Farmington Hills, MI 48331-3535

Phone: (248)699-4253

Toll-free: 800-347-GALE

Fax: (248)699-8075

Email: blue.book@gale.com

Web site: www.gale.cengage.com

The decision to continue education beyond high school years, the selection of a collegiate institution, and the area of study to be pursued are some of the essential experiences necessary for students to determine their futures. Alternatives of choice institutions, work selection, job opportunities, professional training, or even discontinuing any further education are all selective decisions open to the students.

Nearly all students today have opportunities to continue education beyond high school. There are more schools accepting wider ranges of student ability and interest than ever before. This means more effort, more planning, and more personal study in making the college choice.

Self Appraisal

The best place to begin is with oneself. An appraisal with objective, honest answers is necessary. What are the personal potentials as a student? Where has the best performance been? What are the probabilities for improvement? What are the reasons for really wanting to go to college; is it for intellectual development, vocational preparation, or simply to satisfy a desire for status? What are the personal ideas of college? What is expected from the college experience? Have career plans been made? Where are the academic abilities? What subjects are preferred? What is the quality of performance in the preferred areas of study? What is the overall grade average? What is the class rank in high school? In what subject areas is there the greatest interest? What is the quality of work in these areas? Are interests and performance generally consistent? Are the expressed and recorded interests truly and accurately reflecting the inward wishes? What was liked best about the high school experience? Has the college preparatory program been followed in high school? What were the social and cultural experiences during high school years that were most meaningful? What was considered, if anything, to be lacking?

Well-thought-out answers to these and similar questions are helpful. Discussions of such topics with counselors, parents, and teachers increases the probability of success in college selection, attendance, and completion.

The counselor today is an extremely valued resource person available to assist the student. When an effective working team of counselor-student-parent actually exists, the probabilities for the student making selective choices that prove to be the "right" ones are unquestionably the greatest. The better the student and the counselor know one another, the more effective the guidance and counseling program will be. For this to occur, the opportunity for face-to-face student-counselor discussion needs to start in the latter elementary school years and continue through high school and college.

College Appraisals

Research is continuing in the areas of college admissions and student success. The identification and understanding of causes of success and failure need professional study. However, one thing is apparent: the more careful the preparations and planning by the student, the better the chances of college admission and success.

Systemized planning should begin early. The more self-understanding and knowledge about available colleges one has, the better one can plan with corresponding success. Certainly, early in the high school career, students should be reviewing detailed information on colleges and universities with the counselor, noting academic requirements such as scholastic performance, course requirements, costs and other particular qualities of individual collegiate institutions. There is no single one-and-only college for the student. Colleges have personalities just as the students do. There are always several colleges with academic and social climates compatible and acceptable to each student.

Entrance requirements, courses available, costs, size of student body, academic pressure, special programs, geographical location, and specialty schools are some of the considerations of every student in appraising available colleges.

The College Blue Book® is dedicated to providing detailed information regarding collegiate institutions throughout the United States and Canada. Students and counselors should browse through The College Blue Book® and become familiar with the colleges of our country and neighboring Canada. As interest sharpens and narrows, a more selective and in-depth study of institutions should be made.

Where feasible, students should plan visits to college campuses. Campus visiting may begin during the summer between the sophomore and junior years of high school. The best time to be on a college campus, however, is during the regular term with a carefully planned visit in the spring semester of the junior year. Preparatory plans should be made with the high school counselor, reviewing discussions of earlier personal conferences. Advance arrangements should be made with admission officers of the colleges the student expects to visit. The admission officer's name and telephone number will be found in most instances in *The College Blue Book*® volume entitled *Tabular Data*. The admissions officer in many cases will want to know whether the student has actually applied for admission and probably the areas the student may plan to major in or other special interests the student has in the particular institution. The student should have prepared a summary of personal data. If possible, high school students should also talk to students of the colleges they wish to attend.

The growth of community colleges has opened up another avenue for students, especially those of limited finances or those who have not decided on their ultimate educational goals. Students will find many of these community colleges offer an excellent opportunity to gain a solid college background. Then one can choose a four-year institution to complete an undergraduate degree.

Any regular high school graduate can find a school that will accept him or her. Many students need to be encouraged to consider the smaller, private and public colleges of good standing.

Students entering professional training such as engineering or law might consider small schools that have cooperative programs with major universities. A knowledgeable student, through planning and guidance, can avoid unnecessary disappointment. A college career can be quite beneficial to the student who spends three to four years on a small campus and one, two, or three additional years of graduate work on another, larger campus.

Costs

Costs are continuing to rise. Tuition charges as listed herein should only be used as a guide. It would be wise to check with the institution of interest to be sure of having the most up-to-date information available.

Should the need for financial aid be a factor in selecting a college, a college-bound student should be aware that the best single source of financial assistance and information is the financial aid officer or admission director at the college. It is most important for the student to contact the finance office as early as possible during the student's senior year in high school. A principal source of financial assistance is the major federal undergraduate aid programs. Applications can be obtained from the college. Most colleges and universities also offer financial assistance in several forms including academic and general scholarships, grants-in-aid, student loans, and part-time work. For more information, see volume 5 of *The College Blue Book*®: *Scholarships, Fellowships, Grants, and Loans*.

Two-year Colleges

Two-year colleges, referred to as junior colleges or community colleges, both public and private, offer programs that prepare students for technical and semiprofessional careers in business and technology fields, and for transfer to senior colleges. There are hundreds of two-year colleges providing comprehensive programs meeting the lower division requirements of virtually all four-year colleges and universities.

There are decided advantages for some students to enroll in a two-year college. Some of these are: less cost, home residence, availability of highly specialized programs, opportunity for the student to mature, a smaller student body, and generally a closer relationship to the faculty. The development of two-year colleges across the nation is one of the most vital forces in education today. The two-year college is neither an extension of high school, nor a little senior college. It has its own identity, sphere of service, and contribution to make to American education. The comprehensive community college is considered one of the best means of accommodating the demands of higher education, embracing the increasing variety of abilities of students graduating from high schools, preparing students in the technological and semiprofessional occupations, and all in an economical manner.

One very important caution needs to be heeded by students enrolling in two-year colleges who are planning to continue their work through a bachelor's program. Students expecting to transfer should very carefully study the requirements of the institution they ultimately plan to attend. In conference with the junior college counselor, a careful review of the planned program should be made to be sure the contemplated courses at the junior college will satisfy the requirements of the senior institution. Students who depart from prescribed courses stated by the senior institution or fail in any of these courses may experience difficulty with admission or normal progress toward the bachelor degree.

Liberal Arts Colleges

The liberal arts colleges offer four years of college and award the Bachelor of Arts and the Bachelor of Science degrees. The curriculum for the first two years is usually broad with an emphasis in the humanities, natural sciences, and cultural history of our society. The last two years may provide a concentration of specific programs such as premedicine or pre-law leading to graduate professional training.

Students considering professional training at the graduate level should keep this in mind as they plan their work at the liberal arts college. Graduate schools in some cases have strict preparatory requirements. Familiarity with these requirements can greatly assist in making the transfer to graduate level without loss of credit or time.

Specialized Institutions

Four-year institutions of technology are examples of the more specialized schools where concentration in a specialty is intensively pursued throughout the college career. Most of these institutions are quite selective in admission practice and may require more high school mathematics and science than most other schools for entrance. These programs lead to engineering degrees in many fields emphasizing technology and science. Recently there has been a broadening of the program of the first two years, but, in general, such a program is not nearly as comprehensive and varied as the liberal arts college. The demand for engineers and scientists with specially developed skills creates great competition for entrance into schools of technology.

There are other specialized institutions such as conservatories of music, seminaries, medical and law schools, institutions specializing in teacher training, or schools of the fine arts, most of which require specialized preparation for entrance.

Universities

The university is generally composed of a number of degree-granting colleges and schools where both bachelor and graduate degrees are grouped under one administrative head. Bachelor degrees at the university may be earned in liberal arts or one of the professions such as engineering or the physical sciences. The university, to some extent, combines what is available at the liberal arts college with the specialized institution. Complete professional training in such areas as law, medicine, and science is available on the university campus.

As a rule, universities have much larger student bodies than colleges. In order to meet the demand, most state universities have established several campuses. Many state universities are very selective in admitting students. This is particularly true for a student who is applying for admission from out-of-state.

Entrance Examinations

There are more applicants than there is room for students on many campuses. As this demand increases, colleges and universities attempt to identify those applicants who are most likely to succeed on their campuses. A quality scholastic record has more influence on acceptance and admission than any other single factor. High school grades predict with better accuracy than any other single measurement what college grades and success will be. The more selective colleges and universities may choose students who come out highest on quantitative criteria, that is, high school scholastic averages combined with test scores. Some institutions have far more applicants (whose scholastic records and test scores are of a maximum quality) than they can accept. In such cases, applicants are sometimes screened and accepted on the basis of categories according to residence in the state or region, special talents, minority groups, or relationship to alumni. Such procedures are used in an attempt to influence the makeup of the enrollment.

When investigating several schools, one of the most accurate ways for evaluation of an institution is to consider test scores and the high school rank order of the students actually on campus. In many instances this is more informative than the announced admission policies.

College testing is required by many colleges and universities for entering students; some have developed their own tests and over the years have established norms for such tests. Most institutions requiring tests for entrance, however, now use either the test of the American College Testing Program (ACT) or the examinations of the College Entrance Examination Board. The College Entrance Examination Board offers the Preliminary Scholastic Assessment Test/National Merit Scholarship Qualifying Test (PSAT/ NM-SQT), the Scholastic Assessment Test I: Reasoning Test (Verbal and Math), and the SAT II: Subject Tests.

Coaching, tutoring, drill, and memorization of facts can do little to improve the scores of the standardized examinations. It is recommended that students not invest time and money in cramming in hopes of improving test scores. Students can do their best preparation in general reading, completing their school assignments, and arriving on the proper day of the test rested and refreshed.

American College Testing Assessment (ACT)

The ACT Assessment provided by the American College Testing Program covers four subject areas: English, mathematics, reading, and science reasoning. The ACT test is scored on a range of 1 to 36. The ACT is administered at various test sites in the United States and other countries on specified dates throughout the year. Many colleges and universities recommend that prospective students take the examination early in the senior year.

The tests provide estimates of the students' current level of educational development in knowledge skill areas often required in college work. The ACT college testing program was founded in 1959. It is a nonprofit educational service offering programs in testing and financial need analysis.

Scholastic Assessment Tests (SAT)

The SAT I: Reasoning Test is an examination to measure the verbal and mathematics abilities students have developed both in and out of school. The SAT II: Subject Tests, which some colleges require for admission or placement purposes, consist of 22 separate tests that cover subjects such as literature, history, math, languages, chemistry, biology, and physics. Unlike the SAT I, which measures more general abilities, the SAT II tests measure the students' knowledge of a particular subject and their ability to apply that knowledge. Because of this, students should try to take a SAT II Test as soon as possible after completion of their last course in that subject.

The SAT I and II tests are given on certain dates throughout the year at various test centers in the United States and foreign countries. The combination of the student's academic record and the SAT scores, along with other pertinent secondary information enables admissions officers to estimate how well the student will perform on a particular college campus. The SAT is scored on a scale of 200 minimum to 800 maximum.

Admission Policies

One of the most important considerations in planning is to note when colleges and universities request applications, and to be sure that the applications are complete and forwarded during the appropriate periods. Failure in any way in this procedure will usually automatically disqualify a student from acceptance.

Counselors can provide students with freshman profiles on many of the institutions. Studying *The College Blue Book*®, particularly the volume *Tabular Data,* provides a great amount of information on the kind of student bodies found on the campuses of American institutions. There are four general classifications of admission policies. An understanding of these provides valuable guidelines in identifying colleges for consideration.

Most Selective: Many more students apply who meet the announced admission requirements than the college could possibly accept. In addition to requiring outstanding academic records, personal recommendations are required from the high school, and identification of any special qualities of the student should be made known. In this regard, the high school recommendation made to the collegiate institution requires special attention.

Many times, particularly at selective institutions, the high school recommendation actually provides the necessary edge for admission. The recommendation should be on time, carefully providing all information called for, and finally, be precise and detailed in citing personal qualities of the applicant.

All these qualities, however, do not guarantee acceptance. It is strongly recommended that qualified students apply to more than one institution of this type, and that not all applicants should be made to the same type of institution.

Very Selective: Colleges having a very selective procedure in accepting students require ACT scores of 23 or over, or an SAT I score of 600 or more. Students should rank in the top 10 to 12 percent of their high school graduating classes. In addition, strong recommendations stressing particular talents and achievements are necessary. Applications should be made to several institutions of this type.

Selective: An ACT of 20 or over, or an SAT I score of 550 or more is generally necessary. Applications for admission to selective colleges and universities are usually called for in the spring prior to fall entry. In many situations, applications may be submitted in the fall of the senior year with final confirmation to be made after all grades are recorded and confirmed upon graduation from high school.

Least Selective: The fourth classification represents those institutions that will accept students with a C average on their high school work. In certain unusual instances, and under special situations, even the selective institutions may accept students who are in this category, particularly if the scores on the ACT are in the mid-20's or are in excess of 500 on the SAT I. Generally, for acceptance in the less selective schools, students should have an ACT composite score of 17 or a SAT I score of 450.

Entrance examinations may or may not be required. Occasionally, if examinations are required, the results are used for student placement rather than admission. Most high school graduates can meet the requirements for entry and will be accepted. It should be pointed out, however, that in some cases an institution may be liberal in acceptance but carefully screens candidates for graduation. In such an institution, a high attrition rate may occur.

Open Enrollment Policy: This is becoming more common, particularly with the public community colleges. Many students will find this privilege most helpful in continuing their formal education beyond high school. Such a policy enables those students to have a second chance who have failed to perform up to their ability during their high school years. Enrollment and attendance may enable the student to complete a most rewarding vocational program or to later transfer and complete the Bachelor degree, which otherwise might not have been possible because of the deficiency in the high school scholastic record.

A number of colleges and universities, particularly the publicly supported ones, have adopted the open enrollment policy. In response to a feeling of community responsibility, they accept any student who has a diploma (or G.E.D. equivalency certificate) from an accredited high school. This procedure allows students from disadvantaged and minority backgrounds, who might otherwise be denied such an opportunity, to acquire a college education and prepare for a meaningful occupation. These institutions have not lowered their graduation requirements; they have, instead, created opportunities for more students to satisfy these requirements.

Do not assume the erroneous generality that the tougher it is to get into an institution, the better the quality; or the easier to enter, the poorer the school. In fact, there is research evidence available indicating that it may be wise to re-examine some of our traditional notions and attitudes regarding admissions. Not all degree programs on any particular campus are equally outstanding. Every institution has its particular strengths in programs available. Certain institutions are excellent places for some kinds of students in some kinds of programs, but no institution is the one most suited for everyone.

More than 4,400 institutions of higher education, in the United States and Canada, are described in this volume of *The College Blue Book®* including universities, senior colleges, two-year colleges, and specialized institutions. The data has been gathered by direct contact with all institutions as well as by inspection of the most current college catalogues available. The arrangement of information is alphabetical by state and by college within each state.

No judgments or evaluations have been made in these entries, but many applicable facts have been presented to assist the reader in making his or her own.

To assist the user of this volume in making a valid evaluation and comparison of schools, information on each school has been standardized as follows: privately or publicly supported or church-related; level: university, college, graduate school; for whom: men, women, co-educational; type: liberal arts, technological, theological, teacher education, professional; names of degrees granted; fields of specialization, schools, or departments; term system: semester, quarter, trimester; enrollment; size of faculty and faculty-student ratio; regional accreditation; number of volumes in library; cooperative education (work-study) program availability; existence of a ROTC program; entrance requirements; costs per year; collegiate environment; community environment.

There are six regional accrediting commissions covering the United States that evaluate colleges and schools. Gener-

ally, these regional agencies grant accreditation to an entire institution of higher learning. They are as follows: Middle States Association of Colleges and Schools, New England Association of Schools and Colleges, North Central Association of Colleges and Schools, Northwest Association of Schools and Colleges, Southern Association of Colleges and Schools, and Western Association of Schools and Colleges.

An important consideration should be mentioned again, one which *The College Blue Book®* stresses at several points; the "right" college for Student A may not be the "right" college for Student B. A large enrollment, a small teacher-student ratio, an enormous library and exacting entrance requirements do not necessarily mean that this is the best school. Consider all the factors available: is it in a small, rural college town or a huge, vibrating metropolis; does the student need readily available transportation; does this school have specific programs the student is interested in; if seeking a profession, does the school have professional accreditation; does it have on-campus dormitories, or must the student seek other housing arrangements; do expenses fall within the student's budget; can the entrance requirements be met; if accepted, what are the chances of graduating; if the student is not sure just exactly what is wanted in the way of a career, will this school provide opportunities to find out? This revised edition of *The College Blue Book®* has been designed to assist in answering these questions and others that the college bound student may have.

■ **ALABAMA AGRICULTURAL AND MECHANICAL UNIVERSITY**
4900 Meridian St.
Huntsville, AL 35811
Tel: (256)372-5000; Free: 800-553-0816
Fax: (256)372-5881
Web Site: www.aamu.edu/
Description: State-supported, university, coed. Awards bachelor's, master's, and doctoral degrees and post-master's certificates. Founded 1875. Setting: 2,001-acre suburban campus. Endowment: $29.3 million. Research spending for the previous fiscal year: $10.7 million. Educational spending for the previous fiscal year: $3630 per student. Total enrollment: 5,814. Faculty: 290 (289 full-time, 1 part-time). Student-undergrad faculty ratio is 20:1. 5,363 applied, 51% were admitted. Full-time: 4,592 students, 52% women, 48% men. Part-time: 348 students, 54% women, 46% men. 31% from out-of-state. 0.1% American Indian or Alaska Native, non-Hispanic/Latino; 0.3% Hispanic/Latino; 96% African American, non-Hispanic/Latino; 0.2% Asian, non-Hispanic/Latino; 1% international. 13% 25 or older, 4% transferred in. Retention: 75% of full-time freshmen returned the following year. Academic areas with the most degrees conferred: business/marketing; education; biological/life sciences; engineering. Core. Calendar: semesters. Academic remediation for entering students, services for LD students, advanced placement, honors program, independent study, distance learning, double major, summer session for credit, part-time degree program, adult/continuing education programs, co-op programs and internships, graduate courses open to undergrads. Off campus study at Georgia Institute of Technology, Oakwood College, University of Alabama in Huntsville, Calhoun Community College, Athens State College. Study abroad program. ROTC: Army.
Entrance Requirements: Options: electronic application, deferred admission. Required: high school transcript, minimum 2 high school GPA, ACT. Recommended: 1 recommendation. Entrance: minimally difficult. Application deadline: 6/15. Notification: continuous.
Collegiate Environment: Orientation program. Drama-theater group, choral group, marching band, student-run newspaper, radio station. Social organizations: 85 open to all; national fraternities, national sororities, local fraternities, local sororities; 50% of eligible men and 50% of eligible women are members. Most popular organizations: University Voices Gospel Choir, University Choir and Band, Elementary/Early Childhood Club, National Alliance of Business Students. Major annual events: Homecoming, Annual All-Campus Convocation, Women's Week and Men's Week. Student services: health clinic, personal-psychological counseling. Campus security: 24-hour patrols, late night transport-escort service, controlled dormitory access. J. F. Drake Learning Resources Center with 507,500 books, 712,000 microform titles, 2,500 serials, and an OPAC. Operations spending for the previous fiscal year: $2.6 million. 1,000 computers available on campus for general student use. A campuswide network can be accessed from student residence rooms and from off campus. Staffed computer lab on campus.
Community Environment: Population 166,000. Located in the northern part of the state, within the city limits of Huntsville, on U.S. Highways 231 and 431, which pass through the business section of the city. Huntsville may be reached by bus, and Northwest, American, and Delta airlines Taxi service is available to the community from all transportation centers. (See also University of Alabama Huntsville).

■ **ALABAMA SOUTHERN COMMUNITY COLLEGE**
PO Box 2000
Monroeville, AL 36461

Tel: (251)575-3156
E-mail: jhorton@ascc.edu
Web Site: www.ascc.edu/
Description: State-supported, 2-year, coed. Part of Alabama College System. Awards certificates, transfer associate, and terminal associate degrees. Founded 1965. Setting: 80-acre rural campus. Total enrollment: 1,244. 29% 25 or older. Core. Calendar: semesters. Academic remediation for entering students, advanced placement, honors program, summer session for credit, part-time degree program, adult/continuing education programs.
Entrance Requirements: Open admission. Option: early admission. Required: high school transcript. Entrance: noncompetitive. Application deadline: 9/10. Preference given to district residents.
Collegiate Environment: Drama-theater group, choral group. Student services: personal-psychological counseling. Campus security: 24-hour patrols. Dennis Stone Forte Library plus 1 other with 43,000 books and 670 serials.
Community Environment: The campus is located in a rural area with a mild climate. The average temperature is 60 degrees. It is an excellent area for hunting and fishing. Part-time employment is available for students.

■ **ALABAMA STATE UNIVERSITY**
915 S Jackson St.
Montgomery, AL 36101-0271
Tel: (334)229-4100; Free: 800-253-5037
Fax: (334)229-4984
E-mail: admissions@alasu.edu
Web Site: www.alasu.edu/
Description: State-supported, comprehensive, coed. Part of Alabama Commission on Higher Education. Awards bachelor's, master's, and doctoral degrees and post-master's certificates. Founded 1867. Setting: 172-acre urban campus. Total enrollment: 5,816. Faculty: 430 (276 full-time, 154 part-time). Student-undergrad faculty ratio is 16:1. 10,284 applied, 52% were admitted. 2% from top 10% of their high school class, 12% from top quarter, 36% from top half. Full-time: 4,683 students, 59% women, 41% men. Part-time: 447 students, 61% women, 39% men. 28% from out-of-state. 0.1% American Indian or Alaska Native, non-Hispanic/Latino; 1% Hispanic/Latino; 95% African American, non-Hispanic/Latino; 0.1% Asian, non-Hispanic/Latino; 0.1% Native Hawaiian or other Pacific Islander, non-Hispanic/Latino; 1% international. 9% 25 or older, 4% transferred in. Retention: 62% of full-time freshmen returned the following year. Academic areas with the most degrees conferred: education; business/marketing; homeland security, law enforcement, firefighting, and protective services. Core. Calendar: semesters. Academic remediation for entering students, advanced placement, self-designed majors, freshman honors college, honors program, independent study, distance learning, double major, summer session for credit, part-time degree program, co-op programs and internships, graduate courses open to undergrads. ROTC: Army (c), Air Force.
Entrance Requirements: Options: electronic application, early admission, deferred admission. Required: high school transcript, minimum 2 high school GPA, SAT or ACT. Recommended: essay, interview. Entrance: minimally difficult. Application deadline: 7/31. Notification: continuous. SAT Reasoning Test deadline: 7/31. SAT Subject Test deadline: 7/31. Transfer credits accepted: Yes.
Costs Per Year: Application fee: $25. One-time mandatory fee: $150. State resident tuition: $6312 full-time, $263 per credit hour part-time. Nonresident

tuition: $12,624 full-time, $526 per credit hour part-time. Mandatory fees: $213 per term part-time. College room and board: $5366. Room and board charges vary according to board plan and housing facility.

Collegiate Environment: Orientation program. Drama-theater group, choral group, marching band, student-run newspaper, radio station. Social organizations: 64 open to all; national fraternities, national sororities, local fraternities, local sororities; 13% of eligible men and 27% of eligible women are members. Most popular organizations: Alpha Kappa Alpha Sorority Inc., Empower Ministry, Nu Alpha Nu Service Fraternity Inc., Gamma Sigma Sigma National Service Sorority Inc., Delta Sigma Theta Sorority Inc. Major annual events: Founders Day Convocation, The Coronation of Miss ASU and Court, Homecoming Week Activities. Student services: health clinic, personal-psychological counseling. Campus security: 24-hour emergency response devices and patrols, late night transport-escort service, self-defense education, well-lit campus. 2,244 college housing spaces available; 2,087 were occupied in 2012-13. No special consideration for freshman housing applicants. Options: men-only, women-only housing available. Levi Watkins Learning Center plus 1 other with 433,153 books, 2.7 million microform titles, 6,026 serials, 44,581 audiovisual materials, an OPAC, and a Web page. 541 computers available on campus for general student use. A campuswide network can be accessed from student residence rooms and from off campus. Students can access the following: online class registration. Staffed computer lab on campus (open 24 hours a day) provides training in use of computers, software, and the Internet.

Community Environment: Population approximately 200,000. Capital of Alabama. A city known for its stately homes, many of which belong to the antebellum days. The city is also known for its magnolia trees, its southern traditions and culture, and its southern hospitality. Excellent air and highway connections. Montgomery is the home of the Alabama State Capitol Building, the first capital of the Confederacy, the Department of Archives and History, the Montgomery Public Library, Maxwell Air Force Base and Gunter Field, the Air University, and the very large Garrett Coliseum. The South Alabama State Fair, Southern Horse Show, an annual rodeo, an annual indoor track tournament, and other similar functions are held in the Garrett Coliseum. Located here is the First White House of the Confederacy, the home of the Jefferson Davis when Montgomery was the Confederate Capital.

■ **AMRIDGE UNIVERSITY**
1200 Taylor Rd.
Montgomery, AL 36117
Tel: (334)387-3877; Free: 888-790-8080
Fax: (334)387-3878
E-mail: oradavis@amridgeuniversity.edu
Web Site: www.amridgeuniversity.edu/
Description: Independent, university, coed, affiliated with Church of Christ. Awards associate, bachelor's, master's, and doctoral degrees. Founded 1967. Setting: 9-acre urban campus. Endowment: $2.5 million. Educational spending for the previous fiscal year: $3600 per student. Student-undergrad faculty ratio is 11:1. Students come from 48 states and territories, 75% from out-of-state. 85% 25 or older. Retention: 75% of full-time freshmen returned the following year. Academic areas with the most degrees conferred: liberal arts/general studies; theology and religious vocations; business/marketing. Core. Calendar: semesters. Services for LD students, advanced placement, accelerated degree program, distance learning, double major, summer session for credit, part-time degree program, external degree program, adult/continuing education programs, internships.

Entrance Requirements: Open admission. Option: electronic application. Required: high school transcript, minimum 2 high school GPA. Entrance: minimally difficult. Application deadlines: Rolling, Rolling for nonresidents. Transfer credits accepted: Yes.

Costs Per Year: Application fee: $50. Tuition: $6000 full-time, $365 per semester hour part-time. Mandatory fees: $400 per term part-time. Full-time tuition varies according to course load and student level. Part-time tuition and fees vary according to course load and student level.

Collegiate Environment: Orientation program. College housing not available. Southern Christian University Library plus 1 other with 80,000 books, 300 microform titles, 1,200 serials, 800 audiovisual materials, an OPAC, and a Web page. Operations spending for the previous fiscal year: $93,000. 5 computers available on campus for general student use. A computer is required for all students. A campuswide network can be accessed from off-campus. Students can access the following: online class registration, access to over 20 million monographs and journals online. Staffed computer lab on campus.

Community Environment: Southern Christian University is a 9-acre

campus located in Montgomery, the capital city of Alabama adjacent to Interstate 85. This city is strategically located in the central part of the state. Montgomery is the fourth largest city in the state in terms of population, offering residential areas, parks and playgrounds, school and universities, museums, a zoo, and the capitol facilities. Montgomery has two major U.S. Air Force installations, as well as a number of historical sites. The city has an abundance of good housing and a variety of employment opportunities.

■ **ATHENS STATE UNIVERSITY**
300 N Beaty St.
Athens, AL 35611
Tel: (256)233-8100; Free: 800-522-0272
Fax: (256)233-8164
E-mail: necedah.henderson@athens.edu
Web Site: www.athens.edu/
Description: State-supported, upper-level, coed. Awards bachelor's degrees. Founded 1822. Setting: 45-acre small town campus. Total enrollment: 3,415. Faculty: 218 (88 full-time, 130 part-time). Student-undergrad faculty ratio is 17:1. Full-time: 1,533 students, 70% women, 30% men. Part-time: 1,882 students, 61% women, 39% men. Students come from 18 states and territories, 4% from out-of-state. 2% American Indian or Alaska Native, non-Hispanic/Latino; 2% Hispanic/Latino; 12% African American, non-Hispanic/Latino; 1% Asian, non-Hispanic/Latino; 0.03% Native Hawaiian or other Pacific Islander, non-Hispanic/Latino; 1% international. 66% 25 or older, 25% transferred in. Academic areas with the most degrees conferred: business/marketing; education; English. Core. Calendar: semesters. Advanced placement, independent study, distance learning, double major, summer session for credit, part-time degree program, adult/continuing education programs, co-op programs and internships. Off campus study at Oakwood College, Alabama Agricultural and Mechanical University, University of Alabama in Huntsville. Study abroad program.

Costs Per Year: Application fee: $30. State resident tuition: $4590 full-time. Nonresident tuition: $9180 full-time. Mandatory fees: $750 full-time.

Collegiate Environment: Drama-theater group, student-run newspaper. Social organizations: national sororities, local sororities. Major annual events: Homecoming, welcome back cookouts, Halloween carnival. Student services: personal-psychological counseling. College housing not available. Athens State University Library with 178,390 books, 38,332 serials, an OPAC, and a Web page. 210 computers available on campus for general student use. A campuswide network can be accessed. Students can access the following: online class registration, grades, transcripts, schedules, e-mail. Staffed computer lab on campus.

Community Environment: Located in the Tennessee Valley, Athens (population 20,972) is in Limestone County which has an overall population of 72,446. The town is noted for its fine antebellum homes, including the large Founders Hall, built in 1843. With an average temperature of 60 degrees and convenient to air (Huntsville), rail, and within two hours of Nashville and Birmingham, this is a rich, rapidly growing area for farming and industry. State Parks at Wheeler, Wilson Lakes, and Guntersville Reservoir provide for swimming, boating, fishing, and camping.

■ **AUBURN UNIVERSITY**
Auburn University, AL 36849
Tel: (334)844-4000; Free: 800-AUBURN9
E-mail: admissions@auburn.edu
Web Site: www.auburn.edu/
Description: State-supported, university, coed. Awards bachelor's, master's, and doctoral degrees and post-master's certificates. Founded 1856. Setting: 1,875-acre small town campus with easy access to Atlanta, Birmingham. Endowment: $498.8 million. Research spending for the previous fiscal year: $102.2 million. Educational spending for the previous fiscal year: $9213 per student. Total enrollment: 25,134. Faculty: 1,368 (1,192 full-time, 176 part-time). Student-undergrad faculty ratio is 18:1. 17,463 applied, 77% were admitted. 32% from top 10% of their high school class, 68% from top quarter, 90% from top half. 63 National Merit Scholars. Full-time: 18,449 students, 50% women, 50% men. Part-time: 1,726 students, 37% women, 63% men. Students come from 53 states and territories, 44 other countries, 38% from out-of-state. 1% American Indian or Alaska Native, non-Hispanic/Latino; 3% Hispanic/Latino; 7% African American, non-Hispanic/Latino; 2% Asian, non-Hispanic/Latino; 1% international. 4% 25 or older, 20% live on campus, 6% transferred in. Retention: 90% of full-time freshmen returned the following year. Academic areas with the most degrees conferred: business/marketing; engineering; education. Core. Calendar: semesters. ESL program, services for LD students, advanced placement, accelerated degree program, fresh-

man honors college, honors program, independent study, distance learning, double major, summer session for credit, part-time degree program, adult/continuing education programs, co-op programs and internships, graduate courses open to undergrads. Off campus study. Study abroad program. ROTC: Army, Naval, Air Force.

Entrance Requirements: Options: electronic application, early admission, early action, deferred admission, international baccalaureate accepted. Required: essay, high school transcript, minimum 2 high school GPA, SAT or ACT. Recommended: minimum 3 high school GPA. Required for some: minimum 3 high school GPA. Entrance: moderately difficult. Application deadlines: 2/1, 2/1 for nonresidents, 10/1 for early action. Notification: 2/15, 2/15 for nonresidents, 10/15 for early action. SAT Reasoning Test deadline: 2/1. Transfer credits accepted: Yes.

Costs Per Year: Application fee: $50. State resident tuition: $7872 full-time, $328 per semester hour part-time. Nonresident tuition: $23,616 full-time, $984 per semester hour part-time. Mandatory fees: $1574 full-time, $787 per term part-time. Full-time tuition and fees vary according to program and reciprocity agreements. Part-time tuition and fees vary according to course load, program, and reciprocity agreements. College room and board: $10,606. College room only: $5500. Room and board charges vary according to board plan and housing facility.

Collegiate Environment: Orientation program. Drama-theater group, choral group, marching band, student-run newspaper, radio station. Social organizations: 329 open to all; national fraternities, national sororities; 21% of eligible men and 31% of eligible women are members. Most popular organizations: Student Government Association, University Program Council, IMPACT (volunteer opportunities), International Student Organization, student media (AU Plainsman newspaper, WEGL radio, Glomerata yearbook, Eagle Eye television, AU Circle literary journal). Major annual events: Tigermania (Homecoming), Tiger Walk (student rally), Hey Day. Student services: health clinic, personal-psychological counseling. Campus security: 24-hour emergency response devices and patrols, late night transport-escort service, controlled dormitory access. 3,974 college housing spaces available; 3,923 were occupied in 2012-13. Options: coed, men-only, women-only housing available. R. B. Draughon Library plus 2 others with 4.3 million books, 2.7 million microform titles, 256,354 serials, 122,201 audiovisual materials, an OPAC, and a Web page. Operations spending for the previous fiscal year: $8.5 million. 1,722 computers available on campus for general student use. Computer purchase/lease plans available. A campuswide network can be accessed from student residence rooms and from off campus. Students can access the following: online class registration, pay Bursar online, course materials available online. Staffed computer lab on campus provides training in use of computers, software, and the Internet.

Community Environment: Auburn (population 50,000) is located on U.S. 29 and Interstate 85, 55 miles east of Montgomery, 120 miles southeast of Birmingham, and 120 miles southwest of Atlanta, Georgia. Auburn University is the pride of the city. With the many churches in the area there is a cultural atmosphere which makes for pleasant living. Chewacla State Park is nearby for swimming and picnicking. The city has two well-equipped parks, a country club and 2 public courses for golf, a stadium for athletic games and many facilities for intramural sports including fields, swimming pools, racquetball and tennis courts, and a student activities building. Azaleas and camellias may be seen on the grounds of the university and many of the beautiful homes.

■ **AUBURN UNIVERSITY AT MONTGOMERY**
PO Box 244023
Montgomery, AL 36124-4023
Tel: (334)244-3000; Free: 800-227-2649
Fax: (334)244-3795
E-mail: rmckinne@aum.edu
Web Site: www.aum.edu/

Description: State-supported, comprehensive, coed. Part of Auburn University. Awards bachelor's, master's, and doctoral degrees and post-master's certificates. Founded 1967. Setting: 500-acre suburban campus. Endowment: $40.6 million. Research spending for the previous fiscal year: $495,817. Educational spending for the previous fiscal year: $3238 per student. Total enrollment: 4,989. Faculty: 333 (223 full-time, 110 part-time). Student-undergrad faculty ratio is 15:1. 2,386 applied, 72% were admitted. 19% from top 10% of their high school class, 43% from top quarter, 76% from top half. Full-time: 2,906 students, 60% women, 40% men. Part-time: 1,319 students, 61% women, 39% men. 6% from out-of-state. 1% American Indian or Alaska Native, non-Hispanic/Latino; 0.4% Hispanic/Latino; 28%

African American, non-Hispanic/Latino; 2% Asian, non-Hispanic/Latino; 0% Native Hawaiian or other Pacific Islander, non-Hispanic/Latino; 4% international. 28% 25 or older, 12% live on campus, 6% transferred in. Retention: 58% of full-time freshmen returned the following year. Academic areas with the most degrees conferred: business/marketing; education; biological/life sciences. Core. Calendar: semesters. Academic remediation for entering students, ESL program, services for LD students, advanced placement, honors program, independent study, distance learning, double major, summer session for credit, part-time degree program, adult/continuing education programs, co-op programs and internships, graduate courses open to undergrads. Off campus study at Huntingdon College, Alabama State University, Faulkner University. Study abroad program. ROTC: Army, Air Force (c).

Entrance Requirements: Options: electronic application, deferred admission. Required: high school transcript, ACT. Recommended: SAT. Entrance: moderately difficult. Application deadline: Rolling. Notification: continuous. SAT Reasoning Test deadline: 8/1.

Costs Per Year: State resident tuition: $7500 full-time, $250 per credit hour part-time. Nonresident tuition: $22,500 full-time, $750 per credit hour part-time. Mandatory fees: $650 full-time. Full-time tuition and fees vary according to course load. Part-time tuition varies according to course load. College room only: $3270. Room charges vary according to housing facility.

Collegiate Environment: Orientation program. Drama-theater group, choral group, student-run newspaper. Social organizations: 52 open to all; national fraternities, national sororities. Major annual events: AUMFest, Shriek Week, Homecoming. Student services: health clinic, personal-psychological counseling. Campus security: 24-hour emergency response devices and patrols, student patrols, late night transport-escort service, controlled dormitory access. 711 college housing spaces available. No special consideration for freshman housing applicants. Option: coed housing available. Auburn University at Montgomery Library with an OPAC and a Web page. Operations spending for the previous fiscal year: $2.8 million. 705 computers available on campus for general student use. A campuswide network can be accessed from student residence rooms and from off campus. Students can access the following: online class registration. Staffed computer lab on campus provides training in use of computers, software, and the Internet.

Community Environment: See Alabama State University.

■ **BEVILL STATE COMMUNITY COLLEGE**
1411 Indiana Ave.
Jasper, AL 35501
Tel: (205)387-0511
Web Site: www.bscc.edu/

Description: State-supported, 2-year, coed. Part of Alabama College System. Awards certificates, transfer associate, and terminal associate degrees. Founded 1969. Setting: 245-acre rural campus with easy access to Birmingham. Endowment: $142,934. Total enrollment: 4,069. Faculty: 337 (114 full-time, 223 part-time). Student-undergrad faculty ratio is 16:1. Full-time: 2,258 students, 61% women, 39% men. Part-time: 1,811 students, 68% women, 32% men. 0.3% American Indian or Alaska Native, non-Hispanic/Latino; 1% Hispanic/Latino; 16% African American, non-Hispanic/Latino; 0.5% Asian, non-Hispanic/Latino; 0.02% Native Hawaiian or other Pacific Islander, non-Hispanic/Latino; 0.05% international. 36% 25 or older. Core. Calendar: semesters. Academic remediation for entering students, services for LD students, advanced placement, honors program, distance learning, summer session for credit, part-time degree program, adult/continuing education programs, co-op programs. Off campus study at University of Alabama at Birmingham, Wallace State Community College, Shelton State Community College, Northwest Alabama State Technical College.

Entrance Requirements: Open admission. Options: electronic application, early admission, deferred admission. Required: high school transcript. Entrance: noncompetitive. Application deadline: Rolling. Transfer credits accepted: Yes.

Costs Per Year: State resident tuition: $2616 full-time, $109 per credit hour part-time. Nonresident tuition: $5232 full-time, $218 per credit hour part-time. Mandatory fees: $711 full-time, $29 per credit hour part-time. Full-time tuition and fees vary according to course load and program. Part-time tuition and fees vary according to course load and program. College room and board: $2695. Room and board charges vary according to board plan and location.

Collegiate Environment: Choral group. Social organizations: 6 open to all. Most popular organizations: Student Government Association, Campus Ministries, Circle K, Outdoors men Club, Students Against Destructive Decisions. Major annual events: Spring Fling, Homecoming, National Alcohol

Awareness Week. Campus security: 24-hour emergency response devices. 138 college housing spaces available. Option: coed housing available. 141,434 books, 23,905 serials, an OPAC, and a Web pageOperations spending for the previous fiscal year: $605,526. 1,200 computers available on campus for general student use. A campuswide network can be accessed from off-campus. Students can access the following: online class registration, Business Office Payments. Staffed computer lab on campus provides training in use of computers, software, and the Internet.

Community Environment: The Sumiton and Jasper Campuses are in urban areas. The Fayette and Hamilton Campuses are in small towns.

■ BIRMINGHAM-SOUTHERN COLLEGE

900 Arkadelphia Rd.
Birmingham, AL 35254
Tel: (205)226-4600; Free: 800-523-5793
Fax: (205)226-3074
E-mail: jwaters@bsc.edu
Web Site: www.bsc.edu/

Description: Independent Methodist, 4-year, coed. Awards bachelor's degrees. Founded 1856. Setting: 196-acre urban campus with easy access to Birmingham. Endowment: $51.7 million. Educational spending for the previous fiscal year: $8624 per student. Total enrollment: 1,231. Faculty: 114 (86 full-time, 28 part-time). Student-undergrad faculty ratio is 13:1. 1,846 applied, 65% were admitted. 29% from top 10% of their high school class, 61% from top quarter, 82% from top half. 1 National Merit Scholar. Full-time: 1,208 students, 47% women, 53% men. Part-time: 23 students, 52% women, 48% men. Students come from 33 states and territories, 18 other countries, 41% from out-of-state. 1% American Indian or Alaska Native, non-Hispanic/Latino; 3% Hispanic/Latino; 8% African American, non-Hispanic/Latino; 4% Asian, non-Hispanic/Latino; 0% Native Hawaiian or other Pacific Islander, non-Hispanic/Latino; 0% international. 2% 25 or older, 85% live on campus, 2% transferred in. Retention: 81% of full-time freshmen returned the following year. Academic areas with the most degrees conferred: business/marketing; visual and performing arts; psychology. Core. Calendar: 4-1-4. Advanced placement, self-designed majors, honors program, independent study, double major, summer session for credit, part-time degree program, co-op programs and internships. Off campus study at University of Alabama at Birmingham, Samford University, Miles College, Montevallo. Study abroad program. ROTC: Army (c), Air Force (c).

Entrance Requirements: Options: electronic application, early action, deferred admission, international baccalaureate accepted. Required: essay, high school transcript, minimum 2 high school GPA, 1 recommendation, SAT or ACT. Recommended: interview. Required for some: interview. Entrance: moderately difficult. Application deadline: 11/15 for early action. Notification: 3/1, 12/15 for early action. SAT Reasoning Test deadline: 3/1. SAT Subject Test deadline: 3/1. Transfer credits accepted: Yes.

Costs Per Year: Application fee: $40. Comprehensive fee: $41,400 includes full-time tuition ($29,600), mandatory fees ($1100), and college room and board ($10,700). College room only: $6200. Full-time tuition and fees vary according to program and reciprocity agreements. Room and board charges vary according to board plan, housing facility, and location.

Collegiate Environment: Orientation program. Drama-theater group, choral group, marching band, student-run newspaper. Social organizations: 84 open to all; national fraternities, national sororities; 35% of eligible men and 53% of eligible women are members. Most popular organizations: Black Student Union, Southern Bouldering Club, Student Government Association, Multi- Cultural Awareness Organization, BSC Chapter of Habitat for Humanity. Major annual events: Fall Concert, Halloween on the Hilltop Community Event, Homecoming. Student services: health clinic, personal-psychological counseling. Campus security: 24-hour emergency response devices and patrols, late night transport-escort service, controlled dormitory access, vehicle safety inspections for students, emergency phone stations throughout campus. 1,597 college housing spaces available; 1,179 were occupied in 2012-13. Freshmen guaranteed college housing. On-campus residence required through sophomore year. Options: coed, men-only, women-only housing available. Charles Andrew Rush Learning Center/N. E. Miles Library with 309,127 books, 90,629 microform titles, 46,349 serials, 33,032 audiovisual materials, an OPAC, and a Web page. Operations spending for the previous fiscal year: $1 million. 306 computers available on campus for general student use. Computer purchase/lease plans available. A campuswide network can be accessed from student residence rooms and from off campus. Students can access the following: online class registration.

Community Environment: See Birmingham Southern College.

■ BISHOP STATE COMMUNITY COLLEGE

351 N Broad St.
Mobile, AL 36603-5898
Tel: (251)690-6801
Fax: (251)438-5403
E-mail: admiss@bishop.edu
Web Site: www.bishop.edu/

Description: State-supported, 2-year, coed. Part of Alabama College System. Awards certificates, transfer associate, and terminal associate degrees. Founded 1965. Setting: 9-acre urban campus. Total enrollment: 3,598. Student-undergrad faculty ratio is 18:1. 2% from out-of-state. 40% 25 or older. Core. Calendar: semesters. Academic remediation for entering students, services for LD students, distance learning, summer session for credit, part-time degree program, adult/continuing education programs, co-op programs and internships.

Entrance Requirements: Open admission. Options: early admission, deferred admission. Required: high school transcript. Entrance: noncompetitive. Application deadline: Rolling. Notification: continuous until 9/17.

Costs Per Year: Application fee: $0. State resident tuition: $4140 full-time, $109 per credit hour part-time. Nonresident tuition: $6540 full-time, $218 per credit hour part-time. Mandatory fees: $870 full-time, $29 per credit hour part-time. Full-time tuition and fees vary according to course load. Part-time tuition and fees vary according to course load.

Collegiate Environment: Drama-theater group, choral group, student-run radio station. Student services: health clinic. Campus security: 24-hour emergency response devices and patrols.

Community Environment: See University of South Alabama.

■ BROWN MACKIE COLLEGE–BIRMINGHAM

105 Vulcan Rd.
Ste. 400
Birmingham, AL 35209
Tel: (205)299-4699; Free: 888-299-4699
Web Site: www.brownmackie.edu/birmingham

Description: Proprietary, 4-year, coed. Part of Education Management Corporation. Awards associate and bachelor's degrees.

■ CALHOUN COMMUNITY COLLEGE

PO Box 2216
Decatur, AL 35609-2216
Tel: (256)306-2500
Fax: (256)306-2877
E-mail: admissions@calhoun.edu
Web Site: www.calhoun.edu/

Description: State-supported, 2-year, coed. Part of Alabama College System. Awards certificates, transfer associate, and terminal associate degrees. Founded 1965. Setting: suburban campus. Total enrollment: 11,212. Student-undergrad faculty ratio is 26:1. 2% from out-of-state. 39% 25 or older. Core. Calendar: semesters. Academic remediation for entering students, ESL program, services for LD students, advanced placement, accelerated degree program, independent study, distance learning, summer session for credit, part-time degree program, adult/continuing education programs, co-op programs.

Entrance Requirements: Open admission except for nursing, dental services programs. Required for some: high school transcript, SAT or ACT. Entrance: noncompetitive. Application deadline: Rolling. Notification: continuous.

Collegiate Environment: Drama-theater group, choral group, student-run newspaper. Student services: personal-psychological counseling. Campus security: 24-hour patrols. Brewer Library plus 2 others with an OPAC and a Web page.

■ CENTRAL ALABAMA COMMUNITY COLLEGE

1675 Cherokee Rd.
Alexander City, AL 35011-0699
Tel: (256)234-6346
Fax: (256)234-0384
Web Site: www.cacc.edu/

Description: State-supported, 2-year, coed. Part of Alabama College System. Awards certificates, transfer associate, and terminal associate degrees. Founded 1965. Setting: 100-acre small town campus. Research spending for the previous fiscal year: $34,245. Total enrollment: 2,177. Faculty: 193 (52 full-time, 141 part-time). Student-undergrad faculty ratio is 15:1. Full-time: 1,304 students, 63% women, 38% men. Part-time: 873

students, 73% women, 27% men. Students come from 6 states and territories. 16% 25 or older. Core. Calendar: semesters. Academic remediation for entering students, services for LD students, advanced placement, distance learning, summer session for credit, part-time degree program, adult/continuing education programs, co-op programs and internships.
Entrance Requirements: Open admission. Option: early admission. Required: high school transcript. Required for some: interview, SAT or ACT. Entrance: noncompetitive. Application deadline: 9/9.
Collegiate Environment: Orientation program. Drama-theater group, choral group, student-run radio station. Social organizations: 6 open to all. Most popular organizations: Cultural Unity, Baptist Campus Ministry, Student Government Association, Phi Theta Kappa. Major annual events: Fall Fest, Spring Fest. Student services: personal-psychological counseling. Campus security: evening security. Thomas D. Russell Library with 35,000 books and 455 serials. Operations spending for the previous fiscal year: $235,461. 70 computers available on campus for general student use. A campuswide network can be accessed from off-campus. Students can access the following: online class registration. Staffed computer lab on campus.
Community Environment: Alexander City (population 14,957) is recognized as a city with great civic pride and a sound business climate. It is a pivotal point of transportation: 78 miles southeast of Birmingham, 55 miles northeast of Montgomery, 123 miles southwest of Atlanta, and 70 miles northwest of Columbus, GA. Childersburg is strategically located on Highway 280, 35 miles southeast of Birmingham, 76 miles north of Montgomery, and 42 miles southwest of Anniston. Both campuses are located in one of the South's principal industrial areas. Industries are diversified yet bolstered by the large payrolls of two leading textile corporations and a leading paper products company. Electrical energy, various foundries, emerging high tech companies, and many small businesses comprise the economic base of the College's service area. Both cities are favored with a mild climate year round, with outstanding recreational and sports facilities. In Alexander City, Lake Martin is the focus of boating, swimming, fishing, and camping. In Childersburg, Logan Martin Lake and Lay Lake allow for sports and recreational activities.

■ **CHATTAHOOCHEE VALLEY COMMUNITY COLLEGE**
2602 College Dr.
Phenix City, AL 36869-7928
Tel: (334)291-4900
Fax: (334)291-4994
E-mail: admissions@cv.edu
Web Site: www.cv.edu/
Description: State-supported, 2-year, coed. Part of Alabama College System. Awards certificates, transfer associate, and terminal associate degrees. Founded 1974. Setting: 103-acre small town campus. Total enrollment: 1,697. Faculty: 124 (35 full-time, 89 part-time). Student-undergrad faculty ratio is 20:1. 405 applied, 100% were admitted. Full-time: 944 students, 63% women, 37% men. Part-time: 753 students, 65% women, 35% men. 1% American Indian or Alaska Native, non-Hispanic/Latino; 4% Hispanic/Latino; 42% African American, non-Hispanic/Latino; 1% Asian, non-Hispanic/Latino; 0.2% Native Hawaiian or other Pacific Islander, non-Hispanic/Latino; 0% international. 38% 25 or older, 16% transferred in. Retention: 54% of full-time freshmen returned the following year. Core. Calendar: semesters. Academic remediation for entering students, services for LD students, advanced placement, self-designed majors, honors program, distance learning, summer session for credit, part-time degree program, adult/continuing education programs. Off campus study at Troy State University.
Entrance Requirements: Open admission. Option: early admission. Required: high school transcript. Entrance: noncompetitive. Application deadline: Rolling. Notification: continuous. Preference given to state residents. Transfer credits accepted: Yes.
Collegiate Environment: Orientation program. Drama-theater group, choral group. Student services: personal-psychological counseling. Campus security: 24-hour emergency response devices and patrols. Estelle Bain Owens Learning Resource Center and Library with 56,307 books, 88 serials, and a Web page.

■ **COLUMBIA SOUTHERN UNIVERSITY**
21982 University Ln.
Orange Beach, AL 36561
Tel: (251)981-3771; Free: 800-977-8449
Fax: (251)981-3815
E-mail: admissions@columbiasouthern.edu

Web Site: www.columbiasouthern.edu/
Description: Proprietary, comprehensive, coed. Awards associate, bachelor's, master's, and doctoral degrees (offers only distance learning degree programs). Founded 1993. Setting: small town campus. Total enrollment: 22,658. Faculty: 285 (40 full-time, 245 part-time). Student-undergrad faculty ratio is 67:1. 7,656 applied, 100% were admitted. Full-time: 6,594 students, 42% women, 58% men. Part-time: 12,598 students, 34% women, 66% men. Students come from 55 states and territories, 62 other countries, 95% from out-of-state. 1% American Indian or Alaska Native, non-Hispanic/Latino; 6% Hispanic/Latino; 21% African American, non-Hispanic/Latino; 2% Asian, non-Hispanic/Latino; 0.2% Native Hawaiian or other Pacific Islander, non-Hispanic/Latino; 0.04% international. 90% 25 or older, 11% transferred in. Retention: 84% of full-time freshmen returned the following year. Academic areas with the most degrees conferred: business/marketing; homeland security, law enforcement, firefighting, and protective services; engineering technologies. Core. Calendar: modular. Academic remediation for entering students, services for LD students, distance learning, part-time degree program, adult/continuing education programs, internships. Off campus study.
Entrance Requirements: Open admission. Option: electronic application. Required for some: high school transcript. Entrance: noncompetitive. Application deadline: Rolling. Transfer credits accepted: Yes.
Costs Per Year: Application fee: $25. Tuition: $4800 full-time, $200 per credit hour part-time. Mandatory fees: $95 full-time. Full-time tuition and fees vary according to course load and degree level. Part-time tuition varies according to course load and degree level.
Collegiate Environment: CSU Online Library with a Web page.

■ **COMMUNITY COLLEGE OF THE AIR FORCE**
CCAF/DESS
100 S Turner Blvd.
Maxwell Gunter Air Force Base, AL 36114-3011
Tel: (334)649-5000
E-mail: teresa.amatuzzi@maxwell.af.mil
Web Site: www.au.af.mil/au/ccaf/
Description: Federally supported, 2-year, coed. Part of Air University. Awards certificates and terminal associate degrees (courses conducted at 125 branch locations worldwide for members of the U.S. Air Force). Founded 1972. Setting: suburban campus. Total enrollment: 314,962. Faculty: 6,293 (all full-time). 29,486 applied, 100% were admitted. Full-time: 314,962 students, 18% women, 82% men. 64% 25 or older. Core. Calendar: continuous. Academic remediation for entering students, advanced placement, independent study, distance learning, adult/continuing education programs, internships.
Entrance Requirements: Open admission. Option: electronic application. Required: high school transcript, interview, military physical, good character, criminal background check, Armed Services Vocational Aptitude Battery. Entrance: noncompetitive. Application deadline: Rolling. Notification: continuous.
Collegiate Environment: Major annual events: Armed Forces Day activities, Memorial Day activities, Veteran's Day activities. Student services: legal services, health clinic, personal-psychological counseling. Campus security: 24-hour emergency response devices and patrols. Freshmen given priority for college housing. On-campus residence required in freshman year. Option: coed housing available. Air Force Library Service with 5 million books, 56,654 serials, an OPAC, and a Web page.

■ **CONCORDIA COLLEGE ALABAMA**
1712 Broad St.
Selma, AL 36701
Tel: (334)874-5700
Fax: (334)874-3728
E-mail: prichardson@ccal.edu
Web Site: www.ccal.edu/
Description: Independent Lutheran, 4-year, coed. Part of Concordia University System. Awards associate and bachelor's degrees. Founded 1922. Setting: 59-acre small town campus with easy access to Birmingham. Educational spending for the previous fiscal year: $2977 per student. Total enrollment: 611. Faculty: 46 (22 full-time, 24 part-time). Student-undergrad faculty ratio is 19:1. 2,377 applied. Full-time: 565 students, 38% women, 62% men. Part-time: 46 students, 89% women, 11% men. Students come from 21 states and territories, 5 other countries, 23% from out-of-state. 0% American Indian or Alaska Native, non-Hispanic/Latino; 1% Hispanic/Latino; 86% African American, non-Hispanic/Latino; 0% Asian, non-Hispanic/Latino;

0% Native Hawaiian or other Pacific Islander, non-Hispanic/Latino; 2% international. 22% 25 or older, 12% transferred in. Retention: 50% of full-time freshmen returned the following year. Academic areas with the most degrees conferred: business/marketing; education. Core. Calendar: semesters. Academic remediation for entering students, services for LD students, advanced placement, honors program, independent study, double major, summer session for credit, part-time degree program, adult/continuing education programs, internships. Off campus study at Concordia University System. Study abroad program. ROTC: Army.

Entrance Requirements: Options: electronic application, deferred admission. Required: high school transcript, minimum 2 high school GPA. Recommended: SAT or ACT. Entrance: moderately difficult. Application deadline: 8/15. Notification: continuous. Transfer credits accepted: Yes.

Costs Per Year: Application fee: $10. Comprehensive fee: $12,930 includes full-time tuition ($7920), mandatory fees ($670), and college room and board ($4340). College room only: $1800. Full-time tuition and fees vary according to course load. Room and board charges vary according to board plan and housing facility. Part-time tuition: $330 per credit hour. Part-time mandatory fees: $170 per term. Part-time tuition and fees vary according to course load.

Collegiate Environment: Orientation program. Drama-theater group, choral group, marching band, student-run newspaper. Social organizations: 5 open to all; national fraternities, Religious organizations; 26% of eligible men and 34% of eligible women are members. Most popular organizations: Music Ensemble, Rotaract, Phi Theta Kappa, Spiritual Life, Red Cross. Major annual events: Spiritual Life Praise Worship, Choir's Annual Concert, Homecoming Activities. Student services: personal-psychological counseling. Campus security: 24-hour patrols. Freshmen given priority for college housing. Option: coed housing available. Ellwinger-Hunt Learning Resource Center with 56,000 books, 105 microform titles, 105 serials, 400 audiovisual materials, an OPAC, and a Web page. 90 computers available on campus for general student use. A campuswide network can be accessed from student residence rooms and from off campus. Staffed computer lab on campus provides training in use of computers, software, and the Internet.

■ **ENTERPRISE STATE COMMUNITY COLLEGE**
PO Box 1300
Enterprise, AL 36331-1300
Tel: (334)347-2623
E-mail: gdeas@eocc.edu
Web Site: www.escc.edu/
Description: State-supported, 2-year, coed. Part of Alabama College System. Awards certificates, transfer associate, and terminal associate degrees. Founded 1965. Setting: 100-acre small town campus. Total enrollment: 2,189. 37% 25 or older. Core. Calendar: semesters. Academic remediation for entering students, ESL program, services for LD students, advanced placement, honors program, summer session for credit, part-time degree program, adult/continuing education programs, internships.
Entrance Requirements: Open admission. Options: early admission, deferred admission. Required: high school transcript. Entrance: noncompetitive. Application deadline: Rolling. Notification: continuous.
Collegiate Environment: Orientation program. Choral group, student-run newspaper. Student services: personal-psychological counseling, women's center. Campus security: security personnel. Snuggs Hall with 45,076 books and 349 serials.
Community Environment: Population 23,000, Enterprise has a cosmopolitan atmosphere. Due to its proximity to Fort Rucker, approximately 35% of its populace hail from all states in the union and many foreign countries. It enjoys a mild climate. Bus, railroad and a local airport serve the area. There is excellent shopping downtown, plus three shopping centers in the area. The college has a summer work program arranged with the city and local firms; part-time jobs are also available at Fort Rucker, six miles from Enterprise. The community contains many churches, a community center, and most major social, civic, and service groups as well as many city-sponsored programs for recreation.

■ **FAULKNER UNIVERSITY**
5345 Atlanta Hwy.
Montgomery, AL 36109-3398
Tel: (334)386-7324; Free: 800-879-9816
Fax: (334)386-7268
E-mail: nscott@faulkner.edu
Web Site: www.faulkner.edu/
Description: Independent, comprehensive, coed, affiliated with Church of Christ. Awards associate, bachelor's, master's, and doctoral degrees.

Founded 1942. Setting: 75-acre urban campus. Endowment: $18.3 million. Educational spending for the previous fiscal year: $4920 per student. Total enrollment: 3,327. Faculty: 349 (117 full-time, 232 part-time). Student-undergrad faculty ratio is 15:1. 1,305 applied, 60% were admitted. 6% from top 10% of their high school class, 22% from top quarter, 59% from top half. Full-time: 1,993 students, 60% women, 40% men. Part-time: 770 students, 70% women, 30% men. Students come from 35 states and territories, 27 other countries, 14% from out-of-state. 1% American Indian or Alaska Native, non-Hispanic/Latino; 1% Hispanic/Latino; 47% African American, non-Hispanic/Latino; 1% Asian, non-Hispanic/Latino; 0.3% Native Hawaiian or other Pacific Islander, non-Hispanic/Latino; 2% international. 53% 25 or older, 19% live on campus, 20% transferred in. Retention: 54% of full-time freshmen returned the following year. Academic areas with the most degrees conferred: business/marketing; homeland security, law enforcement, firefighting, and protective services; health professions and related sciences. Core. Calendar: semesters. Academic remediation for entering students, ESL program, services for LD students, advanced placement, accelerated degree program, freshman honors college, honors program, independent study, distance learning, double major, summer session for credit, part-time degree program, adult/continuing education programs, internships. Off campus study at the following Montgomery area institutions: Huntingdon College and Auburn University Montgomery. Faulkner's main campus also has a cooperative agreement for ROTC students with Auburn University Montgomery and Alabama State University. Study abroad program. ROTC: Army (c), Air Force (c).

Entrance Requirements: Options: electronic application, early admission, deferred admission, international baccalaureate accepted. Required: high school transcript, minimum 2 high school GPA, SAT or ACT. Recommended: essay, 2 recommendations, interview. Entrance: minimally difficult. Application deadlines: Rolling, Rolling for nonresidents. Notification: continuous, continuous for nonresidents. SAT Reasoning Test deadline: 7/31. SAT Subject Test deadline: 7/31. Transfer credits accepted: Yes.

Costs Per Year: Application fee: $25. Comprehensive fee: $24,030 includes full-time tuition ($15,730), mandatory fees ($1650), and college room and board ($6650). College room only: $3250. Full-time tuition and fees vary according to class time, course load, degree level, location, and program. Room and board charges vary according to board plan and housing facility. Part-time tuition: $530 per semester hour. Part-time tuition and fees vary according to class time, degree level, and location.

Collegiate Environment: Orientation program. Drama-theater group, choral group, marching band, student-run newspaper. Social organizations: 21 open to all; local fraternities, local sororities, social clubs; 15% of eligible men and 9% of eligible women are members. Most popular organizations: student government, Marching Band, Dinner Theatre, Acappella Chorus, Phi Lambda/Kappa Social Clubs. Major annual events: Homecoming, Jamboree, Lectureships. Student services: health clinic, personal-psychological counseling. Campus security: 24-hour emergency response devices and patrols, late night transport-escort service. 648 college housing spaces available; 630 were occupied in 2012-13. Freshmen guaranteed college housing. On-campus residence required through junior year. Options: men-only, women-only housing available. Gus Nichols Library System plus 4 others with 837,316 books, 368,156 microform titles, 3,480 serials, 3,056 audiovisual materials, an OPAC, and a Web page. Operations spending for the previous fiscal year: $2.1 million. 480 computers available on campus for general student use. A campuswide network can be accessed from student residence rooms and from off campus. Students can access the following: online class registration, student account access. Staffed computer lab on campus.
Community Environment: See Alabama State University.

■ **GADSDEN STATE COMMUNITY COLLEGE**
PO Box 227
Gadsden, AL 35902-0227
Tel: (256)549-8200; Free: 800-226-5563
Fax: (256)549-8444
E-mail: info@gadsdenstate.edu
Web Site: www.gadsdenstate.edu/
Description: State-supported, 2-year, coed. Part of Alabama Community College System. Awards certificates, transfer associate, and terminal associate degrees. Founded 1965. Setting: 275-acre small town campus with easy access to Birmingham. Total enrollment: 5,882. Faculty: 345 (154 full-time, 191 part-time). Student-undergrad faculty ratio is 19:1. Full-time: 3,158 students, 57% women, 43% men. Part-time: 2,724 students, 68% women, 32% men. Students come from 17 states and territories, 60 other countries,

1% from out-of-state. 1% American Indian or Alaska Native, non-Hispanic/Latino; 2% Hispanic/Latino; 20% African American, non-Hispanic/Latino; 0.5% Asian, non-Hispanic/Latino; 0.1% Native Hawaiian or other Pacific Islander, non-Hispanic/Latino; 1% international. 37% 25 or older, 2% live on campus, 6% transferred in. Core. Calendar: semesters. Academic remediation for entering students, ESL program, services for LD students, advanced placement, honors program, distance learning, summer session for credit, part-time degree program, external degree program, adult/continuing education programs, co-op programs and internships. Study abroad program. ROTC: Army.

Entrance Requirements: Open admission. Options: electronic application, early admission, deferred admission. Required: high school transcript. Entrance: noncompetitive. Application deadline: Rolling.

Costs Per Year: Application fee: $0. State resident tuition: $3270 full-time, $109 per credit hour part-time. Nonresident tuition: $6540 full-time, $218 per credit hour part-time. Mandatory fees: $684 full-time, $19 per credit hour part-time. Full-time tuition and fees vary according to reciprocity agreements. Part-time tuition and fees vary according to reciprocity agreements. College room and board: $3200.

Collegiate Environment: Orientation program. Drama-theater group, choral group. Social organizations: 13 open to all; Service/civic, faith-based, spirit, academic; 10% of eligible men and 10% of eligible women are members. Most popular organizations: National Society of Leadership and Success, Student Government Association, Circle K, International Club, Cardinal Spirit Club. Major annual events: Get on Board Day, G-Day, Constitution Week. Student services: personal-psychological counseling. Campus security: 24-hour patrols. 110 college housing spaces available; 105 were occupied in 2012-13. No special consideration for freshman housing applicants. Option: coed housing available. Meadows Library with 115,901 books, 144 serials, 7,080 audiovisual materials, an OPAC, and a Web page. 2,240 computers available on campus for general student use. Computer purchase/lease plans available. A campuswide network can be accessed. Students can access the following: online class registration. Staffed computer lab on campus provides training in use of computers, software, and the Internet.

Community Environment: Gadsden (population 37,405) is the county seat, and is the 6th largest in Alabama. Buses and railroads serve the area. Noccalula Falls is located in the City. Industry includes steel, rubber, farm machinery, and cotton mills.

■ **GEORGE C. WALLACE COMMUNITY COLLEGE**
1141 Wallace Dr.
Dothan, AL 36303-9234
Tel: (334)983-3521; Free: 800-543-2426
Fax: (334)983-3600
E-mail: ksaulsberry@wallace.edu
Web Site: www.wallace.edu/
Description: State-supported, 2-year, coed. Part of The Alabama Community College System. Awards certificates, diplomas, transfer associate, and terminal associate degrees. Founded 1949. Setting: 258-acre rural campus. Total enrollment: 4,655. Faculty: 241 (126 full-time, 115 part-time). Full-time: 2,633 students, 65% women, 35% men. Part-time: 2,022 students, 69% women, 31% men. 5% transferred in. Core. Calendar: semesters. Academic remediation for entering students, ESL program, advanced placement, independent study, distance learning, part-time degree program, adult/continuing education programs, co-op programs. Off campus study at University of Alabama at Birmingham.
Entrance Requirements: Open admission. Option: early admission. Required: high school transcript. Recommended: SAT or ACT. Entrance: noncompetitive. Application deadline: Rolling.
Collegiate Environment: Orientation program. Drama-theater group, student-run newspaper. Student services: personal-psychological counseling. Campus security: 24-hour patrols. Learning Resources Centers with 45,000 books, 200 serials, 1,300 audiovisual materials, and an OPAC. 240 computers available on campus for general student use. A campuswide network can be accessed from off-campus. Staffed computer lab on campus provides training in use of computers, software, and the Internet.

■ **GEORGE CORLEY WALLACE STATE COMMUNITY COLLEGE**
PO Box 2530
Selma, AL 36702
Tel: (334)876-9227
Fax: (334)876-9250
Web Site: www.wccs.edu/
Description: State-supported, 2-year, coed. Part of Alabama College

System. Awards certificates, diplomas, transfer associate, and terminal associate degrees. Founded 1966. Setting: small town campus. Total enrollment: 1,781. 31% 25 or older. Core. Calendar: semesters. Academic remediation for entering students, services for LD students, advanced placement, independent study, summer session for credit, part-time degree program, adult/continuing education programs.
Entrance Requirements: Open admission. Options: early admission, deferred admission. Entrance: noncompetitive. Application deadline: Rolling.
Collegiate Environment: Orientation program. Choral group. Campus security: 24-hour patrols. George Corley Wallace Library with 16,598 books, 2,683 microform titles, 2,240 serials, 913 audiovisual materials, an OPAC, and a Web page.
Community Environment: Selma, population 19,400 enjoys a temperate climate. Railroad, bus and air service is available for the area. There are many churches in the city, as well as hospitals, a library, and theaters. Gulf beaches are only 180 miles away. Part-time employment is available. Major civic, fraternal and veteran's organizations are represented. A traditional Market Day is held in October.

■ **H. COUNCILL TRENHOLM STATE TECHNICAL COLLEGE**
1225 Air Base Blvd.
Montgomery, AL 36108-2699
Tel: (334)420-4200; Free: 866-753-4544
Fax: (334)420-4201
E-mail: tmcbryde@trenholmstate.edu
Web Site: www.trenholmstate.edu/
Description: State-supported, 2-year, coed. Part of Alabama Department of Postsecondary Education. Awards certificates, diplomas, and terminal associate degrees. Founded 1962. Setting: 81-acre urban campus. Educational spending for the previous fiscal year: $2363 per student. Total enrollment: 1,721. Faculty: 134 (69 full-time, 65 part-time). Student-undergrad faculty ratio is 10:1. 1,133 applied, 48% were admitted. Students come from 2 states and territories, 1% from out-of-state. 0.3% American Indian or Alaska Native, non-Hispanic/Latino; 1% Hispanic/Latino; 62% African American, non-Hispanic/Latino; 1% Asian, non-Hispanic/Latino; 0% international. 48% 25 or older. Retention: 50% of full-time freshmen returned the following year. Core. Calendar: semesters. Academic remediation for entering students, services for LD students, advanced placement, independent study, distance learning, summer session for credit, part-time degree program, external degree program, adult/continuing education programs, co-op programs and internships.
Entrance Requirements: Open admission except for nursing program. Option: early admission. Required: high school transcript. Required for some: ACT. Entrance: noncompetitive. Application deadlines: Rolling, Rolling for nonresidents. Transfer credits accepted: Yes.
Costs Per Year: Application fee: $0. State resident tuition: $2784 full-time, $116 per unit part-time. Nonresident tuition: $5568 full-time, $232 per unit part-time. Mandatory fees: $456 full-time, $19 per unit part-time.
Collegiate Environment: Orientation program. Student-run newspaper. Most popular organizations: Student Government Association, College Ambassadors, Photography Club, Skills USA - VICA, Student Leadership Academy. Major annual events: Career Expo, Graduation, Honors Day. Student services: personal-psychological counseling. Campus security: 24-hour emergency response devices and patrols, late night transport-escort service. Trenholm State Learning Resources plus 1 other with 61,245 books, 1 microform title, 9,135 serials, 1,097 audiovisual materials, an OPAC, and a Web page. Operations spending for the previous fiscal year: $483,603. 700 computers available on campus for general student use. A campuswide network can be accessed from off-campus. Students can access the following: online class registration. Staffed computer lab on campus provides training in use of computers, software, and the Internet.

■ **HERITAGE CHRISTIAN UNIVERSITY**
PO Box HCU
Florence, AL 35630
Tel: (256)766-6610; Free: 800-367-3565
Fax: (256)760-0981
E-mail: bmckinnon@hcu.edu
Web Site: www.hcu.edu/
Description: Independent, comprehensive, coed, affiliated with Church of Christ. Awards associate, bachelor's, and master's degrees. Founded 1971. Setting: 43-acre small town campus. Endowment: $6 million. Research spending for the previous fiscal year: $8142. Educational spending for the previous fiscal year: $6552 per student. Total enrollment: 88. Faculty: 20 (5

full-time, 15 part-time). Student-undergrad faculty ratio is 5:1. 8 applied, 100% were admitted. Full-time: 27 students, 19% women, 81% men. Part-time: 36 students, 14% women, 86% men. Students come from 14 states and territories, 1 other country, 48% from out-of-state. 0% American Indian or Alaska Native, non-Hispanic/Latino; 3% Hispanic/Latino; 8% African American, non-Hispanic/Latino; 0% Asian, non-Hispanic/Latino; 0% Native Hawaiian or other Pacific Islander, non-Hispanic/Latino; 3% international. 66% 25 or older, 60% live on campus, 19% transferred in. Retention: 33% of full-time freshmen returned the following year. Core. Calendar: semesters. Academic remediation for entering students, accelerated degree program, independent study, distance learning, summer session for credit, part-time degree program, external degree program, adult/continuing education programs, co-op programs and internships, graduate courses open to undergrads.

Entrance Requirements: Open admission. Options: electronic application, early admission, deferred admission, international baccalaureate accepted. Required: high school transcript, minimum 2 high school GPA, 3 recommendations. Recommended: interview. Required for some: TOEFL (Test of English as a Foreign Language) for international students. Entrance: noncompetitive. Application deadline: Rolling. Notification: 7/1. Preference given to applicants interested in preaching in Churches of Christ. Transfer credits accepted: Yes.

Costs Per Year: Application fee: $25. One-time mandatory fee: $300. Comprehensive fee: $18,202 includes full-time tuition ($11,936), mandatory fees ($840), and college room and board ($5426). College room only: $3000. Room and board charges vary according to housing facility. Part-time tuition: $373 per credit hour. Part-time mandatory fees: $35 per credit hour.

Collegiate Environment: Most popular organizations: Missions Club, Preachers Club, Student Government Association, Christian Ladies Organization, HCU Skit Team. Major annual events: Evangelism Seminar, Area-Wide Singing, Annual Theatre Event. Student services: personal-psychological counseling. Overton Memorial Library with 86,000 books, 1,303 microform titles, 176 serials, 2,213 audiovisual materials, and an OPAC. Operations spending for the previous fiscal year: $121,227. 12 computers available on campus for general student use. Computer purchase/lease plans available. A campuswide network can be accessed from student residence rooms. Students can access the following: online class registration. Staffed computer lab on campus provides training in use of computers, software, and the Internet.

■ **HERZING UNIVERSITY**
280 W Valley Ave.
Birmingham, AL 35209
Tel: (205)916-2800; Free: 800-596-0724
Fax: (205)916-2807
E-mail: admiss@bhm.herzing.edu
Web Site: www.herzing.edu/birmingham/
Description: Proprietary, 4-year, coed. Part of Herzing Institutes, Inc. Awards associate and bachelor's degrees. Founded 1965. Setting: 4-acre urban campus. Total enrollment: 371. 91 applied. 66% 25 or older. Core. Calendar: semesters. Advanced placement, self-designed majors, summer session for credit, external degree program, adult/continuing education programs, co-op programs and internships.
Entrance Requirements: Options: early admission, deferred admission. Entrance: minimally difficult. Application deadline: Rolling. Notification: continuous.
Collegiate Environment: Student services: personal-psychological counseling, women's center. Campus security: 24-hour emergency response devices, late night transport-escort service, security guard.

■ **HUNTINGDON COLLEGE**
1500 E Fairview Ave.
Montgomery, AL 36106-2148
Tel: (334)833-4222; Free: 800-763-0313
Fax: (334)833-4347
E-mail: admiss@huntingdon.edu
Web Site: www.huntingdon.edu/
Description: Independent United Methodist, 4-year, coed. Awards bachelor's degrees. Founded 1854. Setting: 71-acre suburban campus with easy access to Birmingham. Endowment: $40.1 million. Educational spending for the previous fiscal year: $6937 per student. Total enrollment: 1,118. Faculty: 120 (51 full-time, 69 part-time). Student-undergrad faculty ratio is 13:1. 13% from top 10% of their high school class, 32% from top quarter, 69% from top half. Full-time: 896 students, 43% women, 57% men. Part-

time: 222 students, 77% women, 23% men. Students come from 27 states and territories, 3 other countries, 17% from out-of-state. 0.4% American Indian or Alaska Native, non-Hispanic/Latino; 2% Hispanic/Latino; 19% African American, non-Hispanic/Latino; 1% Asian, non-Hispanic/Latino; 0.2% Native Hawaiian or other Pacific Islander, non-Hispanic/Latino; 0.4% international. 21% 25 or older, 47% live on campus, 9% transferred in. Retention: 55% of full-time freshmen returned the following year. Academic areas with the most degrees conferred: business/marketing; biological/life sciences; parks and recreation. Core. Calendar: semesters. Services for LD students, advanced placement, accelerated degree program, self-designed majors, freshman honors college, honors program, independent study, distance learning, double major, summer session for credit, part-time degree program, adult/continuing education programs, internships. Off campus study at Auburn University Montgomery, Faulkner University, Marine Environmental Sciences Consortium. Study abroad program. ROTC: Army (c), Air Force (c).
Entrance Requirements: Required: high school transcript, SAT or ACT. Required for some: essay, 3 recommendations, interview, auditions for music students; portfolios for art.
Costs Per Year: Comprehensive fee: $30,750 includes full-time tuition ($21,500), mandatory fees ($1000), and college room and board ($8250). Full-time tuition and fees vary according to course load, program, and student level. Room and board charges vary according to housing facility. Part-time tuition: $900 per credit hour. Part-time tuition varies according to course load and program. Tuition guaranteed not to increase for student's term of enrollment.
Collegiate Environment: Orientation program. Drama-theater group, choral group, marching band, student-run newspaper. Social organizations: 54 open to all; national fraternities, national sororities; 22% of eligible men and 31% of eligible women are members. Most popular organizations: Student Government Association, Campus Activities Board, Voice of Justice, Freshman Forum, Exchange Club. Major annual events: Countess of Huntingdon Ball, Red Pride Night, CloverJam. Student services: health clinic, personal-psychological counseling. Campus security: 24-hour emergency response devices and patrols, student patrols, late night transport-escort service, controlled dormitory access, electronic video surveillance. 544 college housing spaces available; 521 were occupied in 2012-13. Freshmen guaranteed college housing. On-campus residence required through junior year. Option: coed housing available. Houghton Memorial Library plus 1 other with 113,776 books, 61,551 microform titles, 193 serials, 4,345 audiovisual materials, an OPAC, and a Web page. Operations spending for the previous fiscal year: $142,197. 13 computers available on campus for general student use. Computer purchase/lease plans available. A computer is required for all students. A campuswide network can be accessed from student residence rooms and from off campus. Students can access the following: online class registration, online library, student web hosting.
Community Environment: Huntingdon's location in Montgomery gives students easy access to Gulf beaches (3 hours south), mountains (2 hours north), and major metropolitan areas (Birmingham, 90 miles; Atlanta, 180 miles; New Orleans 300 miles). Montgomery, Alabama's capital city, is an historic area rich in tradition and culture.

■ **ITT TECHNICAL INSTITUTE (BESSEMER)**
6270 Park S Dr.
Bessemer, AL 35022
Tel: (205)497-5700; Free: 800-488-7033
Fax: (205)991-5025
Web Site: www.itt-tech.edu/
Description: Proprietary, primarily 2-year, coed. Part of ITT Educational Services, Inc. Awards terminal associate and bachelor's degrees. Founded 1994. Setting: suburban campus.
Entrance Requirements: Entrance: minimally difficult.
Collegiate Environment: Campus security: 24-hour emergency response devices.

■ **ITT TECHNICAL INSTITUTE (MADISON)**
9238 Madison Blvd., Ste. 500
Madison, AL 35758
Tel: (256)542-2900; Free: 877-628-5960
Web Site: www.itt-tech.edu/
Description: Proprietary, primarily 2-year, coed. Part of ITT Educational Services, Inc. Awards terminal associate and bachelor's degrees.
Entrance Requirements: Entrance: minimally difficult.

■ **ITT TECHNICAL INSTITUTE (MOBILE)**
Office Mall S
3100 Cottage Hill Rd., Bldg. 3
Mobile, AL 36606
Tel: (251)472-4760; Free: 877-327-1013
Web Site: www.itt-tech.edu/
Description: Proprietary, primarily 2-year, coed. Part of ITT Educational Services, Inc. Awards terminal associate and bachelor's degrees.
Entrance Requirements: Entrance: minimally difficult.

■ **J. F. DRAKE STATE TECHNICAL COLLEGE**
3421 Meridian St. N
Huntsville, AL 35811-1584
Tel: (256)539-8161; Free: 888-413-7253
E-mail: sudeall@drakestate.edu
Web Site: www.drakestate.edu/
Description: State-supported, 2-year, coed. Part of Alabama Community College System of the Alabama Department of Postsecondary Education. Awards certificates, transfer associate, and terminal associate degrees. Founded 1961. Setting: 6-acre urban campus. Educational spending for the previous fiscal year: $2010 per student. Total enrollment: 1,258. Faculty: 72 (25 full-time, 47 part-time). Student-undergrad faculty ratio is 17:1. 1,010 applied, 69% were admitted. 33% from top 10% of their high school class, 48% from top quarter. Full-time: 754 students, 59% women, 41% men. Part-time: 504 students, 50% women, 50% men. Students come from 2 other countries, 4% from out-of-state. 57% 25 or older, 23% transferred in. Core. Calendar: semesters. Academic remediation for entering students, services for LD students, part-time degree program, co-op programs and internships.
Entrance Requirements: Open admission. Options: electronic application, deferred admission. Required: high school transcript. Entrance: noncompetitive. Application deadline: Rolling. Notification: continuous. Transfer credits accepted: Yes.
Costs Per Year: Application fee: $0. State resident tuition: $3270 full-time, $109 per credit hour part-time. Nonresident tuition: $6540 full-time, $218 per credit hour part-time. Mandatory fees: $720 full-time, $24 per credit hour part-time.
Collegiate Environment: Orientation program. Social organizations: 4 open to all. Most popular organizations: Phi Beta Lambda, SKILLS - USA. Major annual events: Student Government Election, Miss Drake Pageant, Spring Fling. Campus security: 24-hour patrols. College housing not available. S.C. O'Neal Library Technology Center with 24,676 books, 150 serials, 2,247 audiovisual materials, an OPAC, and a Web page. Operations spending for the previous fiscal year: $997,798. 380 computers available on campus for general student use. A campuswide network can be accessed from off-campus. Staffed computer lab on campus provides training in use of software.

■ **JACKSONVILLE STATE UNIVERSITY**
700 Pelham Rd., N
Jacksonville, AL 36265-1602
Tel: (256)782-5781; Free: 800-231-5291
Fax: (256)782-5291
E-mail: info@jsu.edu
Web Site: www.jsu.edu/
Description: State-supported, comprehensive, coed. Awards bachelor's, master's, and doctoral degrees and post-master's certificates. Founded 1883. Setting: 459-acre small town campus with easy access to Birmingham. Research spending for the previous fiscal year: $548,131. Total enrollment: 9,161. Faculty: 497 (319 full-time, 178 part-time). Student-undergrad faculty ratio is 18:1. 3,161 applied, 82% were admitted. 20% from top 10% of their high school class, 26% from top quarter, 28% from top half. Full-time: 6,044 students, 57% women, 43% men. Part-time: 1,947 students, 63% women, 37% men. 20% from out-of-state. 0.4% American Indian or Alaska Native, non-Hispanic/Latino; 1% Hispanic/Latino; 28% African American, non-Hispanic/Latino; 1% Asian, non-Hispanic/Latino; 0.1% Native Hawaiian or other Pacific Islander, non-Hispanic/Latino; 2% international. 24% 25 or older, 25% live on campus, 8% transferred in. Retention: 67% of full-time freshmen returned the following year. Academic areas with the most degrees conferred: health professions and related sciences; education; business/marketing. Core. Calendar: semesters. Academic remediation for entering students, services for LD students, advanced placement, accelerated degree program, honors program, independent study, distance learning, double major, summer session for credit, part-time degree program, adult/continuing education programs, co-op programs and internships, graduate courses open to undergrads. ROTC: Army.

Entrance Requirements: Options: electronic application, early admission, deferred admission. Required: high school transcript, SAT or ACT. Entrance: minimally difficult. Application deadlines: Rolling, Rolling for nonresidents. Notification: continuous, continuous for nonresidents. Transfer credits accepted: Yes.
Costs Per Year: Application fee: $30. State resident tuition: $7950 full-time. Nonresident tuition: $15,900 full-time. College room and board: $6300. College room only: $3550. Room and board charges vary according to board plan and housing facility.
Collegiate Environment: Orientation program. Drama-theater group, choral group, marching band, student-run newspaper, radio station. Social organizations: 97 open to all; national fraternities, national sororities, local fraternities, local sororities; 10% of eligible men and 11% of eligible women are members. Most popular organizations: Student Government Association, Archaeology Club, Campus Fellowship Clubs, Computer Science Club, Biology Club. Major annual events: Homecoming, Parents' Day. Student services: health clinic, personal-psychological counseling. Campus security: 24-hour emergency response devices and patrols, student patrols, late night transport-escort service, controlled dormitory access, night security officer in female residence halls. No special consideration for freshman housing applicants. Options: coed, men-only, women-only housing available. Houston Cole Library with 685,991 books, 1.4 million microform titles, 14,376 serials, an OPAC, and a Web page. 350 computers available on campus for general student use. A campuswide network can be accessed from student residence rooms and from off campus. Students can access the following: online class registration. Staffed computer lab on campus.
Community Environment: Population 8,800, Jacksonville is relatively small and free from the many distractions of a large city. The community is easily accessible by good roads and is 6 miles from Fort McClellan (a military installation), 12 miles from Anniston, 22 miles from Gadsden, 75 miles from Birmingham, and 100 miles from Atlanta, GA. The climate is pleasant.

■ **JAMES H. FAULKNER STATE COMMUNITY COLLEGE**
1900 Hwy. 31 S
Bay Minette, AL 36507
Tel: (251)580-2100; Free: 800-231-3752
Fax: (251)580-2285
E-mail: cmikkelsen@faulknerstate.edu
Web Site: www.faulknerstate.edu/
Description: State-supported, 2-year, coed. Part of Alabama College System. Awards certificates, transfer associate, and terminal associate degrees. Founded 1965. Setting: 105-acre small town campus. Total enrollment: 3,323. Faculty: 193 (63 full-time, 130 part-time). Student-undergrad faculty ratio is 15:1. Full-time: 2,139 students, 61% women, 39% men. Part-time: 1,184 students, 67% women, 33% men. 3% from out-of-state. 39% 25 or older, 9% live on campus. Calendar: semesters. Academic remediation for entering students, services for LD students, advanced placement, honors program, part-time degree program, adult/continuing education programs, co-op programs and internships.
Entrance Requirements: Open admission. Options: early admission, deferred admission. Required: high school transcript. Entrance: noncompetitive. Application deadline: Rolling. Notification: continuous until 8/18.
Collegiate Environment: Orientation program. Drama-theater group, choral group, student-run newspaper. Social organizations: national fraternities. Most popular organizations: Student Government Association, Pow-Wow Leadership Society, Phi Theta Kappa, Association of Computational Machinery, Phi Beta Lambda. Major annual events: Back-to-School Luau and Dance, Spring Fling, Homecoming Week activities. Student services: personal-psychological counseling. Campus security: 24-hour emergency response devices and patrols, controlled dormitory access. Austin R. Meadows Library with 53,100 books, 1,949 microform titles, 200 serials, and an OPAC. 208 computers available on campus for general student use. A campuswide network can be accessed. Staffed computer lab on campus.

■ **JEFFERSON DAVIS COMMUNITY COLLEGE**
PO Box 958
Brewton, AL 36427-0958
Tel: (251)867-4832
Fax: (251)809-0178
Web Site: www.jdcc.edu/
Description: State-supported, 2-year, coed. Awards certificates, transfer associate, and terminal associate degrees. Founded 1965. Setting: 100-acre small town campus. Total enrollment: 1,257. 49% 25 or older. Calendar: semesters. Academic remediation for entering students, services for LD

students, advanced placement, honors program, summer session for credit, part-time degree program, adult/continuing education programs.
Entrance Requirements: Open admission. Option: early admission. Required: high school transcript. Entrance: noncompetitive. Application deadline: Rolling.
Collegiate Environment: Orientation program. Drama-theater group. Student services: personal-psychological counseling. 926 books and 330 serials.

■ JEFFERSON STATE COMMUNITY COLLEGE
2601 Carson Rd.
Birmingham, AL 35215-3098
Tel: (205)853-1200; Free: 800-239-5900
Fax: (205)856-8547
E-mail: lowens@jeffstateonline.com
Web Site: www.jeffstateonline.com/
Description: State-supported, 2-year, coed. Part of Alabama Community College System. Awards certificates, transfer associate, and terminal associate degrees. Founded 1965. Setting: 351-acre suburban campus. Endowment: $1.1 million. Total enrollment: 8,878. Faculty: 405 (128 full-time, 277 part-time). Student-undergrad faculty ratio is 26:1. 4,046 applied, 100% were admitted. Full-time: 3,062 students, 56% women, 44% men. Part-time: 5,816 students, 63% women, 37% men. 0.2% American Indian or Alaska Native, non-Hispanic/Latino; 3% Hispanic/Latino; 21% African American, non-Hispanic/Latino; 2% Asian, non-Hispanic/Latino; 0.05% Native Hawaiian or other Pacific Islander, non-Hispanic/Latino; 1% international. 37% 25 or older, 48% transferred in. Core. Calendar: semesters. Academic remediation for entering students, ESL program, services for LD students, advanced placement, honors program, independent study, distance learning, summer session for credit, part-time degree program, adult/continuing education programs, internships. ROTC: Army (c), Air Force (c).
Entrance Requirements: Open admission except for allied health programs. Options: electronic application, early admission, early action, deferred admission. Required for some: high school transcript. Entrance: noncompetitive. Application deadline: Rolling. Notification: continuous. Transfer credits accepted: Yes.
Costs Per Year: Application fee: $0. State resident tuition: $4200 full-time, $140 per semester hour part-time. Nonresident tuition: $7470 full-time, $249 per semester hour part-time. Full-time tuition varies according to course load. Part-time tuition varies according to course load.
Collegiate Environment: Choral group. Social organizations: 23 open to all. Most popular organizations: Student Government Association, Phi Theta Kappa, Sigma Kappa Delta, Jefferson State Ambassadors, Students in Free Enterprise (SIFE). Major annual events: Black History Month Program, Spring Fling, Jeff Fest. Campus security: 24-hour patrols. College housing not available. Jefferson State Libraries plus 4 others with 217,609 books, 2,255 microform titles, 301 serials, 1,478 audiovisual materials, an OPAC, and a Web page. Operations spending for the previous fiscal year: $814,591. 295 computers available on campus for general student use. A campuswide network can be accessed from off-campus. Students can access the following: online class registration. Staffed computer lab on campus provides training in use of computers, software, and the Internet.
Community Environment: See University of Alabama Birmingham.

■ JUDSON COLLEGE
302 Bibb St.
Marion, AL 36756
Tel: (334)683-5100; Free: 800-447-9472
Fax: (334)683-5158
E-mail: admissions@judson.edu
Web Site: www.judson.edu/
Description: Independent Baptist, 4-year, coed. Awards associate and bachelor's degrees. Founded 1838. Setting: 118-acre rural campus with easy access to Birmingham. Endowment: $14.1 million. Educational spending for the previous fiscal year: $7835 per student. Total enrollment: 357. Faculty: 40 (29 full-time, 11 part-time). Student-undergrad faculty ratio is 9:1. 309 applied, 82% were admitted. 14% from top 10% of their high school class, 37% from top quarter, 79% from top half. 2 valedictorians. Full-time: 293 students, 99% women, 0.3% men. Part-time: 64 students, 86% women, 14% men. Students come from 21 states and territories, 1 other country, 19% from out-of-state. 0.3% American Indian or Alaska Native, non-Hispanic/Latino; 1% Hispanic/Latino; 21% African American, non-Hispanic/Latino; 1% Asian, non-Hispanic/Latino; 0% Native Hawaiian or other Pacific Islander, non-Hispanic/Latino; 1% international. 23% 25 or older, 63% live on

campus, 14% transferred in. Retention: 72% of full-time freshmen returned the following year. Academic areas with the most degrees conferred: psychology; biological/life sciences; business/marketing. Core. Calendar: semesters plus 2-month term. Academic remediation for entering students, services for LD students, advanced placement, accelerated degree program, self-designed majors, honors program, independent study, distance learning, double major, summer session for credit, part-time degree program, external degree program, adult/continuing education programs, internships. Off campus study at Judson College students enroll and participate in the ROTC classes at Marion Military Institute, a cross-town institution. Study abroad program. ROTC: Army (c).
Entrance Requirements: Options: electronic application, early admission, deferred admission, international baccalaureate accepted. Required: high school transcript, minimum 2 high school GPA, SAT or ACT. Entrance: moderately difficult. Application deadlines: Rolling, Rolling for nonresidents. Notification: continuous, continuous for nonresidents. SAT Reasoning Test deadline: 8/8. SAT Subject Test deadline: 8/8. Transfer credits accepted: Yes.
Costs Per Year: Application fee: $35. Comprehensive fee: $24,940 includes full-time tuition ($14,800), mandatory fees ($940), and college room and board ($9200). College room only: $5150. Full-time tuition and fees vary according to degree level. Part-time tuition: $500 per hour. Part-time mandatory fees: $470 per term. Part-time tuition and fees vary according to degree level.
Collegiate Environment: Orientation program. Drama-theater group, choral group, marching band, student-run newspaper. Social organizations: 26 open to all. Most popular organizations: Student Government Association, Campus Ministries, Faith-Based Service Learning Activities, Ambassadors, Science Club. Major annual events: Marion Matters, Pageant, Rose Sunday. Student services: personal-psychological counseling. Campus security: 24-hour emergency response devices and patrols, late night transport-escort service, controlled dormitory access. 264 college housing spaces available; 229 were occupied in 2012-13. Freshmen guaranteed college housing. On-campus residence required through senior year. Option: women-only housing available. Bowling Library with 59,409 books, 2,012 microform titles, 33,538 serials, 1,187 audiovisual materials, an OPAC, and a Web page. Operations spending for the previous fiscal year: $176,231. 50 computers available on campus for general student use. A campuswide network can be accessed from student residence rooms.

■ LAWSON STATE COMMUNITY COLLEGE
3060 Wilson Rd., SW
Birmingham, AL 35221-1798
Tel: (205)925-2515
Fax: (205)929-6316
E-mail: jshelley@lawsonstate.edu
Web Site: www.lawsonstate.edu/
Description: State-supported, 2-year, coed. Part of Alabama Community College System. Awards certificates, transfer associate, and terminal associate degrees. Founded 1949. Setting: 30-acre urban campus. Total enrollment: 3,419. Faculty: 223 (88 full-time, 135 part-time). Student-undergrad faculty ratio is 18:1. 1,596 applied, 82% were admitted. 2 class presidents. Full-time: 1,957 students, 61% women, 39% men. Part-time: 1,462 students, 58% women, 42% men. Students come from 14 states and territories, 1 other country, 1% from out-of-state. 0.1% American Indian or Alaska Native, non-Hispanic/Latino; 1% Hispanic/Latino; 75% African American, non-Hispanic/Latino; 1% Asian, non-Hispanic/Latino; 0.1% Native Hawaiian or other Pacific Islander, non-Hispanic/Latino; 0.2% international. 35% 25 or older, 1% live on campus, 6% transferred in. Retention: 51% of full-time freshmen returned the following year. Core. Calendar: semesters. Academic remediation for entering students, services for LD students, advanced placement, distance learning, summer session for credit, part-time degree program, adult/continuing education programs, co-op programs and internships.
Entrance Requirements: Open admission except for nursing, medical technology programs. Options: electronic application, international baccalaureate accepted. Required: high school transcript. Entrance: noncompetitive. Application deadline: Rolling. Notification: continuous. Transfer credits accepted: Yes.
Costs Per Year: Application fee: $0. State resident tuition: $3360 full-time. Nonresident tuition: $3720 full-time. Mandatory fees: $850 full-time. College room and board: $4000. College room only: $3000.
Collegiate Environment: Choral group. Social organizations: 8 open to all. Most popular organizations: Student Government Association, Phi Theta

Kappa, Kappa Beta Delta Honor Society, Phi Beta Lambda, Social Work Club. Major annual events: Homecoming, Miss Lawson State, L Week Activities. Student services: personal-psychological counseling. Campus security: 24-hour emergency response devices and patrols, controlled dormitory access. 110 college housing spaces available; all were occupied in 2012-13. No special consideration for freshman housing applicants. Option: coed housing available. Lawson State Library with 51,627 books, 27,004 microform titles, 261 serials, and an OPAC. Operations spending for the previous fiscal year: $152,193. 470 computers available on campus for general student use. Computer purchase/lease plans available. A campuswide network can be accessed from student residence rooms. Students can access the following: online class registration. Staffed computer lab on campus provides training in use of computers, software, and the Internet.
Community Environment: See University of Alabama - Birmingham.

■ **LURLEEN B. WALLACE COMMUNITY COLLEGE**
PO Box 1418
Andalusia, AL 36420-1418
Tel: (334)222-6591
E-mail: jriley@lbwcc.edu
Web Site: www.lbwcc.edu/
Description: State-supported, 2-year, coed. Part of Alabama Community College System. Awards certificates, transfer associate, and terminal associate degrees. Founded 1969. Setting: 200-acre small town campus. Educational spending for the previous fiscal year: $3971 per student. Total enrollment: 1,646. Faculty: 91 (64 full-time, 27 part-time). Student-undergrad faculty ratio is 17:1. Full-time: 1,000 students, 63% women, 37% men. Part-time: 646 students, 63% women, 37% men. 4% from out-of-state. 0.4% American Indian or Alaska Native, non-Hispanic/Latino; 1% Hispanic/Latino; 22% African American, non-Hispanic/Latino; 1% Asian, non-Hispanic/Latino; 0% Native Hawaiian or other Pacific Islander, non-Hispanic/Latino; 0% international. 28% 25 or older, 5% transferred in. Calendar: semesters. Academic remediation for entering students, honors program, independent study, distance learning, summer session for credit, part-time degree program, co-op programs.
Entrance Requirements: Open admission. Required: high school transcript. Entrance: noncompetitive. Application deadline: Rolling. Transfer credits accepted: Yes.
Costs Per Year: Application fee: $0. State resident tuition: $3270 full-time, $109 per credit hour part-time. Nonresident tuition: $6540 full-time, $218 per credit hour part-time. Mandatory fees: $690 full-time. Full-time tuition and fees vary according to course load. Part-time tuition varies according to course load.
Collegiate Environment: Orientation program. Drama-theater group, choral group. Most popular organizations: Student Government Association, Student Ambassadors, Interclub Council, Campus Civitan, Christian Student Ministries. Major annual events: Saints' Day, Blue/White Day. Student services: personal-psychological counseling. College housing not available. Lurleen B. Wallace Library plus 2 others with 40,088 books, 2,345 audiovisual materials, an OPAC, and a Web page. Operations spending for the previous fiscal year: $309,990.

■ **MARION MILITARY INSTITUTE**
1101 Washington St.
Marion, AL 36756
Tel: (334)683-2306; Free: 800-664-1842
Fax: (334)683-2380
Web Site: www.marionmilitary.edu/
Description: State-supported, 2-year, coed. Awards transfer associate and terminal associate degrees. Founded 1842. Setting: 130-acre small town campus. Endowment: $1.2 million. Total enrollment: 165. Faculty: 44 (40 full-time, 4 part-time). Student-undergrad faculty ratio is 6:1. 269 applied, 84% were admitted. 25% from top 10% of their high school class, 50% from top quarter, 96% from top half. Students come from 35 states and territories, 3 other countries, 8% from out-of-state. 0% 25 or older, 97% live on campus. Core. Calendar: semesters. Academic remediation for entering students, part-time degree program. Off campus study at Judson College. ROTC: Army, Air Force.
Entrance Requirements: Option: deferred admission. Required: high school transcript, minimum 2.0 high school GPA, 2 recommendations. Recommended: interview. Entrance: moderately difficult. Application deadline: 8/30.
Costs Per Year: Application fee: $35. State resident tuition: $6000 full-time,

$200 per credit hour part-time. Nonresident tuition: $12,000 full-time, $400 per credit hour part-time. College room and board: $3950.
Collegiate Environment: Orientation program. Drama-theater group, choral group, marching band, student-run newspaper. Social organizations: 12 open to all. Most popular organizations: Swamp Foxes, White Knights, marching band, Drama Club, Scabbard and Blade. Major annual events: Military Ball, Gymkhana, Red Carpet Day. Student services: health clinic, personal-psychological counseling. Campus security: night patrols by trained security personnel. Baer Memorial Library with 36,000 books, 140 serials, and 8,471 audiovisual materials. 21 computers available on campus for general student use. A campuswide network can be accessed. Staffed computer lab on campus.
Community Environment: See Judson College.

■ **MILES COLLEGE**
5500 Myron Massey Blvd.
Fairfield, AL 35064
Tel: (205)929-1000; Free: 800-445-0708
E-mail: admissions@miles.edu
Web Site: www.miles.edu/
Description: Independent Christian Methodist Episcopal, 4-year, coed. Awards bachelor's degrees. Founded 1905. Setting: 76-acre suburban campus. Endowment: $13.1 million. Research spending for the previous fiscal year: $1.2 million. Educational spending for the previous fiscal year: $4196 per student. Total enrollment: 1,738. Faculty: 147 (105 full-time, 42 part-time). Student-undergrad faculty ratio is 14:1. 2,905 applied, 26% were admitted. Full-time: 1,589 students, 53% women, 47% men. Part-time: 149 students, 66% women, 34% men. Students come from 23 states and territories, 21% from out-of-state. 20% 25 or older, 40% live on campus, 23% transferred in. Retention: 60% of full-time freshmen returned the following year. Academic areas with the most degrees conferred: business/marketing; foreign languages and literature; public administration and social services. Core. Calendar: semesters. Academic remediation for entering students, services for LD students, accelerated degree program, honors program, double major, summer session for credit, part-time degree program, adult/continuing education programs, co-op programs and internships. Off campus study at BACHE: UAB, Samford, Birmingham Southern. ROTC: Army (c), Air Force (c).
Entrance Requirements: Open admission. Recommended: ACT. Required for some: essay, high school transcript. Entrance: noncompetitive. Application deadline: 8/23. Notification: continuous.
Collegiate Environment: Orientation program. Drama-theater group, choral group, marching band, student-run newspaper. Social organizations: 20 open to all; national fraternities, national sororities, local fraternities, local sororities; 18% of eligible men and 22% of eligible women are members. Most popular organizations: choir, Education Club, Student Government Association, Phi Beta Lambda Business Club, Communications Club. Major annual events: Founders' Day, Homecoming, M-Day. Student services: health clinic, personal-psychological counseling. Campus security: 24-hour emergency response devices and patrols. C.A. Kirkeedoll Learning Resources Center with 180,000 books, 250 serials, 250 audiovisual materials, and an OPAC. Operations spending for the previous fiscal year: $262,000. 50 computers available on campus for general student use. Staffed computer lab on campus.
Community Environment: See University of Alabama - Birmingham.

■ **NORTHEAST ALABAMA COMMUNITY COLLEGE**
PO Box 159
Rainsville, AL 35986-0159
Tel: (256)228-6001
E-mail: niblettt@nacc.edu
Web Site: www.nacc.edu/
Description: State-supported, 2-year, coed. Part of Alabama Community College System. Awards certificates, transfer associate, and terminal associate degrees. Founded 1963. Setting: 117-acre rural campus. Total enrollment: 3,294. Faculty: 177 (59 full-time, 118 part-time). Student-undergrad faculty ratio is 24:1. Full-time: 1,805 students, 57% women, 43% men. Part-time: 1,489 students, 65% women, 35% men. 3% American Indian or Alaska Native, non-Hispanic/Latino; 4% Hispanic/Latino; 2% African American, non-Hispanic/Latino; 0.4% Asian, non-Hispanic/Latino; 0.1% Native Hawaiian or other Pacific Islander, non-Hispanic/Latino; 0.4% international. Retention: 58% of full-time freshmen returned the following year. Core. Academic remediation for entering students, ESL program, services for LD students, advanced placement, accelerated degree program, honors program,

distance learning, double major, summer session for credit, part-time degree program, adult/continuing education programs.

Entrance Requirements: Open admission. Entrance: noncompetitive. Application deadline: Rolling. Notification: continuous. Transfer credits accepted: Yes.

Costs Per Year: Application fee: $0. State resident tuition: $3270 full-time, $109 per credit hour part-time. Nonresident tuition: $6540 full-time, $218 per credit hour part-time. Mandatory fees: $870 full-time, $29 per credit hour part-time.

Collegiate Environment: Orientation program. Drama-theater group, choral group. Student services: personal-psychological counseling. Campus security: 24-hour emergency response devices and patrols, late night transport-escort service. Cecil B. Word Learning Resources Center with 62,648 books, 115 serials, and an OPAC. 515 computers available on campus for general student use. A campuswide network can be accessed from off-campus. Students can access the following: online class registration. Staffed computer lab on campus provides training in use of computers, software, and the Internet.

Community Environment: Rainsville, population 5,000, is in a mountainous area with a very pleasant temperate climate. The town is 58 miles from commercial airline service, six miles from Interstate 59, and eight miles from rail service. Protestant churches, and hospitals in Fort Payne and Scottsboro service the community. Recreational activities include good fishing, boating, camping, and hiking at nearby state parks.

■ NORTHWEST-SHOALS COMMUNITY COLLEGE

PO Box 2545
Muscle Shoals, AL 35662
Tel: (256)331-5200; Free: 800-645-8967
Fax: (256)331-5366
E-mail: taylor@nwscc.edu
Web Site: www.nwscc.edu/

Description: State-supported, 2-year, coed. Part of Alabama Department of Postsecondary Education. Awards certificates and transfer associate degrees. Founded 1963. Setting: 210-acre small town campus. Endowment: $311,484. Total enrollment: 3,717. Faculty: 156 (75 full-time, 81 part-time). Student-undergrad faculty ratio is 22:1. Full-time: 1,915 students, 54% women, 46% men. Part-time: 1,802 students, 59% women, 41% men. Students come from 7 states and territories, 1 other country, 1% from out-of-state. 1% American Indian or Alaska Native, non-Hispanic/Latino; 3% Hispanic/Latino; 10% African American, non-Hispanic/Latino; 0.4% Asian, non-Hispanic/Latino; 0.1% Native Hawaiian or other Pacific Islander, non-Hispanic/Latino; 0.03% international. 28% 25 or older, 5% transferred in. Core. Calendar: semesters. Academic remediation for entering students, services for LD students, advanced placement, accelerated degree program, honors program, independent study, distance learning, summer session for credit, part-time degree program, adult/continuing education programs, co-op programs.

Entrance Requirements: Open admission except for nursing program. Option: electronic application. Required: high school transcript, COMPASS Placement Test for English and Math. Entrance: noncompetitive. Application deadline: Rolling. Transfer credits accepted: Yes.

Costs Per Year: Application fee: $0. State resident tuition: $3270 full-time, $109 per credit hour part-time. Nonresident tuition: $6540 full-time, $218 per credit hour part-time. Mandatory fees: $810 full-time, $27 per credit hour part-time.

Collegiate Environment: Choral group. Social organizations: 20 open to all. Most popular organizations: Student Government Association, Science Club, Phi Theta Kappa, Baptist Campus Ministry, Northwest-Shoals Singers. Major annual events: Back-to-School Cookout, Spring Fling, Blood Drive. Student services: personal-psychological counseling. Campus security: 24-hour emergency response devices. College housing not available. Larry W. McCoy Learning Resource Center and James Glasgow Library with 70,248 books, 376 microform titles, 50 serials, 1,499 audiovisual materials, and an OPAC. Operations spending for the previous fiscal year: $436,250. 850 computers available on campus for general student use. A campuswide network can be accessed from off-campus. Students can access the following: online class registration. Staffed computer lab on campus.

■ OAKWOOD UNIVERSITY

7000 Adventist Blvd.
Huntsville, AL 35896
Tel: (256)726-7000; Free: 800-824-5312
Fax: (256)726-7404

E-mail: admission@oakwood.edu
Web Site: www.oakwood.edu/

Description: Independent Seventh-day Adventist, comprehensive, coed. Awards associate, bachelor's, and master's degrees. Founded 1896. Setting: 1,200-acre campus. Total enrollment: 1,824. Faculty: 171 (103 full-time, 68 part-time). Student-undergrad faculty ratio is 14:1. 1,492 applied, 57% were admitted. 12% from top 10% of their high school class, 26% from top quarter, 50% from top half. Full-time: 1,712 students, 58% women, 42% men. Part-time: 112 students, 65% women, 35% men. Students come from 43 states and territories, 21 other countries, 81% from out-of-state. 13% 25 or older, 64% live on campus, 6% transferred in. Retention: 69% of full-time freshmen returned the following year. Academic areas with the most degrees conferred: business/marketing; biological/life sciences; psychology. Core. Calendar: semesters. Academic remediation for entering students, advanced placement, honors program, double major, part-time degree program, internships. Off campus study at members of the Alabama Center for Higher Education, The University of Alabama in Huntsville. Study abroad program.

Entrance Requirements: Options: early action, deferred admission. Required: high school transcript, minimum 2 high school GPA, SAT or ACT. Required for some: essay. Entrance: minimally difficult. Application deadlines: Rolling, 3/30 for early action. Notification: 4/15 for early action.

Costs Per Year: Application fee: $25. Comprehensive fee: $23,950 includes full-time tuition ($14,530), mandatory fees ($884), and college room and board ($8536). College room only: $3578. Room and board charges vary according to board plan and housing facility. Part-time tuition: $627 per semester hour.

Collegiate Environment: Orientation program. Choral group, student-run newspaper, radio station. Most popular organization: United Student Movement. Major annual events: Homecoming, Graduation, Youth Motivational Task Force Week. Student services: health clinic, personal-psychological counseling. Campus security: 24-hour patrols, student patrols, late night transport-escort service. Eva B. Dykes Library with 133,106 books, 2,150 microform titles, 726 serials, and 6,704 audiovisual materials. 350 computers available on campus for general student use. A campuswide network can be accessed from student residence rooms and from off campus. Students can access the following: online class registration. Staffed computer lab on campus.

Community Environment: See University of Alabama - Huntsville.

■ PRINCE INSTITUTE OF PROFESSIONAL STUDIES

7735 Atlanta Hwy.
Montgomery, AL 36117-4231
Tel: (334)271-1670; Free: 877-853-5569
Fax: (334)271-1671
E-mail: admissions@princeinstitute.edu
Web Site: www.princeinstitute.edu/

Description: Proprietary, 2-year, coed. Awards certificates and terminal associate degrees. Founded 1976. Setting: 150 suburban campus. Educational spending for the previous fiscal year: $1800 per student. Total enrollment: 63. Faculty: 16 (4 full-time, 12 part-time). Student-undergrad faculty ratio is 13:1. 23 applied, 100% were admitted. 0% from out-of-state. 68% 25 or older. Retention: 100% of full-time freshmen returned the following year. Core.

Entrance Requirements: Option: electronic application. Required: high school transcript, interview. Entrance: noncompetitive. Application deadline: 10/1. Transfer credits accepted: Yes.

Collegiate Environment: Student services: personal-psychological counseling. Library plus 1 other with an OPAC and a Web page. Operations spending for the previous fiscal year: $2100. 54 computers available on campus for general student use. A campuswide network can be accessed from student residence rooms and from off campus. Students can access the following: online class registration.

■ REID STATE TECHNICAL COLLEGE

PO Box 588
Evergreen, AL 36401-0588
Tel: (251)578-1313
Fax: (251)578-5355
E-mail: akstuart@rstc.edu
Web Site: www.rstc.edu/

Description: State-supported, 2-year, coed. Part of Alabama Community College System. Awards certificates, diplomas, and terminal associate degrees. Founded 1966. Setting: 26-acre rural campus. Total enrollment: 495. Faculty: 37 (27 full-time, 10 part-time). Student-undergrad faculty ratio is 12:1. 122 applied, 100% were admitted. Full-time: 312 students, 57% women, 43% men. Part-time: 183 students, 66% women, 34% men. Students come from 2 states and territories, 1% from out-of-state. 0.4% American Indian or Alaska Native, non-Hispanic/Latino; 0.4% Hispanic/Latino; 53% African American, non-Hispanic/Latino; 0% Asian, non-Hispanic/Latino; 0.2% Native Hawaiian or other Pacific Islander, non-Hispanic/Latino; 0% international. 13% 25 or older. Calendar: semesters. Academic remediation for entering students, services for LD students, independent study, double major, summer session for credit, part-time degree program, adult/continuing education programs, internships.

Entrance Requirements: Open admission. Option: early admission. Required: high school transcript. Entrance: noncompetitive. Application deadline: Rolling.

Costs Per Year: Application fee: $0. State resident tuition: $3270 full-time, $109 per credit hour part-time. Nonresident tuition: $6540 full-time, $218 per credit hour part-time. Mandatory fees: $930 full-time, $30 per credit hour part-time. Full-time tuition and fees vary according to course load and program. Part-time tuition and fees vary according to course load and program.

Collegiate Environment: Orientation program. Social organizations: 2 open to all. Most popular organizations: Student Government Association, Phi Beta Lambda, National Vocational-Technical Society, Ambassadors, Who's Who. Major annual events: Challenge Cup Ambassadors, Talent Show, Hair Show. Student services: personal-psychological counseling. Campus security: 24-hour emergency response devices, day and evening security guard. College housing not available. Edith A. Gray Library with 4,157 books, 99 serials, 298 audiovisual materials, and a Web page. 80 computers available on campus for general student use. A campuswide network can be accessed from off-campus. Staffed computer lab on campus (open 24 hours a day).

■ **REMINGTON COLLEGE–MOBILE CAMPUS**

828 Downtowner Loop W
Mobile, AL 36609-5404
Tel: (251)343-8200; Free: 800-560-6192
Fax: (251)343-0577
E-mail: david.helveston@remingtoncollege.edu
Web Site: www.remingtoncollege.edu/
Description: Proprietary, primarily 2-year, coed. Awards diplomas, transfer associate, terminal associate, and bachelor's degrees. Setting: 5-acre suburban campus. Services for LD students, adult/continuing education programs, co-op programs.
Entrance Requirements: Entrance: noncompetitive.

■ **SAMFORD UNIVERSITY**

800 Lakeshore Dr.
Birmingham, AL 35229
Tel: (205)726-2011; Free: 800-888-7218
Fax: (205)726-2171
E-mail: blkenned@samford.edu
Web Site: www.samford.edu/
Description: Independent Baptist, university, coed. Awards bachelor's, master's, and doctoral degrees and post-master's certificates. Founded 1841. Setting: 212-acre suburban campus. Endowment: $241.2 million. Educational spending for the previous fiscal year: $12,807 per student. Total enrollment: 4,758. Faculty: 487 (301 full-time, 186 part-time). Student-undergrad faculty ratio is 12:1. 3,234 applied, 76% were admitted. 34% from top 10% of their high school class, 61% from top quarter, 84% from top half. 3 National Merit Scholars, 34 class presidents, 13 valedictorians, 148 student government officers. Full-time: 2,769 students, 65% women, 35% men. Part-time: 196 students, 69% women, 31% men. Students come from 38 states and territories, 12 other countries, 62% from out-of-state. 0.3% American Indian or Alaska Native, non-Hispanic/Latino; 5% Hispanic/Latino; 7% African American, non-Hispanic/Latino; 1% Asian, non-Hispanic/Latino; 0.1% Native Hawaiian or other Pacific Islander, non-Hispanic/Latino; 2% international. 6% 25 or older, 68% live on campus, 4% transferred in. Retention: 87% of full-time freshmen returned the following year. Academic areas with the most degrees conferred: business/marketing; health professions and related sciences; communication/journalism. Core. Calendar: 4-1-4. ESL program, services for LD students, accelerated degree program, honors program, independent study, distance learning, double major, summer session for credit, part-time degree program, adult/continuing education programs, co-op programs and internships, graduate courses open to undergrads. Off campus study at University of Alabama at Birmingham,

Birmingham-Southern College, Miles College, and University of Montevallo. Study abroad program. ROTC: Army (c), Air Force.
Entrance Requirements: Options: electronic application, early admission, deferred admission, international baccalaureate accepted. Required: essay, high school transcript, 1 recommendation, SAT or ACT. Required for some: interview. Entrance: moderately difficult. Application deadlines: Rolling, Rolling for nonresidents. Notification: continuous, continuous for nonresidents. SAT Reasoning Test deadline: 3/15. Transfer credits accepted: Yes. Applicants placed on waiting list: 0. Wait-listed applicants offered admission: 0.
Costs Per Year: Application fee: $35. Comprehensive fee: $33,400 includes full-time tuition ($24,570), mandatory fees ($580), and college room and board ($8250). College room only: $4250. Full-time tuition and fees vary according to course load, location, and program. Room and board charges vary according to board plan, housing facility, and location. Part-time tuition: $821 per credit hour. Part-time mandatory fees: $210 per term. Part-time tuition and fees vary according to course load and program.
Collegiate Environment: Orientation program. Drama-theater group, choral group, marching band, student-run newspaper, radio station. Social organizations: 116 open to all; national fraternities, national sororities; 27% of eligible men and 42% of eligible women are members. Most popular organizations: Alpha Delta Pi sorority, Chi Omega sorority, Phi Mu Sorority, Zeta Tau Alpha sorority, Alpha Omicron Pi sorority. Major annual events: Step Sing, Homecoming, Spring Fling. Student services: health clinic, personal-psychological counseling. Campus security: 24-hour emergency response devices and patrols, late night transport-escort service, self defense education, security escort services, and lighted pathways/sidewalks. College housing designed to accommodate 2,015 students; 2,075 undergraduates lived in college housing during 2012-13. Freshmen guaranteed college housing. On-campus residence required through sophomore year. Options: men-only, women-only housing available. Samford University Library plus 4 others with 688,371 books, 1.4 million microform titles, 85,762 serials, 51,132 audiovisual materials, an OPAC, and a Web page. Operations spending for the previous fiscal year: $5 million. 330 computers available on campus for general student use. A campuswide network can be accessed from student residence rooms and from off campus. Students can access the following: online class registration, free online storage and tech support. Staffed computer lab on campus provides training in use of computers, software, and the Internet.
Community Environment: See University of Alabama - Birmingham.

■ **SELMA UNIVERSITY**

1501 Lapsley St.
Selma, AL 36701-5299
Tel: (334)872-2533
Web Site: www.selmauniversity.org/
Description: Independent Baptist, 4-year, coed. Founded 1878. Calendar: semesters.

■ **SHELTON STATE COMMUNITY COLLEGE**

9500 Old Greensboro Rd.
Tuscaloosa, AL 35405
Tel: (205)391-2211
Fax: (205)391-2426
E-mail: ljones@sheltonstate.edu
Web Site: www.sheltonstate.edu/
Description: State-supported, 2-year, coed. Part of Alabama Community College System. Awards certificates, diplomas, transfer associate, and terminal associate degrees. Founded 1979. Setting: 202-acre small town campus with easy access to Birmingham. Total enrollment: 5,104. Faculty: 254 (97 full-time, 157 part-time). Student-undergrad faculty ratio is 24:1. Full-time: 2,699 students, 54% women, 46% men. Part-time: 2,405 students, 61% women, 39% men. 3% from out-of-state. 0.2% American Indian or Alaska Native, non-Hispanic/Latino; 1% Hispanic/Latino; 34% African American, non-Hispanic/Latino; 1% Asian, non-Hispanic/Latino; 0.02% Native Hawaiian or other Pacific Islander, non-Hispanic/Latino; 0.2% international. 24% 25 or older, 9% transferred in. Retention: 53% of full-time freshmen returned the following year. Core. Calendar: semesters. Academic remediation for entering students, services for LD students, advanced placement, accelerated degree program, distance learning, double major, summer session for credit, part-time degree program, adult/continuing education programs, co-op programs. ROTC: Army (c), Air Force (c).
Entrance Requirements: Open admission Open admission except for practical nursing, registered nursing, and respiratory technician programs.

Option: electronic application. Required: high school transcript. Entrance: noncompetitive. Application deadline: Rolling. Transfer credits accepted: Yes.

Costs Per Year: Application fee: $0. State resident tuition: $3270 full-time, $109 per credit part-time. Nonresident tuition: $6450 full-time, $218 per credit part-time. Mandatory fees: $870 full-time, $18 per credit part-time. Full-time tuition and fees vary according to course load and reciprocity agreements. Part-time tuition and fees vary according to course load and reciprocity agreements.

Collegiate Environment: Orientation program. Drama-theater group, choral group. Social organizations: 20 open to all. Most popular organizations: Phi Theta Kappa, Student Government Association, African American Cultural Association, Red Cross Club. Campus security: 24-hour emergency response devices and patrols. College housing not available. Brooks-Cork Library plus 1 other with an OPAC and a Web page.

■ SNEAD STATE COMMUNITY COLLEGE

220 N Walnut St.
Boaz, AL 35957-0734
Tel: (256)593-5120
Fax: (256)593-7180
E-mail: gchapman@snead.edu
Web Site: www.snead.edu/

Description: State-supported, 2-year, coed. Part of Alabama College System. Awards certificates, transfer associate, and terminal associate degrees. Founded 1898. Setting: 42-acre small town campus with easy access to Birmingham. Total enrollment: 2,483. 2% from out-of-state. 31% 25 or older. Core. Calendar: semesters. Academic remediation for entering students, services for LD students, advanced placement, accelerated degree program, self-designed majors, independent study, distance learning, summer session for credit, part-time degree program, adult/continuing education programs, internships.

Entrance Requirements: Open admission. Options: early admission, deferred admission. Required: high school transcript. Required for some: interview. Entrance: noncompetitive. Application deadline: 8/24. Notification: 8/20.

Collegiate Environment: Choral group, student-run newspaper. Social organizations: 15 open to all. Most popular organizations: Phi Theta Kappa, Snead Agricultural Organization, North American Veterinary Technician Association, Ambassadors, Baptist Campus Ministry. Major annual events: Ham and Biscuit Day, Mocktail Party, Homecoming. Student services: personal-psychological counseling. Campus security: 24-hour patrols, student patrols. McCain Learning Resource Center with an OPAC and a Web page.

Community Environment: Boaz (population 7,893) is located 60 miles north of Birmingham, and has an average temperature of 65 degrees. Employment is available in industry and business. Churches, civic and social organizations are located in the city. Guntersville Lake is ten miles from Boaz. The town is a shopping outlet center, one of the largest in the U.S.

■ SOUTH UNIVERSITY

5355 Vaughn Rd.
Montgomery, AL 36116-1120
Tel: (334)395-8800; Free: 866-629-2962
Fax: (334)395-8859
Web Site: www.southuniversity.edu/montgomery/

Description: Proprietary, comprehensive, coed. Part of Education Management Corporation. Awards associate, bachelor's, and master's degrees. Founded 1887.

■ SOUTHEASTERN BIBLE COLLEGE

2545 Valleydale Rd.
Birmingham, AL 35244-2083
Tel: (205)970-9200; Free: 800-749-8878
Fax: (205)970-9207
E-mail: deidra.whitfield@sebc.edu
Web Site: www.sebc.edu/

Description: Independent nondenominational, 4-year, coed. Awards associate and bachelor's degrees. Founded 1935. Setting: 22-acre suburban campus. Total enrollment: 179. Faculty: 27 (7 full-time, 20 part-time). Student-undergrad faculty ratio is 11:1. 22 applied, 100% were admitted. Full-time: 146 students, 40% women, 60% men. Part-time: 33 students, 45% women, 55% men. Students come from 9 states and territories, 1 other country, 8% from out-of-state. 1% American Indian or Alaska Native, non-

Hispanic/Latino; 1% Hispanic/Latino; 33% African American, non-Hispanic/Latino; 0% Asian, non-Hispanic/Latino; 0% Native Hawaiian or other Pacific Islander, non-Hispanic/Latino; 1% international. 55% 25 or older, 33% live on campus, 25% transferred in. Retention: 67% of full-time freshmen returned the following year. Academic area with the most degrees conferred: theology and religious vocations. Core. Calendar: semesters. Academic remediation for entering students, services for LD students, advanced placement, independent study, distance learning, double major, summer session for credit, part-time degree program, adult/continuing education programs, internships.

Entrance Requirements: Options: electronic application, deferred admission, international baccalaureate accepted. Required: essay, high school transcript, minimum 1.5 high school GPA, 2 recommendations, SAT or ACT. Entrance: noncompetitive. Transfer credits accepted: Yes.

Collegiate Environment: Orientation program. Choral group. Most popular organizations: Student Council, Student Missions Fellowship, chorale. Major annual event: Missions Conference. Campus security: controlled dormitory access. 98 college housing spaces available; 59 were occupied in 2012-13. No special consideration for freshman housing applicants. Options: men-only, women-only housing available. Gannett-Estes Library with 50,000 books, 150 serials, an OPAC, and a Web page. 30 computers available on campus for general student use.

Community Environment: See University of Alabama Birmingham.

■ SOUTHERN UNION STATE COMMUNITY COLLEGE

PO Box 1000, Roberts St.
Wadley, AL 36276
Tel: (256)395-2211
Fax: (256)395-2215
E-mail: info@suscc.edu
Web Site: www.suscc.edu/

Description: State-supported, 2-year, coed. Part of Alabama College System. Awards certificates, diplomas, transfer associate, and terminal associate degrees. Founded 1922. Setting: rural campus. Total enrollment: 4,971. Student-undergrad faculty ratio is 25:1. 12% from out-of-state. 23% 25 or older. Retention: 58% of full-time freshmen returned the following year. Calendar: semesters. Academic remediation for entering students, advanced placement, distance learning, summer session for credit, part-time degree program, adult/continuing education programs. ROTC: Air Force (c).

Entrance Requirements: Open admission. Options: early admission, deferred admission. Required: high school transcript. Entrance: noncompetitive. Application deadline: Rolling. Notification: continuous.

Collegiate Environment: Campus security: 24-hour patrols, controlled dormitory access.

Community Environment: Population 648. Located in East Central Alabama approximately 90 miles southwest of Atlanta, and the same distance southeast of Birmingham. Wadley is on Alabama State Highways 22 and 77. Gently rolling farm and woodland, healthful country atmosphere. Easy access to neighboring cities for shopping and recreation. Hospital in Roanoke.

■ SPRING HILL COLLEGE

4000 Dauphin St.
Mobile, AL 36608-1791
Tel: (251)380-4000; Free: 800-SHC-6704
Fax: (251)460-2186
E-mail: eruscin@shc.edu
Web Site: www.shc.edu/

Description: Independent Roman Catholic (Jesuit), comprehensive, coed. Awards bachelor's and master's degrees and post-master's certificates. Founded 1830. Setting: 450-acre suburban campus. Total enrollment: 1,328. Faculty: 134 (78 full-time, 56 part-time). Student-undergrad faculty ratio is 12:1. 2,817 applied, 47% were admitted. 20% from top 10% of their high school class, 47% from top quarter, 80% from top half. Full-time: 1,119 students, 60% women, 40% men. Part-time: 83 students, 70% women, 30% men. Students come from 39 states and territories, 12 other countries, 60% from out-of-state. 1% American Indian or Alaska Native, non-Hispanic/Latino; 8% Hispanic/Latino; 17% African American, non-Hispanic/Latino; 1% Asian, non-Hispanic/Latino; 0.1% Native Hawaiian or other Pacific Islander, non-Hispanic/Latino; 1% international. 8% 25 or older, 80% live on campus, 3% transferred in. Retention: 74% of full-time freshmen returned the following year. Academic areas with the most degrees conferred: business/marketing; biological/life sciences; psychology. Core. Calendar: semesters. Academic remediation for entering students, services for LD students, advanced placement, accelerated degree program, self-designed majors, honors program, independent study, distance learning, double major, summer session for credit, part-time degree program, adult/continuing education programs, internships. Off campus study at Marine Environmental Sciences Consortium. Study abroad program. ROTC: Army (c), Air Force (c).

Entrance Requirements: Options: electronic application, early admission, deferred admission, international baccalaureate accepted. Required: essay, high school transcript, 1 recommendation, SAT or ACT. Recommended: minimum 2.5 high school GPA, interview. Entrance: moderately difficult. Application deadlines: 7/15, 7/15 for nonresidents. Notification: continuous, continuous for nonresidents. SAT Reasoning Test deadline: 7/15. Transfer credits accepted: Yes.

Costs Per Year: Application fee: $25. Comprehensive fee: $40,746 includes full-time tuition ($27,670), mandatory fees ($1780), and college room and board ($11,296). College room only: $5900. Room and board charges vary according to housing facility. Part-time tuition: $975 per credit hour. Part-time mandatory fees: $50 per credit hour.

Collegiate Environment: Orientation program. Drama-theater group, choral group, student-run newspaper. Social organizations: 47 open to all; national fraternities, national sororities; 20% of eligible men and 28% of eligible women are members. Most popular organizations: Fraternities and sororities, SHAPe, National Society of Leadership and Success, Peer One Project, Chemistry Club. Major annual events: CajunFest, Christmas on the Hill, Campus Mardi Gras. Student services: health clinic, personal-psychological counseling. Campus security: 24-hour emergency response devices and patrols, late night transport-escort service, controlled dormitory access. 1,016 college housing spaces available; 946 were occupied in 2012-13. Freshmen guaranteed college housing. On-campus residence required through senior year. Option: coed housing available. Marnie and John Burke Memorial Library plus 1 other with an OPAC and a Web page. 194 computers available on campus for general student use. A campuswide network can be accessed from student residence rooms and from off campus. Students can access the following: online class registration. Staffed computer lab on campus provides training in use of computers, software, and the Internet.

Community Environment: See University of South Alabama.

■ **STILLMAN COLLEGE**
PO Drawer 1430, 3600 Stillman Blvd.
Tuscaloosa, AL 35403-9990
Tel: (205)349-4240; Free: 800-841-5722
Fax: (205)366-8996
E-mail: vboman@stillman.edu
Web Site: www.stillman.edu/
Description: Independent, 4-year, coed, affiliated with Presbyterian Church (U.S.A.). Awards bachelor's degrees. Founded 1876. Setting: 100-acre urban campus with easy access to Birmingham. Endowment: $18.2 million. Educational spending for the previous fiscal year: $3897 per student. Total enrollment: 1,072. Faculty: 61 (54 full-time, 7 part-time). Student-undergrad faculty ratio is 18:1. 3,491 applied, 44% were admitted. 12% from top 10% of their high school class, 38% from top quarter, 69% from top half. 4 valedictorians. Full-time: 1,032 students, 53% women, 47% men. Part-time: 40 students, 60% women, 40% men. Students come from 25 states and territories, 10 other countries, 35% from out-of-state. 0.1% American Indian or Alaska Native, non-Hispanic/Latino; 1% Hispanic/Latino; 93% African American, non-Hispanic/Latino; 0% Asian, non-Hispanic/Latino; 0% Native Hawaiian or other Pacific Islander, non-Hispanic/Latino; 0% international. 5% 25 or older, 63% live on campus, 13% transferred in. Retention: 61% of full-time freshmen returned the following year. Academic areas with the most degrees conferred: health professions and related sciences; biological/life sciences; business/marketing. Core. Calendar: semesters. Academic remediation for entering students, advanced placement, honors program, independent study, distance learning, double major, summer session for credit, co-op programs and internships. ROTC: Army (c).

Entrance Requirements: Options: electronic application, early admission, early decision, deferred admission, international baccalaureate accepted. Required: high school transcript, minimum 2.5 high school GPA, SAT or ACT, SAT and SAT Subject Tests or ACT. Recommended: essay, interview, SAT, ACT, SAT Subject Tests. Entrance: minimally difficult. Application deadlines: Rolling, 7/1 for early decision. Notification: 7/15 for early decision. Transfer credits accepted: Yes.

Costs Per Year: Application fee: $15. Comprehensive fee: $22,721 includes full-time tuition ($13,548), mandatory fees ($2117), and college room and board ($7056). College room only: $3404. Room and board charges vary

according to housing facility. Part-time tuition: $534 per credit. Part-time mandatory fees: $2117 per term. Tuition guaranteed not to increase for student's term of enrollment.

Collegiate Environment: Orientation program. Drama-theater group, choral group, marching band, student-run newspaper. Social organizations: 15 open to all; national fraternities, national sororities; 3% of eligible men and 5% of eligible women are members. Most popular organizations: Stillman Blue Pride Marching Band, Sophisticated Unlimited Modeling Troupe, Christian Student Association, Student Government Association, Students in Free Enterprise (SIFE). Major annual events: Homecoming, Founders' Day, Christmas Concert. Student services: health clinic, personal-psychological counseling. Campus security: 24-hour patrols, 24-hour patrols by trained campus police. Sheppard Library with 116,945 books, 6,368 microform titles, 31,867 serials, 1,380 audiovisual materials, and an OPAC. Operations spending for the previous fiscal year: $238,840. 150 computers available on campus for general student use. A campuswide network can be accessed from student residence rooms. Students can access the following: online class registration. Staffed computer lab on campus.

Community Environment: See University of Alabama.

■ **STRAYER UNIVERSITY - BIRMINGHAM CAMPUS**
3570 Grandview Pky.
Ste. 200
Birmingham, AL 35243
Tel: (205)453-6300
Fax: (205)453-6330
Web Site: www.strayer.edu/campus/birmingham/
Description: Proprietary, comprehensive, coed. Awards associate, bachelor's, and master's degrees.

■ **STRAYER UNIVERSITY - HUNTSVILLE CAMPUS**
4955 Corporate Dr., NW
Ste. 200
Huntsville, AL 35805
Tel: (256)665-9800
Fax: (256)665-9730
Web Site: www.strayer.edu/campus/huntsville/
Description: Proprietary, comprehensive, coed. Awards associate, bachelor's, and master's degrees.

■ **TALLADEGA COLLEGE**
627 W Battle St.
Talladega, AL 35160-2354
Tel: (256)362-0206; Free: 866-540-3956
Fax: (256)362-2268
E-mail: fdortch@talladega.edu
Web Site: www.talladega.edu/
Description: Independent, 4-year, coed. Awards bachelor's degrees. Founded 1867. Setting: 130-acre small town campus with easy access to Birmingham. Total enrollment: 706. Faculty: 43 (34 full-time, 9 part-time). Student-undergrad faculty ratio is 18:1. 1,771 applied, 51% were admitted. Full-time: 650 students, 57% women, 43% men. Part-time: 56 students, 59% women, 41% men. Students come from 31 states and territories, 3 other countries, 39% from out-of-state. 0% American Indian or Alaska Native, non-Hispanic/Latino; 2% Hispanic/Latino; 89% African American, non-Hispanic/Latino; 0.4% Asian, non-Hispanic/Latino; 0% Native Hawaiian or other Pacific Islander, non-Hispanic/Latino; 0% international. 16% 25 or older, 80% live on campus. Retention: 54% of full-time freshmen returned the following year. Academic areas with the most degrees conferred: business/marketing; biological/life sciences; psychology. Core. Calendar: semesters. Academic remediation for entering students, ESL program, accelerated degree program, independent study, double major, part-time degree program, adult/continuing education programs, co-op programs and internships. Off campus study at 7 members of the Alabama Center for Higher Education. Study abroad program. ROTC: Army (c).

Entrance Requirements: Options: electronic application, early admission. Required: essay, high school transcript, minimum 2 high school GPA, 1 recommendation. Recommended: SAT or ACT. Entrance: moderately difficult. Application deadline: Rolling. Notification: continuous.

Collegiate Environment: Orientation program. Drama-theater group, choral group, student-run newspaper. Social organizations: 31 open to all; national fraternities, national sororities; 15% of eligible men and 25% of eligible women are members. Most popular organizations: Student Government Association, Crimson Ambassadors, Students in Free Enterprise (SIFE),

Talladega College Choir, Social Work Club. Major annual events: Dega Day, Founder's Weekend, Alumni Weekend. Student services: health clinic, personal-psychological counseling. Campus security: 24-hour patrols, late night transport-escort service, campus police. 105 computers available on campus for general student use. A campuswide network can be accessed from student residence rooms and from off campus. Staffed computer lab on campus provides training in use of computers.

Community Environment: Population 17,149, Talladega is at the heart of a fertile valley in the foothills of the Blue Ridge Mountains, 55 miles to Birmingham. Bus service is available and the closest airline is in Anniston, 20 miles away. Its elevation gives it a healthy climate with an average temperature of 63.3 degrees, and annual rainfall of 54.3 inches. The highest point in Alabama, Cheaha Mountain, is 17 miles north in Talladega National Forest. Home of the Alabama School for Blind, and Alabama School for Deaf, the community has theatres, supervised playgrounds, and parks, with hunting, fishing, and hiking facilities.

■ TROY UNIVERSITY

University Ave.
Troy, AL 36082
Tel: (334)670-3000; Free: 800-551-9716
Fax: (334)670-3815
E-mail: bstar@troy.edu
Web Site: www.troy.edu/

Description: State-supported, comprehensive, coed. Part of Troy University System. Awards associate, bachelor's, master's, and doctoral degrees and post-master's certificates. Founded 1887. Setting: 906-acre small town campus. Endowment: $32.9 million. Research spending for the previous fiscal year: $143,153. Educational spending for the previous fiscal year: $3714 per student. Total enrollment: 22,554. Faculty: 1,284 (552 full-time, 732 part-time). Student-undergrad faculty ratio is 19:1. 5,646 applied, 72% were admitted. 54% from top quarter of their high school class, 84% from top half. Full-time: 9,634 students, 62% women, 38% men. Part-time: 8,281 students, 63% women, 37% men. Students come from 52 states and territories, 52 other countries, 40% from out-of-state. 1% American Indian or Alaska Native, non-Hispanic/Latino; 3% Hispanic/Latino; 39% African American, non-Hispanic/Latino; 1% Asian, non-Hispanic/Latino; 0.1% Native Hawaiian or other Pacific Islander, non-Hispanic/Latino; 2% international. 56% 25 or older, 29% live on campus, 8% transferred in. Retention: 71% of full-time freshmen returned the following year. Academic areas with the most degrees conferred: business/marketing; homeland security, law enforcement, firefighting, and protective services; psychology. Core. Calendar: semesters. Academic remediation for entering students, ESL program, services for LD students, advanced placement, accelerated degree program, honors program, independent study, distance learning, double major, summer session for credit, part-time degree program, internships, graduate courses open to undergrads. ROTC: Army, Air Force.

Entrance Requirements: Options: electronic application, deferred admission. Required: high school transcript, SAT or ACT. Recommended: interview. Entrance: moderately difficult. Application deadline: Rolling. Transfer credits accepted: Yes.

Costs Per Year: Application fee: $30. State resident tuition: $7470 full-time, $249 per credit hour part-time. Nonresident tuition: $14,940 full-time, $498 per credit hour part-time. Mandatory fees: $1600 full-time, $32 per credit hour part-time, $50 per term part-time. Full-time tuition and fees vary according to location and program. Part-time tuition and fees vary according to location and program. College room and board: $7071. College room only: $3686. Room and board charges vary according to board plan and housing facility.

Collegiate Environment: Orientation program. Drama-theater group, choral group, marching band, student-run newspaper. Social organizations: 151 open to all; national fraternities, national sororities; 13% of eligible men and 15% of eligible women are members. Most popular organizations: T-Day/Athletic Events (Homecoming), Activities Council, Pep Rallies. Major annual events: Homecoming, Honors Convocation, Commencement. Student services: health clinic, personal-psychological counseling. Campus security: 24-hour emergency response devices and patrols, student patrols, late night transport-escort service, controlled dormitory access. 2,033 college housing spaces available; 1,859 were occupied in 2012-13. Freshmen guaranteed college housing. On-campus residence required in freshman year. Options: coed, men-only, women-only housing available. Lurleen B. Wallace Library (Troy Campus) plus 2 others with 612,668 books, 2.2 million microform titles, 30,072 serials, 39,045 audiovisual materials, an OPAC, and a Web page. Operations spending for the previous fiscal year: $3.6 million. 12,792

computers available on campus for general student use. A campuswide network can be accessed from student residence rooms and from off campus. Students can access the following: online class registration. Staffed computer lab on campus.

Community Environment: Population 13,935, Troy is located at the junction of U.S. Highways 231 and 29 and is 50 miles from Montgomery, the state capital. There is regular bus service. The citizens take great interest in the University, and extend a cordial welcome to students. There are numerous social, church, civic and school organizations which provide cultural enrichment for the citizens and for the students of the University. Recreational facilities include parks for swimming, tennis courts, a lake for fishing, and two golf courses.

■ TUSKEGEE UNIVERSITY

Tuskegee Institute, AL 36088
Tel: (334)727-8011; Free: 800-622-6531
Web Site: www.tuskegee.edu/

Description: Independent, comprehensive, coed. Awards bachelor's, master's, and doctoral degrees. Founded 1881. Setting: 5,000-acre small town campus. Endowment: $113.7 million. Research spending for the previous fiscal year: $19 million. Total enrollment: 3,152. Faculty: 297 (271 full-time, 26 part-time). Student-undergrad faculty ratio is 12:1. 2,815 applied, 65% were admitted. 17% from top 10% of their high school class, 44% from top quarter, 82% from top half. Full-time: 2,614 students, 57% women, 43% men. Part-time: 70 students, 61% women, 39% men. Students come from 44 states and territories, 19 other countries, 72% from out-of-state. 0.1% American Indian or Alaska Native, non-Hispanic/Latino; 0.2% Hispanic/Latino; 87% African American, non-Hispanic/Latino; 0.04% Asian, non-Hispanic/Latino; 1% international. 4% 25 or older, 63% live on campus, 6% transferred in. Retention: 71% of full-time freshmen returned the following year. Academic areas with the most degrees conferred: engineering; business/marketing; agriculture. Core. Calendar: semesters. Academic remediation for entering students, ESL program, honors program, summer session for credit, part-time degree program, co-op programs and internships, graduate courses open to undergrads. Off campus study at Alabama Center for Higher Education. ROTC: Army, Air Force.

Entrance Requirements: Options: electronic application, early admission. Required: high school transcript, minimum 3 high school GPA, SAT or ACT. Entrance: moderately difficult. Application deadline: 4/15. Transfer credits accepted: Yes.

Costs Per Year: Application fee: $25. One-time mandatory fee: $500. Comprehensive fee: $27,350 includes full-time tuition ($18,100), mandatory fees ($800), and college room and board ($8450). College room only: $4190. Full-time tuition and fees vary according to course level, course load, degree level, and program. Room and board charges vary according to housing facility. Part-time tuition: $750 per hour. Part-time mandatory fees: $800 per year. Part-time tuition and fees vary according to course level, course load, degree level, and program.

Collegiate Environment: Orientation program. Drama-theater group, choral group, marching band, student-run newspaper. Social organizations: 6 open to all; national fraternities, national sororities; 7% of eligible men and 8% of eligible women are members. Most popular organizations: student government, Marching Band, State Clubs, Fraternities, Sororities. Major annual events: Homecoming, Choir Christmas Concert, Scholarship Night. Student services: health clinic, personal-psychological counseling. Campus security: 24-hour emergency response devices and patrols, late night transport-escort service. 2,040 college housing spaces available; 55 were occupied in 2012-13. Freshmen given priority for college housing. On-campus residence required through sophomore year. Options: coed, men-only, women-only housing available. Hollis B. Frissell Library plus 3 others with 623,824 books, 287,500 microform titles, 81,157 serials, and an OPAC. Operations spending for the previous fiscal year: $1.1 million. 1,000 computers available on campus for general student use. Computer purchase/lease plans available. A campuswide network can be accessed from student residence rooms and from off campus. Students can access the following: online class registration. Staffed computer lab on campus provides training in use of computers, software, and the Internet.

Community Environment: Tuskegee, population 11,590, is approximately 40 miles east of Montgomery, AL, the state capital, and 120 miles south of Atlanta, GA. Travelers may fly to Montgomery's Dannelly Field and drive to Tuskegee via Interstate 85 north or fly to Atlanta and drive to Tuskegee via Interstate 85 south. Dannelly field is served by American, Delta, Northwest Airlink, and USA Express airlines. Commercial bus transportation is available to Tuskegee from Montgomery, Atlanta, and other nearby cities. Churches of all major denominations, a library and a museum contribute to the cultural atmosphere of the town. Motels and hotels are located in the area. The town also has various fraternal, civic, and veteran's organizations.

■ **UNITED STATES SPORTS ACADEMY**
One Academy Dr.
Daphne, AL 36526-7055
Tel: (251)626-3303; Free: 800-223-2668
Fax: (251)621-2527
Web Site: www.ussa.edu/
Description: Independent, upper-level, coed. Awards bachelor's, master's, and doctoral degrees. Founded 1972. Setting: 10-acre suburban campus. Total enrollment: 546. Student-undergrad faculty ratio is 18:1. 78% 25 or older. Calendar: continuous. Distance learning.

■ **THE UNIVERSITY OF ALABAMA**
Tuscaloosa, AL 35487
Tel: (205)348-6010; Free: 800-933-BAMA
Fax: (205)348-9046
E-mail: admissions@ua.edu
Web Site: www.ua.edu/
Description: State-supported, university, coed. Part of University of Alabama System. Awards bachelor's, master's, and doctoral degrees and post-master's certificates. Founded 1831. Setting: 1,000-acre suburban campus with easy access to Birmingham. Endowment: $616.9 million. Research spending for the previous fiscal year: $55.1 million. Educational spending for the previous fiscal year: $10,197 per student. Total enrollment: 33,503. Faculty: 1,663 (1,202 full-time, 461 part-time). Student-undergrad faculty ratio is 20:1. 26,409 applied, 53% were admitted. 43% from top 10% of their high school class, 60% from top quarter, 82% from top half. 239 National Merit Scholars. Full-time: 25,430 students, 53% women, 47% men. Part-time: 2,596 students, 58% women, 42% men. Students come from 52 states and territories, 47 other countries, 40% from out-of-state. 0.4% American Indian or Alaska Native, non-Hispanic/Latino; 3% Hispanic/Latino; 12% African American, non-Hispanic/Latino; 1% Asian, non-Hispanic/Latino; 0.1% Native Hawaiian or other Pacific Islander, non-Hispanic/Latino; 2% international. 8% 25 or older, 27% live on campus, 5% transferred in. Retention: 85% of full-time freshmen returned the following year. Academic areas with the most degrees conferred: business/marketing; communication/journalism; health professions and related sciences. Core. Calendar: semesters. Academic remediation for entering students, ESL program, services for LD students, advanced placement, accelerated degree program, self-designed majors, freshman honors college, honors program, independent study, distance learning, double major, summer session for credit, part-time degree program, external degree program, adult/continuing education programs, co-op programs and internships, graduate courses open to undergrads. Off campus study at UA is a members of the Academic Common Market of the Southern Regional Education Board which allows students of member institutions to pursue specified degrees outside their state of resident. The UA System Cooperative Exchange Program permits a student on one UA system campus to enroll in a course on another UA system campus. Through the National Student Exchange (NSE) program qualified students have the opportunity to study for a semester or an academic year at other participating universities. Study abroad program. ROTC: Army, Air Force.
Entrance Requirements: Options: electronic application, early admission, international baccalaureate accepted. Required: high school transcript, minimum 3 high school GPA, SAT or ACT. Required for some: essay, 2 recommendations. Entrance: moderately difficult. Application deadlines: 5/1, 5/1 for nonresidents. Notification: continuous, continuous for nonresidents. SAT Reasoning Test deadline: 4/1. Transfer credits accepted: Yes.
Costs Per Year: Application fee: $40. State resident tuition: $9200 full-time. Nonresident tuition: $22,950 full-time. Full-time tuition varies according to course load. College room and board: $8650. College room only: $5600. Room and board charges vary according to board plan and housing facility.
Collegiate Environment: Orientation program. Drama-theater group, choral group, marching band, student-run newspaper, radio station. Social organizations: 423 open to all; national fraternities, national sororities, local fraternities, local sororities; 22% of eligible men and 33% of eligible women are members. Most popular organizations: SOURCE Board of Governors, Association of Residence Communities, International Student Association, Student Government Association, Black Student Union. Major annual events: Homecoming/Football, Get On Board / University Programs Events, Honors Week. Student services: legal services, health clinic, personal-psychological counseling, women's center. Campus security: 24-hour emergency response devices and patrols, late night transport-escort service, controlled dormitory access, 24-hour patrols by University of Alabama Police (UAPD), certified law enforcement personnel. 8,050 college housing spaces available; 7,696 were occupied in 2012-13. Freshmen guaranteed college housing. On-campus residence required in freshman year. Options: coed, men-only, women-only housing available. Amelia Gayle Gorgas Library plus 8 others with 4 million books, 4 million microform titles, 118,753 serials, 34,086 audiovisual materials, an OPAC, and a Web page. Operations spending for the previous fiscal year: $19.2 million. 1,500 computers available on campus for general student use. A campuswide network can be accessed from student residence rooms and from off campus. Students can access the following: online class registration. Staffed computer lab on campus provides training in use of computers and software.
Community Environment: Tuscaloosa, with a population of approximately 81,000, is the fifth largest city in Alabama. The city is located 50 miles southwest of Birmingham, 100 miles northwest of Montgomery, the state capital, and 220 miles east of Atlanta, GA. The community is served by major bus, rail, and air services. Modern shopping and service facilities are accessible in the immediate area.

■ **THE UNIVERSITY OF ALABAMA AT BIRMINGHAM**
1530 3rd Ave. S
Birmingham, AL 35294
Tel: (205)934-4011; Free: 800-421-8743
Fax: (205)975-7114
E-mail: undergradadmit@uab.edu
Web Site: www.uab.edu/
Description: State-supported, university, coed. Part of University of Alabama System. Awards bachelor's, master's, and doctoral degrees and post-master's certificates. Founded 1969. Setting: 323-acre urban campus with easy access to Birmingham. Total enrollment: 17,999. Faculty: 943 (858 full-time, 85 part-time). Student-undergrad faculty ratio is 18:1. 6,026 applied, 74% were admitted. 26% from top 10% of their high school class, 56% from top quarter, 80% from top half. 11 National Merit Scholars. Full-time: 8,295 students, 57% women, 43% men. Part-time: 2,996 students, 59% women, 41% men. Students come from 47 states and territories, 52 other countries, 7% from out-of-state. 0.3% American Indian or Alaska Native, non-Hispanic/Latino; 2% Hispanic/Latino; 27% African American, non-Hispanic/Latino; 5% Asian, non-Hispanic/Latino; 0.1% Native Hawaiian or other Pacific Islander, non-Hispanic/Latino; 2% international. 24% 25 or older, 21% live on campus, 11% transferred in. Retention: 80% of full-time freshmen returned the following year. Academic areas with the most degrees conferred: health professions and related sciences; business/marketing; psychology. Core. Calendar: semesters. Academic remediation for entering students, ESL program, services for LD students, advanced placement, accelerated degree program, self-designed majors, freshman honors college, honors program, independent study, distance learning, double major, summer session for credit, part-time degree program, adult/continuing education programs, co-op programs and internships, graduate courses open to undergrads. Off campus study at University of Alabama in Huntsville, University of Alabama, Birmingham Area Consortium for Higher Education. Study abroad program. ROTC: Army, Air Force (c).
Entrance Requirements: Options: electronic application, early admission, deferred admission, international baccalaureate accepted. Required: high school transcript, SAT or ACT. Entrance: moderately difficult. Application deadline: 5/1. Notification: continuous. SAT Reasoning Test deadline: 5/1. Transfer credits accepted: Yes.
Costs Per Year: Application fee: $30. State resident tuition: $8400 full-time, $267 per credit hour part-time. Nonresident tuition: $19,230 full-time, $628 per credit hour part-time. Full-time tuition varies according to program. Part-time tuition varies according to program. College room only: $5400. Room charges vary according to housing facility.
Collegiate Environment: Orientation program. Drama-theater group, choral group, marching band, student-run newspaper, radio station. Social organizations: 150 open to all; national fraternities, national sororities; 2% of eligible men and 3% of eligible women are members. Most popular organizations: campus ministries, service-oriented groups, sports-affiliated groups. Major annual events: Spring Fest, Homecoming, Talent Search. Student services: health clinic, personal-psychological counseling, women's center. Campus security: 24-hour emergency response devices and patrols, late night transport-escort service, controlled dormitory access. College housing designed to accommodate 2,150 students; 2,301 undergraduates lived in college housing during 2012-13. Freshmen given priority for college housing.

Option: coed housing available. Mervyn Sterne Library plus 1 other with 1.1 million books, 1.3 million microform titles, 36,371 serials, 28,620 audiovisual materials, an OPAC, and a Web page.

■ THE UNIVERSITY OF ALABAMA IN HUNTSVILLE
301 Sparkman Dr.
Huntsville, AL 35899
Tel: (256)824-1000; Free: 800-UAH-CALL
Fax: (256)824-6073
E-mail: admitme@email.uah.edu
Web Site: www.uah.edu/
Description: State-supported, university, coed. Part of University of Alabama System. Awards bachelor's, master's, and doctoral degrees and post-master's certificates. Founded 1950. Setting: 400-acre suburban campus. Endowment: $56.4 million. Research spending for the previous fiscal year: $72.2 million. Educational spending for the previous fiscal year: $9335 per student. Total enrollment: 7,629. Faculty: 486 (306 full-time, 180 part-time). Student-undergrad faculty ratio is 15:1. 1,952 applied, 64% were admitted. 29% from top 10% of their high school class, 50% from top quarter, 80% from top half. 14 National Merit Scholars, 12 valedictorians. Full-time: 4,461 students, 47% women, 53% men. Part-time: 1,474 students, 43% women, 57% men. Students come from 40 states and territories, 68 other countries, 10% from out-of-state. 2% American Indian or Alaska Native, non-Hispanic/Latino; 3% Hispanic/Latino; 14% African American, non-Hispanic/Latino; 4% Asian, non-Hispanic/Latino; 0.03% Native Hawaiian or other Pacific Islander, non-Hispanic/Latino; 3% international. 25% 25 or older, 20% live on campus, 13% transferred in. Retention: 79% of full-time freshmen returned the following year. Academic areas with the most degrees conferred: engineering; business/marketing; health professions and related sciences. Core. Calendar: semesters. Academic remediation for entering students, ESL program, services for LD students, advanced placement, self-designed majors, honors program, independent study, distance learning, double major, summer session for credit, part-time degree program, co-op programs and internships, graduate courses open to undergrads. Off campus study at Alabama Agricultural and Mechanical University, Oakwood College, Athens State College, John C. Calhoun State Community College. Study abroad program. ROTC: Army (c).
Entrance Requirements: Options: electronic application, deferred admission, international baccalaureate accepted. Required: high school transcript, SAT or ACT. Entrance: moderately difficult. Application deadlines: 8/22, 8/22 for nonresidents. Notification: continuous. SAT Reasoning Test deadline: 8/21. Transfer credits accepted: Yes.
Costs Per Year: Application fee: $30. State resident tuition: $8794 full-time, $339.26 per credit hour part-time. Nonresident tuition: $21,108 full-time, $814.89 per credit hour part-time. Full-time tuition varies according to course load. Part-time tuition varies according to course load. College room and board: $8070. College room only: $5480. Room and board charges vary according to board plan and housing facility.
Collegiate Environment: Orientation program. Drama-theater group, choral group, student-run newspaper. Social organizations: 118 open to all; national fraternities, national sororities; 6% of eligible men and 7% of eligible women are members. Most popular organizations: Black Student Association, Chinese Students and Scholars Association, Baptist Campus Ministry, Indian Student Organization, American Society of Civil Engineers. Major annual events: Froshmosh, FallFest, SpringFest. Student services: health clinic, personal-psychological counseling. Campus security: 24-hour emergency response devices and patrols, late night transport-escort service, controlled dormitory access, Sworn Police Department with state certified police officers; 24/7 dispatch center; community policing efforts. Louis Salmon Library with 302,503 books, 554,303 microform titles, 628 serials, 2,677 audiovisual materials, an OPAC, and a Web page. Operations spending for the previous fiscal year: $2.6 million. 1,227 computers available on campus for general student use. A campuswide network can be accessed from student residence rooms and from off campus. Students can access the following: online class registration. Staffed computer lab on campus provides training in use of computers, software, and the Internet.

■ UNIVERSITY OF MOBILE
5735 College Pky.
Mobile, AL 36613
Tel: (251)442-2773; Free: 800-946-7267
Fax: (251)442-2498
E-mail: cwittner@umobile.edu
Web Site: www.umobile.edu/

Description: Independent Southern Baptist, comprehensive, coed. Awards associate, bachelor's, and master's degrees. Founded 1961. Setting: 830-acre suburban campus. Endowment: $18.9 million. Educational spending for the previous fiscal year: $7029 per student. Total enrollment: 1,719. Faculty: 178 (88 full-time, 90 part-time). Student-undergrad faculty ratio is 12:1. 789 applied, 80% were admitted. 23% from top 10% of their high school class, 52% from top quarter, 80% from top half. Full-time: 1,274 students, 66% women, 34% men. Part-time: 278 students, 84% women, 16% men. Students come from 31 states and territories, 26 other countries, 18% from out-of-state. 2% American Indian or Alaska Native, non-Hispanic/Latino; 1% Hispanic/Latino; 24% African American, non-Hispanic/Latino; 1% Asian, non-Hispanic/Latino; 0.1% Native Hawaiian or other Pacific Islander, non-Hispanic/Latino; 2% international. 34% 25 or older, 38% live on campus, 11% transferred in. Retention: 73% of full-time freshmen returned the following year. Academic areas with the most degrees conferred: education; business/marketing; health professions and related sciences. Core. Calendar: semesters. Academic remediation for entering students, services for LD students, advanced placement, accelerated degree program, honors program, independent study, double major, summer session for credit, part-time degree program, adult/continuing education programs, internships, graduate courses open to undergrads. ROTC: Army (c), Air Force (c).
Entrance Requirements: Options: electronic application, deferred admission, international baccalaureate accepted. Required: high school transcript, minimum 2.75 high school GPA, SAT or ACT. Recommended: SAT and SAT Subject Tests or ACT, SAT Subject Tests. Required for some: interview. Entrance: moderately difficult. Application deadline: Rolling. Notification: continuous. SAT Reasoning Test deadline: 8/1. SAT Subject Test deadline: 8/1. Transfer credits accepted: Yes.
Costs Per Year: Application fee: $50. Comprehensive fee: $26,330 includes full-time tuition ($17,110), mandatory fees ($570), and college room and board ($8650). College room only: $5100. Full-time tuition and fees vary according to course load. Room and board charges vary according to housing facility. Part-time tuition: $609 per credit hour. Part-time mandatory fees: $346 per year. Part-time tuition and fees vary according to course load.
Collegiate Environment: Orientation program. Drama-theater group, choral group. Social organizations: 30 open to all. Most popular organizations: Campus Activity Board, Baptist Campus Ministry, Student Government Association, Fellowship of Christian Athletes. Major annual events: True Spin, Ram Rush, Christmas Spectacular. Student services: health clinic, personal-psychological counseling. Campus security: 24-hour emergency response devices and patrols, controlled dormitory access, text alerts. 655 college housing spaces available; 594 were occupied in 2012-13. Freshmen guaranteed college housing. On-campus residence required in freshman year. Options: men-only, women-only housing available. J. L. Bedsole Library with 211,625 books, 169,252 microform titles, 207 serials, 1,733 audiovisual materials, an OPAC, and a Web page. 120 computers available on campus for general student use. A campuswide network can be accessed from student residence rooms and from off campus. Students can access the following: online class registration. Staffed computer lab on campus.
Community Environment: See University of South Alabama.

■ UNIVERSITY OF MONTEVALLO
Station 6001
Montevallo, AL 35115
Tel: (205)665-6000; Free: 800-292-4349
E-mail: admissions@montevallo.edu
Web Site: www.montevallo.edu/
Description: State-supported, comprehensive, coed. Awards bachelor's and master's degrees and post-master's certificates. Founded 1896. Setting: 160-acre small town campus with easy access to Birmingham. Total enrollment: 3,085. Faculty: 223 (142 full-time, 81 part-time). Student-undergrad faculty ratio is 16:1. 1,385 applied, 87% were admitted. Full-time: 2,319 students, 65% women, 35% men. Part-time: 279 students, 63% women, 37% men. Students come from 20 other countries, 5% from out-of-state. 1% American Indian or Alaska Native, non-Hispanic/Latino; 3% Hispanic/Latino; 14% African American, non-Hispanic/Latino; 1% Asian, non-Hispanic/Latino; 0% Native Hawaiian or other Pacific Islander, non-Hispanic/Latino; 2% international. 13% 25 or older, 47% live on campus, 7% transferred in. Retention: 78% of full-time freshmen returned the following year. Academic areas with the most degrees conferred: visual and performing arts; business/marketing; education. Core. Calendar: semesters. Academic remediation for entering students, services for LD students, advanced placement, accelerated degree program, honors program, independent study, distance learn-

ing, double major, summer session for credit, part-time degree program, internships, graduate courses open to undergrads. Study abroad program. ROTC: Army (c), Air Force (c).

Entrance Requirements: Options: electronic application, early admission, deferred admission, international baccalaureate accepted. Required: high school transcript, minimum 2 high school GPA, SAT or ACT. Recommended: interview, ACT. Entrance: moderately difficult. Application deadline: 8/1. Notification: 9/1. Transfer credits accepted: Yes.

Costs Per Year: Application fee: $30. State resident tuition: $8790 full-time, $293 per credit hour part-time. Nonresident tuition: $17,580 full-time, $586 per credit hour part-time. Mandatory fees: $490 full-time. College room and board: $5522. Room and board charges vary according to housing facility.

Collegiate Environment: Orientation program. Drama-theater group, choral group, student-run newspaper. Social organizations: 97 open to all; national fraternities, national sororities; 23% of eligible men and 18% of eligible women are members. Most popular organizations: Student Government Association, University Programming Council, Campus Ministries, Greek Life, Environmental Club. Major annual events: College Night, Spring Fest, Back to School Bash. Student services: health clinic, personal-psychological counseling. Campus security: 24-hour emergency response devices and patrols, late night transport-escort service, controlled dormitory access. 1,253 college housing spaces available; 1,144 were occupied in 2012-13. Freshmen guaranteed college housing. On-campus residence required in freshman year. Options: coed, men-only, women-only housing available. Carmichael Library with 266,236 books, 800,000 microform titles, 27,962 serials, 4,693 audiovisual materials, an OPAC, and a Web page. 340 computers available on campus for general student use. A campuswide network can be accessed from student residence rooms and from off campus. Students can access the following: online class registration. Staffed computer lab on campus.

Community Environment: Montevallo (population 5,092) is near the center of the state, and is accessible by automobile. Montevallo is 32 miles south of Birmingham and 68 miles north of Montgomery, and has a mild year-round climate. There are a library, golf course, municipal park, and many churches in the city. Recreational activities include hunting, lake and stream fishing, boating and water skiing on nearby lakes. Students belonging to church denominations that are not represented in Montevallo hold services in the Religious Association Room of the Student Union Building.

■ **UNIVERSITY OF NORTH ALABAMA**
One Harrison Plz.
Florence, AL 35632-0001
Tel: (256)765-4100; Free: 800-TALK-UNA
Fax: (256)765-4329
E-mail: admissions@una.edu
Web Site: www.una.edu/

Description: State-supported, comprehensive, coed. Awards bachelor's and master's degrees and post-master's certificates. Founded 1830. Setting: 200-acre urban campus with easy access to Huntsville, AL. Endowment: $23.6 million. Research spending for the previous fiscal year: $201,679. Total enrollment: 7,016. Faculty: 331 (237 full-time, 94 part-time). Student-undergrad faculty ratio is 21:1. 2,419 applied, 88% were admitted. Full-time: 4,941 students, 57% women, 43% men. Part-time: 1,141 students, 60% women, 40% men. Students come from 38 states and territories, 34 other countries, 15% from out-of-state. 1% American Indian or Alaska Native, non-Hispanic/Latino; 2% Hispanic/Latino; 13% African American, non-Hispanic/Latino; 0.5% Asian, non-Hispanic/Latino; 0.1% Native Hawaiian or other Pacific Islander, non-Hispanic/Latino; 4% international. 17% 25 or older, 23% live on campus, 10% transferred in. Retention: 69% of full-time freshmen returned the following year. Academic areas with the most degrees conferred: business/marketing; health professions and related sciences; education. Core. Calendar: semesters. Academic remediation for entering students, ESL program, services for LD students, advanced placement, accelerated degree program, self-designed majors, freshman honors college, honors program, independent study, distance learning, double major, summer session for credit, part-time degree program, co-op programs and internships, graduate courses open to undergrads. Off campus study. Study abroad program. ROTC: Army.

Entrance Requirements: Options: electronic application, early admission, deferred admission. Required: high school transcript, SAT or ACT. Entrance: minimally difficult. Application deadlines: Rolling, Rolling for nonresidents. Transfer credits accepted: Yes.

Costs Per Year: Application fee: $25. State resident tuition: $6660 full-time, $222 per credit hour part-time. Nonresident tuition: $13,320 full-time, $444

per credit hour part-time. Mandatory fees: $1488 full-time. Full-time tuition and fees vary according to course load and program. Part-time tuition varies according to course load and program. College room and board: $5678. Room and board charges vary according to board plan and housing facility.

Collegiate Environment: Orientation program. Drama-theater group, choral group, marching band, student-run newspaper, radio station. Social organizations: national fraternities, national sororities; 5% of eligible men and 6% of eligible women are members. Most popular organizations: Student Government Association, University Program Council, Baptist campus ministries, Physical Education Majors Club, Residence Hall Association. Major annual events: Homecoming, Spring Fling, Step Sing. Student services: health clinic, personal-psychological counseling, women's center. Campus security: 24-hour emergency response devices and patrols, student patrols, late night transport-escort service, controlled dormitory access. 1,314 undergraduates lived in college housing during 2012-13. No special consideration for freshman housing applicants. Options: coed, men-only, women-only housing available. Collier Library plus 3 others with 670,168 books, 1.1 million microform titles, 24,421 serials, 14,996 audiovisual materials, an OPAC, and a Web page. Operations spending for the previous fiscal year: $178,882. 1,000 computers available on campus for general student use. A campuswide network can be accessed from student residence rooms. Students can access the following: online class registration. Staffed computer lab on campus provides training in use of computers, software, and the Internet.

Community Environment: Population 36,480. Florence is contiguous to the towns of Sheffield, Tuscumbia, and Muscle Shoals City; it is part of an urban center with a population of 142,000. Area lakes and camping sites attract vacationists and sportsmen from all over the nation. Florence is served by buses and airlines; has excellent public schools, churches, libraries, recreation facilities, cultural centers; several radio stations and a television station.

■ **UNIVERSITY OF PHOENIX–BIRMINGHAM CAMPUS**
One Corporate Ctr., Ste. 400
Birmingham, AL 35244
Free: 866-766-0766
Web Site: www.phoenix.edu/

Description: Proprietary, comprehensive, coed. Awards bachelor's, master's, and doctoral degrees.

■ **UNIVERSITY OF SOUTH ALABAMA**
307 University Blvd.
Mobile, AL 36688-0002
Tel: (251)460-6101; Free: 800-872-5247
Fax: (251)460-7025
E-mail: admiss@usouthal.edu
Web Site: www.southalabama.edu/

Description: State-supported, university, coed. Awards bachelor's, master's, and doctoral degrees and post-master's certificates. Founded 1963. Setting: 1,225-acre suburban campus. Endowment: $126.7 million. Research spending for the previous fiscal year: $27.2 million. Educational spending for the previous fiscal year: $10,493 per student. Total enrollment: 14,636. Faculty: 858 (529 full-time, 329 part-time). Student-undergrad faculty ratio is 21:1. 4,770 applied, 87% were admitted. Full-time: 8,708 students, 55% women, 45% men. Part-time: 2,607 students, 59% women, 41% men. Students come from 54 states and territories, 87 other countries, 18% from out-of-state. 1% American Indian or Alaska Native, non-Hispanic/Latino; 3% Hispanic/Latino; 22% African American, non-Hispanic/Latino; 3% Asian, non-Hispanic/Latino; 0.2% Native Hawaiian or other Pacific Islander, non-Hispanic/Latino; 4% international. 27% 25 or older, 25% live on campus, 9% transferred in. Retention: 66% of full-time freshmen returned the following year. Academic areas with the most degrees conferred: health professions and related sciences; business/marketing; education. Core. Calendar: semesters. Academic remediation for entering students, ESL program, services for LD students, advanced placement, accelerated degree program, freshman honors college, honors program, distance learning, double major, summer session for credit, part-time degree program, adult/continuing education programs, co-op programs, graduate courses open to undergrads. Study abroad program. ROTC: Army, Air Force.

Entrance Requirements: Options: electronic application, early admission. Required: high school transcript. Recommended: minimum 2 high school GPA. Required for some: 1 recommendation, SAT or ACT. Entrance: moderately difficult. Application deadlines: 7/15, 7/15 for nonresidents. Notification: continuous until 8/18, continuous until 8/18 for nonresidents. Preference given to state residents in certain Allied Health programs.

Costs Per Year: Application fee: $35. State resident tuition: $7950 full-time, $265 per hour part-time. Nonresident tuition: $15,900 full-time, $530 per hour part-time. Full-time tuition varies according to course load and program. Part-time tuition varies according to course load and program. College room and board: $7150. College room only: $3900. Room and board charges vary according to board plan and housing facility.

Collegiate Environment: Orientation program. Drama-theater group, choral group, marching band, student-run newspaper. Social organizations: 200 open to all; national fraternities, national sororities; 10% of eligible men and 10% of eligible women are members. Most popular organizations: Student Government Association, African American Student Association, Council of International Student Organizations, Alpha Epsilon Delta Pre-Health Professions, Panhellenic Council. Major annual events: Homecoming, Oozeball, Greek Week. Student services: legal services, health clinic, personal-psychological counseling. Campus security: 24-hour emergency response devices and patrols, late night transport-escort service. 3,098 college housing spaces available; 1,901 were occupied in 2012-13. No special consideration for freshman housing applicants. Option: coed housing available. University Library plus 3 others with 794,249 books, 937,931 microform titles, 980 serials, 11,346 audiovisual materials, an OPAC, and a Web page. 500 computers available on campus for general student use. A computer is required for all students. A campuswide network can be accessed from student residence rooms and from off campus. Students can access the following: online class registration. Staffed computer lab on campus provides training in use of computers, software, and the Internet.

Community Environment: Mobile, with a population 564,000 in the greater metropolitan area, has a temperate climate. In July and August the average high temperature is 91 degrees, and the average low temperature is 73. Airlines, buses and railroads serve the area. The city has libraries, churches of all major denominations, theaters, and museums. Excellent facilities for boating, fishing, and swimming are available. Mobile hosts the annual Senior Bowl, Alabama Deep Sea Fishing Rodeo, Azalea Trail Run, and the oldest Mardi Gras celebration in the country. Part-time work is available.

■ **THE UNIVERSITY OF WEST ALABAMA**
Livingston, AL 35470
Tel: (205)652-3400; Free: 800-621-8044
E-mail: dbuckalew@uwa.edu
Web Site: www.uwa.edu/
Description: State-supported, comprehensive, coed. Awards associate, bachelor's, and master's degrees and post-master's certificates. Founded 1835. Setting: 514-acre small town campus. Total enrollment: 4,943. Faculty: 268 (127 full-time, 141 part-time). Student-undergrad faculty ratio is 26:1. 467 applied, 97% were admitted. Full-time: 1,793 students, 58% women, 42% men. Part-time: 315 students, 69% women, 31% men. Students come from 37 states and territories, 18 other countries, 21% from out-of-state. 1% American Indian or Alaska Native, non-Hispanic/Latino; 1% Hispanic/Latino; 44% African American, non-Hispanic/Latino; 0.5% Asian, non-Hispanic/Latino; 0.3% Native Hawaiian or other Pacific Islander, non-Hispanic/Latino; 5% international. 21% 25 or older, 39% live on campus, 14% transferred in. Retention: 56% of full-time freshmen returned the following year. Academic areas with the most degrees conferred: education; business/marketing; biological/life sciences. Core. Calendar: semesters. Academic remediation for entering students, services for LD students, advanced placement, accelerated degree program, honors program, independent study, distance learning, double major, summer session for credit, part-time degree program, co-op programs and internships. Off campus study at Wallace State Community College, Auburn University, The University of Alabama, Mississippi State University, University of Alabama at Birmingham. ROTC: Army (c), Air Force (c).
Entrance Requirements: Options: electronic application, early admission, deferred admission. Required: high school transcript, minimum 2 high school GPA, SAT or ACT. Entrance: minimally difficult. Application deadline: Rolling. Notification: continuous. SAT Reasoning Test deadline: 8/12. SAT Subject Test deadline: 8/12. Transfer credits accepted: Yes.
Costs Per Year: Application fee: $35. State resident tuition: $6170 full-time, $263 per credit part-time. Nonresident tuition: $12,340 full-time, $526 per credit part-time. Mandatory fees: $1150 full-time. Full-time tuition and fees vary according to course load, degree level, and program. Part-time tuition varies according to course load, degree level, and program. College room and board: $5920. College room only: $3640. Room and board charges vary according to board plan and housing facility.
Collegiate Environment: Orientation program. Drama-theater group, choral group, marching band, student-run newspaper. Social organizations: 30

open to all; national fraternities, national sororities; 8% of eligible men and 11% of eligible women are members. Most popular organizations: The Student Government Association, The UWA Band, The UWA Choir, Fellowship of Christian Athletes (FCA), Livingston's Early Alumni Development (LEAD). Major annual events: Spring Fest, Homecoming, Serendipity Talent Show. Student services: health clinic, personal-psychological counseling. Campus security: 24-hour patrols, late night transport-escort service. 851 college housing spaces available; 790 were occupied in 2012-13. No special consideration for freshman housing applicants. On-campus residence required through sophomore year. Option: coed housing available. Julia Tutwiler Library with 167,500 books, 474,000 microform titles, 62,000 serials, 3,100 audiovisual materials, an OPAC, and a Web page. 400 computers available on campus for general student use. A campuswide network can be accessed from student residence rooms. Students can access the following: online class registration, Wireless intranet is available campuswide for all students. Staffed computer lab on campus.
Community Environment: Livingston (population 3,000) is the Sumter County Seat, and is located on Interstate 59/20 and Alabama Highway 28. It is 116 miles southwest of Birmingham, 130 miles west of Montgomery, and 37 miles east of Meridian, Mississippi. The climate is mild. Fishing and hunting are excellent.

■ **VIRGINIA COLLEGE IN BIRMINGHAM**
488 Palisades Blvd.
Birmingham, AL 35209
Tel: (205)802-1200
Fax: (205)802-1597
Web Site: www.vc.edu/
Description: Proprietary, comprehensive, coed. Awards associate, bachelor's, and master's degrees. Founded 1989. Setting: 1-acre urban campus. Total enrollment: 3,826. 1,512 applied. 71% 25 or older. Core.
Entrance Requirements: Required: high school transcript. Entrance: moderately difficult. Application deadline: Rolling. Notification: continuous.
Collegiate Environment: Orientation program. Student services: personal-psychological counseling. Elma Bell Library plus 2 others with 3,900 books, 120 serials, 40 audiovisual materials, and an OPAC.

■ **VIRGINIA COLLEGE IN HUNTSVILLE**
2021 Drake Ave. SW
Huntsville, AL 35801
Tel: (256)533-7387
Fax: (256)533-7785
Web Site: www.vc.edu/
Description: Proprietary, primarily 2-year, coed. Awards certificates, terminal associate, and bachelor's degrees. Founded 1989. Total enrollment: 731. 224 applied. 4% from out-of-state. 64% 25 or older. Retention: 34% of full-time freshmen returned the following year.
Entrance Requirements: Required: high school transcript. Entrance: minimally difficult. Application deadline: Rolling. Notification: continuous.

■ **WALLACE STATE COMMUNITY COLLEGE**
801 Main St.
Hanceville, AL 35077-2000
Tel: (256)352-8000; Free: 866-350-9722
Fax: (256)352-8228
Web Site: www.wallacestate.edu/
Description: State-supported, 2-year, coed. Awards diplomas, transfer associate, and terminal associate degrees. Founded 1966. Setting: 216-acre rural campus with easy access to Birmingham. Total enrollment: 6,311. Student-undergrad faculty ratio is 23:1. 2% from out-of-state. 35% 25 or older. Retention: 49% of full-time freshmen returned the following year. Calendar: semesters. Academic remediation for entering students, advanced placement, summer session for credit, part-time degree program, co-op programs.
Entrance Requirements: Open admission for technical, liberal arts programs. Options: early admission, deferred admission. Required: high school transcript. Entrance: noncompetitive. Application deadline: Rolling. Notification: continuous.
Collegiate Environment: Orientation program. Choral group. Student services: personal-psychological counseling. Wallace State College Library with an OPAC.
Community Environment: Hanceville is a rural community with a population of approximately 3,100, situated midway between Birmingham and

Decatur. It is located on state highway 31 with easy access to I-65, both of which connect Decatur and Birmingham.

■ ALASKA BIBLE COLLEGE

200 College Rd.
Glennallen, AK 99588-0289
Tel: (907)822-3201; Free: 800-478-7884
Fax: (907)822-5027
E-mail: npalmer@akbible.edu
Web Site: www.akbible.edu/
Description: Independent nondenominational, 4-year, coed. Awards associate and bachelor's degrees. Founded 1966. Setting: 97-acre rural campus. Endowment: $46,833. Educational spending for the previous fiscal year: $12,132 per student. Total enrollment: 34. Faculty: 11 (8 full-time, 3 part-time). Student-undergrad faculty ratio is 3:1. Full-time: 28 students, 36% women, 64% men. Part-time: 6 students, 83% women, 17% men. Students come from 14 states and territories, 57% from out-of-state. 15% American Indian or Alaska Native, non-Hispanic/Latino; 3% Hispanic/Latino; 3% African American, non-Hispanic/Latino. 15% 25 or older, 93% live on campus, 0% transferred in. Retention: 20% of full-time freshmen returned the following year. Academic area with the most degrees conferred: theology and religious vocations. Core. Calendar: semesters. Academic remediation for entering students, advanced placement, independent study, distance learning, double major, part-time degree program, internships. Off campus study.
Entrance Requirements: Open admission. Options: electronic application, deferred admission. Required: essay, high school transcript, minimum 2 high school GPA, interview, 3 reference forms, SAT or ACT. Entrance: minimally difficult. Application deadline: 7/1. Notification: continuous until 7/15. SAT Subject Test deadline: 8/15. Transfer credits accepted: Yes.
Costs Per Year: Application fee: $35. Comprehensive fee: $14,790 includes full-time tuition ($9000), mandatory fees ($390), and college room and board ($5400). Room and board charges vary according to housing facility. Part-time tuition: $375 per credit.
Collegiate Environment: Orientation program. Student-run radio station. Campus security: 24-hour emergency response devices. 32 college housing spaces available; 20 were occupied in 2012-13. Freshmen guaranteed college housing. On-campus residence required through sophomore year. Options: men-only, women-only housing available. Alaska Bible College Ball Memorial Library with an OPAC. Operations spending for the previous fiscal year: $11,250. 8 computers available on campus for general student use. A campuswide network can be accessed from student residence rooms and from off campus. Students can access the following: online class registration.
Community Environment: Glennallen is a rural community that has developed on the crossroads between Anchorage, Fairbanks, and Valdez. The original impetus for the community's growth was the construction of the Alcan Highway for communication during the war years. The climate of Glennallen area runs to extremes with the temperature falling to 50 degrees or more below zero for short periods in midwinter, and rising to 70 degrees or more above zero by the close of the school year in May. Sports such as hunting, fishing, hiking, rafting, and cross country skiing are common recreational activities.

■ ALASKA CAREER COLLEGE

1415 E Tudor Rd.
Anchorage, AK 99507
Tel: (907)563-7575
Web Site: www.alaskacareercollege.edu/

■ ALASKA PACIFIC UNIVERSITY

4101 University Dr.
Anchorage, AK 99508-4672
Tel: (907)561-1266; Free: 800-252-7528
Fax: (907)564-8317
E-mail: admissions@alaskapacific.edu
Web Site: www.alaskapacific.edu/
Description: Independent, comprehensive, coed. Awards associate, bachelor's, master's, and doctoral degrees. Founded 1959. Setting: 170-acre urban campus. Endowment: $42.7 million. Research spending for the previous fiscal year: $390,659. Educational spending for the previous fiscal year: $10,433 per student. Total enrollment: 693. Faculty: 115 (50 full-time, 65 part-time). Student-undergrad faculty ratio is 17:1. 180 applied, 62% were admitted. 10% from top 10% of their high school class, 25% from top quarter, 29% from top half. Full-time: 277 students, 61% women, 39% men. Part-time: 159 students, 71% women, 29% men. Students come from 15 states and territories, 31% from out-of-state. 12% American Indian or Alaska Native, non-Hispanic/Latino; 3% Hispanic/Latino; 2% African American, non-Hispanic/Latino; 2% Asian, non-Hispanic/Latino; 1% Native Hawaiian or other Pacific Islander, non-Hispanic/Latino; 0% international. 47% 25 or older, 26% live on campus, 6% transferred in. Retention: 65% of full-time freshmen returned the following year. Academic areas with the most degrees conferred: business/marketing; biological/life sciences; parks and recreation. Core. Calendar: semesters. Academic remediation for entering students, services for LD students, advanced placement, self-designed majors, independent study, distance learning, double major, summer session for credit, part-time degree program, adult/continuing education programs, internships, graduate courses open to undergrads. Study abroad program. ROTC: Army (c), Air Force (c).
Entrance Requirements: Options: electronic application, deferred admission, international baccalaureate accepted. Required: essay, high school transcript, minimum 2.5 high school GPA, 2 recommendations, SAT or ACT. Required for some: interview. Entrance: moderately difficult. Application deadline: 8/15. SAT Reasoning Test deadline: 8/15. SAT Subject Test deadline: 8/15. Transfer credits accepted: Yes.
Costs Per Year: Application fee: $25. Comprehensive fee: $39,180 includes full-time tuition ($29,700), mandatory fees ($180), and college room and board ($9300). College room only: $4400. Full-time tuition and fees vary according to course load, degree level, program, and reciprocity agreements. Room and board charges vary according to board plan and housing facility. Part-time tuition: $1240 per semester hour. Part-time tuition varies according to course load, degree level, and program.
Collegiate Environment: Orientation program. Drama-theater group, choral group, student-run newspaper. Social organizations: 13 open to all. Most popular organizations: ASAPU (Associated Students of Alaska Pacific University), Photography Club, Dive Club, basketball club, Spectrum Club. Major annual events: Octoberfest, Winter Ball, Spring Dance. Student services: personal-psychological counseling. Campus security: 24-hour emergency response devices, student patrols, late night transport-escort service, controlled dormitory access. 170 college housing spaces available; 110 were occupied in 2012-13. Freshmen guaranteed college housing. On-campus residence required in freshman year. Option: coed housing available. Consortium Library with 945,948 books, 632,420 microform titles, 5,877 serials, 17,932 audiovisual materials, an OPAC, and a Web page. Operations spending for the previous fiscal year: $95,000. 105 computers available on campus for general student use. A campuswide network can be

accessed from student residence rooms and from off campus. Students can access the following: online class registration. Staffed computer lab on campus provides training in use of computers, software, and the Internet.

Community Environment: Alaska Pacific University is located in Anchorage, a modern, dynamic city with half the population of Alaska. To the west is Cook Inlet, named for the famous English explorer, while mountains rise to the south, east, and north, creating a mild climate. The drive south leads to the ski resort at Alyeska, the glacier at Portage and the famous fishing of the Kenai. To the north lie the Alaska Range and Mount McKinley. Anchorage is a young city on the move. Anchorage's per capita income is twice the national average. Anchorage is lively. Dog teams race down Fourth Avenue during the winter Fur Rendezvous while opera, symphony, theater and a steady stream of rock stars, dance troupes, and artists provide cultural events for every taste. Winters are moderated by the warm Japanese current while summers are blessed with a sun that never sets. Daily intercontinental flights link Anchorage to Hawaii, Tokyo, Beijing, Moscow, Stockholm, London, and New York.

■ **CHARTER COLLEGE**
2221 E Northern Lights Blvd.
Ste. 120
Anchorage, AK 99508
Tel: (907)277-1000; Free: 888-200-9942
Fax: (907)274-3342
Web Site: www.chartercollege.edu/

Description: Proprietary, primarily 2-year, coed. Awards certificates, transfer associate, terminal associate, and bachelor's degrees. Founded 1985. Setting: urban campus. Total enrollment: 516. Faculty: 43 (10 full-time, 33 part-time). Student-undergrad faculty ratio is 15:1. 69% 25 or older. Summer session for credit, part-time degree program, adult/continuing education programs, internships.

Entrance Requirements: Open admission. Required: high school transcript, interview. Entrance: noncompetitive. Application deadline: Rolling. Notification: continuous.

Collegiate Environment: Orientation program. Campus security: 24-hour emergency response devices. Charter College Library with 1,000 books, 50 serials, and a Web page.

■ **ILISAGVIK COLLEGE**
UIC/Narl
Barrow, AK 99723
Tel: (907)852-3333
Fax: (907)852-2729
E-mail: janelle.everett@ilisagvik.edu
Web Site: www.ilisagvik.edu/

Description: State-supported, 2-year, coed. Awards certificates, diplomas, and transfer associate degrees. Founded 1995. Setting: rural campus. Total enrollment: 288. Student-undergrad faculty ratio is 6:1. Full-time: 39 students, 56% women, 44% men. Part-time: 249 students, 69% women, 31% men. Students come from 3 states and territories, 3 other countries. Core. Calendar: semesters. Academic remediation for entering students, ESL program, services for LD students, independent study, distance learning, double major, summer session for credit, part-time degree program, co-op programs and internships. Off campus study.

Entrance Requirements: Required: high school transcript, minimum 2 high school GPA, ACT ASSET. Required for some: copy of Alaska Native Shareholder/Native American Tribal Affiliation card if native. Transfer credits accepted: Yes.

Collegiate Environment: Orientation program. Campus security: 24-hour emergency response devices and patrols, controlled dormitory access. Tuzzy Consortium Library with an OPAC and a Web page.

■ **UNIVERSITY OF ALASKA ANCHORAGE**
3211 Providence Dr.
Anchorage, AK 99508
Tel: (907)786-1800
Fax: (907)786-4888
E-mail: enroll@uaa.alaska.edu
Web Site: www.uaa.alaska.edu/

Description: State-supported, comprehensive, coed. Part of University of Alaska System. Awards associate, bachelor's, master's, and doctoral degrees and post-master's certificates. Founded 1954. Setting: 428-acre urban campus. Total enrollment: 18,107. Faculty: 1,390 (680 full-time, 710 part-time). Student-undergrad faculty ratio is 12:1. 3,924 applied, 76% were

admitted. 13% from top 10% of their high school class, 32% from top quarter, 62% from top half. Full-time: 7,936 students, 54% women, 46% men. Part-time: 9,193 students, 62% women, 38% men. 10% from out-of-state. 12% American Indian or Alaska Native, non-Hispanic/Latino; 7% Hispanic/Latino; 4% African American, non-Hispanic/Latino; 7% Asian, non-Hispanic/Latino; 1% Native Hawaiian or other Pacific Islander, non-Hispanic/Latino; 1% international. 50% 25 or older, 4% transferred in. Retention: 73% of full-time freshmen returned the following year. Academic areas with the most degrees conferred: business/marketing; health professions and related sciences; psychology. Core. Calendar: semesters. Academic remediation for entering students, ESL program, services for LD students, advanced placement, self-designed majors, honors program, independent study, distance learning, double major, summer session for credit, part-time degree program, adult/continuing education programs, co-op programs and internships, graduate courses open to undergrads. Off campus study at members of the National Student Exchange, Western Interstate Commission for Higher Education, Western Undergraduate Exchange. Study abroad program. ROTC: Army, Air Force.

Entrance Requirements: Open admission selective admission to some programs. Options: electronic application, deferred admission. Required: minimum 2 high school GPA, SAT or ACT, Completion of either SAT, ACT or a UAA approved test required. Required for some: high school transcript. Entrance: noncompetitive. Application deadline: 6/15. Notification: continuous.

Costs Per Year: Application fee: $50. State resident tuition: $4950 full-time. Nonresident tuition: $17,400 full-time. Full-time tuition varies according to course level and location. College room and board: $9780. College room only: $5980. Room and board charges vary according to board plan and housing facility.

Collegiate Environment: Orientation program. Drama-theater group, choral group, student-run newspaper, radio station. Social organizations: national fraternities, national sororities. Most popular organizations: Accounting Club, African-American Students Association, Association of Latin-American Spanish Students, Inter-Varsity Christian Fellowship, Student Nurses Association. Major annual events: UAA orientation programs, Great Alaska Shootout Basketball Tournament. Student services: health clinic, personal-psychological counseling, women's center. Campus security: 24-hour emergency response devices and patrols, student patrols, late night transport-escort service, controlled dormitory access. Option: coed housing available.

Community Environment: Anchorage, population 275,000, is a friendly, modern progressive city and the largest in Alaska. Summertime temperatures range between 60 and 70 degrees. The winters are less severe in Anchorage than in many U.S. cities. Anchorage is the major stopover point for most international transpolar flights. Living costs are higher than in the continental U.S., with an average living cost (plus tuition) of approximately $11,000 to $14,000 per year. The city bustles with growth and activity; cultural interests are wide range and include a symphony orchestra, museums, a theater group and a dance company. Recreation facilities include theaters, golf courses, bowling alleys, swimming pools, public beaches, skating rinks, ball parks, and several excellent ski areas. Hunting and fishing are easily accessible. There are several hospitals within the city which is near Ft. Richardson Army Post and Elmendorf AFB.

■ **UNIVERSITY OF ALASKA ANCHORAGE, KENAI PENINSULA COLLEGE**
156 College Rd.
Soldotna, AK 99669-9798
Tel: (907)262-0300; Free: 877-262-0330
Fax: (907)262-0322
Web Site: www.kpc.alaska.edu/

Description: State-supported, primarily 2-year, coed. Part of University of Alaska System. Awards certificates, transfer associate, terminal associate, and bachelor's degrees. Founded 1964. Setting: 360-acre rural campus. Total enrollment: 2,733. Core. Calendar: semesters. Academic remediation for entering students, ESL program, services for LD students, advanced placement, distance learning, part-time degree program, adult/continuing education programs, co-op programs.

Entrance Requirements: Open admission. Option: electronic application. Required: high school transcript, ACT, SAT or ACCUPLACER scores. Entrance: noncompetitive. Application deadline: Rolling.

Collegiate Environment: Orientation program. Student services: health clinic. Campus security: 24-hour emergency response devices. 96 college housing spaces available. Option: coed housing available.

Community Environment: Soldotna, population 4,000, is located on the coast and enjoys a cool climate during the spring and summer months. Public transportation in and out of Kenai is mainly by air and highway with some bus service available. The city has a library, museum, many churches, and a full-service hospital. Recreation includes hunting, fishing, boating, water sports, and clam digging. Annual Kenai days around the middle of July is a traditional event. Part-time employment is available.

■ **UNIVERSITY OF ALASKA ANCHORAGE, KODIAK COLLEGE**
117 Benny Benson Dr.
Kodiak, AK 99615-6643
Tel: (907)486-4161; Free: 800-486-7660
Fax: (907)486-1257
E-mail: jmyrick@kodiak.alaska.edu
Web Site: www.koc.alaska.edu/
Description: State-supported, 2-year, coed. Part of University of Alaska System. Awards certificates, transfer associate, and terminal associate degrees. Founded 1968. Setting: 68-acre rural campus. Total enrollment: 479. Faculty: 41 (11 full-time, 30 part-time). Student-undergrad faculty ratio is 13:1. 56 applied, 77% were admitted. Students come from 18 states and territories, 3 other countries. 12% American Indian or Alaska Native, non-Hispanic/Latino; 8% Hispanic/Latino; 2% African American, non-Hispanic/Latino; 6% Asian, non-Hispanic/Latino; 1% Native Hawaiian or other Pacific Islander, non-Hispanic/Latino; 2% international. Retention: 0% of full-time freshmen returned the following year. Core. Calendar: semesters. Academic remediation for entering students, advanced placement, distance learning, double major, summer session for credit, part-time degree program, adult/continuing education programs. Study abroad program.
Entrance Requirements: Open admission. Option: electronic application. Required: ACCUPLACER. Required for some: high school transcript. Entrance: noncompetitive. Application deadlines: Rolling, Rolling for nonresidents. Transfer credits accepted: Yes.
Costs Per Year: Application fee: $40. State resident tuition: $4320 full-time, $144 per credit part-time. Nonresident tuition: $13,450 full-time, $580 per credit part-time. Mandatory fees: $340 full-time, $8 per credit part-time, $5 per term part-time.
Collegiate Environment: Orientation program. Social organizations: 2 open to all. Most popular organizations: PHI THETA KAPPA, student government. Carolyn Floyd Library with 21,000 books, 30 microform titles, 39 serials, 2,400 audiovisual materials, an OPAC, and a Web page. 40 computers available on campus for general student use. Computer purchase/lease plans available. A campuswide network can be accessed. Students can access the following: online class registration. Staffed computer lab on campus provides training in use of computers, software, and the Internet.
Community Environment: Population 6,200. Kodiak, located in the Gulf of Alaska on Kodiak Island, was once a Russian settlement. It has always looked to the sea for its livelihood and in 1968 became the largest fishing port in dollar volume in the United States. Transportation to Kodiak is an interesting trip by automobile. The Alaska Marine Highway ferry, Tustumena, serves Kodiak regularly. There is direct flight service from Anchorage. The city of Kodiak is the largest town in the Kodiak Island group and is the oldest permanent settlement in Alaska. The city is situated on the northeastern corner of Kodiak Island nestled at the foot of the 1,400 foot Pillar Mountain, overlooking the island-studded harbor of St. Paul. This northerly section of the City of Kodiak was rebuilt following the Good Friday earthquake and tidal wave of 1964. The average temperature in January is 30 degrees and in August, 55 degrees. The annual rainfall is 60 inches spread throughout the year. A number of churches, and service organizations are found in the city.

■ **UNIVERSITY OF ALASKA ANCHORAGE, MATANUSKA-SUSITNA COLLEGE**
PO Box 2889
Palmer, AK 99645-2889
Tel: (907)745-9774
Fax: (907)745-9747
E-mail: info@matsu.alaska.edu
Web Site: www.matsu.alaska.edu/
Description: State-supported, 2-year, coed. Part of University of Alaska System. Awards certificates, transfer associate, and terminal associate degrees. Founded 1958. Setting: 950-acre small town campus with easy access to Anchorage. Total enrollment: 1,782. Faculty: 116 (26 full-time, 90 part-time). Student-undergrad faculty ratio is 16:1. 45% 25 or older. Retention: 55% of full-time freshmen returned the following year. Core. Calendar: semesters. Academic remediation for entering students, advanced place-

ment, independent study, distance learning, double major, summer session for credit, part-time degree program, adult/continuing education programs, co-op programs and internships. Off campus study at Alaska Pacific University, University of Alaska Anchorage.
Entrance Requirements: Open admission. Option: electronic application. Required: high school transcript. Entrance: noncompetitive. Application deadline: 9/15. Notification: 9/30. Transfer credits accepted: Yes.
Collegiate Environment: Orientation program. Choral group, student-run newspaper. Most popular organizations: student government, Math Club, Phi Theta Kappa, Basketball, Students for Christ. Major annual events: Fall BBQ and resource fair, Spring BBQ. Campus security: 24-hour patrols. Al Okeson Library with 50,000 books, 292 microform titles, 280 serials, 1,840 audiovisual materials, an OPAC, and a Web page. 207 computers available on campus for general student use. A campuswide network can be accessed. Students can access the following: online class registration. Staffed computer lab on campus provides training in use of computers.
Community Environment: Population 6,920, Palmer is a rural town with subarctic climate. A branch of the Alaska Railroad and bus service to Anchorage serve this area. There are churches, a library, museum, hospital, and a health center in the town. Recreational activities include fishing, boating, ice skating and some swimming. There are good shopping facilities available. Palmer has the usual civic organizations found in most U.S. cities. The Alaska State Fair is the fourth weekend of August through Labor Day weekend each year.

■ **UNIVERSITY OF ALASKA FAIRBANKS**
PO Box 757500
Fairbanks, AK 99775-7520
Tel: (907)474-7211; Free: 800-478-1823
Fax: (907)474-5379
E-mail: admissions@uaf.edu
Web Site: www.uaf.edu/
Description: State-supported, university, coed. Part of University of Alaska System. Awards associate, bachelor's, master's, and doctoral degrees. Founded 1917. Setting: 2,250-acre small town campus. Endowment: $74.1 million. Research spending for the previous fiscal year: $128.2 million. Educational spending for the previous fiscal year: $14,866 per student. Total enrollment: 9,314. Faculty: 1,060 (344 full-time, 716 part-time). Student-undergrad faculty ratio is 11:1. 1,541 applied, 75% were admitted. 14% from top 10% of their high school class, 34% from top quarter, 61% from top half. Full-time: 3,727 students, 51% women, 49% men. Part-time: 4,404 students, 64% women, 36% men. Students come from 49 states and territories, 49 other countries, 12% from out-of-state. 14% American Indian or Alaska Native, non-Hispanic/Latino; 5% Hispanic/Latino; 3% African American, non-Hispanic/Latino; 1% Asian, non-Hispanic/Latino; 0.2% Native Hawaiian or other Pacific Islander, non-Hispanic/Latino; 1% international. 38% 25 or older, 24% live on campus, 6% transferred in. Retention: 74% of full-time freshmen returned the following year. Academic areas with the most degrees conferred: engineering; business/marketing; psychology. Core. Calendar: semesters. Academic remediation for entering students, ESL program, services for LD students, advanced placement, accelerated degree program, self-designed majors, honors program, independent study, distance learning, double major, summer session for credit, part-time degree program, external degree program, co-op programs and internships, graduate courses open to undergrads. Off campus study at National Student Exchange. Study abroad program. ROTC: Army.
Entrance Requirements: Open admission Students who do not meet the minimum requirements for acceptance into a baccalaureate program can be admitted with pre-major status. Options: electronic application, deferred admission, international baccalaureate accepted. Required: high school transcript, minimum 2.5 high school GPA, SAT or ACT. Entrance: minimally difficult. Application deadlines: 7/1, 7/1 for nonresidents. Notification: continuous, continuous for nonresidents. SAT Reasoning Test deadline: 8/1. Transfer credits accepted: Yes.
Costs Per Year: Application fee: $50. State resident tuition: $5580 full-time, $168 per credit part-time. Nonresident tuition: $18,270 full-time, $591 per credit part-time. Full-time tuition varies according to course level, course load, location, and reciprocity agreements. Part-time tuition varies according to course level, course load, location, and reciprocity agreements. College room and board: $7200. College room only: $3680. Room and board charges vary according to board plan and housing facility.
Collegiate Environment: Orientation program. Drama-theater group, choral group, student-run newspaper, radio station. Social organizations: 87 open to all; national fraternities, national sororities; 1% of eligible men and 1% of

eligible women are members. Most popular organizations: Alpha Phi Omega, Festival of Native Arts, Socratic Society, Parkour and Free Running Club, Gay-Straight Alliance. Major annual events: Starvation Gulch, Melt Down, Winter Carnival. Student services: legal services, health clinic, personal-psychological counseling, women's center. Campus security: 24-hour emergency response devices and patrols, student patrols, late night transport-escort service, controlled dormitory access, ID check at door of residence halls, crime prevention and safety workshops. 1,578 college housing spaces available; 1,535 were occupied in 2012-13. Freshmen given priority for college housing. Option: coed housing available. Rasmuson Library plus 2 others with 966,394 books, 133,755 microform titles, 55,685 serials, 95,528 audiovisual materials, an OPAC, and a Web page. Operations spending for the previous fiscal year: $9.5 million. 125 computers available on campus for general student use. A campuswide network can be accessed from student residence rooms and from off campus. Students can access the following: online class registration, university portal, campus wireless access. Staffed computer lab on campus provides training in use of computers, software, and the Internet.

Community Environment: The campus overlooks the Tanana Valley and the city of Fairbanks. Offering the amenities of larger communities, Fairbanks maintains the atmosphere of smaller, more personal towns. One hundred miles south is Denali National Park, home to North America's tallest mountain—Mt. McKinley. Closer lay the vast wilderness that makes up the Great Interior of Alaska. Adventure is unlimited here—hiking, biking, climbing, canoeing, skiing, dog mushing, and other recreational activities abound. Winters are cold, with an annual snowfall of 70 inches. Summers bring temperatures in the 80s and 24 hours of daylight, perfect weather for the activities Alaska has to offer.

■ UNIVERSITY OF ALASKA, PRINCE WILLIAM SOUND COMMUNITY COLLEGE

PO Box 97
Valdez, AK 99686-0097
Tel: (907)834-1600; Free: 800-478-8800
Fax: (907)834-1627
E-mail: studentservices@pwscc.edu
Web Site: www.pwscc.edu/

Description: State-supported, 2-year, coed. Part of University of Alaska System. Administratively affiliated with University of Alaska Anchorage. Awards certificates, diplomas, transfer associate, and terminal associate degrees. Founded 1978. Setting: small town campus. Endowment: $62,630. Research spending for the previous fiscal year: $5000. Educational spending for the previous fiscal year: $283 per student. Total enrollment: 527. Faculty: 53 (7 full-time, 46 part-time). Student-undergrad faculty ratio is 8:1. 107 applied, 89% were admitted. Full-time: 69 students, 46% women, 54% men. Part-time: 458 students, 68% women, 32% men. Students come from 1 other country, 4% from out-of-state. 5% American Indian or Alaska Native, non-Hispanic/Latino; 4% Hispanic/Latino; 0% African American, non-Hispanic/Latino; 3% Asian, non-Hispanic/Latino; 0% Native Hawaiian or other Pacific Islander, non-Hispanic/Latino; 1% international. 76% 25 or older, 2% live on campus. Core. Calendar: semesters. Academic remediation for entering students, ESL program, advanced placement, independent study, distance learning, double major, summer session for credit, adult/continuing education programs, co-op programs and internships.

Entrance Requirements: Open admission. Options: electronic application, early admission. Required: high school transcript. Recommended: SAT or ACT, ACCUPLACER. Entrance: noncompetitive. Application deadlines: Rolling, Rolling for nonresidents. Transfer credits accepted: Yes.

Costs Per Year: Application fee: $25. Area resident tuition: $3480 full-time, $145 per credit part-time. State resident tuition: $3480 full-time, $145 per credit part-time. Nonresident tuition: $3480 full-time, $145 per credit part-time. Mandatory fees: $300 full-time, $32 per credit part-time. Full-time tuition and fees vary according to course load, location, and program. Part-time tuition and fees vary according to course load, location, and program. College room only: $4230. Room charges vary according to housing facility.

Collegiate Environment: Drama-theater group. Social organizations: 4 open to all. Most popular organizations: student government, Phi Theta Kappa Honor Society, Theatre, Archery Team and/or Club. Major annual events: Student Government Sponsored Halloween Dance, Leadership Retreat, New School-Year Glacier and Wildlife Cruise. Student services: personal-psychological counseling. Campus security: student patrols, controlled dormitory access, housing manager supervision. 40 college housing spaces available; 20 were occupied in 2012-13. No special consideration for freshman housing applicants. Option: coed housing available. Valdez

Consortium Library with 40,870 books, 137 serials, an OPAC, and a Web page. Operations spending for the previous fiscal year: $40,000. 30 computers available on campus for general student use. A campuswide network can be accessed from student residence rooms. Students can access the following: online class registration. Staffed computer lab on campus provides training in use of computers, software, and the Internet.

■ UNIVERSITY OF ALASKA SOUTHEAST

11120 Glacier Hwy.
Juneau, AK 99801
Tel: (907)796-6457; Free: 877-465-4827
Fax: (907)796-6365
E-mail: admissions@uas.alaska.edu
Web Site: www.uas.alaska.edu/

Description: State-supported, comprehensive, coed. Part of University of Alaska System. Awards associate, bachelor's, and master's degrees and post-master's certificates. Founded 1972. Setting: 198-acre small town campus. Research spending for the previous fiscal year: $1.1 million. Educational spending for the previous fiscal year: $11,035 per student. Total enrollment: 3,458. Faculty: 229 (102 full-time, 127 part-time). Student-undergrad faculty ratio is 9:1. 655 applied. 8% from top 10% of their high school class, 28% from top quarter, 52% from top half. Full-time: 860 students, 57% women, 43% men. Part-time: 2,213 students, 68% women, 32% men. Students come from 42 states and territories, 7 other countries, 11% from out-of-state. 46% 25 or older, 17% live on campus, 8% transferred in. Retention: 61% of full-time freshmen returned the following year. Academic areas with the most degrees conferred: business/marketing; liberal arts/general studies; social sciences. Core. Calendar: semesters. Academic remediation for entering students, services for LD students, advanced placement, self-designed majors, independent study, distance learning, double major, summer session for credit, part-time degree program, adult/continuing education programs, co-op programs and internships, graduate courses open to undergrads. Off campus study at National Student Exchange. Study abroad program.

Entrance Requirements: Open admission. Options: electronic application, deferred admission. Required: high school transcript, minimum 2 high school GPA. Recommended: SAT or ACT. Required for some: essay. Entrance: noncompetitive. Application deadlines: 9/9, 9/9 for nonresidents. Notification: continuous, continuous for nonresidents. Transfer credits accepted: Yes.

Collegiate Environment: Orientation program. Student-run newspaper, radio station. Most popular organizations: Wooch.een, Native Student Club, Sustainability Club, Alpha Phi Omega, The Beatniks, UAS Improv Club. Major annual events: Orientation Week, Banff Mountain Film Festival, Bonfire. Student services: health clinic, personal-psychological counseling. Campus security: 24-hour emergency response devices and patrols, late night transport-escort service, controlled dormitory access. Egan Memorial Library with an OPAC and a Web page. Operations spending for the previous fiscal year: $1.9 million.

Community Environment: Situated on the shores of scenic Auke Lake, with the famous Mendenhall Glacier in clear sight, the main campus is only a few miles from the heart of downtown Juneau, the capital of Alaska. Nestled between 4,000-foot snow-capped peaks on one side and the sparkling water of Gastineau Channel on the other, Juneau was the first Alaskan city founded after the American purchase of Alaska in 1867. The city is centrally located in the Tongass National Forest, the nation's largest. The combined city and borough encompass 3,108 square miles of land, ranging from tundra, to moss-draped forests, to wind-blown mountain peaks. Juneau's population is approximately 30,900 and provides numerous cultural, academic, and professional opportunities.

■ UNIVERSITY OF ALASKA SOUTHEAST, KETCHIKAN CAMPUS

2600 7th Ave.
Ketchikan, AK 99901-5798
Tel: (907)225-6177
Fax: (907)225-3624
E-mail: ketch.info@uas.alaska.edu
Web Site: www.ketch.alaska.edu/

Description: State and locally supported, 2-year, coed. Part of University of Alaska System. Awards transfer associate and terminal associate degrees. Founded 1954. Setting: 51-acre small town campus. Calendar: semesters. Part-time degree program, adult/continuing education programs. Off campus study at University of Alaska Southeast, Sheldon Jackson College.

Entrance Requirements: Required: high school transcript. Required for some: essay. Entrance: noncompetitive. Application deadline: Rolling.

Collegiate Environment: Orientation program. Campus security: 24-hour emergency response devices. Ketchikan Campus Library with an OPAC.
Community Environment: Population 7,400. Located on the Revillagigedo Island 600 miles northwest of Seattle; climate is very wet - 13 feet of rain per year. Airlines and water transportation serves the area. Extensive access to the Tongass National Forest and intercoastal waterways.

■ **UNIVERSITY OF ALASKA SOUTHEAST, SITKA CAMPUS**
1332 Seward Ave.
Sitka, AK 99835-9418
Tel: (907)747-6653; Free: 800-478-6653
Fax: (907)747-7747
E-mail: cynthia.rogers@uas.alaska.edu
Web Site: www.uas.alaska.edu/
Description: State-supported, 2-year, coed. Part of University of Alaska System. Awards certificates, diplomas, transfer associate, and terminal associate degrees. Founded 1962. Setting: small town campus. Total enrollment: 1,552. Faculty: 105. Student-undergrad faculty ratio is 13:1. Students come from 10 states and territories, 2 other countries. 65% 25 or older. Core. Calendar: semesters. Academic remediation for entering students, ESL program, summer session for credit, part-time degree program, adult/ continuing education programs, co-op programs and internships. Off campus study at Sheldon Jackson College, University of Alaska Southeast.
Entrance Requirements: Open admission. Option: early admission.

Required: high school transcript, minimum 2.0 high school GPA. Required for some: essay. Entrance: noncompetitive. Application deadline: Rolling. Notification: continuous.
Collegiate Environment: Social organizations: 2 open to all. Most popular organizations: Student Government Association, Tai Chi Club. Major annual events: campus-wide picnic, Christmas tree lighting, bi-annual stress fair. Campus security: 24-hour emergency response devices. Stratton Library with 80,050 books, 306 serials, an OPAC, and a Web page. 45 computers available on campus for general student use. A campuswide network can be accessed from student residence rooms and from off campus. Staffed computer lab on campus.
Community Environment: Population 8,980. Sitka is the original capital of Russian-America and was the site of the transfer of Alaska from Russia to the United States in 1867. Many historic sites and museums convey these historic origins, as well as the strong Northwest Coast Native heritage of the region. The rainy climate is mild and comparable to that of Seattle or Portland. Located on Baranof Island, adjacent to the mainland coast of the Southeast Alaskan panhandle, Sitka is surrounded by the heavily forested mountains of the Tongass National Forest. It is served by daily jet service, as well as small regional air carriers. The Alaska Marine Highway System provides weekly passenger and vehicle transportation from the southern terminal of Bellingham, Washington, and the northern terminal of Haines, Alaska. A regional center for health services, business, and education, Sitka has two hospitals, several small but important museums, two colleges, and a State-operated boarding high school.

■ **ACACIA UNIVERSITY**
7665 S Research Dr.
Tempe, AZ 85284
Tel: (480)428-6034
Web Site: www.acacia.edu/
Description: Private, 2-year, coed.

■ **AMERICAN INDIAN COLLEGE OF THE ASSEMBLIES OF GOD, INC.**
10020 N Fifteenth Ave.
Phoenix, AZ 85021-2199
Tel: (602)944-3335
E-mail: sgonzales@aicag.edu
Web Site: www.aicag.edu/
Description: Independent, 4-year, coed, affiliated with Assemblies of God. Awards associate and bachelor's degrees. Founded 1957. Setting: 10-acre urban campus. Total enrollment: 68. 26 applied. 28% 25 or older. Core. Calendar: semesters. Academic remediation for entering students, independent study, distance learning, double major, internships.
Entrance Requirements: Required: essay, high school transcript, 1 recommendation, SAT or ACT. Entrance: minimally difficult. Application deadline: 8/15. Preference given to members of Assemblies of God and other evangelical churches.
Costs Per Year: Application fee: $0. Comprehensive fee: $22,242 includes full-time tuition ($11,700), mandatory fees ($4340), and college room and board ($6202). College room only: $3510. Full-time tuition and fees vary according to course load. Room and board charges vary according to housing facility. Part-time tuition: $390 per credit hour. Part-time tuition varies according to course load.
Collegiate Environment: Orientation program. Drama-theater group. Student services: personal-psychological counseling. Campus security: student patrols. Cummings Memorial Library with 19,899 books, 120 serials, and an OPAC.

■ **ANTHEM COLLEGE–PHOENIX**
1515 E Indian School Rd.
Phoenix, AZ 85014-4901
Tel: (602)279-9700; Free: 855-331-7767
Fax: (602)279-2999
Web Site: anthem.edu/phoenix-arizona/
Description: Proprietary, primarily 2-year, coed. Awards diplomas, terminal associate, and bachelor's degrees. Founded 1982. Setting: 4-acre urban campus. Total enrollment: 5,742. 70% 25 or older. Calendar: semesters.
Entrance Requirements: Open admission. Required: high school transcript. Entrance: noncompetitive. Application deadline: Rolling.

■ **ARGOSY UNIVERSITY, PHOENIX**
2233 W Dunlap Ave.
Phoenix, AZ 85021
Tel: (602)216-2600; Free: 866-216-2777
Fax: (602)216-2601
Web Site: www.argosy.edu/phoenix/
Description: Proprietary, university, coed. Awards bachelor's, master's, and doctoral degrees. Founded 1997. Setting: urban campus. Calendar: semesters.

■ **ARIZONA AUTOMOTIVE INSTITUTE**
6829 N 46th Ave.
Glendale, AZ 85301-3597
Tel: (602)934-7273; Free: 800-321-5961
Fax: (602)937-5000
E-mail: info@azautoinst.com
Web Site: www.aai.edu/
Description: Proprietary, 2-year, coed. Awards diplomas and terminal associate degrees. Total enrollment: 582. 71% 25 or older.
Entrance Requirements: Open admission. Required: high school transcript. Application deadline: Rolling.

■ **ARIZONA CHRISTIAN UNIVERSITY**
2625 E Cactus Rd.
Phoenix, AZ 85032-7042
Tel: (602)992-6101; Free: 800-247-2697
E-mail: brant.nyhart@arizonachristian.edu
Web Site: arizonachristian.edu/
Description: Independent Conservative Baptist, 4-year, coed. Awards associate and bachelor's degrees. Founded 1960. Setting: 19-acre urban campus with easy access to Phoenix. Total enrollment: 683. 310 applied, 71% were admitted. Full-time: 509 students, 47% women, 53% men. Part-time: 174 students, 49% women, 51% men. Students come from 31 states and territories, 5 other countries, 17% from out-of-state. 1% American Indian or Alaska Native, non-Hispanic/Latino; 6% Hispanic/Latino; 5% African American, non-Hispanic/Latino; 1% Asian, non-Hispanic/Latino; 1% Native Hawaiian or other Pacific Islander, non-Hispanic/Latino; 1% international. 15% 25 or older, 17% transferred in. Retention: 68% of full-time freshmen returned the following year. Academic areas with the most degrees conferred: theology and religious vocations; psychology; business/marketing. Core. Calendar: 4-4-1. Academic remediation for entering students, services for LD students, advanced placement, independent study, double major, summer session for credit, adult/continuing education programs, co-op programs and internships. Study abroad program. ROTC: Air Force (c).
Entrance Requirements: Options: electronic application, deferred admission. Required: essay, high school transcript, minimum 2 high school GPA, 1 recommendation, SAT or ACT. Required for some: interview. Entrance: minimally difficult. Application deadline: 8/1. Notification: continuous. Transfer credits accepted: Yes.
Collegiate Environment: Orientation program. Drama-theater group, choral group, student-run newspaper. Most popular organization: Student Leadership Council. Major annual events: Homecoming, Welcome Week. Student services: personal-psychological counseling. Campus security: student patrols, controlled dormitory access. Freshmen guaranteed college housing. Options: men-only, women-only housing available. R. S. Beal Library with 29,948 books, 20,446 microform titles, 808 serials, 2,866 audiovisual materials, and an OPAC. 44 computers available on campus for general student use. A campuswide network can be accessed from student residence rooms.

■ **ARIZONA COLLEGE**
4425 W Olive Ave.
Ste. 300
Glendale, AZ 85302-3843
Tel: (602)222-9300

Fax: (602)200-8726

E-mail: lhicks@arizonacollege.edu

Web Site: www.arizonacollege.edu/

Description: Proprietary, 2-year, coed. Awards terminal associate degrees. Founded 1992. Total enrollment: 740. Student-undergrad faculty ratio is 16:1. 0% from out-of-state. 62% 25 or older.

Entrance Requirements: Required: interview. Entrance: noncompetitive.

■ **ARIZONA STATE UNIVERSITY**

Tempe, AZ 85287

Tel: (480)965-9011

Fax: (482)965-1608

E-mail: admissions@asu.edu

Web Site: www.asu.edu/

Description: State-supported, university, coed. Part of Arizona State University System. Awards bachelor's, master's, and doctoral degrees and post-master's certificates (profile includes data for the West, Polytechnic and Downtown Phoenix campuses). Founded 1885. Setting: 1,952-acre urban campus with easy access to Phoenix. Total enrollment: 73,378. Faculty: 2,762 (2,546 full-time, 216 part-time). Student-undergrad faculty ratio is 23:1. 30,696 applied, 88% were admitted. 30% from top 10% of their high school class, 59% from top quarter, 86% from top half. 97 National Merit Scholars. Full-time: 49,945 students, 50% women, 50% men. Part-time: 9,437 students, 52% women, 48% men. Students come from 54 states and territories, 93 other countries, 25% from out-of-state. 2% American Indian or Alaska Native, non-Hispanic/Latino; 19% Hispanic/Latino; 5% African American, non-Hispanic/Latino; 6% Asian, non-Hispanic/Latino; 0.3% Native Hawaiian or other Pacific Islander, non-Hispanic/Latino; 4% international. 23% 25 or older, 20% live on campus, 12% transferred in. Retention: 80% of full-time freshmen returned the following year. Academic areas with the most degrees conferred: business/marketing; social sciences; education. Core. Calendar: semesters. ESL program, services for LD students, advanced placement, accelerated degree program, self-designed majors, freshman honors college, honors program, independent study, distance learning, double major, summer session for credit, part-time degree program, adult/continuing education programs, co-op programs and internships, graduate courses open to undergrads. Off campus study. Study abroad program. ROTC: Army, Naval, Air Force.

Entrance Requirements: Options: electronic application, international baccalaureate accepted. Required: high school transcript, minimum 3 high school GPA. Recommended: SAT or ACT. Required for some: application fee is $65 for nonresidents, SAT or ACT, SAT and SAT Subject Tests or ACT. Entrance: moderately difficult. Application deadline: Rolling. Notification: continuous. Transfer credits accepted: Yes.

Costs Per Year: Application fee: $50. State resident tuition: $9208 full-time, $658 per credit hour part-time. Nonresident tuition: $22,461 full-time, $936 per credit hour part-time. Mandatory fees: $516 full-time, $154 per term part-time. Full-time tuition and fees vary according to program. Part-time tuition and fees vary according to program. College room and board: $9094. College room only: $5998. Room and board charges vary according to board plan, housing facility, and location.

Collegiate Environment: Orientation program. Drama-theater group, choral group, marching band, student-run newspaper, radio station. Social organizations: 850 open to all; national fraternities, national sororities, local fraternities; 6% of eligible men and 7% of eligible women are members. Most popular organizations: Interfraternity Council, Panhellenic Council, Undergraduate Student Government, Business School Council, Residence Hall Association. Major annual events: Welcome Week/Passport to ASU/Fall Welcome Concert, Homecoming, MLK Day of Service. Student services: legal services, health clinic, personal-psychological counseling. Campus security: 24-hour emergency response devices and patrols, late night transport-escort service. 11,214 college housing spaces available. Freshmen given priority for college housing. On-campus residence required in freshman year. Option: coed housing available. Hayden Library plus 8 others with 4.5 million books, 7.7 million microform titles, 53,524 serials, 110,955 audiovisual materials, an OPAC, and a Web page. Operations spending for the previous fiscal year: $24.3 million. 4,500 computers available on campus for general student use. Computer purchase/lease plans available. A campuswide network can be accessed from student residence rooms and from off campus. Students can access the following: online class registration, My Apps offers enrolled students, faculty and staff access to software applications for use online, in the classroom, by download, or for purchase. My Apps is free of charge and is accessible from any computer using your

ASURITE UserID and password. Staffed computer lab on campus (open 24 hours a day) provides training in use of computers, software, and the Internet.

■ **ARIZONA WESTERN COLLEGE**

PO Box 929

Yuma, AZ 85366-0929

Tel: (928)317-6000; Free: 888-293-0392

Fax: (928)344-7730

E-mail: amy.pignatore@azwestern.edu

Web Site: www.azwestern.edu/

Description: State and locally supported, 2-year, coed. Part of Arizona State Community College System. Awards certificates, transfer associate, and terminal associate degrees. Founded 1962. Setting: 640-acre rural campus. Total enrollment: 7,854. Faculty: 444 (114 full-time, 330 part-time). Student-undergrad faculty ratio is 20:1. Full-time: 2,725 students, 54% women, 46% men. Part-time: 5,129 students, 59% women, 41% men. Students come from 37 states and territories, 31 other countries, 3% from out-of-state. 1% American Indian or Alaska Native, non-Hispanic/Latino; 63% Hispanic/Latino; 3% African American, non-Hispanic/Latino; 1% Asian, non-Hispanic/Latino; 0.3% Native Hawaiian or other Pacific Islander, non-Hispanic/Latino; 8% international. 27% 25 or older, 3% live on campus. Core. Calendar: semesters. Academic remediation for entering students, ESL program, services for LD students, advanced placement, honors program, independent study, distance learning, summer session for credit, part-time degree program, adult/continuing education programs, co-op programs.

Entrance Requirements: Open admission except for the nursing program, massage therapy program, and radiologic technology program. Options: electronic application, early admission, deferred admission, international baccalaureate accepted. Required for some: SAT or ACT. Entrance: noncompetitive. Application deadlines: Rolling, Rolling for nonresidents. Transfer credits accepted: Yes.

Costs Per Year: Application fee: $0. State resident tuition: $1776 full-time, $74 per credit hour part-time. Nonresident tuition: $7224 full-time, $301 per credit hour part-time. Full-time tuition varies according to course load and program. Part-time tuition varies according to course load and program. College room and board: $5828. College room only: $2152. Room and board charges vary according to board plan.

Collegiate Environment: Orientation program. Drama-theater group, choral group, student-run newspaper, radio station. Social organizations: 15 open to all; national fraternities, national sororities. Most popular organizations: Student Government Association, Spirit Squad, Dance Team, Students in Free Enterprise (SIFE), International Students Team. Major annual events: Job Fair, Transfer Fair, Family Night. Student services: health clinic, personal-psychological counseling. Campus security: 24-hour emergency response devices and patrols, student patrols, late night transport-escort service. 335 college housing spaces available. Option: coed housing available. Arizona Western College Library with 109,016 books, 47,941 microform titles, 290 serials, 5,109 audiovisual materials, an OPAC, and a Web page. 500 computers available on campus for general student use. A campuswide network can be accessed from student residence rooms and from off campus. Students can access the following: online class registration. Staffed computer lab on campus provides training in use of computers, software, and the Internet.

Community Environment: Yuma, population 84,700, is on the bank of the Colorado River, midway between Phoenix and San Diego. This is a metropolitan area with a warm, dry climate. Rail, air, and all other modes of transportation are available. There are over 50 churches of major denominations, a public library, historic Yuma Territorial Prison and Museum, Yuma Fine Arts Association, Community Concert Association, the St. Thomas Mission, and many civic, fraternal, and veteran's organizations. Recreational activities include boating, fishing, water skiing, and hunting. The Silver Spur Rodeo is in February; the County Fair is in April. Part-time employment is available.

■ **THE ART INSTITUTE OF PHOENIX**

2233 W Dunlap Ave.

Phoenix, AZ 85021-2859

Tel: (602)331-7500; Free: 800-474-2479

Fax: (602)331-5301

Web Site: www.artinstitutes.edu/phoenix/

Description: Proprietary, 4-year, coed. Part of Education Management Corporation. Awards associate and bachelor's degrees. Founded 1995. Setting: suburban campus.

■ **THE ART INSTITUTE OF TUCSON**
5099 E Grant Rd.
Ste. 100
Tucson, AZ 85712
Tel: (520)881-2900; Free: 866-690-8850
Fax: (520)881-4234
Web Site: www.artinstitutes.edu/tucson/
Description: Proprietary, 4-year, coed. Awards associate and bachelor's degrees. Founded 2007.

■ **BROOKLINE COLLEGE (PHOENIX)**
2445 W Dunlap Ave., Ste. 100
Phoenix, AZ 85021
Tel: (602)242-6265; Free: 800-793-2428
Fax: (602)973-2572
E-mail: tdean@brooklinecollege.edu
Web Site: brooklinecollege.edu/
Description: Proprietary, 4-year, coed. Awards associate and bachelor's degrees. Founded 1979. Setting: urban campus with easy access to Phoenix. Total enrollment: 1,072. Faculty: 43 (22 full-time, 21 part-time). Student-undergrad faculty ratio is 25:1. 66% 25 or older. Academic area with the most degrees conferred: business/marketing. Core. Calendar: continuous. Accelerated degree program, distance learning, part-time degree program.
Entrance Requirements: Open admission. Option: electronic application. Required: interview. Entrance: noncompetitive. Application deadlines: Rolling, Rolling for nonresidents. Notification: continuous, continuous for nonresidents. Transfer credits accepted: Yes.
Collegiate Environment: Orientation program. Major annual events: job fairs, holiday-themed student gatherings. Campus security: 24-hour emergency response devices. Learning Resource Center with an OPAC and a Web page. 25 computers available on campus for general student use. A campuswide network can be accessed from off-campus. Staffed computer lab on campus provides training in use of computers, software, and the Internet.

■ **BROOKLINE COLLEGE (TEMPE)**
1140-1150 S Priest Dr.
Tempe, AZ 85281
Tel: (480)545-8755; Free: 888-886-2428
Fax: (480)926-1371
E-mail: ckindred@brooklinecollege.edu
Web Site: brooklinecollege.edu/
Description: Proprietary, 4-year, coed. Awards associate and bachelor's degrees. Founded 1982. Setting: urban campus with easy access to Phoenix. Total enrollment: 415. Faculty: 37 (15 full-time, 22 part-time). Student-undergrad faculty ratio is 11:1. 62% 25 or older. Core. Calendar: continuous. Accelerated degree program, part-time degree program.
Entrance Requirements: Open admission. Option: electronic application. Required: interview. Entrance: noncompetitive. Application deadlines: Rolling, Rolling for nonresidents. Notification: continuous, continuous for nonresidents. Transfer credits accepted: Yes.
Collegiate Environment: Orientation program. Campus security: 24-hour emergency response devices. Learning Resource Center with an OPAC and a Web page. 20 computers available on campus for general student use. A campuswide network can be accessed from off-campus. Staffed computer lab on campus provides training in use of computers, software, and the Internet.

■ **BROOKLINE COLLEGE (TUCSON)**
5441 E 22nd St.
Ste. 125
Tucson, AZ 85711
Tel: (520)748-9799; Free: 888-292-2428
Fax: (520)748-9355
E-mail: lpechota@brooklinecollege.edu
Web Site: brooklinecollege.edu/
Description: Proprietary, 4-year, coed. Awards associate and bachelor's degrees. Founded 1979. Setting: urban campus with easy access to Tucson. Total enrollment: 645. Faculty: 41 (23 full-time, 18 part-time). Student-undergrad faculty ratio is 16:1. 48% 25 or older. Core. Calendar: continuous. Accelerated degree program, part-time degree program.
Entrance Requirements: Open admission. Option: electronic application. Required: interview. Entrance: noncompetitive. Application deadlines: Roll-

ing, Rolling for nonresidents. Notification: continuous, continuous for nonresidents. Transfer credits accepted: Yes.
Collegiate Environment: Orientation program. Campus security: 24-hour emergency response devices. Learning Resource Center with an OPAC and a Web page. 25 computers available on campus for general student use. A campuswide network can be accessed from off-campus. Staffed computer lab on campus provides training in use of computers, software, and the Internet.

■ **BROWN MACKIE COLLEGE–PHOENIX**
13430 N Black Canyon Hwy.
Ste. 190
Phoenix, AZ 85029
Tel: (602)337-3044; Free: 866-824-4793
Web Site: www.brownmackie.edu/phoenix/
Description: Proprietary, primarily 2-year, coed. Part of Education Management Corporation. Awards diplomas, terminal associate, and bachelor's degrees.

■ **BROWN MACKIE COLLEGE–TUCSON**
4585 E Speedway, Ste. 204
Tucson, AZ 85712
Tel: (520)319-3300
Fax: (520)325-0108
Web Site: www.brownmackie.edu/tucson/
Description: Proprietary, primarily 2-year, coed. Part of Education Management Corporation. Awards diplomas, transfer associate, terminal associate, and bachelor's degrees. Founded 1972. Setting: suburban campus.

■ **THE BRYMAN SCHOOL OF ARIZONA**
2250 W Peoria Ave.
Phoenix, AZ 85029
Tel: (602)274-4300; Free: 866-391-6383
Fax: (602)248-9087
Web Site: www.brymanschool.edu/
Description: Proprietary, 2-year, coed. Awards diplomas and terminal associate degrees. Founded 1964. Setting: urban campus. Total enrollment: 744. Faculty: 59 (all full-time). Student-undergrad faculty ratio is 18:1. 3% from out-of-state. 38% 25 or older. Core. Calendar: continuous.
Entrance Requirements: Open admission. Required: high school transcript, interview. Entrance: minimally difficult. Application deadline: Rolling.
Collegiate Environment: Campus security: late night transport-escort service.

■ **CARRINGTON COLLEGE–MESA**
1001 W Southern Ave.
Ste. 130
Mesa, AZ 85210
Tel: (480)586-2787
Web Site: carrington.edu/
Description: Proprietary, 2-year, coed. Part of Carrington Colleges Group, Inc. Awards certificates and terminal associate degrees. Founded 1977. Setting: suburban campus. Total enrollment: 685. Faculty: 45 (19 full-time, 26 part-time). Student-undergrad faculty ratio is 25:1. Full-time: 685 students, 81% women, 19% men. 11% American Indian or Alaska Native, non-Hispanic/Latino; 24% Hispanic/Latino; 7% African American, non-Hispanic/Latino; 1% Asian, non-Hispanic/Latino; 1% Native Hawaiian or other Pacific Islander, non-Hispanic/Latino; 0% international. 46% 25 or older. Calendar: semesters.
Entrance Requirements: Required: essay, high school transcript, interview, Entrance test administered by Carrington College. Entrance: noncompetitive.
Collegiate Environment: College housing not available.

■ **CARRINGTON COLLEGE–PHOENIX**
8503 N 27th Ave.
Phoenix, AZ 85051
Tel: (602)393-5900
Web Site: carrington.edu/
Description: Proprietary, 2-year, coed. Part of Carrington Colleges Group, Inc. Awards certificates and terminal associate degrees. Founded 1976. Setting: urban campus. Total enrollment: 560. Faculty: 27 (16 full-time, 11 part-time). Student-undergrad faculty ratio is 28:1. Full-time: 560 students, 85% women, 15% men. 9% American Indian or Alaska Native, non-Hispanic/

Latino; 47% Hispanic/Latino; 5% African American, non-Hispanic/Latino; 1% Asian, non-Hispanic/Latino; 1% Native Hawaiian or other Pacific Islander, non-Hispanic/Latino; 0% international. 30% 25 or older. Academic area with the most degrees conferred: health professions and related sciences. Calendar: continuous.

Entrance Requirements: Required: essay, high school transcript, interview, Entrance test administered by Carrington College. Entrance: noncompetitive.

Collegiate Environment: College housing not available.

■ **CARRINGTON COLLEGE–PHOENIX WESTSIDE**
2701 W Bethany Home Rd.
Phoenix, AZ 85017
Tel: (602)433-1333
Web Site: carrington.edu/
Description: Proprietary, 2-year, coed. Part of Carrington Colleges Group, Inc. Awards certificates and terminal associate degrees. Setting: urban campus. Total enrollment: 542. Faculty: 40 (16 full-time, 24 part-time). Student-undergrad faculty ratio is 23:1. Full-time: 542 students, 63% women, 37% men. 4% American Indian or Alaska Native, non-Hispanic/Latino; 28% Hispanic/Latino; 8% African American, non-Hispanic/Latino; 3% Asian, non-Hispanic/Latino; 0.4% Native Hawaiian or other Pacific Islander, non-Hispanic/Latino; 0% international. 64% 25 or older. Calendar: semesters.
Entrance Requirements: Open admission. Required: essay, high school transcript, interview, Entrance test administered by Carrington College. Entrance: noncompetitive. Application deadline: Rolling. Notification: continuous.
Collegiate Environment: College housing not available.

■ **CARRINGTON COLLEGE–TUCSON**
3550 N Oracle Rd.
Tucson, AZ 85705
Tel: (520)888-5885
Web Site: carrington.edu/
Description: Proprietary, 2-year, coed. Part of Carrington Colleges Group, Inc. Awards certificates and terminal associate degrees. Founded 1984. Setting: suburban campus. Total enrollment: 399. Faculty: 16 (9 full-time, 7 part-time). Student-undergrad faculty ratio is 35:1. Full-time: 399 students, 79% women, 21% men. 5% American Indian or Alaska Native, non-Hispanic/Latino; 57% Hispanic/Latino; 3% African American, non-Hispanic/Latino; 1% Asian, non-Hispanic/Latino; 0% Native Hawaiian or other Pacific Islander, non-Hispanic/Latino; 0% international. 43% 25 or older. Calendar: semesters modular courses are offered.
Entrance Requirements: Required: essay, high school transcript, interview, Entrance test administered by Carrington College. Entrance: noncompetitive.
Collegiate Environment: Student services: legal services, personal-psychological counseling. College housing not available. 35 computers available on campus for general student use. A campuswide network can be accessed. Staffed computer lab on campus provides training in use of computers, software, and the Internet.

■ **CENTRAL ARIZONA COLLEGE**
8470 N Overfield Rd.
Coolidge, AZ 85128
Tel: (520)494-5444; Free: 800-237-9814
Fax: (520)426-4234
E-mail: james.moore@centralaz.edu
Web Site: www.centralaz.edu/
Description: Public, 2-year, coed. Awards certificates, transfer associate, and terminal associate degrees. Founded 1961. Setting: 850-acre rural campus with easy access to Phoenix. Total enrollment: 7,913. Faculty: 210 (94 full-time, 116 part-time). Student-undergrad faculty ratio is 14:1. Full-time: 2,976 students, 63% women, 37% men. Part-time: 4,937 students, 59% women, 41% men. Students come from 4 other countries. 13% 25 or older, 17% live on campus. Core. Calendar: semesters. Academic remediation for entering students, services for LD students, self-designed majors, honors program, independent study, distance learning, summer session for credit, part-time degree program, adult/continuing education programs, internships. Study abroad program.
Entrance Requirements: Open admission except for nursing program. Options: electronic application, early admission, deferred admission. Entrance: noncompetitive. Application deadline: Rolling. Notification: continuous. Transfer credits accepted: Yes.

Collegiate Environment: Orientation program. Drama-theater group, choral group, student-run newspaper. Major annual events: Track and Field Events, Basketball Games, Baseball Games. Student services: personal-psychological counseling. Campus security: 24-hour emergency response devices and patrols, late night transport-escort service. Learning Resource Center with 77,709 books, 104,000 microform titles, 16,306 serials, 4,784 audiovisual materials, an OPAC, and a Web page. 1,500 computers available on campus for general student use. A campuswide network can be accessed from student residence rooms. Students can access the following: online class registration. Staffed computer lab on campus provides training in use of computers, software, and the Internet.

Community Environment: Population 8,000. Coolidge is located in Pinal County near the intersection of two major interstate freeways that serve the areas of Southern California and Arizona's two principal cities, Phoenix and Tucson. One can be in the heart of either city within an hour. There are four Native American Reservations in the county. The area is rich in history of mining, cattle and agriculture. Few places on earth have more hours of sunshine a year than south-central Pinal County, which averages approximately 4,000 hours per year according to U.S. Weather Bureau records.

■ **CHAMBERLAIN COLLEGE OF NURSING**
2149 W Dunlap Ave.
Phoenix, AZ 85021
Tel: (602)331-2720; Free: 888-556-8CCN
Web Site: www.chamberlain.edu/
Description: Proprietary, 4-year, coed. Awards bachelor's degrees. Total enrollment: 531. Faculty: 60 (11 full-time, 49 part-time). Student-undergrad faculty ratio is 14:1. Full-time: 296 students, 86% women, 14% men. Part-time: 235 students, 86% women, 14% men. 8% from out-of-state. 1% American Indian or Alaska Native, non-Hispanic/Latino; 11% Hispanic/Latino; 6% African American, non-Hispanic/Latino; 6% Asian, non-Hispanic/Latino; 1% Native Hawaiian or other Pacific Islander, non-Hispanic/Latino; 0.2% international. 60% 25 or older, 0% live on campus, 39% transferred in. Academic area with the most degrees conferred: health professions and related sciences. Calendar: semesters.
Entrance Requirements: Required: SAT or ACT.
Costs Per Year: Tuition: $16,360 full-time, $665 per credit hour part-time. Mandatory fees: $600 full-time. Full-time tuition and fees vary according to course load and program. Part-time tuition varies according to course load and program.

■ **CHANDLER-GILBERT COMMUNITY COLLEGE**
2626 E Pecos Rd.
Chandler, AZ 85225-2479
Tel: (480)732-7000
E-mail: ryan.cain@cgcmail.maricopa.edu
Web Site: www.cgc.maricopa.edu/
Description: State and locally supported, 2-year, coed. Part of Maricopa County Community College District System. Awards certificates, diplomas, transfer associate, and terminal associate degrees. Founded 1985. Setting: 80-acre suburban campus with easy access to Phoenix. Total enrollment: 14,030. Faculty: 645 (129 full-time, 516 part-time). Student-undergrad faculty ratio is 25:1. Full-time: 4,424 students, 48% women, 52% men. Part-time: 9,606 students, 55% women, 45% men. Students come from 38 states and territories, 37 other countries, 2% from out-of-state. 1% American Indian or Alaska Native, non-Hispanic/Latino; 19% Hispanic/Latino; 4% African American, non-Hispanic/Latino; 5% Asian, non-Hispanic/Latino; 0.3% Native Hawaiian or other Pacific Islander, non-Hispanic/Latino; 1% international. 25% 25 or older, 4% transferred in. Retention: 61% of full-time freshmen returned the following year. Core. Calendar: semesters. Academic remediation for entering students, ESL program, services for LD students, advanced placement, freshman honors college, honors program, independent study, summer session for credit, part-time degree program. Study abroad program.
Entrance Requirements: Open admission except for nursing and aviation programs. Option: electronic application. Entrance: noncompetitive.
Costs Per Year: Application fee: $0. Area resident tuition: $1824 full-time, $76 per credit hour part-time. State resident tuition: $7200 full-time, $300 per credit hour part-time. Nonresident tuition: $7608 full-time, $317 per credit hour part-time. Mandatory fees: $30 full-time, $15 per term part-time. Full-time tuition and fees vary according to reciprocity agreements. Part-time tuition and fees vary according to reciprocity agreements.
Collegiate Environment: Orientation program. Choral group, student-run

newspaper, radio station. Student services: personal-psychological counseling. Campus security: 24-hour emergency response devices and patrols, late night transport-escort service. Chandler-Gilbert Community College Library with an OPAC.

■ **COCHISE COLLEGE**
901 N Colombo Ave.
Sierra Vista, AZ 85635-2317
Tel: (520)515-0500; Free: 800-593-9567
Fax: (520)364-0206
E-mail: quickd@cochise.edu
Web Site: www.cochise.edu/
Description: State and locally supported, 2-year, coed. Awards certificates, transfer associate, and terminal associate degrees. Founded 1977. Setting: 518-acre small town campus with easy access to Tucson. Educational spending for the previous fiscal year: $1790 per student. Total enrollment: 4,516. Faculty: 349 (86 full-time, 263 part-time). 1,758 applied, 100% were admitted. Full-time: 1,507 students, 53% women, 47% men. Part-time: 3,009 students, 55% women, 45% men. Students come from 40 states and territories, 2 other countries, 9% from out-of-state. 1% American Indian or Alaska Native, non-Hispanic/Latino; 43% Hispanic/Latino; 6% African American, non-Hispanic/Latino; 2% Asian, non-Hispanic/Latino; 1% Native Hawaiian or other Pacific Islander, non-Hispanic/Latino; 0.2% international. 46% 25 or older, 3% live on campus, 20% transferred in. Retention: 55% of full-time freshmen returned the following year. Core. Calendar: semesters. Academic remediation for entering students, ESL program, services for LD students, advanced placement, honors program, independent study, distance learning, summer session for credit, part-time degree program, adult/continuing education programs, co-op programs and internships.
Entrance Requirements: Open admission Admission to nursing program requires regular college admission, nursing program application and satisfactory score on HESI entrance exam. Aviation students must be TSA approved and have Airman Medical Exam. class two or three to start training. Options: electronic application, deferred admission, international baccalaureate accepted. Recommended: high school transcript. Entrance: noncompetitive. Application deadlines: Rolling, Rolling. for nonresidents. Notification: continuous, continuous for nonresidents. Transfer credits accepted: Yes.
Costs Per Year: State resident tuition: $2190 full-time, $73 per credit hour part-time. Nonresident tuition: $7500 full-time, $250 per credit hour part-time. Full-time tuition varies according to course load, program, and reciprocity agreements. Part-time tuition varies according to course load, program, and reciprocity agreements. College room and board: $6160. Room and board charges vary according to housing facility.
Collegiate Environment: Orientation program. Drama-theater group, choral group, student-run newspaper. Social organizations: 27 open to all. Most popular organizations: Student Nurses, Phi Theta Kappa, Strong Oak. Major annual events: Haunted Union, Back to School BBQ, Springfest. Student services: personal-psychological counseling. Campus security: 24-hour emergency response devices and patrols. 184 college housing spaces available. No special consideration for freshman housing applicants. Option: coed housing available. Charles DiPeso and Andrea Cracchiolo Libraries with 101,262 books, 6,041 microform titles, 6,364 serials, 3,508 audiovisual materials, an OPAC, and a Web page. Operations spending for the previous fiscal year: $771,382. 700 computers available on campus for general student use. A campuswide network can be accessed from student residence rooms and from off campus. Students can access the following: online class registration. Staffed computer lab on campus provides training in use of computers, software, and the Internet.

■ **COCONINO COMMUNITY COLLEGE**
2800 S Lonetree Rd.
Flagstaff, AZ 86001
Tel: (928)527-1222; Free: 800-350-7122
Fax: (928)526-1821
E-mail: veronica.hipolito@coconino.edu
Web Site: www.coconino.edu/
Description: State-supported, 2-year, coed. Awards certificates, transfer associate, and terminal associate degrees. Founded 1991. Setting: 5-acre small town campus. Endowment: $264,023. Educational spending for the previous fiscal year: $3838 per student. Total enrollment: 3,751. Faculty: 271 (41 full-time, 230 part-time). Student-undergrad faculty ratio is 14:1. Full-time: 840 students, 56% women, 44% men. Part-time: 2,911 students, 58% women, 42% men. Students come from 10 states and territories, 3% from

out-of-state. 41% 25 or older, 9% transferred in. Core. Calendar: semesters. Academic remediation for entering students, honors program, independent study, distance learning, summer session for credit, part-time degree program, adult/continuing education programs, internships. Study abroad program. ROTC: Army, Air Force.
Entrance Requirements: Open admission. Option: electronic application. Entrance: noncompetitive. Application deadline: Rolling. Notification: continuous.
Costs Per Year: Application fee: $0. State resident tuition: $2550 full-time, $85 per credit hour part-time. Nonresident tuition: $8925 full-time, $297.50 per credit hour part-time. Mandatory fees: $150 full-time.
Collegiate Environment: Orientation program. Social organizations: 10 open to all. Most popular organizations: Art Club, Clay Club, Dance Club, Native American Club, Video Gaming Club. Major annual events: Registration Celebration, student, staff, and visiting artists exhibits, Student cultural, music and dance performances. Campus security: 24-hour emergency response devices, student patrols, late night transport-escort service, security patrols while campuses are open; electronic access throughout the campuses with security cards. Information Resources and Library Services with 5,905 books, 3,515 serials, 2,358 audiovisual materials, an OPAC, and a Web page. Operations spending for the previous fiscal year: $197,435. 100 computers available on campus for general student use. A campuswide network can be accessed. Students can access the following: online class registration. Staffed computer lab on campus.

■ **COLLEGEAMERICA–FLAGSTAFF**
3012 E Rte. 66
Flagstaff, AZ 86004
Tel: (928)526-0763; Free: 800-622-2894
Fax: (928)526-3468
Web Site: www.collegeamerica.edu/
Description: Private, primarily 2-year, coed. Awards terminal associate and bachelor's degrees. Total enrollment: 200. 0% from out-of-state. 0% 25 or older. Retention: 0% of full-time freshmen returned the following year.
Entrance Requirements: Open admission. Entrance: noncompetitive.

■ **DEVRY UNIVERSITY (MESA)**
1201 S Alma School Rd.
Mesa, AZ 85210-2011
Tel: (480)827-1511; Free: 866-338-7941
Fax: (480)827-2552
Web Site: www.devry.edu/
Description: Proprietary, comprehensive, coed. Awards associate, bachelor's, and master's degrees. Calendar: semesters.

■ **DEVRY UNIVERSITY (PHOENIX)**
2149 W Dunlap Ave.
Phoenix, AZ 85021-2995
Tel: (602)870-9222; Free: 866-338-7941
Web Site: www.devry.edu/
Description: Proprietary, comprehensive, coed. Part of DeVry University. Awards associate, bachelor's, and master's degrees. Founded 1967. Setting: urban campus. Total enrollment: 1,318. Faculty: 157 (32 full-time, 125 part-time). Student-undergrad faculty ratio is 11:1. Full-time: 521 students, 32% women, 68% men. Part-time: 590 students, 30% women, 70% men. 17% from out-of-state. 4% American Indian or Alaska Native, non-Hispanic/Latino; 24% Hispanic/Latino; 6% African American, non-Hispanic/Latino; 3% Asian, non-Hispanic/Latino; 0.4% Native Hawaiian or other Pacific Islander, non-Hispanic/Latino; 0.5% international. 57% 25 or older, 19% transferred in. Academic areas with the most degrees conferred: business/marketing; computer and information sciences; engineering technologies. Calendar: semesters. Part-time degree program, adult/continuing education programs.
Entrance Requirements: Required: high school transcript, interview. Entrance: minimally difficult. Application deadline: Rolling. Notification: continuous.
Costs Per Year: Application fee: $40. Tuition: $16,076 full-time, $609 per credit hour part-time. Mandatory fees: $80 full-time.
Collegiate Environment: Orientation program. College housing not available.

■ **DINÉ COLLEGE**
PO Box 98
Tsaile, AZ 86556
Tel: (520)724-6600; Free: 877-988-DINE

Fax: (520)724-3349
E-mail: louise@dinecollege.edu
Web Site: www.dinecollege.edu/
Description: Federally supported, 2-year, coed. Awards certificates, transfer associate, and terminal associate degrees. Founded 1968. Setting: 1,200-acre rural campus. Total enrollment: 1,657. Full-time: 815 students, 69% women, 31% men. Part-time: 842 students, 79% women, 21% men. 46% 25 or older. Core. Calendar: semesters. Academic remediation for entering students, services for LD students, summer session for credit, part-time degree program, adult/continuing education programs. Off campus study at members of the American Indian Higher Education Consortium, Arizona State University.
Entrance Requirements: Open admission. Option: early admission. Required: high school transcript, certificate of Indian Blood form for Native American Students. Entrance: noncompetitive. Application deadline: Rolling. Notification: continuous. Preference given to Native Americans.
Collegiate Environment: Orientation program. Social organizations: 7 open to all. Most popular organizations: Associate Students of Navajo Community College, Bar-N-Rodeo Club, Red Dawn Indian Club, Native American Church. Major annual events: Fall Bash, Spring Fling, Farewell Dance. Student services: health clinic, personal-psychological counseling. Campus security: 24-hour emergency response devices and patrols, student patrols, late night transport-escort service. Tsaile-Navajo Community College Library plus 1 other with 50,000 books, 329 serials, and a Web page. 418 computers available on campus for general student use. A campuswide network can be accessed from student residence rooms and from off campus. Staffed computer lab on campus provides training in use of computers.

■ **DUNLAP-STONE UNIVERSITY**
19820 N 7th St.
Ste. No.100
Phoenix, AZ 85024
Tel: (602)648-5750; Free: 800-474-8013
Fax: (602)648-5755
E-mail: director@expandglobal.com
Web Site: www.dunlap-stone.edu/
Description: Proprietary, 4-year, coed. Awards associate and bachelor's degrees. Founded 1995. Setting: urban campus with easy access to Phoenix. Total enrollment: 500. Faculty: 100 (all part-time). Student-undergrad faculty ratio is 15:1. Students come from 25 states and territories. 75% 25 or older. Core. Calendar: semesters 3 semesters per year (fall, spring, summer). Academic remediation for entering students, advanced placement, accelerated degree program, independent study, distance learning, internships.
Entrance Requirements: Open admission. Options: electronic application, deferred admission, international baccalaureate accepted. Application deadlines: Rolling, Rolling for nonresidents. Notification: continuous, continuous for nonresidents. Transfer credits accepted: Yes.

■ **EASTERN ARIZONA COLLEGE**
615 N Stadium Ave.
Thatcher, AZ 85552-0769
Tel: (928)428-8322; Free: 800-678-3808
Fax: (928)428-8462
E-mail: admissions@eac.edu
Web Site: www.eac.edu/
Description: State and locally supported, 2-year, coed. Part of Arizona State Community College System. Awards certificates, transfer associate, and terminal associate degrees. Founded 1888. Setting: small town campus. Endowment: $3.6 million. Research spending for the previous fiscal year: $184,436. Educational spending for the previous fiscal year: $4242 per student. Total enrollment: 6,997. Faculty: 276 (88 full-time, 188 part-time). Student-undergrad faculty ratio is 25:1. 1,100 applied, 100% were admitted. Full-time: 2,154 students, 51% women, 49% men. Part-time: 4,843 students, 55% women, 45% men. Students come from 34 states and territories, 25 other countries, 5% from out-of-state. 7% American Indian or Alaska Native, non-Hispanic/Latino; 19% Hispanic/Latino; 4% African American, non-Hispanic/Latino; 1% Asian, non-Hispanic/Latino; 0.1% Native Hawaiian or other Pacific Islander, non-Hispanic/Latino; 1% international. 55% 25 or older, 5% live on campus, 2% transferred in. Core. Calendar: semesters. Academic remediation for entering students, services for LD students, advanced placement, independent study, distance learning, double major, summer session for credit, part-time degree program, adult/continuing education programs, co-op programs and internships. Study abroad program.

Entrance Requirements: Open admission except for nursing program, some emergency medical technology programs. Options: electronic application, early admission, deferred admission. Recommended: high school transcript. Entrance: noncompetitive. Application deadline: Rolling. Notification: continuous.
Costs Per Year: Application fee: $0. State resident tuition: $1760 full-time. Nonresident tuition: $8360 full-time. College room and board: $5390. Room and board charges vary according to board plan.
Collegiate Environment: Orientation program. Drama-theater group, choral group, marching band. Social organizations: 20 open to all. Most popular organizations: Latter-Day Saints Student Association, Criminal Justice Student Association, Multicultural Council, Phi Theta Kappa, Mark Allen Dorm Club. Major annual events: Fall Homecoming, Fall Campus Picnic, Yearbook Party. Student services: personal-psychological counseling. Campus security: 24-hour emergency response devices, late night transport-escort service, controlled dormitory access, 20-hour patrols by trained security personnel. Alumni Library with an OPAC and a Web page. Operations spending for the previous fiscal year: $287,464. 458 computers available on campus for general student use. A campuswide network can be accessed from student residence rooms and from off campus. Students can access the following: online class registration. Staffed computer lab on campus provides training in use of computers, software, and the Internet.
Community Environment: Population over 4,000. Thatcher is located in the broad valley of the Gila River. It is on Highway 70 about 75 miles east of the junction of Highways 60 and 70 at Globe, about 165 miles east of Phoenix, and 250 miles west of El Paso. Nearby Safford, with a population of over 8,900, is the county seat of government for Graham County. In addition, it serves as the hotel and shopping center for the upper Gila Valley. The area enjoys an invigorating climate with sunshine 90% of the year; rainfall is approximately nine inches during the year. The valley is flanked by the 10,000-foot Graham Mountains, Gila Mountain Range, Indian Hot Springs, Red Knolls Desert Theatre, Coolidge Dam, and the Great Surface copper mines. All are within easy driving distance. Elevation: 3,000.

■ **EMBRY-RIDDLE AERONAUTICAL UNIVERSITY–PRESCOTT**
3700 Willow Creek Rd.
Prescott, AZ 86301-3720
Tel: (928)777-3728; Free: 800-888-3728
Fax: (928)777-3740
E-mail: pradmit@erau.edu
Web Site: www.embryriddle.edu/
Description: Independent, comprehensive, coed. Awards bachelor's and master's degrees. Founded 1978. Setting: 547-acre small town campus with easy access to Phoenix. Endowment: $80.9 million. Research spending for the previous fiscal year: $1.8 million. Educational spending for the previous fiscal year: $13,555 per student. Total enrollment: 1,724. Faculty: 136 (97 full-time, 39 part-time). Student-undergrad faculty ratio is 15:1. 36% from top 10% of their high school class, 64% from top quarter, 91% from top half. Full-time: 1,576 students, 18% women, 82% men. Part-time: 102 students, 17% women, 83% men. Students come from 48 states and territories, 25 other countries, 72% from out-of-state. 1% American Indian or Alaska Native, non-Hispanic/Latino; 10% Hispanic/Latino; 2% African American, non-Hispanic/Latino; 5% Asian, non-Hispanic/Latino; 0.4% Native Hawaiian or other Pacific Islander, non-Hispanic/Latino; 6% international. 14% 25 or older, 47% live on campus, 6% transferred in. Retention: 76% of full-time freshmen returned the following year. Academic areas with the most degrees conferred: transportation and materials moving; engineering; social sciences. Core. Calendar: semesters. Academic remediation for entering students, services for LD students, advanced placement, accelerated degree program, self-designed majors, honors program, independent study, distance learning, double major, summer session for credit, part-time degree program, adult/continuing education programs, co-op programs and internships. Study abroad program. ROTC: Army, Air Force.
Entrance Requirements: Options: electronic application, deferred admission, international baccalaureate accepted. Required: high school transcript, minimum 2 high school GPA, 2 recommendations, medical examination for flight students. Recommended: essay, interview, SAT or ACT. Required for some: minimum 3 high school GPA. Entrance: moderately difficult. Application deadlines: Rolling, Rolling for nonresidents. Notification: continuous, continuous for nonresidents. SAT Subject Test deadline: 7/1. Transfer credits accepted: Yes.
Costs Per Year: Application fee: $50. Comprehensive fee: $40,584 includes full-time tuition ($30,120), mandatory fees ($914), and college room and

board ($9550). College room only: $5600. Room and board charges vary according to board plan and housing facility. Part-time tuition: $1255 per credit hour.

Collegiate Environment: Orientation program. Student-run newspaper, radio station. Social organizations: 86 open to all; national fraternities, national sororities; 9% of eligible men and 12% of eligible women are members. Most popular organizations: Hawaii Club, Strike Eagles, Theta XI, American Institute of Aeronautics and Astronautics (AIAA), Arnold Air Society. Major annual events: October West/Homecoming, Spring Fling, Hawaii Club Luau. Student services: health clinic, personal-psychological counseling. Campus security: 24-hour emergency response devices and patrols, student patrols, late night transport-escort service. 777 college housing spaces available; 769 were occupied in 2012-13. Freshmen guaranteed college housing. On-campus residence required in freshman year. Option: coed housing available. Christine & Steven F. Udvar-Hazy Library & Learning Center with 44,905 books, 192,655 microform titles, 252 serials, 2,604 audiovisual materials, an OPAC, and a Web page. Operations spending for the previous fiscal year: $969,360. 470 computers available on campus for general student use. A campuswide network can be accessed from student residence rooms and from off campus. Students can access the following: online class registration. Staffed computer lab on campus provides training in use of software.

Community Environment: The Prescott area is one of the most colorful areas of the Bradshaw Mountains and has an approximate population of 40,400. The campus is surrounded by a national forest, rolling ranchlands, hiking trails, and wilderness areas. The city of Phoenix is approximately 90 miles away.

■ **ESTRELLA MOUNTAIN COMMUNITY COLLEGE**
3000 N Dysart Rd.
Avondale, AZ 85392
Tel: (623)935-8000
E-mail: debbie.kushibab@emcmail.maricopa.edu
Web Site: www.emc.maricopa.edu/
Description: State and locally supported, 2-year, coed. Part of Maricopa County Community College District System. Awards certificates, transfer associate, and terminal associate degrees. Founded 1992. Setting: urban campus with easy access to Phoenix. Total enrollment: 6,358. Faculty: 356 (70 full-time, 286 part-time). Student-undergrad faculty ratio is 22:1. 6,358 applied, 100% were admitted. Full-time: 1,631 students, 58% women, 42% men. Part-time: 4,727 students, 64% women, 36% men. Core. Calendar: semesters. Academic remediation for entering students, ESL program, services for LD students, advanced placement, honors program, independent study, distance learning, summer session for credit, part-time degree program, adult/continuing education programs, co-op programs. ROTC: Air Force (c).
Entrance Requirements: Open admission. Option: electronic application. Entrance: noncompetitive.
Collegiate Environment: Orientation program. Social organizations: 18 open to all. Most popular organizations: Phi Theta Kappa, Men Of Color Association (M.O.C.A.), Movimiento Estudiantil Chicano de Aztlan (M.E.Ch.A), Savings and Investment Club. Major annual events: Spring Fling, Hispanic Heritage Month, Welcome Week. Student services: personal-psychological counseling. Campus security: 24-hour emergency response devices and patrols, late night transport-escort service. Estrella Mountain Library with 57,000 books, 50 serials, 3,000 audiovisual materials, an OPAC, and a Web page. 500 computers available on campus for general student use. A campuswide network can be accessed. Students can access the following: online class registration. Staffed computer lab on campus provides training in use of computers and the Internet.

■ **EVEREST COLLEGE**
10400 N 25th Ave.
Ste. 190
Phoenix, AZ 85021
Tel: (602)942-4141; Free: 888-741-4270
Fax: (602)943-0960
E-mail: jaskins@cci.edu
Web Site: www.everest.edu/
Description: Proprietary, primarily 2-year, coed. Part of Corinthian Colleges, Inc. Awards diplomas, transfer associate, terminal associate, and bachelor's degrees. Founded 1982. Setting: urban campus. Total enrollment: 552. Faculty: 50 (15 full-time, 35 part-time). Student-undergrad faculty ratio is 16:1. 672 applied, 78% were admitted. Full-time: 347 students, 81% women,

19% men. Part-time: 205 students, 82% women, 18% men. 62% 25 or older. Retention: 62% of full-time freshmen returned the following year. Core. Calendar: six-week terms. Academic remediation for entering students, services for LD students, independent study, distance learning, double major, adult/continuing education programs. Study abroad program.
Entrance Requirements: Option: deferred admission. Required: high school transcript, minimum 2.0 high school GPA, interview. Required for some: essay. Entrance: noncompetitive. Application deadline: Rolling. Notification: continuous.
Collegiate Environment: Orientation program. Social organizations: 2 open to all. Most popular organizations: Collegiate Secretaries International, Toastmasters. Major annual event: picnic. Student services: personal-psychological counseling. Campus security: 24-hour emergency response devices and patrols. Everest College Library with 17,515 books, 48 serials, 514 audiovisual materials, and a Web page. 50 computers available on campus for general student use. Staffed computer lab on campus provides training in use of computers, software, and the Internet.

■ **EVEREST ONLINE**
8150 S Hardy Dr. No.102
Tempe, AZ 85284-1117
Tel: (888)391-8881
Web Site: www.everestonline.edu/
Description: Proprietary, comprehensive, coed. Awards associate, bachelor's, and master's degrees.

■ **GATEWAY COMMUNITY COLLEGE**
108 N 40th St.
Phoenix, AZ 85034-1795
Tel: (602)286-8000
Fax: (602)286-8003
E-mail: enroll@gatewaycc.edu
Web Site: www.gatewaycc.edu/
Description: State and locally supported, 2-year, coed. Part of Maricopa County Community College District System. Administratively affiliated with GateWay Community College. Awards certificates, diplomas, transfer associate, and terminal associate degrees. Founded 1968. Setting: 20-acre urban campus. Total enrollment: 6,801. Faculty: 490 (99 full-time, 391 part-time). Student-undergrad faculty ratio is 18:1. 716 applied, 100% were admitted. Full-time: 191 students, 52% women, 48% men. Part-time: 525 students, 43% women, 57% men. 4% American Indian or Alaska Native, non-Hispanic/Latino; 26% Hispanic/Latino; 11% African American, non-Hispanic/Latino; 4% Asian, non-Hispanic/Latino; 0.2% Native Hawaiian or other Pacific Islander, non-Hispanic/Latino; 1% international. Core. Calendar: semesters. Academic remediation for entering students, ESL program, services for LD students, advanced placement, accelerated degree program, freshman honors college, honors program, independent study, distance learning, double major, summer session for credit, part-time degree program, adult/continuing education programs, co-op programs and internships. Off campus study. Study abroad program. ROTC: Army (c), Air Force (c).
Entrance Requirements: Open admission except for health science, nursing programs. Options: electronic application, early admission, deferred admission. Required for some: high school transcript, interview. Entrance: noncompetitive. Application deadline: Rolling. Notification: continuous. Transfer credits accepted: Yes.
Costs Per Year: Application fee: $0. State resident tuition: $1824 full-time, $76 per credit hour part-time. Nonresident tuition: $7608 full-time, $317 per credit hour part-time. Mandatory fees: $30 full-time.
Collegiate Environment: Orientation program. Student services: personal-psychological counseling, women's center. Campus security: 24-hour emergency response devices and patrols, student patrols, late night transport-escort service. GateWay Library with an OPAC.

■ **GLENDALE COMMUNITY COLLEGE**
6000 W Olive Ave.
Glendale, AZ 85302-3090
Tel: (623)845-3000
Fax: (623)845-3329
E-mail: info@gc.maricopa.edu
Web Site: www.gc.maricopa.edu/
Description: State and locally supported, 2-year, coed. Part of Maricopa County Community College District System. Awards certificates, transfer associate, and terminal associate degrees. Founded 1965. Setting: 222-acre

suburban campus with easy access to Phoenix. Endowment: $1.2 million. Educational spending for the previous fiscal year: $6818 per student. Total enrollment: 20,154. Student-undergrad faculty ratio is 24:1. Full-time: 7,126 students, 48% women, 52% men. Part-time: 13,028 students, 56% women, 44% men. Students come from 51 states and territories, 92 other countries, 8% from out-of-state. 7% transferred in. Retention: 64% of full-time freshmen returned the following year. Core. Calendar: semesters. Academic remediation for entering students, ESL program, services for LD students, advanced placement, freshman honors college, honors program, distance learning, double major, summer session for credit, part-time degree program, adult/continuing education programs, co-op programs and internships. Off campus study. Study abroad program. ROTC: Army (c), Air Force (c).

Entrance Requirements: Open admission. Options: electronic application, international baccalaureate accepted. Required for some: high school transcript. Entrance: noncompetitive. Application deadline: 8/20. Notification: continuous until 8/20. Transfer credits accepted: Yes.

Costs Per Year: Application fee: $0. State resident tuition: $1824 full-time, $76 per semester hour part-time. Nonresident tuition: $7608 full-time, $317 per semester hour part-time. Mandatory fees: $30 full-time, $15 per term part-time. Full-time tuition and fees vary according to program and reciprocity agreements. Part-time tuition and fees vary according to course load, program, and reciprocity agreements.

Collegiate Environment: Orientation program. Drama-theater group, choral group, marching band, student-run newspaper. Most popular organizations: Phi Theta Kappa, M.E.Ch.A. (Movimiento Estudiantil Chicano de Aztlan), Associated Student Government, Biotechnology Club, Compass. Student services: legal services, personal-psychological counseling. Campus security: 24-hour patrols, student patrols, late night transport-escort service. College housing not available. Library/Media Center plus 1 other with 97,768 books, 206,762 microform titles, 30,094 serials, 6,032 audiovisual materials, an OPAC, and a Web page. Operations spending for the previous fiscal year: $2.3 million. 2,500 computers available on campus for general student use. A campuswide network can be accessed from off-campus. Students can access the following: online class registration. Staffed computer lab on campus provides training in use of computers, software, and the Internet.

■ **GOLF ACADEMY OF AMERICA**
2031 N Arizona Ave.
Ste. 2
Chandler, AZ 85225
Tel: (480)857-1574
Web Site: www.golfacademy.edu/
Description: Proprietary, 2-year, coed. Calendar: semesters.

■ **GRAND CANYON UNIVERSITY**
3300 W Camelback Rd.
Phoenix, AZ 85017-1097
Tel: (602)249-3300; Free: 800-800-9776
Fax: (602)589-2580
E-mail: admissionsonline@gcu.edu
Web Site: www.gcu.edu/
Description: Independent Southern Baptist, comprehensive, coed. Awards bachelor's, master's, and doctoral degrees and post-master's certificates. Founded 1949. Setting: 100-acre urban campus with easy access to Phoenix. 1% American Indian or Alaska Native, non-Hispanic/Latino; 6% Hispanic/Latino; 22% African American, non-Hispanic/Latino; 2% Asian, non-Hispanic/Latino; 0.2% Native Hawaiian or other Pacific Islander, non-Hispanic/Latino; 0.1% international. 40% live on campus. Academic areas with the most degrees conferred: education; health professions and related sciences; business/marketing. Core. Calendar: semesters. Academic remediation for entering students, ESL program, advanced placement, accelerated degree program, freshman honors college, honors program, independent study, distance learning, double major, summer session for credit, part-time degree program, adult/continuing education programs, co-op programs and internships, graduate courses open to undergrads. Off campus study at Coalition for Christian Colleges and Universities. Study abroad program. ROTC: Army, Air Force (c).
Entrance Requirements: Options: electronic application, early admission, deferred admission, international baccalaureate accepted. Required: high school transcript, minimum 2.75 high school GPA. Recommended: SAT or ACT. Entrance: moderately difficult. Application deadline: Rolling. Notification: continuous. Transfer credits accepted: Yes.
Costs Per Year: Comprehensive fee: $27,100 includes full-time tuition

($16,500), mandatory fees ($2500), and college room and board ($8100). College room only: $4000. Full-time tuition and fees vary according to course load. Room and board charges vary according to board plan and housing facility. Part-time tuition: $687.50 per credit. Part-time tuition varies according to course load.
Collegiate Environment: Orientation program. Drama-theater group, choral group. Social organizations: 24 open to all. Most popular organizations: International Student Association, Fellowship of Christian Athletes, Student Nurses Association, Canyon Crazies, AZ Hosa. Major annual events: Welcome Week, ASGCU events, home basketball games. Student services: health clinic, personal-psychological counseling. Campus security: 24-hour emergency response devices and patrols, late night transport-escort service, controlled dormitory access, staffed gates to enter campus after non-business hours. Fleming Library with 158,587 books, 57,802 serials, 56,750 audiovisual materials, an OPAC, and a Web page. 65 computers available on campus for general student use. A campuswide network can be accessed from student residence rooms and from off campus. Students can access the following: online class registration. Staffed computer lab on campus.
Community Environment: See Phoenix College.

■ **HARRISON MIDDLETON UNIVERSITY**
1105 E Broadway
Tempe, AZ 85282
Tel: (480)317-5955; Free: 877-248-6724
Fax: (480)829-4999
E-mail: information@hmu.edu
Web Site: www.hmu.edu/
Description: Independent, comprehensive, coed. Awards associate, bachelor's, master's, and doctoral degrees. Founded 1998. Setting: suburban campus with easy access to Phoenix. Total enrollment: 157. Faculty: 23 (17 full-time, 6 part-time). Core. Calendar: continuous. Advanced placement, self-designed majors, independent study, distance learning, double major, summer session for credit.
Entrance Requirements: Open admission. Option: electronic application. Required: high school transcript, interview. Required for some: essay, 2 recommendations. Application deadlines: Rolling, Rolling for nonresidents. Notification: continuous, continuous for nonresidents. Transfer credits accepted: Yes.
Costs Per Year: Application fee: $50. One-time mandatory fee: $400. Tuition: $6000 full-time, $250 per contact hour part-time.

■ **INTERNATIONAL BAPTIST COLLEGE**
2211 W Germann Rd.
Chandler, AZ 85286
Tel: (480)245-7903; Free: 800-422-4858
E-mail: admissions@ibconline.edu
Web Site: www.ibcs.edu/
Description: Independent Baptist, comprehensive, coed. Awards associate, bachelor's, and master's degrees. Founded 1980. Setting: 12-acre suburban campus with easy access to Phoenix. Total enrollment: 91. Student-undergrad faculty ratio is 7:1. 33% from out-of-state. 22% 25 or older. Core. Calendar: 4-1-4. Part-time degree program, graduate courses open to undergrads.
Entrance Requirements: Open admission. Option: early admission. Required: essay, high school transcript, 3 recommendations. Application deadline: 8/20.
Collegiate Environment: Choral group. Social organizations: local fraternities, local sororities.

■ **ITT TECHNICAL INSTITUTE (PHOENIX)**
1840 N 95th Ave.
Ste. 132
Phoenix, AZ 85037
Tel: (623)474-7900; Free: 800-210-1178
Web Site: www.itt-tech.edu/
Description: Proprietary, primarily 2-year, coed. Part of ITT Educational Services, Inc. Awards terminal associate and bachelor's degrees.

■ **ITT TECHNICAL INSTITUTE (PHOENIX)**
10220 N 25th Ave., Ste. 100
Phoenix, AZ 85021
Tel: (602)749-7900; Free: 877-221-1132
Web Site: www.itt-tech.edu/

Description: Proprietary, primarily 2-year, coed. Part of ITT Educational Services, Inc. Awards terminal associate and bachelor's degrees. Founded 1972. Setting: urban campus.
Entrance Requirements: Entrance: minimally difficult.

■ **ITT TECHNICAL INSTITUTE (TEMPE)**
5005 S Wendler Dr.
Tempe, AZ 85282
Tel: (602)437-7500; Free: 800-879-4881
Web Site: www.itt-tech.edu/
Description: Proprietary, 4-year, coed. Part of ITT Educational Services, Inc. Awards associate and bachelor's degrees. Founded 1963.
Entrance Requirements: Entrance: minimally difficult.

■ **ITT TECHNICAL INSTITUTE (TUCSON)**
1455 W River Rd.
Tucson, AZ 85704
Tel: (520)408-7488; Free: 800-870-9730
Fax: (520)292-9899
Web Site: www.itt-tech.edu/
Description: Proprietary, primarily 2-year, coed. Part of ITT Educational Services, Inc. Awards terminal associate and bachelor's degrees. Founded 1984. Setting: urban campus.
Entrance Requirements: Entrance: minimally difficult.

■ **LE CORDON BLEU COLLEGE OF CULINARY ARTS IN SCOTTSDALE**
8100 E Camelback Rd.
Ste. 1001
Scottsdale, AZ 85251-3940
Tel: (480)990-3773; Free: 888-557-4222
Fax: (480)990-0351
Web Site: www.chefs.edu/SCOTTSDALE
Description: Proprietary, primarily 2-year, coed. Awards certificates, terminal associate, and bachelor's degrees. Founded 1986. Total enrollment: 1,275. 40% 25 or older. Calendar: semesters.

■ **MESA COMMUNITY COLLEGE**
1833 W Southern Ave.
Mesa, AZ 85202-4866
Tel: (480)461-7000; Free: 866-532-4983
Fax: (480)461-7805
E-mail: admissionsandrecords@mesacc.edu
Web Site: www.mesacc.edu/
Description: State and locally supported, 2-year, coed. Part of Maricopa County Community College District System. Awards certificates, transfer associate, and terminal associate degrees. Founded 1965. Setting: 160-acre urban campus with easy access to Phoenix. Total enrollment: 23,000. Core. Calendar: semesters. Academic remediation for entering students, ESL program, services for LD students, advanced placement, self-designed majors, freshman honors college, honors program, independent study, distance learning, summer session for credit, part-time degree program, adult/continuing education programs, co-op programs. Off campus study at Servicemembers Opportunity Colleges. Study abroad program. ROTC: Army (c), Air Force (c).
Entrance Requirements: Open admission. Options: electronic application, early admission, deferred admission. Entrance: noncompetitive. Application deadline: 8/22. Notification: continuous. Transfer credits accepted: Yes.
Costs Per Year: Application fee: $0. Area resident tuition: $1944 full-time. State resident tuition: $7608 full-time. Nonresident tuition: $7728 full-time. Full-time tuition varies according to course load and reciprocity agreements.
Collegiate Environment: Orientation program. Drama-theater group, choral group, student-run newspaper. Social organizations: 25 open to all. Most popular organizations: MECHA, International Student Association, American Indian Association, Asian/Pacific Islander Club. Major annual events: Bash, Homecoming. Student services: legal services, personal-psychological counseling. Campus security: 24-hour emergency response devices and patrols, student patrols. College housing not available. Information Commons with an OPAC and a Web page. 600 computers available on campus for general student use. A campuswide network can be accessed from off-campus. Staffed computer lab on campus.
Community Environment: Population 442,780, Arizona's third largest city, located 16 miles east of Phoenix, adjacent to Tempe, and near the Superstition Mountains. The average yearly temperature is 68.3 degrees, low humid-

ity and 86 percent of the daylight hours are sunny. Mesa is a beautiful and friendly city; there are part-time jobs available for the college students. Most kinds of sports and recreation facilities available, plus many cultural activities.

■ **MOHAVE COMMUNITY COLLEGE**
1971 Jagerson Ave.
Kingman, AZ 86409
Tel: (928)757-4331; Free: 888-664-2832
Fax: (928)757-0808
E-mail: amasterson@mohave.edu
Web Site: www.mohave.edu/
Description: State-supported, 2-year, coed. Awards certificates, transfer associate, and terminal associate degrees. Founded 1971. Setting: 160-acre small town campus. Total enrollment: 5,220. Faculty: 400 (78 full-time, 322 part-time). Student-undergrad faculty ratio is 16:1. Full-time: 1,412 students, 62% women, 38% men. Part-time: 3,808 students, 66% women, 34% men. Students come from 16 states and territories, 4% from out-of-state. 2% American Indian or Alaska Native, non-Hispanic/Latino; 18% Hispanic/Latino; 1% African American, non-Hispanic/Latino; 2% Asian, non-Hispanic/Latino; 1% Native Hawaiian or other Pacific Islander, non-Hispanic/Latino; 0% international. 51% 25 or older. Core. Calendar: semesters. Academic remediation for entering students, ESL program, independent study, distance learning, summer session for credit, part-time degree program, adult/continuing education programs, co-op programs.
Entrance Requirements: Open admission except for nursing, dental hygiene, surgical technology. Options: electronic application, early admission, deferred admission. Entrance: noncompetitive. Application deadline: Rolling. Notification: continuous.
Costs Per Year: State resident tuition: $2340 full-time, $78 per credit hour part-time. Nonresident tuition: $9360 full-time, $312 per credit hour part-time. Mandatory fees: $210 full-time, $7 per credit hour part-time. Full-time tuition and fees vary according to program. Part-time tuition and fees vary according to program.
Collegiate Environment: Orientation program. Social organizations: 10 open to all. Most popular organizations: Art Club, Phi Theta Kappa, Computer Club (MC4), Science Club, student government. Major annual events: Career Fair, Brighter Future Festival, New Student BBQ. Campus security: late night transport-escort service. College housing not available. Mohave Community College Library with 45,849 books, 476 serials, an OPAC, and a Web page. 120 computers available on campus for general student use. Staffed computer lab on campus provides training in use of computers, software, and the Internet.
Community Environment: The College campuses are accessible by all forms of transportation: bus, rail and air. The area is a rapidly expanding one, offering a variety of year-round activities due to its arid climate. Lake Havasu City boasts the famous London Bridge and English Village. The areas provide opportunities for hunting, fishing, camping and water sports.

■ **NATIONAL PARALEGAL COLLEGE**
6516 N 7th St.
Ste. 103
Phoenix, AZ 85014
Tel: (845)371-9101; Free: 800-371-6105
E-mail: info@nationalparalegal.edu
Web Site: nationalparalegal.edu/
Description: Proprietary, 4-year, coed. Awards associate and bachelor's degrees.

■ **NORTHCENTRAL UNIVERSITY**
10000 E University Dr.
Prescott Valley, AZ 86314
Tel: (928)541-7777; Free: 866-776-0331
Fax: (928)541-7817
E-mail: info@ncu.edu
Web Site: www.ncu.edu/
Description: Proprietary, upper-level, coed. Awards bachelor's, master's, and doctoral degrees and post-master's certificates (offers only distance learning programs). Total enrollment: 9,252. Faculty: 481 (44 full-time, 437 part-time). Student-undergrad faculty ratio is 9:1. Full-time: 78 students, 68% women, 32% men. Part-time: 251 students, 63% women, 37% men. Students come from 45 states and territories, 2 other countries. 0.3% American Indian or Alaska Native, non-Hispanic/Latino; 4% Hispanic/Latino; 11% African American, non-Hispanic/Latino; 2% Asian, non-Hispanic/Latino;

0.3% Native Hawaiian or other Pacific Islander, non-Hispanic/Latino. 88% 25 or older, 100% transferred in. Academic areas with the most degrees conferred: business/marketing; psychology; education. Core. Calendar: continuous. Services for LD students, accelerated degree program, distance learning.

Entrance Requirements: Transfer credits accepted: Yes.

Costs Per Year: Application fee: $0. Tuition: $9760 full-time.

Collegiate Environment: Northcentral University Library (Virtual) with a Web page.

■ **NORTHERN ARIZONA UNIVERSITY**

S San Francisco St.

Flagstaff, AZ 86011

Tel: (928)523-9011; Free: 888-MORE-NAU

Fax: (928)523-0226

E-mail: Admissions@nau.edu

Web Site: www.nau.edu/

Description: State-supported, university, coed. Part of Arizona University System, under the Arizona Board of Regents. Awards bachelor's, master's, and doctoral degrees. Founded 1899. Setting: 740-acre small town campus. Endowment: $108.3 million. Research spending for the previous fiscal year: $21.8 million. Educational spending for the previous fiscal year: $5547 per student. Total enrollment: 26,002. Faculty: 1,539 (900 full-time, 639 part-time). Student-undergrad faculty ratio is 20:1. 34,461 applied, 76% were admitted. 19% from top 10% of their high school class, 48% from top quarter, 81% from top half. Full-time: 18,386 students, 57% women, 43% men. Part-time: 3,388 students, 61% women, 39% men. Students come from 51 states and territories, 42 other countries, 26% from out-of-state. 4% American Indian or Alaska Native, non-Hispanic/Latino; 18% Hispanic/Latino; 3% African American, non-Hispanic/Latino; 1% Asian, non-Hispanic/Latino; 0.3% Native Hawaiian or other Pacific Islander, non-Hispanic/Latino; 4% international. 23% 25 or older, 33% live on campus, 11% transferred in. Retention: 76% of full-time freshmen returned the following year. Academic areas with the most degrees conferred: business/marketing; education; liberal arts/general studies. Core. Calendar: semesters. ESL program, services for LD students, advanced placement, accelerated degree program, freshman honors college, honors program, independent study, distance learning, double major, summer session for credit, part-time degree program, co-op programs and internships, graduate courses open to undergrads. Off campus study at National Student Exchange. Study abroad program. ROTC: Army, Air Force.

Entrance Requirements: Options: electronic application, deferred admission, international baccalaureate accepted. Required: high school transcript, minimum 3 high school GPA, Completion of 16 required college preparatory courses with minimum 2.0 in each subject area. Required for some: SAT, ACT, SAT or ACT, SAT and SAT Subject Tests or ACT, SAT Subject Tests, ACT/SAT test scores required for home-schooled students. Entrance: moderately difficult. Application deadlines: Rolling, Rolling for nonresidents. Notification: continuous, continuous for nonresidents. Transfer credits accepted: Yes.

Costs Per Year: Application fee: $25. State resident tuition: $8453 full-time, $363 per credit hour part-time. Nonresident tuition: $20,808 full-time, $749 per credit hour part-time. Mandatory fees: $818 full-time, $6 per credit hour part-time, $322 per term part-time. Full-time tuition and fees vary according to degree level, location, and program. Part-time tuition and fees vary according to course load, degree level, location, and program. College room and board: $8784. College room only: $4824. Room and board charges vary according to board plan and housing facility. Tuition guaranteed not to increase for student's term of enrollment.

Collegiate Environment: Orientation program. Drama-theater group, choral group, marching band, student-run newspaper, radio station. Social organizations: 317 open to all; national fraternities, national sororities. Most popular organizations: Northern Arizona Snow Association, Golden Key Honor Society, Younglife, Astronomy/Astrobiology Club, IEEE Student Chapter. Major annual events: Welcome Week, Family Weekend, Homecoming Week. Student services: legal services, health clinic, personal-psychological counseling. Campus security: 24-hour emergency response devices and patrols, late night transport-escort service, controlled dormitory access. 7,314 college housing spaces available; 7,202 were occupied in 2012-13. Freshmen guaranteed college housing. Options: coed, men-only, women-only housing available. Cline Library with 892,809 books, 378,717 microform titles, 59,863 serials, 37,039 audiovisual materials, an OPAC, and a Web page. Operations spending for the previous fiscal year: $6.8 million. 400 computers available on campus for general student use. Computer

purchase/lease plans available. A campuswide network can be accessed from student residence rooms and from off campus. Students can access the following: online class registration. Staffed computer lab on campus (open 24 hours a day) provides training in use of computers, software, and the Internet.

Community Environment: Flagstaff, population 57,300, is a city of Seven Wonders in the heart of the Coconino National Forest located at the foot of the San Francisco Peaks. Mountain slopes, canyons, buttes, Indian ruins, forests, and deserts mingle in a setting forever challenging in its appeal. The elevation, the protection provided by the forest, and the Arizona sunshine give Flagstaff unsurpassed year round climate. Recreational activities include hiking, bicycling, boating, fishing, and hunting. Skiing is nearby as are the Grand Canyon, the Petrified forest, numerous Indian villages, and national monuments.

■ **NORTHERN ARIZONA UNIVERSITY–YUMA**

2020 S Ave. 8E

Yuma, AZ 85365

Tel: (928)317-6400; Free: 888-NAU-Yuma

E-mail: eileen.knight@nau.edu

Web Site: www.yuma.nau.edu/

Description: State-supported, upper-level, coed. Administratively affiliated with Northern Arizona University. Awards bachelor's and master's degrees. Total enrollment: 631. Core.

■ **NORTHLAND PIONEER COLLEGE**

PO Box 610

Holbrook, AZ 86025

Tel: (928)524-7311; Free: 800-266-7845

Fax: (928)524-7612

Web Site: www.npc.edu/

Description: State and locally supported, 2-year, coed. Part of Arizona State Community College System. Awards certificates, transfer associate, and terminal associate degrees. Founded 1974. Setting: 50-acre rural campus. Educational spending for the previous fiscal year: $5000 per student. Total enrollment: 4,636. Faculty: 226 (73 full-time, 153 part-time). Student-undergrad faculty ratio is 17:1. Full-time: 946 students, 63% women, 37% men. Part-time: 3,690 students, 67% women, 33% men. Students come from 17 states and territories, 3 other countries, 0.01% from out-of-state. 67% 25 or older, 1% transferred in. Core. Calendar: semesters. ESL program, services for LD students, advanced placement, freshman honors college, honors program, independent study, distance learning, double major, summer session for credit, part-time degree program, co-op programs and internships.

Entrance Requirements: Open admission. Option: early admission. Entrance: noncompetitive. Application deadline: Rolling. Transfer credits accepted: Yes.

Collegiate Environment: Drama-theater group, choral group. Campus security: evening security. Northland Pioneer College Library with 60,000 books, 240 serials, and an OPAC. Operations spending for the previous fiscal year: $506,078. 200 computers available on campus for general student use. A campuswide network can be accessed from off-campus. Students can access the following: online class registration. Staffed computer lab on campus provides training in use of computers, software, and the Internet.

Community Environment: The service area of 21,000 square miles has a population of approximately 154,000 people. The service area includes parts of three Indian reservations. The economy is based primarily on agriculture, tourism, and the lumber industry.

■ **PARADISE VALLEY COMMUNITY COLLEGE**

18401 N 32nd St.

Phoenix, AZ 85032-1200

Tel: (602)787-6500

Fax: (602)787-6625

E-mail: shirley.green@pvmail.maricopa.edu

Web Site: www.pvc.maricopa.edu/

Description: State and locally supported, 2-year, coed. Part of Maricopa County Community College District System. Awards certificates, transfer associate, and terminal associate degrees. Founded 1985. Setting: urban campus. Total enrollment: 9,951. Faculty: 542 (98 full-time, 444 part-time). 4% from out-of-state. Core. Calendar: semesters. Academic remediation for entering students, ESL program, services for LD students, advanced placement, accelerated degree program, honors program, independent study, distance learning, summer session for credit, part-time degree program, adult/continuing education programs, co-op programs and internships. Off campus study. Study abroad program. ROTC: Army (c).

Entrance Requirements: Open admission. Option: early admission. Entrance: noncompetitive. Application deadline: Rolling. Transfer credits accepted: Yes.

Collegiate Environment: Orientation program. Drama-theater group, choral group, student-run newspaper. Social organizations: 16 open to all; national fraternities, Phi Theta Kappa. Most popular organizations: Phi Theta Kappa, International Student Club, Recreational Outing Club, AWARE, Student Christian Association. Major annual events: International Education Week, Black American Month/Hispanic Week/Women's Week. Student services: personal-psychological counseling. Campus security: 24-hour emergency response devices and patrols, late night transport-escort service. Paradise Valley Community College Library plus 1 other with an OPAC and a Web page. 500 computers available on campus for general student use. A campuswide network can be accessed from off-campus. Students can access the following: online class registration. Staffed computer lab on campus provides training in use of computers, software, and the Internet.

■ **THE PARALEGAL INSTITUTE, INC.**
2933 W Indian School Rd.
Phoenix, AZ 85017
Tel: (602)212-0501; Free: 800-354-1254
E-mail: paralegalinst@mindspring.com
Web Site: www.theparalegalinstitute.edu/
Description: Proprietary, 2-year, coed. Awards diplomas and terminal associate degrees. Founded 1974. Faculty: 4 (1 full-time, 3 part-time). 500 applied, 25% were admitted.

■ **PENN FOSTER COLLEGE**
14300 N Northsight Blvd.
Ste. 120
Scottsdale, AZ 85260
Tel: (480)947-6644; Free: 800-471-3232
Web Site: www.pennfostercollege.edu/
Description: Proprietary, 4-year, coed. Awards associate and bachelor's degrees. Faculty: 63 (31 full-time, 32 part-time). Core. Academic remediation for entering students, services for LD students, accelerated degree program, independent study, distance learning, part-time degree program, external degree program, co-op programs and internships. Off campus study.
Entrance Requirements: Open admission. Option: electronic application. Required: high school transcript. Application deadlines: Rolling, Rolling for nonresidents. Transfer credits accepted: Yes.
Collegiate Environment: Orientation program.

■ **PHOENIX COLLEGE**
1202 W Thomas Rd.
Phoenix, AZ 85013-4234
Tel: (602)285-7800
Fax: (602)285-7700
E-mail: kathy.french@pcmail.maricopa.edu
Web Site: www.pc.maricopa.edu/
Description: County-supported, 2-year, coed. Part of Maricopa County Community College District System. Awards certificates, diplomas, transfer associate, and terminal associate degrees. Founded 1920. Setting: 52-acre urban campus. Total enrollment: 12,565. Faculty: 718 (163 full-time, 555 part-time). Student-undergrad faculty ratio is 18:1. 4% American Indian or Alaska Native, non-Hispanic/Latino; 38% Hispanic/Latino; 12% African American, non-Hispanic/Latino; 3% Asian, non-Hispanic/Latino; 0.1% Native Hawaiian or other Pacific Islander, non-Hispanic/Latino; 0.4% international. Core. Calendar: semesters. Academic remediation for entering students, ESL program, services for LD students, advanced placement, freshman honors college, honors program, independent study, distance learning, summer session for credit, part-time degree program, adult/continuing education programs, co-op programs and internships. Off campus study. Study abroad program. ROTC: Army (c), Naval (c), Air Force (c).
Entrance Requirements: Open admission. Options: electronic application, early admission, deferred admission. Entrance: noncompetitive. Application deadlines: Rolling, Rolling for nonresidents. Notification: continuous, continuous for nonresidents. Transfer credits accepted: Yes.
Costs Per Year: Application fee: $0. Area resident tuition: $912 full-time. State resident tuition: $3804 full-time. Nonresident tuition: $3804 full-time. Mandatory fees: $30 full-time.
Collegiate Environment: Orientation program. Drama-theater group, choral

group. Social organizations: 27 open to all. Most popular organizations: Student Leadership Council (SLC), MEChA Movimiento Estudiantil Chicanos de Aztlan, ALE Asociacion Latina Estudiantil, Rainbow Spectrum - Gay, Straight, Whatever alliance, International Club. Major annual events: Homecoming Week, Bear Day, Hispanic Heritage Month. Student services: personal-psychological counseling. Campus security: 24-hour emergency response devices and patrols, student patrols, late night transport-escort service. College housing not available. Fannin Library with 67,370 books, 210 serials, 7,667 audiovisual materials, an OPAC, and a Web page. Operations spending for the previous fiscal year: $1.3 million. 1,277 computers available on campus for general student use. A campuswide network can be accessed from off-campus. Students can access the following: online class registration. Staffed computer lab on campus provides training in use of computers.

Community Environment: Phoenix, population over one million, is a thriving industrial and agricultural city. Easily accessible, served by railroads, buses and airlines, the city has many churches, libraries, museums, and theatres, as well as numerous fine restaurants, hotels, and motels. It is located in proximity to many scenic and historical places of interest including the Grand Canyon, the Petrified Forest, Montezuma Castle, and Oak Creek Canyon. It is one of the outstanding winter resorts of America with The Valley of the Sun nearby.

■ **PIMA COMMUNITY COLLEGE**
4905 E Broadway Blvd.
Tucson, AZ 85709-1010
Tel: (520)206-4666
Fax: (520)884-6728
E-mail: tbenson@pima.edu
Web Site: www.pima.edu/
Description: State and locally supported, 2-year, coed. Awards certificates, diplomas, transfer associate, and terminal associate degrees. Founded 1966. Setting: 486-acre urban campus with easy access to Tucson, Arizona. Endowment: $4.3 million. Educational spending for the previous fiscal year: $2343 per student. Total enrollment: 36,969. Faculty: 1,495 (315 full-time, 1,180 part-time). Student-undergrad faculty ratio is 29:1. Full-time: 13,730 students, 51% women, 49% men. Part-time: 23,239 students, 56% women, 44% men. Students come from 53 states and territories, 63 other countries, 3% from out-of-state. 3% American Indian or Alaska Native, non-Hispanic/Latino; 35% Hispanic/Latino; 5% African American, non-Hispanic/Latino; 3% Asian, non-Hispanic/Latino; 0.3% Native Hawaiian or other Pacific Islander, non-Hispanic/Latino; 1% international. 43% 25 or older, 7% transferred in. Retention: 60% of full-time freshmen returned the following year. Core. Calendar: semesters. Academic remediation for entering students, ESL program, services for LD students, advanced placement, self-designed majors, honors program, independent study, distance learning, summer session for credit, part-time degree program, adult/continuing education programs, co-op programs and internships. Off campus study. ROTC: Army (c), Naval (c), Air Force (c).
Entrance Requirements: Open admission Open admission is for all non-degree seeking students. Degree-seeking students must demonstrate college-readiness by: assessments, proof of completing a college credential, or proof of prior success in college-level math and writing coursework. Options: electronic application, international baccalaureate accepted. Entrance: noncompetitive. Application deadlines: Rolling, Rolling for nonresidents. Transfer credits accepted: Yes.
Costs Per Year: Application fee: $0. State resident tuition: $1524 full-time, $63.50 per credit hour part-time. Nonresident tuition: $7656 full-time, $106 per credit hour part-time. Mandatory fees: $128 full-time, $4.50 per credit hour part-time, $10 per term part-time. Full-time tuition and fees vary according to course load and program. Part-time tuition and fees vary according to course load and program.
Collegiate Environment: Orientation program. Drama-theater group, choral group, student-run newspaper. Social organizations: 31 open to all. Most popular organizations: Student Social Services Organization, Spanish Language Club, Student Nurses Association at Pima, Gay-Straight Student Alliance (GSA), Pima Photography Club. Major annual events: Welcome Week Activities, Blood Drives, Health and Wellness Fairs. Student services: health clinic. Campus security: 24-hour emergency response devices and patrols, late night transport-escort service. Pima Community College Library with 287,262 books, 15,410 microform titles, 771 serials, 19,232 audiovisual materials, an OPAC, and a Web page. Operations spending for the previous fiscal year: $3.2 million. 3,912 computers available on campus for general student use. A campuswide network can be accessed from off-campus.

Students can access the following: online class registration. Staffed computer lab on campus provides training in use of computers, software, and the Internet.
Community Environment: See University of Arizona.

■ **PIMA MEDICAL INSTITUTE (MESA)**
2160 S Power Rd.
Mesa, AZ 85209
Tel: (480)898-9898
E-mail: sbuckley@pmi.edu
Web Site: www.pmi.edu/
Description: Proprietary, 2-year, coed. Setting: urban campus. Core. Distance learning, co-op programs and internships.
Entrance Requirements: Required: high school transcript, interview, Wonderlic Scholastic Level Exam (SLE).
Collegiate Environment: Orientation program.

■ **PIMA MEDICAL INSTITUTE (MESA)**
957 S Dobson Rd.
Mesa, AZ 85202
Tel: (480)644-0267; Free: 888-477-PIMA·
Fax: (480)649-5249
Web Site: www.pmi.edu/
Description: Proprietary, primarily 2-year, coed. Part of Vocational Training Institutes, Inc. Awards certificates, terminal associate, and bachelor's degrees. Founded 1985. Setting: urban campus. Total enrollment: 958. 58% 25 or older. Calendar: modular. Distance learning.
Entrance Requirements: Required: interview, Wonderlic aptitude test. Required for some: high school transcript. Entrance: minimally difficult.

■ **PIMA MEDICAL INSTITUTE (TUCSON)**
3350 E Grant Rd.
Tucson, AZ 85716
Tel: (520)326-1600; Free: 888-477-PIMA
Fax: (520)326-4125
Web Site: www.pmi.edu/
Description: Proprietary, primarily 2-year, coed. Part of Vocational Training Institutes, Inc. Awards certificates, terminal associate, and bachelor's degrees. Founded 1972. Setting: urban campus. Total enrollment: 900. 45% 25 or older. Calendar: modular. Academic remediation for entering students, accelerated degree program, distance learning, adult/continuing education programs, co-op programs and internships.
Entrance Requirements: Option: early admission. Required: interview, Wonderlic Scholastic Level Exam (SLE). Required for some: high school transcript. Entrance: minimally difficult.
Collegiate Environment: Orientation program. E-Global with an OPAC and a Web page.

■ **PRESCOTT COLLEGE**
220 Grove Ave.
Prescott, AZ 86301
Tel: (928)778-2090; Free: 877-350-2100
Fax: (928)776-5157
E-mail: admissions@prescott.edu
Web Site: www.prescott.edu/
Description: Independent, comprehensive, coed. Awards bachelor's, master's, and doctoral degrees and post-master's certificates. Founded 1966. Setting: 13-acre small town campus. Endowment: $1.1 million. Research spending for the previous fiscal year: $920,263. Educational spending for the previous fiscal year: $3433 per student. Total enrollment: 1,065. Faculty: 149 (72 full-time, 77 part-time). Student-undergrad faculty ratio is 8:1. 551 applied, 73% were admitted. 14% from top 10% of their high school class, 28% from top quarter, 86% from top half. Full-time: 541 students, 53% women, 47% men. Part-time: 132 students, 72% women, 28% men. Students come from 45 states and territories, 11 other countries, 75% from out-of-state. 3% American Indian or Alaska Native, non-Hispanic/Latino; 7% Hispanic/Latino; 2% African American, non-Hispanic/Latino; 1% Asian, non-Hispanic/Latino; 0.1% Native Hawaiian or other Pacific Islander, non-Hispanic/Latino; 2% international. 40% 25 or older, 17% live on campus, 23% transferred in. Retention: 73% of full-time freshmen returned the following year. Academic areas with the most degrees conferred: education; natural resources/environmental science; psychology. Core. Calendar: (4-week blocks followed by 10-week terms for each quarter). Services for LD students, advanced placement, self-designed majors, independent study,

distance learning, double major, summer session for credit, external degree program, adult/continuing education programs, internships. Off campus study at Eco League, a five-college consortium of schools that includes Alaska Pacific University, Green Mountain College, Northland College, and College of the Atlantic. Consortium for Innovative Environments in Learning (CIEL), is an eleven-college consortium consisting of: Alverno College, Berea College, Daemen College, The Evergreen State College, Fairhaven College at Western Washington University, Gallatin School of Individualized Study, Hampshire College, Johnson C. Smith University, New College of Florida, Pitzer College. Study abroad program.
Entrance Requirements: Options: electronic application, early decision, deferred admission, international baccalaureate accepted. Required: essay, high school transcript, 1 recommendation, SAT or ACT. Required for some: interview. Entrance: moderately difficult. Application deadlines: 8/15, 8/15 for nonresidents, 12/1 for early decision. Notification: continuous, continuous for nonresidents, 12/15 for early decision. SAT Reasoning Test deadline: 8/15. Transfer credits accepted: Yes. Early decision applicants: 6. Early decision applicants admitted: 6.
Costs Per Year: Application fee: $25. Comprehensive fee: $33,919 includes full-time tuition ($27,408), mandatory fees ($611), and college room and board ($5900). College room only: $4230. Full-time tuition and fees vary according to course load, degree level, and reciprocity agreements. Room and board charges vary according to board plan and housing facility. Part-time tuition: $1142 per credit. Part-time mandatory fees: $306 per term. Part-time tuition and fees vary according to course load, degree level, and reciprocity agreements.
Collegiate Environment: Orientation program. Drama-theater group, choral group, student-run newspaper. Social organizations: 16 open to all; 45% of eligible men and 55% of eligible women are members. Most popular organizations: Student Union, Catalyst, WEB (Women's Empowerment Breakthrough), HUB (Helping Understand Bikes), Aztlan Center. Major annual events: Drag Show, Earth Day Week, Student Awards Ceremony. Student services: personal-psychological counseling. Campus security: 24-hour emergency response devices, late night transport-escort service, controlled dormitory access. 120 college housing spaces available; all were occupied in 2012-13. Freshmen guaranteed college housing. On-campus residence required in freshman year. Option: coed housing available. Prescott College Library with 116,420 books, 160 microform titles, 28,582 serials, 1,844 audiovisual materials, an OPAC, and a Web page. Operations spending for the previous fiscal year: $486,865. 80 computers available on campus for general student use. A campuswide network can be accessed from student residence rooms. Students can access the following: Learning Management System (Moodle), free E-portfolios. Staffed computer lab on campus provides training in use of computers, software, and the Internet.
Community Environment: Located a mile high in the forested mountains of central Arizona, Prescott has a moderate climate and four seasons. Described by"Arizona Highways" magazine as"Everybody's Hometown," the community is known for its friendly atmosphere and small town charm. It was the capital of the Territory of Arizona back in the 1800s and the old governor's mansion still stands today. The town is rich in local history including gold-mining lore, cowboys, and the historic Roughriders. Classic Victorian homes line the streets. With clean air, abundant sunshine, and natural beauty in every direction, the Prescott area is truly an enjoyable place to live.

■ **THE REFRIGERATION SCHOOL**
4210 E Washington St.
Phoenix, AZ 85034-1816
Tel: (602)275-7133; Free: 888-943-4822
E-mail: heather@rsiaz.edu
Web Site: www.refrigerationschool.com/
Description: Proprietary, 2-year, coed. Awards certificates, diplomas, and terminal associate degrees. Founded 1965. Setting: urban campus. Total enrollment: 492. Student-undergrad faculty ratio is 27:1. 1% from out-of-state. 76% 25 or older. Retention: 73% of full-time freshmen returned the following year. Calendar: continuous.

■ **RIO SALADO COLLEGE**
2323 W 14th St.
Tempe, AZ 85281-6950
Tel: (480)517-8000; Free: 800-729-1197
Fax: (480)517-8199
E-mail: admission@riomail.maricopa.edu
Web Site: www.rio.maricopa.edu/

Description: State and locally supported, 2-year, coed. Part of Maricopa County Community College District System. Awards certificates, transfer associate, and terminal associate degrees. Founded 1978. Setting: urban campus. Educational spending for the previous fiscal year: $1807 per student. Total enrollment: 20,865. Faculty: 1,004. Student-undergrad faculty ratio is 25:1. Students come from 44 states and territories, 38 other countries, 4% from out-of-state. 43% 25 or older. Core. Calendar: semesters. Academic remediation for entering students, ESL program, services for LD students, advanced placement, accelerated degree program, honors program, independent study, distance learning, double major, summer session for credit, part-time degree program, external degree program, adult/continuing education programs, co-op programs and internships.

Entrance Requirements: Open admission except for dental hygiene program. Options: electronic application, early admission, deferred admission. Entrance: noncompetitive. Application deadline: Rolling.

Collegiate Environment: Student services: personal-psychological counseling. Campus security: 24-hour emergency response devices, late night transport-escort service. Rio Salado Library and Information Center with 16,000 books, 125 serials, 8,000 audiovisual materials, an OPAC, and a Web page. Operations spending for the previous fiscal year: $197,853. 500 computers available on campus for general student use. A campuswide network can be accessed from off-campus. Students can access the following: online class registration. Staffed computer lab on campus provides training in use of computers, software, and the Internet.

■ **SCOTTSDALE COMMUNITY COLLEGE**
9000 E Chaparral Rd.
Scottsdale, AZ 85256-2626
Tel: (480)423-6000
Fax: (480)423-6200
E-mail: fran.watkins@scottsdalecc.edu
Web Site: www.scottsdalecc.edu/

Description: State and locally supported, 2-year, coed. Part of Maricopa County Community College District System. Awards certificates, diplomas, transfer associate, and terminal associate degrees. Founded 1969. Setting: 160-acre urban campus with easy access to Phoenix. Total enrollment: 10,895. Faculty: 681 (165 full-time, 516 part-time). Student-undergrad faculty ratio is 18:1. Full-time: 3,468 students, 46% women, 54% men. Part-time: 7,427 students, 55% women, 45% men. Students come from 56 states and territories, 42 other countries, 1% from out-of-state. 5% American Indian or Alaska Native, non-Hispanic/Latino; 15% Hispanic/Latino; 5% African American, non-Hispanic/Latino; 2% Asian, non-Hispanic/Latino; 0.4% Native Hawaiian or other Pacific Islander, non-Hispanic/Latino; 1% international. 30% 25 or older, 72% transferred in. Core. Calendar: semesters. Academic remediation for entering students, ESL program, services for LD students, advanced placement, honors program, summer session for credit, part-time degree program, adult/continuing education programs, co-op programs and internships. Off campus study at Servicemembers Opportunity Colleges. Study abroad program.

Entrance Requirements: Open admission. Options: electronic application, early admission. Entrance: noncompetitive. Application deadline: Rolling. Notification: continuous. Transfer credits accepted: Yes.

Costs Per Year: Application fee: $0. Area resident tuition: $2280 full-time, $76 per credit part-time. State resident tuition: $8550 full-time, $285 per credit part-time. Nonresident tuition: $9510 full-time, $317 per credit part-time. Mandatory fees: $30 full-time. Full-time tuition and fees vary according to program and reciprocity agreements. Part-time tuition varies according to program and reciprocity agreements.

Collegiate Environment: Orientation program. Drama-theater group, choral group, student-run newspaper, radio station. Social organizations: 20 open to all. Most popular organizations: Student Leadership Forum, International Community Club, Phi Theta Kappa, Music Industry Club, SCC ASID-Interior Design group. Major annual events: Commencement, Excellence Under the Stars, College to the Community. Student services: personal-psychological counseling. Campus security: 24-hour emergency response devices and patrols, student patrols, late night transport-escort service, 24-hour automatic surveillance cameras. College housing not available. Scottsdale Community College Library with an OPAC and a Web page. 202 computers available on campus for general student use. A campuswide network can be accessed from off-campus. Students can access the following: online class registration. Staffed computer lab on campus provides training in use of software and the Internet.

Community Environment: See Phoenix College.

■ **SESSIONS COLLEGE FOR PROFESSIONAL DESIGN**
398 S MIll Ave., Ste. 300
Tempe, AZ 85281
Tel: (480)212-1704; Free: 800-258-4115
Fax: (480)212-1705
E-mail: admissions@sessions.edu
Web Site: www.sessions.edu/

Description: Proprietary, 2-year, coed. Awards certificates and terminal associate degrees.

Entrance Requirements: Required: essay, high school transcript, 2 recommendations, portfolio, SAT or ACT scores for recent high school graduates or resume of professional work.

■ **SOUTH MOUNTAIN COMMUNITY COLLEGE**
7050 S Twenty-fourth St.
Phoenix, AZ 85040
Tel: (602)243-8000
Fax: (602)243-8329
Web Site: www.southmountaincc.edu/

Description: State and locally supported, 2-year, coed. Part of Maricopa County Community College District System. Awards certificates, transfer associate, and terminal associate degrees. Founded 1979. Setting: 108-acre suburban campus. Total enrollment: 5,138. Student-undergrad faculty ratio is 20:1. 6% from out-of-state. 44% 25 or older. Retention: 55% of full-time freshmen returned the following year. Calendar: semesters. Academic remediation for entering students, advanced placement, summer session for credit, part-time degree program, adult/continuing education programs. ROTC: Air Force (c).

Entrance Requirements: Open admission. Entrance: noncompetitive. Application deadline: 8/22. Notification: continuous until 8/22.

Collegiate Environment: Campus security: late night transport-escort service, 18-hour patrols, campus lockdown.

Community Environment: Located near both downtown Phoenix and Tempe, the college is just minutes from I-10 and Superstition freeways and Arizona State University. Ample parking is available. The college is served by the Phoenix Transit Bus System. Affordable housing, shopping, and services are within easy commuting distance. The campus is located in the shadow of South Mountain Park, the largest municipal park in the United States.

■ **SOUTHWEST INSTITUTE OF HEALING ARTS**
1100 E Apache Blvd.
Tempe, AZ 85281
Tel: (480)994-9244; Free: 888-504-9106
Fax: (480)994-3228
E-mail: joannl@swiha.net
Web Site: www.swiha.org/

Description: Proprietary, 2-year, coed. Awards terminal associate degrees. Founded 1992. Total enrollment: 1,752.

Entrance Requirements: Entrance: noncompetitive.

■ **SOUTHWEST UNIVERSITY OF VISUAL ARTS**
2525 N Country Club Rd.
Tucson, AZ 85716-2505
Tel: (520)325-0123; Free: 800-825-8753
Fax: (520)325-5535
Web Site: www.suva.edu/

Description: Proprietary, comprehensive, coed. Awards associate, bachelor's, and master's degrees. Founded 1983. Setting: suburban campus with easy access to Tucson. Total enrollment: 226. Full-time: 164 students, 64% women, 36% men. Part-time: 62 students, 24% women, 76% men. Core. Calendar: semester with a full summer program. Services for LD students, double major, summer session for credit, part-time degree program. Study abroad program. ROTC: Army (c).

Entrance Requirements: Required: essay, high school transcript, interview. Required for some: ACT ASSET. Entrance: moderately difficult. Application deadline: Rolling. Transfer credits accepted: Yes.

Collegiate Environment: Orientation program.

■ **TOHONO O'ODHAM COMMUNITY COLLEGE**
PO Box 3129
Sells, AZ 85634
Tel: (520)383-8401
Fax: (520)383-8403

E-mail: info@tocc.cc.az.us

Web Site: www.tocc.cc.az.us/

Description: Public, 2-year, coed. Awards certificates, diplomas, transfer associate, and terminal associate degrees. Founded 1998. Setting: 10-acre rural campus. Endowment: $138,720. Research spending for the previous fiscal year: $62,546. Educational spending for the previous fiscal year: $5808 per student. Total enrollment: 254. Faculty: 28 (17 full-time, 11 part-time). Student-undergrad faculty ratio is 4:1. Full-time: 25 students, 68% women, 32% men. Part-time: 229 students, 58% women, 42% men. 0% from out-of-state. 74% 25 or older, 0% transferred in. Retention: 100% of full-time freshmen returned the following year. Core. Calendar: semesters. Academic remediation for entering students, services for LD students, distance learning, double major, summer session for credit, part-time degree program, adult/continuing education programs, co-op programs.

Entrance Requirements: Open admission. Required: high school transcript. Application deadline: Rolling. Notification: continuous. Transfer credits accepted: Yes.

Collegiate Environment: Orientation program. Student services: personal-psychological counseling. Tohono O'odham Community College Library plus 2 others with 7,886 books, 80 serials, 1,398 audiovisual materials, an OPAC, and a Web page. Operations spending for the previous fiscal year: $160,000. 50 computers available on campus for general student use. A campuswide network can be accessed from off-campus. Staffed computer lab on campus provides training in use of computers and the Internet.

■ **UNIVERSAL TECHNICAL INSTITUTE**

10695 W Pierce St.

Avondale, AZ 85323

Tel: (602)264-4164; Free: 800-510-5072

Fax: (602)264-6412

Web Site: www.uti.edu/

Description: Proprietary, 2-year, coed. Awards terminal associate degrees. Founded 1965. Total enrollment: 1,730. Student-undergrad faculty ratio is 23:1. 49% from out-of-state. 14% 25 or older. Retention: 78% of full-time freshmen returned the following year.

Entrance Requirements: Open admission. Required: interview. Entrance: minimally difficult.

■ **UNIVERSITY OF ADVANCING TECHNOLOGY**

2625 W Baseline Rd.

Tempe, AZ 85283-1042

Tel: (602)383-8228; Free: 800-658-5744

Fax: (602)383-8222

E-mail: admissions@uat.edu

Web Site: www.uat.edu/

Description: Proprietary, comprehensive, coed. Awards associate, bachelor's, and master's degrees. Founded 1983. Setting: urban campus. Total enrollment: 1,073. Faculty: 60 (31 full-time, 29 part-time). Student-undergrad faculty ratio is 14:1. Full-time: 1,013 students, 8% women, 92% men. 1% American Indian or Alaska Native, non-Hispanic/Latino; 7% Hispanic/Latino; 7% African American, non-Hispanic/Latino; 3% Asian, non-Hispanic/Latino; 0.3% Native Hawaiian or other Pacific Islander, non-Hispanic/Latino; 2% international. 22% live on campus. Calendar: semesters. Independent study, distance learning, double major, summer session for credit, co-op programs and internships, graduate courses open to undergrads.

Entrance Requirements: Option: electronic application. Required: essay, high school transcript. Required for some: minimum 2.5 high school GPA, SAT or ACT. Application deadline: Rolling. Transfer credits accepted: Yes.

Collegiate Environment: Orientation program. Student-run newspaper. Most popular organizations: Web Club, Gaming Club, Animation Club, Video Club, student government. Major annual events: technology forums, LAN parties, luncheons. Campus security: 24-hour patrols. University of Advancing Computer Technology Library with 27,500 books, 92 serials, 1,200 audiovisual materials, an OPAC, and a Web page. 400 computers available on campus for general student use. Computer purchase/lease plans available. A campuswide network can be accessed from student residence rooms and from off campus. Students can access the following: online class registration. Staffed computer lab on campus provides training in use of computers, software, and the Internet.

■ **THE UNIVERSITY OF ARIZONA**

Tucson, AZ 85721

Tel: (520)621-2211

Fax: (520)621-9799

E-mail: admissions@arizona.edu

Web Site: www.arizona.edu/

Description: State-supported, university, coed. Part of Arizona Board of Regents. Awards bachelor's, master's, and doctoral degrees and post-master's certificates. Founded 1885. Setting: 391-acre urban campus. Endowment: $563.7 million. Research spending for the previous fiscal year: $425,993. Total enrollment: 40,223. Student-undergrad faculty ratio is 22:1. 26,329 applied, 77% were admitted. 32% from top 10% of their high school class, 63% from top quarter, 90% from top half. 81 National Merit Scholars. Full-time: 28,210 students, 53% women, 47% men. Part-time: 3,355 students, 48% women, 52% men. Students come from 116 other countries, 29% from out-of-state. 1% American Indian or Alaska Native, non-Hispanic/Latino; 23% Hispanic/Latino; 3% African American, non-Hispanic/Latino; 6% Asian, non-Hispanic/Latino; 0.2% Native Hawaiian or other Pacific Islander, non-Hispanic/Latino; 5% international. 9% 25 or older, 21% live on campus, 6% transferred in. Retention: 80% of full-time freshmen returned the following year. Academic areas with the most degrees conferred: business/marketing; social sciences; biological/life sciences. Core. Calendar: semesters. ESL program, services for LD students, advanced placement, accelerated degree program, self-designed majors, freshman honors college, honors program, independent study, distance learning, double major, summer session for credit, part-time degree program, external degree program, adult/continuing education programs, co-op programs and internships, graduate courses open to undergrads. Off campus study. Study abroad program. ROTC: Army, Naval, Air Force.

Entrance Requirements: Options: electronic application, early admission, international baccalaureate accepted. Required: essay, high school transcript. Recommended: SAT or ACT. Required for some: minimum 3 high school GPA, interview. Entrance: moderately difficult. Application deadline: 5/1. Notification: continuous. Preference given to state residents. Transfer credits accepted: Yes.

Costs Per Year: Application fee: $50. State resident tuition: $9114 full-time, $651 per credit hour part-time. Nonresident tuition: $25,310 full-time, $1055 per credit hour part-time. Mandatory fees: $921 full-time, $80 per credit hour part-time. Full-time tuition and fees vary according to course level, course load, degree level, location, program, reciprocity agreements, and student level. Part-time tuition and fees vary according to course level, course load, degree level, location, program, reciprocity agreements, and student level. College room and board: $9714. College room only: $6784. Room and board charges vary according to board plan and housing facility.

Collegiate Environment: Orientation program. Drama-theater group, choral group, marching band, student-run newspaper, radio station. Social organizations: 644 open to all; national fraternities, national sororities, local fraternities, local sororities. Major annual events: Spring Fling Carnival, Cultural Programs, Family Weekend. Student services: legal services, health clinic, personal-psychological counseling, women's center. Campus security: 24-hour patrols, student patrols, late night transport-escort service, emergency telephones. 7,209 college housing spaces available. Freshmen given priority for college housing. Options: coed, women-only housing available. University of Arizona Main Library plus 6 others with an OPAC and a Web page. Operations spending for the previous fiscal year: $28.3 million.

Community Environment: Tucson is in a valley of the Sonoran Desert, and is surrounded by mountain ranges. Approximately 700,000 reside in the metropolitan area. Just north of the city are ski slopes and ponderosa pines as well as canyons and grassy meadows, which are popular with hikers and climbers. Yet Tucson has mild winters (average yearly temperature of 85 degrees) and attracts golf, tennis, and other sports enthusiasts year-round. The city has a professional symphony orchestra, opera company, theater company, and ballet, in addition to outstanding medical facilities. Located sixty miles north of Mexico, the community reflects the cultures of its Native American, Spanish, Mexican, and pioneer forefathers.

■ **UNIVERSITY OF PHOENIX–ONLINE CAMPUS**

3157 E Elwood St.

Phoenix, AZ 85034-7209

Tel: (602)387-7000; Free: 866-766-0766

Web Site: www.uopxonline.com/

Description: Proprietary, comprehensive, coed. Awards associate, bachelor's, master's, and doctoral degrees and post-master's certificates. Founded 1989. Total enrollment: 292,797. Faculty: 11,477 (158 full-time, 11,319 part-time). Full-time: 236,109 students, 69% women, 31% men. 80% 25 or older. Academic areas with the most degrees conferred: business/marketing; computer and information sciences; health professions and related sciences. Core. Calendar: continuous. Services for LD students, advanced placement, accelerated degree program, independent study, distance learning, external degree program, adult/continuing education programs, graduate courses open to undergrads.

Entrance Requirements: Open admission. Options: electronic application, deferred admission, international baccalaureate accepted. Required: 1 recommendation. Required for some: high school transcript. Entrance: noncompetitive. Application deadline: Rolling.

Collegiate Environment: University Library with 16,781 serials, an OPAC, and a Web page. Operations spending for the previous fiscal year: $6.8 million.

■ **UNIVERSITY OF PHOENIX–PHOENIX MAIN CAMPUS**
1625 W Fountainhead Pky.
Tempe, AZ 85282-2371
Tel: (602)557-2000; Free: 866-766-0766
Web Site: www.phoenix.edu/

Description: Proprietary, comprehensive, coed. Awards bachelor's and master's degrees and post-master's certificates. Founded 1976. Setting: urban campus. Total enrollment: 5,379. Faculty: 985 (76 full-time, 909 part-time). Full-time: 3,718 students, 59% women, 41% men. 82% 25 or older. Academic areas with the most degrees conferred: business/marketing; computer and information sciences; health professions and related sciences. Core. Calendar: continuous. Services for LD students, advanced placement, accelerated degree program, independent study, distance learning, external degree program, adult/continuing education programs, graduate courses open to undergrads.

Entrance Requirements: Open admission. Options: electronic application, deferred admission. Required: 1 recommendation. Required for some: high school transcript. Entrance: noncompetitive. Application deadline: Rolling.

Collegiate Environment: Campus security: 24-hour patrols, late night transport-escort service. University Library with 16,781 serials, 3,000 audiovisual materials, an OPAC, and a Web page. Operations spending for the previous fiscal year: $6.8 million.

■ **UNIVERSITY OF PHOENIX–SOUTHERN ARIZONA CAMPUS**
300 S Craycroft Rd.
Tucson, AZ 85711
Tel: (520)881-6512; Free: 866-766-0766
Fax: (520)795-6177
Web Site: www.phoenix.edu/

Description: Proprietary, comprehensive, coed. Awards bachelor's and master's degrees and post-master's certificates. Founded 1979. Setting: urban campus. Total enrollment: 2,229. Faculty: 284 (14 full-time, 270 part-time). Full-time: 1,631 students, 63% women, 37% men. 80% 25 or older. Academic areas with the most degrees conferred: business/marketing; computer and information sciences; public administration and social services. Core. Calendar: continuous. Services for LD students, advanced placement, accelerated degree program, independent study, distance learning, external degree program, adult/continuing education programs, graduate courses open to undergrads.

Entrance Requirements: Open admission. Options: electronic application, deferred admission. Required: 1 recommendation. Required for some: high school transcript. Entrance: noncompetitive. Application deadline: Rolling.

Collegiate Environment: Campus security: late night transport-escort service. University Library with 16,781 serials, an OPAC, and a Web page. Operations spending for the previous fiscal year: $6.8 million.

■ **WESTERN INTERNATIONAL UNIVERSITY**
9215 N Black Canyon Hwy.
Phoenix, AZ 85021-2718
Tel: (602)943-2311
E-mail: Melissa.Machuca@west.edu
Web Site: www.west.edu/

Description: Proprietary, comprehensive, coed. Part of Apollo Global and Apollo Group. Awards associate, bachelor's, and master's degrees. Founded 1978. Setting: 4-acre urban campus with easy access to Phoenix. Total enrollment: 2,993. Faculty: 369 (2 full-time, 367 part-time). Student-undergrad faculty ratio is 24:1. Full-time: 2,322 students, 64% women, 36% men. Students come from 59 states and territories, 10 other countries. 2% American Indian or Alaska Native, non-Hispanic/Latino; 12% Hispanic/Latino; 17% African American, non-Hispanic/Latino; 1% Asian, non-Hispanic/Latino; 0.1% Native Hawaiian or other Pacific Islander, non-Hispanic/Latino; 1% international. 94% 25 or older, 0.3% transferred in. Core. Calendar: continuous. Academic remediation for entering students, advanced placement, accelerated degree program, independent study, distance learning, double major, summer session for credit, part-time degree program, adult/continuing education programs.

Entrance Requirements: Options: electronic application, deferred admission. Required: high school transcript, minimum 2.5 high school GPA. Entrance: moderately difficult. Application deadline: Rolling.

Collegiate Environment: Campus security: 24-hour emergency response devices and patrols, late night transport-escort service. Learning Resource Center with a Web page.

■ **YAVAPAI COLLEGE**
1100 E Sheldon St.
Prescott, AZ 86301-3297
Tel: (928)445-7300; Free: 800-922-6787
Fax: (928)776-2151
E-mail: registration@yc.edu
Web Site: www.yc.edu/

Description: State and locally supported, 2-year, coed. Part of Arizona State Community College System. Awards certificates, transfer associate, and terminal associate degrees. Founded 1966. Setting: 100-acre small town campus. Educational spending for the previous fiscal year: $4772 per student. Total enrollment: 8,276. Faculty: 404 (112 full-time, 292 part-time). Student-undergrad faculty ratio is 15:1. Full-time: 1,917 students, 55% women, 45% men. Part-time: 6,359 students, 61% women, 39% men. Students come from 30 states and territories, 18% from out-of-state. 70% 25 or older, 5% live on campus. Core. Calendar: semesters. Academic remediation for entering students, ESL program, services for LD students, advanced placement, honors program, independent study, distance learning, summer session for credit, part-time degree program, adult/continuing education programs, co-op programs and internships. Off campus study at Northern Arizona University, Old Dominion University. ROTC: Army (c), Air Force (c).

Entrance Requirements: Open admission except for nursing, gunsmithing and independent filmmaking. Options: early admission, deferred admission. Required: high school transcript. Required for some: essay. Entrance: noncompetitive. Application deadline: Rolling.

Collegiate Environment: Orientation program. Drama-theater group, choral group, student-run newspaper. Social organizations: 20 open to all. Most popular organizations: Re-Entry Club, Student Nurses Association, Native American Club, International Club, VICA (Vocational Industrial Clubs of America). Major annual events: Welcome Week, Homecoming/Parents' Weekend, Earth Day. Student services: health clinic, personal-psychological counseling, women's center. Campus security: 24-hour emergency response devices and patrols, student patrols, late night transport-escort service, controlled dormitory access. Yavapai College Library with 81,144 books, 1,091 serials, an OPAC, and a Web page. Operations spending for the previous fiscal year: $1 million. 651 computers available on campus for general student use. A campuswide network can be accessed from student residence rooms and from off campus. Staffed computer lab on campus.

Community Environment: Population 40,360. The city of Prescott is imbued with thoroughly Western informality. The city is easily reached from all parts of the United States by regularly scheduled airlines and bus service. Climate is ideal, embracing four seasons, but without the extremes of heat, cold, dryness, or dampness. Employment opportunities are average for a community of this size. Prescott has a community concert program, and an active interest in the arts provides cultural atmosphere. Prescott Frontier Days are held during the July Fourth weekend; this is the original cowboy rodeo of America. The Yavapai County Fair is held during September. There is horse racing at Prescott Downs on weekends from Memorial Day through Labor Day.

■ ARKANSAS BAPTIST COLLEGE

1621 Dr. Martin Luther King, Jr. Dr.
Little Rock, AR 72202-6067
Tel: (501)374-7856
Web Site: www.arkansasbaptist.edu/
Description: Independent Baptist, 4-year, coed. Awards associate and bachelor's degrees. Founded 1884. Setting: urban campus. Total enrollment: 626. Faculty: 38 (18 full-time, 20 part-time). Student-undergrad faculty ratio is 22:1. 3% from top 10% of their high school class, 25% from top quarter, 30% from top half. Students come from 29 states and territories, 1 other country, 17% from out-of-state. 32% 25 or older, 13% live on campus. Retention: 34% of full-time freshmen returned the following year. Core. Calendar: semesters. Academic remediation for entering students, independent study, summer session for credit, part-time degree program, co-op programs and internships.
Entrance Requirements: Open admission. Options: electronic application, deferred admission. Required: high school transcript. Recommended: ACT. Required for some: COMPASS. Entrance: minimally difficult. Application deadline: Rolling.
Collegiate Environment: Orientation program. Choral group, marching band. Social organizations: national fraternities, national sororities; 25% of eligible men and 75% of eligible women are members. Most popular organizations: Phi Beta Lambda, International Club, Student Government Association, Choral/Band Organization. Major annual events: Arkansas Baptist College Health Fair, Arkansas Baptist College Honors Convocation, Arts/Beats and Cuisines. 35 computers available on campus for general student use. A campuswide network can be accessed from student residence rooms and from off campus. Staffed computer lab on campus.

■ ARKANSAS NORTHEASTERN COLLEGE

PO Box 1109
Blytheville, AR 72316-1109
Tel: (870)762-1020
Fax: (870)763-3704
E-mail: lwells@anc.edu
Web Site: www.anc.edu/
Description: State-supported, 2-year, coed. Awards certificates, transfer associate, and terminal associate degrees. Founded 1975. Setting: 80-acre rural campus with easy access to Memphis. Endowment: $187,500. Educational spending for the previous fiscal year: $5048 per student. Total enrollment: 1,800. Faculty: 141 (76 full-time, 65 part-time). Student-undergrad faculty ratio is 18:1. 501 applied, 100% were admitted. 17% from top 10% of their high school class. 3 valedictorians. Full-time: 726 students, 66% women, 34% men. Part-time: 1,074 students, 66% women, 34% men. Students come from 4 states and territories, 17% from out-of-state. 45% 25 or older, 6% transferred in. Retention: 50% of full-time freshmen returned the following year. Core. Calendar: semesters. Academic remediation for entering students, advanced placement, distance learning, double major, summer session for credit, part-time degree program, adult/continuing education programs.
Entrance Requirements: Open admission except for nursing program. Option: deferred admission. Recommended: high school transcript. Entrance: noncompetitive. Application deadline: Rolling. Notification: continuous.
Collegiate Environment: Orientation program. Choral group. Social organizations: 10 open to all. Most popular organizations: Gamma Beta Phi, Association of Childhood Education International, Nursing Club, Cultural Diversity, Adult Student Association. Major annual events: Fall Funfest, Spring Funfest, Evening Student Appreciation Night. Campus security: 24-hour patrols. Adams/Vines Library with 15,493 books, 3,704 microform titles, 165 serials, 682 audiovisual materials, and an OPAC. Operations spending for the previous fiscal year: $326,910. 280 computers available on campus for general student use. A campuswide network can be accessed. Students can access the following: online class registration. Staffed computer lab on campus provides training in use of computers and the Internet.
Community Environment: In a rural area with a population of 16,600.

■ ARKANSAS STATE UNIVERSITY

PO Box 600
State University, AR 72467
Tel: (870)972-2100; Free: 800-382-3030
Fax: (870)972-2090
E-mail: admissions@astate.edu
Web Site: www.astate.edu/
Description: State-supported, comprehensive, coed. Part of Arkansas State University System. Awards associate, bachelor's, master's, and doctoral degrees and post-master's certificates. Founded 1909. Setting: 1,376-acre small town campus with easy access to Memphis. Endowment: $39.4 million. Research spending for the previous fiscal year: $12.9 million. Educational spending for the previous fiscal year: $4680 per student. Total enrollment: 13,877. Faculty: 660 (487 full-time, 173 part-time). Student-undergrad faculty ratio is 19:1. 5,289 applied, 71% were admitted. 24% from top 10% of their high school class, 45% from top quarter, 69% from top half. Full-time: 7,822 students, 57% women, 43% men. Part-time: 2,346 students, 60% women, 40% men. Students come from 40 states and territories, 48 other countries, 11% from out-of-state. 0.4% American Indian or Alaska Native, non-Hispanic/Latino; 2% Hispanic/Latino; 16% African American, non-Hispanic/Latino; 1% Asian, non-Hispanic/Latino; 0.1% Native Hawaiian or other Pacific Islander, non-Hispanic/Latino; 6% international. 24% 25 or older, 27% live on campus, 10% transferred in. Retention: 70% of full-time freshmen returned the following year. Academic areas with the most degrees conferred: education; health professions and related sciences; business/marketing. Core. Calendar: semesters. Academic remediation for entering students, ESL program, services for LD students, advanced placement, accelerated degree program, honors program, independent study, distance learning, double major, summer session for credit, part-time degree program, internships, graduate courses open to undergrads. Off campus study at Arkansas State University-Beebe, East Arkansas Community College, Mid-South Community College, ASU Continuing Education and Community Outreach, ASU-Mountain Home, ASU-Paragould, Arkansas Northeastern College. Study abroad program. ROTC: Army.
Entrance Requirements: Options: electronic application, early admission, international baccalaureate accepted. Required: high school transcript, minimum 2.75 high school GPA, For Fall 2013, ACT composite score of 21 plus a 2.75 high school GPA, immunization, selective service, SAT or ACT. Recommended: ACT. Required for some: ACT ASSET; ACT COMPASS; TOEFL, IELTS, PTE or Proof of English Proficiency for international students. Entrance: moderately difficult. Application deadline: Rolling. Notification: continuous. SAT Reasoning Test deadline: 8/19. SAT Subject Test deadline: 8/19. Transfer credits accepted: Yes.
Costs Per Year: Application fee: $15. State resident tuition: $5430 full-time, $181 per credit hour part-time. Nonresident tuition: $10,860 full-time, $362 per credit hour part-time. Mandatory fees: $1750 full-time, $56 per credit

hour part-time, $25 per term part-time. Full-time tuition and fees vary according to course load, location, and program. Part-time tuition and fees vary according to course load, location, and program. College room and board: $7150. Room and board charges vary according to board plan, housing facility, and student level.

Collegiate Environment: Orientation program. Drama-theater group, choral group, marching band, student-run newspaper, radio station. Social organizations: 139 open to all; national fraternities, national sororities; 12% of eligible men and 10% of eligible women are members. Most popular organizations: ASU Rugby, Black Student Association, Student Activities Board, Honors College Association, Student Government Association. Major annual events: Welcome Week, Order of the Pack, Homecoming. Student services: health clinic, personal-psychological counseling. Campus security: 24-hour emergency response devices and patrols, student patrols, late night transport-escort service, controlled dormitory access, check-in desk; video surveillance cameras. 3,036 college housing spaces available; 2,842 were occupied in 2012-13. No special consideration for freshman housing applicants. On-campus residence required in freshman year. Options: coed, men-only, women-only housing available. Dean B. Ellis Library with 787,237 books, 40,264 serials, 29,429 audiovisual materials, an OPAC, and a Web page. Operations spending for the previous fiscal year: $4.2 million. 600 computers available on campus for general student use. Computer purchase/lease plans available. A campuswide network can be accessed from student residence rooms and from off campus. Students can access the following: online class registration. Staffed computer lab on campus (open 24 hours a day) provides training in use of computers, software, and the Internet.

Community Environment: Jonesboro is located on Crowley's Ridge, bordering the rich Mississippi Delta Agricultural and Industrial Center. Buses, railroads and airlines service the area. Jonesboro is 65 miles from Memphis, 133 miles from Little Rock, and 261 miles from St. Louis. The mean temperature is 60 degrees, and the average annual rainfall is 50 inches. There are more than 102 active clubs, and organizations, theaters, a Community Center, and several city parks in the city. Lake Frierson State Park and Craighead Forest Park and lake are nearby.

■ **ARKANSAS STATE UNIVERSITY–BEEBE**
PO Box 1000
Beebe, AR 72012-1000
Tel: (501)882-3600; Free: 800-632-9985
Fax: (501)882-8370
E-mail: rdhudson@asub.edu
Web Site: www.asub.edu/
Description: State-supported, 2-year, coed. Part of Arkansas State University System. Awards certificates, transfer associate, and terminal associate degrees. Founded 1927. Setting: 320-acre small town campus with easy access to Memphis. Total enrollment: 4,491. Faculty: 97 (63 full-time, 34 part-time). Student-undergrad faculty ratio is 30:1. 3,451 applied, 54% were admitted. 2 class presidents, 1 valedictorian, 20 student government officers. Full-time: 2,601 students, 60% women, 40% men. Part-time: 1,890 students, 59% women, 41% men. Students come from 20 states and territories, 1% from out-of-state. 32% 25 or older, 12% live on campus, 6% transferred in. Retention: 64% of full-time freshmen returned the following year. Core. Calendar: semesters. Academic remediation for entering students, advanced placement, honors program, distance learning, summer session for credit, part-time degree program, adult/continuing education programs. ROTC: Army.
Entrance Requirements: Open admission. Options: electronic application, deferred admission. Required: high school transcript. Entrance: noncompetitive. Application deadline: Rolling. Notification: continuous. Transfer credits accepted: No.
Collegiate Environment: Orientation program. Drama-theater group, choral group. Social organizations: 19 open to all. Most popular organizations: Student Arkansas Education Association, Art Club, Agri Club, Social Science Club, Leadership Council. Major annual events: Organizational Fair, Harvestfest/Spring Dance, Leadership Council activities. Student services: personal-psychological counseling. Campus security: 24-hour emergency response devices and patrols. Abington Library with 90,000 books, 500 serials, and 10 audiovisual materials. 375 computers available on campus for general student use. A campuswide network can be accessed from student residence rooms and from off campus. Students can access the following: online class registration. Staffed computer lab on campus.

■ **ARKANSAS STATE UNIVERSITY–MOUNTAIN HOME**
1600 S College St.
Mountain Home, AR 72653
Tel: (870)508-6100
E-mail: dparrish@asumh.edu
Web Site: www.asumh.edu/
Description: State-supported, 2-year, coed. Part of Arkansas State University System. Awards certificates and terminal associate degrees. Founded 2000. Setting: 136-acre small town campus. Core. Calendar: semesters. Academic remediation for entering students, ESL program, services for LD students, advanced placement, honors program, independent study, distance learning, summer session for credit, part-time degree program, co-op programs and internships. ROTC: Army.
Entrance Requirements: Open admission. Option: electronic application. Required: high school transcript. Recommended: placement scores, GED scores accepted, SAT or ACT, COMPASS, ASSET. Entrance: noncompetitive. Notification: continuous. Transfer credits accepted: Yes.
Costs Per Year: Application fee: $0. State resident tuition: $2112 full-time, $88 per credit hour part-time. Nonresident tuition: $3600 full-time, $150 per credit hour part-time. Mandatory fees: $504 full-time, $21 per credit hour part-time. Full-time tuition and fees vary according to course load. Part-time tuition and fees vary according to course load.
Collegiate Environment: Orientation program. Social organizations: 13 open to all; Phi Theta Kappa Honor Society. Most popular organizations: Phi Theta Kappa, Circle K, Criminal Justice Club, Mortuary Science Club, Student Ambassadors. Major annual events: Gaston Lecture Club events, Jingle-on-the-Green, Arvest Concert Series. Campus security: during operation hours security is present and available as needed. College housing not available. Norma Wood Library with an OPAC and a Web page.

■ **ARKANSAS STATE UNIVERSITY–NEWPORT**
7648 Victory Blvd.
Newport, AR 72112
Tel: (870)512-7800; Free: 800-976-1676
E-mail: robert.summers@asun.edu
Web Site: www.asun.edu/
Description: State-supported, 2-year, coed. Part of Arkansas State University System. Awards certificates, diplomas, transfer associate, and terminal associate degrees. Founded 1989. Total enrollment: 2,037. Student-undergrad faculty ratio is 19:1. 8% from out-of-state. 35% 25 or older. Core. Calendar: semesters. Academic remediation for entering students, ESL program, services for LD students, independent study, external degree program, adult/continuing education programs, internships. Off campus study.
Entrance Requirements: Open admission. Required: high school transcript, interview, SAT or ACT or COMPASS. Entrance: noncompetitive.
Collegiate Environment: Orientation program.

■ **ARKANSAS TECH UNIVERSITY**
Russellville, AR 72801
Tel: (479)968-0389; Free: 800-582-6953
Fax: (479)964-0522
E-mail: tech.enroll@atu.edu
Web Site: www.atu.edu/
Description: State-supported, comprehensive, coed. Awards associate, bachelor's, and master's degrees and post-master's certificates. Founded 1909. Setting: 559-acre small town campus. Endowment: $17 million. Research spending for the previous fiscal year: $1.1 million. Educational spending for the previous fiscal year: $4061 per student. Total enrollment: 10,950. Faculty: 519 (330 full-time, 189 part-time). Student-undergrad faculty ratio is 20:1. 3,857 applied, 88% were admitted. 14% from top 10% of their high school class, 34% from top quarter, 64% from top half. Full-time: 7,068 students, 54% women, 46% men. Part-time: 3,021 students, 57% women, 43% men. Students come from 41 states and territories, 32 other countries, 4% from out-of-state. 2% American Indian or Alaska Native, non-Hispanic/Latino; 5% Hispanic/Latino; 7% African American, non-Hispanic/Latino; 2% Asian, non-Hispanic/Latino; 0.05% Native Hawaiian or other Pacific Islander, non-Hispanic/Latino; 2% international. 28% 25 or older, 30% live on campus, 6% transferred in. Retention: 67% of full-time freshmen returned the following year. Academic areas with the most degrees conferred: education; health professions and related sciences; interdisciplinary studies. Core. Calendar: semesters. Academic remediation for entering students, ESL program, services for LD students, advanced placement, accelerated degree program, honors program, independent study, distance learning, double major, sum-

mer session for credit, part-time degree program, adult/continuing education programs, internships, graduate courses open to undergrads. Off campus study. Study abroad program. ROTC: Army (c).

Entrance Requirements: Options: electronic application, early action, deferred admission, international baccalaureate accepted. Required: high school transcript, minimum 2 high school GPA, SAT or ACT. Entrance: moderately difficult. Notification: continuous. SAT Reasoning Test deadline: 8/15. SAT Subject Test deadline: 8/15. Transfer credits accepted: Yes.

Costs Per Year: Application fee: $0. State resident tuition: $5610 full-time, $187 per credit hour part-time. Nonresident tuition: $11,220 full-time, $374 per credit hour part-time. Mandatory fees: $1188 full-time, $20 per credit hour part-time, $159 per term part-time. Full-time tuition and fees vary according to course load and location. Part-time tuition and fees vary according to course load and location. College room and board: $5846. College room only: $3582. Room and board charges vary according to board plan, housing facility, and location.

Collegiate Environment: Orientation program. Drama-theater group, choral group, marching band, student-run newspaper, radio station. Social organizations: 114 open to all; national fraternities, national sororities, local fraternities, local sororities; 6% of eligible men and 5% of eligible women are members. Student services: health clinic, personal-psychological counseling. Campus security: 24-hour emergency response devices and patrols, student patrols, late night transport-escort service, controlled dormitory access. Freshmen guaranteed college housing. On-campus residence required through sophomore year. Options: coed, men-only, women-only housing available. Ross Pendergraft Library and Technology Center with 288,317 books, 900,529 microform titles, 758 serials, 14,430 audiovisual materials, an OPAC, and a Web page. Operations spending for the previous fiscal year: $1.6 million. 1,124 computers available on campus for general student use. Computer purchase/lease plans available. A campuswide network can be accessed from student residence rooms and from off campus. Students can access the following: online class registration. Staffed computer lab on campus provides training in use of computers, software, and the Internet.

Community Environment: Russellville, the crossroads for State Highways 7, 22, 124, and 64, is located equidistant from Little Rock, Hot Springs, Harrison, and Fort Smith. Interstate 40 passes just north of Russellville, a city of 25,000. A 36,600 acre lake, formed by a lock and dam on the navigable Arkansas River, lies southwest of the city. The area, served by airplane, rail, and bus lines, is experiencing vigorous industrial development, which includes the construction of the first nuclear power plant in the Southwest. Recreational facilities in the area include lakes, picnic areas, city parks, swimming pools, tennis courts, and private country clubs. There are the usual civic organizations of a city. Part-time employment is available in stores and on campus.

■ **BLACK RIVER TECHNICAL COLLEGE**
1410 Hwy. 304 E
Pocahontas, AR 72455
Tel: (870)248-4000
Fax: (870)248-4100
Web Site: www.blackrivertech.edu/
Description: State-supported, 2-year, coed. Awards transfer associate and terminal associate degrees. Founded 1972. Setting: 55-acre small town campus. Total enrollment: 1,933. 50% 25 or older. Calendar: semesters. Academic remediation for entering students, services for LD students, self-designed majors, honors program, summer session for credit, part-time degree program, co-op programs and internships.
Entrance Requirements: Open admission except for nursing program. Required for some: high school transcript, interview, ACT, ACT ASSET, or SAT. Entrance: noncompetitive. Application deadline: Rolling.
Collegiate Environment: Orientation program. Campus security: night patrol. Black River Technical College Library with 10,000 books, 200 serials, and an OPAC.

■ **CENTRAL BAPTIST COLLEGE**
1501 College Ave.
Conway, AR 72032
Tel: (501)329-6872; Free: 800-205-6872
E-mail: tmobly@cbc.edu
Web Site: www.cbc.edu/
Description: Independent Baptist, 4-year, coed. Awards associate and bachelor's degrees. Founded 1952. Setting: 11-acre small town campus. Endowment: $1.5 million. Total enrollment: 832. Faculty: 70 (26 full-time, 44

part-time). Student-undergrad faculty ratio is 20:1. 16% from top 10% of their high school class, 24% from top quarter, 34% from top half. Full-time: 686 students, 48% women, 52% men. Part-time: 147 students, 48% women, 52% men. Students come from 19 states and territories, 13 other countries, 13% from out-of-state. 1% American Indian or Alaska Native, non-Hispanic/Latino; 2% Hispanic/Latino; 21% African American, non-Hispanic/Latino; 1% Asian, non-Hispanic/Latino; 0.2% Native Hawaiian or other Pacific Islander, non-Hispanic/Latino; 3% international. 38% 25 or older, 14% transferred in. Retention: 50% of full-time freshmen returned the following year. Academic areas with the most degrees conferred: business/marketing; theology and religious vocations; liberal arts/general studies. Core. Calendar: semesters. Academic remediation for entering students, advanced placement, summer session for credit, part-time degree program, adult/continuing education programs, internships. ROTC: Army (c).
Entrance Requirements: Options: electronic application, early admission. Required: high school transcript, minimum 2.5 high school GPA, ACT. Entrance: minimally difficult. Application deadline: 8/15.
Collegiate Environment: Orientation program. Drama-theater group, choral group. Major annual events: Harvest Party, Discovery Day, Spring Fling. Student services: personal-psychological counseling. On-campus residence required through senior year. J. E. Cobb Library with 50,448 books, 27,268 microform titles, and 330 serials. Operations spending for the previous fiscal year: $94,035. 70 computers available on campus for general student use. A campuswide network can be accessed. Staffed computer lab on campus.
Community Environment: See University of Central Arkansas.

■ **COLLEGE OF THE OUACHITAS**
One College Cir.
Malvern, AR 72104
Tel: (501)337-5000
Fax: (501)337-9382
E-mail: klazenby@coto.edu
Web Site: www.coto.edu/
Description: State-supported, 2-year, coed. Awards certificates, transfer associate, and terminal associate degrees. Founded 1972. Setting: 11-acre small town campus. Educational spending for the previous fiscal year: $2800 per student. Total enrollment: 1,407. Faculty: 98 (39 full-time, 59 part-time). Full-time: 592 students, 73% women, 27% men. Part-time: 815 students, 51% women, 49% men. 0.4% American Indian or Alaska Native, non-Hispanic/Latino; 3% Hispanic/Latino; 12% African American, non-Hispanic/Latino; 0.4% Asian, non-Hispanic/Latino; 0.1% Native Hawaiian or other Pacific Islander, non-Hispanic/Latino; 0.2% international. 0% transferred in. Core. Calendar: semesters. Academic remediation for entering students, services for LD students, advanced placement, accelerated degree program, independent study, distance learning, double major, summer session for credit, part-time degree program, co-op programs and internships.
Entrance Requirements: Open admission except for nursing program. Options: electronic application, early admission, deferred admission. Required: high school transcript. Recommended: SAT or ACT, ACT COMPASS or ASSET. Entrance: noncompetitive. Application deadline: Rolling.
Costs Per Year: State resident tuition: $1950 full-time, $65 per credit hour part-time. Nonresident tuition: $3900 full-time, $130 per credit hour part-time. Mandatory fees: $557 full-time, $17 per credit part-time, $16. Full-time tuition and fees vary according to program. Part-time tuition and fees vary according to program. Tuition guaranteed not to increase for student's term of enrollment.
Collegiate Environment: Orientation program. Major annual event: awards ceremony. Student services: personal-psychological counseling. Campus security: 24-hour patrols. Ouachita Technical College Library/Learning Resource Center with 8,000 books, 6,151 microform titles, 100 serials, 1,200 audiovisual materials, an OPAC, and a Web page. Operations spending for the previous fiscal year: $118,492. 225 computers available on campus for general student use. A campuswide network can be accessed from off-campus. Staffed computer lab on campus.

■ **COSSATOT COMMUNITY COLLEGE OF THE UNIVERSITY OF ARKANSAS**
183 College Dr.
De Queen, AR 71832
Tel: (870)584-4471; Free: 800-844-4471
E-mail: Jwhite@cccua.edu
Web Site: www.cccua.edu/
Description: State-supported, 2-year, coed. Part of University of Arkansas System. Awards certificates, transfer associate, and terminal associate

degrees. Founded 1991. Setting: 30-acre rural campus. Endowment: $108,167. Total enrollment: 1,542. Faculty: 74 (34 full-time, 40 part-time). Student-undergrad faculty ratio is 14:1. Students come from 6 states and territories, 1 other country, 2% from out-of-state. 2% American Indian or Alaska Native, non-Hispanic/Latino; 16% Hispanic/Latino; 13% African American, non-Hispanic/Latino; 1% Asian, non-Hispanic/Latino; 0.3% Native Hawaiian or other Pacific Islander, non-Hispanic/Latino; 0% international. 33% 25 or older. Calendar: semesters. Academic remediation for entering students, services for LD students, advanced placement, accelerated degree program, independent study, distance learning, double major, summer session for credit, part-time degree program, adult/continuing education programs, co-op programs and internships. Off campus study.
Entrance Requirements: Open admission. Option: electronic application. Recommended: high school transcript. Entrance: noncompetitive. Transfer credits accepted: Yes.
Collegiate Environment: Orientation program. Student-run radio station. Social organizations: 6 open to all. Most popular organizations: Students 4 Students, Phi Theta Kappa, ALPNA, VICA (Vocational Industrial Clubs of America). Major annual events: Thanksgiving Dinner, Relay for Life. Student services: personal-psychological counseling. College housing not available. Operations spending for the previous fiscal year: $105,155.

■ **CROWLEY'S RIDGE COLLEGE**
100 College Dr.
Paragould, AR 72450-9731
Tel: (870)236-6901; Free: 800-264-1096
Fax: (870)236-7748
E-mail: njoneshi@crc.pioneer.paragould.ar.us
Web Site: www.crc.edu/
Description: Independent, 2-year, coed, affiliated with Church of Christ. Awards transfer associate and terminal associate degrees. Founded 1964. Setting: 112-acre small town campus. Total enrollment: 168. 4% 25 or older. Calendar: semesters. Academic remediation for entering students, honors program, independent study, double major, summer session for credit, part-time degree program.
Entrance Requirements: Open admission. Option: electronic application. Required: high school transcript, recommendation form filled out by high school. Required for some: interview. Entrance: noncompetitive. Application deadline: Rolling.
Collegiate Environment: Orientation program. Drama-theater group, choral group, student-run newspaper. Learning Center with an OPAC and a Web page.

■ **EAST ARKANSAS COMMUNITY COLLEGE**
1700 Newcastle Rd.
Forrest City, AR 72335-2204
Tel: (870)633-4480; Free: 877-797-3222
Fax: (870)633-7222
E-mail: dadams@eacc.edu
Web Site: www.eacc.edu/
Description: State-supported, 2-year, coed. Awards certificates, transfer associate, and terminal associate degrees. Founded 1974. Setting: 40-acre small town campus with easy access to Memphis. Total enrollment: 1,547. Faculty: 95 (39 full-time, 56 part-time). Student-undergrad faculty ratio is 18:1. Full-time: 779 students, 73% women, 27% men. Part-time: 768 students, 69% women, 31% men. 45% 25 or older. Core. Calendar: semesters. Academic remediation for entering students, services for LD students, advanced placement, honors program, summer session for credit, part-time degree program, adult/continuing education programs.
Entrance Requirements: Open admission. Options: early admission, deferred admission. Required: high school transcript. Entrance: minimally difficult. Application deadline: Rolling. Notification: continuous.
Collegiate Environment: Drama-theater group, choral group. Social organizations: 4 open to all. Most popular organizations: Gamma Beta Phi, Baptist Student Union, Student Activities Committee, Lambda Alpha Epsilon. Major annual events: Spring Barbecue, Homecoming. Student services: personal-psychological counseling. Campus security: 24-hour emergency response devices, 16-hour patrols by trained security personnel. Learning Resource Center plus 1 other with 21,908 books and 109 serials. 35 computers available on campus for general student use. A campuswide network can be accessed. Students can access the following: online class registration. Staffed computer lab on campus provides training in use of computers, software, and the Internet.

Community Environment: Forrest City, with a population of 14,078, is the county seat of St. Francis County.

■ **ECCLESIA COLLEGE**
9653 Nations Dr.
Springdale, AR 72762
Tel: (479)248-7236
E-mail: myfuture@ecollege.edu
Web Site: www.ecollege.edu/
Description: Independent Christian, 4-year, coed. Awards associate and bachelor's degrees. Founded 1995. Setting: 200-acre suburban campus. Total enrollment: 235. Student-undergrad faculty ratio is 10;1. 65 applied. Core. Calendar: semesters. Independent study, distance learning, internships.
Entrance Requirements: Required: essay, high school transcript, minimum 2 high school GPA, 1 recommendation, interview, SAT or ACT, COMPASS. Entrance: noncompetitive. Transfer credits accepted: Yes.
Collegiate Environment: Orientation program. Drama-theater group, choral group. Campus security: student patrols.

■ **HARDING UNIVERSITY**
915 E Market Ave.
Searcy, AR 72149-0001
Tel: (501)279-4000; Free: 800-477-4407
Fax: (501)279-4865
E-mail: admissions@harding.edu
Web Site: www.harding.edu/
Description: Independent, university, coed, affiliated with Church of Christ. Awards bachelor's, master's, and doctoral degrees and post-master's certificates. Founded 1924. Setting: 350-acre small town campus with easy access to Little Rock. Endowment: $99.3 million. Research spending for the previous fiscal year: $438,074. Educational spending for the previous fiscal year: $9802 per student. Total enrollment: 6,672. Faculty: 585 (288 full-time, 297 part-time). Student-undergrad faculty ratio is 17:1. 2,477 applied, 75% were admitted. 29% from top 10% of their high school class, 54% from top quarter, 80% from top half. 13 National Merit Scholars, 31 valedictorians. Full-time: 4,007 students, 54% women, 46% men. Part-time: 286 students, 49% women, 51% men. Students come from 49 states and territories, 53 other countries, 71% from out-of-state. 0.5% American Indian or Alaska Native, non-Hispanic/Latino; 3% Hispanic/Latino; 4% African American, non-Hispanic/Latino; 1% Asian, non-Hispanic/Latino; 0.05% Native Hawaiian or other Pacific Islander, non-Hispanic/Latino; 7% international. 6% 25 or older, 72% live on campus, 5% transferred in. Retention: 81% of full-time freshmen returned the following year. Academic areas with the most degrees conferred: business/marketing; health professions and related sciences; education. Core. Calendar: semesters. Academic remediation for entering students, ESL program, services for LD students, advanced placement, accelerated degree program, self-designed majors, freshman honors college, honors program, independent study, distance learning, double major, summer session for credit, part-time degree program, adult/continuing education programs, co-op programs and internships, graduate courses open to undergrads. Study abroad program.
Entrance Requirements: Options: electronic application, early admission, early action, deferred admission, international baccalaureate accepted. Required: essay, high school transcript, 2 recommendations, SAT or ACT. Entrance: moderately difficult. Application deadlines: Rolling, Rolling for nonresidents. Notification: continuous, continuous for nonresidents. SAT Reasoning Test deadline: 7/1. Transfer credits accepted: Yes.
Costs Per Year: Application fee: $40. Comprehensive fee: $21,432 includes full-time tuition ($14,790), mandatory fees ($450), and college room and board ($6192). College room only: $3094. Full-time tuition and fees vary according to course load. Room and board charges vary according to board plan and housing facility. Part-time tuition: $493 per credit hour. Part-time mandatory fees: $25 per credit hour. Part-time tuition and fees vary according to course load.
Collegiate Environment: Orientation program. Drama-theater group, choral group, marching band, student-run newspaper, radio station. Social organizations: local fraternities, local sororities; 45% of eligible men and 51% of eligible women are members. Most popular organizations: Bisons for Christ, Harding in Action, Spring Break Campaigns, HUmanity. Major annual events: Spring Sing Festival, Homecoming, Bisons for Christ. Student services: health clinic, personal-psychological counseling. Campus security: 24-hour emergency response devices and patrols, student patrols, late night transport-escort service, controlled dormitory access. 3,136 college housing

spaces available; 3,104 were occupied in 2012-13. Freshmen guaranteed college housing. On-campus residence required through senior year. Options: men-only, women-only housing available. Brackett Library plus 1 other with 236,641 books, 243,193 microform titles, 72,726 serials, 11,019 audiovisual materials, an OPAC, and a Web page. Operations spending for the previous fiscal year: $1.1 million. 482 computers available on campus for general student use. A campuswide network can be accessed from student residence rooms and from off campus. Students can access the following: online class registration. Staffed computer lab on campus provides training in use of computers, software, and the Internet.

Community Environment: Searcy is a small town located approximately 50 miles from Little Rock. The climate is temperate. A public library, two large hospitals, many churches, and a variety of shops serve the city of 20,000. Greer's Ferry Lake, with approximately 400 miles of shoreline, is located within 30 miles of campus. The Little Red River, which is famous for its rainbow trout, runs through the edge of Searcy. About 45 minutes from Harding, the University owns a 1,200 acre camp consisting of many log buildings, bluffs, and horse stables.

■ **HENDERSON STATE UNIVERSITY**
1100 Henderson St.
Arkadelphia, AR 71999-0001
Tel: (870)230-5000; Free: 800-228-7333
Fax: (870)230-5144
E-mail: hardwrv@hsu.edu
Web Site: www.hsu.edu/

Description: State-supported, comprehensive, coed. Awards bachelor's and master's degrees and post-master's certificates. Founded 1890. Setting: 151-acre small town campus with easy access to Little Rock. Endowment: $12.3 million. Research spending for the previous fiscal year: $403,319. Educational spending for the previous fiscal year: $2421 per student. Total enrollment: 3,771. Faculty: 259 (173 full-time, 86 part-time). Student-undergrad faculty ratio is 16:1. 3,383 applied, 61% were admitted. 14% from top 10% of their high school class, 39% from top quarter, 72% from top half. Full-time: 3,017 students, 55% women, 45% men. Part-time: 346 students, 62% women, 38% men. Students come from 25 states and territories, 15 other countries, 13% from out-of-state. 0.3% American Indian or Alaska Native, non-Hispanic/Latino; 3% Hispanic/Latino; 23% African American, non-Hispanic/Latino; 1% Asian, non-Hispanic/Latino; 0.03% Native Hawaiian or other Pacific Islander, non-Hispanic/Latino; 1% international. 17% 25 or older, 41% live on campus, 10% transferred in. Retention: 59% of full-time freshmen returned the following year. Academic areas with the most degrees conferred: education; business/marketing; visual and performing arts. Core. Calendar: semesters. Academic remediation for entering students, ESL program, services for LD students, advanced placement, freshman honors college, honors program, distance learning, summer session for credit, part-time degree program, internships, graduate courses open to undergrads. Off campus study at Ouachita Baptist University. ROTC: Army (c).

Entrance Requirements: Options: electronic application, deferred admission. Required: high school transcript, SAT or ACT. Recommended: minimum 2.5 high school GPA, ACT. Required for some: essay, 3 recommendations. Entrance: moderately difficult. Application deadline: 7/15. Notification: continuous. Transfer credits accepted: Yes.

Costs Per Year: Application fee: $0. State resident tuition: $5880 full-time, $196 per credit hour part-time. Nonresident tuition: $11,760 full-time, $392 per credit hour part-time. Mandatory fees: $1104 full-time. Full-time tuition and fees vary according to course load, degree level, and student level. Part-time tuition varies according to course load, degree level, and student level. College room and board: $5332. Room and board charges vary according to board plan and housing facility.

Collegiate Environment: Orientation program. Drama-theater group, choral group, marching band, student-run newspaper, radio station. Social organizations: 85 open to all; national fraternities, national sororities, local fraternities, local sororities. Most popular organizations: Heart and Key, Student Government Association, Residence Hall Association. Major annual events: Homecoming, Spring Fling, Parents' Weekend. Student services: health clinic, personal-psychological counseling. Campus security: 24-hour emergency response devices and patrols, late night transport-escort service, controlled dormitory access. College housing designed to accommodate 1,244 students; 1,338 undergraduates lived in college housing during 2012-13. Freshmen given priority for college housing. On-campus residence required in freshman year. Options: coed, men-only, women-only housing available. Huie Library with 270,989 books, 212,986 microform titles, 20,733 audiovisual materials, an OPAC, and a Web page. Operations spending for

the previous fiscal year: $894,131. 125 computers available on campus for general student use. A campuswide network can be accessed from student residence rooms and from off campus. Students can access the following: online class registration. Staffed computer lab on campus.

Community Environment: Arkadelphia is 55 miles southwest of Little Rock, and 35 miles south of Hot Springs, America's oldest national park. Arkadelphia is a modern, progressive city, and a well-known educational center. The Missouri Pacific Railroad, U.S. Interstate 30, U.S. Highway 67, and state highways make this city easily accessible from all parts of the state.

■ **HENDRIX COLLEGE**
1600 Washington Ave.
Conway, AR 72032-3080
Tel: (501)329-6811; Free: 800-277-9017
Fax: (501)450-3843
E-mail: baker@hendrix.edu
Web Site: www.hendrix.edu/

Description: Independent United Methodist, comprehensive, coed. Awards bachelor's and master's degrees. Founded 1876. Setting: 180-acre suburban campus with easy access to Little Rock. Endowment: $158 million. Research spending for the previous fiscal year: $1.2 million. Educational spending for the previous fiscal year: $12,890 per student. Total enrollment: 1,388. Faculty: 142 (108 full-time, 34 part-time). Student-undergrad faculty ratio is 11:1. 1,656 applied, 83% were admitted. 51% from top 10% of their high school class, 77% from top quarter, 96% from top half. 5 National Merit Scholars, 21 valedictorians, 21 student government officers. Full-time: 1,356 students, 57% women, 43% men. Part-time: 17 students, 47% women, 53% men. Students come from 45 states and territories, 11 other countries, 55% from out-of-state. 1% American Indian or Alaska Native, non-Hispanic/Latino; 5% Hispanic/Latino; 3% African American, non-Hispanic/Latino; 3% Asian, non-Hispanic/Latino; 0% Native Hawaiian or other Pacific Islander, non-Hispanic/Latino; 5% international. 1% 25 or older, 91% live on campus, 1% transferred in. Retention: 86% of full-time freshmen returned the following year. Academic areas with the most degrees conferred: social sciences; biological/life sciences; psychology. Core. Calendar: semesters. ESL program, services for LD students, advanced placement, self-designed majors, independent study, double major, external degree program, co-op programs and internships, graduate courses open to undergrads. Off campus study at American University, Associated Colleges of the South. Study abroad program. ROTC: Army (c).

Entrance Requirements: Options: electronic application, early action, international baccalaureate accepted. Required: essay, high school transcript, SAT or ACT. Recommended: 1 recommendation. Required for some: interview. Entrance: very difficult. Application deadline: 6/1. Notification: continuous, 4/30 for nonresidents. SAT Reasoning Test deadline: 6/1. SAT Subject Test deadline: 6/1. Applicants placed on waiting list: 11. Wait-listed applicants offered admission: 3. Early action applicants: 932. Early action applicants admitted: 844.

Costs Per Year: Application fee: $40. Comprehensive fee: $48,436 includes full-time tuition ($37,516), mandatory fees ($300), and college room and board ($10,620). College room only: $5480. Full-time tuition and fees vary according to course load and student level. Room and board charges vary according to board plan and housing facility.

Collegiate Environment: Orientation program. Drama-theater group, choral group, student-run newspaper, radio station. Social organizations: 85 open to all. Most popular organizations: Volunteer Action Center, student government, Music ensembles, Unity, Social Committee. Major annual events: Shirt Tails, Miss Hendrix, Campus Kitty Week. Student services: health clinic, personal-psychological counseling. Campus security: 24-hour emergency response devices and patrols, late night transport-escort service, controlled dormitory access. College housing designed to accommodate 1,210 students; 1,228 undergraduates lived in college housing during 2012-13. Freshmen guaranteed college housing. On-campus residence required through senior year. Options: coed, men-only, women-only housing available. Olin C. and Marjorie H. Bailey Library with 231,003 books, 82,346 microform titles, 42,408 serials, 3,319 audiovisual materials, an OPAC, and a Web page. Operations spending for the previous fiscal year: $836,662. 75 computers available on campus for general student use. A campuswide network can be accessed from student residence rooms and from off campus. Students can access the following: online class registration. Staffed computer lab on campus (open 24 hours a day) provides training in use of computers, software, and the Internet.

Community Environment: See University of Central Arkansas.

■ **ITT TECHNICAL INSTITUTE**
12200 Westhaven Dr.
Little Rock, AR 72211
Tel: (501)565-5550; Free: 800-359-4429
Web Site: www.itt-tech.edu/
Description: Proprietary, primarily 2-year, coed. Part of ITT Educational Services, Inc. Awards terminal associate and bachelor's degrees. Founded 1993. Setting: urban campus.
Entrance Requirements: Entrance: minimally difficult.

■ **JOHN BROWN UNIVERSITY**
2000 W University St.
Siloam Springs, AR 72761-2121
Tel: (479)524-9500; Free: 877-JBU-INFO
Fax: (479)524-9548
E-mail: JBurgess@jbu.edu
Web Site: www.jbu.edu/
Description: Independent interdenominational, comprehensive, coed. Awards associate, bachelor's, and master's degrees. Founded 1919. Setting: 200-acre small town campus. Total enrollment: 2,215. Faculty: 156 (84 full-time, 72 part-time). Student-undergrad faculty ratio is 14:1. 1,170 applied, 66% were admitted. 33% from top 10% of their high school class, 60% from top quarter, 84% from top half. Full-time: 1,563 students, 55% women, 45% men. Part-time: 216 students, 60% women, 40% men. Students come from 40 states and territories, 39 other countries, 62% from out-of-state. 1% American Indian or Alaska Native, non-Hispanic/Latino; 8% Hispanic/Latino; 2% African American, non-Hispanic/Latino; 1% Asian, non-Hispanic/Latino; 0.1% Native Hawaiian or other Pacific Islander, non-Hispanic/Latino; 6% international. 4% 25 or older, 74% live on campus, 4% transferred in. Retention: 84% of full-time freshmen returned the following year. Academic areas with the most degrees conferred: business/marketing; visual and performing arts; education. Core. Calendar: semesters. ESL program, services for LD students, accelerated degree program, honors program, independent study, distance learning, double major, external degree program, adult/continuing education programs, internships, graduate courses open to undergrads. Study abroad program. ROTC: Army (c), Air Force (c).
Entrance Requirements: Options: electronic application, deferred admission. Required: essay, high school transcript, minimum 2.5 high school GPA, 2 recommendations, SAT or ACT. Recommended: interview. Entrance: moderately difficult. Application deadline: Rolling. Notification: continuous.
Costs Per Year: Application fee: $25. Comprehensive fee: $30,996 includes full-time tuition ($21,736), mandatory fees ($998), and college room and board ($8262). Full-time tuition and fees vary according to course load. Room and board charges vary according to board plan and housing facility. Part-time tuition: $694 per credit. Part-time tuition varies according to course load.
Collegiate Environment: Orientation program. Drama-theater group, choral group, student-run newspaper, radio station. Social organizations: 20 open to all. Most popular organizations: Student Government Association, Student Ministries Organization, Student Activities Club, Student Missionary Fellowship. Major annual events: Homecoming, Christmas Candlelight Service, Parents' Weekend. Student services: health clinic, personal-psychological counseling. Campus security: 24-hour emergency response devices and patrols, late night transport-escort service, controlled dormitory access. 1,000 college housing spaces available; 931 were occupied in 2012-13. Freshmen guaranteed college housing. On-campus residence required through junior year. Options: coed, men-only, women-only housing available. Arutunoff Learning Resource Center plus 4 others with 106,283 books, 66,748 microform titles, 7,319 serials, and 4,501 audiovisual materials. 100 computers available on campus for general student use. A campuswide network can be accessed from student residence rooms and from off campus. Students can access the following: online class registration. Staffed computer lab on campus provides training in use of computers, software, and the Internet.
Community Environment: Located in the Benton County foothills of the beautiful Ozarks. The town is easily accessible from all parts of the state. The seasons are delightfully mild. Siloam Springs is far enough south to insure mild winters, and the summer nights are pleasantly cool. Northwest Arkansas is considered a very healthful location, and is noted as a summer retreat for many tourists from all sections of the United States.

■ **LYON COLLEGE**
PO Box 2317
Batesville, AR 72503-2317
Tel: (870)793-9813; Free: 800-423-2542
Fax: (870)698-4622
E-mail: admissions@lyon.edu
Web Site: www.lyon.edu/
Description: Independent Presbyterian, 4-year, coed. Awards bachelor's degrees. Founded 1872. Setting: 136-acre small town campus. Endowment: $37.1 million. Research spending for the previous fiscal year: $164,084. Educational spending for the previous fiscal year: $10,711 per student. Total enrollment: 600. Faculty: 75 (41 full-time, 34 part-time). Student-undergrad faculty ratio is 11:1. 500 applied, 98% were admitted. 36% from top 10% of their high school class, 63% from top quarter, 86% from top half. Full-time: 573 students, 52% women, 48% men. Part-time: 27 students, 74% women, 26% men. Students come from 21 states and territories, 13 other countries, 24% from out-of-state. 1% American Indian or Alaska Native, non-Hispanic/Latino; 5% Hispanic/Latino; 4% African American, non-Hispanic/Latino; 1% Asian, non-Hispanic/Latino; 0% Native Hawaiian or other Pacific Islander, non-Hispanic/Latino; 4% international. 7% 25 or older, 78% live on campus, 9% transferred in. Retention: 72% of full-time freshmen returned the following year. Academic areas with the most degrees conferred: psychology; biological/life sciences; business/marketing; English. Core. Calendar: semesters. Advanced placement, accelerated degree program, self-designed majors, independent study, double major, summer session for credit, part-time degree program, internships. Off campus study at University of Arkansas Community College at Batesville (UACCB). Study abroad program.
Entrance Requirements: Options: electronic application, early admission, early action, deferred admission, international baccalaureate accepted. Required: high school transcript, minimum 2.5 high school GPA, SAT or ACT. Required for some: essay, 2 recommendations. Entrance: moderately difficult. Application deadline: Rolling. Notification: continuous. Transfer credits accepted: Yes.
Costs Per Year: Application fee: $25. Comprehensive fee: $31,154 includes full-time tuition ($23,370), mandatory fees ($224), and college room and board ($7560). Room and board charges vary according to board plan and housing facility. Part-time tuition: $780 per credit hour.
Collegiate Environment: Orientation program. Drama-theater group, choral group, student-run newspaper. Social organizations: 53 open to all; national fraternities, national sororities, local fraternities, local sororities; 37% of eligible men and 29% of eligible women are members. Most popular organizations: Wesley Fellowship, Gay-Straight Alliance, Alpha Xi Delta Sorority, Fellowship of Christian Athletes, Young Democrats/Japanese Culture Club. Major annual events: Service Day, Arkansas Scottish Festival, Homecoming Weekend. Student services: health clinic, personal-psychological counseling. Campus security: 24-hour patrols, late night transport-escort service, controlled dormitory access. 467 college housing spaces available; 444 were occupied in 2012-13. Freshmen guaranteed college housing. On-campus residence required through junior year. Options: coed, men-only, women-only housing available. Mabee-Simpson Library with 205,451 books, 2,928 microform titles, 334 serials, 6,795 audiovisual materials, an OPAC, and a Web page. Operations spending for the previous fiscal year: $436,354. 101 computers available on campus for general student use. A campuswide network can be accessed from student residence rooms and from off campus. Students can access the following: online class registration. Staffed computer lab on campus provides training in use of computers and software.
Community Environment: Batesville is located on the banks of the White River, in the foothills of the Ozarks 90 miles north of Little Rock, and 120 miles northwest of Memphis. The climate is mild, summer mean is 78 degrees and the winter mean is 40 degrees. Average annual rainfall is 48 inches. There are many churches in the area, a fine city library, hospitals, and 4 radio stations and cable TV.

■ **MID-SOUTH COMMUNITY COLLEGE**
2000 W Broadway
West Memphis, AR 72301
Tel: (870)733-6722; Free: 866-733-6722
Fax: (870)733-6719
E-mail: jreece@midsouthcc.edu
Web Site: www.midsouthcc.edu/
Description: State-supported, 2-year, coed. Awards certificates, transfer associate, and terminal associate degrees. Founded 1993. Setting: 80-acre suburban campus with easy access to Memphis. Endowment: $967,261. Educational spending for the previous fiscal year: $3581 per student. Total enrollment: 1,654. Faculty: 104 (35 full-time, 69 part-time). Student-

undergrad faculty ratio is 16:1. 307 applied, 100% were admitted. Full-time: 408 students, 72% women, 28% men. Part-time: 1,246 students, 60% women, 40% men. Students come from 2 states and territories, 3 other countries, 5% from out-of-state. 55% 25 or older, 7% transferred in. Retention: 38% of full-time freshmen returned the following year. Core. Calendar: semesters. Academic remediation for entering students, independent study, distance learning, summer session for credit, part-time degree program, adult/continuing education programs, internships.
Entrance Requirements: Open admission. Option: early admission. Required: high school transcript. Entrance: noncompetitive. Application deadline: Rolling. Notification: continuous.
Collegiate Environment: Orientation program. Choral group. Most popular organizations: Phi Theta Kappa, Baptist Collegiate Ministry, Skills USA - VICA. Major annual events: Student Appreciation Day, Stress Free Zone, Job Fair. Campus security: 24-hour emergency response devices, security during class hours. Mid-South Community College Library/Media Center with 14,672 books, 88 serials, 2,151 audiovisual materials, an OPAC, and a Web page. Operations spending for the previous fiscal year: $146,944. 60 computers available on campus for general student use. A campuswide network can be accessed. Students can access the following: online class registration. Staffed computer lab on campus.

■ **NATIONAL PARK COMMUNITY COLLEGE**
101 College Dr.
Hot Springs, AR 71913
Tel: (501)760-4222
Fax: (501)760-4100
E-mail: bmoody@npcc.edu
Web Site: www.npcc.edu/
Description: State and locally supported, 2-year, coed. Part of Arkansas Department of Higher Education. Awards certificates, diplomas, transfer associate, and terminal associate degrees. Founded 1973. Setting: 50-acre suburban campus with easy access to Little Rock. Endowment: $11.3 million. Total enrollment: 2,996. Faculty: 147 (64 full-time, 83 part-time). Student-undergrad faculty ratio is 21:1. 4,969 applied, 100% were admitted. Full-time: 1,237 students, 59% women, 41% men. Part-time: 1,759 students, 61% women, 39% men. 2% from out-of-state. 63% 25 or older, 17% transferred in. Retention: 100% of full-time freshmen returned the following year. Core. Calendar: semesters. Academic remediation for entering students, services for LD students, advanced placement, self-designed majors, honors program, independent study, distance learning, double major, summer session for credit, part-time degree program, external degree program, adult/continuing education programs, co-op programs and internships. Study abroad program.
Entrance Requirements: Open admission except for nursing, allied health programs. Options: early admission, deferred admission. Required: high school transcript, SAT and SAT Subject Tests or ACT. Recommended: ACT ASSET. Entrance: noncompetitive. Application deadline: Rolling.
Collegiate Environment: Orientation program. Choral group, student-run newspaper. Most popular organizations: student newspaper, choral group. Student services: health clinic, personal-psychological counseling, women's center. Campus security: 24-hour emergency response devices and patrols. Garland County Community College Library with 17,800 books, 290 serials, and an OPAC. Operations spending for the previous fiscal year: $280,000. 270 computers available on campus for general student use. A campuswide network can be accessed from off-campus. Staffed computer lab on campus.

■ **NORTH ARKANSAS COLLEGE**
1515 Pioneer Dr.
Harrison, AR 72601
Tel: (870)743-3000; Free: 800-679-6622
Fax: (870)391-3339
E-mail: charlam@northark.edu
Web Site: www.northark.edu/
Description: State and locally supported, 2-year, coed. Awards certificates, transfer associate, and terminal associate degrees. Founded 1974. Setting: 40-acre small town campus. Total enrollment: 2,429. Faculty: 139. Student-undergrad faculty ratio is 19:1. 927 applied, 100% were admitted. Full-time: 1,491 students, 59% women, 41% men. Part-time: 938 students, 61% women, 39% men. Students come from 1 other country, 2% from out-of-state. 44% 25 or older, 10% transferred in. Retention: 50% of full-time freshmen returned the following year. Core. Calendar: semesters. Academic remediation for entering students, services for LD students, advanced placement, freshman honors college, honors program, independent study,

distance learning, summer session for credit, part-time degree program, adult/continuing education programs, internships.
Entrance Requirements: Open admission. Option: deferred admission. Required for some: high school transcript. Application deadlines: Rolling, Rolling for nonresidents. Notification: continuous, continuous for nonresidents. Transfer credits accepted: Yes.
Collegiate Environment: Orientation program. Drama-theater group. Social organizations: 8 open to all. Most popular organizations: Phi Beta Lambda, Phi Theta Kappa, Student Nurses Association, VICA (Vocational Industrial Clubs of America), Baptist Student Union. Major annual events: Cookouts, Homecoming, plays. Student services: personal-psychological counseling. Campus security: 24-hour emergency response devices. North Arkansas College Library plus 1 other with 28,751 books, 5,714 microform titles, 219 serials, 1,235 audiovisual materials, an OPAC, and a Web page. 270 computers available on campus for general student use. A campuswide network can be accessed from off-campus. Students can access the following: online class registration, Portal. Staffed computer lab on campus provides training in use of computers, software, and the Internet.

■ **NORTHWEST ARKANSAS COMMUNITY COLLEGE**
One College Dr.
Bentonville, AR 72712
Tel: (479)636-9222; Free: 800-995-6922
Fax: (479)619-4116
E-mail: admissions@nwacc.edu
Web Site: www.nwacc.edu/
Description: State and locally supported, 2-year, coed. Awards certificates, transfer associate, and terminal associate degrees. Founded 1989. Setting: 77-acre urban campus. Educational spending for the previous fiscal year: $3438 per student. Total enrollment: 8,341. Faculty: 491 (141 full-time, 350 part-time). Student-undergrad faculty ratio is 19:1. Full-time: 3,095 students, 54% women, 46% men. Part-time: 5,246 students, 59% women, 41% men. Students come from 21 states and territories, 2% from out-of-state. 47% 25 or older, 9% transferred in. Retention: 55% of full-time freshmen returned the following year. Core. Calendar: semesters. Academic remediation for entering students, ESL program, services for LD students, advanced placement, accelerated degree program, self-designed majors, honors program, independent study, distance learning, double major, summer session for credit, part-time degree program, adult/continuing education programs, co-op programs and internships. ROTC: Army (c), Air Force (c).
Entrance Requirements: Open admission. Option: electronic application. Required: high school transcript. Application deadline: Rolling. Notification: continuous. Transfer credits accepted: Yes.
Costs Per Year: Application fee: $10. Area resident tuition: $2250 full-time, $75 per credit hour part-time. State resident tuition: $3675 full-time, $122.50 per credit hour part-time. Nonresident tuition: $5250 full-time, $175 per credit hour part-time. Mandatory fees: $665 full-time, $18.50 per credit hour part-time, $55 per term part-time.
Collegiate Environment: Orientation program. Drama-theater group, choral group, student-run newspaper. Social organizations: 18 open to all. Most popular organizations: Student Advisory Activity Council, Gamma Beta Phi, Phi Beta Lambda, Student Nurses Association, Students in Free Enterprise (SIFE). Major annual events: Pizza with the President, Student Organization Fair, Fall Festival. Student services: personal-psychological counseling. Campus security: 24-hour emergency response devices and patrols. College housing not available. Library Resource Center plus 1 other with 15,500 books, 159 serials, an OPAC, and a Web page. 100 computers available on campus for general student use. A campuswide network can be accessed. Students can access the following: online class registration. Staffed computer lab on campus.

■ **OUACHITA BAPTIST UNIVERSITY**
410 Ouachita St.
Arkadelphia, AR 71998-0001
Tel: (870)245-5000; Free: 800-342-5628
Fax: (870)245-5500
E-mail: motll@obu.edu
Web Site: www.obu.edu/
Description: Independent Baptist, 4-year, coed. Awards bachelor's degrees. Founded 1886. Setting: 200-acre small town campus with easy access to Little Rock. Endowment: $81.3 million. Research spending for the previous fiscal year: $223,694. Educational spending for the previous fiscal year: $6819 per student. Total enrollment: 1,532. Faculty: 155 (110 full-time, 45 part-time). Student-undergrad faculty ratio is 12:1. 1,822 applied, 69% were

admitted. 38% from top 10% of their high school class, 61% from top quarter, 86% from top half. 15 National Merit Scholars, 16 valedictorians. Full-time: 1,496 students, 54% women, 46% men. Part-time: 36 students, 53% women, 47% men. Students come from 29 states and territories, 36 other countries, 40% from out-of-state. 1% American Indian or Alaska Native, non-Hispanic/Latino; 3% Hispanic/Latino; 7% African American, non-Hispanic/Latino; 1% Asian, non-Hispanic/Latino; 0.1% Native Hawaiian or other Pacific Islander, non-Hispanic/Latino; 2% international. 1% 25 or older, 96% live on campus, 3% transferred in. Retention: 76% of full-time freshmen returned the following year. Academic areas with the most degrees conferred: business/marketing; theology and religious vocations; biological/life sciences. Core. Calendar: semesters. Academic remediation for entering students, ESL program, advanced placement, accelerated degree program, honors program, independent study, distance learning, double major, summer session for credit, part-time degree program, co-op programs and internships. Off campus study at Henderson State University. Study abroad program. ROTC: Army.

Entrance Requirements: Options: deferred admission, international baccalaureate accepted. Required: high school transcript, minimum 2.75 high school GPA, SAT or ACT. Recommended: interview. Entrance: moderately difficult. Application deadline: 8/15. Notification: continuous. SAT Reasoning Test deadline: 8/15. SAT Subject Test deadline: 8/15. Transfer credits accepted: Yes.

Costs Per Year: Application fee: $0. Comprehensive fee: $28,980 includes full-time tuition ($21,860), mandatory fees ($480), and college room and board ($6640). Room and board charges vary according to housing facility. Part-time tuition: $605 per semester hour.

Collegiate Environment: Orientation program. Drama-theater group, choral group, marching band, student-run newspaper. Social organizations: 60 open to all; local fraternities, local sororities; 25% of eligible men and 35% of eligible women are members. Most popular organizations: Phi Beta Lambda, Campus Activities Board, Student Education Association, Student Foundation, International Club. Major annual events: Tiger Tunes, Tiger Traks, Homecoming. Student services: health clinic, personal-psychological counseling. Campus security: 24-hour emergency response devices and patrols, controlled dormitory access. 1,537 college housing spaces available; 1,507 were occupied in 2012-13. Freshmen guaranteed college housing. On-campus residence required through senior year. Options: men-only, women-only housing available. Riley-Hickinbotham Library plus 1 other with 837,885 books, 318,115 microform titles, 5,088 serials, 3,393 audiovisual materials, an OPAC, and a Web page. Operations spending for the previous fiscal year: $530,737. 275 computers available on campus for general student use. Computer purchase/lease plans available. A campuswide network can be accessed from student residence rooms and from off campus. Students can access the following: student Web portal. Staffed computer lab on campus (open 24 hours a day) provides training in use of computers, software, and the Internet.

Community Environment: Ouachita Baptist University is located in Arkadelphia, Arkansas, about 70 miles southwest of Little Rock on I-30 and 35 miles south of Hot Springs. There is frequent Amtrak service to and from the city. Facilities for air transportation are available both in Hot Springs and Little Rock. Arkadelphia has a population of more than 10,000, including the students of Ouachita and Henderson State University.

■ **OZARKA COLLEGE**
PO Box 10
Melbourne, AR 72556
Tel: (870)368-7371; Free: 800-821-4335
Fax: (870)368-4733
E-mail: dmmowery@ozarka.edu
Web Site: www.ozarka.edu/
Description: State-supported, 2-year, coed. Awards certificates, transfer associate, and terminal associate degrees. Founded 1973. Setting: 40-acre rural campus. Total enrollment: 1,600. Faculty: 71 (31 full-time, 40 part-time). Student-undergrad faculty ratio is 20:1. 1% from out-of-state. 43% 25 or older. Core. Calendar: semesters. Academic remediation for entering students, services for LD students, advanced placement, distance learning, summer session for credit, external degree program, internships.
Entrance Requirements: Open admission except for nursing and information science technology programs. Options: electronic application, deferred admission. Required: high school transcript. Recommended: minimum 2 high school GPA. Required for some: essay, interview. Entrance: noncompetitive. Application deadline: 8/19.
Collegiate Environment: Orientation program. Drama-theater group. Social

organizations: 7 open to all. Most popular organizations: VICA (Vocational Industrial Clubs of America), Phi Beta Lambda, Drama Club, HOSA, Phi Theta Kappa. Major annual events: Community Service Day, Career Day. Student services: personal-psychological counseling. Campus security: security patrols after business hours. College housing not available. Ozarka College Library with 10,500 books, 4,000 serials, and an OPAC. Operations spending for the previous fiscal year: $171,858. 114 computers available on campus for general student use. A campuswide network can be accessed from off-campus. Students can access the following: online class registration. Staffed computer lab on campus.

■ **PHILANDER SMITH COLLEGE**
812 W 13th St.
Little Rock, AR 72202-3799
Tel: (501)375-9845; Free: 800-446-6772
Fax: (501)370-5225
E-mail: ggray@philander.edu
Web Site: www.philander.edu/
Description: Independent United Methodist, 4-year, coed. Awards bachelor's degrees. Founded 1877. Setting: 25-acre urban campus. Total enrollment: 732. Faculty: 84 (47 full-time, 37 part-time). Student-undergrad faculty ratio is 13:1. 2,906 applied, 68% were admitted. 16% from top 10% of their high school class, 32% from top quarter, 65% from top half. Full-time: 680 students, 65% women, 35% men. Part-time: 52 students, 58% women, 42% men. 42% from out-of-state. 0% American Indian or Alaska Native, non-Hispanic/Latino; 1% Hispanic/Latino; 92% African American, non-Hispanic/Latino; 0.1% Asian, non-Hispanic/Latino; 0.1% Native Hawaiian or other Pacific Islander, non-Hispanic/Latino; 5% international. 20% 25 or older, 40% live on campus, 8% transferred in. Retention: 60% of full-time freshmen returned the following year. Academic areas with the most degrees conferred: business/marketing; social sciences; biological/life sciences. Calendar: semesters. Adult/continuing education programs.
Entrance Requirements: Open admission. Option: deferred admission. Required: high school transcript, minimum 2 high school GPA, SAT or ACT. Required for some: essay, interview. Entrance: minimally difficult. Application deadline: 7/1. Notification: continuous. SAT Reasoning Test deadline: 7/15.
Costs Per Year: Application fee: $25. Comprehensive fee: $19,510 includes full-time tuition ($11,350), mandatory fees ($560), and college room and board ($7600). Full-time tuition and fees vary according to course load, program, and student level. Room and board charges vary according to housing facility. Part-time tuition: $400 per credit hour. Part-time tuition varies according to course load, program, and student level.
Collegiate Environment: Orientation program. Campus security: 24-hour emergency response devices and patrols, student patrols, controlled dormitory access.
Community Environment: See University of Arkansas - Little Rock.

■ **PHILLIPS COMMUNITY COLLEGE OF THE UNIVERSITY OF ARKANSAS**
PO Box 785
Helena, AR 72342-0785
Tel: (870)338-6474
Fax: (870)338-7542
Web Site: www.pccua.edu/
Description: State and locally supported, 2-year, coed. Part of University of Arkansas System. Awards certificates, transfer associate, and terminal associate degrees. Founded 1965. Setting: 80-acre small town campus with easy access to Memphis. Total enrollment: 2,337. 32% 25 or older. Core. Calendar: semesters. Academic remediation for entering students, services for LD students, advanced placement, summer session for credit, part-time degree program, adult/continuing education programs.
Entrance Requirements: Open admission except for nursing, medical laboratory technician programs. Option: early admission. Entrance: noncompetitive. Application deadline: 8/25. Notification: continuous until 8/25.
Collegiate Environment: Drama-theater group, choral group, student-run newspaper. Student services: personal-psychological counseling. Campus security: 24-hour patrols. 39,000 books and 352 serials.
Community Environment: Helena is in a suburban area, and blessed with a mild, warm climate. There are churches of major denominations, libraries, a museum, an accredited general hospital, and major civic and service organizations.

■ **PULASKI TECHNICAL COLLEGE**
3000 W Scenic Dr.
North Little Rock, AR 72118

Tel: (501)812-2200
Fax: (501)812-2316
E-mail: catkins@pulaskitech.edu
Web Site: www.pulaskitech.edu/
Description: State-supported, 2-year, coed. Awards certificates, transfer associate, and terminal associate degrees. Founded 1945. Setting: 40-acre urban campus with easy access to Little Rock. Educational spending for the previous fiscal year: $1145 per student. Total enrollment: 10,255. Faculty: 473 (153 full-time, 320 part-time). Student-undergrad faculty ratio is 25:1. 3,193 applied, 100% were admitted. Full-time: 4,856 students, 62% women, 38% men. Part-time: 5,399 students, 70% women, 30% men. Students come from 5 states and territories, 1% from out-of-state. 60% 25 or older, 6% transferred in. Core. Calendar: semesters. Academic remediation for entering students, services for LD students, advanced placement, distance learning, summer session for credit, part-time degree program.
Entrance Requirements: Open admission except for allied health programs. Option: electronic application. Required: high school transcript. Entrance: noncompetitive. Application deadline: Rolling. Transfer credits accepted: Yes.
Collegiate Environment: Orientation program. Drama-theater group, choral group. Major annual events: Spanish Language Department's Fiesta, Spring Fling, Fall Carnival. Campus security: certified law enforcement personnel 7 am to 11 pm. Ottenheimer Library with 35,406 books, 276 serials, 1,994 audiovisual materials, an OPAC, and a Web page. Operations spending for the previous fiscal year: $706,478. 233 computers available on campus for general student use. A campuswide network can be accessed from off-campus. Students can access the following: online class registration, online registration for continuing students only. Staffed computer lab on campus provides training in use of computers, software, and the Internet.

■ **REMINGTON COLLEGE–LITTLE ROCK CAMPUS**
19 Remington Dr.
Little Rock, AR 72204
Tel: (501)312-0007
Fax: (501)225-3819
E-mail: brian.maggio@remingtoncollege.edu
Web Site: www.remingtoncollege.edu/
Description: Proprietary, 2-year, coed. Awards terminal associate degrees.

■ **RICH MOUNTAIN COMMUNITY COLLEGE**
1100 College Dr.
Mena, AR 71953
Tel: (479)394-7622
Fax: (479)394-2628
Web Site: www.rmcc.edu/
Description: State and locally supported, 2-year, coed. Awards certificates, transfer associate, and terminal associate degrees. Founded 1983. Setting: 40-acre small town campus. Total enrollment: 1,004. 46% 25 or older. Core. Calendar: semesters. Academic remediation for entering students, ESL program, services for LD students, advanced placement, distance learning, double major, summer session for credit, part-time degree program, adult/continuing education programs.
Entrance Requirements: Open admission. Option: early admission. Required: high school transcript. Entrance: noncompetitive. Application deadline: 8/25. Notification: continuous until 8/25.
Collegiate Environment: Student services: personal-psychological counseling. Campus security: administrator on night duty. St. John Library with 13,299 books, 417 microform titles, 81 serials, 674 audiovisual materials, and an OPAC.

■ **SOUTH ARKANSAS COMMUNITY COLLEGE**
PO Box 7010
El Dorado, AR 71731-7010
Tel: (870)862-8131; Free: 800-955-2289
Fax: (870)864-7122
E-mail: dinman@southark.edu
Web Site: www.southark.edu/
Description: State-supported, 2-year, coed. Part of Arkansas Department of Higher Education. Awards certificates, transfer associate, and terminal associate degrees. Founded 1975. Setting: 4-acre small town campus. Endowment: $1 million. Educational spending for the previous fiscal year: $2511 per student. Total enrollment: 1,368. Full-time: 612 students, 75% women, 25% men. Part-time: 756 students, 67% women, 33% men. Students come from 2 states and territories, 40% from out-of-state. 43% 25 or older. Reten-

tion: 46% of full-time freshmen returned the following year. Core. Calendar: semesters. Academic remediation for entering students, services for LD students, advanced placement, summer session for credit, part-time degree program, adult/continuing education programs, internships.
Entrance Requirements: Open admission. Options: early admission, deferred admission. Required: high school transcript. Recommended: SAT or ACT. Entrance: noncompetitive. Application deadline: 8/25.
Collegiate Environment: Orientation program. Choral group. Student services: personal-psychological counseling. Campus security: security guard. South Arkansas Community College Library with 22,652 books and 223 serials. 75 computers available on campus for general student use. A campuswide network can be accessed from off-campus. Students can access the following: online class registration. Staffed computer lab on campus provides training in use of computers, software, and the Internet.
Community Environment: El Dorado is the seat of Union County, lying 117 miles south of Little Rock. Important industries are timber, poultry, oil, and chemicals. Bus and air service is available. Community services include a public library, two hospitals, several churches, an arts center, and good shopping facilities. There is good hunting and fishing in the general area, and water sports on nearby lakes and rivers.

■ **SOUTHEAST ARKANSAS COLLEGE**
1900 Hazel St.
Pine Bluff, AR 71603
Tel: (870)543-5900; Free: 888-SEARC TC
E-mail: bdunn@seark.edu
Web Site: www.seark.edu/
Description: State-supported, 2-year, coed. Awards certificates, transfer associate, and terminal associate degrees. Founded 1991. Setting: urban campus with easy access to Little Rock. Total enrollment: 2,187. Faculty: 141 (63 full-time, 78 part-time). Student-undergrad faculty ratio is 16:1. Full-time: 1,157 students, 70% women, 30% men. Part-time: 1,033 students, 66% women, 34% men. Students come from 3 states and territories, 0% from out-of-state. 1% American Indian or Alaska Native, non-Hispanic/Latino; 1% Hispanic/Latino; 58% African American, non-Hispanic/Latino; 0.4% Asian, non-Hispanic/Latino; 0.2% Native Hawaiian or other Pacific Islander, non-Hispanic/Latino; 0% international. 52% 25 or older, 2% transferred in. Retention: 31% of full-time freshmen returned the following year. Calendar: semesters. Academic remediation for entering students, services for LD students, advanced placement, accelerated degree program, honors program, independent study, distance learning, double major, summer session for credit, part-time degree program, co-op programs and internships.
Entrance Requirements: Open admission. Option: early admission. Required: high school transcript, ACT. Recommended: SAT or ACT, SAT and SAT Subject Tests or ACT, SAT Subject Tests, Compass. Entrance: noncompetitive. Notification: continuous. Transfer credits accepted: Yes.
Collegiate Environment: Orientation program. Choral group. Most popular organizations: Phi Beta Lambda, HOSA, Phi Theta Kappa, Student Senate. Major annual events: Spring Fling, Back to School Bash, Honors and Awards Program. Student services: personal-psychological counseling. Campus security: 24-hour patrols. Southeast Arkansas Technical College Library with 5,000 books and 75 serials. 62 computers available on campus for general student use. Staffed computer lab on campus provides training in use of computers, software, and the Internet.

■ **SOUTHERN ARKANSAS UNIVERSITY TECH**
100 Carr Rd.
Camden, AR 71701
Tel: (870)574-4500
E-mail: bellis@sautech.edu
Web Site: www.sautech.edu/
Description: State-supported, 2-year, coed. Part of Southern Arkansas University System. Awards certificates, transfer associate, and terminal associate degrees. Founded 1967. Setting: 96-acre rural campus. Endowment: $403,394. Educational spending for the previous fiscal year: $5250 per student. Total enrollment: 1,817. Faculty: 105 (29 full-time, 76 part-time). Student-undergrad faculty ratio is 19:1. 555 applied, 100% were admitted. 4% from top 10% of their high school class, 50% from top quarter, 84% from top half. Full-time: 589 students, 47% women, 53% men. Part-time: 1,228 students, 50% women, 50% men. Students come from 12 states and territories, 8 other countries, 10% from out-of-state. 47% 25 or older, 2% live on campus, 16% transferred in. Core. Calendar: semesters. Academic remediation for entering students, services for LD students, advanced placement, honors program, independent study, distance learning, double major,

summer session for credit, part-time degree program, external degree program, adult/continuing education programs, internships. Off campus study at Arkansas Fire Training Academy, Arkansas Environmental Training Academy.

Entrance Requirements: Open admission except for nursing program which requires testing and rank ordering. Options: electronic application, deferred admission. Required: high school transcript. Application deadlines: 8/15, 8/15 for nonresidents. Notification: continuous.

Costs Per Year: Application fee: $0. State resident tuition: $2940 full-time, $98 per credit hour part-time. Nonresident tuition: $4260 full-time, $142 per credit hour part-time. Mandatory fees: $1232 full-time, $21 per credit hour part-time, $10. Full-time tuition and fees vary according to course load, location, program, and reciprocity agreements. Part-time tuition and fees vary according to course load, location, program, and reciprocity agreements. College room and board: $5541. College room only: $3000. Room and board charges vary according to housing facility.

Collegiate Environment: Orientation program. Student-run radio station. Social organizations: 11 open to all. Most popular organizations: Phi Beta Lambda, TEC@Tech, Allied Health Student Club, Aviation Club, Multimedia Club. Major annual events: Student Appreciation Day, Ed-U-Fest, Fall EXPO. Student services: personal-psychological counseling. Campus security: 24-hour emergency response devices and patrols. Southern Arkansas University Tech Learning Resource Center with 17,389 books, 250 microform titles, 115 serials, 960 audiovisual materials, and an OPAC. Operations spending for the previous fiscal year: $95,778. 200 computers available on campus for general student use. A campuswide network can be accessed from student residence rooms and from off campus. Students can access the following: online class registration. Staffed computer lab on campus provides training in use of computers, software, and the Internet.

■ SOUTHERN ARKANSAS UNIVERSITY–MAGNOLIA

100 E University
Magnolia, AR 71753
Tel: (870)235-4000; Free: 800-332-7286
Fax: (870)235-5005
E-mail: sejennings@saumag.edu
Web Site: www.saumag.edu/

Description: State-supported, comprehensive, coed. Part of Southern Arkansas University System. Awards associate, bachelor's, and master's degrees. Founded 1909. Setting: 781-acre small town campus. Endowment: $22.2 million. Research spending for the previous fiscal year: $359,725. Educational spending for the previous fiscal year: $4803 per student. Total enrollment: 3,383. Faculty: 174 (all full-time). Student-undergrad faculty ratio is 16:1. 2,631 applied, 65% were admitted. 14% from top 10% of their high school class, 39% from top quarter, 73% from top half. Full-time: 2,457 students, 57% women, 43% men. Part-time: 461 students, 65% women, 35% men. Students come from 26 states and territories, 25 other countries, 23% from out-of-state. 1% American Indian or Alaska Native, non-Hispanic/Latino; 3% Hispanic/Latino; 29% African American, non-Hispanic/Latino; 1% Asian, non-Hispanic/Latino; 1% Native Hawaiian or other Pacific Islander, non-Hispanic/Latino; 3% international. 18% 25 or older, 46% live on campus, 8% transferred in. Retention: 60% of full-time freshmen returned the following year. Academic areas with the most degrees conferred: business/marketing; education; liberal arts/general studies. Core. Calendar: semesters, Academic remediation for entering students, ESL program, services for LD students, advanced placement, accelerated degree program, freshman honors college, honors program, independent study, distance learning, double major, summer session for credit, part-time degree program, adult/continuing education programs, internships, graduate courses open to undergrads. Study abroad program.

Entrance Requirements: Options: electronic application, early admission, deferred admission, international baccalaureate accepted. Required: high school transcript, SAT or ACT. Recommended: ACT. Required for some: interview. Entrance: moderately difficult. Application deadline: 8/27. Transfer credits accepted: Yes.

Costs Per Year: Application fee: $0. State resident tuition: $5880 full-time, $196 per hour part-time. Nonresident tuition: $8910 full-time, $297 per hour part-time. Mandatory fees: $1466 full-time, $39 per hour part-time, $18 per term part-time. Full-time tuition and fees vary according to course load. Part-time tuition and fees vary according to course load. College room and board: $4974. College room only: $2440. Room and board charges vary according to board plan and housing facility.

Collegiate Environment: Orientation program. Drama-theater group, choral group, marching band, student-run newspaper, radio station. Social

organizations: 120 open to all; national fraternities, national sororities; 11% of eligible men and 11% of eligible women are members. Most popular organizations: Student Government Association, Student Activities Board, Resident Hall Association, Residential College, International Student Association. Major annual events: Homecoming, Parents' Day, Spring Fling. Student services: health clinic, personal-psychological counseling. Campus security: 24-hour emergency response devices, student patrols, late night transport-escort service, controlled dormitory access. 1,495 college housing spaces available; 1,346 were occupied in 2012-13. Freshmen guaranteed college housing. On-campus residence required through sophomore year. Options: coed, men-only, women-only housing available. Magale Library with 185,522 books, 385,782 microform titles, 2,896 serials, 9,888 audiovisual materials, an OPAC, and a Web page. Operations spending for the previous fiscal year: $1.1 million. 199 computers available on campus for general student use. A campuswide network can be accessed from student residence rooms and from off campus. Students can access the following: online class registration. Staffed computer lab on campus provides training in use of computers, software, and the Internet.

■ STRAYER UNIVERSITY - LITTLE ROCK CAMPUS

10825 Financial Centre Pky.
Ste. 131
Little Rock, AR 72211
Web Site: www.strayer.edu/campus/little-rock

Description: Proprietary, comprehensive, coed. Awards bachelor's and master's degrees.

■ UNIVERSITY OF ARKANSAS

800 Hotz Hall
Fayetteville, AR 72701-1201
Tel: (479)575-2000; Free: 800-377-8632
Fax: (479)575-7515
E-mail: uofa@uark.edu
Web Site: www.uark.edu/

Description: State-supported, university, coed. Part of University of Arkansas System. Awards bachelor's, master's, and doctoral degrees and post-master's certificates. Founded 1871. Setting: 410-acre suburban campus. Endowment: $673.1 million. Research spending for the previous fiscal year: $119 million. Total enrollment: 23,199. Faculty: 1,087 (989 full-time, 98 part-time). Student-undergrad faculty ratio is 18:1. 16,633 applied, 61% were admitted. 31% from top 10% of their high school class, 58% from top quarter, 87% from top half. Full-time: 16,617 students, 50% women, 50% men. Part-time: 2,410 students, 45% women, 55% men. Students come from 50 states and territories, 120 other countries, 33% from out-of-state. 1% American Indian or Alaska Native, non-Hispanic/Latino; 5% Hispanic/Latino; 5% African American, non-Hispanic/Latino; 3% Asian, non-Hispanic/Latino; 0.1% Native Hawaiian or other Pacific Islander, non-Hispanic/Latino; 3% international. 11% 25 or older, 33% live on campus, 8% transferred in. Retention: 83% of full-time freshmen returned the following year. Academic areas with the most degrees conferred: business/marketing; engineering; social sciences. Core. Calendar: semesters. ESL program, services for LD students, advanced placement, accelerated degree program, freshman honors college, honors program, independent study, distance learning, double major, summer session for credit, part-time degree program, co-op programs and internships, graduate courses open to undergrads. Study abroad program. ROTC: Army, Air Force.

Entrance Requirements: Options: electronic application, early admission, early action, international baccalaureate accepted. Required: high school transcript, SAT or ACT. Recommended: minimum 3 high school GPA. Entrance: moderately difficult. Application deadlines: 8/1, 11/15 for early action. Notification: continuous until 9/1, 12/15 for early action. SAT Reasoning Test deadline: 8/1. SAT Subject Test deadline: 8/1.

Costs Per Year: Application fee: $40. State resident tuition: $6141 full-time. Nonresident tuition: $17,022 full-time. Mandatory fees: $1412 full-time. Full-time tuition and fees vary according to course load and program. College room and board: $8672. College room only: $5494. Room and board charges vary according to board plan and housing facility.

Collegiate Environment: Orientation program. Drama-theater group, choral group, marching band, student-run newspaper, radio station. Social organizations: 313 open to all; national fraternities, national sororities; 17% of eligible men and 26% of eligible women are members. Most popular organizations: Gamma Beta Phi, University Baptist Collegiate Ministry, Associated Student Government, Black Students Association, Hot Pink Ribbon Club. Major annual events: Welcome Week, MLK Holiday Celebration,

Homecoming. Student services: legal services, health clinic, personal-psychological counseling, women's center. Campus security: 24-hour emergency response devices and patrols, student patrols, late night transport-escort service, controlled dormitory access, RAD (Rape Aggression Defense program). David W. Mullins Library plus 5 others with 1.9 million books, 5.6 million microform titles, 27,518 serials, 33,640 audiovisual materials, an OPAC, and a Web page. 3,335 computers available on campus for general student use. Computer purchase/lease plans available. A campuswide network can be accessed from student residence rooms and from off campus. Students can access the following: online class registration. Staffed computer lab on campus provides training in use of computers, software, and the Internet.

■ **UNIVERSITY OF ARKANSAS COMMUNITY COLLEGE AT BATESVILLE**
PO Box 3350
Batesville, AR 72503
Tel: (870)793-7581; Free: 800-508-7878
Fax: (870)793-4988
E-mail: sgage@uaccb.edu
Web Site: www.uaccb.edu/
Description: State-supported, 2-year, coed. Part of University of Arkansas System. Awards certificates, transfer associate, and terminal associate degrees. Setting: small town campus. Total enrollment: 1,725. Student-undergrad faculty ratio is 19:1. 0% from out-of-state. 51% 25 or older. Retention: 58% of full-time freshmen returned the following year. Core. Calendar: semesters. Academic remediation for entering students, ESL program, services for LD students, advanced placement, self-designed majors, independent study, distance learning, double major, summer session for credit, part-time degree program, external degree program, adult/continuing education programs, co-op programs and internships. Off campus study.
Entrance Requirements: Open admission. Required: high school transcript, immunization records. Entrance: noncompetitive. Application deadline: Rolling. Notification: continuous.
Collegiate Environment: Orientation program. Student services: personal-psychological counseling. Campus security: student patrols, security cameras, County Deputy Sheriff Patrol. University of Arkansas Community College at Batesville Library with an OPAC and a Web page.

■ **UNIVERSITY OF ARKANSAS COMMUNITY COLLEGE AT HOPE**
PO Box 140
Hope, AR 71802
Tel: (870)777-5722
Fax: (870)722-5957
E-mail: janderson@uacch.edu
Web Site: www.uacch.edu/
Description: State-supported, 2-year, coed. Part of University of Arkansas System. Awards certificates, diplomas, transfer associate, and terminal associate degrees. Founded 1966. Setting: 60-acre rural campus. Total enrollment: 1,256. Student-undergrad faculty ratio is 17:1. 1% from out-of-state. 41% 25 or older. Retention: 65% of full-time freshmen returned the following year. Calendar: semesters. Academic remediation for entering students, advanced placement, distance learning, summer session for credit, part-time degree program.
Entrance Requirements: Open admission. Option: early admission. Required: high school transcript. Entrance: noncompetitive. Application deadline: Rolling.
Costs Per Year: Application fee: $0. Area resident tuition: $1416 full-time, $59 per credit hour part-time. State resident tuition: $1536 full-time, $64 per credit hour part-time. Nonresident tuition: $3024 full-time, $126 per credit hour part-time. Mandatory fees: $288 full-time, $12 per credit hour part-time, $3 per term part-time. Full-time tuition and fees vary according to reciprocity agreements. Part-time tuition and fees vary according to course load and reciprocity agreements.
Collegiate Environment: Orientation program. Campus security: on-campus security during class hours. University of Arkansas Community College at Hope Library with a Web page.

■ **UNIVERSITY OF ARKANSAS COMMUNITY COLLEGE AT MORRILTON**
1537 University Blvd.
Morrilton, AR 72110
Tel: (501)977-2000; Free: 800-264-1094
Fax: (501)354-9948

E-mail: mullins@uaccm.edu
Web Site: www.uaccm.edu/
Description: State-supported, 2-year, coed. Part of University of Arkansas System. Awards certificates, transfer associate, and terminal associate degrees. Founded 1961. Setting: 79-acre rural campus. Educational spending for the previous fiscal year: $1409 per student. Total enrollment: 2,139. Faculty: 98 (62 full-time, 36 part-time). Student-undergrad faculty ratio is 21:1. 1,405 applied, 64% were admitted. 0% from top 10% of their high school class, 0% from top quarter, 0% from top half. Full-time: 1,267 students, 54% women, 46% men. Part-time: 872 students, 64% women, 36% men. Students come from 5 states and territories, 1 other country, 1% from out-of-state. 0.4% American Indian or Alaska Native, non-Hispanic/Latino; 5% Hispanic/Latino; 10% African American, non-Hispanic/Latino; 1% Asian, non-Hispanic/Latino; 0.1% Native Hawaiian or other Pacific Islander, non-Hispanic/Latino; 2% international. 36% 25 or older, 8% transferred in. Calendar: semesters. Academic remediation for entering students, services for LD students, advanced placement, distance learning, double major, summer session for credit, part-time degree program, internships.
Entrance Requirements: Open admission. Options: electronic application, early admission, deferred admission. Required: high school transcript. Recommended: SAT or ACT, ACT COMPASS. Required for some: immunization records and prior college transcript(s). Entrance: noncompetitive. Application deadline: Rolling. Notification: continuous. Transfer credits accepted: Yes.
Costs Per Year: Application fee: $0. Area resident tuition: $2340 full-time, $78 per credit hour part-time. State resident tuition: $2550 full-time, $85 per credit hour part-time. Nonresident tuition: $3660 full-time, $122 per credit hour part-time. Mandatory fees: $810 full-time, $26 per credit hour part-time, $15 per term part-time. Full-time tuition and fees vary according to course load and program. Part-time tuition and fees vary according to course load and program.
Collegiate Environment: Orientation program. Drama-theater group, choral group. Social organizations: 20 open to all; Phi Theta Kappa and Phi Beta Lambda Academic Honor. Most popular organizations: Student Government Association, Phi Beta Lambda, Student Practical Nurses Organization, Computer Information Systems Organization, Early Childhood Development Organization. Major annual events: Spring Fling, Fall Fest, Intramural Sport Tournaments in volleyball, 5K walk/run, table tennis, and basketball (three-on-three). Student services: personal-psychological counseling. Campus security: 24-hour emergency response devices, campus alert system through mass e-mail. College housing not available. E. Allen Gordon Library with 18,365 books, 55 serials, 1,602 audiovisual materials, an OPAC, and a Web page. Operations spending for the previous fiscal year: $210,835. 510 computers available on campus for general student use. A campuswide network can be accessed from off-campus. Students can access the following: online class registration. Staffed computer lab on campus provides training in use of computers, software, and the Internet.

■ **UNIVERSITY OF ARKANSAS AT LITTLE ROCK**
2801 S University Ave.
Little Rock, AR 72204-1099
Tel: (501)569-3000; Free: 800-482-8892
Fax: (501)569-8915
E-mail: twharrison@ualn.edu
Web Site: www.ualr.edu/
Description: State-supported, university, coed. Part of University of Arkansas System. Awards associate, bachelor's, master's, and doctoral degrees and post-master's certificates. Founded 1927. Setting: 229-acre urban campus. Endowment: $70.1 million. Research spending for the previous fiscal year: $15.4 million. Educational spending for the previous fiscal year: $6629 per student. Total enrollment: 12,872. Faculty: 804 (491 full-time, 313 part-time). Student-undergrad faculty ratio is 14:1. 923 applied, 97% were admitted. Full-time: 5,749 students, 56% women, 44% men. Part-time: 4,562 students, 63% women, 37% men. Students come from 45 states and territories, 50 other countries, 3% from out-of-state. 0.4% American Indian or Alaska Native, non-Hispanic/Latino; 5% Hispanic/Latino; 26% African American, non-Hispanic/Latino; 2% Asian, non-Hispanic/Latino; 0% Native Hawaiian or other Pacific Islander, non-Hispanic/Latino; 3% international. 29% 25 or older, 10% live on campus, 12% transferred in. Retention: 67% of full-time freshmen returned the following year. Academic areas with the most degrees conferred: business/marketing; health professions and related sciences; psychology. Core. Calendar: semesters. Academic remediation for entering students, ESL program, advanced placement, accelerated degree program, self-designed majors, freshman honors

college, honors program, independent study, distance learning, double major, summer session for credit, part-time degree program, adult/continuing education programs, co-op programs and internships, graduate courses open to undergrads. Study abroad program. ROTC: Army.

Entrance Requirements: Options: electronic application, early admission, deferred admission. Required: high school transcript, minimum 2.5 high school GPA, proof of immunization, SAT or ACT. Entrance: minimally difficult. Application deadline: Rolling. Notification: continuous. SAT Reasoning Test deadline: 8/1. SAT Subject Test deadline: 8/1. Transfer credits accepted: Yes.

Costs Per Year: Application fee: $40. One-time mandatory fee: $40. State resident tuition: $5348 full-time, $191 per credit part-time. Nonresident tuition: $14,560 full-time, $520 per credit part-time. Mandatory fees: $1506 full-time, $807 per term part-time. Full-time tuition and fees vary according to degree level and program. Part-time tuition and fees vary according to degree level and program. College room and board: $8989. Room and board charges vary according to board plan and housing facility.

Collegiate Environment: Orientation program. Drama-theater group, student-run newspaper, radio station. Social organizations: national fraternities, national sororities, local fraternities, local sororities; 3% of eligible men and 3% of eligible women are members. Most popular organizations: student government, University Program Council, Housing Activities Council, International Student Organization, Panhellenic Council. Major annual events: Homecoming Week, Greek Week, Black History Month. Student services: health clinic. Campus security: 24-hour emergency response devices and patrols, student patrols, late night transport-escort service, controlled dormitory access. 1,350 college housing spaces available; 975 were occupied in 2012-13. Freshmen given priority for college housing. On-campus residence required in freshman year. Option: coed housing available. Ottenheimer Library plus 1 other with 812,167 books, 179,770 microform titles, 95,870 serials, 11,682 audiovisual materials, an OPAC, and a Web page. 3,500 computers available on campus for general student use. A campuswide network can be accessed from student residence rooms and from off campus. Students can access the following: online class registration. Staffed computer lab on campus provides training in use of software and the Internet.

■ **UNIVERSITY OF ARKANSAS FOR MEDICAL SCIENCES**
4301 W Markham
Little Rock, AR 72205-7199
Tel: (501)686-5000
E-mail: StilesMonnaL@uams.edu
Web Site: www.uams.edu/
Description: State-supported, university, coed. Part of University of Arkansas System. Awards associate, bachelor's, master's, and doctoral degrees (bachelor's degree is upper-level). Founded 1879. Setting: 5-acre urban campus with easy access to Little Rock. Endowment: $27.4 million. Research spending for the previous fiscal year: $112.3 million. Total enrollment: 2,809. Faculty: 1,271. Student-undergrad faculty ratio is 2:1. 3,854 applied, 31% were admitted. 8% from out-of-state. 1% American Indian or Alaska Native, non-Hispanic/Latino; 3% Hispanic/Latino; 12% African American, non-Hispanic/Latino; 2% Asian, non-Hispanic/Latino; 0% Native Hawaiian or other Pacific Islander, non-Hispanic/Latino; 0.5% international. 52% 25 or older. Academic area with the most degrees conferred: health professions and related sciences. Calendar: semesters. Services for LD students, part-time degree program, graduate courses open to undergrads. ROTC: Army (c).
Collegiate Environment: Student services: health clinic, personal-psychological counseling. Campus security: 24-hour emergency response devices and patrols, late night transport-escort service, controlled dormitory access. 200 college housing spaces available. Option: coed housing available. Medical Sciences Library with 183,975 books, 1,567 serials, an OPAC, and a Web page.

■ **UNIVERSITY OF ARKANSAS AT MONTICELLO**
Monticello, AR 71656
Tel: (870)367-6811; Free: 800-844-1826
Fax: (870)460-1321
E-mail: admissions@uamont.edu
Web Site: www.uamont.edu/
Description: State-supported, comprehensive, coed. Part of University of Arkansas System. Awards associate, bachelor's, and master's degrees. Founded 1909. Setting: 1,600-acre small town campus. Endowment: $2.5 million. Research spending for the previous fiscal year: $120,040.

Educational spending for the previous fiscal year: $2456 per student. Total enrollment: 3,920. Faculty: 240 (172 full-time, 68 part-time). Student-undergrad faculty ratio is 16:1. 2,761 applied, 46% were admitted. Full-time: 2,676 students, 57% women, 43% men. Part-time: 1,126 students, 69% women, 31% men. 12% from out-of-state. 0.4% American Indian or Alaska Native, non-Hispanic/Latino; 2% Hispanic/Latino; 33% African American, non-Hispanic/Latino; 0.3% Asian, non-Hispanic/Latino; 0.4% international. 31% 25 or older, 25% live on campus, 0% transferred in. Retention: 40% of full-time freshmen returned the following year. Academic areas with the most degrees conferred: business/marketing; health professions and related sciences; parks and recreation. Core. Calendar: semesters. Academic remediation for entering students, services for LD students, advanced placement, accelerated degree program, independent study, distance learning, double major, summer session for credit, part-time degree program, graduate courses open to undergrads. Off campus study. ROTC: Army.

Entrance Requirements: Open admission except for nursing program. Options: early admission, deferred admission. Required: high school transcript, proof of immunization. Recommended: used for placement. Entrance: noncompetitive. Application deadline: 8/1. Transfer credits accepted: Yes.

Costs Per Year: Application fee: $0. State resident tuition: $3960 full-time, $132 per semester hour part-time. Nonresident tuition: $9450 full-time, $315 per semester hour part-time. Mandatory fees: $1740 full-time, $58 per semester hour part-time. Full-time tuition and fees vary according to location and program. Part-time tuition and fees vary according to location and program. College room and board: $4880. Room and board charges vary according to board plan and housing facility.

Collegiate Environment: Orientation program. Drama-theater group, choral group, marching band, student-run newspaper. Social organizations: 84 open to all; national fraternities, national sororities; 10% of eligible men and 10% of eligible women are members. Major annual events: Homecoming events, Greek Week. Student services: health clinic, personal-psychological counseling. Campus security: 24-hour emergency response devices and patrols. Fred J. Taylor Library and Technology Center with 241,822 books, 17,052 microform titles, and 956 serials. Operations spending for the previous fiscal year: $883,554. 400 computers available on campus for general student use. A campuswide network can be accessed from student residence rooms and from off campus. Students can access the following: online class registration. Staffed computer lab on campus.

■ **UNIVERSITY OF ARKANSAS AT PINE BLUFF**
1200 N University Dr.
Pine Bluff, AR 71601-2799
Tel: (870)575-8000; Free: 800-621-7440
Fax: (870)543-2021
E-mail: jonesm@uapb.edu
Web Site: www.uapb.edu/
Description: State-supported, comprehensive, coed. Part of University of Arkansas System. Awards associate, bachelor's, and master's degrees. Founded 1873. Setting: 327-acre urban campus. Total enrollment: 3,428. Faculty: 234 (171 full-time, 63 part-time). Student-undergrad faculty ratio is 17:1. 4,988 applied, 30% were admitted. Full-time: 3,002 students, 56% women, 44% men. Part-time: 281 students, 59% women, 41% men. Students come from 37 states and territories, 20 other countries, 37% from out-of-state. 15% 25 or older, 46% live on campus, 5% transferred in. Retention: 57% of full-time freshmen returned the following year. Academic areas with the most degrees conferred: business/marketing; homeland security, law enforcement, firefighting, and protective services; family and consumer sciences; liberal arts/general studies. Core. Calendar: semesters. Academic remediation for entering students, ESL program, services for LD students, advanced placement, accelerated degree program, honors program, independent study, distance learning, double major, summer session for credit, part-time degree program, external degree program, adult/continuing education programs, co-op programs and internships, graduate courses open to undergrads. Off campus study at University of Arkansas, University of Arkansas at Little Rock, University of Arkansas at Monticello, University of Arkansas Community College at Hope. ROTC: Army.

Entrance Requirements: Open admission. Options: electronic application, early admission, deferred admission, international baccalaureate accepted. Required: high school transcript, minimum 2 high school GPA, SAT or ACT. Application deadline: Rolling. Notification: continuous.

Collegiate Environment: Orientation program. Drama-theater group, choral group, marching band, student-run newspaper. Social organizations: national fraternities, national sororities, local fraternities, local sororities; 6% of eligible men and 6% of eligible women are members. Most popular organizations: Pre-Alumni Club, Honors College. Major annual events: Unity Fest, Homecoming, Convocation. Student services: health clinic, personal-psychological counseling. Campus security: 24-hour emergency response devices and patrols. Watson Memorial Library with 187,582 books, 175,547 microform titles, 3,041 serials, and an OPAC. 1,000 computers available on campus for general student use. A campuswide network can be accessed from student residence rooms and from off campus. Students can access the following: online class registration. Staffed computer lab on campus provides training in use of computers, software, and the Internet.

■ UNIVERSITY OF ARKANSAS–FORT SMITH

PO Box 3649
Fort Smith, AR 72913-3649
Tel: (479)788-7000; Free: 888-512-5466
Fax: (479)788-7003
E-mail: information@uafortsmith.edu
Web Site: www.uafortsmith.edu/

Description: State and locally supported, 4-year, coed. Part of University of Arkansas System. Awards associate and bachelor's degrees. Founded 1928. Setting: 120-acre suburban campus. Endowment: $63.3 million. Educational spending for the previous fiscal year: $3871 per student. Total enrollment: 7,352. Faculty: 449 (246 full-time, 203 part-time). Student-undergrad faculty ratio is 19:1. 4,126 applied, 54% were admitted. 11% from top 10% of their high school class, 31% from top quarter, 62% from top half. Full-time: 5,136 students, 58% women, 42% men. Part-time: 2,216 students, 57% women, 43% men. Students come from 33 states and territories, 17 other countries, 9% from out-of-state. 3% American Indian or Alaska Native, non-Hispanic/Latino; 7% Hispanic/Latino; 4% African American, non-Hispanic/Latino; 4% Asian, non-Hispanic/Latino; 0.1% Native Hawaiian or other Pacific Islander, non-Hispanic/Latino; 1% international. 30% 25 or older, 12% live on campus, 6% transferred in. Retention: 64% of full-time freshmen returned the following year. Academic areas with the most degrees conferred: business/marketing; interdisciplinary studies; education. Core. Calendar: semesters. Academic remediation for entering students, ESL program, services for LD students, advanced placement, accelerated degree program, honors program, distance learning, double major, summer session for credit, part-time degree program, external degree program, adult/continuing education programs, co-op programs and internships. Off campus study. Study abroad program. ROTC: Army, Air Force (c).
Entrance Requirements: Open admission except for health career and education programs. Options: electronic application, early admission, deferred admission. Required: high school transcript, SAT or ACT, COMPASS (in lieu of SAT or ACT). Entrance: minimally difficult. Application deadline: Rolling. Transfer credits accepted: Yes.
Costs Per Year: Application fee: $0. State resident tuition: $3900 full-time, $130 per credit hour part-time. Nonresident tuition: $10,650 full-time, $355 per credit hour part-time. Mandatory fees: $1536 full-time, $45 per credit hour part-time, $93. Full-time tuition and fees vary according to course load and program. Part-time tuition and fees vary according to course load and program. College room and board: $7828. College room only: $4848. Room and board charges vary according to board plan and housing facility.
Collegiate Environment: Orientation program. Drama-theater group, choral group, student-run newspaper. Social organizations: 68 open to all; national fraternities, national sororities; 5% of eligible men and 5% of eligible women are members. Most popular organizations: Campus Activities Board, Phi Beta Lambda, Student Alumni Association, Non-Traditional Students, Baptist Collegiate Ministry. Major annual events: Campus Picnic and Block Party, Season of Entertainment, Homecoming. Student services: health clinic, personal-psychological counseling. Campus security: 24-hour emergency response devices and patrols, student patrols, late night transport-escort service, controlled dormitory access, student patrols; new dormitory facilities have electronic card readers entrances. 940 college housing spaces available; 876 were occupied in 2012-13. No special consideration for freshman housing applicants. Option: coed housing available. Boreham Library with 164,876 books, 60,510 microform titles, 23,000 serials, 5,241 audiovisual materials, an OPAC, and a Web page. Operations spending for the previous fiscal year: $1.2 million. 1,553 computers available on campus for general student use. Computer purchase/lease plans available. A campuswide network can be accessed from student residence rooms and from off campus. Students can access the following: online class registration, online subscription databases, information portal, online course management system and online courses. Staffed computer lab on campus provides training in use of computers, software, and the Internet.

■ UNIVERSITY OF CENTRAL ARKANSAS

201 Donaghey Ave.
Conway, AR 72035-0001
Tel: (501)450-5000; Free: 800-243-8245
Fax: (501)450-5228
E-mail: rpatterson@uca.edu
Web Site: www.uca.edu/

Description: State-supported, university, coed. Awards bachelor's, master's, and doctoral degrees and post-master's certificates. Founded 1907. Setting: 365-acre small town campus. Total enrollment: 11,107. Faculty: 726 (541 full-time, 185 part-time). Student-undergrad faculty ratio is 16:1. 3,659 applied, 90% were admitted. 18% from top 10% of their high school class, 43% from top quarter, 76% from top half. Full-time: 8,136 students, 58% women, 42% men. Part-time: 1,468 students, 53% women, 47% men. Students come from 43 states and territories, 60 other countries, 8% from out-of-state. 1% American Indian or Alaska Native, non-Hispanic/Latino; 3% Hispanic/Latino; 18% African American, non-Hispanic/Latino; 2% Asian, non-Hispanic/Latino; 0.1% Native Hawaiian or other Pacific Islander, non-Hispanic/Latino; 3% international. 11% 25 or older, 6% transferred in. Retention: 70% of full-time freshmen returned the following year. Academic areas with the most degrees conferred: health professions and related sciences; business/marketing; education. Core. Calendar: semesters. Academic remediation for entering students, ESL program, services for LD students, advanced placement, accelerated degree program, freshman honors college, honors program, independent study, distance learning, double major, summer session for credit, part-time degree program, co-op programs and internships, graduate courses open to undergrads. ROTC: Army.
Entrance Requirements: Options: electronic application, early admission, deferred admission, international baccalaureate accepted. Required: high school transcript, SAT or ACT. Entrance: moderately difficult. Application deadline: Rolling. Notification: continuous. Transfer credits accepted: Yes.
Costs Per Year: Application fee: $25. State resident tuition: $5,498 full-time, $183.25 per credit hour part-time. Nonresident tuition: $10,995 full-time, $366.50 per credit hour part-time. Mandatory fees: $1,835 full-time, $52.72 per credit hour part-time, $126.50 per term part-time. Full-time tuition and fees vary according to course load. Part-time tuition and fees vary according to course load. College room and board: $5270. College room only: $3030. Room and board charges vary according to board plan and housing facility.
Collegiate Environment: Orientation program. Drama-theater group, choral group, marching band, student-run newspaper, radio station. Social organizations: national fraternities, national sororities. Most popular organization: Student Government Association. Major annual events: Homecoming, Miss UCA. Student services: health clinic, personal-psychological counseling, women's center. Campus security: 24-hour emergency response devices and patrols, student patrols, late night transport-escort service, controlled dormitory access. 3,927 college housing spaces available. Freshmen guaranteed college housing. On-campus residence required in freshman year. Options: coed, men-only, women-only housing available. Torreyson Library plus 1 other with 585,928 books, 621,665 microform titles, 49,556 serials, 3,492 audiovisual materials, an OPAC, and a Web page. 608 computers available on campus for general student use. A campuswide network can be accessed from student residence rooms and from off campus. Students can access the following: online class registration. Staffed computer lab on campus (open 24 hours a day).
Community Environment: Conway, population 52,000, is a growing center served by major highways, the Union Pacific Railway, and Little Rock National Airport which is 35 miles away. It is within a few miles of the geographic center of the state. Lake Conway, which covers approximately 6,500 acres, between Conway and Little Rock, is one of the principal resorts of the state. The Arkansas River, the largest to cross the state, is less than ten miles from Conway. Conway is a city with three colleges and is the government seat of Faulkner County. It has a diverse economic background, which includes manufacturers, education, government and service industries. Several major manufacturing firms including Kimberly Clark, Nucor Steel, Touksen and AmTran have facilities here. Axiom, a data processing center, has its corporation headquarters located in Conway and employs approximately 2,000 people. The city has many beautiful residences, churches, businesses, and public buildings.

■ UNIVERSITY OF THE OZARKS

415 N College Ave.
Clarksville, AR 72830-2880
Tel: (479)979-1000; Free: 800-264-8636

Fax: (479)979-1355
E-mail: admiss@ozarks.edu
Web Site: www.ozarks.edu/
Description: Independent Presbyterian, 4-year, coed. Awards bachelor's degrees. Founded 1834. Setting: small town campus. Total enrollment: 630. Faculty: 79 (48 full-time, 31 part-time). Student-undergrad faculty ratio is 11:1. 929 applied, 85% were admitted. 20% from top 10% of their high school class, 37% from top quarter, 79% from top half. Full-time: 595 students, 52% women, 48% men. Part-time: 35 students, 57% women, 43% men. 32% from out-of-state. 1% American Indian or Alaska Native, non-Hispanic/Latino; 8% Hispanic/Latino; 5% African American, non-Hispanic/Latino; 0.3% Asian, non-Hispanic/Latino; 11% international. 0% 25 or older, 70% live on campus, 3% transferred in. Retention: 59% of full-time freshmen returned the following year. Academic areas with the most degrees conferred: business/marketing; education; biological/life sciences. Calendar: semesters. Part-time degree program.
Entrance Requirements: Options: deferred admission, international baccalaureate accepted. Required: minimum 2 high school GPA, SAT or ACT. Required for some: essay, high school transcript, interview. Entrance: moderately difficult. Application deadline: Rolling. Notification: continuous. SAT Reasoning Test deadline: 8/15. Transfer credits accepted: Yes.
Costs Per Year: Application fee: $30. Comprehensive fee: $29,950 includes full-time tuition ($22,650), mandatory fees ($600), and college room and board ($6700). College room only: $3100. Room and board charges vary according to board plan and housing facility. Part-time tuition: $950 per credit hour.
Collegiate Environment: Orientation program. Campus security: 24-hour emergency response devices and patrols, late night transport-escort service. Freshmen guaranteed college housing. On-campus residence required through sophomore year. Options: coed, women-only housing available.
Community Environment: Clarksville is the county seat of Johnson County. The town lies 105 miles northwest of Little Rock on Interstate 40, & is 65 miles east of Fort Smith. The Continental bus line serves this area. Primarily an agricultural community, it also has some manufacturing. There are motel accommodations, and a hospital. A swimming pool, athletic fields, baseball park, football field, tennis courts, and all the outdoor sports are available. Annual events include the Peach Festival.

■ **UNIVERSITY OF PHOENIX–LITTLE ROCK CAMPUS**
10800 Financial Ctr. Pky.
Little Rock, AR 72211-3500
Tel: (501)225-9337; Free: 866-766-0766
Web Site: www.phoenix.edu/
Description: Proprietary, comprehensive, coed. Awards bachelor's and master's degrees. Founded 2003. Setting: urban campus. Total enrollment: 773. Faculty: 122 (13 full-time, 109 part-time). Full-time: 622 students, 68% women, 32% men. 81% 25 or older. Academic areas with the most degrees conferred: business/marketing; computer and information sciences. Core. Calendar: continuous. Services for LD students, advanced placement, accelerated degree program, independent study, distance learning, graduate courses open to undergrads.
Entrance Requirements: Open admission. Options: electronic application, deferred admission. Required: 1 recommendation. Required for some: high school transcript. Entrance: noncompetitive. Application deadline: Rolling.
Collegiate Environment: Campus security: late night transport-escort service.

■ **UNIVERSITY OF PHOENIX–NORTHWEST ARKANSAS CAMPUS**
903 N 47th St. - Barrington Centre 2
Rogers, AR 72756-9615
Tel: (479)986-0385; Free: 866-766-0766
Web Site: www.phoenix.edu/
Description: Proprietary, comprehensive, coed. Awards bachelor's, master's, and doctoral degrees.

■ **WILLIAMS BAPTIST COLLEGE**
60 W Fulbright Ave.
Walnut Ridge, AR 72476
Tel: (870)886-6741; Free: 800-722-4434
E-mail: admissions@wbcoll.edu
Web Site: www.wbcoll.edu/
Description: Independent Southern Baptist, 4-year, coed. Awards associate and bachelor's degrees. Founded 1941. Setting: 180-acre rural campus. Total enrollment: 619. Student-undergrad faculty ratio is 13:1. 17% from out-of-state. 19% 25 or older. Retention: 60% of full-time freshmen returned the following year. Core. Calendar: semesters. Advanced placement, self-designed majors, independent study, double major, summer session for credit, part-time degree program, adult/continuing education programs, internships. Off campus study at Coalition for Christian Colleges and Universities. Study abroad program. ROTC: Army (c).
Entrance Requirements: Option: electronic application. Required: high school transcript, minimum 2.5 high school GPA, SAT or ACT. Recommended: interview. Required for some: essay. Entrance: minimally difficult. Application deadline: Rolling.
Collegiate Environment: Orientation program. Drama-theater group, choral group. Student services: personal-psychological counseling. Campus security: 24-hour emergency response devices, student patrols. Felix Goodson Library with an OPAC.
Community Environment: Walnut Ridge is a rural area with a temperate climate. Railroads serve the area as well as a city airport. There are churches of major denominations, a public library, and a hospital. Recreational activities include boating and water sports. The city has Lions and Kiwanis organizations. An annual county fair is held. Part-time employment opportunities are limited.

■ **ACADEMY OF ART UNIVERSITY**
79 New Montgomery St.
San Francisco, CA 94105-3410
Tel: (415)274-2200; Free: 800-544-ARTS
Fax: (415)263-4130
E-mail: info@academyart.edu
Web Site: www.academyart.edu/
Description: Proprietary, comprehensive, coed. Awards bachelor's and master's degrees. Founded 1929. Setting: 3-acre urban campus. Total enrollment: 18,115. Faculty: 1,468 (264 full-time, 1,204 part-time). Student-undergrad faculty ratio is 19:1. 3,055 applied, 100% were admitted. Full-time: 6,623 students, 54% women, 46% men. Part-time: 5,369 students, 59% women, 41% men. Students come from 55 states and territories, 118 other countries, 41% from out-of-state. 1% American Indian or Alaska Native, non-Hispanic/Latino; 9% Hispanic/Latino; 6% African American, non-Hispanic/Latino; 8% Asian, non-Hispanic/Latino; 0.3% Native Hawaiian or other Pacific Islander, non-Hispanic/Latino; 20% international. 43% 25 or older, 13% live on campus, 9% transferred in. Retention: 71% of full-time freshmen returned the following year. Academic areas with the most degrees conferred: visual and performing arts; communication technologies; communication/journalism. Core. Calendar: semesters. Academic remediation for entering students, ESL program, services for LD students, independent study, distance learning, summer session for credit, part-time degree program, adult/continuing education programs, internships.
Entrance Requirements: Open admission. Options: electronic application, early admission, deferred admission, international baccalaureate accepted. Required: high school transcript. Recommended: minimum 2 high school GPA, interview, Undergraduate applicants are not required to submit a portfolio, but may do so for possible waiver of foundation or major classes for graduate admissions. Entrance: noncompetitive. Application deadline: Rolling. Transfer credits accepted: Yes.
Costs Per Year: Application fee: $100. Comprehensive fee: $37,240 includes full-time tuition ($23,550), mandatory fees ($290), and college room and board ($13,400). Full-time tuition and fees vary according to course load. Room and board charges vary according to board plan and housing facility. Part-time tuition: $785 per credit. Part-time tuition varies according to course load.
Collegiate Environment: Orientation program. Drama-theater group, student-run radio station. Social organizations: 40 open to all; national fraternities, national sororities. Most popular organizations: Tea Time Animation, Beyond the Front Row, Children's Book Club, Comic Book Club, Ideation Club. Major annual events: Spring Show, Industry on Campus Series, Halloweek. Campus security: 24-hour emergency response devices and patrols, late night transport-escort service, controlled dormitory access, ID check at all buildings. 1,873 college housing spaces available; 1,740 were occupied in 2012-13. Freshmen guaranteed college housing. Options: coed, men-only, women-only housing available. Academy of Art University Library with 47,800 books, 275 serials, 4,250 audiovisual materials, an OPAC, and a Web page. 1,720 computers available on campus for general student use. A campuswide network can be accessed. Students can access the following: online class registration, Provide support for students taking online courses. Staffed computer lab on campus provides training in use of computers, software, and the Internet.
Community Environment: Lining the street between the Powell and Sutter buildings are several of San Francisco's finest art galleries. The area provides an ideal environment for studying and developing as an artist.

■ **ACADEMY OF COUTURE ART**
Pacific Design Ctr.
8687 Melrose Ave., Ste. G520
West Hollywood, CA 90069
Tel: (310)360-8888
Fax: (310)967-8888
Web Site: www.academyofcoutureart.edu/
Description: Proprietary, primarily 2-year, coed. Awards terminal associate and bachelor's degrees.

■ **ALLAN HANCOCK COLLEGE**
800 S College Dr.
Santa Maria, CA 93454-6399
Tel: (805)922-6966; Free: 866-342-5242
Fax: (805)922-3477
Web Site: www.hancockcollege.edu/
Description: State and locally supported, 2-year, coed. Awards certificates, transfer associate, and terminal associate degrees. Founded 1920. Setting: 120-acre small town campus. Endowment: $1.1 million. Research spending for the previous fiscal year: $78,392. Educational spending for the previous fiscal year: $1690 per student. Total enrollment: 10,387. Faculty: 594 (152 full-time, 442 part-time). Student-undergrad faculty ratio is 17:1. Full-time: 2,996 students, 54% women, 46% men. Part-time: 7,391 students, 56% women, 44% men. Students come from 27 states and territories, 12 other countries. Core. Calendar: semesters. ESL program, services for LD students, advanced placement, distance learning, summer session for credit, part-time degree program, adult/continuing education programs, co-op programs. Study abroad program.
Entrance Requirements: Open admission except for nursing, drama, fire technology programs. Option: electronic application. Entrance: noncompetitive. Application deadline: Rolling. Notification: continuous. Transfer credits accepted: Yes.
Collegiate Environment: Orientation program. Drama-theater group, choral group, student-run newspaper. Social organizations: 10 open to all. Most popular organizations: MECHA, AHC Student Club, Club Med (medical), Hancock Christian Fellowship, VICA (Vocational Industrial Clubs of America). Major annual events: Chili Cook-Off, Blood Drive, Spring Fest. Student services: legal services, health clinic, personal-psychological counseling. Campus security: 24-hour emergency response devices and patrols, student patrols, late night transport-escort service. Learning Resources Center with 47,370 books, 51,225 microform titles, 397 serials, 2,463 audiovisual materials, an OPAC, and a Web page. Operations spending for the previous fiscal year: $252,771. 200 computers available on campus for general student use. Staffed computer lab on campus.
Community Environment: Santa Maria is located in the Central Coast region on United States Highway 101, 175 miles north of Los Angeles and 262 miles south of San Francisco. Average temperature ranges from 45 degrees minimum to 68.2 degrees maximum. Greyhound Bus and United Airlines serve the area. Santa Maria has a hospital, churches, a library, and a number of manufacturing firms. A municipal swimming pool, golf courses, parks and playgrounds provide facilities for sports. Hunting and fishing opportunities are good.

■ **ALLIANT INTERNATIONAL UNIVERSITY**
10455 Pomerado Rd.
San Diego, CA 92131-1799

Tel: (858)271-4300; Free: 866-825-5426
Fax: (858)635-4739
E-mail: admissions@alliant.edu
Web Site: www.alliant.edu/
Description: Independent, university, coed. Part of Alliant International University. Awards bachelor's, master's, and doctoral degrees. Founded 1952. Setting: 60-acre suburban campus with easy access to San Diego. Total enrollment: 3,554. Faculty: 670 (236 full-time, 434 part-time). Student-undergrad faculty ratio is 9:1. Students come from 8 states and territories, 17 other countries, 5% from out-of-state. 0% American Indian or Alaska Native, non-Hispanic/Latino; 20% Hispanic/Latino; 8% African American, non-Hispanic/Latino; 4% Asian, non-Hispanic/Latino; 0% Native Hawaiian or other Pacific Islander, non-Hispanic/Latino; 27% international. 60% 25 or older, 40% live on campus. Academic areas with the most degrees conferred: business/marketing; psychology; social sciences; education. Core. Calendar: semesters. Academic remediation for entering students, ESL program, services for LD students, advanced placement, honors program, independent study, distance learning, summer session for credit, part-time degree program, internships, graduate courses open to under-grads.
Entrance Requirements: Options: electronic application, deferred admission, international baccalaureate accepted. Required: high school transcript, minimum 2 high school GPA. Transfer credits accepted: Yes.
Costs Per Year: Application fee: $45. Comprehensive fee: $24,270 includes full-time tuition ($16,740), mandatory fees ($190), and college room and board ($7340). Full-time tuition and fees vary according to course load and location. Room and board charges vary according to board plan. Part-time tuition: $620 per unit. Part-time tuition varies according to course load and location.
Collegiate Environment: Orientation program. Student-run newspaper. Social organizations: 12 open to all. Most popular organizations: Residence Hall Association, Latino Students Association, Finance Club, student government, Sigma Iota Epsilon. Major annual events: International Friendship Festival, Winter Ball, Snow Day in Big Bear. Student services: health clinic, personal-psychological counseling. Campus security: 24-hour emergency response devices and patrols, student patrols, late night transport-escort service. 250 college housing spaces available; 50 were occupied in 2012-13. Option: coed housing available. Walter Library with 156,245 books, 2,978 serials, 4,076 audiovisual materials, an OPAC, and a Web page. 100 computers available on campus for general student use. A campuswide network can be accessed from student residence rooms and from off campus. Students can access the following: online class registration. Staffed computer lab on campus.

■ **ALLIED AMERICAN UNIVERSITY**
22952 Alcade Dr.
Laguna Hills, CA 92653
Free: 888-384-0849
Fax: (949)707-2978
E-mail: info@allied.edu
Web Site: allied.edu/
Description: Proprietary, 4-year, coed. Awards associate and bachelor's degrees. Founded 2007. Distance learning.
Entrance Requirements: Option: electronic application. Required: high school transcript.

■ **AMERICAN ACADEMY OF DRAMATIC ARTS**
1336 N La Brea Ave.
Hollywood, CA 90028
Tel: (323)464-2777; Free: 800-222-2867
Fax: (323)464-1250
E-mail: shong@aada.edu
Web Site: www.aada.org/
Description: Independent, 2-year, coed. Awards certificates, diplomas, and transfer associate degrees. Founded 1974. Setting: 4-acre suburban campus with easy access to Los Angeles. Endowment: $1.7 million. Total enrollment: 188. Faculty: 41 (9 full-time, 32 part-time). Student-undergrad faculty ratio is 12:1. 419 applied, 22% were admitted. Full-time: 188 students, 56% women, 44% men. Students come from 37 states and territories, 15 other countries, 59% from out-of-state. 1% American Indian or Alaska Native, non-Hispanic/Latino; 11% Hispanic/Latino; 7% African American, non-Hispanic/Latino; 2% Asian, non-Hispanic/Latino; 0% Native Hawaiian or other Pacific Islander, non-Hispanic/Latino; 20% international. 25% 25 or older, 0% transferred in. Core. Calendar: continuous. Internships.

Entrance Requirements: Option: deferred admission. Required: essay, high school transcript, 2 recommendations, interview, audition. Recommended: minimum 2 high school GPA. Entrance: moderately difficult. Application deadline: Rolling. Notification: continuous. Transfer credits accepted: Yes.
Collegiate Environment: Campus security: 24-hour emergency response devices, 8-hour patrols by trained security personnel. Bryn Morgan Library with 12,500 books, 6 serials, and 1,500 audiovisual materials. Operations spending for the previous fiscal year: $40,362. 8 computers available on campus for general student use. A campuswide network can be accessed. Staffed computer lab on campus provides training in use of computers, software, and the Internet.

■ **AMERICAN CAREER COLLEGE (ANAHEIM)**
1200 N Magnolia Ave.
Anaheim, CA 92801
Tel: (714)763-9066; Free: 877-832-0790
E-mail: info@americancareer.com
Web Site: americancareercollege.edu/
Description: Proprietary, 2-year, coed. Awards certificates, diplomas, and terminal associate degrees. Total enrollment: 1,808. Student-undergrad faculty ratio is 16:1. 685 applied, 77% were admitted. 0% from out-of-state. 48% 25 or older.
Entrance Requirements: Required: high school transcript.

■ **AMERICAN CAREER COLLEGE (LOS ANGELES)**
4021 Rosewood Ave.
Los Angeles, CA 90004-2932
Tel: (323)668-7555; Free: 877-832-0790
E-mail: info@americancareer.com
Web Site: americancareercollege.edu/
Description: Proprietary, 2-year, coed. Awards certificates, diplomas, and terminal associate degrees. Founded 1978. Total enrollment: 1,764. Student-undergrad faculty ratio is 15:1. 676 applied, 86% were admitted. 0% from out-of-state. 39% 25 or older.
Entrance Requirements: Required: high school transcript.

■ **AMERICAN CAREER COLLEGE (ONTARIO)**
3130 E Sedona Ct.
Ontario, CA 91764
Tel: (909)218-3253; Free: 877-832-0790
E-mail: info@amerciancareer.com
Web Site: americancareercollege.edu/
Description: Proprietary, 2-year, coed. Awards certificates, diplomas, and terminal associate degrees. Total enrollment: 1,115. Student-undergrad faculty ratio is 31:1. 352 applied, 76% were admitted. 0% from out-of-state. 42% 25 or older.
Entrance Requirements: Required: high school transcript.

■ **AMERICAN JEWISH UNIVERSITY**
15600 Mulholland Dr.
Bel Air, CA 90077-1599
Tel: (310)476-9777; Free: 888-853-6763
Fax: (310)471-3657
E-mail: admissions@ajula.edu
Web Site: www.ajula.edu/
Description: Independent Jewish, comprehensive, coed. Awards bachelor's and master's degrees. Founded 1947. Setting: 28-acre suburban campus with easy access to Los Angeles. Endowment: $21.6 million. Educational spending for the previous fiscal year: $28,462 per student. Total enrollment: 257. Faculty: 38 (8 full-time, 30 part-time). Student-undergrad faculty ratio is 7:1. 28 applied, 96% were admitted. 0% from top 10% of their high school class, 33% from top quarter, 67% from top half. Full-time: 114 students, 50% women, 50% men. Part-time: 11 students, 45% women, 55% men. Students come from 7 states and territories, 5 other countries, 15% from out-of-state. 2% American Indian or Alaska Native, non-Hispanic/Latino; 3% Hispanic/Latino; 2% African American, non-Hispanic/Latino; 2% Asian, non-Hispanic/Latino; 0% Native Hawaiian or other Pacific Islander, non-Hispanic/Latino; 5% international. 16% 25 or older, 34% live on campus, 24% transferred in. Retention: 58% of full-time freshmen returned the following year. Academic areas with the most degrees conferred: health professions and related sciences; business/marketing; social sciences. Core. Calendar: semesters. Academic remediation for entering students, services for LD students, advanced placement, self-designed majors, independent study, double

major, summer session for credit, part-time degree program, adult/continuing education programs, co-op programs and internships, graduate courses open to undergrads. Study abroad program.

Entrance Requirements: Options: electronic application, deferred admission, international baccalaureate accepted. Required: essay, high school transcript, 2 recommendations, SAT or ACT. Recommended: interview. Entrance: moderately difficult. Application deadlines: 5/31, 5/31 for nonresidents. Notification: continuous, continuous for nonresidents. SAT Reasoning Test deadline: 5/31. SAT Subject Test deadline: 5/31. Transfer credits accepted: Yes.

Costs Per Year: Application fee: $35. Comprehensive fee: $42,578 includes full-time tuition ($26,784), mandatory fees ($1712), and college room and board ($14,082). College room only: $7098. Full-time tuition and fees vary according to course load and degree level. Room and board charges vary according to board plan and housing facility. Part-time tuition: $1116 per unit. Part-time tuition varies according to course load and degree level.

Collegiate Environment: Orientation program. Drama-theater group, student-run newspaper. Social organizations: 12 open to all. Most popular organizations: Investment Club, Hiking Club, Film Club, AJU Sangha, Social Action Committee. Major annual events: Red Ribbon Week, Israel Week, Annual Student Scholarship Fundraiser & Gala. Student services: health clinic, personal-psychological counseling. Campus security: 24-hour emergency response devices, controlled dormitory access. 200 college housing spaces available; 45 were occupied in 2012-13. Freshmen guaranteed college housing. Option: coed housing available. Ostrow Library with an OPAC and a Web page. Operations spending for the previous fiscal year: $357,607. 38 computers available on campus for general student use. A campuswide network can be accessed from student residence rooms and from off campus.

Community Environment: A suburb of Los Angeles, Bel Air enjoys a mild and delightful climate. The city is served by all modes of transportation and freeways. The Hollywood Bowl has special summer-long programs of music and the lively arts. There are many theaters, both movie and stage, the Griffith Park Zoo, Planetarium, the Getty Museum and Skirball Cultural Center, all offering broad cultural and recreational activities. Within the city are excellent world-famous restaurants, night clubs and fine hotels providing outstanding accommodations and service. Employment is usually available on full- or part-time basis.

■ **AMERICAN MUSICAL AND DRAMATIC ACADEMY, LOS ANGELES**
6305 Yucca St.
Los Angeles, CA 90028
Tel: (323)469-3300; Free: 888-474-9444
Fax: (323)469-3350
E-mail: kjackson@amda.edu
Web Site: www.amda.edu/
Description: Proprietary, 4-year, coed. Awards bachelor's degrees.
Entrance Requirements: Required: high school transcript, 2 recommendations, audition.

■ **AMERICAN RIVER COLLEGE**
4700 College Oak Dr.
Sacramento, CA 95841-4286
Tel: (916)484-8011
E-mail: nealr@arc.losrios.edu
Web Site: www.arc.losrios.edu/
Description: District-supported, 2-year, coed. Part of Los Rios Community College District System. Awards certificates, transfer associate, and terminal associate degrees. Founded 1955. Setting: 153-acre suburban campus. Total enrollment: 33,821. 55% 25 or older. Core. Calendar: semesters. Academic remediation for entering students, ESL program, services for LD students, advanced placement, summer session for credit, part-time degree program, adult/continuing education programs, co-op programs.
Entrance Requirements: Open admission except for nursing, respiratory therapy programs. Options: early admission, deferred admission. Entrance: noncompetitive. Application deadline: Rolling.
Costs Per Year: One-time mandatory fee: $35. State resident tuition: $0 full-time. Nonresident tuition: $4992 full-time, $208 per unit part-time. Mandatory fees: $1104 full-time, $46 per unit part-time. Full-time tuition and fees vary according to course load. Part-time tuition and fees vary according to course load.
Collegiate Environment: Drama-theater group, student-run newspaper. Student services: health clinic, personal-psychological counseling, women's

center. Campus security: 24-hour emergency response devices and patrols, student patrols, late night transport-escort service. 78,400 books and 75 serials.
Community Environment: See California State University - Sacramento.

■ **AMERICAN UNIVERSITY OF HEALTH SCIENCES**
1600 E Hill St.
Bldg. No.1
Signal Hill, CA 90755
Tel: (562)988-2278
Fax: (562)988-1791
Web Site: www.auhs.edu/
Description: Proprietary, comprehensive, coed.

■ **ANTELOPE VALLEY COLLEGE**
3041 W Ave. K
Lancaster, CA 93536-5426
Tel: (661)722-6300
Fax: (661)943-5573
Web Site: www.avc.edu/
Description: State and locally supported, 2-year, coed. Part of California Community College System. Awards certificates, transfer associate, and terminal associate degrees. Founded 1929. Setting: 135-acre suburban campus with easy access to Los Angeles. Endowment: $299,569. Research spending for the previous fiscal year: $69,540. Educational spending for the previous fiscal year: $4565 per student. Total enrollment: 15,108. Faculty: 618 (195 full-time, 423 part-time). Student-undergrad faculty ratio is 45:1. 2,830 applied, 100% were admitted. Full-time: 4,802 students, 58% women, 42% men. Part-time: 10,306 students, 61% women, 39% men. Students come from 7 states and territories, 1% from out-of-state. 32% 25 or older, 16% transferred in. Retention: 68% of full-time freshmen returned the following year. Core. Calendar: semesters. Academic remediation for entering students, ESL program, services for LD students, advanced placement, self-designed majors, honors program, independent study, distance learning, summer session for credit, part-time degree program, adult/continuing education programs, co-op programs. ROTC: Air Force (c).
Entrance Requirements: Open admission. Options: electronic application, early admission. Required: high school transcript. Recommended: assessment. Entrance: noncompetitive. Application deadline: Rolling. Notification: continuous. Transfer credits accepted: Yes.
Collegiate Environment: Orientation program. Drama-theater group, choral group, student-run newspaper. Major annual events: Cinco de Mayo, Women's Workshop, Transfer Colleges Day. Student services: personal-psychological counseling. Campus security: 24-hour emergency response devices and patrols, late night transport-escort service. Antelope Valley College Library with 43,000 books, 175 serials, and an OPAC. Operations spending for the previous fiscal year: $946,564. 75 computers available on campus for general student use. A campuswide network can be accessed from off-campus. Students can access the following: online class registration. Staffed computer lab on campus.
Community Environment: Population 134,000. Lancaster is located in the center of the Antelope Valley in a semidesert region. Lancaster has over 350 days of sunshine a year and the climate is the reason that the United States Air Force and almost every manufacturer of aircraft build and maintain establishments in this area. There has been a great increase in population and excellent employment opportunities have developed in proportion to the growth.

■ **ANTHEM COLLEGE–SACRAMENTO**
9738 Lincoln Village Dr.
Ste. 100
Sacramento, CA 95827
Tel: (916)929-9700; Free: 855-331-7768
Fax: (916)929-9703
Web Site: anthem.edu/sacramento-california/
Description: Proprietary, 2-year, coed. Awards terminal associate degrees. Founded 1992. Total enrollment: 716.
Entrance Requirements: Entrance: noncompetitive.

■ **ANTIOCH UNIVERSITY LOS ANGELES**
400 Corporate Pointe
Culver City, CA 90230
Tel: (310)578-1080; Free: 800-726-8462
Fax: (310)827-4742

E-mail: admissions@antiochla.edu
Web Site: www.antiochla.edu/
Description: Independent, upper-level, coed. Part of Antioch University. Awards bachelor's, master's, and doctoral degrees and post-master's certificates. Founded 1972. Setting: 1-acre urban campus with easy access to Los Angeles. Total enrollment: 495. Faculty: 172 (21 full-time, 151 part-time). Student-undergrad faculty ratio is 14:1. 70 applied, 90% were admitted. Part-time: 139 students, 68% women, 32% men. 0% from out-of-state. 97% 25 or older, 36% transferred in. Core. Academic remediation for entering students, services for LD students, advanced placement, accelerated degree program, self-designed majors, independent study, distance learning, double major, summer session for credit, part-time degree program, adult/continuing education programs, co-op programs and internships, graduate courses open to undergrads.
Collegiate Environment: Orientation program. Student-run newspaper, radio station. Student services: personal-psychological counseling. Campus security: 24-hour emergency response devices, late night transport-escort service. 12 computers available on campus for general student use. A campuswide network can be accessed from off-campus. Students can access the following: online class registration. Staffed computer lab on campus.

■ ANTIOCH UNIVERSITY SANTA BARBARA
602 Anacapa St.
Santa Barbara, CA 93101-1581
Tel: (805)962-8179; Free: 866-526-8462
Fax: (805)962-4786
E-mail: sestomo@antioch.edu
Web Site: www.antiochsb.edu/
Description: Independent, upper-level, coed. Part of Antioch University. Awards bachelor's, master's, and doctoral degrees. Founded 1977. Setting: small town campus. Total enrollment: 382. Faculty: 75 (12 full-time, 63 part-time). Student-undergrad faculty ratio is 9:1. Full-time: 64 students, 77% women, 23% men. Part-time: 84 students, 69% women, 31% men. Students come from 3 other countries. 2% American Indian or Alaska Native, non-Hispanic/Latino; 33% Hispanic/Latino; 3% African American, non-Hispanic/Latino; 2% Asian, non-Hispanic/Latino; 1% Native Hawaiian or other Pacific Islander, non-Hispanic/Latino; 3% international. 62% 25 or older. Academic area with the most degrees conferred: liberal arts/general studies. Core. Academic remediation for entering students, accelerated degree program, self-designed majors, independent study, distance learning, summer session for credit, part-time degree program, external degree program, internships, graduate courses open to undergrads. Off campus study.
Entrance Requirements: Transfer credits accepted: Yes.
Costs Per Year: Application fee: $60. Tuition: $453 per unit part-time. Part-time tuition varies according to degree level.
Collegiate Environment: Orientation program. Student-run newspaper. Campus security: late night transport-escort service. College housing not available. Sage Library with 3,254 books, an OPAC, and a Web page. 16 computers available on campus for general student use. A campuswide network can be accessed from off-campus. Students can access the following: online class registration. Staffed computer lab on campus provides training in use of computers, software, and the Internet.

■ APPLIED PROFESSIONAL TRAINING, INC.
5751 Palmer Way, Ste. D
Carlsbad, CA 92013
Free: 800-431-8488
Fax: (888)431-8588
E-mail: aptc@aptc.com
Web Site: www.aptc.edu/
Description: Proprietary, 2-year, coed. Awards certificates and terminal associate degrees. Founded 1993.

■ ARGOSY UNIVERSITY, INLAND EMPIRE
3401 Centre Lake Dr., Ste. 200
Ontario, CA 91761
Tel: (909)472-0800; Free: 866-217-9075
Web Site: www.argosy.edu/inland-empire/
Description: Proprietary, university, coed. Awards bachelor's, master's, and doctoral degrees. Founded 2006.

■ ARGOSY UNIVERSITY, LOS ANGELES
5230 Pacific Concourse, Ste. 200
Santa Monica, CA 90045

Tel: (310)866-4000; Free: 866-505-0332
Web Site: www.argosy.edu/los-angeles/
Description: Proprietary, university, coed. Awards bachelor's, master's, and doctoral degrees.

■ ARGOSY UNIVERSITY, ORANGE COUNTY
601 S Lewis St.
Orange, CA 92868
Tel: (714)338-6200; Free: 800-716-9598
Web Site: www.argosy.edu/locations/los-angeles-orange-county/
Description: Proprietary, university, coed. Awards associate, bachelor's, master's, and doctoral degrees. Setting: urban campus. Calendar: semesters.

■ ARGOSY UNIVERSITY, SAN DIEGO
1615 Murray Canyon Rd., Ste. 100
San Diego, CA 92108
Tel: (619)321-3000; Free: 866-505-0333
Web Site: www.argosy.edu/sandiego/
Description: Proprietary, university, coed. Awards bachelor's, master's, and doctoral degrees.

■ ARGOSY UNIVERSITY, SAN FRANCISCO BAY AREA
1005 Atlantic Ave.
Alameda, CA 94501
Tel: (510)217-4700; Free: 866-215-2777
Fax: (510)217-4806
Web Site: www.argosy.edu/sanfrancisco/
Description: Proprietary, university, coed. Part of Education Management Corporation. Awards bachelor's, master's, and doctoral degrees. Founded 1998. Calendar: semesters.

■ ART CENTER COLLEGE OF DESIGN
1700 Lida St.
Pasadena, CA 91103
Tel: (626)396-2200
Fax: (626)795-0578
E-mail: kit.baron@artcenter.edu
Web Site: www.artcenter.edu/
Description: Independent, comprehensive, coed. Awards bachelor's and master's degrees. Founded 1930. Setting: 175-acre suburban campus with easy access to Los Angeles. Total enrollment: 1,869. Faculty: 431 (94 full-time, 337 part-time). Student-undergrad faculty ratio is 9:1. 450 applied, 81% were admitted. Full-time: 1,443 students, 50% women, 50% men. Part-time: 214 students, 44% women, 56% men. 0.1% American Indian or Alaska Native, non-Hispanic/Latino; 10% Hispanic/Latino; 1% African American, non-Hispanic/Latino; 36% Asian, non-Hispanic/Latino; 0.5% Native Hawaiian or other Pacific Islander, non-Hispanic/Latino; 21% international. 30% 25 or older, 0% live on campus, 11% transferred in. Retention: 83% of full-time freshmen returned the following year. Academic areas with the most degrees conferred: visual and performing arts; communication/journalism; architecture; communication technologies. Calendar: trimesters.
Entrance Requirements: Options: electronic application, deferred admission, international baccalaureate accepted. Required: essay, high school transcript, portfolio. Recommended: interview. Required for some: SAT, ACT, SAT or ACT. Entrance: very difficult. Application deadline: Rolling. Notification: continuous. Transfer credits accepted: Yes.
Costs Per Year: Application fee: $50. Tuition: $35,052 full-time. Mandatory fees: $500 full-time.
Collegiate Environment: Orientation program. Campus security: 24-hour emergency response devices and patrols. College housing not available.
Community Environment: See California Institute of Technology.

■ THE ART INSTITUTE OF CALIFORNIA–HOLLYWOOD, A CAMPUS OF ARGOSY UNIVERSITY
5250 Lankershim Blvd.
North Hollywood, CA 91601
Tel: (818)299-5100; Free: 877-468-6232
Web Site: www.artinstitutes.edu/hollywood/
Description: Proprietary, 4-year, coed. Part of Education Management Corporation. Awards associate and bachelor's degrees. Founded 1992. Setting: urban campus.

THE ART INSTITUTE OF CALIFORNIA–INLAND EMPIRE, A CAMPUS OF ARGOSY UNIVERSITY
674 E Brier Dr.
San Bernardino, CA 92408
Tel: (909)915-2100; Free: 800-353-0812
Web Site: www.artinstitutes.edu/inlandempire/
Description: Proprietary, 4-year, coed. Part of Education Management Corporation. Awards associate and bachelor's degrees. Setting: suburban campus.

THE ART INSTITUTE OF CALIFORNIA–LOS ANGELES, A CAMPUS OF ARGOSY UNIVERSITY
2900 31st St.
Santa Monica, CA 90405-3035
Tel: (310)752-4700; Free: 888-646-4610
Fax: (310)752-4708
Web Site: www.artinstitutes.edu/losangeles/
Description: Proprietary, 4-year, coed. Part of Education Management Corporation. Awards associate and bachelor's degrees. Setting: urban campus.

THE ART INSTITUTE OF CALIFORNIA–ORANGE COUNTY, A CAMPUS OF ARGOSY UNIVERSITY
3601 W Sunflower Ave.
Santa Ana, CA 92704
Tel: (714)830-0200; Free: 888-549-3055
Web Site: www.artinstitutes.edu/orangecounty/
Description: Proprietary, 4-year, coed. Part of Education Management Corporation. Awards associate and bachelor's degrees. Founded 2000. Setting: urban campus with easy access to Orange County.

THE ART INSTITUTE OF CALIFORNIA–SACRAMENTO, A CAMPUS OF ARGOSY UNIVERSITY
2850 Gateway Oaks Dr., Ste. 100
Sacramento, CA 95833
Free: 800-477-1957
Web Site: www.artinstitutes.edu/sacramento/
Description: Proprietary, 4-year, coed. Awards associate and bachelor's degrees.

THE ART INSTITUTE OF CALIFORNIA–SAN DIEGO, A CAMPUS OF ARGOSY UNIVERSITY
7650 Mission Valley Rd.
San Diego, CA 92108
Tel: (858)598-1399; Free: 866-275-2422
Web Site: www.artinstitutes.edu/sandiego/
Description: Proprietary, 4-year, coed. Part of Education Management Corporation. Awards associate and bachelor's degrees. Founded 1981. Setting: urban campus.

THE ART INSTITUTE OF CALIFORNIA–SAN FRANCISCO, A CAMPUS OF ARGOSY UNIVERSITY
1170 Market St.
San Francisco, CA 94102
Tel: (415)865-0198; Free: 888-493-3261
Fax: (415)863-6344
Web Site: www.artinstitutes.edu/sanfrancisco/
Description: Proprietary, comprehensive, coed. Part of Education Management Corporation. Awards associate, bachelor's, and master's degrees. Founded 1939. Setting: urban campus.

THE ART INSTITUTE OF CALIFORNIA–SILICON VALLEY, A CAMPUS OF ARGOSY UNIVERSITY
1120 Kifer Rd.
Sunnyvale, CA 94086
Tel: (408)962-6400; Free: 866-583-7961
Web Site: www.artinstitutes.edu/silicon-valley/
Description: Proprietary, 4-year, coed. Awards associate and bachelor's degrees.

AVIATION & ELECTRONIC SCHOOLS OF AMERICA
111 S Railroad St.
Colfax, CA 95713-1810
Tel: (530)346-6792; Free: 800-345-2742
Fax: (530)346-8466
E-mail: aesa@aesa.com
Web Site: www.aesa.com/
Description: Proprietary, 2-year, coed. Awards certificates and terminal associate degrees. Founded 1988. Calendar: continuous.

AZUSA PACIFIC UNIVERSITY
901 E Alosta Ave.
Azusa, CA 91702-7000
Tel: (626)969-3434; Free: 800-TALK-APU
E-mail: admissions@apu.edu
Web Site: www.apu.edu/
Description: Independent nondenominational, university, coed. Awards bachelor's, master's, and doctoral degrees and post-master's certificates. Founded 1899. Setting: 60-acre suburban campus with easy access to Los Angeles. Total enrollment: 10,184. Faculty: 1,020 (407 full-time, 613 part-time). Student-undergrad faculty ratio is 14:1. 8,515 applied, 52% were admitted. 7% from top 10% of their high school class, 16% from top quarter, 31% from top half. Full-time: 5,412 students, 64% women, 36% men. Part-time: 812 students, 63% women, 37% men. 0% from out-of-state. 0.3% American Indian or Alaska Native, non-Hispanic/Latino; 20% Hispanic/Latino; 5% African American, non-Hispanic/Latino; 8% Asian, non-Hispanic/Latino; 1% Native Hawaiian or other Pacific Islander, non-Hispanic/Latino; 2% international. 0% 25 or older, 58% live on campus, 0% transferred in. Retention: 83% of full-time freshmen returned the following year. Academic areas with the most degrees conferred: health professions and related sciences; business/marketing; liberal arts/general studies. Core. Calendar: semesters. Academic remediation for entering students, ESL program, services for LD students, advanced placement, accelerated degree program, honors program, independent study, distance learning, double major, summer session for credit, part-time degree program, adult/continuing education programs, co-op programs and internships, graduate courses open to undergrads. Off campus study. Study abroad program. ROTC: Army, Air Force (c).
Entrance Requirements: Options: electronic application, early admission, early action. Required: essay, high school transcript, 1 recommendation, SAT or ACT. Required for some: interview. Entrance: moderately difficult. Application deadlines: 6/1, 11/15 for early action. Notification: continuous until 10/1, 1/15 for early action. SAT Reasoning Test deadline: 6/1. Transfer credits accepted: Yes. Applicants placed on waiting list: 0. Wait-listed applicants offered admission: 0.
Costs Per Year: Application fee: $45. Tuition: $30,236 full-time, $1261 per credit part-time. Mandatory fees: $840 full-time. College room only: $4242. Room charges vary according to housing facility.
Collegiate Environment: Orientation program. Drama-theater group, choral group, marching band, student-run newspaper, radio station. Most popular organizations: community service groups, choir, outreach ministries groups, Habitat for Humanity, Multi-Ethnic Student Alliance (MESA). Major annual events: Mega Weekend (Homecoming/dinner rally), Mexicali Outreach, Night of Champions. Student services: health clinic, personal-psychological counseling. Campus security: 24-hour emergency response devices and patrols, student patrols, late night transport-escort service, controlled dormitory access. Freshmen given priority for college housing. On-campus residence required through sophomore year. Options: coed, men-only, women-only housing available. Marshburn Memorial Library plus 3 others with 254,337 books, 703,979 microform titles, 56,262 serials, 24,911 audiovisual materials, an OPAC, and a Web page.
Community Environment: Azusa is in a suburban area 26 miles east of Los Angeles with a temperate climate. Bus, air, and rail services are nearby. The city has a public library, churches of major denominations, hospitals, and clinics within a 10-mile radius. Mountains and beaches are within easy driving distance and Azusa is close to the cultural and recreational advantages of Los Angeles County.

BAKERSFIELD COLLEGE
1801 Panorama Dr.
Bakersfield, CA 93305-1299
Tel: (661)395-4011
Fax: (661)395-4230
E-mail: svaughn@bakersfieldcollege.edu
Web Site: www.bakersfieldcollege.edu/
Description: State and locally supported, 2-year, coed. Part of California Community College System. Awards transfer associate and terminal associate degrees. Founded 1913. Setting: 175-acre urban campus. Total enroll-

ment: 15,001. 50% 25 or older. Core. Calendar: semesters. Academic remediation for entering students, ESL program, services for LD students, advanced placement, accelerated degree program, summer session for credit, part-time degree program, adult/continuing education programs, co-op programs and internships.
Entrance Requirements: Open admission except for registered nursing, radiologic technology programs. Entrance: noncompetitive. Application deadline: Rolling. Preference given to district residents for nursing, radiologic technology programs.
Collegiate Environment: Orientation program. Drama-theater group, choral group, student-run newspaper, radio station. Student services: health clinic, women's center. Campus security: 24-hour patrols, late night transport-escort service. College housing not available. Grace Van Dyke Bird Library with 93,500 books, 298 serials, an OPAC, and a Web page. 650 computers available on campus for general student use. A campuswide network can be accessed. Staffed computer lab on campus.
Community Environment: See California State University Bakersfield.

■ **BARSTOW COMMUNITY COLLEGE**
2700 Barstow Rd.
Barstow, CA 92311-6699
Tel: (760)252-2411
Fax: (760)252-1875
E-mail: hcaldon@barstow.edu
Web Site: www.barstow.edu/
Description: State and locally supported, 2-year, coed. Part of California Community College System. Awards transfer associate and terminal associate degrees. Founded 1959. Setting: 50-acre small town campus. Total enrollment: 4,791. Student-undergrad faculty ratio is 35:1. 0% from out-of-state. 56% 25 or older. Core. Calendar: semesters. Academic remediation for entering students, ESL program, services for LD students, self-designed majors, summer session for credit, part-time degree program, external degree program, adult/continuing education programs, co-op programs.
Entrance Requirements: Open admission except for allied health programs. Options: early admission, deferred admission. Recommended: high school transcript. Entrance: noncompetitive. Application deadline: Rolling.
Collegiate Environment: Drama-theater group, student-run newspaper. Student services: personal-psychological counseling. Campus security: evening security personnel. Thomas Kimball Library with an OPAC and a Web page.
Community Environment: This is a desert community with a dry, warm climate. The Santa Fe and Union Pacific Railroads meet here. Greyhound and Orange Belt bus service is also available. The city has a county library, hospital, many churches, including numerous Protestant Churches, an Episcopal Church, a Roman Catholic Church, a Jewish Synagogue. There is a Community Players Association, which presents locally produced programs. Lectures and concerts are presented throughout the year. Part-time employment is available. Barstow has 4 parks and swimming pools for recreation. There are 82 civic, fraternal, and veterans organizations.

■ **BERGIN UNIVERSITY OF CANINE STUDIES**
5860 Labath Ave.
Rohnert Park, CA 94928
Tel: (707)545-3647
Web Site: www.berginu.edu/
Description: Independent, comprehensive, coed. Founded 1991. Calendar: semesters.

■ **BERKELEY CITY COLLEGE**
2050 Ctr. St.
Berkeley, CA 94704-5102
Tel: (510)981-2800
Fax: (510)841-7333
E-mail: mrivas@peralta.edu
Web Site: www.berkeleycitycollege.edu/
Description: State and locally supported, 2-year, coed. Part of California Community College System. Administratively affiliated with Peralta Community College District. Awards certificates, transfer associate, and terminal associate degrees. Founded 1974. Setting: urban campus with easy access to San Francisco. Educational spending for the previous fiscal year: $5609 per student. Total enrollment: 7,645. Faculty: 287 (62 full-time, 250 part-time). Student-undergrad faculty ratio is 35:1. 1% from out-of-state. 0.5% American Indian or Alaska Native, non-Hispanic/Latino; 12% Hispanic/

Latino; 18% African American, non-Hispanic/Latino; 16% Asian, non-Hispanic/Latino; 0.5% Native Hawaiian or other Pacific Islander, non-Hispanic/Latino. 65% 25 or older. Core. Calendar: semesters. Academic remediation for entering students, ESL program, services for LD students, self-designed majors, independent study, distance learning, double major, summer session for credit, part-time degree program, adult/continuing education programs, co-op programs and internships. Off campus study at University of California, Berkeley; California State University, East Bay; and Mills College, Oakland. Study abroad program.
Entrance Requirements: Required: Berkeley City College requires an assessment test in Math and English for Matriculating students, Matriculating students must take a math and English assessment test. Recommended: high school transcript.
Costs Per Year: State resident tuition: $1380 full-time, $46 per unit part-time. Nonresident tuition: $7080 full-time, $236 per unit part-time. Mandatory fees: $170 full-time, $46 per unit part-time, $690 per term part-time. Full-time tuition and fees vary according to class time, course load, and program. Part-time tuition and fees vary according to class time, course load, and program.
Collegiate Environment: Orientation program. Choral group, student-run newspaper. Social organizations: 20 open to all; Phi Theta Kappa, Community College Honor Students. Most popular organizations: Civic Engagement Club, Global Studies Club, Indigenous Student Alliance, The National Society of Leadership and Success, The Digital Arts Club (DAC). Major annual events: Club Rush, Global Awareness Day, Earth Day. Student services: health clinic, personal-psychological counseling. Campus security: 24-hour patrols. College housing not available. Susan A. Duncan Library plus 1 other with an OPAC and a Web page. 300 computers available on campus for general student use. Computer purchase/lease plans available. A campuswide network can be accessed from off-campus. Students can access the following: online class registration. Staffed computer lab on campus provides training in use of computers, software, and the Internet.

■ **BETHESDA UNIVERSITY OF CALIFORNIA**
730 N Euclid St.
Anaheim, CA 92801
Tel: (714)517-1945
Fax: (714)517-1948
E-mail: admission@bcu.edu
Web Site: www.buc.edu/
Description: Independent, comprehensive, coed, affiliated with Full Gospel World Mission. Awards bachelor's, master's, and doctoral degrees. Founded 1978. Setting: suburban campus with easy access to Los Angeles. Total enrollment: 345. 19 applied, 95% were admitted. 35% 25 or older, 0% live on campus. Core. Calendar: semesters. ESL program, accelerated degree program, independent study, double major, summer session for credit, part-time degree program, adult/continuing education programs, internships. Study abroad program.
Entrance Requirements: Open admission. Options: early admission, international baccalaureate accepted. Required: essay, high school transcript, minimum 2.0 high school GPA, 2 recommendations, interview, 2 photographs. Entrance: minimally difficult. Application deadline: 8/11. Notification: continuous until 8/25.
Collegiate Environment: Orientation program. Student services: personal-psychological counseling. Campus security: student patrols, late night transport-escort service, 24-hour security monitor. Library plus 1 other with 27,763 books, 99 serials, and 3,042 audiovisual materials.

■ **BIOLA UNIVERSITY**
13800 Biola Ave.
La Mirada, CA 90639-0001
Tel: (562)903-6000; Free: 800-652-4652
Fax: (562)903-4709
E-mail: admissions@biola.edu
Web Site: www.biola.edu/
Description: Independent interdenominational, university, coed. Awards bachelor's, master's, and doctoral degrees and post-master's certificates. Founded 1908. Setting: 95-acre suburban campus with easy access to Los Angeles. Endowment: $79.3 million. Educational spending for the previous fiscal year: $5995 per student. Total enrollment: 1,965. Faculty: 515 (255 full-time, 260 part-time). Student-undergrad faculty ratio is 16:1. 3,528 applied, 75% were admitted. 34% from top 10% of their high school class, 64% from top quarter, 88% from top half. Full-time: 8,314 students, 62% women, 38% men. Part-time: 360 students, 51% women, 49% men. Students come

from 44 states and territories, 18 other countries, 22% from out-of-state. 0.3% American Indian or Alaska Native, non-Hispanic/Latino; 17% Hispanic/Latino; 2% African American, non-Hispanic/Latino; 15% Asian, non-Hispanic/Latino; 0.5% Native Hawaiian or other Pacific Islander, non-Hispanic/Latino; 2% international. 4% 25 or older, 61% live on campus, 4% transferred in. Retention: 86% of full-time freshmen returned the following year. Academic areas with the most degrees conferred: business/marketing; theology and religious vocations; visual and performing arts. Core. Calendar: 4-1-4. ESL program, services for LD students, advanced placement, honors program, independent study, distance learning, double major, summer session for credit, part-time degree program, co-op programs and internships. Off campus study at the Biola Department of Physical Science, in cooperation with the University of Southern California's School of Engineering and Boston University's School of Engineering, offers a program allowing students interested in engineering, biblical studies and liberal arts to receive two degrees in five years. Students can earn credit at USC and work toward their degrees while also enrolled and taking classes here at Biola. Study abroad program. ROTC: Army (c), Air Force (c).

Entrance Requirements: Options: electronic application, early action, deferred admission, international baccalaureate accepted. Required: essay, high school transcript, minimum 3 high school GPA, 1 recommendation, The student must be an evangelical believer in the Christian faith, SAT or ACT. Required for some: interview. Entrance: moderately difficult. Application deadlines: 3/1, 3/1 for nonresidents, 11/15 for early action. Notification: 4/1, 4/1 for nonresidents, 1/15 for early action. SAT Reasoning Test deadline: 5/1. Transfer credits accepted: Yes. Early action applicants: 2,629. Early action applicants admitted: 2,163.

Costs Per Year: Application fee: $45. Comprehensive fee: $38,916 includes full-time tuition ($31,004) and college room and board ($7912). College room only: $4732. Full-time tuition varies according to course load. Room and board charges vary according to board plan, housing facility, and location. Part-time tuition: $1292 per unit. Part-time tuition varies according to course load.

Collegiate Environment: Orientation program. Drama-theater group, choral group, student-run newspaper, radio station. Social organizations: 63 open to all; 50% of eligible men and 55% of eligible women are members. Most popular organizations: Adventure Club, Guerilla Film Society, Biola CrossFit, Xopoc Dance Team, Honorable Cheese Society. Major annual events: Mock Rock, Nationball, The Eddy. Student services: health clinic, personal-psychological counseling. Campus security: 24-hour emergency response devices and patrols, late night transport-escort service, controlled dormitory access. 2,700 college housing spaces available; 2,515 were occupied in 2012-13. Freshmen guaranteed college housing. On-campus residence required in freshman year. Options: coed, men-only, women-only housing available. Biola University Library plus 1 other with 545,611 books, 578,540 microform titles, 994 serials, 11,585 audiovisual materials, an OPAC, and a Web page. Operations spending for the previous fiscal year: $5.6 million. 200 computers available on campus for general student use. A campuswide network can be accessed from student residence rooms and from off campus. Students can access the following: online class registration. Staffed computer lab on campus provides training in use of computers, software, and the Internet.

Community Environment: Population 50,000. La Mirada is a suburban area less than one hour from the Los Angeles International Airport. The Santa Fe Railroad and buses serve the area as does the Santa Ana Freeway. There are libraries, churches, and a hospital. Part-time employment is available. The beaches are 20 miles away and the mountains are an hour and half drive with Knott's Berry Farm and Disneyland a few minutes from campus.

■ BRANDMAN UNIVERSITY
16355 Laguna Canyon Rd.
Irvine, CA 92618
Tel: (949)753-4774; Free: 800-746-0082
Fax: (949)753-7875
Web Site: www.brandman.edu/irvine/
Description: Independent, university, coed. Founded 2009. Calendar: trimesters.

■ BROOKS INSTITUTE
27 E Cota St.
Santa Barbara, CA 93101
Tel: (805)966-3888; Free: 888-276-4999
Fax: (805)564-1475

E-mail: admissions@brooks.edu
Web Site: www.brooks.edu/
Description: State and locally supported, 2-year, coed. Part of State University of New York System. Awards certificates, transfer associate, and terminal associate degrees. Founded 1946. Setting: 223-acre suburban campus. Endowment: $1.3 million. Educational spending for the previous fiscal year: $4349 per student. Total enrollment: 6,877. Faculty: 406 (141 full-time, 265 part-time). 538 applied. Full-time: 4,655 students, 52% women, 48% men. Part-time: 2,222 students, 61% women, 39% men. Students come from 26 states and territories, 43 other countries, 1% from out-of-state. 29% 25 or older, 6% transferred in. Core. Calendar: semesters. Academic remediation for entering students, ESL program, services for LD students, advanced placement, self-designed majors, honors program, independent study, distance learning, summer session for credit, part-time degree program, external degree program, adult/continuing education programs, internships. Off campus study at State University of New York at Binghamton. Study abroad program.

Entrance Requirements: Open admission except for allied health, engineering technology, computer science programs. Options: electronic application, early admission. Required: high school transcript. Required for some: interview. Entrance: noncompetitive. Application deadline: Rolling. Notification: continuous. Preference given to county residents.

Collegiate Environment: Orientation program. Choral group, student-run newspaper. Social organizations: 44 open to all. Most popular organizations: Broome Early Childhood Organization, Differentially Disabled Student Association, Ecology Club, Phi Theta Kappa, Criminal Justice Club. Major annual events: Student Activities Day, Convocation, Festival of the Arts. Student services: health clinic, personal-psychological counseling. Campus security: 24-hour emergency response devices and patrols. Cecil C. Tyrrell Learning Resources Center with an OPAC and a Web page. Operations spending for the previous fiscal year: $833,029. 550 computers available on campus for general student use. A campuswide network can be accessed from off-campus. Students can access the following: online class registration. Staffed computer lab on campus.

■ BRYAN COLLEGE
2317 Gold Meadow Way
Gold River, CA 95670
Tel: (916)649-2400; Free: 866-649-2400
E-mail: studentinfo@bryancollege.edu
Web Site: www.bryancollege.edu/
Description: Proprietary, 2-year, coed. Awards terminal associate degrees. Founded 1995. Total enrollment: 436. Student-undergrad faculty ratio is 11:1. 374 applied, 63% were admitted. 3% from out-of-state. 60% 25 or older.
Entrance Requirements: Required: interview.

■ BUTTE COLLEGE
3536 Butte Campus Dr.
Oroville, CA 95965-8399
Tel: (530)895-2511
Fax: (530)895-2345
Web Site: www.butte.edu/
Description: District-supported, 2-year, coed. Part of California Community College System. Awards certificates, transfer associate, and terminal associate degrees. Founded 1966. Setting: 900-acre rural campus. Total enrollment: 12,719. 5% from top 10% of their high school class, 60% from top half. 36% 25 or older, 0% live on campus. Core. Calendar: semesters. Academic remediation for entering students, ESL program, services for LD students, advanced placement, accelerated degree program, honors program, independent study, distance learning, double major, summer session for credit, part-time degree program, adult/continuing education programs, co-op programs and internships. Study abroad program.

Entrance Requirements: Open admission except for allied health, criminal justice, fire science programs. Options: electronic application, early admission, deferred admission. Required for some: high school transcript. Entrance: noncompetitive. Application deadline: Rolling. Transfer credits accepted: No.

Costs Per Year: Application fee: $0. State resident tuition: $1104 full-time, $46 per unit part-time. Nonresident tuition: $5904 full-time, $246 per unit part-time. Mandatory fees: $252 full-time, $126 per term part-time. Full-time tuition and fees vary according to course level, course load, location, and program. Part-time tuition and fees vary according to course level, course load, location, and program.

Collegiate Environment: Orientation program. Drama-theater group, student-run newspaper. Student services: health clinic, personal-psychological counseling. Campus security: 24-hour emergency response devices and patrols, student patrols. College housing not available. 50,000 books, 300 serials, an OPAC, and a Web page.

Community Environment: Butte College is located in the geographical center of Butte County, population 215,881, at the edge of the Sierra Foothills. The county's amenities include a clean environment, moderate climate, ready access to necessities and luxuries and proximity to recreational areas, including the huge Lake Oroville.

■ **CABRILLO COLLEGE**
6500 Soquel Dr.
Aptos, CA 95003-3194
Tel: (831)479-6100
Fax: (831)479-6425
E-mail: tabolton@cabrillo.edu
Web Site: www.cabrillo.edu/

Description: District-supported, 2-year, coed. Part of California Community College System. Awards certificates, transfer associate, and terminal associate degrees. Founded 1959. Setting: 120-acre small town campus with easy access to San Jose. Total enrollment: 15,974. Student-undergrad faculty ratio is 26:1. 0% from out-of-state. 46% 25 or older. Core. Calendar: semesters. Academic remediation for entering students, ESL program, services for LD students, advanced placement, honors program, independent study, distance learning, double major, summer session for credit, part-time degree program, adult/continuing education programs, co-op programs and internships. Study abroad program.

Entrance Requirements: Open admission except for international applicants. Option: early admission. Required for some: high school transcript. Entrance: noncompetitive. Application deadline: Rolling.

Collegiate Environment: Drama-theater group, student-run newspaper. Student services: health clinic, personal-psychological counseling, women's center. Campus security: 24-hour emergency response devices and patrols, late night transport-escort service. Cabrillo College Library with an OPAC and a Web page.

Community Environment: Aptos is a suburban area nine miles from Santa Cruz, with a temperate climate. There is a municipal library, churches of major denominations within a ten mile area, and 2 hospitals in the county. Excellent water sports area for swimming, surfing and deep sea fishing. Fine shopping facilities are available. The University of California at Santa Cruz is nearby.

■ **CALIFORNIA BAPTIST UNIVERSITY**
8432 Magnolia Ave.
Riverside, CA 92504-3206
Tel: (951)689-5771; Free: 877-228-8866
E-mail: admissions@calbaptist.edu
Web Site: www.calbaptist.edu/

Description: Independent Southern Baptist, comprehensive, coed. Awards bachelor's and master's degrees. Founded 1950. Setting: 131-acre suburban campus with easy access to Los Angeles. Endowment: $12.3 million. Research spending for the previous fiscal year: $7733. Educational spending for the previous fiscal year: $6590 per student. Total enrollment: 6,031. Faculty: 531 (227 full-time, 304 part-time). Student-undergrad faculty ratio is 17:1. 2,916 applied, 73% were admitted. 18% from top 10% of their high school class, 49% from top quarter, 82% from top half. 12 valedictorians. Full-time: 4,342 students, 62% women, 38% men. Part-time: 612 students, 68% women, 32% men. Students come from 43 states and territories, 29 other countries, 6% from out-of-state. 1% American Indian or Alaska Native, non-Hispanic/Latino; 27% Hispanic/Latino; 9% African American, non-Hispanic/Latino; 5% Asian, non-Hispanic/Latino; 0.4% Native Hawaiian or other Pacific Islander, non-Hispanic/Latino; 2% international. 20% 25 or older, 44% live on campus, 14% transferred in. Retention: 78% of full-time freshmen returned the following year. Academic areas with the most degrees conferred: business/marketing; psychology; liberal arts/general studies. Core. Calendar: 2-4-4-2. ESL program, services for LD students, advanced placement, accelerated degree program, honors program, independent study, distance learning, double major, summer session for credit, part-time degree program, adult/continuing education programs, internships, graduate courses open to undergrads. Off campus study at Council for Christian Colleges and Universities, Los Angeles Film Institute, The Washington Semester. Study abroad program. ROTC: Army, Air Force (c).

Entrance Requirements: Options: electronic application, early action,

deferred admission, international baccalaureate accepted. Required: essay, minimum 2 high school GPA, 2 recommendations, SAT or ACT. Recommended: SAT Subject Tests. Required for some: high school transcript. Entrance: minimally difficult. Application deadlines: Rolling, Rolling for nonresidents, 12/15 for early action. Notification: continuous until 11/9, continuous for nonresidents, 1/31 for early action. SAT Reasoning Test deadline: 8/1. SAT Subject Test deadline: 8/1. Transfer credits accepted: Yes.

Costs Per Year: Application fee: $45. Comprehensive fee: $35,890 includes full-time tuition ($25,090), mandatory fees ($1810), and college room and board ($8990). College room only: $4560. Full-time tuition and fees vary according to course load, location, and program. Room and board charges vary according to board plan and housing facility. Part-time tuition: $5790 per year. Part-time mandatory fees: $350 per year. Part-time tuition and fees vary according to course load, location, and program.

Collegiate Environment: Orientation program. Drama-theater group, choral group, student-run newspaper. Social organizations: 34 open to all. Most popular organizations: International Service Projects, United States Service Projects and Summer of Service, CBU Crazies (Campus Spirit), Associated Students of California Baptist University (government and leadership), Students of Nursing Association. Major annual events: Fortuna Bowl / Homecoming, Midnight Madness, Campus Day (recreational games). Student services: health clinic, personal-psychological counseling. Campus security: 24-hour emergency response devices and patrols, student patrols, late night transport-escort service, controlled dormitory access. 2,448 college housing spaces available; 2,195 were occupied in 2012-13. Freshmen given priority for college housing. On-campus residence required in freshman year. Options: men-only, women-only housing available. Annie Gabriel Library with 232,039 books, 54,853 microform titles, 24,506 serials, 8,979 audiovisual materials, an OPAC, and a Web page. Operations spending for the previous fiscal year: $1.2 million. 279 computers available on campus for general student use. Computer purchase/lease plans available. A campuswide network can be accessed from student residence rooms and from off campus. Students can access the following: online class registration. Staffed computer lab on campus provides training in use of computers, software, and the Internet.

Community Environment: See University of California Riverside.

■ **CALIFORNIA CHRISTIAN COLLEGE**
4881 E University Ave.
Fresno, CA 93703-3533
Tel: (559)251-4215
E-mail: cccadmissions@sbcglobal.net
Web Site: www.calchristiancollege.edu/

Description: Independent Free Will Baptist, 4-year, coed. Awards associate and bachelor's degrees. Setting: 5-acre urban campus. Endowment: $122,093. Educational spending for the previous fiscal year: $2983 per student. Total enrollment: 20. Faculty: 5 (all part-time). Student-undergrad faculty ratio is 4:1. 3 applied, 100% were admitted. Full-time: 17 students, 47% women, 53% men. Part-time: 3 students, 33% women, 67% men. Students come from 1 other country, 0% from out-of-state. 0% American Indian or Alaska Native, non-Hispanic/Latino; 40% Hispanic/Latino; 20% African American, non-Hispanic/Latino; 10% Asian, non-Hispanic/Latino; 0% Native Hawaiian or other Pacific Islander, non-Hispanic/Latino; 5% international. 32% 25 or older, 25% live on campus, 10% transferred in. Academic area with the most degrees conferred: theology and religious vocations. Core. Calendar: semesters. Academic remediation for entering students, independent study, distance learning, part-time degree program, co-op programs.

Entrance Requirements: Open admission. Options: electronic application, international baccalaureate accepted. Required: essay, high school transcript, minimum 2 high school GPA, 2 recommendations, statement of faith, moral/ethical statement, standardized Bible content tests. Recommended: interview, SAT or ACT. Entrance: noncompetitive. Application deadline: Rolling. Notification: continuous. Transfer credits accepted: Yes.

Costs Per Year: Application fee: $40. Comprehensive fee: $12,210 includes full-time tuition ($7440), mandatory fees ($570), and college room and board ($4200). Part-time tuition: $310 per credit hour.

Collegiate Environment: Orientation program. Major annual events: College Days, CCC Banquet. Student services: personal-psychological counseling. Cortese Library with 23,000 books, 25 serials, 250 audiovisual materials, and an OPAC. Operations spending for the previous fiscal year: $33,868. 5 computers available on campus for general student use. A campuswide network can be accessed from student residence rooms.

Students can access the following: wireless Internet access. Staffed computer lab on campus provides training in use of computers, software, and the Internet.

■ CALIFORNIA COAST UNIVERSITY

925 N Spurgeon St.
Santa Ana, CA 92701
Tel: (714)547-9625; Free: 888-CCU-UNIV
E-mail: admissions@calcoast.edu
Web Site: www.calcoast.edu/
Description: Proprietary, comprehensive, coed. Awards associate, bachelor's, master's, and doctoral degrees (distance learning only). Founded 1973.
Entrance Requirements: Required: resume, high school transcript or GED equivalent.

■ CALIFORNIA COLLEGE

6602 Convoy Ct.
Ste. 100
San Diego, CA 92111
Tel: (619)293-0190; Free: 800-622-3188
E-mail: tana.sanderson@cc-sd.edu
Web Site: www.cc-sd.edu/
Description: Proprietary, 4-year, coed. Awards associate and bachelor's degrees. Total enrollment: 1,299. Student-undergrad faculty ratio is 19:1. 0% from out-of-state. 62% 25 or older. Retention: 89% of full-time freshmen returned the following year.
Entrance Requirements: Open admission.

■ CALIFORNIA COLLEGE OF THE ARTS

1111 Eighth St.
San Francisco, CA 94107
Tel: (415)703-9500; Free: 800-447-1ART
Fax: (415)703-9539
E-mail: enroll@cca.edu
Web Site: www.cca.edu/
Description: Independent, comprehensive, coed. Awards bachelor's and master's degrees. Founded 1907. Setting: 4-acre urban campus with easy access to San Francisco, Oakland. Endowment: $28.6 million. Educational spending for the previous fiscal year: $12,691 per student. Total enrollment: 1,932. Faculty: 466 (81 full-time, 385 part-time). Student-undergrad faculty ratio is 10:1. 1,231 applied, 90% were admitted. Full-time: 1,362 students, 60% women, 40% men. Part-time: 103 students, 73% women, 27% men. Students come from 44 states and territories, 47 other countries, 33% from out-of-state. 0.3% American Indian or Alaska Native, non-Hispanic/Latino; 13% Hispanic/Latino; 5% African American, non-Hispanic/Latino; 16% Asian, non-Hispanic/Latino; 1% Native Hawaiian or other Pacific Islander, non-Hispanic/Latino; 19% international. 16% 25 or older, 20% live on campus, 11% transferred in. Retention: 78% of full-time freshmen returned the following year. Academic areas with the most degrees conferred: visual and performing arts; architecture; communication/journalism. Core. Calendar: semesters. Academic remediation for entering students, ESL program, services for LD students, advanced placement, self-designed majors, honors program, independent study, double major, summer session for credit, co-op programs and internships, graduate courses open to undergrads. Off campus study at Mills College, Holy Names College, AICAD Mobility Program. Study abroad program.
Entrance Requirements: Options: electronic application, deferred admission, international baccalaureate accepted. Required: essay, high school transcript, 2 recommendations, portfolio of creative work and statement of artistic and professional goals. Recommended: SAT or ACT. Required for some: interview. Entrance: moderately difficult. Application deadline: Rolling. Notification: continuous. SAT Reasoning Test deadline: 8/1. SAT Subject Test deadline: 8/1. Transfer credits accepted: Yes.
Costs Per Year: Application fee: $60. Tuition: $39,984 full-time, $1666 per unit part-time. Mandatory fees: $350 full-time. Full-time tuition and fees vary according to degree level. Part-time tuition varies according to course load and degree level. College room only: $8000. Room charges vary according to housing facility.
Collegiate Environment: Orientation program. Social organizations: 11 open to all; national fraternities, national sororities, Alpha Rho Chi (coed); 1% of eligible men and 1% of eligible women are members. Most popular organizations: Social Projects and Communal Environments (SPACE), Queer/Straight Alliance (QSA), Animation Study Group, Students of Color

Coalition, Cossutius Chapter of Alpha Rho Chi Fraternity. Major annual events: Winter and Spring Art and Craft Fairs, Chimeratopia: Community Resource Fair, Holiday Lunch. Student services: personal-psychological counseling. Campus security: 24-hour emergency response devices and patrols, late night transport-escort service, controlled dormitory access, student taxi vouchers for emergencies. 314 college housing spaces available; 288 were occupied in 2012-13. Freshmen given priority for college housing. Option: coed housing available. Meyer Library plus 1 other with 56,874 books, 10,571 serials, 3,685 audiovisual materials, an OPAC, and a Web page. Operations spending for the previous fiscal year: $807,000. 400 computers available on campus for general student use. Computer purchase/lease plans available. A campuswide network can be accessed from student residence rooms and from off campus. Students can access the following: online class registration. Staffed computer lab on campus (open 24 hours a day) provides training in use of computers and the Internet.
Community Environment: See Laney College.

■ CALIFORNIA CULINARY ACADEMY

625 Polk St.
San Francisco, CA 94102-3368
Tel: (415)771-3500; Free: 800-BAYCHEF
Fax: (415)771-2194
Web Site: www.baychef.com/
Description: Proprietary, 2-year, coed. Awards certificates and terminal associate degrees. Founded 1977. Setting: urban campus. Total enrollment: 997. 37% 25 or older. Core. Calendar: continuous. Services for LD students, co-op programs.
Entrance Requirements: Open admission. Option: electronic application. Required: high school transcript, interview. Entrance: minimally difficult. Application deadline: Rolling. Notification: continuous.
Collegiate Environment: Orientation program. Social organizations: dining club. Campus security: 24-hour emergency response devices and patrols, controlled dormitory access. Academy Library plus 1 other with 3,000 books and 70 serials.

■ CALIFORNIA INSTITUTE OF THE ARTS

24700 McBean Pky.
Valencia, CA 91355-2340
Tel: (661)255-1050; Free: 800-545-2787
E-mail: admiss@calarts.edu
Web Site: www.calarts.edu/
Description: Independent, comprehensive, coed. Awards bachelor's, master's, and doctoral degrees. Founded 1961. Setting: 60-acre suburban campus with easy access to Los Angeles. Endowment: $101.6 million. Educational spending for the previous fiscal year: $20,789 per student. Total enrollment: 1,454. Faculty: 314 (161 full-time, 153 part-time). Student-undergrad faculty ratio is 7:1. 1,237 applied, 31% were admitted. Full-time: 887 students, 49% women, 51% men. Part-time: 8 students, 25% women, 75% men. Students come from 42 states and territories, 23 other countries, 51% from out-of-state. 1% American Indian or Alaska Native, non-Hispanic/Latino; 12% Hispanic/Latino; 8% African American, non-Hispanic/Latino; 11% Asian, non-Hispanic/Latino; 0.1% Native Hawaiian or other Pacific Islander, non-Hispanic/Latino; 7% international. 10% 25 or older, 40% live on campus, 16% transferred in. Retention: 79% of full-time freshmen returned the following year. Academic area with the most degrees conferred: visual and performing arts. Core. Calendar: semesters. Services for LD students, advanced placement, self-designed majors, independent study, double major, co-op programs and internships, graduate courses open to undergrads. Study abroad program.
Entrance Requirements: Options: electronic application, international baccalaureate accepted. Required: essay, high school transcript, 2 recommendations, portfolio or audition. Required for some: interview. Entrance: very difficult. Application deadline: 1/5. Notification: continuous until 4/1. Transfer credits accepted: Yes. Applicants placed on waiting list: 63. Waitlisted applicants offered admission: 8.
Collegiate Environment: Orientation program. Drama-theater group, choral group, student-run radio station. Social organizations: 15 open to all. Most popular organizations: Student Council, FISK - Graphic Arts Club, Soccer Club, Korean Bible Study, Black Student Union. Major annual events: Spring Event, Town Hall Meetings, Tea & Sympathy. Student services: health clinic, personal-psychological counseling. Campus security: 24-hour emergency response devices and patrols, late night transport-escort service, controlled dormitory access. Division of Library and Information Resources with 203,471 books, 4,124 microform titles, 665 serials, 32,804 audiovisual

materials, an OPAC, and a Web page. Operations spending for the previous fiscal year: $1.4 million. 42 computers available on campus for general student use. A campuswide network can be accessed from student residence rooms and from off campus. Students can access the following: online class registration. Staffed computer lab on campus provides training in use of computers, software, and the Internet.

Community Environment: Valencia is located on the Golden State Freeway (Interstate 5) 35 miles north of Los Angeles, and historically has been devoted to agriculture and cattle ranching. The area, encompassing the towns of Newhall, Saugus, Valencia and Castaic, is surrounded by the Tehachapi Mountains to the North, the San Gabriel to the east and the Santa Susana to the west. In the last 10 years light industry and numerous housing developments have contributed to the city's growth.

■ CALIFORNIA INSTITUTE OF INTEGRAL STUDIES

1453 Mission St.
San Francisco, CA 94103
Tel: (415)575-6100
Fax: (415)575-1264
E-mail: admissions@ciis.edu
Web Site: www.ciis.edu/
Description: Independent, upper-level, coed. Awards bachelor's, master's, and doctoral degrees. Founded 1968. Total enrollment: 1,166. Student-undergrad faculty ratio is 18:1. 91% 25 or older. Core. Calendar: semesters. External degree program, adult/continuing education programs, graduate courses open to undergrads.
Collegiate Environment: Orientation program. Drama-theater group.
Community Environment: See San Francisco State University.

■ CALIFORNIA INSTITUTE OF TECHNOLOGY

1200 E California Blvd.
Pasadena, CA 91125-0001
Tel: (626)395-6811
Fax: (626)683-3026
Web Site: www.caltech.edu/
Description: Independent, university, coed. Awards bachelor's, master's, and doctoral degrees and post-master's certificates. Founded 1891. Setting: 124-acre suburban campus with easy access to Los Angeles. Endowment: $1.5 billion. Research spending for the previous fiscal year: $237 million. Educational spending for the previous fiscal year: $93,427 per student. Total enrollment: 2,243. Faculty: 341 (324 full-time, 17 part-time). Student-undergrad faculty ratio is 3:1. 5,537 applied, 12% were admitted. 94% from top 10% of their high school class, 99% from top quarter, 100% from top half. Full-time: 997 students, 38% women. 63% men. 63% from out-of-state. 0.3% American Indian or Alaska Native, non-Hispanic/Latino; 10% Hispanic/Latino; 2% African American, non-Hispanic/Latino; 40% Asian, non-Hispanic/Latino; 0.3% Native Hawaiian or other Pacific Islander, non-Hispanic/Latino; 11% international. 0% 25 or older, 85% live on campus, 0.3% transferred in. Retention: 96% of full-time freshmen returned the following year. Academic areas with the most degrees conferred: engineering; physical sciences; computer and information sciences. Core. Calendar: 3 ten-week terms. ESL program, services for LD students, self-designed majors, independent study, double major, co-op programs, graduate courses open to undergrads. Off campus study at Occidental College, Art Center College of Design. Study abroad program. ROTC: Army (c), Air Force (c).
Entrance Requirements: Options: electronic application, early admission, early action, deferred admission. Required: essay, high school transcript, 2 recommendations, SAT or ACT, SAT Subject Tests. Entrance: most difficult. Application deadlines: 1/3, 11/1 for early action. Notification: 4/1, 12/15 for early action. SAT Reasoning Test deadline: 12/31. SAT Subject Test deadline: 12/31. Applicants placed on waiting list: 651. Wait-listed applicants offered admission: 0. Early action applicants: 1,468. Early action applicants admitted: 277.
Costs Per Year: Application fee: $65. One-time mandatory fee: $500. Comprehensive fee: $54,045 includes full-time tuition ($39,990), mandatory fees ($1548), and college room and board ($12,507). College room only: $7035. Full-time tuition and fees vary according to course load. Part-time tuition: $1111 per credit hour. Part-time tuition varies according to course load.
Collegiate Environment: Orientation program. Drama-theater group, choral group, student-run newspaper. Social organizations: 150 open to all. Most popular organizations: Instrumental music groups, Entrepreneur's Club, Glee Club, theater arts, Ultimate Disc Club. Major annual events: Ditch Day, International Day, Pre-Frosh Weekend. Student services: health clinic,

personal-psychological counseling, women's center. Campus security: 24-hour emergency response devices and patrols, late night transport-escort service, controlled dormitory access. 907 college housing spaces available; 847 were occupied in 2012-13. Freshmen guaranteed college housing. On-campus residence required in freshman year. Option: coed housing available. Sherman Fairchild Library plus 6 others with 615,347 books, 23,122 microform titles, 2,737 serials, 2,981 audiovisual materials, an OPAC, and a Web page. Operations spending for the previous fiscal year: $6.5 million.
Community Environment: Population 143,700, Pasadena is located at the foot of the San Gabriel Mountains, the center of a large metropolitan area with ideal climate throughout the year. The famous Huntington Library, located in nearby San Marino, is open to the public and makes available its rich resources for scholarly research work in numerous fields. Pasadena has many cultural activities in the fields of art, music, and literature. The finest talent in America can be seen and heard in Pasadena and Los Angeles. Exhibits of famous artists and art instruction are provided by the community. The annual New Year's Day Tournament of Roses is held in the winter, and nearby is the Rose Bowl that seats 104,000 people.

■ CALIFORNIA INTERCONTINENTAL UNIVERSITY

1470 Valley Vista Dr., Ste. 150
Diamond Bar, CA 91765
Tel: (909)396-6090; Free: 866-687-2258
Fax: (909)804-5151
E-mail: admissions@caluniversity.com
Web Site: caluniversity.edu/
Description: Proprietary, comprehensive, coed. Awards bachelor's and master's degrees.
Entrance Requirements: Required: high school transcript.

■ CALIFORNIA LUTHERAN UNIVERSITY

60 W Olsen Rd.
Thousand Oaks, CA 91360-2787
Tel: (805)492-2411; Free: 877-258-3678
Fax: (805)493-3114
E-mail: cluadm@clunet.edu
Web Site: www.callutheran.edu/
Description: Independent Lutheran, comprehensive, coed. Awards bachelor's, master's, and doctoral degrees and post-master's certificates. Founded 1959. Setting: 290-acre suburban campus with easy access to Los Angeles. Endowment: $55.5 million. Educational spending for the previous fiscal year: $8275 per student. Total enrollment: 4,103. Faculty: 373 (163 full-time, 210 part-time). Student-undergrad faculty ratio is 15:1. 7,245 applied, 44% were admitted. 37% from top 10% of their high school class, 68% from top quarter, 95% from top half. Full-time: 2,480 students, 56% women, 44% men. Part-time: 233 students, 60% women, 40% men. Students come from 38 states and territories, 50 other countries, 15% from out-of-state. 1% American Indian or Alaska Native, non-Hispanic/Latino; 20% Hispanic/Latino; 4% African American, non-Hispanic/Latino; 6% Asian, non-Hispanic/Latino; 1% Native Hawaiian or other Pacific Islander, non-Hispanic/Latino; 4% international. 4% 25 or older, 56% live on campus, 9% transferred in. Retention: 85% of full-time freshmen returned the following year. Academic areas with the most degrees conferred: business/marketing; biological/life sciences; communication/journalism. Core. Calendar: semesters. Services for LD students, advanced placement, accelerated degree program, self-designed majors, honors program, independent study, double major, summer session for credit, part-time degree program, adult/continuing education programs, co-op programs and internships, graduate courses open to undergrads. Off campus study at Wagner College, American University (Washington Semester). Study abroad program. ROTC: Army (c), Air Force (c).
Entrance Requirements: Options: electronic application, early action, deferred admission, international baccalaureate accepted. Required: essay, high school transcript, minimum 2.8 high school GPA, 1 recommendation, SAT or ACT. Recommended: minimum 3 high school GPA, interview. Entrance: moderately difficult. Application deadline: 3/15. Notification: 12/1. SAT Reasoning Test deadline: 5/1. Applicants placed on waiting list: 533. Wait-listed applicants offered admission: 129. Early action applicants: 3,082. Early action applicants admitted: 1,656.
Costs Per Year: Application fee: $45. Comprehensive fee: $45,870 includes full-time tuition ($33,910), mandatory fees ($450), and college room and board ($11,510). College room only: $6220. Room and board charges vary according to board plan. Part-time tuition: $1090 per credit hour. Part-time mandatory fees: $225 per term.

Collegiate Environment: Orientation program. Drama-theater group, choral group, student-run newspaper, radio station. Social organizations: 77 open to all. Most popular organizations: student government, recreation, sports fan, or club sports related, service organizations, campus ministry or other religiously affiliated organization, multicultural organizations. Major annual events: Club Lu, Midnight Madness, Involvement Fair. Student services: health clinic, personal-psychological counseling, women's center. Campus security: 24-hour emergency response devices and patrols, late night transport-escort service, controlled dormitory access, escort service; shuttle service. 1,355 college housing spaces available; 1,304 were occupied in 2012-13. Freshmen guaranteed college housing. On-campus residence required through junior year. Option: coed housing available. Pearson Library with 132,744 books, 22,200 microform titles, 1,497 serials, an OPAC, and a Web page. Operations spending for the previous fiscal year: $1.5 million. 300 computers available on campus for general student use. A campuswide network can be accessed from student residence rooms and from off campus. Students can access the following: online class registration. Staffed computer lab on campus (open 24 hours a day) provides training in use of computers, software, and the Internet.

Community Environment: Located in the Conejo Valley, Thousand Oaks has a mild pleasant climate with temperatures ranging from a mean low of 57 degrees in winter to a mean high of 77 degrees in summer. Average rainfall is 14 inches, the rainy season being between October and April. Buses, trains and airlines serve the area. Principal industries are electronics, aerospace, research, insurance and manufacturing. There are numerous shopping areas in Thousand Oaks. Recreational facilities include the community center, theatres, championship golf courses, Lake Sherwood, and the marinas in Oxnard and Ventura. Pacific Ocean Beaches are thirty minutes from The Campus.

■ **CALIFORNIA MARITIME ACADEMY**
200 Maritime Academy Dr.
Vallejo, CA 94590
Tel: (707)654-1000; Free: 800-561-1945
Fax: (707)648-4204
E-mail: admission@csum.edu
Web Site: www.csum.edu/
Description: State-supported, comprehensive, coed. Part of California State University System. Awards bachelor's and master's degrees. Founded 1929. Setting: 64-acre suburban campus with easy access to San Francisco. Total enrollment: 863. Full-time: 838 students, 14% women, 86% men. Part-time: 25 students, 16% women, 84% men. 15% from out-of-state. 17% 25 or older, 77% live on campus, 13% transferred in. Retention: 86% of full-time freshmen returned the following year. Core. Calendar: semesters. Academic remediation for entering students, advanced placement, summer session for credit, internships. Study abroad program. ROTC: Naval (c).
Entrance Requirements: Option: electronic application. Required: high school transcript, minimum 2 high school GPA, health form, SAT or ACT. Entrance: moderately difficult. Notification: continuous. Preference given to California residents who meet the admissions resident index. SAT Reasoning Test deadline: 12/31.
Collegiate Environment: Orientation program. Choral group, student-run newspaper. Most popular organizations: Sailing Club, Dive Club, drill team. Major annual events: Changeover Dance, Homecoming, open house. Student services: health clinic, personal-psychological counseling. Campus security: 24-hour patrols, student patrols. 75 computers available on campus for general student use. A campuswide network can be accessed from student residence rooms and from off campus. Students can access the following: online class registration. Staffed computer lab on campus.
Community Environment: Vallejo has a population of 117,500 and is located on the north shore of the Carquinez Strait, adjacent to San Pablo Bay.

■ **CALIFORNIA MIRAMAR UNIVERSITY**
9750 Miramar Rd.
Ste. 180
San Diego, CA 92126
Tel: (858)653-3000; Free: 877-570-5678
Fax: (858)653-6786
E-mail: admissions@calmu.edu
Web Site: www.calmu.edu/
Description: Proprietary, comprehensive, coed. Awards associate, bachelor's, and master's degrees.
Entrance Requirements: Required: high school transcript, resume.

■ **CALIFORNIA NATIONAL UNIVERSITY FOR ADVANCED STUDIES**
8550 Balboa Blvd., Ste. 210
Northridge, CA 91325
Tel: (818)830-2411; Free: 800-782-2422
Fax: (818)830-2418
E-mail: cnuadms@mail.cnuas.edu
Web Site: www.cnuas.edu/
Description: Proprietary, comprehensive, coed. Awards bachelor's and master's degrees. Founded 1993. Setting: urban campus. Total enrollment: 500. Faculty: 98 (all part-time). Student-undergrad faculty ratio is 10:1. Students come from 25 other countries, 0% from out-of-state. Core. Calendar: trimesters. Advanced placement, accelerated degree program, independent study, distance learning, double major, part-time degree program, external degree program, adult/continuing education programs, internships. Off campus study.
Entrance Requirements: Open admission. Options: electronic application, deferred admission, international baccalaureate accepted. Required: essay, high school transcript. Required for some: interview. Application deadline: Rolling. Notification: continuous.

■ **CALIFORNIA POLYTECHNIC STATE UNIVERSITY, SAN LUIS OBISPO**
1 Grand Ave.
San Luis Obispo, CA 93407
Tel: (805)756-1111
E-mail: admissions@calpoly.edu
Web Site: www.calpoly.edu/
Description: State-supported, comprehensive, coed. Part of California State University System. Awards bachelor's and master's degrees. Founded 1901. Setting: 6,000-acre suburban campus. Total enrollment: 18,679. Faculty: 1,259 (815 full-time, 444 part-time). Student-undergrad faculty ratio is 19:1. 36,941 applied, 31% were admitted. 50% from top 10% of their high school class, 83% from top quarter, 98% from top half. Full-time: 17,027 students, 45% women, 55% men. Part-time: 653 students, 38% women, 62% men. 9% from out-of-state. 0.3% American Indian or Alaska Native, non-Hispanic/Latino; 14% Hispanic/Latino; 1% African American, non-Hispanic/Latino; 11% Asian, non-Hispanic/Latino; 0.2% Native Hawaiian or other Pacific Islander, non-Hispanic/Latino; 1% international. 3% 25 or older, 36% live on campus, 5% transferred in. Retention: 93% of full-time freshmen returned the following year. Academic areas with the most degrees conferred: engineering; business/marketing; agriculture. Core. Academic remediation for entering students, ESL program, services for LD students, advanced placement, honors program, distance learning, double major, summer session for credit, part-time degree program, co-op programs and internships, graduate courses open to undergrads. Off campus study at other units of the California State University System. Study abroad program. ROTC: Army.
Entrance Requirements: Options: electronic application, early admission, early decision. Required: high school transcript, SAT or ACT. Entrance: moderately difficult. Application deadlines: 11/30, 10/31 for early decision. Notification: 4/1, 12/15 for early decision. SAT Reasoning Test deadline: 12/1. Applicants placed on waiting list: 2,555. Wait-listed applicants offered admission: 1,064.
Costs Per Year: Application fee: $55. State resident tuition: $5472 full-time. Nonresident tuition: $16,632 full-time, $248 per unit part-time. Mandatory fees: $3051 full-time. Full-time tuition and fees vary according to course load, degree level, and program. Part-time tuition varies according to course load, degree level, and program. College room and board: $10,679. College room only: $6123. Room and board charges vary according to housing facility.
Collegiate Environment: Orientation program. Drama-theater group, choral group, marching band, student-run newspaper, radio station. Social organizations: national fraternities, national sororities, local fraternities, local sororities. Student services: legal services, health clinic, personal-psychological counseling, women's center. Campus security: 24-hour emergency response devices and patrols, student patrols, late night transport-escort service, controlled dormitory access. No special consideration for freshman housing applicants. Option: coed housing available. Robert E. Kennedy Library with an OPAC and a Web page.
Community Environment: San Luis Obispo, located midway between San Francisco and Los Angeles, is 12 miles from the Pacific Ocean. The average high winter temperature is in the 60s, and the summer high average is in the 70s. Buses, trains and airlines serve the area. There are 3 hospitals and a student health center. Student housing is available in campus dormitories and college approved housing in the city. Part time work is available in the

community. Recreation includes surfing, fishing, clamming, golfing, hunting, boating and swimming. The Mission San Luis Obispo de Tolosa was founded in 1772, named for the Bishop of Toulouse, an Italian saint of the 13th century.

■ CALIFORNIA STATE POLYTECHNIC UNIVERSITY, POMONA

3801 W Temple Ave.
Pomona, CA 91768-2557
Tel: (909)869-7659
Fax: (909)869-4529
E-mail: admissions@csupomona.edu
Web Site: www.csupomona.edu/
Description: State-supported, comprehensive, coed. Part of California State University System. Awards bachelor's, master's, and doctoral degrees. Founded 1938. Setting: 1,400-acre urban campus with easy access to Los Angeles. Endowment: $55.6 million. Educational spending for the previous fiscal year: $5226 per student. Total enrollment: 22,156. Faculty: 1,077 (532 full-time, 545 part-time). Student-undergrad faculty ratio is 25:1. 40,456 applied, 54% were admitted. Full-time: 17,837 students, 44% women, 56% men. Part-time: 2,705 students, 37% women, 63% men. Students come from 48 states and territories, 35 other countries, 1% from out-of-state. 0.2% American Indian or Alaska Native, non-Hispanic/Latino; 35% Hispanic/Latino; 3% African American, non-Hispanic/Latino; 25% Asian, non-Hispanic/Latino; 0.4% Native Hawaiian or other Pacific Islander, non-Hispanic/Latino; 4% international. 15% 25 or older, 12% live on campus, 10% transferred in. Retention: 92% of full-time freshmen returned the following year. Academic areas with the most degrees conferred: business/marketing; engineering; social sciences. Core. Academic remediation for entering students, ESL program, services for LD students, advanced placement, honors program, distance learning, double major, summer session for credit, part-time degree program, adult/continuing education programs, co-op programs and internships, graduate courses open to undergrads. Off campus study at other units of the California State University System, Desert Studies Consortium, Southern California Ocean Studies Consortium. Study abroad program. ROTC: Army.
Entrance Requirements: Option: electronic application. Required: high school transcript, minimum 2 high school GPA, SAT or ACT. Entrance: moderately difficult. Application deadline: 11/30. Notification: continuous until 10/2. Transfer credits accepted: Yes.
Costs Per Year: Application fee: $55. State resident tuition: $5970 full-time. Nonresident tuition: $17,130 full-time. Mandatory fees: $653 full-time, $248 per credit part-time. Full-time tuition and fees vary according to course load, degree level, and program. Part-time fees vary according to course load, degree level, and program. College room and board: $11,615. College room only: $6921. Room and board charges vary according to board plan and housing facility.
Collegiate Environment: Orientation program. Drama-theater group, choral group, student-run newspaper. Social organizations: 290 open to all; national fraternities, national sororities, local fraternities, local sororities; 2% of eligible men and 1% of eligible women are members. Most popular organizations: Rose Float Club, Ridge Runners Ski Club, Barkada (Asian club), American Marketing Association, Cal Poly Society of Accountants. Major annual events: Rose Float, Founder's Day, Bronco Days. Student services: health clinic, personal-psychological counseling, women's center. Campus security: 24-hour emergency response devices and patrols, student patrols, late night transport-escort service, controlled dormitory access, video camera surveillance. 3,785 college housing spaces available; 3,464 were occupied in 2012-13. Freshmen given priority for college housing. On-campus residence required in freshman year. Option: coed housing available. University Library with 833,428 books, 1.4 million microform titles, 39,992 serials, 11,377 audiovisual materials, an OPAC, and a Web page. Operations spending for the previous fiscal year: $5 million. 1,875 computers available on campus for general student use. Computer purchase/lease plans available. A campuswide network can be accessed from student residence rooms and from off campus. Students can access the following: online class registration. Staffed computer lab on campus provides training in use of computers, software, and the Internet.
Community Environment: Cal Poly Pomona is located just 35 miles southeast of downtown Los Angeles in the heart of Southern California. Near business and industry, the university's location is ideal for internships and/or employment. Cal Poly Pomona is also suitable for recreation; the beach, the desert, ski slopes, museums, Disneyland, and much more are just a short drive away.

■ CALIFORNIA STATE UNIVERSITY, BAKERSFIELD

9001 Stockdale Hwy.
Bakersfield, CA 93311
Tel: (661)664-2011; Free: 800-788-2782
Fax: (661)664-3188
E-mail: admissions@csub.edu
Web Site: www.csub.edu/
Description: State-supported, comprehensive, coed. Part of California State University System. Awards bachelor's and master's degrees. Founded 1970. Setting: 575-acre urban campus. Total enrollment: 8,002. Student-undergrad faculty ratio is 27:1. Full-time: 6,022 students, 62% women, 38% men. Part-time: 715 students, 61% women, 39% men. 1% from out-of-state. 1% American Indian or Alaska Native, non-Hispanic/Latino; 45% Hispanic/Latino; 7% African American, non-Hispanic/Latino; 7% Asian, non-Hispanic/Latino; 1% Native Hawaiian or other Pacific Islander, non-Hispanic/Latino; 2% international, 25% 25 or older, 13% transferred in. Academic areas with the most degrees conferred: business/marketing; liberal arts/general studies; psychology. Part-time degree program, external degree program, adult/continuing education programs.
Entrance Requirements: Options: electronic application, deferred admission. Required: high school transcript. Required for some: SAT or ACT. Entrance: moderately difficult. Application deadline: 3/1. Notification: continuous. Preference given to state residents.
Costs Per Year: State resident tuition: $5472 full-time. Nonresident tuition: $16,632 full-time. Mandatory fees: $1237 full-time. Full-time tuition and fees vary according to course load, degree level, and reciprocity agreements. College room and board: $8787. Room and board charges vary according to board plan.
Collegiate Environment: Orientation program. Campus security: 24-hour emergency response devices and patrols, late night transport-escort service. Walter W. Stiern Library with a Web page.
Community Environment: Bakersfield is the county seat of Kern County which is noted for its rich agriculture, petroleum, and light industries. The city is located 112 miles north of Los Angeles and 295 miles south of San Francisco. Airline, bus, transcontinental railroad, and Amtrak services are available in the area. Bakersfield is considered the trading center of the Southern San Joaquin Valley. Central California beaches are located approximately 100 miles west of the campus. Shirley Meadow ski area is 51 miles northeast of Bakersfield, 20 minutes from Lake Isebella. The county is home to world-famous Edwards Air Force Base. Part-time employment is available.

■ CALIFORNIA STATE UNIVERSITY CHANNEL ISLANDS

One University Dr.
Camarillo, CA 93012
Tel: (805)437-8400
Fax: (805)437-8951
E-mail: prospective.student@csuci.edu
Web Site: www.csuci.edu/
Description: State-supported, comprehensive, coed. Part of California State University System. Awards bachelor's, master's, and doctoral degrees. Founded 2002. Setting: suburban campus. Total enrollment: 3,599. Faculty: 294 (89 full-time, 205 part-time). Student-undergrad faculty ratio is 15:1. 5,562 applied, 53% were admitted. 3% from out-of-state. 25% 25 or older, 23% live on campus. Retention: 76% of full-time freshmen returned the following year. Academic areas with the most degrees conferred: liberal arts/general studies; psychology; business/marketing. Academic remediation for entering students, services for LD students, advanced placement, double major. Study abroad program.
Entrance Requirements: Required: high school transcript, minimum 2.0 high school GPA, SAT or ACT. Recommended: minimum 3.0 high school GPA. Entrance: noncompetitive.
Collegiate Environment: Student-run newspaper. Social organizations: local fraternities, local sororities. Student services: health clinic, personal-psychological counseling, women's center. Campus security: 24-hour emergency response devices and patrols, late night transport-escort service, controlled dormitory access. John Spoor Broome Library at Channel Islands with an OPAC and a Web page.

■ CALIFORNIA STATE UNIVERSITY, CHICO

400 W First St.
Chico, CA 95929-0722
Tel: (530)898-6116; Free: 800-542-4426
Fax: (530)898-6456

E-mail: info@csuchico.edu

Web Site: www.csuchico.edu/

Description: State-supported, comprehensive, coed. Part of California State University System. Awards bachelor's and master's degrees and post-master's certificates. Founded 1887. Setting: 119-acre small town campus. Endowment: $43 million. Research spending for the previous fiscal year: $3.1 million. Educational spending for the previous fiscal year: $5663 per student. Total enrollment: 16,470. Faculty: 862 (451 full-time, 411 part-time). Student-undergrad faculty ratio is 25:1. 15,568 applied, 79% were admitted. 35% from top 10% of their high school class, 76% from top quarter, 100% from top half. Full-time: 14,103 students, 52% women, 48% men. Part-time: 1,213 students, 50% women, 50% men. Students come from 36 states and territories, 39 other countries, 2% from out-of-state. 1% American Indian or Alaska Native, non-Hispanic/Latino; 20% Hispanic/Latino; 2% African American, non-Hispanic/Latino; 6% Asian, non-Hispanic/Latino; 0.2% Native Hawaiian or other Pacific Islander, non-Hispanic/Latino; 4% international. 12% 25 or older, 1% live on campus, 9% transferred in. Retention: 86% of full-time freshmen returned the following year. Academic areas with the most degrees conferred: business/marketing; social sciences; parks and recreation. Core. Calendar: semesters. Academic remediation for entering students, ESL program, services for LD students, advanced placement, self-designed majors, honors program, independent study, distance learning, double major, summer session for credit, part-time degree program, external degree program, adult/continuing education programs, co-op programs and internships, graduate courses open to undergrads. Off campus study at other units of the California State University System, National Student Exchange. Study abroad program.

Entrance Requirements: Options: electronic application, deferred admission, international baccalaureate accepted. Required: high school transcript, GPA of 10th /11th grade college preparatory courses only, SAT or ACT. Required for some: minimum 2 high school GPA. Entrance: moderately difficult. Application deadline: 11/30. Notification: 3/1. SAT Reasoning Test deadline: 12/31. SAT Subject Test deadline: 12/31. Transfer credits accepted: Yes.

Costs Per Year: Application fee: $55. State resident tuition: $7438 full-time. Nonresident tuition: $18,598 full-time. Mandatory fees: $1468 full-time. Full-time tuition and fees vary according to degree level. College room and board: $11,208. Room and board charges vary according to board plan and housing facility.

Collegiate Environment: Orientation program. Drama-theater group, choral group, student-run newspaper, radio station. Social organizations: 250 open to all; national fraternities, national sororities, local fraternities, local sororities; 1% of eligible men and 1% of eligible women are members. Most popular organizations: Scour and Devour, Panhellenic Council, The Edge Campus Christian Fellowship, Golden Key International Honor Society, Music and Entertainment Industry. Major annual events: Greek Week, Community Challenge, Multicultural Night. Student services: legal services, health clinic, personal-psychological counseling, women's center. Campus security: 24-hour emergency response devices and patrols, student patrols, late night transport-escort service, controlled dormitory access, crime prevention workshops, RAD self-defense program, Chico Safe Rides, blue light emergency phones, freshmen safety orientation. 2,100 college housing spaces available; all were occupied in 2012-13. Freshmen given priority for college housing. Options: coed, women-only housing available. Meriam Library with 942,304 books, 1.2 million microform titles, 22,000 serials, 25,765 audiovisual materials, an OPAC, and a Web page. Operations spending for the previous fiscal year: $3.9 million. 1,212 computers available on campus for general student use. Computer purchase/lease plans available. A campuswide network can be accessed from student residence rooms and from off campus. Students can access the following: online class registration, student account information, calendar, transcripts. Staffed computer lab on campus (open 24 hours a day) provides training in use of computers, software, and the Internet.

Community Environment: Chico is located close to the northern end of the Sacramento Valley and is one of the oldest communities in the state. Today Chico has a population of 71,427 (105,000 in the Greater Chico area) and Butte county has a population of 215,800. It is considered the business center for a large agricultural area, which produces an abundance of rice, grains, nuts, and fruits. Winters are mild and summers are hot, averaging 95-105 degrees. Regional airlines connect Chico with adjacent cities, including San Francisco and Sacramento. Greyhound Bus service is available. Chico is the home of Bidwell Park, one of the largest and most beautiful municipal parks in the nation. Lower Bidwell Park starts near the campus and extends 10 miles east along the Big Chico creek. The park offers swimming, hiking, a municipal golf course, horseback riding, a children's park, picnic areas, and softball fields among its recreational facilities. Biking is a favorite (and practical) means of transportation. Local Public Bus transportation is free to university students and personnel. Skiing facilities are only two hours away. Bidwell Mansion, located on campus, is now a historical site maintained by the Department of Parks and Recreation. Part-time employment is available but scarce.

■ **CALIFORNIA STATE UNIVERSITY, DOMINGUEZ HILLS**
1000 E Victoria St.
Carson, CA 90747-0001
Tel: (310)243-3300
Web Site: www.csudh.edu/

Description: State-supported, comprehensive, coed. Part of California State University System. Awards bachelor's and master's degrees and post-master's certificates. Founded 1960. Setting: 350-acre urban campus with easy access to Los Angeles. Endowment: $10.2 million. Educational spending for the previous fiscal year: $5151 per student. Total enrollment: 13,933. Faculty: 743 (262 full-time, 481 part-time). Student-undergrad faculty ratio is 25:1. 9,358 applied, 87% were admitted. Full-time: 7,800 students, 63% women, 37% men. Part-time: 3,627 students, 68% women, 32% men. Students come from 16 states and territories, 31 other countries, 0% from out-of-state. 0.3% American Indian or Alaska Native, non-Hispanic/Latino; 52% Hispanic/Latino; 18% African American, non-Hispanic/Latino; 9% Asian, non-Hispanic/Latino; 0.5% Native Hawaiian or other Pacific Islander, non-Hispanic/Latino; 2% international. 39% 25 or older, 6% live on campus, 16% transferred in. Retention: 77% of full-time freshmen returned the following year. Academic areas with the most degrees conferred: business/marketing; health professions and related sciences; social sciences. Core. Calendar: semesters. Academic remediation for entering students, services for LD students, advanced placement, accelerated degree program, self-designed majors, honors program, independent study, distance learning, double major, summer session for credit, part-time degree program, external degree program, co-op programs and internships, graduate courses open to undergrads. Off campus study at other institutions of the California State University System, National Student Exchange. Study abroad program. ROTC: Army, Air Force (c).

Entrance Requirements: Options: electronic application, international baccalaureate accepted. Required: high school transcript. Required for some: SAT or ACT. Entrance: moderately difficult. Application deadline: Rolling. Notification: continuous. Preference given to state residents. SAT Reasoning Test deadline: 2/15. Transfer credits accepted: Yes.

Costs Per Year: Application fee: $55. State resident tuition: $5472 full-time. Nonresident tuition: $16,632 full-time, $372 per credit part-time. Mandatory fees: $623 full-time. College room and board: $10,733. Room and board charges vary according to housing facility.

Collegiate Environment: Orientation program. Drama-theater group, choral group, student-run newspaper, radio station. Social organizations: 72 open to all; national fraternities, national sororities. Most popular organizations: Latino Student Business Association, Espirito de Nuestro Futuro, Organization of African Studies, American Marketing Association, Circle K. Major annual events: Welcome Week, Toro Days, Unity Fest. Student services: health clinic, personal-psychological counseling, women's center. Campus security: 24-hour emergency response devices, student patrols, late night transport-escort service, Campus Police Patrol Division is staffed 24 hours a day, 7 days a week. Officers are vested with full police powers. 652 college housing spaces available; 647 were occupied in 2012-13. No special consideration for freshman housing applicants. Option: coed housing available. Leo F. Cain Educational Resource Center with 454,476 books, 656 serials, 4,304 audiovisual materials, an OPAC, and a Web page. Operations spending for the previous fiscal year: $2.6 million. 1,100 computers available on campus for general student use. A campuswide network can be accessed from student residence rooms and from off campus. Students can access the following: online class registration. Staffed computer lab on campus provides training in use of computers and the Internet.

Community Environment: This is a metropolitan area in Los Angeles County with a Mediterranean climate. Trains, buses and airlines serve the area. Carson is surrounded by freeways, which makes the larger nearby cities easy to reach. The city has churches, hospitals, a YMCA building and library. The State Department of Employment, which is located in Torrance, has established a program designed to aid students in finding employment.

■ **CALIFORNIA STATE UNIVERSITY, EAST BAY**
25800 Carlos Bee Blvd.
Hayward, CA 94542-3000

Tel: (510)885-3000
Fax: (510)885-3816
E-mail: admissions@csueeastbay.edu
Web Site: www.csueastbay.edu/
Description: State-supported, comprehensive, coed. Part of California State University System. Awards bachelor's, master's, and doctoral degrees. Founded 1957. Setting: 343-acre suburban campus with easy access to San Francisco Bay Area. Endowment: $9.2 million. Research spending for the previous fiscal year: $8.7 million. Educational spending for the previous fiscal year: $11,622 per student. Total enrollment: 13,851. Faculty: 709 (306 full-time, 403 part-time). Student-undergrad faculty ratio is 31:1. 11,625 applied, 58% were admitted. Full-time: 9,975 students, 61% women, 39% men. Part-time: 1,475 students, 60% women, 40% men. Students come from 33 states and territories, 62 other countries, 1% from out-of-state. 0.3% American Indian or Alaska Native, non-Hispanic/Latino; 22% Hispanic/Latino; 12% African American, non-Hispanic/Latino; 20% Asian, non-Hispanic/Latino; 3% Native Hawaiian or other Pacific Islander, non-Hispanic/Latino; 7% international. 36% 25 or older, 11% transferred in. Retention: 75% of full-time freshmen returned the following year. Academic areas with the most degrees conferred: business/marketing; health professions and related sciences; social sciences. Core. Academic remediation for entering students, ESL program, services for LD students, advanced placement, accelerated degree program, self-designed majors, honors program, independent study, distance learning, double major, summer session for credit, part-time degree program, adult/continuing education programs, co-op programs and internships, graduate courses open to undergrads. Off campus study at Regional Association of East Bay Colleges and Universities, National Student Exchange. Study abroad program.
Entrance Requirements: Options: electronic application, international baccalaureate accepted. Required: high school transcript, minimum 2 high school GPA, California State University eligibility index. Required for some: SAT or ACT. Entrance: moderately difficult. Application deadline: 11/30. Notification: continuous.
Costs Per Year: Application fee: $55. State resident tuition: $5472 full-time. Nonresident tuition: $16,632 full-time. Mandatory fees: $837 full-time. College room and board: $11,321.
Collegiate Environment: Orientation program. Drama-theater group, choral group, student-run newspaper, radio station. Social organizations: 90 open to all; national fraternities, national sororities, local sororities. Most popular organizations: Vietnamese Student Association, Accounting Association, Filipino-American Students Association, Movimiento Estudiantil Chicano, Hayward Orientation Team. Major annual events: Al Fresco, Pioneer Days, Club Days. Student services: legal services, health clinic, personal-psychological counseling. Campus security: 24-hour emergency response devices and patrols, late night transport-escort service. 800 college housing spaces available; all were occupied in 2012-13. Option: coed housing available. Hayward Campus Library with an OPAC and a Web page. Operations spending for the previous fiscal year: $3.4 million. 700 computers available on campus for general student use. Computer purchase/lease plans available. A campuswide network can be accessed from student residence rooms and from off campus. Students can access the following: online class registration. Staffed computer lab on campus (open 24 hours a day).
Community Environment: Population 140,000 in a metropolitan area of 5 1/2 million. Hayward is a suburban area near Oakland, Berkeley, San Francisco and San Jose. The climate is mild. All modes of transportation serve the area. The university's proximity to all major Bay Area cities provides access to museums, art galleries, plays, concerts, and libraries as well as to the recreational opportunities of the bay. The climate makes outdoor recreation a year-round activity. Its nearness to ocean and mountain areas offer recreational diversity.

■ **CALIFORNIA STATE UNIVERSITY, FRESNO**
5241 N Maple Ave.
Fresno, CA 93740-8027
Tel: (559)278-4240
Fax: (559)278-4715
E-mail: andyhe@csufresno.edu
Web Site: www.csufresno.edu/
Description: State-supported, comprehensive, coed. Part of California State University System. Awards bachelor's, master's, and doctoral degrees and post-master's certificates. Founded 1911. Setting: 1,399-acre urban campus. Total enrollment: 22,565. Faculty: 1,186 (625 full-time, 561 part-time). Student-undergrad faculty ratio is 22:1. 16,242 applied, 58% were admitted. 15% from top 10% of their high school class, 80% from top quarter, 100%

from top half. Full-time: 17,156 students, 57% women, 43% men. Part-time: 2,563 students, 54% women, 46% men. 0.4% from out-of-state. 0.4% American Indian or Alaska Native, non-Hispanic/Latino; 40% Hispanic/Latino; 4% African American, non-Hispanic/Latino; 15% Asian, non-Hispanic/Latino; 0.4% Native Hawaiian or other Pacific Islander, non-Hispanic/Latino; 3% international. 16% 25 or older, 5% live on campus, 8% transferred in. Retention: 84% of full-time freshmen returned the following year. Academic areas with the most degrees conferred: business/marketing; health professions and related sciences; liberal arts/general studies. Core. Calendar: semesters. Academic remediation for entering students, ESL program, services for LD students, advanced placement, accelerated degree program, self-designed majors, freshman honors college, honors program, independent study, distance learning, double major, summer session for credit, part-time degree program, adult/continuing education programs, co-op programs and internships, graduate courses open to undergrads. Off campus study at other units of the California State University System. Study abroad program. ROTC: Army, Air Force.
Entrance Requirements: Options: electronic application, international baccalaureate accepted. Required: high school transcript, minimum 2 high school GPA, SAT or ACT. Entrance: minimally difficult. Application deadline: 11/30. Notification: continuous. Preference given to state residents. SAT Reasoning Test deadline: 1/15. SAT Subject Test deadline: 1/15. Transfer credits accepted: Yes.
Costs Per Year: Application fee: $55. State resident tuition: $6274 full-time. Nonresident tuition: $14,400 full-time, $372 per credit hour part-time. College room and board: $10,192. Room and board charges vary according to board plan.
Collegiate Environment: Orientation program. Drama-theater group, choral group, marching band, student-run newspaper, radio station. Social organizations: 200 open to all; national fraternities, national sororities, local fraternities, local sororities. Major annual events: Vintage Day, Welcome Week, Commencement. Student services: health clinic, personal-psychological counseling, women's center. Campus security: 24-hour emergency response devices and patrols, late night transport-escort service, controlled dormitory access. No special consideration for freshman housing applicants. Options: coed, men-only, women-only housing available. Henry Madden Library with an OPAC and a Web page.
Community Environment: Fresno (population 461,000) is located in the heart of the San Joaquin Valley, at the center of the state. The climate is mild all year. All modes of transportation serve the area. Fresno is in an agricultural area producing figs, grapes and cotton. Roma Winery and several other wineries are located here; other industries include processing and packing of fruit, the manufacture of cottonseed oil, livestock and poultry feed, agricultural equipment and aircraft parts. There are facilities in the area for swimming, fishing, sailing, water skiing, horseback riding, hiking, rock climbing and all the winter sports. Three national parks and two national forests are nearby.

■ **CALIFORNIA STATE UNIVERSITY, FULLERTON**
PO Box 34080
Fullerton, CA 92834-9480
Tel: (657)278-2011
E-mail: admissions@fullerton.edu
Web Site: www.fullerton.edu/
Description: State-supported, comprehensive, coed. Part of California State University System. Awards bachelor's, master's, and doctoral degrees and post-master's certificates. Founded 1957. Setting: 236-acre suburban campus with easy access to Los Angeles. Endowment: $32.3 million. Research spending for the previous fiscal year: $2.5 million. Educational spending for the previous fiscal year: $7494 per student. Total enrollment: 37,677. Faculty: 1,680 (848 full-time, 832 part-time). Student-undergrad faculty ratio is 26:1. 38,909 applied, 46% were admitted. 19% from top 10% of their high school class, 60% from top quarter, 92% from top half. Full-time: 26,079 students, 56% women, 44% men. Part-time: 6,300 students, 55% women, 45% men. Students come from 36 states and territories, 51 other countries, 1% from out-of-state. 0.3% American Indian or Alaska Native, non-Hispanic/Latino; 35% Hispanic/Latino; 2% African American, non-Hispanic/Latino; 22% Asian, non-Hispanic/Latino; 0.3% Native Hawaiian or other Pacific Islander, non-Hispanic/Latino; 4% international. 19% 25 or older, 6% live on campus, 13% transferred in. Retention: 88% of full-time freshmen returned the following year. Academic areas with the most degrees conferred: business/marketing; communication/journalism; social sciences. Core. Calendar: semesters. Academic remediation for entering students, services for LD students, advanced placement, self-designed majors, honors

program, independent study, distance learning, double major, summer session for credit, part-time degree program, adult/continuing education programs, co-op programs and internships. Off campus study at other institutions of the California State University System. Study abroad program. ROTC: Army.

Entrance Requirements: Options: electronic application, international baccalaureate accepted. Required: high school transcript, minimum 2 high school GPA, SAT, SAT or ACT. Entrance: moderately difficult. Application deadline: 11/30. Notification: continuous. Preference given to state residents. SAT Reasoning Test deadline: 1/15. Transfer credits accepted: Yes.

Costs Per Year: Application fee: $55. State resident tuition: $0 full-time. Nonresident tuition: $11,160 full-time, $372 per unit part-time. Mandatory fees: $6182 full-time, $1945 part-time. Full-time tuition and fees vary according to course load. Part-time tuition and fees vary according to course load. College room and board: $12,096. Room and board charges vary according to board plan and housing facility.

Collegiate Environment: Orientation program. Drama-theater group, choral group, student-run newspaper, radio station. Social organizations: 297 open to all; national fraternities, national sororities, local fraternities, local sororities. Most popular organizations: Pan-Hellenic Council, American Marketing Association, Lacrosse Club, Samaritans (volunteer service club), Human Services Student Association. Major annual events: Block Party (celebrating start of year), spring concert, Snow Day. Student services: legal services, health clinic, personal-psychological counseling, women's center. Campus security: 24-hour emergency response devices and patrols, student patrols, late night transport-escort service, controlled dormitory access. 2,000 college housing spaces available; all were occupied in 2012-13. Freshmen given priority for college housing. Option: coed housing available. Pollak Library with 1.3 million books, 1.1 million microform titles, 55,756 serials, 34,276 audiovisual materials, an OPAC, and a Web page. Operations spending for the previous fiscal year: $5.8 million. 2,000 computers available on campus for general student use. A campuswide network can be accessed from student residence rooms and from off campus. Students can access the following: online class registration. Staffed computer lab on campus provides training in use of computers, software, and the Internet.

Community Environment: Fullerton is in a metropolitan area with a temperate climate. Airlines, buses and trains serve the area. Freeways make all neighboring cities easily accessible. Fullerton is an area of many cultural interests, in art, music and theatre. The city is near Disneyland and the California Angel Stadium; 35 miles from Hollywood and Los Angeles. Recreational facilities include the beaches and the mountains which are both within easy driving distance. Part-time work is available. The major service clubs are represented in the city.

■ **CALIFORNIA STATE UNIVERSITY, LONG BEACH**
1250 Bellflower Blvd.
Long Beach, CA 90840
Tel: (562)985-4111
Web Site: www.csulb.edu/

Description: State-supported, comprehensive, coed. Part of California State University System. Awards bachelor's, master's, and doctoral degrees. Founded 1949. Setting: 320-acre suburban campus with easy access to Los Angeles. Endowment: $42.5 million. Research spending for the previous fiscal year: $14.9 million. Educational spending for the previous fiscal year: $6624 per student. Total enrollment: 36,279. Faculty: 1,908 (917 full-time, 991 part-time). Student-undergrad faculty ratio is 22:1. 54,970 applied, 31% were admitted. 84% from top quarter of their high school class, 100% from top half. Full-time: 25,880 students, 58% women, 42% men. Part-time: 5,051 students, 56% women, 44% men. Students come from 40 states and territories, 85 other countries, 1% from out-of-state. 1% American Indian or Alaska Native, non-Hispanic/Latino; 35% Hispanic/Latino; 4% African American, non-Hispanic/Latino; 22% Asian, non-Hispanic/Latino; 2% Native Hawaiian or other Pacific Islander, non-Hispanic/Latino; 5% international. 16% 25 or older, 30% live on campus, 13% transferred in. Retention: 88% of full-time freshmen returned the following year. Academic areas with the most degrees conferred: business/marketing; visual and performing arts; English. Core. Calendar: semesters. Academic remediation for entering students, ESL program, services for LD students, advanced placement, accelerated degree program, self-designed majors, honors program, independent study, distance learning, double major, summer session for credit, part-time degree program, adult/continuing education programs, internships, graduate courses open to undergrads. Off campus study at other institutions of the California State University System. Study abroad program. ROTC: Army.

Entrance Requirements: Option: electronic application. Required: high school transcript, SAT or ACT. Required for some: minimum 2 high school GPA. Entrance: moderately difficult. Application deadline: 11/30. Notification: continuous. Preference given to local residents. SAT Reasoning Test deadline: 1/15.

Costs Per Year: Application fee: $55. State resident tuition: $0 full-time. Nonresident tuition: $11,160 full-time, $372 per unit part-time. Mandatory fees: $6240 full-time. Full-time tuition and fees vary according to degree level and program. Part-time tuition varies according to course load, degree level, and program. College room and board: $11,300. Room and board charges vary according to board plan.

Collegiate Environment: Orientation program. Drama-theater group, choral group, student-run newspaper, radio station. Social organizations: 300 open to all; national fraternities, national sororities, local fraternities, local sororities; 7% of eligible men and 5% of eligible women are members. Major annual events: Kaleidoscope Spring Festival, Odyssey Theme Year. Student services: legal services, health clinic, personal-psychological counseling, women's center. Campus security: 24-hour emergency response devices and patrols, student patrols, late night transport-escort service. 2,400 college housing spaces available; all were occupied in 2012-13. No special consideration for freshman housing applicants. Option: coed housing available. University Library with 2 million books, 1.5 million microform titles, 99,416 serials, 39,314 audiovisual materials, an OPAC, and a Web page. 2,000 computers available on campus for general student use. A campuswide network can be accessed from off-campus. Staffed computer lab on campus.

Community Environment: Long Beach is approximately 20 miles south of Los Angeles and has a Mediterranean climate. The eight mile beach area provides the finest and safest public bathing on the Pacific Coast, having the largest protected harbor in North America. All modes of transportation serve the area. There are 25 city parks which provide facilities for golf, tennis, baseball, swimming, shuffleboard, and lawn bowling, as well as a sports arena and a municipal auditorium.

■ **CALIFORNIA STATE UNIVERSITY, LOS ANGELES**
5151 State University Dr.
Los Angeles, CA 90032-8530
Tel: (323)343-3000
Fax: (323)343-2670
E-mail: admission@calstatela.edu
Web Site: www.calstatela.edu/

Description: State-supported, comprehensive, coed. Part of California State University System. Awards bachelor's, master's, and doctoral degrees. Founded 1947. Setting: 173-acre urban campus. Endowment: $15.8 million. Research spending for the previous fiscal year: $3.1 million. Educational spending for the previous fiscal year: $6699 per student. Total enrollment: 21,755. Faculty: 1,117 (533 full-time, 584 part-time). Student-undergrad faculty ratio is 25:1. 27,321 applied, 65% were admitted. 3% from top quarter of their high school class, 100% from top half. Full-time: 14,991 students, 60% women, 40% men. Part-time: 3,083 students, 57% women, 43% men. Students come from 50 states and territories, 44 other countries, 0.4% from out-of-state. 0.1% American Indian or Alaska Native, non-Hispanic/Latino; 58% Hispanic/Latino; 5% African American, non-Hispanic/Latino; 17% Asian, non-Hispanic/Latino; 0.4% Native Hawaiian or other Pacific Islander, non-Hispanic/Latino; 4% international. 25% 25 or older, 5% live on campus, 12% transferred in. Retention: 81% of full-time freshmen returned the following year. Academic areas with the most degrees conferred: business/marketing; health professions and related sciences; social sciences. Core. Academic remediation for entering students, ESL program, services for LD students, advanced placement, accelerated degree program, self-designed majors, honors program, independent study, distance learning, double major, summer session for credit, part-time degree program, adult/continuing education programs, co-op programs and internships, graduate courses open to undergrads. Off campus study at other units of the California State University System. Study abroad program. ROTC: Army (c), Air Force (c).

Entrance Requirements: Options: electronic application, early admission. Required: high school transcript. Required for some: SAT or ACT. Entrance: moderately difficult. Application deadline: 11/30. Notification: 8/30. SAT Reasoning Test deadline: 7/13. SAT Subject Test deadline: 7/13.

Costs Per Year: Application fee: $55. State resident tuition: $0 full-time. Nonresident tuition: $15,263 full-time, $248 per unit part-time. Mandatory fees: $6335 full-time. Full-time tuition and fees vary according to course level and course load. Part-time tuition varies according to course level and course load. College room and board: $9728. College room only: $5895. Room and board charges vary according to housing facility.

Collegiate Environment: Orientation program. Drama-theater group, choral group, student-run newspaper. Social organizations: 130 open to all; national fraternities, national sororities, local fraternities, local sororities; 1% of eligible men and 1% of eligible women are members. Most popular organizations: Society of Hispanic Engineering and Science Students, Institute of Electrical and Electronics Engineer, Sigma Delta PI, Asian Unified, Society of Automotive Engineers. Major annual events: Haunted Union, Mardi Gras, Spring Student Fest. Student services: legal services, health clinic, personal-psychological counseling, women's center. Campus security: 24-hour emergency response devices, student patrols, late night transport-escort service. 1,000 college housing spaces available; 867 were occupied in 2012-13. Option: coed housing available. John F. Kennedy Memorial Library plus 1 other with 2 million books, 1.1 million microform titles, 140 serials, 35,987 audiovisual materials, an OPAC, and a Web page. Operations spending for the previous fiscal year: $62.6 million. 1,500 computers available on campus for general student use. A campuswide network can be accessed from student residence rooms and from off campus. Students can access the following: online class registration. Staffed computer lab on campus provides training in use of computers, software, and the Internet.
Community Environment: See University of California - Los Angeles.

■ **CALIFORNIA STATE UNIVERSITY, MONTEREY BAY**
100 Campus Ctr.
Seaside, CA 93955-8001
Tel: (831)582-3000
Fax: (831)582-3540
E-mail: admissions@csumb.edu
Web Site: www.csumb.edu/
Description: State-supported, comprehensive, coed. Part of California State University System. Awards bachelor's and master's degrees. Founded 1994. Setting: 1,387-acre small town campus with easy access to San Jose. Endowment: $13.9 million. Research spending for the previous fiscal year: $5.9 million. Educational spending for the previous fiscal year: $5348 per student. Total enrollment: 5,609. Faculty: 383 (121 full-time, 262 part-time). Student-undergrad faculty ratio is 26:1. 12,562 applied, 44% were admitted. 15% from top 10% of their high school class, 48% from top quarter, 87% from top half. 3 valedictorians. Full-time: 4,879 students, 62% women, 38% men. Part-time: 315 students, 57% women, 43% men. Students come from 37 states and territories, 19 other countries, 3% from out-of-state. 1% American Indian or Alaska Native, non-Hispanic/Latino; 33% Hispanic/Latino; 6% African American, non-Hispanic/Latino; 5% Asian, non-Hispanic/Latino; 1% Native Hawaiian or other Pacific Islander, non-Hispanic/Latino; 2% international. 0% 25 or older, 60% live on campus, 13% transferred in. Retention: 80% of full-time freshmen returned the following year. Academic areas with the most degrees conferred: liberal arts/general studies; business/marketing; social sciences. Core. Calendar: semesters. Academic remediation for entering students, services for LD students, advanced placement, self-designed majors, independent study, distance learning, double major, summer session for credit, part-time degree program, co-op programs and internships, graduate courses open to undergrads. Off campus study at Monterey Institute of International Studies (MIIS). Study abroad program.
Entrance Requirements: Options: electronic application, deferred admission, international baccalaureate accepted. Required: high school transcript, minimum 2 high school GPA, SAT or ACT. Entrance: moderately difficult. Application deadlines: 11/30, 11/30 for nonresidents. Notification: continuous, continuous for nonresidents. SAT Reasoning Test deadline: 1/15. SAT Subject Test deadline: 1/15. Transfer credits accepted: Yes. Applicants placed on waiting list: 0. Wait-listed applicants offered admission: 0.
Costs Per Year: Application fee: $55. State resident tuition: $0 full-time. Nonresident tuition: $11,160 full-time, $372 per credit hour part-time. Mandatory fees: $5963 full-time. Full-time tuition and fees vary according to course load and degree level. Part-time tuition varies according to course load and degree level. College room and board: $9498. Room and board charges vary according to board plan and housing facility.
Collegiate Environment: Orientation program. Student-run newspaper, radio station. Social organizations: 77 open to all; national fraternities, national sororities, local sororities; 5% of eligible men and 5% of eligible women are members. Most popular organizations: National Society for Leadership & Success, Math & Statistics Club, National Association for the Advancement of Colored People (NAACP), Robotics Club, Black Students United. Major annual events: Homecoming events, Welcome week events (Otter Days), Eggs After Dark (Midnight Breakfast). Student services: health clinic, personal-psychological counseling, women's center. Campus security: 24-hour emergency response devices and patrols, student patrols, late night

transport-escort service, controlled dormitory access. 3,168 college housing spaces available. Freshmen given priority for college housing. On-campus residence required through sophomore year. Option: coed housing available. The Tanimura & Antle Family Memorial Library with 160,693 books, 175 microform titles, 53,690 serials, 3,085 audiovisual materials, an OPAC, and a Web page. Operations spending for the previous fiscal year: $1.8 million. 994 computers available on campus for general student use. Computer purchase/lease plans available. A campuswide network can be accessed from student residence rooms and from off campus. Students can access the following: online class registration. Staffed computer lab on campus provides training in use of computers, software, and the Internet.

■ **CALIFORNIA STATE UNIVERSITY, NORTHRIDGE**
18111 Nordhoff St.
Northridge, CA 91330
Tel: (818)677-1200
Fax: (818)677-3766
E-mail: admissions.records@csun.edu
Web Site: www.csun.edu/
Description: State-supported, comprehensive, coed. Part of California State University System. Awards bachelor's and master's degrees. Founded 1958. Setting: 356-acre urban campus with easy access to Los Angeles. Total enrollment: 36,164. Faculty: 1,857 (860 full-time, 997 part-time). Student-undergrad faculty ratio is 26:1. 29,339 applied, 46% were admitted. Full-time: 25,460 students, 55% women, 45% men. Part-time: 5,659 students, 52% women, 48% men. 3% from out-of-state. 0.2% American Indian or Alaska Native, non-Hispanic/Latino; 38% Hispanic/Latino; 7% African American, non-Hispanic/Latino; 11% Asian, non-Hispanic/Latino; 0.3% Native Hawaiian or other Pacific Islander, non-Hispanic/Latino; 7% international. 20% 25 or older, 13% transferred in. Retention: 75% of full-time freshmen returned the following year. Academic areas with the most degrees conferred: business/marketing; social sciences; psychology. Core. Calendar: semesters. Academic remediation for entering students, ESL program, services for LD students, advanced placement, self-designed majors, independent study, distance learning, double major, summer session for credit, part-time degree program, adult/continuing education programs, internships, graduate courses open to undergrads. Off campus study at other units of the California State University System, National Student Exchange. Study abroad program. ROTC: Army (c), Air Force (c).
Entrance Requirements: Option: electronic application. Required: high school transcript, SAT or ACT. Entrance: moderately difficult. Application deadline: 11/30. Notification: continuous. Preference given to state residents for business administration, engineering, computer science, economics programs. SAT Reasoning Test deadline: 1/15.
Costs Per Year: Application fee: $55. State resident tuition: $0 full-time. Nonresident tuition: $11,160 full-time, $372 per credit hour part-time. Mandatory fees: $6520 full-time. College room and board: $12,404. Room and board charges vary according to board plan and housing facility.
Collegiate Environment: Orientation program. Drama-theater group, choral group, student-run newspaper, radio station. Social organizations: national fraternities, national sororities. Student services: health clinic, personal-psychological counseling, women's center. Campus security: 24-hour emergency response devices, late night transport-escort service. Oviatt Library with an OPAC and a Web page.
Community Environment: Located north of Los Angeles and part of the Los Angeles metropolitan area. Climate is mild; all modes of transportation available in the Los Angeles area. The community facilities include churches, library, hospitals and all the service organizations are represented. Part-time employment available in this center for electronic and space research and development; about three-quarters of the students work. Northridge enjoys the cultural and recreational advantages of Los Angeles and is 20 miles from the Pacific Ocean and near the mountain areas for winter sports.

■ **CALIFORNIA STATE UNIVERSITY, SACRAMENTO**
6000 J St.
Sacramento, CA 95819
Tel: (916)278-6011
E-mail: admissions@csus.edu
Web Site: www.csus.edu/
Description: State-supported, comprehensive, coed. Part of California State University System. Awards bachelor's, master's, and doctoral degrees. Founded 1947. Setting: 300-acre urban campus. Total enrollment: 28,016. Faculty: 1,400 (703 full-time, 697 part-time). Student-undergrad faculty ratio is 26:1. 18,617 applied, 67% were admitted. 100% from top half of their high

school class. Full-time: 20,410 students, 57% women, 43% men. Part-time: 4,291 students, 54% women, 46% men. 0% from out-of-state. 1% American Indian or Alaska Native, non-Hispanic/Latino; 18% Hispanic/Latino; 6% African American, non-Hispanic/Latino; 20% Asian, non-Hispanic/Latino; 1% Native Hawaiian or other Pacific Islander, non-Hispanic/Latino; 1% international. 23% 25 or older, 5% live on campus, 14% transferred in. Retention: 83% of full-time freshmen returned the following year. Academic areas with the most degrees conferred: business/marketing; homeland security, law enforcement, firefighting, and protective services; communication/journalism. Calendar: semesters. Part-time degree program. Off campus study at other units of the California State University System. ROTC: Army, Air Force.

Entrance Requirements: Options: electronic application, early action, deferred admission, international baccalaureate accepted. Required: minimum 2 high school GPA, SAT or ACT. Required for some: high school transcript. Entrance: moderately difficult. SAT Subject Test deadline: 3/1.

Costs Per Year: Application fee: $55. State resident tuition: $5472 full-time. Nonresident tuition: $16,632 full-time. Mandatory fees: $1148 full-time. College room and board: $11,724. Room and board charges vary according to board plan and housing facility.

Collegiate Environment: Orientation program. Campus security: 24-hour emergency response devices and patrols, student patrols, late night transport-escort service, controlled dormitory access.

Community Environment: Sacramento, the capital of California, is the gateway to historic Gold Rush country and the High Sierra vacation regions. All modes of transportation serve the area; San Francisco is a two-hour drive on the freeway. The cultural center of Northern California, Sacramento has the historic Crocker Art Gallery, symphony orchestra, summer theater series, state library, a state museum, a state railroad museum and the Sacramento History Center. Numerous part time jobs on campus and in the city are available through the Student Placement Office and the California Department of Employment. There are many post-college vocational opportunities with defense industries, two air bases, state and local government and other growing industrial and high-tech firms. Off campus housing is available to students. There are many points of interest and a great number of recreational facilities in the Sacramento area; parks, zoo, golf courses, boating and fishing on the American and Sacramento Rivers. Squaw Valley, 100 miles away, was the home of the 1960 Olympics for winter sports. There are good health facilities and a wide range of fraternal and civic organizations.

■ **CALIFORNIA STATE UNIVERSITY, SAN BERNARDINO**
5500 University Pky.
San Bernardino, CA 92407-2397
Tel: (909)537-5000
E-mail: moreinfo@mail.csusb.edu
Web Site: www.csusb.edu/

Description: State-supported, comprehensive, coed. Part of California State University System. Awards bachelor's, master's, and doctoral degrees. Founded 1965. Setting: 430-acre suburban campus with easy access to Los Angeles. Total enrollment: 18,234. Faculty: 730 (430 full-time, 300 part-time). Student-undergrad faculty ratio is 26:1. 12,241 applied, 58% were admitted. Full-time: 14,075 students, 62% women, 38% men. Part-time: 1,810 students, 59% women, 41% men. 0.3% American Indian or Alaska Native, non-Hispanic/Latino; 53% Hispanic/Latino; 8% African American, non-Hispanic/Latino; 6% Asian, non-Hispanic/Latino; 0.2% Native Hawaiian or other Pacific Islander, non-Hispanic/Latino; 5% international. Retention: 88% of full-time freshmen returned the following year. Academic areas with the most degrees conferred: business/marketing; psychology; liberal arts/general studies. Core. Services for LD students, accelerated degree program, self-designed majors, honors program, independent study, distance learning, double major, summer session for credit, part-time degree program, co-op programs and internships. Off campus study at National Student Exchange. Study abroad program. ROTC: Army, Air Force.

Entrance Requirements: Options: electronic application, early admission, early action. Required: high school transcript, minimum 2 high school GPA. Recommended: SAT or ACT. Entrance: moderately difficult. Application deadline: Rolling. Notification: continuous. SAT Reasoning Test deadline: 6/30. SAT Subject Test deadline: 9/1.

Costs Per Year: Application fee: $55. State resident tuition: $5472 full-time. Nonresident tuition: $11,160 full-time. Mandatory fees: $6549 full-time. College room and board: $9972. Room and board charges vary according to board plan and housing facility.

Collegiate Environment: Orientation program. Drama-theater group, choral group, student-run newspaper, radio station. Social organizations: national

fraternities, national sororities, local fraternities, local sororities; 3% of eligible men and 4% of eligible women are members. Major annual events: Earth Day, SOAR Days, International Day. Student services: legal services, health clinic, personal-psychological counseling, women's center. Campus security: 24-hour emergency response devices and patrols, student patrols, late night transport-escort service, residence staff on call 24 hours. 1,500 college housing spaces available; 1,100 were occupied in 2012-13. Options: coed, women-only housing available. Pfau Library with 731,259 books, 643,292 microform titles, 2,028 serials, and an OPAC. 1,300 computers available on campus for general student use. Computer purchase/lease plans available. A campuswide network can be accessed from student residence rooms and from off campus. Students can access the following: online class registration. Staffed computer lab on campus provides training in use of computers, software, and the Internet.

Community Environment: Population 198,550. San Bernardino is located 58 miles east of Los Angeles at the foot of the San Bernardino Mountains. Climate is ideal with 312 days of sunshine a year. Citrus groves surround the city. Greyhound and Trailways bus lines and Santa Fe Railroad serve the area. The nearest airport is Ontario International. San Bernardino has art galleries, Swing Auditorium, theaters, many churches, and a library. Pacific Ocean beaches provide water sports. Resort areas of Lake Arrowhead and Big Bear Lake in the mountains have facilities for water sports and winter sports. Cajon Pass offers a scenic drive through the mountains into the Mojave Desert; City Creek Highway connects with the Rim of the World Drive at Running Springs.

■ **CALIFORNIA STATE UNIVERSITY, SAN MARCOS**
333 S Twin Oaks Valley Rd.
San Marcos, CA 92096-0001
Tel: (760)750-4000
Fax: (760)750-4030
E-mail: apply@csusm.edu
Web Site: www.csusm.edu/

Description: State-supported, comprehensive, coed. Part of California State University System. Awards bachelor's and master's degrees. Founded 1990. Setting: 304-acre suburban campus with easy access to San Diego. Total enrollment: 10,363. Faculty: 609 (238 full-time, 371 part-time). Student-undergrad faculty ratio is 25:1. 10,848 applied, 62% were admitted. Full-time: 7,801 students, 61% women, 39% men. Part-time: 2,127 students, 56% women, 44% men. 2% from out-of-state. 0.5% American Indian or Alaska Native, non-Hispanic/Latino; 32% Hispanic/Latino; 3% African American, non-Hispanic/Latino; 10% Asian, non-Hispanic/Latino; 2% international. 21% 25 or older, 14% transferred in. Retention: 83% of full-time freshmen returned the following year. Academic areas with the most degrees conferred: business/marketing; liberal arts/general studies; social sciences. Core. Calendar: semesters. Academic remediation for entering students, ESL program, services for LD students, advanced placement, self-designed majors, independent study, distance learning, double major, summer session for credit, part-time degree program, adult/continuing education programs, internships. Off campus study at San Diego State University, Palomar College, Mira Costa College. Study abroad program. ROTC: Army (c), Naval (c), Air Force (c).

Entrance Requirements: Options: electronic application, international baccalaureate accepted. Required: high school transcript, minimum 3 high school GPA. Recommended: SAT or ACT. Entrance: moderately difficult. Application deadline: 11/30. Notification: continuous.

Costs Per Year: Application fee: $55. State resident tuition: $0 full-time. Nonresident tuition: $11,762 full-time, $372 per unit part-time. Mandatory fees: $7298 full-time, $2251 per term part-time. Part-time tuition and fees vary according to course load.

Collegiate Environment: Orientation program. Drama-theater group, choral group, student-run newspaper. Social organizations: 30 open to all; national fraternities, national sororities. Most popular organizations: Accounting Club, Liberal Studies Club, MECHA, Sigma IOTA Epsilon. Major annual events: Pow-Wow, Welcome Week, Awards Dinner. Student services: health clinic, personal-psychological counseling, women's center. Campus security: 24-hour emergency response devices and patrols, student patrols, late night transport-escort service. Kellogg Library with 406,748 books, 987,161 microform titles, 43,681 serials, 12,942 audiovisual materials, an OPAC, and a Web page. 1,400 computers available on campus for general student use. A campuswide network can be accessed from student residence rooms and from off campus. Students can access the following: online class registration. Staffed computer lab on campus.

■ CALIFORNIA STATE UNIVERSITY, STANISLAUS

One University Cir.
Turlock, CA 95382
Tel: (209)667-3122; Free: 800-300-7420
Fax: (209)667-3333
E-mail: outreach_help_desk@csustan.edu
Web Site: www.csustan.edu/
Description: State-supported, comprehensive, coed. Part of California State University System. Awards bachelor's, master's, and doctoral degrees and post-master's certificates. Founded 1957. Setting: 228-acre small town campus. Endowment: $8.1 million. Research spending for the previous fiscal year: $1.4 million. Total enrollment: 8,882. Faculty: 446 (258 full-time, 188 part-time). Student-undergrad faculty ratio is 21:1. 5,763 applied, 72% were admitted. Full-time: 6,321 students, 64% women, 36% men. Part-time: 1,300 students, 63% women, 37% men. Students come from 18 states and territories, 22 other countries, 1% from out-of-state. 0.4% American Indian or Alaska Native, non-Hispanic/Latino; 42% Hispanic/Latino; 3% African American, non-Hispanic/Latino; 11% Asian, non-Hispanic/Latino; 1% Native Hawaiian or other Pacific Islander, non-Hispanic/Latino; 1% international. 21% 25 or older, 8% live on campus, 11% transferred in. Retention: 83% of full-time freshmen returned the following year. Academic areas with the most degrees conferred: business/marketing; social sciences; psychology. Core. Calendar: semesters. Academic remediation for entering students, ESL program, services for LD students, advanced placement, self-designed majors, honors program, independent study, distance learning, double major, summer session for credit, part-time degree program, adult/continuing education programs, co-op programs and internships, graduate courses open to undergrads. Off campus study at other units of the California State University System. Study abroad program.
Entrance Requirements: Option: electronic application. Required: high school transcript. Recommended: minimum 3 high school GPA. Required for some: interview, SAT or ACT. Entrance: moderately difficult. Application deadline: 11/30. Notification: continuous. SAT Reasoning Test deadline: 7/2.
Costs Per Year: Application fee: $55. State resident tuition: $5472 full-time. Nonresident tuition: $16,632 full-time. Mandatory fees: $1112 full-time. Full-time tuition and fees vary according to course load and reciprocity agreements. College room and board: $9056. Room and board charges vary according to board plan and housing facility.
Collegiate Environment: Orientation program. Drama-theater group, choral group, student-run newspaper, radio station. Social organizations: 83 open to all; national fraternities, national sororities, local fraternities, local sororities; 6% of eligible men and 7% of eligible women are members. Most popular organizations: Alpha Xi Delta, Phi Sigma Sigma, Kappa Sigma, Tau Kappa Epsilon, Theta Chi. Major annual events: Warrior Day, Welcome Back Concert, Warriors Up All Night. Student services: health clinic, personal-psychological counseling, women's center. Campus security: 24-hour emergency response devices and patrols, student patrols, late night transport-escort service, controlled dormitory access. 689 college housing spaces available; 603 were occupied in 2012-13. No special consideration for freshman housing applicants. Option: coed housing available. Vasche Library with 502,279 books, 1.1 million microform titles, 62,850 serials, 5,829 audiovisual materials, an OPAC, and a Web page. Operations spending for the previous fiscal year: $2.1 million. 200 computers available on campus for general student use. A campuswide network can be accessed from student residence rooms and from off campus. Students can access the following: online class registration. Staffed computer lab on campus.
Community Environment: Population 67,700. This is a growing and prosperous residential community in a rural area of central California. Dairying is of major importance; turkeys, melons, grapes and peaches are the chief products. The area is served by bus and railroad. One general hospital, one clinic, many churches, three libraries and most all of the major fraternal and civic organizations are represented in Turlock. Part-time employment opportunities are average. Special events are the Stanislaus County Fair and the Annual Chamber of Commerce Roundup Week in the fall. A summer concert series is held at the university.

■ CALIFORNIA UNIVERSITY OF MANAGEMENT AND SCIENCES

721 N Euclid St.
Anaheim, CA 92801
Tel: (714)533-3946
Web Site: www.calums.edu/
Description: Independent, comprehensive, coed. Founded 1998.

■ CAMBRIDGE JUNIOR COLLEGE

990-A Klamath Ln.
Yuba City, CA 95993
Tel: (530)674-9199
Web Site: cambridge.edu/
Description: Proprietary, 2-year, coed. Awards certificates and terminal associate degrees. Setting: suburban campus with easy access to Sacramento. Total enrollment: 162. 147 applied. Full-time: 162 students, 91% women, 9% men. 0% from out-of-state. 49% 25 or older, 0% transferred in. Retention: 89% of full-time freshmen returned the following year.
Entrance Requirements: Required: high school transcript, interview.
Collegiate Environment: 80 computers available on campus for general student use.

■ CAÑADA COLLEGE

4200 Farm Hill Blvd.
Redwood City, CA 94061-1099
Tel: (650)306-3100
Fax: (650)306-3457
E-mail: miller@smccd.edu
Web Site: www.canadacollege.edu/
Description: State and locally supported, 2-year, coed. Part of San Mateo County Community College District System. Awards certificates, transfer associate, and terminal associate degrees. Founded 1968. Setting: 131-acre suburban campus with easy access to San Francisco, San Jose. Total enrollment: 7,280. Student-undergrad faculty ratio is 27:1. 0% from out-of-state. 55% 25 or older. Core. Calendar: semesters. Academic remediation for entering students, ESL program, services for LD students, advanced placement, accelerated degree program, summer session for credit, part-time degree program, adult/continuing education programs, co-op programs and internships. Study abroad program.
Entrance Requirements: Open admission except for radiologic technology programs. Option: early admission. Entrance: noncompetitive. Application deadline: Rolling.
Collegiate Environment: Drama-theater group, choral group. Student services: health clinic, personal-psychological counseling. Campus security: 12-hour patrols by trained security personnel.

■ CARRINGTON COLLEGE OF CALIFORNIA–ANTIOCH

2157 Country Hills Dr.
Antioch, CA 94509
Tel: (916)388-2800
Web Site: carrington.edu/
Description: Proprietary, 2-year, coed. Part of Carrington Colleges Group, Inc. Awards certificates and terminal associate degrees. Founded 1997. Total enrollment: 318. Faculty: 18 (11 full-time, 7 part-time). Student-undergrad faculty ratio is 24:1. Full-time: 318 students, 81% women, 19% men. 0.3% American Indian or Alaska Native, non-Hispanic/Latino; 30% Hispanic/Latino; 27% African American, non-Hispanic/Latino; 3% Asian, non-Hispanic/Latino; 3% Native Hawaiian or other Pacific Islander, non-Hispanic/Latino; 1% international. 37% 25 or older. Calendar: continuous.
Entrance Requirements: Required: essay, high school transcript, interview, Entrance exam administered by Carrington College California. Required for some: essay. Notification: continuous.
Collegiate Environment: College housing not available.

■ CARRINGTON COLLEGE OF CALIFORNIA–CITRUS HEIGHTS

7301 Greenback Ln.
Ste. A
Citrus Heights, CA 95621
Tel: (916)722-8200
Web Site: carrington.edu/
Description: Proprietary, 2-year, coed. Part of Carrington Colleges Group, Inc. Awards certificates and terminal associate degrees. Total enrollment: 412. Faculty: 16 (10 full-time, 6 part-time). Student-undergrad faculty ratio is 34:1. Full-time: 412 students, 84% women, 16% men. Students come from 4 states and territories, 1% from out-of-state. 2% American Indian or Alaska Native, non-Hispanic/Latino; 12% Hispanic/Latino; 5% African American, non-Hispanic/Latino; 2% Asian, non-Hispanic/Latino; 1% Native Hawaiian or other Pacific Islander, non-Hispanic/Latino; 0% international. 43% 25 or older.
Entrance Requirements: Required: essay, high school transcript, interview, Entrance test administered by Carrington College California.
Collegiate Environment: College housing not available.

■ **CARRINGTON COLLEGE OF CALIFORNIA–EMERYVILLE**
6001 Shellmound St.
Ste. 145
Emeryville, CA 94608
Tel: (510)420-1500
Web Site: carrington.edu/
Description: Proprietary, 2-year, coed. Awards certificates and terminal associate degrees. Founded 2001. Total enrollment: 423. 79 applied, 100% were admitted. 0% from out-of-state. 42% 25 or older. Retention: 57% of full-time freshmen returned the following year. Calendar: semesters.
Entrance Requirements: Required: interview, ACT. Required for some: high school transcript.

■ **CARRINGTON COLLEGE CALIFORNIA–PLEASANT HILL**
380 Civic Dr.
Ste. 300
Pleasant Hill, CA 94523
Tel: (925)609-6650
Web Site: carrington.edu/
Description: Proprietary, 2-year, coed. Part of Carrington Colleges Group, Inc. Awards certificates and terminal associate degrees. Founded 1997. Total enrollment: 346. Faculty: 15 (8 full-time, 7 part-time). Student-undergrad faculty ratio is 33:1. Full-time: 346 students, 75% women, 25% men. 1% American Indian or Alaska Native, non-Hispanic/Latino; 24% Hispanic/Latino; 8% African American, non-Hispanic/Latino; 15% Asian, non-Hispanic/Latino; 3% Native Hawaiian or other Pacific Islander, non-Hispanic/Latino; 0.3% international. 45% 25 or older. Calendar: semesters.
Entrance Requirements: Required: essay, high school transcript, interview.
Collegiate Environment: College housing not available.

■ **CARRINGTON COLLEGE OF CALIFORNIA–SACRAMENTO**
8909 Folsom Blvd.
Sacramento, CA 95826
Tel: (916)361-1660
Web Site: carrington.edu/
Description: Proprietary, 2-year, coed. Part of Carrington Colleges Group, Inc. Awards certificates and terminal associate degrees. Founded 1967. Total enrollment: 1,392. Faculty: 97 (23 full-time, 74 part-time). Student-undergrad faculty ratio is 29:1. Full-time: 1,392 students, 85% women, 15% men. 24% from out-of-state. 1% American Indian or Alaska Native, non-Hispanic/Latino; 20% Hispanic/Latino; 17% African American, non-Hispanic/Latino; 9% Asian, non-Hispanic/Latino; 2% Native Hawaiian or other Pacific Islander, non-Hispanic/Latino; 0.1% international. 55% 25 or older. Calendar: semesters.
Entrance Requirements: Required: essay, high school transcript, interview, Entrance test administered by Carrington College California.

■ **CARRINGTON COLLEGE CALIFORNIA–SAN JOSE**
6201 San Ignacio Ave.
San Jose, CA 95119
Tel: (408)360-0840
Web Site: carrington.edu/
Description: Proprietary, 2-year, coed. Part of Carrington Colleges Group, Inc. Awards certificates and terminal associate degrees. Founded 1999. Total enrollment: 646. Faculty: 56 (17 full-time, 39 part-time). Student-undergrad faculty ratio is 22:1. Full-time: 646 students, 85% women, 15% men. 0.3% American Indian or Alaska Native, non-Hispanic/Latino; 44% Hispanic/Latino; 4% African American, non-Hispanic/Latino; 15% Asian, non-Hispanic/Latino; 3% Native Hawaiian or other Pacific Islander, non-Hispanic/Latino; 0.3% international. 44% 25 or older. Retention: 64% of full-time freshmen returned the following year. Calendar: semesters.
Entrance Requirements: Required: essay, high school transcript, interview, Entrance test administered by Carrington College California.
Collegiate Environment: College housing not available.

■ **CARRINGTON COLLEGE CALIFORNIA–SAN LEANDRO**
15555 E 14th St.
Ste. 500
San Leandro, CA 94578
Tel: (510)276-3888
Web Site: carrington.edu/
Description: Proprietary, 2-year, coed. Part of Carrington Colleges Group, Inc. Awards certificates and terminal associate degrees. Founded 1986. Total enrollment: 471. Faculty: 22 (12 full-time, 10 part-time). Student-

undergrad faculty ratio is 31:1. Full-time: 471 students, 89% women, 11% men. 0.2% American Indian or Alaska Native, non-Hispanic/Latino; 39% Hispanic/Latino; 23% African American, non-Hispanic/Latino; 11% Asian, non-Hispanic/Latino; 3% Native Hawaiian or other Pacific Islander, non-Hispanic/Latino; 0% international. 35% 25 or older. Calendar: semesters.
Entrance Requirements: Required: essay, high school transcript, interview, Entrance test administered by Carrington Colleges California.
Collegiate Environment: College housing not available.

■ **CERRITOS COLLEGE**
11110 Alondra Blvd.
Norwalk, CA 90650-6298
Tel: (562)860-2451
E-mail: smurguia@cerritos.edu
Web Site: www.cerritos.edu/
Description: State and locally supported, 2-year, coed. Part of California Community College System. Awards transfer associate and terminal associate degrees. Founded 1956. Setting: 140-acre suburban campus with easy access to Los Angeles. Total enrollment: 19,780. Faculty: 690 (250 full-time, 440 part-time). Full-time: 5,107 students, 55% women, 45% men. Part-time: 14,673 students, 57% women, 43% men. Students come from 32 other countries, 1% from out-of-state. 46% 25 or older, 3% transferred in. Retention: 61% of full-time freshmen returned the following year. Core. Calendar: semesters. Academic remediation for entering students, ESL program, services for LD students, advanced placement, summer session for credit, part-time degree program, adult/continuing education programs. Study abroad program.
Entrance Requirements: Open admission. Options: early admission, deferred admission. Entrance: noncompetitive. Application deadline: Rolling.
Collegiate Environment: Drama-theater group, student-run newspaper, radio station. Social organizations: local fraternities, local sororities. Student services: legal services, health clinic, personal-psychological counseling, women's center. Wilford Michael Library with 74,502 books and 396 serials. 400 computers available on campus for general student use. A campuswide network can be accessed from off-campus.
Community Environment: Norwalk is an urban area 17 miles from Los Angeles. The climate is subtropical. There is bus and rail service to Los Angeles, where other major transportation facilities are located. The city has many community facilities, industrial firms and retail outlets. Part-time work is available.

■ **CERRO COSO COMMUNITY COLLEGE**
3000 College Heights Blvd.
Ridgecrest, CA 93555-9571
Tel: (760)384-6100
Fax: (760)375-4776
E-mail: hostash@cerrocoso.edu
Web Site: www.cerrocoso.edu/
Description: State-supported, 2-year, coed. Part of Kern Community College District System. Awards certificates, transfer associate, and terminal associate degrees. Founded 1973. Setting: 320-acre small town campus. Total enrollment: 4,577. 61% 25 or older. Core. Calendar: semesters. Academic remediation for entering students, ESL program, services for LD students, honors program, distance learning, summer session for credit, part-time degree program, adult/continuing education programs, co-op programs.
Entrance Requirements: Open admission except for nursing program. Option: early admission. Recommended: high school transcript. Entrance: noncompetitive. Application deadline: Rolling.
Collegiate Environment: Orientation program. Student services: personal-psychological counseling. Campus security: patrols by trained security personnel. Walter Stiern Memorial Library with 25,000 books, 800 serials, an OPAC, and a Web page.

■ **CHABOT COLLEGE**
25555 Hesperian Blvd.
Hayward, CA 94545-5001
Tel: (510)723-6600
Web Site: www.chabotcollege.edu/
Description: State-supported, 2-year, coed. Part of California Community College System. Awards certificates, transfer associate, and terminal associate degrees. Founded 1961. Setting: 245-acre suburban campus with easy access to San Francisco. Total enrollment: 13,229. 43% 25 or older. Core. Calendar: semesters. Academic remediation for entering students, ESL program, services for LD students, advanced placement, self-designed

majors, distance learning, double major, summer session for credit, part-time degree program, adult/continuing education programs, internships. Off campus study at Mills College; California State University, Hayward. Study abroad program. ROTC: Army (c), Air Force (c).

Entrance Requirements: Open admission except for dental hygiene, nursing, emergency medical technician programs. Option: electronic application. Required: high school transcript. Entrance: noncompetitive. Notification: continuous. Preference given to state residents.

Collegiate Environment: Orientation program. Drama-theater group, choral group, student-run newspaper, radio station. Student services: legal services, personal-psychological counseling. Campus security: 24-hour emergency response devices, late night transport-escort service. Chabot Library with 100,000 books and 160 serials.

Community Environment: See California State University - Hayward.

■ **CHAFFEY COLLEGE**
5885 Haven Ave.
Rancho Cucamonga, CA 91737-3002
Tel: (909)652-6000
E-mail: erlinda.martinez@chaffey.edu
Web Site: www.chaffey.edu/
Description: District-supported, 2-year, coed. Part of California Community College System. Awards certificates, transfer associate, and terminal associate degrees. Founded 1883. Setting: 200-acre suburban campus with easy access to Los Angeles. Total enrollment: 21,399. Student-undergrad faculty ratio is 24:1. 0% from out-of-state. 34% 25 or older. Core. Calendar: semesters. Academic remediation for entering students, ESL program, services for LD students, advanced placement, honors program, summer session for credit, part-time degree program, adult/continuing education programs, co-op programs and internships. Study abroad program. ROTC: Army (c).

Entrance Requirements: Open admission. Option: early admission. Entrance: noncompetitive. Application deadline: Rolling. Notification: continuous.

Collegiate Environment: Drama-theater group, choral group, student-run newspaper, radio station. Student services: health clinic, personal-psychological counseling. Campus security: 24-hour emergency response devices, late night transport-escort service.

Community Environment: Rancho Cucamonga is a suburban community 44 miles east of Los Angeles. With the west end of San Bernardino County the area has a population of 1,999,300. It has dry climate conditions, with temperatures ranging from 25 to 112 degrees during the year. Farming, namely citrus and grapes, is the main economy. Rail, bus, and air (Ontario International Airport) serve the area. There are four hospitals nearby.

■ **CHAPMAN UNIVERSITY**
One University Dr.
Orange, CA 92866
Tel: (714)997-6815; Free: 888-CUAPPLY
Fax: (714)997-6713
E-mail: admit@chapman.edu
Web Site: www.chapman.edu/
Description: Independent, comprehensive, coed, affiliated with Christian Church (Disciples of Christ). Administratively affiliated with Brandman University. Awards bachelor's, master's, and doctoral degrees. Founded 1861. Setting: 78-acre suburban campus with easy access to Los Angeles. Endowment: $188.1 million. Total enrollment: 7,566. Faculty: 781 (367 full-time, 414 part-time). Student-undergrad faculty ratio is 14:1. 10,489 applied, 44% were admitted. 53% from top 10% of their high school class, 90% from top quarter, 98% from top half. Full-time: 5,446 students, 58% women, 42% men. Part-time: 231 students, 50% women, 50% men. Students come from 51 states and territories, 60 other countries, 27% from out-of-state. 0.3% American Indian or Alaska Native, non-Hispanic/Latino; 13% Hispanic/Latino; 2% African American, non-Hispanic/Latino; 9% Asian, non-Hispanic/Latino; 0.3% Native Hawaiian or other Pacific Islander, non-Hispanic/Latino; 4% international. 3% 25 or older, 34% live on campus, 7% transferred in. Retention: 91% of full-time freshmen returned the following year. Academic areas with the most degrees conferred: visual and performing arts; business/marketing; communication/journalism. Core. Calendar: 4-1-4. Academic remediation for entering students, services for LD students, advanced placement, self-designed majors, honors program, independent study, distance learning, double major, summer session for credit, part-time degree program, adult/continuing education programs, internships, graduate courses open to undergrads. Off campus study. Study abroad program. ROTC: Army (c), Air Force (c).

Entrance Requirements: Options: electronic application, early action, international baccalaureate accepted. Required: essay, high school transcript, 1 recommendation, SAT or ACT. Recommended: SAT Subject Tests. Required for some: Audition required for music, dance, and theatre majors. Portfolio required for art and film majors. Supplemental application required for all talent-based majors. Entrance: very difficult. Application deadlines: 1/15, 11/1 for early action. Notification: 3/15, 1/10 for early action. SAT Reasoning Test deadline: 1/31. SAT Subject Test deadline: 6/1. Transfer credits accepted: Yes. Applicants placed on waiting list: 1,200. Wait-listed applicants offered admission: 45. Early action applicants: 4,188. Early action applicants admitted: 2,244.

Costs Per Year: Application fee: $65. Comprehensive fee: $55,777 includes full-time tuition ($42,890), mandatory fees ($683), and college room and board ($12,204). College room only: $8238. Room and board charges vary according to board plan and housing facility. Part-time tuition: $1330 per credit.

Collegiate Environment: Orientation program. Drama-theater group, choral group, student-run newspaper, radio station. Social organizations: 145 open to all; national fraternities, national sororities; 26% of eligible men and 30% of eligible women are members. Most popular organizations: Gamma Beta Phi, Alpha Kappa Psi Professional Business Fraternity, Public Relations Student Society of America, Black Student Union, Disciples on Campus. Major annual events: Homecoming, Spring Sizzle, Midnight Breakfast. Student services: health clinic, personal-psychological counseling. Campus security: 24-hour emergency response devices and patrols, late night transport-escort service, controlled dormitory access, full safety education program. 1,955 undergraduates lived in college housing during 2012-13. Freshmen guaranteed college housing. Option: coed housing available. Leatherby Libraries plus 1 other with 291,400 books, 688,857 microform titles, 60,220 serials, 21,805 audiovisual materials, an OPAC, and a Web page.

Community Environment: Orange is located 32 miles southeast of Los Angeles and 94 miles north of San Diego. Its climate is mild with a very low rainfall. It is accessible by car, bus or train and plane. Orange County Airport is a short distance away, and Los Angeles International Airport is a 45-minute drive away. As the name implies, Orange lies in a vast citrus belt; avocados are also grown here. All the necessary facilities of a city are available as well as many recreational facilities for swimming, golf, surfing, skiing, fishing, hunting, and boating. Beaches and mountain resorts are nearby.

■ **CHARLES DREW UNIVERSITY OF MEDICINE AND SCIENCE**
1731 E 120th St.
Los Angeles, CA 90059
Tel: (323)563-4800
E-mail: yvettelane@cdrewu.edu
Web Site: www.cdrewu.edu/
Description: Independent, comprehensive, coed. Awards associate, bachelor's, master's, and doctoral degrees. Founded 1966. Setting: urban campus with easy access to Los Angeles. Total enrollment: 261. Faculty: 25 (22 full-time, 3 part-time). Student-undergrad faculty ratio is 9:1. 872 applied, 21% were admitted. Full-time: 126 students, 62% women, 38% men. Part-time: 104 students, 62% women, 38% men. Academic area with the most degrees conferred: health professions and related sciences. Calendar: semesters. Academic remediation for entering students, services for LD students, independent study, part-time degree program, internships.

Entrance Requirements: Required: essay, high school transcript, minimum 2 high school GPA, 3 recommendations, interview. Recommended: SAT or ACT. Required for some: pre-admission assessment exams. Entrance: moderately difficult. Application deadline: 4/30. Notification: continuous.

Collegiate Environment: Student services: personal-psychological counseling. Health Sciences Library with 84,336 books, 36,693 serials, 2,117 audiovisual materials, an OPAC, and a Web page. 79 computers available on campus for general student use. A campuswide network can be accessed from off-campus. Students can access the following: online class registration. Staffed computer lab on campus provides training in use of computers, software, and the Internet.

■ **CITRUS COLLEGE**
1000 W Foothill Blvd.
Glendora, CA 91741-1899
Tel: (626)963-0323
E-mail: admissions@citruscollege.edu
Web Site: www.citruscollege.edu/
Description: State and locally supported, 2-year, coed. Part of California

Community College System. Awards certificates, diplomas, transfer associ- ate, and terminal associate degrees. Founded 1915. Setting: 104-acre small town campus with easy access to Los Angeles. Total enrollment: 11,576. Faculty: 447 (171 full-time, 276 part-time). Student-undergrad faculty ratio is 26:1. Full-time: 4,957 students, 53% women, 47% men. Part-time: 6,619 students, 60% women, 40% men. 17% from out-of-state. 25% 25 or older. Core. Calendar: semesters. Academic remediation for entering students, ESL program, services for LD students, advanced placement, honors program, distance learning, summer session for credit, part-time degree program, co-op programs. Study abroad program.
Entrance Requirements: Open admission. Required: high school transcript. Entrance: noncompetitive.
Collegiate Environment: Orientation program. Drama-theater group, choral group, student-run newspaper. Social organizations: 40 open to all. Most popular organizations: student government, AGS Honor Society, Interna- tional Student Association, Cosmetology Club. Major annual events: Fall Fest, Spring Fest, Club Rush. Student services: legal services, health clinic, personal-psychological counseling. Campus security: 24-hour patrols, student patrols, late night transport-escort service. Hayden Library with 45,091 books, 133 serials, an OPAC, and a Web page. 1,100 computers available on campus for general student use. A campuswide network can be accessed. Students can access the following: online class registration. Staffed computer lab on campus.
Community Environment: See Azusa Pacific University.

■ **CITY COLLEGE OF SAN FRANCISCO**
50 Phelan Ave.
San Francisco, CA 94112-1821
Tel: (415)239-3000
Fax: (415)239-3936
E-mail: mleyba@ccsf.edu
Web Site: www.ccsf.edu/
Description: State and locally supported, 2-year, coed. Part of California Community College System. Awards certificates, diplomas, transfer associ- ate, and terminal associate degrees. Founded 1935. Setting: 56-acre urban campus. Total enrollment: 32,950. Student-undergrad faculty ratio is 23:1. 0% from out-of-state. 53% 25 or older. Core. Calendar: semesters. Academic remediation for entering students, ESL program, services for LD students, advanced placement, summer session for credit, part-time degree program, adult/continuing education programs, internships. Off campus study at members of The San Francisco Consortium. Study abroad program.
Entrance Requirements: Open admission. Option: early admission. Entrance: noncompetitive. Application deadlines: 8/9, 8/9 for nonresidents. Notification: continuous, continuous for nonresidents.
Collegiate Environment: Orientation program. Drama-theater group, student-run newspaper. Student services: health clinic, personal- psychological counseling, women's center. Campus security: 24-hour emergency response devices and patrols, late night transport-escort service. Louise and Claude Rosenberg, Jr. Library plus 2 others with a Web page.
Community Environment: See San Francisco State University.

■ **CLAREMONT MCKENNA COLLEGE**
500 E 9th St.
Claremont, CA 91711
Tel: (909)621-8000
E-mail: jennifer.sandoval@cmc.edu
Web Site: www.claremontmckenna.edu/
Description: Independent, comprehensive, coed. Awards bachelor's and master's degrees. Founded 1946. Setting: 69-acre suburban campus with easy access to Los Angeles. Endowment: $520.6 million. Research spend- ing for the previous fiscal year: $6.6 million. Educational spending for the previous fiscal year: $24,610 per student. Total enrollment: 1,295. Faculty: 162 (138 full-time, 24 part-time). Student-undergrad faculty ratio is 8:1. 5,058 applied, 14% were admitted. 63% from top 10% of their high school class, 93% from top quarter, 100% from top half. Full-time: 1,260 students, 48% women, 52% men. Part-time: 4 students, 75% women, 25% men. Students come from 45 states and territories, 32 other countries, 56% from out-of- state. 0.1% American Indian or Alaska Native, non-Hispanic/Latino; 9% Hispanic/Latino; 3% African American, non-Hispanic/Latino; 11% Asian, non- Hispanic/Latino; 0.2% Native Hawaiian or other Pacific Islander, non- Hispanic/Latino; 12% international. 0% 25 or older, 94% live on campus, 3% transferred in. Retention: 95% of full-time freshmen returned the following year. Academic areas with the most degrees conferred: social sciences; psychology; biological/life sciences. Core. Calendar: semesters. Services for

LD students, advanced placement, self-designed majors, independent study, double major, summer session for credit, internships, graduate courses open to undergrads. Off campus study at 5 members of The Claremont Colleges; Haverford College; Spelman College; Woods Hole, MA and Shipboard. Study abroad program. ROTC: Army, Air Force (c).
Entrance Requirements: Options: electronic application, early decision, deferred admission, international baccalaureate accepted. Required: essay, high school transcript, 3 recommendations, SAT or ACT. Recommended: interview. Required for some: SAT Subject Tests. Entrance: most difficult. Application deadlines: 1/2, 11/1 for early decision plan 1, 1/2 for early deci- sion plan 2. Notification: 4/1, 12/15 for early decision plan 1, 2/15 for early decision plan 2. Transfer credits accepted: Yes. Applicants placed on waiting list: 549. Wait-listed applicants offered admission: 54. Early decision ap- plicants: 535. Early decision applicants admitted: 152.
Costs Per Year: Application fee: $60. Comprehensive fee: $58,065 includes full-time tuition ($43,840), mandatory fees ($245), and college room and board ($13,980). College room only: $7380. Full-time tuition and fees vary according to course load. Room and board charges vary according to board plan and housing facility. Part-time tuition: $7,306.67 per course. Part-time tuition varies according to course load.
Collegiate Environment: Orientation program. Drama-theater group, choral group, student-run newspaper, radio station. Social organizations: 110 open to all. Most popular organizations: The Forum - student newspaper, ASCMC - student government, Debate/Forensics Club, SOURCE, Rotaract. Major annual events: Athenaeum Lectures, International Festival, Monte Carlo Night/Homecoming. Student services: health clinic, personal-psychological counseling. Campus security: 24-hour emergency response devices and patrols, student patrols, late night transport-escort service, controlled dormi- tory access. 1,129 college housing spaces available; 1,086 were occupied in 2012-13. Freshmen guaranteed college housing. On-campus residence required in freshman year. Option: coed housing available. Honnold Library plus 2 others with 1.4 million books, 980,340 microform titles, 22,978 serials, 10,287 audiovisual materials, an OPAC, and a Web page. Operations spending for the previous fiscal year: $1.7 million. 289 computers available on campus for general student use. Computer purchase/lease plans avail- able. A campuswide network can be accessed from student residence rooms and from off campus. Students can access the following: online class registration. Staffed computer lab on campus (open 24 hours a day) provides training in use of computers, software, and the Internet.

■ **COASTLINE COMMUNITY COLLEGE**
11460 Warner Ave.
Fountain Valley, CA 92708-2597
Tel: (714)546-7600
Fax: (714)241-6288
Web Site: www.coastline.edu/
Description: State and locally supported, 2-year, coed. Part of Coast Com- munity College District System. Awards certificates and transfer associate degrees. Founded 1976. Setting: urban campus with easy access to Los Angeles. Total enrollment: 9,316. 72% 25 or older. Core. Calendar: semesters. Academic remediation for entering students, ESL program, services for LD students, advanced placement, distance learning, summer session for credit, part-time degree program, external degree program, adult/ continuing education programs, co-op programs and internships.
Entrance Requirements: Open admission. Option: early admission. Recommended: high school transcript. Entrance: noncompetitive. Applica- tion deadline: Rolling.
Collegiate Environment: Student services: health clinic. Campus security: 24-hour emergency response devices.

■ **COGSWELL POLYTECHNICAL COLLEGE**
1175 Bordeaux Dr.
Sunnyvale, CA 94089-1299
Tel: (408)541-0100; Free: 800-264-7955
Fax: (408)747-0764
E-mail: achacko@cogswell.edu
Web Site: www.cogswell.edu/
Description: Independent, comprehensive, coed. Awards bachelor's and master's degrees. Founded 1887. Setting: 2-acre suburban campus with easy access to San Francisco, San Jose. Total enrollment: 11. Faculty: 72 (16 full-time, 56 part-time). Student-undergrad faculty ratio is 9:1. 162 ap- plied, 49% were admitted. Full-time: 252 students, 25% women, 75% men. Part-time: 140 students, 14% women, 86% men. Students come from 13 states and territories, 3 other countries, 13% from out-of-state. 1% American

Indian or Alaska Native, non-Hispanic/Latino; 13% Hispanic/Latino; 5% African American, non-Hispanic/Latino; 8% Asian, non-Hispanic/Latino; 3% Native Hawaiian or other Pacific Islander, non-Hispanic/Latino; 3% international. 9% 25 or older, 29% live on campus, 19% transferred in. Retention: 68% of full-time freshmen returned the following year. Academic areas with the most degrees conferred: visual and performing arts; homeland security, law enforcement, firefighting, and protective services; engineering. Core. Calendar: semesters. Advanced placement, self-designed majors, distance learning, double major, summer session for credit, part-time degree program, internships.

Entrance Requirements: Options: electronic application, deferred admission. Required: essay, high school transcript, minimum 2 high school GPA. Recommended: minimum 2.7 high school GPA, interview, SAT or ACT. Required for some: portfolio for Digital Art and Animation and Digital Audio Technology majors. Entrance: moderately difficult. Application deadlines: Rolling, Rolling for nonresidents. Notification: continuous, continuous for nonresidents. Transfer credits accepted: Yes.

Costs Per Year: Application fee: $0. Tuition: $19,488 full-time, $812 per credit hour part-time. Mandatory fees: $180 full-time. Full-time tuition and fees vary according to course load and degree level. Part-time tuition varies according to course load and degree level. College room only: $6000. Room charges vary according to housing facility.

Collegiate Environment: Orientation program. Choral group. Most popular organizations: ASB, Game Development club, Audio Production and Engineering club, Comic Club, Women's club. Major annual events: Founders' Day, Fusion Awards, game nights, clubs competitions, Friday night concerts. Student services: personal-psychological counseling. Campus security: 24-hour emergency response devices. 113 college housing spaces available; all were occupied in 2012-13. Freshmen guaranteed college housing. Option: coed housing available. 224 computers available on campus for general student use. A campuswide network can be accessed from off-campus. Students can access the following: online class registration. Staffed computer lab on campus provides training in use of computers, software, and the Internet.

■ **THE COLBURN SCHOOL CONSERVATORY OF MUSIC**
200 S Grand Ave.
Los Angeles, CA 90012
Tel: (213)621-2200
Fax: (213)621-2110
E-mail: admissions@colburnschool.edu
Web Site: www.colburnschool.edu/
Description: Independent, 4-year, coed. Awards bachelor's degrees. Founded 1980. Setting: urban campus with easy access to Los Angeles. Total enrollment: 67. Faculty: 29 (8 full-time, 21 part-time). Student-undergrad faculty ratio is 4:1. 227 applied, 11% were admitted. Full-time: 67 students, 55% women, 45% men. Students come from 18 states and territories, 10 other countries. 0% 25 or older, 100% live on campus, 4% transferred in. Retention: 95% of full-time freshmen returned the following year. Academic area with the most degrees conferred: visual and performing arts. Core. Calendar: semesters. ESL program.

Entrance Requirements: Options: electronic application, deferred admission, international baccalaureate accepted. Required: essay, high school transcript, 2 recommendations, interview, pre-screening DVD, in-person audition by invitation. Recommended: SAT or ACT. Entrance: most difficult. Application deadline: 1/15. Notification: 4/1. Transfer credits accepted: Yes.

Collegiate Environment: Orientation program. Student services: personal-psychological counseling. Campus security: 24-hour emergency response devices and patrols, controlled dormitory access. Colburn School Library with 20,171 books, 40 serials, 6,903 audiovisual materials, and an OPAC. 12 computers available on campus for general student use. A campuswide network can be accessed from student residence rooms.

■ **COLEMAN UNIVERSITY (SAN DIEGO)**
8888 Balboa Ave.
San Diego, CA 92123
Tel: (858)499-0202; Free: 800-430-2030
Fax: (858)499-0233
E-mail: jschafer@cts.com
Web Site: www.coleman.edu/
Description: Independent, comprehensive, coed. Awards associate, bachelor's, and master's degrees. Founded 1963. Setting: 3-acre suburban campus. Total enrollment: 488. 12 applied, 100% were admitted. 64% 25 or

older. Core. Services for LD students, accelerated degree program, distance learning, summer session for credit, part-time degree program.

Entrance Requirements: Option: deferred admission. Required: high school transcript, interview. Entrance: moderately difficult. Application deadline: 8/1. Notification: continuous.

Collegiate Environment: Student services: personal-psychological counseling. Campus security: 24-hour emergency response devices and patrols, late night transport-escort service. Coleman College LaMesa Library with 66,800 books and 69 serials.

■ **COLEMAN UNIVERSITY (SAN MARCOS)**
1284 W San Marcos Blvd.
San Marcos, CA 92078
Tel: (760)747-3990
Fax: (760)752-9808
Web Site: www.coleman.edu/
Description: Independent, primarily 2-year, coed. Awards certificates, terminal associate, and bachelor's degrees. Founded 1967. Setting: suburban campus.

■ **COLLEGE OF ALAMEDA**
555 Ralph Appezzato Memorial Pky.
Alameda, CA 94501-2109
Tel: (510)522-7221
E-mail: kcompton@peralta.edu
Web Site: alameda.peralta.edu/
Description: State and locally supported, 2-year, coed. Part of Peralta Community College District System. Awards certificates, transfer associate, and terminal associate degrees. Founded 1970. Setting: 62-acre urban campus with easy access to San Francisco. Total enrollment: 7,302. Student-undergrad faculty ratio is 32:1. 0% from out-of-state. 44% 25 or older. Calendar: semesters. Academic remediation for entering students, services for LD students, summer session for credit, part-time degree program, adult/continuing education programs, co-op programs. Off campus study at other units of the Peralta Community College District System.

Entrance Requirements: Open admission. Entrance: noncompetitive. Application deadline: Rolling.

Collegiate Environment: Student-run newspaper. Student services: women's center.

Community Environment: See Laney College.

■ **COLLEGE OF THE CANYONS**
26455 Rockwell Canyon Rd.
Santa Clarita, CA 91355
Tel: (661)259-7800
Fax: (661)362-5300
E-mail: jasmine.ruys@canyons.edu
Web Site: www.canyons.edu/
Description: State and locally supported, 2-year, coed. Part of California Community College System. Awards certificates, transfer associate, and terminal associate degrees. Founded 1969. Setting: 224-acre suburban campus with easy access to Los Angeles. Total enrollment: 16,844. Faculty: 703 (177 full-time, 526 part-time). Student-undergrad faculty ratio is 35:1. Full-time: 5,285 students, 50% women, 50% men. Part-time: 11,559 students, 47% women, 53% men. 4% from out-of-state. 0.3% American Indian or Alaska Native, non-Hispanic/Latino; 40% Hispanic/Latino; 5% African American, non-Hispanic/Latino; 9% Asian, non-Hispanic/Latino; 0.2% Native Hawaiian or other Pacific Islander, non-Hispanic/Latino. Core. Calendar: semesters. Academic remediation for entering students, ESL program, services for LD students, advanced placement, accelerated degree program, honors program, distance learning, double major, summer session for credit, part-time degree program, adult/continuing education programs, co-op programs and internships.

Entrance Requirements: Open admission. Options: electronic application, early admission. Recommended: high school transcript. Entrance: noncompetitive. Application deadline: Rolling. Notification: continuous. Transfer credits accepted: Yes.

Costs Per Year: Application fee: $0. State resident tuition: $1152 full-time, $46 per unit part-time. Nonresident tuition: $5450 full-time, $225 per unit part-time. Mandatory fees: $50 full-time.

Collegiate Environment: Orientation program. Drama-theater group, choral group. Social organizations: 47 open to all. Most popular organizations: Gamma Beta Phi, Phi Theta Kappa, Welding Club, Communication Studies Club, Ice Hockey Club, Psychology Club. Major annual events: Job Fair,

MajorQuest, Welcome Week. Student services: health clinic, personal-psychological counseling, women's center. Campus security: 24-hour emergency response devices, late night transport-escort service. College housing not available. College of the Canyons Library with an OPAC and a Web page. Operations spending for the previous fiscal year: $851,003. 1,838 computers available on campus for general student use. A campus-wide network can be accessed. Students can access the following: online class registration. Staffed computer lab on campus provides training in use of computers, software, and the Internet.

Community Environment: The Valencia-Newhall-Saugus-Canyon Country communities comprise the city of Santa Clarita located 32 miles northwest of Los Angeles near the San Fernando Valley. The average mean temperature is 65 degrees. Community facilities include hospitals, churches, a library, newspapers and banks. Recreational facilities include theaters, parks, a riding stable and golf courses. Desert area and many secluded canyons are nearby. The Castaic Reservoir water recreation area opened in 1970.

■ **COLLEGE OF THE DESERT**
43-500 Monterey Ave.
Palm Desert, CA 92260-9305
Tel: (760)346-8041
E-mail: srodriguez@collegeofthedesert.edu
Web Site: www.collegeofthedesert.edu/

Description: State and locally supported, 2-year, coed. Part of California Community College System. Awards certificates, diplomas, transfer associate, and terminal associate degrees. Founded 1959. Setting: 160-acre small town campus. Total enrollment: 10,099. Faculty: 403 (104 full-time, 299 part-time). Student-undergrad faculty ratio is 30:1. 0% from out-of-state. 0.4% American Indian or Alaska Native, non-Hispanic/Latino; 65% Hispanic/Latino; 4% African American, non-Hispanic/Latino; 4% Asian, non-Hispanic/Latino; 1% Native Hawaiian or other Pacific Islander, non-Hispanic/Latino. 37% 25 or older. Core. Calendar: semesters. Academic remediation for entering students, ESL program, services for LD students, freshman honors college, honors program, distance learning, summer session for credit, part-time degree program, adult/continuing education programs.

Entrance Requirements: Open admission except for international applicants or nursing program. Options: electronic application, early admission. Entrance: noncompetitive. Application deadline: Rolling. Notification: continuous. Preference given to district residents.

Costs Per Year: Application fee: $0. State resident tuition: $1288 full-time, $46 per unit part-time. Nonresident tuition: $6496 full-time, $232 per unit part-time. Mandatory fees: $37 full-time, $.25 per unit part-time, $15 per term part-time. Full-time tuition and fees vary according to course load and program. Part-time tuition and fees vary according to course load and program.

Collegiate Environment: Drama-theater group, choral group, student-run newspaper, radio station. Social organizations: 30 open to all; Phi Theta Kappa. Most popular organizations: Student Nursing Association, Phi Theta Kappa, Dramatic Arts Company, International Club, World Beat. Major annual events: International Day, Homecoming Activities. Student services: health clinic, personal-psychological counseling. Campus security: 24-hour emergency response devices and patrols, late night transport-escort service. College housing not available. College of the Desert Library plus 1 other with an OPAC and a Web page. 100 computers available on campus for general student use. A campuswide network can be accessed from off-campus. Students can access the following: online class registration, Online Catalogs; free Wi-Fi campus wide. Staffed computer lab on campus.

Community Environment: Palm Desert is a resort area with a population of 47,000, where the climate is temperate. Buses and planes serve the area; Highway 111 goes through town. There are churches of major denominations, civic and service groups, and hospitals are nearby. Indio and Palm Springs have such recreational activities as boating, fishing, water skiing, and hiking. There are nearby mountains for winter sports. The area is a major center for golf and tennis tournaments.

■ **COLLEGE OF MARIN**
835 College Ave.
Kentfield, CA 94904
Tel: (415)457-8811
Fax: (415)883-2632
E-mail: patricia.gant@marin.edu
Web Site: www.marin.edu/

Description: State and locally supported, 2-year, coed. Part of California Community College System. Awards certificates, transfer associate, and

terminal associate degrees. Founded 1926. Setting: 410-acre suburban campus with easy access to San Francisco. Total enrollment: 7,000. Faculty: 330. Core. Calendar: semesters. Academic remediation for entering students, ESL program, services for LD students, advanced placement, distance learning, summer session for credit, part-time degree program, co-op programs.

Entrance Requirements: Open admission. Options: electronic application, early admission. Entrance: noncompetitive. Application deadline: Rolling. Transfer credits accepted: Yes.

Costs Per Year: State resident tuition: $0 full-time. Nonresident tuition: $7568 full-time, $251 per unit part-time. Mandatory fees: $1418 full-time, $46 per unit part-time. Full-time tuition and fees vary according to course load. Part-time tuition and fees vary according to course load.

Collegiate Environment: Drama-theater group, student-run newspaper. Student services: health clinic, personal-psychological counseling. Campus security: 24-hour emergency response devices and patrols. College housing not available.

Community Environment: Kentfield is suburban community in a beautiful countryside across the Golden Gate from San Francisco. Located on a peninsula with the Pacific Ocean on one side and San Francisco Bay on the other. A mild climate averaging 70 degrees; average rainfall 36 inches per year. The Golden Gate bus line serves the area. Entertainment and recreational facilities are close by and shopping facilities are good. Good opportunities for part-time employment.

■ **COLLEGE OF THE REDWOODS**
7351 Tompkins Hill Rd.
Eureka, CA 95501-9300
Tel: (707)476-4100; Free: 800-641-0400
Web Site: www.redwoods.edu/

Description: State and locally supported, 2-year, coed. Part of California Community College System. Awards certificates, transfer associate, and terminal associate degrees. Founded 1964. Setting: 322-acre small town campus. Total enrollment: 7,634. Student-undergrad faculty ratio is 23:1. 0% from out-of-state. 47% 25 or older. Core. Calendar: semesters. Academic remediation for entering students, ESL program, services for LD students, advanced placement, honors program, distance learning, summer session for credit, part-time degree program, adult/continuing education programs, co-op programs. Off campus study at Oregon Institute of Technology, Rogue Community College, Southern Oregon University.

Entrance Requirements: Open admission except for nursing program or international students. Option: early admission. Entrance: noncompetitive. Application deadline: Rolling.

Collegiate Environment: Student services: health clinic, personal-psychological counseling. Campus security: 24-hour emergency response devices and patrols, late night transport-escort service. College of the Redwoods Library with an OPAC and a Web page.

Community Environment: Eureka is located on the north coast of Humboldt Bay, 283 miles north of San Francisco; the climate is cool and humid. Buses and railroads serve the area, airlines to connecting flights in San Francisco, Oakland, Sacramento and Portland are available. Community facilities include two hospitals, a medical center, churches, libraries, and a good downtown shopping area. The city provides a park, a community recreation building and an 18 hole golf course. Fishing and hunting are excellent; mountain area very near. In Summer, salmon fishing is good in Humboldt and Trinidad Bay north of the city; in early fall, steelhead and salmon are caught in the Eel Mud, and Trinity Rivers nearby. Eureka sponsors an annual Rhododendron Festival and two fairs each year.

■ **COLLEGE OF SAN MATEO**
1700 W Hillsdale Blvd.
San Mateo, CA 94402-3784
Tel: (650)574-6161
E-mail: csmadmission@smccd.edu
Web Site: www.collegeofsanmateo.edu/

Description: State and locally supported, 2-year, coed. Part of California Community College System. Awards certificates, transfer associate, and terminal associate degrees. Founded 1922. Setting: 150-acre suburban campus. Total enrollment: 11,310. Student-undergrad faculty ratio is 26:1. 0% from out-of-state. 45% 25 or older. Core. Calendar: semesters. Academic remediation for entering students, ESL program, services for LD students, advanced placement, accelerated degree program, honors program, summer session for credit, part-time degree program, adult/

continuing education programs, co-op programs and internships. Study abroad program. ROTC: Army (c), Naval (c), Air Force (c).

Entrance Requirements: Open admission except for nursing program. Option: early admission. Entrance: noncompetitive. Application deadline: Rolling.

Collegiate Environment: Orientation program. Student-run newspaper. Student services: health clinic, personal-psychological counseling. Campus security: 24-hour emergency response devices and patrols. College of San Mateo Library with an OPAC and a Web page.

Community Environment: San Mateo, located on picturesque El Camino Real, is an attractive residential suburb, 19 miles south of San Francisco. Climate is moderate and the city claims to have an average of 258 days of sunshine each year. San Mateo has access to all major forms of transportation and has a municipal transit system. There are many churches, hospitals, and libraries. An outstanding retail shopping center is found on the Peninsula. Recreational facilities include golf courses, yacht harbor, public beach, public parks and the Bay Meadows Race Track.

■ **COLLEGE OF THE SEQUOIAS**
915 S Mooney Blvd.
Visalia, CA 93277-2234
Tel: (559)730-3700
Web Site: www.cos.edu/

Description: State and locally supported, 2-year, coed. Part of California Community College System. Awards certificates, transfer associate, and terminal associate degrees. Founded 1925. Setting: 215-acre small town campus with easy access to Fresno. Endowment: $3 million. Educational spending for the previous fiscal year: $2900 per student. Total enrollment: 13,449. Faculty: 510 (185 full-time, 325 part-time). Student-undergrad faculty ratio is 27:1. Full-time: 5,147 students, 54% women, 46% men. Part-time: 8,302 students, 57% women, 43% men. Students come from 15 states and territories, 6 other countries, 0.1% from out-of-state. 41% 25 or older, 53% transferred in. Core. Calendar: semesters. Academic remediation for entering students, ESL program, services for LD students, advanced placement, accelerated degree program, freshman honors college, honors program, distance learning, double major, summer session for credit, part-time degree program, adult/continuing education programs, co-op programs and internships. Off campus study. Study abroad program. ROTC: Air Force (c).

Entrance Requirements: Open admission except for nursing, engineering, chemistry, math, English programs. Required: high school transcript. Entrance: noncompetitive. Application deadline: 8/15. Notification: continuous.

Collegiate Environment: Orientation program. Drama-theater group, choral group, student-run newspaper. Social organizations: 35 open to all. Most popular organizations: MECHA, Ag Club, Alpha Gamma Sigma, Paralegal Association, Sports Medicine Club. Major annual events: Homecoming, Multicultural Fair, Tech Prep Expo. Student services: health clinic, personal-psychological counseling, women's center. Campus security: 24-hour emergency response devices and patrols, student patrols, late night transport-escort service, 18 hour patrols by trained security personnel. College of the Sequoias Library with 73,557 books, 430 serials, an OPAC, and a Web page. Operations spending for the previous fiscal year: $620,000. 250 computers available on campus for general student use. A campuswide network can be accessed from off-campus. Students can access the following: online class registration. Staffed computer lab on campus provides training in use of computers, software, and the Internet.

Community Environment: Visalia is 42 miles southeast of Fresno. It is the Tulare County seat and is situated in the fertile San Joaquin Valley. It ranks highest in the world in agricultural production of citrus fruits, dairy products, olives, cotton, and walnuts. A number of manufacturers and industrial plants are located here. Bus, rail, and air lines serve the area. The community has churches, hospitals, a symphony orchestra, ballet, theatres, 20 city parks, and 5 golf courses. Tulare County Park provides recreational facilities for picnicking and water sports. Nearby is the High Sierra mountain wonderland in the Sierra National Forest.

■ **COLLEGE OF THE SISKIYOUS**
800 College Ave.
Weed, CA 96094-2899
Tel: (530)938-5555; Free: 888-397-4339
Fax: (530)938-5227
E-mail: admissions-weed@siskyous.edu
Web Site: www.siskiyous.edu/

Description: State and locally supported, 2-year, coed. Part of California Community College System. Awards certificates, transfer associate, and terminal associate degrees. Founded 1957. Setting: 260-acre rural campus. Total enrollment: 3,045. Student-undergrad faculty ratio is 20:1. 0% from out-of-state. 54% 25 or older. Core. Calendar: semesters. Academic remediation for entering students, ESL program, services for LD students, advanced placement, self-designed majors, honors program, independent study, distance learning, double major, summer session for credit, part-time degree program, adult/continuing education programs, co-op programs and internships.

Entrance Requirements: Open admission. Options: early admission, deferred admission. Entrance: noncompetitive. Application deadline: Rolling. Notification: continuous.

Collegiate Environment: Orientation program. Drama-theater group, choral group, student-run newspaper. Student services: legal services, health clinic, personal-psychological counseling, women's center. Campus security: 24-hour emergency response devices, controlled dormitory access. College of the Siskiyou Library with an OPAC and a Web page.

Community Environment: Centrally located in Siskiyou County, just off Interstate 5, the historic lumber town of Weed lies nestled at the base of majestic 14,162-foot Mt. Shasta. At the midpoint between two major population centers - Medford, Oregon, to the north and Redding to the south - Weed is easily accessible by airline, train and bus services. The climate features four distinct seasons with an average snowfall of 24 inches. Outdoor enthusiasts will delight in the spectacular alpine environment of this rural northern California region, which provides for a wide variety of recreational activities including downhill and cross-country skiing, snowboarding, hunting, fishing, hiking, rock climbing, wind surfing, and more.

■ **COLUMBIA COLLEGE**
11600 Columbia College Dr.
Sonora, CA 95370
Tel: (209)588-5100
E-mail: ccadmissions@yosemite.edu
Web Site: www.gocolumbia.edu/

Description: State and locally supported, 2-year, coed. Part of Yosemite Community College District System. Awards certificates, transfer associate, and terminal associate degrees. Founded 1968. Setting: 200-acre rural campus. Total enrollment: 3,629. Student-undergrad faculty ratio is 23:1. 0% from out-of-state. 46% 25 or older. Core. Calendar: semesters. Academic remediation for entering students, ESL program, services for LD students, advanced placement, independent study, distance learning, double major, summer session for credit, part-time degree program, adult/continuing education programs, co-op programs and internships. Off campus study.

Entrance Requirements: Open admission. Options: electronic application, early admission. Required for some: high school transcript. Entrance: noncompetitive. Application deadline: Rolling. Notification: continuous. Preference given to EOPS students, students with disabilities.

Collegiate Environment: Orientation program. Drama-theater group, choral group, student-run newspaper. Student services: health clinic, personal-psychological counseling. Campus security: 24-hour emergency response devices and patrols, late night transport-escort service. Columbia College Library with an OPAC and a Web page.

■ **COLUMBIA COLLEGE HOLLYWOOD**
18618 Oxnard St.
Tarzana, CA 91356
Tel: (818)345-8414; Free: 800-785-0585
Fax: (818)345-9053
E-mail: admissions@columbiacollege.edu
Web Site: www.columbiacollege.edu/

Description: Independent, 4-year, coed. Awards associate and bachelor's degrees. Founded 1952. Setting: 1-acre urban campus with easy access to Los Angeles. Total enrollment: 359. Faculty: (52 full-time). Student-undergrad faculty ratio is 33:1. 196 applied, 57% were admitted. 8% from top 10% of their high school class, 23% from top quarter, 44% from top half. 1 class president. Students come from 5 other countries, 42% from out-of-state. 0% American Indian or Alaska Native, non-Hispanic/Latino; 17% Hispanic/Latino; 16% African American, non-Hispanic/Latino; 7% Asian, non-Hispanic/Latino; 0% Native Hawaiian or other Pacific Islander, non-Hispanic/Latino; 0% international. 10% 25 or older. Retention: 81% of full-time freshmen returned the following year. Core. Accelerated degree program, summer session for credit, part-time degree program, adult/continuing education programs.

Entrance Requirements: Options: electronic application, deferred admission. Required: essay, high school transcript, minimum 2 high school GPA, 2 recommendations, interview. Recommended: portfolio. Entrance: minimally difficult. Application deadline: Rolling. Notification: continuous. Transfer credits accepted: Yes.

Costs Per Year: Application fee: $50. One-time mandatory fee: $95. Comprehensive fee: $48,141 includes full-time tuition ($18,375), mandatory fees ($18,804), and college room and board ($10,962). Room and board charges vary according to housing facility. Part-time tuition: $550 per unit.

Collegiate Environment: Orientation program. Drama-theater group. Social organizations: 20% of eligible men and 30% of eligible women are members. Major annual event: Alumni Weekend. Student services: personal-psychological counseling. Campus security: 24-hour emergency response devices and patrols, late night transport-escort service. 700 college housing spaces available. Option: coed housing available. Columbia College Hollywood Library plus 1 other with 9,000 books, 23 serials, 3,000 audiovisual materials, and an OPAC. 12 computers available on campus for general student use. A computer is required for all students. Students can access the following: online class registration. Staffed computer lab on campus.

Community Environment: The college is located close to freeways, public transportation, housing, and major recreational areas in Southern California.

■ **COMMUNITY CHRISTIAN COLLEGE**
251 Tennessee St.
Redlands, CA 92373
Tel: (909)335-8863
Fax: (909)335-9101
E-mail: emelendez@cccollege.edu
Web Site: www.cccollege.edu/
Description: Independent Christian, 2-year, coed. Awards transfer associate and terminal associate degrees. Founded 1994. Total enrollment: 74. Student-undergrad faculty ratio is 5:1. 0% from out-of-state. 35% 25 or older. Retention: 41% of full-time freshmen returned the following year.
Entrance Requirements: Open admission.

■ **CONCORDE CAREER COLLEGE (GARDEN GROVE)**
12951 Euclid St.
Ste. 101
Garden Grove, CA 92840
Tel: (714)703-1900
Fax: (714)530-4737
E-mail: cbecker@concorde.edu
Web Site: www.concorde.edu/
Description: Proprietary, 2-year, coed. Awards terminal associate degrees. Total enrollment: 698. Student-undergrad faculty ratio is 22:1. 216 applied, 100% were admitted. 0% from out-of-state. 56% 25 or older.
Entrance Requirements: Required: high school transcript.

■ **CONCORDE CAREER COLLEGE (NORTH HOLLYWOOD)**
12412 Victory Blvd.
North Hollywood, CA 91606
Tel: (818)766-8151
Fax: (818)766-1587
E-mail: mvolker@concorde.edu
Web Site: www.concorde.edu/
Description: Proprietary, 2-year, coed. Awards terminal associate degrees. Founded 1955. Total enrollment: 650. Student-undergrad faculty ratio is 20:1. 253 applied, 100% were admitted. 0% from out-of-state. 45% 25 or older.
Entrance Requirements: Required: high school transcript.

■ **CONCORDIA UNIVERSITY**
1530 Concordia W
Irvine, CA 92612-3299
Tel: (949)854-8002; Free: 800-229-1200
Fax: (949)854-6894
E-mail: admission@cui.edu
Web Site: www.cui.edu/
Description: Independent, comprehensive, coed, affiliated with Lutheran Church-Missouri Synod. Part of The Concordia University System. Awards associate, bachelor's, and master's degrees (associate's degree for international students only). Founded 1972. Setting: 70-acre suburban campus with easy access to Los Angeles. System endowment: $12.2 million. Educational spending for the previous fiscal year: $6357 per student. Total

enrollment: 3,519. Faculty: 319 (84 full-time, 235 part-time). Student-undergrad faculty ratio is 19:1. 1,808 applied, 69% were admitted. Full-time: 1,592 students, 61% women, 39% men. Part-time: 146 students, 73% women, 27% men. Students come from 30 states and territories, 22 other countries, 11% from out-of-state. 0.5% American Indian or Alaska Native, non-Hispanic/Latino; 19% Hispanic/Latino; 4% African American, non-Hispanic/Latino; 6% Asian, non-Hispanic/Latino; 0.3% Native Hawaiian or other Pacific Islander, non-Hispanic/Latino; 3% international. 14% 25 or older, 50% live on campus, 12% transferred in. Retention: 78% of full-time freshmen returned the following year. Academic areas with the most degrees conferred: business/marketing; liberal arts/general studies; health professions and related sciences. Core. Calendar: semesters. Academic remediation for entering students, services for LD students, advanced placement, accelerated degree program, honors program, independent study, distance learning, double major, summer session for credit, part-time degree program, adult/continuing education programs, internships. Off campus study at all other universities in the Concordia University System. Study abroad program.

Entrance Requirements: Options: electronic application, early action, deferred admission, international baccalaureate accepted. Required: essay, high school transcript, 1 recommendation, SAT or ACT. Recommended: minimum 2.8 high school GPA, interview. Entrance: moderately difficult. Application deadlines: Rolling, 12/1 for early action. Notification: continuous, 12/15 for early action. SAT Reasoning Test deadline: 6/1. Transfer credits accepted: Yes.

Costs Per Year: Application fee: $50. Comprehensive fee: $38,680 includes full-time tuition ($29,000), mandatory fees ($630), and college room and board ($9050). College room only: $5100. Full-time tuition and fees vary according to course load. Room and board charges vary according to board plan and housing facility. Part-time tuition: $900 per unit. Part-time mandatory fees: $315 per term. Part-time tuition and fees vary according to course load.

Collegiate Environment: Orientation program. Drama-theater group, choral group, student-run newspaper. Social organizations: 15 open to all; FCA, Black Student Union, Hawaii Club, Nuestra Voz; 40% of eligible men and 60% of eligible women are members. Most popular organizations: intramurals, Screaming Eagles, Lacrosse, Abbey West, student activities. Major annual events: Midnight Madness (fall), CultureFest (spring), Homecoming (winter). Student services: health clinic, personal-psychological counseling. Campus security: 24-hour emergency response devices and patrols, student patrols, late night transport-escort service, lighted walkways, 24-hour dispatch. 1,024 college housing spaces available; 840 were occupied in 2012-13. Freshmen guaranteed college housing. Option: coed housing available. Concordia University Library with 81,602 books, 54,600 microform titles, 31,209 serials, 1,760 audiovisual materials, an OPAC, and a Web page. Operations spending for the previous fiscal year: $441,367. 89 computers available on campus for general student use. A campuswide network can be accessed from student residence rooms. Students can access the following: online class registration. Staffed computer lab on campus (open 24 hours a day).

■ **CONTRA COSTA COLLEGE**
2600 Mission Bell Dr.
San Pablo, CA 94806-3195
Tel: (510)235-7800
E-mail: A&R@contracosta.edu
Web Site: www.contracosta.edu/
Description: State and locally supported, 2-year, coed. Part of Contra Costa Community College District and California Community College System. Awards certificates, transfer associate, and terminal associate degrees. Founded 1948. Setting: 83-acre small town campus with easy access to San Francisco. Total enrollment: 8,316. Student-undergrad faculty ratio is 26:1. 0% from out-of-state. 44% 25 or older. Core. Calendar: semesters. Academic remediation for entering students, ESL program, services for LD students, accelerated degree program, self-designed majors, honors program, independent study, distance learning, summer session for credit, part-time degree program, adult/continuing education programs, co-op programs and internships. Off campus study at University of California, Berkeley; members of the Regional Association of East Bay Colleges and Universities. Study abroad program.

Entrance Requirements: Open admission. Option: early admission. Entrance: noncompetitive. Application deadline: Rolling.

Collegiate Environment: Drama-theater group, student-run newspaper. Student services: personal-psychological counseling, women's center.

Campus security: 24-hour emergency response devices and patrols, student patrols, late night transport-escort service. Contra Costa College Library with a Web page.

Community Environment: San Pablo is located on San Francisco Bay north of Richmond and Oakland on Highway 40. Buses and railroads serve the area. The city has 70 major industries; skilled and unskilled labor opportunities are available. San Pablo community facilities include churches, library and hospitals. Recreational facilities are provided by the beaches nearby and the mountain resort area for winter sports, which are approximately a three hour drive.

■ **COPPER MOUNTAIN COLLEGE**

6162 Rotary Way
Joshua Tree, CA 92252
Tel: (760)366-3791; Free: 866-366-3791
Web Site: www.cmccd.edu/

Description: State-supported, 2-year, coed. Awards certificates, transfer associate, and terminal associate degrees. Founded 1966. Total enrollment: 1,673. 52% 25 or older. Calendar: semesters.

Entrance Requirements: Open admission.

■ **COSUMNES RIVER COLLEGE**

8401 Ctr. Pky.
Sacramento, CA 95823-5799
Tel: (916)691-7344
Fax: (916)691-7375
Web Site: www.crc.losrios.edu/

Description: District-supported, 2-year, coed. Part of Los Rios Community College District System. Awards certificates, transfer associate, and terminal associate degrees. Founded 1970. Setting: 180-acre rural campus. Total enrollment: 15,946. Student-undergrad faculty ratio is 34:1. 0% from out-of-state. 41% 25 or older. Calendar: semesters. Academic remediation for entering students, ESL program, services for LD students, advanced placement, honors program, summer session for credit, part-time degree program, adult/continuing education programs, co-op programs. Study abroad program.

Entrance Requirements: Open admission except for international applicants. Option: early admission. Entrance: noncompetitive. Application deadline: 8/1. Notification: continuous until 8/15.

Collegiate Environment: Drama-theater group, choral group, student-run newspaper, radio station. Student services: health clinic, personal-psychological counseling, women's center. Campus security: 24-hour emergency response devices and patrols, student patrols, late night transport-escort service.

Community Environment: See California State University - Sacramento.

■ **CRAFTON HILLS COLLEGE**

11711 Sand Canyon Rd.
Yucaipa, CA 92399-1799
Tel: (909)794-2161
Fax: (909)389-9141
E-mail: laycock@craftonhills.edu
Web Site: www.craftonhills.edu/

Description: State and locally supported, 2-year, coed. Part of California Community College System. Awards certificates, transfer associate, and terminal associate degrees. Founded 1972. Setting: 526-acre small town campus with easy access to Los Angeles. Total enrollment: 6,380. Student-undergrad faculty ratio is 33:1. 0% from out-of-state. 32% 25 or older. Core. Calendar: semesters. Academic remediation for entering students, services for LD students, advanced placement, self-designed majors, distance learning, summer session for credit, part-time degree program, adult/continuing education programs, co-op programs.

Entrance Requirements: Open admission. Options: early admission, deferred admission. Required for some: high school transcript. Entrance: noncompetitive. Application deadline: Rolling. Notification: continuous. Preference given to district residents.

Collegiate Environment: Drama-theater group. Student services: health clinic, personal-psychological counseling, women's center. Campus security: 24-hour patrols, late night transport-escort service.

Community Environment: See California State University - San Bernardino.

■ **CUESTA COLLEGE**

PO Box 8106
San Luis Obispo, CA 93403-8106

Tel: (805)546-3100
E-mail: jchamber@cuesta.edu
Web Site: www.cuesta.edu/

Description: District-supported, 2-year, coed. Administratively affiliated with San Luis Obispo County Community College District. Awards certificates, transfer associate, and terminal associate degrees. Founded 1964. Setting: 129-acre rural campus. Total enrollment: 12,025. Student-undergrad faculty ratio is 27:1. 0% from out-of-state. 31% 25 or older. Core. Calendar: semesters. Academic remediation for entering students, ESL program, services for LD students, advanced placement, honors program, independent study, distance learning, double major, summer session for credit, part-time degree program, adult/continuing education programs, co-op programs and internships. Off campus study. Study abroad program. ROTC: Army (c).

Entrance Requirements: Open admission. Options: electronic application, early admission, deferred admission. Required: high school transcript. Recommended: essay. Entrance: noncompetitive. Application deadline: Rolling. Notification: continuous. Preference given to district residents.

Collegiate Environment: Orientation program. Drama-theater group, choral group, student-run newspaper, radio station. Student services: legal services, health clinic, personal-psychological counseling. Campus security: 24-hour emergency response devices and patrols, late night transport-escort service. Cuesta College Library with an OPAC and a Web page.

Community Environment: See California Polytechnic State University - San Luis Obispo.

■ **CUYAMACA COLLEGE**

900 Rancho San Diego Pky.
El Cajon, CA 92019-4304
Tel: (619)660-4000
E-mail: susan.topham@gcccd.edu
Web Site: www.cuyamaca.net/

Description: State-supported, 2-year, coed. Part of Grossmont-Cuyamaca Community College District. Awards certificates, diplomas, transfer associate, and terminal associate degrees. Founded 1978. Setting: 165-acre suburban campus with easy access to San Diego. Educational spending for the previous fiscal year: $2692 per student. Total enrollment: 7,706. Faculty: 645 (84 full-time, 561 part-time). Full-time: 1,636 students, 56% women, 44% men. Part-time: 6,070 students, 56% women, 44% men. Students come from 8 other countries. Core. Calendar: semesters. Academic remediation for entering students, ESL program, services for LD students, advanced placement, self-designed majors, honors program, distance learning, double major, summer session for credit, part-time degree program, adult/continuing education programs, co-op programs and internships. Off campus study. Study abroad program. ROTC: Army (c), Air Force (c).

Entrance Requirements: Open admission. Options: electronic application, early admission. Entrance: noncompetitive. Application deadline: Rolling. Transfer credits accepted: Yes.

Collegiate Environment: Orientation program. Drama-theater group, student-run newspaper. Student services: health clinic, personal-psychological counseling. Campus security: 24-hour emergency response devices and patrols, late night transport-escort service. Library plus 1 other with 81,304 books, 72 serials, 2,068 audiovisual materials, an OPAC, and a Web page. Operations spending for the previous fiscal year: $1.9 million. 396 computers available on campus for general student use. A campuswide network can be accessed from off-campus. Students can access the following: online class registration. Staffed computer lab on campus provides training in use of computers, software, and the Internet.

■ **CYPRESS COLLEGE**

9200 Valley View
Cypress, CA 90630-5897
Tel: (714)484-7000
Fax: (714)761-3934
E-mail: admissions@cypresscollege.edu
Web Site: www.cypresscollege.edu/

Description: State and locally supported, 2-year, coed. Part of California Community College System. Awards certificates, transfer associate, and terminal associate degrees. Founded 1966. Setting: 108-acre suburban campus with easy access to Los Angeles. Total enrollment: 15,439. Student-undergrad faculty ratio is 26:1. 0% from out-of-state. 33% 25 or older. Core. Calendar: semesters. Academic remediation for entering students, ESL program, services for LD students, advanced placement, freshman honors college, honors program, independent study, distance learning, double major, summer session for credit, part-time degree program, adult/continuing education programs, co-op programs and internships. Off campus study. Study abroad program.

Entrance Requirements: Open admission. Recommended: high school transcript. Entrance: noncompetitive. Application deadline: 8/25.

Collegiate Environment: Orientation program. Drama-theater group, choral group, student-run newspaper. Student services: legal services, health clinic, personal-psychological counseling, women's center. Campus security: 24-hour emergency response devices. Cypress College Library plus 1 other with an OPAC and a Web page.

Community Environment: Cypress is a rapidly growing suburban city, 20 miles east of Los Angeles. The climate is dry and mild. Buses, trains, freeway system and the Los Angeles International Airport 20 miles away all serve the area. The city has three private hospitals, twelve churches, a library, and an amphitheater. There are city parks, a golf course, swimming pool and a gymnasium for those interested in sports. Anaheim Stadium is seven miles away, Disneyland five and one-half miles, Knotts Berry Farm and Movieland Wax Museum two and one-half miles. Beaches and mountain areas provide additional recreational facilities and are within easy driving distance. Many universities and colleges are nearby.

■ **DE ANZA COLLEGE**
21250 Stevens Creek Blvd.
Cupertino, CA 95014-5793
Tel: (408)864-5678
Fax: (408)864-8329
E-mail: webregda@mercury.fhda.edu
Web Site: www.deanza.fhda.edu/

Description: State and locally supported, 2-year, coed. Part of California Community College System. Awards certificates, diplomas, transfer associate, and terminal associate degrees. Founded 1967. Setting: 112-acre suburban campus with easy access to San Francisco, San Jose. Faculty: 794 (300 full-time, 494 part-time). Student-undergrad faculty ratio is 36:1. 1% American Indian or Alaska Native, non-Hispanic/Latino; 22% Hispanic/Latino; 5% African American, non-Hispanic/Latino; 37% Asian, non-Hispanic/Latino; 1% Native Hawaiian or other Pacific Islander, non-Hispanic/Latino. 52% 25 or older. Core. Academic remediation for entering students, ESL program, services for LD students, advanced placement, self-designed majors, honors program, independent study, distance learning, summer session for credit, part-time degree program, external degree program, adult/continuing education programs, co-op programs and internships. Study abroad program. ROTC: Army (c), Air Force (c).

Costs Per Year: State resident tuition: $1116 full-time. Nonresident tuition: $6084 full-time. Mandatory fees: $167 full-time. Full-time tuition and fees vary according to course load.

Collegiate Environment: Orientation program. Drama-theater group, choral group, student-run newspaper. Social organizations: 45 open to all. Most popular organizations: Student Nurses Association, Phi Theta Kappa, Automotive Club, Vietnamese Club, Filipino Club. Major annual events: Graduation, Orientation, Club Day. Student services: legal services, health clinic, personal-psychological counseling. Campus security: 24-hour emergency response devices, student patrols, late night transport-escort service. College housing not available. A. Robert DeHart Learning Center with 80,000 books, 927 serials, an OPAC, and a Web page. 800 computers available on campus for general student use. Computer purchase/lease plans available. A campuswide network can be accessed. Students can access the following: online class registration. Staffed computer lab on campus provides training in use of computers, software, and the Internet.

Community Environment: Cupertino, population 52,171, is within an hour's drive from San Francisco. Buses and trains serve the area and the San Jose International Airport is nearby for air transportation. There are parks, playgrounds and nearby beaches for recreational activities as well as the cultural advantages of the San Francisco Bay Area.

■ **DEEP SPRINGS COLLEGE**
HC 72, Box 45001
Deep Springs, CA 89010-9803
Tel: (760)872-2000
E-mail: apcom@deepsprings.edu
Web Site: www.deepsprings.edu/

Description: Independent, 2-year, men only. Awards transfer associate degrees. Founded 1917. Setting: 3,000-acre rural campus. Endowment: $18 million. Educational spending for the previous fiscal year: $14,230 per student. Total enrollment: 26. Faculty: 8 (3 full-time, 5 part-time). Student-

undergrad faculty ratio is 5:1. 83% from top 10% of their high school class, 100% from top quarter. 1 National Merit Scholar, 1 class president, 1 valedictorian, 3 student government officers. Full-time: 26 students. Students come from 18 states and territories, 3 other countries, 80% from out-of-state. 0% 25 or older, 100% live on campus, 62% transferred in. Retention: 100% of full-time freshmen returned the following year. Calendar: 6 seven-week terms. Services for LD students, advanced placement, freshman honors college, honors program, independent study, distance learning, summer session for credit, internships.

Entrance Requirements: Required: essay, high school transcript, interview, SAT and SAT Subject Tests or ACT.

Costs Per Year: Comprehensive fee: $800 includes full-time tuition ($0), mandatory fees ($800), and college room and board ($0). Every student accepted to Deep Springs receives a scholarship covering tuition, room, and board.

Collegiate Environment: Orientation program. Drama-theater group, choral group. Most popular organizations: Student Self-Government, Labor Program, Applications Committee, Review Committee, Curriculum Committee. Major annual events: Potato Harvest, Cattle Round-up, Thanksgiving Football Game. Student services: legal services, personal-psychological counseling. Campus security: 24-hour emergency response devices, late night transport-escort service. 30 college housing spaces available; 26 were occupied in 2012-13. Freshmen guaranteed college housing. On-campus residence required through sophomore year. Option: men-only housing available. Mossner Library of Deep Springs with 20,000 books and 60 serials. Operations spending for the previous fiscal year: $5000. 6 computers available on campus for general student use.

■ **DESIGN INSTITUTE OF SAN DIEGO**
8555 Commerce Ave.
San Diego, CA 92121-2685
Tel: (858)566-1200; Free: 800-619-4337
Fax: (858)566-2711
E-mail: admissions@disd.edu
Web Site: www.disd.edu/

Description: Proprietary, 4-year, coed. Awards bachelor's degrees. Founded 1977. Setting: urban campus. Total enrollment: 457. 24 applied, 54% were admitted. 52% 25 or older. Core. Calendar: semesters. Part-time degree program, internships. Study abroad program.

Entrance Requirements: Required: high school transcript, minimum 2.0 high school GPA. Recommended: interview. Entrance: noncompetitive. Application deadline: Rolling.

Collegiate Environment: 5,000 books, 90 serials, and an OPAC.

■ **DEVRY UNIVERSITY (ALHAMBRA)**
Unit 100, Bldg. A-11, First Fl.
1000 S Fremont Ave.
Alhambra, CA 91803
Tel: (626)293-4300; Free: 866-338-7941
Web Site: www.devry.edu/

Description: Proprietary, comprehensive, coed. Awards bachelor's and master's degrees.

■ **DEVRY UNIVERSITY (ANAHEIM)**
1900 S State College Blvd., Ste. 150
Anaheim, CA 92806-6136
Tel: (714)935-3200; Free: 866-338-7941
Web Site: www.devry.edu/

Description: Proprietary, comprehensive, coed. Awards bachelor's and master's degrees.

■ **DEVRY UNIVERSITY (BAKERSFIELD)**
3000 Ming Ave.
Bakersfield, CA 93304-4136
Tel: (661)833-7120; Free: 866-338-7941
Web Site: www.devry.edu/

Description: Proprietary, 4-year, coed. Awards associate and bachelor's degrees.

■ **DEVRY UNIVERSITY (DALY CITY)**
2001 Junipero Serra Blvd.
Ste. 161
Daly City, CA 94014-3899
Tel: (650)991-3520; Free: 866-338-7941

Web Site: www.devry.edu/

Description: Proprietary, comprehensive, coed. Awards associate, bachelor's, and master's degrees.

■ **DEVRY UNIVERSITY (ELK GROVE)**

Sacramento Ctr.

2216 Kausen Dr.

Elk Grove, CA 95758

Tel: (916)478-2847; Free: 866-338-7941

Fax: (916)478-2849

Web Site: www.devry.edu/

Description: Proprietary, comprehensive, coed. Awards associate, bachelor's, and master's degrees. Calendar: semesters.

■ **DEVRY UNIVERSITY (FREMONT)**

6600 Dumbarton Cir.

Fremont, CA 94555

Tel: (510)574-1100; Free: 866-338-7941

Fax: (510)742-0868

Web Site: www.devry.edu/

Description: Proprietary, comprehensive, coed. Part of DeVry University. Awards associate, bachelor's, and master's degrees. Founded 1998. Setting: 17-acre suburban campus with easy access to San Francisco. Total enrollment: 1,553. Faculty: 231 (35 full-time, 196 part-time). Student-undergrad faculty ratio is 10:1. Full-time: 754 students, 27% women, 73% men. Part-time: 587 students, 36% women, 64% men. 4% from out-of-state. 49% 25 or older, 15% transferred in. Academic areas with the most degrees conferred: business/marketing; engineering technologies; engineering. Calendar: semesters. Academic remediation for entering students, services for LD students, advanced placement, accelerated degree program, distance learning, summer session for credit, part-time degree program, adult/continuing education programs.

Entrance Requirements: Options: electronic application, early admission, deferred admission, international baccalaureate accepted. Required: high school transcript, interview. Entrance: minimally difficult. Application deadline: Rolling. Notification: continuous. SAT Reasoning Test deadline: 10/31.

Collegiate Environment: Orientation program. Most popular organizations: Latino-American Student Organization, Telecommunications Club, Chess Club. Major annual events: Thanksgiving Dinner, summer barbecue, book fair. Campus security: 24-hour emergency response devices and patrols, late night transport-escort service, lighted pathways/sidewalks. Learning Resource Center with an OPAC and a Web page.

■ **DEVRY UNIVERSITY (IRVINE)**

430 Exchange, Ste. 250

Irvine, CA 92602-1303

Tel: (949)752-5631; Free: 866-338-7941

Fax: (949)752-5637

Web Site: www.devry.edu/

Description: Proprietary, comprehensive, coed. Awards bachelor's and master's degrees. Calendar: semesters.

■ **DEVRY UNIVERSITY (LONG BEACH)**

3880 Kilroy Airport Way

Long Beach, CA 90806

Tel: (562)427-0861; Free: 866-338-7941

Web Site: www.devry.edu/

Description: Proprietary, comprehensive, coed. Part of DeVry University. Awards associate, bachelor's, and master's degrees. Founded 1984. Setting: 23-acre urban campus with easy access to Los Angeles. Total enrollment: 1,172. Faculty: 101 (20 full-time, 81 part-time). Student-undergrad faculty ratio is 14:1. Full-time: 405 students, 35% women, 65% men. Part-time: 512 students, 29% women, 71% men. 1% from out-of-state. 58% 25 or older, 9% transferred in. Academic areas with the most degrees conferred: business/marketing; computer and information sciences; engineering technologies. Calendar: semesters. Academic remediation for entering students, services for LD students, advanced placement, accelerated degree program, distance learning, summer session for credit, part-time degree program, adult/continuing education programs.

Entrance Requirements: Options: electronic application, early admission, deferred admission, international baccalaureate accepted. Required: high

school transcript, interview. Entrance: minimally difficult. Application deadline: Rolling. Notification: continuous. SAT Reasoning Test deadline: 10/31.

Collegiate Environment: Orientation program. Most popular organizations: Teamnet, Society of Hispanic Professional Engineers, National Society of Black Engineers, Institute of Electronics and Electrical Engineers, United Islands. Major annual events: Welcome Back, New Horizons Retreat, Winter Formal. Campus security: 24-hour emergency response devices and patrols, late night transport-escort service, motion detectors, closed hours. Learning Resource Center with an OPAC and a Web page.

■ **DEVRY UNIVERSITY (OAKLAND)**

505 14th St.

Oakland, CA 94612

Tel: (866)473-3879; Free: 866-338-7941

Web Site: www.devry.edu/

Description: Proprietary, comprehensive, coed. Awards bachelor's and master's degrees.

■ **DEVRY UNIVERSITY (PALMDALE)**

One 39115 Trade Ctr. Dr.

Ste. 100

Palmdale, CA 93551

Free: 866-338-7941

Web Site: www.devry.edu/

Description: Proprietary, comprehensive, coed. Part of DeVry University. Awards associate, bachelor's, and master's degrees. Founded 1999. Setting: 20-acre suburban campus. Total enrollment: 769. Faculty: 61 (17 full-time, 44 part-time). Student-undergrad faculty ratio is 16:1. Full-time: 329 students, 26% women, 74% men. Part-time: 342 students, 26% women, 74% men. Students come from 10 states and territories, 13 other countries. 42% 25 or older. Retention: 53% of full-time freshmen returned the following year. Academic areas with the most degrees conferred: computer and information sciences; business/marketing; engineering technologies. Calendar: semesters. Academic remediation for entering students, services for LD students, advanced placement, accelerated degree program, distance learning, summer session for credit, part-time degree program, adult/continuing education programs, co-op programs.

Entrance Requirements: Options: electronic application, deferred admission, international baccalaureate accepted. Required: high school transcript, interview. Entrance: minimally difficult. Application deadline: Rolling. Notification: continuous.

Collegiate Environment: Orientation program. Social organizations: 10 open to all. Most popular organizations: Associated Student Body, Computer Information Systems/Telecommunication Association, Women's Caucus, United Island Student Association, Institute of Electronics and Electrical Engineers. Major annual events: Welcome BBQ, Winter Formal, Cosmic Bowling. Campus security: 24-hour emergency response devices, late night transport-escort service, lighted pathways/sidewalks. Learning Resource Center with 16,177 books, 130 serials, 597 audiovisual materials, an OPAC, and a Web page. 390 computers available on campus for general student use. Computer purchase/lease plans available. A campuswide network can be accessed from off-campus. Students can access the following: online class registration. Staffed computer lab on campus.

■ **DEVRY UNIVERSITY (POMONA)**

901 Corporate Ctr. Dr.

Pomona, CA 91768-2642

Tel: (909)622-8866; Free: 866-338-7941

Fax: (909)623-5666

Web Site: www.devry.edu/

Description: Proprietary, comprehensive, coed. Part of DeVry University. Awards associate, bachelor's, and master's degrees. Founded 1983. Setting: urban campus. Total enrollment: 2,637. Faculty: 98 (21 full-time, 77 part-time). Student-undergrad faculty ratio is 31:1. Full-time: 812 students, 36% women, 64% men. Part-time: 1,511 students, 45% women, 55% men. 9% from out-of-state. 1% American Indian or Alaska Native, non-Hispanic/Latino; 38% Hispanic/Latino; 9% African American, non-Hispanic/Latino; 10% Asian, non-Hispanic/Latino; 2% Native Hawaiian or other Pacific Islander, non-Hispanic/Latino; 1% international. 68% 25 or older, 18% transferred in. Academic areas with the most degrees conferred: business/marketing; computer and information sciences; engineering; engineering technologies. Calendar: semesters. Part-time degree program, adult/continuing education programs.

Entrance Requirements: Required: high school transcript, interview. Entrance: minimally difficult. Application deadline: Rolling. Notification: continuous.

Costs Per Year: Application fee: $40. Tuition: $16,076 full-time, $609 per credit hour part-time. Mandatory fees: $80 full-time.

Collegiate Environment: College housing not available.

■ **DEVRY UNIVERSITY (SAN DIEGO)**
2655 Camino Del Rio N, Ste. 201
San Diego, CA 92108-1633
Tel: (619)683-2446; Free: 866-338-7941
Fax: (619)683-2448
Web Site: www.devry.edu/
Description: Proprietary, comprehensive, coed. Awards associate, bachelor's, and master's degrees. Calendar: semesters.

■ **DEVRY UNIVERSITY (SHERMAN OAKS)**
15301 Ventura Blvd., D-100
Sherman Oaks, CA 91403
Tel: (888)610-0800; Free: 866-338-7941
Web Site: www.devry.edu/
Description: Proprietary, comprehensive, coed. Awards associate, bachelor's, and master's degrees. Total enrollment: 931. Faculty: 69 (8 full-time, 61 part-time). Student-undergrad faculty ratio is 23:1. Full-time: 456 students, 34% women, 66% men. Part-time: 272 students, 34% women, 66% men. 2% from out-of-state. 54% 25 or older, 16% transferred in. Academic areas with the most degrees conferred: business/marketing; computer and information sciences; engineering technologies. Accelerated degree program, distance learning.
Entrance Requirements: Options: electronic application, early admission, deferred admission. Application deadline: Rolling. Notification: continuous. SAT Reasoning Test deadline: 10/31.

■ **DIABLO VALLEY COLLEGE**
321 Golf Club Rd.
Pleasant Hill, CA 94523
Tel: (925)685-1230
Fax: (925)685-1551
E-mail: idorn@dvc.edu
Web Site: www.dvc.edu/
Description: State and locally supported, 2-year, coed. Part of Contra Costa Community College District. Awards certificates, transfer associate, and terminal associate degrees. Founded 1949. Setting: 100-acre suburban campus with easy access to San Francisco. Total enrollment: 22,567. Faculty: 805 (255 full-time, 550 part-time). Student-undergrad faculty ratio is 17:1. Students come from 16 states and territories, 68 other countries, 0.2% from out-of-state. 38% 25 or older. Retention: 61% of full-time freshmen returned the following year. Core. Calendar: semesters. Academic remediation for entering students, services for LD students, advanced placement, self-designed majors, summer session for credit, part-time degree program, adult/continuing education programs, co-op programs. Study abroad program. ROTC: Air Force (c).
Entrance Requirements: Open admission. Option: early admission. Recommended: high school transcript. Entrance: noncompetitive. Application deadline: 8/15.
Collegiate Environment: Drama-theater group, choral group, student-run newspaper. Student services: women's center. Campus security: 24-hour emergency response devices and patrols, student patrols. Diablo Valley College Library with 88,286 books and 298 serials. 450 computers available on campus for general student use. A campuswide network can be accessed from off-campus. Students can access the following: online class registration. Staffed computer lab on campus.
Community Environment: Population 33,000. Pleasant Hill is a suburban residential community that has an average winter temperature of 46.4 degrees and summer temperature of 71.8 degrees. It is located 22 miles from San Francisco. All transportation facilities are available nearby. Churches representing 14 denominations, a hospital and excellent shopping facilities comprise the town. Employment opportunities are available. Pleasant Hill enjoys the cultural atmosphere of the San Francisco Bay Area. A nearby beach area provides recreational facilities; the mountain area for winter sports is accessible for a weekend trip.

■ **DOMINICAN UNIVERSITY OF CALIFORNIA**
50 Acacia Ave.
San Rafael, CA 94901-2298

Tel: (415)457-4440; Free: 888-323-6763
Fax: (415)485-3214
E-mail: enroll@dominican.edu
Web Site: www.dominican.edu/
Description: Independent, comprehensive, coed, affiliated with Roman Catholic Church. Awards bachelor's and master's degrees. Founded 1890. Setting: 85-acre suburban campus with easy access to San Francisco. Endowment: $26.1 million. Research spending for the previous fiscal year: $931,134. Educational spending for the previous fiscal year: $9252 per student. Total enrollment: 2,278. Faculty: 371 (99 full-time, 272 part-time). Student-undergrad faculty ratio is 11:1. 3,093 applied, 54% were admitted. 29% from top 10% of their high school class, 56% from top quarter, 91% from top half. Full-time: 1,364 students, 73% women, 27% men. Part-time: 298 students, 71% women, 29% men. Students come from 31 states and territories, 17 other countries, 7% from out-of-state. 1% American Indian or Alaska Native, non-Hispanic/Latino; 19% Hispanic/Latino; 4% African American, non-Hispanic/Latino; 19% Asian, non-Hispanic/Latino; 2% Native Hawaiian or other Pacific Islander, non-Hispanic/Latino; 2% international. 22% 25 or older, 31% live on campus, 8% transferred in. Retention: 84% of full-time freshmen returned the following year. Academic areas with the most degrees conferred: health professions and related sciences; business/marketing; liberal arts/general studies. Core. Calendar: semesters. Academic remediation for entering students, ESL program, services for LD students, advanced placement, self-designed majors, honors program, independent study, double major, summer session for credit, part-time degree program, external degree program, adult/continuing education programs, internships, graduate courses open to undergrads. Off campus study at University of California, Berkeley, Aquinas College, St. Thomas Aquinas College, Barry University. Study abroad program.
Entrance Requirements: Options: electronic application, deferred admission, international baccalaureate accepted. Required: essay, high school transcript, 1 recommendation, SAT or ACT. Recommended: interview. Entrance: moderately difficult. Application deadline: 2/1. Notification: continuous. SAT Reasoning Test deadline: 8/1.
Costs Per Year: Application fee: $40. Comprehensive fee: $52,990 includes full-time tuition ($38,600), mandatory fees ($450), and college room and board ($13,940). College room only: $7880. Full-time tuition and fees vary according to course load. Room and board charges vary according to board plan. Part-time tuition: $1560 per credit. Part-time mandatory fees: $150 per term.
Collegiate Environment: Orientation program. Drama-theater group, choral group, student-run newspaper, radio station. Social organizations: 19 open to all. Most popular organizations: Students Promoting Dominican Islands, Perceptions, Science Club, Filipino Club, Scripture Union. Major annual events: Shield Day, Boat Dance, Ecumenical Thanksgiving Dinner. Student services: health clinic, personal-psychological counseling. Campus security: 24-hour emergency response devices and patrols, late night transport-escort service, controlled dormitory access. Archbishop Alemany Library with 114,625 books, 3,430 microform titles, 93,144 serials, 1,489 audiovisual materials, an OPAC, and a Web page. Operations spending for the previous fiscal year: $1.2 million. 200 computers available on campus for general student use. A campuswide network can be accessed from student residence rooms. Students can access the following: online class registration, Microsoft Office Applications (Word, Excel, PowerPoint). Staffed computer lab on campus provides training in use of computers, software, and the Internet.
Community Environment: Located in the hills of Marin County 25 minutes from San Francisco across the Golden Gate Bridge, Dominican is close enough to permit easy access to the city's diverse cultural attractions - the opera, symphony, theaters and playhouses. The campus adjoins San Rafael (pop. 55,700), with a climate rated as one of the six most ideal in the world, in addition to a wide variety of libraries, museums and churches. The nearby cities of Mill Valley, Bolinas, and Sausalito harbor a large community of writers, painters and other artists, and a diverse collection of shops, restaurants and galleries. Five state parks and beaches lie within easy reach, including Muir Woods, the Golden Gate National Recreational Area, and the Point Reyes National Seashore.

■ **EAST LOS ANGELES COLLEGE**
1301 Avenida Cesar Chavez
Monterey Park, CA 91754
Tel: (323)265-8650
Fax: (323)265-8763
E-mail: allredjp@elac.edu

Web Site: www.elac.edu/
Description: State and locally supported, 2-year, coed. Part of Los Angeles Community College District System. Awards certificates, transfer associate, and terminal associate degrees. Founded 1945. Setting: 84-acre urban campus with easy access to Los Angeles. Total enrollment: 31,749. Faculty: 829 (231 full-time, 598 part-time). Full-time: 8,063 students, 56% women, 44% men. Part-time: 23,686 students, 56% women, 44% men. Students come from 17 states and territories, 0.1% from out-of-state. 33% 25 or older, 11% transferred in. Core. Calendar: semesters. Academic remediation for entering students, ESL program, services for LD students, advanced placement, accelerated degree program, self-designed majors, freshman honors college, honors program, independent study, distance learning, double major, summer session for credit, part-time degree program, adult/continuing education programs, co-op programs and internships. Off campus study at Respiratory Therapy at Santa Monica City College. Study abroad program.
Entrance Requirements: Open admission. Options: electronic application, early admission. Required: mathematics and English placement tests, international students require TOEFL score of 450, CBT score 133, IBT score 45 or higher. Recommended: high school transcript, English and mathematics placement test. Entrance: noncompetitive. Application deadline: Rolling. Notification: continuous until 9/2. Transfer credits accepted: Yes.
Collegiate Environment: Orientation program. Drama-theater group, choral group, marching band, student-run newspaper. Social organizations: 22 open to all. Most popular organizations: Administration of Justice, American Society of Engineers and Architects, Society of Hispanic Professional Engineers, MENTE, Asian Student Intercultural Association (A.S.I.A) and the International Student Club, Chicano/Community for Creative Medicine, Science Associations, Advocates and Educators for Young Children, Child Development Club. Major annual events: Cinco de Mayo, Dia De Los Muertos, Scholarship Awards Banquet, Vincent Price Art Museum exhibits. Student services: health clinic, personal-psychological counseling. Campus security: 24-hour emergency response devices and patrols, late night transport-escort service, Los Angeles County Sheriff Sub-station. ELAC Helen Miller Bailey Library plus 2 others with 102,000 books, 3,370 microform titles, 228 serials, an OPAC, and a Web page. 1,000 computers available on campus for general student use. A campuswide network can be accessed from off-campus. Students can access the following: online class registration, subject specific computer labs and specialized computer/software. Staffed computer lab on campus provides training in use of computers, software, and the Internet.

■ **EL CAMINO COLLEGE**
16007 Crenshaw Blvd.
Torrance, CA 90506-0001
Tel: (310)532-3670; Free: 866-ELCAMINO
Fax: (310)660-3818
E-mail: wmulrooney@elcamino.edu
Web Site: www.elcamino.edu/
Description: State-supported, 2-year, coed. Part of California Community College System. Awards certificates, diplomas, and transfer associate degrees. Founded 1947. Setting: 15-acre urban campus with easy access to Los Angeles. Total enrollment: 24,895. Faculty: 983 (333 full-time, 650 part-time). Student-undergrad faculty ratio is 15:1. Full-time: 7,729 students, 51% women, 49% men. Part-time: 17,166 students, 56% women, 44% men. Students come from 17 states and territories, 30 other countries, 10% from out-of-state. 42% 25 or older, 22% transferred in. Retention: 78% of full-time freshmen returned the following year. Core. Calendar: semesters. Academic remediation for entering students, ESL program, services for LD students, advanced placement, freshman honors college, honors program, independent study, distance learning, summer session for credit, part-time degree program, co-op programs and internships. Study abroad program.
Entrance Requirements: Open admission. Options: electronic application, early admission. Required: high school transcript. Entrance: noncompetitive. Application deadline: Rolling. Notification: continuous.
Collegiate Environment: Orientation program. Drama-theater group, choral group, marching band, student-run newspaper. Social organizations: 20 open to all. Most popular organizations: Hispanic Club, Kiwanis International, North American Indian Club, Math Club, Cinema Club. Major annual events: Homecoming, Student Elections, College Transfer Fairs. Student services: health clinic, personal-psychological counseling, women's center. Campus security: 24-hour emergency response devices and patrols, late night transport-escort service. El Camino College Schauerman Library with 116,051 books and 864 serials. 151 computers available on campus for

general student use. A campuswide network can be accessed. Students can access the following: online class registration. Staffed computer lab on campus.
Community Environment: Torrance, situated in southwest Los Angeles County, is a suburb of Los Angeles and does enjoy the advantages of the city's cultural and recreational facilities. All forms of commercial transportation are convenient. Outstanding shopping centers are in the city as well as all the other usual community facilities. Climate is normally sunny and mild. Beaches and mountains are within easy driving distance for recreation.

■ **EMPIRE COLLEGE**
3035 Cleveland Ave.
Santa Rosa, CA 95403
Tel: (707)546-4000; Free: 877-395-8535
Fax: (707)546-4058
Web Site: www.empcol.edu/
Description: Proprietary, 2-year, coed. Awards certificates, diplomas, and terminal associate degrees. Founded 1961. Setting: suburban campus with easy access to San Francisco. Total enrollment: 900. 72% 25 or older. Calendar: continuous. Double major.
Entrance Requirements: Option: international baccalaureate accepted. Required: high school transcript, interview, Wonderlic aptitude test. Required for some: essay. Entrance: minimally difficult. Application deadline: Rolling.
Collegiate Environment: Orientation program. Campus security: 24-hour emergency response devices.

■ **EPIC BIBLE COLLEGE**
5225 Hillsdale Blvd.
Sacramento, CA 95842
Tel: (916)348-4689
Fax: (916)334-2315
E-mail: kclarke@tlbc.edu
Web Site: epic.edu/
Description: Independent nondenominational, 4-year, coed. Awards associate and bachelor's degrees. Founded 1974. Total enrollment: 242. 216 applied. 61% 25 or older.
Entrance Requirements: Required: high school transcript.

■ **EVEREST COLLEGE (CITY OF INDUSTRY)**
12801 Crossroads Pky. S
City of Industry, CA 91746
Tel: (562)908-2500; Free: 888-741-4270
Fax: (562)908-7656
Web Site: www.everest.edu/
Description: Proprietary, 2-year, coed. Awards certificates and terminal associate degrees. Founded 1969. Total enrollment: 314. Student-undergrad faculty ratio is 20:1. 283 applied. 0% from out-of-state. 38% 25 or older. Retention: 73% of full-time freshmen returned the following year.
Entrance Requirements: Required: high school transcript.

■ **EVEREST COLLEGE (ONTARIO)**
1819 S Excise Ave.
Ontario, CA 91761
Tel: (909)484-4311; Free: 888-741-4270
Fax: (909)484-1162
Web Site: www.everest.edu/
Description: Proprietary, primarily 2-year, coed. Awards terminal associate and bachelor's degrees. Total enrollment: 986. Student-undergrad faculty ratio is 20:1. 163 applied, 89% were admitted. 0% from out-of-state. 52% 25 or older. Retention: 52% of full-time freshmen returned the following year.

■ **EVERGREEN VALLEY COLLEGE**
3095 Yerba Buena Rd.
San Jose, CA 95135-1598
Tel: (408)274-7900
Fax: (408)223-9351
E-mail: octavio.cruz@evc.edu
Web Site: www.evc.edu/
Description: State and locally supported, 2-year, coed. Part of California Community College System. Awards certificates, transfer associate, and terminal associate degrees. Founded 1975. Setting: 175-acre urban campus. Total enrollment: 11,186. Student-undergrad faculty ratio is 32:1. 0% from out-of-state. 44% 25 or older. Core. Calendar: semesters. Academic remediation for entering students, ESL program, services for LD

students, advanced placement, accelerated degree program, freshman honors college, honors program, independent study, distance learning, summer session for credit, part-time degree program, adult/continuing education programs, co-op programs. Off campus study at other community colleges in the area. ROTC: Army (c).

Entrance Requirements: Open admission except for nursing program. Option: early admission. Entrance: noncompetitive. Application deadline: Rolling. Notification: continuous.

Collegiate Environment: Drama-theater group, choral group. Student services: health clinic, personal-psychological counseling. Campus security: 24-hour emergency response devices, late night transport-escort service, patrols by trained security personnel.

Community Environment: See San Jose State University.

■ **EX'PRESSION COLLEGE FOR DIGITAL ARTS**
6601 Shellmound St.
Emeryville, CA 94608
Tel: (510)654-2934; Free: 877-833-8800
Web Site: www.expression.edu/
Description: Proprietary, 4-year, coed. Awards bachelor's degrees.

■ **FEATHER RIVER COLLEGE**
570 Golden Eagle Ave.
Quincy, CA 95971-9124
Tel: (530)283-0202; Free: 800-442-9799
Fax: (530)283-3757
E-mail: lmikesell@frc.edu
Web Site: www.frc.edu/
Description: State and locally supported, 2-year, coed. Part of California Community College System. Awards certificates, diplomas, transfer associate, and terminal associate degrees. Founded 1968. Setting: 150-acre rural campus. Total enrollment: 2,267. Student-undergrad faculty ratio is 27:1. 0% from out-of-state. 53% 25 or older. Core. Calendar: semesters. Academic remediation for entering students, services for LD students, advanced placement, honors program, independent study, distance learning, double major, summer session for credit, part-time degree program, adult/continuing education programs, co-op programs.

Entrance Requirements: Open admission. Option: electronic application. Entrance: noncompetitive.

Costs Per Year: Application fee: $0. State resident tuition: $1446 full-time, $46 per credit part-time. Nonresident tuition: $6846 full-time, $226 per credit part-time. Mandatory fees: $1 per credit part-time, $18 per term part-time. Full-time tuition varies according to course load. Part-time tuition and fees vary according to course load. College room only: $4250. Room charges vary according to housing facility.

Collegiate Environment: Orientation program. Drama-theater group, choral group. Campus security: student patrols. Feather River Library with 21,598 books, 125 serials, and an OPAC.

■ **FIDM/THE FASHION INSTITUTE OF DESIGN & MERCHANDISING, LOS ANGELES CAMPUS**
919 S Grand Ave.
Los Angeles, CA 90015-1421
Tel: (213)624-1200; Free: 800-624-1200
Fax: (213)624-4799
E-mail: saronson@fidm.com
Web Site: www.fidm.edu/
Description: Proprietary, primarily 2-year, coed. Part of The Fashion Institute of Design and Merchandising/FIDM. Awards transfer associate, terminal associate, and bachelor's degrees (also includes Orange County Campus). Founded 1969. Setting: urban campus. Total enrollment: 3,743. Faculty: 326 (68 full-time, 258 part-time). Student-undergrad faculty ratio is 21:1. 1,777 applied, 57% were admitted. 10% from top 10% of their high school class, 25% from top quarter, 65% from top half. Full-time: 3,288 students, 89% women, 11% men. Part-time: 455 students, 87% women, 13% men. 0.3% American Indian or Alaska Native, non-Hispanic/Latino; 23% Hispanic/Latino; 6% African American, non-Hispanic/Latino; 12% Asian, non-Hispanic/Latino; 1% Native Hawaiian or other Pacific Islander, non-Hispanic/Latino; 12% international. Retention: 91% of full-time freshmen returned the following year. Academic area with the most degrees conferred: business/marketing. Core. Academic remediation for entering students, ESL program, services for LD students, advanced placement, independent study, distance

learning, summer session for credit, part-time degree program, adult/continuing education programs, co-op programs and internships. Study abroad program.

Entrance Requirements: Options: electronic application, deferred admission, international baccalaureate accepted. Required: essay, high school transcript, minimum 2 high school GPA, 3 recommendations, interview, major-determined project. Recommended: SAT or ACT. Entrance: moderately difficult. Application deadlines: Rolling, Rolling for nonresidents. Transfer credits accepted: Yes.

Costs Per Year: Application fee: $225. Tuition: $23,965 full-time. Mandatory fees: $225 full-time. Full-time tuition and fees vary according to degree level and program.

Collegiate Environment: Orientation program. Student-run newspaper. Most popular organizations: ASID (student chapter), Design Council, Phi Theta Kappa Honor Society, Student Council, MODE. Major annual events: Debut Fashion Show, Industry Lunch Connections, Career Connection. Student services: personal-psychological counseling. Campus security: 24-hour emergency response devices and patrols, late night transport-escort service. FIDM Los Angeles Campus Library plus 1 other with 39,205 books, 243 serials, 6,243 audiovisual materials, and an OPAC.

■ **FIDM/THE FASHION INSTITUTE OF DESIGN & MERCHANDISING, ORANGE COUNTY CAMPUS**
17590 Gillette Ave.
Irvine, CA 92614
Tel: (949)851-6200; Free: 888-974-3436
Fax: (949)851-6808
Web Site: www.fidm.edu/
Description: Proprietary, 2-year, coed. Part of The Fashion Institute of Design and Merchandising/FIDM. Awards transfer associate and terminal associate degrees. Founded 1981. Total enrollment: 293. Faculty: 33 (8 full-time, 25 part-time). Student-undergrad faculty ratio is 21:1. 376 applied, 69% were admitted. 10% from top 10% of their high school class, 25% from top quarter, 65% from top half. Full-time: 286 students, 91% women, 9% men. Part-time: 7 students, 100% women. Students come from 8 states and territories, 1 other country, 11% from out-of-state. 1% American Indian or Alaska Native, non-Hispanic/Latino; 31% Hispanic/Latino; 2% African American, non-Hispanic/Latino; 13% Asian, non-Hispanic/Latino; 2% Native Hawaiian or other Pacific Islander, non-Hispanic/Latino; 3% international. 6% 25 or older, 31% transferred in. Core. Academic remediation for entering students, ESL program, services for LD students, advanced placement, independent study, distance learning, summer session for credit, part-time degree program, adult/continuing education programs, co-op programs and internships. Study abroad program.

Entrance Requirements: Options: deferred admission, international baccalaureate accepted. Required: essay, high school transcript, minimum 2 high school GPA, 3 recommendations, interview, entrance requirement project. Entrance: moderately difficult. Application deadlines: Rolling, Rolling for nonresidents. Notification: continuous, continuous for nonresidents.

Costs Per Year: Application fee: $225. Tuition: $23,965 full-time. Mandatory fees: $225 full-time. Full-time tuition and fees vary according to program.

Collegiate Environment: Orientation program. Student-run newspaper. Social organizations: Student Council, Honor Society. Most popular organizations: ASID (student chapter), Design Council, Association of Manufacturing Students. Student services: personal-psychological counseling. Campus security: 24-hour emergency response devices, late night transport-escort service. FIDM Orange County Campus Library plus 1 other with 7,300 books, 84 serials, and 3,010 audiovisual materials.

■ **FIDM/THE FASHION INSTITUTE OF DESIGN & MERCHANDISING, SAN DIEGO CAMPUS**
350 Tenth Ave.
3rd Fl.
San Diego, CA 92101
Tel: (619)235-2049; Free: 800-243-3436
Fax: (619)232-4322
E-mail: info@fidm.com
Web Site: www.fidm.edu/
Description: Proprietary, 2-year, coed. Part of The Fashion Institute of Design and Merchandising/FIDM. Awards transfer associate and terminal associate degrees. Founded 1985. Setting: urban campus. Total enrollment: 181. Faculty: 27 (3 full-time, 24 part-time). Student-undergrad faculty ratio is 15:1. 353 applied, 69% were admitted. 10% from top 10% of their high school class, 25% from top quarter, 65% from top half. Full-time: 174

students, 91% women, 9% men. Part-time: 9 students, 78% women, 22% men. 1% American Indian or Alaska Native, non-Hispanic/Latino; 37% Hispanic/Latino; 4% African American, non-Hispanic/Latino; 12% Asian, non-Hispanic/Latino; 4% Native Hawaiian or other Pacific Islander, non-Hispanic/Latino; 4% international. Core. Academic remediation for entering students, ESL program, services for LD students, advanced placement, independent study, distance learning, summer session for credit, part-time degree program, adult/continuing education programs, co-op programs and internships. Study abroad program.
Entrance Requirements: Options: electronic application, deferred admission, international baccalaureate accepted. Required: essay, high school transcript, minimum 2 high school GPA, 3 recommendations, interview, major-determined project. Recommended: SAT or ACT. Entrance: moderately difficult. Application deadlines: Rolling, Rolling for nonresidents. Transfer credits accepted: Yes.
Costs Per Year: Application fee: $225. Tuition: $22,965 full-time. Mandatory fees: $225 full-time. Full-time tuition and fees vary according to program.
Collegiate Environment: Orientation program. Social organizations: Student Council, Honor Society. Most popular organizations: Student Council, Phi Theta Kappa. Major annual events: Debut Fashion Show, International Food Fair, Career Connection. Student services: personal-psychological counseling. Campus security: 24-hour emergency response devices and patrols. FIDM San Diego Campus Library plus 1 other with 10,145 books, 124 serials, 3,497 audiovisual materials, and an OPAC.

■ **FIDM/THE FASHION INSTITUTE OF DESIGN & MERCHANDISING, SAN FRANCISCO CAMPUS**
55 Stockton St.
San Francisco, CA 94108-5829
Tel: (415)675-5200; Free: 800-422-3436
Fax: (415)296-7299
E-mail: info@fidm.com
Web Site: www.fidm.edu/
Description: Proprietary, 2-year, coed. Part of The Fashion Institute of Design and Merchandising/FIDM. Awards transfer associate and terminal associate degrees. Founded 1973. Setting: urban campus. Total enrollment: 750. Faculty: 74 (9 full-time, 65 part-time). Student-undergrad faculty ratio is 20:1. 316 applied, 63% were admitted. 10% from top 10% of their high school class, 25% from top quarter, 65% from top half. Full-time: 651 students, 92% women, 8% men. Part-time: 102 students, 90% women, 10% men. 0.3% American Indian or Alaska Native, non-Hispanic/Latino; 22% Hispanic/Latino; 7% African American, non-Hispanic/Latino; 2% Asian, non-Hispanic/Latino; 2% Native Hawaiian or other Pacific Islander, non-Hispanic/Latino; 4% international. Core. Academic remediation for entering students, ESL program, services for LD students, advanced placement, honors program, independent study, distance learning, summer session for credit, part-time degree program, adult/continuing education programs, co-op programs and internships. Off campus study at Fashion Institute of Design and Merchandising, Los Angeles Campus. Study abroad program.
Entrance Requirements: Options: electronic application, deferred admission, international baccalaureate accepted. Required: essay, high school transcript, 3 recommendations, interview, major-determined project. Recommended: SAT or ACT. Entrance: moderately difficult. Application deadlines: Rolling, Rolling for nonresidents. Transfer credits accepted: Yes.
Costs Per Year: Application fee: $225. Tuition: $23,965 full-time. Mandatory fees: $225 full-time. Full-time tuition and fees vary according to degree level and program.
Collegiate Environment: Orientation program. Most popular organizations: ASID (student chapter), Student Council, Premiere Marketing Group, Phi Theta Kappa. Major annual events: Career Connection, Industry Lunch Connections. Student services: personal-psychological counseling. Campus security: 24-hour emergency response devices and patrols. College housing not available. FIDM San Francisco Library plus 1 other with 12,540 books, 175 serials, 3,500 audiovisual materials, and an OPAC.

■ **FOLSOM LAKE COLLEGE**
10 College Pky.
Folsom, CA 95630
Tel: (916)608-6500
Web Site: www.flc.losrios.edu/
Description: State-supported, 2-year, coed. Part of Los Rios Community College District System. Awards certificates, diplomas, transfer associate, and terminal associate degrees. Founded 2004. Setting: suburban campus with easy access to Sacramento. Total enrollment: 9,352. Faculty: 295 (109

full-time, 186 part-time). Student-undergrad faculty ratio is 32:1. Core. Academic remediation for entering students, ESL program, services for LD students, advanced placement, independent study, distance learning, summer session for credit, co-op programs and internships. Study abroad program.
Entrance Requirements: Option: electronic application. Recommended: high school transcript. Application deadline: Rolling. Transfer credits accepted: Yes.
Collegiate Environment: Orientation program. Drama-theater group, choral group. Social organizations: Phi Theta Kappa. Student services: health clinic, personal-psychological counseling. Campus security: 24-hour emergency response devices and patrols, late night transport-escort service. Library with 26,100 books, 62 serials, 5 audiovisual materials, an OPAC, and a Web page. 131 computers available on campus for general student use. Computer purchase/lease plans available. A campuswide network can be accessed from off-campus. Students can access the following: online class registration. Staffed computer lab on campus provides training in use of computers, software, and the Internet.

■ **FOOTHILL COLLEGE**
12345 El Monte Rd.
Los Altos Hills, CA 94022-4599
Tel: (650)949-7777
E-mail: acedshawna@hda.edu
Web Site: www.foothill.edu/
Description: State and locally supported, 2-year, coed. Part of Foothill-DeAnza Community College District. Awards certificates, transfer associate, and terminal associate degrees. Founded 1958. Setting: 122-acre suburban campus with easy access to San Jose. System endowment: $15 million. Educational spending for the previous fiscal year: $908 per student. Total enrollment: 15,765. Faculty: 538 (184 full-time, 354 part-time). Student-undergrad faculty ratio is 45:1. 5,697 applied, 100% were admitted. 10% from top 10% of their high school class, 35% from top quarter, 50% from top half. Students come from 16 states and territories, 109 other countries, 1% from out-of-state. 0.3% American Indian or Alaska Native, non-Hispanic/Latino; 19% Hispanic/Latino; 4% African American, non-Hispanic/Latino; 22% Asian, non-Hispanic/Latino; 1% Native Hawaiian or other Pacific Islander, non-Hispanic/Latino; 6% international. Core. Academic remediation for entering students, ESL program, services for LD students, advanced placement, accelerated degree program, self-designed majors, honors program, independent study, distance learning, summer session for credit, part-time degree program, adult/continuing education programs, co-op programs and internships. Off campus study at DeAnza College. Study abroad program. ROTC: Army (c), Air Force (c).
Entrance Requirements: Open admission except for allied health programs. Option: electronic application. Recommended: high school transcript. Entrance: noncompetitive. Application deadlines: Rolling, Rolling for nonresidents. Notification: continuous, continuous for nonresidents. Transfer credits accepted: Yes.
Costs Per Year: State resident tuition: $1224 full-time. Nonresident tuition: $6192 full-time. Full-time tuition varies according to course load.
Collegiate Environment: Orientation program. Drama-theater group, choral group, student-run newspaper, radio station. Social organizations: 45 open to all. Major annual events: Career Day, Club Day, Transfer Day. Student services: legal services, health clinic, personal-psychological counseling. Campus security: 24-hour emergency response devices and patrols, late night transport-escort service. College housing not available. Hubert H. Semans Library with 70,000 books, 6,300 microform titles, 450 serials, 5,150 audiovisual materials, an OPAC, and a Web page. Operations spending for the previous fiscal year: $238,000. 400 computers available on campus for general student use. A campuswide network can be accessed from off-campus. Students can access the following: online class registration. Staffed computer lab on campus.
Community Environment: This is a suburban area with temperate climate averaging 50 to 80 degrees. Los Altos Hills is strictly residential but all recreational and commercial facilities and services may be found in the neighboring cities of Palo Alto, Los Altos, Mountain View and Sunnyvale.

■ **FRESNO CITY COLLEGE**
1101 E University Ave.
Fresno, CA 93741-0002
Tel: (559)442-4600
E-mail: fcc.admissions@fresnocitycollege.edu
Web Site: www.fresnocitycollege.edu/

Description: District-supported, 2-year, coed. Part of California Community College System. Awards certificates, transfer associate, and terminal associate degrees. Founded 1910. Setting: 103-acre urban campus. Total enrollment: 25,511. Student-undergrad faculty ratio is 28:1. 0% from out-of-state. 40% 25 or older. Core. Calendar: semesters. Academic remediation for entering students, ESL program, services for LD students, advanced placement, freshman honors college, honors program, summer session for credit, part-time degree program, co-op programs. Off campus study at Reedley College; California State University, Fresno. Study abroad program. ROTC: Army (c), Air Force (c).

Entrance Requirements: Open admission. Options: early admission, deferred admission. Required: high school transcript. Entrance: noncompetitive. Application deadline: Rolling. Notification: continuous.

Collegiate Environment: Orientation program. Drama-theater group, choral group, marching band, student-run newspaper. Student services: health clinic, personal-psychological counseling. Campus security: 24-hour emergency response devices and patrols, late night transport-escort service. Fresno City College Library with an OPAC and a Web page.

Community Environment: See California State University - Fresno.

■ **FRESNO PACIFIC UNIVERSITY**
1717 S Chestnut Ave.
Fresno, CA 93702-4709
Tel: (559)453-2000; Free: 800-660-6089
Fax: (559)453-2007
E-mail: andy.johnson@fresno.edu
Web Site: www.fresno.edu/
Description: Independent, comprehensive, coed, affiliated with Mennonite Brethren Church. Awards bachelor's and master's degrees. Founded 1944. Setting: 50-acre suburban campus with easy access to Fresno, CA. Endowment: $11.3 million. Total enrollment: 3,759. Faculty: 353 (95 full-time, 258 part-time). Student-undergrad faculty ratio is 14:1. 619 applied, 82% were admitted. 33% from top 10% of their high school class, 62% from top quarter, 91% from top half. Full-time: 2,299 students, 66% women, 34% men. Part-time: 525 students, 48% women, 52% men. Students come from 40 other countries, 1% from out-of-state. 1% American Indian or Alaska Native, non-Hispanic/Latino; 39% Hispanic/Latino; 5% African American, non-Hispanic/Latino; 3% Asian, non-Hispanic/Latino; 0.2% Native Hawaiian or other Pacific Islander, non-Hispanic/Latino; 2% international. 0.3% 25 or older. 61% live on campus, 17% transferred in. Retention: 78% of full-time freshmen returned the following year. Academic areas with the most degrees conferred: business/marketing; education; psychology. Core. Calendar: semesters. ESL program, services for LD students, advanced placement, accelerated degree program, self-designed majors, honors program, independent study, distance learning, double major, summer session for credit, part-time degree program, adult/continuing education programs, co-op programs and internships, graduate courses open to undergrads. Off campus study at California State University, Fresno; Mennonite Brethren Biblical Seminary; San Joaquin College of Law. Study abroad program.

Entrance Requirements: Options: electronic application, early admission, deferred admission. Required: essay, high school transcript, 1 recommendation, SAT and SAT Subject Tests or ACT. Recommended: minimum 3.1 high school GPA. Required for some: interview. Entrance: moderately difficult. Application deadline: Rolling. Notification: continuous until 7/31. SAT Reasoning Test deadline: 7/31. SAT Subject Test deadline: 7/31. Transfer credits accepted: Yes.

Costs Per Year: Application fee: $40. One-time mandatory fee: $2277. Comprehensive fee: $57,956 includes full-time tuition ($25,334), mandatory fees ($25,334), and college room and board ($7288). Full-time tuition and fees vary according to program. Room and board charges vary according to board plan and housing facility. Part-time tuition: $905 per credit. Part-time tuition varies according to program.

Collegiate Environment: Orientation program. Drama-theater group, choral group, student-run newspaper. Social organizations: 20 open to all. Major annual events: Homecoming, M.C.C. Sale. Student services: health clinic, personal-psychological counseling. Campus security: 24-hour emergency response devices and patrols, student patrols, late night transport-escort service, controlled dormitory access, 24-hour monitored closed-circuit security cameras. 537 college housing spaces available; 510 were occupied in 2012-13. Freshmen guaranteed college housing. On-campus residence required through junior year. Options: men-only, women-only housing available. Hiebert Library with 197,032 books, 330,000 microform titles, 16,000 serials, 2,558 audiovisual materials, an OPAC, and a Web page. 90 computers available on campus for general student use. Computer purchase/lease

plans available. A campuswide network can be accessed from student residence rooms and from off campus. Students can access the following: online class registration. Staffed computer lab on campus provides training in use of computers and the Internet.

Community Environment: See California State University Fresno.

■ **FULLERTON COLLEGE**
321 E Chapman Ave.
Fullerton, CA 92832-2095
Tel: (714)992-7000
E-mail: aabutin@fullcoll.edu
Web Site: www.fullcoll.edu/
Description: State and locally supported, 2-year, coed. Part of California Community College System. Awards certificates, transfer associate, and terminal associate degrees. Founded 1913. Setting: 79-acre suburban campus with easy access to Los Angeles. Total enrollment: 22,469. Student-undergrad faculty ratio is 29:1. 0% from out-of-state. 25% 25 or older. Core. Calendar: semesters. Academic remediation for entering students, ESL program, services for LD students, advanced placement, honors program, summer session for credit, part-time degree program, adult/continuing education programs, co-op programs. Study abroad program. ROTC: Army (c), Naval (c), Air Force (c).

Entrance Requirements: Open admission. Option: early admission. Entrance: noncompetitive. Application deadline: Rolling.

Collegiate Environment: Drama-theater group, student-run newspaper, radio station. Student services: legal services, health clinic, personal-psychological counseling, women's center.

Community Environment: See California State University - Fullerton.

■ **GAVILAN COLLEGE**
5055 Santa Teresa Blvd.
Gilroy, CA 95020-9599
Tel: (408)847-1400
Fax: (408)848-4801
E-mail: cwhitney@gavilan.edu
Web Site: www.gavilan.edu/
Description: State and locally supported, 2-year, coed. Part of California Community College System. Awards certificates, diplomas, transfer associate, and terminal associate degrees. Founded 1919. Setting: 150-acre rural campus with easy access to San Jose. Total enrollment: 8,382. Faculty: 324 (74 full-time, 250 part-time). Student-undergrad faculty ratio is 30:1. 0% from out-of-state. 1% American Indian or Alaska Native, non-Hispanic/Latino; 43% Hispanic/Latino; 5% African American, non-Hispanic/Latino; 4% Asian, non-Hispanic/Latino; 2% Native Hawaiian or other Pacific Islander, non-Hispanic/Latino. 56% 25 or older. Retention: 70% of full-time freshmen returned the following year. Core. Calendar: semesters. Academic remediation for entering students, ESL program, services for LD students, advanced placement, honors program, independent study, distance learning, summer session for credit, part-time degree program, adult/continuing education programs, co-op programs and internships. Study abroad program.

Entrance Requirements: Open admission. Option: international baccalaureate accepted. Entrance: noncompetitive. Application deadlines: Rolling, Rolling for nonresidents. Notification: continuous, continuous for nonresidents. Transfer credits accepted: Yes.

Costs Per Year: Application fee: $0. State resident tuition: $36 per unit part-time. Nonresident tuition: $216 per unit part-time. Mandatory fees: $36 per unit part-time. Part-time tuition and fees vary according to course load.

Collegiate Environment: Orientation program. Drama-theater group, choral group, student-run newspaper. Social organizations: 23 open to all. Most popular organizations: EOPS, Rho Alpha Mu (Honor Society), Science Alliance, TADAA Drama Club, Vets Club. Major annual events: ASB back to school events first week of each term, Science Alive, Career Fair. Student services: health clinic, personal-psychological counseling. Campus security: 24-hour emergency response devices. Gavilan Library with 60,587 books, 2,541 serials, an OPAC, and a Web page. 50 computers available on campus for general student use. A campuswide network can be accessed. Students can access the following: online class registration. Staffed computer lab on campus provides training in use of computers, software, and the Internet.

Community Environment: Gilroy has a population of 45,700 and is located 77 miles south of San Francisco; served by buses and railroads. There are churches, a hospital, a library, and radio station. Gilroy has theatres, parks, civic organizations, and a public swimming pool for recreational activities; nearby are beaches and five state parks.

■ GLENDALE COMMUNITY COLLEGE
1500 N Verdugo Rd.
Glendale, CA 91208-2894
Tel: (818)240-1000
Fax: (818)549-9436
E-mail: scombs@glendale.edu
Web Site: www.glendale.edu/

Description: State and locally supported, 2-year, coed. Part of California Community College System. Awards certificates, transfer associate, and terminal associate degrees. Founded 1927. Setting: 119-acre urban campus with easy access to Los Angeles. Total enrollment: 16,781. Student-undergrad faculty ratio is 28:1. 0% from out-of-state. 40% 25 or older. Core. Calendar: semesters. Academic remediation for entering students, ESL program, services for LD students, advanced placement, honors program, independent study, distance learning, summer session for credit, part-time degree program, adult/continuing education programs, co-op programs and internships. Study abroad program.

Entrance Requirements: Open admission. Options: electronic application, early admission, deferred admission. Recommended: high school transcript. Entrance: noncompetitive. Application deadline: Rolling.

Collegiate Environment: Orientation program. Drama-theater group, choral group, student-run newspaper. Student services: health clinic, personal-psychological counseling. Campus security: student patrols, late night transport-escort service. Glendale Community College Library with 123,348 books, 188 serials, an OPAC, and a Web page.

■ GOLDEN GATE UNIVERSITY
536 Mission St.
San Francisco, CA 94105-2968
Tel: (415)442-7000; Free: 800-448-3381
Fax: (415)442-7807
E-mail: info@ggu.edu
Web Site: www.ggu.edu/

Description: Independent, university, coed. Awards bachelor's, master's, and doctoral degrees. Founded 1901. Setting: urban campus. Endowment: $29.8 million. Educational spending for the previous fiscal year: $7600 per student. Total enrollment: 3,528. Faculty: 489 (30 full-time, 459 part-time). Student-undergrad faculty ratio is 16:1. Students come from 18 states and territories, 50 other countries, 5% from out-of-state. 76% 25 or older. Retention: 80% of full-time freshmen returned the following year. Academic areas with the most degrees conferred: business/marketing; computer and information sciences; liberal arts/general studies. Core. Calendar: trimesters. Academic remediation for entering students, ESL program, advanced placement, accelerated degree program, distance learning, summer session for credit, part-time degree program, adult/continuing education programs, internships, graduate courses open to undergrads. Off campus study at The San Francisco Consortium.

Entrance Requirements: Options: electronic application, deferred admission, international baccalaureate accepted. Required: high school transcript, minimum 2.0 high school GPA. Recommended: essay, minimum 3.0 high school GPA. Required for some: minimum 3.2 high school GPA, interview. Entrance: moderately difficult. Application deadline: Rolling. Notification: continuous.

Collegiate Environment: Student-run newspaper. Social organizations: 16 open to all. Most popular organizations: American Marketing Association, Korean Student Association, Japanese Student Association, Thai Student Association, Computing Society. Major annual events: International Cultural Celebration Day, Welcome party, Farewell party. Student services: personal-psychological counseling. Campus security: late night transport-escort service. Golden Gate University Library plus 1 other with 79,204 books, 442,800 microform titles, 3,335 serials, and an OPAC. Operations spending for the previous fiscal year: $470,711. 52 computers available on campus for general student use. Computer purchase/lease plans available. A campuswide network can be accessed. Students can access the following: online class registration. Staffed computer lab on campus provides training in use of computers, software, and the Internet.

Community Environment: See San Francisco State University.

■ GOLDEN WEST COLLEGE
PO Box 2748, 15744 Golden W St.
Huntington Beach, CA 92647-2748
Tel: (714)892-7711
Web Site: www.goldenwestcollege.edu/

Description: State and locally supported, 2-year, coed. Part of Coast Community College District System. Awards certificates, transfer associate, and terminal associate degrees. Founded 1966. Setting: 122-acre suburban campus with easy access to Los Angeles. Endowment: $880,684. Educational spending for the previous fiscal year: $1831 per student. Total enrollment: 13,226. Faculty: 455 (144 full-time, 311 part-time). Student-undergrad faculty ratio is 34:1. Students come from 28 other countries. 44% 25 or older. Core. Calendar: semesters (summer session). Academic remediation for entering students, ESL program, services for LD students, advanced placement, self-designed majors, honors program, independent study, distance learning, summer session for credit, part-time degree program, external degree program, adult/continuing education programs, co-op programs and internships. Study abroad program. ROTC: Air Force (c).

Entrance Requirements: Open admission except for nursing program. Option: early admission. Recommended: high school transcript. Required for some: essay. Entrance: noncompetitive. Application deadline: Rolling. Notification: continuous.

Collegiate Environment: Orientation program. Drama-theater group, choral group, student-run newspaper. Major annual events: College Transfer Day, Gold Rush Days. Student services: legal services, health clinic, personal-psychological counseling. Campus security: 24-hour emergency response devices and patrols, late night transport-escort service. Golden West College Library plus 1 other with 95,000 books, 410 serials, an OPAC, and a Web page. Operations spending for the previous fiscal year: $750,639. 680 computers available on campus for general student use. Computer purchase/lease plans available. A campuswide network can be accessed. Students can access the following: online class registration. Staffed computer lab on campus provides training in use of computers, software, and the Internet.

Community Environment: Huntington Beach is located in the northern coastal region of Orange County, which is 35 miles southeast of Los Angeles. The climate is moderate with a mean yearly temperature of 70 degrees. All major transportation facilities available. Eight miles of the finest, safest beach in California is located here. The city has three public golf courses and parks for recreational activities. This is one of the fastest growing cities in the west.

■ GOLF ACADEMY OF AMERICA
1950 Camino Vida Roble, Ste. 125
Carlsbad, CA 92008
Tel: (760)734-1208; Free: 800-342-7342
Fax: (760)734-1642
E-mail: sdga@sdgagolf.com
Web Site: www.golfacademy.edu/

Description: Proprietary, 2-year, coed. Awards transfer associate and terminal associate degrees. Founded 1974. Total enrollment: 230. 35 applied. 37% 25 or older. Calendar: semesters.

Entrance Requirements: Entrance: moderately difficult. Application deadline: Rolling.

■ GROSSMONT COLLEGE
8800 Grossmont College Dr.
El Cajon, CA 92020-1799
Tel: (619)644-7000
Fax: (619)644-7922
Web Site: www.grossmont.edu/

Description: State and locally supported, 2-year, coed. Part of California Community College System. Awards certificates, transfer associate, and terminal associate degrees. Founded 1961. Setting: 135-acre suburban campus with easy access to San Diego. Total enrollment: 20,335. Student-undergrad faculty ratio is 29:1. 0% from out-of-state. 35% 25 or older. Core. Calendar: semesters. Academic remediation for entering students, ESL program, services for LD students, advanced placement, self-designed majors, honors program, summer session for credit, part-time degree program, adult/continuing education programs, co-op programs and internships. ROTC: Army (c), Air Force (c).

Entrance Requirements: Open admission. Option: early admission. Entrance: noncompetitive. Application deadline: 8/12. Notification: continuous until 8/12.

Collegiate Environment: Drama-theater group, choral group, student-run newspaper, radio station. Student services: legal services, health clinic, personal-psychological counseling. Campus security: 24-hour emergency response devices, student patrols, late night transport-escort service. Lewis F. Smith Learning Resource Center with an OPAC and a Web page.

Community Environment: El Cajon is situated east of San Diego in a suburban community with a Mediterranean climate. Gillespie Airport and buses serve the area. The County Branch Library is located here; there are churches of all denominations. Employment is available through the California Department of Employment which is located on the Grossmont college campus. There are recreational facilities at both the beaches and in the nearby mountain area. Annual festivities include the "Mother Goose Parade.".

■ **HARTNELL COLLEGE**

411 Central Ave.

Salinas, CA 93901

Tel: (831)755-6700

Web Site: www.hartnell.edu/

Description: District-supported, 2-year, coed. Part of California Community College System. Awards certificates, transfer associate, and terminal associate degrees. Founded 1920. Setting: 50-acre small town campus with easy access to San Jose. Total enrollment: 10,451. Student-undergrad faculty ratio is 35:1. 0% from out-of-state. 46% 25 or older. Core. Calendar: semesters. Academic remediation for entering students, ESL program, services for LD students, self-designed majors, honors program, summer session for credit, part-time degree program, adult/continuing education programs, co-op programs. Study abroad program.

Entrance Requirements: Open admission except for allied health programs. Options: early admission, deferred admission. Required for some: high school transcript. Entrance: noncompetitive. Application deadline: Rolling. Notification: continuous.

Collegiate Environment: Drama-theater group, choral group, student-run newspaper. Student services: women's center. Campus security: 24-hour emergency response devices, student patrols, late night transport-escort service.

Community Environment: Population 146,400. Salinas is the county seat of Monterey County, 106 miles south of San Francisco on Highway 101. Southern Pacific Railroad, Greyhound bus and United Airlines serve the area. The Santa Lucia Mountains are to the west of Salinas and the Gabilan foothills to the east. Agriculture is the chief factor of economy in Salinas with new industries designed to take advantage of the abundant harvest. The climate is comfortable, the average temperature being 57 degrees. Salinas has a great number of churches, YMCA, theatres, community concert association, Monterey County symphony, a variety of civic, fraternal and veteran's organizations. John Steinbeck was born here. Part-time employment opportunities for students available in nearby recreational areas, agriculture, industrial and commercial firms. The recreational facilities include nine municipal recreation centers, a municipal golf course, private country clubs, the Monterey Peninsula playland area, the famous white sandy beaches of Carmel, a 20-minute drive away, flying clubs, a ski club, and many hobby clubs. This is the location of the oldest and largest four-day California Rodeo.

■ **HARVEY MUDD COLLEGE**

301 Platt Blvd.

Claremont, CA 91711-5994

Tel: (909)621-8000

Fax: (909)621-8360

E-mail: admission@hmc.edu

Web Site: www.hmc.edu/

Description: Independent, 4-year, coed. Part of The Claremont Colleges Consortium. Awards bachelor's degrees. Founded 1955. Setting: 33-acre suburban campus with easy access to Los Angeles. Endowment: $225.5 million. Research spending for the previous fiscal year: $3.1 million. Educational spending for the previous fiscal year: $27,464 per student. Total enrollment: 783. Faculty: 106 (88 full-time, 18 part-time). Student-undergrad faculty ratio is 8:1. 3,336 applied, 19% were admitted. 96% from top 10% of their high school class, 100% from top quarter, 100% from top half. 55 National Merit Scholars, 17 valedictorians. Full-time: 782 students, 44% women, 56% men. Part-time: 1 student, 100% men. Students come from 42 states and territories, 19 other countries, 63% from out-of-state. 0.4% American Indian or Alaska Native, non-Hispanic/Latino; 7% Hispanic/Latino; 1% African American, non-Hispanic/Latino; 22% Asian, non-Hispanic/Latino; 0% Native Hawaiian or other Pacific Islander, non-Hispanic/Latino; 8% international. 1% 25 or older, 98% live on campus, 0.3% transferred in. Retention: 98% of full-time freshmen returned the following year. Academic areas with the most degrees conferred: engineering; computer and information sciences; physical sciences. Core. Calendar: semesters. Services for

LD students, self-designed majors, double major, internships. Off campus study at other members of The Claremont Colleges, Swarthmore College, Rensselaer Polytechnic Institute. Study abroad program. ROTC: Army (c), Air Force:

Entrance Requirements: Options: electronic application, early admission, early decision, deferred admission. Required: essay, high school transcript, 3 recommendations, SAT or ACT, SAT Subject Tests, SAT or ACT and the SAT Subject Test in Math 2 and a second SAT Subject exam. Recommended: interview. Entrance: most difficult. Application deadlines: 1/1, 11/15 for early decision plan 1, 1/1 for early decision plan 2. Notification: 4/1, 12/15 for early decision plan 1, 2/15 for early decision plan 2. SAT Reasoning Test deadline: 2/1. SAT Subject Test deadline: 2/1. Applicants placed on waiting list: 501. Wait-listed applicants offered admission: 27. Early decision applicants: 315. Early decision applicants admitted: 63.

Costs Per Year: Application fee: $70. One-time mandatory fee: $100. Comprehensive fee: $58,913 includes full-time tuition ($44,159), mandatory fees ($283), and college room and board ($14,471). College room only: $7763. Room and board charges vary according to board plan.

Collegiate Environment: Orientation program. Drama-theater group, choral group, student-run newspaper, radio station. Social organizations: 50 open to all. Most popular organizations: Ballroom Dancing, Delta-H (outdoors club), Intervarsity Christian Fellowship, Science Bus, SWE (Society of Women Engineers). Major annual events: 5-Class Competition, Noisy Minutes, Bed Races. Student services: health clinic, personal-psychological counseling, women's center. Campus security: 24-hour emergency response devices and patrols, late night transport-escort service. 752 college housing spaces available; 745 were occupied in 2012-13. Freshmen guaranteed college housing. On-campus residence required in freshman year. Option: coed housing available. Honnold Mudd Library plus 1 other with 2.7 million books, 980,340 microform titles, 17,836 serials, 4,677 audiovisual materials, an OPAC, and a Web page. Operations spending for the previous fiscal year: $1.2 million. 120 computers available on campus for general student use. A campuswide network can be accessed from student residence rooms and from off campus. Students can access the following: online class registration. Staffed computer lab on campus.

■ **HEALD COLLEGE–CONCORD**

5130 Commercial Cir.

Concord, CA 94520

Tel: (925)288-5800; Free: 800-88-HEALD

Fax: (925)288-5896

E-mail: concordinfo@heald.edu

Web Site: www.heald.edu/

Description: Independent, 2-year, coed. Awards certificates, diplomas, transfer associate, and terminal associate degrees. Founded 1863. Setting: 5-acre small town campus with easy access to San Francisco. Total enrollment: 1,371. Student-undergrad faculty ratio is 30:1. 0% from out-of-state. 43% 25 or older. Retention: 66% of full-time freshmen returned the following year. Academic remediation for entering students, advanced placement, summer session for credit, part-time degree program, internships.

Entrance Requirements: Open admission. Required: high school transcript, interview. Entrance: minimally difficult. Application deadline: Rolling. Notification: continuous.

Collegiate Environment: Campus security: 24-hour emergency response devices. Learning Resource Center with an OPAC.

■ **HEALD COLLEGE–FRESNO**

255 W Bullard Ave.

Fresno, CA 93704-1706

Tel: (559)438-4222; Free: 800-88-HEALD

E-mail: fresnoinfo@heald.edu

Web Site: www.heald.edu/

Description: Independent, 2-year, coed. Awards certificates, diplomas, transfer associate, and terminal associate degrees. Founded 1863. Setting: 3-acre suburban campus. Total enrollment: 1,430. Student-undergrad faculty ratio is 30:1. 0% from out-of-state. 41% 25 or older. Academic remediation for entering students, advanced placement, summer session for credit, part-time degree program, internships.

Entrance Requirements: Open admission. Options: early admission, deferred admission. Required: high school transcript, interview. Entrance: minimally difficult. Application deadline: Rolling. Notification: continuous.

Collegiate Environment: Learning Resource Center with an OPAC.

■ **HEALD COLLEGE–HAYWARD**

25500 Industrial Blvd.

Hayward, CA 94545

Tel: (510)783-2100; Free: 800-88-HEALD
Fax: (510)783-3287
E-mail: harwardinfo@heald.edu
Web Site: www.heald.edu/
Description: Independent, 2-year, coed. Awards certificates, diplomas, transfer associate, and terminal associate degrees. Founded 1863. Setting: urban campus with easy access to San Francisco. Total enrollment: 1,660. Student-undergrad faculty ratio is 34:1. 0% from out-of-state. 42% 25 or older. Academic remediation for entering students, advanced placement, summer session for credit, part-time degree program, internships.
Entrance Requirements: Open admission. Options: early admission, deferred admission. Required: high school transcript, interview. Entrance: minimally difficult. Application deadline: Rolling. Notification: continuous.
Collegiate Environment: Campus security: 24-hour emergency response devices and patrols. Learning Resource Center (LRC) with an OPAC.

■ **HEALD COLLEGE–MODESTO**
5260 Pirrone Ct.
Salida, CA 95368
Tel: (209)416-3700
Web Site: www.heald.edu/
Description: Proprietary, 2-year, coed.

■ **HEALD COLLEGE–RANCHO CORDOVA**
2910 Prospect Park Dr.
Rancho Cordova, CA 95670-6005
Tel: (916)638-1616; Free: 800-88-HEALD
Fax: (916)853-8282
E-mail: ranchocordovainfo@heald.edu
Web Site: www.heald.edu/
Description: Independent, 2-year, coed. Awards certificates, diplomas, transfer associate, and terminal associate degrees. Founded 1863. Setting: 1-acre suburban campus with easy access to Sacramento. Total enrollment: 1,058. Student-undergrad faculty ratio is 24:1. 0% from out-of-state. 52% 25 or older. Academic remediation for entering students, advanced placement, summer session for credit, part-time degree program, internships.
Entrance Requirements: Open admission. Options: early admission, deferred admission. Required: high school transcript, interview. Entrance: minimally difficult. Application deadline: Rolling. Notification: continuous.
Collegiate Environment: Campus security: late night transport-escort service. Learning Resource Center with an OPAC.

■ **HEALD COLLEGE–ROSEVILLE**
Seven Sierra Gate Plz.
Roseville, CA 95678
Tel: (916)789-8600; Free: 800-88-HEALD
E-mail: rosevilleinfo@heald.edu
Web Site: www.heald.edu/
Description: Independent, 2-year, coed. Awards certificates, diplomas, transfer associate, and terminal associate degrees. Founded 1863. Setting: 5-acre urban campus. Total enrollment: 1,039. Student-undergrad faculty ratio is 23:1. 0% from out-of-state. 54% 25 or older. Academic remediation for entering students, advanced placement, summer session for credit, part-time degree program, internships.
Entrance Requirements: Open admission. Options: early admission, deferred admission. Required: high school transcript, interview. Entrance: minimally difficult.
Collegiate Environment: Orientation program. Campus security: 24-hour emergency response devices, evening security guard. Learning Resource Center with an OPAC.

■ **HEALD COLLEGE–SALINAS**
1450 N Main St.
Salinas, CA 93906
Tel: (831)443-1700; Free: 800-88-HEALD
Fax: (831)443-1050
E-mail: salinasinfo@heald.edu
Web Site: www.heald.edu/
Description: Independent, 2-year, coed. Awards certificates, diplomas, transfer associate, and terminal associate degrees. Founded 1863. Setting: small town campus with easy access to San Jose. Total enrollment: 1,069. Student-undergrad faculty ratio is 29:1. 1% from out-of-state. 32% 25 or older. Academic remediation for entering students, advanced placement, summer session for credit, part-time degree program, internships.

Entrance Requirements: Open admission. Options: early admission, deferred admission. Required: high school transcript, interview. Entrance: minimally difficult. Application deadline: Rolling. Notification: continuous.
Collegiate Environment: Orientation program. Campus security: 24-hour emergency response devices, evening security personnel. Learning Resource Center with an OPAC.

■ **HEALD COLLEGE–SAN FRANCISCO**
350 Mission St.
San Francisco, CA 94105-2206
Tel: (415)808-3000; Free: 800-88-HEALD
Fax: (415)808-3003
E-mail: sanfranciscoinfo@heald.edu
Web Site: www.heald.edu/
Description: Independent, 2-year, coed. Awards certificates, diplomas, transfer associate, and terminal associate degrees. Founded 1863. Setting: urban campus. Total enrollment: 1,083. Student-undergrad faculty ratio is 25:1. 1% from out-of-state. 48% 25 or older. Academic remediation for entering students, advanced placement, summer session for credit, part-time degree program, internships.
Entrance Requirements: Open admission. Options: early admission, deferred admission. Required: high school transcript, interview. Entrance: minimally difficult. Application deadline: Rolling. Notification: continuous.
Collegiate Environment: Orientation program. Learning Resource Center with an OPAC.

■ **HEALD COLLEGE–SAN JOSE**
341 Great Mall Pky.
Milpitas, CA 95035
Tel: (408)934-4900; Free: 800-88-HEALD
Fax: (408)934-7777
E-mail: sanjoseinfo@heald.edu
Web Site: www.heald.edu/
Description: Independent, 2-year, coed. Awards certificates, diplomas, transfer associate, and terminal associate degrees. Founded 1863. Setting: 5-acre small town campus with easy access to San Jose. Total enrollment: 1,273. Student-undergrad faculty ratio is 37:1. 0% from out-of-state. 47% 25 or older. Academic remediation for entering students, advanced placement, summer session for credit, part-time degree program, internships.
Entrance Requirements: Open admission. Options: early admission, deferred admission. Required: high school transcript, interview. Entrance: minimally difficult. Application deadline: Rolling. Notification: continuous.
Collegiate Environment: Orientation program. Learning Resource Center with an OPAC.

■ **HEALD COLLEGE–STOCKTON**
1605 E March Ln.
Stockton, CA 95210
Tel: (209)473-5200; Free: 800-88-HEALD
Fax: (209)477-2739
E-mail: stocktoninfo@heald.edu
Web Site: www.heald.edu/
Description: Independent, 2-year, coed. Awards certificates, diplomas, transfer associate, and terminal associate degrees. Founded 1863. Total enrollment: 1,545. Student-undergrad faculty ratio is 23:1. 0% from out-of-state. 44% 25 or older. Academic remediation for entering students, advanced placement, summer session for credit, part-time degree program, internships.
Entrance Requirements: Open admission. Options: early admission, deferred admission. Required: high school transcript, interview. Entrance: minimally difficult. Application deadline: Rolling. Notification: continuous.
Collegiate Environment: Learning Resource Center with an OPAC.

■ **HENLEY-PUTNAM UNIVERSITY**
2804 Mission College Blvd.
Ste. 240
Santa Clara, CA 95054
Tel: (408)453-9900; Free: 888-852-8746
Fax: (408)453-9700
E-mail: nreggio@henley-putnam.edu
Web Site: www.henley-putnam.edu/
Description: Proprietary, comprehensive, coed. Awards bachelor's,

master's, and doctoral degrees (offers only online degree programs). Founded 1991. Core. Part-time degree program, external degree program, adult/continuing education programs.

Entrance Requirements: Open admission. Options: electronic application, international baccalaureate accepted. Required for some: essay, high school transcript, interview, official transcripts from all colleges and universities attended; background checks. Application deadlines: Rolling, Rolling for nonresidents. Transfer credits accepted: Yes.

Costs Per Year: Application fee: $0. Tuition: $264 per unit part-time. Part-time tuition varies according to course level and degree level. Tuition guaranteed not to increase for student's term of enrollment.

Collegiate Environment: Orientation program.

■ **HOLY NAMES UNIVERSITY**
3500 Mountain Blvd.
Oakland, CA 94619-1699
Tel: (510)436-1000; Free: 800-430-1321
Fax: (510)436-1325
E-mail: spencer@hnu.edu
Web Site: www.hnu.edu/

Description: Independent Roman Catholic, comprehensive, coed. Awards bachelor's and master's degrees and post-master's certificates. Founded 1868. Setting: 60-acre urban campus with easy access to San Francisco. Endowment: $10.8 million. Educational spending for the previous fiscal year: $7015 per student. Total enrollment: 1,353. Faculty: 209 (55 full-time, 154 part-time). Student-undergrad faculty ratio is 14:1. 742 applied, 51% were admitted. Full-time: 695 students, 66% women, 34% men. Part-time: 192 students, 86% women, 14% men. Students come from 24 states and territories, 34 other countries, 6% from out-of-state. 1% American Indian or Alaska Native, non-Hispanic/Latino; 24% Hispanic/Latino; 23% African American, non-Hispanic/Latino; 14% Asian, non-Hispanic/Latino; 4% Native Hawaiian or other Pacific Islander, non-Hispanic/Latino; 3% international. 36% 25 or older, 66% live on campus, 16% transferred in. Retention: 70% of full-time freshmen returned the following year. Academic areas with the most degrees conferred: business/marketing; psychology; health professions and related sciences. Core. Calendar: semesters. Academic remediation for entering students, ESL program, services for LD students, advanced placement, accelerated degree program, self-designed majors, honors program, independent study, distance learning, double major, summer session for credit, part-time degree program, adult/continuing education programs, internships, graduate courses open to undergrads. Study abroad program. ROTC: Army (c), Air Force (c).

Entrance Requirements: Options: electronic application, deferred admission, international baccalaureate accepted. Required: essay, high school transcript, 1 recommendation, 1 recommendation minimum, 3 maximum. Letters must be in English, SAT or ACT. Required for some: interview. Entrance: moderately difficult. Application deadlines: Rolling, Rolling for nonresidents. Notification: continuous, continuous for nonresidents.

Collegiate Environment: Orientation program. Drama-theater group, choral group. Most popular organizations: Drama Club, Latinos Unidos, Black Student Union, Biology Club, Hiking Club. Major annual events: CORE Festival, Founders' Day, Convocation. Student services: personal-psychological counseling. Campus security: 24-hour emergency response devices, late night transport-escort service, controlled dormitory access, 24-hour security main gate. 444 college housing spaces available; 396 were occupied in 2012-13. Freshmen guaranteed college housing. Option: coed housing available. Cushing Library with 86,954 books, 27,803 serials, 75 audiovisual materials, an OPAC, and a Web page. Operations spending for the previous fiscal year: $502,441. 92 computers available on campus for general student use. A campuswide network can be accessed from student residence rooms. Students can access the following: online class registration. Staffed computer lab on campus (open 24 hours a day) provides training in use of computers, software, and the Internet.

Community Environment: The College is located in the Oakland hills, overlooking San Francisco Bay and San Francisco itself. The campus is within 15-45 minutes of all the rich cultural, recreational, and sports activities of San Francisco, Berkeley and Oakland. Easy day trips can be made to the wine country, beaches, ski areas and National Parks.

■ **HOPE INTERNATIONAL UNIVERSITY**
2500 E Nutwood Ave.
Fullerton, CA 92831-3138
Tel: (714)879-3901; Free: 866-722-HOPE
Fax: (714)526-0231

E-mail: mfmadden@hiu.edu
Web Site: www.hiu.edu/

Description: Independent, comprehensive, coed, affiliated with Christian Churches and Churches of Christ. Awards associate, bachelor's, and master's degrees. Founded 1928. Setting: 16-acre suburban campus with easy access to Los Angeles. Total enrollment: 1,652. Faculty: 208 (40 full-time, 168 part-time). Student-undergrad faculty ratio is 10:1. 439 applied, 56% were admitted. Full-time: 798 students, 56% women, 44% men. Part-time: 369 students, 57% women, 43% men. 11% from out-of-state. 0.4% American Indian or Alaska Native, non-Hispanic/Latino; 16% Hispanic/Latino; 7% African American, non-Hispanic/Latino; 3% Asian, non-Hispanic/Latino; 1% Native Hawaiian or other Pacific Islander, non-Hispanic/Latino; 9% international. 25% live on campus, 13% transferred in. Retention: 72% of full-time freshmen returned the following year. Academic areas with the most degrees conferred: theology and religious vocations; business/marketing; family and consumer sciences. Core. Calendar: 4-1-4. Academic remediation for entering students, ESL program, services for LD students, advanced placement, accelerated degree program, independent study, distance learning, double major, part-time degree program, adult/continuing education programs, internships, graduate courses open to undergrads. Off campus study. Study abroad program. ROTC: Army (c).

Entrance Requirements: Options: electronic application, international baccalaureate accepted. Required: essay, high school transcript, minimum 2.5 high school GPA, 2 recommendations, rank in upper 50% of high school class, SAT or ACT. Required for some: interview. Entrance: moderately difficult. Application deadline: 2/1. Transfer credits accepted: Yes.

Costs Per Year: Application fee: $40. One-time mandatory fee: $160. Comprehensive fee: $34,650 includes full-time tuition ($25,550), mandatory fees ($500), and college room and board ($8600). College room only: $4610. Full-time tuition and fees vary according to course level, course load, degree level, location, program, and reciprocity agreements. Room and board charges vary according to board plan and student level. Part-time tuition: $1075 per unit. Part-time mandatory fees: $500 per year. Part-time tuition and fees vary according to course level, course load, degree level, location, program, and reciprocity agreements.

Collegiate Environment: Orientation program. Drama-theater group, choral group, student-run newspaper. Most popular organizations: Campus Ministries, International Student Organization, Musical Theater, student government, student publications. Student services: personal-psychological counseling. Campus security: 24-hour emergency response devices and patrols, student patrols. Freshmen guaranteed college housing. On-campus residence required through sophomore year. Options: men-only, women-only housing available. Darling Library with 171,005 books, 36 microform titles, 227 serials, 2,500 audiovisual materials, an OPAC, and a Web page. 30 computers available on campus for general student use. A campuswide network can be accessed from student residence rooms and from off campus. Students can access the following: online class registration. Staffed computer lab on campus provides training in use of computers, software, and the Internet.

Community Environment: See California State University - Fullerton.

■ **HORIZON COLLEGE SAN DIEGO**
5331 Mt. Alifan Dr.
San Diego, CA 92111
Tel: (858)695-8587
Web Site: www.horizoncollege.org/
Description: Independent, 4-year, coed. Founded 1993. Calendar: semesters.

■ **HUMBOLDT STATE UNIVERSITY**
1 Harpst St.
Arcata, CA 95521-8299
Tel: (707)826-3011; Free: 866-850-9556
Fax: (707)826-6194
E-mail: hsuinfo@humboldt.edu
Web Site: www.humboldt.edu/

Description: State-supported, comprehensive, coed. Part of California State University System. Awards bachelor's and master's degrees and post-master's certificates. Founded 1913. Setting: 161-acre rural campus. Total enrollment: 8,116. Faculty: 538 (228 full-time, 310 part-time). Student-undergrad faculty ratio is 23:1. 9,979 applied, 80% were admitted. 11% from top 10% of their high school class, 39% from top quarter, 78% from top half. Full-time: 7,047 students, 53% women, 47% men. Part-time: 550 students, 49% women, 51% men. Students come from 48 states and territories, 41 other countries, 12% from out-of-state. 1% American Indian or Alaska Native, non-Hispanic/Latino; 23% Hispanic/Latino; 4% African American, non-Hispanic/Latino; 3% Asian, non-Hispanic/Latino; 0.3% Native Hawaiian or other Pacific Islander, non-Hispanic/Latino; 1% international. 19% 25 or older, 26% live on campus, 12% transferred in. Retention: 73% of full-time freshmen returned the following year. Academic areas with the most degrees conferred: natural resources/environmental science; visual and performing arts; biological/life sciences. Core. Calendar: semesters. Academic remediation for entering students, ESL program, services for LD students, advanced placement, self-designed majors, honors program, independent study, distance learning, double major, summer session for credit, part-time degree program, adult/continuing education programs, co-op programs and internships, graduate courses open to undergrads. Off campus study at members of the National Student Exchange, California State University System. Study abroad program.

Entrance Requirements: Options: electronic application, international baccalaureate accepted. Required: high school transcript, minimum 2 high school GPA. Required for some: SAT or ACT. Entrance: moderately difficult. Application deadlines: 11/30, 11/30 for nonresidents. Notification: continuous, continuous for nonresidents. Preference given to state residents. SAT Reasoning Test deadline: 7/1. SAT Subject Test deadline: 7/1. Transfer credits accepted: Yes.

Costs Per Year: Application fee: $55. State resident tuition: $0 full-time. Nonresident tuition: $11,160 full-time, $372 per credit hour part-time. Mandatory fees: $7130 full-time, $2208 per term part-time. Full-time tuition and fees vary according to degree level. Part-time tuition and fees vary according to course load and degree level. College room and board: $11,440. Room and board charges vary according to board plan and housing facility.

Collegiate Environment: Orientation program. Drama-theater group, choral group, marching band, student-run newspaper, radio station. Social organizations: 160 open to all; national fraternities, national sororities, local sororities; 1% of eligible men and 1% of eligible women are members. Most popular organizations: Bicycle Learning Center, Campus Center for Appropriate Technology (CCAT), Youth Educational Services, HOLA, MECHA. Major annual events: Homecoming, Dialogue on Race (seminars and guest speakers), film festival. Student services: health clinic, personal-psychological counseling, women's center. Campus security: 24-hour emergency response devices and patrols, late night transport-escort service, controlled dormitory access. 1,965 college housing spaces available; 1,958 were occupied in 2012-13. Freshmen given priority for college housing. Option: coed housing available. Humbolt State University Library with 2 million books, 603,245 microform titles, 864 serials, 23,756 audiovisual materials, an OPAC, and a Web page. 1,098 computers available on campus for general student use. Computer purchase/lease plans available. A campuswide network can be accessed from student residence rooms and from off campus. Students can access the following: online class registration. Staffed computer lab on campus.

Community Environment: Arcata, population 16,900, is located on the north shore of Humboldt Bay in northwestern California with an unrestricted panorama of mountains, bay, dairy and farm lands, sand dunes, and the Pacific Ocean. It is eight miles north of Eureka, and 275 miles north of San Francisco. Industry includes lumbering, manufacturing of wood products, tourism and dairy products. Humboldt Bay region climate is moist, but stimulating, with no extremes of heat or cold. Summer and fall are considered particularly delightful seasons. Buses and airlines serve the area. The city has a library, churches and the usual service clubs. Recreational opportunities include river rafting, kayaking, backpacking, hunting, trout fishing in mountain streams, salmon fishing in Humboldt and Trinidad Bays, and deep sea fishing. There is an Azalea Reserve, three miles north.

■ **HUMPHREYS COLLEGE**
6650 Inglewood Ave.
Stockton, CA 95207-3896
Tel: (209)478-0800
Fax: (209)478-8721
E-mail: ugadmission@humphreys.edu
Web Site: www.humphreys.edu/
Description: Independent, comprehensive, coed. Awards associate, bachelor's, master's, and doctoral degrees. Founded 1896. Setting: 10-acre suburban campus with easy access to San Francisco. Total enrollment: 756. 71% 25 or older. Core. Academic remediation for entering students, advanced placement, accelerated degree program, self-designed majors, summer session for credit, part-time degree program, adult/continuing education programs, co-op programs and internships.

Entrance Requirements: Open admission. Options: early admission, deferred admission. Required: high school transcript, minimum 2.0 high school GPA. Recommended: interview. Entrance: noncompetitive. Application deadline: Rolling.
Costs Per Year: Application fee: $35. Tuition: $7440 full-time.
Collegiate Environment: Most popular organizations: Business Club, Paralegal Club, Student Council, Collegiate Secretaries International. Major annual events: Hot Dog Day (quarterly BBQ), Annual Christmas Dinner, Students Versus Staff Softball. Campus security: 24-hour patrols, late night transport-escort service. Humphreys College Library plus 1 other with 20,500 books and 115 serials. 40 computers available on campus for general student use. Staffed computer lab on campus.
Community Environment: See University of the Pacific.

■ **ICDC COLLEGE**
5422 W Sunset Blvd.
Los Angeles, CA 90027
Tel: (323)655-9100
Web Site: icdccollege.edu/
Description: Proprietary, 2-year, coed.

■ **IMPERIAL VALLEY COLLEGE**
380 E Aten Rd.
Imperial, CA 92251-0158
Tel: (760)352-8320
Web Site: www.imperial.edu/
Description: State and locally supported, 2-year, coed. Part of California Community College System. Awards certificates, transfer associate, and terminal associate degrees. Founded 1922. Setting: 160-acre rural campus. Endowment: $832,061. Educational spending for the previous fiscal year: $2672 per student. Total enrollment: 7,413. Students come from 12 states and territories, 3% from out-of-state. Calendar: semesters. Academic remediation for entering students, ESL program, services for LD students, advanced placement, accelerated degree program, self-designed majors, double major, summer session for credit, part-time degree program, adult/continuing education programs.

Entrance Requirements: Open admission. Recommended: high school transcript. Required for some: high school transcript. Entrance: noncompetitive. Application deadline: Rolling. Notification: continuous.
Collegiate Environment: Orientation program. Drama-theater group, choral group, student-run newspaper. Social organizations: 12 open to all. Most popular organizations: Student Support Services Club, Pre-School Mothers, Care Club, Christian Club, Nursing Club. Major annual events: College and University Day, Career Fair, Life's a Beach. Student services: personal-psychological counseling, women's center. Campus security: student patrols. Spencer Library with 55,875 books, 13,324 microform titles, 425 serials, 3,383 audiovisual materials, an OPAC, and a Web page. Operations spending for the previous fiscal year: $743,156. 235 computers available on campus for general student use. A campuswide network can be accessed from off-campus. Staffed computer lab on campus.
Community Environment: Imperial is in the southern desert area of California known as the Imperial Valley. It has a very dry climate. The Chocolate Mountains are separated from Imperial by a ribbon of sand dunes. Buses and airlines serve the area. The surrounding Imperial Valley is a large and abundant agricultural area. There are six small cities in surrounding area that provide additional employment opportunities. The annual midwinter fair and the Christmas Parade are here at Imperial.

■ **INTERIOR DESIGNERS INSTITUTE**
1061 Camelback Rd.
Newport Beach, CA 92660
Tel: (949)675-4451
Fax: (949)759-0667
E-mail: contact@idi.edu
Web Site: www.idi.edu/
Description: Proprietary, comprehensive, coed. Awards associate, bachelor's, and master's degrees. Founded 1984. Setting: 1-acre suburban campus with easy access to Los Angeles, San Diego. Total enrollment: 468. 67% 25 or older. Part-time degree program.
Entrance Requirements: Required: high school transcript.
Collegiate Environment: Social organizations: ASID, IIDA student chapters.

■ **IRVINE VALLEY COLLEGE**
5500 Irvine Ctr. Dr.
Irvine, CA 92618

Tel: (949)451-5100
Fax: (949)559-3443
Web Site: www.ivc.edu/
Description: State and locally supported, 2-year, coed. Part of Saddleback Community College District. Awards certificates, transfer associate, and terminal associate degrees. Founded 1979. Setting: 20-acre suburban campus with easy access to Los Angeles. Total enrollment: 10,511. Faculty: 344 (94 full-time, 250 part-time). 55% 25 or older. Core. Calendar: semesters. Academic remediation for entering students, ESL program, services for LD students, advanced placement, summer session for credit, part-time degree program, adult/continuing education programs, co-op programs.
Entrance Requirements: Open admission. Option: early admission. Entrance: noncompetitive. Application deadline: Rolling. Notification: continuous.
Collegiate Environment: Drama-theater group, student-run newspaper. Student services: health clinic, personal-psychological counseling, women's center. Campus security: late night transport-escort service. Irvine Valley College Library with 24,000 books and 250 serials. 125 computers available on campus for general student use. Staffed computer lab on campus.

■ **ITT TECHNICAL INSTITUTE (CLOVIS)**
362 N Clovis Ave.
Clovis, CA 93612
Tel: (559)325-5400; Free: 800-564-9771
Web Site: www.itt-tech.edu/
Description: Proprietary, 4-year, coed. Part of ITT Educational Services, Inc. Awards associate and bachelor's degrees. Founded 2005.
Entrance Requirements: Entrance: minimally difficult.

■ **ITT TECHNICAL INSTITUTE (CONCORD)**
1140 Galaxy Way
Ste. 400
Concord, CA 94520
Tel: (925)674-8200; Free: 800-211-7062
Web Site: www.itt-tech.edu/
Description: Proprietary, 4-year, coed. Part of ITT Educational Services, Inc. Awards associate and bachelor's degrees.
Entrance Requirements: Entrance: minimally difficult.

■ **ITT TECHNICAL INSTITUTE (CORONA)**
4160 Temescal Canyon Rd.
Ste. 100
Corona, CA 92883
Tel: (951)277-5400; Free: 877-764-9661
Web Site: www.itt-tech.edu/
Description: Proprietary, 4-year, coed. Awards associate and bachelor's degrees.
Entrance Requirements: Entrance: minimally difficult.

■ **ITT TECHNICAL INSTITUTE (CULVER CITY)**
6101 W Centinela Ave.
Ste. 180
Culver City, CA 90230
Tel: (310)417-5800; Free: 800-215-6151
Web Site: www.itt-tech.edu/
Description: Proprietary, primarily 2-year, coed. Part of ITT Educational Services, Inc. Awards terminal associate and bachelor's degrees.

■ **ITT TECHNICAL INSTITUTE (LATHROP)**
16916 S Harlan Rd.
Lathrop, CA 95330
Tel: (209)858-0077; Free: 800-346-1786
Web Site: www.itt-tech.edu/
Description: Proprietary, primarily 2-year, coed. Part of ITT Educational Services, Inc. Awards terminal associate and bachelor's degrees. Founded 1997.
Entrance Requirements: Entrance: minimally difficult.

■ **ITT TECHNICAL INSTITUTE (OAKLAND)**
7901 Oakport St.
Ste. 3000
Oakland, CA 94621
Tel: (510)553-2800; Free: 877-442-5833

Web Site: www.itt-tech.edu/
Description: Proprietary, primarily 2-year, coed. Part of ITT Educational Services, Inc. Awards terminal associate and bachelor's degrees.

■ **ITT TECHNICAL INSTITUTE (ORANGE)**
4000 W Metropolitan Dr.
Ste. 100
Orange, CA 92868
Tel: (714)941-2400
Web Site: www.itt-tech.edu/
Description: Proprietary, primarily 2-year, coed. Part of ITT Educational Services, Inc. Awards terminal associate and bachelor's degrees. Founded 1982. Setting: suburban campus.
Entrance Requirements: Entrance: minimally difficult.

■ **ITT TECHNICAL INSTITUTE (OXNARD)**
2051 Solar Dr., Ste. 150
Oxnard, CA 93036
Tel: (805)988-0143; Free: 800-530-1582
Fax: (805)988-1813
Web Site: www.itt-tech.edu/
Description: Proprietary, primarily 2-year, coed. Part of ITT Educational Services, Inc. Awards transfer associate, terminal associate, and bachelor's degrees. Founded 1993. Setting: urban campus.
Entrance Requirements: Entrance: minimally difficult.

■ **ITT TECHNICAL INSTITUTE (RANCHO CORDOVA)**
10863 Gold Ctr. Dr.
Rancho Cordova, CA 95670-6034
Tel: (916)851-3900; Free: 800-488-8466
Fax: (916)366-9225
Web Site: www.itt-tech.edu/
Description: Proprietary, primarily 2-year, coed. Part of ITT Educational Services, Inc. Awards terminal associate and bachelor's degrees. Founded 1954. Setting: urban campus.
Entrance Requirements: Entrance: minimally difficult.

■ **ITT TECHNICAL INSTITUTE (SAN BERNARDINO)**
670 E Carnegie Dr.
San Bernardino, CA 92408
Tel: (909)806-4600; Free: 800-888-3801
Fax: (909)888-6970
Web Site: www.itt-tech.edu/
Description: Proprietary, primarily 2-year, coed. Part of ITT Educational Services, Inc. Awards terminal associate and bachelor's degrees. Founded 1987. Setting: urban campus.
Entrance Requirements: Entrance: minimally difficult.

■ **ITT TECHNICAL INSTITUTE (SAN DIEGO)**
9680 Granite Ridge Dr.
San Diego, CA 92123
Tel: (858)571-8500; Free: 800-883-0380
Fax: (858)571-1277
Web Site: www.itt-tech.edu/
Description: Proprietary, primarily 2-year, coed. Part of ITT Educational Services, Inc. Awards terminal associate and bachelor's degrees. Founded 1981. Setting: suburban campus.
Entrance Requirements: Entrance: minimally difficult.

■ **ITT TECHNICAL INSTITUTE (SAN DIMAS)**
650 W Cienega Ave.
San Dimas, CA 91773
Tel: (909)971-2300; Free: 800-414-6522
Web Site: www.itt-tech.edu/
Description: Proprietary, primarily 2-year, coed. Part of ITT Educational Services, Inc. Awards terminal associate and bachelor's degrees. Founded 1982. Setting: suburban campus.
Entrance Requirements: Entrance: minimally difficult.

■ **ITT TECHNICAL INSTITUTE (SYLMAR)**
12669 Encinitas Ave.
Sylmar, CA 91342-3664
Tel: (818)364-5151; Free: 800-636-2086
Web Site: www.itt-tech.edu/

Description: Proprietary, primarily 2-year, coed. Part of ITT Educational Services, Inc. Awards terminal associate and bachelor's degrees. Founded 1982. Setting: urban campus.
Entrance Requirements: Entrance: minimally difficult.

■ **ITT TECHNICAL INSTITUTE (TORRANCE)**
2555 W 190th St.
Ste. 125
Torrance, CA 90504
Tel: (310)965-5900
Fax: (310)380-1557
Web Site: www.itt-tech.edu/
Description: Proprietary, primarily 2-year, coed. Part of ITT Educational Services, Inc. Awards terminal associate and bachelor's degrees. Founded 1987. Setting: urban campus.
Entrance Requirements: Entrance: minimally difficult.

■ **ITT TECHNICAL INSTITUTE (WEST COVINA)**
1530 W Cameron Ave.
West Covina, CA 91790
Tel: (626)813-3681; Free: 877-480-2766
Web Site: www.itt-tech.edu/
Description: Proprietary, primarily 2-year, coed. Part of ITT Educational Services, Inc. Awards terminal associate and bachelor's degrees.

■ **JOHN F. KENNEDY UNIVERSITY**
100 Ellinwood Way
Pleasant Hill, CA 94523-4817
Tel: (925)969-3300; Free: 800-696-JFKU
Fax: (925)254-6964
E-mail: jmhogg@jfku.edu
Web Site: www.jfku.edu/
Description: Independent, upper-level, coed. Administratively affiliated with National University System. Awards bachelor's, master's, and doctoral degrees. Founded 1964. Setting: 5-acre suburban campus with easy access to San Francisco. Endowment: $1.5 million. Educational spending for the previous fiscal year: $5881 per student. Total enrollment: 1,580. Faculty: 237. Student-undergrad faculty ratio is 8:1. Full-time: 54 students, 57% women, 43% men. Part-time: 233 students, 78% women, 22% men. 0% from out-of-state. 89% 25 or older, 7% transferred in. Academic areas with the most degrees conferred: psychology; law/legal studies; business/marketing. Core. Calendar: semesters for law school. Services for LD students, advanced placement, self-designed majors, independent study, summer session for credit, part-time degree program, adult/continuing education programs, graduate courses open to undergrads. Off campus study at University of California, Berkeley, California State University, Hayward, Contra Costa College, Laney College.
Collegiate Environment: Student services: personal-psychological counseling. Campus security: late night transport-escort service. Robert M. Fisher Library plus 1 other with 104,360 books, 507 microform titles, 788 serials, 1,604 audiovisual materials, an OPAC, and a Web page. Operations spending for the previous fiscal year: $1.4 million. 50 computers available on campus for general student use. Students can access the following: online class registration. Staffed computer lab on campus.
Community Environment: Orinda, population 18,259, is located just east of the Oakland-Berkeley Hills. Oakland, 10 miles away, and San Francisco, 20 miles, are easily accessed. Climate is mild the year round, with the average temperature 65-70 degrees.

■ **JOHN PAUL THE GREAT CATHOLIC UNIVERSITY**
10174 Old Grove Rd.
Ste. 200
San Diego, CA 92131
Tel: (858)653-6740
Web Site: www.jpcatholic.com/
Description: Independent religious, comprehensive, coed. Founded 2006.

■ **KAPLAN COLLEGE, BAKERSFIELD CAMPUS**
1914 Wible Rd.
Bakersfield, CA 93304
Tel: (661)836-6300; Free: 800-935-1857
Web Site: bakersfield.kaplancollege.com/
Description: Proprietary, 2-year, coed. Awards diplomas and terminal associate degrees.

■ **KAPLAN COLLEGE, CHULA VISTA CAMPUS**
555 Broadway
Chula Vista, CA 91910
Free: 800-935-1857
Web Site: chulavista.kaplancollege.com/
Description: Proprietary, 2-year, coed. Awards diplomas and terminal associate degrees.

■ **KAPLAN COLLEGE, FRESNO CAMPUS**
44 Shaw Ave.
Clovis, CA 93612
Tel: (559)325-5100; Free: 800-935-1857
Web Site: fresno.kaplancollege.com/
Description: Proprietary, 2-year, coed. Awards diplomas and terminal associate degrees.

■ **KAPLAN COLLEGE, MODESTO CAMPUS**
5172 Kiernan Ct.
Salida, CA 95368
Tel: (209)543-7000; Free: 800-935-1857
Fax: (209)571-9836
Web Site: modesto.kaplancollege.com/
Description: Proprietary, 2-year, coed. Awards diplomas and terminal associate degrees. Calendar: semesters.

■ **KAPLAN COLLEGE, PALM SPRINGS CAMPUS**
2475 E Tahquitz Canyon Way
Palm Springs, CA 92262
Tel: (760)778-3540; Free: 800-935-1857
Web Site: palm-springs.kaplancollege.com/
Description: Proprietary, 2-year, coed. Awards diplomas and terminal associate degrees.

■ **KAPLAN COLLEGE, RIVERSIDE CAMPUS**
4040 Vine St.
Riverside, CA 92507
Tel: (951)276-1704; Free: 800-935-1857
Web Site: riverside.kaplancollege.com/
Description: Proprietary, 2-year, coed. Awards diplomas and terminal associate degrees.

■ **KAPLAN COLLEGE, SACRAMENTO CAMPUS**
4330 Watt Ave.
Ste. 400
Sacramento, CA 95821
Tel: (916)649-8168; Free: 800-935-1857
Fax: (916)649-8344
Web Site: sacramento.kaplancollege.com/
Description: Proprietary, 2-year, coed. Awards diplomas and terminal associate degrees. Calendar: semesters.

■ **KAPLAN COLLEGE, SAN DIEGO CAMPUS**
9055 Balboa Ave.
San Diego, CA 92123
Tel: (858)279-4500; Free: 800-935-1857
Fax: (858)279-4885
Web Site: san-diego.kaplancollege.com/
Description: Proprietary, 2-year, coed. Awards diplomas and terminal associate degrees (also includes Vista campus). Founded 1976. Setting: urban campus. Calendar: semesters.

■ **KAPLAN COLLEGE, VISTA CAMPUS**
2022 University Dr.
Vista, CA 92083
Tel: (760)630-1555; Free: 800-935-1857
Fax: (760)630-1656
Web Site: vista.kaplancollege.com/
Description: Proprietary, 2-year, coed. Awards diplomas and terminal associate degrees.

■ **KING'S UNIVERSITY**
14800 Sherman Way
Van Nuys, CA 91405-8040
Tel: (818)779-8040; Free: 888-779-8040

Fax: (818)779-8241
E-mail: mchappell@kingscollege.edu
Web Site: kingsuniversity.edu/
Description: Independent, comprehensive, coed, affiliated with International Church of the Foursquare Gospel. Awards associate, bachelor's, and master's degrees. Total enrollment: 531. 11 applied. 73% 25 or older.
Entrance Requirements: Required: high school transcript.

■ LA SIERRA UNIVERSITY

4500 Riverwalk Pky.
Riverside, CA 92515
Tel: (951)785-2000; Free: 800-874-5587
Fax: (951)785-2901
E-mail: iteheda@lasierra.edu
Web Site: www.lasierra.edu/
Description: Independent Seventh-day Adventist, comprehensive, coed. Part of Seventh-Day Adventist Education System. Administratively affiliated with WASC (Western Association of Schools and Colleges). Awards bachelor's, master's, and doctoral degrees and post-master's certificates. Founded 1922. Setting: 100-acre suburban campus with easy access to Los Angeles. Endowment: $15 million. Research spending for the previous fiscal year: $7815. Educational spending for the previous fiscal year: $32,443 per student. Total enrollment: 2,393. Faculty: 212 (99 full-time, 113 part-time). Student-undergrad faculty ratio is 16:1. 3,208 applied, 48% were admitted. 10% from top 10% of their high school class, 41% from top quarter, 74% from top half. Full-time: 1,872 students, 57% women, 43% men. Part-time: 176 students, 61% women, 39% men. Students come from 16 states and territories, 8 other countries, 9% from out-of-state. 0.05% American Indian or Alaska Native, non-Hispanic/Latino; 40% Hispanic/Latino; 8% African American, non-Hispanic/Latino; 15% Asian, non-Hispanic/Latino; 2% Native Hawaiian or other Pacific Islander, non-Hispanic/Latino; 13% international. 10% 25 or older, 31% live on campus, 12% transferred in. Retention: 77% of full-time freshmen returned the following year. Academic areas with the most degrees conferred: health professions and related sciences; business/marketing; biological/life sciences. Core. Academic remediation for entering students, ESL program, services for LD students, advanced placement, accelerated degree program, self-designed majors, honors program, independent study, distance learning, double major, summer session for credit, part-time degree program, adult/continuing education programs, internships, graduate courses open to undergrads. Off campus study at Loma Linda University. Study abroad program.
Entrance Requirements: Options: electronic application, deferred admission, international baccalaureate accepted. Required: essay, high school transcript, minimum 2 high school GPA, 2 recommendations, Eligibility Index Table (combination of GPA and test scores), SAT or ACT. Required for some: interview. Entrance: minimally difficult. Application deadlines: 2/1, 2/1 for nonresidents. Notification: continuous, continuous for nonresidents. Preference given to Seventh-day Adventists. SAT Reasoning Test deadline: 1/7. SAT Subject Test deadline: 1/7. Transfer credits accepted: Yes.
Costs Per Year: Application fee: $30. Comprehensive fee: $35,694 includes full-time tuition ($27,180), mandatory fees ($1134), and college room and board ($7380). Full-time tuition and fees vary according to course load, degree level, and location. Room and board charges vary according to board plan and housing facility. Part-time tuition: $755 per quarter hour. Part-time tuition varies according to course load, degree level, and location.
Collegiate Environment: Orientation program. Drama-theater group, choral group, student-run newspaper. Social organizations: 51 open to all. Most popular organizations: Student Association of LSU, Korean Student Association, Students In Free Enterprise (SIFE), OI Club, Black Student Association. Major annual events: Christmas Candlelight Concert, Festival of Nations, Annual Convocation. Student services: health clinic, personal-psychological counseling, women's center. Campus security: 24-hour emergency response devices and patrols, student patrols, late night transport-escort service. 850 college housing spaces available; 646 were occupied in 2012-13. Freshmen guaranteed college housing. On-campus residence required in freshman year. Options: men-only, women-only housing available. University Library plus 1 other with 262,554 books, 648,664 microform titles, 825 serials, an OPAC, and a Web page. Operations spending for the previous fiscal year: $421,482. 300 computers available on campus for general student use. Computer purchase/lease plans available. A computer is required for all students. A campuswide network can be accessed from student residence rooms and from off campus. Students can access the following: online class registration. Staffed computer lab on campus provides training in use of computers, software, and the Internet.

Community Environment: See University of California Riverside.

■ LAGUNA COLLEGE OF ART & DESIGN

2222 Laguna Canyon Rd.
Laguna Beach, CA 92651-1136
Tel: (949)376-6000; Free: 800-255-0762
Fax: (949)376-6009
Web Site: www.lcad.edu/
Description: Independent, comprehensive, coed. Awards bachelor's and master's degrees. Founded 1962. Setting: 9-acre small town campus with easy access to Los Angeles. Endowment: $411,000. Educational spending for the previous fiscal year: $6512 per student. Total enrollment: 310. Faculty: 72 (10 full-time, 62 part-time). Student-undergrad faculty ratio is 10:1. 245 applied, 88% were admitted. 15 National Merit Scholars, 5 class presidents, 12 valedictorians, 31 student government officers. Full-time: 310 students, 47% women, 53% men. Students come from 32 states and territories, 42% from out-of-state. 22% 25 or older. Retention: 83% of full-time freshmen returned the following year. Core. Calendar: semesters. Academic remediation for entering students, ESL program, advanced placement, independent study, summer session for credit, part-time degree program, adult/continuing education programs, internships. Off campus study at Art College Exchange, Association of Independent Colleges of Art and Design.
Entrance Requirements: Options: electronic application, deferred admission, international baccalaureate accepted. Required: high school transcript, portfolio, SAT or ACT. Entrance: very difficult. Notification: 5/1.
Collegiate Environment: Orientation program. Student-run newspaper. Major annual event: Student Juried Art Exhibition. Student services: personal-psychological counseling. Campus security: 24-hour emergency response devices. Ruth Salyer Library plus 1 other with 16,000 books, 30 microform titles, 100 serials, 8 audiovisual materials, and an OPAC. Operations spending for the previous fiscal year: $85,000. 85 computers available on campus for general student use. Computer purchase/lease plans available. A computer is required for all students. A campuswide network can be accessed from off-campus. Staffed computer lab on campus provides training in use of computers.

■ LAKE TAHOE COMMUNITY COLLEGE

One College Dr.
South Lake Tahoe, CA 96150-4524
Tel: (530)541-4660
Fax: (530)541-7852
E-mail: admissions@ltcc.edu
Web Site: www.ltcc.edu/
Description: State and locally supported, 2-year, coed. Part of California Community College System. Awards transfer associate and terminal associate degrees. Founded 1975. Setting: 164-acre small town campus. Total enrollment: 3,000. Faculty: 200 (41 full-time, 159 part-time). 450 applied, 100% were admitted. 68% 25 or older. Core. Academic remediation for entering students, ESL program, services for LD students, advanced placement, independent study, distance learning, double major, summer session for credit, part-time degree program, co-op programs and internships. Study abroad program.
Entrance Requirements: Open admission. Option: early admission. Recommended: high school transcript. Entrance: noncompetitive. Application deadline: Rolling. Notification: continuous.
Collegiate Environment: Drama-theater group, choral group. Social organizations: 8 open to all. Most popular organizations: Associated Student Council, Alpha Gamma Sigma, Foreign Language Club, Art Club, Performing Arts League. Major annual events: AIDS Awareness Day, Club Day, Multicultural Day. Student services: personal-psychological counseling. Campus security: 24-hour emergency response devices, late night transport-escort service. Lake Tahoe Community College Library with 20,000 books, 10,000 serials, 5,000 audiovisual materials, an OPAC, and a Web page. Operations spending for the previous fiscal year: $307,421. 135 computers available on campus for general student use. A campuswide network can be accessed. Staffed computer lab on campus.

■ LANEY COLLEGE

900 Fallon St.
Oakland, CA 94607-4893
Tel: (510)834-5740
Web Site: www.laney.edu/
Description: State and locally supported, 2-year, coed. Part of Peralta Community College District System. Awards certificates, transfer associate, and

terminal associate degrees. Founded 1953. Setting: urban campus with easy access to San Francisco. Research spending for the previous fiscal year: $68,724. Total enrollment: 13,463. Faculty: 451 (118 full-time, 333 part-time). Full-time: 2,424 students, 57% women, 43% men. Part-time: 11,039 students, 58% women, 42% men. 57% 25 or older. Core. Calendar: semesters. Academic remediation for entering students, services for LD students, summer session for credit, part-time degree program, adult/continuing education programs.

Entrance Requirements: Open admission. Option: early admission. Entrance: noncompetitive. Application deadline: Rolling.

Collegiate Environment: Drama-theater group, student-run newspaper. Most popular organizations: La Raza Club, African Student Union, Vision Christian Society, Asian/Pacific Islander Club, Vietnamese Student Club. Major annual events: Cinco de Mayo, Black History Month, Multicultural Day. Laney Library with 78,054 books and 209 serials. 30 computers available on campus for general student use.

Community Environment: Oakland is the fourth largest city in the state. Located on the mainland side of San Francisco Bay; adjoined on the north by Berkeley; on the south by Alameda and San Leandro. Climate is mild and the average temperature is 65.9 degrees. All modes of transportation are available; the Oakland Airport is a 12-minute drive. Oakland has all the advantages of a large metropolitan area, being a part of the San Francisco Bay Area. Numerous churches, museums, libraries, hospitals, service groups, and organizations are in the city. Oakland has many tourist attractions and recreational facilities. Lake Merritt, a 160-acre body of salt water, is the only tidal lake in the heart of any American city. There are parks, golf courses, swimming pools within a short distance.

■ **LAS POSITAS COLLEGE**
3000 Campus Hill Dr.
Livermore, CA 94551
Tel: (925)424-1000
Fax: (925)443-0742
Web Site: www.laspositascollege.edu/

Description: State-supported, 2-year, coed. Part of California Community College System. Awards certificates, diplomas, transfer associate, and terminal associate degrees. Founded 1988. Setting: 150-acre suburban campus with easy access to Oakland, San Francisco. Total enrollment: 8,044. 50% 25 or older. Core. Calendar: semesters. Academic remediation for entering students, ESL program, services for LD students, advanced placement, self-designed majors, summer session for credit, part-time degree program, internships.

Entrance Requirements: Open admission. Recommended: high school transcript. Entrance: noncompetitive.

Collegiate Environment: Drama-theater group, choral group, student-run newspaper. Social organizations: 23 open to all. Student services: health clinic, personal-psychological counseling. Campus security: 24-hour emergency response devices, late night transport-escort service.

■ **LASSEN COMMUNITY COLLEGE DISTRICT**
Hwy. 139
Susanville, CA 96130
Tel: (530)257-6181
Fax: (530)257-8964
Web Site: www.lassencollege.edu/

Description: State and locally supported, 2-year, coed. Part of California Community College System. Awards certificates, transfer associate, and terminal associate degrees. Founded 1925. Setting: 100-acre rural campus. Total enrollment: 2,161. Faculty: 204 (44 full-time, 160 part-time). Students come from 12 states and territories, 3 other countries. 58% 25 or older. Core. Calendar: semesters. Academic remediation for entering students, ESL program, services for LD students, advanced placement, summer session for credit, part-time degree program, adult/continuing education programs, co-op programs and internships. Off campus study at members of the Northeastern California Higher Education Council.

Entrance Requirements: Open admission. Option: early admission. Recommended: high school transcript. Entrance: noncompetitive. Application deadline: Rolling. Notification: continuous.

Collegiate Environment: Drama-theater group, student-run newspaper. Most popular organization: Lassen Student Union. Major annual events: Career Day, Vocational Olympics, Skunk Days. Student services: legal services, health clinic. Lassen College Library with 15,000 books and 100 serials. 30 computers available on campus for general student use. Staffed computer lab on campus.

■ **LE CORDON BLEU COLLEGE OF CULINARY ARTS IN LOS ANGELES**
521 E Green St.
Pasadena, CA 91101
Tel: (626)229-1300
E-mail: nsandoval@la.chefs.edu
Web Site: www.chefs.edu/Los-Angeles

Description: Proprietary, 2-year, coed. Awards diplomas and terminal associate degrees. Founded 1994. Total enrollment: 2,253. Student-undergrad faculty ratio is 16:1. 3% from out-of-state. 42% 25 or older.

Entrance Requirements: Entrance: noncompetitive.

■ **LIFE PACIFIC COLLEGE**
1100 Covina Blvd.
San Dimas, CA 91773-3298
Tel: (909)599-5433; Free: 877-886-5433
Fax: (909)599-6690
E-mail: adm@lifepacific.edu
Web Site: www.lifepacific.edu/

Description: Independent, 4-year, coed, affiliated with International Church of the Foursquare Gospel. Awards associate and bachelor's degrees. Founded 1923. Setting: 9-acre suburban campus with easy access to Los Angeles. Endowment: $2.6 million. Educational spending for the previous fiscal year: $4570 per student. Total enrollment: 514. Faculty: 38 (16 full-time, 22 part-time). Student-undergrad faculty ratio is 16:1. 75 applied, 100% were admitted. 8% from top 10% of their high school class, 21% from top quarter, 42% from top half. Students come from 39 states and territories, 3 other countries, 44% from out-of-state. 27% 25 or older, 50% live on campus. Retention: 77% of full-time freshmen returned the following year. Academic area with the most degrees conferred: theology and religious vocations. Core. Calendar: semesters. Services for LD students, advanced placement, accelerated degree program, independent study, distance learning, summer session for credit, part-time degree program, external degree program, adult/continuing education programs, co-op programs and internships. Study abroad program.

Entrance Requirements: Options: electronic application, deferred admission, international baccalaureate accepted. Required: essay, high school transcript, minimum 2.0 high school GPA, 1 recommendation, Christian testimony, SAT or ACT. Entrance: minimally difficult. Application deadline: 5/1. Notification: continuous.

Costs Per Year: Application fee: $35. One-time mandatory fee: $100. Comprehensive fee: $19,700 includes full-time tuition ($12,600), mandatory fees ($500), and college room and board ($6600). Full-time tuition and fees vary according to course load. Part-time tuition: $420 per credit hour. Part-time mandatory fees: $280 per term. Part-time tuition and fees vary according to course load.

Collegiate Environment: Orientation program. Drama-theater group, choral group. Major annual events: Spring/Fall Retreats, Winter Social, Spring Social. Student services: personal-psychological counseling. Campus security: 24-hour emergency response devices, student patrols, part-time security personnel. Life Pacific College Alumni Library with an OPAC. Operations spending for the previous fiscal year: $223,812. 46 computers available on campus for general student use. A campuswide network can be accessed from student residence rooms. Students can access the following: online class registration. Staffed computer lab on campus provides training in use of computers, software, and the Internet.

Community Environment: San Dimas is a suburban community approximately 45 minutes from Los Angeles, located at the foothills of the San Gabriel Mountains.

■ **LINCOLN UNIVERSITY**
401 15th St.
Oakland, CA 94612
Tel: (510)628-8010; Free: 888-810-9998
Fax: (510)628-8026
E-mail: admissions@lincolnuca.edu
Web Site: www.lincolnuca.edu/

Description: Independent, comprehensive, coed. Awards associate, bachelor's, master's, and doctoral degrees. Founded 1919. Setting: 2-acre urban campus. Educational spending for the previous fiscal year: $17 per student. Total enrollment: 375. Faculty: 25 (10 full-time, 15 part-time). Student-undergrad faculty ratio is 20:1. 174 applied, 52% were admitted. 3 student government officers. Full-time: 55 students, 51% women, 49% men. Part-time: 48 students, 67% women, 33% men. Students come from 44 other countries, 0% from out-of-state. 20% 25 or older, 8% transferred in. Retention: 5% of full-time freshmen returned the following year. Academic area with the most degrees conferred: business/marketing. Core. Calendar: semesters. ESL program, advanced placement, double major, summer session for credit, co-op programs and internships.

Entrance Requirements: Options: electronic application, deferred admission. Required: high school transcript, minimum 2 high school GPA. Required for some: essay, interview. Entrance: minimally difficult. Application deadline: 8/22. Transfer credits accepted: Yes.

Collegiate Environment: Orientation program. Major annual events: Annual Ski Trip, Welcome Barbeque, Welcome Free Lunch. Student services: personal-psychological counseling. Campus security: 24-hour emergency response devices. Lincoln University Library with 19,752 books and 856 serials. 32 computers available on campus for general student use. A campuswide network can be accessed. Staffed computer lab on campus provides training in use of computers, software, and the Internet.

■ **LOMA LINDA UNIVERSITY**
Loma Linda, CA 92350
Tel: (909)558-1000; Free: 800-422-4558
Fax: (909)558-4577
Web Site: www.llu.edu/

Description: Independent Seventh-day Adventist, university, coed. Awards associate, bachelor's, master's, and doctoral degrees and post-master's certificates (associate degree and nursing students may enter at the sophomore level). Founded 1905. Setting: small town campus with easy access to Los Angeles. Endowment: $135.9 million. Research spending for the previous fiscal year: $31.6 million. Educational spending for the previous fiscal year: $27,730 per student. Total enrollment: 4,270. Faculty: 840 (557 full-time, 283 part-time). Student-undergrad faculty ratio is 8:1. Full-time: 885 students, 70% women, 30% men. Part-time: 347 students, 76% women, 24% men. Students come from 29 states and territories, 30 other countries, 12% from out-of-state. 50% 25 or older, 27% live on campus, 18% transferred in. Academic area with the most degrees conferred: health professions and related sciences. ESL program, independent study, distance learning, internships. Off campus study.

Entrance Requirements: Option: deferred admission.

Collegiate Environment: Most popular organizations: Students for International Mission Services, Black Health Professional Association, Association of Latin American Students. Major annual events: Annual Convocation, Welcome Back Bash. Student services: health clinic, personal-psychological counseling. Campus security: 24-hour emergency response devices and patrols, late night transport-escort service. Del E. Webb Memorial Library with 338,418 books, 1,671 serials, an OPAC, and a Web page. Operations spending for the previous fiscal year: $3.6 million, 160 computers available on campus for general student use. A campuswide network can be accessed from student residence rooms and from off campus. Students can access the following: online class registration, online courses. Staffed computer lab on campus provides training in use of computers, software, and the Internet.

Community Environment: Loma Linda is located 56 miles east of Los Angeles, between Redlands, San Bernardino, and Riverside. The climate is pleasant and mild. Loma Linda is a medical center that has three hospitals, including the 515-bed University Medical Center and the 500-bed Jerry L. Pettis Memorial Veterans Hospital. Pacific ocean beaches, ski slopes, and lakes for boating and water skiing are all within a one-hour drive. Part-time and full-time work is available.

■ **LONG BEACH CITY COLLEGE**
4901 E Carson St.
Long Beach, CA 90808-1780
Tel: (562)938-4353
Web Site: www.lbcc.edu/

Description: State-supported, 2-year, coed. Part of California Community College System. Awards certificates, transfer associate, and terminal associate degrees. Founded 1927. Setting: 40-acre urban campus with easy access to Los Angeles. Total enrollment: 27,894. Student-undergrad faculty ratio is 30:1. 45% 25 or older. Core. Calendar: semesters. Academic remediation for entering students, ESL program, services for LD students, advanced placement, honors program, distance learning, summer session for credit, part-time degree program, adult/continuing education programs, internships.

Entrance Requirements: Open admission except for nursing program. Option: early admission. Recommended: high school transcript. Entrance: noncompetitive. Application deadline: Rolling.

Collegiate Environment: Drama-theater group, choral group, student-run newspaper, radio station. Social organizations: local fraternities, local sororities. Student services: legal services, health clinic, personal-psychological counseling, women's center. Campus security: 24-hour emergency response devices and patrols, student patrols, late night transport-escort service. Long Beach City College Library plus 1 other with an OPAC and a Web page.

■ **LOS ANGELES CITY COLLEGE**
855 N Vermont Ave.
Los Angeles, CA 90029-3590
Tel: (323)953-4000
Fax: (323)953-4536
Web Site: www.lacitycollege.edu/

Description: District-supported, 2-year, coed. Part of Los Angeles Community College District System. Awards certificates, diplomas, transfer associate, and terminal associate degrees. Founded 1929. Setting: 42-acre urban campus. Total enrollment: 25,000. Faculty: 572 (249 full-time, 323 part-time). Students come from 52 states and territories. 62% 25 or older. Core. Calendar: semesters. Academic remediation for entering students, ESL program, services for LD students, advanced placement, honors program, summer session for credit, part-time degree program, adult/continuing education programs. Study abroad program. ROTC: Army (c), Air Force (c).

Entrance Requirements: Open admission except for international applicants or optics, radiological technology programs. Entrance: noncompetitive. Application deadline: 9/5. Notification: continuous until 9/5.

Collegiate Environment: Drama-theater group, choral group, marching band, student-run newspaper. Student services: health clinic, personal-psychological counseling. Campus security: 24-hour emergency response devices and patrols, student patrols, late night transport-escort service. 150,000 books and 150 serials 200 computers available on campus for general student use. A campuswide network can be accessed from off-campus. Students can access the following: online class registration, telephone registration. Staffed computer lab on campus.

Community Environment: See University of California - Los Angeles.

■ **LOS ANGELES COUNTY COLLEGE OF NURSING AND ALLIED HEALTH**
1237 N Mission Rd.
Los Angeles, CA 90033
Tel: (323)226-4911
Fax: (323)226-6427
Web Site: www.ladhs.org/wps/portal/CollegeOfNursing

Description: County-supported, 2-year, coed. Awards terminal associate degrees. Founded 1895. Total enrollment: 333. Student-undergrad faculty ratio is 4:1. 82% 25 or older. Calendar: semesters.

Entrance Requirements: Required: TEAS, version V.

■ **LOS ANGELES FILM SCHOOL**
6363 Sunset Blvd.
Hollywood, CA 90028
Tel: (323)860-0789; Free: 877-952-3456
Web Site: www.lafilm.edu/
Description: Proprietary, 2-year, coed.

■ **LOS ANGELES HARBOR COLLEGE**
1111 Figueroa Pl.
Wilmington, CA 90744-2397
Tel: (310)233-4000
Fax: (310)233-4223
E-mail: chingdm@lahc.edu
Web Site: www.lahc.edu/

Description: State and locally supported, 2-year, coed. Part of Los Angeles Community College District System. Awards certificates, transfer associate, and terminal associate degrees. Founded 1949. Setting: 80-acre suburban campus with easy access to Los Angeles. Research spending for the previous fiscal year: $206,773. Educational spending for the previous fiscal year: $2057 per student. Total enrollment: 10,181. Faculty: 422 (113 full-time, 309 part-time). Student-undergrad faculty ratio is 47:1. Full-time: 2,812 students, 57% women, 43% men. Part-time: 7,369 students, 62% women, 38% men. Students come from 14 states and territories, 15 other countries. 35% 25 or older. Core. Calendar: semesters. Academic remediation for entering students, ESL program, services for LD students, advanced placement, accelerated degree program, freshman honors college, honors program, independent study, distance learning, double major, summer session for credit, part-time degree program, adult/continuing education programs, co-op programs. Off campus study at California State University, Dominguez Hills. Study abroad program.

Entrance Requirements: Open admission except for nursing program. Options: electronic application, early admission, deferred admission. Entrance: noncompetitive. Application deadlines: 9/3, 9/3 for nonresidents. Transfer credits accepted: Yes.

Costs Per Year: Application fee: $0. State resident tuition: $1380 full-time, $46 per unit part-time. Nonresident tuition: $7080 full-time, $236 per unit part-time. Mandatory fees: $24 full-time, $12 per term part-time.

Collegiate Environment: Orientation program. Drama-theater group, choral group, student-run newspaper. Social organizations: 13 open to all. Most popular organizations: Alpha Gamma Sigma, EOP&S, Creando Un Nuevo Futuro, Psychology Club, Honors Transfer Program. Major annual events: ASO Elections, Blood Drives, Club Rush Day. Student services: legal services, health clinic, personal-psychological counseling. Campus security: 24-hour emergency response devices and patrols, late night transport-escort service. Harbor College Library with 89,768 books, 118 microform titles, 21 serials, 35 audiovisual materials, an OPAC, and a Web page. Operations spending for the previous fiscal year: $738,905. 725 computers available on campus for general student use. A campuswide network can be accessed from off-campus. Students can access the following: online class registration. Staffed computer lab on campus provides training in use of computers and software.

Community Environment: The Harbor College service area encompasses a multicultural population of 369,907 persons who live in the communities of San Pedro, Wilmington, Carson, Gardena, Lomita, Harbor City, and on the Palos Verdes Peninsula and parts of South Los Angeles. A business, industrial, shipping and civic center of the Port of Los Angeles, Wilmington is located in the heart of the Southern California oil refining district. Points of interest are Marineland, the Queen Mary, Ports O' Call Village, and a Korean Liberty Bell, all within easy driving distance.

■ **LOS ANGELES MISSION COLLEGE**
13356 Eldridge Ave.
Sylmar, CA 91342-3245
Tel: (818)364-7600
Web Site: www.lamission.edu/
Description: State and locally supported, 2-year, coed. Part of Los Angeles Community College District System. Awards transfer associate and terminal associate degrees. Founded 1974. Setting: 22-acre small town campus with easy access to Los Angeles. Educational spending for the previous fiscal year: $890 per student. Total enrollment: 7,617. Faculty: 270 (85 full-time, 185 part-time). Student-undergrad faculty ratio is 33:1. Students come from 8 other countries. 55% 25 or older. Core. Calendar: semesters. Academic remediation for entering students, ESL program, services for LD students, advanced placement, summer session for credit, part-time degree program, external degree program, adult/continuing education programs, co-op programs.
Entrance Requirements: Open admission. Option: early admission. Entrance: noncompetitive. Notification: continuous until 9/25.
Collegiate Environment: Orientation program. Drama-theater group, student-run newspaper. Student services: personal-psychological counseling, women's center. Campus security: 24-hour emergency response devices and patrols, student patrols. Los Angeles Mission College with 40,000 books, 450 serials, an OPAC, and a Web page. Operations spending for the previous fiscal year: $70,000. 103 computers available on campus for general student use. A campuswide network can be accessed. Staffed computer lab on campus.

■ **LOS ANGELES PIERCE COLLEGE**
6201 Winnetka Ave.
Woodland Hills, CA 91371-0001
Tel: (818)710-4123
Fax: (818)710-9844
Web Site: www.piercecollege.edu/
Description: State and locally supported, 2-year, coed. Part of Los Angeles Community College District System. Awards certificates, transfer associate, and terminal associate degrees. Founded 1947. Setting: 425-acre suburban campus with easy access to Los Angeles. Total enrollment: 16,255. Faculty: 558. 26,070 applied, 100% were admitted. Students come from 2 states and territories, 48 other countries. 48% 25 or older. Core. Calendar: semesters. Academic remediation for entering students, ESL program, services for LD

students, advanced placement, honors program, independent study, distance learning, summer session for credit, part-time degree program, adult/continuing education programs, co-op programs and internships. Study abroad program.

Entrance Requirements: Open admission except for nursing, honors programs. Options: electronic application, early admission. Entrance: noncompetitive. Application deadline: 8/20.

Collegiate Environment: Orientation program. Drama-theater group, choral group, student-run newspaper. Social organizations: 28 open to all. Most popular organizations: Alpha Gamma Sigma, Club Latino United for Education, United African-American Student Association, Hillel, Filipino Club. Major annual events: Club Day, Job Fair, University Day. Student services: health clinic, personal-psychological counseling, women's center. Campus security: 24-hour patrols, late night transport-escort service. Pierce College Library plus 1 other with 106,122 books and 395 serials. 60 computers available on campus for general student use. A campuswide network can be accessed. Staffed computer lab on campus.

Community Environment: Woodland Hills is a suburban area of Los Angeles with a subtropical climate, and known as a beautiful residential area. Buses serve the area. The community has a library, hospital, churches, and civic and service organizations. Nearby are shopping centers, theatres, and a public park with a swimming pool. The Pacific Ocean is within easy driving distance. Part-time employment is available.

■ **LOS ANGELES SOUTHWEST COLLEGE**
1600 W Imperial Hwy.
Los Angeles, CA 90047-4810
Tel: (323)241-5225
Web Site: www.lasc.edu/
Description: State and locally supported, 2-year, coed. Part of Los Angeles Community College District System. Awards certificates, diplomas, transfer associate, and terminal associate degrees. Founded 1967. Setting: 69-acre urban campus. Research spending for the previous fiscal year: $321,616. Total enrollment: 6,000. Faculty: 223 (75 full-time, 148 part-time). Students come from 20 states and territories, 4 other countries. 63% 25 or older. Core. Calendar: semesters. Academic remediation for entering students, ESL program, services for LD students, accelerated degree program, freshman honors college, honors program, summer session for credit, part-time degree program, adult/continuing education programs, co-op programs and internships.
Entrance Requirements: Open admission except for nursing program. Option: early admission. Recommended: essay, minimum 2.0 high school GPA. Required for some: high school transcript. Entrance: noncompetitive. Application deadline: 9/9. Notification: continuous until 9/9.
Collegiate Environment: Choral group, student-run newspaper. Social organizations: 8 open to all. Campus security: 24-hour emergency response devices and patrols, student patrols, late night transport-escort service. Main library plus 1 other with 60,000 books, 600 serials, an OPAC, and a Web page. Operations spending for the previous fiscal year: $329,727. 40 computers available on campus for general student use. A campuswide network can be accessed from off-campus. Staffed computer lab on campus.
Community Environment: See University of California - Los Angeles.

■ **LOS ANGELES TRADE-TECHNICAL COLLEGE**
400 W Washington Blvd.
Los Angeles, CA 90015-4108
Tel: (213)744-9500
Fax: (213)748-7334
E-mail: CardozaRJ@lattc.edu
Web Site: www.lattc.edu/
Description: State and locally supported, 2-year, coed. Part of Los Angeles Community College District System. Awards certificates, diplomas, transfer associate, and terminal associate degrees. Founded 1925. Setting: 25-acre urban campus. Total enrollment: 13,194. Faculty: 443 (200 full-time, 243 part-time). Full-time: 4,160 students, 56% women, 44% men. Part-time: 9,034 students, 49% women, 51% men. 47% 25 or older. Core. Calendar: semesters. Academic remediation for entering students, ESL program, services for LD students, advanced placement, summer session for credit, part-time degree program, adult/continuing education programs, co-op programs.
Entrance Requirements: Recommended: high school transcript. Entrance: noncompetitive. Application deadline: 9/7.
Collegiate Environment: Orientation program. Student services: health clinic, personal-psychological counseling, women's center. Campus security:

24-hour patrols, student patrols, late night transport-escort service. 98,000 books and 367 serials 200 computers available on campus for general student use. A campuswide network can be accessed. Students can access the following: online class registration. Staffed computer lab on campus.
Community Environment: See University of California - Los Angeles.

■ LOS ANGELES VALLEY COLLEGE
5800 Fulton Ave.
Van Nuys, CA 91401-4096
Tel: (818)947-2600
Fax: (818)947-2610
E-mail: manzanf@lavc.edu
Web Site: www.lavc.cc.ca.us/
Description: State and locally supported, 2-year, coed. Part of Los Angeles Community College District System. Awards certificates, transfer associate, and terminal associate degrees. Founded 1949. Setting: 105-acre suburban campus. Total enrollment: 17,264. 41% 25 or older. Core. Calendar: semesters. Academic remediation for entering students, ESL program, services for LD students, self-designed majors, honors program, independent study, distance learning, double major, summer session for credit, part-time degree program, adult/continuing education programs, co-op programs and internships.
Entrance Requirements: Open admission except for allied health programs. Options: electronic application, early admission. Recommended: high school transcript. Entrance: noncompetitive. Application deadline: Rolling.
Collegiate Environment: Orientation program. Drama-theater group, choral group, student-run newspaper, radio station. Student services: legal services, health clinic, personal-psychological counseling, women's center. Campus security: 24-hour emergency response devices and patrols, student patrols, late night transport-escort service. Los Angeles Valley Library with 124,000 books, 7,300 microform titles, 400 serials, an OPAC, and a Web page.

■ LOS MEDANOS COLLEGE
2700 E Leland Rd.
Pittsburg, CA 94565-5197
Tel: (925)439-2181
Fax: (925)439-8797
Web Site: www.losmedanos.net/
Description: District-supported, 2-year, coed. Part of California Community College System. Awards certificates, transfer associate, and terminal associate degrees. Founded 1974. Setting: 120-acre suburban campus with easy access to San Francisco. Research spending for the previous fiscal year: $70,348. Educational spending for the previous fiscal year: $1873 per student. Total enrollment: 7,152. Faculty: 244 (104 full-time, 140 part-time). Students come from 3 states and territories, 15 other countries, 0.2% from out-of-state. 56% 25 or older. Core. Calendar: semesters. Academic remediation for entering students, ESL program, services for LD students, advanced placement, honors program, independent study, double major, summer session for credit, part-time degree program, co-op programs. Study abroad program.
Entrance Requirements: Open admission. Required for some: high school transcript. Entrance: noncompetitive. Application deadline: 8/29. Notification: continuous until 8/29.
Collegiate Environment: Orientation program. Choral group, student-run newspaper. Social organizations: 16 open to all. Most popular organizations: Alpha Gamma Sigma, Christian Fellowship Club, Student Nurses Association, La Raza Club. Student services: women's center. Campus security: 24-hour patrols, student patrols, late night transport-escort service. Learning Resource Center with 15,439 books and 205 serials. Operations spending for the previous fiscal year: $926,689. 200 computers available on campus for general student use. Students can access the following: online class registration. Staffed computer lab on campus.

■ LOYOLA MARYMOUNT UNIVERSITY
One LMU Dr.
Los Angeles, CA 90045-2659
Tel: (310)338-2700; Free: 800-LMU-INFO
Fax: (310)338-2797
E-mail: admissions@lmu.edu
Web Site: www.lmu.edu/
Description: Independent Roman Catholic, comprehensive, coed. Awards bachelor's, master's, and doctoral degrees and post-master's certificates.

Founded 1911. Setting: 142-acre suburban campus with easy access to Los Angeles. Endowment: $358.9 million. Research spending for the previous fiscal year: $5.4 million. Educational spending for the previous fiscal year: $13,658 per student. Total enrollment: 9,492. Faculty: 1,115 (544 full-time, 571 part-time). Student-undergrad faculty ratio is 11:1. 11,913 applied, 50% were admitted. 36% from top 10% of their high school class, 70% from top quarter, 96% from top half. Full-time: 5,834 students, 58% women, 42% men. Part-time: 251 students, 42% women, 58% men. Students come from 48 states and territories, 65 other countries, 24% from out-of-state. 0.3% American Indian or Alaska Native, non-Hispanic/Latino; 22% Hispanic/Latino; 6% African American, non-Hispanic/Latino; 10% Asian, non-Hispanic/Latino; 0.2% Native Hawaiian or other Pacific Islander, non-Hispanic/Latino; 4% international. 2% 25 or older, 52% live on campus, 5% transferred in. Retention: 89% of full-time freshmen returned the following year. Academic areas with the most degrees conferred: business/marketing; visual and performing arts; social sciences. Core. Calendar: semesters. Academic remediation for entering students, ESL program, services for LD students, advanced placement, accelerated degree program, self-designed majors, honors program, independent study, double major, summer session for credit, part-time degree program, co-op programs and internships, graduate courses open to undergrads. Study abroad program. ROTC: Army (c), Naval (c), Air Force.
Entrance Requirements: Options: electronic application, early admission, early action, deferred admission, international baccalaureate accepted. Required: essay, high school transcript, 1 recommendation, SAT or ACT. Recommended: interview. Required for some: portfolios or auditions for animation, dance, music, or theatre arts majors. Entrance: very difficult. Application deadlines: 1/15, 11/1 for early action. Notification: continuous, 12/20 for early action. SAT Reasoning Test deadline: 2/1. Transfer credits accepted: Yes. Applicants placed on waiting list: 1,477. Wait-listed applicants offered admission: 21. Early action applicants: 3,051. Early action applicants admitted: 1,968.
Costs Per Year: Application fee: $60. One-time mandatory fee: $225. Comprehensive fee: $53,295 includes full-time tuition ($38,212), mandatory fees ($688), and college room and board ($14,395). College room only: $9995. Full-time tuition and fees vary according to reciprocity agreements. Room and board charges vary according to board plan and housing facility. Part-time tuition: $1594 per credit hour. Part-time mandatory fees: $8 per credit hour, $64 per term. Part-time tuition and fees vary according to course load.
Collegiate Environment: Orientation program. Drama-theater group, choral group, student-run newspaper, radio station. Social organizations: 140 open to all; national fraternities, national sororities; 16% of eligible men and 33% of eligible women are members. Most popular organizations: Greeks, Christian Life Community, intramurals, Black Student Union, Na Kolea Hawaii Club. Major annual events: College Fest Concert, Madness at Midnight (athletic spirit event), Charity Ball. Student services: health clinic, personal-psychological counseling. Campus security: 24-hour emergency response devices and patrols, late night transport-escort service, controlled dormitory access. 3,210 college housing spaces available; all were occupied in 2012-13. Freshmen given priority for college housing. Options: coed, men-only, women-only housing available. William H. Hannon Library with 598,443 books, 130,185 microform titles, 49,746 serials, 29,700 audiovisual materials, an OPAC, and a Web page. Operations spending for the previous fiscal year: $12.7 million. 780 computers available on campus for general student use. Computer purchase/lease plans available. A campuswide network can be accessed from student residence rooms and from off campus. Students can access the following: online class registration. Staffed computer lab on campus.
Community Environment: See University of California - Los Angeles.

■ MARYMOUNT COLLEGE, PALOS VERDES, CALIFORNIA
30800 Palos Verdes Dr. E
Rancho Palos Verdes, CA 90275-6299
Tel: (310)377-5501
Fax: (310)377-6223
E-mail: admissions@marymountpv.edu
Web Site: www.marymountpv.edu/
Description: Independent Roman Catholic, 4-year, coed. Awards associate and bachelor's degrees. Founded 1932. Setting: 26-acre suburban campus with easy access to Los Angeles. Endowment: $7.8 million. Educational spending for the previous fiscal year: $6892 per student. Total enrollment: 1,001. Faculty: 105 (35 full-time, 70 part-time). Student-undergrad faculty ratio is 17:1. 2,476 applied, 58% were admitted. Full-time: 958 students,

55% women, 45% men. Part-time: 43 students, 49% women, 51% men. Students come from 24 states and territories, 23 other countries, 7% from out-of-state. 0.2% American Indian or Alaska Native, non-Hispanic/Latino; 28% Hispanic/Latino; 9% African American, non-Hispanic/Latino; 4% Asian, non-Hispanic/Latino; 2% Native Hawaiian or other Pacific Islander, non-Hispanic/Latino; 8% international. 1% 25 or older, 43% live on campus, 7% transferred in. Retention: 66% of full-time freshmen returned the following year. Academic areas with the most degrees conferred: liberal arts/general studies; business/marketing. Core. Calendar: semesters. Academic remediation for entering students, ESL program, services for LD students, advanced placement, honors program, independent study, distance learning, summer session for credit, part-time degree program, adult/continuing education programs, internships. Off campus study. Study abroad program.

Entrance Requirements: Options: electronic application, early admission, international baccalaureate accepted. Required: high school transcript. Recommended: SAT or ACT. Required for some: essay, interview. Entrance: minimally difficult. Application deadline: 7/1. Notification: continuous until 9/1. SAT Reasoning Test deadline: 8/31. Transfer credits accepted: Yes.

Costs Per Year: Application fee: $40. Comprehensive fee: $40,942 includes full-time tuition ($28,217), mandatory fees ($650), and college room and board ($12,075). Room and board charges vary according to board plan and housing facility. Part-time tuition: $1066 per credit hour.

Collegiate Environment: Orientation program. Drama-theater group, choral group, student-run newspaper, radio station. Social organizations: 25 open to all; Phi Theta Kappa; 5% of eligible men and 5% of eligible women are members. Major annual events: Service Days, Club days, Spring Formal. Student services: health clinic, personal-psychological counseling. Campus security: 24-hour emergency response devices and patrols, late night transport-escort service, controlled dormitory access. 450 college housing spaces available; 432 were occupied in 2012-13. Freshmen guaranteed college housing. On-campus residence required in freshman year. Option: coed housing available. College Library plus 1 other with 24,406 books, 32,459 serials, 1,077 audiovisual materials, an OPAC, and a Web page. Operations spending for the previous fiscal year: $444,919. 200 computers available on campus for general student use. Computer purchase/lease plans available. A computer is required for all students. A campuswide network can be accessed from student residence rooms and from off campus. Students can access the following: online class registration. Staffed computer lab on campus provides training in use of computers, software, and the Internet.

■ **THE MASTER'S COLLEGE AND SEMINARY**
21726 Placerita Canyon Rd.
Santa Clarita, CA 91321-1200
Tel: (661)259-3540; Free: 800-568-6248
E-mail: admissions@masters.edu
Web Site: www.masters.edu/

Description: Independent nondenominational, comprehensive, coed. Awards bachelor's, master's, and doctoral degrees. Founded 1927. Setting: 110-acre suburban campus with easy access to Los Angeles. Endowment: $14.4 million. Educational spending for the previous fiscal year: $8163 per student. Total enrollment: 1,534. Faculty: 191 (54 full-time, 137 part-time). Student-undergrad faculty ratio is 19:1. 849 applied, 61% were admitted. 31% from top 10% of their high school class, 59% from top quarter, 84% from top half. 3 valedictorians. Full-time: 998 students, 49% women, 51% men. Part-time: 136 students, 32% women, 68% men. Students come from 42 states and territories, 25 other countries, 29% from out-of-state. 1% American Indian or Alaska Native, non-Hispanic/Latino; 10% Hispanic/Latino; 3% African American, non-Hispanic/Latino; 6% Asian, non-Hispanic/Latino; 1% Native Hawaiian or other Pacific Islander, non-Hispanic/Latino; 5% international. 14% 25 or older, 75% live on campus, 8% transferred in. Retention: 77% of full-time freshmen returned the following year. Academic areas with the most degrees conferred: theology and religious vocations; business/marketing; liberal arts/general studies. Core. Calendar: semesters. Academic remediation for entering students, services for LD students, advanced placement, accelerated degree program, independent study, distance learning, double major, summer session for credit, part-time degree program, external degree program, adult/continuing education programs, co-op programs and internships. Study abroad program.

Entrance Requirements: Options: electronic application, early admission, early action, deferred admission, international baccalaureate accepted. Required: essay, high school transcript, minimum 2.75 high school GPA, 2 recommendations, SAT or ACT. Recommended: interview. Entrance: moderately difficult. Application deadlines: 9/1, 9/1 for nonresidents, 11/15 for early action. Notification: 3/15, 12/22 for early action. Early action applicants: 353. Early action applicants admitted: 207.

Costs Per Year: Application fee: $40. Comprehensive fee: $38,840 includes full-time tuition ($28,380), mandatory fees ($1100), and college room and board ($9360). Full-time tuition and fees vary according to course load, degree level, and program. Room and board charges vary according to board plan. Part-time tuition: $1190 per credit hour. Part-time mandatory fees: $1190 per credit hour. Part-time tuition and fees vary according to course load, degree level, and program.

Collegiate Environment: Orientation program. Drama-theater group, choral group. Social organizations: 15 open to all. Most popular organizations: College Chorale, Summer Missions, intramurals, Church Ministries, Drama Club. Major annual events: Mission Truth and Life Conference, Spring Sing, Disney Day. Student services: health clinic, personal-psychological counseling. Campus security: 24-hour patrols. 808 college housing spaces available; 704 were occupied in 2012-13. Freshmen guaranteed college housing. On-campus residence required through junior year. Options: men-only, women-only housing available. Robert L. Powell Library plus 1 other with 193,130 books, 34,685 serials, 2,723 audiovisual materials, an OPAC, and a Web page. Operations spending for the previous fiscal year: $1.3 million. 57 computers available on campus for general student use. A computer is required for all students. A campuswide network can be accessed from student residence rooms and from off campus. Students can access the following: online class registration. Staffed computer lab on campus provides training in use of the Internet.

■ **MENDOCINO COLLEGE**
1000 Hensley Creek Rd.
Ukiah, CA 95482-0300
Tel: (707)468-3000
Fax: (707)468-3430
E-mail: asimpson@mendocino.edu
Web Site: www.mendocino.edu/

Description: State and locally supported, 2-year, coed. Part of California Community College System. Awards certificates, transfer associate, and terminal associate degrees. Founded 1973. Setting: 127-acre rural campus. Endowment: $6.4 million. Educational spending for the previous fiscal year: $4088 per student. Total enrollment: 3,614. Faculty: 294 (51 full-time, 243 part-time). Student-undergrad faculty ratio is 16:1. 660 applied, 100% were admitted. Full-time: 1,296 students, 55% women, 45% men. Part-time: 2,318 students, 63% women, 37% men. Students come from 16 states and territories, 2 other countries. 5% American Indian or Alaska Native, non-Hispanic/Latino; 23% Hispanic/Latino; 3% African American, non-Hispanic/Latino; 3% Asian, non-Hispanic/Latino; 1% Native Hawaiian or other Pacific Islander, non-Hispanic/Latino; 0% international. 40% 25 or older, 4% transferred in. Core. Calendar: semesters. Academic remediation for entering students, ESL program, services for LD students, advanced placement, honors program, independent study, distance learning, summer session for credit, part-time degree program, adult/continuing education programs, co-op programs and internships.

Entrance Requirements: Open admission. Options: electronic application, early admission, deferred admission. Required: high school transcript. Entrance: noncompetitive. Application deadline: Rolling. Notification: continuous. Preference given to state residents. Transfer credits accepted: Yes.

Costs Per Year: Application fee: $0. State resident tuition: $1380 full-time. Nonresident tuition: $7380 full-time. Mandatory fees: $32 full-time. Full-time tuition and fees vary according to course load.

Collegiate Environment: Orientation program. Drama-theater group, choral group, student-run radio station. Social organizations: 14 open to all. Campus security: late night transport-escort service, security patrols 6 pm to 10 pm. College housing not available. Lowery Library with 27,441 books, 275 serials, and a Web page. Operations spending for the previous fiscal year: $404,311. 90 computers available on campus for general student use. A campuswide network can be accessed from off-campus. Students can access the following: online class registration. Staffed computer lab on campus provides training in use of computers, software, and the Internet.

■ **MENLO COLLEGE**
1000 El Camino Real
Atherton, CA 94027-4301
Tel: (650)688-3753; Free: 800-556-3656
Fax: (650)617-2395
E-mail: admissions@menlo.edu
Web Site: www.menlo.edu/

Description: Independent, 4-year, coed. Awards bachelor's degrees.

Founded 1927. Setting: 45-acre small town campus with easy access to San Francisco. Endowment: $27.2 million. Educational spending for the previous fiscal year: $8228 per student. Total enrollment: 681. Faculty: 78 (31 full-time, 47 part-time). Student-undergrad faculty ratio is 15:1. 1,856 applied, 92% were admitted. Full-time: 670 students, 37% women, 63% men. Part-time: 11 students, 18% women, 82% men. Students come from 20 states and territories, 24 other countries, 23% from out-of-state. 0.4% American Indian or Alaska Native, non-Hispanic/Latino; 21% Hispanic/Latino; 6% African American, non-Hispanic/Latino; 6% Asian, non-Hispanic/Latino; 4% Native Hawaiian or other Pacific Islander, non-Hispanic/Latino; 12% international. 4% 25 or older, 67% live on campus, 13% transferred in. Retention: 74% of full-time freshmen returned the following year. Academic areas with the most degrees conferred: business/marketing; communication/journalism; psychology. Core. Calendar: semesters. ESL program, services for LD students, advanced placement, accelerated degree program, self-designed majors, independent study, double major, summer session for credit, part-time degree program, adult/continuing education programs, co-op programs and internships. Study abroad program. ROTC: Army (c), Air Force (c).

Entrance Requirements: Options: electronic application, early admission, early action, deferred admission, international baccalaureate accepted. Required: essay, high school transcript, 1 recommendation, SAT or ACT. Recommended: minimum 2.5 high school GPA, interview. Entrance: moderately difficult. Application deadlines: Rolling, Rolling for nonresidents, 12/1 for early action. Notification: continuous, continuous for nonresidents, 12/15 for early action. Transfer credits accepted: Yes. Applicants placed on waiting list: 98. Wait-listed applicants offered admission: 32.

Costs Per Year: Application fee: $40. Comprehensive fee: $49,002 includes full-time tuition ($36,500), mandatory fees ($600), and college room and board ($11,902). Room and board charges vary according to housing facility. Part-time tuition: $1521 per credit.

Collegiate Environment: Orientation program. Choral group. Social organizations: 47 open to all. Most popular organizations: International Club, student government, SERV, Finance Club, Hawaiian Club. Major annual events: Homecoming, Luau, Mystery Dance. Student services: personal-psychological counseling, women's center. Campus security: 24-hour emergency response devices and patrols, controlled dormitory access. 470 college housing spaces available; 458 were occupied in 2012-13. No special consideration for freshman housing applicants. On-campus residence required through sophomore year. Options: coed, men-only, women-only housing available. Bowman Library with 57,000 books, 34,000 serials, 1,100 audiovisual materials, an OPAC, and a Web page. Operations spending for the previous fiscal year: $607,881. 200 computers available on campus for general student use. A campuswide network can be accessed from student residence rooms and from off campus. Students can access the following: online class registration. Staffed computer lab on campus provides training in use of computers, software, and the Internet.

Community Environment: This is a residential community 30 miles south of San Francisco and 20 miles north of San Jose. The climate is moderate. The Southern Pacific Railroad, and Pacific Greyhound Bus serve the area with San Francisco International Airport 16 miles north. Activities are planned for all ages at the recreation center and many parks and playgrounds.

■ **MERCED COLLEGE**
3600 M St.
Merced, CA 95348-2898
Tel: (209)384-6000
Fax: (209)384-6339
Web Site: www.mccd.edu/
Description: State and locally supported, 2-year, coed. Part of California Community College System. Awards certificates, transfer associate, and terminal associate degrees. Founded 1962. Setting: 269-acre small town campus. Research spending for the previous fiscal year: $65,602. Total enrollment: 12,525. Faculty: 421 (145 full-time, 276 part-time). 2,593 applied, 100% were admitted. Students come from 30 states and territories, 2% from out-of-state. 51% 25 or older. Core. Calendar: semesters. Academic remediation for entering students, ESL program, advanced placement, self-designed majors, honors program, summer session for credit, part-time degree program, adult/continuing education programs, co-op programs and internships. Off campus study at several local community colleges. Study abroad program. ROTC: Army (c).
Entrance Requirements: Open admission except for allied health programs or international students. Option: early admission. Recommended: high school transcript. Entrance: noncompetitive. Application deadline: Rolling. Notification: continuous.

Collegiate Environment: Drama-theater group, choral group, student-run newspaper. Social organizations: 30 open to all. Student services: legal services, health clinic, personal-psychological counseling, women's center. Campus security: 24-hour patrols, late night transport-escort service. Lesher Library with 45,000 books, 1,500 microform titles, 200 serials, 300 audiovisual materials, and an OPAC. Operations spending for the previous fiscal year: $666,963. 400 computers available on campus for general student use.

Community Environment: Merced is a rural, suburban area with a dry temperate climate. All forms of transportation serve the area. The community has a library, churches, theatres, a symphony, two general hospitals and all national service clubs. Merced is located at the foot of the Sierra Nevada Mountains and near Yosemite National Park, which provides recreational facilities for camping, hiking, fishing, and skiing, the major winter sport. Job opportunities are good during the summer.

■ **MERRITT COLLEGE**
12500 Campus Dr.
Oakland, CA 94619-3196
Tel: (510)531-4911
E-mail: hperdue@peralta.cc.ca.us
Web Site: www.merritt.edu/
Description: State and locally supported, 2-year, coed. Part of Peralta Community College District System. Awards certificates, transfer associate, and terminal associate degrees. Founded 1953. Setting: 130-acre urban campus with easy access to San Francisco. Total enrollment: 6,944. 65% 25 or older. Core. Calendar: semesters. Academic remediation for entering students, ESL program, services for LD students, summer session for credit, part-time degree program, adult/continuing education programs, co-op programs. Off campus study at Holy Names College; Mills College; University of California, Berkeley.
Entrance Requirements: Open admission. Options: early admission, deferred admission. Entrance: noncompetitive. Application deadline: 8/28. Notification: continuous.
Collegiate Environment: Student-run newspaper. Student services: women's center. Merritt College Library with 80,000 books and 200 serials.
Community Environment: See Laney College.

■ **MILLS COLLEGE**
5000 MacArthur Blvd.
Oakland, CA 94613-1000
Tel: (510)430-2255; Free: 800-87-MILLS
Fax: (510)430-3314
E-mail: admission@mills.edu
Web Site: www.mills.edu/
Description: Independent, comprehensive. Awards bachelor's, master's, and doctoral degrees. Founded 1852. Setting: 135-acre urban campus with easy access to San Francisco. Endowment: $165.8 million. Research spending for the previous fiscal year: $2.9 million. Educational spending for the previous fiscal year: $16,318 per student. Total enrollment: 1,533. Faculty: 211 (102 full-time, 109 part-time). Student-undergrad faculty ratio is 10:1. 2,031 applied, 63% were admitted. 33% from top 10% of their high school class, 65% from top quarter, 92% from top half. 6 National Merit Scholars, 1 class president, 3 valedictorians, 19 student government officers. Full-time: 894 students, 100% women. Part-time: 43 students, 100% women. Students come from 34 states and territories, 14 other countries, 19% from out-of-state. 0.1% American Indian or Alaska Native, non-Hispanic/Latino; 21% Hispanic/Latino; 6% African American, non-Hispanic/Latino; 12% Asian, non-Hispanic/Latino; 1% Native Hawaiian or other Pacific Islander, non-Hispanic/Latino; 2% international. 16% 25 or older, 55% live on campus, 14% transferred in. Retention: 77% of full-time freshmen returned the following year. Academic areas with the most degrees conferred: social sciences; visual and performing arts; psychology. Core. Calendar: semesters. ESL program, services for LD students, advanced placement, accelerated degree program, self-designed majors, independent study, double major, part-time degree program, adult/continuing education programs, internships, graduate courses open to undergrads. Off campus study at University of California, Berkeley, California State University, Hayward, Sonoma State University, 9 other California colleges, American University, Agnes Scott College, Barnard College, Fisk University, Hollins College, Howard University, Manhattanville College, Mount Holyoke College, Simmons College, Spelman College, Swarthmore College, Wellesley College, Wheaton College. Study abroad program. ROTC: Army (c).
Entrance Requirements: Options: electronic application, early action,

deferred admission, international baccalaureate accepted. Required: high school transcript, 2 recommendations, essay or graded paper, SAT or ACT. Recommended: interview, SAT Subject Tests. Entrance: moderately difficult. Application deadlines: 2/1, 11/15 for early action. Notification: 3/30, 12/1 for early action. SAT Reasoning Test deadline: 2/1. Transfer credits accepted: Yes. Early action applicants: 1,008. Early action applicants admitted: 405.

Costs Per Year: Application fee: $50. Comprehensive fee: $54,119 includes full-time tuition ($40,210), mandatory fees ($1284), and college room and board ($12,625). College room only: $6495. Full-time tuition and fees vary according to course load. Room and board charges vary according to board plan and housing facility. Part-time tuition: $6702 per course. Part-time mandatory fees: $1284 per year. Part-time tuition and fees vary according to course load.

Collegiate Environment: Orientation program. Drama-theater group, choral group, student-run newspaper, radio station. Social organizations: 45 open to all. Most popular organizations: Mujeres Unidas, Black Women's Collective, Student Athlete Advisory Committee, Women's Health Resource Center, Phi Alpha Delta Pre-Law Fraternity. Major annual events: Black and White Ball, Midnight Breakfast, Spring Fling. Student services: health clinic, personal-psychological counseling, women's center. Campus security: 24-hour emergency response devices and patrols, late night transport-escort service, controlled dormitory access. 704 college housing spaces available; 514 were occupied in 2012-13. Freshmen guaranteed college housing. Options: coed, women-only housing available. F. W. Olin Library plus 1 other with 228,425 books, 28,498 microform titles, 43,560 serials, 13,641 audiovisual materials, an OPAC, and a Web page. Operations spending for the previous fiscal year: $1.5 million. 320 computers available on campus for general student use. Computer purchase/lease plans available. A campuswide network can be accessed from student residence rooms and from off campus. Students can access the following: online class registration, online degree audit. Staffed computer lab on campus provides training in use of computers, software, and the Internet.

Community Environment: See Laney College.

■ MIRACOSTA COLLEGE

One Barnard Dr.
Oceanside, CA 92056-3899
Tel: (760)757-2121; Free: 888-201-8480
Fax: (760)795-6609
E-mail: admissions@miracosta.edu
Web Site: www.miracosta.edu/

Description: State-supported, 2-year, coed. Part of California Community College System. Awards certificates, diplomas, transfer associate, and terminal associate degrees. Founded 1934. Setting: 131-acre suburban campus with easy access to San Diego. Total enrollment: 13,537. Student-undergrad faculty ratio is 28:1. 0% from out-of-state. 40% 25 or older. Core. Calendar: semesters. Academic remediation for entering students, ESL program, services for LD students, advanced placement, accelerated degree program, self-designed majors, freshman honors college, honors program, independent study, distance learning, double major, summer session for credit, part-time degree program, adult/continuing education programs, co-op programs and internships. Study abroad program.

Entrance Requirements: Open admission except for nursing program. Options: early admission, deferred admission, international baccalaureate accepted. Entrance: noncompetitive. Application deadline: Rolling.

Collegiate Environment: Orientation program. Drama-theater group, choral group, student-run newspaper. Student services: health clinic, personal-psychological counseling, women's center. Campus security: 24-hour emergency response devices, student patrols, late night transport-escort service, trained security personnel during class hours. MiraCosta College Library with an OPAC and a Web page.

■ MISSION COLLEGE

3000 Mission College Blvd.
Santa Clara, CA 95054-1897
Tel: (408)988-2200
Web Site: www.missioncollege.org/

Description: State and locally supported, 2-year, coed. Part of California Community College System. Awards certificates, diplomas, transfer associate, and terminal associate degrees. Founded 1977. Setting: 167-acre urban campus with easy access to San Francisco, San Jose. Total enrollment: 10,500. Faculty: 390 (180 full-time, 210 part-time). Student-undergrad faculty ratio is 26:1. Full-time: 4,000 students, 52% women, 48% men. Part-time: 6,500 students, 52% women, 48% men. Students come from 18 other

countries, 0.3% from out-of-state. 60% 25 or older, 0.5% transferred in. Core. Calendar: semesters. Academic remediation for entering students, ESL program, services for LD students, independent study, distance learning, double major, summer session for credit, part-time degree program, adult/continuing education programs, co-op programs and internships. ROTC: Army (c), Air Force (c).

Entrance Requirements: Open admission except for nursing program. Options: electronic application, early admission. Entrance: noncompetitive. Application deadline: Rolling. Notification: continuous. Preference given to district residents.

Collegiate Environment: Orientation program. Student services: personal-psychological counseling. Campus security: 24-hour emergency response devices, late night transport-escort service. 43,456 books and 323 serialsOperations spending for the previous fiscal year: $900,000. 120 computers available on campus for general student use. A campuswide network can be accessed from off-campus. Students can access the following: online class registration. Staffed computer lab on campus.

■ MODESTO JUNIOR COLLEGE

435 College Ave.
Modesto, CA 95350-5800
Tel: (209)575-6498
E-mail: mjcadmissions@mail.yosemite.cc.ca.us
Web Site: www.mjc.edu/

Description: State and locally supported, 2-year, coed. Part of Yosemite Community College District System. Awards certificates, transfer associate, and terminal associate degrees. Founded 1921. Setting: 229-acre urban campus. Educational spending for the previous fiscal year: $4217 per student. Total enrollment: 19,307. Faculty: 612 (267 full-time, 345 part-time). Student-undergrad faculty ratio is 29:1. Full-time: 6,874 students, 55% women, 45% men. Part-time: 12,433 students, 61% women, 39% men. 36% 25 or older, 4% transferred in. Retention: 73% of full-time freshmen returned the following year. Core. Calendar: semesters. Academic remediation for entering students, ESL program, services for LD students, advanced placement, honors program, independent study, distance learning, summer session for credit, part-time degree program, adult/continuing education programs, co-op programs. Study abroad program.

Entrance Requirements: Open admission. Option: electronic application. Recommended: high school transcript. Entrance: noncompetitive. Application deadline: Rolling. Notification: continuous.

Collegiate Environment: Orientation program. Drama-theater group, choral group, student-run newspaper, radio station. Social organizations: 24 open to all. Most popular organizations: Young Farmers, Red Nations, Psychology Club, Alpha Gamma Sigma, MECHA. Major annual events: Transfer Day/College Night, Job Fair, Club Fair. Student services: health clinic, personal-psychological counseling. Campus security: 24-hour emergency response devices and patrols, late night transport-escort service. Modesto Junior College Library with 69,865 books, 5,600 microform titles, 4,161 audiovisual materials, an OPAC, and a Web page. 137 computers available on campus for general student use. A campuswide network can be accessed from off-campus. Students can access the following: online class registration. Staffed computer lab on campus provides training in use of computers, software, and the Internet.

Community Environment: Modesto is located in the heart of the San Joaquin Valley and is the access point for the Sonora Pass vacationland in the Stanislaus National Forest, Mother Lode Country and the Big Oak Flat route to Yosemite. Modesto is the county seat of Stanislaus County. Churches of all denominations, a library, hospitals, plus the usual businesses make up the City of Modesto. There are 20 parks, playgrounds, golf courses, tennis courts, swimming pools for recreational facilities plus areas where there is boating, fishing, hunting and skiing. Part-time employment is available.

■ MONTEREY PENINSULA COLLEGE

980 Fremont St.
Monterey, CA 93940-4799
Tel: (831)646-4000
Fax: (831)655-2627
E-mail: vcoleman@mpc.edu
Web Site: www.mpc.edu/

Description: State-supported, 2-year, coed. Part of California Community College System. Awards certificates, transfer associate, and terminal associate degrees. Founded 1947. Setting: 87-acre small town campus. Total enrollment: 14,074. Faculty: 317 (136 full-time, 181 part-time). Students come from 29 states and territories, 47 other countries. Core. Calendar: semesters. Academic remediation for entering students, ESL program, services for LD students, advanced placement, summer session for credit, part-time degree program, adult/continuing education programs, co-op programs.

Entrance Requirements: Open admission except for nonresident aliens. Option: early admission. Entrance: noncompetitive. Application deadline: Rolling. Notification: continuous.

Collegiate Environment: Drama-theater group, choral group, student-run newspaper. Student services: health clinic, personal-psychological counseling, women's center. Campus security: 24-hour emergency response devices, late night transport-escort service. Monterey Peninsula College Library with 52,000 books, 137,300 microform titles, 281 serials, 2,623 audiovisual materials, an OPAC, and a Web page. 120 computers available on campus for general student use. A campuswide network can be accessed from off-campus. Staffed computer lab on campus.

Community Environment: Monterey Peninsula's population is approximately 150,000 including the cities of Carmel, Carmel Valley, Marina, Monterey, Pacific Grove, Pebble Beach, and Seaside. Monterey is a good two hour drive south of San Francisco on Highway 1. Airlines and buses serve the area. The climate is pleasing; average summer temperature is 60 and winter average is 51 degrees. This is the home of the Bach Festival, Golf Tournaments, Sports Car Races, the Monterey Jazz and Blues Festivals, and the County Fair. Artists, photographers, and writers enjoy Monterey for its beautiful scenery and good weather. Little theatre groups, music groups, art council and symphony guilds make up the cultural atmosphere of the city. Monterey Peninsula is a popular playground with several golf courses, facilities for fishing, boating, hunting and tennis. There are twelve championship golf courses in the area.

■ MOORPARK COLLEGE

7075 Campus Rd.
Moorpark, CA 93021-1695
Tel: (805)378-1400
Web Site: www.moorparkcollege.edu/

Description: County-supported, 2-year, coed. Part of Ventura County Community College District System. Awards certificates, transfer associate, and terminal associate degrees. Founded 1967. Setting: 121-acre small town campus with easy access to Los Angeles. Total enrollment: 13,750. Faculty: 577 (176 full-time, 401 part-time). Student-undergrad faculty ratio is 30:1. Students come from 45 states and territories, 50 other countries. 28% 25 or older. Core. Calendar: semesters. Academic remediation for entering students, ESL program, services for LD students, advanced placement, honors program, independent study, distance learning, summer session for credit, part-time degree program, adult/continuing education programs, co-op programs and internships.

Entrance Requirements: Open admission except for nursing, exotic animal training programs. Options: electronic application, early admission, deferred admission. Recommended: high school transcript. Required for some: high school transcript. Entrance: noncompetitive. Application deadline: Rolling. Notification: continuous.

Collegiate Environment: Student-run newspaper. Major annual event: Multicultural Day. Student services: health clinic, personal-psychological counseling, women's center. Campus security: 24-hour patrols. 50,000 books and 100 serials 80 computers available on campus for general student use. Students can access the following: online class registration. Staffed computer lab on campus.

Community Environment: See California Lutheran University.

■ MORENO VALLEY COLLEGE

16130 Lasselle St.
Moreno Valley, CA 92551
Tel: (951)571-6100
E-mail: admissions@mvc.edu
Web Site: www.rcc.edu/morenovalley/index.cfm

Description: State and locally supported, 2-year, coed. Awards transfer associate and terminal associate degrees. Founded 2010. Setting: suburban campus. Total enrollment: 10,413. Faculty: 437 (75 full-time, 362 part-time). Academic remediation for entering students, ESL program, honors program, distance learning.

Entrance Requirements: Open admission. Option: electronic application. Application deadline: Rolling. Notification: continuous.

Costs Per Year: State resident tuition: $1380 full-time, $46 per unit part-time. Nonresident tuition: $6660 full-time, $222 per unit part-time. Full-time tuition varies according to course load. Part-time tuition varies according to course load.

Collegiate Environment: Campus security: late night transport-escort service.

■ MOUNT ST. MARY'S COLLEGE

12001 Chalon Rd.
Los Angeles, CA 90049-1599
Tel: (310)954-4000; Free: 800-999-9893
E-mail: admissions@msmc.la.edu
Web Site: www.msmc.la.edu/

Description: Independent Roman Catholic, comprehensive, coed. Administratively affiliated with Sisters of St. Joseph Carondelet. Awards associate, bachelor's, master's, and doctoral degrees and post-master's certificates. Founded 1925. Setting: 49-acre urban campus with easy access to Los Angeles. Endowment: $97.7 million. Research spending for the previous fiscal year: $645,593. Educational spending for the previous fiscal year: $6510 per student. Total enrollment: 3,146. Faculty: 347 (99 full-time, 248 part-time). Student-undergrad faculty ratio is 13:1. 2,244 applied, 71% were admitted. Full-time: 1,919 students, 96% women, 4% men. Part-time: 539 students, 86% women, 14% men. Students come from 18 states and territories, 7 other countries, 2% from out-of-state. 1% American Indian or Alaska Native, non-Hispanic/Latino; 55% Hispanic/Latino; 8% African American, non-Hispanic/Latino; 17% Asian, non-Hispanic/Latino; 1% Native Hawaiian or other Pacific Islander, non-Hispanic/Latino; 1% international. 32% 25 or older, 20% live on campus, 4% transferred in. Retention: 79% of full-time freshmen returned the following year. Academic areas with the most degrees conferred: health professions and related sciences; social sciences; psychology. Core. Calendar: semesters. Academic remediation for entering students, ESL program, services for LD students, advanced placement, accelerated degree program, self-designed majors, freshman honors college, honors program, independent study, distance learning, double major, summer session for credit, part-time degree program, internships, graduate courses open to undergrads. Off campus study at University of Southern California, University of California, Los Angeles, Sisters of Saint Joseph College Consortium, University of Judaism. Study abroad program.

Entrance Requirements: Options: electronic application, early action, international baccalaureate accepted. Required: essay, high school transcript, minimum 2.5 high school GPA, 1 recommendation, SAT or ACT. Recommended: 2 recommendations, interview. Entrance: moderately difficult. Application deadlines: 2/15, 12/1 for early action. Notification: continuous, 1/1 for early action. SAT Reasoning Test deadline: 2/15. Transfer credits accepted: Yes. Early action applicants: 1,679. Early action applicants admitted: 673.

Costs Per Year: Application fee: $50. Comprehensive fee: $44,382 includes full-time tuition ($32,882), mandatory fees ($970), and college room and board ($10,530). College room only: $6318. Full-time tuition and fees vary according to course load, degree level, and program. Room and board charges vary according to board plan and housing facility. Part-time tuition: $1370 per unit. Part-time tuition varies according to course load, degree level, and program.

Collegiate Environment: Orientation program. Drama-theater group, choral group, student-run newspaper. Social organizations: 33 open to all; local sororities. Most popular organizations: Na Pua O Ka Aina, Pangkat Pilipino, Alpha Tau Delta, California Nursing Student Association, Mount Movement. Major annual events: Charity Ball, Spring Carnival, Mount Community Night. Student services: health clinic, personal-psychological counseling, women's center. Campus security: 24-hour emergency response devices and patrols, late night transport-escort service, controlled dormitory access. 659 college housing spaces available; 579 were occupied in 2012-13. Freshmen given priority for college housing. Options: men-only, women-only housing available. Coe Library plus 1 other with 150,000 books, 150,000 serials, 9,000 audiovisual materials, an OPAC, and a Web page. Operations spending for the previous fiscal year: $2 million. 170 computers available on campus for general student use. A campuswide network can be accessed from student residence rooms and from off campus. Students can access the following: online class registration. Staffed computer lab on campus.

■ MT. SAN ANTONIO COLLEGE

1100 N Grand Ave.
Walnut, CA 91789-1399
Tel: (909)594-5611
Web Site: www.mtsac.edu/

Description: District-supported, 2-year, coed. Part of California Community College System. Awards certificates, diplomas, transfer associate, and terminal associate degrees. Founded 1946. Setting: 421-acre suburban campus with easy access to Los Angeles. Total enrollment: 28,036. Faculty: 1,191 (398 full-time, 793 part-time). Full-time: 10,749 students, 49% women, 51% men. Part-time: 17,287 students, 52% women, 48% men. Students come from 21 states and territories, 139 other countries, 1% from out-of-state. 0.2% American Indian or Alaska Native, non-Hispanic/Latino; 56% Hispanic/Latino; 5% African American, non-Hispanic/Latino; 18% Asian, non-Hispanic/Latino; 0.4% Native Hawaiian or other Pacific Islander, non-Hispanic/Latino; 2% international. Retention: 79% of full-time freshmen returned the following year. Core. Calendar: semesters. Academic remediation for entering students, ESL program, services for LD students, advanced placement, honors program, independent study, distance learning, double major, summer session for credit, part-time degree program, adult/continuing education programs, co-op programs. Study abroad program. ROTC: Army, Air Force.

Entrance Requirements: Open admission. Options: electronic application, early admission, deferred admission. Required for some: high school transcript. Notification: continuous.

Costs Per Year: State resident tuition: $1104 full-time. Nonresident tuition: $6000 full-time. Mandatory fees: $60 full-time. Full-time tuition and fees vary according to course load and program.

Collegiate Environment: Orientation program. Drama-theater group, choral group, student-run radio station. Social organizations: 40 open to all. Most popular organizations: Alpha Gamma Sigma, Muslim Student Association, student government, Asian Student Association, Kasama-Filipino Student Organization. Major annual events: Cinco de Mayo, Asian Awareness Week, Join-a-Club. Student services: health clinic, personal-psychological counseling, women's center. Campus security: 24-hour emergency response devices and patrols, late night transport-escort service. College housing not available. Learning Resources Center with 97,996 books, 118 microform titles, 986 serials, 9,933 audiovisual materials, an OPAC, and a Web page. 1,200 computers available on campus for general student use. A campus-wide network can be accessed from off-campus. Students can access the following: online class registration, library databases. Staffed computer lab on campus provides training in use of computers, software, and the Internet.

■ **MT. SAN JACINTO COLLEGE**
1499 N State St.
San Jacinto, CA 92583-2399
Tel: (909)487-6752
Fax: (909)654-6738
E-mail: SLoomis@msjc.edu
Web Site: www.msjc.edu/
Description: State and locally supported, 2-year, coed. Part of California Community College System. Awards certificates, diplomas, transfer associate, and terminal associate degrees. Founded 1963. Setting: 180-acre suburban campus with easy access to San Diego. Total enrollment: 17,583. Full-time: 6,356 students, 57% women, 43% men. Part-time: 11,227 students, 60% women, 40% men. 38% 25 or older. Core. Calendar: semesters. Academic remediation for entering students, ESL program, services for LD students, advanced placement, honors program, distance learning, double major, summer session for credit, part-time degree program, adult/continuing education programs. Off campus study at Citrus College. Study abroad program.
Entrance Requirements: Open admission except for nursing program. Option: early admission. Recommended: high school transcript. Entrance: noncompetitive. Application deadline: Rolling.
Collegiate Environment: Drama-theater group. Student services: personal-psychological counseling. Campus security: part-time trained security personnel. Milo P. Johnson Library plus 1 other with 28,000 books and 330 serials.

■ **MT. SIERRA COLLEGE**
101 E Huntington Dr.
Monrovia, CA 91016
Tel: (626)873-2144; Free: 888-828-8000
Fax: (626)359-5528
E-mail: enroll@mtsierra.edu
Web Site: www.mtsierra.edu/
Description: Proprietary, 4-year, coed. Awards bachelor's degrees. Founded 1990. Setting: 5-acre suburban campus. Total enrollment: 511. 66

applied. 45% 25 or older. Core. Accelerated degree program, independent study, distance learning, summer session for credit, adult/continuing education programs, internships.
Entrance Requirements: Options: electronic application, international baccalaureate accepted. Required: essay, high school transcript, interview. Entrance: moderately difficult. Notification: 10/1.
Collegiate Environment: Orientation program. Campus security: 24-hour emergency response devices, student patrols, late night transport-escort service. Mt. Sierra College Learning Resource Center with 6,000 books, 5,000 serials, and 100 audiovisual materials.

■ **MTI COLLEGE**
5221 Madison Ave.
Sacramento, CA 95841
Tel: (916)339-1500
Fax: (916)339-0305
Web Site: www.mticollege.edu/
Description: Proprietary, 2-year, coed. Awards diplomas, transfer associate, and terminal associate degrees. Founded 1965. Setting: 5-acre suburban campus with easy access to Sacramento. Total enrollment: 900. Student-undergrad faculty ratio is 15:1. 629 applied, 62% were admitted. 0% from out-of-state. 62% 25 or older. Calendar: continuous.
Entrance Requirements: Required: essay, high school transcript, interview, MTI Assessment. Transfer credits accepted: Yes.

■ **MUSICIANS INSTITUTE**
1655 N McCadden Pl.
Hollywood, CA 90028
Tel: (323)462-1384; Free: 800-255-PLAY
Fax: (323)462-6978
E-mail: admissions@mi.edu
Web Site: www.mi.edu/
Description: Proprietary, 4-year, coed. Awards associate and bachelor's degrees. Founded 1976. Setting: urban campus. Total enrollment: 1,337. Faculty: 204 (108 full-time, 96 part-time). Student-undergrad faculty ratio is 10:1. 1,201 applied, 98% were admitted. Students come from 54 other countries. 1% American Indian or Alaska Native, non-Hispanic/Latino; 13% Hispanic/Latino; 7% African American, non-Hispanic/Latino; 4% Asian, non-Hispanic/Latino; 1% Native Hawaiian or other Pacific Islander, non-Hispanic/Latino; 25% international. 32% 25 or older. Services for LD students, summer session for credit, part-time degree program, internships.
Entrance Requirements: Options: electronic application, deferred admission, international baccalaureate accepted. Required: high school transcript, 1 recommendation. Required for some: essay, 2 recommendations, SAT or ACT. Entrance: minimally difficult. Application deadline: Rolling. Notification: continuous. SAT Reasoning Test deadline: 7/31. SAT Subject Test deadline: 7/31. Transfer credits accepted: Yes.
Costs Per Year: Application fee: $100. Tuition: $24,720 full-time. Mandatory fees: $5700 full-time. Full-time tuition and fees vary according to course load, degree level, and program.
Collegiate Environment: Orientation program. Student services: personal-psychological counseling. Campus security: 24-hour emergency response devices and patrols.

■ **NAPA VALLEY COLLEGE**
2277 Napa-Vallejo Hwy.
Napa, CA 94558-6236
Tel: (707)253-3000; Free: 800-826-1077
Fax: (707)253-3064
E-mail: odeharo@napavalley.edu
Web Site: www.napavalley.edu/
Description: State and locally supported, 2-year, coed. Part of California Community College System. Awards certificates, transfer associate, and terminal associate degrees. Founded 1942. Setting: 188-acre suburban campus with easy access to San Francisco. Total enrollment: 6,908. Faculty: 311 (99 full-time, 212 part-time). Student-undergrad faculty ratio is 22:1. 2,000 applied, 100% were admitted. Full-time: 1,909 students, 57% women, 43% men. Part-time: 4,999 students, 62% women, 38% men. Retention: 66% of full-time freshmen returned the following year. Core. Calendar: semesters. Academic remediation for entering students, ESL program, services for LD students, advanced placement, distance learning, summer session for credit, part-time degree program, co-op programs. Study abroad program.
Entrance Requirements: Open admission except for allied health

programs. Required for some: high school transcript. Entrance: noncompetitive. Application deadlines: Rolling, Rolling for nonresidents.

Collegiate Environment: Drama-theater group, choral group, student-run newspaper. Most popular organizations: Hispano-Americano Club, African-American Club, Environmental Action Coalition, International Student Club, Phi Theta Kappa. Major annual events: Black History Month, Cinco de Mayo, Native American Pow Wow. Student services: personal-psychological counseling, women's center. Campus security: late night transport-escort service. Napa Valley College Library plus 1 other with 42,000 books, 250 serials, and an OPAC. 90 computers available on campus for general student use. Staffed computer lab on campus.

Community Environment: Population 74,700. The town of Napa, in the southern wine district, is the center of a fruit and nut raising region as well as the southeastern entrance to the Redwood Empire. Located in the Napa Valley area, there are numerous wineries, most of which are open to the public for tours. The climate is delightful. Buses and trains serve the area. Napa has churches of all denominations, hospitals, clinics, and libraries. Recreation includes parks, picnic grounds, swimming pools, and golf courses.

■ **THE NATIONAL HISPANIC UNIVERSITY**
14271 Story Rd.
San Jose, CA 95127-3823
Tel: (408)254-6900
E-mail: chernandez@nhu.edu
Web Site: www.nhu.edu/

Description: Independent, 4-year, coed. Awards associate and bachelor's degrees. Founded 1981. Setting: 1-acre urban campus. Total enrollment: 551. 271 applied. 33% 25 or older. Core. Calendar: semesters. Academic remediation for entering students, ESL program, advanced placement, accelerated degree program, summer session for credit, part-time degree program, adult/continuing education programs, co-op programs and internships. Off campus study at California State University, Hayward, San Jose City College, Lincoln University, San Jose State University. Study abroad program.

Entrance Requirements: Option: electronic application. Required: essay, high school transcript, minimum 2.0 high school GPA, interview. Recommended: SAT and SAT Subject Tests or ACT. Entrance: minimally difficult. Application deadline: 8/15. Notification: continuous.

Collegiate Environment: Orientation program. Student services: personal-psychological counseling. Campus security: 24-hour emergency response devices and patrols. University Library with 10,000 books and 40 serials.

■ **NATIONAL UNIVERSITY**
11255 N Torrey Pines Rd.
La Jolla, CA 92037-1011
Tel: (619)563-7100; Free: 800-NAT-UNIV
Fax: (619)563-7299
E-mail: mmoses@nu.edu
Web Site: www.nu.edu/

Description: Independent, comprehensive, coed. Part of National University System. Awards associate, bachelor's, master's, and doctoral degrees. Founded 1971. Setting: urban campus. Endowment: $403 million. Research spending for the previous fiscal year: $4.5 million. Educational spending for the previous fiscal year: $4291 per student. Total enrollment: 17,898. Faculty: 2,756 (261 full-time, 2,495 part-time). Student-undergrad faculty ratio is 11:1. 1,659 applied, 100% were admitted. Full-time: 5,248 students, 59% women, 41% men. Part-time: 4,234 students, 58% women, 42% men. Students come from 51 states and territories, 43 other countries, 9% from out-of-state. 1% American Indian or Alaska Native, non-Hispanic/Latino; 25% Hispanic/Latino; 11% African American, non-Hispanic/Latino; 10% Asian, non-Hispanic/Latino; 2% Native Hawaiian or other Pacific Islander, non-Hispanic/Latino; 1% international. 78% 25 or older, 53% transferred in. Retention: 58% of full-time freshmen returned the following year. Academic areas with the most degrees conferred: business/marketing; health professions and related sciences; psychology. Core. Calendar: continuous. ESL program, services for LD students, advanced placement, accelerated degree program, independent study, distance learning, double major, summer session for credit, part-time degree program, adult/continuing education programs, internships. Off campus study at Servicemembers Opportunity Colleges. ROTC: Army (c), Air Force (c).

Entrance Requirements: Open admission. Options: electronic application, deferred admission. Required: high school transcript, minimum 2 high school GPA, interview. Required for some: essay, TEAS Exam for BSN Students.

Entrance: minimally difficult. Application deadline: Rolling. Notification: continuous. Transfer credits accepted: Yes.

Costs Per Year: Application fee: $60. Tuition: $14,670 full-time, $326 per quarter hour part-time. Full-time tuition varies according to location and program. Part-time tuition varies according to location and program.

Collegiate Environment: Campus security: 24-hour emergency response devices and patrols, late night transport-escort service. College housing not available. National University Library with 371,040 books, 411,963 microform titles, 39,475 serials, 22,138 audiovisual materials, an OPAC, and a Web page. Operations spending for the previous fiscal year: $3.1 million. 2,800 computers available on campus for general student use. A campuswide network can be accessed from off-campus. Students can access the following: online class registration. Staffed computer lab on campus provides training in use of computers and the Internet.

■ **NEW CHARTER UNIVERSITY**
543 Howard St., 5th Fl.
San Francisco, CA 94105
Tel: (415)813-5970; Free: 888-639-1388
Fax: (415)813-5980
E-mail: admissions@aju.edu
Web Site: www.new.edu/

Description: Private, comprehensive, coed. Awards associate, bachelor's, master's, and doctoral degrees (offers primarily external degree programs). Founded 1994. Setting: suburban campus with easy access to Birmingham. Total enrollment: 472. Faculty: 50 (all part-time). Student-undergrad faculty ratio is 11:1. 115 applied, 87% were admitted. Part-time: 230 students, 31% women, 69% men. 95% from out-of-state. 95% 25 or older. Academic areas with the most degrees conferred: business/marketing; social sciences; communication/journalism. Core. Advanced placement, accelerated degree program, independent study, distance learning, summer session for credit, part-time degree program, external degree program, adult/continuing education programs. Off campus study.

Entrance Requirements: Open admission. Option: electronic application. Required: interview. Required for some: essay, high school transcript. Entrance: noncompetitive. Transfer credits accepted: Yes.

Costs Per Year: Application fee: $75. Tuition: $1592 full-time. Tuition guaranteed not to increase for student's term of enrollment.

Collegiate Environment: Orientation program.

■ **NEW YORK FILM ACADEMY**
3801 Barham Blvd.
Los Angeles, CA 90068
Tel: (818)733-2600
Fax: (818)733-4074
E-mail: studios@nyfa.edu
Web Site: www.nyfa.com/

Description: Independent, comprehensive, coed. Awards associate, bachelor's, and master's degrees. Founded 1992.

Entrance Requirements: Required: essay, high school transcript, 2 recommendations, portfolio, SAT or ACT.

■ **NEWSCHOOL OF ARCHITECTURE & DESIGN**
1249 F St.
San Diego, CA 92101-6634
Tel: (619)235-4100; Free: 800-490-7081
Web Site: www.newschoolarch.edu/

Description: Proprietary, comprehensive, coed. Awards bachelor's and master's degrees. Founded 1980. Setting: 1-acre urban campus. Total enrollment: 463. 67 applied, 100% were admitted. 36% 25 or older. Core. Academic remediation for entering students, ESL program, advanced placement, summer session for credit, part-time degree program, adult/continuing education programs, co-op programs and internships, graduate courses open to undergrads. Off campus study. Study abroad program.

Entrance Requirements: Options: early decision, international baccalaureate accepted. Required: essay, high school transcript, minimum 2.5 high school GPA, interview. Required for some: portfolio. Entrance: moderately difficult. Application deadlines: Rolling, 8/30 for nonresidents, 7/1 for early decision. Notification: continuous, continuous for nonresidents.

Collegiate Environment: Orientation program. Student-run newspaper. Student services: personal-psychological counseling. Campus security: 24-hour emergency response devices. Newschool of Arts Foundation Library with 7,500 books, 50 serials, and 250 audiovisual materials.

■ **NORCO COLLEGE**

2001 Third St.

Norco, CA 92860

Tel: (951)372-7000

E-mail: admissionsnorco@norcocollege.edu

Web Site: www.rcc.edu/norco/index.cfm

Description: State and locally supported, 2-year, coed. Awards transfer associate and terminal associate degrees. Founded 2010. Setting: 141-acre urban campus with easy access to Los Angeles. Total enrollment: 9,674. Faculty: 271 (68 full-time, 203 part-time). Academic remediation for entering students, ESL program, honors program, distance learning.

Entrance Requirements: Open admission. Option: electronic application. Application deadline: Rolling. Notification: continuous.

Costs Per Year: State resident tuition: $1380 full-time, $46 per unit part-time. Nonresident tuition: $6660 full-time, $222 per unit part-time. Full-time tuition varies according to course load. Part-time tuition varies according to course load.

■ **NORTHWESTERN POLYTECHNIC UNIVERSITY**

47671 Westinghouse Dr.

Fremont, CA 94539-7482

Tel: (510)657-5913

Fax: (510)657-8975

E-mail: admission@npu.edu

Web Site: www.npu.edu/

Description: Independent, comprehensive, coed. Awards bachelor's, master's, and doctoral degrees. Founded 1984. Setting: 3-acre urban campus with easy access to San Francisco, San Jose. Total enrollment: 927. Faculty: 87 (31 full-time, 56 part-time). Student-undergrad faculty ratio is 16:1. 249 applied, 99% were admitted. Students come from 7 states and territories, 11 other countries, 7% from out-of-state. 45% 25 or older, 12% live on campus. Retention: 89% of full-time freshmen returned the following year. Core. Calendar: trimesters. ESL program, advanced placement, distance learning, summer session for credit, part-time degree program, adult/continuing education programs, graduate courses open to undergrads.

Entrance Requirements: Options: electronic application, deferred admission, international baccalaureate accepted. Required: high school transcript, minimum 2 high school GPA. Recommended: SAT. Required for some: essay, interview. Application deadlines: 8/2, 8/2 for nonresidents. Notification: continuous.

Collegiate Environment: Orientation program. Most popular organizations: NPU Student Association, Table Tennis Club, IEEE Student Chapter, softball club. Major annual events: Halloween party, dance party, picnic. Campus security: late night transport-escort service. Northwest Polytechnic University Library with 12,000 books, 100 microform titles, 200 serials, an OPAC, and a Web page. Operations spending for the previous fiscal year: $750,000. 200 computers available on campus for general student use. A campuswide network can be accessed from student residence rooms and from off campus. Students can access the following: online class registration, online learning resource services. Staffed computer lab on campus.

■ **NOTRE DAME DE NAMUR UNIVERSITY**

1500 Ralston Ave.

Belmont, CA 94002-1908

Tel: (650)508-3500; Free: 800-263-0545

Fax: (650)508-3660

E-mail: jpmurray@ndnu.edu

Web Site: www.ndnu.edu/

Description: Independent Roman Catholic, comprehensive, coed. Awards bachelor's, master's, and doctoral degrees. Founded 1851. Setting: 50-acre suburban campus with easy access to San Francisco. Endowment: $12.1 million. Educational spending for the previous fiscal year: $7249 per student. Total enrollment: 2,001. Faculty: 226 (58 full-time, 168 part-time). Student-undergrad faculty ratio is 12:1. 2,209 applied, 75% were admitted. 10% from top 10% of their high school class, 29% from top quarter, 62% from top half. Full-time: 802 students, 64% women, 36% men. Part-time: 381 students, 70% women, 30% men. Students come from 30 states and territories, 29 other countries, 7% from out-of-state. 1% American Indian or Alaska Native, non-Hispanic/Latino; 30% Hispanic/Latino; 7% African American, non-Hispanic/Latino; 11% Asian, non-Hispanic/Latino; 3% Native Hawaiian or other Pacific Islander, non-Hispanic/Latino; 3% international. 36% 25 or older, 39% live on campus, 16% transferred in. Retention: 81% of full-time freshmen returned the following year. Academic areas with the most degrees conferred: business/marketing; public administration and social services;

biological/life sciences. Core. Calendar: semesters. Academic remediation for entering students, ESL program, services for LD students, advanced placement, accelerated degree program, self-designed majors, independent study, double major, summer session for credit, part-time degree program, adult/continuing education programs, co-op programs and internships, graduate courses open to undergrads. Off campus study at Trinity College (DC), Emmanuel College (MA). Study abroad program. ROTC: Air Force (c).

Entrance Requirements: Options: electronic application, early admission, early action, deferred admission, international baccalaureate accepted. Required: essay, high school transcript, SAT or ACT. Required for some: interview, audition for music programs. Entrance: moderately difficult. Application deadline: Rolling. Notification: continuous. SAT Reasoning Test deadline: 8/1. Transfer credits accepted: Yes.

Costs Per Year: Application fee: $50. Comprehensive fee: $43,358 includes full-time tuition ($30,806), mandatory fees ($400), and college room and board ($12,152). College room only: $7878. Full-time tuition and fees vary according to degree level and program. Room and board charges vary according to board plan and housing facility. Part-time tuition: $994 per unit. Part-time tuition varies according to degree level and program.

Collegiate Environment: Orientation program. Drama-theater group, choral group, student-run newspaper. Social organizations: 20 open to all. Most popular organizations: Associated Students of Notre Dame de Namur University, BizCom, Rotaract, Students for Sustainability, International Club. Major annual events: Spring Formal, Viva Las Vegas, Activities Fair. Student services: health clinic, personal-psychological counseling. Campus security: 24-hour emergency response devices and patrols, late night transport-escort service, controlled dormitory access. 475 college housing spaces available; 464 were occupied in 2012-13. Freshmen guaranteed college housing. On-campus residence required through sophomore year. Option: coed housing available. The Carl Gellert and Celia Berta Gellert Library with 91,389 books, 503,834 microform titles, 14,000 serials, 9,122 audiovisual materials, an OPAC, and a Web page. 80 computers available on campus for general student use. A campuswide network can be accessed from student residence rooms and from off campus. Students can access the following: online class registration. Staffed computer lab on campus provides training in use of computers, software, and the Internet.

Community Environment: Population 24,500, Belmont is located 25 miles south of San Francisco, and has the advantages of a suburban location. The climate is ideal. The average high is 69.5 degrees, the low 47 degrees and the average rainfall is 19.8 inches. It is on the main line of Southern Pacific Railroad and San Francisco International Airport is 12 miles away. Students attending Notre Dame are close enough to San Francisco to enjoy all the cultural and recreational benefits such as major drama, music, and opera productions, films, rock group performances, and professional and collegiate sports. The beaches of the Pacific Ocean are 12 miles away. Two hours to the north is the wine country, and a few hours' drive east are the historic gold country, Lake Tahoe, and the Sierra Nevada Range with famous facilities for skiing and other winter sports.

■ **OCCIDENTAL COLLEGE**

1600 Campus Rd.

Los Angeles, CA 90041-3314

Tel: (323)259-2500; Free: 800-825-5262

Fax: (323)341-4875

E-mail: srichmond@oxy.edu

Web Site: www.oxy.edu/

Description: Independent, comprehensive, coed. Awards bachelor's and master's degrees. Founded 1887. Setting: 120-acre urban campus with easy access to Los Angeles. Endowment: $330.7 million. Total enrollment: 2,178. Faculty: 265 (184 full-time, 81 part-time). Student-undergrad faculty ratio is 10:1. 6,135 applied, 39% were admitted. 60% from top 10% of their high school class, 91% from top quarter, 100% from top half. 59 student government officers. Full-time: 2,154 students, 56% women, 44% men. Part-time: 22 students, 45% women, 55% men. Students come from 45 states and territories, 25 other countries, 53% from out-of-state. 0.4% American Indian or Alaska Native, non-Hispanic/Latino; 15% Hispanic/Latino; 4% African American, non-Hispanic/Latino; 13% Asian, non-Hispanic/Latino; 0.1% Native Hawaiian or other Pacific Islander, non-Hispanic/Latino; 3% international. 1% 25 or older, 78% live on campus, 2% transferred in. Retention: 94% of full-time freshmen returned the following year. Academic areas with the most degrees conferred: social sciences; biological/life sciences; visual and performing arts. Core. Calendar: semesters. Services for LD students, advanced placement, self-designed majors, honors program, independent study, double major, internships, graduate courses open to undergrads. Off campus study at California Institute of Technology, Art Center College of Design, Columbia University School of Engineering. Study abroad program. ROTC: Army (c), Air Force (c).

Entrance Requirements: Options: electronic application, early admission, early decision, deferred admission, international baccalaureate accepted. Required: essay, high school transcript, 1 recommendation, At least 2 SAT subject tests recommended, SAT or ACT. Recommended: SAT Subject Tests. Entrance: very difficult. Application deadlines: 1/10, 1/10 for nonresidents, 11/5 for early decision plan 1, 1/2 for early decision plan 2. Notification: 4/1, 4/1 for nonresidents, 12/5 for early decision plan 1, 2/1 for early decision plan 2. SAT Reasoning Test deadline: 1/10. SAT Subject Test deadline: 1/10. Transfer credits accepted: Yes. Applicants placed on waiting list: 970. Wait-listed applicants offered admission: 43. Early decision applicants: 260. Early decision applicants admitted: 111.

Costs Per Year: Application fee: $60. Comprehensive fee: $59,210 includes full-time tuition ($45,190), mandatory fees ($1080), and college room and board ($12,940). Room and board charges vary according to board plan.

Collegiate Environment: Orientation program. Drama-theater group, choral group, student-run newspaper, radio station. Social organizations: 86 open to all; national fraternities, national sororities, local fraternities, local sororities; 10% of eligible men and 13% of eligible women are members. Most popular organizations: Dance Production, Vagina Monologues, MEChA/ALAS, FEAST Garden, Queer Straight Alliance. Major annual events: Dance Production, Springfest, Founders Day. Student services: health clinic, personal-psychological counseling, women's center. Campus security: 24-hour emergency response devices and patrols, late night transport-escort service, controlled dormitory access. 1,671 college housing spaces available; all were occupied in 2012-13. Freshmen guaranteed college housing. On-campus residence required through junior year. Options: coed, women-only housing available. Mary Norton Clapp Library plus 2 others with 435,538 books, 428,452 microform titles, 47,576 serials, 13,134 audiovisual materials, an OPAC, and a Web page. 257 computers available on campus for general student use. Computer purchase/lease plans available. A campuswide network can be accessed from student residence rooms and from off campus. Students can access the following: online class registration. Staffed computer lab on campus (open 24 hours a day) provides training in use of computers, software, and the Internet.

Community Environment: See University of California - Los Angeles.

■ **OHLONE COLLEGE**
43600 Mission Blvd.
Fremont, CA 94539-5884
Tel: (510)659-6000
E-mail: cwilliamson@ohlone.edu
Web Site: www.ohlone.edu/

Description: State and locally supported, 2-year, coed. Part of California Community College System. Awards transfer associate and terminal associate degrees. Founded 1967. Setting: 530-acre suburban campus with easy access to San Francisco. Total enrollment: 10,867. Faculty: 430 (144 full-time, 286 part-time). Student-undergrad faculty ratio is 24:1. Full-time: 3,473 students, 60% women, 40% men. Part-time: 7,394 students, 49% women, 51% men. 49% 25 or older. Core. Calendar: semesters. Academic remediation for entering students, ESL program, services for LD students, self-designed majors, honors program, summer session for credit, part-time degree program, adult/continuing education programs, co-op programs. Off campus study at Contra Costa Community College District, Cabot College, members of the California State University System. Study abroad program. ROTC: Army (c), Air Force (c).

Entrance Requirements: Open admission except for nursing, respiratory therapy, physical therapy assistant, interpreter preparation programs. Option: early admission. Required: high school transcript. Entrance: noncompetitive. Application deadline: Rolling. Notification: continuous.

Collegiate Environment: Orientation program. Drama-theater group, choral group, student-run newspaper. Student services: health clinic, personal-psychological counseling. Campus security: 24-hour emergency response devices and patrols, late night transport-escort service. Ohlone College Library with 65,000 books and 410 serials. 250 computers available on campus for general student use. A campuswide network can be accessed from off-campus. Students can access the following: online class registration. Staffed computer lab on campus.

Community Environment: The Fremont area is one of the faster growing areas of California. Mild climate is enjoyed in this city located on the San Francisco Bay. Fremont is within easy driving distance of San Francisco, Berkeley, Oakland and Palo Alto, and enjoys the cultural advantages of those cities. Beaches are nearby for swimming, boating and fishing. There are numerous golf courses and parks for recreational facilities. Shopping facilities are good.

■ **ORANGE COAST COLLEGE**
2701 Fairview Rd.
Costa Mesa, CA 92628-5005
Tel: (714)432-0202
Fax: (714)432-5072
E-mail: egalvan@occ.cccd.edu
Web Site: www.orangecoastcollege.edu/

Description: State and locally supported, 2-year, coed. Part of Coast Community College District System. Awards certificates, transfer associate, and terminal associate degrees. Founded 1947. Setting: 164-acre suburban campus with easy access to Los Angeles. Endowment: $10.8 million. Research spending for the previous fiscal year: $210,218. Educational spending for the previous fiscal year: $1752 per student. Total enrollment: 24,239. Faculty: 758 (215 full-time, 543 part-time). Student-undergrad faculty ratio is 34:1. Full-time: 10,094 students, 47% women, 53% men. Part-time: 14,145 students, 50% women, 50% men. Students come from 52 states and territories, 69 other countries, 2% from out-of-state. 0.4% American Indian or Alaska Native, non-Hispanic/Latino; 25% Hispanic/Latino; 2% African American, non-Hispanic/Latino; 23% Asian, non-Hispanic/Latino; 0.5% Native Hawaiian or other Pacific Islander, non-Hispanic/Latino; 3% international. 70% 25 or older, 8% transferred in. Retention: 79% of full-time freshmen returned the following year. Core. Calendar: semesters plus summer session. Academic remediation for entering students, ESL program, services for LD students, advanced placement, self-designed majors, freshman honors college, honors program, distance learning, double major, summer session for credit, part-time degree program, external degree program, adult/continuing education programs, co-op programs and internships. Off campus study at Golden West College, Coastline Community College. Study abroad program. ROTC: Army (c), Air Force (c).

Entrance Requirements: Open admission. Option: electronic application. Entrance: noncompetitive. Application deadline: Rolling. Notification: continuous. Transfer credits accepted: Yes.

Costs Per Year: Application fee: $0. State resident tuition: $1112 full-time, $36 per unit part-time. Nonresident tuition: $6992 full-time, $232 per unit part-time. Mandatory fees: $902 full-time, $61.

Collegiate Environment: Orientation program. Drama-theater group, choral group, student-run newspaper. Social organizations: 68 open to all. Most popular organizations: Architecture Club, Circle K, Doctors of Tomorrow, Speech, Theater, and Debate, Vietnamese Student Association. Major annual events: Club Rush, ASOCC Angel Tree Gift Drive, Coast Days. Student services: legal services, health clinic, personal-psychological counseling. Campus security: 24-hour emergency response devices and patrols, student patrols, late night transport-escort service. College housing not available. Library with 112,276 books, 55 microform titles, 210 serials, 3,462 audiovisual materials, an OPAC, and a Web page. Operations spending for the previous fiscal year: $1.6 million. 1,515 computers available on campus for general student use. Computer purchase/lease plans available. A campuswide network can be accessed from off-campus. Students can access the following: online class registration. Staffed computer lab on campus.

Community Environment: Costa Mesa, three miles inland from the Pacific Ocean and Highway 101-A, is at the edge of Newport Beach. The city has a moderate climate - mild winters, and cool summer breezes from the ocean. Orange County's economy is derived from defense manufacture, electronics, light industry, housing, business, agriculture, and tourism. The campus is located within 15 minutes of the Orange County Performing Arts Center; Irvine Industrial Center (home of many high-tech industries); South Coast Plaza (one of the nation's largest shopping malls); and the University of California at Irvine (a major educational and research institution). The Los Angeles Museum, Pasadena Art Gallery, and the Griffith Park Observatory and planetarium are 50 miles away. The mountains and the desert are an easy two-hour drive. Recreational activities locally are boating, fishing, and all forms of water sports to be found on its beaches, canals, and waterways. Part-time employment is available.

■ **OTIS COLLEGE OF ART AND DESIGN**
9045 Lincoln Blvd.
Los Angeles, CA 90045-9785
Tel: (310)665-6800; Free: 800-527-OTIS
Fax: (310)665-6805

E-mail: admissions@otis.edu

Web Site: www.otis.edu/

Description: Independent, comprehensive, coed. Awards bachelor's and master's degrees. Founded 1918. Setting: 5-acre urban campus. Educational spending for the previous fiscal year: $36,350 per student. Total enrollment: 1,165. Faculty: 544 (55 full-time, 489 part-time). Student-undergrad faculty ratio is 5:1. 1,493 applied, 55% were admitted. Full-time: 1,085 students, 65% women, 35% men. Part-time: 20 students, 75% women, 25% men. Students come from 26 states and territories, 15 other countries, 19% from out-of-state. 0.4% American Indian or Alaska Native, non-Hispanic/Latino; 14% Hispanic/Latino; 4% African American, non-Hispanic/Latino; 33% Asian, non-Hispanic/Latino; 0.4% Native Hawaiian or other Pacific Islander, non-Hispanic/Latino; 17% international. 9% live on campus, 7% transferred in. Retention: 77% of full-time freshmen returned the following year. Academic areas with the most degrees conferred: visual and performing arts; architecture. Core. Calendar: semesters. Academic remediation for entering students, services for LD students, advanced placement, self-designed majors, freshman honors college, honors program, independent study, double major, summer session for credit, adult/continuing education programs, co-op programs and internships. Off campus study at the Consortium of East Coast Art Schools. Study abroad program.

Entrance Requirements: Options: electronic application, early admission. Required: essay, high school transcript, minimum 2.5 high school GPA, portfolio, SAT or ACT. Recommended: interview. Entrance: moderately difficult. Application deadline: Rolling. Notification: continuous.

Collegiate Environment: Orientation program. Social organizations: 15 open to all. Most popular organizations: Student Government Association, international students organization, Otis Students in Service (OASIS), Literary Magazine Club, Campus Crusade. Major annual events: Otis Scholarship Benefit Fashion Show, senior exhibitions, Orientation. Student services: personal-psychological counseling. Campus security: 24-hour patrols. 100 college housing spaces available; all were occupied in 2012-13. Freshmen given priority for college housing. Milliard Sheets Library 1 other with 42,000 books, 150 serials, an OPAC, and a Web page. 400 computers available on campus for general student use. A campuswide network can be accessed. Students can access the following: online class registration. Staffed computer lab on campus provides training in use of computers, software, and the Internet.

■ **OXNARD COLLEGE**

4000 S Rose Ave.

Oxnard, CA 93033-6699

Tel: (805)986-5800

Fax: (805)986-5806

E-mail: jdiaz@vcccd.edu

Web Site: www.oxnardcollege.edu/

Description: State-supported, 2-year, coed. Part of Ventura County Community College District System. Awards certificates, diplomas, and transfer associate degrees. Founded 1975. Setting: 119-acre urban campus. Endowment: $1.7 million. Total enrollment: 7,060. Faculty: 184 (89 full-time, 95 part-time). Full-time: 1,920 students, 55% women, 45% men. Part-time: 5,140 students, 56% women, 44% men. 0.4% American Indian or Alaska Native, non-Hispanic/Latino; 69% Hispanic/Latino; 3% African American, non-Hispanic/Latino; 6% Asian, non-Hispanic/Latino; 0.4% Native Hawaiian or other Pacific Islander, non-Hispanic/Latino; 0.05% international. 55% 25 or older, 12% transferred in. Retention: 56% of full-time freshmen returned the following year. Calendar: semesters. Core. Academic remediation for entering students, ESL program, services for LD students, advanced placement, accelerated degree program, honors program, independent study, distance learning, double major, summer session for credit, part-time degree program.

Entrance Requirements: Open admission. Options: electronic application, early admission. Recommended: high school transcript. Entrance: noncompetitive. Application deadline: Rolling. Notification: continuous. Transfer credits accepted: Yes.

Collegiate Environment: Orientation program. Drama-theater group. Student services: health clinic, personal-psychological counseling, women's center. Campus security: 24-hour patrols. College housing not available. Oxnard College Library with 31,500 books, 107 serials, an OPAC, and a Web page. 116 computers available on campus for general student use. A campuswide network can be accessed. Students can access the following: online class registration. Staffed computer lab on campus provides training in use of computers, software, and the Internet.

Community Environment: The city of Oxnard has a population of approximately 183,600 people, and is located on the Gold Coast of California, situated about 45 miles south of Santa Barbara and 60 miles north of Los Angeles. The climate has been described as Mediterranean. Oxnard has seven miles of shoreline with wide, uncrowded beaches. It is a paradise for people who love to boat, surf and sport-fish. There are many museums and points of historical interest. Some of the major annual events include the California Strawberry Festival in May, Fiestas Patrias Celebration in September, and the Parade of Lights in December.

■ **PACIFIC OAKS COLLEGE**

5 Westmoreland Pl.

Pasadena, CA 91103

Tel: (626)397-1300; Free: 877-314-2380

Fax: (626)397-1317

E-mail: admissions@pacificoaks.edu

Web Site: www.pacificoaks.edu/

Description: Independent, upper-level, coed. Part of The Chicago School Education System. Awards bachelor's and master's degrees and post-master's certificates. Founded 1945. Setting: 2-acre small town campus with easy access to Los Angeles, San Gabriel Valley. Endowment: $7.3 million. Research spending for the previous fiscal year: $236,517. Educational spending for the previous fiscal year: $9523 per student. Total enrollment: 1,028. Faculty: 125 (27 full-time, 98 part-time). Student-undergrad faculty ratio is 22:1. 339 applied, 77% were admitted. Full-time: 17 students, 88% women, 12% men. Part-time: 240 students, 96% women, 4% men. 91% 25 or older, 21% transferred in. Core. Calendar: semesters summer sessions and 2 intensive sessions. Independent study, distance learning, summer session for credit, part-time degree program, adult/continuing education programs, internships, graduate courses open to undergrads. Off campus study at Four College Consortium.

Entrance Requirements: Transfer credits accepted: Yes.

Collegiate Environment: Orientation program. Social organizations: 4 open to all. Most popular organizations: Latina/o Support Group, Student Empowerment Group, Teacher Education Student Association, Marriage, Family Therapy Student Association. Andrew Norman Library plus 1 other with 36,000 books, 87 serials, 125 audiovisual materials, an OPAC, and a Web page. Operations spending for the previous fiscal year: $188,124. 25 computers available on campus for general student use. A campuswide network can be accessed from off-campus. Students can access the following: online class listings. Staffed computer lab on campus.

Community Environment: See California Institute of Technology.

■ **PACIFIC STATES UNIVERSITY**

3450 Wilshire Blvd.

Ste. No.500

Los Angeles, CA 90006

Tel: (323)731-2383; Free: 888-200-0383

Fax: (323)731-7276

E-mail: admissions@psuca.edu

Web Site: www.psuca.edu/

Description: Independent, comprehensive, coed. Awards bachelor's, master's, and doctoral degrees. Founded 1928. Setting: 1-acre urban campus. Total enrollment: 175. Faculty: 34 (7 full-time, 27 part-time). Student-undergrad faculty ratio is 5:1. Full-time: 19 students, 37% women, 63% men. Students come from 6 other countries, 0% from out-of-state. 16% Asian, non-Hispanic/Latino; 79% international. 50% 25 or older, 21% transferred in. Retention: 90% of full-time freshmen returned the following year. Academic area with the most degrees conferred: business/marketing. Core. Academic remediation for entering students, ESL program, accelerated degree program, independent study, distance learning, double major, adult/continuing education programs.

Entrance Requirements: Open admission. Options: electronic application, deferred admission, international baccalaureate accepted. Required: high school transcript, minimum 2.5 high school GPA, proof of English proficiency (i.e. TOEFL, IBT, IELTS). Recommended: essay, SAT or ACT. Required for some: TOEFL or IELTS. Entrance: noncompetitive. Application deadlines: Rolling, Rolling for nonresidents. Notification: continuous, continuous for nonresidents. Transfer credits accepted: Yes.

Costs Per Year: Application fee: $100. Tuition: $14,055 full-time. Mandatory fees: $540 full-time. Full-time tuition and fees vary according to course load, degree level, and program. College room only: $7200. Room charges vary according to housing facility. Tuition guaranteed not to increase for student's term of enrollment.

Collegiate Environment: Orientation program. Campus security: patrols by trained security personnel during campus hours. 5 college housing spaces available. No special consideration for freshman housing applicants. Option: coed housing available. University Library plus 1 other with an OPAC and a Web page. 50 computers available on campus for general student use. A campuswide network can be accessed. Staffed computer lab on campus provides training in use of the Internet.

■ PACIFIC UNION COLLEGE
One Angwin Ave.
Angwin, CA 94508-9707
Tel: (707)965-6311; Free: 800-862-7080
Fax: (707)965-6390
E-mail: enroll@puc.edu
Web Site: www.puc.edu/
Description: Independent Seventh-day Adventist, comprehensive, coed. Awards associate, bachelor's, and master's degrees. Founded 1882. Setting: 200-acre rural campus with easy access to San Francisco Bay Area. Total enrollment: 1,564. Faculty: 139 (92 full-time, 47 part-time). Student-undergrad faculty ratio is 13:1. 2,105 applied, 47% were admitted. Full-time: 1,364 students, 54% women, 46% men. Part-time: 200 students, 66% women, 35% men. 18% from out-of-state. 1% American Indian or Alaska Native, non-Hispanic/Latino; 23% Hispanic/Latino; 7% African American, non-Hispanic/Latino; 18% Asian, non-Hispanic/Latino; 2% Native Hawaiian or other Pacific Islander, non-Hispanic/Latino; 3% international. 16% 25 or older, 71% live on campus, 7% transferred in. Retention: 78% of full-time freshmen returned the following year. Academic areas with the most degrees conferred: business/marketing; health professions and related sciences; biological/life sciences. Core. Academic remediation for entering students, services for LD students, advanced placement, honors program, independent study, double major, summer session for credit, part-time degree program, adult/continuing education programs, co-op programs and internships, graduate courses open to undergrads. Off campus study. Study abroad program.
Entrance Requirements: Options: electronic application, deferred admission, international baccalaureate accepted. Required: high school transcript, minimum 2.3 high school GPA, 3 recommendations, SAT or ACT. Entrance: moderately difficult. Application deadline: Rolling. Transfer credits accepted: Yes.
Costs Per Year: Comprehensive fee: $34,335 includes full-time tuition ($26,550), mandatory fees ($300), and college room and board ($7485). Full-time tuition and fees vary according to course load. Tuition guaranteed not to increase for student's term of enrollment.
Collegiate Environment: Orientation program. Drama-theater group, choral group, student-run newspaper. Social organizations: 24 open to all. Most popular organizations: Student Association, Business Club, Asian Student Association, Korean Adventist Student Association, Student Organization of Latinos. Major annual events: Fall Festival, All College Get Acquainted Party, Talent show. Student services: health clinic, personal-psychological counseling, women's center. Campus security: 24-hour emergency response devices and patrols, late night transport-escort service. 1,150 college housing spaces available. No special consideration for freshman housing applicants. On-campus residence required through senior year. Options: men-only, women-only housing available. W.E. Nelson Memorial Library with an OPAC and a Web page. 150 computers available on campus for general student use. A campuswide network can be accessed from student residence rooms and from off campus. Students can access the following: online class registration, student financial information. Staffed computer lab on campus provides training in use of computers, software, and the Internet.
Community Environment: This is a rural un-incorporated area on Howell Mountain, an extinct volcano, 80 miles from San Francisco. The climate is not extreme, although it is not unusual to have as much as 60 inches of rain in the winter. Bus service is available in St. Helena; railroads and airlines serve the San Francisco Bay area. Freeways are nearby. A hospital is located five miles from Angwin. Employment is available for students.

■ PALO VERDE COLLEGE
One College Dr.
Blythe, CA 92225
Tel: (760)921-5500
Fax: (760)921-5590
E-mail: diana.rodriguez@paloverde.edu
Web Site: www.paloverde.edu/
Description: State and locally supported, 2-year, coed. Part of California Community College System. Awards transfer associate and terminal associ-

ate degrees. Founded 1947. Setting: 10-acre small town campus. Total enrollment: 3,516. Student-undergrad faculty ratio is 23:1. 0% from out-of-state. 74% 25 or older. Core. Calendar: semesters. Academic remediation for entering students, ESL program, services for LD students, advanced placement, summer session for credit, part-time degree program, adult/continuing education programs, internships.
Entrance Requirements: Open admission. Option: early admission. Recommended: high school transcript. Entrance: noncompetitive. Application deadline: Rolling. Notification: continuous.
Collegiate Environment: Drama-theater group, student-run newspaper. Student services: personal-psychological counseling. Campus security: student patrols, security personnel during open hours.
Community Environment: Blythe, in the Palo Verde Valley, is on Interstate 10, 225 miles east of Los Angeles and 165 miles west of Phoenix. The climate is dry and temperate. It is an agricultural region with year-round farming. Greyhound Bus serves the area. There is a public library, 30 churches, a hospital, 2 clinics and the usual civic organizations. Recreation includes hunting, boating, and fishing on the Colorado River. There are good part-time employment opportunities.

■ PALOMAR COLLEGE
1140 W Mission Rd.
San Marcos, CA 92069-1487
Tel: (760)744-1150
Fax: (760)744-2932
E-mail: admissions@palomar.edu
Web Site: www.palomar.edu/
Description: State and locally supported, 2-year, coed. Part of California Community College System. Awards certificates and transfer associate degrees. Founded 1946. Setting: 156-acre suburban campus with easy access to San Diego. Total enrollment: 27,222. 37% 25 or older. Core. Calendar: semesters. Academic remediation for entering students, ESL program, services for LD students, advanced placement, distance learning, summer session for credit, part-time degree program, co-op programs and internships. Study abroad program.
Entrance Requirements: Open admission. Option: electronic application. Entrance: noncompetitive. Application deadline: Rolling. Notification: continuous.
Collegiate Environment: Orientation program. Drama-theater group, choral group, student-run newspaper, radio station. Student services: health clinic, personal-psychological counseling. Campus security: 24-hour patrols, student patrols, late night transport-escort service. Palomar Library with 108,000 books, an OPAC, and a Web page.

■ PASADENA CITY COLLEGE
1570 E Colorado Blvd.
Pasadena, CA 91106-2041
Tel: (626)585-7123
Fax: (626)585-7915
E-mail: rhbell@pasadena.edu
Web Site: www.pasadena.edu/
Description: State and locally supported, 2-year, coed. Part of California Community College System. Awards certificates, transfer associate, and terminal associate degrees. Founded 1924. Setting: 55-acre urban campus with easy access to Los Angeles. Total enrollment: 22,859. Faculty: 1,014 (378 full-time, 636 part-time). Student-undergrad faculty ratio is 22:1. 6,853 applied, 98% were admitted. Full-time: 8,092 students, 49% women, 51% men. Part-time: 14,767 students, 53% women, 47% men. Students come from 271 other countries, 0% from out-of-state. 0.2% American Indian or Alaska Native, non-Hispanic/Latino; 42% Hispanic/Latino; 4% African American, non-Hispanic/Latino; 25% Asian, non-Hispanic/Latino; 0.2% Native Hawaiian or other Pacific Islander, non-Hispanic/Latino; 4% international. 28% 25 or older, 4% transferred in. Retention: 80% of full-time freshmen returned the following year. Core. Calendar: semesters. Academic remediation for entering students, ESL program, services for LD students, advanced placement, honors program, independent study, distance learning, double major, summer session for credit, part-time degree program, adult/continuing education programs, internships. Study abroad program.
Entrance Requirements: Open admission except for international students. Option: electronic application. Entrance: noncompetitive. Application deadline: Rolling. Notification: continuous. Transfer credits accepted: Yes.
Costs Per Year: State resident tuition: $1152 full-time. Nonresident tuition: $6120 full-time. Mandatory fees: $48 full-time.
Collegiate Environment: Orientation program. Drama-theater group, choral

group, marching band, student-run newspaper. Social organizations: 72 open to all. Student services: health clinic, personal-psychological counseling. Campus security: 24-hour emergency response devices and patrols, late night transport-escort service, cadet patrols. College housing not available. Pasadena City College Library plus 1 other with 137,945 books, 3,429 microform titles, 19,326 serials, 12,079 audiovisual materials, an OPAC, and a Web page. 500 computers available on campus for general student use. A campuswide network can be accessed from off-campus. Students can access the following: online class registration. Staffed computer lab on campus provides training in use of computers, software, and the Internet.

Community Environment: See California Institute of Technology.

■ **PATTEN UNIVERSITY**
2433 Coolidge Ave.
Oakland, CA 94601-2699
Tel: (510)261-8500; Free: 877-4PATTEN
Fax: (510)534-8564
Web Site: www.patten.edu/

Description: Independent interdenominational, comprehensive, coed. Awards associate, bachelor's, and master's degrees. Founded 1944. Setting: 5-acre urban campus with easy access to San Francisco. Endowment: $1.3 million. Educational spending for the previous fiscal year: $13,340 per student. Total enrollment: 1,050. Faculty: 125 (26 full-time, 99 part-time). Student-undergrad faculty ratio is 17:1. 7 National Merit Scholars, 6 student government officers. Full-time: 487 students, 53% women, 47% men. Part-time: 507 students, 35% women, 65% men. Students come from 12 states and territories, 6 other countries, 5% from out-of-state. 59% 25 or older, 34% live on campus. Academic areas with the most degrees conferred: theology and religious vocations; psychology; business/marketing. Core. Calendar: semesters. Services for LD students, advanced placement, accelerated degree program, honors program, distance learning, double major, summer session for credit, part-time degree program, internships.

Entrance Requirements: Open admission. Options: early admission, deferred admission, international baccalaureate accepted. Required: essay, high school transcript, minimum 2.5 high school GPA, 2 recommendations, SAT or ACT. Recommended: interview. Entrance: noncompetitive. Application deadline: Rolling. Notification: continuous.

Collegiate Environment: Orientation program. Drama-theater group, choral group, student-run newspaper. Most popular organizations: Student Council, Patten Singers, Patten Symphonette. Major annual events: Patten Christmas Party, Campus Day, Graduation Banquet. Student services: personal-psychological counseling. Campus security: 24-hour emergency response devices, student patrols, late night transport-escort service. 36,160 books, 398 microform titles, 164 serials, 700 audiovisual materials, and an OPACOperations spending for the previous fiscal year: $124,610. 24 computers available on campus for general student use. A campuswide network can be accessed from student residence rooms and from off campus. Staffed computer lab on campus provides training in use of computers and the Internet.

Community Environment: The Oakland Bay Area is beautiful and there is easy access to San Francisco, Berkeley, and the Regional Park System. There is a variety of cultural, sporting, religious, and recreational activities available.

■ **PEPPERDINE UNIVERSITY**
24255 Pacific Coast Hwy.
Malibu, CA 90263
Tel: (310)506-4000
Fax: (310)506-4861
E-mail: laura.reisert@pepperdine.edu
Web Site: www.pepperdine.edu/

Description: Independent, university, coed, affiliated with Church of Christ. Awards bachelor's, master's, and doctoral degrees. Founded 1937. Setting: 830-acre suburban campus with easy access to Los Angeles. Endowment: $583.3 million. Research spending for the previous fiscal year: $2.5 million. Educational spending for the previous fiscal year: $13,457 per student. Total enrollment: 7,319. Faculty: 707 (385 full-time, 322 part-time). Student-undergrad faculty ratio is 13:1. 8,567 applied, 38% were admitted. 44% from top 10% of their high school class, 81% from top quarter, 96% from top half. Full-time: 3,086 students, 59% women, 41% men. Part-time: 402 students, 42% women, 58% men. Students come from 50 states and territories, 50 other countries, 38% from out-of-state. 1% American Indian or Alaska Native, non-Hispanic/Latino; 15% Hispanic/Latino; 7% African American, non-Hispanic/Latino; 12% Asian, non-Hispanic/Latino; 0.5% Native Hawaiian or

other Pacific Islander, non-Hispanic/Latino; 8% international. 9% 25 or older, 58% live on campus, 2% transferred in. Retention: 91% of full-time freshmen returned the following year. Academic areas with the most degrees conferred: business/marketing; communication/journalism; social sciences. Core. Calendar: semesters. Advanced placement, self-designed majors, honors program, independent study, double major, summer session for credit, part-time degree program, adult/continuing education programs, internships, graduate courses open to undergrads. Study abroad program. ROTC: Army (c), Air Force (c).

Entrance Requirements: Options: electronic application, international baccalaureate accepted. Required: essay, high school transcript, 2 recommendations, SAT or ACT. Entrance: very difficult. Application deadlines: 1/5, 1/5 for nonresidents. Notification: 4/1, 4/1 for nonresidents. SAT Reasoning Test deadline: 1/5. Transfer credits accepted: Yes.

Costs Per Year: Application fee: $65. Comprehensive fee: $55,372 includes full-time tuition ($42,520), mandatory fees ($252), and college room and board ($12,600). College room only: $9600. Room and board charges vary according to board plan and housing facility. Part-time tuition: $1330 per credit hour.

Collegiate Environment: Orientation program. Drama-theater group, choral group, student-run newspaper, radio station. Social organizations: national fraternities, national sororities; 18% of eligible men and 31% of eligible women are members. Most popular organizations: Latino Student Association, Black Student Union, Panhellenic Council, Interfraternity Council, International Justice Mission. Major annual events: Homecoming, Songfest, Family Weekend. Student services: health clinic, personal-psychological counseling. Campus security: 24-hour emergency response devices and patrols, student patrols, late night transport-escort service, controlled dormitory access, front gate security, 24-hour security in residence halls, controlled access, crime prevention programs. 2,109 college housing spaces available; 2,018 were occupied in 2012-13. Freshmen guaranteed college housing. On-campus residence required through sophomore year. Options: men-only, women-only housing available. Payson Library plus 7 others with 609,024 books, 505,727 microform titles, 7,779 serials, 12,524 audiovisual materials, an OPAC, and a Web page. Operations spending for the previous fiscal year: $7 million. 218 computers available on campus for general student use. Computer purchase/lease plans available. A campuswide network can be accessed from student residence rooms and from off campus. Students can access the following: online class registration. Staffed computer lab on campus provides training in use of computers, software, and the Internet.

Community Environment: See University of California - Los Angeles.

■ **PERELANDRA COLLEGE**
8697-C La Mesa Blvd.
PMB 21
La Mesa, CA 91941
Tel: (619)677-3308
Fax: (619)677-3304
E-mail: admin@perelandra.edu

Description: Independent Christian, comprehensive, coed. Awards bachelor's and master's degrees. Setting: suburban campus with easy access to San Diego. Educational spending for the previous fiscal year: $1000 per student. Total enrollment: 18. Faculty: 11 (all part-time). Student-undergrad faculty ratio is 3:1. Part-time: 6 students, 67% women, 33% men. Students come from 10 states and territories, 3 other countries, 90% from out-of-state. 90% 25 or older, 83% transferred in. Retention: 100% of full-time freshmen returned the following year. Core. Services for LD students, advanced placement, accelerated degree program, independent study, distance learning, summer session for credit, part-time degree program, external degree program, adult/continuing education programs, graduate courses open to undergrads. Off campus study.

Entrance Requirements: Options: electronic application, international baccalaureate accepted. Required: essay, minimum 2.5 high school GPA, 2 recommendations, letter of intent. Required for some: high school transcript. Entrance: minimally difficult. Notification: continuous, continuous for nonresidents. Transfer credits accepted: Yes.

Collegiate Environment: Student services: personal-psychological counseling. Operations spending for the previous fiscal year: $500.

■ **PIMA MEDICAL INSTITUTE**
780 Bay Blvd.
Ste. 101
Chula Vista, CA 91910

Tel: (619)425-3200; Free: 888-477-PIMA

Fax: (619)425-3450

Web Site: www.pmi.edu/

Description: Proprietary, primarily 2-year, coed. Administratively affiliated with Vocational Training Institutes, Inc. Awards certificates, terminal associate, and bachelor's degrees. Founded 1998. Setting: urban campus. Total enrollment: 813. 42% 25 or older. Core. Calendar: modular. Distance learning, co-op programs and internships.

Entrance Requirements: Required: high school transcript, interview, Wonderlic Scholastic Level Exam (SLE). Entrance: minimally difficult.

Collegiate Environment: Orientation program.

■ **PITZER COLLEGE**

1050 N Mills Ave.

Claremont, CA 91711-6101

Tel: (909)621-8000; Free: 800-748-9371

Fax: (909)621-8770

E-mail: admission@pitzer.edu

Web Site: www.pitzer.edu/

Description: Independent, 4-year, coed. Part of The Claremont Colleges Consortium. Awards bachelor's degrees. Founded 1963. Setting: 35-acre suburban campus with easy access to Los Angeles. Endowment: $113.7 million. Research spending for the previous fiscal year: $258,346. Educational spending for the previous fiscal year: $22,628 per student. Total enrollment: 1,084. Faculty: 121 (83 full-time, 38 part-time). Student-undergrad faculty ratio is 10:1. 4,227 applied, 16% were admitted. Full-time: 1,041 students, 61% women, 39% men. Part-time: 43 students, 67% women, 33% men. Students come from 40 states and territories, 17 other countries, 52% from out-of-state. 1% American Indian or Alaska Native, non-Hispanic/Latino; 15% Hispanic/Latino; 5% African American, non-Hispanic/Latino; 8% Asian, non-Hispanic/Latino; 0.1% Native Hawaiian or other Pacific Islander, non-Hispanic/Latino; 4% international. 7% 25 or older, 74% live on campus, 1% transferred in. Retention: 93% of full-time freshmen returned the following year. Academic areas with the most degrees conferred: social sciences; liberal arts/general studies; interdisciplinary studies; psychology. Core. Calendar: semesters. ESL program, services for LD students, advanced placement, self-designed majors, honors program, independent study, double major, summer session for credit, part-time degree program, adult/continuing education programs, co-op programs and internships. Off campus study at The Claremont Colleges, Colby College, Haverford College, Spelman College, Morehouse College. Study abroad program. ROTC: Army (c), Air Force (c).

Entrance Requirements: Options: electronic application, early decision, deferred admission, international baccalaureate accepted. Required: essay, high school transcript, minimum 2 high school GPA, 3 recommendations. Recommended: interview. Required for some: SAT or ACT. Entrance: very difficult. Application deadlines: 1/1, 11/15 for early decision. Notification: 4/1, 1/1 for early decision. SAT Reasoning Test deadline: 1/1. SAT Subject Test deadline: 1/1.

Costs Per Year: Application fee: $60. Comprehensive fee: $57,266 includes full-time tuition ($43,136), mandatory fees ($266), and college room and board ($13,864). College room only: $8028. Full-time tuition and fees vary according to course load. Room and board charges vary according to board plan. Part-time tuition: $5392 per course. Part-time tuition varies according to course load.

Collegiate Environment: Orientation program. Drama-theater group, choral group, student-run newspaper, radio station. Social organizations: 75 open to all. Most popular organizations: Student Senate, The Other Side, Without A Box, Residence Hall Association. Major annual events: Kohoutek Festival, Senior Celebration, Groove at the Grove. Student services: health clinic, personal-psychological counseling, women's center. Campus security: 24-hour emergency response devices and patrols, late night transport-escort service, controlled dormitory access. 770 college housing spaces available; all were occupied in 2012-13. Freshmen guaranteed college housing. On-campus residence required in freshman year. Options: coed, women-only housing available. Honnold Library plus 3 others with 2.5 million books, 1.1 million microform titles, 16,000 serials, an OPAC, and a Web page. Operations spending for the previous fiscal year: $1.4 million. 100 computers available on campus for general student use. A campuswide network can be accessed from student residence rooms and from off campus. Students can access the following: online class registration. Staffed computer lab on campus provides training in use of computers, software, and the Internet.

■ **PLATT COLLEGE (ALHAMBRA)**

1000 S Fremont A9W

Alhambra, CA 91803

Tel: (323)258-8050; Free: 888-80-PLATT

Fax: (323)258-8532

Web Site: www.plattcollege.edu/

Description: Proprietary, primarily 2-year, coed. Awards certificates, diplomas, transfer associate, terminal associate, and bachelor's degrees. Founded 1987. Setting: suburban campus. Total enrollment: 116. 43% 25 or older. Core. Calendar: continuous. Academic remediation for entering students, accelerated degree program, summer session for credit, internships.

Entrance Requirements: Required: interview, CPAt. Required for some: essay. Entrance: minimally difficult. Application deadline: Rolling. Notification: continuous.

Collegiate Environment: Orientation program. Campus security: parking lot security. Platt College Library with 808 books, 20 serials, and 70 audiovisual materials.

■ **PLATT COLLEGE (ONTARIO)**

3700 Inland Empire Blvd.

Ste. 400

Ontario, CA 91764

Tel: (909)941-9410; Free: 888-80-PLATT

Fax: (909)989-8974

Web Site: www.plattcollege.edu/

Description: Proprietary, primarily 2-year, coed. Awards certificates, diplomas, transfer associate, terminal associate, and bachelor's degrees. Total enrollment: 604. 39% 25 or older. Calendar: continuous. Academic remediation for entering students, accelerated degree program, honors program, independent study, summer session for credit, internships.

Entrance Requirements: Required: essay, interview, CPAt. Entrance: minimally difficult. Application deadline: Rolling. Notification: continuous.

Collegiate Environment: Orientation program. Main Library-Platt College with 2,800 books, 12 serials, and 35 audiovisual materials.

■ **PLATT COLLEGE SAN DIEGO**

6250 El Cajon Blvd.

San Diego, CA 92115-3919

Tel: (619)265-0107; Free: 866-752-8826

Fax: (619)265-8655

E-mail: sgallup@platt.edu

Web Site: www.platt.edu/

Description: Proprietary, 4-year, coed. Awards associate and bachelor's degrees. Founded 1879. Setting: 1-acre suburban campus. Educational spending for the previous fiscal year: $18,220 per student. Total enrollment: 292. Faculty: 29 (6 full-time, 23 part-time). Student-undergrad faculty ratio is 21:1. Full-time: 292 students, 25% women, 75% men. Students come from 4 states and territories, 5% from out-of-state. 44% 25 or older, 46% transferred in. Retention: 98% of full-time freshmen returned the following year. Academic area with the most degrees conferred: visual and performing arts. Core. Calendar: continuous. Academic remediation for entering students, accelerated degree program, adult/continuing education programs, co-op programs. Study abroad program.

Entrance Requirements: Open admission. Options: early admission, deferred admission, international baccalaureate accepted. Required: essay, high school transcript, interview, Wonderlic aptitude test. Recommended: SAT or ACT, SAT and SAT Subject Tests or ACT, SAT Subject Tests. Application deadlines: Rolling, Rolling for nonresidents. Notification: continuous, continuous for nonresidents.

Costs Per Year: Application fee: $110. Tuition: $15,200 full-time.

Collegiate Environment: Major annual events: art show on campus, Graduation Ceremonies. Student services: personal-psychological counseling. Campus security: 24-hour emergency response devices, surveillance cameras, security guard for evening session. Platt College San Diego Library with 775 books, 28 serials, 403 audiovisual materials, an OPAC, and a Web page. Operations spending for the previous fiscal year: $60,200.

■ **POINT LOMA NAZARENE UNIVERSITY**

3900 Lomaland Dr.

San Diego, CA 92106-2899

Tel: (619)849-2200; Free: 800-733-7770

Fax: (619)849-2579

E-mail: admissions@pointloma.edu

Web Site: www.pointloma.edu/

Description: Independent Nazarene, comprehensive, coed. Awards bachelor's and master's degrees and post-master's certificates. Founded 1902. Setting: 93-acre suburban campus with easy access to San Diego. Endowment: $35.7 million. Research spending for the previous fiscal year: $396,642. Educational spending for the previous fiscal year: $9563 per student. Total enrollment: 3,192. Faculty: 362 (142 full-time, 220 part-time). Student-undergrad faculty ratio is 14:1. 3,545 applied, 56% were admitted. 31% from top 10% of their high school class, 69% from top quarter, 92% from top half. Full-time: 2,350 students, 62% women, 38% men. Part-time: 65 students, 62% women, 38% men. 18% from out-of-state. 2% American Indian or Alaska Native, non-Hispanic/Latino; 19% Hispanic/Latino; 2% African American, non-Hispanic/Latino; 6% Asian, non-Hispanic/Latino; 1% Native Hawaiian or other Pacific Islander, non-Hispanic/Latino; 0.4% international. 3% 25 or older, 68% live on campus, 6% transferred in. Retention: 83% of full-time freshmen returned the following year. Academic areas with the most degrees conferred: business/marketing; health professions and related sciences; visual and performing arts. Core. Calendar: semesters. Academic remediation for entering students, services for LD students, advanced placement, honors program, independent study, double major, summer session for credit, part-time degree program, internships, graduate courses open to undergrads. Off campus study at American University, Coalition for Christian Colleges and Universities. Study abroad program. ROTC: Army (c), Naval (c), Air Force (c).

Entrance Requirements: Options: electronic application, early action, international baccalaureate accepted. Required: essay, high school transcript, minimum 2.8 high school GPA, 2 recommendations, SAT or ACT. Recommended: SAT, ACT. Entrance: moderately difficult. Application deadlines: 2/15, 11/15 for early action. Notification: 4/1, 12/21 for early action. SAT Reasoning Test deadline: 3/1. Transfer credits accepted: Yes. Applicants placed on waiting list: 186. Wait-listed applicants offered admission: 0.

Costs Per Year: Application fee: $50. Comprehensive fee: $39,060 includes full-time tuition ($28,900), mandatory fees ($610), and college room and board ($9550). College room only: $5440. Full-time tuition and fees vary according to course load. Room and board charges vary according to board plan. Part-time tuition: $1205 per credit hour. Part-time tuition varies according to course load.

Collegiate Environment: Orientation program. Drama-theater group, choral group, student-run newspaper, radio station. Social organizations: local fraternities, local sororities. Major annual event: homecoming. Student services: health clinic, personal-psychological counseling, women's center. Campus security: 24-hour patrols, student patrols, late night transport-escort service. Freshmen guaranteed college housing. On-campus residence required through junior year. Options: men-only, women-only housing available. Ryan Library with an OPAC and a Web page.

Community Environment: San Diego is an area of matchless climate and spectacular scenery. Resident institutions provide ample resources in research, culture, entertainment, and recreation. They involve the University of California, San Diego; San Diego State University; University of San Diego; San Diego Symphony; San Diego Opera; Scripps Institute of Oceanography; Palomar Observatory; and Balboa Park with its world famous Zoo, Natural History Museum, Fine Arts Gallery, Old Globe Theatre, Museum of Man, Photographic Arts Museum, Aerospace Museum, Starlight Opera, and Reuben H. Fleet Space Theatre and Museum. Los Angeles is two and one-half hours driving time to the north and Mexico thirty minutes to the south. The Laguna Mountains are to the east.

■ POMONA COLLEGE

333 N College Way
Claremont, CA 91711
Tel: (909)621-8000
Fax: (909)621-8403
E-mail: admissions@pomona.edu
Web Site: www.pomona.edu/

Description: Independent, 4-year, coed. Awards bachelor's degrees. Founded 1887. Setting: 140-acre suburban campus with easy access to Los Angeles. Endowment: $1.7 billion. Total enrollment: 1,607. Faculty: 241 (192 full-time, 49 part-time). Student-undergrad faculty ratio is 8:1. 7,456 applied, 13% were admitted. 91% from top 10% of their high school class, 97% from top quarter, 100% from top half. 22 valedictorians, 47 student government officers. Full-time: 1,589 students, 52% women, 48% men. Part-time: 18 students, 50% women, 50% men. Students come from 49 states and territories, 24 other countries, 66% from out-of-state. 0.1% American Indian or

Alaska Native, non-Hispanic/Latino; 14% Hispanic/Latino; 6% African American, non-Hispanic/Latino; 11% Asian, non-Hispanic/Latino; 0% Native Hawaiian or other Pacific Islander, non-Hispanic/Latino; 7% international. 0% 25 or older, 98% live on campus, 1% transferred in. Retention: 97% of full-time freshmen returned the following year. Academic areas with the most degrees conferred: social sciences; mathematics and statistics; interdisciplinary studies; physical sciences. Core. Calendar: semesters. Services for LD students, advanced placement, self-designed majors, independent study, double major, internships. Off campus study at other members of The Claremont Colleges, plus Swarthmore College, Colby College, Smith College, and Spelman College. Study abroad program. ROTC: Army (c), Air Force (c).

Entrance Requirements: Options: electronic application, early admission, early decision, deferred admission, international baccalaureate accepted. Required: essay, high school transcript, 3 recommendations, SAT and SAT Subject Tests or ACT. Recommended: interview, Supplemental forms for visual and performing arts, athletics, and science research are available. Entrance: most difficult. Application deadlines: 1/1, 11/1 for early decision plan 1, 1/1 for early decision plan 2. Notification: 4/1, 12/15 for early decision plan 1, 2/15 for early decision plan 2. SAT Reasoning Test deadline: 1/1. SAT Subject Test deadline: 1/1. Transfer credits accepted: Yes. Applicants placed on waiting list: 634. Wait-listed applicants offered admission: 11. Early decision applicants: 734. Early decision applicants admitted: 150.

Costs Per Year: Application fee: $70. Comprehensive fee: $54,964 includes full-time tuition ($41,120), mandatory fees ($318), and college room and board ($13,526). Room and board charges vary according to board plan.

Collegiate Environment: Orientation program. Drama-theater group, choral group, student-run newspaper, radio station. Social organizations: 220 open to all; local fraternities; 5% of men are members. Most popular organizations: student government, music/choral organizations, service organizations, intramural sports, outdoor activities club. Major annual events: Harwood Halloween Costume Party, Ski/Beach Day, Smiley Dorm '80s-Themed Party. Student services: health clinic, personal-psychological counseling, women's center. Campus security: 24-hour emergency response devices and patrols, late night transport-escort service, controlled dormitory access. 1,399 college housing spaces available; 1,370 were occupied in 2012-13. Freshmen guaranteed college housing. On-campus residence required in freshman year. Option: coed housing available. Honnold/Mudd Library plus 4 others with 2 million books, 70,000 serials, an OPAC, and a Web page. 180 computers available on campus for general student use. A campuswide network can be accessed from student residence rooms and from off campus. Students can access the following: online class registration. Staffed computer lab on campus (open 24 hours a day).

■ PORTERVILLE COLLEGE

100 E College Ave.
Porterville, CA 93257-6058
Tel: (559)791-2200
Fax: (559)791-2349
Web Site: www.pc.cc.ca.us/

Description: State-supported, 2-year, coed. Part of Kern Community College District System. Awards certificates, transfer associate, and terminal associate degrees. Founded 1927. Setting: 60-acre rural campus. Endowment: $1.3 million. Total enrollment: 5,024. Faculty: 140 (60 full-time, 80 part-time). 3,586 applied, 100% were admitted. Students come from 4 other countries. 48% 25 or older. Core. Calendar: semesters. Academic remediation for entering students, services for LD students, advanced placement, distance learning, summer session for credit, part-time degree program, adult/continuing education programs.

Entrance Requirements: Open admission. Options: electronic application, early admission. Required: high school transcript. Entrance: noncompetitive. Application deadline: Rolling.

Collegiate Environment: Orientation program. Drama-theater group, choral group. Student services: health clinic, personal-psychological counseling. Campus security: 24-hour emergency response devices, student patrols. Porterville College Library/Media Center with 31,557 books, 297 serials, and an OPAC. Operations spending for the previous fiscal year: $404,219. 350 computers available on campus for general student use. A campuswide network can be accessed. Students can access the following: online class registration. Staffed computer lab on campus.

Community Environment: Population 45,000, Porterville is located in southeastern Tulare County and is in a vast olive, grape, peach, walnut, cotton, and citrus growing area. The annual rainfall is 11.47 inches with an annual mean temperature of 62.8 degrees. Bus transportation is available to the airports and rail stations. The community has many churches, a library, auditorium, a community concert and theatre series each year, and an excellent shopping center with several new shopping centers in outlying areas. Recreational activities include fishing, camping, hunting in season, golf, boating, tennis, and skiing. Porterville is a 1 1/2 hour drive from Sequoia National Park; 2 1/2 hours from Kings Canyon National Park; and 3 hours from Yosemite National Park. Employment opportunities are good.

■ **PROFESSIONAL GOLFERS CAREER COLLEGE**
26109 Ynez Rd.
Temecula, CA 92591
Tel: (909)693-2963; Free: 800-877-4380
Fax: (909)693-2863
E-mail: garygilleon@golfcollege.edu
Web Site: www.golfcollege.edu/
Description: Independent, 2-year, coed. Awards terminal associate degrees. Setting: rural campus. Total enrollment: 282. Faculty: 23 (5 full-time, 18 part-time). Student-undergrad faculty ratio is 15:1. 40 applied, 100% were admitted. Full-time: 282 students, 4% women, 96% men. Students come from 50 states and territories, 13 other countries, 75% from out-of-state. 1% American Indian or Alaska Native, non-Hispanic/Latino; 4% Hispanic/Latino; 1% African American, non-Hispanic/Latino; 2% Asian, non-Hispanic/Latino; 1% Native Hawaiian or other Pacific Islander, non-Hispanic/Latino; 12% international. 50% 25 or older, 26% live on campus, 0% transferred in. Retention: 69% of full-time freshmen returned the following year. Core. Calendar: semesters. ESL program.
Entrance Requirements: Open admission. Options: early admission, deferred admission. Required: high school transcript, 3 recommendations. Application deadline: Rolling. Transfer credits accepted: Yes.
Costs Per Year: Application fee: $75. Tuition: $26,800 full-time. Mandatory fees: $2000 full-time. Tuition guaranteed not to increase for student's term of enrollment.
Collegiate Environment: Orientation program. Major annual events: Semester Golf Tournament, International Cup, President's Cup. Student services: personal-psychological counseling. 96 college housing spaces available; 92 were occupied in 2012-13. No special consideration for freshman housing applicants. Option: coed housing available. Professional Golfers Career College with 2,291 books, 45 serials, 115 audiovisual materials, and a Web page. Operations spending for the previous fiscal year: $24,325. 20 computers available on campus for general student use. Staffed computer lab on campus (open 24 hours a day).

■ **REEDLEY COLLEGE**
995 N Reed Ave.
Reedley, CA 93654-2099
Tel: (559)638-3641
Web Site: www.reedleycollege.edu/
Description: State and locally supported, 2-year, coed. Part of State Center Community College District System. Awards certificates, diplomas, transfer associate, and terminal associate degrees. Founded 1926. Setting: 350-acre rural campus. Total enrollment: 14,573. Faculty: 844 (194 full-time, 650 part-time). Students come from 15 states and territories. 0.1% American Indian or Alaska Native, non-Hispanic/Latino; 41% Hispanic/Latino; 2% African American, non-Hispanic/Latino; 5% Asian, non-Hispanic/Latino; 0% Native Hawaiian or other Pacific Islander, non-Hispanic/Latino; 0% international. Core. Calendar: semesters. Academic remediation for entering students, ESL program, services for LD students, advanced placement, freshman honors college, honors program, independent study, distance learning, summer session for credit, part-time degree program, adult/continuing education programs, co-op programs. Study abroad program. ROTC: Air Force (c).
Entrance Requirements: Open admission. Option: international baccalaureate accepted. Required: high school transcript. Entrance: noncompetitive. Application deadline: Rolling. Notification: continuous until 8/1.
Collegiate Environment: Orientation program. Drama-theater group, choral group, student-run newspaper. Student services: personal-psychological counseling. Campus security: 24-hour emergency response devices, late night transport-escort service, 24-hour on-campus police dispatcher. Reedley College Library with 36,000 books, 8,400 microform titles, 217 serials, and an OPAC. 303 computers available on campus for general student use. A campuswide network can be accessed from student residence rooms and from off campus. Students can access the following: online class registration. Staffed computer lab on campus.
Community Environment: Population 22,300. Reedley is in a rural area southeast of Fresno with a temperate climate. The rich farmlands around

Reedley produce a diversity of crops, including citrus fruits, plums, peaches, grapes, tomatoes, celery and walnuts. The community has 19 packing houses, two wineries, and a sawmill. There are a number of churches, a public library and a hospital. Part-time employment is available. Reedley is near Kings Canyon and Sequoia National Parks which provide recreational activities. Major civic, fraternal and veteran's organizations are part of the town.

■ **RIO HONDO COLLEGE**
3600 Workman Mill Rd.
Whittier, CA 90601-1699
Tel: (562)692-0921
Fax: (562)692-9318
Web Site: www.riohondo.edu/
Description: State and locally supported, 2-year, coed. Part of California Community College System. Awards certificates, transfer associate, and terminal associate degrees. Founded 1960. Setting: 128-acre suburban campus with easy access to Los Angeles. Total enrollment: 15,000. Faculty: 710 (210 full-time, 500 part-time). Students come from 5 states and territories, 40 other countries. 40% 25 or older. Core. Calendar: semesters. Academic remediation for entering students, ESL program, services for LD students, advanced placement, honors program, summer session for credit, part-time degree program, adult/continuing education programs. Study abroad program. ROTC: Army (c), Naval (c), Air Force (c).
Entrance Requirements: Open admission. Option: early admission. Entrance: noncompetitive. Application deadline: 7/10. Notification: continuous.
Collegiate Environment: Drama-theater group, choral group, student-run newspaper, radio station. Social organizations: 15 open to all. Student services: legal services, health clinic, personal-psychological counseling, women's center. Campus security: 24-hour patrols, late night transport-escort service. Main library plus 1 other with 94,143 books, 479 serials, and a Web page. 150 computers available on campus for general student use.
Community Environment: Small ex-urban community, 23 miles from downtown Los Angeles. Population of approximately 84,400. Small business and manufacturing predominate.

■ **RIVERSIDE CITY COLLEGE**
4800 Magnolia Ave.
Riverside, CA 92506-1299
Tel: (909)222-8000
Fax: (909)222-8037
E-mail: admissionsriverside@rcc.edu
Web Site: www.rcc.edu/
Description: State and locally supported, 2-year, coed. Part of California Community College System. Awards certificates and terminal associate degrees. Founded 1916. Setting: 108-acre suburban campus with easy access to Los Angeles. Total enrollment: 18,586. Faculty: 665 (222 full-time, 443 part-time). 33% 25 or older. Calendar: semesters. Academic remediation for entering students, ESL program, honors program, distance learning. Study abroad program.
Entrance Requirements: Open admission except for nursing program. Option: electronic application. Application deadline: Rolling. Notification: continuous.
Costs Per Year: Application fee: $0. State resident tuition: $1380 full-time, $46 per unit part-time. Nonresident tuition: $6660 full-time, $222 per unit part-time. Full-time tuition varies according to course load. Part-time tuition varies according to course load.
Collegiate Environment: Campus security: late night transport-escort service.
Community Environment: See University of California Riverside.

■ **SACRAMENTO CITY COLLEGE**
3835 Freeport Blvd.
Sacramento, CA 95822-1386
Tel: (916)558-2111
Fax: (916)558-2190
Web Site: www.scc.losrios.edu/
Description: State and locally supported, 2-year, coed. Part of California Community College System. Awards certificates, diplomas, transfer associate, and terminal associate degrees. Founded 1916. Setting: 60-acre urban campus. Total enrollment: 21,890. Faculty: 554. Student-undergrad faculty ratio is 30:1. 5% from top 10% of their high school class, 10% from top quarter, 25% from top half. Students come from 35 states and territories.

50% 25 or older. Core. Calendar: semesters. Academic remediation for entering students, ESL program, services for LD students, advanced placement, self-designed majors, honors program, summer session for credit, part-time degree program, adult/continuing education programs, co-op programs. Off campus study at University of California, Davis; California State University, Sacramento. Study abroad program.

Entrance Requirements: Open admission. Entrance: noncompetitive. Application deadline: Rolling. Notification: continuous.

Collegiate Environment: Orientation program. Drama-theater group, choral group, student-run newspaper. Most popular organizations: BOSS, African Student Alliance, Asian Pacific Club, MECHA, SMEC. Major annual events: Welcome Back Day, Peoples' Day. Student services: personal-psychological counseling, women's center. Campus security: 24-hour emergency response devices and patrols, student patrols, late night transport-escort service. Sacramento City College Library with 68,462 books, 415 serials, an OPAC, and a Web page. Operations spending for the previous fiscal year: $995,408. 450 computers available on campus for general student use. A campuswide network can be accessed from off-campus. Staffed computer lab on campus.

■ **SADDLEBACK COLLEGE**
28000 Marguerite Pky.
Mission Viejo, CA 92692
Tel: (949)582-4500
Fax: (949)347-8315
E-mail: earaiza@saddleback.edu
Web Site: www.saddleback.edu/
Description: State and locally supported, 2-year, coed. Awards certificates and transfer associate degrees. Founded 1967. Setting: 200-acre suburban campus with easy access to Los Angeles, San Diego. Total enrollment: 18,371. Faculty: 754 (215 full-time, 539 part-time). Full-time: 6,621 students, 50% women, 50% men. Part-time: 11,750 students, 58% women, 42% men. Students come from 37 states and territories, 23 other countries. 61% 25 or older. Core. Calendar: semesters. Academic remediation for entering students, ESL program, services for LD students, advanced placement, honors program, distance learning, summer session for credit, part-time degree program, adult/continuing education programs, co-op programs. Off campus study at Irvine Valley College. Study abroad program.
Entrance Requirements: Open admission. Option: early admission. Entrance: noncompetitive. Application deadline: Rolling.
Collegiate Environment: Drama-theater group, choral group, student-run newspaper, radio station. Social organizations: 19 open to all. Student services: legal services, health clinic, personal-psychological counseling, women's center. Campus security: 24-hour emergency response devices and patrols, late night transport-escort service. James B. Utt Memorial Library with 109,000 books and 132 serials. 200 computers available on campus for general student use. A campuswide network can be accessed. Staffed computer lab on campus.
Community Environment: Mission Viejo is largely a residential community located in the rolling hills midway between Los Angeles and San Diego. This is one of Orange County's fast growing areas, with a dry temperate climate. Good shopping facilities are available with most major department stores represented. Buses serve the area and Orange County Airport is only a short drive away. Beach resorts are located nearby for all water sports. The mountains are approximately a two-hour drive and ski slopes abound in the Big Bear area.

■ **SAGE COLLEGE**
12125 Day St., Bldg. L
Moreno Valley, CA 92557-6720
Tel: (951)781-2727; Free: 888-755-SAGE
Fax: (951)781-0570
Web Site: www.sagecollege.edu/
Description: Proprietary, 2-year, coed. Awards terminal associate degrees. Founded 1973. Total enrollment: 387. 12 applied, 100% were admitted.

■ **SAINT MARY'S COLLEGE OF CALIFORNIA**
1928 Saint Mary's Rd.
Moraga, CA 94556
Tel: (925)631-4000; Free: 800-800-4SMC
Fax: (925)376-7193
E-mail: smcadmit@stmarys-ca.edu
Web Site: www.stmarys-ca.edu/
Description: Independent Roman Catholic, upper-level, coed. Awards

bachelor's, master's, and doctoral degrees. Founded 1863. Setting: 420-acre suburban campus with easy access to San Francisco. Endowment: $124.2 million. Educational spending for the previous fiscal year: $11,319 per student. Total enrollment: 4,228. Faculty: 458 (194 full-time, 264 part-time). Student-undergrad faculty ratio is 13:1. 5,256 applied, 66% were admitted. Full-time: 2,781 students, 60% women, 40% men. Part-time: 254 students, 60% women, 40% men. Students come from 40 states and territories, 22 other countries, 10% from out-of-state. 0.5% American Indian or Alaska Native, non-Hispanic/Latino; 25% Hispanic/Latino; 4% African American, non-Hispanic/Latino; 10% Asian, non-Hispanic/Latino; 1% Native Hawaiian or other Pacific Islander, non-Hispanic/Latino; 2% international. 3% 25 or older, 53% live on campus, 7% transferred in. Retention: 88% of full-time entering class returned the following year. Academic areas with the most degrees conferred: business/marketing; communication/journalism; social sciences. Core. Calendar: 4-1-4. Services for LD students, advanced placement, self-designed majors, honors program, independent study, double major, summer session for credit, part-time degree program, adult/continuing education programs, internships, graduate courses open to undergrads. Off campus study at members of the January Interim Program. Study abroad program. ROTC: Army (c), Air Force (c).
Entrance Requirements: SAT Reasoning Test deadline: 2/15. Transfer credits accepted: Yes. Applicants placed on waiting list: 894. Wait-listed applicants offered admission: 167. Early action applicants: 1,698. Early action applicants admitted: 1,255.
Costs Per Year: Application fee: $55. Comprehensive fee: $53,550 includes full-time tuition ($39,740), mandatory fees ($150), and college room and board ($13,660). College room only: $7450. Room and board charges vary according to board plan and housing facility. Part-time tuition: $4972 per course. Part-time tuition varies according to course load and program.
Collegiate Environment: Orientation program. Drama-theater group, choral group, student-run newspaper, radio station. Social organizations: 41 open to all. Most popular organizations: Gael Force, Student Alumni Association, LASA-Latin American Student Association-Black Student Union, Inter-Varsity Christian Fellowship, Asian Pacific America Student Association. Major annual events: Gaelpalooza, Cultural Nights, Oasis. Student services: health clinic, personal-psychological counseling, women's center. Campus security: 24-hour emergency response devices and patrols, late night transport-escort service. College housing designed to accommodate 1,559 students; 1,599 undergraduates lived in college housing during 2012-13. Options: coed, men-only, women-only housing available. St. Albert Hall Library with 252,527 books, 446,888 microform titles, 10,181 serials, 39,190 audiovisual materials, an OPAC, and a Web page. 244 computers available on campus for general student use. A campuswide network can be accessed from student residence rooms and from off campus. Students can access the following: online class registration, student accounts. Staffed computer lab on campus provides training in use of computers, software, and the Internet.

■ **THE SALVATION ARMY COLLEGE FOR OFFICER TRAINING AT CRESTMONT**
30840 Hawthorne Blvd.
Rancho Palos Verdes, CA 90275
Tel: (310)377-0481
Fax: (310)265-6565
Web Site: www.crestmont.edu/
Description: Independent Salvation Army, 2-year, coed. Administratively affiliated with The Salvation Army. Awards transfer associate and terminal associate degrees. Founded 1878. Setting: 44-acre suburban campus with easy access to Los Angeles. Endowment: $85.5 million. Research spending for the previous fiscal year: $32. Total enrollment: 124. Faculty: 35 (13 full-time, 22 part-time). Student-undergrad faculty ratio is 1:1. Full-time: 61 students, 100% men. Part-time: 63 students, 100% women. Students come from 14 states and territories, 1 other country, 67% from out-of-state. 22% Hispanic/Latino; 4% African American, non-Hispanic/Latino; 7% Asian, non-Hispanic/Latino; 6% Native Hawaiian or other Pacific Islander, non-Hispanic/Latino. 100% 25 or older, 100% live on campus. Retention: 98% of full-time freshmen returned the following year. Academic area with the most degrees conferred: theology and religious vocations. Core. Academic remediation for entering students, ESL program, accelerated degree program, self-designed majors, independent study, distance learning, external degree program, co-op programs and internships. Off campus study.
Entrance Requirements: Required: essay, high school transcript, 2 recommendations, interview. Entrance: noncompetitive. Application deadline: 6/1. Notification: 8/20. Preference given to Members of the Salvation Army.
Collegiate Environment: Orientation program. Drama-theater group, choral

group. Major annual event: performing arts production. Student services: health clinic, personal-psychological counseling. Campus security: 24-hour emergency response devices and patrols. 60 college housing spaces available. On-campus residence required through sophomore year. The Salvation Army Elfman Memorial Library with 40,000 books, 500 serials, and an OPAC. Operations spending for the previous fiscal year: $194,700. 65 computers available on campus for general student use. Computer purchase/lease plans available. A campuswide network can be accessed from student residence rooms and from off campus. Students can access the following: online class registration. Staffed computer lab on campus.

■ SAMUEL MERRITT UNIVERSITY

3100 Telegraph Ave.
Oakland, CA 94609-3108
Tel: (510)869-6511; Free: 800-607-MERRITT
Fax: (510)869-6525
E-mail: admission@samuelmerritt.edu
Web Site: www.samuelmerritt.edu/
Description: Independent, upper-level, coed. Awards bachelor's, master's, and doctoral degrees (bachelor's degree offered jointly with Saint Mary's College of California). Founded 1909. Setting: 1-acre urban campus with easy access to San Francisco. Endowment: $38.2 million. Research spending for the previous fiscal year: $11,060. Educational spending for the previous fiscal year: $8969 per student. Total enrollment: 1,530. Faculty: 271 (109 full-time, 162 part-time). Student-undergrad faculty ratio is 10:1. Full-time: 513 students, 83% women, 17% men. Part-time: 71 students, 76% women, 24% men. Students come from 2 states and territories, 1 other country, 1% from out-of-state. 1% American Indian or Alaska Native, non-Hispanic/Latino; 13% Hispanic/Latino; 4% African American, non-Hispanic/Latino; 29% Asian, non-Hispanic/Latino; 2% Native Hawaiian or other Pacific Islander, non-Hispanic/Latino; 0% international. 66% 25 or older, 41% transferred in. Academic area with the most degrees conferred: health professions and related sciences. Core. Calendar: trimesters. Academic remediation for entering students, services for LD students, advanced placement, accelerated degree program, independent study, distance learning, summer session for credit, part-time degree program, co-op programs and internships. Off campus study at Saint Mary's College of California, Holy Names University, Mills College. ROTC: Army (c), Air Force (c).
Entrance Requirements: Transfer credits accepted: Yes.
Costs Per Year: Application fee: $50. Tuition: $39,456 full-time, $1663 per unit part-time. Full-time tuition varies according to degree level and program. Part-time tuition varies according to degree level and program.
Collegiate Environment: Orientation program. Student-run newspaper. Social organizations: local fraternities. Most popular organizations: Student Body Association, Green Team, International Health Club, Multicultural Group. Major annual events: Welcome Back BBQ and the Spring Fling BBQ, Diversity Day, Halloween Dance. Student services: health clinic, personal-psychological counseling. Campus security: 24-hour emergency response devices and patrols, late night transport-escort service, controlled dormitory access, 24-hour controlled access. College housing not available. John A. Graziano Memorial Library plus 1 other with 34,729 books, 9,188 serials, 1,760 audiovisual materials, an OPAC, and a Web page. Operations spending for the previous fiscal year: $940,891. 102 computers available on campus for general student use. A campuswide network can be accessed from student residence rooms. Students can access the following: online class registration. Staffed computer lab on campus.

■ SAN BERNARDINO VALLEY COLLEGE

701 S Mount Vernon Ave.
San Bernardino, CA 92410-2748
Tel: (909)384-4400
Web Site: www.valleycollege.edu/
Description: State and locally supported, 2-year, coed. Part of San Bernardino Community College District System. Awards certificates, diplomas, transfer associate, and terminal associate degrees. Founded 1926. Setting: 82-acre campus with easy access to Los Angeles. Total enrollment: 1,540. Faculty: 375 (175 full-time, 200 part-time). Students come from 2 states and territories. 55% 25 or older. Core. Calendar: semesters. Academic remediation for entering students, services for LD students, summer session for credit, part-time degree program, co-op programs.
Entrance Requirements: Open admission. Entrance: noncompetitive. Application deadline: 8/29.
Collegiate Environment: Drama-theater group, student-run newspaper, radio station. Student services: health clinic, personal-psychological counsel-

ing, women's center. 122,802 books and 657 serials 180 computers available on campus for general student use. Staffed computer lab on campus.
Community Environment: See California State University - San Bernardino.

■ SAN DIEGO CHRISTIAN COLLEGE

2100 Greenfield Dr.
El Cajon, CA 92019-1157
Tel: (619)441-2200; Free: 800-676-2242
Fax: (619)440-0209
E-mail: cdelgiudice@sdcc.edu
Web Site: www.sdcc.edu/
Description: Independent nondenominational, 4-year, coed. Awards associate and bachelor's degrees. Founded 1970. Setting: 55-acre suburban campus with easy access to San Diego. Endowment: $532,546. Educational spending for the previous fiscal year: $5547 per student. Total enrollment: 752. Faculty: 94 (16 full-time, 78 part-time). Student-undergrad faculty ratio is 17:1. 596 applied, 43% were admitted. 5% from top 10% of their high school class, 27% from top quarter, 53% from top half. Full-time: 652 students, 49% women, 51% men. Part-time: 87 students, 59% women, 41% men. Students come from 44 states and territories, 5 other countries, 31% from out-of-state. 1% American Indian or Alaska Native, non-Hispanic/Latino; 15% Hispanic/Latino; 15% African American, non-Hispanic/Latino; 2% Asian, non-Hispanic/Latino; 1% Native Hawaiian or other Pacific Islander, non-Hispanic/Latino; 1% international. 45% 25 or older, 42% live on campus, 30% transferred in. Retention: 66% of full-time freshmen returned the following year. Academic areas with the most degrees conferred: family and consumer sciences; business/marketing; theology and religious vocations. Core. Calendar: semesters. Academic remediation for entering students, ESL program, services for LD students, advanced placement, accelerated degree program, self-designed majors, honors program, independent study, distance learning, double major, summer session for credit, part-time degree program, adult/continuing education programs, internships. Off campus study. Study abroad program. ROTC: Army (c), Air Force (c).
Entrance Requirements: Options: electronic application, deferred admission. Required: essay, high school transcript, 2 recommendations. Recommended: minimum 2.75 high school GPA, interview. Required for some: SAT or ACT. Entrance: moderately difficult. Application deadline: 7/1. Notification: continuous. SAT Reasoning Test deadline: 8/15. Transfer credits accepted: Yes.
Costs Per Year: Application fee: $25. Comprehensive fee: $35,166 includes full-time tuition ($24,540), mandatory fees ($1348), and college room and board ($9278). Full-time tuition and fees vary according to class time, course load, location, and program. Room and board charges vary according to location.
Collegiate Environment: Orientation program. Drama-theater group, choral group. Social organizations: 15 open to all. Most popular organizations: ASB - Student Government, Service & Community Engagement, Ministry Teams, Flight team, SALSA. Major annual events: International Outreach Festival, Bible Conference, Homecoming. Student services: health clinic, personal-psychological counseling. Campus security: 24-hour emergency response devices and patrols. 206 college housing spaces available; 182 were occupied in 2012-13. Freshmen guaranteed college housing. On-campus residence required through sophomore year. Options: men-only, women-only housing available. San Diego Christian College with 163,210 books, 161 serials, 1,995 audiovisual materials, an OPAC, and a Web page. Operations spending for the previous fiscal year: $363,084. 65 computers available on campus for general student use. A campuswide network can be accessed from student residence rooms and from off campus. Students can access the following: online class registration. Staffed computer lab on campus provides training in use of computers, software, and the Internet.
Community Environment: The campus is two miles from the center of El Cajon, a suburb of San Diego. The location of the college affords short travel distances to nearby mountain, desert and beach resorts.

■ SAN DIEGO CITY COLLEGE

1313 Park Blvd.
San Diego, CA 92101-4787
Tel: (619)388-3400
Fax: (619)388-3063
E-mail: lhumphri@sdccd.edu
Web Site: www.sdcity.edu/
Description: State and locally supported, 2-year, coed. Part of San Diego Community College District System. Awards certificates and transfer associ-

ate degrees. Founded 1914. Setting: 60-acre urban campus with easy access to San Diego, Tijuana. Endowment: $166,270. Educational spending for the previous fiscal year: $11,466 per student. Total enrollment: 17,681. Faculty: 803 (167 full-time, 636 part-time). Student-undergrad faculty ratio is 35:1. 0.4% American Indian or Alaska Native, non-Hispanic/Latino; 46% Hispanic/Latino; 12% African American, non-Hispanic/Latino; 9% Asian, non-Hispanic/Latino; 0.5% Native Hawaiian or other Pacific Islander, non-Hispanic/Latino. Core. Calendar: semesters. Academic remediation for entering students, ESL program, services for LD students, self-designed majors, honors program, independent study, distance learning, summer session for credit, part-time degree program, external degree program, adult/continuing education programs, co-op programs. Off campus study at San Diego State University. ROTC: Air Force (c).

Entrance Requirements: Open admission. Option: electronic application. Required for some: high school transcript. Entrance: noncompetitive. Application deadline: Rolling. Transfer credits accepted: Yes.

Costs Per Year: Application fee: $0. State resident tuition: $1380 full-time, $46 per unit part-time. Nonresident tuition: $6870 full-time, $229 per unit part-time. Mandatory fees: $38 full-time. Full-time tuition and fees vary according to course load. Part-time tuition varies according to course load.

Collegiate Environment: Orientation program. Drama-theater group, choral group, student-run newspaper, radio station. Social organizations: 34 open to all. Most popular organizations: Alpha Gamma Sigma, Association of United Latin American Students, MECHA, Afrikan Student Union, Student Nurses Association. Major annual events: World Cultures Day I, World Cultures Day II, Entrepreneurs' Day. Student services: health clinic, personal-psychological counseling. Campus security: 24-hour emergency response devices and patrols, late night transport-escort service. College housing not available. San Diego City College Library with 88,000 books, 191 serials, 950 audiovisual materials, and an OPAC. Operations spending for the previous fiscal year: $1.2 million. 150 computers available on campus for general student use. A campuswide network can be accessed from student residence rooms and from off campus. Students can access the following: online class registration. Staffed computer lab on campus provides training in use of computers, software, and the Internet.

Community Environment: See San Diego State University.

■ SAN DIEGO MESA COLLEGE

7250 Mesa College Dr.
San Diego, CA 92111-4998
Tel: (619)388-2600
Fax: (619)388-2968
E-mail: csawyer@sdccd.edu
Web Site: www.sdmesa.edu/

Description: State and locally supported, 2-year, coed. Part of San Diego Community College District System. Awards certificates, diplomas, and transfer associate degrees. Founded 1964. Setting: 104-acre suburban campus. Total enrollment: 25,464. Faculty: 723 (199 full-time, 524 part-time). 0.4% American Indian or Alaska Native, non-Hispanic/Latino; 31% Hispanic/Latino; 7% African American, non-Hispanic/Latino; 16% Asian, non-Hispanic/Latino; 1% Native Hawaiian or other Pacific Islander, non-Hispanic/Latino. 38% 25 or older. Core. Calendar: semesters. Academic remediation for entering students, ESL program, services for LD students, honors program, independent study, summer session for credit, part-time degree program, external degree program, adult/continuing education programs.

Costs Per Year: State resident tuition: $552 full-time, $46 per unit part-time. Nonresident tuition: $2196 full-time, $229 per unit part-time. Mandatory fees: $1104 full-time. College room and board: $10,962.

Collegiate Environment: Drama-theater group, choral group, student-run newspaper. Social organizations: 30 open to all. Most popular organizations: Alpha Gamma Sigma, Black Student Union, MECHA, Associated Student Government, Vietnamese Student Association. Major annual events: Festival of Colors, Job Fair, Club Rush/Back to School Reception. Student services: health clinic, personal-psychological counseling. Campus security: 24-hour emergency response devices and patrols, late night transport-escort service. College housing not available. Learning Resource Center- Library with 99,806 books, 147,982 microform titles, 104 serials, 1,923 audiovisual materials, and an OPAC. 350 computers available on campus for general student use. Students can access the following: online class registration. Staffed computer lab on campus provides training in use of computers.

Community Environment: See San Diego State University.

■ SAN DIEGO MIRAMAR COLLEGE

10440 Black Mountain Rd.
San Diego, CA 92126-2999
Tel: (619)388-7800
Fax: (619)388-7801
E-mail: dmaxwell@sdccd.cc.ca.us
Web Site: www.sdmiramar.edu/

Description: State and locally supported, 2-year, coed. Part of San Diego Community College District System. Awards transfer associate degrees. Founded 1969. Setting: 120-acre suburban campus. Total enrollment: 10,650. 48% 25 or older. Calendar: semesters. Academic remediation for entering students, ESL program, services for LD students, advanced placement, accelerated degree program, self-designed majors, honors program, independent study, distance learning, double major, summer session for credit, part-time degree program, adult/continuing education programs, co-op programs. Study abroad program.

Entrance Requirements: Open admission. Option: electronic application. Entrance: noncompetitive.

Collegiate Environment: Student-run newspaper. Student services: health clinic, personal-psychological counseling. Campus security: 24-hour emergency response devices and patrols. Miramar College Library with 19,301 books, 95,586 microform titles, 135 serials, 901 audiovisual materials, and an OPAC.

■ SAN DIEGO STATE UNIVERSITY

5500 Campanile Dr.
San Diego, CA 92182
Tel: (619)594-5200
E-mail: admissions@sdsu.edu
Web Site: www.sdsu.edu/

Description: State-supported, university, coed. Part of California State University System. Awards bachelor's, master's, and doctoral degrees. Founded 1897. Setting: 300-acre urban campus with easy access to San Diego. Endowment: $136.4 million. Research spending for the previous fiscal year: $2.9 million. Educational spending for the previous fiscal year: $5688 per student. Total enrollment: 31,597. Faculty: 1,370 (742 full-time, 628 part-time). Student-undergrad faculty ratio is 23:1. 51,364 applied, 31% were admitted. 29% from top 10% of their high school class, 72% from top quarter, 96% from top half. Full-time: 20,105 students, 57% women, 43% men. Part-time: 2,709 students, 56% women, 44% men. Students come from 53 states and territories, 66 other countries, 7% from out-of-state. 0.3% American Indian or Alaska Native, non-Hispanic/Latino; 30% Hispanic/Latino; 4% African American, non-Hispanic/Latino; 7% Asian, non-Hispanic/Latino; 7% Native Hawaiian or other Pacific Islander, non-Hispanic/Latino; 4% international. 16% 25 or older, 14% live on campus, 15% transferred in. Retention: 89% of full-time freshmen returned the following year. Academic areas with the most degrees conferred: business/marketing; social sciences; psychology. Core. Calendar: semesters. Academic remediation for entering students, ESL program, services for LD students, advanced placement, honors program, independent study, distance learning, double major, summer session for credit, part-time degree program, external degree program, internships, graduate courses open to undergrads. Off campus study at other units of the California State University System. Study abroad program. ROTC: Army, Naval, Air Force.

Entrance Requirements: Options: electronic application, early action, international baccalaureate accepted. Required: high school transcript, minimum 2 high school GPA, 2.5 GPA for non-California residents, SAT or ACT. Entrance: moderately difficult. Application deadline: 11/30. Notification: 3/1. SAT Reasoning Test deadline: 11/30. SAT Subject Test deadline: 11/30. Transfer credits accepted: Yes. Applicants placed on waiting list: 2,120. Waitlisted applicants offered admission: 299. Early action applicants admitted: 1,021.

Costs Per Year: Application fee: $55. State resident tuition: $0 full-time. Nonresident tuition: $11,160 full-time, $372 per unit part-time. Mandatory fees: $6766 full-time, $2140 per term part-time. Full-time tuition and fees vary according to degree level, location, and program. Part-time tuition and fees vary according to course load, degree level, location, and program. College room and board: $13,812. Room and board charges vary according to board plan and housing facility.

Collegiate Environment: Orientation program. Drama-theater group, choral group, marching band, student-run newspaper, radio station. Social organizations: 300 open to all; national fraternities, national sororities, local fraternities, local sororities. Most popular organizations: AB Samahan, Asian Pacific Student Alliance, Enviro-Business Society, M.E.Ch.A de SDSU, Social fraternities and Sororities, including both general and culturally based organizations. Major annual events: Student Involvement Expo (showcasing student organizations, community service, involvement activities), Welcome

Week, Aztec Nights. Student services: health clinic, personal-psychological counseling, women's center. Campus security: 24-hour emergency response devices and patrols, student patrols, late night transport-escort service. 3,805 college housing spaces available; 3,633 were occupied in 2012-13. Freshmen given priority for college housing. On-campus residence required in freshman year. Option: coed housing available. Malcolm A. Love Library with 2.2 million books, 4.6 million microform titles, 75,661 serials, 42,724 audiovisual materials, an OPAC, and a Web page. Operations spending for the previous fiscal year: $11.3 million. 400 computers available on campus for general student use. A campuswide network can be accessed from student residence rooms and from off campus. Students can access the following: online class registration, Blackboard. Staffed computer lab on campus (open 24 hours a day) provides training in use of computers, software, and the Internet.

Community Environment: San Diego lies along and around one of the world's ten most beautiful protected natural harbors. It has 19 miles of beautiful beaces and a very special "sea-washed, air-conditioned climate." The maximum average temperature of 70.8 degrees and a minimum of 55.4 degrees make the climate very special. The population of San Diego is 1,255,540 with a greater metropolitan area population of 2,166,200. The Santa Fe Railroad, buses, and a number of major airlines serve the area. The city is a manufacturing and shipping center, with its main industries being tourism, agriculture, and defense. The county is the country's largest producer of avocados. It has a public library with 30 branches, nine general hospitals, numerous museums, galleries, and churches. Residents and visitors will find many golf courses, all aquatic sports, hiking, mountain climbing, horseback riding, fishing and hunting, and other snow sports nearby. This area is home of the San Diego Chargers professional football team, and the San Diego Padres professional baseball team. Known as a winter playground, it has 19 miles of Pacific Ocean shores with beautiful beaches.

■ **SAN DIEGO STATE UNIVERSITY–IMPERIAL VALLEY CAMPUS**
720 Heber Ave.
Calexico, CA 92231
Tel: (760)768-5500
E-mail: transfer@mail.sdsu.edu
Web Site: www.ivcampus.sdsu.edu/
Description: State-supported, comprehensive, coed. Awards bachelor's and master's degrees. Total enrollment: 1,003. 50,100 applied. 0% from out-of-state. 38% 25 or older. Distance learning. Study abroad program.

■ **SAN FRANCISCO ART INSTITUTE**
800 Chestnut St.
San Francisco, CA 94133
Tel: (415)771-7020; Free: 800-345-SFAI
E-mail: admissions@sfai.edu
Web Site: www.sfai.edu/
Description: Independent, comprehensive, coed. Awards bachelor's and master's degrees. Founded 1871. Setting: 3-acre urban campus with easy access to San Francisco. Endowment: $8.2 million. Research spending for the previous fiscal year: $744,899. Educational spending for the previous fiscal year: $8564 per student. Total enrollment: 670. Faculty: 130 (19 full-time, 111 part-time). Student-undergrad faculty ratio is 11:1. 511 applied, 63% were admitted. Full-time: 418 students, 59% women, 41% men. Part-time: 35 students, 63% women, 37% men. Students come from 14 other countries. 1% American Indian or Alaska Native, non-Hispanic/Latino; 14% Hispanic/Latino; 2% African American, non-Hispanic/Latino; 3% Asian, non-Hispanic/Latino; 0.5% Native Hawaiian or other Pacific Islander, non-Hispanic/Latino; 9% international. 22% 25 or older, 29% live on campus, 22% transferred in. Retention: 63% of full-time freshmen returned the following year. Academic areas with the most degrees conferred: visual and performing arts; social sciences. Core. Calendar: semesters. Academic remediation for entering students, ESL program, services for LD students, advanced placement, honors program, independent study, double major, summer session for credit, part-time degree program, external degree program, adult/continuing education programs, internships. Off campus study at Association of Independent Colleges of Art and Design; Academy of Fine Arts, Prague; Bezalel Academy of Arts and Design, Jerusalem; Chelsea College of Art & Design, London; Ecole Nationale Superieure des Beaux-Arts, Paris; Gerrit Rietveld Academy, Amsterdam; Glasgow School of Art, Glasgow; Korea National University of the Arts, Seoul; University of Fine Arts of Hamburg, Hamburg; Valand School of Fine Arts in Gothenburg. Study abroad program.

Entrance Requirements: Options: electronic application, deferred admission, international baccalaureate accepted. Required: essay, high school transcript, portfolio. Recommended: minimum 2 high school GPA, 2 recommendations, interview, SAT or ACT. Entrance: moderately difficult. Application deadlines: Rolling, Rolling for nonresidents. Notification: continuous, continuous for nonresidents. Transfer credits accepted: Yes.

Costs Per Year: Application fee: $65. Comprehensive fee: $50,462 includes full-time tuition ($35,748), mandatory fees ($870), and college room and board ($13,844). College room only: $9974. Full-time tuition and fees vary according to degree level. Room and board charges vary according to housing facility. Part-time tuition: $1566 per credit. Part-time tuition varies according to degree level.

Collegiate Environment: Orientation program. Student-run newspaper, radio station. Social organizations: 12 open to all. Most popular organizations: Docuphoto, The Tower 102.5 fm, Film Salon, Indigenous Arts Coalition, Chinese Student Association. Major annual events: Vernissage Art Exhibition, Spring Art Show, Winter Art Sale. Student services: personal-psychological counseling. Campus security: 24-hour patrols, security cameras. 145 college housing spaces available; 127 were occupied in 2012-13. Freshmen given priority for college housing. On-campus residence required in freshman year. Option: coed housing available. Anne Bremer Memorial Library with 32,500 books, 210 serials, 3,370 audiovisual materials, an OPAC, and a Web page. Operations spending for the previous fiscal year: $263,882. 70 computers available on campus for general student use. A campuswide network can be accessed. Students can access the following: online class registration. Staffed computer lab on campus provides training in use of computers, software, and the Internet.

Community Environment: See San Francisco State University.

■ **SAN FRANCISCO CONSERVATORY OF MUSIC**
50 Oak St.
San Francisco, CA 94102
Tel: (415)864-7326
Fax: (415)503-6299
E-mail: admit@sfcm.edu
Web Site: www.sfcm.edu/
Description: Independent, comprehensive, coed. Awards bachelor's and master's degrees and post-master's certificates. Founded 1917. Setting: 2-acre urban campus. Endowment: $35.2 million. Educational spending for the previous fiscal year: $20,016 per student. Total enrollment: 415. Faculty: 121 (32 full-time, 89 part-time). Student-undergrad faculty ratio is 7:1. 10% from top 10% of their high school class, 30% from top quarter, 70% from top half. Full-time: 182 students, 48% women, 52% men. Part-time: 4 students, 50% women, 50% men. Students come from 26 states and territories, 18 other countries, 36% from out-of-state. 1% American Indian or Alaska Native, non-Hispanic/Latino; 5% Hispanic/Latino; 5% African American, non-Hispanic/Latino; 8% Asian, non-Hispanic/Latino; 22% international. 7% 25 or older, 42% live on campus, 8% transferred in. Retention: 82% of full-time freshmen returned the following year. Academic area with the most degrees conferred: visual and performing arts. Core. Calendar: semesters. Academic remediation for entering students, advanced placement, independent study, part-time degree program, internships.

Entrance Requirements: Required: essay, high school transcript, minimum 2.5 high school GPA, 2 recommendations, audition, pre-screen recording in select areas. Recommended: SAT or ACT.

Costs Per Year: Tuition: $37,600 full-time, $1660 per credit part-time. Mandatory fees: $540 full-time, $270 per term part-time. Part-time tuition and fees vary according to course load and program.

Collegiate Environment: Orientation program. Drama-theater group, choral group. Social organizations: 3 open to all. Most popular organizations: Yoga Group, Meditation Group, Conservatory Ball Planning Committee. Major annual events: Halloween Party, Conservatory Ball, Start-of-the-year Activities, SF Giants Baseball Game. Student services: personal-psychological counseling. Campus security: 24-hour emergency response devices and patrols, controlled dormitory access, resident assistant on-call for residential hall residents. 130 college housing spaces available; 71 were occupied in 2012-13. No special consideration for freshman housing applicants. Option: coed housing available. Conservatory Library with 65,000 books, 75 serials, 14,891 audiovisual materials, an OPAC, and a Web page. Operations spending for the previous fiscal year: $304,000. 15 computers available on campus for general student use. A campuswide network can be accessed. Staffed computer lab on campus provides training in use of computers, software, and the Internet.

Community Environment: See San Francisco State University.

■ SAN FRANCISCO STATE UNIVERSITY

1600 Holloway Ave.
San Francisco, CA 94132-1722
Tel: (415)338-1100
E-mail: ugadmit@sfsu.edu
Web Site: www.sfsu.edu/

Description: State-supported, university, coed. Part of California State University System. Awards bachelor's, master's, and doctoral degrees and post-master's certificates. Founded 1899. Setting: 142-acre urban campus. Endowment: $49 million. Educational spending for the previous fiscal year: $5413 per student. Total enrollment: 30,500. Faculty: 1,712 (778 full-time, 934 part-time). Student-undergrad faculty ratio is 25:1. 31,439 applied, 64% were admitted. Full-time: 22,510 students, 57% women, 43% men. Part-time: 3,939 students, 54% women, 46% men. 1% from out-of-state. 0.2% American Indian or Alaska Native, non-Hispanic/Latino; 22% Hispanic/Latino; 5% African American, non-Hispanic/Latino; 28% Asian, non-Hispanic/Latino; 1% Native Hawaiian or other Pacific Islander, non-Hispanic/Latino; 7% international. 21% 25 or older, 12% live on campus, 13% transferred in. Retention: 80% of full-time freshmen returned the following year. Academic areas with the most degrees conferred: business/marketing; social sciences; visual and performing arts. Core. Calendar: semesters. Academic remediation for entering students, ESL program, services for LD students, advanced placement, self-designed majors, honors program, independent study, distance learning, double major, summer session for credit, part-time degree program, adult/continuing education programs, co-op programs and internships, graduate courses open to undergrads. Off campus study at The San Francisco Consortium, 18 other institutions of the California State University System. Study abroad program. ROTC: Army (c), Air Force (c).

Entrance Requirements: Options: electronic application, international baccalaureate accepted. Required: high school transcript, SAT or ACT. Entrance: moderately difficult. Application deadline: 11/30. Notification: 10/1. SAT Reasoning Test deadline: 1/31.

Costs Per Year: Application fee: $55. State resident tuition: $5472 full-time. Nonresident tuition: $16,632 full-time, $372 per unit part-time. Mandatory fees: $968 full-time. Full-time tuition and fees vary according to course load. Part-time tuition varies according to course load. College room and board: $11,576. Room and board charges vary according to board plan and housing facility.

Collegiate Environment: Orientation program. Drama-theater group, choral group, student-run newspaper, radio station. Social organizations: 183 open to all; national fraternities, national sororities, local fraternities, local sororities; 1% of eligible men and 1% of eligible women are members. Most popular organizations: International Education Exchange Council, Graduate Students Association, Accounting Students Organization, Improv Nation @ San Francisco State University, Asian Student Union. Major annual events: Cultural/Activities Fair, Associated Students Craft Fair, Campus Health Fairs. Student services: legal services, health clinic, personal-psychological counseling, women's center. Campus security: 24-hour emergency response devices and patrols, student patrols, late night transport-escort service, controlled dormitory access. 3,000 college housing spaces available. Freshmen given priority for college housing. Option: coed housing available. J. Paul Leonard Library with 921,744 books, 1.7 million microform titles, 73,735 serials, 264,128 audiovisual materials, an OPAC, and a Web page. Operations spending for the previous fiscal year: $9.6 million. 2,800 computers available on campus for general student use. Computer purchase/lease plans available. A campuswide network can be accessed from student residence rooms and from off campus. Students can access the following: online class registration. Staffed computer lab on campus (open 24 hours a day) provides training in use of computers, software, and the Internet.

Community Environment: San Francisco is one of the most cosmopolitan cities in the United States. It is the financial center of the west, and an important industrial city. A great port, it serves as the terminus for Trans-Pacific and coastwise steamship lines and airlines. The city is located on hills at the end of a narrow peninsula with the Pacific Ocean on one side and the San Francisco Bay on the other. The annual temperature averages 57 degrees. San Francisco Bay is the largest landlocked harbor in the world, and is the home of the beautiful Golden Gate Bridge. All modes of transportation serve the area. A large civic center includes the city hall, public library, civic auditorium, state building, federal office building, health center, opera house and war memorial building. The opera house is the only municipally owned opera house in America. Job opportunities vary considerably but are available. San Francisco has 438 churches, 52 public parks, and 100 theaters. Recreational facilities are numerous for all water sports, hiking, and fishing. Mountain resort areas are approximately a three hour drive. Famous Chinatown is located here, as is the picturesque Fisherman's Wharf.

■ SAN JOAQUIN DELTA COLLEGE

5151 Pacific Ave.
Stockton, CA 95207-6370
Tel: (209)954-5151
Fax: (209)954-5600
E-mail: admissions@deltacollege.edu
Web Site: www.deltacollege.edu/

Description: District-supported, 2-year, coed. Part of California Community College System. Awards certificates, transfer associate, and terminal associate degrees. Founded 1935. Setting: 165-acre urban campus with easy access to Sacramento. Educational spending for the previous fiscal year: $3500 per student. Total enrollment: 20,190. Faculty: 643 (235 full-time, 408 part-time). Student-undergrad faculty ratio is 31:1. 3,741 applied, 100% were admitted. Students come from 20 states and territories, 0.2% from out-of-state. 27% 25 or older. Retention: 72% of full-time freshmen returned the following year. Core. Calendar: semesters. Academic remediation for entering students, ESL program, services for LD students, advanced placement, honors program, independent study, distance learning, summer session for credit, part-time degree program, adult/continuing education programs, co-op programs.

Entrance Requirements: Open admission except for nursing. Options: electronic application, early admission, international baccalaureate accepted. Entrance: noncompetitive. Application deadline: Rolling. Notification: continuous.

Collegiate Environment: Orientation program. Drama-theater group, choral group, student-run newspaper, radio station. Student services: legal services, personal-psychological counseling. Campus security: 24-hour emergency response devices and patrols, late night transport-escort service. Goleman Library plus 1 other with 124,755 books, 113,723 microform titles, 67,450 serials, 6,184 audiovisual materials, an OPAC, and a Web page. Operations spending for the previous fiscal year: $1.4 million. 400 computers available on campus for general student use. A campuswide network can be accessed from off-campus. Students can access the following: online class registration. Staffed computer lab on campus.

Community Environment: See University of the Pacific.

■ SAN JOAQUIN VALLEY COLLEGE (BAKERSFIELD)

201 New Stine Rd.
Bakersfield, CA 93309
Tel: (661)834-0126; Free: 866-544-7898
E-mail: admissions@sjvc.edu
Web Site: www.sjvc.edu/

Description: Proprietary, 2-year, coed. Part of San Joaquin Valley College. Awards certificates and terminal associate degrees. Founded 1977. Total enrollment: 743. 59% 25 or older. Core.

Entrance Requirements: Required for some: essay, high school transcript, interview. Entrance: noncompetitive. Application deadline: Rolling. Notification: continuous.

Costs Per Year: Tuition: $29,750 per degree program. Tuition guaranteed not to increase for student's term of enrollment.

Collegiate Environment: Orientation program. Social organizations: 6 open to all. Most popular organizations: CAMA Club, RACT Club, Business Club, Student Council, National Technical Honor Society. Major annual events: Thanksgiving Turkey Feed, All School Luau, student celebrations.

■ SAN JOAQUIN VALLEY COLLEGE (CHULA VISTA)

303 H St.
Chula Vista, CA 91910
Tel: (619)426-7582
Web Site: www.sjvc.edu/

Description: Proprietary, 2-year, coed. Founded 2012.

■ SAN JOAQUIN VALLEY COLLEGE (FRESNO)

295 E Sierra Ave.
Fresno, CA 93710-3616
Tel: (209)448-8282
Fax: (209)448-8250
E-mail: admissions@sjvc.edu
Web Site: www.sjvc.edu/

Description: Proprietary, 2-year, coed. Part of San Joaquin Valley College.

Awards certificates and terminal associate degrees. Total enrollment: 694. 1% American Indian or Alaska Native, non-Hispanic/Latino; 50% Hispanic/Latino; 12% African American, non-Hispanic/Latino; 1% Asian, non-Hispanic/Latino; 1% Native Hawaiian or other Pacific Islander, non-Hispanic/Latino; 1% international. 32% 25 or older. Core.
Entrance Requirements: Required for some: essay, 1 recommendation, interview. Entrance: noncompetitive. Application deadline: Rolling. Notification: continuous.
Costs Per Year: Tuition: $15,500 full-time. Full-time tuition varies according to location and program.
Collegiate Environment: Orientation program. Social organizations: 4 open to all. Most popular organizations: Associated Student Body, American Medical Technologists, State and County Dental Assistants Association, Arts and Entertainment. Major annual events: March of Dimes Fundraiser, Christmas Toy Drive, Thanksgiving Food Drive. College housing not available.

■ **SAN JOAQUIN VALLEY COLLEGE (HANFORD)**
215 W 7th St.
Hanford, CA 93230
Tel: (866)544-7898
Web Site: www.sjvc.edu/
Description: Proprietary, 2-year, coed. Awards certificates degrees.
Costs Per Year: Tuition: $29,750 per degree program.

■ **SAN JOAQUIN VALLEY COLLEGE (HESPERIA)**
9331 Mariposa Rd.
Hesperia, CA 92344
Tel: (760)948-1947
Web Site: www.sjvc.edu/
Description: Proprietary, 2-year, coed.
Costs Per Year: Tuition: $31,950 per degree program.

■ **SAN JOAQUIN VALLEY COLLEGE (LANCASTER)**
42135 10th St. W
Lancaster, CA 93534
Tel: (661)974-8282
Web Site: www.sjvc.edu/
Description: Proprietary, 2-year, coed. Founded 2012.

■ **SAN JOAQUIN VALLEY COLLEGE (RANCHO CORDOVA)**
11050 Olson Dr.
Ste. 100
Rancho Cordova, CA 95670
E-mail: admissions@sjvc.edu
Web Site: www.sjvc.edu/
Description: Proprietary, 2-year, coed. Part of San Joaquin Valley College. Awards certificates and terminal associate degrees. Total enrollment: 114. 0% American Indian or Alaska Native, non-Hispanic/Latino; 6% Hispanic/Latino; 4% African American, non-Hispanic/Latino; 21% Asian, non-Hispanic/Latino; 6% Native Hawaiian or other Pacific Islander, non-Hispanic/Latino; 5% international. 72% 25 or older. Core.
Entrance Requirements: Required for some: essay, interview. Entrance: noncompetitive. Application deadline: Rolling. Notification: continuous.
Costs Per Year: Tuition: $21,560 full-time. Full-time tuition varies according to location and program.
Collegiate Environment: Most popular organizations: Associated Student Body, Diversity Committee. Major annual events: Constitution Day Activities, Campus Dress Down Day, Christmas Toy Drive. College housing not available.

■ **SAN JOAQUIN VALLEY COLLEGE (RANCHO CUCAMONGA)**
10641 Church St.
Rancho Cucamonga, CA 91730
Tel: (909)948-7582
E-mail: admissions@sjvc.edu
Web Site: www.sjvc.edu/
Description: Proprietary, 2-year, coed. Part of San Joaquin Valley College. Awards certificates and terminal associate degrees. Total enrollment: 746. 1% American Indian or Alaska Native, non-Hispanic/Latino; 61% Hispanic/Latino; 6% African American, non-Hispanic/Latino; 4% Asian, non-Hispanic/Latino; 3% Native Hawaiian or other Pacific Islander, non-Hispanic/Latino; 3% international. 27% 25 or older. Core.
Entrance Requirements: Required for some: essay, interview. Entrance: noncompetitive. Application deadline: Rolling. Notification: continuous.

Costs Per Year: Tuition: $16,650 full-time. Full-time tuition varies according to location and program.
Collegiate Environment: Orientation program. Most popular organizations: Students in Free Enterprise (SIFE), Associated Student Body, Fitness Club, Ambassador Club, Diversity Club. Major annual events: Career Expo: Job Fair, Awards Ceremony, Spring Fling. College housing not available.

■ **SAN JOAQUIN VALLEY COLLEGE (SALIDA)**
5380 Pirrone Rd.
Salida, CA 95368
E-mail: admissions@sjvc.edu
Web Site: www.sjvc.edu/
Description: Proprietary, 2-year, coed. Part of San Joaquin Valley College. Awards certificates and terminal associate degrees. Total enrollment: 322. 1% American Indian or Alaska Native, non-Hispanic/Latino; 52% Hispanic/Latino; 3% African American, non-Hispanic/Latino; 4% Asian, non-Hispanic/Latino; 2% Native Hawaiian or other Pacific Islander, non-Hispanic/Latino; 4% international. 34% 25 or older. Core.
Entrance Requirements: Required for some: essay, interview. Entrance: noncompetitive. Application deadline: Rolling. Notification: continuous.
Costs Per Year: Tuition: $15,500 full-time. Full-time tuition varies according to location and program.
Collegiate Environment: Orientation program. Social organizations: 2 open to all. Most popular organizations: Associated Student Body, Book Club. Major annual events: Student Appreciation Day, March of Dimes, Cancer Relay.

■ **SAN JOAQUIN VALLEY COLLEGE (TEMECULA)**
27270 Madison Ave.
Ste. 305
Temecula, CA 92590
Tel: (866)544-7898
Web Site: www.sjvc.edu/
Description: Proprietary, 2-year, coed.
Costs Per Year: Tuition: $31,950 per degree program.

■ **SAN JOAQUIN VALLEY COLLEGE (VISALIA)**
8400 W Mineral King Ave.
Visalia, CA 93291
Tel: (559)651-2500
E-mail: admissions@sjvc.edu
Web Site: www.sjvc.edu/
Description: Proprietary, 2-year, coed. Part of San Joaquin Valley College. Awards certificates and terminal associate degrees. Founded 1977. Setting: small town campus. Total enrollment: 1,892. 1% American Indian or Alaska Native, non-Hispanic/Latino; 40% Hispanic/Latino; 14% African American, non-Hispanic/Latino; 4% Asian, non-Hispanic/Latino; 1% Native Hawaiian or other Pacific Islander, non-Hispanic/Latino; 3% international. 53% 25 or older. Core. Calendar: semesters. Academic remediation for entering students.
Entrance Requirements: Required for some: essay, high school transcript, interview. Entrance: noncompetitive. Application deadline: Rolling. Notification: continuous.
Costs Per Year: Tuition: $29,750 per degree program. Tuition guaranteed not to increase for student's term of enrollment.
Collegiate Environment: Orientation program. Social organizations: 4 open to all. Most popular organizations: Associated Student Body, Students in Free Enterprise (SIFE), American Medical Technologists, National and Technical Honor Society. Major annual events: Student Appreciation Day, March of Dimes Fundraiser, Constitution Day. Campus security: late night transport-escort service, full-time security personnel. College housing not available.

■ **SAN JOAQUIN VALLEY COLLEGE–FRESNO AVIATION CAMPUS**
4985 E Anderson Ave.
Fresno, CA 93727
E-mail: admissions@sjvc.edu
Web Site: www.sjvc.edu/
Description: Proprietary, 2-year, coed. Part of San Joaquin Valley College. Awards terminal associate degrees. Total enrollment: 83. 0% American Indian or Alaska Native, non-Hispanic/Latino; 30% Hispanic/Latino; 4% African American, non-Hispanic/Latino; 12% Asian, non-Hispanic/Latino; 0% Native Hawaiian or other Pacific Islander, non-Hispanic/Latino; 4% international. 65% 25 or older. Core.

Entrance Requirements: Required for some: essay, high school transcript, interview. Entrance: noncompetitive. Application deadline: Rolling. Notification: continuous.

Costs Per Year: Tuition: $27,265 per degree program. Tuition guaranteed not to increase for student's term of enrollment.

Collegiate Environment: Orientation program. Most popular organization: RC Club (radio controlled airplane). Major annual events: AMT Day, Student Appreciation Day, Veteran's Day. College housing not available.

■ **SAN JOAQUIN VALLEY COLLEGE–ONLINE**
801 S Akers St.
Ste. 150
Visalia, CA 93277
Tel: (559)734-7582
Fax: (559)735-0219
E-mail: admissions@sjvc.edu
Web Site: www.sjvc.edu/campus/SJVC_Online/

Description: Proprietary, 2-year, coed. Part of San Joaquin Valley College. Awards certificates and terminal associate degrees. Setting: suburban campus. Total enrollment: 1,892. 1% American Indian or Alaska Native, non-Hispanic/Latino; 40% Hispanic/Latino; 14% African American, non-Hispanic/Latino; 4% Asian, non-Hispanic/Latino; 1% Native Hawaiian or other Pacific Islander, non-Hispanic/Latino; 3% international. 53% 25 or older. Core.

Entrance Requirements: Option: electronic application. Required for some: essay, interview. Application deadline: Rolling. Notification: continuous.

Costs Per Year: Tuition: $30,800 per degree program. Tuition guaranteed not to increase for student's term of enrollment.

Collegiate Environment: Orientation program.

■ **SAN JOSE CITY COLLEGE**
2100 Moorpark Ave.
San Jose, CA 95128-2799
Tel: (408)298-2181
Web Site: www.sjcc.edu/

Description: District-supported, 2-year, coed. Part of San Jose/Evergreen Community College District System. Awards transfer associate and terminal associate degrees. Founded 1921. Setting: 58-acre urban campus. Total enrollment: 9,805. 50% 25 or older. Core. Calendar: semesters. Academic remediation for entering students, ESL program, services for LD students, advanced placement, self-designed majors, summer session for credit, part-time degree program, adult/continuing education programs, co-op programs. ROTC: Army (c), Air Force (c).

Entrance Requirements: Open admission. Options: early admission, deferred admission. Entrance: noncompetitive. Application deadline: Rolling. Preference given to district residents.

Collegiate Environment: Drama-theater group, student-run newspaper, radio station. Student services: health clinic. San Jose City College Library with 54,075 books and 345 serials.

Community Environment: See San Jose State University.

■ **SAN JOSE STATE UNIVERSITY**
One Washington Sq.
San Jose, CA 95192-0001
Tel: (408)924-1000
Fax: (408)924-2050
E-mail: admissions@sjsu.edu
Web Site: www.sjsu.edu/

Description: State-supported, comprehensive, coed. Part of California State University System. Awards bachelor's and master's degrees. Founded 1857. Setting: 152-acre urban campus. Total enrollment: 30,448. Faculty: 1,656 (619 full-time, 1,037 part-time). Student-undergrad faculty ratio is 27:1. 25,155 applied, 63% were admitted. Full-time: 20,320 students, 50% women, 50% men. Part-time: 4,837 students, 50% women, 50% men. 0% from out-of-state. 0.2% American Indian or Alaska Native, non-Hispanic/Latino; 23% Hispanic/Latino; 4% African American, non-Hispanic/Latino; 35% Asian, non-Hispanic/Latino; 1% Native Hawaiian or other Pacific Islander, non-Hispanic/Latino; 4% international. 21% 25 or older, 14% live on campus, 12% transferred in. Retention: 83% of full-time freshmen returned the following year. Academic areas with the most degrees conferred: business/marketing; health professions and related sciences; engineering. Core. Calendar: semesters. Academic remediation for entering students, services for LD students, advanced placement, self-designed majors, honors program, independent study, distance learning, double major, summer session for credit, part-time degree program, adult/continuing education

programs, internships, graduate courses open to undergrads. Off campus study at other institutions of the California State University System. Study abroad program. ROTC: Army, Air Force.

Entrance Requirements: Option: electronic application. Required: high school transcript. Required for some: SAT or ACT. Entrance: very difficult. Application deadline: 11/30. Notification: continuous. Preference given to state residents. SAT Reasoning Test deadline: 11/30.

Costs Per Year: Application fee: $55. State resident tuition: $6852 full-time. Nonresident tuition: $11,160 full-time. Mandatory fees: $6852 full-time. College room and board: $11,733. College room only: $6633.

Collegiate Environment: Orientation program. Drama-theater group, choral group, marching band, student-run newspaper, radio station. Social organizations: national fraternities, national sororities, local fraternities, local sororities. Student services: health clinic, personal-psychological counseling, women's center. Campus security: 24-hour emergency response devices and patrols, student patrols, late night transport-escort service. No special consideration for freshman housing applicants. Options: coed, men-only, women-only housing available. Dr. Martin Luther King Jr. Library plus 1 other with 1.3 million books, 1.3 million microform titles, 109,730 serials, 36,680 audiovisual materials, an OPAC, and a Web page.

Community Environment: Population 912,332. 15th largest city in U.S. Located in the Santa Clara Valley, known worldwide as"Silicon Valley". 50 miles south of San Francisco, and 30 miles from the Pacific Ocean. The Mount Hamilton Range rises to 4,209 feet on the east, and the Santa Cruz Range provides the western view. San Jose was the first capital of California. Recreational facilities are numerous, including Alum Rock Park, six miles away which includes a museum, picnic grounds, active mineral springs, a large swimming pool, mineral baths, and several miles of marked trails. Mountain resort areas are within easy driving distance for the major winter sports. Points of interest are Lick Observatory on the summit of Mount Hamilton, Rosicrucian Egyptian Temple, Oriental Museum, Winchester Mystery House.

■ **SANTA ANA COLLEGE**
1530 W 17th St.
Santa Ana, CA 92706-3398
Tel: (714)564-6000
Web Site: www.sac.edu/

Description: State-supported, 2-year, coed. Part of California Community College System. Awards certificates, transfer associate, and terminal associate degrees. Founded 1915. Setting: 58-acre urban campus with easy access to Los Angeles. Total enrollment: 22,189. Faculty: 1,296 (249 full-time, 1,047 part-time). Student-undergrad faculty ratio is 20:1. Students come from 50 states and territories, 4% from out-of-state. 63% 25 or older. Core. Calendar: semesters. Academic remediation for entering students, ESL program, services for LD students, advanced placement, accelerated degree program, freshman honors college, honors program, distance learning, summer session for credit, part-time degree program, external degree program, adult/continuing education programs, co-op programs. Study abroad program. ROTC: Air Force (c).

Entrance Requirements: Open admission. Option: early admission. Entrance: noncompetitive. Application deadline: 8/21.

Collegiate Environment: Drama-theater group, choral group, student-run newspaper. Social organizations: 23 open to all. Most popular organizations: Students of Diverse Cultures, Students United for Better Education, Phi Beta Kappa, Alpha Gamma Sigma, Puente. Major annual events: International Festival, Club Rush, Cinco de Mayo. Student services: legal services, health clinic, personal-psychological counseling, women's center. Campus security: late night transport-escort service. McNeally Library with 99,473 books, 99,473 microform titles, and 7,690 audiovisual materials. 100 computers available on campus for general student use. A campuswide network can be accessed. Staffed computer lab on campus.

■ **SANTA BARBARA CITY COLLEGE**
721 Cliff Dr.
Santa Barbara, CA 93109-2394
Tel: (805)965-0581
Fax: (805)963-SBCC
E-mail: admissions@sbcc.edu
Web Site: www.sbcc.edu/

Description: State and locally supported, 2-year, coed. Part of California Community College System. Awards certificates and terminal associate degrees. Founded 1908. Setting: 65-acre small town campus. Endowment: $21.1 million. Educational spending for the previous fiscal year: $2587 per student. Total enrollment: 18,092. Faculty: 806 (266 full-time, 540 part-time). Student-undergrad faculty ratio is 27:1. 4,448 applied, 100% were admitted. Full-time: 7,952 students, 50% women, 50% men. Part-time: 10,140 students, 56% women, 44% men. Students come from 46 states and territories, 66 other countries, 6% from out-of-state. 1% American Indian or Alaska Native, non-Hispanic/Latino; 29% Hispanic/Latino; 3% African American, non-Hispanic/Latino; 3% Asian, non-Hispanic/Latino; 1% Native Hawaiian or other Pacific Islander, non-Hispanic/Latino; 10% international. 29% 25 or older, 5% transferred in. Core. Calendar: semesters. Academic remediation for entering students, ESL program, services for LD students, advanced placement, honors program, independent study, distance learning, double major, summer session for credit, part-time degree program, adult/continuing education programs, co-op programs and internships. Study abroad program. ROTC: Army (c).

Entrance Requirements: Open admission. Options: electronic application, early admission. Recommended: high school transcript. Entrance: noncompetitive. Application deadline: 8/19. Notification: continuous. Transfer credits accepted: Yes.

Collegiate Environment: Orientation program. Choral group. Social organizations: 50 open to all. Most popular organizations: IDEAS, Video Game Club, Glee Club, Marketing Club, Project H.O.P.E. Major annual events: Commencement, Dorantes Lecture, President's Honor Roll Reception. Student services: health clinic, personal-psychological counseling. Campus security: 24-hour emergency response devices and patrols, late night transport-escort service. Eli Luria Library with 140,471 books, 89,603 microform titles, 976 serials, 57 audiovisual materials, an OPAC, and a Web page. Operations spending for the previous fiscal year: $1.1 million. 1,340 computers available on campus for general student use. A campuswide network can be accessed from off-campus. Students can access the following: online class registration, online application process. Staffed computer lab on campus provides training in use of computers, software, and the Internet.

Community Environment: See University of California Santa Barbara.

■ **SANTA CLARA UNIVERSITY**
500 El Camino Real
Santa Clara, CA 95053
Tel: (408)554-4000
Fax: (408)554-5255
E-mail: ugadmissions@scu.edu
Web Site: www.scu.edu/
Description: Independent Roman Catholic (Jesuit), university, coed. Awards bachelor's, master's, and doctoral degrees and post-master's certificates. Founded 1851. Setting: 106-acre suburban campus with easy access to San Francisco, San Jose. Endowment: $688.1 million. Research spending for the previous fiscal year: $4.3 million. Educational spending for the previous fiscal year: $14,205 per student. Total enrollment: 8,519. Faculty: 839 (504 full-time, 335 part-time). Student-undergrad faculty ratio is 12:1. 14,339 applied, 51% were admitted. 44% from top 10% of their high school class, 81% from top quarter, 96% from top half. 5 National Merit Scholars. Full-time: 5,141 students, 50% women, 50% men. Part-time: 109 students, 61% women, 39% men. Students come from 46 states and territories, 40 other countries, 37% from out-of-state. 0.2% American Indian or Alaska Native, non-Hispanic/Latino; 18% Hispanic/Latino; 3% African American, non-Hispanic/Latino; 14% Asian, non-Hispanic/Latino; 0.3% Native Hawaiian or other Pacific Islander, non-Hispanic/Latino; 3% international. 2% 25 or older, 53% live on campus, 3% transferred in. Retention: 95% of full-time freshmen returned the following year. Academic areas with the most degrees conferred: business/marketing; social sciences; engineering. Core. Services for LD students, advanced placement, self-designed majors, honors program, independent study, double major, summer session for credit, co-op programs and internships, graduate courses open to undergrads. Study abroad program. ROTC: Army, Air Force (c).

Entrance Requirements: Options: electronic application, early decision, early action, deferred admission, international baccalaureate accepted. Required: essay, high school transcript, 1 recommendation, SAT or ACT. Entrance: moderately difficult. Application deadlines: 1/7, 11/1 for early decision, 11/1 for early action. Notification: continuous until 4/1, 12/15 for early decision, 12/23 for early action. SAT Reasoning Test deadline: 1/7. Transfer credits accepted: Yes. Applicants placed on waiting list: 2,057. Wait-listed applicants offered admission: 71. Early action applicants: 4,268. Early action applicants admitted: 2,839.

Costs Per Year: Application fee: $55. Comprehensive fee: $52,848 includes full-time tuition ($40,572) and college room and board ($12,276). Room and

board charges vary according to board plan, housing facility, location, and student level. Part-time tuition: $1127 per unit. Part-time tuition varies according to course load.

Collegiate Environment: Orientation program. Drama-theater group, choral group, student-run newspaper, radio station. Social organizations: 128 open to all. Most popular organizations: Ruff Riders, Associated Student Government (ASG), The Multicultural Center (MCC), The SCU Radio Station (KSCU), Santa Clara Community Action Program (SCCAP). Major annual events: Bronco Spirit Week, Family Weekend, Grand Reunion Weekend. Student services: health clinic, personal-psychological counseling. Campus security: 24-hour emergency response devices and patrols, late night transport-escort service, controlled dormitory access. 2,819 college housing spaces available; 2,776 were occupied in 2012-13. Freshmen given priority for college housing. Option: coed housing available. University Library plus 1 other with 1.2 million books, 2.4 million microform titles, 28,022 serials, 26,002 audiovisual materials, an OPAC, and a Web page. Operations spending for the previous fiscal year: $6.9 million. 826 computers available on campus for general student use. Computer purchase/lease plans available. A campuswide network can be accessed from student residence rooms and from off campus. Students can access the following: online class registration. Staffed computer lab on campus provides training in use of computers, software, and the Internet.

Community Environment: Santa Clara is known as the"Mission City." It has an ideal climate, with a mean temperature of 71 degrees. Buses, trains and airlines serve the area. Community facilities include churches, a community symphony orchestra and an art gallery. Santa Clara is in the heart of"Silicon Valley," a dynamic center of high technology and progressive businesses. There are numerous part-time work opportunities. Recreational facilities include miles of beaches within a 30-minute drive of the university. San Francisco is 50 miles to the north.

■ **SANTA MONICA COLLEGE**
1900 Pico Blvd.
Santa Monica, CA 90405-1628
Tel: (310)434-4000
Web Site: www.smc.edu/
Description: State and locally supported, 2-year, coed. Part of California Community College System. Awards certificates, transfer associate, and terminal associate degrees. Founded 1929. Setting: 40-acre urban campus with easy access to Los Angeles. Total enrollment: 31,138. Faculty: 1,303 (309 full-time, 994 part-time). Full-time: 11,160 students, 52% women, 48% men. Part-time: 19,978 students, 57% women, 43% men. 0.3% American Indian or Alaska Native, non-Hispanic/Latino; 32% Hispanic/Latino; 10% African American, non-Hispanic/Latino; 12% Asian, non-Hispanic/Latino; 0.3% Native Hawaiian or other Pacific Islander, non-Hispanic/Latino; 10% international. 23% 25 or older. Core. Calendar: semester plus optional winter and summer terms. Academic remediation for entering students, ESL program, services for LD students, advanced placement, honors program, independent study, distance learning, summer session for credit, part-time degree program, adult/continuing education programs, co-op programs and internships. Study abroad program. ROTC: Army (c).

Entrance Requirements: Open admission. Option: early admission. Required: high school transcript. Entrance: noncompetitive. Application deadline: 8/30. Notification: continuous until 8/30.

Costs Per Year: Application fee: $0. State resident tuition: $1080 full-time, $36 per unit part-time. Nonresident tuition: $8250 full-time, $275 per unit part-time. Mandatory fees: $48 full-time. Full-time tuition and fees vary according to course load. Part-time tuition varies according to course load.

Collegiate Environment: Orientation program. Drama-theater group, choral group, student-run newspaper. Student services: legal services, health clinic, personal-psychological counseling, women's center. Campus security: 24-hour emergency response devices and patrols, student patrols, late night transport-escort service. Santa Monica College Library with 101,317 books, 77,458 microform titles, 389 serials, an OPAC, and a Web page.

Community Environment: A residential city and beach resort, Santa Monica is part of the Los Angeles metropolitan area. The temperature averages 64.2 degrees. All forms of major transportation serve the area. Excellent shopping facilities are in the city. Part-time employment is available. Beach area includes Ocean Park, Malibu Beach, and Will Rogers State Beach, providing recreational activities in addition to the city facilities for outdoor sports.

■ **SANTA ROSA JUNIOR COLLEGE**
1501 Mendocino Ave.
Santa Rosa, CA 95401-4395

Tel: (707)527-4011
E-mail: admininfo@santarosa.edu
Web Site: www.santarosa.edu/
Description: State and locally supported, 2-year, coed. Part of California Community College System. Awards certificates, transfer associate, and terminal associate degrees. Founded 1918. Setting: 100-acre urban campus with easy access to San Francisco. Endowment: $35.5 million. Educational spending for the previous fiscal year: $3099 per student. Total enrollment: 21,878. Faculty: 1,188 (279 full-time, 909 part-time). Student-undergrad faculty ratio is 23:1. 5,474 applied, 100% were admitted. Students come from 40 other countries, 2% from out-of-state. 1% American Indian or Alaska Native, non-Hispanic/Latino; 22% Hispanic/Latino; 2% African American, non-Hispanic/Latino; 4% Asian, non-Hispanic/Latino; 1% Native Hawaiian or other Pacific Islander, non-Hispanic/Latino. 54% 25 or older. Core. Calendar: semesters. Academic remediation for entering students, ESL program, services for LD students, advanced placement, independent study, distance learning, summer session for credit, part-time degree program, adult/continuing education programs, co-op programs and internships. Off campus study. Study abroad program.
Entrance Requirements: Open admission except for allied health programs. Options: electronic application, early admission. Entrance: noncompetitive. Application deadlines: Rolling, Rolling for nonresidents. Notification: continuous, continuous for nonresidents. Transfer credits accepted: Yes.
Costs Per Year: Application fee: $0. One-time mandatory fee: $38. State resident tuition: $0 full-time. Nonresident tuition: $4728 full-time, $197 per unit part-time. Mandatory fees: $1104 full-time, $46 per unit part-time, $19 per term part-time. Full-time tuition and fees vary according to course load. Part-time tuition and fees vary according to course load.
Collegiate Environment: Orientation program. Drama-theater group, choral group, student-run newspaper. Social organizations: 32 open to all. Most popular organizations: AG Ambassadors, MECHA, Alpha Gamma Sigma, Phi Theta Kappa, Puente. Major annual events: Day Under the Oaks-College Open House, Club Days. Student services: health clinic, personal-psychological counseling. Campus security: 24-hour emergency response devices and patrols, student patrols. College housing not available. Doyle Library plus 1 other with 185,461 books, 195,928 microform titles, 29,932 serials, 18,173 audiovisual materials, an OPAC, and a Web page. Operations spending for the previous fiscal year: $2.5 million. 1,700 computers available on campus for general student use. A campuswide network can be accessed from off-campus. Students can access the following: online class registration, library databases. Staffed computer lab on campus provides training in use of computers, software, and the Internet.
Community Environment: Sonama County, located 50 miles north of San Francisco, is well known for its rolling hills, grassy valleys, vineyards and spectacular coast. The county's moderate climate is characterized by average afternoon temperatures in the lower 80's during the summer and mid-50's in the winter. Average annual rainfall is approximately 30 inches. Santa Rosa is the county seat and commercial center for the north coast's Redwood Empire. The city enjoys an abundance of urban amenities including schools and colleges, business centers, three general hospitals and a family residency program as well as local theatres, the Santa Rosa Symphony, and the Luther Burbank Center for the Performing Arts. Nearby parks offer miles of hiking and riding trails as well as facilities for sailing, swimming, fishing, picnicking and camping.

■ SANTIAGO CANYON COLLEGE
8045 E Chapman Ave.
Orange, CA 92869
Tel: (714)628-4900
Fax: (714)564-4379
Web Site: www.sccollege.edu/
Description: State-supported, 2-year, coed. Part of California Community College System. Awards certificates, transfer associate, and terminal associate degrees. Founded 2000. Setting: suburban campus with easy access to Los Angeles. Total enrollment: 8,371. Faculty: 417 (92 full-time, 325 part-time). Student-undergrad faculty ratio is 23:1. Full-time: 7,987 students, 44% women, 56% men. Part-time: 6,096 students, 47% women, 53% men. Students come from 6 other countries, 6% from out-of-state. 50% 25 or older, 0.2% transferred in. Core. Calendar: semesters. Academic remediation for entering students, ESL program, services for LD students, advanced placement, freshman honors college, honors program, distance learning, summer session for credit, part-time degree program, external degree program, adult/continuing education programs, co-op programs.

Costs Per Year: State resident tuition: $46 full-time. Nonresident tuition: $205 full-time.
Collegiate Environment: Orientation program. Campus security: 24-hour emergency response devices, late night transport-escort service. College housing not available. Santiago Canyon College Library with 31,000 books, 135 microform titles, 2,260 serials, 4,082 audiovisual materials, an OPAC, and a Web page. 45 computers available on campus for general student use.

■ SCHOOL OF URBAN MISSIONS
735 105th Ave.
Oakland, CA 94603
Tel: (510)567-6174; Free: 888-567-6174
Web Site: www.sum.edu/
Description: Independent interdenominational, primarily 2-year, coed. Awards terminal associate and bachelor's degrees. Founded 1991. Total enrollment: 139. Faculty: 22 (4 full-time, 18 part-time). Student-undergrad faculty ratio is 11:1. 111 applied, 59% were admitted. Full-time: 133 students, 44% women, 56% men. Part-time: 6 students, 17% women, 83% men. 45% transferred in. Calendar: trimesters. Distance learning.
Entrance Requirements: Option: deferred admission. Required: essay, 2 recommendations, interview, pastoral recommendation. Application deadline: Rolling. Notification: continuous.

■ SCRIPPS COLLEGE
1030 Columbia Ave.
Claremont, CA 91711-3948
Tel: (909)621-8000; Free: 800-770-1333
Fax: (909)621-8323
E-mail: admission@scrippscollege.edu
Web Site: www.scrippscollege.edu/
Description: Independent, 4-year, women only. Awards bachelor's degrees. Founded 1926. Setting: 37-acre suburban campus with easy access to Los Angeles. Endowment: $258.7 million. Research spending for the previous fiscal year: $750,000. Educational spending for the previous fiscal year: $30,000 per student. Total enrollment: 962. Faculty: 115 (81 full-time, 34 part-time). Student-undergrad faculty ratio is 10:1. 2,373 applied, 32% were admitted. 70% from top 10% of their high school class, 96% from top quarter, 100% from top half. Full-time: 940 students. Part-time: 5 students. Students come from 47 states and territories, 19 other countries, 52% from out-of-state. 0.2% American Indian or Alaska Native, non-Hispanic/Latino; 9% Hispanic/Latino; 4% African American, non-Hispanic/Latino; 18% Asian, non-Hispanic/Latino; 0.3% Native Hawaiian or other Pacific Islander, non-Hispanic/Latino; 5% international. 0% 25 or older, 95% live on campus, 1% transferred in. Retention: 92% of full-time freshmen returned the following year. Academic areas with the most degrees conferred: psychology; social sciences; area and ethnic studies. Core. Calendar: semesters. Advanced placement, accelerated degree program, self-designed majors, independent study, double major, part-time degree program, internships. Off campus study at Five members of The Claremont Colleges, Colby College, Spelman College, American University (Washington Semester), George Washington University. Study abroad program. ROTC: Army (c), Air Force (c).
Entrance Requirements: Options: early admission, early decision, deferred admission, international baccalaureate accepted. Required: essay, high school transcript, interview, graded writing sample, SAT or ACT. Recommended: minimum 3 high school GPA. Entrance: very difficult. Application deadlines: 1/2, 1/2 for nonresidents, 11/15 for early decision plan 1, 1/2 for early decision plan 2. Notification: 4/1, 4/1 for nonresidents, 12/15 for early decision plan 1, 2/15 for early decision plan 2. SAT Reasoning Test deadline: 1/2. Transfer credits accepted: Yes. Applicants placed on waiting list: 499. Wait-listed applicants offered admission: 55. Early decision applicants: 186. Early decision applicants admitted: 72.
Costs Per Year: Application fee: $60. Comprehensive fee: $57,088 includes full-time tuition ($43,406), mandatory fees ($214), and college room and board ($13,468). College room only: $7280. Full-time tuition and fees vary according to course load. Room and board charges vary according to board plan. Part-time tuition: $5426 per course. Part-time tuition varies according to course load.
Collegiate Environment: Orientation program. Drama-theater group, choral group, student-run newspaper, radio station. Social organizations: 200 open to all. Most popular organizations: Scripps Associated Students, Asian/Black/Latina clubs, National Organization for Women, Sexual Assault Task Force. Major annual events: Spring Formal, Holiday Dinners, 5-College Carnival. Student services: health clinic, personal-psychological counseling, women's

center. Campus security: 24-hour emergency response devices and patrols, late night transport-escort service, controlled dormitory access. 853 college housing spaces available. Freshmen guaranteed college housing. On-campus residence required in freshman year. Option: women-only housing available. Honnold Library plus 2 others with 2.7 million books, 980,340 microform titles, 15,588 serials, 4,597 audiovisual materials, an OPAC, and a Web page. Operations spending for the previous fiscal year: $1.6 million. 151 computers available on campus for general student use. A campuswide network can be accessed from student residence rooms and from off campus. Students can access the following: online class registration, 2 ports per dorm room. Staffed computer lab on campus (open 24 hours a day) provides training in use of software.

Community Environment: The Claremont consortium consists of five undergraduate institutions and the Claremont Graduate University — all located in an area approximately one square mile in size.

■ SHASTA BIBLE COLLEGE

2951 Goodwater Ave.
Redding, CA 96002
Tel: (530)221-4275; Free: 800-800-4SBC
E-mail: registrar@shasta.edu
Web Site: www.shasta.edu/

Description: Independent nondenominational, comprehensive, coed. Awards associate, bachelor's, and master's degrees. Founded 1971. Setting: 55-acre small town campus. Educational spending for the previous fiscal year: $2502 per student. Total enrollment: 59. Faculty: 37 (9 full-time, 28 part-time). Student-undergrad faculty ratio is 3:1. 18 applied, 83% were admitted. Full-time: 36 students, 56% women, 44% men. Part-time: 13 students, 62% women, 38% men. Students come from 6 states and territories, 3 other countries, 25% from out-of-state. 53% 25 or older, 77% live on campus, 27% transferred in. Retention: 63% of full-time freshmen returned the following year. Core. Calendar: semesters. Academic remediation for entering students, accelerated degree program, independent study, distance learning, double major, summer session for credit, part-time degree program, adult/continuing education programs, co-op programs.

Entrance Requirements: Open admission. Options: electronic application, early admission, international baccalaureate accepted. Required: essay, high school transcript, 4 recommendations. Required for some: interview. Entrance: noncompetitive. Application deadlines: Rolling, Rolling for nonresidents. Notification: continuous, continuous for nonresidents. Transfer credits accepted: Yes.

Collegiate Environment: Orientation program. Choral group, student-run newspaper. Social organizations: 1 open to all. Most popular organization: Associated Student Body. Major annual events: Weekend Retreat, Associated Student Body Monthly Activities. Student services: personal-psychological counseling. Campus security: 24-hour emergency response devices, student patrols. Faye Messler Library with 30,983 books, 52 serials, 349 audiovisual materials, and an OPAC. Operations spending for the previous fiscal year: $37,953. 7 computers available on campus for general student use. A campuswide network can be accessed. Staffed computer lab on campus.

■ SHASTA COLLEGE

11555 Old Oregon Trl.
Redding, CA 96049-6006
Tel: (530)242-7500
Web Site: www.shastacollege.edu/

Description: State and locally supported, 2-year, coed. Part of California Community College System. Awards certificates, transfer associate, and terminal associate degrees. Founded 1948. Setting: 336-acre rural campus. Endowment: $1.3 million. Research spending for the previous fiscal year: $175,040. Educational spending for the previous fiscal year: $1944 per student. Total enrollment: 10,240. Faculty: 491 (146 full-time, 345 part-time). 3,586 applied, 100% were admitted. Full-time: 4,336 students, 59% women, 41% men. Part-time: 5,904 students, 62% women, 38% men. 2% from out-of-state. 56% 25 or older. Core. Calendar: semesters. Academic remediation for entering students, ESL program, services for LD students, advanced placement, honors program, distance learning, double major, summer session for credit, part-time degree program, adult/continuing education programs, co-op programs and internships.

Entrance Requirements: Open admission. Option: early admission. Required: high school transcript. Entrance: noncompetitive. Application deadline: Rolling. Notification: continuous.

Collegiate Environment: Orientation program. Drama-theater group, choral

group, student-run newspaper. Social organizations: 8 open to all. Most popular organizations: Associated Student Body, Environmental Resource Leadership Club, Intercultural Club, Inter-Varsity Christian Fellowship, Music Education National Conference. Major annual events: Cinco De Mayo, 'Tis The Season, Halloween Festivities. Student services: health clinic, personal-psychological counseling. Campus security: 24-hour emergency response devices, student patrols, late night transport-escort service, 16-hour patrols by trained security personnel. Shasta College Learning Resource Center with 67,500 books, 55,486 microform titles, 1,700 serials, 4,859 audiovisual materials, an OPAC, and a Web page. Operations spending for the previous fiscal year: $885,790. 154 computers available on campus for general student use. A campuswide network can be accessed from off-campus. Staffed computer lab on campus.

Community Environment: Redding is located at the northern end of the Sacramento Valley and is served by buses, railroads and airlines. The city provides unlimited recreational opportunities; Shasta National Forest, Sacramento Canyon, Mount Shasta, Shasta Dam which is the second largest concrete dam in the world and Shasta Lake which encompasses 30,000 acres. Excellent fishing, camping, picnicking and swimming in the area. Redding is a trade center with good shopping facilities.

■ SIERRA COLLEGE

5000 Rocklin Rd.
Rocklin, CA 95677-3397
Tel: (916)624-3333
E-mail: gmodder@sierracollege.edu
Web Site: www.sierracollege.edu/

Description: State-supported, 2-year, coed. Part of California Community College System. Awards certificates, transfer associate, and terminal associate degrees. Founded 1936. Setting: 327-acre suburban campus with easy access to Sacramento. Research spending for the previous fiscal year: $192,586. Total enrollment: 19,416. Faculty: 870 (158 full-time, 712 part-time). Student-undergrad faculty ratio is 25:1. 24,000 applied, 100% were admitted. Full-time: 5,355 students, 54% women, 46% men. Part-time: 14,061 students, 57% women, 43% men. 1% from out-of-state. 32% 25 or older, 1% live on campus, 4% transferred in. Core. Calendar: semesters. Academic remediation for entering students, ESL program, services for LD students, advanced placement, accelerated degree program, honors program, independent study, distance learning, double major, summer session for credit, part-time degree program, internships. Off campus study. Study abroad program.

Entrance Requirements: Open admission. Options: electronic application, early admission. Entrance: noncompetitive. Application deadline: Rolling. Notification: continuous. Transfer credits accepted: Yes.

Collegiate Environment: Orientation program. Drama-theater group, choral group, student-run newspaper. Social organizations: 32 open to all. Most popular organizations: Drama Club, student government, Art Club, band, Aggie Club. Major annual events: Scholarship Awards Banquet, Kids' Day, Sierra Daze. Student services: health clinic, personal-psychological counseling. Campus security: 24-hour emergency response devices and patrols, late night transport-escort service. 148 college housing spaces available; 135 were occupied in 2012-13. No special consideration for freshman housing applicants. Option: coed housing available. Leary Resource Center plus 1 other with 69,879 books, 189 serials, an OPAC, and a Web page. Operations spending for the previous fiscal year: $865,210. 430 computers available on campus for general student use. A campuswide network can be accessed from off-campus. Students can access the following: online class registration. Staffed computer lab on campus provides training in use of computers, software, and the Internet.

Community Environment: Population 49,626. Rocklin is located on Interstate 80 in the Loomis Basin, 23 miles northeast of Sacramento; the center of a large deciduous fruit-raising area. All forms of transportation available at nearby cities of Auburn and Roseville. Rocklin has libraries, hospitals, clinics, a health department, churches, and civic, fraternal, and veteran's organizations. Industry includes three lumber mills and a granite quarry. Recreational activities include swimming, picnicking, skiing, fishing and hunting. Seasonal and part-time employment is available.

■ SILICON VALLEY UNIVERSITY

2160 Lundy Ave.
Ste. 110
San Jose, CA 95131
Tel: (408)435-8989
Fax: (408)435-8989

E-mail: admission-office@svuca.edu

Web Site: www.svuca.edu/

Description: Proprietary, comprehensive, coed. Awards bachelor's and master's degrees. Setting: 1-acre suburban campus with easy access to San Jose. Research spending for the previous fiscal year: $100,000. Educational spending for the previous fiscal year: $3000 per student. Total enrollment: 1,090. Faculty: 31 (1 full-time, 30 part-time). Student-undergrad faculty ratio is 24:1. 0% from out-of-state. 65% 25 or older. Retention: 100% of full-time freshmen returned the following year. Core. Calendar: trimesters. ESL program, accelerated degree program, honors program, independent study, double major, summer session for credit, part-time degree program, co-op programs and internships, graduate courses open to undergrads.

Entrance Requirements: Options: electronic application, deferred admission, international baccalaureate accepted. Required: high school transcript, copy of diploma, TOEFL for students whose first language is not English. Recommended: essay, SAT, ACT, SAT or ACT. Required for some: interview. Transfer credits accepted: Yes.

Collegiate Environment: Orientation program. Social organizations: 1 open to all. Most popular organization: Student Association Club. Major annual events: Graduation Ceremony, Student Association New Student Welcoming Party. Campus security: 24-hour emergency response devices and patrols. SVU Library plus 1 other with 1,683 books, 3 serials, an OPAC, and a Web page. Operations spending for the previous fiscal year: $68,000. 24 computers available on campus for general student use. Computer purchase/lease plans available. A campuswide network can be accessed. Staffed computer lab on campus provides training in use of computers, software, and the Internet.

■ SIMPSON UNIVERSITY

2211 College View Dr.

Redding, CA 96003-8606

Tel: (530)226-4606; Free: 888-9-SIMPSON

Fax: (530)226-4861

E-mail: admissions@simpsonu.edu

Web Site: www.simpsonu.edu/

Description: Independent, comprehensive, coed, affiliated with The Christian and Missionary Alliance. Awards associate, bachelor's, and master's degrees. Founded 1921. Setting: 100-acre suburban campus. Endowment: $5 million. Educational spending for the previous fiscal year: $6242 per student. Total enrollment: 1,297. Faculty: 154 (52 full-time, 102 part-time). Student-undergrad faculty ratio is 14:1. 544 applied, 62% were admitted. 24% from top 10% of their high school class, 58% from top quarter, 86% from top half. Full-time: 1,007 students, 66% women, 34% men. Part-time: 26 students, 58% women, 42% men. Students come from 31 states and territories, 6 other countries, 15% from out-of-state. 2% American Indian or Alaska Native, non-Hispanic/Latino; 12% Hispanic/Latino; 3% African American, non-Hispanic/Latino; 6% Asian, non-Hispanic/Latino; 1% Native Hawaiian or other Pacific Islander, non-Hispanic/Latino; 0.1% international. 31% 25 or older, 61% live on campus, 12% transferred in. Retention: 63% of full-time freshmen returned the following year. Academic areas with the most degrees conferred: business/marketing; psychology; liberal arts/general studies. Core. Calendar: semesters. Academic remediation for entering students, services for LD students, advanced placement, accelerated degree program, self-designed majors, honors program, independent study, distance learning, double major, summer session for credit, part-time degree program, adult/continuing education programs, internships, graduate courses open to undergrads. Off campus study at Coalition for Christian Colleges and Universities. Study abroad program. ROTC: Army.

Entrance Requirements: Options: electronic application, deferred admission. Required: essay, high school transcript, 2 recommendations, Christian commitment, SAT or ACT. Recommended: SAT Subject Tests. Required for some: interview. Entrance: moderately difficult. Application deadline: Rolling. Notification: continuous.

Costs Per Year: Application fee: $25. Comprehensive fee: $30,800 includes full-time tuition ($23,300) and college room and board ($7500). College room only: $4200. Full-time tuition varies according to course load. Room and board charges vary according to board plan. Part-time tuition: $975 per credit. Part-time tuition varies according to course load.

Collegiate Environment: Orientation program. Drama-theater group, choral group, student-run newspaper. Social organizations: 17 open to all. Most popular organizations: Summer Missions Trips, Social Action Committee, Asian Fellowship, Vida, Psychology Club. Major annual events: Homecoming Weekend/Airband, Exposure Film Festival, Genesis Youth Conference/Nite Life. Student services: health clinic, personal-psychological counseling.

Campus security: 24-hour emergency response devices and patrols, student patrols, late night transport-escort service, controlled dormitory access, emergency whistle program and monthly campus safety meetings. 580 college housing spaces available; 471 were occupied in 2012-13. Freshmen guaranteed college housing. On-campus residence required through junior year. Options: men-only, women-only housing available. Start-Kilgour Memorial Library with 176,640 books, 242,910 microform titles, 24,334 serials, 3,283 audiovisual materials, an OPAC, and a Web page. Operations spending for the previous fiscal year: $356,741. 50 computers available on campus for general student use. A campuswide network can be accessed from student residence rooms. Students can access the following: online class registration.

■ SKYLINE COLLEGE

3300 College Dr.

San Bruno, CA 94066-1698

Tel: (650)738-4100

E-mail: stats@smccd.net

Web Site: skylinecollege.net/

Description: State and locally supported, 2-year, coed. Part of San Mateo County Community College District System. Awards certificates, transfer associate, and terminal associate degrees. Founded 1969. Setting: 125-acre suburban campus with easy access to San Francisco. Total enrollment: 8,359. Faculty: 333 (119 full-time, 214 part-time). Student-undergrad faculty ratio is 25:1. Full-time: 2,486 students, 47% women, 53% men. Part-time: 5,873 students, 56% women, 44% men. Students come from 9 other countries, 2% from out-of-state. 9% 25 or older. Core. Calendar: semesters. Academic remediation for entering students, ESL program, services for LD students, advanced placement, honors program, distance learning, summer session for credit, part-time degree program, adult/continuing education programs, co-op programs. Study abroad program.

Entrance Requirements: Open admission except for international students or auto technology, respiratory therapy, cosmetology, concurrent high school, emergency medical, surgical technician programs. Required for some: high school transcript. Entrance: noncompetitive. Application deadline: Rolling.

Collegiate Environment: Choral group, student-run newspaper. Social organizations: 15 open to all. Student services: health clinic, personal-psychological counseling. Campus security: security guards during open hours. Skyline College Library with 50,000 books, 230 serials, and an OPAC. 220 computers available on campus for general student use. Computer purchase/lease plans available. A campuswide network can be accessed from off-campus. Students can access the following: online class registration, student account information. Staffed computer lab on campus provides training in use of computers, software, and the Internet.

Community Environment: Population 39,750. San Bruno, located 12 miles south of San Francisco, is known as "The Airport City." The climate is temperate all year long, with cool, often foggy summers. All modes of transportation serve the area. This is a residential community with regional shopping centers, churches, library, and hospitals in nearby cities. Cultural advantages of San Francisco are appreciated by the people in San Bruno since it is so near.

■ SOKA UNIVERSITY OF AMERICA

1 University Dr.

Aliso Viejo, CA 92656

Tel: (949)480-4000; Free: 888-600-SOKA

Fax: (949)480-4001

E-mail: jserna@soka.edu

Web Site: www.soka.edu/

Description: Independent, comprehensive, coed. Awards bachelor's and master's degrees. Founded 2001. Setting: 103-acre suburban campus with easy access to Los Angeles, San Diego. Endowment: $950 million. Total enrollment: 438. Faculty: 65 (41 full-time, 24 part-time). Student-undergrad faculty ratio is 9:1. 345 applied, 46% were admitted. 39% from top 10% of their high school class, 78% from top quarter, 94% from top half. Full-time: 435 students, 65% women, 35% men. Part-time: 1 student, 100% women. Students come from 32 states and territories, 27 other countries, 33% from out-of-state. 0.5% American Indian or Alaska Native, non-Hispanic/Latino; 9% Hispanic/Latino; 3% African American, non-Hispanic/Latino; 21% Asian, non-Hispanic/Latino; 0.2% Native Hawaiian or other Pacific Islander, non-Hispanic/Latino; 39% international. 1% 25 or older, 99% live on campus, 0% transferred in. Retention: 99% of full-time freshmen returned the following year. Academic area with the most degrees conferred: liberal arts/general studies. Core. Calendar: semesters. ESL program, services for LD students, honors program, independent study, double major, co-op programs and internships. Off campus study at Study abroad is required of all undergraduate degree seeking students during one semester of their junior year. Study abroad program.

Entrance Requirements: Options: electronic application, early admission, early action, deferred admission, international baccalaureate accepted. Required: essay, high school transcript, 2 recommendations, Applications will be evaluated only when all required materials have been received. It is the students responsibility to ensure that all of the required documents have been requested of the school they are attending and submitted, SAT or ACT. Recommended: interview, SAT Subject Tests. Entrance: very difficult. Application deadlines: 1/15, 1/15 for nonresidents, 10/15 for early action. Notification: 3/1, 3/1 for nonresidents, 12/1 for early action. SAT Reasoning Test deadline: 1/15. Transfer credits accepted: No. Applicants placed on waiting list: 24. Wait-listed applicants offered admission: 6. Early action applicants: 62. Early action applicants admitted: 21.

Costs Per Year: Application fee: $30. Comprehensive fee: $39,724 includes full-time tuition ($27,950), mandatory fees ($858), and college room and board ($10,916). Full-time tuition and fees vary according to class time, course load, and program. Room and board charges vary according to board plan. Part-time tuition: $1164 per credit. Part-time tuition varies according to class time, course load, and program.

Collegiate Environment: Orientation program. Choral group, student-run newspaper. Social organizations: 29 open to all. Most popular organizations: Josho Daiko (Japanese Drum Club), Rhythmission (Hip Hop Dance Club), Sualseros (Salsa Dance Club), Ka Pilina Ho'olokahi (Hawaiian Dance Club), Soul Wings (Choir). Major annual events: The Festivals (In celebration of art as it is expressed through film, poetry and music), The ASB: (Students become involved as volunteers in community-based service projects), Winter Formal: (Student organized party/dance). Student services: health clinic, personal-psychological counseling. Campus security: 24-hour emergency response devices and patrols, student patrols, late night transport-escort service, controlled dormitory access. 500 college housing spaces available; 435 were occupied in 2012-13. Freshmen guaranteed college housing. On-campus residence required through senior year. Options: coed, men-only, women-only housing available. Daisaku and Kaneko Ikeda Library with 63,806 books, 3,780 microform titles, 11,141 serials, an OPAC, and a Web page. 100 computers available on campus for general student use. Computer purchase/lease plans available. A computer is required for all students. A campuswide network can be accessed from student residence rooms and from off campus. Students can access the following: online class registration, Angel courseware/PeopleSoft Portal. Staffed computer lab on campus (open 24 hours a day) provides training in use of computers, software, and the Internet.

■ SOLANO COMMUNITY COLLEGE

4000 Suisun Valley Rd.
Fairfield, CA 94534
Tel: (707)864-7000
Fax: (707)864-7175
E-mail: barbara.fountain@solano.edu
Web Site: www.solano.edu/

Description: State and locally supported, 2-year, coed. Part of California Community College System. Awards certificates, diplomas, transfer associate, and terminal associate degrees. Founded 1945. Setting: 192-acre suburban campus with easy access to Sacramento, San Francisco. Total enrollment: 10,927. Faculty: 374 (147 full-time, 227 part-time). Student-undergrad faculty ratio is 27:1. 10,927 applied. Students come from 43 states and territories, 6 other countries, 1% from out-of-state. 46% 25 or older. Core. Calendar: semesters. Academic remediation for entering students, ESL program, services for LD students, advanced placement, honors program, independent study, distance learning, double major, summer session for credit, part-time degree program, adult/continuing education programs, co-op programs. Off campus study at California State University, Hayward; University of California, Davis; University of California, Berkeley. Study abroad program.

Entrance Requirements: Open admission. Options: electronic application, early admission, deferred admission. Entrance: noncompetitive. Application deadline: Rolling. Transfer credits accepted: Yes.

Collegiate Environment: Orientation program. Drama-theater group, choral group, student-run newspaper. Social organizations: national fraternities. Student services: health clinic, personal-psychological counseling. Campus security: 24-hour patrols, student patrols, late night transport-escort service. Solano Community College Library with 32,000 books. 300 computers avail-able on campus for general student use. A campuswide network can be accessed from off-campus. Students can access the following: online class registration. Staffed computer lab on campus.

■ SONOMA STATE UNIVERSITY

1801 E Cotati Ave.
Rohnert Park, CA 94928-3609
Tel: (707)664-2880
E-mail: gustavo.flores@sonoma.edu
Web Site: www.sonoma.edu/

Description: State-supported, comprehensive, coed. Part of California State University System. Awards bachelor's and master's degrees. Founded 1960. Setting: 280-acre small town campus with easy access to San Francisco. Endowment: $28 million. Educational spending for the previous fiscal year: $5498 per student. Total enrollment: 9,021. Faculty: 514 (241 full-time, 273 part-time). Student-undergrad faculty ratio is 25:1. 13,142 applied, 82% were admitted. Full-time: 7,288 students, 60% women, 40% men. Part-time: 834 students, 58% women, 42% men. Students come from 28 states and territories, 20 other countries, 1% from out-of-state. 1% American Indian or Alaska Native, non-Hispanic/Latino; 17% Hispanic/Latino; 2% African American, non-Hispanic/Latino; 5% Asian, non-Hispanic/Latino; 1% Native Hawaiian or other Pacific Islander, non-Hispanic/Latino; 1% international. 11% 25 or older, 37% live on campus, 10% transferred in. Retention: 79% of full-time freshmen returned the following year. Academic areas with the most degrees conferred: business/marketing; psychology; social sciences; liberal arts/general studies. Core. Calendar: semesters. Academic remediation for entering students, ESL program, services for LD students, advanced placement, accelerated degree program, self-designed majors, honors program, independent study, distance learning, double major, summer session for credit, part-time degree program, adult/continuing education programs, co-op programs and internships, graduate courses open to undergrads. Off campus study at other units of the California State University System, National Student Exchange, Mills College. Study abroad program. ROTC: Army (c), Air Force (c).

Entrance Requirements: Options: electronic application, early admission. Required: high school transcript, SAT or ACT. Entrance: moderately difficult. Application deadline: Rolling. Notification: continuous. SAT Reasoning Test deadline: 12/30.

Costs Per Year: Application fee: $55. State resident tuition: $5970 full-time. Nonresident tuition: $10,434 full-time, $372 per unit part-time. Mandatory fees: $1426 full-time. Full-time tuition and fees vary according to course load and degree level. Part-time tuition varies according to course load and degree level. College room and board: $11,241. Room and board charges vary according to housing facility.

Collegiate Environment: Orientation program. Drama-theater group, choral group, student-run newspaper, radio station. Social organizations: 100 open to all; national fraternities, national sororities, local fraternities, local sororities; 11% of eligible men and 5% of eligible women are members. Most popular organizations: Accounting Forum, Sonoma Earth Action, Re-Entry Student Association, Lacrosse Club, Inter-Varsity Christian Fellowship. Major annual events: Welcome Week, Student Orientation, Science Night. Student services: legal services, health clinic, personal-psychological counseling, women's center. Campus security: 24-hour emergency response devices and patrols, student patrols, late night transport-escort service, controlled dormitory access. 3,054 college housing spaces available; 2,016 were occupied in 2012-13. Freshmen given priority for college housing. Options: coed, women-only housing available. Jean and Charles Schultz Information Center with 647,168 books, 1.7 million microform titles, 116,888 serials, 56,870 audiovisual materials, an OPAC, and a Web page. Operations spending for the previous fiscal year: $3.5 million. 400 computers available on campus for general student use. A computer is required for all students. A campuswide network can be accessed from student residence rooms and from off campus. Students can access the following: online class registration. Staffed computer lab on campus (open 24 hours a day) provides training in use of computers, software, and the Internet.

Community Environment: Population 41,100. Rohnert Park is a rapidly growing suburban community with temperate climate. Located near Santa Rosa (pop. 153,000) in Sonoma County. Buses and airlines serve the area. Community facilities include many shopping centers, civic and sports clubs. Recreational facilities include swimming pools, baseball parks, a community park, golf courses and others within a 20 mile radius. Rohnert Park has the annual Founders Day Parade. There are five hospitals within a 10 mile radius. The Valley of the Moon, San Francisco, the Russian River recreation areas, Redwood National Park and Lake Tahoe are all within driving distance from an hour to a half day. Sonoma county produces premium wine and is the location of many famous wineries.

■ **SOUTH COAST COLLEGE**
2011 W Chapman Ave.
Orange, CA 92868
Tel: (714)867-5009; Free: 877-568-6130
Fax: (714)867-5026
Web Site: www.southcoastcollege.com/
Description: Proprietary, 2-year, coed. Awards terminal associate degrees. Founded 1961. Total enrollment: 368.
Entrance Requirements: Entrance: noncompetitive.

■ **SOUTHERN CALIFORNIA INSTITUTE OF ARCHITECTURE**
960 E Third St.
Los Angeles, CA 90013
Tel: (213)613-2200
Fax: (213)613-0524
E-mail: admissions@sciarc.edu
Web Site: www.sciarc.edu/
Description: Independent, comprehensive, coed. Awards bachelor's and master's degrees. Founded 1972. Setting: urban campus with easy access to Los Angeles. Total enrollment: 528. Faculty: 75 (28 full-time, 47 part-time). Student-undergrad faculty ratio is 15:1. 227 applied, 70% were admitted. Full-time: 261 students, 34% women, 66% men. Part-time: 17 students, 24% women, 76% men. Students come from 21 other countries, 10% from out-of-state. 0% American Indian or Alaska Native, non-Hispanic/Latino; 23% Hispanic/Latino; 1% African American, non-Hispanic/Latino; 26% Asian, non-Hispanic/Latino; 1% Native Hawaiian or other Pacific Islander, non-Hispanic/Latino; 28% international. 41% 25 or older, 9% transferred in. Retention: 78% of full-time freshmen returned the following year. Academic area with the most degrees conferred: architecture. Core. Calendar: semesters. Academic remediation for entering students, ESL program, advanced placement, summer session for credit, co-op programs and internships, graduate courses open to undergrads, Study abroad program.
Entrance Requirements: Options: electronic application, deferred admission, international baccalaureate accepted. Required: essay, high school transcript, 3 recommendations, portfolio of creative visual work, resume, statement of purpose, application, application fee, test score (SAT/ACT and TOEFL/IELTS for international students), SAT or ACT. Recommended: minimum 3 high school GPA. Required for some: interview. Entrance: moderately difficult. Application deadline: 1/15. Notification: continuous until 4/1. SAT Reasoning Test deadline: 1/15. Transfer credits accepted: Yes. Applicants placed on waiting list: 47. Wait-listed applicants offered admission: 14.
Costs Per Year: Application fee: $85. Tuition: $36,600 full-time. Mandatory fees: $700 full-time. Full-time tuition and fees vary according to course load.
Collegiate Environment: Orientation program. Social organizations: 1 open to all; Student Union (STUN). Most popular organization: Student Union. Major annual events: Commencement, End-of-Year Exhibition. Student services: personal-psychological counseling. Campus security: 24-hour emergency response devices and patrols, electronically operated school entrances (e.g., access only with key/security card available to students 24/7). College housing not available. Kappe Library plus 1 other with 105,705 books, 96 serials, 1,770 audiovisual materials, and an OPAC. 85 computers available on campus for general student use. A campuswide network can be accessed from off-campus. Students can access the following: online class registration. Staffed computer lab on campus (open 24 hours a day) provides training in use of computers, software, and the Internet.

■ **SOUTHERN CALIFORNIA INSTITUTE OF TECHNOLOGY**
525 N Muller St.
Anaheim, CA 92801
Tel: (714)520-5552
E-mail: admissions@scitech.edu
Web Site: www.scitech.edu/
Description: Proprietary, 4-year, coed. Awards associate and bachelor's degrees. Founded 1987. Setting: urban campus with easy access to Anaheim, Los Angeles. Total enrollment: 538. Full-time: 538 students, 7% women, 93% men. 0% from out-of-state. 0.2% American Indian or Alaska Native, non-Hispanic/Latino; 46% Hispanic/Latino; 8% African American, non-Hispanic/Latino; 15% Asian, non-Hispanic/Latino; 1% Native Hawaiian or other Pacific Islander, non-Hispanic/Latino; 0% international. 69% 25 or older, 0% transferred in. Retention: 86% of full-time freshmen returned the

following year. Core. ESL program, accelerated degree program, double major, adult/continuing education programs.
Entrance Requirements: Open admission. Required: interview, entrance exam. Required for some: high school transcript.
Collegiate Environment: Orientation program. College housing not available. 300 computers available on campus for general student use. A campuswide network can be accessed. Staffed computer lab on campus (open 24 hours a day) provides training in use of computers, software, and the Internet.

■ **SOUTHERN CALIFORNIA SEMINARY**
2075 E Madison Ave.
El Cajon, CA 92019
Tel: (619)442-9841
Fax: (619)442-4510
E-mail: thpittman@socalsem.edu
Web Site: www.socalsem.edu/
Description: Independent interdenominational, comprehensive, coed. Awards associate, bachelor's, and master's degrees. Founded 1946. Endowment: $114,070. Total enrollment: 283. Faculty: 55 (11 full-time, 44 part-time). Student-undergrad faculty ratio is 10:1. 25 applied, 88% were admitted. Students come from 14 states and territories, 7 other countries, 20% from out-of-state. 60% 25 or older, 9% live on campus. Academic area with the most degrees conferred: theology and religious vocations. Core.
Entrance Requirements: Options: electronic application, early admission, deferred admission, international baccalaureate accepted. Required: essay, high school transcript, minimum 2.5 high school GPA, 3 recommendations, interview. Entrance: moderately difficult. Application deadline: 8/13. Notification: 8/28.
Collegiate Environment: Orientation program. 12 computers available on campus for general student use. A campuswide network can be accessed from off-campus. Students can access the following: online class registration. Staffed computer lab on campus (open 24 hours a day) provides training in use of computers and software.

■ **SOUTHWESTERN COLLEGE**
900 Otay Lakes Rd.
Chula Vista, CA 91910-7299
Tel: (619)421-6700
Web Site: www.swc.edu/
Description: State and locally supported, 2-year, coed. Part of California Community College System. Awards certificates, transfer associate, and terminal associate degrees. Founded 1961. Setting: 158-acre suburban campus with easy access to San Diego. Total enrollment: 22,030. Student-undergrad faculty ratio is 22:1. 0% from out-of-state. 34% 25 or older. Retention: 59% of full-time freshmen returned the following year. Calendar: semesters. Academic remediation for entering students, advanced placement, distance learning, summer session for credit, part-time degree program, external degree program, adult/continuing education programs. Study abroad program.
Entrance Requirements: Open admission. Option: early admission. Required for some: high school transcript. Entrance: noncompetitive. Application deadline: Rolling. Notification: continuous.
Collegiate Environment: Social organizations: national fraternities. Student services: personal-psychological counseling. Campus security: 24-hour emergency response devices, student patrols, late night transport-escort service. Southwestern College Library with an OPAC and a Web page.

■ **STANBRIDGE COLLEGE**
2041 Business Ctr. Dr.
Irvine, CA 92612
Tel: (949)794-9090
Fax: (949)794-9094
Web Site: www.stanbridge.edu/
Description: Proprietary, 2-year, coed. Awards terminal associate degrees. Total enrollment: 28. 65 applied, 95% were admitted.

■ **STANFORD UNIVERSITY**
Stanford, CA 94305-9991
Tel: (650)723-2300
Fax: (650)725-2846
E-mail: admission@stanford.edu
Web Site: www.stanford.edu/
Description: Independent, university, coed. Awards bachelor's, master's,

and doctoral degrees and post-master's certificates. Founded 1891. Setting: 8,180-acre suburban campus with easy access to San Francisco, San Jose. Endowment: $17 billion. Research spending for the previous fiscal year: $1.2 billion. Educational spending for the previous fiscal year: $73,894 per student. Total enrollment: 18,217. Faculty: 1,508 (1,486 full-time, 22 part-time). Student-undergrad faculty ratio is 5:1. 36,632 applied, 7% were admitted. 94% from top 10% of their high school class, 99% from top quarter, 100% from top half. Full-time: 7,003 students, 48% women, 52% men. Part-time: 60 students, 70% women, 30% men. Students come from 52 states and territories, 89 other countries, 53% from out-of-state. 1% American Indian or Alaska Native, non-Hispanic/Latino; 17% Hispanic/Latino; 6% African American, non-Hispanic/Latino; 19% Asian, non-Hispanic/Latino; 0.4% Native Hawaiian or other Pacific Islander, non-Hispanic/Latino; 7% international. 1% 25 or older, 91% live on campus, 0.4% transferred in. Retention: 98% of full-time freshmen returned the following year. Academic areas with the most degrees conferred: social sciences; engineering; interdisciplinary studies. Core. ESL program, services for LD students, advanced placement, self-designed majors, honors program, independent study, distance learning, double major, summer session for credit, internships, graduate courses open to undergrads. Off campus study at Howard University; Spelman College; Morehouse College, Dartmouth College. Study abroad program. ROTC: Army (c), Naval (c), Air Force (c).
Entrance Requirements: Options: electronic application, early action, deferred admission, international baccalaureate accepted. Required: essay, high school transcript, 2 recommendations, SAT or ACT. Recommended: SAT Subject Tests. Entrance: most difficult. Application deadlines: 1/1, 11/1 for early action. Notification: 4/1, 12/15 for early action. SAT Reasoning Test deadline: 1/1. SAT Subject Test deadline: 1/1. Transfer credits accepted: Yes. Applicants placed on waiting list: 789. Wait-listed applicants offered admission: 0. Early action applicants: 5,929. Early action applicants admitted: 755.
Costs Per Year: Application fee: $90. Comprehensive fee: $55,856 includes full-time tuition ($42,690) and college room and board ($13,166). Room and board charges vary according to board plan.
Collegiate Environment: Orientation program. Drama-theater group, choral group, marching band, student-run newspaper, radio station. Social organizations: 650 open to all; national fraternities, national sororities; 24% of eligible men and 28% of eligible women are members. Most popular organizations: Ram's Head (theatre club), Axe Committee (athletic support), Business Association of Engineering Students, Asian-American Student Association, Stanford Daily. Major annual events: Big Game, Gaieties, Full Moon on the Quad. Student services: legal services, health clinic, personal-psychological counseling, women's center. Campus security: 24-hour emergency response devices and patrols, late night transport-escort service, controlled dormitory access. 6,394 college housing spaces available; all were occupied in 2012-13. Freshmen guaranteed college housing. On-campus residence required in freshman year. Options: coed, women-only housing available. Green Library plus 19 others with 9 million books, 6 million microform titles, 75,000 serials, 1.5 million audiovisual materials, an OPAC, and a Web page. Operations spending for the previous fiscal year: $109 million. 1,000 computers available on campus for general student use. Computer purchase/lease plans available. A campuswide network can be accessed from student residence rooms and from off campus. Students can access the following: online class registration. Staffed computer lab on campus (open 24 hours a day) provides training in use of computers, software, and the Internet.
Community Environment: Stanford is an unincorporated campus adjacent to Palo Alto. Palo Alto with a population of 56,900 is located 30 miles south of San Francisco with an ideal climate, the summer average being 70 degrees and the winter average 55 degrees. The average rainfall is 15.5 inches. The city is served by all modes of transportation, the San Francisco Airport being 18 miles north. Palo Alto has three libraries, a museum, art gallery, hotels, hospitals, and churches. The Silicon Valley, in large part an offspring of Stanford, begins at campus edge. The cultural and recreation opportunities of San Francisco and San Jose are added to the many of the Stanford campus and the surrounding area. The Pacific Ocean is 32 miles to the west; the Monterey peninsula is 75 miles to the south. The Sierra Nevada, 160 miles away and the site of several national parks, are a popular resort area for camping, hiking, and skiing.

■ **TAFT COLLEGE**
29 Emmons Park Dr.
Taft, CA 93268-2317
Tel: (661)763-7700
Fax: (661)763-7705

E-mail: ncook@taftcollege.edu
Web Site: www.taftcollege.edu/
Description: State and locally supported, 2-year, coed. Part of California Community College System. Awards certificates, transfer associate, and terminal associate degrees. Founded 1922. Setting: 15-acre small town campus. Endowment: $14,405. Total enrollment: 9,500. Faculty: 91 (37 full-time, 54 part-time). 812 applied, 100% were admitted. Full-time: 505 students, 60% women, 40% men. Part-time: 8,995 students, 18% women, 82% men. Students come from 1 other country, 5% from out-of-state. 47% 25 or older, 6% live on campus, 3% transferred in. Core. Calendar: semesters. Academic remediation for entering students, ESL program, services for LD students, advanced placement, honors program, independent study, distance learning, summer session for credit, part-time degree program, adult/continuing education programs.
Entrance Requirements: Open admission. Option: electronic application. Required for some: high school transcript. Entrance: noncompetitive. Application deadline: Rolling. Transfer credits accepted: Yes.
Costs Per Year: Application fee: $0. State resident tuition: $0 full-time. Nonresident tuition: $7080 full-time, $190 per unit part-time. Mandatory fees: $1380 full-time, $46 per unit part-time. Full-time tuition and fees vary according to course load and program. Part-time tuition and fees vary according to course load.
Collegiate Environment: Orientation program. Student-run newspaper. Social organizations: 4 open to all; Phi Theta Kappa. Most popular organizations: International Club, Alpha Gamma Sigma, Rotaract, ASB Club. Major annual events: International Day, Spring Fling. Student services: personal-psychological counseling. Campus security: 24-hour emergency response devices, controlled dormitory access, parking lot security. 160 college housing spaces available; 93 were occupied in 2012-13. No special consideration for freshman housing applicants. Option: coed housing available. Taft College Library with 28,500 books, 150 serials, 1,500 audiovisual materials, an OPAC, and a Web page. Operations spending for the previous fiscal year: $263,133. 91 computers available on campus for general student use. A campuswide network can be accessed. Students can access the following: online class registration. Staffed computer lab on campus provides training in use of computers.
Community Environment: The population of Taft is 9,100. Centrally located two and one-half hours north of Los Angeles, Taft has a mild climate with hot summers. The city, surrounded by oilfields, is an important supply point for field equipment. Churches of all denominations, hospital, library, and shopping facilities make up the town. Part-time employment is available. Recreational facilities include a theatre, golf course, and more. Apartments are available.

■ **THOMAS AQUINAS COLLEGE**
10000 N Ojai Rd.
Santa Paula, CA 93060
Tel: (805)525-4417; Free: 800-634-9797
Fax: (805)525-9342
E-mail: admissions@thomasaquinas.edu
Web Site: www.thomasaquinas.edu/
Description: Independent Roman Catholic, 4-year, coed. Awards bachelor's degrees. Founded 1971. Setting: 131-acre rural campus with easy access to Los Angeles. System endowment: $13.9 million. Educational spending for the previous fiscal year: $13,263 per student. Total enrollment: 370. Faculty: 36 (30 full-time, 6 part-time). Student-undergrad faculty ratio is 12:1. 165 applied, 81% were admitted. 44% from top 10% of their high school class, 67% from top quarter, 100% from top half. 1 National Merit Scholar, 5 valedictorians, 8 student government officers. Full-time: 370 students, 51% women, 49% men. Students come from 39 states and territories, 5 other countries, 60% from out-of-state. 0.3% American Indian or Alaska Native, non-Hispanic/Latino; 12% Hispanic/Latino; 0% African American, non-Hispanic/Latino; 1% Asian, non-Hispanic/Latino; 0% Native Hawaiian or other Pacific Islander, non-Hispanic/Latino; 4% international. 2% 25 or older, 99% live on campus, 0% transferred in. Retention: 85% of full-time freshmen returned the following year. Academic area with the most degrees conferred: liberal arts/general studies. Core. Calendar: semesters. Co-op programs.
Entrance Requirements: Options: electronic application, international baccalaureate accepted. Required: essay, high school transcript, 3 recommendations, SAT or ACT. Recommended: minimum 3 high school GPA. Required for some: interview. Entrance: very difficult. Application deadlines: Rolling, Rolling for nonresidents. Notification: continuous, continuous for nonresidents. Transfer credits accepted: No. Applicants placed on waiting list: 35. Wait-listed applicants offered admission: 14.

Costs Per Year: Application fee: $0. Comprehensive fee: $32,450 includes full-time tuition ($24,500) and college room and board ($7950).
Collegiate Environment: Orientation program. Drama-theater group, choral group. Social organizations: 5 open to all. Most popular organizations: Musical Groups (Choir, Chamber Orchestra), Theatre Groups, Language Clubs, Pro-Life Ministry, religious groups. Major annual events: St. Thomas Aquinas Day, Presidents Day Formal Dinner, St. Patrick's Day Celebration. Student services: personal-psychological counseling. Campus security: daily security patrol. 398 college housing spaces available; 367 were occupied in 2012-13. Freshmen guaranteed college housing. On-campus residence required through senior year. Options: men-only, women-only housing available. St. Bernardine Library with 65,302 books, 60 serials, and 2,865 audiovisual materials. Operations spending for the previous fiscal year: $176,445. 20 computers available on campus for general student use. A campuswide network can be accessed. Staffed computer lab on campus provides training in use of computers, software, and the Internet.
Community Environment: The college is located in a rural setting 60 miles from Los Angeles and 45 miles from Santa Barbara. It is bordered on three sides by Los Padres National Forest.

■ **TOURO COLLEGE LOS ANGELES**
1317 N Crescent Heights Blvd.
West Hollywood, CA 90046
Tel: (323)822-9700
Web Site: www.touro.edu/losangeles/
Description: Independent, 4-year, coed. Founded 2005. Calendar: semesters.

■ **TRIDENT UNIVERSITY INTERNATIONAL**
5757 Plz. Dr., Ste. 100
Cypress, CA 90630
Tel: (714)816-0366
Fax: (714)816-0367
E-mail: admissions@trident.edu
Web Site: www.trident.edu/
Description: Independent, university, coed. Awards bachelor's, master's, and doctoral degrees and post-master's certificates (offers only online degree programs). Setting: urban campus. Student-undergrad faculty ratio is 25:1. Academic areas with the most degrees conferred: business/marketing; health professions and related sciences; computer and information sciences. Core. Calendar: four 12 week sessions per year. Accelerated degree program, honors program, distance learning, double major, summer session for credit, part-time degree program, adult/continuing education programs.
Entrance Requirements: Open admission. Options: electronic application, international baccalaureate accepted. Required: high school transcript. Required for some: essay. Entrance: minimally difficult. Application deadlines: Rolling, Rolling for nonresidents. Notification: continuous, continuous for nonresidents. Transfer credits accepted: Yes.
Collegiate Environment: College housing not available. Trident University International Library with a Web page.

■ **UNITED STATES UNIVERSITY (CHULA VISTA)**
830 Bay Blvd.
Chula Vista, CA 91911
Tel: (619)477-6310; Free: 888-422-3381
Fax: (619)477-7340
Web Site: www.usuniversity.edu/sd/
Description: Proprietary, comprehensive, coed. Awards bachelor's and master's degrees.
Entrance Requirements: Required: high school transcript, interview.
Collegiate Environment: Orientation program.

■ **UNITED STATES UNIVERSITY (CYPRESS)**
6251 Katella Ave.
Cypress, CA 90630
Tel: (714)252-8592; Free: 888-422-3381
Web Site: www.usuniversity.edu/oc/
Description: Proprietary, comprehensive, coed. Awards bachelor's and master's degrees.

■ **UNITEK COLLEGE**
4670 Auto Mall Pky.
Fremont, CA 94538
Tel: (510)249-1060

Fax: (510)249-9125
Web Site: www.unitekcollege.edu/
Description: Proprietary, 2-year, coed. Awards certificates and terminal associate degrees.

■ **UNIVERSITY OF ANTELOPE VALLEY**
44055 N Sierra Hwy.
Lancaster, CA 93534
Tel: (661)726-1911
Web Site: www.uav.edu/
Description: Proprietary, comprehensive, coed.

■ **UNIVERSITY OF CALIFORNIA, BERKELEY**
Berkeley, CA 94720-1500
Tel: (510)642-6000
Fax: (510)642-7333
Web Site: www.berkeley.edu/
Description: State-supported, university, coed. Part of University of California. Awards bachelor's, master's, and doctoral degrees. Founded 1868. Setting: 1,232-acre urban campus with easy access to San Francisco. Endowment: $3 billion. Research spending for the previous fiscal year: $550 million. Total enrollment: 35,899. Student-undergrad faculty ratio is 17:1. 61,731 applied, 18% were admitted. 98% from top 10% of their high school class, 100% from top quarter, 100% from top half. 11% from out-of-state. 1% American Indian or Alaska Native, non-Hispanic/Latino; 13% Hispanic/Latino; 3% African American, non-Hispanic/Latino; 39% Asian, non-Hispanic/Latino; 0.2% Native Hawaiian or other Pacific Islander, non-Hispanic/Latino; 10% international. 7% 25 or older, 26% live on campus. Retention: 96% of full-time freshmen returned the following year. Academic areas with the most degrees conferred: social sciences; biological/life sciences; engineering. Core. Calendar: semesters. ESL program, services for LD students, advanced placement, accelerated degree program, self-designed majors, honors program, independent study, double major, summer session for credit, adult/continuing education programs, internships, graduate courses open to undergrads. Off campus study at Holy Names College, Mills College, Dominican College, John F. Kennedy University, San Francisco State University, Sonoma State University, California State University, Hayward. Study abroad program. ROTC: Army, Naval, Air Force.
Entrance Requirements: Options: electronic application, international baccalaureate accepted. Required: essay, SAT or ACT. Recommended: SAT Subject Tests. Application deadline: 11/30. Notification: 3/31. Preference given to state residents. SAT Reasoning Test deadline: 12/31. SAT Subject Test deadline: 12/31. Applicants placed on waiting list: 161. Wait-listed applicants offered admission: 107.
Costs Per Year: Application fee: $70. State resident tuition: $11,220 full-time. Nonresident tuition: $34,098 full-time. Mandatory fees: $1654 full-time. College room and board: $15,000. Room and board charges vary according to board plan and housing facility.
Collegiate Environment: Orientation program. Drama-theater group, choral group, marching band, student-run newspaper, radio station. Social organizations: national fraternities, national sororities, local fraternities, local sororities. Student services: legal services, health clinic, personal-psychological counseling, women's center. Campus security: 24-hour emergency response devices and patrols, late night transport-escort service, controlled dormitory access, Office of Emergency Preparedness. Freshmen guaranteed college housing. Options: coed, men-only, women-only housing available. Doe Library with an OPAC and a Web page. Operations spending for the previous fiscal year: $58.6 million.
Community Environment: The City of Berkeley (population 100,744) has a long history as one of America's most lively, culturally diverse, and politically adventurous cities. The surrounding San Francisco Bay Area offers culture, entertainment, and natural beauty without rival, much of it within easy reach by BART (Bay Area Rapid Transit).

■ **UNIVERSITY OF CALIFORNIA, DAVIS**
One Shields Ave.
Davis, CA 95616
Tel: (530)752-1011
Fax: (530)752-6363
E-mail: undergraduateadmissions@ucdavis.edu
Web Site: www.ucdavis.edu/
Description: State-supported, university, coed. Part of University of California System. Awards bachelor's, master's, and doctoral degrees and post-master's certificates. Founded 1905. Setting: 5,993-acre suburban

campus with easy access to San Francisco. Total enrollment: 32,354. Faculty: 1,620 (1,471 full-time, 149 part-time). Student-undergrad faculty ratio is 17:1. 49,333 applied, 46% were admitted. Full-time: 25,446 students, 55% women, 45% men. Part-time: 313 students, 50% women, 50% men. 2% from out-of-state. 0.3% American Indian or Alaska Native, non-Hispanic/Latino; 16% Hispanic/Latino; 2% African American, non-Hispanic/Latino; 37% Asian, non-Hispanic/Latino; 0.5% Native Hawaiian or other Pacific Islander, non-Hispanic/Latino; 4% international. 5% 25 or older, 25% live on campus, 11% transferred in. Retention: 92% of full-time freshmen returned the following year. Academic areas with the most degrees conferred: biological/life sciences; social sciences; psychology. Core. Academic remediation for entering students, ESL program, services for LD students, advanced placement, self-designed majors, freshman honors college, honors program, independent study, double major, summer session for credit, part-time degree program, adult/continuing education programs, internships, graduate courses open to undergrads. Study abroad program. ROTC: Army, Naval (c), Air Force (c).

Entrance Requirements: Option: electronic application. Required: essay, high school transcript, minimum 2.8 high school GPA, high school subject requirements, SAT or ACT, SAT Subject Tests. Entrance: very difficult. Application deadline: 11/30. Notification: 3/15. Preference given to state residents for certain programs. SAT Subject Test deadline: 1/31. Applicants placed on waiting list: 6,911. Wait-listed applicants offered admission: 12.

Costs Per Year: Application fee: $70. State resident tuition: $15,727 full-time. Nonresident tuition: $38,605 full-time.

Collegiate Environment: Orientation program. Drama-theater group, choral group, marching band, student-run newspaper, radio station. Social organizations: 320 open to all; national fraternities, national sororities, state fraternities and sororities; 9% of eligible men and 8% of eligible women are members. Most popular organizations: Filipino Student Organization, Vietnamese Student Association, Jewish Student Union, Alpha Phi Omega. Major annual events: Picnic Day, Whole Earth Festival, Cultural Days. Student services: legal services, health clinic, personal-psychological counseling, women's center. Campus security: 24-hour emergency response devices and patrols, student patrols, late night transport-escort service, controlled dormitory access, Campus Violence Prevention Program (CVPP). Freshmen guaranteed college housing. Options: coed, women-only housing available. Peter J. Shields Library plus 6 others with 4.3 million microform titles, 104,999 serials, 11,982 audiovisual materials, an OPAC, and a Web page.

Community Environment: Population 60,700. Located in the center of the Sacramento Valley, the climate is typical of the Great Central Valley of California - cool in the winter and warm in the long dry summer season. January average temperatures range from a low of 37 to a high of 54 degrees; July average temperatures range 57 to 97 degrees. The average annual rainfall is 17 inches. The agricultural region surrounding Davis produces numerous crops including tomatoes, alfalfa, wheat and corn. Berkeley and San Francisco are within one hour by train, bus or car. Part-time employment is available either on or off campus. Davis is only 2-3 hours from the Lake Tahoe vacation area in the Sierra Nevada Mountains.

■ **UNIVERSITY OF CALIFORNIA, IRVINE**
Irvine, CA 92697
Tel: (949)824-5011
E-mail: admissions@uci.edu
Web Site: www.uci.edu/

Description: State-supported, university, coed. Part of University of California System. Awards bachelor's, master's, and doctoral degrees. Founded 1965. Setting: 1,477-acre suburban campus with easy access to Los Angeles. Research spending for the previous fiscal year: $246 million. Educational spending for the previous fiscal year: $16,036 per student. Total enrollment: 27,479. Faculty: 1,906 (1,467 full-time, 439 part-time). Student-undergrad faculty ratio is 19:1. 56,508 applied, 42% were admitted. 96% from top 10% of their high school class, 100% from top quarter, 100% from top half. Full-time: 21,878 students, 54% women, 46% men. Part-time: 338 students, 42% women, 58% men. Students come from 43 states and territories, 70 other countries, 1% from out-of-state. 0.2% American Indian or Alaska Native, non-Hispanic/Latino; 20% Hispanic/Latino; 2% African American, non-Hispanic/Latino; 47% Asian, non-Hispanic/Latino; 0.1% Native Hawaiian or other Pacific Islander, non-Hispanic/Latino; 6% international. 4% 25 or older, 38% live on campus, 8% transferred in. Retention: 93% of full-time freshmen returned the following year. Academic areas with the most degrees conferred: social sciences; biological/life sciences; psychology. Core. ESL program, services for LD students, advanced placement, acceler-

ated degree program, honors program, independent study, distance learning, double major, summer session for credit, internships, graduate courses open to undergrads. Off campus study at other campuses of University of California System. Study abroad program. ROTC: Army, Air Force (c).

Entrance Requirements: Options: electronic application, international baccalaureate accepted. Required: essay, high school transcript, SAT or ACT. Recommended: SAT Subject Tests. Entrance: very difficult. Application deadline: 11/30. Notification: 3/31. SAT Reasoning Test deadline: 12/31. SAT Subject Test deadline: 12/31. Transfer credits accepted: Yes. Applicants placed on waiting list: 3,732. Wait-listed applicants offered admission: 1,621.

Costs Per Year: Application fee: $70. State resident tuition: $11,220 full-time. Nonresident tuition: $34,098 full-time. Mandatory fees: $3006 full-time. College room and board: $11,735. Room and board charges vary according to board plan and housing facility.

Collegiate Environment: Orientation program. Drama-theater group, choral group, marching band, student-run newspaper, radio station. Social organizations: 526 open to all; national fraternities, national sororities, local fraternities, local sororities; 9% of eligible men and 10% of eligible women are members. Major annual events: Celebrate UCI (open house), Homecoming, Shocktoberfest. Student services: health clinic, personal-psychological counseling. Campus security: 24-hour emergency response devices and patrols, student patrols, late night transport-escort service, controlled dormitory access. 10,199 college housing spaces available; 8,434 were occupied in 2012-13. Freshmen guaranteed college housing. Options: coed, men-only, women-only housing available. Langson Library plus 4 others with 3.2 million books, 2.2 million microform titles, 132,134 serials, 123,396 audiovisual materials, an OPAC, and a Web page. Operations spending for the previous fiscal year: $22.3 million. 1,500 computers available on campus for general student use. A campuswide network can be accessed from student residence rooms and from off campus. Students can access the following: online class registration. Staffed computer lab on campus (open 24 hours a day) provides training in use of computers, software, and the Internet.

Community Environment: UCI's location combines the cultural and economic resources of an urban area along with access to the scenic, recreational areas of Southern California. Located 50 miles south of Los Angeles, five miles from the Pacific Ocean, and nestled in 1,477 acres of coastal foothills near Newport Beach, UCI lies amid rapidly growing residential communities and a dynamic international business environment of Orange County and the surrounding region. The sailing and surfing beaches of Newport, Laguna, and Huntington are a 10-minute bike ride from campus, while hiking trails, desert camping, or mountain resorts for snow boarding and skiing are within two-hour's travel distance from Irvine. The campus itself is a natural arboretum of native species, as well as trees and shrubs from all over the world. Adjacent to the campus, the San Joaquin Freshwater Marsh serves as a natural classroom or peaceful refuge, with trails for viewing the rich diversity of wildlife. Within walking distance of the University are shops and restaurants, bookstores, markets, a post office, and a theatre. Complementing UCI cultural events throughout the academic year is the Orange County arts and entertainment environment. It offers everything from small venues for bands and performers to galleries, museums, the Irvine Barclay Theater, the Orange County Performing Arts Center, and the Pacific Symphony. Within a one- to two-hour drive are the metropolitan attractions of Los Angeles and San Diego, as well as desert and mountain recreational opportunities.

■ **UNIVERSITY OF CALIFORNIA, LOS ANGELES**
405 Hilgard Ave.
Los Angeles, CA 90095
Tel: (310)825-4321
E-mail: ugadm@saonet.ucla.edu
Web Site: www.ucla.edu/

Description: State-supported, university, coed. Part of University of California System. Awards bachelor's, master's, and doctoral degrees. Founded 1919. Setting: 419-acre urban campus with easy access to Los Angeles. Total enrollment: 41,341. Faculty: 2,553 (1,989 full-time, 564 part-time). Student-undergrad faculty ratio is 17:1. 72,697 applied, 22% were admitted. 97% from top 10% of their high school class, 100% from top quarter, 100% from top half. Full-time: 27,365 students, 55% women, 45% men. Part-time: 583 students, 47% women, 53% men. Students come from 51 states and territories, 119 other countries, 7% from out-of-state. 0.2% American Indian or Alaska Native, non-Hispanic/Latino; 18% Hispanic/Latino; 3% African American, non-Hispanic/Latino; 32% Asian, non-Hispanic/Latino; 0.3% Native Hawaiian or other Pacific Islander, non-Hispanic/Latino; 10% international. 5% 25 or older, 45% live on campus, 11% transferred in.

Retention: 96% of full-time freshmen returned the following year. Academic areas with the most degrees conferred: social sciences; biological/life sciences; psychology. Core. Services for LD students, advanced placement, accelerated degree program, self-designed majors, freshman honors college, honors program, independent study, double major, summer session for credit, internships, graduate courses open to undergrads. Off campus study. Study abroad program. ROTC: Army, Naval, Air Force.

Entrance Requirements: Options: electronic application, international baccalaureate accepted. Required: essay, high school transcript, SAT or ACT. Entrance: very difficult. Application deadlines: 11/30, 11/30 for nonresidents. Notification: 3/31, 3/31 for nonresidents. SAT Reasoning Test deadline: 1/15. SAT Subject Test deadline: 1/15.

Costs Per Year: Application fee: $70. State resident tuition: $11,220 full-time. Nonresident tuition: $34,098 full-time. Mandatory fees: $1472 full-time. College room and board: $12,675. Room and board charges vary according to board plan and housing facility.

Collegiate Environment: Orientation program. Drama-theater group, choral group, marching band, student-run newspaper, radio station. Social organizations: 1,000 open to all; national fraternities, national sororities, local fraternities, local sororities; 13% of eligible men and 13% of eligible women are members. Major annual events: Bruin Bash, Blue and Gold Week, Spring Sing. Student services: legal services, health clinic, personal-psychological counseling, women's center. Campus security: 24-hour emergency response devices and patrols, student patrols, late night transport-escort service, controlled dormitory access. 10,453 undergraduates lived in college housing during 2012-13. Freshmen guaranteed college housing. Option: coed housing available. Charles E. Young Research Library plus 13 others with 9 million books, 6.2 million microform titles, 38,975 serials, 316,523 audiovisual materials, an OPAC, and a Web page. 3,930 computers available on campus for general student use. A campuswide network can be accessed from student residence rooms and from off campus. Students can access the following: online class registration. Staffed computer lab on campus (open 24 hours a day) provides training in use of computers, software, and the Internet.

Community Environment: Los Angeles is a major metropolitan center with a semiarid climate. There are very fine museums and libraries in the city, and a music center, which contribute to the cultural atmosphere of the city. Los Angeles has many points of interest, and is near enough to the beaches and to the mountains for all sports. There are excellent metropolitan shopping centers.

■ **UNIVERSITY OF CALIFORNIA, MERCED**

5200 N Lake Rd.
Merced, CA 95343
Tel: (209)228-4400
E-mail: admissions@ucmerced.edu
Web Site: www.ucmerced.edu/

Description: State-supported, university, coed. Part of University of California System. Awards bachelor's, master's, and doctoral degrees. Setting: 815-acre small town campus with easy access to Fresno, CA. Endowment: $26.8 million. Research spending for the previous fiscal year: $15.9 million. Educational spending for the previous fiscal year: $5515 per student. Total enrollment: 5,760. Faculty: 306 (260 full-time, 46 part-time). Student-undergrad faculty ratio is 20:1. 13,959 applied, 76% were admitted. Full-time: 5,363 students, 50% women, 50% men. Part-time: 68 students, 35% women, 65% men. Students come from 19 states and territories, 17 other countries, 1% from out-of-state. 0.3% American Indian or Alaska Native, non-Hispanic/Latino; 40% Hispanic/Latino; 7% African American, non-Hispanic/Latino; 28% Asian, non-Hispanic/Latino; 1% Native Hawaiian or other Pacific Islander, non-Hispanic/Latino; 2% international. 4% 25 or older, 29% live on campus, 2% transferred in. Retention: 83% of full-time freshmen returned the following year. Academic areas with the most degrees conferred: biological/life sciences; psychology; engineering. Core. Academic remediation for entering students, services for LD students, advanced placement, independent study, double major, summer session for credit, part-time degree program, internships. Off campus study at UC Merced and Merced College have created an Intersegmental Cross-Enrollment agreement that allows approved full-time undergraduate students from either institution to cross-enroll. Enrollment is limited to one course per term and participating students need the approval of both the home and the host campus. Study abroad program.

Entrance Requirements: Options: electronic application, international baccalaureate accepted. Required: essay, high school transcript, minimum 3.0 high school GPA for California residents, SAT or ACT. Entrance: moderately

difficult. Application deadline: 11/30. Notification: 3/1. SAT Reasoning Test deadline: 1/15. SAT Subject Test deadline: 1/15. Transfer credits accepted: Yes.

Costs Per Year: Application fee: $70. State resident tuition: $13,070 full-time. Nonresident tuition: $35,948 full-time. College room and board: $14,272.

Collegiate Environment: Orientation program. Drama-theater group, choral group, marching band, student-run newspaper, radio station. Social organizations: 140 open to all; national fraternities, national sororities; 7% of eligible men and 9% of eligible women are members. Most popular organizations: Philipino American Alliance, Vietnamese Student Association, Intervarsity Christian Fellowship, Latino Associated Students, Hip Hop Movement. Major annual events: Asian Fest, Bobcat Day, Dance Off. Student services: legal services, health clinic, personal-psychological counseling, women's center. Campus security: 24-hour emergency response devices and patrols, student patrols, late night transport-escort service, controlled dormitory access. College housing designed to accommodate 1,328 students; 1,570 undergraduates lived in college housing during 2012-13. Freshmen guaranteed college housing. Option: coed housing available. Kolligian with 997,705 books, 80,886 serials, 1,584 audiovisual materials, an OPAC, and a Web page. Operations spending for the previous fiscal year: $3.7 million. 226 computers available on campus for general student use. A campuswide network can be accessed from student residence rooms and from off campus. Students can access the following: online class registration. Staffed computer lab on campus provides training in use of computers, software, and the Internet.

■ **UNIVERSITY OF CALIFORNIA, RIVERSIDE**

900 University Ave.
Riverside, CA 92521-0102
Tel: (951)827-1012
Fax: (951)827-6344
E-mail: discover@ucr.edu
Web Site: www.ucr.edu/

Description: State-supported, university, coed. Part of University of California System. Awards bachelor's, master's, and doctoral degrees. Founded 1954. Setting: 1,200-acre urban campus with easy access to Los Angeles. Endowment: $138.8 million. Research spending for the previous fiscal year: $99 million. Educational spending for the previous fiscal year: $9731 per student. Total enrollment: 21,005. Faculty: 902 (751 full-time, 151 part-time). Student-undergrad faculty ratio is 22:1. 30,395 applied, 63% were admitted. 94% from top 10% of their high school class, 100% from top quarter, 100% from top half. Full-time: 18,054 students, 52% women, 48% men. Part-time: 485 students, 39% women, 61% men. Students come from 35 states and territories, 43 other countries, 1% from out-of-state. 0.2% American Indian or Alaska Native, non-Hispanic/Latino; 35% Hispanic/Latino; 6% African American, non-Hispanic/Latino; 36% Asian, non-Hispanic/Latino; 0.4% Native Hawaiian or other Pacific Islander, non-Hispanic/Latino; 2% international. 5% 25 or older, 31% live on campus, 7% transferred in. Retention: 88% of full-time freshmen returned the following year. Academic areas with the most degrees conferred: social sciences; business/marketing; biological/life sciences. Core. Services for LD students, advanced placement, accelerated degree program, honors program, independent study, distance learning, double major, summer session for credit, adult/continuing education programs, internships, graduate courses open to undergrads. Off campus study at University of California, Santa Barbara, University of California, Davis, University of California, Los Angeles, Cal State San Bernardino. Study abroad program. ROTC: Army (c), Air Force (c).

Entrance Requirements: Options: electronic application, international baccalaureate accepted. Required: essay, high school transcript, minimum 3 high school GPA, SAT or ACT. Recommended: SAT Subject Tests. Entrance: very difficult. Application deadline: 11/30. Notification: continuous until 2/1. SAT Reasoning Test deadline: 7/15. SAT Subject Test deadline: 7/15. Transfer credits accepted: Yes. Applicants placed on waiting list: 3,694. Waitlisted applicants offered admission: 0.

Costs Per Year: Application fee: $70. State resident tuition: $11,220 full-time. Nonresident tuition: $34,098 full-time. Mandatory fees: $1740 full-time. Full-time tuition and fees vary according to course load. College room and board: $13,200. Room and board charges vary according to board plan and housing facility.

Collegiate Environment: Orientation program. Drama-theater group, choral group, student-run newspaper, radio station. Social organizations: 350 open to all; national fraternities, national sororities, local fraternities, local sororities, coed fraternities; 1% of eligible men and 1% of eligible women are members. Most popular organizations: Associated Students, Student Alumni Association, Health Careers Organization. Major annual events: HEAT Festival, Homecoming, Annual Block Party. Student services: legal services, health clinic, personal-psychological counseling, women's center. Campus security: 24-hour emergency response devices and patrols, student patrols, late night transport-escort service, controlled dormitory access. 6,045 undergraduates lived in college housing during 2012-13. Freshmen guaranteed college housing. Option: coed housing available. Tomas Rivera Library plus 4 others with 3.3 million books, 2.3 million microform titles, 128,594 serials, 61,553 audiovisual materials, an OPAC, and a Web page. Operations spending for the previous fiscal year: $14.2 million. 556 computers available on campus for general student use. Computer purchase/lease plans available. A campuswide network can be accessed from student residence rooms and from off campus. Students can access the following: online class registration, online viewing of financial information. Staffed computer lab on campus provides training in use of computers, software, and the Internet.

Community Environment: Population 290,000. A suburban area 60 miles east of Los Angeles with a temperate climate, Riverside is an important residential and commercial center in Riverside County. This city launched the navel orange industry in southern California. Major transportation facilities are available. Riverside has churches of the major denominations, a library, hospitals and all public health services. Recreational activities include all water sports. Beaches, desert and mountain/ski resort areas are nearby.

■ **UNIVERSITY OF CALIFORNIA, SAN DIEGO**
9500 Gilman Dr.
La Jolla, CA 92093
Tel: (858)534-2230
E-mail: admissionsreply@ucsd.edu
Web Site: www.ucsd.edu/

Description: State-supported, university, coed. Part of University of California System. Awards bachelor's, master's, and doctoral degrees. Founded 1959. Setting: 1,976-acre suburban campus with easy access to San Diego. Research spending for the previous fiscal year: $387.9 million. Total enrollment: 26,723. Faculty: 1,144 (943 full-time, 201 part-time). Student-undergrad faculty ratio is 19:1. 47,365 applied, 42% were admitted. 100% from top 10% of their high school class, 100% from top quarter, 100% from top half. 49 National Merit Scholars. Full-time: 22,205 students, 52% women, 48% men. Part-time: 313 students, 49% women, 51% men. 3% from out-of-state. 4% 25 or older, 8% transferred in. Retention: 93% of full-time freshmen returned the following year. Academic areas with the most degrees conferred: social sciences; biological/life sciences; engineering. Core. ESL program, services for LD students, advanced placement, accelerated degree program, self-designed majors, freshman honors college, honors program, independent study, double major, summer session for credit, co-op programs and internships, graduate courses open to undergrads. Off campus study at Dartmouth College, Spelman College, Morehouse College. Study abroad program. ROTC: Army (c).

Entrance Requirements: Options: electronic application, international baccalaureate accepted. Required: essay, high school transcript, minimum 2.8 high school GPA, SAT or ACT, ACT Assessment with Writing or SAT Reasoning Test, plus two SAT Subject Tests. Required for some: minimum 3.4 high school GPA. Entrance: very difficult. Application deadline: 11/30. Notification: 3/31. Preference given to state residents.

Costs Per Year: Application fee: $60. State resident tuition: $12,192 full-time. Nonresident tuition: $35,070 full-time. Mandatory fees: $1042 full-time. College room and board: $11,924. Room and board charges vary according to board plan and housing facility.

Collegiate Environment: Orientation program. Drama-theater group, choral group, marching band, student-run newspaper, radio station. Social organizations: national fraternities, national sororities; 10% of eligible men and 10% of eligible women are members. Most popular organizations: cultural organizations, recreational clubs, service organizations, spiritual/religious organizations. Major annual events: Sun God Festival, Winterfest, Fall Festival on the Green. Student services: legal services, health clinic, personal-psychological counseling, women's center. Campus security: 24-hour emergency response devices and patrols, student patrols, late night transport-escort service, crime prevention programs. Geisel Library plus 9 others with an OPAC. Operations spending for the previous fiscal year: $20.4 million. 1,500 computers available on campus for general student use. A campuswide network can be accessed from student residence rooms and from off campus. Students can access the following: online class registration. Staffed computer lab on campus.

Community Environment: La Jolla is within the corporate limits of San Diego and is a popular resort with a rocky coast and fine beaches. San Diego lies along and around one of the world's ten most beautiful protected natural harbors, and has a very special seawashed, air-conditioned climate. The maximum average temperature of 70.8 degrees and a minimum of 55.4 degrees makes the climate very special. Amtrak, buses, a trolley system, and major airlines all serve the area. The city is a major center for biomedical, high technology electronics and wireless communication industries. Other industries include shipbuilding, shipping, and fishing. San Diego County is the country's largest producer of avocados. San Diego has a large public library system, hospitals, museums, galleries, and churches. Within San Diego County are numerous golf courses, all aquatic sports, hiking, camping, mountain climbing, horseback riding, snow sports, fishing and hunting. Sea World, the world-famous San Diego Zoo and Wild Animal Park, Balboa Park, and the Anza Borrego Desert State Park also provide recreational opportunities. This is the home of the 1994 AFC Champion San Diego Chargers, the professional football team, and the 1998 National League Champion San Diego Padres professional baseball team. Known as a winter playground, it has 70 miles of beautiful beaches. Population of San Diego is 1,255,500, with a greater metropolitan area population of 2,853,00.

■ **UNIVERSITY OF CALIFORNIA, SANTA BARBARA**
1210 Cheadle Hall
Santa Barbara, CA 93106-2014
Tel: (805)893-8000
E-mail: admissions@sa.ucsb.edu
Web Site: www.ucsb.edu/

Description: State-supported, university, coed. Part of University of California System. Awards bachelor's, master's, and doctoral degrees and post-master's certificates. Founded 1909. Setting: 989-acre suburban campus. Endowment: $109 million. Research spending for the previous fiscal year: $169.2 million. Educational spending for the previous fiscal year: $35,782 per student. Total enrollment: 21,927. Faculty: 1,050 (880 full-time, 170 part-time). Student-undergrad faculty ratio is 17:1. 54,762 applied, 44% were admitted. 96% from top 10% of their high school class, 98% from top quarter, 100% from top half. Full-time: 18,715 students, 53% women, 47% men. Part-time: 262 students, 43% women, 57% men. Students come from 50 states and territories, 76 other countries, 3% from out-of-state. 1% American Indian or Alaska Native, non-Hispanic/Latino; 24% Hispanic/Latino; 4% African American, non-Hispanic/Latino; 23% Asian, non-Hispanic/Latino; 0.2% Native Hawaiian or other Pacific Islander, non-Hispanic/Latino; 3% international. 2% 25 or older, 37% live on campus, 9% transferred in. Retention: 91% of full-time freshmen returned the following year. Academic areas with the most degrees conferred: social sciences; biological/life sciences; psychology. Core. Calendar: plus 6-week summer term. ESL program, services for LD students, advanced placement, accelerated degree program, self-designed majors, honors program, independent study, double major, summer session for credit, co-op programs and internships, graduate courses open to undergrads. Off campus study at other campuses of the University of California System. Study abroad program. ROTC: Army, Air Force (c).

Entrance Requirements: Options: electronic application, international baccalaureate accepted. Required: essay, high school transcript, SAT or ACT. Recommended: SAT Subject Tests. Required for some: interview. Entrance: very difficult. Application deadline: 11/30. Notification: 3/15. SAT Reasoning Test deadline: 1/31. SAT Subject Test deadline: 1/31. Transfer credits accepted: Yes. Applicants placed on waiting list: 3,262. Wait-listed applicants offered admission: 330.

Costs Per Year: Application fee: $70. State resident tuition: $12,192 full-time. Nonresident tuition: $34,213 full-time. Mandatory fees: $2844 full-time. College room and board: $13,275. Room and board charges vary according to board plan and housing facility.

Collegiate Environment: Orientation program. Drama-theater group, choral group, student-run newspaper, radio station. Social organizations: 421 open to all; national fraternities, national sororities, local fraternities, local sororities; 8% of eligible men and 12% of eligible women are members. Major annual event: Extravaganza (spring concert with national acts). Student services: legal services, health clinic, personal-psychological counseling, women's center. Campus security: 24-hour emergency response devices and patrols, student patrols, late night transport-escort service, controlled dormitory access. 6,300 college housing spaces available. Freshmen given priority for college housing. On-campus residence required in freshman year. Option: coed housing available. Davidson Library plus 1 other with 2.9 million books, 3.8 million microform titles, 92,139 serials, 5.5 million audiovisual materials, an OPAC, and a Web page. Operations spending for the previous fiscal year: $16.3 million. 700 computers available on campus for general student use. A campuswide network can be accessed from student residence rooms and from off campus. Students can access the following: online class registration. Staffed computer lab on campus provides training in use of computers, software, and the Internet.

Community Environment: The University is located in Goleta, a suburb of Santa Barbara. Santa Barbara is a county seat, the largest city between Los Angeles and San Francisco, and is known as the"Riviera of the Pacific." The city lies at the foot of the Santa Ynez Mountains, facing the Pacific Ocean. The climate is moderate, and the temperature varies only 7 degrees in summer and winter. All modes of transportation serve the area, and hotel and motel accommodations are numerous. Santa Barbara has all the community facilities plus many points of interest, a planetarium, botanic garden, natural history, art, historical museums, and more. The annual horse show, Old Spanish Days, August Fiesta, Semana Nautica (Marine sports week), and flower shows are the highlights of the year. Active music organizations and the Symphony Orchestra are an important part of the cultural life of the city. Recreational facilities include golf courses, tennis courts, water sports at the beach, and many other activities.

■ **UNIVERSITY OF CALIFORNIA, SANTA CRUZ**

1156 High St.
Santa Cruz, CA 95064
Tel: (831)459-0111
Fax: (831)459-4452
E-mail: admissions@ucsc.edu
Web Site: www.ucsc.edu/

Description: State-supported, university, coed. Part of University of California System. Awards bachelor's, master's, and doctoral degrees. Founded 1965. Setting: 2,000-acre small town campus with easy access to San Francisco, San Jose. Endowment: $121.9 million. Research spending for the previous fiscal year: $108.2 million. Total enrollment: 17,404. Faculty: 804 (548 full-time, 256 part-time). Student-undergrad faculty ratio is 18:1. 33,142 applied, 61% were admitted. 96% from top 10% of their high school class, 100% from top quarter, 100% from top half. Full-time: 15,721 students, 53% women, 47% men. Part-time: 257 students, 58% women, 42% men. Students come from 41 states and territories, 14 other countries, 2% from out-of-state. 0.3% American Indian or Alaska Native, non-Hispanic/Latino; 28% Hispanic/Latino; 2% African American, non-Hispanic/Latino; 21% Asian, non-Hispanic/Latino; 0.2% Native Hawaiian or other Pacific Islander, non-Hispanic/Latino; 0.3% international. 4% 25 or older, 45% live on campus, 7% transferred in. Retention: 89% of full-time freshmen returned the following year. Academic areas with the most degrees conferred: social sciences; biological/life sciences; psychology. Core. Services for LD students, advanced placement, accelerated degree program, self-designed majors, freshman honors college, honors program, independent study, double major, summer session for credit, co-op programs and internships, graduate courses open to undergrads. Off campus study at other campuses of the University of California System, University of New Hampshire, University of New Mexico. Study abroad program. ROTC: Army (c), Naval (c), Air Force (c).

Entrance Requirements: Options: electronic application, international baccalaureate accepted. Required: essay, high school transcript, minimum high school GPA of 3.0 for California residents, 3.4 for non-residents, SAT or ACT. Entrance: very difficult. Application deadline: 11/30. Notification: 3/31. Preference given to qualified state residents. Transfer credits accepted: Yes. Applicants placed on waiting list: 2,173. Wait-listed applicants offered admission: 0.

Costs Per Year: Application fee: $70. State resident tuition: $12,192 full-time. Nonresident tuition: $35,070 full-time. Mandatory fees: $1225 full-time. College room and board: $14,856. Room and board charges vary according to board plan and housing facility.

Collegiate Environment: Orientation program. Drama-theater group, choral group, student-run newspaper, radio station. Social organizations: 150 open to all; national fraternities, national sororities, local fraternities, local sororities; 1% of eligible men and 1% of eligible women are members. Most popular organizations: Filipino Student Association, Movimiento Estudiantil Chicano de Aztlan, CSA (Chinese Student Association), A/BSA (African/Black Student Alliance), SEC (Student Environmental Center). Major annual events: Martin Luther King Jr. Convocation, Multicultural Festival, Banana Slug Spring Fair. Student services: health clinic, personal-psychological counseling, women's center. Campus security: 24-hour emergency response devices and patrols, late night transport-escort service, controlled dormitory

access, evening main gate security, campus police force and fire station. 7,880 college housing spaces available; 7,382 were occupied in 2012-13. Freshmen guaranteed college housing. Options: coed, men-only, women-only housing available. UCSC Library with 2.3 million books, 68,757 microform titles, 56,757 audiovisual materials, an OPAC, and a Web page. Operations spending for the previous fiscal year: $13.4 million.

Community Environment: The City of Santa Cruz, population 54,760, and other nearby communities are easily accessible via the local bus system. The area has long been a popular resort because of its recreational offerings, which include 10 miles of beaches, a widely varied coastal zone, and the densely wooded Santa Cruz Mountains. The temperate climate is characterized by sunny summer days with foggy mornings and rain in the winter. Many of the city's Victorian houses have been restored in recent years, and its main shopping street has been revitalized. For its size, Santa Cruz has a remarkable variety of outstanding restaurants in all price ranges. Numerous cultural activities are sponsored by the University, the local junior college, and community organizations.

■ **UNIVERSITY OF LA VERNE**

1950 Third St.
La Verne, CA 91750-4443
Tel: (909)593-3511; Free: 800-876-4858
Fax: (909)593-0965
E-mail: admissions@ulv.edu
Web Site: www.laverne.edu/

Description: Independent, university, coed. Awards associate, bachelor's, master's, and doctoral degrees (also offers continuing education program with significant enrollment not reflected in profile). Founded 1891. Setting: 38-acre suburban campus with easy access to Los Angeles. Endowment: $37.6 million. Total enrollment: 4,973. Faculty: 665 (225 full-time, 440 part-time). Student-undergrad faculty ratio is 12:1. 6,989 applied, 39% were admitted. 24% from top 10% of their high school class, 61% from top quarter, 88% from top half. Full-time: 2,413 students, 61% women, 39% men. Part-time: 86 students, 45% women, 55% men. Students come from 18 states and territories, 9 other countries, 4% from out-of-state. 0.3% American Indian or Alaska Native, non-Hispanic/Latino; 50% Hispanic/Latino; 5% African American, non-Hispanic/Latino; 6% Asian, non-Hispanic/Latino; 0.4% Native Hawaiian or other Pacific Islander, non-Hispanic/Latino; 4% international. 2% 25 or older, 33% live on campus, 9% transferred in. Retention: 85% of full-time freshmen returned the following year. Academic areas with the most degrees conferred: business/marketing; social sciences; liberal arts/general studies. Core. Calendar: 4-1-4. Academic remediation for entering students, ESL program, services for LD students, advanced placement, accelerated degree program, self-designed majors, freshman honors college, honors program, independent study, distance learning, double major, summer session for credit, part-time degree program, adult/continuing education programs, internships, graduate courses open to undergrads. Off campus study. Study abroad program. ROTC: Army (c).

Entrance Requirements: Options: electronic application, deferred admission, international baccalaureate accepted. Required: essay, high school transcript, 2 recommendations, SAT or ACT. Recommended: interview. Entrance: moderately difficult. Application deadline: 2/1. Notification: continuous. SAT Reasoning Test deadline: 8/31. SAT Subject Test deadline: 8/31. Transfer credits accepted: Yes.

Costs Per Year: Application fee: $50. Comprehensive fee: $46,910 includes full-time tuition ($33,628), mandatory fees ($1372), and college room and board ($11,910). College room only: $6100. Full-time tuition and fees vary according to degree level and location. Room and board charges vary according to board plan and housing facility. Part-time tuition: $979 per unit. Part-time tuition varies according to degree level and location.

Collegiate Environment: Orientation program. Drama-theater group, choral group, student-run newspaper, radio station. Social organizations: 50 open to all; national fraternities, national sororities, local sororities; 5% of eligible men and 13% of eligible women are members. Most popular organizations: Latino Student Forum, Black Student Union, Associated Students of La Verne, Alpha Kappa Psi, Voices in Action. Major annual events: Homecoming, International Fair, Spring Formal. Student services: health clinic, personal-psychological counseling. Campus security: 24-hour emergency response devices and patrols, late night transport-escort service, controlled dormitory access. 837 college housing spaces available; 819 were occupied in 2012-13. Freshmen guaranteed college housing. Options: coed, men-only, women-only housing available. Wilson Library with 181,576 books, 1,068 microform titles, 37,287 serials, 1,640 audiovisual materials, an OPAC, and a Web page. 520 computers available on campus for general student use. A campuswide network can be accessed from student residence rooms and from off campus. Students can access the following: online class registration, MyLaVerne (online). Staffed computer lab on campus provides training in use of computers, software, and the Internet.

Community Environment: La Verne is a suburban area approximately 35 miles east of Los Angeles, Pasadena, Beverly Hills and Hollywood. MetroLink railroad system and the Metropolitan Bus Lines provide access in and out of Los Angeles. La Verne is overshadowed on the north by the snowcapped San Gabriel Mountains, which rise to a height of 10,000 feet. La Verne is within easy driving distance of the beaches and mountains which provide both summer and winter recreational activities.

■ UNIVERSITY OF THE PACIFIC

3601 Pacific Ave.
Stockton, CA 95211-0197
Tel: (209)946-2344
Fax: (209)946-2413
E-mail: admissions@pacific.edu
Web Site: www.pacific.edu/

Description: Independent, university, coed. Awards bachelor's, master's, and doctoral degrees. Founded 1851. Setting: 175-acre suburban campus with easy access to Sacramento. Total enrollment: 6,652. Faculty: 812 (453 full-time, 359 part-time). Student-undergrad faculty ratio is 13:1. 22,972 applied, 38% were admitted. 44% from top 10% of their high school class, 75% from top quarter, 93% from top half. Full-time: 3,761 students, 53% women, 47% men. Part-time: 106 students, 46% women, 54% men. 8% from out-of-state. 1% American Indian or Alaska Native, non-Hispanic/Latino; 19% Hispanic/Latino; 3% African American, non-Hispanic/Latino; 32% Asian, non-Hispanic/Latino; 0.2% Native Hawaiian or other Pacific Islander, non-Hispanic/Latino; 5% international. 7% 25 or older, 46% live on campus, 7% transferred in. Retention: 82% of full-time freshmen returned the following year. Academic areas with the most degrees conferred: business/marketing; biological/life sciences; health professions and related sciences. Core. Calendar: semesters. Academic remediation for entering students, ESL program, services for LD students, advanced placement, accelerated degree program, self-designed majors, honors program, independent study, double major, summer session for credit, part-time degree program, co-op programs and internships. ROTC: Air Force (c).

Entrance Requirements: Options: electronic application, early action, international baccalaureate accepted. Required: essay, high school transcript, minimum 2.5 high school GPA, 1 recommendation, SAT or ACT. Recommended: minimum 3 high school GPA, SAT Subject Tests. Required for some: audition for music program. Entrance: moderately difficult. Notification: continuous. SAT Reasoning Test deadline: 1/31. Applicants placed on waiting list: 1,840. Wait-listed applicants offered admission: 45.

Costs Per Year: Comprehensive fee: $50,358 includes full-time tuition ($37,800), mandatory fees ($520), and college room and board ($12,038). Room and board charges vary according to board plan and housing facility.

Collegiate Environment: Orientation program. Drama-theater group, choral group, student-run newspaper, radio station. Social organizations: national fraternities, national sororities, local fraternities. Student services: legal services, health clinic, personal-psychological counseling. Campus security: 24-hour emergency response devices and patrols, late night transport-escort service, controlled dormitory access. Freshmen guaranteed college housing. On-campus residence required through sophomore year. Option: coed housing available. University of the Pacific Library plus 1 other with an OPAC and a Web page.

Community Environment: Stockton, population 286,900, is located 80 miles east of San Francisco and 40 miles south of Sacramento. The city is located in a rich agricultural region. All major forms of transportation serve the area. Stockton has 110 churches, general hospitals, a library, museum, and fine shopping facilities. Recreational facilities include theaters, parks, playgrounds, stadiums, a large events center, and a baseball stadium. The city is only a short drive away from facilities for water skiing, sailing, and golf, and the Sierra Nevada mountain range is also nearby.

■ UNIVERSITY OF PHOENIX–BAY AREA CAMPUS

3590 N First Sreet
San Jose, CA 95134-1805
Tel: (925)416-4100; Free: 866-766-0766
Web Site: www.phoenix.edu/

Description: Proprietary, comprehensive, coed. Awards bachelor's and master's degrees. Setting: urban campus. Total enrollment: 2,240. Faculty: 318 (29 full-time, 289 part-time). Full-time: 1,676 students, 64% women,

36% men. 82% 25 or older. Core. Calendar: continuous. Services for LD students, advanced placement, accelerated degree program, independent study, distance learning, external degree program, adult/continuing education programs, graduate courses open to undergrads.

Entrance Requirements: Open admission. Options: electronic application, deferred admission. Required: 1 recommendation. Required for some: high school transcript. Entrance: noncompetitive. Application deadline: Rolling.

Collegiate Environment: Campus security: late night transport-escort service. University Library with 16,781 serials, an OPAC, and a Web page. Operations spending for the previous fiscal year: $6.8 million.

■ UNIVERSITY OF PHOENIX–CENTRAL VALLEY CAMPUS

45 River Park Pl. W
Ste. 101
Fresno, CA 93720-1562
Free: 866-766-0766
Web Site: www.phoenix.edu/

Description: Proprietary, comprehensive, coed. Awards bachelor's and master's degrees. Founded 2004. Setting: urban campus. Total enrollment: 2,235. Faculty: 272 (31 full-time, 241 part-time). Full-time: 1,928 students, 71% women, 29% men. 3% from out-of-state. 73% 25 or older. Academic areas with the most degrees conferred: business/marketing; public administration and social services; homeland security, law enforcement, firefighting, and protective services. Core. Services for LD students, advanced placement, accelerated degree program, independent study, distance learning, graduate courses open to undergrads.

Entrance Requirements: Open admission. Options: electronic application, deferred admission. Required: 1 recommendation. Required for some: high school transcript. Entrance: noncompetitive. Application deadline: Rolling.

Collegiate Environment: Campus security: late night transport-escort service.

■ UNIVERSITY OF PHOENIX–SACRAMENTO VALLEY CAMPUS

2890 Gateway Oaks Dr.
Ste. 200
Sacramento, CA 95833-3632
Tel: (916)923-2107; Free: 866-766-0766
Fax: (916)923-3914
Web Site: www.phoenix.edu/

Description: Proprietary, comprehensive, coed. Awards bachelor's and master's degrees. Founded 1993. Setting: urban campus. Total enrollment: 3,842. Faculty: 518 (49 full-time, 469 part-time). Full-time: 3,162 students, 69% women, 31% men. 81% 25 or older. Core. Calendar: continuous. Services for LD students, advanced placement, accelerated degree program, independent study, distance learning, external degree program, adult/continuing education programs, graduate courses open to undergrads.

Entrance Requirements: Open admission. Options: electronic application, deferred admission. Required: 1 recommendation. Required for some: high school transcript. Entrance: noncompetitive. Application deadline: Rolling.

Collegiate Environment: Campus security: late night transport-escort service. University Library with 16,781 serials, an OPAC, and a Web page. Operations spending for the previous fiscal year: $6.8 million.

■ UNIVERSITY OF PHOENIX–SAN DIEGO CAMPUS

3870 Murphy Canyon Rd.
San Diego, CA 92123
Tel: (800)473-4346; Free: 866-766-0766
Fax: (858)576-0032
Web Site: www.phoenix.edu/

Description: Proprietary, comprehensive, coed. Awards bachelor's and master's degrees. Founded 1988. Setting: urban campus. Total enrollment: 3,212. Faculty: 399 (30 full-time, 369 part-time). Full-time: 2,500 students, 59% women, 41% men. 79% 25 or older. Core. Calendar: continuous. Services for LD students, advanced placement, accelerated degree program, independent study, distance learning, external degree program, adult/continuing education programs, graduate courses open to undergrads.

Entrance Requirements: Open admission. Options: electronic application, deferred admission. Required: 1 recommendation. Required for some: high school transcript. Entrance: noncompetitive. Application deadline: Rolling.

Collegiate Environment: Campus security: late night transport-escort service. University Library with 16,781 serials, an OPAC, and a Web page. Operations spending for the previous fiscal year: $6.8 million.

■ UNIVERSITY OF PHOENIX–SOUTHERN CALIFORNIA CAMPUS

3150 Bristol St.
Ste. 340
Costa Mesa, CA 92626
Tel: (800)GO-TO-UOP; Free: 866-766-0766
Web Site: www.phoenix.edu/

Description: Proprietary, comprehensive, coed. Awards bachelor's and master's degrees. Founded 1980. Setting: urban campus. Total enrollment: 11,780. Faculty: 1,340 (64 full-time, 1,276 part-time). Full-time: 9,196 students, 67% women, 33% men. 80% 25 or older. Academic areas with the most degrees conferred: business/marketing; public administration and social services; computer and information sciences. Core. Calendar: continuous. Services for LD students, advanced placement, accelerated degree program, independent study, distance learning, external degree program, adult/continuing education programs, graduate courses open to undergrads.

Entrance Requirements: Open admission. Options: electronic application, deferred admission. Required: 1 recommendation. Required for some: high school transcript. Entrance: noncompetitive. Application deadline: Rolling.

Collegiate Environment: Campus security: late night transport-escort service. University Library with 16,781 serials, an OPAC, and a Web page. Operations spending for the previous fiscal year: $6.8 million.

■ UNIVERSITY OF REDLANDS

1200 E Colton Ave.
Redlands, CA 92373-0999
Tel: (909)793-2121; Free: 800-455-5064
Fax: (909)335-4089
E-mail: admissions@redlands.edu
Web Site: www.redlands.edu/

Description: Independent, comprehensive, coed. Awards bachelor's, master's, and doctoral degrees and post-master's certificates. Founded 1907. Setting: 140-acre small town campus with easy access to Los Angeles. Endowment: $103.8 million. Educational spending for the previous fiscal year: $10,200 per student. Total enrollment: 4,956. Faculty: 492 (198 full-time, 294 part-time). Student-undergrad faculty ratio is 14:1. 4,501 applied, 69% were admitted. 28% from top 10% of their high school class, 64% from top quarter, 91% from top half. Full-time: 2,611 students, 57% women, 43% men. Part-time: 749 students, 52% women, 48% men. Students come from 43 states and territories, 8 other countries, 24% from out-of-state. 1% American Indian or Alaska Native, non-Hispanic/Latino; 25% Hispanic/Latino; 5% African American, non-Hispanic/Latino; 4% Asian, non-Hispanic/Latino; 1% Native Hawaiian or other Pacific Islander, non-Hispanic/Latino; 1% international. 2% 25 or older, 69% live on campus, 2% transferred in. Retention: 91% of full-time freshmen returned the following year. Academic areas with the most degrees conferred: business/marketing; social sciences; liberal arts/general studies. Core. Calendar: 4-4-1. Academic remediation for entering students, services for LD students, advanced placement, self-designed majors, freshman honors college, honors program, independent study, double major, part-time degree program, adult/continuing education programs, internships, graduate courses open to undergrads. Off campus study at members of the Association for Innovation in Higher Education, American University. Study abroad program. ROTC: Army (c), Air Force (c).

Entrance Requirements: Options: electronic application, deferred admission, international baccalaureate accepted. Required: essay, high school transcript, 2 recommendations, SAT or ACT. Recommended: interview. Entrance: moderately difficult. Application deadline: Rolling. Notification: continuous until 12/1. SAT Reasoning Test deadline: 4/1. Transfer credits accepted: Yes.

Costs Per Year: Application fee: $30. Comprehensive fee: $51,262 includes full-time tuition ($39,038), mandatory fees ($300), and college room and board ($11,924). Full-time tuition and fees vary according to program. Room and board charges vary according to board plan and housing facility. Part-time mandatory fees: $150 per term. Part-time fees vary according to course load and program.

Collegiate Environment: Orientation program. Drama-theater group, choral group, student-run newspaper, radio station. Social organizations: 120 open to all; local fraternities, local sororities; 10% of eligible men and 13% of eligible women are members. Most popular organizations: Associated Students, service organizations, cultural organizations, social awareness groups. Major annual events: Homecoming, Living on Common Ground Multicultural Festival, Convocation Lecture Series. Student services: health clinic, personal-psychological counseling, women's center. Campus security: 24-hour emergency response devices and patrols, student patrols, late night

transport-escort service, controlled dormitory access. 1,659 college housing spaces available; 1,645 were occupied in 2012-13. Freshmen guaranteed college housing. On-campus residence required through senior year. Options: coed, men-only, women-only housing available. Armacost Library with 305,207 books, 314,333 microform titles, 37,005 serials, 11,049 audiovisual materials, an OPAC, and a Web page. 804 computers available on campus for general student use. A campuswide network can be accessed from student residence rooms and from off campus. Students can access the following: online class registration. Staffed computer lab on campus provides training in use of computers, software, and the Internet.

Community Environment: Redlands is located halfway between Los Angeles and Palm Springs. It has a mild climate. The average yearly temperature is 65 degrees, and the average rainfall 14.45 inches. Once a principal center for navel oranges, the city has developed a more diversified economy in recent years. There are 60 churches, a community hospital and satellite clinics, a city library, fraternal and social service organizations, and museums. Buses serve the area, and the Ontario International Airport is 30 minutes from the campus. Through the Office of Community Service Learning and other organizations, students at the university have many opportunities to interact with community members.

■ UNIVERSITY OF SAN DIEGO

5998 Alcala Park
San Diego, CA 92110-2492
Tel: (619)260-4600; Free: 800-248-4873
E-mail: admissions@sandiego.edu
Web Site: www.sandiego.edu/

Description: Independent Roman Catholic, university, coed. Awards bachelor's, master's, and doctoral degrees and post-master's certificates. Founded 1949. Setting: 180-acre urban campus with easy access to San Diego. Endowment: $345.6 million. Total enrollment: 8,105. Faculty: 875 (400 full-time, 475 part-time). Student-undergrad faculty ratio is 16:1. 16,578 applied, 43% were admitted. 46% from top 10% of their high school class, 77% from top quarter, 95% from top half. Full-time: 5,269 students, 55% women, 45% men. Part-time: 188 students, 53% women, 47% men. Students come from 52 states and territories, 58 other countries, 38% from out-of-state. 0.3% American Indian or Alaska Native, non-Hispanic/Latino; 18% Hispanic/Latino; 3% African American, non-Hispanic/Latino; 6% Asian, non-Hispanic/Latino; 0.3% Native Hawaiian or other Pacific Islander, non-Hispanic/Latino; 6% international. 5% 25 or older, 45% live on campus, 7% transferred in. Retention: 90% of full-time freshmen returned the following year. Academic areas with the most degrees conferred: business/marketing; social sciences; communication/journalism. Core. Calendar: 4-1-4. ESL program, services for LD students, advanced placement, honors program, independent study, double major, summer session for credit, part-time degree program, internships. Study abroad program. ROTC: Army (c), Naval, Air Force (c).

Entrance Requirements: Options: electronic application, deferred admission, international baccalaureate accepted. Required: essay, high school transcript, 1 recommendation, SAT or ACT. Entrance: very difficult. Application deadline: 12/15. Notification: 4/1. SAT Reasoning Test deadline: 1/15. Transfer credits accepted: Yes. Applicants placed on waiting list: 2,382. Waitlisted applicants offered admission: 457.

Costs Per Year: Application fee: $55. Comprehensive fee: $53,302 includes full-time tuition ($40,900), mandatory fees ($492), and college room and board ($11,910). Room and board charges vary according to board plan and housing facility. Part-time tuition: $1410 per unit. Part-time tuition varies according to course load.

Collegiate Environment: Orientation program. Drama-theater group, choral group, student-run newspaper, radio station. Social organizations: 119 open to all; national fraternities, national sororities; 20% of eligible men and 32% of eligible women are members. Most popular organizations: Panhellenic Council, Interfraternity Council, Residence Hall Association, Kappa Kappa Gamma Sorority, Accounting Society. Major annual events: Alcala Bazaar (clubs and organizations fair), major concert, Homecoming. Student services: legal services, health clinic, personal-psychological counseling, women's center. Campus security: 24-hour emergency response devices and patrols, late night transport-escort service, controlled dormitory access. 2,500 college housing spaces available; 2,450 were occupied in 2012-13. Freshmen guaranteed college housing. On-campus residence required in freshman year. Options: coed, men-only, women-only housing available. Helen K. and James S. Copley Library plus 1 other with 1 million books, 1.2 million microform titles, 38,368 serials, 16,860 audiovisual materials, and an OPAC. Operations spending for the previous fiscal year: $7.1 million. 946

computers available on campus for general student use. Computer purchase/lease plans available. A campuswide network can be accessed from student residence rooms and from off campus. Students can access the following: online class registration. Staffed computer lab on campus provides training in use of computers, software, and the Internet.

Community Environment: Known for many reasons as"America's Finest City," San Diego has an almost perfect climate with warm, sunny days and cool evenings. Throughout the year, students can take advantage of San Diego's many outdoor recreational and cultural opportunities. The museums of Balboa Park, the Old Globe Theatre, the Zoo, Sea World, the beaches, the opera, and downtown San Diego and La Jolla are only minutes away. The rapidly developing economy of Greater San Diego provides varied employment opportunities for the USD graduate.

■ **UNIVERSITY OF SAN FRANCISCO**
2130 Fulton St.
San Francisco, CA 94117-1080
Tel: (415)422-5555; Free: 800-CALL-USF
Fax: (415)422-2217
E-mail: admissions@usfca.edu
Web Site: www.usfca.edu/
Description: Independent Roman Catholic (Jesuit), university, coed. Awards bachelor's, master's, and doctoral degrees and post-master's certificates. Founded 1855. Setting: 55-acre urban campus. Endowment: $206.5 million. Research spending for the previous fiscal year: $3.2 million. Educational spending for the previous fiscal year: $29,637 per student. Total enrollment: 10,017. Faculty: 1,043 (430 full-time, 613 part-time). Student-undergrad faculty ratio is 15:1. 11,223 applied, 69% were admitted. 26% from top 10% of their high school class, 59% from top quarter, 91% from top half. Full-time: 6,077 students, 63% women, 37% men. Part-time: 267 students, 53% women, 47% men. Students come from 51 states and territories, 67 other countries, 20% from out-of-state. 0.3% American Indian or Alaska Native, non-Hispanic/Latino; 19% Hispanic/Latino; 3% African American, non-Hispanic/Latino; 19% Asian, non-Hispanic/Latino; 0.4% Native Hawaiian or other Pacific Islander, non-Hispanic/Latino; 16% international. 5% 25 or older, 34% live on campus, 7% transferred in. Retention: 88% of full-time freshmen returned the following year. Academic areas with the most degrees conferred: business/marketing; social sciences; psychology; health professions and related sciences. Core. Calendar: 4-1-4. ESL program, services for LD students, advanced placement, self-designed majors, honors program, independent study, distance learning, double major, summer session for credit, part-time degree program, external degree program, adult/continuing education programs, co-op programs and internships, graduate courses open to undergrads. Off campus study at American University, Jackson State University. Study abroad program. ROTC: Army, Naval (c), Air Force (c).
Entrance Requirements: Options: electronic application, early action, deferred admission, international baccalaureate accepted. Required: essay, high school transcript, 1 recommendation, Test scores are required for first-year applicants, SAT or ACT, Sat Writing and Reading are used for Core Curriculum placement in the Foundation of Communication Core requirements. Recommended: minimum 3 high school GPA. Entrance: moderately difficult. Application deadlines: 1/15, 11/15 for early action. Notification: continuous, 12/31 for early action. SAT Reasoning Test deadline: 1/2. Transfer credits accepted: Yes. Applicants placed on waiting list: 618. Waitlisted applicants offered admission: 4. Early action applicants: 3,051. Early action applicants admitted: 1,754.
Costs Per Year: Application fee: $55. Comprehensive fee: $53,284 includes full-time tuition ($39,840), mandatory fees ($454), and college room and board ($12,990). College room only: $8730. Full-time tuition and fees vary according to course load, degree level, program, and reciprocity agreements. Room and board charges vary according to housing facility. Part-time tuition: $1415 per credit. Part-time mandatory fees: $454 per term. Part-time tuition and fees vary according to course load, degree level, program, and reciprocity agreements.
Collegiate Environment: Orientation program. Drama-theater group, choral group, student-run newspaper, radio station. Social organizations: 102 open to all; national fraternities, national sororities, local fraternities, local sororities; 2% of eligible men and 2% of eligible women are members. Most popular organizations: student leadership, student media, College Players, sports. Major annual events: Homecoming, Founders' Week, Welcome Week. Student services: health clinic, personal-psychological counseling, women's center. Campus security: 24-hour emergency response devices and patrols, student patrols, late night transport-escort service, controlled

dormitory access. 2,400 college housing spaces available; 2,162 were occupied in 2012-13. Freshmen guaranteed college housing. On-campus residence required in freshman year. Options: coed, women-only housing available. Gleeson Library plus 2 others with 1.1 million books, 742,844 microform titles, 5,560 serials, an OPAC, and a Web page. Operations spending for the previous fiscal year: $3.3 million. 250 computers available on campus for general student use. Computer purchase/lease plans available. A campuswide network can be accessed from student residence rooms and from off campus. Students can access the following: online class registration. Staffed computer lab on campus provides training in use of computers, software, and the Internet.

Community Environment: The University of San Francisco is located in the heart of one the world's most dynamic cities. San Francisco's diversity and geographical compactness afford opportunities for community involvement and employment experiences that few other cities can match.

■ **UNIVERSITY OF SOUTHERN CALIFORNIA**
University Park Campus
Los Angeles, CA 90089
Tel: (213)740-2311
Fax: (213)740-6364
E-mail: admitusc@usc.edu
Web Site: www.usc.edu/
Description: Independent, university, coed. Awards bachelor's, master's, and doctoral degrees and post-master's certificates. Founded 1880. Setting: 229-acre urban campus with easy access to Los Angeles. Endowment: $3.5 billion. Total enrollment: 39,958. Faculty: 3,264 (1,768 full-time, 1,496 part-time). Student-undergrad faculty ratio is 9:1. 46,104 applied, 20% were admitted. 251 National Merit Scholars. Full-time: 17,619 students, 51% women, 49% men. Part-time: 697 students, 43% women, 57% men. Students come from 56 states and territories, 95 other countries, 32% from out-of-state. 0.2% American Indian or Alaska Native, non-Hispanic/Latino; 13% Hispanic/Latino; 4% African American, non-Hispanic/Latino; 23% Asian, non-Hispanic/Latino; 0.2% Native Hawaiian or other Pacific Islander, non-Hispanic/Latino; 12% international. 4% 25 or older, 38% live on campus, 9% transferred in. Retention: 97% of full-time freshmen returned the following year. Academic areas with the most degrees conferred: business/marketing; social sciences; visual and performing arts. Core. Calendar: semesters. ESL program, services for LD students, advanced placement, accelerated degree program, self-designed majors, freshman honors college, honors program, independent study, distance learning, double major, summer session for credit, part-time degree program, co-op programs and internships, graduate courses open to undergrads. Off campus study at Hebrew Union College-Jewish Institute of Religion, Howard University, American University. Study abroad program. ROTC: Army, Naval, Air Force.
Entrance Requirements: Options: electronic application, deferred admission, international baccalaureate accepted. Required: essay, high school transcript, SAT or ACT. Entrance: most difficult. Application deadlines: 1/10, 1/10 for nonresidents. Notification: 4/1, 4/1 for nonresidents. SAT Reasoning Test deadline: 2/15. SAT Subject Test deadline: 2/15. Transfer credits accepted: Yes.
Costs Per Year: Application fee: $80. One-time mandatory fee: $150. Comprehensive fee: $56,903 includes full-time tuition ($43,722), mandatory fees ($741), and college room and board ($12,440). College room only: $7340. Full-time tuition and fees vary according to program. Room and board charges vary according to board plan and housing facility. Part-time tuition: $1473 per unit. Part-time tuition varies according to course load and program.
Collegiate Environment: Orientation program. Drama-theater group, choral group, marching band, student-run newspaper, radio station. Social organizations: 725 open to all; national fraternities, national sororities, local fraternities, local sororities. Most popular organizations: Troy Camp, USC Helenes, Alpha Phi Omega, Student Bar Association, USC Accounting Society. Major annual events: CONQUEST, Welcome Week, Springfest. Student services: legal services, health clinic, personal-psychological counseling, women's center. Campus security: 24-hour emergency response devices and patrols, student patrols, late night transport-escort service, controlled dormitory access. 5,950 college housing spaces available; 5,880 were occupied in 2012-13. Freshmen guaranteed college housing. Option: coed housing available. Doheny Memorial Library plus 23 others with 4.8 million books, 6.6 million microform titles, 84,953 audiovisual materials, an OPAC, and a Web page. 2,000 computers available on campus for general student use. Computer purchase/lease plans available. A campuswide network can be accessed from student residence rooms and from off

campus. Students can access the following: online class registration, online degree progress, financial aid applications, document sharing, calendars, personal Web space, customizable Web portal, course management systems (including data and video). Staffed computer lab on campus (open 24 hours a day) provides training in use of computers, software, and the Internet.

Community Environment: Located in the heart of Los Angeles, USC exposes undergraduates to one of the world's great cosmopolitan centers. Students take advantage of this setting through internships with major corporations, new technology ventures, the entertainment industry, museums and galleries, non-profit organizations, and government agencies. Across the street from the campus in Exposition Park are museums, gardens, and the Memorial Coliseum. The nearby Figueroa Boulevard "Sports and Entertainment Corridor" includes the Shrine Auditorium, frequent host to the Grammy and Oscar events; the enormous Los Angeles Convention Center; the Staples Arena, which hosts the Lakers, Kings, and Clippers, and the 2000 Democratic Convention; and the Los Angeles Music Center, which offers world-class theatre, concerts, and opera. The campus is minutes away from the beaches of Santa Monica and Venice and also offers easy access to the hiking and bike trails of the Santa Monica Mountains. Local ski resorts are about a 90-minute drive from the campus.

■ **UNIVERSITY OF THE WEST**

1409 N Walnut Grove Ave.
Rosemead, CA 91770
Tel: (626)571-8811
Fax: (626)571-1413
E-mail: graceh@uwest.edu
Web Site: www.uwest.edu/

Description: Independent, comprehensive, coed. Awards bachelor's, master's, and doctoral degrees and post-master's certificates. Founded 1991. Setting: 10-acre suburban campus. Total enrollment: 212. Faculty: 62 (10 full-time, 52 part-time). Student-undergrad faculty ratio is 9:1. 235 applied, 85% were admitted. Full-time: 54 students, 56% women, 44% men. Part-time: 17 students, 59% women, 41% men. Students come from 5 states and territories, 14 other countries, 6% from out-of-state. 19% 25 or older, 35% live on campus. Academic areas with the most degrees conferred: business/marketing; liberal arts/general studies; English. Core. Calendar: semesters. ESL program, accelerated degree program, independent study, double major, summer session for credit, part-time degree program, adult/continuing education programs, co-op programs and internships, graduate courses open to undergrads.

Entrance Requirements: Options: electronic application, deferred admission, international baccalaureate accepted. Required: essay, high school transcript, minimum 2 high school GPA, 3 recommendations. Entrance: moderately difficult. Application deadlines: 6/15, 6/15 for nonresidents. Notification: 7/15, 7/15 for nonresidents. Transfer credits accepted: Yes.

Costs Per Year: Application fee: $50. One-time mandatory fee: $75. Comprehensive fee: $14,720 includes full-time tuition ($8400), mandatory fees ($250), and college room and board ($6070). Full-time tuition and fees vary according to course level, course load, degree level, and program. Room and board charges vary according to board plan and housing facility. Part-time tuition: $350 per credit hour. Part-time mandatory fees: $250 per term. Part-time tuition and fees vary according to course level, course load, degree level, and program.

Collegiate Environment: Orientation program. Social organizations: 10 open to all. Most popular organizations: Buddhawest Club, Music Club, Explorer Club, Badminton Club, Chaplaincy Club. Major annual events: Opening BBQ, Christmas Holiday celebration. Student services: personal-psychological counseling. Campus security: 24-hour patrols. University of the West Library plus 1 other with 84,398 books, 12,565 serials, 1,375 audiovisual materials, an OPAC, and a Web page. Operations spending for the previous fiscal year: $206,907. 501 computers available on campus for general student use. A campuswide network can be accessed from student residence rooms. Students can access the following: online class registration. Staffed computer lab on campus (open 24 hours a day) provides training in use of software.

■ **VANGUARD UNIVERSITY OF SOUTHERN CALIFORNIA**

55 Fair Dr.
Costa Mesa, CA 92626-9601
Tel: (714)556-3610; Free: 800-722-6279
Fax: (714)966-5460
E-mail: admissions@vanguard.edu

Web Site: www.vanguard.edu/

Description: Independent, comprehensive, coed, affiliated with Assemblies of God. Awards bachelor's and master's degrees. Founded 1920. Setting: 38-acre suburban campus with easy access to Los Angeles. Endowment: $5 million. Educational spending for the previous fiscal year: $6381 per student. Total enrollment: 2,197. Faculty: 203 (63 full-time, 140 part-time). Student-undergrad faculty ratio is 17:1. 787 applied, 79% were admitted. 21% from top 10% of their high school class, 25% from top quarter, 29% from top half. Full-time: 1,461 students, 63% women, 37% men. Part-time: 493 students, 68% women, 32% men. Students come from 37 states and territories, 13 other countries, 14% from out-of-state. 1% American Indian or Alaska Native, non-Hispanic/Latino; 26% Hispanic/Latino; 5% African American, non-Hispanic/Latino; 5% Asian, non-Hispanic/Latino; 0.4% Native Hawaiian or other Pacific Islander, non-Hispanic/Latino; 1% international. 9% 25 or older, 68% live on campus, 11% transferred in. Retention: 73% of full-time freshmen returned the following year. Academic areas with the most degrees conferred: business/marketing; psychology; communication/journalism. Core. Calendar: semesters. Services for LD students, advanced placement, accelerated degree program, independent study, double major, summer session for credit, part-time degree program, adult/continuing education programs, internships, graduate courses open to undergrads. Off campus study at Council for Christian Colleges and Universities, Los Angeles Film Studies Center. Study abroad program. ROTC: Air Force (c).

Entrance Requirements: Options: electronic application, early admission, early action, deferred admission, international baccalaureate accepted. Required: essay, high school transcript, minimum 2.8 high school GPA, 2 recommendations, SAT or ACT. Required for some: interview. Entrance: moderately difficult. Application deadlines: 1/15, 12/1 for early action. Notification: continuous until 3/1, 1/15 for early action. Preference given to Christians. SAT Reasoning Test deadline: 8/30. Early action applicants: 680. Early action applicants admitted: 480.

Costs Per Year: Application fee: $45. Comprehensive fee: $37,200 includes full-time tuition ($28,500) and college room and board ($8700). Full-time tuition varies according to course load. Room and board charges vary according to board plan and housing facility.

Collegiate Environment: Orientation program. Drama-theater group, choral group, student-run newspaper, radio station. Most popular organizations: local outreach, Global Missions, student organizations/clubs, choral groups. Major annual events: Harvest Party, All School Party, Mr. VU. Student services: personal-psychological counseling, women's center. Campus security: 24-hour emergency response devices and patrols, student patrols, late night transport-escort service. O. Cope Budge Library with 164,333 books, 13,870 microform titles, 17,342 serials, 6,023 audiovisual materials, an OPAC, and a Web page. Operations spending for the previous fiscal year: $554,554. 100 computers available on campus for general student use. A campuswide network can be accessed from student residence rooms and from off campus. Students can access the following: online class registration. Staffed computer lab on campus.

Community Environment: The college is adjacent to Newport Beach, the pleasure boat harbor of the West. See Orange Coast College.

■ **VENTURA COLLEGE**

4667 Telegraph Rd.
Ventura, CA 93003-3899
Tel: (805)654-6400
Fax: (805)654-6466
E-mail: sbricker@vcccd.net
Web Site: www.venturacollege.edu/

Description: State and locally supported, 2-year, coed. Part of California Community College System. Awards certificates, diplomas, transfer associate, and terminal associate degrees. Founded 1925. Setting: 103-acre suburban campus with easy access to Los Angeles. Total enrollment: 13,551. Faculty: 522 (136 full-time, 386 part-time). Student-undergrad faculty ratio is 26:1. 2,652 applied. 11% from out-of-state. Core. Calendar: semesters. Academic remediation for entering students, ESL program, services for LD students, advanced placement, independent study, summer session for credit, part-time degree program, adult/continuing education programs, internships.

Entrance Requirements: Open admission. Required: high school transcript. Entrance: noncompetitive. Application deadline: Rolling. Notification: continuous.

Collegiate Environment: Orientation program. Drama-theater group, choral group, student-run newspaper. Most popular organizations: Pan American Student Union, MECHA, Automotive Technology Club, Campus Christian

Fellowship, Asian-American Club. Major annual events: ASB Welcome Barbecue, Cinco de Mayo, Native American International Pow Wow. Student services: health clinic, personal-psychological counseling, women's center. Campus security: 24-hour emergency response devices and patrols, student patrols. Ventura College Library with 63,529 books, 341 serials, an OPAC, and a Web page. 500 computers available on campus for general student use. Students can access the following: online class registration. Staffed computer lab on campus.

Community Environment: Ventura is the county seat of Ventura County as well as one of the oldest settlements on the coast. The climate is pleasant and smog-free all year with rain during a few months in the winter and spring. The city is located in the South Central Coast Region, 63 miles northwest of Los Angeles and is served by the Southern Pacific Railroad, Greyhound Bus Lines, and various airlines. Community facilities include hospitals, libraries, churches, and many civic and service organizations. Other facilities include recreation centers, a golf course, and the county fair grounds. An extensive ocean coastline, forest reserves, and mountains all combine to make the area ideal for outdoor recreation.

■ **VICTOR VALLEY COLLEGE**
18422 Bear Valley Rd.
Victorville, CA 92395
Tel: (760)245-4271
Fax: (760)245-9745
E-mail: moong@vvc.edu
Web Site: www.vvc.edu/
Description: State-supported, 2-year, coed. Part of California Community College System. Awards certificates, diplomas, transfer associate, and terminal associate degrees. Founded 1961. Setting: 253-acre small town campus with easy access to Los Angeles. Total enrollment: 6,790. Faculty: 565 (123 full-time, 442 part-time). Student-undergrad faculty ratio is 27:1. Full-time: 2,668 students, 53% women, 47% men. Part-time: 4,122 students, 57% women, 43% men. 3% from out-of-state. 44% American Indian or Alaska Native, non-Hispanic/Latino; 0.5% Hispanic/Latino; 1% African American, non-Hispanic/Latino; 0.1% Asian, non-Hispanic/Latino; 0.3% Native Hawaiian or other Pacific Islander, non-Hispanic/Latino; 14% international. 34% 25 or older, 6% transferred in. Retention: 66% of full-time freshmen returned the following year. Core. Calendar: semesters. Academic remediation for entering students, ESL program, services for LD students, advanced placement, accelerated degree program, honors program, independent study, distance learning, double major, summer session for credit, part-time degree program, co-op programs and internships. Off campus study. Study abroad program.
Entrance Requirements: Open admission except for allied health programs. Entrance: noncompetitive. Application deadline: Rolling. Notification: continuous.
Costs Per Year: State resident tuition: $1104 full-time. Nonresident tuition: $4296 full-time.
Collegiate Environment: Orientation program. Drama-theater group, choral group, student-run newspaper. Most popular organizations: Black Student Union, Drama Club, rugby, Phi Theta Kappa. Major annual events: Back to School BBQ, MLK Day, Cinco de Mayo. Student services: health clinic, personal-psychological counseling. Campus security: 24-hour emergency response devices and patrols, late night transport-escort service, part-time trained security personnel. College housing not available. Learning Resource Center with an OPAC and a Web page.
Community Environment: Victorville is a suburban area with a dry temperate climate. Amtrak, Santa Fe and Union Pacific Railroads, and Greyhound bus lines serve the area. The town has a library, churches of major denominations, hospitals, major civic organizations, and shopping facilities. Part-time employment opportunities are good. Victorville is the distributing point for an irrigated agricultural area. The San Bernardino County Fair is held here each year around Labor Day.

■ **WEST COAST UNIVERSITY (ANAHEIM)**
1477 S Manchester Ave.
Anaheim, CA 92802
Tel: (714)782-1700
Web Site: westcoastuniversity.edu/
Description: Proprietary, 4-year, coed. Calendar: semesters.

■ **WEST COAST UNIVERSITY (NORTH HOLLYWOOD)**
12215 Victory Blvd.
North Hollywood, CA 91606

Tel: (323)315-5207; Free: 866-508-2684
E-mail: info@katz.wcula.edu
Web Site: www.westcoastuniversity.edu/
Description: Proprietary, 4-year, coed. Awards bachelor's degrees. Founded 1909. Total enrollment: 1,792. 24 applied, 83% were admitted. 69% 25 or older.

■ **WEST COAST UNIVERSITY (ONTARIO)**
2855 E Guasti Rd.
Ontario, CA 91761
Tel: (909)467-6100
Web Site: westcoastuniversity.edu/
Description: Proprietary, 4-year, coed. Calendar: semesters.

■ **WEST HILLS COMMUNITY COLLEGE**
300 Cherry Ln.
Coalinga, CA 93210-1399
Tel: (559)934-2000; Free: 800-266-1114
Fax: (559)934-1511
E-mail: sandradagnino@westhillscollege.com
Web Site: www.westhillscollege.com/
Description: State-supported, 2-year, coed. Part of California Community College System. Awards certificates, diplomas, transfer associate, and terminal associate degrees. Founded 1932. Setting: 193-acre small town campus. Total enrollment: 2,965. Student-undergrad faculty ratio is 24:1. 0% from out-of-state. 35% 25 or older. Core. Calendar: semesters. Academic remediation for entering students, ESL program, services for LD students, advanced placement, independent study, distance learning, summer session for credit, part-time degree program, adult/continuing education programs, co-op programs. Off campus study at Central California Consortium. Study abroad program.
Entrance Requirements: Open admission. Option: early admission. Recommended: high school transcript. Entrance: noncompetitive. Application deadline: Rolling. Notification: continuous. Preference given to district residents.
Collegiate Environment: Orientation program. Drama-theater group. Student services: personal-psychological counseling.

■ **WEST LOS ANGELES COLLEGE**
9000 Overland Ave.
Culver City, CA 90230-3519
Tel: (310)287-4200
Fax: (310)841-0396
Web Site: www.lacolleges.net/
Description: State and locally supported, 2-year, coed. Part of Los Angeles Community College District System. Awards transfer associate and terminal associate degrees. Founded 1969. Setting: 69-acre urban campus with easy access to Los Angeles. Total enrollment: 11,866. Student-undergrad faculty ratio is 37:1. 0% from out-of-state. 50% 25 or older. Retention: 61% of full-time freshmen returned the following year. Core. Calendar: semesters. Academic remediation for entering students, ESL program, services for LD students, advanced placement, honors program, summer session for credit, part-time degree program, adult/continuing education programs, co-op programs. ROTC: Army (c), Air Force (c).
Entrance Requirements: Open admission. Option: early admission. Recommended: high school transcript. Entrance: noncompetitive. Application deadline: 8/16.
Collegiate Environment: Choral group. Student services: health clinic, personal-psychological counseling. Campus security: 24-hour patrols.
Community Environment: Culver City is an industrial and residential city located near Los Angeles. The world's largest motion picture studio, Metro-Goldwyn-Mayer, was located here, as well as the Desilu Studios. All forms of transportation serve the area; Los Angeles International Airport is near. Churches of all major denominations are in the area; there are excellent shopping facilities available.

■ **WEST VALLEY COLLEGE**
14000 Fruitvale Ave.
Saratoga, CA 95070-5698
Tel: (408)867-2200
Fax: (408)867-5033
E-mail: barbara_ogilvie@westvalley.edu
Web Site: www.westvalley.edu/
Description: State and locally supported, 2-year, coed. Part of California

Community College System. Awards certificates, transfer associate, and terminal associate degrees. Founded 1963. Setting: 143-acre small town campus with easy access to San Francisco, San Jose. Total enrollment: 12,893. Student-undergrad faculty ratio is 28:1. 0% from out-of-state. 46% 25 or older. Retention: 75% of full-time freshmen returned the following year. Core. Calendar: semesters. Academic remediation for entering students, ESL program, services for LD students, honors program, summer session for credit, part-time degree program, adult/continuing education programs, co-op programs and internships. ROTC: Army (c), Air Force (c).

Entrance Requirements: Open admission. Option: early admission. Entrance: noncompetitive. Application deadline: Rolling. Notification: continuous. Preference given to district residents.

Collegiate Environment: Orientation program. Drama-theater group, student-run newspaper. Student services: health clinic, personal-psychological counseling.

Community Environment: See San Jose State University.

■ WESTMONT COLLEGE

955 La Paz Rd.
Santa Barbara, CA 93108-1099
Tel: (805)565-6000; Free: 800-777-9011
Fax: (805)565-6234
E-mail: admissions@westmont.edu
Web Site: www.westmont.edu/

Description: Independent nondenominational, 4-year, coed. Awards bachelor's degrees. Founded 1937. Setting: 113-acre suburban campus with easy access to Los Angeles. Endowment: $60 million. Total enrollment: 1,378. Faculty: 151 (95 full-time, 56 part-time). Student-undergrad faculty ratio is 12:1. 1,877 applied, 75% were admitted. 42% from top 10% of their high school class, 73% from top quarter, 93% from top half. 4 National Merit Scholars. Full-time: 1,369 students, 64% women, 36% men. Part-time: 9 students, 67% women, 33% men. Students come from 37 states and territories, 10 other countries, 35% from out-of-state. 1% 25 or older, 80% live on campus, 4% transferred in. Retention: 87% of full-time freshmen returned the following year. Academic areas with the most degrees conferred: business/marketing; English; social sciences. Core. Calendar: semesters. Academic remediation for entering students, services for LD students, advanced placement, accelerated degree program, self-designed majors, honors program, double major, summer session for credit, internships. Off campus study at 13 members of the Christian College Consortium, 90 members of the Christian Colleges and Universities, American University (Washington Semester). Study abroad program. ROTC: Army (c), Air Force (c).

Entrance Requirements: Options: electronic application, early action, international baccalaureate accepted. Required: essay, high school transcript, 1 recommendation, SAT or ACT. Recommended: interview. Required for some: interview. Entrance: moderately difficult. Application deadlines: 2/20, 11/1 for early action. Notification: 4/1, 12/20 for early action. Transfer credits accepted: Yes. Applicants placed on waiting list: 98. Wait-listed applicants offered admission: 0.

Collegiate Environment: Orientation program. Drama-theater group, choral group, student-run newspaper, radio station. Social organizations: 31 open to all. Most popular organizations: student ministries, student government, competitive athletics, music and theater ensembles, intramural athletics. Major annual events: Potter's Clay service project to Mexico, Spring Sing campus-wide talent competition, Fall/Spring Formal Dances. Student services: health clinic, personal-psychological counseling, women's center. Campus security: 24-hour emergency response devices and patrols, late night transport-escort service, controlled dormitory access. Roger John Voskuyl Library with 174,246 books, 15,590 microform titles, 380 serials, 11,375 audiovisual materials, an OPAC, and a Web page. 100 computers available on campus for general student use. A campuswide network can be accessed from student residence rooms and from off campus. Staffed computer lab on campus provides training in use of computers, software, and the Internet.

Community Environment: See University of California - Santa Barbara.

■ WESTWOOD COLLEGE–ANAHEIM

1551 S Douglass Rd.
Anaheim, CA 92806
Tel: (714)704-2721; Free: 877-840-8999
Web Site: www.westwood.edu/

Description: Proprietary, 4-year, coed. Awards associate and bachelor's degrees. Total enrollment: 1,206. Faculty: 82. Calendar: continuous.

■ WESTWOOD COLLEGE–INLAND EMPIRE

20 W 7th St.
Upland, CA 91786
Tel: (909)931-7599; Free: 866-221-5632
Web Site: www.westwood.edu/

Description: Proprietary, 4-year, coed. Awards associate and bachelor's degrees. Total enrollment: 1,140. Faculty: 94. Calendar: continuous.

■ WESTWOOD COLLEGE–LOS ANGELES

3250 Wilshire Blvd., 4th Fl.
Los Angeles, CA 90010
Tel: (213)382-2328; Free: 866-930-9256
Web Site: www.westwood.edu/

Description: Proprietary, 4-year, coed. Awards associate and bachelor's degrees. Total enrollment: 948. Faculty: 79. Calendar: continuous.

■ WESTWOOD COLLEGE–SOUTH BAY CAMPUS

19700 S Vermont Ave.
Ste. 100
Torrance, CA 90502
Tel: (310)522-2088; Free: 888-403-3308
Fax: (310)522-4318
Web Site: www.westwood.edu/

Description: Proprietary, 4-year, coed. Part of Association of Independent Technological Universities (AITU). Awards associate and bachelor's degrees. Founded 2002. Total enrollment: 724. Faculty: 69. Calendar: continuous.

■ WHITTIER COLLEGE

13406 E Philadelphia St.
Whittier, CA 90608-0634
Tel: (562)907-4200
Fax: (562)907-4870
E-mail: admission@whittier.edu
Web Site: www.whittier.edu/

Description: Independent, comprehensive, coed. Awards bachelor's, master's, and doctoral degrees. Founded 1887. Setting: 95-acre suburban campus with easy access to Los Angeles. Total enrollment: 2,448. Faculty: 169 (109 full-time, 60 part-time). Student-undergrad faculty ratio is 13:1. 4,123 applied, 64% were admitted. 28% from top 10% of their high school class, 44% from top quarter, 92% from top half. Full-time: 1,632 students, 53% women, 47% men. Part-time: 38 students, 55% women, 45% men. Students come from 27 states and territories, 20 other countries, 21% from out-of-state. 1% American Indian or Alaska Native, non-Hispanic/Latino; 37% Hispanic/Latino; 6% African American, non-Hispanic/Latino; 11% Asian, non-Hispanic/Latino; 3% international. 3% 25 or older, 49% live on campus, 4% transferred in. Retention: 86% of full-time freshmen returned the following year. Academic areas with the most degrees conferred: social sciences; business/marketing; psychology. Core. Calendar: 4-1-4. Academic remediation for entering students, services for LD students, advanced placement, accelerated degree program, self-designed majors, independent study, double major, summer session for credit, adult/continuing education programs, internships, graduate courses open to undergrads. Off campus study. Study abroad program. ROTC: Army (c), Air Force (c).

Entrance Requirements: Options: electronic application, early action, deferred admission, international baccalaureate accepted. Required: essay, high school transcript, minimum 2 high school GPA, 2 recommendations, SAT or ACT. Recommended: minimum 2.5 high school GPA, interview, SAT Subject Tests. Required for some: minimum 3.5 high school GPA. Entrance: moderately difficult. Application deadlines: Rolling, 12/1 for early action. Notification: continuous, 12/31 for early action. Transfer credits accepted: Yes. Early action applicants: 1,026. Early action applicants admitted: 716.

Costs Per Year: Application fee: $50. One-time mandatory fee: $200. Comprehensive fee: $51,590 includes full-time tuition ($39,736), mandatory fees ($360), and college room and board ($11,494). College room only: $6412. Room and board charges vary according to board plan. Part-time tuition: $1610 per unit.

Collegiate Environment: Orientation program. Drama-theater group, choral group, student-run newspaper, radio station. Social organizations: 56 open to all; local fraternities, local sororities; 10% of eligible men and 13% of eligible women are members. Most popular organizations: Hispanic Students Association, Hawaiian Islander Club, choir, Asian Students Association, Students Organized for Multicultural Awareness. Major annual events: Spring Sing, Sportsfest, Homecoming. Student services: health clinic, personal-psychological counseling. Campus security: 24-hour emergency response devices and patrols, late night transport-escort service, controlled dormitory access. Freshmen guaranteed college housing. On-campus residence required through junior year. Option: coed housing available. Bonnie Bell Wardman Library plus 1 other with 225,337 books, 1,357 serials, an OPAC, and a Web page. 150 computers available on campus for general student use. A campuswide network can be accessed from student residence rooms and from off campus. Students can access the following: online class registration. Staffed computer lab on campus.

Community Environment: Whittier enjoys a beautiful setting at the foot of the Puente Hills, in a suburban area in southeast Los Angeles County. The climate is pleasant with a minimum temperature of 53 degrees, a maximum temperature of 73 degrees, and an average rainfall of 15 inches. Buses and railroads serve the area with connection to the Los Angeles International Airport via helicopter, and to the metropolitan area via the freeway system. Modern shopping facilities are available in addition to many manufacturing plants. Recreational facilities include parks, theaters, nearby Disneyland, beaches, and mountains less than one hour away. The Whittier College School of Law is the only ABA accredited Law School in Orange County, California.

■ **WILLIAM JESSUP UNIVERSITY**
333 Sunset Blvd.
Rocklin, CA 95765
Tel: (916)577-2200; Free: 800-355-7522
Fax: (916)577-1813
E-mail: admissions@jessup.edu
Web Site: www.jessup.edu/
Description: Independent nondenominational, 4-year, coed. Awards associate and bachelor's degrees. Founded 1939. Setting: 126-acre suburban campus with easy access to Sacramento. Total enrollment: 896. Faculty: 114 (27 full-time, 87 part-time). Student-undergrad faculty ratio is 13:1. 389 applied, 65% were admitted. 15% from top 10% of their high school class, 44% from top quarter, 75% from top half. Full-time: 700 students, 61% women, 39% men. Part-time: 169 students, 53% women, 47% men. Students come from 13 states and territories, 15 other countries, 9% from out-of-state. 2% American Indian or Alaska Native, non-Hispanic/Latino; 9% Hispanic/Latino; 6% African American, non-Hispanic/Latino; 3% Asian, non-Hispanic/Latino; 1% Native Hawaiian or other Pacific Islander, non-Hispanic/Latino; 0.3% international. 10% 25 or older, 60% live on campus, 17% transferred in. Retention: 78% of full-time freshmen returned the following year. Academic areas with the most degrees conferred: psychology; theology and religious vocations; business/marketing. Core. Calendar: semesters. Services for LD students, advanced placement, independent study, double major, summer session for credit, part-time degree program, adult/continuing education programs, internships. Off campus study at Council for Christian Colleges and Universities. Study abroad program.
Entrance Requirements: Options: electronic application, international baccalaureate accepted. Required: essay, high school transcript, minimum 2.5 high school GPA, SAT or ACT. Recommended: 1 recommendation, interview. Required for some: 1 recommendation, interview. Entrance: moderately difficult. Application deadline: 8/15. Notification: continuous. SAT Reasoning Test deadline: 8/15. Transfer credits accepted: Yes.
Costs Per Year: Application fee: $45. Comprehensive fee: $31,970 includes full-time tuition ($22,900) and college room and board ($9070). Full-time tuition varies according to course load. Room and board charges vary according to board plan and housing facility. Part-time tuition: $970 per credit hour. Part-time tuition varies according to course load.
Collegiate Environment: Orientation program. Drama-theater group, choral group, student-run newspaper. Major annual events: Homecoming Weekend, Fall Week of Welcome, The Roommate Game. Student services: personal-psychological counseling. Campus security: student patrols, late night transport-escort service, controlled dormitory access, day and evening patrols by trained security personnel. Paul Nystrom Library plus 1 other with 120,845 books, 90 microform titles, 11,532 serials, 79,968 audiovisual materials, an OPAC, and a Web page. 44 computers available on campus for general student use. A campuswide network can be accessed from student residence rooms. Students can access the following: online class registration. Staffed computer lab on campus provides training in use of computers, software, and the Internet.
Community Environment: See San Jose State University.

■ **WOODBURY UNIVERSITY**
7500 Glenoaks Blvd.
Burbank, CA 91504-1099

Tel: (818)767-0888; Free: 800-784-WOOD
Fax: (818)504-9320
E-mail: admissions@woodbury.edu
Web Site: www.woodbury.edu/
Description: Independent, comprehensive, coed. Awards bachelor's and master's degrees. Founded 1884. Setting: 22-acre suburban campus with easy access to Los Angeles. Endowment: $16.9 million. Educational spending for the previous fiscal year: $13,739 per student. Total enrollment: 1,771. Faculty: 315 (83 full-time, 232 part-time). Student-undergrad faculty ratio is 10:1. 661 applied, 65% were admitted. Full-time: 1,236 students, 50% women, 50% men. Part-time: 252 students, 51% women, 49% men. Students come from 30 states and territories, 9 other countries. 0.5% American Indian or Alaska Native, non-Hispanic/Latino; 30% Hispanic/Latino; 4% African American, non-Hispanic/Latino; 9% Asian, non-Hispanic/Latino; 1% Native Hawaiian or other Pacific Islander, non-Hispanic/Latino; 15% international. 25% 25 or older, 16% live on campus, 61% transferred in. Retention: 83% of full-time freshmen returned the following year. Academic areas with the most degrees conferred: architecture; business/marketing; visual and performing arts. Core. Calendar: semesters. Academic remediation for entering students, ESL program, services for LD students, advanced placement, accelerated degree program, self-designed majors, independent study, double major, summer session for credit, part-time degree program, adult/continuing education programs, internships. Study abroad program.
Entrance Requirements: Options: electronic application, deferred admission, international baccalaureate accepted. Required: minimum 2 high school GPA, SAT or ACT. Recommended: essay, minimum 3 high school GPA, 2 recommendations. Required for some: high school transcript. Entrance: moderately difficult. Application deadline: Rolling. Notification: continuous. Transfer credits accepted: Yes.
Costs Per Year: Application fee: $50. Comprehensive fee: $41,396 includes full-time tuition ($31,054), mandatory fees ($390), and college room and board ($9952). College room only: $6200. Full-time tuition and fees vary according to course load, degree level, and program. Room and board charges vary according to board plan, housing facility, and location.
Collegiate Environment: Orientation program. Social organizations: 26 open to all; national fraternities, national sororities, local fraternities, local sororities; 10% of eligible men and 10% of eligible women are members. Most popular organizations: Associated Student Government, American Institute of Architecture Students, Armenian Student Association, La Voz Unida, Collegiate Entrepreneurs' Organization (CEO). Major annual events: Welcome Week, Woodstock, Winter Formal. Student services: health clinic, personal-psychological counseling. Campus security: 24-hour patrols, late night transport-escort service, controlled dormitory access. 219 college housing spaces available; 200 were occupied in 2012-13. Freshmen given priority for college housing. Option: coed housing available. Los Angeles Times Library with 68,666 books, 13,257 microform titles, 250 serials, 12,554 audiovisual materials, an OPAC, and a Web page. Operations spending for the previous fiscal year: $951,832. 225 computers available on campus for general student use. A campuswide network can be accessed from off-campus. Students can access the following: online class registration. Staffed computer lab on campus provides training in use of computers, software, and the Internet.
Community Environment: Southern California is famous for the variety of terrain it offers and the array of activities available to its residents. Valleys, mountains, beaches, and deserts enable Woodbury students to escape to practically any climate they wish. Woodbury is surrounded by a residential neighborhood in a city known as the heart of the entertainment industry. Students are just minutes away from the many benefits of southern California: historical and cultural events and museums, world-class entertainment, professional sporting events, and vast beaches, deserts, mountains, and valleys for recreational leisure.

■ **WOODLAND COMMUNITY COLLEGE**
2300 E Gibson Rd.
Woodland, CA 95776
Tel: (530)661-5700
Web Site: www.yccd.edu/woodland/
Description: County-supported, 2-year, coed. Total enrollment: 3,188. 39% 25 or older.

■ **WYOTECH FREMONT**
200 Whitney Pl.
Fremont, CA 94539-7663

Tel: (510)490-6900; Free: 888-577-7559
Fax: (510)490-8599
Web Site: www.wyotech.edu/
Description: Proprietary, 2-year, coed. Administratively affiliated with Corinthian Colleges, Inc. Awards certificates, diplomas, and terminal associate degrees. Founded 1966. Setting: urban campus. Total enrollment: 1,596. Faculty: 92 (80 full-time, 12 part-time). Student-undergrad faculty ratio is 25:1. 560 applied, 80% were admitted. Calendar: continuous. Academic remediation for entering students.
Collegiate Environment: Campus security: security personnel. Learning Resource Center with 1,000 audiovisual materials.

■ **WYOTECH LONG BEACH**
2161 Technology Pl.
Long Beach, CA 90810
Tel: (562)624-9530; Free: 888-577-7559
Fax: (562)437-8111
Web Site: www.wyotech.edu/
Description: Proprietary, 2-year, coed. Awards terminal associate degrees. Founded 1969. Total enrollment: 2,166. Student-undergrad faculty ratio is 30:1. 539 applied, 55% were admitted. 0% from out-of-state. 51% 25 or older.

■ **WYOTECH SACRAMENTO**
980 Riverside Pky.
West Sacramento, CA 95605-1507
Tel: (916)376-8888; Free: 888-577-7559
Web Site: www.wyotech.edu/
Description: Proprietary, 2-year, coed. Awards certificates and terminal associate degrees. Founded 2003. Total enrollment: 737. 27% from out-of-state. 27% 25 or older. Calendar: 9-month program.
Entrance Requirements: Open admission.

■ **YESHIVA OHR ELCHONON CHABAD/WEST COAST TALMUDICAL SEMINARY**
7215 Waring Ave.
Los Angeles, CA 90046-7660
Tel: (213)937-3763
E-mail: roshyeshiva@yoec.edu
Web Site: www.yoec.edu/
Description: Independent Jewish, 4-year, men only. Awards bachelor's degrees. Founded 1953. Setting: 4-acre urban campus. Total enrollment: 135. 68 applied, 100% were admitted. Core. Calendar: semesters. Academic remediation for entering students, honors program, summer session for credit, adult/continuing education programs, internships. Off campus study at Central Yeshiva Tomchei Tmimim-Lubavitch, Rabbinical College of America, Talmudical Seminary Oholei Torah.
Entrance Requirements: Options: early admission, deferred admission. Required: high school transcript, minimum 2.0 high school GPA, interview, oral examination. Entrance: moderately difficult. Application deadline: Rolling. Notification: continuous. Preference given to applicants with religious commitment.
Collegiate Environment: Student services: personal-psychological counseling. Campus security: 24-hour emergency response devices, student patrols. Yeshiva Ohr Elchonon Chabad Library plus 3 others with 12,000 books and 200 serials.

■ **YUBA COLLEGE**
2088 N Beale Rd.
Marysville, CA 95901-7699
Tel: (530)741-6700
Fax: (530)741-3541
Web Site: www.yccd.edu/
Description: State and locally supported, 2-year, coed. Part of California Community College System. Awards certificates and transfer associate degrees. Founded 1927. Setting: 160-acre rural campus with easy access to Sacramento. Total enrollment: 8,564. Student-undergrad faculty ratio is 29:1. 45% 25 or older. Retention: 63% of full-time freshmen returned the following year. Core. Calendar: semesters. Academic remediation for entering students, ESL program, services for LD students, advanced placement, distance learning, double major, summer session for credit, part-time degree program.
Entrance Requirements: Open admission. Option: electronic application. Required: high school transcript. Entrance: noncompetitive. Application deadline: Rolling.
Collegiate Environment: Orientation program. Drama-theater group, choral group. Student services: health clinic, personal-psychological counseling, women's center. Campus security: 24-hour patrols, student patrols. Learning Resource Center and Library with an OPAC.
Community Environment: Marysville is 50 miles north of Sacramento, has a moderate climate, and is the center of a rich agricultural area. Amtrak serves the area. The city has a hospital, churches, shopping center, and civic organizations. Excellent boating, hunting and fishing facilities are available.

■ **ADAMS STATE UNIVERSITY**
208 Edgemont Blvd.
Alamosa, CO 81102
Tel: (719)587-7011; Free: 800-824-6494
Fax: (719)587-7522
E-mail: admissions@adams.edu
Web Site: www.adams.edu/
Description: State-supported, comprehensive, coed. Awards associate, bachelor's, and master's degrees. Founded 1921. Setting: 90-acre small town campus with easy access to Pueblo. Endowment: $643,931. Research spending for the previous fiscal year: $1200. Educational spending for the previous fiscal year: $6073 per student. Total enrollment: 3,283. Faculty: 177 (112 full-time, 65 part-time). Student-undergrad faculty ratio is 15:1. 2,569 applied, 66% were admitted. 9% from top 10% of their high school class, 23% from top quarter, 53% from top half. Full-time: 1,909 students, 49% women, 51% men. Part-time: 522 students, 60% women, 40% men. Students come from 52 states and territories, 12 other countries, 20% from out-of-state. 1% American Indian or Alaska Native, non-Hispanic/Latino; 31% Hispanic/Latino; 6% African American, non-Hispanic/Latino; 1% Asian, non-Hispanic/Latino; 0.4% Native Hawaiian or other Pacific Islander, non-Hispanic/Latino. 24% 25 or older, 47% live on campus, 9% transferred in. Retention: 55% of full-time freshmen returned the following year. Academic areas with the most degrees conferred: liberal arts/general studies; business/marketing; social sciences. Core. Calendar: semesters. Academic remediation for entering students, services for LD students, advanced placement, accelerated degree program, self-designed majors, independent study, distance learning, double major, summer session for credit, part-time degree program, adult/continuing education programs, internships, graduate courses open to undergrads. Off campus study at members of the Consortium of State Colleges in Colorado, National Student Exchange. Study abroad program.
Entrance Requirements: Options: electronic application, early admission, deferred admission, international baccalaureate accepted. Required: high school transcript, minimum 2 high school GPA, SAT or ACT. Required for some: essay, interview, audition for music majors, portfolio for art majors. Entrance: moderately difficult. Application deadlines: 8/1, 8/10 for nonresidents. Notification: continuous, continuous for nonresidents. SAT Reasoning Test deadline: 8/15. Transfer credits accepted: Yes.
Costs Per Year: Application fee: $30. State resident tuition: $3816 full-time. Nonresident tuition: $14,784 full-time. Mandatory fees: $2,632 full-time. Full-time tuition and fees vary according to course load. College room and board: $7900. College room only: $4200. Room and board charges vary according to board plan and housing facility.
Collegiate Environment: Orientation program. Drama-theater group, choral group, marching band, student-run newspaper, radio station. Social organizations: 40 open to all. Most popular organizations: Student Programming Board, student government, Semillas de la Tierra, Newman Club, Fellowship of Christian Athletes. Major annual events: Homecoming, Martin Luther King Week, ASC Cares Days. Student services: personal-psychological counseling. Campus security: 24-hour emergency response devices and patrols, student patrols, late night transport-escort service, controlled dormitory access. 874 undergraduates lived in college housing during 2012-13. Freshmen guaranteed college housing. On-campus residence required through sophomore year. Options: coed, men-only, women-only housing available. Nielsen Library with 127,024 books, 338 serials, 2,748 audiovisual materials, an OPAC, and a Web page. Operations

spending for the previous fiscal year: $533,936. 326 computers available on campus for general student use. A campuswide network can be accessed from student residence rooms and from off campus. Students can access the following: online class registration. Staffed computer lab on campus (open 24 hours a day) provides training in use of computers, software, and the Internet.
Community Environment: Located in the center of San Luis Valley, an extensive grazing and farming area larger than the state of Connecticut, Alamosa is completely surrounded by mountain ranges. It has an ideal climate, with an average yearly temperature of 65 degrees. A commuter airline and a bus line serve the area. Alamosa has churches, radio stations, libraries, hotels and motels, a hospital and a number of civic, social, cultural, fraternal and veterans organizations.

■ **AIMS COMMUNITY COLLEGE**
Box 69
5401 W 20th St.
Greeley, CO 80632-0069
Tel: (970)330-8008
E-mail: wgreen@chiron.aims.edu
Web Site: www.aims.edu/
Description: District-supported, 2-year, coed. Awards certificates, diplomas, transfer associate, and terminal associate degrees. Founded 1967. Setting: 185-acre urban campus with easy access to Denver. Total enrollment: 4,588. Faculty: 273 (91 full-time, 182 part-time). Student-undergrad faculty ratio is 18:1. Full-time: 1,701 students, 50% women, 50% men. Part-time: 2,887 students, 61% women, 39% men. 48% 25 or older. Retention: 80% of full-time freshmen returned the following year. Core. Calendar: semesters. Academic remediation for entering students, ESL program, advanced placement, self-designed majors, freshman honors college, honors program, summer session for credit, part-time degree program, external degree program, adult/continuing education programs, co-op programs. ROTC: Air Force (c).
Entrance Requirements: Open admission. Options: early admission, deferred admission. Entrance: noncompetitive. Application deadline: Rolling.
Collegiate Environment: Drama-theater group, choral group, student-run newspaper, radio station. Major annual events: Fall-In Activity, Winter Fest, Spring-Fest/Blowout Activity. Student services: personal-psychological counseling, women's center. Campus security: 24-hour emergency response devices, day and evening patrols by trained security personnel. Aims Community College Library with 39,129 books, 258 serials, and an OPAC. 1,000 computers available on campus for general student use. Computer purchase/lease plans available. A campuswide network can be accessed from off-campus. Students can access the following: online class registration. Staffed computer lab on campus provides training in use of computers, software, and the Internet.
Community Environment: See University of Northern Colorado.

■ **AMERICAN SENTINEL UNIVERSITY**
2260 S Xanadu Way, Ste. 310
Aurora, CO 80014
Free: 800-729-2427
E-mail: natalie.nixon@AmericanSentinel.edu
Web Site: www.americansentinel.edu/
Description: Private, comprehensive, coed. Awards associate, bachelor's, and master's degrees. Founded 1988.

Entrance Requirements: Required: high school transcript, resume.

■ **ANTHEM COLLEGE–AURORA**
350 Blackhawk St.
Aurora, CO 80011
Tel: (720)859-7900; Free: 855-268-4363
Web Site: www.anthem.edu/aurora-colorado/
Description: Proprietary, 2-year, coed. Awards certificates and terminal associate degrees. Total enrollment: 352. Student-undergrad faculty ratio is 35:1. 5% from out-of-state. 62% 25 or older.
Entrance Requirements: Entrance: noncompetitive.

■ **ARAPAHOE COMMUNITY COLLEGE**
5900 S Santa Fe Dr.
Littleton, CO 80160-9002
Tel: (303)797-4222
Fax: (303)797-5970
E-mail: darcy.briggs@arapahoe.edu
Web Site: www.arapahoe.edu/
Description: State-supported, 2-year, coed. Part of Colorado Community College and Occupational Education System. Awards certificates, diplomas, transfer associate, and terminal associate degrees. Founded 1965. Setting: 52-acre suburban campus with easy access to Denver. Educational spending for the previous fiscal year: $6001 per student. Total enrollment: 9,963. Faculty: 473 (96 full-time, 377 part-time). Student-undergrad faculty ratio is 18:1. 2,389 applied, 100% were admitted. Full-time: 2,644 students, 55% women, 45% men. Part-time: 7,319 students, 61% women, 39% men. Students come from 38 states and territories, 54 other countries, 8% from out-of-state. 2% American Indian or Alaska Native, non-Hispanic/Latino; 10% Hispanic/Latino; 4% African American, non-Hispanic/Latino; 3% Asian, non-Hispanic/Latino; 0.4% Native Hawaiian or other Pacific Islander, non-Hispanic/Latino; 1% international. 53% 25 or older, 7% transferred in. Retention: 55% of full-time freshmen returned the following year. Core. Calendar: semesters. Academic remediation for entering students, ESL program, services for LD students, advanced placement, accelerated degree program, self-designed majors, honors program, independent study, distance learning, double major, summer session for credit, part-time degree program, adult/continuing education programs, co-op programs and internships. Off campus study. Study abroad program. ROTC: Army (c), Naval (c), Air Force (c).
Entrance Requirements: Open admission medical laboratory technology, medical assistant technology, nursing, medical records technology, police academy and mortuary science programs require high school diploma or GED. Options: electronic application, early admission, deferred admission, international baccalaureate accepted. Recommended: ACT, SAT or ACT. Entrance: noncompetitive. Application deadlines: Rolling, Rolling for nonresidents. Notification: continuous, continuous for nonresidents. Transfer credits accepted: Yes.
Costs Per Year: Application fee: $0. State resident tuition: $1,449 full-time, $174.75 per hour part-time. Nonresident tuition: $5,647 full-time, $462.55 per hour part-time. Mandatory fees: $182 full-time.
Collegiate Environment: Orientation program. Drama-theater group, choral group, student-run newspaper. Social organizations: 28 open to all. Most popular organizations: History Club, Science Club, Phi Theta Kappa, Outdoor Club, Frisbee Golf. Major annual events: Breakfast with the President, End of Year BBQ, Beginning of the Year Pizza. Student services: personal-psychological counseling. Campus security: 24-hour emergency response devices and patrols, late night transport-escort service. College housing not available. Weber Center for Learning Resources plus 1 other with 48,693 books, 194 serials, an OPAC, and a Web page.
Community Environment: Littleton is a suburban area 10 miles from Denver with seasonal variations in temperature. There are churches of all denominations, shopping centers, and medical clinics, with all forms of transportation available. Community facilities include parks with playground equipment, public swimming pools, indoor tennis courts, fairgrounds, golf courses and an ice rink. Skiing in the nearby mountains is excellent. Part-time employment is available.

■ **ARGOSY UNIVERSITY, DENVER**
7600 E Eastman Ave.
Denver, CO 80231
Tel: (303)923-4110; Free: 866-431-5981
Fax: (303)923-4111
Web Site: www.argosy.edu/denver/

Description: Proprietary, university, coed. Awards bachelor's, master's, and doctoral degrees.

■ **THE ART INSTITUTE OF COLORADO**
1200 Lincoln St.
Denver, CO 80203
Tel: (303)837-0825; Free: 800-275-2420
Fax: (303)860-8520
Web Site: www.artinstitutes.edu/denver/
Description: Proprietary, 4-year, coed. Part of Education Management Corporation. Awards associate and bachelor's degrees. Founded 1952. Setting: urban campus.

■ **ASPEN UNIVERSITY**
501 S Cherry St., Ste. 350
Denver, CO 80246
Tel: (303)333-4224; Free: 800-441-4746
Fax: (303)336-1144
E-mail: admissions@aspen.edu
Web Site: www.aspen.edu/
Description: Independent, comprehensive, coed. Awards bachelor's and master's degrees. Founded 1987. Calendar: 5 terms per year.
Costs Per Year: Application fee: $50. Tuition: $750 per course part-time. Part-time tuition varies according to course level, course load, degree level, and program.

■ **BEL–REA INSTITUTE OF ANIMAL TECHNOLOGY**
1681 S Dayton St.
Denver, CO 80247
Tel: (303)751-8700; Free: 800-950-8001
Fax: (303)751-9969
E-mail: admissions@bel-rea.com
Web Site: www.bel-rea.com/
Description: Proprietary, 2-year, coed. Awards terminal associate degrees. Founded 1971. Setting: 4-acre suburban campus. Total enrollment: 644. 414 applied. 28% 25 or older. Core. Academic remediation for entering students, internships.
Entrance Requirements: Required: high school transcript, minimum 2.5 high school GPA. Recommended: interview. Entrance: moderately difficult. Application deadline: Rolling.
Collegiate Environment: Student services: personal-psychological counseling. 1,800 books and 57 serials.

■ **BOULDER COLLEGE OF MASSAGE THERAPY**
6255 Longbow Dr.
Boulder, CO 80301
Tel: (303)530-2100; Free: 800-442-5131
Fax: (303)530-2204
E-mail: admissions@bcmt.org
Web Site: www.bcmt.org/
Description: Independent, 2-year, coed. Awards certificates and terminal associate degrees. Founded 1975. Total enrollment: 149. Student-undergrad faculty ratio is 18:1. 46% from out-of-state. 78% 25 or older.
Entrance Requirements: Entrance: noncompetitive.

■ **COLLEGEAMERICA–COLORADO SPRINGS**
3645 Citadel Dr. S
Colorado Springs, CO 80909
Tel: (719)637-0600; Free: 800-622-2894
Fax: (719)637-0806
Web Site: www.collegeamerica.edu/
Description: Proprietary, primarily 2-year, coed. Awards terminal associate and bachelor's degrees. Total enrollment: 675. Student-undergrad faculty ratio is 22:1. 0% from out-of-state. 61% 25 or older.

■ **COLLEGEAMERICA–DENVER**
1385 S Colorado Blvd.
Denver, CO 80222
Tel: (303)691-9756; Free: 800-622-2894
Fax: (303)692-9156
Web Site: www.collegeamerica.edu/
Description: Proprietary, primarily 2-year, coed. Awards certificates,

terminal associate, and bachelor's degrees. Founded 1962. Setting: urban campus. Total enrollment: 681. Student-undergrad faculty ratio is 16:1. 0% from out-of-state. 59% 25 or older.

Entrance Requirements: Entrance: noncompetitive.

■ **COLLEGEAMERICA–FORT COLLINS**
4601 S Mason St.
Fort Collins, CO 80525-3740
Tel: (970)223-6060; Free: 800-622-2894
Fax: (970)223-6060
Web Site: www.collegeamerica.edu/

Description: Proprietary, primarily 2-year, coed. Awards terminal associate and bachelor's degrees. Founded 1962. Setting: suburban campus. Total enrollment: 116. 57% 25 or older. Core. Calendar: continuous. Independent study, internships.

Entrance Requirements: Open admission. Option: international baccalaureate accepted. Required: essay, high school transcript, interview. Recommended: minimum 2.0 high school GPA. Entrance: noncompetitive. Notification: continuous.

Collegiate Environment: Orientation program.

■ **COLORADO CHRISTIAN UNIVERSITY**
8787 W Alameda
Lakewood, CO 80226
Tel: (303)202-0100; Free: 800-44-FAITH
Fax: (303)238-2191
E-mail: jomartin@ccu.edu
Web Site: www.ccu.edu/

Description: Independent interdenominational, comprehensive, coed. Awards associate, bachelor's, and master's degrees. Founded 1914. Setting: 26-acre suburban campus with easy access to Denver. Total enrollment: 2,511. Student-undergrad faculty ratio is 9:1. 5,552 applied. 32% from out-of-state. 53% 25 or older. Retention: 94% of full-time freshmen returned the following year. Core. Calendar: semesters. Academic remediation for entering students, services for LD students, advanced placement, accelerated degree program, self-designed majors, honors program, independent study, distance learning, double major, summer session for credit, part-time degree program, adult/continuing education programs, co-op programs and internships, graduate courses open to undergrads. Off campus study at Colorado Institute of Art, Metropolitan State College, University of Colorado at Denver, Red Rocks Community College. Study abroad program. ROTC: Army (c).

Entrance Requirements: Options: electronic application, deferred admission, international baccalaureate accepted. Required: essay, high school transcript, 2 recommendations, interview, SAT or ACT. Required for some: minimum 2.8 high school GPA, 3 recommendations, interview. Entrance: moderately difficult. Application deadline: 8/21. Notification: 11/1.

Collegiate Environment: Orientation program. Drama-theater group, choral group, student-run newspaper. Student services: health clinic, personal-psychological counseling, women's center. Campus security: 24-hour emergency response devices and patrols, student patrols. Clifton Fowler Library plus 1 other with an OPAC and a Web page.

Community Environment: See University of Denver.

■ **THE COLORADO COLLEGE**
14 E Cache La Poudre
Colorado Springs, CO 80903-3294
Tel: (719)389-6000; Free: 800-542-7214
Fax: (719)389-6282
E-mail: admission@coloradocollege.edu
Web Site: www.coloradocollege.edu/

Description: Independent, comprehensive, coed. Awards bachelor's and master's degrees (master's degree in education only). Founded 1874. Setting: 90-acre urban campus with easy access to Denver. Endowment: $507 million. Research spending for the previous fiscal year: $1.2 million. Educational spending for the previous fiscal year: $21,586 per student. Total enrollment: 2,026. Faculty: 198 (167 full-time, 31 part-time). Student-undergrad faculty ratio is 10:1. 5,606 applied, 23% were admitted. 62% from top 10% of their high school class, 90% from top quarter, 98% from top half. Full-time: 1,983 students, 54% women, 46% men. Part-time: 25 students, 68% women, 32% men. Students come from 51 states and territories, 58 other countries, 80% from out-of-state. 0.3% American Indian or Alaska Native, non-Hispanic/Latino; 7% Hispanic/Latino; 2% African American, non-Hispanic/Latino; 4% Asian, non-Hispanic/Latino; 0% Native Hawaiian or

other Pacific Islander, non-Hispanic/Latino; 5% international. 78% live on campus, 2% transferred in. Retention: 95% of full-time freshmen returned the following year. Academic areas with the most degrees conferred: social sciences; biological/life sciences; visual and performing arts. Core. Calendar: modular. ESL program, services for LD students, advanced placement, self-designed majors, independent study, double major, summer session for credit. Off campus study at American University; Woods Hole Marine Biological Laboratory Ecosystems Center; Associated Colleges of the Midwest Programs (5). Study abroad program. ROTC: Army (c).

Entrance Requirements: Options: electronic application, early decision, early action, deferred admission, international baccalaureate accepted. Required: essay, high school transcript, 2 recommendations. Recommended: interview. Required for some: SAT and SAT Subject Tests or ACT. Entrance: very difficult. Application deadlines: 1/15, 11/15 for early decision plan 1, 1/1 for early decision plan 2, 11/15 for early action. Notification: 4/1, 12/15 for early decision plan 1, 2/10 for early decision plan 2, 12/20 for early action. SAT Reasoning Test deadline: 1/15. Applicants placed on waiting list: 1,064. Wait-listed applicants offered admission: 6. Early decision applicants: 552. Early decision applicants admitted: 200. Early action applicants: 1,856. Early action applicants admitted: 580.

Costs Per Year: Application fee: $60. One-time mandatory fee: $150. Comprehensive fee: $51,670 includes full-time tuition ($41,742), mandatory fees ($200), and college room and board ($9728). College room only: $5496. Room and board charges vary according to board plan and housing facility. Part-time tuition: $6957 per course. Part-time tuition varies according to course load.

Collegiate Environment: Orientation program. Drama-theater group, choral group, student-run newspaper. Social organizations: 144 open to all; national fraternities, national sororities; 7% of eligible men and 11% of eligible women are members. Major annual events: Homecoming, Winter Ball, Annual Arts and Crafts. Student services: health clinic, personal-psychological counseling. Campus security: 24-hour emergency response devices and patrols, late night transport-escort service, controlled dormitory access, whistle program, student escort service, good campus lighting. 1,541 college housing spaces available. Freshmen guaranteed college housing. On-campus residence required through junior year. Options: coed, men-only, women-only housing available. Tutt Library plus 1 other with 566,379 books, 136,114 microform titles, 45,422 serials, 41,960 audiovisual materials, an OPAC, and a Web page. Operations spending for the previous fiscal year: $798,615. 396 computers available on campus for general student use. A campuswide network can be accessed from student residence rooms and from off campus. Students can access the following: online class registration. Staffed computer lab on campus provides training in use of computers, software, and the Internet.

Community Environment: Colorado Springs, metropolitan population of 587,500, is located 70 miles south of Denver at the foot of Pikes Peak. It is known for its healthful climate and spectacular scenery. the area averages more than 310 days of sunshine each year, has clean air, low humidity, cool summer nights, and mild winters. Bus, air, and good highways serve the area. The city has a fine arts center, opera, symphony, theatre, museums, art galleries, and numerous fine hotels, and motels. Areas for skiing, hunting, fishing, backpacking, and camping are nearby.

■ **COLORADO HEIGHTS UNIVERSITY**
3001 S Federal Blvd.
Denver, CO 80236-2711
Tel: (303)937-4200
E-mail: admissions@tlhu.edu
Web Site: www.chu.edu/

Description: Independent, 4-year, coed. Part of Teikyo University Group. Awards associate and bachelor's degrees. Founded 1989. Total enrollment: 504. 327 applied, 100% were admitted. 58% 25 or older.

Entrance Requirements: Required: high school transcript.

■ **COLORADO MESA UNIVERSITY**
1100 N Ave.
Grand Junction, CO 81501-3122
Tel: (970)248-1020; Free: 800-982-MESA
Fax: (970)248-1973
E-mail: admissions@coloradomesa.edu
Web Site: www.coloradomesa.edu/

Description: State-supported, comprehensive, coed. Awards associate, bachelor's, master's, and doctoral degrees. Founded 1925. Setting: 78-acre small town campus. Total enrollment: 9,482. Faculty: 607 (265 full-time, 342 part-time). Student-undergrad faculty ratio is 22:1. 5,840 applied, 82% were admitted. 7% from top 10% of their high school class, 22% from top quarter, 51% from top half. Full-time: 8,017 students, 46% women, 54% men. Part-time: 2,376 students, 61% women, 39% men. Students come from 43 states and territories, 14 other countries, 12% from out-of-state. 1% American Indian or Alaska Native, non-Hispanic/Latino; 13% Hispanic/Latino; 2% African American, non-Hispanic/Latino; 1% Asian, non-Hispanic/Latino; 1% Native Hawaiian or other Pacific Islander, non-Hispanic/Latino; 1% international. 27% 25 or older, 21% live on campus, 6% transferred in. Retention: 64% of full-time freshmen returned the following year. Academic areas with the most degrees conferred: business/marketing; health professions and related sciences; parks and recreation. Core. Calendar: semesters. Academic remediation for entering students, services for LD students, advanced placement, accelerated degree program, honors program, independent study, distance learning, double major, summer session for credit, part-time degree program, adult/continuing education programs, internships, graduate courses open to undergrads. Off campus study at National Student Exchange Program. Study abroad program.

Entrance Requirements: Options: electronic application, deferred admission. Required: high school transcript, SAT or ACT. Recommended: essay, 2 recommendations. Entrance: minimally difficult. Application deadlines: Rolling, Rolling for nonresidents. Notification: continuous, continuous for nonresidents. SAT Reasoning Test deadline: 8/15. SAT Subject Test deadline: 8/15. Transfer credits accepted: Yes.

Costs Per Year: Application fee: $30. State resident tuition: $6102 full-time, $203.41 per credit hour part-time. Nonresident tuition: $16,280 full-time, $542.69 per credit hour part-time. Mandatory fees: $768 full-time, $25.61 per credit hour part-time. Full-time tuition and fees vary according to course load. Part-time tuition and fees vary according to course load. College room and board: $9103. Room and board charges vary according to board plan and housing facility.

Collegiate Environment: Orientation program. Drama-theater group, choral group, marching band, student-run newspaper, radio station. Social organizations: 76 open to all. Most popular organizations: Environmental Club, Student Body Association, KMSA radio station, Rodeo Club, Campus Residents Association. Major annual events: Homecoming, Spring Fling, Unityfest. Student services: legal services, health clinic, personal-psychological counseling. Campus security: 24-hour emergency response devices and patrols, late night transport-escort service, controlled dormitory access. 2,251 college housing spaces available; all were occupied in 2012-13. Freshmen given priority for college housing. On-campus residence required through sophomore year. Options: coed, women-only housing available. John U. Tomlinson Library with 545,373 books, 58,348 microform titles, 76,724 serials, 19,149 audiovisual materials, an OPAC, and a Web page. 525 computers available on campus for general student use. A campuswide network can be accessed from student residence rooms and from off campus. Students can access the following: online class registration. Staffed computer lab on campus provides training in use of computers, software, and the Internet.

Community Environment: Grand Junction is located in an irrigated valley in the heart of a vast vacationland that is also rich in energy-related natural resources. The climate is invigorating, sunny, and mild. The community has churches of many denominations, excellent public schools, library facilities, cultural programs, city parks, golf courses, tennis courts, 4 hospitals, and good transportation services including three major airlines. Recreational activities in the nearby mountains and deserts include hiking, camping, boating, river rafting, fishing, hunting, cross-country and downhill skiing; and more.

■ **COLORADO MOUNTAIN COLLEGE**
3000 CR 114
Glenwood Springs, CO 81601
Tel: (970)945-7481; Free: 800-621-8559
E-mail: Vvalentine@coloradomtn.edu
Web Site: www.coloradomtn.edu/

Description: District-supported, 4-year, coed. Part of Colorado Mountain College District System. Awards associate and bachelor's degrees. Founded 1965. Setting: 680-acre rural campus. Total enrollment: 2,465. Faculty: (28 full-time). Student-undergrad faculty ratio is 12:1. 70% 25 or older, 44% live on campus. Core. Calendar: semesters. Academic remediation for entering students, ESL program, services for LD students, advanced placement, honors program, independent study, distance learning, double major, summer session for credit, part-time degree program, adult/continuing education programs, co-op programs and internships. Study abroad program.

Entrance Requirements: Open admission except for nursing, photography, and veterinary technology programs, Law Enforcement Training Academy. Options: electronic application, early admission, deferred admission, international baccalaureate accepted. Required: high school transcript. Recommended: SAT or ACT. Entrance: noncompetitive. Application deadlines: Rolling, Rolling for nonresidents. Transfer credits accepted: Yes.

Costs Per Year: Application fee: $0. Area resident tuition: $1680 full-time, $56 per credit part-time. State resident tuition: $2850 full-time, $95 per credit part-time. Nonresident tuition: $9970 full-time, $299 per credit part-time. Mandatory fees: $180 full-time. Full-time tuition and fees vary according to course level. Part-time tuition varies according to course level. College room and board: $8164.

Collegiate Environment: Orientation program. Drama-theater group, student-run newspaper. Most popular organizations: student government, Outdoor activities, World Awareness Society, Peer Mentors, Student Activities Board. Major annual events: Spring Fest, Outdoor activities, X Games. Student services: health clinic, personal-psychological counseling. Campus security: 24-hour emergency response devices, student patrols, controlled dormitory access. 237 college housing spaces available; 200 were occupied in 2012-13. Freshmen given priority for college housing. On-campus residence required in freshman year. Option: coed housing available. Quigley Library with 36,000 books, 70 serials, an OPAC, and a Web page. 65 computers available on campus for general student use. A campuswide network can be accessed from student residence rooms. Students can access the following: online class registration. Staffed computer lab on campus provides training in use of computers, software, and the Internet.

Community Environment: Glenwood Springs is an urban area with a moderate climate; a beautiful place to live. Railroads and buses serve the area and charter air service is available. Glenwood Springs is the county seat of Garfield County, and has the best shopping facilities in the county. The city has churches of all major denominations, library, museum, theatres, hospital and many of the civic clubs. Hot mineral springs have made Glenwood Springs a popular resort. Seven miles above the town is the Shoshone Hydroelectric Plant. The Colorado employment office is located here; several businesses hire part-time workers. Over 1,000 miles of fishing streams and more than 100 lakes are accessible from Glenwood Springs. The Sunlight Ski area is located nine miles south of the town; it has a 7,000 foot double chair lift. Aspen and Snowmass are 45 miles away. Other recreational activities include fishing, hiking, hunting and tennis. Strawberry day is an annual event in June.

■ **COLORADO MOUNTAIN COLLEGE, ALPINE CAMPUS**
1330 Bob Adams Dr.
Steamboat Springs, CO 80487
Tel: (970)870-4444; Free: 800-621-8559
E-mail: stephaniefletcher@coloradomtn.edu
Web Site: www.coloradomtn.edu/

Description: District-supported, 4-year, coed. Part of Colorado Mountain College District System. Awards associate and bachelor's degrees. Founded 1965. Setting: 10-acre small town campus. Total enrollment: 1,550. Faculty: (25 full-time). Student-undergrad faculty ratio is 12:1. 30% 25 or older, 44% live on campus. Core. Calendar: semesters. Academic remediation for entering students, ESL program, services for LD students, advanced placement, honors program, independent study, distance learning, double major, summer session for credit, part-time degree program, adult/continuing education programs, co-op programs and internships. Off campus study. Study abroad program.

Entrance Requirements: Open admission. Options: electronic application, early admission, deferred admission, international baccalaureate accepted. Required: high school transcript. Recommended: SAT or ACT. Entrance: noncompetitive. Application deadlines: Rolling, Rolling for nonresidents. Transfer credits accepted: Yes.

Costs Per Year: Application fee: $0. Area resident tuition: $1680 full-time, $56 per credit part-time. State resident tuition: $2850 full-time, $95 per quarter hour part-time. Nonresident tuition: $8970 full-time, $299 per credit part-time. Mandatory fees: $180 full-time. Full-time tuition and fees vary according to course level. Part-time tuition varies according to course level. College room and board: $8164. Room and board charges vary according to board plan.

Collegiate Environment: Orientation program. Student-run newspaper. Social organizations: 8 open to all. Most popular organizations: student government, Sky Club, Ski Club, International Club, Phi Theta Kappa. Major annual events: Spring Fling, Winter Carnival, Rail Jam. Student services: health clinic, personal-psychological counseling. Campus security: 24-hour emergency response devices, student patrols, controlled dormitory access. 225 college housing spaces available; 221 were occupied in 2012-13. On-campus residence required in freshman year. Option: coed housing available. Main library plus 1 other with 25,000 books, 50 serials, an OPAC, and a Web page. 60 computers available on campus for general student use. A campuswide network can be accessed from student residence rooms and from off campus. Students can access the following: online class registration. Staffed computer lab on campus provides training in use of computers, software, and the Internet.

Community Environment: Steamboat Springs is 175 miles northwest of Denver. A permanent population of 9,000 swells to over 25,000 on Christmas Eve, largely due to the attraction of the town's famous champagne powder. The town flourishes with the contrasting influences of working cattle ranches and a world-class ski resort. The surrounding area offers unlimited opportunities for downhill and cross-country skiing, and hunting. Students learn additional outdoor skills through college-sponsored activities such as winter survival, desert camping, and orienteering.

■ COLORADO MOUNTAIN COLLEGE, TIMBERLINE CAMPUS

901 S Hwy. 24
Leadville, CO 80461
Tel: (719)486-2015; Free: 800-621-8559
E-mail: joinus@coloradomtn.edu
Web Site: www.coloradomtn.edu/

Description: District-supported, 4-year, coed. Part of Colorado Mountain College District System. Awards associate and bachelor's degrees. Founded 1965. Setting: 200-acre rural campus. Total enrollment: 1,209. Faculty: (16 full-time). Student-undergrad faculty ratio is 12:1. 55% 25 or older, 30% live on campus. Core. Calendar: semesters. Academic remediation for entering students, ESL program, services for LD students, advanced placement, self-designed majors, honors program, independent study, distance learning, double major, summer session for credit, part-time degree program, adult/continuing education programs, co-op programs and internships. Off campus study. Study abroad program.

Entrance Requirements: Open admission. Options: electronic application, early admission, deferred admission, international baccalaureate accepted. Required: high school transcript. Recommended: SAT or ACT. Entrance: noncompetitive. Application deadlines: Rolling, Rolling for nonresidents. Transfer credits accepted: Yes.

Costs Per Year: Application fee: $0. Area resident tuition: $1680 full-time, $56 per credit part-time. State resident tuition: $2850 full-time, $95 per credit part-time. Nonresident tuition: $8970 full-time, $299 per credit part-time. Mandatory fees: $180 full-time. Full-time tuition and fees vary according to course level. Part-time tuition varies according to course level. College room and board: $8164. Room and board charges vary according to board plan.

Collegiate Environment: Orientation program. Most popular organizations: Environmental Club, Outdoor Club, Student Activities Board. Major annual events: Rail Jam, Winter Skjol, Leadville 100. Student services: health clinic, personal-psychological counseling. Campus security: 24-hour emergency response devices, student patrols, controlled dormitory access. 130 college housing spaces available; 100 were occupied in 2012-13. Freshmen given priority for college housing. On-campus residence required in freshman year. Option: coed housing available. Leadville Campus Library plus 1 other with 25,000 books, 50 serials, an OPAC, and a Web page. 30 computers available on campus for general student use. A campuswide network can be accessed from student residence rooms. Students can access the following: online class registration. Staffed computer lab on campus provides training in use of computers, software, and the Internet.

Community Environment: Leadville, situated at an altitude of 10,000 feet, is a rural community with a dry climate. Leadville has been the center of a famous mining district since the Placer Mines were opened in 1860. It became the silver capital and one of Colorado's greatest mining camps. Mining and tourism are major industries at the present. The city has a library, branch museum of the Colorado State Historical Society, churches, medical clinic and a hospital. Part-time work opportunities are available nearby. Recreation activities are numerous and include ice skating, golfing, tennis, fishing, soccer, bowling, swimming. There is skiing at Ski Cooper on the top of Tennessee Pass 12 miles north of Leadville and at nearby Copper Mountain, Vail, Keystone, Breckenridge and A-Basin. The World's Championship Pack Burro Race is an annual event the first weekend in August.

■ COLORADO NORTHWESTERN COMMUNITY COLLEGE

500 Kennedy Dr.
Rangely, CO 81648-3598

Tel: (970)675-2261; Free: 800-562-1105
Fax: (970)675-3343
E-mail: tresa.england@cncc.edu
Web Site: www.cncc.edu/

Description: State-supported, 2-year, coed. Part of Colorado Community College and Occupational Education System. Awards certificates, transfer associate, and terminal associate degrees. Founded 1962. Setting: 150-acre rural campus. Total enrollment: 1,291. Faculty: 92 (33 full-time, 59 part-time). Student-undergrad faculty ratio is 14:1. 1,009 applied, 100% were admitted. Full-time: 504 students, 62% women, 38% men. Part-time: 787 students, 56% women, 44% men. Students come from 17 states and territories, 3 other countries, 38% from out-of-state. 2% American Indian or Alaska Native, non-Hispanic/Latino; 9% Hispanic/Latino; 5% African American, non-Hispanic/Latino; 2% Asian, non-Hispanic/Latino; 0.1% Native Hawaiian or other Pacific Islander, non-Hispanic/Latino; 0.5% international. 47% 25 or older, 5% transferred in. Retention: 51% of full-time freshmen returned the following year. Academic areas with the most degrees conferred: liberal arts/general studies; health professions and related sciences; engineering technologies. Core. Calendar: semesters. Academic remediation for entering students, services for LD students, advanced placement, self-designed majors, independent study, distance learning, double major, summer session for credit, part-time degree program, adult/continuing education programs, internships.

Entrance Requirements: Open admission except for dental hygiene programs and nursing programs. Options: electronic application, early admission, deferred admission. Required: high school transcript. Recommended: ACT. Required for some: essay, 3 recommendations, interview. Entrance: noncompetitive. Application deadlines: Rolling, Rolling for nonresidents. Notification: continuous, continuous for nonresidents. Transfer credits accepted: Yes.

Costs Per Year: Application fee: $0. State resident tuition: $2540 full-time, $106 per credit hour part-time. Nonresident tuition: $5035 full-time, $210 per credit hour part-time. Mandatory fees: $200 full-time. Full-time tuition and fees vary according to program. Part-time tuition varies according to program. College room and board: $5988. College room only: $2306. Room and board charges vary according to board plan and housing facility.

Collegiate Environment: Orientation program. Choral group, student-run newspaper. Student services: personal-psychological counseling. Campus security: student patrols, late night transport-escort service. Freshmen given priority for college housing. On-campus residence required in freshman year. Option: coed housing available. Colorado Northwestern Community College Library plus 1 other with 20,063 books, 5,525 microform titles, 230 serials, 3,559 audiovisual materials, and an OPAC. 83 computers available on campus for general student use. A campuswide network can be accessed from student residence rooms and from off campus. Students can access the following: online class registration. Staffed computer lab on campus.

Community Environment: Rangely is a rural community (population 2,000) located on the western slope of Colorado, 300 miles northwest of Denver and 130 miles west of Steamboat Springs. It is a friendly community that offers a sharp change of pace from the urban areas. Excellent area for cross-country skiing, backpacking, river rafting, fishing and hunting. Close to Dinosaur National Monument and Flaming Gorge Dam and Reservoir. The area is two hours from downhill skiing at Steamboat Springs, Powder Horn and Sunlight Mountain. Community recreation facilities include: The Taylor Draw Dam Reservoir, a nine-hole golf course, tennis courts, a fitness trail, an ice skating rink, an indoor Olympic-size swimming pool, racquetball courts, and a dance and aerobics room. Bus and airport facilities are nearby.

■ COLORADO SCHOOL OF HEALING ARTS

7655 W Mississippi Ave.
Ste. 100
Lakewood, CO 80226
Tel: (303)986-2320; Free: 800-233-7114
Fax: (303)980-6594
Web Site: www.csha.net/

Description: Proprietary, 2-year, coed. Awards certificates and terminal associate degrees. Founded 1986. Total enrollment: 225. Student-undergrad faculty ratio is 16:1. 5% from out-of-state. 63% 25 or older.

Entrance Requirements: Required: high school transcript, interview. Entrance: noncompetitive.

Collegiate Environment: Student services: personal-psychological counseling.

■ COLORADO SCHOOL OF MINES

1500 Illinois St.
Golden, CO 80401-1887
Tel: (303)273-3000; Free: 800-446-9488
Fax: (303)273-3509
E-mail: admit@mines.edu
Web Site: www.mines.edu/

Description: State-supported, university, coed. Awards bachelor's, master's, and doctoral degrees and post-master's certificates. Founded 1874. Setting: 491-acre small town campus with easy access to Denver, Boulder, Colorado Springs. Endowment: $196 million. Research spending for the previous fiscal year: $42.4 million. Educational spending for the previous fiscal year: $9457 per student. Total enrollment: 5,632. Faculty: 368 (251 full-time, 117 part-time). Student-undergrad faculty ratio is 16:1. 11,682 applied, 37% were admitted. 60% from top 10% of their high school class, 91% from top quarter, 100% from top half. 18 National Merit Scholars, 83 valedictorians. Full-time: 3,953 students, 26% women, 74% men. Part-time: 216 students, 26% women, 74% men. Students come from 55 states and territories, 54 other countries, 38% from out-of-state. 0.3% American Indian or Alaska Native, non-Hispanic/Latino; 7% Hispanic/Latino; 1% African American, non-Hispanic/Latino; 5% Asian, non-Hispanic/Latino; 0.02% Native Hawaiian or other Pacific Islander, non-Hispanic/Latino; 6% international. 6% 25 or older, 43% live on campus, 3% transferred in. Retention: 89% of full-time freshmen returned the following year. Academic areas with the most degrees conferred: engineering; mathematics and statistics; physical sciences. Core. Calendar: semesters. Services for LD students, advanced placement, accelerated degree program, honors program, independent study, double major, summer session for credit, co-op programs and internships, graduate courses open to undergrads. Off campus study at Red Rocks Community College (studio art courses may be taken as free electives). Study abroad program. ROTC: Army, Air Force.

Entrance Requirements: Options: electronic application, deferred admission. Required: high school transcript, SAT or ACT. Recommended: minimum 3.8 high school GPA, rank in upper quartile of high school class. Required for some: essay, interview. Entrance: very difficult. Application deadline: 5/1. Notification: continuous until 10/1. SAT Reasoning Test deadline: 2/1. Transfer credits accepted: Yes. Applicants placed on waiting list: 1,533. Wait-listed applicants offered admission: 2.

Collegiate Environment: Orientation program. Drama-theater group, choral group, marching band, student-run newspaper, radio station. Social organizations: 170 open to all; national fraternities, national sororities; 16% of eligible men and 20% of eligible women are members. Most popular organizations: Society of Women Engineers, Residence Hall Association, Associated Students of Colorado School of Mines, Student Professional Societies/ and/ Religious Organizations, Multicultural Engineering Program. Major annual events: Engineers' Days (E-Days), Celebration of Mines, Career Day (Fall and Spring). Student services: health clinic, personal-psychological counseling, women's center. Campus security: 24-hour emergency response devices and patrols, late night transport-escort service, controlled dormitory access, full service, community oriented law enforcement agency employing fully trained police officers. 1,509 college housing spaces available; all were occupied in 2012-13. Freshmen guaranteed college housing. On-campus residence required in freshman year. Options: coed, men-only housing available. Arthur Lakes Library with 593,618 books, 452,343 microform titles, 31,570 serials, 728 audiovisual materials, an OPAC, and a Web page. Operations spending for the previous fiscal year: $3.1 million. 508 computers available on campus for general student use. Computer purchase/lease plans available. A campuswide network can be accessed from student residence rooms and from off campus. Students can access the following: online class registration. Staffed computer lab on campus provides training in use of computers, software, and the Internet.

Community Environment: CSM is located in Golden, only 15 miles west of Denver's downtown business district. Golden is a community of 15,000 people nestled in the foothills of the Rocky Mountains. Maintaining a distinct identity from the other Denver suburbs, Golden is also home to the National Earthquake Center and the National Renewable Energy Laboratory. Many CSM students enjoy the outdoors, and favorite summer activities include hiking, jogging, camping, and bicycling. During the winter months, skiing is the major activity with some of the world's best slopes virtually in CSM's backyard. With a population of over two million people, nearby Denver offers all the attractions of a major metropolitan area. As a commercial, transportation, and financial center for the Rocky Mountain region, Denver is home to many government agencies, colleges and universities, and business involved in natural resources, computers, and biotechnology.

■ COLORADO SCHOOL OF TRADES

1575 Hoyt St.
Lakewood, CO 80215-2996
Tel: (303)233-4697; Free: 800-234-4594
Fax: (303)233-4723
E-mail: rm@schooloftrades.edu
Web Site: www.schooloftrades.com/

Description: Proprietary, 2-year, coed. Awards terminal associate degrees. Founded 1947. Setting: suburban campus. Total enrollment: 134. Faculty: (10 full-time). Student-undergrad faculty ratio is 12:1. 174 applied, 87% were admitted. Full-time: 134 students, 1% women, 99% men. 88% from out-of-state.

Entrance Requirements: Required: essay, high school transcript, interview.

Costs Per Year: Application fee: $25. Tuition: $18,900 full-time. Tuition guaranteed not to increase for student's term of enrollment.

Collegiate Environment: 6 computers available on campus for general student use.

■ COLORADO STATE UNIVERSITY

Fort Collins, CO 80523-0015
Tel: (970)491-1101
Fax: (970)491-7799
E-mail: admissions@colostate.edu
Web Site: www.colostate.edu/

Description: State-supported, university, coed. Part of Colorado State University System. Awards bachelor's, master's, and doctoral degrees. Founded 1870. Setting: 582-acre urban campus with easy access to Denver. Endowment: $225.4 million. Research spending for the previous fiscal year: $375.9 million. Educational spending for the previous fiscal year: $9799 per student. Total enrollment: 30,647. Faculty: 966 (940 full-time, 26 part-time). Student-undergrad faculty ratio is 19:1. 17,929 applied, 75% were admitted. 22% from top 10% of their high school class, 51% from top quarter, 88% from top half. 6 National Merit Scholars. Full-time: 21,193 students, 52% women, 48% men. Part-time: 2,286 students, 47% women, 53% men. Students come from 57 states and territories, 55 other countries, 18% from out-of-state. 0.4% American Indian or Alaska Native, non-Hispanic/Latino; 9% Hispanic/Latino; 2% African American, non-Hispanic/Latino; 2% Asian, non-Hispanic/Latino; 0.2% Native Hawaiian or other Pacific Islander, non-Hispanic/Latino; 2% international. 9% 25 or older, 25% live on campus, 6% transferred in. Retention: 84% of full-time freshmen returned the following year. Academic areas with the most degrees conferred: business/marketing; family and consumer sciences; social sciences. Core. Calendar: semesters. ESL program, services for LD students, advanced placement, accelerated degree program, honors program, independent study, distance learning, double major, summer session for credit, part-time degree program, co-op programs and internships, graduate courses open to undergrads. Off campus study at Aims Community College. Study abroad program. ROTC: Army, Air Force.

Entrance Requirements: Options: electronic application, early action, deferred admission, international baccalaureate accepted. Required: essay, high school transcript, 1 recommendation, SAT or ACT. Entrance: moderately difficult. Application deadline: 2/1. Notification: continuous. SAT Reasoning Test deadline: 5/1. Transfer credits accepted: Yes. Early action applicants: 6,084. Early action applicants admitted: 5,723.

Costs Per Year: Application fee: $50. State resident tuition: $6,875 full-time, $312.20 per credit hour part-time. Nonresident tuition: $22,667 full-time, $1,133 per credit hour part-time. Mandatory fees: $1,774 full-time, $29.84 per credit hour part-time, $149.22 per term part-time. Full-time tuition and fees vary according to course load, program, and student level. Part-time tuition and fees vary according to course load, program, and student level. College room and board: $10,278. College room only: $4720. Room and board charges vary according to board plan and housing facility.

Collegiate Environment: Orientation program. Drama-theater group, choral group, marching band, student-run newspaper, radio station. Social organizations: 538 open to all; national fraternities, national sororities, local fraternities, local sororities; 6% of eligible men and 9% of eligible women are members. Most popular organizations: Golden Key International Honor Society, Council of International Student Affairs, Campus Crusade for Christ, Associated Students of CSU (ASCSU Student Government), Snowriders. Major annual events: Homecoming Weekend, Monfort Lecture Series, President's Fall Address and University Picnic. Student services: legal services, health clinic, personal-psychological counseling, women's center. Campus security: 24-hour emergency response devices and patrols, student patrols, late night transport-escort service, controlled dormitory access. College housing designed to accommodate 5,325 students; 5,330 undergraduates lived in college housing during 2012-13. Freshmen guaranteed college housing. On-campus residence required in freshman year. Option: coed housing available. William E. Morgan Library plus 3 others with 2.8 million books, 169,039 microform titles, 76,028 serials, 5,053 audiovisual materials, an OPAC, and a Web page. Operations spending for the previous fiscal year: $16 million. 2,700 computers available on campus for general student use. Computer purchase/lease plans available. A campuswide network can be accessed from student residence rooms and from off campus. Students can access the following: online class registration, personalized portal services including transcripts and financials (billing, financial aid). Staffed computer lab on campus (open 24 hours a day) provides training in use of computers, software, and the Internet.

Community Environment: Fort Collins, a community of 110,000 is situated at the foot of the Rocky Mountains. The excellent climate and beautiful mountains create an ideal college setting about 65 miles north of Denver. The city has many churches, a local airport, hospital, hotels, motels, and is the shopping center of Northern Colorado. Part-time employment is available for students and some full-time employment is available for graduates.

■ **COLORADO STATE UNIVERSITY–PUEBLO**
2200 Bonforte Blvd.
Pueblo, CO 81001-4901
Tel: (719)549-2100
Fax: (719)549-2419
E-mail: dana.trujillo@colostate-pueblo.edu
Web Site: www.colostate-pueblo.edu/

Description: State-supported, comprehensive, coed. Part of Colorado State University System. Awards bachelor's and master's degrees. Founded 1933. Setting: 275-acre small town campus with easy access to Colorado Springs. Endowment: $7.3 million. Research spending for the previous fiscal year: $194,908. Educational spending for the previous fiscal year: $3806 per student. Total enrollment: 5,049. Faculty: 418 (192 full-time, 226 part-time). Student-undergrad faculty ratio is 16:1. 2,758 applied, 95% were admitted. 2% from top 10% of their high school class, 7% from top quarter, 30% from top half. Students come from 40 states and territories, 23 other countries, 7% from out-of-state. 33% 25 or older, 19% live on campus. Retention: 65% of full-time freshmen returned the following year. Academic areas with the most degrees conferred: social sciences; business/marketing; health professions and related sciences. Core. Calendar: semesters. Academic remediation for entering students, ESL program, services for LD students, advanced placement, accelerated degree program, honors program, independent study, distance learning, double major, summer session for credit, part-time degree program, external degree program, co-op programs and internships, graduate courses open to undergrads. Off campus study at Adams State College, Colorado State University, University of Colorado at Denver. Study abroad program. ROTC: Army.

Entrance Requirements: Options: electronic application, deferred admission, international baccalaureate accepted. Required: minimum 2 high school GPA, SAT or ACT. Required for some: high school transcript. Entrance: moderately difficult. Application deadline: 8/1. Notification: continuous. SAT Reasoning Test deadline: 8/1. Transfer credits accepted: Yes.

Costs Per Year: Application fee: $25. State resident tuition: $5494 full-time, $203.91 per credit hour part-time. Nonresident tuition: $15,816 full-time, $613 per credit hour part-time. Mandatory fees: $1833 full-time, $61.10 per credit hour part-time. Full-time tuition and fees vary according to course load. Part-time tuition and fees vary according to course load. College room and board: $8600. College room only: $5200. Room and board charges vary according to board plan.

Collegiate Environment: Orientation program. Choral group, marching band, student-run newspaper, radio station. Social organizations: 60 open to all; national fraternities, national sororities; 2% of eligible men and 2% of eligible women are members. Most popular organizations: Belmont Residence Hall Association, Associated Student Government. Major annual events: Student Welcome Back Activities, Casino Night, Homecoming Week activities. Student services: health clinic, personal-psychological counseling. Campus security: 24-hour emergency response devices and patrols, late night transport-escort service, controlled dormitory access. CSU-Pueblo University Library plus 1 other with 274,890 books, 14,142 microform titles, 14,672 serials, 13,034 audiovisual materials, an OPAC, and a Web page. 702 computers available on campus for general student use. A campuswide network can be accessed. Students can access the following: online class registration. Staffed computer lab on campus.

Community Environment: Pueblo is a city of approximately 100,000

people located on the Arkansas River on the eastern slope of the Rocky Mountains. The city is a manufacturing and retail center for southeastern Colorado with a mild and semiarid climate. Recreational activities including skiing, hiking, camping, boating, fishing, and swimming are available in Pueblo and its immediate vicinity. The city and the university cooperate to provide cultural activities including a symphony orchestra and theatrical productions.

■ **COLORADO TECHNICAL UNIVERSITY COLORADO SPRINGS**
4435 N Chestnut St.
Colorado Springs, CO 80907-3896
Tel: (719)598-0200; Free: 866-942-6555
E-mail: bbraaten@coloradotech.edu
Web Site: www.coloradotech.edu/

Description: Proprietary, university, coed. Administratively affiliated with Colorado Technical University. Awards associate, bachelor's, master's, and doctoral degrees. Founded 1965. Setting: 14-acre suburban campus with easy access to Denver. Total enrollment: 2,359. Faculty: 343. 5% from out-of-state. 80% 25 or older. Academic areas with the most degrees conferred: computer and information sciences; business/marketing; homeland security, law enforcement, firefighting, and protective services. Core. Academic remediation for entering students, services for LD students, advanced placement, accelerated degree program, independent study, distance learning, double major, summer session for credit, part-time degree program, adult/continuing education programs, co-op programs and internships, graduate courses open to undergrads. ROTC: Army (c).

Entrance Requirements: Options: electronic application, deferred admission, international baccalaureate accepted. Required: interview. Entrance: minimally difficult. Application deadline: Rolling. Notification: continuous.

Collegiate Environment: Orientation program. Campus security: 24-hour emergency response devices, late night transport-escort service. 400 computers available on campus for general student use. A campuswide network can be accessed. Staffed computer lab on campus.

Community Environment: Colorado Tech is located at the foot of beautiful Pikes Peak. This ideal location provides convenient access to Colorado's magnificent outdoor recreational facilities: skiing, camping, hunting, fishing, and backpacking. Beautiful Colorado Springs and its environs constitute a progressive, growing city of approximately 400,000.

■ **COLORADO TECHNICAL UNIVERSITY DENVER SOUTH**
3151 S Vaughn Way
Aurora, CO 80014
Tel: (303)632-2300; Free: 888-309-6555
E-mail: rgiboney@coloradotech.edu
Web Site: www.coloradotech.edu/

Description: Proprietary, comprehensive, coed. Administratively affiliated with Colorado Technical University. Awards associate, bachelor's, and master's degrees. Founded 1965. Setting: 1-acre urban campus with easy access to Denver. Total enrollment: 733. Faculty: 163. Full-time: 229 students, 45% women, 55% men. Part-time: 344 students, 49% women, 51% men. 6% from out-of-state. 68% 25 or older, 13% transferred in. Academic areas with the most degrees conferred: computer and information sciences; business/marketing; homeland security, law enforcement, firefighting, and protective services. Core. Academic remediation for entering students, services for LD students, advanced placement, accelerated degree program, independent study, distance learning, double major, summer session for credit, part-time degree program, adult/continuing education programs, co-op programs and internships, graduate courses open to undergrads.

Entrance Requirements: Options: electronic application, deferred admission, international baccalaureate accepted. Required: interview. Application deadline: Rolling. Notification: continuous.

Collegiate Environment: Orientation program. Campus security: 24-hour emergency response devices and patrols, late night transport-escort service. 230 computers available on campus for general student use. A campuswide network can be accessed. Staffed computer lab on campus.

■ **COLORADO TECHNICAL UNIVERSITY ONLINE**
4435 N Chestnut St.
Ste. E
Colorado Springs, CO 80907
Tel: (303)362-2900
Fax: (303)362-2945
Web Site: www.coloradotech.edu/

Description: Proprietary, comprehensive, coed. Administratively affiliated with Colorado Technical University. Awards associate, bachelor's, and master's degrees. Total enrollment: 25,797. Faculty: 613. Full-time: 23,094 students, 65% women, 35% men. 83% 25 or older, 22% transferred in. Academic areas with the most degrees conferred: business/marketing; homeland security, law enforcement, firefighting, and protective services; computer and information sciences. Core. Academic remediation for entering students, services for LD students, advanced placement, accelerated degree program, distance learning, double major, part-time degree program, adult/continuing education programs, graduate courses open to undergrads.
Entrance Requirements: Options: electronic application, deferred admission, international baccalaureate accepted. Required: interview. Entrance: minimally difficult. Application deadline: Rolling. Notification: continuous.
Collegiate Environment: Orientation program.

■ **COMMUNITY COLLEGE OF AURORA**
16000 E Centre Tech Pky.
Aurora, CO 80011-9036
Tel: (303)360-4700
E-mail: kristen.cusack@ccaurora.edu
Web Site: www.ccaurora.edu/
Description: State-supported, 2-year, coed. Awards certificates, transfer associate, and terminal associate degrees. Founded 1983. Setting: suburban campus with easy access to Denver. Total enrollment: 6,293. Student-undergrad faculty ratio is 20:1. 1% from out-of-state. 53% 25 or older. Core. Calendar: semesters. Academic remediation for entering students, ESL program, services for LD students, independent study, distance learning, summer session for credit, part-time degree program, external degree program, adult/continuing education programs, internships. Off campus study at T. H. Pickens Technical Vocational Center.
Entrance Requirements: Open admission. Option: early admission. Required for some: high school transcript. Entrance: noncompetitive. Application deadline: Rolling. Notification: continuous.
Collegiate Environment: Drama-theater group. Student services: women's center. Campus security: late night transport-escort service. 6,727 books, 105 serials, an OPAC, and a Web page.

■ **COMMUNITY COLLEGE OF DENVER**
PO Box 173363
Denver, CO 80217-3363
Tel: (303)556-2600
E-mail: enrollment_services@ccd.edu
Web Site: www.ccd.edu/
Description: State-supported, 2-year, coed. Part of Colorado Community College System. Awards certificates, transfer associate, and terminal associate degrees. Founded 1970. Setting: 124-acre urban campus. Total enrollment: 10,918. Faculty: 436 (90 full-time, 346 part-time). Student-undergrad faculty ratio is 27:1. Full-time: 2,740 students, 58% women, 42% men. Part-time: 8,178 students, 59% women, 41% men. 9% from out-of-state. 49% 25 or older. Academic areas with the most degrees conferred: liberal arts/general studies; health professions and related sciences; business/marketing. Core. Calendar: semesters. Academic remediation for entering students, ESL program, services for LD students, advanced placement, accelerated degree program, freshman honors college, honors program, independent study, distance learning, double major, summer session for credit, part-time degree program, external degree program, adult/continuing education programs, co-op programs and internships. Off campus study at Metropolitan State College, University of Colorado at Denver. Study abroad program. ROTC: Army (c), Air Force (c).
Entrance Requirements: Open admission except for health occupation, essential skills programs, and computer information systems programs. Options: electronic application, early admission, deferred admission. Entrance: noncompetitive. Application deadline: Rolling. Notification: continuous.
Collegiate Environment: Orientation program. Choral group, student-run newspaper. Most popular organizations: Phi Theta Kappa, Black Student Alliance, La Mision, SAFI, Chinese Culture Club. Major annual events: Haunted Harvest, Cinco de Mayo, Welcome Back Picnic. Student services: health clinic, personal-psychological counseling. Campus security: 24-hour emergency response devices and patrols, late night transport-escort service. Auraria Library with an OPAC and a Web page.
Community Environment: See University of Denver.

■ **DENVER SCHOOL OF NURSING**
1401 19th St.
Denver, CO 80202

Tel: (303)292-0015; Free: 888-479-5550
Fax: (720)974-0290
Web Site: www.denverschoolofnursing.edu/
Description: Proprietary, 4-year, coed. Awards bachelor's degrees.

■ **DEVRY UNIVERSITY (COLORADO SPRINGS)**
1175 Kelly Johnson Blvd.
Colorado Springs, CO 80920
Tel: (719)632-3000; Free: 866-338-7941
Web Site: www.devry.edu/
Description: Proprietary, comprehensive, coed. Part of DeVry University. Awards associate, bachelor's, and master's degrees. Founded 2001. Setting: 9-acre urban campus. Total enrollment: 275. Faculty: 42 (1 full-time, 41 part-time). Student-undergrad faculty ratio is 9:1. Full-time: 89 students, 39% women, 61% men. Part-time: 127 students, 31% women, 69% men. Students come from 12 states and territories, 1 other country. 63% 25 or older. Retention: 36% of full-time freshmen returned the following year. Academic areas with the most degrees conferred: business/marketing; computer and information sciences. Calendar: semesters. Academic remediation for entering students, services for LD students, advanced placement, accelerated degree program, distance learning, summer session for credit, part-time degree program, adult/continuing education programs, co-op programs.
Entrance Requirements: Options: electronic application, deferred admission, international baccalaureate accepted. Required: high school transcript, interview. Entrance: minimally difficult. Application deadline: Rolling. Notification: continuous.
Collegiate Environment: Orientation program. Social organizations: 1 open to all. Most popular organization: Association for Information Technology Professionals. Major annual event: various food events. Campus security: 24-hour emergency response devices and patrols, late night transport-escort service, safety pamphlets, lighted sidewalks/pathways. Learning Resource Center with an OPAC and a Web page.

■ **DEVRY UNIVERSITY (WESTMINSTER)**
1870 W 122nd Ave.
Westminster, CO 80234-2010
Tel: (303)280-7400; Free: 866-338-7941
Web Site: www.devry.edu/
Description: Proprietary, comprehensive, coed. Awards associate, bachelor's, and master's degrees. Founded 1945. Setting: urban campus. Total enrollment: 723. Faculty: 72 (12 full-time, 60 part-time). Student-undergrad faculty ratio is 12:1. Full-time: 188 students, 31% women, 69% men. Part-time: 425 students, 39% women, 61% men. 14% from out-of-state. 1% American Indian or Alaska Native, non-Hispanic/Latino; 14% Hispanic/Latino; 6% African American, non-Hispanic/Latino; 4% Asian, non-Hispanic/Latino; 0.5% Native Hawaiian or other Pacific Islander, non-Hispanic/Latino; 0.2% international. 76% 25 or older, 17% transferred in. Academic areas with the most degrees conferred: business/marketing; computer and information sciences; engineering technologies. Calendar: semesters. Adult/continuing education programs.
Entrance Requirements: Required: high school transcript. Required for some: essay, interview. Entrance: noncompetitive. Application deadline: Rolling. Notification: continuous.
Costs Per Year: Application fee: $40. Tuition: $16,076 full-time, $609 per credit hour part-time. Mandatory fees: $80 full-time.
Collegiate Environment: Orientation program. College housing not available.

■ **EVEREST COLLEGE (AURORA)**
14280 E Jewell Ave.
Ste. 100
Aurora, CO 80014
Tel: (303)745-6244
Fax: (303)745-6245
Web Site: www.everest.edu/
Description: Proprietary, 2-year, coed. Awards terminal associate degrees. Founded 1989. Total enrollment: 1,272. 251 applied. 0% from out-of-state. 53% 25 or older.

■ **EVEREST COLLEGE (COLORADO SPRINGS)**
1815 Jet Wing Dr.
Colorado Springs, CO 80916
Tel: (719)638-6580; Free: 888-741-4270

Fax: (719)638-6818
Web Site: www.everest.edu/
Description: Proprietary, 2-year, coed. Part of Corinthian Colleges, Inc. Awards diplomas, transfer associate, and terminal associate degrees. Founded 1897. Setting: 5-acre suburban campus with easy access to Denver. Total enrollment: 632. 116 applied. 0% from out-of-state. 49% 25 or older. Retention: 79% of full-time freshmen returned the following year.
Entrance Requirements: Required: high school transcript, CPAt. Entrance: minimally difficult. Application deadline: Rolling. Notification: continuous.
Collegiate Environment: Campus security: 24-hour emergency response devices.
Community Environment: See The Colorado College.

■ **EVEREST COLLEGE (THORNTON)**
9065 Grant St.
Thornton, CO 80229-4339
Tel: (303)457-2757; Free: 888-741-4270
Web Site: www.everest.edu/
Description: Proprietary, 2-year, coed. Awards certificates and terminal associate degrees. Founded 1895. Setting: 11-acre campus. Total enrollment: 850. 321 applied. 1% from out-of-state. 54% 25 or older. Retention: 94% of full-time freshmen returned the following year. Summer session for credit.
Entrance Requirements: Required: CPAt. Entrance: moderately difficult. Application deadline: Rolling.

■ **FORT LEWIS COLLEGE**
1000 Rim Dr.
Durango, CO 81301-3999
Tel: (970)247-7010; Free: 877-FLC-COLO
Fax: (970)247-7179
E-mail: admission@fortlewis.edu
Web Site: www.fortlewis.edu/
Description: State-supported, 4-year, coed. Awards bachelor's degrees. Founded 1911. Setting: 350-acre small town campus. Endowment: $4.7 million. Total enrollment: 3,891. Faculty: 205 (160 full-time, 45 part-time). Student-undergrad faculty ratio is 19:1. 2,417 applied, 87% were admitted. 11% from top 10% of their high school class, 31% from top quarter, 35% from top half. Full-time: 3,565 students, 49% women, 51% men. Part-time: 326 students, 48% women, 52% men. Students come from 47 states and territories, 19 other countries, 41% from out-of-state. 20% American Indian or Alaska Native, non-Hispanic/Latino; 9% Hispanic/Latino; 1% African American, non-Hispanic/Latino; 0.4% Asian, non-Hispanic/Latino; 0.3% Native Hawaiian or other Pacific Islander, non-Hispanic/Latino; 2% international. 15% 25 or older, 37% live on campus, 10% transferred in. Retention: 62% of full-time freshmen returned the following year. Academic areas with the most degrees conferred: business/marketing; social sciences; visual and performing arts; parks and recreation. Core. Calendar: modified trimesters. Academic remediation for entering students, services for LD students, advanced placement, self-designed majors, honors program, independent study, double major, summer session for credit, internships. Study abroad program.
Entrance Requirements: Options: early action, deferred admission, international baccalaureate accepted. Required: high school transcript, SAT or ACT. Recommended: essay, 2 recommendations. Required for some: interview. Entrance: moderately difficult. Application deadline: 8/1.
Costs Per Year: Application fee: $40. State resident tuition: $5232 full-time, $218 per credit hour part-time. Nonresident tuition: $16,072 full-time, $670 per credit hour part-time. Mandatory fees: $1691 full-time. Full-time tuition and fees vary according to course load and reciprocity agreements. Part-time tuition varies according to course load and reciprocity agreements. College room and board: $8590. College room only: $4270. Room and board charges vary according to board plan and housing facility.
Collegiate Environment: Orientation program. Drama-theater group, student-run newspaper, radio station. Student services: health clinic, personal-psychological counseling. Campus security: 24-hour emergency response devices and patrols, late night transport-escort service, controlled dormitory access. 1,396 college housing spaces available; 1,331 were occupied in 2012-13. Freshmen given priority for college housing. On-campus residence required in freshman year. Option: coed housing available. John F. Reed Library plus 1 other with 178,602 books, 344,586 microform titles, 44,061 serials, 8,562 audiovisual materials, an OPAC, and a Web page. 786 computers available on campus for general student use. A campuswide network can be accessed from student residence rooms and from off campus. Students can access the following: online class registration. Staffed

computer lab on campus (open 24 hours a day) provides training in use of computers, software, and the Internet.
Community Environment: Durango is located in the Four-Corners region where the states of Colorado, Utah, Arizona, and New Mexico come to a common point. Durango has magnificent mountain landscapes and glistening sunshine at an elevation of 6,700 feet. A modern jet port serves the area. Near Durango nestled in the spruce of the high country gleam thousands of mountain lakes, including two of the larger, Lemon and Vallecito. A few miles south is Navajo Lake, which extends into New Mexico. Agriculture and tourism are an integral part of the economy, as is retailing education, medicine, and law. La Plata County is home to over 47,000 people, and Durango has a population of over 15,500. Purgatory ski area offers complete ski resort facilities.

■ **FRONT RANGE COMMUNITY COLLEGE**
3645 W 112th Ave.
Westminster, CO 80030
Tel: (303)466-8811
E-mail: yolanda.espinoza@frontrange.edu
Web Site: www.frontrange.edu/
Description: State-supported, 2-year, coed. Part of Community Colleges of Colorado System. Awards certificates, transfer associate, and terminal associate degrees. Founded 1968. Setting: 90-acre suburban campus with easy access to Denver. Endowment: $294,302. Educational spending for the previous fiscal year: $722 per student. Total enrollment: 20,092. Faculty: 1,118 (212 full-time, 906 part-time). Student-undergrad faculty ratio is 23:1. 8,187 applied, 100% were admitted. Full-time: 7,445 students, 51% women, 49% men. Part-time: 12,647 students, 60% women, 40% men. Students come from 44 states and territories, 26 other countries, 2% from out-of-state. 1% American Indian or Alaska Native, non-Hispanic/Latino; 13% Hispanic/Latino; 2% African American, non-Hispanic/Latino; 3% Asian, non-Hispanic/Latino; 0.4% Native Hawaiian or other Pacific Islander, non-Hispanic/Latino; 1% international. 43% 25 or older, 9% transferred in. Retention: 43% of full-time freshmen returned the following year. Core. Calendar: semesters. Academic remediation for entering students, ESL program, services for LD students, advanced placement, self-designed majors, freshman honors college, honors program, independent study, distance learning, double major, summer session for credit, part-time degree program, co-op programs and internships. Off campus study at Metropolitan State College, University of Colorado at Denver, Colorado State University. Study abroad program. ROTC: Army (c), Air Force (c).
Entrance Requirements: Open admission. Options: electronic application, early admission, deferred admission. Entrance: noncompetitive. Application deadlines: Rolling, Rolling for nonresidents. Notification: continuous, continuous for nonresidents. Transfer credits accepted: Yes.
Collegiate Environment: Orientation program. Drama-theater group, student-run newspaper. Social organizations: 15 open to all. Most popular organizations: Student Government Association, Student Colorado Registry of Interpreters for the Deaf, Students in Free Enterprise (SIFE), Gay Straight Alliance, Recycling Club. Major annual events: Spring Fling, Chili Cook-Off, culture days. Student services: personal-psychological counseling. Campus security: 24-hour patrols, late night transport-escort service. College Hill Library with an OPAC and a Web page. 233 computers available on campus for general student use. Computer purchase/lease plans available. A campuswide network can be accessed from off-campus. Students can access the following: online class registration. Staffed computer lab on campus provides training in use of computers and software.
Community Environment: See University of Denver.

■ **HERITAGE COLLEGE**
12 Lakeside Ln.
Denver, CO 80212-7413
Tel: (303)477-7240
Fax: (303)477-7276
Web Site: www.heritage-education.com/
Description: Proprietary, 2-year, coed. Awards terminal associate degrees. Founded 1986. Total enrollment: 496. 329 applied, 53% were admitted.
Entrance Requirements: Recommended: high school transcript.

■ **INSTITUTE OF BUSINESS & MEDICAL CAREERS**
3842 S Mason St.
Fort Collins, CO 80525
Tel: (970)223-2669; Free: 800-495-2669
E-mail: kmcneil@ibmc.edu

Web Site: www.ibmc.edu/

Description: Private, 2-year, coed. Administratively affiliated with Institute of Business and Medical Careers- Greeley, Colorado and Cheyenne, Wyoming. Awards certificates, diplomas, and terminal associate degrees. Founded 1987. Setting: suburban campus with easy access to Denver. Educational spending for the previous fiscal year: $4440 per student. Total enrollment: 302. Faculty: 34 (11 full-time, 23 part-time). Student-undergrad faculty ratio is 14:1. 366 applied, 100% were admitted. Full-time: 302 students, 89% women, 11% men. 2% from out-of-state. 20% 25 or older. Retention: 69% of full-time freshmen returned the following year. Core. Calendar: continuous. Accelerated degree program, honors program, co-op programs and internships.

Entrance Requirements: Open admission. Required: high school transcript, interview. Application deadline: Rolling. Transfer credits accepted: Yes.

Costs Per Year: Application fee: $75. Tuition: $11,340 full-time. Full-time tuition varies according to course load and program. Tuition guaranteed not to increase for student's term of enrollment.

Collegiate Environment: Orientation program. Student-run newspaper. Most popular organizations: Alpha Beta Kappa, Circle of Hope, Relay for Life. Major annual events: Nine News Health Fair, Student Assembly. 118 computers available on campus for general student use. A campuswide network can be accessed from off-campus. Staffed computer lab on campus provides training in use of computers, software, and the Internet.

■ INTELLITEC COLLEGE (COLORADO SPRINGS)

2315 E Pikes Peak Ave.
Colorado Springs, CO 80909-6030
Tel: (719)632-7626; Free: 800-748-2282
Fax: (719)632-7451
Web Site: www.intelliteccollege.edu/

Description: Proprietary, 2-year, coed. Part of Technical Trades Institute, Inc. Awards certificates, diplomas, and terminal associate degrees. Founded 1965. Setting: 2-acre urban campus with easy access to Denver. Total enrollment: 587. 57% 25 or older. Core. Calendar: 6-week terms. Advanced placement, double major.

Entrance Requirements: Open admission. Required: high school transcript, interview. Entrance: noncompetitive. Application deadline: Rolling.

Collegiate Environment: Orientation program. Campus security: 24-hour emergency response devices. 274 books and 28 serials.

■ INTELLITEC COLLEGE (GRAND JUNCTION)

772 Horizon Dr.
Grand Junction, CO 81506
Tel: (970)245-8101; Free: 800-748-2282
Fax: (970)243-8074
Web Site: www.intelliteccollege.edu/

Description: Proprietary, 2-year, coed. Awards certificates, diplomas, and transfer associate degrees. Setting: small town campus. Total enrollment: 729. Student-undergrad faculty ratio is 22:1. 2% from out-of-state. 57% 25 or older. Calendar: continuous.

Entrance Requirements: Required: high school transcript, interview. Entrance: noncompetitive.

■ INTELLITEC MEDICAL INSTITUTE

2345 N Academy Blvd.
Colorado Springs, CO 80909
Tel: (719)596-7400; Free: 800-748-2282
Fax: (719)596-2464
Web Site: www.intelliteccollege.edu/

Description: Proprietary, 2-year, coed. Awards diplomas and terminal associate degrees. Founded 1966. Setting: suburban campus. Total enrollment: 434. 56% 25 or older. Calendar: clock hours. Services for LD students, advanced placement, independent study, part-time degree program, co-op programs and internships.

Entrance Requirements: Open admission. Option: electronic application. Required: high school transcript, interview. Entrance: noncompetitive. Application deadline: Rolling.

■ ITT TECHNICAL INSTITUTE (AURORA)

12500 E Iliff Ave.
Ste. 100
Aurora, CO 80014
Tel: (303)695-6317; Free: 877-832-8460
Web Site: www.itt-tech.edu/

Description: Proprietary, primarily 2-year, coed. Awards terminal associate and bachelor's degrees.

Entrance Requirements: Entrance: minimally difficult.

■ ITT TECHNICAL INSTITUTE (WESTMINSTER)

8620 Wolff Ct.
Ste. 100
Westminster, CO 80031
Tel: (303)288-4488; Free: 800-395-4488
Fax: (303)288-8166
Web Site: www.itt-tech.edu/

Description: Proprietary, primarily 2-year, coed. Part of ITT Educational Services, Inc. Awards terminal associate and bachelor's degrees. Founded 1984. Setting: suburban campus.

Entrance Requirements: Entrance: minimally difficult.

■ JOHNSON & WALES UNIVERSITY

7150 Montview Blvd.
Denver, CO 80220
Tel: (303)256-9300; Free: 877-598-3368
Fax: (303)256-9333
E-mail: den@admissions.jwu.edu
Web Site: www.jwu.edu/denver/

Description: Independent, 4-year, coed. Administratively affiliated with Johnson & Wales University (RI). Awards associate and bachelor's degrees. Founded 1993. Setting: small town campus. Total enrollment: 1,532. Faculty: 87 (48 full-time, 39 part-time). Student-undergrad faculty ratio is 24:1. 3,019 applied, 64% were admitted. Full-time: 1,462 students, 58% women, 42% men. Part-time: 70 students, 50% women, 50% men. 60% from out-of-state. 1% American Indian or Alaska Native, non-Hispanic/Latino; 9% Hispanic/Latino; 3% African American, non-Hispanic/Latino; 2% Asian, non-Hispanic/Latino; 0.1% Native Hawaiian or other Pacific Islander, non-Hispanic/Latino; 1% international. 11% 25 or older, 38% live on campus, 11% transferred in. Retention: 67% of full-time freshmen returned the following year. Academic areas with the most degrees conferred: personal and culinary services; business/marketing; family and consumer sciences. Core. Academic remediation for entering students, ESL program, services for LD students, advanced placement, accelerated degree program, honors program, independent study, summer session for credit, part-time degree program, adult/continuing education programs, co-op programs and internships. Study abroad program.

Entrance Requirements: Options: electronic application, early admission, deferred admission, international baccalaureate accepted. Required: high school transcript. Recommended: minimum 2 high school GPA. Required for some: essay, minimum 2.75 high school GPA, interview, SAT or ACT. Entrance: moderately difficult. Application deadline: Rolling. Notification: continuous.

Collegiate Environment: Orientation program. Drama-theater group, student-run newspaper. Campus security: 24-hour emergency response devices and patrols, student patrols, late night transport-escort service. Johnson & Wales University Library with an OPAC and a Web page.

■ JONES INTERNATIONAL UNIVERSITY

9697 E Mineral Ave.
Centennial, CO 80112
Tel: (303)784-8904; Free: 800-811-5663
Fax: (303)784-8547
Web Site: www.jiu.edu/

Description: Proprietary, university, coed. Awards associate, bachelor's, master's, and doctoral degrees (offers only online degree programs). Founded 1995. Setting: suburban campus. Total enrollment: 3,196. Faculty: 111 (12 full-time, 99 part-time). Full-time: 638 students, 61% women, 39% men. Part-time: 1,092 students, 63% women, 37% men. Students come from 54 states and territories, 20 other countries, 95% from out-of-state. 1% American Indian or Alaska Native, non-Hispanic/Latino; 4% Hispanic/Latino; 32% African American, non-Hispanic/Latino; 1% Asian, non-Hispanic/Latino; 0.1% Native Hawaiian or other Pacific Islander, non-Hispanic/Latino; 0% international. 76% 25 or older. Academic area with the most degrees conferred: business/marketing. Core. Calendar: continuous. Academic remediation for entering students, services for LD students, advanced placement, independent study, distance learning, part-time degree program, internships, graduate courses open to undergrads.

Entrance Requirements: Open admission. Options: electronic application, early admission, deferred admission, international baccalaureate accepted.

Required: high school transcript, minimum 2 high school GPA. Entrance: noncompetitive. Application deadlines: Rolling, Rolling for nonresidents. Notification: continuous, continuous for nonresidents. Transfer credits accepted: Yes.

Costs Per Year: Application fee: $0. Tuition: $12,720 full-time, $530 per credit hour part-time. Full-time tuition varies according to course level, course load, degree level, and program. Part-time tuition varies according to course level, course load, degree level, and program.

Collegiate Environment: Orientation program. Social organizations: National Society of Collegiate Scholars. Jones International University Library with 245,000 books, 29,000 serials, 3,922 audiovisual materials, and a Web page.

■ LAMAR COMMUNITY COLLEGE

2401 S Main St.
Lamar, CO 81052-3999
Tel: (719)336-2248; Free: 800-968-6920
Fax: (719)336-2448
E-mail: admissions@lamarcc.edu
Web Site: www.lamarcc.edu/
Description: State-supported, 2-year, coed. Part of Colorado Community College and Occupational Education System. Awards certificates, diplomas, transfer associate, and terminal associate degrees. Founded 1937. Setting: 125-acre small town campus. Endowment: $136,000. Total enrollment: 1,084. Faculty: 50 (18 full-time, 32 part-time). Student-undergrad faculty ratio is 15:1. 517 applied, 100% were admitted. Full-time: 485 students, 60% women, 40% men. Part-time: 599 students, 56% women, 44% men. Students come from 28 states and territories, 4 other countries, 16% from out-of-state. 43% 25 or older, 20% live on campus, 4% transferred in. Core. Calendar: semesters. Academic remediation for entering students, ESL program, services for LD students, advanced placement, self-designed majors, independent study, distance learning, double major, summer session for credit, part-time degree program, adult/continuing education programs, co-op programs and internships.
Entrance Requirements: Open admission. Options: electronic application, early admission. Entrance: noncompetitive. Application deadline: 9/16. Preference given to state residents. Transfer credits accepted: Yes.
Collegiate Environment: Orientation program. Major annual event: Antelope Night. Student services: health clinic, personal-psychological counseling. Campus security: 24-hour emergency response devices and patrols, student patrols, late night transport-escort service, controlled dormitory access. Learning Resources Center with 27,729 books, 172 serials, and an OPAC. Operations spending for the previous fiscal year: $127,718. 60 computers available on campus for general student use. A campuswide network can be accessed. Students can access the following: online class registration.
Community Environment: Lamar is an All-America City located at the junction of U.S. Highways 50, 287, and 385 with a dry climate and a population of 8,400. Livestock and poultry are primary concerns in this extensively irrigated area for which Lamar is a trading center. Airlines, railroads and buses serve the area. The community facilities include churches, a hospital and clinics, a library and various civic clubs. Part-time employment is available. The recreational activities include hunting, fishing, boating, golfing, swimming, and baseball.

■ LINCOLN COLLEGE OF TECHNOLOGY

11194 E 45th Ave.
Denver, CO 80239
Tel: (303)722-5724
Fax: (303)778-8264
Web Site: www.lincolnedu.com/campus/denver-co/
Description: Proprietary, 2-year, coed. Awards diplomas and terminal associate degrees. Founded 1963. Setting: urban campus. Total enrollment: 863. 272 applied, 100% were admitted. 25% 25 or older. Core. Calendar: 8 six-week terms. Services for LD students, summer session for credit.
Entrance Requirements: Entrance: moderately difficult. Application deadline: Rolling.
Collegiate Environment: Orientation program. Student services: personal-psychological counseling. Campus security: 24-hour emergency response devices and patrols. Denver Automotive and Diesel College Library plus 1 other with 1,050 books, 8 serials, and a Web page.

■ METROPOLITAN STATE UNIVERSITY OF DENVER

PO Box 173362
Denver, CO 80217-3362

Tel: (303)556-2400
Fax: (303)556-6345
Web Site: www.msudenver.edu/
Description: State-supported, comprehensive, coed. Awards bachelor's and master's degrees and post-master's certificates. Founded 1963. Setting: 175-acre urban campus with easy access to Denver. Educational spending for the previous fiscal year: $1015 per student. Total enrollment: 23,381. Faculty: 1,494 (533 full-time, 961 part-time). Student-undergrad faculty ratio is 20:1. 5,867 applied, 71% were admitted. 6% from top 10% of their high school class, 22% from top quarter, 55% from top half. Full-time: 13,335 students, 52% women, 48% men. Part-time: 9,684 students, 56% women, 44% men. 4% from out-of-state. 1% American Indian or Alaska Native, non-Hispanic/Latino; 20% Hispanic/Latino; 6% African American, non-Hispanic/Latino; 3% Asian, non-Hispanic/Latino; 0.3% Native Hawaiian or other Pacific Islander, non-Hispanic/Latino; 0.5% international. 45% 25 or older, 0% live on campus, 9% transferred in. Retention: 66% of full-time freshmen returned the following year. Academic areas with the most degrees conferred: business/marketing; interdisciplinary studies; psychology. Core. Calendar: semesters. Services for LD students, advanced placement, accelerated degree program, self-designed majors, honors program, independent study, distance learning, double major, summer session for credit, part-time degree program, external degree program, adult/continuing education programs, co-op programs and internships. Off campus study at 3 members of the Consortium of State Colleges in Colorado, University of Colorado at Denver, Community College of Denver. Study abroad program. ROTC: Army (c), Air Force (c).
Entrance Requirements: Open admission for applicants 20 years or older who are high school graduates, have GED, or have 30 transferable credits from another college. Options: electronic application, deferred admission, international baccalaureate accepted. Required: high school transcript, SAT or ACT. Recommended: minimum 2 high school GPA. Required for some: SAT, ACT. Entrance: minimally difficult. Notification: continuous. SAT Reasoning Test deadline: 8/1. Transfer credits accepted: Yes.
Collegiate Environment: Orientation program. Drama-theater group, choral group, student-run newspaper, radio station. Social organizations: national fraternities, national sororities. Student services: legal services, health clinic, personal-psychological counseling, women's center. Campus security: 24-hour emergency response devices and patrols, late night transport-escort service. College housing not available. Auraria Library with 607,971 books, 1 million microform titles, 2,380 serials, 16,309 audiovisual materials, an OPAC, and a Web page. 808 computers available on campus for general student use. A campuswide network can be accessed from off-campus. Students can access the following: online class registration. Staffed computer lab on campus provides training in use of computers, software, and the Internet.
Community Environment: See University of Denver.

■ MORGAN COMMUNITY COLLEGE

920 Barlow Rd.
Fort Morgan, CO 80701-4399
Tel: (970)542-3100; Free: 800-622-0216
E-mail: kim.maxwell@morgancc.edu
Web Site: www.morgancc.edu/
Description: State-supported, 2-year, coed. Part of Colorado Community College and Occupational Education System. Awards certificates, transfer associate, and terminal associate degrees. Founded 1967. Setting: 20-acre small town campus with easy access to Denver. Total enrollment: 1,643. Faculty: 150 (36 full-time, 114 part-time). Student-undergrad faculty ratio is 11:1. 197 applied, 100% were admitted. Full-time: 501 students, 76% women, 24% men. Part-time: 1,142 students, 77% women, 23% men. Students come from 5 states and territories, 4% from out-of-state. 30% 25 or older, 2% transferred in. Retention: 41% of full-time freshmen returned the following year. Core. Calendar: semesters. Academic remediation for entering students, services for LD students, advanced placement, distance learning, double major, summer session for credit, part-time degree program, adult/continuing education programs, internships.
Entrance Requirements: Open admission. Options: electronic application, early admission, deferred admission. Recommended: high school transcript. Entrance: noncompetitive. Application deadline: Rolling.
Collegiate Environment: Student-run newspaper. Learning Resource Center with 13,800 books, 80 serials, 1,096 audiovisual materials, an OPAC, and a Web page. 60 computers available on campus for general student use. A campuswide network can be accessed from off-campus. Students can access the following: online class registration. Staffed computer lab on campus.

Community Environment: Morgan County has an abundant supply of facilities for recreational enjoyment. In addition to the athletic activities close at hand, the students have access to the metropolitan offerings in Denver, one hour away, and the beautiful Rocky Mountains, a two hour drive on Interstate highways.

■ **NAROPA UNIVERSITY**
2130 Arapahoe Ave.
Boulder, CO 80302-6697
Tel: (303)444-0202; Free: 800-772-6951
Fax: (303)444-0410
E-mail: jmakowsky@naropa.edu
Web Site: www.naropa.edu/
Description: Independent, comprehensive, coed. Awards bachelor's and master's degrees. Founded 1974. Setting: 12-acre urban campus with easy access to Denver. Endowment: $5.6 million. Educational spending for the previous fiscal year: $8657 per student. Total enrollment: 1,019. Faculty: 164 (43 full-time, 121 part-time). Student-undergrad faculty ratio is 9:1. 93 applied, 83% were admitted. Full-time: 361 students, 62% women, 38% men. Part-time: 42 students, 55% women, 45% men. Students come from 47 states and territories, 8 other countries, 64% from out-of-state. 0% American Indian or Alaska Native, non-Hispanic/Latino; 8% Hispanic/Latino; 1% African American, non-Hispanic/Latino; 1% Asian, non-Hispanic/Latino; 0% Native Hawaiian or other Pacific Islander, non-Hispanic/Latino; 1% international. 39% 25 or older, 18% live on campus, 24% transferred in. Retention: 50% of full-time freshmen returned the following year. Academic areas with the most degrees conferred: psychology; interdisciplinary studies; visual and performing arts. Core. Calendar: semesters. Services for LD students, advanced placement, self-designed majors, independent study, double major, summer session for credit, part-time degree program, co-op programs and internships, graduate courses open to undergrads. Off campus study at University of Colorado-Boulder Extended Studies Consortium. Study abroad program.
Entrance Requirements: Options: electronic application, deferred admission, international baccalaureate accepted. Required: essay, high school transcript, 2 recommendations, interview. Required for some: supplemental application and/or art samples for applicants to performance, environmental studies, INTD studies, music, visual arts and writing and literature programs. Entrance: moderately difficult. Application deadlines: 1/15, 1/15 for nonresidents. Notification: continuous, continuous for nonresidents. Transfer credits accepted: Yes.
Costs Per Year: Application fee: $50. Comprehensive fee: $37,770 includes full-time tuition ($28,620), mandatory fees ($170), and college room and board ($8980). Full-time tuition and fees vary according to course load. Part-time tuition: $936 per hour. Part-time mandatory fees: $335 per term. Part-time tuition and fees vary according to course load.
Collegiate Environment: Orientation program. Drama-theater group, choral group, student-run newspaper. Social organizations: 30 open to all. Most popular organizations: Team Asana, ROOT: Reconnecting on Outdoor Terrain, United Naropa. Major annual events: Open Mic Coffee House Night, Sustainability/Earth Days, Community Practice Days. Student services: personal-psychological counseling. Campus security: late night transport-escort service, controlled dormitory access, foot and vehicle patrol 4:30 pm to midnight, 24 hour on-call Safety and Security Manager. 103 college housing spaces available; 69 were occupied in 2012-13. Freshmen guaranteed college housing. On-campus residence required in freshman year. Option: coed housing available. Allen Ginsberg Library with 31,497 books, 76 serials, 5,677 audiovisual materials, an OPAC, and a Web page. Operations spending for the previous fiscal year: $319,795. 37 computers available on campus for general student use. A campuswide network can be accessed from student residence rooms and from off campus. Students can access the following: online class registration. Staffed computer lab on campus provides training in use of computers, software, and the Internet.

■ **NATIONAL AMERICAN UNIVERSITY (COLORADO SPRINGS)**
5125 N Academy Blvd.
Colorado Springs, CO 80918
Tel: (719)277-0588
Fax: (719)277-0589
E-mail: csadmissions@national.edu
Web Site: www.national.edu/
Description: Proprietary, 4-year, coed. Awards associate and bachelor's degrees. Founded 1941. Setting: 1-acre suburban campus with easy access to Denver. Total enrollment: 285. 88% 25 or older. Core. Academic remediation for entering students, ESL program, accelerated degree program, independent study, distance learning, double major, summer session for credit, part-time degree program, external degree program, adult/continuing education programs, internships. Off campus study.
Entrance Requirements: Open admission. Option: deferred admission. Required: high school transcript, interview. Entrance: noncompetitive. Application deadline: Rolling.
Collegiate Environment: Orientation program. Campus security: late night transport-escort service. National American University Library with 15,000 books and 100 serials.

■ **NATIONAL AMERICAN UNIVERSITY (DENVER)**
1325 S Colorado Blvd., Ste. 100
Denver, CO 80222
Tel: (303)758-6700
Fax: (303)758-6810
E-mail: jhaack@national.edu
Web Site: www.national.edu/
Description: Proprietary, comprehensive, coed. Awards associate, bachelor's, and master's degrees. Founded 1974. Setting: urban campus. Total enrollment: 206. Faculty: 35 (all part-time). Student-undergrad faculty ratio is 10:1. Students come from 6 other countries. 85% 25 or older. Retention: 60% of full-time freshmen returned the following year. Core. Academic remediation for entering students, ESL program, advanced placement, accelerated degree program, independent study, distance learning, double major, summer session for credit, part-time degree program, adult/continuing education programs, internships.
Entrance Requirements: Open admission. Options: electronic application, early admission, deferred admission. Required: high school transcript, interview. Entrance: noncompetitive. Application deadline: Rolling.
Collegiate Environment: Orientation program. Campus security: 24-hour emergency response devices and patrols. NAU Library with 400 books and 33 serials. 47 computers available on campus for general student use. A campuswide network can be accessed from off-campus. Staffed computer lab on campus.

■ **NAZARENE BIBLE COLLEGE**
1111 Academy Park Loop
Colorado Springs, CO 80910-3704
Tel: (719)884-5000; Free: 800-873-3873
Fax: (719)884-5199
Web Site: www.nbc.edu/
Description: Independent, 4-year, coed, affiliated with Church of the Nazarene. Awards associate and bachelor's degrees. Founded 1967. Setting: 64-acre urban campus with easy access to Colorado Springs. Endowment: $2.3 million. Educational spending for the previous fiscal year: $3416 per student. Total enrollment: 995. Faculty: 79 (14 full-time, 65 part-time). Student-undergrad faculty ratio is 10:1. 1,063 applied, 20% were admitted. Full-time: 212 students, 40% women, 60% men. Part-time: 783 students, 40% women, 60% men. Students come from 50 states and territories, 1 other country, 55% from out-of-state. 89% 25 or older, 7% transferred in. Retention: 65% of full-time freshmen returned the following year. Academic area with the most degrees conferred: theology and religious vocations. Core. Academic remediation for entering students, independent study, distance learning, double major, summer session for credit, part-time degree program, internships.
Entrance Requirements: Open admission. Options: electronic application, deferred admission. Required: essay, high school transcript, 2 recommendations. Entrance: noncompetitive. Application deadline: 7/31.
Costs Per Year: Application fee: $0. Tuition: $10,050 full-time, $335 per credit hour part-time. Mandatory fees: $750 full-time, $25 per credit hour part-time.
Collegiate Environment: Orientation program. Choral group, student-run newspaper. Student services: personal-psychological counseling. Campus security: student patrols. Trimble Library with 64,651 books, 10,995 microform titles, 1,756 serials, 8,580 audiovisual materials, and an OPAC. Operations spending for the previous fiscal year: $164,477. 10 computers available on campus for general student use. A campuswide network can be accessed from off-campus. Staffed computer lab on campus.
Community Environment: See The Colorado College.

■ **NORTHEASTERN JUNIOR COLLEGE**
100 College Ave.
Sterling, CO 80751-2399

Tel: (970)521-6600; Free: 800-626-4637
Fax: (970)522-4945
E-mail: andy.long@njc.edu
Web Site: www.njc.edu/
Description: State-supported, 2-year, coed. Part of Colorado Community College and Occupational Education System. Awards certificates, transfer associate, and terminal associate degrees. Founded 1941. Setting: 65-acre small town campus. Endowment: $5.6 million. Educational spending for the previous fiscal year: $4130 per student. Total enrollment: 1,486. Faculty: 98 (48 full-time, 50 part-time). Student-undergrad faculty ratio is 18:1. 1,290 applied, 100% were admitted. Full-time: 979 students, 51% women, 49% men. Part-time: 507 students, 71% women, 29% men. Students come from 26 states and territories, 4 other countries, 5% from out-of-state. 1% American Indian or Alaska Native, non-Hispanic/Latino; 9% Hispanic/Latino; 6% African American, non-Hispanic/Latino; 1% Asian, non-Hispanic/Latino; 0.2% Native Hawaiian or other Pacific Islander, non-Hispanic/Latino; 1% international. 22% 25 or older, 37% live on campus, 56% transferred in. Retention: 48% of full-time freshmen returned the following year. Core. Calendar: semesters. Academic remediation for entering students, ESL program, services for LD students, advanced placement, accelerated degree program, honors program, independent study, distance learning, double major, summer session for credit, part-time degree program, adult/continuing education programs, co-op programs and internships.
Entrance Requirements: Open admission. Options: electronic application, early admission, deferred admission, international baccalaureate accepted. Required: high school transcript. Entrance: noncompetitive. Application deadlines: Rolling, Rolling for nonresidents. Notification: continuous until 8/1, continuous for nonresidents. Preference given to state residents. Transfer credits accepted: Yes.
Costs Per Year: Application fee: $0. State resident tuition: $3,382 full-time, $112.75 per credit hour part-time. Nonresident tuition: $11,098 full-time, $369.95 per credit hour part-time. Mandatory fees: $596 full-time, $21.97 per credit hour part-time, $12.05 per term part-time. Full-time tuition and fees vary according to course load. Part-time tuition and fees vary according to course load. College room and board: $6190. College room only: $2732. Room and board charges vary according to board plan and housing facility.
Collegiate Environment: Orientation program. Drama-theater group, choral group. Social organizations: 25 open to all. Most popular organizations: Associated Student Government, Post Secondary Agriculture (PAS), Crossroads, Students in Free Enterprise (SIFE), NJC Ambassadors. Major annual events: Region Nine Basketball Games and Volleyball Games, Frederick Winters (hypnotist), $2 movie nights on Thursday nights. Student services: health clinic, personal-psychological counseling. Campus security: 24-hour emergency response devices, late night transport-escort service, controlled dormitory access. 545 college housing spaces available; 508 were occupied in 2012-13. Freshmen guaranteed college housing. On-campus residence required in freshman year. Options: coed, women-only housing available. Monahan Library with 96,871 books, 116 serials, an OPAC, and a Web page. Operations spending for the previous fiscal year: $152,000. 145 computers available on campus for general student use. A campuswide network can be accessed from student residence rooms. Students can access the following: online class registration. Staffed computer lab on campus provides training in use of computers, software, and the Internet.
Community Environment: Sterling, population 12,500, in northeastern Colorado on the South Platte River, has a mild climate. Trains and buses serve the area. Community facilities include churches, hospitals, libraries, a health center, and museum. Recreational activities include golf, tennis, swimming, bowling, roller skating, and boating. Rooming houses and private homes are available for student housing. The County Fair and Overland Trail Roundup are annual events. Part-time work is available.

■ **OTERO JUNIOR COLLEGE**
1802 Colorado Ave.
La Junta, CO 81050-3415
Tel: (719)384-6831
Fax: (719)384-6880
E-mail: jan.schiro@ojc.edu
Web Site: www.ojc.edu/
Description: State-supported, 2-year, coed. Part of Colorado Community College System. Awards certificates, transfer associate, and terminal associate degrees. Founded 1941. Setting: 40-acre rural campus. Total enrollment: 1,660. Faculty: 75 (33 full-time, 42 part-time). Full-time: 870 students, 57% women, 43% men. Part-time: 790 students, 66% women, 34% men. 25% 25 or older, 17% live on campus. Core. Calendar: semesters. Academic

remediation for entering students, advanced placement, distance learning, summer session for credit, part-time degree program, external degree program, adult/continuing education programs, internships.
Entrance Requirements: Open admission except for nursing program. Options: electronic application, early admission. Recommended: high school transcript. Entrance: noncompetitive. Application deadline: 8/30. Notification: continuous.
Costs Per Year: Application fee: $0. State resident tuition: $2706 full-time. Nonresident tuition: $5362 full-time. Mandatory fees: $263 full-time. College room and board: $5536. Room and board charges vary according to board plan and housing facility.
Collegiate Environment: Orientation program. Drama-theater group, choral group, student-run newspaper. Social organizations: 6 open to all. Student services: personal-psychological counseling. Campus security: 24-hour patrols, late night transport-escort service. Wheeler Library with 36,701 books, 183 serials, and an OPAC. 100 computers available on campus for general student use. A campuswide network can be accessed from student residence rooms. Staffed computer lab on campus.
Community Environment: La Junta is located in the rich agricultural and stock-raising territory of the Arkansas River Valley with a mild year-round climate; the average mean temperature being 54.1 degrees, and the average yearly precipitation, 13.61 inches. The community facilities include a library, churches, many shopping facilities, hotels, motels, hospital and a community sponsored concert association. La Junta has many civic and service organizations. Industries include canning, manufacture of copper tubings and the renovation of railroad cars. The Kid's Rodeo is held here each year in August.

■ **PIKES PEAK COMMUNITY COLLEGE**
5675 S Academy Blvd.
Colorado Springs, CO 80906-5498
Tel: (719)576-7711; Free: 866-411-7722
Fax: (719)540-7614
Web Site: www.ppcc.edu/
Description: State-supported, 2-year, coed. Part of Colorado Community College and Occupational Education System. Awards certificates, transfer associate, and terminal associate degrees. Founded 1968. Setting: 287-acre urban campus with easy access to Denver. Total enrollment: 13,572. 45% 25 or older. Core. Calendar: semesters. Academic remediation for entering students, ESL program, services for LD students, advanced placement, independent study, distance learning, double major, summer session for credit, part-time degree program, adult/continuing education programs, co-op programs and internships. ROTC: Army (c).
Entrance Requirements: Open admission. Option: international baccalaureate accepted. Required for some: high school transcript. Entrance: noncompetitive. Application deadline: Rolling.
Collegiate Environment: Orientation program. Drama-theater group, student-run newspaper. Student services: women's center. Campus security: 24-hour emergency response devices and patrols, late night transport-escort service. PPCC Library plus 1 other with 34,332 books, 4,505 microform titles, 311 serials, 3,832 audiovisual materials, and an OPAC.
Community Environment: Colorado Springs, a community of approximately 278,000 people, is situated 70 miles south of Denver. The dry, temperate climate and 310 days of sunshine annually make it a highly desirable place to live year-round. Many high technology industries are located in Colorado Springs. Housing is readily available and buses serve all parts of the city. Skiing, hiking, fishing, hunting, backpacking, and camping can be enjoyed within a one-half hour to one hour drive from Colorado Springs.

■ **PIMA MEDICAL INSTITUTE (COLORADO SPRINGS)**
3770 Citadel Dr. N
Colorado Springs, CO 80909
Tel: (719)482-7462
E-mail: jalbers@pmi.edu
Web Site: www.pmi.edu/
Description: Proprietary, 2-year, coed. Setting: urban campus. Core. Distance learning, co-op programs and internships.
Entrance Requirements: Required: high school transcript, interview, Wonderlic Scholastic Level Exam (SLE).
Collegiate Environment: Orientation program.

■ **PIMA MEDICAL INSTITUTE (DENVER)**
7475 Dakin St.
Denver, CO 80221

Tel: (303)426-1800; Free: 888-477-PIMA
Fax: (303)412-8752
Web Site: www.pmi.edu/
Description: Proprietary, primarily 2-year, coed. Part of Vocational Training Institutes, Inc. Awards certificates, terminal associate, and bachelor's degrees. Founded 1988. Setting: urban campus. Total enrollment: 922. 59% 25 or older. Calendar: modular. Academic remediation for entering students, distance learning, co-op programs and internships.
Entrance Requirements: Required: interview, Wonderlic Scholastic Level Exam (SLE). Required for some: high school transcript. Entrance: minimally difficult.

■ **PLATT COLLEGE**
3100 S Parker Rd., Ste. 200
Aurora, CO 80014-3141
Tel: (303)369-5151
Web Site: www.plattcolorado.edu/
Description: Proprietary, 4-year, coed. Awards associate and bachelor's degrees. Founded 1986. Setting: suburban campus. Total enrollment: 134. 15 applied. 64% 25 or older. Calendar: continuous. Academic remediation for entering students, advanced placement.
Entrance Requirements: Required: high school transcript, interview. Entrance: noncompetitive. Application deadline: Rolling.
Collegiate Environment: Orientation program.

■ **PRINCE INSTITUTE–ROCKY MOUNTAINS CAMPUS**
9051 Harlan St., Unit 20
Westminster, CO 80031
Tel: (303)427-5292; Free: 866-712-2425
Fax: (303)427-5383
Web Site: www.princeinstitute.edu/
Description: Proprietary, 2-year, coed. Awards terminal associate degrees. Founded 1975. Setting: urban campus. Total enrollment: 150. 69% 25 or older. Core. Double major, part-time degree program, external degree program, adult/continuing education programs, internships.
Entrance Requirements: Open admission. Required: high school transcript. Recommended: interview. Entrance: noncompetitive. Application deadline: Rolling.
Collegiate Environment: Orientation program. Campus security: 24-hour emergency response devices, late night transport-escort service.

■ **PUEBLO COMMUNITY COLLEGE**
900 W Orman Ave.
Pueblo, CO 81004-1499
Tel: (719)549-3200; Free: 888-642-6017
Fax: (719)549-3012
Web Site: www.pueblocc.edu/
Description: State-supported, 2-year, coed. Part of Colorado Community College System. Awards certificates, transfer associate, and terminal associate degrees. Founded 1933. Setting: 35-acre urban campus. Endowment: $1.1 million. Educational spending for the previous fiscal year: $3487 per student. Total enrollment: 7,736. Faculty: 427 (110 full-time, 317 part-time). Student-undergrad faculty ratio is 19:1. 2,833 applied, 100% were admitted. Students come from 24 states and territories, 6 other countries, 1% from out-of-state. 3% American Indian or Alaska Native, non-Hispanic/Latino; 31% Hispanic/Latino; 3% African American, non-Hispanic/Latino; 1% Asian, non-Hispanic/Latino; 0.02% international. 57% 25 or older. Retention: 59% of full-time freshmen returned the following year. Core. Calendar: semesters. Academic remediation for entering students, ESL program, services for LD students, advanced placement, accelerated degree program, honors program, independent study, distance learning, double major, summer session for credit, part-time degree program, co-op programs and internships.
Entrance Requirements: Open admission except for allied health programs. Options: electronic application, early admission, deferred admission. Entrance: noncompetitive. Application deadlines: Rolling, Rolling for nonresidents. Notification: continuous until 9/1, continuous until 9/1 for nonresidents.
Collegiate Environment: Orientation program. Drama-theater group, choral group. Social organizations: 23 open to all. Most popular organizations: Phi Theta Kappa, Welding Club, Culinary Arts Club, Performing Arts Club, Art Club. Major annual events: Welcome Back Week, Fall Festival, Spring Fling. Student services: personal-psychological counseling. Campus security: 24-hour emergency response devices, late night transport-escort service. The Library with 38,719 books, 824 microform titles, 8,586 serials, 15,870

audiovisual materials, and an OPAC. Operations spending for the previous fiscal year: $377,895. 1,180 computers available on campus for general student use. A campuswide network can be accessed from off-campus. Students can access the following: online class registration. Staffed computer lab on campus provides training in use of computers, software, and the Internet.
Community Environment: Pueblo, population 103,500, is 42 miles south of Colorado Springs and 112 miles south of Denver on I-25. The original site of Pueblo was a crossroad for Indians, Spanish troops, friars, fur trappers, and explorers. A trading post was built in 1842 and served travelers on their way to California. Pueblo's location as the focal point for travel to the Rocky Mountain Empire continues to serve business and industry in the area. Puebloans enjoy clean air, uncrowded highways, and nearby water and mountain recreation set in the warm pleasant atmosphere of the Southwest. Pueblo boasts a fine community college, a university, symphony orchestra, chorale, ballet, theatrical groups, and a beautiful arts center.

■ **RED ROCKS COMMUNITY COLLEGE**
13300 W 6th Ave.
Lakewood, CO 80228-1255
Tel: (303)914-6600
Fax: (303)914-6666
E-mail: admissions@rrcc.edu
Web Site: www.rrcc.edu/
Description: State-supported, 2-year, coed. Part of Colorado Community College and Occupational Education System. Awards certificates, transfer associate, and terminal associate degrees. Founded 1969. Setting: 141-acre urban campus with easy access to Denver. Educational spending for the previous fiscal year: $2770 per student. Total enrollment: 9,028. Faculty: 511 (93 full-time, 418 part-time). Student-undergrad faculty ratio is 23:1. 3,258 applied, 100% were admitted. Full-time: 2,854 students, 45% women, 55% men. Part-time: 6,174 students, 52% women, 48% men. Students come from 38 states and territories, 27 other countries, 6% from out-of-state. 1% American Indian or Alaska Native, non-Hispanic/Latino; 13% Hispanic/Latino; 2% African American, non-Hispanic/Latino; 2% Asian, non-Hispanic/Latino; 0.3% Native Hawaiian or other Pacific Islander, non-Hispanic/Latino; 1% international. 53% 25 or older, 22% transferred in. Calendar: semesters. Academic remediation for entering students, ESL program, services for LD students, honors program, distance learning, summer session for credit, part-time degree program, adult/continuing education programs, co-op programs. Off campus study at Metropolitan State College, University of Colorado at Denver, Colorado School of Mines. Study abroad program. ROTC: Army (c), Air Force (c).
Entrance Requirements: Open admission. Options: electronic application, early admission, international baccalaureate accepted. Entrance: noncompetitive. Application deadlines: Rolling, Rolling for nonresidents. Notification: continuous, continuous for nonresidents. Transfer credits accepted: Yes.
Costs Per Year: Application fee: $0. State resident tuition: $3383 full-time, $115 per credit hour part-time. Nonresident tuition: $13,877 full-time, $465 per credit hour part-time. Mandatory fees: $285 full-time, $10.50 per credit hour part-time, $35 per term part-time. Full-time tuition and fees vary according to program and reciprocity agreements. Part-time tuition and fees vary according to program and reciprocity agreements.
Collegiate Environment: Orientation program. Drama-theater group. Student services: health clinic, personal-psychological counseling. Campus security: 24-hour emergency response devices and patrols. College housing not available. Marvin Buckels Library with 38,204 books, 84 serials, 4,098 audiovisual materials, an OPAC, and a Web page. Operations spending for the previous fiscal year: $140,278. 128 computers available on campus for general student use. A campuswide network can be accessed. Students can access the following: online class registration. Staffed computer lab on campus provides training in use of computers, software, and the Internet.
Community Environment: See Colorado School of Mines.

■ **REDSTONE COLLEGE–DENVER**
10851 W 120th Ave.
Broomfield, CO 80021
Tel: (303)466-1714; Free: 877-801-1025
Fax: (303)469-3797
Web Site: www.redstone.edu/
Description: Proprietary, 2-year, coed. Awards certificates, diplomas, and terminal associate degrees. Founded 1965. Total enrollment: 590. Faculty: 48. Calendar: continuous.

■ REGIS UNIVERSITY

3333 Regis Blvd.
Denver, CO 80221-1099
Tel: (303)458-4100; Free: 800-388-2366
Fax: (303)964-5534
E-mail: regisadm@regis.edu
Web Site: www.regis.edu/

Description: Independent Roman Catholic (Jesuit), comprehensive, coed. Awards bachelor's, master's, and doctoral degrees and post-master's certificates. Founded 1877. Setting: 90-acre suburban campus with easy access to Denver. Educational spending for the previous fiscal year: $5801 per student. Total enrollment: 10,683. Faculty: 1,181 (288 full-time, 893 part-time). Student-undergrad faculty ratio is 12:1. 2,531 applied, 90% were admitted. 34% from top 10% of their high school class, 64% from top quarter, 90% from top half. Full-time: 2,555 students, 64% women, 36% men. Part-time: 3,195 students, 63% women, 37% men. 33% from out-of-state. 1% American Indian or Alaska Native, non-Hispanic/Latino; 16% Hispanic/Latino; 6% African American, non-Hispanic/Latino; 4% Asian, non-Hispanic/Latino; 0.1% Native Hawaiian or other Pacific Islander, non-Hispanic/Latino; 1% international. 62% 25 or older, 8% live on campus, 6% transferred in. Retention: 88% of full-time freshmen returned the following year. Academic areas with the most degrees conferred: health professions and related sciences; business/marketing; liberal arts/general studies. Core. Calendar: semesters. Academic remediation for entering students, services for LD students, advanced placement, accelerated degree program, self-designed majors, freshman honors college, honors program, independent study, distance learning, double major, summer session for credit, part-time degree program, external degree program, adult/continuing education programs, co-op programs and internships, graduate courses open to undergrads. Off campus study at other Jesuit colleges and universities. Study abroad program. ROTC: Army (c), Naval (c), Air Force (c).

Entrance Requirements: Options: electronic application, deferred admission, international baccalaureate accepted. Required: essay, high school transcript, minimum 2.5 high school GPA, SAT or ACT. Required for some: 1 recommendation, interview. Entrance: moderately difficult. Application deadlines: Rolling, Rolling for nonresidents. Notification: continuous. SAT Reasoning Test deadline: 8/1. Transfer credits accepted: Yes.

Costs Per Year: Application fee: $40. Comprehensive fee: $41,804 includes full-time tuition ($31,824), mandatory fees ($600), and college room and board ($9380). College room only: $5200. Full-time tuition and fees vary according to course load, location, program, and reciprocity agreements. Room and board charges vary according to board plan and housing facility. Part-time tuition: $995 per credit hour. Part-time tuition varies according to location, program, and reciprocity agreements.

Collegiate Environment: Orientation program. Drama-theater group, choral group, student-run newspaper, radio station. Social organizations: 45 open to all. Most popular organizations: Musical Theater Club, student government, Club Sports, Outdoor Adventure, Black Student Association. Major annual events: Welcome Week, Snow Week, Ranger Week. Student services: health clinic, personal-psychological counseling. Campus security: 24-hour emergency response devices and patrols, student patrols, late night transport-escort service, controlled dormitory access. 720 college housing spaces available. Freshmen given priority for college housing. On-campus residence required through sophomore year. Option: coed housing available. Dayton Memorial Library with 618,544 books, 88,000 microform titles, 35,000 serials, 180,000 audiovisual materials, an OPAC, and a Web page. 450 computers available on campus for general student use. Computer purchase/lease plans available. A campuswide network can be accessed from student residence rooms and from off campus. Students can access the following: online class registration. Staffed computer lab on campus (open 24 hours a day) provides training in use of computers, software, and the Internet.

Community Environment: See University of Denver.

■ ROCKY MOUNTAIN COLLEGE OF ART + DESIGN

1600 Pierce St.
Lakewood, CO 80214
Tel: (303)753-6046; Free: 800-888-ARTS
Fax: (303)759-4970
E-mail: alatkins@rmcad.edu
Web Site: www.rmcad.edu/

Description: Proprietary, comprehensive, coed. Awards bachelor's and master's degrees. Founded 1963. Setting: 23-acre suburban campus with easy access to Denver. Total enrollment: 651. Faculty: 119 (51 full-time, 68 part-time). Student-undergrad faculty ratio is 8:1. 171 applied, 50% were admitted. Full-time: 573 students, 64% women, 36% men. Part-time: 50 students, 60% women, 40% men. Students come from 44 states and territories, 5 other countries, 23% from out-of-state. 1% American Indian or Alaska Native, non-Hispanic/Latino; 9% Hispanic/Latino; 2% African American, non-Hispanic/Latino; 3% Asian, non-Hispanic/Latino; 0% Native Hawaiian or other Pacific Islander, non-Hispanic/Latino; 1% international. 19% 25 or older, 14% transferred in. Retention: 100% of full-time freshmen returned the following year. Academic areas with the most degrees conferred: visual and performing arts; communication technologies; education. Core. Calendar: trimesters. Academic remediation for entering students, services for LD students, advanced placement, accelerated degree program, honors program, independent study, distance learning, double major, summer session for credit, part-time degree program, co-op programs and internships. Off campus study. Study abroad program.

Entrance Requirements: Options: electronic application, international baccalaureate accepted. Required: minimum 2 high school GPA, interview, portfolio, SAT or ACT. Required for some: essay, high school transcript. Entrance: moderately difficult. Application deadline: Rolling. Notification: continuous. Transfer credits accepted: Yes.

Costs Per Year: Application fee: $50. Tuition: $27,648 full-time, $1152 per credit hour part-time. Full-time tuition varies according to degree level and location. Part-time tuition varies according to course load, degree level, and location. Tuition guaranteed not to increase for student's term of enrollment.

Collegiate Environment: Orientation program. Social organizations: 10 open to all; student government, special-interest social groups. Most popular organizations: The American Institute of Graphic Arts, The American Society of Interior Designers. Major annual events: Annual Student Exhibition, Welcome Back Week, Art + Music Festival. Student services: personal-psychological counseling. Campus security: 24-hour emergency response devices, late night transport-escort service. College housing not available. Rocky Mountain College of Art and Design Library plus 1 other with 17,000 books, 86 serials, 3,600 audiovisual materials, an OPAC, and a Web page. Operations spending for the previous fiscal year: $130,000. 300 computers available on campus for general student use. Computer purchase/lease plans available. A campuswide network can be accessed from off-campus. Students can access the following: online class registration, computer assistance, online library, wireless network, discounted software/hardware. Staffed computer lab on campus provides training in use of computers, software, and the Internet.

■ TRINIDAD STATE JUNIOR COLLEGE

600 Prospect
Trinidad, CO 81082-2396
Tel: (719)846-5011; Free: 800-621-8752
Fax: (719)846-5667
E-mail: sandy.veltri@trinidadstate.edu
Web Site: www.trinidadstate.edu/

Description: State-supported, 2-year, coed. Part of Colorado Community College and Occupational Education System. Awards certificates, diplomas, transfer associate, and terminal associate degrees. Founded 1925. Setting: 17-acre small town campus. Total enrollment: 1,760. Faculty: 122 (37 full-time, 85 part-time). Student-undergrad faculty ratio is 17:1. Full-time: 794 students, 49% women, 51% men. Part-time: 966 students, 61% women, 39% men. 43% 25 or older. Retention: 60% of full-time freshmen returned the following year. Calendar: semesters. Academic remediation for entering students, ESL program, services for LD students, advanced placement, accelerated degree program, self-designed majors, honors program, independent study, distance learning, double major, summer session for credit, part-time degree program, adult/continuing education programs, co-op programs and internships.

Entrance Requirements: Open admission except for practical nursing program. Option: deferred admission. Required: high school transcript. Entrance: noncompetitive. Application deadline: Rolling. Notification: continuous.

Collegiate Environment: Orientation program. Campus security: 24-hour emergency response devices and patrols, late night transport-escort service. Frendenthal Library plus 1 other with 54,255 books, 17,076 microform titles, 105 serials, 1,574 audiovisual materials, and an OPAC. 125 computers available on campus for general student use. A campuswide network can be accessed from student residence rooms and from off campus. Students can access the following: online class registration. Staffed computer lab on campus.

Community Environment: Located in South Central Colorado, Trinidad is the County Seat of Las Animas County and was a trading post on the Old Santa Fe Trail. Good highways, busses, and the railroad serve the area. Leading industries are coal production, farming, and ranching. The area offers Monument Lake, a 1,200-acre city owned park with fishing, boating and camping; Trinidad Lake, located 36 miles west of Trinidad in scenic Stonewall Valley, with water skiing, fishing, boating, camping, hiking and a recreation area; Cuchara Ski Area, located 50 miles west of Trinidad in scenic Cuchara valley.

■ **UNITED STATES AIR FORCE ACADEMY**
HQ USAFA/A9A
2304 Cadet Dr., Ste. 3800
USAF Academy, CO 80840-5025
Tel: (719)333-1818; Free: 800-443-9266
Fax: (719)333-3012
Web Site: www.usafa.edu/
Description: Federally supported, 4-year, coed. Awards bachelor's degrees. Founded 1954. Setting: 18,000-acre suburban campus with easy access to Colorado Springs, Denver. Research spending for the previous fiscal year: $22.2 million. Educational spending for the previous fiscal year: $57,523 per student. Total enrollment: 4,120. Faculty: 523 (516 full-time, 7 part-time). Student-undergrad faculty ratio is 8:1. 12,274 applied, 8% were admitted. 62% from top 10% of their high school class, 88% from top quarter, 97% from top half. 67 National Merit Scholars, 113 class presidents, 82 valedictorians, 163 student government officers. Full-time: 4,120 students, 22% women, 78% men. Students come from 54 states and territories, 38 other countries, 91% from out-of-state. 1% American Indian or Alaska Native, non-Hispanic/Latino; 9% Hispanic/Latino; 7% African American, non-Hispanic/Latino; 7% Asian, non-Hispanic/Latino; 1% Native Hawaiian or other Pacific Islander, non-Hispanic/Latino; 1% international. 1% 25 or older, 100% live on campus, 0% transferred in. Retention: 93% of full-time freshmen returned the following year. Academic areas with the most degrees conferred: engineering; social sciences; interdisciplinary studies. Core. Calendar: semesters. Academic remediation for entering students, ESL program, advanced placement, honors program, independent study, double major, summer session for credit, internships. Off campus study at other United States service academies: U.S. Military Academy (West Point), U.S. Naval Academy (Annapolis). Study abroad program.
Entrance Requirements: Options: electronic application, international baccalaureate accepted. Required: essay, high school transcript, minimum 2 high school GPA, interview, authorized nomination, SAT or ACT. Recommended: 3 recommendations. Entrance: most difficult. Application deadline: 12/31. Notification: 10/15. SAT Reasoning Test deadline: 12/31. SAT Subject Test deadline: 12/31. Transfer credits accepted: Yes.
Costs Per Year: Application fee: $0. Comprehensive fee: $0. Tuition, room and board, and medical and dental care are provided by the U.S. government. Each cadet receives a salary from which to pay for uniforms, supplies, and personal expenses.
Collegiate Environment: Drama-theater group, choral group, marching band, student-run radio station. Social organizations: 78 open to all. Most popular organizations: Cadet Ski Club, Men's and Women's Rugby Club, Cadet Cycling Club, Aviation Club, Drum and Bugle Corps. Major annual events: National Character and Leadership Symposium (NCLS), Football games, Graduation. Student services: legal services, health clinic, personal-psychological counseling, women's center. Campus security: 24-hour emergency response devices and patrols, late night transport-escort service, controlled dormitory access, self-defense education, well-lit campus. 4,500 college housing spaces available; 4,120 were occupied in 2012-13. Freshmen guaranteed college housing. On-campus residence required through senior year. Option: coed housing available. McDermott Library plus 1 other with 806,321 books, 777,003 microform titles, 108,978 serials, 10,140 audiovisual materials, an OPAC, and a Web page. Operations spending for the previous fiscal year: $5 million. 400 computers available on campus for general student use. Computer purchase/lease plans available. A computer is required for all students. A campuswide network can be accessed from student residence rooms and from off campus. Students can access the following: online class registration. Staffed computer lab on campus provides training in use of computers, software, and the Internet.

■ **UNIVERSITY OF COLORADO BOULDER**
Boulder, CO 80309
Tel: (303)492-1411
Fax: (303)492-7115
E-mail: apply@colorado.edu

Web Site: www.colorado.edu/
Description: State-supported, university, coed. Part of University of Colorado System. Awards bachelor's, master's, and doctoral degrees and post-master's certificates. Founded 1876. Setting: 600-acre suburban campus with easy access to Denver. Endowment: $385.7 million. Research spending for the previous fiscal year: $393 million. Educational spending for the previous fiscal year: $13,678 per student. Total enrollment: 31,725. Faculty: 1,899 (1,384 full-time, 515 part-time). Student-undergrad faculty ratio is 18:1. 21,744 applied, 84% were admitted. 25% from top 10% of their high school class, 56% from top quarter, 88% from top half. 15 National Merit Scholars, 140 valedictorians. Full-time: 23,582 students, 46% women, 54% men. Part-time: 2,223 students, 44% women, 56% men. Students come from 53 states and territories, 94 other countries, 37% from out-of-state. 0.5% American Indian or Alaska Native, non-Hispanic/Latino; 9% Hispanic/Latino; 2% African American, non-Hispanic/Latino; 5% Asian, non-Hispanic/Latino; 0.05% Native Hawaiian or other Pacific Islander, non-Hispanic/Latino; 3% international. 6% 25 or older, 28% live on campus, 4% transferred in. Retention: 84% of full-time freshmen returned the following year. Academic areas with the most degrees conferred: social sciences; biological/life sciences; business/marketing. Core. Calendar: semesters. ESL program, services for LD students, advanced placement, accelerated degree program, self-designed majors, freshman honors college, honors program, independent study, distance learning, double major, summer session for credit, part-time degree program, adult/continuing education programs, co-op programs and internships, graduate courses open to undergrads. Off campus study at other units of the University of Colorado System. Study abroad program. ROTC: Army, Naval, Air Force.
Entrance Requirements: Options: electronic application, early action, deferred admission, international baccalaureate accepted. Required: essay, high school transcript, SAT or ACT. Recommended: minimum 3 high school GPA, 2 recommendations. Required for some: audition for music program. Entrance: moderately difficult. Application deadlines: 1/15, 12/1 for early action. Notification: 4/1, 1/15 for early action. SAT Reasoning Test deadline: 1/15. Transfer credits accepted: Yes. Applicants placed on waiting list: 841. Early action applicants: 11,447. Early action applicants admitted: 10,653.
Costs Per Year: Application fee: $50. One-time mandatory fee: $182. State resident tuition: $8056 full-time. Nonresident tuition: $29,952 full-time. Mandatory fees: $1426 full-time. Full-time tuition and fees vary according to program. College room and board: $11,730. Room and board charges vary according to board plan, housing facility, and location.
Collegiate Environment: Orientation program. Drama-theater group, choral group, marching band, student-run newspaper, radio station. Social organizations: 600 open to all; national fraternities, national sororities, local sororities; 11% of eligible men and 16% of eligible women are members. Most popular organizations: student government, Environmental Center, Ski and Snowboard Club, AIESEC (international leadership organization), Program Council. Major annual events: Conference on World Affairs, Parents' Weekend, Global Jam. Student services: legal services, health clinic, personal-psychological counseling, women's center. Campus security: 24-hour emergency response devices and patrols, student patrols, late night transport-escort service, controlled dormitory access, University police department. 7,408 college housing spaces available; 7,174 were occupied in 2012-13. Freshmen guaranteed college housing. On-campus residence required in freshman year. Option: coed housing available. Norlin Library plus 5 others with 6.1 million books, an OPAC, and a Web page. Operations spending for the previous fiscal year: $21 million. 2,800 computers available on campus for general student use. Computer purchase/lease plans available. A campuswide network can be accessed from student residence rooms and from off campus. Students can access the following: online class registration, training, tutorials, workshops, and seminars; standard and academic software; student government voting. Staffed computer lab on campus provides training in use of computers, software, and the Internet.

■ **UNIVERSITY OF COLORADO COLORADO SPRINGS**
1420 Austin Bluffs Pky.
Colorado Springs, CO 80933-7150
Tel: (719)255-3000; Free: 800-990-8227
E-mail: cbeiswan@uccs.edu
Web Site: www.uccs.edu/
Description: State-supported, university, coed. Part of University of Colorado System. Awards bachelor's, master's, and doctoral degrees. Founded 1965. Setting: 532-acre urban campus with easy access to Colorado Springs. Endowment: $31.3 million. Research spending for the previous fiscal year: $10.2 million. Educational spending for the previous fis-

cal year: $5774 per student. Total enrollment: 10,257. Faculty: 712 (353 full-time, 359 part-time). Student-undergrad faculty ratio is 18:1. 5,612 applied, 92% were admitted. 14% from top 10% of their high school class, 39% from top quarter, 75% from top half. Full-time: 6,439 students, 54% women, 46% men. Part-time: 1,915 students, 54% women, 46% men. Students come from 48 states and territories, 18 other countries, 11% from out-of-state. 1% American Indian or Alaska Native, non-Hispanic/Latino; 13% Hispanic/Latino; 4% African American, non-Hispanic/Latino; 4% Asian, non-Hispanic/Latino; 0.2% Native Hawaiian or other Pacific Islander, non-Hispanic/Latino; 0.5% international. 25% 25 or older, 13% live on campus, 13% transferred in. Retention: 66% of full-time freshmen returned the following year. Academic areas with the most degrees conferred: business/marketing; social sciences; health professions and related sciences. Core. Calendar: semesters. Academic remediation for entering students, ESL program, services for LD students, advanced placement, accelerated degree program, self-designed majors, honors program, independent study, distance learning, double major, summer session for credit, part-time degree program, adult/continuing education programs, co-op programs and internships, graduate courses open to undergrads. Off campus study at Pikes Peak Community College, Otero Community College, Lamar Community College, University of Colorado Denver, University of Colorado Boulder. Study abroad program. ROTC: Army.

Entrance Requirements: Options: electronic application, deferred admission, international baccalaureate accepted. Required: high school transcript, SAT or ACT. Required for some: minimum 2 high school GPA, GED certificate in lieu of high school transcript; SAT or ACT test scores are required for most new students. Entrance: moderately difficult. Application deadlines: Rolling, Rolling for nonresidents. Notification: continuous, continuous for nonresidents. Transfer credits accepted: Yes.

Costs Per Year: Application fee: $50. State resident tuition: $7051 full-time, $297 per credit hour part-time. Nonresident tuition: $16,720 full-time, $848 per credit hour part-time. Mandatory fees: $1288 full-time, $27.85 per contact hour part-time, $242.85 per term part-time. Full-time tuition and fees vary according to course level, course load, degree level, location, program, reciprocity agreements, and student level. Part-time tuition and fees vary according to course level, course load, degree level, location, program, reciprocity agreements, and student level. College room and board: $8300. College room only: $7250. Room and board charges vary according to board plan and housing facility.

Collegiate Environment: Orientation program. Drama-theater group, choral group, student-run newspaper, radio station. Social organizations: 200 open to all; national fraternities, national sororities. Most popular organizations: Fans Initiating Growth Honor and Tradition (spirit club), Pi Beta Phi, Sustainability Club, Gamers (computing), El Circulo. Major annual events: Black Out Night (Basketball), Disorientation Week, Back to the Bluffs Homecoming. Student services: health clinic, personal-psychological counseling. Campus security: 24-hour emergency response devices and patrols, student patrols, late night transport-escort service, controlled dormitory access, emergency text messaging. 900 college housing spaces available; 895 were occupied in 2012-13. Freshmen given priority for college housing. Options: coed, men-only, women-only housing available. Kraemer Family Library with 415,808 books, 451,925 microform titles, 4,776 serials, 9,720 audiovisual materials, an OPAC, and a Web page. Operations spending for the previous fiscal year: $1.4 million. 672 computers available on campus for general student use. Computer purchase/lease plans available. A campuswide network can be accessed from student residence rooms and from off campus. Students can access the following: online class registration, wireless network, student portal, learning management system. Staffed computer lab on campus provides training in use of computers, software, and the Internet.

■ **UNIVERSITY OF COLORADO DENVER**
PO Box 173364
Denver, CO 80217-3364
Tel: (303)556-2400
Fax: (303)556-2398
E-mail: admissions@ucdenver.edu
Web Site: www.ucdenver.edu/
Description: State-supported, university, coed. Part of University of Colorado System. Awards bachelor's, master's, and doctoral degrees and post-master's certificates. Founded 1912. Setting: 171-acre urban campus with easy access to Denver. Endowment: $282.8 million. Research spending for the previous fiscal year: $250 million. Total enrollment: 22,396. Faculty: 3,417 (2,863 full-time, 554 part-time). Student-undergrad faculty ratio is 17:1.

3,075 applied, 76% were admitted. 20% from top 10% of their high school class, 47% from top quarter, 79% from top half. Full-time: 7,741 students, 53% women, 47% men. Part-time: 5,362 students, 55% women, 45% men. Students come from 49 states and territories, 66 other countries, 7% from out-of-state. 1% American Indian or Alaska Native, non-Hispanic/Latino; 15% Hispanic/Latino; 5% African American, non-Hispanic/Latino; 10% Asian, non-Hispanic/Latino; 0.1% Native Hawaiian or other Pacific Islander, non-Hispanic/Latino; 9% international. 32% 25 or older, 5% live on campus, 12% transferred in. Retention: 76% of full-time freshmen returned the following year. Academic areas with the most degrees conferred: business/marketing; social sciences; health professions and related sciences. Core. Calendar: semesters. ESL program, services for LD students, advanced placement, accelerated degree program, self-designed majors, honors program, independent study, distance learning, double major, summer session for credit, part-time degree program, adult/continuing education programs, co-op programs and internships, graduate courses open to undergrads. Off campus study at Metropolitan State College, Community College of Denver, University of Northern Colorado, Colorado State University, University of Colorado Colorado Springs, University of Colorado Boulder. Study abroad program. ROTC: Army (c), Air Force (c).

Entrance Requirements: Options: electronic application, deferred admission, international baccalaureate accepted. Required: high school transcript, minimum 2.5 high school GPA, SAT or ACT. Recommended: essay. Required for some: essay, minimum 3 high school GPA, audition, portfolio, entrance exam for some programs. Entrance: moderately difficult. Application deadlines: 7/22, 7/22 for nonresidents. Notification: continuous, continuous for nonresidents. SAT Reasoning Test deadline: 7/22. SAT Subject Test deadline: 7/22. Transfer credits accepted: Yes.

Costs Per Year: Application fee: $50. State resident tuition: $6384 full-time, $266 per credit hour part-time. Nonresident tuition: $19,896 full-time, $829 per credit hour part-time. Mandatory fees: $1110 full-time, $266 per credit hour part-time, $550 per term part-time. Full-time tuition and fees vary according to course level, course load, degree level, location, program, reciprocity agreements, and student level. Part-time tuition and fees vary according to course level, course load, degree level, location, program, reciprocity agreements, and student level. College room and board: $10,410. College room only: $7110. Room and board charges vary according to board plan.

Collegiate Environment: Orientation program. Drama-theater group, choral group, student-run newspaper. Social organizations: 199 open to all. Most popular organizations: Veterans Student Organization (Service), Golden Key Honor Society (Academic), Minority Association for Pre-Health Students (Health), Future Doctors of Denver, Intercultural Club Beijing (Cultural and Social). Major annual events: Distinguished Lecture Series, Fall Fest, Spring Fling. Student services: health clinic, personal-psychological counseling. Campus security: 24-hour emergency response devices and patrols, student patrols, late night transport-escort service. 685 college housing spaces available; 507 were occupied in 2012-13. Freshmen given priority for college housing. On-campus residence required in freshman year. Option: coed housing available. Auraria Library (UCD) and Health Sciences Library (AMC) with 653,885 books, 1 million microform titles, 75,585 serials, 26,114 audiovisual materials, an OPAC, and a Web page. Operations spending for the previous fiscal year: $9.1 million. 750 computers available on campus for general student use. A campuswide network can be accessed from student residence rooms and from off campus. Students can access the following: online class registration. Staffed computer lab on campus provides training in use of computers, software, and the Internet.

■ **UNIVERSITY OF DENVER**
2199 S University Blvd.
Denver, CO 80208
Tel: (303)871-2000; Free: 800-525-9495
Fax: (303)871-3301
E-mail: admission@du.edu
Web Site: www.du.edu/
Description: Independent, university, coed. Awards bachelor's, master's, and doctoral degrees and post-master's certificates. Founded 1864. Setting: 125-acre urban campus with easy access to Denver. Endowment: $373.4 million. Research spending for the previous fiscal year: $14.5 million. Educational spending for the previous fiscal year: $13,695 per student. Total enrollment: 11,656. Faculty: 1,349 (671 full-time, 678 part-time). Student-undergrad faculty ratio is 11:1. 11,448 applied, 68% were admitted. 44% from top 10% of their high school class, 78% from top quarter, 97% from top half. Full-time: 4,965 students, 55% women, 45% men. Part-time: 429

students, 71% women, 29% men. Students come from 50 states and territories, 54 other countries, 50% from out-of-state. 1% American Indian or Alaska Native, non-Hispanic/Latino; 8% Hispanic/Latino; 3% African American, non-Hispanic/Latino; 4% Asian, non-Hispanic/Latino; 0.1% Native Hawaiian or other Pacific Islander, non-Hispanic/Latino; 9% international. 9% 25 or older, 44% live on campus, 3% transferred in. Retention: 86% of full-time freshmen returned the following year. Academic areas with the most degrees conferred: business/marketing; social sciences; visual and performing arts. Core. Calendar: quarters; semesters for law school. ESL program, services for LD students, advanced placement, accelerated degree program, self-designed majors, freshman honors college, honors program, independent study, distance learning, double major, summer session for credit, part-time degree program, adult/continuing education programs, co-op programs and internships, graduate courses open to undergrads. Off campus study. Study abroad program. ROTC: Army (c), Air Force (c).

Entrance Requirements: Options: electronic application, early admission, early action, deferred admission, international baccalaureate accepted. Required: essay, high school transcript, 2 recommendations, SAT or ACT. Recommended: interview. Required for some: minimum 2 high school GPA. Entrance: moderately difficult. Application deadlines: 1/15, 11/1 for early action. Notification: 3/15, 1/15 for early action. SAT Reasoning Test deadline: 2/1. Transfer credits accepted: Yes. Applicants placed on waiting list: 926. Wait-listed applicants offered admission: 103. Early action applicants: 4,552. Early action applicants admitted: 3,579.

Costs Per Year: Application fee: $60. Comprehensive fee: $51,787 includes full-time tuition ($39,744), mandatory fees ($963), and college room and board ($11,080). College room only: $6780. Full-time tuition and fees vary according to class time, course load, and program. Room and board charges vary according to board plan and housing facility. Part-time tuition: $1104 per quarter hour. Part-time tuition varies according to class time, course load, and program.

Collegiate Environment: Orientation program. Drama-theater group, choral group, student-run newspaper, radio station. Social organizations: 90 open to all; national fraternities, national sororities; 11% of eligible men and 14% of eligible women are members. Most popular organizations: Club Sports Council, Alpine Club, DU Programs Board, Greek Life Council, Residence Hall Association. Major annual events: Homecoming, Winter Carnival, May Days. Student services: health clinic, personal-psychological counseling, women's center. Campus security: 24-hour emergency response devices and patrols, late night transport-escort service, controlled dormitory access, 24-hour locked residence hall entrances. 2,400 college housing spaces available; 2,325 were occupied in 2012-13. Freshmen guaranteed college housing. On-campus residence required through sophomore year. Options: coed, men-only, women-only housing available. Penrose Library plus 1 other with 4.7 million books, 1.3 million microform titles, 39,271 serials, 21,215 audiovisual materials, an OPAC, and a Web page. Operations spending for the previous fiscal year: $13.4 million. 150 computers available on campus for general student use. Computer purchase/lease plans available. A computer is required for all students. A campuswide network can be accessed from student residence rooms and from off campus. Students can access the following: online class registration. Staffed computer lab on campus provides training in use of computers, software, and the Internet.

Community Environment: Denver is a metropolitan area, capital of Colorado, situated at the foot of the Rocky Mountains. The climate is temperate and considered healthful. The State Museum, Art Museum, Museum of Natural History, many public and private hospitals, churches, and the fine shopping areas make up the city. Part-time employment opportunities are good. Denver is the gateway to the playgrounds of the mountains; the city's mountain parks of 20,000 acres include the Genesee Mountain with its game preserve. There are lakes in the area for water sports and fishing. Denver has become a great center for snow sports activities, with several of the best known ski areas located 55 to 85 miles from Denver in the Arapaho National Forest. The annual National Western Stock Show is in January.

■ **UNIVERSITY OF NORTHERN COLORADO**
Greeley, CO 80639
Tel: (970)351-1890; Free: 888-700-4UNC
E-mail: admissions@unco.edu
Web Site: www.unco.edu/
Description: State-supported, university, coed. Awards bachelor's, master's, and doctoral degrees. Founded 1890. Setting: 240-acre suburban campus with easy access to Denver. Endowment: $71.5 million. Research spending for the previous fiscal year: $2.5 million. Educational spending for the previous fiscal year: $6425 per student. Total enrollment: 12,497. Faculty: 737

(483 full-time, 254 part-time). Student-undergrad faculty ratio is 19:1. 6,823 applied, 89% were admitted. 12% from top 10% of their high school class, 35% from top quarter, 71% from top half. Full-time: 9,110 students, 62% women, 38% men. Part-time: 992 students, 65% women, 35% men. Students come from 50 states and territories, 37 other countries, 12% from out-of-state. 0.4% American Indian or Alaska Native, non-Hispanic/Latino; 15% Hispanic/Latino; 4% African American, non-Hispanic/Latino; 1% Asian, non-Hispanic/Latino; 0.3% Native Hawaiian or other Pacific Islander, non-Hispanic/Latino; 1% international. 10% 25 or older, 30% live on campus, 8% transferred in. Retention: 65% of full-time freshmen returned the following year. Academic areas with the most degrees conferred: business/marketing; interdisciplinary studies; health professions and related sciences. Core. Calendar: semesters. Academic remediation for entering students, ESL program, services for LD students, advanced placement, accelerated degree program, self-designed majors, honors program, independent study, distance learning, double major, summer session for credit, part-time degree program, external degree program, adult/continuing education programs, co-op programs and internships, graduate courses open to undergrads. Off campus study at National Student Exchange. Study abroad program. ROTC: Army, Air Force.

Entrance Requirements: Options: electronic application, deferred admission, international baccalaureate accepted. Required: high school transcript, minimum 2.9 high school GPA, SAT or ACT. Entrance: moderately difficult. Application deadlines: 8/1, 8/1 for nonresidents. Notification: continuous. SAT Reasoning Test deadline: 8/1. Transfer credits accepted: Yes.

Costs Per Year: Application fee: $45. One-time mandatory fee: $225. State resident tuition: $5214 full-time, $217.25 per credit hour part-time. Nonresident tuition: $16,488 full-time, $687 per credit hour part-time. Mandatory fees: $1,300 full-time, $62.59 per credit hour part-time. Full-time tuition and fees vary according to course load and program. Part-time tuition and fees vary according to course load and program. College room and board: $10,040. College room only: $4914. Room and board charges vary according to board plan, housing facility, and student level.

Collegiate Environment: Orientation program. Drama-theater group, choral group, marching band, student-run newspaper, radio station. Social organizations: 120 open to all; national fraternities, national sororities; 33% of eligible men and 67% of eligible women are members. Most popular organizations: Fraternities and Sororities, Club Sports, Campus Religious/Spiritual Organizations, Academic Clubs, Services Clubs. Major annual events: Homecoming, Spring Concert, Welcome Week. Student services: legal services, health clinic, personal-psychological counseling, women's center. Campus security: 24-hour emergency response devices and patrols, student patrols, late night transport-escort service, controlled dormitory access. 3,176 college housing spaces available; 2,933 were occupied in 2012-13. Freshmen guaranteed college housing. On-campus residence required in freshman year. Options: coed, women-only housing available. James A. Michener Library plus 2 others with 1.2 million books, 2.1 million microform titles, 43,646 serials, 55,184 audiovisual materials, an OPAC, and a Web page. Operations spending for the previous fiscal year: $3 million. 1,736 computers available on campus for general student use. Computer purchase/lease plans available. A campuswide network can be accessed from student residence rooms and from off campus. Students can access the following: online class registration. Staffed computer lab on campus (open 24 hours a day) provides training in use of computers, software, and the Internet.

Community Environment: Located one hour north of Denver and one hour east of Rocky Mountain National Park, the city of Greeley has a population of more than 87,500. It has a symphony, rock and jazz concerts, community theatre, and the largest 4th of July rodeo in the country. The dry, desert climate produces sunny days and cool nights. There is some snow and very little rain.

■ **UNIVERSITY OF PHOENIX–DENVER CAMPUS**
10004 Park Meadows Dr.
Lone Tree, CO 80124-5453
Tel: (303)694-9093; Free: 866-766-0766
Web Site: www.phoenix.edu/
Description: Proprietary, comprehensive, coed. Awards bachelor's and master's degrees and post-master's certificates. Setting: urban campus. Total enrollment: 2,264. Faculty: 302 (27 full-time, 275 part-time). Full-time: 1,289 students, 67% women, 33% men. 88% 25 or older. Academic areas with the most degrees conferred: business/marketing; computer and information sciences; homeland security, law enforcement, firefighting, and protective services. Core. Calendar: continuous. Services for LD students,

advanced placement, accelerated degree program, independent study, distance learning, external degree program, adult/continuing education programs, graduate courses open to undergrads.

Entrance Requirements: Open admission. Options: electronic application, deferred admission. Required: 1 recommendation. Required for some: high school transcript. Entrance: noncompetitive. Application deadline: Rolling.

Collegiate Environment: Campus security: late night transport-escort service. University Library with 16,781 serials, an OPAC, and a Web page. Operations spending for the previous fiscal year: $6.8 million.

■ **UNIVERSITY OF PHOENIX–SOUTHERN COLORADO CAMPUS**
5725 Mark Dabling Blvd.
Ste. 150
Colorado Springs, CO 80919-2335
Tel: (719)599-5282; Free: 866-766-0766
Web Site: www.phoenix.edu/

Description: Proprietary, comprehensive, coed. Awards bachelor's and master's degrees. Founded 1999. Setting: urban campus. Total enrollment: 560. Faculty: 126 (9 full-time, 117 part-time). 84% 25 or older. Retention: 36% of full-time freshmen returned the following year. Academic areas with the most degrees conferred: business/marketing; computer and information sciences; interdisciplinary studies. Core. Calendar: continuous. Services for LD students, advanced placement, accelerated degree program, independent study, distance learning, external degree program, adult/continuing education programs, graduate courses open to undergrads.

Entrance Requirements: Open admission. Options: electronic application, deferred admission. Required: 1 recommendation. Required for some: high school transcript. Entrance: noncompetitive. Application deadline: Rolling.

Collegiate Environment: Campus security: late night transport-escort service. University Library with 16,781 serials, an OPAC, and a Web page. Operations spending for the previous fiscal year: $6.8 million.

■ **WESTERN STATE COLORADO UNIVERSITY**
600 N Adams St.
Gunnison, CO 81231
Tel: (970)943-0120; Free: 800-876-5309
Fax: (970)943-7069
E-mail: admissions@western.edu
Web Site: www.western.edu/

Description: State-supported, comprehensive, coed. Awards bachelor's and master's degrees. Founded 1901. Setting: 381-acre rural campus. Research spending for the previous fiscal year: $26,507. Educational spending for the previous fiscal year: $5778 per student. Total enrollment: 2,301. Faculty: 163 (112 full-time, 51 part-time). Student-undergrad faculty ratio is 15:1. 1,515 applied, 96% were admitted. 9% from top 10% of their high school class, 27% from top quarter, 56% from top half. 3 valedictorians. Full-time: 1,853 students, 38% women, 62% men. Part-time: 252 students, 48% women, 52% men. Students come from 50 states and territories, 8 other countries, 25% from out-of-state. 0.3% American Indian or Alaska Native, non-Hispanic/Latino; 7% Hispanic/Latino; 2% African American, non-Hispanic/Latino; 1% Asian, non-Hispanic/Latino; 0.5% Native Hawaiian or other Pacific Islander, non-Hispanic/Latino; 1% international. 12% 25 or older, 37% live on campus, 8% transferred in. Retention: 64% of full-time freshmen returned the following year. Academic areas with the most degrees conferred: business/marketing; parks and recreation; social sciences. Core. Calendar: semesters. Academic remediation for entering students, services for LD students, advanced placement, honors program, independent study, double major, summer session for credit, part-time degree program, adult/continuing education programs, internships, graduate courses open to undergrads. Off campus study at State Colleges of Colorado, National Student Exchange. Study abroad program.

Entrance Requirements: Options: electronic application, deferred admission, international baccalaureate accepted. Required: high school transcript, SAT or ACT. Recommended: minimum 2.5 high school GPA. Required for some: essay, interview. Entrance: moderately difficult. Notification: continuous until 11/15, continuous until 11/15 for nonresidents. Transfer credits accepted: Yes.

Costs Per Year: Application fee: $30. State resident tuition: $5275 full-time, $219.80 per credit hour part-time. Nonresident tuition: $15,216 full-time, $634 per credit hour part-time. Mandatory fees: $2068 full-time. Full-time tuition and fees vary according to course load and reciprocity agreements.

Part-time tuition varies according to course load and reciprocity agreements. College room and board: $8792. College room only: $4700. Room and board charges vary according to board plan and housing facility.

Collegiate Environment: Orientation program. Drama-theater group, choral group, student-run newspaper, radio station. Social organizations: 20% of eligible men and 22% of eligible women are members. Most popular organizations: Mountain Search and Rescue Team, Student Government Association, Rodeo Club, wilderness pursuits, Peak Productions. Major annual events: Earth Day, Homecoming, Family Weekend. Student services: health clinic, personal-psychological counseling. Campus security: 24-hour emergency response devices and patrols, student patrols, late night transport-escort service, controlled dormitory access. 1,200 college housing spaces available; 1,000 were occupied in 2012-13. Freshmen guaranteed college housing. On-campus residence required through sophomore year. Options: coed, men-only, women-only housing available. Leslie J. Savage Library with 444,840 books, 787,130 microform titles, 6,000 serials, 9,323 audiovisual materials, an OPAC, and a Web page. Operations spending for the previous fiscal year: $614,970. 181 computers available on campus for general student use. A campuswide network can be accessed from student residence rooms and from off campus. Students can access the following: online class registration. Staffed computer lab on campus provides training in use of computers, software, and the Internet.

Community Environment: Gunnison is a community with a population of about 5,200. Western State students are welcome to participate in all kinds of cultural, political, recreational, and religious activities offered by the community. The summer climate and the natural beauties of the region annually attract millions of tourists. Winter sports enthusiasts enjoy excellent skiing at Crested Butte Mountain Resort and Monarch Ski Area and ice fishing on Colorado's Blue Mesa Reservoir, which is located just 9 miles from the campus.

■ **WESTWOOD COLLEGE–DENVER NORTH**
7350 N Broadway
Denver, CO 80221-3653
Tel: (303)650-5050; Free: 800-281-2978
Fax: (303)426-0702
Web Site: www.westwood.edu/

Description: Proprietary, 4-year, coed. Awards associate and bachelor's degrees. Founded 1953. Setting: suburban campus. Total enrollment: 829. Faculty: 84. Calendar: 5 terms.

■ **WESTWOOD COLLEGE–DENVER SOUTH**
3150 S Sheridan Blvd.
Denver, CO 80227
Tel: (303)934-1122; Free: 800-281-2978
Web Site: www.westwood.edu/

Description: Proprietary, 4-year, coed. Awards associate and bachelor's degrees. Total enrollment: 445. Faculty: 44. Calendar: continuous.

■ **WESTWOOD COLLEGE–ONLINE CAMPUS**
10249 Church Ranch Way
Broomfield, CO 80021
Tel: (720)887-8888
Web Site: www.westwood.edu/

Description: Proprietary, comprehensive, coed. Awards associate, bachelor's, and master's degrees. Total enrollment: 7,584. Faculty: 281.

■ **YESHIVA TORAS CHAIM TALMUDICAL SEMINARY**
1555 Stuart St.
Denver, CO 80204-1415
Tel: (303)629-8200
Fax: (303)623-5949

Description: Independent Jewish, comprehensive, men only. Awards bachelor's and master's degrees. Founded 1967. Setting: urban campus. Total enrollment: 11. 6 applied, 100% were admitted. Core. Calendar: trimesters. Academic remediation for entering students, services for LD students, honors program, adult/continuing education programs, graduate courses open to undergrads.

Entrance Requirements: Option: early admission. Recommended: high school transcript. Entrance: moderately difficult.

■ ALBERTUS MAGNUS COLLEGE

700 Prospect St.
New Haven, CT 06511-1189
Tel: (203)773-8550; Free: 800-578-9160
Fax: (203)785-8652
E-mail: admissions@albertus.edu
Web Site: www.albertus.edu/

Description: Independent Roman Catholic, comprehensive, coed. Awards associate, bachelor's, and master's degrees. Founded 1925. Setting: 55-acre suburban campus. Endowment: $6.1 million. Total enrollment: 2,010. Faculty: 76 (42 full-time, 34 part-time). Student-undergrad faculty ratio is 15:1. 722 applied, 67% were admitted. 8% from top 10% of their high school class, 19% from top quarter, 70% from top half. 1 valedictorian. Full-time: 1,376 students, 66% women, 34% men. Part-time: 228 students, 68% women, 32% men. Students come from 7 states and territories, 2 other countries, 17% from out-of-state. 1% American Indian or Alaska Native, non-Hispanic/Latino; 11% Hispanic/Latino; 22% African American, non-Hispanic/Latino; 1% Asian, non-Hispanic/Latino; 0.1% Native Hawaiian or other Pacific Islander, non-Hispanic/Latino; 0.1% international. 54% 25 or older, 46% live on campus, 9% transferred in. Retention: 76% of full-time freshmen returned the following year. Academic areas with the most degrees conferred: business/marketing; social sciences; psychology. Core. Calendar: semesters. Academic remediation for entering students, ESL program, services for LD students, advanced placement, accelerated degree program, self-designed majors, freshman honors college, honors program, independent study, distance learning, double major, summer session for credit, part-time degree program, internships, graduate courses open to undergrads.

Entrance Requirements: Options: electronic application, deferred admission. Required: high school transcript, 1 recommendation, SAT or ACT. Recommended: essay, minimum 2.5 high school GPA, interview, SAT Subject Tests. Required for some: minimum 2.5 high school GPA. Entrance: moderately difficult. Application deadline: 8/30. Notification: continuous. SAT Reasoning Test deadline: 8/30. Transfer credits accepted: Yes.

Costs Per Year: Application fee: $35. Comprehensive fee: $40,112 includes full-time tuition ($27,888), mandatory fees ($470), and college room and board ($11,754). Full-time tuition and fees vary according to program.

Collegiate Environment: Orientation program. Drama-theater group, choral group. Most popular organizations: Student Government Association, College Drama, Campus ministry. Major annual events: Candlelight Ceremony, Fall Festival, Spring Semi-Formal/Winter Wonderland. Student services: health clinic, personal-psychological counseling. Campus security: 24-hour emergency response devices and patrols, late night transport-escort service, controlled dormitory access. 300 college housing spaces available; 230 were occupied in 2012-13. Freshmen given priority for college housing. Options: coed, women-only housing available. Rosary Hall with 120,276 books, 7,368 microform titles, 25,777 serials, an OPAC, and a Web page. Operations spending for the previous fiscal year: $72,202. 146 computers available on campus for general student use. A campuswide network can be accessed from student residence rooms and from off campus. Students can access the following: online class registration, online class sessions - Moodle. Staffed computer lab on campus provides training in use of computers, software, and the Internet.

Community Environment: See Yale University.

■ ASNUNTUCK COMMUNITY COLLEGE

170 Elm St.
Enfield, CT 06082-3800
Tel: (860)253-3000
Fax: (860)253-9310
E-mail: tstjames@acc.commnet.edu
Web Site: www.acc.commnet.edu/

Description: State-supported, 2-year, coed. Part of Connecticut Community-Technical College System. Awards certificates, transfer associate, and terminal associate degrees. Founded 1972. Setting: 4-acre suburban campus. Total enrollment: 1,808. Student-undergrad faculty ratio is 20:1. 14% from out-of-state. 46% 25 or older. Core. Calendar: semesters. Academic remediation for entering students, ESL program, services for LD students, advanced placement, self-designed majors, independent study, distance learning, double major, summer session for credit, part-time degree program, adult/continuing education programs, co-op programs and internships.

Entrance Requirements: Open admission. Option: deferred admission. Required: high school transcript, Basic Skills Assessment. Entrance: noncompetitive. Application deadline: Rolling. Notification: continuous.

Collegiate Environment: Orientation program. Drama-theater group, student-run newspaper, radio station. Student services: women's center. Campus security: 24-hour patrols, late night transport-escort service. ACTC Learning Resource Center with an OPAC.

■ BAIS BINYOMIN ACADEMY

132 Prospect St.
Stamford, CT 06901-1202
Tel: (203)325-4351

Description: Independent Jewish, 4-year, men only. Awards bachelor's degrees. Founded 1976. Total enrollment: 63. Student-undergrad faculty ratio is 9:1. 26 applied, 100% were admitted. 96% from out-of-state. 0% 25 or older. Retention: 77% of full-time freshmen returned the following year. Calendar: trimesters.

■ CAPITAL COMMUNITY COLLEGE

950 Main St.
Hartford, CT 06103
Tel: (860)906-5000
E-mail: jphillips@ccc.commnet.edu
Web Site: www.ccc.commnet.edu/

Description: State-supported, 2-year, coed. Part of Connecticut Community-Technical College System. Awards certificates, transfer associate, and terminal associate degrees. Founded 1946. Setting: 10-acre urban campus. Total enrollment: 4,280. Student-undergrad faculty ratio is 46:1. 0% from out-of-state. 54% 25 or older. Calendar: semesters. Academic remediation for entering students, ESL program, services for LD students, advanced placement, accelerated degree program, independent study, distance learning, double major, summer session for credit, part-time degree program, adult/continuing education programs, internships.

Entrance Requirements: Open admission except for nursing, emergency medical technology, radiological technology programs. Recommended: high school transcript. Entrance: noncompetitive. Application deadline: Rolling. Notification: continuous until 9/1.

Collegiate Environment: Drama-theater group, choral group. Student services: personal-psychological counseling. Campus security: late night transport-escort service, security staff during hours of operation, emergency telephones 7 am - 11 pm. Arthur C. Banks, Jr. Library plus 1 other with an OPAC and a Web page.

■ CENTRAL CONNECTICUT STATE UNIVERSITY

1615 Stanley St.
New Britain, CT 06050-4010
Tel: (860)832-2278
Fax: (860)832-2522
E-mail: admissions@ccsu.edu
Web Site: www.ccsu.edu/

Description: State-supported, comprehensive, coed. Part of Connecticut State University System. Awards bachelor's, master's, and doctoral degrees and post-master's certificates. Founded 1849. Setting: 294-acre suburban campus. Endowment: $38.2 million. Research spending for the previous fiscal year: $2 million. Educational spending for the previous fiscal year: $8559 per student. Total enrollment: 12,521. Faculty: 968 (440 full-time, 528 part-time). Student-undergrad faculty ratio is 16:1. 5,699 applied, 64% were admitted. 9% from top 10% of their high school class, 21% from top quarter, 73% from top half. Full-time: 7,823 students, 48% women, 52% men. Part-time: 2,269 students, 49% women, 51% men. Students come from 29 states and territories, 41 other countries, 3% from out-of-state. 0.2% American Indian or Alaska Native, non-Hispanic/Latino; 9% Hispanic/Latino; 10% African American, non-Hispanic/Latino; 3% Asian, non-Hispanic/Latino; 0.1% Native Hawaiian or other Pacific Islander, non-Hispanic/Latino; 1% international. 16% 25 or older, 23% live on campus, 11% transferred in. Retention: 76% of full-time freshmen returned the following year. Academic areas with the most degrees conferred: business/marketing; social sciences; education. Core. Calendar: semesters. Academic remediation for entering students, ESL program, services for LD students, advanced placement, self-designed majors, honors program, independent study, distance learning, summer session for credit, part-time degree program, adult/continuing education programs, co-op programs and internships, graduate courses open to undergrads. Off campus study at members of the Inter-Institutional Student Exchange Program. Study abroad program. ROTC: Army (c), Air Force (c).

Entrance Requirements: Option: electronic application. Required: essay, high school transcript, minimum 2 high school GPA, SAT. Recommended: minimum 3 high school GPA, 1 recommendation. Required for some: interview. Entrance: moderately difficult. Application deadline: 5/1. Notification: continuous until 10/15.

Costs Per Year: Application fee: $50. State resident tuition: $4285 full-time, $179 per credit part-time. Nonresident tuition: $13,866 full-time, $182 per credit part-time. Mandatory fees: $4036 full-time, $218 per credit part-time, $223. Full-time tuition and fees vary according to course level, course load, program, and reciprocity agreements. Part-time tuition and fees vary according to course level, course load, and program. College room and board: $10,056. College room only: $5850. Room and board charges vary according to board plan.

Collegiate Environment: Orientation program. Drama-theater group, choral group, student-run newspaper, radio station. Social organizations: 100 open to all; national fraternities, national sororities, local fraternities, local sororities; 1% of eligible men and 1% of eligible women are members. Most popular organizations: Inter-Residence Council, student radio station, Program Council, Outing Club, NAACP. Major annual events: Homecoming, Film Series, Spring Weekend. Student services: health clinic, personal-psychological counseling, women's center. Campus security: 24-hour emergency response devices and patrols, student patrols, late night transport-escort service, controlled dormitory access. 2,142 college housing spaces available; 2,130 were occupied in 2012-13. No special consideration for freshman housing applicants. Options: coed, women-only housing available. Elihu Burritt Library plus 1 other with 734,780 books, 557,275 microform titles, 55,879 serials, 15,096 audiovisual materials, an OPAC, and a Web page. Operations spending for the previous fiscal year: $6.7 million. 750 computers available on campus for general student use. A campuswide network can be accessed from student residence rooms and from off campus. Students can access the following: online class registration. Staffed computer lab on campus provides training in use of computers, software, and the Internet.

Community Environment: Population 71,250. Known as the"Hardware City of the World," New Britain is located nine miles southwest of Hartford. Sleigh bells were the first items manufactured here. Now there are 250 manufacturing establishments and over 600 retail outlets. Access to New York City is by train, and there is commercial air service nearby. New Britain has 44 churches of major denominations, outstanding hospital facilities and is now undertaking urban renewal projects. Points of interest are the New Britain Institute and Art Museum, memorial monuments, municipal golf course and the parks.

■ CHARTER OAK STATE COLLEGE

55 Paul Manafort Dr.
New Britain, CT 06053-2142
Tel: (860)832-3800
Fax: (860)832-3999
E-mail: admissions@charteroak.edu
Web Site: www.charteroak.edu/

Description: State-supported, 4-year, coed. Awards associate and bachelor's degrees (offers only external degree programs). Founded 1973. Setting: small town campus. Total enrollment: 1,644. Faculty: 153 (all part-time). Student-undergrad faculty ratio is 14:1. Full-time: 276 students, 68% women, 32% men. Part-time: 1,368 students, 67% women, 33% men. Students come from 43 states and territories, 25% from out-of-state. 0.1% American Indian or Alaska Native, non-Hispanic/Latino; 11% Hispanic/Latino; 17% African American, non-Hispanic/Latino; 2% Asian, non-Hispanic/Latino; 0.1% Native Hawaiian or other Pacific Islander, non-Hispanic/Latino; 0.3% international. 89% 25 or older, 0% live on campus, 28% transferred in. Academic area with the most degrees conferred: liberal arts/general studies. Core. Calendar: continuous. Services for LD students, advanced placement, accelerated degree program, self-designed majors, independent study, distance learning, summer session for credit, part-time degree program, external degree program, adult/continuing education programs.

Entrance Requirements: Open admission. Options: electronic application, deferred admission. Entrance: noncompetitive. Transfer credits accepted: Yes.

Costs Per Year: Application fee: $75. State resident tuition: $7350 full-time, $245 per credit hour part-time. Nonresident tuition: $9660 full-time, $322 per credit hour part-time. Mandatory fees: $342 full-time, $171 per term part-time.

Collegiate Environment: College housing not available.

■ CONNECTICUT COLLEGE

270 Mohegan Ave.
New London, CT 06320-4196
Tel: (860)447-1911
Fax: (860)439-4301
E-mail: admission@conncoll.edu
Web Site: www.connecticutcollege.edu/

Description: Independent, comprehensive, coed. Awards bachelor's and master's degrees. Founded 1911. Setting: 702-acre small town campus. Endowment: $211.2 million. Educational spending for the previous fiscal year: $18,822 per student. Total enrollment: 1,933. Faculty: 249 (179 full-time, 70 part-time). Student-undergrad faculty ratio is 9:1. 4,837 applied, 36% were admitted. 56% from top 10% of their high school class, 95% from top quarter, 100% from top half. Full-time: 1,884 students, 60% women, 40% men. Part-time: 42 students, 62% women, 38% men. Students come from 42 states and territories, 74 other countries, 83% from out-of-state. 0.1% American Indian or Alaska Native, non-Hispanic/Latino; 7% Hispanic/Latino; 4% African American, non-Hispanic/Latino; 3% Asian, non-Hispanic/Latino; 0% Native Hawaiian or other Pacific Islander, non-Hispanic/Latino; 4% international. 0% 25 or older, 99% live on campus, 1% transferred in. Retention: 92% of full-time freshmen returned the following year. Academic areas with the most degrees conferred: social sciences; biological/life sciences; visual and performing arts. Core. Calendar: semesters. Services for LD students, advanced placement, accelerated degree program, self-designed majors, independent study, double major, part-time degree program, adult/continuing education programs, internships. Off campus study at members of the Twelve-College Exchange Program, exchanges with United States Coast Guard Academy, American University, Trinity College, Wesleyan University, National Theater Institute, Williams College. Study abroad program.

Entrance Requirements: Options: electronic application, early decision, deferred admission, international baccalaureate accepted. Required: essay, high school transcript, minimum 2 high school GPA, 1 recommendation, Supplement to Common Application. Recommended: interview. Entrance: very difficult. Application deadlines: 1/1, 11/15 for early decision plan 1, 1/1 for early decision plan 2. Notification: 3/31, 12/15 for early decision plan 1, 2/15 for early decision plan 2. SAT Reasoning Test deadline: 2/15. SAT

Subject Test deadline: 2/15. Transfer credits accepted: Yes. Applicants placed on waiting list: 1,152. Wait-listed applicants offered admission: 31. Early decision applicants: 416. Early decision applicants admitted: 268.

Costs Per Year: Application fee: $60. Comprehensive fee: $58,780 includes full-time tuition ($45,765), mandatory fees ($320), and college room and board ($12,695). College room only: $7325. Part-time tuition: $1364 per credit hour.

Collegiate Environment: Orientation program. Drama-theater group, choral group, student-run newspaper, radio station. Social organizations: 60 open to all; about 65 student clubs. Most popular organizations: Student Government Association, Student Activity Council, Unity House organizations, sports clubs, student radio station. Major annual events: Floralia, Harvestfest, Winter Formal. Student services: health clinic, personal-psychological counseling, women's center. Campus security: 24-hour emergency response devices and patrols, late night transport-escort service, controlled dormitory access. 1,791 college housing spaces available; 1,764 were occupied in 2012-13. Freshmen guaranteed college housing. On-campus residence required through sophomore year. Option: coed housing available. Charles Shain Library plus 1 other with 821,589 books, 153,545 microform titles, 6,973 serials, 95,917 audiovisual materials, an OPAC, and a Web page.

Community Environment: On the west bank of the Thames River, three miles from Long Island Sound, known historically as "The Whaling City." New London is a maritime center located midway between Boston and New York. It is a popular summer resort. Ocean Beach Park, a fifty-acre tract, borders a half-mile-long beach and provides recreational facilities. New London is the location of the annual Yale-Harvard Crew Races held each June.

■ **EASTERN CONNECTICUT STATE UNIVERSITY**
83 Windham St.
Willimantic, CT 06226-2295
Tel: (860)465-5000
E-mail: admissions@easternct.edu
Web Site: www.easternct.edu/

Description: State-supported, comprehensive, coed. Part of Connecticut State Colleges and Universities (ConnSCU). Awards associate, bachelor's, and master's degrees. Founded 1889. Setting: 182-acre small town campus with easy access to Hartford. Endowment: $12.1 million. Research spending for the previous fiscal year: $133,305. Educational spending for the previous fiscal year: $8163 per student. Total enrollment: 5,440. Faculty: 478 (195 full-time, 283 part-time). Student-undergrad faculty ratio is 16:1. 4,387 applied, 67% were admitted. 9% from top 10% of their high school class, 30% from top quarter, 70% from top half. Full-time: 4,420 students, 54% women, 46% men. Part-time: 838 students, 57% women, 43% men. Students come from 26 states and territories, 44 other countries, 4% from out-of-state. 0.3% American Indian or Alaska Native, non-Hispanic/Latino; 8% Hispanic/Latino; 7% African American, non-Hispanic/Latino; 2% Asian, non-Hispanic/Latino; 0.1% Native Hawaiian or other Pacific Islander, non-Hispanic/Latino; 1% international. 11% 25 or older, 53% live on campus, 9% transferred in. Retention: 76% of full-time freshmen returned the following year. Academic areas with the most degrees conferred: business/marketing; social sciences; liberal arts/general studies. Core. Calendar: semesters. Academic remediation for entering students, services for LD students, advanced placement, accelerated degree program, self-designed majors, honors program, independent study, distance learning, double major, summer session for credit, part-time degree program, external degree program, adult/continuing education programs, co-op programs and internships, graduate courses open to undergrads. Off campus study at International and National Exchange programs. Study abroad program. ROTC: Army (c), Air Force (c).

Entrance Requirements: Options: electronic application, deferred admission. Required: high school transcript, SAT or ACT. Recommended: essay, rank in upper 50% of high school class. Required for some: interview. Entrance: moderately difficult. Application deadline: Rolling. Notification: continuous. Transfer credits accepted: Yes. Applicants placed on waiting list: 166. Wait-listed applicants offered admission: 15.

Costs Per Year: Application fee: $50. State resident tuition: $4510 full-time. Nonresident tuition: $14,594 full-time. Mandatory fees: $4866 full-time. Full-time tuition and fees vary according to reciprocity agreements. College room and board: $11,168. College room only: $6392. Room and board charges vary according to board plan.

Collegiate Environment: Orientation program. Drama-theater group, choral group, student-run newspaper, radio station. Social organizations: 65 open to all. Most popular organizations: Bowling Club, People Helping People, M.A.L.E.S, Education Club, West Indian Society. Major annual events: Open

Rec Night, Spring Fest, Family Day. Student services: health clinic, personal-psychological counseling, women's center. Campus security: 24-hour emergency response devices and patrols, student patrols, late night transport-escort service, controlled dormitory access. College housing designed to accommodate 2,527 students; 2,609 undergraduates lived in college housing during 2012-13. Freshmen guaranteed college housing. Option: coed housing available. J. Eugene Smith Library with 239,218 books, 1 million microform titles, 1,729 serials, an OPAC, and a Web page. Operations spending for the previous fiscal year: $3.1 million. 637 computers available on campus for general student use. Computer purchase/lease plans available. A campuswide network can be accessed from student residence rooms and from off campus. Students can access the following: online class registration. Staffed computer lab on campus provides training in use of computers, software, and the Internet.

Community Environment: Located 28 miles from Hartford and New London and halfway between Boston and New York, Willimantic, with a population of approximately 16,000, is primarily a retail and service center for eastern Connecticut. Bus service connects the city with major transportation facilities in Hartford, Providence, and New York. Willimantic has excellent health and hospital services and recreational facilities include the Willimantic Golf Course and nearby lakes and state parks.

■ **FAIRFIELD UNIVERSITY**
1073 N Benson Rd.
Fairfield, CT 06824-5195
Tel: (203)254-4000
Fax: (203)254-4199
E-mail: admis@fairfield.edu
Web Site: www.fairfield.edu/

Description: Independent Roman Catholic (Jesuit), comprehensive, coed. Awards bachelor's, master's, and doctoral degrees and post-master's certificates. Founded 1942. Setting: 200-acre suburban campus with easy access to New York City. Endowment: $245.3 million. Research spending for the previous fiscal year: $6.5 million. Educational spending for the previous fiscal year: $14,304 per student. Total enrollment: 4,999. Faculty: 587 (263 full-time, 324 part-time). Student-undergrad faculty ratio is 11:1. 9,254 applied, 71% were admitted. 34% from top 10% of their high school class, 64% from top quarter, 91% from top half. Full-time: 3,471 students, 59% women, 41% men. Part-time: 408 students, 54% women, 46% men. Students come from 31 states and territories, 24 other countries, 64% from out-of-state. 0.1% American Indian or Alaska Native, non-Hispanic/Latino; 8% Hispanic/Latino; 3% African American, non-Hispanic/Latino; 2% Asian, non-Hispanic/Latino; 0.1% Native Hawaiian or other Pacific Islander, non-Hispanic/Latino; 1% international. 6% 25 or older, 82% live on campus, 1% transferred in. Retention: 87% of full-time freshmen returned the following year. Academic areas with the most degrees conferred: business/marketing; social sciences; health professions and related sciences. Core. Calendar: semesters. Services for LD students, advanced placement, self-designed majors, honors program, independent study, distance learning, double major, summer session for credit, part-time degree program, adult/continuing education programs, internships, graduate courses open to undergrads. Off campus study. Study abroad program. ROTC: Army (c), Air Force (c).

Entrance Requirements: Options: electronic application, early admission, early decision, early action, deferred admission, international baccalaureate accepted. Required: essay, high school transcript, 1 recommendation. Recommended: interview. Entrance: moderately difficult. Application deadlines: 1/15, 1/1 for early decision, 11/1 for early action. Notification: 4/1, 2/1 for early decision, 1/1 for early action. SAT Reasoning Test deadline: 1/15. Transfer credits accepted: Yes. Applicants placed on waiting list: 1,668. Wait-listed applicants offered admission: 43. Early decision applicants: 95. Early decision applicants admitted: 55. Early action applicants: 4,365. Early action applicants admitted: 3,214.

Costs Per Year: Application fee: $60. One-time mandatory fee: $230. Comprehensive fee: $54,240 includes full-time tuition ($41,090), mandatory fees ($600), and college room and board ($12,550). College room only: $7690. Room and board charges vary according to board plan and housing facility. Part-time tuition: $700 per credit hour. Part-time mandatory fees: $60 per term. Part-time tuition and fees vary according to course load.

Collegiate Environment: Orientation program. Drama-theater group, choral group, student-run newspaper, radio station. Social organizations: 86 open to all. Most popular organizations: student government, Glee Club, Residence Hall Council, Stags in the Stands, Campus Ministry. Major annual events: Annual Midnight Breakfast, Presidential Ball, Spring concert. Student services: health clinic, personal-psychological counseling, women's center.

Campus security: 24-hour emergency response devices and patrols, late night transport-escort service, controlled dormitory access, bicycle patrols. 2,795 college housing spaces available; 2,790 were occupied in 2012-13. Freshmen guaranteed college housing. On-campus residence required through senior year. Option: coed housing available. DiMenna-Nyselius Library with 375,927 books, 886,674 microform titles, 60,156 serials, 15,416 audiovisual materials, an OPAC, and a Web page. Operations spending for the previous fiscal year: $1.7 million. 101 computers available on campus for general student use. Computer purchase/lease plans available. A campuswide network can be accessed from student residence rooms and from off campus. Students can access the following: online class registration. Staffed computer lab on campus provides training in use of computers, software, and the Internet.

Community Environment: Population 58,000. Fairfield is a suburban area one hour north of New York City on the Long Island Sound. The climate is temperate. The Metro-North New Haven branch railroad serves the area, as well as the Connecticut Turnpike and Merritt Parkway. Community facilities include libraries, churches and shopping areas. Part-time employment opportunities are available. Beaches are nearby for water sports; other sports include golf and tennis. A special annual event is the Dogwood Festival.

■ **GATEWAY COMMUNITY COLLEGE**
60 Sargent Dr.
New Haven, CT 06511
Tel: (203)285-2000; Free: 800-390-7723
Fax: (203)285-2018
E-mail: gateway_ctc@commnet.edu
Web Site: www.gwcc.commnet.edu/
Description: State-supported, 2-year, coed. Part of Connecticut Community-Technical College System. Awards certificates, transfer associate, and terminal associate degrees. Founded 1992. Setting: 5-acre urban campus with easy access to New York City. Total enrollment: 7,261. Faculty: 443 (63 full-time, 380 part-time). Student-undergrad faculty ratio is 20:1. 3,522 applied, 97% were admitted. Full-time: 2,490 students, 52% women, 48% men. Part-time: 4,771 students, 63% women, 37% men. 42% 25 or older. Core. Calendar: semesters. Academic remediation for entering students, ESL program, services for LD students, advanced placement, independent study, distance learning, summer session for credit, part-time degree program, external degree program, adult/continuing education programs, internships. Off campus study at Southern Connecticut State University.
Entrance Requirements: Open admission except for radiological technology, pharmacy technology, engineering technologies programs. Options: early admission, deferred admission. Required: high school transcript. Required for some: essay, interview. Entrance: noncompetitive. Application deadline: 9/1. Notification: continuous until 9/1. Transfer credits accepted: Yes. Applicants placed on waiting list: 124. Wait-listed applicants offered admission: 124.
Costs Per Year: Application fee: $20. State resident tuition: $3168 full-time, $132 per credit part-time. Nonresident tuition: $9504 full-time, $396 per credit part-time. Mandatory fees: $402 full-time.
Collegiate Environment: Drama-theater group, student-run newspaper. Student services: personal-psychological counseling, women's center. Campus security: late night transport-escort service. Gateway Community College Library plus 2 others with 46,090 books, 1,239 microform titles, 275 serials, 3,121 audiovisual materials, an OPAC, and a Web page. 556 computers available on campus for general student use. A campuswide network can be accessed from off-campus. Students can access the following: online class registration. Staffed computer lab on campus provides training in use of computers, software, and the Internet.

■ **GOODWIN COLLEGE**
One Riverside Dr.
East Hartford, CT 06118
Tel: (860)528-4111; Free: 800-889-3282
Fax: (860)291-9550
E-mail: nlantino@goodwin.edu
Web Site: www.goodwin.edu/
Description: Independent, primarily 2-year, coed. Awards certificates, transfer associate, terminal associate, and bachelor's degrees. Founded 1999. Setting: 660-acre suburban campus with easy access to Hartford. Endowment: $3.4 million. Educational spending for the previous fiscal year: $8866 per student. Total enrollment: 3,317. Faculty: 275 (63 full-time, 212 part-time). Student-undergrad faculty ratio is 11:1. 604 applied, 100% were admitted. Full-time: 495 students, 77% women, 23% men. Part-time: 2,822

students, 84% women, 16% men. 2% from out-of-state. 0.4% American Indian or Alaska Native, non-Hispanic/Latino; 19% Hispanic/Latino; 22% African American, non-Hispanic/Latino; 2% Asian, non-Hispanic/Latino; 0.03% Native Hawaiian or other Pacific Islander, non-Hispanic/Latino; 0.1% international. 65% 25 or older, 15% transferred in. Retention: 57% of full-time freshmen returned the following year. Academic areas with the most degrees conferred: health professions and related sciences; family and consumer sciences. Core. Calendar: semesters. Academic remediation for entering students, ESL program, services for LD students, advanced placement, distance learning, double major, summer session for credit, part-time degree program, adult/continuing education programs, internships. Off campus study.
Entrance Requirements: Open admission selective admission for out-of-state students. Options: electronic application, early admission, early decision, early action, deferred admission, international baccalaureate accepted. Required: essay, high school transcript, minimum 2 high school GPA, medical exam. Recommended: 2 recommendations, interview. Entrance: minimally difficult. Application deadlines: Rolling, 3/1 for early decision, 6/1 for early action. Notification: continuous, 3/15 for early decision, 6/15 for early action. Transfer credits accepted: Yes.
Costs Per Year: Application fee: $50. Tuition: $18,900 full-time, $590 per credit hour part-time. Mandatory fees: $500 full-time. Full-time tuition and fees vary according to course load and program. Part-time tuition varies according to course load and program.
Collegiate Environment: Orientation program. Choral group, student-run newspaper. Student services: personal-psychological counseling. Campus security: 24-hour emergency response devices, evening security patrolman. College housing not available. Hoffman Family Library with an OPAC. 204 computers available on campus for general student use. Computer purchase/lease plans available. A campuswide network can be accessed from off-campus. Students can access the following: online class registration. Staffed computer lab on campus provides training in use of computers, software, and the Internet.

■ **HOLY APOSTLES COLLEGE AND SEMINARY**
33 Prospect Hill Rd.
Cromwell, CT 06416-2005
Tel: (860)632-3010
Fax: (860)632-3030
E-mail: admissions@holyapostles.edu
Web Site: www.holyapostles.edu/
Description: Independent Roman Catholic, comprehensive, coed. Awards associate, bachelor's, and master's degrees and post-master's certificates. Founded 1956. Setting: 17-acre suburban campus with easy access to Hartford, New Haven. Endowment: $657,367. Educational spending for the previous fiscal year: $3460 per student. Total enrollment: 343. Faculty: 30 (17 full-time, 13 part-time). Student-undergrad faculty ratio is 2:1. 10 applied, 100% were admitted. Full-time: 26 students, 23% women, 77% men. Part-time: 32 students, 81% women, 19% men. 9% transferred in. Retention: 60% of full-time freshmen returned the following year. Core. Calendar: semesters. Academic remediation for entering students, ESL program, services for LD students, independent study, summer session for credit, part-time degree program, external degree program, adult/continuing education programs, graduate courses open to undergrads.
Entrance Requirements: Open admission. Options: deferred admission, international baccalaureate accepted. Required: high school transcript. Recommended: SAT. Required for some: interview. Entrance: noncompetitive. Application deadlines: Rolling, Rolling for nonresidents. Transfer credits accepted: Yes.
Costs Per Year: Application fee: $50. Tuition: $10,080 full-time, $420 per credit part-time. Mandatory fees: $35 full-time. Full-time tuition and fees vary according to course load and degree level. Part-time tuition varies according to degree level.
Collegiate Environment: Orientation program. Most popular organizations: Toastmasters, Pro-Life Organization, Student Council, Schola Choir. Major annual events: Christmas Party, Graduation. Student services: personal-psychological counseling. College housing not available. Holy Apostles College and Seminary Library with 85,000 books, 210 microform titles, 250 serials, 400 audiovisual materials, an OPAC, and a Web page. Operations spending for the previous fiscal year: $21,450. 10 computers available on campus for general student use. A campuswide network can be accessed from student residence rooms. Staffed computer lab on campus provides training in use of computers, software, and the Internet.

■ HOUSATONIC COMMUNITY COLLEGE

900 Lafayette Blvd.
Bridgeport, CT 06604-4704
Tel: (203)332-5000
Web Site: www.hctc.commnet.edu/
Description: State-supported, 2-year, coed. Part of Connecticut Community Colleges and State Universities Board of Regents. Awards certificates, transfer associate, and terminal associate degrees. Founded 1965. Setting: 4-acre urban campus with easy access to New York City. Total enrollment: 6,097. Faculty: 377 (68 full-time, 309 part-time). Student-undergrad faculty ratio is 16:1. 1% American Indian or Alaska Native, non-Hispanic/Latino; 30% African American, non-Hispanic/Latino; 2% Asian, non-Hispanic/Latino; 0.1% Native Hawaiian or other Pacific Islander, non-Hispanic/Latino. Core. Calendar: semesters. Academic remediation for entering students, ESL program, services for LD students, advanced placement, honors program, independent study, distance learning, double major, summer session for credit, part-time degree program, adult/continuing education programs, co-op programs and internships. ROTC: Army (c).
Entrance Requirements: Open admission except for medical laboratory technician, allied health, nursing, physical therapy programs. Options: electronic application, deferred admission. Required: high school transcript. Required for some: interview. Entrance: noncompetitive. Application deadline: Rolling. Notification: continuous. Transfer credits accepted: Yes.
Costs Per Year: Application fee: $20. State resident tuition: $3598 full-time. Nonresident tuition: $10,754 full-time. Full-time tuition varies according to program.
Collegiate Environment: Orientation program. Drama-theater group, student-run newspaper. Social organizations: Honor Societies, various clubs. Most popular organizations: Student Senate, Association of Latin American Students, Community Action Network, Drama Club. Major annual events: Spring Outing, cultural 3rd Thursdays, jazz concerts. Student services: health clinic, personal-psychological counseling, women's center. Campus security: 24-hour emergency response devices, late night transport-escort service. College housing not available. Housatonic Community College Library with 30,000 books, 300 serials, an OPAC, and a Web page. 700 computers available on campus for general student use. A campuswide network can be accessed from off-campus. Students can access the following: online class registration, online catalog, online refresher option in math, computer labs. Staffed computer lab on campus provides training in use of computers, software, and the Internet.
Community Environment: See University of Bridgeport.

■ LINCOLN COLLEGE OF NEW ENGLAND (SOUTHINGTON)

2279 Mount Vernon Rd.
Southington, CT 06489-1057
Tel: (860)628-4751; Free: 800-825-0087
Fax: (860)628-6444
E-mail: areich@lincolncollegene.edu
Web Site: www.lincolncollegene.edu/
Description: Proprietary, 4-year, coed. Awards associate and bachelor's degrees. Founded 1966. Setting: 32-acre small town campus with easy access to Boston, Hartford. Endowment: $27,595. Total enrollment: 772. Faculty: 95 (29 full-time, 66 part-time). Student-undergrad faculty ratio is 8:1. 607 applied, 73% were admitted. 4% from top 10% of their high school class, 7% from top quarter, 24% from top half. Full-time: 378 students, 78% women, 22% men. Part-time: 394 students, 78% women, 22% men. Students come from 10 states and territories, 2 other countries, 7% from out-of-state. 38% 25 or older, 21% live on campus, 13% transferred in. Retention: 43% of full-time freshmen returned the following year. Core. Calendar: semesters. Academic remediation for entering students, ESL program, services for LD students, advanced placement, accelerated degree program, independent study, double major, summer session for credit, part-time degree program, adult/continuing education programs, internships.
Entrance Requirements: Option: electronic application. Required: high school transcript. Recommended: essay. Required for some: essay, interview. Entrance: minimally difficult. Application deadlines: Rolling, Rolling for nonresidents.
Collegiate Environment: Orientation program. Student-run radio station. Most popular organizations: student government, yearbook committee, Student Ambassador Club. Major annual event: Class Night. Student services: personal-psychological counseling. Campus security: 24-hour patrols, late night transport-escort service. Pupillo Library with 11,500 books, 154 serials, and a Web page. Operations spending for the previous fiscal year: $70,283. 54 computers available on campus for general student use. Staffed computer lab on campus.

■ LINCOLN COLLEGE OF NEW ENGLAND (SUFFIELD)

1760 Mapleton Ave.
Suffield, CT 06078
Tel: (860)668-3515; Free: 800-825-0087
Fax: (860)668-7369
E-mail: admissions@lincolncollegene.edu
Web Site: www.lincolncollegene.edu/
Description: Proprietary, 2-year, coed. Awards certificates, transfer associate, and terminal associate degrees. Founded 1992. Setting: 56-acre small town campus with easy access to New York City, Boston. Total enrollment: 98. Student-undergrad faculty ratio is 10:1. 78 applied, 95% were admitted. 41% from out-of-state. 9% 25 or older. Core. Calendar: continuous. Academic remediation for entering students, ESL program, services for LD students, advanced placement, accelerated degree program, independent study, distance learning, part-time degree program, adult/continuing education programs, co-op programs and internships. Study abroad program.
Entrance Requirements: Options: electronic application, deferred admission. Required: high school transcript, 2 recommendations. Recommended: interview, SAT. Required for some: essay, interview. Entrance: minimally difficult. Application deadline: Rolling. Notification: continuous.
Collegiate Environment: Orientation program. Student-run newspaper. Student services: health clinic, personal-psychological counseling. Campus security: 24-hour emergency response devices, student patrols, late night transport-escort service, controlled dormitory access, weekend patrols by trained security personnel. International College of Hospitality Management Library with 10,000 books, 50 serials, and an OPAC.

■ LYME ACADEMY COLLEGE OF FINE ARTS

84 Lyme St.
Old Lyme, CT 06371
Tel: (860)434-5232
Fax: (860)434-8725
E-mail: kholzenthal@lymeacademy.edu
Web Site: www.lymeacademy.edu/
Description: Independent, 4-year, coed. Awards bachelor's degrees. Founded 1976. Setting: 47-acre rural campus with easy access to New Haven, Hartford. Endowment: $4 million. Educational spending for the previous fiscal year: $11,173 per student. Total enrollment: 85. Faculty: 21 (9 full-time, 12 part-time). Student-undergrad faculty ratio is 4:1. 111 applied, 41% were admitted. Full-time: 66 students, 58% women, 42% men. Part-time: 17 students, 71% women, 29% men. Students come from 21 states and territories, 2 other countries, 47% from out-of-state. 32% 25 or older, 7% transferred in. Retention: 89% of full-time freshmen returned the following year. Academic area with the most degrees conferred: visual and performing arts. Core. Calendar: semesters. Services for LD students, advanced placement, independent study, part-time degree program, adult/continuing education programs, internships. Study abroad program.
Entrance Requirements: Options: electronic application, early admission, early decision, deferred admission. Required: high school transcript, art portfolio of at least 5 pieces but recommend 10-12 pieces, SAT or ACT. Recommended: essay, 2 recommendations, interview. Entrance: moderately difficult. Application deadlines: Rolling, Rolling for nonresidents, 2/15 for early decision. Notification: continuous, continuous for nonresidents. SAT Reasoning Test deadline: 8/31. SAT Subject Test deadline: 8/31. Transfer credits accepted: Yes.
Costs Per Year: Application fee: $55. Comprehensive fee: $39,336 includes full-time tuition ($26,904), mandatory fees ($1632), and college room and board ($10,800). College room only: $7200. Part-time tuition: $1121 per credit. Part-time mandatory fees: $68 per credit. Part-time tuition and fees vary according to course load.
Collegiate Environment: Orientation program. Social organizations: 1 open to all. Most popular organization: Student Organization. Major annual events: Halloween Costume Party, Welcome Back Barbeque, Spring Fling. Student services: personal-psychological counseling. Campus security: student patrols. The Krieble Library with 13,000 books, 70 serials, 70 audiovisual materials, an OPAC, and a Web page. Operations spending for the previous fiscal year: $124,009. 24 computers available on campus for general student use. A campuswide network can be accessed. Staffed computer lab on campus provides training in use of computers, software, and the Internet.

■ MANCHESTER COMMUNITY COLLEGE

PO Box 1046
Manchester, CT 06045-1046
Tel: (860)512-3000

Fax: (860)647-6238
Web Site: www.mcc.commnet.edu/
Description: State-supported, 2-year, coed. Part of Connecticut Community-Technical College System. Awards certificates, transfer associate, and terminal associate degrees. Founded 1963. Setting: small town campus. Total enrollment: 7,692. Faculty: 509 (104 full-time, 405 part-time). Student-undergrad faculty ratio is 18:1. 2,874 applied, 99% were admitted. Full-time: 2,721 students, 50% women, 50% men. Part-time: 4,971 students, 54% women, 46% men. 0.1% American Indian or Alaska Native, non-Hispanic/Latino; 15% Hispanic/Latino; 15% African American, non-Hispanic/Latino; 4% Asian, non-Hispanic/Latino; 0.1% Native Hawaiian or other Pacific Islander, non-Hispanic/Latino; 0.5% international. 32% 25 or older, 16% transferred in. Retention: 64% of full-time freshmen returned the following year. Calendar: semesters. Part-time degree program, adult/continuing education programs.
Entrance Requirements: Open admission. Option: electronic application. Required: high school transcript. Entrance: noncompetitive. Application deadline: Rolling. Notification: continuous.
Costs Per Year: Application fee: $20. State resident tuition: $3598 full-time. Nonresident tuition: $10,754 full-time. Mandatory fees: $406 full-time.
Collegiate Environment: Orientation program. College housing not available.

■ **MIDDLESEX COMMUNITY COLLEGE**
100 Training Hill Rd.
Middletown, CT 06457-4889
Tel: (860)343-5800
Fax: (860)344-7488
E-mail: mshabazz@mxcc.commnet.edu
Web Site: www.mxcc.commnet.edu/
Description: State-supported, 2-year, coed. Part of Connecticut Community-Technical College System. Awards certificates, transfer associate, and terminal associate degrees. Founded 1966. Setting: 38-acre suburban campus with easy access to Hartford. Endowment: $287,691. Educational spending for the previous fiscal year: $2500 per student. Total enrollment: 2,952. Faculty: 147 (44 full-time, 103 part-time). Student-undergrad faculty ratio is 22:1. 993 applied. Full-time: 1,186 students, 50% women, 50% men. Part-time: 1,766 students, 63% women, 37% men. Students come from 6 states and territories, 10 other countries, 1% from out-of-state. 37% 25 or older, 9% transferred in. Retention: 54% of full-time freshmen returned the following year. Core. Calendar: semesters. Academic remediation for entering students, ESL program, services for LD students, advanced placement, honors program, independent study, distance learning, double major, summer session for credit, part-time degree program, adult/continuing education programs, co-op programs and internships. Off campus study at other units of the Connecticut Community College System.
Entrance Requirements: Open admission except for radiological technology, human services, drug and alcohol counseling, broadcast journalism, ophthalmic design and dispensing programs. Options: electronic application, early admission, deferred admission. Required: high school transcript, CPT. Entrance: noncompetitive. Application deadline: Rolling. Transfer credits accepted: Yes.
Costs Per Year: Application fee: $20. State resident tuition: $3192 full-time, $133 per credit part-time. Nonresident tuition: $9576 full-time, $399 per credit part-time. Mandatory fees: $406 full-time, $83 per course part-time. Full-time tuition and fees vary according to course load, degree level, and program. Part-time tuition and fees vary according to course load, degree level, and program.
Collegiate Environment: Orientation program. Drama-theater group, student-run newspaper. Social organizations: 10 open to all; Student Senate, student clubs. Most popular organizations: Phi Theta Kappa, Human Services Association, Peace and Justice Club, Poetry Club, International Student Club. Major annual events: International Day, Spring Festival, Senior Art Exhibit. Campus security: 24-hour emergency response devices and patrols. Jean Burr Smith Library with 70,773 books, 6,180 microform titles, 32,235 serials, 2,285 audiovisual materials, an OPAC, and a Web page. 80 computers available on campus for general student use. Computer purchase/lease plans available. A campuswide network can be accessed from off-campus. Students can access the following: online class registration. Staffed computer lab on campus provides training in use of computers, software, and the Internet.

■ **MITCHELL COLLEGE**
437 Pequot Ave.
New London, CT 06320-4498

Tel: (860)701-5000; Free: 800-443-2811
Fax: (860)444-1209
E-mail: admissions@mitchell.edu
Web Site: www.mitchell.edu/
Description: Independent, 4-year, coed. Awards associate and bachelor's degrees. Founded 1938. Setting: 67-acre suburban campus with easy access to Hartford (CT), Providence (RI). Total enrollment: 858. Faculty: 94 (35 full-time, 59 part-time). Student-undergrad faculty ratio is 14:1. 1,041 applied, 60% were admitted. Full-time: 731 students, 46% women, 54% men. Part-time: 127 students, 54% women, 46% men. 43% from out-of-state. 2% American Indian or Alaska Native, non-Hispanic/Latino; 12% Hispanic/Latino; 10% African American, non-Hispanic/Latino; 2% Asian, non-Hispanic/Latino; 0.1% Native Hawaiian or other Pacific Islander, non-Hispanic/Latino; 0.4% international. 1% 25 or older, 56% live on campus, 9% transferred in. Retention: 56% of full-time freshmen returned the following year. Academic areas with the most degrees conferred: liberal arts/general studies; business/marketing; homeland security, law enforcement, firefighting, and protective services. Core. Calendar: semesters. Services for LD students, advanced placement, self-designed majors, independent study, double major, summer session for credit, part-time degree program, co-op programs and internships.
Entrance Requirements: Options: electronic application, early admission, early decision, deferred admission. Required: essay, high school transcript, minimum 2 high school GPA, 1 recommendation. Recommended: interview. Entrance: moderately difficult. Application deadlines: Rolling, Rolling for nonresidents, 11/15 for early decision. Notification: continuous, continuous for nonresidents, 12/1 for early decision.
Costs Per Year: Application fee: $30. Comprehensive fee: $40,986 includes full-time tuition ($26,774), mandatory fees ($1720), and college room and board ($12,492). College room only: $6496. Part-time mandatory fees: $300 per credit. Part-time fees vary according to course load.
Collegiate Environment: Orientation program. Drama-theater group, choral group, student-run radio station. Social organizations: 29 open to all. Most popular organizations: Mitchell College Drama Society, Sigma Alpha Pi Leadership Society, Behavioral Science, Early Childhood, Gaming Club. Major annual events: Founder's Day/Picnic/Activities Fair, Leadership Speakers Series, Awards Ceremony/Strawberry Festival. Student services: health clinic, personal-psychological counseling. Campus security: 24-hour emergency response devices and patrols, student patrols, late night transport-escort service, controlled dormitory access. 598 college housing spaces available; 485 were occupied in 2012-13. Freshmen given priority for college housing. On-campus residence required through senior year. Options: coed, men-only, women-only housing available. Mitchell College Library with 94,542 books, 70 serials, 1,658 audiovisual materials, an OPAC, and a Web page. 176 computers available on campus for general student use. Computer purchase/lease plans available. A campuswide network can be accessed from student residence rooms and from off campus. Students can access the following: online student portfolios, online course requests. Staffed computer lab on campus provides training in use of computers, software, and the Internet.
Community Environment: Small city of 30,000. Southern Connecticut is one of the country's fastest-growing tourist attractions. Campus is located at the confluence of the Thames River and Long Island Sound. The college maintains its own beach and 26-acre wooded park.

■ **NAUGATUCK VALLEY COMMUNITY COLLEGE**
750 Chase Pky.
Waterbury, CT 06708-3000
Tel: (203)575-8040
Fax: (203)596-8766
E-mail: lsveda@nvcc.commnet.edu
Web Site: www.nvcc.commnet.edu/
Description: State-supported, 2-year, coed. Part of Connecticut Community-Technical College System. Awards certificates, transfer associate, and terminal associate degrees. Founded 1992. Setting: 110-acre urban campus. Total enrollment: 5,659. Faculty: 210. Student-undergrad faculty ratio is 5:1. 3,499 applied, 39% were admitted. Full-time: 2,266 students, 54% women, 46% men. Part-time: 3,393 students, 66% women, 34% men. 6% from out-of-state. 39% 25 or older, 0.2% transferred in. Core. Calendar: semesters. Academic remediation for entering students, ESL program, services for LD students, advanced placement, accelerated degree program, self-designed majors, independent study, summer session for credit, part-time degree program, external degree program, adult/continuing education programs, co-op programs and internships. Off campus study at other institutions in the Connecticut Public Higher Education System. Study abroad program.

Entrance Requirements: Open admission except for nursing, allied health, technician programs. Option: deferred admission. Required: high school transcript, ACCUPLACER. Required for some: interview. Entrance: noncompetitive. Application deadline: Rolling. Notification: continuous.

Collegiate Environment: Orientation program. Drama-theater group, choral group, student-run newspaper. Social organizations: 35 open to all. Most popular organizations: Student Senate, Choral Society, Automotive Technician Club, Human Service Club, Legal Assistant Club. Major annual events: Awards Ceremony, Spring Picnic, Club Expo. Student services: health clinic, personal-psychological counseling. Campus security: 24-hour emergency response devices and patrols, late night transport-escort service, security escort service. Max R. Traurig Learning Resource Center with 35,000 books, 520 serials, an OPAC, and a Web page. Operations spending for the previous fiscal year: $618,484. 450 computers available on campus for general student use. A campuswide network can be accessed. Staffed computer lab on campus.

Community Environment: See Teikyo Post University.

■ **NORTHWESTERN CONNECTICUT COMMUNITY COLLEGE**
Park Pl. E
Winsted, CT 06098-1798
Tel: (860)738-6300
Fax: (860)379-4465
E-mail: admissions@nwcc.commnet.edu
Web Site: www.nwcc.commnet.edu/
Description: State-supported, 2-year, coed. Part of Connecticut State Colleges and Universities (ConnSCU). Awards certificates, transfer associate, and terminal associate degrees. Founded 1965. Setting: 5-acre small town campus with easy access to Hartford. Total enrollment: 1,701. Full-time: 511 students, 64% women, 36% men. Part-time: 1,190 students, 69% women, 31% men. Students come from 3 states and territories, 1% from out-of-state. 0% American Indian or Alaska Native, non-Hispanic/Latino; 7% Hispanic/Latino; 2% African American, non-Hispanic/Latino; 1% Asian, non-Hispanic/Latino; 0.1% Native Hawaiian or other Pacific Islander, non-Hispanic/Latino; 0.2% international. 40% 25 or older, 10% transferred in. Retention: 60% of full-time freshmen returned the following year. Core. Calendar: semesters. Academic remediation for entering students, ESL program, services for LD students, advanced placement, independent study, distance learning, double major, summer session for credit, part-time degree program, adult/continuing education programs, co-op programs and internships.
Entrance Requirements: Open admission except for physical therapy assistant, drug and alcohol counseling programs. Option: deferred admission. Entrance: noncompetitive. Application deadline: Rolling. Notification: continuous.
Collegiate Environment: Student-run newspaper. Campus security: evening security patrols. Northwestern Connecticut Community-Technical College Learning Center with an OPAC.
Community Environment: Population 7,321. Winsted is a suburban community with a temperate climate. It has shopping areas, library, churches, and a YMCA. Airport facilities are 30 miles away, but easy to reach. Recreational facilities are good, including excellent fishing in surrounding areas, boating on Highland Lake, and winter sports at Sundown ski area about three miles southeast.

■ **NORWALK COMMUNITY COLLEGE**
188 Richards Ave.
Norwalk, CT 06854-1655
Tel: (203)857-7000
Fax: (203)857-3335
E-mail: admissions@ncc.commnet.edu
Web Site: www.ncc.commnet.edu/
Description: State-supported, 2-year, coed. Part of Connecticut Community-Technical College System. Awards certificates, transfer associate, and terminal associate degrees. Founded 1961. Setting: 30-acre suburban campus with easy access to New York City. Total enrollment: 6,810. Faculty: 428 (103 full-time, 325 part-time). Student-undergrad faculty ratio is 16:1. 2,162 applied, 100% were admitted. Full-time: 2,267 students, 50% women, 50% men. Part-time: 4,543 students, 63% women, 37% men. Students come from 6 states and territories, 44 other countries, 4% from out-of-state. 0.2% American Indian or Alaska Native, non-Hispanic/Latino; 30% Hispanic/Latino; 17% African American, non-Hispanic/Latino; 4% Asian, non-Hispanic/Latino; 0.2% Native Hawaiian or other Pacific Islander, non-Hispanic/Latino; 2% international. 37% 25 or older, 6% transferred in. Core. Calendar: semesters. Academic remediation for entering students, ESL program,

services for LD students, advanced placement, honors program, independent study, distance learning, summer session for credit, part-time degree program, adult/continuing education programs, co-op programs and internships.
Entrance Requirements: Open admission except for allied health programs. Options: electronic application, deferred admission. Required: high school transcript. Entrance: noncompetitive. Application deadline: Rolling. Notification: continuous. Transfer credits accepted: Yes.
Costs Per Year: Application fee: $20. State resident tuition: $3360 full-time. Nonresident tuition: $10,080 full-time. Mandatory fees: $426 full-time, $70 per contact hour part-time, $25 per term part-time.
Collegiate Environment: Orientation program. Drama-theater group, choral group, student-run newspaper. Social organizations: 36 open to all; Honor society. Most popular organizations: Student World Assembly, Archaeology Club, Literature Club, Art Club, Phi Theta Kappa. Major annual events: Awards Ceremony, Welcome Back Club Fair, Spring Fling. Student services: personal-psychological counseling, women's center. Campus security: late night transport-escort service, all buildings are secured each evening; there are foot patrols and vehicle patrols by security from 8am to 11pm. College housing not available. Everett I. L. Baker Library with 64,878 books, 1,516 microform titles, 120 serials, 10,704 audiovisual materials, an OPAC, and a Web page. 300 computers available on campus for general student use. A campuswide network can be accessed. Students can access the following: online class registration, college wireless network. Staffed computer lab on campus.
Community Environment: Norwalk is a urban community located on Long Island Sound and is 50 minutes by rail from Grand Central Station in New York City. Community facilities include major shopping areas, libraries, churches, a symphony orchestra, and the Silvermine Guild Artists.

■ **PAIER COLLEGE OF ART, INC.**
20 Gorham Ave.
Hamden, CT 06514-3902
Tel: (203)287-3030
E-mail: paier.admission@snet.net
Web Site: www.paiercollegeofart.edu/
Description: Proprietary, 4-year, coed. Awards bachelor's degrees. Founded 1946. Setting: 3-acre suburban campus with easy access to New York City. Total enrollment: 192. Faculty: 39 (10 full-time, 29 part-time). Student-undergrad faculty ratio is 5:1. 0% from top 10% of their high school class, 20% from top quarter, 20% from top half. Full-time: 141 students, 62% women, 38% men. Part-time: 51 students, 57% women, 43% men. Students come from 5 states and territories, 1 other country, 0% from out-of-state. 0% American Indian or Alaska Native, non-Hispanic/Latino; 8% Hispanic/Latino; 5% African American, non-Hispanic/Latino; 1% Asian, non-Hispanic/Latino; 0% Native Hawaiian or other Pacific Islander, non-Hispanic/Latino; 0% international. 19% 25 or older, 9% transferred in. Retention: 89% of full-time freshmen returned the following year. Academic area with the most degrees conferred: visual and performing arts. Core. Calendar: semesters plus 1 summer session. Academic remediation for entering students, services for LD students, advanced placement, independent study, part-time degree program. Study abroad program.
Entrance Requirements: Required: high school transcript, minimum 2 high school GPA, 2 recommendations, interview, Portfolio Interview, SAT or ACT. Recommended: essay.
Costs Per Year: Tuition: $12,000 full-time, $400 per credit part-time. Mandatory fees: $360 full-time, $400 per credit part-time, $125. Full-time tuition and fees vary according to degree level. Part-time tuition and fees vary according to course load.
Collegiate Environment: Orientation program. Student-run newspaper. Social organizations: 2 open to all. Most popular organizations: Student Council, School Newspaper. Major annual events: Winter Art Show and Sale, Spring Art Show and Sale, Fall Paier Picnic. Campus security: evening patrols by security. College housing not available. Adele K. Paier Memorial Library with 13,000 books and 87 serials. 48 computers available on campus for general student use. Computer purchase/lease plans available. Staffed computer lab on campus provides training in use of computers, software, and the Internet.

■ **POST UNIVERSITY**
800 Country Club Rd.
Waterbury, CT 06723-2540
Tel: (203)596-4500; Free: 800-345-2562
Fax: (203)756-5810

E-mail: admiss@post.edu
Web Site: www.post.edu/

Description: Independent, comprehensive, coed. Awards associate, bachelor's, and master's degrees. Founded 1890. Setting: 70-acre suburban campus with easy access to Hartford. Total enrollment: 722. Faculty: 165 (43 full-time, 122 part-time). Student-undergrad faculty ratio is 9:1. 1,861 applied, 13% were admitted. 5% from top 10% of their high school class, 20% from top quarter, 50% from top half. Full-time: 700 students, 49% women, 51% men. Part-time: 22 students, 64% women, 36% men. Students come from 26 states and territories, 11 other countries, 31% from out-of-state. 1% American Indian or Alaska Native, non-Hispanic/Latino; 12% Hispanic/Latino; 28% African American, non-Hispanic/Latino; 2% Asian, non-Hispanic/Latino; 0.1% Native Hawaiian or other Pacific Islander, non-Hispanic/Latino; 2% international. 10% 25 or older, 52% live on campus, 11% transferred in. Retention: 58% of full-time freshmen returned the following year. Academic areas with the most degrees conferred: business/marketing; homeland security, law enforcement, firefighting, and protective services; public administration and social services. Core. Calendar: semesters (modular courses offered in the evening). ESL program, services for LD students, advanced placement, accelerated degree program, freshman honors college, honors program, independent study, distance learning, double major, summer session for credit, part-time degree program, adult/continuing education programs, co-op programs and internships, graduate courses open to undergrads. Off campus study at Students may prepare for the prestigious British Horse Society Assistant Instructor Examination through a training semester at a riding center in the United Kingdom. The BHSAI Certificate is internationally recognized. It confirms achievement at a standardized level of excellence for which there is no current equivalent in the United States. Study abroad program.

Entrance Requirements: Options: electronic application, deferred admission, international baccalaureate accepted. Required: high school transcript, 1 recommendation, SAT or ACT. Recommended: essay, minimum 2 high school GPA, interview. Entrance: moderately difficult. Application deadline: Rolling. Notification: continuous. SAT Reasoning Test deadline: 8/1. Transfer credits accepted: Yes.

Costs Per Year: Application fee: $40. Comprehensive fee: $37,880 includes full-time tuition ($26,250), mandatory fees ($1200), and college room and board ($10,430). Full-time tuition and fees vary according to degree level and program. Room and board charges vary according to housing facility. Part-time tuition: $875 per credit. Part-time tuition varies according to class time, course load, degree level, and program.

Collegiate Environment: Orientation program. Drama-theater group, choral group. Social organizations: 18 open to all. Most popular organizations: Equine Club, Newman Club, GSA, Accounting Club, Choir. Major annual events: Fall Weekend, Winter Weekend, Spring Weekend. Student services: health clinic, personal-psychological counseling. Campus security: 24-hour emergency response devices and patrols, late night transport-escort service, controlled dormitory access. 450 college housing spaces available; 378 were occupied in 2012-13. Freshmen guaranteed college housing. Option: coed housing available. Trauriq Library and Resource Center with 92,061 books, 305 serials, 1,214 audiovisual materials, and an OPAC. Operations spending for the previous fiscal year: $249,484. 150 computers available on campus for general student use. Computer purchase/lease plans available. A campuswide network can be accessed from student residence rooms and from off campus. Students can access the following: online class registration, software applications. Staffed computer lab on campus.

Community Environment: Waterbury is a city of approximately 110,000, located in the northwest part of the state. There are three other colleges in the area and 15 other institutions of higher learning within a 30-minute drive. The Greater Waterbury area offers ample opportunities for cultural, athletic, and recreational activities.

■ **QUINEBAUG VALLEY COMMUNITY COLLEGE**
742 Upper Maple St.
Danielson, CT 06239-1440
Tel: (860)774-1130
Fax: (860)774-7768
E-mail: qu_isd@commnet.edu
Web Site: www.qvcc.commnet.edu/
Description: State-supported, 2-year, coed. Part of Connecticut Community-Technical College System. Awards certificates, transfer associate, and terminal associate degrees. Founded 1971. Setting: 60-acre rural campus. Total enrollment: 1,779. Faculty: 126 (29 full-time, 97 part-time). Student-undergrad faculty ratio is 18:1. 586 applied, 98% were admitted. Full-time:

669 students, 60% women, 40% men. Part-time: 1,110 students, 73% women, 27% men. Students come from 3 states and territories, 1% from out-of-state. 41% 25 or older, 9% transferred in. Core. Calendar: semesters. Academic remediation for entering students, ESL program, advanced placement, independent study, distance learning, summer session for credit, part-time degree program, external degree program, adult/continuing education programs, internships. Study abroad program.

Entrance Requirements: Open admission. Options: electronic application, early admission, deferred admission. Recommended: high school transcript. Required for some: high school transcript. Entrance: noncompetitive. Application deadline: 9/1. Notification: continuous until 9/1.

Collegiate Environment: Orientation program. Campus security: evening security guard. Audrey Beck Library with 31,000 books, 130 serials, and an OPAC. 80 computers available on campus for general student use. A campuswide network can be accessed. Staffed computer lab on campus.

Community Environment: Population, 4,285. Located in Northeastern Connecticut, Danielson is in the midst of a semi-rural area which is supported by poultry and dairy industries. Outdoor recreational possibilities abound. The Connecticut turnpike provides easy access to New London, Old Mystic, Massachusetts and Rhode Island.

■ **QUINNIPIAC UNIVERSITY**
275 Mount Carmel Ave.
Hamden, CT 06518-1940
Tel: (203)582-8200; Free: 800-462-1944
Fax: (203)582-6347
E-mail: admissions@quinnipiac.edu
Web Site: www.quinnipiac.edu/
Description: Independent, comprehensive, coed. Awards bachelor's, master's, and doctoral degrees and post-master's certificates. Founded 1929. Setting: 600-acre suburban campus with easy access to New Haven, Hartford. Endowment: $275.5 million. Research spending for the previous fiscal year: $2.2 million. Educational spending for the previous fiscal year: $10,075 per student. Total enrollment: 8,614. Faculty: 942 (369 full-time, 573 part-time). Student-undergrad faculty ratio is 12:1. 18,825 applied, 69% were admitted. 24% from top 10% of their high school class, 69% from top quarter, 91% from top half. Full-time: 6,231 students, 62% women, 38% men. Part-time: 199 students, 53% women, 47% men. Students come from 28 states and territories, 22 other countries, 73% from out-of-state. 0.3% American Indian or Alaska Native, non-Hispanic/Latino; 8% Hispanic/Latino; 4% African American, non-Hispanic/Latino; 2% Asian, non-Hispanic/Latino; 0.1% Native Hawaiian or other Pacific Islander, non-Hispanic/Latino; 1% international. 5% 25 or older, 78% live on campus, 3% transferred in. Retention: 85% of full-time freshmen returned the following year. Academic areas with the most degrees conferred: health professions and related sciences; business/marketing; communication/journalism. Core. Calendar: semesters. Services for LD students, advanced placement, accelerated degree program, self-designed majors, honors program, independent study, distance learning, double major, summer session for credit, part-time degree program, internships, graduate courses open to undergrads. Study abroad program. ROTC: Army (c), Naval (c), Air Force (c).

Entrance Requirements: Options: electronic application, early decision, deferred admission, international baccalaureate accepted. Required: essay, high school transcript, 1 recommendation, SAT or ACT. Recommended: minimum 3 high school GPA, interview. Required for some: minimum 3 high school GPA. Entrance: moderately difficult. Application deadlines: 2/1, 2/1 for nonresidents, 11/1 for early decision. Notification: continuous, continuous for nonresidents, Rolling for early decision. SAT Reasoning Test deadline: 2/1. Transfer credits accepted: Yes. Applicants placed on waiting list: 1,710. Waitlisted applicants offered admission: 185. Early decision applicants: 340. Early decision applicants admitted: 178.

Costs Per Year: Application fee: $45. Comprehensive fee: $53,580 includes full-time tuition ($37,830), mandatory fees ($1500), and college room and board ($14,250). Room and board charges vary according to housing facility. Part-time tuition: $900 per credit. Part-time mandatory fees: $37 per credit. Part-time tuition and fees vary according to class time and course load.

Collegiate Environment: Orientation program. Drama-theater group, choral group, student-run newspaper, radio station. Social organizations: 100 open to all; national fraternities, national sororities, local sororities; 11% of eligible men and 12% of eligible women are members. Most popular organizations: student government, Social Programming Board, Drama Club, Chronicle (student newspaper), dance company. Major annual events: Campus Concerts, Student/Faculty Holiday Dinner, Midnight Madness (athletics). Student services: health clinic, personal-psychological counseling. Campus security: 24-hour emergency response devices and patrols, late night transport-escort service, controlled dormitory access, text message emergency notification system. 4,970 college housing spaces available; 4,685 were occupied in 2012-13. Freshmen guaranteed college housing. Option: coed housing available. Arnold Bernhard Library plus 1 other with 311,000 books, 592,900 microform titles, 44,700 serials, 6,000 audiovisual materials, an OPAC, and a Web page. Operations spending for the previous fiscal year: $4.7 million. 600 computers available on campus for general student use. Computer purchase/lease plans available. A computer is required for all students. A campuswide network can be accessed from student residence rooms and from off campus. Students can access the following: online class registration, e-commerce 'Q' card for local merchants, food service, dorm card access. Staffed computer lab on campus provides training in use of computers, software, and the Internet.

Community Environment: Hamden, population 58,180. Sleeping Giant Mountain State Park is adjacent to the campus and has 1700 acres for walking and hiking.

■ SACRED HEART UNIVERSITY

5151 Park Ave.
Fairfield, CT 06825-1000
Tel: (203)371-7999
Fax: (203)371-7889
E-mail: higginsk2288@sacredheart.edu
Web Site: www.sacredheart.edu/

Description: Independent Roman Catholic, comprehensive, coed. Awards bachelor's, master's, and doctoral degrees and post-master's certificates (also offers part-time program with significant enrollment not reflected in profile). Founded 1963. Setting: 71-acre suburban campus with easy access to New York City. Endowment: $112.7 million. Educational spending for the previous fiscal year: $7828 per student. Total enrollment: 6,347. Faculty: 634 (237 full-time, 397 part-time). Student-undergrad faculty ratio is 13:1. 8,221 applied, 76% were admitted. 15% from top 10% of their high school class, 40% from top quarter, 77% from top half. 11 class presidents, 3 valedictorians. Full-time: 3,399 students, 61% women, 39% men. Part-time: 693 students, 69% women, 31% men. Students come from 35 states and territories, 14 other countries, 59% from out-of-state. 0.3% American Indian or Alaska Native, non-Hispanic/Latino; 6% Hispanic/Latino; 4% African American, non-Hispanic/Latino; 2% Asian, non-Hispanic/Latino; 0.1% Native Hawaiian or other Pacific Islander, non-Hispanic/Latino; 1% international. 13% 25 or older, 51% live on campus. Retention: 83% of full-time freshmen returned the following year. Academic areas with the most degrees conferred: business/marketing; health professions and related sciences; psychology. Core. Calendar: semesters. Academic remediation for entering students, ESL program, services for LD students, advanced placement, accelerated degree program, self-designed majors, honors program, independent study, distance learning, double major, summer session for credit, part-time degree program, adult/continuing education programs, co-op programs and internships, graduate courses open to undergrads. Off campus study at Dingle County Kerry, Ireland and the Grand Duchy of Luxembourg. Study abroad program. ROTC: Army (c).

Entrance Requirements: Options: electronic application, early admission, early decision, international baccalaureate accepted. Required: essay, high school transcript, 1 recommendation. Recommended: minimum 3.2 high school GPA, interview, Test-Optional Admissions Policy, SAT/ACT scores will be considered if submitted. Required for some: interview, interview for Early Decision candidates. Entrance: moderately difficult. Application deadline: 12/1 for early decision. Notification: continuous, 12/15 for early decision. SAT Reasoning Test deadline: 3/1. Transfer credits accepted: Yes. Applicants placed on waiting list: 581. Wait-listed applicants offered admission: 221. Early decision applicants: 187. Early decision applicants admitted: 142.

Costs Per Year: Application fee: $70. Comprehensive fee: $47,260 includes full-time tuition ($33,780), mandatory fees ($250), and college room and board ($13,230). College room only: $9380. Full-time tuition and fees vary according to course load, location, and program. Room and board charges vary according to board plan, housing facility, and student level. Part-time tuition: $515 per credit. Part-time mandatory fees: $90 per term. Part-time tuition and fees vary according to location and program.

Collegiate Environment: Orientation program. Drama-theater group, choral group, marching band, student-run newspaper, radio station. Social organizations: 52 open to all; national fraternities, national sororities, local fraternities, local sororities; 4% of eligible men and 12% of eligible women are members. Most popular organizations: Habitat for Humanity, student government, Performing Arts Program, Student Athletic Training Organiza-

tion, Student Nurses Association. Major annual events: Campus Spring Concert, Big Red BBQ, Pack the Pitt. Student services: health clinic, personal-psychological counseling. Campus security: 24-hour emergency response devices and patrols, late night transport-escort service, controlled dormitory access, Campus Emergency Plan, Personal Safety Escort Program, Security Alarm Systems, Crime Prevention Announcements, Security Surveys. 2,208 college housing spaces available; 2,035 were occupied in 2012-13. Freshmen guaranteed college housing. On-campus residence required through sophomore year. Options: coed, men-only, women-only housing available. Ryan-Matura Library with 132,062 books, 223,560 microform titles, 39,306 serials, 1,197 audiovisual materials, an OPAC, and a Web page. Operations spending for the previous fiscal year: $1.8 million. 111 computers available on campus for general student use. Computer purchase/lease plans available. A computer is required for all students. A campuswide network can be accessed from student residence rooms and from off campus. Students can access the following: online class registration. Staffed computer lab on campus (open 24 hours a day) provides training in use of computers, software, and the Internet.

Community Environment: Sacred Heart University is located in coastal Fairfield, Connecticut, one hour northeast of New York City. Numerous Fortune 500 companies are headquartered in Fairfield County providing students with unique opportunities for outside learning and hands-on experience. Transportation, restaurants, shopping malls, movies, theaters, and beaches are all easily accessible.

■ ST. VINCENT'S COLLEGE

2800 Main St.
Bridgeport, CT 06606-4292
Tel: (203)576-5235; Free: 800-873-1013
E-mail: jmarrone@stvincentscollege.edu
Web Site: www.stvincentscollege.edu/

Description: Independent, 2-year, coed, affiliated with Roman Catholic Church. Awards certificates and transfer associate degrees. Founded 1991. Setting: urban campus with easy access to New York City. Total enrollment: 427. Student-undergrad faculty ratio is 7:1. 565 applied. 0% from out-of-state. 66% 25 or older. Retention: 100% of full-time freshmen returned the following year. Core. Calendar: semesters. Academic remediation for entering students, advanced placement, distance learning, summer session for credit, part-time degree program.

Entrance Requirements: Option: deferred admission. Required: essay, high school transcript. Recommended: minimum 3.0 high school GPA. Required for some: interview. Entrance: moderately difficult. Application deadline: Rolling.

Collegiate Environment: Orientation program. Campus security: 24-hour patrols, late night transport-escort service.

■ SOUTHERN CONNECTICUT STATE UNIVERSITY

501 Crescent St.
New Haven, CT 06515-1355
Tel: (203)392-5200
Fax: (203)392-5727
Web Site: www.southernct.edu/

Description: State-supported, comprehensive, coed. Part of Connecticut State Colleges and Universities (ConnSCU). Awards bachelor's, master's, and doctoral degrees and post-master's certificates. Founded 1893. Setting: 168-acre suburban campus with easy access to New York City. Endowment: $14.7 million. Research spending for the previous fiscal year: $2.1 million. Educational spending for the previous fiscal year: $8748 per student. Total enrollment: 11,117. Faculty: 1,055 (434 full-time, 621 part-time). Student-undergrad faculty ratio is 14:1. 4,978 applied, 75% were admitted. 5% from top 10% of their high school class, 21% from top quarter, 60% from top half. Full-time: 7,289 students, 62% women, 38% men. Part-time: 1,236 students, 53% women, 47% men. Students come from 27 states and territories, 10 other countries, 4% from out-of-state. 0.3% American Indian or Alaska Native, non-Hispanic/Latino; 10% Hispanic/Latino; 16% African American, non-Hispanic/Latino; 3% Asian, non-Hispanic/Latino; 0.1% Native Hawaiian or other Pacific Islander, non-Hispanic/Latino; 0.4% international. 19% 25 or older, 31% live on campus, 10% transferred in. Retention: 73% of full-time freshmen returned the following year. Academic areas with the most degrees conferred: health professions and related sciences; psychology; business/marketing; liberal arts/general studies. Core. Calendar: semesters. Academic remediation for entering students, services for LD students, advanced placement, accelerated degree program, self-designed majors, freshman honors college, honors program, independent study, distance learning, double major, summer session for credit, part-time degree program, co-op programs and internships, graduate courses open to undergrads. Off campus study at New England Board of Higher Education. Study abroad program. ROTC: Army (c), Air Force (c).

Entrance Requirements: Options: electronic application, deferred admission, international baccalaureate accepted. Required: essay, high school transcript, SAT or ACT. Entrance: moderately difficult. Application deadline: 4/1. Notification: continuous. SAT Reasoning Test deadline: 4/1. Transfer credits accepted: Yes.

Costs Per Year: Application fee: $50. State resident tuition: $4285 full-time, $427 per credit hour part-time. Nonresident tuition: $13,866 full-time, $441 per credit hour part-time. Mandatory fees: $4285 full-time, $55 per term part-time. Full-time tuition and fees vary according to course load and reciprocity agreements. Part-time tuition and fees vary according to course load. College room and board: $10,641. College room only: $5859. Room and board charges vary according to board plan and housing facility.

Collegiate Environment: Orientation program. Drama-theater group, choral group, marching band, student-run newspaper, radio station. Social organizations: 153 open to all; national fraternities, national sororities, local sororities; 1% of eligible men and 1% of eligible women are members. Most popular organizations: Student Government Association, Psychology Club, Habitat for Humanity, Crescent Players, Black Student Union. Major annual events: Spring Week, Homecoming Week, Convocation. Student services: health clinic, personal-psychological counseling, women's center. Campus security: 24-hour emergency response devices and patrols, late night transport-escort service, controlled dormitory access. College housing designed to accommodate 2,610 students; 2,612 undergraduates lived in college housing during 2012-13. Freshmen guaranteed college housing. Option: coed housing available. Hilton C. Buley Library with 428,990 books, 40,957 microform titles, 59,264 serials, 9,840 audiovisual materials, an OPAC, and a Web page. Operations spending for the previous fiscal year: $5.3 million. 800 computers available on campus for general student use. A campuswide network can be accessed from student residence rooms and from off campus. Students can access the following: online class registration. Staffed computer lab on campus provides training in use of computers, software, and the Internet.

Community Environment: Metropolitan.

■ **THREE RIVERS COMMUNITY COLLEGE**
574 New London Tpke.
Norwich, CT 06360
Tel: (860)886-0177
Fax: (860)886-0691
E-mail: admissions@trcc.commnet.edu
Web Site: www.trcc.commnet.edu/

Description: State-supported, 2-year, coed. Part of Connecticut Community-Technical College System. Awards certificates, transfer associate, and terminal associate degrees (engineering technology programs are offered on the Thames Valley Campus; liberal arts, transfer and career programs are offered on the Mohegan Campus). Founded 1963. Setting: 40-acre suburban campus with easy access to Hartford. Total enrollment: 5,154. Faculty: 315 (76 full-time, 239 part-time). Student-undergrad faculty ratio is 18:1. 511 applied, 99% were admitted. Full-time: 1,650 students, 49% women, 51% men. Part-time: 3,504 students, 62% women, 38% men. 1% from out-of-state. 1% American Indian or Alaska Native, non-Hispanic/Latino; 13% Hispanic/Latino; 8% African American, non-Hispanic/Latino; 3% Asian, non-Hispanic/Latino; 0.2% Native Hawaiian or other Pacific Islander, non-Hispanic/Latino; 0.1% international. 7% transferred in. Calendar: semesters. Part-time degree program, adult/continuing education programs.

Entrance Requirements: Open admission except for nursing, drug and alcohol rehabilitation counseling, paramedic programs. Options: electronic application, early admission, deferred admission. Recommended: high school transcript. Required for some: minimum 3 high school GPA. Entrance: noncompetitive. Application deadline: Rolling. Notification: continuous. Transfer credits accepted: Yes.

Costs Per Year: State resident tuition: $3192 full-time, $133 per credit hour part-time. Nonresident tuition: $10,348 full-time, $399 per credit hour part-time. Mandatory fees: $386 full-time, $78 per course part-time. Full-time tuition and fees vary according to course load and reciprocity agreements. Part-time tuition and fees vary according to course load and reciprocity agreements.

Collegiate Environment: Orientation program. Campus security: 24-hour emergency response devices, late night transport-escort service, 14-hour patrols by trained security personnel. Three Rivers Community College Learning Resource Center plus 1 other with an OPAC.

■ **TRINITY COLLEGE**
300 Summit St.
Hartford, CT 06106-3100
Tel: (860)297-2000
Fax: (860)297-2287
E-mail: admissions.office@trincoll.edu
Web Site: www.trincoll.edu/

Description: Independent, comprehensive, coed. Awards bachelor's and master's degrees. Founded 1823. Setting: 100-acre urban campus. Endowment: $439.1 million. Total enrollment: 2,387. Faculty: 250 (175 full-time, 75 part-time). Student-undergrad faculty ratio is 10:1. 7,720 applied, 34% were admitted. 69% from top 10% of their high school class, 90% from top quarter, 100% from top half. Full-time: 2,195 students, 48% women, 52% men. Part-time: 106 students, 52% women, 48% men. Students come from 48 states and territories, 53 other countries, 83% from out-of-state. 0.05% American Indian or Alaska Native, non-Hispanic/Latino; 7% Hispanic/Latino; 6% African American, non-Hispanic/Latino; 5% Asian, non-Hispanic/Latino; 0% Native Hawaiian or other Pacific Islander, non-Hispanic/Latino; 8% international. 0% 25 or older, 90% live on campus, 1% transferred in. Retention: 88% of full-time freshmen returned the following year. Academic areas with the most degrees conferred: social sciences; area and ethnic studies; biological/life sciences. Core. Calendar: semesters. Advanced placement, accelerated degree program, self-designed majors, honors program, independent study, double major, summer session for credit, adult/continuing education programs, internships, graduate courses open to undergrads. Off campus study at members of the Twelve College Exchange Program, Hartford Consortium for Higher Education. Study abroad program. ROTC: Army (c).

Entrance Requirements: Options: electronic application, early admission, early decision, deferred admission, international baccalaureate accepted. Required: essay, high school transcript, 3 recommendations. Recommended: interview. Required for some: SAT or ACT, SAT Subject Tests. Entrance: most difficult. Application deadlines: 1/1, 11/15 for early decision plan 1, 1/1 for early decision plan 2. Notification: 4/1, 12/15 for early decision plan 1, 2/15 for early decision plan 2. SAT Reasoning Test deadline: 1/15. SAT Subject Test deadline: 1/15. Applicants placed on waiting list: 1,885. Wait-listed applicants offered admission: 33. Early decision applicants: 487. Early decision applicants admitted: 307.

Costs Per Year: Application fee: $60. One-time mandatory fee: $25. Comprehensive fee: $57,530 includes full-time tuition ($43,570), mandatory fees ($2160), and college room and board ($11,800). College room only: $7660. Full-time tuition and fees vary according to course load and program. Room and board charges vary according to board plan. Part-time tuition: $4841 per course. Part-time tuition varies according to course load and program.

Collegiate Environment: Orientation program. Drama-theater group, choral group, student-run newspaper, radio station. Social organizations: 104 open to all; national fraternities, national sororities, local fraternities, local sororities, coed fraternities; 20% of eligible men and 16% of eligible women are members. Most popular organizations: Friends Active in Community Engagement and Service (FACES), The Mill, Student Government Association, Relay for Life, Multi-Cultural Affairs Council. Major annual events: Spring Weekend, Homecoming. Student services: health clinic, personal-psychological counseling, women's center. Campus security: 24-hour emergency response devices and patrols, late night transport-escort service, controlled dormitory access. 1,900 college housing spaces available; 1,883 were occupied in 2012-13. Freshmen guaranteed college housing. On-campus residence required in freshman year. Option: coed housing available. Trinity College Library plus 1 other with 986,184 books, 381,055 microform titles, 1,407 serials, 101,249 audiovisual materials, an OPAC, and a Web page. 249 computers available on campus for general student use. A campuswide network can be accessed from student residence rooms and from off campus. Students can access the following: online class registration, Web pages. Staffed computer lab on campus provides training in use of computers, software, and the Internet.

■ **TUNXIS COMMUNITY COLLEGE**
271 Scott Swamp Rd.
Farmington, CT 06032-3026
Tel: (860)255-3500
E-mail: pmccluskey@tunxis.edu
Web Site: www.tunxis.commnet.edu/

Description: State-supported, 2-year, coed. Part of Connecticut State Colleges and Universities (ConnSCU), Board of Regents for Higher Education.

Awards certificates, transfer associate, and terminal associate degrees. Founded 1969. Setting: 12-acre suburban campus with easy access to Hartford. Total enrollment: 4,764. Faculty: 239 (67 full-time, 172 part-time). Student-undergrad faculty ratio is 19:1. Full-time: 1,783 students, 51% women, 49% men. Part-time: 2,981 students, 61% women, 39% men. Students come from 6 states and territories, 2% from out-of-state. 0.2% American Indian or Alaska Native, non-Hispanic/Latino; 14% Hispanic/Latino; 7% African American, non-Hispanic/Latino; 3% Asian, non-Hispanic/Latino; 0.1% Native Hawaiian or other Pacific Islander, non-Hispanic/Latino; 1% international. 38% 25 or older. Retention: 61% of full-time freshmen returned the following year. Core. Calendar: semesters. Academic remediation for entering students, ESL program, services for LD students, honors program, independent study, distance learning, double major, summer session for credit, part-time degree program, adult/continuing education programs, co-op programs and internships.

Entrance Requirements: Open admission except for dental hygiene, physical therapist assistant. Option: deferred admission. Required: high school transcript. Entrance: noncompetitive. Application deadline: Rolling. Transfer credits accepted: Yes.

Costs Per Year: Application fee: $20. State resident tuition: $3192 full-time, $133 per credit hour part-time. Nonresident tuition: $9576 full-time, $399 per credit hour part-time. Mandatory fees: $446 full-time, $114 per term part-time, $332 per term part-time.

Collegiate Environment: Orientation program. Drama-theater group, student-run newspaper. Social organizations: 14 open to all; student clubs. Most popular organizations: Phi Theta Kappa, Student American Dental Hygiene Association (SADHA), Human Services Club, student newspaper, Criminal Justice Club. Major annual events: Writer's Festival, Campus Barbecue, International Students' Day. Campus security: 24-hour emergency response devices. College housing not available. Tunxis Community College Library with 33,866 books, 106,400 microform titles, 285 serials, and an OPAC. 354 computers available on campus for general student use. A campuswide network can be accessed from off-campus. Students can access the following: online class registration. Staffed computer lab on campus provides training in use of computers, software, and the Internet.

Community Environment: Farmington was settled in 1640 and incorporated in 1645. It is a suburban, residential town with a population of 25,000.

■ UNITED STATES COAST GUARD ACADEMY

15 Mohegan Ave.
New London, CT 06320-8100
Tel: (860)444-8444; Free: 800-883-8724
Fax: (860)444-8289
E-mail: admissions@uscga.edu
Web Site: www.uscga.edu/

Description: Federally supported, 4-year, coed. Awards bachelor's degrees. Founded 1876. Setting: 110-acre suburban campus with easy access to Providence, Hartford. Endowment: $1.3 million. Research spending for the previous fiscal year: $1.7 million. Educational spending for the previous fiscal year: $47,236 per student. Total enrollment: 1,045. Faculty: 143 (133 full-time, 10 part-time). Student-undergrad faculty ratio is 8:1. 2,374 applied, 16% were admitted. 52% from top 10% of their high school class, 85% from top quarter, 99% from top half. 11 class presidents, 8 valedictorians, 36 student government officers. Full-time: 1,045 students, 30% women, 70% men. Students come from 53 states and territories, 19 other countries, 94% from out-of-state. 1% American Indian or Alaska Native, non-Hispanic/Latino; 10% Hispanic/Latino; 3% African American, non-Hispanic/Latino; 4% Asian, non-Hispanic/Latino; 1% Native Hawaiian or other Pacific Islander, non-Hispanic/Latino; 2% international. 0% 25 or older, 100% live on campus, 0% transferred in. Retention: 95% of full-time freshmen returned the following year. Academic areas with the most degrees conferred: engineering; social sciences; biological/life sciences. Core. Calendar: semesters. Academic remediation for entering students, ESL program, honors program, independent study, double major, summer session for credit, internships. Off campus study at Connecticut College, U.S. Military Academy (West Point), U.S. Naval Academy and the U.S. Air Force Academy.

Entrance Requirements: Options: electronic application, early action. Required: essay, high school transcript, 3 recommendations, medical examination, physical fitness examination, SAT or ACT. Recommended: interview. Entrance: very difficult. Application deadlines: 2/1, 2/1 for nonresidents, 11/1 for early action. Notification: continuous until 4/15, continuous until 4/15 for nonresidents, 1/15 for early action. SAT Reasoning Test deadline: 3/15. SAT Subject Test deadline: 3/15. Transfer credits ac-

cepted: No. Applicants placed on waiting list: 479. Wait-listed applicants offered admission: 54. Early action applicants: 1,017. Early action applicants admitted: 196.

Costs Per Year: Application fee: $0. Comprehensive fee: $0. Tuition, room and board, and medical and dental care are provided by the US government. Each cadet receives a salary from which to pay for uniforms, supplies, and personal expenses.

Collegiate Environment: Orientation program. Drama-theater group, choral group, marching band. Social organizations: 70 open to all. Most popular organizations: Companneros Club - Latino culture and traditions, Genesis Club - Multicultural awareness, Men's and Women's Lacrosse Club, Men's and Women's Rugby Club, Officers' Christian Fellowship. Major annual events: Homecoming, Parents' Weekend, Community Service Day. Student services: legal services, health clinic, personal-psychological counseling. Campus security: 24-hour patrols, student patrols, late night transport-escort service. 1,045 college housing spaces available; all were occupied in 2012-13. Freshmen guaranteed college housing. On-campus residence required through senior year. Option: coed housing available. USCG Academy Library with 178,000 books, 410,645 microform titles, 55,000 serials, 2,478 audiovisual materials, an OPAC, and a Web page. Operations spending for the previous fiscal year: $1.2 million. 325 computers available on campus for general student use. A computer is required for all students. A campuswide network can be accessed from student residence rooms and from off campus. Students can access the following: online class registration. Staffed computer lab on campus provides training in use of computers, software, and the Internet.

■ UNIVERSITY OF BRIDGEPORT

126 Park Ave.
Bridgeport, CT 06604
Tel: (203)576-4000; Free: 800-EXCEL-UB
Fax: (203)576-4941
E-mail: admit@bridgeport.edu
Web Site: www.bridgeport.edu/

Description: Independent, comprehensive, coed. Awards associate, bachelor's, master's, and doctoral degrees and post-master's certificates. Founded 1927. Setting: 86-acre urban campus with easy access to New York City. Endowment: $24.9 million. Research spending for the previous fiscal year: $670,000. Educational spending for the previous fiscal year: $7822 per student. Total enrollment: 4,877. Faculty: 470 (121 full-time, 349 part-time). Student-undergrad faculty ratio is 15:1. 5,736 applied, 63% were admitted. 10% from top 10% of their high school class, 32% from top quarter, 69% from top half. Full-time: 1,852 students, 61% women, 39% men. Part-time: 836 students, 83% women, 17% men. Students come from 35 states and territories, 51 other countries, 38% from out-of-state. 1% American Indian or Alaska Native, non-Hispanic/Latino; 18% Hispanic/Latino; 37% African American, non-Hispanic/Latino; 3% Asian, non-Hispanic/Latino; 0.1% Native Hawaiian or other Pacific Islander, non-Hispanic/Latino; 11% international. 36% 25 or older, 48% live on campus, 8% transferred in. Retention: 62% of full-time freshmen returned the following year. Academic areas with the most degrees conferred: business/marketing; liberal arts/general studies; psychology. Core. Calendar: semesters. Academic remediation for entering students, ESL program, services for LD students, advanced placement, accelerated degree program, self-designed majors, honors program, independent study, distance learning, double major, summer session for credit, part-time degree program, adult/continuing education programs, co-op programs and internships, graduate courses open to undergrads. Off campus study at Fairfield University, Sacred Heart University. Study abroad program. ROTC: Army.

Entrance Requirements: Options: electronic application, early admission, early decision, deferred admission. Required: essay, high school transcript, minimum 2 high school GPA, SAT or ACT. Recommended: 1 recommendation, interview. Required for some: 2 recommendations, interview, portfolio, audition. Entrance: moderately difficult. Application deadlines: Rolling, Rolling for nonresidents. Notification: continuous, continuous for nonresidents. Transfer credits accepted: Yes.

Costs Per Year: Application fee: $25. Comprehensive fee: $40,190 includes full-time tuition ($25,950), mandatory fees ($2190), and college room and board ($12,050). Full-time tuition and fees vary according to course load and program. Room and board charges vary according to board plan, housing facility, and student level. Part-time tuition: $865 per credit hour. Part-time mandatory fees: $200 per term. Part-time tuition and fees vary according to course load and program.

Collegiate Environment: Orientation program. Choral group, student-run

newspaper. Social organizations: 44 open to all; national fraternities, national sororities, local fraternities, local sororities; 1% of eligible men and 2% of eligible women are members. Most popular organizations: Student Congress, International Relations Club, Black Students Alliance, Latin America Club, Martial Arts Club. Major annual events: International Festival, Spring Week Events, Halloween Bash. Student services: health clinic, personal-psychological counseling, women's center. Campus security: 24-hour emergency response devices and patrols, student patrols, late night transport-escort service, controlled dormitory access. 1,440 college housing spaces available; 885 were occupied in 2012-13. Freshmen guaranteed college housing. On-campus residence required through sophomore year. Option: coed housing available. Wahlstrom Library with 243,586 books, 1.1 million microform titles, 45,712 serials, 3,342 audiovisual materials, an OPAC, and a Web page. Operations spending for the previous fiscal year: $1.4 million. 200 computers available on campus for general student use. A campuswide network can be accessed from student residence rooms. Students can access the following: online class registration. Staffed computer lab on campus provides training in use of computers, software, and the Internet.

Community Environment: Bridgeport is named for the first drawbridge erected over the Pequonock River and is easily accessible by auto, bus and train, automobiles using the Merrit Parkway and the Connecticut Thruway. Bridgeport is the home of P.T. Barnum. Barnum Institute of Science and History and the Museum of Art, Science and Industry is located in Bridgeport. Seaside Park, a 225-acre park stretching two and one half miles along Long Island Sound, offers opportunities for swimming and field sports. Beardsley Park has woodland walks and drives, a large lake and a zoo. Sixty-five percent of Connecticut's largest corporations are located in Fairfield County. These companies provide students with excellent opportunities for employment, before and after graduation.

■ UNIVERSITY OF CONNECTICUT

Storrs, CT 06269
Tel: (860)486-2000
Fax: (860)486-1476
E-mail: beahusky@uconnvm.uconn.edu
Web Site: www.uconn.edu/

Description: State-supported, university, coed. Awards associate, bachelor's, master's, and doctoral degrees and post-master's certificates. Founded 1881. Setting: 4,108-acre rural campus. Endowment: $329 million. Research spending for the previous fiscal year: $162.9 million. Total enrollment: 25,483. Faculty: 1,421 (1,096 full-time, 325 part-time). Student-undergrad faculty ratio is 17:1. 29,966 applied, 45% were admitted. 48% from top 10% of their high school class, 86% from top quarter, 98% from top half. 146 valedictorians. Full-time: 16,736 students, 49% women, 51% men. Part-time: 792 students, 41% women, 59% men. Students come from 44 states and territories, 58 other countries, 27% from out-of-state. 0.1% American Indian or Alaska Native, non-Hispanic/Latino; 7% Hispanic/Latino; 6% African American, non-Hispanic/Latino; 8% Asian, non-Hispanic/Latino; 0.1% Native Hawaiian or other Pacific Islander, non-Hispanic/Latino; 3% international. 3% 25 or older, 72% live on campus, 5% transferred in. Retention: 93% of full-time freshmen returned the following year. Academic areas with the most degrees conferred: business/marketing; social sciences; health professions and related sciences. Core. Calendar: semesters. ESL program, services for LD students, advanced placement, accelerated degree program, self-designed majors, honors program, independent study, distance learning, double major, summer session for credit, part-time degree program, adult/continuing education programs, co-op programs and internships, graduate courses open to undergrads. Off campus study at other public institutions in Connecticut. Study abroad program. ROTC: Army, Air Force.

Entrance Requirements: Options: electronic application, deferred admission. Required: essay, high school transcript, SAT or ACT. Recommended: 1 recommendation. Entrance: moderately difficult. Application deadline: 1/15. Notification: 3/1. SAT Reasoning Test deadline: 2/1. Transfer credits accepted: Yes. Applicants placed on waiting list: 1,600. Wait-listed applicants offered admission: 436.

Costs Per Year: Application fee: $70. State resident tuition: $9256 full-time, $386 per credit part-time. Nonresident tuition: $28,204 full-time, $1175 per credit part-time. Mandatory fees: $2766 full-time. Part-time tuition varies according to course load. College room and board: $11,722. College room only: $6278. Room and board charges vary according to board plan and housing facility.

Collegiate Environment: Orientation program. Drama-theater group, choral group, marching band, student-run newspaper, radio station. Social organizations: 582 open to all; national fraternities, national sororities, local fraternities, local sororities; 10% of eligible men and 13% of eligible women are members. Major annual events: Husky WOW (Week of Welcome), Homecoming, Winter Weekend/One Ton Sundae. Student services: health clinic, personal-psychological counseling, women's center. Campus security: 24-hour emergency response devices, late night transport-escort service. 12,076 undergraduates lived in college housing during 2012-13. Freshmen guaranteed college housing. Options: coed, men-only, women-only housing available. Homer Babbidge Library plus 3 others with 3.5 million books, 3.2 million microform titles, 87,556 serials, 312,139 audiovisual materials, an OPAC, and a Web page. Operations spending for the previous fiscal year: $19 million. 2,220 computers available on campus for general student use. Computer purchase/lease plans available. A campuswide network can be accessed from student residence rooms and from off campus. Students can access the following: online class registration. Staffed computer lab on campus provides training in use of computers, software, and the Internet.

Community Environment: Storrs, population 11,000, is in a rural area 25 miles east of Hartford and 70 miles south of Boston. The climate is temperate. Buses serve the area with other modes of transportation available in Hartford. Community facilities include various houses of worship and a small shopping area. Willimantic, nine miles away, has a hospital and additional shopping facilities. There are recreational activities at nearby lakes and State Parks. Part-time employment opportunities are limited.

■ UNIVERSITY OF HARTFORD

200 Bloomfield Ave.
West Hartford, CT 06117-1599
Tel: (860)768-4100; Free: 800-947-4303
Fax: (860)768-4961
E-mail: admissions@hartford.edu
Web Site: www.hartford.edu/

Description: Independent, comprehensive, coed. Awards associate, bachelor's, master's, and doctoral degrees and post-master's certificates. Founded 1877. Setting: 320-acre suburban campus with easy access to Hartford. Endowment: $114.6 million. Research spending for the previous fiscal year: $3.6 million. Educational spending for the previous fiscal year: $13,509 per student. Total enrollment: 6,894. Faculty: 846 (347 full-time, 499 part-time). Student-undergrad faculty ratio is 11:1. 13,040 applied, 70% were admitted. Full-time: 4,503 students, 49% women, 51% men. Part-time: 781 students, 60% women, 40% men. Students come from 46 states and territories, 39 other countries, 57% from out-of-state. 0.3% American Indian or Alaska Native, non-Hispanic/Latino; 8% Hispanic/Latino; 13% African American, non-Hispanic/Latino; 3% Asian, non-Hispanic/Latino; 0.1% Native Hawaiian or other Pacific Islander, non-Hispanic/Latino; 4% international. 9% 25 or older, 62% live on campus, 4% transferred in. Retention: 72% of full-time freshmen returned the following year. Academic areas with the most degrees conferred: visual and performing arts; business/marketing; health professions and related sciences. Core. Calendar: semesters. Academic remediation for entering students, ESL program, services for LD students, advanced placement, self-designed majors, honors program, independent study, distance learning, double major, summer session for credit, part-time degree program, adult/continuing education programs, co-op programs and internships, graduate courses open to undergrads. Off campus study at members of the Hartford Consortium for Higher Education. Study abroad program. ROTC: Army (c), Air Force (c).

Entrance Requirements: Options: electronic application, early admission, deferred admission. Required: high school transcript, SAT or ACT. Recommended: essay, 2 recommendations, interview. Entrance: moderately difficult. Application deadline: Rolling. Notification: continuous. Transfer credits accepted: Yes.

Costs Per Year: Application fee: $40. Comprehensive fee: $45,606 includes full-time tuition ($31,804), mandatory fees ($1554), and college room and board ($12,248). College room only: $7328. Full-time tuition and fees vary according to program. Room and board charges vary according to board plan and housing facility. Part-time tuition: $480 per credit. Part-time tuition varies according to course load and program.

Collegiate Environment: Orientation program. Drama-theater group, choral group, student-run newspaper, radio station. Social organizations: 45 open to all; national fraternities, national sororities; 17% of eligible men and 21% of eligible women are members. Most popular organizations: Program Council, Brothers and Sisters United, Hillel, Student Government Association, Residence Hall Association. Major annual events: Hawks Fest, Lacrosse Under the Light, Midnight Mania. Student services: legal services, health clinic, personal-psychological counseling, women's center. Campus security: 24-hour emergency response devices and patrols, late night transport-escort service, controlled dormitory access, bicycle patrols. 3,530 college housing spaces available; 3,123 were occupied in 2012-13. Freshmen guaranteed college housing. Options: coed, women-only housing available. Mortenson Library plus 1 other with 590,724 books, 383,386 microform titles, 49,600 serials, an OPAC, and a Web page. Operations spending for the previous fiscal year: $3.3 million. 400 computers available on campus for general student use. A campuswide network can be accessed from student residence rooms and from off campus. Students can access the following: online class registration, student Web pages. Staffed computer lab on campus.

Community Environment: The University is located in a suburban area of West Hartford, four miles from the center of Hartford. In addition to the many activities available on campus, the proximity to a metropolitan area affords a multitude of cultural, educational and recreational opportunities.

■ **UNIVERSITY OF NEW HAVEN**
300 Boston Post Rd.
West Haven, CT 06516-1916
Tel: (203)932-7000; Free: 800-DIAL-UNH
Fax: (203)937-0756
E-mail: adminfo@newhaven.edu
Web Site: www.newhaven.edu/
Description: Independent, comprehensive, coed. Awards associate, bachelor's, master's, and doctoral degrees and post-master's certificates. Founded 1920. Setting: 75-acre suburban campus with easy access to Hartford, New Haven. Total enrollment: 6,351. Faculty: 572 (209 full-time, 363 part-time). Student-undergrad faculty ratio is 17:1. 10,028 applied, 71% were admitted. Full-time: 4,267 students, 51% women, 49% men. Part-time: 426 students, 44% women, 56% men. Students come from 40 states and territories, 26 other countries, 55% from out-of-state. 0.3% American Indian or Alaska Native, non-Hispanic/Latino; 3% Hispanic/Latino; 8% African American, non-Hispanic/Latino; 2% Asian, non-Hispanic/Latino; 0.1% Native Hawaiian or other Pacific Islander, non-Hispanic/Latino; 6% international. 9% 25 or older, 56% live on campus, 5% transferred in. Retention: 76% of full-time freshmen returned the following year. Academic areas with the most degrees conferred: homeland security, law enforcement, firefighting, and protective services; business/marketing; visual and performing arts. Core. Calendar: 4-1-4. Academic remediation for entering students, ESL program, services for LD students, advanced placement, accelerated degree program, honors program, independent study, distance learning, double major, summer session for credit, part-time degree program, adult/continuing education programs, co-op programs and internships, graduate courses open to undergrads. Off campus study at OCICU. Study abroad program. ROTC: Army, Air Force (c).
Entrance Requirements: Options: electronic application, early action. Required: essay, high school transcript, SAT or ACT. Recommended: interview. Entrance: moderately difficult. Application deadlines: Rolling, 11/15 for early action. Notification: continuous, 12/17 for early action. SAT Reasoning Test deadline: 9/11. Transfer credits accepted: Yes.
Costs Per Year: Application fee: $75. Comprehensive fee: $46,450 includes full-time tuition ($31,500), mandatory fees ($1250), and college room and board ($13,700). Full-time tuition and fees vary according to course load and program. Room and board charges vary according to board plan and housing facility.
Collegiate Environment: Orientation program. Drama-theater group, choral group, marching band, student-run newspaper, radio station. Social organizations: 165 open to all; national fraternities, national sororities, local fraternities, local sororities. Most popular organizations: student government, Criminal Justice Club, Music Entertainment and Industry Association, Black Student Union, Fire Science Club. Major annual events: Homecoming, Spring Weekend, Snowball Formal Dance. Student services: health clinic, personal-psychological counseling. Campus security: 24-hour emergency response devices and patrols, student patrols, late night transport-escort service, controlled dormitory access, escort service, vehicle, bicycle and foot patrols, crime prevention programs. College housing designed to accommodate 2,346 students; 2,363 undergraduates lived in college housing during 2012-13. Freshmen given priority for college housing. Option: coed housing available. Marvin K. Peterson Library with 370,346 books, 404,175 microform titles, 34,026 serials, 1,392 audiovisual materials, an OPAC, and a Web page. 300 computers available on campus for general student use. Computer purchase/lease plans available. A campuswide network can be accessed from student residence rooms. Students can access the following:

online class registration, computer repair services. Staffed computer lab on campus provides training in use of computers, software, and the Internet.
Community Environment: Located in West Haven, a town with a population of 52,900; ten minutes from downtown New Haven. Cultural attractions include the Shubert Theater, The Palace, Long Wharf Theater, Yale Repertory Theater. The university is accessible to many shopping malls and the beaches of Long Island Sound.

■ **UNIVERSITY OF PHOENIX–FAIRFIELD COUNTY CAMPUS**
535 Connecticut Ave. Ste. 400
Norwalk, CT 06854-1799
Tel: (203)523-4700; Free: 866-766-0766
Web Site: www.phoenix.edu/
Description: Proprietary, comprehensive, coed. Awards bachelor's, master's, and doctoral degrees.

■ **UNIVERSITY OF SAINT JOSEPH**
1678 Asylum Ave.
West Hartford, CT 06117-2700
Tel: (860)232-4571; Free: 866-442-8752
Fax: (860)233-5695
E-mail: admissions@usj.edu
Web Site: www.usj.edu/
Description: Independent Roman Catholic, comprehensive. Awards bachelor's, master's, and doctoral degrees and post-master's certificates. Founded 1932. Setting: 84-acre suburban campus with easy access to Hartford. Endowment: $21.7 million. Total enrollment: 2,525. Faculty: 309 (117 full-time, 192 part-time). Student-undergrad faculty ratio is 10:1. 679 applied, 80% were admitted. 8% from top 10% of their high school class, 45% from top quarter, 86% from top half. Full-time: 831 students, 99% women, 1% men. Part-time: 236 students, 96% women, 4% men. 6% from out-of-state. 0.2% American Indian or Alaska Native, non-Hispanic/Latino; 11% Hispanic/Latino; 10% African American, non-Hispanic/Latino; 3% Asian, non-Hispanic/Latino; 0.1% Native Hawaiian or other Pacific Islander, non-Hispanic/Latino; 0.2% international. 13% 25 or older, 47% live on campus, 11% transferred in. Retention: 75% of full-time freshmen returned the following year. Academic areas with the most degrees conferred: psychology; health professions and related sciences; biological/life sciences. Core. Calendar: semesters. Services for LD students, advanced placement, accelerated degree program, self-designed majors, honors program, independent study, distance learning, double major, summer session for credit, part-time degree program, adult/continuing education programs, internships, graduate courses open to undergrads. Off campus study. Study abroad program.
Entrance Requirements: Options: electronic application, deferred admission. Required: high school transcript, SAT or ACT. Recommended: essay, interview, SAT. Entrance: moderately difficult. Application deadlines: Rolling, Rolling for nonresidents. Notification: continuous, continuous for nonresidents. Transfer credits accepted: Yes.
Costs Per Year: Application fee: $50. Comprehensive fee: $45,424 includes full-time tuition ($30,408), mandatory fees ($1418), and college room and board ($13,598). College room only: $6274. Full-time tuition and fees vary according to course load, degree level, location, program, and student level. Room and board charges vary according to board plan and housing facility. Part-time tuition: $688 per credit. Part-time mandatory fees: $45 per credit. Part-time tuition and fees vary according to course load, degree level, location, program, and student level.
Collegiate Environment: Orientation program. Drama-theater group, choral group. Student services: health clinic, personal-psychological counseling. Campus security: 24-hour emergency response devices and patrols, late night transport-escort service, controlled dormitory access. 422 college housing spaces available; 357 were occupied in 2012-13. No special consideration for freshman housing applicants. Option: women-only housing available. Pope Pius XII Library with 92,813 books, 903 microform titles, 11,208 serials, 3,175 audiovisual materials, an OPAC, and a Web page.
Community Environment: The campus is located in a suburban community within 5 miles of Hartford, the capital of Connecticut. Known as the Insurance City, Hartford offers multiple internship and employment possibilities and diverse attractions such as ballet, opera, theater, symphony, museums, historic landmarks, sporting events, shopping, churches, and hospitals. Many volunteer opportunities are also available.

■ **WESLEYAN UNIVERSITY**
Middletown, CT 06459
Tel: (860)685-2000

Fax: (860)685-3001
E-mail: admissions@wesleyan.edu
Web Site: www.wesleyan.edu/
Description: Independent, university, coed. Awards bachelor's, master's, and doctoral degrees and post-master's certificates. Founded 1831. Setting: 240-acre small town campus. Endowment: $616.2 million. Research spending for the previous fiscal year: $10.7 million. Educational spending for the previous fiscal year: $27,074 per student. Total enrollment: 3,262. Faculty: 389 (338 full-time, 51 part-time). Student-undergrad faculty ratio is 9:1. 10,046 applied, 21% were admitted. 69% from top 10% of their high school class, 92% from top quarter, 98% from top half. Full-time: 2,932 students, 52% women, 48% men. Part-time: 8 students, 50% women, 50% men. 92% from out-of-state. 0.1% American Indian or Alaska Native, non-Hispanic/Latino; 10% Hispanic/Latino; 7% African American, non-Hispanic/Latino; 9% Asian, non-Hispanic/Latino; 0.1% Native Hawaiian or other Pacific Islander, non-Hispanic/Latino; 8% international. 0% 25 or older, 98% live on campus, 2% transferred in. Retention: 95% of full-time freshmen returned the following year. Academic areas with the most degrees conferred: social sciences; psychology; area and ethnic studies. Calendar: semesters. Services for LD students, advanced placement, self-designed majors, honors program, independent study, double major, summer session for credit, adult/continuing education programs, graduate courses open to undergrads. Off campus study at members of the Twelve College Exchange Program, American University. Study abroad program. ROTC: Air Force (c).
Entrance Requirements: Options: electronic application, early admission, early decision, deferred admission, international baccalaureate accepted. Required: essay, high school transcript, 2 recommendations, SAT and SAT Subject Tests or ACT. Recommended: interview. Required for some: interview. Entrance: most difficult. Application deadlines: 1/1, 11/15 for early decision plan 1, 1/1 for early decision plan 2. Notification: 4/1, 12/15 for early decision plan 1, 2/15 for early decision plan 2. SAT Reasoning Test deadline: 2/15. SAT Subject Test deadline: 2/15. Applicants placed on waiting list: 2,234. Wait-listed applicants offered admission: 48. Early decision applicants: 814. Early decision applicants admitted: 372.
Costs Per Year: Application fee: $55. One-time mandatory fee: $300. Comprehensive fee: $58,202 includes full-time tuition ($45,358), mandatory fees ($270), and college room and board ($12,574). Room and board charges vary according to board plan and housing facility.
Collegiate Environment: Orientation program. Drama-theater group, choral group, student-run newspaper, radio station. Social organizations: 260 open to all; national fraternities, national sororities, local fraternities. Most popular organizations: Environmental Organizers Network, WesDems, Ajuacampos (Latino affinity group). Major annual events: WesFest (Annual festival celebrating all things Wesleyan for admitted students), Homecoming/Family Weekend, The Common Moment during new student orientation. Student services: health clinic, personal-psychological counseling, women's center. Campus security: 24-hour emergency response devices and patrols, student patrols, late night transport-escort service, controlled dormitory access. 2,840 college housing spaces available. Freshmen guaranteed college housing. On-campus residence required through senior year. Option: coed housing available. Olin Memorial Library with an OPAC and a Web page. Operations spending for the previous fiscal year: $10.3 million. 1,600 computers available on campus for general student use. Computer purchase/lease plans available. A campuswide network can be accessed from student residence rooms and from off campus. Students can access the following: online class registration, electronic portfolio, online course drop/add, Blackboard course management system. Staffed computer lab on campus (open 24 hours a day) provides training in use of computers.
Community Environment: Population 47,400. In central Connecticut, 15 miles south of Hartford and 20 miles north of New Haven, Middletown is an important research and manufacturing center. Buses and railroads serve the area with an airline service nearby. Middletown has 21 churches of all denominations, hospital, three libraries with branches, several inns, motels, theatres and a shopping area. The various civic, fraternal and veterans organizations are active within the city. Parks, tennis courts, basketball courts, ball fields, picnic grounds and swimming pool provide facilities for recreation.

■ **WESTERN CONNECTICUT STATE UNIVERSITY**
181 White St.
Danbury, CT 06810-6885
Tel: (203)837-8200; Free: 877-837-WCSU
Fax: (203)837-8320
E-mail: admissions@wcsu.edu

Web Site: www.wcsu.edu/
Description: State-supported, comprehensive, coed. Part of Connecticut State Colleges and Universities (ConnSCU). Awards associate, bachelor's, master's, and doctoral degrees and post-master's certificates. Founded 1903. Setting: 340-acre urban campus with easy access to New York City. Endowment: $10.5 million. Research spending for the previous fiscal year: $370,616. Educational spending for the previous fiscal year: $10,256 per student. Total enrollment: 6,176. Faculty: 588 (228 full-time, 360 part-time). Student-undergrad faculty ratio is 14:1. 4,016 applied, 59% were admitted. 7% from top 10% of their high school class, 24% from top quarter, 58% from top half. Full-time: 4,501 students, 53% women, 47% men. Part-time: 1,082 students, 57% women, 43% men. Students come from 17 states and territories, 4 other countries, 7% from out-of-state. 0.4% American Indian or Alaska Native, non-Hispanic/Latino; 13% Hispanic/Latino; 9% African American, non-Hispanic/Latino; 3% Asian, non-Hispanic/Latino; 0.4% Native Hawaiian or other Pacific Islander, non-Hispanic/Latino; 0.1% international. 15% 25 or older, 29% live on campus, 10% transferred in. Retention: 68% of full-time freshmen returned the following year. Academic areas with the most degrees conferred: business/marketing; health professions and related sciences; education. Core. Calendar: semesters. Services for LD students, self-designed majors, honors program, independent study, distance learning, summer session for credit, part-time degree program, co-op programs and internships, graduate courses open to undergrads. Study abroad program. ROTC: Army (c), Air Force (c).
Entrance Requirements: Options: electronic application, early admission, deferred admission. Required: high school transcript, 2 recommendations, SAT or ACT. Required for some: essay, interview. Entrance: moderately difficult. Application deadline: Rolling. Notification: continuous. Preference given to state residents.
Costs Per Year: Application fee: $50. State resident tuition: $4510 full-time, $188 per credit part-time. Nonresident tuition: $14,594 full-time, $192 per credit part-time. Mandatory fees: $4383 full-time, $222 per credit part-time. Full-time tuition and fees vary according to course load, program, and reciprocity agreements. College room and board: $10,907. College room only: $6445. Room and board charges vary according to board plan and housing facility.
Collegiate Environment: Orientation program. Drama-theater group, choral group, student-run newspaper, radio station. Social organizations: 89 open to all; national fraternities, national sororities, local sororities; 3% of eligible men and 3% of eligible women are members. Most popular organizations: National Society of Collegiate Scholars, Criminology Club, Jazz Club, American Marketing Club, Meteorology. Major annual events: The President's Lecture Series, WCSU Annual 'Roots & Shoots' hosting of renowned Dr. Jane Goodall, The WCSU Theatre Arts Department productions. Student services: health clinic, personal-psychological counseling. Campus security: 24-hour emergency response devices and patrols, student patrols, late night transport-escort service, controlled dormitory access. 1,675 college housing spaces available; 1,459 were occupied in 2012-13. Freshmen guaranteed college housing. Options: coed, women-only housing available. Ruth Haas Library with 213,314 books, 3,516 microform titles, 1,089 serials, 17,970 audiovisual materials, an OPAC, and a Web page. Operations spending for the previous fiscal year: $1 million. 834 computers available on campus for general student use. A campuswide network can be accessed from student residence rooms and from off campus. Students can access the following: online class registration, 100% wireless, on-line payment. Staffed computer lab on campus provides training in use of computers, software, and the Internet.
Community Environment: Population 78,700, Danbury is within easy commuting distance of Stamford, Waterbury, Bridgeport, New Haven, and Torrington. Cultural centers in Danbury and in the surrounding cities are within easy reach. Trains and buses serve the area. Recreational facilities include nearby Candlewood Lake for swimming, boating, and fishing. Part time work is available in the community.

■ **YALE UNIVERSITY**
New Haven, CT 06520
Tel: (203)432-4771
Fax: (203)432-9392
E-mail: student.questions@yale.edu
Web Site: www.yale.edu/
Description: Independent, university, coed. Awards bachelor's, master's, and doctoral degrees and post-master's certificates. Founded 1701. Setting: 342-acre urban campus with easy access to New York City. Endowment: $19.3 billion. Total enrollment: 11,906. Faculty: 1,666 (1,176 full-time, 490

part-time). Student-undergrad faculty ratio is 5:1. 28,977 applied, 7% were admitted. 95% from top 10% of their high school class, 99% from top quarter, 100% from top half. Full-time: 5,393 students, 50% women, 50% men. Part-time: 12 students, 33% women, 67% men. Students come from 50 states and territories, 86 other countries, 94% from out-of-state. 1% American Indian or Alaska Native, non-Hispanic/Latino; 10% Hispanic/Latino; 7% African American, non-Hispanic/Latino; 16% Asian, non-Hispanic/Latino; 0.1% Native Hawaiian or other Pacific Islander, non-Hispanic/Latino; 10% international. 1% 25 or older, 88% live on campus, 0.4% transferred in. Retention: 99% of full-time freshmen returned the following year. Academic areas with the most degrees conferred: social sciences; area and ethnic studies; biological/life sciences; interdisciplinary studies. Core. Calendar: semesters. Services for LD students, advanced placement, self-designed majors, independent study, double major, summer session for credit, part-time degree program, graduate courses open to undergrads. Study abroad program. ROTC: Army (c), Naval, Air Force.

Entrance Requirements: Options: electronic application, early admission, early action, deferred admission, international baccalaureate accepted. Required: essay, high school transcript, 3 recommendations, SAT and SAT Subject Tests or ACT. Recommended: interview. Entrance: most difficult. Application deadlines: 12/31, 11/1 for early action. Notification: 4/1, 12/15 for early action. SAT Reasoning Test deadline: 3/1. SAT Subject Test deadline: 3/1. Transfer credits accepted: Yes. Wait-listed applicants offered admission: 70.

Costs Per Year: Application fee: $75. Comprehensive fee: $57,500 includes full-time tuition ($44,000) and college room and board ($13,500). Room and board charges vary according to board plan.

Collegiate Environment: Orientation program. Drama-theater group, choral group, marching band, student-run newspaper, radio station. Social organizations: 400 open to all; national fraternities, national sororities. Major annual events: Spring Fling Concert, Fall Show, Yale Symphony Orchestra Halloween Show. Student services: health clinic, personal-psychological counseling, women's center. Campus security: 24-hour emergency response devices and patrols, late night transport-escort service, controlled dormitory access. Freshmen guaranteed college housing. On-campus residence required through sophomore year. Option: coed housing available. Sterling Memorial Library plus 15 others with 15 million books, 1 million microform titles, 450,000 serials, and 400,000 audiovisual materials. 450 computers available on campus for general student use. Computer purchase/lease plans available. A campuswide network can be accessed from student residence rooms and from off campus. Students can access the following: online class registration. Staffed computer lab on campus (open 24 hours a day) provides training in use of computers, software, and the Internet.

Community Environment: Southern Connecticut's major city, New Haven is in many respects a college town. The average temperature is 50.7 degrees. Buses, railroads, and airlines serve the area. New Haven is engaged in one of the most successful urban renewal projects in the country, restoring and rebuilding housing, community facilities and commercial redevelopment. Points of interest are the museums and libraries. New Haven also has the usual civic organizations, hospitals, shopping centers, hotels and motels. Employment is available. The recreational facilities include theaters, swimming areas, tennis courts, archery ranges, indoor swimming pool, bowling alleys, riding stables, roller skating rinks, municipal golf course and many parks. Important manufacturing establishments are located here.

■ DELAWARE COLLEGE OF ART AND DESIGN

600 N Market St.
Wilmington, DE 19801
Tel: (302)622-8000
Fax: (302)622-8870
E-mail: agullo@dcad.edu
Web Site: www.dcad.edu/

Description: Independent, 2-year, coed. Administratively affiliated with Corcoran College of Art and Design. Awards transfer associate degrees. Founded 1997. Setting: 1-acre urban campus. Endowment: $65,295. Educational spending for the previous fiscal year: $4884 per student. Total enrollment: 210. Faculty: 27 (7 full-time, 20 part-time). Student-undergrad faculty ratio is 8:1. 322 applied, 58% were admitted. Full-time: 192 students, 52% women, 48% men. Part-time: 18 students, 78% women, 22% men. Students come from 9 states and territories, 45% from out-of-state. 19% 25 or older, 50% live on campus, 10% transferred in. Retention: 54% of full-time freshmen returned the following year. Core. Calendar: semesters. Academic remediation for entering students, services for LD students, advanced placement, double major, summer session for credit, part-time degree program, adult/continuing education programs. Off campus study at regional galleries and museums. Study abroad program.

Entrance Requirements: Options: electronic application, deferred admission. Required: essay, high school transcript, minimum 2.0 high school GPA, interview, portfolio. Entrance: moderately difficult. Application deadline: Rolling. Notification: continuous until 8/15.

Collegiate Environment: Orientation program. Information Resource Center plus 1 other with 8,000 books, 76 serials, 500 audiovisual materials, and an OPAC. Operations spending for the previous fiscal year: $33,247. 68 computers available on campus for general student use. A campuswide network can be accessed from student residence rooms and from off campus. Students can access the following: student Web space. Staffed computer lab on campus.

■ DELAWARE STATE UNIVERSITY

1200 N DuPont Hwy.
Dover, DE 19901-2277
Tel: (302)857-6290; Free: 800-845-2544
Fax: (302)857-6352
E-mail: ehill@desu.edu
Web Site: www.desu.edu/

Description: State-supported, university, coed. Part of Delaware Higher Education Commission. Awards bachelor's, master's, and doctoral degrees. Founded 1891. Setting: 400-acre small town campus. Total enrollment: 4,178. Faculty: 357 (211 full-time, 146 part-time). Student-undergrad faculty ratio is 15:1. 9,221 applied, 43% were admitted. 7% from top 10% of their high school class, 28% from top quarter, 67% from top half. Full-time: 3,467 students, 63% women, 37% men. Part-time: 277 students, 56% women, 44% men. Students come from 31 states and territories, 22 other countries, 49% from out-of-state. 0.2% American Indian or Alaska Native, non-Hispanic/Latino; 5% Hispanic/Latino; 73% African American, non-Hispanic/Latino; 3% Asian, non-Hispanic/Latino; 0.2% Native Hawaiian or other Pacific Islander, non-Hispanic/Latino; 2% international. 8% 25 or older, 64% live on campus, 6% transferred in. Retention: 71% of full-time freshmen returned the following year. Academic areas with the most degrees conferred: business/marketing; psychology; communication/journalism. Core. Calendar: semesters. Academic remediation for entering students,

ESL program, services for LD students, advanced placement, accelerated degree program, honors program, distance learning, double major, summer session for credit, part-time degree program, adult/continuing education programs, co-op programs and internships, graduate courses open to undergrads. Off campus study at University of Delaware. Study abroad program. ROTC: Army, Air Force (c).

Entrance Requirements: Options: electronic application, early admission. Required: high school transcript, minimum 2 high school GPA, SAT or ACT. Entrance: moderately difficult. Preference given to state residents. Transfer credits accepted: Yes.

Costs Per Year: Application fee: $35. State resident tuition: $6481 full-time. Nonresident tuition: $13,742 full-time. Full-time tuition varies according to course load. College room and board: $9386. College room only: $6114. Room and board charges vary according to board plan and housing facility.

Collegiate Environment: Orientation program. Drama-theater group, choral group, marching band, student-run newspaper, radio station. Social organizations: 67 open to all; national fraternities, national sororities; 5% of eligible men and 15% of eligible women are members. Most popular organizations: SGA, NPHC, Women's Senate, RHA, Men's Council. Major annual events: Welcome Week, Commencement, Homecoming Week. Student services: health clinic, personal-psychological counseling, women's center. Campus security: 24-hour emergency response devices and patrols, student patrols, late night transport-escort service, controlled dormitory access. William C. Jason Library plus 1 other with 190,613 books, 120,899 microform titles, 74,881 serials, 5,104 audiovisual materials, an OPAC, and a Web page. 641 computers available on campus for general student use. Computer purchase/lease plans available. A campuswide network can be accessed from student residence rooms and from off campus. Students can access the following: online class registration. Staffed computer lab on campus provides training in use of software.

Community Environment: Dover, the capital of Delaware, is 75 miles from Philadelphia, 85 miles from Baltimore, 90 miles from Washington, DC, and 160 miles from New York City. Railway and bus are available in the area. Dover is an agricultural section noted for fruit, produce, grains and poultry. Many fine old colonial homes steeped in the traditions of the activity of the old town are found in the area."The Green" is the center of activity of the old town and still the hub from which radiate many of the political and government activities of both the city and the state. Located 10 miles south of"The Green" is Barratt's Chapel, often called the"Cradle of Methodism in America." Each year on Dover Days, the first Saturday and Sunday in May, many historic homes are open to the public for a small fee. Dover is the home of the largest air freight terminal in the world. General Food's multimillion-dollar Jell-O plant and Playtex Corporation are also located here.

■ DELAWARE TECHNICAL & COMMUNITY COLLEGE, JACK F. OWENS CAMPUS

PO Box 610
Georgetown, DE 19947
Tel: (302)856-5400
Fax: (302)856-9461
Web Site: www.dtcc.edu/

Description: State-supported, 2-year, coed. Part of Delaware Technical and Community College System. Awards certificates, diplomas, transfer associate, and terminal associate degrees. Founded 1967. Setting: small town campus. Total enrollment: 4,611. 1,627 applied, 100% were admitted. Full-time: 1,979 students, 57% women, 43% men. Part-time: 2,632 students,

68% women, 32% men. 0.3% American Indian or Alaska Native, non-Hispanic/Latino; 7% Hispanic/Latino; 17% African American, non-Hispanic/Latino; 2% Asian, non-Hispanic/Latino; 0.1% Native Hawaiian or other Pacific Islander, non-Hispanic/Latino; 2% international. 57% 25 or older, 4% transferred in. Retention: 59% of full-time freshmen returned the following year. Calendar: semesters. Part-time degree program.

Entrance Requirements: Open admission except for nursing, allied health, and energy programs. Options: electronic application, early admission, deferred admission. Required for some: high school transcript. Entrance: noncompetitive. Application deadline: Rolling. Notification: continuous. Preference given to state residents.

Collegiate Environment: Orientation program. Campus security: 24-hour emergency response devices, late night transport-escort service. College housing not available.

■ **DELAWARE TECHNICAL & COMMUNITY COLLEGE, STANTON/ WILMINGTON CAMPUS**

400 Stanton-Christiana Rd.
Newark, DE 19713
Tel: (302)454-3900
Fax: (302)577-2548
Web Site: www.dtcc.edu/
Description: State-supported, 2-year, coed. Part of Delaware Technical and Community College System. Awards certificates, diplomas, transfer associate, and terminal associate degrees. Founded 1968. Setting: urban campus. Total enrollment: 7,216. 2,806 applied, 100% were admitted. Full-time: 2,600 students, 54% women, 46% men. Part-time: 4,616 students, 63% women, 37% men. 0.2% American Indian or Alaska Native, non-Hispanic/Latino; 9% Hispanic/Latino; 25% African American, non-Hispanic/Latino; 4% Asian, non-Hispanic/Latino; 0.2% Native Hawaiian or other Pacific Islander, non-Hispanic/Latino; 2% international. 35% 25 or older, 4% transferred in. Retention: 62% of full-time freshmen returned the following year. Calendar: semesters. Part-time degree program. ROTC: Air Force (c).
Entrance Requirements: Open admission Selective admission for Allied Health, Nursing and Energy programs. Options: electronic application, early admission, deferred admission. Required for some: high school transcript. Entrance: noncompetitive. Application deadline: Rolling. Notification: continuous. Transfer credits accepted: Yes.
Collegiate Environment: Orientation program. Campus security: 24-hour emergency response devices, late night transport-escort service. College housing not available.

■ **DELAWARE TECHNICAL & COMMUNITY COLLEGE, TERRY CAMPUS**

100 Campus Dr.
Dover, DE 19901
Tel: (302)857-1000
Fax: (302)857-1296
E-mail: terry-info@dtcc.edu
Web Site: www.dtcc.edu/
Description: State-supported, 2-year, coed. Part of Delaware Technical and Community College System. Awards certificates, diplomas, transfer associate, and terminal associate degrees. Founded 1972. Setting: small town campus. Total enrollment: 3,107. 1,235 applied, 100% were admitted. Full-time: 1,436 students, 60% women, 40% men. Part-time: 1,671 students, 67% women, 33% men. 0.3% American Indian or Alaska Native, non-Hispanic/Latino; 5% Hispanic/Latino; 28% African American, non-Hispanic/Latino; 3% Asian, non-Hispanic/Latino; 0.2% Native Hawaiian or other Pacific Islander, non-Hispanic/Latino; 1% international. 39% 25 or older, 5% transferred in. Retention: 56% of full-time freshmen returned the following year. Calendar: semesters. Part-time degree program. ROTC: Air Force (c).
Entrance Requirements: Open admission except for allied health, nursing, and energy. Options: electronic application, early admission, deferred admission. Required for some: high school transcript. Entrance: noncompetitive. Application deadline: Rolling. Notification: continuous. Preference given to state residents.
Collegiate Environment: Orientation program. Campus security: 24-hour emergency response devices, late night transport-escort service. College housing not available.
Community Environment: See Delaware State University.

■ **GOLDEY-BEACOM COLLEGE**

4701 Limestone Rd.
Wilmington, DE 19808-1999

Tel: (302)998-8814; Free: 800-833-4877
Fax: (302)996-5408
E-mail: admissions@gbc.edu
Web Site: www.gbc.edu/
Description: Independent, comprehensive, coed. Awards associate, bachelor's, and master's degrees. Founded 1886. Setting: 24-acre suburban campus with easy access to Philadelphia. Endowment: $47.4 million. Total enrollment: 1,352. Faculty: 56 (18 full-time, 38 part-time). Student-undergrad faculty ratio is 26:1. Full-time: 462 students, 55% women, 45% men. Part-time: 163 students, 57% women, 43% men. Students come from 12 states and territories, 24 other countries, 33% from out-of-state. 0.2% American Indian or Alaska Native, non-Hispanic/Latino; 8% Hispanic/Latino; 24% African American, non-Hispanic/Latino; 5% Asian, non-Hispanic/Latino; 0% Native Hawaiian or other Pacific Islander, non-Hispanic/Latino; 9% international. 29% 25 or older, 32% live on campus, 9% transferred in. Retention: 85% of full-time freshmen returned the following year. Academic areas with the most degrees conferred: business/marketing; social sciences; psychology. Core. Calendar: semesters. Academic remediation for entering students, advanced placement, accelerated degree program, honors program, double major, summer session for credit, part-time degree program, co-op programs and internships, graduate courses open to undergrads.
Entrance Requirements: Required: high school transcript, minimum 2 high school GPA, SAT or ACT. Required for some: 1 recommendation, interview.
Costs Per Year: Tuition: $21,840 full-time, $728 per credit part-time. Mandatory fees: $300 full-time, $10 per credit part-time. Full-time tuition and fees vary according to course load. Part-time tuition and fees vary according to course load. College room only: $5353. Room charges vary according to housing facility.
Collegiate Environment: Orientation program. Student-run newspaper. Social organizations: 14 open to all. Most popular organizations: Student Athletic Advisory Committee, Alpha Chi, Resident Student Association, Student Ambassadors, International Student Association. Major annual events: Drive In Movie Night, Homecoming, New York City Trip. Campus security: 24-hour emergency response devices and patrols, student patrols, late night transport-escort service. 271 college housing spaces available; 199 were occupied in 2012-13. No special consideration for freshman housing applicants. Option: coed housing available. J. Wilbur Hirons Library with 167,656 books, 17,434 serials, 38,854 audiovisual materials, and a Web page. Operations spending for the previous fiscal year: $282,032. 159 computers available on campus for general student use. A campuswide network can be accessed from student residence rooms and from off campus. Students can access the following: campus Web. Staffed computer lab on campus provides training in use of computers, software, and the Internet.
Community Environment: Known as the"Chemical Capital of the World," Wilmington (pop. 72,786) lies on the west bank of the Delaware River in northern Delaware. Railroads and airlines serve the area. Almost 300 industries are located in the area. A great variety of items are shipped from Wilmington, including such products as automobiles, airplanes, steel, clothing, hosiery, machinery, paper and paper products. Points of interest include Holy Trinity Church (Old Swedes), Wilmington Institute, Free Library, Brandywine Park, Fort Christian State Park, Delaware Art Center, Hagley Museum, Old Town Hall, and the Henry Francis du Pont Winterthur Museum. Nearby are Longwood Gardens and the Brandywine Museum.

■ **STRAYER UNIVERSITY - CHRISTIANA CAMPUS**

240 Continental Dr.
Ste. 108
Newark, DE 19713
Tel: (302)292-6100
Fax: (302)292-6130
Web Site: www.strayer.edu/campus/christiana
Description: Proprietary, comprehensive, coed. Awards associate, bachelor's, and master's degrees.

■ **UNIVERSITY OF DELAWARE**

Newark, DE 19716
Tel: (302)831-2000
Fax: (302)831-6905
E-mail: admissions@udel.edu
Web Site: www.udel.edu/
Description: State-related, university, coed. Awards associate, bachelor's, master's, and doctoral degrees. Founded 1743. Setting: 1,000-acre small

town campus with easy access to Philadelphia, Baltimore. Total enrollment: 21,081. Faculty: 1,484 (1,190 full-time, 294 part-time). Student-undergrad faculty ratio is 13:1. 26,225 applied, 57% were admitted. 40% from top 10% of their high school class, 76% from top quarter, 97% from top half. Full-time: 15,899 students, 58% women, 42% men. Part-time: 1,528 students, 54% women, 46% men. 58% from out-of-state. 0.1% American Indian or Alaska Native, non-Hispanic/Latino; 6% Hispanic/Latino; 5% African American, non-Hispanic/Latino; 4% Asian, non-Hispanic/Latino; 0.1% Native Hawaiian or other Pacific Islander, non-Hispanic/Latino; 4% international. 3% 25 or older, 44% live on campus, 3% transferred in. Retention: 92% of full-time freshmen returned the following year. Academic areas with the most degrees conferred: business/marketing; social sciences; health professions and related sciences. Core. Calendar: 4-1-4. Academic remediation for entering students, ESL program, services for LD students, advanced placement, accelerated degree program, self-designed majors, honors program, independent study, distance learning, double major, summer session for credit, part-time degree program, adult/continuing education programs, internships, graduate courses open to undergrads. Off campus study. Study abroad program. ROTC: Army, Air Force.

Entrance Requirements: Options: electronic application, early admission, deferred admission, international baccalaureate accepted. Required: essay, high school transcript, 1 recommendation, SAT or ACT. Recommended: SAT Subject Tests. Required for some: SAT Subject Tests. Entrance: moderately difficult. Application deadline: 1/15. Notification: 3/15. Preference given to state residents. SAT Reasoning Test deadline: 1/15. SAT Subject Test deadline: 1/15. Applicants placed on waiting list: 2,502. Wait-listed applicants offered admission: 640.

Costs Per Year: Application fee: $75. State resident tuition: $10,150 full-time, $423 per credit hour part-time. Nonresident tuition: $27,240 full-time, $1135 per credit hour part-time. Mandatory fees: $1532 full-time. College room and board: $10,758. College room only: $6516. Room and board charges vary according to board plan, housing facility, and student level.

Collegiate Environment: Orientation program. Drama-theater group, choral group, marching band, student-run newspaper, radio station. Social organizations: 350 open to all; national fraternities, national sororities, local fraternities. Student services: health clinic, personal-psychological counseling, women's center. Campus security: 24-hour emergency response devices and patrols, student patrols, late night transport-escort service, controlled dormitory access. 7,222 college housing spaces available; 7,187 were occupied in 2012-13. Freshmen guaranteed college housing. On-campus residence required in freshman year. Options: coed, women-only housing available. Hugh Morris Library plus 3 others with 2.8 million books, 3.1 million microform titles, 42,000 serials, an OPAC, and a Web page.

Community Environment: The campus is located in Newark, Delaware, a city of 24,000, which is situated halfway between Philadelphia and Baltimore on I-95. The location is ideal for students who want the advantages of a small community and easy access to the educational, cultural, and social opportunities offered in nearby metropolitan area.

■ **WESLEY COLLEGE**
120 N State St.
Dover, DE 19901-3875
Tel: (302)736-2300; Free: 800-937-5398
Fax: (302)736-2301
E-mail: christopher.jester@wesley.edu
Web Site: www.wesley.edu/
Description: Independent United Methodist, comprehensive, coed. Awards associate, bachelor's, and master's degrees and post-master's certificates. Founded 1873. Setting: 40-acre small town campus. Total enrollment: 1,770. Faculty: 170 (70 full-time, 100 part-time). 2,933 applied, 63% were admitted. Full-time: 1,345 students, 51% women, 49% men. Part-time: 316 students, 44% women, 56% men. Students come from 28 states and territories, 4 other countries, 57% from out-of-state. 1% American Indian or Alaska Native, non-Hispanic/Latino; 6% Hispanic/Latino; 37% African American, non-Hispanic/Latino; 1% Asian, non-Hispanic/Latino; 0% Native Hawaiian or other Pacific Islander, non-Hispanic/Latino; 0% international. 13% 25 or older, 66% live on campus, 2% transferred in. Retention: 46% of full-time freshmen returned the following year. Academic areas with the most degrees conferred: business/marketing; health professions and related sciences; education. Core. Calendar: semesters. Academic remediation for entering students, ESL program, services for LD students, advanced placement, freshman honors college, independent study, summer session for credit,

part-time degree program, external degree program, adult/continuing education programs, co-op programs and internships, graduate courses open to undergrads. Off campus study. Study abroad program. ROTC: Army (c).

Entrance Requirements: Option: electronic application. Required: essay, high school transcript, minimum 2.2 high school GPA, 1 recommendation, SAT. Recommended: interview. Required for some: special test for nursing. Entrance: moderately difficult. Application deadline: Rolling.

Costs Per Year: Application fee: $25. Comprehensive fee: $32,830 includes full-time tuition ($21,512), mandatory fees ($880), and college room and board ($10,438). College room only: $5096. Full-time tuition and fees vary according to class time. Room and board charges vary according to board plan and housing facility.

Collegiate Environment: Orientation program. Drama-theater group, choral group, student-run newspaper. Social organizations: 20 open to all; national fraternities, national sororities, local fraternities, local sororities; 3% of eligible men and 3% of eligible women are members. Most popular organizations: Student Activity Board, Student Government Association, National Coeducation Community Service Organization. Major annual events: Homecoming, Families' Day, reunion. Student services: health clinic, personal-psychological counseling. Campus security: 24-hour patrols, controlled dormitory access. 846 college housing spaces available; all were occupied in 2012-13. Freshmen guaranteed college housing. On-campus residence required in freshman year. Options: coed, men-only, women-only housing available. Robert H. Parker Library with 104,636 books, 178,073 microform titles, 252 serials, 946 audiovisual materials, an OPAC, and a Web page. 225 computers available on campus for general student use. Computer purchase/lease plans available. A campuswide network can be accessed from student residence rooms and from off campus. Students can access the following: online class registration. Staffed computer lab on campus provides training in use of computers, software, and the Internet.

■ **WILMINGTON UNIVERSITY**
320 N DuPont Hwy.
New Castle, DE 19720-6491
Tel: (302)328-9401; Free: 877-967-5464
Fax: (302)328-5902
E-mail: undergradadmissions@wilmu.edu
Web Site: www.wilmu.edu/
Description: Independent, comprehensive, coed. Awards associate, bachelor's, master's, and doctoral degrees and post-master's certificates. Founded 1967. Setting: 17-acre suburban campus with easy access to Philadelphia. Endowment: $15.5 million. Educational spending for the previous fiscal year: $3487 per student. Total enrollment: 11,795. Faculty: 1,116 (92 full-time, 1,024 part-time). Student-undergrad faculty ratio is 14:1. 1,466 applied, 97% were admitted. Full-time: 5,205 students, 61% women, 39% men. Part-time: 3,033 students, 71% women, 29% men. Students come from 41 states and territories, 25 other countries, 23% from out-of-state. 1% American Indian or Alaska Native, non-Hispanic/Latino; 3% Hispanic/Latino; 22% African American, non-Hispanic/Latino; 2% Asian, non-Hispanic/Latino; 0.1% Native Hawaiian or other Pacific Islander, non-Hispanic/Latino. 57% 25 or older, 19% transferred in. Retention: 64% of full-time freshmen returned the following year. Academic areas with the most degrees conferred: business/marketing; liberal arts/general studies; education. Core. Calendar: semesters. Academic remediation for entering students, accelerated degree program, independent study, distance learning, double major, summer session for credit, part-time degree program, external degree program, adult/continuing education programs, co-op programs and internships. ROTC: Army (c), Air Force (c).

Entrance Requirements: Open admission. Options: early admission, deferred admission. Required: high school transcript. Recommended: interview. Entrance: noncompetitive. Application deadline: Rolling. Notification: continuous. Transfer credits accepted: Yes.

Collegiate Environment: Orientation program. Most popular organizations: Student Government Association, Green Team, Photography Club, WU Student United Way, Wildcat Cheerleaders. Major annual event: Commencement. Campus security: 24-hour emergency response devices and patrols, late night transport-escort service. College housing not available. Robert C. and Dorothy M. Peoples Library plus 1 other with 98,713 books, 99,418 microform titles, 425 serials, and an OPAC. 600 computers available on campus for general student use. A campuswide network can be accessed. Students can access the following: online class registration. Staffed computer lab on campus.

District of Columbia

■ **AMERICAN UNIVERSITY**
4400 Massachusetts Ave., NW
Washington, DC 20016-8001
Tel: (202)885-1000
Fax: (202)885-6014
E-mail: admissions@american.edu
Web Site: www.american.edu/
Description: Independent Methodist, university, coed. Awards associate, bachelor's, master's, and doctoral degrees. Founded 1893. Setting: 84-acre suburban campus with easy access to Washington, DC. Endowment: $466 million. Research spending for the previous fiscal year: $39.3 million. Educational spending for the previous fiscal year: $21,277 per student. Total enrollment: 12,904. Faculty: 1,327 (733 full-time, 594 part-time). Student-undergrad faculty ratio is 12:1. 17,039 applied, 44% were admitted. 45% from top 10% of their high school class, 80% from top quarter, 97% from top half. Full-time: 6,970 students, 60% women, 40% men. Part-time: 329 students, 57% women, 43% men. Students come from 55 states and territories, 89 other countries, 86% from out-of-district. 0.2% American Indian or Alaska Native, non-Hispanic/Latino; 9% Hispanic/Latino; 6% African American, non-Hispanic/Latino; 6% Asian, non-Hispanic/Latino; 0.1% Native Hawaiian or other Pacific Islander, non-Hispanic/Latino; 7% international. 2% 25 or older, 3% transferred in. Retention: 90% of full-time freshmen returned the following year. Academic areas with the most degrees conferred: social sciences; business/marketing; communication/journalism. Core. Calendar: semesters. ESL program, services for LD students, advanced placement, accelerated degree program, self-designed majors, honors program, independent study, distance learning, double major, summer session for credit, part-time degree program, co-op programs and internships, graduate courses open to undergrads. Off campus study. Study abroad program. ROTC: Army (c), Air Force (c).
Entrance Requirements: Options: electronic application, early decision, deferred admission, international baccalaureate accepted. Required: essay, high school transcript, SAT or ACT. Recommended: 2 recommendations. Required for some: If home schooled: A description of why home-schooling was chosen for the applicant and the home-school philosophy and a detailed description of curriculum. At least two SAT Subject Tests are recommended but not required. An additional letter of recommendation is recommended but not required. Entrance: very difficult. Application deadlines: 1/15, 11/15 for early decision. Notification: 4/1, 12/31 for early decision. SAT Reasoning Test deadline: 1/15. SAT Subject Test deadline: 6/1. Transfer credits accepted: Yes. Applicants placed on waiting list: 1,379. Wait-listed applicants offered admission: 0. Early decision applicants: 582. Early decision applicants admitted: 484.
Costs Per Year: Application fee: $65. Comprehensive fee: $53,419 includes full-time tuition ($38,982), mandatory fees ($517), and college room and board ($13,920). College room only: $9290. Full-time tuition and fees vary according to location. Room and board charges vary according to board plan, housing facility, and location. Part-time tuition: $1299 per credit hour. Part-time mandatory fees: $170 per term. Part-time tuition and fees vary according to course load and location.
Collegiate Environment: Orientation program. Drama-theater group, choral group, student-run newspaper, radio station. Social organizations: 200 open to all; national fraternities, national sororities, student clubs and intramural athletics. Most popular organizations: Kennedy Political Union, Habitat for Humanity, student government, Amnesty International, Ethnic and religious organizations. Major annual events: Kennedy Political Union award-wining

speaker series, Founder's Day Ball, Campus Beautification Day. Student services: health clinic, personal-psychological counseling, women's center. Campus security: 24-hour emergency response devices and patrols, late night transport-escort service, controlled dormitory access, e-mail and text emergency notification system. 3,800 college housing spaces available. Freshmen guaranteed college housing. Option: coed housing available. Bender Library plus 1 other with 979,518 books, 45,000 serials, 55,245 audiovisual materials, an OPAC, and a Web page. 650 computers available on campus for general student use. A campuswide network can be accessed from student residence rooms and from off campus. Students can access the following: online class registration. Staffed computer lab on campus (open 24 hours a day) provides training in use of computers, software, and the Internet.
Community Environment: Washington, D.C., is located on the Potomac River between Maryland and Virginia. It is a beautiful and historic city of impressive buildings and residential neighborhoods, with a vibrant, diverse international character. All major forms of transportation are available: the Metro bus and subway system, historic Union Railroad Station, and three major airports serve Washington. The National Zoo, Rock Creek Park, and the C&O Canal are some of the city's finest recreation areas. Shopping facilities are excellent. Points of interest for students include government sites such as the U.S. Capitol, Senate and House office buildings, U.S. Treasury, Supreme Court, Federal Bureau of Investigation, and the White House; cultural institutions such as the Folger Shakespeare Library, Library of Congress, Smithsonian Institute, U.S. Holocaust Memorial Museum, Frederick Douglass Museum, National Gallery of Art, National Archives, Islamic Center, Washington Cathedral, and John F. Kennedy Center for the Performing Arts; scientific institutions such as the National Bureau of Standards, Naval Observatory, and the nearby National Institutes of Health; and international organizations such as the World Bank, Pan American Union, and the embassies and legations of many nations.

■ **THE CATHOLIC UNIVERSITY OF AMERICA**
Cardinal Station
Washington, DC 20064
Tel: (202)319-5000; Free: 800-673-2772
Fax: (202)319-6533
E-mail: cua-admissions@cua.edu
Web Site: www.cua.edu/
Description: Independent, university, coed, affiliated with Roman Catholic Church. Awards associate, bachelor's, master's, and doctoral degrees and post-master's certificates. Founded 1887. Setting: 184-acre urban campus. Total enrollment: 6,838. Faculty: 814 (398 full-time, 416 part-time). Student-undergrad faculty ratio is 9:1. 6,361 applied, 63% were admitted. Full-time: 3,422 students; 54% women, 46% men. Part-time: 272 students, 61% women, 39% men. Students come from 48 states and territories, 41 other countries, 96% from out-of-district. 0.2% American Indian or Alaska Native, non-Hispanic/Latino; 9% Hispanic/Latino; 5% African American, non-Hispanic/Latino; 3% Asian, non-Hispanic/Latino; 0.2% Native Hawaiian or other Pacific Islander, non-Hispanic/Latino; 4% international. 7% 25 or older, 59% live on campus, 2% transferred in. Retention: 84% of full-time freshmen returned the following year. Academic areas with the most degrees conferred: social sciences; architecture; business/marketing. Core. Calendar: semesters. ESL program, services for LD students, advanced placement, accelerated degree program, honors program, independent study, distance learning, double major, summer session for credit, part-time

The College Blue Book, 41st Edition   185 degree program, adult/continuing education programs, co-op programs and internships, graduate courses open to undergrads. Off campus study at members of the Consortium of Universities of the Washington Metropolitan Area. Study abroad program. ROTC: Army (c), Naval (c), Air Force (c).

Entrance Requirements: Options: electronic application, early action, deferred admission, international baccalaureate accepted. Required: essay, high school transcript, 1 recommendation, SAT or ACT. Recommended: minimum 3 high school GPA, SAT Subject Tests. Required for some: interview. Entrance: moderately difficult. Application deadlines: 2/15, 11/15 for early action. Notification: 3/15, 12/15 for early action. SAT Reasoning Test deadline: 2/15. SAT Subject Test deadline: 2/15. Transfer credits accepted: Yes.

Costs Per Year: Application fee: $55. One-time mandatory fee: $425. Comprehensive fee: $51,094 includes full-time tuition ($36,320), mandatory fees ($500), and college room and board ($14,274). College room only: $8876. Full-time tuition and fees vary according to program. Room and board charges vary according to board plan and housing facility. Part-time tuition: $1420 per credit hour. Part-time mandatory fees: $290 per year. Part-time tuition and fees vary according to course load and program.

Collegiate Environment: Orientation program. Drama-theater group, choral group, student-run newspaper, radio station. Social organizations: 89 open to all; national fraternities, national sororities; 1% of eligible men and 1% of eligible women are members. Most popular organizations: Student Nursing Association, College Republicans, CU Film Society, Alpha Phi Omega, Program Board. Major annual events: Luaupalooza, Fall Fiesta, Late night breakfast. Student services: legal services, health clinic, personal-psychological counseling. Campus security: 24-hour emergency response devices and patrols, late night transport-escort service, controlled dormitory access, controlled access of academic buildings. 2,187 college housing spaces available; 2,160 were occupied in 2012-13. Freshmen guaranteed college housing. On-campus residence required through sophomore year. Options: coed, men-only, women-only housing available. Mullen Library plus 7 others with 1.7 million books, 2.4 million microform titles, 8,418 serials, 42,911 audiovisual materials, an OPAC, and a Web page. 500 computers available on campus for general student use. Computer purchase/lease plans available. A campuswide network can be accessed from student residence rooms and from off campus. Students can access the following: online class registration, Internet2, video streaming, online voting, pedagogical software. Staffed computer lab on campus (open 24 hours a day) provides training in use of computers, software, and the Internet.

Community Environment: See American University.

■ CORCORAN COLLEGE OF ART AND DESIGN

500 17th St. NW
Washington, DC 20006-4804
Tel: (202)639-1800; Free: 888-CORCORAN
E-mail: admissions@corcoran.org
Web Site: www.corcoran.edu/

Description: Independent, comprehensive, coed. Awards associate, bachelor's, and master's degrees. Founded 1890. Setting: 7-acre urban campus with easy access to Washington, DC. Endowment: $19.2 million. Educational spending for the previous fiscal year: $14,365 per student. Total enrollment: 640. Faculty: 214 (26 full-time, 188 part-time). Student-undergrad faculty ratio is 10:1. 609 applied, 31% were admitted. 0% from top 10% of their high school class, 0% from top quarter, 0% from top half. Full-time: 268 students, 63% women, 37% men. Part-time: 118 students, 81% women, 19% men. Students come from 21 states and territories, 32 other countries, 79% from out-of-district. 1% American Indian or Alaska Native, non-Hispanic/Latino; 10% Hispanic/Latino; 10% African American, non-Hispanic/Latino; 8% Asian, non-Hispanic/Latino; 1% Native Hawaiian or other Pacific Islander, non-Hispanic/Latino; 6% international. 40% 25 or older, 20% live on campus, 8% transferred in. Retention: 87% of full-time freshmen returned the following year. Academic areas with the most degrees conferred: visual and performing arts; communication/journalism. Core. Calendar: semesters. Academic remediation for entering students, services for LD students, advanced placement, independent study, summer session for credit, part-time degree program, adult/continuing education programs, internships, graduate courses open to undergrads. Off campus study at Association of Independent Colleges of Art and Design, Consortium of Universities of the Washington Metropolitan Area. Study abroad program.

Entrance Requirements: Options: electronic application, early admission, early action, deferred admission, international baccalaureate accepted. Required: high school transcript, minimum 2.5 high school GPA, portfolio. Recommended: essay, minimum 3 high school GPA, 1 recommendation,

interview, SAT or ACT. Required for some: essay, 1 recommendation, interview. Entrance: moderately difficult. Application deadlines: Rolling, 11/15 for early action. Notification: continuous until 3/15, 12/15 for early action. Transfer credits accepted: Yes. Early action applicants: 225. Early action applicants admitted: 34.

Costs Per Year: Application fee: $45. Comprehensive fee: $44,030 includes full-time tuition ($30,930), mandatory fees ($200), and college room and board ($12,900). College room only: $10,400.

Collegiate Environment: Orientation program. Most popular organizations: Student Activities Programming Board, American Society of Interior Designers, National Art Education Association, Corcoran Student Council, Society of Environmental Designers. Major annual events: Spirit Week, Off the Wall Art Sale, Cinco de Mayo party. Student services: personal-psychological counseling. Campus security: 24-hour emergency response devices and patrols, controlled dormitory access, ID check at all entrances. 89 college housing spaces available; 63 were occupied in 2012-13. Freshmen given priority for college housing. Option: coed housing available. Corcoran Library with 35,716 books, 17,623 serials, 1,682 audiovisual materials, an OPAC, and a Web page. Operations spending for the previous fiscal year: $395,075. 154 computers available on campus for general student use. Staffed computer lab on campus provides training in use of computers and software.

■ GALLAUDET UNIVERSITY

800 Florida Ave., NE
Washington, DC 20002-3625
Tel: (202)651-5000; Free: 800-995-0550
Fax: (202)651-5774
E-mail: charity.reedy-hines@gallaudet.edu
Web Site: www.gallaudet.edu/

Description: Independent, university, coed. Awards bachelor's, master's, and doctoral degrees and post-master's certificates (undergraduate programs are open primarily to the students with hearing-impairments). Founded 1864. Setting: 99-acre urban campus. Total enrollment: 1,546. Faculty: 185 (all full-time). Student-undergrad faculty ratio is 8:1. 413 applied, 69% were admitted. Full-time: 1,029 students, 53% women, 47% men. Part-time: 89 students, 60% women, 40% men. Students come from 47 states and territories, 21 other countries, 96% from out-of-district. 0.3% American Indian or Alaska Native, non-Hispanic/Latino; 8% Hispanic/Latino; 11% African American, non-Hispanic/Latino; 4% Asian, non-Hispanic/Latino; 0.1% Native Hawaiian or other Pacific Islander, non-Hispanic/Latino; 5% international. 25% 25 or older, 9% transferred in. Retention: 70% of full-time freshmen returned the following year. Academic areas with the most degrees conferred: communication/journalism; business/marketing; foreign languages and literature. Core. Calendar: semesters. Academic remediation for entering students, ESL program, services for LD students, advanced placement, accelerated degree program, self-designed majors, honors program, independent study, distance learning, double major, summer session for credit, part-time degree program, adult/continuing education programs, internships, graduate courses open to undergrads. Off campus study at Consortium of Universities of the Washington Metropolitan Area. Study abroad program.

Entrance Requirements: Options: electronic application, deferred admission. Required: essay, high school transcript, 2 recommendations, audiogram, SAT or ACT. Recommended: ACT. Required for some: interview. Entrance: moderately difficult. Application deadline: Rolling. Notification: continuous. Transfer credits accepted: Yes.

Costs Per Year: Application fee: $50. Comprehensive fee: $23,596 includes full-time tuition ($12,430), mandatory fees ($376), and college room and board ($10,790). College room only: $5960. Full-time tuition and fees vary according to degree level. Room and board charges vary according to board plan. Part-time tuition: $621.50 per credit hour. Part-time tuition varies according to degree level.

Collegiate Environment: Orientation program. Drama-theater group, student-run newspaper. Social organizations: 30 open to all; national fraternities, national sororities, local fraternities, local sororities; 22% of eligible men and 21% of eligible women are members. Most popular organizations: Student Body Government, Delta Epsilon, Rainbow Society, Black Deaf Student Union. Major annual events: Homecoming, RIT/Gallaudet Weekend. Student services: health clinic, personal-psychological counseling. Campus security: 24-hour emergency response devices and patrols, late night transport-escort service, controlled dormitory access. 990 college housing spaces available; 815 were occupied in 2012-13. Option:

coed housing available. Merrill Learning Center with 260,000 books, 623,982 microform titles, 2,000 serials, 8,000 audiovisual materials, an OPAC, and a Web page.

Community Environment: See American University.

■ THE GEORGE WASHINGTON UNIVERSITY

2121 I St., NW
Washington, DC 20052
Tel: (202)994-1000
E-mail: gwadm@gwis2.circ.gwu.edu
Web Site: www.gwu.edu/

Description: Independent, university, coed. Awards associate, bachelor's, master's, and doctoral degrees and post-master's certificates. Founded 1821. Setting: 36-acre urban campus. Total enrollment: 25,653. 21,756 applied, 33% were admitted. 58% from top 10% of their high school class, 86% from top quarter, 99% from top half. Full-time: 9,758 students, 56% women, 44% men. Part-time: 706 students, 47% women, 53% men. Students come from 54 states and territories, 87 other countries, 98% from out-of-district. 0.3% American Indian or Alaska Native, non-Hispanic/Latino; 7% Hispanic/Latino; 7% African American, non-Hispanic/Latino; 10% Asian, non-Hispanic/Latino; 0.1% Native Hawaiian or other Pacific Islander, non-Hispanic/Latino; 8% international. 6% 25 or older, 67% live on campus, 4% transferred in. Retention: 93% of full-time freshmen returned the following year. Academic areas with the most degrees conferred: social sciences; business/marketing; health professions and related sciences. Core. Calendar: semesters. Services for LD students, advanced placement, accelerated degree program, self-designed majors, honors program, independent study, distance learning, double major, summer session for credit, part-time degree program, adult/continuing education programs, co-op programs and internships, graduate courses open to undergrads. Off campus study at members of the Consortium of Universities of the Washington Metropolitan Area. Study abroad program. ROTC: Army (c), Naval, Air Force (c).

Entrance Requirements: Options: electronic application, early admission, early decision, deferred admission. Required: essay, high school transcript, 2 recommendations, SAT or ACT. Recommended: interview. Entrance: very difficult. Application deadlines: 1/10, 11/10 for early decision plan 1, 1/10 for early decision plan 2. Notification: 4/1, 12/15 for early decision plan 1, 2/1 for early decision plan 2. SAT Reasoning Test deadline: 1/10. SAT Subject Test deadline: 1/10. Applicants placed on waiting list: 2,865. Wait-listed applicants offered admission: 26. Early decision applicants: 2,316. Early decision applicants admitted: 927.

Costs Per Year: Application fee: $75. Comprehensive fee: $58,713 includes full-time tuition ($47,290), mandatory fees ($45), and college room and board ($11,378). Full-time tuition and fees vary according to student level. Room and board charges vary according to housing facility. Part-time tuition: $1,315.25 per credit hour. Part-time mandatory fees: $1.75 per credit hour. Part-time tuition and fees vary according to course load. Tuition guaranteed not to increase for student's term of enrollment.

Collegiate Environment: Orientation program. Drama-theater group, choral group, marching band, student-run newspaper, radio station. Social organizations: national fraternities, national sororities. Most popular organizations: Program Board, Student Association, Residence Hall Association, College Democrats, College Republicans. Major annual events: Homecoming, Welcome Week, Colonial Inauguration. Student services: legal services, health clinic, personal-psychological counseling. Campus security: 24-hour emergency response devices and patrols, late night transport-escort service, controlled dormitory access. 6,966 undergraduates lived in college housing during 2012-13. Freshmen guaranteed college housing. On-campus residence required through sophomore year. Option: coed housing available. Gelman Library with an OPAC and a Web page.

Community Environment: See American University.

■ GEORGETOWN UNIVERSITY

37th and O Sts., NW
Washington, DC 20057
Tel: (202)687-5055
Fax: (202)687-6660
Web Site: www.georgetown.edu/

Description: Independent Roman Catholic (Jesuit), university, coed. Awards bachelor's, master's, and doctoral degrees. Founded 1789. Setting: 110-acre urban campus. Total enrollment: 17,357. Faculty: 1,757 (961 full-time, 796 part-time). Student-undergrad faculty ratio is 11:1. 20,115 applied, 17% were admitted. 92% from top 10% of their high school class, 99% from top quarter, 100% from top half. Full-time: 7,242 students, 56% women, 44% men. Part-

time: 310 students, 54% women, 46% men. Students come from 52 states and territories, 106 other countries, 97% from out-of-district. 0.1% American Indian or Alaska Native, non-Hispanic/Latino; 8% Hispanic/Latino; 6% African American, non-Hispanic/Latino; 9% Asian, non-Hispanic/Latino; 0.1% Native Hawaiian or other Pacific Islander, non-Hispanic/Latino; 11% international. 4% 25 or older, 71% live on campus, 2% transferred in. Retention: 96% of full-time freshmen returned the following year. Academic areas with the most degrees conferred: social sciences; business/marketing; health professions and related sciences. Core. Calendar: semesters. Academic remediation for entering students, ESL program, services for LD students, advanced placement, self-designed majors, honors program, independent study, distance learning, double major, summer session for credit, adult/continuing education programs, internships, graduate courses open to undergrads. Off campus study at members of the Consortium of Universities of the Washington Metropolitan Area. Study abroad program. ROTC: Army, Naval (c), Air Force (c).

Entrance Requirements: Options: electronic application, early action, deferred admission, international baccalaureate accepted. Required: essay, high school transcript, 2 recommendations, interview, SAT or ACT. Recommended: SAT Subject Tests. Entrance: most difficult. Application deadlines: 1/10, 11/1 for early action. Notification: 4/1, 12/15 for early action. SAT Reasoning Test deadline: 1/10. SAT Subject Test deadline: 1/10. Applicants placed on waiting list: 2,217. Wait-listed applicants offered admission: 84.

Costs Per Year: Application fee: $70. Comprehensive fee: $56,382 includes full-time tuition ($42,360), mandatory fees ($710), and college room and board ($13,312). Full-time tuition and fees vary according to course load and program. Room and board charges vary according to board plan and housing facility.

Collegiate Environment: Orientation program. Drama-theater group, choral group, student-run newspaper, radio station. Social organizations: 162 open to all. Major annual events: Homecoming Block Party, GU Day, Student Activities Fair. Student services: health clinic, personal-psychological counseling, women's center. Campus security: 24-hour emergency response devices and patrols, late night transport-escort service, controlled dormitory access, student guards at residence halls and academic facilities. 5,053 college housing spaces available; 4,889 were occupied in 2012-13. Freshmen guaranteed college housing. On-campus residence required through sophomore year. Option: coed housing available. Lauinger Library plus 6 others with an OPAC and a Web page.

Community Environment: See American University.

■ HOWARD UNIVERSITY

2400 Sixth St., NW
Washington, DC 20059-0002
Tel: (202)806-6100; Free: 800-822-6363
E-mail: lsanders-hawkins@howard.edu
Web Site: www.howard.edu/

Description: Independent, university, coed. Awards bachelor's, master's, and doctoral degrees and post-master's certificates. Founded 1867. Setting: 256-acre urban campus. Endowment: $490.6 million. Research spending for the previous fiscal year: $38.7 million. Educational spending for the previous fiscal year: $8676 per student. Total enrollment: 10,288. Faculty: 1,520 (1,064 full-time, 456 part-time). Student-undergrad faculty ratio is 8:1. 9,750 applied, 49% were admitted. 26% from top 10% of their high school class, 55% from top quarter, 84% from top half. 12 class presidents, 10 valedictorians, 32 student government officers. Students come from 50 states and territories, 65 other countries, 97% from out-of-district. 9% 25 or older, 56% live on campus. Retention: 85% of full-time freshmen returned the following year. Academic areas with the most degrees conferred: health professions and related sciences; business/marketing; communication/journalism. Core. Calendar: semesters. Academic remediation for entering students, services for LD students, advanced placement, accelerated degree program, self-designed majors, freshman honors college, honors program, independent study, distance learning, double major, summer session for credit, part-time degree program, co-op programs and internships, graduate courses open to undergrads. Off campus study at 9 members of the Consortium of Universities of the Washington Metropolitan Area; over 21 colleges and universities including Duke University; University of California, Berkeley; Smith College; Vassar College; Williams College. ROTC: Army, Air Force.

Entrance Requirements: Options: electronic application, early admission, early action, deferred admission. Required: high school transcript, SAT or ACT. Required for some: 2 recommendations. Entrance: moderately difficult. Application deadlines: 2/15, 11/1 for early action. Notification: continuous, 12/24 for early action.

Costs Per Year: Application fee: $45. Comprehensive fee: $32,225 includes full-time tuition ($21,450), mandatory fees ($1433), and college room and board ($9342). College room only: $5388. Full-time tuition and fees vary according to course load. Room and board charges vary according to board plan and housing facility.

Collegiate Environment: Orientation program. Drama-theater group, choral group, marching band, student-run newspaper, radio station. Social organizations: 155 open to all; national fraternities, national sororities, local fraternities; 2% of eligible men and 1% of eligible women are members. Most popular organizations: Howard University Student Association, Undergraduate Student Assembly, Campus Pals, International Student Organization, Entrepreneurial Society, Howard University. Major annual events: Homecoming, Spring Black Arts Festival, Residence Hall Week. Student services: health clinic, personal-psychological counseling. Campus security: 24-hour emergency response devices and patrols, student patrols, late night transport-escort service, controlled dormitory access, security lighting. Howard University Libraries plus 7 others with 2.5 million books, 4.2 million microform titles, 26,382 serials, 194,000 audiovisual materials, an OPAC, and a Web page. Operations spending for the previous fiscal year: $9.4 million. 6,343 computers available on campus for general student use. A campuswide network can be accessed from student residence rooms and from off campus. Students can access the following: online class registration, student residential network. Staffed computer lab on campus (open 24 hours a day) provides training in use of computers, software, and the Internet.

Community Environment: See American University.

■ POTOMAC COLLEGE

4000 Chesapeake St., NW
Washington, DC 20016
Tel: (202)686-0876; Free: 888-686-0876
Fax: (202)686-0818
E-mail: admissions@potomac.edu
Web Site: www.potomac.edu/

Description: Proprietary, 4-year, coed. Awards associate, bachelor's, and master's degrees. Founded 1991. Setting: urban campus with easy access to Washington, DC. Educational spending for the previous fiscal year: $3488 per student. Total enrollment: 298. Faculty: 38 (5 full-time, 33 part-time). Student-undergrad faculty ratio is 10:1. 81 applied, 100% were admitted. Full-time: 253 students, 58% women, 42% men. Part-time: 45 students, 53% women, 47% men. Students come from 29 states and territories, 0% from out-of-district. 0.3% American Indian or Alaska Native, non-Hispanic/Latino; 6% Hispanic/Latino; 60% African American, non-Hispanic/Latino; 1% Asian, non-Hispanic/Latino; 0% Native Hawaiian or other Pacific Islander, non-Hispanic/Latino; 0.3% international. 85% 25 or older, 0% transferred in. Retention: 88% of full-time freshmen returned the following year. Academic areas with the most degrees conferred: business/marketing; health professions and related sciences. Core. Calendar: 6-week modules. Services for LD students, honors program, independent study, distance learning, part-time degree program, external degree program, adult/continuing education programs.

Entrance Requirements: Open admission. Options: electronic application, international baccalaureate accepted. Required: interview. Entrance: noncompetitive. Application deadline: Rolling. Notification: continuous. Transfer credits accepted: Yes.

Costs Per Year: Application fee: $0. Tuition: $11,760 full-time, $490 per credit part-time. Mandatory fees: $450 full-time, $450 per term part-time. Tuition guaranteed not to increase for student's term of enrollment.

Collegiate Environment: Orientation program. Major annual events: Student Government Association Elections, Annual SGA and alumni cookout and Career Fair, Rock the Vote - Voter Registration. Campus security: late night transport-escort service. College housing not available. Operations spending for the previous fiscal year: $109,703. 28 computers available on campus for general student use. Students can access the following: Student Portal and access to Course Management System.

■ STRAYER UNIVERSITY - TAKOMA PARK CAMPUS

6830 Laurel St., NW
Washington, DC 20012
Tel: (202)722-8100
Web Site: www.strayer.edu/campus/takoma-park

Description: Proprietary, comprehensive, coed. Awards associate, bachelor's, and master's degrees.

■ STRAYER UNIVERSITY - WASHINGTON CAMPUS

1133 15th St., NW
Washington, DC 20005
Tel: (202)408-2400
Fax: (202)419-1425
Web Site: www.strayer.edu/campus/washington

Description: Proprietary, comprehensive, coed. Awards associate, bachelor's, and master's degrees.

■ TRINITY WASHINGTON UNIVERSITY

125 Michigan Ave., NE
Washington, DC 20017-1094
Tel: (202)884-9000; Free: 800-IWANTTC
Fax: (202)884-9229
E-mail: admissions@trinitydc.edu
Web Site: www.trinitydc.edu/

Description: Independent Roman Catholic, comprehensive. Awards bachelor's and master's degrees. Founded 1897. Setting: 26-acre urban campus. Total enrollment: 1,630. 800 applied. 38% 25 or older. Core. Calendar: semesters. Academic remediation for entering students, ESL program, services for LD students, advanced placement, accelerated degree program, self-designed majors, honors program, independent study, double major, summer session for credit, part-time degree program, external degree program, adult/continuing education programs, co-op programs and internships, graduate courses open to undergrads. Off campus study at Georgetown University; George Washington University; American University; Catholic University of America; University of Maryland, College Park; University of the District of Columbia; Marymount University. Study abroad program. ROTC: Army (c).

Entrance Requirements: Options: electronic application, early action, deferred admission, international baccalaureate accepted. Required: essay, high school transcript, minimum 2.0 high school GPA, 1 recommendation. Recommended: interview, SAT or ACT. Entrance: moderately difficult. Application deadlines: 3/1, 12/1 for early action. Notification: 1/1 for early action.

Collegiate Environment: Orientation program. Drama-theater group, choral group, student-run newspaper. Student services: health clinic, personal-psychological counseling. Campus security: 24-hour emergency response devices and patrols, late night transport-escort service, controlled dormitory access. Sister Helen Sheehan Library plus 1 other with 207,000 books, 6,754 microform titles, 498 serials, 13,760 audiovisual materials, an OPAC, and a Web page.

■ UNIVERSITY OF THE DISTRICT OF COLUMBIA

4200 Connecticut Ave., NW
Washington, DC 20008-1175
Tel: (202)274-5000
E-mail: scarter@udc.edu
Web Site: www.udc.edu/

Description: District-supported, comprehensive, coed. Awards associate, bachelor's, and master's degrees. Founded 1976. Setting: 28-acre urban campus. Endowment: $36.7 million. Research spending for the previous fiscal year: $6.9 million. Total enrollment: 5,110. Faculty: (218 full-time). Student-undergrad faculty ratio is 13:1. 7,412 applied, 50% were admitted. 13% from top 10% of their high school class. Full-time: 2,087 students, 59% women, 41% men. Part-time: 2,770 students, 65% women, 35% men. Students come from 39 states and territories, 95 other countries, 20% from out-of-district. 0.1% American Indian or Alaska Native, non-Hispanic/Latino; 3% Hispanic/Latino; 37% African American, non-Hispanic/Latino; 0.4% Asian, non-Hispanic/Latino; 0% Native Hawaiian or other Pacific Islander, non-Hispanic/Latino; 6% international. 57% 25 or older, 9% transferred in. Retention: 54% of full-time freshmen returned the following year. Academic areas with the most degrees conferred: business/marketing; social sciences; parks and recreation. Core. Calendar: semesters. Academic remediation for entering students, ESL program, services for LD students, accelerated degree program, honors program, summer session for credit, part-time degree program, external degree program, adult/continuing education programs, co-op programs and internships, graduate courses open to undergrads. Off campus study at members of the Consortium of Universities of the Washington Metropolitan Area. ROTC: Army (c), Air Force (c).

Entrance Requirements: Open admission students in the Community College. Options: electronic application, deferred admission. Required: high school transcript. Recommended: SAT. Required for some: GED. Entrance: noncompetitive. Application deadline: 8/1. Notification: continuous until 8/15.

Preference given to district residents. Applicants placed on waiting list: 207. Wait-listed applicants offered admission: 197.

Costs Per Year: Application fee: $35. District resident tuition: $6635 full-time, $276 per credit part-time. Nonresident tuition: $13,915 full-time, $580 per credit part-time. Mandatory fees: $620 full-time, $30 per credit part-time. Full-time tuition and fees vary according to course load. Part-time tuition and fees vary according to course load. College room and board: $6600.

Collegiate Environment: Drama-theater group, choral group, marching band, student-run newspaper. Social organizations: 61 open to all; national fraternities, national sororities, local fraternities, local sororities; 4% of eligible men and 6% of eligible women are members. Most popular organizations: Caribbean Student Association, Theater Arts Ensemble, National Association for the Advancement of Colored People. Major annual events: Homecoming, basketball games, Miss UDC Pageant. Student services: health clinic, personal-psychological counseling. Campus security: 24-hour emergency response devices and patrols. Learning Resources Division Library plus 1 other with 554,412 books, 607,332 microform titles, 647 serials, an OPAC, and a Web page. 1,586 computers available on campus for general student use. A campuswide network can be accessed. Students can access the following: online class registration. Staffed computer lab on campus.

Community Environment: See American University.

■ **UNIVERSITY OF PHOENIX–WASHINGTON D.C. CAMPUS**
25 Massachusetts Ave. NW, Ste. 150
Washington, DC 20001
Free: 866-766-0766
Web Site: www.phoenix.edu/

Description: Proprietary, comprehensive, coed. Awards bachelor's and master's degrees. Total enrollment: 27. Faculty: 25 (3 full-time, 22 part-time). Full-time: 14 students, 64% women, 36% men. 71% 25 or older. Academic area with the most degrees conferred: business/marketing. Core. Graduate courses open to undergrads.

Entrance Requirements: Open admission. Options: electronic application, deferred admission, international baccalaureate accepted.

■ ADVENTIST UNIVERSITY OF HEALTH SCIENCES

671 Winyah Dr.
Orlando, FL 32803
Tel: (407)303-7747; Free: 800-500-7747
E-mail: katie.shaw@adu.edu
Web Site: www.adu.edu/

Description: Independent, comprehensive, coed. Awards associate, bachelor's, and master's degrees. Founded 1913. Setting: 9-acre urban campus with easy access to Orlando. Endowment: $6 million. Total enrollment: 2,671. Faculty: 252 (62 full-time, 190 part-time). 358 applied, 96% were admitted. Full-time: 594 students, 78% women, 22% men. Part-time: 1,982 students, 80% women, 20% men. Students come from 52 states and territories, 35% from out-of-state. 1% American Indian or Alaska Native, non-Hispanic/Latino; 19% Hispanic/Latino; 15% African American, non-Hispanic/Latino; 5% Asian, non-Hispanic/Latino; 1% Native Hawaiian or other Pacific Islander, non-Hispanic/Latino; 1% international. 66% 25 or older, 24% transferred in. Core. Calendar: semesters. Academic remediation for entering students, services for LD students, advanced placement, independent study, distance learning. ROTC: Air Force (c).

Entrance Requirements: Open admission. Option: electronic application. Required: minimum 2.7 high school GPA. Required for some: essay, high school transcript, 3 recommendations, SAT or ACT. Entrance: minimally difficult. Application deadlines: 7/1, 7/1 for nonresidents. Notification: continuous until 8/30, continuous until 8/30 for nonresidents. SAT Reasoning Test deadline: 7/1. SAT Subject Test deadline: 7/1. Transfer credits accepted: Yes.

Collegiate Environment: Orientation program. Drama-theater group, student-run newspaper. Major annual events: Convocation, International Food Festival, Spring Picnic. Student services: personal-psychological counseling. Campus security: 24-hour emergency response devices and patrols, late night transport-escort service, controlled dormitory access. 184 college housing spaces available. No special consideration for freshman housing applicants. Option: coed housing available. The R. A. Williams Library plus 1 other with 76,000 books, 142 serials, 6,000 audiovisual materials, an OPAC, and a Web page. 43 computers available on campus for general student use. Computer purchase/lease plans available. A computer is required for all students. A campuswide network can be accessed. Students can access the following: online class registration, Online registration. Staffed computer lab on campus provides training in use of computers, software, and the Internet.

■ AMERICAN INTERCONTINENTAL UNIVERSITY SOUTH FLORIDA

2250 N Commerce Pky., Ste. 100
Weston, FL 33326
Tel: (954)446-6100; Free: 888-603-4888
Fax: (954)835-1020
Web Site: www.aiuniv.edu/

Description: Proprietary, comprehensive, coed. Administratively affiliated with American InterContinental University. Awards associate, bachelor's, and master's degrees. Founded 1998. Setting: 3-acre suburban campus. Total enrollment: 887. Faculty: 45. Full-time: 671 students, 62% women, 38% men. Part-time: 127 students, 60% women, 40% men. 48% 25 or older, 12% transferred in. Academic areas with the most degrees conferred: business/marketing; visual and performing arts; computer and information sciences. Core. Calendar: five 10-week terms. Academic remediation for entering students, accelerated degree program, distance learning, summer session

for credit, part-time degree program, adult/continuing education programs, co-op programs. Off campus study at Cecore.

Entrance Requirements: Options: electronic application, deferred admission, international baccalaureate accepted. Required: essay, high school transcript, interview. Application deadline: Rolling. Notification: continuous.

Collegiate Environment: Orientation program. 40 computers available on campus for general student use. A campuswide network can be accessed. Students can access the following: online class registration. Staffed computer lab on campus.

■ ANTHEM COLLEGE–ORLANDO

3710 Maguire Blvd.
Orlando, FL 32803
Tel: (407)893-7400; Free: 855-824-0055
Fax: (407)895-1804
Web Site: anthem.edu/orlando-florida/

Description: Proprietary, 2-year, coed. Awards terminal associate degrees. Founded 1998. Total enrollment: 1,066.

Entrance Requirements: Entrance: noncompetitive.

■ ARGOSY UNIVERSITY, SARASOTA

5250 17th St.
Sarasota, FL 34235
Tel: (941)379-0404; Free: 800-331-5995
Fax: (941)379-9464
Web Site: www.argosy.edu/sarasota/

Description: Proprietary, university, coed. Part of Education Management Corporation. Awards bachelor's, master's, and doctoral degrees. Founded 1974. Calendar: semesters.

■ ARGOSY UNIVERSITY, TAMPA

1403 N Howard Ave.
Tampa, FL 33607
Tel: (813)393-5290; Free: 800-850-6488
Fax: (813)246-4045
Web Site: www.argosy.edu/tampa/

Description: Proprietary, university, coed. Part of Education Management Corporation. Awards bachelor's, master's, and doctoral degrees. Setting: urban campus. Calendar: semesters.

■ THE ART INSTITUTE OF FORT LAUDERDALE

1799 SE 17th St.
Fort Lauderdale, FL 33316
Tel: (954)527-1799; Free: 800-275-7603
Fax: (954)728-8637
Web Site: www.artinstitutes.edu/fortlauderdale/

Description: Proprietary, 4-year, coed. Part of Education Management Corporation. Awards associate and bachelor's degrees. Founded 1968. Setting: urban campus.

Community Environment: AIFL is located in Broward County, Fort Lauderdale, pop. 167,380. It has a diverse mix of culture and lifestyles with a stimulating, creative learning environment nestled between 23 miles of beaches and 3,000 annual hours of sunshine.

■ THE ART INSTITUTE OF JACKSONVILLE

8775 Baypine Rd.
Jacksonville, FL 32256
Tel: (904)732-9393; Free: 800-924-1589
Fax: (904)732-9423
Web Site: www.artinstitutes.edu/jacksonville/
Description: Proprietary, 4-year, coed. Part of Education Management Corporation. Awards associate and bachelor's degrees. Founded 2006. Setting: suburban campus.

■ THE ART INSTITUTE OF TAMPA

Parkside at Tampa Bay Park
4401 N Himes Ave., Ste. 150
Tampa, FL 33614
Tel: (813)873-2112; Free: 866-703-3277
Fax: (813)873-2171
Web Site: www.artinstitutes.edu/tampa/
Description: Proprietary, 4-year, coed. Part of Education Management Corporation. Awards associate and bachelor's degrees. Setting: suburban campus.

■ ATI CAREER TRAINING CENTER

2890 NW 62nd St.
Fort Lauderdale, FL 33309
Tel: (954)973-4760; Free: 888-209-8264
Fax: (954)973-6422
Web Site: www.aticareertraining.edu/
Description: Proprietary, 2-year, coed. Awards terminal associate degrees. Setting: suburban campus. Total enrollment: 312. 343 applied, 100% were admitted. 19% 25 or older.

■ ATI COLLEGE OF HEALTH

1395 NW 167th St., Ste. 200
Miami, FL 33169-5742
Tel: (305)628-1000; Free: 888-209-8264
E-mail: admissions@atienterprises.edu
Web Site: www.aticareertraining.edu/
Description: Proprietary, 2-year, coed. Part of ATI Enterprises, Inc. of Florida. Awards transfer associate and terminal associate degrees. Founded 1976. Setting: 1-acre urban campus. Total enrollment: 1,191. 64% 25 or older. Calendar: semesters. Academic remediation for entering students.
Entrance Requirements: Open admission. Required: high school transcript, interview. Entrance: minimally difficult. Application deadline: Rolling. Notification: continuous.
Collegiate Environment: Student services: health clinic, personal-psychological counseling.

■ AVE MARIA UNIVERSITY

5050 Ave. Maria Blvd.
Ave Maria, FL 34142
Tel: (239)280-2556; Free: 877-283-8648
Fax: (239)352-2392
E-mail: brett.ormandy@avemaria.edu
Web Site: www.avemaria.edu/
Description: Independent Roman Catholic, comprehensive, coed. Awards bachelor's and master's degrees. Founded 2002. Setting: suburban campus. Total enrollment: 672. Faculty: 73 (56 full-time, 17 part-time). Student-undergrad faculty ratio is 10:1. 1,464 applied, 56% were admitted. Full-time: 525 students, 54% women, 46% men. Part-time: 7 students, 43% women, 57% men. Students come from 45 states and territories, 28 other countries, 75% from out-of-state. 1% 25 or older, 90% live on campus, 19% transferred in. Retention: 60% of full-time freshmen returned the following year. Academic areas with the most degrees conferred: theology and religious vocations; biological/life sciences; history. Core. Calendar: semesters. Services for LD students, accelerated degree program, independent study, double major, summer session for credit, internships, graduate courses open to undergrads. Study abroad program.
Entrance Requirements: Options: electronic application, early admission, early decision, deferred admission, international baccalaureate accepted. Required: essay, high school transcript, minimum 2.8 high school GPA, 2 recommendations, activities list, SAT or ACT. Entrance: moderately difficult. Application deadlines: Rolling, 11/1 for early decision. Notification: continuous.
Costs Per Year: Application fee: $0. Comprehensive fee: $30,263 includes full-time tuition ($20,800), mandatory fees ($696), and college room and board ($8767). College room only: $4961.
Collegiate Environment: Orientation program. Drama-theater group, choral group, student-run newspaper. Social organizations: 25 open to all. Most popular organizations: Students for Life, Chastity Team, Student Government Association, Habitat for Humanity, Faith in Action Ministry. Major annual events: semi-formal dance, Parents' Weekend, open house. Student services: health clinic, personal-psychological counseling. Campus security: 24-hour patrols, controlled dormitory access, County Sheriff workstation on campus with deputy patrols. Canizaro Library with 200,000 books, 164 serials, an OPAC, and a Web page.

■ THE BAPTIST COLLEGE OF FLORIDA

5400 College Dr.
Graceville, FL 32440-1898
Tel: (850)263-3261; Free: 800-328-2660
Fax: (850)263-7506
E-mail: skrichards@baptistcollege.edu
Web Site: www.baptistcollege.edu/
Description: Independent Southern Baptist, comprehensive, coed. Awards associate, bachelor's, and master's degrees. Founded 1943. Setting: 250-acre small town campus. Endowment: $5.8 million. Educational spending for the previous fiscal year: $4461 per student. Total enrollment: 606. Faculty: 63 (26 full-time, 37 part-time). Student-undergrad faculty ratio is 13:1. 162 applied, 40% were admitted. Full-time: 438 students, 40% women, 60% men. Part-time: 158 students, 37% women, 63% men. Students come from 20 states and territories, 37% from out-of-state. 0.2% American Indian or Alaska Native, non-Hispanic/Latino; 3% Hispanic/Latino; 6% African American, non-Hispanic/Latino; 0.2% Asian, non-Hispanic/Latino; 0% Native Hawaiian or other Pacific Islander, non-Hispanic/Latino; 0% international. 35% 25 or older, 44% live on campus, 12% transferred in. Retention: 82% of full-time freshmen returned the following year. Academic areas with the most degrees conferred: theology and religious vocations; visual and performing arts; psychology. Core. Calendar: semesters. Academic remediation for entering students, services for LD students, advanced placement, independent study, distance learning, double major, summer session for credit, part-time degree program, internships.
Entrance Requirements: Open admission. Options: electronic application, deferred admission, international baccalaureate accepted. Required: essay, high school transcript, 2 recommendations, Christian/Church Member for 1 year minimum, SAT or ACT. Recommended: interview. Entrance: noncompetitive. Application deadline: 8/11. Notification: continuous. Preference given to professing Christians who are members of an evangelical church. Transfer credits accepted: Yes.
Costs Per Year: Application fee: $25. Comprehensive fee: $13,538 includes full-time tuition ($9000), mandatory fees ($400), and college room and board ($4138). Room and board charges vary according to board plan and housing facility. Part-time tuition: $300 per credit hour.
Collegiate Environment: Orientation program. Drama-theater group, choral group, student-run radio station. Social organizations: 3 open to all. Most popular organizations: Baptist Collegiate Ministry, College Choir, AACC. Major annual events: Halloween Carnival & Brain Bowl, Dorm Wars, Spring/Christmas Concert. Student services: personal-psychological counseling. Campus security: student patrols, patrols by police officers 11 pm to 7 am. 250 college housing spaces available; 234 were occupied in 2012-13. Freshmen guaranteed college housing. On-campus residence required through sophomore year. Options: men-only, women-only housing available. Ida J. MacMillan Library with 125,760 books, 9,844 microform titles, 380 serials, 2,322 audiovisual materials, an OPAC, and a Web page. Operations spending for the previous fiscal year: $305,483. 25 computers available on campus for general student use. A campuswide network can be accessed from student residence rooms. Students can access the following: online class registration. Staffed computer lab on campus provides training in use of computers, software, and the Internet.
Community Environment: Graceville is in northwest Florida near the borders of Alabama, Florida and Georgia. 23 miles north is Dothan, Alabama, and 20 miles southeast is Marianna, Florida. Railroads and buses serve the area. One excellent shopping center is available.

■ BARRY UNIVERSITY

11300 NE Second Ave.
Miami Shores, FL 33161-6695
Tel: (305)899-3000; Free: 800-695-2279
Fax: (305)899-2971

E-mail: admissions@mail.barry.edu

Web Site: www.barry.edu/

Description: Independent Roman Catholic, university, coed. Awards bachelor's, master's, and doctoral degrees and post-master's certificates. Founded 1940. Setting: 122-acre suburban campus with easy access to Miami. Endowment: $29.7 million. Educational spending for the previous fiscal year: $11,071 per student. Total enrollment: 9,070. Faculty: 838 (370 full-time, 468 part-time). Student-undergrad faculty ratio is 12:1. 7,645 applied, 52% were admitted. 0% from top 10% of their high school class, 100% from top quarter, 0% from top half. Full-time: 3,824 students, 64% women, 36% men. Part-time: 795 students, 57% women, 43% men. 0.3% American Indian or Alaska Native, non-Hispanic/Latino; 17% Hispanic/Latino; 19% African American, non-Hispanic/Latino; 1% Asian, non-Hispanic/Latino; 0.1% Native Hawaiian or other Pacific Islander, non-Hispanic/Latino; 7% international. 8% transferred in. Retention: 62% of full-time freshmen returned the following year. Academic areas with the most degrees conferred: public administration and social services; computer and information sciences; education; visual and performing arts; psychology. Core. Calendar: semesters. Academic remediation for entering students, ESL program, services for LD students, advanced placement, accelerated degree program, honors program, independent study, distance learning, double major, summer session for credit, part-time degree program, adult/continuing education programs, internships, graduate courses open to undergrads. Off campus study at St. Thomas Aquinas College, Dominican College of San Rafael. Study abroad program. ROTC: Army (c), Air Force (c).

Entrance Requirements: Options: electronic application, early admission, deferred admission. Required: high school transcript, minimum 2 high school GPA, SAT or ACT. Recommended: interview. Required for some: essay. Entrance: moderately difficult. Application deadline: Rolling. Notification: continuous.

Costs Per Year: Application fee: $30. Tuition: $28,160 full-time. College room only: $11,988.

Collegiate Environment: Orientation program. Drama-theater group, choral group, student-run newspaper, radio station. Social organizations: 27 open to all; national fraternities, national sororities. Most popular organizations: Student Government Association, Campus Activities Board, SCUBA Society, Caribbean Students Association, Jamaican Association. Major annual events: Founders' Day, Spring and Fall Formals, Festival of Nations. Student services: health clinic, personal-psychological counseling. Campus security: 24-hour emergency response devices and patrols, late night transport-escort service. On-campus residence required in freshman year. Options: coed, men-only, women-only housing available. Monsignor William Barry Memorial Library plus 1 other with 352,609 books, an OPAC, and a Web page. 368 computers available on campus for general student use. A campuswide network can be accessed from student residence rooms and from off campus. Students can access the following: online class registration, Blackboard. Staffed computer lab on campus.

Community Environment: Located only minutes from the cities of Miami and Ft. Lauderdale, Barry University offers easy access to the recreational facilities and cultural opportunities of Florida's Gold Coast area. Golf, tennis, swimming, skin and scuba diving, sailing and waterskiing are available all year long. Professional football, basketball, soccer, and hockey teams play in South Florida. The Miami Beach Theater of the Performing Arts, Coconut Grove Playhouse and the New World Symphony provide a full season of highly acclaimed performances. Well known personalities entertain regularly in the area. The Miami/Ft. Lauderdale area provides ready access to beaches, recreational, and ecological features including the Florida Keys, the Everglades, and National, State and Marine parks.

■ **BEACON COLLEGE**

105 E Main St.

Leesburg, FL 34748

Tel: (352)787-7660

Fax: (352)787-0721

E-mail: bmeli@beaconcollege.edu

Web Site: www.beaconcollege.edu/

Description: Independent, 4-year, coed. Awards associate and bachelor's degrees. Founded 1989. Setting: 5-acre small town campus with easy access to Orlando. Endowment: $50,000. Educational spending for the previous fiscal year: $9053 per student. Total enrollment: 186. Faculty: 24 (14 full-time, 10 part-time). Student-undergrad faculty ratio is 11:1. 138 applied, 36% were admitted. Full-time: 182 students, 34% women, 66% men. Part-time: 2 students, 100% men. Students come from 31 states and territories, 4 other countries, 72% from out-of-state. 1% American Indian or Alaska Na-

tive, non-Hispanic/Latino; 6% Hispanic/Latino; 13% African American, non-Hispanic/Latino; 2% Asian, non-Hispanic/Latino; 1% Native Hawaiian or other Pacific Islander, non-Hispanic/Latino; 3% international. 4% 25 or older, 86% live on campus, 11% transferred in. Retention: 80% of full-time freshmen returned the following year. Academic areas with the most degrees conferred: health professions and related sciences; liberal arts/general studies; computer and information sciences. Core. Calendar: semesters. Academic remediation for entering students, services for LD students, advanced placement, independent study, double major, summer session for credit, adult/continuing education programs, co-op programs and internships.

Entrance Requirements: Options: early admission, deferred admission, international baccalaureate accepted. Required: essay, high school transcript, 3 recommendations, Psycho-educational evaluation. Recommended: minimum 2.5 high school GPA, SAT or ACT. Entrance: moderately difficult. Application deadline: Rolling. Notification: 8/1. Transfer credits accepted: Yes.

Costs Per Year: Application fee: $50. Tuition: $30,396 full-time.

Collegiate Environment: Orientation program. Drama-theater group, student-run newspaper. Social organizations: 16 open to all; local fraternities, local sororities; 70% of eligible men and 50% of eligible women are members. Most popular organizations: Florida Christian Athletes, Performance Club, Theater Goers Club, Camping Club, Beach Goers Club. Major annual events: Parents' Weekend, Convocation, College Annual Gala. Student services: health clinic, personal-psychological counseling. Campus security: 24-hour emergency response devices, student patrols, late night transport-escort service. 173 college housing spaces available; 162 were occupied in 2012-13. Freshmen guaranteed college housing. Option: coed housing available. Beacon College Library with 139,545 books, 99 serials, 1,195 audiovisual materials, and a Web page. Operations spending for the previous fiscal year: $140,913. 72 computers available on campus for general student use. A campuswide network can be accessed from student residence rooms and from off campus. Staffed computer lab on campus provides training in use of computers, software, and the Internet.

■ **BELHAVEN UNIVERSITY**

5200 Vineland Rd.

Ste. 100

Orlando, FL 32811

Tel: (407)804-1424; Free: 877-804-1424

Fax: (407)661-1732

E-mail: orlando@belhaven.edu

Web Site: orlando.belhaven.edu/

Description: Independent Presbyterian, comprehensive, coed. Awards associate, bachelor's, and master's degrees. Founded 1999. Calendar: semesters.

Entrance Requirements: Required: high school transcript. Required for some: essay, resume.

■ **BETHUNE-COOKMAN UNIVERSITY**

640 Dr. Mary McLeod Bethune Blvd.

Daytona Beach, FL 32114-3099

Tel: (386)481-2000; Free: 800-448-0228

Fax: (386)481-2010

E-mail: brownr@cookman.edu

Web Site: www.cookman.edu/

Description: Independent Methodist, comprehensive, coed. Awards bachelor's and master's degrees. Founded 1904. Setting: 60-acre urban campus with easy access to Orlando. Endowment: $41.8 million. Educational spending for the previous fiscal year: $5748 per student. Total enrollment: 3,543. Faculty: 248 (178 full-time, 70 part-time). Student-undergrad faculty ratio is 17:1. 5,380 applied, 73% were admitted. 8% from top 10% of their high school class, 24% from top quarter, 54% from top half. 14 valedictorians. Full-time: 3,348 students, 59% women, 41% men. Part-time: 138 students, 49% women, 51% men. Students come from 44 states and territories, 28 other countries, 33% from out-of-state. 0.1% American Indian or Alaska Native, non-Hispanic/Latino; 2% Hispanic/Latino; 79% African American, non-Hispanic/Latino; 0.2% Asian, non-Hispanic/Latino; 0.5% Native Hawaiian or other Pacific Islander, non-Hispanic/Latino; 1% international. 6% 25 or older, 55% live on campus, 14% transferred in. Retention: 64% of full-time freshmen returned the following year. Academic areas with the most degrees conferred: business/marketing; homeland security, law enforcement, firefighting, and protective services; education; psychology. Core. Calendar: semesters. Academic remediation for entering students, advanced placement, accelerated degree program, honors program, independent study, distance learning, double major, summer session for credit, part-time degree program, adult/continuing education programs, co-op programs and internships, graduate courses open to undergrads. Study abroad program. ROTC: Army (c), Air Force (c).

Entrance Requirements: Options: electronic application, early admission, deferred admission, international baccalaureate accepted. Required: high school transcript, minimum 2.25 high school GPA, 1 recommendation, medical history, SAT or ACT. Recommended: essay. Required for some: interview. Entrance: minimally difficult. Application deadline: 6/30. Notification: continuous. SAT Reasoning Test deadline: 7/30.

Costs Per Year: Application fee: $25. Comprehensive fee: $22,958 includes full-time tuition ($14,410) and college room and board ($8548). Full-time tuition varies according to course load and degree level. Room and board charges vary according to housing facility. Part-time tuition: $600 per credit hour. Part-time tuition varies according to course load and degree level.

Collegiate Environment: Orientation program. Drama-theater group, choral group, marching band, student-run newspaper, radio station. Social organizations: 40 open to all; national fraternities, national sororities, local fraternities, local sororities; 3% of eligible men and 5% of eligible women are members. Most popular organizations: Concert Chorale, marching band, Inspirational Gospel Choir, Student Government Association. Major annual events: Homecoming, Founders' Day, Career Day. Student services: health clinic, personal-psychological counseling. Campus security: 24-hour emergency response devices and patrols, student patrols, late night transport-escort service. 1,881 college housing spaces available; 1,725 were occupied in 2012-13. Freshmen guaranteed college housing. On-campus residence required in freshman year. Options: coed, men-only, women-only housing available. Carl S. Swisher Library plus 1 other with 149,194 books, 53,000 microform titles, 91 serials, 1,344 audiovisual materials, an OPAC, and a Web page. Operations spending for the previous fiscal year: $1 million. 966 computers available on campus for general student use. A campuswide network can be accessed from student residence rooms and from off campus. Students can access the following: online class registration. Staffed computer lab on campus provides training in use of computers, software, and the Internet.

Community Environment: Daytona Beach is a resort area located on the Atlantic Ocean with a subtropical climate. All modes of transportation serve the area. The community facilities include two libraries, two museums, many churches, a hospital and major civic organizations. Part-time employment opportunities are available. Recreational activities include water sports, stock car racing, motor bike racing, and archery. Beach drivers almost outnumber swimmers. Spring vacation brings an influx of college students. Special events include the Antique Car Meet and car racing known as the Speed Week.

■ **BREVARD COMMUNITY COLLEGE**
1519 Clearlake Rd.
Cocoa, FL 32922-6597
Tel: (321)632-1111
Fax: (321)633-4565
E-mail: cocoaadmissions@brevardcc.edu
Web Site: www.brevardcc.edu/

Description: State-supported, 2-year, coed. Part of Florida Community College System. Awards certificates, transfer associate, and terminal associate degrees. Founded 1960. Setting: 100-acre suburban campus with easy access to Orlando. Total enrollment: 15,607. Faculty: 1,037 (215 full-time, 822 part-time). Student-undergrad faculty ratio is 19:1. 6,586 applied, 100% were admitted. Full-time: 6,125 students, 55% women, 45% men. Part-time: 9,482 students, 61% women, 39% men. Students come from 42 states and territories, 67 other countries. 33% 25 or older. Core. Calendar: semesters. Academic remediation for entering students, ESL program, services for LD students, advanced placement, accelerated degree program, honors program, independent study, distance learning, double major, summer session for credit, part-time degree program, external degree program, adult/continuing education programs, co-op programs and internships. Study abroad program. ROTC: Army, Air Force.

Entrance Requirements: Open admission. Options: electronic application, early admission, international baccalaureate accepted. Required: high school transcript. Entrance: noncompetitive. Application deadline: Rolling. Notification: continuous.

Collegiate Environment: Orientation program. Drama-theater group, choral group, student-run newspaper. Most popular organizations: Phi Theta Kappa, The Green Team, African-American Student Union, Student Govern-

ment Association, Cosmetology in Action. Major annual events: Spring Festival, Black History month, Student Welcome Back Days. Student services: women's center. Campus security: 24-hour emergency response devices and patrols. UCF Library with 213,873 books, 216,720 microform titles, 904 serials, an OPAC, and a Web page. Operations spending for the previous fiscal year: $1.8 million. 2,051 computers available on campus for general student use. A campuswide network can be accessed from off-campus. Students can access the following: online class registration. Staffed computer lab on campus.

Community Environment: Cocoa, a suburban area with a subtropical climate, is the leading shipping point for the famous Indian River citrus fruits, and a resort town. Airline and bus service provide transportation for the area. Community facilities include four hospitals, two clinics and many churches. Recreational activities are water sports, golf, bowling and fishing. Part-time employment is limited.

■ **BROWARD COLLEGE**
225 E Las Olas Blvd.
Fort Lauderdale, FL 33301-2298
Tel: (954)761-7450
Fax: (954)761-7484
E-mail: walexand@broward.edu
Web Site: www.broward.edu/

Description: State-supported, primarily 2-year, coed. Part of Florida Community College System. Awards certificates, diplomas, transfer associate, terminal associate, and bachelor's degrees. Founded 1960. Setting: urban campus with easy access to Miami. Total enrollment: 37,360. Student-undergrad faculty ratio is 30:1. 1% from out-of-state. 35% 25 or older. Retention: 75% of full-time freshmen returned the following year. Core. Calendar: trimesters. Academic remediation for entering students, ESL program, services for LD students, advanced placement, self-designed majors, honors program, summer session for credit, part-time degree program, adult/continuing education programs, co-op programs. Study abroad program. ROTC: Army.

Entrance Requirements: Open admission. Options: early admission, deferred admission. Required for some: high school transcript, minimum 2.75 high school GPA. Entrance: noncompetitive. Preference given to state residents.

Collegiate Environment: Drama-theater group, choral group, student-run newspaper. Social organizations: local fraternities, local sororities. Student services: personal-psychological counseling, women's center. Campus security: 24-hour emergency response devices and patrols, late night transport-escort service. South Regional/Broward Community College Library with an OPAC.

Community Environment: Fort Lauderdale, population 167,000, is located on the Atlantic Ocean coastline, 25 miles north of Miami. The climate is subtropical and the average year-round temperature is 75 degrees.

■ **BROWN MACKIE COLLEGE–MIAMI**
One Herald Plz.
Miami, FL 33132
Tel: (305)341-6600; Free: 866-505-0335
Web Site: www.brownmackie.edu/miami/

Description: Proprietary, primarily 2-year, coed. Part of Education Management Corporation. Awards diplomas, terminal associate, and bachelor's degrees.

■ **CAMBRIDGE INSTITUTE OF ALLIED HEALTH AND TECHNOLOGY**
5150 Linton Blvd.
Ste. 340
Delray Beach, FL 33484
Tel: (561)381-4990
Web Site: www.cambridgehealth.edu/
Description: Proprietary, 2-year, coed.

■ **CARLOS ALBIZU UNIVERSITY, MIAMI CAMPUS**
2173 NW 99th Ave.
Miami, FL 33172-2209
Tel: (305)593-1223; Free: 800-GO-TO-CAU
Fax: (305)592-7930
E-mail: mtriana@albizu.edu
Web Site: www.mia.albizu.edu/

Description: Independent, comprehensive, coed. Part of Carlos Albizu University. Awards bachelor's, master's, and doctoral degrees. Founded

1980. Setting: 18-acre urban campus. Educational spending for the previous fiscal year: $4407 per student. Total enrollment: 1,046. Faculty: 48 (5 full-time, 43 part-time). Student-undergrad faculty ratio is 12:1. 18 applied, 56% were admitted. Full-time: 178 students, 65% women, 35% men. Part-time: 144 students, 73% women, 27% men. 0% from out-of-state. 0% American Indian or Alaska Native, non-Hispanic/Latino; 41% Hispanic/Latino; 3% African American, non-Hispanic/Latino; 0% Asian, non-Hispanic/Latino; 0% Native Hawaiian or other Pacific Islander, non-Hispanic/Latino; 1% international. 66% 25 or older, 20% transferred in. Retention: 63% of full-time freshmen returned the following year. Academic areas with the most degrees conferred: psychology; business/marketing; education. Core. Calendar: trimesters. Academic remediation for entering students, ESL program, services for LD students, advanced placement, accelerated degree program, independent study, distance learning, double major, summer session for credit, part-time degree program, adult/continuing education programs, co-op programs and internships.

Entrance Requirements: Open admission. Options: electronic application, international baccalaureate accepted. Required: high school transcript, minimum 2 high school GPA. Recommended: interview. Entrance: moderately difficult. Application deadline: Rolling. Notification: continuous. Transfer credits accepted: Yes.

Costs Per Year: Application fee: $25. Tuition: $11,304 full-time, $314 per credit part-time. Mandatory fees: $744 full-time, $248 per term part-time. Full-time tuition and fees vary according to course load, degree level, and program. Part-time tuition and fees vary according to course load, degree level, and program.

Collegiate Environment: Orientation program. Student-run newspaper. Social organizations: 6 open to all. Most popular organizations: Student Council, Psi Chi, Kappa Delta Pi, Nu Sigma Si, Future Educators of America. Major annual events: Albizu Student Excellence Awards Banquet, Student Council Elections, Town Hall Meetings. Campus security: 24-hour emergency response devices and patrols, late night transport-escort service. College housing not available. Albizu Library with 24,545 books, 346 serials, 2,308 audiovisual materials, an OPAC, and a Web page. Operations spending for the previous fiscal year: $462,730. 187 computers available on campus for general student use. Students can access the following: online class registration, Campus Portal. Staffed computer lab on campus provides training in use of computers, software, and the Internet.

■ CENTRAL FLORIDA INSTITUTE

30522 US Hwy. 19 N
Ste. 300
Palm Harbor, FL 34684
Tel: (727)786-4707; Free: 888-831-8303
Fax: (727)781-9421
Web Site: www.cfinstitute.com/
Description: Proprietary, 2-year, coed. Awards certificates, diplomas, and terminal associate degrees. Founded 1997. Setting: urban campus. Total enrollment: 545. 61% 25 or older. Calendar: continuous.
Entrance Requirements: Open admission.

■ CENTURA INSTITUTE

6359 Edgewater Dr.
Orlando, FL 32810
Tel: (407)275-9696; Free: 888-312-1320
Fax: (407)275-4499
E-mail: admcircorl@centura.edu
Web Site: www.centurainstitute.edu/
Description: Proprietary, 2-year, coed. Awards diplomas and terminal associate degrees. Total enrollment: 185. Student-undergrad faculty ratio is 16:1. 0% from out-of-state. 69% 25 or older.

■ CHAMBERLAIN COLLEGE OF NURSING (JACKSONVILLE)

5200 Belfort Rd.
Jacksonville, FL 32256-6040
Tel: (904)251-8100; Free: 888-556-8CCN
Web Site: www.chamberlain.edu/
Description: Proprietary, 4-year, coed. Awards bachelor's degrees. Total enrollment: 312. Faculty: 33 (11 full-time, 22 part-time). Student-undergrad faculty ratio is 11:1. Full-time: 148 students, 84% women, 16% men. Part-time: 164 students, 87% women, 13% men. 9% from out-of-state. 0% American Indian or Alaska Native, non-Hispanic/Latino; 7% Hispanic/Latino; 27% African American, non-Hispanic/Latino; 9% Asian, non-Hispanic/Latino; 1% Native Hawaiian or other Pacific Islander, non-Hispanic/Latino; 1%

international. 67% 25 or older, 0% live on campus, 40% transferred in. Academic area with the most degrees conferred: health professions and related sciences. Calendar: semesters.
Entrance Requirements: Required: SAT or ACT.
Costs Per Year: Tuition: $16,360 full-time, $665 per credit hour part-time. Mandatory fees: $600 full-time. Full-time tuition and fees vary according to course load. Part-time tuition varies according to course load.

■ CHAMBERLAIN COLLEGE OF NURSING (MIRAMAR)

2300 SW 145th Ave.
Miramar, FL 33027
Tel: (954)885-3510
Web Site: www.chamberlain.edu/
Description: Proprietary, 4-year, coed. Awards bachelor's degrees. Total enrollment: 274. Faculty: 21 (6 full-time, 15 part-time). Student-undergrad faculty ratio is 16:1. Full-time: 120 students, 88% women, 12% men. Part-time: 154 students, 91% women, 9% men. 7% from out-of-state. 0% American Indian or Alaska Native, non-Hispanic/Latino; 39% Hispanic/Latino; 22% African American, non-Hispanic/Latino; 3% Asian, non-Hispanic/Latino; 0% Native Hawaiian or other Pacific Islander, non-Hispanic/Latino; 3% international. 53% 25 or older, 0% live on campus, 62% transferred in.
Entrance Requirements: Required: SAT or ACT. Entrance: moderately difficult. Application deadline: Rolling. Notification: continuous.
Costs Per Year: Application fee: $95. Tuition: $16,360 full-time, $665 per credit hour part-time. Mandatory fees: $600 full-time. Full-time tuition and fees vary according to course load. Part-time tuition varies according to course load.
Collegiate Environment: College housing not available.

■ CHIPOLA COLLEGE

3094 Indian Cir.
Marianna, FL 32446-3065
Tel: (850)526-2761
Fax: (850)718-2388
E-mail: rehbergk@chipola.edu
Web Site: www.chipola.edu/
Description: State-supported, primarily 2-year, coed. Awards certificates, transfer associate, terminal associate, and bachelor's degrees. Founded 1947. Setting: 105-acre rural campus. Total enrollment: 2,292. Faculty: 127 (39 full-time, 88 part-time). Student-undergrad faculty ratio is 24:1. Full-time: 964 students, 58% women, 42% men. Part-time: 1,328 students, 66% women, 34% men. Students come from 7 states and territories, 6 other countries, 8% from out-of-state. 1% American Indian or Alaska Native, non-Hispanic/Latino; 3% Hispanic/Latino; 17% African American, non-Hispanic/Latino; 1% Asian, non-Hispanic/Latino; 0.04% Native Hawaiian or other Pacific Islander, non-Hispanic/Latino. 37% 25 or older, 6% transferred in. Core. Calendar: semesters. Academic remediation for entering students, services for LD students, advanced placement, honors program, independent study, distance learning, summer session for credit, part-time degree program, adult/continuing education programs.
Entrance Requirements: Open admission. Option: early admission. Required: high school transcript. Entrance: noncompetitive. Application deadline: Rolling. Notification: continuous. Transfer credits accepted: Yes.
Costs Per Year: Application fee: $0. State resident tuition: $3060 full-time, $102 per semester hour part-time. Nonresident tuition: $8,890 full-time, $296.35 per semester hour part-time. Mandatory fees: $40 full-time. Full-time tuition and fees vary according to degree level. Part-time tuition varies according to degree level.
Collegiate Environment: Drama-theater group, choral group, student-run newspaper. Most popular organization: Drama/Theater Group. Major annual events: Fall Festival, Homecoming, Spring Frolics. Campus security: night security personnel. College housing not available. Chipola Library with 37,740 books and 226 serials. 80 computers available on campus for general student use. A campuswide network can be accessed from off-campus. Staffed computer lab on campus.
Community Environment: Marianna, located in northwest Florida, has an annual average temperature of 68.1 degrees and an average rainfall of 54.51 inches. Buses serve the area along the U.S. Highway 90. Community facilities include a hospital, several motels, a library, churches, and two radio stations. The Florida Caverns State Park, three miles north, has extensive limestone caverns with guided trips available. Picnic areas, campsites, rock gardens, a museum, and golf course are located here. There are fine beaches for all water sports, and excellent hunting in the area.

■ **CITY COLLEGE (ALMONTE SPRINGS)**

177 Montgomery Rd.

Almonte Springs, FL 32714

Tel: (407)831-9816

Fax: (407)831-1147

E-mail: kbowden@citycollege.edu

Web Site: www.citycollege.edu/

Description: Independent, primarily 2-year, coed. Awards diplomas, terminal associate, and bachelor's degrees. Total enrollment: 217. Faculty: 37 (2 full-time, 35 part-time). Student-undergrad faculty ratio is 17:1. Full-time: 217 students, 84% women, 16% men. 62% 25 or older. Retention: 47% of full-time freshmen returned the following year. Calendar: semesters.

Entrance Requirements: Required: high school transcript, interview, TABE. Entrance: noncompetitive.

Collegiate Environment: Orientation program. 50 computers available on campus for general student use. A campuswide network can be accessed. Staffed computer lab on campus provides training in use of computers, software, and the Internet.

■ **CITY COLLEGE (FORT LAUDERDALE)**

2000 W Commercial Blvd.

Ste. 200

Fort Lauderdale, FL 33309

Tel: (954)492-5353; Free: 866-314-5681

Fax: (954)491-1965

E-mail: tcarpenter@citycollege.edu

Web Site: www.citycollege.edu/

Description: Independent, primarily 2-year, coed. Awards certificates, terminal associate, and bachelor's degrees. Founded 1984. Total enrollment: 677. Student-undergrad faculty ratio is 20:1. 129 applied, 91% were admitted. 0% from out-of-state. 64% 25 or older. Calendar: semesters.

Entrance Requirements: Required: high school transcript, interview, TABE.

■ **CITY COLLEGE (GAINESVILLE)**

7001 NW 4th Blvd.

Gainesville, FL 32607

Tel: (352)335-4000

Fax: (352)335-4303

Web Site: www.citycollege.edu/

Description: Independent, primarily 2-year, coed. Awards certificates, terminal associate, and bachelor's degrees. Founded 1986. Total enrollment: 426. Student-undergrad faculty ratio is 15:1. 43 applied, 98% were admitted. 0% from out-of-state. 67% 25 or older. Calendar: semesters.

Entrance Requirements: Required: high school transcript, interview, TABE.

■ **CITY COLLEGE (MIAMI)**

9300 S Dadeland Blvd.

Ste. PH

Miami, FL 33156

Tel: (305)666-9242

Fax: (305)666-9243

Web Site: www.citycollege.edu/

Description: Independent, primarily 2-year, coed. Awards certificates, terminal associate, and bachelor's degrees. Founded 1997. Total enrollment: 416. Student-undergrad faculty ratio is 22:1. 107 applied, 62% were admitted. 0% from out-of-state. 54% 25 or older. Calendar: semesters.

Entrance Requirements: Required: high school transcript, interview, TABE.

■ **CLEARWATER CHRISTIAN COLLEGE**

3400 Gulf-to-Bay Blvd.

Clearwater, FL 33759-4595

Tel: (727)726-1153; Free: 800-348-4463

Fax: (727)726-8597

E-mail: admissions@clearwater.edu

Web Site: www.clearwater.edu/

Description: Independent nondenominational, comprehensive, coed. Awards associate, bachelor's, and master's degrees. Founded 1966. Setting: 138-acre suburban campus with easy access to Tampa-St. Petersburg. Endowment: $577,109. Educational spending for the previous fiscal year: $5285 per student. Total enrollment: 498. Faculty: 43 (30 full-time, 13 part-time). Student-undergrad faculty ratio is 14:1. 353 applied, 72% were admitted. 11% from top 10% of their high school class, 24% from top quarter, 50% from top half. Full-time: 470 students, 49% women, 51% men. Part-time: 15 students, 53% women, 47% men. Students come from 38 states and ter-

ritories, 8 other countries, 46% from out-of-state. 0% American Indian or Alaska Native, non-Hispanic/Latino; 10% Hispanic/Latino; 5% African American, non-Hispanic/Latino; 1% Asian, non-Hispanic/Latino; 0% Native Hawaiian or other Pacific Islander, non-Hispanic/Latino; 2% international. 3% 25 or older, 75% live on campus, 7% transferred in. Retention: 68% of full-time freshmen returned the following year. Academic areas with the most degrees conferred: business/marketing; biological/life sciences; education. Core. Calendar: semesters. Academic remediation for entering students, services for LD students, advanced placement, independent study, distance learning, double major, summer session for credit, part-time degree program, internships. Off campus study. Study abroad program. ROTC: Army (c), Naval (c), Air Force (c).

Entrance Requirements: Options: electronic application, early admission, deferred admission, international baccalaureate accepted. Required: essay, high school transcript, minimum 2 high school GPA, 2 recommendations, Christian testimony, SAT or ACT. Recommended: interview. Entrance: minimally difficult. Application deadline: Rolling. Notification: continuous. Transfer credits accepted: Yes.

Costs Per Year: Application fee: $35. Comprehensive fee: $25,360 includes full-time tuition ($17,060) and college room and board ($8300). College room only: $5050. Full-time tuition varies according to student level. Room and board charges vary according to board plan. Tuition guaranteed not to increase for student's term of enrollment.

Collegiate Environment: Orientation program. Drama-theater group, choral group, student-run newspaper. Social organizations: 19 open to all; Social groups that are non-fraternity; 100% of eligible men and 100% of eligible women are members. Most popular organizations: Drama Club, Alpha Chi, College Republicans, Science Club, Student Missionary Fellowship. Major annual events: Homecoming, Christmas Banquet, Christian Life Conference. Student services: personal-psychological counseling. Campus security: 24-hour emergency response devices and patrols. 600 college housing spaces available. Freshmen guaranteed college housing. On-campus residence required through senior year. Options: men-only, women-only housing available. Easter Library with 112,000 books, 3,400 microform titles, 12,000 serials, 7,600 audiovisual materials, and an OPAC. Operations spending for the previous fiscal year: $227,662. 45 computers available on campus for general student use. A campuswide network can be accessed from student residence rooms and from off campus. Students can access the following: online class registration. Staffed computer lab on campus provides training in use of computers, software, and the Internet.

Community Environment: Clearwater is located on Pinellas Peninsula, between Clearwater and Old Tampa Bays, 20 miles west of Tampa. The area is an all-year resort and citrus center. Amtrak, all major airlines, and buses serve the area. Airports are in St. Petersburg and Tampa. Community facilities include churches of all denominations, a library, museums, hotels, motels, two hospitals, a health center, city parks, floral gardens, a civic center, a maritime center and the usual fraternal civic and veterans organizations. Employment is available in the citrus packing and canning industries. The broad white sand beach on the gulf is the main attraction in the city. This beautiful beach provides for water sports, deep sea fishing, boating, etc. The Philadelphia Phillies baseball team comes here for spring training. The Clearwater Yacht Club and four golf courses including the Professional Golfers Association Club provide additional recreational facilities.

■ **COLLEGE OF BUSINESS AND TECHNOLOGY**

8991 SW 107th Ave.

Miami, FL 33176

Tel: (305)273-4499; Free: 866-626-8842

Fax: (305)273-5216

E-mail: admissions@cbt.edu

Web Site: www.cbt.edu/

Description: Proprietary, primarily 2-year, coed. Awards certificates, diplomas, transfer associate, and bachelor's degrees. Founded 1988. Total enrollment: 1,098. Faculty: 28 (12 full-time, 16 part-time). Student-undergrad faculty ratio is 15:1. 1,463 applied, 75% were admitted. 4 National Merit Scholars, 4 valedictorians, 2 student government officers. Full-time: 1,098 students, 37% women, 63% men. Students come from 4 states and territories, 0% from out-of-state. 1% American Indian or Alaska Native, non-Hispanic/Latino; 85% Hispanic/Latino; 11% African American, non-Hispanic/Latino; 0.1% Asian, non-Hispanic/Latino; 0.1% Native Hawaiian or other Pacific Islander, non-Hispanic/Latino. 70% 25 or older, 3% transferred in. Core. Calendar: semesters. Academic remediation for entering students, ESL program, services for LD students, advanced placement, accelerated degree program, honors program, independent study, distance learning, double major, summer session for credit, part-time degree program, adult/ continuing education programs, co-op programs and internships. Off campus study.

Entrance Requirements: Open admission. Option: electronic application. Required: essay, high school transcript, minimum 2.6 high school GPA, 2 recommendations, interview. Entrance: minimally difficult.

Costs Per Year: Application fee: $25. Tuition: $10,920 full-time. Mandatory fees: $1400 full-time.

Collegiate Environment: Orientation program. Student-run newspaper. The Bill Clinton Library plus 1 other with 700,000 books, 200,000 serials, 1,200 audiovisual materials, an OPAC, and a Web page. 150 computers available on campus for general student use. A campuswide network can be accessed from student residence rooms and from off campus. Students can access the following: online class registration. Staffed computer lab on campus.

■ COLLEGE OF CENTRAL FLORIDA

3001 SW College Rd.
Ocala, FL 34474
Tel: (352)854-2322
Fax: (352)237-3747
E-mail: sewelld@cf.edu
Web Site: www.cf.edu/

Description: State and locally supported, primarily 2-year, coed. Part of Florida Community College System. Awards certificates, diplomas, transfer associate, terminal associate, and bachelor's degrees. Founded 1957. Setting: 139-acre small town campus. Endowment: $40.1 million. Total enrollment: 8,766. Faculty: 611 (131 full-time, 480 part-time). Student-undergrad faculty ratio is 18:1. Full-time: 3,666 students, 59% women, 41% men. Part-time: 5,100 students, 65% women, 35% men. 32% 25 or older. Core. Calendar: semesters. Academic remediation for entering students, ESL program, services for LD students, advanced placement, freshman honors college, honors program, independent study, distance learning, summer session for credit, part-time degree program, adult/continuing education programs, co-op programs and internships.

Entrance Requirements: Open admission. Option: early admission. Required: high school transcript. Recommended: SAT, ACT, SAT or ACT, SAT and SAT Subject Tests or ACT, SAT Subject Tests. Entrance: noncompetitive. Application deadline: Rolling. Notification: continuous. Transfer credits accepted: Yes.

Costs Per Year: Application fee: $30. State resident tuition: $2388 full-time, $79.60 per credit hour part-time. Nonresident tuition: $9552 full-time, $421.88 per credit hour part-time. Mandatory fees: $765 full-time, $25.50 per credit hour part-time. Full-time tuition and fees vary according to course level, degree level, and program. Part-time tuition and fees vary according to course level, degree level, and program.

Collegiate Environment: Orientation program. Drama-theater group, choral group, student-run newspaper. Social organizations: 31 open to all. Most popular organizations: Student Activities Board, African-American Student Union, ROC (Realizing Our Cause), Gay Straight Alliance, Musagettas. Major annual events: Homecoming, Student Activities Week, Student Activities Banquet. Student services: personal-psychological counseling. Campus security: 24-hour emergency response devices and patrols, student patrols, late night transport-escort service. Learning Resources Center plus 1 other with 60,558 books, 412 serials, 6,244 audiovisual materials, an OPAC, and a Web page. 737 computers available on campus for general student use. Computer purchase/lease plans available. A campuswide network can be accessed from off-campus. Students can access the following: online class registration. Staffed computer lab on campus provides training in use of computers, software, and the Internet.

Community Environment: Ocala, the county seat, is the largest city in Marion County, and the hub of local economic and cultural activity. Service and light manufacturing industries provide the majority of employment opportunities, although agriculture is also important to the area. The 450 horse farms in the Ocala area rival Kentucky as the home of the best American thoroughbreds. Ocala boasts a mild climate, beautiful countryside, and is in close proximity to major tourist and recreational facilities. Numerous lakes provide fishing and other water sports. Ocala has 16 parks and playgrounds, two municipal swimming pools, and an 18-hole public golf course. The Sunshine Christmas Parade is an annual event.

■ DAYTONA STATE COLLEGE

1200 W International Speedway Blvd.
Daytona Beach, FL 32114
Tel: (386)506-3000

E-mail: sanderk@daytonastate.edu
Web Site: www.daytonastate.edu/

Description: State-supported, primarily 2-year, coed. Part of Florida Community College System. Awards certificates, diplomas, transfer associate, terminal associate, and bachelor's degrees. Founded 1958. Setting: 100-acre suburban campus with easy access to Orlando. Endowment: $9.4 million. Educational spending for the previous fiscal year: $6022 per student. Total enrollment: 15,708. Faculty: 931 (325 full-time, 606 part-time). Student-undergrad faculty ratio is 26:1. 4,684 applied, 99% were admitted. Full-time: 6,429 students, 55% women, 45% men. Part-time: 9,279 students, 64% women, 36% men. Students come from 51 states and territories, 130 other countries, 4% from out-of-state. 1% American Indian or Alaska Native, non-Hispanic/Latino; 11% Hispanic/Latino; 13% African American, non-Hispanic/Latino; 2% Asian, non-Hispanic/Latino; 0.1% Native Hawaiian or other Pacific Islander, non-Hispanic/Latino; 0% international. 40% 25 or older, 7% transferred in. Academic areas with the most degrees conferred: business/marketing; education; engineering. Core. Calendar: semesters. Academic remediation for entering students, ESL program, services for LD students, advanced placement, freshman honors college, honors program, independent study, distance learning, double major, summer session for credit, part-time degree program, external degree program, adult/continuing education programs, co-op programs and internships. Off campus study. Study abroad program. ROTC: Army (c), Air Force (c).

Entrance Requirements: Open admission except for nursing, allied health, public services programs, limited access and bachelor's programs. Options: electronic application, early admission, deferred admission, international baccalaureate accepted. Required: high school transcript. Entrance: noncompetitive. Application deadline: Rolling. Notification: continuous. Transfer credits accepted: Yes.

Collegiate Environment: Orientation program. Drama-theater group, choral group, student-run newspaper. Social organizations: 50 open to all; national fraternities, national sororities, local fraternities, local sororities; 10% of eligible men and 15% of eligible women are members. Most popular organizations: Florida Student Nursing Association, Phi Theta Kappa, Mu Rho Chapter, Student Government Association, Campus Crusade for Christ, Student Paralegal Association. Major annual events: Cultural Festival, Outstanding Student Awards/Honors Reception, Welcome Back Student Days. Student services: personal-psychological counseling, women's center. Campus security: 24-hour emergency response devices and patrols, late night transport-escort service. College housing not available. Mary Karl Memorial Learning Resources Center plus 1 other with 91,000 books, 735 serials, 5,000 audiovisual materials, an OPAC, and a Web page. Operations spending for the previous fiscal year: $3.3 million. 3,208 computers available on campus for general student use. A campuswide network can be accessed. Students can access the following: online class registration. Staffed computer lab on campus provides training in use of computers and software.

Community Environment: See Bethune-Cookman College.

■ DEVRY UNIVERSITY (JACKSONVILLE)

5200 Belfort Rd.
Jacksonville, FL 32256-6040
Web Site: www.devry.edu/locations/campuses/loc_jacksonville.jsp
Description: Proprietary, comprehensive, coed. Awards associate, bachelor's, and master's degrees.

■ DEVRY UNIVERSITY (MIAMI)

8700 W Flagler St., Ste. 100
Miami, FL 33174-2535
Tel: (305)229-4833; Free: 866-338-7941
Web Site: www.devry.edu/
Description: Proprietary, comprehensive, coed. Awards bachelor's and master's degrees. Calendar: semesters.

■ DEVRY UNIVERSITY (MIRAMAR)

2300 SW 145th Ave.
Miramar, FL 33027-4150
Tel: (954)499-9775; Free: 866-338-7941
Web Site: www.devry.edu/
Description: Proprietary, comprehensive, coed. Part of DeVry University. Awards associate, bachelor's, and master's degrees. Founded 2002. Total enrollment: 881. Faculty: 61 (18 full-time, 43 part-time). Student-undergrad faculty ratio is 16:1. Full-time: 295 students, 35% women, 65% men. Part-time: 419 students, 41% women, 59% men. 11% from out-of-state. 0% American Indian or Alaska Native, non-Hispanic/Latino; 43% Hispanic/

Latino; 22% African American, non-Hispanic/Latino; 1% Asian, non-Hispanic/Latino; 0.3% Native Hawaiian or other Pacific Islander, non-Hispanic/Latino; 4% international. 69% 25 or older, 16% transferred in. Academic areas with the most degrees conferred: business/marketing; computer and information sciences; engineering technologies. Calendar: semesters. Part-time degree program.

Entrance Requirements: Required: high school transcript, interview. Entrance: minimally difficult. Application deadline: Rolling. Notification: continuous.

Costs Per Year: Application fee: $40. Tuition: $16,076 full-time, $609 per credit hour part-time. Mandatory fees: $80 full-time.

Collegiate Environment: College housing not available.

■ **DEVRY UNIVERSITY (ORLANDO)**
4000 Millenia Blvd.
Orlando, FL 32839
Tel: (407)345-2800; Free: 866-338-7941
Web Site: www.devry.edu/
Description: Proprietary, comprehensive, coed. Part of DeVry University. Awards associate, bachelor's, and master's degrees. Founded 2000. Setting: urban campus. Total enrollment: 1,594. Faculty: 98 (25 full-time, 73 part-time). Student-undergrad faculty ratio is 19:1. Full-time: 543 students, 36% women, 64% men. Part-time: 787 students, 43% women; 57% men. 15% from out-of-state. 0.2% American Indian or Alaska Native, non-Hispanic/Latino; 22% Hispanic/Latino; 21% African American, non-Hispanic/Latino; 2% Asian, non-Hispanic/Latino; 0.3% Native Hawaiian or other Pacific Islander, non-Hispanic/Latino; 2% international. 72% 25 or older, 20% transferred in. Academic areas with the most degrees conferred: business/marketing; computer and information sciences; engineering. Calendar: semesters. Part-time degree program, adult/continuing education programs.

Entrance Requirements: Required: high school transcript, interview. Entrance: minimally difficult. Application deadline: Rolling. Notification: continuous.

Costs Per Year: Application fee: $40. Tuition: $16,076 full-time, $609 per credit hour part-time. Mandatory fees: $80 full-time.

Collegiate Environment: Orientation program. College housing not available. Learning Resource Center with a Web page.

■ **DEVRY UNIVERSITY (TAMPA)**
3030 N Rocky Point Dr. W, Ste. 100
Tampa, FL 33607-5901
Tel: (813)288-8994; Free: 866-338-7941
Fax: (813)288-8980
Web Site: www.devry.edu/
Description: Proprietary, comprehensive, coed. Awards associate, bachelor's, and master's degrees. Calendar: semesters.

■ **ECKERD COLLEGE**
4200 54th Ave. S
Saint Petersburg, FL 33711
Tel: (727)867-1166; Free: 800-456-9009
Fax: (727)866-2304
E-mail: admissions@eckerd.edu
Web Site: www.eckerd.edu/
Description: Independent Presbyterian, 4-year, coed. Awards bachelor's degrees. Founded 1958. Setting: 188-acre suburban campus with easy access to Tampa. Endowment: $45.6 million. Research spending for the previous fiscal year: $403,815. Total enrollment: 1,893. Faculty: 164 (117 full-time, 47 part-time). Student-undergrad faculty ratio is 13:1. 3,713 applied, 68% were admitted. Full-time: 1,849 students, 59% women, 41% men. Part-time: 44 students, 61% women, 39% men. Students come from 47 states and territories, 35 other countries, 80% from out-of-state. 0.4% American Indian or Alaska Native, non-Hispanic/Latino; 8% Hispanic/Latino; 3% African American, non-Hispanic/Latino; 1% Asian, non-Hispanic/Latino; 0.2% Native Hawaiian or other Pacific Islander, non-Hispanic/Latino; 4% international. 1% 25 or older, 81% live on campus, 3% transferred in. Retention: 81% of full-time freshmen returned the following year. Academic areas with the most degrees conferred: biological/life sciences; business/marketing; psychology. Core. Calendar: 4-1-4. Services for LD students, advanced placement, accelerated degree program, self-designed majors, honors program, independent study, double major, summer session for credit, part-time degree program, external degree program, adult/continuing education programs, internships. Off campus study at other colleges having a 4-1-4 calendar. Study abroad program. ROTC: Army (c), Air Force (c).

Entrance Requirements: Options: electronic application, early action, deferred admission, international baccalaureate accepted. Required: essay, high school transcript, 1 recommendation, SAT or ACT. Recommended: minimum 3 high school GPA, interview, SAT Subject Tests. Entrance: moderately difficult. Application deadlines: Rolling, 11/15 for early action. Notification: continuous, 12/15 for early action. SAT Reasoning Test deadline: 3/15. SAT Subject Test deadline: 3/15. Transfer credits accepted: Yes. Applicants placed on waiting list: 111. Wait-listed applicants offered admission: 34. Early action applicants: 1,109. Early action applicants admitted: 978.

Costs Per Year: Application fee: $40. Comprehensive fee: $47,506 includes full-time tuition ($37,046), mandatory fees ($316), and college room and board ($10,144). College room only: $5106. Room and board charges vary according to board plan and housing facility. Part-time tuition: $4361 per course.

Collegiate Environment: Orientation program. Drama-theater group, choral group, student-run newspaper, radio station. Social organizations: 90 open to all. Most popular organizations: Earth Society, Water Search and Rescue Team, The Current (student newspaper), College Choir, Organization of Students. Major annual events: Festival of Hope, Kappa Carnival, Midnight Madness/Triton Tip-Off. Student services: health clinic, personal-psychological counseling, women's center. Campus security: 24-hour emergency response devices and patrols, student patrols, late night transport-escort service, controlled dormitory access. 1,501 college housing spaces available; all were occupied in 2012-13. Freshmen guaranteed college housing. On-campus residence required in freshman year. Options: coed, women-only housing available. Peter Armacost Library with 181,031 books, 14,388 microform titles, 6,775 serials, 3,415 audiovisual materials, an OPAC, and a Web page. 300 computers available on campus for general student use. A campuswide network can be accessed from student residence rooms and from off campus. Students can access the following: online class registration, free computer repair shop. Staffed computer lab on campus (open 24 hours a day) provides training in use of computers, software, and the Internet.

Community Environment: St. Petersburg, known as the"Sunshine City," has a wonderful semitropical climate. The city is the state's fourth largest, and is the most important tourist center on the west coast of Florida. The city has 33 miles of shoreline on the Gulf of Mexico and several fresh water lakes: an excellent location for all water sports. Other sports are baseball, basketball, soccer, cross country, volleyball, softball, golf, and tennis. This is the spring training area for several major league baseball teams. The Tampa Bay area also is home to football's Buccaneers, baseball's Devil Rays, hockey's Lightning, and the international headquarters of the Women's Tennis Association. Numerous points of interest include the Florida International Museum, Fort DeSoto Park, Sunshine Skyway, the St. Petersburg Museum of Fine Arts, the Dali Museum, and Tropicana Field.

■ **EDISON STATE COLLEGE**
8099 College Pky.
Fort Myers, FL 33919
Tel: (239)489-9300; Free: 800-749-2ECC
Fax: (239)489-9399
E-mail: Lauren.Willison@edison.edu
Web Site: www.edison.edu/
Description: State and locally supported, primarily 2-year, coed. Part of Florida Community College System. Awards certificates, diplomas, transfer associate, terminal associate, and bachelor's degrees. Founded 1962. Setting: 80-acre urban campus. Total enrollment: 13,007. Full-time: 4,570 students, 57% women, 43% men. Part-time: 8,437 students, 63% women, 37% men. Students come from 36 other countries, 0% from out-of-state. 34% 25 or older, 7% transferred in. Retention: 52% of full-time freshmen returned the following year. Academic area with the most degrees conferred: homeland security, law enforcement, firefighting, and protective services. Core. Calendar: semesters. Academic remediation for entering students, ESL program, services for LD students, advanced placement, accelerated degree program, honors program, independent study, distance learning, summer session for credit, part-time degree program, adult/continuing education programs, co-op programs and internships.

Entrance Requirements: Open admission. Options: electronic application, early admission, deferred admission, international baccalaureate accepted. Required: high school transcript. Recommended: SAT or ACT. Entrance: noncompetitive. Application deadline: 8/18. Notification: continuous.

Collegiate Environment: Orientation program. Drama-theater group, choral group. Social organizations: national fraternities, national sororities. Campus security: 24-hour emergency response devices and patrols, student patrols, late night transport-escort service. Richard H. Rush Library with 181,085 books and 10,297 audiovisual materials.

Community Environment: Edison Community College campuses are located on the sunny coast of southwest Florida, between Naples and Tampa. The climate is semitropical. The offshore islands have many attractive beaches, and majestic Royal Palms line the streets. All modes of transportation serve the area. Tourism, commercial fishing, shrimping and livestock production are important industries. The community facilities include churches of all denominations, hospitals, little theater groups, dances, and lecture halls. The saltwater bays and freshwater lakes nearby are among the finest fishing grounds anywhere. Other sports include boating, hunting, horseback riding, golf, bowling, tennis, shuffleboard and greyhound racing in Bonita Springs. TECO Arena is home to minor league hockey and basketball teams. A minor league baseball team also plays in Fort Myers. The Boston Red Sox and Minnesota Twins have their spring training camps in Fort Myers.

■ EDWARD WATERS COLLEGE

1658 Kings Rd.
Jacksonville, FL 32209-6199
Tel: (904)470-8000; Free: 888-898-3191
Fax: (904)470-8039
E-mail: edward.alexander@ewc.edu
Web Site: www.ewc.edu/

Description: Independent African Methodist Episcopal, 4-year, coed. Awards bachelor's degrees. Founded 1866. Setting: 50-acre urban campus. Total enrollment: 751. Faculty: 81 (36 full-time, 45 part-time). Student-undergrad faculty ratio is 9:1. 1,611 applied, 23% were admitted. Students come from 21 states and territories, 4 other countries, 19% from out-of-state. 0.3% American Indian or Alaska Native, non-Hispanic/Latino; 1% Hispanic/Latino; 94% African American, non-Hispanic/Latino; 0.1% Native Hawaiian or other Pacific Islander, non-Hispanic/Latino. Retention: 53% of full-time freshmen returned the following year. Academic areas with the most degrees conferred: business/marketing; homeland security, law enforcement, firefighting, and protective services; biological/life sciences. Core. Calendar: semesters. Academic remediation for entering students, services for LD students, self-designed majors, honors program, summer session for credit, part-time degree program, adult/continuing education programs, co-op programs and internships. Off campus study at University of North Florida. ROTC: Army (c).

Entrance Requirements: Open admission. Option: electronic application. Required: high school transcript, 2 recommendations, medical forms, SAT or ACT. Entrance: noncompetitive. Application deadline: Rolling. Notification: continuous. Transfer credits accepted: Yes.

Costs Per Year: Application fee: $25. Comprehensive fee: $18,028 includes full-time tuition ($11,158) and college room and board ($6870). College room only: $3280.

Collegiate Environment: Drama-theater group, choral group, marching band. Social organizations: national fraternities, national sororities. Student services: health clinic, personal-psychological counseling. Campus security: 24-hour emergency response devices and patrols, student patrols, late night transport-escort service, controlled dormitory access. Centennial Library with 65,798 books, 1,350 serials, and 2,900 audiovisual materials. 200 computers available on campus for general student use. A campuswide network can be accessed. Students can access the following: online class registration. Staffed computer lab on campus (open 24 hours a day) provides training in use of computers, software, and the Internet.

Community Environment: See Jacksonville University.

■ EMBRY-RIDDLE AERONAUTICAL UNIVERSITY–DAYTONA

600 S Clyde Morris Blvd.
Daytona Beach, FL 32114-3900
Tel: (386)226-6000; Free: 800-862-2416
Fax: (386)226-7070
E-mail: dbadmit@erau.edu
Web Site: www.embryriddle.edu/

Description: Independent, comprehensive, coed. Awards associate, bachelor's, master's, and doctoral degrees. Founded 1926. Setting: 168-acre suburban campus with easy access to Orlando. Endowment: $80.9 million. Research spending for the previous fiscal year: $14.5 million. Educational spending for the previous fiscal year: $13,918 per student. Total enrollment: 5,120. Faculty: 392 (312 full-time, 80 part-time). Student-undergrad faculty ratio is 13:1. 21% from top 10% of their high school class,

51% from top quarter, 82% from top half. Full-time: 4,225 students, 16% women, 84% men. Part-time: 309 students, 18% women, 82% men. Students come from 52 states and territories, 100 other countries, 59% from out-of-state. 1% American Indian or Alaska Native, non-Hispanic/Latino; 8% Hispanic/Latino; 6% African American, non-Hispanic/Latino; 5% Asian, non-Hispanic/Latino; 0.2% Native Hawaiian or other Pacific Islander, non-Hispanic/Latino; 15% international. 14% 25 or older, 40% live on campus, 6% transferred in. Retention: 77% of full-time freshmen returned the following year. Academic areas with the most degrees conferred: transportation and materials moving; engineering; business/marketing. Core. Calendar: semesters. Academic remediation for entering students, ESL program, services for LD students, advanced placement, accelerated degree program, honors program, independent study, distance learning, double major, summer session for credit, part-time degree program, adult/continuing education programs, co-op programs and internships, graduate courses open to undergrads. Study abroad program. ROTC: Army, Naval, Air Force.

Entrance Requirements: Options: electronic application, deferred admission, international baccalaureate accepted. Required: high school transcript, minimum 2 high school GPA, 2 recommendations, SAT or ACT. Recommended: essay, interview. Required for some: minimum 3 high school GPA, medical examination for flight students. Entrance: moderately difficult. Application deadlines: Rolling, Rolling for nonresidents. Notification: continuous, continuous for nonresidents. SAT Reasoning Test deadline: 7/1. SAT Subject Test deadline: 7/1. Transfer credits accepted: Yes.

Costs Per Year: Application fee: $50. Comprehensive fee: $40,884 includes full-time tuition ($30,120), mandatory fees ($1214), and college room and board ($9550). College room only: $5600. Room and board charges vary according to board plan and housing facility. Part-time tuition: $1255 per credit hour.

Collegiate Environment: Orientation program. Drama-theater group, choral group, student-run newspaper, radio station. Social organizations: 151 open to all; national fraternities, national sororities; 12% of eligible men and 19% of eligible women are members. Most popular organizations: Eagle Wing, Future Professional Pilots Association, African Student Association, Caribbean Student Association, Sigma Gamma Tau. Major annual events: Homecoming, spring concert, hypnotist performance. Student services: health clinic, personal-psychological counseling, women's center. Campus security: 24-hour emergency response devices and patrols, student patrols, late night transport-escort service, controlled dormitory access. 1,986 college housing spaces available; 1,855 were occupied in 2012-13. Freshmen guaranteed college housing. On-campus residence required in freshman year. Option: coed housing available. Jack R. Hunt Memorial Library with 146,360 books, 317,003 microform titles, 840 serials, 5,831 audiovisual materials, an OPAC, and a Web page. Operations spending for the previous fiscal year: $1.9 million. 1,049 computers available on campus for general student use. A campuswide network can be accessed from student residence rooms and from off campus. Students can access the following: online class registration. Staffed computer lab on campus (open 24 hours a day).

Community Environment: Daytona Beach has a population of approximately 500,000 in the immediate vicinity, and the campus itself has approximately 4,500 students. Boasting one of the finest recreational beaches in the world, it is also home to the Daytona International Speedway. Other major attractions include Walt Disney World and Sea World near Orlando (approximately 80 miles away). The area provides ample housing and excellent opportunities for part-time employment for ERAU students. The Prescott area is one of the more colorful areas of the old"Wild West," with a population in the immediate area approaching 100,000. The Prescott Campus of approximately 1,500 students is surrounded by a national forest and is close to mountains and excellent outdoor recreational areas. The city of Phoenix is about 90 miles away.

■ EMBRY-RIDDLE AERONAUTICAL UNIVERSITY–WORLDWIDE

600 S Clyde Morris Blvd.
Daytona Beach, FL 32114-3900
Tel: (386)226-6910; Free: 800-522-6787
Fax: (386)226-6984
E-mail: ecinfo@erau.edu
Web Site: www.embryriddle.edu/

Description: Independent, comprehensive, coed. Awards associate, bachelor's, master's, and doctoral degrees (programs offered at 100 military bases worldwide). Founded 1970. Endowment: $80.9 million. Research spending for the previous fiscal year: $51,000. Educational spending for the previous fiscal year: $4645 per student. Total enrollment: 16,482. Faculty:

2,711 (138 full-time, 2,573 part-time). Full-time: 2,875 students, 12% women, 88% men. Part-time: 8,242 students, 11% women, 89% men. 0.4% American Indian or Alaska Native, non-Hispanic/Latino; 9% Hispanic/Latino; 7% African American, non-Hispanic/Latino; 2% Asian, non-Hispanic/Latino; 0.5% Native Hawaiian or other Pacific Islander, non-Hispanic/Latino; 1% international. 5% transferred in. Academic areas with the most degrees conferred: transportation and materials moving; business/marketing; mechanic and repair technologies. Core. Calendar: 5 9-week terms. Services for LD students, advanced placement, independent study, distance learning, summer session for credit, part-time degree program, external degree program, adult/continuing education programs, co-op programs, graduate courses open to undergrads. Off campus study at Servicemembers Opportunity Colleges.

Entrance Requirements: Options: electronic application, deferred admission. Required: minimum 2 high school GPA. Required for some: essay, high school transcript, 2 recommendations, SAT with a minimum score of 1000 or ACT with a minimum score of 21; 300-500 word essay, SAT or ACT. Entrance: minimally difficult. Application deadline: Rolling. Notification: continuous. Transfer credits accepted: Yes.

Costs Per Year: Application fee: $50. Tuition: $7032 full-time, $305 per credit part-time. Full-time tuition varies according to program and reciprocity agreements. Part-time tuition varies according to program and reciprocity agreements.

Collegiate Environment: Orientation program. College housing not available. Jack R. Hunt Memorial Library with 116,440 books, 310,331 microform titles, 1,003 serials, 5,260 audiovisual materials, an OPAC, and a Web page. Operations spending for the previous fiscal year: $1.5 million.

■ EVEREST INSTITUTE (FORT LAUDERDALE)
1040 Bayview Dr.
Fort Lauderdale, FL 33304
Tel: (954)630-0066; Free: 888-741-4270
Fax: (954)630-0076
Web Site: www.everest.edu/
Description: Proprietary, 2-year, coed. Awards terminal associate degrees. Founded 2003. Total enrollment: 131. Student-undergrad faculty ratio is 7:1. 297 applied. 0% from out-of-state. 39% 25 or older. Calendar: continuous.
Entrance Requirements: Required: high school transcript.

■ EVEREST INSTITUTE (HIALEAH)
530 W 49th St.
Hialeah, FL 33012
Tel: (305)558-9500; Free: 888-741-4270
Fax: (305)558-4419
Web Site: www.everest.edu/
Description: Proprietary, 2-year, coed. Awards terminal associate degrees. Founded 1977. Total enrollment: 1,349. Student-undergrad faculty ratio is 19:1. 252 applied, 87% were admitted. 0% from out-of-state. 45% 25 or older. Calendar: continuous.

■ EVEREST INSTITUTE (MIAMI)
9020 SW 137th Ave.
Miami, FL 33186
Tel: (305)386-9900; Free: 888-741-4270
Fax: (305)388-1740
Web Site: www.everest.edu/
Description: Proprietary, 2-year, coed. Awards diplomas and terminal associate degrees. Founded 1977. Setting: urban campus. Total enrollment: 222. Student-undergrad faculty ratio is 8:1. 165 applied. 0% from out-of-state. 45% 25 or older. Retention: 59% of full-time freshmen returned the following year. Calendar: continuous.
Entrance Requirements: Required: high school transcript. Entrance: minimally difficult.

■ EVEREST INSTITUTE (MIAMI)
111 NW 183rd St., Second Fl.
Miami, FL 33169
Tel: (305)949-9500; Free: 888-741-4270
Fax: (305)956-5758
Web Site: www.everest.edu/
Description: Proprietary, 2-year, coed. Awards diplomas and terminal associate degrees. Founded 1977. Total enrollment: 1,052. 495 applied. 0% from out-of-state. 45% 25 or older. Retention: 60% of full-time freshmen returned the following year. Calendar: continuous.

■ EVEREST UNIVERSITY (JACKSONVILLE)
8226 Phillips Hwy.
Jacksonville, FL 32256
Tel: (904)731-4949; Free: 888-741-4270
Fax: (904)731-0599
E-mail: rmanning@cci.edu
Web Site: www.everest.edu/
Description: Proprietary, comprehensive, coed. Awards associate, bachelor's, and master's degrees. Founded 2000. Total enrollment: 409. 233 applied. 49% 25 or older.
Entrance Requirements: Entrance: minimally difficult.

■ EVEREST UNIVERSITY (LAKELAND)
995 E Memorial Blvd.
Ste. 110
Lakeland, FL 33801
Tel: (863)686-1444; Free: 888-741-4270
Fax: (863)688-9881
E-mail: psabol@cci.edu
Web Site: www.everest.edu/
Description: Proprietary, 4-year, coed. Part of Corinthian Colleges, Inc. Awards associate and bachelor's degrees (bachelor's degree in business administration only). Founded 1890. Setting: 3-acre urban campus with easy access to Orlando, Tampa-St. Petersburg. Total enrollment: 691. Faculty: 36 (10 full-time, 26 part-time). Student-undergrad faculty ratio is 18:1. Full-time: 343 students, 80% women, 20% men. Part-time: 340 students, 79% women, 21% men. Students come from 5 states and territories, 1% from out-of-state. 1% American Indian or Alaska Native, non-Hispanic/Latino; 13% Hispanic/Latino; 28% African American, non-Hispanic/Latino; 1% Asian, non-Hispanic/Latino; 0% Native Hawaiian or other Pacific Islander, non-Hispanic/Latino; 0% international. 70% 25 or older, 1% transferred in. Retention: 3% of full-time freshmen returned the following year. Academic areas with the most degrees conferred: business/marketing; law/legal studies. Core. Academic remediation for entering students, services for LD students, accelerated degree program, independent study, distance learning, summer session for credit, part-time degree program, external degree program, adult/continuing education programs, internships.
Entrance Requirements: Options: early admission, international baccalaureate accepted. Required: high school transcript, interview, CPAt. Recommended: essay, high school transcript, SAT or ACT. Entrance: minimally difficult. Transfer credits accepted: Yes.
Costs Per Year: Application fee: $0. Tuition: $452 per credit part-time. Part-time tuition varies according to course load, degree level, and program.
Collegiate Environment: Social organizations: 4 open to all. Most popular organizations: C. J. Association, Paralegal Society, Club Med, Phi Beta Lambda. Major annual events: Student Appreciation Week, Academic Event Weeks. Campus security: 24-hour patrols. Everest University Learning Resource Center with 5,000 books and 30 serials. 50 computers available on campus for general student use. Staffed computer lab on campus.

■ EVEREST UNIVERSITY (LARGO)
1199 E Bay Dr.
Largo, FL 33770
Tel: (727)725-2688; Free: 888-741-4270
Fax: (727)796-3722
E-mail: kbuskirk@cci.edu
Web Site: www.everest.edu/
Description: Proprietary, comprehensive, coed. Part of Corinthian Colleges, Inc. Awards associate, bachelor's, and master's degrees. Founded 1890. Setting: 3-acre urban campus with easy access to Tampa-St. Petersburg. Total enrollment: 261. 152 applied. 63% 25 or older. Core. Academic remediation for entering students, services for LD students, advanced placement, accelerated degree program, honors program, double major, summer session for credit, part-time degree program, adult/continuing education programs, co-op programs and internships.
Entrance Requirements: Options: early admission, deferred admission, international baccalaureate accepted. Required: high school transcript, interview, CPAt. Recommended: minimum 2.0 high school GPA, SAT or ACT. Entrance: minimally difficult. Application deadline: Rolling.
Collegiate Environment: Orientation program. Student-run newspaper. Campus security: 24-hour emergency response devices, late night transport-escort service, evening patrols by security. Laurel Raffel Memorial Library with 6,721 books and 51 serials.

■ **EVEREST UNIVERSITY (MELBOURNE)**

2401 N Harbor City Blvd.

Melbourne, FL 32935-6657

Tel: (321)253-2929

Fax: (321)255-2017

Web Site: www.everest.edu/

Description: Proprietary, comprehensive, coed. Part of Corinthian Colleges, Inc. Awards associate, bachelor's, and master's degrees. Founded 1953. Setting: 5-acre small town campus with easy access to Orlando. Total enrollment: 291. 152 applied. 60% 25 or older. Core. Academic remediation for entering students, advanced placement, accelerated degree program, summer session for credit, part-time degree program, internships, graduate courses open to undergrads.

Entrance Requirements: Option: deferred admission. Required: high school transcript, interview, CPAt. Entrance: minimally difficult. Application deadline: Rolling.

Collegiate Environment: Student services: personal-psychological counseling. Campus security: 24-hour emergency response devices. 5,000 books and 51 serials.

■ **EVEREST UNIVERSITY (ORANGE PARK)**

805 Wells Rd.

Orange Park, FL 32073

Tel: (904)264-9122

Fax: (904)264-9952

Web Site: www.everest.edu/

Description: Proprietary, primarily 2-year, coed. Awards terminal associate and bachelor's degrees. Founded 2003. Total enrollment: 1,359. Student-undergrad faculty ratio is 14:1. 269 applied, 65% were admitted. 2% from out-of-state. 67% 25 or older. Retention: 54% of full-time freshmen returned the following year.

■ **EVEREST UNIVERSITY - NORTH ORLANDO (ORLANDO)**

5421 Diplomat Cir.

Orlando, FL 32810-5674

Tel: (407)628-5870; Free: 800-628-5870

Fax: (407)628-2616

Web Site: www.everest.edu/

Description: Proprietary, comprehensive, coed. Part of Corinthian Colleges, Inc. Awards associate, bachelor's, and master's degrees. Founded 1953. Setting: 1-acre urban campus. Total enrollment: 527. Faculty: 96 (10 full-time, 86 part-time). Student-undergrad faculty ratio is 15:1. 145 applied. 43% 25 or older. Core. Advanced placement, independent study, double major, summer session for credit, part-time degree program, external degree program, internships.

Entrance Requirements: Option: deferred admission. Required: high school transcript, interview, entrance evaluation. Entrance: minimally difficult. Application deadline: Rolling. Notification: continuous.

Collegiate Environment: Orientation program. Campus security: door alarms. FMU North Orlando Library with 18,000 books, 78 serials, 337 audiovisual materials, an OPAC, and a Web page.

■ **EVEREST UNIVERSITY - SOUTH ORLANDO (ORLANDO)**

9200 S Park Ctr. Loop

Orlando, FL 32819

Tel: (407)851-2525; Free: 888-471-4270

Fax: (407)851-1477

Web Site: www.everest.edu/

Description: Proprietary, comprehensive, coed. Awards associate, bachelor's, and master's degrees. Founded 1987. Total enrollment: 823. 755 applied. 48% 25 or older. Core. Academic remediation for entering students, services for LD students, accelerated degree program, distance learning, double major, part-time degree program, adult/continuing education programs, co-op programs and internships.

Entrance Requirements: Required: high school transcript, interview. Entrance: minimally difficult. Application deadline: Rolling. Notification: continuous.

Collegiate Environment: Orientation program. 5,113 books, 79 serials, 441 audiovisual materials, and a Web page.

■ **EVEREST UNIVERSITY (POMPANO BEACH)**

225 N Federal Hwy.

Pompano Beach, FL 33062

Tel: (954)783-7339

Fax: (954)568-2008

Web Site: www.everest.edu/

Description: Proprietary, comprehensive, coed. Part of Corinthian Colleges, Inc. Awards associate, bachelor's, and master's degrees. Founded 1940. Setting: urban campus with easy access to Miami. Total enrollment: 1,633. Student-undergrad faculty ratio is 16:1. 314 applied, 69% were admitted. 1% from out-of-state. 63% 25 or older. Retention: 42% of full-time freshmen returned the following year. Core. ESL program, distance learning, summer session for credit, part-time degree program, adult/continuing education programs, internships.

Entrance Requirements: Options: electronic application, deferred admission. Required: CPAt. Recommended: SAT or ACT. Entrance: minimally difficult. Application deadline: Rolling. Notification: continuous.

Collegiate Environment: Orientation program. Student-run newspaper. Student services: personal-psychological counseling. Campus security: late night transport-escort service, building security.

■ **EVEREST UNIVERSITY (TAMPA)**

3319 W Hillsborough Ave.

Tampa, FL 33614-5899

Tel: (813)879-6000

Fax: (813)871-2483

Web Site: www.everest.edu/

Description: Proprietary, comprehensive, coed. Part of Corinthian Colleges, Inc. Awards associate, bachelor's, and master's degrees. Founded 1890. Setting: 4-acre urban campus. Total enrollment: 3,430. Faculty: 61 (13 full-time, 48 part-time). Student-undergrad faculty ratio is 20:1. 2,225 applied, 74% were admitted. Full-time: 2,750 students, 63% women, 37% men. Part-time: 636 students, 69% women, 31% men. Students come from 15 states and territories, 3 other countries. 51% 25 or older, 1% transferred in. Core. ESL program, advanced placement, accelerated degree program, self-designed majors, independent study, distance learning, double major, summer session for credit, part-time degree program, external degree program, adult/continuing education programs, co-op programs and internships.

Entrance Requirements: Options: deferred admission, international baccalaureate accepted. Required: high school transcript, CPAt. Required for some: SAT, ACT. Entrance: minimally difficult. Application deadline: Rolling. Notification: continuous.

Collegiate Environment: Social organizations: 6 open to all; coed fraternity; 7% of eligible men and 13% of eligible women are members. Most popular organizations: Legal Network, Phi Beta Lambda, Ambassadors Club. Major annual events: Clean City Day, Health Fair. Campus security: 24-hour emergency response devices, evening and Saturday afternoon patrols by trained security personnel. Tampa College Library with 4,000 books, 95 microform titles, 130 serials, 260 audiovisual materials, an OPAC, and a Web page. Operations spending for the previous fiscal year: $90,000. 113 computers available on campus for general student use. Staffed computer lab on campus.

■ **EVEREST UNIVERSITY - BRANDON (TAMPA)**

3924 Coconut Palm Dr.

Tampa, FL 33619

Tel: (813)621-0041; Free: 888-741-4270

E-mail: spointer@cci.edu

Web Site: www.everest.edu/

Description: Proprietary, comprehensive, coed. Part of Corinthian Colleges, Inc. Awards associate, bachelor's, and master's degrees. Founded 1890. Setting: 5-acre urban campus with easy access to Tampa. Total enrollment: 12,695. Faculty: 61 (25 full-time, 36 part-time). Student-undergrad faculty ratio is 17:1. 0.5% American Indian or Alaska Native, non-Hispanic/Latino; 25% Hispanic/Latino; 31% African American, non-Hispanic/Latino; 1% Asian, non-Hispanic/Latino; 0.4% Native Hawaiian or other Pacific Islander, non-Hispanic/Latino; 0% international. 68% 25 or older. Academic areas with the most degrees conferred: business/marketing; homeland security, law enforcement, firefighting, and protective services; law/legal studies. Core. Academic remediation for entering students, ESL program, services for LD students, accelerated degree program, distance learning, double major, summer session for credit, part-time degree program, external degree program, adult/continuing education programs, co-op programs.

Entrance Requirements: Options: early admission, deferred admission, international baccalaureate accepted. Required: high school transcript, interview. Entrance: minimally difficult. Application deadline: Rolling. Notification: continuous.

Collegiate Environment: Orientation program. Social organizations: 12

open to all. Most popular organizations: Accounting Club, Medical Assistants Club, Paralegal Club, Criminal Justice Club, Surgical Technology Club. Major annual events: Toys For Tots, Student Appreciation Days, Thanksgiving and Christmas food drives. Campus security: 24-hour emergency response devices, on-campus security guard on duty during business hours. Everest University Library with 73,608 books, 103 serials, 338 audiovisual materials, an OPAC, and a Web page. 200 computers available on campus for general student use. A campuswide network can be accessed. Staffed computer lab on campus provides training in use of computers, software, and the Internet.

■ **EVERGLADES UNIVERSITY (ALTAMONTE SPRINGS)**
887 E Altamonte Dr.
Altamonte Springs, FL 32701
Tel: (407)277-0311; Free: 866-289-1078
Fax: (407)482-9801
E-mail: admissions-orl@evergladesuniversity.edu
Web Site: www.evergladesuniversity.edu/
Description: Independent, comprehensive, coed. Awards bachelor's and master's degrees.

■ **EVERGLADES UNIVERSITY (BOCA RATON)**
5002 T-Rex Ave., Ste. 100
Boca Raton, FL 33431
Tel: (561)912-1211; Free: 888-772-6077
Fax: (561)912-1191
E-mail: admissions-boca@evergladesuniversity.edu
Web Site: www.evergladesuniversity.edu/
Description: Independent, comprehensive, coed. Awards bachelor's and master's degrees. Founded 1989. Setting: suburban campus. Total enrollment: 1,039. Student-undergrad faculty ratio is 10:1. 354 applied, 84% were admitted. 37% from out-of-state. 81% 25 or older. Calendar: continuous. Summer session for credit.
Entrance Requirements: Open admission. Required: high school transcript. Required for some: SAT or ACT. Application deadlines: Rolling, Rolling for nonresidents. Notification: continuous, continuous for nonresidents.
Collegiate Environment: Orientation program. Campus security: 24-hour emergency response devices and patrols, late night transport-escort service.

■ **EVERGLADES UNIVERSITY (SARASOTA)**
6001 Lake Osprey Dr. No.110
Sarasota, FL 34240
Tel: (941)907-2262; Free: 866-907-2262
Fax: (941)907-6634
E-mail: admissions-sar@evergladesuniversity.edu
Web Site: www.evergladesuniversity.edu/
Description: Independent, comprehensive, coed. Awards bachelor's and master's degrees. Founded 2003. Calendar: continuous.

■ **FLAGLER COLLEGE**
74 King St.
Saint Augustine, FL 32085-1027
Tel: (904)829-6481; Free: 800-304-4208
Fax: (904)826-0094
E-mail: admiss@flagler.edu
Web Site: www.flagler.edu/
Description: Independent, 4-year, coed. Awards bachelor's degrees. Founded 1968. Setting: 32-acre small town campus with easy access to Jacksonville. Endowment: $54.9 million. Educational spending for the previous fiscal year: $5054 per student. Total enrollment: 2,847. Faculty: 228 (108 full-time, 120 part-time). Student-undergrad faculty ratio is 18:1. 5,347 applied, 41% were admitted. 14% from top 10% of their high school class, 45% from top quarter, 90% from top half. Full-time: 2,764 students, 59% women, 41% men. Part-time: 83 students, 64% women, 36% men. Students come from 43 states and territories, 32 other countries, 36% from out-of-state. 1% American Indian or Alaska Native, non-Hispanic/Latino; 7% Hispanic/Latino; 4% African American, non-Hispanic/Latino; 1% Asian, non-Hispanic/Latino; 0.1% Native Hawaiian or other Pacific Islander, non-Hispanic/Latino; 3% international. 8% 25 or older, 36% live on campus, 6% transferred in. Retention: 69% of full-time freshmen returned the following year. Academic areas with the most degrees conferred: business/marketing; communication/journalism; education; visual and performing arts; psychology. Core. Calendar: semesters. Academic remediation for entering students, services

for LD students, advanced placement, independent study, double major, summer session for credit, internships. Study abroad program.
Entrance Requirements: Options: electronic application, early admission, early decision, deferred admission, international baccalaureate accepted. Required: essay, high school transcript, SAT or ACT. Recommended: minimum 2 high school GPA, 1 recommendation, interview, rank in upper 50% of high school class. Entrance: moderately difficult. Application deadlines: 3/1, 12/1 for early decision. Notification: 3/30, 12/15 for early decision. SAT Reasoning Test deadline: 3/30. Transfer credits accepted: Yes. Applicants placed on waiting list: 809. Wait-listed applicants offered admission: 61. Early decision applicants: 695. Early decision applicants admitted: 302.
Costs Per Year: Application fee: $40. Comprehensive fee: $23,690 includes full-time tuition ($15,340) and college room and board ($8350). College room only: $4070. Room and board charges vary according to board plan and housing facility. Part-time tuition: $510 per credit hour.
Collegiate Environment: Orientation program. Drama-theater group, choral group, student-run newspaper, radio station. Social organizations: 36 open to all. Most popular organizations: Student Government Association, InterVarsity, Campus Crusade, Mu Epsilon Nu (men's service club), Phi Alpha Omega (women's service club). Major annual events: Midnight Breakfast, Bachelor Bid, Spring Formal. Student services: health clinic, personal-psychological counseling. Campus security: 24-hour emergency response devices and patrols, late night transport-escort service, controlled dormitory access. 1,030 college housing spaces available; 969 were occupied in 2012-13. Freshmen guaranteed college housing. On-campus residence required in freshman year. Options: men-only, women-only housing available. Proctor Library with 225,004 books, 1,877 microform titles, 598 serials, 4,922 audiovisual materials, an OPAC, and a Web page. Operations spending for the previous fiscal year: $743,399. 265 computers available on campus for general student use. A campuswide network can be accessed from student residence rooms and from off campus. Students can access the following: online class registration. Staffed computer lab on campus provides training in use of computers and the Internet.
Community Environment: St. Augustine, the nation's oldest city, has a very mild climate; average high temperature is 79.9 degrees and the average low is 58.3 degrees. The city is located approximately 40 miles south of Jacksonville, near the Atlantic coast. St. Augustine is undergoing a restoration program to extend over a twenty-year period that will return the entire area to an authentic likeness of its colonial days. The leading industries are tourist trade, airplane rebuilding, aluminum extrusion, boat-building, food processing, and shrimp fishing. Recreation facilities include championship golf courses, beaches, tennis courts, and the ocean for deep sea fishing. The Matanzas River affords miles of protected waters for boating and fishing. The city has churches of all denominations, numerous hotels and motels, 2 hospitals, and a library. All major civic and fraternal organizations are represented. Sightseeing tours are available by trains and horse-drawn carriages. There are many points of interest, some of which are the Cathedral of St. Augustine, Lightner Museum, Marineland, Alligator Farm, Casa Del Hidalgo, the World Golf Village, Fountain of Youth, Mission of Nombre De Dios, Oldest Schoolhouse, the Zimenes House, Memorial Presbyterian Church, and the Castillo de San Marcos.

■ **FLORIDA AGRICULTURAL AND MECHANICAL UNIVERSITY**
Tallahassee, FL 32307-3200
Tel: (850)599-3000; Free: 866-642-1198
Fax: (850)561-2428
E-mail: ugrdadmissions@famu.edu
Web Site: www.famu.edu/
Description: State-supported, university, coed. Part of State University System of Florida. Awards associate, bachelor's, master's, and doctoral degrees and post-master's certificates. Founded 1887. Setting: 419-acre urban campus with easy access to Jacksonville. Endowment: $79.9 million. Research spending for the previous fiscal year: $35.3 million. Educational spending for the previous fiscal year: $7224 per student. Total enrollment: 12,057. Faculty: 724 (550 full-time, 174 part-time). Student-undergrad faculty ratio is 19:1. 5,747 applied, 49% were admitted. 11% from top 10% of their high school class, 36% from top quarter, 74% from top half. 1 National Merit Scholar. Full-time: 9,086 students, 62% women, 38% men. Part-time: 967 students, 58% women, 42% men. Students come from 42 states and territories, 50 other countries, 16% from out-of-state. 0.1% American Indian or Alaska Native, non-Hispanic/Latino; 1% Hispanic/Latino; 94% African American, non-Hispanic/Latino; 1% Asian, non-Hispanic/Latino; 0% Native Hawaiian or other Pacific Islander, non-Hispanic/Latino; 1% international.

11% 25 or older, 27% live on campus, 5% transferred in. Retention: 80% of full-time freshmen returned the following year. Academic areas with the most degrees conferred: health professions and related sciences; business/marketing; homeland security, law enforcement, firefighting, and protective services. Core. Calendar: semesters. Academic remediation for entering students, services for LD students, advanced placement, accelerated degree program, honors program, independent study, distance learning, double major, summer session for credit, part-time degree program, adult/continuing education programs, co-op programs and internships, graduate courses open to undergrads. Off campus study at Florida State University. Study abroad program. ROTC: Army, Naval, Air Force (c).

Entrance Requirements: Options: electronic application, early admission, international baccalaureate accepted. Required: essay, high school transcript, minimum 2.5 high school GPA, 3 recommendations, SAT or ACT. Recommended: minimum 3 high school GPA. Required for some: interview, audition for music major applicants. Entrance: moderately difficult. Application deadlines: 5/15, 5/15 for nonresidents. Notification: continuous, continuous for nonresidents. Preference given to state residents, extracurricular activities, volunteer work, work experience, and alumni/ae relations. SAT Reasoning Test deadline: 5/15. Transfer credits accepted: Yes.

Costs Per Year: Application fee: $30. State resident tuition: $4929 full-time, $164.29 per credit part-time. Nonresident tuition: $16,869 full-time, $562.31 per credit part-time. Mandatory fees: $258 full-time, $129 per term part-time. College room and board: $8754. College room only: $4928. Room and board charges vary according to board plan and housing facility.

Collegiate Environment: Orientation program. Drama-theater group, choral group, marching band, student-run newspaper, radio station. Social organizations: 135 open to all; national fraternities, national sororities; 2% of eligible men and 3% of eligible women are members. Most popular organizations: National Council of Negro Women, FAMU Chapter, American Society of Mechanical Engineers, Psi Chi International Honor Society, Caribbean Student Association, Academy of Student Pharmacists/Student National Pharmaceutical Association. Major annual events: Homecoming Convocation, Career Expo, Welcome Week. Student services: health clinic, personal-psychological counseling. Campus security: 24-hour emergency response devices and patrols, late night transport-escort service, controlled dormitory access. 2,697 college housing spaces available; 2,319 were occupied in 2012-13. Freshmen given priority for college housing. On-campus residence required in freshman year. Options: coed, men-only, women-only housing available. Coleman Memorial Library plus 4 others with 1.1 million books, 509,940 microform titles, 201,405 serials, 77,145 audiovisual materials, an OPAC, and a Web page. Operations spending for the previous fiscal year: $4.5 million. 4,000 computers available on campus for general student use. A campuswide network can be accessed from student residence rooms and from off campus. Students can access the following: online class registration. Staffed computer lab on campus provides training in use of computers, software, and the Internet.

Community Environment: Tallahassee, a community of varied interests, provides an ideal setting for a thriving comprehensive university. The community abounds in a broad range of programs and activities, including three institutions of higher education; city, county, and state government; civic and community organizations; art galleries; theater and music archives, libraries and museums; state parks and recreational facilities; tree-shaded streets and highways; and a 13,500-seat Civic Center.

■ **FLORIDA ATLANTIC UNIVERSITY**
777 Glades Rd.
Boca Raton, FL 33431-0991
Tel: (561)297-3000
Web Site: www.fau.edu/
Description: State-supported, university, coed. Part of State University System of Florida. Awards associate, bachelor's, master's, and doctoral degrees and post-master's certificates. Founded 1961. Setting: 850-acre suburban campus with easy access to Miami, Fort Lauderdale, Palm Beach. Total enrollment: 30,038. Faculty: 1,226 (730 full-time, 496 part-time). Student-undergrad faculty ratio is 22:1. 27,888 applied, 39% were admitted. 11% from top 10% of their high school class, 35% from top quarter, 78% from top half. Full-time: 15,593 students, 55% women, 45% men. Part-time: 9,230 students, 58% women, 42% men. Students come from 50 states and territories, 135 other countries, 5% from out-of-state. 0.2% American Indian or Alaska Native, non-Hispanic/Latino; 24% Hispanic/Latino; 18% African American, non-Hispanic/Latino; 4% Asian, non-Hispanic/Latino; 0.1% Native Hawaiian or other Pacific Islander, non-Hispanic/Latino; 1% international. 27% 25 or older, 6% live on campus, 13% transferred in. Retention: 78% of

full-time freshmen returned the following year. Academic areas with the most degrees conferred: business/marketing; education; social sciences. Core. Calendar: semesters. ESL program, services for LD students, advanced placement, accelerated degree program, freshman honors college, honors program, independent study, distance learning, double major, summer session for credit, part-time degree program, adult/continuing education programs, co-op programs and internships, graduate courses open to undergrads. Off campus study at other members of the State University System of Florida. Study abroad program. ROTC: Army, Air Force (c).

Entrance Requirements: Options: electronic application, early admission, deferred admission, international baccalaureate accepted. Required: high school transcript, SAT or ACT. Entrance: moderately difficult. Application deadline: 5/1. SAT Reasoning Test deadline: 5/1.

Costs Per Year: Application fee: $30. State resident tuition: $5986 full-time, $199.54 per credit hour part-time. Nonresident tuition: $21,543 full-time, $718.09 per credit hour part-time. Full-time tuition varies according to course load. Part-time tuition varies according to course load. College room and board: $11,353. Room and board charges vary according to board plan and housing facility.

Collegiate Environment: Orientation program. Drama-theater group, choral group, marching band, student-run newspaper, radio station. Social organizations: 230 open to all; national fraternities, national sororities, local fraternities, local sororities; 2% of eligible men and 2% of eligible women are members. Most popular organizations: American Society of Civil Engineers, Dive Club, Pre-Law Society, Submarine Club, American Criminal Justice Society. Major annual events: Homecoming, Fall Festival, Festival of Nations. Student services: health clinic, personal-psychological counseling, women's center. Campus security: 24-hour emergency response devices and patrols, student patrols, late night transport-escort service, controlled dormitory access. 3,800 college housing spaces available; 3,705 were occupied in 2012-13. Freshmen guaranteed college housing. On-campus residence required in freshman year. Options: coed, women-only housing available. S. E. Wimberly Library plus 2 others with 1.3 million books, 2.1 million microform titles, 12,811 serials, an OPAC, and a Web page. 1,000 computers available on campus for general student use. A campuswide network can be accessed from student residence rooms and from off campus. Students can access the following: online class registration. Staffed computer lab on campus (open 24 hours a day) provides training in use of computers, software, and the Internet.

Community Environment: A resort and suburban area located on Florida's east coast, Boca Raton is 40 miles north of Miami and 25 miles from Ft. Lauderdale and Palm Beach airports. The area enjoys a subtropical climate. Local industry includes large regional centers for Sensormatic, Siemens, Motorola and other high tech multinational corporations. Several shopping centers, a library, many houses of worship, and two hospitals are some of the community facilities. Cultural activities are many. Recreational activities include swimming, tennis, golf, surf casting, and deep-sea fishing. There are three public beaches and numerous superior golf courses nearby. Everglades National Park lies to the west and south.

■ **FLORIDA CAREER COLLEGE**
1321 SW 107 Ave.
Ste. 201B
Miami, FL 33174
Tel: (305)553-6065; Free: 888-852-7272
Fax: (305)225-0128
Web Site: www.careercollege.edu/
Description: Proprietary, 2-year, coed. Awards certificates, diplomas, and terminal associate degrees. Founded 1982. Setting: urban campus. Total enrollment: 3,952. 45% 25 or older. Core. Academic remediation for entering students, independent study, summer session for credit, part-time degree program.

Entrance Requirements: Open admission. Option: deferred admission. Required: high school transcript, interview. Entrance: noncompetitive. Application deadline: Rolling. Notification: continuous.

Collegiate Environment: Orientation program. Campus security: 24-hour emergency response devices. Resource Center plus 1 other with 1,200 books and 200 serials.

■ **FLORIDA COLLEGE**
119 N Glen Arven Ave.
Temple Terrace, FL 33617
Tel: (813)988-5131
Fax: (813)899-6772

E-mail: admissions@floridacollege.edu

Web Site: www.floridacollege.edu/

Description: Independent, 4-year, coed. Awards associate and bachelor's degrees. Founded 1944. Setting: 95-acre small town campus with easy access to Tampa. Endowment: $11.9 million. Educational spending for the previous fiscal year: $3623 per student. Total enrollment: 532. Faculty: 60 (39 full-time, 21 part-time). Student-undergrad faculty ratio is 11:1. 322 applied, 73% were admitted. Full-time: 507 students, 52% women, 48% men. Part-time: 25 students, 56% women, 44% men. Students come from 34 states and territories, 5 other countries, 68% from out-of-state. 2% American Indian or Alaska Native, non-Hispanic/Latino; 6% Hispanic/Latino; 5% African American, non-Hispanic/Latino; 1% Asian, non-Hispanic/Latino; 0.4% Native Hawaiian or other Pacific Islander, non-Hispanic/Latino; 1% international. 81% live on campus, 6% transferred in. Academic areas with the most degrees conferred: liberal arts/general studies; business/marketing; education. Core. Calendar: semesters. Academic remediation for entering students, advanced placement, independent study, summer session for credit. ROTC: Army (c), Air Force (c).

Entrance Requirements: Options: electronic application, international baccalaureate accepted. Required: high school transcript, minimum 2 high school GPA, 2 recommendations, SAT or ACT. Required for some: essay for international students. Entrance: moderately difficult. Application deadline: 8/1. Notification: continuous. SAT Reasoning Test deadline: 8/1. Transfer credits accepted: Yes.

Costs Per Year: Application fee: $30. One-time mandatory fee: $150. Comprehensive fee: $21,390 includes full-time tuition ($13,020), mandatory fees ($800), and college room and board ($7570). College room only: $3880. Room and board charges vary according to board plan and housing facility. Part-time tuition: $520 per credit hour. Part-time tuition varies according to course load.

Collegiate Environment: Orientation program. Drama-theater group, choral group. Social organizations: 16 open to all; coed societies; 75% of eligible men and 75% of eligible women are members. Most popular organizations: Co-ed Societies, Circle K, NAFME, SBGA, Footlighters. Major annual events: Beach Devotionals, Spring Banquet, MOSI Singings. Student services: health clinic, personal-psychological counseling. Campus security: controlled dormitory access, evening patrols by trained security personnel. 669 college housing spaces available; 429 were occupied in 2012-13. Freshmen guaranteed college housing. On-campus residence required through sophomore year. Options: men-only, women-only housing available. Chatlos Library with 136,125 books, 7,601 microform titles, 284 serials, 6,111 audiovisual materials, an OPAC, and a Web page. Operations spending for the previous fiscal year: $198,290. 36 computers available on campus for general student use. A campuswide network can be accessed from student residence rooms and from off campus. Staffed computer lab on campus provides training in use of computers, software, and the Internet.

Community Environment: Located near Tampa, Temple Terrace has a subtropical climate. Buses serve the area. Community facilities include a library, churches, and one community college and two universities. Part-time employment is limited. Sport activities include boating, fishing, golf, professional baseball, football and soccer. Cultural and recreational facilities, broad and varied, are also available in Tampa.

■ **FLORIDA COLLEGE OF NATURAL HEALTH (BRADENTON)**

616 67th St. Cir. E

Bradenton, FL 34208

Tel: (941)744-1244; Free: 800-966-7117

Fax: (941)744-1242

Web Site: www.fcnh.com/

Description: Proprietary, 2-year, coed. Awards terminal associate degrees. Founded 1998. Total enrollment: 251. Student-undergrad faculty ratio is 25:1. 0% from out-of-state. 67% 25 or older.

Entrance Requirements: Entrance: noncompetitive.

■ **FLORIDA COLLEGE OF NATURAL HEALTH (MAITLAND)**

2600 Lake Lucien Dr.

Ste. 140

Maitland, FL 32751

Tel: (407)261-0319; Free: 800-393-7337

Fax: (407)261-0342

Web Site: www.fcnh.com/

Description: Proprietary, 2-year, coed. Awards terminal associate degrees. Founded 1995. Total enrollment: 467. Student-undergrad faculty ratio is 25:1. 1% from out-of-state. 64% 25 or older.

Entrance Requirements: Entrance: noncompetitive.

■ **FLORIDA COLLEGE OF NATURAL HEALTH (MIAMI)**

7925 NW 12th St.

Ste. 201

Miami, FL 33126

Tel: (305)597-9599; Free: 800-599-9599

Fax: (305)597-9110

Web Site: www.fcnh.com/

Description: Proprietary, 2-year, coed. Awards terminal associate degrees. Founded 1993. Total enrollment: 349. Student-undergrad faculty ratio is 25:1. 1% from out-of-state. 70% 25 or older.

Entrance Requirements: Entrance: noncompetitive.

■ **FLORIDA COLLEGE OF NATURAL HEALTH (POMPANO BEACH)**

2001 W Sample Rd.

Ste. 100

Pompano Beach, FL 33064

Tel: (954)975-6400; Free: 800-541-9299

Fax: (954)975-9633

Web Site: www.fcnh.com/

Description: Proprietary, 2-year, coed. Awards terminal associate degrees. Founded 1986. Total enrollment: 448. Student-undergrad faculty ratio is 25:1. 2% from out-of-state. 67% 25 or older.

Entrance Requirements: Entrance: noncompetitive.

■ **FLORIDA GATEWAY COLLEGE**

149 SE College Pl.

Lake City, FL 32025

Tel: (386)752-1822

Fax: (386)755-1521

E-mail: admissions@fgc.edu

Web Site: www.fgc.edu/

Description: State-supported, primarily 2-year, coed. Part of Florida Community College System. Awards certificates, diplomas, transfer associate, terminal associate, and bachelor's degrees. Founded 1962. Setting: 132-acre small town campus with easy access to Jacksonville. Total enrollment: 3,073. Faculty: 179 (68 full-time, 111 part-time). Student-undergrad faculty ratio is 16:1. Full-time: 1,040 students, 61% women, 39% men. Part-time: 2,033 students, 68% women, 32% men. Students come from 4 states and territories, 0% from out-of-state. 0.4% American Indian or Alaska Native, non-Hispanic/Latino; 4% Hispanic/Latino; 10% African American, non-Hispanic/Latino; 1% Asian, non-Hispanic/Latino; 0% Native Hawaiian or other Pacific Islander, non-Hispanic/Latino; 0.1% international. 35% 25 or older, 4% transferred in. Core. Calendar: semesters. Academic remediation for entering students, ESL program, services for LD students, advanced placement, independent study, distance learning, summer session for credit, part-time degree program, adult/continuing education programs, co-op programs and internships. Off campus study.

Entrance Requirements: Open admission Nursing is a limited access program and is therefore not open admit. EMS, golf course operations, physical therapist assistant, practical nursing, paramedic, phlebotomy, and patient care assistant have special admissions requirements. Required for some: high school transcript. Entrance: noncompetitive. Application deadline: Rolling. Notification: continuous. Transfer credits accepted: Yes.

Costs Per Year: Application fee: $0. State resident tuition: $2,480 full-time, $103.32 per credit hour part-time. Nonresident tuition: $11,747 full-time, $391.57 per credit hour part-time. Mandatory fees: $731 full-time, $24.38 per credit hour part-time. Full-time tuition and fees vary according to course level, course load, degree level, program, and reciprocity agreements. Part-time tuition and fees vary according to course level, course load, degree level, program, and reciprocity agreements.

Collegiate Environment: Orientation program. Drama-theater group, choral group. Student services: personal-psychological counseling. Campus security: 24-hour emergency response devices and patrols. College housing not available. Wilson S. Rivers Library and Media Center with 43,811 books, 180 serials, an OPAC, and a Web page. 150 computers available on campus for general student use. A campuswide network can be accessed. Students can access the following: online class registration. Staffed computer lab on campus.

Community Environment: Lake City is the county seat of Columbia County, located midway between Atlanta and Miami. It has a temperate climate. Community facilities include excellent hospital and health facilities and fine motel accommodations. Annual deer and bear hunting is staged in nearby Osceola National Forest. Numerous lakes and streams are well stocked with bass, bream, and speckled perch. Tubing on the nearby Ichetucknee River is popular with students.

■ FLORIDA GULF COAST UNIVERSITY

10501 FGCU Blvd. S
Fort Myers, FL 33965-6565
Tel: (239)590-1000; Free: 888-889-1095
Fax: (239)590-7894
Web Site: www.fgcu.edu/
Description: State-supported, comprehensive, coed. Part of State University System of Florida. Awards associate, bachelor's, master's, and doctoral degrees. Founded 1991. Setting: 760-acre suburban campus. Endowment: $55.6 million. Total enrollment: 13,471. Faculty: 630 (398 full-time, 232 part-time). Student-undergrad faculty ratio is 22:1. 10,073 applied, 68% were admitted. 9% from top 10% of their high school class, 35% from top quarter, 76% from top half. Full-time: 9,704 students, 56% women, 44% men. Part-time: 2,451 students, 53% women, 47% men. Students come from 44 states and territories, 87 other countries, 7% from out-of-state. 0.2% American Indian or Alaska Native, non-Hispanic/Latino; 18% Hispanic/Latino; 7% African American, non-Hispanic/Latino; 2% Asian, non-Hispanic/Latino; 0.1% Native Hawaiian or other Pacific Islander, non-Hispanic/Latino; 1% international. 13% 25 or older, 34% live on campus, 9% transferred in. Retention: 76% of full-time freshmen returned the following year. Academic areas with the most degrees conferred: business/marketing; communication/journalism; education. Core. Calendar: semesters. Academic remediation for entering students, services for LD students, advanced placement, accelerated degree program, honors program, independent study, distance learning, double major, summer session for credit, part-time degree program, co-op programs and internships, graduate courses open to undergrads. Off campus study. Study abroad program.
Entrance Requirements: Options: electronic application, deferred admission, international baccalaureate accepted. Required: high school transcript, minimum 2 high school GPA, SAT or ACT. Entrance: moderately difficult. Application deadline: 5/1. Notification: continuous.
Costs Per Year: Application fee: $30. State resident tuition: $4,855 full-time. Nonresident tuition: $20,090 full-time. Full-time tuition varies according to course load. College room and board: $9424. Room and board charges vary according to board plan.
Collegiate Environment: Orientation program. Drama-theater group, student-run newspaper. Social organizations: 125 open to all; national fraternities, national sororities; 3% of eligible men and 5% of eligible women are members. Most popular organizations: student government, Ignite (Religious Organization), International Club, Martial Arts Club, Physical Therapy Association. Major annual events: Nest Fest (Annual Concert), Fright Night (Halloween Party), Eaglepalooza (Campus Recreation Festival). Student services: health clinic, personal-psychological counseling. Campus security: 24-hour emergency response devices and patrols, late night transport-escort service. 4,200 college housing spaces available. No special consideration for freshman housing applicants. Option: coed housing available. Library Services plus 1 other with 396,625 books, 843,772 microform titles, 94,274 serials, 319,285 audiovisual materials, an OPAC, and a Web page. 871 computers available on campus for general student use. Computer purchase/lease plans available. A campuswide network can be accessed from student residence rooms and from off campus. Students can access the following: online class registration, online admissions and advising. Staffed computer lab on campus.

■ FLORIDA INSTITUTE OF TECHNOLOGY

150 W University Blvd.
Melbourne, FL 32901-6975
Tel: (321)674-8000; Free: 800-888-4348
Fax: (321)723-9468
E-mail: admission@fit.edu
Web Site: www.fit.edu/
Description: Independent, university, coed. Awards bachelor's, master's, and doctoral degrees and post-master's certificates. Founded 1958. Setting: 130-acre small town campus with easy access to Orlando. Endowment: $47.1 million. Research spending for the previous fiscal year: $17.3 million. Educational spending for the previous fiscal year: $12,907 per student. Total enrollment: 5,384. Faculty: 467 (246 full-time, 221 part-time). Student-undergrad faculty ratio is 14:1. 7,428 applied, 59% were admitted. 31% from top 10% of their high school class, 58% from top quarter, 85% from top half. 17 valedictorians. Full-time: 2,794 students, 27% women, 73% men. Part-

time: 184 students, 30% women, 70% men. Students come from 49 states and territories, 97 other countries, 47% from out-of-state. 0.1% American Indian or Alaska Native, non-Hispanic/Latino; 6% Hispanic/Latino; 5% African American, non-Hispanic/Latino; 2% Asian, non-Hispanic/Latino; 0.1% Native Hawaiian or other Pacific Islander, non-Hispanic/Latino; 29% international. 9% 25 or older, 47% live on campus, 7% transferred in. Retention: 79% of full-time freshmen returned the following year. Academic areas with the most degrees conferred: engineering; biological/life sciences; business/marketing. Core. Calendar: semesters. Academic remediation for entering students, ESL program, services for LD students, advanced placement, accelerated degree program, self-designed majors, independent study, distance learning, double major, summer session for credit, part-time degree program, adult/continuing education programs, co-op programs and internships, graduate courses open to undergrads. Study abroad program. ROTC: Army.
Entrance Requirements: Options: electronic application, deferred admission, international baccalaureate accepted. Required: essay, high school transcript, minimum 2.6 high school GPA, 2 recommendations, SAT or ACT, SAT or ACT. Recommended: minimum 3.3 high school GPA, interview. Entrance: moderately difficult. Application deadline: Rolling. Notification: continuous. SAT Reasoning Test deadline: 5/1. Transfer credits accepted: Yes.
Costs Per Year: Comprehensive fee: $48,290 includes full-time tuition ($35,460), mandatory fees ($560), and college room and board ($12,270). College room only: $7150. Full-time tuition and fees vary according to course load, program, and student level. Room and board charges vary according to board plan and housing facility. Part-time tuition: $1025 per credit hour.
Collegiate Environment: Orientation program. Drama-theater group, choral group, student-run newspaper, radio station. Social organizations: 147 open to all; national fraternities, national sororities; 14% of eligible men and 11% of eligible women are members. Most popular organizations: FITSSFF, College Players, Saudi Student House, Squamish, Phi Eta Sigma National Honor Society. Major annual events: Homecoming, Relay for Life, International Festival. Student services: health clinic, personal-psychological counseling. Campus security: 24-hour emergency response devices and patrols, late night transport-escort service, controlled dormitory access. 1,676 college housing spaces available; 1,480 were occupied in 2012-13. Freshmen guaranteed college housing. On-campus residence required through sophomore year. Option: coed housing available. Evans Library with 527,223 books, 310,337 microform titles, 68,007 serials, 10,319 audiovisual materials, an OPAC, and a Web page. Operations spending for the previous fiscal year: $2.7 million. 440 computers available on campus for general student use. A campuswide network can be accessed from student residence rooms and from off campus. Students can access the following: online class registration. Staffed computer lab on campus provides training in use of computers, software, and the Internet.
Community Environment: Florida Tech is located in the city of Melbourne, Brevard County, on Florida's space coast, approximately 30 miles south of Spaceport, 60 miles east of Orlando and 170 miles north of Miami. It is 5 minutes from the Melbourne International Airport, which is host to 2 major airlines. Recreation includes public swimming pools, golf courses, a tourist club with facilities for a number of sports, a harbor, and a yacht basin. Fresh and salt water fishing are available.

■ FLORIDA INTERNATIONAL UNIVERSITY

11200 SW 8th St.
Miami, FL 33199
Tel: (305)348-2000
Fax: (305)348-3648
E-mail: admiss@fiu.edu
Web Site: www.fiu.edu/
Description: State-supported, university, coed. Part of State University System of Florida. Awards bachelor's, master's, and doctoral degrees. Founded 1965. Setting: 582-acre urban campus with easy access to Miami. Endowment: $132.5 million. Research spending for the previous fiscal year: $77.9 million. Total enrollment: 46,261. Faculty: 2,052 (1,116 full-time, 936 part-time). Student-undergrad faculty ratio is 25:1. 15,863 applied, 40% were admitted. 16% from top 10% of their high school class, 44% from top quarter, 80% from top half. Full-time: 24,001 students, 56% women, 44% men. Part-time: 13,467 students, 54% women, 46% men. Students come from 49 states and territories, 133 other countries, 3% from out-of-state. 0.1% American Indian or Alaska Native, non-Hispanic/Latino; 66% Hispanic/Latino; 12% African American, non-Hispanic/Latino; 3% Asian, non-Hispanic/

Latino; 0.1% Native Hawaiian or other Pacific Islander, non-Hispanic/Latino; 5% international. 25% 25 or older, 7% live on campus, 11% transferred in. Retention: 82% of full-time freshmen returned the following year. Academic areas with the most degrees conferred: business/marketing; psychology; social sciences. Core. Calendar: semesters. Services for LD students, advanced placement, accelerated degree program, freshman honors college, honors program, independent study, distance learning, double major, summer session for credit, part-time degree program, adult/continuing education programs, co-op programs and internships, graduate courses open to undergrads. Off campus study at National Student Exchange Program. Study abroad program. ROTC: Army, Air Force.

Entrance Requirements: Options: electronic application, international baccalaureate accepted. Required: high school transcript, minimum 3 high school GPA, SAT or ACT, TOEFL is required of all applicants whose native language is not English. Recommended: SAT Subject Tests. Required for some: portfolio, audition. Entrance: moderately difficult. Application deadlines: Rolling, Rolling for nonresidents. Notification: continuous, continuous for nonresidents. SAT Reasoning Test deadline: 5/1. SAT Subject Test deadline: 5/1. Transfer credits accepted: Yes.

Costs Per Year: Application fee: $30. State resident tuition: $6,050 full-time, $201.66 per credit hour part-time. Nonresident tuition: $18,449 full-time, $614.96 per credit hour part-time. Mandatory fees: $367 full-time. Full-time tuition and fees vary according to course load. Part-time tuition varies according to course load. College room and board: $11,330. Room and board charges vary according to board plan and housing facility.

Collegiate Environment: Orientation program. Drama-theater group, choral group, marching band, student-run newspaper, radio station. Social organizations: 193 open to all; national fraternities, national sororities. Most popular organizations: Students for Community Service, Black Student Leadership Council, Hospitality Management Student Club, Hispanic Students Association, Haitian Students Organization. Major annual events: Relay for Life (fund-raising event), Dance Marathon (fund-raising event), Welcome Week. Student services: health clinic, personal-psychological counseling, women's center. Campus security: 24-hour emergency response devices and patrols, late night transport-escort service, controlled dormitory access. 3,016 college housing spaces available; 2,543 were occupied in 2012-13. No special consideration for freshman housing applicants. Option: coed housing available. Steven and Dorothea Green Library plus 4 others with 2 million books, 4.3 million microform titles, 149,685 serials, 211,603 audiovisual materials, an OPAC, and a Web page. Operations spending for the previous fiscal year: $18.6 million.

Community Environment: The Greater Miami area offers cultural diversity and a dynamic economic and aesthetic climate. South Florida is a major center of higher education and stands at the forefront of international trading, finance and banking, as well as tourism and a developing high technology industry. Miami International Airport is served by more airlines than any other airport in the country. One of the most culturally diverse cities in America, Miami has many distinctive neighborhoods. Both visual and performing arts thrive in Miami. The Metro-Dade Cultural Complex in downtown Miami houses the Metropolitan Library, the Museum of South Florida, and the Center for the Fine Arts. The city also maintains both an opera and three ballet companies. A wealth of galleries, libraries, and theaters are valuable resources. The greater Miami area also hosts many professional sports events and offers year round recreation activities such as fishing, boating, scuba diving, wind surfing, snorkeling, swimming, and deep-sea fishing.

■ FLORIDA KEYS COMMUNITY COLLEGE

5901 College Rd.
Key West, FL 33040-4397
Tel: (305)296-9081
Web Site: www.fkcc.edu/

Description: State-supported, 2-year, coed. Part of Florida Community College System. Awards certificates, transfer associate, and terminal associate degrees. Founded 1965. Setting: 20-acre small town campus. Total enrollment: 1,012. 49% 25 or older. Core. Calendar: trimesters. Academic remediation for entering students, ESL program, services for LD students, advanced placement, self-designed majors, independent study, distance learning, double major, summer session for credit, part-time degree program, adult/continuing education programs, co-op programs and internships.

Entrance Requirements: Open admission except for nursing program. Options: early admission, deferred admission. Required for some: high school transcript. Entrance: noncompetitive. Application deadline: Rolling. Notification: continuous.

Collegiate Environment: Orientation program. Choral group. Student services: personal-psychological counseling. Campus security: 24-hour patrols. Florida Keys Community College Library with 29,402 books, 81,675 microform titles, 330 serials, 1,001 audiovisual materials, and an OPAC.

Community Environment: Key West is the southernmost city in the continental United States. It is a tropical island 157 miles southwest of Miami with an Old-World atmosphere. The setting is a blend of Cuban, West Indian, and Bahamian. The climate is warm and the air is almost pollen free. A rich and colorful history is retained in a thriving modern city. All forms of transportation serve the area. Searstown and four shopping centers are among the nation's most unique, all having a tropical flair. Year-round outdoor recreation includes a coral reef several miles offshore and provides some of the world's finest fishing and diving. Numerous points of interest are the Audubon house, Ernest Hemingway Home and Museum, Martello Gallery and Museum, the Lighthouse and the Military Museum.

■ FLORIDA MEMORIAL UNIVERSITY

15800 NW 42nd Ave.
Miami Gardens, FL 33054
Tel: (305)626-3600; Free: 800-822-1362
Web Site: www.fmuniv.edu/

Description: Independent, comprehensive, coed, affiliated with Baptist Church. Awards bachelor's and master's degrees. Founded 1879. Setting: 77-acre suburban campus. Endowment: $6.7 million. Total enrollment: 1,750. Faculty: 173 (105 full-time, 68 part-time). Student-undergrad faculty ratio is 12:1. 5,286 applied, 39% were admitted. Full-time: 1,516 students, 63% women, 37% men. Part-time: 153 students, 56% women, 44% men. Students come from 37 states and territories, 15 other countries, 12% from out-of-state. 30% 25 or older, 8% transferred in. Retention: 70% of full-time freshmen returned the following year. Academic areas with the most degrees conferred: education; business/marketing; law/legal studies. Core. Calendar: semesters. Academic remediation for entering students, ESL program, freshman honors college, honors program, summer session for credit, part-time degree program, external degree program, co-op programs and internships. Off campus study. ROTC: Army, Air Force (c).

Entrance Requirements: Open admission. Options: electronic application, international baccalaureate accepted. Required: essay, high school transcript, minimum 2.2 high school GPA, 2 recommendations. Recommended: SAT or ACT. Entrance: noncompetitive. Application deadline: 7/1. Notification: continuous.

Collegiate Environment: Orientation program. Drama-theater group, student-run newspaper. Social organizations: national fraternities, national sororities. Student services: health clinic. Florida Memorial College Library with 122,919 books and 405 serials. 200 computers available on campus for general student use. A campuswide network can be accessed from student residence rooms and from off campus. Students can access the following: online class registration. Staffed computer lab on campus provides training in use of computers and software.

■ FLORIDA NATIONAL UNIVERSITY

4425 W 20th Ave.
Hialeah, FL 33012
Tel: (305)821-3333
Fax: (305)362-0595
E-mail: jforton@fnu.edu
Web Site: www.fnu.edu/

Description: Proprietary, comprehensive, coed. Awards associate, bachelor's, and master's degrees. Founded 1982. Setting: 4-acre urban campus with easy access to Miami. Educational spending for the previous fiscal year: $1327 per student. Total enrollment: 2,506. Faculty: 150 (91 full-time, 59 part-time). Student-undergrad faculty ratio is 19:1. 1,394 applied, 83% were admitted. 5 student government officers. Full-time: 1,825 students, 71% women, 29% men. Part-time: 662 students, 70% women, 30% men. Students come from 16 states and territories, 16 other countries, 1% from out-of-state. 0.2% American Indian or Alaska Native, non-Hispanic/Latino; 91% Hispanic/Latino; 3% African American, non-Hispanic/Latino; 1% Asian, non-Hispanic/Latino; 0% Native Hawaiian or other Pacific Islander, non-Hispanic/Latino; 4% international. 65% 25 or older, 4% transferred in. Retention: 78% of full-time freshmen returned the following year. Academic areas with the most degrees conferred: business/marketing; homeland security, law enforcement, firefighting, and protective services; law/legal studies. Core. Calendar: semesters. Academic remediation for entering students, ESL program, services for LD students, advanced placement, accelerated degree program, independent study, distance learning, summer session for credit, part-time degree program, adult/continuing education programs, co-op programs and internships.

Entrance Requirements: Options: electronic application, deferred admission. Required: high school transcript, interview, SAT or ACT. Entrance: moderately difficult. Application deadline: Rolling. Notification: continuous. Transfer credits accepted: Yes.

Costs Per Year: Application fee: $0. Tuition: $12,600 full-time, $525 per credit part-time. Mandatory fees: $630 full-time. Tuition guaranteed not to increase for student's term of enrollment.

Collegiate Environment: Orientation program. Student-run newspaper. Social organizations: 5 open to all; national fraternities, Honor Society; 2% of eligible men and 3% of eligible women are members. Most popular organizations: Student Government Association, Bible Club, Salsa Club, W.I.C.S (Women Community Service), Criminal Justice Society. Major annual events: Founders Week, Celebration of Independence Day 4 of July, Thanksgiving Day. Campus security: 24-hour emergency response devices. College housing not available. Hialeah Campus Library with 409,386 books, 3,852 audiovisual materials, an OPAC, and a Web page. Operations spending for the previous fiscal year: $458,413. 225 computers available on campus for general student use. A campuswide network can be accessed from off-campus. Students can access the following: online class registration. Staffed computer lab on campus provides training in use of computers, software, and the Internet.

■ THE FLORIDA SCHOOL OF TRADITIONAL MIDWIFERY

810 E University Ave., 2nd Fl.
Gainseville, FL 32601
Tel: (352)338-0766
Fax: (352)338-2013
E-mail: info@midwiferyschool.org
Web Site: www.midwiferyschool.org/
Description: Independent, 2-year, women only. Awards terminal associate degrees. Founded 1993.

■ FLORIDA SOUTHERN COLLEGE

111 Lake Hollingsworth Dr.
Lakeland, FL 33801-5698
Tel: (863)680-4111; Free: 800-274-4131
Fax: (863)680-4120
E-mail: eervin@flsouthern.edu
Web Site: www.flsouthern.edu/
Description: Independent, comprehensive, coed, affiliated with United Methodist Church. Awards bachelor's and master's degrees. Founded 1885. Setting: 113-acre suburban campus with easy access to Tampa, Orlando. Endowment: $78.7 million. Educational spending for the previous fiscal year: $5975 per student. Total enrollment: 2,238. Faculty: 229 (123 full-time, 106 part-time). Student-undergrad faculty ratio is 13:1. 4,448 applied, 56% were admitted. 21% from top 10% of their high school class, 42% from top quarter, 75% from top half. 2 valedictorians. Full-time: 1,987 students, 59% women, 41% men. Part-time: 53 students, 53% women, 47% men. Students come from 45 states and territories, 40 other countries, 33% from out-of-state. 0.4% American Indian or Alaska Native, non-Hispanic/Latino; 9% Hispanic/Latino; 6% African American, non-Hispanic/Latino; 2% Asian, non-Hispanic/Latino; 0.05% Native Hawaiian or other Pacific Islander, non-Hispanic/Latino; 5% international. 4% 25 or older, 70% live on campus, 5% transferred in. Retention: 76% of full-time freshmen returned the following year. Academic areas with the most degrees conferred: business/marketing; health professions and related sciences; education. Core. Calendar: semesters. Advanced placement, accelerated degree program, self-designed majors, honors program, independent study, double major, summer session for credit, part-time degree program, external degree program, adult/continuing education programs, internships. Off campus study at United Nations Semester, USF Medical School Honor's Program, American University, Drew University, Washington Center. Study abroad program. ROTC: Army, Air Force (c).

Entrance Requirements: Options: electronic application, early admission, early decision, deferred admission, international baccalaureate accepted. Required: essay, high school transcript, 1 recommendation, SAT or ACT. Recommended: minimum 2 high school GPA, interview. Entrance: moderately difficult. Application deadlines: 3/1, 12/1 for early decision. Notification: continuous, 12/15 for early decision. Transfer credits accepted: Yes. Early decision applicants: 97. Early decision applicants admitted: 53.

Costs Per Year: Application fee: $30. Comprehensive fee: $36,300 includes full-time tuition ($26,600), mandatory fees ($600), and college room and

board ($9100). College room only: $5000. Full-time tuition and fees vary according to student level. Room and board charges vary according to board plan and housing facility. Part-time tuition: $780 per semester hour. Part-time tuition varies according to class time.

Collegiate Environment: Orientation program. Drama-theater group, choral group, student-run newspaper. Social organizations: 85 open to all; national fraternities, national sororities; 31% of eligible men and 27% of eligible women are members. Most popular organizations: Student Government Association, Toastmasters, Association of Campus Entertainment, Beyond (Campus Ministry), Fellowship of Christian Athletes. Major annual events: Fairwell Festival, Blast-off, Convocation. Student services: health clinic, personal-psychological counseling. Campus security: 24-hour emergency response devices and patrols, student patrols, late night transport-escort service, controlled dormitory access. 1,526 college housing spaces available; 1,426 were occupied in 2012-13. Freshmen guaranteed college housing. On-campus residence required through senior year. Options: coed, men-only, women-only housing available. Roux Library plus 1 other with 153,456 books, 445,000 microform titles, 119,861 serials, 7,862 audiovisual materials, an OPAC, and a Web page. Operations spending for the previous fiscal year: $956,583. 500 computers available on campus for general student use. Computer purchase/lease plans available. A campuswide network can be accessed from student residence rooms and from off campus. Students can access the following: online class registration, campus portal. Staffed computer lab on campus provides training in use of computers, software, and the Internet.

Community Environment: Lakeland is located in the geographical center of Florida, 35 miles East of Tampa, 50 miles west of Orlando, 100 miles from the Atlantic Ocean, 35 miles from Disney World and 60 miles from the Gulf of Mexico. The Seaboard Coast Line Railroad serves the area. The"World's Citrus Center" is the permanent spring training headquarters of the Detroit Tigers. Excellent shopping facilities in the city; a civic center, concert association, and community theatre are part of the lively community. Recreational facilities include 12 lakes within the city for excellent fishing, golf courses, boating, hiking, and waterskiing. The annual Orange Cup Regatta Hydroplane Race is held the weekend closest to February 1st.

■ FLORIDA STATE COLLEGE AT JACKSONVILLE

501 W State St.
Jacksonville, FL 32202-4030
Tel: (904)632-3000; Free: 888-873-1145
Fax: (904)632-3393
E-mail: pbiegel@fscj.edu
Web Site: www.fscj.edu/
Description: State-supported, primarily 2-year, coed. Part of Florida College System. Awards certificates, diplomas, transfer associate, terminal associate, and bachelor's degrees. Founded 1963. Setting: 825-acre urban campus. Endowment: $28.8 million. Educational spending for the previous fiscal year: $5464 per student. Total enrollment: 30,863. Faculty: 1,205 (407 full-time, 798 part-time). Student-undergrad faculty ratio is 29:1. 8,562 applied, 48% were admitted. Full-time: 10,778 students, 58% women, 42% men. Part-time: 20,085 students, 61% women, 39% men. 0.5% American Indian or Alaska Native, non-Hispanic/Latino; 4% Hispanic/Latino; 28% African American, non-Hispanic/Latino; 3% Asian, non-Hispanic/Latino; 1% Native Hawaiian or other Pacific Islander, non-Hispanic/Latino; 1% international. 46% 25 or older, 7% transferred in. Retention: 36% of full-time freshmen returned the following year. Academic areas with the most degrees conferred: business/marketing; health professions and related sciences; education. Core. Calendar: semesters. Academic remediation for entering students, ESL program, services for LD students, advanced placement, accelerated degree program, honors program, independent study, distance learning, double major, summer session for credit, part-time degree program, adult/continuing education programs, co-op programs and internships. Off campus study at Jacksonville Naval Station, Jacksonville, FL; Mayport Naval Air Station, Jacksonville, FL; Cecil Field Naval Air Station, Jacksonville, FL; Naval Aviation Technical Training Center, Pensacola, FL. Study abroad program. ROTC: Naval (c).

Entrance Requirements: Open admission. Options: electronic application, early admission, deferred admission, international baccalaureate accepted. Required: high school transcript. Entrance: noncompetitive. Application deadlines: Rolling, Rolling for nonresidents. Transfer credits accepted: Yes.

Collegiate Environment: Orientation program. Drama-theater group, choral group, student-run newspaper, radio station. Most popular organizations: Phi Theta Kappa, Forensic Team, Brain Bowl Team, International Student Association, DramaWorks. Major annual event: FSCJ Talent/Variety Show.

Student services: personal-psychological counseling, women's center. Campus security: 24-hour emergency response devices and patrols, late night transport-escort service. Florida State College at Jacksonville Library and Learning Commons plus 7 others with 211,361 books, 6,860 microform titles, 3,299 serials, 21,541 audiovisual materials, an OPAC, and a Web page. Operations spending for the previous fiscal year: $2.4 million. 2,500 computers available on campus for general student use. A campuswide network can be accessed from off-campus. Students can access the following: online class registration. Staffed computer lab on campus provides training in use of computers, software, and the Internet.

■ **FLORIDA STATE UNIVERSITY**

Tallahassee, FL 32306

Tel: (850)644-2525

Fax: (850)644-0197

E-mail: admissions@admin.fsu.edu

Web Site: www.fsu.edu/

Description: State-supported, university, coed. Part of State University System of Florida. Awards associate, bachelor's, master's, and doctoral degrees and post-master's certificates. Founded 1851. Setting: 451-acre suburban campus. Endowment: $497.7 million. Research spending for the previous fiscal year: $136.7 million. Educational spending for the previous fiscal year: $8555 per student. Total enrollment: 40,695. Faculty: 1,624 (1,248 full-time, 376 part-time). Student-undergrad faculty ratio is 26:1. 30,040 applied, 54% were admitted. 41% from top 10% of their high school class, 80% from top quarter, 98% from top half. 19 National Merit Scholars. Full-time: 28,733 students, 56% women, 44% men. Part-time: 3,438 students, 47% women, 53% men. Students come from 52 states and territories, 109 other countries, 9% from out-of-state. 0.3% American Indian or Alaska Native, non-Hispanic/Latino; 16% Hispanic/Latino; 9% African American, non-Hispanic/Latino; 3% Asian, non-Hispanic/Latino; 0.03% Native Hawaiian or other Pacific Islander, non-Hispanic/Latino; 1% international. 7% 25 or older, 20% live on campus, 6% transferred in. Retention: 91% of full-time freshmen returned the following year. Academic areas with the most degrees conferred: business/marketing; social sciences; homeland security, law enforcement, firefighting, and protective services. Core. Calendar: semesters. ESL program, services for LD students, advanced placement, accelerated degree program, honors program, independent study, distance learning, double major, summer session for credit, part-time degree program, co-op programs and internships, graduate courses open to undergrads. Off campus study at Florida Agricultural and Mechanical University, Tallahassee Community College. Study abroad program. ROTC: Army, Naval (c), Air Force.

Entrance Requirements: Options: electronic application, early admission, international baccalaureate accepted. Required: high school transcript, SAT or ACT. Recommended: essay. Entrance: very difficult. Application deadlines: 1/14, 1/14 for nonresidents. Notification: 3/20, 3/20 for nonresidents. SAT Reasoning Test deadline: 1/14. Transfer credits accepted: Yes.

Costs Per Year: Application fee: $30. State resident tuition: $3397 full-time, $113.24 per credit hour part-time. Nonresident tuition: $18,564 full-time, $618.79 per credit hour part-time. Mandatory fees: $3005 full-time, $98.85 per credit hour part-time, $20 per term part-time. Full-time tuition and fees vary according to course load, degree level, and location. Part-time tuition and fees vary according to course load, degree level, and location. College room and board: $9626. College room only: $5694. Room and board charges vary according to board plan and housing facility.

Collegiate Environment: Orientation program, Drama-theater group, choral group, marching band, student-run newspaper, radio station. Social organizations: 550 open to all; national fraternities, national sororities, local fraternities, local sororities; 18% of eligible men and 16% of eligible women are members. Most popular organizations: student government, honors program, Golden Key Honor Society, Marching Chiefs, intramural sports. Major annual events: Family Weekend, Homecoming, Dance Marathon. Student services: legal services, health clinic, personal-psychological counseling, women's center. Campus security: 24-hour emergency response devices and patrols, late night transport-escort service, controlled dormitory access. College housing designed to accommodate 6,387 students; 6,424 undergraduates lived in college housing during 2012-13. Freshmen given priority for college housing. Housing: coed, women-only housing available. Robert Manning Strozier Library plus 8 others with 3 million books, 9.8 million microform titles, 83,241 serials, 1.1 million audiovisual materials, and an OPAC. 3,821 computers available on campus for general student use. A campuswide network can be accessed from student residence rooms and

from off campus. Students can access the following: online class registration, course home pages, course search, online fee payment. Staffed computer lab on campus.

Community Environment: Situated in north Florida, FSU is nestled in the heart of Tallahassee, the state's capital city. A classic college town, Tallahassee is not only one of Florida's oldest and fastest growing cities, it is also part of the"other Florida" with its rolling hills, canopy roads, mild climate, and southern hospitality. More than 100 state and federal agencies furnish students with opportunities for internships, research, and work-study programs that match all areas of academic interest. Part-time jobs are plentiful. In addition, Tallahassee affords a rich offering of social, cultural, and recreational activities, making it an excellent place to live, study, and grow.

■ **FLORIDA TECH UNIVERSITY ONLINE**

9417 Princess Palm Ave.

Tampa, FL 33619

Free: 855-300-1469

Web Site: floridatechonline.com/

Description: Proprietary, comprehensive, coed.

■ **FLORIDA TECHNICAL COLLEGE (DELAND)**

1199 S Woodland Blvd., 3rd Fl.

DeLand, FL 32720

Tel: (904)734-3303

Fax: (904)734-5150

Web Site: www.ftccollege.edu/

Description: Proprietary, 2-year, coed. Awards transfer associate and terminal associate degrees. Total enrollment: 260. Faculty: 13 (11 full-time, 2 part-time). Student-undergrad faculty ratio is 22:1. Full-time: 260 students, 58% women, 42% men.

■ **FLORIDA TECHNICAL COLLEGE (ORLANDO)**

12900 Challenger Pky.

Orlando, FL 32826

Tel: (407)678-5600

Fax: (407)678-1149

Web Site: www.ftccollege.edu/

Description: Proprietary, 2-year, coed. Part of Fore Front Education, Inc. Awards certificates, diplomas, and terminal associate degrees. Founded 1982. Setting: 1-acre urban campus. Total enrollment: 1,355. 379 applied. 56% 25 or older. Core. Advanced placement, accelerated degree program, independent study, distance learning, double major, external degree program.

Entrance Requirements: Option: international baccalaureate accepted. Required: high school transcript, interview. Recommended: essay. Entrance: minimally difficult.

Collegiate Environment: Orientation program. Student-run newspaper.

■ **FORTIS COLLEGE (LARGO)**

6565 Ulmerton Rd.

Largo, FL 33771

Tel: (727)531-5900

Web Site: www.fortis.edu/

Description: Proprietary, 2-year, coed.

■ **FORTIS COLLEGE (TAMPA)**

3910 US Hwy. 301 N

Ste. 200

Tampa, FL 33619-1259

Tel: (813)620-1446; Free: 855-4-FORTIS

Web Site: www.fortis.edu/

Description: Private, 2-year, coed. Awards diplomas and terminal associate degrees. Founded 1978. Setting: 2-acre urban campus. Total enrollment: 181. Student-undergrad faculty ratio is 15:1. 0% from out-of-state. 75% 25 or older. Core. Advanced placement, accelerated degree program, internships.

Entrance Requirements: Open admission. Option: electronic application. Required: interview. Entrance: noncompetitive.

Collegiate Environment: Orientation program. Student services: personal-psychological counseling. Campus security: 24-hour emergency response devices, evening security guard.

■ **FORTIS COLLEGE (WINTER PARK)**

1573 W Fairbanks Ave.

Ste. 100

Winter Park, FL 32789
Tel: (407)843-3984; Free: 855-4-FORTIS
Fax: (407)843-9828
Web Site: www.fortis.edu/
Description: Proprietary, 2-year, coed. Awards terminal associate degrees. Founded 1984. Total enrollment: 475. Student-undergrad faculty ratio is 12:1. 27% from out-of-state. 53% 25 or older.
Entrance Requirements: Entrance: noncompetitive.

■ FULL SAIL UNIVERSITY
3300 University Blvd.
Winter Park, FL 32792-7437
Tel: (407)679-6333; Free: 800-226-7625
Fax: (407)678-0070
E-mail: admissions@fullsail.com
Web Site: www.fullsail.edu/
Description: Proprietary, comprehensive, coed. Awards associate, bachelor's, and master's degrees. Founded 1979. Setting: 190-acre suburban campus with easy access to Orlando. Total enrollment: 8,921. Faculty: 702. Student-undergrad faculty ratio is 8:1. Students come from 50 states and territories, 40 other countries, 70% from out-of-state. Retention: 84% of full-time freshmen returned the following year. Core. Calendar: modular. Academic remediation for entering students, services for LD students, summer session for credit, co-op programs and internships.
Entrance Requirements: Open admission. Option: electronic application. Required: high school transcript. Required for some: minimum 'A' average in Algebra II. Application deadline: Rolling.
Collegiate Environment: Orientation program. Most popular organizations: Student Chapter of Audio Engineering Society, Digital Art and Design Association, International Film Society, Student Art League, Student Association of Real-World Advancement. Major annual events: Annual Speech Tournament, Success Seminar, Entertainment Business. Student services: personal-psychological counseling. Campus security: 24-hour patrols. Full Sail Library plus 1 other with 2,531 books, 84 serials, 784 audiovisual materials, and an OPAC.

■ GOLF ACADEMY OF AMERICA
510 S Hunt Club Blvd.
Apopka, FL 32703
Tel: (407)699-1990
Web Site: www.golfacademy.edu/
Description: Proprietary, 2-year, coed. Calendar: semesters.

■ GULF COAST STATE COLLEGE
5230 W Hwy. 98
Panama City, FL 32401-1058
Tel: (850)769-1551
Fax: (850)913-3308
E-mail: jkuczenski@gulfcoast.edu
Web Site: www.gulfcoast.edu/
Description: State-supported, primarily 2-year, coed. Awards certificates, transfer associate, terminal associate, and bachelor's degrees. Founded 1957. Setting: 80-acre suburban campus. Endowment: $25.9 million. Educational spending for the previous fiscal year: $3209 per student. Total enrollment: 6,436. Faculty: 304 (114 full-time, 190 part-time). Student-undergrad faculty ratio is 21:1. Full-time: 2,414 students, 60% women, 40% men. Part-time: 4,022 students, 64% women, 36% men. Students come from 21 states and territories, 6% from out-of-state. 0.5% American Indian or Alaska Native, non-Hispanic/Latino; 8% Hispanic/Latino; 11% African American, non-Hispanic/Latino; 2% Asian, non-Hispanic/Latino; 0.2% Native Hawaiian or other Pacific Islander, non-Hispanic/Latino; 1% international. 44% 25 or older, 4% transferred in. Core. Calendar: semesters. Academic remediation for entering students, ESL program, services for LD students, advanced placement, accelerated degree program, honors program, independent study, distance learning, double major, summer session for credit, part-time degree program, external degree program, adult/continuing education programs, co-op programs. Off campus study.
Entrance Requirements: Open admission. Options: electronic application, early admission, deferred admission, international baccalaureate accepted. Required: high school transcript. Entrance: noncompetitive. Application deadline: Rolling. Notification: continuous. Transfer credits accepted: Yes.
Costs Per Year: Application fee: $20. One-time mandatory fee: $20. State resident tuition: $2370 full-time, $98.75 per credit hour part-time.

Nonresident tuition: $8635 full-time, $359.71 per credit hour part-time. Full-time tuition varies according to degree level. Part-time tuition varies according to degree level.
Collegiate Environment: Orientation program. Drama-theater group, choral group, student-run newspaper. Social organizations: 30 open to all; Phi Theta Kappa Honor Society. Major annual events: Annual Luau, Drive in Movies. Student services: personal-psychological counseling. Campus security: late night transport-escort service, patrols by trained security personnel during campus hours. Gulf Coast State College Library with 117,901 books, 4,655 microform titles, 124 serials, 5,204 audiovisual materials, an OPAC, and a Web page. 1,000 computers available on campus for general student use. A campuswide network can be accessed. Students can access the following: online class registration. Staffed computer lab on campus provides training in use of computers, software, and the Internet.
Community Environment: Panama City is an urban area with a temperate climate and is recognized as one of the most progressive industrial and resort cities in the state. A municipal marina includes a city hall, an auditorium, a library, and berths for about 400 boats. Community facilities include libraries, churches of major denominations, two hospitals and several clinics; shopping facilities are excellent. Some part-time employment is available. The city's industries include tourism, oil companies, wholesale fisheries, chemical production, boat manufacturing. Outdoor sports include golfing, yachting, sailing, water skiing and swimming. Panama City is a noted sport fishing center for both fresh and salt water fish.

■ HERZING UNIVERSITY
1595 S Semoran Blvd.
Winter Park, FL 32792
Tel: (407)478-0500; Free: 800-596-0724
Fax: (407)478-0501
Web Site: www.herzing.edu/
Description: Proprietary, 4-year, coed. Awards associate and bachelor's degrees. Founded 1989. Total enrollment: 209. 60% 25 or older. Calendar: semesters.

■ HILLSBOROUGH COMMUNITY COLLEGE
PO Box 31127
Tampa, FL 33631-3127
Tel: (813)253-7000
Fax: (813)253-7196
E-mail: kdurkee@hccfl.edu
Web Site: www.hccfl.edu/
Description: State-supported, 2-year, coed. Part of Florida College System. Awards certificates, transfer associate, and terminal associate degrees. Founded 1968. Setting: urban campus with easy access to Tampa, Clearwater, St. Petersburg. Total enrollment: 27,754. Faculty: 1,613 (278 full-time, 1,335 part-time). Student-undergrad faculty ratio is 24:1. Full-time: 12,098 students, 54% women, 46% men. Part-time: 15,656 students, 60% women, 40% men. Students come from 43 states and territories, 133 other countries, 1% from out-of-state. 0.4% American Indian or Alaska Native, non-Hispanic/Latino; 25% Hispanic/Latino; 18% African American, non-Hispanic/Latino; 3% Asian, non-Hispanic/Latino; 0.2% Native Hawaiian or other Pacific Islander, non-Hispanic/Latino; 2% international. 38% 25 or older, 24% transferred in. Core. Calendar: semesters. Academic remediation for entering students, ESL program, services for LD students, advanced placement, honors program, independent study, distance learning, summer session for credit, part-time degree program, co-op programs and internships. Off campus study. Study abroad program. ROTC: Army (c), Air Force (c).
Entrance Requirements: Open admission Some allied health area programs are limited due to capacity. Options: electronic application, early admission, international baccalaureate accepted. Required: high school transcript, Entrance exams are required for assessing student readiness for college level courses. Florida's Postsecondary Education Readiness Test (PERT) is the primary entrance exam used. Hillsborough Community College is an open-access institution. Entrance: noncompetitive. Application deadlines: Rolling, Rolling for nonresidents. Transfer credits accepted: Yes.
Costs Per Year: Application fee: $0. State resident tuition: $2505 full-time, $104.39 per credit hour part-time. Nonresident tuition: $9112 full-time, $379.61 per credit hour part-time.
Collegiate Environment: Orientation program. Drama-theater group, choral group, student-run newspaper, radio station. Social organizations: 53 open to all; Radiography Club. Most popular organizations: Student Government Association, Student Nursing Association, Phi Theta Kappa, International

Students. Student services: personal-psychological counseling. Campus security: 24-hour emergency response devices and patrols, late night transport-escort service, emergency call boxes. 420 college housing spaces available. Dale Mabry plus 4 others with 170,615 books, 88,182 microform titles, 1,283 serials, 50,000 audiovisual materials, an OPAC, and a Web page. 2,300 computers available on campus for general student use. A campuswide network can be accessed from student residence rooms and from off campus. Students can access the following: online class registration. Staffed computer lab on campus.

Community Environment: See University of South Florida.

■ **HOBE SOUND BIBLE COLLEGE**

PO Box 1065
Hobe Sound, FL 33475-1065
Tel: (561)546-5534
Fax: (561)545-1422
E-mail: info@hsbc.edu
Web Site: www.hsbc.edu/

Description: Independent nondenominational, 4-year, coed. Awards associate and bachelor's degrees. Founded 1960. Setting: 84-acre small town campus. Total enrollment: 119. Student-undergrad faculty ratio is 10:1. 67% from out-of-state. 21% 25 or older. Retention: 75% of full-time freshmen returned the following year. Core. Calendar: semesters. Academic remediation for entering students, ESL program, advanced placement, independent study, distance learning, double major, summer session for credit, external degree program, internships.

Entrance Requirements: Open admission. Option: early admission. Required: essay, high school transcript, 3 recommendations, photograph, medical report, SAT or ACT. Entrance: noncompetitive. Application deadline: Rolling. Notification: continuous until 8/30. Preference given to applicants committed to Wesleyan-Armenian theological position.

Collegiate Environment: Orientation program. Choral group. Campus security: student patrols, late night transport-escort service, controlled dormitory access. College Library with a Web page.

■ **HODGES UNIVERSITY**

2655 Northbrooke Dr.
Naples, FL 34119
Tel: (239)513-1122; Free: 800-466-8017
Fax: (239)513-9071
E-mail: rlampus@hodges.edu
Web Site: www.hodges.edu/

Description: Independent, comprehensive, coed. Awards associate, bachelor's, and master's degrees. Founded 1990. Setting: 31-acre suburban campus with easy access to Miami. Endowment: $4.5 million. Total enrollment: 2,255. Faculty: 157 (92 full-time, 65 part-time). Student-undergrad faculty ratio is 14:1. 240 applied, 86% were admitted. Full-time: 1,409 students, 63% women, 37% men. Part-time: 658 students, 70% women, 30% men. Students come from 7 states and territories, 6% from out-of-state. 1% American Indian or Alaska Native, non-Hispanic/Latino; 34% Hispanic/Latino; 16% African American, non-Hispanic/Latino; 2% Asian, non-Hispanic/Latino; 0.3% Native Hawaiian or other Pacific Islander, non-Hispanic/Latino; 0% international. 71% 25 or older, 15% transferred in. Academic areas with the most degrees conferred: business/marketing; interdisciplinary studies; health professions and related sciences. Core. Calendar: trimesters. Academic remediation for entering students, ESL program, services for LD students, advanced placement, accelerated degree program, independent study, distance learning, double major, summer session for credit, part-time degree program, external degree program, adult/continuing education programs, co-op programs and internships.

Entrance Requirements: Options: electronic application, deferred admission, international baccalaureate accepted. Required: essay, high school transcript, interview. Required for some: 2 recommendations, CPAt. Entrance: minimally difficult. Application deadline: Rolling. Notification: continuous. Transfer credits accepted: Yes.

Costs Per Year: Application fee: $20. Tuition: $11,760 full-time. Mandatory fees: $500 full-time.

Collegiate Environment: Orientation program. Most popular organizations: Ambassadors, Paralegal Club, Institute of Managerial Accountants, running club, Entrepreneurial Club. Major annual events: Student Recognition Banquet, Salvation Army food drive, seasonal socials. Student services: personal-psychological counseling. Campus security: late night transport-escort service, building security. College housing not available. Terry P. McMahan Libraries plus 1 other with 172,626 books, 93,004 serials, an

OPAC, and a Web page. Operations spending for the previous fiscal year: $884,876. 1,020 computers available on campus for general student use. A campuswide network can be accessed. Students can access the following: Our campus intranet takes the form of a student portal that is accessible via the internet. The portal provides single sign on access to all of the above as well as our Learning Management System, online storage, library resources, a student calendar, etc. Staffed computer lab on campus provides training in use of computers, software, and the Internet.

■ **INDIAN RIVER STATE COLLEGE**

3209 Virginia Ave.
Fort Pierce, FL 34981-5596
Tel: (772)462-4700; Free: 866-792-4772
Fax: (772)462-4796
E-mail: spayne@ircc.edu
Web Site: www.irsc.edu/

Description: State-supported, 4-year, coed. Part of Florida Community College System. Awards associate and bachelor's degrees. Founded 1960. Setting: 713-acre small town campus. Total enrollment: 17,806. Faculty: 874 (228 full-time, 647 part-time). Student-undergrad faculty ratio is 22:1. 1,734 applied, 100% were admitted. Full-time: 6,097 students, 54% women, 46% men. Part-time: 11,709 students, 63% women, 37% men. Students come from 28 states and territories, 120 other countries, 15% from out-of-state. 17% American Indian or Alaska Native, non-Hispanic/Latino; 15% Hispanic/Latino; 0.2% African American, non-Hispanic/Latino; 0.2% Asian, non-Hispanic/Latino; 61% Native Hawaiian or other Pacific Islander, non-Hispanic/Latino; 1% international. 44% 25 or older, 14% transferred in. Core. Calendar: semesters. Academic remediation for entering students, ESL program, services for LD students, advanced placement, independent study, distance learning, summer session for credit, part-time degree program, adult/continuing education programs.

Entrance Requirements: Open admission. Options: early admission, deferred admission. Required: high school transcript. Entrance: noncompetitive. Application deadline: Rolling. Notification: continuous. Transfer credits accepted: Yes.

Collegiate Environment: Orientation program. Drama-theater group, choral group. Social organizations: local fraternities, local sororities. Student services: health clinic, personal-psychological counseling, women's center. Campus security: 24-hour emergency response devices and patrols. College housing not available. Charles S. Miley Learning Resource Center with 73,566 books, 205 serials, 3,116 audiovisual materials, an OPAC, and a Web page. 3,200 computers available on campus for general student use. A campuswide network can be accessed. Students can access the following: online class registration. Staffed computer lab on campus.

Community Environment: A midsize city on the east coast of Florida with a subtropical climate, the area is known for citrus fruits and winter vegetables. Florida's Turnpike, I-95, the Florida East Coast Railroad and the Greyhound bus line serve the area. Community facilities include public libraries, YMCA, churches, hospitals, mental health centers, beaches and recreational activities. Part-time employment opportunities are moderate. Swimming from two ocean beaches, golf and sports fishing are the principal outdoor sports.

■ **INTERNATIONAL ACADEMY OF DESIGN & TECHNOLOGY**

5104 Eisenhower Blvd.
Tampa, FL 33634-7350
Tel: (813)881-0007; Free: 888-315-6111
Fax: (813)881-0008
E-mail: dwolff@academy.edu
Web Site: www.academy.edu/

Description: Proprietary, 4-year, coed. Part of Career Education Corporation. Awards associate and bachelor's degrees. Founded 1984. Setting: 1-acre urban campus. Faculty: 91. Student-undergrad faculty ratio is 21:1. Core. Academic remediation for entering students, services for LD students, accelerated degree program, independent study, distance learning, summer session for credit, part-time degree program, co-op programs and internships. Study abroad program.

Entrance Requirements: Options: electronic application, early admission, deferred admission, international baccalaureate accepted. Required: interview, Portfolio review for fashion design program; Wonderlic assessment, Wonderlic Assessment. Recommended: high school transcript. Entrance: noncompetitive. Application deadlines: Rolling, Rolling for nonresidents. Notification: continuous, continuous for nonresidents. Transfer credits accepted: Yes.

Costs Per Year: Application fee: $50. Tuition: $14,400 full-time.

Collegiate Environment: Orientation program. Social organizations: 3 open to all. Most popular organizations: Student Chapter ASID, IIDA, Emerging Professionals, United States Greenbuilding Council (USGBC), American Advertising Federation. Major annual event: Annual Fashion Show/Portfolio Review. Campus security: 24-hour emergency response devices, late night patrols by trained security personnel. College housing not available. International Academy Learning Resource Center with 6,000 books, 140 serials, 70 audiovisual materials, and an OPAC. 485 computers available on campus for general student use. A campuswide network can be accessed. Staffed computer lab on campus.

■ ITT TECHNICAL INSTITUTE (BRADENTON)

8039 Cooper Creek Blvd.
Bradenton, FL 34201
Tel: (941)309-9200; Free: 800-342-8684
Web Site: www.itt-tech.edu/
Description: Proprietary, primarily 2-year, coed. Part of ITT Educational Services, Inc. Awards terminal associate and bachelor's degrees.

■ ITT TECHNICAL INSTITUTE (DEERFIELD BEACH)

700 W Hillsboro Blvd.
Ste. 100, Bldg. 1
Deerfield Beach, FL 33441
Tel: (954)360-4701; Free: 877-243-8548
Web Site: www.itt-tech.edu/
Description: Proprietary, 4-year, coed. Awards associate and bachelor's degrees.
Entrance Requirements: Entrance: minimally difficult.

■ ITT TECHNICAL INSTITUTE (FORT LAUDERDALE)

3401 S University Dr.
Fort Lauderdale, FL 33328-2021
Tel: (954)476-9300; Free: 800-488-7797
Fax: (954)476-6889
Web Site: www.itt-tech.edu/
Description: Proprietary, primarily 2-year, coed. Part of ITT Educational Services, Inc. Awards terminal associate and bachelor's degrees. Founded 1991. Setting: suburban campus.
Entrance Requirements: Entrance: minimally difficult.

■ ITT TECHNICAL INSTITUTE (FORT MYERS)

13500 Powers Ct.
Ste. 100
Fort Myers, FL 33912
Tel: (239)603-8700; Free: 877-485-5313
Web Site: www.itt-tech.edu/
Description: Proprietary, primarily 2-year, coed. Awards terminal associate and bachelor's degrees.
Entrance Requirements: Entrance: minimally difficult.

■ ITT TECHNICAL INSTITUTE (JACKSONVILLE)

7011 A.C. Skinner Pky.
Ste. 140
Jacksonville, FL 32256
Tel: (904)573-9100; Free: 800-318-1264
Web Site: www.itt-tech.edu/
Description: Proprietary, primarily 2-year, coed. Part of ITT Educational Services, Inc. Awards terminal associate and bachelor's degrees. Founded 1991. Setting: urban campus.
Entrance Requirements: Entrance: minimally difficult.

■ ITT TECHNICAL INSTITUTE (LAKE MARY)

1400 S International Pky.
Lake Mary, FL 32746
Tel: (407)660-2900; Free: 866-489-8441
Web Site: www.itt-tech.edu/
Description: Proprietary, primarily 2-year, coed. Part of ITT Educational Services, Inc. Awards terminal associate and bachelor's degrees. Founded 1989. Setting: suburban campus.
Entrance Requirements: Entrance: minimally difficult.

■ ITT TECHNICAL INSTITUTE (MIAMI)

7955 NW 12th St.
Ste. 119
Miami, FL 33126
Tel: (305)477-3080
Web Site: www.itt-tech.edu/
Description: Proprietary, primarily 2-year, coed. Part of ITT Educational Services, Inc. Awards terminal associate and bachelor's degrees. Founded 1996.
Entrance Requirements: Entrance: minimally difficult.

■ ITT TECHNICAL INSTITUTE (ORLANDO)

8301 Southpark Cir.
Ste. 100
Orlando, FL 32819
Tel: (407)371-6000; Free: 877-201-4367
Web Site: www.itt-tech.edu/
Description: Proprietary, primarily 2-year, coed. Part of ITT Educational Services, Inc. Awards terminal associate and bachelor's degrees.

■ ITT TECHNICAL INSTITUTE (SAINT PETERSBURG)

877 Executive Ctr. Dr. W
Ste. 100
Saint Petersburg, FL 33702
Tel: (727)209-4700; Free: 866-488-5084
Web Site: www.itt-tech.edu/
Description: Proprietary, primarily 2-year, coed. Part of ITT Educational Services, Inc. Awards terminal associate and bachelor's degrees.
Entrance Requirements: Entrance: minimally difficult.

■ ITT TECHNICAL INSTITUTE (TALLAHASSEE)

2639 N Monroe St.
Bldg. A, Ste. 100
Tallahassee, FL 32303
Tel: (850)422-6300; Free: 877-230-3559
Web Site: www.itt-tech.edu/
Description: Proprietary, primarily 2-year, coed. Awards terminal associate and bachelor's degrees.
Entrance Requirements: Entrance: minimally difficult.

■ ITT TECHNICAL INSTITUTE (TAMPA)

4809 Memorial Hwy.
Tampa, FL 33634-7151
Tel: (813)885-2244; Free: 800-825-2831
Fax: (813)888-6078
Web Site: www.itt-tech.edu/
Description: Proprietary, primarily 2-year, coed. Part of ITT Educational Services, Inc. Awards terminal associate and bachelor's degrees. Founded 1981. Setting: suburban campus.
Entrance Requirements: Entrance: minimally difficult.

■ ITT TECHNICAL INSTITUTE (WEST PALM BEACH)

1756 N Congress Ave.
West Palm Beach, FL 33409
Tel: (561)233-4900; Free: 877-236-8164
Web Site: www.itt-tech.edu/
Description: Proprietary, 4-year, coed. Awards associate and bachelor's degrees.
Entrance Requirements: Entrance: minimally difficult.

■ JACKSONVILLE UNIVERSITY

2800 University Blvd. N
Jacksonville, FL 32211
Tel: (904)256-8000; Free: 800-225-2027
Fax: (904)256-7086
E-mail: admissions@ju.edu
Web Site: www.ju.edu/
Description: Independent, comprehensive, coed. Awards bachelor's, master's, and doctoral degrees and post-master's certificates. Founded 1934. Setting: 198-acre suburban campus with easy access to Jacksonville and Saint Augustine FL. Endowment: $35.4 million. Research spending for the previous fiscal year: $1.6 million. Educational spending for the previous fiscal year: $21,230 per student. Total enrollment: 3,936. Faculty: 335 (182 full-time, 153 part-time). Student-undergrad faculty ratio is 12:1. 3,365 applied, 45% were admitted. Full-time: 2,154 students, 51% women, 49% men. Part-time: 1,165 students, 81% women, 19% men. Students come from 49 states and territories, 4 other countries, 89% from out-of-state. 1% American

Indian or Alaska Native, non-Hispanic/Latino; 7% Hispanic/Latino; 19% African American, non-Hispanic/Latino; 4% Asian, non-Hispanic/Latino; 0.4% Native Hawaiian or other Pacific Islander, non-Hispanic/Latino; 2% international. 44% 25 or older, 42% live on campus, 1% transferred in. Retention: 61% of full-time freshmen returned the following year. Academic areas with the most degrees conferred: health professions and related sciences; business/marketing; visual and performing arts. Core. Calendar: semesters. Academic remediation for entering students, ESL program, services for LD students, advanced placement, accelerated degree program, self-designed majors, honors program, independent study, distance learning, double major, summer session for credit, part-time degree program, adult/continuing education programs, co-op programs and internships, graduate courses open to undergrads. Off campus study at Florida Coastal School of Law. Study abroad program. ROTC: Army, Naval.

Entrance Requirements: Options: electronic application, early admission, deferred admission, international baccalaureate accepted. Required: high school transcript, minimum 2 high school GPA, SAT or ACT. Recommended: interview. Required for some: essay. Entrance: moderately difficult. Application deadline: Rolling. Notification: continuous. SAT Reasoning Test deadline: 6/1. SAT Subject Test deadline: 6/1. Transfer credits accepted: Yes.

Costs Per Year: Application fee: $30. Comprehensive fee: $99,730 includes full-time tuition ($29,900), mandatory fees ($29,900), and college room and board ($39,930). College room only: $6190. Room and board charges vary according to board plan and housing facility. Part-time tuition: $498 per credit hour. Part-time mandatory fees: $498 per credit hour.

Collegiate Environment: Orientation program. Drama-theater group, choral group, marching band, student-run newspaper, radio station. Social organizations: 115 open to all; national fraternities, national sororities, local fraternities, local sororities, Professional, Religious, Multicultural, Honorary. Most popular organizations: Honors Student Association- Academic, Greek Life (Panhellenic and IFC Councils)- Social, Black Student Union- Multicultural, International Student Association- Multicultural, Political Science Society- Political. Major annual events: Homecoming, Win the Fin Spirit Competition, Amphitheater Concerts. Student services: health clinic, personal-psychological counseling. Campus security: 24-hour emergency response devices and patrols, student patrols, late night transport-escort service, controlled dormitory access, code lock doors in residence halls, trained security patrols during evening hours. 1,205 college housing spaces available; 1,026 were occupied in 2012-13. Freshmen guaranteed college housing. On-campus residence required through sophomore year. Options: coed, men-only, women-only housing available. Carl S. Swisher Library with an OPAC and a Web page. Operations spending for the previous fiscal year: $2.6 million. 400 computers available on campus for general student use. Computer purchase/lease plans available. A campuswide network can be accessed from student residence rooms and from off campus. Students can access the following: online class registration, Blackboard and Web Advisor. Staffed computer lab on campus provides training in use of computers.

Community Environment: Jacksonville is located on the St. John's River near the Atlantic Ocean and has a temperate climate characterized by short mild winters and long relatively warm summers with the average temperature being 67.8 degrees. The city functions as the financial, industrial, transportation, and commercial center of Florida. Along with the usual community facilities, there are seven hospitals, churches of almost all denominations, excellent shopping facilities, a civic performing arts center which features the finest of concerts, plays, and ballet, and many little theatre groups. Jacksonville and the surrounding area provide ample beaches and facilities for yachting, swimming, fishing, and golfing. The Friendship Park on the south side of the St. Johns River contains the spectacular Friendship Fountain and marina. A sports complex consists of the Coliseum, Alltell, Stadium, home of the NFL Jacksonville Jaguars; and Wolfson Park, home of the minor league baseball Jacksonville Suns. Part-time employment is available.

■ **JOHNSON UNIVERSITY FLORIDA**
1011 Bill Beck Blvd.
Kissimmee, FL 34744-5301
Tel: (407)847-8966; Free: 888-GO-TO-FCC
Fax: (407)847-3925
E-mail: admissionsforms@fcc.edu
Web Site: www.johnsonu.edu/
Description: Independent, 4-year, coed, affiliated with Christian Churches and Churches of Christ. Awards associate and bachelor's degrees. Founded 1976. Setting: 40-acre small town campus with easy access to Orlando,

Florida. Total enrollment: 380. Faculty: 29 (12 full-time, 17 part-time). Student-undergrad faculty ratio is 18:1. 526 applied, 35% were admitted. Full-time: 281 students, 42% women, 58% men. Part-time: 99 students, 52% women, 48% men. Students come from 21 states and territories, 2 other countries, 12% from out-of-state. 0% American Indian or Alaska Native, non-Hispanic/Latino; 16% Hispanic/Latino; 17% African American, non-Hispanic/Latino; 0% Asian, non-Hispanic/Latino; 0% Native Hawaiian or other Pacific Islander, non-Hispanic/Latino; 0.3% international. 22% 25 or older, 62% live on campus, 11% transferred in. Retention: 60% of full-time freshmen returned the following year. Academic areas with the most degrees conferred: theology and religious vocations; education. Core. Calendar: semesters. Academic remediation for entering students, advanced placement, distance learning, double major, summer session for credit, part-time degree program, adult/continuing education programs, internships. Study abroad program.

Entrance Requirements: Options: early admission, deferred admission. Required: essay, high school transcript, 3 recommendations, SAT or ACT. Required for some: interview. Entrance: minimally difficult. Application deadline: 7/15. Notification: continuous until 8/25. SAT Reasoning Test deadline: 5/1. SAT Subject Test deadline: 5/1. Transfer credits accepted: Yes.

Costs Per Year: Application fee: $35. One-time mandatory fee: $920. Tuition: $11,400 full-time. Mandatory fees: $1170 full-time. College room only: $3200. Tuition guaranteed not to increase for student's term of enrollment.

Collegiate Environment: Orientation program. Choral group. Campus security: controlled dormitory access, late night trained security patrol. 230 college housing spaces available; 209 were occupied in 2012-13. No special consideration for freshman housing applicants. Options: men-only, women-only housing available. FCC Library plus 1 other with 31,000 books, 285 serials, an OPAC, and a Web page.

■ **JOHNSON & WALES UNIVERSITY**
1701 NE 127th St.
North Miami, FL 33181
Tel: (305)892-7000; Free: 866-598-3567
Fax: (305)892-7030
E-mail: mia@admissions.jwu.edu
Web Site: www.jwu.edu/northmiami/
Description: Independent, 4-year, coed. Administratively affiliated with Johnson & Wales University (RI). Awards associate and bachelor's degrees. Founded 1992. Setting: 8-acre suburban campus with easy access to Miami. Total enrollment: 2,098. Faculty: 90 (62 full-time, 28 part-time). Student-undergrad faculty ratio is 28:1. 6,764 applied, 58% were admitted. Full-time: 2,008 students, 57% women, 43% men. Part-time: 90 students, 50% women, 50% men. 44% from out-of-state. 0.3% American Indian or Alaska Native, non-Hispanic/Latino; 18% Hispanic/Latino; 17% African American, non-Hispanic/Latino; 1% Asian, non-Hispanic/Latino; 8% international. 10% 25 or older, 47% live on campus, 7% transferred in. Retention: 69% of full-time freshmen returned the following year. Academic areas with the most degrees conferred: business/marketing; family and consumer sciences; parks and recreation. Core. Academic remediation for entering students, ESL program, services for LD students, advanced placement, accelerated degree program, honors program, independent study, summer session for credit, part-time degree program, co-op programs and internships. Study abroad program.

Entrance Requirements: Options: early admission, deferred admission, international baccalaureate accepted. Required: high school transcript. Recommended: minimum 2 high school GPA. Required for some: essay, interview, SAT or ACT. Entrance: moderately difficult. Application deadline: Rolling. Notification: continuous.

Collegiate Environment: Orientation program. Social organizations: national fraternities, national sororities, local fraternities, local sororities. Student services: personal-psychological counseling. Campus security: 24-hour emergency response devices and patrols, video camera surveillance throughout campus. Florida Campus Library with an OPAC.

■ **JONES COLLEGE**
5353 Arlington Expy.
Jacksonville, FL 32211
Tel: (904)743-1122; Free: 800-631-4056
E-mail: admissions@jones.edu
Web Site: www.jones.edu/
Description: Independent, 4-year, coed. Awards associate and bachelor's

degrees. Founded 1918. Setting: 5-acre urban campus. Total enrollment: 496. Faculty: 73 (9 full-time, 64 part-time). Student-undergrad faculty ratio is 7:1. Full-time: 240 students, 75% women, 25% men. Part-time: 256 students, 63% women, 37% men. Students come from 16 states and territories, 1 other country, 8% from out-of-state. 1% American Indian or Alaska Native, non-Hispanic/Latino; 5% Hispanic/Latino; 71% African American, non-Hispanic/Latino; 1% Asian, non-Hispanic/Latino; 0% Native Hawaiian or other Pacific Islander, non-Hispanic/Latino; 0.4% international. 84% 25 or older, 11% transferred in. Retention: 0% of full-time freshmen returned the following year. Academic areas with the most degrees conferred: business/marketing; health professions and related sciences; law/legal studies. Core. Calendar: trimesters. Academic remediation for entering students, advanced placement, accelerated degree program, self-designed majors, distance learning, double major, summer session for credit, part-time degree program, adult/continuing education programs, co-op programs and internships.

Entrance Requirements: Open admission. Option: electronic application. Required: interview. Required for some: high school transcript, CPAt. Entrance: noncompetitive. Application deadline: Rolling. Transfer credits accepted: Yes.

Costs Per Year: Application fee: $0. Tuition: $7320 full-time, $305 per credit hour part-time. Mandatory fees: $90 full-time, $45 per term part-time.

Collegiate Environment: Orientation program. Campus security: late night transport-escort service, emergency notification system through email/texting/phones. College housing not available. James V. Forrestal Library plus 1 other with 34,000 books, 161 serials, an OPAC, and a Web page. 100 computers available on campus for general student use. A campuswide network can be accessed. Students can access the following: online class registration. Staffed computer lab on campus provides training in use of computers, software, and the Internet.

Community Environment: See Jacksonville University.

■ **JOSE MARIA VARGAS UNIVERSITY**
8300 S Palm Dr.
Pembroke Pines, FL 33025
Tel: (954)322-4446
Web Site: www.jmvu.edu/
Description: Proprietary, comprehensive, coed.

■ **KAPLAN COLLEGE, JACKSONVILLE CAMPUS**
7450 Beach Blvd.
Jacksonville, FL 32216
Tel: (904)855-2405
Web Site: jacksonville.kaplancollege.com/
Description: Proprietary, 2-year, coed. Awards diplomas and terminal associate degrees.

■ **KEISER UNIVERSITY (FORT LAUDERDALE)**
1500 NW 49th St.
Fort Lauderdale, FL 33309
Tel: (954)776-4456; Free: 888-534-7379
Web Site: www.keiseruniversity.edu/
Description: Independent, comprehensive, coed. Awards associate, bachelor's, master's, and doctoral degrees (profile includes data from campuses located in Daytona Beach, Fort Lauderdale, Fort Myers, Jacksonville, Lakeland, Melbourne, Miami, Orlando, Pembroke Pines, Port St. Lucie, Sarasota, Tallahassee, Tampa, and West Palm Beach; not all programs offered at all locations, but many classes offered 100% online). Founded 1977. Faculty: 837 (352 full-time, 485 part-time). Student-undergrad faculty ratio is 11:1. Calendar: 3 semesters per year. Adult/continuing education programs.

Entrance Requirements: Open admission. Required: high school transcript, interview, SAT, ACT, Wonderlic Test. Application deadline: Rolling. Notification: continuous.

Collegiate Environment: Orientation program. Social organizations: national fraternities. Most popular organizations: Student Government Association, Phi Theta Kappa, Sigma Beta Delta International Honor Society, Alpha Phi Sigma National Honor Society, Student Nurses Association. Major annual events: Cystic Fibrosis Foundation, American Cancer Society, American Diabetes Association. Student services: personal-psychological counseling. Campus security: 24-hour emergency response devices, AlertNow Rapid Communications Service.

■ **KEISER UNIVERSITY (FORT MYERS)**
9100 Forum Corporate Pky.
Fort Myers, FL 33905

Tel: (239)277-1336
Web Site: www.keiseruniversity.edu/
Description: Independent, 4-year, coed.

■ **KEY COLLEGE**
225 E Dania Beach Blvd.
Dania Beach, FL 33004
Tel: (954)581-2223; Free: 800-581-8292
Fax: (954)583-9458
Web Site: www.keycollege.edu/
Description: Proprietary, 2-year, coed. Awards certificates, diplomas, transfer associate, and terminal associate degrees. Founded 1881. Setting: suburban campus with easy access to Miami. Total enrollment: 100. 11 applied, 100% were admitted. 46% 25 or older. Core. Advanced placement, honors program, double major, external degree program, adult/continuing education programs, internships.

Entrance Requirements: Options: electronic application, deferred admission. Required: high school transcript, interview. Required for some: CPAt, SAT, or ACT. Entrance: minimally difficult. Application deadline: Rolling. Notification: continuous.

Collegiate Environment: Orientation program. Campus security: 24-hour emergency response devices.

■ **LAKE-SUMTER STATE COLLEGE**
9501 US Hwy. 441
Leesburg, FL 34788-8751
Tel: (352)787-3747
E-mail: admissinquiry@lscc.edu
Web Site: www.lscc.edu/
Description: State and locally supported, 2-year, coed. Part of Florida College System. Awards certificates, diplomas, and transfer associate degrees. Founded 1962. Setting: 112-acre suburban campus with easy access to Orlando. Endowment: $3.9 million. Total enrollment: 4,929. Faculty: 428 (84 full-time, 344 part-time). Student-undergrad faculty ratio is 17:1. 1,353 applied, 100% were admitted. Full-time: 1,641 students, 59% women, 41% men. Part-time: 3,288 students, 64% women, 36% men. 1% from out-of-state. 29% 25 or older, 5% transferred in. Core. Calendar: semesters. Academic remediation for entering students, services for LD students, advanced placement, independent study, distance learning, double major, summer session for credit, part-time degree program, adult/continuing education programs, co-op programs and internships. Off campus study.

Entrance Requirements: Open admission except for nursing program. Option: electronic application. Required: high school transcript. Entrance: noncompetitive. Application deadline: Rolling. Notification: continuous. Transfer credits accepted: Yes.

Collegiate Environment: Orientation program. Drama-theater group, choral group, student-run newspaper. Social organizations: 19 open to all. Most popular organizations: Phi Theta Kappa, Student Government Association, Theatre Arts Society, Nursing Student's Association, Safire. Student services: women's center. Campus security: 24-hour emergency response devices. Lake-Sumter Community College Library with 82,023 books, 167 serials, 1,761 audiovisual materials, an OPAC, and a Web page. Operations spending for the previous fiscal year: $699,594. 825 computers available on campus for general student use. A campuswide network can be accessed from off-campus. Students can access the following: online class registration. Staffed computer lab on campus provides training in use of computers, software, and the Internet.

Community Environment: Leesburg is a rapidly growing rural area with a temperate climate, located in central Florida near the shores of Lakes Griffin and Harris, within easy driving distance of metropolitan areas. Community facilities include numerous libraries, churches, general hospitals, active major civic and service groups. Part-time and full-time employment are available. Many forms of recreation are found, including fishing, swimming, golf, tennis, shuffleboard, water skiing and hunting. Lake Griffin State Park nearby provides additional recreational facilities.

■ **LAUREL UNIVERSITY**
14540 SW 136th St.
Ste. 108
Miami, FL 33186
Tel: (305)232-5880; Free: 888-376-3538
Fax: (305)232-3592
E-mail: admissiones@flet.edu
Web Site: laureluniversity.edu/academics/division-academica-en-espanol/

Description: Independent interdenominational, comprehensive, coed. Awards associate, bachelor's, and master's degrees. Founded 1977. Setting: urban campus. Educational spending for the previous fiscal year: $2000 per student. Total enrollment: 902. Faculty: 20 (4 full-time, 16 part-time). Student-undergrad faculty ratio is 33:1. Part-time: 696 students, 39% women, 61% men. 80% 25 or older. Academic area with the most degrees conferred: theology and religious vocations. Core. Part-time degree program, external degree program, adult/continuing education programs.
Entrance Requirements: Open admission. Options: electronic application, international baccalaureate accepted. Required: high school transcript.

■ **LE CORDON BLEU COLLEGE OF CULINARY ARTS, MIAMI**
3221 Enterprise Way
Miramar, FL 33025
Free: 888-569-3222
Web Site: www.miamiculinary.com/
Description: Proprietary, 2-year, coed. Awards terminal associate degrees. Total enrollment: 1,114. Student-undergrad faculty ratio is 71:1. 6% from out-of-state. 59% 25 or older.
Entrance Requirements: Open admission.

■ **LE CORDON BLEU COLLEGE OF CULINARY ARTS IN ORLANDO**
8511 Commodity Cir.
Ste. 100
Orlando, FL 32819
Tel: (407)888-4000; Free: 888-793-3222
Fax: (407)888-4019
Web Site: www.chefs.edu/Orlando
Description: Proprietary, 2-year, coed. Awards terminal associate degrees. Founded 2002. Total enrollment: 951.
Entrance Requirements: Entrance: noncompetitive.

■ **LINCOLN COLLEGE OF TECHNOLOGY**
2410 Metrocentre Blvd.
West Palm Beach, FL 33407
Tel: (561)842-8324
Fax: (561)842-9503
Web Site: www.lincolnedu.com/
Description: Proprietary, primarily 2-year, coed. Awards certificates, diplomas, transfer associate, terminal associate, and bachelor's degrees. Founded 1983. Setting: 7-acre urban campus with easy access to Miami. Total enrollment: 1,521. 39% 25 or older. Academic remediation for entering students, internships.
Entrance Requirements: Open admission. Option: early admission. Required: high school transcript. Entrance: noncompetitive. Application deadline: Rolling. Notification: continuous.
Collegiate Environment: Student services: personal-psychological counseling.

■ **LINCOLN CULINARY INSTITUTE**
2410 Metrocentre Blvd.
West Palm Beach, FL 33407
Tel: (561)842-8324
E-mail: info@floridaculinary.com
Web Site: www.lincolnedu.com/campus/west-palm-beach-culinary-fl
Description: Proprietary, 4-year, coed. Administratively affiliated with Lincoln Educational Services. Awards associate and bachelor's degrees (degree in science only (18 or 24 month program). Setting: 14-acre urban campus with easy access to West Palm Beach, Fort Lauderdale, Miami. Total enrollment: 600. Faculty: 19.

■ **LINCOLN TECHNICAL INSTITUTE**
7275 Estapona Cir.
Fern Park, FL 32730
Tel: (407)673-7406
Web Site: www.lincolnedu.com/
Description: Proprietary, 2-year, coed.

■ **LYNN UNIVERSITY**
3601 N Military Trl.
Boca Raton, FL 33431-5598
Tel: (561)237-7000; Free: 800-888-5966
Fax: (561)241-3552
E-mail: spapaleo@lynn.edu

Web Site: www.lynn.edu/
Description: Independent, comprehensive, coed. Administratively affiliated with American College Dublin. Awards bachelor's, master's, and doctoral degrees and post-master's certificates. Founded 1962. Setting: 123-acre suburban campus with easy access to Fort Lauderdale. System endowment: $21.1 million. Educational spending for the previous fiscal year: $9352 per student. Total enrollment: 2,097. Faculty: 181 (93 full-time, 88 part-time). Student-undergrad faculty ratio is 15:1. 2,162 applied, 95% were admitted. 3% from top 10% of their high school class, 22% from top quarter, 52% from top half. Full-time: 1,499 students, 47% women, 53% men. Part-time: 158 students, 56% women, 44% men. Students come from 42 states and territories, 77 other countries, 55% from out-of-state. 0.2% American Indian or Alaska Native, non-Hispanic/Latino; 10% Hispanic/Latino; 8% African American, non-Hispanic/Latino; 1% Asian, non-Hispanic/Latino; 0.3% Native Hawaiian or other Pacific Islander, non-Hispanic/Latino; 22% international. 12% 25 or older, 48% live on campus, 10% transferred in. Retention: 69% of full-time freshmen returned the following year. Academic areas with the most degrees conferred: business/marketing; communication/journalism; homeland security, law enforcement, firefighting, and protective services. Core. Calendar: semesters plus 3 summer sessions. Academic remediation for entering students, ESL program, services for LD students, advanced placement, accelerated degree program, freshman honors college, honors program, independent study, distance learning, double major, summer session for credit, part-time degree program, adult/continuing education programs, co-op programs and internships, graduate courses open to undergrads. Study abroad program. ROTC: Air Force (c).
Entrance Requirements: Options: electronic application, early admission, deferred admission, international baccalaureate accepted. Required: essay, high school transcript, minimum 2 high school GPA, SAT or ACT. Recommended: minimum 3 high school GPA, interview, Interview and essay, portfolio for art and graphic design majors. Entrance: moderately difficult. Application deadline: Rolling. Notification: continuous. Transfer credits accepted: Yes.
Costs Per Year: Application fee: $45. Comprehensive fee: $44,300 includes full-time tuition ($31,900), mandatory fees ($1500), and college room and board ($10,900). Full-time tuition and fees vary according to reciprocity agreements. Room and board charges vary according to board plan and housing facility. Part-time tuition: $925 per credit. Part-time tuition varies according to class time and course load.
Collegiate Environment: Orientation program. Drama-theater group, student-run newspaper, radio station. Social organizations: national fraternities, national sororities. Most popular organizations: Knights of the Round Table, intramural groups, student newspaper, Residence Hall Council, Activities Board. Major annual events: Fall Fest, Homecoming, Spring Fling. Student services: health clinic, personal-psychological counseling, women's center. Campus security: 24-hour emergency response devices and patrols, late night transport-escort service, video monitor at residence entrances. 922 college housing spaces available; 780 were occupied in 2012-13. Freshmen guaranteed college housing. On-campus residence required in freshman year. Options: coed, women-only housing available. Eugene M. and Christine E. Lynn Library with 240,000 books, an OPAC, and a Web page. Operations spending for the previous fiscal year: $545,192.
Community Environment: See Florida Atlantic University.

■ **MEDVANCE INSTITUTE**
1630 S Congress Ave.
Palm Springs, FL 33461
Tel: (561)304-3466; Free: 877-606-3382
Fax: (561)304-3471
Web Site: www.medvance.edu/
Description: Proprietary, 2-year, coed. Awards certificates and transfer associate degrees. Founded 1970. Total enrollment: 1,067. Student-undergrad faculty ratio is 37:1. 0% from out-of-state. 54% 25 or older.

■ **MERIDIAN COLLEGE**
7020 Professional Pky. E
Sarasota, FL 34240
Tel: (941)377-4880
Web Site: www.meridian.edu/
Description: Proprietary, 2-year, coed. Founded 1982.

■ **MIAMI DADE COLLEGE**
300 NE Second Ave.
Miami, FL 33132

Tel: (305)237-3000
Fax: (305)237-3761
E-mail: dbeltran@mdc.edu
Web Site: www.mdc.edu/
Description: State and locally supported, primarily 2-year, coed. Part of Florida College System. Awards certificates, transfer associate, terminal associate, and bachelor's degrees. Founded 1960. Setting: urban campus. Endowment: $165.5 million. Educational spending for the previous fiscal year: $2234 per student. Total enrollment: 66,701. Faculty: 2,558 (710 full-time, 1,848 part-time). Student-undergrad faculty ratio is 30:1. 10,575 applied, 100% were admitted. Full-time: 26,211 students, 57% women, 43% men. Part-time: 40,490 students, 59% women, 41% men. Students come from 43 states and territories, 185 other countries, 1% from out-of-state. 0.1% American Indian or Alaska Native, non-Hispanic/Latino; 70% Hispanic/Latino; 17% African American, non-Hispanic/Latino; 1% Asian, non-Hispanic/Latino; 0.1% Native Hawaiian or other Pacific Islander, non-Hispanic/Latino; 2% international. 36% 25 or older, 3% transferred in. Academic areas with the most degrees conferred: business/marketing; homeland security, law enforcement, firefighting, and protective services; education. Core. Calendar: 16-16-6-6. Academic remediation for entering students, ESL program, services for LD students, advanced placement, accelerated degree program, freshman honors college, honors program, independent study, distance learning, summer session for credit, part-time degree program, adult/continuing education programs, co-op programs and internships. Off campus study. Study abroad program. ROTC: Army, Air Force.
Entrance Requirements: Open admission. Options: electronic application, early admission, international baccalaureate accepted. Required: high school transcript. Required for some: Some programs such as Honors College and Medical programs have additional admissions requirements. Entrance: noncompetitive. Application deadlines: Rolling, Rolling for nonresidents. Notification: continuous, continuous for nonresidents. Transfer credits accepted: Yes.
Costs Per Year: Application fee: $30. One-time mandatory fee: $30. State resident tuition: $2,483 full-time, $82.78 per credit hour part-time. Nonresident tuition: $9,933 full-time, $331.11 per credit hour part-time. Mandatory fees: $883 full-time, $29.44 per credit hour part-time. Full-time tuition and fees vary according to course load, degree level, and program. Part-time tuition and fees vary according to course load, degree level, and program.
Collegiate Environment: Orientation program. Drama-theater group, choral group, student-run newspaper, radio station. Social organizations: 40 open to all; national fraternities, local fraternities; 40% of eligible men and 60% of eligible women are members. Most popular organizations: Student Government Association, Phi Theta Kappa, Phi Beta Lambda (Business), Future Educators of America Professional, Kappa Delta Pi Honor Society (Education). Major annual events: Miami International Film Festival, Miami Book Fair International, Graduation. Student services: personal-psychological counseling. Campus security: 24-hour emergency response devices and patrols, mass communication emergency notification systems. College housing not available. Miami Dade College Learning Resources plus 8 others with 367,687 books, 750 serials, 32,428 audiovisual materials, an OPAC, and a Web page. Operations spending for the previous fiscal year: $444,939. 9,655 computers available on campus for general student use. A campuswide network can be accessed. Students can access the following: online class registration, admissions; student feedback of faculty; financial aid; IRS Form 1098. Staffed computer lab on campus provides training in use of computers, software, and the Internet.
Community Environment: See Florida International University.

■ **MIAMI INTERNATIONAL UNIVERSITY OF ART & DESIGN**
1501 Biscayne Blvd., Ste. 100
Miami, FL 33132-1418
Tel: (305)428-5700; Free: 800-225-9023
Fax: (305)374-7946
Web Site: www.artinstitutes.edu/miami/
Description: Proprietary, comprehensive, coed. Part of Education Management Corporation. Awards associate, bachelor's, and master's degrees. Founded 1965. Setting: urban campus.
Community Environment: See Barry University.

■ **MILLENNIA ATLANTIC UNIVERSITY**
3801 NW 97th Ave.
Doral, FL 33178
Tel: (786)331-1000

Web Site: www.maufl.edu/
Description: Proprietary, comprehensive, coed. Calendar: semesters.

■ **NEW COLLEGE OF FLORIDA**
5800 Bay Shore Rd.
Sarasota, FL 34243
Tel: (941)359-4269
Fax: (941)359-4435
E-mail: admissions@ncf.edu
Web Site: www.ncf.edu/
Description: State-supported, 4-year, coed. Part of State University System of Florida. Awards bachelor's degrees. Founded 1960. Setting: 119-acre suburban campus with easy access to Tampa-St. Petersburg. Endowment: $28.2 million. Research spending for the previous fiscal year: $930,717. Educational spending for the previous fiscal year: $10,344 per student. Total enrollment: 832. Faculty: 105 (68 full-time, 37 part-time). Student-undergrad faculty ratio is 10:1. 1,348 applied, 60% were admitted. 35% from top 10% of their high school class, 76% from top quarter, 97% from top half. Full-time: 832 students, 59% women, 41% men. Students come from 37 states and territories, 20 other countries, 18% from out-of-state. 0.2% American Indian or Alaska Native, non-Hispanic/Latino; 14% Hispanic/Latino; 2% African American, non-Hispanic/Latino; 2% Asian, non-Hispanic/Latino; 0.1% Native Hawaiian or other Pacific Islander, non-Hispanic/Latino; 1% international. 2% 25 or older, 75% live on campus, 3% transferred in. Retention: 83% of full-time freshmen returned the following year. Academic area with the most degrees conferred: liberal arts/general studies. Core. Calendar: 4-1-4. Services for LD students, self-designed majors, honors program, independent study, double major, co-op programs and internships. Off campus study at National Student Exchange. Study abroad program.
Entrance Requirements: Options: electronic application, early admission, deferred admission, international baccalaureate accepted. Required: essay, high school transcript, 1 recommendation, SAT or ACT. Recommended: minimum 3 high school GPA. Required for some: interview. Entrance: very difficult. Application deadlines: 4/15, 4/15 for nonresidents. Notification: 4/25, 4/25 for nonresidents. SAT Reasoning Test deadline: 4/15. Transfer credits accepted: Yes. Applicants placed on waiting list: 141. Wait-listed applicants offered admission: 16.
Costs Per Year: Application fee: $30. State resident tuition: $6783 full-time. Nonresident tuition: $29,812 full-time. Full-time tuition varies according to course load. College room and board: $8856. College room only: $6078. Room and board charges vary according to board plan and housing facility.
Collegiate Environment: Orientation program. Drama-theater group, choral group, student-run newspaper, radio station. Social organizations: 90 open to all. Most popular organizations: PRIDE, Interfaith groups, New College Student Alliance, Feminist Majority Leadership Alliance, Sailing Club. Major annual events: Halloween Palm Court Party, Towne Meetings, Dance Tutorial Performances. Student services: health clinic, personal-psychological counseling, women's center. Campus security: 24-hour emergency response devices and patrols, student patrols, late night transport-escort service, controlled dormitory access, campus police are state certified police officers and available 24/7. 636 college housing spaces available; all were occupied in 2012-13. Freshmen guaranteed college housing. On-campus residence required through senior year. Option: coed housing available. Jane Bancroft Cook Library with 288,555 books, 198,287 microform titles, 24,099 serials, 7,777 audiovisual materials, an OPAC, and a Web page. Operations spending for the previous fiscal year: $924,737. 41 computers available on campus for general student use. A campuswide network can be accessed from student residence rooms and from off campus. Students can access the following: online class registration. Staffed computer lab on campus provides training in use of computers, software, and the Internet.

■ **NEW WORLD SCHOOL OF THE ARTS**
300 NE 2nd Ave.
Miami, FL 33132
Tel: (305)237-3135
Fax: (305)237-3794
E-mail: nwsaadm@mdc.edu
Web Site: www.mdc.edu/nwsa/
Description: State-supported, 4-year, coed. Part of New World School of the Arts is a partnership of Miami Dade County Public Schools, Miami Dade College and the University of Florida. Awards associate and bachelor's degrees. Founded 1984. Setting: 5-acre urban campus with easy access to Broward, Palm Beach Counties. Endowment: $8.3 million. Total enrollment: 335. Faculty: 77 (22 full-time, 55 part-time). Student-undergrad faculty ratio

is 5:1. 384 applied, 52% were admitted. Full-time: 335 students, 57% women, 43% men. Students come from 12 states and territories, 9 other countries, 4% from out-of-state. 62% Hispanic/Latino; 13% African American, non-Hispanic/Latino; 4% Asian, non-Hispanic/Latino. 12% 25 or older, 6% transferred in. Retention: 70% of full-time freshmen returned the following year. Academic area with the most degrees conferred: visual and performing arts. Core. Calendar: semesters. Academic remediation for entering students, ESL program, services for LD students, advanced placement, freshman honors college, independent study, distance learning, double major, summer session for credit, co-op programs and internships. Study abroad program.

Entrance Requirements: Option: early decision. Required: essay, high school transcript, 2 recommendations, interview, audition. Recommended: SAT or ACT. Entrance: noncompetitive. Application deadline: Rolling. Notification: continuous, continuous for nonresidents, Rolling for early decision. Transfer credits accepted: Yes.

Collegiate Environment: Orientation program. Most popular organization: student government. Major annual event: Rising Stars. Student services: personal-psychological counseling. Campus security: 24-hour patrols. Miami Dade Community College library (Wolfson Campus) plus 1 other with an OPAC and a Web page. 100 computers available on campus for general student use. A campuswide network can be accessed from off-campus. Students can access the following: online class registration. Staffed computer lab on campus.

■ NORTH FLORIDA COMMUNITY COLLEGE

325 NW Turner Davis Dr.
Madison, FL 32340
Tel: (850)973-2288; Free: 866-937-6322
Fax: (850)973-1696
Web Site: www.nfcc.edu/

Description: State-supported, 2-year, coed. Awards certificates, transfer associate, and terminal associate degrees. Founded 1958. Setting: 109-acre small town campus. Total enrollment: 1,297. Faculty: 44 (25 full-time, 19 part-time). Student-undergrad faculty ratio is 18:1. Full-time: 593 students, 64% women, 36% men. Part-time: 704 students, 65% women, 35% men. 31% 25 or older. Core. Calendar: semesters. Academic remediation for entering students, services for LD students, advanced placement, accelerated degree program, honors program, distance learning, summer session for credit, part-time degree program, adult/continuing education programs.

Entrance Requirements: Open admission. Option: early admission. Required: high school transcript, minimum 2.0 high school GPA. Entrance: noncompetitive. Application deadline: Rolling.

Costs Per Year: Application fee: $20. State resident tuition: $2994 full-time, $99.80 per semester hour part-time. Nonresident tuition: $11,910 full-time, $397 per semester hour part-time. Full-time tuition varies according to course load and program. Part-time tuition varies according to course load and program.

Collegiate Environment: Drama-theater group, choral group, student-run newspaper. Social organizations: 7 open to all; local sororities. Most popular organizations: Student Government Association, Sentinel Ambassadors, Phi Theta Kappa, African-American Student Union, Fellowship of Christian Athletes. Major annual event: Octoberfest. Student services: women's center. Campus security: 24-hour emergency response devices. Dr. Marshall Hamilton Library with 30,137 books, 125 serials, an OPAC, and a Web page. 275 computers available on campus for general student use. A campuswide network can be accessed. Students can access the following: online class registration. Staffed computer lab on campus.

Community Environment: Madison is located in a rural area with a temperate climate. Railroads and buses serve the area along with three highways. Community facilities include a public library, hospital, ten churches, and major civic and fraternal organizations. Within easy reach are large shopping and cultural centers. Recreational facilities include a golf course, recreation center, and many facilities for all water sports. Part-time employment opportunities are limited.

■ NORTHWEST FLORIDA STATE COLLEGE

100 College Blvd.
Niceville, FL 32578-1295
Tel: (850)678-5111
E-mail: registrar@nwfsc.edu
Web Site: www.nwfsc.edu/

Description: State and locally supported, primarily 2-year, coed. Part of Florida Colleges System. Awards certificates, transfer associate, terminal as-

sociate, and bachelor's degrees. Founded 1963. Setting: 264-acre small town campus. Endowment: $28.6 million. Educational spending for the previous fiscal year: $5136 per student. Total enrollment: 10,317. Faculty: 310 (95 full-time, 215 part-time). Student-undergrad faculty ratio is 15:1. Students come from 18 states and territories. 44% 25 or older. Core. Calendar: semesters plus summer sessions. Academic remediation for entering students, ESL program, services for LD students, advanced placement, accelerated degree program, independent study, distance learning, summer session for credit, part-time degree program, adult/continuing education programs. ROTC: Army.

Entrance Requirements: Open admission. Option: electronic application. Required: high school transcript. Required for some: ACT, SAT I, ACT ASSET, MAPS, or Florida College Entry Placement Test are used for placement not admission. Entrance: noncompetitive. Application deadline: Rolling. Notification: continuous. Preference given to state residents.

Costs Per Year: Application fee: $0. One-time mandatory fee: $30. State resident tuition: $3234 full-time, $107.80 per credit part-time. Nonresident tuition: $11,604 full-time, $386.80 per credit part-time. Full-time tuition varies according to course level, course load, degree level, and reciprocity agreements. Part-time tuition varies according to course level, course load, degree level, and reciprocity agreements.

Collegiate Environment: Drama-theater group, choral group. Social organizations: 24 open to all. Major annual events: College Night, Student Government Association Picnic (Fall), Student Government Association Picnic (Spring). Student services: women's center. Northwest Florida State College Learning Resources Center with 106,383 books, 139,142 microform titles, 399 serials, 10,219 audiovisual materials, an OPAC, and a Web page. Operations spending for the previous fiscal year: $908,962. 643 computers available on campus for general student use. A campuswide network can be accessed. Students can access the following: online class registration. Staffed computer lab on campus.

Community Environment: Twin cities with temperate climate, largely residential in nature. Many residents are military retirees or civil service personnel. Airlines and Greyhound and AmTrak buses serve the area. Large shopping centers are within easy driving distance. Part-time job opportunities for students are limited.

■ NORTHWOOD UNIVERSITY, FLORIDA CAMPUS

2600 N Military Trl.
West Palm Beach, FL 33409-2911
Tel: (561)478-5500; Free: 800-622-9000
Fax: (561)640-3328
E-mail: fladmit@northwood.edu
Web Site: www.northwood.edu/

Description: Private, comprehensive, coed. Administratively affiliated with Northwood University (MI). Awards bachelor's and master's degrees. Founded 1982. Setting: 90-acre suburban campus. Endowment: $31.1 million. Educational spending for the previous fiscal year: $5339 per student. Total enrollment: 537. Faculty: 44 (16 full-time, 28 part-time). Student-undergrad faculty ratio is 20:1. 628 applied, 54% were admitted. 11% from top 10% of their high school class, 35% from top quarter, 32% from top half. Full-time: 484 students, 36% women, 64% men. Part-time: 13 students, 31% women, 69% men. 38% from out-of-state. 1% American Indian or Alaska Native, non-Hispanic/Latino; 11% Hispanic/Latino; 10% African American, non-Hispanic/Latino; 1% Asian, non-Hispanic/Latino; 0% Native Hawaiian or other Pacific Islander, non-Hispanic/Latino; 39% international. 6% 25 or older, 41% live on campus, 25% transferred in. Retention: 56% of full-time freshmen returned the following year. Academic areas with the most degrees conferred: business/marketing; parks and recreation. Core. Academic remediation for entering students, advanced placement, accelerated degree program, honors program, distance learning, double major, summer session for credit, part-time degree program, external degree program, adult/continuing education programs, internships. Off campus study. Study abroad program.

Entrance Requirements: Options: electronic application, deferred admission, international baccalaureate accepted. Required: SAT or ACT. Recommended: minimum 2 high school GPA, SAT Subject Tests. Required for some: essay, high school transcript, interview. Entrance: moderately difficult. Application deadlines: 8/1, 8/1 for nonresidents. Notification: continuous, continuous for nonresidents. SAT Reasoning Test deadline: 8/1. Transfer credits accepted: Yes.

Costs Per Year: Application fee: $25. Comprehensive fee: $32,171 includes full-time tuition ($21,000), mandatory fees ($1130), and college room and board ($10,041). Part-time tuition: $811 per credit hour.

Collegiate Environment: Orientation program. Drama-theater group. Social organizations: 24 open to all. Most popular organizations: Student Government Association, International Club, Auto Show. Major annual events: Homecoming, Auto Show, Spring Fling. Student services: health clinic, personal-psychological counseling. Campus security: 24-hour emergency response devices and patrols, student patrols, late night transport-escort service. 432 college housing spaces available; 257 were occupied in 2012-13. Freshmen guaranteed college housing. On-campus residence required in freshman year. Options: coed, men-only housing available. Peter C. Cook Library plus 1 other with 793 books, an OPAC, and a Web page. 89 computers available on campus for general student use. A campuswide network can be accessed from student residence rooms and from off campus. Students can access the following: online class registration. Staffed computer lab on campus.

■ **NOVA SOUTHEASTERN UNIVERSITY**
3301 College Ave.
Fort Lauderdale, FL 33314-7796
Tel: (954)262-7300; Free: 800-541-NOVA
Fax: (954)262-3967
E-mail: nsuinfo@nova.edu
Web Site: www.nova.edu/
Description: Independent, university, coed. Awards associate, bachelor's, master's, and doctoral degrees and post-master's certificates. Founded 1964. Setting: 300-acre suburban campus. Endowment: $69.6 million. Research spending for the previous fiscal year: $11.8 million. Educational spending for the previous fiscal year: $13,077 per student. Total enrollment: 26,808. Faculty: 1,725 (816 full-time, 909 part-time). Student-undergrad faculty ratio is 18:1. 4,257 applied, 56% were admitted. 21% from top 10% of their high school class, 49% from top quarter, 79% from top half. Full-time: 3,592 students, 66% women, 34% men. Part-time: 2,147 students, 76% women, 24% men. Students come from 45 states and territories, 67 other countries, 16% from out-of-state. 0.2% American Indian or Alaska Native, non-Hispanic/Latino; 33% Hispanic/Latino; 22% African American, non-Hispanic/Latino; 6% Asian, non-Hispanic/Latino; 0.2% Native Hawaiian or other Pacific Islander, non-Hispanic/Latino; 6% international. 41% 25 or older, 16% live on campus, 14% transferred in. Retention: 72% of full-time freshmen returned the following year. Academic areas with the most degrees conferred: health professions and related sciences; business/marketing; biological/life sciences. Core. Calendar: trimesters. Academic remediation for entering students, services for LD students, advanced placement, honors program, independent study, distance learning, double major, summer session for credit, part-time degree program, adult/continuing education programs, internships. Off campus study. Study abroad program.
Entrance Requirements: Options: electronic application, deferred admission, international baccalaureate accepted. Required: SAT or ACT. Recommended: minimum 2.6 high school GPA, essay and transcript of high school record recommended of some. Entrance: moderately difficult. Application deadlines: Rolling, Rolling for nonresidents. Notification: continuous, continuous for nonresidents. SAT Reasoning Test deadline: 8/1.
Costs Per Year: Application fee: $50. Comprehensive fee: $34,016 includes full-time tuition ($23,850), mandatory fees ($650), and college room and board ($9516). College room only: $6916. Full-time tuition and fees vary according to class time and program. Room and board charges vary according to board plan and housing facility. Part-time tuition: $795 per credit hour. Part-time tuition varies according to class time, course load, and program.
Collegiate Environment: Orientation program. Drama-theater group, choral group, student-run newspaper, radio station. Social organizations: national fraternities, national sororities; 4% of eligible men and 2% of eligible women are members. Most popular organizations: Delta Epsilon Iota, Students for Stress Resilience, International Muslim Association at NSU (IMAN), Preventative Medicine Initiative (PMI), Pre-Med Society. Major annual events: Orientation, Homecoming, Sharkapalooza. Student services: health clinic, personal-psychological counseling, women's center. Campus security: 24-hour emergency response devices and patrols, late night transport-escort service, controlled dormitory access, shuttle bus service. 1,099 college housing spaces available; 946 were occupied in 2012-13. Freshmen guaranteed college housing. On-campus residence required through sophomore year. Option: coed housing available. Alvin Sherman Library, Research, and Information Technology Center plus 4 others with 1 million books, 1.6 million microform titles, 197,340 serials, 52,176 audiovisual materials, an OPAC, and a Web page. Operations spending for the previous fiscal year: $10 million. 3,000 computers available on campus for general student use. A campuswide network can be accessed from student

residence rooms and from off campus. Students can access the following: online class registration. Staffed computer lab on campus (open 24 hours a day) provides training in use of computers, software, and the Internet.
Community Environment: Nova Southeastern University is located on a 227-acre site west of Fort Lauderdale in the town of Davie, 10 miles inland from the Atlantic Ocean and easily accessible from major U.S. and state highways including the Sunshine State Parkway. The climate is subtropical and the average year-round temperature is 75 degrees. Nova Southeastern University is situated in close proximity to Broward Community College and to the Nova complex of elementary, middle and high schools.

■ **PALM BEACH ATLANTIC UNIVERSITY**
901 S Flagler Dr.
West Palm Beach, FL 33416-4708
Tel: (561)803-2000; Free: 888-GO-TO-PBA
E-mail: admissions_admissions@pba.edu
Web Site: www.pba.edu/
Description: Independent nondenominational, comprehensive, coed. Awards associate, bachelor's, master's, and doctoral degrees. Founded 1968. Setting: 93-acre urban campus with easy access to Orlando, the Caribbean. Endowment: $70 million. Research spending for the previous fiscal year: $23,720. Educational spending for the previous fiscal year: $7565 per student. Total enrollment: 3,579. Faculty: 332 (165 full-time, 167 part-time). Student-undergrad faculty ratio is 13:1. 1,380 applied, 96% were admitted. Full-time: 2,188 students, 65% women, 35% men. Part-time: 563 students, 57% women, 43% men. Students come from 49 states and territories, 41 other countries, 27% from out-of-state. 0.5% American Indian or Alaska Native, non-Hispanic/Latino; 14% Hispanic/Latino; 15% African American, non-Hispanic/Latino; 1% Asian, non-Hispanic/Latino; 0.1% Native Hawaiian or other Pacific Islander, non-Hispanic/Latino; 4% international. 20% 25 or older, 38% live on campus, 12% transferred in. Retention: 68% of full-time freshmen returned the following year. Academic areas with the most degrees conferred: business/marketing; health professions and related sciences; theology and religious vocations; visual and performing arts; psychology. Core. Calendar: semesters. Academic remediation for entering students, services for LD students, advanced placement, accelerated degree program, self-designed majors, honors program, independent study, distance learning, double major, summer session for credit, part-time degree program, adult/continuing education programs, internships, graduate courses open to undergrads. Off campus study at PBA London Semester; Best Semester Programs through the Council of Christian Colleges and Universities; New College at the University of Edinburgh, Scotland; and University of Aberdeen Exchange Program (International Christian College). Study abroad program. ROTC: Army (c).
Entrance Requirements: Options: electronic application, early admission, early action, deferred admission, international baccalaureate accepted. Required: essay, high school transcript, SAT or ACT. Required for some: interview. Entrance: moderately difficult. Application deadline: Rolling. Notification: continuous. SAT Reasoning Test deadline: 8/1. SAT Subject Test deadline: 8/1. Transfer credits accepted: Yes. Applicants placed on waiting list: 130. Wait-listed applicants offered admission: 101.
Costs Per Year: Application fee: $50. Comprehensive fee: $33,882 includes full-time tuition ($25,232), mandatory fees ($300), and college room and board ($8350). College room only: $4700. Full-time tuition and fees vary according to course load, degree level, location, and program. Room and board charges vary according to board plan and housing facility. Part-time tuition: $590 per credit. Part-time mandatory fees: $99 per term. Part-time tuition and fees vary according to course load, degree level, location, and program.
Collegiate Environment: Orientation program. Drama-theater group, choral group, student-run newspaper, radio station. Social organizations: 35 open to all. Most popular organizations: Christian Pharmacist Fellowship International, American Latino Intercultural Coalition, N.O.W. (Night of Worship), student government, Club S.A.I.L. Major annual events: Welcome Week, Paradise Weekend, Sailfish Cup. Student services: health clinic, personal-psychological counseling. Campus security: 24-hour emergency response devices and patrols, late night transport-escort service, controlled dormitory access, Security Escort Services; Lighted pathways/sidewalks; Self-defense education; Closed-circuit television system. 1,133 college housing spaces available; 1,035 were occupied in 2012-13. Freshmen given priority for college housing. On-campus residence required through sophomore year. Options: men-only, women-only housing available. Warren Library with 265,745 books, 79,097 microform titles, 28,841 serials, 5,925 audiovisual materials, an OPAC, and a Web page. Operations spending for

the previous fiscal year: $1.2 million. 600 computers available on campus for general student use. A campuswide network can be accessed from student residence rooms and from off campus. Students can access the following: online class registration. Staffed computer lab on campus (open 24 hours a day) provides training in use of computers, software, and the Internet.

Community Environment: West Palm Beach is the county seat of Palm Beach County, one of the fastest-growing areas in Florida. The campus is minutes away from the Atlantic Ocean and just across the Intracoastal Waterway from Palm Beach. Cultural, athletic and recreational events abound, and a railway system offers easy access to Fort Lauderdale and Miami.

■ PALM BEACH STATE COLLEGE

4200 Congress Ave.
Lake Worth, FL 33461-4796
Tel: (561)967-7222
E-mail: enrollmt@palmbeachstate.edu
Web Site: www.palmbeachstate.edu/

Description: State-supported, 4-year, coed. Part of Florida College System. Awards associate and bachelor's degrees. Founded 1933. Setting: 150-acre urban campus with easy access to West Palm Beach. Endowment: $23 million. Total enrollment: 29,974. Faculty: 1,473 (283 full-time, 1,190 part-time). Student-undergrad faculty ratio is 43:1. 4,153 applied, 100% were admitted. 5% from top 10% of their high school class, 60% from top half. Full-time: 10,177 students, 53% women, 47% men. Part-time: 19,797 students, 59% women, 41% men. Students come from 49 states and territories, 146 other countries, 5% from out-of-state. 0.2% American Indian or Alaska Native, non-Hispanic/Latino; 24% Hispanic/Latino; 24% African American, non-Hispanic/Latino; 3% Asian, non-Hispanic/Latino; 0.2% Native Hawaiian or other Pacific Islander, non-Hispanic/Latino; 2% international. 33% 25 or older, 4% transferred in. Core. Calendar: semesters. Academic remediation for entering students, ESL program, services for LD students, advanced placement, self-designed majors, freshman honors college, honors program, independent study, distance learning, double major, summer session for credit, part-time degree program, adult/continuing education programs, co-op programs and internships. Off campus study. Study abroad program.

Entrance Requirements: Open admission except for nursing, dental hygiene programs, radiography, respiratory therapy, firefighter, police and corrections. Options: electronic application, early admission, deferred admission. Recommended: SAT and SAT Subject Tests or ACT. Entrance: noncompetitive. Application deadline: 8/20. Notification: continuous until 8/20. Preference given to state residents.

Collegiate Environment: Orientation program. Drama-theater group, choral group, student-run newspaper. Social organizations: 27 open to all; national fraternities; 3% of eligible men and 3% of eligible women are members. Most popular organizations: student government, Phi Theta Kappa, Students for International Understanding, Black Student Union, Drama Club. Major annual event: Graduation. Student services: health clinic, women's center. Campus security: 24-hour emergency response devices and patrols. College housing not available. Harold C. Manor Library plus 3 others with 151,000 books, 685,608 microform titles, 1,474 serials, an OPAC, and a Web page. Operations spending for the previous fiscal year: $1.9 million. 2,300 computers available on campus for general student use. A campuswide network can be accessed from off-campus. Students can access the following: online class registration. Staffed computer lab on campus provides training in use of computers, software, and the Internet.

Community Environment: Located south of West Palm Beach, Lake Worth has an annual average temperature of 75 degrees and an average rainfall of 61.72 inches. All modes of transportation serve the area. Recreational activities are golfing, shuffleboard, polo, tennis, swimming, water skiing, jai alai, deep sea and fresh water fishing. Deep sea fishing for sailfish, surf fishing for pompano and blue fish are excellent; fresh water fishing at Lake Osborne. Points of interest are the Palm Beach Speedway, Kennel Club Race Track, and art galleries.

■ PASCO-HERNANDO COMMUNITY COLLEGE

10230 Ridge Rd.
New Port Richey, FL 34654-5199
Tel: (727)847-2727; Free: 877-TRY-PHCC
Fax: (727)816-3450
E-mail: carrioe@phcc.edu
Web Site: www.phcc.edu/

Description: State-supported, 2-year, coed. Part of Florida College System. Awards certificates, diplomas, transfer associate, and terminal associate

degrees. Founded 1972. Setting: 142-acre suburban campus with easy access to Tampa. Endowment: $35.2 million. Educational spending for the previous fiscal year: $4543 per student. Total enrollment: 10,795. Faculty: 377 (125 full-time, 252 part-time). Student-undergrad faculty ratio is 29:1. 661 applied. Full-time: 3,893 students, 58% women, 42% men. Part-time: 6,902 students, 64% women, 36% men. Students come from 6 states and territories, 51 other countries, 1% from out-of-state. 1% American Indian or Alaska Native, non-Hispanic/Latino; 14% Hispanic/Latino; 5% African American, non-Hispanic/Latino; 3% Asian, non-Hispanic/Latino; 0.2% international. 35% 25 or older, 3% transferred in. Retention: 60% of full-time freshmen returned the following year. Core. Calendar: semesters. Academic remediation for entering students, services for LD students, advanced placement, accelerated degree program, honors program, independent study, distance learning, double major, summer session for credit, part-time degree program, adult/continuing education programs, co-op programs and internships. Off campus study at other members of the Florida College System and the State University System of Florida. ROTC: Army (c).

Entrance Requirements: Open admission. Option: electronic application. Required: high school transcript. Recommended: SAT and SAT Subject Tests or ACT, CPT. Entrance: noncompetitive. Application deadlines: Rolling, Rolling for nonresidents. Notification: continuous, continuous for nonresidents. Transfer credits accepted: Yes.

Costs Per Year: Application fee: $25. State resident tuition: $101.18 per credit hour part-time. Nonresident tuition: $385.05 per credit hour part-time. Part-time tuition varies according to program.

Collegiate Environment: Orientation program. Drama-theater group, choral group. Social organizations: 38 open to all. Most popular organizations: Student Government Association, Phi Theta Kappa, Phi Beta Lambda, Human Services, PHCC Cares. Major annual events: Peace Week, Welcome Back activities, Spring Fling. Student services: personal-psychological counseling. Campus security: late night transport-escort service. College housing not available. Alric Pottberg Library plus 3 others with an OPAC and a Web page. Operations spending for the previous fiscal year: $265,064.

Community Environment: See Saint Leo University.

■ PENSACOLA STATE COLLEGE

1000 College Blvd.
Pensacola, FL 32504-8998
Tel: (850)484-1000
Fax: (850)484-1826
Web Site: www.pensacolastate.edu/

Description: State-supported, primarily 2-year, coed. Part of Florida College System. Awards certificates, diplomas, transfer associate, terminal associate, and bachelor's degrees. Founded 1948. Setting: 130-acre urban campus. Total enrollment: 11,862. Faculty: 632 (187 full-time, 445 part-time). Student-undergrad faculty ratio is 25:1. Full-time: 4,865 students, 57% women, 43% men. Part-time: 6,997 students, 63% women, 37% men. Students come from 25 states and territories, 1% from out-of-state. 1% American Indian or Alaska Native, non-Hispanic/Latino; 5% Hispanic/Latino; 15% African American, non-Hispanic/Latino; 3% Asian, non-Hispanic/Latino; 0.4% Native Hawaiian or other Pacific Islander, non-Hispanic/Latino; 0.4% international. 39% 25 or older, 6% transferred in. Academic area with the most degrees conferred: business/marketing. Core. Calendar: semesters. Academic remediation for entering students, ESL program, services for LD students, advanced placement, honors program, independent study, distance learning, double major, summer session for credit, part-time degree program, external degree program, adult/continuing education programs, co-op programs. ROTC: Army.

Entrance Requirements: Open admission except for some health-related programs. Options: electronic application, early admission. Required: high school transcript. Entrance: noncompetitive. Application deadline: 8/30. Notification: continuous until 8/30. Transfer credits accepted: Yes.

Costs Per Year: Application fee: $30. One-time mandatory fee: $30. State resident tuition: $2510 full-time, $104.58 per credit hour part-time. Nonresident tuition: $10,075 full-time, $419.76 per credit hour part-time. Full-time tuition varies according to degree level. Part-time tuition varies according to degree level.

Collegiate Environment: Orientation program. Drama-theater group, choral group, student-run newspaper. Student services: health clinic, personal-psychological counseling, women's center. Campus security: 24-hour emergency response devices and patrols, late night transport-escort service. College housing not available. Edward M. Chadbourne Library plus 4 others with 116,312 books, 93 serials, 7,702 audiovisual materials, an OPAC, and a Web page. 500 computers available on campus for general student use.

Computer purchase/lease plans available. A campuswide network can be accessed. Students can access the following: online class registration. Staffed computer lab on campus provides training in use of computers, software, and the Internet.

Community Environment: Pensacola Junior College offers courses at five locations in Escambia and Santa Rosa counties in northwest Florida. Famous for the white sand beaches of the Emerald Coast, Pensacola is the center of a growing metropolitan area of a third of a million residents. Pensacola is the "Cradle of Naval Aviation" and several Navy bases are located in the area, including the Pensacola Naval Air Station, Whiting Field, Corry Field, and Saufley Field. The white beaches of the Gulf of Mexico are a mecca for tourists. The area is served by the University of West Florida as well as Pensacola Junior College. In addition, the city has numerous museums, galleries, and historical areas, including Seville Quarter, a part of Pensacola dating back to the mid 1700s. Florida's First Place City continues to grow and expand.

■ POLK STATE COLLEGE

999 Ave. H, NE
Winter Haven, FL 33881-4299
Tel: (863)297-1000
Fax: (863)297-1060
E-mail: kbucklew@polk.edu
Web Site: www.polk.edu/

Description: State-supported, 4-year, coed. Part of Florida College System. Awards associate and bachelor's degrees. Founded 1964. Setting: 98-acre suburban campus with easy access to Orlando, Tampa. Endowment: $10.8 million. Total enrollment: 11,862. Faculty: 623 (186 full-time, 437 part-time). Student-undergrad faculty ratio is 20:1. Full-time: 3,849 students, 59% women, 41% men. Part-time: 8,013 students, 63% women, 37% men. Students come from 13 states and territories, 60 other countries, 1% from out-of-state. 0.2% American Indian or Alaska Native, non-Hispanic/Latino; 16% Hispanic/Latino; 17% African American, non-Hispanic/Latino; 2% Asian, non-Hispanic/Latino; 0.1% Native Hawaiian or other Pacific Islander, non-Hispanic/Latino; 1% international. 36% 25 or older, 4% transferred in. Retention: 55% of full-time freshmen returned the following year. Academic area with the most degrees conferred: public administration and social services. Core. Calendar: semesters 16-16-6-6. Academic remediation for entering students, ESL program, services for LD students, advanced placement, accelerated degree program, honors program, independent study, distance learning, double major, summer session for credit, part-time degree program, adult/continuing education programs, co-op programs. Off campus study. Study abroad program. ROTC: Army (c).

Entrance Requirements: Open admission. Options: electronic application, early admission, deferred admission, international baccalaureate accepted. Required: high school transcript. Entrance: noncompetitive. Application deadline: Rolling. Notification: continuous. Transfer credits accepted: Yes.

Costs Per Year: Application fee: $0. State resident tuition: $3,307 full-time, $110.22 per credit hour part-time. Nonresident tuition: $12,212 full-time, $407.06 per credit hour part-time. Full-time tuition varies according to course level, course load, and degree level. Part-time tuition varies according to course level, course load, and degree level.

Collegiate Environment: Orientation program. Drama-theater group, choral group. Social organizations: 20 open to all. Most popular organizations: Florida Student Nursing Association, SLAM (Student's Living a Message), Eagleteers, Student Government Association, SALO (Student Activities and Leadership Office). Major annual events: Welcome Week, Casino Night, Black Out Basketball Game. Student services: personal-psychological counseling. Campus security: 24-hour emergency response devices and patrols. College housing not available. Polk State College Libraries plus 1 other with 162,767 books, 217 serials, 3,434 audiovisual materials, an OPAC, and a Web page. Operations spending for the previous fiscal year: $1.2 million. 250 computers available on campus for general student use. A campuswide network can be accessed. Students can access the following: online class registration. Staffed computer lab on campus provides training in use of computers, software, and the Internet.

■ POLYTECHNIC UNIVERSITY OF PUERTO RICO, MIAMI CAMPUS

8180 NW 36th St.
Ste. 401
Miami, FL 33166
Tel: (305)592-7659; Free: 888-729-7659
Web Site: www.pupr.edu/miami/

Description: Independent, comprehensive, coed. Awards bachelor's and master's degrees. Total enrollment: 185. Student-undergrad faculty ratio is 10:1. 92% 25 or older.

■ POLYTECHNIC UNIVERSITY OF PUERTO RICO, ORLANDO CAMPUS

4800 Howell Branch Rd.
Winter Park, FL 32792
Tel: (407)677-5661; Free: 888-577-POLY
Fax: (407)677-5082
Web Site: www.pupr.edu/orlando/

Description: Independent, comprehensive, coed. Awards bachelor's and master's degrees. Total enrollment: 192. Student-undergrad faculty ratio is 8:1. 75 applied, 89% were admitted. 68% 25 or older.

■ RASMUSSEN COLLEGE FORT MYERS

9160 Forum Corporate Pky.
Ste. 100
Fort Myers, FL 33905
Tel: (239)477-2100; Free: 888-549-6755
Fax: (239)477-2101
E-mail: susan.hammerstrom@rasmussen.edu
Web Site: www.rasmussen.edu/

Description: Proprietary, primarily 2-year, coed. Part of Rasmussen College System. Awards certificates, diplomas, transfer associate, terminal associate, and bachelor's degrees. Setting: suburban campus. Total enrollment: 798. Student-undergrad faculty ratio is 22:1. 84% 25 or older. Core. Academic remediation for entering students, accelerated degree program, distance learning, double major, summer session for credit, part-time degree program, adult/continuing education programs, internships.

Entrance Requirements: Options: electronic application, early admission, deferred admission. Required: high school transcript, minimum 2 high school GPA, Internal Exam. Required for some: interview. Entrance: minimally difficult. Application deadline: Rolling. Transfer credits accepted: Yes.

Costs Per Year: Tuition: $12,600 full-time. Mandatory fees: $1800 full-time. Full-time tuition and fees vary according to course level, course load, degree level, location, and program.

Collegiate Environment: Orientation program. College housing not available. Rasmussen College Library - Fort Myers with 2,367 books, 17 serials, 155 audiovisual materials, an OPAC, and a Web page. 129 computers available on campus for general student use. A campuswide network can be accessed from off-campus.

■ RASMUSSEN COLLEGE LAND O' LAKES

18600 Fernview St.
Land O' Lakes, FL 34638
Tel: (813)435-3601; Free: 888-549-6755
E-mail: susan.hammerstrom@rasmussen.edu
Web Site: www.rasmussen.edu/

Description: Proprietary, 4-year, coed. Part of Rasmussen College System. Awards associate and bachelor's degrees. Setting: suburban campus. Total enrollment: 182. Student-undergrad faculty ratio is 22:1. 81% 25 or older. Core. Academic remediation for entering students, accelerated degree program, distance learning, double major, summer session for credit, part-time degree program, adult/continuing education programs, internships.

Entrance Requirements: Options: electronic application, early admission, deferred admission. Required: high school transcript, minimum 2 high school GPA, Internal Exam. Required for some: interview. Entrance: minimally difficult. Application deadline: Rolling. Transfer credits accepted: Yes.

Costs Per Year: Tuition: $12,600 full-time. Mandatory fees: $1800 full-time. Full-time tuition and fees vary according to course level, course load, degree level, location, and program.

Collegiate Environment: Orientation program. College housing not available. Rasmussen College Library - Land O' Lakes with 2,984 books, 13 serials, 4 audiovisual materials, an OPAC, and a Web page. 61 computers available on campus for general student use. A campuswide network can be accessed from off-campus.

■ RASMUSSEN COLLEGE NEW PORT RICHEY

8661 Citizens Dr.
New Port Richey, FL 34654
Tel: (727)942-0069; Free: 888-549-6755
Fax: (727)938-5709
E-mail: susan.hammerstrom@rasmussen.edu

Web Site: www.rasmussen.edu/

Description: Proprietary, primarily 2-year, coed. Part of Rasmussen College System. Awards certificates, diplomas, transfer associate, terminal associate, and bachelor's degrees. Setting: suburban campus. Total enrollment: 893. Student-undergrad faculty ratio is 22:1. 84% 25 or older. Core. Academic remediation for entering students, accelerated degree program, distance learning, double major, summer session for credit, part-time degree program, adult/continuing education programs, internships.

Entrance Requirements: Options: electronic application, early admission, deferred admission. Required: high school transcript, minimum 2 high school GPA, Internal Exam. Required for some: interview. Entrance: minimally difficult. Application deadline: Rolling. Transfer credits accepted: Yes.

Costs Per Year: Tuition: $12,600 full-time. Mandatory fees: $1800 full-time. Full-time tuition and fees vary according to course level, course load, degree level, location, and program.

Collegiate Environment: Orientation program. College housing not available. Rasmussen College Library - New Port Richey with 2,228 books, 16 serials, 87 audiovisual materials, an OPAC, and a Web page. 118 computers available on campus for general student use. A campuswide network can be accessed from off-campus.

■ **RASMUSSEN COLLEGE OCALA**
4755 SW 46th Ct.
Ocala, FL 34471
Tel: (352)629-1941; Free: 888-549-6755
Fax: (352)629-0926
E-mail: susan.hammerstrom@rasmussen.edu
Web Site: www.rasmussen.edu/

Description: Proprietary, primarily 2-year, coed. Part of Rasmussen College System. Awards certificates, diplomas, transfer associate, terminal associate, and bachelor's degrees. Founded 1984. Setting: suburban campus with easy access to Orlando. Total enrollment: 1,266. Student-undergrad faculty ratio is 22:1. 84% 25 or older. Core. Academic remediation for entering students, accelerated degree program, distance learning, double major, summer session for credit, part-time degree program, adult/continuing education programs, internships.

Entrance Requirements: Open admission. Options: electronic application, early admission, deferred admission. Required: high school transcript, minimum 2 high school GPA, Internal Exam. Required for some: interview. Entrance: minimally difficult. Application deadline: Rolling. Transfer credits accepted: Yes.

Costs Per Year: Tuition: $12,600 full-time. Mandatory fees: $1800 full-time. Full-time tuition and fees vary according to course level, course load, degree level, location, and program.

Collegiate Environment: Orientation program. College housing not available. Rasmussen College Library - Ocala with 1,868 books, 6 serials, 159 audiovisual materials, an OPAC, and a Web page. 124 computers available on campus for general student use. A campuswide network can be accessed from off-campus.

■ **RASMUSSEN COLLEGE OCALA SCHOOL OF NURSING**
2100 SW 22nd Pl.
Ocala, FL 34471
Tel: (352)291-8560; Free: 888-549-6755
E-mail: susan.hammerstrom@rasmussen.edu
Web Site: www.rasmussen.edu/

Description: Proprietary, 4-year, coed. Part of Rasmussen College System. Awards associate and bachelor's degrees. Setting: suburban campus. Student-undergrad faculty ratio is 22:1. Core. Academic remediation for entering students, accelerated degree program, distance learning, double major, summer session for credit, part-time degree program, adult/continuing education programs, internships.

Entrance Requirements: Options: electronic application, early admission, deferred admission. Required: high school transcript, minimum 2 high school GPA, Internal Exam. Required for some: interview. Entrance: minimally difficult. Application deadline: Rolling. Transfer credits accepted: Yes.

Costs Per Year: Tuition: $14,220 full-time. Mandatory fees: $1800 full-time. Full-time tuition and fees vary according to course level, course load, degree level, location, and program.

Collegiate Environment: Orientation program. College housing not available. Rasmussen College Library - Ocala with 1,868 books, 6 serials, 159 audiovisual materials, an OPAC, and a Web page.

■ **RASMUSSEN COLLEGE TAMPA/BRANDON**
4042 Park Oaks Blvd.
Tampa, FL 33610

Tel: (813)246-7600; Free: 888-549-6755
E-mail: susan.hammerstrom@rasmussen.edu
Web Site: www.rasmussen.edu/

Description: Proprietary, 4-year, coed. Part of Rasmussen College System. Awards associate and bachelor's degrees. Setting: suburban campus. Total enrollment: 300. Student-undergrad faculty ratio is 22:1. 88% 25 or older. Core. Academic remediation for entering students, accelerated degree program, distance learning, double major, summer session for credit, part-time degree program, adult/continuing education programs, internships.

Entrance Requirements: Options: electronic application, early admission, deferred admission. Required: high school transcript, minimum 2 high school GPA, Internal Exam. Required for some: interview. Entrance: minimally difficult. Application deadline: Rolling. Transfer credits accepted: Yes.

Costs Per Year: Tuition: $12,600 full-time. Mandatory fees: $1800 full-time. Full-time tuition and fees vary according to course level, course load, degree level, location, and program.

Collegiate Environment: Orientation program. College housing not available. Rasmussen College Library - Tampa with 925 books, 11 serials, 11 audiovisual materials, an OPAC, and a Web page. 47 computers available on campus for general student use. A campuswide network can be accessed from off-campus.

■ **REMINGTON COLLEGE–TAMPA CAMPUS**
6302 E Dr. Martin Luther King, Jr. Blvd., Ste. 400
Tampa, FL 33619
Tel: (813)932-0701; Free: 800-560-6192
Fax: (813)935-7415
E-mail: raymond.johnson@remingtoncollege.edu
Web Site: www.remingtoncollege.edu/

Description: Proprietary, primarily 2-year, coed. Awards diplomas, transfer associate, and bachelor's degrees. Founded 1948. Setting: 10-acre urban campus. Academic remediation for entering students, accelerated degree program, internships.

Collegiate Environment: Campus security: late night transport-escort service. Tampa Technical Institute Library with 4,100 books, 124 serials, 340 audiovisual materials, and an OPAC.

■ **RINGLING COLLEGE OF ART AND DESIGN**
2700 N Tamiami Trl.
Sarasota, FL 34234-5895
Tel: (941)351-5100; Free: 800-255-7695
Fax: (941)359-7517
E-mail: admissions@ringling.edu
Web Site: www.ringling.edu/

Description: Independent, 4-year, coed. Awards bachelor's degrees. Founded 1931. Setting: 49-acre small town campus with easy access to Tampa-St. Petersburg. Endowment: $26.6 million. Total enrollment: 1,364. Faculty: 152 (92 full-time, 60 part-time). Student-undergrad faculty ratio is 12:1. 1,255 applied, 75% were admitted. Full-time: 1,313 students, 61% women, 39% men. Part-time: 51 students, 65% women, 35% men. Students come from 47 states and territories, 53 other countries, 46% from out-of-state. 0.4% American Indian or Alaska Native, non-Hispanic/Latino; 14% Hispanic/Latino; 3% African American, non-Hispanic/Latino; 7% Asian, non-Hispanic/Latino; 0.3% Native Hawaiian or other Pacific Islander, non-Hispanic/Latino; 11% international. 7% 25 or older, 60% live on campus, 7% transferred in. Retention: 79% of full-time freshmen returned the following year. Academic areas with the most degrees conferred: visual and performing arts; communication technologies. Core. Calendar: semesters. Academic remediation for entering students, services for LD students, advanced placement, independent study, part-time degree program, internships. Off campus study at Association of Independent Colleges of Art and Design, New York Studio Program. Study abroad program.

Entrance Requirements: Options: electronic application, deferred admission, international baccalaureate accepted. Required: essay, high school transcript, minimum 2 high school GPA, 2 recommendations, portfolio, resume. Recommended: interview. Entrance: moderately difficult. Application deadline: Rolling. Notification: continuous. Transfer credits accepted: Yes.

Costs Per Year: Application fee: $70. Comprehensive fee: $47,530 includes full-time tuition ($33,960), mandatory fees ($1340), and college room and board ($12,230). College room only: $6670. Full-time tuition and fees vary according to course load, program, and student level. Room and board charges vary according to board plan and housing facility. Part-time tuition: $1583 per credit hour. Part-time tuition varies according to course load, program, and student level.

Collegiate Environment: Orientation program. Drama-theater group. Social organizations: 29 open to all. Most popular organizations: Student Government Association, Digital Painting Sketch Club, Resident Student Association, MOSAIC, Quidditch Team. Major annual events: Illest of Illustrators, Best of Ringling Opening, International Harvest Fest. Student services: legal services, personal-psychological counseling. Campus security: 24-hour emergency response devices and patrols, late night transport-escort service, controlled dormitory access, lighted campus. 850 college housing spaces available; 825 were occupied in 2012-13. Freshmen given priority for college housing. Options: coed, men-only, women-only housing available. Verman Kimbrough Memorial Library with 149,147 books, 375 serials, 10,494 audiovisual materials, an OPAC, and a Web page. Operations spending for the previous fiscal year: $857,870. 879 computers available on campus for general student use. A campuswide network can be accessed from student residence rooms and from off campus. Students can access the following: online class registration, central file storage, high performance computing labs. Staffed computer lab on campus provides training in use of computers, software, and the Internet.

■ **ROLLINS COLLEGE**
1000 Holt Ave.
Winter Park, FL 32789-4499
Tel: (407)646-2000
Fax: (407)646-2600
E-mail: admission@rollins.edu
Web Site: www.rollins.edu/

Description: Independent, comprehensive, coed. Awards bachelor's and master's degrees. Founded 1885. Setting: 80-acre suburban campus with easy access to Orlando. Endowment: $335.6 million. Research spending for the previous fiscal year: $118,215. Educational spending for the previous fiscal year: $12,238 per student. Total enrollment: 2,459. Faculty: 216 (all full-time). Student-undergrad faculty ratio is 10:1. 4,542 applied, 56% were admitted. 38% from top 10% of their high school class, 69% from top quarter, 95% from top half. Full-time: 1,884 students, 59% women, 41% men. Students come from 44 states and territories, 39 other countries, 45% from out-of-state. 0.1% American Indian or Alaska Native, non-Hispanic/Latino; 13% Hispanic/Latino; 4% African American, non-Hispanic/Latino; 3% Asian, non-Hispanic/Latino; 0.2% Native Hawaiian or other Pacific Islander, non-Hispanic/Latino; 5% international. 2% 25 or older, 68% live on campus, 3% transferred in. Retention: 84% of full-time freshmen returned the following year. Academic areas with the most degrees conferred: social sciences; communication/journalism; psychology. Core. Calendar: semesters. Academic remediation for entering students, services for LD students, advanced placement, accelerated degree program, self-designed majors, honors program, independent study, double major, summer session for credit, part-time degree program, adult/continuing education programs, internships. Off campus study at American University. Study abroad program.

Entrance Requirements: Options: electronic application, early admission, early decision, deferred admission, international baccalaureate accepted. Required: essay, high school transcript, 1 recommendation. Recommended: minimum 2 high school GPA, interview. Required for some: SAT or ACT, Selection of Test Score Waived Option (TSWO) or official SAT/ACT scores (TSWO is not appropriate for applicants seeking academic merit scholarship, Honors Program, or 3/2 Accelerated Management Program consideration). Entrance: moderately difficult. Application deadlines: 2/15, 11/15 for early decision plan 1, 1/15 for early decision plan 2. Notification: 4/1, 12/15 for early decision plan 1, 2/1 for early decision plan 2. SAT Reasoning Test deadline: 2/15. Transfer credits accepted: Yes. Applicants placed on waiting list: 188. Wait-listed applicants offered admission: 13. Early decision applicants admitted: 200.

Costs Per Year: Application fee: $40. Comprehensive fee: $52,370 includes full-time tuition ($39,900) and college room and board ($12,470). College room only: $7340. Room and board charges vary according to housing facility.

Collegiate Environment: Orientation program. Drama-theater group, choral group, student-run newspaper, radio station. Social organizations: 100 open to all; national fraternities, national sororities, local fraternities, local sororities; 29% of eligible men and 35% of eligible women are members. Most popular organizations: Interfraternity Council, Panhellenic Association, Student Government Association, Rollins Entertainment Programs, National Society of Collegiate Scholars. Major annual events: R-Big Event, Campus Movie Fest, Lip Sync. Student services: health clinic, personal-psychological counseling, women's center. Campus security: 24-hour emergency response devices and patrols, late night transport-escort service, controlled dormitory access. 1,264 college housing spaces available; 1,205 were occupied in 2012-13. Freshmen guaranteed college housing. On-campus residence required through sophomore year. Options: coed, men-only, women-only housing available. Olin Library with 366,684 books, 43,923 microform titles, 63,495 serials, 5,239 audiovisual materials, an OPAC, and a Web page. Operations spending for the previous fiscal year: $2.3 million. 240 computers available on campus for general student use. Computer purchase/lease plans available. A campuswide network can be accessed from student residence rooms and from off campus. Students can access the following: online class registration. Staffed computer lab on campus (open 24 hours a day) provides training in use of computers, software, and the Internet.

Community Environment: Within the metropolitan area of which Orlando is the center, Winter Park is a residential area of great beauty. This area of Florida is popularly known as"The Lake Region." Orange groves, subtropical forest, flowering shrubs and trees are the dominant features of the landscape. Scenic boat trips may be taken through a chain of four lakes. Annual events are the Sidewalk Arts Festival and a Bach festival held on the campus of Rollins College.

■ **ST. JOHN VIANNEY COLLEGE SEMINARY**
2900 SW 87th Ave.
Miami, FL 33165-3244
Tel: (305)223-4561
Web Site: www.sjvcs.edu/

Description: Independent Roman Catholic, 4-year, coed. Awards bachelor's degrees. Founded 1959. Setting: 33-acre urban campus. 10 applied, 100% were admitted. 24% 25 or older. Core. Calendar: semesters. Academic remediation for entering students, ESL program, advanced placement, internships.

Entrance Requirements: Required: high school transcript, minimum 2.0 high school GPA, 1 recommendation, psychological examination. Recommended: interview, SAT or ACT. Entrance: moderately difficult. Application deadline: Rolling. Preference given to candidates for the priesthood.

Collegiate Environment: Orientation program. Choral group. Student services: legal services, personal-psychological counseling. Campus security: 24-hour emergency response devices, student patrols. Maytag Memorial Library with 54,000 books, 150 serials, and an OPAC.

■ **ST. JOHNS RIVER STATE COLLEGE**
5001 Saint Johns Ave.
Palatka, FL 32177-3897
Tel: (386)312-4200
Fax: (386)312-4292
Web Site: www.sjrstate.edu/

Description: State-supported, 2-year, coed. Awards certificates, diplomas, transfer associate, and terminal associate degrees. Founded 1958. Setting: 105-acre small town campus with easy access to Jacksonville. Total enrollment: 6,086. Faculty: 265 (111 full-time, 154 part-time). Student-undergrad faculty ratio is 24:1. Core. Calendar: semesters. Academic remediation for entering students, services for LD students, advanced placement, accelerated degree program, distance learning, summer session for credit, part-time degree program, adult/continuing education programs.

Entrance Requirements: Open admission. Option: early admission. Required: high school transcript. Entrance: noncompetitive. Application deadline: Rolling. Notification: continuous.

Collegiate Environment: Orientation program. Choral group, student-run newspaper. Campus security: 24-hour patrols. 56,925 books, 90,725 microform titles, 7,015 audiovisual materials, an OPAC, and a Web page 450 computers available on campus for general student use. A campuswide network can be accessed. Students can access the following: online class registration. Staffed computer lab on campus.

■ **SAINT LEO UNIVERSITY**
PO Box 6665
Saint Leo, FL 33574-6665
Tel: (352)588-8200; Free: 800-334-5532
Fax: (352)588-8257
E-mail: admissions@saintleo.edu
Web Site: www.saintleo.edu/

Description: Independent Roman Catholic, comprehensive, coed. Awards associate, bachelor's, and master's degrees. Founded 1889. Setting: 259-acre rural campus with easy access to Tampa, Orlando. Endowment: $35.1 million. Total enrollment: 5,383. Faculty: 190 (111 full-time, 79 part-time).

Student-undergrad faculty ratio is 15:1. 2,648 applied, 85% were admitted. 9% from top 10% of their high school class, 26% from top quarter, 65% from top half. 3 valedictorians. Full-time: 2,098 students, 50% women, 50% men. Part-time: 69 students, 49% women, 51% men. Students come from 44 states and territories, 56 other countries, 28% from out-of-state. 0.3% American Indian or Alaska Native, non-Hispanic/Latino; 14% Hispanic/Latino; 11% African American, non-Hispanic/Latino; 1% Asian, non-Hispanic/Latino; 0.1% Native Hawaiian or other Pacific Islander, non-Hispanic/Latino; 13% international. 9% 25 or older, 62% live on campus, 7% transferred in. Retention: 73% of full-time freshmen returned the following year. Academic areas with the most degrees conferred: business/marketing; homeland security, law enforcement, firefighting, and protective services; psychology. Core. Calendar: semesters. Academic remediation for entering students, ESL program, services for LD students, advanced placement, honors program, independent study, distance learning, double major, summer session for credit, part-time degree program, adult/continuing education programs, internships. Study abroad program. ROTC: Army, Air Force (c).

Entrance Requirements: Options: electronic application, early admission, deferred admission, international baccalaureate accepted. Required: high school transcript, minimum 2.7 high school GPA, 1 recommendation. Recommended: minimum 3 high school GPA, interview, SAT or ACT. Entrance: moderately difficult. Application deadline: 7/1. Notification: continuous. SAT Reasoning Test deadline: 8/10. Transfer credits accepted: Yes.

Costs Per Year: Application fee: $40. Comprehensive fee: $24,610 includes full-time tuition ($19,240), mandatory fees ($370), and college room and board ($5000). College room only: $4680.

Collegiate Environment: Orientation program. Drama-theater group, choral group, student-run newspaper, radio station. Social organizations: 80 open to all; national fraternities, national sororities, local fraternities; 17% of eligible men and 16% of eligible women are members. Most popular organizations: Student Government Union, Campus Activities Board, Caribbean Student Association, The Quest, Intercultural Student Association. Major annual events: Fall Family Festival, Spring Fling, Fall Community Service Day. Student services: health clinic, personal-psychological counseling. Campus security: 24-hour emergency response devices and patrols, late night transport-escort service, controlled dormitory access, surveillance cameras in parking lots. 1,579 college housing spaces available; 1,345 were occupied in 2012-13. Freshmen given priority for college housing. On-campus residence required through junior year. Options: coed, men-only, women-only housing available. Cannon Memorial Library plus 1 other with 275,049 books, 26,208 microform titles, 148,546 serials, 3,164 audiovisual materials, an OPAC, and a Web page. Operations spending for the previous fiscal year: $1.7 million. 150 computers available on campus for general student use. Computer purchase/lease plans available. A campuswide network can be accessed from student residence rooms and from off campus. Students can access the following: online class registration, campus residents are issued a laptop for their personal use. Staffed computer lab on campus provides training in use of computers, software, and the Internet.

Community Environment: Saint Leo is located 25 miles north of Tampa, and 38 miles from Tampa International Airport. Semitropical climate. Orlando and Disney World are 65 miles to the east.

■ ST. PETERSBURG COLLEGE

PO Box 13489
Saint Petersburg, FL 33733-3489
Tel: (727)341-3600
Fax: (727)341-3150
E-mail: information@spcollege.edu
Web Site: www.spcollege.edu/

Description: State and locally supported, 4-year, coed. Awards associate and bachelor's degrees. Founded 1927. Setting: 410-acre suburban campus with easy access to Tampa. Endowment: $25.8 million. Educational spending for the previous fiscal year: $3260 per student. Total enrollment: 31,793. Faculty: 1,731 (325 full-time, 1,406 part-time). Full-time: 10,297 students, 56% women, 44% men. Part-time: 21,496 students, 63% women, 37% men. Students come from 23 states and territories, 120 other countries, 3% from out-of-state. 51% 25 or older, 72% transferred in. Academic areas with the most degrees conferred: health professions and related sciences; education; business/marketing. Core. Calendar: semesters. Academic remediation for entering students, ESL program, services for LD students, advanced placement, accelerated degree program, freshman honors college, honors program, distance learning, summer session for credit, part-time degree program, adult/continuing education programs, co-op programs and internships. Off campus study. Study abroad program.

Entrance Requirements: Open admission. Options: electronic application, early admission, international baccalaureate accepted. Required: high school transcript. Entrance: noncompetitive. Application deadline: Rolling. Notification: continuous. Transfer credits accepted: Yes.

Collegiate Environment: Orientation program. Drama-theater group, choral group, student-run newspaper. Student services: women's center. Campus security: late night transport-escort service. M. M. Bennett Library plus 6 others with 241,761 books, 1,987 serials, 14,495 audiovisual materials, an OPAC, and a Web page. Operations spending for the previous fiscal year: $3.5 million. 4,555 computers available on campus for general student use. Computer purchase/lease plans available. A campuswide network can be accessed from off-campus. Students can access the following: online class registration. Staffed computer lab on campus provides training in use of computers, software, and the Internet.

■ ST. THOMAS UNIVERSITY

16401 NW 37th Ave.
Miami Gardens, FL 33054-6459
Tel: (305)625-6000; Free: 800-367-9010
Fax: (305)628-6591
E-mail: signup@stu.edu
Web Site: www.stu.edu/

Description: Independent Roman Catholic, comprehensive, coed. Awards bachelor's, master's, and doctoral degrees and post-master's certificates. Founded 1961. Setting: 140-acre suburban campus. Total enrollment: 2,472. Faculty: 238 (102 full-time, 136 part-time). Student-undergrad faculty ratio is 14:1. 681 applied, 39% were admitted. 5% from top 10% of their high school class, 19% from top quarter, 46% from top half. Full-time: 1,013 students, 55% women, 45% men. Part-time: 72 students, 65% women, 35% men. Students come from 25 states and territories, 52 other countries, 20% from out-of-state. 0.2% American Indian or Alaska Native, non-Hispanic/Latino; 41% Hispanic/Latino; 26% African American, non-Hispanic/Latino; 0.4% Asian, non-Hispanic/Latino; 0% Native Hawaiian or other Pacific Islander, non-Hispanic/Latino; 13% international. 23% 25 or older, 25% live on campus, 16% transferred in. Retention: 67% of full-time freshmen returned the following year. Academic areas with the most degrees conferred: business/marketing; homeland security, law enforcement, firefighting, and protective services; psychology. Core. Calendar: semesters. Academic remediation for entering students, services for LD students, advanced placement, freshman honors college, honors program, independent study, distance learning, double major, summer session for credit, part-time degree program, adult/continuing education programs, internships, graduate courses open to undergrads.

Entrance Requirements: Options: electronic application, deferred admission, international baccalaureate accepted. Required: high school transcript, minimum 2 high school GPA, SAT or ACT. Recommended: essay, 1 recommendation, interview. Entrance: minimally difficult. Application deadline: Rolling. Notification: continuous. SAT Reasoning Test deadline: 8/15. Transfer credits accepted: Yes.

Costs Per Year: Application fee: $40. Comprehensive fee: $32,250 includes full-time tuition ($25,110) and college room and board ($7140). Full-time tuition varies according to program. Room and board charges vary according to board plan and housing facility. Part-time tuition: $502 per credit hour. Part-time tuition varies according to program.

Collegiate Environment: Orientation program. Choral group. Social organizations: 16 open to all. Most popular organizations: Psychology Club, National Society of Leadership and Success (NSLS), Criminal Justice, Kreyol Nation, Gay Strait Alliance (GSA). Student services: health clinic, personal-psychological counseling. Campus security: 24-hour emergency response devices and patrols, late night transport-escort service, controlled dormitory access. 281 undergraduates lived in college housing during 2012-13. No special consideration for freshman housing applicants. Options: men-only, women-only housing available. St. Thomas University Library plus 1 other with 343,423 books, 11 microform titles, 512 serials, 4,550 audiovisual materials, an OPAC, and a Web page. 80 computers available on campus for general student use. A campuswide network can be accessed from student residence rooms. Students can access the following: online class registration. Staffed computer lab on campus.

■ SANFORD-BROWN INSTITUTE (FORT LAUDERDALE)

1201 W Cypress Creek Rd.
Fort Lauderdale, FL 33309
Tel: (954)733-8900; Free: 888-742-0333
Fax: (954)733-8994

E-mail: snelowet@sbjacksonville.com

Web Site: www.sanfordbrown.edu/Fort-Lauderdale

Description: Proprietary, 2-year, coed. Part of Career Education Corporation. Awards terminal associate degrees. Setting: urban campus. Educational spending for the previous fiscal year: $9500 per student. Total enrollment: 303. Faculty: 30 (25 full-time, 5 part-time). Student-undergrad faculty ratio is 10:1. 1,028 applied, 29% were admitted. 26% from top 10% of their high school class, 45% from top quarter, 47% from top half. Students come from 6 states and territories, 3 other countries, 16% from out-of-state. 46% 25 or older. Retention: 29% of full-time freshmen returned the following year. Academic remediation for entering students, services for LD students, advanced placement, adult/continuing education programs, internships.

Entrance Requirements: Required: high school transcript, interview. Application deadline: Rolling. Notification: continuous.

Collegiate Environment: Campus security: 24-hour emergency response devices and patrols, late night transport-escort service. SBI Library plus 1 other with 4,000 books, 67 serials, 34 audiovisual materials, an OPAC, and a Web page.

■ SANFORD-BROWN INSTITUTE (JACKSONVILLE)

10255 Fortune Pky.

Ste. 501

Jacksonville, FL 32256

Tel: (904)363-6221; Free: 888-577-5333

Fax: (904)363-6824

E-mail: dneal@sbjacksonville.com

Web Site: www.sanfordbrown.edu/Jacksonville

Description: Proprietary, 2-year, coed. Awards diplomas and terminal associate degrees. Founded 1992. Educational spending for the previous fiscal year: $2802 per student. Total enrollment: 418. Faculty: 35. 887 applied, 52% were admitted. 7% from out-of-state. 41% 25 or older. Core.

Entrance Requirements: Open admission. Options: electronic application, early admission. Required: high school transcript, interview.

■ SANFORD-BROWN INSTITUTE (TAMPA)

5701 E Hillsborough Ave.

Tampa, FL 33610

Tel: (813)393-4250; Free: 888-450-0333

Fax: (813)626-0392

Web Site: www.sanfordbrown.edu/Tampa

Description: Proprietary, 2-year, coed. Awards terminal associate degrees. Total enrollment: 473.

Entrance Requirements: Entrance: noncompetitive.

■ SANTA FE COLLEGE

3000 NW 83rd St.

Gainesville, FL 32606

Tel: (352)395-5000

Fax: (352)395-5581

E-mail: michael.hutley@sfcollege.edu

Web Site: www.sfcollege.edu/

Description: State and locally supported, 4-year, coed. Part of Florida College System. Awards associate and bachelor's degrees (offers bachelor's degrees in conjunction with Saint Leo College). Founded 1966. Setting: 187-acre suburban campus with easy access to Jacksonville. Total enrollment: 15,745. Faculty: 829 (245 full-time, 584 part-time). Student-undergrad faculty ratio is 25:1. Full-time: 6,777 students, 53% women, 47% men. Part-time: 8,968 students, 57% women, 43% men. Students come from 28 states and territories, 61 other countries, 2% from out-of-state. 1% American Indian or Alaska Native, non-Hispanic/Latino; 12% Hispanic/Latino; 16% African American, non-Hispanic/Latino; 2% Asian, non-Hispanic/Latino; 0.4% Native Hawaiian or other Pacific Islander, non-Hispanic/Latino; 1% international. 30% 25 or older, 11% transferred in. Core. Calendar: semesters. Academic remediation for entering students, ESL program, services for LD students, advanced placement, honors program, independent study, distance learning, summer session for credit, part-time degree program, adult/continuing education programs, co-op programs and internships. Study abroad program. ROTC: Army (c), Air Force (c).

Entrance Requirements: Open admission. Options: electronic application, early admission, international baccalaureate accepted. Required: high school transcript. Required for some: essay, high school transcript, interview. Entrance: noncompetitive. Application deadline: Rolling. Notification: continuous. Transfer credits accepted: Yes.

Collegiate Environment: Orientation program. Drama-theater group, choral

group, student-run newspaper. Student services: legal services, health clinic, personal-psychological counseling, women's center. Campus security: 24-hour emergency response devices and patrols. Lawrence W. Tyree Library with 81,832 books, 624 serials, an OPAC, and a Web page.

Community Environment: See University of Florida.

■ SCHILLER INTERNATIONAL UNIVERSITY

300 E Bay Dr.

Largo, FL 33770

Tel: (727)736-5082; Free: 800-261-9751

Fax: (727)734-0359

E-mail: admissions@schiller.edu

Web Site: www.schiller.edu/

Description: Independent, comprehensive, coed. Part of Schiller International University. Awards associate, bachelor's, and master's degrees. Founded 1991. Setting: 4-acre suburban campus with easy access to Tampa. Total enrollment: 673. Faculty: 66 (2 full-time, 64 part-time). Student-undergrad faculty ratio is 16:1. Full-time: 153 students, 37% women, 63% men. Part-time: 38 students, 50% women, 50% men. Students come from 11 states and territories, 50 other countries. 85% live on campus. Academic areas with the most degrees conferred: business/marketing; interdisciplinary studies; psychology. Core. Calendar: semesters. ESL program, advanced placement, accelerated degree program, self-designed majors, honors program, independent study, distance learning, double major, summer session for credit, part-time degree program, adult/continuing education programs, co-op programs and internships, graduate courses open to undergrads. Off campus study. Study abroad program.

Entrance Requirements: Options: electronic application, deferred admission, international baccalaureate accepted. Required: essay, high school transcript. Recommended: minimum 2.0 high school GPA, interview. Entrance: minimally difficult. Application deadlines: Rolling, Rolling for nonresidents. Notification: continuous, continuous for nonresidents.

Collegiate Environment: Orientation program. Most popular organizations: student government, Model United Nations. Major annual events: International Food Festivals, Picnic in the Park, Horse Back Riding. Student services: personal-psychological counseling. Campus security: night patrols. SIU Library with 1,918 books and 34 serials. 42 computers available on campus for general student use. A campuswide network can be accessed. Staffed computer lab on campus provides training in use of computers, software, and the Internet.

■ SEMINOLE STATE COLLEGE OF FLORIDA

100 Weldon Blvd.

Sanford, FL 32773-6199

Tel: (407)708-4722

Fax: (407)328-2395

E-mail: admissions@scc-fl.edu

Web Site: www.seminolestate.edu/

Description: State and locally supported, primarily 2-year, coed. Awards certificates, diplomas, transfer associate, terminal associate, and bachelor's degrees. Founded 1966. Setting: 200-acre small town campus with easy access to Orlando. Endowment: $12.5 million. Educational spending for the previous fiscal year: $2436 per student. Total enrollment: 19,450. Faculty: 795 (238 full-time, 557 part-time). Student-undergrad faculty ratio is 27:1. 9,901 applied, 100% were admitted. Full-time: 7,559 students, 53% women, 47% men. Part-time: 11,891 students, 62% women, 38% men. Students come from 88 other countries, 1% from out-of-state. 0.3% American Indian or Alaska Native, non-Hispanic/Latino; 22% Hispanic/Latino; 18% African American, non-Hispanic/Latino; 3% Asian, non-Hispanic/Latino; 0.3% Native Hawaiian or other Pacific Islander, non-Hispanic/Latino; 2% international. 42% 25 or older, 6% transferred in. Core. Calendar: semesters. Academic remediation for entering students, ESL program, services for LD students, advanced placement, accelerated degree program, honors program, independent study, distance learning, double major, summer session for credit, part-time degree program, external degree program, adult/continuing education programs, co-op programs and internships. Study abroad program. ROTC: Army.

Entrance Requirements: Open admission except for physical therapy, respiratory therapy, nursing programs. Options: electronic application, early admission, deferred admission, international baccalaureate accepted. Required: high school transcript, minimum 2 high school GPA, CPT, PERT. Recommended: ACT. Entrance: noncompetitive. Application deadline: Rolling. Notification: continuous. Transfer credits accepted: Yes.

Costs Per Year: Application fee: $0. State resident tuition: $3131 full-time. Nonresident tuition: $11,456 full-time. Full-time tuition varies according to degree level and program.

Collegiate Environment: Orientation program. Drama-theater group, choral group, student-run newspaper. Social organizations: 50 open to all. Most popular organizations: Phi Beta Lambda, Phi Theta Kappa, Student Government Association, Sigma Phi Gamma, Hispanic Student Association. Major annual events: Welcome Back, Career Fair, Club Rush. Student services: personal-psychological counseling. Campus security: 24-hour emergency response devices and patrols. College housing not available. Seminole State College Library - SLM plus 8 others with 110,331 books, 245 serials, 7,401 audiovisual materials, an OPAC, and a Web page. Operations spending for the previous fiscal year: $506,679. 250 computers available on campus for general student use. A campuswide network can be accessed from off-campus. Students can access the following: online class registration, Online Syallabii. Staffed computer lab on campus provides training in use of computers, software, and the Internet.

Community Environment: A residential city with subtropical climate. Sanford is located 20 miles northeast of Orlando. Air service is available through Orlando International Airport, and Amtrak serves the area. Part-time employment for students is available in the metropolitan Orlando Area. Lake Monroe is a recreation area nearby with a municipal zoo, picnic facilities and playground. Other sports include boating, fishing, tennis, and more. The close proximity to Orlando offers many convenient cultural and recreational activities.

■ **SOUTH FLORIDA STATE COLLEGE**
600 W College Dr.
Avon Park, FL 33825-9356
Tel: (863)453-6661
Fax: (863)453-0165
Web Site: www.southflorida.edu/
Description: State-supported, primarily 2-year, coed. Part of Florida State College System. Awards certificates, diplomas, transfer associate, terminal associate, and bachelor's degrees. Founded 1965. Setting: 228-acre rural campus with easy access to Tampa-St. Petersburg, Orlando. Endowment: $4.7 million. Educational spending for the previous fiscal year: $5463 per student. Total enrollment: 2,800. Faculty: 156 (66 full-time, 90 part-time). Student-undergrad faculty ratio is 16:1. 1,086 applied, 100% were admitted. 8% from top 10% of their high school class, 23% from top quarter, 63% from top half. Full-time: 1,042 students, 53% women, 47% men. Part-time: 1,748 students, 61% women, 39% men. 3% from out-of-state. 0.1% American Indian or Alaska Native, non-Hispanic/Latino; 28% Hispanic/Latino; 11% African American, non-Hispanic/Latino; 2% Asian, non-Hispanic/Latino; 0.3% Native Hawaiian or other Pacific Islander, non-Hispanic/Latino; 1% international. 35% 25 or older, 4% transferred in. Core. Calendar: semesters. Academic remediation for entering students, ESL program, services for LD students, advanced placement, distance learning, summer session for credit, part-time degree program, adult/continuing education programs, co-op programs and internships.

Entrance Requirements: Open admission. Options: electronic application, early admission, deferred admission, international baccalaureate accepted. Required: high school transcript. Entrance: noncompetitive. Application deadline: Rolling. Notification: continuous. Transfer credits accepted: Yes.

Costs Per Year: Application fee: $15. One-time mandatory fee: $25. Area resident tuition: $3136 full-time, $104.52 per credit hour part-time. State resident tuition: $3136 full-time, $104.52 per credit hour part-time. Nonresident tuition: $11,831 full-time, $394.31 per credit hour part-time. Mandatory fees: $25 full-time. Full-time tuition and fees vary according to degree level. Part-time tuition varies according to degree level. College room and board: $5821. College room only: $1500.

Collegiate Environment: Orientation program. Drama-theater group, choral group, student-run newspaper. Social organizations: 30 open to all; 45% of eligible men and 55% of eligible women are members. Most popular organizations: Phi Theta Kappa, Phi Beta Lambda, Soccer Club, Anime & Gaming Club, Basketball Club. Major annual events: Fall Fest, Club Rush (Fall and Spring), College Week. Student services: personal-psychological counseling, women's center. Campus security: 24-hour emergency response devices and patrols. 70 college housing spaces available; 47 were occupied in 2012-13. Learning Resource Center with 49,252 books, 47 serials, 1,753 audiovisual materials, an OPAC, and a Web page. Operations spending for the previous fiscal year: $295,838. 81 computers available on campus for general student use. Computer purchase/lease plans available. A campuswide network can be accessed. Students can access the following:

online class registration. Staffed computer lab on campus provides training in use of computers, software, and the Internet.

Community Environment: An urban area in south central Florida; semitropical climate and a tourist center. Trains and buses serve the area. Citrus production is the main source of income. Part time employment is limited to eating establishments and grocery stores. Recreational activities are numerous; they include golfing, bowling, tennis, shuffleboard, water sports, hunting, fishing and camping. Avon Park has many active civic organizations. The annual International Jamboree and Cultural Series is a special event.

■ **SOUTH UNIVERSITY (ROYAL PALM BEACH)**
University Centre
9801 Belvedere Rd.
Royal Palm Beach, FL 33411
Tel: (561)697-9200; Free: 866-629-2902
Fax: (561)697-9944
Web Site: www.southuniversity.edu/west-palm-beach/
Description: Proprietary, comprehensive, coed. Part of Education Management Corporation. Awards associate, bachelor's, and master's degrees. Founded 1899.

■ **SOUTH UNIVERSITY (TAMPA)**
4401 N Himes Ave.
Ste. 175
Tampa, FL 33614
Tel: (813)393-3800; Free: 800-846-1472
Web Site: www.southuniversity.edu/tampa/
Description: Proprietary, comprehensive, coed. Part of Education Management Corporation. Awards associate, bachelor's, and master's degrees.

■ **SOUTHEASTERN COLLEGE–GREENACRES**
6812 Forest Hill Blvd.
Ste. D-1
Greenacres, FL 33413
Tel: (561)433-2330
Web Site: www.sec.edu/
Description: Proprietary, 2-year, coed. Awards certificates and terminal associate degrees. Total enrollment: 433. 536 applied, 98% were admitted.
Entrance Requirements: Required: high school transcript.

■ **SOUTHEASTERN COLLEGE–MIAMI LAKES**
17395 NW 59th Ave.
Miami Lakes, FL 33015
Tel: (305)820-5003
Fax: (305)820-5455
Web Site: www.sec.edu/
Description: Proprietary, 2-year, coed. Awards certificates and terminal associate degrees.

■ **SOUTHEASTERN COLLEGE–ST. PETERSBURG**
11208 Blue Heron Blvd., Ste. A
Saint Petersburg, FL 33716
Tel: (727)576-6500
Fax: (727)576-6589
Web Site: www.sec.edu/
Description: Proprietary, 2-year, coed. Awards certificates and terminal associate degrees.

■ **SOUTHEASTERN UNIVERSITY**
1000 Longfellow Blvd.
Lakeland, FL 33801-6099
Tel: (863)667-5000; Free: 800-500-8760
Fax: (863)667-5200
E-mail: admission@seu.edu
Web Site: www.seu.edu/
Description: Independent, comprehensive, coed, affiliated with Assemblies of God. Awards associate, bachelor's, and master's degrees. Founded 1935. Setting: 87-acre suburban campus with easy access to Tampa, Orlando. Endowment: $5.8 million. Educational spending for the previous fiscal year: $5510 per student. Total enrollment: 2,703. Faculty: 169 (96 full-time, 73 part-time). Student-undergrad faculty ratio is 19:1. 1,234 applied, 70% were admitted. Full-time: 2,106 students, 57% women, 43% men. Part-time: 342 students, 46% women, 54% men. Students come from 49 states and ter-

ritories, 20 other countries, 33% from out-of-state. 0.4% American Indian or Alaska Native, non-Hispanic/Latino; 14% Hispanic/Latino; 11% African American, non-Hispanic/Latino; 1% Asian, non-Hispanic/Latino; 0.2% Native Hawaiian or other Pacific Islander, non-Hispanic/Latino; 1% international. 15% 25 or older, 54% live on campus, 6% transferred in. Retention: 66% of full-time freshmen returned the following year. Academic areas with the most degrees conferred: theology and religious vocations; business/marketing; public administration and social services. Calendar: semesters. Part-time degree program, adult/continuing education programs. ROTC: Army (c).

Entrance Requirements: Open admission for those of the Christian Faith. Options: early admission, deferred admission, international baccalaureate accepted. Required: essay, high school transcript, 2 recommendations, SAT or ACT. Required for some: interview. Entrance: minimally difficult. Application deadline: 5/1. Notification: 6/1.

Costs Per Year: Application fee: $40. Comprehensive fee: $27,202 includes full-time tuition ($17,996), mandatory fees ($600), and college room and board ($8606). Full-time tuition and fees vary according to class time, degree level, and reciprocity agreements. Room and board charges vary according to board plan and housing facility. Part-time tuition: $750 per credit hour. Part-time mandatory fees: $150 per term. Part-time tuition and fees vary according to class time, course load, degree level, and reciprocity agreements.

Collegiate Environment: Orientation program. Drama-theater group, choral group, student-run newspaper, radio station. Student services: health clinic, personal-psychological counseling. Campus security: 24-hour emergency response devices and patrols, late night transport-escort service. Freshmen guaranteed college housing. On-campus residence required through senior year. Options: men-only, women-only housing available.

■ **SOUTHERN TECHNICAL COLLEGE (AUBURNDALE)**

298 Havendale Blvd.
Auburndale, FL 33823
Tel: (863)967-8822
Fax: (863)967-4972
Web Site: www.southerntech.edu/
Description: Proprietary, 2-year, coed. Awards certificates, diplomas, transfer associate, and terminal associate degrees. Total enrollment: 185. Faculty: 8 (5 full-time, 3 part-time). 175 applied, 100% were admitted.
Entrance Requirements: Entrance: moderately difficult.

■ **SOUTHERN TECHNICAL COLLEGE (ORLANDO)**

1485 Florida Mall Ave.
Orlando, FL 32809
Tel: (407)438-6000
Web Site: www.southerntech.edu/
Description: Proprietary, 2-year, coed.

■ **SOUTHWEST FLORIDA COLLEGE (FORT MYERS)**

1685 Medical Ln.
Fort Myers, FL 33907
Tel: (239)939-4766; Free: 877-793-5147
Fax: (239)936-4040
E-mail: kreynolds@swfc.edu
Web Site: www.swfc.edu/
Description: Independent, 4-year, coed. Awards associate and bachelor's degrees. Founded 1940. Setting: urban campus. Total enrollment: 1,263. Academic remediation for entering students, advanced placement, accelerated degree program, distance learning, double major, co-op programs and internships.
Entrance Requirements: Open admission. Recommended: high school transcript. Entrance: noncompetitive. Application deadline: Rolling. Notification: continuous.
Collegiate Environment: Orientation program. Campus security: day and evening security guards. Learning Resource Center with 1,000 books, 20 serials, an OPAC, and a Web page. 80 computers available on campus for general student use. A campuswide network can be accessed from off-campus. Staffed computer lab on campus.

■ **SOUTHWEST FLORIDA COLLEGE (TAMPA)**

3910 Riga Blvd.
Tampa, FL 33619
Tel: (813)630-4401; Free: 877-493-5147
Web Site: www.swfc.edu/

Description: Independent, primarily 2-year, coed. Awards diplomas, terminal associate, and bachelor's degrees. Founded 1974.

■ **STATE COLLEGE OF FLORIDA MANATEE-SARASOTA**

5840 26th St. W
Bradenton, FL 34206-7046
Tel: (941)752-5000
Fax: (941)727-6177
E-mail: lewym@scf.edu
Web Site: www.scf.edu/
Description: State-supported, 4-year, coed. Part of Florida Community College System. Awards associate and bachelor's degrees. Founded 1957. Setting: 100-acre suburban campus with easy access to Tampa-St. Petersburg. Total enrollment: 10,765. Faculty: 445 (153 full-time, 292 part-time). 2,729 applied, 100% were admitted. Full-time: 4,600 students, 56% women, 44% men. Part-time: 6,165 students, 63% women, 37% men. Students come from 31 states and territories, 38 other countries, 3% from out-of-state. 0.4% American Indian or Alaska Native, non-Hispanic/Latino; 13% Hispanic/Latino; 9% African American, non-Hispanic/Latino; 2% Asian, non-Hispanic/Latino; 0.01% Native Hawaiian or other Pacific Islander, non-Hispanic/Latino; 1% international. 39% 25 or older, 4% transferred in. Retention: 61% of full-time freshmen returned the following year. Core. Calendar: semesters. Academic remediation for entering students, ESL program, services for LD students, advanced placement, honors program, independent study, distance learning, summer session for credit, part-time degree program, co-op programs.
Entrance Requirements: Open admission except for allied health programs. Option: early admission. Required: high school transcript. Entrance: noncompetitive. Application deadline: 8/20. Notification: continuous.
Costs Per Year: Application fee: $0. State resident tuition: $2,460 full-time, $102.48 per credit part-time. Nonresident tuition: $9,276 full-time, $386.52 per credit part-time.
Collegiate Environment: Orientation program. Drama-theater group, choral group, student-run newspaper. Social organizations: 36 open to all. Most popular organizations: Student Government Association, Phi Theta Kappa, American Chemical Society Student Affiliate, Campus Ministry, Medical Community Club. Major annual events: Fall Frolic, Spring Fling, Great Safe Holiday Break Campaign. Campus security: 24-hour emergency response devices and patrols, late night transport-escort service. College housing not available. Sara Harlee Library plus 1 other with 65,386 books, 125,726 microform titles, 378 serials, an OPAC, and a Web page. 1,000 computers available on campus for general student use. A campuswide network can be accessed from off-campus. Students can access the following: online class registration. Staffed computer lab on campus.
Community Environment: A suburban area with a subtropical climate, Bradenton is located on the west coast and is known as"The Friendly City;" the hub of activities are in Manatee County. Air service at the Bradenton-Sarasota airport are available. Shopping centers, hospital, city parks, theaters and a modern municipal auditorium are part of the community facilities. The city is a rich agricultural area, producing, processing and shipping citrus fruits, winter vegetables and gladiola. Recreational facilities include beaches, a municipal pier, yacht basin, boat launching, and fishing. Points of interest are the South Florida Museum and Planetarium, and the De Soto National Memorial. The Pittsburgh Pirates baseball team trains here. A De Soto celebration is an annual event in March. Venice, Florida, is located approximately 42 miles south of the Bradenton campus. Some part-time employment is available.

■ **STETSON UNIVERSITY**

421 N Woodland Blvd.
DeLand, FL 32723
Tel: (386)822-7000; Free: 800-688-0101
Fax: (386)822-8832
E-mail: admissions@stetson.edu
Web Site: www.stetson.edu/
Description: Independent, comprehensive, coed. Awards bachelor's, master's, and doctoral degrees and post-master's certificates. Founded 1883. Setting: 140-acre small town campus with easy access to Orlando. Endowment: $147.7 million. Research spending for the previous fiscal year: $297,792. Educational spending for the previous fiscal year: $10,369 per student. Total enrollment: 3,961. Faculty: 381 (243 full-time, 138 part-time). Student-undergrad faculty ratio is 12:1. 4,862 applied, 60% were admitted. 51% from top 10% of their high school class, 18% from top quarter, 89%

from top half. 9 valedictorians. Full-time: 2,477 students, 56% women, 44% men. Part-time: 39 students, 49% women, 51% men. Students come from 42 states and territories, 47 other countries, 22% from out-of-state. 0.1% American Indian or Alaska Native, non-Hispanic/Latino; 15% Hispanic/Latino; 7% African American, non-Hispanic/Latino; 2% Asian, non-Hispanic/Latino; 0.04% Native Hawaiian or other Pacific Islander, non-Hispanic/Latino; 4% international. 5% 25 or older, 67% live on campus, 4% transferred in. Retention: 79% of full-time freshmen returned the following year. Academic areas with the most degrees conferred: business/marketing; visual and performing arts; social sciences. Core. Calendar: semesters. Services for LD students, advanced placement, accelerated degree program, self-designed majors, honors program, independent study, distance learning, double major, summer session for credit, part-time degree program, adult/continuing education programs, internships, graduate courses open to undergrads. Off campus study at American University. Study abroad program. ROTC: Army (c).

Entrance Requirements: Options: electronic application, early admission, deferred admission, international baccalaureate accepted. Required: essay, high school transcript, 1 recommendation. Recommended: interview. Required for some: SAT or ACT. Entrance: moderately difficult. Application deadlines: Rolling, Rolling for nonresidents. Notification: continuous, continuous for nonresidents. SAT Reasoning Test deadline: 7/15. Transfer credits accepted: Yes.

Costs Per Year: Application fee: $50. Comprehensive fee: $47,332 includes full-time tuition ($36,344), mandatory fees ($300), and college room and board ($10,688). College room only: $6088. Room and board charges vary according to board plan and housing facility. Part-time tuition: $3785 per course. Part-time tuition varies according to course load, location, and program.

Collegiate Environment: Orientation program. Drama-theater group, choral group, student-run newspaper, radio station. Social organizations: 120 open to all; national fraternities, national sororities; 28% of eligible men and 24% of eligible women are members. Most popular organizations: Hatter Harvest, Wesley House, Invisible Children, Kaleidoscope, Student Government Association. Major annual events: Homecoming, Greenfeather, Winter Wonderland. Student services: health clinic, personal-psychological counseling, women's center. Campus security: 24-hour emergency response devices and patrols, late night transport-escort service, controlled dormitory access. 1,791 college housing spaces available; 1,734 were occupied in 2012-13. Freshmen guaranteed college housing. On-campus residence required through junior year. Options: coed, men-only, women-only housing available. duPont-Ball Library plus 1 other with 481,595 books, 304,740 microform titles, 69,374 serials, 18,423 audiovisual materials, an OPAC, and a Web page. Operations spending for the previous fiscal year: $1.5 million. 500 computers available on campus for general student use. A campuswide network can be accessed from student residence rooms and from off campus. Students can access the following: online class registration. Staffed computer lab on campus (open 24 hours a day) provides training in use of computers, software, and the Internet.

■ STRAYER UNIVERSITY - BAYMEADOWS CAMPUS
8375 Dix Ellis Trl.
Ste. 200
Jacksonville, FL 32256
Tel: (904)538-1000
Fax: (904)538-1030
Web Site: www.strayer.edu/campus/baymeadows/
Description: Proprietary, comprehensive, coed. Awards associate, bachelor's, and master's degrees.

■ STRAYER UNIVERSITY - BRICKELL CAMPUS
1201 Brickell Ave.
Ste. 700
Miami, FL 33131
Tel: (305)507-5800
Fax: (305)416-2970
Web Site: www.strayer.edu/campus/brickell
Description: Proprietary, comprehensive, coed. Awards associate, bachelor's, and master's degrees.

■ STRAYER UNIVERSITY - CORAL SPRINGS CAMPUS
5830 Coral Ridge Dr.
Ste. 300
Coral Springs, FL 33076

Tel: (954)369-0700
Fax: (954)369-0730
Web Site: www.strayer.edu/campus/coral-springs/
Description: Proprietary, comprehensive, coed. Awards associate, bachelor's, and master's degrees.

■ STRAYER UNIVERSITY - DORAL CAMPUS
11430 NW 20th St.
Ste. 150
Miami, FL 33172
Tel: (305)507-5700
Fax: (305)470-3988
Web Site: www.strayer.edu/campus/doral
Description: Proprietary, comprehensive, coed. Awards associate, bachelor's, and master's degrees.

■ STRAYER UNIVERSITY - FORT LAUDERDALE CAMPUS
2307 W Broward Blvd.
Ste. 100
Fort Lauderdale, FL 33312
Tel: (954)745-6960
Fax: (954)745-6930
Web Site: www.strayer.edu/campus/fort-lauderdale/
Description: Proprietary, comprehensive, coed. Awards associate, bachelor's, and master's degrees.

■ STRAYER UNIVERSITY - MAITLAND CAMPUS
850 Trafalgar Ct.
Ste. 360
Maitland, FL 32751
Tel: (407)618-5900
Fax: (407)618-5930
Web Site: www.strayer.edu/campus/maitland/
Description: Proprietary, comprehensive, coed. Awards associate, bachelor's, and master's degrees.

■ STRAYER UNIVERSITY - MIRAMAR CAMPUS
15620 SW 29th St.
Miramar, FL 33027
Tel: (954)378-2400
Fax: (305)207-3042
Web Site: www.strayer.edu/campus/miramar
Description: Proprietary, comprehensive, coed. Awards associate, bachelor's, and master's degrees.

■ STRAYER UNIVERSITY - ORLANDO EAST CAMPUS
2200 N Alafaya Trl.
Ste. 500
Orlando, FL 32826
Tel: (407)926-2000
Fax: (407)926-2030
Web Site: www.strayer.edu/campus/orlando-east/
Description: Proprietary, comprehensive, coed. Awards associate, bachelor's, and master's degrees.

■ STRAYER UNIVERSITY - PALM BEACH GARDENS CAMPUS
11025 RCA Ctr. Dr.
Ste. 200
Palm Beach Gardens, FL 33410
Tel: (561)904-3000
Fax: (561)904-3030
Web Site: www.strayer.edu/campus/palm-beach-gardens
Description: Proprietary, comprehensive, coed. Awards associate, bachelor's, and master's degrees.

■ STRAYER UNIVERSITY - SAND LAKE CAMPUS
8541 S Park Cir.
Bldg. 900
Orlando, FL 32819
Tel: (407)264-9400
Fax: (407)264-9430
Web Site: www.strayer.edu/campus/sand-lake/
Description: Proprietary, comprehensive, coed. Awards associate, bachelor's, and master's degrees.

■ **STRAYER UNIVERSITY - TAMPA EAST CAMPUS**
6302 E Martin Luther King Blvd., Ste. 450
Tampa, FL 33619
Tel: (813)663-0100
Fax: (813)626-2245
Web Site: www.strayer.edu/campus/tampa-east
Description: Proprietary, comprehensive, coed. Awards associate, bachelor's, and master's degrees.

■ **STRAYER UNIVERSITY - TAMPA WESTSHORE CAMPUS**
4902 Eisenhower Blvd., Ste. 100
Tampa, FL 33634
Tel: (813)882-0100
Fax: (813)249-2483
Web Site: www.strayer.edu/campus/tampa-westshore
Description: Proprietary, comprehensive, coed. Awards associate, bachelor's, and master's degrees.

■ **TALLAHASSEE COMMUNITY COLLEGE**
444 Appleyard Dr.
Tallahassee, FL 32304-2895
Tel: (850)201-6200
E-mail: admissions@tcc.fl.edu
Web Site: www.tcc.fl.edu/
Description: State and locally supported, 2-year, coed. Part of Florida College System. Awards certificates, transfer associate, and terminal associate degrees. Founded 1966. Setting: 258-acre suburban campus. Endowment: $7.9 million. Educational spending for the previous fiscal year: $2478 per student. Total enrollment: 14,237. Faculty: 868 (187 full-time, 681 part-time). Student-undergrad faculty ratio is 23:1. 2,628 applied, 100% were admitted. Full-time: 6,840 students, 48% women, 52% men. Part-time: 7,397 students, 58% women, 42% men. 7% from out-of-state. 0.2% American Indian or Alaska Native, non-Hispanic/Latino; 9% Hispanic/Latino; 33% African American, non-Hispanic/Latino; 1% Asian, non-Hispanic/Latino; 0.1% Native Hawaiian or other Pacific Islander, non-Hispanic/Latino; 1% international. 24% 25 or older, 8% transferred in. Core. Calendar: semesters. Academic remediation for entering students, ESL program, services for LD students, advanced placement, accelerated degree program, honors program, independent study, distance learning, summer session for credit, part-time degree program, external degree program, adult/continuing education programs. Off campus study at Florida Agricultural and Mechanical University, Florida State University. Study abroad program. ROTC: Army (c), Naval (c), Air Force (c).
Entrance Requirements: Open admission except for allied health programs. Options: electronic application, early admission, deferred admission. Required: high school transcript. Entrance: noncompetitive. Application deadline: 8/1. Transfer credits accepted: Yes.
Costs Per Year: Application fee: $0. State resident tuition: $2518 full-time, $96.83 per credit hour part-time. Nonresident tuition: $9724 full-time, $373 per credit hour part-time. Full-time tuition varies according to course load. Part-time tuition varies according to course load. Tuition guaranteed not to increase for student's term of enrollment.
Collegiate Environment: Orientation program. Drama-theater group, choral group, student-run newspaper. Social organizations: 22 open to all. Most popular organizations: Student Government Association, International Student Organization, Phi Theta Kappa, Model United Nations, Honors Council. Major annual events: Student/Faculty days, Volunteer Fair, Career Expo. Student services: personal-psychological counseling. Campus security: 24-hour emergency response devices and patrols, late night transport-escort service. College housing not available. Tallahassee Community College Library with 126,904 books, 4,742 microform titles, 7,965 audiovisual materials, and an OPAC. Operations spending for the previous fiscal year: $1.8 million. 2,244 computers available on campus for general student use. A campuswide network can be accessed from off-campus. Students can access the following: online class registration. Staffed computer lab on campus provides training in use of computers, software, and the Internet.
Community Environment: See Florida State University.

■ **TALMUDIC COLLEGE OF FLORIDA**
1910 Alton Rd.
Miami Beach, FL 33139
Tel: (305)534-7050
Fax: (305)534-8444

E-mail: yandtg@gmail.com
Web Site: www.talmudicu.edu/
Description: Independent Jewish, comprehensive, men only. Awards bachelor's and master's degrees. Founded 1974. Setting: urban campus with easy access to Miami. Educational spending for the previous fiscal year: $10,000 per student. Total enrollment: 35. Faculty: 6 (all full-time). Student-undergrad faculty ratio is 5:1. 10 applied, 80% were admitted. Full-time: 30 students. Students come from 5 states and territories, 5 other countries, 95% from out-of-state. 1% 25 or older, 99% live on campus, 83% transferred in. Retention: 50% of full-time freshmen returned the following year. Core. Calendar: semesters. Academic remediation for entering students, ESL program, honors program, independent study, summer session for credit, part-time degree program, adult/continuing education programs, graduate courses open to undergrads. Study abroad program.
Entrance Requirements: Options: early admission, deferred admission, international baccalaureate accepted. Required: high school transcript, interview, placement exam. Recommended: essay. Required for some: high school transcript. Entrance: moderately difficult. Application deadline: Rolling. Notification: continuous.
Collegiate Environment: Student services: personal-psychological counseling. Beis Medrash plus 1 other with 25,000 books, 10,000 audiovisual materials, and a Web page.

■ **TRINITY BAPTIST COLLEGE**
800 Hammond Blvd.
Jacksonville, FL 32221
Tel: (904)596-2400; Free: 800-786-2206
Fax: (904)596-2531
E-mail: trinity@tbc.edu
Web Site: www.tbc.edu/
Description: Independent Baptist, comprehensive, coed. Awards associate, bachelor's, and master's degrees. Founded 1974. Setting: 148-acre urban campus with easy access to Jacksonville. Total enrollment: 280. Faculty: 50. Student-undergrad faculty ratio is 9:1. 130 applied. Core. Calendar: semesters. Academic remediation for entering students, services for LD students, advanced placement, accelerated degree program, independent study, distance learning, double major, summer session for credit, part-time degree program, adult/continuing education programs, internships, graduate courses open to undergrads.
Entrance Requirements: Option: electronic application. Required: essay, high school transcript, minimum 2 high school GPA, 2 recommendations, SAT or ACT. Entrance: moderately difficult. Application deadline: Rolling. Notification: continuous until 8/15. Transfer credits accepted: Yes.
Costs Per Year: Application fee: $30. Comprehensive fee: $14,550 includes full-time tuition ($7990), mandatory fees ($1050), and college room and board ($5510). College room only: $2510. Room and board charges vary according to board plan. Part-time tuition: $335 per credit hour.
Collegiate Environment: Orientation program. Drama-theater group, choral group, student-run newspaper. Student services: health clinic, personal-psychological counseling. Campus security: 24-hour emergency response devices and patrols, controlled dormitory access. Travis Hudson Library with 39,000 books and a Web page. 30 computers available on campus for general student use. A campuswide network can be accessed from student residence rooms and from off campus. Students can access the following: online class registration. Staffed computer lab on campus.

■ **TRINITY COLLEGE OF FLORIDA**
2430 Welbilt Blvd.
New Port Richey, FL 34655
Tel: (727)376-6911; Free: 800-388-0869
Fax: (727)376-0781
E-mail: kofarrell@trinitycollege.edu
Web Site: www.trinitycollege.edu/
Description: Independent nondenominational, 4-year, coed. Awards associate and bachelor's degrees. Founded 1932. Setting: 40-acre small town campus with easy access to Tampa. Endowment: $606,874. Educational spending for the previous fiscal year: $5268 per student. Total enrollment: 219. Faculty: 23 (8 full-time, 15 part-time). Student-undergrad faculty ratio is 10:1. 107 applied, 25% were admitted. Full-time: 189 students, 46% women, 54% men. Part-time: 30 students, 33% women, 67% men. Students come from 8 states and territories, 7 other countries, 3% from out-of-state. 0% American Indian or Alaska Native, non-Hispanic/Latino; 18% Hispanic/Latino; 10% African American, non-Hispanic/Latino; 0.5% Asian, non-Hispanic/Latino; 0% Native Hawaiian or other Pacific Islander, non-Hispanic/

Latino; 4% international. 47% 25 or older, 27% live on campus, 26% transferred in. Retention: 45% of full-time freshmen returned the following year. Academic areas with the most degrees conferred: theology and religious vocations; education; liberal arts/general studies; business/marketing. Core. Calendar: semesters. Academic remediation for entering students, services for LD students, advanced placement, accelerated degree program, self-designed majors, independent study, distance learning, double major, summer session for credit, part-time degree program, adult/continuing education programs, co-op programs and internships. Off campus study.

Entrance Requirements: Options: electronic application, early admission, deferred admission, international baccalaureate accepted. Required: essay, high school transcript, 2 recommendations, interview, SAT or ACT. Recommended: minimum 2 high school GPA. Entrance: minimally difficult. Application deadlines: 12/17, 12/17 for nonresidents. Notification: continuous until 12/17, continuous for nonresidents. SAT Reasoning Test deadline: 12/17. SAT Subject Test deadline: 12/17. Transfer credits accepted: Yes.

Costs Per Year: Application fee: $25. Comprehensive fee: $19,870 includes full-time tuition ($12,520), mandatory fees ($800), and college room and board ($6550). College room only: $4450. Part-time tuition: $522 per credit hour. Part-time mandatory fees: $400 per term. Part-time tuition and fees vary according to course load.

Collegiate Environment: Drama-theater group, choral group, student-run newspaper. Social organizations: 4 open to all. Most popular organizations: Great Commission Missionary Fellowship, Trinity Tribune (School Newspaper), student government. Major annual events: Commencement, Missions Conference, Campus Preview. Student services: personal-psychological counseling. Campus security: student patrols. College housing designed to accommodate 42 students; 59 undergraduates lived in college housing during 2012-13. Freshmen guaranteed college housing. On-campus residence required through senior year. Options: men-only, women-only housing available. Raymond H. Center, M.D. Library with 41,120 books, 264 serials, 2,574 audiovisual materials, and an OPAC. Operations spending for the previous fiscal year: $124,415. 17 computers available on campus for general student use. A campuswide network can be accessed from student residence rooms. Students can access the following: online class registration. Staffed computer lab on campus provides training in use of computers, software, and the Internet.

Community Environment: See Clearwater Christian College.

■ UNIVERSITY OF CENTRAL FLORIDA

4000 Central Florida Blvd.
Orlando, FL 32816
Tel: (407)823-2000
Fax: (407)823-3419
E-mail: admission@ucf.edu
Web Site: www.ucf.edu/

Description: State-supported, university, coed. Part of State University System of Florida. Awards associate, bachelor's, master's, and doctoral degrees. Founded 1963. Setting: 1,415-acre suburban campus with easy access to Orlando. Endowment: $121.1 million. Research spending for the previous fiscal year: $98.3 million. Total enrollment: 59,767. Faculty: 1,842 (1,318 full-time, 524 part-time). Student-undergrad faculty ratio is 32:1. 33,281 applied, 46% were admitted. 32% from top 10% of their high school class, 75% from top quarter, 97% from top half. 67 National Merit Scholars, 51 valedictorians. Full-time: 36,731 students, 54% women, 46% men. Part-time: 14,237 students, 55% women, 45% men. Students come from 50 states and territories, 134 other countries, 5% from out-of-state. 0.3% American Indian or Alaska Native, non-Hispanic/Latino; 20% Hispanic/Latino; 10% African American, non-Hispanic/Latino; 5% Asian, non-Hispanic/Latino; 0.2% Native Hawaiian or other Pacific Islander, non-Hispanic/Latino; 1% international. 21% 25 or older, 17% live on campus, 12% transferred in. Retention: 88% of full-time freshmen returned the following year. Academic areas with the most degrees conferred: business/marketing; health professions and related sciences; psychology. Core. Calendar: semesters. ESL program, services for LD students, advanced placement, accelerated degree program, freshman honors college, honors program, independent study, distance learning, double major, summer session for credit, part-time degree program, adult/continuing education programs, co-op programs and internships, graduate courses open to undergrads. Off campus study. Study abroad program. ROTC: Army, Air Force.

Entrance Requirements: Options: electronic application, early admission, international baccalaureate accepted. Required: high school transcript, minimum 2 high school GPA, SAT or ACT. Recommended: essay. Entrance: moderately difficult. Application deadline: 3/1. Notification: continuous.

Preference given to state residents who are designated as Talented 20. SAT Reasoning Test deadline: 5/1. Transfer credits accepted: Yes. Applicants placed on waiting list: 2,029. Wait-listed applicants offered admission: 190.

Costs Per Year: Application fee: $30. State resident tuition: $6247 full-time, $208.23 per credit hour part-time. Nonresident tuition: $22,345 full-time, $744.84 per credit hour part-time. Full-time tuition varies according to course load. Part-time tuition varies according to course load. College room and board: $9357. College room only: $5400. Room and board charges vary according to board plan and housing facility.

Collegiate Environment: Orientation program. Drama-theater group, choral group, marching band, student-run newspaper, radio station. Social organizations: 450 open to all; national fraternities, national sororities, local fraternities, local sororities; 6% of eligible men and 7% of eligible women are members. Most popular organizations: Volunteer UCF, intramural sports, Recreation and Wellness Center Group Exercise Programs, Multicultural Student Center and Organizations, Campus Religious Organizations. Major annual events: Homecoming Week (includes Concert, Comedy Show, Skits, Parade and Game), Pegasus Palooza (AKA Welcome Week), Study Union (SU open 24/7 during finals week - nationally recognized partnership with academic units. Student services: legal services, health clinic, personal-psychological counseling, women's center. Campus security: 24-hour emergency response devices and patrols, late night transport-escort service, controlled dormitory access. 10,276 college housing spaces available; 8,701 were occupied in 2012-13. Freshmen given priority for college housing. Options: coed, men-only, women-only housing available. University Library with 2.5 million books, 3.2 million microform titles, 44,976 serials, 51,168 audiovisual materials, an OPAC, and a Web page. Operations spending for the previous fiscal year: $14.1 million. 3,200 computers available on campus for general student use. Computer purchase/lease plans available. A campuswide network can be accessed from student residence rooms and from off campus. Students can access the following: online class registration. Staffed computer lab on campus provides training in use of computers, software, and the Internet.

Community Environment: Orlando has become a focal point for business and major industry, easily accessible by major forms of public transportation, and serves as a regional retail market for eight counties and over a million people. The area's reputation as a tourism mecca has brought a resultant surge in the hospitality industry as well. It also is an important agricultural center, noted for citrus and truck gardening. The temperate climate year-round provides ideal conditions for numerous recreational opportunities: fishing, boating, dog and horse racing, Jai-Alai, golf, tennis, and other outdoor activities. Points of interest include Walt Disney World, Epcot Center, MGM Studios, Universal Studios, Sea World, plus such seasonal attractions as the Church Street Station, Citrus Open Golf Tournament, Walt Disney World Golf Classic, Orlando Horse Show, Central Florida Fair, Orlando Magic Pro-Basketball, and Citrus Bowl. Cultural activities are widespread in the Orlando-Winter Park area, and include annual Sidewalk Art Festivals, Orlando Shakespeare Festival, the Florida Symphony Orchestra, Central Florida Civic Theatre, and the John Young Museum and Planetarium, located adjacent to the Loch Haven Art Center.

■ UNIVERSITY OF FLORIDA

Gainesville, FL 32611
Tel: (352)392-3261
Web Site: www.ufl.edu/

Description: State-supported, university, coed. Part of Board of Trustees. Awards bachelor's, master's, and doctoral degrees. Founded 1853. Setting: 2,000-acre suburban campus with easy access to Jacksonville. Endowment: $1.3 billion. Research spending for the previous fiscal year: $558.2 million. Educational spending for the previous fiscal year: $8875 per student. Total enrollment: 49,913. Faculty: 3,701 (3,438 full-time, 263 part-time). Student-undergrad faculty ratio is 21:1. 27,419 applied, 44% were admitted. 77% from top 10% of their high school class, 98% from top quarter, 100% from top half. 129 National Merit Scholars. Full-time: 30,241 students, 56% women, 44% men. Part-time: 2,535 students, 47% women, 53% men. Students come from 51 states and territories, 127 other countries, 3% from out-of-state. 0.3% American Indian or Alaska Native, non-Hispanic/Latino; 18% Hispanic/Latino; 8% African American, non-Hispanic/Latino; 8% Asian, non-Hispanic/Latino; 1% Native Hawaiian or other Pacific Islander, non-Hispanic/Latino; 1% international. 5% 25 or older, 23% live on campus, 6% transferred in. Retention: 96% of full-time freshmen returned the following year. Academic areas with the most degrees conferred: social sciences; business/marketing; engineering. Core. Calendar: semesters. ESL program, services for LD students, advanced placement, accelerated degree program, self-designed majors, honors program, independent study, distance learning, double major, summer session for credit, part-time degree program, external degree program, adult/continuing education programs, co-op programs and internships, graduate courses open to undergrads. Off campus study at Miami New World School of the Arts, Miami-Dade Community College. Study abroad program. ROTC: Army, Naval, Air Force.

Entrance Requirements: Options: electronic application, early admission, international baccalaureate accepted. Required: essay, high school transcript, SAT or ACT. Entrance: very difficult. Application deadline: 11/1. Notification: 2/8. SAT Reasoning Test deadline: 12/31. SAT Subject Test deadline: 12/31. Transfer credits accepted: Yes.

Costs Per Year: Application fee: $30. State resident tuition: $6143 full-time, $147.49 per credit hour part-time. Nonresident tuition: $28,420 full-time, $854.70 per credit hour part-time. Mandatory fees: $57.27 per credit hour part-time, $92.63. Full-time tuition varies according to course level, location, program, and reciprocity agreements. Part-time tuition and fees vary according to course level, location, program, and reciprocity agreements. College room and board: $9370. College room only: $5240. Room and board charges vary according to board plan and housing facility.

Collegiate Environment: Orientation program. Drama-theater group, choral group, marching band, student-run newspaper, radio station. Social organizations: 985 open to all; national fraternities, national sororities; 23% of eligible men and 15% of eligible women are members. Most popular organizations: VISA - Volunteers for International Student Affairs, Fellowship of Christian Athletes, Black Student Union, Hispanic Student Association, Asian American Student Union. Major annual events: Gator Growl/ Homecoming, New Student Convocation, Welcome Assemblies. Student services: legal services, health clinic, personal-psychological counseling. Campus security: 24-hour emergency response devices and patrols, student patrols, late night transport-escort service, controlled dormitory access, crime and rape prevention programs. College housing designed to accommodate 7,572 students; 7,801 undergraduates lived in college housing during 2012-13. Freshmen given priority for college housing. Option: coed housing available. George A. Smathers Libraries plus 9 others with 4.8 million books, 8.1 million microform titles, 141,195 serials, 78,686 audiovisual materials, an OPAC, and a Web page. Operations spending for the previous fiscal year: $24.7 million. 2,200 computers available on campus for general student use. A campuswide network can be accessed from student residence rooms and from off campus. Students can access the following: online class registration, course management system. Staffed computer lab on campus (open 24 hours a day) provides training in use of computers, software, and the Internet.

Community Environment: Gainesville is the county seat of Alachua County located on the rolling highlands of north-central Florida midway between the Gulf of Mexico and the Atlantic Ocean. The climate is subtropical with an average mean temperature of 70 degrees. Railroads, buses and airlines serve the area. Gainesville is the focal point of diversified industrial and agricultural activities. The city facilities include churches of many denominations, center for science, education and medicine, medical center with hospital, museum and numerous civic organizations. Recreational facilities include golf courses, swimming at nearby springs, boating and freshwater fishing in surrounding lakes and rivers. Both the Atlantic Ocean and the Gulf of Mexico are within a two-hour drive. Off-campus housing is available for over 20,000 students in addition to university housing.

■ **UNIVERSITY OF FORT LAUDERDALE**
4093 NW 16th St.
Lauderhill, FL 33313
Tel: (954)486-7728
Web Site: uftl.edu/
Description: Independent religious, comprehensive, coed. Founded 1995. Calendar: semesters.

■ **UNIVERSITY OF MIAMI**
PO Box 248025
Coral Gables, FL 33124
Tel: (305)284-2211
Fax: (305)284-2507
E-mail: admission@miami.edu
Web Site: www.miami.edu/
Description: Independent, university, coed. Awards bachelor's, master's, and doctoral degrees and post-master's certificates. Founded 1925. Setting: 239-acre suburban campus with easy access to Miami. Total enrollment: 16,172. Faculty: 1,452 (1,043 full-time, 409 part-time). Student-undergrad faculty ratio is 11:1. 27,757 applied, 40% were admitted. 69% from top 10%

of their high school class, 90% from top quarter, 96% from top half. 47 National Merit Scholars, 33 valedictorians. Full-time: 9,979 students, 51% women, 49% men. Part-time: 611 students, 58% women, 42% men. Students come from 54 states and territories, 99 other countries, 52% from out-of-state. 0.2% American Indian or Alaska Native, non-Hispanic/Latino; 23% Hispanic/Latino; 7% African American, non-Hispanic/Latino; 6% Asian, non-Hispanic/Latino; 0.1% Native Hawaiian or other Pacific Islander, non-Hispanic/Latino; 12% international. 5% 25 or older, 39% live on campus, 5% transferred in. Retention: 91% of full-time freshmen returned the following year. Academic areas with the most degrees conferred: business/marketing; biological/life sciences; social sciences. Core. Calendar: semesters. Academic remediation for entering students, ESL program, services for LD students, advanced placement, accelerated degree program, self-designed majors, honors program, independent study, distance learning, double major, summer session for credit, part-time degree program, co-op programs and internships, graduate courses open to undergrads. Off campus study at Washington Semester Program, American University. Study abroad program. ROTC: Army, Air Force.

Entrance Requirements: Options: electronic application, early admission, early decision, early action, deferred admission, international baccalaureate accepted. Required: essay, 1 recommendation, College transcript(s) and statement of good standing from prior institution(s), SAT or ACT. Required for some: high school transcript, SAT Subject Tests. Entrance: very difficult. Application deadlines: 1/1, 11/1 for early decision, 11/1 for early action. Notification: 4/15, 12/15 for early decision, 2/1 for early action. SAT Reasoning Test deadline: 1/1. SAT Subject Test deadline: 11/1. Transfer credits accepted: Yes. Early decision applicants: 681. Early decision applicants admitted: 181. Early action applicants: 11,169. Early action applicants admitted: 5,474.

Costs Per Year: Application fee: $70. Comprehensive fee: $55,166 includes full-time tuition ($41,580), mandatory fees ($1272), and college room and board ($12,314). College room only: $7122. Room and board charges vary according to board plan and housing facility. Part-time tuition: $1730 per credit hour. Part-time tuition varies according to course load. Tuition guaranteed not to increase for student's term of enrollment.

Collegiate Environment: Orientation program. Drama-theater group, choral group, marching band, student-run newspaper, radio station. Social organizations: national fraternities, national sororities. Major annual events: Alumni Weekend and Homecoming Festivities, Annual Canes Film Festival, Earth Day's 'Hug the Lake'. Student services: health clinic, personal-psychological counseling, women's center. Campus security: 24-hour emergency response devices and patrols, student patrols, late night transport-escort service, controlled dormitory access, Programs, seminars, activities, classes and publications are available to students, faculty, staff, parents and friends. 4,344 college housing spaces available; 4,216 were occupied in 2012-13. Freshmen guaranteed college housing. On-campus residence required in freshman year. Option: coed housing available. Otto G. Richter Library plus 6 others with 3.6 million books, 3.2 million microform titles, 81,066 serials, 176,130 audiovisual materials, an OPAC, and a Web page. 400 computers available on campus for general student use. Computer purchase/lease plans available. A campuswide network can be accessed from student residence rooms and from off campus. Students can access the following: online class registration, Online bill payment, online housing registration. Staffed computer lab on campus provides training in use of computers, software, and the Internet.

Community Environment: A part of the metropolitan Miami area, Coral Gables is known as"City Beautiful" with the mildest climate in the United States. The Miami International Airport is nearby. The city offers a distinguished retail shopping district, the opera, theatre, ballet, concerts, the Vizcaya Museum, and Lowe Art Gallery. Recreational activities are numerous including swimming, golf, tennis, boating, sport fishing, and snorkeling and scuba diving among the only coral reefs in the continental United States, in the Florida Keys. The Everglades National Park is 1 hour away.

■ **UNIVERSITY OF NORTH FLORIDA**
1 UNF Dr.
Jacksonville, FL 32224
Tel: (904)620-1000
Fax: (904)620-1040
E-mail: admissions@unf.edu
Web Site: www.unf.edu/
Description: State-supported, comprehensive, coed. Part of State University System of Florida. Awards associate, bachelor's, master's, and doctoral degrees and post-master's certificates (doctoral degree in education

only). Founded 1965. Setting: 1,300-acre urban campus. Research spending for the previous fiscal year: $8.8 million. Educational spending for the previous fiscal year: $5037 per student. Total enrollment: 16,201. Faculty: 827 (539 full-time, 288 part-time). Student-undergrad faculty ratio is 20:1. 10,412 applied, 52% were admitted. 24% from top 10% of their high school class, 56% from top quarter, 87% from top half. Full-time: 10,308 students, 57% women, 43% men. Part-time: 4,090 students, 54% women, 46% men. Students come from 41 states and territories, 53 other countries, 2% from out-of-state. 0.2% American Indian or Alaska Native, non-Hispanic/Latino; 9% Hispanic/Latino; 10% African American, non-Hispanic/Latino; 5% Asian, non-Hispanic/Latino; 0.1% Native Hawaiian or other Pacific Islander, non-Hispanic/Latino; 2% international. 24% 25 or older, 20% live on campus, 9% transferred in. Retention: 83% of full-time freshmen returned the following year. Academic areas with the most degrees conferred: business/marketing; health professions and related sciences; communication/journalism. Core. Calendar: semesters. ESL program, services for LD students, advanced placement, accelerated degree program, self-designed majors, honors program, independent study, distance learning, double major, summer session for credit, part-time degree program, adult/continuing education programs, co-op programs and internships, graduate courses open to undergrads. Off campus study at State University System of Florida. Study abroad program. ROTC: Army, Naval (c).

Entrance Requirements: Options: electronic application, deferred admission, international baccalaureate accepted. Required: high school transcript, minimum 2.5 high school GPA, meet minimum test score requirements (460 SAT Critical Reading, 460 SAT Math, 440 SAT Writing; or 19 ACT Reading, 19 ACT Math, 18 ACT English/Writing), SAT or ACT. Recommended: minimum 3 high school GPA. Required for some: essay. Entrance: very difficult. Application deadline: Rolling. Notification: continuous until 1/3. SAT Reasoning Test deadline: 5/10. Transfer credits accepted: Yes.

Costs Per Year: Application fee: $30. State resident tuition: $4229 full-time, $207.83 per credit hour part-time. Nonresident tuition: $17,999 full-time, $689.80 per credit hour part-time. Mandatory fees: $2006 full-time. Full-time tuition and fees vary according to course load. Part-time tuition varies according to course load. College room and board: $8190. Room and board charges vary according to board plan and housing facility.

Collegiate Environment: Orientation program. Drama-theater group, choral group, student-run newspaper, radio station. Social organizations: 198 open to all; national fraternities, national sororities. Most popular organizations: Student Government Association, African American Student Association, International Student Association, Filipino Student Association, National Education Association. Major annual events: Homecoming, Earth Music Fest, Toga Party. Student services: health clinic, personal-psychological counseling, women's center. Campus security: 24-hour emergency response devices and patrols, late night transport-escort service, controlled dormitory access, electronic parking lot security. 3,000 college housing spaces available; 2,911 were occupied in 2012-13. Freshmen guaranteed college housing. On-campus residence required in freshman year. Option: coed housing available. Thomas G. Carpenter Library with 864,706 books, 1.5 million microform titles, 37,919 serials, 59,205 audiovisual materials, an OPAC, and a Web page. Operations spending for the previous fiscal year: $2.6 million. 750 computers available on campus for general student use. Computer purchase/lease plans available. A campuswide network can be accessed from student residence rooms and from off campus. Students can access the following: online class registration, applications software. Staffed computer lab on campus provides training in use of computers.

Community Environment: See Jacksonville University.

■ **UNIVERSITY OF PHOENIX–CENTRAL FLORIDA CAMPUS**
2290 Lucien Way
Ste. 400
Maitland, FL 32751-7057
Tel: (407)667-0555; Free: 866-766-0766
Web Site: www.phoenix.edu/
Description: Proprietary, comprehensive, coed. Awards bachelor's and master's degrees. Founded 1996. Setting: urban campus. Total enrollment: 1,537. Faculty: 215 (33 full-time, 182 part-time). Full-time: 1,174 students, 66% women, 34% men. 86% 25 or older. Academic areas with the most degrees conferred: business/marketing; computer and information sciences; health professions and related sciences. Core. Calendar: continuous. Services for LD students, advanced placement, accelerated degree program, independent study, distance learning, external degree program, adult/continuing education programs, graduate courses open to undergrads.
Entrance Requirements: Open admission. Options: electronic application,

deferred admission. Required: 1 recommendation. Required for some: high school transcript. Entrance: noncompetitive. Application deadline: Rolling.
Collegiate Environment: Campus security: late night transport-escort service. University Library with 16,781 serials, an OPAC, and a Web page. Operations spending for the previous fiscal year: $6.8 million.

■ **UNIVERSITY OF PHOENIX–NORTH FLORIDA CAMPUS**
4500 Salisbury Rd.
Jacksonville, FL 32216-0959
Tel: (904)636-6645; Free: 866-766-0766
Web Site: www.phoenix.edu/
Description: Proprietary, comprehensive, coed. Awards bachelor's and master's degrees. Founded 1976. Setting: urban campus. Total enrollment: 1,276. Faculty: 210 (24 full-time, 186 part-time). Full-time: 1,019 students, 63% women, 37% men. 91% 25 or older. Academic areas with the most degrees conferred: business/marketing; computer and information sciences; health professions and related sciences. Core. Calendar: continuous. Services for LD students, advanced placement, accelerated degree program, independent study, distance learning, graduate courses open to undergrads.
Entrance Requirements: Open admission. Options: electronic application, deferred admission. Required: 1 recommendation. Required for some: high school transcript. Entrance: noncompetitive. Application deadline: Rolling.
Collegiate Environment: Campus security: late night transport-escort service.

■ **UNIVERSITY OF PHOENIX–SOUTH FLORIDA CAMPUS**
600 N Pine Island Rd.
Fort Lauderdale, FL 33309
Tel: (954)382-5303; Free: 866-766-0766
Web Site: www.phoenix.edu/
Description: Proprietary, comprehensive, coed. Awards bachelor's and master's degrees. Setting: urban campus. Total enrollment: 2,439. Faculty: 233 (22 full-time, 211 part-time). Full-time: 1,961 students, 73% women, 27% men. 84% 25 or older. Academic areas with the most degrees conferred: business/marketing; health professions and related sciences; computer and information sciences. Core. Calendar: continuous. Services for LD students, advanced placement, accelerated degree program, independent study, distance learning, external degree program, adult/continuing education programs, graduate courses open to undergrads.
Entrance Requirements: Open admission. Options: electronic application, deferred admission. Required: 1 recommendation. Required for some: high school transcript. Entrance: noncompetitive. Application deadline: Rolling.
Collegiate Environment: Campus security: late night transport-escort service. University Library with 16,781 serials, an OPAC, and a Web page. Operations spending for the previous fiscal year: $6.8 million.

■ **UNIVERSITY OF PHOENIX–WEST FLORIDA CAMPUS**
12802 Tampa Oaks Blvd.
Ste. 200
Temple Terrace, FL 33637
Tel: (813)626-7911; Free: 866-766-0766
Fax: (813)977-1449
Web Site: www.phoenix.edu/
Description: Proprietary, comprehensive, coed. Awards bachelor's and master's degrees. Setting: urban campus. Total enrollment: 894. Faculty: 201 (25 full-time, 176 part-time). 57 applied, 100% were admitted. Full-time: 740 students, 63% women, 37% men. 90% 25 or older. Academic areas with the most degrees conferred: business/marketing; computer and information sciences; health professions and related sciences. Core. Calendar: continuous. Services for LD students, advanced placement, accelerated degree program, independent study, distance learning, external degree program, adult/continuing education programs, graduate courses open to undergrads.
Entrance Requirements: Open admission. Options: electronic application, deferred admission, international baccalaureate accepted. Required: 1 recommendation. Required for some: high school transcript. Entrance: noncompetitive. Application deadline: Rolling.
Collegiate Environment: Campus security: late night transport-escort service. University Library with 16,781 serials, an OPAC, and a Web page. Operations spending for the previous fiscal year: $6.8 million.

■ **UNIVERSITY OF SOUTH FLORIDA**
4202 E Fowler Ave.
Tampa, FL 33620-9951

Tel: (813)974-2011
Fax: (813)974-9689
E-mail: admissions@usf.edu
Web Site: www.usf.edu/

Description: State-supported, university, coed. Part of State University System of Florida. Awards associate, bachelor's, master's, and doctoral degrees. Founded 1956. Setting: 1,562-acre urban campus. System endowment: $334.1 million. Total enrollment: 40,111. Faculty: 1,188 (1,104 full-time, 84 part-time). Student-undergrad faculty ratio is 27:1. 28,544 applied, 43% were admitted. 33% from top 10% of their high school class, 61% from top quarter, 73% from top half. 24 National Merit Scholars. Full-time: 23,407 students, 57% women, 43% men. Part-time: 5,882 students, 47% women, 53% men. Students come from 51 states and territories, 153 other countries, 7% from out-of-state. 0.3% American Indian or Alaska Native, non-Hispanic/Latino; 19% Hispanic/Latino; 11% African American, non-Hispanic/Latino; 6% Asian, non-Hispanic/Latino; 0.2% Native Hawaiian or other Pacific Islander, non-Hispanic/Latino; 3% international. 18% 25 or older, 17% live on campus, 13% transferred in. Retention: 87% of full-time freshmen returned the following year. Academic areas with the most degrees conferred: business/marketing; social sciences; psychology; biological/life sciences. Core. Calendar: semesters. Academic remediation for entering students, ESL program, services for LD students, advanced placement, accelerated degree program, self-designed majors, freshman honors college, honors program, independent study, distance learning, double major, summer session for credit, part-time degree program, adult/continuing education programs, co-op programs and internships, graduate courses open to undergrads. Off campus study at members of the National Student Exchange, State University System of Florida. Study abroad program. ROTC: Army, Naval, Air Force.

Entrance Requirements: Options: electronic application, early admission, international baccalaureate accepted. Required: minimum 2 high school GPA, SAT or ACT. Required for some: high school transcript, 1 recommendation. Entrance: moderately difficult. Application deadline: 3/1. Notification: continuous. SAT Reasoning Test deadline: 4/15. Applicants placed on waiting list: 16.

Costs Per Year: Application fee: $30. State resident tuition: $4506 full-time, $209 per credit hour part-time. Nonresident tuition: $14,429 full-time, $539 per credit hour part-time. Mandatory fees: $1828 full-time, $37. Full-time tuition and fees vary according to course level, course load, and location. Part-time tuition and fees vary according to course level, course load, and location. College room and board: $8960. College room only: $5460. Room and board charges vary according to board plan, housing facility, and location.

Collegiate Environment: Orientation program. Drama-theater group, choral group, marching band, student-run newspaper, radio station. Social organizations: national fraternities, national sororities. Most popular organizations: student government, Campus Activities Board, USF Ambassadors, Student Admissions Representatives. Major annual events: Homecoming, Welcome Week, University lecture series. Student services: legal services, health clinic, personal-psychological counseling, women's center. Campus security: 24-hour emergency response devices and patrols, student patrols, late night transport-escort service, controlled dormitory access, residence hall lobby personnel 8 pm to 6 am. 5,373 college housing spaces available; 5,249 were occupied in 2012-13. Freshmen guaranteed college housing. On-campus residence required in freshman year. Options: coed, men-only, women-only housing available. Tampa Campus Library plus 5 others with 2.2 million books, 83,938 serials, an OPAC, and a Web page. 500 computers available on campus for general student use. Computer purchase/lease plans available. A campuswide network can be accessed from student residence rooms and from off campus. Students can access the following: online class registration. Staffed computer lab on campus provides training in use of computers, software, and the Internet.

Community Environment: Tampa, located on the west coast of Florida, is the seventh largest port in the nation. It is a significant industrial and commercial center; the second largest city in the state. A fine harbor with a 34 foot channel to the Gulf of Mexico is located here. It is important in trade and travel to and from Central and South America. Annual mean temperature is 72.3 degrees, the average rainfall is 49 inches. All modes of travel serve the area. Industries include cigar manufacturing, phosphate, beer, cement, cans, wire and cable, and canned citrus fruits and vegetables. Tampa is a tourist city with many recreational facilities; yacht basin, golf courses, tennis clubs, saddle clubs, swimming pools, bowling alleys, baseball diamonds, and basketball courts. Salt water fishing is excellent. Swimming is excellent all year in Tampa Bay, and at the municipal beach on Courtney Campbell

Causeway. The Tampa Bay Buccaneers is the local NFL team and the Cincinnati Reds make Tampa their spring training quarters. Points of interest are the Busch Gardens, Lowry Park, Tampa Art Institute, and the Tampa Museum.

■ **UNIVERSITY OF SOUTH FLORIDA SARASOTA-MANATEE**
8350 N Tamiami Trl.
Sarasota, FL 34243
Tel: (941)359-4200
E-mail: pngoodwin@sar.usf.edu
Web Site: www.sarasota.usf.edu/

Description: State-supported, upper-level, coed. Part of University of South Florida System. Awards bachelor's and master's degrees and post-master's certificates. Founded 1956. Setting: 31-acre urban campus. System endowment: $347 million. Research spending for the previous fiscal year: $189,895. Educational spending for the previous fiscal year: $4939 per student. Total enrollment: 1,943. Faculty: 121 (57 full-time, 64 part-time). Student-undergrad faculty ratio is 15:1. Full-time: 813 students, 61% women, 39% men. Part-time: 967 students, 62% women, 38% men. Students come from 8 states and territories, 5 other countries, 1% from out-of-state. 0.3% American Indian or Alaska Native, non-Hispanic/Latino; 13% Hispanic/Latino; 7% African American, non-Hispanic/Latino; 2% Asian, non-Hispanic/Latino; 0% Native Hawaiian or other Pacific Islander, non-Hispanic/Latino; 0.4% international. 61% 25 or older, 24% transferred in. Academic areas with the most degrees conferred: business/marketing; social sciences; psychology. Core. Calendar: semesters. Services for LD students, honors program, independent study, distance learning, double major, summer session for credit, part-time degree program, co-op programs and internships. Study abroad program.

Costs Per Year: State resident tuition: $5519 full-time, $184 per credit part-time. Nonresident tuition: $15,442 full-time, $515 per credit part-time. Mandatory fees: $10 full-time, $5 per term part-time. Full-time tuition and fees vary according to course load and program. Part-time tuition and fees vary according to course load and program.

Collegiate Environment: Orientation program. Social organizations: 28 open to all. Most popular organizations: Accounting Society, USF Sarasota-Manatee Sharing Math, Promoting Recruiting Increasing Diverse Educators, Phi Beta Lambda, Finance Club. Major annual events: Week of Welcome, USF Spirit Week, Get on The Bus. Student services: health clinic, personal-psychological counseling. Campus security: 24-hour emergency response devices and patrols, late night transport-escort service. Jane Bancroft Cook Library with 2.5 million books, 727,000 microform titles, 24,700 serials, 1,748 audiovisual materials, an OPAC, and a Web page. Operations spending for the previous fiscal year: $759,406. 45 computers available on campus for general student use. Computer purchase/lease plans available. A campuswide network can be accessed from off-campus. Students can access the following: online class registration. Staffed computer lab on campus provides training in use of computers, software, and the Internet.

■ **UNIVERSITY OF SOUTH FLORIDA–ST. PETERSBURG CAMPUS**
140 Seventh Ave. S
Saint Petersburg, FL 33701
Tel: (727)873-4873
E-mail: admissions@usfsp.edu
Web Site: www.stpt.usf.edu/

Description: State-supported, comprehensive, coed. Part of University of South Florida System. Awards bachelor's and master's degrees. Founded 1965. Setting: 50-acre urban campus with easy access to Tampa. Total enrollment: 4,391. Faculty: 255 (144 full-time, 111 part-time). Student-undergrad faculty ratio is 13:1. Full-time: 2,542 students, 60% women, 40% men. Part-time: 1,383 students, 60% women, 40% men. Students come from 28 states and territories, 2% from out-of-state. 0.3% American Indian or Alaska Native, non-Hispanic/Latino; 12% Hispanic/Latino; 7% African American, non-Hispanic/Latino; 4% Asian, non-Hispanic/Latino; 0.3% Native Hawaiian or other Pacific Islander, non-Hispanic/Latino; 0.5% international. 30% 25 or older, 16% transferred in. Retention: 68% of full-time freshmen returned the following year. Academic areas with the most degrees conferred: business/marketing; social sciences; psychology. Core. Calendar: semesters. Services for LD students, freshman honors college, honors program, independent study, distance learning, double major, summer session for credit, internships, graduate courses open to undergrads. Study abroad program. ROTC: Army.

Entrance Requirements: Required: high school transcript, minimum 2.5 high school GPA, SAT or ACT.

Costs Per Year: State resident tuition: $5189 full-time, $172.96 per credit hour part-time. Nonresident tuition: $14,377 full-time, $392.24 per credit hour part-time. Mandatory fees: $10 full-time. College room only: $7570.

Collegiate Environment: Orientation program. Student-run newspaper. Social organizations: 100 open to all. Major annual events: Welcome Week, Spring Fling, Leadership Retreats. Student services: personal-psychological counseling. Campus security: 24-hour emergency response devices and patrols, late night transport-escort service, controlled dormitory access. Nelson Poynter Memorial Library with 236,793 books, 919,481 microform titles, 52,812 serials, 9,337 audiovisual materials, an OPAC, and a Web page. 125 computers available on campus for general student use. Computer purchase/lease plans available. A campuswide network can be accessed from student residence rooms and from off campus. Students can access the following: online class registration. Staffed computer lab on campus.

■ **THE UNIVERSITY OF TAMPA**
401 W Kennedy Blvd.
Tampa, FL 33606-1490
Tel: (813)253-3333; Free: 888-MINARET
Fax: (813)254-4955
E-mail: admissions@ut.edu
Web Site: www.ut.edu/

Description: Independent, comprehensive, coed. Awards associate, bachelor's, and master's degrees and post-master's certificates. Founded 1931. Setting: 100-acre urban campus with easy access to Tampa-St. Petersburg, Clearwater. Total enrollment: 6,912. Faculty: 564 (263 full-time, 301 part-time). Student-undergrad faculty ratio is 16:1. 14,704 applied, 59% were admitted. 18% from top 10% of their high school class, 46% from top quarter, 85% from top half. Full-time: 5,799 students, 56% women, 44% men. Part-time: 344 students, 55% women, 45% men. Students come from 50 states and territories, 122 other countries, 63% from out-of-state. 0.1% American Indian or Alaska Native, non-Hispanic/Latino; 11% Hispanic/Latino; 6% African American, non-Hispanic/Latino; 1% Asian, non-Hispanic/Latino; 0.2% Native Hawaiian or other Pacific Islander, non-Hispanic/Latino; 10% international. 7% 25 or older, 60% live on campus, 7% transferred in. Retention: 74% of full-time freshmen returned the following year. Academic areas with the most degrees conferred: business/marketing; communication/journalism; social sciences. Core. Calendar: semesters. Academic remediation for entering students, ESL program, services for LD students, advanced placement, honors program, independent study, double major, summer session for credit, part-time degree program, adult/continuing education programs, co-op programs and internships. Study abroad program. ROTC: Army, Naval (c), Air Force (c).

Entrance Requirements: Options: electronic application, early admission, early action, deferred admission, international baccalaureate accepted. Required: essay, high school transcript, minimum 2 high school GPA, SAT or ACT. Recommended: interview. Required for some: 1 recommendation. Entrance: moderately difficult. Application deadlines: Rolling, Rolling for nonresidents, 5/1 for early action. Notification: continuous, continuous for nonresidents, 12/15 for early action. Transfer credits accepted: Yes. Applicants placed on waiting list: 1,789. Early action applicants: 11,901. Early action applicants admitted: 5,036.

Costs Per Year: Application fee: $40. One-time mandatory fee: $85. Comprehensive fee: $34,338 includes full-time tuition ($23,520), mandatory fees ($1702), and college room and board ($9116). College room only: $4852. Full-time tuition and fees vary according to class time. Room and board charges vary according to board plan and housing facility. Part-time tuition: $500 per credit hour. Part-time mandatory fees: $40 per term. Part-time tuition and fees vary according to class time.

Collegiate Environment: Orientation program. Drama-theater group, choral group, student-run newspaper, radio station. Social organizations: 160 open to all; national fraternities, national sororities; 11% of eligible men and 20% of eligible women are members. Most popular organizations: Greek Life, student government, PEACE (volunteer organization), Student Productions, Minaret. Major annual events: Student Productions Major Concert, Homecoming game, Greek Sing. Student services: health clinic, personal-psychological counseling, women's center. Campus security: 24-hour emergency response devices and patrols, student patrols, late night transport-escort service, controlled dormitory access. 3,656 college housing spaces available; all were occupied in 2012-13. No special consideration for freshman housing applicants. Option: coed housing available. Macdonald Kelce Library with 243,334 books, 65,230 microform titles, 56,220 serials, 11,309 audiovisual materials, an OPAC, and a Web page. 800 computers available on campus for general student use. Computer purchase/lease plans available. A campuswide network can be accessed from student residence rooms and from off campus. Students can access the following: online class registration. Staffed computer lab on campus (open 24 hours a day) provides training in use of computers, software, and the Internet.

Community Environment: The university is situated along the Hillsborough River adjacent to the downtown area of Tampa, Florida. The city of Tampa (population 326,000) is part of the Tampa Bay metropolitan area of over 2 million. This rapidly growing area is a business and resort center featuring year-round sunshine with school year temperatures averaging 60-80 degrees Fahrenheit and excellent job prospects. Tampa's ultramodern international airport is just 15 minutes from campus. The city is easily accessible by interstate highway, bus or rail. Tampa is 30 minutes from the beaches of the Gulf of Mexico and 60 minutes from Central Florida's parks and amusement areas such as Walt Disney World.

■ **UNIVERSITY OF WEST FLORIDA**
11000 University Pky.
Pensacola, FL 32514-5750
Tel: (850)474-2000; Free: 800-263-1074
Fax: (850)474-2096
E-mail: admissions@uwf.edu
Web Site: www.uwf.edu/

Description: State-supported, comprehensive, coed. Part of State University System of Florida. Awards associate, bachelor's, master's, and doctoral degrees and post-master's certificates. Founded 1963. Setting: 1,600-acre suburban campus. Endowment: $49.2 million. Research spending for the previous fiscal year: $14.7 million. Educational spending for the previous fiscal year: $4785 per student. Total enrollment: 12,651. Faculty: 603 (314 full-time, 289 part-time). Student-undergrad faculty ratio is 23:1. 13,623 applied, 61% were admitted. 9% from top 10% of their high school class, 35% from top quarter, 76% from top half. Full-time: 7,559 students, 57% women, 43% men. Part-time: 2,773 students, 58% women, 42% men. Students come from 50 states and territories, 92 other countries, 9% from out-of-state. 1% American Indian or Alaska Native, non-Hispanic/Latino; 8% Hispanic/Latino; 12% African American, non-Hispanic/Latino; 3% Asian, non-Hispanic/Latino; 0.4% Native Hawaiian or other Pacific Islander, non-Hispanic/Latino; 2% international. 28% 25 or older, 20% live on campus, 12% transferred in. Retention: 70% of full-time freshmen returned the following year. Academic areas with the most degrees conferred: business/marketing; health professions and related sciences; communication/journalism. Core. Calendar: semesters. ESL program, services for LD students, advanced placement, honors program, independent study, distance learning, summer session for credit, part-time degree program, co-op programs and internships, graduate courses open to undergrads. Off campus study at other members of the State University System of Florida. Study abroad program. ROTC: Army, Air Force.

Entrance Requirements: Options: electronic application, early admission, deferred admission, international baccalaureate accepted. Required: high school transcript, minimum 2 high school GPA, SAT or ACT, SAT and SAT Subject Tests or ACT. Entrance: moderately difficult. Application deadline: 6/30. Notification: continuous. Preference given to applicants with associate degrees from Florida public junior colleges. SAT Reasoning Test deadline: 6/30. SAT Subject Test deadline: 6/30.

Costs Per Year: Application fee: $30. State resident tuition: $5072 full-time, $207.95 per semester hour part-time. Nonresident tuition: $17,954 full-time, $637.34 per semester hour part-time. Mandatory fees: $1950 full-time, $207.95 per semester hour part-time. Full-time tuition and fees vary according to location and reciprocity agreements. Part-time tuition and fees vary according to location and reciprocity agreements. College room and board: $9210. Room and board charges vary according to housing facility.

Collegiate Environment: Orientation program. Drama-theater group, choral group, student-run newspaper. Social organizations: 220 open to all; national fraternities, national sororities, local sororities; 5% of eligible men and 5% of eligible women are members. Most popular organizations: Marketing Association, Student Council for Exceptional Children, Inter-Varsity Christian Fellowship, Baptist Student Ministry, Golden Key Honor Society. Major annual events: Homecoming, Exam Jam, Love Fest (Valentine's celebration). Student services: health clinic, personal-psychological counseling. Campus security: 24-hour emergency response devices and patrols, student patrols, late night transport-escort service, controlled dormitory access. 1,850 college housing spaces available; all were occupied in 2012-13. No special consideration for freshman housing applicants. Option: coed housing available. John C. Pace Library plus 2 others with 510,494 books, 1.7 million microform titles, 6,715 serials, 7,018 audiovisual materials, an OPAC, and a Web page. Operations spending for the previous fiscal year: $3.3 million. 1,067 computers available on campus for general student use. Computer purchase/lease plans available. A campuswide network can be accessed from student residence rooms and from off campus. Students can access the following: online class registration. Staffed computer lab on campus provides training in use of computers, software, and the Internet.

Community Environment: Pensacola is Florida's westernmost metropolitan area, situated approximately 50 miles east of Mobile, Alabama. A mild climate and more than 200 miles of Gulf and bay shoreline combine to produce an environment perfect for outdoor recreation. Pensacola is the home of the largest naval air training facility in the United States and of Florida's largest industrial plant. Boating, skin diving, swimming, surfing, and sailing are among the numerous water-related sports enjoyed practically year-round. More than 20 miles of Pensacola Beach are within the confines of the National Seashore, including historic Fort Pickens. Numerous museums and related facilities provide amateur historians with a wealth of exploring. The U.S. Naval Air Training museum provides a historical compendium of naval aviation in the United States. Such annual events as the Fiesta of Five Flags, the Gulf Coast Fine Arts Festival and the West Florida Music Festival draw thousands of people annually.

■ VALENCIA COLLEGE
PO Box 3028
Orlando, FL 32802-3028
Tel: (407)299-5000
E-mail: rsimpson@valenciacollege.edu
Web Site: valenciacollege.edu/

Description: State-supported, 4-year, coed. Part of Florida College System. Awards associate and bachelor's degrees. Founded 1967. Setting: 629-acre urban campus with easy access to Orlando. Endowment: $55.6 million. Educational spending for the previous fiscal year: $2643 per student. Total enrollment: 42,915. Faculty: 1,602 (400 full-time, 1,202 part-time). Student-undergrad faculty ratio is 16:1. 11,235 applied, 90% were admitted. Full-time: 16,998 students, 54% women, 46% men. Part-time: 25,917 students, 58% women, 42% men. Students come from 59 other countries, 3% from out-of-state. 0.3% American Indian or Alaska Native, non-Hispanic/Latino; 31% Hispanic/Latino; 17% African American, non-Hispanic/Latino; 4% Asian, non-Hispanic/Latino; 0.4% Native Hawaiian or other Pacific Islander, non-Hispanic/Latino; 1% international. 37% 25 or older, 9% transferred in. Retention: 65% of full-time freshmen returned the following year. Core. Calendar: semesters. Academic remediation for entering students, ESL program, services for LD students, advanced placement, accelerated degree program, freshman honors college, honors program, independent study, distance learning, double major, summer session for credit, part-time degree program, external degree program, adult/continuing education programs, co-op programs and internships. Study abroad program. ROTC: Army (c), Naval (c).

Entrance Requirements: Open admission Selective admissions for high school dual enrollment, The Criminal Justice Institute, Dance Performance, Film Production, Allied Health Sciences programs and Bachelor's programs. Options: electronic application, early admission, deferred admission, international baccalaureate accepted. Required: $35 Application fee for lower level (1000 and 2000 level courses) students and $50 application fee for Bachelor level students. Required for some: high school transcript. Application deadlines: 8/12, 8/12 for nonresidents. Transfer credits accepted: Yes.

Costs Per Year: Application fee: $35. State resident tuition: $2377 full-time, $99.06 per credit part-time. Nonresident tuition: $9005 full-time, $375.22 per credit part-time. Full-time tuition varies according to course level, degree level, and program. Part-time tuition varies according to course level, degree level, and program.

Collegiate Environment: Orientation program. Drama-theater group, choral group, student-run newspaper. Social organizations: Honors Society, Phi Theta Kappa. Student services: legal services, personal-psychological counseling. Campus security: 24-hour emergency response devices and patrols, student patrols, late night transport-escort service. College housing not available. Learning Resources Center plus 4 others with 183,323 books, 41,380 serials, 18,271 audiovisual materials, an OPAC, and a Web page. Operations spending for the previous fiscal year: $2.9 million.

Community Environment: See University of Central Florida.

■ WARNER UNIVERSITY
13895 US Hwy. 27
Lake Wales, FL 33859

Tel: (863)638-1426; Free: 800-309-9563
E-mail: admissions@warner.edu
Web Site: www.warner.edu/

Description: Independent, comprehensive, coed, affiliated with Church of God. Awards associate, bachelor's, and master's degrees. Founded 1968. Setting: 320-acre rural campus with easy access to Tampa, Orlando. Endowment: $3 million. Educational spending for the previous fiscal year: $3468 per student. Total enrollment: 970. Faculty: 99 (35 full-time, 64 part-time). Student-undergrad faculty ratio is 16:1. 391 applied, 58% were admitted. 10% from top 10% of their high school class, 30% from top quarter, 66% from top half. 1 National Merit Scholar. Full-time: 778 students, 57% women, 43% men. Part-time: 143 students, 62% women, 38% men. Students come from 27 states and territories, 17 other countries, 13% from out-of-state. 46% 25 or older, 41% live on campus, 8% transferred in. Retention: 57% of full-time freshmen returned the following year. Academic areas with the most degrees conferred: business/marketing; education; theology and religious vocations. Core. Calendar: semesters. Academic remediation for entering students, ESL program, advanced placement, accelerated degree program, independent study, distance learning, double major, summer session for credit, part-time degree program, adult/continuing education programs, internships. Study abroad program.

Entrance Requirements: Options: electronic application, deferred admission. Required: high school transcript, minimum 2.25 high school GPA, 1 recommendation, SAT or ACT. Recommended: essay. Required for some: interview. Entrance: minimally difficult. Application deadline: Rolling. Notification: continuous.

Costs Per Year: Application fee: $20. One-time mandatory fee: $50. Comprehensive fee: $25,202 includes full-time tuition ($17,480), mandatory fees ($300), and college room and board ($7422). College room only: $3636. Full-time tuition and fees vary according to course load, degree level, and program. Room and board charges vary according to board plan and housing facility. Part-time tuition: $335 per credit hour. Part-time mandatory fees: $25 per term. Part-time tuition and fees vary according to course load, degree level, and program.

Collegiate Environment: Orientation program. Choral group, student-run newspaper. Social organizations: 4 open to all. Most popular organizations: concert choir, Fellowship of Christian Athletes, Young Americans, Student Government Association. Major annual events: Spring Banquet, Warner Weekend. Student services: health clinic, personal-psychological counseling. Campus security: 24-hour emergency response devices and patrols, late night transport-escort service, controlled dormitory access. Pontious Learning Resource Center with 56,419 books, 8,140 microform titles, 224 serials, 14,935 audiovisual materials, an OPAC, and a Web page. Operations spending for the previous fiscal year: $336,106. 75 computers available on campus for general student use. A campuswide network can be accessed. Staffed computer lab on campus.

Community Environment: See Webber College.

■ WEBBER INTERNATIONAL UNIVERSITY
PO Box 96, 1200 N Scenic Hwy.
Babson Park, FL 33827-0096
Tel: (863)638-1431; Free: 800-741-1844
Fax: (863)638-2823
E-mail: admissions@webber.edu
Web Site: www.webber.edu/

Description: Independent, comprehensive, coed. Awards associate, bachelor's, and master's degrees. Founded 1927. Setting: 110-acre small town campus with easy access to Orlando. Endowment: $4.4 million. Total enrollment: 717. Faculty: 43 (20 full-time, 23 part-time). Student-undergrad faculty ratio is 22:1. 586 applied, 69% were admitted. 5% from top 10% of their high school class, 15% from top quarter, 50% from top half. Full-time: 628 students, 32% women, 68% men. Part-time: 27 students, 41% women, 59% men. 8% from out-of-state. 0.2% American Indian or Alaska Native, non-Hispanic/Latino; 9% Hispanic/Latino; 24% African American, non-Hispanic/Latino; 1% Asian, non-Hispanic/Latino; 24% international. 30% 25 or older, 52% live on campus, 0% transferred in. Retention: 52% of full-time freshmen returned the following year. Academic areas with the most degrees conferred: business/marketing; parks and recreation; communication/journalism. Core. Calendar: semesters. Academic remediation for entering students, ESL program, services for LD students, advanced placement, accelerated degree program, distance learning, double major, summer session for credit, part-time degree program, adult/continuing education programs, co-op programs and internships. Study abroad program.

Entrance Requirements: Options: electronic application, early action, international baccalaureate accepted. Required: high school transcript, minimum 2 high school GPA, SAT or ACT. Recommended: essay. Required for some: interview. Entrance: moderately difficult. Application deadlines: 8/1, 4/1 for early action.

Costs Per Year: Application fee: $35. Comprehensive fee: $28,318 includes full-time tuition ($20,418) and college room and board ($7900). College room only: $5072. Full-time tuition varies according to class time and course load. Room and board charges vary according to board plan, gender, and housing facility. Part-time tuition: $294 per credit hour. Part-time tuition varies according to course load.

Collegiate Environment: Orientation program. Marching band, student-run newspaper. Social organizations: 10 open to all. Most popular organizations: Student Leadership Association, Phi Beta Lambda, Society of International Students, Fellowship of Christian Athletes, Marketing Club. Major annual events: Homecoming, Halloween Party, Beach Party. Student services: health clinic, personal-psychological counseling. Campus security: 24-hour emergency response devices and patrols, late night transport-escort service,

controlled dormitory access. 352 college housing spaces available; all were occupied in 2012-13. Freshmen guaranteed college housing. On-campus residence required in freshman year. Options: men-only, women-only housing available. Grace and Roger Babson Library with 15,000 books, 11 serials, 106 audiovisual materials, and an OPAC. Operations spending for the previous fiscal year: $127,345. 89 computers available on campus for general student use. A campuswide network can be accessed from off-campus.

■ **YESHIVA GEDOLAH RABBINICAL COLLEGE**
1140 Alton Rd.
Miami Beach, FL 33139
Tel: (305)673-5664
Fax: (305)532-9820
Description: Independent Jewish, comprehensive, men only. Awards bachelor's and master's degrees. Total enrollment: 47.
Entrance Requirements: Open admission.

■ **ABRAHAM BALDWIN AGRICULTURAL COLLEGE**
2802 Moore Hwy.
Tifton, GA 31793
Tel: (229)391-5001; Free: 800-733-3653
Fax: (229)386-7006
E-mail: dwebb@abac.edu
Web Site: www.abac.edu/
Description: State-supported, 4-year, coed. Part of University System of Georgia. Awards associate and bachelor's degrees. Founded 1933. Setting: 421-acre small town campus. Endowment: $7.5 million. Educational spending for the previous fiscal year: $3626 per student. Total enrollment: 3,327. Faculty: 162 (94 full-time, 68 part-time). Student-undergrad faculty ratio is 24:1. 2,927 applied, 79% were admitted. 8% from top 10% of their high school class, 23% from top quarter, 43% from top half. Full-time: 2,475 students, 50% women, 50% men. Part-time: 852 students, 67% women, 33% men. Students come from 17 states and territories, 11 other countries, 2% from out-of-state. 18% 25 or older, 32% live on campus, 18% transferred in. Retention: 67% of full-time freshmen returned the following year. Academic area with the most degrees conferred: agriculture. Core. Calendar: semesters. Academic remediation for entering students, services for LD students, advanced placement, honors program, double major, summer session for credit, part-time degree program, internships. Off campus study at East Central Technical College (ECTC), Moultrie Technical College (MTC). Study abroad program.
Entrance Requirements: Open admission. Options: electronic application, early admission, deferred admission. Required: high school transcript. Required for some: minimum high school GPA of 2.0 for College Prep Diploma and 2.2 for Tech Prep Diploma. Entrance: noncompetitive.
Costs Per Year: Application fee: $20. State resident tuition: $2846 full-time. Nonresident tuition: $10,514 full-time. Mandatory fees: $1002 full-time. College room and board: $7117. College room only: $4547.
Collegiate Environment: Orientation program. Drama-theater group, choral group, student-run newspaper, radio station. Social organizations: 40 open to all; national fraternities, Kappa Sigma and Alpha Gamma Rho. Most popular organizations: Campus Activities Board, Baptist Collegiate Ministry, Forestry/Wildlife Club, Agriculture Engineering Technology, Residence Hall Association. Major annual events: Welcome Week, George Scott Day. Student services: health clinic, personal-psychological counseling. Campus security: 24-hour emergency response devices and patrols, controlled dormitory access. Baldwin Library with 72,149 books, 164 serials, 1,664 audiovisual materials, an OPAC, and a Web page. Operations spending for the previous fiscal year: $399,149.
Community Environment: A rural area between Macon and Valdosta having a temperate climate. All modes of transportation serve the area. Scheduled airlines are nearby at Moultrie and Albany. Tifton is an agricultural area; plants are grown here and then sent north for transplanting. Other products are tobacco, cotton, peanuts, melons, commercial grasses and livestock. Part and full-time employment is good. Recreational activities include hunting, tennis, golf, swimming and other water sports.

■ **AGNES SCOTT COLLEGE**
141 E College Ave.
Decatur, GA 30030-3797
Tel: (404)471-6000; Free: 800-868-8602
Fax: (404)471-6414
E-mail: admission@agnesscott.edu

Web Site: www.agnesscott.edu/
Description: Independent, 4-year, affiliated with Presbyterian Church (U.S. A.). Awards bachelor's degrees. Founded 1889. Setting: 100-acre urban campus with easy access to Atlanta. Endowment: $239.3 million. Research spending for the previous fiscal year: $51,170. Educational spending for the previous fiscal year: $892 per student. Total enrollment: 885. Faculty: 89 (70 full-time, 19 part-time). Student-undergrad faculty ratio is 11:1. 1,554 applied, 62% were admitted. 39% from top 10% of their high school class, 69% from top quarter, 92% from top half. Full-time: 869 students, 99% women, 1% men. Part-time: 16 students, 100% women. Students come from 43 states and territories, 29 other countries, 37% from out-of-state. 0% American Indian or Alaska Native, non-Hispanic/Latino; 8% Hispanic/Latino; 35% African American, non-Hispanic/Latino; 3% Asian, non-Hispanic/Latino; 0% Native Hawaiian or other Pacific Islander, non-Hispanic/Latino; 9% international. 4% 25 or older, 85% live on campus, 1% transferred in. Retention: 82% of full-time freshmen returned the following year. Academic areas with the most degrees conferred: social sciences; psychology; English. Core. Calendar: semesters. Services for LD students, advanced placement, accelerated degree program, self-designed majors, independent study, double major, summer session for credit, part-time degree program, adult/continuing education programs, internships. Off campus study at Mills College, American University, members of Atlanta Regional Consortium for Higher Education and Public Leadership Education Network. Study abroad program. ROTC: Army (c), Air Force (c).
Entrance Requirements: Options: electronic application, early admission, early action, deferred admission, international baccalaureate accepted. Required: essay, high school transcript, 2 recommendations, SAT or ACT scores or graded writing sample, home-schooled students must submit SAT or ACT. Recommended: interview. Required for some: SAT and SAT Subject Tests or ACT. Entrance: very difficult. Application deadlines: 3/1, 11/15 for early action. Notification: 12/15 for early action. SAT Subject Test deadline: 12/31. Transfer credits accepted: Yes. Applicants placed on waiting list: 0. Early action applicants: 550. Early action applicants admitted: 396.
Costs Per Year: Application fee: $35. Comprehensive fee: $45,321 includes full-time tuition ($34,546), mandatory fees ($240), and college room and board ($10,535). Full-time tuition and fees vary according to course load. Room and board charges vary according to board plan and housing facility.
Collegiate Environment: Orientation program. Drama-theater group, choral group, marching band, student-run newspaper. Social organizations: 86 open to all. Most popular organizations: Programming Board, Witkaze (African-American Student organization), Student Senate, ASC-TV, International Students Association. Major annual events: Black Cat, Agnes Scott Writers' Festival, Spring Annual Research Conference (SpARC). Student services: health clinic, personal-psychological counseling. Campus security: 24-hour emergency response devices and patrols, late night transport-escort service, controlled dormitory access, security systems in apartments, public safety facility, surveillance equipment, key required for residence hall entry. 795 college housing spaces available; 724 were occupied in 2012-13. Freshmen guaranteed college housing. On-campus residence required through senior year. Option: women-only housing available. McCain Library with 236,819 books, 41,122 serials, 26,755 audiovisual materials, an OPAC, and a Web page. 458 computers available on campus for general student use. A campuswide network can be accessed from student residence rooms and from off campus. Students can access the following: online class registration. Staffed computer lab on campus (open 24 hours a day) provides training in use of software.

Community Environment: See Clark Atlanta University.

■ **ALBANY STATE UNIVERSITY**
504 College Dr.
Albany, GA 31705-2717
Tel: (229)430-4600; Free: 866-579-3498
Fax: (229)430-3936
E-mail: enrollmentservices@asurams.edu
Web Site: www.asurams.edu/
Description: State-supported, comprehensive, coed. Part of University System of Georgia. Awards bachelor's and master's degrees and post-master's certificates. Founded 1903. Setting: 232-acre urban campus. Endowment: $1.5 million. Research spending for the previous fiscal year: $1.7 million. Educational spending for the previous fiscal year: $5048 per student. Total enrollment: 4,663. Faculty: 270 (164 full-time, 106 part-time). Student-undergrad faculty ratio is 21:1. 6,554 applied, 29% were admitted. 10% from top 10% of their high school class, 30% from top quarter, 67% from top half. Full-time: 3,662 students, 65% women, 35% men. Part-time: 525 students, 78% women, 22% men. Students come from 32 states and territories, 18 other countries, 4% from out-of-state. 0.1% American Indian or Alaska Native, non-Hispanic/Latino; 1% Hispanic/Latino; 83% African American, non-Hispanic/Latino; 0.1% Asian, non-Hispanic/Latino; 0.02% Native Hawaiian or other Pacific Islander, non-Hispanic/Latino; 0.3% international. 25% 25 or older, 43% live on campus, 6% transferred in. Retention: 65% of full-time freshmen returned the following year. Academic areas with the most degrees conferred: education; business/marketing; homeland security, law enforcement, firefighting, and protective services. Core. Calendar: semesters. Academic remediation for entering students, services for LD students, advanced placement, honors program, independent study, distance learning, double major, summer session for credit, part-time degree program, co-op programs and internships, graduate courses open to undergrads. Off campus study at Abraham Baldwin Agricultural College, Bainbridge College, Waycross College. Study abroad program. ROTC: Army.
Entrance Requirements: Options: electronic application, early admission, deferred admission, international baccalaureate accepted. Required: high school transcript, minimum 2.22 high school GPA, SAT or ACT. Required for some: COMPASS Test. Entrance: minimally difficult. Application deadlines: 6/1, 6/1 for nonresidents. Notification: continuous, continuous for nonresidents. SAT Reasoning Test deadline: 8/1. Transfer credits accepted: Yes.
Costs Per Year: Application fee: $20. State resident tuition: $4512 full-time. Nonresident tuition: $16,416 full-time. Mandatory fees: $1400 full-time. Full-time tuition and fees vary according to course load and degree level. College room and board: $7388. College room only: $2734. Room and board charges vary according to board plan and housing facility.
Collegiate Environment: Orientation program. Drama-theater group, choral group, marching band, student-run newspaper, radio station. Social organizations: 50 open to all; national fraternities, national sororities; 28% of eligible men and 20% of eligible women are members. Most popular organizations: ASU Anointed Gospel Choir, ASU Pan-Hellenic Council (Greeks), Peer Educators, SIFE (Students In Free Enterprise), Student Government Association. Major annual events: Homecoming Week/Convocation, SGA Leadership Conference, Founder's Day/Collegiate Relay for Life. Student services: health clinic, personal-psychological counseling. Campus security: 24-hour emergency response devices and patrols, late night transport-escort service, controlled dormitory access, Connect Ed.-Emergency E-mail, Emergency sirens, Active Shooter Team, Certified Police Officers. James Pendergrast Memorial Library with 201,063 books, 800,831 microform titles, 327 serials, 2,805 audiovisual materials, an OPAC, and a Web page. Operations spending for the previous fiscal year: $1 million.
Community Environment: The campus is situated in a progressive community that affords a variety of advantages. Albany is located on the Flint River. Air transportation is accessible at the Southwest Georgia Regional Airport. The Marine Corps Supply Center is located here. Albany's economy is broadly based on agriculture, manufacturing, and business from the nearby military bases. The most notable industry is the production of papershell pecans; more than 700,000 pecan trees cover 60,000 acres in the vicinity. The Spanish peanut industry and other diversified businesses and farming contribute to the city's high rating in retail sales. Part-time employment is available. Radium Springs, four miles south, has the largest natural spring in the state.

■ **ALBANY TECHNICAL COLLEGE**
1704 S Slappey Blvd.
Albany, GA 31701

Tel: (229)430-3500; Free: 877-261-3113
Fax: (229)430-5155
E-mail: ldejesus@albanytech.edu
Web Site: www.albanytech.edu/
Description: State-supported, 2-year, coed. Part of Technical College System of Georgia. Awards certificates, diplomas, and terminal associate degrees. Founded 1961. Total enrollment: 3,935. Full-time: 2,198 students, 61% women, 39% men. Part-time: 1,737 students, 61% women, 39% men. 0.4% from out-of-state. 0.3% American Indian or Alaska Native, non-Hispanic/Latino; 1% Hispanic/Latino; 78% African American, non-Hispanic/Latino; 0.2% Asian, non-Hispanic/Latino; 0.2% Native Hawaiian or other Pacific Islander, non-Hispanic/Latino; 0% international. 64% 25 or older. Retention: 76% of full-time freshmen returned the following year. Distance learning.
Entrance Requirements: Open admission selective admission to some programs. Option: early admission. Required: high school transcript. Entrance: noncompetitive.
Collegiate Environment: College housing not available.

■ **ALTAMAHA TECHNICAL COLLEGE**
1777 W Cherry St.
Jesup, GA 31545
Tel: (912)427-5800; Free: 800-645-8284
Fax: (912)427-5823
E-mail: cjeancake@altamahatech.edu
Web Site: www.altamahatech.edu/
Description: State-supported, 2-year, coed. Part of Technical College System of Georgia. Awards certificates, diplomas, and terminal associate degrees. Total enrollment: 1,405. Full-time: 391 students, 56% women, 44% men. Part-time: 1,014 students, 55% women, 45% men. 0% from out-of-state. 0.3% American Indian or Alaska Native, non-Hispanic/Latino; 6% Hispanic/Latino; 27% African American, non-Hispanic/Latino; 1% Asian, non-Hispanic/Latino; 1% Native Hawaiian or other Pacific Islander, non-Hispanic/Latino; 0% international. 55% 25 or older. Retention: 72% of full-time freshmen returned the following year. Distance learning.
Entrance Requirements: Open admission selective admission to some programs. Option: early admission. Required: high school transcript. Entrance: noncompetitive.
Collegiate Environment: College housing not available.

■ **AMERICAN INTERCONTINENTAL UNIVERSITY ATLANTA**
6600 Peachtree-Dunwoody Rd.
500 Embassy Row
Atlanta, GA 30328
Tel: (404)965-6500; Free: 800-353-1744
Fax: (404)965-6501
Web Site: www.aiuniv.edu/
Description: Proprietary, comprehensive, coed. Administratively affiliated with American InterContinental University. Awards associate, bachelor's, and master's degrees. Founded 1970. Setting: 2-acre urban campus. Total enrollment: 585. Faculty: 55. Full-time: 315 students, 56% women, 44% men. Part-time: 119 students, 69% women, 31% men. 47% 25 or older, 10% transferred in. Academic areas with the most degrees conferred: business/marketing; homeland security, law enforcement, firefighting, and protective services; computer and information sciences. Core. Academic remediation for entering students, accelerated degree program, distance learning, part-time degree program, adult/continuing education programs, co-op programs.
Entrance Requirements: Options: electronic application, deferred admission, international baccalaureate accepted. Required: essay, high school transcript, interview. Application deadline: Rolling. Notification: continuous.
Collegiate Environment: Orientation program.

■ **ANDREW COLLEGE**
501 College St.
Cuthbert, GA 39840
Tel: (229)732-2171; Free: 800-664-9250
Fax: (229)732-2176
E-mail: admissions@andrewcollege.edu
Web Site: www.andrewcollege.edu/
Description: Independent United Methodist, 2-year, coed. Awards certificates and transfer associate degrees. Founded 1854. Setting: 40-acre rural campus. Faculty: 22 (17 full-time, 5 part-time). Student-undergrad faculty ratio is 12:1. Students come from 13 other countries. 1% 25 or older. Core. Calendar: semesters. Academic remediation for entering students,

ESL program, services for LD students, advanced placement, honors program, summer session for credit, part-time degree program.

Entrance Requirements: Options: electronic application, early admission, deferred admission. Required: high school transcript, SAT or ACT. Recommended: minimum 2 high school GPA. Required for some: essay, 1 recommendation, interview. Entrance: moderately difficult. Application deadline: 8/15.

Collegiate Environment: Orientation program. Drama-theater group, choral group. Campus security: 24-hour patrols, controlled dormitory access, campus police. Pitts Library with 40,000 books and 100 serials. 50 computers available on campus for general student use. A campuswide network can be accessed from student residence rooms and from off campus. Staffed computer lab on campus provides training in use of computers.

Community Environment: Cuthbert is a rural community 40 miles from Albany, and 55 miles from Columbus. Its climate is ideal. Airline services are available one hour away. Part-time employment exists for students. Community facilities include a library, churches, and good shopping. A public recreation center, two swimming pools, golf course and nearby lakes provide facilities for fishing, boating and water skiing.

■ **ANTHEM COLLEGE–ATLANTA**
2450 Piedmont Rd. NE
Atlanta, GA 30324
Free: 855-268-4360
E-mail: ckusema@hightechschools.com
Web Site: anthem.edu/atlanta-georgia/
Description: Proprietary, 2-year, coed. Awards terminal associate degrees. Founded 2010. Calendar: semesters.

■ **ARGOSY UNIVERSITY, ATLANTA**
980 Hammond Dr.
Ste. 100
Atlanta, GA 30328
Tel: (770)671-1200; Free: 888-671-4777
Fax: (770)671-0476
Web Site: www.argosy.edu/atlanta/
Description: Proprietary, university, coed. Part of Education Management Corporation. Awards bachelor's, master's, and doctoral degrees and post-master's certificates. Founded 1990. Setting: suburban campus. Calendar: semesters.

■ **ARMSTRONG ATLANTIC STATE UNIVERSITY**
11935 Abercorn St.
Savannah, GA 31419-1997
Tel: (912)927-5211; Free: 800-633-2349
Fax: (912)921-5462
E-mail: adm-info@mail.armstrong.edu
Web Site: www.armstrong.edu/
Description: State-supported, comprehensive, coed. Part of University System of Georgia. Awards associate, bachelor's, master's, and doctoral degrees and post-master's certificates. Founded 1935. Setting: 267-acre suburban campus. Endowment: $9 million. Research spending for the previous fiscal year: $66,643. Educational spending for the previous fiscal year: $4730 per student. Total enrollment: 7,439. Faculty: 424 (258 full-time, 166 part-time). Student-undergrad faculty ratio is 19:1. 2,790 applied, 70% were admitted. Full-time: 4,839 students, 65% women, 35% men. Part-time: 1,892 students, 65% women, 35% men. Students come from 43 states and territories, 67 other countries, 11% from out-of-state. 0.3% American Indian or Alaska Native, non-Hispanic/Latino; 6% Hispanic/Latino; 23% African American, non-Hispanic/Latino; 3% Asian, non-Hispanic/Latino; 0.2% Native Hawaiian or other Pacific Islander, non-Hispanic/Latino; 2% international. 30% 25 or older, 20% live on campus, 9% transferred in. Retention: 69% of full-time freshmen returned the following year. Academic areas with the most degrees conferred: health professions and related sciences; education; liberal arts/general studies. Core. Calendar: semesters. Academic remediation for entering students, services for LD students, advanced placement, honors program, independent study, distance learning, double major, summer session for credit, part-time degree program, adult/continuing education programs, co-op programs and internships, graduate courses open to undergrads. Off campus study at Savannah State University. Study abroad program. ROTC: Army, Naval (c).

Entrance Requirements: Options: electronic application, early admission, deferred admission, international baccalaureate accepted. Required: high school transcript, minimum 2.5 high school GPA, ACT/SAT Scores, SAT or

ACT. Required for some: SAT Subject Tests. Entrance: minimally difficult. Application deadline: 7/15. Notification: continuous. SAT Reasoning Test deadline: 8/1. SAT Subject Test deadline: 8/1. Transfer credits accepted: Yes.

Costs Per Year: Application fee: $25. State resident tuition: $4512 full-time, $150.40 per credit hour part-time. Nonresident tuition: $16,416 full-time, $547.02 per credit hour part-time. Mandatory fees: $1332 full-time, $666 per term part-time. Full-time tuition and fees vary according to course load, location, and program. Part-time tuition and fees vary according to course load, location, and program. College room and board: $9770. College room only: $5908. Room and board charges vary according to board plan and housing facility.

Collegiate Environment: Orientation program. Drama-theater group, choral group, student-run newspaper. Social organizations: 82 open to all; national fraternities, national sororities, local fraternities, local sororities; 3% of eligible men and 4% of eligible women are members. Most popular organizations: Wesley Fellowship, Hispanic Outreach and Leadership at Armstrong (HOLA), Ebony Coalition, American Chemical Society, Phi Alpha Theta. Major annual events: Celebrate Armstrong, Saint Patrick's Day, Beach Bash. Student services: health clinic, personal-psychological counseling. Campus security: 24-hour emergency response devices and patrols, student patrols, late night transport-escort service, controlled dormitory access. 1,411 college housing spaces available; 1,330 were occupied in 2012-13. Freshmen given priority for college housing. On-campus residence required in freshman year. Option: coed housing available. Lane Library with 254,777 books, 535,080 microform titles, 496 serials, 9,532 audiovisual materials, an OPAC, and a Web page. Operations spending for the previous fiscal year: $492,012. 300 computers available on campus for general student use. A campuswide network can be accessed from student residence rooms. Students can access the following: online class registration.

Community Environment: The college is located on the southside of Savannah, 30 miles from the Atlantic Ocean. All modes of transportation are available. Savannah is a highly industrialized metropolitan area with only minor agricultural activities. Industrial plants number over 350. This city is considered to be one of the first planned cities in North America. The charm of the city comes from the cobblestoned riverfront, and the many squares shaded by majestic oak trees. Points of interest include Factor's Walk, Savannah riverfront shopping, Johnson Square, Pink House, Owens-Thomas House, Cathedral of St. John the Baptist, Independent Presbyterian Church, Colonial Park, and many others.

■ **THE ART INSTITUTE OF ATLANTA**
6600 Peachtree Dunwoody Rd., NE
100 Embassy Row
Atlanta, GA 30328
Tel: (770)394-8300; Free: 800-275-4242
Fax: (770)394-0008
Web Site: www.artinstitutes.edu/atlanta/
Description: Proprietary, 4-year, coed. Part of Education Management Corporation. Awards associate and bachelor's degrees. Founded 1949. Setting: 7-acre suburban campus.

Community Environment: Just north of Atlanta's city limits, the campus is located in one of Atlanta's fastest growing business and residential districts and provides easy access to public transportation, shopping, housing, restaurants, and jobs for students.

■ **THE ART INSTITUTE OF ATLANTA–DECATUR**
One W Ct. Sq., Ste. 110
Decatur, GA 30030
Free: 866-856-6203
Web Site: www.artinstitutes.edu/decatur/
Description: Proprietary, 4-year, coed. Part of Education Management Corporation. Awards associate and bachelor's degrees. Founded 2007.

■ **ASHWORTH COLLEGE**
6625 The Corners Pky.
Ste. 500
Norcross, GA 30092
Tel: (770)729-8400; Free: 800-957-5412
Fax: (770)729-9296
Web Site: www.ashworthcollege.edu/
Description: Proprietary, comprehensive, coed. Administratively affiliated with Professional Career Development, LLC. Awards associate, bachelor's, and master's degrees and post-master's certificates. Setting: suburban

campus with easy access to Atlanta. Total enrollment: 57,650. Students come from 50 states and territories, 32 other countries, 90% from out-of-state. Core. Calendar: semesters. Advanced placement, accelerated degree program, independent study, distance learning, summer session for credit, part-time degree program, external degree program, adult/continuing education programs. Off campus study.

Entrance Requirements: Open admission. Option: electronic application. Required: high school transcript. Entrance: noncompetitive. Notification: continuous, continuous for nonresidents. Transfer credits accepted: Yes.

Collegiate Environment: Orientation program. Social organizations: honor society.

■ ATHENS TECHNICAL COLLEGE
800 US Hwy. 29 N
Athens, GA 30601-1500
Tel: (706)355-5000
Fax: (706)369-5753
E-mail: lreid@athenstech.edu
Web Site: www.athenstech.edu/

Description: State-supported, 2-year, coed. Part of Technical College System of Georgia. Awards certificates, diplomas, and terminal associate degrees. Founded 1958. Setting: suburban campus. Total enrollment: 4,788. Full-time: 1,340 students, 62% women, 38% men. Part-time: 3,448 students, 68% women, 32% men. 0.1% from out-of-state. 0.3% American Indian or Alaska Native, non-Hispanic/Latino; 4% Hispanic/Latino; 24% African American, non-Hispanic/Latino; 1% Asian, non-Hispanic/Latino; 0.1% Native Hawaiian or other Pacific Islander, non-Hispanic/Latino; 0% international. 45% 25 or older. Retention: 70% of full-time freshmen returned the following year. Distance learning.

Entrance Requirements: Open admission selective admission to some programs. Option: early admission. Required: high school transcript. Entrance: noncompetitive.

Collegiate Environment: College housing not available.

■ ATLANTA METROPOLITAN STATE COLLEGE
1630 Metropolitan Pky., SW
Atlanta, GA 30310-4498
Tel: (404)756-4000
E-mail: admissions@atlm.edu
Web Site: www.atlm.edu/

Description: State-supported, 2-year, coed. Part of University System of Georgia. Awards transfer associate and terminal associate degrees. Founded 1974. Setting: 68-acre urban campus. Total enrollment: 2,241. Student-undergrad faculty ratio is 23:1. 22% from out-of-state. 40% 25 or older. Retention: 56% of full-time freshmen returned the following year. Core. Calendar: semesters. Academic remediation for entering students, services for LD students, independent study, distance learning, summer session for credit, part-time degree program, adult/continuing education programs, co-op programs. Study abroad program.

Entrance Requirements: Option: electronic application. Required: high school transcript, certificate of immunization, COMPASS placement exam. Entrance: minimally difficult. Application deadline: 7/15. Notification: continuous until 8/12.

Collegiate Environment: Orientation program. Drama-theater group, choral group, student-run newspaper. Student services: personal-psychological counseling. Campus security: 24-hour emergency response devices and patrols. Atlanta Metropolitan College Library with 50,147 books, 101 serials, an OPAC, and a Web page.

Community Environment: The College, though within view of the city, is situated on a 83-acre wooded tract. It is located next to Atlanta Technical College, and is convenient to major bus lines and Hartsfield International Airport, and is adjacent to Interstate 75-85 South.

■ ATLANTA TECHNICAL COLLEGE
1560 Metropolitan Pky., SW
Atlanta, GA 30310
Tel: (404)225-4400
Fax: (404)752-0809
E-mail: vbillups@atlantatech.edu
Web Site: www.atlantatech.edu/

Description: State-supported, 2-year, coed. Part of Technical College System of Georgia. Awards certificates, diplomas, and terminal associate degrees. Founded 1945. Total enrollment: 4,874. Full-time: 1,779 students, 52% women, 48% men. Part-time: 3,095 students, 64% women, 36% men.

0.1% from out-of-state. 0.2% American Indian or Alaska Native, non-Hispanic/Latino; 1% Hispanic/Latino; 95% African American, non-Hispanic/Latino; 0.3% Asian, non-Hispanic/Latino; 0% Native Hawaiian or other Pacific Islander, non-Hispanic/Latino; 0% international. 66% 25 or older. Retention: 67% of full-time freshmen returned the following year. Distance learning. Study abroad program.

Entrance Requirements: Open admission selective admission to some programs. Option: early admission. Required: high school transcript. Entrance: noncompetitive.

Collegiate Environment: College housing not available.

■ AUGUSTA TECHNICAL COLLEGE
3200 Augusta Tech Dr.
Augusta, GA 30906
Tel: (706)771-4000
Fax: (706)771-4016
E-mail: dwendt@augustatech.edu
Web Site: www.augustatech.edu/

Description: State-supported, 2-year, coed. Part of Technical College System of Georgia. Awards certificates, diplomas, and terminal associate degrees. Founded 1961. Setting: urban campus. Total enrollment: 4,339. Full-time: 1,504 students, 56% women, 44% men. Part-time: 2,835 students, 63% women, 37% men. 4% from out-of-state. 0.1% American Indian or Alaska Native, non-Hispanic/Latino; 2% Hispanic/Latino; 51% African American, non-Hispanic/Latino; 1% Asian, non-Hispanic/Latino; 0.1% Native Hawaiian or other Pacific Islander, non-Hispanic/Latino; 0% international. 54% 25 or older. Retention: 60% of full-time freshmen returned the following year. Distance learning.

Entrance Requirements: Open admission selective admission to some programs. Option: early admission. Required: high school transcript. Entrance: noncompetitive.

Collegiate Environment: College housing not available.

■ BAINBRIDGE COLLEGE
2500 E Shotwell St.
Bainbridge, GA 39819
Tel: (229)248-2500; Free: 888-825-1715
Fax: (229)248-2525
E-mail: sstewart@bainbridge.edu
Web Site: www.bainbridge.edu/

Description: State-supported, 2-year, coed. Part of University System of Georgia. Awards certificates, transfer associate, and terminal associate degrees. Founded 1972. Setting: 160-acre small town campus. Total enrollment: 2,938. Faculty: 179 (73 full-time, 106 part-time). 1,030 applied, 67% were admitted. Students come from 5 states and territories, 2% from out-of-state. 0.2% American Indian or Alaska Native, non-Hispanic/Latino; 1% Hispanic/Latino; 56% African American, non-Hispanic/Latino; 0.3% Asian, non-Hispanic/Latino. 57% 25 or older. Core. Calendar: semesters. Academic remediation for entering students, services for LD students, advanced placement, independent study, distance learning, double major, summer session for credit, part-time degree program, adult/continuing education programs. Study abroad program.

Entrance Requirements: Options: electronic application, early admission. Required for some: high school transcript, minimum 1.8 high school GPA, 3 recommendations, interview, immunizations/waivers, medical records and criminal, SAT or ACT, ACT COMPASS. Entrance: noncompetitive. Application deadline: Rolling. Notification: continuous. Transfer credits accepted: Yes.

Costs Per Year: Application fee: $0. State resident tuition: $2,026 full-time, $84.40 per credit hour part-time. Nonresident tuition: $7,666 full-time, $319.40 per credit hour part-time. Mandatory fees: $888 full-time, $444 per term part-time. Full-time tuition and fees vary according to course load. Part-time tuition and fees vary according to course load.

Collegiate Environment: Orientation program. Drama-theater group, choral group. Social organizations: 32 open to all; 18% of eligible men and 21% of eligible women are members. Most popular organizations: Honors Club, Alpha Beta Gamma, Sigma Kappa Delta, History Club, Student Government Association. Major annual events: Welcome Back Bash, Spring Lecture, Fall Carnival. Student services: personal-psychological counseling. Campus security: 24-hour patrols. College housing not available. Bainbridge College Library with 45,366 books, 140 microform titles, 83 serials, 3,958 audiovisual materials, and an OPAC. 640 computers available on campus for general student use. A campuswide network can be accessed. Students can access the following: online class registration. Staffed computer lab on campus provides training in use of computers, software, and the Internet.

■ BAUDER COLLEGE
384 Northyards Blvd. NW
Suites 190 and 400
Atlanta, GA 30313
Tel: (404)237-7573; Free: 800-935-1857
Fax: (404)237-1642
Web Site: atlanta.bauder.edu/
Description: Proprietary, 4-year, coed. Administratively affiliated with Kaplan Higher Education. Awards associate and bachelor's degrees. Founded 1964. Setting: urban campus.

■ BERRY COLLEGE
PO Box 490159
Mount Berry, GA 30149-0159
Tel: (706)232-5374; Free: 800-237-7942
Fax: (706)236-2248
E-mail: admissions@berry.edu
Web Site: www.berry.edu/
Description: Independent interdenominational, comprehensive, coed. Awards bachelor's and master's degrees. Founded 1902. Setting: 27,000-acre suburban campus with easy access to Atlanta. Endowment: $822 million. Research spending for the previous fiscal year: $507,085. Educational spending for the previous fiscal year: $14,409 per student. Total enrollment: 2,166. Faculty: 207 (154 full-time, 53 part-time). Student-undergrad faculty ratio is 13:1. 3,485 applied, 66% were admitted. 33% from top 10% of their high school class, 67% from top quarter, 91% from top half. 1 National Merit Scholar, 17 valedictorians. Full-time: 2,007 students, 67% women, 33% men. Part-time: 34 students, 68% women, 32% men. Students come from 35 states and territories, 17 other countries, 27% from out-of-state. 0.2% American Indian or Alaska Native, non-Hispanic/Latino; 5% Hispanic/Latino; 4% African American, non-Hispanic/Latino; 2% Asian, non-Hispanic/Latino; 0.1% Native Hawaiian or other Pacific Islander, non-Hispanic/Latino; 1% international. 1% 25 or older, 86% live on campus, 2% transferred in. Retention: 75% of full-time freshmen returned the following year. Academic areas with the most degrees conferred: biological/life sciences; social sciences; psychology; business/marketing. Core. Calendar: semesters. Advanced placement, self-designed majors, honors program, independent study, double major, summer session for credit, part-time degree program, adult/continuing education programs, internships, graduate courses open to undergrads. Study abroad program.
Entrance Requirements: Options: electronic application, early admission, international baccalaureate accepted. Required: essay, high school transcript, 1 recommendation, SAT or ACT. Recommended: interview. Required for some: 2 recommendations, Home-school applicants must meet or exceed academic profile of previous freshmen class. Entrance: moderately difficult. Application deadline: 7/26. Notification: continuous. SAT Reasoning Test deadline: 7/26.
Costs Per Year: Application fee: $50. Comprehensive fee: $37,329 includes full-time tuition ($27,450), mandatory fees ($200), and college room and board ($9679). College room only: $5456. Room and board charges vary according to board plan and housing facility. Part-time tuition: $915 per credit hour.
Collegiate Environment: Orientation program. Drama-theater group, choral group, student-run newspaper. Social organizations: 80 open to all. Most popular organizations: Student Government Association, Campus Outreach, Block-n-Bridle, Allied Health, Athletes Bettering the Community. Major annual events: Mountain Day, Conson Wilson Lecture Series, BCTC Theatre Season. Student services: health clinic, personal-psychological counseling. Campus security: 24-hour emergency response devices and patrols, controlled dormitory access, lighted pathways, gated campus, mobile police patrols, identification of valuables, limited access to campus, on campus police officers. 1,793 college housing spaces available; 1,755 were occupied in 2012-13. Freshmen guaranteed college housing. On-campus residence required through senior year. Options: coed, men-only, women-only housing available. Memorial Library plus 1 other with 343,347 books, 821,504 microform titles, 3,552 serials, 5,509 audiovisual materials, an OPAC, and a Web page. Operations spending for the previous fiscal year: $1.8 million. 200 computers available on campus for general student use. A campuswide network can be accessed from student residence rooms and from off campus. Students can access the following: online class registration. Staffed computer lab on campus provides training in use of computers, software, and the Internet.

Community Environment: Located on Highway 27 between Chattanooga and Atlanta, Mount Berry is in the mountains of North Georgia in Floyd County, adjoining Rome. Recreation, cultural facilities and transportation are found in Rome.

■ BEULAH HEIGHTS UNIVERSITY
892 Berne St., SE
Atlanta, GA 30316
Tel: (404)627-2681; Free: 888-777-BHBC
Fax: (404)627-0702
E-mail: john.dreher@beulah.org
Web Site: www.beulah.org/
Description: Independent Pentecostal, comprehensive, coed. Awards associate, bachelor's, and master's degrees. Founded 1918. Setting: 10-acre urban campus with easy access to Atlanta. Educational spending for the previous fiscal year: $1136 per student. Total enrollment: 846. Faculty: 64 (26 full-time, 38 part-time). Student-undergrad faculty ratio is 13:1. 78 applied, 100% were admitted. Full-time: 329 students, 53% women, 47% men. Part-time: 312 students, 59% women, 41% men. Students come from 22 states and territories, 12 other countries, 30% from out-of-state. 98% 25 or older, 10% live on campus, 8% transferred in. Retention: 57% of full-time freshmen returned the following year. Academic area with the most degrees conferred: theology and religious vocations. Core. Calendar: semesters. Academic remediation for entering students, services for LD students, advanced placement, accelerated degree program, independent study, distance learning, double major, summer session for credit, part-time degree program, adult/continuing education programs, co-op programs and internships. Off campus study.
Entrance Requirements: Open admission. Options: electronic application, early admission, international baccalaureate accepted. Required: essay, high school transcript, minimum 2 high school GPA, 2 recommendations, Statement of Faith, TOFEL required for international students. Recommended: interview, SAT or ACT. Entrance: noncompetitive. Application deadline: Rolling. Notification: continuous. Transfer credits accepted: Yes.
Costs Per Year: Application fee: $30. Tuition: $5760 full-time, $240 per credit part-time. Full-time tuition varies according to course load. College room only: $2500. Room charges vary according to housing facility.
Collegiate Environment: Orientation program. Choral group, student-run newspaper. Social organizations: 2 open to all; BHU (Beta Eta Kappa Honor Society). Most popular organizations: Chapel Choir, student government, Club Give. Major annual events: Discovery Days, Annual College Banquet, International Day. Student services: personal-psychological counseling. Campus security: 24-hour emergency response devices and patrols. Barth Memorial Library with 48,000 books, 308 serials, 2,337 audiovisual materials, and an OPAC. Operations spending for the previous fiscal year: $134,547. 28 computers available on campus for general student use. A campuswide network can be accessed from student residence rooms and from off campus. Students can access the following: online class registration. Staffed computer lab on campus provides training in use of computers and the Internet.
Community Environment: See Clark Atlanta University.

■ BRENAU UNIVERSITY
500 Washington St., SE
Gainesville, GA 30501
Tel: (770)534-6299; Free: 800-252-5119
Fax: (770)534-6114
E-mail: admissions@brenau.edu
Web Site: www.brenau.edu/
Description: Independent, comprehensive, women only. Awards associate, bachelor's, and master's degrees (also offers coed evening and weekend programs with significant enrollment not reflected in profile). Founded 1878. Setting: 57-acre small town campus with easy access to Atlanta. Endowment: $31.7 million. Educational spending for the previous fiscal year: $6361 per student. Total enrollment: 864. Faculty: 115 (71 full-time, 44 part-time). Student-undergrad faculty ratio is 9:1. 2,696 applied, 47% were admitted. Full-time: 715 students. Part-time: 87 students. Students come from 13 states and territories, 12 other countries, 8% from out-of-state. 0.4% American Indian or Alaska Native, non-Hispanic/Latino; 9% Hispanic/Latino; 21% African American, non-Hispanic/Latino; 2% Asian, non-Hispanic/Latino; 0% Native Hawaiian or other Pacific Islander, non-Hispanic/Latino; 5% international. 22% 25 or older, 58% live on campus, 17% transferred in. Retention: 69% of full-time freshmen returned the following year. Academic areas with the most degrees conferred: health professions and related sci-

ences; visual and performing arts; business/marketing. Core. Calendar: semesters. Academic remediation for entering students, ESL program, services for LD students, advanced placement, self-designed majors, honors program, independent study, distance learning, double major, summer session for credit, part-time degree program, internships, graduate courses open to undergrads. Study abroad program.

Entrance Requirements: Options: electronic application, deferred admission, international baccalaureate accepted. Required: high school transcript, minimum 2.5 high school GPA, SAT or ACT. Required for some: interview. Entrance: moderately difficult. Application deadlines: Rolling, Rolling for nonresidents. Notification: continuous, continuous for nonresidents. SAT Reasoning Test deadline: 9/1. Transfer credits accepted: Yes.

Costs Per Year: Application fee: $35. Comprehensive fee: $32,792 includes full-time tuition ($21,908) and college room and board ($10,884). Full-time tuition varies according to location and program.

Collegiate Environment: Orientation program. Drama-theater group, choral group, student-run newspaper, radio station. Social organizations: 52 open to all; national sororities; 23% of eligible undergrads are members. Most popular organizations: Sigma Alpha Pi Leadership Society, Student Government Association/Student Activities Board, Circle K, Silhouettes, International Club. Major annual events: May Day, Convocation, Winter Weekend. Student services: health clinic, personal-psychological counseling. Campus security: 24-hour emergency response devices and patrols, late night transport-escort service. Trustee Library with 86,590 books, 107,024 microform titles, 20,128 serials, 3,349 audiovisual materials, an OPAC, and a Web page. 130 computers available on campus for general student use. A campuswide network can be accessed from student residence rooms. Students can access the following: online class registration, students can create own Web sites, videos and other things made possible by Google apps. Staffed computer lab on campus provides training in use of computers, software, and the Internet.

■ **BREWTON-PARKER COLLEGE**
201 David-Eliza Fountain Cir.
Mount Vernon, GA 30445
Tel: (912)583-2241; Free: 800-342-1087
Fax: (912)583-4498
E-mail: admissions@bpc.edu
Web Site: www.bpc.edu/
Description: Independent Southern Baptist, 4-year, coed. Awards associate and bachelor's degrees. Founded 1904. Setting: 280-acre rural campus. Total enrollment: 629. Faculty: 85 (31 full-time, 54 part-time). Student-undergrad faculty ratio is 11:1. 293 applied. 24% from top 10% of their high school class, 40% from top quarter, 66% from top half. Full-time: 468 students, 49% women, 51% men. Part-time: 161 students, 51% women, 49% men. Students come from 11 states and territories, 12 other countries, 12% from out-of-state. 0.3% American Indian or Alaska Native, non-Hispanic/Latino; 5% Hispanic/Latino; 24% African American, non-Hispanic/Latino; 0.5% Asian, non-Hispanic/Latino; 0.5% Native Hawaiian or other Pacific Islander, non-Hispanic/Latino; 4% international. 20% 25 or older, 55% live on campus. Retention: 41% of full-time freshmen returned the following year. Academic areas with the most degrees conferred: business/marketing; education; psychology. Core. Calendar: semesters. Academic remediation for entering students, services for LD students, advanced placement, accelerated degree program, honors program, independent study, summer session for credit, part-time degree program, co-op programs and internships.

Entrance Requirements: Options: electronic application, international baccalaureate accepted. Required: high school transcript, minimum 2 high school GPA, SAT or ACT. Entrance: minimally difficult. Application deadlines: 8/1, Rolling for nonresidents. Notification: continuous, continuous for nonresidents. Transfer credits accepted: Yes.

Costs Per Year: Application fee: $35. One-time mandatory fee: $200. Comprehensive fee: $21,030 includes full-time tuition ($12,670), mandatory fees ($760), and college room and board ($7600). College room only: $3000. Full-time tuition and fees vary according to course load, location, and program. Room and board charges vary according to board plan and housing facility. Part-time tuition: $360 per credit hour. Part-time mandatory fees: $360 per credit hour. Part-time tuition and fees vary according to course load, location, and program.

Collegiate Environment: Orientation program. Drama-theater group, student-run newspaper. Social organizations: 26 open to all. Most popular organizations: Council of Intramural Activities, Student Activities Council, Student Government Association, Circle K, Baptist Student Union. Major an-

nual events: Homecoming Weekend, Fall Festival, Black History Month. Student services: personal-psychological counseling. Campus security: 24-hour emergency response devices, controlled dormitory access, Campus security is provided from 6 pm to 6 am. Fountain-New Library with 89,800 books, 1,623 microform titles, 132 serials, 6,945 audiovisual materials, an OPAC, and a Web page. 104 computers available on campus for general student use. A campuswide network can be accessed from student residence rooms. Students can access the following: online class registration. Staffed computer lab on campus.

■ **BROWN MACKIE COLLEGE–ATLANTA**
4370 Peachtree Rd., NE
Atlanta, GA 30319
Tel: (404)799-4500
Web Site: www.brownmackie.edu/atlanta/
Description: Proprietary, 2-year, coed. Part of Education Management Corporation. Awards diplomas and terminal associate degrees. Setting: urban campus.

■ **CARVER COLLEGE**
437 Nelson St.
Atlanta, GA 30313
Tel: (404)527-4520
Fax: (404)527-4526
E-mail: info@carver.edu
Web Site: www.carver.edu/
Description: Independent nondenominational, 4-year, coed. Awards associate and bachelor's degrees. Founded 1943. Setting: 16-acre urban campus. Total enrollment: 104. Faculty: 19 (2 full-time, 17 part-time). Student-undergrad faculty ratio is 6:1. 49 applied, 100% were admitted. Students come from 4 states and territories, 4 other countries, 1% from out-of-state. 65% African American, non-Hispanic/Latino; 1% Asian, non-Hispanic/Latino; 34% international. 72% 25 or older, 35% live on campus. Retention: 56% of full-time freshmen returned the following year. Academic area with the most degrees conferred: theology and religious vocations. Core. Calendar: semesters. Part-time degree program.

Entrance Requirements: Required: essay, high school transcript, minimum 2 high school GPA, 2 recommendations. Recommended: interview. Required for some: interview. Entrance: noncompetitive. Application deadline: 8/1. Transfer credits accepted: Yes.

Costs Per Year: Application fee: $35. Comprehensive fee: $11,840 includes full-time tuition ($6960) and college room and board ($4880). Part-time tuition: $290 per credit hour.

Collegiate Environment: Orientation program. Social organizations: 3 open to all. Most popular organizations: Student Government Association, Student Missions Organization, Carver Praise Team. Major annual events: Carver Homecoming, W.D. Hungerpiller Bible Conference, Herman Conley Missions Conference. Carver Bible College Library plus 1 other with 150 serials and 1,000 audiovisual materials. 7 computers available on campus for general student use. Staffed computer lab on campus.

■ **CENTRAL GEORGIA TECHNICAL COLLEGE**
3300 Macon Tech Dr.
Macon, GA 31206
Tel: (478)757-3400; Free: 866-430-0135
Fax: (478)757-3454
E-mail: tcarter@centralgatech.edu
Web Site: www.centralgatech.edu/
Description: State-supported, 2-year, coed. Part of Technical College System of Georgia. Awards certificates, diplomas, and terminal associate degrees. Founded 1966. Setting: suburban campus. Total enrollment: 4,631. Full-time: 2,116 students, 64% women, 36% men. Part-time: 2,515 students, 63% women, 37% men. 1% from out-of-state. 0.4% American Indian or Alaska Native, non-Hispanic/Latino; 3% Hispanic/Latino; 61% African American, non-Hispanic/Latino; 1% Asian, non-Hispanic/Latino; 0% Native Hawaiian or other Pacific Islander, non-Hispanic/Latino; 0.1% international. 57% 25 or older. Retention: 67% of full-time freshmen returned the following year. Distance learning.

Entrance Requirements: Open admission selective admission to some programs. Option: early admission. Required: high school transcript. Entrance: noncompetitive.

Collegiate Environment: College housing not available.

■ **CHAMBERLAIN COLLEGE OF NURSING**
5775 Peachtree-Dunwoody Rd., NE
Ste. A100
Atlanta, GA 30342
Tel: (404)250-8500
Web Site: www.chamberlain.edu/
Description: Proprietary, 4-year, coed. Awards bachelor's degrees. Total enrollment: 381. Faculty: 15 (9 full-time, 6 part-time). Student-undergrad faculty ratio is 22:1. Full-time: 165 students, 95% women, 5% men. Part-time: 216 students, 93% women, 7% men. 2% from out-of-state. 0% American Indian or Alaska Native, non-Hispanic/Latino; 2% Hispanic/Latino; 28% African American, non-Hispanic/Latino; 4% Asian, non-Hispanic/Latino; 0% Native Hawaiian or other Pacific Islander, non-Hispanic/Latino; 7% international. 76% 25 or older, 0% live on campus, 82% transferred in.
Entrance Requirements: Required: SAT or ACT.
Costs Per Year: Application fee: $95. Tuition: $16,360 full-time, $665 per credit hour part-time. Mandatory fees: $600 full-time.

■ **CHATTAHOOCHEE TECHNICAL COLLEGE**
980 S Cobb Dr., SE
Marietta, GA 30060
Tel: (770)528-4545
Fax: (770)528-4578
E-mail: mcusack@chattahoocheetech.edu
Web Site: www.chattahoocheetech.edu/
Description: State-supported, 2-year, coed. Part of Technical College System of Georgia. Awards certificates, diplomas, and terminal associate degrees. Founded 1961. Setting: suburban campus. Total enrollment: 11,679. Full-time: 3,731 students, 53% women, 47% men. Part-time: 7,948 students, 61% women, 39% men. 0.3% from out-of-state. 0.5% American Indian or Alaska Native, non-Hispanic/Latino; 8% Hispanic/Latino; 30% African American, non-Hispanic/Latino; 2% Asian, non-Hispanic/Latino; 0.1% Native Hawaiian or other Pacific Islander, non-Hispanic/Latino; 1% international. 47% 25 or older. Retention: 69% of full-time freshmen returned the following year. Distance learning.
Entrance Requirements: Open admission selective admission to some programs. Option: early admission. Required: high school transcript. Entrance: noncompetitive.
Collegiate Environment: College housing not available.

■ **CLARK ATLANTA UNIVERSITY**
223 James P. Brawley Dr., SW
Atlanta, GA 30314
Tel: (404)880-8000; Free: 800-688-3228
Fax: (404)880-6174
E-mail: cauadmissions@cau.edu
Web Site: www.cau.edu/
Description: Independent United Methodist, university, coed. Awards bachelor's, master's, and doctoral degrees and post-master's certificates. Founded 1865. Setting: 126-acre urban campus. Endowment: $53.7 million. Research spending for the previous fiscal year: $9.1 million. Educational spending for the previous fiscal year: $7264 per student. Total enrollment: 3,419. Faculty: 320 (170 full-time, 150 part-time). Student-undergrad faculty ratio is 15:1. 5,801 applied, 69% were admitted. 11% from top 10% of their high school class, 29% from top quarter, 68% from top half. Full-time: 2,484 students, 75% women, 25% men. Part-time: 148 students, 64% women, 36% men. Students come from 43 states and territories, 10 other countries, 63% from out-of-state. 0.3% American Indian or Alaska Native, non-Hispanic/Latino; 0.4% Hispanic/Latino; 90% African American, non-Hispanic/Latino; 0.2% Asian, non-Hispanic/Latino; 0% Native Hawaiian or other Pacific Islander, non-Hispanic/Latino; 1% international. 3% 25 or older, 55% live on campus, 5% transferred in. Retention: 61% of full-time freshmen returned the following year. Academic areas with the most degrees conferred: communication/journalism; business/marketing; psychology. Core. Calendar: semesters. Academic remediation for entering students, services for LD students, advanced placement, accelerated degree program, honors program, independent study, double major, summer session for credit, part-time degree program, adult/continuing education programs, co-op programs and internships. Off campus study at University Center in Georgia, Atlanta University Center. Study abroad program. ROTC: Army (c), Naval (c).
Entrance Requirements: Options: electronic application, early admission, deferred admission, international baccalaureate accepted. Required: essay, high school transcript, minimum 2.5 high school GPA, 2 recommendations,

SAT or ACT. Required for some: interview. Entrance: moderately difficult. Application deadlines: 6/1, 6/1 for nonresidents. Notification: continuous, continuous for nonresidents. SAT Reasoning Test deadline: 5/1. Transfer credits accepted: Yes.
Costs Per Year: Application fee: $35. Comprehensive fee: $28,786 includes full-time tuition ($19,012), mandatory fees ($818), and college room and board ($8956). Room and board charges vary according to board plan and housing facility. Part-time tuition: $792 per credit hour. Part-time mandatory fees: $409 per term.
Collegiate Environment: Orientation program. Drama-theater group, choral group, marching band, student-run newspaper, radio station. Social organizations: 80 open to all; national fraternities, national sororities; 3% of eligible men and 12% of eligible women are members. Most popular organizations: Spirit Boosters, Pre-Alumni Council, Campus Activities Board, Orientation Guides, National Association for the Advancement of Colored People. Major annual events: Homecoming, Greek Symposium, Miss Clark Atlanta University Pageants. Student services: health clinic, personal-psychological counseling. Campus security: 24-hour emergency response devices and patrols, late night transport-escort service, controlled dormitory access. 2,448 college housing spaces available; 1,438 were occupied in 2012-13. Freshmen given priority for college housing. On-campus residence required through sophomore year. Options: coed, men-only, women-only housing available. Robert W. Woodruff Library with 347,984 books, 853,037 microform titles, 30,554 serials, 7,731 audiovisual materials, an OPAC, and a Web page. 741 computers available on campus for general student use. A campuswide network can be accessed from student residence rooms. Students can access the following: online class registration. Staffed computer lab on campus provides training in use of computers, software, and the Internet.
Community Environment: One mile east of the campus lie the mirrored skyscrapers and modern expressways of Atlanta. The World Congress Center, the Civic Center, the Arts Alliance Center (home of the Atlanta Symphony Orchestra and the Atlantic Ballet Company), the Martin Luther King, Jr. Center for Nonviolent Social Change, the Dome (home of the Atlanta Falcons football team), the Jimmy Carter Presidential Library, and outstanding entertainment features, such as Underground Atlanta, Stone Mountain Park, and Six Flags Over Georgia amusement park, mark Atlanta as the capital of the Sun Belt.

■ **CLAYTON STATE UNIVERSITY**
2000 Clayton State Blvd.
Morrow, GA 30260-0285
Tel: (678)466-4000
E-mail: csc-info@clayton.edu
Web Site: www.clayton.edu/
Description: State-supported, comprehensive, coed. Part of University System of Georgia. Awards associate, bachelor's, and master's degrees. Founded 1969. Setting: 163-acre suburban campus with easy access to Atlanta. Endowment: $1.1 million. Research spending for the previous fiscal year: $2276. Educational spending for the previous fiscal year: $4288 per student. Total enrollment: 7,140. Faculty: 367 (224 full-time, 143 part-time). Student-undergrad faculty ratio is 19:1. 2,556 applied, 39% were admitted. 12% from top 10% of their high school class, 40% from top quarter, 69% from top half. Full-time: 3,924 students, 70% women, 30% men. Part-time: 2,884 students, 71% women, 29% men. Students come from 34 states and territories, 34 other countries, 2% from out-of-state. 0.2% American Indian or Alaska Native, non-Hispanic/Latino; 2% Hispanic/Latino; 63% African American, non-Hispanic/Latino; 0.4% Asian, non-Hispanic/Latino; 0.01% Native Hawaiian or other Pacific Islander, non-Hispanic/Latino; 1% international. 37% 25 or older, 10% live on campus, 1% transferred in. Retention: 68% of full-time freshmen returned the following year. Academic areas with the most degrees conferred: health professions and related sciences; business/marketing; liberal arts/general studies. Core. Calendar: semesters. Academic remediation for entering students, ESL program, services for LD students, advanced placement, self-designed majors, freshman honors college, honors program, independent study, distance learning, double major, summer session for credit, part-time degree program, adult/continuing education programs, co-op programs and internships. Off campus study at University Center in Georgia. Study abroad program. ROTC: Army, Naval (c), Air Force (c).
Entrance Requirements: Options: electronic application, early admission, deferred admission. Required: high school transcript, proof of immunization, SAT or ACT. Required for some: SAT Subject Tests. Entrance: minimally difficult. Application deadline: 7/17. Notification: continuous.

Costs Per Year: Application fee: $40. State resident tuition: $4512 full-time, $150.40 per credit hour part-time. Nonresident tuition: $16,416 full-time, $547.20 per credit hour part-time. Mandatory fees: $1404 full-time, $702 per term part-time. Full-time tuition and fees vary according to course load. Part-time tuition and fees vary according to course load. College room and board: $8862. College room only: $5574. Room and board charges vary according to board plan and housing facility.

Collegiate Environment: Orientation program. Drama-theater group, choral group, student-run newspaper. Social organizations: 26 open to all; national fraternities, national sororities; 10% of eligible men and 15% of eligible women are members. Most popular organizations: Accounting Club, International Awareness Club, Black Cultural Awareness Association, Student Government Association, music club. Major annual events: Homecoming, Spring Fling. Student services: health clinic, personal-psychological counseling. Campus security: 24-hour emergency response devices and patrols, late night transport-escort service, controlled dormitory access, lighted pathways. 1,275 college housing spaces available; 725 were occupied in 2012-13. Freshmen given priority for college housing. On-campus residence required in freshman year. Option: coed housing available. Clayton State University Library with 148,798 books, 285,858 microform titles, 618 serials, an OPAC, and a Web page. Operations spending for the previous fiscal year: $1.2 million. 3,500 computers available on campus for general student use. A computer is required for all students. A campuswide network can be accessed from student residence rooms and from off campus. Students can access the following: online class registration.

Community Environment: See Clark Atlanta University.

■ **COLLEGE OF COASTAL GEORGIA**
One College Dr.
Brunswick, GA 31520
Tel: (912)264-7235; Free: 800-675-7235
Fax: (912)262-3072
E-mail: admiss@ccga.edu
Web Site: www.ccga.edu/
Description: State-supported, 4-year, coed. Part of University System of Georgia. Awards associate and bachelor's degrees. Founded 1961. Setting: 193-acre small town campus with easy access to Jacksonville. Endowment: $6.4 million. Educational spending for the previous fiscal year: $3799 per student. Total enrollment: 3,156. Faculty: 186 (86 full-time, 100 part-time). Student-undergrad faculty ratio is 19:1. 983 applied, 88% were admitted. Full-time: 1,792 students, 66% women, 34% men. Part-time: 1,364 students, 71% women, 29% men. Students come from 38 states and territories, 8% from out-of-state. 0.4% American Indian or Alaska Native, non-Hispanic/Latino; 4% Hispanic/Latino; 18% African American, non-Hispanic/Latino; 1% Asian, non-Hispanic/Latino; 0.2% Native Hawaiian or other Pacific Islander, non-Hispanic/Latino; 1% international. 33% 25 or older, 11% live on campus, 8% transferred in. Retention: 55% of full-time freshmen returned the following year. Academic areas with the most degrees conferred: education; health professions and related sciences; business/marketing. Core. Calendar: semesters. Academic remediation for entering students, services for LD students, advanced placement, distance learning, double major, summer session for credit, part-time degree program, internships. Study abroad program.
Entrance Requirements: Options: electronic application, early admission, deferred admission, international baccalaureate accepted. Required: high school transcript, minimum 2 high school GPA, Immunization records, proof of residency and SAT or ACT scores(for applicants graduating from high school within the last five years). Required for some: SAT or ACT, Applicants graduating from high school within the last five years must submit SAT or ACT scores. Entrance: minimally difficult. Application deadline: 7/15. Notification: continuous. SAT Reasoning Test deadline: 7/15. SAT Subject Test deadline: 7/15. Transfer credits accepted: Yes.
Costs Per Year: Application fee: $25. State resident tuition: $2,277 full-time, $94.87 per credit hour part-time. Nonresident tuition: $8,411 full-time, $350.47 per credit hour part-time. Mandatory fees: $1650 full-time, $830 per term part-time. Full-time tuition and fees vary according to course load. Part-time tuition and fees vary according to course load. College room and board: $8126. College room only: $5126. Room and board charges vary according to board plan, housing facility, and location.
Collegiate Environment: Orientation program. Student-run newspaper. Social organizations: 31 open to all. Most popular organizations: Phi Theta Kappa, Urban Gaming Club, Biology Club, Psychology Club, International Association. Major annual events: Welcome Back and Student Organiza-

tions Fair, Homecoming Dance, Halloween Dance. Student services: health clinic, personal-psychological counseling. Campus security: 24-hour emergency response devices and patrols, late night transport-escort service, controlled dormitory access. 350 college housing spaces available; 330 were occupied in 2012-13. Freshmen guaranteed college housing. Option: coed housing available. Clara Wood Gould Memorial Library plus 1 other with 15.3 million books, 38,977 microform titles, 330 serials, 6,635 audiovisual materials, an OPAC, and a Web page. Operations spending for the previous fiscal year: $743,011. 395 computers available on campus for general student use. A campuswide network can be accessed from student residence rooms. Students can access the following: online class registration. Staffed computer lab on campus provides training in use of computers, software, and the Internet.
Community Environment: Brunswick is the county seat of Glynn County, which includes the historic resort islands of St. Simons, Sea Island, and Jekyll Island. The climate is mild with a mean temperature of 68 degrees. Bus and rail serve the area. Besides being a tourist center, it is an industrial city. Recreational activities are unlimited including golf, bowling, fresh, salt water, and deep sea fishing, tennis, picnicking, surfing, and water skiing at excellent beaches. Numerous points of historical interest are in or near Brunswick. Kings Bay Naval Submarine Base and the Federal Law Enforcement Training Center are nearby.

■ **COLUMBUS STATE UNIVERSITY**
4225 University Ave.
Columbus, GA 31907-5645
Tel: (706)568-2001; Free: 866-264-2035
Fax: (706)568-2123
E-mail: lovell_susan@columbusstate.edu
Web Site: www.columbusstate.edu/
Description: State-supported, comprehensive, coed. Part of University System of Georgia. Awards associate, bachelor's, master's, and doctoral degrees and post-master's certificates. Founded 1958. Setting: 132-acre suburban campus with easy access to Atlanta. Endowment: $1.8 million. Research spending for the previous fiscal year: $420,275. Educational spending for the previous fiscal year: $5544 per student. Total enrollment: 8,239. Faculty: 511 (280 full-time, 231 part-time). Student-undergrad faculty ratio is 17:1. 3,672 applied, 53% were admitted. 16% from top 10% of their high school class, 41% from top quarter, 71% from top half. Full-time: 4,947 students, 61% women, 39% men. Part-time: 2,078 students, 54% women, 46% men. Students come from 44 states and territories, 45 other countries, 15% from out-of-state. 1% American Indian or Alaska Native, non-Hispanic/Latino; 5% Hispanic/Latino; 36% African American, non-Hispanic/Latino; 2% Asian, non-Hispanic/Latino; 0.3% Native Hawaiian or other Pacific Islander, non-Hispanic/Latino; 1% international. 26% 25 or older, 21% live on campus, 9% transferred in. Retention: 67% of full-time freshmen returned the following year. Academic areas with the most degrees conferred: business/marketing; health professions and related sciences; education. Core. Calendar: semesters. Academic remediation for entering students, ESL program, services for LD students, advanced placement, freshman honors college, honors program, independent study, distance learning, double major, summer session for credit, part-time degree program, adult/continuing education programs, co-op programs and internships, graduate courses open to undergrads. Off campus study. Study abroad program. ROTC: Army.
Entrance Requirements: Options: electronic application, early admission, deferred admission, international baccalaureate accepted. Required: high school transcript, minimum 2.4 high school GPA, proof of immunization, SAT or ACT. Entrance: minimally difficult. Application deadline: 6/30. Notification: continuous. SAT Reasoning Test deadline: 6/30.
Costs Per Year: Application fee: $40. State resident tuition: $4852 full-time, $161.74 per semester hour part-time. Nonresident tuition: $17,128 full-time, $570.94 per semester hour part-time. Mandatory fees: $1740 full-time, $870 per term part-time. College room and board: $8542. Room and board charges vary according to board plan.
Collegiate Environment: Orientation program. Drama-theater group, choral group, student-run newspaper. Social organizations: 90 open to all; national fraternities, national sororities, local sororities; 2% of eligible men and 2% of eligible women are members. Most popular organizations: Student Government Association, Student Activities Council, Campus Ministry Association, African Students Association, SABER Student Newspaper. Major annual events: Homecoming, Greek Week, Black History Month. Student services: health clinic, personal-psychological counseling. Campus security: 24-hour emergency response devices and patrols, late night transport-escort service, controlled dormitory access. 1,300 college housing spaces available; 1,289

were occupied in 2012-13. Freshmen given priority for college housing. On-campus residence required in freshman year. Options: coed, men-only, women-only housing available. Simon Schwob Memorial Library plus 2 others with 376,614 books, 1.1 million microform titles, 1,392 serials, 12,348 audiovisual materials, an OPAC, and a Web page. Operations spending for the previous fiscal year: $1.4 million. 1,135 computers available on campus for general student use. A campuswide network can be accessed from student residence rooms and from off campus. Students can access the following: online class registration. Staffed computer lab on campus (open 24 hours a day) provides training in use of computers, software, and the Internet.

Community Environment: Columbus, Georgia's second largest city, is located in the Chattahoochee Valley, 100 miles south of Atlanta on the Georgia-Alabama border, having an annual mean temperature of 65 degrees and annual rainfall of 37 inches. All forms of transportation serve the area. Columbus is one of the South's largest textile centers, a regional retail center, and manufacturers high-tech industrial products, iron and metal goods, hosiery, processed foods, soft drinks, candy and peanut products. Cultural facilities are the churches, libraries, symphony orchestra, Museum of Arts and Sciences, Fort Benning Little Theatre, and Springer Opera House which is the State Theatre. With the completion of the dam projects on the Chattahoochee River and the Apalachicola River in Florida, Columbus became a port city. A navigable waterway extends to the Gulf of Mexico and the Intracoastal Canal. Oliver Dam provides facilities for all water sports. There are recreational facilities at community centers, golf courses, bowling alleys, and swimming pools.

■ **COLUMBUS TECHNICAL COLLEGE**

928 Manchester Expy.
Columbus, GA 31904-6572
Tel: (706)649-1800
Fax: (706)649-1937
E-mail: taskew@columbustech.edu
Web Site: www.columbustech.edu/

Description: State-supported, 2-year, coed. Part of Technical College System of Georgia. Awards certificates, diplomas, and terminal associate degrees. Founded 1961. Setting: urban campus. Total enrollment: 4,267. Full-time: 1,430 students, 64% women, 36% men. Part-time: 2,837 students, 69% women, 31% men. 15% from out-of-state. 0.1% American Indian or Alaska Native, non-Hispanic/Latino; 5% Hispanic/Latino; 48% African American, non-Hispanic/Latino; 0.1% Asian, non-Hispanic/Latino; 1% Native Hawaiian or other Pacific Islander, non-Hispanic/Latino; 0% international. 52% 25 or older. Retention: 62% of full-time freshmen returned the following year. Distance learning.

Entrance Requirements: Open admission selective admission to some programs. Option: early admission. Required: high school transcript. Entrance: noncompetitive.

Collegiate Environment: College housing not available.

■ **COVENANT COLLEGE**

14049 Scenic Hwy.
Lookout Mountain, GA 30750
Tel: (706)820-1560; Free: 888-451-2683
E-mail: admissions@covenant.edu
Web Site: www.covenant.edu/

Description: Independent, comprehensive, coed, affiliated with Presbyterian Church in America. Awards associate, bachelor's, and master's degrees (master's degree in education only). Founded 1955. Setting: 350-acre suburban campus. Endowment: $25.1 million. Educational spending for the previous fiscal year: $6760 per student. Total enrollment: 1,135. Faculty: 101 (67 full-time, 34 part-time). Student-undergrad faculty ratio is 13:1. 1,129 applied, 57% were admitted. 31% from top 10% of their high school class, 47% from top quarter, 84% from top half. Full-time: 1,011 students, 57% women, 43% men. Part-time: 54 students, 59% women, 41% men. 76% from out-of-state. 0.5% American Indian or Alaska Native, non-Hispanic/Latino; 2% Hispanic/Latino; 3% African American, non-Hispanic/Latino; 2% Asian, non-Hispanic/Latino; 0% Native Hawaiian or other Pacific Islander, non-Hispanic/Latino; 2% international. 5% 25 or older, 83% live on campus, 3% transferred in. Retention: 87% of full-time freshmen returned the following year. Academic areas with the most degrees conferred: education; social sciences; visual and performing arts. Core. Calendar: semesters. Academic remediation for entering students, services for LD students, advanced placement, self-designed majors, independent study, double major, summer ses-

sion for credit, part-time degree program, adult/continuing education programs, internships. Off campus study. Study abroad program. ROTC: Army (c).

Entrance Requirements: Options: electronic application, early admission, deferred admission, international baccalaureate accepted. Required: essay, high school transcript, minimum 2.5 high school GPA, 2 recommendations, interview, SAT or ACT. Entrance: moderately difficult. Application deadline: Rolling. Notification: continuous. SAT Reasoning Test deadline: 8/15.

Costs Per Year: Application fee: $35. Comprehensive fee: $36,310 includes full-time tuition ($27,500), mandatory fees ($770), and college room and board ($8040). Full-time tuition and fees vary according to course load. Part-time tuition: $1150 per credit hour. Part-time tuition varies according to course load.

Collegiate Environment: Orientation program. Drama-theater group, choral group, student-run newspaper, radio station. Social organizations: 43 open to all. Student services: health clinic, personal-psychological counseling, women's center. Campus security: controlled dormitory access, night security guards. 912 college housing spaces available. Freshmen guaranteed college housing. On-campus residence required through junior year. Options: men-only, women-only housing available. Kresge Memorial Library with an OPAC and a Web page. Operations spending for the previous fiscal year: $679,076.

Community Environment: Located 5 miles from Chattanooga, TN, and 120 miles from Atlanta, GA, Lookout Mountain is a suburban community that enjoys the cultural, recreational and social facilities of Chattanooga. The community has churches of all denominations, a library, various cultural opportunities, an aquarium, several hospitals, and health center at nearby Chattanooga. Part-time jobs are available.

■ **DALTON STATE COLLEGE**

650 College Dr.
Dalton, GA 30720
Tel: (706)272-4436; Free: 800-829-4436
Fax: (706)272-2530
Web Site: www.daltonstate.edu/

Description: State-supported, 4-year, coed. Part of University System of Georgia. Awards associate and bachelor's degrees. Founded 1963. Setting: 144-acre small town campus. Endowment: $29.8 million. Educational spending for the previous fiscal year: $3580 per student. Total enrollment: 5,047. Faculty: 215 (160 full-time, 55 part-time). Student-undergrad faculty ratio is 21:1. 3,067 applied, 36% were admitted. Full-time: 2,976 students, 59% women, 41% men. Part-time: 2,071 students, 68% women, 32% men. Students come from 6 states and territories, 40 other countries, 1% from out-of-state. 0.5% American Indian or Alaska Native, non-Hispanic/Latino; 17% Hispanic/Latino; 4% African American, non-Hispanic/Latino; 1% Asian, non-Hispanic/Latino; 0.2% Native Hawaiian or other Pacific Islander, non-Hispanic/Latino; 1% international. 29% 25 or older, 4% live on campus, 5% transferred in. Retention: 61% of full-time freshmen returned the following year. Academic areas with the most degrees conferred: business/marketing; education; public administration and social services. Core. Calendar: semesters. Academic remediation for entering students, ESL program, services for LD students, advanced placement, double major, summer session for credit, part-time degree program, adult/continuing education programs, co-op programs and internships. Off campus study. Study abroad program.

Entrance Requirements: Open admission. Options: electronic application, deferred admission. Required: high school transcript, SAT or ACT. Entrance: noncompetitive. Application deadline: 7/1. Notification: continuous. SAT Reasoning Test deadline: 7/1. Transfer credits accepted: Yes.

Costs Per Year: Application fee: $30. One-time mandatory fee: $300. State resident tuition: $2276 full-time, $93 per credit hour part-time. Nonresident tuition: $8411 full-time, $350 per credit hour part-time. Mandatory fees: $886 full-time. Full-time tuition and fees vary according to course load. Part-time tuition varies according to course load. College room and board: $6320. College room only: $4970. Room and board charges vary according to housing facility.

Collegiate Environment: Orientation program. Student-run newspaper. Social organizations: 25 open to all. Most popular organizations: Kappa Delta Pi, Phi Theta Kappa, Phi Beta Lambda, Environmental Club, Radiological Technology Club. Major annual events: Week of Welcome, Day for Dalton, Volunteer Fair. Campus security: 24-hour emergency response devices and patrols. Option: coed housing available. Derrell C. Roberts Library with 242,996 books, 213,789 microform titles, 10,205 audiovisual materials, an OPAC, and a Web page. Operations spending for the previous fiscal year: $583,755. 730 computers available on campus for general student use. A campuswide network can be accessed from student residence rooms. Students can access the following: online class registration. Staffed computer lab on campus provides training in use of computers, software, and the Internet.

Community Environment: Dalton is an urban area 20 miles south of the Tennessee line. The climate is mild year-round. This is known as the"Carpet Capital of the World." Railroads and buses serve the area. Commercial air transportation is available at Chattanooga, 31 miles distant. Fishing is excellent in the many surrounding lakes. Nearby mountains offer opportunities for hunting, fishing, hiking, and other sports. Recreation within the city includes a supervised recreation program at the center with swimming, football, baseball, softball, tennis, and an indoor picnic area.

■ DARTON STATE COLLEGE
2400 Gillionville Rd.
Albany, GA 31707-3098
Tel: (229)317-6000; Free: 866-775-1214
Fax: (229)430-2926
E-mail: info@darton.edu
Web Site: www.darton.edu/
Description: State-supported, primarily 2-year, coed. Part of University System of Georgia. Awards certificates, transfer associate, terminal associate, and bachelor's degrees. Founded 1965. Setting: 185-acre urban campus. Endowment: $978,169. Educational spending for the previous fiscal year: $3072 per student. Total enrollment: 6,396. Faculty: 282 (121 full-time, 161 part-time). Student-undergrad faculty ratio is 21:1. Full-time: 3,137 students, 64% women, 36% men. Part-time: 3,259 students, 75% women, 25% men. Students come from 33 states and territories, 46 other countries, 7% from out-of-state. 0.4% American Indian or Alaska Native, non-Hispanic/Latino; 2% Hispanic/Latino; 45% African American, non-Hispanic/Latino; 1% Asian, non-Hispanic/Latino; 0.2% Native Hawaiian or other Pacific Islander, non-Hispanic/Latino; 1% international. 47% 25 or older, 15% transferred in. Retention: 53% of full-time freshmen returned the following year. Calendar: semesters. Academic remediation for entering students, ESL program, services for LD students, advanced placement, accelerated degree program, self-designed majors, honors program, independent study, distance learning, double major, summer session for credit, part-time degree program, adult/continuing education programs, co-op programs. Off campus study. Study abroad program. ROTC: Army (c).
Entrance Requirements: Open admission. Options: electronic application, deferred admission. Required: minimum 2 high school GPA, proof of immunization, non-traditional students must take the COMPASS test. Recommended: SAT or ACT, SAT Subject Tests. Required for some: high school transcript, SAT or ACT, SAT Subject Tests. Entrance: minimally difficult. Application deadline: 7/20. Notification: continuous until 7/27.
Costs Per Year: Application fee: $20. State resident tuition: $2,026 full-time, $84.40 per credit hour part-time. Nonresident tuition: $7,666 full-time, $319.40 per credit hour part-time. Mandatory fees: $1144 full-time, $395. College room and board: $8730. Room and board charges vary according to board plan and housing facility.
Collegiate Environment: Orientation program. Drama-theater group, choral group. Social organizations: 11 open to all. Most popular organizations: Cultural Exchange Club, Democratic, Independent, & Republican Team (D.I.R.T.), Human Services Club, Outdoor Adventure Club (OAC), Music Club. Major annual event: Beach Party. Student services: health clinic, personal-psychological counseling. Campus security: 24-hour emergency response devices and patrols, student patrols, late night transport-escort service, controlled dormitory access. 457 college housing spaces available; all were occupied in 2012-13. No special consideration for freshman housing applicants. Option: coed housing available. Weatherbee Learning Resources Center with 101,612 books, 37,056 microform titles, 125 serials, 5,182 audiovisual materials, an OPAC, and a Web page. Operations spending for the previous fiscal year: $513,106. 450 computers available on campus for general student use. A campuswide network can be accessed from student residence rooms and from off campus. Students can access the following: online class registration. Staffed computer lab on campus provides training in use of computers and software.

■ DEVRY UNIVERSITY (ALPHARETTA)
2555 Northwinds Pky.
Alpharetta, GA 30009
Tel: (770)521-4900; Free: 866-338-7941
Web Site: www.devry.edu/

Description: Proprietary, comprehensive, coed. Part of DeVry University. Awards associate, bachelor's, and master's degrees. Founded 1997. Setting: 9-acre suburban campus with easy access to Atlanta. Total enrollment: 892. Faculty: 58 (27 full-time, 31 part-time). Student-undergrad faculty ratio is 14:1. Full-time: 343 students, 38% women, 62% men. Part-time: 369 students, 43% women, 57% men. 6% from out-of-state. 72% 25 or older, 18% transferred in. Academic areas with the most degrees conferred: business/marketing; computer and information sciences; engineering. Calendar: semesters. Academic remediation for entering students, advanced placement, accelerated degree program, distance learning, summer session for credit, part-time degree program, adult/continuing education programs.
Entrance Requirements: Options: electronic application, early admission, deferred admission, international baccalaureate accepted. Required: high school transcript, interview. Entrance: minimally difficult. Application deadline: Rolling. Notification: continuous. SAT Reasoning Test deadline: 10/31.
Collegiate Environment: Orientation program. Most popular organizations: Epsilon Delta Pi, International Student Organization, Programming Club, Alpha Sigma Lambda, National Society of Black Engineers. Major annual events: Fall Festival, Spring Fling, Thanksgiving Dinner. Campus security: 24-hour emergency response devices, late night transport-escort service, lighted pathways, video recorder (CCTV). Learning Resource Center with an OPAC and a Web page.

■ DEVRY UNIVERSITY (DECATUR)
1 W Ct. Sq.
Ste. 100
Decatur, GA 30030-2556
Tel: (404)292-7900; Free: 866-338-7941
Fax: (404)292-2321
Web Site: www.devry.edu/
Description: Proprietary, comprehensive, coed. Part of DeVry University. Awards associate, bachelor's, and master's degrees. Founded 1969. Setting: suburban campus. Total enrollment: 2,554. Faculty: 152 (41 full-time, 111 part-time). Student-undergrad faculty ratio is 18:1. Full-time: 703 students, 54% women, 46% men. Part-time: 1,537 students, 57% women, 43% men. 13% from out-of-state. 0.2% American Indian or Alaska Native, non-Hispanic/Latino; 3% Hispanic/Latino; 54% African American, non-Hispanic/Latino; 1% Asian, non-Hispanic/Latino; 0.2% Native Hawaiian or other Pacific Islander, non-Hispanic/Latino; 1% international. 76% 25 or older, 24% transferred in. Academic areas with the most degrees conferred: business/marketing; computer and information sciences; engineering technologies. Calendar: semesters. Part-time degree program, adult/continuing education programs.
Entrance Requirements: Required: high school transcript, interview. Entrance: minimally difficult. Application deadline: Rolling. Notification: continuous.
Costs Per Year: Application fee: $40. Tuition: $16,076 full-time, $609 per credit hour part-time. Mandatory fees: $80 full-time.
Collegiate Environment: Orientation program. College housing not available.

■ DEVRY UNIVERSITY (DULUTH)
3505 Koger Blvd., Ste. 170
Duluth, GA 30096-7671
Tel: (678)380-9780; Free: 866-338-7941
Fax: (678)924-0958
Web Site: www.devry.edu/
Description: Proprietary, comprehensive, coed. Awards associate, bachelor's, and master's degrees. Calendar: semesters.

■ EAST GEORGIA STATE COLLEGE
131 College Cir.
Swainsboro, GA 30401-2699
Tel: (478)289-2000
Fax: (478)289-2038
E-mail: kjones@ega.edu
Web Site: www.ega.edu/
Description: State-supported, 2-year, coed. Part of University System of Georgia. Awards certificates, transfer associate, and terminal associate degrees. Founded 1973. Setting: 207-acre rural campus. Total enrollment: 2,754. Student-undergrad faculty ratio is 26:1. 1% from out-of-state. 14% 25 or older. Core. Calendar: semesters. Academic remediation for entering students, services for LD students, advanced placement, honors program,

independent study, distance learning, summer session for credit, part-time degree program, adult/continuing education programs. Off campus study. Study abroad program.

Entrance Requirements: Options: early admission, deferred admission. Required: high school transcript. Entrance: minimally difficult. Application deadline: Rolling. Notification: continuous.

Costs Per Year: Application fee: $20. State resident tuition: $2532 full-time, $84.40 per credit hour part-time. Nonresident tuition: $9582 full-time, $319.40 per credit hour part-time. Mandatory fees: $836 full-time, $418 per term part-time. Full-time tuition and fees vary according to course load and location. Part-time tuition and fees vary according to course load and location. College room and board: $7232.

Collegiate Environment: Orientation program. Drama-theater group, choral group, student-run newspaper. Student services: personal-psychological counseling. Campus security: 24-hour patrols. East Georgia College Library with an OPAC and a Web page.

Community Environment: Swainsboro, the county seat of Emanuel County, is located in the southeast section of Georgia near the Center of the vast southern pine forest. The climate is mild with an annual mean temperature of 66 degrees; the average rainfall is 42 inches. Transportation is provided by the Georgia and Florida Railroad and Greyhound. Community facilities include one hospital, 24 churches, restaurants, hotels, motels, and shopping areas. Industry, agriculture, and forestry are important to the economy of the area. Agricultural products include cotton, tobacco, peanuts, soybeans, corn, and potatoes. Some of the industries manufacture sprinkler system valves, furniture, dressed lumber, seed processing, playground equipment, knitwear, molded plastics, screws, rivets, and component parts. A well-staffed and budgeted recreation department offers many recreational opportunities to youth. Fish ponds are in abundance in Emanuel County. Many fresh water streams are filled with trout and bream. Quail and wild turkeys abound and there are excellent reserves for hunting. The first week in May is set aside for the annual Emanuel County Pine Tree Festival.

■ **EMMANUEL COLLEGE**
181 Springs St.
Franklin Springs, GA 30639-0129
Tel: (706)245-7226; Free: 800-860-8800
E-mail: admissions@ec.edu
Web Site: www.ec.edu/

Description: Independent, 4-year, coed, affiliated with Pentecostal Holiness Church. Awards associate and bachelor's degrees. Founded 1919. Setting: 90-acre rural campus with easy access to Atlanta, Georgia. Endowment: $3.2 million. Educational spending for the previous fiscal year: $4593 per student. Total enrollment: 806. Faculty: 82 (50 full-time, 32 part-time). Student-undergrad faculty ratio is 12:1. 1,144 applied, 51% were admitted. Full-time: 711 students, 50% women, 50% men. Part-time: 95 students, 57% women, 43% men. Students come from 20 states and territories, 18 other countries, 24% from out-of-state. 0% American Indian or Alaska Native, non-Hispanic/Latino; 4% Hispanic/Latino; 17% African American, non-Hispanic/Latino; 1% Asian, non-Hispanic/Latino; 0% Native Hawaiian or other Pacific Islander, non-Hispanic/Latino; 4% international. 12% 25 or older, 56% live on campus, 7% transferred in. Retention: 67% of full-time freshmen returned the following year. Academic areas with the most degrees conferred: education; parks and recreation; theology and religious vocations. Core. Calendar: semesters. Academic remediation for entering students, services for LD students, advanced placement, accelerated degree program, honors program, independent study, distance learning, summer session for credit, part-time degree program, internships. Study abroad program.

Entrance Requirements: Options: electronic application, early admission, deferred admission, international baccalaureate accepted. Required: essay, high school transcript, SAT or ACT. Required for some: interview. Entrance: moderately difficult. Application deadline: 8/1. Notification: 8/1. SAT Reasoning Test deadline: 8/1. Transfer credits accepted: Yes.

Costs Per Year: Application fee: $25. Comprehensive fee: $22,140 includes full-time tuition ($15,700) and college room and board ($6440). Room and board charges vary according to housing facility. Part-time tuition: $630 per credit hour.

Collegiate Environment: Orientation program. Drama-theater group, choral group. Social organizations: 15 open to all. Most popular organizations: Students in Free Enterprise (SIFE), Fellowship of Christian Athletes, SOS, BSU, International Students Club. Major annual events: Feast of Ingathering, Homecoming Weekend, Spring Musical. Student services: personal-psychological counseling. Campus security: 24-hour patrols. 525 college housing spaces available; 451 were occupied in 2012-13. Freshmen

guaranteed college housing. On-campus residence required through sophomore year. Options: men-only, women-only housing available. Shaw-Leslie Library plus 1 other with 90,594 books, 6,297 microform titles, 91 serials, 1,055 audiovisual materials, an OPAC, and a Web page. Operations spending for the previous fiscal year: $226,164. 50 computers available on campus for general student use. A campuswide network can be accessed from student residence rooms and from off campus. Students can access the following: online class registration. Staffed computer lab on campus.

■ **EMORY UNIVERSITY**
201 Dowman Dr.
Atlanta, GA 30322-1100
Tel: (404)727-6123; Free: 800-727-6036
E-mail: admiss@emory.edu
Web Site: www.emory.edu/

Description: Independent Methodist, university, coed. Awards associate, bachelor's, master's, and doctoral degrees and post-master's certificates (enrollment figures include Emory University, Oxford College; application data for main campus only). Founded 1836. Setting: 634-acre suburban campus with easy access to Atlanta. Endowment: $5.5 billion. Research spending for the previous fiscal year: $409.1 million. Educational spending for the previous fiscal year: $29,806 per student. Total enrollment: 14,236. Faculty: 1,452 (1,004 full-time, 448 part-time). Student-undergrad faculty ratio is 7:1. 17,475 applied, 26% were admitted. 80% from top 10% of their high school class, 98% from top quarter, 100% from top half. 43 National Merit Scholars. Full-time: 7,567 students, 56% women, 44% men. Part-time: 89 students, 63% women, 37% men. Students come from 55 states and territories, 49 other countries, 72% from out-of-state. 0.2% American Indian or Alaska Native, non-Hispanic/Latino; 6% Hispanic/Latino; 10% African American, non-Hispanic/Latino; 23% Asian, non-Hispanic/Latino; 0.04% Native Hawaiian or other Pacific Islander, non-Hispanic/Latino; 13% international. 3% 25 or older, 67% live on campus, 2% transferred in. Retention: 95% of full-time freshmen returned the following year. Academic areas with the most degrees conferred: social sciences; business/marketing; biological/life sciences. Core. Calendar: semesters. ESL program, services for LD students, advanced placement, honors program, independent study, double major, summer session for credit, internships, graduate courses open to undergrads. Off campus study at Atlanta Regional Council for Higher Education (ARCHE); Washington Semester, American University. Study abroad program. ROTC: Army (c), Naval (c), Air Force (c).

Entrance Requirements: Options: electronic application, early admission, early decision, deferred admission, international baccalaureate accepted. Required: essay, high school transcript, 2 recommendations, SAT or ACT. Recommended: SAT Subject Tests. Entrance: most difficult. Application deadlines: 1/15, 11/1 for early decision plan 1, 1/1 for early decision plan 2. Notification: 4/1, 12/15 for early decision plan 1, 2/15 for early decision plan 2. SAT Reasoning Test deadline: 1/15. SAT Subject Test deadline: 1/15. Transfer credits accepted: Yes. Applicants placed on waiting list: 3,457. Waitlisted applicants offered admission: 37. Early decision applicants: 1,789. Early decision applicants admitted: 682.

Costs Per Year: Application fee: $50. Comprehensive fee: $56,368 includes full-time tuition ($43,400), mandatory fees ($608), and college room and board ($12,360). College room only: $7360. Full-time tuition and fees vary according to degree level and location. Room and board charges vary according to board plan, housing facility, location, and student level. Part-time tuition: $1808 per credit hour.

Collegiate Environment: Orientation program. Drama-theater group, choral group, student-run newspaper, radio station. Social organizations: 320 open to all; national fraternities, national sororities; 29% of eligible men and 32% of eligible women are members. Most popular organizations: Volunteer Emory, music/theater, student government, Outdoor Emory, Hillel. Major annual events: Heritage/Homecoming Week, Wonderful Wednesdays, Dooley's Ball and Spring Festival. Student services: legal services, health clinic, personal-psychological counseling, women's center. Campus security: 24-hour emergency response devices and patrols, student patrols, late night transport-escort service, controlled dormitory access. Freshmen guaranteed college housing. On-campus residence required through sophomore year. Option: coed housing available. Robert W. Woodruff Library plus 8 others with 3.9 million books, 6.3 million microform titles, 117,143 audiovisual materials, an OPAC, and a Web page. Operations spending for the previous fiscal year: $37.7 million. 875 computers available on campus for general student use. Computer purchase/lease plans available. A campuswide network can be accessed from student residence rooms and from off campus. Students can access the following: online class registration,

Computer Repair System, Online Library, iTunes University. Staffed computer lab on campus provides training in use of computers, software, and the Internet.

Community Environment: Emory is located in a residential area of Atlanta, 6 miles from downtown. Atlanta, capital of Georgia, is the commercial, industrial and financial giant of the southeast. It is located in the foothills of the Blue Ridge Mountains. Atlanta was host to the 1996 Olympic Games. Atlanta's moderate climate permits year-round golf, fishing and outdoor living. All major forms of public transportation are available. Peachtree Street is experiencing one of the biggest building booms in the country. Peachtree Center includes the Atlanta Merchandise Mart, and the 22-story regency Hyatt Hotel. Bridges 22 stories above the street connect buildings on the Peachtree Center. The city is the cultural center of the South with a symphony, art center, and theaters. Atlanta is a major business and manufacturing center that produces more that 3,500 different commodities. Excellent part-time employment opportunities are available. Recreational activities include all major sports, swimming, golfing, boating, horseback riding, tennis, and fishing. Many spectator sports events take place in the Atlanta Stadium.

■ **EMORY UNIVERSITY, OXFORD COLLEGE**
100 Hamill St.
Oxford, GA 30054
Tel: (770)784-8888; Free: 800-723-8328
Fax: (770)784-8359
E-mail: oxadmission@emory.edu
Web Site: oxford.emory.edu/

Description: Independent Methodist, primarily 2-year, coed. Administratively affiliated with Emory University. Awards transfer associate and bachelor's degrees. Founded 1836. Setting: 150-acre small town campus with easy access to Atlanta. Endowment: $39 million. Research spending for the previous fiscal year: $95,391. Educational spending for the previous fiscal year: $5765 per student. Total enrollment: 936. Faculty: 85 (57 full-time, 28 part-time). Student-undergrad faculty ratio is 14:1. 3,683 applied, 55% were admitted. 40% from top 10% of their high school class, 77% from top quarter, 96% from top half. Full-time: 936 students, 53% women, 47% men. Students come from 45 states and territories, 29 other countries, 61% from out-of-state. 0.3% American Indian or Alaska Native, non-Hispanic/Latino; 6% Hispanic/Latino; 14% African American, non-Hispanic/Latino; 29% Asian, non-Hispanic/Latino; 0.1% Native Hawaiian or other Pacific Islander, non-Hispanic/Latino; 15% international. 0% 25 or older, 99% live on campus. Retention: 90% of full-time freshmen returned the following year. Core. Calendar: semesters. Services for LD students, advanced placement, independent study, double major, summer session for credit, internships. Off campus study at Theory Practice Service Learning courses with classroom and field components. Study abroad program. ROTC: Army (c), Naval (c), Air Force (c).

Entrance Requirements: Options: electronic application, early admission, early action, deferred admission, international baccalaureate accepted. Required: essay, high school transcript, 1 recommendation, SAT or ACT. Recommended: minimum 3 high school GPA, 2 recommendations. Required for some: interview, SAT Subject Tests. Entrance: very difficult. Application deadlines: 1/15, 11/1 for early action. Notification: continuous until 4/1, 12/15 for early action. SAT Reasoning Test deadline: 3/29. SAT Subject Test deadline: 3/29. Transfer credits accepted: Yes. Applicants placed on waiting list: 746. Wait-listed applicants offered admission: 47. Early action applicants: 576. Early action applicants admitted: 486.

Costs Per Year: Application fee: $50. Comprehensive fee: $47,054 includes full-time tuition ($36,100), mandatory fees ($478), and college room and board ($10,476). College room only: $7196. Part-time tuition: $1504 per contact hour.

Collegiate Environment: Orientation program. Drama-theater group, choral group, student-run newspaper. Social organizations: 70 open to all; local coed social organizations. Most popular organizations: Residence Hall Association, intramurals/junior varsity sports, Student Government Association, Student Admissions Association, Volunteer Oxford. Major annual events: Fall Formal, Spirit week, Dance Company. Student services: health clinic, personal-psychological counseling. Campus security: 24-hour emergency response devices and patrols, student patrols, late night transport-escort service, controlled dormitory access. Hoke O'Kelly Library with 92,681 books, 167 serials, 1,352 audiovisual materials, an OPAC, and a Web page. Operations spending for the previous fiscal year: $236,745. 110 computers available on campus for general student use. Computer purchase/lease plans available. A campuswide network can be accessed from student

residence rooms and from off campus. Students can access the following: online class registration. Staffed computer lab on campus (open 24 hours a day) provides training in use of computers, software, and the Internet.

■ **FORT VALLEY STATE UNIVERSITY**
1005 State University Dr.
Fort Valley, GA 31030
Tel: (478)825-6211; Free: 877-462-3878
Fax: (478)825-6394
E-mail: admissap@fvsu.edu
Web Site: www.fvsu.edu/

Description: State-supported, comprehensive, coed. Part of University System of Georgia. Awards associate, bachelor's, master's, and doctoral degrees. Founded 1895. Setting: 1,365-acre small town campus. Total enrollment: 3,571. Faculty: 202 (153 full-time, 49 part-time). Student-undergrad faculty ratio is 19:1. 5,343 applied, 40% were admitted. 5% from top 10% of their high school class, 13% from top quarter, 41% from top half. Full-time: 3,001 students, 56% women, 44% men. Part-time: 420 students, 58% women, 42% men. 4% from out-of-state. 9% 25 or older, 62% live on campus, 4% transferred in. Retention: 73% of full-time freshmen returned the following year. Core. Calendar: semesters. Academic remediation for entering students, services for LD students, advanced placement, freshman honors college, honors program, independent study, distance learning, double major, summer session for credit, part-time degree program, adult/continuing education programs, internships, graduate courses open to undergrads. Off campus study. ROTC: Army.

Entrance Requirements: Options: electronic application, early admission, deferred admission. Required: high school transcript, SAT or ACT. Entrance: moderately difficult. Application deadline: 7/19. Notification: continuous.

Collegiate Environment: Orientation program. Drama-theater group, choral group, marching band, student-run newspaper, radio station. Social organizations: national fraternities, national sororities. Most popular organizations: Drama Group, Christian Student Organization, Habitat for Humanity, Debate Club. Major annual events: Founders' Day, Black History Observance, Annual Fall Convocation. Student services: health clinic, personal-psychological counseling. Campus security: 24-hour emergency response devices and patrols, student patrols, late night transport-escort service. Henry A. Hunt Memorial Library with an OPAC.

Community Environment: Fort Valley is a small town with a temperate climate. It is the main peach-growing section of the state. Miles of blooming peach orchards adorn the roadways in the spring. Community facilities include churches of major denominations, a library, and hospital. The Blue Bird Body Company, manufacturers of school bus bodies, is also located here. Part-time employment opportunities are available in Peach and surrounding counties. The Massee Lane Farms located five miles southwest of the City has one of the finest collections of camellias in the country.

■ **GEORGIA COLLEGE & STATE UNIVERSITY**
Hancock St.
Milledgeville, GA 31061
Tel: (478)445-5004
Fax: (478)445-6795
E-mail: admissions@gcsu.edu
Web Site: www.gcsu.edu/

Description: State-supported, comprehensive, coed. Part of University System of Georgia. Awards bachelor's, master's, and doctoral degrees and post-master's certificates. Founded 1889. Setting: 602-acre small town campus. Endowment: $25.3 million. Research spending for the previous fiscal year: $356,113. Educational spending for the previous fiscal year: $5838 per student. Total enrollment: 6,444. Faculty: 446 (319 full-time, 127 part-time). Student-undergrad faculty ratio is 17:1. 3,878 applied, 66% were admitted. Full-time: 5,131 students, 61% women, 39% men. Part-time: 437 students, 55% women, 45% men. Students come from 24 states and territories, 40 other countries, 1% from out-of-state. 0.2% American Indian or Alaska Native, non-Hispanic/Latino; 5% Hispanic/Latino; 5% African American, non-Hispanic/Latino; 1% Asian, non-Hispanic/Latino; 0.1% Native Hawaiian or other Pacific Islander, non-Hispanic/Latino; 1% international. 4% 25 or older, 37% live on campus, 6% transferred in. Retention: 86% of full-time freshmen returned the following year. Academic areas with the most degrees conferred: business/marketing; health professions and related sciences; psychology. Core. Calendar: semesters. ESL program, services for LD students, advanced placement, accelerated degree program, self-designed majors, freshman honors college, honors program, independent study, distance learning, double major, summer session for credit, part-time degree program, external degree program, internships, graduate courses open to undergrads. Study abroad program. ROTC: Army (c).

Entrance Requirements: Options: electronic application, early admission, early action, deferred admission, international baccalaureate accepted. Required: essay, proof of immunization, SAT or ACT. Required for some: high school transcript, SAT Subject Tests. Entrance: moderately difficult. Application deadlines: 4/1, 4/1 for nonresidents, 11/1 for early action. Notification: continuous, continuous for nonresidents, 12/1 for early action. SAT Reasoning Test deadline: 4/1. Transfer credits accepted: Yes.

Costs Per Year: Application fee: $40. State resident tuition: $6634 full-time. Nonresident tuition: $24,098 full-time. Mandatory fees: $1984 full-time, $992 per term part-time. Full-time tuition and fees vary according to course load, location, and program. Part-time fees vary according to course load, location, and program. College room and board: $9268. College room only: $5268. Room and board charges vary according to board plan, housing facility, and location.

Collegiate Environment: Orientation program. Drama-theater group, choral group, student-run newspaper, radio station. Social organizations: 146 open to all; national fraternities, national sororities; 20% of eligible men and 26% of eligible women are members. Most popular organizations: Alpha Lambda Delta, Campus Activities Board, Alpha Delta Pi, Zeta au Alpha Sorority, Georgia College Miracle. Major annual events: Fall Freshman Convocation/Week of Welcome, Midnight Breakfast, Homecoming Week. Student services: health clinic, personal-psychological counseling, women's center. Campus security: 24-hour emergency response devices and patrols, student patrols, late night transport-escort service, controlled dormitory access. 2,237 college housing spaces available; 2,048 were occupied in 2012-13. Freshmen given priority for college housing. On-campus residence required in freshman year. Option: coed housing available. Ina Dillard Russell Library with 210,609 books, 24,459 microform titles, 43,000 serials, 12,963 audiovisual materials, an OPAC, and a Web page. Operations spending for the previous fiscal year: $2.2 million. 900 computers available on campus for general student use. Computer purchase/lease plans available. A campuswide network can be accessed from student residence rooms and from off campus. Students can access the following: online class registration. Staffed computer lab on campus provides training in use of computers, software, and the Internet.

■ **GEORGIA GWINNETT COLLEGE**
1000 University Ctr. Ln.
Lawrenceville, GA 60043
Tel: (678)407-5000; Free: 877-704-4422
E-mail: ggcadmissions@ggc.edu
Web Site: www.ggc.edu/

Description: State-supported, 4-year, coed. Part of University System of Georgia. Awards bachelor's degrees. Setting: 260-acre suburban campus with easy access to Atlanta. Research spending for the previous fiscal year: $328,802. Total enrollment: 9,397. Faculty: 562 (342 full-time, 220 part-time). Student-undergrad faculty ratio is 20:1. 4,593 applied, 91% were admitted. 2% from top 10% of their high school class, 12% from top quarter, 38% from top half. Full-time: 6,648 students, 53% women, 47% men. Part-time: 2,749 students, 54% women, 46% men. Students come from 26 states and territories, 92 other countries, 1% from out-of-state. 0.2% American Indian or Alaska Native, non-Hispanic/Latino; 12% Hispanic/Latino; 30% African American, non-Hispanic/Latino; 8% Asian, non-Hispanic/Latino; 0.2% Native Hawaiian or other Pacific Islander, non-Hispanic/Latino; 1% international. 19% 25 or older, 8% live on campus, 9% transferred in. Retention: 60% of full-time freshmen returned the following year. Academic areas with the most degrees conferred: business/marketing; psychology; biological/life sciences. Core. ESL program, services for LD students, advanced placement, summer session for credit, internships. ROTC: Army.

Entrance Requirements: Open admission. Option: electronic application. Required: high school transcript, minimum 2 high school GPA. Recommended: SAT or ACT. Application deadlines: 6/1, 6/1 for nonresidents. SAT Reasoning Test deadline: 6/8. Transfer credits accepted: Yes.

Costs Per Year: Application fee: $20. State resident tuition: $3378 full-time, $112.60 per credit hour part-time. Nonresident tuition: $12,604 full-time, $420.14 per credit hour part-time. Mandatory fees: $1704 full-time, $1704 per year part-time. College room and board: $12,350. College room only: $9650. Room and board charges vary according to board plan. Tuition guaranteed not to increase for student's term of enrollment.

Collegiate Environment: Orientation program. Social organizations: 85 open to all. Major annual events: March through the Arch, Common Reading Initiative, GGC Idol. Student services: personal-psychological counseling.

Campus security: 24-hour emergency response devices and patrols. 1,029 college housing spaces available; 672 were occupied in 2012-13. No special consideration for freshman housing applicants. Option: coed housing available. Library and Learning Center with 134,772 books, 270 serials, 2,595 audiovisual materials, an OPAC, and a Web page. Operations spending for the previous fiscal year: $1.7 million. 243 computers available on campus for general student use. A campuswide network can be accessed from student residence rooms and from off campus. Students can access the following: online class registration. Staffed computer lab on campus provides training in use of computers, software, and the Internet.

■ **GEORGIA HIGHLANDS COLLEGE**
3175 Cedartown Hwy.
Rome, GA 30161
Tel: (706)802-5000; Free: 800-332-2406
Fax: (706)295-6610
E-mail: sdavis@highlands.edu
Web Site: www.highlands.edu/

Description: State-supported, 2-year, coed. Part of University System of Georgia. Awards transfer associate and terminal associate degrees. Founded 1970. Setting: 226-acre suburban campus with easy access to Atlanta. Endowment: $31,769. Educational spending for the previous fiscal year: $3210 per student. Total enrollment: 5,532. Faculty: 245 (136 full-time, 109 part-time). Student-undergrad faculty ratio is 22:1. Full-time: 2,756 students, 59% women, 41% men. Part-time: 2,776 students, 67% women, 33% men. Students come from 10 states and territories, 48 other countries, 1% from out-of-state. 0.2% American Indian or Alaska Native, non-Hispanic/Latino; 7% Hispanic/Latino; 17% African American, non-Hispanic/Latino; 1% Asian, non-Hispanic/Latino; 0.2% Native Hawaiian or other Pacific Islander, non-Hispanic/Latino. 28% 25 or older, 9% transferred in. Retention: 56% of full-time freshmen returned the following year. Core. Calendar: semesters. Academic remediation for entering students, services for LD students, advanced placement, honors program, independent study, distance learning, double major, summer session for credit, part-time degree program, co-op programs. Study abroad program.

Entrance Requirements: Options: electronic application, deferred admission, international baccalaureate accepted. Required: high school transcript, minimum 2 high school GPA. Required for some: minimum 2.2 high school GPA. Entrance: noncompetitive. Application deadlines: Rolling, Rolling for nonresidents. Notification: continuous, continuous for nonresidents. Transfer credits accepted: Yes.

Costs Per Year: Application fee: $20. State resident tuition: $2532 full-time, $84 per credit hour part-time. Nonresident tuition: $9582 full-time, $319 per credit hour part-time. Mandatory fees: $934 full-time, $467 per term part-time. Full-time tuition and fees vary according to course load. Part-time tuition and fees vary according to course load.

Collegiate Environment: Orientation program. Drama-theater group, student-run newspaper. Social organizations: 43 open to all. Most popular organizations: Highlands Association of Nursing Students, Green Highlands, Black Awareness Society, Political Science Association, Phi Theta Kappa. Major annual events: Fall Frenzy, Spring Fling, Family Fun Night. Student services: personal-psychological counseling. Campus security: 24-hour emergency response devices and patrols, emergency phone/email alert system. College housing not available. Georgia Highlands College Library - Floyd Campus plus 1 other with 139,861 books, 102 serials, 9,247 audiovisual materials, an OPAC, and a Web page. Operations spending for the previous fiscal year: $957,401. 202 computers available on campus for general student use. A campuswide network can be accessed from off-campus. Students can access the following: online class registration, Wi-Fi. Staffed computer lab on campus provides training in use of software.

Community Environment: See Shorter College.

■ **GEORGIA INSTITUTE OF TECHNOLOGY**
225 N Ave., NW
Atlanta, GA 30332-0001
Tel: (404)894-2000
Fax: (404)853-9163
E-mail: admission@gatech.edu
Web Site: www.gatech.edu/

Description: State-supported, university, coed. Part of University System of Georgia. Awards bachelor's, master's, and doctoral degrees. Founded 1885. Setting: 400-acre urban campus. Endowment: $1.6 billion. Research spending for the previous fiscal year: $688.9 million. Educational spending for the previous fiscal year: $11,479 per student. Total enrollment: 21,557. Faculty:

1,251 (1,059 full-time, 192 part-time). Student-undergrad faculty ratio is 18:1. 14,645 applied, 55% were admitted. 74% from top 10% of their high school class, 94% from top quarter, 99% from top half. 119 National Merit Scholars. Full-time: 13,272 students, 33% women, 67% men. Part-time: 1,255 students, 32% women, 68% men. Students come from 53 states and territories, 82 other countries, 28% from out-of-state. 0.1% American Indian or Alaska Native, non-Hispanic/Latino; 6% Hispanic/Latino; 6% African American, non-Hispanic/Latino; 18% Asian, non-Hispanic/Latino; 0.1% Native Hawaiian or other Pacific Islander, non-Hispanic/Latino; 9% international. 4% 25 or older, 56% live on campus, 4% transferred in. Retention: 95% of full-time freshmen returned the following year. Academic areas with the most degrees conferred: engineering; business/marketing; computer and information sciences. Core. Calendar: semesters. Academic remediation for entering students, ESL program, services for LD students, advanced placement, accelerated degree program, self-designed majors, honors program, independent study, distance learning, double major, summer session for credit, part-time degree program, co-op programs and internships, graduate courses open to undergrads. Off campus study at Dual Degree Programs are in many of the schools in the University System of Georgia, including Morehouse College, Spelman College, Clark Atlanta University, and other historically African American colleges and universities (HBCU); and predominantly women's colleges in the southeast and ARCHE-Atlanta Regional Council for Higher Education. Study abroad program. ROTC: Army, Naval, Air Force.

Entrance Requirements: Options: electronic application, early admission, early action, deferred admission, international baccalaureate accepted. Required: essay, high school transcript, SAT or ACT. Entrance: very difficult. Application deadlines: 1/10, 10/15 for early action. Notification: 3/9, 12/15 for early action. Preference given to qualified state residents and non residents who are legacies of the Institute. SAT Reasoning Test deadline: 1/10. Transfer credits accepted: Yes. Applicants placed on waiting list: 978. Waitlisted applicants offered admission: 43. Early action applicants: 8,344. Early action applicants admitted: 5,060.

Costs Per Year: Application fee: $65. State resident tuition: $7718 full-time, $2293 per term part-time. Nonresident tuition: $27,022 full-time, $8017 per term part-time. Mandatory fees: $2380 full-time, $1190 per term part-time, $1190 per term part-time. Part-time tuition and fees vary according to course load. College room and board: $9236. College room only: $5574. Room and board charges vary according to board plan and housing facility.

Collegiate Environment: Orientation program. Drama-theater group, choral group, marching band, student-run newspaper, radio station. Social organizations: 480 open to all; national fraternities, national sororities, local sororities; 23% of eligible men and 29% of eligible women are members. Major annual events: Team Buzz, Tech Beautification Day, Relay for Life. Student services: legal services, health clinic, personal-psychological counseling, women's center. Campus security: 24-hour emergency response devices and patrols, late night transport-escort service, controlled dormitory access, self defense education, lighted pathways and walks, video cameras, email and phone alerts of emergency situations. 10,033 college housing spaces available; 10,003 were occupied in 2012-13. Freshmen guaranteed college housing. Options: coed, men-only, women-only housing available. Georgia Institute of Technology Library plus 1 other with 2.6 million books, 4.7 million microform titles, 46,017 serials, 327,196 audiovisual materials, an OPAC, and a Web page. Operations spending for the previous fiscal year: $13.8 million. 1,000 computers available on campus for general student use. Computer purchase/lease plans available. A computer is required for all students. A campuswide network can be accessed from student residence rooms and from off campus. Students can access the following: online class registration. Staffed computer lab on campus (open 24 hours a day) provides training in use of computers, software, and the Internet.

Community Environment: See Clark Atlanta University.

■ **GEORGIA MILITARY COLLEGE**
201 E Greene St.
Old Capitol Bldg.
Milledgeville, GA 31061-3398
Tel: (478)387-4900; Free: 800-342-0413
Fax: (478)445-2688
E-mail: dfindley@gmc.cc.ga.us
Web Site: www.gmc.cc.ga.us/
Description: State and locally supported, 2-year, coed. Part of Georgia Independent College Association (GICA). Awards transfer associate degrees. Founded 1879. Setting: small town campus. System endowment: $12.8 million. Educational spending for the previous fiscal year: $2478 per

student. Total enrollment: 8,071. Faculty: 429 (126 full-time, 303 part-time). Student-undergrad faculty ratio is 25:1. Full-time: 5,384 students, 60% women, 40% men. Part-time: 2,687 students, 63% women, 37% men. Students come from 8 states and territories, 1% from out-of-state. 1% American Indian or Alaska Native, non-Hispanic/Latino; 5% Hispanic/Latino; 43% African American, non-Hispanic/Latino; 1% Asian, non-Hispanic/Latino; 0% Native Hawaiian or other Pacific Islander, non-Hispanic/Latino; 0% international. 37% 25 or older, 10% live on campus, 14% transferred in. Retention: 55% of full-time freshmen returned the following year. Core. Academic remediation for entering students, services for LD students, advanced placement, self-designed majors, independent study, distance learning, double major, summer session for credit, part-time degree program, co-op programs. Off campus study. Study abroad program. ROTC: Army.

Entrance Requirements: Open admission Cadet Corps are not open admission. Options: electronic application, early admission, deferred admission. Required for some: essay, high school transcript, interview. Entrance: noncompetitive. Application deadlines: Rolling, Rolling for nonresidents. Transfer credits accepted: Yes.

Collegiate Environment: Orientation program. Drama-theater group, choral group, student-run newspaper. Social organizations: 20 open to all; Phi Theta Kappa Honors Society. Most popular organizations: Student Government Association, Alpha Phi Omega National Service Fraternity, Phi Theta Kappa, Drama Club, Biology Club. Major annual events: Military parades, Convocation, Musical and theater performances. Student services: health clinic. Campus security: 24-hour emergency response devices and patrols, controlled dormitory access. 248 college housing spaces available; all were occupied in 2012-13. On-campus residence required through sophomore year. Option: coed housing available.

Community Environment: Milledgeville, an educational center, was the state capital from 1807 to 1867. Georgia Military College occupies the old state house. Railroads and buses serve the area. Some of the industries are spinning, canning, manufacture of clay products, and mobile homes. Job opportunities are numerous in textile plants. Nearby Lake Sinclair provides boating, fishing and water skiing. The early nineteenth-century homes add atmosphere and beauty to community life.

■ **GEORGIA NORTHWESTERN TECHNICAL COLLEGE**
One Maurice Culberson Dr.
Rome, GA 30161
Tel: (706)295-6963; Free: 866-983-GNTC
Fax: (706)295-6944
E-mail: dmcburnett@gntc.edu
Web Site: www.gntc.edu/
Description: State-supported, 2-year, coed. Part of Technical College System of Georgia. Awards certificates, diplomas, and terminal associate degrees. Founded 1962. Total enrollment: 6,036. Full-time: 2,284 students, 64% women, 36% men. Part-time: 3,752 students, 69% women, 31% men. 1% from out-of-state. 0.4% American Indian or Alaska Native, non-Hispanic/Latino; 7% Hispanic/Latino; 11% African American, non-Hispanic/Latino; 1% Asian, non-Hispanic/Latino; 0% Native Hawaiian or other Pacific Islander, non-Hispanic/Latino; 0% international. 49% 25 or older. Retention: 70% of full-time freshmen returned the following year. Distance learning.

Entrance Requirements: Open admission selective admission to some programs. Option: early admission. Required: high school transcript. Entrance: noncompetitive.

Collegiate Environment: College housing not available.

■ **GEORGIA PERIMETER COLLEGE**
3251 Panthersville Rd.
Decatur, GA 30034-3897
Tel: (404)244-5090; Free: 888-696-2780
Fax: (404)244-2996
Web Site: www.gpc.edu/
Description: State-supported, 2-year, coed. Part of University System of Georgia. Awards certificates, transfer associate, and terminal associate degrees. Founded 1964. Setting: 100-acre suburban campus with easy access to Atlanta. Total enrollment: 24,549. Faculty: 914 (351 full-time, 563 part-time). Student-undergrad faculty ratio is 24:1. 9,475 applied, 59% were admitted. Full-time: 11,522 students, 56% women, 44% men. Part-time: 13,027 students, 66% women, 34% men. 10% from out-of-state. 34% 25 or older, 5% transferred in. Core. Calendar: semesters. Academic remediation for entering students, ESL program, services for LD students, advanced

placement, honors program, distance learning, summer session for credit, part-time degree program, adult/continuing education programs. Study abroad program. ROTC: Army (c).

Entrance Requirements: Options: electronic application, early admission. Required: high school transcript. Recommended: SAT or ACT. Entrance: minimally difficult. Application deadline: 7/1. Notification: continuous.

Collegiate Environment: Orientation program. Drama-theater group, choral group, student-run newspaper. Student services: personal-psychological counseling. Campus security: 24-hour emergency response devices and patrols, late night transport-escort service. Georgia Perimeter College Library with 369,969 books, 36,511 microform titles, 2,032 serials, 15,500 audiovisual materials, and an OPAC.

■ **GEORGIA PIEDMONT TECHNICAL COLLEGE**

495 N Indian Creek Dr.
Clarkston, GA 30021-2397
Tel: (404)297-9522
Fax: (404)294-4234
E-mail: richardt@dekalbtech.edu
Web Site: www.gptc.edu/

Description: State-supported, 2-year, coed. Part of Technical College System of Georgia. Awards certificates, diplomas, and terminal associate degrees. Founded 1961. Setting: suburban campus. Total enrollment: 4,283. Full-time: 1,220 students, 55% women, 45% men. Part-time: 3,063 students, 64% women, 36% men. 0% from out-of-state. 0% American Indian or Alaska Native, non-Hispanic/Latino; 4% Hispanic/Latino; 74% African American, non-Hispanic/Latino; 3% Asian, non-Hispanic/Latino; 0% Native Hawaiian or other Pacific Islander, non-Hispanic/Latino; 0.2% international. 62% 25 or older. Retention: 63% of full-time freshmen returned the following year. Distance learning.

Entrance Requirements: Open admission selective admission to some programs. Option: early admission. Required: high school transcript. Entrance: noncompetitive.

Collegiate Environment: College housing not available.

■ **GEORGIA REGENTS UNIVERSITY**

1120 15th St.
Augusta, GA 30912
Tel: (706)721-0211; Free: 800-519-3388
Fax: (706)721-3461
E-mail: ksweeney@gru.edu
Web Site: www.gru.edu/

Description: State-supported, comprehensive, coed. Part of University System of Georgia. Awards associate, bachelor's, master's, and doctoral degrees and post-master's certificates. Founded 1828. Setting: 650-acre urban campus. Academic areas with the most degrees conferred: library science; business/marketing; education. Core. Calendar: semesters. Academic remediation for entering students, services for LD students, advanced placement, honors program, independent study, distance learning, double major, summer session for credit, adult/continuing education programs, co-op programs and internships, graduate courses open to undergrads. Off campus study. Study abroad program. ROTC: Army.

Entrance Requirements: Option: electronic application. Transfer credits accepted: Yes.

Costs Per Year: Application fee: $50. State resident tuition: $7434 full-time, $249 per credit hour part-time. Nonresident tuition: $26,130 full-time, $871 per credit hour part-time. Mandatory fees: $1646 full-time. Full-time tuition and fees vary according to course load, location, and program. Part-time tuition varies according to course load, location, and program. College room only: $2308.

Collegiate Environment: Orientation program. Drama-theater group, choral group, student-run newspaper. Social organizations: national fraternities, national sororities. Most popular organization: Student Government Association. Student services: health clinic, personal-psychological counseling. Campus security: 24-hour emergency response devices and patrols, late night transport-escort service. No special consideration for freshman housing applicants. Option: coed housing available.

Community Environment: Augusta is the second largest city in Georgia with a metropolitan-area population of around 500,000. The city offers a wide array of cultural and recreational activities, including a world-class Riverwalk, the site of many activities including the Augusta Invitation Regatta (a national collegiate rowing event) and the Augusta Southern Nationals, dubbed the World's Richest Drag Boat Race. The city also is a short drive from the huge Lake Thurmond Reservoir. Outdoor activities such as water-skiing, swim-

ming, boating, and camping abound. Kid-friendly sites include the Funsville Amusement Park, Krystal River Water Park, and Augusta Iceforum, an ice-skating rink. Attractions that promise both fun and enlightenment include the National Science Center's Fort Discovery, the Morris Museum of Art, the Georgia Golf Hall of Fame, the Lucy Craft Laney Museum of Black History, the Augusta Cotton Exchange Welcome Center and Museum, and the Augusta Museum of History. Augusta has many association dedicated to the performing and visual arts, including the Fort Gordon Dinner Theater, Augusta Opera Association, the Augusta Ballet, the Augusta Players, the Augusta Symphony, and the Augusta Art Association. The Medical College of Georgia, Augusta State University, and Paine College often bring prestigious films, speakers, and special events to the city. Augusta is within an easy three-hour drive of Atlanta, the University of Georgia, the Atlantic Ocean, and the mountains. The sporting life is ubiquitous throughout Augusta, whether you consider yourself an athlete or spectator. The city is home to professional baseball and ice hockey teams. The city annually hosts the Augusta Futurity, the largest cutting-horse futurity in the eastern United States. And of course, Augusta is world-renowned as the home of the Masters Golf Tournament. Augusta is a leading health care center of the Southeast and has a rapidly developing and diversified industrial base. The area's nine hospitals serve the Southeast and beyond.

■ **GEORGIA SOUTHERN UNIVERSITY**

1332 Southern Dr.
Statesboro, GA 30460
Tel: (912)681-5611
Fax: (912)681-5635
E-mail: admissions@georgiasouthern.edu
Web Site: www.georgiasouthern.edu/

Description: State-supported, university, coed. Part of University System of Georgia. Awards bachelor's, master's, and doctoral degrees and post-master's certificates. Founded 1906. Setting: 900-acre small town campus. Endowment: $36 million. Research spending for the previous fiscal year: $4.4 million. Educational spending for the previous fiscal year: $5182 per student. Total enrollment: 20,574. Faculty: 884 (761 full-time, 123 part-time). Student-undergrad faculty ratio is 22:1. 10,525 applied, 52% were admitted. 17% from top 10% of their high school class, 42% from top quarter, 75% from top half. Full-time: 15,818 students, 50% women, 50% men. Part-time: 2,175 students, 50% women, 50% men. Students come from 50 states and territories, 69 other countries, 4% from out-of-state. 1% American Indian or Alaska Native, non-Hispanic/Latino; 4% Hispanic/Latino; 25% African American, non-Hispanic/Latino; 1% Asian, non-Hispanic/Latino; 0.2% Native Hawaiian or other Pacific Islander, non-Hispanic/Latino; 1% international. 9% 25 or older, 28% live on campus, 6% transferred in. Retention: 77% of full-time freshmen returned the following year. Academic areas with the most degrees conferred: business/marketing; education; health professions and related sciences; engineering technologies. Core. Calendar: semesters. Academic remediation for entering students, ESL program, services for LD students, advanced placement, accelerated degree program, self-designed majors, honors program, independent study, distance learning, double major, summer session for credit, part-time degree program, adult/continuing education programs, co-op programs and internships, graduate courses open to undergrads. Off campus study at WebBSIT (a consortium of institutions including Georgia Southern University, Armstrong Atlantic State University, Clayton State University, Columbus State University, Georgia Southwestern State University, and Southern Polytechnic State University). The WebBSIT is offered fully online and is not campus based. Study abroad program. ROTC: Army.

Entrance Requirements: Options: electronic application, early admission, deferred admission, international baccalaureate accepted. Required: minimum 2 high school GPA, proof of immunization prior to enrollment, SAT or ACT. Required for some: high school transcript. Entrance: moderately difficult. Application deadlines: 5/1, 5/1 for nonresidents. Notification: continuous, continuous for nonresidents. SAT Reasoning Test deadline: 5/1. SAT Subject Test deadline: 5/1. Transfer credits accepted: Yes.

Costs Per Year: Application fee: $30. State resident tuition: $4852 full-time, $162 per credit hour part-time. Nonresident tuition: $17,128 full-time, $571 per credit hour part-time. Mandatory fees: $1872 full-time, $936 per term part-time. Full-time tuition and fees vary according to degree level, location, and program. Part-time tuition and fees vary according to course load, degree level, location, and program. College room and board: $9290. College room only: $5582. Room and board charges vary according to board plan and housing facility.

Collegiate Environment: Orientation program. Drama-theater group, choral

group, marching band, student-run newspaper, radio station. Social organizations: 215 open to all; national fraternities, national sororities, local fraternities, local sororities; 10% of eligible men and 15% of eligible women are members. Most popular organizations: Residence Hall Association, Campus Religious Ministries, Student Government Association, Club Sports and Recreation, Greek Life. Major annual events: Boro Browse (student organizations, local vender, ministry, and departmental fair), Homecoming Week, Welcome Week. Student services: legal services, health clinic, personal-psychological counseling, women's center. Campus security: 24-hour emergency response devices and patrols, student patrols, late night transport-escort service, controlled dormitory access, bike police and environmental safety services. 4,775 college housing spaces available; 4,662 were occupied in 2012-13. Freshmen given priority for college housing. On-campus residence required in freshman year. Option: coed housing available. Henderson Library with 631,881 books, 896,453 microform titles, 42,688 serials, 29,526 audiovisual materials, an OPAC, and a Web page. Operations spending for the previous fiscal year: $4.4 million. 3,320 computers available on campus for general student use. Computer purchase/lease plans available. A campuswide network can be accessed from student residence rooms and from off campus. Students can access the following: online class registration, online degree audit, online career services, and online healthcare. Staffed computer lab on campus (open 24 hours a day) provides training in use of computers, software, and the Internet.

Community Environment: Georgia Southern ranks among the safest college communities in the country. Its hometown of Statesboro is a neighborly college town and the seat of Bulloch County (50,000 residents). Because the campus and community have grown up together over the past century, shopping, services, and housing are tuned to student's needs. Just an hour down the road are the historic seaside city of Savannah and the beaches of Tybee Island.

■ **GEORGIA SOUTHWESTERN STATE UNIVERSITY**
800 Georgia Southwestern State University Dr.
Americus, GA 31709-4693
Tel: (229)928-1273; Free: 800-338-0082
Fax: (229)931-2983
E-mail: gswapps@canes.gsw.edu
Web Site: www.gsw.edu/

Description: State-supported, comprehensive, coed. Part of University System of Georgia. Awards bachelor's and master's degrees and post-master's certificates. Founded 1906. Setting: 400-acre small town campus. Endowment: $345,315. Research spending for the previous fiscal year: $66,379. Educational spending for the previous fiscal year: $4899 per student. Total enrollment: 2,973. Faculty: 169 (111 full-time, 58 part-time). Student-undergrad faculty ratio is 19:1. 1,308 applied, 66% were admitted. 20% from top 10% of their high school class, 37% from top quarter, 73% from top half. Full-time: 1,982 students, 63% women, 37% men. Part-time: 767 students, 68% women, 32% men. Students come from 25 states and territories, 38 other countries, 3% from out-of-state. 0.2% American Indian or Alaska Native, non-Hispanic/Latino; 2% Hispanic/Latino; 30% African American, non-Hispanic/Latino; 1% Asian, non-Hispanic/Latino; 0.1% Native Hawaiian or other Pacific Islander, non-Hispanic/Latino; 3% international. 30% 25 or older, 29% live on campus, 12% transferred in. Retention: 63% of full-time freshmen returned the following year. Academic areas with the most degrees conferred: business/marketing; education; health professions and related sciences. Core. Calendar: semesters. Academic remediation for entering students, ESL program, services for LD students, advanced placement, accelerated degree program, honors program, distance learning, double major, summer session for credit, part-time degree program, internships, graduate courses open to undergrads. Off campus study at Abraham Baldwin Agricultural College, Middle Georgia State College, Georgia Perimeter College, Bainbridge State College, East Georgia State College, South Georgia State College. Study abroad program.

Entrance Requirements: Options: electronic application, early admission, early decision, deferred admission, international baccalaureate accepted. Required: high school transcript, minimum 2 high school GPA, proof of immunization; SAT or ACT scores, SAT or ACT. Recommended: interview. Entrance: moderately difficult. Application deadlines: 7/21, 12/15 for early decision. Notification: continuous, 1/15 for early decision. SAT Reasoning Test deadline: 7/21. SAT Subject Test deadline: 7/21.

Costs Per Year: Application fee: $25. State resident tuition: $4512 full-time. Nonresident tuition: $16,416 full-time. Mandatory fees: $1268 full-time. Full-time tuition and fees vary according to course load. College room and board: $7378. College room only: $4620. Room and board charges vary according to board plan and housing facility.

Collegiate Environment: Orientation program. Drama-theater group, choral group, student-run newspaper. Social organizations: 60 open to all; national fraternities, national sororities; 17% of eligible men and 10% of eligible women are members. Most popular organizations: SUAVE - Strong United Assertive Virtuous Educated, BOLD - Beautiful Outstanding Ladies of Distinction, Residence Hall Association, Baptist Collegiate Ministries. Major annual events: Homecoming, Student Appreciation Day, Welcome Week. Student services: health clinic, personal-psychological counseling. Campus security: 24-hour emergency response devices and patrols, late night transport-escort service, controlled dormitory access. 950 college housing spaces available; 786 were occupied in 2012-13. Freshmen guaranteed college housing. On-campus residence required through sophomore year. Option: coed housing available. James Earl Carter Library with 787,018 books, 1.6 million microform titles, 237 serials, 14,335 audiovisual materials, an OPAC, and a Web page. Operations spending for the previous fiscal year: $628,996. 250 computers available on campus for general student use. A campuswide network can be accessed from student residence rooms and from off campus. Students can access the following: online class registration. Staffed computer lab on campus.

Community Environment: Americus is located 135 miles south of Atlanta, the climate is mild with a yearly mean temperature of 65.7 degrees, and an annual rainfall of 49 inches. Airlines serve the area. The usual community facilities include a hospital, library, the newly restored Rylander Theatre, daily newspaper, radio stations, clinics, and shopping centers. Manufactured products include shirts, lumber, nails, auto parts, and paper products. Kaolin and Bauxite mines are nearby. Outdoor sports include tennis, baseball, golf and basketball. Historic sites in Americus include Plains, home of President Jimmy Carter, Andersonville National Cemetery and Civil War prison site, and Souther field where Charles Lindbergh made his first solo flight. Americus is also home to International Habitat for Humanity.

■ **GEORGIA STATE UNIVERSITY**
33 Gilmer St.
Atlanta, GA 30302-3083
Tel: (404)651-2000
E-mail: onestopshop@gsu.edu
Web Site: www.gsu.edu/

Description: State-supported, university, coed. Part of University System of Georgia. Awards bachelor's, master's, and doctoral degrees and post-master's certificates. Founded 1913. Setting: 67-acre urban campus with easy access to Atlanta. Endowment: $112.1 million. Research spending for the previous fiscal year: $98.7 million. Educational spending for the previous fiscal year: $7024 per student. Total enrollment: 32,092. Faculty: 1,658 (1,174 full-time, 484 part-time). Student-undergrad faculty ratio is 21:1. 12,774 applied, 57% were admitted. 481 student government officers. Full-time: 18,060 students, 58% women, 42% men. Part-time: 6,605 students, 60% women, 40% men. Students come from 57 states and territories, 152 other countries, 3% from out-of-state. 0.2% American Indian or Alaska Native, non-Hispanic/Latino; 8% Hispanic/Latino; 39% African American, non-Hispanic/Latino; 11% Asian, non-Hispanic/Latino; 0.1% Native Hawaiian or other Pacific Islander, non-Hispanic/Latino; 2% international. 7% 25 or older, 17% live on campus, 11% transferred in. Retention: 83% of full-time freshmen returned the following year. Academic areas with the most degrees conferred: business/marketing; social sciences; education. Core. Calendar: semesters. ESL program, services for LD students, advanced placement, honors program, independent study, distance learning, double major, summer session for credit, part-time degree program, co-op programs and internships. Study abroad program. ROTC: Army, Naval (c), Air Force (c).

Entrance Requirements: Options: electronic application, early admission, early action, deferred admission, international baccalaureate accepted. Required: high school transcript, minimum 2.8 high school GPA, college preparatory curriculum as specified by the University System of Georgia Board of Regents. Combined SAT of 830. Freshman Index of 2500 or higher, SAT or ACT. Entrance: moderately difficult. Application deadlines: 3/1, 11/1 for early action. Notification: 5/1, 1/30 for early action. SAT Reasoning Test deadline: 3/1. Transfer credits accepted: Yes. Applicants placed on waiting list: 0. Wait-listed applicants offered admission: 0. Early action applicants: 4,763. Early action applicants admitted: 2,240.

Costs Per Year: Application fee: $60. State resident tuition: $7536 full-time, $251.20 per credit hour part-time. Nonresident tuition: $25,746 full-time, $858.20 per credit hour part-time. Mandatory fees: $2128 full-time, $1064 per term part-time. Part-time tuition and fees vary according to course load. College room and board: $11,546. College room only: $7956. Room and board charges vary according to housing facility.

Collegiate Environment: Orientation program. Drama-theater group, choral group, marching band, student-run newspaper, radio station. Social organizations: 338 open to all; national fraternities, national sororities; 3% of eligible men and 7% of eligible women are members. Most popular organizations: Spotlight Programs Board, Greek Organizations, International Student Associations Council, Academic Clubs, Sports Clubs. Major annual events: Welcome Week, Panther Prowl, Homecoming. Student services: health clinic, personal-psychological counseling. Campus security: 24-hour emergency response devices and patrols, late night transport-escort service, controlled dormitory access, Emergency Notification Center. 4,120 college housing spaces available; 4,000 were occupied in 2012-13. Freshmen given priority for college housing. Option: coed housing available. University Library plus 1 other with 1.7 million books, 2.6 million microform titles, 18,639 serials, 26,320 audiovisual materials, an OPAC, and a Web page. Operations spending for the previous fiscal year: $12.9 million. 685 computers available on campus for general student use. A campuswide network can be accessed from student residence rooms and from off campus. Students can access the following: online class registration. Staffed computer lab on campus provides training in use of computers, software, and the Internet.
Community Environment: See Clark Atlanta University.

■ **GORDON STATE COLLEGE**
419 College Dr.
Barnesville, GA 30204-1762
Tel: (678)359-5555; Free: 800-282-6504
E-mail: benf@gdn.edu
Web Site: www.gordonstate.edu/
Description: State-supported, primarily 2-year, coed. Part of University System of Georgia. Awards certificates, transfer associate, terminal associate, and bachelor's degrees. Founded 1852. Setting: 125-acre small town campus with easy access to Atlanta. Endowment: $7.5 million. Educational spending for the previous fiscal year: $3040 per student. Total enrollment: 4,171. Faculty: 207 (124 full-time, 83 part-time). Student-undergrad faculty ratio is 24:1. 2,871 applied, 43% were admitted. Students come from 9 states and territories, 1 other country, 0.1% from out-of-state. 16% 25 or older. Core. Calendar: semesters. Academic remediation for entering students, advanced placement, accelerated degree program, honors program, summer session for credit, part-time degree program, adult/continuing education programs, co-op programs and internships. Off campus study. Study abroad program.
Entrance Requirements: Open admission. Options: electronic application, early admission, deferred admission. Required: high school transcript. Entrance: minimally difficult. Application deadline: Rolling.
Collegiate Environment: Orientation program. Drama-theater group, choral group, student-run newspaper. Social organizations: 35 open to all; 39% of eligible men and 61% of eligible women are members. Most popular organizations: Campus Activity Board, Student Government Association, Earth wind fire (Science Club), Student African American Brotherhood (SAAB), Swazi Step Team. Major annual events: Spring Fling (April), October Fest (October), Turkey Trot. Student services: health clinic, personal-psychological counseling. Campus security: 24-hour emergency response devices and patrols, student patrols, late night transport-escort service, controlled dormitory access, RA's and RDs (housing) and Parking Patrol (Public Safety). 994 college housing spaces available; 857 were occupied in 2012-13. Freshmen given priority for college housing. On-campus residence required in freshman year. Option: coed housing available. Hightower Library with 150,062 books, 10,056 microform titles, 55,588 serials, 5,037 audiovisual materials, an OPAC, and a Web page. Operations spending for the previous fiscal year: $560,970. 466 computers available on campus for general student use. A campuswide network can be accessed from student residence rooms. Students can access the following: online class registration. Staffed computer lab on campus provides training in use of computers, software, and the Internet.

■ **GUPTON-JONES COLLEGE OF FUNERAL SERVICE**
5141 Snapfinger Woods Dr.
Decatur, GA 30035-4022
Tel: (770)593-2257; Free: 800-848-5352
Fax: (770)593-1891
Web Site: www.gupton-jones.edu/
Description: Independent, 2-year, coed. Part of Pierce Mortuary Colleges, Inc. Awards terminal associate degrees. Founded 1920. Setting: 3-acre suburban campus with easy access to Atlanta. Total enrollment: 149. 48% 25 or older. Core. Academic remediation for entering students, distance learning, summer session for credit.

Entrance Requirements: Open admission. Option: electronic application. Required: high school transcript, health certificate. Recommended: minimum 3.0 high school GPA. Entrance: noncompetitive. Application deadline: Rolling.
Collegiate Environment: Social organizations: national fraternities. Russell Millison Library with 3,500 books, 15 serials, and an OPAC.

■ **GWINNETT TECHNICAL COLLEGE**
5150 Sugarloaf Pky.
Lawrenceville, GA 30043-5702
Tel: (770)962-7580
E-mail: fhalloran@gwinnetttech.edu
Web Site: www.gwinnetttech.edu/
Description: State-supported, 2-year, coed. Part of Technical College System of Georgia. Awards certificates, diplomas, and terminal associate degrees. Founded 1984. Setting: suburban campus. Total enrollment: 6,682. Full-time: 2,244 students, 58% women, 42% men. Part-time: 4,438 students, 64% women, 36% men. 1% from out-of-state. 0% American Indian or Alaska Native, non-Hispanic/Latino; 15% Hispanic/Latino; 31% African American, non-Hispanic/Latino; 4% Asian, non-Hispanic/Latino; 0.1% Native Hawaiian or other Pacific Islander, non-Hispanic/Latino; 0% international. 61% 25 or older. Retention: 69% of full-time freshmen returned the following year. Distance learning.
Entrance Requirements: Open admission selective admission to some programs. Option: early admission. Required: high school transcript. Entrance: noncompetitive.
Collegiate Environment: College housing not available.

■ **HERZING UNIVERSITY**
3393 Peachtree Rd.
Ste. 1003
Atlanta, GA 30326
Tel: (404)816-4533; Free: 800-596-0724
Fax: (404)816-5576
E-mail: aelder@atl.herzing.edu
Web Site: www.herzing.edu/atlanta/
Description: Proprietary, 4-year, coed. Part of Herzing, Inc. Awards associate and bachelor's degrees. Founded 1949. Setting: urban campus with easy access to Atlanta. Total enrollment: 609. Faculty: 25 (10 full-time, 15 part-time). Student-undergrad faculty ratio is 8:1. 279 applied, 75% were admitted. Full-time: 426 students, 65% women, 35% men. Part-time: 183 students, 70% women, 30% men. Students come from 5 states and territories, 10 other countries, 0% from out-of-state. 56% 25 or older, 7% transferred in. Retention: 89% of full-time freshmen returned the following year. Calendar: semesters. Academic remediation for entering students, ESL program, honors program, internships.
Entrance Requirements: Required: high school transcript, interview, Wonderlic aptitude test. Entrance: moderately difficult. Application deadline: Rolling. Notification: continuous. Transfer credits accepted: Yes.
Collegiate Environment: Orientation program. Student services: personal-psychological counseling, women's center. Campus security: 24-hour patrols. Herzing University Library with 6,000 books, 25 serials, an OPAC, and a Web page. Operations spending for the previous fiscal year: $40,000. 125 computers available on campus for general student use. A campuswide network can be accessed from student residence rooms.

■ **INTERACTIVE COLLEGE OF TECHNOLOGY**
5303 New Peachtree Rd.
Chamblee, GA 30341
Tel: (770)216-2960; Free: 800-447-2011
Fax: (770)216-2989
Web Site: www.ict-ils.edu/
Description: Proprietary, 2-year, coed. Part of Interactive Learning Systems. Awards certificates, diplomas, and terminal associate degrees. Total enrollment: 312. Student-undergrad faculty ratio is 25:1. 0% from out-of-state. 80% 25 or older. Core. Academic remediation for entering students, ESL program, advanced placement, accelerated degree program, independent study, double major, part-time degree program, adult/continuing education programs, internships.
Entrance Requirements: Open admission. Option: international baccalaureate accepted. Required: high school transcript, interview. Application deadline: Rolling.
Collegiate Environment: Orientation program. 4,589 books, 25 serials, and an OPAC.

■ **ITT TECHNICAL INSTITUTE (ATLANTA)**
485 Oak Pl.
Ste. 800
Atlanta, GA 30349
Tel: (404)765-4600; Free: 877-788-6102
Web Site: www.itt-tech.edu/
Description: Proprietary, primarily 2-year, coed. Part of ITT Educational Services, Inc. Awards terminal associate and bachelor's degrees.
Entrance Requirements: Entrance: minimally difficult.

■ **ITT TECHNICAL INSTITUTE (DULUTH)**
10700 Abbotts Bridge Rd.
Duluth, GA 30097
Tel: (678)957-8510; Free: 866-489-8818
Web Site: www.itt-tech.edu/
Description: Proprietary, primarily 2-year, coed. Part of ITT Educational Services, Inc. Awards terminal associate and bachelor's degrees. Founded 2003.
Entrance Requirements: Entrance: minimally difficult.

■ **ITT TECHNICAL INSTITUTE (KENNESAW)**
2065 ITT Tech Way NW
Kennesaw, GA 30144
Tel: (770)426-2300; Free: 800-231-6415
Web Site: www.itt-tech.edu/
Description: Proprietary, primarily 2-year, coed. Part of ITT Educational Services, Inc. Awards terminal associate and bachelor's degrees. Founded 2004.
Entrance Requirements: Entrance: minimally difficult.

■ **KENNESAW STATE UNIVERSITY**
1000 Chastain Rd.
Kennesaw, GA 30144-5591
Tel: (770)423-6000
Fax: (770)423-6541
E-mail: ksuadmit@kennesaw.edu
Web Site: www.kennesaw.edu/
Description: State-supported, comprehensive, coed. Part of University System of Georgia. Awards bachelor's, master's, and doctoral degrees and post-master's certificates. Founded 1963. Setting: 384-acre suburban campus with easy access to Atlanta. Endowment: $24.8 million. Research spending for the previous fiscal year: $1.8 million. Educational spending for the previous fiscal year: $5921 per student. Total enrollment: 24,604. Faculty: 1,356 (747 full-time, 609 part-time). Student-undergrad faculty ratio is 21:1. 9,471 applied, 57% were admitted. 21% from top 10% of their high school class, 53% from top quarter, 81% from top half. Full-time: 16,954 students, 58% women, 42% men. Part-time: 5,730 students, 58% women, 42% men. 6% from out-of-state. 0.2% American Indian or Alaska Native, non-Hispanic/Latino; 7% Hispanic/Latino; 16% African American, non-Hispanic/Latino; 3% Asian, non-Hispanic/Latino; 0.1% Native Hawaiian or other Pacific Islander, non-Hispanic/Latino; 2% international. 27% 25 or older, 14% live on campus. Retention: 76% of full-time freshmen returned the following year. Academic areas with the most degrees conferred: business/marketing; education; communication/journalism. Core. Calendar: semesters. ESL program, services for LD students, advanced placement, honors program, distance learning, double major, summer session for credit, part-time degree program, adult/continuing education programs, co-op programs and internships, graduate courses open to undergrads. Off campus study at University Center in Georgia, 19 colleges and universities in the Atlanta area. Study abroad program. ROTC: Army (c), Air Force (c).
Entrance Requirements: Options: electronic application, early admission, deferred admission. Required: high school transcript, minimum 2.5 high school GPA, proof of immunization, SAT or ACT. Entrance: moderately difficult. Application deadline: 5/10. Notification: continuous. SAT Reasoning Test deadline: 5/10. SAT Subject Test deadline: 5/10. Transfer credits accepted: Yes.
Costs Per Year: Application fee: $40. State resident tuition: $4852 full-time, $162 per credit hour part-time. Nonresident tuition: $17,128 full-time, $571 per credit hour part-time. Mandatory fees: $1634 full-time, $817 per term part-time. Part-time tuition and fees vary according to course load. College room and board: $7966. Room and board charges vary according to board plan and housing facility.
Collegiate Environment: Orientation program. Drama-theater group, choral group, student-run newspaper, radio station. Social organizations: 180 open

to all; national fraternities, national sororities; 4% of eligible men and 5% of eligible women are members. Most popular organizations: Global Society, Student Government Association, Kennesaw Activities Board, African-American Student Alliance, International Student Association. Major annual events: KSU Day, Homecoming, International Festival. Student services: health clinic, personal-psychological counseling. Campus security: 24-hour emergency response devices and patrols, student patrols, late night transport-escort service, controlled dormitory access. 3,494 college housing spaces available; all were occupied in 2012-13. Freshmen given priority for college housing. Option: coed housing available. Horace W. Sturgis Library plus 1 other with 573,000 books, 1.3 million microform titles, 55,000 serials, 9,000 audiovisual materials, an OPAC, and a Web page. Operations spending for the previous fiscal year: $3.5 million. 1,650 computers available on campus for general student use. Computer purchase/lease plans available. A campuswide network can be accessed from student residence rooms and from off campus. Students can access the following: online class registration. Staffed computer lab on campus provides training in use of computers, software, and the Internet.
Community Environment: A suburban area of Marietta, the average winter temperature is 45 degrees, the average summer temperature is 80 degrees, with an average rainfall of 50 inches. Community facilities include churches, and civic organizations with hospitals and shopping areas in Marietta. In view is Kennesaw Mountain, site of Civil War battles and the"The Great Locomotive Chase.".

■ **LAGRANGE COLLEGE**
601 Broad St.
LaGrange, GA 30240-2999
Tel: (706)880-8000; Free: 800-593-2885
Fax: (706)880-8040
E-mail: mthomas@lagrange.edu
Web Site: www.lagrange.edu/
Description: Independent United Methodist, comprehensive, coed. Awards bachelor's and master's degrees. Founded 1831. Setting: 120-acre small town campus with easy access to Atlanta. Endowment: $52.5 million. Research spending for the previous fiscal year: $7636. Educational spending for the previous fiscal year: $8217 per student. Total enrollment: 902. Faculty: 109 (70 full-time, 39 part-time). Student-undergrad faculty ratio is 10:1. 1,288 applied, 49% were admitted. 22% from top 10% of their high school class, 48% from top quarter, 87% from top half. 6 class presidents, 22 student government officers. Full-time: 823 students, 57% women, 43% men. Part-time: 11 students, 55% women, 45% men. Students come from 17 states and territories, 10 other countries, 15% from out-of-state. 0.5% American Indian or Alaska Native, non-Hispanic/Latino; 3% Hispanic/Latino; 23% African American, non-Hispanic/Latino; 1% Asian, non-Hispanic/Latino; 0% Native Hawaiian or other Pacific Islander, non-Hispanic/Latino; 1% international. 18% 25 or older, 64% live on campus, 10% transferred in. Retention: 60% of full-time freshmen returned the following year. Academic areas with the most degrees conferred: health professions and related sciences; business/marketing; visual and performing arts. Core. Calendar: 4-1-4. Services for LD students, advanced placement, accelerated degree program, self-designed majors, independent study, double major, summer session for credit, part-time degree program, adult/continuing education programs, internships, graduate courses open to undergrads. Study abroad program.
Entrance Requirements: Options: electronic application, early admission, early action, deferred admission, international baccalaureate accepted. Required: essay, high school transcript, SAT or ACT, SAT or ACT. Required for some: minimum 2.5 high school GPA, 1 recommendation, interview. Entrance: moderately difficult. Application deadlines: Rolling, 12/31 for early action. Notification: continuous. SAT Reasoning Test deadline: 3/1. Transfer credits accepted: Yes. Early action applicants: 0. Early action applicants admitted: 0.
Costs Per Year: Application fee: $30. Comprehensive fee: $34,640 includes full-time tuition ($24,302), mandatory fees ($160), and college room and board ($10,178). College room only: $5816. Full-time tuition and fees vary according to class time, course load, degree level, and program. Room and board charges vary according to board plan and housing facility. Part-time tuition: $1000 per semester hour. Part-time tuition varies according to class time, course load, degree level, and program.
Collegiate Environment: Orientation program. Drama-theater group, choral group, student-run newspaper. Social organizations: 55 open to all; national fraternities, national sororities; 19% of eligible men and 19% of eligible women are members. Most popular organizations: Student Government As-

sociation, Greek Life, Baptist Collegiate Ministries, Wesley Fellowship, Fellowship of Christian Athletes. Major annual events: Spirit and Traditions Kickoff, Family Weekend, Christmas on the Hill. Student services: health clinic, personal-psychological counseling. Campus security: 24-hour patrols, controlled dormitory access, A mass notification system, called e2Campus, allows the college to automatically send emergency messages to students and employees. 632 college housing spaces available; 533 were occupied in 2012-13. Freshmen guaranteed college housing. On-campus residence required through senior year. Options: coed, men-only, women-only housing available. Frank and Laura Lewis Library with 402,389 books, 119,677 microform titles, 493 serials, 7,763 audiovisual materials, an OPAC, and a Web page. Operations spending for the previous fiscal year: $763,629. 175 computers available on campus for general student use. A campuswide network can be accessed from student residence rooms and from off campus. Students can access the following: online class registration. Staffed computer lab on campus provides training in use of computers, software, and the Internet.

■ **LANIER TECHNICAL COLLEGE**
2990 Landrum Education Dr.
Oakwood, GA 30566
Tel: (770)531-6300
Fax: (770)531-6328
E-mail: mike@laniertech.edu
Web Site: www.laniertech.edu/
Description: State-supported, 2-year, coed. Part of Technical College System of Georgia. Awards certificates, diplomas, and terminal associate degrees. Founded 1964. Total enrollment: 3,389. Full-time: 922 students, 67% women, 33% men. Part-time: 2,467 students, 63% women, 37% men. 0.2% from out-of-state. 0% American Indian or Alaska Native, non-Hispanic/Latino; 14% Hispanic/Latino; 9% African American, non-Hispanic/Latino; 1% Asian, non-Hispanic/Latino; 0.2% Native Hawaiian or other Pacific Islander, non-Hispanic/Latino; 0.4% international. 54% 25 or older. Retention: 70% of full-time freshmen returned the following year. Distance learning.
Entrance Requirements: Open admission selective admission to some programs. Option: early admission. Required: high school transcript. Entrance: noncompetitive.
Collegiate Environment: College housing not available.

■ **LE CORDON BLEU COLLEGE OF CULINARY ARTS, ATLANTA**
1957 Lakeside Pky.
Tucker, GA 30084
Tel: (770)938-4711; Free: 888-549-8222
Web Site: www.atlantaculinary.com/
Description: Proprietary, 2-year, coed. Awards terminal associate degrees. Total enrollment: 763.
Entrance Requirements: Entrance: noncompetitive.

■ **LIFE UNIVERSITY**
1269 Barclay Cir.
Marietta, GA 30060-2903
Tel: (770)426-2600; Free: 800-543-3202
E-mail: admissions@life.edu
Web Site: www.life.edu/
Description: Independent, comprehensive, coed. Awards associate, bachelor's, master's, and doctoral degrees. Founded 1974. Setting: 96-acre suburban campus. Total enrollment: 2,655. Faculty: 181 (126 full-time, 55 part-time). Student-undergrad faculty ratio is 17:1. 809 applied, 75% were admitted. Full-time: 598 students, 46% women, 54% men. Part-time: 245 students, 56% women, 44% men. Students come from 52 states and territories, 39 other countries, 54% from out-of-state. 1% American Indian or Alaska Native, non-Hispanic/Latino; 8% Hispanic/Latino; 32% African American, non-Hispanic/Latino; 3% Asian, non-Hispanic/Latino; 4% international. 49% 25 or older, 15% transferred in. Retention: 70% of full-time freshmen returned the following year. Academic areas with the most degrees conferred: biological/life sciences; business/marketing; psychology. Core. Academic remediation for entering students, ESL program, services for LD students, advanced placement, accelerated degree program, independent study, double major, summer session for credit, internships, graduate courses open to undergrads. Off campus study.
Entrance Requirements: Options: electronic application, international baccalaureate accepted. Required: high school transcript, minimum 2 high school GPA, SAT or ACT. Entrance: minimally difficult. Application deadline: 9/1. Notification: continuous. Transfer credits accepted: Yes.

Costs Per Year: Application fee: $50. Comprehensive fee: $24,832 includes full-time tuition ($11,231), mandatory fees ($747), and college room and board ($12,854). Full-time tuition and fees vary according to course load. Part-time tuition: $191 per credit hour. Part-time mandatory fees: $249 per term. Part-time tuition and fees vary according to course load.
Collegiate Environment: Orientation program. Student-run newspaper. Student services: health clinic. Campus security: 24-hour emergency response devices and patrols, controlled dormitory access. 300 college housing spaces available. No special consideration for freshman housing applicants. Library & Learning Services with an OPAC.

■ **LUTHER RICE UNIVERSITY**
3038 Evans Mill Rd.
Lithonia, GA 30038-2454
Tel: (770)484-1204; Free: 800-442-1577
E-mail: admissions@lru.edu
Web Site: www.lru.edu/
Description: Independent Baptist, comprehensive, coed. Awards bachelor's and master's degrees. Founded 1962. Setting: 5-acre urban campus with easy access to Atlanta. Total enrollment: 1,650. 360 applied, 81% were admitted. 31% from out-of-state. 90% 25 or older. Core. Calendar: semesters. Academic remediation for entering students, advanced placement, independent study, distance learning, part-time degree program, external degree program, adult/continuing education programs, co-op programs and internships, graduate courses open to undergrads. Study abroad program.
Entrance Requirements: Open admission. Options: electronic application, early admission, international baccalaureate accepted. Required: high school transcript, Bible examination. Entrance: noncompetitive. Application deadline: Rolling.
Costs Per Year: Application fee: $50. Tuition: $5352 full-time.
Collegiate Environment: Student services: personal-psychological counseling. Campus security: 24-hour emergency response devices, late night transport-escort service. College housing not available. Bertha Smith Library with 45,200 books and 70 serials.

■ **MERCER UNIVERSITY**
1400 Coleman Ave.
Macon, GA 31207-0003
Tel: (478)301-2700; Free: 800-MERCER-U
Fax: (478)301-2828
E-mail: sosa_ac@mercer.edu
Web Site: www.mercer.edu/
Description: Independent Baptist, university, coed. Awards bachelor's, master's, and doctoral degrees and post-master's certificates. Founded 1833. Setting: 150-acre suburban campus with easy access to Atlanta. Endowment: $191.7 million. Research spending for the previous fiscal year: $28.9 million. Total enrollment: 6,288. Faculty: 685 (371 full-time, 314 part-time). Student-undergrad faculty ratio is 13:1. 3,519 applied, 63% were admitted. 42% from top 10% of their high school class, 70% from top quarter, 92% from top half. Full-time: 2,318 students, 49% women, 51% men. Part-time: 64 students, 53% women, 47% men. Students come from 41 states and territories, 37 other countries, 16% from out-of-state. 0.3% American Indian or Alaska Native, non-Hispanic/Latino; 4% Hispanic/Latino; 19% African American, non-Hispanic/Latino; 7% Asian, non-Hispanic/Latino; 0% Native Hawaiian or other Pacific Islander, non-Hispanic/Latino; 4% international. 4% 25 or older, 67% live on campus, 4% transferred in. Retention: 82% of full-time freshmen returned the following year. Academic areas with the most degrees conferred: biological/life sciences; business/marketing; engineering. Core. Calendar: semesters. ESL program, services for LD students, advanced placement, accelerated degree program, self-designed majors, honors program, independent study, distance learning, double major, summer session for credit, part-time degree program, adult/continuing education programs, co-op programs and internships, graduate courses open to undergrads. Off campus study at Wesleyan College (GA). Study abroad program. ROTC: Army.
Entrance Requirements: Options: electronic application, early admission, early action, deferred admission, international baccalaureate accepted. Required: high school transcript, minimum 3 high school GPA, SAT or ACT. Recommended: interview, counselor's evaluation. Required for some: 2 recommendations, interview. Entrance: moderately difficult. Application deadlines: 7/1, 11/1 for early action. Notification: continuous, 11/15 for early action. SAT Reasoning Test deadline: 7/1.
Costs Per Year: Application fee: $50. Comprehensive fee: $43,163 includes

full-time tuition ($32,166), mandatory fees ($300), and college room and board ($10,697). College room only: $5244. Full-time tuition and fees vary according to class time and location. Room and board charges vary according to board plan, housing facility, and location. Part-time tuition: $1,072 per credit hour. Part-time mandatory fees: $10 per credit hour. Part-time tuition and fees vary according to class time, course load, and location.

Collegiate Environment: Orientation program. Drama-theater group, choral group, marching band, student-run newspaper, radio station. Social organizations: 104 open to all; national fraternities, national sororities, local sororities; 21% of eligible men and 26% of eligible women are members. Major annual events: Mercer Madness, Homecoming, Founders' Day. Student services: health clinic, personal-psychological counseling. Campus security: 24-hour emergency response devices and patrols, student patrols, late night transport-escort service, controlled dormitory access, patrols by police officers. 1,647 college housing spaces available; 1,578 were occupied in 2012-13. Freshmen guaranteed college housing. On-campus residence required through sophomore year. Options: coed, men-only, women-only housing available. Jack Tarver Library plus 3 others with 796,693 books, 3 million microform titles, 25,037 serials, 68,619 audiovisual materials, an OPAC, and a Web page.

■ **MIDDLE GEORGIA STATE COLLEGE**
1100 Second St., SE
Cochran, GA 31014-1599
Tel: (478)934-6221
Fax: (478)934-3199
E-mail: admissions@mgc.edu
Web Site: www.mgc.edu/

Description: State-supported, 4-year, coed. Part of University System of Georgia. Awards associate and bachelor's degrees. Founded 1884. Setting: 165-acre small town campus. Endowment: $847,031. Educational spending for the previous fiscal year: $4761 per student. Total enrollment: 3,614. Faculty: 170 (115 full-time, 55 part-time). Student-undergrad faculty ratio is 22:1. 2,188 applied, 89% were admitted. Full-time: 2,586 students, 52% women, 48% men. Part-time: 1,028 students, 61% women, 39% men. Students come from 36 states and territories, 31 other countries, 4% from out-of-state. 21% 25 or older, 35% live on campus, 7% transferred in. Retention: 63% of full-time freshmen returned the following year. Core. Calendar: semesters. Academic remediation for entering students, advanced placement, accelerated degree program, self-designed majors, honors program, distance learning, double major, summer session for credit, part-time degree program, co-op programs and internships. Study abroad program.

Entrance Requirements: Options: electronic application, early admission, deferred admission, international baccalaureate accepted. Required: high school transcript, minimum 2 high school GPA. Recommended: SAT or ACT. Required for some: essay, minimum 3.5 high school GPA, 3 recommendations, interview, SAT or ACT. Entrance: minimally difficult. Application deadline: Rolling. Notification: continuous.

Collegiate Environment: Orientation program. Drama-theater group, choral group, marching band. Social organizations: 20 open to all. Most popular organizations: Baptist Student Union, Student Government Association, MGC Ambassadors, Encore Productions, United Voices of Praise. Major annual events: Movie Night, Homecoming, Spring Fling. Student services: health clinic, personal-psychological counseling. Campus security: 24-hour emergency response devices and patrols, late night transport-escort service, controlled dormitory access, patrols by police officers. Roberts Memorial Library with 105,568 books, 17,200 microform titles, 220 serials, 1,000 audiovisual materials, an OPAC, and a Web page. Operations spending for the previous fiscal year: $687,987. 650 computers available on campus for general student use. A campuswide network can be accessed from student residence rooms and from off campus. Students can access the following: online class registration. Staffed computer lab on campus (open 24 hours a day).

Community Environment: Cochran is 40 miles south of Macon, between interstate highways 75 and 16, almost squarely in the center of the state. Both mountain and beach resorts are about three hours away.

■ **MIDDLE GEORGIA TECHNICAL COLLEGE**
80 Cohen Walker Dr.
Warner Robbins, GA 31088
Tel: (478)988-6800; Free: 800-474-1031
E-mail: dwebb@middlegatech.edu
Web Site: www.middlegatech.edu/
Description: State-supported, 2-year, coed. Part of Technical College

System of Georgia. Awards certificates, diplomas, and terminal associate degrees. Founded 1973. Total enrollment: 3,771. Full-time: 1,342 students, 61% women, 39% men. Part-time: 2,429 students, 57% women, 43% men. 4% from out-of-state. 0.2% American Indian or Alaska Native, non-Hispanic/Latino; 2% Hispanic/Latino; 46% African American, non-Hispanic/Latino; 1% Asian, non-Hispanic/Latino; 0.1% Native Hawaiian or other Pacific Islander, non-Hispanic/Latino; 0.1% international. 54% 25 or older. Retention: 72% of full-time freshmen returned the following year. Distance learning.

Entrance Requirements: Open admission selective admission to some programs. Option: early admission. Required: high school transcript. Entrance: noncompetitive.

Collegiate Environment: College housing not available.

■ **MOREHOUSE COLLEGE**
830 Westview Dr., SW
Atlanta, GA 30314
Tel: (404)681-2800; Free: 800-851-1254
Fax: (404)659-6536
E-mail: kwilliams@morehouse.edu
Web Site: www.morehouse.edu/

Description: Independent, 4-year, men only. Awards bachelor's degrees. Founded 1867. Setting: 61-acre urban campus. Endowment: $129.4 million. Research spending for the previous fiscal year: $5.9 million. Educational spending for the previous fiscal year: $9676 per student. Total enrollment: 2,377. Faculty: 223 (164 full-time, 59 part-time). Student-undergrad faculty ratio is 12:1. 2,576 applied, 66% were admitted. 20% from top 10% of their high school class, 45% from top quarter, 71% from top half. 5 National Merit Scholars, 25 class presidents, 6 valedictorians, 100 student government officers. Full-time: 2,221 students. Part-time: 156 students. Students come from 44 states and territories, 14 other countries, 71% from out-of-state. 0% American Indian or Alaska Native, non-Hispanic/Latino; 0.2% Hispanic/Latino; 96% African American, non-Hispanic/Latino; 0% Asian, non-Hispanic/Latino; 0% Native Hawaiian or other Pacific Islander, non-Hispanic/Latino; 2% international. 5% 25 or older, 96% live on campus, 3% transferred in. Retention: 80% of full-time freshmen returned the following year. Academic areas with the most degrees conferred: business/marketing; social sciences; psychology. Core. Calendar: semesters. Academic remediation for entering students, services for LD students, advanced placement, honors program, double major, summer session for credit, part-time degree program, co-op programs and internships. Off campus study at Atlanta University Center (AUC); Clark Atlanta University, Spelman College. Study abroad program. ROTC: Army, Naval, Air Force.

Entrance Requirements: Options: electronic application, early admission, early decision, early action, deferred admission. Required: essay, high school transcript, SAT or ACT. Recommended: minimum 3 high school GPA, interview. Entrance: moderately difficult. Application deadlines: 2/15, 11/1 for early decision, 11/1 for early action. Notification: 4/1, 12/15 for early decision, 12/15 for early action. SAT Reasoning Test deadline: 2/15. SAT Subject Test deadline: 2/15. Transfer credits accepted: Yes. Early decision applicants: 99. Early decision applicants admitted: 38. Early action applicants: 380. Early action applicants admitted: 153.

Costs Per Year: Application fee: $50. Comprehensive fee: $37,416 includes full-time tuition ($22,482), mandatory fees ($2262), and college room and board ($12,672). College room only: $7220. Full-time tuition and fees vary according to course load and student level. Room and board charges vary according to board plan.

Collegiate Environment: Orientation program. Drama-theater group, choral group, marching band, student-run newspaper. Social organizations: 50 open to all; national fraternities; 60% of eligible undergrads are members. Most popular organizations: Morehouse College Glee Club, Morehouse Business Association, NAACP, Morehouse Public Health Association, Pre-Law Society. Major annual events: Homecoming, Founders' Week, Commencement/Reunion. Student services: health clinic, personal-psychological counseling. Campus security: 24-hour emergency response devices and patrols, late night transport-escort service, controlled dormitory access. 1,587 college housing spaces available; 1,525 were occupied in 2012-13. Freshmen guaranteed college housing. On-campus residence required in freshman year. Option: men-only housing available. Atlanta University Center Robert R. Woodruff Library with 419,575 books, 853,037 microform titles, 293,961 serials, 7,437 audiovisual materials, an OPAC, and a Web page. 500 computers available on campus for general student use. A campuswide network can be accessed from student residence rooms and from off campus. Students can access the following: online class registration. Staffed computer lab on campus (open 24 hours a day) provides training in use of computers, software, and the Internet.

Community Environment: See Clark Atlanta University.

■ MOULTRIE TECHNICAL COLLEGE

800 Veterans Pky. N
Moultrie, GA 31788
Tel: (229)891-7000
Fax: (229)891-7010
E-mail: lgriffin@moultrietech.edu
Web Site: www.moultrietech.edu/

Description: State-supported, 2-year, coed. Part of Technical College System of Georgia. Awards certificates, diplomas, and terminal associate degrees. Founded 1964. Total enrollment: 1,999. Full-time: 809 students, 63% women, 37% men. Part-time: 1,190 students, 65% women, 35% men. 0% from out-of-state. 0.4% American Indian or Alaska Native, non-Hispanic/Latino; 7% Hispanic/Latino; 32% African American, non-Hispanic/Latino; 0.4% Asian, non-Hispanic/Latino; 0% Native Hawaiian or other Pacific Islander, non-Hispanic/Latino; 0% international. 42% 25 or older. Retention: 65% of full-time freshmen returned the following year. Distance learning.

Entrance Requirements: Open admission selective admission to some programs. Option: early admission. Required: high school transcript. Entrance: noncompetitive.

Collegiate Environment: College housing not available.

■ NORTH GEORGIA TECHNICAL COLLEGE

1500 Georgia Hwy. 197, N
Clarkesville, GA 30523
Tel: (706)754-7700
Fax: (706)754-7777
E-mail: amitchell@northgatech.edu
Web Site: www.northgatech.edu/

Description: State-supported, 2-year, coed. Part of Technical College System of Georgia. Awards certificates, diplomas, and terminal associate degrees. Founded 1943. Total enrollment: 2,369. Full-time: 1,072 students, 57% women, 43% men. Part-time: 1,297 students, 62% women, 38% men. 1% from out-of-state. 0% American Indian or Alaska Native, non-Hispanic/Latino; 5% Hispanic/Latino; 6% African American, non-Hispanic/Latino; 0.4% Asian, non-Hispanic/Latino; 0% Native Hawaiian or other Pacific Islander, non-Hispanic/Latino; 0.2% international. 41% 25 or older. Retention: 68% of full-time freshmen returned the following year. Distance learning.

Entrance Requirements: Open admission selective admission to some programs. Option: early admission. Required: high school transcript. Entrance: noncompetitive.

Collegiate Environment: Option: coed housing available.

■ OCONEE FALL LINE TECHNICAL COLLEGE–NORTH CAMPUS

1189 Deepstep Rd.
Sandersville, GA 31082
Tel: (478)553-2050; Free: 877-399-8324
Fax: (478)553-2118
Web Site: www.oftc.edu/

Description: State-supported, 2-year, coed. Part of Technical College System of Georgia. Awards certificates, diplomas, and terminal associate degrees. Total enrollment: 1,886. Full-time: 505 students, 68% women, 32% men. Part-time: 1,381 students, 56% women, 44% men. 0% from out-of-state. 0% American Indian or Alaska Native, non-Hispanic/Latino; 2% Hispanic/Latino; 35% African American, non-Hispanic/Latino; 1% Asian, non-Hispanic/Latino; 0% Native Hawaiian or other Pacific Islander, non-Hispanic/Latino; 0% international. 44% 25 or older. Distance learning.

Entrance Requirements: Open admission selective admission to some programs. Option: early admission. Required: high school transcript. Entrance: noncompetitive.

Collegiate Environment: College housing not available.

■ OCONEE FALL LINE TECHNICAL COLLEGE–SOUTH CAMPUS

560 Pinehill Rd.
Dublin, GA 31021
Tel: (478)275-6589; Free: 800-200-4484
Fax: (478)275-6642
E-mail: bedingfield@heartofgatech.edu
Web Site: www.oftc.edu/

Description: State-supported, 2-year, coed. Part of Technical College System of Georgia. Awards certificates, diplomas, and terminal associate degrees. Founded 1984. Setting: small town campus with easy access to Atlanta. Total enrollment: 1,817. Full-time: 875 students, 65% women, 35%

men. Part-time: 942 students, 51% women, 49% men. 0% from out-of-state. 0.2% American Indian or Alaska Native, non-Hispanic/Latino; 0.3% Hispanic/Latino; 44% African American, non-Hispanic/Latino; 0.1% Asian, non-Hispanic/Latino; 0.3% Native Hawaiian or other Pacific Islander, non-Hispanic/Latino; 0% international. 49% 25 or older. Retention: 54% of full-time freshmen returned the following year. Distance learning.

Entrance Requirements: Open admission selective admission to some programs. Option: early admission. Required: high school transcript. Entrance: noncompetitive.

■ OGEECHEE TECHNICAL COLLEGE

One Joe Kennedy Blvd.
Statesboro, GA 30458
Tel: (912)681-5500; Free: 800-646-1316
E-mail: lsaunders@ogeecheetech.edu
Web Site: www.ogeecheetech.edu/

Description: State-supported, 2-year, coed. Part of Technical College System of Georgia. Awards certificates, diplomas, and terminal associate degrees. Founded 1989. Setting: small town campus. Total enrollment: 2,236. Full-time: 878 students, 61% women, 39% men. Part-time: 1,358 students, 72% women, 28% men. 0.3% from out-of-state. 0% American Indian or Alaska Native, non-Hispanic/Latino; 3% Hispanic/Latino; 39% African American, non-Hispanic/Latino; 0% Asian, non-Hispanic/Latino; 0% Native Hawaiian or other Pacific Islander, non-Hispanic/Latino; 0% international. 43% 25 or older. Retention: 71% of full-time freshmen returned the following year. Distance learning.

Entrance Requirements: Open admission selective admission to some programs. Option: early admission. Required: high school transcript. Entrance: noncompetitive.

Collegiate Environment: College housing not available.

■ OGLETHORPE UNIVERSITY

4484 Peachtree Rd., NE
Atlanta, GA 30319-2797
Tel: (404)261-1441; Free: 800-428-4484
Fax: (404)364-8500
E-mail: admission@oglethorpe.edu
Web Site: www.oglethorpe.edu/

Description: Independent, comprehensive, coed. Awards bachelor's and master's degrees. Founded 1835. Setting: 102-acre suburban campus with easy access to Atlanta. Endowment: $17.4 million. Total enrollment: 1,079. Faculty: 116 (55 full-time, 61 part-time). Student-undergrad faculty ratio is 13:1. 2,463 applied, 83% were admitted. 25% from top 10% of their high school class, 54% from top quarter, 81% from top half. Full-time: 971 students, 58% women, 42% men. Part-time: 82 students, 65% women, 35% men. Students come from 32 states and territories, 27 other countries, 29% from out-of-state. 0.2% American Indian or Alaska Native, non-Hispanic/Latino; 8% Hispanic/Latino; 21% African American, non-Hispanic/Latino; 3% Asian, non-Hispanic/Latino; 0.1% Native Hawaiian or other Pacific Islander, non-Hispanic/Latino; 5% international. 14% 25 or older, 57% live on campus, 4% transferred in. Retention: 80% of full-time freshmen returned the following year. Academic areas with the most degrees conferred: English; business/marketing; psychology. Core. Calendar: semesters. Services for LD students, advanced placement, accelerated degree program, self-designed majors, honors program, independent study, double major, summer session for credit, part-time degree program, adult/continuing education programs, co-op programs and internships, graduate courses open to undergrads. Off campus study at Atlanta Regional Consortium for Higher Education, 19 colleges and universities in the Atlanta area. Study abroad program. ROTC: Air Force (c).

Entrance Requirements: Options: electronic application, early admission, early action, deferred admission, international baccalaureate accepted. Required: essay, high school transcript, 1 recommendation, SAT or ACT. Recommended: minimum 2.5 high school GPA, interview. Required for some: interview. Entrance: very difficult. Application deadlines: Rolling, 12/5 for early action. Notification: continuous, 12/20 for early action. Transfer credits accepted: Yes.

Costs Per Year: Application fee: $40. Comprehensive fee: $42,580 includes full-time tuition ($31,000), mandatory fees ($280), and college room and board ($11,300). Full-time tuition and fees vary according to degree level. Room and board charges vary according to housing facility and location. Part-time tuition: $1260 per credit hour. Part-time tuition varies according to class time, course load, and degree level.

Collegiate Environment: Orientation program. Drama-theater group, choral

group, student-run newspaper, radio station. Social organizations: national fraternities, national sororities. Student services: health clinic, personal-psychological counseling. Campus security: 24-hour emergency response devices and patrols, late night transport-escort service, controlled dormitory access. 57 undergraduates lived in college housing during 2012-13. Freshmen guaranteed college housing. On-campus residence required through sophomore year. Option: coed housing available. Philip Weltner Library with an OPAC and a Web page. Operations spending for the previous fiscal year: $187,000.

Community Environment: Oglethorpe students enjoy the scenic setting of a suburban campus combined with the opportunities of a great international city. Atlanta offers professional and amateur art and entertainment, professional and amateur sports, renowned intellectual and research activities, and world-class dining and enjoyment opportunities. It also offers small town values of friendliness, courtesy, and respect. Students can find part-time employment, internships, cultural activities, and an active job placement program, all of which are enhanced by the Atlanta location.

■ **OKEFENOKEE TECHNICAL COLLEGE**
1701 Carswell Ave.
Waycross, GA 31503
Tel: (912)287-6584; Free: 877-ED-AT-OTC
Fax: (912)287-4865
E-mail: nmurphy@okefenokeetech.edu
Web Site: www.okefenokeetech.edu/
Description: State-supported, 2-year, coed. Part of Technical College System of Georgia. Awards certificates, diplomas, and terminal associate degrees. Setting: small town campus. Total enrollment: 1,347. Full-time: 434 students, 68% women, 32% men. Part-time: 913 students, 67% women, 33% men. 0% from out-of-state. 0.4% American Indian or Alaska Native, non-Hispanic/Latino; 3% Hispanic/Latino; 22% African American, non-Hispanic/Latino; 0% Asian, non-Hispanic/Latino; 0% Native Hawaiian or other Pacific Islander, non-Hispanic/Latino; 0.4% international. 49% 25 or older. Retention: 64% of full-time freshmen returned the following year. Distance learning.
Entrance Requirements: Open admission selective admission to some programs. Option: early admission. Required: high school transcript. Entrance: noncompetitive.
Collegiate Environment: College housing not available.

■ **PAINE COLLEGE**
1235 15th St.
Augusta, GA 30901-3182
Tel: (706)821-8200; Free: 800-476-7703
Fax: (706)821-8293
E-mail: mrainey@paine.edu
Web Site: www.paine.edu/
Description: Independent Methodist, 4-year, coed. Awards bachelor's degrees. Founded 1882. Setting: 65-acre urban campus with easy access to Atlanta. Endowment: $8.1 million. Total enrollment: 837. Faculty: 79 (53 full-time, 26 part-time). Student-undergrad faculty ratio is 13:1. 2,142 applied, 78% were admitted. 5% from top 10% of their high school class, 16% from top quarter, 59% from top half. Full-time: 765 students, 62% women, 38% men. Part-time: 72 students, 63% women, 38% men. Students come from 28 states and territories, 5 other countries, 25% from out-of-state. 0.1% American Indian or Alaska Native, non-Hispanic/Latino; 1% Hispanic/Latino; 91% African American, non-Hispanic/Latino; 0.4% Asian, non-Hispanic/Latino; 0.2% Native Hawaiian or other Pacific Islander, non-Hispanic/Latino; 2% international. 13% 25 or older, 48% live on campus, 7% transferred in. Retention: 52% of full-time freshmen returned the following year. Academic areas with the most degrees conferred: business/marketing; social sciences; communication/journalism. Core. Calendar: semesters. Academic remediation for entering students, services for LD students, advanced placement, accelerated degree program, honors program, independent study, distance learning, double major, summer session for credit, part-time degree program, internships. Off campus study at Georgia Regents University. Study abroad program. ROTC: Army (c).
Entrance Requirements: Options: electronic application, early admission, deferred admission. Required: essay, high school transcript, minimum 2 high school GPA, 3 recommendations, SAT or ACT. Required for some: score of 500 on each Georgia high school exit exam. Entrance: minimally difficult. Application deadlines: 7/1, 7/1 for nonresidents. Notification: continuous, continuous for nonresidents. SAT Reasoning Test deadline: 7/15. SAT Subject Test deadline: 7/15. Transfer credits accepted: Yes.

Costs Per Year: Application fee: $35. Comprehensive fee: $18,594 includes full-time tuition ($11,550), mandatory fees ($952), and college room and board ($6092). Full-time tuition and fees vary according to course load, location, and reciprocity agreements. Room and board charges vary according to housing facility. Part-time tuition: $481 per semester hour. Part-time tuition varies according to course load, location, and reciprocity agreements.
Collegiate Environment: Orientation program. Drama-theater group, choral group, student-run newspaper. Social organizations: 17 open to all; national fraternities, national sororities; 7% of eligible men and 4% of eligible women are members. Most popular organizations: Wesley Fellowship, Alpha Kappa Mu National Honor Society, Pre-Alumni Council, Honda All-Stars, Creme de la Creme Models. Major annual events: Homecoming, Painefest, Conference on the Black Experience. Student services: health clinic, personal-psychological counseling. Campus security: 24-hour emergency response devices and patrols, late night transport-escort service. 589 college housing spaces available; 405 were occupied in 2012-13. Freshmen given priority for college housing. Options: men-only, women-only housing available. Collins-Callaway Library with 6,979 microform titles, 3,348 serials, 574 audiovisual materials, an OPAC, and a Web page. Operations spending for the previous fiscal year: $338,840. 130 computers available on campus for general student use. Computer purchase/lease plans available. A campuswide network can be accessed from student residence rooms and from off campus. Students can access the following: online class registration. Staffed computer lab on campus provides training in use of computers, software, and the Internet.
Community Environment: Augusta, located on the Savannah River in east central Georgia, is a river port and industrial center, and is the third leading producer of clay products in the southeast. All forms of transportation are available. Recreational facilities include lakes for fishing, boating and hunting, golf courses, horseback riding, and polo. The famous Augusta National Golf Club course, home of the Masters Golf Tournament, is located here. Some of the points of interest are the Mackay Trading Post, Meadow Garden, Fort Augusta, Confederate Monument, New Savannah Bluff Lock and Dam System, churches of historic interest, and two large enclosed shopping malls, one of which is the largest in Georgia.

■ **PIEDMONT COLLEGE**
165 Central Ave.
Demorest, GA 30535-0010
Tel: (706)778-3000; Free: 800-277-7020
Fax: (706)776-6635
E-mail: bboonstra@piedmont.edu
Web Site: www.piedmont.edu/
Description: Independent, comprehensive, coed, affiliated with United Church of Christ. Awards bachelor's, master's, and doctoral degrees and post-master's certificates. Founded 1897. Setting: 186-acre rural campus with easy access to Atlanta. Endowment: $49.7 million. Educational spending for the previous fiscal year: $6370 per student. Total enrollment: 1,170. Faculty: 245 (113 full-time, 132 part-time). Student-undergrad faculty ratio is 16:1. 901 applied, 56% were admitted. 22% from top 10% of their high school class, 47% from top quarter, 83% from top half. Full-time: 1,127 students, 67% women, 33% men. Part-time: 167 students, 76% women, 24% men. Students come from 21 states and territories, 7 other countries, 6% from out-of-state. 1% American Indian or Alaska Native, non-Hispanic/Latino; 3% Hispanic/Latino; 10% African American, non-Hispanic/Latino; 1% Asian, non-Hispanic/Latino; 0.1% Native Hawaiian or other Pacific Islander, non-Hispanic/Latino; 0.2% international. 28% 25 or older, 45% live on campus, 9% transferred in. Retention: 75% of full-time freshmen returned the following year. Academic areas with the most degrees conferred: education; business/marketing; health professions and related sciences. Core. Calendar: semesters. Services for LD students, advanced placement, accelerated degree program, self-designed majors, honors program, independent study, distance learning, double major, summer session for credit, part-time degree program, adult/continuing education programs, co-op programs and internships, graduate courses open to undergrads. Off campus study at Piedmont College, Athens, GA. Study abroad program.
Entrance Requirements: Options: electronic application, early admission, deferred admission, international baccalaureate accepted. Required: high school transcript, minimum 2 high school GPA, SAT or ACT. Recommended: essay. Required for some: interview. Entrance: moderately difficult. Application deadline: 7/1. Transfer credits accepted: Yes.
Costs Per Year: Application fee: $0. Comprehensive fee: $29,260 includes full-time tuition ($20,730) and college room and board ($8530). College room only: $4744. Full-time tuition varies according to course load, degree level,

location, and program. Part-time tuition: $864 per credit. Part-time tuition varies according to course load, degree level, location, and program.

Collegiate Environment: Orientation program. Drama-theater group, choral group, student-run newspaper, radio station. Social organizations: 32 open to all. Most popular organizations: Campus Activity Board, Residence Hall Council, Outdoor Club, Team Piedmont, Alpha PSI Omega. Major annual events: Homecoming/Piedmont Pride Week, Welcome Back Blowout, Spring Formal. Student services: personal-psychological counseling. Campus security: 24-hour emergency response devices and patrols, late night transport-escort service. 594 college housing spaces available; 577 were occupied in 2012-13. Freshmen guaranteed college housing. On-campus residence required through sophomore year. Options: coed, men-only, women-only housing available. Arrendale Library plus 1 other with 311,722 books, 290 serials, 2,677 audiovisual materials, an OPAC, and a Web page. Operations spending for the previous fiscal year: $590,578. 150 computers available on campus for general student use. A campuswide network can be accessed from student residence rooms and from off campus. Staffed computer lab on campus provides training in use of computers, software, and the Internet.

Community Environment: Demorest, located in Habersham County in the northeastern corner of Georgia, is in the foothills of the southern Blue Ridge Mountains. The climate is considered unusually healthful. Buses serve the area with rail service in Toccoa, eighteen miles away and Hartfield International Airport in Atlanta, 75 miles southwest by major highway.

■ POINT UNIVERSITY
2605 Ben Hill Rd.
East Point, GA 30344-1999
Tel: (404)761-8861; Free: 855-37-POINT
E-mail: admissions@point.edu
Web Site: point.edu/

Description: Independent Christian, 4-year, coed. Awards associate and bachelor's degrees. Founded 1937. Setting: 52-acre small town campus with easy access to Atlanta, Georgia. Total enrollment: 1,483. Faculty: 129 (31 full-time, 98 part-time). Student-undergrad faculty ratio is 22:1. 721 applied, 56% were admitted. 8% from top 10% of their high school class, 25% from top quarter, 60% from top half. Full-time: 1,306 students, 58% women, 42% men. Part-time: 177 students, 64% women, 36% men. 16% from out-of-state. 0.1% American Indian or Alaska Native, non-Hispanic/Latino; 3% Hispanic/Latino; 59% African American, non-Hispanic/Latino; 0.5% Asian, non-Hispanic/Latino; 0.2% Native Hawaiian or other Pacific Islander, non-Hispanic/Latino; 0% international. 75% live on campus, 13% transferred in. Retention: 50% of full-time freshmen returned the following year. Academic areas with the most degrees conferred: theology and religious vocations; social sciences; business/marketing. Core. Calendar: semesters. Academic remediation for entering students, services for LD students, advanced placement, accelerated degree program, independent study, distance learning, double major, summer session for credit, part-time degree program, adult/continuing education programs, co-op programs and internships. Study abroad program.

Entrance Requirements: Options: electronic application, early admission, deferred admission. Required: high school transcript, minimum 2 high school GPA, 1 recommendation, SAT or ACT for some, COMPASS for some, college transcript if applicable, SAT or ACT. Required for some: essay, interview. Entrance: moderately difficult. Application deadlines: 8/5, 8/5 for nonresidents. Notification: continuous, continuous for nonresidents. SAT Reasoning Test deadline: 8/5. Transfer credits accepted: Yes.

Collegiate Environment: Orientation program. Drama-theater group, choral group, student-run newspaper. Most popular organizations: Student Government Association, Global Mission Conference, Campus Life Ministers, Student Transition Team, Sunday Night Live. Major annual events: Homecoming, Global Mission Conference, Honors Chapel. Student services: health clinic, personal-psychological counseling. Campus security: 24-hour patrols, student patrols. 450 college housing spaces available; 424 were occupied in 2012-13. Freshmen given priority for college housing. On-campus residence required through sophomore year. Options: men-only, women-only housing available. Point University Library plus 1 other with 48,806 books, 245 microform titles, 13,500 serials, 637 audiovisual materials, and an OPAC. 115 computers available on campus for general student use. A campuswide network can be accessed from student residence rooms and from off campus. Students can access the following: online class registration. Staffed computer lab on campus provides training in use of computers, software, and the Internet.

Community Environment: A suburban area with temperate climate, East

Point is served by all major forms of transportation. Along with the usual community facilities, the opportunities are excellent for part-time employment.

■ REINHARDT UNIVERSITY
7300 Reinhardt Cir.
Waleska, GA 30183-2981
Tel: (770)720-5600
Fax: (770)720-5602
E-mail: admissions@mail.reinhardt.edu
Web Site: www.reinhardt.edu/

Description: Independent, comprehensive, coed, affiliated with United Methodist Church. Awards associate, bachelor's, and master's degrees. Founded 1883. Setting: 600-acre rural campus with easy access to Atlanta. Endowment: $41.5 million. Educational spending for the previous fiscal year: $6559 per student. Total enrollment: 1,154. Faculty: 157 (62 full-time, 95 part-time). Student-undergrad faculty ratio is 12:1. 1,310 applied, 59% were admitted. 63% from top half of their high school class. Full-time: 938 students, 56% women, 44% men. Part-time: 97 students, 59% women, 41% men. Students come from 4 states and territories, 40 other countries, 27% from out-of-state. 0.5% American Indian or Alaska Native, non-Hispanic/Latino; 4% Hispanic/Latino; 12% African American, non-Hispanic/Latino; 1% Asian, non-Hispanic/Latino. 22% 25 or older, 43% live on campus, 9% transferred in. Retention: 58% of full-time freshmen returned the following year. Academic areas with the most degrees conferred: business/marketing; education; visual and performing arts. Core. Calendar: semesters. Academic remediation for entering students, services for LD students, advanced placement, self-designed majors, freshman honors college, honors program, independent study, distance learning, double major, summer session for credit, part-time degree program, adult/continuing education programs, co-op programs and internships. Off campus study. Study abroad program.

Entrance Requirements: Options: electronic application, early admission, deferred admission. Required: high school transcript, minimum 2 high school GPA, SAT or ACT. Entrance: moderately difficult. Application deadline: Rolling. Notification: continuous. SAT Reasoning Test deadline: 8/24.

Costs Per Year: Application fee: $25. Comprehensive fee: $25,248 includes full-time tuition ($17,950), mandatory fees ($340), and college room and board ($6958). Full-time tuition and fees vary according to location and program. Room and board charges vary according to board plan and housing facility. Part-time tuition: $598 per credit hour. Part-time mandatory fees: $85 per term. Part-time tuition and fees vary according to course load, location, and program.

Collegiate Environment: Orientation program. Drama-theater group, choral group, student-run newspaper. Social organizations: 38 open to all. Most popular organizations: Real Deal, International and Historical Film Society, Student Government Association, SOAR (Student Orientation Leaders), Communication Club. Major annual events: Spring Formal, Fall Day, Spring Day. Student services: health clinic, personal-psychological counseling. Campus security: 24-hour emergency response devices and patrols, late night transport-escort service, controlled dormitory access. Hill Freeman Library/Spruill Learning Center plus 1 other with 70,000 books, 2,200 microform titles, 140,000 serials, 12,000 audiovisual materials, an OPAC, and a Web page. Operations spending for the previous fiscal year: $458,141. 164 computers available on campus for general student use. Computer purchase/lease plans available. A campuswide network can be accessed from student residence rooms and from off campus. Students can access the following: online class registration. Staffed computer lab on campus provides training in use of computers, software, and the Internet.

Community Environment: Waleska is located on the summit of a ridge, an hour's drive from metropolitan Atlanta. The high altitude assures a crisp, dry atmosphere and a year-round climate never excelled in its healthful and invigorating qualities. The picturesque southern foothills of the Blue Ridge Mountains surround Waleska.

■ SAVANNAH COLLEGE OF ART AND DESIGN
342 Bull St.
Savannah, GA 31402-3146
Tel: (912)525-5000; Free: 800-869-7223
Fax: (912)238-2436
E-mail: admission@scad.edu
Web Site: www.scad.edu/

Description: Independent, comprehensive, coed. Awards bachelor's and master's degrees. Founded 1978. Setting: urban campus. Total enrollment: 11,415. Faculty: 657 (519 full-time, 138 part-time). Student-undergrad faculty ratio is 18:1. 8,977 applied, 62% were admitted. 16% from top 10% of their high school class, 42% from top quarter, 77% from top half. Full-time: 7,754 students, 64% women, 36% men. Part-time: 1,428 students, 63% women, 37% men. Students come from 54 states and territories, 101 other countries, 77% from out-of-state. 0.5% American Indian or Alaska Native, non-Hispanic/Latino; 6% Hispanic/Latino; 9% African American, non-Hispanic/Latino; 5% Asian, non-Hispanic/Latino; 0.2% Native Hawaiian or other Pacific Islander, non-Hispanic/Latino; 11% international. 10% 25 or older, 41% live on campus, 7% transferred in. Retention: 81% of full-time freshmen returned the following year. Academic areas with the most degrees conferred: visual and performing arts; communication technologies; architecture. Core. ESL program, services for LD students, advanced placement, independent study, distance learning, double major, summer session for credit, part-time degree program, internships. Off campus study at Savannah College of Art and Design Atlanta. Study abroad program. ROTC: Army (c).

Entrance Requirements: Options: electronic application, early admission, deferred admission, international baccalaureate accepted. Required: high school transcript, SAT or ACT. Recommended: essay, minimum 3 high school GPA, 3 recommendations, interview. Required for some: essay, high school transcript, College transcripts required for transfer students; Portfolio/audition recommended for all performing arts, riding, writing, or visual arts applicants. Entrance: moderately difficult. Application deadline: Rolling. Notification: continuous. Transfer credits accepted: Yes.

Costs Per Year: Application fee: $35. Comprehensive fee: $45,395 includes full-time tuition ($31,905), mandatory fees ($500), and college room and board ($12,990). College room only: $8220. Full-time tuition and fees vary according to course load and degree level. Room and board charges vary according to board plan, housing facility, and location. Part-time tuition: $709 per quarter hour. Part-time tuition varies according to course load and degree level.

Collegiate Environment: Orientation program. Drama-theater group, choral group, student-run newspaper, radio station. Social organizations: 109 open to all. Most popular organizations: Gamers' Guild, Contemporary Animation Society, Circus Club, Expressions Dance Club, Queers and Allies. Major annual events: Sidewalk Arts Festival, Savannah Film Festival, International Festival. Student services: health clinic, personal-psychological counseling. Campus security: 24-hour emergency response devices and patrols, student patrols, late night transport-escort service, controlled dormitory access, video camera surveillance. 4,167 college housing spaces available; 3,737 were occupied in 2012-13. Freshmen given priority for college housing. Options: coed, women-only housing available. Jen Library plus 4 others with 215,014 books, 7,016 microform titles, 87,439 serials, 5,014 audiovisual materials, an OPAC, and a Web page. 3,400 computers available on campus for general student use. Computer purchase/lease plans available. A campuswide network can be accessed from student residence rooms and from off campus. Students can access the following: online class registration. Staffed computer lab on campus (open 24 hours a day) provides training in use of computers, software, and the Internet.

Community Environment: The college is located in the downtown historic district of Savannah, Georgia, only minutes from Georgia's golden coast. The metropolitan area population is 313,000. Savannah is a popular tourist area, creating activities available to students throughout the year. Students enjoy new-age technology in an old-world evironment. A free campus bus service transports students to and from classes.

■ **SAVANNAH STATE UNIVERSITY**
3219 College St.
Savannah, GA 31404
Tel: (912)356-2186; Free: 800-788-0478
Fax: (912)356-2529
E-mail: dolanc@savannahstate.edu
Web Site: www.savannahstate.edu/
Description: State-supported, comprehensive, coed. Part of University System of Georgia. Awards bachelor's and master's degrees. Founded 1890. Setting: 173-acre suburban campus. Endowment: $3.7 million. Research spending for the previous fiscal year: $1.2 million. Educational spending for the previous fiscal year: $3906 per student. Total enrollment: 4,080. Faculty: 200 (157 full-time, 43 part-time). Student-undergrad faculty ratio is 23:1. 5,680 applied, 35% were admitted. Full-time: 3,421 students, 55% women, 45% men. Part-time: 520 students, 56% women, 44% men. Students come from 37 states and territories, 33 other countries, 8% from out-of-state. 0.1% American Indian or Alaska Native, non-Hispanic/Latino; 1% Hispanic/Latino; 90% African American, non-Hispanic/Latino; 0.3%

Asian, non-Hispanic/Latino; 0.03% Native Hawaiian or other Pacific Islander, non-Hispanic/Latino; 1% international. 13% 25 or older, 5% transferred in. Retention: 72% of full-time freshmen returned the following year. Academic areas with the most degrees conferred: business/marketing; social sciences; communication/journalism. Core. Calendar: semesters. Academic remediation for entering students, services for LD students, advanced placement, accelerated degree program, honors program, independent study, double major, summer session for credit, part-time degree program, adult/continuing education programs, co-op programs and internships. Off campus study at Armstrong Atlantic State University. Study abroad program. ROTC: Army, Naval.

Entrance Requirements: Options: electronic application, early admission, deferred admission, international baccalaureate accepted. Required: high school transcript, minimum 2.3 high school GPA, SAT or ACT. Recommended: SAT. Required for some: essay, interview, SAT Subject Tests. Entrance: minimally difficult. Application deadline: 7/15. Notification: continuous. Transfer credits accepted: Yes.

Collegiate Environment: Orientation program. Drama-theater group, choral group, marching band, student-run newspaper, radio station. Social organizations: 45 open to all; national fraternities, national sororities, local fraternities, local sororities; 35% of eligible men and 38% of eligible women are members. Most popular organizations: Marching band, Gospel Choir, Concert Choir, Student Orientation Leaders (SOL), Tiger Ambassadors. Major annual events: Homecoming, Spring Fling Activities, Martin Luther King Observance Day. Student services: health clinic, personal-psychological counseling. Campus security: 24-hour emergency response devices and patrols, late night transport-escort service, controlled dormitory access. Asa H. Gordon Library with 278,141 books, 586,633 microform titles, 586,933 serials, 3,725 audiovisual materials, an OPAC, and a Web page. Operations spending for the previous fiscal year: $279,542. 420 computers available on campus for general student use. A campuswide network can be accessed from student residence rooms. Students can access the following: online class registration. Staffed computer lab on campus provides training in use of computers, software, and the Internet.
Community Environment: See Armstrong Atlantic State University.

■ **SAVANNAH TECHNICAL COLLEGE**
5717 White Bluff Rd.
Savannah, GA 31405
Tel: (912)443-5700; Free: 800-769-6362
Fax: (912)352-4362
E-mail: gmoore@savannahtech.edu
Web Site: www.savannahtech.edu/
Description: State-supported, 2-year, coed. Part of Technical College System of Georgia. Awards certificates, diplomas, and terminal associate degrees. Founded 1929. Setting: urban campus. Total enrollment: 4,747. Full-time: 1,771 students, 61% women, 39% men. Part-time: 2,976 students, 66% women, 34% men. 2% from out-of-state. 0.2% American Indian or Alaska Native, non-Hispanic/Latino; 6% Hispanic/Latino; 46% African American, non-Hispanic/Latino; 2% Asian, non-Hispanic/Latino; 0.1% Native Hawaiian or other Pacific Islander, non-Hispanic/Latino; 1% international. 54% 25 or older. Retention: 65% of full-time freshmen returned the following year. Distance learning.
Entrance Requirements: Open admission selective admission to some programs. Option: early admission. Required: high school transcript. Entrance: noncompetitive.
Collegiate Environment: College housing not available.

■ **SHORTER UNIVERSITY**
315 Shorter Ave.
Rome, GA 30165
Tel: (706)291-2121; Free: 800-868-6980
Fax: (706)236-1515
E-mail: admissions@shorter.edu
Web Site: www.shorter.edu/
Description: Independent Baptist, comprehensive, coed. Awards associate, bachelor's, and master's degrees. Founded 1873. Setting: 155-acre small town campus with easy access to Atlanta. Endowment: $20.1 million. Educational spending for the previous fiscal year: $7431 per student. Total enrollment: 1,696. Faculty: 186 (92 full-time, 94 part-time). Student-undergrad faculty ratio is 13:1. 1,944 applied, 65% were admitted. 21% from top 10% of their high school class, 47% from top quarter, 77% from top half. Full-time: 1,510 students, 54% women, 46% men. Part-time: 132 students, 52% women, 48% men. Students come from 35 states and territories, 23

other countries, 14% from out-of-state. 0.2% American Indian or Alaska Native, non-Hispanic/Latino; 4% Hispanic/Latino; 17% African American, non-Hispanic/Latino; 1% Asian, non-Hispanic/Latino; 0.1% Native Hawaiian or other Pacific Islander, non-Hispanic/Latino; 3% international. 14% 25 or older, 54% live on campus, 10% transferred in. Retention: 68% of full-time freshmen returned the following year. Academic areas with the most degrees conferred: business/marketing; education; visual and performing arts. Core. Calendar: semesters. Academic remediation for entering students, services for LD students, advanced placement, self-designed majors, honors program, independent study, double major, summer session for credit, part-time degree program, adult/continuing education programs, internships. Off campus study at Berry College. Study abroad program.

Entrance Requirements: Options: electronic application, early admission, deferred admission. Required: essay, high school transcript, SAT or ACT. Recommended: minimum 2 high school GPA, 1 recommendation, interview. Required for some: interview, audition for music and theater programs. Entrance: moderately difficult. Application deadline: 8/25. Notification: continuous. SAT Reasoning Test deadline: 8/11. Transfer credits accepted: Yes.

Collegiate Environment: Orientation program. Drama-theater group, choral group, marching band, student-run newspaper, radio station. Social organizations: 15 open to all; national fraternities, national sororities, local sororities; 9% of eligible men and 23% of eligible women are members. Most popular organizations: Baptist Collegiate Ministries, Student Government Association, Fellowship of Christian Athletes, Habitat for Humanity, SAVE (Students Advocating Volunteer Efforts). Major annual events: Celebrate Shorter, Midnight Breakfast and Welcome Week, Convocation. Student services: health clinic, personal-psychological counseling. Campus security: 24-hour emergency response devices and patrols. Livingston Library with 144,475 books, 8,099 microform titles, 8,511 serials, 12,134 audiovisual materials, an OPAC, and a Web page. Operations spending for the previous fiscal year: $474,360. 100 computers available on campus for general student use. A campuswide network can be accessed from student residence rooms. Students can access the following: online class registration. Staffed computer lab on campus (open 24 hours a day) provides training in use of computers, software, and the Internet.

■ **SOUTH GEORGIA STATE COLLEGE (DOUGLAS)**
100 W College Park Dr.
Douglas, GA 31533-5098
Tel: (912)260-4200; Free: 800-342-6364
Fax: (912)389-4392
E-mail: danielle.buehrer@sgc.edu
Web Site: www.sgc.edu/
Description: State-supported, 2-year, coed. Part of University System of Georgia. Awards certificates, transfer associate, and terminal associate degrees. Founded 1906. Setting: 250-acre small town campus. Endowment: $153,798. Total enrollment: 2,000. Faculty: 100 (42 full-time, 58 part-time). Student-undergrad faculty ratio is 27:1. Full-time: 1,487 students, 58% women, 42% men. Part-time: 513 students, 77% women, 23% men. Students come from 13 states and territories, 2% from out-of-state. 22% 25 or older, 6% transferred in. Core. Calendar: semesters. Academic remediation for entering students, services for LD students, advanced placement, summer session for credit, part-time degree program, adult/continuing education programs. Study abroad program.
Entrance Requirements: Options: electronic application, early admission, deferred admission. Required: high school transcript. Entrance: minimally difficult. Application deadline: Rolling. Notification: continuous.
Costs Per Year: Application fee: $20. State resident tuition: $2532 full-time, $84.40 per credit hour part-time. Nonresident tuition: $9582 full-time, $319.40 per credit hour part-time. Mandatory fees: $1030 full-time, $515 per term part-time. College room and board: $7750. College room only: $4500. Room and board charges vary according to board plan.
Collegiate Environment: Orientation program. Drama-theater group, student-run newspaper. Campus security: 24-hour emergency response devices and patrols, controlled dormitory access. William S. Smith Library with an OPAC and a Web page.
Community Environment: Douglas is situated in the southern part of Georgia; having a delightful climate, winters are mild, and the summers pleasant. This community is one of the largest tobacco markets in the South. Livestock, poultry, naval stores, light industry, and the manufacture of mobile homes. Part-time employment is available for students. The community facilities include churches of all denominations, regional library, hospital, community concert association. Recreational facilities are the golf course, recreation center, tennis courts, pools, etc.

■ **SOUTH GEORGIA STATE COLLEGE (WAYCROSS)**
2001 S Georgia Pky.
Waycross, GA 31503-9248
Tel: (912)285-6133
Fax: (912)287-4909
E-mail: rwing@waycross.edu
Web Site: www.waycross.edu/
Description: State-supported, 2-year, coed. Part of University System of Georgia. Awards certificates, transfer associate, and terminal associate degrees. Founded 1976. Setting: 150-acre small town campus. Total enrollment: 1,118. Student-undergrad faculty ratio is 19:1. 1,118 applied, 100% were admitted. 3% from out-of-state. 38% 25 or older. Retention: 58% of full-time freshmen returned the following year. Core. Calendar: semesters. Academic remediation for entering students, advanced placement, distance learning, summer session for credit, part-time degree program, adult/continuing education programs. Off campus study at South Georgia College, Valdosta State University, Albany State College, Okefenokee Technical College. Study abroad program.
Entrance Requirements: Options: electronic application, early admission, deferred admission, international baccalaureate accepted. Required: high school transcript. Recommended: SAT or ACT. Entrance: noncompetitive. Application deadline: Rolling. Notification: continuous. Transfer credits accepted: Yes.
Collegiate Environment: Orientation program. Campus security: late night transport-escort service, security guards.

■ **SOUTH GEORGIA TECHNICAL COLLEGE**
900 S Georgia Tech Pky.
Americus, GA 31709
Tel: (229)931-2394
Fax: (229)931-2459
E-mail: wcrisp@southgatech.edu
Web Site: www.southgatech.edu/
Description: State-supported, 2-year, coed. Part of Technical College System of Georgia. Awards certificates, diplomas, and terminal associate degrees. Founded 1948. Total enrollment: 1,901. Full-time: 892 students, 54% women, 46% men. Part-time: 1,009 students, 53% women, 47% men. 6% from out-of-state. 0.2% American Indian or Alaska Native, non-Hispanic/Latino; 1% Hispanic/Latino; 57% African American, non-Hispanic/Latino; 0.5% Asian, non-Hispanic/Latino; 0% Native Hawaiian or other Pacific Islander, non-Hispanic/Latino; 0% international. 41% 25 or older. Retention: 68% of full-time freshmen returned the following year. Distance learning.
Entrance Requirements: Open admission selective admission to some programs. Option: early admission. Required: high school transcript. Entrance: noncompetitive.

■ **SOUTH UNIVERSITY**
709 Mall Blvd.
Savannah, GA 31406
Tel: (912)201-8000; Free: 866-629-2901
Fax: (912)201-8070
Web Site: www.southuniversity.edu/savannah/
Description: Proprietary, comprehensive, coed. Part of Education Management Corporation. Awards associate, bachelor's, master's, and doctoral degrees. Founded 1899.

■ **SOUTHEASTERN TECHNICAL COLLEGE**
3001 E First St.
Vidalia, GA 30474
Tel: (912)538-3100
Fax: (912)538-3156
E-mail: brhart @southeasterntech.edu
Web Site: www.southeasterntech.edu/
Description: State-supported, 2-year, coed. Part of Technical College System of Georgia. Awards certificates, diplomas, and terminal associate degrees. Founded 1989. Total enrollment: 1,747. Full-time: 466 students, 64% women, 36% men. Part-time: 1,281 students, 75% women, 25% men. 0% from out-of-state. 0.4% American Indian or Alaska Native, non-Hispanic/Latino; 5% Hispanic/Latino; 26% African American, non-Hispanic/Latino; 0% Asian, non-Hispanic/Latino; 0% Native Hawaiian or other Pacific Islander, non-Hispanic/Latino; 0% international. 48% 25 or older. Retention: 72% of full-time freshmen returned the following year. Distance learning.

Entrance Requirements: Open admission selective admission to some programs. Option: early admission. Required: high school transcript. Entrance: noncompetitive.

Collegiate Environment: College housing not available.

■ SOUTHERN CRESCENT TECHNICAL COLLEGE

501 Varsity Rd.
Griffin, GA 30223
Tel: (770)228-7348
Fax: (770)229-3227
E-mail: tkinard@sctech.edu
Web Site: www.sctech.edu/

Description: State-supported, 2-year, coed. Part of Technical College System of Georgia. Awards certificates, diplomas, and terminal associate degrees. Founded 1965. Setting: small town campus. Total enrollment: 5,543. Full-time: 2,228 students, 62% women, 38% men. Part-time: 3,315 students, 71% women, 29% men. 0% from out-of-state. 0.1% American Indian or Alaska Native, non-Hispanic/Latino; 3% Hispanic/Latino; 36% African American, non-Hispanic/Latino; 1% Asian, non-Hispanic/Latino; 0.1% Native Hawaiian or other Pacific Islander, non-Hispanic/Latino; 0% international. 52% 25 or older, 0% live on campus. Retention: 66% of full-time freshmen returned the following year. Distance learning.

Entrance Requirements: Open admission selective admission to some programs. Option: early admission. Required: high school transcript. Entrance: noncompetitive.

■ SOUTHERN POLYTECHNIC STATE UNIVERSITY

1100 S Marietta Pky.
Marietta, GA 30060-2896
Tel: (678)915-7778; Free: 800-635-3204
E-mail: gbush@spsu.edu
Web Site: www.spsu.edu/

Description: State-supported, comprehensive, coed. Part of University System of Georgia. Awards associate, bachelor's, and master's degrees. Founded 1948. Setting: 198-acre suburban campus with easy access to Atlanta. Endowment: $3.1 million. Research spending for the previous fiscal year: $655,184. Educational spending for the previous fiscal year: $4219 per student. Total enrollment: 6,202. Faculty: 309 (219 full-time, 90 part-time). Student-undergrad faculty ratio is 19:1. 1,535 applied, 79% were admitted. 12% from top 10% of their high school class, 42% from top quarter, 79% from top half. Full-time: 3,863 students, 17% women, 83% men. Part-time: 1,539 students, 21% women, 79% men. Students come from 41 states and territories, 51 other countries, 2% from out-of-state. 0.2% American Indian or Alaska Native, non-Hispanic/Latino; 8% Hispanic/Latino; 22% African American, non-Hispanic/Latino; 6% Asian, non-Hispanic/Latino; 0.1% Native Hawaiian or other Pacific Islander, non-Hispanic/Latino; 4% international. 31% 25 or older, 25% live on campus, 13% transferred in. Retention: 76% of full-time freshmen returned the following year. Academic areas with the most degrees conferred: engineering technologies; business/marketing; computer and information sciences. Core. Calendar: semesters. Services for LD students, advanced placement, self-designed majors, honors program, independent study, distance learning, double major, summer session for credit, part-time degree program, co-op programs and internships. Off campus study at Atlanta Regional Council for Higher Education. Study abroad program. ROTC: Army (c), Naval (c), Air Force (c).

Entrance Requirements: Options: electronic application, deferred admission, international baccalaureate accepted. Required: high school transcript, minimum 2.5 high school GPA, proof of immunization, international students have additional requirements, 19 academic CPC units, SAT or ACT. Entrance: moderately difficult. Application deadlines: 7/1, 7/1 for nonresidents. Notification: continuous, continuous for nonresidents. SAT Reasoning Test deadline: 7/1. Transfer credits accepted: Yes.

Costs Per Year: Application fee: $40. State resident tuition: $5256 full-time, $175.20 per semester hour part-time. Nonresident tuition: $18,704 full-time, $623.47 per semester hour part-time. Mandatory fees: $1422 full-time, $711 per term part-time. Full-time tuition and fees vary according to course load. Part-time tuition and fees vary according to course load. College room and board: $7280. College room only: $4020. Room and board charges vary according to board plan and housing facility.

Collegiate Environment: Orientation program. Drama-theater group, student-run newspaper, radio station. Social organizations: 128 open to all; national fraternities, national sororities; 7% of eligible men and 8% of eligible women are members. Most popular organizations: International Student Association, Campus Activities Board, National Society of Black Engineers,

Baptist Collegiate Ministries, American Society of Civil Engineers. Major annual events: SPSU Live Fall Concert, Casino Night, Spring Fling. Student services: health clinic, personal-psychological counseling. Campus security: 24-hour emergency response devices and patrols, late night transport-escort service, controlled dormitory access. 1,673 college housing spaces available; 1,538 were occupied in 2012-13. Freshmen given priority for college housing. On-campus residence required in freshman year. Options: coed, men-only, women-only housing available. Lawrence V. Johnson Library with 126,779 books, 3,493 microform titles, 510 serials, 355 audiovisual materials, an OPAC, and a Web page. Operations spending for the previous fiscal year: $1 million. 1,400 computers available on campus for general student use. A campuswide network can be accessed from student residence rooms and from off campus. Students can access the following: online class registration. Staffed computer lab on campus provides training in use of computers, software, and the Internet.

Community Environment: Nestled between the Chattahoochee National Recreation Area and Kennesaw National Battlefield Park on the Piedmont Plateau of north central Georgia lies historic Marietta, Georgia. Incorporated in 1834, Marietta is the heart of Cobb County, Georgia, and serves as the seat of Cobb County Government. Marietta, the"Gem City of the South," is the second largest municipality in the Atlantic area (15 miles from downtown Atlanta), but has the lowest tax rate. Cobb is one of the twenty-five fastest growing counties in the country with a population of 679,000. Lockheed Martin is the county's largest single employer. Cobb has one of the metro area's highest per family incomes at $46,119. College-educated residents make up 33 percent of the population. Five colleges and two technical institutes serve the area, as do two public school systems.

■ SOUTHWEST GEORGIA TECHNICAL COLLEGE

15689 US 19 N
Thomasville, GA 31792
Tel: (229)225-4096
Fax: (229)225-4330
E-mail: whancock@southwestgatech.edu
Web Site: www.southwestgatech.edu/

Description: State-supported, 2-year, coed. Part of Technical College System of Georgia. Awards certificates, diplomas, and terminal associate degrees. Founded 1963. Total enrollment: 1,632. Full-time: 442 students, 67% women, 33% men. Part-time: 1,190 students, 70% women, 30% men. 2% from out-of-state. 1% American Indian or Alaska Native, non-Hispanic/Latino; 2% Hispanic/Latino; 34% African American, non-Hispanic/Latino; 0% Asian, non-Hispanic/Latino; 0% Native Hawaiian or other Pacific Islander, non-Hispanic/Latino; 0% international. 45% 25 or older. Retention: 74% of full-time freshmen returned the following year. Distance learning.

Entrance Requirements: Open admission selective admission to some programs. Options: electronic application, early admission. Required: high school transcript. Entrance: noncompetitive.

Collegiate Environment: College housing not available.

■ SPELMAN COLLEGE

350 Spelman Ln., SW
Atlanta, GA 30314-4399
Tel: (404)681-3643; Free: 800-982-2411
Fax: (404)215-7788
E-mail: admiss@spelman.edu
Web Site: www.spelman.edu/

Description: Independent, 4-year, women only. Awards bachelor's degrees. Founded 1881. Setting: 39-acre urban campus with easy access to Atlanta. Total enrollment: 2,145. Faculty: 247 (174 full-time, 73 part-time). Student-undergrad faculty ratio is 11:1. 6,081 applied, 38% were admitted. 30% from top 10% of their high school class, 64% from top quarter, 90% from top half. Full-time: 2,074 students. Part-time: 71 students. Students come from 9 states and territories, 45 other countries, 73% from out-of-state. 0.05% American Indian or Alaska Native, non-Hispanic/Latino; 0.4% Hispanic/Latino; 82% African American, non-Hispanic/Latino; 0.1% Asian, non-Hispanic/Latino; 0% Native Hawaiian or other Pacific Islander, non-Hispanic/Latino; 1% international. 3% 25 or older, 65% live on campus, 1% transferred in. Retention: 90% of full-time freshmen returned the following year. Academic areas with the most degrees conferred: social sciences; psychology; biological/life sciences. Core. Calendar: semesters. Services for LD students, self-designed majors, honors program, independent study, double major, part-time degree program, adult/continuing education programs, internships. Study abroad program. ROTC: Army (c), Naval (c), Air Force (c).

Entrance Requirements: Options: electronic application, early admission, early decision, early action, deferred admission, international baccalaureate accepted. Required: essay, high school transcript, minimum 2 high school GPA, 2 recommendations, SAT or ACT. Required for some: interview. Entrance: very difficult. Application deadlines: 2/1, 11/1 for early decision, 11/15 for early action. Notification: 4/1, 12/15 for early decision, 12/31 for early action. Transfer credits accepted: Yes. Applicants placed on waiting list: 637. Wait-listed applicants offered admission: 265. Early decision applicants: 387. Early decision applicants admitted: 146. Early action applicants: 1,618. Early action applicants admitted: 869.

Costs Per Year: Application fee: $35. One-time mandatory fee: $250. Comprehensive fee: $35,335 includes full-time tuition ($20,569), mandatory fees ($3225), and college room and board ($11,541). Full-time tuition and fees vary according to course load. Room and board charges vary according to board plan and housing facility. Part-time tuition: $860 per credit hour. Part-time mandatory fees: $1,613 per term. Part-time tuition and fees vary according to course load. $1,612.50 per term fees are optional if a student registers for less than six semester hours.

Collegiate Environment: Orientation program. Drama-theater group, choral group, marching band, student-run newspaper. Social organizations: 95 open to all; national sororities, local sororities; 10% of eligible undergrads are members. Major annual events: Founder's Day, Market Friday, Homecoming. Student services: health clinic, women's center. Campus security: 24-hour emergency response devices and patrols, late night transport-escort service, controlled dormitory access, lighted pathways/sidewalks. 1,398 college housing spaces available; 1,386 were occupied in 2012-13. Freshmen given priority for college housing. On-campus residence required in freshman year. Option: women-only housing available. Robert Woodruff Library with 513,213 books, 853,037 microform titles, 1,946 serials, 7,731 audiovisual materials, an OPAC, and a Web page. 770 computers available on campus for general student use. A campuswide network can be accessed from off-campus. Students can access the following: online class registration. Staffed computer lab on campus.

Community Environment: See Clark Atlanta University.

■ STRAYER UNIVERSITY - AUGUSTA CAMPUS

1330 Augusta W Pky.
Augusta, GA 30909
Tel: (706)855-8233
Fax: (706)855-8234
Web Site: www.strayer.edu/campus/augusta/
Description: Proprietary, comprehensive, coed. Awards associate, bachelor's, and master's degrees.

■ STRAYER UNIVERSITY - CHAMBLEE CAMPUS

3355 NE Expy.
Ste. 100
Atlanta, GA 30341
Tel: (770)454-9270
Fax: (770)457-6958
Web Site: www.strayer.edu/campus/chamblee/
Description: Proprietary, comprehensive, coed. Awards associate, bachelor's, and master's degrees.

■ STRAYER UNIVERSITY - COBB COUNTY CAMPUS

3101 Towercreek Pky., SE
Ste. 700
Atlanta, GA 30339-3256
Tel: (770)612-2170
Fax: (770)956-7241
Web Site: www.strayer.edu/campus/cobb-county/
Description: Proprietary, comprehensive, coed. Awards associate, bachelor's, and master's degrees.

■ STRAYER UNIVERSITY - COLUMBUS CAMPUS

6003 Veterans Pky.
Ste. 100
Columbus, GA 31909
Tel: (706)225-5300
Web Site: www.strayer.edu/campus/columbus_ga
Description: Proprietary, comprehensive, coed. Awards associate, bachelor's, and master's degrees.

■ STRAYER UNIVERSITY - DOUGLASVILLE CAMPUS

4655 Timber Ridge Dr.
Douglasville, GA 30135
Tel: (678)715-2200
Fax: (678)715-2230
Web Site: www.strayer.edu/campus/douglasville/
Description: Proprietary, comprehensive, coed. Awards associate, bachelor's, and master's degrees.

■ STRAYER UNIVERSITY - LITHONIA CAMPUS

3120 Stonecrest Blvd.
Ste. 200
Lithonia, GA 30038
Tel: (678)323-7700
Fax: (678)323-7730
Web Site: www.strayer.edu/campus/lithonia/
Description: Proprietary, comprehensive, coed. Awards associate, bachelor's, and master's degrees.

■ STRAYER UNIVERSITY - MORROW CAMPUS

3000 Corporate Ctr. Dr., Ste. 100
Morrow, GA 30260
Tel: (678)422-4100
Fax: (678)422-4130
Web Site: www.strayer.edu/campus/morrow
Description: Proprietary, comprehensive, coed. Awards associate, bachelor's, and master's degrees.

■ STRAYER UNIVERSITY - ROSWELL CAMPUS

100 Mansell Ct. E, Ste. 100
Roswell, GA 30076
Tel: (770)650-3000
Fax: (770)650-3030
Web Site: www.strayer.edu/campus/roswell
Description: Proprietary, comprehensive, coed. Awards associate, bachelor's, and master's degrees.

■ STRAYER UNIVERSITY - SAVANNAH CAMPUS

20 Martin Ct.
Savannah, GA 31419
Tel: (912)921-2900
Fax: (912)291-2930
Web Site: www.strayer.edu/campus/savannah/
Description: Proprietary, comprehensive, coed. Awards associate, bachelor's, and master's degrees.

■ THOMAS UNIVERSITY

1501 Millpond Rd.
Thomasville, GA 31792-7499
Tel: (229)226-1621; Free: 800-538-9784
E-mail: kknight@thomasu.edu
Web Site: www.thomasu.edu/
Description: Independent, comprehensive, coed. Awards associate, bachelor's, and master's degrees. Founded 1950. Setting: 24-acre small town campus. Endowment: $4.2 million. Educational spending for the previous fiscal year: $13,286 per student. Total enrollment: 1,124. Faculty: 53 (51 full-time, 2 part-time). Student-undergrad faculty ratio is 6:1. 71 applied. Full-time: 519 students, 51% women, 49% men. Part-time: 363 students, 63% women, 37% men. Students come from 14 states and territories, 10 other countries, 26% from out-of-state. 1% American Indian or Alaska Native, non-Hispanic/Latino; 4% Hispanic/Latino; 27% African American, non-Hispanic/Latino; 1% Asian, non-Hispanic/Latino; 0.1% Native Hawaiian or other Pacific Islander, non-Hispanic/Latino; 2% international. 48% 25 or older, 9% live on campus, 22% transferred in. Core. Calendar: semesters. Academic remediation for entering students, services for LD students, advanced placement, accelerated degree program, independent study, distance learning, double major, summer session for credit, part-time degree program, adult/continuing education programs, co-op programs and internships. Study abroad program.

Entrance Requirements: Open admission. Options: electronic application, early admission, deferred admission, international baccalaureate accepted. Required: high school transcript. Recommended: SAT, SAT and SAT Subject Tests or ACT. Entrance: minimally difficult. Application deadline: Rolling. Notification: continuous.

Collegiate Environment: Orientation program. Drama-theater group, choral group, student-run newspaper. Social organizations: 7 open to all. Most popular organizations: Student Government Association, Professional Management Association, National Society for Leadership and Success. Major annual events: Homecoming, Fall Harvest Festival, Spring Fling. Student services: personal-psychological counseling. Campus security: late night transport-escort service, controlled dormitory access, evening security guards. 64 college housing spaces available; all were occupied in 2012-13. Freshmen given priority for college housing. Option: coed housing available. Thomas University Library with 41,467 books, 451 serials, 560 audiovisual materials, and an OPAC. 80 computers available on campus for general student use. A campuswide network can be accessed from student residence rooms and from off campus. Staffed computer lab on campus provides training in use of computers, software, and the Internet.

■ **TOCCOA FALLS COLLEGE**
107 N Chapel Dr.
Toccoa Falls, GA 30598
Tel: (706)886-6831
Fax: (706)282-6012
E-mail: admissions@tfc.edu
Web Site: www.tfc.edu/
Description: Independent interdenominational, 4-year, coed. Awards associate and bachelor's degrees. Founded 1907. Setting: 500-acre small town campus. Total enrollment: 859. Faculty: 76 (46 full-time, 30 part-time). Student-undergrad faculty ratio is 14:1. Full-time: 788 students, 55% women, 45% men. Part-time: 71 students, 49% women, 51% men. Students come from 42 states and territories, 21 other countries, 45% from out-of-state. 14% 25 or older, 63% live on campus. Retention: 60% of full-time freshmen returned the following year. Academic areas with the most degrees conferred: psychology; area and ethnic studies; education. Core. Calendar: 4-1-4. Services for LD students, advanced placement, accelerated degree program, independent study, distance learning, double major, summer session for credit, part-time degree program, internships. Study abroad program.
Entrance Requirements: Options: electronic application, early admission, deferred admission, international baccalaureate accepted. Required: essay, high school transcript, minimum 2.0 high school GPA, 1 recommendation, SAT or ACT. Required for some: interview. Entrance: moderately difficult. Application deadline: Rolling. Notification: continuous.
Collegiate Environment: Orientation program. Drama-theater group, choral group, student-run newspaper, radio station. Social organizations: 10 open to all. Most popular organizations: Outdoor Club, Hmong Student Fellowship, Impact, Student Missionary Fellowship, Fellowship of Christian Athletes. Major annual events: Spiritual Emphasis Week, lecture series, World Outreach Conference. Student services: health clinic, personal-psychological counseling. Campus security: student patrols. Seby Jones Library with 142,674 books, 23,447 microform titles, 25,305 serials, 2,171 audiovisual materials, an OPAC, and a Web page. 60 computers available on campus for general student use. A campuswide network can be accessed from student residence rooms and from off campus. Students can access the following: online class registration. Staffed computer lab on campus provides training in use of computers, software, and the Internet.
Community Environment: Toccoa is in a rural area in the foothills of the Blue Ridge Mountains. The Southern Railway and Greyhound Bus provide public transportation. Industries located here are the manufacturing of machinery, garments, furniture and thread. Toccoa has a municipal recreation center and golf course. Mountain lakes and resorts are within a short distance, providing fishing, hunting, water sports, and picnicking.

■ **TRUETT-MCCONNELL COLLEGE**
100 Alumni Dr.
Cleveland, GA 30528
Tel: (706)865-2134; Free: 800-226-8621
Fax: (706)219-3339
E-mail: nraynor@truett.edu
Web Site: www.truett.edu/
Description: Independent Baptist, 4-year, coed. Awards associate and bachelor's degrees. Founded 1946. Setting: 310-acre rural campus with easy access to Atlanta. Total enrollment: 921. Faculty: 89 (34 full-time, 55 part-time). Student-undergrad faculty ratio is 13:1. 400 applied, 83% were admitted. Full-time: 586 students, 44% women, 56% men. Part-time: 335 students, 55% women, 45% men. Students come from 17 states and territories, 7 other countries, 6% from out-of-state. 1% American Indian or

Alaska Native, non-Hispanic/Latino; 4% Hispanic/Latino; 8% African American, non-Hispanic/Latino; 0% Asian, non-Hispanic/Latino; 0% Native Hawaiian or other Pacific Islander, non-Hispanic/Latino; 3% international. 7% 25 or older, 49% live on campus, 6% transferred in. Retention: 74% of full-time freshmen returned the following year. Academic areas with the most degrees conferred: education; history; visual and performing arts. Core. Calendar: semesters. Academic remediation for entering students, services for LD students, advanced placement, accelerated degree program, distance learning, double major, summer session for credit.
Entrance Requirements: Options: electronic application, early admission, deferred admission. Required: essay, high school transcript, minimum 2 high school GPA, SAT or ACT. Required for some: 1 recommendation, interview. Entrance: minimally difficult. Application deadline: 8/1. Notification: continuous. Transfer credits accepted: Yes.
Collegiate Environment: Orientation program. Choral group. Student services: health clinic. Campus security: 24-hour weekday patrols, 10-hour weekend patrols by trained security personnel. Cofer Library with an OPAC.
Community Environment: Cleveland is in the mountains of north Georgia, a few miles south of the famous Vogel State Park. Bus service is available. The community, with its inspiring mountain scenery, provides a wholesome environment for young people. The Chattahoochee National Forest is 10 miles away.

■ **UNIVERSITY OF ATLANTA**
6685 Peachtree Industrial Blvd.
Atlanta, GA 30360
Tel: (770)368-8877; Free: 800-533-3378
Fax: (888)368-8667
E-mail: bkay@uofa.edu
Web Site: www.uofa.edu/
Description: Independent, comprehensive, coed. Awards bachelor's, master's, and doctoral degrees. Total enrollment: 1,410. Faculty: 299 (73 full-time, 226 part-time). Student-undergrad faculty ratio is 6:1. 467 applied, 48% were admitted. 4 National Merit Scholars, 11 class presidents, 11 valedictorians, 19 student government officers. Students come from 24 states and territories, 33 other countries, 90% from out-of-state. 61% 25 or older. Retention: 79% of full-time freshmen returned the following year. Academic areas with the most degrees conferred: business/marketing; social sciences; law/legal studies. Core. Accelerated degree program, honors program, independent study, distance learning, adult/continuing education programs, internships. Off campus study.
Entrance Requirements: Options: electronic application, early admission, deferred admission, international baccalaureate accepted. Required: essay, high school transcript, minimum 3 high school GPA. Recommended: SAT or ACT. Entrance: moderately difficult. Application deadline: Rolling. Notification: continuous.
Collegiate Environment: Orientation program.

■ **UNIVERSITY OF GEORGIA**
Athens, GA 30602
Tel: (706)542-3000
E-mail: admproc@uga.edu
Web Site: www.uga.edu/
Description: State-supported, comprehensive, coed. Part of University System of Georgia. Awards bachelor's, master's, and doctoral degrees and post-master's certificates. Founded 1785. Setting: 759-acre suburban campus with easy access to Atlanta. Endowment: $744.3 million. Research spending for the previous fiscal year: $318.2 million. Educational spending for the previous fiscal year: $7519 per student. Total enrollment: 34,519. Faculty: 2,205 (1,841 full-time, 364 part-time). Student-undergrad faculty ratio is 18:1. 18,458 applied, 56% were admitted. 48% from top 10% of their high school class, 90% from top quarter, 99% from top half. Full-time: 24,514 students, 58% women, 42% men. Part-time: 1,745 students, 53% women, 47% men. Students come from 55 states and territories, 121 other countries, 9% from out-of-state. 0.1% American Indian or Alaska Native, non-Hispanic/Latino; 5% Hispanic/Latino; 7% African American, non-Hispanic/Latino; 8% Asian, non-Hispanic/Latino; 0.1% Native Hawaiian or other Pacific Islander, non-Hispanic/Latino; 1% international. 4% 25 or older, 28% live on campus, 5% transferred in. Retention: 94% of full-time freshmen returned the following year. Academic areas with the most degrees conferred: business/ marketing; social sciences; communication/journalism. Core. Calendar: semesters. Academic remediation for entering students, services for LD students, advanced placement, accelerated degree program, self-designed majors, honors program, independent study, distance learning, double major,

summer session for credit, part-time degree program, adult/continuing education programs, co-op programs and internships, graduate courses open to undergrads. Off campus study at National Student Exchange. Study abroad program. ROTC: Army, Air Force.

Entrance Requirements: Options: electronic application, early admission, early action, deferred admission, international baccalaureate accepted. Required: high school transcript, counselor evaluation, SAT or ACT. Recommended: essay, minimum 2 high school GPA, SAT Subject Tests. Entrance: moderately difficult. Application deadlines: 1/15, 10/15 for early action. Notification: 4/1, 12/1 for early action. SAT Reasoning Test deadline: 1/15. SAT Subject Test deadline: 1/15. Applicants placed on waiting list: 1,131. Wait-listed applicants offered admission: 158. Early action applicants: 10,689. Early action applicants admitted: 5,689.

Costs Per Year: Application fee: $60. State resident tuition: $9842 full-time. Nonresident tuition: $28,052 full-time. Full-time tuition varies according to course load, location, and program. College room and board: $8970. College room only: $5088. Room and board charges vary according to board plan and housing facility.

Collegiate Environment: Orientation program. Drama-theater group, choral group, marching band, student-run newspaper, radio station. Social organizations: 600 open to all; national fraternities, national sororities, local fraternities, local sororities; 20% of eligible men and 25% of eligible women are members. Most popular organizations: intramurals, Recreational sports program, Communiversity, University Union, Red Coat Band. Major annual events: Concerts at Legion Field, Homecoming, UGA Health Fair. Student services: legal services, health clinic, personal-psychological counseling, women's center. Campus security: 24-hour emergency response devices and patrols, late night transport-escort service, controlled dormitory access. 7,218 college housing spaces available. Freshmen guaranteed college housing. On-campus residence required in freshman year. Options: coed, women-only housing available. Ilah Dunlap Little Memorial Library plus 4 others with 4.9 million books, 6.7 million microform titles, 97,296 serials, an OPAC, and a Web page. Operations spending for the previous fiscal year: $23.6 million. 3,046 computers available on campus for general student use. A campuswide network can be accessed from student residence rooms and from off campus. Students can access the following: online class registration. Staffed computer lab on campus (open 24 hours a day) provides training in use of computers, software, and the Internet.

Community Environment: Athens, the largest city in the rolling Piedmont area of northeast Georgia, is 70 miles northeast of Atlanta. Many of its building exemplify Greek Revival architecture characteristic of the Old South. It enjoys a mild climate, with an annual mean temperature of 60 degrees. Recreational facilities include parks, golf courses, swimming pools, tennis courts, baseball parks, a bowling center, and skating rinks, as well as areas for hunting, fishing and boating. Athens, serviced by buses and an airline, has numerous lodging accommodations and restaurants both in town and on campus. Its manufactured products include textiles, plastics, metals, electrical equipment, dairy products, and paper goods.

■ UNIVERSITY OF NORTH GEORGIA

82 College Cir.
Dahlonega, GA 30597
Tel: (706)864-1400; Free: 800-498-9581
Fax: (706)864-1478
E-mail: admissions@northgeorgia.edu
Web Site: www.ung.edu/

Description: State-supported, comprehensive, coed. Part of University System of Georgia. Awards associate, bachelor's, master's, and doctoral degrees and post-master's certificates. Founded 1873. Setting: 140-acre small town campus with easy access to Atlanta. Endowment: $21.8 million. Total enrollment: 6,413. Faculty: 353 (247 full-time, 106 part-time). Student-undergrad faculty ratio is 20:1. 4,226 applied, 56% were admitted. Full-time: 4,889 students, 55% women, 45% men. Part-time: 962 students, 67% women, 33% men. Students come from 39 states and territories, 47 other countries, 6% from out-of-state. 0.2% American Indian or Alaska Native, non-Hispanic/Latino; 4% Hispanic/Latino; 3% African American, non-Hispanic/Latino; 2% Asian, non-Hispanic/Latino; 0.1% Native Hawaiian or other Pacific Islander, non-Hispanic/Latino; 1% international. 13% 25 or older, 37% live on campus, 8% transferred in. Retention: 78% of full-time freshmen returned the following year. Academic areas with the most degrees conferred: business/marketing; education; homeland security, law enforcement, firefighting, and protective services. Core. Calendar: semesters. Academic remediation for entering students, ESL program, services for LD students, advanced placement, accelerated degree program, freshman

honors college, honors program, independent study, distance learning, double major, summer session for credit, part-time degree program, external degree program, co-op programs and internships. Study abroad program. ROTC: Army.

Entrance Requirements: Options: electronic application, early admission, international baccalaureate accepted. Required: high school transcript, minimum 2 high school GPA, proof of immunization, SAT or ACT. Required for some: SAT and SAT Subject Tests or ACT. Entrance: moderately difficult. Application deadline: 7/1. Notification: continuous. SAT Reasoning Test deadline: 7/1. SAT Subject Test deadline: 7/1. Transfer credits accepted: Yes.

Costs Per Year: Application fee: $30. State resident tuition: $4852 full-time, $161.74 per credit hour part-time. Nonresident tuition: $17,128 full-time, $570.94 per credit hour part-time. Mandatory fees: $1718 full-time. Part-time tuition varies according to course load. College room and board: $8430. College room only: $4760. Room and board charges vary according to board plan and housing facility.

Collegiate Environment: Orientation program. Drama-theater group, choral group, student-run newspaper. Social organizations: 160 open to all; national fraternities, national sororities; 11% of eligible men and 13% of eligible women are members. Most popular organizations: Student Government Association, Commuter Council, Graduate Student Senate, Student Activities Board, Greek organizations. Major annual events: Parents'/Alumni Weekend, Homecoming, Fall Jam. Student services: health clinic, personal-psychological counseling. Campus security: 24-hour emergency response devices and patrols, late night transport-escort service, controlled dormitory access. 2,230 college housing spaces available; 2,172 were occupied in 2012-13. Freshmen guaranteed college housing. On-campus residence required through sophomore year. Options: coed, men-only, women-only housing available. Library Technology Center with 275,898 books, 366,785 microform titles, 9,000 serials, 2,175 audiovisual materials, an OPAC, and a Web page. 707 computers available on campus for general student use. A campuswide network can be accessed from student residence rooms and from off campus. Students can access the following: online class registration. Staffed computer lab on campus.

■ UNIVERSITY OF PHOENIX–ATLANTA CAMPUS

8200 Roberts Dr., Ste. 300
Sandy Springs, GA 30350-4153
Tel: (678)731-0555; Free: 866-766-0766
Fax: (770)821-5399
Web Site: www.phoenix.edu/

Description: Proprietary, comprehensive, coed. Awards bachelor's and master's degrees. Setting: urban campus. Total enrollment: 1,573. Faculty: 220 (17 full-time, 203 part-time). Full-time: 1,196 students, 71% women, 29% men. 89% 25 or older. Academic areas with the most degrees conferred: business/marketing; computer and information sciences; health professions and related sciences. Core. Calendar: continuous. Services for LD students, advanced placement, accelerated degree program, independent study, distance learning, external degree program, adult/continuing education programs, graduate courses open to undergrads.

Entrance Requirements: Open admission. Options: electronic application, deferred admission. Required: 1 recommendation. Required for some: high school transcript. Entrance: noncompetitive. Application deadline: Rolling.

Collegiate Environment: Campus security: late night transport-escort service. University Library with 16,781 serials, an OPAC, and a Web page. Operations spending for the previous fiscal year: $6.8 million.

■ UNIVERSITY OF PHOENIX–AUGUSTA CAMPUS

3150 Perimeter Pky.
Augusta, GA 30909-4583
Tel: (706)868-2000; Free: 866-766-0766
Web Site: www.phoenix.edu/

Description: Proprietary, comprehensive, coed. Awards associate, bachelor's, master's, and doctoral degrees.

■ UNIVERSITY OF PHOENIX–COLUMBUS GEORGIA CAMPUS

4747 Hamilton Rd., Ste. E
Columbus, GA 31904-6321
Tel: (706)320-1266; Free: 866-766-0766
Web Site: www.phoenix.edu/

Description: Proprietary, comprehensive, coed. Awards associate, bachelor's, and master's degrees. Founded 2003. Setting: urban campus. Total enrollment: 764. Faculty: 107 (12 full-time, 95 part-time). Full-time: 704

students, 75% women, 25% men. 76% 25 or older. Academic areas with the most degrees conferred: business/marketing; health professions and related sciences; homeland security, law enforcement, firefighting, and protective services. Core. Calendar: continuous. Services for LD students, advanced placement, accelerated degree program, independent study, distance learning, graduate courses open to undergrads.

Entrance Requirements: Open admission. Options: electronic application, deferred admission. Required: 1 recommendation. Required for some: high school transcript. Entrance: noncompetitive. Application deadline: Rolling.

Collegiate Environment: Campus security: late night transport-escort service. 16,781 microform titles, 3,000 audiovisual materials, and an OPACOperations spending for the previous fiscal year: $6.8 million.

■ **UNIVERSITY OF PHOENIX–SAVANNAH CAMPUS**

8001 Chatham Ctr. Dr., Ste. 200
Savannah, GA 31405-7400
Tel: (912)232-0531; Free: 866-766-0766
Web Site: www.phoenix.edu/

Description: Proprietary, comprehensive, coed. Awards bachelor's, master's, and doctoral degrees.

■ **UNIVERSITY OF WEST GEORGIA**

1601 Maple St.
Carrollton, GA 30118
Tel: (678)839-5000
E-mail: admiss@westga.edu
Web Site: www.westga.edu/

Description: State-supported, comprehensive, coed. Part of University System of Georgia. Awards bachelor's, master's, and doctoral degrees and post-master's certificates. Founded 1933. Setting: 645-acre small town campus with easy access to Atlanta. Endowment: $19.7 million. Research spending for the previous fiscal year: $1.6 million. Educational spending for the previous fiscal year: $6597 per student. Total enrollment: 11,769. Faculty: 644 (453 full-time, 191 part-time). Student-undergrad faculty ratio is 19:1. 6,435 applied, 56% were admitted. Full-time: 8,178 students, 61% women, 39% men. Part-time: 1,785 students, 62% women, 38% men. Students come from 41 states and territories, 56 other countries, 3% from out-of-state. 0.2% American Indian or Alaska Native, non-Hispanic/Latino; 4% Hispanic/Latino; 31% African American, non-Hispanic/Latino; 1% Asian, non-Hispanic/Latino; 0.1% Native Hawaiian or other Pacific Islander, non-Hispanic/Latino; 1% international. 14% 25 or older, 27% live on campus, 6% transferred in. Retention: 70% of full-time freshmen returned the following year. Academic areas with the most degrees conferred: business/marketing; education; health professions and related sciences. Core. Calendar: semesters. Academic remediation for entering students, ESL program, services for LD students, advanced placement, accelerated degree program, honors program, independent study, distance learning, double major, summer session for credit, part-time degree program, external degree program, adult/continuing education programs, co-op programs and internships, graduate courses open to undergrads. Off campus study at UWG/Newnan Center, Georgia Highlands College, Dalton State College, Piedmont-South Atlantic Coast Cooperative Ecosystem Studies Unit (PSAC-CESU), The Inter-University Consortium for Political and Social Research (ICPSR), Atlanta Regional Council for Higher Education (ARCHE) Cross Registration members. Study abroad program. ROTC: Air Force (c).

Entrance Requirements: Options: electronic application, early admission, deferred admission, international baccalaureate accepted. Required: high school transcript, minimum 2.4 high school GPA, proof of immunization, SAT or ACT. Entrance: minimally difficult. Application deadlines: 6/1, 6/1 for nonresidents. Notification: continuous, continuous for nonresidents. SAT Reasoning Test deadline: 6/1. Transfer credits accepted: Yes.

Costs Per Year: Application fee: $40. State resident tuition: $4852 full-time, $161.74 per semester hour part-time. Nonresident tuition: $17,128 full-time, $570.94 per semester hour part-time. Mandatory fees: $1858 full-time, $46.35 per semester hour part-time, $512 per term part-time. Full-time tuition and fees vary according to course load and location. Part-time tuition and fees vary according to course load and location. College room and board: $7482. College room only: $4100. Room and board charges vary according to board plan and housing facility.

Collegiate Environment: Orientation program. Drama-theater group, choral group, marching band, student-run newspaper, radio station. Social organizations: 159 open to all; national fraternities, national sororities; 3% of eligible men and 3% of eligible women are members. Most popular organizations: Black Student Alliance, Student Activities Council, Baptist Student

Union, Campus Outreach, United Voices Gospel Choir. Major annual events: Homecoming, Annual Campus Awards Program, Spring Fling. Student services: health clinic, personal-psychological counseling. Campus security: 24-hour emergency response devices and patrols, late night transport-escort service, controlled dormitory access. 3,000 college housing spaces available; 2,728 were occupied in 2012-13. Freshmen guaranteed college housing. On-campus residence required in freshman year. Options: coed, women-only housing available. Irvine Sullivan Ingram Library plus 1 other with 671,683 books, 21,052 microform titles, 77,717 serials, 23,935 audiovisual materials, an OPAC, and a Web page. Operations spending for the previous fiscal year: $2.9 million. 1,200 computers available on campus for general student use. A campuswide network can be accessed from student residence rooms and from off campus. Students can access the following: online class registration. Staffed computer lab on campus provides training in use of computers, software, and the Internet.

Community Environment: Located in northwest Georgia, 48 miles southwest of the state capital, Atlanta, Carrollton has a mild climate with an average temperature of 63 degrees. Part-time employment is available. The benefits of this unique area include a safe, peaceful small town atmosphere, offering educational excellence in a personal environment, within 45 minutes of the cultural and social diversities of Atlanta. Private housing is available.

■ **VALDOSTA STATE UNIVERSITY**

1500 N Patterson St.
Valdosta, GA 31698
Tel: (229)333-5800; Free: 800-618-1878
Fax: (229)333-5482
E-mail: admissions@valdosta.edu
Web Site: www.valdosta.edu/

Description: State-supported, university, coed. Part of University System of Georgia. Awards associate, bachelor's, master's, and doctoral degrees and post-master's certificates. Founded 1906. Setting: 180-acre small town campus. Endowment: $23.3 million. Research spending for the previous fiscal year: $530,627. Educational spending for the previous fiscal year: $4745 per student. Total enrollment: 12,515. Faculty: 644 (486 full-time, 158 part-time). Student-undergrad faculty ratio is 21:1. 6,268 applied, 59% were admitted. Full-time: 8,859 students, 60% women, 40% men. Part-time: 1,431 students, 56% women, 44% men. Students come from 47 states and territories, 68 other countries, 5% from out-of-state. 0.2% American Indian or Alaska Native, non-Hispanic/Latino; 4% Hispanic/Latino; 35% African American, non-Hispanic/Latino; 1% Asian, non-Hispanic/Latino; 0.2% Native Hawaiian or other Pacific Islander, non-Hispanic/Latino; 2% international. 14% 25 or older, 28% live on campus, 6% transferred in. Retention: 67% of full-time freshmen returned the following year. Academic areas with the most degrees conferred: business/marketing; education; health professions and related sciences. Core. Calendar: semesters. ESL program, services for LD students, advanced placement, accelerated degree program, honors program, independent study, distance learning, double major, summer session for credit, part-time degree program, external degree program, adult/continuing education programs, co-op programs and internships, graduate courses open to undergrads. Off campus study at ABAC/ABAC on the Square-Moultrie, Albany State, Columbus State, Darton College, Georgia College, Georgia State, Macon State, Moultrie Tech, Okefenokee Technical, SW RESA, Southwest Technical, Waycross College, and Wiregrass Georgia Technical. Study abroad program. ROTC: Air Force.

Entrance Requirements: Options: electronic application, early admission, deferred admission, international baccalaureate accepted. Required: high school transcript, SAT or ACT. Entrance: moderately difficult. Application deadlines: 6/15, 6/15 for nonresidents. Notification: continuous until 8/1, continuous until 8/1 for nonresidents. SAT Reasoning Test deadline: 6/15. Transfer credits accepted: Yes.

Costs Per Year: Application fee: $40. State resident tuition: $3882 full-time, $161.74 per credit hour part-time. Nonresident tuition: $13,703 full-time, $570.94 per credit hour part-time. Mandatory fees: $1910 full-time, $955 per term part-time. Full-time tuition and fees vary according to course load, location, program, and reciprocity agreements. Part-time tuition and fees vary according to course load, location, program, and reciprocity agreements. College room and board: $7070. College room only: $3560. Room and board charges vary according to board plan and housing facility.

Collegiate Environment: Orientation program. Drama-theater group, choral group, marching band, student-run newspaper, radio station. Social organizations: 199 open to all; national fraternities, national sororities; 12% of eligible men and 14% of eligible women are members. Most popular organizations: Interfraternity Council, College Panhellenic Council, Black

Student League, Residence Hall Association, Alpha Lambda Delta Freshmen Honor Society. Major annual events: The Happening, Homecoming activities, Fall Explosion. Student services: health clinic, personal-psychological counseling. Campus security: 24-hour emergency response devices and patrols, late night transport-escort service, controlled dormitory access, bicycle patrols, security cameras. 2,856 college housing spaces available; 2,839 were occupied in 2012-13. Freshmen given priority for college housing. On-campus residence required in freshman year. Option: coed housing available. Odum Library plus 1 other with 728,261 books, 1.1 million microform titles, 2,558 serials, 25,294 audiovisual materials, an OPAC, and a Web page. Operations spending for the previous fiscal year: $3.8 million. 1,225 computers available on campus for general student use. Computer purchase/lease plans available. A campuswide network can be accessed from student residence rooms and from off campus. Students can access the following: online class registration. Staffed computer lab on campus (open 24 hours a day) provides training in use of computers and the Internet.
Community Environment: Valdosta, located in the south-central section of Georgia, is the largest city of the 16-county area that it serves. Buses and railroads serve the area, and airlines are available in Valdosta, Tallahassee, Jacksonville and Atlanta. Average temperature for the year is 67 degrees. Valdosta is the largest inland naval stores market in the world. Industries are tobacco, lumber, mobile homes, cotton, paper and metal goods. Valdosta Entertainment Association brings outstanding cultural events to the city. The Gulf of Mexico and the Atlantic Ocean are within 125 miles. Near the city are numerous freshwater lakes that provide fishing, boating, water skiing, beaches for swimming and picnic areas. Valdosta boasts a congenial atmosphere and friendly spirit. Newcomers and visitors are welcomed. Part-time employment is available.

■ VIRGINIA COLLEGE IN MACON
1901 Paul Walsh Dr.
Macon, GA 31206
Tel: (478)803-4802
Web Site: www.vc.edu/
Description: Proprietary, 2-year, coed. Founded 2010.

■ WESLEYAN COLLEGE
4760 Forsyth Rd.
Macon, GA 31210-4462
Tel: (478)477-1110; Free: 800-447-6610
Fax: (478)757-4030
E-mail: admissions@wesleyancollege.edu
Web Site: www.wesleyancollege.edu/
Description: Independent United Methodist, comprehensive. Awards bachelor's and master's degrees. Founded 1836. Setting: 200-acre suburban campus with easy access to Atlanta. Endowment: $55 million. Educational spending for the previous fiscal year: $11,537 per student. Total enrollment: 710. Faculty: 114 (51 full-time, 63 part-time). Student-undergrad faculty ratio is 8:1. 690 applied, 51% were admitted. 0% from top 10% of their high school class, 1% from top quarter, 13% from top half. Full-time: 439 students, 100% women. Part-time: 209 students, 100% women. Students come from 21 states and territories, 27 other countries, 14% from out-of-state. 0% American Indian or Alaska Native, non-Hispanic/Latino; 4% Hispanic/Latino; 31% African American, non-Hispanic/Latino; 1% Asian, non-Hispanic/Latino; 0.2% Native Hawaiian or other Pacific Islander, non-Hispanic/Latino; 18% international. 35% 25 or older, 82% live on campus, 3% transferred in. Retention: 83% of full-time freshmen returned the following year. Academic areas with the most degrees conferred: business/marketing; psychology; social sciences. Core. Calendar: semesters. Services for LD students, advanced placement, self-designed majors, honors program, independent study, double major, summer session for credit, part-time degree program, adult/continuing education programs, co-op programs and internships. Off campus study at Mercer University, National Student Exchange. Study abroad program. ROTC: Army (c).
Entrance Requirements: Options: electronic application, early admission, early decision, early action, deferred admission, international baccalaureate accepted. Required: high school transcript, minimum 2 high school GPA, 1 recommendation, SAT or ACT. Recommended: essay, 2 recommendations. Required for some: interview. Entrance: moderately difficult. Application deadlines: 2/15, 11/15 for early decision, 1/15 for early action. Notification: continuous, 12/15 for early decision. SAT Reasoning Test deadline: 6/1. Transfer credits accepted: Yes.
Costs Per Year: Application fee: $30. Comprehensive fee: $27,400 includes full-time tuition ($19,000) and college room and board ($8400). Full-time

tuition varies according to degree level, program, and reciprocity agreements. Room and board charges vary according to board plan and housing facility.
Collegiate Environment: Orientation program. Drama-theater group, choral group, student-run newspaper. Social organizations: 37 open to all. Most popular organizations: Student Recreation Council, Campus Activities Board, Student Government Association, Council on Religious Concerns, Christian Fellowship. Major annual events: Homecoming, Stunt, Holiday Banquet. Student services: health clinic, women's center. Campus security: 24-hour emergency response devices and patrols, late night transport-escort service, controlled dormitory access. 622 college housing spaces available; 316 were occupied in 2012-13. Freshmen guaranteed college housing. On-campus residence required through senior year. Option: women-only housing available. Willet Memorial Library with 145,571 books, 33,912 microform titles, 431 serials, 4,420 audiovisual materials, an OPAC, and a Web page. Operations spending for the previous fiscal year: $358,273. 40 computers available on campus for general student use. A campuswide network can be accessed from student residence rooms and from off campus. Students can access the following: online class registration, online payment. Staffed computer lab on campus provides training in use of computers, software, and the Internet.
Community Environment: The college is located in suburban Macon. There are 5 other coed colleges within a 60-mile radius of Macon.

■ WEST GEORGIA TECHNICAL COLLEGE
176 Murphy Campus Blvd.
Waco, GA 30182
Tel: (770)537-6000
E-mail: mary.aderhold@westgatech.edu
Web Site: www.westgatech.edu/
Description: State-supported, 2-year, coed. Part of Technical College System of Georgia. Awards certificates, diplomas, and terminal associate degrees. Founded 1966. Total enrollment: 6,645. Full-time: 2,037 students, 69% women, 31% men. Part-time: 4,608 students, 67% women, 33% men. 3% from out-of-state. 1% American Indian or Alaska Native, non-Hispanic/Latino; 3% Hispanic/Latino; 28% African American, non-Hispanic/Latino; 1% Asian, non-Hispanic/Latino; 0.1% Native Hawaiian or other Pacific Islander, non-Hispanic/Latino; 0.1% international. 46% 25 or older. Retention: 66% of full-time freshmen returned the following year. Distance learning.
Entrance Requirements: Open admission selective admission to some programs. Option: early admission. Required: high school transcript. Entrance: noncompetitive.
Collegiate Environment: College housing not available.

■ WESTWOOD COLLEGE–ATLANTA MIDTOWN
1100 Spring St.
Ste. 102
Atlanta, GA 30309
Tel: (404)745-9862; Free: 800-613-4595
Web Site: www.westwood.edu/
Description: Proprietary, 4-year, coed. Awards associate and bachelor's degrees. Founded 2003. Total enrollment: 675. Faculty: 68. Calendar: continuous.

■ WESTWOOD COLLEGE–ATLANTA NORTHLAKE
2309 Parklake Dr., NE
Bldg. 10
Atlanta, GA 30345
Tel: (404)962-2998; Free: 866-821-6145
Web Site: www.westwood.edu/
Description: Proprietary, 4-year, coed. Part of Alta College, Inc. Awards associate and bachelor's degrees. Total enrollment: 490. Faculty: 50.

■ WIREGRASS GEORGIA TECHNICAL COLLEGE
4089 Val Tech Rd.
Valdosta, GA 31602
Tel: (229)333-2100
Fax: (229)333-2129
E-mail: teresa.spires@wiregrass.edu
Web Site: www.wiregrass.edu/
Description: State-supported, 2-year, coed. Part of Technical College System of Georgia. Awards certificates, diplomas, and terminal associate degrees. Founded 1963. Setting: suburban campus. Total enrollment: 4,143. Full-time: 1,532 students, 62% women, 38% men. Part-time: 2,611 students,

67% women, 33% men. 1% from out-of-state. 0.4% American Indian or Alaska Native, non-Hispanic/Latino; 4% Hispanic/Latino; 32% African American, non-Hispanic/Latino; 1% Asian, non-Hispanic/Latino; 0.1% Native Hawaiian or other Pacific Islander, non-Hispanic/Latino; 0% international. 49% 25 or older. Retention: 63% of full-time freshmen returned the following year. Distance learning.

Entrance Requirements: Open admission selective admission to some programs. Option: early admission. Required: high school transcript. Entrance: noncompetitive.

Collegiate Environment: College housing not available.

■ **YOUNG HARRIS COLLEGE**
1 College St.
Young Harris, GA 30582
Tel: (706)379-3111
Fax: (706)379-4306
E-mail: admissions@yhc.edu
Web Site: www.yhc.edu/

Description: Independent United Methodist, 4-year, coed. Awards bachelor's degrees. Founded 1886. Setting: 800-acre small town campus. Endowment: $93.7 million. Educational spending for the previous fiscal year: $8823 per student. Total enrollment: 1,034. Faculty: 105 (77 full-time, 28 part-time). Student-undergrad faculty ratio is 12:1. 2,061 applied, 48% were admitted. Full-time: 999 students, 53% women, 47% men. Part-time: 35 students, 74% women, 26% men. Students come from 24 states and territories, 26 other countries, 14% from out-of-state. 0.2% American Indian or Alaska Native, non-Hispanic/Latino; 6% Hispanic/Latino; 6% African American, non-Hispanic/Latino; 1% Asian, non-Hispanic/Latino; 0.4% Native Hawaiian or other Pacific Islander, non-Hispanic/Latino. 1% 25 or older, 87% live on campus, 3% transferred in. Retention: 65% of full-time freshmen returned the following year. Academic areas with the most degrees conferred: business/marketing; biological/life sciences; visual and performing arts. Core. Calendar: semesters. Services for LD students, advanced placement, honors program, double major, summer session for credit, part-time degree program, adult/continuing education programs, co-op programs and internships. Study abroad program.

Entrance Requirements: Option: electronic application. Required: high school transcript, SAT or ACT. Entrance: moderately difficult. Application deadlines: Rolling, Rolling for nonresidents. Notification: continuous, continuous for nonresidents. Transfer credits accepted: Yes.

Costs Per Year: Application fee: $0. Comprehensive fee: $34,940 includes full-time tuition ($24,500), mandatory fees ($780), and college room and board ($9660). Full-time tuition and fees vary according to course load. Room and board charges vary according to housing facility. Part-time tuition: $675 per credit hour. Part-time tuition varies according to course load.

Collegiate Environment: Orientation program. Drama-theater group, choral group, student-run newspaper. Social organizations: 56 open to all; national fraternities, national sororities, local fraternities, local sororities; 13% of eligible men and 15% of eligible women are members. Most popular organizations: Greek life, religious organizations/Bible study, intramural sports, Student Government Association, Campus Activities Board. Major annual events: Spring Formal, Organizational Fair, Fall Fest. Student services: health clinic, personal-psychological counseling. Campus security: 24-hour emergency response devices and patrols, student patrols, late night transport-escort service, controlled dormitory access. 889 college housing spaces available; 812 were occupied in 2012-13. Freshmen guaranteed college housing. On-campus residence required through senior year. Options: coed, men-only, women-only housing available. Duckworth Library with 104,432 books, 138 microform titles, 126 serials, 5,415 audiovisual materials, an OPAC, and a Web page. Operations spending for the previous fiscal year: $768,687. 99 computers available on campus for general student use. A campuswide network can be accessed from student residence rooms and from off campus. Students can access the following: online class registration. Staffed computer lab on campus.

Community Environment: Young Harris is situated in the Blue Ridge Mountains of northeast Georgia where the climate is moderate. Atlanta, Asheville, Chattanooga, and Greenville, South Carolina, are all within one hundred miles. Various religious denominations, a Lions Club, a clinic, and two hospitals serve the community. As part of a resort area the recreational activities include fishing, boating, hiking, horseback riding, picnicking, swimming, tennis, and golf. The county fair is an annual event.

■ ARGOSY UNIVERSITY, HAWAI'I

400 ASB Twr., 1001 Bishop St.
Honolulu, HI 96813
Tel: (808)536-5555; Free: 888-323-2777
Fax: (808)536-5505
Web Site: www.argosy.edu/hawaii/
Description: Proprietary, university, coed. Part of Education Management Corporation. Awards bachelor's, master's, and doctoral degrees. Founded 1994. Calendar: semesters.

■ BRIGHAM YOUNG UNIVERSITY–HAWAII

55-220 Kulanui St.
Laie, HI 96762-1294
Tel: (808)293-3211
E-mail: admissions@byuh.edu
Web Site: www.byuh.edu/
Description: Independent Latter-day Saints, 4-year, coed. Administratively affiliated with Brigham Young University. Awards associate and bachelor's degrees. Founded 1955. Setting: 60-acre small town campus with easy access to Honolulu. Total enrollment: 2,555. Faculty: 228 (121 full-time, 107 part-time). Student-undergrad faculty ratio is 15:1. 1,295 applied, 58% were admitted. Full-time: 2,380 students, 54% women, 46% men. Part-time: 175 students, 57% women, 43% men. Students come from 48 states and territories, 71 other countries, 75% from out-of-state. 26% 25 or older, 57% live on campus, 10% transferred in. Retention: 62% of full-time freshmen returned the following year. Academic areas with the most degrees conferred: business/marketing; education; interdisciplinary studies. Core. Calendar: semesters two semesters and three terms. Academic remediation for entering students, ESL program, services for LD students, advanced placement, accelerated degree program, freshman honors college, honors program, double major, summer session for credit, part-time degree program, adult/continuing education programs, co-op programs and internships. Off campus study. ROTC: Army (c), Naval (c), Air Force (c).
Entrance Requirements: Options: electronic application, early admission, deferred admission, international baccalaureate accepted. Required: essay, high school transcript, minimum 3 high school GPA, resume of activities, ecclesiastical endorsement, SAT or ACT. Recommended: ACT. Entrance: moderately difficult. Application deadline: 2/15. Notification: continuous. Preference given to Latter-Day Saints Church members. Transfer credits accepted: Yes.
Costs Per Year: Application fee: $30. Comprehensive fee: $9678 includes full-time tuition ($4630) and college room and board ($5048). Room and board charges vary according to board plan and housing facility.
Collegiate Environment: Orientation program. Drama-theater group, choral group, student-run newspaper. Social organizations: 46 open to all. Most popular organizations: Tonga Club, Samoa Club, Hawaiian Club, Hong Kong Club, Japanese Club. Major annual events: Culture Night, Foodfest, Songfest. Student services: health clinic, personal-psychological counseling. Campus security: 24-hour patrols, late night transport-escort service. Joseph F. Smith Library plus 1 other with 358,513 books, 450,000 microform titles, 37,901 serials, 11,383 audiovisual materials, an OPAC, and a Web page. 640 computers available on campus for general student use. A campuswide network can be accessed from student residence rooms. Students can access the following: online class registration. Staffed computer lab on campus provides training in use of computers, software, and the Internet.

■ CHAMINADE UNIVERSITY OF HONOLULU

3140 Waialae Ave.
Honolulu, HI 96816-1578
Tel: (808)735-4711; Free: 800-735-3733
Fax: (808)739-4647
E-mail: admissions@chaminade.edu
Web Site: www.chaminade.edu/
Description: Independent Roman Catholic, comprehensive, coed. Awards associate, bachelor's, and master's degrees. Founded 1955. Setting: 62-acre urban campus with easy access to Honolulu. Endowment: $10.2 million. Educational spending for the previous fiscal year: $7300 per student. Total enrollment: 2,144. Student-undergrad faculty ratio is 13:1. 950 applied, 87% were admitted. 9% from top 10% of their high school class, 34% from top quarter, 75% from top half. Full-time: 1,327 students, 66% women, 34% men. Part-time: 45 students, 76% women, 24% men. Students come from 41 states and territories, 25 other countries, 35% from out-of-state. 0.3% American Indian or Alaska Native, non-Hispanic/Latino; 6% Hispanic/Latino; 3% African American, non-Hispanic/Latino; 30% Asian, non-Hispanic/Latino; 15% Native Hawaiian or other Pacific Islander, non-Hispanic/Latino; 3% international. 11% 25 or older, 32% live on campus, 9% transferred in. Retention: 69% of full-time freshmen returned the following year. Academic areas with the most degrees conferred: homeland security, law enforcement, firefighting, and protective services; education; psychology. Core. Calendar: semesters. Academic remediation for entering students, advanced placement, accelerated degree program, self-designed majors, independent study, distance learning, double major, summer session for credit, part-time degree program, adult/continuing education programs, internships, graduate courses open to undergrads. Off campus study at University of Hawaii at Manoa, Brigham Young University, Hawaii Pacific University. Study abroad program. ROTC: Army (c), Air Force (c).
Entrance Requirements: Options: electronic application, deferred admission, international baccalaureate accepted. Required: essay, high school transcript, minimum 2.5 high school GPA, SAT or ACT, TOEFL for international students. Recommended: minimum 3 high school GPA, 2 recommendations. Required for some: minimum 2.75 high school GPA, 2 recommendations, interview. Entrance: moderately difficult. Application deadline: Rolling. Notification: continuous. Transfer credits accepted: Yes.
Costs Per Year: Application fee: $50. Comprehensive fee: $30,620 includes full-time tuition ($19,200), mandatory fees ($130), and college room and board ($11,290). Full-time tuition and fees vary according to course load. Room and board charges vary according to board plan and housing facility. Part-time tuition: $640 per credit hour. Part-time tuition varies according to course load.
Collegiate Environment: Orientation program. Drama-theater group, choral group, student-run newspaper. Social organizations: 32 open to all. Most popular organizations: Lumana O Samoa (Samoan Club), Kaimi Lalakea (Hawaiian Club), Rotaract, Residence Hall Association, Chaminade Student Government Association. Major annual events: International Extravaganza, Campus Ministry Awakening Retreats, Club Fest. Student services: personal-psychological counseling. Campus security: 24-hour emergency response devices and patrols, late night transport-escort service, controlled dormitory access. 397 college housing spaces available; 346 were occupied in 2012-13. No special consideration for freshman housing applicants. Options: coed, women-only housing available. Sullivan Library with 78,000 books, 6,361 microform titles, 6,730 serials, 566 audiovisual materials, an OPAC, and a Web page. 100 computers available on campus for general

student use. A campuswide network can be accessed from student residence rooms and from off campus. Students can access the following: online class registration. Staffed computer lab on campus provides training in use of computers, software, and the Internet.
Community Environment: See University of Hawaii - Manoa.

■ HAWAII COMMUNITY COLLEGE
200 W Kawili St.
Hilo, HI 96720-4091
Tel: (808)974-7611
Fax: (808)974-7692
Web Site: www.hawcc.hawaii.edu/
Description: State-supported, 2-year, coed. Part of University of Hawaii System. Awards certificates, diplomas, transfer associate, and terminal associate degrees. Founded 1954. Setting: small town campus. Total enrollment: 2,603. 34% 25 or older. Calendar: semesters. ESL program, services for LD students, advanced placement, honors program, summer session for credit, part-time degree program, co-op programs.
Entrance Requirements: Open admission. Option: early admission. Entrance: noncompetitive. Application deadline: 8/1.
Collegiate Environment: Orientation program. Campus security: 24-hour patrols.

■ HAWAI'I PACIFIC UNIVERSITY
1164 Bishop St.
Honolulu, HI 96813
Tel: (808)544-0200; Free: 866-225-5478
Fax: (808)544-1136
E-mail: admissions@hpu.edu
Web Site: www.hpu.edu/
Description: Independent, comprehensive, coed. Awards associate, bachelor's, and master's degrees and post-master's certificates. Founded 1965. Setting: 140-acre urban campus. Endowment: $61 million. Research spending for the previous fiscal year: $5.2 million. Educational spending for the previous fiscal year: $4639 per student. Total enrollment: 7,463. Faculty: 696 (262 full-time, 434 part-time). Student-undergrad faculty ratio is 14:1. 4,129 applied, 72% were admitted. 25% from top 10% of their high school class, 53% from top quarter, 85% from top half. Full-time: 3,944 students, 60% women, 40% men. Part-time: 2,224 students, 46% women, 54% men. Students come from 51 states and territories, 65 other countries, 30% from out-of-state. 1% American Indian or Alaska Native, non-Hispanic/Latino; 14% Hispanic/Latino; 6% African American, non-Hispanic/Latino; 21% Asian, non-Hispanic/Latino; 3% Native Hawaiian or other Pacific Islander, non-Hispanic/Latino; 10% international. 44% 25 or older, 10% live on campus, 12% transferred in. Retention: 69% of full-time freshmen returned the following year. Academic areas with the most degrees conferred: business/marketing; health professions and related sciences; social sciences. Core. Calendar: semesters. Academic remediation for entering students, ESL program, services for LD students, advanced placement, accelerated degree program, self-designed majors, freshman honors college, honors program, independent study, distance learning, double major, summer session for credit, part-time degree program, adult/continuing education programs, co-op programs and internships, graduate courses open to undergrads. Off campus study at Carroll College, Creighton University, Samuel Merritt College, Southern California University of Health Sciences. Study abroad program. ROTC: Army (c), Air Force (c).
Entrance Requirements: Options: electronic application, early admission, deferred admission, international baccalaureate accepted. Required: high school transcript, minimum 2.5 high school GPA, SAT or ACT. Recommended: essay, 2 recommendations. Required for some: interview. Entrance: moderately difficult. Application deadline: Rolling. Transfer credits accepted: Yes.
Costs Per Year: Application fee: $50. Comprehensive fee: $33,210 includes full-time tuition ($19,980) and college room and board ($13,230). Full-time tuition varies according to course level, course load, degree level, location, program, and student level. Room and board charges vary according to housing facility.
Collegiate Environment: Orientation program. Drama-theater group, choral group, student-run newspaper. Social organizations: 51 open to all; Student Life Club. Most popular organizations: Student Government Association, Circle K International, Psychology Club, Student Nurses Association, Outspoken LGBT Cooperative. Major annual events: Intercultural Day, Club Carnival, Spring Talent Show. Student services: personal-psychological counseling. Campus security: 24-hour emergency response devices and

patrols, student patrols, late night transport-escort service, controlled dormitory access, Rave Alert System. 200 college housing spaces available; all were occupied in 2012-13. Freshmen given priority for college housing. Option: coed housing available. Meader Library plus 2 others with 175,000 books, 415,000 microform titles, 45,000 serials, 6,300 audiovisual materials, an OPAC, and a Web page. Operations spending for the previous fiscal year: $3 million. 590 computers available on campus for general student use. A campuswide network can be accessed from student residence rooms and from off campus. Students can access the following: online class registration. Staffed computer lab on campus provides training in use of computers, software, and the Internet.
Community Environment: Honolulu, the travel capital of the world and nexus of the Pacific Basin, is a cosmopolitan city of some 800,000. Its leading industries are the travel industry, agriculture, and government-related services. Positions are available for HPU students in a wide variety of fields via the university's Cooperative Education and Internship Program. Such cultural institutions as the Bishop Museum, the Honolulu Academy of Arts, and the Honolulu Symphony are located within two to four miles of the campus. Recreation facilities, most of them free, are widely available throughout Hawaii and are among the finest in the world; also among the world's finest are Hawaii's many major restaurants and hotels.

■ HAWAII TOKAI INTERNATIONAL COLLEGE
2241 Kapiolani Blvd.
Honolulu, HI 96826-4310
Tel: (808)983-4100
Fax: (808)983-4107
E-mail: studentservices@tokai.edu
Web Site: www.hawaiitokai.edu/
Description: Independent, 2-year, coed. Part of Tokai University Educational System (Japan). Awards certificates, diplomas, transfer associate, and terminal associate degrees. Founded 1992. Setting: urban campus. Endowment: $1.3 million. Research spending for the previous fiscal year: $3.7 million. Educational spending for the previous fiscal year: $13,795 per student. Total enrollment: 64. Faculty: 39 (12 full-time, 27 part-time). 22 applied, 100% were admitted. 0.01% from top 10% of their high school class, 25% from top quarter, 50% from top half. 8 National Merit Scholars, 7 student government officers. Full-time: 64 students, 55% women, 45% men. Students come from 2 states and territories, 3 other countries, 0.01% from out-of-state. 75% international. 0.01% 25 or older, 60% live on campus, 0% transferred in. Retention: 93% of full-time freshmen returned the following year. Core. ESL program, summer session for credit, part-time degree program. Study abroad program.
Entrance Requirements: Options: electronic application, deferred admission, international baccalaureate accepted. Required: essay, high school transcript, minimum 2.5 high school GPA. Recommended: 1 recommendation. Required for some: interview, TOEFL score of 450 PBT for international students. Entrance: minimally difficult. Application deadlines: Rolling, Rolling for nonresidents. Notification: continuous, continuous for nonresidents. Transfer credits accepted: Yes.
Costs Per Year: Application fee: $50. Comprehensive fee: $21,240. Room and board charges vary according to board plan. Part-time tuition: $450 per credit.
Collegiate Environment: Orientation program. Social organizations: 5 open to all. Most popular organizations: Running Club, Kendo Club, Music Club, Baseball Club, Phi Theta Kappa International Honor Society, Student Government. Major annual events: Convocation, Student Presentation Day, Town Hall. Campus security: 24-hour patrols. 250 college housing spaces available; 140 were occupied in 2012-13. Freshmen given priority for college housing. Options: men-only, women-only housing available. The Learning Center with 7,000 books, 35 serials, 500 audiovisual materials, and an OPAC. Operations spending for the previous fiscal year: $119,378. 45 computers available on campus for general student use. A campuswide network can be accessed from student residence rooms and from off campus. Staffed computer lab on campus provides training in use of computers, software, and the Internet.

■ HEALD COLLEGE–HONOLULU
1500 Kapiolani Blvd.
Honolulu, HI 96814-3797
Tel: (808)955-1500; Free: 800-88-HEALD
Fax: (808)955-6964
E-mail: honoluluinfo@heald.edu
Web Site: www.heald.edu/

Description: Independent, 2-year, coed. Awards certificates, diplomas, transfer associate, and terminal associate degrees. Founded 1863. Setting: urban campus. Total enrollment: 1,376. Student-undergrad faculty ratio is 26:1. 1% from out-of-state. 35% 25 or older. Academic remediation for entering students, advanced ,placement, summer session for credit, part-time degree program, internships.
Entrance Requirements: Open admission. Options: early admission, deferred admission. Required: high school transcript, interview. Entrance: minimally difficult. Application deadline: Rolling. Notification: continuous.
Collegiate Environment: Learning Resource Center with an OPAC.
Community Environment: Heald is conveniently located in the Ala Moana/Kapiolani Business District just one block from the huge Ala Moana shopping, hotel, and office complex. Its location offers favorable transportation factors: Kapiolani Boulevard is a primary traffic artery that provides a direct link with both downtown and Waikiki, freeway access is excellent, and Ala Moana is a focal point of the bus system providing public transportation to all parts of the island.

■ **HONOLULU COMMUNITY COLLEGE**
874 Dillingham Blvd.
Honolulu, HI 96817-4598
Tel: (808)845-9211
E-mail: honcc@hawaii.edu
Web Site: www.honolulu.hawaii.edu/
Description: State-supported, 2-year, coed. Part of University of Hawaii System. Awards certificates, transfer associate, and terminal associate degrees. Founded 1920. Setting: 20-acre urban campus. Total enrollment: 4,567. Faculty: 205 (129 full-time, 76 part-time). Full-time: 1,640 students, 37% women, 63% men. Part-time: 2,927 students, 48% women, 52% men. Students come from 32 states and territories, 16 other countries, 2% from out-of-state. 10% transferred in. Retention: 55% of full-time freshmen returned the following year. Core. Calendar: semesters. Academic remediation for entering students, ESL program, services for LD students, advanced placement, accelerated degree program, self-designed majors, distance learning, summer session for credit, part-time degree program, co-op programs and internships. ROTC: Army (c), Air Force (c).
Entrance Requirements: Open admission. Option: early admission. Required for some: TOEFL required for international applicants. Entrance: noncompetitive. Application deadline: 8/15. Notification: continuous until 8/15.
Costs Per Year: Application fee: $0. State resident tuition: $2424 full-time, $101 per semester hour part-time. Nonresident tuition: $7104 full-time, $296 per semester hour part-time. Mandatory fees: $30 full-time, $.50 per semester hour part-time, $10 per term part-time. Full-time tuition and fees vary according to course load. Part-time tuition and fees vary according to course load.
Collegiate Environment: Orientation program. Student-run newspaper. Most popular organizations: Phi Theta Kappa, Hui 'Oiwi, Fashion Society. Major annual events: Campus Awareness Day, HCC Week. Student services: health clinic, personal-psychological counseling. Campus security: 24-hour emergency response devices. Honolulu Community College Library plus 1 other with 54,902 books, 65,679 microform titles, 1,280 serials, 858 audiovisual materials, an OPAC, and a Web page. 120 computers available on campus for general student use. A campuswide network can be accessed from off-campus. Students can access the following: online class registration. Staffed computer lab on campus.
Community Environment: See University of Hawaii - Manoa.

■ **KAPIOLANI COMMUNITY COLLEGE**
4303 Diamond Head Rd.
Honolulu, HI 96816-4421
Tel: (808)734-9111
E-mail: kapinfo@hawaii.edu
Web Site: kapiolani.hawaii.edu/page/home
Description: State-supported, 2-year, coed. Part of University of Hawaii System. Awards certificates, transfer associate, and terminal associate degrees. Founded 1957. Setting: 52-acre urban campus. Total enrollment: 9,102. Student-undergrad faculty ratio is 21:1. 3% from out-of-state. 34% 25 or older. Core. Calendar: semesters. Academic remediation for entering students, ESL program, services for LD students, advanced placement, self-designed majors, honors program, distance learning, summer session for credit, part-time degree program, adult/continuing education programs, co-op programs and internships. Off campus study at other units of the University of Hawaii System. ROTC: Army (c), Air Force (c).

Entrance Requirements: Open admission except for nursing, health sciences, paralegal programs. Option: early admission. Entrance: noncompetitive. Application deadline: 7/15. Notification: continuous until 8/15. Preference given to state residents.
Collegiate Environment: Orientation program. Choral group, student-run newspaper. Campus security: 24-hour patrols. Lama Library with 74,456 books and 209 serials.
Community Environment: See University of Hawaii - Manoa.

■ **KAUAI COMMUNITY COLLEGE**
3-1901 Kaumualii Hwy.
Lihue, HI 96766
Tel: (808)245-8311
Fax: (808)245-8297
E-mail: arkauai@hawaii.edu
Web Site: kauai.hawaii.edu/
Description: State-supported, 2-year, coed. Part of University of Hawaii System. Awards certificates and transfer associate degrees. Founded 1965. Setting: 100-acre small town campus. Total enrollment: 1,345. Core. Calendar: semesters. ESL program, services for LD students, advanced placement, accelerated degree program, distance learning, summer session for credit, part-time degree program, co-op programs and internships.
Entrance Requirements: Open admission except for nursing, electrical installation and maintenance, electronics technology, facilities engineering programs. Option: early admission. Recommended: high school transcript. Required for some: high school transcript. Entrance: noncompetitive. Application deadline: 8/1. Notification: continuous until 8/1. Preference given to state residents.
Collegiate Environment: Choral group, student-run newspaper. Social organizations: 8 open to all. Most popular organizations: Food Service Club, Hui O Hana Po'okela (Hoper Club), Nursing Club, Phi Theta Kappa, Pamantasan Club. Student services: health clinic, personal-psychological counseling. Campus security: student patrols, 6-hour evening patrols by trained security personnel. S. W. Wilcox II Learning Resource Center plus 1 other with 51,875 books, 16,946 microform titles, 165 serials, 1,248 audiovisual materials, an OPAC, and a Web page. 173 computers available on campus for general student use. A campuswide network can be accessed. Staffed computer lab on campus.
Community Environment: Kauai is known as the"Garden Island," offering magnificent scenery and lush vegetation, beautiful waterfalls, the spectacular Waimea Canyon, the great"hidden" valley of Kalalau, and colorful tropical plants and flowers. Airlines and boats serve the area. Honolulu is 100 nautical miles away. Industries are sugar and tourism; oceanography research and development is conducted here. Community facilities include five public libraries and many churches of all denominations. Several county beach parks and one major state park provide recreation facilities for boating, swimming, scuba diving, deepsea and surf fishing. Wild boar, goat and pheasant hunting are favorite sports.

■ **LEEWARD COMMUNITY COLLEGE**
96-045 Ala Ike
Pearl City, HI 96782-3393
Tel: (808)455-0011
Fax: (808)455-0471
Web Site: www.lcc.hawaii.edu/
Description: State-supported, 2-year, coed. Part of University of Hawaii System. Awards certificates, transfer associate, and terminal associate degrees. Founded 1968. Setting: 49-acre suburban campus with easy access to Honolulu. Total enrollment: 7,942. Faculty: 283 (178 full-time, 105 part-time). Student-undergrad faculty ratio is 23:1. 2,013 applied, 100% were admitted. Full-time: 3,296 students, 56% women, 44% men. Part-time: 4,646 students, 63% women, 37% men. Students come from 31 states and territories, 13 other countries, 1% from out-of-state. 0.3% American Indian or Alaska Native, non-Hispanic/Latino; 11% Hispanic/Latino; 2% African American, non-Hispanic/Latino; 37% Asian, non-Hispanic/Latino; 12% Native Hawaiian or other Pacific Islander, non-Hispanic/Latino; 0.5% international. 29% 25 or older, 7% transferred in. Retention: 65% of full-time freshmen returned the following year. Core. Calendar: semesters. Academic remediation for entering students, ESL program, services for LD students, advanced placement, honors program, independent study, distance learning, summer session for credit, part-time degree program, co-op programs and internships. Off campus study at University of Hawaii - Manoa, University of Hawaii - Hilo, University of Hawaii - West Oahu, University of Hawaii Community Colleges (Hawaii Community College, Honolulu Community College,

Kapiolani Community College, Kauai Community College, Maui College, Windward Community College). Study abroad program. ROTC: Air Force (c).

Entrance Requirements: Open admission except for Running Start, Early Admission. Options: electronic application, early admission, international baccalaureate accepted. Required for some: high school transcript. Entrance: noncompetitive. Application deadline: 7/15. Notification: continuous. Preference given to state residents. Transfer credits accepted: Yes.

Collegiate Environment: Orientation program. Drama-theater group, choral group, student-run newspaper. Social organizations: 19 open to all. Most popular organizations: Soccer Club, Japan Circle, Future Teachers Club, Leeward Campus Crusade For Christ, 4n Tongues (Hip Hop). Major annual events: College Bash, Leeward Discovery Fair, Career, College and Job Fair. Student services: health clinic, personal-psychological counseling. Campus security: 24-hour emergency response devices and patrols, late night transport-escort service. 66,000 books, 45 microform titles, 147 serials, 1,062 audiovisual materials, an OPAC, and a Web page 670 computers available on campus for general student use. A campuswide network can be accessed from off-campus. Students can access the following: online class registration, degree planning. Staffed computer lab on campus provides training in use of computers, software, and the Internet.

Community Environment: See University of Hawaii - Manoa.

■ **REMINGTON COLLEGE–HONOLULU CAMPUS**
1111 Bishop St.
Ste. 400
Honolulu, HI 96813
Tel: (808)942-1000
Fax: (808)533-3064
E-mail: louis.lamair@remingtoncollege.edu
Web Site: www.remingtoncollege.edu/

Description: Proprietary, primarily 2-year, coed. Awards diplomas, transfer associate, terminal associate, and bachelor's degrees.

■ **UNIVERSITY OF HAWAII AT HILO**
200 W Kawili St.
Hilo, HI 96720-4091
Tel: (808)974-7311; Free: 800-897-4456
Fax: (808)933-0861
E-mail: uhhao@hawaii.edu
Web Site: www.uhh.hawaii.edu/

Description: State-supported, comprehensive, coed. Part of University of Hawaii System. Awards bachelor's, master's, and doctoral degrees. Founded 1970. Setting: 115-acre small town campus. Endowment: $2.8 million. Research spending for the previous fiscal year: $7.9 million. Educational spending for the previous fiscal year: $6998 per student. Total enrollment: 4,157. Faculty: 300 (227 full-time, 73 part-time). Student-undergrad faculty ratio is 14:1. 1,639 applied, 28% were admitted. 18% from top 10% of their high school class, 53% from top quarter, 88% from top half. Full-time: 2,818 students, 58% women, 42% men. Part-time: 750 students, 64% women, 36% men. Students come from 50 states and territories, 26 other countries, 23% from out-of-state. 0.4% American Indian or Alaska Native, non-Hispanic/Latino; 10% Hispanic/Latino; 1% African American, non-Hispanic/Latino; 19% Asian, non-Hispanic/Latino; 12% Native Hawaiian or other Pacific Islander, non-Hispanic/Latino; 5% international. 24% 25 or older, 22% live on campus, 18% transferred in. Retention: 70% of full-time freshmen returned the following year. Academic areas with the most degrees conferred: social sciences; biological/life sciences; business/marketing. Core. Calendar: semesters. ESL program, services for LD students, advanced placement, self-designed majors, honors program, independent study, distance learning, double major, summer session for credit, part-time degree program, internships. Off campus study at members of the National Student Exchange. Study abroad program.

Entrance Requirements: Options: electronic application, deferred admission, international baccalaureate accepted. Required: high school transcript, SAT or ACT. Recommended: minimum 3 high school GPA. Entrance: moderately difficult. Application deadline: 7/1. Notification: 7/31.

Costs Per Year: Application fee: $50. State resident tuition: $6192 full-time, $258 per credit part-time. Nonresident tuition: $17,952 full-time, $748 per credit part-time. Mandatory fees: $304 full-time. Full-time tuition and fees vary according to reciprocity agreements. Part-time tuition varies according to course load.

Collegiate Environment: Orientation program. Drama-theater group, choral group, student-run newspaper. Social organizations: 43 open to all. Most popular organizations: International Student Association, Hawaiian Leadership and Development, Delta Sigma Pi Business Fraternity, University Canoe Club, Samoan Club. Major annual events: International Night, Homecoming, Hilo Basketball Classic. Student services: health clinic, personal-psychological counseling, women's center. Campus security: 24-hour emergency response devices and patrols, controlled dormitory access. 620 college housing spaces available; 600 were occupied in 2012-13. No special consideration for freshman housing applicants. Option: coed housing available. Edwin H. Mookini Library with 250,000 books, 2,500 serials, an OPAC, and a Web page. Operations spending for the previous fiscal year: $1.7 million. 600 computers available on campus for general student use. A campuswide network can be accessed from student residence rooms and from off campus. Students can access the following: online class registration. Staffed computer lab on campus.

■ **UNIVERSITY OF HAWAII AT MANOA**
2500 Campus Rd.
Honolulu, HI 96822
Tel: (808)956-8111; Free: 800-823-9771
E-mail: ar-info@hawaii.edu
Web Site: manoa.hawaii.edu/

Description: State-supported, university, coed. Part of University of Hawaii System. Awards bachelor's, master's, and doctoral degrees. Founded 1907. Setting: 320,300-acre urban campus with easy access to Honolulu. System endowment: $201.5 million. Total enrollment: 20,426. Faculty: 1,265 (1,201 full-time, 64 part-time). Student-undergrad faculty ratio is 14:1. 6,810 applied, 81% were admitted. 27% from top 10% of their high school class, 59% from top quarter, 91% from top half. 53 valedictorians. Full-time: 11,975 students, 55% women, 45% men. Part-time: 2,680 students, 53% women, 47% men. Students come from 63 states and territories, 50 other countries, 23% from out-of-state. 0.3% American Indian or Alaska Native, non-Hispanic/Latino; 2% Hispanic/Latino; 2% African American, non-Hispanic/Latino; 40% Asian, non-Hispanic/Latino; 17% Native Hawaiian or other Pacific Islander, non-Hispanic/Latino; 3% international. 18% 25 or older, 23% live on campus, 13% transferred in. Retention: 79% of full-time freshmen returned the following year. Academic areas with the most degrees conferred: business/marketing; social sciences; education. Core. Calendar: semesters. ESL program, services for LD students, advanced placement, accelerated degree program, self-designed majors, honors program, independent study, distance learning, double major, summer session for credit, part-time degree program, co-op programs and internships, graduate courses open to undergrads. Off campus study at Members of the National Student Exchange. Study abroad program. ROTC: Army, Air Force.

Entrance Requirements: Options: electronic application, international baccalaureate accepted. Required: high school transcript, minimum 2.8 high school GPA, SAT or ACT. Entrance: moderately difficult. Application deadline: 5/1. Notification: continuous. Preference given to state residents. SAT Reasoning Test deadline: 5/1. SAT Subject Test deadline: 5/1. Transfer credits accepted: Yes.

Costs Per Year: Application fee: $70. State resident tuition: $9144 full-time, $381 per credit part-time. Nonresident tuition: $26,712 full-time, $1113 per credit part-time. Mandatory fees: $740 full-time. Full-time tuition and fees vary according to class time, course level, course load, degree level, program, reciprocity agreements, and student level. Part-time tuition varies according to class time, course level, course load, degree level, program, reciprocity agreements, and student level. College room and board: $10,029. College room only: $6820. Room and board charges vary according to board plan and housing facility.

Collegiate Environment: Orientation program. Drama-theater group, choral group, marching band, student-run newspaper, radio station. Social organizations: 150 open to all; national fraternities, national sororities, local fraternities, local sororities; 1% of eligible men and 1% of eligible women are members. Most popular organizations: Associated Students of University of Hawaii (ASUH), Campus Center Board, Broadcast Communication Authority, Board of Publications, Student Activities and Program Fee Board. Major annual events: Sustainability Festival in Honor of Earth Day, Aloha Bash, Manoa Moonlight Madness. Student services: health clinic, personal-psychological counseling, women's center. Campus security: 24-hour emergency response devices and patrols, student patrols, late night transport-escort service, controlled dormitory access. College housing designed to accommodate 3,065 students; 3,300 undergraduates lived in college housing during 2012-13. Freshmen given priority for college housing. Option: coed housing available. Hamilton Library plus 6 others with 3.4 million books, 2.3 million microform titles, 58,434 serials, 72,147 audiovisual materials, an OPAC, and a Web page. 400 computers available on campus for general student use. Computer purchase/lease plans available. A campuswide network can be accessed from student residence rooms and from off campus. Students can access the following: online class registration. Staffed computer lab on campus provides training in use of computers, software, and the Internet.

■ UNIVERSITY OF HAWAII MAUI COLLEGE

310 Kaahumanu Ave.
Kahului, HI 96732
Tel: (808)984-3500; Free: 800-479-6692
Fax: (808)242-9618
E-mail: kameda@hawaii.edu
Web Site: maui.hawaii.edu/

Description: State-supported, primarily 2-year, coed. Part of University of Hawaii System. Awards certificates, transfer associate, terminal associate, and bachelor's degrees. Founded 1967. Setting: 77-acre rural campus. Total enrollment: 3,254. Faculty: 117 (116 full-time, 1 part-time). 992 applied. Full-time: 1,258 students, 62% women, 38% men. Part-time: 1,996 students, 67% women, 33% men. Students come from 15 other countries. 43% 25 or older, 1% live on campus. Core. Calendar: semesters. Academic remediation for entering students, ESL program, services for LD students, summer session for credit, part-time degree program, external degree program, adult/continuing education programs, co-op programs.

Entrance Requirements: Open admission. Options: electronic application, early admission. Required for some: high school transcript. Entrance: noncompetitive. Application deadline: Rolling.

Collegiate Environment: Student-run newspaper. Student services: health clinic, personal-psychological counseling. Campus security: 24-hour emergency response devices and patrols. Maui Community College Library plus 1 other with 49,812 books, 7,993 microform titles, 631 serials, 1,333 audiovisual materials, an OPAC, and a Web page. Operations spending for the previous fiscal year: $412,000. 487 computers available on campus for general student use. A campuswide network can be accessed from off-campus. Staffed computer lab on campus.

Community Environment: Kahului is an urban community on the Island of Maui enjoying an average temperature of 74.9 degrees. Both airlines and boats serve the area. The community facilities include churches of most denominations, hospital, clinic and shopping center. The pineapple and sugar industries provide work during the summer. Recreational activities are mainly surfing and swimming. The Island of Maui has three golf courses; the Maui Country Club, Royal Kaanapali Golf Course and the Waiehu Golf Course.

■ UNIVERSITY OF HAWAII–WEST OAHU

96-129 Ala Ike
Pearl City, HI 96782-3366
Tel: (808)454-4700; Free: 866-299-8656
E-mail: admissions@hawaii.edu
Web Site: www.uhwo.hawaii.edu/

Description: State-supported, 4-year, coed. Part of University of Hawaii System. Awards bachelor's degrees. Founded 1976. Setting: small town campus with easy access to Honolulu. Total enrollment: 1,997. Faculty: 101 (51 full-time, 50 part-time). Student-undergrad faculty ratio is 18:1. 908 applied, 51% were admitted. 16% from top 10% of their high school class, 47% from top quarter, 80% from top half. Full-time: 830 students, 66% women, 34% men. Part-time: 1,167 students, 67% women, 33% men. 20% from out-of-state. 0.3% American Indian or Alaska Native, non-Hispanic/Latino; 1% Hispanic/Latino; 2% African American, non-Hispanic/Latino; 41% Asian, non-Hispanic/Latino; 28% Native Hawaiian or other Pacific Islander, non-Hispanic/Latino; 0.4% international. 35% 25 or older, 25% transferred in.

Retention: 67% of full-time freshmen returned the following year. Academic areas with the most degrees conferred: business/marketing; public administration and social services; education. Calendar: semesters. Part-time degree program. ROTC: Army (c), Air Force (c).

Entrance Requirements: Option: deferred admission. Required: minimum 2.7 high school GPA. Required for some: high school transcript, 2 recommendations, college transcripts, SAT, ACT, SAT or ACT. Entrance: moderately difficult. Application deadline: 3/1. Notification: continuous. Preference given to state residents. SAT Reasoning Test deadline: 8/1. SAT Subject Test deadline: 8/1.

Costs Per Year: Application fee: $50. State resident tuition: $5592 full-time, $254 per credit hour part-time. Nonresident tuition: $16,656 full-time, $734 per credit hour part-time.

Collegiate Environment: Orientation program. Student services: personal-psychological counseling. Campus security: 24-hour emergency response devices and patrols, late night transport-escort service. College housing not available. University of Hawaii-West Oahu Library with an OPAC and a Web page.

■ UNIVERSITY OF PHOENIX–HAWAII CAMPUS

827 Fort St.
Honolulu, HI 96813-4317
Tel: (808)536-2686; Free: 866-766-0766
Web Site: www.phoenix.edu/

Description: Proprietary, comprehensive, coed. Awards bachelor's and master's degrees (courses conducted at 121 campuses and learning centers in 25 states). Setting: urban campus. Total enrollment: 955. Faculty: 178 (20 full-time, 158 part-time). Full-time: 743 students, 71% women, 29% men. 75% 25 or older. Academic areas with the most degrees conferred: business/marketing; health professions and related sciences; computer and information sciences. Core. Calendar: continuous. Services for LD students, advanced placement, accelerated degree program, independent study, distance learning, external degree program, adult/continuing education programs, graduate courses open to undergrads.

Entrance Requirements: Open admission. Options: electronic application, deferred admission. Required: 1 recommendation. Required for some: high school transcript. Entrance: noncompetitive. Application deadline: Rolling.

Collegiate Environment: Campus security: late night transport-escort service. University Library with 16,781 serials, an OPAC, and a Web page. Operations spending for the previous fiscal year: $6.8 million.

■ WINDWARD COMMUNITY COLLEGE

45-720 Keaahala Rd.
Kaneohe, HI 96744-3528
Tel: (808)235-7400
E-mail: gerii@hawaii.edu
Web Site: www.wcc.hawaii.edu/

Description: State-supported, 2-year, coed. Part of University of Hawaii System. Awards certificates, transfer associate, and terminal associate degrees. Founded 1972. Setting: 78-acre small town campus with easy access to Honolulu. Total enrollment: 1,959. Student-undergrad faculty ratio is 15:1. 1% from out-of-state. 31% 25 or older. Retention: 57% of full-time freshmen returned the following year. Calendar: semesters. Academic remediation for entering students, advanced placement, distance learning, summer session for credit, part-time degree program, adult/continuing education programs. ROTC: Army (c), Air Force (c).

Entrance Requirements: Open admission. Option: early admission. Entrance: noncompetitive. Application deadline: Rolling. Notification: continuous until 8/1. Preference given to state residents.

Collegiate Environment: Orientation program.

■ **BOISE BIBLE COLLEGE**
8695 W Marigold St.
Boise, ID 83714-1220
Tel: (208)376-7731; Free: 800-893-7755
Fax: (208)376-7743
E-mail: rgrove@boisebible.edu
Web Site: www.boisebible.edu/
Description: Independent nondenominational, 4-year, coed. Awards associate and bachelor's degrees. Founded 1945. Setting: 17-acre suburban campus. Total enrollment: 174. Student-undergrad faculty ratio is 15:1. 77 applied, 100% were admitted. 56% from out-of-state. 16% 25 or older. Retention: 53% of full-time freshmen returned the following year. Core. Calendar: semesters. Academic remediation for entering students, advanced placement, independent study, distance learning, double major, part-time degree program, adult/continuing education programs, internships.
Entrance Requirements: Option: deferred admission. Required: essay, high school transcript, minimum 2.0 high school GPA, SAT or ACT. Entrance: minimally difficult. Application deadline: 8/1. Notification: continuous.
Collegiate Environment: Orientation program. Choral group. Student services: personal-psychological counseling. Campus security: controlled dormitory access, patrols by police officers.

■ **BOISE STATE UNIVERSITY**
1910 University Dr.
Boise, ID 83725-0399
Tel: (208)426-1011; Free: 800-824-7017
E-mail: bsuinfo@boisestate.edu
Web Site: www.boisestate.edu/
Description: State-supported, university, coed. Part of Idaho System of Higher Education. Awards associate, bachelor's, master's, and doctoral degrees. Founded 1932. Setting: 216-acre urban campus. Endowment: $75.3 million. Research spending for the previous fiscal year: $26.1 million. Educational spending for the previous fiscal year: $6442 per student. Total enrollment: 22,674. Faculty: 1,272 (615 full-time, 657 part-time). Student-undergrad faculty ratio is 20:1. 5,184 applied, 85% were admitted. 14% from top 10% of their high school class, 38% from top quarter, 73% from top half. Full-time: 12,783 students, 51% women, 49% men. Part-time: 6,870 students, 57% women, 43% men. Students come from 50 states and territories, 68 other countries, 12% from out-of-state. 1% American Indian or Alaska Native, non-Hispanic/Latino; 8% Hispanic/Latino; 2% African American, non-Hispanic/Latino; 2% Asian, non-Hispanic/Latino; 0.5% Native Hawaiian or other Pacific Islander, non-Hispanic/Latino; 3% international. 33% 25 or older, 12% live on campus, 15% transferred in. Retention: 71% of full-time freshmen returned the following year. Academic areas with the most degrees conferred: business/marketing; health professions and related sciences; education. Core. Calendar: semesters. Academic remediation for entering students, ESL program, services for LD students, advanced placement, self-designed majors, freshman honors college, honors program, independent study, distance learning, double major, summer session for credit, part-time degree program, adult/continuing education programs, co-op programs and internships, graduate courses open to undergrads. Off campus study at National Student Exchange. Study abroad program. ROTC: Army.
Entrance Requirements: Option: electronic application. Required: SAT or ACT. Required for some: high school transcript. Entrance: moderately dif-

ficult. Application deadline: 5/15. Notification: continuous. SAT Reasoning Test deadline: 5/15. SAT Subject Test deadline: 5/15. Transfer credits accepted: Yes.
Costs Per Year: Application fee: $50. State resident tuition: $3990 full-time, $239 per credit hour part-time. Nonresident tuition: $15,430 full-time, $331 per credit hour part-time. Mandatory fees: $1894 full-time, $92 per credit hour part-time, $92. Full-time tuition and fees vary according to reciprocity agreements. College room and board: $7174. College room only: $3674. Room and board charges vary according to board plan and housing facility.
Collegiate Environment: Orientation program. Drama-theater group, choral group, marching band, student-run newspaper, radio station. Social organizations: 242 open to all; national fraternities, national sororities, local fraternities, local sororities; 1% of eligible men and 1% of eligible women are members. Most popular organizations: Latter-Day Saints Student Association, Residence Hall Association, Organization of Student Social Workers, Marching Band Association, Teacher Education Association. Major annual events: Homecoming, Student Organizational Fair, Spring Fling. Student services: legal services, health clinic, personal-psychological counseling, women's center. Campus security: 24-hour emergency response devices and patrols, late night transport-escort service. 2,200 college housing spaces available; 1,900 were occupied in 2012-13. Freshmen given priority for college housing. Options: coed, men-only, women-only housing available. Albertsons Library with 1 million books, 1.5 million microform titles, 96,687 serials, 32,613 audiovisual materials, an OPAC, and a Web page. Operations spending for the previous fiscal year: $7.8 million. 900 computers available on campus for general student use. A campuswide network can be accessed from student residence rooms and from off campus. Students can access the following: online class registration. Staffed computer lab on campus provides training in use of computers, software, and the Internet.
Community Environment: Boise, the capital of Idaho and its largest city, is located on the Boise River at the upper end of the Boise Valley. It enjoys mild winters with very little snow and temperate summers with cool nights. Community facilities include hospitals and libraries. The Idaho Concert and Artists Association features artists of national and international fame. Points of interest are the State Capitol, Ann Morrison and Julia Davis Parks, Platt Gardens, State Historical Museum, Pioneer Village, Urquides Village, Boise Heights, Idaho City, and Silver City. The latter two are pioneer gold rush communities. Year-round recreational opportunities are available in and around Boise.

■ **BRIGHAM YOUNG UNIVERSITY–IDAHO**
Rexburg, ID 83460
Tel: (208)496-2011
Fax: (208)496-1220
E-mail: williamst@byui.edu
Web Site: www.byui.edu/
Description: Independent, 4-year, coed, affiliated with The Church of Jesus Christ of Latter-day Saints. Awards associate and bachelor's degrees. Founded 1888. Setting: 255-acre small town campus. Total enrollment: 14,944. Student-undergrad faculty ratio is 23:1. 6,887 applied, 97% were admitted. 73% from out-of-state. 15% 25 or older. Core. Calendar: semesters. Academic remediation for entering students, services for LD students, advanced placement, accelerated degree program, honors program, summer session for credit, part-time degree program, adult/continuing education programs, internships. ROTC: Army.
Entrance Requirements: Option: electronic application. Required: essay,

high school transcript, interview, SAT or ACT. Entrance: moderately difficult. Application deadline: 2/15. Notification: 4/1. Preference given to Latter-Day Saints Church members.
Collegiate Environment: Orientation program. Drama-theater group, choral group, student-run newspaper, radio station. Social organizations: national fraternities, national sororities. Student services: legal services, health clinic, personal-psychological counseling. Campus security: 24-hour emergency response devices and patrols, late night transport-escort service. David O. McKay Library with an OPAC.

■ **BROADVIEW UNIVERSITY–BOISE**
2750 E Gala Ct.
Meridian, ID 83642
Tel: (208)577-2900; Free: 877-572-5757
Fax: (208)577-2901
E-mail: jchiddy@broadviewuniversity.edu
Web Site: www.broadviewuniversity.edu/
Description: Proprietary, 4-year, coed. Part of Globe Education Network (GEN) which is composed of Globe University, Minnesota School of Business, Broadview University, The Institute of Production and Recording and Minnesota School of Cosmetology. Awards associate and bachelor's degrees. Setting: 4-acre small town campus. Faculty: 16 (4 full-time, 12 part-time). Student-undergrad faculty ratio is 5:1. 0% from out-of-state. 0% 25 or older. Retention: 0% of full-time freshmen returned the following year. Core. Academic remediation for entering students, services for LD students, advanced placement, accelerated degree program, summer session for credit, part-time degree program, adult/continuing education programs, internships.
Entrance Requirements: Option: electronic application. Required: high school transcript, interview, ACCUPLACER is required of all applicants unless documentation of a minimum ACT composite score of 21 or documentation of a minimum composite score of 1485 on the SAT is presented. Required for some: essay, 2 recommendations, GED certificate in lieu of high school transcript. Application deadlines: Rolling, Rolling for nonresidents. Notification: continuous, continuous for nonresidents. Transfer credits accepted: Yes.
Costs Per Year: Application fee: $50. Tuition: $14,400 full-time, $435 per credit part-time. Mandatory fees: $1548 full-time, $43 per credit part-time. Full-time tuition and fees vary according to course level, course load, degree level, location, and program. Part-time tuition and fees vary according to course level, course load, degree level, location, and program.
Collegiate Environment: Orientation program. Social organizations: Program specific student led organizations. Major annual events: Service Learning Projects, Applied Learning Projects, Student Appreciation Events. Campus security: 24-hour emergency response devices, late night transport-escort service. Boise Campus Library with 1,784 books, 53,138 serials, 5 audiovisual materials, an OPAC, and a Web page. 45 computers available on campus for general student use. A campuswide network can be accessed. Students can access the following: online class registration. Staffed computer lab on campus provides training in use of computers, software, and the Internet.

■ **BROWN MACKIE COLLEGE–BOISE**
9050 W Overland Rd., Ste. 100
Boise, ID 83709
Web Site: www.brownmackie.edu/boise/
Description: Proprietary, primarily 2-year, coed. Part of Education Management Corporation. Awards diplomas, terminal associate, and bachelor's degrees.

■ **CARRINGTON COLLEGE–BOISE**
1122 N Liberty St.
Boise, ID 83704
Tel: (208)377-8080
Web Site: carrington.edu/
Description: Proprietary, 2-year, coed. Part of Carrington Colleges Group, Inc. Awards certificates and terminal associate degrees. Founded 1980. Total enrollment: 508. Faculty: 45 (19 full-time, 26 part-time). Student-undergrad faculty ratio is 18:1. Full-time: 508 students, 82% women, 18% men. 1% American Indian or Alaska Native, non-Hispanic/Latino; 13% Hispanic/Latino; 2% African American, non-Hispanic/Latino; 3% Asian, non-Hispanic/Latino; 1% Native Hawaiian or other Pacific Islander, non-Hispanic/Latino; 0% international. 65% 25 or older. Calendar: semesters.

Entrance Requirements: Required: essay, high school transcript, interview, Entrance test administered by Carrington College. Entrance: minimally difficult.
Collegiate Environment: Orientation program. College housing not available.

■ **THE COLLEGE OF IDAHO**
2112 Cleveland Blvd.
Caldwell, ID 83605
Tel: (208)459-5011; Free: 800-244-3246
Fax: (208)454-2077
E-mail: admission@collegeofidaho.edu
Web Site: www.collegeofidaho.edu/
Description: Independent, comprehensive, coed. Awards bachelor's and master's degrees. Founded 1891. Setting: 50-acre suburban campus. Endowment: $91.7 million. Research spending for the previous fiscal year: $539,457. Educational spending for the previous fiscal year: $7341 per student. Total enrollment: 1,059. Faculty: 113 (75 full-time, 38 part-time). Student-undergrad faculty ratio is 12:1. 1,388 applied, 65% were admitted. 25% from top 10% of their high school class, 56% from top quarter, 88% from top half. Full-time: 1,003 students, 58% women, 42% men. Part-time: 39 students, 49% women, 51% men. Students come from 29 states and territories, 53 other countries, 17% from out-of-state. 1% American Indian or Alaska Native, non-Hispanic/Latino; 14% Hispanic/Latino; 1% African American, non-Hispanic/Latino; 3% Asian, non-Hispanic/Latino; 1% Native Hawaiian or other Pacific Islander, non-Hispanic/Latino; 10% international. 0.3% 25 or older, 62% live on campus, 3% transferred in. Retention: 83% of full-time freshmen returned the following year. Academic areas with the most degrees conferred: business/marketing; visual and performing arts; health professions and related sciences. Core. Calendar: 12-6-12 week calendar. ESL program, services for LD students, advanced placement, honors program, independent study, double major, part-time degree program, co-op programs and internships, graduate courses open to undergrads. Off campus study. Study abroad program. ROTC: Army (c).
Entrance Requirements: Options: electronic application, early admission, early action, deferred admission, international baccalaureate accepted. Required: essay, high school transcript, 1 recommendation, SAT or ACT. Recommended: interview, class rank, extracurricular resume. Entrance: moderately difficult. Application deadlines: 8/1, 11/15 for early action. Notification: continuous, 11/15 for early action. SAT Reasoning Test deadline: 8/1. Transfer credits accepted: Yes.
Costs Per Year: Application fee: $0. One-time mandatory fee: $355. Comprehensive fee: $31,646 includes full-time tuition ($22,600), mandatory fees ($400), and college room and board ($8646). Room and board charges vary according to board plan and housing facility. Part-time tuition: $940 per credit. Part-time tuition varies according to course load.
Collegiate Environment: Orientation program. Drama-theater group, choral group, student-run newspaper. Social organizations: national fraternities, national sororities, local sororities. Most popular organizations: ISO-International Student Organization, ALAS- Association of Latino American Students, Potter's Clay, GSCA- Gay-Straight Campus Alliance, AFRO-Africans Friends Relatives and Others. Major annual events: Winterfest, Spring Fling, Fall Fling. Student services: health clinic, personal-psychological counseling, women's center. Campus security: 24-hour emergency response devices and patrols, student patrols, late night transport-escort service, controlled dormitory access. 668 college housing spaces available; 642 were occupied in 2012-13. Freshmen guaranteed college housing. On-campus residence required through junior year. Option: coed housing available. Terteling Library with 155,000 books, 27,535 microform titles, 1,975 serials, 1,700 audiovisual materials, an OPAC, and a Web page. Operations spending for the previous fiscal year: $350,279. 475 computers available on campus for general student use. A campuswide network can be accessed from student residence rooms and from off campus. Students can access the following: online class registration, online course syllabi, course assignments, course discussion, College of Idaho catalog.

■ **COLLEGE OF SOUTHERN IDAHO**
PO Box 1238
Twin Falls, ID 83303-1238
Tel: (208)733-9554; Free: 800-680-0274
Fax: (208)736-3014
Web Site: www.csi.edu/
Description: State and locally supported, 2-year, coed. Awards certificates,

diplomas, transfer associate, and terminal associate degrees. Founded 1964. Setting: 287-acre small town campus. Endowment: $15 million. Educational spending for the previous fiscal year: $6220 per student. Total enrollment: 7,118. Faculty: 361 (160 full-time, 201 part-time). Student-undergrad faculty ratio is 19:1. Full-time: 2,812 students, 59% women, 41% men. Part-time: 4,306 students, 69% women, 31% men. Students come from 29 states and territories, 27 other countries, 3% from out-of-state. 10% live on campus. Core. Calendar: semesters. Academic remediation for entering students, ESL program, services for LD students, advanced placement, honors program, independent study, distance learning, summer session for credit, part-time degree program, adult/continuing education programs, co-op programs and internships.

Entrance Requirements: Open admission except for nursing program. Required: high school transcript, ACT COMPASS. Required for some: interview, ACT. Entrance: noncompetitive. Application deadline: Rolling.

Collegiate Environment: Drama-theater group, choral group, student-run newspaper, radio station. Social organizations: 60 open to all. Most popular organizations: BPA, Delta Epsilon Chi, Chi Alpha (Christian Group), Vet Tech Club, Equine Club. Major annual events: Lane of Trees, Halloween Carnival, Ski Day. Student services: legal services, health clinic, personal-psychological counseling, women's center. Campus security: 24-hour emergency response devices and patrols, controlled dormitory access. College of Southern Idaho Library with 62,556 books, 374 serials, 4,216 audiovisual materials, an OPAC, and a Web page. Operations spending for the previous fiscal year: $549,680. 750 computers available on campus for general student use. Computer purchase/lease plans available. A campuswide network can be accessed from student residence rooms and from off campus. Students can access the following: online class registration. Staffed computer lab on campus.

Community Environment: Twin Falls, a pleasant residential town with a population of 38,600, is the county seat of Twin Falls County, the cultural and trade center of South Central Idaho's Magic Valley. The city is located at the junction of Transcontinental Highway 30 and International Highway 93. Buses, railroads, and airlines serve the area. Due to the climate, location, and natural surroundings, there are an unlimited variety of outdoor recreational facilities and activities. The city serves as headquarters for the Sawtooth National Forest.

■ **COLLEGE OF WESTERN IDAHO**
2407 Caldwell Blvd.
Nampa, ID 83651
Tel: (208)562-3000
Web Site: cwidaho.cc/
Description: State-supported, 2-year, coed. Founded 2007. Calendar: semesters.

■ **EASTERN IDAHO TECHNICAL COLLEGE**
1600 S 25th E
Idaho Falls, ID 83404-5788
Tel: (208)524-3000; Free: 800-662-0261
Fax: (208)524-3007
E-mail: Annalea.avery@my.eitc.edu
Web Site: www.eitc.edu/
Description: State-supported, 2-year, coed. Awards certificates and terminal associate degrees. Founded 1970. Setting: 40-acre small town campus. Endowment: $789,503. Educational spending for the previous fiscal year: $6622 per student. Total enrollment: 702. Faculty: 68 (40 full-time, 28 part-time). Student-undergrad faculty ratio is 13:1. 527 applied, 50% were admitted. Full-time: 278 students, 50% women, 50% men. Part-time: 424 students, 72% women, 28% men. Students come from 2 states and territories, 1 other country, 0% from out-of-state. 1% American Indian or Alaska Native, non-Hispanic/Latino; 11% Hispanic/Latino; 0.4% African American, non-Hispanic/Latino; 1% Asian, non-Hispanic/Latino; 1% Native Hawaiian or other Pacific Islander, non-Hispanic/Latino; 1% international. 62% 25 or older, 22% transferred in. Retention: 0% of full-time freshmen returned the following year. Calendar: semesters. Academic remediation for entering students, ESL program, services for LD students, advanced placement, summer session for credit, part-time degree program, adult/continuing education programs.

Entrance Requirements: Open admission. Option: deferred admission. Required: high school transcript, interview, COMPASS. Required for some: essay. Entrance: noncompetitive. Application deadline: Rolling. Transfer credits accepted: Yes.

Costs Per Year: Application fee: $10. State resident tuition: $1932 full-time,

$90 per credit part-time. Nonresident tuition: $7078 full-time, $180 per credit part-time. Mandatory fees: $15 per term part-time.

Collegiate Environment: Orientation program. Major annual events: Fall BBQ, Spring Banquet, Halloween Party. Student services: personal-psychological counseling. Campus security: 24-hour patrols. College housing not available. Richard and Lila Jordan Library plus 1 other with 18,000 books, 64,350 microform titles, 125 serials, 150 audiovisual materials, an OPAC, and a Web page. Operations spending for the previous fiscal year: $144,364. 105 computers available on campus for general student use. A campuswide network can be accessed. Students can access the following: online class registration. Staffed computer lab on campus provides training in use of computers and the Internet.

■ **IDAHO STATE UNIVERSITY**
921 S 8th Ave.
Pocatello, ID 83209
Tel: (208)282-0211
E-mail: info@isu.edu
Web Site: www.isu.edu/
Description: State-supported, university, coed. Awards associate, bachelor's, master's, and doctoral degrees and post-master's certificates. Founded 1901. Setting: 1,100-acre urban campus. Endowment: $39.3 million. Research spending for the previous fiscal year: $20.9 million. Educational spending for the previous fiscal year: $8293 per student. Total enrollment: 14,209. Faculty: 787 (590 full-time, 197 part-time). Student-undergrad faculty ratio is 16:1. 3,184 applied, 92% were admitted. 12% from top 10% of their high school class, 29% from top quarter, 61% from top half. Full-time: 7,441 students, 51% women, 49% men. Part-time: 4,702 students, 59% women, 41% men. Students come from 48 states and territories, 62 other countries, 6% from out-of-state. 1% American Indian or Alaska Native, non-Hispanic/Latino; 8% Hispanic/Latino; 1% African American, non-Hispanic/Latino; 1% Asian, non-Hispanic/Latino; 0.2% Native Hawaiian or other Pacific Islander, non-Hispanic/Latino; 4% international. 39% 25 or older, 8% live on campus, 4% transferred in. Retention: 62% of full-time freshmen returned the following year. Academic areas with the most degrees conferred: health professions and related sciences; education; business/marketing. Core. Calendar: semesters. Academic remediation for entering students, ESL program, services for LD students, advanced placement, accelerated degree program, self-designed majors, honors program, independent study, distance learning, double major, summer session for credit, part-time degree program, adult/continuing education programs, co-op programs and internships, graduate courses open to undergrads. Off campus study at Domestic exchange programs with more than 200 colleges universities. Study abroad program. ROTC: Army.

Entrance Requirements: Options: electronic application, early admission, deferred admission, international baccalaureate accepted. Required: high school transcript, minimum 2 high school GPA, SAT or ACT. Recommended: ACT. Entrance: minimally difficult. Application deadline: Rolling. Notification: continuous. Transfer credits accepted: Yes.

Costs Per Year: Application fee: $40. One-time mandatory fee: $40. State resident tuition: $4418 full-time, $304 per credit hour part-time. Nonresident tuition: $16,218 full-time, $494 per credit hour part-time. Mandatory fees: $1652 full-time. Full-time tuition and fees vary according to course load, program, and reciprocity agreements. Part-time tuition varies according to course load and reciprocity agreements. College room and board: $5838. College room only: $2520. Room and board charges vary according to board plan and housing facility.

Collegiate Environment: Orientation program. Choral group, marching band, student-run newspaper, radio station. Social organizations: 156 open to all; national fraternities, national sororities, over 156 social organizations. Major annual events: Chrome in the Dome, Rodeo, Monster Truck Show. Student services: health clinic, personal-psychological counseling, women's center. Campus security: 24-hour emergency response devices and patrols, late night transport-escort service, controlled dormitory access. 866 college housing spaces available. No special consideration for freshman housing applicants. Options: coed, men-only, women-only housing available. Eli M. Oboler Library with 6 million books, 2 million microform titles, 3,981 serials, 6,170 audiovisual materials, an OPAC, and a Web page. Operations spending for the previous fiscal year: $4.8 million. 697 computers available on campus for general student use. A campuswide network can be accessed from student residence rooms and from off campus. Students can access the following: online class registration. Staffed computer lab on campus (open 24 hours a day) provides training in use of computers, software, and the Internet.

Community Environment: Pocatello is located in a farming and industrial area of southeastern Idaho where the climate is dry and sunny. Planes and buses provide transportation. The community facilities include many churches, two hospitals, the district health department, hotels, motels, etc. The municipal park has facilities for archery, baseball, field games, and includes a swimming pool and a zoo. Other facilities outside of Pocatello are in the intermountain region, which offers some of the best hunting and fishing in the United States. Camping, hiking, snowmobiling, swimming, boating, horseback riding and skiing available for the outdoor life. Rodeos and the Indian Sun Dances are special annual events.

■ ITT TECHNICAL INSTITUTE
12302 W Explorer Dr.
Boise, ID 83713
Tel: (208)322-8844; Free: 800-666-4888
Fax: (208)322-0173
Web Site: www.itt-tech.edu/
Description: Proprietary, primarily 2-year, coed. Part of ITT Educational Services, Inc. Awards terminal associate and bachelor's degrees. Founded 1906. Setting: urban campus.
Entrance Requirements: Entrance: minimally difficult.

■ LEWIS-CLARK STATE COLLEGE
500 Eighth Ave.
Lewiston, ID 83501-2698
Tel: (208)792-5272; Free: 800-933-5272
Fax: (208)799-2063
E-mail: admissions@lcsc.edu
Web Site: www.lcsc.edu/
Description: State-supported, 4-year, coed. Awards associate and bachelor's degrees. Founded 1893. Setting: 44-acre small town campus. Total enrollment: 4,525. Faculty: 260 (168 full-time, 92 part-time). Student-undergrad faculty ratio is 16:1. 1,006 applied, 99% were admitted. 8% from top 10% of their high school class, 16% from top quarter, 29% from top half. Full-time: 2,549 students, 58% women, 42% men. Part-time: 1,976 students, 62% women, 38% men. 20% from out-of-state. 2% American Indian or Alaska Native, non-Hispanic/Latino; 5% Hispanic/Latino; 1% African American, non-Hispanic/Latino; 1% Asian, non-Hispanic/Latino; 0.2% Native Hawaiian or other Pacific Islander, non-Hispanic/Latino; 2% international. 34% 25 or older, 9% transferred in. Retention: 50% of full-time freshmen returned the following year. Academic areas with the most degrees conferred: business/marketing; health professions and related sciences; education. Calendar: semesters. Part-time degree program, adult/continuing education programs. Study abroad program. ROTC: Army (c), Naval (c), Air Force (c).
Entrance Requirements: Options: electronic application, deferred admission, international baccalaureate accepted. Required: high school transcript, minimum 2 high school GPA. Required for some: interview, SAT or ACT. Entrance: minimally difficult. Application deadline: Rolling. Notification: continuous.
Costs Per Year: Application fee: $35. State resident tuition: $5562 full-time. Nonresident tuition: $15,476 full-time. Full-time tuition varies according to course load and reciprocity agreements.
Collegiate Environment: Orientation program. Campus security: 24-hour emergency response devices and patrols, student patrols, late night transport-escort service. No special consideration for freshman housing applicants. Option: coed housing available.
Community Environment: Lewiston is a small urban area that is a major community in the Nez Perce National Park area; climate is temperate. It is the center of a vast lumbering, mining, farming and ranching territory. Planes, buses and trains serve the area. Community facilities include libraries, museums, YWCA, hospital, clinics, community concert series and shopping areas. Part-time employment opportunities are good. Facilities are good for boating, fishing and big game hunting. Boat trips up Hell's Canyon of the Snake River are spectacular journeys; shorter trips are available. The Lewiston Roundup and Dogwood festival are special events.

■ NEW SAINT ANDREWS COLLEGE
PO Box 9025
Moscow, ID 83843
Tel: (208)882-1566
Fax: (208)882-4293
E-mail: info@nsa.edu
Web Site: www.nsa.edu/

Description: Independent Christian, comprehensive, coed. Awards associate, bachelor's, and master's degrees. Founded 1993. Setting: small town campus. Educational spending for the previous fiscal year: $3734 per student. Total enrollment: 175. Faculty: 16 (6 full-time, 10 part-time). Student-undergrad faculty ratio is 15:1. 89 applied, 78% were admitted. 2 National Merit Scholars. Full-time: 130 students, 62% women, 38% men. Part-time: 19 students, 74% women, 26% men. Students come from 29 states and territories, 5 other countries, 75% from out-of-state. 2% American Indian or Alaska Native, non-Hispanic/Latino; 1% Hispanic/Latino; 1% African American, non-Hispanic/Latino; 1% Asian, non-Hispanic/Latino; 0% Native Hawaiian or other Pacific Islander, non-Hispanic/Latino; 4% international. 3% 25 or older, 3% transferred in. Retention: 87% of full-time freshmen returned the following year. Academic area with the most degrees conferred: liberal arts/general studies. Core. Calendar: 4 8-week terms. Advanced placement, independent study, summer session for credit, part-time degree program, graduate courses open to undergrads.
Entrance Requirements: Options: electronic application, deferred admission, international baccalaureate accepted. Required: essay, high school transcript, 2 recommendations, SAT or ACT. Required for some: interview. Entrance: moderately difficult. Application deadline: 2/15. Notification: 3/15. SAT Reasoning Test deadline: 8/1. Transfer credits accepted: Yes. Applicants placed on waiting list: 0.
Costs Per Year: Application fee: $40. Tuition: $11,200 full-time, $950 per course part-time. Full-time tuition varies according to program. Part-time tuition varies according to program. Tuition guaranteed not to increase for student's term of enrollment.
Collegiate Environment: Orientation program. Drama-theater group, choral group. Most popular organizations: Students for the Relief of the Oppressed, Nursing Home Visits and Elderly Assistance (snow and leaf removal), Blood Drives, Fall Carnival, St. Andrews Day Food Bank Drive. Major annual events: Dances and Banquets, student-organized basketball, football, pumpkin rugby, soccer, tennis, volleyball, Concerts, talent shows, dramatic productions. Student services: personal-psychological counseling. Campus security: 24-hour emergency response devices. College housing not available. Tyndale Library plus 1 other with 59,850 books, 25 serials, 302 audiovisual materials, an OPAC, and a Web page. Operations spending for the previous fiscal year: $118,017. 6 computers available on campus for general student use. A campuswide network can be accessed from off-campus. Students can access the following: online class registration.

■ NORTH IDAHO COLLEGE
1000 W Garden Ave.
Coeur d'Alene, ID 83814-2199
Tel: (208)769-3300; Free: 877-404-4536
Fax: (208)769-3273
E-mail: admit@nic.edu
Web Site: www.nic.edu/
Description: State and locally supported, 2-year, coed. Awards certificates, transfer associate, and terminal associate degrees. Founded 1933. Setting: 42-acre small town campus. Total enrollment: 5,723. Faculty: 447 (160 full-time, 287 part-time). Student-undergrad faculty ratio is 17:1. 2,684 applied, 58% were admitted. Full-time: 3,437 students, 54% women, 46% men. Part-time: 2,286 students, 67% women, 33% men. 2% American Indian or Alaska Native, non-Hispanic/Latino; 3% Hispanic/Latino; 1% African American, non-Hispanic/Latino; 1% Asian, non-Hispanic/Latino; 0.3% Native Hawaiian or other Pacific Islander, non-Hispanic/Latino. Core. Calendar: semesters. Academic remediation for entering students, ESL program, services for LD students, advanced placement, independent study, distance learning, summer session for credit, part-time degree program, adult/continuing education programs, co-op programs and internships. Off campus study at Lewis-Clark State College, University of Idaho. ROTC: Army (c).
Entrance Requirements: Options: electronic application, early admission, deferred admission. Required for some: essay, high school transcript, county residency certificate. Entrance: noncompetitive. Application deadline: 8/20.
Collegiate Environment: Orientation program. Drama-theater group, choral group, student-run newspaper. Social organizations: 25 open to all. Most popular organizations: Ski Club, Fusion, Baptist student ministries, Journalism Club, Phi Theta Kappa. Student services: legal services, health clinic, personal-psychological counseling, women's center. Campus security: 24-hour emergency response devices and patrols, late night transport-escort service. Molstead Library Computer Center with 60,893 books, 751 serials, an OPAC, and a Web page. 145 computers available on campus for general student use. A campuswide network can be accessed. Students can access the following: online student information, records, grades. Staffed computer lab on campus.

Community Environment: Coeur d'Alene is located on the north shore of Lake Coeur d'Alene, 33 miles east of Spokane, Washington. The area is a popular resort for summer and winter events. Two major ski areas are only minutes away from downtown and the lake offers many water sports activities. Average summer high temperature is 82 degrees and average summer lows are 51 degrees, average winter high temperature is 38 degrees and the average low is 26 degrees. There is an average of 50 inches of snow each year and total average precipitation is 26 inches. Transportation facilities for the Spokane/Coeur d'Alene area include bus, train and airline. Facilities of the community include library, hospital, county health unit and active civic clubs. The college hosts art and music programs for the community in its 1,200 seat Boswell Hall auditorium. Coeur d'Alene draws its industry from tourism, high tech, forestry products and agricultural. Outdoor sports are boating, biking, hunting, fishing, golfing, water and snow skiing, sailing, windsurfing, swimming, and mountain biking.

■ **NORTHWEST NAZARENE UNIVERSITY**

623 S University Blvd.

Nampa, ID 83686-5897

Tel: (208)467-8011; Free: 877-668-4968

Fax: (208)467-8645

E-mail: mmarston@nnu.edu

Web Site: www.nnu.edu/

Description: Independent, comprehensive, coed, affiliated with Church of the Nazarene. Awards bachelor's, master's, and doctoral degrees and post-master's certificates. Founded 1913. Setting: 85-acre small town campus with easy access to Boise. Endowment: $25.9 million. Research spending for the previous fiscal year: $449,828. Educational spending for the previous fiscal year: $6943 per student. Total enrollment: 2,232. Faculty: 107 (103 full-time, 4 part-time). Student-undergrad faculty ratio is 14:1. 993 applied, 67% were admitted. 29% from top 10% of their high school class, 52% from top quarter, 81% from top half. Full-time: 1,154 students, 59% women, 41% men. Part-time: 323 students, 41% women, 59% men. 51% from out-of-state. 1% American Indian or Alaska Native, non-Hispanic/Latino; 6% Hispanic/Latino; 1% African American, non-Hispanic/Latino; 2% Asian, non-Hispanic/Latino; 0.4% Native Hawaiian or other Pacific Islander, non-Hispanic/Latino; 3% international. 19% 25 or older, 67% live on campus, 5% transferred in. Retention: 80% of full-time freshmen returned the following year. Academic areas with the most degrees conferred: business/marketing; health professions and related sciences; education. Core. Calendar: semesters. Academic remediation for entering students, ESL program, services for LD students, advanced placement, accelerated degree program, self-designed majors, freshman honors college, honors program, independent study, distance learning, double major, summer session for credit, part-time degree program, adult/continuing education programs, co-op programs and internships, graduate courses open to undergrads. Off campus study at CCCU Exchange programs. Study abroad program. ROTC: Army.

Entrance Requirements: Options: electronic application, early action, deferred admission, international baccalaureate accepted. Required: essay, high school transcript, minimum 2.5 high school GPA, 2 recommendations, SAT or ACT. Required for some: interview. Entrance: moderately difficult. Application deadlines: 8/15, 12/15 for early action. Notification: continuous, 1/15 for early action. SAT Reasoning Test deadline: 8/15. SAT Subject Test deadline: 8/15. Transfer credits accepted: Yes. Early action applicants: 246. Early action applicants admitted: 244.

Costs Per Year: Application fee: $25. Comprehensive fee: $32,950 includes full-time tuition ($26,150), mandatory fees ($400), and college room and board ($6400). Full-time tuition and fees vary according to course load, degree level, program, and reciprocity agreements. Room and board charges vary according to board plan. Part-time tuition: $1130 per semester hour.

Collegiate Environment: Orientation program. Drama-theater group, choral group, student-run newspaper. Social organizations: 40 open to all. Most popular organizations: Students in Free Enterprise (SIFE), Student Government Association, Fellowship of Christian Athletes, The Crusader newspaper, The Oasis yearbook. Major annual events: Fresheree talent show, TWIRP (The Woman is Required to Pay), Mr. NNU Pageant. Student services: health clinic, personal-psychological counseling. Campus security: 24-hour emergency response devices and patrols, student patrols, late night transport-escort service, controlled dormitory access, residence hall check-in system, on-campus police hub. Freshmen guaranteed college housing. On-campus residence required through sophomore year. Options: men-only, women-only housing available. John E. Riley Library with 141,947 books, 149,265 microform titles, 548 serials, 2,875 audiovisual materials, an OPAC,

and a Web page. Operations spending for the previous fiscal year: $339,732. 213 computers available on campus for general student use. Computer purchase/lease plans available. A campuswide network can be accessed from student residence rooms. Students can access the following: online class registration. Staffed computer lab on campus provides training in use of computers, software, and the Internet.

Community Environment: Nampa, located in southwestern Idaho, has a mild climate with an average mean temperature of 51 degrees and average rainfall of 13 inches. It is the agricultural, industrial and transportation center of southwest Idaho. Industries are processing and packing food, building mobile homes, feed mills, and seed houses; Zilog, a computer chip manufacturer is located here. Community facilities include excellent library, churches representing 22 denominations, hospitals, motels and hotels. One hundred fifty civic, fraternal, and veterans organizations are active. Part-time employment is available. Recreational facilities consist of a state-of-the-art recreation center, six parks, softball and baseball fields, horseshoe courts, tennis courts, roller skating rink and bowling alleys; other facilities are Lake Lowell for swimming, boating, fishing and hunting. A ski run is within 35 miles. Points of interest are the Deer Flat National Wildlife Refuge, Givens' Hot Springs, Lakeview Park and Silver City and De Lamar, old mining towns. The Snake River Stampede, a rodeo, is an annual event held in July.

■ **STEVENS-HENAGER COLLEGE–BOISE**

1444 S Entertainment Ave.

Boise, ID 83709

Tel: (801)345-0700; Free: 800-622-2640

Fax: (801)621-0866

Web Site: www.stevenshenager.edu/

Description: Proprietary, 4-year, coed. Awards associate and bachelor's degrees. Founded 2004.

■ **UNIVERSITY OF IDAHO**

875 Perimeter Dr.

Moscow, ID 83844-2282

Tel: (208)885-6111; Free: 888-884-3246

Fax: (208)885-6911

E-mail: admissions@uidaho.edu

Web Site: www.uidaho.edu/

Description: State-supported, university, coed. Awards bachelor's, master's, and doctoral degrees and post-master's certificates. Founded 1889. Setting: 1,450-acre small town campus. Endowment: $187.6 million. Research spending for the previous fiscal year: $97.2 million. Educational spending for the previous fiscal year: $5355 per student. Total enrollment: 12,420. Faculty: 687 (545 full-time, 142 part-time). Student-undergrad faculty ratio is 18:1. 7,467 applied, 66% were admitted. 18% from top 10% of their high school class, 44% from top quarter, 77% from top half. 12 National Merit Scholars. Full-time: 8,138 students, 46% women, 54% men. Part-time: 1,790 students, 52% women, 48% men. Students come from 45 states and territories, 46 other countries, 26% from out-of-state. 1% American Indian or Alaska Native, non-Hispanic/Latino; 8% Hispanic/Latino; 1% African American, non-Hispanic/Latino; 2% Asian, non-Hispanic/Latino; 0.3% Native Hawaiian or other Pacific Islander, non-Hispanic/Latino; 3% international. 16% 25 or older, 39% live on campus, 7% transferred in. Retention: 77% of full-time freshmen returned the following year. Academic areas with the most degrees conferred: business/marketing; education; engineering. Core. Calendar: semesters. Academic remediation for entering students, ESL program, services for LD students, advanced placement, accelerated degree program, honors program, independent study, distance learning, double major, summer session for credit, part-time degree program, adult/continuing education programs, co-op programs and internships, graduate courses open to undergrads. Off campus study at National Student Exchange. Study abroad program. ROTC: Army, Naval, Air Force (c).

Entrance Requirements: Options: electronic application, deferred admission, international baccalaureate accepted. Required: high school transcript, minimum 2.2 high school GPA, SAT or ACT. Required for some: essay. Entrance: moderately difficult. Application deadline: 8/1. Notification: continuous. Transfer credits accepted: Yes.

Costs Per Year: Application fee: $50. State resident tuition: $4230 full-time, $253 per credit hour part-time. Nonresident tuition: $17,018 full-time, $892 per credit hour part-time. Mandatory fees: $1982 full-time, $59 per credit hour part-time. Full-time tuition and fees vary according to course load, degree level, program, and reciprocity agreements. Part-time tuition and fees vary according to course load, degree level, and program. College room and board: $7682. Room and board charges vary according to board plan and housing facility.

Collegiate Environment: Orientation program. Drama-theater group, choral group, marching band, student-run newspaper, radio station. Social organizations: 200 open to all; national fraternities, national sororities; 17% of eligible men and 18% of eligible women are members. Most popular organizations: Pre-Med club, Student Alumni Relations Board, Vandal Volunteers Club, National Society of Collegiate Scholars, University of Idaho Polo. Major annual events: Vandal Fridays, Palouse-A-Fest, Homecoming. Student services: health clinic, personal-psychological counseling, women's center. Campus security: 24-hour emergency response devices and patrols, late night transport-escort service, controlled dormitory access, contracted services with the city of Moscow police department. 2,034 college housing spaces available; 1,648 were occupied in 2012-13. Freshmen guaranteed college housing. On-campus residence required in freshman year. Options: coed, men-only, women-only housing available. University of Idaho Library plus 1 other with 1.4 million books, 2.6 million microform titles, 45,769 serials, 11,329 audiovisual materials, an OPAC, and a Web page. Operations spending for the previous fiscal year: $6.4 million. 530 computers available on campus for general student use. Computer purchase/lease plans available. A campuswide network can be accessed from student residence rooms. Students can access the following: online class registration. Staffed computer lab on campus provides training in use of computers, software, and the Internet.

Community Environment: The location is rural, combining the peace, calm, and simplicity of the country with the intellectual atmosphere of a progressive college town. Moscow is in Idaho's Palouse Hill country and leads the nation in the production and processing of seed peas and lentils. Community facilities include a library, churches, clinics, hospital, hotels and motels and 2 shopping malls. Air, bus and railroads serve the area. Part-time work is available. Apartments and rooms may be rented. Eight miles away is Washington State University, the land grant institution for the state of Washington. There is an active faculty exchange, cross registration, and multiple library resources.

■ **UNIVERSITY OF PHOENIX–IDAHO CAMPUS**
1422 S Tech Ln.
Meridian, ID 83642-5114
Tel: (208)898-2000; Free: 866-766-0766
Fax: (208)895-9728
Web Site: www.phoenix.edu/

Description: Proprietary, comprehensive, coed. Awards bachelor's and master's degrees. Setting: urban campus. Total enrollment: 545. Faculty: 120 (22 full-time, 98 part-time). Full-time: 456 students, 59% women, 41% men. 89% 25 or older. Academic areas with the most degrees conferred: business/marketing; computer and information sciences; health professions and related sciences. Core. Calendar: continuous. Services for LD students, advanced placement, accelerated degree program, independent study, distance learning, external degree program, adult/continuing education programs, graduate courses open to undergrads.

Entrance Requirements: Open admission. Options: electronic application, deferred admission. Required: 1 recommendation. Required for some: high school transcript. Entrance: noncompetitive. Application deadline: Rolling.

Collegiate Environment: Campus security: late night transport-escort service. University Library with 16,781 serials, an OPAC, and a Web page. Operations spending for the previous fiscal year: $6.8 million.

■ **AMERICAN ACADEMY OF ART**
332 S Michigan Ave., Ste. 300
Chicago, IL 60604-4302
Tel: (312)461-0600; Free: 888-461-0600
E-mail: srosenbloom@aaart.edu
Web Site: www.aaart.edu/
Description: Proprietary, 4-year, coed. Awards bachelor's degrees. Founded 1923. Setting: urban campus with easy access to Chicago. Total enrollment: 432. Student-undergrad faculty ratio is 15:1. 20% from out-of-state. 5% 25 or older. Retention: 78% of full-time freshmen returned the following year. Academic area with the most degrees conferred: visual and performing arts. Core. Calendar: trimesters. Academic remediation for entering students, accelerated degree program, independent study, summer session for credit, part-time degree program, adult/continuing education programs, internships. Study abroad program.
Entrance Requirements: Option: electronic application. Required: high school transcript, interview. Entrance: moderately difficult. Application deadline: Rolling. Transfer credits accepted: Yes.
Collegiate Environment: Orientation program. Campus security: 24-hour emergency response devices. College housing not available.
Community Environment: See University of Chicago.

■ **AMERICAN INTERCONTINENTAL UNIVERSITY ONLINE**
5550 Prairie Stone Pky., Ste. 400
Hoffman Estates, IL 60192
Tel: (847)851-5000; Free: 877-701-3800
Fax: (847)851-6002
E-mail: jziegenmier@aiuonline.edu
Web Site: www.aiuniv.edu/
Description: Proprietary, comprehensive, coed. Administratively affiliated with American InterContinental University. Awards associate, bachelor's, and master's degrees (offers online degree programs only). Founded 1970. Setting: 1-acre suburban campus. Total enrollment: 22,424. Faculty: 396. Full-time: 20,341 students, 67% women, 33% men. 78% 25 or older, 20% transferred in. Academic areas with the most degrees conferred: business/marketing; computer and information sciences; homeland security, law enforcement, firefighting, and protective services. Core. Calendar: five 10-week terms. Academic remediation for entering students, advanced placement, accelerated degree program, distance learning, part-time degree program, adult/continuing education programs.
Entrance Requirements: Options: electronic application, deferred admission, international baccalaureate accepted. Required: essay, high school transcript, interview. Entrance: minimally difficult. Application deadlines: Rolling, Rolling for nonresidents. Notification: continuous, continuous for nonresidents.
Collegiate Environment: Orientation program.

■ **ARGOSY UNIVERSITY, CHICAGO**
225 N Michigan Ave., Ste. 1300
Chicago, IL 60601
Tel: (312)777-7600; Free: 800-626-4123
Fax: (312)201-1907
Web Site: www.argosy.edu/chicago/
Description: Proprietary, university, coed. Awards bachelor's, master's, and doctoral degrees. Founded 1976. Setting: urban campus. Calendar: semesters.

■ **ARGOSY UNIVERSITY, SCHAUMBURG**
999 N Plz. Dr., Ste. 111
Schaumburg, IL 60173-5403
Tel: (847)969-4900; Free: 866-290-2777
Fax: (847)598-6191
Web Site: www.argosy.edu/schaumburg/
Description: Proprietary, university, coed. Awards bachelor's, master's, and doctoral degrees and post-master's certificates. Founded 1979. Calendar: semesters.

■ **AUGUSTANA COLLEGE**
639 38th St.
Rock Island, IL 61201-2296
Tel: (309)794-7000; Free: 800-798-8100
Fax: (309)794-7431
E-mail: admissions@augustana.edu
Web Site: www.augustana.edu/
Description: Independent, 4-year, coed, affiliated with Evangelical Lutheran Church in America. Awards bachelor's degrees. Founded 1860. Setting: 115-acre suburban campus. Endowment: $115.9 million. Research spending for the previous fiscal year: $502,377. Educational spending for the previous fiscal year: $8316 per student. Total enrollment: 2,551. Faculty: 286 (178 full-time, 108 part-time). Student-undergrad faculty ratio is 12:1. 4,230 applied, 69% were admitted. 29% from top 10% of their high school class, 59% from top quarter, 88% from top half. Full-time: 2,532 students, 58% women, 42% men. Part-time: 19 students, 42% women, 58% men. Students come from 34 states and territories, 25 other countries, 15% from out-of-state. 0.4% American Indian or Alaska Native, non-Hispanic/Latino; 7% Hispanic/Latino; 4% African American, non-Hispanic/Latino; 2% Asian, non-Hispanic/Latino; 0.1% Native Hawaiian or other Pacific Islander, non-Hispanic/Latino; 2% international. 1% 25 or older, 73% live on campus, 2% transferred in. Retention: 84% of full-time freshmen returned the following year. Academic areas with the most degrees conferred: business/marketing; biological/life sciences; social sciences. Core. Services for LD students, advanced placement, self-designed majors, honors program, independent study, double major, summer session for credit, part-time degree program, internships. Study abroad program.
Entrance Requirements: Options: electronic application, deferred admission, international baccalaureate accepted. Required: high school transcript. Recommended: essay, 1 recommendation, interview, SAT or ACT. Required for some: essay, interview, SAT or ACT. Entrance: moderately difficult. Application deadline: Rolling. Notification: continuous. SAT Reasoning Test deadline: 4/1. SAT Subject Test deadline: 4/1.
Costs Per Year: Application fee: $30. Comprehensive fee: $43,398 includes full-time tuition ($34,614) and college room and board ($8784). Full-time tuition varies according to student level. Room and board charges vary according to board plan and housing facility.
Collegiate Environment: Orientation program. Drama-theater group, choral group, student-run newspaper, radio station. Social organizations: 117 open to all; local fraternities, local sororities; 23% of eligible men and 34% of eligible women are members. Most popular organizations: College Union Board of Managers, Student Government Association, student newspaper, student radio station, service organizations (APO, Dance Marathon committee). Major annual events: Homecoming, All Campus Volunteer Day, Diversity Week. Student services: health clinic, personal-psychological counseling, women's center. Campus security: 24-hour emergency response

devices and patrols, late night transport-escort service, controlled dormitory access. College housing designed to accommodate 1,800 students; 1,855 undergraduates lived in college housing during 2012-13. Freshmen guaranteed college housing. On-campus residence required through junior year. Options: coed, men-only, women-only housing available. Thomas Tredway Library plus 1 other with 131,821 books, 3,504 microform titles, 28,503 serials, 3,527 audiovisual materials, an OPAC, and a Web page. Operations spending for the previous fiscal year: $1.7 million. 600 computers available on campus for general student use. A campuswide network can be accessed from student residence rooms and from off campus. Students can access the following: online class registration. Staffed computer lab on campus provides training in use of computers, software, and the Internet.

■ **AURORA UNIVERSITY**
347 S Gladstone Ave.
Aurora, IL 60506-4892
Tel: (630)892-6431; Free: 800-742-5281
Fax: (630)844-5535
E-mail: admission@aurora.edu
Web Site: www.aurora.edu/
Description: Independent, comprehensive, coed. Awards bachelor's, master's, and doctoral degrees and post-master's certificates. Founded 1893. Setting: 32-acre suburban campus with easy access to Chicago. Endowment: $38.5 million. Research spending for the previous fiscal year: $135,470. Educational spending for the previous fiscal year: $5917 per student. Total enrollment: 4,702. Faculty: 382 (121 full-time, 261 part-time). Student-undergrad faculty ratio is 17:1. 2,219 applied, 75% were admitted. 14% from top 10% of their high school class, 37% from top quarter, 71% from top half. Full-time: 2,629 students, 62% women, 38% men. Part-time: 386 students, 73% women, 27% men. Students come from 25 states and territories, 5 other countries, 9% from out-of-state. 0.2% American Indian or Alaska Native, non-Hispanic/Latino; 17% Hispanic/Latino; 8% African American, non-Hispanic/Latino; 2% Asian, non-Hispanic/Latino; 0.1% Native Hawaiian or other Pacific Islander, non-Hispanic/Latino; 0.2% international. 23% 25 or older, 23% live on campus, 16% transferred in. Retention: 70% of full-time freshmen returned the following year. Academic areas with the most degrees conferred: business/marketing; health professions and related sciences; education. Core. Calendar: semesters. Academic remediation for entering students, services for LD students, advanced placement, accelerated degree program, self-designed majors, honors program, independent study, distance learning, double major, summer session for credit, part-time degree program, adult/continuing education programs, internships. Off campus study at 3 members of the Council of West Suburban Colleges. Study abroad program. ROTC: Army (c).
Entrance Requirements: Options: electronic application, deferred admission. Required: high school transcript, minimum 2 high school GPA, SAT or ACT. Recommended: essay, interview. Required for some: 2 recommendations, interview. Entrance: moderately difficult. Application deadlines: 5/1, 5/1 for nonresidents. SAT Reasoning Test deadline: 6/1. Transfer credits accepted: Yes.
Costs Per Year: Application fee: $25. Comprehensive fee: $30,262 includes full-time tuition ($20,500), mandatory fees ($220), and college room and board ($9542). Full-time tuition and fees vary according to location. Room and board charges vary according to board plan, housing facility, and location. Part-time tuition: $590 per semester hour. Part-time tuition varies according to course load, location, and program.
Collegiate Environment: Orientation program. Drama-theater group, choral group, student-run newspaper, radio station. Social organizations: 55 open to all; national fraternities, national sororities, local fraternities, local sororities; 22% of eligible men and 23% of eligible women are members. Most popular organizations: Aurora University Student Association, Latin American Student Organization, Student Nursing Association, Social Work Association, Future Educators Association. Major annual events: Homecoming Weekend, Spring Fling, Finals Week Pancake Night. Student services: health clinic, personal-psychological counseling. Campus security: 24-hour emergency response devices and patrols, late night transport-escort service, controlled dormitory access. 701 college housing spaces available; 649 were occupied in 2012-13. Freshmen given priority for college housing. Option: coed housing available. Charles B. Phillips Library with 95,869 books, 500 microform titles, 30,124 serials, 7,100 audiovisual materials, an OPAC, and a Web page. Operations spending for the previous fiscal year: $1.3 million. 167 computers available on campus for general student use. A campuswide network can be accessed from student residence rooms and from off campus. Students can access the following: online class registration, Moodle

Learning Management System. Staffed computer lab on campus provides training in use of computers, software, and the Internet.
Community Environment: Aurora is a large suburb in the Chicago metropolitan area but retains its own distinctive community life and atmosphere. The city is located in the Fox River Valley, 40 miles west of Chicago. Aurora is a city of schools, churches, libraries, and beautiful homes. Phillips Park provides facilities for tennis, swimming and golf.

■ **BENEDICTINE UNIVERSITY**
5700 College Rd.
Lisle, IL 60532-0900
Tel: (630)829-6000; Free: 888-829-6363
Fax: (630)960-1126
E-mail: admissions@ben.edu
Web Site: www.ben.edu/
Description: Independent Roman Catholic, comprehensive, coed. Awards associate, bachelor's, master's, and doctoral degrees. Founded 1887. Setting: 108-acre suburban campus with easy access to Chicago. Endowment: $28.5 million. Research spending for the previous fiscal year: $312,668. Total enrollment: 6,516. Faculty: 702 (146 full-time, 556 part-time). Student-undergrad faculty ratio is 18:1. 1,586 applied, 39% were admitted. 14% from top 10% of their high school class, 39% from top quarter, 71% from top half. 4 valedictorians. Full-time: 2,916 students, 60% women, 40% men. Part-time: 808 students, 66% women, 34% men. Students come from 50 states and territories, 17 other countries, 8% from out-of-state. 0.3% American Indian or Alaska Native, non-Hispanic/Latino; 7% Hispanic/Latino; 10% African American, non-Hispanic/Latino; 14% Asian, non-Hispanic/Latino; 0.4% Native Hawaiian or other Pacific Islander, non-Hispanic/Latino; 2% international. 29% 25 or older, 18% live on campus, 8% transferred in. Retention: 73% of full-time freshmen returned the following year. Academic areas with the most degrees conferred: business/marketing; health professions and related sciences; psychology. Core. Calendar: semesters. Academic remediation for entering students, ESL program, services for LD students, advanced placement, accelerated degree program, honors program, independent study, distance learning, double major, summer session for credit, part-time degree program, adult/continuing education programs, internships, graduate courses open to undergrads. Off campus study at 3 members of the Council of West Suburban Colleges. Study abroad program. ROTC: Army (c).
Entrance Requirements: Options: electronic application, deferred admission. Required: essay, high school transcript, SAT or ACT. Recommended: rank in upper 50% of high school class. Required for some: interview. Entrance: moderately difficult. Application deadline: Rolling. Notification: continuous.
Costs Per Year: Application fee: $40. Comprehensive fee: $34,230 includes full-time tuition ($24,850), mandatory fees ($1000), and college room and board ($8380). College room only: $5860. Full-time tuition and fees vary according to class time, degree level, and location. Room and board charges vary according to board plan, housing facility, and location. Part-time tuition: $830 per credit hour. Part-time mandatory fees: $15 per credit hour. Part-time tuition and fees vary according to class time and degree level.
Collegiate Environment: Orientation program. Choral group, student-run newspaper. Social organizations: 46 open to all. Most popular organizations: Student Senate, MSA-Muslim Student Association, AMSA-American Medical Student Association, The Candor-Student Newspaper, Programming Board. Major annual events: Thanksgiving and Christmas Dinner, Quad Day, Spring Ball. Student services: health clinic, personal-psychological counseling. Campus security: 24-hour emergency response devices and patrols, late night transport-escort service, controlled dormitory access. 774 college housing spaces available; 682 were occupied in 2012-13. Freshmen guaranteed college housing. Options: coed, men-only, women-only housing available. Benedictine Library with 292,602 books, 23,383 microform titles, 50,305 serials, 4,049 audiovisual materials, an OPAC, and a Web page. Operations spending for the previous fiscal year: $1.5 million. 200 computers available on campus for general student use. A campuswide network can be accessed from student residence rooms and from off campus. Students can access the following: online class registration. Staffed computer lab on campus.
Community Environment: Lisle (population 23,000) is a suburban city located in Greater Chicago between Downers Grove and Naperville; it enjoys a temperate climate. Trains and buses serve the area. Ten shopping centers are located within 10 miles of the campus. Part-time employment is available for students. Recreational activities include varsity and intramural

sports. Lisle is the home of the world famous Morton Arboretum. Benedictine University is located in DuPage County, one of the fastest growing areas in the Midwest.

■ BENEDICTINE UNIVERSITY AT SPRINGFIELD

1500 N Fifth St.
Springfield, IL 62702
Tel: (217)525-1420; Free: 800-635-7289
Fax: (217)789-1698
E-mail: khinkle@sci.edu
Web Site: www1.ben.edu/springfield/

Description: Independent, 2-year, coed, affiliated with Roman Catholic Church. Awards transfer associate degrees (the college partners with Benedictine University, offering baccalaureate and master degree programs at Springfield College's campus). Founded 1929. Setting: 8-acre urban campus. Total enrollment: 608. Faculty: 69 (25 full-time, 44 part-time). Student-undergrad faculty ratio is 10:1. Full-time: 286 students, 60% women, 40% men. Part-time: 322 students, 78% women, 22% men. 37% 25 or older. Calendar: semesters. Academic remediation for entering students, advanced placement, self-designed majors, summer session for credit, part-time degree program, adult/continuing education programs. Off campus study at Illinois College, MacMurray College, Sangamon State University, Lincoln Land Community College.

Entrance Requirements: Required: high school transcript, SAT and SAT Subject Tests or ACT. Recommended: minimum 2.0 high school GPA. Required for some: interview. Entrance: moderately difficult. Application deadline: Rolling. Notification: continuous.

Collegiate Environment: Orientation program. Student services: personal-psychological counseling. Campus security: 24-hour emergency response devices. Charles E. Becker Library plus 1 other with 19,951 books, 15,398 microform titles, 146 serials, 2,490 audiovisual materials, an OPAC, and a Web page. 45 computers available on campus for general student use. A campuswide network can be accessed. Staffed computer lab on campus.

■ BLACK HAWK COLLEGE

6600 34th Ave.
Moline, IL 61265-5899
Tel: (309)796-5000; Free: 800-334-1311
E-mail: berryv@bhc.edu
Web Site: www.bhc.edu/

Description: State and locally supported, 2-year, coed. Part of Black Hawk College District System. Awards certificates, transfer associate, and terminal associate degrees. Founded 1946. Setting: 161-acre urban campus. Educational spending for the previous fiscal year: $2722 per student. Total enrollment: 6,267. Faculty: 329 (134 full-time, 195 part-time). Student-undergrad faculty ratio is 19:1. 732 applied, 100% were admitted. 2% from top 10% of their high school class, 11% from top quarter, 40% from top half. Full-time: 2,715 students, 58% women, 42% men. Part-time: 3,552 students, 62% women, 38% men. Students come from 14 states and territories, 9 other countries, 6% from out-of-state. 40% 25 or older, 3% transferred in. Core. Calendar: semesters. Academic remediation for entering students, ESL program, services for LD students, advanced placement, accelerated degree program, independent study, distance learning, summer session for credit, part-time degree program, adult/continuing education programs, co-op programs and internships. Off campus study at Scott Community College, WEIC. Study abroad program.

Entrance Requirements: Open admission special requirements for health care-related programs, such as nursing and physical therapy. Options: electronic application, early admission, deferred admission. Recommended: high school transcript. Entrance: noncompetitive. Application deadline: Rolling. Notification: continuous. Transfer credits accepted: Yes.

Collegiate Environment: Orientation program. Drama-theater group, choral group, student-run newspaper. Social organizations: 30 open to all. Student services: personal-psychological counseling. Campus security: 24-hour patrols. Quad City Campus Library plus 1 other with 59,840 books, 8,340 microform titles, 612 serials, 140 audiovisual materials, an OPAC, and a Web page. 800 computers available on campus for general student use. Computer purchase/lease plans available. A campuswide network can be accessed from off-campus. Students can access the following: online class registration, college portal called myBlackHawk. Staffed computer lab on campus.

■ BLACKBURN COLLEGE

700 College Ave.
Carlinville, IL 62626-1498

Tel: (217)854-3231; Free: 800-233-3550
Fax: (217)854-3713
E-mail: admit@mail.blackburn.edu
Web Site: www.blackburn.edu/

Description: Independent Presbyterian, 4-year, coed. Awards bachelor's degrees. Founded 1837. Setting: 80-acre small town campus with easy access to St. Louis. Endowment: $11.1 million. Educational spending for the previous fiscal year: $5861 per student. Total enrollment: 546. Faculty: 73 (38 full-time, 35 part-time). Student-undergrad faculty ratio is 12:1. 423 applied, 70% were admitted. 16% from top 10% of their high school class, 40% from top quarter, 69% from top half. Full-time: 531 students, 58% women, 42% men. Part-time: 15 students, 60% women, 40% men. Students come from 18 states and territories, 2 other countries, 9% from out-of-state. 1% American Indian or Alaska Native, non-Hispanic/Latino; 1% Hispanic/Latino; 9% African American, non-Hispanic/Latino; 1% Asian, non-Hispanic/Latino; 1% Native Hawaiian or other Pacific Islander, non-Hispanic/Latino; 0.4% international. 6% 25 or older, 67% live on campus, 11% transferred in. Retention: 71% of full-time freshmen returned the following year. Academic areas with the most degrees conferred: education; biological/life sciences; business/marketing. Core. Calendar: semesters. Services for LD students, advanced placement, self-designed majors, honors program, independent study, double major, summer session for credit, co-op programs and internships. Off campus study at American University. Study abroad program.

Entrance Requirements: Options: electronic application, deferred admission. Required: high school transcript, minimum 2 high school GPA, SAT or ACT. Recommended: minimum 2.5 high school GPA. Required for some: essay, 3 recommendations, interview. Entrance: moderately difficult. Application deadlines: Rolling, Rolling for nonresidents. Notification: continuous, continuous for nonresidents. Transfer credits accepted: Yes.

Costs Per Year: Application fee: $20. Comprehensive fee: $24,906 includes full-time tuition ($18,146), mandatory fees ($300), and college room and board ($6460). College room only: $3748. Full-time tuition and fees vary according to student level. Room and board charges vary according to board plan and housing facility. Part-time tuition: $605 per credit hour. Part-time tuition varies according to student level.

Collegiate Environment: Orientation program. Drama-theater group, choral group, student-run newspaper, radio station. Social organizations: 30 open to all. Most popular organizations: Habitat for Humanity, Residence Hall Association, Newman Club, Blackburn Common Ground. Major annual events: Homecoming Dance, Founder's Day Convocation, Platinum Bingo. Student services: personal-psychological counseling. Campus security: student patrols, late night transport-escort service. 475 college housing spaces available; 386 were occupied in 2012-13. Freshmen guaranteed college housing. On-campus residence required through junior year. Options: coed, men-only, women-only housing available. Lumpkin Library with 75,754 books, 10,921 microform titles, 88 serials, 2,893 audiovisual materials, and an OPAC. Operations spending for the previous fiscal year: $235,398. 202 computers available on campus for general student use. A campuswide network can be accessed from student residence rooms and from off campus. Students can access the following: online class registration. Staffed computer lab on campus provides training in use of computers, software, and the Internet.

■ BLESSING-RIEMAN COLLEGE OF NURSING

Broadway at 11th St.
Quincy, IL 62305-7005
Tel: (217)228-5520; Free: 800-877-9140
Fax: (217)223-6400
E-mail: admissions@brcn.edu
Web Site: www.brcn.edu/

Description: Independent, comprehensive, coed. Awards bachelor's and master's degrees. Founded 1985. Setting: 1-acre small town campus. Endowment: $6.7 million. Educational spending for the previous fiscal year: $5799 per student. Total enrollment: 282. Faculty: 18 (all full-time). Student-undergrad faculty ratio is 12:1. 39 applied, 77% were admitted. Full-time: 221 students, 90% women, 10% men. Part-time: 45 students, 93% women, 7% men. Students come from 10 states and territories, 32% from out-of-state. 35% 25 or older, 82% live on campus, 10% transferred in. Academic area with the most degrees conferred: health professions and related sciences. Core. Calendar: semesters. Academic remediation for entering students, advanced placement, honors program, distance learning, double major, summer session for credit, part-time degree program, adult/continuing education programs, internships.

Entrance Requirements: Options: electronic application, deferred admis-

sion. Required: high school transcript, minimum 3 high school GPA, SAT or ACT. Recommended: essay, interview. Entrance: moderately difficult. Application deadline: Rolling.

Collegiate Environment: Orientation program. Drama-theater group, choral group, student-run newspaper, radio station. Social organizations: national fraternities, national sororities; 40% of women are members. Most popular organization: Student Nurses Organization. Major annual events: Teddy Bear Clinic, Health Fair, Convocation. Student services: health clinic, personal-psychological counseling. Campus security: 24-hour patrols, late night transport-escort service, controlled dormitory access. Blessing Health Professions Library plus 1 other with 3,767 books, 125 serials, an OPAC, and a Web page. Operations spending for the previous fiscal year: $315,714. 28 computers available on campus for general student use. A campuswide network can be accessed. Staffed computer lab on campus provides training in use of computers, software, and the Internet.

■ **BRADLEY UNIVERSITY**
1501 W Bradley Ave.
Peoria, IL 61625-0002
Tel: (309)676-7611; Free: 800-447-6460
E-mail: admissions@bradley.edu
Web Site: www.bradley.edu/
Description: Independent, comprehensive, coed. Awards bachelor's, master's, and doctoral degrees. Founded 1897. Setting: 85-acre suburban campus. Endowment: $243 million. Research spending for the previous fiscal year: $8.1 million. Educational spending for the previous fiscal year: $10,246 per student. Total enrollment: 5,451. Faculty: 579 (352 full-time, 227 part-time). Student-undergrad faculty ratio is 12:1. 7,562 applied, 63% were admitted. 35% from top 10% of their high school class, 69% from top quarter, 94% from top half. 2 National Merit Scholars, 48 valedictorians. Full-time: 4,631 students, 53% women, 47% men. Part-time: 241 students, 50% women, 50% men. Students come from 41 states and territories, 38 other countries, 12% from out-of-state. 0.3% American Indian or Alaska Native, non-Hispanic/Latino; 6% Hispanic/Latino; 7% African American, non-Hispanic/Latino; 4% Asian, non-Hispanic/Latino; 0.1% Native Hawaiian or other Pacific Islander, non-Hispanic/Latino; 1% international. 5% 25 or older, 66% live on campus, 6% transferred in. Retention: 86% of full-time freshmen returned the following year. Academic areas with the most degrees conferred: business/marketing; engineering; health professions and related sciences. Core. Calendar: semesters. Services for LD students, advanced placement, self-designed majors, honors program, independent study, distance learning, double major, summer session for credit, part-time degree program, co-op programs and internships, graduate courses open to undergrads. Off campus study. Study abroad program. ROTC: Army.
Entrance Requirements: Options: electronic application, early admission, deferred admission, international baccalaureate accepted. Required: essay, high school transcript, 1 recommendation, SAT or ACT. Recommended: interview. Entrance: moderately difficult. Application deadlines: Rolling, Rolling for nonresidents. SAT Reasoning Test deadline: 8/15. Transfer credits accepted: Yes. Applicants placed on waiting list: 0. Wait-listed applicants offered admission: 0.
Costs Per Year: Application fee: $35. One-time mandatory fee: $200. Comprehensive fee: $38,714 includes full-time tuition ($29,320), mandatory fees ($344), and college room and board ($9050). College room only: $5250. Full-time tuition and fees vary according to course load and program. Room and board charges vary according to board plan. Part-time tuition: $740 per credit. Part-time tuition varies according to course load and program.
Collegiate Environment: Orientation program. Drama-theater group, choral group, student-run newspaper, radio station. Social organizations: 237 open to all; national fraternities, national sororities; 32% of eligible men and 27% of eligible women are members. Most popular organizations: Habitat for Humanity, Alpha Phi Omega Co-Ed Service Fraternity, Activities Council of Bradley University, CRU (Campus Christian group), Dance Marathon. Major annual events: Latenight BU, Student Organization Fair, Taste of Bradley. Student services: health clinic, personal-psychological counseling. Campus security: 24-hour emergency response devices and patrols, late night transport-escort service, controlled dormitory access, emergency text messaging, mass notification/emergency communication system in 20 academic buildings. 2,187 college housing spaces available; 2,100 were occupied in 2012-13. Freshmen guaranteed college housing. On-campus residence required through sophomore year. Option: coed housing available. Cullom-Davis Library plus 1 other with 511,000 books, 86,504 microform titles, 41,689 serials, 13,775 audiovisual materials, an OPAC, and a Web page.

Operations spending for the previous fiscal year: $2.6 million. 2,500 computers available on campus for general student use. Computer purchase/lease plans available. A campuswide network can be accessed from student residence rooms and from off campus. Students can access the following: online class registration. Staffed computer lab on campus provides training in use of computers, software, and the Internet.
Community Environment: Bradley benefits tremendously from its location in Peoria, the state's second largest metropolitan area. (350,000) Students find manifold opportunities in terms of professional internships, cooperative education programs, research opportunities, social and cultural life and employment, and they also benefit from adjunct professors employed in various professors employed in various Peoria area businesses, professions, and other organizations. Peoria is a mecca for the arts and medical sciences. The city's three major health care facilities and the University of Illinois School of Medicine are known collectively as the Downstate Medical Center of Illinois. Together they have built one of the most modern, comprehensive health systems in the Midwest. With a symphony orchestra, civic opera, ballet company and a rich theater and gallery life, Peoria is the center of arts activity in central Illinois. Peoria is blessed with natural beauty, clean air and water, numerous parks, an all-season sports arena and a wealth of recreational opportunities. Peoria is within easy driving distance of two great cities: Three hours from Chicago and from St. Louis.

■ **CARL SANDBURG COLLEGE**
2400 Tom L. Wilson Blvd.
Galesburg, IL 61401-9576
Tel: (309)344-2518
Fax: (309)344-1395
Web Site: www.sandburg.edu/
Description: State and locally supported, 2-year, coed. Part of Illinois Community College Board. Awards certificates, transfer associate, and terminal associate degrees. Founded 1967. Setting: 105-acre small town campus. Total enrollment: 2,693. 40% 25 or older. Calendar: semesters. Academic remediation for entering students, ESL program, services for LD students, advanced placement, self-designed majors, summer session for credit, part-time degree program, adult/continuing education programs, co-op programs and internships. ROTC: Army (c).
Entrance Requirements: Open admission for district residents. Options: early admission, deferred admission. Required: high school transcript. Entrance: noncompetitive. Application deadline: Rolling.
Collegiate Environment: Drama-theater group, choral group. Student services: personal-psychological counseling. Campus security: 24-hour emergency response devices and patrols. Learning Resource Center plus 1 other with 39,900 books and 290 serials. 110 computers available on campus for general student use. Staffed computer lab on campus.
Community Environment: Galesburg (population 32,000), once selected as one of the four ideal American cities by noted editor and author, Edward Bok, is located 180 miles southwest of Chicago on the main lines of the Burlington and Santa Fe Railroads. The Carl Sandburg birthplace preserves the early home of the poet and contains interesting Sandburg and Lincoln memoirs.

■ **CHAMBERLAIN COLLEGE OF NURSING (ADDISON)**
1221 N Swift Rd.
Addison, IL 60101-6106
Tel: (630)953-3680; Free: 888-556-8CCN
Web Site: www.chamberlain.edu/
Description: Proprietary, 4-year, coed. Awards bachelor's and master's degrees. Total enrollment: 11,120. Faculty: 353 (60 full-time, 293 part-time). Student-undergrad faculty ratio is 30:1. Full-time: 1,470 students, 90% women, 10% men. Part-time: 7,629 students, 93% women, 7% men. 80% from out-of-state. 0.3% American Indian or Alaska Native, non-Hispanic/Latino; 5% Hispanic/Latino; 12% African American, non-Hispanic/Latino; 5% Asian, non-Hispanic/Latino; 1% Native Hawaiian or other Pacific Islander, non-Hispanic/Latino; 1% international. 90% 25 or older, 0% live on campus, 45% transferred in. Academic area with the most degrees conferred: health professions and related sciences. Calendar: semesters.
Entrance Requirements: Required: SAT or ACT.
Costs Per Year: Tuition: $16,360 full-time, $665 per credit hour part-time. Mandatory fees: $600 full-time. Full-time tuition and fees vary according to course load. Part-time tuition varies according to course load.

■ **CHAMBERLAIN COLLEGE OF NURSING (CHICAGO)**
3300 N Campbell Ave.
Chicago, IL 60618

Tel: (773)961-3000; Free: 888-556-8CCN

Web Site: www.chamberlain.edu/

Description: Proprietary, 4-year, coed. Awards bachelor's degrees. Total enrollment: 778. Faculty: 57 (19 full-time, 38 part-time). Student-undergrad faculty ratio is 16:1. Full-time: 392 students, 85% women, 15% men. Part-time: 386 students, 85% women, 15% men. 2% from out-of-state. 0.1% American Indian or Alaska Native, non-Hispanic/Latino; 20% Hispanic/Latino; 18% African American, non-Hispanic/Latino; 18% Asian, non-Hispanic/Latino; 2% Native Hawaiian or other Pacific Islander, non-Hispanic/Latino; 2% international. 52% 25 or older, 0% live on campus, 35% transferred in. Calendar: semesters.

Entrance Requirements: Required: SAT or ACT.

Costs Per Year: Tuition: $16,360 full-time, $665 per credit hour part-time. Mandatory fees: $600 full-time. Full-time tuition and fees vary according to course load. Part-time tuition varies according to course load.

■ CHICAGO STATE UNIVERSITY

9501 S King Dr.

Chicago, IL 60628

Tel: (773)995-2000

E-mail: jmarti21@csu.edu

Web Site: www.csu.edu/

Description: State-supported, comprehensive, coed. Awards bachelor's, master's, and doctoral degrees. Founded 1867. Setting: 161-acre urban campus. Endowment: $2 million. Research spending for the previous fiscal year: $5.8 million. Educational spending for the previous fiscal year: $3302 per student. Total enrollment: 6,107. Faculty: 291 (282 full-time, 9 part-time). Student-undergrad faculty ratio is 11:1. 3,702 applied, 32% were admitted. 17% from top 10% of their high school class, 28% from top quarter, 48% from top half. Full-time: 3,012 students, 70% women, 30% men. Part-time: 1,606 students, 76% women, 24% men. Students come from 29 states and territories, 2 other countries, 2% from out-of-state. 0.2% American Indian or Alaska Native, non-Hispanic/Latino; 7% Hispanic/Latino; 83% African American, non-Hispanic/Latino; 1% Asian, non-Hispanic/Latino; 0.02% Native Hawaiian or other Pacific Islander, non-Hispanic/Latino; 0.02% international. 57% 25 or older, 12% transferred in. Retention: 54% of full-time freshmen returned the following year. Academic areas with the most degrees conferred: liberal arts/general studies; business/marketing; psychology. Core. Calendar: semesters. Academic remediation for entering students, services for LD students, advanced placement, accelerated degree program, self-designed majors, freshman honors college, honors program, independent study, distance learning, double major, summer session for credit, part-time degree program, external degree program, adult/continuing education programs, co-op programs and internships, graduate courses open to undergrads. Off campus study. Study abroad program. ROTC: Army, Naval (c), Air Force (c).

Entrance Requirements: Option: electronic application. Required: high school transcript, minimum 2.5 high school GPA, SAT or ACT. Required for some: essay, interview. Entrance: minimally difficult. Notification: continuous.

Costs Per Year: Application fee: $25. State resident tuition: $6840 full-time. Nonresident tuition: $13,606 full-time. Mandatory fees: $2414 full-time. College room and board: $8,221. Tuition guaranteed not to increase for student's term of enrollment.

Collegiate Environment: Orientation program. Drama-theater group, choral group, student-run newspaper, radio station. Social organizations: 75 open to all; national fraternities, national sororities, local fraternities, local sororities. Most popular organizations: Math/Computer Science Club, Geographic Society Club, Gospel Choir, Movie Club. Student services: health clinic, personal-psychological counseling, women's center. Campus security: 24-hour emergency response devices and patrols, student patrols, late night transport-escort service, controlled dormitory access. 310 college housing spaces available; 291 were occupied in 2012-13. No special consideration for freshman housing applicants. Option: coed housing available. Paul and Emily Douglas Library with 426,691 books, 29,738 microform titles, 1,654 serials, 1,688 audiovisual materials, an OPAC, and a Web page. Operations spending for the previous fiscal year: $3.6 million. 75 computers available on campus for general student use. Computer purchase/lease plans available. A campuswide network can be accessed from student residence rooms and from off campus. Students can access the following: online class registration. Staffed computer lab on campus provides training in use of computers, software, and the Internet.

Community Environment: See University of Chicago.

■ CHRISTIAN LIFE COLLEGE

400 E Gregory St.

Mount Prospect, IL 60056

Tel: (847)259-1840

E-mail: mbell@christianlifecollege.edu

Web Site: www.christianlifecollege.edu/

Description: Independent Christian, 4-year, coed. Awards associate and bachelor's degrees. Founded 1950. Setting: 5-acre suburban campus with easy access to Chicago. Total enrollment: 40. Faculty: 8 (2 full-time, 6 part-time). Student-undergrad faculty ratio is 4:1. 25% from top 10% of their high school class, 50% from top half. Full-time: 33 students, 42% women, 58% men. Part-time: 7 students, 57% women, 43% men. Students come from 5 states and territories, 3 other countries, 10% from out-of-state. 0% American Indian or Alaska Native, non-Hispanic/Latino; 15% Hispanic/Latino; 10% African American, non-Hispanic/Latino; 13% Asian, non-Hispanic/Latino; 0% Native Hawaiian or other Pacific Islander, non-Hispanic/Latino; 30% international. 60% 25 or older, 13% transferred in. Academic area with the most degrees conferred: theology and religious vocations. Core. Academic remediation for entering students, independent study, part-time degree program, external degree program, adult/continuing education programs, co-op programs and internships. Off campus study.

Entrance Requirements: Options: early admission, deferred admission. Required: high school transcript, minimum 2 high school GPA, SAT or ACT. Recommended: minimum 2.5 high school GPA. Required for some: essay, minimum 2.5 high school GPA, interview. Entrance: noncompetitive. Application deadlines: Rolling, Rolling for nonresidents. Notification: continuous, continuous for nonresidents. SAT Reasoning Test deadline: 8/14. SAT Subject Test deadline: 8/14. Transfer credits accepted: Yes.

Collegiate Environment: Orientation program. Campus security: controlled dormitory access. 7 computers available on campus for general student use. Staffed computer lab on campus provides training in use of computers, software, and the Internet.

■ CITY COLLEGES OF CHICAGO, HAROLD WASHINGTON COLLEGE

30 E Lake St.

Chicago, IL 60601-2449

Tel: (312)553-5600

Fax: (312)553-6077

Web Site: hwashington.ccc.edu/

Description: State and locally supported, 2-year, coed. Part of City Colleges of Chicago. Awards certificates, transfer associate, and terminal associate degrees. Founded 1962. Setting: 1-acre urban campus. Total enrollment: 8,464. Student-undergrad faculty ratio is 33:1. 0% from out-of-state. 42% 25 or older. Core. Calendar: semesters. Academic remediation for entering students, ESL program, services for LD students, advanced placement, accelerated degree program, independent study, distance learning, double major, summer session for credit, part-time degree program, adult/continuing education programs, co-op programs and internships. Off campus study at Governors State University, Roosevelt University.

Entrance Requirements: Open admission. Options: early admission, deferred admission. Entrance: noncompetitive. Application deadline: Rolling. Notification: continuous.

Collegiate Environment: Orientation program. Drama-theater group, choral group, student-run newspaper. Student services: personal-psychological counseling, women's center. Campus security: 24-hour emergency response devices and patrols.

Community Environment: See University of Chicago.

■ CITY COLLEGES OF CHICAGO, HARRY S. TRUMAN COLLEGE

1145 W Wilson Ave.

Chicago, IL 60640-5616

Tel: (773)907-4000

Fax: (773)907-4464

E-mail: mlatuszek@ccc.edu

Web Site: www.trumancollege.edu/

Description: State and locally supported, 2-year, coed. Part of City Colleges of Chicago. Awards certificates, diplomas, transfer associate, and terminal associate degrees. Founded 1956. Setting: 5-acre urban campus. Total enrollment: 13,174. Student-undergrad faculty ratio is 34:1. 0% from out-of-state. 65% 25 or older. Core. Calendar: semesters. Academic remediation for entering students, ESL program, services for LD students, advanced placement, honors program, distance learning, summer session for credit, part-time degree program, adult/continuing education programs, co-op programs and internships.

Entrance Requirements: Open admission. Options: early admission, deferred admission. Entrance: noncompetitive. Application deadline: Rolling. Notification: continuous until 9/8.
Collegiate Environment: Orientation program. Drama-theater group. Student services: personal-psychological counseling. Campus security: 24-hour patrols, late night transport-escort service.
Community Environment: See University of Chicago.

■ **CITY COLLEGES OF CHICAGO, KENNEDY-KING COLLEGE**
6301 S Halstead St.
Chicago, IL 60621
Tel: (773)602-5000
Web Site: kennedyking.ccc.edu/
Description: State and locally supported, 2-year, coed. Part of City Colleges of Chicago. Awards certificates, transfer associate, and terminal associate degrees. Founded 1935. Setting: 18-acre urban campus. Total enrollment: 7,180. Student-undergrad faculty ratio is 30:1. 0% from out-of-state. 52% 25 or older. Core. Calendar: semesters. Academic remediation for entering students, ESL program, advanced placement, honors program, distance learning, summer session for credit, part-time degree program, adult/continuing education programs, co-op programs and internships.
Entrance Requirements: Open admission. Option: electronic application. Required: high school transcript. Entrance: noncompetitive. Application deadline: Rolling. Preference given to city residents.
Collegiate Environment: Orientation program. Drama-theater group, choral group, student-run newspaper, radio station. Social organizations: national fraternities. Student services: personal-psychological counseling. Campus security: late night transport-escort service. Harold Washington College Library with an OPAC and a Web page.
Community Environment: See University of Chicago.

■ **CITY COLLEGES OF CHICAGO, MALCOLM X COLLEGE**
1900 W Van Buren St.
Chicago, IL 60612-3145
Tel: (312)850-7000
Fax: (312)850-7092
E-mail: khollingsworth@ccc.edu
Web Site: malcolmx.ccc.edu/
Description: State and locally supported, 2-year, coed. Part of City Colleges of Chicago. Awards certificates, transfer associate, and terminal associate degrees. Founded 1911. Setting: 20-acre urban campus. Total enrollment: 6,031. Faculty: 240 (75 full-time, 165 part-time). Student-undergrad faculty ratio is 25:1. Full-time: 2,522 students, 69% women, 31% men. Part-time: 3,509 students, 64% women, 36% men. 60% 25 or older. Core. Calendar: semesters. Academic remediation for entering students, ESL program, services for LD students, advanced placement, distance learning, summer session for credit, part-time degree program, adult/continuing education programs, co-op programs.
Entrance Requirements: Open admission except for allied health programs. Option: electronic application. Required: high school transcript, minimum 2 high school GPA. Required for some: essay, interview. Entrance: noncompetitive. Application deadline: Rolling. Notification: continuous. Preference given to state residents. Transfer credits accepted: Yes.
Collegiate Environment: Orientation program. Student-run newspaper. Social organizations: 11 open to all. Most popular organizations: Student Government Association, Phi Theta Kappa, Phi Beta Lambda, Chess Club, Latino Leadership Council. Major annual events: Homecoming Parade, African-American History Month, Hispanic Heritage Month. Student services: personal-psychological counseling. Campus security: 24-hour emergency response devices and patrols. The Carter G. Woodson Library with 50,000 books, 250 serials, an OPAC, and a Web page. 275 computers available on campus for general student use. A campuswide network can be accessed. Students can access the following: online class registration. Staffed computer lab on campus provides training in use of computers and the Internet.
Community Environment: See University of Chicago.

■ **CITY COLLEGES OF CHICAGO, OLIVE-HARVEY COLLEGE**
10001 S Woodlawn Ave.
Chicago, IL 60628-1645
Tel: (773)291-6100
Fax: (773)291-6304
E-mail: gbarksdale@ccc.edu
Web Site: oliveharvey.ccc.edu/

Description: State and locally supported, 2-year, coed. Part of City Colleges of Chicago. Awards certificates, transfer associate, and terminal associate degrees. Founded 1970. Setting: 67-acre urban campus. Total enrollment: 4,777. Student-undergrad faculty ratio is 35:1. 0% from out-of-state. 52% 25 or older. Core. Calendar: semesters. Academic remediation for entering students, services for LD students, advanced placement, accelerated degree program, self-designed majors, distance learning, summer session for credit, part-time degree program, adult/continuing education programs, co-op programs. Study abroad program.
Entrance Requirements: Open admission except for nursing, computer electronics, respiratory care programs. Options: early admission, deferred admission. Entrance: noncompetitive. Application deadline: Rolling. Preference given to city residents.
Collegiate Environment: Drama-theater group. Student services: personal-psychological counseling, women's center. Campus security: 24-hour emergency response devices and patrols.
Community Environment: See University of Chicago.

■ **CITY COLLEGES OF CHICAGO, RICHARD J. DALEY COLLEGE**
7500 S Pulaski Rd.
Chicago, IL 60652-1242
Tel: (773)838-7500
Fax: (773)838-7524
E-mail: mwright@ccc.edu
Web Site: daley.ccc.edu/
Description: State and locally supported, 2-year, coed. Part of City Colleges of Chicago. Awards certificates, transfer associate, and terminal associate degrees. Founded 1960. Setting: 25-acre urban campus. Research spending for the previous fiscal year: $50,000. Educational spending for the previous fiscal year: $3469 per student. Total enrollment: 9,711. Faculty: 162 (56 full-time, 106 part-time). Student-undergrad faculty ratio is 44:1. 837 applied, 100% were admitted. Full-time: 3,507 students, 59% women, 41% men. Part-time: 6,204 students, 61% women, 39% men. Students come from 2 states and territories. 53% 25 or older. Retention: 52% of full-time freshmen returned the following year. Core. Calendar: semesters. Academic remediation for entering students, ESL program, services for LD students, advanced placement, honors program, distance learning, summer session for credit, part-time degree program, adult/continuing education programs. Off campus study at Governors State University, Chicago State University. Study abroad program. ROTC: Air Force (c).
Entrance Requirements: Open admission except for nursing program. Options: early admission, deferred admission. Required: high school transcript. Recommended: interview. Required for some: essay. Entrance: noncompetitive. Application deadline: Rolling. Preference given to city residents. Transfer credits accepted: Yes.
Collegiate Environment: Drama-theater group. Most popular organizations: Latin Student Organization, Student Government Association, African-American Culture Club. Campus security: 24-hour emergency response devices and patrols. Learning Resource Center plus 1 other with 53,201 books, 275 serials, an OPAC, and a Web page. Operations spending for the previous fiscal year: $550,000. 325 computers available on campus for general student use. A campuswide network can be accessed. Students can access the following: online class registration. Staffed computer lab on campus provides training in use of software.
Community Environment: See University of Chicago.

■ **CITY COLLEGES OF CHICAGO, WILBUR WRIGHT COLLEGE**
4300 N Narragansett Ave.
Chicago, IL 60634-1591
Tel: (773)777-7900
E-mail: aaiello@ccc.edu
Web Site: wright.ccc.edu/
Description: State and locally supported, 2-year, coed. Part of City Colleges of Chicago. Awards certificates, transfer associate, and terminal associate degrees. Founded 1934. Setting: 20-acre urban campus. Educational spending for the previous fiscal year: $2375 per student. Total enrollment: 6,826. Faculty: 262 (112 full-time, 150 part-time). Student-undergrad faculty ratio is 23:1. 2,550 applied, 100% were admitted. 5% from top 10% of their high school class, 20% from top quarter, 50% from top half. 0% from out-of-state. 45% 25 or older. Core. Calendar: semesters. Academic remediation for entering students, ESL program, accelerated degree program, distance learning, summer session for credit, part-time degree program, adult/continuing education programs.
Entrance Requirements: Open admission. Options: electronic application,

early admission, deferred admission. Entrance: noncompetitive. Application deadline: Rolling. Notification: continuous. Preference given to city residents. **Collegiate Environment:** Orientation program. Drama-theater group, choral group, student-run newspaper. Social organizations: 23 open to all. Most popular organizations: student government, Circle K, Phi Theta Kappa, Black Student Union. Major annual events: Ethnic Food Fair, Hispanic-American History Month, graduation. Student services: legal services. Campus security: 24-hour emergency response devices and patrols, student patrols, late night transport-escort service. Learning Resource Center plus 1 other with 60,000 books and 350 serials. Operations spending for the previous fiscal year: $822,000. 700 computers available on campus for general student use. A campuswide network can be accessed. Students can access the following: online class registration. Staffed computer lab on campus provides training in use of computers, software, and the Internet.

■ **COLLEGE OF DUPAGE**
425 Fawell Blvd.
Glen Ellyn, IL 60137-6599
Tel: (630)942-2800
Fax: (630)790-2686
E-mail: admissions@cod.edu
Web Site: www.cod.edu/
Description: State and locally supported, 2-year, coed. Awards certificates, transfer associate, and terminal associate degrees. Founded 1967. Setting: 297-acre suburban campus with easy access to Chicago. Endowment: $7.4 million. Total enrollment: 26,209. Faculty: 1,134 (273 full-time, 861 part-time). Student-undergrad faculty ratio is 21:1. 3,360 applied, 87% were admitted. Full-time: 9,464 students, 46% women, 54% men. Part-time: 16,745 students, 57% women, 43% men. Students come from 24 states and territories, 1% from out-of-state. 0.2% American Indian or Alaska Native, non-Hispanic/Latino; 22% Hispanic/Latino; 7% African American, non-Hispanic/Latino; 9% Asian, non-Hispanic/Latino; 0.03% Native Hawaiian or other Pacific Islander, non-Hispanic/Latino; 0.4% international. 13% transferred in. Retention: 60% of full-time freshmen returned the following year. Core. Calendar: semesters. Academic remediation for entering students, ESL program, services for LD students, advanced placement, accelerated degree program, self-designed majors, honors program, independent study, distance learning, double major, summer session for credit, part-time degree program, external degree program, adult/continuing education programs, co-op programs and internships. Off campus study at other colleges of the Illinois Community College System. Study abroad program.
Entrance Requirements: Open admission except for allied health programs. Options: early admission, deferred admission. Recommended: ACT. Entrance: noncompetitive. Application deadlines: Rolling, Rolling for nonresidents. Notification: continuous, continuous for nonresidents. Transfer credits accepted: Yes.
Costs Per Year: Application fee: $20. Area resident tuition: $4080 full-time, $136 per credit hour part-time. State resident tuition: $9690 full-time, $323 per credit hour part-time. Nonresident tuition: $11,790 full-time, $393 per credit hour part-time. Full-time tuition varies according to program. Part-time tuition varies according to program.
Collegiate Environment: Orientation program. Drama-theater group, choral group, student-run newspaper. Social organizations: 37 open to all. Most popular organizations: Latino Ethnic Awareness Association, The Christian Group, Phi Theta Kappa, International Students Organization, Muslim Student Association. Major annual events: international students year-end cruise, Annual Pool Tournament, Street Fair. Student services: health clinic, personal-psychological counseling. Campus security: 24-hour emergency response devices and patrols, student patrols, late night transport-escort service. College of DuPage Library with 203,300 books, 312,000 microform titles, 6,005 serials, an OPAC, and a Web page. 3,058 computers available on campus for general student use. A campuswide network can be accessed from off-campus. Students can access the following: online class registration. Staffed computer lab on campus.
Community Environment: Glen Ellyn is an attractive residential village with trees, rolling terrain, and well-landscaped dwellings; a suburban area near Wheaton, served by the regional commuter rail system, the shopping facilities are excellent. Glen Ellyn also has a library, YMCA, clinic in town, and hospitals nearby. Lake Ellyn is nearby for recreation, boating, swimming, etc.

■ **COLLEGE OF LAKE COUNTY**
19351 W Washington St.
Grayslake, IL 60030-1198

Tel: (847)543-2000
Fax: (847)223-1017
Web Site: www.clcillinois.edu/
Description: District-supported, 2-year, coed. Part of Illinois Community College Board. Awards certificates, transfer associate, and terminal associate degrees. Founded 1967. Setting: 226-acre suburban campus with easy access to Chicago, Milwaukee. Total enrollment: 17,577. Faculty: 1,032 (210 full-time, 822 part-time). Student-undergrad faculty ratio is 17:1. Full-time: 4,945 students, 49% women, 51% men. Part-time: 12,632 students, 58% women, 42% men. Students come from 42 other countries, 1% from out-of-state. 0.2% American Indian or Alaska Native, non-Hispanic/Latino; 29% Hispanic/Latino; 9% African American, non-Hispanic/Latino; 5% Asian, non-Hispanic/Latino; 0.1% Native Hawaiian or other Pacific Islander, non-Hispanic/Latino; 0% international. 43% 25 or older. Core. Calendar: semesters. Academic remediation for entering students, ESL program, services for LD students, advanced placement, self-designed majors, honors program, independent study, distance learning, double major, summer session for credit, part-time degree program, adult/continuing education programs, co-op programs and internships. Off campus study at McHenry County College, Gateway Technical College, Oakton Community College, William Rainey Harper College, Elgin Community College, College of DuPage. Study abroad program.
Entrance Requirements: Open admission except for health programs. Options: electronic application, early admission, deferred admission. Required for some: high school transcript, interview. Entrance: noncompetitive. Application deadline: Rolling. Notification: continuous. Preference given to district residents.
Costs Per Year: Application fee: $0. Area resident tuition: $2790 full-time, $93 per credit hour part-time. State resident tuition: $7200 full-time, $240 per credit hour part-time. Nonresident tuition: $9705 full-time, $323.50 per credit hour part-time. Mandatory fees: $570 full-time, $19 per credit hour part-time.
Collegiate Environment: Orientation program. Drama-theater group, choral group, student-run newspaper, radio station. Social organizations: 40 open to all. Most popular organizations: Latino Alliance, Men of Vision, Asian Student Alliance, Student Government Association, Anime. Major annual events: Welcome Week activities, Spring Fling, New Student Orientation. Student services: health clinic, personal-psychological counseling, women's center. Campus security: 24-hour emergency response devices and patrols, late night transport-escort service. College housing not available. College of Lake County Library plus 1 other with 99,037 books, 457 serials, an OPAC, and a Web page. 1,500 computers available on campus for general student use. A campuswide network can be accessed from off-campus. Students can access the following: online class registration. Staffed computer lab on campus.
Community Environment: The college has 2 campuses. The main campus centrally located in Grayslake (population 21,100), and the second campus situated in Waukegan (population 91,396). Waukegan is situated in the northeast corner of Illinois on the scenic shores of Lake Michigan. Excellent transportation facilities are available. Waukegan is an industrial city and is part of the metropolitan area of Chicago. Two of the principal industrial products are pharmaceutical supplies and outboard motors. Community facilities include over 50 churches of various denominations and municipal libraries. Recreation and sports include fishing, swimming, skiing, and hunting in the forest preserves. There are more than 60 lakes located in the county.

■ **THE COLLEGE OF OFFICE TECHNOLOGY**
1520 W Division St.
Chicago, IL 60622
Tel: (773)278-0042; Free: 800-953-6161
Fax: (773)278-0143
E-mail: bbolton@cot.edu
Web Site: www.cot.edu/
Description: Private, 2-year, coed. Awards terminal associate degrees. Total enrollment: 276. Student-undergrad faculty ratio is 10:1. 0% from out-of-state. 62% 25 or older.
Entrance Requirements: Entrance: noncompetitive.

■ **COLUMBIA COLLEGE CHICAGO**
600 S Michigan Ave.
Chicago, IL 60605-1996
Tel: (312)663-1600
E-mail: admissions@colum.edu
Web Site: www.colum.edu/

Description: Independent, comprehensive, coed. Awards bachelor's and master's degrees. Founded 1890. Setting: urban campus with easy access to Chicago. Endowment: $109.2 million. Research spending for the previous fiscal year: $2.3 million. Educational spending for the previous fiscal year: $11,893 per student. Total enrollment: 10,783. Faculty: 1,675 (380 full-time, 1,295 part-time). Student-undergrad faculty ratio is 11:1. 7,416 applied, 85% were admitted. 8% from top 10% of their high school class, 24% from top quarter, 55% from top half. Full-time: 9,224 students, 53% women, 47% men. Part-time: 1,086 students, 52% women, 48% men. Students come from 52 states and territories, 46 other countries, 37% from out-of-state. 0.3% American Indian or Alaska Native, non-Hispanic/Latino; 13% Hispanic/Latino; 17% African American, non-Hispanic/Latino; 3% Asian, non-Hispanic/Latino; 0.1% Native Hawaiian or other Pacific Islander, non-Hispanic/Latino; 2% international. 12% 25 or older, 18% live on campus, 9% transferred in. Retention: 64% of full-time freshmen returned the following year. Academic areas with the most degrees conferred: visual and performing arts; business/marketing; communication/journalism. Core. Calendar: semesters. Academic remediation for entering students, ESL program, services for LD students, advanced placement, self-designed majors, honors program, independent study, distance learning, summer session for credit, part-time degree program, adult/continuing education programs, co-op programs and internships. Off campus study at College Columbia Consortium. Study abroad program.

Entrance Requirements: Options: electronic application, deferred admission, international baccalaureate accepted. Required: essay, high school transcript, 1 recommendation. Recommended: minimum 2 high school GPA, interview, SAT or ACT. Entrance: moderately difficult. Application deadlines: Rolling, Rolling for nonresidents. Notification: continuous, continuous for nonresidents. Transfer credits accepted: Yes.

Costs Per Year: Application fee: $35. Comprehensive fee: $33,670 includes full-time tuition ($21,200), mandatory fees ($550), and college room and board ($11,920). Full-time tuition and fees vary according to course load. Room and board charges vary according to housing facility. Part-time tuition: $732 per credit hour. Part-time tuition varies according to course load.

Collegiate Environment: Orientation program. Drama-theater group, choral group, student-run newspaper, radio station. Social organizations: 39 open to all. Most popular organizations: Columbia Urban Music Association, International Student Organization, Acianza Latina, Marketing Club. Major annual events: Student Organizations Day, Welcome Back Dance, CUMBA Annual Music Conference. Student services: health clinic, personal-psychological counseling. Campus security: 24-hour emergency response devices and patrols, late night transport-escort service, controlled dormitory access, escort upon request. 2,700 college housing spaces available; 2,283 were occupied in 2012-13. Freshmen given priority for college housing. Option: coed housing available. Columbia College Chicago Library plus 2 others with 290,556 books, 40,838 serials, 33,067 audiovisual materials, an OPAC, and a Web page. Operations spending for the previous fiscal year: $5.4 million. 851 computers available on campus for general student use. Computer purchase/lease plans available. A campuswide network can be accessed from student residence rooms and from off campus. Students can access the following: online class registration. Staffed computer lab on campus provides training in use of computers, software, and the Internet.

Community Environment: The college is located in the dynamic South Loop neighborhood. It is within walking distance of the Art Institute of Chicago, the Shedd Aquarium, major theaters, and the Orchestra Hall. Across the street from the campus are beautiful Grant Park and Lake Michigan.

■ CONCORDIA UNIVERSITY CHICAGO

7400 Augusta St.
River Forest, IL 60305-1499
Tel: (708)771-8300; Free: 800-285-2668
Fax: (708)209-3176
E-mail: gwen.kanelos@cuchicago.edu
Web Site: www.cuchicago.edu/

Description: Independent, comprehensive, coed, affiliated with Lutheran Church-Missouri Synod. Part of Concordia University System. Awards bachelor's, master's, and doctoral degrees and post-master's certificates. Founded 1864. Setting: 40-acre suburban campus with easy access to Chicago. Total enrollment: 5,454. Faculty: 507 (128 full-time, 379 part-time). Student-undergrad faculty ratio is 19:1. 3,524 applied, 55% were admitted. 12% from top 10% of their high school class, 34% from top quarter, 65% from top half. Full-time: 1,407 students, 62% women, 38% men. Part-time: 108 students, 66% women, 34% men. 28% from out-of-state. 21% Hispanic/

Latino; 13% African American, non-Hispanic/Latino; 2% Asian, non-Hispanic/Latino; 0.1% Native Hawaiian or other Pacific Islander, non-Hispanic/Latino; 0.4% international. 11% 25 or older, 55% live on campus, 8% transferred in. Academic areas with the most degrees conferred: education; business/marketing; parks and recreation. Calendar: semesters. Part-time degree program, adult/continuing education programs.

Entrance Requirements: Options: electronic application, deferred admission, international baccalaureate accepted. Required: high school transcript, minimum 2 high school GPA, 1 recommendation, SAT or ACT. Required for some: essay, interview. Entrance: moderately difficult. Application deadline: Rolling.

Costs Per Year: Application fee: $0. Comprehensive fee: $36,452 includes full-time tuition ($27,044), mandatory fees ($744), and college room and board ($8664). College room only: $4264. Full-time tuition and fees vary according to program. Part-time tuition: $845 per credit hour. Part-time tuition varies according to program.

Collegiate Environment: Orientation program. Campus security: 24-hour emergency response devices and patrols, student patrols, late night transport-escort service, controlled dormitory access, emergency call boxes. No special consideration for freshman housing applicants. Option: coed housing available.

■ DANVILLE AREA COMMUNITY COLLEGE

2000 E Main St.
Danville, IL 61832-5199
Tel: (217)443-3222
Fax: (217)443-8560
E-mail: cpeck@dacc.edu
Web Site: www.dacc.edu/

Description: State and locally supported, 2-year, coed. Part of Illinois Community College Board. Awards certificates, transfer associate, and terminal associate degrees. Founded 1946. Setting: 50-acre small town campus. Total enrollment: 4,227. Faculty: 144 (59 full-time, 85 part-time). Student-undergrad faculty ratio is 25:1. Full-time: 1,207 students, 53% women, 47% men. Part-time: 3,020 students, 59% women, 41% men. 12% from out-of-state. Core. Calendar: semesters. Academic remediation for entering students, ESL program, services for LD students, advanced placement, independent study, distance learning, double major, summer session for credit, part-time degree program, adult/continuing education programs, co-op programs and internships.

Entrance Requirements: Open admission. Options: early admission, deferred admission. Required: high school transcript. Entrance: noncompetitive. Application deadline: Rolling.

Costs Per Year: Application fee: $0. Area resident tuition: $3240 full-time, $108 per credit hour part-time. State resident tuition: $5700 full-time, $190 per credit hour part-time. Nonresident tuition: $5700 full-time, $190 per credit hour part-time. Mandatory fees: $360 full-time, $12 per credit hour part-time. Full-time tuition and fees vary according to program. Part-time tuition and fees vary according to program.

Collegiate Environment: Orientation program. Choral group. Social organizations: 10 open to all. Student services: personal-psychological counseling. Campus security: 24-hour emergency response devices and patrols. College housing not available. Library with 50,000 books, 8,790 microform titles, 2,487 audiovisual materials, and an OPAC. 600 computers available on campus for general student use. A campuswide network can be accessed from off-campus. Students can access the following: online class registration. Staffed computer lab on campus provides training in use of computers, software, and the Internet.

Community Environment: Danville, population 33,000, is the county seat of Vermillion County situated in the eastern part of the state, four miles from the Indiana border, and 124 miles south of Chicago. Four railroads serve the area which is in the middle of the cornbelt. The city is the site of the large radio telescope used by the University of Illinois for studying signals a billion light years away. Community facilities include many churches, a newspaper, TV station, YMCA, YWCA, radio stations, and hospitals. Within the city are ten city parks. Nearby is Lake Vermillion for boating, swimming and fishing; Kickapoo State Park is also available for camping and fishing. Annual events are the All Breed Dog Show, boat races, and auto races.

■ DEPAUL UNIVERSITY

1 E Jackson Blvd.
Chicago, IL 60604-2287
Tel: (312)362-8000; Free: 800-4DE-PAUL
Fax: (312)362-3322

E-mail: admission@depaul.edu

Web Site: www.depaul.edu/

Description: Independent Roman Catholic, university, coed. Awards bachelor's, master's, and doctoral degrees and post-master's certificates. Founded 1898. Setting: 36-acre urban campus with easy access to Chicago. Endowment: $349.2 million. Research spending for the previous fiscal year: $10 million. Educational spending for the previous fiscal year: $11,225 per student. Total enrollment: 24,966. Faculty: 1,987 (979 full-time, 1,008 part-time). Student-undergrad faculty ratio is 16:1. 18,160 applied, 62% were admitted. 23% from top 10% of their high school class, 52% from top quarter, 85% from top half. Full-time: 13,657 students, 53% women, 47% men. Part-time: 2,841 students, 55% women, 45% men. Students come from 51 states and territories, 75 other countries, 19% from out-of-state. 0.1% American Indian or Alaska Native, non-Hispanic/Latino; 17% Hispanic/Latino; 8% African American, non-Hispanic/Latino; 7% Asian, non-Hispanic/Latino; 0.3% Native Hawaiian or other Pacific Islander, non-Hispanic/Latino; 2% international. 19% 25 or older, 17% live on campus, 11% transferred in. Retention: 85% of full-time freshmen returned the following year. Academic areas with the most degrees conferred: business/marketing; communication/journalism; social sciences. Core. Calendar: quarters; semesters for law school. Academic remediation for entering students, ESL program, services for LD students, advanced placement, accelerated degree program, self-designed majors, freshman honors college, honors program, independent study, distance learning, double major, summer session for credit, part-time degree program, adult/continuing education programs, co-op programs and internships, graduate courses open to undergrads. Off campus study. Study abroad program. ROTC: Army.

Entrance Requirements: Options: electronic application, early action, deferred admission, international baccalaureate accepted. Required: essay, high school transcript, minimum 2 high school GPA. Recommended: minimum 2.75 high school GPA, SAT and SAT Subject Tests or ACT. Required for some: minimum 3 high school GPA, interview, audition/interviews for the School of Music and Theatre School applicants. Entrance: moderately difficult. Application deadlines: 2/1, 11/15 for early action. Notification: 3/15, 1/15 for early action. SAT Reasoning Test deadline: 2/1. Transfer credits accepted: Yes. Early action applicants: 7,523. Early action applicants admitted: 5,876.

Costs Per Year: Application fee: $40. Comprehensive fee: $44,012 includes full-time tuition ($31,650), mandatory fees ($645), and college room and board ($11,717). College room only: $8486. Full-time tuition and fees vary according to course load and program. Room and board charges vary according to board plan, housing facility, and location. Part-time tuition: $530 per credit hour. Part-time tuition varies according to course load and program.

Collegiate Environment: Orientation program. Drama-theater group, choral group, student-run newspaper, radio station. Social organizations: 313 open to all; national fraternities, national sororities. Most popular organizations: Panhellenic Association, DePaul Activities Board, Student Government Association, Community Service Organizations, Catholic Campus Ministry. Major annual events: FEST, Homecoming, Welcome Week. Student services: legal services, health clinic, personal-psychological counseling, women's center. Campus security: 24-hour emergency response devices and patrols, late night transport-escort service, controlled dormitory access, security lighting, prevention/awareness programs, on-campus police officers, video cameras, smoke detectors in residence halls, etc. College housing designed to accommodate 2,632 students; 2,678 undergraduates lived in college housing during 2012-13. Freshmen given priority for college housing. Option: coed housing available. John T. Richardson Library plus 6 others with 928,933 books, 237,056 microform titles, 30,348 serials, 30,787 audiovisual materials, an OPAC, and a Web page. Operations spending for the previous fiscal year: $12.2 million. 1,800 computers available on campus for general student use. Computer purchase/lease plans available. A campuswide network can be accessed from student residence rooms and from off campus. Students can access the following: online class registration, tuition payments, degree progress, financial aid, transcript requests, housing services, student employment information. Staffed computer lab on campus (open 24 hours a day) provides training in use of computers, software, and the Internet.

Community Environment: DePaul is located in a culturally and academically rich urban environment. The downtown campus is minutes away from the Art Institute, Orchestra Hall, Lake Michigan, and the LaSalle Street business district. Because 75% of DePaul's students work to help finance their education, they find that the downtown location provides many employment opportunities. Facilities of the Colleges of Law and Commerce have undergone extensive remodeling, and further renovations are in progress, thus ensuring DePaul's continuing commitment to the growth and development of downtown Chicago. At the Lincoln Park campus, restoration of the community has paralleled the expansion of University facilities. The potpourri of stores, theaters, musical groups, and events reflects the broad spectrum of interests of the people who live and work in the area. A short walk or local bus ride enables students to browse through neighborhoods of craft shops and fine old Victorian homes or visit the area's conservatory, zoo, and two museums.

■ **DEVRY UNIVERSITY (ADDISON)**

1221 N Swift Rd.

Addison, IL 60101-6106

Tel: (630)953-1300; Free: 866-338-7941

Fax: (630)953-1236

Web Site: www.devry.edu/

Description: Proprietary, 4-year, coed. Part of DeVry University. Awards associate and bachelor's degrees. Founded 1982. Setting: 14-acre suburban campus with easy access to Chicago. Total enrollment: 1,508. Faculty: 154 (45 full-time, 109 part-time). Student-undergrad faculty ratio is 14:1. Full-time: 919 students, 25% women, 75% men. Part-time: 589 students, 30% women, 70% men. 3% from out-of-state. 50% 25 or older, 19% transferred in. Academic areas with the most degrees conferred: business/marketing; computer and information sciences; engineering technologies. Calendar: semesters. Academic remediation for entering students, advanced placement, accelerated degree program, distance learning, summer session for credit, part-time degree program, adult/continuing education programs.

Entrance Requirements: Options: electronic application, early admission, deferred admission, international baccalaureate accepted. Required: high school transcript, interview. Entrance: minimally difficult. Application deadline: Rolling. Notification: continuous. SAT Reasoning Test deadline: 10/31.

Collegiate Environment: Orientation program. Most popular organizations: Epsilon Delta Phi (EDP), International Student Organizations, Muslim Student Association, Institute for Electric and Electronic Engineers. Major annual events: Summer Fest, Casino Night, Santa Day. Campus security: 24-hour emergency response devices, lighted pathways/sidewalks. Learning Resource Center with an OPAC and a Web page.

■ **DEVRY UNIVERSITY (CHICAGO)**

3300 N Campbell Ave.

Chicago, IL 60618-5994

Tel: (773)929-8500; Free: 866-338-7941

Web Site: www.devry.edu/

Description: Proprietary, comprehensive, coed. Part of DeVry University. Awards associate, bachelor's, and master's degrees. Founded 1931. Setting: urban campus. Total enrollment: 1,776. Faculty: 130 (37 full-time, 93 part-time). Student-undergrad faculty ratio is 18:1. Full-time: 915 students, 40% women, 60% men. Part-time: 719 students, 41% women, 59% men. 9% from out-of-state. 0.2% American Indian or Alaska Native, non-Hispanic/Latino; 34% Hispanic/Latino; 31% African American, non-Hispanic/Latino; 6% Asian, non-Hispanic/Latino; 0.4% Native Hawaiian or other Pacific Islander, non-Hispanic/Latino; 2% international. 53% 25 or older, 13% transferred in. Academic areas with the most degrees conferred: business/marketing; computer and information sciences; engineering technologies. Calendar: semesters. Part-time degree program, adult/continuing education programs.

Entrance Requirements: Required: high school transcript, interview. Entrance: minimally difficult. Application deadline: Rolling. Notification: continuous.

Costs Per Year: Application fee: $40. Tuition: $16,076 full-time, $609 per credit hour part-time. Mandatory fees: $80 full-time.

Collegiate Environment: Orientation program. College housing not available.

■ **DEVRY UNIVERSITY (DOWNERS GROVE)**

3005 Highland Pky.

Downers Grove, IL 60515

Tel: (630)515-3000; Free: 866-338-7941

Web Site: www.devry.edu/

Description: Proprietary, comprehensive, coed. Awards bachelor's and master's degrees. Founded 1973. Calendar: semesters.

■ **DEVRY UNIVERSITY (ELGIN)**

Randall Point

2250 Point Blvd., Ste. 250

Elgin, IL 60123
Tel: (847)649-3980; Free: 866-338-7941
Web Site: www.devry.edu/
Description: Proprietary, comprehensive, coed. Awards bachelor's and master's degrees. Calendar: semesters.

■ **DEVRY UNIVERSITY (GURNEE)**
1075 Tri-State Pky., Ste. 800
Gurnee, IL 60031-9126
Tel: (847)855-2649; Free: 866-338-7941
Fax: (847)855-5932
Web Site: www.devry.edu/
Description: Proprietary, comprehensive, coed. Awards bachelor's and master's degrees. Calendar: semesters.

■ **DEVRY UNIVERSITY (NAPERVILLE)**
2056 Westings Ave., Ste. 40
Naperville, IL 60563-2361
Tel: (630)428-9086; Free: 866-338-7941
Fax: (630)428-4721
Web Site: www.devry.edu/
Description: Proprietary, comprehensive, coed. Awards associate, bachelor's, and master's degrees. Total enrollment: 8,828. Faculty: 2,248 (all part-time). Student-undergrad faculty ratio is 6:1. Full-time: 2,196 students, 48% women, 52% men. Part-time: 3,887 students, 47% women, 53% men. 89% from out-of-state. 78% 25 or older. Retention: 35% of full-time freshmen returned the following year. Calendar: semesters. Accelerated degree program, distance learning.
Entrance Requirements: Application deadline: Rolling. Notification: continuous.

■ **DEVRY UNIVERSITY (TINLEY PARK)**
18624 W Creek Dr.
Tinley Park, IL 60477
Tel: (708)342-3300; Free: 866-338-7941
Web Site: www.devry.edu/
Description: Proprietary, comprehensive, coed. Part of DeVry University. Awards associate, bachelor's, and master's degrees. Founded 2000. Setting: 12-acre suburban campus. Total enrollment: 1,471. Faculty: 79 (32 full-time, 47 part-time). Student-undergrad faculty ratio is 19:1. Full-time: 589 students, 33% women, 67% men. Part-time: 552 students, 35% women, 65% men. 9% from out-of-state. 54% 25 or older, 16% transferred in. Academic areas with the most degrees conferred: business/marketing; computer and information sciences; engineering technologies. Calendar: semesters. Academic remediation for entering students, services for LD students, advanced placement, accelerated degree program, distance learning, summer session for credit, part-time degree program, adult/continuing education programs.
Entrance Requirements: Options: electronic application, deferred admission, international baccalaureate accepted. Required: high school transcript, interview. Entrance: minimally difficult. Application deadline: Rolling. Notification: continuous. SAT Reasoning Test deadline: 10/31.
Collegiate Environment: Orientation program. Most popular organizations: Institute of Electrical and Electronic Engineers (IEEE), Student Leadership, Hash Bang Slash, OGRE. Major annual event: Anniversary Celebration. Campus security: 24-hour emergency response devices, late night transport-escort service, lighted pathways/sidewalks, security patrols. Learning Resource Center with an OPAC and a Web page.

■ **DEVRY UNIVERSITY ONLINE**
1221 N Swift Rd.
Addison, IL 60101-6106
Free: 866-338-7941
Web Site: www.devry.edu/
Description: Proprietary, comprehensive, coed. Awards associate, bachelor's, and master's degrees. Founded 2000. Total enrollment: 24,623. Faculty: 2,809 (28 full-time, 2,781 part-time). Student-undergrad faculty ratio is 12:1. Full-time: 3,938 students, 53% women, 47% men. Part-time: 15,166 students, 54% women, 46% men. 89% from out-of-state. 1% American Indian or Alaska Native, non-Hispanic/Latino; 8% Hispanic/Latino; 18% African American, non-Hispanic/Latino; 2% Asian, non-Hispanic/Latino; 0.4% Native Hawaiian or other Pacific Islander, non-Hispanic/Latino; 1% international. 81% 25 or older, 26% transferred in. Academic areas with the

most degrees conferred: business/marketing; computer and information sciences; engineering technologies. Calendar: semesters.
Entrance Requirements: Required: high school transcript, interview. Entrance: minimally difficult. Application deadline: Rolling. Notification: continuous.
Costs Per Year: Application fee: $40. Tuition: $16,076 full-time, $609 per credit hour part-time. Mandatory fees: $80 full-time.

■ **DOMINICAN UNIVERSITY**
7900 W Division St.
River Forest, IL 60305-1099
Tel: (708)366-2490; Free: 800-828-8475
Fax: (708)366-5360
E-mail: domadmis@dom.edu
Web Site: www.dom.edu/
Description: Independent Roman Catholic, comprehensive, coed. Awards bachelor's, master's, and doctoral degrees and post-master's certificates. Founded 1901. Setting: 30-acre suburban campus with easy access to Chicago. Endowment: $23.3 million. Research spending for the previous fiscal year: $156,000. Educational spending for the previous fiscal year: $8333 per student. Total enrollment: 3,589. Faculty: 404 (154 full-time, 250 part-time). Student-undergrad faculty ratio is 11:1. 3,056 applied, 57% were admitted. 21% from top 10% of their high school class, 49% from top quarter, 85% from top half. 2 valedictorians. Full-time: 1,794 students, 68% women, 32% men. Part-time: 201 students, 72% women, 28% men. Students come from 31 states and territories, 23 other countries, 8% from out-of-state. 0.2% American Indian or Alaska Native, non-Hispanic/Latino; 34% Hispanic/Latino; 8% African American, non-Hispanic/Latino; 4% Asian, non-Hispanic/Latino; 0.3% Native Hawaiian or other Pacific Islander, non-Hispanic/Latino; 2% international. 12% 25 or older, 29% live on campus, 5% transferred in. Retention: 80% of full-time freshmen returned the following year. Academic areas with the most degrees conferred: business/marketing; social sciences; psychology. Core. Calendar: semesters. ESL program, services for LD students, advanced placement, accelerated degree program, honors program, independent study, distance learning, double major, summer session for credit, part-time degree program, adult/continuing education programs, internships, graduate courses open to undergrads. Off campus study at Concordia University (IL), Elmhurst College (IL), Illinois Institute of Technology (IL). Study abroad program.
Entrance Requirements: Options: electronic application, deferred admission, international baccalaureate accepted. Required: high school transcript, SAT or ACT. Recommended: essay. Required for some: interview. Entrance: moderately difficult. Application deadline: Rolling. Notification: continuous. SAT Reasoning Test deadline: 8/15. SAT Subject Test deadline: 8/15. Transfer credits accepted: Yes.
Costs Per Year: Application fee: $25. One-time mandatory fee: $250. Comprehensive fee: $37,508 includes full-time tuition ($28,440), mandatory fees ($250), and college room and board ($8818). Full-time tuition and fees vary according to course load. Room and board charges vary according to board plan and housing facility. Part-time tuition: $948 per credit hour. Part-time tuition and fees vary according to course load.
Collegiate Environment: Orientation program. Drama-theater group, choral group, student-run newspaper. Social organizations: 34 open to all; 38% of eligible men and 38% of eligible women are members. Most popular organizations: Polish Club, Commuter Student Association, Nutrition Club, Organization of Latin American Students, Fashion Club. Major annual events: DUfest, Homecoming, Caritas Veritas. Student services: health clinic, personal-psychological counseling. Campus security: 24-hour emergency response devices and patrols, student patrols, late night transport-escort service, controlled dormitory access, door alarms. 604 college housing spaces available; 587 were occupied in 2012-13. Freshmen guaranteed college housing. Option: coed housing available. Rebecca Crown Library with 250,000 books, 50,000 microform titles, 35,000 serials, 5,000 audiovisual materials, an OPAC, and a Web page. Operations spending for the previous fiscal year: $1.8 million. 550 computers available on campus for general student use. Computer purchase/lease plans available. A campuswide network can be accessed from student residence rooms and from off campus. Students can access the following: online class registration. Staffed computer lab on campus provides training in use of computers, software, and the Internet.
Community Environment: The university is located in River Forest, a quiet, tree-lined residential suburb of Chicago; public transportation is easily accessible to downtown Chicago.

■ EAST-WEST UNIVERSITY

816 S Michigan Ave.
Chicago, IL 60605-2103
Tel: (312)939-0111
Fax: (312)939-0083
Web Site: www.eastwest.edu/

Description: Independent, 4-year, coed. Awards associate and bachelor's degrees. Founded 1978. Setting: 1-acre urban campus with easy access to Chicago. Endowment: $56.1 million. Educational spending for the previous fiscal year: $9379 per student. Total enrollment: 755. Faculty: 67 (18 full-time, 49 part-time). Student-undergrad faculty ratio is 15:1. 1,008 applied, 89% were admitted. 14% from top 10% of their high school class, 23% from top quarter, 70% from top half. Full-time: 737 students, 55% women, 45% men. Part-time: 18 students, 17% women, 83% men. Students come from 7 states and territories, 14 other countries, 7% from out-of-state. 1% American Indian or Alaska Native, non-Hispanic/Latino; 15% Hispanic/Latino; 65% African American, non-Hispanic/Latino; 12% Asian, non-Hispanic/Latino; 1% Native Hawaiian or other Pacific Islander, non-Hispanic/Latino. 31% 25 or older, 12% transferred in. Retention: 71% of full-time freshmen returned the following year. Academic areas with the most degrees conferred: business/marketing; social sciences; computer and information sciences. Core. Academic remediation for entering students, ESL program, advanced placement, honors program, double major, summer session for credit, part-time degree program, external degree program, co-op programs and internships.

Entrance Requirements: Options: electronic application, early decision. Required: essay, high school transcript, minimum 2 high school GPA, interview, ACT. Required for some: 1 recommendation. Entrance: minimally difficult. Application deadlines: Rolling, 7/1 for early decision.

Costs Per Year: Application fee: $40. Tuition: $17,550 full-time. Mandatory fees: $1470 full-time. College room only: $7641.

Collegiate Environment: Orientation program. Drama-theater group, choral group, student-run newspaper. Social organizations: 9 open to all. Most popular organizations: student government, performing arts, Black Student Union, Latino Student Association, Multicultural Student Association. Major annual events: Holiday Revue, Black History Month Events, International Day. Student services: personal-psychological counseling. East-West University Library with 32,820 books, 1,300 microform titles, 3,474 serials, 6 audiovisual materials, and an OPAC. Operations spending for the previous fiscal year: $278,850. 144 computers available on campus for general student use. A campuswide network can be accessed from off-campus. Students can access the following: online class registration. Staffed computer lab on campus provides training in use of computers, software, and the Internet.

Community Environment: Located in Chicago's South Loop (Burnham Park) District, East-West overlooks scenic Grant Park and is within walking distance of the Field Museum, Shedd Aquarium, Adler Planetarium, Art Institute and Buckingham Fountain. Also within walking distance of the University is the"Loop" (Chicago's main business and banking district) and the historic Printer's Row area. The accessibility of such cultural landmarks adds to the overall education of the students.

■ EASTERN ILLINOIS UNIVERSITY

600 Lincoln Ave.
Charleston, IL 61920-3099
Tel: (217)581-5000; Free: 800-252-5711
Fax: (217)581-7060
E-mail: admissions@eiu.edu
Web Site: www.eiu.edu/

Description: State-supported, comprehensive, coed. Awards bachelor's and master's degrees and post-master's certificates. Founded 1895. Setting: 320-acre small town campus. Endowment: $51.6 million. Research spending for the previous fiscal year: $1.2 million. Educational spending for the previous fiscal year: $10,180 per student. Total enrollment: 10,417. Faculty: 720 (586 full-time, 134 part-time). Student-undergrad faculty ratio is 15:1. 6,710 applied, 65% were admitted. 11% from top 10% of their high school class, 31% from top quarter, 66% from top half. Full-time: 7,906 students, 59% women, 41% men. Part-time: 1,069 students, 64% women, 36% men. Students come from 35 states and territories, 30 other countries, 2% from out-of-state. 0.2% American Indian or Alaska Native, non-Hispanic/Latino; 4% Hispanic/Latino; 17% African American, non-Hispanic/Latino; 1% Asian, non-Hispanic/Latino; 0.1% Native Hawaiian or other Pacific Islander, non-Hispanic/Latino; 1% international. 14% 25 or older, 36% live on campus, 11% transferred in. Retention: 79% of full-time freshmen returned the following year. Academic areas with the most degrees conferred: education;

business/marketing; liberal arts/general studies. Core. Calendar: semesters. Academic remediation for entering students, services for LD students, advanced placement, accelerated degree program, freshman honors college, honors program, independent study, distance learning, double major, summer session for credit, part-time degree program, adult/continuing education programs, co-op programs and internships, graduate courses open to undergrads. Off campus study at Olney Central College, Kaskaskia College, Parkland College, Danville Area Community College, Richland Community College, Lake Land College, Frontier Community College, Lincoln Trail College, Triton College, Lincoln Land Community College, Rend Lake College, University Center of Lake County. Study abroad program. ROTC: Army.

Entrance Requirements: Options: electronic application, deferred admission, international baccalaureate accepted. Required: high school transcript, minimum 2.25 high school GPA, standardized test scores, audition for music program, SAT or ACT. Required for some: essay, 2 recommendations, standardized test scores, audition for music program. Entrance: moderately difficult. Application deadlines: Rolling, Rolling for nonresidents. Notification: continuous, continuous for nonresidents. SAT Reasoning Test deadline: 8/15. SAT Subject Test deadline: 8/15. Transfer credits accepted: Yes.

Costs Per Year: Application fee: $30. State resident tuition: $8370 full-time, $279 per credit hour part-time. Nonresident tuition: $25,110 full-time, $837 per credit hour part-time. Mandatory fees: $2560 full-time, $92 per credit hour part-time. Full-time tuition and fees vary according to course load and student level. Part-time tuition and fees vary according to course load and student level. College room and board: $9174. Room and board charges vary according to board plan and housing facility. Tuition guaranteed not to increase for student's term of enrollment.

Collegiate Environment: Orientation program. Drama-theater group, choral group, marching band, student-run newspaper, radio station. Social organizations: 260 open to all; national fraternities, national sororities; 20% of eligible men and 17% of eligible women are members. Most popular organizations: Illinois Student Education Association, Math Energy at Eastern Illinois University, Black Student Union, Alpha Gamma, Alpha Phi. Major annual events: Family Weekend, Homecoming, Celebration of the Arts. Student services: legal services, health clinic, personal-psychological counseling, women's center. Campus security: 24-hour emergency response devices and patrols, student patrols, late night transport-escort service, AlertEIU and warning sirens. 5,410 college housing spaces available; 3,357 were occupied in 2012-13. Freshmen guaranteed college housing. On-campus residence required in freshman year. Options: coed, men-only, women-only housing available. Booth Library with 1.1 million books, 94,203 microform titles, 46,047 serials, 42,550 audiovisual materials, an OPAC, and a Web page. Operations spending for the previous fiscal year: $5.2 million. 582 computers available on campus for general student use. Computer purchase/lease plans available. A campuswide network can be accessed from student residence rooms and from off campus. Students can access the following: online class registration. Staffed computer lab on campus provides training in use of computers, software, and the Internet.

Community Environment: Located in east central Illinois, 50 miles south of the University of Illinois at Urbana-Champaign, Charleston (population 20,000) is second only to Springfield in Lincoln Lore. Airline service is available at the county airport. Within the community are churches of all denominations, medical facilities, library, and motels. Part-time employment is available. Fox Ridge and Lincoln Log Cabin State Parks nearby are of historical, scenic, and recreational interest.

■ ELGIN COMMUNITY COLLEGE

1700 Spartan Dr.
Elgin, IL 60123-7193
Tel: (847)697-1000
E-mail: admissions@elgin.edu
Web Site: www.elgin.edu/

Description: State and locally supported, 2-year, coed. Part of Illinois Community College Board. Awards certificates, diplomas, transfer associate, and terminal associate degrees. Founded 1949. Setting: 145-acre suburban campus with easy access to Chicago. Total enrollment: 11,554. Faculty: 598 (130 full-time, 468 part-time). Student-undergrad faculty ratio is 23:1. 7% from top 10% of their high school class, 22% from top quarter, 51% from top half. Full-time: 3,910 students, 51% women, 49% men. Part-time: 7,644 students, 57% women, 43% men. Students come from 4 states and territories, 15 other countries, 0.2% from out-of-state. 0.3% American Indian or Alaska Native, non-Hispanic/Latino; 36% Hispanic/Latino; 5% African American, non-Hispanic/Latino; 7% Asian, non-Hispanic/Latino; 0.1% Native

Hawaiian or other Pacific Islander, non-Hispanic/Latino; 1% international. 42% 25 or older, 4% transferred in. Core. Calendar: semesters. Academic remediation for entering students, ESL program, services for LD students, advanced placement, accelerated degree program, honors program, independent study, distance learning, double major, summer session for credit, part-time degree program, co-op programs and internships. Off campus study at McHenry County College, Waubonsee Community College, College of DuPage, William Rainey Harper College, Rock Valley College, Illinois Valley Community College, College of Lake County. Study abroad program.

Entrance Requirements: Open admission except for nursing, selected health programs. Option: electronic application. Required for some: high school transcript, some academic programs have additional departmental admission requirements that students must meet. Entrance: noncompetitive. Application deadline: Rolling. Notification: continuous. Transfer credits accepted: Yes.

Collegiate Environment: Orientation program. Drama-theater group, choral group, student-run newspaper. Social organizations: 33 open to all. Most popular organizations: Phi Theta Kappa Honor Society, Organization of Latin American Students, Asian Filipino Club, Amnesty International, student government. Major annual events: Relay for Life, PB Jam (Service Event), ChiliRama (Club involvement expo). Student services: legal services, personal-psychological counseling. Campus security: grounds are patrolled Sunday-Saturday 7am-11pm during the academic year. College housing not available. Renner Learning Resource Center with an OPAC and a Web page. 1,145 computers available on campus for general student use. A campuswide network can be accessed from off-campus. Students can access the following: online class registration. Staffed computer lab on campus provides training in use of computers, software, and the Internet.

Community Environment: See Judson College.

■ ELMHURST COLLEGE

190 Prospect Ave.
Elmhurst, IL 60126-3296
Tel: (630)617-3500; Free: 800-697-1871
Fax: (630)617-5501
E-mail: admit@elmhurst.edu
Web Site: www.elmhurst.edu/

Description: Independent, comprehensive, coed, affiliated with United Church of Christ. Awards bachelor's and master's degrees. Founded 1871. Setting: 38-acre suburban campus with easy access to Chicago. Endowment: $85.2 million. Total enrollment: 3,298. Faculty: 392 (151 full-time, 241 part-time). Student-undergrad faculty ratio is 13:1. 3,056 applied, 68% were admitted. 19% from top 10% of their high school class, 47% from top quarter, 82% from top half. Full-time: 2,864 students, 62% women, 38% men. Part-time: 188 students, 56% women, 44% men. Students come from 19 states and territories, 38 other countries, 9% from out-of-state. 0.4% American Indian or Alaska Native, non-Hispanic/Latino; 11% Hispanic/Latino; 5% African American, non-Hispanic/Latino; 4% Asian, non-Hispanic/Latino; 0.3% Native Hawaiian or other Pacific Islander, non-Hispanic/Latino; 1% international. 10% 25 or older, 40% live on campus, 10% transferred in. Retention: 78% of full-time freshmen returned the following year. Academic areas with the most degrees conferred: business/marketing; health professions and related sciences; education. Core. Calendar: 4-1-4. Academic remediation for entering students, services for LD students, advanced placement, accelerated degree program, honors program, independent study, double major, summer session for credit, part-time degree program, adult/continuing education programs, co-op programs and internships. Off campus study. Study abroad program. ROTC: Army (c), Air Force (c).

Entrance Requirements: Options: electronic application, deferred admission, international baccalaureate accepted. Required: high school transcript, SAT or ACT. Recommended: essay, interview. Required for some: essay, interview. Entrance: moderately difficult. Application deadline: Rolling. Notification: continuous. Transfer credits accepted: Yes.

Costs Per Year: Application fee: $0. Comprehensive fee: $42,057 includes full-time tuition ($32,720), mandatory fees ($225), and college room and board ($9112). College room only: $5520. Room and board charges vary according to board plan and housing facility. Part-time tuition: $993 per semester hour. Part-time tuition varies according to course load.

Collegiate Environment: Orientation program. Drama-theater group, choral group, student-run newspaper, radio station. Social organizations: 100 open to all; national fraternities, national sororities, local sororities; 7% of eligible men and 11% of eligible women are members. Most popular organizations: Programming Board and Student Government, theater and music groups,

Black Student Union, residence life groups, Hablamos. Major annual events: Homecoming, Orientation/Welcome Week, Spring Fling. Student services: health clinic, personal-psychological counseling. Campus security: 24-hour emergency response devices and patrols, late night transport-escort service, controlled dormitory access. 1,166 college housing spaces available; all were occupied in 2012-13. Freshmen given priority for college housing. Option: coed housing available. Buehler Library with 230,055 books, 49,874 microform titles, 1,859 serials, 8,327 audiovisual materials, an OPAC, and a Web page. 800 computers available on campus for general student use. A campuswide network can be accessed from student residence rooms and from off campus. Students can access the following: online class registration. Staffed computer lab on campus.

Community Environment: A beautiful residential suburb of Chicago, 16 miles west of the Loop, Elmhurst has a population of approximately 45,000. Residents enjoy the advantages of life in a small city and the resources of a large city with its social and cultural facilities.

■ EUREKA COLLEGE

300 E College Ave.
Eureka, IL 61530
Tel: (309)467-3721; Free: 888-4-EUREKA
Fax: (309)467-6576
E-mail: admissions@eureka.edu
Web Site: www.eureka.edu/

Description: Independent, 4-year, coed, affiliated with Christian Church (Disciples of Christ). Awards bachelor's degrees. Founded 1855. Setting: 112-acre small town campus. Total enrollment: 672. 772 applied. 16% 25 or older. Calendar: 4 8-week terms. Advanced placement, self-designed majors, honors program, independent study, double major, summer session for credit, part-time degree program, co-op programs and internships. Study abroad program.

Entrance Requirements: Options: electronic application, deferred admission. Required: high school transcript, minimum 2.3 high school GPA, 1 recommendation, SAT or ACT. Recommended: essay, interview. Required for some: essay, 3 recommendations. Entrance: moderately difficult. Application deadline: 8/1. Notification: continuous.

Collegiate Environment: Orientation program. Campus security: 24-hour emergency response devices, late night patrols. Melick Library with 75,000 books, 6,127 microform titles, 330 serials, 500 audiovisual materials, and an OPAC.

Community Environment: A small community in central Illinois, between Bloomington and Peoria, Eureka, population 5,000, is 140 miles southwest of Chicago. The community provides a public library, churches, and a hospital. A lake more than a mile long offers boating and fishing. Part-time employment is available.

■ FOX COLLEGE

6640 S Cicero
Bedford Park, IL 60638
Tel: (708)636-7700
Fax: (708)636-8078
Web Site: www.foxcollege.edu/

Description: Private, 2-year, coed. Awards diplomas and terminal associate degrees. Founded 1932. Setting: suburban campus. Total enrollment: 447. 1,071 applied, 62% were admitted. Accelerated degree program, internships.

Collegiate Environment: College housing not available.

■ GEM CITY COLLEGE

PO Box 179
Quincy, IL 62301
Tel: (217)222-0391
Fax: (217)222-1557
Web Site: www.gemcitycollege.com/

Description: Proprietary, 2-year, coed. Awards diplomas and terminal associate degrees. Founded 1870. Setting: small town campus. Total enrollment: 67. 54% 25 or older. Academic remediation for entering students, summer session for credit, part-time degree program, adult/continuing education programs, internships.

Entrance Requirements: Open admission. Options: early admission, deferred admission. Entrance: noncompetitive. Application deadline: Rolling.

Collegiate Environment: Student services: personal-psychological counseling. 2,700 books and 40 serials.

■ **GOVERNORS STATE UNIVERSITY**
One University Pky.
University Park, IL 60484
Tel: (708)534-5000; Free: 800-GSU-8GSU
Fax: (708)534-1640
E-mail: ydaniels@govst.edu
Web Site: www.govst.edu/
Description: State-supported, upper-level, coed. Awards bachelor's, master's, and doctoral degrees and post-master's certificates. Founded 1969. Setting: 750-acre suburban campus with easy access to Chicago. Total enrollment: 5,609. Faculty: 413 (208 full-time, 205 part-time). Student-undergrad faculty ratio is 11:1. Full-time: 1,269 students, 66% women, 34% men. Part-time: 1,909 students, 70% women, 30% men. 3% from out-of-state. 0.4% American Indian or Alaska Native, non-Hispanic/Latino; 9% Hispanic/Latino; 37% African American, non-Hispanic/Latino; 1% Asian, non-Hispanic/Latino; 0.1% Native Hawaiian or other Pacific Islander, non-Hispanic/Latino; 0.5% international. 68% 25 or older, 29% transferred in. Academic areas with the most degrees conferred: liberal arts/general studies; health professions and related sciences; business/marketing. Core. Calendar: trimesters. Services for LD students, advanced placement, self-designed majors, honors program, independent study, distance learning, double major, summer session for credit, part-time degree program, adult/continuing education programs, internships, graduate courses open to undergrads. Off campus study at Chicago State University, Northeastern Illinois University, Western Illinois University, Eastern Illinois University.
Entrance Requirements: Transfer credits accepted: Yes.
Costs Per Year: State resident tuition: $7470 full-time, $249 per credit hour part-time. Nonresident tuition: $14,940 full-time, $498 per credit hour part-time. Mandatory fees: $1646 full-time, $46 per credit hour part-time, $133 per term part-time. Full-time tuition and fees vary according to course load, reciprocity agreements, and student level. Part-time tuition and fees vary according to course load, reciprocity agreements, and student level. Tuition guaranteed not to increase for student's term of enrollment.
Collegiate Environment: Orientation program. Choral group, student-run newspaper. Student services: personal-psychological counseling. Campus security: 24-hour emergency response devices and patrols, late night transport-escort service. College housing not available. University Library with 465,000 books, 1 million microform titles, 51,000 serials, 4,500 audiovisual materials, an OPAC, and a Web page.
Community Environment: Located in University Park, Illinois, on 750 acres, the University is in a suburban/rural setting. However, it is about 35 miles from downtown Chicago and thirty miles from Kankakee or Joliet, Illinois, in the Southern metropolitan area of Chicago. The campus is accessible via public transportation, from the city and most of the southern suburbs. Governors State University is a commuter institution. There is no student housing available.

■ **GREENVILLE COLLEGE**
315 E College Ave.
Greenville, IL 62246-0159
Tel: (618)664-2800; Free: 800-345-4440
Fax: (618)664-9841
E-mail: admissions@greenville.edu
Web Site: www.greenville.edu/
Description: Independent Free Methodist, comprehensive, coed. Awards bachelor's and master's degrees. Founded 1892. Setting: 12-acre small town campus with easy access to St. Louis. Endowment: $13.8 million. Total enrollment: 1,463. Faculty: 185 (63 full-time, 122 part-time). Student-undergrad faculty ratio is 14:1. 1,101 applied, 74% were admitted. 14% from top 10% of their high school class, 38% from top quarter, 69% from top half. 23 valedictorians. Full-time: 1,155 students, 49% women, 51% men. Part-time: 69 students, 51% women, 49% men. Students come from 40 states and territories, 8 other countries, 32% from out-of-state. 1% American Indian or Alaska Native, non-Hispanic/Latino; 4% Hispanic/Latino; 8% African American, non-Hispanic/Latino; 1% Asian, non-Hispanic/Latino; 0% Native Hawaiian or other Pacific Islander, non-Hispanic/Latino; 2% international. 13% 25 or older, 76% live on campus, 10% transferred in. Retention: 62% of full-time freshmen returned the following year. Academic areas with the most degrees conferred: business/marketing; education; visual and performing arts. Core. Calendar: 4-1-4. Academic remediation for entering students, advanced placement, accelerated degree program, self-designed majors, honors program, independent study, distance learning, double major, summer session for credit, part-time degree program, external degree program, adult/continuing education programs, co-op programs and internships. Off

campus study at 13 members of the Christian College Consortium; 100 members of the Council for Christian Colleges and Universities. Study abroad program.
Entrance Requirements: Options: electronic application, early admission, deferred admission, international baccalaureate accepted. Required: essay, high school transcript, minimum 2.25 high school GPA, agreement to code of conduct, SAT or ACT. Required for some: interview. Entrance: moderately difficult. Application deadline: Rolling. Notification: continuous.
Costs Per Year: Application fee: $0. Comprehensive fee: $30,496 includes full-time tuition ($22,750), mandatory fees ($170), and college room and board ($7576). College room only: $3664. Full-time tuition and fees vary according to degree level. Room and board charges vary according to housing facility. Part-time tuition: $482 per credit hour. Part-time tuition varies according to course load and degree level.
Collegiate Environment: Orientation program. Drama-theater group, choral group, marching band, student-run newspaper, radio station. Social organizations: 25 open to all. Most popular organizations: Campus Activity Board, Greenville Student Outreach, Greenville College Student Association, Circle K, Music and Entertainment Industry Student Association. Major annual events: Back to School Bash, Agape Music Festival, All-College Hike. Student services: personal-psychological counseling. Campus security: 24-hour emergency response devices and patrols, late night transport-escort service, controlled dormitory access. 792 college housing spaces available; 770 were occupied in 2012-13. Freshmen guaranteed college housing. On-campus residence required through senior year. Options: men-only, women-only housing available. Ruby E. Dare Library with 143,697 books, 17,868 microform titles, 10,758 serials, 4,376 audiovisual materials, an OPAC, and a Web page. Operations spending for the previous fiscal year: $443,167. 65 computers available on campus for general student use. A campuswide network can be accessed from student residence rooms and from off campus. Students can access the following: online class registration. Staffed computer lab on campus provides training in use of computers, software, and the Internet.

■ **HARPER COLLEGE**
1200 W Algonquin Rd.
Palatine, IL 60067-7398
Tel: (847)925-6000
Fax: (847)925-6044
E-mail: admissions@harpercollege.edu
Web Site: goforward.harpercollege.edu/
Description: State and locally supported, 2-year, coed. Part of Illinois Community College Board. Awards certificates, transfer associate, and terminal associate degrees. Founded 1965. Setting: 200-acre suburban campus with easy access to Chicago. Endowment: $4 million. Research spending for the previous fiscal year: $508,686. Educational spending for the previous fiscal year: $1959 per student. Total enrollment: 14,673. Faculty: 827 (205 full-time, 622 part-time). Student-undergrad faculty ratio is 19:1. 3,274 applied, 100% were admitted. Full-time: 5,550 students, 48% women, 52% men. Part-time: 9,123 students, 60% women, 40% men. Students come from 9 states and territories, 1% from out-of-state. 0.2% American Indian or Alaska Native, non-Hispanic/Latino; 18% Hispanic/Latino; 4% African American, non-Hispanic/Latino; 9% Asian, non-Hispanic/Latino; 0.02% international. 38% 25 or older, 4% transferred in. Retention: 67% of full-time freshmen returned the following year. Core. Calendar: semesters. Academic remediation for entering students, ESL program, services for LD students, advanced placement, accelerated degree program, honors program, independent study, distance learning, summer session for credit, part-time degree program, adult/continuing education programs, co-op programs and internships. Study abroad program.
Entrance Requirements: Open admission. Options: electronic application, early admission, deferred admission. Required: high school transcript. Entrance: noncompetitive. Application deadline: Rolling. Notification: continuous. Preference given to for district residents for nursing, dental hygiene and cardiac technology programs.
Costs Per Year: Application fee: $25. Area resident tuition: $3255 full-time, $108.50 per credit hour part-time. State resident tuition: $10,965 full-time, $365.50 per credit hour part-time. Nonresident tuition: $13,230 full-time, $441 per credit hour part-time. Full-time tuition varies according to course load and program. Part-time tuition varies according to course load and program. Tuition guaranteed not to increase for student's term of enrollment.
Collegiate Environment: Orientation program. Drama-theater group, choral group, student-run newspaper, radio station. Social organizations: 48 open to all. Most popular organizations: Student Radio Station, Program Board,

Student Senate, Nursing Club, Phi Theta Kappa. Major annual events: Transfer Information Week, Wellness Week, Career Expo. Student services: legal services, health clinic, personal-psychological counseling, women's center. Campus security: 24-hour emergency response devices and patrols, late night transport-escort service. College housing not available. Harper College Library with 128,068 books, 10,528 microform titles, 242 serials, 17,540 audiovisual materials, an OPAC, and a Web page. Operations spending for the previous fiscal year: $2 million. 250 computers available on campus for general student use. A campuswide network can be accessed from off-campus. Students can access the following: online class registration, payments, applications, course management system (Blackboard). Staffed computer lab on campus.

Community Environment: Palatine, population 67,200, is a suburban community located 30 miles northwest of Chicago. It enjoys a temperate Midwestern climate. Rail and bus services are available. Community facilities include churches of major denominations, a public library, and hospitals nearby. Many active organizations provide social, recreational, and cultural programs and functions.

■ HARRINGTON COLLEGE OF DESIGN
200 W Madison St.
Chicago, IL 60605-1496
Tel: (312)939-4975; Free: 877-939-4975
Fax: (312)939-8005
E-mail: jmcewen@harrington.edu
Web Site: www.harrington.edu/

Description: Proprietary, comprehensive, coed. Part of Career Education Corporation. Awards associate, bachelor's, and master's degrees. Founded 1931. Setting: urban campus with easy access to Chicago. Educational spending for the previous fiscal year: $4363 per student. Total enrollment: 773. Faculty: 77 (17 full-time, 60 part-time). Student-undergrad faculty ratio is 14:1. 73 applied, 89% were admitted. Full-time: 247 students, 77% women, 23% men. Part-time: 398 students, 76% women, 24% men. Students come from 17 states and territories, 11 other countries, 11% from out-of-state. 0.2% American Indian or Alaska Native, non-Hispanic/Latino; 16% Hispanic/Latino; 13% African American, non-Hispanic/Latino; 3% Asian, non-Hispanic/Latino; 1% Native Hawaiian or other Pacific Islander, non-Hispanic/Latino; 2% international. 49% 25 or older, 10% transferred in. Retention: 69% of full-time freshmen returned the following year. Academic area with the most degrees conferred: visual and performing arts. Core. Calendar: semesters. Academic remediation for entering students, summer session for credit, part-time degree program, internships. Study abroad program.

Entrance Requirements: Options: electronic application, international baccalaureate accepted. Required: high school transcript, interview. Recommended: essay, 1 recommendation, SAT or ACT. Entrance: noncompetitive. Application deadlines: Rolling, Rolling for nonresidents. Notification: continuous, continuous for nonresidents. Transfer credits accepted: Yes.

Costs Per Year: Application fee: $50. Tuition: $18,250 full-time, $4750 per term part-time. Mandatory fees: $1050 full-time, $410 per term part-time. Full-time tuition and fees vary according to course load, degree level, and program. Part-time tuition and fees vary according to course load, degree level, and program.

Collegiate Environment: Orientation program. Student-run newspaper. Social organizations: 5 open to all. Most popular organizations: American Society of Interior Designers, International Interior Design Association, American Industry of Graphic Artists, student government, Digital Photography Focus Group. Major annual events: Imagine Charity Art Auction, Senior and Faculty Show, Fall All Student Welcome. Student services: personal-psychological counseling. Campus security: 24-hour emergency response devices and patrols. Harrington College of Design Library with 27,000 books, 95 serials, 500 audiovisual materials, an OPAC, and a Web page. Operations spending for the previous fiscal year: $199,691. 249 computers available on campus for general student use. A campuswide network can be accessed. Students can access the following: online class registration, wireless access for student use and network file storage for students. Staffed computer lab on campus provides training in use of computers, software, and the Internet.

■ HEARTLAND COMMUNITY COLLEGE
1500 W Raab Rd.
Normal, IL 61761
Tel: (309)268-8000
Fax: (309)268-7999

E-mail: candace.brownlee@heartland.edu
Web Site: www.heartland.edu/

Description: State and locally supported, 2-year, coed. Part of Illinois Community College Board. Awards certificates, transfer associate, and terminal associate degrees. Founded 1990. Setting: urban campus. Educational spending for the previous fiscal year: $4920 per student. Total enrollment: 4,667. Faculty: 253 (70 full-time, 183 part-time). Student-undergrad faculty ratio is 19:1. Students come from 5 states and territories, 2 other countries, 1% from out-of-state. 38% 25 or older. Retention: 55% of full-time freshmen returned the following year. Core. Calendar: semesters. Academic remediation for entering students, ESL program, services for LD students, advanced placement, honors program, independent study, distance learning, double major, summer session for credit, part-time degree program, adult/continuing education programs, co-op programs and internships. Study abroad program. ROTC: Army (c).

Entrance Requirements: Open admission except for nursing program, network administration program. Option: electronic application. Recommended: high school transcript. Entrance: noncompetitive. Application deadline: Rolling. Notification: continuous.

Collegiate Environment: Orientation program. Drama-theater group, choral group, student-run newspaper. Social organizations: 21 open to all. Most popular organizations: Environmental Club, Early Childhood Club, student government, Nursing Club, Phi Theta Kappa. Major annual events: Fall Fest, Spring Fest, Diversity Day. Student services: personal-psychological counseling. Campus security: 24-hour emergency response devices and patrols. Heartland Community College Library with 5,000 books, 188 serials, 4,000 audiovisual materials, an OPAC, and a Web page. Operations spending for the previous fiscal year: $401,420. 400 computers available on campus for general student use. A campuswide network can be accessed. Staffed computer lab on campus.

■ HEBREW THEOLOGICAL COLLEGE
7135 N Carpenter Rd.
Skokie, IL 60077-3263
Tel: (847)982-2500
Web Site: www.htc.edu/

Description: Independent Jewish, 4-year. Awards bachelor's degrees. Founded 1922. Setting: 13-acre suburban campus with easy access to Chicago. Total enrollment: 422. 331 applied. 2% 25 or older. Core. Calendar: semesters. Academic remediation for entering students, advanced placement, accelerated degree program, independent study, double major, summer session for credit, part-time degree program, internships. Study abroad program.

Entrance Requirements: Required: essay, high school transcript, 2 recommendations, interview, SAT or ACT. Entrance: moderately difficult. Application deadline: 8/15.

Collegiate Environment: Orientation program. Campus security: controlled dormitory access. Saul Silber Memorial Library plus 2 others with 63,000 books and 60 serials.

Community Environment: A suburb of Chicago and adjacent to Evanston, Skokie has all the usual community facilities as well as good shopping areas.

■ HIGHLAND COMMUNITY COLLEGE
2998 W Pearl City Rd.
Freeport, IL 61032-9341
Tel: (815)235-6121
Fax: (815)235-6130
E-mail: jeremy.bradt@highland.edu
Web Site: www.highland.edu/

Description: State and locally supported, 2-year, coed. Part of Illinois Community College Board. Awards certificates, transfer associate, and terminal associate degrees. Founded 1962. Setting: 240-acre rural campus. Total enrollment: 2,064. Faculty: 140 (45 full-time, 95 part-time). Student-undergrad faculty ratio is 18:1. 710 applied, 100% were admitted. 5% from top 10% of their high school class, 17% from top quarter, 46% from top half. Full-time: 1,062 students, 59% women, 41% men. Part-time: 1,002 students, 66% women, 34% men. 3% from out-of-state. 2% American Indian or Alaska Native, non-Hispanic/Latino; 2% Hispanic/Latino; 10% African American, non-Hispanic/Latino; 1% Asian, non-Hispanic/Latino; 0.1% Native Hawaiian or other Pacific Islander, non-Hispanic/Latino. 39% 25 or older, 4% transferred in. Core. Calendar: semesters. Academic remediation for entering students, ESL program, services for LD students, advanced placement, self-designed majors, honors program, independent study, distance learning, summer session for credit, part-time degree program, external degree program, adult/continuing education programs, co-op programs and internships.

Entrance Requirements: Open admission except for nursing program; based on points accumulated by taking prerequisite courses, class rank, and test scores considered. Special criteria for Wind Turbine program; based on prerequisites, GPA, and letters of recommendation. Options: electronic application, early admission, deferred admission, international baccalaureate accepted. Recommended: high school transcript. Required for some: high school transcript, 1 recommendation. Entrance: noncompetitive. Application deadline: Rolling. Preference given to district residents for medical programs (if they qualify); nursing, paramedic, CPN, medical assistant programs all have deadlines for application. Transfer credits accepted: Yes.

Costs Per Year: Application fee: $0. Area resident tuition: $3150 full-time, $105 per credit hour part-time. State resident tuition: $4530 full-time, $151 per credit hour part-time. Nonresident tuition: $5250 full-time, $175 per credit hour part-time. Mandatory fees: $270 full-time, $9 per credit hour part-time. Full-time tuition and fees vary according to program and reciprocity agreements. Part-time tuition and fees vary according to program and reciprocity agreements.

Collegiate Environment: Orientation program. Drama-theater group, choral group, student-run newspaper, radio station. Social organizations: 21 open to all. Most popular organizations: Phi Theta Kappa, Royal Scots, Prairie Wind, intramurals, Collegiate Choir. Major annual events: Spring Fling, Welcome Back to Campus Day. Student services: personal-psychological counseling. Campus security: 24-hour emergency response devices and patrols. College housing not available. Clarence Mitchell Library with 71 serials, 6,843 audiovisual materials, an OPAC, and a Web page. Operations spending for the previous fiscal year: $334,709. 426 computers available on campus for general student use. Computer purchase/lease plans available. A campuswide network can be accessed from off-campus. Students can access the following: online class registration. Staffed computer lab on campus provides training in use of computers, software, and the Internet.

■ **ILLINOIS CENTRAL COLLEGE**
One College Dr.
East Peoria, IL 61635-0001
Tel: (309)694-5011
Fax: (309)694-5450
E-mail: Angela.Dreessen@icc.edu
Web Site: www.icc.edu/

Description: State and locally supported, 2-year, coed. Part of Illinois Community College Board. Awards certificates, transfer associate, and terminal associate degrees. Founded 1967. Setting: 430-acre suburban campus. Total enrollment: 11,125. Faculty: 633 (183 full-time, 450 part-time). Student-undergrad faculty ratio is 18:1. 4,829 applied, 41% were admitted. Full-time: 4,123 students, 50% women, 50% men. Part-time: 7,002 students, 61% women, 39% men. Students come from 31 states and territories, 4 other countries, 1% from out-of-state. 0.3% American Indian or Alaska Native, non-Hispanic/Latino; 4% Hispanic/Latino; 12% African American, non-Hispanic/Latino; 2% Asian, non-Hispanic/Latino; 0.1% Native Hawaiian or other Pacific Islander, non-Hispanic/Latino; 0% international. 38% 25 or older, 2% transferred in. Retention: 59% of full-time freshmen returned the following year. Core. Calendar: semesters. Academic remediation for entering students, ESL program, services for LD students, advanced placement, honors program, independent study, summer session for credit, part-time degree program, adult/continuing education programs, internships.

Entrance Requirements: Open admission except for college transfer associate degree, health applied science programs. Options: electronic application, early admission. Required: high school transcript. Entrance: noncompetitive. Application deadlines: Rolling, Rolling for nonresidents. Notification: continuous, continuous for nonresidents. Transfer credits accepted: Yes.

Costs Per Year: Application fee: $0. Area resident tuition: $2760 full-time, $115 per credit hour part-time. State resident tuition: $6120 full-time, $255 per credit hour part-time. Nonresident tuition: $6120 full-time, $255 per credit hour part-time. Full-time tuition varies according to course load. Part-time tuition varies according to course load.

Collegiate Environment: Orientation program. Drama-theater group, choral group, student-run newspaper, radio station. Student services: health clinic, personal-psychological counseling. Campus security: 24-hour emergency response devices and patrols, late night transport-escort service. Illinois Central College Library plus 2 others with 92,550 books, 5,341 audiovisual materials, an OPAC, and a Web page.

Community Environment: Illinois Central College is located in rural Tazewell County on the outskirts of East Peoria, IL. Primarily a commuter college, adequate bus transportation is available from the city of Peoria. The large rolling campus of 434 acres provides an open feeling for attending students. With the surrounding wooded areas, the beautiful campus provides easy access to classrooms, laboratories, bookstore, cafeteria, and other student services. Illinois Central faculty and staff are committed to student learning and take pride in the large number of successful graduates. Over the 25-year history of the college, approximately 225,000 different individuals have taken classes, and more than 20,000 have received degrees and certificates. Illinois Central College offers a diverse curriculum including college transfer, career education, developmental assistance and continuing community education.

■ **ILLINOIS COLLEGE**
1101 W College Ave.
Jacksonville, IL 62650-2299
Tel: (217)245-3000; Free: 866-464-5265
Fax: (217)245-3034
E-mail: admissions@ic.edu
Web Site: www.ic.edu/

Description: Independent interdenominational, comprehensive, coed. Awards bachelor's and master's degrees. Founded 1829. Setting: 62-acre small town campus with easy access to St. Louis. Total enrollment: 987. Faculty: 104 (80 full-time, 24 part-time). Student-undergrad faculty ratio is 11:1. 2,357 applied, 58% were admitted. 30% from top 10% of their high school class, 57% from top quarter, 89% from top half. Full-time: 961 students, 49% women, 51% men. Part-time: 9 students, 44% women, 56% men. 13% from out-of-state. 0% American Indian or Alaska Native, non-Hispanic/Latino; 5% Hispanic/Latino; 8% African American, non-Hispanic/Latino; 0.4% Asian, non-Hispanic/Latino; 0.1% Native Hawaiian or other Pacific Islander, non-Hispanic/Latino; 3% international. 1% 25 or older, 84% live on campus, 5% transferred in. Retention: 72% of full-time freshmen returned the following year. Academic areas with the most degrees conferred: biological/life sciences; interdisciplinary studies; education. Calendar: semesters.

Entrance Requirements: Options: electronic application, early admission, early action, deferred admission. Required: high school transcript, 1 recommendation. Recommended: essay, minimum 2.5 high school GPA, interview. Required for some: essay. Entrance: moderately difficult. Application deadlines: Rolling, 12/15 for early action. Notification: continuous.

Costs Per Year: Application fee: $0. Comprehensive fee: $35,000 includes full-time tuition ($26,000), mandatory fees ($500), and college room and board ($8500). College room only: $4600. Room and board charges vary according to board plan and housing facility. Part-time tuition: $800 per semester hour. Part-time mandatory fees: $125 per term.

Collegiate Environment: Orientation program. Campus security: 24-hour emergency response devices and patrols, late night transport-escort service, controlled dormitory access. Freshmen guaranteed college housing. On-campus residence required through sophomore year. Options: coed, men-only, women-only housing available. Schewe Library with an OPAC and a Web page.

Community Environment: Jacksonville, population 19,470, is located in the west-central part of Illinois. It is the home of the only ferris wheel factory in the United States. Within the community are a library, many churches, hospitals, movie theaters, golf courses, and lakes for boating and fishing. Part-time jobs are available.

■ **ILLINOIS EASTERN COMMUNITY COLLEGES, FRONTIER COMMUNITY COLLEGE**
Frontier Dr.
Fairfield, IL 62837-2601
Tel: (618)842-3711
Fax: (618)842-6340
E-mail: atkinsm@iecc.edu
Web Site: www.iecc.edu/fcc/

Description: State and locally supported, 2-year, coed. Part of Illinois Eastern Community College System. Awards certificates, transfer associate, and terminal associate degrees. Founded 1976. Setting: 8-acre rural campus. Total enrollment: 2,597. Faculty: 218 (6 full-time, 212 part-time). Student-undergrad faculty ratio is 21:1. Full-time: 278 students, 62% women, 38% men. Part-time: 2,319 students, 64% women, 36% men. 1% from out-of-state. 0.3% American Indian or Alaska Native, non-Hispanic/Latino; 1% Hispanic/Latino; 1% African American, non-Hispanic/Latino; 0.4% Asian,

non-Hispanic/Latino; 0.04% Native Hawaiian or other Pacific Islander, non-Hispanic/Latino; 0.04% international. 60% 25 or older. Core. Calendar: semesters. Academic remediation for entering students, ESL program, services for LD students, advanced placement, self-designed majors, independent study, distance learning, double major, summer session for credit, part-time degree program, external degree program, adult/continuing education programs, co-op programs.
Entrance Requirements: Open admission. Options: early admission, deferred admission. Required: high school transcript. Entrance: noncompetitive. Application deadline: Rolling. Notification: continuous. Preference given to district residents.
Costs Per Year: Area resident tuition: $2464 full-time, $77 per semester hour part-time. State resident tuition: $7840 full-time, $245 per semester hour part-time. Nonresident tuition: $9920 full-time, $310 per semester hour part-time. Mandatory fees: $490 full-time, $15 per semester hour part-time, $5 per term part-time.
Collegiate Environment: College housing not available. 19,244 books, 96 serials, and 2,659 audiovisual materialsOperations spending for the previous fiscal year: $99,612. 42 computers available on campus for general student use. Staffed computer lab on campus.

■ **ILLINOIS EASTERN COMMUNITY COLLEGES, LINCOLN TRAIL COLLEGE**
11220 State Hwy. 1
Robinson, IL 62454
Tel: (618)544-8657
Fax: (618)544-7423
E-mail: mikeworthb@iecc.edu
Web Site: www.iecc.edu/ltc/
Description: State and locally supported, 2-year, coed. Part of Illinois Eastern Community College System. Awards certificates, transfer associate, and terminal associate degrees. Founded 1969. Setting: 120-acre rural campus. Total enrollment: 1,055. Faculty: 81 (18 full-time, 63 part-time). Student-undergrad faculty ratio is 18:1. Full-time: 436 students, 53% women, 47% men. Part-time: 619 students, 63% women, 37% men. 4% from out-of-state. 0.1% American Indian or Alaska Native, non-Hispanic/Latino; 1% Hispanic/Latino; 2% African American, non-Hispanic/Latino; 1% Asian, non-Hispanic/Latino; 0% Native Hawaiian or other Pacific Islander, non-Hispanic/Latino; 0% international. 38% 25 or older. Core. Calendar: semesters. Academic remediation for entering students, ESL program, services for LD students, advanced placement, self-designed majors, independent study, distance learning, double major, summer session for credit, part-time degree program, external degree program, adult/continuing education programs, co-op programs and internships.
Entrance Requirements: Open admission. Options: early admission, deferred admission. Required: high school transcript. Entrance: noncompetitive. Application deadline: Rolling. Notification: continuous. Preference given to district residents.
Costs Per Year: Area resident tuition: $2464 full-time, $77 per semester hour part-time. State resident tuition: $7840 full-time, $245 per semester hour part-time. Nonresident tuition: $9920 full-time, $310 per semester hour part-time. Mandatory fees: $490 full-time, $15 per semester hour part-time, $5 per term part-time.
Collegiate Environment: Drama-theater group, choral group. Social organizations: national fraternities. College housing not available. Eagleton Learning Resource Center plus 1 other with 15,563 books, 34 serials, and 652 audiovisual materials. Operations spending for the previous fiscal year: $71,723. 96 computers available on campus for general student use. Staffed computer lab on campus.

■ **ILLINOIS EASTERN COMMUNITY COLLEGES, OLNEY CENTRAL COLLEGE**
305 NW St.
Olney, IL 62450
Tel: (618)395-7777
Fax: (618)392-5212
E-mail: webberc@iecc.edu
Web Site: www.iecc.edu/occ/
Description: State and locally supported, 2-year, coed. Part of Illinois Eastern Community College System. Awards certificates, transfer associate, and terminal associate degrees. Founded 1962. Setting: 128-acre rural campus. Total enrollment: 1,477. Faculty: 108 (42 full-time, 66 part-time). Student-undergrad faculty ratio is 16:1. Full-time: 692 students, 60% women, 40% men. Part-time: 785 students, 73% women, 27% men. 2% from out-of-

state. 0.2% American Indian or Alaska Native, non-Hispanic/Latino; 1% Hispanic/Latino; 2% African American, non-Hispanic/Latino; 1% Asian, non-Hispanic/Latino; 0% Native Hawaiian or other Pacific Islander, non-Hispanic/Latino; 0% international. 41% 25 or older. Core. Calendar: semesters. Academic remediation for entering students, ESL program, services for LD students, advanced placement, self-designed majors, independent study, distance learning, double major, summer session for credit, part-time degree program, external degree program, adult/continuing education programs, co-op programs and internships.
Entrance Requirements: Open admission. Options: early admission, deferred admission. Required: high school transcript. Entrance: noncompetitive. Application deadline: Rolling. Notification: continuous. Preference given to district residents.
Costs Per Year: Area resident tuition: $2464 full-time, $77 per semester hour part-time. State resident tuition: $7840 full-time, $245 per semester hour part-time. Nonresident tuition: $9920 full-time, $310 per semester hour part-time. Mandatory fees: $490 full-time, $15 per semester hour part-time, $5 per term part-time.
Collegiate Environment: Drama-theater group, choral group, student-run newspaper. College housing not available. Anderson Learning Resources Center plus 1 other with 21,020 books, 22 serials, and 1,156 audiovisual materials. Operations spending for the previous fiscal year: $142,586. 125 computers available on campus for general student use. Staffed computer lab on campus.

■ **ILLINOIS EASTERN COMMUNITY COLLEGES, WABASH VALLEY COLLEGE**
2200 College Dr.
Mount Carmel, IL 62863-2657
Tel: (618)262-8641
Fax: (618)262-8641
E-mail: speard@iecc.edu
Web Site: www.iecc.edu/wvc/
Description: State and locally supported, 2-year, coed. Part of Illinois Eastern Community College System. Awards certificates, transfer associate, and terminal associate degrees. Founded 1960. Setting: 40-acre rural campus. Total enrollment: 4,706. Faculty: 120 (35 full-time, 85 part-time). Student-undergrad faculty ratio is 43:1. Full-time: 585 students, 42% women, 58% men. Part-time: 4,121 students, 42% women, 58% men. 4% from out-of-state. 0.3% American Indian or Alaska Native, non-Hispanic/Latino; 1% Hispanic/Latino; 4% African American, non-Hispanic/Latino; 1% Asian, non-Hispanic/Latino; 0.02% Native Hawaiian or other Pacific Islander, non-Hispanic/Latino; 0.02% international. 52% 25 or older. Core. Calendar: semesters. Academic remediation for entering students, ESL program, services for LD students, advanced placement, self-designed majors, independent study, distance learning, double major, summer session for credit, part-time degree program, external degree program, adult/continuing education programs, co-op programs and internships.
Entrance Requirements: Open admission. Options: early admission, deferred admission. Required: high school transcript. Entrance: noncompetitive. Application deadline: Rolling. Notification: continuous. Preference given to district residents.
Costs Per Year: Area resident tuition: $2464 full-time, $77 per semester hour part-time. State resident tuition: $7840 full-time, $245 per semester hour part-time. Nonresident tuition: $9920 full-time, $310 per semester hour part-time. Mandatory fees: $490 full-time, $15 per semester hour part-time, $5 per term part-time.
Collegiate Environment: Drama-theater group, choral group, student-run newspaper, radio station. College housing not available. Bauer Media Center plus 1 other with 32,811 books, 21,649 serials, and 1,480 audiovisual materials. Operations spending for the previous fiscal year: $129,484. 100 computers available on campus for general student use. Staffed computer lab on campus.

■ **THE ILLINOIS INSTITUTE OF ART–CHICAGO**
350 N Orleans St.
Chicago, IL 60654
Tel: (312)280-3500; Free: 800-351-3450
Fax: (312)280-3528
Web Site: www.artinstitutes.edu/chicago/
Description: Proprietary, 4-year, coed. Part of Education Management Corporation. Awards associate and bachelor's degrees. Founded 1916. Setting: urban campus.

■ THE ILLINOIS INSTITUTE OF ART–SCHAUMBURG

1000 N Plz. Dr., Ste. 100
Schaumburg, IL 60173
Tel: (847)619-3450; Free: 800-314-3450
Fax: (847)619-3064
Web Site: www.artinstitutes.edu/schaumburg/
Description: Proprietary, 4-year, coed. Part of Education Management Corporation. Awards associate and bachelor's degrees. Setting: suburban campus.

■ THE ILLINOIS INSTITUTE OF ART–TINLEY PARK

18670 Graphic Dr.
Tinley Park, IL 60477
Tel: (708)781-4201; Free: 877-342-3298
Web Site: www.artinstitutes.edu/tinleypark
Description: Proprietary, 4-year, coed. Part of Education Management Corporation. Awards associate and bachelor's degrees.

■ ILLINOIS INSTITUTE OF TECHNOLOGY

3300 S Federal St.
Chicago, IL 60616-3793
Tel: (312)567-3000; Free: 866-472-3448
Fax: (312)567-6939
E-mail: admission@iit.edu
Web Site: www.iit.edu/
Description: Independent, comprehensive, coed. Awards bachelor's, master's, and doctoral degrees. Founded 1890. Setting: 120-acre urban campus with easy access to Chicago. Endowment: $180.2 million. Research spending for the previous fiscal year: $64.8 million. Educational spending for the previous fiscal year: $11,422 per student. Total enrollment: 7,684. Faculty: 742 (411 full-time, 331 part-time). Student-undergrad faculty ratio is 12:1. 2,597 applied, 55% were admitted. 51% from top 10% of their high school class, 82% from top quarter, 98% from top half. Full-time: 2,610 students, 31% women, 69% men. Part-time: 191 students, 23% women, 77% men. Students come from 51 states and territories, 72 other countries, 23% from out-of-state. 0.4% American Indian or Alaska Native, non-Hispanic/Latino; 13% Hispanic/Latino; 7% African American, non-Hispanic/Latino; 10% Asian, non-Hispanic/Latino; 1% Native Hawaiian or other Pacific Islander, non-Hispanic/Latino; 23% international. 14% 25 or older, 60% live on campus, 10% transferred in. Retention: 92% of full-time freshmen returned the following year. Academic areas with the most degrees conferred: engineering; architecture; computer and information sciences. Core. Calendar: semesters. ESL program, services for LD students, advanced placement, independent study, distance learning, double major, summer session for credit, part-time degree program, co-op programs and internships, graduate courses open to undergrads. Off campus study at Shimer College; VanderCook College of Music. Study abroad program. ROTC: Army, Naval, Air Force.
Entrance Requirements: Options: electronic application, early admission, early action, deferred admission, international baccalaureate accepted. Required: essay, high school transcript, 1 recommendation, SAT or ACT. Recommended: interview. Entrance: moderately difficult. Application deadlines: 8/1, 12/1 for early action. Notification: continuous, 11/15 for early action. SAT Reasoning Test deadline: 7/1. SAT Subject Test deadline: 7/1. Transfer credits accepted: Yes.
Costs Per Year: Application fee: $0. Tuition: $38,512 full-time, $1204 per credit part-time. Full-time tuition varies according to student level. Part-time tuition varies according to course load and student level.
Collegiate Environment: Orientation program. Drama-theater group, choral group, student-run newspaper, radio station. Social organizations: 105 open to all; national fraternities, national sororities, local sororities; 14% of eligible men and 13% of eligible women are members. Most popular organizations: Union Board, International Students Association, Student Government Association, Greek Council, Commuter Student Associate. Major annual events: Homecoming, International Fest, Spring Formal. Student services: legal services, health clinic, personal-psychological counseling, women's center. Campus security: 24-hour emergency response devices and patrols, late night transport-escort service, controlled dormitory access. College housing designed to accommodate 1,440 students; 1,628 undergraduates lived in college housing during 2012-13. Freshmen given priority for college housing. On-campus residence required in freshman year. Option: coed housing available. Paul V. Galvin Library plus 5 others with 1.8 million books, 337,505 microform titles, 34,652 serials, 1,162 audiovisual materials, an OPAC, and a Web page. Operations spending for the previous fiscal year:

$6.3 million. 500 computers available on campus for general student use. A campuswide network can be accessed from student residence rooms and from off campus. Students can access the following: online class registration. Staffed computer lab on campus provides training in use of computers, software, and the Internet.
Community Environment: See University of Chicago.

■ ILLINOIS STATE UNIVERSITY

Normal, IL 61790-2200
Tel: (309)438-2111; Free: 800-366-2478
Fax: (309)438-3932
E-mail: admissions@ilstu.edu
Web Site: www.illinoisstate.edu/
Description: State-supported, university, coed. Awards bachelor's, master's, and doctoral degrees and post-master's certificates. Founded 1857. Setting: 490-acre urban campus. Endowment: $67.3 million. Research spending for the previous fiscal year: $16.6 million. Educational spending for the previous fiscal year: $6303 per student. Total enrollment: 20,706. Faculty: 1,212 (860 full-time, 352 part-time). Student-undergrad faculty ratio is 19:1. 12,407 applied, 74% were admitted. Full-time: 17,140 students, 55% women, 45% men. Part-time: 1,117 students, 50% women, 50% men. Students come from 43 states and territories, 39 other countries, 3% from out-of-state. 0.2% American Indian or Alaska Native, non-Hispanic/Latino; 7% Hispanic/Latino; 6% African American, non-Hispanic/Latino; 2% Asian, non-Hispanic/Latino; 0.1% Native Hawaiian or other Pacific Islander, non-Hispanic/Latino; 0.5% international. 6% 25 or older, 34% live on campus, 10% transferred in. Retention: 82% of full-time freshmen returned the following year. Academic areas with the most degrees conferred: business/marketing; education; health professions and related sciences. Core. Calendar: semesters. Academic remediation for entering students, ESL program, services for LD students, advanced placement, accelerated degree program, self-designed majors, honors program, independent study, distance learning, double major, summer session for credit, part-time degree program, adult/continuing education programs, co-op programs and internships, graduate courses open to undergrads. Off campus study at National Student Exchange. Study abroad program. ROTC: Army.
Entrance Requirements: Options: electronic application, deferred admission, international baccalaureate accepted. Required: essay, high school transcript, SAT or ACT. Entrance: moderately difficult. Application deadline: 3/1. Notification: continuous. SAT Reasoning Test deadline: 3/1. Transfer credits accepted: Yes. Applicants placed on waiting list: 364.
Costs Per Year: Application fee: $40. State resident tuition: $12,726 full-time. Nonresident tuition: $20,887 full-time. Full-time tuition varies according to course load and degree level. College room and board: $9364. Room and board charges vary according to board plan, housing facility, and location. Tuition guaranteed not to increase for student's term of enrollment.
Collegiate Environment: Orientation program. Drama-theater group, choral group, marching band, student-run newspaper, radio station. Social organizations: 299 open to all; national fraternities, national sororities; 8% of eligible men and 11% of eligible women are members. Major annual events: Spring Fest, Passages, Homecoming. Student services: legal services, health clinic, personal-psychological counseling, women's center. Campus security: 24-hour emergency response devices and patrols, late night transport-escort service, controlled dormitory access. 5,800 college housing spaces available; 5,747 were occupied in 2012-13. Freshmen guaranteed college housing. On-campus residence required through sophomore year. Options: coed, women-only housing available. Milner Library with 1.6 million books, 84,798 microform titles, 83,375 serials, 38,098 audiovisual materials, an OPAC, and a Web page. Operations spending for the previous fiscal year: $9.6 million. 2,445 computers available on campus for general student use. Computer purchase/lease plans available. A computer is required for all students. A campuswide network can be accessed from student residence rooms and from off campus. Students can access the following: online class registration. Staffed computer lab on campus (open 24 hours a day) provides training in use of computers, software, and the Internet.
Community Environment: Bloomington-Normal, with a combined population of 119,676, has a strong agricultural base with many business and industrial affiliations. Located at the intersection of Interstates 55 and 74, it is 132 miles from Chicago, 65 miles from Springfield, and 168 miles from St. Louis. Winters are moderately cold, summers are warm, and spring and fall are delightful. Both the twin-cities offer business districts for shopping, banking, and professional services, as well as year-round municipal recreational programs.

■ **ILLINOIS VALLEY COMMUNITY COLLEGE**
815 N Orlando Smith Ave.
Oglesby, IL 61348-9692
Tel: (815)224-2720
Fax: (815)224-3033
E-mail: mark_grzybowski@ivcc.edu
Web Site: www.ivcc.edu/
Description: District-supported, 2-year, coed. Part of Illinois Community
College Board. Awards certificates, transfer associate, and terminal associ-
ate degrees. Founded 1924. Setting: 410-acre rural campus with easy ac-
cess to Chicago. Endowment: $3.7 million. Educational spending for the
previous fiscal year: $3460 per student. Total enrollment: 4,355. Faculty: 270
(91 full-time, 179 part-time). Student-undergrad faculty ratio is 18:1. Full-
time: 1,881 students, 55% women, 45% men. Part-time: 2,474 students,
63% women, 37% men. 1% from out-of-state. 0.3% American Indian or
Alaska Native, non-Hispanic/Latino; 9% Hispanic/Latino; 2% African
American, non-Hispanic/Latino; 1% Asian, non-Hispanic/Latino; 0.03% Native Hawaiian or other Pacific Islander, non-Hispanic/Latino; 0% international.
33% 25 or older, 37% transferred in. Retention: 52% of full-time freshmen
returned the following year. Core. Calendar: semesters. Academic
remediation for entering students, ESL program, services for LD students,
advanced placement, self-designed majors, honors program, independent
study, distance learning, summer session for credit, part-time degree
program, internships. Off campus study at Sauk Valley Community College,
Kishwaukee College, Kankakee Community College, Joliet Junior College,
Rock Valley College, Elgin Community College, Waubonsee Community College, Illinois Central College. Study abroad program.
Entrance Requirements: Open admission except for nursing, dental assistant programs, therapeutic massage. Options: electronic application, early
admission, deferred admission. Required: high school transcript. Recommended: ACT. Entrance: noncompetitive. Application deadline: Rolling.
Notification: continuous. Transfer credits accepted: Yes.
Costs Per Year: Area resident tuition: $2720 full-time, $84.38 per credit
part-time. State resident tuition: $7808 full-time, $244 per credit part-time.
Nonresident tuition: $8720 full-time, $272.50 per credit part-time. Mandatory
fees: $247 full-time, $7.39 per credit hour part-time, $5. Full-time tuition and
fees vary according to course load. Part-time tuition and fees vary according
to course load.
Collegiate Environment: Orientation program. Drama-theater group, choral
group, student-run newspaper. Social organizations: 40 open to all. Most
popular organizations: Chemistry Club, Student Embassadors, Phi Theta
Kappa, Illinois Valley Leaders for Service, Student Veterans Association.
Major annual events: New Student Convocation, Spirit Day. Student
services: personal-psychological counseling. Campus security: 24-hour
emergency response devices and patrols, late night transport-escort service.
Jacobs Library with 55,473 books, 45,547 microform titles, 14,981 serials,
1,379 audiovisual materials, an OPAC, and a Web page. Operations spending for the previous fiscal year: $374,611. 242 computers available on
campus for general student use. A campuswide network can be accessed.
Students can access the following: online class registration, Bookstore,
library, transcripts, payments, scholarship application, career assessment.
Staffed computer lab on campus provides training in use of computers,
software, and the Internet.
Community Environment: Oglesby (population 3,621) is almost 75 miles
southwest of Chicago, 50 miles northeast of Peoria.

■ **ILLINOIS WESLEYAN UNIVERSITY**
PO Box 2900
Bloomington, IL 61702-2900
Tel: (309)556-1000; Free: 800-332-2498
Fax: (309)556-3411
E-mail: iwuadmit@iwu.edu
Web Site: www.iwu.edu/
Description: Independent, 4-year, coed. Awards bachelor's degrees.
Founded 1850. Setting: 79-acre suburban campus. Total enrollment: 2,013.
Faculty: 226 (162 full-time, 64 part-time). Student-undergrad faculty ratio is
11:1. 3,297 applied, 60% were admitted. 45% from top 10% of their high
school class, 82% from top quarter, 98% from top half. Full-time: 2,008
students, 58% women, 42% men. Part-time: 5 students, 40% women, 60%
men. 12% from out-of-state. 0.4% American Indian or Alaska Native, non-
Hispanic/Latino; 5% Hispanic/Latino; 5% African American, non-Hispanic/
Latino; 5% Asian, non-Hispanic/Latino; 0.05% Native Hawaiian or other
Pacific Islander, non-Hispanic/Latino; 4% international. 0% 25 or older, 71%
live on campus, 2% transferred in. Retention: 89% of full-time freshmen

returned the following year. Academic areas with the most degrees
conferred: business/marketing; visual and performing arts; psychology.
Calendar: 4-4-1. ROTC: Army (c).
Entrance Requirements: Options: electronic application, early admission,
early action, deferred admission, international baccalaureate accepted.
Required: essay, high school transcript, minimum 2 high school GPA, 1
recommendation, SAT or ACT. Recommended: minimum 3 high school GPA,
2 recommendations, interview. Entrance: very difficult. Application deadlines:
Rolling, 11/15 for early action. Notification: continuous, 1/15 for early action.
SAT Reasoning Test deadline: 4/1. SAT Subject Test deadline: 4/1. Applicants placed on waiting list: 200. Wait-listed applicants offered admission:
5.
Costs Per Year: Application fee: $0. Comprehensive fee: $46,792 includes
full-time tuition ($37,774), mandatory fees ($180), and college room and
board ($8838). College room only: $5584. Part-time tuition: $1180 per credit
hour.
Collegiate Environment: Orientation program. Campus security: 24-hour
emergency response devices and patrols, late night transport-escort service,
controlled dormitory access, emergency response team. Freshmen
guaranteed college housing. On-campus residence required through
sophomore year. Option: coed housing available. The Ames Library with an
OPAC and a Web page.
Community Environment: Illinois Wesleyan University is located in
Bloomington, Illinois, which is known as a research, insurance, retail, education and business center. Situated in a corporate community of 100,000
people, Bloomington is now one of the fastest growing communities in the
country and is listed among the most desirable places to live in the nation.

■ **INTERNATIONAL ACADEMY OF DESIGN & TECHNOLOGY**
One N State St., Ste. 500
Chicago, IL 60602-9736
Tel: (312)980-9200; Free: 877-458-6111
Fax: (312)828-9405
E-mail: sreichart@iadtchicago.edu
Web Site: www.iadtchicago.edu/
Description: Proprietary, 4-year, coed. Part of Career Education Corpora-
tion. Awards associate and bachelor's degrees. Founded 1977. Setting:
1-acre urban campus. Educational spending for the previous fiscal year:
$4056 per student. Total enrollment: 1,832. Faculty: 113 (14 full-time, 99
part-time). Student-undergrad faculty ratio is 27:1. 600 applied, 52% were
admitted. 5% from top 10% of their high school class, 15% from top quarter,
45% from top half. Full-time: 1,482 students, 61% women, 39% men. Part-
time: 350 students, 62% women, 38% men. Students come from 15 states
and territories, 11 other countries, 6% from out-of-state. 39% 25 or older,
10% transferred in. Retention: 44% of full-time freshmen returned the following year. Core. Academic remediation for entering students, services for LD
students, advanced placement, independent study, summer session for
credit, part-time degree program, adult/continuing education programs,
internships. Study abroad program.
Entrance Requirements: Options: electronic application, early admission,
international baccalaureate accepted. Required: high school transcript,
interview. Recommended: essay, minimum 2 high school GPA. Required for
some: GED. Entrance: minimally difficult. Application deadline: Rolling.
Collegiate Environment: Orientation program. Student-run newspaper.
Most popular organizations: Fashion Council, GLBT (Gay, Lesbian, Bi,
Transgender), Gamers Anonymous, Image Consulting, ASA (Anime Student
Alliance). Major annual events: Annual Fashion Show, Academic Achievement Reception, Job Fairs. Student services: personal-psychological
counseling. Campus security: 24-hour emergency response devices, building security during hours of operation. International Academy of Design and
Technology Library with 10,000 books, 90 serials, 1,500 audiovisual materials, an OPAC, and a Web page. Operations spending for the previous fiscal
year: $91,977. 425 computers available on campus for general student use.
A campuswide network can be accessed from off-campus. Students can access the following: online class registration, student Web site. Staffed
computer lab on campus (open 24 hours a day) provides training in use of
computers, software, and the Internet.

■ **ITT TECHNICAL INSTITUTE (MOUNT PROSPECT)**
1401 Feehanville Dr.
Mount Prospect, IL 60056
Tel: (847)375-8800
Web Site: www.itt-tech.edu/

Description: Proprietary, primarily 2-year, coed. Part of ITT Educational Services, Inc. Awards terminal associate and bachelor's degrees. Founded 1986. Setting: suburban campus.

Entrance Requirements: Entrance: minimally difficult.

■ ITT TECHNICAL INSTITUTE (OAK BROOK)
800 Jorie Blvd.
Ste. 100
Oak Brook, IL 60523
Tel: (630)472-7000; Free: 877-488-0001
Web Site: www.itt-tech.edu/
Description: Proprietary, primarily 2-year, coed. Part of ITT Educational Services, Inc. Awards terminal associate and bachelor's degrees. Founded 1998.

Entrance Requirements: Entrance: minimally difficult.

■ ITT TECHNICAL INSTITUTE (ORLAND PARK)
11551 184th Pl.
Orland Park, IL 60467
Tel: (708)326-3200
Web Site: www.itt-tech.edu/
Description: Proprietary, primarily 2-year, coed. Part of ITT Educational Services, Inc. Awards terminal associate and bachelor's degrees. Founded 1993. Setting: suburban campus.

Entrance Requirements: Entrance: minimally difficult.

■ ITT TECHNICAL INSTITUTE (SPRINGFIELD)
2501 Wabash Ave.
Springfield, IL 62704
Tel: (217)547-5700; Free: 877-263-2374
Web Site: www.itt-tech.edu/
Description: Proprietary, 4-year, coed. Awards associate and bachelor's degrees.

Entrance Requirements: Entrance: minimally difficult.

■ JOHN A. LOGAN COLLEGE
700 Logan College Rd.
Carterville, IL 62918-9900
Tel: (618)985-3741
Fax: (618)985-2248
E-mail: terrycrain@jalc.edu
Web Site: www.jalc.edu/
Description: State and locally supported, 2-year, coed. Part of Illinois Community College Board. Awards certificates and transfer associate degrees. Founded 1967. Setting: 160-acre rural campus. Total enrollment: 7,559. Faculty: 313 (103 full-time, 210 part-time). Student-undergrad faculty ratio is 24:1. Full-time: 2,368 students, 51% women, 49% men. Part-time: 5,191 students, 62% women, 38% men. 44% 25 or older. Core. Calendar: semesters. Academic remediation for entering students, services for LD students, advanced placement, distance learning, summer session for credit, part-time degree program, adult/continuing education programs, co-op programs and internships. Off campus study at Belleville Area College, Rend Lake College, Illinois Eastern Community Colleges, Shawnee Community College, Southern Illinois University Carbondale, Southeastern Illinois College. Study abroad program. ROTC: Army (c), Air Force (c).

Entrance Requirements: Open admission except for allied health, veterinary technology, and massage therapy programs. Option: early admission. Required: high school transcript. Entrance: noncompetitive. Application deadline: 8/25. Notification: continuous.

Collegiate Environment: Campus security: 24-hour emergency response devices and patrols. Learning Resource Center with 33,306 books, 298 serials, and a Web page. 150 computers available on campus for general student use. A campuswide network can be accessed from off-campus. Students can access the following: online class registration. Staffed computer lab on campus provides training in use of computers, software, and the Internet.

■ JOHN HANCOCK UNIVERSITY
111 N Canal St.
Ste. 380
Chicago, IL 60606-7204
Free: 877-355-4762
E-mail: admissions@ellis.edu
Web Site: www.hancocku.edu/

Description: Proprietary, comprehensive, coed. Awards associate, bachelor's, and master's degrees. Total enrollment: 1,950. Student-undergrad faculty ratio is 8:1. 76% 25 or older.

■ JOHN WOOD COMMUNITY COLLEGE
1301 S 48th St.
Quincy, IL 62301-9147
Tel: (217)224-6500
Fax: (217)224-4208
E-mail: admissions@jwcc.edu
Web Site: www.jwcc.edu/
Description: District-supported, 2-year, coed. Part of Illinois Community College Board. Awards certificates, transfer associate, and terminal associate degrees. Founded 1974. Setting: small town campus. Educational spending for the previous fiscal year: $4162 per student. Total enrollment: 2,390. Faculty: 258 (56 full-time, 202 part-time). Student-undergrad faculty ratio is 13:1. 5% from top 10% of their high school class, 9% from top quarter, 35% from top half. Full-time: 1,178 students, 53% women, 47% men. Part-time: 1,212 students, 66% women, 34% men. Students come from 18 states and territories, 7% from out-of-state. 0.4% American Indian or Alaska Native, non-Hispanic/Latino; 1% Hispanic/Latino; 4% African American, non-Hispanic/Latino; 1% Asian, non-Hispanic/Latino; 0.1% Native Hawaiian or other Pacific Islander, non-Hispanic/Latino; 0% international. 37% 25 or older, 9% transferred in. Core. Calendar: semesters. Academic remediation for entering students, ESL program, services for LD students, advanced placement, accelerated degree program, self-designed majors, independent study, distance learning, summer session for credit, part-time degree program, external degree program, adult/continuing education programs, co-op programs and internships. Off campus study at members of the Quincy Area Education Consortium, Southeastern Community College (IA), Blessing Hospital, Quincy Area Vocational Technical Center. Study abroad program.

Entrance Requirements: Open admission except for nursing (ADN). Options: electronic application, early admission. Required: high school transcript. Recommended: ACT. Entrance: noncompetitive. Application deadlines: Rolling, Rolling for nonresidents. Notification: continuous, continuous for nonresidents. Preference given to district residents. Transfer credits accepted: Yes.

Costs Per Year: Application fee: $0. Area resident tuition: $3690 full-time, $123 per credit hour part-time. State resident tuition: $6900 full-time, $233 per credit hour part-time. Nonresident tuition: $6990 full-time, $233 per credit hour part-time. Mandatory fees: $300 full-time, $10 per credit hour part-time. Full-time tuition and fees vary according to program and reciprocity agreements. Part-time tuition and fees vary according to program and reciprocity agreements.

Collegiate Environment: Orientation program. Choral group. Social organizations: 12 open to all; Phi Theta Kappa, Circle K, BACCHUS, Multi-Cultural. Most popular organizations: Phi Theta Kappa, Agriculture Club, BACCHUS, Music Educators National Conference, Student Nurses Organization. Major annual events: Welcome Back Barbeque, Community College Month, including Student Appreciation Week, United Way events, including student-staff competitions. Campus security: 24-hour emergency response devices, late night transport-escort service, campus police department, 911-enhanced phone system. Academic Support Center with 18,000 books, 160 serials, 2,000 audiovisual materials, an OPAC, and a Web page. Operations spending for the previous fiscal year: $228,402. 400 computers available on campus for general student use. A campuswide network can be accessed. Students can access the following: online class registration. Staffed computer lab on campus provides training in use of computers, software, and the Internet.

Community Environment: See Quincy University.

■ JOLIET JUNIOR COLLEGE
1215 Houbolt Rd.
Joliet, IL 60431-8938
Tel: (815)729-9020
E-mail: admission@jjc.edu
Web Site: www.jjc.edu/
Description: State and locally supported, 2-year, coed. Part of Illinois Community College Board. Awards certificates, diplomas, transfer associate, and terminal associate degrees. Founded 1901. Setting: 463-acre suburban campus with easy access to Chicago. Total enrollment: 15,288. Student-undergrad faculty ratio is 25:1. 1% from out-of-state. 38% 25 or older. Core. Calendar: semesters. Academic remediation for entering students, ESL

program, services for LD students, advanced placement, honors program, independent study, distance learning, summer session for credit, part-time degree program, adult/continuing education programs, internships.

Entrance Requirements: Open admission except for nursing program. Options: early admission, deferred admission. Required: high school transcript. Entrance: noncompetitive. Application deadline: Rolling. Preference given to district residents.

Collegiate Environment: Orientation program. Drama-theater group, choral group, student-run newspaper. Social organizations: national fraternities. Student services: personal-psychological counseling, women's center. Campus security: 24-hour emergency response devices and patrols, student patrols, late night transport-escort service. Learning Resource Center with an OPAC.

Community Environment: Joliet is a leading industrial area 38 miles southwest of Chicago's Loop. Railroads and buses are accessible; Midway and O'Hare Airports serve the area. Industries are steel, petroleum products, chemicals, wallpaper, machinery, and greeting cards. Shipping is also a major industry. Community facilities include excellent libraries, churches of almost every denomination, hospitals, YMCA, hotels and private rooming houses. Outdoor sports include hunting, boating, fishing, golf, and other sports.

■ **JUDSON UNIVERSITY**
1151 N State St.
Elgin, IL 60123-1498
Tel: (847)628-2500; Free: 800-879-5376
Fax: (847)695-0712
E-mail: nbinger@judsonu.edu
Web Site: www.judsonu.edu/

Description: Independent Baptist, comprehensive, coed. Awards bachelor's and master's degrees. Founded 1963. Setting: 90-acre suburban campus with easy access to Chicago. Endowment: $11.4 million. Research spending for the previous fiscal year: $183. Educational spending for the previous fiscal year: $11,573 per student. Total enrollment: 1,128. Faculty: 218 (62 full-time, 156 part-time). Student-undergrad faculty ratio is 8:1. 711 applied, 65% were admitted. 15% from top 10% of their high school class, 44% from top quarter, 75% from top half. Full-time: 747 students, 50% women, 50% men. Part-time: 271 students, 68% women, 32% men. Students come from 35 states and territories, 24 other countries, 18% from out-of-state. 0% American Indian or Alaska Native, non-Hispanic/Latino; 9% Hispanic/Latino; 6% African American, non-Hispanic/Latino; 1% Asian, non-Hispanic/Latino; 0.2% Native Hawaiian or other Pacific Islander, non-Hispanic/Latino; 3% international. 24% 25 or older, 65% live on campus, 16% transferred in. Retention: 73% of full-time freshmen returned the following year. Academic areas with the most degrees conferred: business/marketing; education; public administration and social services. Core. Calendar: semesters. Academic remediation for entering students, services for LD students, advanced placement, accelerated degree program, self-designed majors, honors program, independent study, distance learning, double major, summer session for credit, part-time degree program, adult/continuing education programs, internships, graduate courses open to undergrads. Off campus study at Council for Christian Colleges & Universities (Best Semester), Chicago Semester, AuSable Institute, Wesley Inst. for Music/the Arts (Australia), Anhalt Univ (Germany), Harlaxton College (UK), Inholland Univ (Netherlands), New York Center for Art & Media Studies, Japan Tokyo Christian Univ. Study abroad program. ROTC: Army (c).

Entrance Requirements: Options: electronic application, international baccalaureate accepted. Required: high school transcript, minimum 2.5 high school GPA, Minimum 21 ACT; lifestyle statement; portfolios for some majors, SAT or ACT. Required for some: essay, 1 recommendation. Entrance: moderately difficult. Application deadlines: Rolling, Rolling for nonresidents. Notification: continuous, continuous for nonresidents. SAT Reasoning Test deadline: 8/20. SAT Subject Test deadline: 8/20. Transfer credits accepted: Yes.

Costs Per Year: Application fee: $50. Comprehensive fee: $36,520 includes full-time tuition ($26,750), mandatory fees ($780), and college room and board ($8990). Full-time tuition and fees vary according to course load and program. Room and board charges vary according to board plan. Part-time tuition: $1100 per credit. Part-time tuition varies according to course load and program.

Collegiate Environment: Orientation program. Drama-theater group, choral group. Social organizations: 28 open to all. Most popular organizations: Judson Student Organization, University Ministries, Judson Choir, Fellowship of Christian Athletes, Judson Business Network. Major annual events:

Homecoming, Spiritual Enrichment Week, spring dance. Student services: health clinic, personal-psychological counseling. Campus security: 24-hour emergency response devices and patrols, controlled dormitory access. 596 college housing spaces available. Freshmen guaranteed college housing. On-campus residence required through senior year. Options: coed, men-only, women-only housing available. Benjamin P. Browne Library with 117,762 books, 20,025 microform titles, 229 serials, 540 audiovisual materials, an OPAC, and a Web page. Operations spending for the previous fiscal year: $571,810. 90 computers available on campus for general student use. A campuswide network can be accessed from student residence rooms and from off campus. Students can access the following: online class registration. Staffed computer lab on campus.

■ **KANKAKEE COMMUNITY COLLEGE**
100 College Dr.
Kankakee, IL 60901
Tel: (815)802-8100
Fax: (815)933-0217
E-mail: ocarpenterwilliams@kcc.edu
Web Site: www.kcc.edu/

Description: State and locally supported, 2-year, coed. Part of Illinois Community College Board. Awards certificates, diplomas, transfer associate, and terminal associate degrees (also offers continuing education program with significant enrollment not reflected in profile). Founded 1966. Setting: 178-acre small town campus with easy access to Chicago. Endowment: $4.5 million. Total enrollment: 3,913. Faculty: 198 (71 full-time, 127 part-time). Student-undergrad faculty ratio is 17:1. 1,765 applied. 5% from top 10% of their high school class, 18% from top quarter, 50% from top half. Full-time: 1,613 students, 56% women, 44% men. Part-time: 2,300 students, 66% women, 34% men. Students come from 14 states and territories, 6 other countries, 1% from out-of-state. 1% American Indian or Alaska Native, non-Hispanic/Latino; 8% Hispanic/Latino; 18% African American, non-Hispanic/Latino; 1% Asian, non-Hispanic/Latino; 0.2% Native Hawaiian or other Pacific Islander, non-Hispanic/Latino; 0% international. 42% 25 or older, 47% transferred in. Retention: 59% of full-time freshmen returned the following year. Core. Calendar: semesters. Academic remediation for entering students, ESL program, services for LD students, advanced placement, self-designed majors, honors program, independent study, distance learning, summer session for credit, part-time degree program, internships. Off campus study at Olivet Nazarene University, University of Illinois-Urbana (Agriculture program only), Franklin University. Study abroad program. ROTC: Army (c).

Entrance Requirements: Open admission except for health occupations programs. Options: electronic application, early admission, international baccalaureate accepted. Required: high school transcript. Entrance: noncompetitive. Application deadlines: Rolling, Rolling for nonresidents. Notification: continuous, continuous for nonresidents. Preference given to district residents for health occupations programs. Transfer credits accepted: Yes.

Costs Per Year: Application fee: $0. Area resident tuition: $3000 full-time. State resident tuition: $5681 full-time. Nonresident tuition: $13,600 full-time. Mandatory fees: $390 full-time.

Collegiate Environment: Orientation program. Drama-theater group. Social organizations: 17 open to all. Most popular organizations: Phi Theta Kappa, Hort, Student Nursing, Gay Straight Alliance, Student Advisory Council. Major annual events: Fall Club Rush, National Coming Out Day, Wealth Watchers. Campus security: 24-hour patrols, late night transport-escort service. College housing not available. Kankakee Community College Learning Resource Center with 35,308 books, 120 serials, 2,299 audiovisual materials, an OPAC, and a Web page. 1,100 computers available on campus for general student use. A campuswide network can be accessed. Students can access the following: online class registration, online transcripts. Staffed computer lab on campus provides training in use of computers, software, and the Internet.

Community Environment: Kankakee (population 26,600), one of the fastest growing cities of Illinois and the U.S., has beautiful residential sections along the banks of the picturesque Kankakee River. Kankakee is located 60 miles southwest of Chicago and is the seat of Kankakee County. Some of the world's largest gladiolus fields are nearby. The manufacturing plants offer ample opportunity for employment. Nearby Chicago provides the cultural facilities for the outlying area. Kankakee County Fair and Championship Rodeo is an annual event in August.

■ **KASKASKIA COLLEGE**
27210 College Rd.
Centralia, IL 62801-7878

Tel: (618)545-3000; Free: 800-642-0859

Fax: (618)532-1135

E-mail: jripperda@kaskaskia.edu

Web Site: www.kaskaskia.edu/

Description: State and locally supported, 2-year, coed. Part of Illinois Community College Board. Awards certificates, transfer associate, and terminal associate degrees. Founded 1966. Setting: 195-acre rural campus with easy access to St. Louis. Endowment: $5.1 million. Total enrollment: 5,104. Faculty: 253 (76 full-time, 177 part-time). Student-undergrad faculty ratio is 21:1. 284 applied, 100% were admitted. Full-time: 2,006 students, 60% women, 40% men. Part-time: 3,098 students, 62% women, 38% men. Students come from 10 states and territories, 3 other countries, 1% from out-of-state. 0.4% American Indian or Alaska Native, non-Hispanic/Latino; 2% Hispanic/Latino; 7% African American, non-Hispanic/Latino; 1% Asian, non-Hispanic/Latino; 0% Native Hawaiian or other Pacific Islander, non-Hispanic/Latino; 0.2% international. 40% 25 or older, 36% transferred in. Core. Calendar: semesters. Academic remediation for entering students, ESL program, services for LD students, accelerated degree program, honors program, independent study, distance learning, double major, summer session for credit, part-time degree program, adult/continuing education programs, co-op programs and internships. Off campus study at Southern Illinois Collegiate Common Market (SICCM), University Alliance, Career Comprehensive Agreement with other colleges listed in our catalog, Cooperative Agreements. Study abroad program.

Entrance Requirements: Open admission except for allied health programs. Options: electronic application, early admission, deferred admission. Required: high school transcript. Recommended: ACT. Required for some: interview. Entrance: noncompetitive. Application deadline: Rolling. Notification: continuous. Preference given to district residents. Transfer credits accepted: Yes.

Costs Per Year: Application fee: $0. Area resident tuition: $2944 full-time, $92 per credit hour part-time. State resident tuition: $5728 full-time, $179 per credit hour part-time. Nonresident tuition: $12,480 full-time, $390 per credit hour part-time. Mandatory fees: $384 full-time, $12 per credit hour part-time. Full-time tuition and fees vary according to program. Part-time tuition and fees vary according to program.

Collegiate Environment: Orientation program. Drama-theater group, choral group, student-run newspaper. Social organizations: 44 open to all; student congress; 9% of eligible men and 8% of eligible women are members. Most popular organizations: Student Nurse Organization, Student Practical Nurses, Student Radiology Club, Agriculture Club, Cosmetology Club. Major annual event: Student Picnic. Student services: personal-psychological counseling. Campus security: 24-hour emergency response devices and patrols, late night transport-escort service. College housing not available. Kaskaskia College Library with 19,007 books, 479 microform titles, 77 serials, 545 audiovisual materials, an OPAC, and a Web page. Operations spending for the previous fiscal year: $306,948. 198 computers available on campus for general student use. A campuswide network can be accessed from off-campus. Students can access the following: online class registration. Staffed computer lab on campus provides training in use of computers, software, and the Internet.

Community Environment: Centralia, located 60 miles east of St. Louis, has mild winters and warm summers. Buses and planes serve the area. Community facilities include a hospital, library, hotels, motels, rooming houses, and a good shopping area. Three lakes are located nearby, for hunting and fishing, and there are three golf courses. The local merchants and civic organizations sponsor a Halloween Parade each year.

■ **KENDALL COLLEGE**

900 N N Branch St.

Chicago, IL 60201-2899

Tel: (312)752-2000; Free: 888-90-KENDALL

E-mail: admissions@kendall.edu

Web Site: www.kendall.edu/

Description: Proprietary, 4-year, coed. Part of Laureate International Universities. Awards associate and bachelor's degrees. Founded 1934. Setting: urban campus with easy access to Chicago. Total enrollment: 2,545. Faculty: 209 (45 full-time, 164 part-time). Student-undergrad faculty ratio is 18:1. 361 applied, 98% were admitted. Full-time: 1,480 students, 66% women, 34% men. Part-time: 1,065 students, 85% women, 15% men. Students come from 58 other countries, 23% from out-of-state. 25% 25 or older, 14% transferred in. Retention: 52% of full-time freshmen returned the following year. Academic areas with the most degrees conferred: education; personal and culinary services. Core. Academic remediation for entering

students, accelerated degree program, distance learning, summer session for credit, part-time degree program, internships. Off campus study at University Center of Lake County. Study abroad program.

Entrance Requirements: Options: electronic application, deferred admission, international baccalaureate accepted. Required: essay, high school transcript, interview. Recommended: minimum 2 high school GPA. Required for some: SAT or ACT. Entrance: minimally difficult. Application deadlines: Rolling, Rolling for nonresidents. Notification: continuous, continuous for nonresidents. Transfer credits accepted: Yes.

Collegiate Environment: Orientation program. Social organizations: 15 open to all. Major annual events: International Fair, Fall Festival, Spring Dance. Student services: personal-psychological counseling. Campus security: 24-hour emergency response devices and patrols, controlled dormitory access, late night security in dorms. Library with 36,293 books, 187 serials, 453 audiovisual materials, an OPAC, and a Web page.

Community Environment: See Northwestern University.

■ **KISHWAUKEE COLLEGE**

21193 Malta Rd.

Malta, IL 60150

Tel: (815)825-2086

Fax: (815)825-2306

Web Site: www.kishwaukeecollege.edu/

Description: State and locally supported, 2-year, coed. Part of Illinois Community College Board. Awards certificates, transfer associate, and terminal associate degrees. Founded 1967. Setting: 120-acre rural campus with easy access to Chicago. Total enrollment: 4,466. 29% 25 or older. Core. Calendar: semesters. Academic remediation for entering students, ESL program, services for LD students, advanced placement, independent study, distance learning, double major, summer session for credit, part-time degree program, external degree program, adult/continuing education programs, co-op programs and internships. Off campus study at 6 other Illinois community colleges. Study abroad program.

Entrance Requirements: Open admission except for nursing, radiological technology programs. Options: early admission, deferred admission. Required: high school transcript, transcripts from all other colleges or universities previously attended. Recommended: minimum 2.0 high school GPA. Required for some: minimum 2.0 high school GPA. Entrance: noncompetitive. Application deadline: Rolling. Notification: continuous.

Collegiate Environment: Orientation program. Drama-theater group, choral group, student-run newspaper. Student services: health clinic, personal-psychological counseling. Campus security: 24-hour patrols. Learning Resource Center with 52,075 books, 13,003 microform titles, 248 serials, 3,500 audiovisual materials, an OPAC, and a Web page.

Community Environment: See Northern Illinois University.

■ **KNOX COLLEGE**

2 E S St.

Galesburg, IL 61401

Tel: (309)341-7000; Free: 800-678-KNOX

Fax: (309)341-7070

E-mail: admission@knox.edu

Web Site: www.knox.edu/

Description: Independent, 4-year, coed. Awards bachelor's degrees. Founded 1837. Setting: 82-acre small town campus with easy access to Peoria; Quad Cities. Endowment: $84.4 million. Educational spending for the previous fiscal year: $13,257 per student. Total enrollment: 1,430. Faculty: 140 (110 full-time, 30 part-time). Student-undergrad faculty ratio is 12:1. 2,208 applied, 78% were admitted. 30% from top 10% of their high school class, 66% from top quarter, 90% from top half. 4 National Merit Scholars, 10 class presidents, 11 valedictorians. Full-time: 1,392 students, 57% women, 43% men. Part-time: 38 students, 55% women, 45% men. Students come from 45 states and territories, 36 other countries, 55% from out-of-state. 0.3% American Indian or Alaska Native, non-Hispanic/Latino; 9% Hispanic/Latino; 6% African American, non-Hispanic/Latino; 5% Asian, non-Hispanic/Latino; 0% Native Hawaiian or other Pacific Islander, non-Hispanic/Latino; 11% international. 1% 25 or older, 85% live on campus, 3% transferred in. Retention: 88% of full-time freshmen returned the following year. Academic areas with the most degrees conferred: social sciences; English; biological/life sciences. Core. Calendar: trimesters. Services for LD students, advanced placement, self-designed majors, honors program, independent study, double major, part-time degree program, internships. Off campus study at Argonne Science Semester; ACM Chicago Urban Studies, Arts, and Business, Entrepreneurship & Society programs; Newberry Library Program in the Humanities; Oak Ridge Science Semester; American University Washington Semester Program; other ACM/GLCA international programs. Study abroad program.

Entrance Requirements: Options: electronic application, early admission, early action, deferred admission, international baccalaureate accepted. Required: essay, high school transcript, 2 recommendations. Recommended: interview. Required for some: SAT or ACT. Entrance: very difficult. Application deadlines: 2/1, 12/1 for early action. Notification: 3/31, 12/31 for early action. SAT Reasoning Test deadline: 2/1. Transfer credits accepted: Yes. Applicants placed on waiting list: 30. Wait-listed applicants offered admission: 1. Early action applicants: 1,084. Early action applicants admitted: 813.

Costs Per Year: Application fee: $40. Comprehensive fee: $47,352 includes full-time tuition ($38,286), mandatory fees ($666), and college room and board ($8400). College room only: $4206. Full-time tuition and fees vary according to course load. Room and board charges vary according to housing facility.

Collegiate Environment: Orientation program. Drama-theater group, choral group, student-run newspaper, radio station. Social organizations: 95 open to all; national fraternities, national sororities, local fraternities; 21% of eligible men and 16% of eligible women are members. Most popular organizations: Student-Run Radio Station (WVKC), International Club, Student Newspaper (The Knox Student), Common Ground, Terpsichore (Dance Collective). Major annual events: International Fair, 'Flunk Day' (College Spring Carnival), Pumphandle. Student services: health clinic, personal-psychological counseling. Campus security: 24-hour emergency response devices and patrols, late night transport-escort service. 1,911 college housing spaces available. Freshmen guaranteed college housing. On-campus residence required through sophomore year. Options: coed, men-only, women-only housing available. Henry M. Seymour Library plus 2 others with 338,746 books, 98,733 microform titles, 11,943 serials, 13,574 audiovisual materials, an OPAC, and a Web page. Operations spending for the previous fiscal year: $1.7 million. 200 computers available on campus for general student use. A campuswide network can be accessed from student residence rooms and from off campus. Students can access the following: online class registration, Transcripts, EDR, Moodle. Staffed computer lab on campus (open 24 hours a day) provides training in use of computers, software, and the Internet.

Community Environment: Knox College is situated in the small city of Galesburg, Illinois, with a population of 32,017. It is 180 miles west of Chicago and easily accessible by Amtrak, Interstate Highway 74, and Greyhound bus lines.

■ **LAKE FOREST COLLEGE**
555 N Sheridan Rd.
Lake Forest, IL 60045
Tel: (847)234-3100; Free: 800-828-4751
Fax: (847)735-6271
E-mail: admissions@lakeforest.edu
Web Site: www.lakeforest.edu/

Description: Independent, comprehensive, coed. Awards bachelor's and master's degrees. Founded 1857. Setting: 107-acre suburban campus with easy access to Chicago. Endowment: $70.9 million. Research spending for the previous fiscal year: $602,400. Educational spending for the previous fiscal year: $10,849 per student. Total enrollment: 1,516. Faculty: 161 (94 full-time, 67 part-time). Student-undergrad faculty ratio is 13:1. 3,198 applied, 54% were admitted. 33% from top 10% of their high school class, 62% from top quarter, 90% from top half. Full-time: 1,481 students, 59% women, 41% men. Part-time: 16 students, 50% women, 50% men. Students come from 49 states and territories, 78 other countries, 40% from out-of-state. 0.2% American Indian or Alaska Native, non-Hispanic/Latino; 12% Hispanic/Latino; 6% African American, non-Hispanic/Latino; 4% Asian, non-Hispanic/Latino; 0.1% Native Hawaiian or other Pacific Islander, non-Hispanic/Latino; 12% international. 1% 25 or older, 80% live on campus, 4% transferred in. Retention: 84% of full-time freshmen returned the following year. Academic areas with the most degrees conferred: social sciences; business/marketing; communication/journalism. Core. Calendar: semesters. Services for LD students, advanced placement, accelerated degree program, self-designed majors, honors program, independent study, double major, summer session for credit, part-time degree program, internships. Off campus study at 14 members of the Associated Colleges of the Midwest (ACM); Washington Semester at American University; approved programs include: AIFS, AIU, API, ASA, CC-CS, CCIS, CEA, CIEE, CIS, Global Leadership Program, AsiaLearn, AustraLearn, EuroLearn, IAU, IES, IIE, InterStudy, ISA, OSAP, Semester at Sea Univ. of Virginia, SIT. Study abroad program.

Entrance Requirements: Options: electronic application, early decision, early action, deferred admission, international baccalaureate accepted. Required: essay, high school transcript, 1 recommendation. Recommended: interview. Required for some: SAT or ACT. Entrance: moderately difficult. Application deadlines: 2/15, 12/1 for early decision, 12/1 for early action. Notification: 3/20, Rolling for early decision, 1/20 for early action. Transfer credits accepted: Yes. Early decision applicants: 79. Early decision applicants admitted: 47.

Costs Per Year: Application fee: $0. Comprehensive fee: $47,350 includes full-time tuition ($37,660), mandatory fees ($640), and college room and board ($9050). College room only: $4440.

Collegiate Environment: Orientation program. Drama-theater group, choral group, student-run newspaper, radio station. Social organizations: 45 open to all; national fraternities, national sororities; 7% of eligible men and 19% of eligible women are members. Most popular organizations: WMXM, eTeam, Habitat for Humanity, United Black Association, International Student Organization. Major annual events: Relay for Life, Gates Day of Community Service, spring concert. Student services: health clinic, personal-psychological counseling. Campus security: 24-hour emergency response devices and patrols, student patrols, late night transport-escort service, controlled dormitory access. Donnelley and Lee Library with 292 books, 108,774 microform titles, 3,289 serials, 9,035 audiovisual materials, an OPAC, and a Web page. Operations spending for the previous fiscal year: $1.7 million. 130 computers available on campus for general student use. Computer purchase/lease plans available. A campuswide network can be accessed from student residence rooms and from off campus. Students can access the following: online class registration, file storage. Staffed computer lab on campus (open 24 hours a day) provides training in use of computers, software, and the Internet.

■ **LAKE LAND COLLEGE**
5001 Lake Land Blvd.
Mattoon, IL 61938-9366
Tel: (217)234-5253
E-mail: admissions@lakeland.cc.il.us
Web Site: www.lakelandcollege.edu/

Description: State and locally supported, 2-year, coed. Part of Illinois Community College Board. Awards certificates, transfer associate, and terminal associate degrees. Founded 1966. Setting: 308-acre rural campus. Endowment: $2.7 million. Educational spending for the previous fiscal year: $2016 per student. Total enrollment: 7,431. Faculty: 191 (116 full-time, 75 part-time). Student-undergrad faculty ratio is 21:1. 3,266 applied, 100% were admitted. Full-time: 3,160 students, 51% women, 49% men. Part-time: 4,271 students, 43% women, 57% men. Students come from 25 states and territories, 20 other countries, 1% from out-of-state. 36% 25 or older, 6% transferred in. Retention: 56% of full-time freshmen returned the following year. Core. Calendar: semesters. Academic remediation for entering students, ESL program, services for LD students, accelerated degree program, honors program, distance learning, summer session for credit, part-time degree program, external degree program, adult/continuing education programs, co-op programs and internships.

Entrance Requirements: Open admission except for dental services, nursing, physical therapy, civil engineering technology, and agricultural technology programs. Options: electronic application, early admission. Recommended: high school transcript, ACT. Entrance: noncompetitive. Application deadline: Rolling. Notification: continuous.

Collegiate Environment: Choral group, student-run newspaper, radio station. Social organizations: 25 open to all. Most popular organizations: Agriculture Production and Management Club, Cosmetology Club, Agriculture Transfer Club, Phi Theta Kappa, Civil Engineering Technology Club. Major annual events: Spring Carnival, Alcohol Awareness Week, Blood Drives. Student services: personal-psychological counseling. Campus security: 24-hour patrols. Virgil H. Judge Learning Resource Center with 28,000 books, 21,723 microform titles, 225 serials, 1,939 audiovisual materials, and an OPAC. Operations spending for the previous fiscal year: $439,600. 1,800 computers available on campus for general student use. A campuswide network can be accessed. Students can access the following: online class registration. Staffed computer lab on campus.

Community Environment: Mattoon (population 17,000) is an agricultural, commercial, industrial, oil, and transportation center with an average temperature of 53 degrees and an annual rainfall of 39 inches. Bus, train, and air service is available. Community facilities include churches of all denominations, many civic, service, and fraternal organizations, a civic center, hospital, nursing center, clinic, and excellent shopping facilities.

Recreational facilities include golf courses, swimming pools, bowling lanes, theatres, skating rinks, and Lakes Paradise and Mattoon with swimming, boating, fishing, and an amusement park. Mattoon is located in the heart of the Lincoln-Lore Lane with many historic points of interest in the area. Part-time employment is available.

■ LAKEVIEW COLLEGE OF NURSING

903 N Logan Ave.
Danville, IL 61832
Tel: (217)443-5238
Fax: (217)431-4015
E-mail: admission@lakeviewcol.edu
Web Site: www.lakeviewcol.edu/
Description: Independent, upper-level, coed. Awards bachelor's degrees. Founded 1987. Setting: 1-acre small town campus. Total enrollment: 239. Faculty: 51 (25 full-time, 26 part-time). Student-undergrad faculty ratio is 7:1. Full-time: 239 students, 81% women, 19% men. 31% 25 or older. Core. Calendar: semesters. Academic remediation for entering students, distance learning, summer session for credit, part-time degree program. Off campus study at Eastern Illinois University branch campus. ROTC: Army (c).
Entrance Requirements: Transfer credits accepted: Yes.
Collegiate Environment: Orientation program. Campus security: 24-hour emergency response devices.

■ LE CORDON BLEU COLLEGE OF CULINARY ARTS IN CHICAGO

361 W Chestnut
Chicago, IL 60610-3050
Tel: (312)944-0882; Free: 888-295-7222
Fax: (312)944-8557
E-mail: mverratti@chicnet.org
Web Site: www.chefs.edu/chicago/
Description: Proprietary, 2-year, coed. Part of Career Education Corporation. Awards transfer associate and terminal associate degrees. Founded 1983. Setting: urban campus. Endowment: $35,000. Educational spending for the previous fiscal year: $4850 per student. Total enrollment: 898. Faculty: 68 (28 full-time, 40 part-time). Student-undergrad faculty ratio is 19:1. Full-time: 721 students, 42% women, 58% men. Part-time: 177 students, 42% women, 58% men. Students come from 13 states and territories, 26% from out-of-state. 36% 25 or older, 0% transferred in. Core. Calendar: continuous. Academic remediation for entering students, services for LD students, advanced placement, internships.
Entrance Requirements: Open admission. Options: electronic application, deferred admission, international baccalaureate accepted. Recommended: essay, high school transcript, interview. Entrance: minimally difficult.
Collegiate Environment: Student-run newspaper. Social organizations: 8 open to all. Most popular organizations: The Student Board, Culinary Competition Club, Recipe Development Association, The Cellar Club, Pastry Display Club. Campus security: 24-hour emergency response devices and patrols. Learning Resource Center with 11,000 books, 40 serials, 150 audiovisual materials, and an OPAC. Operations spending for the previous fiscal year: $75,000. 25 computers available on campus for general student use. A campuswide network can be accessed from off-campus. Staffed computer lab on campus.

■ LEWIS AND CLARK COMMUNITY COLLEGE

5800 Godfrey Rd.
Godfrey, IL 62035-2466
Tel: (618)466-7000; Free: 800-YES-LCCC
Fax: (618)466-2798
Web Site: www.lc.edu/
Description: District-supported, 2-year, coed. Part of Illinois Community College Board. Awards certificates, transfer associate, and terminal associate degrees. Founded 1970. Setting: 275-acre small town campus with easy access to St. Louis. Total enrollment: 8,179. Core. Calendar: semesters. Academic remediation for entering students, ESL program, services for LD students, advanced placement, independent study, distance learning, double major, summer session for credit, part-time degree program, adult/continuing education programs, co-op programs and internships. Off campus study at Blackburn College. ROTC: Army.
Entrance Requirements: Open admission except for nursing, dental assisting, dental hygiene, occupational therapy, paramedicine, and therapeutic massage. Options: early admission, deferred admission. Recommended: high school transcript. Required for some: interview. Entrance: noncompetitive. Application deadline: Rolling. Notification: continuous.

Collegiate Environment: Orientation program. Choral group, student-run newspaper, radio station. Student services: health clinic, personal-psychological counseling. Campus security: 24-hour emergency response devices and patrols. Reid Memorial Library with 47,000 books, 2,500 microform titles, 3,500 serials, 1,700 audiovisual materials, an OPAC, and a Web page.
Community Environment: Godfrey (population 16,996) is near Alton (population 29,433), an industrial city just north of St. Louis. Industries include glass production, oil refineries, and manufacturing of steel products, brass, bronze, and copper goods. Railroads serve the area and air service is available at St. Louis airport, approximately 17 miles away. Alton has a community concert association, civic orchestra, little theater, and other similar facilities at nearby colleges. Recreational activities include golf, water sports, tennis, and spectator sports. Hunting and fishing opportunities are outstanding. Part-time work is available in industrial and commercial establishments.

■ LEWIS UNIVERSITY

One University Pky.
Romeoville, IL 60446
Tel: (815)838-0500; Free: 800-897-9000
Fax: (815)838-9456
E-mail: admissions@lewisu.edu
Web Site: www.lewisu.edu/
Description: Independent, comprehensive, coed, affiliated with Roman Catholic Church. Awards associate, bachelor's, master's, and doctoral degrees and post-master's certificates. Founded 1932. Setting: 410-acre suburban campus with easy access to Chicago. Endowment: $40.8 million. Educational spending for the previous fiscal year: $8266 per student. Total enrollment: 6,539. Faculty: 662 (212 full-time, 450 part-time). Student-undergrad faculty ratio is 13:1. 5,568 applied, 56% were admitted. 13% from top 10% of their high school class, 40% from top quarter, 77% from top half. 19 valedictorians. Full-time: 3,611 students, 55% women, 45% men. Part-time: 968 students, 61% women, 39% men. Students come from 37 states and territories, 21 other countries, 6% from out-of-state. 0.4% American Indian or Alaska Native, non-Hispanic/Latino; 16% Hispanic/Latino; 8% African American, non-Hispanic/Latino; 3% Asian, non-Hispanic/Latino; 0.2% Native Hawaiian or other Pacific Islander, non-Hispanic/Latino; 1% international. 25% 25 or older, 28% live on campus, 9% transferred in. Retention: 82% of full-time freshmen returned the following year. Academic areas with the most degrees conferred: business/marketing; health professions and related sciences; homeland security, law enforcement, firefighting, and protective services. Core. Calendar: semesters. Academic remediation for entering students, ESL program, services for LD students, advanced placement, accelerated degree program, self-designed majors, honors program, independent study, distance learning, double major, summer session for credit, part-time degree program, adult/continuing education programs, internships, graduate courses open to undergrads. Off campus study. Study abroad program. ROTC: Army (c), Air Force (c).
Entrance Requirements: Options: electronic application, deferred admission, international baccalaureate accepted. Required: high school transcript, minimum 2 high school GPA, SAT or ACT. Required for some: interview. Entrance: moderately difficult. Application deadlines: 8/1, 8/1 for nonresidents. Notification: continuous, continuous for nonresidents. SAT Reasoning Test deadline: 8/1. Transfer credits accepted: Yes.
Costs Per Year: Application fee: $40. Comprehensive fee: $36,310 includes full-time tuition ($26,780) and college room and board ($9530). College room only: $6160. Full-time tuition varies according to course load and program. Room and board charges vary according to board plan and housing facility. Part-time tuition: $780 per credit. Part-time mandatory fees: $780 per credit. Part-time tuition and fees vary according to course load and program.
Collegiate Environment: Orientation program. Drama-theater group, choral group, student-run newspaper, radio station. Social organizations: 103 open to all; national fraternities, national sororities, local fraternities, local sororities; 3% of eligible men and 4% of eligible women are members. Most popular organizations: Student Governing Board, Student Nurses Association, Latin American Student Organization, Theta Kappa Pi Sorority, Delta Sigma Pi (business fraternity). Major annual events: Homecoming and Family Day, Fall/Spring Formal, International Student Food Festival. Student services: health clinic, personal-psychological counseling. Campus security: 24-hour emergency response devices and patrols, student patrols, late night transport-escort service, controlled dormitory access. 1,348 college housing spaces available; 1,257 were occupied in 2012-13. Freshmen guaranteed college housing. Option: coed housing available. Lewis University Library with 169,371 books, 79,425 microform titles, 47,529 serials, 800 audiovisual

materials, an OPAC, and a Web page. Operations spending for the previous fiscal year: $1.3 million. 350 computers available on campus for general student use. A campuswide network can be accessed from student residence rooms and from off campus. Students can access the following: online class registration, online help, online billing, online financial aid, online payments, online application for admission, online housing application, online application for graduation, Blackboard course management system. Staffed computer lab on campus provides training in use of computers, software, and the Internet.

Community Environment: Romeoville, located 35 miles southwest of Chicago, enjoys a seasonal climate. The Regional Transportation Authority between Chicago and Joliet serves the area, as well as Amtrak. Romeoville has the usual civic, fraternal, and veterans' organizations. Part-time employment is available.

■ **LEXINGTON COLLEGE**
310 S Peoria St., Ste. 512
Chicago, IL 60607-3534
Tel: (312)226-6294
Fax: (312)226-6405
E-mail: admissions@lexingtoncollege.edu
Web Site: www.lexingtoncollege.edu/

Description: Independent, 4-year, women only. Awards associate and bachelor's degrees. Founded 1977. Setting: urban campus. Endowment: $29,600. Educational spending for the previous fiscal year: $19,725 per student. Total enrollment: 54. Faculty: 19 (4 full-time, 15 part-time). Student-undergrad faculty ratio is 6:1. 62 applied, 47% were admitted. 22% from top 10% of their high school class, 33% from top quarter, 56% from top half. 2 student government officers. Full-time: 52 students. Part-time: 2 students. Students come from 8 states and territories, 1 other country, 20% from out-of-state. 35% 25 or older, 11% transferred in. Retention: 71% of full-time freshmen returned the following year. Core. Calendar: semesters. Academic remediation for entering students, advanced placement, independent study, part-time degree program, co-op programs and internships. Study abroad program.

Entrance Requirements: Open admission. Option: electronic application. Required: essay, high school transcript, minimum 2 high school GPA. Recommended: interview. Required for some: SAT or ACT. Entrance: noncompetitive. Application deadline: Rolling. Notification: continuous. Transfer credits accepted: Yes.

Collegiate Environment: Orientation program. Student-run newspaper. Social organizations: 5 open to all. Most popular organizations: student government, Dinner Club, student service program, Student Mentors, student tutoring. Major annual events: cultural appreciation events, Taste of Lexington, College Fall Benefit. Campus security: 24-hour emergency response devices and patrols, patrols by municipal security personnel. 3,500 books, 30 serials, 50 audiovisual materials, an OPAC, and a Web page 30 computers available on campus for general student use. A campuswide network can be accessed from off-campus. Students can access the following: academic, coursework-supporting software. Staffed computer lab on campus provides training in use of computers, software, and the Internet.

■ **LINCOLN CHRISTIAN UNIVERSITY**
100 Campus View Dr.
Lincoln, IL 62656-2167
Tel: (217)732-3168; Free: 888-522-5228
Fax: (217)732-5914
E-mail: admissions@lincolnchristian.edu
Web Site: www.lincolnchristian.edu/

Description: Independent, 4-year, coed, affiliated with Christian Churches and Churches of Christ. Awards associate, bachelor's, master's, and doctoral degrees. Founded 1944. Setting: 227-acre small town campus. Endowment: $4.2 million. Educational spending for the previous fiscal year: $5663 per student. Total enrollment: 1,071. Faculty: 118 (36 full-time, 82 part-time). Student-undergrad faculty ratio is 14:1. 335 applied, 67% were admitted. Full-time: 580 students, 54% women, 46% men. Part-time: 99 students, 52% women, 48% men. Students come from 33 states and territories, 3 other countries, 31% from out-of-state. 1% American Indian or Alaska Native, non-Hispanic/Latino; 3% Hispanic/Latino; 6% African American, non-Hispanic/Latino; 1% Asian, non-Hispanic/Latino; 0% Native Hawaiian or other Pacific Islander, non-Hispanic/Latino; 2% international. 9% 25 or older, 51% live on campus, 12% transferred in. Retention: 75% of full-time freshmen returned the following year. Academic areas with the most degrees confered: theology and religious vocations; business/marketing;

public administration and social services. Core. Calendar: semesters. Academic remediation for entering students, services for LD students, advanced placement, honors program, independent study, distance learning, double major, summer session for credit, part-time degree program, external degree program, adult/continuing education programs, internships. Off campus study at University of Illinois at Springfield, Illinois State University, Greenville College. Study abroad program.

Entrance Requirements: Options: electronic application, deferred admission. Required: essay, high school transcript, 3 recommendations, SAT or ACT. Required for some: interview. Entrance: moderately difficult. Application deadlines: Rolling, Rolling for nonresidents. Notification: continuous, continuous for nonresidents. Preference given to Christian applicants interested in religious studies. SAT Reasoning Test deadline: 8/1. Transfer credits accepted: Yes.

Costs Per Year: Application fee: $25. One-time mandatory fee: $240. Comprehensive fee: $22,140 includes full-time tuition ($15,060) and college room and board ($7080). College room only: $3398. Full-time tuition varies according to location. Part-time tuition: $502 per credit hour. Part-time mandatory fees: $8 per credit hour. Part-time tuition and fees vary according to location.

Collegiate Environment: Orientation program. Drama-theater group, choral group. Social organizations: 4 open to all. Most popular organizations: Chorale, Student Cabinet, American Association of Christian Counselors (AACC) - Student Chapter, Cheerleading. Major annual events: Christmas in the Chapel, Lectureships, Convocation. Student services: personal-psychological counseling. Campus security: 24-hour emergency response devices, student patrols, controlled dormitory access. 622 college housing spaces available; 311 were occupied in 2012-13. Freshmen guaranteed college housing. On-campus residence required through senior year. Options: men-only, women-only housing available. Jessie Eury Library with 141,763 books, 26,621 serials, 20,909 audiovisual materials, an OPAC, and a Web page. Operations spending for the previous fiscal year: $436,244. 51 computers available on campus for general student use. A campuswide network can be accessed from student residence rooms and from off campus. Students can access the following: online class registration. Staffed computer lab on campus.

Community Environment: See Lincoln College.

■ **LINCOLN COLLEGE**
300 Keokuk St.
Lincoln, IL 62656-1699
Tel: (217)732-3155; Free: 800-569-0558
Fax: (217)732-8859
E-mail: gbree@lincolncollege.edu
Web Site: www.lincolncollege.edu/

Description: Independent, 2-year, coed. Awards transfer associate degrees. Founded 1865. Setting: 42-acre small town campus. Total enrollment: 1,304. Student-undergrad faculty ratio is 15:1. 1,537 applied, 68% were admitted. 4% from out-of-state. 22% 25 or older. Core. Calendar: semesters. Academic remediation for entering students, accelerated degree program, freshman honors college, honors program, independent study, summer session for credit, part-time degree program.

Entrance Requirements: Options: early admission, deferred admission. Required: high school transcript, SAT or ACT. Recommended: interview. Required for some: 1 recommendation. Entrance: minimally difficult. Application deadline: Rolling.

Collegiate Environment: Orientation program. Drama-theater group, choral group, student-run newspaper, radio station. Student services: health clinic. Campus security: 24-hour emergency response devices and patrols, controlled dormitory access. McKinstry Library with an OPAC and a Web page.

Community Environment: Lincoln (population 14,971) was founded in 1852, the only one of 24 similarly named cities of the United States that was named for Abraham Lincoln before he became famous. He assisted in planning the city and performed law work necessary for its incorporation. Lincoln christened the town with the juice of a watermelon when the first lots were sold in 1853. Lincoln is midway between Chicago and St. Louis on the main line of Alton route of GM & O Railroad. Churches of many denominations are located here.

■ **LINCOLN COLLEGE–NORMAL**
715 W Raab Rd.
Normal, IL 61761
Tel: (309)452-0500; Free: 800-569-0558

Fax: (309)454-5652
E-mail: spuck@lincolncollege.edu
Web Site: www.lincolncollege.edu/normal/
Description: Independent, 4-year, coed. Awards associate and bachelor's degrees. Founded 1865. Setting: 10-acre suburban campus with easy access to Bloomington/Normal, IL. Total enrollment: 527. Faculty: 58 (9 full-time, 49 part-time). Student-undergrad faculty ratio is 14:1. 1,417 applied, 72% were admitted. Students come from 9 states and territories, 1 other country, 2% from out-of-state. 39% 25 or older, 35% live on campus. Academic areas with the most degrees conferred: business/marketing; liberal arts/general studies; homeland security, law enforcement, firefighting, and protective services. Core. Calendar: some programs are semester; some are continuous. Academic remediation for entering students, accelerated degree program, honors program, independent study, distance learning, summer session for credit, part-time degree program, adult/continuing education programs, co-op programs and internships.
Entrance Requirements: Options: electronic application, deferred admission. Required: high school transcript. Recommended: minimum 2 high school GPA. Required for some: essay, 1 recommendation, interview, SAT or ACT. ACT score required for some programs. Entrance: minimally difficult. Application deadlines: 9/1, 9/1 for nonresidents. Notification: continuous, continuous for nonresidents. SAT Reasoning Test deadline: 9/1. Transfer credits accepted: Yes.
Collegiate Environment: Orientation program. Social organizations: local fraternities, local sororities; 40% of eligible men and 60% of eligible women are members. Most popular organizations: Residence Hall Association, MCC Student Government, Black Student Union, BACCHUS. Campus security: 24-hour emergency response devices and patrols, student patrols, late night transport-escort service, controlled dormitory access. Milner Library at Illinois State University with 1.8 million books, 2 million microform titles, 25,000 audiovisual materials, an OPAC, and a Web page. 63 computers available on campus for general student use. A campuswide network can be accessed from student residence rooms and from off campus. Staffed computer lab on campus (open 24 hours a day).

■ **LINCOLN LAND COMMUNITY COLLEGE**
5250 Shepherd Rd.
Springfield, IL 62794-9256
Tel: (217)786-2200; Free: 800-727-4161
Fax: (217)786-2492
E-mail: ron.gregoire@llcc.edu
Web Site: www.llcc.edu/
Description: District-supported, 2-year, coed. Part of Illinois Community College Board. Awards certificates, transfer associate, and terminal associate degrees. Founded 1967. Setting: 441-acre suburban campus. Endowment: $2.6 million. Educational spending for the previous fiscal year: $3299 per student. Total enrollment: 7,193. Faculty: 382 (129 full-time, 253 part-time). Student-undergrad faculty ratio is 21:1. Full-time: 3,047 students, 53% women, 47% men. Part-time: 4,146 students, 62% women, 38% men. Students come from 12 states and territories, 0% from out-of-state. 0.2% American Indian or Alaska Native, non-Hispanic/Latino; 2% Hispanic/Latino; 9% African American, non-Hispanic/Latino; 2% Asian, non-Hispanic/Latino; 0.1% Native Hawaiian or other Pacific Islander, non-Hispanic/Latino; 0.1% international. 44% 25 or older, 1% transferred in. Retention: 50% of full-time freshmen returned the following year. Core. Calendar: semesters. Academic remediation for entering students, ESL program, services for LD students, advanced placement, accelerated degree program, honors program, independent study, distance learning, summer session for credit, part-time degree program, external degree program, adult/continuing education programs, internships. Off campus study at Foreign Language/International Studies Consortium. Study abroad program.
Entrance Requirements: Open admission except for allied health programs. Options: electronic application, early admission, deferred admission. Recommended: high school transcript. Entrance: noncompetitive. Application deadline: Rolling. Notification: continuous. Transfer credits accepted: Yes.
Costs Per Year: Application fee: $0. Area resident tuition: $2304 full-time, $96 per credit hour part-time. State resident tuition: $4608 full-time, $192 per credit hour part-time. Nonresident tuition: $6912 full-time, $288 per credit hour part-time. Mandatory fees: $264 full-time, $11 per credit hour part-time. Full-time tuition and fees vary according to program. Part-time tuition and fees vary according to program.
Collegiate Environment: Orientation program. Drama-theater group, choral group, student-run newspaper. Social organizations: 41 open to all. Most

popular organizations: Student Government Association, Phi Theta Kappa, Agriculture Club, Epicurean Club, Veteran's Club. Major annual events: Graduation, Loggerpalooza, Club & Vendor Day. Student services: health clinic, personal-psychological counseling. Campus security: 24-hour emergency response devices and patrols, late night transport-escort service. College housing not available. Learning Resource Center with 64,916 books, 3,000 microform titles, 2,860 serials, 2,057 audiovisual materials, an OPAC, and a Web page. Operations spending for the previous fiscal year: $925,938. 525 computers available on campus for general student use. A campuswide network can be accessed from off-campus. Students can access the following: online class registration. Staffed computer lab on campus.

■ **LINDENWOOD UNIVERSITY–BELLEVILLE**
2600 W Main St.
Belleville, IL 62226
Tel: (618)239-6000
Web Site: belleville.lindenwood.edu/
Description: Independent religious, comprehensive, coed. Founded 2003.

■ **LOYOLA UNIVERSITY CHICAGO**
1032 W Sheridan Rd.
Chicago, IL 60660
Tel: (773)274-3000; Free: 800-262-2373
Fax: (773)915-6414
E-mail: admission@luc.edu
Web Site: www.luc.edu/
Description: Independent Roman Catholic (Jesuit), university, coed. Awards bachelor's, master's, and doctoral degrees and post-master's certificates (also offers adult part-time program with significant enrollment not reflected in profile). Founded 1870. Setting: 105-acre urban campus. Endowment: $406 million. Research spending for the previous fiscal year: $44.1 million. Educational spending for the previous fiscal year: $10,289 per student. Total enrollment: 15,720. Faculty: 1,463 (719 full-time, 744 part-time). Student-undergrad faculty ratio is 14:1. 19,657 applied, 58% were admitted. 35% from top 10% of their high school class, 69% from top quarter, 94% from top half. 10 National Merit Scholars, 7 class presidents, 24 valedictorians, 265 student government officers. Full-time: 8,952 students, 63% women, 37% men. Part-time: 771 students, 61% women, 39% men. Students come from 50 states and territories, 77 other countries, 34% from out-of-state. 0.1% American Indian or Alaska Native, non-Hispanic/Latino; 12% Hispanic/Latino; 4% African American, non-Hispanic/Latino; 10% Asian, non-Hispanic/Latino; 0.1% Native Hawaiian or other Pacific Islander, non-Hispanic/Latino; 2% international. 9% 25 or older, 41% live on campus, 7% transferred in. Retention: 87% of full-time freshmen returned the following year. Academic areas with the most degrees conferred: business/marketing; biological/life sciences; psychology. Core. Calendar: semesters. Academic remediation for entering students, ESL program, services for LD students, advanced placement, accelerated degree program, freshman honors college, honors program, independent study, distance learning, double major, summer session for credit, part-time degree program, adult/continuing education programs, co-op programs and internships, graduate courses open to undergrads. Off campus study at Washington interns; Marquette. Study abroad program. ROTC: Army (c), Naval (c), Air Force (c).
Entrance Requirements: Options: electronic application, international baccalaureate accepted. Required: essay, high school transcript, minimum 2 high school GPA, SAT or ACT. Recommended: interview. Entrance: moderately difficult. Notification: continuous, continuous for nonresidents. SAT Reasoning Test deadline: 2/1. Transfer credits accepted: Yes.
Costs Per Year: Application fee: $0. Comprehensive fee: $48,403 includes full-time tuition ($34,343), mandatory fees ($1160), and college room and board ($12,900). College room only: $8114. Full-time tuition and fees vary according to location, program, and student level. Room and board charges vary according to board plan, housing facility, and location. Part-time tuition: $690 per credit. Part-time mandatory fees: $158 per term. Part-time tuition and fees vary according to course load.
Collegiate Environment: Orientation program. Drama-theater group, student-run newspaper, radio station. Social organizations: 195 open to all; national fraternities, national sororities; 68% of eligible men and 72% of eligible women are members. Most popular organizations: Department of Programming, Panhellenic Sororities, American Medical Association, Habitat for Humanity, Globe Med. Major annual events: President's Ball, Department of Programming Concert/Mainstage Events, New Year's Festival. Student services: health clinic, personal-psychological counseling, women's center.

Campus security: 24-hour emergency response devices and patrols, late night transport-escort service, controlled dormitory access, Loyola Alert (special service to provide personalized, time-sensitive alerts to students, faculty, staff and other personnel at Loyola). 4,070 college housing spaces available; 3,851 were occupied in 2012-13. Freshmen guaranteed college housing. On-campus residence required through sophomore year. Option: coed housing available. Cudahy Library plus 7 others with 1.4 million books, 1.4 million microform titles, 52,535 serials, 15,754 audiovisual materials, an OPAC, and a Web page. Operations spending for the previous fiscal year: $14 million. 1,464 computers available on campus for general student use. Computer purchase/lease plans available. A campuswide network can be accessed from student residence rooms and from off campus. Students can access the following: online class registration. Staffed computer lab on campus provides training in use of computers, software, and the Internet.

Community Environment: See University of Chicago.

■ MACCORMAC COLLEGE

506 S Wabash Ave.
Chicago, IL 60605-1667
Tel: (312)922-1884
Fax: (312)922-3196
Web Site: www.maccormac.edu/

Description: Independent, 2-year, coed. Awards certificates, diplomas, transfer associate, and terminal associate degrees. Founded 1904. Setting: urban campus. Total enrollment: 377. Faculty: 34 (4 full-time, 30 part-time). Student-undergrad faculty ratio is 9:1. Full-time: 159 students, 86% women, 14% men. Part-time: 218 students, 89% women, 11% men. Students come from 7 states and territories, 8 other countries, 1% from out-of-state. 20% 25 or older. Core. Calendar: semesters. Academic remediation for entering students, ESL program, advanced placement, honors program, summer session for credit, part-time degree program, adult/continuing education programs, internships.

Entrance Requirements: Option: deferred admission. Required: high school transcript, ACT. Recommended: interview, SAT. Entrance: moderately difficult. Application deadline: Rolling. Notification: continuous.

Collegiate Environment: Orientation program. Social organizations: 2 open to all. Major annual events: Halloween Party, Christmas Dance, All-College Picnic. Student services: personal-psychological counseling. Campus security: late night transport-escort service. MacCormac College Library with 11,000 books and 140 serials. 180 computers available on campus for general student use. A campuswide network can be accessed.

Community Environment: See University of Chicago.

■ MACMURRAY COLLEGE

447 E College Ave.
Jacksonville, IL 62650
Tel: (217)479-7000; Free: 800-252-7485
Fax: (217)245-0405
E-mail: alicia.zeone@mac.edu
Web Site: www.mac.edu/

Description: Independent United Methodist, 4-year, coed. Awards associate and bachelor's degrees. Founded 1846. Setting: 60-acre small town campus. Endowment: $7.1 million. Educational spending for the previous fiscal year: $5644 per student. Total enrollment: 528. Faculty: 56 (33 full-time, 23 part-time). Student-undergrad faculty ratio is 11:1. 539 applied, 77% were admitted. 11% from top 10% of their high school class, 13% from top quarter, 48% from top half. Full-time: 435 students, 60% women, 40% men. Part-time: 93 students, 72% women, 28% men. Students come from 21 states and territories, 1 other country, 12% from out-of-state. 15% 25 or older, 49% live on campus, 12% transferred in. Retention: 49% of full-time freshmen returned the following year. Academic areas with the most degrees conferred: personal and culinary services; social sciences; psychology. Core. Calendar: 4-1-4. Academic remediation for entering students, services for LD students, advanced placement, self-designed majors, independent study, double major, summer session for credit, part-time degree program, adult/continuing education programs, co-op programs and internships. Off campus study at 5 members of the Western Illinois Foreign Language Consortium. Study abroad program.

Entrance Requirements: Options: electronic application, early admission, international baccalaureate accepted. Required: high school transcript. Recommended: SAT or ACT. Required for some: essay, minimum 2.5 high school GPA, 1 recommendation, interview. Entrance: moderately difficult. Application deadline: Rolling. Notification: continuous. Transfer credits accepted: Yes.

Costs Per Year: Application fee: $0. Comprehensive fee: $29,050 includes full-time tuition ($20,900), mandatory fees ($500), and college room and board ($7650). Full-time tuition and fees vary according to course load. Room and board charges vary according to housing facility. Part-time tuition: $693 per credit hour. Part-time mandatory fees: $30 per credit hour. Part-time tuition and fees vary according to course load.

Collegiate Environment: Orientation program. Drama-theater group, choral group. Social organizations: 35 open to all; national fraternities, local sororities; 10% of eligible men and 15% of eligible women are members. Most popular organizations: Campus Activity Board, MacMurray Student Association, Sigma Tau Gamma, Alpha Phi Omega, Circle K. Major annual event: Homecoming. Student services: health clinic, personal-psychological counseling. Campus security: 24-hour emergency response devices and patrols, late night transport-escort service. Henry Pfeiffer Library with 150,000 books, 25,000 microform titles, 125 serials, an OPAC, and a Web page. Operations spending for the previous fiscal year: $261,952. 100 computers available on campus for general student use. Staffed computer lab on campus provides training in use of computers, software, and the Internet.

Community Environment: See Illinois College.

■ MCHENRY COUNTY COLLEGE

8900 US Hwy. 14
Crystal Lake, IL 60012-2761
Tel: (815)455-3700
E-mail: admissions@mchenry.edu
Web Site: www.mchenry.edu/

Description: State and locally supported, 2-year, coed. Part of Illinois Community College Board. Awards certificates, transfer associate, and terminal associate degrees. Founded 1967. Setting: 168-acre suburban campus with easy access to Chicago. Endowment: $856,341. Educational spending for the previous fiscal year: $3988 per student. Total enrollment: 5,618. Faculty: 401 (100 full-time, 301 part-time). Student-undergrad faculty ratio is 18:1. 2,630 applied, 100% were admitted. Full-time: 2,375 students, 50% women, 50% men. Part-time: 3,243 students, 58% women, 42% men. 1% from out-of-state. 0.4% American Indian or Alaska Native, non-Hispanic/Latino; 10% Hispanic/Latino; 2% African American, non-Hispanic/Latino; 2% Asian, non-Hispanic/Latino; 0.2% Native Hawaiian or other Pacific Islander, non-Hispanic/Latino; 0.2% international. 33% 25 or older, 0% transferred in. Core. Calendar: semesters. Academic remediation for entering students, ESL program, services for LD students, advanced placement, accelerated degree program, honors program, independent study, distance learning, summer session for credit, part-time degree program, adult/continuing education programs, co-op programs and internships. Study abroad program.

Entrance Requirements: Open admission. Options: electronic application, early admission, deferred admission. Recommended: high school transcript. Entrance: noncompetitive. Application deadlines: Rolling, Rolling for nonresidents. Notification: continuous, continuous for nonresidents. Transfer credits accepted: Yes.

Costs Per Year: Application fee: $15. Area resident tuition: $2700 full-time, $90 per credit hour part-time. State resident tuition: $8010 full-time, $267 per credit hour part-time. Nonresident tuition: $9780 full-time, $326 per credit hour part-time. Mandatory fees: $229 full-time, $9 per credit hour part-time, $7. Full-time tuition and fees vary according to course load. Part-time tuition and fees vary according to course load.

Collegiate Environment: Orientation program. Drama-theater group, choral group, student-run newspaper. Social organizations: 31 open to all. Most popular organizations: Phi Theta Kappa, Student Senate, Equality Club, Writer's Block, Latinos Unidos. Major annual events: Welcome Week Picnic & Convocation, Student Organization Fair, Spring Fling Week. Student services: personal-psychological counseling. Campus security: 24-hour emergency response devices and patrols, late night transport-escort service. College housing not available. McHenry County College Library with 60,000 books, 125 serials, 5,042 audiovisual materials, an OPAC, and a Web page. Operations spending for the previous fiscal year: $1 million. 153 computers available on campus for general student use. A campuswide network can be accessed. Students can access the following: online class registration. Staffed computer lab on campus.

Community Environment: Crystal Lake after which the city (population 40,900) was named, is the only natural spring-fed lake between Chicago and Wisconsin. Within the city are 27 large industrial firms and 45 smaller ones, churches, library, medical center, hospitals, and 350 apartment units ranging from small to luxury townhouses. Recreational facilities include the 400 acres of parks and beaches along the lake for all types of water sports and other recreation.

■ **MCKENDREE UNIVERSITY**
701 College Rd.
Lebanon, IL 62254-1299
Tel: (618)537-4481; Free: 800-232-7228
Fax: (618)537-6259
E-mail: jlblasdel@mckendree.edu
Web Site: www.mckendree.edu/
Description: Independent, comprehensive, coed, affiliated with United Methodist Church. Awards associate, bachelor's, master's, and doctoral degrees and post-master's certificates. Founded 1828. Setting: 234-acre suburban campus with easy access to St. Louis, MO; Belleville, IL. Endowment: $28.6 million. Educational spending for the previous fiscal year: $8588 per student. Total enrollment: 3,308. Faculty: 313 (98 full-time, 215 part-time). Student-undergrad faculty ratio is 13:1. 1,359 applied, 68% were admitted. 13% from top 10% of their high school class, 41% from top quarter, 71% from top half. 4 valedictorians. Full-time: 1,667 students, 54% women, 46% men. Part-time: 689 students, 60% women, 40% men. Students come from 24 states and territories, 9 other countries, 32% from out-of-state. 0.2% American Indian or Alaska Native, non-Hispanic/Latino; 2% Hispanic/Latino; 9% African American, non-Hispanic/Latino; 1% Asian, non-Hispanic/Latino; 0% Native Hawaiian or other Pacific Islander, non-Hispanic/Latino; 1% international. 30% 25 or older, 60% live on campus, 5% transferred in. Retention: 81% of full-time freshmen returned the following year. Academic areas with the most degrees conferred: business/marketing; education; health professions and related sciences. Core. Calendar: semesters. Academic remediation for entering students, services for LD students, advanced placement, accelerated degree program, self-designed majors, honors program, independent study, distance learning, double major, summer session for credit, part-time degree program, adult/continuing education programs, co-op programs and internships, graduate courses open to undergrads. Off campus study. Study abroad program. ROTC: Army (c), Air Force (c).
Entrance Requirements: Options: electronic application, deferred admission. Required: essay, high school transcript, minimum 2.5 high school GPA, 1 recommendation, rank in upper 50% of high school class, ACT score of 20 or higher, SAT or ACT. Required for some: interview. Entrance: moderately difficult. Application deadline: Rolling. Notification: continuous. SAT Reasoning Test deadline: 8/13. Transfer credits accepted: Yes. Applicants placed on waiting list: 15. Wait-listed applicants offered admission: 3.
Costs Per Year: Comprehensive fee: $34,740 includes full-time tuition ($25,050), mandatory fees ($1000), and college room and board ($8690). College room only: $4620. Full-time tuition and fees vary according to course load, degree level, and location. Room and board charges vary according to board plan and housing facility. Part-time tuition: $830 per credit hour. Part-time tuition varies according to course load, degree level, and location.
Collegiate Environment: Orientation program. Drama-theater group, choral group, marching band, student-run newspaper, radio station. Social organizations: 60 open to all; national fraternities, national sororities, local sororities; 7% of eligible men and 10% of eligible women are members. Most popular organizations: Wonders of Wellness, Center for Public Service, Campus Ministries, APO, Debate. Major annual events: Homecoming, Involvement Fair, Commencement. Student services: health clinic, personal-psychological counseling. Campus security: 24-hour emergency response devices and patrols, student patrols, late night transport-escort service, controlled dormitory access. 888 college housing spaces available; 835 were occupied in 2012-13. Freshmen guaranteed college housing. On-campus residence required through junior year. Option: coed housing available. Holman Library with 112,000 books, 39,000 microform titles, 1,500 serials, 7,742 audiovisual materials, an OPAC, and a Web page. Operations spending for the previous fiscal year: $511,971. 168 computers available on campus for general student use. A campuswide network can be accessed from student residence rooms and from off campus. Students can access the following: online class registration. Staffed computer lab on campus provides training in use of computers, software, and the Internet.
Community Environment: Lebanon, population 3,700, is 23 miles east of St. Louis. The city has the usual Mississippi Valley climate, neither too hot nor too cold but unpredictable. Scott Air Force Base is six miles from downtown. Employment is available in Belleville, 12 miles away, Fairview Heights, 12 miles away, and in St. Louis proper. Hospital facilities are in

Belleville, Highland, Breese and St. Louis. Local recreational activities are tennis, hunting, fishing, golfing, picnicking, and community theater.

■ **MIDSTATE COLLEGE**
411 W Northmoor Rd.
Peoria, IL 61614
Tel: (309)692-4092; Free: 800-251-4299
Fax: (309)692-3893
E-mail: jhancock2@midstate.edu
Web Site: www.midstate.edu/
Description: Proprietary, 4-year, coed. Awards associate and bachelor's degrees. Founded 1888. Setting: 1-acre urban campus. Total enrollment: 641. 49 applied. 82% 25 or older. Core. Academic remediation for entering students, freshman honors college, honors program, summer session for credit, part-time degree program, co-op programs and internships.
Entrance Requirements: Options: early admission, deferred admission. Required: high school transcript, Wonderlic aptitude test. Recommended: interview. Entrance: moderately difficult. Application deadline: Rolling.
Collegiate Environment: Social organizations: national sororities, local fraternities. Campus security: late night transport-escort service. Barbara Fields Library with 8,724 books, 104 serials, and an OPAC.
Community Environment: Peoria is the third largest city of downstate Illinois. All modes of transportation are available. It is the hub of the central area of the state for cultural, business and professional activities. Peoria is a manufacturing and shipping center located in the heart of the farm belt. Community facilities include good shopping areas and recreational opportunities. Job opportunities are good, particularly for summer work. Points of interest are Fort Creve Coer, Indian burial mounds, Peoria Historical Society Museum, Lakeview Center for Arts Sciences, the Planetarium, the Peoria Civic Center, and Wildlife Prairie Park.

■ **MILLIKIN UNIVERSITY**
1184 W Main St.
Decatur, IL 62522-2084
Tel: (217)424-6211; Free: 800-373-7733
Fax: (217)425-4669
E-mail: admis@millikin.edu
Web Site: www.millikin.edu/
Description: Independent, comprehensive, coed, affiliated with Presbyterian Church (U.S.A.). Awards bachelor's and master's degrees. Founded 1901. Setting: 75-acre suburban campus. Endowment: $105.5 million. Educational spending for the previous fiscal year: $17,502 per student. Total enrollment: 2,347. Faculty: 305 (154 full-time, 151 part-time). Student-undergrad faculty ratio is 11:1. 3,998 applied, 55% were admitted. 16% from top 10% of their high school class, 40% from top quarter, 77% from top half. Full-time: 2,161 students, 59% women, 41% men. Part-time: 103 students, 66% women, 34% men. Students come from 32 states and territories, 13 other countries, 11% from out-of-state. 0.3% American Indian or Alaska Native, non-Hispanic/Latino; 5% Hispanic/Latino; 12% African American, non-Hispanic/Latino; 1% Asian, non-Hispanic/Latino; 0.2% Native Hawaiian or other Pacific Islander, non-Hispanic/Latino; 1% international. 13% 25 or older, 61% live on campus, 6% transferred in. Retention: 78% of full-time freshmen returned the following year. Academic areas with the most degrees conferred: business/marketing; visual and performing arts; education. Core. Calendar: semesters. ESL program, services for LD students, advanced placement, accelerated degree program, self-designed majors, honors program, independent study, double major, summer session for credit, part-time degree program, adult/continuing education programs, internships. Off campus study at Drew University, American University, Urban Life Center. Study abroad program.
Entrance Requirements: Options: electronic application, deferred admission, international baccalaureate accepted. Required: high school transcript, minimum 2 high school GPA, 2 recommendations, SAT or ACT. Recommended: interview. Required for some: audition for music/theatre, art portfolio review. Entrance: moderately difficult. Application deadlines: Rolling, Rolling for nonresidents. Notification: continuous, continuous for nonresidents. SAT Reasoning Test deadline: 5/1. Transfer credits accepted: Yes.
Costs Per Year: Application fee: $0. Comprehensive fee: $37,614 includes full-time tuition ($27,852), mandatory fees ($792), and college room and board ($8970). College room only: $5000. Room and board charges vary according to board plan and housing facility. Part-time tuition: $931 per credit hour. Part-time mandatory fees: $22 per credit hour.
Collegiate Environment: Orientation program. Drama-theater group, choral group, student-run newspaper, radio station. Social organizations: 110 open

to all; national fraternities, national sororities; 19% of eligible men and 17% of eligible women are members. Most popular organizations: University Center Board, Multicultural Student Council, Student Housing Council, Panhellenic Council, Interfraternity Council. Major annual events: Homecoming, Fall Family Weekend, Performing Arts Series. Student services: health clinic, personal-psychological counseling. Campus security: 24-hour emergency response devices and patrols, late night transport-escort service, controlled dormitory access. 1,452 college housing spaces available; 1,069 were occupied in 2012-13. Freshmen guaranteed college housing. On-campus residence required through junior year. Options: coed, women-only housing available. Staley Library with 220,402 books, 21,394 microform titles, 237 serials, 13,345 audiovisual materials, an OPAC, and a Web page. Operations spending for the previous fiscal year: $671,799. 282 computers available on campus for general student use. A campuswide network can be accessed from student residence rooms. Students can access the following: online class registration, online degree audit; online financials (view and pay bills; view financial aid). Staffed computer lab on campus provides training in use of computers, software, and the Internet.

Community Environment: Decatur is a diversified industrial community. Bus and air service are available. Many part-time jobs are available. A well-developed park system provides varied recreational opportunities. South of Decatur is the Lincoln Trail Homestead State Park, which marks the first homestead site of the Lincoln family in Illinois.

■ MONMOUTH COLLEGE
700 E Broadway
Monmouth, IL 61462-1998
Tel: (309)457-2311; Free: 800-747-2687
Fax: (309)457-2141
E-mail: admissions@monmouthcollege.edu
Web Site: www.monm.edu/

Description: Independent, 4-year, coed, affiliated with Presbyterian Church. Awards bachelor's degrees. Founded 1853. Setting: 106-acre small town campus. Endowment: $77.7 million. Educational spending for the previous fiscal year: $9197 per student. Total enrollment: 1,247. Faculty: 118 (86 full-time, 32 part-time). Student-undergrad faculty ratio is 13:1. 1,930 applied, 62% were admitted. 13% from top 10% of their high school class, 37% from top quarter, 72% from top half. Full-time: 1,234 students, 54% women, 46% men. Part-time: 13 students, 62% women, 38% men. Students come from 19 states and territories, 9 other countries, 7% from out-of-state. 1% American Indian or Alaska Native, non-Hispanic/Latino; 9% Hispanic/Latino; 13% African American, non-Hispanic/Latino; 1% Asian, non-Hispanic/Latino; 0.3% Native Hawaiian or other Pacific Islander, non-Hispanic/Latino; 1% international. 0% 25 or older, 92% live on campus, 4% transferred in. Retention: 75% of full-time freshmen returned the following year. Academic areas with the most degrees conferred: business/marketing; education; communication/journalism. Core. Calendar: semesters. Academic remediation for entering students, ESL program, services for LD students, advanced placement, self-designed majors, honors program, independent study, double major, part-time degree program, internships. Off campus study at Associated Colleges of the Midwest study abroad programs, American College of Thessaloniki, American University in Paris, Augsburg College (Mexico and Central America), Beloit (Estonia, Morocco and Senegal), Central (Granada), Ecole Normale Superieure de Gestion et Commerce, International Student Exchange Program (ISTEP), Irish-American Scholars Program, University of Highlands and Islands (Scotland), Umea University (Sweden), American University - Washington Semester. Study abroad program. ROTC: Army (c).

Entrance Requirements: Options: electronic application, deferred admission, international baccalaureate accepted. Required: high school transcript, SAT or ACT. Recommended: essay, minimum 2.7 high school GPA, interview. Required for some: interview. Entrance: moderately difficult. Application deadline: Rolling. Notification: continuous. SAT Reasoning Test deadline: 5/1. SAT Subject Test deadline: 5/1. Transfer credits accepted: Yes.

Costs Per Year: Application fee: $0. One-time mandatory fee: $190. Comprehensive fee: $39,100 includes full-time tuition ($31,500) and college room and board ($7600). Full-time tuition varies according to course load. Room and board charges vary according to board plan and housing facility.

Collegiate Environment: Orientation program. Drama-theater group, choral group, marching band, student-run newspaper, radio station. Social organizations: 46 open to all; national fraternities, national sororities; 24% of eligible men and 25% of eligible women are members. Most popular organizations: Fighting Scots Marching Band and Jazz Band, Associated

Students of Monmouth College, Crimson Masque (theatre), Alternative Spring Break, Coalition for Ethnic Awareness. Major annual events: Homecoming, Scots Day (Founders Day), Family Weekend. Student services: personal-psychological counseling. Campus security: 24-hour emergency response devices, late night transport-escort service, controlled dormitory access, night security. 1,435 college housing spaces available; 1,144 were occupied in 2012-13. Freshmen guaranteed college housing. On-campus residence required through senior year. Options: coed, men-only, women-only housing available. Hewes Library plus 2 others with 199,087 books, 266,956 microform titles, 3,053 serials, 12,019 audiovisual materials, an OPAC, and a Web page. Operations spending for the previous fiscal year: $772,911. 140 computers available on campus for general student use. A campuswide network can be accessed from student residence rooms and from off campus. Students can access the following: online class registration, 11 PC labs and 3 specialized Mac labs. Staffed computer lab on campus (open 24 hours a day) provides training in use of computers, software, and the Internet.

Community Environment: Monmouth is located about 180 miles southwest of Chicago and 180 miles north of St. Louis in the heart of the rich corn belt of the Midwest. Although agriculture is the backbone of the economy in the area, numerous small businesses and light industry firms are located here. As a region noted for beef cattle feeding, Monmouth holds a three-day Prime Beef Festival in September. Monmouth Park, a natural forest at the outskirts of the city, has playground equipment, picnic facilities, and an 18-hole municipal golf course.

■ MOODY BIBLE INSTITUTE
820 N LaSalle Blvd.
Chicago, IL 60610-3284
Tel: (312)329-4000; Free: 800-967-4MBI
Fax: (312)329-8987
E-mail: admissions@moody.edu
Web Site: www.moody.edu/

Description: Independent nondenominational, comprehensive, coed. Awards associate, bachelor's, and master's degrees. Founded 1886. Setting: 25-acre urban campus with easy access to Chicago. Endowment: $27.8 million. Educational spending for the previous fiscal year: $10,100 per student. Total enrollment: 3,349. Faculty: 211 (90 full-time, 121 part-time). Student-undergrad faculty ratio is 20:1. 816 applied, 89% were admitted. Full-time: 2,275 students, 47% women, 53% men. Part-time: 653 students, 36% women, 64% men. Students come from 24 other countries. 0.2% American Indian or Alaska Native, non-Hispanic/Latino; 4% Hispanic/Latino; 4% African American, non-Hispanic/Latino; 3% Asian, non-Hispanic/Latino; 0.1% Native Hawaiian or other Pacific Islander, non-Hispanic/Latino; 6% international. Retention: 78% of full-time freshmen returned the following year. Academic areas with the most degrees conferred: theology and religious vocations; communication/journalism; visual and performing arts. Core. Calendar: semesters. ESL program, advanced placement, independent study, distance learning, double major, summer session for credit, part-time degree program, external degree program, adult/continuing education programs, internships, graduate courses open to undergrads. Off campus study at Roosevelt University, University of Illinois at Chicago, City Colleges of Chicago, Harold Washington College. Study abroad program.

Entrance Requirements: Options: electronic application, early admission, early decision, international baccalaureate accepted. Required: essay, high school transcript, minimum 2 high school GPA, 4 recommendations, Christian testimony, SAT and SAT Subject Tests or ACT. Required for some: interview. Entrance: moderately difficult. Application deadlines: 3/1, 12/1 for early decision. Notification: continuous until 4/1, 1/15 for early decision. SAT Reasoning Test deadline: 3/1. SAT Subject Test deadline: 3/1. Transfer credits accepted: Yes. Applicants placed on waiting list: 68. Wait-listed applicants offered admission: 0. Early decision applicants: 734. Early decision applicants admitted: 262.

Collegiate Environment: Orientation program. Drama-theater group, choral group, student-run newspaper, radio station. Student services: health clinic, personal-psychological counseling. Campus security: 24-hour emergency response devices and patrols, student patrols, late night transport-escort service, controlled dormitory access. Henry Crowell Learning Center plus 1 other with 135,000 books and 987 serials. Operations spending for the previous fiscal year: $640,660.

Community Environment: See University of Chicago.

■ MORAINE VALLEY COMMUNITY COLLEGE
9000 W College Pky.
Palos Hills, IL 60465

Tel: (708)974-4300

Fax: (708)974-0681

E-mail: roselli@morainevalley.edu

Web Site: www.morainevalley.edu/

Description: State and locally supported, 2-year, coed. Part of Illinois Community College Board. Awards certificates, transfer associate, and terminal associate degrees. Founded 1967. Setting: 294-acre suburban campus with easy access to Chicago. Endowment: $13.5 million. Educational spending for the previous fiscal year: $3202 per student. Total enrollment: 16,650. Faculty: 812 (209 full-time, 603 part-time). Student-undergrad faculty ratio is 25:1. Full-time: 6,983 students, 51% women, 49% men. Part-time: 9,667 students, 54% women, 46% men. Students come from 3 states and territories, 39 other countries, 0.1% from out-of-state. 0.2% American Indian or Alaska Native, non-Hispanic/Latino; 17% Hispanic/Latino; 10% African American, non-Hispanic/Latino; 2% Asian, non-Hispanic/Latino; 0.02% Native Hawaiian or other Pacific Islander, non-Hispanic/Latino; 2% international. 30% 25 or older, 7% transferred in. Retention: 58% of full-time freshmen returned the following year. Core. Calendar: semesters. Academic remediation for entering students, ESL program, services for LD students, advanced placement, accelerated degree program, honors program, independent study, distance learning, double major, summer session for credit, part-time degree program, adult/continuing education programs, co-op programs and internships. Off campus study. Study abroad program.

Entrance Requirements: Open admission except for allied health, nursing programs. Options: electronic application, early admission, deferred admission. Recommended: high school transcript. Entrance: noncompetitive. Application deadline: Rolling. Notification: continuous. Preference given to district residents for allied health, nursing programs. Transfer credits accepted: Yes.

Costs Per Year: Application fee: $0. Area resident tuition: $3120 full-time, $104 per credit part-time. State resident tuition: $7740 full-time, $258 per hour part-time. Nonresident tuition: $9060 full-time, $302 per hour part-time. Mandatory fees: $516 full-time, $17 per credit hour part-time, $3 per term part-time.

Collegiate Environment: Orientation program. Drama-theater group, choral group, student-run newspaper. Social organizations: 30 open to all. Most popular organizations: student newspaper, Speech Team, Alliance of Latin American Students, Phi Theta Kappa, Arab Student Union. Major annual events: Back to School Fest, Phi Theta Kappa initiation, Student Activities Awards Banquet. Student services: personal-psychological counseling, women's center. Campus security: 24-hour emergency response devices and patrols, late night transport-escort service, safety and security programs. College housing not available. Library with 70,878 books, 231,768 microform titles, 412 serials, 8,076 audiovisual materials, an OPAC, and a Web page. Operations spending for the previous fiscal year: $1.7 million. 2,000 computers available on campus for general student use. A campuswide network can be accessed from off-campus. Students can access the following: online class registration. Staffed computer lab on campus provides training in use of computers, software, and the Internet.

Community Environment: Palos Hills is located 20 miles south of downtown Chicago near Oak Lawn, a suburban area that has access to all the cultural, educational, and recreational opportunities of Chicago. All major forms of transportation are available. The climate is seasonal. Part-time employment is available.

■ MORRISON INSTITUTE OF TECHNOLOGY

701 Portland Ave.

Morrison, IL 61270-0410

Tel: (815)772-7218

Fax: (815)772-7584

E-mail: admissions@morrison.tec.il.us

Web Site: www.morrisontech.edu/

Description: Independent, 2-year, coed. Awards transfer associate and terminal associate degrees. Founded 1973. Setting: 17-acre small town campus. Endowment: $76,000. Total enrollment: 144. Faculty: 11 (10 full-time, 1 part-time). Student-undergrad faculty ratio is 13:1. 94 applied, 100% were admitted. 3% from top 10% of their high school class, 16% from top quarter, 38% from top half. 1 National Merit Scholar, 4 student government officers. Full-time: 142 students, 8% women, 92% men. Part-time: 2 students, 50% women, 50% men. Students come from 3 states and territories, 1 other country, 5% from out-of-state. 11% 25 or older, 55% live on campus, 7% transferred in. Core. Calendar: semesters. Academic remediation for entering students, double major, part-time degree program, internships.

Entrance Requirements: Open admission. Option: deferred admission. Required: high school transcript, proof of immunization. Recommended: SAT or ACT. Entrance: noncompetitive. Application deadline: Rolling. Notification: continuous until 9/1.

Collegiate Environment: Major annual events: Turkey Day, Harvest Hammer. Campus security: late night transport-escort service, controlled dormitory access. Milikan Library with 7,946 books and 39 serials. Operations spending for the previous fiscal year: $22,000. 60 computers available on campus for general student use. Computer purchase/lease plans available. A campuswide network can be accessed from student residence rooms. Staffed computer lab on campus.

Community Environment: Morrison is located 130 miles west of Chicago and 10 miles east of the Mississippi River. It is close to the Chestnut Lodge Winter Ski Area. Students are welcome in the local Theater Association and recreation leagues. Morrison also has two city parks and a state park with a lake. Community facilities include shopping areas, 16 churches, a public library, and two medical centers. A very safe campus environment.

■ MORTON COLLEGE

3801 S Central Ave.

Cicero, IL 60804-4398

Tel: (708)656-8000

Fax: (708)656-9592

Web Site: www.morton.edu/

Description: State and locally supported, 2-year, coed. Part of Illinois Community College Board. Awards certificates, transfer associate, and terminal associate degrees. Founded 1924. Setting: 25-acre suburban campus with easy access to Chicago. Educational spending for the previous fiscal year: $3286 per student. Faculty: 270 (52 full-time, 218 part-time). Student-undergrad faculty ratio is 23:1, 412 applied, 100% were admitted. Students come from 7 states and territories, 8 other countries, 1% from out-of-state. 0% American Indian or Alaska Native, non-Hispanic/Latino; 74% Hispanic/Latino; 5% African American, non-Hispanic/Latino; 1% Asian, non-Hispanic/Latino; 0.1% Native Hawaiian or other Pacific Islander, non-Hispanic/Latino; 0.1% international. 29% 25 or older. Retention: 57% of full-time freshmen returned the following year. Core. Calendar: semesters. Academic remediation for entering students, ESL program, services for LD students, advanced placement, self-designed majors, distance learning, summer session for credit, part-time degree program, adult/continuing education programs, internships.

Entrance Requirements: Open admission except for nursing, physical therapy assistant programs. Entrance: noncompetitive. Application deadline: Rolling. Preference given to district residents for nursing, physical therapy assistant programs, therapeutic massage. Transfer credits accepted: Yes.

Collegiate Environment: Orientation program. Drama-theater group, student-run newspaper. Most popular organizations: Morton Ambassador Program, Campus Activities Board, Student Government Association, Nursing Club. Major annual events: Welcome Week, Success Workshop Series, Club Day. Campus security: 24-hour patrols, security cameras. Learning Resource Center with 55,000 books, 327 serials, an OPAC, and a Web page. Operations spending for the previous fiscal year: $580,000. 250 computers available on campus for general student use. Computer purchase/lease plans available. A campuswide network can be accessed from off-campus. Staffed computer lab on campus provides training in use of computers.

Community Environment: Cicero, (population 82,700), is a residential and industrial suburb on the west side of the greater Chicago area.

■ NATIONAL LOUIS UNIVERSITY

122 S Michigan Ave.

Chicago, IL 60603

Tel: (312)621-9650; Free: 888-658-8632

Fax: (312)261-3057

Web Site: www.nl.edu/

Description: Independent, university, coed. Awards bachelor's, master's, and doctoral degrees and post-master's certificates. Founded 1886. Setting: 12-acre urban campus. Endowment: $29 million. Total enrollment: 5,737. Faculty: 521 (213 full-time, 308 part-time). Student-undergrad faculty ratio is 8:1. 161 applied, 30% were admitted. Full-time: 849 students, 79% women, 21% men. Part-time: 588 students, 80% women, 20% men. Students come from 6 states and territories. 0.4% American Indian or Alaska Native, non-Hispanic/Latino; 20% Hispanic/Latino; 39% African American, non-Hispanic/Latino; 2% Asian, non-Hispanic/Latino; 0.2% Native Hawaiian or other Pacific Islander, non-Hispanic/Latino; 1% international. 79% 25 or older.

Academic areas with the most degrees conferred: business/marketing; interdisciplinary studies; education. Core. Academic remediation for entering students, ESL program, services for LD students, advanced placement, accelerated degree program, honors program, independent study, distance learning, summer session for credit, adult/continuing education programs, internships, graduate courses open to undergrads.
Entrance Requirements: Options: electronic application, deferred admission, international baccalaureate accepted. Required: high school transcript, minimum 2 high school GPA. Recommended: interview. Required for some: 2 recommendations, SAT or ACT. Entrance: minimally difficult. Application deadline: Rolling. Notification: continuous. Transfer credits accepted: Yes.
Collegiate Environment: Orientation program. Drama-theater group. Student services: personal-psychological counseling. Campus security: 24-hour emergency response devices and patrols. NLU Library plus 5 others with 106,402 microform titles, 4,857 audiovisual materials, and an OPAC. 165 computers available on campus for general student use. A campuswide network can be accessed from off-campus. Students can access the following: online class registration. Staffed computer lab on campus provides training in use of computers.
Community Environment: See Northwestern University.

■ NORTH CENTRAL COLLEGE
30 N Brainard St.
Naperville, IL 60566-7063
Tel: (630)637-5100; Free: 800-411-1861
E-mail: admissions@noctrl.edu
Web Site: www.northcentralcollege.edu/
Description: Independent United Methodist, comprehensive, coed. Awards bachelor's and master's degrees. Founded 1861. Setting: 63-acre suburban campus with easy access to Chicago. Endowment: $91.3 million. Educational spending for the previous fiscal year: $8380 per student. Total enrollment: 3,042. Faculty: 256 (130 full-time, 126 part-time). Student-undergrad faculty ratio is 16:1. 3,987 applied, 60% were admitted. 25% from top 10% of their high school class, 55% from top quarter, 87% from top half. 5 valedictorians. Full-time: 2,560 students, 57% women, 43% men. Part-time: 195 students, 54% women, 46% men. Students come from 30 states and territories, 22 other countries, 7% from out-of-state. 0.2% American Indian or Alaska Native, non-Hispanic/Latino; 8% Hispanic/Latino; 4% African American, non-Hispanic/Latino; 2% Asian, non-Hispanic/Latino; 0.1% Native Hawaiian or other Pacific Islander, non-Hispanic/Latino; 1% international. 6% 25 or older, 54% live on campus, 10% transferred in. Retention: 78% of full-time freshmen returned the following year. Academic areas with the most degrees conferred: business/marketing; social sciences; education. Core. Academic remediation for entering students, ESL program, services for LD students, advanced placement, accelerated degree program, self-designed majors, honors program, independent study, double major, summer session for credit, part-time degree program, internships, graduate courses open to undergrads. Off campus study at Aurora University, Benedictine University, Northwestern Memorial Hospital, Hooke College of Applied Sciences. Study abroad program. ROTC: Army (c), Air Force (c).
Entrance Requirements: Options: electronic application, deferred admission, international baccalaureate accepted. Required: high school transcript, minimum 2.5 high school GPA, SAT or ACT. Recommended: essay, 1 recommendation, ACT. Required for some: interview. Entrance: moderately difficult. Application deadlines: Rolling, Rolling for nonresidents. Notification: continuous, continuous for nonresidents. SAT Reasoning Test deadline: 6/1. SAT Subject Test deadline: 6/1. Transfer credits accepted: Yes.
Costs Per Year: Application fee: $25. Comprehensive fee: $39,954 includes full-time tuition ($30,891), mandatory fees ($180), and college room and board ($8883). Room and board charges vary according to housing facility. Part-time tuition: $750 per credit hour. Part-time mandatory fees: $20 per term. Part-time tuition and fees vary according to course load.
Collegiate Environment: Orientation program. Drama-theater group, choral group, student-run newspaper, radio station. Social organizations: 60 open to all. Most popular organizations: College Union Activities Board, WONC (student radio station), Cardinals in Action (service group), Students in Free Enterprise (SIFE), Residence Hall Association. Major annual events: Jim Wand (annual hypnotist show), Taste of Asia, Springfest. Student services: health clinic, personal-psychological counseling. Campus security: 24-hour emergency response devices and patrols, late night transport-escort service, controlled dormitory access. 1,537 college housing spaces available; 1,436 were occupied in 2012-13. Freshmen given priority for college housing. Options: coed, men-only, women-only housing available. Oesterle Library with 138,968 books, 105,494 microform titles, 11,821 serials, 4,405 audiovisual

materials, an OPAC, and a Web page. Operations spending for the previous fiscal year: $1.2 million. 254 computers available on campus for general student use. A campuswide network can be accessed from student residence rooms and from off campus. Students can access the following: online class registration, software packages. Staffed computer lab on campus provides training in use of computers.
Community Environment: Naperville, population 141,500, is a suburban community 29 miles west of Chicago on the Burlington Northern Railroad route. It has a moderate, temperate climate, is the site of many corporate and scientific research installations, and is in the "Research and Development Corridor of Illinois." The community facilities include public and college libraries, a YMCA, hospital, many churches, motels, restaurants, shopping, entertainment, and numerous civic organizations. Many parks and attractive natural surroundings provide for outdoor sports and recreation. Part-time employment for students is generally available.

■ NORTH PARK UNIVERSITY
3225 W Foster Ave.
Chicago, IL 60625-4895
Tel: (773)244-6200; Free: 800-888-NPC8
Fax: (773)583-0858
E-mail: afao@northpark.edu
Web Site: www.northpark.edu/
Description: Independent, comprehensive, coed, affiliated with Evangelical Covenant Church. Awards bachelor's, master's, and doctoral degrees. Founded 1891. Setting: 30-acre urban campus. Total enrollment: 2,181. 1,452 applied. Full-time: 1,252 students, 60% women, 40% men. Part-time: 321 students, 67% women, 33% men. 22% 25 or older. Core. Calendar: semesters. Academic remediation for entering students, ESL program, advanced placement, accelerated degree program, self-designed majors, freshman honors college, honors program, summer session for credit, part-time degree program, adult/continuing education programs, internships. Off campus study at Christian College Coalition. Study abroad program.
Entrance Requirements: Option: early admission. Required: essay, high school transcript, minimum 2.0 high school GPA, 2 recommendations, SAT or ACT. Recommended: minimum 3.0 high school GPA. Required for some: interview. Entrance: moderately difficult. Application deadline: Rolling. Notification: continuous.
Costs Per Year: Application fee: $40. Comprehensive fee: $30,130 includes full-time tuition ($22,090) and college room and board ($8040). Full-time tuition varies according to program. Room and board charges vary according to board plan and housing facility.
Collegiate Environment: Orientation program. Drama-theater group, choral group, student-run newspaper. Student services: health clinic, personal-psychological counseling. Campus security: 24-hour emergency response devices and patrols, late night transport-escort service. Consolidated Library plus 4 others with 260,685 books, 254,468 microform titles, 1,178 serials, an OPAC, and a Web page.
Community Environment: See University of Chicago.

■ NORTHEASTERN ILLINOIS UNIVERSITY
5500 N St. Louis Ave.
Chicago, IL 60625-4699
Tel: (773)583-4050
Fax: (773)794-6243
E-mail: admrec@neiu.edu
Web Site: www.neiu.edu/
Description: State-supported, comprehensive, coed. Awards bachelor's and master's degrees. Founded 1961. Setting: 67-acre urban campus with easy access to Chicago. Endowment: $2.9 million. Research spending for the previous fiscal year: $1 million. Educational spending for the previous fiscal year: $7604 per student. Total enrollment: 11,149. Faculty: 669 (411 full-time, 258 part-time). Student-undergrad faculty ratio is 16:1. 5,295 applied, 63% were admitted. 8% from top 10% of their high school class, 24% from top quarter, 61% from top half. Full-time: 5,464 students, 54% women, 46% men. Part-time: 3,676 students, 58% women, 42% men. Students come from 15 states and territories, 104 other countries, 1% from out-of-state. 0.2% American Indian or Alaska Native, non-Hispanic/Latino; 34% Hispanic/Latino; 10% African American, non-Hispanic/Latino; 9% Asian, non-Hispanic/Latino; 0.3% Native Hawaiian or other Pacific Islander, non-Hispanic/Latino; 4% international. 44% 25 or older, 0% live on campus, 15% transferred in. Retention: 62% of full-time freshmen returned the following year. Academic areas with the most degrees conferred: education; business/marketing; social sciences. Core. Calendar: semesters. Academic remediation for enter-

ing students, ESL program, services for LD students, advanced placement, honors program, independent study, distance learning, double major, summer session for credit, part-time degree program, external degree program, adult/continuing education programs, co-op programs and internships. Off campus study at National Student Exchange. Study abroad program. ROTC: Army (c), Air Force (c).

Entrance Requirements: Options: electronic application, deferred admission, international baccalaureate accepted. Required: high school transcript, SAT or ACT. Entrance: minimally difficult. Application deadline: 7/1. Notification: 9/1. SAT Reasoning Test deadline: 7/1. Transfer credits accepted: Yes.

Costs Per Year: Application fee: $30. State resident tuition: $8610 full-time, $287 per credit hour part-time. Nonresident tuition: $14,700 full-time, $550 per credit hour part-time. Mandatory fees: $1316 full-time. Full-time tuition and fees vary according to student level. Part-time tuition varies according to student level. Tuition guaranteed not to increase for student's term of enrollment.

Collegiate Environment: Orientation program. Drama-theater group, choral group, student-run newspaper, radio station. Social organizations: 102 open to all; national fraternities, national sororities, local fraternities, local sororities, Ethnic, religious, special interest associations; 2% of eligible men and 3% of eligible women are members. Most popular organizations: Student Government Association, United Greek Council, Anime Club, Honors Society, Latinas in Power. Major annual events: Talent Show, Student Organization Fair, Welcome Week. Student services: health clinic, personal-psychological counseling, women's center. Campus security: 24-hour emergency response devices and patrols, late night transport-escort service. College housing not available. Ronald Williams Library with 747,663 books, 352,943 microform titles, 73,208 serials, 10,919 audiovisual materials, an OPAC, and a Web page. Operations spending for the previous fiscal year: $4.1 million. 520 computers available on campus for general student use. A campuswide network can be accessed from off-campus. Students can access the following: online class registration, productivity software. Staffed computer lab on campus.

Community Environment: See University of Chicago.

■ **NORTHERN ILLINOIS UNIVERSITY**
De Kalb, IL 60115-2854
Tel: (815)753-1000; Free: 800-892-3050
E-mail: admission-info@niu.edu
Web Site: www.niu.edu/

Description: State-supported, university, coed. Awards bachelor's, master's, and doctoral degrees. Founded 1895. Setting: 650-acre small town campus with easy access to Chicago. Endowment: $3 million. Research spending for the previous fiscal year: $23.7 million. Educational spending for the previous fiscal year: $7658 per student. Total enrollment: 21,869. Faculty: 1,148 (891 full-time, 257 part-time). Student-undergrad faculty ratio is 17:1. 17,842 applied, 52% were admitted. 11% from top 10% of their high school class, 33% from top quarter, 70% from top half. Full-time: 14,494 students, 50% women, 50% men. Part-time: 2,058 students, 52% women, 48% men. Students come from 28 states and territories, 91 other countries, 2% from out-of-state. 0.2% American Indian or Alaska Native, non-Hispanic/Latino; 12% Hispanic/Latino; 16% African American, non-Hispanic/Latino; 5% Asian, non-Hispanic/Latino; 0.1% Native Hawaiian or other Pacific Islander, non-Hispanic/Latino; 1% international. 16% 25 or older, 28% live on campus, 12% transferred in. Retention: 70% of full-time freshmen returned the following year. Academic areas with the most degrees conferred: business/marketing; health professions and related sciences; social sciences; education. Core. Calendar: semesters. Services for LD students, advanced placement, accelerated degree program, self-designed majors, honors program, independent study, double major, summer session for credit, part-time degree program, adult/continuing education programs, co-op programs and internships, graduate courses open to undergrads. Off campus study at Rockford Regional Academic Center. Study abroad program. ROTC: Army, Air Force (c).

Entrance Requirements: Option: electronic application. Required: high school transcript, high school rank, SAT or ACT. Entrance: moderately difficult. Application deadline: 8/1. Notification: continuous. Transfer credits accepted: Yes.

Costs Per Year: Application fee: $40. State resident tuition: $11,484 full-time. Nonresident tuition: $20,377 full-time. Mandatory fees: $1,577 full-time. Full-time tuition and fees vary according to course load, location, and student level. College room and board: $10,648. Room and board charges vary according to board plan and housing facility. Tuition guaranteed not to increase for student's term of enrollment.

Collegiate Environments: Orientation program. Drama-theater group, choral

group, marching band, student-run newspaper, radio station. Social organizations: 200 open to all; national fraternities, national sororities; 9% of eligible men and 6% of eligible women are members. Most popular organizations: American Marketing Association, Delta Sigma Pi, Pi Sigma Epsilon, Black Choir, Student Volunteer Choir. Major annual events: Homecoming, NIU Cares Day, Welcome Day. Student services: legal services, health clinic, personal-psychological counseling, women's center. Campus security: 24-hour emergency response devices and patrols, student patrols, late night transport-escort service, controlled dormitory access. 6,200 college housing spaces available; 6,000 were occupied in 2012-13. Freshmen given priority for college housing. On-campus residence required in freshman year. Option: coed housing available. Founders Memorial Library plus 4 others with 3.4 million books, 3.6 million microform titles, 69,843 serials, 60,088 audiovisual materials, an OPAC, and a Web page. Operations spending for the previous fiscal year: $11 million. 1,500 computers available on campus for general student use. A campuswide network can be accessed from student residence rooms and from off campus. Students can access the following: online class registration. Staffed computer lab on campus.

■ **NORTHWESTERN COLLEGE**
9700 W Higgins Rd.
Ste. 750
Rosemont, IL 60018
Tel: (847)318-8550; Free: 888-205-2283
Web Site: www.northwesterncollege.edu/

Description: Proprietary, 2-year, coed. Awards certificates, transfer associate, and terminal associate degrees (profile includes branch campuses in Bridgeview and Naperville, IL). Founded 1902. Setting: 3-acre urban campus. Total enrollment: 1,762. 981 applied. 61% 25 or older. Core. Academic remediation for entering students, honors program, independent study, double major, summer session for credit, part-time degree program, co-op programs and internships.

Entrance Requirements: Required: high school transcript, SAT or ACT. Entrance: minimally difficult. Application deadline: Rolling.

Collegiate Environment: Edward G. Schumacher Memorial Library with 2,000 books and 20 serials.

■ **NORTHWESTERN UNIVERSITY**
Evanston, IL 60208
Tel: (847)491-3741
E-mail: ug-admission@northwestern.edu
Web Site: www.northwestern.edu/

Description: Independent, university, coed. Awards bachelor's, master's, and doctoral degrees and post-master's certificates. Founded 1851. Setting: 250-acre suburban campus with easy access to Chicago. Endowment: $7.2 billion. Total enrollment: 18,431. Faculty: 1,153 (1,027 full-time, 126 part-time). Student-undergrad faculty ratio is 7:1. 25,013 applied, 26% were admitted. 85% from top 10% of their high school class, 96% from top quarter, 99% from top half. 239 National Merit Scholars, 259 valedictorians. Full-time: 8,273 students, 52% women, 48% men. Part-time: 203 students, 52% women, 48% men. Students come from 51 states and territories, 55 other countries, 75% from out-of-state. 1% 25 or older, 65% live on campus, 2% transferred in. Retention: 97% of full-time freshmen returned the following year. Academic areas with the most degrees conferred: communication/journalism; social sciences; engineering. Core. Calendar: semesters. Services for LD students, advanced placement, accelerated degree program, self-designed majors, honors program, independent study, double major, summer session for credit, part-time degree program, adult/continuing education programs, co-op programs and internships, graduate courses open to undergrads. Study abroad program. ROTC: Army (c), Naval, Air Force (c).

Entrance Requirements: Options: electronic application, early admission, early decision, deferred admission. Required: essay, high school transcript, 1 recommendation, SAT or ACT. Recommended: SAT Subject Tests. Required for some: audition for music program, SAT Subject Tests. Entrance: most difficult. Application deadlines: 1/1, 11/1 for early decision. Notification: 4/15, 12/15 for early decision.

Costs Per Year: Application fee: $65. Comprehensive fee: $57,108 includes full-time tuition ($43,380), mandatory fees ($399), and college room and board ($13,329). Room and board charges vary according to board plan and housing facility.

Collegiate Environment: Orientation program. Drama-theater group, choral group, marching band, student-run newspaper, radio station. Social organizations: 415 open to all; national fraternities, national sororities; 32%

of eligible men and 38% of eligible women are members. Most popular organizations: Associated Student Government, Northwestern Community Development Corp, Activities and Organization Board, Dance Marathon, Arts Alliance. Major annual events: Alternative Student Break Trips, dance marathon, Armadillo Day. Student services: health clinic, personal-psychological counseling, women's center. Campus security: 24-hour emergency response devices and patrols, late night transport-escort service, controlled dormitory access. University Library plus 6 others with 4.8 million books, 4.6 million microform titles, 77,933 serials, an OPAC, and a Web page. Operations spending for the previous fiscal year: $26.3 million. 678 computers available on campus for general student use. A campuswide network can be accessed from student residence rooms and from off campus. Students can access the following: online class registration. Staffed computer lab on campus.

Community Environment: Evanston is a residential city on Lake Michigan, adjoining the northern limits of the city of Chicago. With Lake Michigan forming an impressive backdrop, an abundance of oak, elm, and maple trees enhance the beauty of the community. Situated 12 miles from the center of Chicago, Evanston offers the advantages of a quiet, modern community close to a great thriving city. Excellent shopping facilities are available.

■ **OAKTON COMMUNITY COLLEGE**
1600 E Golf Rd.
Des Plaines, IL 60016-1268
Tel: (847)635-1600
Fax: (847)635-1706
E-mail: dcohen@oakton.edu
Web Site: www.oakton.edu/

Description: District-supported, 2-year, coed. Part of Illinois Community College Board. Awards certificates, transfer associate, and terminal associate degrees. Founded 1969. Setting: 193-acre suburban campus with easy access to Chicago. Total enrollment: 10,406. 48% 25 or older. Core. Calendar: semesters. Academic remediation for entering students, ESL program, services for LD students, advanced placement, honors program, independent study, distance learning, summer session for credit, part-time degree program, adult/continuing education programs. Study abroad program.

Entrance Requirements: Open admission except for health care programs. Option: electronic application. Recommended: high school transcript. Required for some: interview. Entrance: noncompetitive. Application deadline: Rolling. Notification: continuous.

Costs Per Year: Application fee: $25. Area resident tuition: $2,288 full-time, $95.34 per semester hour part-time. State resident tuition: $6,909 full-time, $287.88 per semester hour part-time. Nonresident tuition: $8,881 full-time, $370.05 per semester hour part-time. Mandatory fees: $167 full-time.

Collegiate Environment: Orientation program. Drama-theater group, choral group, student-run newspaper. Student services: health clinic, personal-psychological counseling. Campus security: 24-hour emergency response devices and patrols, student patrols, late night transport-escort service. College housing not available. Oakton Community College Library plus 1 other with 92,000 books, 7,800 microform titles, 586 serials, 10,500 audiovisual materials, an OPAC, and a Web page.

Community Environment: Des Plaines, population 56,551, is a suburban community situated about 12 miles from the center of Chicago, the third largest city in the nation. Cultural facilities of Chicago include museums which cover a wide variety of fields, art galleries, research libraries, theaters, opera, and symphony orchestra.

■ **OLIVET NAZARENE UNIVERSITY**
One University Ave.
Bourbonnais, IL 60914
Tel: (815)939-5011; Free: 800-648-1463
E-mail: swolff@olivet.edu
Web Site: www.olivet.edu/

Description: Independent, comprehensive, coed, affiliated with Church of the Nazarene. Awards associate, bachelor's, and master's degrees. Founded 1907. Setting: 200-acre small town campus with easy access to Chicago. Total enrollment: 4,636. 2,454 applied. 20% 25 or older. Core. Calendar: semesters. Academic remediation for entering students, advanced placement, independent study, double major, summer session for credit, part-time degree program, adult/continuing education programs, internships, graduate courses open to undergrads. Study abroad program. ROTC: Army.

Entrance Requirements: Options: electronic application, deferred admission. Required: high school transcript, minimum 2.0 high school GPA, 2

recommendations, ACT. Recommended: essay, interview. Entrance: minimally difficult. Application deadline: Rolling. Notification: continuous.

Costs Per Year: Application fee: $25. Comprehensive fee: $35,990 includes full-time tuition ($27,250), mandatory fees ($840), and college room and board ($7900). Full-time tuition and fees vary according to course load. Room and board charges vary according to board plan. Part-time tuition: $1135 per credit hour. Part-time tuition varies according to course load.

Collegiate Environment: Orientation program. Drama-theater group, choral group, student-run newspaper, radio station. Social organizations: 30 open to all. Most popular organizations: Fellowship of Christian Athletes, C.A.U. S.E. (College and University Serving and Enabling), Diakonia, Student Education Association, Women's Residence Association. Major annual events: All-School Christmas Banquet, Junior/Senior Banquet, Homecoming Coronation. Student services: health clinic, personal-psychological counseling. Campus security: 24-hour patrols, late night transport-escort service. Benner Library with 160,039 books, 240,846 microform titles, 925 serials, 6,818 audiovisual materials, an OPAC, and a Web page.

Community Environment: The campus is in the historic village of Bourbonnais (16,000) on the north edge of Kankakee, Illinois (100,000). This is the growing edge of the community, with excellent schools and small businesses. A shopping mall and numerous stores provide shopping convenience and employment opportunities. Major industries in the area include Armour Pharmaceutical, Armstrong Tile, Quaker Oats, General Foods, and a variety of metal working plants. The proximity to the Chicago metropolitan area is a definite asset.

■ **PARKLAND COLLEGE**
2400 W Bradley Ave.
Champaign, IL 61821-1899
Tel: (217)351-2200; Free: 800-346-8089
Fax: (217)351-7640
Web Site: www.parkland.edu/

Description: District-supported, 2-year, coed. Part of Illinois Community College Board. Awards certificates, transfer associate, and terminal associate degrees. Founded 1967. Setting: 233-acre suburban campus. Total enrollment: 9,368. Faculty: 521 (174 full-time, 347 part-time). 6,780 applied, 100% were admitted. Full-time: 3,432 students, 50% women, 50% men. Part-time: 5,936 students, 56% women, 44% men. 1% from out-of-state. 0.5% American Indian or Alaska Native, non-Hispanic/Latino; 4% Hispanic/Latino; 16% African American, non-Hispanic/Latino; 3% Asian, non-Hispanic/Latino; 0.1% Native Hawaiian or other Pacific Islander, non-Hispanic/Latino; 1% international. 34% 25 or older, 4% transferred in. Core. Calendar: semesters. Academic remediation for entering students, ESL program, services for LD students, advanced placement, accelerated degree program, self-designed majors, honors program, independent study, distance learning, double major, summer session for credit, part-time degree program, adult/continuing education programs, co-op programs and internships. Off campus study at University of Illinois at Urbana-Champaign. Study abroad program. ROTC: Army (c), Naval (c), Air Force (c).

Entrance Requirements: Open admission except for allied health, nursing programs. Option: deferred admission. Recommended: high school transcript. Required for some: ACT. Entrance: noncompetitive. Application deadline: Rolling. Notification: continuous.

Collegiate Environment: Orientation program. Drama-theater group, choral group, student-run newspaper, radio station. Student services: personal-psychological counseling. Campus security: 24-hour emergency response devices and patrols, late night transport-escort service. College housing not available. Parkland College Library with an OPAC and a Web page. 1,200 computers available on campus for general student use. A campuswide network can be accessed. Students can access the following: online class registration. Staffed computer lab on campus.

Community Environment: See University of Illinois at Urbana-Champaign.

■ **PRAIRIE STATE COLLEGE**
202 S Halsted St.
Chicago Heights, IL 60411-8226
Tel: (708)709-3500
E-mail: jmmiller@prairiestate.edu
Web Site: www.prairiestate.edu/

Description: State and locally supported, 2-year, coed. Part of Illinois Community College Board. Awards certificates, transfer associate, and terminal associate degrees. Founded 1958. Setting: 68-acre suburban campus with easy access to Chicago. Total enrollment: 5,854. Student-undergrad faculty ratio is 17:1. 5% from out-of-state. 45% 25 or older. Core. Calendar:

semesters. Academic remediation for entering students, ESL program, services for LD students, advanced placement, self-designed majors, honors program, distance learning, summer session for credit, part-time degree program, adult/continuing education programs, internships.

Entrance Requirements: Open admission except for nursing, dental hygiene programs. Option: deferred admission. Required: high school transcript. Entrance: noncompetitive. Application deadline: Rolling.

Collegiate Environment: Orientation program. Drama-theater group, choral group, student-run newspaper. Student services: personal-psychological counseling. Campus security: 24-hour emergency response devices and patrols, student patrols, late night transport-escort service. Learning Resource Center with an OPAC.

Community Environment: Chicago Heights is a metropolitan area located 25 miles south of the Chicago loop. Railroads and buses serve the area. Within the city are shopping centers, many churches, a library, and a hospital. For recreation, there are many parks, a community center with an educational, recreational and social service program, and a Forest Preserve of 1,350 acres.

■ **PRINCIPIA COLLEGE**
One Maybeck Pl.
Elsah, IL 62028-9799
Tel: (618)374-2131; Free: 800-277-4648
Fax: (618)374-4000
Web Site: www.principiacollege.edu/

Description: Independent Christian Science, 4-year, coed. Awards bachelor's degrees. Founded 1910. Setting: 2,600-acre rural campus with easy access to St. Louis. Endowment: $458.7 million. Total enrollment: 489. Faculty: 85 (76 full-time, 9 part-time). Student-undergrad faculty ratio is 7:1. 195 applied, 59% were admitted. 17% from top 10% of their high school class, 39% from top quarter, 69% from top half. Full-time: 476 students, 55% women, 45% men. Part-time: 13 students, 46% women, 54% men. Students come from 36 states and territories, 22 other countries, 91% from out-of-state. 0% American Indian or Alaska Native, non-Hispanic/Latino; 0% Hispanic/Latino; 1% African American, non-Hispanic/Latino; 0.4% Asian, non-Hispanic/Latino; 0% Native Hawaiian or other Pacific Islander, non-Hispanic/Latino; 15% international. 4% 25 or older, 100% live on campus, 5% transferred in. Retention: 79% of full-time freshmen returned the following year. Academic areas with the most degrees conferred: social sciences; education; computer and information sciences. Core. Advanced placement, accelerated degree program, self-designed majors, honors program, independent study, double major, internships. Off campus study. Study abroad program.

Entrance Requirements: Options: electronic application, deferred admission, international baccalaureate accepted. Required: essay, high school transcript, minimum 2.3 high school GPA, 3 recommendations, Christian Science commitment, SAT or ACT. Recommended: interview, SAT Subject Tests. Required for some: interview. Entrance: moderately difficult. Application deadline: Rolling. Notification: continuous. Transfer credits accepted: Yes.

Costs Per Year: Application fee: $0. Comprehensive fee: $36,480 includes full-time tuition ($25,500), mandatory fees ($480), and college room and board ($10,500). College room only: $5000. Full-time tuition and fees vary according to course load.

Collegiate Environment: Orientation program. Drama-theater group, choral group, student-run newspaper, radio station. Social organizations: 36 open to all. Most popular organizations: Christian Science Organization, student newspaper, International Students Association, student radio station, student government. Major annual events: Whole World Festival, Public Affairs Conference, Speakers Series. Student services: health clinic. Campus security: 24-hour patrols. 600 college housing spaces available; 489 were occupied in 2012-13. Freshmen guaranteed college housing. On-campus residence required through senior year. Options: men-only, women-only housing available. Marshall Brooks Library plus 1 other with 211,460 books, 187,434 microform titles, 11,876 serials, 7,792 audiovisual materials, an OPAC, and a Web page. 200 computers available on campus for general student use. A campuswide network can be accessed from student residence rooms and from off campus. Students can access the following: online class registration. Staffed computer lab on campus.

Community Environment: Principia College is located on 2,600 acres of the highest and loveliest section of the Piasa Bluffs above the Mississippi River. In a setting rich in beauty and historical significance, three great rivers may be seen from the bluffs: the Mississippi below, the Missouri to the southeast, and the Illinois, which joins the Mississippi to the west several miles upstream. Mean temperatures are 28-78 degrees, and rainfall averages 35 inches. Recreation, entertainment, and shopping are found in Alton and St. Louis. Part-time student employment is available at the college.

■ **QUINCY UNIVERSITY**
1800 College Ave.
Quincy, IL 62301-2699
Tel: (217)222-8020; Free: 800-688-4295
Fax: (217)228-5479
E-mail: admissions@quincy.edu
Web Site: www.quincy.edu/

Description: Independent Roman Catholic, comprehensive, coed. Awards associate, bachelor's, and master's degrees. Founded 1860. Setting: 70-acre small town campus. Endowment: $15.9 million. Educational spending for the previous fiscal year: $4759 per student. Total enrollment: 1,632. Faculty: 165 (54 full-time, 111 part-time). Student-undergrad faculty ratio is 14:1. 1,034 applied, 91% were admitted. 12% from top 10% of their high school class, 36% from top quarter, 74% from top half. 6 valedictorians. Full-time: 1,102 students, 56% women, 44% men. Part-time: 124 students, 76% women, 24% men. Students come from 23 states and territories, 3 other countries, 25% from out-of-state. 1% American Indian or Alaska Native, non-Hispanic/Latino; 1% Hispanic/Latino; 10% African American, non-Hispanic/Latino; 1% Asian, non-Hispanic/Latino; 0.3% Native Hawaiian or other Pacific Islander, non-Hispanic/Latino; 1% international. 10% 25 or older, 63% live on campus, 7% transferred in. Retention: 70% of full-time freshmen returned the following year. Academic areas with the most degrees conferred: business/marketing; education; health professions and related sciences. Core. Calendar: semesters. Academic remediation for entering students, advanced placement, accelerated degree program, self-designed majors, honors program, independent study, distance learning, double major, summer session for credit, part-time degree program, adult/continuing education programs, internships, graduate courses open to undergrads. Off campus study at American University (Washington Semester Program). Study abroad program.

Entrance Requirements: Options: electronic application, deferred admission, international baccalaureate accepted. Required: essay, high school transcript, minimum 2.5 high school GPA, SAT or ACT. Recommended: interview. Required for some: 1 recommendation, audition for music majors, portfolio recommended for art majors. Entrance: moderately difficult. Application deadlines: Rolling, Rolling for nonresidents. Notification: continuous, continuous for nonresidents. SAT Reasoning Test deadline: 8/15. Transfer credits accepted: Yes.

Costs Per Year: Application fee: $25. Comprehensive fee: $35,714 includes full-time tuition ($24,974), mandatory fees ($860), and college room and board ($9880). College room only: $5500. Room and board charges vary according to board plan, housing facility, and student level. Part-time tuition: $585 per semester hour. Part-time mandatory fees: $30 per semester hour. Part-time tuition and fees vary according to course load.

Collegiate Environment: Orientation program. Drama-theater group, choral group, marching band, student-run newspaper. Social organizations: 45 open to all; national fraternities, national sororities; 6% of eligible men and 8% of eligible women are members. Most popular organizations: Student Senate, Kappa Kappa Psi, Student Programming Board, Minority Student Association, Students in Free Enterprise (SIFE). Major annual events: Homecoming, Hawk Wild Weekend, Hawk Back Weekend. Student services: health clinic, personal-psychological counseling. Campus security: 24-hour emergency response devices and patrols, student patrols, late night transport-escort service, controlled dormitory access, self-defense education, shuttle buses, lighted pathways/sidewalks. 736 college housing spaces available; 667 were occupied in 2012-13. Freshmen guaranteed college housing. On-campus residence required through junior year. Option: coed housing available. Brenner Library with 207,881 books, 176,805 microform titles, 305 serials, 9,342 audiovisual materials, an OPAC, and a Web page. Operations spending for the previous fiscal year: $451,514. 131 computers available on campus for general student use. A campuswide network can be accessed from student residence rooms and from off campus. Students can access the following: online class registration.

Community Environment: The University is located in a residential section of Quincy, a city of 50,000, located on the bluffs of the Mississippi River. It is within easy traveling distance of St. Louis (2 1/2 hours), Kansas City (4 hours), and Chicago (4 hours).

■ **RASMUSSEN COLLEGE AURORA**
2363 Sequoia Dr.
Aurora, IL 60506

Tel: (630)888-3500; Free: 888-549-6755
Fax: (630)888-3501
E-mail: susan.hammerstrom@rasmussen.edu
Web Site: www.rasmussen.edu/
Description: Proprietary, primarily 2-year, coed. Part of Rasmussen College System. Awards certificates, diplomas, transfer associate, terminal associate, and bachelor's degrees. Setting: suburban campus. Total enrollment: 366. Student-undergrad faculty ratio is 22:1. 82% 25 or older. Core. Academic remediation for entering students, accelerated degree program, distance learning, double major, summer session for credit, part-time degree program, adult/continuing education programs, internships.
Entrance Requirements: Options: electronic application, early admission, deferred admission. Required: high school transcript, minimum 2 high school GPA, Internal Exam. Required for some: interview. Entrance: minimally difficult. Application deadline: Rolling. Transfer credits accepted: Yes.
Costs Per Year: Tuition: $12,600 full-time. Mandatory fees: $1800 full-time. Full-time tuition and fees vary according to course level, course load, degree level, location, and program.
Collegiate Environment: Orientation program. College housing not available. Rasmussen College Library - Aurora with 2,543 books, 4 serials, 322 audiovisual materials, an OPAC, and a Web page. 87 computers available on campus for general student use. A campuswide network can be accessed from off-campus.

■ **RASMUSSEN COLLEGE MOKENA/TINLEY PARK**
8650 W Spring Lake Rd.
Mokena, IL 60448
Tel: (815)534-3300; Free: 888-549-6755
Web Site: www.rasmussen.edu/
Description: Proprietary, 4-year, coed. Part of Rasmussen College System. Awards associate and bachelor's degrees. Setting: suburban campus. Total enrollment: 249. Student-undergrad faculty ratio is 22:1. 88% 25 or older. Core. Academic remediation for entering students, accelerated degree program, distance learning, double major, summer session for credit, part-time degree program, adult/continuing education programs, internships.
Entrance Requirements: Options: electronic application, early admission, deferred admission. Required: high school transcript, minimum 2 high school GPA, Internal Exam. Required for some: interview. Entrance: minimally difficult. Application deadline: Rolling. Transfer credits accepted: Yes.
Costs Per Year: Tuition: $12,600 full-time. Mandatory fees: $1800 full-time. Full-time tuition and fees vary according to course level, course load, degree level, location, and program.
Collegiate Environment: Orientation program. College housing not available. Rasmussen College Library - Mokena with 1,128 books, 6 serials, 6 audiovisual materials, an OPAC, and a Web page. 73 computers available on campus for general student use. A campuswide network can be accessed from off-campus.

■ **RASMUSSEN COLLEGE ROCKFORD**
6000 E State St., Fourth Fl.
Rockford, IL 61108-2513
Tel: (815)316-4800; Free: 888-549-6755
Fax: (815)316-4801
E-mail: susan.hammerstrom@rasmussen.edu
Web Site: www.rasmussen.edu/
Description: Proprietary, primarily 2-year, coed. Part of Rasmussen College System. Awards certificates, diplomas, transfer associate, terminal associate, and bachelor's degrees. Setting: suburban campus. Total enrollment: 713. Student-undergrad faculty ratio is 22:1. 85% 25 or older. Core. Academic remediation for entering students, accelerated degree program, distance learning, double major, summer session for credit, part-time degree program, adult/continuing education programs, internships.
Entrance Requirements: Options: electronic application, early admission, deferred admission. Required: high school transcript, minimum 2 high school GPA, Internal Exam. Required for some: interview. Entrance: minimally difficult. Application deadline: Rolling. Transfer credits accepted: Yes.
Costs Per Year: Tuition: $12,600 full-time. Mandatory fees: $1800 full-time. Full-time tuition and fees vary according to course level, course load, degree level, location, and program.
Collegiate Environment: Orientation program. College housing not available. Rasmussen College Library - Rockford with 2,343 books, 6 serials, 195 audiovisual materials, an OPAC, and a Web page. 103 computers available on campus for general student use. A campuswide network can be accessed from off-campus.

■ **RASMUSSEN COLLEGE ROMEOVILLE/JOLIET**
1400 W Normantown Rd.
Romeoville, IL 60446
Tel: (815)306-2600; Free: 888-549-6755
E-mail: susan.hammerstrom@rasmussen.edu
Web Site: www.rasmussen.edu/
Description: Proprietary, 4-year, coed. Part of Rasmussen College System. Awards associate and bachelor's degrees. Setting: suburban campus. Total enrollment: 475. Student-undergrad faculty ratio is 22:1. 75% 25 or older. Core. Academic remediation for entering students, accelerated degree program, distance learning, double major, summer session for credit, part-time degree program, adult/continuing education programs, internships.
Entrance Requirements: Options: electronic application, early admission, deferred admission. Required: high school transcript, minimum 2 high school GPA, Internal Exam. Required for some: interview. Entrance: minimally difficult. Application deadline: Rolling. Transfer credits accepted: Yes.
Costs Per Year: Tuition: $12,600 full-time. Mandatory fees: $1800 full-time. Full-time tuition and fees vary according to course level, course load, degree level, location, and program.
Collegiate Environment: Orientation program. College housing not available. Rasmussen College Library - Romeoville with 1,993 books, 33 serials, 45 audiovisual materials, an OPAC, and a Web page. 87 computers available on campus for general student use. A campuswide network can be accessed from off-campus.

■ **REND LAKE COLLEGE**
468 N Ken Gray Pky.
Ina, IL 62846-9801
Tel: (618)437-5321; Free: 800-369-5321
Fax: (618)437-5677
E-mail: swannj@rlc.edu
Web Site: www.rlc.edu/
Description: State-supported, 2-year, coed. Part of Illinois Community College Board. Awards certificates, transfer associate, and terminal associate degrees. Founded 1967. Setting: 350-acre rural campus. Total enrollment: 5,871. 47% 25 or older. Core. Calendar: semesters. Academic remediation for entering students, services for LD students, advanced placement, honors program, independent study, distance learning, summer session for credit, part-time degree program, adult/continuing education programs, co-op programs and internships. Off campus study at Southern Illinois Collegiate Common Market (SICCM), Murphy-Wall Pinckneyville Center, Reno Lake College Marketplace.
Entrance Requirements: Open admission except for allied health programs. Options: electronic application, deferred admission. Required: high school transcript. Entrance: noncompetitive. Application deadline: 8/18.
Costs Per Year: Application fee: $0. Area resident tuition: $2790 full-time, $93 per credit hour part-time. State resident tuition: $4275 full-time, $142.50 per credit hour part-time. Nonresident tuition: $4500 full-time, $150 per credit hour part-time. Mandatory fees: $90 full-time. Full-time tuition and fees vary according to course load, program, and reciprocity agreements. Part-time tuition varies according to course load, program, and reciprocity agreements. College room and board: $3316.
Collegiate Environment: Orientation program. Drama-theater group, choral group, student-run newspaper. Campus security: 24-hour emergency response devices and patrols, late night transport-escort service. Learning Resource Center with 35,426 books, 68,500 microform titles, 265 serials, 3,770 audiovisual materials, an OPAC, and a Web page.
Community Environment: The college is located in a rural area with all forms of transportation available. Industries in nearby Mount Vernon, population 16,344, include the manufacture of electric equipment, radiators, women's wear, shoes, forest products, boats, automobile tires, and chemicals. Oil production and agriculture are important in the surrounding areas. Cultural opportunities offered by the State Law Library and Museum. Community facilities include 40 churches of major denominations, hospitals, a clinic, and major civic and service organizations. Recreational activities are boating, fishing, swimming, bowling, and golf. Du Quoin State Fair is an annual event.

■ **RESURRECTION UNIVERSITY**
1431 N Claremont Ave.
Chicago, IL 60622
Tel: (708)763-6530
Fax: (708)763-1531
Web Site: www.resu.edu/

Description: Independent, upper-level, coed. Awards bachelor's and master's degrees. Founded 1982. Setting: 10-acre urban campus with easy access to Chicago. Endowment: $1.5 million. Educational spending for the previous fiscal year: $8848 per student. Total enrollment: 515. Faculty: 56 (24 full-time, 32 part-time). Student-undergrad faculty ratio is 13:1. 252 applied, 94% were admitted. Full-time: 323 students, 81% women, 19% men. Part-time: 69 students, 90% women, 10% men. Students come from 2 states and territories, 1 other country, 0.01% from out-of-state. 0% American Indian or Alaska Native, non-Hispanic/Latino; 19% Hispanic/Latino; 13% African American, non-Hispanic/Latino; 18% Asian, non-Hispanic/Latino; 1% Native Hawaiian or other Pacific Islander, non-Hispanic/Latino; 0.3% international. 69% 25 or older, 99% transferred in. Academic area with the most degrees conferred: health professions and related sciences. Calendar: semesters. Academic remediation for entering students, advanced placement, accelerated degree program, independent study, summer session for credit, part-time degree program, graduate courses open to undergrads.

Entrance Requirements: Transfer credits accepted: Yes.

Costs Per Year: Application fee: $50. Tuition: $11,349 full-time, $769 per credit hour part-time. Mandatory fees: $290 full-time, $140 per term part-time.

Collegiate Environment: Student services: personal-psychological counseling. Campus security: 24-hour emergency response devices and patrols, late night transport-escort service. College housing not available. Resurrection University Library with 3,084 books, 7,060 serials, 90 audiovisual materials, an OPAC, and a Web page. Operations spending for the previous fiscal year: $105,723. 36 computers available on campus for general student use. A computer is required for all students. A campuswide network can be accessed. Students can access the following: online class registration. Staffed computer lab on campus provides training in use of computers, software, and the Internet.

■ RICHLAND COMMUNITY COLLEGE

One College Park
Decatur, IL 62521-8513
Tel: (217)875-7200
Fax: (217)875-6991
E-mail: jwirey@richland.edu
Web Site: www.richland.edu/

Description: District-supported, 2-year, coed. Part of Illinois Community College Board. Awards certificates, transfer associate, and terminal associate degrees. Founded 1971. Setting: 117-acre small town campus. Total enrollment: 3,152. Faculty: 242 (96 full-time, 146 part-time). Student-undergrad faculty ratio is 14:1. Full-time: 1,003 students, 58% women, 42% men. Part-time: 2,149 students, 65% women, 35% men. 49% 25 or older. Retention: 59% of full-time freshmen returned the following year. Core. Calendar: semesters. Academic remediation for entering students, ESL program, services for LD students, advanced placement, self-designed majors, freshman honors college, honors program, distance learning, summer session for credit, part-time degree program, adult/continuing education programs.

Entrance Requirements: Open admission. Option: early admission. Required: high school transcript. Recommended: ACT. Entrance: noncompetitive. Application deadline: Rolling.

Collegiate Environment: Orientation program. Student-run newspaper. Social organizations: 35 open to all. Most popular organizations: Student Senate, Forensics Club, Drama Club, Black Student Association, Student Activities Board. Major annual events: Multicultural Fair, Career Fair. Student services: personal-psychological counseling. Campus security: 24-hour emergency response devices and patrols. Kitty Lindsay Library with 39,452 books, 2,635 microform titles, 275 serials, an OPAC, and a Web page. 150 computers available on campus for general student use. A campuswide network can be accessed from off-campus. Students can access the following: online class registration. Staffed computer lab on campus provides training in use of computers, software, and the Internet.

Community Environment: See Millikin University.

■ ROBERT MORRIS UNIVERSITY ILLINOIS

401 S State St.
Chicago, IL 60605
Tel: (312)935-6800; Free: 800-RMC-5960
Fax: (312)836-4599
E-mail: enroll@robertmorris.edu
Web Site: www.robertmorris.edu/

Description: Independent, comprehensive, coed. Awards associate, bachelor's, and master's degrees. Founded 1913. Setting: urban campus with easy access to Chicago. Endowment: $51.1 million. Educational spending for the previous fiscal year: $3278 per student. Total enrollment: 3,802. Faculty: 261 (124 full-time, 137 part-time). Student-undergrad faculty ratio is 20:1. 3,386 applied, 28% were admitted. 6% from top 10% of their high school class, 19% from top quarter, 46% from top half. Full-time: 3,065 students, 53% women, 47% men. Part-time: 165 students, 62% women, 38% men. Students come from 31 states and territories, 20 other countries, 8% from out-of-state. 0.4% American Indian or Alaska Native, non-Hispanic/Latino; 23% Hispanic/Latino; 33% African American, non-Hispanic/Latino; 3% Asian, non-Hispanic/Latino; 0.3% Native Hawaiian or other Pacific Islander, non-Hispanic/Latino; 1% international. 29% 25 or older, 10% live on campus, 15% transferred in. Retention: 49% of full-time freshmen returned the following year. Academic areas with the most degrees conferred: business/marketing; interdisciplinary studies; visual and performing arts. Core. Calendar: 5 ten-week academic sessions per year. Services for LD students, advanced placement, accelerated degree program, honors program, double major, summer session for credit, part-time degree program, adult/continuing education programs, internships, graduate courses open to undergrads. Study abroad program. ROTC: Army (c).

Entrance Requirements: Options: electronic application, deferred admission. Required: ACT scores (Nursing and Surgical Tech applicants). Recommended: interview. Required for some: high school transcript, SAT or ACT. Entrance: minimally difficult. Application deadlines: Rolling, Rolling for nonresidents. Notification: continuous, continuous for nonresidents. Transfer credits accepted: Yes. Applicants placed on waiting list: 0. Wait-listed applicants offered admission: 0.

Costs Per Year: Application fee: $20. Comprehensive fee: $34,554 includes full-time tuition ($22,800) and college room and board ($11,754). College room only: $10,500. Room and board charges vary according to housing facility. Part-time tuition: $633 per credit hour. Part-time tuition varies according to course load.

Collegiate Environment: Orientation program. Choral group, marching band, student-run newspaper. Social organizations: 28 open to all. Most popular organizations: UNA-USA, Architectural Technology Club, Sigma Beta Delta, LEX, Film Club. Major annual events: Fall welcome week, Pack the Place - Basketball game, Pack the Field - Football game. Student services: personal-psychological counseling. Campus security: controlled dormitory access, Roaming security visits our metropolitan campuses on an intermittent schedule and are sent to other campuses as needed. 351 college housing spaces available; 316 were occupied in 2012-13. No special consideration for freshman housing applicants. Option: coed housing available. Information Technology Library with 158,088 books, 5 serials, 65,711 audiovisual materials, an OPAC, and a Web page. Operations spending for the previous fiscal year: $694,700. 1,740 computers available on campus for general student use. A campuswide network can be accessed from student residence rooms. Students can access the following: online class registration, online credentials, online payments, online student accounts, online degree audit.

Community Environment: Located in Chicago's Loop, the main campus is in the heart of the downtown business and financial district.

■ ROCK VALLEY COLLEGE

3301 N Mulford Rd.
Rockford, IL 61114-5699
Tel: (815)921-7821; Free: 800-973-7821
Fax: (815)654-5568
E-mail: p.peyer@rockvalleycollege.edu
Web Site: www.rockvalleycollege.edu/

Description: District-supported, 2-year, coed. Part of Illinois Community College Board. Awards certificates, transfer associate, and terminal associate degrees. Founded 1964. Setting: 217-acre suburban campus with easy access to Chicago. Total enrollment: 8,849. Faculty: 424 (157 full-time, 267 part-time). Student-undergrad faculty ratio is 24:1. Full-time: 4,308 students, 53% women, 47% men. Part-time: 4,541 students, 60% women, 40% men. Students come from 2 states and territories, 3 other countries, 2% from out-of-state. 0.3% American Indian or Alaska Native, non-Hispanic/Latino; 9% Hispanic/Latino; 10% African American, non-Hispanic/Latino; 1% Asian, non-Hispanic/Latino; 0.1% Native Hawaiian or other Pacific Islander, non-Hispanic/Latino; 0.2% international. 40% 25 or older. Retention: 66% of full-time freshmen returned the following year. Core. Calendar: semesters. Academic remediation for entering students, ESL program, services for LD students, advanced placement, self-designed majors, honors program, independent study, distance learning, summer session for credit, part-time degree program, adult/continuing education programs, co-op programs and internships. Study abroad program.

Entrance Requirements: Open admission. Required: high school transcript. Entrance: noncompetitive. Application deadline: 8/29. Notification: continuous.

Costs Per Year: Application fee: $0. Area resident tuition: $2490 full-time, $83 per credit part-time. State resident tuition: $7920 full-time, $264 per credit part-time. Nonresident tuition: $13,950 full-time, $456 per credit part-time. Mandatory fees: $314 full-time. Full-time tuition and fees vary according to course load. Part-time tuition varies according to course load.

Collegiate Environment: Orientation program. Drama-theater group, choral group, student-run newspaper. Social organizations: 12 open to all. Most popular organizations: Black Student Alliance, Phi Theta Kappa, Adults on Campus, Inter-Varsity Club, Christian Fellowship. Major annual events: New Student Week, Homecoming Week, May Fest. Student services: personal-psychological counseling. Campus security: 24-hour emergency response devices and patrols, late night transport-escort service. Educational Resource Center with 67,168 books, an OPAC, and a Web page. Operations spending for the previous fiscal year: $880,000. 130 computers available on campus for general student use. A campuswide network can be accessed from off-campus. Students can access the following: online class registration. Staffed computer lab on campus.

Community Environment: See Rockford College.

■ **ROCKFORD CAREER COLLEGE**
1130 S Alpine Rd.
Ste. 100
Rockford, IL 61108
Tel: (815)965-8616
Fax: (815)965-0360
Web Site: www.rockfordcareercollege.edu/

Description: Independent, 2-year, coed. Awards certificates, diplomas, and terminal associate degrees. Founded 1862. Setting: urban campus with easy access to Chicago. Total enrollment: 428. Faculty: 26 (8 full-time, 18 part-time). Student-undergrad faculty ratio is 15:1. 125 applied. Full-time: 243 students, 90% women, 10% men. Part-time: 185 students, 87% women, 13% men. Students come from 2 states and territories, 1% from out-of-state. 65% 25 or older, 8% transferred in. Core. Academic remediation for entering students, services for LD students, advanced placement, honors program, independent study, summer session for credit, part-time degree program, adult/continuing education programs, co-op programs and internships.

Entrance Requirements: Open admission. Options: electronic application, early admission. Required: high school transcript, interview. Required for some: essay. Entrance: minimally difficult. Application deadline: 9/4.

Collegiate Environment: Orientation program. Student-run newspaper. Most popular organization: International Students Club. Student services: personal-psychological counseling. Campus security: 24-hour patrols, late night transport-escort service. Rockford Business College Library plus 1 other with 1,823 books, 161 serials, and 50 audiovisual materials. 65 computers available on campus for general student use. A campuswide network can be accessed. Staffed computer lab on campus.

Community Environment: See Rockford College.

■ **ROCKFORD COLLEGE**
5050 E State St.
Rockford, IL 61108-2393
Tel: (815)226-4000; Free: 800-892-2984
Fax: (815)226-4119
E-mail: rcadmissions@rockford.edu
Web Site: www.rockford.edu/

Description: Independent, comprehensive, coed. Awards bachelor's and master's degrees. Founded 1847. Setting: 150-acre suburban campus with easy access to Chicago. Endowment: $10.5 million. Educational spending for the previous fiscal year: $5044 per student. Total enrollment: 1,238. Faculty: 162 (71 full-time, 91 part-time). Student-undergrad faculty ratio is 9:1. 1,455 applied, 40% were admitted. Full-time: 881 students, 61% women, 39% men. Part-time: 141 students, 67% women, 33% men. Students come from 25 states and territories, 5 other countries, 9% from out-of-state. 0.2% American Indian or Alaska Native, non-Hispanic/Latino; 6% Hispanic/Latino; 7% African American, non-Hispanic/Latino; 2% Asian, non-Hispanic/Latino; 0.4% Native Hawaiian or other Pacific Islander, non-Hispanic/Latino; 2% international. 31% 25 or older, 41% live on campus, 17% transferred in. Retention: 61% of full-time freshmen returned the follow-

ing year. Academic areas with the most degrees conferred: education; business/marketing; health professions and related sciences. Core. Calendar: semesters. Academic remediation for entering students, ESL program, services for LD students, advanced placement, accelerated degree program, honors program, independent study, double major, summer session for credit, part-time degree program, adult/continuing education programs, internships, graduate courses open to undergrads. Off campus study. Study abroad program. ROTC: Army (c).

Entrance Requirements: Options: electronic application, early admission, deferred admission, international baccalaureate accepted. Required: high school transcript, SAT/ACT score, SAT or ACT. Recommended: minimum 2.65 high school GPA. Required for some: essay, minimum 2.65 high school GPA, 2 recommendations. Entrance: moderately difficult. Application deadlines: Rolling, Rolling for nonresidents. Notification: continuous, continuous for nonresidents. SAT Reasoning Test deadline: 8/15. SAT Subject Test deadline: 8/15. Transfer credits accepted: Yes.

Costs Per Year: Application fee: $0. Comprehensive fee: $33,630 includes full-time tuition ($26,210), mandatory fees ($100), and college room and board ($7320). College room only: $4070. Full-time tuition and fees vary according to course load. Room and board charges vary according to board plan and housing facility. Part-time tuition: $715 per credit. Part-time mandatory fees: $40 per term. Part-time tuition and fees vary according to course load.

Collegiate Environment: Orientation program. Drama-theater group, choral group, student-run newspaper, radio station. Social organizations: 25 open to all. Most popular organizations: Student Government Association, Multicultural Club, RAGE (Regent Athletics Getting Excited), Psychology Society, Nursing Student Organization. Major annual events: Homecoming, April Weekend, Hunger and Homelessness Week Activities. Student services: health clinic, personal-psychological counseling. Campus security: 24-hour emergency response devices and patrols, late night transport-escort service, controlled dormitory access. 396 college housing spaces available; 342 were occupied in 2012-13. No special consideration for freshman housing applicants. Option: coed housing available. Howard Colman Library with 137,000 books, 23,000 serials, 1,670 audiovisual materials, an OPAC, and a Web page. Operations spending for the previous fiscal year: $333,782. 131 computers available on campus for general student use. A campuswide network can be accessed from student residence rooms and from off campus. Students can access the following: online class registration, online bill payment. Staffed computer lab on campus provides training in use of computers, software, and the Internet.

Community Environment: Rockford, population 152,916, is the second largest city in the state. It is 75 miles northwest of Chicago, and is situated in the historic and attractive Rock River Valley close to the Wisconsin border. Rockford is also an important industrial city that produces machine tools, furniture, hardware and automobile accessories.

■ **ROOSEVELT UNIVERSITY**
430 S Michigan Ave.
Chicago, IL 60605
Tel: (312)341-3500; Free: 877-APPLYRU
E-mail: amitchell@roosevelt.edu
Web Site: www.roosevelt.edu/

Description: Independent, comprehensive, coed. Awards bachelor's, master's, and doctoral degrees. Founded 1945. Setting: urban campus with easy access to Chicago. Endowment: $74.4 million. Research spending for the previous fiscal year: $570,931. Educational spending for the previous fiscal year: $9746 per student. Total enrollment: 6,343. Faculty: 722 (243 full-time, 479 part-time). Student-undergrad faculty ratio is 12:1. 3,862 applied, 75% were admitted. 2% from top 10% of their high school class, 10% from top quarter, 35% from top half. Full-time: 2,779 students, 63% women, 37% men. Part-time: 1,016 students, 67% women, 33% men. Students come from 30 states and territories, 41 other countries, 16% from out-of-state. 0.2% American Indian or Alaska Native, non-Hispanic/Latino; 17% Hispanic/Latino; 21% African American, non-Hispanic/Latino; 5% Asian, non-Hispanic/Latino; 0.2% Native Hawaiian or other Pacific Islander, non-Hispanic/Latino; 3% international. 38% 25 or older, 23% live on campus, 19% transferred in. Retention: 58% of full-time freshmen returned the following year. Academic areas with the most degrees conferred: business/marketing; psychology; education. Core. Calendar: semesters. Academic remediation for entering students, ESL program, services for LD students, advanced placement, accelerated degree program, self-designed majors, honors program, independent study, distance learning, double major, summer session for credit, part-time degree program, adult/continuing education programs, internships, graduate courses open to undergrads. Off campus study at School of the Art Institute of Chicago. Study abroad program.

Entrance Requirements: Options: electronic application, deferred admission, international baccalaureate accepted. Required: high school transcript, minimum 2.5 high school GPA, audition for music and theater programs, SAT or ACT. Recommended: essay. Required for some: essay, interview. Entrance: moderately difficult. Application deadline: 8/15. Notification: continuous. SAT Reasoning Test deadline: 8/15. SAT Subject Test deadline: 8/15.

Costs Per Year: Application fee: $25. Comprehensive fee: $38,050 includes full-time tuition ($25,950) and college room and board ($12,100). Full-time tuition varies according to course load, program, and reciprocity agreements. Room and board charges vary according to board plan and housing facility. Part-time tuition: $699 per credit. Part-time tuition varies according to course load, program, and reciprocity agreements.

Collegiate Environment: Orientation program. Student-run newspaper, radio station. Social organizations: 32 open to all; national fraternities, national sororities, local fraternities, local sororities; 1% of eligible men and 2% of eligible women are members. Most popular organizations: International Student Union, RU Proud, Association of Latin Americans (ALAS), student government, Residence Hall Council. Major annual events: International Day, semi-formal dances, Student Involvement Fair. Student services: personal-psychological counseling. Campus security: 24-hour emergency response devices and patrols, late night transport-escort service, controlled dormitory access. 1,000 college housing spaces available; 955 were occupied in 2012-13. Freshmen guaranteed college housing. On-campus residence required through sophomore year. Option: coed housing available. Murray-Green Library plus 4 others with 213,000 books, 188,000 microform titles, 1,500 serials, an OPAC, and a Web page. Operations spending for the previous fiscal year: $2.6 million. 646 computers available on campus for general student use. A campuswide network can be accessed from student residence rooms and from off campus. Students can access the following: online class registration. Staffed computer lab on campus provides training in use of computers, software, and the Internet.

Community Environment: Roosevelt University's downtown location places students only blocks away from such cultural and educational resources as the Art Institute, Orchestra Hall, the Opera House, the Field Museum of Natural History, the Grant Park Band Shell, the Shedd Aquarium and the Adler Planetarium. Roosevelt University is also located in the hub of the city's mercantile and financial districts - the Board of Trade, the State Street department stores, the LaSalle and Dearborn Streets banking houses, law offices, and government buildings all being within easy walking distance of the university. The Schauburg campus is located across from the Chicago area's largest shopping mall and only 15 minutes from O'Hare International Airport. The two campuses are linked by regularly scheduled van service and all academic programs are available at both locations except the Performing Arts (Chicago only).

■ RUSH UNIVERSITY

600 S Paulina
Chicago, IL 60612-3832
Tel: (312)942-5000
Fax: (312)942-2100
E-mail: hicela_castruita@rush.edu
Web Site: www.rushu.rush.edu/

Description: Independent, upper-level, coed. Awards bachelor's, master's, and doctoral degrees and post-master's certificates. Founded 1969. Setting: 35-acre urban campus. Endowment: $340.2 million. Research spending for the previous fiscal year: $41.6 million. Educational spending for the previous fiscal year: $20,780 per student. Total enrollment: 1,566. Faculty: 796 (all full-time). Student-undergrad faculty ratio is 8:1. 398 applied, 37% were admitted. Full-time: 159 students, 87% women, 13% men. Part-time: 7 students, 71% women, 29% men. Students come from 14 states and territories, 4 other countries, 19% from out-of-state. 60% 25 or older, 10% live on campus, 12% transferred in. Academic area with the most degrees conferred: health professions and related sciences. Distance learning.

Collegiate Environment: Most popular organization: Service project to Belize. Major annual events: Octoberfest, TGIFs, Music Recital. Student services: health clinic, personal-psychological counseling. Campus security: 24-hour emergency response devices and patrols, late night transport-escort service, controlled dormitory access. Library of Rush University Medical Center with 120,042 books, 1,100 serials, 4,750 audiovisual materials, an OPAC, and a Web page. Operations spending for the previous fiscal year: $2.8 million. 150 computers available on campus for general student use.

Computer purchase/lease plans available. A campuswide network can be accessed from student residence rooms and from off campus. Staffed computer lab on campus provides training in use of computers, software, and the Internet.

Community Environment: See University of Chicago.

■ SAINT ANTHONY COLLEGE OF NURSING

5658 E State St.
Rockford, IL 61108-2468
Tel: (815)395-5091
E-mail: info@sacn.edu
Web Site: www.sacn.edu/

Description: Independent Roman Catholic, upper-level, coed. Awards bachelor's and master's degrees. Founded 1915. Setting: 17-acre urban campus with easy access to Chicago. Endowment: $600,000. Educational spending for the previous fiscal year: $13,656 per student. Total enrollment: 161. Faculty: 15 (12 full-time, 3 part-time). Student-undergrad faculty ratio is 9:1. Full-time: 129 students, 92% women, 8% men. Part-time: 17 students, 76% women, 24% men. Students come from 2 states and territories, 4% from out-of-state. 49% 25 or older, 22% transferred in. Academic area with the most degrees conferred: health professions and related sciences. Core. Calendar: semesters. Services for LD students, advanced placement, accelerated degree program, independent study, summer session for credit, part-time degree program, internships. Off campus study.

Costs Per Year: Application fee: $50. Tuition: $20,134 full-time, $630 per credit hour part-time. Mandatory fees: $152 full-time, $30 per term part-time. Full-time tuition and fees vary according to course load and degree level. Part-time tuition and fees vary according to course load and degree level.

Collegiate Environment: Orientation program. Social organizations: 1 open to all. Most popular organization: Student Organization. Major annual events: Opening Mass and Breakfast, Welcome Party for new students, Student Organization Activities. Student services: legal services, health clinic, personal-psychological counseling. Campus security: 24-hour emergency response devices and patrols, late night transport-escort service. Sister Mary Linus Learning Resource Center plus 1 other with 1,258 books, 3,136 serials, 321 audiovisual materials, an OPAC, and a Web page. Operations spending for the previous fiscal year: $116,000. 17 computers available on campus for general student use. A campuswide network can be accessed from off-campus. Staffed computer lab on campus.

■ ST. AUGUSTINE COLLEGE

1333-1345 W Argyle
Chicago, IL 60640-3501
Tel: (773)878-8756
E-mail: info@staugustine.edu
Web Site: www.staugustine.edu/

Description: Independent, 4-year, coed. Awards associate and bachelor's degrees (offers bilingual Spanish/English degree programs). Founded 1980. Setting: 4-acre urban campus. Endowment: $501,935. Educational spending for the previous fiscal year: $2514 per student. Total enrollment: 1,430. Faculty: 154 (20 full-time, 134 part-time). Student-undergrad faculty ratio is 20:1. Full-time: 1,218 students, 76% women, 24% men. Part-time: 212 students, 74% women, 26% men. Students come from 2 states and territories, 5 other countries. 69% 25 or older, 3% transferred in. Retention: 68% of full-time freshmen returned the following year. Core. Calendar: semesters. Academic remediation for entering students, ESL program, services for LD students, independent study, double major, summer session for credit, part-time degree program, adult/continuing education programs, co-op programs and internships.

Entrance Requirements: Open admission. Entrance: noncompetitive. Application deadlines: Rolling, Rolling for nonresidents. Notification: continuous, continuous for nonresidents. Transfer credits accepted: Yes.

Collegiate Environment: Orientation program. Major annual events: Student Alliance Week, Hispanic History Week, Mexican Fiesta. Student services: personal-psychological counseling. Campus security: 24-hour patrols, late night transport-escort service. St. Augustine College Library with 24,007 books, 50 serials, 2,358 audiovisual materials, and an OPAC. Operations spending for the previous fiscal year: $121,000. 292 computers available on campus for general student use. A campuswide network can be accessed. Staffed computer lab on campus provides training in use of computers, software, and the Internet.

■ SAINT FRANCIS MEDICAL CENTER COLLEGE OF NURSING

511 NE Greenleaf St.
Peoria, IL 61603-3783

Tel: (309)655-2201

E-mail: janice.farquharson@osfhealthcare.org

Web Site: www.sfmccon.edu/

Description: Independent Roman Catholic, upper-level, coed. Awards bachelor's, master's, and doctoral degrees and post-master's certificates. Founded 1986. Setting: urban campus. Educational spending for the previous fiscal year: $10,577 per student. Total enrollment: 638. Faculty: 62 (35 full-time, 27 part-time). Student-undergrad faculty ratio is 8:1. 190 applied, 49% were admitted. Full-time: 294 students, 87% women, 13% men. Part-time: 108 students, 94% women, 6% men. Students come from 4 states and territories, 2 other countries, 1% from out-of-state. 0.2% American Indian or Alaska Native, non-Hispanic/Latino; 4% Hispanic/Latino; 5% African American, non-Hispanic/Latino; 2% Asian, non-Hispanic/Latino; 0.5% Native Hawaiian or other Pacific Islander, non-Hispanic/Latino; 0.2% international. 49% 25 or older, 3% live on campus, 23% transferred in. Academic area with the most degrees conferred: health professions and related sciences. Core. Calendar: semesters. Advanced placement, accelerated degree program, independent study, distance learning, summer session for credit.

Entrance Requirements: Transfer credits accepted: Yes.

Costs Per Year: Application fee: $50. Tuition: $16,368 full-time, $528 per hour part-time. Mandatory fees: $596 full-time. Full-time tuition and fees vary according to course load. Part-time tuition varies according to course load. College room only: $3200.

Collegiate Environment: Orientation program. Social organizations: 4 open to all. Most popular organizations: Student Senate, SNAI, Minority Student Association, Tau Omicron. Major annual events: Open House, Christmas Dinner, Spring Formal. Student services: health clinic, personal-psychological counseling. Campus security: 24-hour emergency response devices and patrols, controlled dormitory access. 79 college housing spaces available; all were occupied in 2012-13. Option: coed housing available. Sister Mary Ludgera Pieperbeck Learning and Resource Center plus 1 other with 6,790 books, 139 serials, 782 audiovisual materials, an OPAC, and a Web page. 49 computers available on campus for general student use. A computer is required for all students. A campuswide network can be accessed from student residence rooms and from off campus. Students can access the following: online class registration. Staffed computer lab on campus provides training in use of computers, software, and the Internet.

■ ST. JOHN'S COLLEGE

729 E Carpenter St.

Springfield, IL 62702

Tel: (217)525-5628

E-mail: college@st-johns.org

Web Site: www.stjohnscollegespringfield.edu/

Description: Independent Roman Catholic, upper-level, coed. Awards bachelor's degrees. Founded 1886. Setting: urban campus. Total enrollment: 71. Student-undergrad faculty ratio is 6:1. 32% 25 or older. Calendar: semesters. Part-time degree program.

Costs Per Year: Application fee: $50. Tuition: $15,030 full-time, $626 per credit hour part-time. Mandatory fees: $926 full-time. Full-time tuition and fees vary according to course load, program, and student level. Part-time tuition varies according to course load, program, and student level.

Collegiate Environment: Orientation program. Campus security: 24-hour emergency response devices and patrols, late night transport-escort service.

■ SAINT XAVIER UNIVERSITY

3700 W 103rd St.

Chicago, IL 60655-3105

Tel: (773)298-3000; Free: 800-462-9288

Fax: (773)298-3076

E-mail: carlson@sxu.edu

Web Site: www.sxu.edu/

Description: Independent Roman Catholic, comprehensive, coed. Awards bachelor's and master's degrees and post-master's certificates. Founded 1847. Setting: 70-acre urban campus. Endowment: $7.1 million. Total enrollment: 4,709. Faculty: 431 (173 full-time, 258 part-time). Student-undergrad faculty ratio is 14:1. 5,520 applied, 83% were admitted. 22% from top 10% of their high school class, 50% from top quarter, 84% from top half. Full-time: 2,537 students, 68% women, 32% men. Part-time: 456 students, 69% women, 31% men. 5% from out-of-state. 0.5% American Indian or Alaska Native, non-Hispanic/Latino; 17% Hispanic/Latino; 17% African American, non-Hispanic/Latino; 2% Asian, non-Hispanic/Latino; 0% Native Hawaiian or other Pacific Islander, non-Hispanic/Latino; 0.3% international. 19% 25 or older, 29% live on campus, 13% transferred in. Retention: 72% of full-time

freshmen returned the following year. Academic areas with the most degrees conferred: education; business/marketing; health professions and related sciences. Core. Calendar: semesters. Academic remediation for entering students, ESL program, services for LD students, advanced placement, accelerated degree program, self-designed majors, honors program, independent study, double major, summer session for credit, part-time degree program, adult/continuing education programs, co-op programs and internships, graduate courses open to undergrads. Study abroad program. ROTC: Air Force (c).

Entrance Requirements: Options: electronic application, deferred admission, international baccalaureate accepted. Required: high school transcript, SAT or ACT. Recommended: essay, minimum 2.5 high school GPA, interview. Entrance: moderately difficult. Application deadline: Rolling. Notification: continuous. Transfer credits accepted: Yes.

Costs Per Year: Application fee: $25. Comprehensive fee: $37,600 includes full-time tuition ($27,330), mandatory fees ($780), and college room and board ($9490). Room and board charges vary according to board plan and housing facility.

Collegiate Environment: Orientation program. Drama-theater group, choral group, marching band, student-run newspaper, radio station. Social organizations: 37 open to all. Most popular organizations: Student Activities Board, Black Student Union, UNIDOS (Hispanic Organization), Student Nurses Association, Business Students Association. Major annual events: Homecoming Celebrations, Boat Bash. Student services: health clinic, personal-psychological counseling, women's center. Campus security: 24-hour emergency response devices and patrols, late night transport-escort service. Byrne Memorial Library with 179,000 books, 11,327 microform titles, 35,000 serials, 6,000 audiovisual materials, an OPAC, and a Web page. 500 computers available on campus for general student use. A campuswide network can be accessed from student residence rooms and from off campus. Students can access the following: online class registration. Staffed computer lab on campus provides training in use of computers, software, and the Internet.

Community Environment: See University of Chicago.

■ SAUK VALLEY COMMUNITY COLLEGE

173 Illinois Rte. 2

Dixon, IL 61021

Tel: (815)288-5511

E-mail: medemap@svcc.edu

Web Site: www.svcc.edu/

Description: District-supported, 2-year, coed. Part of Illinois Community College Board. Awards certificates, transfer associate, and terminal associate degrees. Founded 1965. Setting: 165-acre rural campus. Endowment: $1.1 million. Educational spending for the previous fiscal year: $2975 per student. Total enrollment: 2,492. Faculty: 144 (43 full-time, 101 part-time). Student-undergrad faculty ratio is 22:1. 585 applied, 100% were admitted. Full-time: 1,269 students, 55% women, 45% men. Part-time: 1,223 students, 64% women, 36% men. 37% 25 or older. Core. Calendar: semesters. Academic remediation for entering students, ESL program, services for LD students, accelerated degree program, self-designed majors, honors program, independent study, distance learning, summer session for credit, part-time degree program, adult/continuing education programs, co-op programs and internships. Off campus study at Highland Community College, Illinois Valley Community College, Rock Valley College, Kishwaukee College.

Entrance Requirements: Open admission except for health programs. Options: electronic application, early admission, deferred admission. Recommended: high school transcript, ACT. Entrance: noncompetitive. Application deadline: Rolling. Notification: continuous.

Collegiate Environment: Orientation program. Drama-theater group, choral group. Social organizations: 10 open to all. Student services: personal-psychological counseling. Campus security: 24-hour emergency response devices and patrols, late night transport-escort service. Learning Resource Center plus 1 other with 55,000 books, 268 serials, and an OPAC. Operations spending for the previous fiscal year: $249,091. 100 computers available on campus for general student use. A campuswide network can be accessed from student residence rooms and from off campus. Students can access the following: online class registration. Staffed computer lab on campus provides training in use of computers, software, and the Internet.

Community Environment: Dixon has a population of 15,372; Sterling (population 15,381) is a small industrial city, enjoying a seasonal climate. Ozark Airlines and Greyhound buses serve the area. Community facilities include a public library, hospital, YMCA, YWCA, many churches, and all the major civic and service groups. Recreational opportunities abound in the many city parks providing swimming, tennis, picnic areas, boating and fishing, along with access to golf, bowling, roller skating, miniature golf and go-carting. Jobs are plentiful in this highly industrialized area.

■ SCHOOL OF THE ART INSTITUTE OF CHICAGO

37 S Wabash
Chicago, IL 60603-3103
Tel: (312)899-5100; Free: 800-232-SAIC
Fax: (312)263-0141
E-mail: ugadmiss@saic.edu
Web Site: www.saic.edu/

Description: Independent, comprehensive, coed. Awards bachelor's and master's degrees. Founded 1866. Setting: 1-acre urban campus with easy access to Chicago. Endowment: $186.3 million. Total enrollment: 3,308. Faculty: 744 (160 full-time, 584 part-time). Student-undergrad faculty ratio is 9:1. 3,004 applied, 78% were admitted. Full-time: 2,387 students, 70% women, 30% men. Part-time: 240 students, 69% women, 31% men. Students come from 50 states and territories, 68 other countries, 62% from out-of-state. 1% American Indian or Alaska Native, non-Hispanic/Latino; 5% Hispanic/Latino; 4% African American, non-Hispanic/Latino; 12% Asian, non-Hispanic/Latino; 0.2% Native Hawaiian or other Pacific Islander, non-Hispanic/Latino; 22% international. 13% 25 or older, 25% live on campus, 10% transferred in. Retention: 79% of full-time freshmen returned the following year. Academic areas with the most degrees conferred: visual and performing arts; architecture. Core. Calendar: semesters. Academic remediation for entering students, ESL program, services for LD students, advanced placement, self-designed majors, independent study, double major, summer session for credit, part-time degree program, co-op programs and internships, graduate courses open to undergrads. Off campus study at Association of Independent Colleges of Art and Design. Study abroad program.

Entrance Requirements: Options: electronic application, early action, deferred admission, international baccalaureate accepted. Required: essay, high school transcript, 1 recommendation, portfolio, SAT or ACT. Recommended: interview. Entrance: very difficult. Application deadlines: 6/1, 1/3 for early action. Notification: continuous, 2/15 for early action. Transfer credits accepted: Yes.

Costs Per Year: Application fee: $65. One-time mandatory fee: $150. Comprehensive fee: $52,830 includes full-time tuition ($38,340), mandatory fees ($680), and college room and board ($13,810). College room only: $10,400. Full-time tuition and fees vary according to course load, degree level, and program. Room and board charges vary according to board plan. Part-time tuition: $1278 per credit hour. Part-time mandatory fees: $235 per term. Part-time tuition and fees vary according to course load, degree level, and program.

Collegiate Environment: Orientation program. Drama-theater group, student-run newspaper, radio station. Social organizations: 45 open to all. Most popular organizations: Student Association/Student Union Galleries, Korean Student Association, InterVarsity, Curatorial Community, Good 'Ol Futbol. Major annual events: Exhibition Openings, Holiday Art Sale, All School BBQ. Student services: health clinic, personal-psychological counseling. Campus security: 24-hour emergency response devices and patrols, late night transport-escort service, controlled dormitory access. 846 college housing spaces available; 499 were occupied in 2012-13. No special consideration for freshman housing applicants. Option: coed housing available. The John M. Flaxman Library plus 1 other with 130,186 books, 150 microform titles, 399 serials, 178,700 audiovisual materials, an OPAC, and a Web page. 300 computers available on campus for general student use. Computer purchase/lease plans available. A computer is required for all students. A campuswide network can be accessed from student residence rooms and from off campus. Students can access the following: online class registration. Staffed computer lab on campus (open 24 hours a day) provides training in use of computers, software, and the Internet.

Community Environment: See University of Chicago.

■ SHAWNEE COMMUNITY COLLEGE

8364 Shawnee College Rd.
Ullin, IL 62992
Tel: (618)634-3200
Fax: (618)634-3300
E-mail: erink@shawneecc.edu
Web Site: www.shawneecc.edu/

Description: State and locally supported, 2-year, coed. Part of Illinois Com-

munity College Board. Awards certificates, diplomas, transfer associate, and terminal associate degrees. Founded 1967. Setting: 163-acre rural campus. Educational spending for the previous fiscal year: $3576 per student. Total enrollment: 2,139. Faculty: 169 (40 full-time, 129 part-time). Student-undergrad faculty ratio is 13:1. 771 applied, 100% were admitted. 5% from top 10% of their high school class, 20% from top quarter, 60% from top half. Full-time: 701 students, 59% women, 41% men. Part-time: 1,438 students, 63% women, 37% men. Students come from 5 states and territories, 2 other countries, 2% from out-of-state. 1% American Indian or Alaska Native, non-Hispanic/Latino; 2% Hispanic/Latino; 17% African American, non-Hispanic/Latino; 0.4% Asian, non-Hispanic/Latino; 0.1% Native Hawaiian or other Pacific Islander, non-Hispanic/Latino. 33% 25 or older. Retention: 0% of full-time freshmen returned the following year. Core. Calendar: semesters. Academic remediation for entering students, ESL program, services for LD students, advanced placement, accelerated degree program, independent study, distance learning, double major, summer session for credit, part-time degree program, external degree program, adult/continuing education programs, co-op programs and internships. Off campus study.

Entrance Requirements: Open admission except for health programs. Options: electronic application, early admission, deferred admission. Required: high school transcript. Recommended: ACT. Required for some: ACT. Entrance: noncompetitive. Application deadlines: Rolling, Rolling for nonresidents. Notification: continuous, continuous for nonresidents. Preference given to district residents. Transfer credits accepted: Yes.

Costs Per Year: Application fee: $0. Area resident tuition: $2208 full-time, $92 per credit hour part-time. State resident tuition: $3312 full-time, $138 per credit hour part-time. Nonresident tuition: $3696 full-time, $154 per credit hour part-time.

Collegiate Environment: Drama-theater group, choral group. Social organizations: 14 open to all. Most popular organizations: Phi Theta Kappa, Phi Beta Lambda, Music Club, Student Senate, Future Teachers Organization. Major annual events: Homecoming, Fall Fest, Spring Fest. Student services: personal-psychological counseling. Campus security: 24-hour patrols. College housing not available. Shawnee Community College Library with 46,313 books, 3,537 microform titles, 148 serials, 1,842 audiovisual materials, an OPAC, and a Web page. Operations spending for the previous fiscal year: $108,105. 165 computers available on campus for general student use. A campuswide network can be accessed from off-campus. Students can access the following: online class registration. Staffed computer lab on campus.

■ SHIMER COLLEGE

3424 S State St.
Chicago, IL 60616
Tel: (312)235-3500; Free: 800-215-7173
Fax: (312)235-3501
E-mail: admission@shimer.edu
Web Site: www.shimer.edu/

Description: Independent, 4-year, coed. Awards bachelor's degrees. Founded 1853. Setting: 3-acre urban campus with easy access to Chicago, Milwaukee. Total enrollment: 127. Faculty: 15 (11 full-time, 4 part-time). Student-undergrad faculty ratio is 9:1. 31 applied, 74% were admitted. Full-time: 105 students, 49% women, 51% men. Part-time: 22 students, 50% women, 50% men. 52% from out-of-state. 0% American Indian or Alaska Native, non-Hispanic/Latino; 4% Hispanic/Latino; 2% African American, non-Hispanic/Latino; 4% Asian, non-Hispanic/Latino; 0% Native Hawaiian or other Pacific Islander, non-Hispanic/Latino; 0% international. 20% 25 or older, 5% live on campus, 12% transferred in. Retention: 84% of full-time freshmen returned the following year. Academic areas with the most degrees conferred: liberal arts/general studies; social sciences; interdisciplinary studies. Core. Calendar: semesters. Self-designed majors, independent study, double major, summer session for credit, part-time degree program, adult/continuing education programs, co-op programs and internships. Off campus study at Illinois Institute of Technology. Study abroad program.

Entrance Requirements: Option: electronic application. Required: essay, high school transcript, 1 recommendation, interview. Required for some: SAT and SAT Subject Tests or ACT. Entrance: moderately difficult. Application deadline: Rolling. Notification: continuous. SAT Reasoning Test deadline: 8/15. SAT Subject Test deadline: 8/15.

Costs Per Year: Application fee: $25. Comprehensive fee: $41,856 includes full-time tuition ($26,510), mandatory fees ($4720), and college room and board ($10,626). Full-time tuition and fees vary according to class time, course load, and program. Room and board charges vary according to housing facility.

Collegiate Environment: Orientation program. Drama-theater group, choral group, student-run newspaper, radio station. Student services: personal-psychological counseling. Campus security: 24-hour emergency response devices, late night transport-escort service. Freshmen guaranteed college housing. Option: coed housing available.

Community Environment: Waukegan (population 91,000) is the county seat of Lake County on Lake Michigan. Excellent public transportation is available to Chicago. Students enjoy all the usual services of a small city, including a nearby state park.

■ **SOLEX COLLEGE**
350 E Dundee Rd.
Wheeling, IL 60090
Tel: (847)229-9595
Web Site: www.solex.edu/
Description: Proprietary, 2-year, coed. Administratively affiliated with The School of Massage Therapy at SOLEX. Awards certificates and terminal associate degrees. Setting: suburban campus with easy access to Chicago. ESL program, summer session for credit, part-time degree program, adult/continuing education programs, internships. Off campus study.
Entrance Requirements: Options: electronic application, international baccalaureate accepted. Required: high school transcript, SAT or ACT.

■ **SOUTH SUBURBAN COLLEGE**
15800 S State St.
South Holland, IL 60473-1270
Tel: (708)596-2000
E-mail: admissionsquestions@ssc.edu
Web Site: www.ssc.edu/
Description: State and locally supported, 2-year, coed. Part of Illinois Community College Board. Awards certificates, transfer associate, and terminal associate degrees. Founded 1927. Setting: suburban campus with easy access to Chicago. Total enrollment: 6,211. Faculty: 364 (117 full-time, 247 part-time). Student-undergrad faculty ratio is 17:1. 873 applied, 100% were admitted. 20% from top 10% of their high school class, 49% from top quarter. 6% from out-of-state. 2% American Indian or Alaska Native, non-Hispanic/Latino; 9% Hispanic/Latino; 68% African American, non-Hispanic/Latino; 0.2% Asian, non-Hispanic/Latino; 0% Native Hawaiian or other Pacific Islander, non-Hispanic/Latino; 1% international. 52% 25 or older. Retention: 58% of full-time freshmen returned the following year. Core. Calendar: semesters. Academic remediation for entering students, ESL program, services for LD students, advanced placement, honors program, distance learning, summer session for credit, part-time degree program, adult/continuing education programs, co-op programs and internships. Off campus study at other colleges of the Illinois Community College System. Study abroad program.
Entrance Requirements: Open admission except for nursing, occupational therapy, court reporting, practical nursing, radiological technology programs. Options: early admission, deferred admission. Required: high school transcript. Recommended: essay, minimum 2 high school GPA. Required for some: essay. Entrance: noncompetitive. Application deadline: Rolling. Notification: continuous. Preference given to district residents for nursing program. Transfer credits accepted: Yes.
Costs Per Year: Area resident tuition: $3300 full-time. State resident tuition: $8640 full-time. Nonresident tuition: $10,290 full-time. Mandatory fees: $473 full-time. Full-time tuition and fees vary according to course load and reciprocity agreements.
Collegiate Environment: Drama-theater group, choral group. Campus security: 24-hour emergency response devices and patrols. College housing not available. South Suburban College Library with 28,500 books, 55 serials, an OPAC, and a Web page.

■ **SOUTHEASTERN ILLINOIS COLLEGE**
3575 College Rd.
Harrisburg, IL 62946-4925
Tel: (618)252-5400; Free: 866-338-2742
Web Site: www.sic.edu/
Description: State-supported, 2-year, coed. Part of Illinois Community College Board. Awards certificates, transfer associate, and terminal associate degrees. Founded 1960. Setting: 140-acre rural campus. Educational spending for the previous fiscal year: $4188 per student. Total enrollment: 2,941. 7% from out-of-state. 40% 25 or older. Core. Calendar: semesters. Academic remediation for entering students, services for LD students, advanced placement, self-designed majors, independent study, distance

learning, summer session for credit, part-time degree program, adult/continuing education programs, internships. Off campus study at Southern Illinois Collegiate Common Market.
Entrance Requirements: Open admission except for nursing, medical records technology, medical lab technology, operating room technology, game management, occupational therapy programs, health information technology. Options: electronic application, early admission, deferred admission. Required: high school transcript. Entrance: noncompetitive. Application deadline: 9/1. Notification: continuous. Preference given to district residents.
Collegiate Environment: Drama-theater group, choral group. Social organizations: 13 open to all. Most popular organizations: Math and Science Club, Phi Theta Kappa, Forestry Club, Phi Beta Lambda, BASIC. Student services: personal-psychological counseling. Campus security: student patrols, evening security guard. Melba Patton Library plus 2 others with an OPAC and a Web page. Operations spending for the previous fiscal year: $277,328.
Community Environment: Harrisburg is an important coal mining, dairying, agricultural, and commercial center. Community facilities include a library, hospital, churches, an historical museum, and TV and radio stations. Recreational facilities are unlimited with Shawnee National Forest and other federal and state recreation areas within five to ten miles, and many large lakes in the area. The Saline County Fair is an annual event each July. Some part-time work is available.

■ **SOUTHERN ILLINOIS UNIVERSITY CARBONDALE**
Carbondale, IL 62901-4701
Tel: (618)453-2121
Fax: (618)453-3250
E-mail: ksuski@siu.edu
Web Site: www.siuc.edu/
Description: State-supported, university, coed. Part of Southern Illinois University. Awards associate, bachelor's, master's, and doctoral degrees. Founded 1869. Setting: 1,136-acre rural campus with easy access to St. Louis. Endowment: $95.9 million. Research spending for the previous fiscal year: $55 million. Total enrollment: 18,847. Faculty: 996 (869 full-time, 127 part-time). Student-undergrad faculty ratio is 15:1. 14,535 applied, 51% were admitted. 9% from top 10% of their high school class, 30% from top quarter, 61% from top half. 21 valedictorians. Full-time: 12,388 students, 45% women, 55% men. Part-time: 1,742 students, 42% women, 58% men. Students come from 47 states and territories, 45 other countries, 13% from out-of-state. 0.3% American Indian or Alaska Native, non-Hispanic/Latino; 6% Hispanic/Latino; 22% African American, non-Hispanic/Latino; 2% Asian, non-Hispanic/Latino; 0.2% Native Hawaiian or other Pacific Islander, non-Hispanic/Latino; 3% international. 22% 25 or older, 29% live on campus, 13% transferred in. Retention: 61% of full-time freshmen returned the following year. Academic areas with the most degrees conferred: education; business/marketing; engineering technologies; health professions and related sciences. Core. Calendar: semesters plus 8-week summer session. Academic remediation for entering students, ESL program, services for LD students, advanced placement, accelerated degree program, self-designed majors, honors program, independent study, distance learning, double major, summer session for credit, part-time degree program, adult/continuing education programs, co-op programs and internships, graduate courses open to undergrads. Off campus study. Study abroad program. ROTC: Army, Air Force.
Entrance Requirements: Options: electronic application, deferred admission, international baccalaureate accepted. Required: high school transcript, SAT or ACT, SAT or ACT. Entrance: moderately difficult. Application deadlines: 5/1, 5/1 for nonresidents. Notification: continuous until 9/1, continuous until 9/1 for nonresidents. SAT Reasoning Test deadline: 5/1. SAT Subject Test deadline: 5/1. Transfer credits accepted: Yes.
Costs Per Year: Application fee: $30. State resident tuition: $8169 full-time, $272 per credit hour part-time. Nonresident tuition: $20,422 full-time, $681 per credit hour part-time. Mandatory fees: $3359 full-time, $156 per credit hour part-time. Full-time tuition and fees vary according to course load, program, and student level. Part-time tuition and fees vary according to course load, program, and student level. College room and board: $9126. Room and board charges vary according to board plan and housing facility. Tuition guaranteed not to increase for student's term of enrollment.
Collegiate Environment: Orientation program. Drama-theater group, choral group, marching band, student-run newspaper, radio station. Social organizations: 450 open to all; national fraternities, national sororities, local fraternities, local sororities; 6% of eligible men and 5% of eligible women are members. Most popular organizations: Undergraduate Student Government,

Graduate Professional Student Government, Interfraternity Council, Student Programming Council, International Student Council. Major annual events: Homecoming, Family Weekend, St. Jude Children's Research Hospital's Up 'til Dawn. Student services: legal services, health clinic, personal-psychological counseling, women's center. Campus security: 24-hour emergency response devices and patrols, student patrols, late night transport-escort service, controlled dormitory access, well-lit pathways, night safety vans, student transit system. 3,828 college housing spaces available; 3,584 were occupied in 2012-13. Freshmen guaranteed college housing. On-campus residence required in freshman year. Options: coed, women-only housing available. Morris Library plus 1 other with 2.9 million books, 3.6 million microform titles, 64,225 serials, 49,584 audiovisual materials, an OPAC, and a Web page. Operations spending for the previous fiscal year: $14.9 million. 1,856 computers available on campus for general student use. Computer purchase/lease plans available. A campuswide network can be accessed from student residence rooms and from off campus. Students can access the following: online class registration. Staffed computer lab on campus provides training in use of computers, software, and the Internet.

Community Environment: Carbondale, an economic center of Southern Illinois, is only a few hours from Chicago, St. Louis, and Memphis. It sits amid rolling hills, farmlands, and orchards just 60 miles above the confluence of the Mississippi and Ohio Rivers. The area from Carbondale south is ruggedly scenic and suitable for a wide range of year-round outdoor activities. Within minutes are four large recreational lakes, the two great rivers, and spectacular 270,000-acre Shawnee National Forest. A large number of smaller lakes, state parks, and recreational areas are within easy driving distance.

■ SOUTHERN ILLINOIS UNIVERSITY EDWARDSVILLE

Edwardsville, IL 62026-0001
Tel: (618)650-2000; Free: 800-447-SIUE
Fax: (618)692-2081
E-mail: admissions@siue.edu
Web Site: www.siue.edu/

Description: State-supported, comprehensive, coed. Part of Southern Illinois University. Awards bachelor's, master's, and doctoral degrees and post-master's certificates. Founded 1957. Setting: 2,660-acre suburban campus with easy access to St. Louis. Endowment: $16.5 million. Research spending for the previous fiscal year: $10.7 million. Educational spending for the previous fiscal year: $11,177 per student. Total enrollment: 14,055. Faculty: 920 (626 full-time, 294 part-time). Student-undergrad faculty ratio is 18:1. 7,660 applied, 82% were admitted. 17% from top 10% of their high school class, 42% from top quarter, 75% from top half. Full-time: 9,648 students, 53% women, 47% men. Part-time: 1,693 students, 52% women, 48% men. 0.3% American Indian or Alaska Native, non-Hispanic/Latino; 4% Hispanic/Latino; 15% African American, non-Hispanic/Latino; 1% Asian, non-Hispanic/Latino; 0.1% Native Hawaiian or other Pacific Islander, non-Hispanic/Latino; 1% international. 15% 25 or older, 30% live on campus, 11% transferred in. Retention: 71% of full-time freshmen returned the following year. Academic areas with the most degrees conferred: business/marketing; health professions and related sciences; education. Core. Calendar: semesters. Academic remediation for entering students, ESL program, services for LD students, advanced placement, accelerated degree program, self-designed majors, honors program, independent study, distance learning, double major, summer session for credit, part-time degree program, co-op programs and internships, graduate courses open to undergrads. Off campus study at University of Missouri-St. Louis, International Student Exchange Program, MBA program at southwestern Illinois College. Study abroad program. ROTC: Army, Air Force (c).

Entrance Requirements: Options: electronic application, deferred admission, international baccalaureate accepted. Required: high school transcript, SAT or ACT. Recommended: minimum 2.5 high school GPA. Entrance: moderately difficult. Application deadline: 5/1. Notification: continuous. SAT Reasoning Test deadline: 5/1. Transfer credits accepted: Yes.

Costs Per Year: Application fee: $30. State resident tuition: $6948 full-time, $231.60 per credit hour part-time. Nonresident tuition: $17,370 full-time. Mandatory fees: $2,303 full-time, $272.80 per credit hour part-time. Full-time tuition and fees vary according to course load. Part-time tuition and fees vary according to course load. College room and board: $8281. Room and board charges vary according to board plan and housing facility. Tuition guaranteed not to increase for student's term of enrollment.

Collegiate Environment: Orientation program. Drama-theater group, choral group, student-run newspaper, radio station. Social organizations: 250 open to all; national fraternities, national sororities. Major annual events: Welcome Week, Homecoming, Springfest. Student services: legal services, health clinic, personal-psychological counseling. Campus security: 24-hour emergency response devices and patrols, student patrols, late night transport-escort service, controlled dormitory access, 24-hour ID check at residence hall entrances, emergency call boxes located throughout campus. 3,587 college housing spaces available; 3,412 were occupied in 2012-13. Freshmen given priority for college housing. Option: coed housing available. Lovejoy Library with 1.4 million books, 1.7 million microform titles, 32,858 serials, 33,438 audiovisual materials, an OPAC, and a Web page. Operations spending for the previous fiscal year: $4.5 million. 600 computers available on campus for general student use. Computer purchase/lease plans available. A campuswide network can be accessed from student residence rooms and from off campus. Students can access the following: online class registration, online job finder. Staffed computer lab on campus.

Community Environment: Edwardsville/Glen Carbon (population more than 24,000) is a suburban St. Louis community with a public library, many churches, museum, YMCA, and hospital facilities nearby. It is located only 30 minutes from Lambert St. Louis International Airport.

■ SOUTHWESTERN ILLINOIS COLLEGE

2500 Carlyle Rd.
Belleville, IL 62221-5899
Tel: (618)235-2700
Fax: (618)235-1578
E-mail: michelle.birk@swic.edu
Web Site: www.southwestern.cc.il.us/

Description: District-supported, 2-year, coed. Part of Illinois Community College Board. Awards certificates, diplomas, transfer associate, and terminal associate degrees. Founded 1946. Setting: 341-acre suburban campus with easy access to St. Louis. Endowment: $5.2 million. Educational spending for the previous fiscal year: $3600 per student. Total enrollment: 12,779. Faculty: 728 (153 full-time, 575 part-time). Student-undergrad faculty ratio is 23:1. 1,147 applied, 100% were admitted. Full-time: 5,276 students, 54% women, 46% men. Part-time: 7,503 students, 58% women, 42% men. Students come from 12 states and territories, 1% from out-of-state. 0.4% American Indian or Alaska Native, non-Hispanic/Latino; 2% Hispanic/Latino; 23% African American, non-Hispanic/Latino; 1% Asian, non-Hispanic/Latino; 0.4% Native Hawaiian or other Pacific Islander, non-Hispanic/Latino; 0.01% international. 41% 25 or older, 4% transferred in. Core. Calendar: semesters. Academic remediation for entering students, ESL program, services for LD students, advanced placement, accelerated degree program, distance learning, double major, summer session for credit, part-time degree program, adult/continuing education programs, co-op programs and internships. Off campus study at other colleges of the Illinois Community College System. Study abroad program. ROTC: Army (c), Air Force (c).

Entrance Requirements: Open admission. Options: early admission, deferred admission. Required: high school transcript. Required for some: ACT, ACT ASSET or ACT COMPASS. Entrance: noncompetitive. Application deadlines: Rolling, Rolling for nonresidents.

Costs Per Year: Area resident tuition: $3120 full-time, $99 per credit hour part-time. State resident tuition: $7440 full-time, $243 per credit hour part-time. Nonresident tuition: $11,100 full-time, $365 per credit hour part-time. Mandatory fees: $150 full-time, $4 per credit hour part-time. Full-time tuition and fees vary according to course load. Part-time tuition and fees vary according to course load.

Collegiate Environment: Orientation program. Drama-theater group, choral group, student-run newspaper. Social organizations: 37 open to all. Most popular organizations: College Activities Board, Phi Theta Kappa, Student Nurses Association, Horticulture Club, Data Processing Management Association. Major annual events: Spring Blast, Fall Fest, Summer Picnic. Student services: personal-psychological counseling. Campus security: 24-hour emergency response devices and patrols, late night transport-escort service. Southwestern Illinois College Library with 85,265 books, 60 serials, 6,902 audiovisual materials, an OPAC, and a Web page. Operations spending for the previous fiscal year: $228,646. 1,700 computers available on campus for general student use. A campuswide network can be accessed. Students can access the following: online class registration. Staffed computer lab on campus provides training in use of computers, software, and the Internet.

■ SPOON RIVER COLLEGE

23235 N County 22
Canton, IL 61520-9801
Tel: (309)647-4645; Free: 800-334-7337

Fax: (309)649-6235
E-mail: info@spoonrivercollege.edu
Web Site: www.src.edu/
Description: State-supported, 2-year, coed. Part of Illinois Community College Board. Awards certificates, transfer associate, and terminal associate degrees. Founded 1959. Setting: 160-acre rural campus. Endowment: $1.4 million. Educational spending for the previous fiscal year: $3464 per student. Total enrollment: 1,966. Faculty: 116 (35 full-time, 81 part-time). Student-undergrad faculty ratio is 17:1. 605 applied, 100% were admitted. Full-time: 872 students, 53% women, 47% men. Part-time: 1,094 students, 63% women, 37% men. 0.5% American Indian or Alaska Native, non-Hispanic/Latino; 2% Hispanic/Latino; 5% African American, non-Hispanic/Latino; 1% Asian, non-Hispanic/Latino; 0% Native Hawaiian or other Pacific Islander, non-Hispanic/Latino; 0% international. 41% 25 or older, 11% transferred in. Retention: 58% of full-time freshmen returned the following year. Core. Calendar: semesters. Academic remediation for entering students, ESL program, services for LD students, advanced placement, accelerated degree program, freshman honors college, honors program, distance learning, summer session for credit, part-time degree program, adult/continuing education programs, internships. ROTC: Army.
Entrance Requirements: Open admission The Open Admission Policy applies for everything with the exception of the Nursing Program. Options: electronic application, early admission, deferred admission. Required: high school transcript. Entrance: noncompetitive. Application deadline: Rolling. Notification: continuous.
Costs Per Year: Application fee: $0. Area resident tuition: $3390 full-time, $113 per semester hour part-time. State resident tuition: $7470 full-time, $249 per semester hour part-time. Nonresident tuition: $8550 full-time, $285 per semester hour part-time. Mandatory fees: $450 full-time. Full-time tuition and fees vary according to course load and program. Part-time tuition varies according to course load and program. College room and board: $4830.
Collegiate Environment: Orientation program. Drama-theater group, student-run newspaper. Social organizations: 11 open to all; 9% of eligible men and 10% of eligible women are members. Most popular organizations: Student Government Association, PEEPS, Intramural Athletics, Habitat for Humanity, Drama Club. Major annual events: Graduation, Homecoming. Student services: personal-psychological counseling. Campus security: 24-hour emergency response devices. College housing not available. Library/Learning Resource Center with 74,252 books, 121 serials, 2,285 audiovisual materials, an OPAC, and a Web page. 600 computers available on campus for general student use. A campuswide network can be accessed from off-campus. Students can access the following: online class registration. Staffed computer lab on campus.
Community Environment: Canton is situated in an extremely fertile agricultural district with a seasonal climate. Planes and buses are available. Air service at Peoria some 30 miles distant. Industries are coal mining and the manufacture of farm implements. The city has a library, YMCA, YWCA, concert association, hospital, a downtown shopping area with over 100 retail outlets. Additional shopping facilities in Peoria. Recreational activities are boating, fishing, hunting, bowling, and golf. At least 12 retail and community-sponsored events are conducted each year.

■ **TAYLOR BUSINESS INSTITUTE**
318 W Adams
Chicago, IL 60606
Tel: (312)658-5100
Fax: (312)658-0867
Web Site: www.tbiil.edu/
Description: Proprietary, 2-year, coed. Awards terminal associate degrees. Founded 1964. Total enrollment: 95. 131 applied, 78% were admitted.

■ **TELSHE YESHIVA–CHICAGO**
3535 W Foster Ave.
Chicago, IL 60625-5598
Tel: (773)463-7738
Description: Independent Jewish, comprehensive, men only. Awards bachelor's and master's degrees. Founded 1960. Total enrollment: 77. 8 applied, 100% were admitted. Core. Calendar: semesters. Summer session for credit, part-time degree program.
Entrance Requirements: Required: interview.
Collegiate Environment: Student services: health clinic, personal-psychological counseling.

■ **TRINITY CHRISTIAN COLLEGE**
6601 W College Dr.
Palos Heights, IL 60463-0929

Tel: (708)597-3000
Fax: (708)239-3995
E-mail: admissions@trnty.edu
Web Site: www.trnty.edu/
Description: Independent Christian Reformed, comprehensive, coed. Awards bachelor's and master's degrees. Founded 1959. Setting: 53-acre suburban campus with easy access to Chicago. Endowment: $7.9 million. Educational spending for the previous fiscal year: $10,496 per student. Total enrollment: 1,369. Faculty: 157 (83 full-time, 74 part-time). Student-undergrad faculty ratio is 11:1. 691 applied, 82% were admitted. 15% from top 10% of their high school class, 34% from top quarter, 62% from top half. Full-time: 1,075 students, 64% women, 36% men. Part-time: 271 students, 72% women, 28% men. 28% from out-of-state. 1% American Indian or Alaska Native, non-Hispanic/Latino; 9% Hispanic/Latino; 9% African American, non-Hispanic/Latino; 2% Asian, non-Hispanic/Latino; 0.2% Native Hawaiian or other Pacific Islander, non-Hispanic/Latino; 2% international. 21% 25 or older, 45% live on campus, 7% transferred in. Retention: 80% of full-time freshmen returned the following year. Academic areas with the most degrees conferred: education; business/marketing; health professions and related sciences. Core. Calendar: semesters plus 2 week interim term. Academic remediation for entering students, ESL program, services for LD students, advanced placement, honors program, independent study, double major, summer session for credit, part-time degree program, adult/continuing education programs, co-op programs and internships. Off campus study. Study abroad program.
Entrance Requirements: Options: electronic application, deferred admission, international baccalaureate accepted. Required: essay, high school transcript, minimum 2.25 high school GPA, interview, SAT or ACT. Recommended: ACT. Required for some: 1 recommendation, SAT, SAT and SAT Subject Tests or ACT, SAT Subject Tests. Entrance: moderately difficult. Application deadline: Rolling. Notification: continuous. SAT Reasoning Test deadline: 8/1. SAT Subject Test deadline: 8/1. Transfer credits accepted: Yes.
Costs Per Year: Application fee: $20. Comprehensive fee: $31,955 includes full-time tuition ($23,098), mandatory fees ($415), and college room and board ($8442). Room and board charges vary according to board plan. Part-time tuition: $772 per credit hour.
Collegiate Environment: Orientation program. Drama-theater group, choral group, student-run newspaper. Social organizations: 15 open to all. Most popular organizations: Student Association, student ministries, campus newspaper, Pro-Life Task Force, PACE (prison tutoring program). Major annual events: OPUS, Trollstock Talent Show, Convocation. Student services: health clinic, personal-psychological counseling. Campus security: 24-hour emergency response devices and patrols, student patrols, late night transport-escort service, security cameras, Code Blue Emergency Phones. 633 college housing spaces available. Freshmen guaranteed college housing. Option: coed housing available. Jennie Huizenga Memorial Library with 71,226 books, 44,165 serials, 2,200 audiovisual materials, an OPAC, and a Web page. Operations spending for the previous fiscal year: $399,881. 170 computers available on campus for general student use. A campuswide network can be accessed from student residence rooms. Students can access the following: online class registration. Staffed computer lab on campus provides training in use of computers, software, and the Internet.
Community Environment: Palos Heights is residential area located 25 miles from downtown Chicago.

■ **TRINITY COLLEGE OF NURSING AND HEALTH SCIENCES**
2122 25th Ave.
Rock Island, IL 61201
Tel: (309)779-7700
Fax: (309)779-7796
E-mail: PerezLJ@ihs.org
Web Site: www.trinitycollegeqc.edu/
Description: Independent, 4-year, coed. Administratively affiliated with Trinity Medical Center. Awards associate and bachelor's degrees (general education requirements are taken off campus, usually at Black Hawk College, Eastern Iowa Community College District and Western Illinois University). Founded 1994. Setting: 2-acre urban campus. Endowment: $1.3 million. Educational spending for the previous fiscal year: $13,341 per student. Total enrollment: 232. Faculty: 26 (16 full-time, 10 part-time). Student-undergrad faculty ratio is 9:1. 4 applied, 50% were admitted. Full-time: 119 students, 93% women, 7% men. Part-time: 113 students, 91% women, 9% men. 46% from out-of-state. 0% American Indian or Alaska Native, non-Hispanic/Latino; 5% Hispanic/Latino; 4% African American, non-

Hispanic/Latino; 2% Asian, non-Hispanic/Latino; 0.4% Native Hawaiian or other Pacific Islander, non-Hispanic/Latino; 0% international. 56% 25 or older, 17% transferred in. Retention: 100% of full-time freshmen returned the following year. Academic area with the most degrees conferred: health professions and related sciences. Calendar: semesters. Services for LD students, advanced placement, accelerated degree program, independent study, distance learning, summer session for credit, part-time degree program, adult/continuing education programs, internships. Off campus study. Study abroad program.

Entrance Requirements: Options: electronic application, early admission, early decision. Required: minimum 2.5 high school GPA. Required for some: essay, high school transcript, minimum 3 high school GPA, interview, ACT, Applicants with 24 or more college credit hours with a grade of 'C' (2.0) or above, may be exempt for submitting ACT and/or SAT scores. Entrance: moderately difficult. Application deadlines: Rolling, Rolling for nonresidents, 12/1 for early decision. Notification: continuous until 2/1, continuous until 2/1 for nonresidents, 12/15 for early decision. Transfer credits accepted: Yes. Applicants placed on waiting list: 33. Wait-listed applicants offered admission: 13. Early decision applicants admitted: 14.

Costs Per Year: Application fee: $50. Tuition: $22,680 full-time, $648 per credit hour part-time. Mandatory fees: $2302 full-time. Full-time tuition and fees vary according to degree level, program, and student level. Part-time tuition varies according to degree level, program, and student level.

Collegiate Environment: Orientation program. Social organizations: 3 open to all. Most popular organizations: Student Government Association, Phi Theta Kappa, BSN Honor Society. Major annual events: Alumni Weekend, Graduation, Orientation. Student services: personal-psychological counseling. Campus security: 24-hour emergency response devices. College housing not available. Trinity Medical Center Library - Rock Island Campus with 8,500 books, 791 serials, an OPAC, and a Web page. Operations spending for the previous fiscal year: $377,031. 20 computers available on campus for general student use. A campuswide network can be accessed from off-campus.

■ **TRINITY INTERNATIONAL UNIVERSITY**
2065 Half Day Rd.
Deerfield, IL 60015-1284
Tel: (847)945-8800; Free: 800-822-3225
Fax: (847)317-7081
E-mail: tcadmissions@tiu.edu
Web Site: www.tiu.edu/
Description: Independent, university, coed, affiliated with Evangelical Free Church of America. Administratively affiliated with Evangelical Free Church of America. Awards bachelor's, master's, and doctoral degrees. Founded 1897. Setting: 108-acre suburban campus with easy access to Chicago. Endowment: $28.7 million. Educational spending for the previous fiscal year: $5205 per student. Total enrollment: 2,671. Faculty: 82 (43 full-time, 39 part-time). Student-undergrad faculty ratio is 12:1. 548 applied, 63% were admitted. 37% from top 10% of their high school class, 43% from top quarter, 68% from top half. 6 valedictorians. Full-time: 841 students, 57% women, 43% men. Part-time: 127 students, 61% women, 39% men. Students come from 38 states and territories, 19 other countries, 41% from out-of-state. 2% 25 or older, 70% live on campus, 8% transferred in. Retention: 66% of full-time freshmen returned the following year. Academic areas with the most degrees conferred: education; business/marketing; theology and religious vocations. Core. Calendar: semesters. Academic remediation for entering students, advanced placement, honors program, independent study, double major, part-time degree program, adult/continuing education programs, internships, graduate courses open to undergrads. Off campus study at 13 members of the Christian College Consortium. Study abroad program.
Entrance Requirements: Options: electronic application, deferred admission, international baccalaureate accepted. Required: essay, high school transcript, minimum 2.5 high school GPA, 1 recommendation, SAT or ACT. Recommended: minimum 3.0 high school GPA. Required for some: interview. Entrance: moderately difficult. Application deadline: Rolling. Notification: continuous until 9/1.
Collegiate Environment: Orientation program. Drama-theater group, choral group, student-run newspaper. Social organizations: 15 open to all. Most popular organizations: student government, College Union, Trinity Summer Mission, student newspaper, yearbook. Major annual events: Homecoming, Santa Lucia, Parents' Weekend. Student services: health clinic, personal-psychological counseling. Campus security: 24-hour patrols, controlled dormitory access. Rolfing Memorial Library with 266,586 books, 40,981 microform titles, 979 serials, an OPAC, and a Web page. Operations spend-

ing for the previous fiscal year: $1.6 million. 130 computers available on campus for general student use. A campuswide network can be accessed from student residence rooms and from off campus. Students can access the following: online class registration. Staffed computer lab on campus provides training in use of computers, software, and the Internet.
Community Environment: Deerfield, population 19,400, is located 25 miles north of Chicago.

■ **TRITON COLLEGE**
2000 5th Ave.
River Grove, IL 60171
Tel: (708)456-0300
Fax: (708)583-3121
E-mail: mpatrice@triton.edu
Web Site: www.triton.edu/
Description: State-supported, 2-year, coed. Part of Illinois Community College Board. Awards certificates, transfer associate, and terminal associate degrees. Founded 1964. Setting: 100-acre suburban campus with easy access to Chicago. Total enrollment: 15,658. Faculty: 644 (123 full-time, 521 part-time). Student-undergrad faculty ratio is 24:1. Full-time: 3,893 students, 51% women, 49% men. Part-time: 11,765 students, 56% women, 44% men. 40% 25 or older. Retention: 56% of full-time freshmen returned the following year. Core. Calendar: semesters. Academic remediation for entering students, ESL program, advanced placement, self-designed majors, freshman honors college, honors program, distance learning, summer session for credit, part-time degree program, adult/continuing education programs, co-op programs and internships.
Entrance Requirements: Open admission except for some allied health programs. Option: deferred admission. Required: high school transcript. Entrance: noncompetitive. Application deadline: Rolling. Preference given to district residents.
Collegiate Environment: Orientation program. Drama-theater group, choral group, student-run newspaper, radio station. Social organizations: 34 open to all. Most popular organizations: student government, Program Board. Major annual events: Triton Spirit Week, World's Largest Sober Party. Student services: health clinic, personal-psychological counseling. Campus security: 24-hour emergency response devices and patrols. Learning Resource Center with 70,859 books, 11,297 microform titles, and 1,247 serials. 500 computers available on campus for general student use. A campuswide network can be accessed. Students can access the following: online class registration. Staffed computer lab on campus provides training in use of computers, software, and the Internet.
Community Environment: Triton college district is in the near west suburbs of Chicago. The college is approximately 15 miles from downtown Chicago.

■ **UNIVERSITY OF CHICAGO**
5801 S Ellis Ave.
Chicago, IL 60637-1513
Tel: (773)702-1234
Fax: (773)702-4199
E-mail: collegeadmissions@uchicago.edu
Web Site: www.uchicago.edu/
Description: Independent, university, coed. Awards bachelor's, master's, and doctoral degrees. Founded 1891. Setting: 215-acre urban campus. Endowment: $6.6 million. Research spending for the previous fiscal year: $270.8 million. Total enrollment: 12,508. Faculty: 1,723 (1,261 full-time, 462 part-time). Student-undergrad faculty ratio is 6:1. 25,273 applied, 13% were admitted. 97% from top 10% of their high school class, 99% from top quarter, 100% from top half. Full-time: 5,531 students, 47% women, 53% men. Part-time: 59 students, 47% women, 53% men. 81% from out-of-state. 0.2% American Indian or Alaska Native, non-Hispanic/Latino; 8% Hispanic/Latino; 5% African American, non-Hispanic/Latino; 18% Asian, non-Hispanic/Latino; 0.04% Native Hawaiian or other Pacific Islander, non-Hispanic/Latino; 9% international. 0% 25 or older, 55% live on campus, 0.3% transferred in. Retention: 99% of full-time freshmen returned the following year. Academic areas with the most degrees conferred: social sciences; biological/life sciences; mathematics and statistics. Core. Advanced placement, accelerated degree program, self-designed majors, independent study, double major, summer session for credit, adult/continuing education programs, internships, graduate courses open to undergrads. Off campus study. Study abroad program. ROTC: Army (c), Air Force (c).
Entrance Requirements: Options: electronic application, early admission, early action, deferred admission, international baccalaureate accepted. Required: essay, high school transcript, 2 recommendations, 2 teacher

recommendations, SAT or ACT. Recommended: interview. Entrance: most difficult. Application deadlines: 1/2, 11/1 for early action. Notification: 4/1, 12/17 for early action. SAT Reasoning Test deadline: 2/3. Early action applicants: 8,633.

Costs Per Year: Application fee: $75. One-time mandatory fee: $1035. Comprehensive fee: $57,711 includes full-time tuition ($43,581), mandatory fees ($993), and college room and board ($13,137). Room and board charges vary according to board plan and housing facility.

Collegiate Environment: Orientation program. Drama-theater group, choral group, student-run newspaper, radio station. Social organizations: 400 open to all; national fraternities, national sororities. Most popular organizations: University Theatre, Model United Nations, Council on University Programming, Documentary Films, South Asian Students Association. Major annual events: Major Activities Board presents Summer Breeze, Scavenger Hunt, Homecoming. Student services: health clinic, personal-psychological counseling, women's center. Campus security: 24-hour emergency response devices and patrols, student patrols, late night transport-escort service, controlled dormitory access. 2,992 college housing spaces available; 2,970 were occupied in 2012-13. Freshmen guaranteed college housing. On-campus residence required in freshman year. Options: coed, men-only, women-only housing available. Joseph Regenstein Library plus 5 others with 11.3 million books, 19 microform titles, 122,000 serials, 6 audiovisual materials, an OPAC, and a Web page. Operations spending for the previous fiscal year: $15.6 million. 300 computers available on campus for general student use. Computer purchase/lease plans available. A campuswide network can be accessed from student residence rooms and from off campus. Students can access the following: online class registration. Staffed computer lab on campus (open 24 hours a day) provides training in use of computers, software, and the Internet.

Community Environment: Chicago, with a population of nearly 3 million and the third largest city in the nation, is a metropolitan area extending along the southern end of Lake Michigan. It is a leading industrial, medical, educational, and cultural center. The University's campus is located in a residential neighborhood along the lake shore fifteen minutes away from the central downtown area. Cultural facilities include museums that cover a wide variety of fields, art galleries, research libraries, public libraries, theaters, opera, and a symphony orchestra. Numerous recreational activities and points of interest exist.

■ **UNIVERSITY OF ILLINOIS AT CHICAGO**
601 S Morgan St.
Chicago, IL 60607-7128
Tel: (312)996-7000
E-mail: uic.admit@uic.edu
Web Site: www.uic.edu/

Description: State-supported, university, coed. Part of University of Illinois System. Awards bachelor's, master's, and doctoral degrees and post-master's certificates. Founded 1946. Setting: 240-acre urban campus with easy access to Chicago. Endowment: $217.2 million. Research spending for the previous fiscal year: $267.3 million. Educational spending for the previous fiscal year: $19,478 per student. Total enrollment: 28,875. Faculty: 1,672 (1,201 full-time, 471 part-time). Student-undergrad faculty ratio is 18:1. 14,380 applied, 64% were admitted. 25% from top 10% of their high school class, 59% from top quarter, 93% from top half. Full-time: 15,381 students, 52% women, 48% men. Part-time: 1,297 students, 50% women, 50% men. Students come from 42 states and territories, 40 other countries, 2% from out-of-state. 0.1% American Indian or Alaska Native, non-Hispanic/Latino; 24% Hispanic/Latino; 8% African American, non-Hispanic/Latino; 22% Asian, non-Hispanic/Latino; 0.5% Native Hawaiian or other Pacific Islander, non-Hispanic/Latino; 2% international. 11% 25 or older, 19% live on campus, 9% transferred in. Retention: 78% of full-time freshmen returned the following year. Academic areas with the most degrees conferred: business/marketing; psychology; biological/life sciences. Core. Calendar: semesters. Academic remediation for entering students, services for LD students, advanced placement, accelerated degree program, self-designed majors, honors program, independent study, distance learning, double major, summer session for credit, part-time degree program, co-op programs and internships, graduate courses open to undergrads. Off campus study. Study abroad program. ROTC: Army, Naval (c), Air Force (c).

Entrance Requirements: Options: electronic application, international baccalaureate accepted. Required: essay, high school transcript, auditions for music and theater majors; portfolios for art majors, SAT or ACT. Entrance: moderately difficult. Application deadline: 1/15. Notification: continuous until 11/30. SAT Reasoning Test deadline: 1/15. SAT Subject Test deadline: 1/15. Transfer credits accepted: Yes.

Costs Per Year: Application fee: $50. State resident tuition: $10,406 full-time. Nonresident tuition: $22,796 full-time. Mandatory fees: $2948 full-time, $1193 per term part-time. Full-time tuition and fees vary according to degree level and program. Part-time fees vary according to course load, degree level, and program. College room and board: $10,882. College room only: $7462. Room and board charges vary according to board plan and housing facility. Tuition guaranteed not to increase for student's term of enrollment.

Collegiate Environment: Orientation program. Drama-theater group, choral group, student-run newspaper, radio station. Social organizations: 370 open to all; national fraternities, national sororities, local fraternities, local sororities; 3% of eligible men and 4% of eligible women are members. Most popular organizations: MBA Association, StudentsMuslim Student Association, Society of Automotive Engineers, Pakistani Student Organization, Society of Future Physicians. Major annual events: Fun Fair, UIC Fashion Show, New Student convocation. Student services: legal services, health clinic, personal-psychological counseling, women's center. Campus security: 24-hour emergency response devices and patrols, student patrols, late night transport-escort service, controlled dormitory access, housing ID stickers, guest escort policy, 24-hour closed circuit videos for exits and entrances, security screen for first floor. 3,800 college housing spaces available; 3,200 were occupied in 2012-13. No special consideration for freshman housing applicants. Option: coed housing available. Richard J. Daley Library plus 3 others with an OPAC and a Web page. Operations spending for the previous fiscal year: $21.4 million. 910 computers available on campus for general student use. A campuswide network can be accessed from student residence rooms and from off campus. Students can access the following: online class registration. Staffed computer lab on campus (open 24 hours a day) provides training in use of computers, software, and the Internet.

■ **UNIVERSITY OF ILLINOIS AT SPRINGFIELD**
One University Plz.
Springfield, IL 62703-5407
Tel: (217)206-6600; Free: 888-977-4847
Fax: (217)206-7279
E-mail: admissions@uis.edu
Web Site: www.uis.edu/

Description: State-supported, comprehensive, coed. Part of University of Illinois System. Awards bachelor's, master's, and doctoral degrees and post-master's certificates. Founded 1969. Setting: 746-acre suburban campus. Endowment: $11.2 million. Total enrollment: 5,048. Faculty: 374 (214 full-time, 160 part-time). Student-undergrad faculty ratio is 12:1. 1,506 applied, 56% were admitted. 19% from top 10% of their high school class, 42% from top quarter, 73% from top half. Full-time: 1,948 students, 54% women, 46% men. Part-time: 1,106 students, 46% women, 54% men. Students come from 50 states and territories, 15 other countries, 11% from out-of-state. 0.3% American Indian or Alaska Native, non-Hispanic/Latino; 6% Hispanic/Latino; 12% African American, non-Hispanic/Latino; 3% Asian, non-Hispanic/Latino; 0.2% Native Hawaiian or other Pacific Islander, non-Hispanic/Latino; 3% international. 43% 25 or older, 28% live on campus, 21% transferred in. Retention: 72% of full-time freshmen returned the following year. Academic areas with the most degrees conferred: business/marketing; psychology; homeland security, law enforcement, firefighting, and protective services; communication/journalism; liberal arts/general studies. Core. Calendar: semesters. Academic remediation for entering students, ESL program, services for LD students, advanced placement, honors program, independent study, distance learning, summer session for credit, part-time degree program, co-op programs and internships, graduate courses open to undergrads. Off campus study. Study abroad program.

Entrance Requirements: Options: electronic application, deferred admission, international baccalaureate accepted. Required: high school transcript, SAT or ACT. Entrance: moderately difficult. Application deadline: Rolling. Transfer credits accepted: Yes. Applicants placed on waiting list: 0. Wait-listed applicants offered admission: 0.

Costs Per Year: Application fee: $50. State resident tuition: $9,248 full-time, $308.25 per credit hour part-time. Nonresident tuition: $18,398 full-time, $613.25 per credit hour part-time. Mandatory fees: $1884 full-time. Full-time tuition and fees vary according to course load. Part-time tuition varies according to course load. College room and board: $10,350. College room only: $7000. Room and board charges vary according to board plan and housing facility. Tuition guaranteed not to increase for student's term of enrollment.

Collegiate Environment: Orientation program. Drama-theater group, choral group, student-run newspaper, radio station. Social organizations: 73 open to all. Most popular organizations: Student Activities Committee, Christian

Student Fellowship, DODGE - Dodge Ball Club, Black Student Union, Black Male Collegiate Society. Major annual events: First Week, Homecoming, Spring Fest. Student services: health clinic, personal-psychological counseling, women's center. Campus security: 24-hour emergency response devices and patrols, late night transport-escort service, controlled dormitory access. Freshmen guaranteed college housing. On-campus residence required in freshman year. Option: coed housing available. Norris L. Brookens Library with 719,956 books, 53,028 microform titles, 54,300 serials, 10,051 audiovisual materials, an OPAC, and a Web page. 390 computers available on campus for general student use. A campuswide network can be accessed from student residence rooms and from off campus. Students can access the following: online class registration. Staffed computer lab on campus provides training in use of computers, software, and the Internet.

■ **UNIVERSITY OF ILLINOIS AT URBANA–CHAMPAIGN**
601 E John St.
Champaign, IL 61820
Tel: (217)333-1000
Fax: (217)244-7278
E-mail: ugradadmissions@uiuc.edu
Web Site: www.illinois.edu/
Description: State-supported, university, coed. Part of University of Illinois System. Awards bachelor's, master's, and doctoral degrees and post-master's certificates. Founded 1867. Setting: 1,783-acre urban campus. System endowment: $24 billion. Educational spending for the previous fiscal year: $17,826 per student. Total enrollment: 44,520. Faculty: 1,854 (1,851 full-time, 3 part-time). Student-undergrad faculty ratio is 19:1. 31,454 applied, 63% were admitted. 54% from top 10% of their high school class, 88% from top quarter, 99% from top half. Full-time: 31,118 students, 45% women, 55% men. Part-time: 1,163 students, 33% women, 67% men. Students come from 52 states and territories, 119 other countries, 8% from out-of-state. 0.1% American Indian or Alaska Native, non-Hispanic/Latino; 7% Hispanic/Latino; 5% African American, non-Hispanic/Latino; 14% Asian, non-Hispanic/Latino; 0.2% Native Hawaiian or other Pacific Islander, non-Hispanic/Latino; 14% international. 2% 25 or older, 50% live on campus, 4% transferred in. Retention: 94% of full-time freshmen returned the following year. Academic areas with the most degrees conferred: engineering; business/marketing; social sciences. Core. Calendar: semesters. Academic remediation for entering students, ESL program, services for LD students, advanced placement, accelerated degree program, self-designed majors, honors program, independent study, distance learning, double major, summer session for credit, co-op programs and internships, graduate courses open to undergrads. Off campus study at members of the Committee on Institutional Cooperation, Midwest Universities Consortium for International Activities. Study abroad program. ROTC: Army, Naval, Air Force.
Entrance Requirements: Options: electronic application, early admission, deferred admission, international baccalaureate accepted. Required: essay, high school transcript, SAT or ACT. Required for some: application essay is required for all potential students. Auditions or portfolios may be required of some applicants depending on their field of study. Entrance: very difficult. Application deadline: 1/2. Notification: 2/17. SAT Reasoning Test deadline: 12/30. Transfer credits accepted: Yes. Applicants placed on waiting list: 2,138. Wait-listed applicants offered admission: 437.
Costs Per Year: Application fee: $50. State resident tuition: $11,834 full-time. Nonresident tuition: $26,216 full-time. Mandatory fees: $3504 full-time. Full-time tuition and fees vary according to program and student level. College room and board: $10,636. Room and board charges vary according to board plan, housing facility, and location. Tuition guaranteed not to increase for student's term of enrollment.
Collegiate Environment: Orientation program. Drama-theater group, choral group, marching band, student-run newspaper, radio station. Social organizations: 1,000 open to all; national fraternities, national sororities, local fraternities, local sororities; 21% of eligible men and 21% of eligible women are members. Most popular organizations: Volunteer Illini Project, October Lovers, Illini Pride Student Board, National Society of Collegiate Scholars, Phi Eta Sigma Freshman Honor Society. Major annual events: Homecoming, Moms' Weekend/Dads' Weekend, Quad Day. Student services: legal services, health clinic, personal-psychological counseling, women's center. Campus security: 24-hour emergency response devices and patrols, student patrols, late night transport-escort service, controlled dormitory access, safety training classes, ID cards with safety numbers. 15,000 college housing spaces available; all were occupied in 2012-13. Freshmen guaranteed college housing. On-campus residence required in freshman year. Options: coed, men-only, women-only housing available. University Library plus 20 others with 24 million books, an OPAC, and a Web page.

■ **UNIVERSITY OF PHOENIX–CHICAGO CAMPUS**
1500 McConner Pky.
Ste. 700
Schaumburg, IL 60173-4399
Tel: (847)413-1922; Free: 866-766-0766
Fax: (847)413-8706
Web Site: www.phoenix.edu/
Description: Proprietary, comprehensive, coed. Awards bachelor's and master's degrees. Founded 2002. Setting: urban campus. Total enrollment: 1,178. Faculty: 191 (16 full-time, 175 part-time). Full-time: 1,025 students, 64% women, 36% men. 78% 25 or older. Academic areas with the most degrees conferred: business/marketing; computer and information sciences; health professions and related sciences. Core. Calendar: continuous. Services for LD students, advanced placement, accelerated degree program, independent study, distance learning, external degree program, adult/continuing education programs, graduate courses open to undergrads.
Entrance Requirements: Open admission. Options: electronic application, deferred admission. Required: 1 recommendation. Required for some: high school transcript. Entrance: noncompetitive. Application deadline: Rolling.
Collegiate Environment: Campus security: late night transport-escort service. University Library with 16,781 serials, an OPAC, and a Web page. Operations spending for the previous fiscal year: $6.8 million.

■ **UNIVERSITY OF ST. FRANCIS**
500 Wilcox St.
Joliet, IL 60435-6169
Tel: (815)740-3400; Free: 800-735-7500
Fax: (815)740-4285
E-mail: ccruz@stfrancis.edu
Web Site: www.stfrancis.edu/
Description: Independent Roman Catholic, comprehensive, coed. Awards bachelor's, master's, and doctoral degrees and post-master's certificates. Founded 1920. Setting: 24-acre suburban campus with easy access to Chicago. Endowment: $10.2 million. Educational spending for the previous fiscal year: $6937 per student. Total enrollment: 2,345. Faculty: 254 (91 full-time, 163 part-time). Student-undergrad faculty ratio is 12:1. 1,718 applied, 51% were admitted. 17% from top 10% of their high school class, 50% from top quarter, 79% from top half. Full-time: 1,361 students, 68% women, 32% men. Part-time: 62 students, 71% women, 29% men. Students come from 17 states and territories, 6% from out-of-state. 0.5% American Indian or Alaska Native, non-Hispanic/Latino; 14% Hispanic/Latino; 8% African American, non-Hispanic/Latino; 2% Asian, non-Hispanic/Latino; 0.4% Native Hawaiian or other Pacific Islander, non-Hispanic/Latino; 1% international. 16% 25 or older, 26% live on campus, 14% transferred in. Retention: 79% of full-time freshmen returned the following year. Academic areas with the most degrees conferred: health professions and related sciences; education; business/marketing. Core. Calendar: semesters. Academic remediation for entering students, ESL program, services for LD students, advanced placement, accelerated degree program, self-designed majors, honors program, independent study, distance learning, double major, summer session for credit, part-time degree program, adult/continuing education programs, internships, graduate courses open to undergrads. Off campus study. Study abroad program. ROTC: Army (c).
Entrance Requirements: Options: electronic application, deferred admission, international baccalaureate accepted. Required: high school transcript, minimum 2.5 high school GPA, SAT or ACT. Required for some: essay, 2 recommendations, interview. Entrance: moderately difficult. Application deadline: 8/1. Notification: continuous. SAT Reasoning Test deadline: 8/1. Transfer credits accepted: Yes.
Costs Per Year: Application fee: $30. Comprehensive fee: $35,092 includes full-time tuition ($26,374), mandatory fees ($450), and college room and board ($8268). Full-time tuition and fees vary according to degree level and location. Room and board charges vary according to board plan and housing facility. Part-time tuition: $795 per credit hour. Part-time tuition varies according to degree level.
Collegiate Environment: Orientation program. Drama-theater group, choral group, student-run newspaper, radio station. Social organizations: 34 open to all. Most popular organizations: Justice League, Student Business Association, International Club, Student Nurses Association, Student Activities Board. Major annual events: Homecoming Dance, Hypnotist Fredrick Winters, Comedians. Student services: health clinic, personal-psychological counseling. Campus security: 24-hour emergency response devices and patrols, student patrols, late night transport-escort service, controlled dormitory access, First Response trained security personnel. 402 college housing

spaces available; 370 were occupied in 2012-13. Freshmen guaranteed college housing. Option: coed housing available. Brown Library with 135,000 books, 1,767 microform titles, 15,250 serials, 4,788 audiovisual materials, an OPAC, and a Web page. Operations spending for the previous fiscal year: $852,135. 476 computers available on campus for general student use. A campuswide network can be accessed from student residence rooms and from off campus. Students can access the following: online class registration, billing/payment. Staffed computer lab on campus (open 24 hours a day) provides training in use of computers, software, and the Internet.

■ VANDERCOOK COLLEGE OF MUSIC

3140 S Federal St.
Chicago, IL 60616-3731
Tel: (312)225-6288
Fax: (312)225-5211
E-mail: admissions@vandercook.edu
Web Site: www.vandercook.edu/

Description: Independent, 4-year, coed. Awards bachelor's and master's degrees. Founded 1909. Setting: 1-acre urban campus with easy access to Downtown Chicago. Total enrollment: 227. Faculty: 33 (9 full-time, 24 part-time). Student-undergrad faculty ratio is 9:1. 8% from top 10% of their high school class, 35% from top quarter, 81% from top half. Full-time: 108 students, 55% women, 45% men. Part-time: 31 students, 32% women, 68% men. Students come from 13 states and territories, 3 other countries, 25% from out-of-state. 5% 25 or older, 15% live on campus, 2% transferred in. Retention: 90% of full-time freshmen returned the following year. Academic area with the most degrees conferred: education. Core. Calendar: semesters. Advanced placement, independent study, distance learning, part-time degree program, internships.

Entrance Requirements: Required: essay, high school transcript, 3 recommendations, interview, audition. Recommended: minimum 3 high school GPA. Required for some: minimum 3 high school GPA, SAT or ACT.

Costs Per Year: Comprehensive fee: $34,742 includes full-time tuition ($22,776), mandatory fees ($1340), and college room and board ($10,626). College room only: $5546. Full-time tuition and fees vary according to course level, course load, degree level, and program. Room and board charges vary according to board plan and housing facility. Part-time tuition: $950 per semester hour. Part-time mandatory fees: $1040 per year. Part-time tuition and fees vary according to course level, course load, degree level, and program.

Collegiate Environment: Orientation program. Choral group. Social organizations: 4 open to all; national fraternities, national sororities, local fraternities, local sororities. Most popular organizations: NAME (National Association for Music Education), ACDA (American Choral Directors Association), NBA (National Band Association), ASTA (American String Teachers Association). Major annual events: Prism Concert, A Night of the Pops benefit concert. Campus security: 24-hour emergency response devices and patrols, late night transport-escort service. 500 college housing spaces available; 21 were occupied in 2012-13. No special consideration for freshman housing applicants. Option: coed housing available. Harry Ruppel Memorial Library plus 1 other with 15,200 books, 200 serials, 5,305 audiovisual materials, an OPAC, and a Web page. 21 computers available on campus for general student use. A campuswide network can be accessed from student residence rooms and from off campus. Staffed computer lab on campus.

Community Environment: Urban.

■ VET TECH INSTITUTE AT FOX COLLEGE

18020 S Oak Park Ave.
Tinley Park, IL 60477
Tel: (708)444-4500; Free: 888-884-3694
Web Site: www.vettechinstitute.edu/chicago

Description: Private, 2-year, coed. Awards terminal associate degrees. Founded 2006. Setting: suburban campus. Total enrollment: 148. 475 applied, 56% were admitted. Accelerated degree program, internships.

Collegiate Environment: College housing not available.

■ WAUBONSEE COMMUNITY COLLEGE

Rte. 47 at Waubonsee Dr.
Sugar Grove, IL 60554-9799
Tel: (630)466-7900
Fax: (630)466-4964
E-mail: admissions@waubonsee.edu
Web Site: www.waubonsee.edu/

Description: District-supported, 2-year, coed. Part of Illinois Community College Board. Awards certificates, transfer associate, and terminal associate degrees. Founded 1966. Setting: 243-acre small town campus with easy access to Chicago. Total enrollment: 11,146. Faculty: 720 (116 full-time, 604 part-time). 2,405 applied, 100% were admitted. Full-time: 3,666 students, 50% women, 50% men. Part-time: 7,480 students, 59% women, 41% men. Students come from 21 states and territories. 0.2% American Indian or Alaska Native, non-Hispanic/Latino; 26% Hispanic/Latino; 8% African American, non-Hispanic/Latino; 2% Asian, non-Hispanic/Latino; 0.1% Native Hawaiian or other Pacific Islander, non-Hispanic/Latino; 0% international. 34% 25 or older, 3% transferred in. Calendar: semesters. Academic remediation for entering students, ESL program, services for LD students, advanced placement, accelerated degree program, honors program, independent study, distance learning, summer session for credit, part-time degree program, internships. Off campus study at Emergency Medical Technician/Paramedic A.A.S. Program is based at Delnor Community Hospital in Geneva, IL is offered as a collaboration with the Southern Fox Valley Emergency Medical Services System (SFVEMSS) Paramedic Training Program. Study abroad program. ROTC: Army (c).

Entrance Requirements: Open admission except for nursing, interpreter training, auto body, certified nurse assistant programs, medical assistant, health care interpreting, therapeutic massage, phlebotomy, translation. Option: electronic application. Entrance: noncompetitive. Application deadline: Rolling. Notification: continuous. Preference given to in-district residents for some health programs. Transfer credits accepted: Yes.

Collegiate Environment: Orientation program. Drama-theater group, choral group, student-run newspaper. Social organizations: 35 open to all; honor societies. Most popular organizations: Phi Theta Kappa, Otaku Gamers Society, Waubonsee Student Education Association (WSEA), Business Club, Latinos Unidos. Major annual events: College Night, Club Fair, Cinco de Mayo Celebration/Party Smart. Campus security: 24-hour emergency response devices and patrols, late night transport-escort service. College housing not available. Todd Library plus 3 others with 81,282 books, 384 serials, 3,248 audiovisual materials, an OPAC, and a Web page. 160 computers available on campus for general student use. A campuswide network can be accessed. Students can access the following: online class registration. Staffed computer lab on campus provides training in use of computers.

Community Environment: See Aurora University.

■ WESTERN ILLINOIS UNIVERSITY

1 University Cir.
Macomb, IL 61455-1390
Tel: (309)298-1414; Free: 877-742-5948
Fax: (309)298-3111
E-mail: aj-borst@wiu.edu
Web Site: www.wiu.edu/

Description: State-supported, comprehensive, coed. Awards bachelor's, master's, and doctoral degrees. Founded 1899. Setting: 1,050-acre small town campus. Endowment: $28.4 million. Research spending for the previous fiscal year: $6.2 million. Total enrollment: 12,205. Faculty: 737 (664 full-time, 73 part-time). Student-undergrad faculty ratio is 15:1. 10,326 applied, 63% were admitted. 8% from top 10% of their high school class, 26% from top quarter, 61% from top half. Full-time: 9,161 students, 48% women, 52% men. Part-time: 1,102 students, 51% women, 49% men. Students come from 36 states and territories, 55 other countries, 6% from out-of-state. 0.2% American Indian or Alaska Native, non-Hispanic/Latino; 7% Hispanic/Latino; 16% African American, non-Hispanic/Latino; 1% Asian, non-Hispanic/Latino; 0.1% Native Hawaiian or other Pacific Islander, non-Hispanic/Latino; 1% international. 13% 25 or older, 42% live on campus, 13% transferred in. Retention: 68% of full-time freshmen returned the following year. Academic areas with the most degrees conferred: homeland security, law enforcement, firefighting, and protective services; business/marketing; liberal arts/general studies. Core. Calendar: semesters. Academic remediation for entering students, ESL program, services for LD students, advanced placement, self-designed majors, freshman honors college, honors program, independent study, distance learning, double major, summer session for credit, part-time degree program, external degree program, adult/continuing education programs, internships, graduate courses open to undergrads. Off campus study at Western Illinois Education Consortium. Study abroad program. ROTC: Army.

Entrance Requirements: Options: electronic application, deferred admission. Required: high school transcript, minimum 2.5 high school GPA, SAT or

ACT. Entrance: moderately difficult. Application deadline: 5/15. Notification: continuous. SAT Reasoning Test deadline: 5/15. Transfer credits accepted: Yes.

Costs Per Year: Application fee: $30. State resident tuition: $8010 full-time. Nonresident tuition: $12,018 full-time. Mandatory fees: $1,945 full-time. Full-time tuition and fees vary according to course load and student level. College room and board: $8820. College room only: $5370. Room and board charges vary according to board plan, housing facility, and student level. Tuition guaranteed not to increase for student's term of enrollment.

Collegiate Environment: Orientation program. Drama-theater group, choral group, marching band, student-run newspaper, radio station. Social organizations: 250 open to all; national fraternities, national sororities, local fraternities, local sororities; 20% of eligible men and 20% of eligible women are members. Most popular organizations: Student Government Association, Black Student Association, University Union Board, International Friendship Club, Bureau of Cultural Affairs. Major annual events: Family Weekend, Homecoming. Student services: legal services, health clinic, personal-psychological counseling, women's center. Campus security: 24-hour emergency response devices and patrols, student patrols, late night transport-escort service, controlled dormitory access. 4,626 college housing spaces available; 4,245 were occupied in 2012-13. Freshmen guaranteed college housing. On-campus residence required through sophomore year. Options: coed, men-only, women-only housing available. Leslie Malpass Library plus 4 others with 998,041 books, 1.3 million microform titles, 3,200 serials, an OPAC, and a Web page. 1,000 computers available on campus for general student use. A campuswide network can be accessed from student residence rooms and from off campus. Students can access the following: online class registration. Staffed computer lab on campus provides training in use of computers, software, and the Internet.

Community Environment: Macomb is located 240 miles southwest of Chicago and 150 miles north of St. Louis on the main line of the Burlington Railroad. Besides agriculture, Macomb's industries produce ball bearings, plastic bags, porcelain insulators, and pottery. This is a friendly, Midwest community balanced by the youthfulness and creativity of the rapidly expanding university. The community facilities include a hospital, library, hotels, motels, and many clubs and organizations in the city. Recreational facilities include a swimming pool, bowling alleys, parks, and movie theaters.

■ WESTWOOD COLLEGE–CHICAGO DU PAGE

7155 Janes Ave.
Woodridge, IL 60517
Tel: (630)434-8250; Free: 866-721-7647
Web Site: www.westwood.edu/
Description: Proprietary, 4-year, coed. Awards associate and bachelor's degrees. Total enrollment: 582. Faculty: 72. Calendar: continuous.

■ WESTWOOD COLLEGE–CHICAGO LOOP CAMPUS

1 N State St., Ste. 1000
Chicago, IL 60602
Tel: (312)739-0890; Free: 800-693-5411
Web Site: www.westwood.edu/
Description: Proprietary, 4-year, coed. Awards associate and bachelor's degrees. Founded 2002. Total enrollment: 885. Faculty: 104.

■ WESTWOOD COLLEGE–CHICAGO O'HARE AIRPORT

8501 W Higgins Rd.
Ste. 100
Chicago, IL 60631
Tel: (773)380-6801; Free: 866-235-2457
Web Site: www.westwood.edu/
Description: Proprietary, 4-year, coed. Awards associate and bachelor's degrees. Total enrollment: 888. Faculty: 99. Calendar: continuous.

■ WESTWOOD COLLEGE–CHICAGO RIVER OAKS

80 River Oaks Dr.
Ste. 111
Calumet City, IL 60409
Tel: (708)832-9760; Free: 888-549-4960
Web Site: www.westwood.edu/
Description: Proprietary, 4-year, coed. Awards associate and bachelor's degrees. Total enrollment: 722. Faculty: 66. Calendar: continuous.

■ WHEATON COLLEGE

501 College Ave.
Wheaton, IL 60187-5593
Tel: (630)752-5000; Free: 800-222-2419
Fax: (630)752-5285
E-mail: admissions@wheaton.edu
Web Site: www.wheaton.edu/
Description: Independent nondenominational, comprehensive, coed. Awards bachelor's, master's, and doctoral degrees. Founded 1860. Setting: 80-acre suburban campus with easy access to Chicago. Endowment: $312.9 million. Research spending for the previous fiscal year: $577,467. Educational spending for the previous fiscal year: $12,401 per student. Total enrollment: 3,034. Faculty: 283 (197 full-time, 86 part-time). Student-undergrad faculty ratio is 12:1. 1,959 applied, 69% were admitted. 58% from top 10% of their high school class, 84% from top quarter, 97% from top half. 25 National Merit Scholars. Full-time: 2,435 students, 51% women, 49% men. Part-time: 73 students, 51% women, 49% men. Students come from 51 states and territories, 37 other countries, 74% from out-of-state. 0.2% American Indian or Alaska Native, non-Hispanic/Latino; 4% Hispanic/Latino; 2% African American, non-Hispanic/Latino; 7% Asian, non-Hispanic/Latino; 0.1% Native Hawaiian or other Pacific Islander, non-Hispanic/Latino; 2% international. 0% 25 or older, 90% live on campus, 3% transferred in. Retention: 95% of full-time freshmen returned the following year. Academic areas with the most degrees conferred: social sciences; theology and religious vocations; visual and performing arts. Core. Calendar: semesters. Services for LD students, advanced placement, self-designed majors, independent study, double major, summer session for credit, internships, graduate courses open to undergrads. Off campus study at members of the Christian College Consortium, Council for Christian Colleges and Universities. Study abroad program. ROTC: Army, Air Force (c).

Entrance Requirements: Options: electronic application, early action, deferred admission, international baccalaureate accepted. Required: essay, high school transcript, 2 recommendations, SAT or ACT. Recommended: interview. Entrance: very difficult. Application deadlines: 1/10, 11/1 for early action. Notification: 4/1, 12/31 for early action. Preference given to Christians. SAT Reasoning Test deadline: 1/10. Transfer credits accepted: Yes. Applicants placed on waiting list: 428. Wait-listed applicants offered admission: 35. Early action applicants: 1,003. Early action applicants admitted: 638.

Costs Per Year: Application fee: $50. Comprehensive fee: $38,680 includes full-time tuition ($30,120) and college room and board ($8560). College room only: $5050. Room and board charges vary according to board plan and housing facility. Part-time tuition: $1255 per credit hour. Part-time tuition varies according to course load.

Collegiate Environment: Orientation program. Drama-theater group, choral group, student-run newspaper. Social organizations: 108 open to all. Most popular organizations: Discipleship small groups, intramurals, Club Sports, Christian Service Council, student government. Major annual events: Mastodon March, Talent Show, Class Films. Student services: health clinic, personal-psychological counseling. Campus security: 24-hour emergency response devices and patrols, student patrols, late night transport-escort service, controlled dormitory access. 2,156 college housing spaces available; 2,126 were occupied in 2012-13. Freshmen guaranteed college housing. On-campus residence required through senior year. Options: coed, men-only, women-only housing available. Buswell Memorial Library with 489,856 books, 202,133 microform titles, 6,325 serials, 36,668 audiovisual materials, an OPAC, and a Web page. Operations spending for the previous fiscal year: $2.5 million. 125 computers available on campus for general student use. A campuswide network can be accessed from student residence rooms and from off campus. Students can access the following: online class registration, financial information, degree requirements evaluation. Staffed computer lab on campus provides training in use of software and the Internet.

■ WORSHAM COLLEGE OF MORTUARY SCIENCE

495 Northgate Pky.
Wheeling, IL 60090-2646
Tel: (847)808-8444
Fax: (847)808-8493
Web Site: www.worshamcollege.com/
Description: Independent, 2-year, coed. Awards terminal associate degrees. Founded 1911. Total enrollment: 91. Student-undergrad faculty ratio is 21:1. 54% 25 or older.

■ ANCILLA COLLEGE

9601 S Union Rd.
Donaldson, IN 46513
Tel: (574)936-8898; Free: 866-ANCILLA
Fax: (574)935-1773
E-mail: admissions@ancilla.edu
Web Site: www.ancilla.edu/

Description: Independent Roman Catholic, 2-year, coed. Awards certificates, transfer associate, and terminal associate degrees. Founded 1937. Setting: 63-acre rural campus with easy access to Chicago. Endowment: $3.7 million. Educational spending for the previous fiscal year: $3597 per student. Total enrollment: 439. Faculty: 39 (21 full-time, 18 part-time). Student-undergrad faculty ratio is 16:1. 547 applied, 55% were admitted. 0% from top 10% of their high school class, 6% from top quarter, 22% from top half. Full-time: 294 students, 59% women, 41% men. Part-time: 146 students, 73% women, 27% men. Students come from 9 states and territories, 3 other countries, 7% from out-of-state. 0.5% American Indian or Alaska Native, non-Hispanic/Latino; 6% Hispanic/Latino; 7% African American, non-Hispanic/Latino; 0% Asian, non-Hispanic/Latino; 0% Native Hawaiian or other Pacific Islander, non-Hispanic/Latino; 0.5% international. 38% 25 or older, 10% transferred in. Retention: 46% of full-time freshmen returned the following year. Core. Calendar: semesters. Academic remediation for entering students, services for LD students, advanced placement, accelerated degree program, self-designed majors, independent study, distance learning, double major, summer session for credit, part-time degree program, adult/continuing education programs, co-op programs and internships.

Entrance Requirements: Open admission. Options: electronic application, international baccalaureate accepted. Required: high school transcript. Recommended: SAT or ACT. Entrance: noncompetitive. Application deadlines: Rolling, Rolling for nonresidents. Transfer credits accepted: Yes.

Costs Per Year: Application fee: $0. Tuition: $13,650 full-time, $455 per credit part-time. Mandatory fees: $230 full-time. Full-time tuition and fees vary according to course load and program. Part-time tuition varies according to course load and program.

Collegiate Environment: Orientation program. Social organizations: 4 open to all. Most popular organizations: Student Government Association, Student Nursing Organization, Ancilla Student Ambassadors, Phi Theta Kappa. Major annual events: Constitution Day, Lampen Lecture Series, Various activities sponsored by Student Government. Student services: personal-psychological counseling. Campus security: 24-hour patrols, late night transport-escort service. College housing not available. Ball Library with 25,313 books, 97 serials, 1,009 audiovisual materials, an OPAC, and a Web page. Operations spending for the previous fiscal year: $170,821. 90 computers available on campus for general student use. A campuswide network can be accessed. Staffed computer lab on campus.

Community Environment: Situated in a rural area with a temperate climate.

■ ANDERSON UNIVERSITY

1100 E Fifth St.
Anderson, IN 46012-3495
Tel: (765)649-9071; Free: 800-428-6414
Fax: (765)641-3851
E-mail: info@anderson.edu
Web Site: www.anderson.edu/

Description: Independent, comprehensive, coed, affiliated with Church of God. Awards associate, bachelor's, master's, and doctoral degrees. Founded 1917. Setting: 163-acre suburban campus with easy access to Indianapolis. Endowment: $21.7 million. Educational spending for the previous fiscal year: $10,922 per student. Total enrollment: 2,516. Faculty: 274 (135 full-time, 139 part-time). Student-undergrad faculty ratio is 11:1. 2,894 applied, 54% were admitted. 22% from top 10% of their high school class, 49% from top quarter, 81% from top half. 8 valedictorians. Full-time: 1,868 students, 59% women, 41% men. Part-time: 166 students, 69% women, 31% men. Students come from 42 states and territories, 21 other countries, 25% from out-of-state. 0.2% American Indian or Alaska Native, non-Hispanic/Latino; 3% Hispanic/Latino; 6% African American, non-Hispanic/Latino; 0.4% Asian, non-Hispanic/Latino; 0.1% Native Hawaiian or other Pacific Islander, non-Hispanic/Latino; 3% international. 13% 25 or older, 62% live on campus, 4% transferred in. Retention: 75% of full-time freshmen returned the following year. Academic areas with the most degrees conferred: business/marketing; education; health professions and related sciences. Core. Calendar: semesters. Academic remediation for entering students, services for LD students, advanced placement, accelerated degree program, self-designed majors, honors program, independent study, distance learning, double major, summer session for credit, part-time degree program, adult/continuing education programs, internships. Off campus study. Study abroad program.

Entrance Requirements: Options: electronic application, deferred admission, international baccalaureate accepted. Required: high school transcript, minimum 2 high school GPA, 2 recommendations, lifestyle statement, SAT or ACT. Recommended: essay. Required for some: interview. Entrance: moderately difficult. Application deadline: 7/1. Notification: 9/1. SAT Reasoning Test deadline: 7/1. Transfer credits accepted: Yes.

Costs Per Year: Application fee: $25. Comprehensive fee: $35,310 includes full-time tuition ($26,120), mandatory fees ($80), and college room and board ($9110). College room only: $5830. Room and board charges vary according to board plan and housing facility. Part-time tuition: $1089 per semester hour. Part-time tuition varies according to course load.

Collegiate Environment: Orientation program. Drama-theater group, choral group, student-run newspaper, radio station. Social organizations: 41 open to all. Most popular organizations: Adult and Continuing Education Students Association, Multicultural Student Union, Campus Ministries. Major annual events: Homecoming, Vision/Revision, Rush Week. Student services: health clinic, personal-psychological counseling. Campus security: 24-hour emergency response devices and patrols, student patrols, late night transport-escort service, controlled dormitory access, 24-hour crime line. 1,378 college housing spaces available; 1,239 were occupied in 2012-13. Freshmen guaranteed college housing. On-campus residence required through junior year. Options: men-only, women-only housing available. Robert A. Nicholson Library with 303,170 books, 76,637 microform titles, 457 serials, 7,851 audiovisual materials, an OPAC, and a Web page. Operations spending for the previous fiscal year: $978,000. 338 computers available on campus for general student use. A campuswide network can be accessed from student residence rooms and from off campus. Students can access the following: online class registration, microcomputer software. Staffed computer lab on campus.

Community Environment: Anderson (population 57,500) is located 35 miles northeast of Indianapolis, and is known for the automotive electrical systems and lighting equipment produced by Delco-Remy Division America. Other industries located here manufacture recreation equipment, files, copper wire, corrugated paper boxes, dairy products and agricultural products. Railroads, buses and airports serve the area. The community has a library, churches, and hospitals. Recreational facilities include five 18-hole golf courses and 17 city parks. Mounds State Park is nearby. Employment opportunities are available.

■ **THE ART INSTITUTE OF INDIANAPOLIS**
3500 Depauw Blvd.
Ste. 1010
Indianapolis, IN 46268
Tel: (317)613-4800; Free: 866-441-9031
Web Site: www.artinstitutes.edu/indianapolis/
Description: Proprietary, 4-year, coed. Part of Education Management Corporation. Awards associate and bachelor's degrees. Setting: suburban campus.

■ **AVIATION INSTITUTE OF MAINTENANCE–INDIANAPOLIS**
7251 W McCarty St.
Indianapolis, IN 46241
Tel: (317)243-4519; Free: 888-349-5387
Fax: (317)243-4569
Web Site: www.aviationmaintenance.edu/
Description: Proprietary, 2-year, coed. Awards terminal associate degrees. Founded 1992. Total enrollment: 205. 69% 25 or older. Calendar: semesters.
Entrance Requirements: Open admission. Entrance: noncompetitive.

■ **BALL STATE UNIVERSITY**
2000 W University Ave.
Muncie, IN 47306-1099
Tel: (765)289-1241; Free: 800-482-4BSU
Fax: (765)285-1632
E-mail: askus@bsu.edu
Web Site: www.bsu.edu/
Description: State-supported, university, coed. Awards associate, bachelor's, master's, and doctoral degrees and post-master's certificates. Founded 1918. Setting: 1,140-acre suburban campus with easy access to Indianapolis. Endowment: $165.5 million. Research spending for the previous fiscal year: $10.2 million. Educational spending for the previous fiscal year: $7913 per student. Total enrollment: 21,053. Faculty: 1,140 (949 full-time, 191 part-time). Student-undergrad faculty ratio is 16:1. 16,896 applied, 61% were admitted. 18% from top 10% of their high school class, 48% from top quarter, 88% from top half. Full-time: 15,597 students, 57% women, 43% men. Part-time: 1,055 students, 58% women, 42% men. Students come from 50 states and territories, 44 other countries, 10% from out-of-state. 0.1% American Indian or Alaska Native, non-Hispanic/Latino; 3% Hispanic/Latino; 6% African American, non-Hispanic/Latino; 1% Asian, non-Hispanic/Latino; 0.1% Native Hawaiian or other Pacific Islander, non-Hispanic/Latino; 2% international. 6% 25 or older, 42% live on campus, 4% transferred in. Retention: 77% of full-time freshmen returned the following year. Academic areas with the most degrees conferred: education; business/marketing; liberal arts/general studies. Core. Calendar: semesters. ESL program, services for LD students, advanced placement, accelerated degree program, self-designed majors, freshman honors college, honors program, independent study, distance learning, double major, summer session for credit, part-time degree program, external degree program, adult/continuing education programs, co-op programs and internships, graduate courses open to undergrads. Study abroad program. ROTC: Army.
Entrance Requirements: Options: electronic application, deferred admission, international baccalaureate accepted. Required: high school transcript. Required for some: essay, SAT or ACT. Entrance: moderately difficult. Application deadline: 8/15. Notification: continuous. SAT Reasoning Test deadline: 6/30. SAT Subject Test deadline: 8/1. Transfer credits accepted: Yes.
Costs Per Year: Application fee: $55. State resident tuition: $8318 full-time, $270 per credit hour part-time. Nonresident tuition: $22,988 full-time, $906 per credit hour part-time. Mandatory fees: $662 full-time. Full-time tuition and fees vary according to course load, program, and reciprocity agreements. Part-time tuition varies according to course load and reciprocity agreements. College room and board: $8870. Room and board charges vary according to board plan and housing facility.
Collegiate Environment: Orientation program. Drama-theater group, choral group, marching band, student-run newspaper, radio station. Social organizations: 369 open to all; national fraternities, national sororities; 10% of eligible men and 11% of eligible women are members. Most popular

organizations: Epsilon Sigma Alpha International, WCRD- Student Radio Station, Golden Key Honor Society, Excellence in Leadership (EIL), Student Voluntary Services. Major annual events: Homecoming, Carnival, Late Nite. Student services: legal services, health clinic, personal-psychological counseling, women's center. Campus security: 24-hour emergency response devices and patrols, late night transport-escort service, controlled dormitory access. 6,906 college housing spaces available; 6,746 were occupied in 2012-13. Freshmen guaranteed college housing. On-campus residence required in freshman year. Options: coed, men-only, women-only housing available. Bracken Library plus 2 others with 1 million books, 1.1 million microform titles, 2,551 serials, 68,188 audiovisual materials, an OPAC, and a Web page. Operations spending for the previous fiscal year: $10.7 million. 888 computers available on campus for general student use. Computer purchase/lease plans available. A campuswide network can be accessed from student residence rooms and from off campus. Students can access the following: online class registration, room reservations, testing and test results, manage and pay tuition, order/buy textbooks, request room repairs, order transcripts, manage meal plan, manage and prepay long distance service, undergraduate degree progress report. Staffed computer lab on campus provides training in use of computers, software, and the Internet.
Community Environment: Muncie is the county seat and the largest city in east-central Indiana. It is located on the White River, 66 miles northeast of Indianapolis. All forms of commercial transportation are available.

■ **BETHEL COLLEGE**
1001 Bethel Cir.
Mishawaka, IN 46545-5591
Tel: (574)259-8511; Free: 800-422-4101
Fax: (574)257-3326
E-mail: admissions@bethelcollege.edu
Web Site: www.bethelcollege.edu/
Description: Independent, comprehensive, coed, affiliated with Missionary Church. Awards associate, bachelor's, and master's degrees. Founded 1947. Setting: 80-acre suburban campus. Endowment: $8.2 million. Educational spending for the previous fiscal year: $7585 per student. Total enrollment: 1,963. Faculty: 221 (82 full-time, 139 part-time). Student-undergrad faculty ratio is 13:1. 956 applied, 73% were admitted. 22% from top 10% of their high school class, 55% from top quarter, 82% from top half. 8 valedictorians. Full-time: 1,416 students, 65% women, 35% men. Part-time: 385 students, 76% women, 24% men. Students come from 31 states and territories, 15 other countries, 24% from out-of-state. 0.3% American Indian or Alaska Native, non-Hispanic/Latino; 5% Hispanic/Latino; 12% African American, non-Hispanic/Latino; 0.5% Asian, non-Hispanic/Latino; 0.1% Native Hawaiian or other Pacific Islander, non-Hispanic/Latino; 2% international. 39% 25 or older, 45% live on campus, 13% transferred in. Retention: 75% of full-time freshmen returned the following year. Academic areas with the most degrees conferred: business/marketing; health professions and related sciences; liberal arts/general studies; education. Core. Calendar: semesters. Academic remediation for entering students, services for LD students, advanced placement, accelerated degree program, self-designed majors, honors program, independent study, distance learning, double major, summer session for credit, part-time degree program, adult/continuing education programs, internships, graduate courses open to undergrads. Off campus study at Northern Indiana Consortium for Education, Council for Christian Colleges and Universities. Study abroad program. ROTC: Army (c), Air Force (c).
Entrance Requirements: Options: electronic application, early admission, deferred admission, international baccalaureate accepted. Required: high school transcript, minimum 2 high school GPA, 1 recommendation, SAT or ACT. Recommended: essay, minimum 2.5 high school GPA, interview. Entrance: minimally difficult. Application deadline: 8/15. Notification: continuous. SAT Reasoning Test deadline: 8/15. SAT Subject Test deadline: 8/15. Transfer credits accepted: Yes.
Costs Per Year: Application fee: $25. Comprehensive fee: $32,430 includes full-time tuition ($24,620), mandatory fees ($350), and college room and board ($7460). College room only: $3560. Full-time tuition and fees vary according to program. Room and board charges vary according to board plan and housing facility. Part-time tuition: $782 per credit. Part-time tuition varies according to program.
Collegiate Environment: Orientation program. Drama-theater group, choral group, student-run newspaper, radio station. Social organizations: 10 open to all. Most popular organizations: International Student Fellowship, Students for Life, Student Council, Spiritual Life Team. Major annual events: Community Service Day, Midnight Breakfast, Spiritual Emphasis Weeks. Student

services: health clinic, personal-psychological counseling. Campus security: 24-hour emergency response devices and patrols, late night transport-escort service, controlled dormitory access. 863 college housing spaces available; 779 were occupied in 2012-13. No special consideration for freshman housing applicants. On-campus residence required through sophomore year. Options: men-only, women-only housing available. Otis and Elizabeth Bowen Library with 146,563 books, 4,577 microform titles, 2,678 serials, 3,252 audiovisual materials, an OPAC, and a Web page. Operations spending for the previous fiscal year: $481,000. 160 computers available on campus for general student use. A campuswide network can be accessed from student residence rooms. Students can access the following: online class registration. Staffed computer lab on campus provides training in use of computers, software, and the Internet.

■ **BROWN MACKIE COLLEGE–FORT WAYNE**
3000 E Coliseum Blvd.
Fort Wayne, IN 46805
Tel: (219)484-4400; Free: 866-433-2289
Fax: (219)484-2678
Web Site: www.brownmackie.edu/fortwayne/
Description: Proprietary, primarily 2-year, coed. Part of Education Management Corporation. Awards certificates, diplomas, terminal associate, and bachelor's degrees.

■ **BROWN MACKIE COLLEGE–INDIANAPOLIS**
1200 N Meridian St.
Ste. 100
Indianapolis, IN 46204
Free: 866-255-0279
Web Site: www.brownmackie.edu/indianapolis/
Description: Proprietary, primarily 2-year, coed. Part of Education Management Corporation. Awards certificates, diplomas, terminal associate, and bachelor's degrees.

■ **BROWN MACKIE COLLEGE–MERRILLVILLE**
1000 E 80th Pl.
Ste. 205S
Merrillville, IN 46410
Tel: (219)769-3321; Free: 800-258-3321
Fax: (219)258-3321
Web Site: www.brownmackie.edu/merrillville/
Description: Proprietary, primarily 2-year, coed. Part of Education Management Corporation. Awards certificates, diplomas, terminal associate, and bachelor's degrees. Founded 1890. Setting: small town campus.

■ **BROWN MACKIE COLLEGE–MICHIGAN CITY**
325 E US Hwy. 20
Michigan City, IN 46360
Tel: (219)877-3100; Free: 800-519-2416
Fax: (219)877-3110
Web Site: www.brownmackie.edu/michigancity/
Description: Proprietary, primarily 2-year, coed. Part of Education Management Corporation. Awards certificates, diplomas, transfer associate, terminal associate, and bachelor's degrees. Setting: rural campus.

■ **BROWN MACKIE COLLEGE–SOUTH BEND**
3454 Douglas Rd.
South Bend, IN 46635
Tel: (574)237-0774; Free: 800-743-2447
Fax: (219)237-3585
Web Site: www.brownmackie.edu/southbend/
Description: Proprietary, primarily 2-year, coed. Part of Education Management Corporation. Awards certificates, transfer associate, terminal associate, and bachelor's degrees. Founded 1882. Setting: urban campus.

■ **BUTLER UNIVERSITY**
4600 Sunset Ave.
Indianapolis, IN 46208-3485
Tel: (317)940-8000; Free: 888-940-8100
Fax: (317)940-8150
E-mail: admission@butler.edu
Web Site: www.butler.edu/
Description: Independent, comprehensive, coed. Awards associate, bachelor's, master's, and doctoral degrees. Founded 1855. Setting: 290-

acre urban campus with easy access to Indianapolis. Endowment: $146 million. Research spending for the previous fiscal year: $727,000. Educational spending for the previous fiscal year: $13,009 per student. Total enrollment: 4,771. Faculty: 480 (341 full-time, 139 part-time). Student-undergrad faculty ratio is 11:1. 9,682 applied, 66% were admitted. 52% from top 10% of their high school class, 77% from top quarter, 97% from top half. 9 National Merit Scholars, 82 class presidents, 257 student government officers. Full-time: 3,943 students, 60% women, 40% men. Part-time: 77 students, 56% women, 44% men. Students come from 45 states and territories, 49 other countries, 48% from out-of-state. 0.4% American Indian or Alaska Native, non-Hispanic/Latino; 3% Hispanic/Latino; 3% African American, non-Hispanic/Latino; 3% Asian, non-Hispanic/Latino; 0% Native Hawaiian or other Pacific Islander, non-Hispanic/Latino; 2% international. 2% 25 or older, 69% live on campus, 3% transferred in. Retention: 91% of full-time freshmen returned the following year. Academic areas with the most degrees conferred: business/marketing; education; communication/journalism. Core. Calendar: semesters. Services for LD students, advanced placement, self-designed majors, honors program, independent study, double major, summer session for credit, part-time degree program, adult/continuing education programs, co-op programs and internships, graduate courses open to undergrads. Off campus study at Franklin College, Marian College, IUPUI, Martin University, Ivy Tech State College, University of Indianapolis. Study abroad program. ROTC: Army, Air Force (c).
Entrance Requirements: Options: electronic application, early action, deferred admission. Required: essay, high school transcript, 1 recommendation, SAT or ACT. Recommended: 1 recommendation. Required for some: Audition/interview/portfolio required for applicants to JCFA. Four years of math and science STRONGLY recommended for students interested in COPHS majors and natural sciences. Entrance: very difficult. Application deadlines: Rolling, Rolling for nonresidents, 11/1 for early action. Notification: continuous, continuous for nonresidents, 12/15 for early action. SAT Reasoning Test deadline: 2/1. Transfer credits accepted: Yes. Applicants placed on waiting list: 276. Wait-listed applicants offered admission: 5. Early action applicants: 5,809. Early action applicants admitted: 4,876.
Costs Per Year: Application fee: $35. One-time mandatory fee: $288. Comprehensive fee: $44,248 includes full-time tuition ($32,280), mandatory fees ($858), and college room and board ($11,110). College room only: $5370. Full-time tuition and fees vary according to course load, degree level, and program. Room and board charges vary according to housing facility.
Collegiate Environment: Orientation program. Drama-theater group, choral group, marching band, student-run newspaper. Social organizations: 153 open to all; national fraternities, national sororities. Most popular organizations: Dawg Pound, Student Government Association, Academic Service Honoraries, Alpha Phi Omega, Mortar Board. Major annual events: Homecoming, Spring Sports Spectacular, Spring Sing. Student services: health clinic, personal-psychological counseling. Campus security: 24-hour emergency response devices and patrols, late night transport-escort service, controlled dormitory access. College housing designed to accommodate 2,064 students; 2,066 undergraduates lived in college housing during 2012-13. Freshmen guaranteed college housing. On-campus residence required through junior year. Options: coed, women-only housing available. Irwin Library System plus 1 other with an OPAC and a Web page. Operations spending for the previous fiscal year: $3 million. 450 computers available on campus for general student use. A campuswide network can be accessed from student residence rooms and from off campus. Students can access the following: online class registration. Staffed computer lab on campus (open 24 hours a day) provides training in use of computers, software, and the Internet.
Community Environment: Indianapolis is the capital city, located in the exact center of the state, enjoying a fine climate. All modes of transportation are available. Excellent city facilities include a library with 21 branches, a museum, churches of all denominations, and 17 hospitals. Recreational facilities consist of 32 parks and eight golf courses with additional facilities for auto races, boating, baseball, basketball, football, riding, swimming, roller skating, boxing, wrestling, and ice skating.

■ **CALUMET COLLEGE OF SAINT JOSEPH**
2400 New York Ave.
Whiting, IN 46394-2195
Tel: (219)473-7770; Free: 877-700-9100
Fax: (219)473-4259
E-mail: admissions@ccsj.edu
Web Site: www.ccsj.edu/
Description: Independent Roman Catholic, comprehensive, coed. Awards

associate, bachelor's, and master's degrees. Founded 1951. Setting: 25-acre urban campus with easy access to Chicago. Endowment: $3.6 million. Total enrollment: 1,030. Faculty: 130 (33 full-time, 97 part-time). Student-undergrad faculty ratio is 10:1. 553 applied, 33% were admitted. 10% from top 10% of their high school class, 25% from top quarter, 50% from top half. Full-time: 438 students, 48% women, 52% men. Part-time: 429 students, 44% women, 56% men. Students come from 2 states and territories, 1% from out-of-state. 1% American Indian or Alaska Native, non-Hispanic/Latino; 31% Hispanic/Latino; 26% African American, non-Hispanic/Latino; 1% Asian, non-Hispanic/Latino; 0% Native Hawaiian or other Pacific Islander, non-Hispanic/Latino; 1% international. 70% 25 or older, 14% transferred in. Retention: 56% of full-time freshmen returned the following year. Academic areas with the most degrees conferred: law/legal studies; business/marketing; education. Core. Calendar: semesters. Academic remediation for entering students, services for LD students, advanced placement, accelerated degree program, honors program, independent study, distance learning, double major, summer session for credit, part-time degree program, external degree program, adult/continuing education programs, co-op programs and internships.

Entrance Requirements: Options: electronic application, deferred admission, international baccalaureate accepted. Required: high school transcript. Recommended: minimum 2 high school GPA, SAT or ACT. Required for some: essay, interview, ACT COMPASS. Entrance: noncompetitive. Application deadlines: Rolling, Rolling for nonresidents. SAT Reasoning Test deadline: 9/1. Transfer credits accepted: Yes.

Costs Per Year: Application fee: $0. Tuition: $15,420 full-time, $490 per credit part-time. Mandatory fees: $200 full-time, $100 per term part-time. Full-time tuition and fees vary according to course load and program. Part-time tuition and fees vary according to course load and program.

Collegiate Environment: Orientation program. Drama-theater group, student-run newspaper. Social organizations: 11 open to all; 5% of eligible men and 15% of eligible women are members. Most popular organizations: student government, Los Amigos Hispanic Club, Criminal Justice Club, Drama Club, GIVE. Major annual events: Welcome Back Week, Homecoming, Spirit Week. Student services: personal-psychological counseling. Campus security: day and night security, emergency alert system. College housing not available. Mary Gorman Specker Memorial Library with 110,000 books, 4,000 serials, 1,200 audiovisual materials, an OPAC, and a Web page. Operations spending for the previous fiscal year: $255,562. 161 computers available on campus for general student use. A campuswide network can be accessed. Students can access the following: online class registration. Staffed computer lab on campus provides training in use of computers and the Internet.

Community Environment: Hammond-Whiting, facing Lake Michigan, is one of the greatest industrial regions in the world. Industries produce pig iron, rolled, forged and casted steel products, petroleum, lead and aluminum products, chemicals, railroad freight cars and building materials. Part-time employment is available.

■ **CHAMBERLAIN COLLEGE OF NURSING**
9100 Keystone Crossing
Ste. 600
Indianapolis, IN 46240
Tel: (317)816-7335
Web Site: www.chamberlain.edu/

Description: Proprietary, 4-year, coed. Awards bachelor's degrees. Total enrollment: 124. Faculty: 3 (all full-time). Student-undergrad faculty ratio is 28:1. Full-time: 66 students, 80% women, 20% men. Part-time: 58 students, 86% women, 14% men. 0% from out-of-state. 1% American Indian or Alaska Native, non-Hispanic/Latino; 3% Hispanic/Latino; 30% African American, non-Hispanic/Latino; 2% Asian, non-Hispanic/Latino; 0% Native Hawaiian or other Pacific Islander, non-Hispanic/Latino; 2% international. 68% 25 or older, 0% live on campus, 93% transferred in.

Entrance Requirements: Required: SAT or ACT.

Costs Per Year: Application fee: $95. Tuition: $16,360 full-time, $665 per credit hour part-time. Mandatory fees: $600 full-time.

■ **COLLEGE OF COURT REPORTING**
111 W Tenth St.
Ste. 111
Hobart, IN 46342
Tel: (219)942-1459; Free: 866-294-3974
Fax: (219)942-1631
E-mail: nrodriquez@ccr.edu

Web Site: www.ccr.edu/

Description: Proprietary, 2-year, coed. Awards certificates, diplomas, transfer associate, and terminal associate degrees. Total enrollment: 275. Student-undergrad faculty ratio is 17:1. 86% from out-of-state. 89% 25 or older.

■ **CROSSROADS BIBLE COLLEGE**
601 N Shortridge Rd.
Indianapolis, IN 46219
Tel: (317)352-8736; Free: 800-822-3119
Fax: (317)352-9145
E-mail: admissions@crossroads.edu
Web Site: www.crossroads.edu/

Description: Independent Baptist, 4-year, coed. Awards associate and bachelor's degrees. Founded 1980. Setting: 6-acre urban campus with easy access to Indianapolis. Educational spending for the previous fiscal year: $10,767 per student. Total enrollment: 232. Faculty: 35 (6 full-time, 29 part-time). Student-undergrad faculty ratio is 7:1. 42 applied, 95% were admitted. 0% from top 10% of their high school class, 0% from top quarter, 0% from top half. Full-time: 127 students, 53% women, 47% men. Part-time: 105 students, 59% women, 41% men. Students come from 12 states and territories, 7 other countries, 9% from out-of-state. 0.4% American Indian or Alaska Native, non-Hispanic/Latino; 2% Hispanic/Latino; 55% African American, non-Hispanic/Latino; 0.4% Asian, non-Hispanic/Latino; 0.4% Native Hawaiian or other Pacific Islander, non-Hispanic/Latino; 0% international. 79% 25 or older, 5% live on campus, 22% transferred in. Retention: 45% of full-time freshmen returned the following year. Core. Calendar: semesters. Academic remediation for entering students, accelerated degree program, independent study, distance learning, double major, summer session for credit, part-time degree program, external degree program, adult/continuing education programs, co-op programs and internships.

Entrance Requirements: Open admission. Options: electronic application, deferred admission. Required: essay, high school transcript. Required for some: interview. Entrance: noncompetitive. Application deadlines: 8/8, Rolling for nonresidents. Notification: continuous, continuous for nonresidents. Transfer credits accepted: Yes.

Costs Per Year: Application fee: $10. Tuition: $9480 full-time, $395 per credit hour part-time. Mandatory fees: $500 full-time, $250 per term part-time. College room only: $3400.

Collegiate Environment: Orientation program. Choral group. Major annual events: Diversity / International Food Fair, Chapel, Move / Game Nights / Discussions. Student services: personal-psychological counseling. Campus security: 24-hour emergency response devices, student patrols, late night transport-escort service. Kathryn Ulmer Library plus 1 other with 33,676 books and 2,094 audiovisual materials. Operations spending for the previous fiscal year: $4621. 15 computers available on campus for general student use. A campuswide network can be accessed from student residence rooms. Students can access the following: online class registration.

■ **DEPAUW UNIVERSITY**
313 S Locust St.
Greencastle, IN 46135
Tel: (765)658-4800; Free: 800-447-2495
Fax: (765)658-4007
E-mail: emacam@depauw.edu
Web Site: www.depauw.edu/

Description: Independent, 4-year, coed, affiliated with United Methodist Church. Awards bachelor's degrees. Founded 1837. Setting: 655-acre small town campus with easy access to Indianapolis. Total enrollment: 2,336. Faculty: 267 (228 full-time, 39 part-time). Student-undergrad faculty ratio is 10:1. 4,835 applied, 63% were admitted. 44% from top 10% of their high school class, 77% from top quarter, 98% from top half. Full-time: 2,307 students, 55% women, 45% men. Part-time: 29 students, 52% women, 48% men. 58% from out-of-state. 0.3% American Indian or Alaska Native, non-Hispanic/Latino; 4% Hispanic/Latino; 6% African American, non-Hispanic/Latino; 3% Asian, non-Hispanic/Latino; 0% Native Hawaiian or other Pacific Islander, non-Hispanic/Latino; 11% international. 1% 25 or older, 95% live on campus, 1% transferred in. Retention: 89% of full-time freshmen returned the following year. Calendar: 4-1-4. Part-time degree program. ROTC: Army (c), Air Force (c).

Entrance Requirements: Options: electronic application, early admission, early decision, early action, deferred admission, international baccalaureate accepted. Required: essay, high school transcript, 1 recommendation, SAT or ACT. Recommended: interview. Entrance: moderately difficult. Application deadlines: 2/1, 11/1 for early decision, 12/1 for early action. Notification: 1/1 for early decision, 1/31 for early action. SAT Reasoning Test deadline: 2/1. Early decision applicants: 62. Early decision applicants admitted: 57.

Costs Per Year: Application fee: $40. Comprehensive fee: $48,950 includes full-time tuition ($38,280), mandatory fees ($470), and college room and board ($10,200). Room and board charges vary according to board plan. Part-time tuition: $1,196.25 per credit hour.

Collegiate Environment: Orientation program. Drama-theater group, choral group, student-run newspaper, radio station. Social organizations: national fraternities, national sororities. Student services: health clinic, personal-psychological counseling, women's center. Campus security: 24-hour emergency response devices and patrols, student patrols, late night transport-escort service, controlled dormitory access. Freshmen guaranteed college housing. On-campus residence required through senior year. Option: coed housing available. Roy O. West Library with an OPAC and a Web page.

Community Environment: Greencastle is located 40 miles west of Indianapolis, and within a 4-hour drive of Chicago, Cincinnati, Columbus, Louisville, and St. Louis. Community facilities include churches and a county hospital. The resort areas of Cataract Lake and Mansfield Lake are within 15 miles, and provide facilities for water sports and fishing.

■ **DEVRY UNIVERSITY (INDIANAPOLIS)**
9100 Keystone Crossing, Ste. 350
Indianapolis, IN 46240-2158
Tel: (317)581-8854; Free: 866-338-7941
Web Site: www.devry.edu/
Description: Proprietary, comprehensive, coed. Part of DeVry University. Awards associate, bachelor's, and master's degrees. Total enrollment: 365. Faculty: 33 (all part-time). Student-undergrad faculty ratio is 18:1. Full-time: 99 students, 37% women, 63% men. Part time: 132 students, 49% women, 51% men. 2% from out-of-state. 81% 25 or older, 30% transferred in. Academic areas with the most degrees conferred: business/marketing; computer and information sciences. Calendar: semesters. Academic remediation for entering students, services for LD students, advanced placement, accelerated degree program, distance learning, summer session for credit, part-time degree program, adult/continuing education programs.
Entrance Requirements: Options: electronic application, deferred admission, international baccalaureate accepted. Required: high school transcript, interview. Entrance: minimally difficult. Application deadline: Rolling. Notification: continuous. SAT Reasoning Test deadline: 10/31.
Collegiate Environment: Orientation program.

■ **DEVRY UNIVERSITY (MERRILLVILLE)**
Twin Towers
1000 E 80th Pl., Ste. 222 Mall
Merrillville, IN 46410-5673
Tel: (219)736-7440; Free: 866-338-7941
Fax: (219)736-7874
Web Site: www.devry.edu/
Description: Proprietary, comprehensive, coed. Awards bachelor's and master's degrees. Calendar: semesters.

■ **EARLHAM COLLEGE**
801 National Rd. W
Richmond, IN 47374-4095
Tel: (765)983-1200; Free: 800-327-5426
Fax: (765)983-1560
E-mail: admission@earlham.edu
Web Site: www.earlham.edu/
Description: Independent, comprehensive, coed, affiliated with Society of Friends. Awards bachelor's and master's degrees. Founded 1847. Setting: 800-acre small town campus with easy access to Cincinnati, Indianapolis, Dayton. Endowment: $289.4 million. Research spending for the previous fiscal year: $469,943. Educational spending for the previous fiscal year: $17,473 per student. Total enrollment: 1,211. Faculty: 120 (104 full-time, 16 part-time). Student-undergrad faculty ratio is 10:1. 1,408 applied, 75% were admitted. 30% from top 10% of their high school class, 61% from top quarter, 93% from top half. Full-time: 1,065 students, 56% women, 44% men. Part-time: 22 students, 45% women, 55% men. Students come from 43 states and territories, 76 other countries, 81% from out-of-state. 1% American Indian or Alaska Native, non-Hispanic/Latino; 6% Hispanic/Latino; 10% African American, non-Hispanic/Latino; 2% Asian, non-Hispanic/Latino; 0.3% Native Hawaiian or other Pacific Islander, non-Hispanic/Latino; 18%

international. 1% 25 or older, 96% live on campus, 1% transferred in. Retention: 83% of full-time freshmen returned the following year. Academic areas with the most degrees conferred: biological/life sciences; interdisciplinary studies; social sciences. Core. Calendar: semesters. ESL program, services for LD students, advanced placement, accelerated degree program, self-designed majors, independent study, double major, internships. Off campus study at members of the Great Lakes Colleges Association. Study abroad program.

Entrance Requirements: Options: electronic application, early admission, early decision, early action, deferred admission, international baccalaureate accepted. Required: essay, high school transcript, minimum 2.8 high school GPA, 2 recommendations. Recommended: interview, SAT or ACT. Entrance: very difficult. Application deadlines: 2/1, 11/1 for early decision, 12/1 for early action. Notification: 3/1, 12/1 for early decision, 2/1 for early action. Preference given to Quakers, children of alumni, state residents, minorities. SAT Reasoning Test deadline: 3/15. Transfer credits accepted: Yes. Applicants placed on waiting list: 37. Wait-listed applicants offered admission: 13. Early decision applicants: 17. Early decision applicants admitted: 16. Early action applicants: 657. Early action applicants admitted: 454.

Costs Per Year: Application fee: $0. Comprehensive fee: $49,710 includes full-time tuition ($40,600), mandatory fees ($850), and college room and board ($8260). College room only: $4190. Room and board charges vary according to board plan. Part-time tuition: $1353 per credit.

Collegiate Environment: Orientation program. Drama-theater group, choral group, student-run newspaper, radio station. Social organizations: 70 open to all. Most popular organizations: Gospel Revelations Chorus, Dance Alloy, club sports, student government, Black Student Union. Major annual events: Spring Fest, African Festival, Convocation. Student services: health clinic, personal-psychological counseling, women's center. Campus security: 24-hour emergency response devices and patrols, student patrols, late night transport-escort service, controlled dormitory access. 1,052 college housing spaces available; 958 were occupied in 2012-13. Freshmen guaranteed college housing. On-campus residence required through senior year. Options: coed, men-only, women-only housing available. Lilly Library plus 2 others with 378,895 books, 191,754 microform titles, 54,038 serials, 9,387 audiovisual materials, an OPAC, and a Web page. Operations spending for the previous fiscal year: $715,770.

Community Environment: The campus lies at the southwest edge of Richmond, IN, a city of 40,000 people. Richmond is 70 miles from Cincinnati, OH, and Indianapolis, IN, and 40 miles from Dayton, OH. Local activities include auctions, the city's arboretum, the pedestrian shopping mall downtown, the symphony orchestra, civic theater and opera companies, a historical museum and the art association. The city is served by buses. Airline service is available in Dayton, OH.

■ **FRANKLIN COLLEGE**
101 Branigin Blvd.
Franklin, IN 46131
Tel: (317)738-8000; Free: 800-852-0232
Fax: (317)738-8274
E-mail: admissions@franklincollege.edu
Web Site: www.franklincollege.edu/
Description: Independent, 4-year, coed, affiliated with American Baptist Churches in the U.S.A. Awards bachelor's degrees. Founded 1834. Setting: 187-acre small town campus with easy access to Indianapolis. Endowment: $80.1 million. Educational spending for the previous fiscal year: $7009 per student. Total enrollment: 1,053. Faculty: 103 (74 full-time, 29 part-time). Student-undergrad faculty ratio is 11:1. 1,926 applied, 60% were admitted. 22% from top 10% of their high school class, 53% from top quarter, 93% from top half. Full-time: 1,006 students, 50% women, 50% men. Part-time: 47 students, 53% women, 47% men. Students come from 20 states and territories, 8 other countries, 7% from out-of-state. 0.5% American Indian or Alaska Native, non-Hispanic/Latino; 1% Hispanic/Latino; 5% African American, non-Hispanic/Latino; 1% Asian, non-Hispanic/Latino; 0% Native Hawaiian or other Pacific Islander, non-Hispanic/Latino; 0% international. 1% 25 or older, 76% live on campus, 3% transferred in. Retention: 77% of full-time freshmen returned the following year. Academic areas with the most degrees conferred: education; communication/journalism; social sciences. Core. Calendar: 4-1-4. Academic remediation for entering students, services for LD students, advanced placement, independent study, double major, summer session for credit, part-time degree program, co-op programs and internships. Off campus study at Marian College, University of Indianapolis, Indiana University-Purdue University at Indianapolis, Butler University, Martin University, Ivy Tech State College. Study abroad program. ROTC: Army (c).

Entrance Requirements: Options: electronic application, deferred admission. Required: essay, high school transcript, SAT or ACT. Required for some: interview. Entrance: moderately difficult. Application deadline: Rolling. Notification: continuous.

Costs Per Year: Application fee: $30. One-time mandatory fee: $380. Comprehensive fee: $34,845 includes full-time tuition ($26,710), mandatory fees ($185), and college room and board ($7950). College room only: $4720. Room and board charges vary according to board plan. Part-time tuition: $380 per credit.

Collegiate Environment: Orientation program. Drama-theater group, choral group, student-run newspaper, radio station. Social organizations: 66 open to all; national fraternities, national sororities; 34% of eligible men and 43% of eligible women are members. Most popular organizations: FLOW, FC Volunteers, Student Entertainment Board, Student Congress. Major annual events: Homecoming, Grizzly Grand Prix Festival. Student services: health clinic, personal-psychological counseling. Campus security: 24-hour emergency response devices and patrols, late night transport-escort service. 700 college housing spaces available; all were occupied in 2012-13. Freshmen guaranteed college housing. On-campus residence required through junior year. Option: coed housing available. Hamilton Library with 25,434 books, 301,815 microform titles, 292 serials, 7,669 audiovisual materials, an OPAC, and a Web page. Operations spending for the previous fiscal year: $531,000. 150 computers available on campus for general student use. Computer purchase/lease plans available. A campuswide network can be accessed from student residence rooms and from off campus. Students can access the following: online class registration. Staffed computer lab on campus (open 24 hours a day) provides training in use of computers, software, and the Internet.

Community Environment: Franklin (population 21,700) is situated 20 miles south of Indianapolis with facilities that include a library, hospital, 15 churches representing major denominations, and various service, fraternal, and veteran's organizations. Recreational activities are fishing, swimming, tennis, and bowling. Part-time job opportunities are available.

■ **GOSHEN COLLEGE**
1700 S Main St.
Goshen, IN 46526-4794
Tel: (574)535-7000; Free: 800-348-7422
Fax: (574)535-7060
E-mail: dankl@goshen.edu
Web Site: www.goshen.edu/

Description: Independent Mennonite, comprehensive, coed. Awards bachelor's and master's degrees. Founded 1894. Setting: 135-acre small town campus. Endowment: $94 million. Research spending for the previous fiscal year: $55,211. Educational spending for the previous fiscal year: $11,065 per student. Total enrollment: 928. Faculty: 94 (71 full-time, 23 part-time). Student-undergrad faculty ratio is 10:1. 608 applied, 60% were admitted. 27% from top 10% of their high school class, 55% from top quarter, 88% from top half. 1 National Merit Scholar, 11 valedictorians. Full-time: 807 students, 59% women, 41% men. Part-time: 77 students, 73% women, 27% men. Students come from 37 states and territories, 37 other countries, 49% from out-of-state. 0% American Indian or Alaska Native, non-Hispanic/Latino; 10% Hispanic/Latino; 3% African American, non-Hispanic/Latino; 1% Asian, non-Hispanic/Latino; 0% Native Hawaiian or other Pacific Islander, non-Hispanic/Latino; 9% international. 8% 25 or older, 70% live on campus, 7% transferred in. Retention: 83% of full-time freshmen returned the following year. Academic areas with the most degrees conferred: health professions and related sciences; business/marketing; visual and performing arts. Core. Calendar: semesters. Academic remediation for entering students, services for LD students, advanced placement, accelerated degree program, self-designed majors, independent study, distance learning, double major, summer session for credit, part-time degree program, adult/continuing education programs, internships, graduate courses open to undergrads. Off campus study at Northern Indiana Consortium for Education. Study abroad program.

Entrance Requirements: Options: electronic application, deferred admission, international baccalaureate accepted. Required: essay, high school transcript, minimum 2 high school GPA, 1 recommendation, SAT or ACT. Recommended: minimum 2.75 high school GPA, interview, rank in upper 50% of high school class. Entrance: moderately difficult. Application deadline: 8/15. Notification: continuous. SAT Reasoning Test deadline: 8/1. SAT Subject Test deadline: 8/1. Transfer credits accepted: Yes.

Costs Per Year: Application fee: $25. Comprehensive fee: $37,960 includes full-time tuition ($28,500) and college room and board ($9460). College room only: $5060. Full-time tuition varies according to degree level and program.

Room and board charges vary according to board plan and housing facility. Part-time tuition: $1190 per credit hour. Part-time tuition varies according to course load, degree level, and program.

Collegiate Environment: Orientation program. Drama-theater group, choral group, student-run newspaper, radio station. Social organizations: 30 open to all. Most popular organizations: International Student Club, Latino Student Union, PAX - Peace Club, Goshen Student Women's Organization, Business Club. Major annual event: Kickoff. Student services: health clinic, personal-psychological counseling. Campus security: 24-hour emergency response devices and patrols, late night transport-escort service. 750 college housing spaces available; 650 were occupied in 2012-13. Freshmen guaranteed college housing. On-campus residence required through junior year. Options: coed, men-only, women-only housing available. The Harold and Wilma Good Library plus 1 other with 135,000 books, 180,000 microform titles, 400 serials, 2,800 audiovisual materials, an OPAC, and a Web page. Operations spending for the previous fiscal year: $509,168. 160 computers available on campus for general student use. A campuswide network can be accessed from student residence rooms and from off campus. Students can access the following: online class registration. Staffed computer lab on campus provides training in use of computers, software, and the Internet.

Community Environment: Goshen,"The Maple City" is a diversified small industry center, situated ten miles south of the Michigan state line. Annual mean temperature is 55 degrees, and the annual rainfall is 34 inches. All forms of transportation are available, and the airport is five miles southeast. Community facilities include a public library, hospital, 24 churches and many civic, service and social organizations. Goshen is noted for its large number of Amish farmers, and hundreds of lakes are within a 40-mile radius.

■ **GRACE COLLEGE**
200 Seminary Dr.
Winona Lake, IN 46590-1294
Tel: (574)372-5100; Free: 800-54-GRACE
Fax: (574)372-5139
E-mail: enroll@grace.edu
Web Site: www.grace.edu/

Description: Independent, comprehensive, coed, affiliated with Fellowship of Grace Brethren Churches. Administratively affiliated with Grace Theological Seminary. Awards associate, bachelor's, master's, and doctoral degrees. Founded 1948. Setting: 160-acre small town campus. Endowment: $8.3 million. Educational spending for the previous fiscal year: $4334 per student. Total enrollment: 1,616. Faculty: 85 (44 full-time, 41 part-time). Student-undergrad faculty ratio is 27:1. 1,821 applied, 95% were admitted. 29% from top 10% of their high school class, 54% from top quarter, 84% from top half. Full-time: 1,078 students, 55% women, 45% men. Part-time: 232 students, 62% women, 38% men. Students come from 34 states and territories, 5 other countries, 42% from out-of-state. 0.3% American Indian or Alaska Native, non-Hispanic/Latino; 3% Hispanic/Latino; 4% African American, non-Hispanic/Latino; 1% Asian, non-Hispanic/Latino; 0.2% Native Hawaiian or other Pacific Islander, non-Hispanic/Latino; 1% international. 13% 25 or older, 61% live on campus, 4% transferred in. Retention: 79% of full-time freshmen returned the following year. Academic areas with the most degrees conferred: business/marketing; psychology; education. Core. Calendar: semesters. Academic remediation for entering students, services for LD students, advanced placement, accelerated degree program, honors program, independent study, distance learning, double major, summer session for credit, part-time degree program, adult/continuing education programs, co-op programs and internships, graduate courses open to undergrads. Off campus study at Coalition for Christian Colleges and Universities. Study abroad program.

Entrance Requirements: Options: electronic application, early admission, early action, deferred admission, international baccalaureate accepted. Required: essay, high school transcript, minimum 2.3 high school GPA, 2 recommendations, personal statement of faith, SAT or ACT. Required for some: interview. Entrance: moderately difficult. Application deadlines: 8/1, 12/1 for early action. Notification: 8/15.

Costs Per Year: Application fee: $30. Comprehensive fee: $30,744 includes full-time tuition ($23,290) and college room and board ($7454). College room only: $3900. Full-time tuition varies according to course load, degree level, location, and program. Room and board charges vary according to board plan and housing facility. Part-time tuition: $775 per credit hour. Part-time tuition varies according to course load, degree level, location, and program.

Collegiate Environment: Orientation program. Drama-theater group, choral group, student-run newspaper. Social organizations: 30 open to all. Most popular organizations: Grace Ministries in Action, Student Activities Board,

Funfest, women's ministries, Breakout. Major annual events: Homecoming, Heart of the Holidays, Halloween Fun Fest. Student services: health clinic, personal-psychological counseling. Campus security: student patrols, late night transport-escort service, controlled dormitory access, evening patrols by trained security personnel. Morgan Library with 140,966 books, 24,891 microform titles, 17,247 serials, 3,806 audiovisual materials, an OPAC, and a Web page. Operations spending for the previous fiscal year: $445,423. 150 computers available on campus for general student use. A campuswide network can be accessed from student residence rooms and from off campus. Students can access the following: online class registration. Staffed computer lab on campus provides training in use of computers, software, and the Internet.

Community Environment: One of the outstanding Christian summer resorts in America, Winona Lake, population 4,000, is situated two miles from Warsaw, Indiana, on the main line of Amtrack Railroad. This is a resort area for the entire family.

■ **HANOVER COLLEGE**
PO Box 108
Hanover, IN 47243-0108
Tel: (812)866-7000; Free: 800-213-2178
Fax: (812)866-7098
E-mail: admission@hanover.edu
Web Site: www.hanover.edu/

Description: Independent Presbyterian, 4-year, coed. Awards bachelor's degrees. Founded 1827. Setting: 630-acre rural campus with easy access to Louisville. Endowment: $127.9 million. Research spending for the previous fiscal year: $101,197. Educational spending for the previous fiscal year: $14,758 per student. Total enrollment: 1,123. Faculty: 101 (96 full-time, 5 part-time). Student-undergrad faculty ratio is 12:1. 3,633 applied, 64% were admitted. 28% from top 10% of their high school class, 67% from top quarter, 93% from top half. 6 valedictorians. Full-time: 1,116 students, 56% women, 44% men. Part-time: 7 students, 57% women, 43% men. Students come from 23 states and territories, 11 other countries, 31% from out-of-state. 0.4% American Indian or Alaska Native, non-Hispanic/Latino; 2% Hispanic/Latino; 4% African American, non-Hispanic/Latino; 1% Asian, non-Hispanic/Latino; 0.1% Native Hawaiian or other Pacific Islander, non-Hispanic/Latino; 3% international. 1% 25 or older, 95% live on campus, 1% transferred in. Retention: 83% of full-time freshmen returned the following year. Academic areas with the most degrees conferred: social sciences; psychology; communication/journalism. Core. Calendar: 4-4-1. Services for LD students, advanced placement, self-designed majors, independent study, double major, co-op programs and internships. Off campus study at City Semesters: Philadelphia Center (through Hope College); Washington Center; Chicago Program (through Associated Colleges of the Midwest). Study abroad program.

Entrance Requirements: Options: electronic application, early admission, early action, deferred admission, international baccalaureate accepted. Required: essay, high school transcript, 1 recommendation, SAT or ACT. Recommended: interview. Entrance: moderately difficult. Application deadlines: 3/1, 12/1 for early action. Notification: continuous, 12/20 for early action. SAT Reasoning Test deadline: 4/1. Transfer credits accepted: Yes. Applicants placed on waiting list: 0. Wait-listed applicants offered admission: 0. Early action applicants: 2,924. Early action applicants admitted: 2,018.

Costs Per Year: Application fee: $40. One-time mandatory fee: $250. Comprehensive fee: $39,498 includes full-time tuition ($29,668), mandatory fees ($600), and college room and board ($9230). College room only: $4588. Full-time tuition and fees vary according to reciprocity agreements. Room and board charges vary according to housing facility and location. Part-time tuition: $3296 per unit. Part-time tuition varies according to course load and reciprocity agreements.

Collegiate Environment: Orientation program. Drama-theater group, choral group, marching band, student-run newspaper, radio station. Social organizations: 60 open to all; national fraternities, national sororities; 40% of eligible men and 40% of eligible women are members. Most popular organizations: Student Senate, Campus Crusade for Christ, Campus Activities Board, People for Peace, Love Out Loud. Major annual events: Homecoming, Parents' Day, Wake Up and Live. Student services: health clinic, personal-psychological counseling. Campus security: 24-hour emergency response devices and patrols, late night transport-escort service, controlled dormitory access. 1,070 college housing spaces available; 1,067 were occupied in 2012-13. Freshmen guaranteed college housing. On-campus residence required through senior year. Options: coed, men-only, women-only housing available. Duggan Library with 224,478 books, 44,770

microform titles, 1,035 serials, 5,080 audiovisual materials, an OPAC, and a Web page. Operations spending for the previous fiscal year: $834,481. 120 computers available on campus for general student use. A campuswide network can be accessed from student residence rooms and from off campus. Students can access the following: online class registration. Staffed computer lab on campus provides training in use of computers, software, and the Internet.

Community Environment: Hanover is located four and one-half miles from Madison, Indiana (population 12,400), overlooking the beautiful Ohio River valley from a hilltop nearly 400 feet above the river. Community facilities include a modern hospital. The Hanover/Madison area is rich in historic lore and antiques. Clifty Falls, a large State Park, well known for its rugged scenery, serves this community.

■ **HARRISON COLLEGE**
550 E Washington St.
Indianapolis, IN 46204
Tel: (317)264-5656; Free: 888-544-4422
Fax: (317)264-5650
E-mail: Admissions@harrison.edu
Web Site: www.harrison.edu/

Description: Proprietary, 4-year, coed. Part of We have additional Indiana locations in Anderson, Columbus, Indianapolis East Side, Evansville, Fort Wayne, Lafayette, Indianapolis Northwest side, Terre Haute, and a fully online campus. Awards associate and bachelor's degrees. Founded 1902. Setting: 1-acre urban campus with easy access to Indianapolis. Total enrollment: 4,547. Faculty: 345 (86 full-time, 259 part-time). Student-undergrad faculty ratio is 14:1. 470 applied, 99% were admitted. Full-time: 2,584 students, 81% women, 19% men. Part-time: 1,963 students, 84% women, 16% men. Students come from 43 states and territories, 1 other country, 14% from out-of-state. 1% American Indian or Alaska Native, non-Hispanic/Latino; 1% Hispanic/Latino; 15% African American, non-Hispanic/Latino; 0.3% Asian, non-Hispanic/Latino; 0.02% Native Hawaiian or other Pacific Islander, non-Hispanic/Latino; 0.02% international. 69% 25 or older, 12% transferred in. Retention: 39% of full-time freshmen returned the following year. Academic areas with the most degrees conferred: business/marketing; health professions and related sciences; homeland security, law enforcement, firefighting, and protective services. Advanced placement, distance learning, double major, summer session for credit, part-time degree program, adult/continuing education programs, co-op programs and internships. Off campus study.

Entrance Requirements: Option: electronic application. Required: high school transcript, interview, Wonderlic Scholastic Level Exam (SLE). Entrance: moderately difficult. Application deadlines: Rolling, Rolling for nonresidents. Notification: continuous, continuous for nonresidents. Transfer credits accepted: Yes.

Collegiate Environment: Orientation program. Most popular organizations: Student Advisory Board, Student Ambassadors, Phi Beta Lambda. Campus security: 24-hour patrols. College housing not available.

■ **HOLY CROSS COLLEGE**
PO Box 308, 54515 State Rd. 933 N
Notre Dame, IN 46556-0308
Tel: (574)239-8400
Fax: (574)239-8323
E-mail: admissions@hcc-nd.edu
Web Site: www.hcc-nd.edu/

Description: Independent Roman Catholic, 4-year, coed. Awards associate and bachelor's degrees. Founded 1966. Setting: 150-acre suburban campus with easy access to Chicago, Indianapolis. Endowment: $1.4 million. Educational spending for the previous fiscal year: $3173 per student. Total enrollment: 450. Faculty: 48 (22 full-time, 26 part-time). Student-undergrad faculty ratio is 14:1. 493 applied, 81% were admitted. Full-time: 420 students, 39% women, 61% men. Part-time: 30 students, 63% women, 37% men. Students come from 29 states and territories, 6 other countries, 47% from out-of-state. 0.2% American Indian or Alaska Native, non-Hispanic/Latino; 10% Hispanic/Latino; 7% African American, non-Hispanic/Latino; 1% Asian, non-Hispanic/Latino; 0% Native Hawaiian or other Pacific Islander, non-Hispanic/Latino; 11% international. 7% 25 or older, 52% live on campus, 7% transferred in. Retention: 64% of full-time freshmen returned the following year. Academic areas with the most degrees conferred: business/marketing; communication/journalism; liberal arts/general studies; education; psychology. Core. Calendar: semesters. Academic remediation for entering students, advanced placement, self-designed majors, freshman honors college, honors program, independent study, double major, summer session for credit, internships. Off campus study at members of the Northern Indiana Consortium for Education. Study abroad program. ROTC: Army (c), Air Force (c).

Entrance Requirements: Options: electronic application, deferred admission, international baccalaureate accepted. Required: high school transcript, Freshmen applicants and Transfer applicants with fewer than 24 transferable credits are required to submit ACT or SAT scores, SAT or ACT. Recommended: minimum 2.5 high school GPA, interview. Required for some: essay. Entrance: moderately difficult. Application deadlines: Rolling, Rolling for nonresidents. Notification: continuous, continuous for nonresidents. SAT Reasoning Test deadline: 8/15. SAT Subject Test deadline: 8/15. Transfer credits accepted: Yes.

Costs Per Year: Application fee: $0. Comprehensive fee: $34,345 includes full-time tuition ($24,500), mandatory fees ($950), and college room and board ($8895). Full-time tuition and fees vary according to course load. Room and board charges vary according to board plan and housing facility. Part-time tuition: $825 per semester hour. Part-time tuition varies according to course load. Tuition guaranteed not to increase for student's term of enrollment.

Collegiate Environment: Orientation program. Drama-theater group, choral group, marching band, student-run newspaper. Social organizations: 30 open to all. Most popular organizations: Student Government Association, Campus Ministry, Intramural athletics, Commuter Student Organization, Circle K. Major annual events: Campus Open House, All College Picnic, Parent/Alumni Weekend. Student services: personal-psychological counseling. Campus security: 24-hour emergency response devices and patrols, late night transport-escort service, controlled dormitory access. 300 college housing spaces available; 230 were occupied in 2012-13. Freshmen given priority for college housing. On-campus residence required in freshman year. Options: men-only, women-only housing available. McKenna Library with 40,000 books, 150 serials, 400 audiovisual materials, and an OPAC. Operations spending for the previous fiscal year: $188,500. 91 computers available on campus for general student use. Computer purchase/lease plans available. A campuswide network can be accessed from student residence rooms and from off campus. Students can access the following: online class registration. Staffed computer lab on campus provides training in use of computers, software, and the Internet.

Community Environment: See University of Notre Dame.

■ **HUNTINGTON UNIVERSITY**
2303 College Ave.
Huntington, IN 46750-1299
Tel: (260)356-6000; Free: 800-642-6493
Fax: (260)356-9448
E-mail: admissions@huntington.edu
Web Site: www.huntington.edu/

Description: Independent, comprehensive, coed, affiliated with Church of the United Brethren in Christ. Administratively affiliated with Church of the United Brethren in Christ. Awards associate, bachelor's, and master's degrees. Founded 1897. Setting: 170-acre small town campus with easy access to Fort Wayne. Endowment: $20.6 million. Educational spending for the previous fiscal year: $8467 per student. Total enrollment: 1,189. Faculty: 109 (58 full-time, 51 part-time). Student-undergrad faculty ratio is 13:1. 824 applied, 97% were admitted. 22% from top 10% of their high school class, 48% from top quarter, 83% from top half. 2 valedictorians. Full-time: 1,041 students, 58% women, 42% men. Part-time: 93 students, 53% women, 47% men. Students come from 36 states and territories, 19 other countries, 38% from out-of-state. 0.4% American Indian or Alaska Native, non-Hispanic/ Latino; 3% Hispanic/Latino; 2% African American, non-Hispanic/Latino; 0.4% Asian, non-Hispanic/Latino; 0.1% Native Hawaiian or other Pacific Islander, non-Hispanic/Latino; 3% international. 1% 25 or older, 74% live on campus, 5% transferred in. Retention: 73% of full-time freshmen returned the following year. Academic areas with the most degrees conferred: business/ marketing; education; health professions and related sciences; theology and religious vocations; visual and performing arts; communication/journalism. Core. Calendar: 4-1-4. Academic remediation for entering students, ESL program, services for LD students, advanced placement, accelerated degree program, independent study, distance learning, double major, summer session for credit, part-time degree program, adult/continuing education programs, internships, graduate courses open to undergrads. Off campus study at American Studies Program in Washington, D.C.; Contemporary Music Center in Nashville; Focus Leadership Institute in Colorado; Los Angeles Film Studies Center; Washington Journalism Center in Washington, DC. Study abroad program.

Entrance Requirements: Options: electronic application, deferred admission. Required: essay, high school transcript, minimum 2.3 high school GPA, SAT or ACT. Recommended: interview. Entrance: moderately difficult. Application deadline: 8/1. Notification: 10/1. SAT Reasoning Test deadline: 8/1. Transfer credits accepted: Yes.

Costs Per Year: Application fee: $20. Comprehensive fee: $32,220 includes full-time tuition ($23,300), mandatory fees ($740), and college room and board ($8180). Full-time tuition and fees vary according to course load, degree level, and program. Room and board charges vary according to board plan. Part-time tuition: $700 per credit. Part-time tuition varies according to course load, degree level, and program.

Collegiate Environment: Orientation program. Drama-theater group, choral group, student-run newspaper, radio station. Social organizations: 14 open to all. Most popular organizations: Film Club, Ultimate Frisbee Club, Mu Kappa, Social Work Student Council, Investment Club. Major annual events: Huntington University Olympiad, Campus Paranoia, Campus hoedown and Stance. Campus security: 24-hour emergency response devices, late night transport-escort service, campus police on duty from 6 pm to 6 am. 820 college housing spaces available; 750 were occupied in 2012-13. Freshmen guaranteed college housing. On-campus residence required through junior year. Options: men-only, women-only housing available. RichLyn Library with 235,824 books, 11,803 microform titles, 51,338 serials, 7,542 audiovisual materials, an OPAC, and a Web page. Operations spending for the previous fiscal year: $562,491. 209 computers available on campus for general student use. A campuswide network can be accessed from student residence rooms and from off campus. Students can access the following: online class registration. Staffed computer lab on campus provides training in use of computers, software, and the Internet.

Community Environment: Huntington (population 17,011) is located 24 miles southwest of Fort Wayne and is 90 miles north of Indianapolis. It is in a grain and industrial region. City facilities include museums, library, many churches, YMCA, hospital and numerous civic organizations. The retail and industrial organizations and citizens of the community appreciate the importance of the college students in the overall well being of the community. Salamonie Reservoir, six miles southwest has facilities for camping, picnicking, fishing, and boating.

■ **INDIANA STATE UNIVERSITY**
210 N Seventh St.
Terre Haute, IN 47809
Tel: (812)237-6311; Free: 800-468-6478
Fax: (812)237-8023
E-mail: admisu@isugw.indstate.edu
Web Site: www.indstate.edu/

Description: State-supported, university, coed. Awards associate, bachelor's, master's, and doctoral degrees and post-master's certificates. Founded 1865. Setting: 91-acre small town campus with easy access to Indianapolis. Endowment: $47.6 million. Research spending for the previous fiscal year: $8.4 million. Educational spending for the previous fiscal year: $6414 per student. Total enrollment: 12,114. Faculty: 689 (485 full-time, 204 part-time). Student-undergrad faculty ratio is 19:1. 10,709 applied, 86% were admitted. 9% from top 10% of their high school class, 28% from top quarter, 68% from top half. 14 valedictorians. Full-time: 8,675 students, 53% women, 47% men. Part-time: 1,401 students, 62% women, 38% men. Students come from 53 states and territories, 43 other countries, 17% from out-of-state. 0.2% American Indian or Alaska Native, non-Hispanic/Latino; 3% Hispanic/Latino; 17% African American, non-Hispanic/Latino; 1% Asian, non-Hispanic/Latino; 0.1% Native Hawaiian or other Pacific Islander, non-Hispanic/Latino; 4% international. 19% 25 or older, 36% live on campus, 7% transferred in. Retention: 61% of full-time freshmen returned the following year. Academic areas with the most degrees conferred: business/marketing; social sciences; health professions and related sciences. Core. Calendar: semesters. Academic remediation for entering students, ESL program, services for LD students, advanced placement, accelerated degree program, freshman honors college, honors program, independent study, distance learning, double major, summer session for credit, part-time degree program, adult/continuing education programs, co-op programs and internships, graduate courses open to undergrads. Off campus study at Saint Mary-of-the-Woods College, Rose-Hulman Institute of Technology. Study abroad program. ROTC: Army, Air Force.

Entrance Requirements: Options: electronic application, deferred admission. Required: high school transcript, SAT or ACT. Required for some: interview. Entrance: moderately difficult. Application deadline: 8/15. Notification: continuous. SAT Reasoning Test deadline: 8/15. SAT Subject Test deadline: 8/15. Transfer credits accepted: Yes.

Costs Per Year: Application fee: $25. State resident tuition: $7898 full-time, $286 per credit hour part-time. Nonresident tuition: $17,444 full-time, $617 per credit hour part-time. Mandatory fees: $200 full-time, $100 per term part-time. Part-time tuition and fees vary according to course load. College room and board: $8262. Room and board charges vary according to board plan, housing facility, and student level.

Collegiate Environment: Orientation program. Drama-theater group, choral group, marching band, student-run newspaper, radio station. Social organizations: 231 open to all; national fraternities, national sororities; 13% of eligible men and 9% of eligible women are members. Most popular organizations: Union Board, Student Government Association, Panhellenic Council (sororities), Interfraternity Council (fraternities), Residence Hall Association. Major annual events: Homecoming, Club Week, Spring Week. Student services: health clinic, personal-psychological counseling, women's center. Campus security: 24-hour emergency response devices and patrols, student patrols, late night transport-escort service. 3,500 college housing spaces available; 3,100 were occupied in 2012-13. Freshmen guaranteed college housing. On-campus residence required in freshman year. Options: coed, men-only, women-only housing available. Cunningham Memorial Library plus 2 others with an OPAC and a Web page. Operations spending for the previous fiscal year: $5 million. 395 computers available on campus for general student use. Computer purchase/lease plans available. A computer is required for all students. A campuswide network can be accessed from student residence rooms and from off campus. Students can access the following: online class registration. Staffed computer lab on campus (open 24 hours a day) provides training in use of computers, software, and the Internet.

Community Environment: Indiana State is located in Terre Haute, a city of 60,000, on the banks of the Wabash River. Terre Haute is within a 500-mile radius of more than half the population of the United States. Chicago, St. Louis, Cincinnati, Louisville, and Nashville are within a half-day drive, and Indianapolis is only an hour and a half away. Terre Haute's cultural attractions include the Terre Haute Symphony Orchestra, Community Theater, the Sheldon Swope Art Museum, the Eugene V. Debs Museum, and the Vigo County Historical Museum. The educational atmosphere of the city is enhanced by Saint Mary-of-the-Woods College, Rose-Hulman Institute of Technology, and Indiana Vocational-Tech College.

■ **INDIANA TECH**

1600 E Washington Blvd.

Fort Wayne, IN 46803-1297

Tel: (260)422-5561; Free: 800-937-2448

Fax: (260)422-7696

E-mail: admissions@indianatech.edu

Web Site: www.indianatech.edu/

Description: Independent, comprehensive, coed. Awards associate, bachelor's, master's, and doctoral degrees. Founded 1930. Setting: 42-acre urban campus. Endowment: $47.1 million. Educational spending for the previous fiscal year: $3688 per student. Total enrollment: 4,912. Faculty: 306 (40 full-time, 266 part-time). Student-undergrad faculty ratio is 19:1. 3,172 applied, 65% were admitted. 8% from top 10% of their high school class, 23% from top quarter, 63% from top half. Full-time: 2,969 students, 59% women, 41% men. Part-time: 1,501 students, 58% women, 42% men. Students come from 41 states and territories, 10 other countries, 16% from out-of-state. 0.3% American Indian or Alaska Native, non-Hispanic/Latino; 3% Hispanic/Latino; 25% African American, non-Hispanic/Latino; 0.4% Asian, non-Hispanic/Latino; 0.2% Native Hawaiian or other Pacific Islander, non-Hispanic/Latino; 0.4% international. 48% live on campus, 2% transferred in. Retention: 73% of full-time freshmen returned the following year. Academic areas with the most degrees conferred: business/marketing; engineering; homeland security, law enforcement, firefighting, and protective services. Core. Calendar: semesters. Academic remediation for entering students, services for LD students, advanced placement, accelerated degree program, self-designed majors, honors program, independent study, distance learning, double major, summer session for credit, part-time degree program, external degree program, adult/continuing education programs, co-op programs and internships, graduate courses open to undergrads. ROTC: Army (c).

Entrance Requirements: Options: electronic application, international baccalaureate accepted. Required: minimum 2 high school GPA, SAT or ACT. Recommended: Interview with the Director of Software Engineering and college-level math courses for the Software Engineering program, Interview with the Director for the Pre-Law program. Required for some: high school transcript, minimum 3 high school GPA, 2 recommendations, Interview with

the Director of Software Engineering and college-level math courses for the Software Engineering program, Interview with the Director for the Pre-Law program. Entrance: moderately difficult. Application deadline: 8/15. Notification: continuous until 8/15. SAT Reasoning Test deadline: 8/15. Transfer credits accepted: Yes.

Costs Per Year: Application fee: $50. Comprehensive fee: $34,240 includes full-time tuition ($24,450), mandatory fees ($410), and college room and board ($9380). Full-time tuition and fees vary according to class time, course load, and program. Room and board charges vary according to housing facility. Part-time tuition: $480 per credit hour. Part-time tuition varies according to class time, course load, and program.

Collegiate Environment: Orientation program. Student-run newspaper. Social organizations: 26 open to all; national fraternities, local sororities. Most popular organizations: Student Board, Student Ambassadors, NSBE, SHRM, Sport Recreation and Leisure Society. Major annual events: Spring Bling Fling, Homecoming, Graduation. Campus security: 24-hour emergency response devices and patrols, student patrols, late night transport-escort service, controlled dormitory access. 470 college housing spaces available; all were occupied in 2012-13. Freshmen guaranteed college housing. On-campus residence required through sophomore year. Option: coed housing available. McMillen Library with 35,000 books, 40 serials, 286 audiovisual materials, and an OPAC. Operations spending for the previous fiscal year: $237,987. 398 computers available on campus for general student use. A campuswide network can be accessed from student residence rooms and from off campus. Students can access the following: online class registration.

Community Environment: Fort Wayne is the hub of the great north central industrial and agricultural America and gateway to the northern Indiana lake region. Gasoline tank and pump manufacturing originated here, and industries now include a General Motors truck plant, electronics, automotive, and agriculture. The city has 147 churches, a civic theatre, and Philharmonic Symphony. Points of interest are the Allen County War Memorial Coliseum, Cathedral of the Immaculate Conception, Concordia Senior College, Fort Wayne Art School and Museum, Lincoln Museum, Lincoln Tower Building, Historical Fort Wayne, and many city parks.

■ **INDIANA UNIVERSITY BLOOMINGTON**

107 S Indiana Ave.

Bloomington, IN 47405-7000

Tel: (812)855-4848

Fax: (812)855-1871

E-mail: iuadmit@indiana.edu

Web Site: www.iub.edu/

Description: State-supported, university, coed. Part of Indiana University System. Awards bachelor's, master's, and doctoral degrees and post-master's certificates. Founded 1820. Setting: 1,937-acre small town campus with easy access to Indianapolis. Endowment: $692.1 million. Total enrollment: 42,133. Faculty: 2,284 (1,941 full-time, 343 part-time). Student-undergrad faculty ratio is 18:1. 35,247 applied, 74% were admitted. 34% from top 10% of their high school class, 70% from top quarter, 95% from top half. Full-time: 30,949 students, 51% women, 49% men. Part-time: 1,422 students, 46% women, 54% men. Students come from 51 states and territories, 135 other countries, 28% from out-of-state. 0.1% American Indian or Alaska Native, non-Hispanic/Latino; 4% Hispanic/Latino; 4% African American, non-Hispanic/Latino; 4% Asian, non-Hispanic/Latino; 0.1% Native Hawaiian or other Pacific Islander, non-Hispanic/Latino; 11% international. 3% 25 or older, 38% live on campus, 3% transferred in. Retention: 88% of full-time freshmen returned the following year. Academic areas with the most degrees conferred: business/marketing; communication/journalism; education. Core. Calendar: semesters plus 2 summer sessions. Academic remediation for entering students, ESL program, services for LD students, advanced placement, accelerated degree program, self-designed majors, freshman honors college, honors program, independent study, distance learning, double major, summer session for credit, part-time degree program, external degree program, adult/continuing education programs, co-op programs and internships, graduate courses open to undergrads. Off campus study. Study abroad program. ROTC: Army, Air Force.

Entrance Requirements: Options: electronic application, deferred admission. Required: high school transcript, SAT or ACT. Recommended: interview, SAT Subject Tests. Entrance: moderately difficult. Application deadline: Rolling. Notification: continuous. Preference given to state residents. SAT Reasoning Test deadline: 4/1. SAT Subject Test deadline: 4/1.

Costs Per Year: Application fee: $55. State resident tuition: $8750 full-time,

$273.40 per credit hour part-time. Nonresident tuition: $30,200 full-time, $943.75 per credit hour part-time. Mandatory fees: $1283 full-time. Full-time tuition and fees vary according to location and program. Part-time tuition varies according to course load, location, and program. College room and board: $8853. College room only: $5853. Room and board charges vary according to board plan and housing facility.

Collegiate Environment: Orientation program. Drama-theater group, choral group, marching band, student-run newspaper, radio station. Social organizations: 650 open to all; national fraternities, national sororities, local fraternities, local sororities. Most popular organizations: Union Board, Student Association, Student Foundation, Habitat for Humanity, Student Athletic Board. Major annual events: Homecoming, Little 500 Bike Race, Founders' Day. Student services: legal services, health clinic, personal-psychological counseling, women's center. Campus security: 24-hour emergency response devices and patrols, late night transport-escort service, safety seminars, lighted pathways, escort service, shuttle bus service, emergency telephones. 12,316 college housing spaces available. Freshmen given priority for college housing. On-campus residence required in freshman year. Options: coed, men-only, women-only housing available. Indiana University Library plus 27 others with 9.1 million books, an OPAC, and a Web page.

Community Environment: The 1,900-acre main campus is located in a community of 66,000 in southern Indiana. Indianapolis, site of the I.U. Medical Center, is 50 miles away. Places of worship are located in the immediate community for all faiths. The city is served by air and bus.

■ **INDIANA UNIVERSITY EAST**
2325 Chester Blvd.
Richmond, IN 47374-1289
Tel: (765)973-8200; Free: 800-959-EAST
Fax: (765)973-8288
E-mail: applynow@iue.edu
Web Site: www.iue.edu/

Description: State-supported, comprehensive, coed. Part of Indiana University System. Awards bachelor's and master's degrees. Founded 1971. Setting: 182-acre small town campus with easy access to Indianapolis. Endowment: $4.1 million. Total enrollment: 4,186. Faculty: 271 (103 full-time, 168 part-time). Student-undergrad faculty ratio is 16:1. 1,266 applied, 60% were admitted. 10% from top 10% of their high school class, 35% from top quarter, 69% from top half. Full-time: 1,988 students, 66% women, 34% men. Part-time: 2,064 students, 64% women, 36% men. Students come from 33 states and territories, 25 other countries, 20% from out-of-state. 0.2% American Indian or Alaska Native, non-Hispanic/Latino; 2% Hispanic/Latino; 3% African American, non-Hispanic/Latino; 1% Asian, non-Hispanic/Latino; 0.05% Native Hawaiian or other Pacific Islander, non-Hispanic/Latino; 0.4% international. 46% 25 or older, 10% transferred in. Retention: 67% of full-time freshmen returned the following year. Academic areas with the most degrees conferred: business/marketing; liberal arts/general studies; health professions and related sciences. Core. Calendar: semesters. Academic remediation for entering students, services for LD students, advanced placement, honors program, independent study, distance learning, double major, summer session for credit, part-time degree program, external degree program, adult/continuing education programs, co-op programs and internships, graduate courses open to undergrads. Off campus study at Earlham College. Study abroad program.

Entrance Requirements: Options: electronic application, early admission, deferred admission. Required: high school transcript, SAT or ACT. Recommended: minimum 2 high school GPA. Entrance: moderately difficult. Application deadline: Rolling. Notification: continuous.

Costs Per Year: Application fee: $35. State resident tuition: $5,964 full-time, $198.79 per credit hour part-time. Nonresident tuition: $16,894 full-time, $563.12 per credit hour part-time. Mandatory fees: $532 full-time. Full-time tuition and fees vary according to course load, location, program, and reciprocity agreements. Part-time tuition varies according to course load, location, program, and reciprocity agreements.

Collegiate Environment: Orientation program. Drama-theater group, student-run newspaper. Social organizations: 30 open to all. Most popular organizations: Student Government Association, Cultural Inclusive Awareness, Psychology Club, Sociology Club, Humanities Club. Major annual events: Spring Fling, Homecoming, Halloween Party. Student services: personal-psychological counseling. Campus security: 24-hour emergency response devices, late night transport-escort service, safety awareness, lighted pathways, 14-hour foot and vehicle patrol. College housing not available. IU East Campus Library with 81,000 books, an OPAC, and a Web page.

Community Environment: The school is located in an outlying area of Richmond, which has a population of about 37,500.

■ **INDIANA UNIVERSITY KOKOMO**
2300 S Washington St.
Kokomo, IN 46904-9003
Tel: (765)453-2000; Free: 888-875-4485
Fax: (765)455-9537
E-mail: iuadmis@iuk.edu
Web Site: www.iuk.edu/

Description: State-supported, comprehensive, coed. Part of Indiana University System. Awards associate, bachelor's, and master's degrees. Founded 1945. Setting: 51-acre small town campus with easy access to Indianapolis. Endowment: $4.1 million. Total enrollment: 3,719. Faculty: 194 (98 full-time, 96 part-time). Student-undergrad faculty ratio is 18:1. 1,023 applied, 70% were admitted. 6% from top 10% of their high school class, 29% from top quarter, 68% from top half. Full-time: 1,869 students, 64% women, 36% men. Part-time: 1,712 students, 64% women, 36% men. Students come from 13 states and territories, 19 other countries, 1% from out-of-state. 0.2% American Indian or Alaska Native, non-Hispanic/Latino; 3% Hispanic/Latino; 4% African American, non-Hispanic/Latino; 1% Asian, non-Hispanic/Latino; 0.1% Native Hawaiian or other Pacific Islander, non-Hispanic/Latino; 0.1% international. 39% 25 or older, 8% transferred in. Retention: 63% of full-time freshmen returned the following year. Academic areas with the most degrees conferred: health professions and related sciences; liberal arts/general studies; education. Core. Calendar: semesters. Academic remediation for entering students, ESL program, services for LD students, advanced placement, accelerated degree program, freshman honors college, honors program, independent study, distance learning, double major, summer session for credit, part-time degree program, external degree program, adult/continuing education programs, internships, graduate courses open to undergrads. Study abroad program. ROTC: Army.

Entrance Requirements: Options: electronic application, deferred admission. Required: high school transcript, SAT or ACT. Entrance: minimally difficult. Application deadline: Rolling. Notification: continuous. SAT Reasoning Test deadline: 8/6.

Costs Per Year: Application fee: $35. State resident tuition: $5,949 full-time, $198.31 per credit hour part-time. Nonresident tuition: $16,894 full-time, $563.12 per credit hour part-time. Mandatory fees: $592 full-time. Full-time tuition and fees vary according to course load, location, and program. Part-time tuition varies according to course load, location, and program.

Collegiate Environment: Orientation program. Drama-theater group, choral group, student-run newspaper, radio station. Social organizations: 30 open to all. Major annual events: Dance-a-Thon, Campus Fall Kick-off BBQ, Campus Beautification Day. Student services: personal-psychological counseling. Campus security: 24-hour patrols, late night transport-escort service, campus police, lighted pathways. College housing not available. IU Kokomo Library with 138,653 books, an OPAC, and a Web page.

Community Environment: Kokomo (population 46,178) is an urban area, enjoying a temperate climate, with excellent community facilities; shopping areas, library, museum, 71 churches and two hospitals. All forms of transportation are available. The General Motors Corp. and Chrysler Corp. plants in Kokomo manufacture car radios, transistors, transmissions, and aluminum die castings. Kokomo is the home of Elwood Haynes who invented one of the first American automobiles in 1893. Part-time employment is available.

■ **INDIANA UNIVERSITY NORTHWEST**
3400 Broadway
Gary, IN 46408-1197
Tel: (219)980-6500; Free: 800-968-7486
Fax: (219)981-4219
E-mail: admit@iun.edu
Web Site: www.iun.edu/

Description: State-supported, comprehensive, coed. Part of Indiana University System. Awards associate, bachelor's, and master's degrees. Founded 1959. Setting: 38-acre urban campus with easy access to Chicago. Endowment: $6.8 million. Total enrollment: 6,184. Faculty: 424 (187 full-time, 237 part-time). Student-undergrad faculty ratio is 15:1. 1,704 applied, 69% were admitted. 6% from top 10% of their high school class, 24% from top quarter, 56% from top half. Full-time: 3,260 students, 67% women, 33% men. Part-time: 2,376 students, 66% women, 34% men. Students come from 14 states and territories, 33 other countries, 2% from out-of-state. 0.2% American Indian or Alaska Native, non-Hispanic/Latino; 15% Hispanic/

Latino; 20% African American, non-Hispanic/Latino; 2% Asian, non-Hispanic/Latino; 0.2% Native Hawaiian or other Pacific Islander, non-Hispanic/Latino; 0.1% international. 38% 25 or older, 6% transferred in. Retention: 67% of full-time freshmen returned the following year. Academic areas with the most degrees conferred: health professions and related sciences; liberal arts/general studies; business/marketing. Core. Calendar: semesters. Academic remediation for entering students, services for LD students, advanced placement, accelerated degree program, self-designed majors, honors program, independent study, distance learning, double major, summer session for credit, part-time degree program, external degree program, adult/continuing education programs, co-op programs and internships, graduate courses open to undergrads. Off campus study. Study abroad program. ROTC: Army.
Entrance Requirements: Options: electronic application, deferred admission. Required: high school transcript, minimum 2 high school GPA, SAT or ACT. Entrance: minimally difficult. Application deadline: Rolling. Notification: continuous.
Costs Per Year: Application fee: $35. State resident tuition: $6,043 full-time, $201.44 per credit hour part-time. Nonresident tuition: $16,894 full-time, $563.12 per credit hour part-time. Mandatory fees: $583 full-time. Full-time tuition and fees vary according to course load, location, and program. Part-time tuition varies according to course load, location, and program.
Collegiate Environment: Orientation program. Drama-theater group, choral group, student-run newspaper, radio station. Social organizations: 50 open to all; national fraternities, national sororities. Most popular organizations: Student Government Association, Student Ambassadors, Student Nurses Association, Dental Education, International Affairs Club. Major annual events: Welcome Back Week, Spring Fest, Communications Week. Student services: health clinic, personal-psychological counseling. Campus security: 24-hour emergency response devices and patrols, late night transport-escort service, lighted pathways. College housing not available. IUN Library with 226,300 books, an OPAC, and a Web page.
Community Environment: Gary (population 98,715) is the second largest city in Indiana, a metropolitan area, and is in one of the country's outstanding steel production areas. The United States Steel Corp. is located here on Lake Michigan. All forms of transportation are available. Community facilities include libraries, churches, hospitals, and shopping areas. Part-time employment is available. Marquette Park nearby has a four-mile beach, a pavilion, piers, and a picnic area.

■ **INDIANA UNIVERSITY SOUTH BEND**
1700 Mishawaka Ave.
South Bend, IN 46634-7111
Tel: (574)520-4872; Free: 877-GO-2-IUSB
Fax: (574)520-4834
E-mail: admissions@iusb.edu
Web Site: www.iusb.edu/
Description: State-supported, comprehensive, coed. Part of Indiana University System. Awards associate, bachelor's, and master's degrees. Founded 1922. Setting: 103-acre suburban campus with easy access to Chicago. Endowment: $8.6 million. Total enrollment: 8,490. Faculty: 535 (286 full-time, 249 part-time). Student-undergrad faculty ratio is 14:1. 2,354 applied, 72% were admitted. 6% from top 10% of their high school class, 27% from top quarter, 66% from top half. Full-time: 4,134 students, 62% women, 38% men. Part-time: 3,726 students, 62% women, 38% men. Students come from 26 states and territories, 76 other countries, 3% from out-of-state. 0.2% American Indian or Alaska Native, non-Hispanic/Latino; 6% Hispanic/Latino; 7% African American, non-Hispanic/Latino; 1% Asian, non-Hispanic/Latino; 0.1% Native Hawaiian or other Pacific Islander, non-Hispanic/Latino; 1% international. 35% 25 or older, 6% live on campus, 5% transferred in. Retention: 63% of full-time freshmen returned the following year. Academic areas with the most degrees conferred: business/marketing; liberal arts/general studies; health professions and related sciences. Core. Calendar: semesters. ESL program, services for LD students, advanced placement, accelerated degree program, freshman honors college, honors program, independent study, distance learning, double major, summer session for credit, part-time degree program, external degree program, adult/continuing education programs, internships, graduate courses open to undergrads. Off campus study at Bethel College, Saint Mary's College (IN), Holy Cross College, Goshen College. Study abroad program. ROTC: Army (c), Naval (c), Air Force (c).
Entrance Requirements: Options: electronic application, deferred admission. Required: high school transcript, minimum 2 high school GPA, SAT or ACT. Required for some: interview. Entrance: moderately difficult. Application deadline: Rolling. Notification: continuous.

Costs Per Year: Application fee: $35. State resident tuition: $6,138 full-time, $204.61 per credit hour part-time. Nonresident tuition: $16,894 full-time, $563.12 per credit hour part-time. Mandatory fees: $590 full-time. Full-time tuition and fees vary according to course load, location, and program. Part-time tuition varies according to course load, location, and program. College room only: $6838. Room charges vary according to housing facility.
Collegiate Environment: Orientation program. Drama-theater group, choral group, student-run newspaper. Social organizations: 90 open to all; national fraternities, national sororities, local sororities. Major annual events: Student Welcome Day, Titan Fest, Red & White Dance. Student services: health clinic, personal-psychological counseling, women's center. Campus security: 24-hour emergency response devices and patrols, late night transport-escort service, safety seminars, lighted pathways. 400 college housing spaces available. Option: coed housing available. Franklin D. Schurz Library with 329,139 books, an OPAC, and a Web page.
Community Environment: See University of Notre Dame.

■ **INDIANA UNIVERSITY SOUTHEAST**
4201 Grant Line Rd.
New Albany, IN 47150-6405
Tel: (812)941-2000; Free: 800-852-8835
E-mail: admissions@ius.edu
Web Site: www.ius.edu/
Description: State-supported, comprehensive, coed. Part of Indiana University System. Awards associate, bachelor's, and master's degrees. Founded 1941. Setting: 178-acre suburban campus with easy access to Louisville. Endowment: $10.5 million. Total enrollment: 6,904. Faculty: 498 (210 full-time, 288 part-time). Student-undergrad faculty ratio is 15:1. 2,147 applied, 78% were admitted. 10% from top 10% of their high school class, 31% from top quarter, 67% from top half. Full-time: 3,751 students, 59% women, 41% men. Part-time: 2,452 students, 57% women, 43% men. Students come from 18 states and territories, 36 other countries, 28% from out-of-state. 0.2% American Indian or Alaska Native, non-Hispanic/Latino; 3% Hispanic/Latino; 6% African American, non-Hispanic/Latino; 1% Asian, non-Hispanic/Latino; 0.1% Native Hawaiian or other Pacific Islander, non-Hispanic/Latino; 0.3% international. 31% 25 or older, 6% live on campus, 8% transferred in. Retention: 59% of full-time freshmen returned the following year. Academic areas with the most degrees conferred: liberal arts/general studies; business/marketing; education. Core. Calendar: semesters. Academic remediation for entering students, services for LD students, advanced placement, accelerated degree program, self-designed majors, honors program, independent study, distance learning, double major, summer session for credit, part-time degree program, external degree program, adult/continuing education programs, internships, graduate courses open to undergrads. Off campus study at the Kentuckiana Metroversity. Study abroad program. ROTC: Army (c), Air Force (c).
Entrance Requirements: Options: electronic application, early admission, deferred admission. Required: high school transcript, SAT or ACT. Required for some: interview. Entrance: minimally difficult. Application deadline: Rolling. Notification: continuous. SAT Reasoning Test deadline: 8/1.
Costs Per Year: Application fee: $35. State resident tuition: $5,960 full-time, $198.65 per credit hour part-time. Nonresident tuition: $16,894 full-time, $563.12 per credit hour part-time. Mandatory fees: $616 full-time. Full-time tuition and fees vary according to course load, location, program, and reciprocity agreements. Part-time tuition varies according to course load, location, program, and reciprocity agreements. College room only: $6570. Room charges vary according to housing facility.
Collegiate Environment: Orientation program. Drama-theater group, choral group, student-run newspaper. Social organizations: 60 open to all; national fraternities, national sororities. Major annual events: Homecoming, Diversity Week, Comedy Series. Student services: personal-psychological counseling. Campus security: 24-hour emergency response devices and patrols, self-defense education, lighted pathways, police department on campus. 399 college housing spaces available. Option: coed housing available. IU Southeast Library with 375,198 books, an OPAC, and a Web page.
Community Environment: New Albany (population 37,000), a highly industrialized area, enjoys a temperate climate. It is one of the Falls Cities, the others being Louisville, Kentucky and Jeffersonville, Indiana. Buses and railroads serve the area with airlines available at Louisville, Kentucky, Airport. The American Commercial Barge Line, one of the largest, has a terminal there. Community facilities include many churches, Steamboat Museum, hospital and parks. Some part-time employment is available. Ohio River provides facilities for all water sports. Derby Week is an annual event.

■ **INDIANA UNIVERSITY–PURDUE UNIVERSITY FORT WAYNE**
2101 E Coliseum Blvd.
Fort Wayne, IN 46805-1499
Tel: (260)481-6100; Free: 800-324-4739
E-mail: morrena@ipfw.edu
Web Site: www.ipfw.edu/
Description: State-supported, comprehensive, coed. Part of Indiana University System and Purdue University System. Awards associate, bachelor's, and master's degrees. Founded 1917. Setting: 683-acre urban campus. Endowment: $41.6 million. Research spending for the previous fiscal year: $701,106. Educational spending for the previous fiscal year: $5683 per student. Total enrollment: 13,771. Faculty: 860 (428 full-time, 432 part-time). Student-undergrad faculty ratio is 17:1. 3,270 applied, 82% were admitted. 11% from top 10% of their high school class, 37% from top quarter, 76% from top half. 9 valedictorians. Full-time: 7,870 students, 55% women, 45% men. Part-time: 5,247 students, 57% women, 43% men. Students come from 43 states and territories, 53 other countries, 3% from out-of-state. 0.3% American Indian or Alaska Native, non-Hispanic/Latino; 5% Hispanic/Latino; 6% African American, non-Hispanic/Latino; 2% Asian, non-Hispanic/Latino; 0.04% Native Hawaiian or other Pacific Islander, non-Hispanic/Latino; 2% international. 24% 25 or older, 6% live on campus, 5% transferred in. Retention: 60% of full-time freshmen returned the following year. Academic areas with the most degrees conferred: business/marketing; liberal arts/general studies; health professions and related sciences. Core. Calendar: semesters. Academic remediation for entering students, ESL program, services for LD students, advanced placement, accelerated degree program, self-designed majors, honors program, independent study, distance learning, double major, summer session for credit, part-time degree program, adult/continuing education programs, co-op programs and internships, graduate courses open to undergrads. Off campus study at National Student Exchange. Study abroad program. ROTC: Army.
Entrance Requirements: Options: electronic application, deferred admission, international baccalaureate accepted. Required: high school transcript, minimum 2.8 high school GPA, SAT or ACT. Recommended: rank in upper 50% of high school class. Entrance: minimally difficult. Application deadlines: 8/1, 8/1 for nonresidents. Notification: continuous, continuous for nonresidents. SAT Reasoning Test deadline: 8/1. Transfer credits accepted: Yes.
Costs Per Year: Application fee: $50. State resident tuition: $6001 full-time, $222.25 per credit hour part-time. Nonresident tuition: $15,640 full-time, $579.25 per credit hour part-time. Mandatory fees: $875 full-time, $32.40 per credit hour part-time. Full-time tuition and fees vary according to course load. Part-time tuition and fees vary according to course load. College room only: $7210. Room charges vary according to housing facility.
Collegiate Environment: Orientation program. Drama-theater group, choral group, student-run newspaper. Social organizations: 127 open to all. Most popular organizations: Campus Ministry, Delta Sigma Pi, Chi Alpha Christian Fellowship, IPFW OUTspoken (previously named United Sexualities), Live Action Combat Club. Major annual events: PIT Theater Performances, Kids' Carnival, IPFW Health Fair. Student services: health clinic, personal-psychological counseling, women's center. Campus security: 24-hour emergency response devices and patrols, late night transport-escort service, controlled dormitory access. 1,204 college housing spaces available; 817 were occupied in 2012-13. No special consideration for freshman housing applicants. Option: coed housing available. Helmke Library with 369,101 books, 537,248 microform titles, 27,840 serials, 4,815 audiovisual materials, an OPAC, and a Web page. Operations spending for the previous fiscal year: $2.3 million. 642 computers available on campus for general student use. Computer purchase/lease plans available. A campuswide network can be accessed from student residence rooms and from off campus. Students can access the following: online class registration, student academic records. Staffed computer lab on campus provides training in use of computers, software, and the Internet.
Community Environment: See Indiana Institute of Technology.

■ **INDIANA UNIVERSITY–PURDUE UNIVERSITY INDIANAPOLIS**
420 University Blvd.
Indianapolis, IN 46202-2896
Tel: (317)274-5555
Fax: (317)278-1862
E-mail: apply@iupui.edu
Web Site: www.iupui.edu/
Description: State-supported, university, coed. Part of Indiana University System. Awards associate, bachelor's, master's, and doctoral degrees. Founded 1969. Setting: 509-acre urban campus. Endowment: $512.1 mil-

lion. Total enrollment: 30,451. Faculty: 3,256 (2,247 full-time, 1,009 part-time). Student-undergrad faculty ratio is 17:1. 11,350 applied, 67% were admitted. 15% from top 10% of their high school class, 44% from top quarter, 86% from top half. Full-time: 16,127 students, 57% women, 43% men. Part-time: 6,144 students, 57% women, 43% men. Students come from 51 states and territories, 141 other countries, 3% from out-of-state. 0.1% American Indian or Alaska Native, non-Hispanic/Latino; 5% Hispanic/Latino; 11% African American, non-Hispanic/Latino; 3% Asian, non-Hispanic/Latino; 0.04% Native Hawaiian or other Pacific Islander, non-Hispanic/Latino; 3% international. 30% 25 or older, 6% live on campus, 8% transferred in. Retention: 72% of full-time freshmen returned the following year. Academic areas with the most degrees conferred: health professions and related sciences; business/marketing; liberal arts/general studies. Core. Calendar: semesters. Academic remediation for entering students, ESL program, services for LD students, advanced placement, accelerated degree program, self-designed majors, freshman honors college, honors program, independent study, distance learning, double major, summer session for credit, part-time degree program, external degree program, adult/continuing education programs, co-op programs and internships, graduate courses open to undergrads. Off campus study at Consortium for Urban Education. Study abroad program. ROTC: Army, Air Force (c).
Entrance Requirements: Options: electronic application, deferred admission, international baccalaureate accepted. Required: high school transcript, SAT or ACT. Recommended: portfolio for art program. Required for some: interview. Entrance: moderately difficult. Application deadline: 5/1. Notification: continuous. SAT Reasoning Test deadline: 5/1.
Costs Per Year: Application fee: $50. State resident tuition: $7623 full-time, $254.10 per credit hour part-time. Nonresident tuition: $28,080 full-time, $936 per credit hour part-time. Mandatory fees: $982 full-time. Full-time tuition and fees vary according to course load, location, and program. Part-time tuition varies according to course load, location, and program. College room and board: $7944. Room and board charges vary according to housing facility.
Collegiate Environment: Orientation program. Drama-theater group, choral group, student-run newspaper. Social organizations: 470 open to all; national fraternities, national sororities. Major annual events: Weeks of Welcome, Spring Dance, IUPUI Regatta. Student services: health clinic, personal-psychological counseling, women's center. Campus security: 24-hour emergency response devices and patrols, late night transport-escort service, controlled dormitory access, lighted pathways, self-defense education. 1,398 college housing spaces available. Option: coed housing available. University Library plus 4 others with 1.7 million books, an OPAC, and a Web page.
Community Environment: See Butler University.

■ **INDIANA WESLEYAN UNIVERSITY**
4201 S Washington St.
Marion, IN 46953-4974
Tel: (765)674-6901; Free: 866-468-6498
Fax: (765)677-2333
E-mail: admissions@indwes.edu
Web Site: www.indwes.edu/
Description: Independent Wesleyan, comprehensive, coed. Awards associate, bachelor's, master's, and doctoral degrees and post-master's certificates (also offers adult program with significant enrollment not reflected in profile). Founded 1920. Setting: 300-acre small town campus with easy access to Indianapolis. Total enrollment: 95. Faculty: 300 (164 full-time, 136 part-time). Student-undergrad faculty ratio is 14:1. 3,429 applied, 66% were admitted. 30% from top 10% of their high school class, 60% from top quarter, 86% from top half. 4 National Merit Scholars, 24 valedictorians. Full-time: 2,798 students, 64% women, 36% men. Part-time: 201 students, 63% women, 37% men. 0.2% American Indian or Alaska Native, non-Hispanic/Latino; 3% Hispanic/Latino; 2% African American, non-Hispanic/Latino; 1% Asian, non-Hispanic/Latino; 0.2% Native Hawaiian or other Pacific Islander, non-Hispanic/Latino; 0.3% international. 80% live on campus. Retention: 74% of full-time freshmen returned the following year. Academic areas with the most degrees conferred: health professions and related sciences; education; theology and religious vocations. Core. Calendar: semesters. Academic remediation for entering students, services for LD students, advanced placement, freshman honors college, honors program, independent study, distance learning, double major, summer session for credit, part-time degree program, internships. Off campus study at Taylor University, Council for Christian Colleges and Universities. Study abroad program. ROTC: Army.
Entrance Requirements: Options: electronic application, deferred admission, international baccalaureate accepted. Required: essay, high school

transcript, minimum 2.5 high school GPA, 2 recommendations, SAT or ACT, TOEFL for non-English speaking, and some non-resident alien students. Entrance: moderately difficult. Application deadlines: Rolling, Rolling for nonresidents. Notification: continuous, continuous for nonresidents. SAT Reasoning Test deadline: 8/15. Transfer credits accepted: Yes.

Costs Per Year: Application fee: $25. Comprehensive fee: $31,188 includes full-time tuition ($23,628) and college room and board ($7560). Full-time tuition varies according to course load and degree level. Room and board charges vary according to board plan. Part-time tuition: $662 per credit hour. Part-time tuition varies according to course load and degree level.

Collegiate Environment: Orientation program. Drama-theater group, choral group, student-run newspaper, radio station. Social organizations: 15 open to all. Most popular organizations: Student Government Organization, Student Activities Council, University Players, World Christian Fellowship, Sixth Man Club. Major annual events: Homecoming, Friday Night Live, Spotted Cow Music Festival. Student services: health clinic, personal-psychological counseling. Campus security: 24-hour emergency response devices and patrols, late night transport-escort service, controlled dormitory access. 2,700 college housing spaces available; 2,437 were occupied in 2012-13. Freshmen guaranteed college housing. On-campus residence required through junior year. Options: men-only, women-only housing available. Lewis A. Jackson Library with 248,819 books, 315,156 microform titles, 101,452 serials, 13,183 audiovisual materials, an OPAC, and a Web page. 691 computers available on campus for general student use. A campuswide network can be accessed from student residence rooms and from off campus. Students can access the following: online class registration. Staffed computer lab on campus provides training in use of computers, software, and the Internet.

Community Environment: Marion is an industrial city in a farming and fruit raising region, located 70 miles northeast of Indianapolis and 50 miles southwest of Ft. Wayne in Grant County. Bus service is available. Major industries located here are Thompson Electronics, BICC Cahles, General Motors, Gencorp., Foster-Forbes Glass, and General Plastics. Part-time employment is abundant. Mississinewa Lake and Salamonie Reservoir and Dam are nearby, providing facilities for many outdoor sports; also the city has facilities for tennis, swimming, and picnics. The Easter Pageant and Christmas Walkway of Lights are an annual event.

■ **INTERNATIONAL BUSINESS COLLEGE (FORT WAYNE)**
5699 Coventry Ln.
Fort Wayne, IN 46804
Tel: (219)459-4500; Free: 800-589-6363
Fax: (219)436-1896
Web Site: www.ibcfortwayne.edu/
Description: Private, 4-year, coed. Awards associate and bachelor's degrees. Founded 1889. Setting: suburban campus. Total enrollment: 559. 860 applied, 72% were admitted. Calendar: semesters. Accelerated degree program, internships.

■ **INTERNATIONAL BUSINESS COLLEGE (INDIANAPOLIS)**
7205 Shadeland Station
Indianapolis, IN 46256
Tel: (317)841-6400; Free: 800-589-6500
Fax: (317)841-6419
Web Site: www.ibcindianapolis.edu/
Description: Private, 2-year, coed. Awards diplomas and terminal associate degrees. Founded 1889. Setting: suburban campus. Total enrollment: 413. 1,054 applied, 73% were admitted. Calendar: semesters. Accelerated degree program, internships.

■ **ITT TECHNICAL INSTITUTE (FORT WAYNE)**
2810 Dupont Commerce Ct.
Fort Wayne, IN 46825
Tel: (260)497-6200; Free: 800-866-4488
Web Site: www.itt-tech.edu/
Description: Proprietary, primarily 2-year, coed. Part of ITT Educational Services, Inc. Awards terminal associate and bachelor's degrees. Founded 1967.
Entrance Requirements: Entrance: minimally difficult.

■ **ITT TECHNICAL INSTITUTE (INDIANAPOLIS)**
9511 Angola Ct.
Indianapolis, IN 46268-1119
Tel: (317)875-8640; Free: 800-937-4488

Fax: (317)875-8641
Web Site: www.itt-tech.edu/
Description: Proprietary, comprehensive, coed. Part of ITT Educational Services, Inc. Awards associate, bachelor's, and master's degrees. Founded 1966. Setting: suburban campus.
Entrance Requirements: Entrance: minimally difficult.

■ **ITT TECHNICAL INSTITUTE (INDIANAPOLIS)**
2525 N Shadeland Ave.
Ste. 103
Indianapolis, IN 46219
Tel: (317)351-3800; Free: 877-264-1057
Web Site: www.itt-tech.edu/
Description: Proprietary, 4-year, coed. Awards associate and bachelor's degrees.
Entrance Requirements: Entrance: minimally difficult.

■ **ITT TECHNICAL INSTITUTE (MERRILLVILLE)**
8488 Georgia St.
Merrillville, IN 46410
Tel: (219)738-6100; Free: 877-418-8134
Web Site: www.itt-tech.edu/
Description: Proprietary, primarily 2-year, coed. Awards terminal associate and bachelor's degrees.
Entrance Requirements: Entrance: minimally difficult.

■ **ITT TECHNICAL INSTITUTE (NEWBURGH)**
10999 Stahl Rd.
Newburgh, IN 47630-7430
Tel: (812)858-1600; Free: 800-832-4488
Web Site: www.itt-tech.edu/
Description: Proprietary, primarily 2-year, coed. Part of ITT Educational Services, Inc. Awards terminal associate and bachelor's degrees. Founded 1966.
Entrance Requirements: Entrance: minimally difficult.

■ **ITT TECHNICAL INSTITUTE (SOUTH BEND)**
17390 Dugdale Dr.
Ste. 100
South Bend, IN 46635
Tel: (574)247-8300; Free: 877-474-1926
Web Site: www.itt-tech.edu/
Description: Proprietary, 4-year, coed. Part of ITT Educational Services, Inc. Awards associate and bachelor's degrees.
Entrance Requirements: Entrance: minimally difficult.

■ **IVY TECH COMMUNITY COLLEGE–BLOOMINGTON**
200 Daniels Way
Bloomington, IN 47404
Tel: (812)332-1559; Free: 888-IVY-LINE
Fax: (812)332-8147
E-mail: nfrederi@ivytech.edu
Web Site: www.ivytech.edu/
Description: State-supported, 2-year, coed. Part of Ivy Tech Community College System. Awards certificates, transfer associate, and terminal associate degrees. Founded 2001. Total enrollment: 5,822. Faculty: 356 (80 full-time, 276 part-time). Student-undergrad faculty ratio is 22:1. 2,141 applied, 100% were admitted. Full-time: 2,705 students, 51% women, 49% men. Part-time: 3,117 students, 63% women, 37% men. 1% from out-of-state. 1% American Indian or Alaska Native, non-Hispanic/Latino; 2% Hispanic/Latino; 4% African American, non-Hispanic/Latino; 2% Asian, non-Hispanic/Latino; 0% international. 46% 25 or older, 6% transferred in. Retention: 45% of full-time freshmen returned the following year. Core. Calendar: semesters. Academic remediation for entering students, services for LD students, advanced placement, distance learning, summer session for credit, part-time degree program, external degree program, adult/continuing education programs, internships.
Entrance Requirements: Open admission. Options: electronic application, deferred admission. Required: high school transcript. Required for some: interview. Entrance: noncompetitive. Application deadline: Rolling. Notification: continuous. Preference given to state residents.
Costs Per Year: Application fee: $0. State resident tuition: $3335 full-time, $111 per credit hour part-time. Nonresident tuition: $7182 full-time, $239 per credit hour part-time. Mandatory fees: $120 full-time, $60 per term part-time.

Collegiate Environment: Orientation program. Most popular organizations: student government, Phi Theta Kappa. Campus security: late night transport-escort service. 5,516 books, 97 serials, 1,281 audiovisual materials, an OPAC, and a Web page 221 computers available on campus for general student use. Students can access the following: online class registration.

■ **IVY TECH COMMUNITY COLLEGE–CENTRAL INDIANA**

50 W Fall Creek Pky. N Dr.

Indianapolis, IN 46206-1763

Tel: (317)921-4800; Free: 888-IVYLINE

E-mail: tfunk@ivytech.edu

Web Site: www.ivytech.edu/

Description: State-supported, 2-year, coed. Part of Ivy Tech Community College System. Awards certificates, transfer associate, and terminal associate degrees. Founded 1963. Setting: 10-acre urban campus. Total enrollment: 21,407. Faculty: 859 (187 full-time, 672 part-time). Student-undergrad faculty ratio is 29:1. Full-time: 7,203 students, 57% women, 43% men. Part-time: 14,204 students, 59% women, 41% men. 2% from out-of-state. 0.4% American Indian or Alaska Native, non-Hispanic/Latino; 5% Hispanic/Latino; 28% African American, non-Hispanic/Latino; 2% Asian, non-Hispanic/Latino; 0.04% international. 53% 25 or older, 5% transferred in. Retention: 46% of full-time freshmen returned the following year. Core. Calendar: semesters. Academic remediation for entering students, ESL program, services for LD students, advanced placement, distance learning, summer session for credit, part-time degree program, adult/continuing education programs, co-op programs and internships. Off campus study at Indiana University-Purdue University at Indianapolis, Butler University, Marian College, University of Indianapolis, Martin University, Franklin College of Indiana.

Entrance Requirements: Open admission except for human services and health technology programs. Options: electronic application, early admission, deferred admission. Required: high school transcript. Required for some: interview. Entrance: noncompetitive. Application deadline: Rolling. Notification: continuous. Preference given to state residents.

Costs Per Year: Application fee: $0. State resident tuition: $3335 full-time, $111 per credit hour part-time. Nonresident tuition: $7182 full-time, $239 per credit hour part-time. Mandatory fees: $120 full-time, $60 per term part-time.

Collegiate Environment: Orientation program. Student-run newspaper. Most popular organizations: student government, Phi Theta Kappa, Human Services Club, Administrative Office Assistants Club, Radiology Club. Student services: personal-psychological counseling. Campus security: 24-hour emergency response devices and patrols, late night transport-escort service. College housing not available. 20,247 books, 138 serials, 2,135 audiovisual materials, an OPAC, and a Web page 407 computers available on campus for general student use. Students can access the following: online class registration. Staffed computer lab on campus.

■ **IVY TECH COMMUNITY COLLEGE–COLUMBUS**

4475 Central Ave.

Columbus, IN 47203-1868

Tel: (812)372-9925; Free: 888-IVY-LINE

Fax: (812)372-0311

E-mail: adeck@ivytech.edu

Web Site: www.ivytech.edu/

Description: State-supported, 2-year, coed. Part of Ivy Tech Community College System. Awards certificates, transfer associate, and terminal associate degrees. Founded 1963. Setting: small town campus with easy access to Indianapolis. Total enrollment: 4,140. Faculty: 275 (55 full-time, 220 part-time). Student-undergrad faculty ratio is 19:1. Full-time: 1,509 students, 65% women, 35% men. Part-time: 2,631 students, 67% women, 33% men. 1% from out-of-state. 0.2% American Indian or Alaska Native, non-Hispanic/Latino; 2% Hispanic/Latino; 2% African American, non-Hispanic/Latino; 1% Asian, non-Hispanic/Latino. 50% 25 or older, 3% transferred in. Retention: 48% of full-time freshmen returned the following year. Core. Calendar: semesters. Academic remediation for entering students, services for LD students, advanced placement, distance learning, summer session for credit, part-time degree program, adult/continuing education programs, internships.

Entrance Requirements: Open admission except for human services and health technology programs. Options: electronic application, early admission, deferred admission. Required: high school transcript. Required for some: interview. Entrance: noncompetitive. Application deadline: Rolling. Notification: continuous. Preference given to state residents.

Costs Per Year: Application fee: $0. State resident tuition: $3335 full-time,

$111 per credit hour part-time. Nonresident tuition: $7182 full-time, $239 per credit hour part-time. Mandatory fees: $120 full-time, $60 per term part-time.

Collegiate Environment: Orientation program. Most popular organizations: student government, Phi Theta Kappa, LPN Club. Campus security: late night transport-escort service, trained evening security personnel, escort service. College housing not available. 7,855 books, 13,382 serials, 989 audiovisual materials, an OPAC, and a Web page 185 computers available on campus for general student use. Students can access the following: online class registration. Staffed computer lab on campus.

■ **IVY TECH COMMUNITY COLLEGE–EAST CENTRAL**

4301 S Cowan Rd.

Muncie, IN 47302-9448

Tel: (765)289-2291; Free: 888-IVY-LINE

E-mail: mlewelle@ivytech.edu

Web Site: www.ivytech.edu/

Description: State-supported, 2-year, coed. Part of Ivy Tech Community College System. Awards certificates, transfer associate, and terminal associate degrees. Founded 1968. Setting: 15-acre suburban campus with easy access to Indianapolis. Total enrollment: 7,471. Faculty: 548 (119 full-time, 428 part-time). Student-undergrad faculty ratio is 19:1. Full-time: 3,589 students, 61% women, 39% men. Part-time: 3,882 students, 65% women, 35% men. 0% from out-of-state. 0.4% American Indian or Alaska Native, non-Hispanic/Latino; 2% Hispanic/Latino; 8% African American, non-Hispanic/Latino; 1% Asian, non-Hispanic/Latino; 0.01% international. 49% 25 or older, 4% transferred in. Retention: 42% of full-time freshmen returned the following year. Core. Calendar: semesters. Academic remediation for entering students, services for LD students, advanced placement, distance learning, part-time degree program, adult/continuing education programs, internships.

Entrance Requirements: Open admission except for allied health programs in human services and health technology. Options: electronic application, early admission, deferred admission. Required: high school transcript. Required for some: interview. Entrance: noncompetitive. Application deadline: Rolling. Notification: continuous. Preference given to state residents.

Costs Per Year: Application fee: $0. State resident tuition: $3335 full-time, $111 per credit hour part-time. Nonresident tuition: $7182 full-time, $239 per credit hour part-time. Mandatory fees: $120 full-time, $60 per term part-time.

Collegiate Environment: Orientation program. Most popular organizations: Business Professionals of America, Skills USA - VICA, student government, Phi Theta Kappa, Human Services Club. College housing not available. 5,779 books, 145 serials, 6,266 audiovisual materials, an OPAC, and a Web page 270 computers available on campus for general student use. A campuswide network can be accessed from off-campus. Students can access the following: online class registration. Staffed computer lab on campus.

■ **IVY TECH COMMUNITY COLLEGE–KOKOMO**

1815 E Morgan St.

Kokomo, IN 46903-1373

Tel: (765)459-0561; Free: 888-IVY-LINE

E-mail: mfedersp@ivytech.edu

Web Site: www.ivytech.edu/

Description: State-supported, 2-year, coed. Part of Ivy Tech Community College System. Awards certificates, transfer associate, and terminal associate degrees. Founded 1968. Setting: 20-acre small town campus with easy access to Indianapolis. Total enrollment: 4,649. Faculty: 364 (72 full-time, 292 part-time). Student-undergrad faculty ratio is 16:1. Full-time: 1,821 students, 63% women, 37% men. Part-time: 2,828 students, 64% women, 36% men. 0% from out-of-state. 1% American Indian or Alaska Native, non-Hispanic/Latino; 3% Hispanic/Latino; 6% African American, non-Hispanic/Latino; 1% Asian, non-Hispanic/Latino. 60% 25 or older, 3% transferred in. Retention: 50% of full-time freshmen returned the following year. Core. Calendar: semesters. Academic remediation for entering students, services for LD students, advanced placement, distance learning, summer session for credit, part-time degree program, adult/continuing education programs, internships.

Entrance Requirements: Open admission except for allied health programs in human services and health technology. Options: electronic application, early admission. Required: high school transcript. Required for some: interview. Entrance: noncompetitive. Application deadline: Rolling. Notification: continuous. Preference given to state residents.

Costs Per Year: Application fee: $0. State resident tuition: $3335 full-time,

$111 per credit hour part-time. Nonresident tuition: $7182 full-time, $239 per credit hour part-time. Mandatory fees: $120 full-time, $60 per term part-time. **Collegiate Environment:** Student-run newspaper. Most popular organizations: student government, Collegiate Secretaries International, Licensed Practical Nursing Club, Phi Theta Kappa. Student services: personal-psychological counseling. Campus security: 24-hour emergency response devices, late night transport-escort service. College housing not available. 5,177 books, 99 serials, 772 audiovisual materials, an OPAC, and a Web page 320 computers available on campus for general student use. A campuswide network can be accessed from off-campus. Students can access the following: online class registration. Staffed computer lab on campus.

■ **IVY TECH COMMUNITY COLLEGE–LAFAYETTE**
3101 S Creasy Ln.
Lafayette, IN 47905-5266
Tel: (765)772-9100; Free: 888-IVY-LINE
E-mail: ihernand@ivytech.edu
Web Site: www.ivytech.edu/
Description: State-supported, 2-year, coed. Part of Ivy Tech Community College System. Awards certificates, transfer associate, and terminal associate degrees. Founded 1968. Setting: suburban campus with easy access to Indianapolis. Total enrollment: 6,666. Faculty: 412 (102 full-time, 310 part-time). Full-time: 2,933 students, 55% women, 45% men. Part-time: 3,733 students, 56% women, 44% men. 1% from out-of-state. 0.5% American Indian or Alaska Native, non-Hispanic/Latino; 6% Hispanic/Latino; 4% African American, non-Hispanic/Latino; 2% Asian, non-Hispanic/Latino; 0.03% international. 43% 25 or older, 5% transferred in. Retention: 49% of full-time freshmen returned the following year. Core. Calendar: semesters. Academic remediation for entering students, services for LD students, advanced placement, distance learning, summer session for credit, part-time degree program, internships.
Entrance Requirements: Open admission except for allied health programs in human services and health technology. Option: electronic application. Required: high school transcript. Required for some: interview. Entrance: noncompetitive. Application deadline: Rolling. Notification: continuous. Preference given to state residents.
Costs Per Year: Application fee: $0. State resident tuition: $3335 full-time, $111 per credit hour part-time. Nonresident tuition: $7182 full-time, $239 per credit hour part-time. Mandatory fees: $120 full-time, $60 per term part-time.
Collegiate Environment: Orientation program. Student-run newspaper. Most popular organizations: student government, Phi Theta Kappa, LPN Club, Accounting Club, Student Computer Technology Association. Student services: personal-psychological counseling. College housing not available. 8,043 books, 200 serials, 2,234 audiovisual materials, an OPAC, and a Web page 267 computers available on campus for general student use. A campuswide network can be accessed. Students can access the following: online class registration. Staffed computer lab on campus.

■ **IVY TECH COMMUNITY COLLEGE–NORTH CENTRAL**
220 Dean Johnson Blvd.
South Bend, IN 46601
Tel: (574)289-7001; Free: 888-IVY-LINE
Fax: (574)236-7181
E-mail: jaustin@ivytech.edu
Web Site: www.ivytech.edu/
Description: State-supported, 2-year, coed. Part of Ivy Tech Community College System. Awards certificates, transfer associate, and terminal associate degrees. Founded 1968. Setting: 4-acre suburban campus. Total enrollment: 7,852. Faculty: 423 (108 full-time, 315 part-time). Student-undergrad faculty ratio is 19:1. Full-time: 2,290 students, 62% women, 38% men. Part-time: 5,562 students, 62% women, 38% men. 2% from out-of-state. 1% American Indian or Alaska Native, non-Hispanic/Latino; 9% Hispanic/Latino; 18% African American, non-Hispanic/Latino; 1% Asian, non-Hispanic/Latino; 0.04% international. 60% 25 or older, 6% transferred in. Retention: 44% of full-time freshmen returned the following year. Core. Calendar: semesters. Academic remediation for entering students, ESL program, services for LD students, advanced placement, distance learning, summer session for credit, part-time degree program, adult/continuing education programs, internships. Off campus study at other members of the Northern Indiana Consortium for Education.
Entrance Requirements: Open admission except for allied health programs, in human services and health technology. Options: electronic application, early admission, deferred admission. Required: high school

transcript. Required for some: interview. Entrance: noncompetitive. Application deadline: Rolling. Notification: continuous. Preference given to state residents.
Costs Per Year: Application fee: $0. State resident tuition: $3335 full-time, $111 per credit hour part-time. Nonresident tuition: $7182 full-time, $239 per credit hour part-time. Mandatory fees: $120 full-time, $60 per term part-time.
Collegiate Environment: Orientation program. Most popular organizations: Phi Theta Kappa, student government, LPN Club. Student services: personal-psychological counseling, women's center. Campus security: 24-hour emergency response devices and patrols, late night transport-escort service, security during open hours. College housing not available. 6,246 books, 90 serials, 689 audiovisual materials, an OPAC, and a Web page 426 computers available on campus for general student use. Students can access the following: online class registration. Staffed computer lab on campus.

■ **IVY TECH COMMUNITY COLLEGE–NORTHEAST**
3800 N Anthony Blvd.
Fort Wayne, IN 46805-1430
Tel: (260)482-9171; Free: 888-IVY-LINE
Fax: (260)480-4177
E-mail: rboss1@ivytech.edu
Web Site: www.ivytech.edu/
Description: State-supported, 2-year, coed. Part of Ivy Tech Community College System. Awards certificates, transfer associate, and terminal associate degrees. Founded 1969. Setting: 22-acre urban campus. Total enrollment: 9,883. Faculty: 506 (133 full-time, 373 part-time). Student-undergrad faculty ratio is 22:1. Full-time: 3,738 students, 60% women, 40% men. Part-time: 6,145 students, 58% women, 42% men. 3% from out-of-state. 1% American Indian or Alaska Native, non-Hispanic/Latino; 5% Hispanic/Latino; 16% African American, non-Hispanic/Latino; 2% Asian, non-Hispanic/Latino; 0.01% international. 54% 25 or older, 6% transferred in. Retention: 42% of full-time freshmen returned the following year. Core. Calendar: semesters. ESL program, services for LD students, advanced placement, distance learning, summer session for credit, part-time degree program, adult/continuing education programs, internships.
Entrance Requirements: Open admission except for allied health programs in human services and health technology. Option: early admission. Required: high school transcript. Required for some: interview. Entrance: noncompetitive. Application deadline: Rolling. Notification: continuous. Preference given to state residents.
Costs Per Year: Application fee: $0. State resident tuition: $3335 full-time, $111 per credit hour part-time. Nonresident tuition: $7182 full-time, $239 per credit hour part-time. Mandatory fees: $120 full-time, $60 per term part-time.
Collegiate Environment: Orientation program. Student-run newspaper. Most popular organizations: student government, LPN Club, Phi Theta Kappa. Campus security: 24-hour emergency response devices and patrols, late night transport-escort service. College housing not available. 18,389 books, 110 serials, 3,397 audiovisual materials, an OPAC, and a Web page 382 computers available on campus for general student use. Students can access the following: online class registration. Staffed computer lab on campus.

■ **IVY TECH COMMUNITY COLLEGE–NORTHWEST**
1440 E 35th Ave.
Gary, IN 46409-1499
Tel: (219)981-1111; Free: 888-IVY-LINE
E-mail: tlewis@ivytech.edu
Web Site: www.ivytech.edu/
Description: State-supported, 2-year, coed. Part of Ivy Tech Community College System. Awards certificates, transfer associate, and terminal associate degrees. Founded 1963. Setting: 13-acre urban campus with easy access to Chicago. Total enrollment: 9,813. Faculty: 482 (126 full-time, 356 part-time). Student-undergrad faculty ratio is 24:1. Full-time: 3,807 students, 60% women, 40% men. Part-time: 6,006 students, 61% women, 39% men. 2% from out-of-state. 0.3% American Indian or Alaska Native, non-Hispanic/Latino; 11% Hispanic/Latino; 26% African American, non-Hispanic/Latino; 1% Asian, non-Hispanic/Latino; 0.03% international. 56% 25 or older, 7% transferred in. Retention: 47% of full-time freshmen returned the following year. Core. Calendar: semesters. Academic remediation for entering students, services for LD students, advanced placement, distance learning, summer session for credit, part-time degree program, adult/continuing education programs, internships.
Entrance Requirements: Open admission except for allied health programs

in human services and health technology. Options: electronic application, deferred admission. Required: high school transcript. Required for some: interview. Entrance: noncompetitive. Application deadline: Rolling. Notification: continuous. Preference given to state residents.
Collegiate Environment: Orientation program. Most popular organizations: Phi Theta Kappa, LPN Club, Computer Club, student government, Business Club. Campus security: 24-hour emergency response devices, late night transport-escort service. College housing not available. 13,805 books, 157 microform titles, 160 serials, 4,295 audiovisual materials, an OPAC, and a Web page 267 computers available on campus for general student use. Students can access the following: online class registration. Staffed computer lab on campus.

■ **IVY TECH COMMUNITY COLLEGE–RICHMOND**
2325 Chester Blvd.
Richmond, IN 47374-1220
Tel: (765)966-2656; Free: 888-IVY-LINE
E-mail: crethlake@ivytech.edu
Web Site: www.ivytech.edu/richmond/
Description: State-supported, 2-year, coed. Part of Ivy Tech Community College System. Awards certificates, transfer associate, and terminal associate degrees. Founded 1963. Setting: 23-acre small town campus with easy access to Indianapolis. Total enrollment: 3,233. Faculty: 196 (41 full-time, 155 part-time). Student-undergrad faculty ratio is 20:1. Full-time: 1,117 students, 63% women, 37% men. Part-time: 2,116 students, 66% women, 34% men. 8% from out-of-state. 1% American Indian or Alaska Native, non-Hispanic/Latino; 1% Hispanic/Latino; 5% African American, non-Hispanic/Latino; 0.3% Asian, non-Hispanic/Latino. 61% 25 or older, 3% transferred in. Retention: 38% of full-time freshmen returned the following year. Core. Calendar: semesters. Academic remediation for entering students, services for LD students, advanced placement, independent study, distance learning, summer session for credit, part-time degree program, adult/continuing education programs, internships. Off campus study at Indiana University East.
Entrance Requirements: Open admission except for human services and health technology programs. Options: electronic application, early admission. Required: high school transcript. Required for some: interview. Entrance: noncompetitive. Application deadline: Rolling. Notification: continuous. Preference given to state residents.
Costs Per Year: Application fee: $0. State resident tuition: $3335 full-time, $111 per credit hour part-time. Nonresident tuition: $7182 full-time, $239 per credit hour part-time. Mandatory fees: $120 full-time, $60 per term part-time.
Collegiate Environment: Orientation program. Student-run newspaper. Most popular organizations: student government, Phi Theta Kappa, LPN Club, CATS 2000, Business Professionals of America. Student services: personal-psychological counseling. Campus security: 24-hour emergency response devices, late night transport-escort service. College housing not available. 169 computers available on campus for general student use. A campuswide network can be accessed. Students can access the following: online class registration. Staffed computer lab on campus.

■ **IVY TECH COMMUNITY COLLEGE–SOUTHEAST**
590 Ivy Tech Dr.
Madison, IN 47250-1883
Tel: (812)265-4028; Free: 888-IVY-LINE
E-mail: chutcher@ivytech.edu
Web Site: www.ivytech.edu/
Description: State-supported, 2-year, coed. Part of Ivy Tech Community College System. Awards certificates, transfer associate, and terminal associate degrees. Founded 1963. Setting: 5-acre small town campus with easy access to Louisville. Total enrollment: 2,778. Faculty: 200 (45 full-time, 155 part-time). Student-undergrad faculty ratio is 17:1. Full-time: 1,106 students, 66% women, 34% men. Part-time: 1,672 students, 70% women, 30% men. 4% from out-of-state. 0.3% American Indian or Alaska Native, non-Hispanic/Latino; 1% Hispanic/Latino; 1% African American, non-Hispanic/Latino; 0.3% Asian, non-Hispanic/Latino. 51% 25 or older, 3% transferred in. Retention: 54% of full-time freshmen returned the following year. Core. Calendar: semesters. Academic remediation for entering students, services for LD students, advanced placement, distance learning, summer session for credit, part-time degree program, internships.
Entrance Requirements: Open admission except for human services and health technology programs. Option: electronic application. Required: high school transcript. Required for some: interview. Entrance: noncompetitive. Application deadline: Rolling. Notification: continuous. Preference given to state residents.

Costs Per Year: Application fee: $0. State resident tuition: $3335 full-time, $111 per credit hour part-time. Nonresident tuition: $7182 full-time, $239 per credit hour part-time. Mandatory fees: $120 full-time, $60 per term part-time.
Collegiate Environment: Orientation program. Most popular organizations: student government, Phi Theta Kappa, LPN Club. Campus security: 24-hour emergency response devices. College housing not available. 9,027 books, 14,299 serials, 1,341 audiovisual materials, an OPAC, and a Web page 123 computers available on campus for general student use. A campuswide network can be accessed. Students can access the following: online class registration. Staffed computer lab on campus.

■ **IVY TECH COMMUNITY COLLEGE–SOUTHERN INDIANA**
8204 Hwy. 311
Sellersburg, IN 47172-1829
Tel: (812)246-3301; Free: 888-IVY-LINE
E-mail: bharris88@ivytech.edu
Web Site: www.ivytech.edu/
Description: State-supported, 2-year, coed. Part of Ivy Tech Community College System. Awards certificates, transfer associate, and terminal associate degrees. Founded 1968. Setting: 63-acre small town campus with easy access to Louisville. Total enrollment: 5,283. Faculty: 240 (60 full-time, 180 part-time). Student-undergrad faculty ratio is 23:1. Full-time: 1,554 students, 64% women, 36% men. Part-time: 3,729 students, 53% women, 47% men. 8% from out-of-state. 1% American Indian or Alaska Native, non-Hispanic/Latino; 2% Hispanic/Latino; 8% African American, non-Hispanic/Latino; 1% Asian, non-Hispanic/Latino. 58% 25 or older, 6% transferred in. Retention: 45% of full-time freshmen returned the following year. Core. Calendar: semesters. Academic remediation for entering students, services for LD students, advanced placement, distance learning, summer session for credit, part-time degree program, adult/continuing education programs, co-op programs and internships.
Entrance Requirements: Open admission except for human services and health programs. Options: electronic application, early admission, deferred admission. Required: high school transcript. Required for some: interview. Entrance: noncompetitive. Application deadline: Rolling. Notification: continuous. Preference given to state residents.
Costs Per Year: Application fee: $0. State resident tuition: $3335 full-time, $111 per credit hour part-time. Nonresident tuition: $7182 full-time, $239 per credit hour part-time. Mandatory fees: $60 per term part-time.
Collegiate Environment: Orientation program. Most popular organizations: Phi Theta Kappa, Practical Nursing Club, Medical Assistant Club, Accounting Club, student government. Campus security: late night transport-escort service. College housing not available. 7,634 books, 66 serials, 648 audiovisual materials, an OPAC, and a Web page 187 computers available on campus for general student use. A campuswide network can be accessed. Students can access the following: online class registration. Staffed computer lab on campus.

■ **IVY TECH COMMUNITY COLLEGE–SOUTHWEST**
3501 First Ave.
Evansville, IN 47710-3398
Tel: (812)426-2865; Free: 888-IVY-LINE
E-mail: ajohnson@ivytech.edu
Web Site: www.ivytech.edu/
Description: State-supported, 2-year, coed. Part of Ivy Tech Community College System. Awards certificates, transfer associate, and terminal associate degrees. Founded 1963. Setting: 15-acre suburban campus. Total enrollment: 5,731. Faculty: 341 (84 full-time, 257 part-time). Student-undergrad faculty ratio is 19:1. Full-time: 2,066 students, 62% women, 38% men. Part-time: 3,665 students, 51% women, 49% men. 3% from out-of-state. 0.4% American Indian or Alaska Native, non-Hispanic/Latino; 2% Hispanic/Latino; 10% African American, non-Hispanic/Latino; 1% Asian, non-Hispanic/Latino; 0.02% international. 56% 25 or older, 5% transferred in. Retention: 45% of full-time freshmen returned the following year. Core. Calendar: semesters. Academic remediation for entering students, services for LD students, advanced placement, independent study, distance learning, summer session for credit, part-time degree program, co-op programs and internships.
Entrance Requirements: Open admission except for human services and health technology programs. Options: electronic application, early admission, deferred admission. Required: high school transcript. Required for some: interview. Entrance: noncompetitive. Application deadline: Rolling. Notification: continuous. Preference given to state residents.
Costs Per Year: Application fee: $0. State resident tuition: $3335 full-time,

$111 per credit hour part-time. Nonresident tuition: $7182 full-time, $239 per credit hour part-time. Mandatory fees: $120 full-time, $60 per term part-time.
Collegiate Environment: Orientation program. Most popular organizations: student government, Phi Theta Kappa, LPN Club, National Association of Industrial Technology, Design Club. Campus security: late night transport-escort service. College housing not available. 7,082 books, 107 serials, 1,755 audiovisual materials, an OPAC, and a Web page 362 computers available on campus for general student use. Students can access the following: online class registration. Staffed computer lab on campus.

■ **IVY TECH COMMUNITY COLLEGE–WABASH VALLEY**
7999 US Hwy. 41, S
Terre Haute, IN 47802
Tel: (812)299-1121; Free: 888-IVY-LINE
E-mail: mfisher@ivytech.edu
Web Site: www.ivytech.edu/
Description: State-supported, 2-year, coed. Part of Ivy Tech Community College System. Awards certificates, transfer associate, and terminal associate degrees. Founded 1966. Setting: 55-acre suburban campus with easy access to Indianapolis. Total enrollment: 5,544. Faculty: 267 (94 full-time, 173 part-time). Student-undergrad faculty ratio is 22:1. Full-time: 2,224 students, 64% women, 36% men. Part-time: 3,320 students, 50% women, 50% men. 5% from out-of-state. 0.3% American Indian or Alaska Native, non-Hispanic/Latino; 1% Hispanic/Latino; 4% African American, non-Hispanic/Latino; 1% Asian, non-Hispanic/Latino; 0% international. 50% 25 or older, 6% transferred in. Retention: 48% of full-time freshmen returned the following year. Core. Calendar: semesters. Academic remediation for entering students, services for LD students, advanced placement, distance learning, summer session for credit, part-time degree program, adult/continuing education programs, internships.
Entrance Requirements: Open admission except for allied health programs in human services and health technology. Options: electronic application, early admission, deferred admission. Required: high school transcript. Required for some: interview. Entrance: noncompetitive. Application deadline: Rolling. Notification: continuous. Preference given to state residents.
Costs Per Year: Application fee: $0. State resident tuition: $3335 full-time, $111 per credit hour part-time. Nonresident tuition: $7182 full-time, $239 per credit hour part-time. Mandatory fees: $120 full-time, $60 per term part-time.
Collegiate Environment: Orientation program. Most popular organizations: student government, Phi Theta Kappa, LPN Club, National Association of Industrial Technology. Student services: personal-psychological counseling, women's center. Campus security: 24-hour emergency response devices. College housing not available. 4,403 books, 77 serials, 406 audiovisual materials, an OPAC, and a Web page 305 computers available on campus for general student use. A campuswide network can be accessed. Students can access the following: online class registration. Staffed computer lab on campus.

■ **KAPLAN COLLEGE, HAMMOND CAMPUS**
7833 Indianapolis Blvd.
Hammond, IN 46324
Tel: (219)844-0100; Free: 800-935-1857
Web Site: hammond.kaplancollege.com/
Description: Proprietary, 2-year, coed. Awards diplomas and terminal associate degrees. Founded 1962. Setting: suburban campus.

■ **KAPLAN COLLEGE, SOUTHEAST INDIANAPOLIS CAMPUS**
4200 SE St.
Indianapolis, IN 46227
Tel: (317)782-0315
Web Site: www.seindianapolis.kaplancollege.com/
Description: Proprietary, 2-year, coed. Awards diplomas and terminal associate degrees.

■ **LINCOLN COLLEGE OF TECHNOLOGY**
7225 Winton Dr.
Bldg. 128
Indianapolis, IN 46268
Tel: (317)632-5553
Web Site: www.lincolnedu.com/
Description: Proprietary, 2-year, coed. Part of Lincoln Technical Institute,

Inc. Awards certificates and terminal associate degrees. Founded 1946. Setting: urban campus. Total enrollment: 1,650. 17% 25 or older. Calendar: modular. Summer session for credit.
Entrance Requirements: Required: high school transcript, interview. Entrance: minimally difficult. Application deadline: Rolling.
Collegiate Environment: Orientation program. Student services: personal-psychological counseling. 800 books and 15 serials.

■ **MANCHESTER UNIVERSITY**
604 E College Ave.
North Manchester, IN 46962-1225
Tel: (260)982-5000; Free: 800-852-3648
Fax: (260)982-5043
E-mail: arhohman@manchester.edu
Web Site: www.manchester.edu/
Description: Independent, comprehensive, coed, affiliated with Church of the Brethren. Awards associate, bachelor's, master's, and doctoral degrees. Founded 1889. Setting: 125-acre small town campus. Endowment: $42.9 million. Educational spending for the previous fiscal year: $5603 per student. Total enrollment: 1,345. Faculty: 102 (74 full-time, 28 part-time). Student-undergrad faculty ratio is 15:1. 3,861 applied, 64% were admitted. 23% from top 10% of their high school class, 52% from top quarter, 87% from top half. Full-time: 1,232 students, 52% women, 48% men. Part-time: 25 students, 36% women, 64% men. Students come from 21 states and territories, 23 other countries, 8% from out-of-state. 0.2% American Indian or Alaska Native, non-Hispanic/Latino; 4% Hispanic/Latino; 3% African American, non-Hispanic/Latino; 1% Asian, non-Hispanic/Latino; 0.1% Native Hawaiian or other Pacific Islander, non-Hispanic/Latino; 2% international. 1% 25 or older, 75% live on campus, 2% transferred in. Retention: 68% of full-time freshmen returned the following year. Academic areas with the most degrees conferred: business/marketing; education; health professions and related sciences. Core. Calendar: 4-1-4. Services for LD students, advanced placement, accelerated degree program, self-designed majors, honors program, independent study, distance learning, double major, summer session for credit, part-time degree program, internships. Off campus study. Study abroad program.
Entrance Requirements: Options: electronic application, international baccalaureate accepted. Required: high school transcript, 1 recommendation, rank in upper 50% of high school class, SAT or ACT. Recommended: minimum 2.3 high school GPA. Required for some: essay, minimum 3 high school GPA. Entrance: moderately difficult. Application deadline: Rolling. Notification: continuous. Transfer credits accepted: Yes.
Costs Per Year: Application fee: $25. One-time mandatory fee: $250. Comprehensive fee: $37,170 includes full-time tuition ($27,000), mandatory fees ($920), and college room and board ($9250). College room only: $5500. Room and board charges vary according to board plan and housing facility. Part-time tuition: $700 per credit hour. Part-time tuition and fees vary according to course load.
Collegiate Environment: Orientation program. Drama-theater group, choral group, student-run newspaper, radio station. Social organizations: 47 open to all. Most popular organizations: Acappella Choir, American Chemical Society, Accounting and Business Club, Circle K, Student Education Association. Major annual events: Homecoming, Relay for Life, May Day Week. Student services: health clinic, personal-psychological counseling. Campus security: 24-hour emergency response devices and patrols, student patrols, late night transport-escort service, alarm system, locked residence hall entrances. 1,000 college housing spaces available; 846 were occupied in 2012-13. Freshmen guaranteed college housing. On-campus residence required through junior year. Option: coed housing available. Funderburg Library with an OPAC and a Web page. Operations spending for the previous fiscal year: $626,611. 222 computers available on campus for general student use. Computer purchase/lease plans available. A campuswide network can be accessed from student residence rooms and from off campus. Students can access the following: online class registration.
Community Environment: North Manchester (population 6,000) is situated in north central Indiana, 35 miles west of Ft. Wayne, and 100 miles north of Indianapolis, and 3 hours from Chicago, enjoying a favorable climate. Bus facilities and airlines are within 30 miles. Community facilities include a library, indoor swimming pool, churches of many denominations, a medical clinic across the street from campus and a hospital within 20 minutes.

■ **MARIAN UNIVERSITY**
3200 Cold Spring Rd.
Indianapolis, IN 46222-1997

Tel: (317)955-6000
E-mail: admissions@marian.edu
Web Site: www.marian.edu/
Description: Independent Roman Catholic, comprehensive, coed. Awards associate, bachelor's, master's, and doctoral degrees. Founded 1851. Setting: 114-acre suburban campus with easy access to Indianapolis. Endowment: $26 million. Educational spending for the previous fiscal year: $20,564 per student. Total enrollment: 2,580. Faculty: 269 (108 full-time, 161 part-time). Student-undergrad faculty ratio is 12:1. 2,012 applied, 55% were admitted. 15% from top 10% of their high school class, 36% from top quarter, 78% from top half. Full-time: 1,672 students, 62% women, 38% men. Part-time: 569 students, 74% women, 26% men. Students come from 29 states and territories, 5 other countries, 10% from out-of-state. 0.1% American Indian or Alaska Native, non-Hispanic/Latino; 3% Hispanic/Latino; 14% African American, non-Hispanic/Latino; 1% Asian, non-Hispanic/Latino; 0.1% Native Hawaiian or other Pacific Islander, non-Hispanic/Latino; 0.3% international. 28% 25 or older, 32% live on campus, 4% transferred in. Retention: 69% of full-time freshmen returned the following year. Academic areas with the most degrees conferred: business/marketing; health professions and related sciences; education. Core. Calendar: semesters. Academic remediation for entering students, services for LD students, advanced placement, accelerated degree program, honors program, independent study, distance learning, double major, summer session for credit, part-time degree program, adult/continuing education programs, co-op programs and internships. Off campus study at Franklin College of Indiana, Indiana University-Purdue University at Indianapolis, University of Indianapolis, Christian Theological Seminary, Butler University. Study abroad program. ROTC: Army (c).
Entrance Requirements: Options: electronic application, deferred admission, international baccalaureate accepted. Required: minimum 2.3 high school GPA, college transcripts, SAT or ACT. Required for some: essay, high school transcript, interview. Entrance: moderately difficult. Application deadlines: 8/1, 8/1 for nonresidents. Notification: continuous, continuous for nonresidents. SAT Reasoning Test deadline: 8/1. Transfer credits accepted: Yes.
Costs Per Year: Application fee: $35. Comprehensive fee: $37,058 includes full-time tuition ($28,400) and college room and board ($8658). Room and board charges vary according to board plan and housing facility. Part-time tuition: $1260 per credit.
Collegiate Environment: Orientation program. Drama-theater group, choral group, marching band, student-run newspaper. Social organizations: 39 open to all. Most popular organizations: Student Government of Marian University, Booster Club, Best Buddies, College Mentors for Kids, Sophia Club. Major annual events: October Fest, Homecoming, Spring and Fall Formal. Student services: health clinic, personal-psychological counseling. Campus security: 24-hour patrols, student patrols, late night transport-escort service, controlled dormitory access. 820 college housing spaces available; 535 were occupied in 2012-13. Freshmen guaranteed college housing. On-campus residence required through junior year. Option: coed housing available. Mother Theresa Hackelmeier Memorial Library with 130,000 books, 337 serials, 2,517 audiovisual materials, an OPAC, and a Web page. 310 computers available on campus for general student use. Computer purchase/lease plans available. A campuswide network can be accessed from student residence rooms. Students can access the following: online class registration. Staffed computer lab on campus provides training in use of computers, software, and the Internet.
Community Environment: See Butler University.

■ MARTIN UNIVERSITY
2171 Avondale Pl.
Indianapolis, IN 46218-3867
Tel: (317)543-3235
Fax: (317)543-3257
Web Site: www.martin.edu/
Description: Independent, comprehensive, coed. Awards bachelor's and master's degrees. Founded 1977. Setting: 5-acre urban campus. Endowment: $128,101. Educational spending for the previous fiscal year: $2759 per student. Total enrollment: 1,236. Faculty: 43 (26 full-time, 17 part-time). Student-undergrad faculty ratio is 21:1. 243 applied, 96% were admitted. Full-time: 336 students, 77% women, 23% men. Part-time: 738 students, 64% women, 36% men. Students come from 2 other countries, 0% from out-of-state. 93% 25 or older. Retention: 75% of full-time freshmen returned the following year. Academic areas with the most degrees conferred: liberal arts/general studies; psychology; business/marketing. Core. Calendar:

semesters. Academic remediation for entering students, advanced placement, accelerated degree program, self-designed majors, honors program, independent study, double major, summer session for credit, part-time degree program, external degree program, adult/continuing education programs, internships, graduate courses open to undergrads. Off campus study at Consortium for Urban Education (CUE).
Entrance Requirements: Open admission. Options: electronic application, early admission, deferred admission. Required: essay, high school transcript, interview, writing sample. Entrance: noncompetitive. Application deadline: Rolling. Notification: continuous.
Collegiate Environment: Orientation program. Major annual events: Orientation, Honors Program, Constitution Day. Campus security: building security, security personnel from 7 am to 9:30 pm. 20 computers available on campus for general student use. Computer purchase/lease plans available. A campuswide network can be accessed. Staffed computer lab on campus provides training in use of computers, software, and the Internet.

■ MEDTECH COLLEGE (FORT WAYNE)
7230 Engle Rd.
Fort Wayne, IN 46804
Tel: (260)436-3272
Web Site: www.medtechcollege.edu/
Description: Proprietary, 2-year, coed. Founded 2008.

■ MEDTECH COLLEGE (GREENWOOD)
1500 American Way
Greenwood, IN 46143
Tel: (317)534-0322
Web Site: www.medtechcollege.edu/
Description: Proprietary, 2-year, coed. Founded 2007.

■ MID-AMERICA COLLEGE OF FUNERAL SERVICE
3111 Hamburg Pke.
Jeffersonville, IN 47130-9630
Tel: (812)288-8878; Free: 800-221-6158
Fax: (812)288-5942
E-mail: macfs@mindspring.com
Web Site: www.mid-america.edu/
Description: Independent, primarily 2-year, coed. Awards terminal associate and bachelor's degrees. Founded 1905. Setting: 3-acre small town campus with easy access to Louisville. Total enrollment: 120. Faculty: 7 (6 full-time, 1 part-time). Student-undergrad faculty ratio is 13:1. Students come from 6 states and territories. 13% 25 or older. Core. Academic remediation for entering students.
Entrance Requirements: Open admission. Option: deferred admission. Required: high school transcript. Entrance: minimally difficult. Application deadline: Rolling.
Collegiate Environment: Orientation program. 1,500 books and 20 serials 15 computers available on campus for general student use. Staffed computer lab on campus.

■ OAKLAND CITY UNIVERSITY
138 N Lucretia St.
Oakland City, IN 47660-1099
Tel: (812)749-4781; Free: 800-737-5125
Fax: (812)749-1233
Web Site: www.oak.edu/
Description: Independent General Baptist, comprehensive, coed. Awards associate, bachelor's, master's, and doctoral degrees. Founded 1885. Setting: 20-acre rural campus. Total enrollment: 2,519. Faculty: 202 (37 full-time, 165 part-time). Student-undergrad faculty ratio is 15:1. 514 applied, 48% were admitted. 8% from top 10% of their high school class, 22% from top quarter, 65% from top half. Full-time: 480 students, 57% women, 43% men. Part-time: 1,821 students, 62% women, 38% men. 15% from out-of-state. 0.4% American Indian or Alaska Native, non-Hispanic/Latino; 4% Hispanic/Latino; 5% African American, non-Hispanic/Latino; 1% Asian, non-Hispanic/Latino; 0.2% Native Hawaiian or other Pacific Islander, non-Hispanic/Latino; 0% international. 15% 25 or older, 33% live on campus, 1% transferred in. Retention: 75% of full-time freshmen returned the following year. Academic areas with the most degrees conferred: computer and information sciences; education; business/marketing. Core. Calendar: semesters. Academic remediation for entering students, services for LD

students, advanced placement, accelerated degree program, summer session for credit, part-time degree program, external degree program, adult/continuing education programs.

Entrance Requirements: Options: electronic application, early admission, deferred admission. Required: essay, high school transcript, minimum 2 high school GPA, SAT or ACT. Recommended: interview. Required for some: SAT or ACT. Entrance: minimally difficult. Application deadline: Rolling. Notification: continuous. SAT Reasoning Test deadline: 8/1. Transfer credits accepted: Yes.

Costs Per Year: Application fee: $35. Comprehensive fee: $26,700 includes full-time tuition ($18,600) and college room and board ($8100). College room only: $2800. Full-time tuition varies according to degree level. Room and board charges vary according to board plan and housing facility. Part-time tuition: $620 per credit hour.

Collegiate Environment: Orientation program. Drama-theater group, choral group, student-run newspaper. Most popular organizations: Student Government Association, Good News Players, Art Guild, FOCUS, intramural sports. Major annual events: Founders' Day, Formal Tea, Homecoming. Student services: personal-psychological counseling. Campus security: 24-hour patrols, student patrols. 320 college housing spaces available. Freshmen guaranteed college housing. On-campus residence required in freshman year. Options: men-only, women-only housing available. Barger-Richardson Library with 87,724 books, 101,963 microform titles, 222 serials, 2,570 audiovisual materials, an OPAC, and a Web page. 92 computers available on campus for general student use. A campuswide network can be accessed from student residence rooms and from off campus. Staffed computer lab on campus provides training in use of computers, software, and the Internet.

Community Environment: Oakland City is a friendly rural-suburban community with a Midwest climate, temperatures ranging from a high of 98 degrees to a low of ten degrees. Average rainfall is over 40 inches annually. Community facilities include six churches, both Protestant and Catholic, numerous civic and service groups, library, individual stores, and a shopping center 15 miles away. Some part time jobs are available for students.

■ **PURDUE UNIVERSITY**
West Lafayette, IN 47907
Tel: (765)494-4600
Fax: (765)494-0544
E-mail: admissions@purdue.edu
Web Site: www.purdue.edu/

Description: State-supported, university, coed. Part of Purdue University System. Awards associate, bachelor's, master's, and doctoral degrees and post-master's certificates. Founded 1869. Setting: 2,602-acre suburban campus with easy access to Indianapolis. Endowment: $1.9 billion. Research spending for the previous fiscal year: $622.4 million. Total enrollment: 39,256. Faculty: 2,314 (2,041 full-time, 273 part-time). Student-undergrad faculty ratio is 14:1. 30,903 applied, 61% were admitted. 41% from top 10% of their high school class, 76% from top quarter, 97% from top half. Full-time: 28,739 students, 42% women, 58% men. Part-time: 1,408 students, 48% women, 52% men. Students come from 52 states and territories, 90 other countries, 31% from out-of-state. 0.2% American Indian or Alaska Native, non-Hispanic/Latino; 4% Hispanic/Latino; 3% African American, non-Hispanic/Latino; 5% Asian, non-Hispanic/Latino; 0.1% Native Hawaiian or other Pacific Islander, non-Hispanic/Latino; 16% international. 4% 25 or older, 35% live on campus, 2% transferred in. Retention: 91% of full-time freshmen returned the following year. Academic areas with the most degrees conferred: engineering; business/marketing; health professions and related sciences. Core. Calendar: semesters. Services for LD students, advanced placement, accelerated degree program, freshman honors college, honors program, independent study, distance learning, double major, summer session for credit, part-time degree program, adult/continuing education programs, co-op programs and internships, graduate courses open to undergrads. Study abroad program. ROTC: Army, Naval, Air Force.

Entrance Requirements: Options: electronic application, early admission, deferred admission. Required: high school transcript, SAT or ACT. Entrance: moderately difficult. Application deadline: 3/1. Notification: continuous. SAT Reasoning Test deadline: 3/1. SAT Subject Test deadline: 3/1. Transfer credits accepted: Yes. Applicants placed on waiting list: 1,393. Wait-listed applicants offered admission: 165.

Costs Per Year: Application fee: $50. State resident tuition: $9900 full-time. Nonresident tuition: $28,702 full-time. Mandatory fees: $566 full-time. Full-time tuition and fees vary according to course load and program. College room and board: $9990. College room only: $5196. Room and board charges vary according to board plan and housing facility.

Collegiate Environment: Orientation program. Drama-theater group, choral group, marching band, student-run newspaper, radio station. Social organizations: 948 open to all; national fraternities, national sororities; 10% of eligible men and 8% of eligible women are members. Most popular organizations: student government, Golden Key National Honor Society, Society of Women Engineers, Purdue student union board, Krannert Graduate Student Association. Major annual events: Grand Prix, homecoming, rush. Student services: health clinic, personal-psychological counseling, women's center. Campus security: 24-hour emergency response devices and patrols, student patrols, late night transport-escort service, controlled dormitory access. 11,104 college housing spaces available; 10,622 were occupied in 2012-13. Freshmen given priority for college housing. Options: coed, men-only, women-only housing available. Humanities Social Science and Education Library plus 13 others with 3.6 million books, an OPAC, and a Web page. Operations spending for the previous fiscal year: $23.2 million. 5,217 computers available on campus for general student use. Computer purchase/lease plans available. A campuswide network can be accessed from student residence rooms and from off campus. Students can access the following: online class registration. Staffed computer lab on campus (open 24 hours a day).

Community Environment: Lafayette is located 65 miles northwest of Indianapolis and 120 miles southeast of Chicago. It is located on the Wabash River, in a rich grain-growing county where livestock and dairying are principal agricultural industries. All forms of commercial transportation are available. The community facilities include libraries, churches that represent 34 denominations, Lafayette Symphony Orchestra, Civic Theatre, museums, hospitals, a TV station, and good shopping at downtown locations and 8 other shopping centers. Many hotel and motel accommodations are available for the conventions at Lafayette.

■ **PURDUE UNIVERSITY CALUMET**
2200 169th St.
Hammond, IN 46323-2094
Tel: (219)989-2400; Free: 800-447-8738
Fax: (219)989-2775
E-mail: adms@purduecal.edu
Web Site: www.purduecal.edu/

Description: State-supported, comprehensive, coed. Part of Purdue University System. Awards associate, bachelor's, and master's degrees and post-master's certificates. Founded 1951. Setting: 202-acre urban campus with easy access to Chicago. Endowment: $12.9 million. Total enrollment: 10,054. Faculty: 606 (310 full-time, 296 part-time). Student-undergrad faculty ratio is 17:1. 3,759 applied, 51% were admitted. 15% from top 10% of their high school class, 38% from top quarter, 74% from top half. Full-time: 5,140 students, 51% women, 49% men. Part-time: 3,772 students, 68% women, 32% men. 20% from out-of-state. 0.3% American Indian or Alaska Native, non-Hispanic/Latino; 15% Hispanic/Latino; 14% African American, non-Hispanic/Latino; 2% Asian, non-Hispanic/Latino; 0.1% Native Hawaiian or other Pacific Islander, non-Hispanic/Latino; 6% international. 41% 25 or older, 6% live on campus, 6% transferred in. Retention: 69% of full-time freshmen returned the following year. Academic areas with the most degrees conferred: business/marketing; health professions and related sciences; engineering technologies. Core. Calendar: semesters. Academic remediation for entering students, ESL program, services for LD students, advanced placement, accelerated degree program, freshman honors college, honors program, independent study, distance learning, double major, summer session for credit, part-time degree program, adult/continuing education programs, co-op programs and internships, graduate courses open to undergrads. Study abroad program. ROTC: Army.

Entrance Requirements: Option: electronic application. Required: high school transcript, minimum 2 high school GPA, SAT or ACT. Entrance: moderately difficult. Application deadlines: 8/9, 8/9 for nonresidents. Notification: continuous, continuous for nonresidents. Transfer credits accepted: Yes.

Costs Per Year: Application fee: $25. State resident tuition: $6991 full-time, $231.95 per credit hour part-time. Nonresident tuition: $15,169 full-time, $524 per credit hour part-time. Full-time tuition varies according to course load and program. Part-time tuition varies according to course load and program. College room and board: $7717. College room only: $5170. Room and board charges vary according to housing facility.

Collegiate Environment: Orientation program. Drama-theater group, choral group, student-run newspaper. Social organizations: 73 open to all; national fraternities, national sororities, multicultural, religious, special interest; 4% of eligible men and 4% of eligible women are members. Most popular organizations: Purdue University Gamers Guild, Biology Club, American Society of Civil Engineers, Purdue Calumet Ambassadors, Society for Human Resources Management. Major annual events: Student Convocation, Welcome Back Week Events, Chinese New Year Celebration. Student services: health clinic, personal-psychological counseling. Campus security: 24-hour emergency response devices and patrols, student patrols, late night transport-escort service. 744 college housing spaces available. No special consideration for freshman housing applicants. Option: coed housing available. Purdue University Calumet Library plus 1 other with 287,564 books, 801,558 microform titles, 6,688 serials, 1,424 audiovisual materials, an OPAC, and a Web page. 1,500 computers available on campus for general student use. A campuswide network can be accessed from student residence rooms and from off campus. Students can access the following: online class registration. Staffed computer lab on campus.

Community Environment: Purdue University - Calumet primarily serves the communities located in the northwestern part of the state, adjacent to metropolitan Chicago. It is situated in the southeastern section of Hammond, just off the Borman Expressway and Indianapolis Boulevard.

■ **PURDUE UNIVERSITY NORTH CENTRAL**
1401 S US Hwy. 421
Westville, IN 46391-9542
Tel: (219)785-5200
Fax: (219)785-5538
E-mail: jwhisler@pnc.edu
Web Site: www.pnc.edu/

Description: State-supported, comprehensive, coed. Part of Purdue University System. Awards associate, bachelor's, and master's degrees. Founded 1967. Setting: 305-acre rural campus with easy access to Chicago. Endowment: $3.5 million. Total enrollment: 6,048. Faculty: 277 (119 full-time, 158 part-time). Student-undergrad faculty ratio is 17:1. 1,582 applied, 72% were admitted. 7% from top 10% of their high school class, 25% from top quarter, 65% from top half. Full-time: 2,701 students, 57% women, 43% men. Part-time: 3,281 students, 61% women, 39% men. Students come from 7 states and territories, 12 other countries, 2% from out-of-state. 0.5% American Indian or Alaska Native, non-Hispanic/Latino; 10% Hispanic/Latino; 5% African American, non-Hispanic/Latino; 1% Asian, non-Hispanic/Latino; 0.1% Native Hawaiian or other Pacific Islander, non-Hispanic/Latino; 0.3% international. 34% 25 or older, 0% live on campus, 5% transferred in. Retention: 62% of full-time freshmen returned the following year. Academic areas with the most degrees conferred: business/marketing; liberal arts/general studies; engineering technologies. Calendar: semesters. Academic remediation for entering students, services for LD students, advanced placement, honors program, independent study, distance learning, double major, summer session for credit, internships, graduate courses open to undergrads. Off campus study. Study abroad program.

Entrance Requirements: Options: electronic application, deferred admission. Required: high school transcript. Recommended: SAT or ACT. Required for some: minimum 2 high school GPA. Entrance: minimally difficult. Application deadline: 8/15. Notification: continuous. SAT Reasoning Test deadline: 8/15. SAT Subject Test deadline: 8/15. Transfer credits accepted: Yes.

Costs Per Year: Application fee: $0. State resident tuition: $6440 full-time, $214.65 per credit hour part-time. Nonresident tuition: $16,164 full-time, $538.80 per credit hour part-time. Mandatory fees: $605 full-time, $20.17 per credit hour part-time. Full-time tuition and fees vary according to reciprocity agreements. Part-time tuition and fees vary according to reciprocity agreements.

Collegiate Environment: Orientation program. Drama-theater group, choral group, student-run newspaper. Social organizations: 42 open to all. Most popular organizations: Dean's Leadership Group, Society of Human Resource Management, PLAYCE (Early Childhood Education), Astronomy Club, PNC Veteran's. Major annual events: Purdue Pride Week-August, Spirit Week-January, Pounce Week-April. Student services: personal-psychological counseling. Campus security: 24-hour emergency response devices and patrols, late night transport-escort service. College housing not available. Purdue University North Central Library with 87,848 books, 42,367 serials, 531 audiovisual materials, an OPAC, and a Web page. 450 computers available on campus for general student use. A campuswide network can be accessed from off-campus. Students can access the following: online class registration. Staffed computer lab on campus provides training in use of computers, software, and the Internet.

Community Environment: This small community (Westville population 5,219) located 12 miles south of Lake Michigan is progressing under a town

and country zoning plan. Community facilities include six major civic organizations, two churches, a library, two parks, good transportation and shopping facilities.

■ **ROSE-HULMAN INSTITUTE OF TECHNOLOGY**
5500 Wabash Ave.
Terre Haute, IN 47803-3999
Tel: (812)877-1511; Free: 800-248-7448
Fax: (812)877-8941
E-mail: admissions@rose-hulman.edu
Web Site: www.rose-hulman.edu/

Description: Independent, comprehensive, coed. Awards bachelor's and master's degrees. Founded 1874. Setting: 200-acre suburban campus with easy access to Indianapolis. Endowment: $165.6 million. Research spending for the previous fiscal year: $3 million. Educational spending for the previous fiscal year: $15,196 per student. Total enrollment: 2,214. Faculty: 181 (165 full-time, 16 part-time). Student-undergrad faculty ratio is 13:1. 4,469 applied, 65% were admitted. 60% from top 10% of their high school class, 90% from top quarter, 100% from top half. 11 National Merit Scholars, 42 valedictorians, 28 student government officers. Full-time: 2,114 students, 21% women, 79% men. Part-time: 7 students, 14% women, 86% men. Students come from 48 states and territories, 14 other countries, 61% from out-of-state. 0.2% American Indian or Alaska Native, non-Hispanic/Latino; 3% Hispanic/Latino; 2% African American, non-Hispanic/Latino; 4% Asian, non-Hispanic/Latino; 0.1% Native Hawaiian or other Pacific Islander, non-Hispanic/Latino; 7% international. 1% 25 or older, 62% live on campus, 2% transferred in. Retention: 94% of full-time freshmen returned the following year. Academic areas with the most degrees conferred: engineering; physical sciences; computer and information sciences. Core. Services for LD students, advanced placement, accelerated degree program, independent study, double major, summer session for credit, adult/continuing education programs, co-op programs and internships, graduate courses open to undergrads. Off campus study at Indiana State University, St. Mary-of-the-Woods College. Study abroad program. ROTC: Army, Air Force.

Entrance Requirements: Options: electronic application, deferred admission, international baccalaureate accepted. Required: high school transcript, 1 recommendation, curricular, SAT or ACT. Recommended: essay, interview. Entrance: very difficult. Application deadline: 3/1. Notification: continuous. Transfer credits accepted: No. Applicants placed on waiting list: 95. Waitlisted applicants offered admission: 3.

Costs Per Year: Application fee: $40. One-time mandatory fee: $2400. Comprehensive fee: $50,013 includes full-time tuition ($38,313), mandatory fees ($765), and college room and board ($10,935). College room only: $6705. Full-time tuition and fees vary according to course load. Room and board charges vary according to board plan. Part-time tuition: $1118 per credit hour. Part-time tuition varies according to course load.

Collegiate Environment: Orientation program. Drama-theater group, choral group, student-run newspaper, radio station. Social organizations: 93 open to all; national fraternities, national sororities; 39% of eligible men and 36% of eligible women are members. Most popular organizations: Drama Club, yoga club, Intervarsity Christian Fellowship, Chinese Culture Club, lacrosse club. Major annual events: Homecoming, Campus Beautification Day, Bikes for Tykes Bicycle Assembly Day. Student services: health clinic, personal-psychological counseling. Campus security: 24-hour emergency response devices and patrols, late night transport-escort service, controlled dormitory access. 1,284 college housing spaces available; all were occupied in 2012-13. Freshmen guaranteed college housing. On-campus residence required in freshman year. Options: coed, men-only housing available. John A. Logan Library with 149,409 books, 9,114 serials, 556 audiovisual materials, an OPAC, and a Web page. Operations spending for the previous fiscal year: $656,492. 45 computers available on campus for general student use. Computer purchase/lease plans available. A computer is required for all students. A campuswide network can be accessed from student residence rooms and from off campus. Students can access the following: online class registration. Staffed computer lab on campus provides training in use of computers, software, and the Internet.

Community Environment: See Indiana State University.

■ **SAINT JOSEPH'S COLLEGE**
1498 S College Ave.
Rensselaer, IN 47978
Tel: (219)866-6000; Free: 800-447-8781
Fax: (219)866-6122
E-mail: admissions@saintjoe.edu

Web Site: www.saintjoe.edu/

Description: Independent Roman Catholic, comprehensive, coed. Awards associate, bachelor's, and master's degrees. Founded 1889. Setting: 180-acre small town campus. Endowment: $24.2 million. Educational spending for the previous fiscal year: $5959 per student. Total enrollment: 1,084. Faculty: 119 (59 full-time, 60 part-time). Student-undergrad faculty ratio is 13:1. 1,718 applied, 62% were admitted. 14% from top 10% of their high school class, 34% from top quarter, 69% from top half. 1 valedictorian. Full-time: 986 students, 60% women, 40% men. Part-time: 88 students, 69% women, 31% men. Students come from 22 states and territories, 9 other countries, 23% from out-of-state. 1% American Indian or Alaska Native, non-Hispanic/Latino; 4% Hispanic/Latino; 10% African American, non-Hispanic/Latino; 1% Asian, non-Hispanic/Latino; 0.1% Native Hawaiian or other Pacific Islander, non-Hispanic/Latino; 0.5% international. 14% 25 or older, 67% live on campus, 4% transferred in. Retention: 67% of full-time freshmen returned the following year. Academic areas with the most degrees conferred: health professions and related sciences; business/marketing; parks and recreation. Core. Calendar: semesters. Academic remediation for entering students, services for LD students, advanced placement, accelerated degree program, self-designed majors, honors program, independent study, double major, summer session for credit, part-time degree program, internships. Study abroad program.

Entrance Requirements: Options: electronic application, deferred admission, international baccalaureate accepted. Required: high school transcript, minimum 2 high school GPA, SAT or ACT. Recommended: interview. Required for some: essay. Entrance: moderately difficult. Application deadline: Rolling. Notification: continuous. SAT Reasoning Test deadline: 8/1. Transfer credits accepted: Yes.

Costs Per Year: Application fee: $25. Comprehensive fee: $35,600 includes full-time tuition ($27,160), mandatory fees ($190), and college room and board ($8250). College room only: $4010. Full-time tuition and fees vary according to reciprocity agreements. Room and board charges vary according to housing facility. Part-time tuition: $910 per credit. Part-time tuition varies according to course load and reciprocity agreements.

Collegiate Environment: Orientation program. Drama-theater group, choral group, marching band, student-run newspaper, radio station. Social organizations: 35 open to all. Most popular organizations: Gallagher Charitable Society, Cup O' Joe, Habitat for Humanity, Science Club, Alpha Lambda Delta. Major annual events: Little 500, Homecoming Weekend, Little Siblings Weekend. Student services: health clinic, personal-psychological counseling. Campus security: 24-hour emergency response devices and patrols, student patrols, late night transport-escort service. 745 college housing spaces available; 646 were occupied in 2012-13. Freshmen guaranteed college housing. On-campus residence required through senior year. Options: coed, men-only, women-only housing available. Robinson Memorial Library with 130,365 books, 67,760 microform titles, 13,262 serials, 16,707 audiovisual materials, an OPAC, and a Web page. Operations spending for the previous fiscal year: $463,312. 69 computers available on campus for general student use. A campuswide network can be accessed from student residence rooms. Students can access the following: online class registration. Staffed computer lab on campus provides training in use of computers, software, and the Internet.

■ SAINT MARY-OF-THE-WOODS COLLEGE

Saint Mary of the Woods, IN 47876

Tel: (812)535-5151; Free: 800-926-SMWC

Fax: (812)535-5215

E-mail: smwcadms@smwc.edu

Web Site: www.smwc.edu/

Description: Independent Roman Catholic, comprehensive, coed. Awards associate, bachelor's, and master's degrees (also offers external degree program with significant enrollment not reflected in profile). Founded 1840. Setting: 67-acre rural campus with easy access to Indianapolis. Endowment: $10.6 million. Educational spending for the previous fiscal year: $10,028 per student. Total enrollment: 956. Faculty: 64 (63 full-time, 1 part-time). Student-undergrad faculty ratio is 8:1. 424 applied, 64% were admitted. 13% from top 10% of their high school class, 44% from top quarter, 70% from top half. Full-time: 431 students, 98% women, 2% men. Part-time: 364 students, 93% women, 7% men. Students come from 36 states and territories, 7 other countries, 24% from out-of-state. 1% American Indian or Alaska Native, non-Hispanic/Latino; 2% Hispanic/Latino; 4% African American, non-Hispanic/Latino; 0.3% Asian, non-Hispanic/Latino; 0% Native Hawaiian or other Pacific Islander, non-Hispanic/Latino; 1% international. 60% 25 or older, 10% transferred in. Retention: 74% of full-time freshmen returned the following

year. Academic areas with the most degrees conferred: education; business/marketing; psychology. Core. Calendar: semesters. Academic remediation for entering students, advanced placement, accelerated degree program, self-designed majors, honors program, independent study, distance learning, double major, summer session for credit, part-time degree program, external degree program, adult/continuing education programs, internships. Off campus study at College Consortium of Western Indiana - Indiana State University, Rose-Hulman Institute of Technology, Saint Mary-of-the-Woods; Indiana College Network (ICN). Study abroad program. ROTC: Army (c), Air Force (c).

Entrance Requirements: Options: electronic application, early admission, deferred admission, international baccalaureate accepted. Required: essay, high school transcript, minimum 2.5 high school GPA, 1 recommendation, SAT or ACT. Required for some: interview. Entrance: moderately difficult. Transfer credits accepted: Yes.

Costs Per Year: Application fee: $30. One-time mandatory fee: $225. Comprehensive fee: $37,472 includes full-time tuition ($26,872), mandatory fees ($800), and college room and board ($9800). College room only: $3826. Full-time tuition and fees vary according to program and student level. Room and board charges vary according to housing facility. Part-time tuition: $482 per credit hour. Part-time mandatory fees: $150 per term. Part-time tuition and fees vary according to course load. Tuition guaranteed not to increase for student's term of enrollment.

Collegiate Environment: Orientation program. Drama-theater group, choral group, student-run newspaper. Social organizations: 30 open to all. Most popular organizations: Student Activities Committee, Chorale, Student Senate, Woods Newspaper. Major annual events: Ring Day, Spring Formal, Homecoming. Student services: health clinic, personal-psychological counseling. Campus security: 24-hour emergency response devices and patrols, late night transport-escort service. 345 college housing spaces available; 190 were occupied in 2012-13. Freshmen guaranteed college housing. On-campus residence required through senior year. Option: women-only housing available. Rooney Library with 96,835 books, 62 serials, 754 audiovisual materials, an OPAC, and a Web page. Operations spending for the previous fiscal year: $229,905. 85 computers available on campus for general student use. A campuswide network can be accessed from student residence rooms.

■ SAINT MARY'S COLLEGE

Notre Dame, IN 46556

Tel: (574)284-4000; Free: 800-551-7621

Fax: (574)284-4713

E-mail: admission@saintmarys.edu

Web Site: www.saintmarys.edu/

Description: Independent Roman Catholic, 4-year, women only. Awards bachelor's degrees. Founded 1844. Setting: 100-acre suburban campus with easy access to Chicago. Endowment: $123.3 million. Educational spending for the previous fiscal year: $14,299 per student. Total enrollment: 1,469. Faculty: 196 (123 full-time, 73 part-time). Student-undergrad faculty ratio is 10:1. 1,482 applied, 85% were admitted. 36% from top 10% of their high school class, 72% from top quarter, 94% from top half. 3 class presidents, 10 valedictorians. Full-time: 1,456 students. Part-time: 13 students. Students come from 42 states and territories, 14 other countries, 73% from out-of-state. 0.1% American Indian or Alaska Native, non-Hispanic/Latino; 10% Hispanic/Latino; 1% African American, non-Hispanic/Latino; 1% Asian, non-Hispanic/Latino; 0% Native Hawaiian or other Pacific Islander, non-Hispanic/Latino; 2% international. 1% 25 or older, 87% live on campus, 2% transferred in. Retention: 88% of full-time freshmen returned the following year. Academic areas with the most degrees conferred: health professions and related sciences; business/marketing; communication/journalism. Core. Calendar: semesters. Academic remediation for entering students, ESL program, services for LD students, advanced placement, accelerated degree program, self-designed majors, independent study, distance learning, double major, summer session for credit, part-time degree program, co-op programs and internships. Off campus study at University of Notre Dame, members of the Northern Indiana Consortium for Education. Study abroad program. ROTC: Army (c), Naval (c), Air Force (c).

Entrance Requirements: Options: electronic application, early admission, early decision, deferred admission, international baccalaureate accepted. Required: essay, high school transcript, 1 recommendation, 16 high school academic units; at least two years of study of the same foreign language, SAT or ACT. Recommended: interview. Entrance: moderately difficult. Application deadlines: 2/15, 11/15 for early decision. Notification: continuous,

12/15 for early decision. SAT Reasoning Test deadline: 3/1. Transfer credits accepted: Yes. Early decision applicants: 63. Early decision applicants admitted: 57.

Costs Per Year: Application fee: $0. Comprehensive fee: $43,420 includes full-time tuition ($32,560), mandatory fees ($720), and college room and board ($10,140). College room only: $6250. Room and board charges vary according to board plan and housing facility. Part-time tuition: $1290 per credit hour. Part-time mandatory fees: $360 per term.

Collegiate Environment: Orientation program. Drama-theater group, choral group, marching band, student-run newspaper, radio station. Social organizations: 76 open to all. Most popular organizations: Student Government Association, Dance Marathon, Class Boards, Residence Hall Association, Student Diversity Board. Major annual events: Back to School Dance, All School Formal, Diverse Student Leadership Conference. Student services: health clinic, personal-psychological counseling, women's center. Campus security: 24-hour emergency response devices and patrols, late night transport-escort service, controlled dormitory access. 1,350 college housing spaces available; 1,202 were occupied in 2012-13. Freshmen guaranteed college housing. On-campus residence required through junior year. Option: women-only housing available. Cushwa-Leighton Library with 244,566 books, 18,612 microform titles, 26,259 serials, 3,333 audiovisual materials, an OPAC, and a Web page. Operations spending for the previous fiscal year: $258,265. 303 computers available on campus for general student use. Computer purchase/lease plans available. A campuswide network can be accessed from student residence rooms and from off campus. Students can access the following: online class registration. Staffed computer lab on campus provides training in use of computers, software, and the Internet.

■ **STRAYER UNIVERSITY - NORTH INDIANAPOLIS CAMPUS**
9025 N River Rd.
Ste. 400
Indianapolis, IN 46240
Tel: (317)810-0600
Fax: (317)574-0003
Web Site: www.strayer.edu/campus/north-indianapolis
Description: Proprietary, comprehensive, coed. Awards bachelor's and master's degrees.

■ **TAYLOR UNIVERSITY**
236 W Reade Ave.
Upland, IN 46989-1001
Tel: (765)998-2751; Free: 800-882-3456
Fax: (765)998-4925
E-mail: admissions@taylor.edu
Web Site: www.taylor.edu/
Description: Independent interdenominational, comprehensive, coed. Awards associate, bachelor's, and master's degrees. Founded 1846. Setting: 950-acre rural campus with easy access to Indianapolis. Endowment: $67.5 million. Research spending for the previous fiscal year: $428,000. Educational spending for the previous fiscal year: $10,208 per student. Total enrollment: 2,358. Faculty: 253 (134 full-time, 119 part-time). Student-undergrad faculty ratio is 12:1. 1,787 applied, 84% were admitted. 44% from top 10% of their high school class, 72% from top quarter, 91% from top half. 2 National Merit Scholars, 16 valedictorians. Full-time: 1,846 students, 54% women, 46% men. Part-time: 391 students, 64% women, 36% men. Students come from 42 states and territories, 27 other countries, 63% from out-of-state. 0.4% American Indian or Alaska Native, non-Hispanic/Latino; 2% Hispanic/Latino; 2% African American, non-Hispanic/Latino; 2% Asian, non-Hispanic/Latino; 0.2% Native Hawaiian or other Pacific Islander, non-Hispanic/Latino; 4% international. 1% 25 or older, 86% live on campus, 2% transferred in. Retention: 88% of full-time freshmen returned the following year. Academic areas with the most degrees conferred: education; business/marketing; social sciences. Core. Calendar: 4-1-4. Academic remediation for entering students, ESL program, services for LD students, advanced placement, self-designed majors, honors program, independent study, distance learning, double major, summer session for credit, part-time degree program, co-op programs and internships, graduate courses open to undergrads. Off campus study at Christian College Coalition and the Christian College Consortium, Bowling Green University, Trinity Christian College, Gordon College. Study abroad program.
Entrance Requirements: Options: electronic application, early action, deferred admission. Required: essay, high school transcript, 2 recommendations, interview, SAT or ACT. Recommended: minimum 2.8 high school GPA.

Entrance: moderately difficult. Application deadlines: Rolling, 12/1 for early action. Notification: continuous, 12/20 for early action. Preference given to Evangelical Christians. SAT Reasoning Test deadline: 6/1. Transfer credits accepted: Yes.

Costs Per Year: Application fee: $25. Comprehensive fee: $35,845 includes full-time tuition ($27,850), mandatory fees ($238), and college room and board ($7757). College room only: $4041. Full-time tuition and fees vary according to course load. Room and board charges vary according to board plan and housing facility. Part-time tuition: $981 per credit hour. Part-time mandatory fees: $36.50 per term. Part-time tuition and fees vary according to course load.

Collegiate Environment: Orientation program. Drama-theater group, choral group, student-run newspaper, radio station. Social organizations: 67 open to all; 10% of eligible men and 12% of eligible women are members. Most popular organizations: TWO (Taylor World Outreach), IFC (Integration of Faith and Culture), Spring Break Mission Trips, Community Outreach, TSO (Taylor Student Organization). Major annual events: Airband, Silent Night Basketball Game and All Campus Christmas Party, Nostalgia Night. Student services: health clinic, personal-psychological counseling. Campus security: 24-hour patrols, student patrols, late night transport-escort service. 1,692 college housing spaces available; 1,644 were occupied in 2012-13. Freshmen guaranteed college housing. On-campus residence required through junior year. Options: men-only, women-only housing available. Zondervan Library with 201,653 books, 14,661 microform titles, 40,225 serials, 15,505 audiovisual materials, an OPAC, and a Web page. Operations spending for the previous fiscal year: $1 million. 437 computers available on campus for general student use. Computer purchase/lease plans available. A campuswide network can be accessed from student residence rooms and from off campus. Students can access the following: online class registration. Staffed computer lab on campus provides training in use of computers, software, and the Internet.

Community Environment: Upland (population 3,700) has all the advantages of quiet, country life with the nearby cities for activities. It is located 14 miles southeast of Marion and 23 miles north of Muncie. Buses and trains are accessible. The communities have churches of many denominations, health services and hospitals. Recreational activities are hunting, tennis, boating, fishing, golf and other sports.

■ **TRINE UNIVERSITY**
1 University Ave.
Angola, IN 46703-1764
Tel: (260)665-4100; Free: 800-347-4TSU
Fax: (260)665-4292
E-mail: admit@trine.edu
Web Site: www.trine.edu/
Description: Independent, comprehensive, coed. Awards associate, bachelor's, and master's degrees. Founded 1884. Setting: 400-acre small town campus. Endowment: $22.7 million. Educational spending for the previous fiscal year: $6898 per student. Total enrollment: 1,948. Faculty: 137 (79 full-time, 58 part-time). Student-undergrad faculty ratio is 15:1. 2,867 applied, 72% were admitted. 22% from top 10% of their high school class, 53% from top quarter, 87% from top half. 19 valedictorians. Full-time: 1,498 students, 30% women, 70% men. Part-time: 445 students, 57% women, 43% men. Students come from 29 states and territories, 14 other countries, 36% from out-of-state. 0.3% American Indian or Alaska Native, non-Hispanic/Latino; 2% Hispanic/Latino; 2% African American, non-Hispanic/Latino; 0.4% Asian, non-Hispanic/Latino; 0.3% Native Hawaiian or other Pacific Islander, non-Hispanic/Latino; 4% international. 3% 25 or older, 56% live on campus, 2% transferred in. Retention: 69% of full-time freshmen returned the following year. Academic areas with the most degrees conferred: engineering; business/marketing; education. Core. Calendar: semesters. Academic remediation for entering students, ESL program, advanced placement, self-designed majors, honors program, distance learning, double major, summer session for credit, part-time degree program, adult/continuing education programs, co-op programs and internships. Study abroad program. ROTC: Air Force (c).
Entrance Requirements: Options: electronic application, deferred admission, international baccalaureate accepted. Required: high school transcript, minimum 2.5 high school GPA, SAT or ACT. Recommended: essay, 2 recommendations, interview. Entrance: moderately difficult. Application deadline: 8/1. Notification: 8/15. SAT Reasoning Test deadline: 8/1. Transfer credits accepted: Yes.
Costs Per Year: Application fee: $0. Comprehensive fee: $38,350 includes full-time tuition ($28,700), mandatory fees ($150), and college room and

board ($9500). Full-time tuition and fees vary according to degree level, location, and program. Room and board charges vary according to board plan and housing facility. Part-time tuition: $890 per credit hour. Part-time tuition varies according to degree level, location, and program.

Collegiate Environment: Orientation program. Drama-theater group, choral group, marching band, student-run newspaper, radio station. Social organizations: 14 open to all; national fraternities, national sororities, local sororities; 23% of eligible men and 24% of eligible women are members. Most popular organizations: Campus Christian House, Fellowship of Christian Athletes, Multicultural Student Organization, Math Club, Trine Disc Golf Collective. Major annual events: Homecoming, Bingo for Bucks, Moonlight Breakfast. Student services: health clinic, personal-psychological counseling. Campus security: 24-hour emergency response devices and patrols, late night transport-escort service, controlled dormitory access. College housing designed to accommodate 1,067 students; 1,078 undergraduates lived in college housing during 2012-13. Freshmen guaranteed college housing. On-campus residence required through senior year. Options: coed, men-only, women-only housing available. Trine University Sponsel Library plus 1 other with 115,719 books, 314 microform titles, 31,993 serials, 3,431 audiovisual materials, an OPAC, and a Web page. Operations spending for the previous fiscal year: $394,708. 700 computers available on campus for general student use. Computer purchase/lease plans available. A campuswide network can be accessed from student residence rooms. Students can access the following: online class registration, online campus billing accounts. Staffed computer lab on campus provides training in use of computers, software, and the Internet.

Community Environment: Angola, population 7,890, is situated at the intersection of U.S. Highways 20, 27, I-69 and the Indiana Toll Road. The city has a small airport. Recreational facilities include three golf courses, including one located on the Tri-State campus, Pokagon State Park five miles north, and many miles of shoreline surrounding more than 100 spring-fed lakes.

■ UNIVERSITY OF EVANSVILLE

1800 Lincoln Ave.
Evansville, IN 47722
Tel: (812)488-2000; Free: 800-423-8633
Fax: (812)474-4076
E-mail: admission@evansville.edu
Web Site: www.evansville.edu/

Description: Independent, comprehensive, coed, affiliated with United Methodist Church. Awards associate, bachelor's, master's, and doctoral degrees. Founded 1854. Setting: 75-acre urban campus. Endowment: $74.4 million. Research spending for the previous fiscal year: $101,030. Educational spending for the previous fiscal year: $10,401 per student. Total enrollment: 2,757. Faculty: 238 (179 full-time, 59 part-time). Student-undergrad faculty ratio is 13:1. 2,879 applied, 80% were admitted. 40% from top 10% of their high school class, 70% from top quarter, 95% from top half. 6 National Merit Scholars, 36 valedictorians. Full-time: 2,418 students, 59% women, 41% men. Part-time: 194 students, 62% women, 38% men. Students come from 42 states and territories, 45 other countries, 43% from out-of-state. 0.1% American Indian or Alaska Native, non-Hispanic/Latino; 3% Hispanic/Latino; 3% African American, non-Hispanic/Latino; 1% Asian, non-Hispanic/Latino; 0.1% Native Hawaiian or other Pacific Islander, non-Hispanic/Latino; 7% international. 4% 25 or older, 66% live on campus, 3% transferred in. Retention: 85% of full-time freshmen returned the following year. Academic areas with the most degrees conferred: business/marketing; visual and performing arts; health professions and related sciences; engineering. Core. Calendar: semesters. ESL program, services for LD students, advanced placement, accelerated degree program, self-designed majors, honors program, independent study, distance learning, double major, summer session for credit, part-time degree program, external degree program, adult/continuing education programs, co-op programs and internships, graduate courses open to undergrads. Study abroad program. ROTC: Army (c).

Entrance Requirements: Options: electronic application, early action, deferred admission, international baccalaureate accepted. Required: essay, high school transcript, 1 recommendation, SAT or ACT. Recommended: minimum 3 high school GPA, interview. Required for some: interview. Entrance: moderately difficult. Application deadlines: 2/1, 12/1 for early action. Notification: 2/15, 12/15 for early action. SAT Reasoning Test deadline: 2/1. Transfer credits accepted: Yes. Early action applicants: 2,754. Early action applicants admitted: 2,361.

Costs Per Year: Application fee: $35. Comprehensive fee: $40,566 includes

full-time tuition ($29,740), mandatory fees ($816), and college room and board ($10,010). College room only: $5230. Room and board charges vary according to board plan and housing facility. Part-time tuition: $830 per credit hour. Part-time mandatory fees: $50 per term. Part-time tuition and fees vary according to course load.

Collegiate Environment: Orientation program. Drama-theater group, choral group, student-run newspaper, radio station. Social organizations: 166 open to all; national fraternities, national sororities, local sororities; 30% of eligible men and 28% of eligible women are members. Most popular organizations: Phi Eta Sigma, International Club, PT Club, Student Christian Fellowship, Alpha Omicron Pi. Major annual events: Labor Day Picnic and Student Organization Fair, Bike Race, Sunset Concert. Student services: health clinic, personal-psychological counseling. Campus security: 24-hour emergency response devices and patrols, student patrols, late night transport-escort service, controlled dormitory access. 1,835 college housing spaces available; 1,555 were occupied in 2012-13. Freshmen guaranteed college housing. On-campus residence required in freshman year. Options: coed, men-only, women-only housing available. University of Evansville Libraries with 282,516 books, 474,391 microform titles, 475 serials, 14,238 audiovisual materials, an OPAC, and a Web page. Operations spending for the previous fiscal year: $1.5 million. 385 computers available on campus for general student use. A campuswide network can be accessed from student residence rooms and from off campus. Students can access the following: online class registration. Staffed computer lab on campus provides training in use of computers, software, and the Internet.

Community Environment: Evansville, population 115,900, is the fourth largest city in Indiana, and the largest in Southern Indiana. Cultural activities include a philharmonic orchestra, art museum, planetarium, zoo, civic and repertory theaters, and the remains of early Indian settlement.

■ UNIVERSITY OF INDIANAPOLIS

1400 E Hanna Ave.
Indianapolis, IN 46227-3697
Tel: (317)788-3368; Free: 800-232-8634
Fax: (317)788-3300
E-mail: admissions@uindy.edu
Web Site: www.uindy.edu/

Description: Independent, comprehensive, coed, affiliated with United Methodist Church. Awards associate, bachelor's, master's, and doctoral degrees. Founded 1902. Setting: 65-acre urban campus with easy access to Indianapolis. Endowment: $72.7 million. Total enrollment: 5,417. Faculty: 493 (218 full-time, 275 part-time). Student-undergrad faculty ratio is 15:1. 5,396 applied, 79% were admitted. 27% from top 10% of their high school class, 56% from top quarter, 88% from top half. Full-time: 3,036 students, 64% women, 36% men. Part-time: 1,169 students, 77% women, 23% men. 9% from out-of-state. 0.2% American Indian or Alaska Native, non-Hispanic/Latino; 2% Hispanic/Latino; 13% African American, non-Hispanic/Latino; 1% Asian, non-Hispanic/Latino; 0.1% Native Hawaiian or other Pacific Islander, non-Hispanic/Latino; 5% international. 28% 25 or older, 36% live on campus, 0% transferred in. Retention: 74% of full-time freshmen returned the following year. Academic areas with the most degrees conferred: business/marketing; health professions and related sciences; education. Core. Calendar: semesters. Academic remediation for entering students, ESL program, services for LD students, advanced placement, accelerated degree program, self-designed majors, freshman honors college, honors program, independent study, distance learning, double major, summer session for credit, part-time degree program, adult/continuing education programs, co-op programs and internships, graduate courses open to undergrads. Off campus study at 7 members of the Consortium for Urban Education, 10 members of the May Term Consortium. Study abroad program. ROTC: Army (c).

Entrance Requirements: Options: electronic application, deferred admission, international baccalaureate accepted. Required: high school transcript, minimum 2 high school GPA, SAT or ACT. Required for some: interview. Entrance: moderately difficult. Application deadlines: Rolling, Rolling for nonresidents. Notification: continuous, continuous for nonresidents. SAT Reasoning Test deadline: 8/1. Transfer credits accepted: Yes.

Costs Per Year: Application fee: $25. Comprehensive fee: $32,920 includes full-time tuition ($23,590), mandatory fees ($240), and college room and board ($9090). College room only: $4300. Room and board charges vary according to board plan and housing facility. Part-time tuition: $982 per credit hour. Part-time tuition varies according to course load.

Collegiate Environment: Orientation program. Drama-theater group, choral group, student-run newspaper, radio station. Social organizations: 37 open

to all. Most popular organizations: Fellowship of Christian Athletes, Intercultural Association, Circle K, Indianapolis Student Government, Residence Hall Association. Major annual events: Late Nights, Winter Formal Dance, Cyclerama. Student services: health clinic, personal-psychological counseling. Campus security: 24-hour emergency response devices and patrols, student patrols, late night transport-escort service, emergency call boxes. Krannert Memorial Library with 173,363 books, 15,551 microform titles, 1,015 serials, an OPAC, and a Web page. 222 computers available on campus for general student use. A campuswide network can be accessed from student residence rooms and from off campus. Staffed computer lab on campus (open 24 hours a day).

Community Environment: The university is located in the southern, residential suburb of Indianapolis known as University Heights. Indianapolis is the nation's third largest capital city and is known as the"Amateur Sports Capital of the World." The metropolitan area has a population of more than one million. Recreational, cultural, and social opportunities abound. Bus, train, and airline services are within minutes of the campus. There are also numerous shops, restaurants, hotels, and a major shopping mall nearby.

■ **UNIVERSITY OF NOTRE DAME**

Notre Dame, IN 46556

Tel: (574)631-5000

Fax: (574)631-8865

E-mail: admissions@nd.edu

Web Site: www.nd.edu/

Description: Independent Roman Catholic, university, coed. Awards bachelor's, master's, and doctoral degrees. Founded 1842. Setting: 1,250-acre suburban campus. Endowment: $7.6 billion. Total enrollment: 12,126. Faculty: 1,221 (1,082 full-time, 139 part-time). Student-undergrad faculty ratio is 11:1. 16,957 applied, 23% were admitted. 89% from top 10% of their high school class, 97% from top quarter, 100% from top half. Full-time: 8,462 students, 47% women, 53% men. Part-time: 13 students, 46% women, 54% men. Students come from 51 states and territories, 40 other countries, 92% from out-of-state. 0.4% American Indian or Alaska Native, non-Hispanic/Latino; 10% Hispanic/Latino; 3% African American, non-Hispanic/Latino; 7% Asian, non-Hispanic/Latino; 0.01% Native Hawaiian or other Pacific Islander, non-Hispanic/Latino; 4% international. 0% 25 or older, 80% live on campus. Retention: 97% of full-time freshmen returned the following year. Academic areas with the most degrees conferred: business/marketing; social sciences; engineering. Core. Calendar: semesters. Services for LD students, advanced placement, self-designed majors, honors program, independent study, double major, summer session for credit, internships, graduate courses open to undergrads. Off campus study at Saint Mary's College (IN). Study abroad program. ROTC: Army, Naval, Air Force.

Entrance Requirements: Options: electronic application, early action, deferred admission, international baccalaureate accepted. Required: essay, high school transcript, 1 recommendation, SAT or ACT. Required for some: SAT Subject Tests. Entrance: most difficult. Application deadlines: 12/31, 11/1 for early action. Notification: 4/10, 12/21 for early action. SAT Reasoning Test deadline: 3/1. SAT Subject Test deadline: 3/1. Applicants placed on waiting list: 2,461. Wait-listed applicants offered admission: 86. Early action applicants: 4,212. Early action applicants admitted: 1,851.

Costs Per Year: Application fee: $75. Comprehensive fee: $54,905 includes full-time tuition ($42,464), mandatory fees ($507), and college room and board ($11,934). Part-time tuition: $1769 per credit hour.

Collegiate Environment: Orientation program. Drama-theater group, choral group, marching band, student-run newspaper, radio station. Most popular organizations: marching band, Circle K, Finance Club, Notre Dame/St. Mary's Right to Life. Major annual events: home football weekends, Bookstore Basketball Tournament, Junior Parents' Weekend. Student services: health clinic, personal-psychological counseling, women's center. Campus security: 24-hour emergency response devices and patrols, student patrols, late night transport-escort service, controlled dormitory access, crime prevention and personal safety workshops, full-time trained police investigators, fire sprinklers in all residence halls. 6,481 college housing spaces available; 6,464 were occupied in 2012-13. Freshmen guaranteed college housing. On-campus residence required in freshman year. Options: men-only, women-only housing available. Hesburgh Library plus 9 others with 3.9 million books, 4 million microform titles, 88,352 serials, 43,368 audiovisual materials, and an OPAC. 200 computers available on campus for general student use. Computer purchase/lease plans available. A campuswide network can be accessed from student residence rooms and from off campus. Students can access the following: online class registration. Staffed computer lab on campus (open 24 hours a day).

Community Environment: The South Bend area has a population of over 100,000. The downtown district, located 3 miles south of the campus, has enjoyed a complete urban renewal and offers attractive services to the students. A world-class water raceway provides excellent opportunities for challenging kayaking, tubing and canoeing. Home of the College Football Hall of Fame. Several major shopping malls with direct bus service to campus are less than 15 minutes away.

■ **UNIVERSITY OF PHOENIX–INDIANAPOLIS CAMPUS**

7999 Knue Rd. Dr.

Ste. 100 and 500

Indianapolis, IN 46250-932

Tel: (317)585-8610; Free: 866-766-0766

Web Site: www.phoenix.edu/

Description: Proprietary, comprehensive, coed. Awards associate, bachelor's, and master's degrees. Founded 2003. Setting: urban campus. Total enrollment: 339. Faculty: 80 (15 full-time, 65 part-time). 43 applied, 100% were admitted. Full-time: 271 students, 73% women, 27% men. 85% 25 or older. Academic areas with the most degrees conferred: business/marketing; health professions and related sciences. Core. Calendar: continuous. Services for LD students, advanced placement, accelerated degree program, independent study, distance learning, graduate courses open to undergrads.

Entrance Requirements: Open admission. Options: electronic application, deferred admission. Required: 1 recommendation. Required for some: high school transcript. Entrance: noncompetitive. Application deadline: Rolling.

Collegiate Environment: Campus security: late night transport-escort service.

■ **UNIVERSITY OF PHOENIX–NORTHWEST INDIANA CAMPUS**

359 E 81st Ave.

Merrillville, IN 46410

Tel: (219)769-6418; Free: 866-766-0766

Web Site: www.phoenix.edu/

Description: Proprietary, comprehensive, coed. Awards associate, bachelor's, master's, and doctoral degrees.

■ **UNIVERSITY OF SAINT FRANCIS**

2701 Spring St.

Fort Wayne, IN 46808-3994

Tel: (260)434-3100; Free: 800-729-4732

E-mail: admis@sf.edu

Web Site: www.sf.edu/

Description: Independent Roman Catholic, comprehensive, coed. Awards associate, bachelor's, and master's degrees. Founded 1890. Setting: 74-acre suburban campus. Endowment: $14.8 million. Total enrollment: 2,464. Faculty: 249 (128 full-time, 121 part-time). Student-undergrad faculty ratio is 15:1. 1,782 applied, 54% were admitted. 10% from top 10% of their high school class, 42% from top quarter, 78% from top half. Full-time: 1,584 students, 65% women, 35% men. Part-time: 417 students, 80% women, 20% men. Students come from 17 states and territories, 12 other countries, 10% from out-of-state. 5% Hispanic/Latino; 7% African American, non-Hispanic/Latino; 1% Asian, non-Hispanic/Latino; 0.3% international. 22% 25 or older, 26% live on campus, 11% transferred in. Academic areas with the most degrees conferred: health professions and related sciences; visual and performing arts; education. Core. Calendar: semesters. Academic remediation for entering students, services for LD students, advanced placement, freshman honors college, honors program, independent study, distance learning, double major, summer session for credit, part-time degree program, co-op programs and internships, graduate courses open to undergrads. Off campus study. Study abroad program. ROTC: Army (c).

Entrance Requirements: Options: electronic application, deferred admission, international baccalaureate accepted. Required: high school transcript, minimum 2.3 high school GPA, SAT or ACT. Recommended: essay. Required for some: interview. Entrance: moderately difficult. Application deadline: Rolling. Notification: 8/15. Transfer credits accepted: Yes.

Costs Per Year: Application fee: $20. Comprehensive fee: $32,730 includes full-time tuition ($23,560), mandatory fees ($1000), and college room and board ($8170). Full-time tuition and fees vary according to course load. Room and board charges vary according to board plan and housing facility. Part-time tuition: $730 per credit hour. Part-time mandatory fees: $20 per credit hour. Part-time tuition and fees vary according to course load.

Collegiate Environment: Orientation program. Drama-theater group, choral group, student-run newspaper. Most popular organizations: Student Activities Council, Art Club, Student Government Organization, Student Nursing Association, Residence Hall Council. Major annual events: Homecoming, Spring Fling. Student services: personal-psychological counseling. Campus security: 24-hour emergency response devices and patrols, late night transport-escort service, controlled dormitory access. Lee and Jim Vann Library with an OPAC and a Web page. 139 computers available on campus for general student use. Computer purchase/lease plans available. A campuswide network can be accessed from student residence rooms. Students can access the following: online class registration. Staffed computer lab on campus provides training in use of computers, software, and the Internet.

■ UNIVERSITY OF SOUTHERN INDIANA

8600 University Blvd.
Evansville, IN 47712-3590
Tel: (812)464-8600; Free: 800-467-1965
Fax: (812)465-7154
E-mail: enroll@usi.edu
Web Site: www.usi.edu/

Description: State-supported, comprehensive, coed. Part of Indiana Commission for Higher Education. Awards associate, bachelor's, master's, and doctoral degrees. Founded 1965. Setting: 330-acre suburban campus. Research spending for the previous fiscal year: $480,018. Educational spending for the previous fiscal year: $2272 per student. Total enrollment: 10,467. Faculty: 681 (332 full-time, 349 part-time). Student-undergrad faculty ratio is 17:1. 6,279 applied, 72% were admitted. 11% from top 10% of their high school class, 25% from top quarter, 74% from top half. 33 valedictorians. Full-time: 7,902 students, 59% women, 41% men. Part-time: 1,600 students, 66% women, 34% men. Students come from 44 states and territories, 37 other countries, 8% from out-of-state. 0.3% American Indian or Alaska Native, non-Hispanic/Latino; 1% Hispanic/Latino; 5% African American, non-Hispanic/Latino; 1% Asian, non-Hispanic/Latino; 0.1% Native Hawaiian or other Pacific Islander, non-Hispanic/Latino; 3% international. 18% 25 or older, 27% live on campus, 7% transferred in. Retention: 67% of full-time freshmen returned the following year. Academic areas with the most degrees conferred: health professions and related sciences; business/marketing; education. Core. Calendar: semesters. Academic remediation for entering students, ESL program, services for LD students, advanced placement, honors program, independent study, distance learning, double major, summer session for credit, part-time degree program, adult/continuing education programs, co-op programs and internships, graduate courses open to undergrads. Study abroad program. ROTC: Army.

Entrance Requirements: Options: electronic application, international baccalaureate accepted. Required: high school transcript, SAT or ACT. Recommended: essay, minimum 2 high school GPA. Required for some: interview. Entrance: moderately difficult. Application deadline: 8/10. Notification: continuous. SAT Reasoning Test deadline: 8/10. Transfer credits accepted: Yes.

Costs Per Year: Application fee: $40. One-time mandatory fee: $100. State resident tuition: $6085 full-time, $202.83 per credit hour part-time. Nonresident tuition: $14,485 full-time, $482.83 per credit hour part-time. Mandatory fees: $240 full-time. Full-time tuition and fees vary according to course load, program, and reciprocity agreements. Part-time tuition varies according to course load, program, and reciprocity agreements. College room and board: $7502. College room only: $4032. Room and board charges vary according to board plan and housing facility.

Collegiate Environment: Orientation program. Drama-theater group, choral group, student-run newspaper, radio station. Social organizations: 122 open to all; national fraternities, national sororities. Most popular organizations: Activities Programming Board, Interfraternity Council, Panhellenic Council, International Student Organization, Habitat for Humanity. Major annual events: Midnight Breakfast, Relay for Life, International Food Expo. Student services: health clinic, personal-psychological counseling. Campus security: 24-hour emergency response devices and patrols, student patrols, late night transport-escort service, controlled dormitory access. 2,808 college housing spaces available; 2,591 were occupied in 2012-13. No special consideration for freshman housing applicants. Option: coed housing available. David L. Rice Library with 373,612 books, 575,614 microform titles, 40,806 serials, 7,164 audiovisual materials, an OPAC, and a Web page. Operations spending for the previous fiscal year: $2.7 million. 306 computers available on campus for general student use. A campuswide network can be accessed from student residence rooms and from off campus. Students can access the following: online class registration. Staffed computer lab on campus provides training in use of computers, software, and the Internet.

Community Environment: See University of Evansville.

■ VALPARAISO UNIVERSITY

1700 Chapel Dr.
Valparaiso, IN 46383
Tel: (219)464-5000; Free: 888-GO-VALPO
Fax: (219)464-6898
E-mail: undergrad.admission@valpo.edu
Web Site: www.valpo.edu/

Description: Independent, university, coed, affiliated with Lutheran Church. Awards associate, bachelor's, master's, and doctoral degrees and post-master's certificates. Founded 1859. Setting: 320-acre small town campus with easy access to Chicago. Endowment: $163.5 million. Research spending for the previous fiscal year: $1.3 million. Educational spending for the previous fiscal year: $11,715 per student. Total enrollment: 4,078. Faculty: 380 (267 full-time, 113 part-time). Student-undergrad faculty ratio is 13:1. 5,555 applied, 80% were admitted. 35% from top 10% of their high school class, 66% from top quarter, 93% from top half. 3 National Merit Scholars, 14 valedictorians. Full-time: 2,855 students, 53% women, 47% men. Part-time: 125 students, 62% women, 38% men. Students come from 46 states and territories, 47 other countries, 59% from out-of-state. 0.2% American Indian or Alaska Native, non-Hispanic/Latino; 7% Hispanic/Latino; 5% African American, non-Hispanic/Latino; 2% Asian, non-Hispanic/Latino; 0.1% Native Hawaiian or other Pacific Islander, non-Hispanic/Latino; 7% international. 6% 25 or older, 65% live on campus, 6% transferred in. Retention: 87% of full-time freshmen returned the following year. Academic areas with the most degrees conferred: business/marketing; health professions and related sciences; engineering. Core. Calendar: semesters. ESL program, services for LD students, advanced placement, accelerated degree program, self-designed majors, freshman honors college, honors program, independent study, distance learning, double major, summer session for credit, part-time degree program, adult/continuing education programs, co-op programs and internships, graduate courses open to undergrads. Off campus study at Associated Colleges of the Midwest, American University, Lutheran College Washington Consortium, Drew University. Study abroad program. ROTC: Army (c), Air Force (c).

Entrance Requirements: Options: electronic application, deferred admission, international baccalaureate accepted. Required: essay, high school transcript, SAT or ACT. Recommended: 2 recommendations, interview. Required for some: interview. Entrance: moderately difficult. Application deadlines: Rolling, Rolling for nonresidents. Notification: continuous, continuous for nonresidents. Transfer credits accepted: Yes.

Costs Per Year: Comprehensive fee: $41,414 includes full-time tuition ($31,170), mandatory fees ($1080), and college room and board ($9164). College room only: $5564. Full-time tuition and fees vary according to course load and program. Room and board charges vary according to housing facility and student level. Part-time tuition: $1400 per credit hour. Part-time mandatory fees: $96 per term. Part-time tuition and fees vary according to course load and program.

Collegiate Environment: Orientation program. Drama-theater group, choral group, student-run newspaper, radio station. Social organizations: 88 open to all; national fraternities, local sororities; 20% of eligible men and 20% of eligible women are members. Most popular organizations: Union Board, student government, student volunteer organization, chapel programs. Major annual events: Homecoming, Spring Weekend, Martin Luther King, Jr. Day. Student services: legal services, health clinic, personal-psychological counseling. Campus security: 24-hour emergency response devices and patrols, late night transport-escort service, controlled dormitory access. 2,064 college housing spaces available; 1,826 were occupied in 2012-13. Freshmen guaranteed college housing. On-campus residence required through junior year. Options: coed, women-only housing available. Christopher Center for Library and Information Resources plus 1 other with 580,732 books, 1.9 million microform titles, 43,700 serials, 11,862 audiovisual materials, an OPAC, and a Web page. Operations spending for the previous fiscal year: $3.7 million. 500 computers available on campus for general student use. A campuswide network can be accessed from student residence rooms and from off campus. Students can access the following: online class registration, Web academic information, degree audit. Staffed computer lab on campus provides training in use of computers, software, and the Internet.

Community Environment: Valparaiso University is located 50 miles southeast of Chicago. For those interested in off-campus recreation and entertainment, it is a 20-minute drive to the Indiana Dunes National Lakeshore and less than an hour to the many theaters, museums, restaurants and athletic events of Chicago.

■ **VET TECH INSTITUTE AT INTERNATIONAL BUSINESS COLLEGE (FORT WAYNE)**

5699 Coventry Ln.
Fort Wayne, IN 46804
Tel: (260)459-4500; Free: 800-589-6363
Web Site: www.vettechinstitute.edu/
Description: Private, 2-year, coed. Awards terminal associate degrees. Founded 2005. Setting: suburban campus. Total enrollment: 125. 360 applied, 48% were admitted. Accelerated degree program, internships.

■ **VET TECH INSTITUTE AT INTERNATIONAL BUSINESS COLLEGE (INDIANAPOLIS)**

7205 Shadeland Station
Indianapolis, IN 46256
Tel: (317)813-2300; Free: 877-835-7297
Fax: (317)841-6419
Web Site: www.vettechinstitute.edu/indianapolis
Description: Private, 2-year, coed. Awards terminal associate degrees. Founded 2007. Setting: suburban campus. Total enrollment: 111. 418 applied, 45% were admitted. Accelerated degree program, internships.

■ **VINCENNES UNIVERSITY**

1002 N First St.
Vincennes, IN 47591-5202
Tel: (812)888-8888; Free: 800-742-9198
Fax: (812)888-5868
Web Site: www.vinu.edu/
Description: State-supported, primarily 2-year, coed. Awards certificates, transfer associate, terminal associate, and bachelor's degrees. Founded 1801. Setting: 100-acre small town campus. Total enrollment: 17,530. Faculty: 1,614 (241 full-time, 1,373 part-time). Student-undergrad faculty ratio is 14:1. Full-time: 6,199 students, 47% women, 53% men. Part-time: 11,331 students, 44% women, 56% men. 0.3% American Indian or Alaska Native, non-Hispanic/Latino; 2% Hispanic/Latino; 11% African American, non-Hispanic/Latino; 0.4% Asian, non-Hispanic/Latino; 0.2% Native Hawaiian or other Pacific Islander, non-Hispanic/Latino; 1% international. Retention: 69% of full-time freshmen returned the following year. Academic areas with the most degrees conferred: education; health professions and related sciences; homeland security, law enforcement, firefighting, and protective services. Core. Calendar: semesters. Academic remediation for entering students, ESL program, services for LD students, advanced placement, honors program, distance learning, double major, summer session for credit, part-time degree program, external degree program, adult/continuing education programs. Off campus study at 30 universities in Indiana. ROTC: Army (c), Air Force (c).
Entrance Requirements: Open admission except for health-related programs. Options: electronic application, early admission, deferred admission. Required: high school transcript. Required for some: interview. Entrance: noncompetitive. Application deadline: Rolling. Notification: continuous until 8/1. Transfer credits accepted: Yes.
Costs Per Year: Application fee: $20. State resident tuition: $4882 full-time, $2013 per year part-time. Nonresident tuition: $11,542 full-time, $4580 per year part-time. Full-time tuition varies according to course level, course load, location, and program. Part-time tuition varies according to course level, course load, location, and program. College room and board: $8152. Room and board charges vary according to board plan, gender, and housing facility.
Collegiate Environment: Orientation program. Drama-theater group, choral group, student-run newspaper, radio station. Social organizations: national fraternities, national sororities, local fraternities, local sororities. Student services: health clinic, personal-psychological counseling. Campus security: 24-hour emergency response devices and patrols, student patrols, late night transport-escort service, controlled dormitory access, surveillance cameras. 2,314 college housing spaces available; 1,864 were occupied in 2012-13. Freshmen guaranteed college housing. On-campus residence required in freshman year. Options: coed, men-only, women-only housing available.
Community Environment: Vincennes (population 18,000) is the oldest city in the state and was the capital of the Old Northwest. On the banks of the Wabash River, Vincennes is the distribution point for this area, which produces peaches, apples, cantaloupes, watermelons, sweet potatoes and wheat. Points of interest are the Cathedral Library, George Rogers Clark National Historic Park, Harrison Mansion, Indiana Territory State Memorial and the Old Cathedral.

■ **VINCENNES UNIVERSITY JASPER CAMPUS**

850 College Ave.
Jasper, IN 47546-9393
Tel: (812)482-3030; Free: 800-809-VUJC
Fax: (812)481-5960
E-mail: lagilbert@vinu.edu
Web Site: vujc.vinu.edu/
Description: State-supported, primarily 2-year, coed. Part of Vincennes University. Awards certificates, transfer associate, terminal associate, and bachelor's degrees. Founded 1970. Setting: 140-acre small town campus. Total enrollment: 915. Faculty: 51 (20 full-time, 31 part-time). Student-undergrad faculty ratio is 16:1. 3% from top 10% of their high school class, 20% from top quarter, 40% from top half. Students come from 1 other country. 50% 25 or older. Core. Calendar: semesters. Academic remediation for entering students, advanced placement, distance learning, summer session for credit, part-time degree program, adult/continuing education programs.
Entrance Requirements: Open admission. Required: high school transcript. Entrance: noncompetitive. Application deadline: Rolling.
Collegiate Environment: Orientation program. Student-run newspaper. Student services: personal-psychological counseling. Vincennes University Jasper Library with 14,000 books, 180 serials, and an OPAC. 140 computers available on campus for general student use. A campuswide network can be accessed from off-campus.

■ **WABASH COLLEGE**

PO Box 352
Crawfordsville, IN 47933-0352
Tel: (765)361-6100; Free: 800-345-5385
Fax: (765)361-6437
E-mail: admissions@wabash.edu
Web Site: www.wabash.edu/
Description: Independent, 4-year, men only. Awards bachelor's degrees. Founded 1832. Setting: 60-acre small town campus with easy access to Indianapolis. Endowment: $322.9 million. Research spending for the previous fiscal year: $2 million. Educational spending for the previous fiscal year: $10,752 per student. Total enrollment: 906. Faculty: 97 (91 full-time, 6 part-time). Student-undergrad faculty ratio is 10:1. 1,331 applied, 67% were admitted. 37% from top 10% of their high school class, 70% from top quarter, 94% from top half. 9 valedictorians, 55 student government officers. Full-time: 904 students. Part-time: 2 students. Students come from 35 states and territories, 11 other countries, 26% from out-of-state. 1% American Indian or Alaska Native, non-Hispanic/Latino; 5% Hispanic/Latino; 6% African American, non-Hispanic/Latino; 1% Asian, non-Hispanic/Latino; 0.4% Native Hawaiian or other Pacific Islander, non-Hispanic/Latino; 7% international. 0% 25 or older, 87% live on campus, 1% transferred in. Retention: 86% of full-time freshmen returned the following year. Academic areas with the most degrees conferred: social sciences; biological/life sciences; foreign languages and literature. Core. Calendar: semesters. Services for LD students, advanced placement, independent study, double major, internships. Off campus study at members of the Great Lakes Colleges Association and Associated Colleges of the Midwest. Study abroad program.
Entrance Requirements: Options: electronic application, early admission, early decision, early action, deferred admission. Required: high school transcript, SAT or ACT. Recommended: essay, 1 recommendation, interview. Entrance: moderately difficult. Application deadlines: Rolling, 11/15 for early decision, 12/1 for early action. Notification: continuous, 12/1 for early decision, 12/22 for early action. Applicants placed on waiting list: 93. Wait-listed applicants offered admission: 1. Early decision applicants: 48. Early decision applicants admitted: 42. Early action applicants: 0. Early action applicants admitted: 0.
Costs Per Year: Application fee: $40. Comprehensive fee: $44,160 includes full-time tuition ($35,000), mandatory fees ($650), and college room and board ($8510). College room only: $4310. Room and board charges vary according to board plan and housing facility. Part-time tuition: $5833 per course.
Collegiate Environment: Orientation program. Drama-theater group, choral group, student-run newspaper, radio station. Social organizations: 75 open to all; national fraternities; 51% of eligible undergrads are members. Most popular organizations: Sphinx Club, Alpha Phi Omega, The Bachelor, Malcolm X Institute of Black Studies, Wabash Christian Fellowship. Major annual events: Homecoming, Monon Bell football game, Pan Hel Weekend. Student services: health clinic, personal-psychological counseling. Campus security: 24-hour emergency response devices and patrols, late night

transport-escort service. 900 college housing spaces available; 783 were occupied in 2012-13. Freshmen guaranteed college housing. On-campus residence required through sophomore year. Option: men-only housing available. Lilly Library with 276,184 books, 26,195 microform titles, 19,900 serials, 17,604 audiovisual materials, an OPAC, and a Web page. Operations spending for the previous fiscal year: $1.3 million. 350 computers available on campus for general student use. Computer purchase/lease plans available. A campuswide network can be accessed from student residence rooms and from off campus. Students can access the following: online course management, degree audit, expenses. Staffed computer lab on campus (open 24 hours a day) provides training in use of computers, software, and the Internet.

Community Environment: Crawfordsville (population 15,155), is located 45 miles northwest of Indianapolis. It is an historic small town community, and has many churches, a hospital, and motels. Recreational facilities include golf courses and swimming pools. Shades State Park is 14 miles away, and Turkey Run State Park is approximately 25 miles distant. Points of interest are the Lane Place Museum and Lew Wallace"Ben Hur" Museum.

■ AIB COLLEGE OF BUSINESS

2500 Fleur Dr.
Des Moines, IA 50321-1799
Tel: (515)244-4221; Free: 800-444-1921
Fax: (515)244-6773
E-mail: pitzm@aib.edu
Web Site: www.aib.edu/

Description: Independent, 4-year, coed. Awards associate and bachelor's degrees. Founded 1921. Setting: 20-acre urban campus. Endowment: $7 million. Educational spending for the previous fiscal year: $3536 per student. Total enrollment: 905. Faculty: 59 (20 full-time, 39 part-time). Student-undergrad faculty ratio is 21:1. 229 applied, 94% were admitted. 6% from top 10% of their high school class, 21% from top quarter, 53% from top half. Full-time: 610 students, 57% women, 43% men. Part-time: 295 students, 65% women, 35% men. Students come from 26 states and territories, 7 other countries, 8% from out-of-state. 1% American Indian or Alaska Native, non-Hispanic/Latino; 4% Hispanic/Latino; 4% African American, non-Hispanic/Latino; 3% Asian, non-Hispanic/Latino; 0.1% Native Hawaiian or other Pacific Islander, non-Hispanic/Latino; 3% international. 36% 25 or older, 36% live on campus, 13% transferred in. Retention: 73% of full-time freshmen returned the following year. Academic areas with the most degrees conferred: business/marketing; law/legal studies. Core. Academic remediation for entering students, services for LD students, advanced placement, independent study, distance learning, double major, summer session for credit, part-time degree program, co-op programs and internships.

Entrance Requirements: Option: electronic application. Required: high school transcript, minimum 2 high school GPA. Recommended: interview, ACT. Required for some: Nelson-Denny if no ACT score. Entrance: minimally difficult. Application deadlines: Rolling, Rolling for nonresidents. Notification: continuous, continuous for nonresidents. SAT Reasoning Test deadline: 8/1. Transfer credits accepted: Yes.

Costs Per Year: Application fee: $0. Tuition: $14,550 full-time, $1275 per course part-time. Mandatory fees: $300 full-time, $100 per term part-time. Full-time tuition and fees vary according to course load. Part-time tuition and fees vary according to course load. College room only: $3984. Room charges vary according to housing facility. Tuition guaranteed not to increase for student's term of enrollment.

Collegiate Environment: Orientation program. Social organizations: 8 open to all; national sororities; 3% of women are members. Most popular organizations: Student Government Association, Business Management Association, Enactus (formerly Students in Free Enterprise), Hospitality and Travel Management Association, Institute of Management Accountants. Major annual events: Welcome Week, Homecoming, Career Fest. Student services: personal-psychological counseling. Campus security: 24-hour emergency response devices and patrols, late night transport-escort service, controlled dormitory access, video security. 488 college housing spaces available; 296 were occupied in 2012-13. No special consideration for freshman housing applicants. Option: coed housing available. AIB Library with 6,806 books, 76 serials, 3,996 audiovisual materials, an OPAC, and a Web page. Operations spending for the previous fiscal year: $75,184. 346 computers available on campus for general student use. Computer purchase/lease plans available. A campuswide network can be accessed from student residence rooms and from off campus.

■ ALLEN COLLEGE

1825 Logan Ave.
Waterloo, IA 50703
Tel: (319)226-2000
Fax: (319)226-2020
E-mail: allencollegeadmissions@ihs.org
Web Site: www.allencollege.edu/

Description: Independent, comprehensive, coed. Awards associate, bachelor's, master's, and doctoral degrees and post-master's certificates (liberal arts and general education courses offered at either University of North Iowa or Wartburg College). Founded 1989. Setting: 20-acre suburban campus. Endowment: $1.9 million. Educational spending for the previous fiscal year: $5905 per student. Total enrollment: 551. Faculty: 42 (28 full-time, 14 part-time). Student-undergrad faculty ratio is 12:1. 9 applied, 11% were admitted. Full-time: 247 students, 91% women, 9% men. Part-time: 138 students, 97% women, 3% men. Students come from 10 states and territories, 1 other country, 5% from out-of-state. 0% American Indian or Alaska Native, non-Hispanic/Latino; 0.3% Hispanic/Latino; 2% African American, non-Hispanic/Latino; 1% Asian, non-Hispanic/Latino; 0% Native Hawaiian or other Pacific Islander, non-Hispanic/Latino; 1% international. 41% 25 or older, 5% live on campus, 38% transferred in. Academic area with the most degrees conferred: health professions and related sciences. Core. Calendar: semesters. Advanced placement, accelerated degree program, honors program, independent study, distance learning, part-time degree program, co-op programs and internships, graduate courses open to undergrads. Off campus study. ROTC: Army (c).

Entrance Requirements: Option: electronic application. Required: minimum 3 high school GPA. Recommended: GPA requirements are based on grades in specific general education courses, not on a cumulative GPA. Required for some: essay, high school transcript, 1 recommendation, interview, SAT or ACT. Entrance: moderately difficult. Application deadline: 2/1. Notification: continuous until 3/1. Transfer credits accepted: Yes.

Costs Per Year: Application fee: $50. Comprehensive fee: $26,110 includes full-time tuition ($16,771), mandatory fees ($2058), and college room and board ($7281). College room only: $3641. Full-time tuition and fees vary according to course load and program. Part-time tuition: $541 per credit. Part-time mandatory fees: $73 per credit. Part-time tuition and fees vary according to course load and program.

Collegiate Environment: Orientation program. Choral group. Social organizations: 4 open to all. Most popular organizations: Allen Student Nurses' Association, Nurses' Christian Fellowship. Student services: health clinic, personal-psychological counseling. Campus security: 24-hour patrols, controlled dormitory access. 16 college housing spaces available; 12 were occupied in 2012-13. No special consideration for freshman housing applicants. Option: coed housing available. Barrett Library with 3,300 books, 214 serials, 400 audiovisual materials, an OPAC, and a Web page. Operations spending for the previous fiscal year: $279,260. 32 computers available on campus for general student use. A campuswide network can be accessed from student residence rooms and from off campus. Staffed computer lab on campus provides training in use of computers, software, and the Internet.

■ ASHFORD UNIVERSITY

400 N Bluff Blvd.
Clinton, IA 52733-2967
Tel: (563)242-4023; Free: 866-711-1700
Fax: (563)242-2003

E-mail: admissns@tfu.edu
Web Site: www.ashford.edu/

Description: Proprietary, comprehensive, coed. Awards associate, bachelor's, and master's degrees. Founded 1918. Setting: 24-acre small town campus with easy access to Chicago. Endowment: $1.4 million. Research spending for the previous fiscal year: $26,474. Educational spending for the previous fiscal year: $3227 per student. Total enrollment: 10,568. Faculty: 748 (45 full-time, 703 part-time). Student-undergrad faculty ratio is 37:1. Full-time: 9,761 students, 77% women, 23% men. Part-time: 105 students, 70% women, 30% men. Students come from 9 states and territories. 0% transferred in. Retention: 45% of full-time freshmen returned the following year. Core. Calendar: semesters. Academic remediation for entering students, advanced placement, freshman honors college, honors program, independent study, distance learning, double major, summer session for credit, part-time degree program, external degree program, internships.

Entrance Requirements: Options: electronic application, early admission, deferred admission. Required: high school transcript. Recommended: minimum 2.0 high school GPA, interview. Required for some: interview, SAT or ACT. Entrance: minimally difficult. Application deadline: Rolling. Notification: continuous.

Collegiate Environment: Orientation program. Drama-theater group, choral group, student-run newspaper. Social organizations: 21 open to all. Most popular organizations: Student Senate, Student Ambassadors, Hall Council, Black Student Union, Student Iowa State Education Association. Major annual events: Brother/Sister Weekend, Matriculation Ceremony, Pep Rally and Homecoming. Student services: health clinic, personal-psychological counseling. Campus security: 24-hour emergency response devices and patrols, student patrols, late night transport-escort service, controlled dormitory access, self-defense education, lighted pathways. The Franciscan University of the Prairies Library with 98,974 books, 73,682 microform titles, 639 serials, an OPAC, and a Web page. Operations spending for the previous fiscal year: $159,661. 109 computers available on campus for general student use. Computer purchase/lease plans available. Students can access the following: online class registration, wireless/laptop campus. Staffed computer lab on campus.

Community Environment: Clinton, Iowa (population 27,000), situated midway between Chicago and Des Moines, is home to a minor league baseball team, a symphony orchestra, a pre-professional ballet company, summer stock theater, art shows, and other cultural events. Clinton is 45 minutes from the Quad Cities, three hours from Chicago, and five hours from Minneapolis. The quality of life in the city and on campus is typical of the wholesome lifestyle the Midwest is known for throughout the country.

■ **BRIAR CLIFF UNIVERSITY**
3303 Rebecca St.
Sioux City, IA 51104-0100
Tel: (712)279-5321; Free: 800-662-3303
Fax: (712)279-5410
E-mail: admissions@briarcliff.edu
Web Site: www.briarcliff.edu/

Description: Independent Roman Catholic, comprehensive, coed. Awards associate, bachelor's, and master's degrees and post-master's certificates. Founded 1930. Setting: 75-acre suburban campus. Endowment: $9.5 million. Educational spending for the previous fiscal year: $5935 per student. Total enrollment: 1,185. Faculty: 106 (61 full-time, 45 part-time). Student-undergrad faculty ratio is 12:1. 2,400 applied, 54% were admitted. 11% from top 10% of their high school class, 31% from top quarter, 67% from top half. Full-time: 851 students, 54% women, 46% men. Part-time: 237 students, 71% women, 29% men. Students come from 32 states and territories, 11 other countries, 42% from out-of-state. 1% American Indian or Alaska Native, non-Hispanic/Latino; 9% Hispanic/Latino; 7% African American, non-Hispanic/Latino; 2% Asian, non-Hispanic/Latino; 0.3% Native Hawaiian or other Pacific Islander, non-Hispanic/Latino; 2% international. 19% 25 or older, 12% transferred in. Retention: 69% of full-time freshmen returned the following year. Academic areas with the most degrees conferred: business/marketing; health professions and related sciences; education. Core. Calendar: (3 10-week terms plus 2 5-week summer sessions). Academic remediation for entering students, services for LD students, advanced placement, accelerated degree program, self-designed majors, honors program, independent study, distance learning, double major, summer session for credit, part-time degree program, adult/continuing education programs, internships. Off campus study at Colleges of Mid-America. Study abroad program. ROTC: Army (c).

Entrance Requirements: Options: electronic application, early admission, deferred admission. Required: high school transcript, minimum 2 high school GPA, SAT or ACT. Required for some: essay, 3 recommendations, interview. Entrance: moderately difficult. Application deadlines: Rolling, Rolling for nonresidents.

Costs Per Year: Application fee: $20. Comprehensive fee: $33,184 includes full-time tuition ($24,520), mandatory fees ($1122), and college room and board ($7542). Room and board charges vary according to board plan and housing facility. Part-time tuition: $810 per hour.

Collegiate Environment: Orientation program. Drama-theater group, choral group, student-run newspaper, radio station. Social organizations: 36 open to all. Most popular organizations: Residence Hall Association, Briar Cliff Student Government, Choices, Blue Crew, Catholic Daughters of America. Major annual events: Glo-Fest, Homecoming dance, Winterfest Dance. Student services: health clinic, personal-psychological counseling. Campus security: 24-hour emergency response devices and patrols, student patrols, late night transport-escort service, controlled dormitory access. Bishop Mueller Library with 82,007 books, 21,664 microform titles, 151 serials, 1,244 audiovisual materials, an OPAC, and a Web page. Operations spending for the previous fiscal year: $334,565. 100 computers available on campus for general student use. A campuswide network can be accessed from student residence rooms and from off campus. Staffed computer lab on campus provides training in use of computers, software, and the Internet.

■ **BROWN MACKIE COLLEGE–QUAD CITIES**
2119 E Kimberly Rd.
Bettendorf, IA 52722
Tel: (563)344-1500; Free: 888-420-1652
Web Site: www.brownmackie.edu/quad-cities/

Description: Proprietary, 2-year, coed. Part of Education Management Corporation. Awards diplomas and terminal associate degrees.

■ **BUENA VISTA UNIVERSITY**
610 W Fourth St.
Storm Lake, IA 50588
Tel: (712)749-2351; Free: 800-383-9600
Fax: (712)749-2037
E-mail: admissions@bvu.edu
Web Site: www.bvu.edu/

Description: Independent, comprehensive, coed, affiliated with Presbyterian Church (U.S.A.). Awards bachelor's and master's degrees. Founded 1891. Setting: 60-acre small town campus. Endowment: $114.2 million. Total enrollment: 971. Faculty: 119 (88 full-time, 31 part-time). Student-undergrad faculty ratio is 9:1. 1,223 applied, 71% were admitted. 17% from top 10% of their high school class, 42% from top quarter, 80% from top half. 7 valedictorians. Full-time: 896 students, 51% women, 49% men. Part-time: 17 students, 47% women, 53% men. Students come from 27 states and territories, 9 other countries, 21% from out-of-state. 0.2% American Indian or Alaska Native, non-Hispanic/Latino; 7% Hispanic/Latino; 3% African American, non-Hispanic/Latino; 1% Asian, non-Hispanic/Latino; 0% Native Hawaiian or other Pacific Islander, non-Hispanic/Latino; 4% international. 3% 25 or older, 87% live on campus, 6% transferred in. Retention: 77% of full-time freshmen returned the following year. Academic areas with the most degrees conferred: business/marketing; interdisciplinary studies; education. Core. Calendar: 4-1-4. Academic remediation for entering students, ESL program, services for LD students, advanced placement, self-designed majors, honors program, independent study, distance learning, double major, summer session for credit, part-time degree program, external degree program, adult/continuing education programs, internships, graduate courses open to undergrads. Off campus study at Washington University in St. Louis. Study abroad program. ROTC: Army.

Entrance Requirements: Options: electronic application, deferred admission, international baccalaureate accepted. Required: high school transcript, SAT or ACT. Recommended: minimum 3 high school GPA. Required for some: essay, interview. Entrance: moderately difficult. Notification: continuous. Transfer credits accepted: Yes.

Costs Per Year: Comprehensive fee: $36,494 includes full-time tuition ($28,314) and college room and board ($8180). Full-time tuition varies according to location. Room and board charges vary according to board plan. Tuition guaranteed not to increase for student's term of enrollment.

Collegiate Environment: Orientation program. Drama-theater group, choral group, student-run newspaper, radio station. Social organizations: 60 open to all. Most popular organizations: Student Activities Board, student orientation staff, Esprit De Corps, Student Senate, Marketing Association. Major annual events: Homecoming, Academic and Cultural Events Series (ACES), Buenafication Day. Student services: health clinic, personal-psychological counseling. Campus security: 24-hour emergency response devices, late night transport-escort service, controlled dormitory access, night security patrols. 1,038 college housing spaces available; 789 were occupied in 2012-13. Freshmen guaranteed college housing. On-campus residence required through senior year. Options: coed, men-only, women-only housing available. BVU Library with 150,000 books, 41,000 microform titles, 632 serials, 6,000 audiovisual materials, an OPAC, and a Web page. 400 computers available on campus for general student use. Computer purchase/lease plans available. A campuswide network can be accessed from student residence rooms and from off campus. Students can access the following: online class registration. Staffed computer lab on campus.

Community Environment: Storm Lake (population 10,000) is the county seat of Buena Vista County, and is located 75 miles east of Sioux City and 160 miles northwest of Des Moines. Bus lines and nearby airport facilities provide adequate transportation. Several churches of various Christian denominations are represented in the community.

■ **CENTRAL COLLEGE**

812 University St.
Pella, IA 50219
Tel: (641)628-9000; Free: 877-462-3687
Fax: (641)628-5316
E-mail: freiburgerc@central.edu
Web Site: www.central.edu/

Description: Independent, 4-year, coed, affiliated with Reformed Church in America. Awards bachelor's degrees. Founded 1853. Setting: 169-acre small town campus with easy access to Des Moines. Endowment: $68.1 million. Educational spending for the previous fiscal year: $12,808 per student. Total enrollment: 1,486. Faculty: 120 (98 full-time, 22 part-time). Student-undergrad faculty ratio is 13:1. 2,471 applied, 65% were admitted. 25% from top 10% of their high school class, 58% from top quarter, 89% from top half. Full-time: 1,461 students, 54% women, 46% men. Part-time: 25 students, 48% women, 52% men. Students come from 32 states and territories, 12 other countries, 19% from out-of-state. 0.3% American Indian or Alaska Native, non-Hispanic/Latino; 3% Hispanic/Latino; 2% African American, non-Hispanic/Latino; 1% Asian, non-Hispanic/Latino; 0.2% Native Hawaiian or other Pacific Islander, non-Hispanic/Latino; 0.4% international. 1% 25 or older, 94% live on campus, 3% transferred in. Retention: 83% of full-time freshmen returned the following year. Academic areas with the most degrees conferred: parks and recreation; business/marketing; social sciences; foreign languages and literature. Core. Calendar: semesters. Services for LD students, self-designed majors, honors program, independent study, double major, summer session for credit, part-time degree program, co-op programs and internships. Off campus study. Study abroad program.

Entrance Requirements: Options: electronic application, deferred admission, international baccalaureate accepted. Required: high school transcript, SAT or ACT. Recommended: minimum 2.7 high school GPA. Required for some: essay, 3 recommendations, interview. Entrance: moderately difficult. Application deadline: 8/15. Notification: continuous. SAT Reasoning Test deadline: 7/1. SAT Subject Test deadline: 7/1. Transfer credits accepted: Yes.

Costs Per Year: Application fee: $25. Comprehensive fee: $40,680 includes full-time tuition ($30,700) and college room and board ($9980). College room only: $4892. Room and board charges vary according to board plan. Part-time tuition: $1279 per credit. Part-time tuition varies according to course load.

Collegiate Environment: Orientation program. Drama-theater group, choral group, student-run newspaper. Social organizations: 60 open to all; local fraternities, local sororities; 3% of eligible men and 3% of eligible women are members. Most popular organizations: Campus Activities Board, Fellowship of Christian Athletes, Central Volunteer Center, Health Professions, Economics, Accounting, Management (EAM) Club. Major annual events: Annual Lemming Race, Homecoming, Campus-wide Service Day. Student services: health clinic, personal-psychological counseling. Campus security: 24-hour emergency response devices and patrols, late night transport-escort service, controlled dormitory access. 1,415 college housing spaces available; 1,204 were occupied in 2012-13. Freshmen guaranteed college housing. On-campus residence required through senior year. Options: coed, men-only, women-only housing available. Geisler Library plus 2 others with 158,193 books, 26,188 microform titles, 379 serials, 6,421 audiovisual materials, an OPAC, and a Web page. Operations spending for the previous fiscal year: $1.1 million. 322 computers available on campus for general student use. A campuswide network can be accessed from student residence rooms and from off campus. Students can access the following: online class registration. Staffed computer lab on campus provides training in use of computers, software, and the Internet.

Community Environment: Pella (population 10,300), a rapidly growing agricultural and industrial community, is located 43 miles southeast of Des Moines. Active churches, libraries, and a community hospital serve the area. Pella is widely known for its attractive homes, gardens, and fine community spirit. Red Rock Dam and Lake is located four miles south. Tulip Time is an annual event here dedicated to preserving the Dutch heritage of the town.

■ **CLARKE UNIVERSITY**

1550 Clarke Dr.
Dubuque, IA 52001-3198
Tel: (563)588-6300; Free: 800-383-2345
Fax: (563)588-6789
E-mail: admissions@clarke.edu
Web Site: www.clarke.edu/

Description: Independent Roman Catholic, comprehensive, coed. Awards associate, bachelor's, master's, and doctoral degrees. Founded 1843. Setting: 55-acre urban campus. Endowment: $28.9 million. Educational spending for the previous fiscal year: $7745 per student. Total enrollment: 1,191. Faculty: 160 (84 full-time, 76 part-time). Student-undergrad faculty ratio is 10:1. 1,034 applied, 74% were admitted. 23% from top 10% of their high school class, 45% from top quarter, 82% from top half. Full-time: 829 students, 67% women, 33% men. Part-time: 138 students, 64% women, 36% men. Students come from 28 states and territories, 8 other countries, 39% from out-of-state. 0.1% American Indian or Alaska Native, non-Hispanic/Latino; 2% Hispanic/Latino; 3% African American, non-Hispanic/Latino; 1% Asian, non-Hispanic/Latino; 0.2% Native Hawaiian or other Pacific Islander, non-Hispanic/Latino; 1% international. 22% 25 or older, 42% live on campus, 9% transferred in. Retention: 81% of full-time freshmen returned the following year. Academic areas with the most degrees conferred: health professions and related sciences; business/marketing; education. Core. Calendar: semesters. ESL program, advanced placement, accelerated degree program, self-designed majors, honors program, independent study, distance learning, double major, summer session for credit, part-time degree program, adult/continuing education programs, co-op programs and internships. Off campus study. Study abroad program. ROTC: Army (c).

Entrance Requirements: Options: electronic application, deferred admission, international baccalaureate accepted. Required: high school transcript, minimum 2 high school GPA, SAT or ACT. Entrance: moderately difficult. Application deadline: Rolling. Notification: 7/15.

Costs Per Year: Application fee: $25. Comprehensive fee: $36,400 includes full-time tuition ($27,100), mandatory fees ($900), and college room and board ($8400). College room only: $4100. Room and board charges vary according to housing facility. Part-time tuition: $690 per credit.

Collegiate Environment: Orientation program. Drama-theater group, choral group, student-run newspaper, radio station. Social organizations: 63 open to all. Most popular organizations: Admissions Student Team, Student Multicultural Organization, concert choir, campus ministry, student government. Major annual events: Homecoming, May Daze, Passport Dance. Student services: health clinic, personal-psychological counseling. Campus security: 24-hour emergency response devices and patrols, late night transport-escort service, controlled dormitory access. 577 college housing spaces available; 364 were occupied in 2012-13. Freshmen guaranteed college housing. On-campus residence required through sophomore year. Options: coed, men-only, women-only housing available. Nicholas J. Schrupp Library with 98,700 books, 6,700 microform titles, 42,000 serials, 1,710 audiovisual materials, an OPAC, and a Web page. Operations spending for the previous fiscal year: $594,233. 237 computers available on campus for general student use. A campuswide network can be accessed from student residence rooms and from off campus. Students can access the following: online class registration. Staffed computer lab on campus.

Community Environment: The small city of Dubuque is located on the Mississippi River where Iowa, Illinois and Wisconsin meet. The oldest city in Iowa, it features rugged bluffs and Victorian architecture. Excellent air connections with Chicago's O'Hare Airport and the Minneapolis-St. Paul Airport are available. The city is the cultural, recreational and commercial center of the tristate area, and offers theater, symphony, art galleries, museums, dog racing, riverboat gambling, and concerts as well as facilities for boating, skiing, golf and tennis.

■ CLINTON COMMUNITY COLLEGE

1000 Lincoln Blvd.

Clinton, IA 52732-6299

Tel: (563)244-7001; Free: 800-462-3255

Fax: (563)244-7107

E-mail: gmohr@eicc.edu

Web Site: www.eicc.edu/ccc/

Description: State and locally supported, 2-year, coed. Part of Eastern Iowa Community College District. Awards certificates, diplomas, transfer associate, and terminal associate degrees. Founded 1946. Setting: 20-acre small town campus. Total enrollment: 1,240. Faculty: 43 (30 full-time, 13 part-time). Student-undergrad faculty ratio is 23:1. 254 applied, 100% were admitted. Full-time: 571 students, 63% women, 37% men. Part-time: 669 students, 68% women, 32% men. Students come from 8 states and territories, 5 other countries, 8% from out-of-state. 30% 25 or older. Retention: 58% of full-time freshmen returned the following year. Core. Calendar: semesters. Academic remediation for entering students, ESL program, services for LD students, advanced placement, self-designed majors, independent study, distance learning, double major, summer session for credit, part-time degree program, adult/continuing education programs, co-op programs and internships. Study abroad program.

Entrance Requirements: Open admission except for nursing program. Options: electronic application, early admission, deferred admission. Entrance: noncompetitive. Application deadline: Rolling. Notification: continuous.

Collegiate Environment: Orientation program. Drama-theater group. Social organizations: Greek honors society. Campus security: 24-hour emergency response devices. Clinton Community College Library with 18,701 books, 155 serials, and an OPAC. 37 computers available on campus for general student use. A campuswide network can be accessed from off-campus. Students can access the following: online class registration. Staffed computer lab on campus provides training in use of computers, software, and the Internet.

■ COE COLLEGE

1220 1st Ave., NE

Cedar Rapids, IA 52402-5092

Tel: (319)399-8000; Free: 877-225-5263

Fax: (319)399-8816

E-mail: admission@coe.edu

Web Site: www.coe.edu/

Description: Independent, comprehensive, coed, affiliated with Presbyterian Church. Awards bachelor's and master's degrees. Founded 1851. Setting: 53-acre urban campus. Endowment: $87.5 million. Research spending for the previous fiscal year: $311,290. Educational spending for the previous fiscal year: $13,963 per student. Total enrollment: 1,367. Faculty: 169 (92 full-time, 77 part-time). Student-undergrad faculty ratio is 11:1. 2,509 applied, 67% were admitted. 27% from top 10% of their high school class, 62% from top quarter, 89% from top half. 98 National Merit Scholars, 80 valedictorians. Full-time: 1,304 students, 53% women, 47% men. Part-time: 60 students, 45% women, 55% men. Students come from 40 states and territories, 15 other countries, 43% from out-of-state. 0.1% American Indian or Alaska Native, non-Hispanic/Latino; 4% Hispanic/Latino; 4% African American, non-Hispanic/Latino; 3% Asian, non-Hispanic/Latino; 0.4% Native Hawaiian or other Pacific Islander, non-Hispanic/Latino; 2% international. 4% 25 or older, 84% live on campus, 2% transferred in. Retention: 81% of full-time freshmen returned the following year. Academic areas with the most degrees conferred: business/marketing; psychology; biological/life sciences. Core. Calendar: 4-4-1. ESL program, services for LD students, advanced placement, accelerated degree program, self-designed majors, honors program, independent study, double major, summer session for credit, part-time degree program, internships. Off campus study at University of Iowa, Mount Mercy College, Associated Colleges of the Midwest, Washington University in St. Louis. Study abroad program. ROTC: Army, Air Force (c).

Entrance Requirements: Options: electronic application, early admission, early action, deferred admission, international baccalaureate accepted. Required: essay, high school transcript, 1 recommendation, SAT or ACT. Recommended: minimum 3 high school GPA, interview. Entrance: moderately difficult. Application deadlines: 3/1, 12/10 for early action. Notification: 3/15. Transfer credits accepted: Yes. Early action applicants: 1,776. Early action applicants admitted: 758.

Costs Per Year: Application fee: $30. Comprehensive fee: $43,480 includes full-time tuition ($35,400), mandatory fees ($330), and college room and board ($7750). College room only: $3450. Room and board charges vary according to housing facility. Part-time tuition: $4035 per course. Part-time tuition varies according to course load.

Collegiate Environment: Orientation program. Drama-theater group, choral group, student-run newspaper, radio station. Social organizations: 80 open to all; national fraternities, national sororities; 13% of eligible men and 12% of eligible women are members. Most popular organizations: Student Activities Committee, Student Senate, Up 'til Dawn, Cedar Rapids Dance Marathon, Alpha Sigma Alpha Sorority. Major annual events: Homecoming, Flunk Day, International Club Cultural Show and Dinner. Student services: health clinic, personal-psychological counseling. Campus security: 24-hour emergency response devices and patrols, late night transport-escort service, controlled dormitory access. 1,150 college housing spaces available; 1,142 were occupied in 2012-13. Freshmen guaranteed college housing. On-campus residence required through senior year. Options: coed, men-only, women-only housing available. Stewart Memorial Library plus 1 other with 301,894 books, 5,979 microform titles, 36,879 serials, 11,423 audiovisual materials, an OPAC, and a Web page. Operations spending for the previous fiscal year: $1.5 million. 300 computers available on campus for general student use. Computer purchase/lease plans available. A campuswide network can be accessed from student residence rooms and from off campus. Students can access the following: online class registration. Staffed computer lab on campus (open 24 hours a day) provides training in use of computers, software, and the Internet.

Community Environment: Cedar Rapids, a metropolitan community of 150,000 is located just 225 miles west of Chicago in east-central Iowa. All forms of commercial transportation are available. Community facilities include over 100 churches, a symphony orchestra, library, hospital, and shopping in the downtown area, plus three shopping centers. Part time employment is available. Cedar Rapids has over 59 city parks which offer a variety of recreational facilities. Points of interest are the Cedar Rapids Art Center, Iowa Masonic Library, Paramount Theater of Performing Arts, Five Seasons Civic Center, and Theatre Cedar Rapids.

■ CORNELL COLLEGE

600 First St. SW

Mount Vernon, IA 52314-1098

Tel: (319)895-4000; Free: 800-747-1112

Fax: (319)895-4492

E-mail: admissions@cornellcollege.edu

Web Site: www.cornellcollege.edu/

Description: Independent Methodist, 4-year, coed. Awards bachelor's degrees. Founded 1853. Setting: 129-acre small town campus. Endowment: $65 million. Research spending for the previous fiscal year: $2.4 million. Educational spending for the previous fiscal year: $10,072 per student. Total enrollment: 1,180. Faculty: 116 (89 full-time, 27 part-time). Student-undergrad faculty ratio is 12:1. 2,716 applied, 53% were admitted. 38% from top 10% of their high school class, 66% from top quarter, 91% from top half. 13 valedictorians. Full-time: 1,171 students, 55% women, 45% men. Part-time: 9 students, 22% women, 78% men. Students come from 49 states and territories, 19 other countries, 83% from out-of-state. 1% American Indian or Alaska Native, non-Hispanic/Latino; 11% Hispanic/Latino; 5% African American, non-Hispanic/Latino; 4% Asian, non-Hispanic/Latino; 0.3% Native Hawaiian or other Pacific Islander, non-Hispanic/Latino; 6% international. 1% 25 or older, 92% live on campus, 3% transferred in. Retention: 84% of full-time freshmen returned the following year. Academic areas with the most degrees conferred: social sciences; visual and performing arts; biological/life sciences. Core. Calendar: 9 3&S1/&I2-week terms. ESL program, services for LD students, advanced placement, self-designed majors, honors program, independent study, double major, internships. Off campus study at Associated Colleges of the Midwest, Fisk University, School for International Training. Study abroad program.

Entrance Requirements: Options: electronic application, early admission, early decision, early action, deferred admission, international baccalaureate accepted. Required: essay, high school transcript, 1 recommendation, SAT or ACT. Recommended: interview, SAT Subject Tests. Entrance: moderately difficult. Application deadlines: 2/1, 11/1 for early decision plan 1, 2/1 for early decision plan 2, 12/1 for early action. Notification: 3/20, 12/15 for early decision plan 1, 3/15 for early decision plan 2, 2/1 for early action. SAT Reasoning Test deadline: 3/1. Transfer credits accepted: Yes. Applicants placed on waiting list: 142. Wait-listed applicants offered admission: 43. Early decision applicants: 115. Early decision applicants admitted: 32. Early action applicants: 1,203. Early action applicants admitted: 659.

Costs Per Year: Application fee: $30. Comprehensive fee: $42,605 includes full-time tuition ($34,480), mandatory fees ($225), and college room and

board ($7900). College room only: $3700. Room and board charges vary according to board plan and housing facility. Part-time tuition: $2586 per course. Part-time mandatory fees: $113 per year. Part-time tuition and fees vary according to course load and reciprocity agreements.

Collegiate Environment: Orientation program. Drama-theater group, choral group, student-run newspaper, radio station. Social organizations: 90 open to all; local fraternities, local sororities; 24% of eligible men and 17% of eligible women are members. Most popular organizations: Student-initiated Living-learning Community, Lunch Buddies/Youth Mentoring, Chess and Games Club, PAAC (Performing Arts and Activities Council), Fellowship of Christian Athletes (FCA). Major annual events: Homecoming, music and cultural events and theatre productions, interactive entertainment. Student services: health clinic, personal-psychological counseling, women's center. Campus security: 24-hour emergency response devices and patrols, late night transport-escort service, controlled dormitory access. 1,118 college housing spaces available; 1,088 were occupied in 2012-13. Freshmen guaranteed college housing. On-campus residence required through senior year. Options: coed, women-only housing available. Cole Library plus 1 other with 234,549 books, 75,688 microform titles, 487 serials, 8,896 audiovisual materials, an OPAC, and a Web page. Operations spending for the previous fiscal year: $1.6 million. 190 computers available on campus for general student use. A campuswide network can be accessed from student residence rooms and from off campus. Students can access the following: online class registration. Staffed computer lab on campus (open 24 hours a day) provides training in use of computers, software, and the Internet.

Community Environment: Mount Vernon is a small town located 15 miles east of Cedar Rapids and 22 miles north of Iowa City. Bus and airline service are available in Cedar Rapids. The community and college share many facilities. Community facilities include churches and various civic, fraternal and veteran's organizations. Opportunities for student employment off campus are limited. Excellent recreational facilities are available at the Palisades State Park, MacBride State Park and Coralville Reservoir, for fishing and boating, golf, bowling, swimming, and cross-country skiing. Downhill skiing facilities are available within 70 miles.

■ DES MOINES AREA COMMUNITY COLLEGE

2006 S Ankeny Blvd.
Ankeny, IA 50021-8995
Tel: (515)964-6200; Free: 800-362-2127
E-mail: mjleutsch@dmacc.edu
Web Site: www.dmacc.edu/

Description: State and locally supported, 2-year, coed. Part of Iowa Area Community Colleges System. Awards certificates, diplomas, transfer associate, and terminal associate degrees (profile also includes information from the Boone, Carroll, Des Moines, and Newton campuses). Founded 1966. Setting: 362-acre small town campus. Endowment: $11.1 million. Total enrollment: 22,324. Faculty: 326 (322 full-time, 4 part-time). Student-undergrad faculty ratio is 33:1. Full-time: 8,947 students, 52% women, 48% men. Part-time: 13,377 students, 56% women, 44% men. Students come from 43 states and territories, 69 other countries. 41% 25 or older. Retention: 58% of full-time freshmen returned the following year. Core. Calendar: semesters. Academic remediation for entering students, ESL program, services for LD students, advanced placement, self-designed majors, honors program, distance learning, summer session for credit, part-time degree program, adult/continuing education programs, co-op programs. Off campus study at Drake University, Grand View College, Iowa State University of Science and Technology, University of Northern Iowa.

Entrance Requirements: Open admission. Options: electronic application, early admission, deferred admission. Required for some: high school transcript, interview, SAT or ACT, ACT COMPASS. Entrance: noncompetitive. Application deadline: Rolling.

Collegiate Environment: Drama-theater group, choral group, student-run newspaper. Social organizations: 30 open to all. Most popular organizations: Agri-Business Club, Horticulture Club, Hospitality Arts Club, Iowa Delta Epsilon Chi, Dental Hygienist Club. Major annual events: Orientation, Drive Into DMACC Days. Student services: health clinic, personal-psychological counseling. Campus security: 24-hour emergency response devices and patrols, late night transport-escort service. DMACC District Library plus 4 others with 62,986 books, 3,784 serials, 7,224 audiovisual materials, an OPAC, and a Web page. Operations spending for the previous fiscal year: $1.2 million. 400 computers available on campus for general student use. A campuswide network can be accessed from off-campus. Students can access the following: online class registration, online classes. Staffed computer lab on campus provides training in use of software.

■ DIVINE WORD COLLEGE

102 Jacoby Dr. SW
Epworth, IA 52045-0380
Tel: (563)876-3353; Free: 800-553-3321
Fax: (563)876-3407
E-mail: luhal@dwci.edu
Web Site: www.dwci.edu/

Description: Independent Roman Catholic, 4-year, coed. Awards associate and bachelor's degrees. Founded 1912. Setting: 35-acre rural campus. Total enrollment: 107. Core. Calendar: semesters. Academic remediation for entering students, ESL program, advanced placement, independent study, double major. Study abroad program.

Entrance Requirements: Option: early admission. Required: essay, high school transcript, 3 recommendations, interview, medical history. Recommended: SAT or ACT. Application deadline: 7/15. Notification: continuous until 8/1. Transfer credits accepted: Yes.

Costs Per Year: Application fee: $25. Comprehensive fee: $15,400 includes full-time tuition ($12,000), mandatory fees ($100), and college room and board ($3300). Part-time tuition: .

Collegiate Environment: Orientation program. Choral group. Student services: personal-psychological counseling. Campus security: controlled dormitory access. Matthew Jacoby Library with 94,583 books, 372 serials, an OPAC, and a Web page.

■ DORDT COLLEGE

498 4th Ave., NE
Sioux Center, IA 51250-1697
Tel: (712)722-6000; Free: 800-343-6738
Fax: (712)722-1967
E-mail: admissions@dordt.edu
Web Site: www.dordt.edu/

Description: Independent Christian Reformed, comprehensive, coed. Awards associate, bachelor's, and master's degrees. Founded 1955. Setting: 110-acre small town campus. Endowment: $29 million. Educational spending for the previous fiscal year: $7774 per student. Total enrollment: 1,400. Faculty: 102 (75 full-time, 27 part-time). Student-undergrad faculty ratio is 14:1. 1,102 applied, 79% were admitted. 13% from top 10% of their high school class, 21% from top quarter, 58% from top half. 6 National Merit Scholars. Full-time: 1,344 students, 47% women, 53% men. Part-time: 35 students, 69% women, 31% men. Students come from 37 states and territories, 18 other countries, 62% from out-of-state. 0.2% American Indian or Alaska Native, non-Hispanic/Latino; 2% Hispanic/Latino; 2% African American, non-Hispanic/Latino; 1% Asian, non-Hispanic/Latino; 0% Native Hawaiian or other Pacific Islander, non-Hispanic/Latino; 9% international. 5% 25 or older, 90% live on campus, 4% transferred in. Retention: 80% of full-time freshmen returned the following year. Academic areas with the most degrees conferred: education; business/marketing; engineering. Core. Calendar: semesters. Academic remediation for entering students, ESL program, services for LD students, advanced placement, self-designed majors, freshman honors college, honors program, independent study, distance learning, double major, part-time degree program, internships. Off campus study at Christian College Coalition, Chicago Metro Program, American Studies Program, Los Angeles Film Studies Program, European Studies program, Nicaragua Studies Program. Study abroad program.

Entrance Requirements: Options: electronic application, deferred admission, international baccalaureate accepted. Required: high school transcript, minimum 2.25 high school GPA, SAT or ACT. Required for some: essay, interview. Entrance: moderately difficult. Application deadline: 8/1. Notification: 8/1.

Costs Per Year: Application fee: $0. Comprehensive fee: $32,750 includes full-time tuition ($25,100), mandatory fees ($420), and college room and board ($7230). College room only: $3700. Full-time tuition and fees vary according to course load. Room and board charges vary according to board plan and housing facility. Part-time tuition: $960 per quarter hour.

Collegiate Environment: Orientation program. Drama-theater group, choral group, student-run newspaper, radio station. Social organizations: 50 open to all. Most popular organizations: PLIA, Future Teachers, Ag Club, Lacrosse Club, Defenders of Life. Major annual events: Talent Extravaganza, Homecoming, Parents' Weekend. Student services: health clinic, personal-psychological counseling. Campus security: 24-hour emergency response devices, student patrols, late night transport-escort service, controlled dormitory access. 1,250 college housing spaces available; 1,200 were occupied in 2012-13. Freshmen guaranteed college housing. On-campus residence required through senior year. Options: men-only, women-only housing available. Dordt College Library plus 1 other with 185,000 books, 121,622 microform titles, 6,597 serials, an OPAC, and a Web page. Operations spending for the previous fiscal year: $574,708. 200 computers available on campus for general student use. A campuswide network can be accessed from student residence rooms and from off campus. Students can access the following: online class registration. Staffed computer lab on campus provides training in use of computers, software, and the Internet.

Community Environment: Sioux Center, population 6,500 is a rural area with a temperate climate. College transportation serves the area. A public library, hospital, churches, clinics and shopping facilities are all available within the community. Recreational activities include swimming, golf, and fishing. Part-time employment may be found.

■ DRAKE UNIVERSITY

2507 University Ave.
Des Moines, IA 50311-4516
Tel: (515)271-2011; Free: 800-44-DRAKE
Fax: (515)271-2831
E-mail: admission@drake.edu
Web Site: www.drake.edu/

Description: Independent, university, coed. Awards bachelor's, master's, and doctoral degrees and post-master's certificates. Founded 1881. Setting: 120-acre urban campus. Endowment: $149.3 million. Research spending for the previous fiscal year: $1.1 million. Total enrollment: 5,270. Faculty: 450 (289 full-time, 161 part-time). Student-undergrad faculty ratio is 12:1. 6,357 applied, 66% were admitted. 42% from top 10% of their high school class, 75% from top quarter, 94% from top half. Full-time: 3,189 students, 57% women, 43% men. Part-time: 176 students, 43% women, 57% men. Students come from 46 states and territories, 39 other countries, 62% from out-of-state. 0.2% American Indian or Alaska Native, non-Hispanic/Latino; 3% Hispanic/Latino; 3% African American, non-Hispanic/Latino; 3% Asian, non-Hispanic/Latino; 0.1% Native Hawaiian or other Pacific Islander, non-Hispanic/Latino; 8% international. 5% 25 or older, 71% live on campus, 4% transferred in. Retention: 88% of full-time freshmen returned the following year. Academic areas with the most degrees conferred: business/marketing; communication/journalism; social sciences; education. Core. Calendar: semesters. ESL program, services for LD students, advanced placement, accelerated degree program, self-designed majors, honors program, independent study, distance learning, double major, summer session for credit, part-time degree program, co-op programs and internships, graduate courses open to undergrads. Off campus study at Des Moines Consortium. Study abroad program. ROTC: Army, Air Force (c).

Entrance Requirements: Options: electronic application, early admission, deferred admission, international baccalaureate accepted. Required: essay, high school transcript, SAT or ACT. Recommended: interview. Entrance: moderately difficult. Application deadline: 3/1. Notification: continuous. SAT Reasoning Test deadline: 5/1.

Costs Per Year: Application fee: $25. Comprehensive fee: $39,580 includes full-time tuition ($30,734), mandatory fees ($146), and college room and board ($8700). College room only: $4470. Full-time tuition and fees vary according to course load, program, and student level. Room and board charges vary according to board plan. Part-time tuition: $610 per hour. Part-time tuition varies according to class time and program.

Collegiate Environment: Orientation program. Drama-theater group, choral group, marching band, student-run newspaper, radio station. Social organizations: 160 open to all; national fraternities, national sororities; 28% of eligible men and 27% of eligible women are members. Most popular organizations: Student Activities Board, Drake Magazine, Dog Pound Pep Squad, Alpha Phi Omega, Residence Hall Association. Major annual events: Drake Relays, Parent/Family Weekend, Homecoming. Student services: legal services, health clinic, personal-psychological counseling. Campus security: 24-hour emergency response devices and patrols, late night transport-escort service, 24-hour desk attendants in residence halls. 1,787 college housing spaces available. Freshmen guaranteed college housing. On-campus residence required through sophomore year. Option: coed housing available. Cowles Library plus 2 others with 1.2 million books, 936,702 microform titles, 93,729 serials, 2,969 audiovisual materials, an OPAC, and a Web page. 1,000 computers available on campus for general student use. A campuswide network can be accessed from student residence rooms and from off campus. Students can access the following: online class registration. Staffed computer lab on campus provides training in use of computers, software, and the Internet.

Community Environment: Des Moines is Iowa's capital city, and its metropolitan population of 456,000 is the largest in the state. The downtown

area includes the Convention Center, a skywalk system linking office buildings and shops, and a major restoration and conversion of historic buildings in the former city market area. A Civic Center offers plays, concerts and other entertainment. The Art Center, in a park setting of trees and gardens, houses a permanent collection of paintings and sculpture, in addition to traveling exhibits. Major business interests include a concentration of home offices of insurance companies and the pivotal operation of a large publishing firm.

■ ELLSWORTH COMMUNITY COLLEGE

1100 College Ave.
Iowa Falls, IA 50126-1199
Tel: (641)648-4611; Free: 800-ECC-9235
Fax: (641)648-3128
Web Site: www.iavalley.cc.ia.us/ecc/

Description: State and locally supported, 2-year, coed. Part of Iowa Valley Community College District System. Awards diplomas, transfer associate, and terminal associate degrees. Founded 1890. Setting: 10-acre small town campus. Total enrollment: 916. 17% 25 or older. Core. Calendar: semesters. Academic remediation for entering students, services for LD students, advanced placement, self-designed majors, honors program, distance learning, summer session for credit, part-time degree program, adult/continuing education programs, co-op programs and internships.

Entrance Requirements: Open admission for state residents. Options: electronic application, early admission, deferred admission. Required: high school transcript. Entrance: noncompetitive. Application deadlines: Rolling, 8/1 for nonresidents. Notification: continuous.

Collegiate Environment: Orientation program. Drama-theater group, choral group, student-run newspaper. Student services: personal-psychological counseling. Campus security: 24-hour emergency response devices and patrols. Osgood Learning Resource Center with 25,500 books and 300 serials.

Community Environment: Iowa Falls (population 5,112) is a rural area situated on the Iowa River. Community facilities include 18 churches of all denominations, a hospital, library, motels, hotels, and various civic and service organizations. Part-time jobs are available. Recreational facilities include a theater, hunting, fishing, water skiing, swimming and two nine-hole golf courses.

■ EMMAUS BIBLE COLLEGE

2570 Asbury Rd.
Dubuque, IA 52001-3097
Tel: (319)588-8000; Free: 800-397-2425
Fax: (319)588-1216
E-mail: ichavez@emmaus.edu
Web Site: www.emmaus.edu/

Description: Independent nondenominational, 4-year, coed. Awards associate and bachelor's degrees. Founded 1941. Setting: 22-acre small town campus. Total enrollment: 244. 162 applied, 74% were admitted. 9% 25 or older. Calendar: semesters. Advanced placement, independent study, double major, part-time degree program, internships. Off campus study.

Entrance Requirements: Open admission. Options: electronic application, deferred admission. Required: essay, high school transcript, 2 recommendations, SAT or ACT. Entrance: noncompetitive. Application deadline: 6/1. Notification: continuous. Transfer credits accepted: Yes.

Costs Per Year: Application fee: $25. Comprehensive fee: $20,700 includes full-time tuition ($13,750), mandatory fees ($750), and college room and board ($6200). Full-time tuition and fees vary according to course load and program.

Collegiate Environment: Orientation program. Choral group. Student services: personal-psychological counseling. Campus security: 24-hour emergency response devices, student patrols, controlled dormitory access. The Emmaus Bible College Library plus 1 other with 86,000 books, 259 microform titles, 330 serials, and an OPAC.

Community Environment: Emmaus Bible College is located in Dubuque, Iowa, a Mississippi River City, of 60,000 people. It serves as the metropolitan center of 300,000 residents in the tri-state trading area. It is a city of traditional values and loyalties reflecting the past with a progressive spirit toward the future. Dubuque provides many wholesome activities for the Emmaus student. The Dubuque Symphony Orchestra performs regularly at the Five Flags Center. The Spirit of Dubuque, a paddlewheeler, plies the Mississippi and provides dining en route. Fall brings out the beauty of the variety of trees and foliage along the river and its tributaries. Dubuque is also a center for education, boasting three colleges in addition to Emmaus, as well as two seminaries. This healthy environment is a suitable setting for the Emmaus education and for the community outreach of Christian service and evangelism.

■ **FAITH BAPTIST BIBLE COLLEGE AND THEOLOGICAL SEMINARY**
1900 NW 4th St.
Ankeny, IA 50023
Tel: (515)964-0601; Free: 888-FAITH 4U
Fax: (515)964-1638
E-mail: admissions@faith.edu
Web Site: www.faith.edu/
Description: Independent, comprehensive, coed, affiliated with General Association of Regular Baptist Churches. Awards associate, bachelor's, and master's degrees. Founded 1921. Setting: 52-acre suburban campus. Endowment: $4 million. Educational spending for the previous fiscal year: $5795 per student. Total enrollment: 300. Faculty: 29 (18 full-time, 11 part-time). Student-undergrad faculty ratio is 11:1. 191 applied, 65% were admitted. 11% from top 10% of their high school class, 43% from top quarter, 66% from top half. 5 valedictorians. Full-time: 234 students, 55% women, 45% men. Part-time: 27 students, 33% women, 67% men. Students come from 26 states and territories, 7 other countries, 44% from out-of-state. 1% American Indian or Alaska Native, non-Hispanic/Latino; 1% Hispanic/Latino; 2% African American, non-Hispanic/Latino; 1% Asian, non-Hispanic/Latino; 1% Native Hawaiian or other Pacific Islander, non-Hispanic/Latino; 0% international. 5% 25 or older, 75% live on campus, 5% transferred in. Retention: 72% of full-time freshmen returned the following year. Academic areas with the most degrees conferred: theology and religious vocations; education; business/marketing. Core. Calendar: semesters. Academic remediation for entering students, advanced placement, independent study, double major, summer session for credit, part-time degree program, adult/continuing education programs, internships, graduate courses open to undergrads.
Entrance Requirements: Options: electronic application, deferred admission. Required: essay, high school transcript, 2 recommendations, SAT or ACT. Recommended: minimum 2 high school GPA. Required for some: interview. Entrance: minimally difficult. Application deadline: 8/1. Notification: 9/1. SAT Reasoning Test deadline: 8/1. SAT Subject Test deadline: 8/1. Transfer credits accepted: Yes.
Costs Per Year: Application fee: $0. One-time mandatory fee: $230. Comprehensive fee: $21,008 includes full-time tuition ($14,560), mandatory fees ($460), and college room and board ($5988). College room only: $2812. Full-time tuition and fees vary according to course load and degree level. Part-time tuition: $532 per credit hour. Part-time mandatory fees: $230 per term. Part-time tuition and fees vary according to course load and degree level.
Collegiate Environment: Orientation program. Drama-theater group, choral group. Social organizations: 6 open to all; 70% of eligible men and 70% of eligible women are members. Most popular organizations: Student Association, Student Missionary Fellowship, Intramural Sports, Photo Club, Chapel Orchestra. Major annual events: Homecoming Week, Student Appreciation Night, Spring Banquet. Student services: personal-psychological counseling. Campus security: 24-hour emergency response devices and patrols, late night transport-escort service. 280 college housing spaces available; 181 were occupied in 2012-13. Freshmen guaranteed college housing. On-campus residence required through senior year. Options: men-only, women-only housing available. Patten Hall with 73,625 books, 3,300 microform titles, 378 serials, 7,283 audiovisual materials, an OPAC, and a Web page. Operations spending for the previous fiscal year: $112,751. 45 computers available on campus for general student use. A campuswide network can be accessed from student residence rooms and from off campus. Students can access the following: online class registration. Staffed computer lab on campus provides training in use of computers, software, and the Internet.

■ **GRACELAND UNIVERSITY**
1 University Pl.
Lamoni, IA 50140
Tel: (641)784-5000; Free: 866-GRACELAND
Fax: (641)784-5480
E-mail: admissions@graceland.edu
Web Site: www.graceland.edu/
Description: Independent Community of Christ, comprehensive, coed. Awards bachelor's, master's, and doctoral degrees and post-master's certificates. Founded 1895. Setting: 170-acre rural campus with easy access to Des Moines. Endowment: $35.3 million. Educational spending for the previous fiscal year: $7689 per student. Total enrollment: 2,318. Faculty: 97 (55 full-time, 42 part-time). Student-undergrad faculty ratio is 13:1. 1,676 applied, 48% were admitted. 18% from top 10% of their high school class, 36% from top quarter, 68% from top half. Full-time: 1,203 students, 53% women, 47% men. Part-time: 312 students, 72% women, 28% men. Students come from 44 states and territories, 40 other countries, 69% from out-of-state. 0.5% American Indian or Alaska Native, non-Hispanic/Latino; 2% Hispanic/Latino; 9% African American, non-Hispanic/Latino; 0.3% Asian, non-Hispanic/Latino; 1% Native Hawaiian or other Pacific Islander, non-Hispanic/Latino; 8% international. 20% 25 or older, 72% live on campus, 6% transferred in. Retention: 68% of full-time freshmen returned the following year. Academic areas with the most degrees conferred: education; health professions and related sciences; business/marketing. Core. Calendar: 4-1-4. Academic remediation for entering students, ESL program, services for LD students, advanced placement, accelerated degree program, self-designed majors, freshman honors college, honors program, independent study, distance learning, double major, summer session for credit, part-time degree program, adult/continuing education programs, co-op programs and internships, graduate courses open to undergrads. Off campus study. Study abroad program.
Entrance Requirements: Options: electronic application, deferred admission, international baccalaureate accepted. Required: high school transcript, minimum 2.5 high school GPA. Students must meet 2 out of the following 3 requirements to be considered for admission: rank in top half of class; score a minimum of 21 on ACT or 960 on the SAT; have a 2.5 high school GPA (on a 4.0 scale), SAT or ACT, TOEFL for all students whose first language is not English. Required for some: essay, 2 recommendations, interview. Entrance: moderately difficult. Application deadlines: Rolling, Rolling for nonresidents. Notification: continuous, continuous for nonresidents. SAT Reasoning Test deadline: 8/28. SAT Subject Test deadline: 8/28. Transfer credits accepted: Yes.
Costs Per Year: Application fee: $0. Comprehensive fee: $31,420 includes full-time tuition ($23,180), mandatory fees ($350), and college room and board ($7890). Full-time tuition and fees vary according to course load. Room and board charges vary according to board plan, housing facility, and location. Part-time tuition: $725 per credit. Part-time tuition varies according to course load.
Collegiate Environment: Orientation program. Drama-theater group, choral group, student-run newspaper, radio station. Social organizations: 52 open to all; Residence Life-run housing system; 100% of eligible men and 100% of eligible women are members. Most popular organizations: International Club, Student Athletic Trainers, Outreach International, Art Student Society, Students in Free Enterprise (SIFE). Major annual events: New Year's in November, Final Fling, Air Band Competition at Homecoming. Student services: health clinic, personal-psychological counseling. Campus security: 24-hour emergency response devices and patrols, late night transport-escort service, controlled dormitory access. 774 college housing spaces available; 656 were occupied in 2012-13. Freshmen guaranteed college housing. On-campus residence required through sophomore year. Options: men-only, women-only housing available. F. M. Smith Library with 143,989 books, 82,874 microform titles, 903 serials, 3,755 audiovisual materials, an OPAC, and a Web page. Operations spending for the previous fiscal year: $569,968. 249 computers available on campus for general student use. A campuswide network can be accessed from student residence rooms and from off campus. Students can access the following: online class registration. Staffed computer lab on campus provides training in use of computers, software, and the Internet.
Community Environment: Lamoni (population 2,470), a picturesque town in the rolling hills of south central Iowa, is within easy driving distance of Des Moines, Omaha, Council Bluffs, and Kansas City. Bus transportation is available to these urban centers. The city has an excellent library and shopping area including several antique malls. Churches play an important part in the life of the community and a county hospital is located in nearby Leon. Citizens enjoy world-renowned artists in concert and theater productions at the college fine arts center, movies, sports, clubs, and lodges. Nine Eagles State Park (12 miles southeast), Central Park, and Foreman Park provide facilities for recreation.

■ **GRAND VIEW UNIVERSITY**
1200 Grandview Ave.
Des Moines, IA 50316-1599
Tel: (515)263-2800; Free: 800-444-6083
Fax: (515)263-2974
E-mail: admissions@grandview.edu
Web Site: www.grandview.edu/

Description: Independent, comprehensive, coed, affiliated with Evangelical Lutheran Church in America. Awards bachelor's and master's degrees. Founded 1896. Setting: 25-acre urban campus. Endowment: $16.4 million. Educational spending for the previous fiscal year: $5700 per student. Total enrollment: 2,232. Faculty: 269 (94 full-time, 175 part-time). Student-undergrad faculty ratio is 14:1. 821 applied, 92% were admitted. 23% from top 10% of their high school class, 40% from top quarter, 63% from top half. 6 valedictorians. Full-time: 1,785 students, 58% women, 42% men. Part-time: 410 students, 65% women, 35% men. Students come from 34 states and territories, 16 other countries, 14% from out-of-state. 0.5% American Indian or Alaska Native, non-Hispanic/Latino; 3% Hispanic/Latino; 7% African American, non-Hispanic/Latino; 3% Asian, non-Hispanic/Latino; 0.2% Native Hawaiian or other Pacific Islander, non-Hispanic/Latino; 2% international. 28% 25 or older, 35% live on campus, 18% transferred in. Retention: 73% of full-time freshmen returned the following year. Academic areas with the most degrees conferred: business/marketing; health professions and related sciences; education. Core. Calendar: semesters. Academic remediation for entering students, services for LD students, advanced placement, accelerated degree program, self-designed majors, freshman honors college, honors program, independent study, distance learning, double major, summer session for credit, part-time degree program, adult/continuing education programs, co-op programs and internships. Off campus study at Drake University, Des Moines Area Community College. Study abroad program. ROTC: Army (c), Air Force (c).
Entrance Requirements: Option: electronic application. Required: high school transcript, SAT or ACT. Recommended: minimum 2 high school GPA. Entrance: minimally difficult. Application deadline: 8/15. Notification: 9/15. Transfer credits accepted: Yes.
Costs Per Year: Application fee: $0. Comprehensive fee: $29,972 includes full-time tuition ($22,208), mandatory fees ($500), and college room and board ($7264). Full-time tuition and fees vary according to class time and course load. Room and board charges vary according to board plan and housing facility. Part-time tuition: $553 per credit hour. Part-time tuition varies according to class time and course load.
Collegiate Environment: Orientation program. Drama-theater group, choral group, student-run newspaper, radio station. Social organizations: 43 open to all. Most popular organizations: Nursing Student Association, Art Club, Science Club, Education Club, Business Club. Major annual event: Homecoming. Student services: health clinic, personal-psychological counseling. Campus security: 24-hour emergency response devices and patrols, late night transport-escort service, controlled dormitory access, night security patrols. 800 college housing spaces available; 757 were occupied in 2012-13. Freshmen given priority for college housing. On-campus residence required through sophomore year. Option: coed housing available. Grand View University Library with 135,448 books, 11,334 microform titles, 27,077 serials, 3,801 audiovisual materials, an OPAC, and a Web page. Operations spending for the previous fiscal year: $517,810. 313 computers available on campus for general student use. A campuswide network can be accessed from student residence rooms and from off campus. Students can access the following: online class registration. Staffed computer lab on campus provides training in use of computers.
Community Environment: See Drake University.

■ **GRINNELL COLLEGE**
1103 Park St.
Grinnell, IA 50112-1690
Tel: (641)269-4000; Free: 800-247-0113
Fax: (641)269-3408
E-mail: askgrin@grinnell.edu
Web Site: www.grinnell.edu/
Description: Independent, 4-year, coed. Awards bachelor's degrees. Founded 1846. Setting: 120-acre small town campus. Endowment: $1.4 billion. Educational spending for the previous fiscal year: $21,779 per student. Total enrollment: 1,674. Faculty: 211 (160 full-time, 51 part-time). Student-undergrad faculty ratio is 9:1. 4,021 applied, 36% were admitted. 68% from top 10% of their high school class, 92% from top quarter, 100% from top half. Full-time: 1,615 students, 55% women, 45% men. Part-time: 59 students, 46% women, 54% men. Students come from 50 states and territories, 54 other countries, 88% from out-of-state. 0% American Indian or Alaska Native, non-Hispanic/Latino; 7% Hispanic/Latino; 5% African American, non-Hispanic/Latino; 7% Asian, non-Hispanic/Latino; 0.2% Native Hawaiian or other Pacific Islander, non-Hispanic/Latino; 12% international. 0% 25 or older, 82% live on campus, 1% transferred in. Retention: 95% of full-time freshmen returned the following year. Academic areas with the most degrees

conferred: social sciences; foreign languages and literature; biological/life sciences. Calendar: semesters. Services for LD students, advanced placement, accelerated degree program, self-designed majors, independent study, double major, internships. Off campus study. Study abroad program.
Entrance Requirements: Options: electronic application, early admission, early decision, deferred admission, international baccalaureate accepted. Required: essay, high school transcript, 3 recommendations, SAT or ACT. Recommended: interview. Entrance: very difficult. Application deadlines: 1/15, 11/15 for early decision plan 1, 1/1 for early decision plan 2. Notification: 4/1, 12/15 for early decision plan 1, 2/1 for early decision plan 2. SAT Reasoning Test deadline: 1/15. Transfer credits accepted: Yes. Applicants placed on waiting list: 1,191. Wait-listed applicants offered admission: 111. Early decision applicants: 286. Early decision applicants admitted: 137.
Costs Per Year: Application fee: $30. Comprehensive fee: $50,618 includes full-time tuition ($40,628), mandatory fees ($376), and college room and board ($9614). College room only: $4504. Room and board charges vary according to board plan and housing facility. Part-time tuition: $1270 per credit hour.
Collegiate Environment: Orientation program. Drama-theater group, choral group, student-run newspaper, radio station. Social organizations: 250 open to all. Most popular organizations: Concerned Black Students, International Student Organization, Student Organization of Latinas/Latinos, Campus Democrats, Ultimate Frisbee. Major annual events: Titular Head Student Film Festival, Mary B. James, Grinnell Relays. Student services: health clinic, personal-psychological counseling. Campus security: 24-hour emergency response devices and patrols, student patrols, late night transport-escort service, controlled dormitory access. College housing designed to accommodate 1,249 students; 1,309 undergraduates lived in college housing during 2012-13. Freshmen guaranteed college housing. On-campus residence required through sophomore year. Option: coed housing available. Burling Library plus 2 others with 1.2 million books, 416,593 microform titles, 26,222 serials, 39,745 audiovisual materials, an OPAC, and a Web page.
Community Environment: Grinnell, population 9,332, is located 1 hour east of Des Moines and 1 hour west of Iowa City, on Interstate 80 and is within a five-hour drive from Chicago, St. Louis, Kansas City, and Minneapolis.

■ **HAMILTON TECHNICAL COLLEGE**
1011 E 53rd St.
Davenport, IA 52807-2653
Tel: (563)386-3570; Free: 866-966-4825
Fax: (563)386-6756
E-mail: servin@hamiltontechcollege.com
Web Site: www.hamiltontechcollege.edu/
Description: Proprietary, 4-year, coed. Awards associate and bachelor's degrees. Founded 1969. Setting: urban campus. Faculty: 12 (11 full-time, 1 part-time). Student-undergrad faculty ratio is 20:1. 95 applied. Academic area with the most degrees conferred: engineering technologies. Calendar: continuous.
Entrance Requirements: Open admission. Option: deferred admission. Required: high school transcript, interview. Entrance: noncompetitive. Application deadline: Rolling.
Collegiate Environment: Campus security: 24-hour emergency response devices. Hamilton Technical College Library with 4,500 books and 30 serials.

■ **HAWKEYE COMMUNITY COLLEGE**
PO Box 8015
Waterloo, IA 50704-8015
Tel: (319)296-2320; Free: 800-670-4769
Fax: (319)296-2874
E-mail: holly.grimm-see@hawkeyecollege.edu
Web Site: www.hawkeyecollege.edu/
Description: State and locally supported, 2-year, coed. Awards certificates, diplomas, transfer associate, and terminal associate degrees. Founded 1966. Setting: 320-acre rural campus. Endowment: $1.9 million. Research spending for the previous fiscal year: $176,136. Educational spending for the previous fiscal year: $5525 per student. Total enrollment: 5,971. Faculty: 346 (117 full-time, 229 part-time). Student-undergrad faculty ratio is 20:1. 2,186 applied, 99.9% were admitted. Full-time: 2,683 students, 54% women, 46% men. Part-time: 3,288 students, 57% women, 43% men. 1% from out-of-state. 0.3% American Indian or Alaska Native, non-Hispanic/Latino; 3% Hispanic/Latino; 8% African American, non-Hispanic/Latino; 1% Asian, non-Hispanic/Latino; 0.1% Native Hawaiian or other Pacific Islander, non-Hispanic/Latino; 0.2% international. 30% 25 or older, 33% transferred in.

Calendar: semesters. Academic remediation for entering students, ESL program, services for LD students, advanced placement, accelerated degree program, distance learning, summer session for credit, part-time degree program, external degree program, adult/continuing education programs, co-op programs. Study abroad program. ROTC: Army (c).

Entrance Requirements: Open admission. Options: electronic application, deferred admission. Required: high school transcript, COMPASS or the equivalent from ACT or accredited college course(s). Required for some: ACT. Entrance: noncompetitive. Application deadlines: Rolling, Rolling for nonresidents. Notification: continuous, continuous for nonresidents. Transfer credits accepted: Yes.

Costs Per Year: Application fee: $0. State resident tuition: $3836 full-time, $137 per credit hour part-time. Nonresident tuition: $4536 full-time, $162 per credit hour part-time. Mandatory fees: $168 full-time, $6 per credit hour part-time. Full-time tuition and fees vary according to course load and program. Part-time tuition and fees vary according to course load and program.

Collegiate Environment: Orientation program. Social organizations: 29 open to all; academic fraternities; 20% of eligible men and 30% of eligible women are members. Most popular organizations: Student Senate, Phi Theta Kappa, Student Ambassadors, Nursing, IAAP. Major annual events: Fall Fest, Diversify Hawkeye Lunch, Health and Wellness Fair. Student services: health clinic, personal-psychological counseling, women's center. Campus security: 24-hour patrols. College housing not available. Hawkeye Community College Library with 125,194 books, 220 serials, 1,800 audiovisual materials, an OPAC, and a Web page. Operations spending for the previous fiscal year: $458,477. 2,100 computers available on campus for general student use. A campuswide network can be accessed. Students can access the following: online class registration. Staffed computer lab on campus provides training in use of computers, software, and the Internet.

Community Environment: Waterloo, population 66,500, is an industrial city. The manufacture of tractors, and the horse racing cart known as the Sulky by the Jerald Sulky Company. Highlights of interest are the Museum of History and Science.

■ INDIAN HILLS COMMUNITY COLLEGE

525 Grandview Ave., Bldg. No.1
Ottumwa, IA 52501-1398
Tel: (641)683-5111; Free: 800-726-2585
Web Site: www.ihcc.cc.ia.us/

Description: State and locally supported, 2-year, coed. Part of Iowa Area Community Colleges System. Awards certificates, diplomas, transfer associate, and terminal associate degrees. Founded 1966. Setting: 400-acre small town campus. Total enrollment: 4,174. 28% 25 or older. Academic remediation for entering students, ESL program, services for LD students, self-designed majors, honors program, summer session for credit, part-time degree program, adult/continuing education programs, co-op programs and internships.

Entrance Requirements: Open admission except for nursing, technology programs. Option: early admission. Required for some: high school transcript. Entrance: noncompetitive. Application deadline: Rolling.

Collegiate Environment: Orientation program. Drama-theater group. Student services: personal-psychological counseling, women's center. Campus security: 24-hour emergency response devices and patrols. Indian Hills Community College Library plus 2 others with 53,073 books, 350 serials, an OPAC, and a Web page.

Community Environment: The population of Ottumwa is 25,000. This community is located about 85 miles southwest of Des Moines. Recreational activities are available at Lake Rathbun, about six miles northwest of Centerville.

■ INSTE BIBLE COLLEGE

2302 SW 3rd St.
Ankeny, IA 50023
Tel: (515)289-9200
Fax: (515)289-9201
E-mail: inste@inste.edu
Web Site: www.inste.edu/

Description: Proprietary, 4-year, coed. Awards bachelor's degrees.

■ IOWA CENTRAL COMMUNITY COLLEGE

330 Ave. M
Fort Dodge, IA 50501-5798
Tel: (515)576-7201; Free: 800-362-2793
Fax: (515)576-7724

E-mail: bahls@iowacentral.com
Web Site: www.iccc.cc.ia.us/

Description: State and locally supported, 2-year, coed. Part of Iowa Department of Education Division of Community Colleges. Awards certificates, diplomas, transfer associate, and terminal associate degrees. Founded 1966. Setting: 110-acre small town campus. Total enrollment: 5,731. Faculty: 280 (73 full-time, 207 part-time). Student-undergrad faculty ratio is 18:1. 10% from top 10% of their high school class, 20% from top quarter, 40% from top half. Full-time: 2,590 students, 47% women, 53% men. Part-time: 3,141 students, 53% women, 47% men. Students come from 25 states and territories, 18 other countries, 5% from out-of-state. 26% 25 or older, 22% live on campus, 2% transferred in. Core. Calendar: semesters. Academic remediation for entering students, services for LD students, advanced placement, independent study, distance learning, summer session for credit, part-time degree program, adult/continuing education programs, co-op programs and internships. Study abroad program.

Entrance Requirements: Open admission except for health occupations programs. Options: early admission, deferred admission. Required: high school transcript. Entrance: noncompetitive. Application deadline: Rolling.

Collegiate Environment: Orientation program. Drama-theater group, choral group, student-run newspaper, radio station. Social organizations: 1 open to all. Most popular organizations: Student Senate, HOSA, BPA, Phi Beta Lambda. Major annual events: first week of fall semester activities, Hypnotist, theater productions. Student services: health clinic, personal-psychological counseling. Campus security: 24-hour emergency response devices and patrols, student patrols, late night transport-escort service, controlled dormitory access. Iowa Central Community College Library plus 1 other with 55,000 books, 350 serials, an OPAC, and a Web page. 510 computers available on campus for general student use. A campuswide network can be accessed from off-campus. Staffed computer lab on campus.

■ IOWA LAKES COMMUNITY COLLEGE

19 S 7th St.
Estherville, IA 51334-2295
Tel: (712)362-2604; Free: 800-521-5054
E-mail: info@iowalakes.edu
Web Site: www.iowalakes.edu/

Description: State and locally supported, 2-year, coed. Part of Iowa Community College System. Awards certificates, diplomas, transfer associate, and terminal associate degrees. Founded 1967. Setting: 20-acre small town campus. Endowment: $6.5 million. Educational spending for the previous fiscal year: $4619 per student. Total enrollment: 3,102. Faculty: 171 (91 full-time, 80 part-time). Student-undergrad faculty ratio is 24:1. 1,425 applied, 92% were admitted. Full-time: 1,663 students, 46% women, 54% men. Part-time: 1,439 students, 62% women, 38% men. Students come from 33 states and territories, 6 other countries. 0.4% American Indian or Alaska Native, non-Hispanic/Latino; 3% Hispanic/Latino; 3% African American, non-Hispanic/Latino; 1% Asian, non-Hispanic/Latino; 0.4% Native Hawaiian or other Pacific Islander, non-Hispanic/Latino; 1% international. 26% 25 or older, 37% live on campus. Retention: 59% of full-time freshmen returned the following year. Core. Calendar: semesters. Academic remediation for entering students, ESL program, services for LD students, advanced placement, accelerated degree program, honors program, independent study, distance learning, summer session for credit, part-time degree program, adult/continuing education programs, co-op programs and internships.

Entrance Requirements: Open admission except for allied health, aviation and wind energy programs. Option: electronic application. Required for some: interview. Entrance: noncompetitive. Application deadlines: Rolling, Rolling for nonresidents. Transfer credits accepted: Yes.

Collegiate Environment: Orientation program. Drama-theater group, choral group, student-run newspaper, radio station. Social organizations: 42 open to all. Most popular organizations: music, Criminal Justice, nursing clubs, Environmental Studies, Business. Major annual events: Homecoming, Convocations, Coffee houses/concerts. Campus security: 24-hour emergency response devices, student patrols. Iowa Lakes Community College Library plus 2 others with 25,305 books, 3,651 serials, 1,175 audiovisual materials, and an OPAC. Operations spending for the previous fiscal year: $483,141. 1,316 computers available on campus for general student use. A campuswide network can be accessed from student residence rooms and from off campus. Students can access the following: online class registration. Staffed computer lab on campus provides training in use of software and the Internet.

■ IOWA STATE UNIVERSITY OF SCIENCE AND TECHNOLOGY

Ames, IA 50011

Tel: (515)294-4111; Free: 800-262-3810

Fax: (515)294-2592

E-mail: admissions@iastate.edu

Web Site: www.iastate.edu/

Description: State-supported, university, coed. Awards bachelor's, master's, and doctoral degrees and post-master's certificates. Founded 1858. Setting: 1,795-acre suburban campus with easy access to Des Moines. Endowment: $604.9 million. Research spending for the previous fiscal year: $171 million. Educational spending for the previous fiscal year: $7720 per student. Total enrollment: 30,748. Faculty: 1,745 (1,446 full-time, 299 part-time). Student-undergrad faculty ratio is 18:1. 16,539 applied, 83% were admitted. 26% from top 10% of their high school class, 56% from top quarter, 90% from top half. Full-time: 24,206 students, 44% women, 56% men. Part-time: 1,349 students, 40% women, 60% men. Students come from 54 states and territories, 101 other countries, 28% from out-of-state. 0.2% American Indian or Alaska Native, non-Hispanic/Latino; 4% Hispanic/Latino; 3% African American, non-Hispanic/Latino; 3% Asian, non-Hispanic/Latino; 0.1% Native Hawaiian or other Pacific Islander, non-Hispanic/Latino; 8% international. 6% 25 or older, 34% live on campus, 7% transferred in. Retention: 86% of full-time freshmen returned the following year. Academic areas with the most degrees conferred: business/marketing; engineering; agriculture. Calendar: semesters. Academic remediation for entering students, ESL program, services for LD students, advanced placement, accelerated degree program, self-designed majors, freshman honors college, honors program, independent study, distance learning, double major, summer session for credit, part-time degree program, external degree program, adult/continuing education programs, co-op programs and internships, graduate courses open to undergrads. Off campus study at Iowa Regents' Universities Student Exchange, National Student Exchange. Study abroad program. ROTC: Army, Naval, Air Force.

Entrance Requirements: Options: electronic application, early admission, deferred admission, international baccalaureate accepted. Required: high school transcript, Regent Admission Index (RAI) of at least 245 and meet minimum HS course requirements, SAT or ACT. Entrance: moderately difficult. Application deadline: 7/1. Notification: continuous. SAT Reasoning Test deadline: 7/1. SAT Subject Test deadline: 7/1. Transfer credits accepted: Yes.

Costs Per Year: Application fee: $40. State resident tuition: $6648 full-time, $277 per semester hour part-time. Nonresident tuition: $18,760 full-time, $782 per semester hour part-time. Mandatory fees: $1078 full-time. Full-time tuition and fees vary according to class time, degree level, and program. Part-time tuition varies according to class time, course load, degree level, and program. College room and board: $7721. College room only: $4093. Room and board charges vary according to board plan and housing facility.

Collegiate Environment: Orientation program. Drama-theater group, choral group, marching band, student-run newspaper, radio station. Social organizations: 825 open to all; national fraternities, national sororities, local fraternities. Most popular organizations: student government, Student Alumni Association, Residence Hall Associations. Major annual events: VEISHEA (student spring festival and university open house), Homecoming, Family Weekend. Student services: legal services, health clinic, personal-psychological counseling, women's center. Campus security: 24-hour emergency response devices and patrols, student patrols, late night transport-escort service, controlled dormitory access, crime prevention programs, threat assessment team, motor vehicle help van. 9,940 college housing spaces available; 9,930 were occupied in 2012-13. Freshmen given priority for college housing. Options: coed, men-only, women-only housing available. University Library plus 1 other with 2.9 million books, 3.5 million microform titles, 100,528 serials, an OPAC, and a Web page. Operations spending for the previous fiscal year: $22.1 million. 2,400 computers available on campus for general student use. Computer purchase/lease plans available. A campuswide network can be accessed from student residence rooms and from off campus. Students can access the following: online class registration, network services. Staffed computer lab on campus provides training in use of computers, software, and the Internet.

■ IOWA WESLEYAN COLLEGE

601 N Main St.

Mount Pleasant, IA 52641-1398

Tel: (319)385-8021; Free: 800-582-2383

Fax: (319)385-6296

E-mail: mpetty@iwc.edu

Web Site: www.iwc.edu/

Description: Independent United Methodist, 4-year, coed. Awards bachelor's degrees. Founded 1842. Setting: 60-acre small town campus. Endowment: $13.1 million. Educational spending for the previous fiscal year: $8539 per student. Total enrollment: 650. Faculty: 105 (48 full-time, 57 part-time). Student-undergrad faculty ratio is 12:1. 1,274 applied, 56% were admitted. Full-time: 497 students, 55% women, 45% men. Part-time: 153 students, 73% women, 27% men. Students come from 30 states and territories, 11 other countries, 36% from out-of-state. 0.3% American Indian or Alaska Native, non-Hispanic/Latino; 6% Hispanic/Latino; 9% African American, non-Hispanic/Latino; 0.3% Asian, non-Hispanic/Latino; 0.3% Native Hawaiian or other Pacific Islander, non-Hispanic/Latino; 7% international. 30% 25 or older, 68% live on campus, 15% transferred in. Retention: 43% of full-time freshmen returned the following year. Academic areas with the most degrees conferred: business/marketing; health professions and related sciences; education. Core. Calendar: semesters. Academic remediation for entering students, services for LD students, advanced placement, self-designed majors, honors program, independent study, distance learning, double major, summer session for credit, part-time degree program, adult/continuing education programs, co-op programs and internships. Off campus study at Southeastern Community College, Muscatine Community College. Study abroad program.

Entrance Requirements: Options: electronic application, early admission, deferred admission. Required: high school transcript, minimum 2.5 high school GPA, minimum ACT score of 19 or SAT of 890, SAT or ACT. Required for some: essay, 1 recommendation, interview. Entrance: moderately difficult. Application deadline: 8/15. SAT Reasoning Test deadline: 8/15. SAT Subject Test deadline: 8/15. Transfer credits accepted: Yes.

Costs Per Year: Application fee: $20. Comprehensive fee: $32,280 includes full-time tuition ($24,300) and college room and board ($7980). College room only: $3140. Room and board charges vary according to board plan and housing facility. Part-time tuition: $610 per credit hour. Part-time tuition varies according to class time, course load, and location.

Collegiate Environment: Orientation program. Choral group, student-run radio station. Social organizations: 32 open to all; national sororities; 12% of women are members. Most popular organizations: Student Union Board, Student Senate, Commuter Club, Choir, Student Ambassadors. Major annual events: Homecoming, Spring Thing, Christmas Thing. Student services: health clinic, personal-psychological counseling. Campus security: late night transport-escort service, controlled dormitory access, evening patrols by trained security personnel. 465 college housing spaces available; 220 were occupied in 2012-13. Freshmen guaranteed college housing. On-campus residence required through senior year. Options: coed, men-only, women-only housing available. Chadwick Library with 84,778 books, 25,441 microform titles, 44 serials, 4,025 audiovisual materials, an OPAC, and a Web page. Operations spending for the previous fiscal year: $248,974. 97 computers available on campus for general student use. A campuswide network can be accessed from student residence rooms. Staffed computer lab on campus provides training in use of computers, software, and the Internet.

Community Environment: Mount Pleasant (population 8,700) is located at the intersection of U.S. Highways 218 and 34; Amtrak and a municipal airport serve the area. Community facilities include many churches, libraries, a hospital, motels, and civic and fraternal organizations. Part time employment is available. Two state parks are nearby which provide facilities for boating and fishing.

■ IOWA WESTERN COMMUNITY COLLEGE

2700 College Rd., Box 4-C

Council Bluffs, IA 51502

Tel: (712)325-3200; Free: 800-432-5852

Fax: (712)325-3720

E-mail: admissions@iwcc.edu

Web Site: www.iwcc.edu/

Description: District-supported, 2-year, coed. Part of Iowa Department of Education Division of Community Colleges. Awards certificates, diplomas, transfer associate, and terminal associate degrees. Founded 1966. Setting: 282-acre suburban campus with easy access to Omaha. Total enrollment: 5,300. 22% 25 or older. Core. Calendar: semesters. Academic remediation for entering students, ESL program, services for LD students, independent study, distance learning, summer session for credit, part-time degree program, adult/continuing education programs, co-op programs and internships. ROTC: Army (c), Air Force (c).

Entrance Requirements: Open admission except for nursing, technical programs. Options: early admission, deferred admission. Required: high school transcript. Entrance: noncompetitive. Application deadline: Rolling.

Collegiate Environment: Orientation program. Drama-theater group, choral group, student-run newspaper, radio station. Student services: personal-psychological counseling. Campus security: 24-hour patrols, late night transport-escort service. 59,200 books, 207 serials, and an OPAC.

■ **ITT TECHNICAL INSTITUTE (CEDAR RAPIDS)**
3735 Queen Ct. SW
Cedar Rapids, IA 52404
Tel: (319)297-3400; Free: 877-320-4625
Web Site: www.itt-tech.edu/
Description: Proprietary, primarily 2-year, coed. Awards terminal associate and bachelor's degrees.
Entrance Requirements: Entrance: minimally difficult.

■ **ITT TECHNICAL INSTITUTE (CLIVE)**
1860 NW 118th St., Ste. 110
Clive, IA 50325
Tel: (515)327-5500; Free: 877-526-7312
Web Site: www.itt-tech.edu/
Description: Proprietary, primarily 2-year, coed. Part of ITT Educational Services, Inc. Awards terminal associate and bachelor's degrees.
Entrance Requirements: Entrance: minimally difficult.

■ **KAPLAN UNIVERSITY, CEDAR FALLS**
7009 Nordic Dr.
Cedar Falls, IA 50613
Tel: (319)277-0220; Free: 800-527-5268
Web Site: www.cedarfalls.kaplanuniversity.edu/
Description: Proprietary, primarily 2-year, coed. Awards certificates, diplomas, transfer associate, terminal associate, and bachelor's degrees. Founded 2000.
Entrance Requirements: Application deadline: Rolling.

■ **KAPLAN UNIVERSITY, CEDAR RAPIDS**
3165 Edgewood Pky., SW
Cedar Rapids, IA 52404
Tel: (319)363-0481; Free: 800-527-5268
Fax: (319)363-3812
Web Site: www.cedarrapids.kaplanuniversity.edu/
Description: Proprietary, primarily 2-year, coed. Administratively affiliated with Kaplan University - Davenport Campus. Awards certificates, diplomas, transfer associate, terminal associate, and bachelor's degrees (branch locations in Des Moines, Mason City, and Cedar Falls with significant enrollment not reflected in profile). Founded 1900. Setting: suburban campus.

■ **KAPLAN UNIVERSITY, COUNCIL BLUFFS**
1751 Madison Ave.
Council Bluffs, IA 51503
Tel: (712)328-4212; Free: 800-527-5268
Web Site: www.councilbluffs.kaplanuniversity.edu/
Description: Proprietary, primarily 2-year, coed. Awards certificates, transfer associate, terminal associate, and bachelor's degrees. Founded 2004.
Entrance Requirements: Required: Wonderlic aptitude test.

■ **KAPLAN UNIVERSITY, DAVENPORT CAMPUS**
1801 E Kimberly Rd.
Ste. 1
Davenport, IA 52807-2095
Tel: (563)355-3500; Free: 800-527-5268
Web Site: www.davenport.kaplanuniversity.edu/
Description: Proprietary, comprehensive, coed. Awards associate, bachelor's, and master's degrees (profile includes both traditional and online students). Founded 1937. Setting: suburban campus.

■ **KAPLAN UNIVERSITY, DES MOINES**
4655 121st St.
Urbandale, IA 50323
Tel: (515)727-2100; Free: 800-527-5268
Web Site: www.desmoines.kaplanuniversity.edu/
Description: Proprietary, primarily 2-year, coed. Awards certificates, diplomas, transfer associate, terminal associate, and bachelor's degrees.

■ **KAPLAN UNIVERSITY, MASON CITY CAMPUS**
2570 4th St., SW
Mason City, IA 50401
Tel: (641)423-2530; Free: 800-527-5268
Web Site: masoncity.kaplanuniversity.edu/
Description: Proprietary, 4-year, coed. Awards associate and bachelor's degrees. Founded 1900.

■ **KIRKWOOD COMMUNITY COLLEGE**
PO Box 2068
Cedar Rapids, IA 52406-2068
Tel: (319)398-5411; Free: 800-332-2055
Fax: (319)398-1244
E-mail: dbannon@kirkwood.cc.ia.us
Web Site: www.kirkwood.edu/
Description: State and locally supported, 2-year, coed. Part of Iowa Department of Education Division of Community Colleges. Awards certificates, diplomas, transfer associate, and terminal associate degrees. Founded 1966. Setting: 630-acre suburban campus. Endowment: $16 million. Total enrollment: 17,841. Faculty: 968 (288 full-time, 680 part-time). Student-undergrad faculty ratio is 24:1. Students come from 37 states and territories, 94 other countries, 3% from out-of-state. 35% 25 or older. Core. Calendar: semesters. Academic remediation for entering students, ESL program, services for LD students, advanced placement, accelerated degree program, self-designed majors, honors program, independent study, distance learning, summer session for credit, part-time degree program, external degree program, adult/continuing education programs, co-op programs and internships. Off campus study at Iowa State University of Science and Technology, University of Northern Iowa, St. Ambrose University.
Entrance Requirements: Open admission. Options: electronic application, early admission. Required: high school transcript. Entrance: noncompetitive. Application deadline: Rolling. Notification: continuous.
Collegiate Environment: Orientation program. Drama-theater group, choral group, student-run newspaper. Social organizations: 45 open to all. Major annual events: Homecoming, Fall Orientation, graduation. Student services: legal services, health clinic, personal-psychological counseling. Campus security: 24-hour emergency response devices and patrols. Library with 60,622 books, 40,377 microform titles, 565 serials, and an OPAC. 1,000 computers available on campus for general student use. A campuswide network can be accessed. Students can access the following: online class registration. Staffed computer lab on campus.
Community Environment: Cedar Rapids/Marion is a dynamic community of 130,000, and Kirkwood students enjoy its many options for recreation, entertainment, and shopping. Located just five minutes north of the campus, downtown Cedar Rapids features Five Seasons Center, which holds an arena accommodating 8,000 persons for rock concerts, sports events, auto and ice shows, and more. Numerous restaurants, night spots, and movie theaters round out the entertainment scene. There are 62 parks for swimming, golfing, tennis, boating, and camping, and there is shopping in two large malls and the thriving downtown business districts of Cedar Rapids and Marion. Cultural activity centers around the Cedar Rapids Symphony, Art Museum, and Community Theater, as well as the area's four colleges. Religious activity is based in more than 125 congregations of all faiths. Apartment and condominium housing is available in all price ranges, and more new units are being built. Cedar Rapids/Marion is an attractive and stimulating place to live as well as learn. In addition to the Cedar Rapids campus, there are Kirkwood learning centers in each of the seven counties in the College's service area.

■ **LORAS COLLEGE**
1450 Alta Vista
Dubuque, IA 52004-0178
Tel: (563)588-7100; Free: 800-245-6727
Fax: (563)588-7964
E-mail: adms@loras.edu
Web Site: www.loras.edu/
Description: Independent Roman Catholic, comprehensive, coed. Awards associate, bachelor's, and master's degrees. Founded 1839. Setting: 60-acre suburban campus. Endowment: $22 million. Research spending for the previous fiscal year: $572,934. Educational spending for the previous fiscal year: $6916 per student. Total enrollment: 1,555. Faculty: 141 (110 full-time, 31 part-time). Student-undergrad faculty ratio is 12:1. 1,540 applied, 76% were admitted. 21% from top 10% of their high school class, 43% from top quarter, 76% from top half. Full-time: 1,467 students, 49% women, 51%

men. Part-time: 47 students, 47% women, 53% men. Students come from 23 states and territories, 13 other countries, 55% from out-of-state. 0.5% American Indian or Alaska Native, non-Hispanic/Latino; 3% Hispanic/Latino; 2% African American, non-Hispanic/Latino; 1% Asian, non-Hispanic/Latino; 0.2% Native Hawaiian or other Pacific Islander, non-Hispanic/Latino; 4% international. 2% 25 or older, 67% live on campus, 4% transferred in. Retention: 79% of full-time freshmen returned the following year. Academic areas with the most degrees conferred: business/marketing; education; social sciences. Core. Calendar: semesters. Academic remediation for entering students, services for LD students, advanced placement, self-designed majors, honors program, independent study, double major, summer session for credit, part-time degree program, co-op programs and internships, graduate courses open to undergrads. Off campus study. Study abroad program. ROTC: Army (c).

Entrance Requirements: Options: electronic application, deferred admission. Required: high school transcript, minimum 2.5 high school GPA. Recommended: essay, 1 recommendation, ACT. Required for some: interview, SAT. Entrance: moderately difficult. Application deadline: Rolling. Notification: continuous. SAT Reasoning Test deadline: 8/15.

Costs Per Year: Application fee: $25. Comprehensive fee: $35,815 includes full-time tuition ($26,813), mandatory fees ($1352), and college room and board ($7650). College room only: $3875. Full-time tuition and fees vary according to course load and degree level. Room and board charges vary according to board plan and housing facility. Part-time tuition: $559 per credit hour.

Collegiate Environment: Orientation program. Drama-theater group, choral group, student-run newspaper, radio station. Social organizations: national sororities. Most popular organizations: Student Senate, Campus Ministry, College Activities Board, residence hall councils. Major annual events: Homecoming, End of Year Bash, Family Weekend. Student services: health clinic, personal-psychological counseling. Campus security: 24-hour emergency response devices and patrols, late night transport-escort service, controlled dormitory access. Loras College Library with 369,009 books, 6,835 microform titles, 67,484 serials, 3,243 audiovisual materials, an OPAC, and a Web page. Operations spending for the previous fiscal year: $681,623. 20 computers available on campus for general student use. A campuswide network can be accessed from student residence rooms and from off campus. Students can access the following: online class registration. Staffed computer lab on campus.

Community Environment: The small city of Dubuque is located on the Mississippi River where Iowa, Illinois, and Wisconsin meet. The oldest city in Iowa, it features rugged bluffs and Victorian architecture. Excellent air connections with Chicago's O'Hare Airport and with the Minneapolis-St. Paul Airport are available. The city is the commercial, cultural, and recreational center of the tri-state area. It offers concerts, theater, symphony, art galleries, museums, and riverboat gambling. Facilities are available for boating, skiing, golf, and tennis.

■ LUTHER COLLEGE

700 College Dr.
Decorah, IA 52101
Tel: (563)387-2000; Free: 800-458-8437
Fax: (563)387-2159
E-mail: admissions@luther.edu
Web Site: www.luther.edu/

Description: Independent, 4-year, coed, affiliated with Evangelical Lutheran Church in America. Awards bachelor's degrees. Founded 1861. Setting: 200-acre small town campus. Endowment: $118.1 million. Research spending for the previous fiscal year: $425,520. Educational spending for the previous fiscal year: $13,190 per student. Total enrollment: 2,473. Faculty: 255 (178 full-time, 77 part-time). Student-undergrad faculty ratio is 12:1. 3,556 applied, 70% were admitted. 32% from top 10% of their high school class, 59% from top quarter, 90% from top half. 2 National Merit Scholars, 16 class presidents, 39 valedictorians, 78 student government officers. Full-time: 2,421 students, 57% women, 43% men. Part-time: 52 students, 42% women, 58% men. Students come from 38 states and territories, 46 other countries, 68% from out-of-state. 0.04% American Indian or Alaska Native, non-Hispanic/Latino; 3% Hispanic/Latino; 1% African American, non-Hispanic/Latino; 2% Asian, non-Hispanic/Latino; 0.04% Native Hawaiian or other Pacific Islander, non-Hispanic/Latino; 5% international. 1% 25 or older, 85% live on campus, 1% transferred in. Retention: 88% of full-time freshmen returned the following year. Academic areas with the most degrees conferred: social sciences; biological/life sciences; visual and performing arts. Core. Calendar: 4-1-4. Academic remediation for entering students,

services for LD students, advanced placement, self-designed majors, honors program, independent study, double major, summer session for credit, part-time degree program, internships. Off campus study. Study abroad program.

Entrance Requirements: Options: electronic application, deferred admission, international baccalaureate accepted. Required: essay, high school transcript, 1 recommendation, SAT or ACT. Recommended: interview. Entrance: moderately difficult. Notification: continuous. Transfer credits accepted: Yes.

Costs Per Year: Application fee: $25. Comprehensive fee: $44,330 includes full-time tuition ($37,330), mandatory fees ($150), and college room and board ($6850). College room only: $3240. Full-time tuition and fees vary according to course load. Room and board charges vary according to board plan and housing facility. Part-time tuition: $1334 per credit hour. Part-time tuition varies according to course load.

Collegiate Environment: Orientation program. Drama-theater group, choral group, student-run newspaper, radio station. Social organizations: 85 open to all; local fraternities, local sororities, National Coed Service Fraternity (APO); 1% of eligible men and 2% of eligible women are members. Most popular organizations: Alpha Phi Omega, college ministries, recreational sports, Student Activities Council, Diversity groups. Major annual events: Open Mic, Jazz Night, Parade, Flamingo Ball, Family Weekend - SAC Soda Shoppe, Christmas at Luther Weekend. Student services: health clinic, personal-psychological counseling, women's center. Campus security: 24-hour emergency response devices and patrols, late night transport-escort service, controlled dormitory access. 2,143 college housing spaces available; 2,121 were occupied in 2012-13. Freshmen guaranteed college housing. On-campus residence required through senior year. Option: coed housing available. Preus Library with 335,949 books, 24,834 microform titles, 38,495 serials, 13,988 audiovisual materials, an OPAC, and a Web page. Operations spending for the previous fiscal year: $1.7 million. 546 computers available on campus for general student use. A campuswide network can be accessed from student residence rooms and from off campus. Students can access the following: online class registration. Staffed computer lab on campus provides training in use of computers, software, and the Internet.

Community Environment: Decorah (population 8,000) is on the banks of the Upper Iowa River, in an area known as Little Switzerland, in northeast Iowa. Twin Springs and Siewer Springs state fish hatcheries are nearby. Decorah has set aside more than 328 acres for recreation. Outdoor activities include golf, skiing, hiking, hunting and fishing.

■ MAHARISHI UNIVERSITY OF MANAGEMENT

1000 N 4th St.
Fairfield, IA 52557
Tel: (641)472-7000; Free: 800-369-6480
Fax: (641)472-1189
E-mail: admissions@mum.edu
Web Site: www.mum.edu/

Description: Independent, university, coed. Awards bachelor's, master's, and doctoral degrees and post-master's certificates. Founded 1971. Setting: small town campus. Total enrollment: 1,132. Faculty: 94 (68 full-time, 26 part-time). Student-undergrad faculty ratio is 12:1. 100 applied, 50% were admitted. Full-time: 336 students, 47% women, 53% men. Part-time: 19 students, 26% women, 74% men. 83% from out-of-state. 1% American Indian or Alaska Native, non-Hispanic/Latino; 14% Hispanic/Latino; 9% African American, non-Hispanic/Latino; 3% Asian, non-Hispanic/Latino; 0.3% Native Hawaiian or other Pacific Islander, non-Hispanic/Latino; 13% international. 44% 25 or older, 68% live on campus, 48% transferred in. Retention: 77% of full-time freshmen returned the following year. Academic areas with the most degrees conferred: natural resources/environmental science; business/marketing; communication/journalism. Calendar: semesters. Adult/continuing education programs.

Entrance Requirements: Options: electronic application, early admission, deferred admission, international baccalaureate accepted. Required: essay, high school transcript, minimum 2.5 high school GPA, 2 recommendations. Recommended: interview. Entrance: moderately difficult. Application deadline: 8/1. Notification: continuous until 8/15. Preference given to graduates of the Maharishi School of the Age of Enlightenment.

Costs Per Year: Application fee: $25. Comprehensive fee: $33,830 includes full-time tuition ($26,000), mandatory fees ($430), and college room and board ($7400). Part-time tuition: $350 per credit hour. Part-time tuition varies according to course load.

Collegiate Environment: Orientation program. Campus security: 24-hour emergency response devices and patrols, late night transport-escort service, controlled dormitory access. Freshmen guaranteed college housing. On-campus residence required through senior year. Options: men-only, women-only housing available.

Community Environment: The University is located in the Fairfield, Iowa, 50 miles west of the Mississippi River in the heartland of the central United States. A thirty percent growth in the population and the appearance of numerous new businesses in Fairfield in recent years have spurred an unprecedented level of economic and cultural growth in the community. Fairfield is viewed as one of the great success stories in Iowa, and is recognized throughout the state for its creativity in business, the arts, and education. Located within easy access of Chicago, St. Louis, and Kansas City, it is only one hour south of Iowa City, home of the University of Iowa.

■ MARSHALLTOWN COMMUNITY COLLEGE

3700 S Ctr. St.
Marshalltown, IA 50158-4760
Tel: (641)752-7106; Free: 866-622-4748
Fax: (641)752-8149
Web Site: www.marshalltowncommunitycollege.com/
Description: District-supported, 2-year, coed. Part of Iowa Valley Community College District System. Awards certificates, diplomas, transfer associate, and terminal associate degrees. Founded 1927. Setting: 200-acre small town campus. Total enrollment: 1,701. 28% 25 or older. Core. Calendar: semesters. Academic remediation for entering students, ESL program, services for LD students, advanced placement, self-designed majors, freshman honors college, honors program, independent study, distance learning, summer session for credit, part-time degree program, adult/continuing education programs, co-op programs and internships. Study abroad program. ROTC: Air Force (c).
Entrance Requirements: Open admission. Options: electronic application, early admission. Required: high school transcript, ACT COMPASS. Recommended: ACT. Required for some: interview. Entrance: noncompetitive. Application deadline: Rolling. Notification: continuous.
Collegiate Environment: Drama-theater group, choral group, student-run newspaper, radio station. Student services: personal-psychological counseling. Learning Resource Center with 39,348 books, 216 serials, and a Web page.
Community Environment: Marshalltown, an industrial city in central Iowa, is an important bus and truck terminal. The community facilities include 32 churches, hospitals, a library and many civic service clubs, as well as a Chamber of Commerce. Opportunities for part time or seasonal employment are excellent. Recreational facilities include an expanding park system; three golf courses; YMCA; two swimming pools; large youth soccer, football, and Little League complexes; a five-mile in-city walk/jog/bike path with greenbelt environment; new playgrounds; two bowling alleys; and three theaters.

■ MERCY COLLEGE OF HEALTH SCIENCES

928 Sixth Ave.
Des Moines, IA 50309-1239
Tel: (515)643-3180; Free: 800-637-2994
Fax: (515)643-6698
E-mail: kdonovan@mercydesmoines.org
Web Site: www.mchs.edu/
Description: Independent, 4-year, coed, affiliated with Roman Catholic Church. Administratively affiliated with Catholic Health Initiatives, Mercy Medial Center. Awards associate and bachelor's degrees. Founded 1995. Setting: 5-acre urban campus. Total enrollment: 846. Faculty: 117 (51 full-time, 66 part-time). Student-undergrad faculty ratio is 7:1. 111 applied, 84% were admitted. Full-time: 390 students, 86% women, 14% men. Part-time: 456 students, 90% women, 10% men. Students come from 13 states and territories, 2% from out-of-state. 1% American Indian or Alaska Native, non-Hispanic/Latino; 3% Hispanic/Latino; 3% African American, non-Hispanic/Latino; 4% Asian, non-Hispanic/Latino; 0% Native Hawaiian or other Pacific Islander, non-Hispanic/Latino; 0% international. 48% 25 or older. Academic area with the most degrees conferred: health professions and related sciences. Calendar: semesters. Academic remediation for entering students, ESL program, services for LD students, advanced placement, accelerated degree program, independent study, distance learning, double major, summer session for credit, part-time degree program, co-op programs. Off campus study.
Entrance Requirements: Option: electronic application. Required: high school transcript, minimum 2.25 high school GPA. Required for some: interview, ACT. Transfer credits accepted: Yes.
Costs Per Year: Application fee: $0. Tuition: $13,900 full-time, $480 per

credit part-time. Full-time tuition varies according to course load. Part-time tuition varies according to course load.
Collegiate Environment: Orientation program. Most popular organizations: student senate, Campus Ministry, Science Club. Major annual events: President's luncheons, Career Fair, Cultural Fair. Student services: personal-psychological counseling. Campus security: 24-hour emergency response devices and patrols, late night transport-escort service. College housing not available. Mercy College Library plus 4 others with an OPAC and a Web page. 46 computers available on campus for general student use. A campuswide network can be accessed from off-campus. Staffed computer lab on campus provides training in use of computers, software, and the Internet.
Community Environment: Des Moines is the setting for MCHS's four-acre campus, which is located just south of Interstate 235 and three blocks south of Mercy Medical Center.

■ MORNINGSIDE COLLEGE

1501 Morningside Ave.
Sioux City, IA 51106
Tel: (712)274-5000; Free: 800-831-0806
E-mail: mscadm@morningside.edu
Web Site: www.morningside.edu/
Description: Independent, comprehensive, coed, affiliated with United Methodist Church. Awards bachelor's and master's degrees. Founded 1894. Setting: 69-acre suburban campus. Endowment: $38.1 million. Educational spending for the previous fiscal year: $5359 per student. Total enrollment: 2,224. Faculty: 180 (78 full-time, 102 part-time). Student-undergrad faculty ratio is 14:1. 2,048 applied, 63% were admitted. 19% from top 10% of their high school class, 43% from top quarter, 78% from top half. Full-time: 1,199 students, 50% women, 50% men. Part-time: 43 students, 74% women, 26% men. Students come from 21 states and territories, 9 other countries, 35% from out-of-state. 0.5% American Indian or Alaska Native, non-Hispanic/Latino; 6% Hispanic/Latino; 1% African American, non-Hispanic/Latino; 0.5% Asian, non-Hispanic/Latino; 0.2% Native Hawaiian or other Pacific Islander, non-Hispanic/Latino; 2% international. 7% 25 or older, 60% live on campus, 6% transferred in. Retention: 68% of full-time freshmen returned the following year. Academic areas with the most degrees conferred: education; business/marketing; biological/life sciences; visual and performing arts. Core. Calendar: semesters. Academic remediation for entering students, ESL program, services for LD students, advanced placement, self-designed majors, honors program, independent study, distance learning, double major, summer session for credit, part-time degree program, adult/continuing education programs, internships, graduate courses open to undergrads. Off campus study at American University, Drew University. Study abroad program. ROTC: Army (c).
Entrance Requirements: Options: electronic application, deferred admission, international baccalaureate accepted. Required: high school transcript, 20 ACT/1410 SAT and either rank in top half of class or 2.5 GPA, SAT or ACT. Recommended: minimum 2.5 high school GPA, interview. Entrance: moderately difficult. Application deadlines: Rolling, Rolling for nonresidents. Notification: continuous, continuous for nonresidents. SAT Reasoning Test deadline: 8/15. Transfer credits accepted: Yes.
Costs Per Year: Application fee: $0. Comprehensive fee: $32,620 includes full-time tuition ($23,780), mandatory fees ($1220), and college room and board ($7620). College room only: $3900. Room and board charges vary according to housing facility.
Collegiate Environment: Orientation program. Drama-theater group, choral group, student-run newspaper, radio station. Social organizations: 45 open to all; national fraternities, national sororities; 4% of eligible men and 2% of eligible women are members. Most popular organizations: Student Government/Activities Council, Student Ambassadors, Homecoming Committee. Major annual events: Homecoming, Honors Assembly, Christmas at Morningside. Student services: health clinic, personal-psychological counseling, women's center. Campus security: 24-hour emergency response devices, student patrols, late night transport-escort service, controlled dormitory access, 20-hour patrols by trained security personnel. 858 college housing spaces available; 719 were occupied in 2012-13. Freshmen guaranteed college housing. On-campus residence required through junior year. Option: coed housing available. Hickman-Johnson-Furrow Learning Center with 72,714 books, 288,382 microform titles, 165 serials, 1,567 audiovisual materials, an OPAC, and a Web page. Operations spending for the previous fiscal year: $411,404. 150 computers available on campus for general student use. Computer purchase/lease plans available. A computer is required for all students. A campuswide network can be accessed from

student residence rooms and from off campus. Students can access the following: online class registration, academic and financial records. Staffed computer lab on campus provides training in use of computers, software, and the Internet.

Community Environment: See Briar Cliff College.

■ **MOUNT MERCY UNIVERSITY**
1330 Elmhurst Dr., NE
Cedar Rapids, IA 52402-4797
Tel: (319)363-8213; Free: 800-248-4504
Fax: (319)368-6492
E-mail: lgarcia@mtmercy.edu
Web Site: www.mtmercy.edu/
Description: Independent Roman Catholic, comprehensive, coed. Awards bachelor's and master's degrees. Founded 1928. Setting: 40-acre suburban campus with easy access to Iowa City. Endowment: $23.1 million. Educational spending for the previous fiscal year: $6819 per student. Total enrollment: 1,810. Faculty: 152 (87 full-time, 65 part-time). Student-undergrad faculty ratio is 13:1. 532 applied, 70% were admitted. 16% from top 10% of their high school class, 36% from top quarter, 75% from top half. Full-time: 915 students, 68% women, 32% men. Part-time: 598 students, 70% women, 30% men. Students come from 6 states and territories, 10 other countries, 4% from out-of-state. 0.2% American Indian or Alaska Native, non-Hispanic/Latino; 3% Hispanic/Latino; 3% African American, non-Hispanic/Latino; 1% Asian, non-Hispanic/Latino; 0.1% Native Hawaiian or other Pacific Islander, non-Hispanic/Latino; 4% international. 44% 25 or older, 38% live on campus, 19% transferred in. Retention: 75% of full-time freshmen returned the following year. Academic areas with the most degrees conferred: business/marketing; health professions and related sciences; education. Core. Calendar: 4-1-4. Academic remediation for entering students, services for LD students, advanced placement, accelerated degree program, honors program, independent study, double major, summer session for credit, part-time degree program, adult/continuing education programs, internships. Off campus study at Coe College. Study abroad program.
Entrance Requirements: Options: electronic application, deferred admission. Required: high school transcript, minimum 2.5 high school GPA, SAT or ACT. Required for some: 1 recommendation. Entrance: moderately difficult. Application deadline: 8/15. Notification: continuous. Transfer credits accepted: Yes.
Costs Per Year: Application fee: $0. Comprehensive fee: $34,385 includes full-time tuition ($26,160), mandatory fees ($150), and college room and board ($8075). Full-time tuition and fees vary according to course load. Room and board charges vary according to board plan and housing facility. Part-time tuition: $710 per semester hour. Part-time mandatory fees: $150 per year. Part-time tuition and fees vary according to course load.
Collegiate Environment: Orientation program. Drama-theater group, choral group, student-run newspaper. Social organizations: 35 open to all. Most popular organizations: Student Ambassadors, Mount Mercy University Association of Nursing Students, Cheerleaders, Best Buddies, Student Government Association. Major annual events: Vegas Night, Christmas Club Friday, Spring Fling Week. Student services: health clinic, personal-psychological counseling. Campus security: 24-hour emergency response devices and patrols, student patrols, late night transport-escort service, controlled dormitory access, The Mount Mercy University Department of Public Safety is operational 24 hours a day, seven days a week. 475 college housing spaces available; 418 were occupied in 2012-13. Freshmen guaranteed college housing. On-campus residence required through sophomore year. Options: coed, men-only, women-only housing available. Busse Center with 131,930 books, 54,823 microform titles, 3,926 serials, 5,322 audiovisual materials, an OPAC, and a Web page. Operations spending for the previous fiscal year: $614,546. 120 computers available on campus for general student use. A campuswide network can be accessed from student residence rooms and from off campus. Students can access the following: online class registration. Staffed computer lab on campus provides training in use of computers and software.
Community Environment: See Kirkwood Community College.

■ **MUSCATINE COMMUNITY COLLEGE**
152 Colorado St.
Muscatine, IA 52761-5396
Tel: (563)288-6001; Free: 800-351-4669
Fax: (563)288-6074
E-mail: gmohr@eicc.edu

Web Site: www.eicc.edu/general/muscatine/
Description: State-supported, 2-year, coed. Part of Eastern Iowa Community College District. Awards diplomas, transfer associate, and terminal associate degrees. Founded 1929. Setting: 25-acre small town campus. Educational spending for the previous fiscal year: $2249 per student. Total enrollment: 1,624. Faculty: 91 (32 full-time, 59 part-time). 311 applied, 100% were admitted. Full-time: 608 students, 56% women, 44% men. Part-time: 1,016 students, 53% women, 47% men. Students come from 6 states and territories, 8 other countries, 3% from out-of-state. 26% 25 or older, 4% live on campus. Retention: 55% of full-time freshmen returned the following year. Core. Calendar: semesters. Academic remediation for entering students, ESL program, services for LD students, advanced placement, self-designed majors, honors program, independent study, distance learning, double major, summer session for credit, part-time degree program, adult/continuing education programs, co-op programs and internships. Off campus study at Black Hawk College, Carl Sandburg Community College, Kirkwood Community College, Northeast Iowa Community College. Study abroad program.
Entrance Requirements: Open admission except for nursing program and vet tech. Option: electronic application. Entrance: noncompetitive. Application deadline: Rolling. Notification: continuous.
Collegiate Environment: Orientation program. Drama-theater group, choral group, student-run newspaper. Campus security: 24-hour emergency response devices. Muscatine Community College Library with 19,588 books, 176 serials, and an OPAC. 57 computers available on campus for general student use. A campuswide network can be accessed from off-campus. Students can access the following: online class registration. Staffed computer lab on campus provides training in use of computers, software, and the Internet.
Community Environment: Muscatine, an industrial center, is located on the Mississippi River, and has an annual mean temperature of 50 degrees, and an average rainfall of 34 inches. Vegetables and melons are raised in the vicinity; over three million bushels of grain are shipped from here each year. Community facilities include many churches and a library. Parks, a golf course, a bowling alley and skating rink offer recreation. The Mississippi River and nearby Cedar and Iowa rivers provide excellent picnicking, fishing and boat launching facilities. Points of interest are the Laura Musser Art Gallery and Museum, and Weed Park.

■ **NORTH IOWA AREA COMMUNITY COLLEGE**
500 College Dr.
Mason City, IA 50401-7299
Tel: (641)423-1264; Free: 888-GO NIACC
Fax: (641)423-1711
E-mail: request@niacc.edu
Web Site: www.niacc.edu/
Description: State and locally supported, 2-year, coed. Part of Iowa Community College System. Awards certificates, diplomas, and transfer associate degrees. Founded 1918. Setting: 320-acre rural campus. Total enrollment: 3,744. Faculty: 256 (84 full-time, 172 part-time). Student-undergrad faculty ratio is 17:1. 2,045 applied, 100% were admitted. 3% from top 10% of their high school class, 11% from top quarter, 38% from top half. Full-time: 1,994 students, 50% women, 50% men. Part-time: 1,750 students, 61% women, 39% men. 23% from out-of-state. 0.4% American Indian or Alaska Native, non-Hispanic/Latino; 3% Hispanic/Latino; 3% African American, non-Hispanic/Latino; 1% Asian, non-Hispanic/Latino; 0% Native Hawaiian or other Pacific Islander, non-Hispanic/Latino; 1% international. 23% 25 or older, 9% live on campus. Core. Calendar: semesters. Academic remediation for entering students, ESL program, services for LD students, advanced placement, self-designed majors, honors program, distance learning, summer session for credit, part-time degree program, external degree program, co-op programs and internships. Study abroad program.
Entrance Requirements: Open admission except for nursing, physical therapy assistant programs. Option: electronic application. Entrance: noncompetitive. Application deadline: Rolling. Notification: continuous. Transfer credits accepted: Yes.
Collegiate Environment: Orientation program. Drama-theater group, choral group, student-run newspaper. Social organizations: 30 open to all. Most popular organizations: Student Senate, intramurals, band/orchestra. Major annual events: Quodlibet, Homecoming. Student services: health clinic, personal-psychological counseling. Campus security: 24-hour emergency response devices. North Iowa Area Community College Library with 29,540 books, 1,905 microform titles, 413 serials, 7,773 audiovisual materials, an OPAC, and a Web page. 365 computers available on campus for general student use. A campuswide network can be accessed from student

residence rooms and from off campus. Students can access the following: online class registration. Staffed computer lab on campus provides training in use of computers, software, and the Internet.

Community Environment: Mason City (population 27,909) is located in the north center of the state midway between Des Moines and Minneapolis - St. Paul, and has an average winter temperature of 28 degrees, summer average 63 degrees. One bus line and an airline offer transportation. The community facilities include hospitals, a library, Art Center, hotels and motels. Brick, tile and Portland cement are manufactured from the deposits of clay, limestone and sand in this area. Part-time work is available. Recreation activities include golf, water sports in summer, ice boating and fishing in winter, ice skating, pheasant deer and duck hunting.

■ NORTHEAST IOWA COMMUNITY COLLEGE
Box 400
Calmar, IA 52132-0480
Tel: (563)562-3263; Free: 800-728-CALMAR
Fax: (563)562-3719
E-mail: mcconnellb@nicc.edu
Web Site: www.nicc.edu/

Description: State and locally supported, 2-year, coed. Part of Iowa Area Community Colleges System. Awards certificates, diplomas, transfer associate, and terminal associate degrees. Founded 1966. Setting: 210-acre rural campus. Total enrollment: 5,018. Faculty: 348 (107 full-time, 241 part-time). Student-undergrad faculty ratio is 16:1. 1,227 applied, 78% were admitted. Full-time: 2,066 students, 59% women, 41% men. Part-time: 2,952 students, 63% women, 37% men. 10% from out-of-state. 0.2% American Indian or Alaska Native, non-Hispanic/Latino; 2% Hispanic/Latino; 3% African American, non-Hispanic/Latino; 0.4% Asian, non-Hispanic/Latino; 0.1% Native Hawaiian or other Pacific Islander, non-Hispanic/Latino. 24% 25 or older, 7% transferred in. Retention: 50% of full-time freshmen returned the following year. Core. Calendar: semesters. Academic remediation for entering students, services for LD students, advanced placement, honors program, distance learning, double major, summer session for credit, part-time degree program, external degree program, adult/continuing education programs, co-op programs and internships. Off campus study at Upper Iowa University, Clarke College, University of Dubuque, Loras College.

Entrance Requirements: Open admission except for allied health programs. Option: electronic application. Recommended: high school transcript. Entrance: noncompetitive. Application deadlines: Rolling, Rolling for nonresidents. Notification: continuous, continuous for nonresidents. Transfer credits accepted: Yes.

Collegiate Environment: Orientation program. Choral group, student-run newspaper. Social organizations: national fraternities, national sororities. Student services: personal-psychological counseling. Campus security: security personnel on weeknights. College housing not available. Wilder Resource Center & Burton Payne Library plus 2 others with 44,835 books, 1,166 microform titles, 341 serials, 7,326 audiovisual materials, an OPAC, and a Web page. 1,054 computers available on campus for general student use. A campuswide network can be accessed from off-campus. Students can access the following: online class registration. Staffed computer lab on campus provides training in use of computers, software, and the Internet.

Community Environment: Calmar is located 10 miles from Decorah, 25 miles from Cresco, 17 miles from Postville, and 24 miles from New Hampton. The town's primary business is agriculture and related fields. Two firms here manufacture furniture and truck racks. Recreational facilities are provided by Calmar Lake, Upper Iowa River, and Turkey River, which furnish great opportunity for fishing and hunting. Northeast Iowa operates a second campus at Peosta, Iowa, which is located approximately ten miles west of the city of Dubuque. The rural area of Peosta is similar to that of Calmar, except that it is close to the metropolitan area of Dubuque, which has a population of nearly 70,000. It offers a wide range of cultural and recreational activities and is situated on the Mississippi River. The popularity of Northeast Iowa is pointed out by the growing numbers of tourists who travel to the area from all over the Midwest.

■ NORTHWEST IOWA COMMUNITY COLLEGE
603 W Park St.
Sheldon, IA 51201-1046
Tel: (712)324-5061; Free: 800-352-4907
Fax: (712)324-4136
E-mail: lstory@nwicc.edu
Web Site: www.nwicc.edu/

Description: State-supported, 2-year, coed. Part of Iowa Department of Education Division of Community Colleges. Awards certificates, diplomas, transfer associate, and terminal associate degrees. Founded 1966. Setting: 263-acre small town campus with easy access to Sioux City, IA and Sioux Falls, SD. Total enrollment: 1,288. Faculty: 139 (40 full-time, 99 part-time). Student-undergrad faculty ratio is 11:1. 22% 25 or older. Retention: 93% of full-time freshmen returned the following year. Calendar: semesters. Academic remediation for entering students, ESL program, services for LD students, distance learning, double major, part-time degree program, adult/continuing education programs, co-op programs. Off campus study. Study abroad program.

Entrance Requirements: Open admission. Option: electronic application. Required: high school transcript, ACT COMPASS. Required for some: minimum 2.0 high school GPA. Entrance: noncompetitive. Application deadline: Rolling. Notification: continuous.

Costs Per Year: Application fee: $10. State resident tuition: $4140 full-time, $138 per credit part-time. Nonresident tuition: $4620 full-time, $154 per credit part-time. Mandatory fees: $840 full-time, $28 per credit part-time. Full-time tuition and fees vary according to program. Part-time tuition and fees vary according to program. College room and board: $4700. College room only: $3400. Room and board charges vary according to housing facility.

Collegiate Environment: Orientation program. Student-run newspaper. Social organizations: 3 open to all. Major annual events: Fall Kick-off BBQ, Free Holiday Meals, SGA Special Entertainment. Student services: personal-psychological counseling. Campus security: 24-hour emergency response devices. Northwest Iowa Community College Library plus 1 other with 16,300 books, 170 serials, 3,800 audiovisual materials, an OPAC, and a Web page. 358 computers available on campus for general student use. A campuswide network can be accessed. Staffed computer lab on campus provides training in use of computers, software, and the Internet.

Community Environment: Sheldon (population 4,800) is the trading center for a rich, five-county farmland area. Bus and train transportation are available, airline service is within 55 miles at Sioux City. Local parks and a golf club provide facilities for recreation. The Iowa Lakes Region is a 50 mile drive. Community facilities include public libraries, churches, a modern hospital, and an indoor swimming pool.

■ NORTHWESTERN COLLEGE
101 Seventh St., SW
Orange City, IA 51041-1996
Tel: (712)707-7000; Free: 800-747-4757
Fax: (712)707-7247
E-mail: admissions@nwciowa.edu
Web Site: www.nwciowa.edu/

Description: Independent, 4-year, coed, affiliated with Reformed Church in America. Awards bachelor's degrees. Founded 1882. Setting: 100-acre small town campus. Endowment: $41.3 million. Educational spending for the previous fiscal year: $7963 per student. Total enrollment: 1,241. Faculty: 126 (84 full-time, 42 part-time). Student-undergrad faculty ratio is 12:1. 1,193 applied, 74% were admitted. 26% from top 10% of their high school class, 54% from top quarter, 79% from top half. 27 valedictorians. Full-time: 1,169 students, 55% women, 45% men. Part-time: 72 students, 85% women, 15% men. Students come from 33 states and territories, 23 other countries, 46% from out-of-state. 1% American Indian or Alaska Native, non-Hispanic/Latino; 5% Hispanic/Latino; 2% African American, non-Hispanic/Latino; 1% Asian, non-Hispanic/Latino; 0% Native Hawaiian or other Pacific Islander, non-Hispanic/Latino; 3% international. 3% 25 or older, 89% live on campus, 4% transferred in. Retention: 77% of full-time freshmen returned the following year. Academic areas with the most degrees conferred: business/marketing; education; health professions and related sciences. Core. Calendar: semesters. Academic remediation for entering students, ESL program, services for LD students, advanced placement, self-designed majors, honors program, independent study, distance learning, double major, summer session for credit, co-op programs and internships. Off campus study at 5 members of the Mid-America States Universities Association, Council for Christian Colleges and Universities. Study abroad program.

Entrance Requirements: Options: electronic application, early admission, deferred admission, international baccalaureate accepted. Required: essay, high school transcript, minimum 2 high school GPA, 1 recommendation, SAT or ACT. Recommended: minimum 2.5 high school GPA, interview. Entrance: moderately difficult. Application deadline: Rolling. Notification: continuous. SAT Reasoning Test deadline: 8/15. SAT Subject Test deadline: 8/15. Transfer credits accepted: Yes.

Costs Per Year: Application fee: $25. Comprehensive fee: $34,848 includes

full-time tuition ($26,614), mandatory fees ($150), and college room and board ($8084). Full-time tuition and fees vary according to program. Room and board charges vary according to board plan and housing facility. Part-time tuition: $570 per credit hour. Part-time mandatory fees: $50 per term. Part-time tuition and fees vary according to course load and program.

Collegiate Environment: Orientation program. Drama-theater group, choral group, student-run newspaper. Social organizations: 30 open to all. Most popular organizations: Drama Ministries Ensemble, Acappella Choir, Psi Chi, Fellowship of Christian Athletes, International Club. Major annual events: Clash of the Classes, RUSH (Student-Organized and Choreographed Dance Performance), Dancing with the Profs. Student services: health clinic, personal-psychological counseling. Campus security: 24-hour emergency response devices, controlled dormitory access. 1,169 college housing spaces available; 1,051 were occupied in 2012-13. Freshmen guaranteed college housing. On-campus residence required through senior year. Options: men-only, women-only housing available. Ramaker Library plus 1 other with 120,000 books, 110,000 microform titles, 840 serials, an OPAC, and a Web page. 250 computers available on campus for general student use. A campuswide network can be accessed from student residence rooms and from off campus. Students can access the following: online class registration, online degree audits. Staffed computer lab on campus provides training in use of computers, software, and the Internet.

■ **PALMER COLLEGE OF CHIROPRACTIC**
1000 Brady St.
Davenport, IA 52803-5287
Tel: (563)884-5000; Free: 800-722-3648
Fax: (563)884-5897
E-mail: lisa.gisel@palmer.edu
Web Site: www.palmer.edu/

Description: Independent, comprehensive, coed. Awards associate, incidental bachelor's, master's, and doctoral degrees. Founded 1897. Setting: 31-acre urban campus. Total enrollment: 2,310. Faculty: 15 (2 full-time, 13 part-time). Student-undergrad faculty ratio is 3:1. 24 applied, 83% were admitted. Full-time: 39 students, 54% women, 46% men. Part-time: 10 students, 40% women, 60% men. Students come from 16 states and territories, 1 other country, 63% from out-of-state. 2% Hispanic/Latino; 2% African American, non-Hispanic/Latino; 2% Asian, non-Hispanic/Latino. 45% 25 or older, 59% transferred in. Retention: 50% of full-time freshmen returned the following year. Academic area with the most degrees conferred: biological/life sciences. Core. Calendar: trimesters. Academic remediation for entering students, services for LD students, summer session for credit, internships.

Entrance Requirements: Open admission. Options: electronic application, deferred admission. Required: high school transcript, minimum 2 high school GPA, minimum 2.0 in math, science, and English courses. Required for some: essay, interview. Entrance: noncompetitive. Application deadlines: Rolling, Rolling for nonresidents. Notification: continuous, continuous for nonresidents. Transfer credits accepted: Yes.

Collegiate Environment: Orientation program. Student-run newspaper. Social organizations: 60 open to all; national fraternities, local fraternities, local sororities. Most popular organizations: Gonstead Club, intramural sports, campus guides, Student International Chiropractic Association, Palmer Student Alumni Foundation. Major annual events: Homecoming, Chili Cook-off, Student Holiday Dance. Student services: health clinic, personal-psychological counseling. Campus security: 24-hour emergency response devices and patrols, late night transport-escort service. David D. Palmer Health Sciences Library with 72,918 books, 2,297 microform titles, 24,697 serials, 1,200 audiovisual materials, an OPAC, and a Web page. Operations spending for the previous fiscal year: $1.3 million. 94 computers available on campus for general student use. A campuswide network can be accessed. Staffed computer lab on campus provides training in use of computers, software, and the Internet.

Community Environment: The Quad-Cities area, a community of about 400,000, offers a wide variety of entertainment options including more than 275 restaurants; professional basketball and ice hockey; Class A baseball; arena football; 60 miles of bike trails; theater, museums and the art galleries.

■ **ST. AMBROSE UNIVERSITY**
518 W Locust St.
Davenport, IA 52803-2898
Tel: (563)333-6000; Free: 800-383-2627
Fax: (563)383-8791
E-mail: higginsmegf@sau.edu

Web Site: www.sau.edu/

Description: Independent Roman Catholic, comprehensive, coed. Awards bachelor's, master's, and doctoral degrees and post-master's certificates. Founded 1882. Setting: 118-acre urban campus. Endowment: $105.2 million. Educational spending for the previous fiscal year: $23,354 per student. Total enrollment: 3,671. Faculty: 425 (214 full-time, 211 part-time). Student-undergrad faculty ratio is 11:1. 3,309 applied, 73% were admitted. 21% from top 10% of their high school class, 44% from top quarter, 74% from top half. 82 valedictorians. Full-time: 2,419 students, 57% women, 43% men. Part-time: 375 students, 68% women, 32% men. Students come from 25 states and territories, 14 other countries, 57% from out-of-state. 0.1% American Indian or Alaska Native, non-Hispanic/Latino; 1% Hispanic/Latino; 3% African American, non-Hispanic/Latino; 1% Asian, non-Hispanic/Latino; 0.1% Native Hawaiian or other Pacific Islander, non-Hispanic/Latino; 1% international. 16% 25 or older, 60% live on campus, 9% transferred in. Retention: 78% of full-time freshmen returned the following year. Academic areas with the most degrees conferred: business/marketing; parks and recreation; health professions and related sciences; education. Core. Calendar: 4-1-4. Academic remediation for entering students, services for LD students, advanced placement, accelerated degree program, self-designed majors, independent study, distance learning, double major, summer session for credit, part-time degree program, external degree program, adult/continuing education programs, co-op programs and internships, graduate courses open to undergrads. Off campus study at Black Hawk College, Eastern Iowa Community Colleges. Study abroad program.

Entrance Requirements: Options: electronic application, deferred admission. Required: high school transcript, minimum 2.5 high school GPA, rank in upper 50% of high school class, SAT or ACT. Recommended: interview, ACT. Required for some: interview. Entrance: moderately difficult. Application deadline: Rolling. Notification: 10/1.

Costs Per Year: Application fee: $25. Comprehensive fee: $35,756 includes full-time tuition ($26,500), mandatory fees ($240), and college room and board ($9016). College room only: $5500. Full-time tuition and fees vary according to course load, location, program, and reciprocity agreements. Room and board charges vary according to board plan and housing facility. Part-time tuition: $820 per credit hour. Part-time tuition varies according to course load and location.

Collegiate Environment: Orientation program. Drama-theater group, choral group, student-run newspaper, radio station. Social organizations: 45 open to all. Most popular organizations: Up 'til Dawn, SOTA, Ambrosinas for Obama, Amnesty International, SPTO. Major annual events: Midnight Breakfast, Last Blast, Big Game Party. Student services: health clinic, personal-psychological counseling, women's center. Campus security: 24-hour emergency response devices and patrols, late night transport-escort service, controlled dormitory access, police officer on campus 10 pm to 6 am. 1,507 college housing spaces available; 1,506 were occupied in 2012-13. Freshmen guaranteed college housing. On-campus residence required through sophomore year. Options: coed, men-only, women-only housing available. SAU Library plus 1 other with 171,113 books, 7,091 microform titles, 563,352 serials, 4,552 audiovisual materials, an OPAC, and a Web page. Operations spending for the previous fiscal year: $1.5 million. 276 computers available on campus for general student use. A campuswide network can be accessed from student residence rooms and from off campus. Students can access the following: online class registration, online course syllabi, online class listings, and online payments. Staffed computer lab on campus provides training in use of computers, software, and the Internet.

■ **ST. LUKE'S COLLEGE**
2720 Stone Park Blvd.
Sioux City, IA 51104
Tel: (712)279-3149; Free: 800-352-4660
Fax: (712)233-8017
E-mail: mccartsj@stlukes.org
Web Site: stlukescollege.edu/

Description: Independent, 2-year, coed. Part of St. Luke's Regional Medical Center. Awards certificates and terminal associate degrees. Founded 1967. Setting: 3-acre rural campus with easy access to Omaha. Endowment: $981,282. Educational spending for the previous fiscal year: $7850 per student. Total enrollment: 203. Faculty: 36 (22 full-time, 14 part-time). Student-undergrad faculty ratio is 8:1. 35 applied, 34% were admitted. 14% from top 10% of their high school class, 86% from top half. Full-time: 165 students, 87% women, 13% men. Part-time: 38 students, 84% women, 16% men. Students come from 14 states and territories, 2 other countries, 43%

from out-of-state. 1% American Indian or Alaska Native, non-Hispanic/Latino; 8% Hispanic/Latino; 0.5% African American, non-Hispanic/Latino; 4% Asian, non-Hispanic/Latino; 0.5% Native Hawaiian or other Pacific Islander, non-Hispanic/Latino; 0% international. 27% 25 or older, 7% transferred in. Retention: 90% of full-time freshmen returned the following year. Core. Calendar: semesters. Advanced placement, summer session for credit, co-op programs.

Entrance Requirements: Option: electronic application. Required: essay, high school transcript, minimum 2.5 high school GPA, interview, SAT or ACT. Entrance: minimally difficult. Application deadline: 8/1. Transfer credits accepted: Yes. Applicants placed on waiting list: 0. Wait-listed applicants offered admission: 0.

Costs Per Year: Application fee: $50. Tuition: $16,740 full-time, $465 per credit hour part-time. Mandatory fees: $1050 full-time, $1050 per year part-time. Full-time tuition and fees vary according to course load, degree level, and program. Part-time tuition and fees vary according to course load, degree level, and program.

Collegiate Environment: Orientation program. Major annual events: Phone-a-thon, Community Service Day. Student services: health clinic, personal-psychological counseling. Campus security: 24-hour emergency response devices and patrols, late night transport-escort service. College housing not available. St. Luke's College with 2,418 books, 100 serials, 249 audiovisual materials, an OPAC, and a Web page. Operations spending for the previous fiscal year: $388,900. 9 computers available on campus for general student use. A campuswide network can be accessed. Staffed computer lab on campus provides training in use of computers, software, and the Internet.

■ **SCOTT COMMUNITY COLLEGE**
500 Belmont Rd.
Bettendorf, IA 52722-6804
Tel: (563)441-4001; Free: 800-895-0811
Fax: (563)441-4066
E-mail: gmohr@eicc.edu
Web Site: www.eicc.edu/scc/

Description: State and locally supported, 2-year, coed. Part of Eastern Iowa Community College District. Awards certificates, diplomas, transfer associate, and terminal associate degrees. Founded 1966. Setting: urban campus. Total enrollment: 4,111. Faculty: 250 (86 full-time, 164 part-time). Student-undergrad faculty ratio is 20:1. 904 applied, 100% were admitted. Full-time: 2,059 students, 62% women, 38% men. Part-time: 2,052 students, 63% women, 37% men. Students come from 26 states and territories, 23 other countries, 9% from out-of-state. 40% 25 or older, 1% transferred in. Retention: 48% of full-time freshmen returned the following year. Core. Calendar: semesters. Academic remediation for entering students, ESL program, services for LD students, advanced placement, self-designed majors, honors program, independent study, distance learning, double major, summer session for credit, part-time degree program, adult/continuing education programs, co-op programs and internships. Off campus study at Black Hawk College, Carl Sandburg College, Northeast Iowa Community College, Kirkwood Community College. Study abroad program.

Entrance Requirements: Open admission except for nursing program. Option: electronic application. Entrance: noncompetitive. Application deadline: Rolling. Notification: continuous.

Collegiate Environment: Orientation program. Drama-theater group. Social organizations: Greek honor society. Most popular organizations: student government, Campus Activities Board. Campus security: 24-hour emergency response devices. Scott Community College Library with 22,700 books, 183 serials, and an OPAC. 200 computers available on campus for general student use. A campuswide network can be accessed from off-campus. Students can access the following: online class registration. Staffed computer lab on campus provides training in use of computers, software, and the Internet.

Community Environment: Davenport (population 98,845), part of the Iowa-Illinois Quad Cities (pop. 375,000), is situated on the north bank of the Mississippi River and has an average temperature of 57 degrees and average rainfall of 50 inches. Commercial transportation is available. Community facilities are excellent and include 91 churches, hotels, hospitals, four local radio stations, four TV stations, a public library, and numerous civic and service organizations. Some of its industries' products are brooms, clothing, food, machinery, foundry products, and aircraft instruments. The 27 city parks offer varied recreational facilities. Vandeer Veer Park has gardens with approximately 2,500 species of roses.

■ **SIMPSON COLLEGE**
701 N C St.
Indianola, IA 50125-1297
Tel: (515)961-6251; Free: 800-362-2454
Fax: (515)961-1498
E-mail: admiss@simpson.edu
Web Site: www.simpson.edu/

Description: Independent United Methodist, comprehensive, coed. Awards bachelor's and master's degrees. Founded 1860. Setting: 80-acre suburban campus with easy access to Des Moines. Endowment: $69.2 million. Educational spending for the previous fiscal year: $9144 per student. Total enrollment: 1,897. Faculty: 202 (99 full-time, 103 part-time). Student-undergrad faculty ratio is 12:1. 1,385 applied, 89% were admitted. 27% from top 10% of their high school class, 56% from top quarter, 85% from top half. 29 valedictorians. Full-time: 1,423 students, 54% women, 46% men. Part-time: 421 students, 52% women, 48% men. Students come from 29 states and territories, 5 other countries, 11% from out-of-state. 0.3% American Indian or Alaska Native, non-Hispanic/Latino; 2% Hispanic/Latino; 2% African American, non-Hispanic/Latino; 1% Asian, non-Hispanic/Latino; 0% Native Hawaiian or other Pacific Islander, non-Hispanic/Latino; 1% international. 21% 25 or older, 87% live on campus, 4% transferred in. Retention: 82% of full-time freshmen returned the following year. Academic areas with the most degrees conferred: business/marketing; social sciences; education. Core. Calendar: 4-4-1. Services for LD students, advanced placement, accelerated degree program, self-designed majors, independent study, double major, summer session for credit, part-time degree program, adult/continuing education programs, co-op programs and internships. Off campus study at Capitol Hill Internship Program, Washington, D.C.; Drew University Semester on the United Nations, Madison, NJ/New York, NY; New York Media Experience Program, Marist College, Poughkeepsie, NY. Study abroad program.

Entrance Requirements: Options: electronic application, deferred admission, international baccalaureate accepted. Required: high school transcript, online or paper application, guidance counselor recommendation form, SAT or ACT. Recommended: minimum 3 high school GPA, interview. Entrance: moderately difficult. Application deadline: 8/15. Notification: continuous. SAT Reasoning Test deadline: 8/15. SAT Subject Test deadline: 8/15. Transfer credits accepted: Yes.

Costs Per Year: Application fee: $0. One-time mandatory fee: $200. Comprehensive fee: $38,962 includes full-time tuition ($30,423), mandatory fees ($576), and college room and board ($7963). College room only: $3860. Full-time tuition and fees vary according to class time, course load, degree level, and program. Room and board charges vary according to board plan and housing facility. Part-time tuition: $355 per credit hour. Part-time tuition varies according to class time, course load, degree level, and program.

Collegiate Environment: Orientation program. Drama-theater group, choral group, student-run newspaper, radio station. Social organizations: 80 open to all; national fraternities, national sororities, local fraternities; 22% of eligible men and 21% of eligible women are members. Most popular organizations: Religious Life Community, Campus Activities Board, Student Government Association, Residence Hall Association, intramurals. Major annual events: Homecoming Week, Campus Day (Campus Beautification/Volunteer Service Day), Back to School Stand-Around. Student services: health clinic, personal-psychological counseling, women's center. Campus security: 24-hour emergency response devices and patrols, student patrols, late night transport-escort service, controlled dormitory access, Safe (Simpson Alert for Emergencies) Students and staff/faculty will receive phone calls in case of campus emergency, including weather. 1,268 college housing spaces available; 1,176 were occupied in 2012-13. Freshmen guaranteed college housing. On-campus residence required through junior year. Option: coed housing available. Dunn Library plus 1 other with 161,611 books, 9,898 microform titles, 292 serials, 4,430 audiovisual materials, an OPAC, and a Web page. Operations spending for the previous fiscal year: $771,328. 374 computers available on campus for general student use. A campuswide network can be accessed from student residence rooms and from off campus. Students can access the following: online class registration, wireless campus. Staffed computer lab on campus provides training in use of computers, software, and the Internet.

Community Environment: Indianola (population 14,000) is located 20 minutes from Des Moines, the state capital, and enjoys the advantages of both a charming small town and a metropolitan center. Major transportation facilities are found in Des Moines, including the Des Moines International Airport. While Des Moines is known as a commercial and industrial city in the heart of a great agricultural state, it is also known for its educational, cultural, philanthropic, and religious institutions.

■ SOUTHEASTERN COMMUNITY COLLEGE

1500 W Agency Rd.
West Burlington, IA 52655-0180
Tel: (319)752-2731; Free: 866-722-4692
Fax: (319)752-4957
E-mail: admoff@scciowa.edu
Web Site: www.scciowa.edu/

Description: State and locally supported, 2-year, coed. Part of Iowa Department of Education Division of Community Colleges. Awards certificates, diplomas, and transfer associate degrees. Founded 1968. Setting: 160-acre small town campus. Total enrollment: 3,112. Faculty: 168 (77 full-time, 91 part-time). Student-undergrad faculty ratio is 20:1. 716 applied, 62% were admitted. 8% from top 10% of their high school class, 32% from top quarter, 66% from top half. Full-time: 1,621 students, 60% women, 40% men. Part-time: 1,491 students, 62% women, 38% men. 15% from out-of-state. 1% American Indian or Alaska Native, non-Hispanic/Latino; 4% Hispanic/Latino; 4% African American, non-Hispanic/Latino; 1% Asian, non-Hispanic/Latino; 0.1% Native Hawaiian or other Pacific Islander, non-Hispanic/Latino; 1% international. 30% 25 or older, 3% live on campus, 3% transferred in. Calendar: semesters. Part-time degree program, adult/continuing education programs.

Entrance Requirements: Open admission except for computer programming, nursing, electronics, medical assistant, medical laboratory technology, manufacturing technology, engineering design, occupational therapy assistant, physical therapy assistant programs. Options: early admission, deferred admission. Entrance: noncompetitive. Application deadline: Rolling. Notification: continuous.

Costs Per Year: Application fee: $0. State resident tuition: $4260 full-time, $142 per credit hour part-time. Nonresident tuition: $4410 full-time, $147 per credit hour part-time. Full-time tuition varies according to course load, program, and reciprocity agreements. Part-time tuition varies according to course load, program, and reciprocity agreements. College room and board: $5800. Room and board charges vary according to board plan and housing facility.

Collegiate Environment: Campus security: controlled dormitory access, night patrols by trained security personnel. Options: coed, men-only housing available.

■ SOUTHWESTERN COMMUNITY COLLEGE

1501 W Townline St.
Creston, IA 50801
Tel: (641)782-7081; Free: 800-247-4023
Fax: (641)782-3312
E-mail: carstens@swcciowa.edu
Web Site: www.swcciowa.edu/

Description: State-supported, 2-year, coed. Part of Iowa Department of Education Division of Community Colleges. Awards certificates, diplomas, transfer associate, and terminal associate degrees. Founded 1966. Setting: 420-acre rural campus. Total enrollment: 1,680. Faculty: 123 (43 full-time, 80 part-time). Student-undergrad faculty ratio is 13:1. 5% from top 10% of their high school class, 19% from top quarter, 48% from top half. 7 valedictorians. Full-time: 839 students, 62% women, 38% men. Part-time: 841 students, 66% women, 34% men. Students come from 21 states and territories, 2 other countries, 5% from out-of-state. 29% 25 or older, 3% live on campus, 6% transferred in. Retention: 57% of full-time freshmen returned the following year. Calendar: semesters. Academic remediation for entering students, advanced placement, distance learning, double major, summer session for credit, part-time degree program, adult/continuing education programs.

Entrance Requirements: Open admission except for allied health programs. Options: electronic application, early admission. Required: high school transcript. Required for some: SAT or ACT, ACT COMPASS. Entrance: noncompetitive. Application deadline: 9/5. Notification: continuous. Transfer credits accepted: Yes.

Collegiate Environment: Choral group. Major annual events: All School Picnic, Job Fair, Orientation. Student services: personal-psychological counseling. Campus security: 24-hour emergency response devices and patrols, controlled dormitory access. Learning Resources Center with 20,500 books. 200 computers available on campus for general student use. A campuswide network can be accessed from off-campus. Staffed computer lab on campus.

■ UNIVERSITY OF DUBUQUE

2000 University Ave.
Dubuque, IA 52001-5099
Tel: (563)589-3000; Free: 800-722-5583
Fax: (563)589-3690
E-mail: admissns@dbq.edu
Web Site: www.dbq.edu/

Description: Independent Presbyterian, comprehensive, coed. Awards associate, bachelor's, master's, and doctoral degrees. Founded 1852. Setting: 77-acre suburban campus. Endowment: $87.1 million. Educational spending for the previous fiscal year: $6970 per student. Total enrollment: 2,003. Faculty: 166 (87 full-time, 79 part-time). Student-undergrad faculty ratio is 15:1. 1,264 applied, 80% were admitted. 8% from top 10% of their high school class, 25% from top quarter, 54% from top half. 1 National Merit Scholar, 15 class presidents, 2 valedictorians, 100 student government officers. Full-time: 1,524 students, 41% women, 59% men. Part-time: 150 students, 64% women, 36% men. Students come from 41 states and territories, 8 other countries, 52% from out-of-state. 2% American Indian or Alaska Native, non-Hispanic/Latino; 1% Hispanic/Latino; 11% African American, non-Hispanic/Latino; 2% Asian, non-Hispanic/Latino; 0.1% Native Hawaiian or other Pacific Islander, non-Hispanic/Latino; 1% international. 15% 25 or older, 42% live on campus, 10% transferred in. Retention: 72% of full-time freshmen returned the following year. Academic areas with the most degrees conferred: business/marketing; transportation and materials moving; computer and information sciences. Core. Calendar: semesters. Academic remediation for entering students, ESL program, services for LD students, advanced placement, accelerated degree program, self-designed majors, honors program, independent study, distance learning, double major, summer session for credit, part-time degree program, adult/continuing education programs, internships, graduate courses open to undergrads. Off campus study. Study abroad program. ROTC: Army.

Entrance Requirements: Options: electronic application, international baccalaureate accepted. Required: essay, high school transcript, minimum 2.5 high school GPA, 2 recommendations, SAT or ACT. Recommended: interview. Entrance: moderately difficult. Application deadline: Rolling. Notification: continuous. SAT Reasoning Test deadline: 8/15. SAT Subject Test deadline: 8/15.

Costs Per Year: Application fee: $25. Comprehensive fee: $32,410 includes full-time tuition ($23,540), mandatory fees ($990), and college room and board ($7880). College room only: $3920. Room and board charges vary according to board plan, housing facility, and location.

Collegiate Environment: Orientation program. Drama-theater group, choral group, student-run newspaper. Social organizations: 58 open to all; local fraternities, local sororities; 22% of eligible men and 27% of eligible women are members. Most popular organizations: Black Student Union, Flight Team, Fellowship of Christian Athletes, Teacher Education Student Organization, Students in Free Enterprise (SIFE). Major annual events: Homecoming, Spring Founders' Day Ball, Christmas Candlelight Ceremony. Student services: health clinic, personal-psychological counseling. Campus security: 24-hour patrols, late night transport-escort service, controlled dormitory access. Charles C. Myers Library with 183,336 books, 3,614 microform titles, 51,859 serials, 4,379 audiovisual materials, an OPAC, and a Web page. Operations spending for the previous fiscal year: $833,324. 220 computers available on campus for general student use. A campuswide network can be accessed from student residence rooms and from off campus. Students can access the following: online class registration. Staffed computer lab on campus provides training in use of software.

■ THE UNIVERSITY OF IOWA

Iowa City, IA 52242-1316
Tel: (319)335-3500; Free: 800-553-4692
Fax: (319)335-1535
E-mail: admissions@uiowa.edu
Web Site: www.uiowa.edu/

Description: State-supported, university, coed. Awards bachelor's, master's, and doctoral degrees and post-master's certificates. Founded 1847. Setting: 1,900-acre small town campus. Endowment: $981.1 million. Research spending for the previous fiscal year: $335.1 million. Educational spending for the previous fiscal year: $14,443 per student. Total enrollment: 30,119. Faculty: 1,635 (1,555 full-time, 80 part-time). Student-undergrad faculty ratio is 16:1. 19,430 applied, 78% were admitted. 24% from top 10% of their high school class, 55% from top quarter, 91% from top half. 21 National Merit Scholars. Full-time: 19,639 students, 51% women, 49% men. Part-time: 2,360 students, 54% women, 46% men. Students come from 53 states and territories, 58 other countries, 39% from out-of-state. 0.2% American Indian or Alaska Native, non-Hispanic/Latino; 5% Hispanic/Latino; 3% African American, non-Hispanic/Latino; 3% Asian, non-Hispanic/Latino; 0.1% Native Hawaiian or other Pacific Islander, non-Hispanic/Latino; 9% international. 9% 25 or older, 31% live on campus, 5% transferred in. Retention: 86% of full-time freshmen returned the following year. Academic areas with the most degrees conferred: business/marketing; social sciences; communication/journalism. Core. Calendar: semesters. ESL program, services for LD students, advanced placement, accelerated degree program, self-designed majors, honors program, independent study, distance learning, double major, summer session for credit, part-time degree program, external degree program, adult/continuing education programs, co-op programs and internships, graduate courses open to undergrads. Off campus study at Iowa State University of Science and Technology, University of Northern Iowa, Committee on Institutional Cooperation. Study abroad program. ROTC: Army, Air Force.

Entrance Requirements: Options: electronic application, early admission, deferred admission, international baccalaureate accepted. Required: high school transcript, Must submit ACT or SAT score; must meet Regent Admission Index (RAI) requirement: residents 245 or above; nonresidents 255 or above, SAT or ACT. Entrance: moderately difficult. Application deadline: 4/1. Notification: continuous. SAT Reasoning Test deadline: 4/1. SAT Subject Test deadline: 4/1. Transfer credits accepted: Yes. Applicants placed on waiting list: 0.

Costs Per Year: Application fee: $40. State resident tuition: $6678 full-time, $279 per semester hour part-time. Nonresident tuition: $25,548 full-time, $1,065 per semester hour part-time. Mandatory fees: $1383 full-time, $72 per semester hour part-time. Full-time tuition and fees vary according to course load, program, and student level. Part-time tuition and fees vary according to course load, program, and student level. College room and board: $9420. Room and board charges vary according to board plan and housing facility.

Collegiate Environment: Orientation program. Drama-theater group, choral group, marching band, student-run newspaper, radio station. Social organizations: 487 open to all; national fraternities, national sororities; 11% of eligible men and 15% of eligible women are members. Most popular organizations: Association of Residence Halls, Graduate Student Senate, National Society of Collegiate Scholars, Organization for the Active Support of International Students (OASIS), Dance Marathon. Major annual events: River Fest Annual Spring Festival, Homecoming, Dance Marathon. Student services: legal services, health clinic, personal-psychological counseling, women's center. Campus security: 24-hour emergency response devices and patrols, late night transport-escort service, controlled dormitory access. 5,731 college housing spaces available; all were occupied in 2012-13. No special consideration for freshman housing applicants. Option: coed housing available. Main Library plus 8 others with 5.3 million books, an OPAC, and a Web page. Operations spending for the previous fiscal year: $24.4 million. 1,386 computers available on campus for general student use. Computer purchase/lease plans available. A campuswide network can be accessed from student residence rooms and from off campus. Students can access the following: online class registration, online degree process, financial aid summary, university bill. Staffed computer lab on campus provides training in use of computers, software, and the Internet.

Community Environment: Greater Iowa City (population 62,887) is located in eastern Iowa. Major transportation facilities are accessible. The university hospital and medical and scientific research departments make Iowa City an important medical center for the area and state. Public and historical libraries and museums, churches of most denominations, hospitals, and civic, fraternal, and veterans' organizations are a part of the community.

■ **UNIVERSITY OF NORTHERN IOWA**
1227 W 27th St.
Cedar Falls, IA 50614
Tel: (319)273-2311; Free: 800-772-2037
Fax: (319)273-2885
E-mail: admissions@uni.edu
Web Site: www.uni.edu/
Description: State-supported, comprehensive, coed. Part of Board of Regents, State of Iowa. Awards bachelor's, master's, and doctoral degrees. Founded 1876. Setting: 916-acre small town campus. Endowment: $75.5 million. Research spending for the previous fiscal year: $3 million. Educational spending for the previous fiscal year: $11,666 per student. Total enrollment: 12,273. Faculty: 788 (602 full-time, 186 part-time). Student-undergrad faculty ratio is 16:1. 4,322 applied, 78% were admitted. 19% from

top 10% of their high school class, 48% from top quarter, 84% from top half. 63 valedictorians. Full-time: 9,679 students, 58% women, 42% men. Part-time: 976 students, 47% women, 53% men. Students come from 38 states and territories, 45 other countries, 5% from out-of-state. 0.2% American Indian or Alaska Native, non-Hispanic/Latino; 3% Hispanic/Latino; 3% African American, non-Hispanic/Latino; 1% Asian, non-Hispanic/Latino; 0.04% Native Hawaiian or other Pacific Islander, non-Hispanic/Latino; 3% international. 9% 25 or older, 34% live on campus, 9% transferred in. Retention: 81% of full-time freshmen returned the following year. Academic areas with the most degrees conferred: business/marketing; education; social sciences. Core. Calendar: semesters. Academic remediation for entering students, ESL program, services for LD students, advanced placement, accelerated degree program, self-designed majors, honors program, independent study, distance learning, double major, summer session for credit, part-time degree program, external degree program, adult/continuing education programs, co-op programs and internships, graduate courses open to undergrads. Off campus study at Iowa Regents' Universities Student Exchange, National Student Exchange. Study abroad program. ROTC: Army.

Entrance Requirements: Options: electronic application, deferred admission, international baccalaureate accepted. Required: high school transcript, Regent Admission Index (RAI) score of 245 guarantees admission. High school requirements include 4 years of English; 3 years each of math, science and social studies, and 2 or more years of electives, which may include foreign language and fine arts, SAT or ACT. Recommended: ACT. Required for some: interview. Entrance: moderately difficult. Application deadline: 8/15. Notification: 9/1. SAT Reasoning Test deadline: 8/15. SAT Subject Test deadline: 8/15. Transfer credits accepted: Yes.

Costs Per Year: Application fee: $40. State resident tuition: $6648 full-time, $277 per hour part-time. Nonresident tuition: $15,734 full-time, $656 per hour part-time. Mandatory fees: $987 full-time. Full-time tuition and fees vary according to course load and program. Part-time tuition varies according to course load and program. College room and board: $7597. College room only: $3703. Room and board charges vary according to board plan and housing facility.

Collegiate Environment: Orientation program. Drama-theater group, choral group, marching band, student-run newspaper, radio station. Social organizations: 263 open to all; national fraternities, national sororities; 5% of eligible men and 5% of eligible women are members. Most popular organizations: Catholic Student Association, National Society of Collegiate Scholars, Accounting Club, Phi Eta Sigma, Students Today Alumni Tomorrow. Major annual events: Homecoming, Family Weekend, Welcome Week. Student services: health clinic, personal-psychological counseling. Campus security: 24-hour emergency response devices and patrols, student patrols, late night transport-escort service, controlled dormitory access. 4,635 college housing spaces available; 4,123 were occupied in 2012-13. Freshmen guaranteed college housing. Options: coed, women-only housing available. Rod Library with 1.2 million books, 1.1 million microform titles, 52,278 serials, 30,680 audiovisual materials, an OPAC, and a Web page. Operations spending for the previous fiscal year: $6.6 million. 1,900 computers available on campus for general student use. Computer purchase/lease plans available. A campuswide network can be accessed from student residence rooms and from off campus. Students can access the following: online class registration, course registration, student account, degree audit, program of study. Staffed computer lab on campus provides training in use of computers, software, and the Internet.

Community Environment: Cedar Falls is an active industrial community on the Cedar River, situated in northeast Iowa. Along with nearby Waterloo, the area population is well over 100,000. All forms of commercial transportation are available. Recreational facilities include many parks, Cedar River for fishing and boating, and two public golf courses. Part-time work is available.

■ **UNIVERSITY OF PHOENIX–DES MOINES CAMPUS**
6600 Westown Pky.
Des Moines, IA 50266
Tel: (515)267-8218; Free: 866-766-0766
Web Site: www.phoenix.edu/
Description: Proprietary, comprehensive, coed. Awards bachelor's, master's, and doctoral degrees.

■ **UPPER IOWA UNIVERSITY**
605 Washington St., Box 1857
Fayette, IA 52142-1857
Tel: (563)425-5200; Free: 800-553-4150

Fax: (563)425-5277
E-mail: schmitts@uiu.edu
Web Site: www.uiu.edu/

Description: Independent, comprehensive, coed. Awards associate, bachelor's, and master's degrees (enrollment figures include extended learning centers and online and distance education programs). Founded 1857. Setting: 80-acre rural campus with easy access to Minneapolis, Chicago. Endowment: $9 million. Educational spending for the previous fiscal year: $3604 per student. Total enrollment: 5,178. Faculty: 586 (80 full-time, 506 part-time). Student-undergrad faculty ratio is 19:1. 1,160 applied, 62% were admitted. 16% from top 10% of their high school class, 35% from top quarter, 65% from top half. Full-time: 3,008 students, 59% women, 41% men. Part-time: 1,637 students, 63% women, 37% men. Students come from 50 states and territories, 35 other countries, 60% from out-of-state. 1% American Indian or Alaska Native, non-Hispanic/Latino; 4% Hispanic/Latino; 16% African American, non-Hispanic/Latino; 1% Asian, non-Hispanic/Latino; 0.1% Native Hawaiian or other Pacific Islander, non-Hispanic/Latino; 3% international. 65% 25 or older, 50% live on campus, 2% transferred in. Retention: 68% of full-time freshmen returned the following year. Academic areas with the most degrees conferred: business/marketing; public administration and social services; social sciences. Core. Calendar: 4 8-week terms. Academic remediation for entering students, ESL program, services for LD students, advanced placement, accelerated degree program, self-designed majors, freshman honors college, honors program, independent study, distance learning, double major, summer session for credit, part-time degree program, external degree program, adult/continuing education programs, co-op programs and internships. Off campus study at North Iowa Community College (agribusiness), North Iowa Community College (industrial technology). Study abroad program.

Entrance Requirements: Option: electronic application. Required: high school transcript, minimum 2 high school GPA, SAT or ACT. Required for some: essay, interview. Entrance: moderately difficult. Application deadlines: Rolling, Rolling for nonresidents. SAT Reasoning Test deadline: 8/23. SAT Subject Test deadline: 8/23. Transfer credits accepted: Yes.

Costs Per Year: Comprehensive fee: $31,910 includes full-time tuition ($24,400) and college room and board ($7510). College room only: $3028. Full-time tuition varies according to degree level, location, and program. Room and board charges vary according to board plan, housing facility, and location.

Collegiate Environment: Orientation program. Drama-theater group, choral group, student-run newspaper. Social organizations: 32 open to all; local fraternities, local sororities; 10% of eligible men and 16% of eligible women are members. Most popular organizations: Beta Phi Omega, Peacock Entertainment Crew, Greek Council, Student Government Association, International Student Association. Major annual events: Family weekend, Homecoming, Backyard BBQ. Student services: health clinic, personal-psychological counseling. Campus security: late night transport-escort service, controlled dormitory access. 740 college housing spaces available; 505 were occupied in 2012-13. Freshmen guaranteed college housing. On-campus residence required through sophomore year. Options: coed, men-only, women-only housing available. Henderson Wilder Library with 74,813 books, 26,313 microform titles, 284 serials, 2,062 audiovisual materials, an OPAC, and a Web page. Operations spending for the previous fiscal year: $374,795. 600 computers available on campus for general student use. Computer purchase/lease plans available. A campuswide network can be accessed from student residence rooms and from off campus. Students can access the following: online class registration.

Community Environment: Fayette (population 1,340) is a rural area in northeastern Iowa, 50 miles from the Mississippi River. Community facilities include five churches and hospital service in the county seat 8 miles away. The city has a Chamber of Commerce and other civic and fraternal organizations. Part-time work is available for students and families. Outdoor sports include hiking, cross-country skiing, hunting, fishing, and golf.

■ **VATTEROTT COLLEGE**
7000 Fleur Dr.
Ste. 290
Des Moines, IA 50321
Tel: (515)309-9000; Free: 888-553-6627
Fax: (515)309-0366
Web Site: www.vatterott.edu/

Description: Proprietary, primarily 2-year, coed. Awards certificates, diplomas, terminal associate, and bachelor's degrees. Setting: 25-acre urban campus. Total enrollment: 336. Faculty: 14 (8 full-time, 6 part-time). Student-undergrad faculty ratio is 15:1. Calendar: ten week periods.

Entrance Requirements: Required: high school transcript, interview.

■ **WALDORF COLLEGE**
106 S 6th St.
Forest City, IA 50436-1713
Tel: (641)585-2450; Free: 800-292-1903
Fax: (641)585-8194
E-mail: admissions@waldorf.edu
Web Site: www.waldorf.edu/

Description: Independent Lutheran, 4-year, coed. Part of Columbia Southern Education Group. Awards associate and bachelor's degrees. Founded 1903. Setting: 51-acre rural campus. Total enrollment: 1,105. Faculty: 41 (38 full-time, 3 part-time). Student-undergrad faculty ratio is 15:1. 1,039 applied, 51% were admitted. 4% from top 10% of their high school class, 20% from top quarter, 28% from top half. Full-time: 925 students, 35% women, 65% men. Part-time: 180 students, 30% women, 70% men. Students come from 46 states and territories, 2 other countries, 82% from out-of-state. 1% American Indian or Alaska Native, non-Hispanic/Latino; 6% Hispanic/Latino; 15% African American, non-Hispanic/Latino; 2% Asian, non-Hispanic/Latino; 0% Native Hawaiian or other Pacific Islander, non-Hispanic/Latino; 0% international. 48% 25 or older, 70% live on campus, 6% transferred in. Retention: 47% of full-time freshmen returned the following year. Academic areas with the most degrees conferred: business/marketing; education; homeland security, law enforcement, firefighting, and protective services. Core. Calendar: semesters. Academic remediation for entering students, services for LD students, advanced placement, freshman honors college, honors program, independent study, distance learning, double major, summer session for credit, part-time degree program, adult/continuing education programs, co-op programs and internships.

Entrance Requirements: Options: electronic application, early admission. Required: high school transcript, ACT or SAT scores, SAT or ACT. Recommended: minimum 2 high school GPA. Required for some: interview. Entrance: moderately difficult. Application deadlines: Rolling, Rolling for nonresidents. Notification: continuous, continuous for nonresidents.

Costs Per Year: Application fee: $0. Comprehensive fee: $27,172 includes full-time tuition ($19,266), mandatory fees ($1050), and college room and board ($6856). Full-time tuition and fees vary according to class time, course load, and program. Room and board charges vary according to board plan and housing facility.

Collegiate Environment: Orientation program. Drama-theater group, choral group, student-run newspaper, radio station. Social organizations: 20 open to all; music and theatre honor societies; 6% of eligible men and 6% of eligible women are members. Most popular organizations: Student Activities Team, Education Club, Campus Ministry groups, intramurals, Radio/TV/Newspaper. Major annual events: Homecoming Week, Live concert (outdoor music and food), Christmas Festival. Student services: health clinic, personal-psychological counseling. Campus security: 24-hour emergency response devices, student patrols, late night transport-escort service, controlled dormitory access, evening and night patrols by trained security personnel, camera surveillance system. 605 college housing spaces available; 350 were occupied in 2012-13. Freshmen guaranteed college housing. On-campus residence required through junior year. Options: coed, men-only, women-only housing available. Luise V. Hanson Library with 181,580 books, 43,920 microform titles, 125 serials, 4,293 audiovisual materials, an OPAC, and a Web page. 500 computers available on campus for general student use. Computer purchase/lease plans available. A campuswide network can be accessed from student residence rooms and from off campus. Students can access the following: all students receive laptops. Staffed computer lab on campus provides training in use of computers, software, and the Internet.

Community Environment: Forest City (population 4,250), so named for the numerous trees covering the slopes of the rolling hills surrounding the city, is in north-central Iowa on the Winnebago River, near Mason City (population 27,900) and midway between Minneapolis and Des Moines. It is also the county seat and serves as both the manufacturing and administrative center for Winnebago Industries. A few miles to the east is Pilot Knob State Park, offering hiking and winter sports. Also available for recreation is the YMCA.

■ **WARTBURG COLLEGE**
100 Wartburg Blvd.
Waverly, IA 50677-0903
Tel: (319)352-8200; Free: 800-772-2085
Fax: (319)352-8279
E-mail: admissions@wartburg.edu
Web Site: www.wartburg.edu/

Description: Independent Lutheran, 4-year, coed. Awards bachelor's degrees. Founded 1852. Setting: 118-acre small town campus. Endowment: $45.7 million. Educational spending for the previous fiscal year: $9645 per student. Total enrollment: 1,747. Faculty: 160 (109 full-time, 51 part-time). Student-undergrad faculty ratio is 11:1. 2,389 applied, 70% were admitted. 27% from top 10% of their high school class, 51% from top quarter, 84% from top half. Full-time: 1,673 students, 53% women, 47% men. Part-time: 74 students, 54% women, 46% men. Students come from 29 states and territories, 52 other countries, 26% from out-of-state. 0.1% American Indian or Alaska Native, non-Hispanic/Latino; 2% Hispanic/Latino; 6% African American, non-Hispanic/Latino; 1% Asian, non-Hispanic/Latino; 0.1% Native Hawaiian or other Pacific Islander, non-Hispanic/Latino; 8% international. 1% 25 or older, 86% live on campus, 1% transferred in. Retention: 76% of full-time freshmen returned the following year. Academic areas with the most degrees conferred: business/marketing; biological/life sciences; education. Core. Calendar: 4-4-1. Academic remediation for entering students, services for LD students, advanced placement, accelerated degree program, self-designed majors, honors program, independent study, double major, summer session for credit, part-time degree program, internships. Off campus study at members of the May Term Consortium. Study abroad program.
Entrance Requirements: Options: electronic application, early action, deferred admission. Required: high school transcript, minimum 2 high school GPA, SAT or ACT. Recommended: secondary school report. Required for some: interview. Entrance: moderately difficult. Application deadlines: Rolling, 12/1 for early action. Notification: continuous. Applicants placed on waiting list: 0. Wait-listed applicants offered admission: 0.
Costs Per Year: Application fee: $0. Tuition: $33,400 full-time. Mandatory fees: $850 full-time. College room only: $4150.
Collegiate Environment: Orientation program. Drama-theater group, choral group, student-run newspaper, radio station. Social organizations: 96 open to all. Most popular organizations: Entertainment To Knight, Student Senate, Campus Ministry, Symphonic Band, Wartburg Choir. Major annual events: Outfly, Homecoming, Christmas with Wartburg. Student services: health clinic, personal-psychological counseling. Campus security: 24-hour emergency response devices and patrols, late night transport-escort service, controlled dormitory access. 1,433 college housing spaces available; 1,382 were occupied in 2012-13. Freshmen guaranteed college housing. On-campus residence required through senior year. Options: coed, men-only, women-only housing available. Vogel Library with 228,905 books, 8,611 microform titles, 74,754 serials, 5,165 audiovisual materials, an OPAC, and a Web page. Operations spending for the previous fiscal year: $873,159. 250 computers available on campus for general student use. A campuswide network can be accessed from student residence rooms and from off campus. Students can access the following: online class registration. Staffed computer lab on campus (open 24 hours a day).
Community Environment: Waverly is a rural Iowa community (population 9,290), within 15 minutes of the Waterloo-Cedar Falls metro area (population 101,000). A variety of cultural events are available. The community provides libraries, a museum, a hospital, churches, clinics, shopping facilities and a community symphony. Part-time employment opportunities are limited.

■ **WESTERN IOWA TECH COMMUNITY COLLEGE**
4647 Stone Ave.
Sioux City, IA 51102-5199
Tel: (712)274-6400; Free: 800-352-4649
Fax: (712)274-6412
Web Site: www.witcc.edu/
Description: State-supported, 2-year, coed. Part of Iowa Department of Education Division of Community Colleges. Awards certificates, diplomas, transfer associate, and terminal associate degrees. Founded 1966. Setting: 143-acre suburban campus. Endowment: $1 million. Research spending for the previous fiscal year: $129,177. Educational spending for the previous fiscal year: $3638 per student. Total enrollment: 6,425. Faculty: 373 (77 full-time, 296 part-time). Student-undergrad faculty ratio is 22:1. Full-time: 2,685 students, 56% women, 44% men. Part-time: 3,740 students, 59% women, 41% men. Students come from 23 states and territories, 4 other countries, 18% from out-of-state. 3% American Indian or Alaska Native, non-Hispanic/Latino; 12% Hispanic/Latino; 4% African American, non-Hispanic/Latino; 2% Asian, non-Hispanic/Latino; 0.2% Native Hawaiian or other Pacific Islander, non-Hispanic/Latino; 0.1% international. 42% 25 or older, 5% live on campus, 20% transferred in. Retention: 41% of full-time freshmen returned the following year. Core. Calendar: semesters. Academic remediation for entering students, ESL program, services for LD students, advanced placement, accelerated degree program, self-designed majors, honors program,

independent study, distance learning, double major, summer session for credit, part-time degree program, co-op programs and internships. Off campus study. Study abroad program.
Entrance Requirements: Open admission except for health occupations programs. Options: electronic application, early admission, deferred admission. Recommended: high school transcript, ACT, SAT or ACT. Entrance: noncompetitive. Application deadlines: Rolling, Rolling for nonresidents. Notification: continuous, continuous for nonresidents. Transfer credits accepted: Yes.
Costs Per Year: Application fee: $0. State resident tuition: $3072 full-time, $128 per credit hour part-time. Nonresident tuition: $3192 full-time, $133 per credit hour part-time. Mandatory fees: $372 full-time, $15.50 per credit hour part-time. Full-time tuition and fees vary according to class time and program. Part-time tuition and fees vary according to class time and program.
Collegiate Environment: Orientation program. Drama-theater group, choral group. Social organizations: 27 open to all. Most popular organizations: Shakespeare Overseas Traveling Club, Habitat for Humanity, Anime Club, Leadership Academy, Police Science Club. Major annual event: WITStock. Student services: personal-psychological counseling. Campus security: 24-hour emergency response devices and patrols, controlled dormitory access. 374 college housing spaces available; 330 were occupied in 2012-13. No special consideration for freshman housing applicants. Option: coed housing available. Western Iowa Tech Community College Library Services plus 1 other with 26,598 books, 210 serials, 5,376 audiovisual materials, an OPAC, and a Web page. Operations spending for the previous fiscal year: $343,137.
Community Environment: See Briar Cliff University.

■ **WILLIAM PENN UNIVERSITY**
201 Trueblood Ave.
Oskaloosa, IA 52577-1799
Tel: (641)673-1001; Free: 800-779-7366
Fax: (641)673-1396
E-mail: admissions@wmpenn.edu
Web Site: www.wmpenn.edu/
Description: Independent, comprehensive, coed, affiliated with Society of Friends. Awards associate, bachelor's, and master's degrees. Founded 1873. Setting: 60-acre rural campus with easy access to Des Moines. Endowment: $6.6 million. Educational spending for the previous fiscal year: $4860 per student. Total enrollment: 1,865. Faculty: 50 (49 full-time, 1 part-time). Student-undergrad faculty ratio is 15:1. 841 applied, 54% were admitted. 9% from top 10% of their high school class, 21% from top quarter, 55% from top half. Full-time: 1,648 students, 49% women, 51% men. Part-time: 49 students, 63% women, 37% men. Students come from 48 states and territories, 15 other countries, 29% from out-of-state. 1% American Indian or Alaska Native, non-Hispanic/Latino; 7% Hispanic/Latino; 1% African American, non-Hispanic/Latino; 1% Asian, non-Hispanic/Latino; 1% Native Hawaiian or other Pacific Islander, non-Hispanic/Latino; 2% international. 40% 25 or older, 40% live on campus, 42% transferred in. Retention: 61% of full-time freshmen returned the following year. Academic areas with the most degrees conferred: business/marketing; social sciences; biological/life sciences. Core. Calendar: semesters. Academic remediation for entering students, services for LD students, advanced placement, honors program, independent study, distance learning, double major, summer session for credit, part-time degree program, adult/continuing education programs, co-op programs and internships. Study abroad program.
Entrance Requirements: Options: electronic application, deferred admission. Required: high school transcript, minimum 2 high school GPA, SAT or ACT. Required for some: essay, interview. Entrance: moderately difficult. Notification: continuous, continuous for nonresidents. Transfer credits accepted: Yes.
Costs Per Year: Application fee: $20. Comprehensive fee: $28,682 includes full-time tuition ($22,750), mandatory fees ($460), and college room and board ($5472). College room only: $2002. Room and board charges vary according to board plan and housing facility. Part-time tuition: $450 per credit hour.
Collegiate Environment: Orientation program. Drama-theater group, choral group, marching band, student-run newspaper, radio station. Social organizations: 30 open to all; local fraternities, local sororities; 5% of eligible men and 5% of eligible women are members. Most popular organizations: Student Government Association, Computer Club, InterVarsity/Campus Ministries, College Republicans, Education Club. Major annual events: Homecoming, Campus Beautification Day, PennStock. Student services: health clinic, personal-psychological counseling. Campus security: 24-hour

emergency response devices and patrols, late night transport-escort service, controlled dormitory access. 540 college housing spaces available; 537 were occupied in 2012-13. Freshmen guaranteed college housing. On-campus residence required through sophomore year. Options: coed, men-only, women-only housing available. Wilcox Library plus 1 other with 72,907 books, 2,718 microform titles, 354 serials, 738 audiovisual materials, an

OPAC, and a Web page. Operations spending for the previous fiscal year: $199,700. 85 computers available on campus for general student use. Computer purchase/lease plans available. A campuswide network can be accessed from student residence rooms and from off campus. Staffed computer lab on campus provides training in use of computers, software, and the Internet.

■ ALLEN COMMUNITY COLLEGE

1801 N Cottonwood St.
Iola, KS 66749-1607
Tel: (620)365-5116
Fax: (620)365-7406
E-mail: bilderback@allencc.edu
Web Site: www.allencc.edu/

Description: State and locally supported, 2-year, coed. Part of Kansas State Board of Regents. Awards certificates, transfer associate, and terminal associate degrees. Founded 1923. Setting: 88-acre small town campus. Total enrollment: 2,277. Faculty: 155 (35 full-time, 120 part-time). Student-undergrad faculty ratio is 17:1. Students come from 20 states and territories, 8 other countries, 9% from out-of-state. 2% American Indian or Alaska Native, non-Hispanic/Latino; 4% Hispanic/Latino; 4% African American, non-Hispanic/Latino; 1% Asian, non-Hispanic/Latino; 1% Native Hawaiian or other Pacific Islander, non-Hispanic/Latino; 1% international. 35% 25 or older. Retention: 56% of full-time freshmen returned the following year. Core. Calendar: semesters. Academic remediation for entering students, ESL program, services for LD students, self-designed majors, independent study, distance learning, summer session for credit, part-time degree program, adult/continuing education programs, co-op programs and internships.

Entrance Requirements: Open admission. Options: electronic application, early admission, deferred admission. Required: high school transcript, SAT or ACT. Entrance: noncompetitive. Application deadline: 8/24. Notification: continuous. Transfer credits accepted: Yes.

Costs Per Year: Application fee: $0. State resident tuition: $1500 full-time, $50 per credit hour part-time. Nonresident tuition: $1500 full-time, $50 per credit hour part-time. Mandatory fees: $540 full-time, $18 per credit hour part-time, $18. Full-time tuition and fees vary according to course load. Part-time tuition and fees vary according to course load. College room and board: $4400. College room only: $4375. Room and board charges vary according to housing facility.

Collegiate Environment: Drama-theater group, choral group. Social organizations: Phi Theta Kappa. Most popular organizations: intramurals, Student Senate, Biology Club, Theatre, Phi Theta Kappa. Major annual events: Homecoming, Outstanding Sophomore, Welcome Week. Student services: personal-psychological counseling. Learning Resource Center plus 1 other with 49,416 books, 159 serials, and an OPAC. 80 computers available on campus for general student use. A campuswide network can be accessed. Students can access the following: online class registration. Staffed computer lab on campus provides training in use of computers and the Internet.

Community Environment: Iola is a rural area with community facilities that provide a library, hospital, many churches and a fine arts center. Part-time employment is available. Fishing, boating, golf and bowling are some of the recreational activities. The County 4-H Fair is an annual event as is the Farm-City Day Celebration.

■ THE ART INSTITUTES INTERNATIONAL–KANSAS CITY

8208 Melrose Dr.
Lenexa, KS 66214
Free: 866-530-8508
Web Site: www.artinstitutes.edu/kansascity/

Description: Proprietary, 4-year, coed. Part of Education Management Corporation. Awards associate and bachelor's degrees. Founded 2008.

■ BAKER UNIVERSITY

PO Box 65
Baldwin City, KS 66006-0065
Tel: (785)594-6451; Free: 800-873-4282
Fax: (785)594-6721
E-mail: admissions@bakeru.edu
Web Site: www.bakeru.edu/

Description: Independent United Methodist, comprehensive, coed. Awards bachelor's, master's, and doctoral degrees (profile includes information primarily for undergraduate residential campus in Baldwin City, KS). Founded 1858. Setting: 26-acre small town campus with easy access to Kansas City. Endowment: $33.8 million. Educational spending for the previous fiscal year: $4473 per student. Total enrollment: 936. Faculty: 98 (57 full-time, 41 part-time). Student-undergrad faculty ratio is 13:1. 775 applied, 85% were admitted. 20% from top 10% of their high school class, 40% from top quarter, 76% from top half. 13 valedictorians. Full-time: 818 students, 45% women, 55% men. Part-time: 118 students, 64% women, 36% men. Students come from 22 states and territories, 9 other countries, 25% from out-of-state. 3% American Indian or Alaska Native, non-Hispanic/Latino; 4% Hispanic/Latino; 10% African American, non-Hispanic/Latino; 1% Asian, non-Hispanic/Latino; 0.5% Native Hawaiian or other Pacific Islander, non-Hispanic/Latino; 2% international. 4% 25 or older, 74% live on campus, 6% transferred in. Retention: 75% of full-time freshmen returned the following year. Academic areas with the most degrees conferred: business/marketing; education; parks and recreation. Core. Calendar: 4-1-4, semesters for nursing program. Services for LD students, advanced placement, self-designed majors, honors program, independent study, double major, summer session for credit, internships. Study abroad program. ROTC: Army (c), Air Force (c).

Entrance Requirements: Options: electronic application, deferred admission, international baccalaureate accepted. Required: high school transcript, 1 recommendation, SAT or ACT. Required for some: essay, interview. Entrance: moderately difficult. Application deadline: Rolling. SAT Reasoning Test deadline: 8/15. Transfer credits accepted: Yes.

Costs Per Year: Application fee: $0. One-time mandatory fee: $80. Comprehensive fee: $32,070 includes full-time tuition ($24,470) and college room and board ($7600). Full-time tuition varies according to course load, degree level, location, and program. Room and board charges vary according to board plan and housing facility. Part-time tuition: $740 per credit hour. Part-time tuition varies according to course load, degree level, location, and program.

Collegiate Environment: Orientation program. Drama-theater group, choral group, student-run newspaper, radio station. Social organizations: 54 open to all; national fraternities, national sororities, local fraternities; 36% of eligible men and 43% of eligible women are members. Most popular organizations: Cardinal Key, Earth We Are, Mungano, Fellowship of Christian Athletes, Student Activities Council. Major annual events: Homecoming, Springfest Week, International Education Week. Student services: health clinic, personal-psychological counseling. Campus security: 24-hour emergency response devices and patrols, student patrols, controlled dormitory access. 582 college housing spaces available; 413 were occupied in 2012-13. Freshmen guaranteed college housing. On-campus residence required through senior year. Options: coed, men-only, women-only housing available. Collins Library with 106,549 books, 160,000 microform titles, 160 serials, 6,366 audiovisual materials, an OPAC, and a Web page. Operations spending for the previous fiscal year: $466,831. 140 computers available on campus for general student use. A campuswide network can be accessed from student residence rooms. Students can access the following: online class registration. Staffed computer lab on campus (open 24 hours a day) provides training in use of computers, software, and the Internet.

Community Environment: A rural town located 30 miles southwest of Kansas City and 15 miles south of Lawrence. The city is 10 miles from Lone Star Lake, which provides recreational facilities. Churches of many denominations are represented here. Shopping, a public library, and a clinic all serve the community. The larger shopping centers of Kansas City and Topeka are excellent as are the cultural advantages of these two cities, which contribute to the enjoyment of the smaller surrounding areas.

■ BARCLAY COLLEGE

607 N Kingman
Haviland, KS 67059-0288
Tel: (620)862-5252; Free: 800-862-0226
Fax: (620)862-5403
E-mail: jkendall@barclaycollege.edu
Web Site: www.barclaycollege.edu/

Description: Independent, comprehensive, coed, affiliated with Society of Friends. Awards associate, bachelor's, and master's degrees. Founded 1917. Setting: 17-acre rural campus. Endowment: $700,000. Educational spending for the previous fiscal year: $5725 per student. Total enrollment: 263. Faculty: 33 (10 full-time, 23 part-time). Student-undergrad faculty ratio is 13:1. 79 applied, 72% were admitted. Full-time: 216 students, 51% women, 49% men. Part-time: 23 students, 48% women, 52% men. Students come from 30 states and territories, 3 other countries, 67% from out-of-state. 0.4% American Indian or Alaska Native, non-Hispanic/Latino; 6% Hispanic/Latino; 4% African American, non-Hispanic/Latino; 1% Asian, non-Hispanic/Latino; 0% Native Hawaiian or other Pacific Islander, non-Hispanic/Latino; 2% international. 22% 25 or older, 78% live on campus, 12% transferred in. Retention: 71% of full-time freshmen returned the following year. Academic areas with the most degrees conferred: theology and religious vocations; psychology; business/marketing; education. Core. Calendar: semesters. Academic remediation for entering students, advanced placement, independent study, distance learning, double major, part-time degree program, external degree program, adult/continuing education programs, internships. Off campus study at with Pratt County Community College (Pratt, KS-joint nursing program), Fort Hays State University (Hays, KS-joint elementary education program).

Entrance Requirements: Options: electronic application, early admission, deferred admission. Required: essay, high school transcript, minimum 2.3 high school GPA, 2 recommendations, interview, SAT or ACT. Entrance: minimally difficult. Application deadline: 9/1. Notification: continuous.

Costs Per Year: Application fee: $15. Comprehensive fee: $21,590 includes full-time tuition ($11,000), mandatory fees ($3590), and college room and board ($7000). College room only: $2800. Room and board charges vary according to board plan and housing facility.

Collegiate Environment: Drama-theater group, choral group. Social organizations: 3 open to all. Most popular organizations: Pep Club, Drama Club, Missions Club. Major annual events: Homecoming, Christmas banquet. Student services: personal-psychological counseling. Campus security: student patrols. 154 college housing spaces available. Freshmen guaranteed college housing. On-campus residence required through senior year. Options: men-only, women-only housing available. Worden Memorial Library with 63,972 books, 404 microform titles, 40,624 serials, 705 audiovisual materials, and an OPAC. Operations spending for the previous fiscal year: $75,000. 28 computers available on campus for general student use. A campuswide network can be accessed from student residence rooms and from off campus. Students can access the following: online class registration. Staffed computer lab on campus provides training in use of computers, software, and the Internet.

Community Environment: Haviland is a small town in a rural area with a friendly and supportive atmosphere. Especially welcoming to young families.

■ BARTON COUNTY COMMUNITY COLLEGE

245 NE 30th Rd.
Great Bend, KS 67530-9283
Tel: (620)792-2701; Free: 800-722-6842
Fax: (620)792-3238
E-mail: admissions@bartonccc.edu
Web Site: www.bartonccc.edu/

Description: State and locally supported, 2-year, coed. Part of Kansas Board of Regents. Awards certificates, transfer associate, and terminal associate degrees. Founded 1969. Setting: 140-acre rural campus. Faculty:

206 (69 full-time, 137 part-time). Student-undergrad faculty ratio is 23:1. 8% live on campus. Calendar: semesters. Academic remediation for entering students, ESL program, services for LD students, advanced placement, accelerated degree program, honors program, independent study, distance learning, double major, summer session for credit, part-time degree program, external degree program, adult/continuing education programs, co-op programs and internships. ROTC: Army.

Entrance Requirements: Open admission. Options: electronic application, early admission. Recommended: high school transcript. Entrance: noncompetitive. Application deadline: Rolling.

Costs Per Year: Application fee: $0. State resident tuition: $1770 full-time, $59 per credit hour part-time. Nonresident tuition: $2700 full-time, $90 per credit hour part-time. Mandatory fees: $960 full-time, $32 per credit hour part-time. Full-time tuition and fees vary according to course load. Part-time tuition and fees vary according to course load.

Collegiate Environment: Orientation program. Drama-theater group, choral group, student-run newspaper. Social organizations: 20 open to all. Most popular organizations: Danceline, Business Professionals, Psychology Club, Agriculture Club, Cougarettes. Major annual events: Homecoming, Parents' Day, Orientation/Welcome Back Days. Student services: health clinic, personal-psychological counseling. Campus security: 24-hour emergency response devices and patrols. 292 college housing spaces available; all were occupied in 2012-13. Freshmen guaranteed college housing. Option: coed housing available. Barton County Community College Library with an OPAC and a Web page. 350 computers available on campus for general student use. A campuswide network can be accessed from student residence rooms and from off campus. Students can access the following: online class registration. Staffed computer lab on campus provides training in use of computers and the Internet.

Community Environment: An urban area, Great Bend (population 15,500) is in the wheat belt and is a large oil producing area. Thirty churches, a library, a hospital and good shopping facilities are a part of the community. Brit Spaugh Park has recreational facilities for tennis, baseball, swimming, and picnicking. Cheyenne Bottoms, nearby, is a wildlife and waterfowl refuge of more than 18,000 acres of which 15,000 acres are covered by water. All forms of commercial transportation are available.

■ BENEDICTINE COLLEGE

1020 N 2nd St.
Atchison, KS 66002-1499
Tel: (913)367-5340; Free: 800-467-5340
Fax: (913)367-3673
E-mail: phelgesen@benedictine.edu
Web Site: www.benedictine.edu/

Description: Independent Roman Catholic, comprehensive, coed. Awards bachelor's and master's degrees. Founded 1859. Setting: 225-acre small town campus with easy access to Kansas City. Endowment: $16.6 million. Research spending for the previous fiscal year: $244,927. Educational spending for the previous fiscal year: $6686 per student. Total enrollment: 2,149. Faculty: 158 (102 full-time, 56 part-time). Student-undergrad faculty ratio is 16:1. 3,347 applied, 61% were admitted. 22% from top 10% of their high school class, 45% from top quarter, 75% from top half. 2 National Merit Scholars, 13 valedictorians. Full-time: 1,735 students, 53% women, 47% men. Part-time: 351 students, 53% women, 47% men. Students come from 42 states and territories, 14 other countries, 71% from out-of-state. 0.4% American Indian or Alaska Native, non-Hispanic/Latino; 7% Hispanic/Latino; 4% African American, non-Hispanic/Latino; 1% Asian, non-Hispanic/Latino; 0.5% Native Hawaiian or other Pacific Islander, non-Hispanic/Latino; 2% international. 1% 25 or older, 82% live on campus, 3% transferred in. Retention: 78% of full-time freshmen returned the following year. Academic areas with the most degrees conferred: business/marketing; education; social sciences. Core. Calendar: semesters. Academic remediation for entering students, ESL program, services for LD students, advanced placement, self-designed majors, independent study, distance learning, double major, summer session for credit, part-time degree program, co-op programs and internships, graduate courses open to undergrads. Off campus study at 16 members of the Kansas City Regional Council for Higher Education, Kansas State University. Study abroad program. ROTC: Army (c).

Entrance Requirements: Options: electronic application, deferred admission, international baccalaureate accepted. Required: high school transcript, minimum 2 high school GPA, 1 recommendation, SAT or ACT. Required for some: interview. Entrance: moderately difficult. Application deadlines: Rolling, Rolling for nonresidents. Notification: continuous. SAT Reasoning Test deadline: 8/15. SAT Subject Test deadline: 8/15. Transfer credits accepted: Yes. Applicants placed on waiting list: 0.

Costs Per Year: Application fee: $50. Comprehensive fee: $31,365 includes full-time tuition ($22,550), mandatory fees ($625), and college room and board ($8190). College room only: $4540. Full-time tuition and fees vary according to course load and degree level. Room and board charges vary according to board plan and housing facility.

Collegiate Environment: Orientation program. Drama-theater group, choral group, marching band, student-run newspaper. Social organizations: 29 open to all. Most popular organizations: student government, Students in Free Enterprise (SIFE), Knights of Columbus, Concert Chorale/Chamber Singers, Ravens Respect Life. Major annual events: Springfest, Homecoming, Family Weekend. Student services: health clinic, personal-psychological counseling. Campus security: 24-hour emergency response devices and patrols, late night transport-escort service, controlled dormitory access. 1,371 college housing spaces available; all were occupied in 2012-13. Freshmen guaranteed college housing. On-campus residence required through senior year. Options: men-only, women-only housing available. Benedictine College Library with 347,829 books, 27,551 microform titles, 27,467 serials, 1,109 audiovisual materials, an OPAC, and a Web page. Operations spending for the previous fiscal year: $421,176. 100 computers available on campus for general student use. Computer purchase/lease plans available. A campuswide network can be accessed from student residence rooms and from off campus. Students can access the following: online class registration. Staffed computer lab on campus provides training in use of computers, software, and the Internet.

Community Environment: Atchison is located on the Kansas-Missouri border, within 30-50 miles of St. Joseph and Kansas City, Missouri, and Topeka and Kansas City, Kansas.

■ BETHANY COLLEGE
335 E Swensson St.
Lindsborg, KS 67456-1897
Tel: (785)227-3311; Free: 800-826-2281
Fax: (785)227-2860
E-mail: cornettv@bethanylb.edu
Web Site: www.bethanylb.edu/

Description: Independent Lutheran, 4-year, coed. Awards bachelor's degrees. Founded 1881. Setting: 80-acre small town campus. Endowment: $23 million. Educational spending for the previous fiscal year: $6763 per student. Total enrollment: 626. Faculty: 72 (35 full-time, 37 part-time). Student-undergrad faculty ratio is 13:1. 831 applied, 60% were admitted. 13% from top 10% of their high school class, 22% from top quarter, 26% from top half. Full-time: 582 students, 46% women, 54% men. Part-time: 44 students, 43% women, 57% men. Students come from 32 states and territories, 15 other countries, 40% from out-of-state. 0.2% American Indian or Alaska Native, non-Hispanic/Latino; 5% Hispanic/Latino; 6% African American, non-Hispanic/Latino; 0% Asian, non-Hispanic/Latino; 1% Native Hawaiian or other Pacific Islander, non-Hispanic/Latino; 4% international. 4% 25 or older, 76% live on campus, 13% transferred in. Retention: 64% of full-time freshmen returned the following year. Academic areas with the most degrees conferred: business/marketing; education; biological/life sciences. Core. Calendar: 4-1-4. Academic remediation for entering students, services for LD students, advanced placement, accelerated degree program, self-designed majors, honors program, independent study, double major, summer session for credit, internships. Off campus study at 6 members of the Associated Colleges of Central Kansas. Study abroad program.

Entrance Requirements: Options: electronic application, deferred admission, international baccalaureate accepted. Required: high school transcript, minimum 2.5 high school GPA, SAT or ACT. Required for some: essay, 1 recommendation, interview. Entrance: moderately difficult. Application deadlines: Rolling, Rolling for nonresidents. Notification: continuous, continuous for nonresidents. SAT Reasoning Test deadline: 8/15. SAT Subject Test deadline: 8/15. Transfer credits accepted: Yes.

Costs Per Year: Application fee: $0. Comprehensive fee: $29,510 includes full-time tuition ($22,024), mandatory fees ($600), and college room and board ($6886). College room only: $3550. Room and board charges vary according to board plan and housing facility. Part-time tuition: $460 per credit hour. Part-time tuition varies according to course load.

Collegiate Environment: Orientation program. Drama-theater group, choral group, student-run newspaper. Social organizations: 35 open to all; local fraternities, local sororities; 11% of eligible men and 10% of eligible women are members. Most popular organizations: Student Activities Board (SAB), Alpha Theta Chi, Alpha Sigma Nu, Fellowship of Christian Athletes (FCA), Bethany Youth Ministries Team. Major annual events: Handel's Messiah by the Bethany Oratorio Society, Homecoming events/talent show, Midnight

Movie and Bowling. Student services: health clinic, personal-psychological counseling. Campus security: 24-hour emergency response devices, late night transport-escort service, controlled dormitory access, night patrols by security personnel. Wallerstedt Library plus 1 other with 103,018 books, 51,442 microform titles, 81 serials, 3,119 audiovisual materials, and an OPAC. Operations spending for the previous fiscal year: $174,491. 65 computers available on campus for general student use. A campuswide network can be accessed from student residence rooms and from off campus. Students can access the following: online class registration. Staffed computer lab on campus provides training in use of computers and software.

■ BETHEL COLLEGE
300 E 27th St.
North Newton, KS 67117
Tel: (316)283-2500; Free: 800-522-1887
Fax: (316)284-5286
E-mail: admissions@bethelks.edu
Web Site: www.bethelks.edu/

Description: Independent, 4-year, coed, affiliated with Mennonite Church USA. Awards bachelor's degrees. Founded 1887. Setting: 60-acre small town campus with easy access to Wichita. Total enrollment: 472. Faculty: 58 (37 full-time, 21 part-time). Student-undergrad faculty ratio is 9:1. 521 applied, 65% were admitted. 17% from top 10% of their high school class, 42% from top quarter, 69% from top half. Full-time: 451 students, 54% women, 46% men. Part-time: 21 students, 62% women, 38% men. 28% from out-of-state. 0.4% American Indian or Alaska Native, non-Hispanic/Latino; 9% Hispanic/Latino; 9% African American, non-Hispanic/Latino; 1% Asian, non-Hispanic/Latino; 2% international. 8% 25 or older, 72% live on campus, 13% transferred in. Retention: 62% of full-time freshmen returned the following year. Academic areas with the most degrees conferred: health professions and related sciences; business/marketing; public administration and social services. Calendar: 4-1-4. Part-time degree program.

Entrance Requirements: Options: deferred admission, international baccalaureate accepted. Required: high school transcript, minimum 2.5 high school GPA, SAT or ACT. Recommended: interview. Required for some: essay, 2 recommendations. Entrance: moderately difficult. Application deadline: Rolling. Notification: continuous. SAT Reasoning Test deadline: 8/1.

Costs Per Year: Application fee: $20. One-time mandatory fee: $200. Comprehensive fee: $31,480 includes full-time tuition ($23,500) and college room and board ($7980). College room only: $4310.

Collegiate Environment: Orientation program. Drama-theater group, choral group, student-run newspaper, radio station. Student services: health clinic, personal-psychological counseling. Freshmen guaranteed college housing. On-campus residence required through senior year. Mantz Library plus 1 other with an OPAC and a Web page.

■ BROWN MACKIE COLLEGE–KANSAS CITY
9705 Lenexa Dr.
Lenexa, KS 66215
Tel: (913)768-1900; Free: 800-635-9101
Fax: (913)823-7448
Web Site: www.brownmackie.edu/kansascity/

Description: Proprietary, 2-year, coed. Part of Education Management Corporation. Awards certificates, diplomas, and terminal associate degrees. Founded 1892. Setting: suburban campus.

■ BROWN MACKIE COLLEGE–SALINA
2106 S 9th St.
Salina, KS 67401-2810
Tel: (785)825-5422; Free: 800-365-0433
Fax: (785)827-7623
Web Site: www.brownmackie.edu/salina/

Description: Proprietary, 2-year, coed. Part of Education Management Corporation. Awards certificates, diplomas, transfer associate, and terminal associate degrees. Founded 1892. Setting: small town campus. Calendar: modular.

■ BUTLER COMMUNITY COLLEGE
901 S Haverhill Rd.
El Dorado, KS 67042-3280
Tel: (316)321-2222
Fax: (316)322-3109
E-mail: admissions@butlercc.edu

Web Site: www.butlercc.edu/

Description: State and locally supported, 2-year, coed. Part of Kansas State Board of Education. Awards transfer associate and terminal associate degrees. Founded 1927. Setting: 80-acre small town campus. Endowment: $5.4 million. Educational spending for the previous fiscal year: $2799 per student. Total enrollment: 8,096. Faculty: 582 (151 full-time, 431 part-time). Student-undergrad faculty ratio is 17:1. Full-time: 3,543 students, 54% women, 46% men. Part-time: 4,553 students, 63% women, 37% men. Students come from 19 states and territories, 34 other countries, 3% from out-of-state. 37% 25 or older, 4% live on campus, 6% transferred in. Retention: 59% of full-time freshmen returned the following year. Core. Calendar: semesters. Academic remediation for entering students, ESL program, services for LD students, advanced placement, accelerated degree program, self-designed majors, honors program, independent study, distance learning, double major, summer session for credit, part-time degree program, adult/continuing education programs, co-op programs.

Entrance Requirements: Open admission. Options: early admission, deferred admission. Required: high school transcript. Entrance: noncompetitive. Application deadline: 8/19. Notification: continuous.

Collegiate Environment: Orientation program. Drama-theater group, choral group, student-run newspaper, radio station. Social organizations: 21 open to all. Most popular organizations: Phi Theta Kappa, HALO (Hispanic American Leadership Organization), Student Nurses Association, Kansas Gaming Association, Colleges Against Cancer. Major annual events: Welcome Week Orientation, Homecoming, Spring Fling. Student services: health clinic, personal-psychological counseling. Campus security: 24-hour emergency response devices and patrols, controlled dormitory access, video cameras at dormitory entrances and parking lot. L.W. Nixon Library with 38,000 books, 36,920 microform titles, 220 serials, 914 audiovisual materials, an OPAC, and a Web page. Operations spending for the previous fiscal year: $114,734. 1,200 computers available on campus for general student use. A campuswide network can be accessed from off-campus. Students can access the following: online class registration. Staffed computer lab on campus.

Community Environment: Butler County attracts visitors because of its location near the scenic Flint Hills in Kansas and the El Dorado Lake, a federal Corps of Engineers Project covering approximately 4,500 acres. Butler County has an approximate population of 63,000 persons in nine communities. Butler County communities offers good schools, numerous musical, writing and civic clubs with an emphasis toward educational and cultural opportunities. Located just 30 minutes east of Wichita, a city of approximately 355,000 residents, Butler County residents and BCCC students are also offered all the advantages of a major metropolitan city.

■ **CENTRAL CHRISTIAN COLLEGE OF KANSAS**
1200 S Main
McPherson, KS 67460-5799
Tel: (620)241-0723; Free: 800-835-0078
Fax: (620)241-6032
E-mail: rick.wyatt@centralchristian.edu
Web Site: www.centralchristian.edu/

Description: Independent Free Methodist, 4-year, coed. Awards associate and bachelor's degrees. Founded 1884. Setting: 16-acre small town campus. Endowment: $6.9 million. Educational spending for the previous fiscal year: $6116 per student. Total enrollment: 466. Faculty: 46 (19 full-time, 27 part-time). Student-undergrad faculty ratio is 14:1. 402 applied, 99% were admitted. 7% from top 10% of their high school class, 28% from top quarter, 67% from top half. 3 valedictorians. Full-time: 328 students, 44% women, 56% men. Part-time: 138 students, 60% women, 40% men. Students come from 26 states and territories, 4 other countries, 47% from out-of-state. 5% 25 or older, 85% live on campus, 6% transferred in. Retention: 72% of full-time freshmen returned the following year. Academic areas with the most degrees conferred: business/marketing; theology and religious vocations; liberal arts/general studies. Core. Calendar: 4-1-4. Academic remediation for entering students, services for LD students, advanced placement, self-designed majors, independent study, distance learning, double major, part-time degree program, adult/continuing education programs, co-op programs and internships. Off campus study at McPherson College, Christian Center for Urban Studies, Focus on the Family Institute, CCCU. Study abroad program.

Entrance Requirements: Options: electronic application, deferred admission, international baccalaureate accepted. Required: high school transcript, minimum 2.5 high school GPA, 2 recommendations, SAT or ACT. Recommended: essay, interview. Entrance: minimally difficult. Application deadline: Rolling. Notification: continuous. Transfer credits accepted: Yes.

Collegiate Environment: Orientation program. Drama-theater group, choral group, student-run newspaper. Social organizations: 9 open to all. Most popular organizations: student government, Outreach Central, Student Activities Committee, Social Awareness Board, Phi Beta Lambda Business Club. Major annual events: All College Picnic, Community Service Day, Christmas Banquet. Student services: health clinic, personal-psychological counseling. Briner Library with 35,027 books, 524 microform titles, 134 serials, 1,186 audiovisual materials, an OPAC, and a Web page. Operations spending for the previous fiscal year: $81,762. 28 computers available on campus for general student use. A campuswide network can be accessed from student residence rooms. Staffed computer lab on campus provides training in use of computers, software, and the Internet.

Community Environment: The community of McPherson, Kansas is an attractive Midwestern agricultural and petroleum based city of 14,000. Located 50 miles north of Wichita, the community is rated the thirty-third best small town in the United States.

■ **CLEVELAND CHIROPRACTIC COLLEGE–KANSAS CITY CAMPUS**
10850 Lowell Ave.
Overland Park, KS 66210
Tel: (913)234-0600; Free: 800-467-2252
Fax: (913)234-0912
E-mail: kc.admissions@cleveland.edu
Web Site: www.cleveland.edu/

Description: Independent, comprehensive, coed. Awards associate, bachelor's, and doctoral degrees. Founded 1922. Setting: 34-acre suburban campus with easy access to Kansas City. Total enrollment: 523. Faculty: 53 (43 full-time, 10 part-time). Student-undergrad faculty ratio is 11:1. 1 applied, 100% were admitted. Full-time: 74 students, 34% women, 66% men. Part-time: 5 students, 40% women, 60% men. Students come from 10 states and territories, 1 other country, 47% from out-of-state. 3% American Indian or Alaska Native, non-Hispanic/Latino; 5% Hispanic/Latino; 0% African American, non-Hispanic/Latino; 3% Asian, non-Hispanic/Latino; 0% Native Hawaiian or other Pacific Islander, non-Hispanic/Latino; 1% international. 57% 25 or older, 41% transferred in. Retention: 50% of full-time freshmen returned the following year. Academic area with the most degrees conferred: biological/life sciences. Core. Calendar: trimesters. Academic remediation for entering students, services for LD students, advanced placement, accelerated degree program, summer session for credit, co-op programs and internships.

Entrance Requirements: Open admission cumulative college GPA of 2.0 required to enter BS degree program for transfer students. Options: electronic application, deferred admission, international baccalaureate accepted. Required: high school transcript, minimum 2.5 high school GPA. Required for some: interview, SAT or ACT. Entrance: noncompetitive. Application deadlines: Rolling, Rolling for nonresidents. Notification: continuous, continuous for nonresidents. Transfer credits accepted: Yes.

Costs Per Year: Application fee: $50. Tuition: . Mandatory fees: $440 full-time. Full-time tuition and fees vary according to course load and program.

Collegiate Environment: Orientation program. Major annual events: Homecoming, Winter Formal, Fun and Sun day. Student services: health clinic, personal-psychological counseling. Campus security: 24-hour patrols. College housing not available. Ruth R. Cleveland Memorial Library with 15,000 books, 73,000 microform titles, 6,100 serials, 12,300 audiovisual materials, an OPAC, and a Web page. 30 computers available on campus for general student use. A campuswide network can be accessed. Students can access the following: educational software.

■ **CLOUD COUNTY COMMUNITY COLLEGE**
2221 Campus Dr.
Concordia, KS 66901-1002
Tel: (785)243-1435; Free: 800-729-5101
Fax: (785)243-1043
Web Site: www.cloud.edu/

Description: State and locally supported, 2-year, coed. Part of Kansas Community College System. Awards certificates, diplomas, transfer associate, and terminal associate degrees. Founded 1965. Setting: 35-acre rural campus. Total enrollment: 2,728. 33% 25 or older. Core. Calendar: semesters. Academic remediation for entering students, services for LD students, advanced placement, summer session for credit, part-time degree program, adult/continuing education programs, co-op programs and internships.

Entrance Requirements: Open admission. Options: early admission, deferred admission. Required: high school transcript. Entrance: noncompetitive. Application deadline: 9/11. Notification: continuous.

Collegiate Environment: Orientation program. Drama-theater group, choral group, student-run newspaper, radio station. Student services: health clinic. Campus security: 24-hour emergency response devices. 18,010 books and 142 serials.

Community Environment: Located in the Republican River Valley, Concordia is a central shopping, industrial and medical district for the citizens of North Central Kansas. The city of approximately 7,000 is home to St. Joseph Hospital, which is operated by the Sisters of St. Joseph. The city features a large municipal swimming complex, a vigorous summer recreational program, tennis courts and spacious parks. Concordia hosts the annual North Central Kansas Rodeo and the annual Fall Fest Celebration, and is the home of the Cloud County Fair. The Brown Grand Theater, which is on the National Register of Historic Sites, features many cultural events throughout the year.

■ **COFFEYVILLE COMMUNITY COLLEGE**
400 W 11th St.
Coffeyville, KS 67337-5063
Tel: (620)251-7700; Free: 877-51-RAVEN
Fax: (620)252-7098
E-mail: staciam@coffeyville.edu
Web Site: www.coffeyville.edu/

Description: State and locally supported, 2-year, coed. Part of Kansas State Board of Education. Awards certificates, transfer associate, and terminal associate degrees. Founded 1923. Setting: 39-acre small town campus with easy access to Tulsa. Total enrollment: 2,056. Student-undergrad faculty ratio is 22:1. 29% from out-of-state. 31% 25 or older. Core. Calendar: semesters. Academic remediation for entering students, ESL program, services for LD students, advanced placement, self-designed majors, honors program, distance learning, double major, summer session for credit, part-time degree program, adult/continuing education programs, co-op programs and internships.

Entrance Requirements: Open admission. Options: early admission, deferred admission. Required: high school transcript. Entrance: noncompetitive. Application deadline: Rolling. Notification: continuous.

Collegiate Environment: Drama-theater group, choral group, marching band. Student services: health clinic, personal-psychological counseling, women's center. Campus security: 24-hour patrols, late night transport-escort service, controlled dormitory access. Russell H. Graham Learning Resource Center plus 1 other with an OPAC and a Web page.

Community Environment: A town of diversified industries, Coffeyville has churches of many denominations, a hospital and numerous civic, service and social organizations. A municipal airport, railroads and bus lines provide transportation. A significant point of interest is the Dalton Defenders Museum. Coffeyville was once the home of the famous baseball pitcher, Walter Johnson; a memorial to Johnson may be seen in Walter Johnson Park.

■ **COLBY COMMUNITY COLLEGE**
1255 S Range
Colby, KS 67701-4099
Tel: (785)462-3984; Free: 888-634-9350
Fax: (785)462-4600
E-mail: admissions@colbycc.edu
Web Site: www.colbycc.edu/

Description: State and locally supported, 2-year, coed. Part of Kansas State Board of Education. Awards certificates, diplomas, transfer associate, and terminal associate degrees. Founded 1964. Setting: 80-acre small town campus. Endowment: $3.4 million. Educational spending for the previous fiscal year: $3780 per student. Total enrollment: 1,451. Faculty: 153 (58 full-time, 95 part-time). Student-undergrad faculty ratio is 11:1. 1,016 applied, 100% were admitted. 3% from top 10% of their high school class, 15% from top quarter, 42% from top half. Full-time: 723 students, 60% women, 40% men. Part-time: 728 students, 69% women, 31% men. Students come from 15 states and territories, 5 other countries, 30% from out-of-state. 1% American Indian or Alaska Native, non-Hispanic/Latino; 7% Hispanic/Latino; 7% African American, non-Hispanic/Latino; 2% Asian, non-Hispanic/Latino; 1% Native Hawaiian or other Pacific Islander, non-Hispanic/Latino; 5% international. 12% 25 or older, 30% live on campus, 6% transferred in. Core. Calendar: semesters. Academic remediation for entering students, services for LD students, advanced placement, self-designed majors, honors

program, distance learning, double major, summer session for credit, part-time degree program, adult/continuing education programs, co-op programs and internships.

Entrance Requirements: Open admission except for animal science, health-related programs. Options: electronic application, early admission, deferred admission. Required: high school transcript, COMPASS or ASSET. Recommended: SAT or ACT. Required for some: interview. Entrance: noncompetitive. Application deadlines: Rolling, Rolling for nonresidents. Notification: continuous, continuous for nonresidents. Transfer credits accepted: Yes.

Costs Per Year: Application fee: $0. State resident tuition: $1920 full-time, $60 per credit part-time. Nonresident tuition: $3648 full-time, $114 per credit part-time. Mandatory fees: $1140 full-time, $38 per credit part-time, $38. Full-time tuition and fees vary according to course load and program. Part-time tuition and fees vary according to course load and program. College room and board: $6090. Room and board charges vary according to board plan and housing facility.

Collegiate Environment: Orientation program. Drama-theater group, choral group, student-run newspaper, radio station. Social organizations: 16 open to all. Most popular organizations: KSNEA, Physical Therapist Assistants Club, Block and Bridle, SVTA, COPNS. Major annual events: Fall Formal, Spring Formal, End of Year Event. Student services: health clinic, personal-psychological counseling. Campus security: 24-hour emergency response devices and patrols. 424 college housing spaces available; 225 were occupied in 2012-13. No special consideration for freshman housing applicants. On-campus residence required in freshman year. Options: coed, men-only, women-only housing available. Davis Library with 34,000 books, 500 microform titles, 463 serials, 600 audiovisual materials, and an OPAC. Operations spending for the previous fiscal year: $116,000. 125 computers available on campus for general student use. Computer purchase/lease plans available. A campuswide network can be accessed from student residence rooms and from off campus. Students can access the following: online class registration. Staffed computer lab on campus provides training in use of computers, software, and the Internet.

Community Environment: Colby is in the state's leading wheat-producing area, the northwest corner of the state. Population 5,030. Community facilities include a fine hospital, library and churches of most faiths. Job opportunities are open with the city and community providing employment for students wherever possible.

■ **COWLEY COUNTY COMMUNITY COLLEGE AND AREA VOCATIONAL–TECHNICAL SCHOOL**
125 S Second
Arkansas City, KS 67005-1147
Tel: (620)442-0430; Free: 800-593-CCCC
Fax: (620)441-5350
E-mail: admissions@cowley.edu
Web Site: www.cowley.edu/

Description: State and locally supported, 2-year, coed. Part of Kansas State Board of Education. Awards certificates, diplomas, transfer associate, and terminal associate degrees. Founded 1922. Setting: 19-acre small town campus. Endowment: $4.7 million. Educational spending for the previous fiscal year: $1173 per student. Total enrollment: 4,328. Faculty: 253 (48 full-time, 205 part-time). Student-undergrad faculty ratio is 26:1. 1,010 applied, 100% were admitted. 6% from top 10% of their high school class, 23% from top quarter, 50% from top half. 13 valedictorians. Full-time: 2,328 students, 59% women, 41% men. Part-time: 2,000 students, 65% women, 35% men. 10% from out-of-state. 13% 25 or older, 12% live on campus. Retention: 58% of full-time freshmen returned the following year. Core. Calendar: semesters. Academic remediation for entering students, services for LD students, advanced placement, accelerated degree program, independent study, distance learning, summer session for credit, part-time degree program, external degree program, adult/continuing education programs, co-op programs. Off campus study.

Entrance Requirements: Open admission. Options: electronic application, early admission. Required: high school transcript. Recommended: ACT. Entrance: noncompetitive. Application deadlines: Rolling, Rolling for nonresidents. Notification: continuous, continuous for nonresidents. Transfer credits accepted: Yes.

Costs Per Year: Application fee: $0. Area resident tuition: $1568 full-time, $49 per credit hour part-time. State resident tuition: $1888 full-time, $59 per credit hour part-time. Nonresident tuition: $3392 full-time, $106 per credit hour part-time. Mandatory fees: $864 full-time, $27 per credit hour part-time. College room and board: $4475. Room and board charges vary according to board plan.

Collegiate Environment: Orientation program. Drama-theater group, choral group, student-run newspaper. Social organizations: 25 open to all. Most popular organizations: Cowley Activity Awareness Team (CAAT), Academic Civic Engagement through Service (ACES), Phi Theta Kappa, Cowley College Student Senate, Creative Claws. Major annual events: Mr. Cinderfella, Spring Break Awareness Week, Homecoming. Student services: health clinic, personal-psychological counseling. Campus security: 24-hour emergency response devices and patrols, student patrols, late night transport-escort service, controlled dormitory access, residence hall entrances are locked at night. 483 college housing spaces available; 450 were occupied in 2012-13. No special consideration for freshman housing applicants. Options: coed, men-only, women-only housing available. Renn Memorial Library with 27,000 books, 50 microform titles, 12,000 serials, 1,000 audiovisual materials, an OPAC, and a Web page. Operations spending for the previous fiscal year: $162,117. 100 computers available on campus for general student use. A campuswide network can be accessed from student residence rooms and from off campus. Students can access the following: online class registration. Staffed computer lab on campus provides training in use of computers, software, and the Internet.

■ **DODGE CITY COMMUNITY COLLEGE**

2501 N 14th Ave.
Dodge City, KS 67801-2399
Tel: (620)225-1321
Fax: (620)225-0918
E-mail: admin@dc3.edu
Web Site: www.dc3.edu/

Description: State and locally supported, 2-year, coed. Part of Kansas State Board of Education. Awards certificates, transfer associate, and terminal associate degrees. Founded 1935. Setting: 143-acre small town campus. Total enrollment: 1,807. Faculty: 163 (55 full-time, 108 part-time). Student-undergrad faculty ratio is 18:1. 5% from top 10% of their high school class, 50% from top half. Students come from 24 states and territories, 10% from out-of-state. 29% 25 or older, 20% live on campus. Core. Calendar: semesters. Academic remediation for entering students, ESL program, advanced placement, self-designed majors, summer session for credit, part-time degree program, external degree program, adult/continuing education programs, co-op programs and internships.

Entrance Requirements: Open admission. Options: electronic application, early admission, deferred admission. Required: high school transcript. Entrance: noncompetitive. Application deadline: Rolling. Notification: continuous.

Costs Per Year: Application fee: $0. State resident tuition: $2240 full-time, $70 per credit hour part-time. Nonresident tuition: $2880 full-time, $90 per credit hour part-time. Full-time tuition varies according to course load. Part-time tuition varies according to course load. College room and board: $4590. Room and board charges vary according to board plan.

Collegiate Environment: Drama-theater group, choral group, student-run newspaper, radio station. Major annual events: Homecoming, Spring Fling, Multicultural Day. Student services: health clinic, personal-psychological counseling. Learning Resource Center with 30,000 books and 225 serials. 125 computers available on campus for general student use. Staffed computer lab on campus.

Community Environment: Dodge City serves as a supply and trade center for a large agricultural area. It is located on the plains of western Kansas. All modes of transportation are accessible. Community facilities include a library, hospitals, churches of all major denominations, community concert association, and many fraternal, civic and veteran's organizations. Sports include golf, bowling, fishing, hunting and boating. Points of interest are Boot Hill, Fort Dodge and Point Rocks. Special events are Dodge City Days rodeo and the Square Dance Festival.

■ **DONNELLY COLLEGE**

608 N 18th St.
Kansas City, KS 66102-4298
Tel: (913)621-8700
Fax: (913)621-0354
E-mail: admissions@donnelly.edu
Web Site: www.donnelly.edu/

Description: Independent Roman Catholic, primarily 2-year, coed. Awards certificates, transfer associate, terminal associate, and bachelor's degrees. Founded 1949. Setting: 4-acre urban campus. Total enrollment: 661. Faculty: 48 (15 full-time, 33 part-time). Student-undergrad faculty ratio is 16:1. Full-time: 291 students, 68% women, 32% men. Part-time: 370

students, 80% women, 20% men. Students come from 2 states and territories, 42 other countries, 15% from out-of-state. 65% 25 or older, 2% live on campus, 2% transferred in. Retention: 48% of full-time freshmen returned the following year. Academic area with the most degrees conferred: public administration and social services. Core. Calendar: semesters. Academic remediation for entering students, ESL program, services for LD students, advanced placement, independent study, distance learning, double major, summer session for credit, part-time degree program, external degree program, internships.

Entrance Requirements: Open admission. Options: electronic application, early admission, deferred admission. Recommended: high school transcript. Entrance: noncompetitive. Application deadline: Rolling. Transfer credits accepted: Yes.

Collegiate Environment: Orientation program. Most popular organizations: Organization of Student Leadership, Student Ambassadors, Healthy Student Task Force, Men's Soccer Club, Women's Soccer Club. Major annual events: Convocation Day, Thanks and Giving Celebration, Multicultural Festival. Student services: personal-psychological counseling. Campus security: 24-hour emergency response devices. Trant Memorial Library with 33,752 books, 114 serials, 1,020 audiovisual materials, an OPAC, and a Web page. 75 computers available on campus for general student use. A campuswide network can be accessed from off-campus. Students can access the following: online class registration. Staffed computer lab on campus provides training in use of computers, software, and the Internet.

■ **EMPORIA STATE UNIVERSITY**

1200 Commercial St.
Emporia, KS 66801-5087
Tel: (620)341-1200; Free: 877-468-6378
E-mail: go2esu@emporia.edu
Web Site: www.emporia.edu/

Description: State-supported, comprehensive, coed. Part of Kansas State Board of Regents. Awards bachelor's, master's, and doctoral degrees and post-master's certificates. Founded 1863. Setting: 207-acre small town campus with easy access to Wichita. Endowment: $59.6 million. Research spending for the previous fiscal year: $498,332. Educational spending for the previous fiscal year: $3134 per student. Total enrollment: 5,867. Faculty: 296 (260 full-time, 36 part-time). Student-undergrad faculty ratio is 16:1. 1,753 applied, 72% were admitted. 13% from top 10% of their high school class, 37% from top quarter, 70% from top half. Full-time: 3,343 students, 60% women, 40% men. Part-time: 428 students, 58% women, 42% men. Students come from 31 states and territories, 19 other countries, 9% from out-of-state. 0.4% American Indian or Alaska Native, non-Hispanic/Latino; 6% Hispanic/Latino; 6% African American, non-Hispanic/Latino; 1% Asian, non-Hispanic/Latino; 0.2% Native Hawaiian or other Pacific Islander, non-Hispanic/Latino; 7% international. 18% 25 or older, 6% live on campus, 12% transferred in. Retention: 70% of full-time freshmen returned the following year. Academic areas with the most degrees conferred: education; business/marketing; health professions and related sciences. Core. Calendar: semesters. Academic remediation for entering students, ESL program, services for LD students, advanced placement, accelerated degree program, honors program, independent study, distance learning, double major, summer session for credit, part-time degree program, adult/continuing education programs, co-op programs and internships, graduate courses open to undergrads. Off campus study. Study abroad program.

Entrance Requirements: Options: electronic application, early admission, deferred admission. Required: high school transcript, SAT or ACT. Recommended: minimum 2 high school GPA. Entrance: noncompetitive. Application deadlines: Rolling, Rolling for nonresidents. Notification: continuous, continuous for nonresidents. SAT Reasoning Test deadline: 12/15. Transfer credits accepted: Yes.

Costs Per Year: Application fee: $30. State resident tuition: $4102 full-time, $137 per credit hour part-time. Nonresident tuition: $15,156 full-time, $505 per credit hour part-time. Mandatory fees: $1170 full-time, $70 per credit hour part-time, $70. Full-time tuition and fees vary according to course load, degree level, and location. Part-time tuition and fees vary according to course load, degree level, and location. College room and board: $6629. College room only: $3438. Room and board charges vary according to board plan, housing facility, and location.

Collegiate Environment: Orientation program. Drama-theater group, choral group, marching band, student-run newspaper, radio station. Social organizations: 117 open to all; national fraternities, national sororities; 5% of eligible men and 5% of eligible women are members. Most popular organizations: Union Activities Council, Associated Student Government, Black

Student Union. Major annual events: Homecoming, Flintstock, Family Day. Student services: legal services, health clinic, personal-psychological counseling, women's center. Campus security: 24-hour emergency response devices and patrols, student patrols, late night transport-escort service, controlled dormitory access, 24-hour residence hall monitoring, safety and self-awareness programs. 802 college housing spaces available; 735 were occupied in 2012-13. Freshmen guaranteed college housing. On-campus residence required in freshman year. Options: coed, men-only, women-only housing available. William Allen White Library with 2.5 million books, 62,442 microform titles, 54,379 serials, 7,515 audiovisual materials, an OPAC, and a Web page. Operations spending for the previous fiscal year: $2.2 million. 410 computers available on campus for general student use. A campuswide network can be accessed from student residence rooms and from off campus. Students can access the following: online class registration. Staffed computer lab on campus provides training in use of computers, software, and the Internet.

Community Environment: Emporia, close to the nation's geographical center, is an industrial city as well as a "university town." From this agricultural area more than 100,000 cattle are sent to market each year. The community facilities include a hospital, libraries, an auditorium and many civic, social and veteran's organizations. All forms of commercial transportation are available. Parks, golf courses, a skating rink, tennis courts, ball fields, bowling alley, and swimming pools are some of the facilities for recreation.

■ FLINT HILLS TECHNICAL COLLEGE
3301 W 18th Ave.
Emporia, KS 66801
Tel: (620)343-4600; Free: 800-711-6947
Web Site: www.fhtc.edu/

Description: State-supported, 2-year, coed. Awards certificates and terminal associate degrees. Founded 1963. Total enrollment: 481. Faculty: 72 (27 full-time, 45 part-time). Student-undergrad faculty ratio is 15:1. Full-time: 259 students, 54% women, 46% men. Part-time: 222 students, 46% women, 54% men. 39% from out-of-state. Retention: 88% of full-time freshmen returned the following year. Calendar: semesters.

Entrance Requirements: Required: high school transcript, SAT or ACT. Recommended: interview. Entrance: noncompetitive.

Collegiate Environment: Orientation program. 86 computers available on campus for general student use. A campuswide network can be accessed from off-campus. Staffed computer lab on campus provides training in use of computers, software, and the Internet.

■ FORT HAYS STATE UNIVERSITY
600 Park St.
Hays, KS 67601-4099
Tel: (785)628-4000; Free: 800-628-FHSU
Fax: (785)628-4014
E-mail: tcline@fhsu.edu
Web Site: www.fhsu.edu/

Description: State-supported, comprehensive, coed. Awards associate, bachelor's, and master's degrees and post-master's certificates. Founded 1902. Setting: 200-acre small town campus. Total enrollment: 12,802. Faculty: 479 (287 full-time, 192 part-time). Student-undergrad faculty ratio is 18:1. 2,536 applied, 68% were admitted. Full-time: 5,224 students, 56% women, 44% men. Part-time: 5,934 students, 59% women, 41% men. 0.3% American Indian or Alaska Native, non-Hispanic/Latino; 4% Hispanic/Latino; 3% African American, non-Hispanic/Latino; 1% Asian, non-Hispanic/Latino; 0.1% Native Hawaiian or other Pacific Islander, non-Hispanic/Latino; 35% international. Core. Calendar: semesters. Academic remediation for entering students, ESL program, self-designed majors, honors program, independent study, distance learning, double major, part-time degree program, internships. Study abroad program.

Entrance Requirements: Open admission. Required: high school transcript, SAT or ACT. Entrance: noncompetitive. Application deadline: Rolling.

Collegiate Environment: Orientation program. Marching band. Student services: health clinic. Campus security: 24-hour emergency response devices and patrols.

Community Environment: Fort Hays, a military post on the old frontier, gave this railroad town its name of Hays. Known as an agricultural, educational, and regional medical center Hays has vast interests in oil and livestock as well. Ellis county, the county in which Hays is located, is the largest oil producing county in the State of Kansas. Fort Hays Experiment Station, one of the largest dryland experiment stations in the world, is located here.

■ FORT SCOTT COMMUNITY COLLEGE
2108 S Horton
Fort Scott, KS 66701
Tel: (316)223-2700; Free: 800-874-3722
Fax: (316)223-4927
Web Site: www.fortscott.edu/

Description: State and locally supported, 2-year, coed. Awards certificates, transfer associate, and terminal associate degrees. Founded 1919. Setting: 147-acre small town campus. Total enrollment: 1,696. 25% 25 or older. Core. Calendar: semesters. Academic remediation for entering students, ESL program, services for LD students, advanced placement, self-designed majors, independent study, distance learning, summer session for credit, part-time degree program, external degree program, adult/continuing education programs, co-op programs and internships. Study abroad program. ROTC: Army (c).

Entrance Requirements: Open admission. Options: early admission, deferred admission. Entrance: minimally difficult. Application deadline: 8/15.

Collegiate Environment: Orientation program. Drama-theater group, choral group, marching band. Student services: personal-psychological counseling. Campus security: controlled dormitory access, evening security from 9 pm to 6 am. Learning Resource Center with 25,308 books, 124 serials, and an OPAC.

Community Environment: FSCC is located in Fort Scott, Kansas, a thriving agricultural-industrial town at the intersection of U.S. highways 69 and 54 in southeast Kansas. About 9,000 persons live in Fort Scott and an additional 6,000 live in the surrounding Bourbon County area. Fort Scott citizens continue to value their historic background, dating from the time the town was established as a military outpost in 1842. The original army post on the Indian frontier, restored and operated by the National Park Service as the Fort Scott National Historic Site, draws thousands of tourists annually. The city is served by major highways and bus lines and has a municipal airport. Superb medical facilities, including a 164-bed hospital, provide medical services for much of southeast Kansas. Numerous cultural opportunities include an active arts council and civic symphony. Outstanding community recreational programs and facilities, 180 acres of parks and several area lakes enhance the college experience for FSCC students.

■ FRIENDS UNIVERSITY
2100 W University Ave.
Wichita, KS 67213
Tel: (316)295-5000; Free: 800-794-6945
Fax: (316)262-5027
E-mail: learn@friends.edu
Web Site: www.friends.edu/

Description: Independent, comprehensive, coed, affiliated with Christian non-denominational. Awards associate, bachelor's, and master's degrees. Founded 1898. Setting: 55-acre urban campus. Endowment: $40.1 million. Educational spending for the previous fiscal year: $2354 per student. Total enrollment: 2,502. Faculty: 206 (75 full-time, 131 part-time). Student-undergrad faculty ratio is 11:1. 786 applied, 58% were admitted. 20% from top 10% of their high school class, 36% from top quarter, 68% from top half. Full-time: 1,428 students, 55% women, 45% men. Part-time: 341 students, 58% women, 42% men. Students come from 18 states and territories, 11 other countries, 19% from out-of-state. 2% American Indian or Alaska Native, non-Hispanic/Latino; 4% Hispanic/Latino; 11% African American, non-Hispanic/Latino; 3% Asian, non-Hispanic/Latino; 0.3% Native Hawaiian or other Pacific Islander, non-Hispanic/Latino; 0% international. 9% 25 or older, 46% live on campus, 6% transferred in. Retention: 60% of full-time freshmen returned the following year. Academic areas with the most degrees conferred: business/marketing; computer and information sciences; biological/life sciences; psychology; education; visual and performing arts. Core. Calendar: semesters. Academic remediation for entering students, services for LD students, advanced placement, accelerated degree program, self-designed majors, honors program, independent study, distance learning, double major, summer session for credit, part-time degree program, adult/continuing education programs, co-op programs and internships. Off campus study at Cross-registration is offered to Friends University students at Newman University, Wichita, Kansas on a space-available basis. The courses are counted as resident credit at Friends University. Most courses are available on both campuses to all students without separate registrations or added costs. The student exchange program is designed to enrich the educational opportunities of Friends and Newman students. Study abroad program.

Entrance Requirements: Options: electronic application, international bac-

calaureate accepted. Required: High school transcripts are not required for adult students enrolling in degree completion programs. Auditions are required for music, dance and theater programs. Portfolios are required for art program. Admission for traditional undergraduate students is based on student's hs GPA x ACT score. Recommended: ACT, SAT and SAT Subject Tests or ACT. Required for some: high school transcript, interview, SAT or ACT. Entrance: moderately difficult. Application deadlines: Rolling, Rolling for nonresidents. Notification: continuous, continuous for nonresidents. SAT Reasoning Test deadline: 8/29. SAT Subject Test deadline: 8/29. Transfer credits accepted: Yes.

Costs Per Year: Application fee: $35. Comprehensive fee: $29,100 includes full-time tuition ($22,320), mandatory fees ($180), and college room and board ($6600). College room only: $3200. Full-time tuition and fees vary according to course load and degree level. Room and board charges vary according to board plan and housing facility. Part-time tuition: $738 per credit hour. Part-time mandatory fees: $6 per credit hour. Part-time tuition and fees vary according to course load and degree level.

Collegiate Environment: Orientation program. Drama-theater group, choral group, student-run newspaper. Social organizations: 24 open to all; Numerous student organizations on campus; 35% of eligible men and 35% of eligible women are members. Most popular organizations: Concert Choir, Singing Quakers, Zoo Science Club, Psychology Club, Spanish Club. Major annual events: Late Night Breakfast, Homecoming Week, Cherry Carnival Week. Student services: health clinic, personal-psychological counseling. Campus security: 24-hour patrols, late night transport-escort service, controlled dormitory access. 423 college housing spaces available; 343 were occupied in 2012-13. No special consideration for freshman housing applicants. Option: coed housing available. Edmund Stanley Library plus 1 other with 166,916 books, 2,173 microform titles, 69,526 serials, 9,208 audiovisual materials, an OPAC, and a Web page. Operations spending for the previous fiscal year: $360,817. 360 computers available on campus for general student use. A campuswide network can be accessed from student residence rooms and from off campus. Students can access the following: online class registration. Staffed computer lab on campus provides training in use of computers, software, and the Internet.

■ **GARDEN CITY COMMUNITY COLLEGE**
801 Campus Dr.
Garden City, KS 67846-6399
Tel: (316)276-7611; Free: 800-658-1696
E-mail: admissions@gcccks.edu
Web Site: www.gcccks.edu/
Description: County-supported, 2-year, coed. Part of Kansas Board of Regents. Awards certificates, transfer associate, and terminal associate degrees. Founded 1919. Setting: 63-acre rural campus. Total enrollment: 2,059. 558 applied, 100% were admitted. 14% from top 10% of their high school class, 18% from top quarter, 46% from top half. Full-time: 1,038 students, 51% women, 49% men. Part-time: 1,021 students, 56% women, 44% men. Students come from 41 states and territories, 6 other countries, 15% from out-of-state. 1% American Indian or Alaska Native, non-Hispanic/Latino; 31% Hispanic/Latino; 6% African American, non-Hispanic/Latino; 3% Asian, non-Hispanic/Latino; 0% Native Hawaiian or other Pacific Islander, non-Hispanic/Latino; 4% international. 24% 25 or older, 4% transferred in. Core. Calendar: semesters. Academic remediation for entering students, ESL program, services for LD students, advanced placement, self-designed majors, distance learning, summer session for credit, part-time degree program, external degree program, adult/continuing education programs.
Entrance Requirements: Open admission except for transfer students. Required: high school transcript, ACT COMPASS. Recommended: ACT. Entrance: noncompetitive. Application deadline: Rolling. Transfer credits accepted: Yes.
Collegiate Environment: Orientation program. Drama-theater group, choral group, student-run newspaper. Social organizations: 19 open to all; 20% of eligible men and 20% of eligible women are members. Most popular organizations: HALO (Hispanic Student Leadership Organization), GC3 Media, Criminal Justice/Tau Epsilon Lambda, SGA (Student Government Association), PTK (Phi Theta Kappa). Major annual events: HALO/SSS Campus Fiesta, SGA Casino Night, Constitution Day Demonstration. Student services: health clinic, personal-psychological counseling. Campus security: 24-hour emergency response devices and patrols, student patrols, late night transport-escort service, controlled dormitory access. 304 college housing spaces available; 302 were occupied in 2012-13. No special consideration for freshman housing applicants. Option: coed housing available. Saffell Library with 15,984 books, 6,221 microform titles, 31 serials,

428 audiovisual materials, an OPAC, and a Web page. 400 computers available on campus for general student use. A campuswide network can be accessed from student residence rooms. Students can access the following: online class registration. Staffed computer lab on campus.
Community Environment: Garden City is on the Arkansas River in a fertile agricultural area. Predominant crops are corn, alfalfa, wheat and grain sorgums, with beef cattle production very strong. Shopping facilities are good. Finnup Park, a large recreational development, contains a swimming pool, picnic sites, museum and zoo. Other facilities for recreation are golf courses and local parks. One of the largest buffalo herds is located at Garden City on the Buffalo Preserve. All forms of commercial transportation are available.

■ **HASKELL INDIAN NATIONS UNIVERSITY**
155 Indian Ave., No.5031
Lawrence, KS 66046-4800
Tel: (785)749-8404
Fax: (785)749-8429
Web Site: www.haskell.edu/
Description: Federally supported, 4-year, coed. Awards associate and bachelor's degrees. Founded 1884. Setting: 320-acre suburban campus. Total enrollment: 894. 544 applied. 24% 25 or older. Core. Calendar: semesters. Academic remediation for entering students, services for LD students, advanced placement, self-designed majors, independent study, distance learning, summer session for credit, part-time degree program, internships. Off campus study at members of the American Indian Higher Education Consortium, Kansas City Regional Council for Higher Education, University of Kansas. ROTC: Air Force (c).
Entrance Requirements: Option: electronic application. Required: high school transcript, minimum 2.0 high school GPA, ACT. Required for some: 2 recommendations. Entrance: minimally difficult. Application deadline: 7/30. Notification: continuous. Preference given to applicants with at least one-fourth Native American ancestry or tribal membership.
Collegiate Environment: Orientation program. Drama-theater group, student-run newspaper. Student services: health clinic, personal-psychological counseling. Campus security: night patrol only. 50,000 books, 400 serials, and an OPAC.
Community Environment: See University of Kansas.

■ **HESSTON COLLEGE**
Box 3000
Hesston, KS 67062-2093
Tel: (620)327-4221; Free: 800-995-2757
Fax: (620)327-8300
E-mail: admissions@hesston.edu
Web Site: www.hesston.edu/
Description: Independent Mennonite, 2-year, coed. Awards transfer associate and terminal associate degrees. Founded 1909. Setting: 50-acre small town campus with easy access to Wichita. Total enrollment: 448. Faculty: 51 (34 full-time, 17 part-time). Student-undergrad faculty ratio is 12:1. 844 applied. Full-time: 396 students, 55% women, 45% men. Part-time: 52 students, 85% women, 15% men. Students come from 30 states and territories, 11 other countries, 45% from out-of-state. 2% American Indian or Alaska Native, non-Hispanic/Latino; 5% Hispanic/Latino; 6% African American, non-Hispanic/Latino; 1% Asian, non-Hispanic/Latino; 0.2% Native Hawaiian or other Pacific Islander, non-Hispanic/Latino; 8% international. 13% 25 or older, 73% live on campus, 9% transferred in. Retention: 78% of full-time freshmen returned the following year. Core. Calendar: semesters. Academic remediation for entering students, ESL program, services for LD students, advanced placement, independent study, double major, summer session for credit, part-time degree program, co-op programs and internships.
Entrance Requirements: Open admission except for nursing and pastoral ministries programs. Options: electronic application, early admission, deferred admission. Required: high school transcript, 2 recommendations, SAT or ACT. Required for some: interview. Entrance: noncompetitive. Application deadline: Rolling. Transfer credits accepted: Yes.
Costs Per Year: Application fee: $15. Comprehensive fee: $30,114 includes full-time tuition ($22,282), mandatory fees ($340), and college room and board ($7492). Full-time tuition and fees vary according to program. Part-time tuition: $928 per hour. Part-time mandatory fees: $85 per term. Part-time tuition and fees vary according to course load and program.
Collegiate Environment: Orientation program. Drama-theater group, choral group, student-run newspaper. Most popular organizations: Peace and

Service Club, intramural sports, Ministry Assistants. Major annual events: Thanksgiving Weekend, Feast of Carols, Mod Olympics. Student services: personal-psychological counseling. Campus security: 24-hour emergency response devices, controlled dormitory access. Mary Miller Library with 35,000 books, 2,000 microform titles, 234 serials, 2,670 audiovisual materials, an OPAC, and a Web page. 115 computers available on campus for general student use. A campuswide network can be accessed from student residence rooms and from off campus. Staffed computer lab on campus provides training in use of computers, software, and the Internet.

Community Environment: Hesston is a small, progressive, south central Kansas town with a population of 3,600. It is located 35 miles north of Wichita, and has ready access to air, rail, and bus transportation. Part-time employment for students is available in the area and is coordinated through the Cooperative Education office on campus. A temperate climate allows considerable outside activity. Recreational facilities located in or near Hesston include an 18-hole golf course, bike trails, tennis courts, year-round swimming pool, and numerous county and state parks and lakes.

■ **HIGHLAND COMMUNITY COLLEGE**
606 W Main St.
Highland, KS 66035
Tel: (785)442-6000
Fax: (785)442-6100
Web Site: www.highlandcc.edu/

Description: State and locally supported, 2-year, coed. Part of Kansas Community College System. Awards certificates, transfer associate, and terminal associate degrees. Founded 1858. Setting: 20-acre rural campus. Total enrollment: 2,810. 21% 25 or older. Core. Calendar: semesters. Academic remediation for entering students, services for LD students, advanced placement, self-designed majors, summer session for credit, part-time degree program, adult/continuing education programs, co-op programs and internships. Off campus study. ROTC: Army (c).

Entrance Requirements: Open admission for state residents. Option: early admission. Required: high school transcript. Entrance: minimally difficult. Application deadline: 8/20. Notification: continuous. Preference given to state residents.

Collegiate Environment: Drama-theater group, student-run newspaper. 30,000 books and 268 serials.

■ **HUTCHINSON COMMUNITY COLLEGE AND AREA VOCATIONAL SCHOOL**
1300 N Plum St.
Hutchinson, KS 67501-5894
Tel: (620)665-3500; Free: 888-GO-HUTCH
Fax: (620)665-3310
E-mail: strobelc@hutchcc.edu
Web Site: www.hutchcc.edu/

Description: State and locally supported, 2-year, coed. Part of Kansas Board of Regents. Awards certificates, transfer associate, and terminal associate degrees. Founded 1928. Setting: 47-acre small town campus. Educational spending for the previous fiscal year: $3976 per student. Total enrollment: 6,159. Faculty: 500 (118 full-time, 382 part-time). Student-undergrad faculty ratio is 15:1. 1,373 applied, 100% were admitted. Full-time: 2,586 students, 52% women, 48% men. Part-time: 3,573 students, 60% women, 40% men. Students come from 46 states and territories, 6 other countries, 7% from out-of-state. 1% American Indian or Alaska Native, non-Hispanic/Latino; 8% Hispanic/Latino; 7% African American, non-Hispanic/Latino; 1% Asian, non-Hispanic/Latino; 0% Native Hawaiian or other Pacific Islander, non-Hispanic/Latino; 0.4% international. 36% 25 or older, 7% live on campus, 8% transferred in. Retention: 57% of full-time freshmen returned the following year. Core. Calendar: semesters. Academic remediation for entering students, ESL program, services for LD students, advanced placement, self-designed majors, honors program, independent study, distance learning, double major, summer session for credit, part-time degree program, adult/continuing education programs, co-op programs and internships. ROTC: Army (c).

Entrance Requirements: Open admission Allied Health programs do not have open admission. Options: electronic application, early admission, deferred admission, international baccalaureate accepted. Required for some: high school transcript, interview. Entrance: noncompetitive. Application deadline: Rolling. Notification: continuous. Transfer credits accepted: Yes.

Costs Per Year: Application fee: $0. State resident tuition: $2144 full-time, $67 per hour part-time. Nonresident tuition: $3136 full-time, $98 per hour

part-time. Mandatory fees: $544 full-time, $17 per hour part-time. College room and board: $5150. Room and board charges vary according to board plan.

Collegiate Environment: Orientation program. Drama-theater group, choral group, student-run newspaper. Most popular organizations: Black Leadership League, Hispanic American Leadership Organization, Campus Crusade for Christ, Circle K, Block and Bridle Club. Major annual events: Football Homecoming, Basketball Homecoming, Spring Fling. Student services: health clinic, personal-psychological counseling. Campus security: 24-hour emergency response devices and patrols, student patrols, late night transport-escort service, controlled dormitory access. 500 college housing spaces available; all were occupied in 2012-13. No special consideration for freshman housing applicants. Options: men-only, women-only housing available. John F. Kennedy Library plus 1 other with 41,510 books, 60,244 microform titles, 132 serials, 2,238 audiovisual materials, an OPAC, and a Web page. Operations spending for the previous fiscal year: $143,793. 500 computers available on campus for general student use. A campuswide network can be accessed from student residence rooms and from off campus. Students can access the following: online class registration. Staffed computer lab on campus provides training in use of computers, software, and the Internet.

■ **INDEPENDENCE COMMUNITY COLLEGE**
Brookside Dr. and College Ave.
Independence, KS 67301-0708
Tel: (620)331-4100; Free: 800-842-6063
Fax: (620)331-5344
E-mail: sciufulescu@indycc.edu
Web Site: www.indycc.edu/

Description: State-supported, 2-year, coed. Part of Kansas State Board of Education. Awards certificates, transfer associate, and terminal associate degrees. Founded 1925. Setting: 68-acre small town campus. Total enrollment: 1,177. Student-undergrad faculty ratio is 13:1. 30% from out-of-state. 27% 25 or older. Core. Calendar: semesters. Academic remediation for entering students, ESL program, advanced placement, honors program, summer session for credit, part-time degree program, adult/continuing education programs, co-op programs and internships.

Entrance Requirements: Open admission. Options: electronic application, early admission. Required: high school transcript. Entrance: noncompetitive. Application deadline: Rolling.

Collegiate Environment: Drama-theater group, choral group, student-run newspaper. Student services: personal-psychological counseling. Campus security: night patrol.

Community Environment: Independence, is in a predominately agricultural region that also produces oil. The community includes a number of churches, a hospital and numerous civic, fraternal and veteran's organizations. An airport is within a ten-minute drive. Montgomery County State Lake and the Elk City Reservoir provide facilities for all water sports. Other recreational activities are golf, tennis and bowling.

■ **ITT TECHNICAL INSTITUTE (OVERLAND PARK)**
7600 W 119th St.
Ste. 100
Overland Park, KS 66213
Tel: (913)253-1300; Free: 877-327-9026
Web Site: www.itt-tech.edu/

Description: Proprietary, 4-year, coed. Awards associate and bachelor's degrees.

Entrance Requirements: Entrance: minimally difficult.

■ **ITT TECHNICAL INSTITUTE (WICHITA)**
8111 E 32nd St. N
Ste. 103
Wichita, KS 67226
Tel: (316)609-4100; Free: 877-207-1047
Web Site: www.itt-tech.edu/

Description: Proprietary, 4-year, coed. Part of ITT Educational Services, Inc. Awards associate and bachelor's degrees.

Entrance Requirements: Entrance: minimally difficult.

■ **JOHNSON COUNTY COMMUNITY COLLEGE**
12345 College Blvd.
Overland Park, KS 66210-1299
Tel: (913)469-8500

Web Site: www.johnco.cc.ks.us/

Description: State and locally supported, 2-year, coed. Part of Kansas State Board of Education. Awards certificates, transfer associate, and terminal associate degrees. Founded 1967. Setting: 220-acre suburban campus with easy access to Kansas City. Total enrollment: 18,897. 34% 25 or older. Core. Calendar: semesters. Academic remediation for entering students, ESL program, services for LD students, advanced placement, self-designed majors, honors program, independent study, distance learning, double major, summer session for credit, part-time degree program, adult/continuing education programs, co-op programs and internships. Off campus study at Metropolitan Community College.

Entrance Requirements: Open admission except for nursing, dental hygiene, paralegal, respiratory care, interpreter training, emergency medical technology programs. Option: early admission. Required for some: high school transcript. Entrance: noncompetitive. Application deadline: Rolling. Notification: continuous.

Collegiate Environment: Drama-theater group, student-run newspaper. Campus security: 24-hour emergency response devices and patrols, late night transport-escort service. Johnson County Community College Library with 89,400 books, 708 serials, 4,770 audiovisual materials, an OPAC, and a Web page.

■ **KANSAS CITY KANSAS COMMUNITY COLLEGE**
7250 State Ave.
Kansas City, KS 66112-3003
Tel: (913)334-1100
Fax: (913)696-9646
E-mail: dmcdowell@kckcc.edu
Web Site: www.kckcc.edu/

Description: State and locally supported, 2-year, coed. Awards certificates, diplomas, transfer associate, and terminal associate degrees. Founded 1923. Setting: 148-acre urban campus. Endowment: $1.1 million. Research spending for the previous fiscal year: $200,072. Educational spending for the previous fiscal year: $3920 per student. Total enrollment: 7,555. Faculty: 480 (148 full-time, 332 part-time). Student-undergrad faculty ratio is 17:1. Full-time: 2,903 students, 58% women, 42% men. Part-time: 4,652 students, 67% women, 33% men. Students come from 27 states and territories, 13 other countries, 5% from out-of-state. 1% American Indian or Alaska Native, non-Hispanic/Latino; 10% Hispanic/Latino; 29% African American, non-Hispanic/Latino; 2% Asian, non-Hispanic/Latino; 0.2% Native Hawaiian or other Pacific Islander, non-Hispanic/Latino; 2% international. 59% 25 or older, 4% transferred in. Core. Calendar: semesters. Academic remediation for entering students, ESL program, services for LD students, advanced placement, freshman honors college, honors program, independent study, distance learning, summer session for credit, part-time degree program, external degree program, adult/continuing education programs, co-op programs and internships.

Entrance Requirements: Open admission except for nursing program. Options: electronic application, international baccalaureate accepted. Required: high school transcript. Entrance: noncompetitive. Application deadline: Rolling. Notification: continuous.

Collegiate Environment: Drama-theater group, choral group, student-run newspaper. Social organizations: 25 open to all. Most popular organizations: Student Senate, Phi Theta Kappa, Drama Club, The African American Student Union, Collegiate Educators Music Club. Major annual events: Last Class Bash, Candle Lighting Program, First Class Bash. Student services: health clinic, personal-psychological counseling, women's center. Campus security: 24-hour emergency response devices and patrols, student patrols, late night transport-escort service. Kansas City Kansas Community College Library plus 1 other with 75,000 books, 250,000 microform titles, 200 serials, 7,000 audiovisual materials, an OPAC, and a Web page. Operations spending for the previous fiscal year: $776,088. 775 computers available on campus for general student use. A campuswide network can be accessed from off-campus. Students can access the following: online class registration. Staffed computer lab on campus.

■ **KANSAS STATE UNIVERSITY**
Manhattan, KS 66506
Tel: (785)532-6011; Free: 800-432-8270
Fax: (785)532-6393
E-mail: k-state@k-state.edu
Web Site: www.k-state.edu/

Description: State-supported, university, coed. Part of Kansas Board of Regents. Awards associate, bachelor's, master's, and doctoral degrees.

Founded 1863. Setting: 668-acre suburban campus. Endowment: $329.2 million. Research spending for the previous fiscal year: $133.1 million. Educational spending for the previous fiscal year: $6227 per student. Total enrollment: 24,378. Faculty: 1,203 (1,001 full-time, 202 part-time). Student-undergrad faculty ratio is 20:1. 9,273 applied, 99% were admitted. 20% from top 10% of their high school class, 45% from top quarter, 74% from top half. 261 valedictorians. Full-time: 17,798 students, 47% women, 53% men. Part-time: 2,055 students, 50% women, 50% men. Students come from 52 states and territories, 79 other countries, 16% from out-of-state. 0.4% American Indian or Alaska Native, non-Hispanic/Latino; 6% Hispanic/Latino; 4% African American, non-Hispanic/Latino; 1% Asian, non-Hispanic/Latino; 0.1% Native Hawaiian or other Pacific Islander, non-Hispanic/Latino; 6% international. 10% 25 or older, 8% transferred in. Retention: 80% of full-time freshmen returned the following year. Academic areas with the most degrees conferred: business/marketing; agriculture; social sciences. Core. Calendar: semesters. Academic remediation for entering students, ESL program, services for LD students, advanced placement, accelerated degree program, freshman honors college, honors program, independent study, distance learning, double major, summer session for credit, part-time degree program, adult/continuing education programs, co-op programs and internships, graduate courses open to undergrads. Off campus study at Manhattan Christian College, University of Missouri-Kansas City, 19 Kansas community colleges. Study abroad program. ROTC: Army, Air Force.

Entrance Requirements: Options: electronic application, early admission. Required: high school transcript, minimum 2 high school GPA. Recommended: SAT or ACT. Required for some: SAT or ACT. Entrance: noncompetitive. Application deadlines: Rolling, Rolling for nonresidents. Notification: continuous, continuous for nonresidents. Transfer credits accepted: Yes.

Costs Per Year: Application fee: $30. State resident tuition: $7317 full-time. Nonresident tuition: $19,416 full-time. Mandatory fees: $730 full-time. Full-time tuition and fees vary according to course load, degree level, location, program, and reciprocity agreements. College room and board: $7450. Room and board charges vary according to board plan, housing facility, and location.

Collegiate Environment: Orientation program. Drama-theater group, choral group, marching band, student-run newspaper, radio station. Social organizations: national fraternities, national sororities. Most popular organizations: athletic department groups, marching band, Union Governing Board, theater productions, debate team. Major annual events: Homecoming, Multicultural Week, open house. Student services: legal services, health clinic, personal-psychological counseling, women's center. Campus security: 24-hour emergency response devices and patrols, late night transport-escort service, controlled dormitory access. No special consideration for freshman housing applicants. Options: coed, men-only, women-only housing available. Hale Library plus 3 others with 2.9 million books, 1.6 million microform titles, 74,394 serials, 144,558 audiovisual materials, an OPAC, and a Web page. Operations spending for the previous fiscal year: $15.5 million.

Community Environment: Manhattan; a beautiful city, situated on the Blue River and Kansas River, enjoys the excellent recreational facilities of Tuttle Creek Dam. The community offers libraries, churches, hospitals, hotels, motels, rooming houses and four attractive shopping centers including Manhattan Town Center. Numerous civic, service and social organizations exist. Part-time work is available. Historic Fort Riley is eight miles away.

■ **KANSAS WESLEYAN UNIVERSITY**
100 E Claflin Ave.
Salina, KS 67401-6196
Tel: (785)827-5541; Free: 800-874-1154
Fax: (785)827-0927
E-mail: lorie.howe@kwu.edu
Web Site: www.kwu.edu/

Description: Independent United Methodist, comprehensive, coed. Awards associate, bachelor's, and master's degrees. Founded 1886. Setting: 28-acre urban campus. Endowment: $19.8 million. Total enrollment: 745. Faculty: 80 (43 full-time, 37 part-time). Student-undergrad faculty ratio is 13:1. 728 applied, 48% were admitted. 13% from top 10% of their high school class, 31% from top quarter, 37% from top half. Full-time: 637 students, 57% women, 43% men. Part-time: 74 students, 68% women, 32% men. Students come from 19 states and territories, 15 other countries, 37% from out-of-state. 1% American Indian or Alaska Native, non-Hispanic/Latino; 10% Hispanic/Latino; 7% African American, non-Hispanic/Latino; 1% Asian, non-Hispanic/Latino; 1% Native Hawaiian or other Pacific Islander, non-Hispanic/Latino; 3% international. 11% 25 or older, 57% live on campus, 12% transferred in. Retention: 48% of full-time freshmen returned the following year. Academic areas with the most degrees conferred: health professions and related sciences; business/marketing; parks and recreation. Core. Calendar: 2 semesters with a summer term. Academic remediation for entering students, ESL program, advanced placement, self-designed majors, honors program, independent study, distance learning, double major, summer session for credit, part-time degree program, adult/continuing education programs, internships, graduate courses open to undergrads. Off campus study at Associated Colleges of Central Kansas. Study abroad program.

Entrance Requirements: Options: electronic application, deferred admission, international baccalaureate accepted. Required: high school transcript, minimum 2.5 high school GPA, SAT or ACT. Entrance: moderately difficult. Application deadline: Rolling. Notification: continuous. Transfer credits accepted: Yes.

Costs Per Year: Application fee: $20. One-time mandatory fee: $100. Comprehensive fee: $31,400 includes full-time tuition ($23,800) and college room and board ($7600). College room only: $2600. Room and board charges vary according to housing facility.

Collegiate Environment: Orientation program. Drama-theater group, choral group, student-run newspaper. Social organizations: local fraternities, local sororities, societies. Most popular organizations: Fellowship of Christian Athletes, student government, Wesleyan Chorale, Multicultural Student Association, Business Club. Major annual events: Homecoming, Sweetheart Dance, Spring Fling. Student services: personal-psychological counseling. Campus security: 24-hour emergency response devices, student patrols, late night transport-escort service, controlled dormitory access, evening patrols by security. 590 college housing spaces available; 367 were occupied in 2012-13. Freshmen guaranteed college housing. On-campus residence required through sophomore year. Options: coed, men-only, women-only housing available. Memorial Library with 97,060 books, 35,058 microform titles, 188 serials, 1,797 audiovisual materials, an OPAC, and a Web page. 130 computers available on campus for general student use. A campuswide network can be accessed from student residence rooms and from off campus. Staffed computer lab on campus provides training in use of computers, software, and the Internet.

Community Environment: Salina (pop. 45,956), situated in the central part of the state, is the fifth largest city in Kansas. Major forms of transportation are available. Community facilities include a public library, municipal shopping center, museum, community theater, and numerous churches. Points of interest include Kanapolis Lake and Rock City.

■ LABETTE COMMUNITY COLLEGE

200 S 14th St.
Parsons, KS 67357-4299
Tel: (620)421-6700; Free: 888-522-3883
Web Site: www.labette.edu/

Description: State and locally supported, 2-year, coed. Part of Kansas State Board of Education. Awards certificates, transfer associate, and terminal associate degrees. Founded 1923. Setting: 4-acre small town campus. Total enrollment: 1,401. Faculty: 208 (31 full-time, 177 part-time). 212 applied, 100% were admitted. 20% from top 10% of their high school class, 59% from top half. Full-time: 466 students, 58% women, 42% men. Part-time: 935 students, 69% women, 31% men. Students come from 7 states and territories, 4 other countries. 40% 25 or older. Calendar: semesters. Academic remediation for entering students, services for LD students, advanced placement, accelerated degree program, independent study, distance learning, double major, summer session for credit, part-time degree program, adult/continuing education programs, co-op programs and internships. Off campus study. ROTC: Army (c).

Entrance Requirements: Open admission except for nursing program. Option: early admission. Recommended: high school transcript. Required for some: interview. Entrance: noncompetitive. Application deadline: Rolling. Notification: continuous.

Collegiate Environment: Choral group. Social organizations: 18 open to all. Most popular organizations: Adult Women Who Are Returning to Education (AWARE), Phi Beta Lambda. Student services: personal-psychological counseling. Labette Community College Library with 26,000 books, 1,770 microform titles, 235 serials, 542 audiovisual materials, an OPAC, and a Web page. 66 computers available on campus for general student use. Staffed computer lab on campus.

Community Environment: This is an agricultural and industrial area, dairying being the principal source of income. Lake Parsons, which is municipally owned, provides facilities for picnicking, fishing and boating. Camping is available at Marvel Park and the Neosho Water Fowl Management Area, 12 miles north of the city, affords fishing and hunting as well.

■ MANHATTAN AREA TECHNICAL COLLEGE

3136 Dickens Ave.
Manhattan, KS 66503
Tel: (785)587-2800; Free: 800-352-7575
Web Site: www.matc.net/

Description: State and locally supported, 2-year, coed. Awards certificates, diplomas, and terminal associate degrees. Founded 1965. Setting: 19-acre suburban campus. Educational spending for the previous fiscal year: $3563 per student. Total enrollment: 473. Faculty: 35 (27 full-time, 8 part-time). Student-undergrad faculty ratio is 11:1. Full-time: 343 students, 40% women, 60% men. Part-time: 130 students, 69% women, 31% men. 32% 25 or older, 23% transferred in. Core. Calendar: semesters.

Entrance Requirements: Recommended: high school transcript. Required for some: high school transcript.

Collegiate Environment: Matc Library with an OPAC.

■ MANHATTAN CHRISTIAN COLLEGE

1415 Anderson Ave.
Manhattan, KS 66502-4081
Tel: (785)539-3571; Free: 877-246-4622
Fax: (785)539-0832
E-mail: admit@mccks.edu
Web Site: www.mccks.edu/

Description: Independent, 4-year, coed, affiliated with Christian Churches and Churches of Christ. Awards associate and bachelor's degrees. Founded 1927. Setting: 10-acre small town campus. Total enrollment: 388. 21% 25 or older. Core. Calendar: semesters. Academic remediation for entering students, advanced placement, independent study, distance learning, double major, summer session for credit, adult/continuing education programs, internships. ROTC: Army (c), Air Force (c).

Entrance Requirements: Options: electronic application, international baccalaureate accepted. Required: essay, high school transcript, minimum 2.0 high school GPA, 3 recommendations, SAT or ACT. Required for some: interview. Entrance: minimally difficult. Application deadline: 8/1. Notification: continuous.

Collegiate Environment: Orientation program. Drama-theater group, choral group, student-run newspaper. Student services: personal-psychological counseling. Manhattan Christian College Library with 3,300 books, 1,800 microform titles, 3,000 serials, 2,200 audiovisual materials, an OPAC, and a Web page.

Community Environment: See Kansas State University.

■ MCPHERSON COLLEGE

1600 E Euclid
McPherson, KS 67460-1402
Tel: (620)241-0731; Free: 800-365-7402
Fax: (620)241-8443
E-mail: admiss@mcpherson.edu
Web Site: www.mcpherson.edu/

Description: Independent, 4-year, coed, affiliated with Church of the Brethren. Awards bachelor's degrees. Founded 1887. Setting: 26-acre small town campus. Total enrollment: 620. Faculty: 65 (39 full-time, 26 part-time). Student-undergrad faculty ratio is 13:1. 487 applied, 86% were admitted. 11% from top 10% of their high school class, 29% from top quarter, 64% from top half. Full-time: 585 students, 39% women, 61% men. Part-time: 35 students, 69% women, 31% men. 1% American Indian or Alaska Native, non-Hispanic/Latino; 7% Hispanic/Latino; 12% African American, non-Hispanic/Latino; 0.5% Asian, non-Hispanic/Latino; 1% Native Hawaiian or other Pacific Islander, non-Hispanic/Latino; 2% international. 74% live on campus, 12% transferred in. Retention: 59% of full-time freshmen returned the following year. Academic areas with the most degrees conferred: health professions and related sciences; engineering technologies; transportation and materials moving. Calendar: 4-1-4. Part-time degree program, adult/continuing education programs.

Entrance Requirements: Options: electronic application, deferred admission. Required: high school transcript, minimum 2 high school GPA, SAT or ACT. Entrance: moderately difficult. Application deadline: 8/12. Notification: continuous. SAT Reasoning Test deadline: 8/1. SAT Subject Test deadline: 8/1. Transfer credits accepted: Yes.

Costs Per Year: Application fee: $25. Comprehensive fee: $29,565 includes full-time tuition ($21,801) and college room and board ($7764). College room only: $3206. Full-time tuition varies according to course load and program.

Collegiate Environment: Orientation program. Campus security: student patrols, controlled dormitory access.

Community Environment: McPherson is a small city of 14,000 located near Highway I-135. The county seat, as well as the business center for the surrounding agricultural area, McPherson's principal industries include oil refining, insulation, plastic pipe, pharmaceuticals, mobile homes, and farm equipment. The community supports many cultural activities such as activities symphony, theatre guild, chorale, and art festival. Air transportation is available at nearby Wichita, Salina and Hutchinson, as well as churches, motels, and several parks.

■ **MIDAMERICA NAZARENE UNIVERSITY**
2030 E College Way
Olathe, KS 66062-1899
Tel: (913)782-3750; Free: 800-800-8887
Fax: (913)791-3481
E-mail: ldowns@mnu.edu
Web Site: www.mnu.edu/

Description: Independent, comprehensive, coed, affiliated with Church of the Nazarene. Awards associate, bachelor's, and master's degrees and post-master's certificates. Founded 1966. Setting: 105-acre suburban campus with easy access to Kansas City. Endowment: $7 million. Total enrollment: 1,978. Faculty: 80 (76 full-time, 4 part-time). Student-undergrad faculty ratio is 10:1. 630 applied, 71% were admitted. Full-time: 1,170 students, 58% women, 42% men. Part-time: 309 students, 59% women, 41% men. Students come from 36 states and territories, 4 other countries, 40% from out-of-state. 1% American Indian or Alaska Native, non-Hispanic/Latino; 5% Hispanic/Latino; 12% African American, non-Hispanic/Latino; 2% Asian, non-Hispanic/Latino; 0.1% Native Hawaiian or other Pacific Islander, non-Hispanic/Latino; 0.1% international. 37% 25 or older, 63% live on campus, 27% transferred in. Retention: 70% of full-time freshmen returned the following year. Core. Calendar: semesters. Academic remediation for entering students, services for LD students, advanced placement, accelerated degree program, honors program, independent study, distance learning, double major, summer session for credit, part-time degree program, adult/continuing education programs, internships. Off campus study at Coalition for Christian Colleges and Universities. Study abroad program. ROTC: Army (c), Air Force (c).

Entrance Requirements: Open admission. Options: electronic application, deferred admission, international baccalaureate accepted. Required: high school transcript, minimum 2 high school GPA, SAT or ACT. Recommended: TOEFL recommended. Entrance: minimally difficult. Application deadline: 8/1. Notification: continuous. SAT Reasoning Test deadline: 8/1. SAT Subject Test deadline: 8/1. Transfer credits accepted: Yes.

Costs Per Year: Application fee: $25. Comprehensive fee: $30,170 includes full-time tuition ($21,500), mandatory fees ($1230), and college room and board ($7440). Full-time tuition and fees vary according to course load and degree level. Room and board charges vary according to board plan and housing facility. Part-time tuition: $725 per credit hour. Part-time mandatory fees: $265 per term. Part-time tuition and fees vary according to course load and degree level.

Collegiate Environment: Orientation program. Drama-theater group, choral group, student-run newspaper, radio station. Student services: personal-psychological counseling. Campus security: 24-hour emergency response devices and patrols, student patrols, late night transport-escort service, controlled dormitory access. 699 college housing spaces available; 599 were occupied in 2012-13. Freshmen guaranteed college housing. Options: men-only, women-only housing available. Mabee Library with 106,268 books, 275 serials, 47 audiovisual materials, an OPAC, and a Web page.

■ **NATIONAL AMERICAN UNIVERSITY**
10310 Mastin
Overland Park, KS 66212
Tel: (913)981-8700
Web Site: www.national.edu/

Description: Independent, 2-year, coed. Awards terminal associate degrees. Total enrollment: 156.
Entrance Requirements: Entrance: noncompetitive.

■ **NEOSHO COUNTY COMMUNITY COLLEGE**
800 W 14th St.
Chanute, KS 66720-2699
Tel: (620)431-6222
Fax: (620)431-0082
E-mail: llast@neosho.edu
Web Site: www.neosho.edu/

Description: State and locally supported, 2-year, coed. Part of Kansas State Board of Education. Awards certificates, diplomas, transfer associate, and terminal associate degrees. Founded 1936. Setting: 50-acre small town campus. Endowment: $370,000. Total enrollment: 1,826. Faculty: 126 (40 full-time, 86 part-time). 573 applied, 100% were admitted. Full-time: 615 students, 61% women, 39% men. Part-time: 1,211 students, 69% women, 31% men. Students come from 15 states and territories. 58% 25 or older, 5% live on campus. Core. Calendar: semesters. Academic remediation for entering students, services for LD students, advanced placement, self-designed majors, summer session for credit, part-time degree program, adult/continuing education programs.

Entrance Requirements: Open admission. Option: early admission. Required: high school transcript. Entrance: noncompetitive. Application deadline: 9/15. Notification: continuous.

Collegiate Environment: Drama-theater group, choral group, student-run newspaper. Most popular organizations: Business Club, Science Club, Student Nurses Association, Fellowship of Christian Athletes, Nontraditional Student Organization. Major annual events: Homecoming, Fun-in-the-Sun Week, Halloween Dance. Student services: personal-psychological counseling. Campus security: controlled dormitory access. Chapman Library with 33,000 books and 200 serials. 100 computers available on campus for general student use. Staffed computer lab on campus.

Community Environment: An industrial city with rural and urban sections, Chanute is the girlhood home of Osa Johnson, famous African and South Seas explorer. Oil production, manufacturing and agriculture are important to the city's economy. The varied industries include a cement plant, an oil field equipment manufacturing company, a garment factory and machine shops. Some part-time employment is available. Chanute has good shopping facilities, a hospital, many churches, a theater, a skating rink, commercial family recreation, a lake and a municipal golf course. A Mexican Fiesta, the Fall Festival, and a Horse Show are special annual events.

■ **NEWMAN UNIVERSITY**
3100 McCormick Ave.
Wichita, KS 67213-2097
Tel: (316)942-4291; Free: 877-NEWMANU
Fax: (316)942-4483
E-mail: reusserj@newmanu.edu
Web Site: www.newmanu.edu/

Description: Independent Roman Catholic, comprehensive, coed. Awards associate, bachelor's, and master's degrees. Founded 1933. Setting: 61-acre urban campus. Endowment: $19.5 million. Educational spending for the previous fiscal year: $4303 per student. Total enrollment: 3,108. Faculty: 233 (89 full-time, 144 part-time). Student-undergrad faculty ratio is 13:1. 2,454 applied, 44% were admitted. 36% from top 10% of their high school class, 65% from top quarter, 88% from top half. Full-time: 1,149 students, 66% women, 34% men. Part-time: 1,235 students, 60% women, 40% men. Students come from 22 states and territories, 25 other countries, 12% from out-of-state. 1% American Indian or Alaska Native, non-Hispanic/Latino; 11% Hispanic/Latino; 6% African American, non-Hispanic/Latino; 4% Asian, non-Hispanic/Latino; 0.1% Native Hawaiian or other Pacific Islander, non-Hispanic/Latino; 5% international. 40% 25 or older, 14% live on campus, 11% transferred in. Retention: 69% of full-time freshmen returned the following year. Academic areas with the most degrees conferred: health professions and related sciences; business/marketing; education. Core. Calendar: semesters. Academic remediation for entering students, services for LD students, advanced placement, accelerated degree program, self-designed majors, honors program, independent study, distance learning, double major, summer session for credit, part-time degree program, adult/continuing education programs, co-op programs and internships. Off campus study at Friends University. Study abroad program.

Entrance Requirements: Options: electronic application, early admission, deferred admission. Required: high school transcript, minimum 2 high school GPA. Recommended: interview. Required for some: SAT or ACT. Entrance: minimally difficult. Application deadlines: Rolling, Rolling for nonresidents. Notification: continuous, continuous for nonresidents. SAT Reasoning Test deadline: 9/9. SAT Subject Test deadline: 9/9. Transfer credits accepted: Yes.

Costs Per Year: Application fee: $20. Comprehensive fee: $28,688 includes full-time tuition ($21,388), mandatory fees ($910), and college room and board ($6390). College room only: $3200. Full-time tuition and fees vary according to class time, course load, location, and program. Room and board charges vary according to board plan and housing facility. Part-time tuition:

$713 per credit hour. Part-time mandatory fees: $15 per credit hour. Part-time tuition and fees vary according to class time, course load, location, and program.

Collegiate Environment: Orientation program. Drama-theater group, choral group, student-run newspaper. Social organizations: 26 open to all. Most popular organizations: Newman University Medical Professionals Club (NUMPC), Hispanic American Leadership Organization (HALO), Chemistry Club, Math Club, Art Club. Major annual events: Weeks of Welcome/ Welcome Back Bash, Homecoming, Family Weekend. Student services: personal-psychological counseling. Campus security: 24-hour emergency response devices and patrols, student patrols, late night transport-escort service, controlled dormitory access. 406 college housing spaces available; 341 were occupied in 2012-13. Freshmen guaranteed college housing. On-campus residence required through sophomore year. Options: coed, men-only, women-only housing available. Dugan Library with 90,129 books, 143,723 microform titles, 7,015 serials, 2,168 audiovisual materials, an OPAC, and a Web page. Operations spending for the previous fiscal year: $262,132. 90 computers available on campus for general student use. A campuswide network can be accessed from student residence rooms and from off campus. Students can access the following: online class registration. Staffed computer lab on campus provides training in use of software and the Internet.

Community Environment: See Wichita State University.

■ **NORTH CENTRAL KANSAS TECHNICAL COLLEGE**
PO Box 507, 3033 US Hwy. 24
Beloit, KS 67420
Tel: (913)738-2276; Free: 800-658-4655
E-mail: jheidrick@ncktc.tec.ks.us
Web Site: www.ncktc.edu/
Description: State-supported, 2-year, coed. Awards terminal associate degrees. Founded 1963. Total enrollment: 513. Calendar: semesters.
Entrance Requirements: Entrance: noncompetitive.

■ **NORTHWEST KANSAS TECHNICAL COLLEGE**
PO Box 668, 1209 Harrison St.
Goodland, KS 67735
Tel: (785)899-3641; Free: 800-316-4127
Fax: (785)899-5711
Web Site: www.nwktc.edu/
Description: State-supported, 2-year, coed. Awards terminal associate degrees. Founded 1964. Total enrollment: 281. Calendar: semesters.
Entrance Requirements: Entrance: noncompetitive.

■ **OTTAWA UNIVERSITY**
1001 S Cedar
Ottawa, KS 66067-3399
Tel: (785)242-5200; Free: 800-755-5200
Fax: (785)242-7429
E-mail: june.unrein@ottawa.edu
Web Site: www.ottawa.edu/
Description: Independent American Baptist Churches in the USA, comprehensive, coed. Awards bachelor's and master's degrees (also offers master's, adult, international and on-line education programs with significant enrollment not reflected in profile). Founded 1865. Setting: 64-acre small town campus with easy access to Kansas City. Endowment: $15.9 million. Educational spending for the previous fiscal year: $5087 per student. Total enrollment: 531. Faculty: 36 (25 full-time, 11 part-time). Student-undergrad faculty ratio is 18:1. 1,419 applied, 70% were admitted. 12% from top 10% of their high school class, 36% from top quarter, 77% from top half. Full-time: 511 students, 48% women, 52% men. Part-time: 20 students, 50% women, 50% men. Students come from 19 states and territories, 4 other countries, 41% from out-of-state. 15% 25 or older, 63% live on campus, 9% transferred in. Retention: 51% of full-time freshmen returned the following year. Academic areas with the most degrees conferred: business/marketing; parks and recreation; communication/journalism; education. Core. Calendar: semesters. Advanced placement, self-designed majors, independent study, distance learning, double major, summer session for credit, part-time degree program, internships. Study abroad program.
Entrance Requirements: Options: electronic application, international baccalaureate accepted. Required: high school transcript, minimum 2.5 high school GPA, rank in upper 50% of high school class, SAT or ACT. Recommended: 2 recommendations, interview. Required for some: essay.

Entrance: moderately difficult. Application deadline: Rolling. Notification: continuous. Transfer credits accepted: Yes.
Collegiate Environment: Orientation program. Drama-theater group, choral group, student-run newspaper, radio station. Social organizations: 20 open to all; Greek Life social clubs. Most popular organizations: Christian Faith In Action, Student Activities Force, Education Club, Whole Earth Club, Fellowship of Christian Athletes. Major annual events: Welcome Week, Casino Night, Late Night Finals Breakfast. Student services: health clinic, personal-psychological counseling. Campus security: 24-hour emergency response devices and patrols, controlled dormitory access, locked residence hall entrances. Myers Library with 82,069 books, 18,483 microform titles, 107 serials, 659 audiovisual materials, an OPAC, and a Web page. Operations spending for the previous fiscal year: $240,142. 40 computers available on campus for general student use. Computer purchase/lease plans available. A campuswide network can be accessed from student residence rooms and from off campus. Students can access the following: online class registration. Staffed computer lab on campus provides training in use of computers and the Internet.
Community Environment: The city is named for the Indians who established a new reservation here in 1834. Pomona Dam and Reservoir, fifteen miles northwest, provides facilities for picnicking, camping, trailering, swimming, boating, fishing and hunting. Forest Park on the Marais des Cygnes River provides additional outdoor recreational facilities. Community facilities include libraries, municipal airport and trains and buses for transportation. Other cultural and recreational activities are enjoyed in Kansas City, which is an hour's drive away.

■ **PITTSBURG STATE UNIVERSITY**
1701 S Broadway
Pittsburg, KS 66762
Tel: (620)231-7000; Free: 800-854-7488
Fax: (620)235-4080
E-mail: psuadmit@pittstate.edu
Web Site: www.pittstate.edu/
Description: State-supported, comprehensive, coed. Part of Kansas State Board of Regents. Awards associate, bachelor's, and master's degrees and post-master's certificates. Founded 1903. Setting: 630-acre small town campus. Endowment: $57.2 million. Research spending for the previous fiscal year: $1.7 million. Educational spending for the previous fiscal year: $4985 per student. Total enrollment: 7,107. Faculty: 411 (313 full-time, 98 part-time). 2,771 applied, 79% were admitted. 13% from top 10% of their high school class, 32% from top quarter, 66% from top half. 53 valedictorians. Full-time: 5,256 students, 48% women, 52% men. Part-time: 728 students, 46% women, 54% men. Students come from 39 states and territories, 41 other countries, 26% from out-of-state. 2% American Indian or Alaska Native, non-Hispanic/Latino; 4% Hispanic/Latino; 3% African American, non-Hispanic/Latino; 1% Asian, non-Hispanic/Latino; 0.2% Native Hawaiian or other Pacific Islander, non-Hispanic/Latino; 5% international. 17% 25 or older, 18% live on campus, 9% transferred in. Retention: 69% of full-time freshmen returned the following year. Academic areas with the most degrees conferred: engineering technologies; business/marketing; education. Core. Calendar: semesters. Academic remediation for entering students, ESL program, services for LD students, advanced placement, self-designed majors, freshman honors college, honors program, independent study, distance learning, double major, summer session for credit, part-time degree program, adult/continuing education programs, co-op programs and internships, graduate courses open to undergrads. Off campus study at Southside Education Center, Wichita, KS, Kansas City Metro Center, Lenexa, KS. Study abroad program. ROTC: Army.
Entrance Requirements: Options: electronic application, deferred admission, international baccalaureate accepted. Required: high school transcript, ACT. Required for some: minimum 2 high school GPA. Entrance: minimally difficult. Application deadline: Rolling. Transfer credits accepted: Yes.
Costs Per Year: Application fee: $30. State resident tuition: $5494 full-time. Nonresident tuition: $15,050 full-time. College room and board: $6758. Room and board charges vary according to board plan and housing facility.
Collegiate Environment: Orientation program. Drama-theater group, choral group, marching band, student-run newspaper, radio station. Social organizations: 150 open to all; national fraternities, national sororities; 7% of eligible men and 8% of eligible women are members. Most popular organizations: Student Government Association, student yearbook, student newspaper, Student Activities Council, Students in Free Enterprise (SIFE). Major annual events: Homecoming, Family Day, Visit the Campus Day. Student services: legal services, health clinic, personal-psychological

counseling. Campus security: 24-hour emergency response devices and patrols, controlled dormitory access. 1,283 college housing spaces available; 1,259 were occupied in 2012-13. Freshmen given priority for college housing. On-campus residence required in freshman year. Option: coed housing available. Leonard H. Axe Library plus 2 others with 712,681 books, 100,614 microform titles, 35,360 serials, 10,151 audiovisual materials, an OPAC, and a Web page. Operations spending for the previous fiscal year: $2.3 million. 425 computers available on campus for general student use. A campuswide network can be accessed from student residence rooms and from off campus. Students can access the following: online class registration. Staffed computer lab on campus provides training in use of computers.

Community Environment: Pittsburg is the largest city in southeast Kansas. It is widely known for its fine homes, large churches, excellent schools, and many municipal facilities. Much of the coal mining in Kansas was done in this area. Some of the abandoned open pits have been flooded and stocked for fishing, swimming, boating, and water skiing. Other recreational activities within the city are bowling, tennis, and golf. Part-time employment opportunities are good.

■ **PRATT COMMUNITY COLLEGE**
348 NE State Rd. 61
Pratt, KS 67124-8317
Tel: (620)672-9800
Fax: (620)672-5288
E-mail: theresaz@prattcc.edu
Web Site: www.prattcc.edu/
Description: State and locally supported, 2-year, coed. Part of Kansas State Board of Education. Awards certificates, transfer associate, and terminal associate degrees. Founded 1938. Setting: 80-acre rural campus with easy access to Wichita. Endowment: $3 million. Educational spending for the previous fiscal year: $3481 per student. Total enrollment: 1,664. Faculty: 45. Student-undergrad faculty ratio is 15:1. Full-time: 751 students, 48% women, 52% men. Part-time: 913 students, 59% women, 41% men. Students come from 32 states and territories, 14 other countries, 14% from out-of-state. 20% 25 or older, 35% live on campus, 8% transferred in. Retention: 60% of full-time freshmen returned the following year. Core. Calendar: semesters. Academic remediation for entering students, advanced placement, distance learning, summer session for credit, part-time degree program, adult/continuing education programs, co-op programs and internships.
Entrance Requirements: Open admission. Options: electronic application, early admission. Required: high school transcript. Required for some: AS-SET. Entrance: noncompetitive. Application deadline: Rolling. Transfer credits accepted: Yes.
Collegiate Environment: Drama-theater group, choral group, student-run newspaper. Social organizations: 14 open to all. Most popular organizations: Phi Theta Kappa, Rotaract, Christian Challenge, Block and Bridle, Kappa Beta Delta. Major annual events: Mr. Cinderfella, Beaver Fever Week, Rodeo Week. Student services: health clinic, personal-psychological counseling. Campus security: 24-hour patrols, late night transport-escort service, controlled dormitory access. The Linda Hunt Memorial Library with 28,700 books, 78 serials, 1,849 audiovisual materials, an OPAC, and a Web page. Operations spending for the previous fiscal year: $139,228. 120 computers available on campus for general student use. A campuswide network can be accessed from off-campus. Students can access the following: online class registration. Staffed computer lab on campus provides training in use of computers, software, and the Internet.

■ **SEWARD COUNTY COMMUNITY COLLEGE AND AREA TECHNICAL SCHOOL**
PO Box 1137
Liberal, KS 67905-1137
Tel: (620)624-1951; Free: 800-373-9951
Fax: (620)629-2725
Web Site: www.sccc.edu/
Description: State and locally supported, 2-year, coed. Part of Kansas State Board of Regents. Awards certificates, diplomas, transfer associate, and terminal associate degrees. Founded 1969. Setting: 120-acre rural campus. Total enrollment: 1,656. 39% 25 or older. Core. Calendar: semesters. Academic remediation for entering students, ESL program, self-designed majors, distance learning, summer session for credit, part-time degree program, external degree program, adult/continuing education programs, co-op programs and internships.
Entrance Requirements: Open admission. Options: early admission, deferred admission. Required: high school transcript. Required for some:

minimum 2.0 high school GPA, 1 recommendation, interview. Entrance: noncompetitive. Application deadline: 8/15. Notification: continuous.
Collegiate Environment: Orientation program. Drama-theater group, choral group, student-run newspaper. Campus security: 24-hour patrols, late night transport-escort service. Learning Resource Center plus 1 other with 32,926 books and 318 serials.
Community Environment: Liberal is the county seat of Seward County. Oil discoveries have added significantly to the economic importance of Liberal. Southwestern Kansas is rich in wheat, oil and gas, and growing agri-related industries such as cattle/swine feed operations and meat packing. Part time employment is available. All forms of commercial transportation are available. A golf course, parks and swimming pools are some of the recreational facilities. Shopping facilities are excellent.

■ **SOUTHWESTERN COLLEGE**
100 College St.
Winfield, KS 67156-2499
Tel: (620)229-6000; Free: 800-846-1543
Fax: (620)229-6224
E-mail: scadmit@sckans.edu
Web Site: www.sckans.edu/
Description: Independent United Methodist, comprehensive, coed. Awards bachelor's and master's degrees and post-master's certificates. Founded 1885. Setting: 70-acre small town campus with easy access to Wichita. Endowment: $19.9 million. Educational spending for the previous fiscal year: $4843 per student. Total enrollment: 1,637. Faculty: 119 (45 full-time, 74 part-time). Student-undergrad faculty ratio is 12:1. 339 applied, 88% were admitted. 21% from top 10% of their high school class, 44% from top quarter, 83% from top half. 8 valedictorians. Full-time: 523 students, 53% women, 47% men. Part-time: 781 students, 40% women, 60% men. Students come from 47 states and territories, 9 other countries, 37% from out-of-state. 2% American Indian or Alaska Native, non-Hispanic/Latino; 7% Hispanic/Latino; 10% African American, non-Hispanic/Latino; 1% Asian, non-Hispanic/Latino; 0.1% Native Hawaiian or other Pacific Islander, non-Hispanic/Latino; 2% international. 5% 25 or older, 72% live on campus, 4% transferred in. Retention: 60% of full-time freshmen returned the following year. Academic areas with the most degrees conferred: business/marketing; education; computer and information sciences. Core. Calendar: semesters. Advanced placement, accelerated degree program, self-designed majors, honors program, independent study, distance learning, double major, summer session for credit, part-time degree program, adult/continuing education programs, internships. Off campus study at Urban Life Center, Chicago; Washington Internship Institute, Washington, DC. Study abroad program.
Entrance Requirements: Options: electronic application, international baccalaureate accepted. Required: high school transcript, minimum 2.5 high school GPA, SAT or ACT. Recommended: essay. Required for some: 2 recommendations, interview. Entrance: minimally difficult. Application deadlines: 8/1, 8/1 for nonresidents. Notification: continuous, continuous for nonresidents. SAT Reasoning Test deadline: 8/25. SAT Subject Test deadline: 8/25. Transfer credits accepted: Yes.
Costs Per Year: Application fee: $25. Comprehensive fee: $30,522 includes full-time tuition ($23,736), mandatory fees ($150), and college room and board ($6636). College room only: $3000. Full-time tuition and fees vary according to class time, course load, degree level, location, and program. Room and board charges vary according to board plan and housing facility. Part-time tuition: $989 per credit hour. Part-time tuition varies according to class time, course load, degree level, location, and program.
Collegiate Environment: Orientation program. Drama-theater group, choral group, student-run newspaper, radio station. Social organizations: 20 open to all; national fraternities, national sororities, local fraternities, local sororities. Most popular organizations: Discipleship SC, Leadership SC, Acappella Choir, Concert Band, Southwestern Singers. Major annual events: Homecoming, Moundbuilding Ceremony, Stau Bau. Student services: health clinic, personal-psychological counseling. Campus security: 24-hour emergency response devices and patrols, late night transport-escort service, controlled dormitory access. 625 college housing spaces available; 371 were occupied in 2012-13. Freshmen guaranteed college housing. On-campus residence required through sophomore year. Options: coed, men-only, women-only housing available. Harold and Mary Ellen Deets Library plus 1 other with 58,146 books, 192 microform titles, 21,638 serials, 9,758 audiovisual materials, an OPAC, and a Web page. 15 computers available on campus for general student use. A computer is required for all students. A campuswide network can be accessed from student residence rooms and

from off campus. Students can access the following: online class registration. Staffed computer lab on campus provides training in use of computers, software, and the Internet.

■ STERLING COLLEGE
125 W Cooper
Sterling, KS 67579-0098
Tel: (620)278-2173; Free: 800-346-1017
Fax: (620)278-3690
E-mail: admissions@sterling.edu
Web Site: www.sterling.edu/

Description: Independent Presbyterian, 4-year, coed. Awards bachelor's degrees. Founded 1887. Setting: 46-acre rural campus. Endowment: $13.3 million. Educational spending for the previous fiscal year: $4679 per student. Total enrollment: 653. Faculty: 63 (40 full-time, 23 part-time). Student-undergrad faculty ratio is 12:1. 806 applied, 51% were admitted. 15% from top 10% of their high school class, 36% from top quarter, 69% from top half. 6 valedictorians. Full-time: 577 students, 44% women, 56% men. Part-time: 76 students, 51% women, 49% men. Students come from 36 states and territories, 2 other countries, 47% from out-of-state. 2% American Indian or Alaska Native, non-Hispanic/Latino; 6% Hispanic/Latino; 9% African American, non-Hispanic/Latino; 0% Asian, non-Hispanic/Latino; 2% Native Hawaiian or other Pacific Islander, non-Hispanic/Latino; 0.5% international. 7% 25 or older, 76% live on campus, 9% transferred in. Retention: 55% of full-time freshmen returned the following year. Academic areas with the most degrees conferred: education; parks and recreation; business/marketing. Core. Calendar: 4-1-4. Services for LD students, advanced placement, self-designed majors, honors program, independent study, distance learning, double major, summer session for credit, internships. Off campus study at 6 members of the Associated Colleges of Central Kansas. Study abroad program.

Entrance Requirements: Options: electronic application, deferred admission. Required: high school transcript, minimum 2.2 high school GPA, SAT or ACT. Recommended: essay, interview. Required for some: 2 recommendations. Entrance: minimally difficult. Application deadline: Rolling. Notification: continuous. SAT Reasoning Test deadline: 8/1. SAT Subject Test deadline: 8/1. Transfer credits accepted: Yes.

Costs Per Year: Application fee: $25. Comprehensive fee: $28,722 includes full-time tuition ($20,950), mandatory fees ($250), and college room and board ($7520). Room and board charges vary according to board plan and housing facility. Part-time tuition: $392 per credit hour.

Collegiate Environment: Orientation program. Drama-theater group, choral group, student-run newspaper, radio station. Social organizations: 18 open to all. Most popular organizations: Fellowship of Christian Athletes, Student Activities Council, Bible study groups, theatre, Mission teams. Major annual events: Homecoming, Last Blast-End of Year outdoor party, Convocations. Student services: health clinic, personal-psychological counseling. Campus security: controlled dormitory access, late night security patrol. 580 college housing spaces available; 497 were occupied in 2012-13. Freshmen guaranteed college housing. On-campus residence required through senior year. Options: men-only, women-only housing available. Mabee Library with 103,284 books, 1,767 microform titles, 105 serials, 1,416 audiovisual materials, an OPAC, and a Web page. Operations spending for the previous fiscal year: $151,795. 50 computers available on campus for general student use. A campuswide network can be accessed from student residence rooms and from off campus. Students can access the following: online class registration. Staffed computer lab on campus.

Community Environment: Sterling is in a rich wheat-growing, oil producing area with community facilities that include churches, Medical Center and many businesses. Opportunities for part time work are good. Train and bus service are available as well as an airport in Hutchinson, 25 miles away. Recreational activities are baseball, fishing, picnicking, and swimming at the municipal lake and college swimming pool.

■ TABOR COLLEGE
400 S Jefferson
Hillsboro, KS 67063
Tel: (620)947-3121; Free: 800-822-6799
Fax: (620)947-2607
E-mail: leew@tabor.edu
Web Site: www.tabor.edu/

Description: Independent Mennonite Brethren, comprehensive, coed. Awards associate, bachelor's, and master's degrees. Founded 1908. Setting: 87-acre small town campus with easy access to Wichita. Endowment:

$6.1 million. Educational spending for the previous fiscal year: $4857 per student. Total enrollment: 768. Faculty: 75 (36 full-time, 39 part-time). Student-undergrad faculty ratio is 16:1. 367 applied, 85% were admitted. 12% from top 10% of their high school class, 26% from top quarter, 28% from top half. 10 valedictorians. Full-time: 580 students, 39% women, 61% men. Part-time: 180 students, 77% women, 23% men. Students come from 31 states and territories, 7 other countries, 52% from out-of-state. 1% American Indian or Alaska Native, non-Hispanic/Latino; 9% Hispanic/Latino; 7% African American, non-Hispanic/Latino; 1% Asian, non-Hispanic/Latino; 1% Native Hawaiian or other Pacific Islander, non-Hispanic/Latino; 1% international. 4% 25 or older, 86% live on campus, 9% transferred in. Retention: 56% of full-time freshmen returned the following year. Academic areas with the most degrees conferred: health professions and related sciences; education; visual and performing arts. Core. Calendar: 4-1-4. Academic remediation for entering students, services for LD students, advanced placement, accelerated degree program, self-designed majors, honors program, independent study, distance learning, double major, part-time degree program, adult/continuing education programs, co-op programs and internships. Off campus study at Associated Colleges of Central Kansas, Focus on the Family Institute, Au Sable Institute, American Studies Program, Contemporary Music Center, Los Angeles Film Studies Center, Washington Journalism Center. Study abroad program.

Entrance Requirements: Options: electronic application, early admission, deferred admission, international baccalaureate accepted. Required: essay, high school transcript, minimum 2 high school GPA, SAT or ACT. Recommended: interview. Required for some: 1 recommendation. Entrance: moderately difficult. Application deadlines: Rolling, Rolling for nonresidents. SAT Reasoning Test deadline: 8/1. Transfer credits accepted: Yes.

Costs Per Year: Application fee: $30. One-time mandatory fee: $175. Comprehensive fee: $29,860 includes full-time tuition ($21,160), mandatory fees ($580), and college room and board ($8120). College room only: $3220. Full-time tuition and fees vary according to course load. Room and board charges vary according to board plan, housing facility, and location. Part-time tuition: $440 per credit hour. Part-time mandatory fees: $15 per credit hour, $140 per term. Part-time tuition and fees vary according to course load.

Collegiate Environment: Orientation program. Drama-theater group, choral group, student-run newspaper. Social organizations: 8 open to all. Most popular organizations: Student Activities Board, Campus Ministries Council, Multi-Cultural Student Union, Business Club, Science Club. Major annual events: Homecoming, Sadie Hawkins Weekend, Christmas Banquet. Student services: personal-psychological counseling. Campus security: Emergency Alert System. 586 college housing spaces available; 505 were occupied in 2012-13. Freshmen guaranteed college housing. On-campus residence required through senior year. Options: men-only, women-only housing available. Tabor College Library with 76,093 books, 436 microform titles, 145 serials, 3,901 audiovisual materials, an OPAC, and a Web page. Operations spending for the previous fiscal year: $245,783. 40 computers available on campus for general student use. A campuswide network can be accessed. Students can access the following: online class registration.

Community Environment: Situated in the wheat and dairy area of central Kansas, Hillsboro is the leading trade center of western Marion County. Community facilities include a hospital, park, swimming pool and golf course.

■ THE UNIVERSITY OF KANSAS
Lawrence, KS 66045
Tel: (785)864-2700
Fax: (785)864-5006
E-mail: adm@ku.edu
Web Site: www.ku.edu/

Description: State-supported, university, coed. Part of Kansas Board of Regents System. Awards bachelor's, master's, and doctoral degrees (University of Kansas is a single institution with academic programs and facilities at two primary locations: Lawrence and Kansas City). Founded 1866. Setting: 1,000-acre suburban campus with easy access to Kansas City. Endowment: $1.6 billion. Research spending for the previous fiscal year: $277 million. Total enrollment: 27,135. Faculty: 1,722 (1,324 full-time, 398 part-time). Student-undergrad faculty ratio is 19:1. 12,389 applied, 92% were admitted. 26% from top 10% of their high school class, 57% from top quarter, 88% from top half. 37 National Merit Scholars. Full-time: 17,130 students, 50% women, 50% men. Part-time: 2,039 students, 47% women, 53% men. Students come from 52 states and territories, 76 other countries, 22% from out-of-state. 1% American Indian or Alaska Native, non-Hispanic/Latino; 6% Hispanic/Latino; 4% African American, non-Hispanic/Latino; 4%

Asian, non-Hispanic/Latino; 0.1% Native Hawaiian or other Pacific Islander, non-Hispanic/Latino; 5% international. 10% 25 or older, 24% live on campus, 7% transferred in. Retention: 79% of full-time freshmen returned the following year. Academic areas with the most degrees conferred: business/marketing; communication/journalism; health professions and related sciences. Core. Calendar: semesters. Academic remediation for entering students, ESL program, services for LD students, advanced placement, accelerated degree program, honors program, independent study, distance learning, double major, summer session for credit, part-time degree program, co-op programs and internships, graduate courses open to undergrads. Study abroad program. ROTC: Army, Naval, Air Force.

Entrance Requirements: Options: electronic application, international baccalaureate accepted. Required: high school transcript, minimum 2 high school GPA, Kansas Board of Regents admissions criteria, SAT or ACT. Required for some: minimum 2.5 high school GPA. Entrance: moderately difficult. Application deadlines: 4/1, 4/1 for nonresidents. Notification: continuous, continuous for nonresidents. SAT Reasoning Test deadline: 5/1. Transfer credits accepted: Yes.

Costs Per Year: Application fee: $30. State resident tuition: $8790 full-time, $293 per credit hour part-time. Nonresident tuition: $22,860 full-time, $762 per credit hour part-time. Mandatory fees: $888 full-time, $74 per credit hour part-time, $74. Full-time tuition and fees vary according to program, reciprocity agreements, and student level. Part-time tuition and fees vary according to program, reciprocity agreements, and student level. College room and board: $7258. College room only: $3804. Room and board charges vary according to board plan and housing facility. Tuition guaranteed not to increase for student's term of enrollment.

Collegiate Environment: Orientation program. Drama-theater group, choral group, marching band, student-run newspaper, radio station. Social organizations: 579 open to all; national fraternities, national sororities; 14% of eligible men and 20% of eligible women are members. Most popular organizations: Hillel, National Society of Collegiate Scholars, International Student Association, Panhellenic Association, Chinese Students & Scholars Friendship Association. Major annual events: Homecoming, Graduation, home football games. Student services: legal services, health clinic, personal-psychological counseling, women's center. Campus security: 24-hour emergency response devices and patrols, late night transport-escort service, controlled dormitory access, University police department. 5,332 college housing spaces available; 4,538 were occupied in 2012-13. No special consideration for freshman housing applicants. Options: coed, women-only housing available. Watson Library plus 11 others with 5.3 million books, an OPAC, and a Web page. Operations spending for the previous fiscal year: $23.3 million. 1,500 computers available on campus for general student use. A campuswide network can be accessed from student residence rooms and from off campus. Students can access the following: online class registration. Staffed computer lab on campus (open 24 hours a day) provides training in use of computers, software, and the Internet.

Community Environment: Lawrence, a town about 70,000, is set among the rolling hills of northeast Kansas. The cosmopolitan quality of the campus extends to the community, making a wide variety of cultural, ethnic, and recreational opportunities available to university students. Lawrence offers shopping areas, restaurants, entertainment, and recreational facilities that are either within easy walking distance of the campus or served by the university bus service. Near Lawrence there are several lakes for boating, fishing, and swimming. Metropolitan Kansas City, with its professional sports, ballet, opera, concerts, night spots, galleries, museums, festivals, and international airport, is about 40 miles east of Lawrence. Topeka, the state capital, is 30 miles west.

■ UNIVERSITY OF PHOENIX–WICHITA CAMPUS
3020 N Cypress Dr., Ste. 150
Wichita, KS 67226-4011
Tel: (316)630-8121; Free: 866-766-0766
Web Site: www.phoenix.edu/

Description: Proprietary, comprehensive, coed. Awards bachelor's and master's degrees. Founded 2003. Setting: urban campus. Total enrollment: 135. Faculty: 49 (4 full-time, 45 part-time). Full-time: 125 students, 57% women, 43% men. 1% from out-of-state. 82% 25 or older. Academic areas with the most degrees conferred: computer and information sciences; business/marketing; health professions and related sciences. Core. Calendar: continuous. Services for LD students, advanced placement, accelerated degree program, independent study, distance learning, graduate courses open to undergrads.

Entrance Requirements: Open admission. Options: electronic application,

deferred admission, international baccalaureate accepted. Required: 1 recommendation. Required for some: high school transcript. Entrance: noncompetitive. Application deadline: Rolling.

Collegiate Environment: Campus security: late night transport-escort service.

■ UNIVERSITY OF SAINT MARY
4100 S Fourth St. Trafficway
Leavenworth, KS 66048-5082
Tel: (913)682-5151; Free: 800-752-7043
Fax: (913)758-6140
E-mail: admiss@stmary.edu
Web Site: www.stmary.edu/

Description: Independent Roman Catholic, comprehensive, coed. Awards associate, bachelor's, master's, and doctoral degrees. Founded 1923. Setting: 240-acre small town campus with easy access to Kansas City. Endowment: $15.6 million. Educational spending for the previous fiscal year: $6467 per student. Total enrollment: 1,044. Faculty: 148 (50 full-time, 98 part-time). Student-undergrad faculty ratio is 10:1. 733 applied, 47% were admitted. 14% from top 10% of their high school class, 39% from top quarter, 80% from top half. Full-time: 544 students, 57% women, 43% men. Part-time: 272 students, 78% women, 22% men. Students come from 25 states and territories, 4 other countries, 40% from out-of-state. 1% American Indian or Alaska Native, non-Hispanic/Latino; 6% Hispanic/Latino; 14% African American, non-Hispanic/Latino; 2% Asian, non-Hispanic/Latino; 0.3% Native Hawaiian or other Pacific Islander, non-Hispanic/Latino; 1% international. 29% 25 or older, 40% live on campus, 10% transferred in. Retention: 64% of full-time freshmen returned the following year. Academic areas with the most degrees conferred: health professions and related sciences; psychology; social sciences. Core. Calendar: semesters. Academic remediation for entering students, services for LD students, advanced placement, self-designed majors, honors program, independent study, distance learning, double major, summer session for credit, part-time degree program, adult/continuing education programs, co-op programs and internships, graduate courses open to undergrads. Off campus study at University of Kansas, members of the Council of Independent Colleges. Study abroad program. ROTC: Army (c), Air Force (c).

Entrance Requirements: Options: electronic application, international baccalaureate accepted. Required: high school transcript, minimum 2.5 high school GPA, SAT or ACT. Recommended: 1 recommendation, interview. Entrance: moderately difficult. Application deadline: Rolling. Notification: continuous. SAT Reasoning Test deadline: 9/1. SAT Subject Test deadline: 9/1. Transfer credits accepted: Yes.

Costs Per Year: Application fee: $25. Comprehensive fee: $29,230 includes full-time tuition ($21,500), mandatory fees ($480), and college room and board ($7250). Full-time tuition and fees vary according to class time, course load, location, and program. Room and board charges vary according to board plan and housing facility. Part-time tuition: $410 per credit. Part-time mandatory fees: $115 per term. Part-time tuition and fees vary according to class time, course load, location, and program.

Collegiate Environment: Orientation program. Drama-theater group, choral group. Social organizations: 25 open to all. Most popular organizations: Student Government Association, BACCHUS, Theatrical Union, campus ministry, Amnesty International. Major annual events: Family Weekend, Heritage Day, Spring Honors Convocation. Student services: personal-psychological counseling. Campus security: 24-hour patrols, late night transport-escort service, controlled dormitory access. 325 college housing spaces available; 227 were occupied in 2012-13. Freshmen guaranteed college housing. On-campus residence required through sophomore year. Option: coed housing available. De Paul Library with 119,545 books, 1 microform title, 124 serials, 4 audiovisual materials, an OPAC, and a Web page. Operations spending for the previous fiscal year: $170,634. 45 computers available on campus for general student use. A campuswide network can be accessed from student residence rooms. Students can access the following: online class registration.

Community Environment: Leavenworth is 26 miles northwest of Kansas City, which contributes to the economic and recreational interest of the community.

■ WASHBURN UNIVERSITY
1700 SW College Ave.
Topeka, KS 66621
Tel: (785)670-1010; Free: 800-332-0291
Fax: (785)231-1089

E-mail: admissions@washburn.edu
Web Site: www.washburn.edu/

Description: City-supported, comprehensive, coed. Awards associate, bachelor's, master's, and doctoral degrees. Founded 1865. Setting: 160-acre urban campus with easy access to Kansas City. Endowment: $120 million. Research spending for the previous fiscal year: $217,296. Total enrollment: 7,204. Faculty: 555 (273 full-time, 282 part-time). Student-undergrad faculty ratio is 15:1. 1,916 applied, 96% were admitted. 16% from top 10% of their high school class, 37% from top quarter, 67% from top half. 30 valedictorians. Full-time: 4,213 students, 58% women, 42% men. Part-time: 2,176 students, 62% women, 38% men. Students come from 43 states and territories, 37 other countries, 7% from out-of-state. 32% 25 or older, 14% live on campus, 9% transferred in. Retention: 67% of full-time freshmen returned the following year. Academic areas with the most degrees conferred: health professions and related sciences; business/marketing; education. Core. Calendar: semesters. Academic remediation for entering students, ESL program, services for LD students, advanced placement, self-designed majors, honors program, independent study, distance learning, double major, summer session for credit, part-time degree program, adult/continuing education programs, co-op programs and internships, graduate courses open to undergrads. Off campus study at PLAN 2+2 (Partner Institutions). Study abroad program. ROTC: Army, Naval (c), Air Force (c).

Entrance Requirements: Open admission Selected admission to some programs. Option: electronic application. Required: high school transcript, ACT. Entrance: noncompetitive. Application deadline: 8/1. Notification: continuous. SAT Reasoning Test deadline: 8/1. Transfer credits accepted: Yes.

Costs Per Year: Application fee: $20. State resident tuition: $5400 full-time, $225 per credit hour part-time. Nonresident tuition: $12,216 full-time, $509 per credit hour part-time. Mandatory fees: $86 full-time, $21 per term part-time. Full-time tuition and fees vary according to program. Part-time tuition and fees vary according to program. College room and board: $6216. College room only: $3501. Room and board charges vary according to board plan and housing facility.

Collegiate Environment: Orientation program. Drama-theater group, choral group, marching band, student-run newspaper. Social organizations: 122 open to all; national fraternities, national sororities, local fraternities; 6% of eligible men and 6% of eligible women are members. Major annual events: Theatre, Family Day, Homecoming. Student services: legal services, health clinic, personal-psychological counseling. Campus security: 24-hour emergency response devices and patrols, student patrols, late night transport-escort service. 674 college housing spaces available; 654 were occupied in 2012-13. No special consideration for freshman housing applicants. Option: coed housing available. Mabee Library plus 1 other with 467,524 books, 92,066 microform titles, 42,657 serials, 4,342 audiovisual materials, an OPAC, and a Web page. 560 computers available on campus for general student use. A campuswide network can be accessed from student residence rooms and from off campus. Students can access the following: online class registration. Staffed computer lab on campus provides training in use of computers, software, and the Internet.

Community Environment: Topeka, the state capital of Kansas, is situated on the edge of the wheat belt approximately 60 miles from Kansas City. The leading industries are meat packing, tire manufacturing, grain milling, printing and publishing, and the manufacture of steel products. Excellent community facilities include libraries, museums, many churches, and outstanding medical facilities. The Topeka Civic Theatre and Topeka Community Concert group provide the citizens with unusual cultural activities. Lake Shawnee is a popular recreation spot; Gage Park is a beautiful park within the city that has the finest facilities for picnicking and swimming, as well as lovely rose gardens. All major forms of commercial transportation are available. The Menninger Clinic located here is one of the world's largest psychiatric research and training centers.

■ **WICHITA AREA TECHNICAL COLLEGE**
301 S Grove St.
Wichita, KS 67211
Tel: (316)677-9282
E-mail: info@watc.edu
Web Site: www.wichitatech.com/

Description: District-supported, 2-year, coed. Awards certificates, diplomas, transfer associate, and terminal associate degrees. Founded 1963. Setting: urban campus. Total enrollment: 2,116. Student-undergrad faculty ratio is 13:1. 0% from out-of-state. 59% 25 or older. Retention: 72% of full-time freshmen returned the following year. Calendar: semesters. Academic remediation for entering students, part-time degree program, internships.

Entrance Requirements: Required for some: high school transcript, WorkKeys, COMPASS and TEAS. Entrance: minimally difficult. Application deadline: Rolling.

Costs Per Year: State resident tuition: $1860 full-time, $62 per credit hour part-time. Nonresident tuition: $2232 full-time, $75 per credit hour part-time. Mandatory fees: $860 full-time, $28 per credit hour part-time. Full-time tuition and fees vary according to location and program. Part-time tuition and fees vary according to location and program.

Collegiate Environment: Campus security: 24-hour emergency response devices. Library and Learning Resource Center with an OPAC and a Web page.

■ **WICHITA STATE UNIVERSITY**
1845 N Fairmount
Wichita, KS 67260
Tel: (316)978-3456; Free: 800-362-2594
Fax: (316)978-3795
E-mail: bobby.gandu@wichita.edu
Web Site: www.wichita.edu/

Description: State-supported, university, coed. Part of Kansas State Board of Education. Awards associate, bachelor's, master's, and doctoral degrees and post-master's certificates. Founded 1895. Setting: 335-acre urban campus. Endowment: $220.1 million. Research spending for the previous fiscal year: $61.6 million. Educational spending for the previous fiscal year: $5405 per student. Total enrollment: 14,893. Faculty: 814 (459 full-time, 355 part-time). Student-undergrad faculty ratio is 20:1. 3,515 applied, 95% were admitted. 22% from top 10% of their high school class, 47% from top quarter, 77% from top half. Full-time: 8,670 students, 53% women, 47% men. Part-time: 3,522 students, 56% women, 44% men. Students come from 47 states and territories, 82 other countries, 4% from out-of-state. 1% American Indian or Alaska Native, non-Hispanic/Latino; 8% Hispanic/Latino; 6% African American, non-Hispanic/Latino; 7% Asian, non-Hispanic/Latino; 0.1% Native Hawaiian or other Pacific Islander, non-Hispanic/Latino; 7% international. 31% 25 or older, 8% live on campus, 11% transferred in. Retention: 70% of full-time freshmen returned the following year. Academic areas with the most degrees conferred: business/marketing; health professions and related sciences; engineering. Core. Calendar: semesters. Academic remediation for entering students, ESL program, services for LD students, advanced placement, accelerated degree program, freshman honors college, honors program, independent study, distance learning, double major, summer session for credit, part-time degree program, co-op programs and internships, graduate courses open to undergrads. Off campus study at National Student Exchange, Student abroad Programs(Pau, France; Feng China University, Taiwan; Sun Ya-Sen University, Guangzhou China; the Berlin School of Economics, Germany; Jonkoping International Business School, Sweden; University of Applied Science, Wiener-Neustadt, Austria; Midwest Student Exchange(Michigan, Minnesota, Missouri; Nebraska, North Dakota, Wisconsin). Study abroad program.

Entrance Requirements: Open admission for state residents who graduated from a Kansas high school before May 2001 or already have a previous bachelor degree. Options: electronic application, deferred admission, international baccalaureate accepted. Recommended: high school transcript, SAT or ACT. Required for some: minimum 2.5 high school GPA, rank in upper one-third of high school class or complete the pre-college curriculum with a minimum 2.0 GPA (2.5 GPA for nonresidents), SAT or ACT. Entrance: noncompetitive. Application deadline: Rolling. Notification: continuous. Transfer credits accepted: Yes.

Costs Per Year: Application fee: $30. State resident tuition: $5205 full-time, $173.50 per credit hour part-time. Nonresident tuition: $13,239 full-time, $441.30 per credit hour part-time. Mandatory fees: $1237 full-time. Full-time tuition and fees vary according to course load, degree level, and student level. Part-time tuition varies according to course load, degree level, and student level. College room and board: $6460. Room and board charges vary according to board plan and housing facility.

Collegiate Environment: Orientation program. Drama-theater group, choral group, student-run newspaper, radio station. Social organizations: 200 open to all; national fraternities, national sororities; 5% of eligible men and 4% of eligible women are members. Most popular organizations: Golden Key Honor Society, WSU Green Group, Criminal Justice Society, Future Health Care Professionals, Students in Free Enterprise (SIFE). Major annual events: Shocktoberfest, Welcome Fest, Convocation. Student services: legal services, health clinic, personal-psychological counseling, women's center. Campus security: 24-hour emergency response devices and patrols, student patrols, late night transport-escort service, controlled dormitory access, bicycle patrols by campus security. 1,453 college housing spaces available; 1,101 were occupied in 2012-13. No special consideration for freshman housing applicants. On-campus residence required in freshman year. Option: coed housing available. Ablah Library plus 2 others with 1.9 million books, 1.2 million microform titles, 61,010 serials, 200,973 audiovisual materials, an OPAC, and a Web page. Operations spending for the previous fiscal year: $328,888. 1,500 computers available on campus for general student use. A campuswide network can be accessed from student residence rooms and from off campus. Students can access the following: online class registration, online Blackboard. Staffed computer lab on campus.

Community Environment: Wichita, population 354,800, is the largest city in Kansas. It is located 161 miles southeast of the center of the U.S. Primary economic factors contributing to the growth and development of the city have been aircraft manufacturing, oil and natural gas, air conditioners, heating and lighting units, as well as camping equipment and agriculture. It is the Aviation Center of the World. WSU is an important resource to the Wichita area business community. The university supports research and develop-

ment through programs such as the Center for Productivity Enhancement and the National Institute for Aviation Research. The corporate community utilizes programs offered by the University's Center for Management for continuing professional development. The Center for Entrepreneurship and Small Business Management encourages development of small businesses, while the Hugo Wall Center for Urban Studies supports local and state government facilities for canoeing, boating, and water skiing. Several theater groups stage productions throughout the year and the Wichita Symphony has provided more than 30 years of professional music. The city's civic and cultural complex offers an outstanding library in addition to a modern convention and performing arts center.

■ **WRIGHT CAREER COLLEGE**
10700 Metcalf Ave.
Overland Park, KS 66210
Tel: (913)385-7700
Web Site: www.wrightcareercollege.com/
Description: Proprietary, 2-year, coed.

■ ALICE LLOYD COLLEGE

100 Purpose Rd.
Pippa Passes, KY 41844
Tel: (606)368-2101; Free: 888-280-4252
Fax: (606)368-2125
E-mail: ronniecollins@alc.edu
Web Site: www.alc.edu/

Description: Independent, 4-year, coed. Awards bachelor's degrees. Founded 1923. Setting: 175-acre rural campus. Endowment: $29 million. Educational spending for the previous fiscal year: $4248 per student. Total enrollment: 608. Faculty: 38 (29 full-time, 9 part-time). Student-undergrad faculty ratio is 18:1. 3,081 applied, 6% were admitted. 14% from top 10% of their high school class, 46% from top quarter, 76% from top half. Full-time: 581 students, 52% women, 48% men. Part-time: 27 students, 56% women, 44% men. Students come from 10 states and territories, 2 other countries, 17% from out-of-state. 0.2% American Indian or Alaska Native, non-Hispanic/Latino; 1% Hispanic/Latino; 1% African American, non-Hispanic/Latino; 0% Asian, non-Hispanic/Latino; 0.2% Native Hawaiian or other Pacific Islander, non-Hispanic/Latino; 0.3% international. 5% 25 or older, 80% live on campus, 6% transferred in. Retention: 54% of full-time freshmen returned the following year. Academic areas with the most degrees conferred: biological/life sciences; education; business/marketing. Core. Calendar: semesters. Academic remediation for entering students, advanced placement, self-designed majors, independent study, double major, part-time degree program, internships.

Entrance Requirements: Option: deferred admission. Required: high school transcript, minimum 2.25 high school GPA, interview, SAT or ACT. Required for some: essay, 2 recommendations. Entrance: moderately difficult. Application deadline: Rolling. Notification: continuous. Applicants placed on waiting list: 0. Wait-listed applicants offered admission: 0.

Costs Per Year: Application fee: $0. Comprehensive fee: $15,240 includes full-time tuition ($8500), mandatory fees ($1600), and college room and board ($5140). College room only: $2470. Full-time tuition and fees vary according to course load, location, and program. Room and board charges vary according to location. Part-time tuition: $212 per credit hour. Part-time tuition varies according to course load and program.

Collegiate Environment: Orientation program. Drama-theater group, choral group, student-run newspaper, radio station. Social organizations: 18 open to all. Most popular organizations: Phi Beta Lambda, ALC Scholastic Society, Math/Science Club, Allied Health Sciences Club, Alpha Chi National Honor Society. Major annual events: Religious Emphasis Week, Alcohol Awareness Week, Appalachia Day Homecoming. Student services: health clinic, personal-psychological counseling. Campus security: 24-hour patrols, late night transport-escort service. 450 college housing spaces available. No special consideration for freshman housing applicants. On-campus residence required through senior year. Options: men-only, women-only housing available. McGaw Library and Learning Center with 72,781 books, 3,512 microform titles, 211 serials, 2,922 audiovisual materials, and an OPAC. Operations spending for the previous fiscal year: $238,585. 85 computers available on campus for general student use. A campuswide network can be accessed from student residence rooms and from off campus. Staffed computer lab on campus.

Community Environment: Located in a small, rural town, the primary industries being coal mining and farming.

■ ASBURY UNIVERSITY

1 Macklem Dr.
Wilmore, KY 40390-1198
Tel: (859)858-3511; Free: 800-888-1818
Fax: (859)858-3921
E-mail: admissions@asbury.edu
Web Site: www.asbury.edu/

Description: Independent nondenominational, comprehensive, coed. Awards associate, bachelor's, and master's degrees. Founded 1890. Setting: 400-acre small town campus with easy access to Lexington. Endowment: $38 million. Educational spending for the previous fiscal year: $7982 per student. Total enrollment: 1,765. Faculty: 187 (86 full-time, 101 part-time). Student-undergrad faculty ratio is 13:1. 1,260 applied, 63% were admitted. 29% from top 10% of their high school class, 56% from top quarter, 83% from top half. Full-time: 1,363 students, 60% women, 40% men. Part-time: 166 students, 66% women, 34% men. Students come from 44 states and territories, 25 other countries, 49% from out-of-state. 0.4% American Indian or Alaska Native, non-Hispanic/Latino; 3% Hispanic/Latino; 3% African American, non-Hispanic/Latino; 0.4% Asian, non-Hispanic/Latino; 0.1% Native Hawaiian or other Pacific Islander, non-Hispanic/Latino; 1% international. 3% 25 or older, 86% live on campus, 3% transferred in. Retention: 84% of full-time freshmen returned the following year. Academic areas with the most degrees conferred: education; communication technologies; parks and recreation; English. Core. Calendar: semesters. Advanced placement, distance learning, double major, summer session for credit, adult/continuing education programs, graduate courses open to undergrads. Off campus study at Consortium of Christian Colleges, Best Semester Programs of the Council for Christian Colleges and Universities, NYCAMS through Bethel University, Focus On The Family Institute, Semester in Spain through Trinity Christian College. Study abroad program. ROTC: Army (c), Air Force (c).

Entrance Requirements: Options: electronic application, early admission, deferred admission, international baccalaureate accepted. Required: essay, high school transcript, minimum 2.5 high school GPA, 1 recommendation, SAT or ACT. Required for some: interview, ACT. Entrance: moderately difficult. Application deadline: Rolling. Notification: continuous. Transfer credits accepted: Yes.

Costs Per Year: Application fee: $0. Comprehensive fee: $32,038 includes full-time tuition ($25,894), mandatory fees ($182), and college room and board ($5962). Full-time tuition and fees vary according to course load, location, and program. Room and board charges vary according to board plan, housing facility, and location. Part-time tuition: $996 per credit. Part-time tuition varies according to course load, location, and program.

Collegiate Environment: Orientation program. Drama-theater group, choral group, student-run newspaper, radio station. Social organizations: 35 open to all. Most popular organizations: Fellowship of Christian Athletes, Impact (community service), Christian Service Association, ministry teams, Student-Faculty Council. Major annual events: Homecoming, Fall Revival, Missions Conference. Student services: health clinic, personal-psychological counseling. Campus security: 24-hour emergency response devices, late night transport-escort service, controlled dormitory access, late night security personnel. 1,168 college housing spaces available; 1,041 were occupied in 2012-13. Freshmen guaranteed college housing. On-campus residence required through senior year. Options: men-only, women-only housing available. Kinlaw Library with 183,785 books, 13,238 microform titles, 299 serials, 7,188 audiovisual materials, and an OPAC. Operations spending for the previous fiscal year: $724,845. 250 computers available on campus for general student use. A campuswide network can be accessed from student residence rooms and from off campus. Students can access the following: online class registration. Staffed computer lab on campus provides training in use of computers, software, and the Internet.

Community Environment: This is rural town with air and bus service available in nearby Lexington, Kentucky. There are several natural and historic points of interest located nearby: High Bridge, Shakertown, Fort Harrod, Boone's Tavern, National Cemetery at Camp Nelson, Kentucky Horse Park, world famous thoroughbred farms and Natural Bridge.

■ ASHLAND COMMUNITY AND TECHNICAL COLLEGE
1400 College Dr.
Ashland, KY 41101-3683
Tel: (606)329-2999; Free: 800-928-4256
Fax: (606)325-8124
E-mail: chandra.kumar@kctcs.edu
Web Site: www.ashland.kctcs.edu/

Description: State-supported, 2-year, coed. Part of Kentucky Community and Technical College System. Awards certificates, diplomas, transfer associate, and terminal associate degrees. Founded 1937. Setting: 47-acre small town campus. Total enrollment: 4,419. Student-undergrad faculty ratio is 17:1. 9% from out-of-state. 37% 25 or older. Core. Calendar: semesters. Academic remediation for entering students, services for LD students, advanced placement, honors program, distance learning, summer session for credit, part-time degree program, adult/continuing education programs, co-op programs and internships. Off campus study at University of Kentucky, other area colleges.

Entrance Requirements: Open admission except for nursing program. Options: early admission, deferred admission. Required: high school transcript. Entrance: noncompetitive. Application deadline: 8/20.

Collegiate Environment: Orientation program. Drama-theater group, choral group, student-run newspaper. Student services: personal-psychological counseling. Campus security: 24-hour emergency response devices and patrols, late night transport-escort service, electronic surveillance of bookstore and business office. Joseph and Sylvia Mansbach Memorial Library with an OPAC.

Community Environment: On the Ohio River, Ashland has a temperate climate with an average annual temperature of 55 degrees. This city has 25 industries including steel, oil refining, a coal and coke-processing plant and a firebrick factory. More than 21 million tons of barge traffic on the river passes the city annually. The Greenup Locks and Dam complex consist of two adjacent chambers which elevate 1,100 foot modern tows in 20 minutes as opposed to the six hours previously required. Transportation is provided by bus and railroad. Part time work is available. City services include a public library, churches of 15 denominations, Y's (no overnight facilities), and hospitals. Recreational facilities easily accessible are indoor theatres, several drive-ins, golf courses, boating, fishing, two state parks, bowling alleys, municipal swimming pool and private swim club, baseball, tennis, and croquet.

■ ATA COLLEGE
10180 Linn Station Rd.
Ste. A200
Louisville, KY 40223
Tel: (502)371-8330
Web Site: www.ata.edu/

Description: Proprietary, 2-year, coed. Awards terminal associate degrees. Total enrollment: 450. Student-undergrad faculty ratio is 14:1. 73 applied, 78% were admitted. 16% from out-of-state. 66% 25 or older. Retention: 74% of full-time freshmen returned the following year.

Entrance Requirements: Open admission.

■ BECKFIELD COLLEGE
16 Spiral Dr.
Florence, KY 41042
Tel: (859)371-9393
Fax: (859)371-5096
E-mail: lboerger@beckfield.edu
Web Site: www.beckfield.edu/

Description: Proprietary, primarily 2-year, coed. Awards certificates, diplomas, terminal associate, and bachelor's degrees. Founded 1984. Setting: suburban campus. Total enrollment: 605. 69% 25 or older.

Entrance Requirements: Open admission.

■ BELLARMINE UNIVERSITY
2001 Newburg Rd.
Louisville, KY 40205-0671
Tel: (502)452-8000; Free: 800-274-4723
Fax: (502)452-8002
E-mail: admissions@bellarmine.edu
Web Site: www.bellarmine.edu/

Description: Independent Roman Catholic, comprehensive, coed. Awards bachelor's, master's, and doctoral degrees. Founded 1950. Setting: 144-acre suburban campus with easy access to Louisville. Total enrollment: 3,602. Faculty: 376 (156 full-time, 220 part-time). Student-undergrad faculty ratio is 12:1. 4,317 applied, 86% were admitted. 21% from top 10% of their high school class, 50% from top quarter, 84% from top half. 12 valedictorians. Full-time: 2,344 students, 63% women, 37% men. Part-time: 386 students, 77% women, 23% men. 33% from out-of-state. 0.2% American Indian or Alaska Native, non-Hispanic/Latino; 4% Hispanic/Latino; 0.2% African American, non-Hispanic/Latino; 4% Asian, non-Hispanic/Latino; 2% Native Hawaiian or other Pacific Islander, non-Hispanic/Latino; 1% international. 9% 25 or older, 44% live on campus, 3% transferred in. Retention: 81% of full-time freshmen returned the following year. Academic areas with the most degrees conferred: health professions and related sciences; business/marketing; psychology. Calendar: semesters. Part-time degree program, adult/continuing education programs. ROTC: Army (c), Air Force (c).

Entrance Requirements: Options: electronic application, early action. Required: high school transcript, minimum 2.5 high school GPA, 1 recommendation, SAT or ACT. Recommended: interview. Required for some: essay. Entrance: moderately difficult. Application deadlines: 8/15, 11/1 for early action. Notification: continuous, 11/15 for early action. SAT Reasoning Test deadline: 8/15. Transfer credits accepted: Yes.

Costs Per Year: Application fee: $25. Comprehensive fee: $42,950 includes full-time tuition ($31,900), mandatory fees ($1280), and college room and board ($9770). College room only: $5990. Room and board charges vary according to board plan and housing facility. Part-time tuition: $755 per credit hour.

Collegiate Environment: Orientation program. Social organizations: 63 open to all. Most popular organizations: student government, Bellarmine Activities Council, Knights Nation, Fellowship of Christian Athletes, Delta Sigma Pi. Major annual events: Ball on the Belle, Homecoming, Late Night Breakfast. Campus security: 24-hour emergency response devices and patrols, student patrols, late night transport-escort service, controlled dormitory access, 24-hour locked residence hall entrances, security cameras. 1,127 college housing spaces available. Freshmen guaranteed college housing. On-campus residence required through junior year. Options: coed, men-only, women-only housing available. W.L. Lyons Brown Library with 136,183 books, 336,315 microform titles, 418 serials, and 5,691 audiovisual materials. Operations spending for the previous fiscal year: $511,880. 434 computers available on campus for general student use. A campuswide network can be accessed from student residence rooms and from off campus. Students can access the following: online class registration. Staffed computer lab on campus provides training in use of computers, software, and the Internet.

■ BEREA COLLEGE
Berea, KY 40404
Tel: (859)985-3000; Free: 800-326-5948
E-mail: admissions@berea.edu
Web Site: www.berea.edu/

Description: Independent, 4-year, coed. Awards bachelor's degrees. Founded 1855. Setting: 140-acre small town campus. Endowment: $978.7 million. Educational spending for the previous fiscal year: $13,078 per student. Total enrollment: 1,658. Faculty: 171 (129 full-time, 42 part-time). Student-undergrad faculty ratio is 11:1. 1,694 applied, 32% were admitted. 29% from top 10% of their high school class, 74% from top quarter, 95% from top half. Full-time: 1,601 students, 57% women, 43% men. Part-time: 57 students, 51% women, 49% men. 56% from out-of-state. 0.3% American Indian or Alaska Native, non-Hispanic/Latino; 4% Hispanic/Latino; 14% African American, non-Hispanic/Latino; 1% Asian, non-Hispanic/Latino; 0% Native Hawaiian or other Pacific Islander, non-Hispanic/Latino; 7% international. 8% 25 or older, 84% live on campus, 3% transferred in. Retention: 82% of full-time freshmen returned the following year. Academic areas with the most degrees conferred: business/marketing; education; visual and performing arts. Core. Calendar: 4-1-4. Academic remediation for entering students, ESL program, services for LD students, advanced placement, self-designed majors, honors program, independent study, double major, summer session for credit, internships. Off campus study. Study abroad program.

Entrance Requirements: Option: electronic application. Required: essay, high school transcript, interview, financial aid application, SAT or ACT. Recommended: 2 recommendations. Entrance: moderately difficult. Application deadline: 4/30. Notification: continuous. Preference given to Appalachian residents with high ability and limited economic resources.

Collegiate Environment: Orientation program. Drama-theater group, choral group, student-run newspaper. Social organizations: 70 open to all. Most popular organizations: Campus Activities Board, Cosmopolitan Club, CELTS (Center for Excellence in Learning through Service), Black Cultural Center, African Student Association. Major annual events: Mountain Day Eve, Graduation, Labor Day. Student services: health clinic, personal-psychological counseling, women's center. Campus security: 24-hour emergency response devices and patrols, late night transport-escort service, controlled dormitory access, crime prevention programs. 1,448 college housing spaces available. Freshmen guaranteed college housing. On-campus residence required through senior year. Options: men-only, women-only housing available. Hutchins Library plus 1 other with 392,752 books, 148,294 microform titles, 1,438 serials, 13,699 audiovisual materials, an OPAC, and a Web page. Operations spending for the previous fiscal year: $931,493.

Community Environment: Nestled in the foothills of the Cumberland Mountains, Berea draws 80% of its students from the Appalachian regions of nine southern states. Excellent motels are found in the community as well as the college hotel. The Churchill Weavers, one of the largest hand-weaving companies in the country, is located here.

■ BIG SANDY COMMUNITY AND TECHNICAL COLLEGE

One Bert T. Combs Dr.
Prestonsburg, KY 41653-1815
Tel: (606)886-3863; Free: 888-641-4132
Fax: (606)886-6943
E-mail: jimmy.wright@kctcs.edu
Web Site: www.bigsandy.kctcs.edu/

Description: State-supported, 2-year, coed. Part of Kentucky Community and Technical College System. Awards transfer associate and terminal associate degrees. Founded 1964. Setting: 50-acre rural campus. Total enrollment: 4,856. 36% 25 or older. Core. Calendar: semesters. Academic remediation for entering students, services for LD students, advanced placement, independent study, distance learning, summer session for credit, part-time degree program, adult/continuing education programs, co-op programs. Off campus study at Morehead State University.

Entrance Requirements: Open admission except for nursing program. Options: early admission, deferred admission. Required: high school transcript. Entrance: noncompetitive. Application deadline: Rolling.

Collegiate Environment: Orientation program. Choral group. Student services: health clinic, personal-psychological counseling. Campus security: 24-hour emergency response devices. Magoffin Learning Resource Center with 34,668 books, 259 serials, and an OPAC.

Community Environment: Prestonsburg is the site of a revolutionary war battle and General Garfield's headquarters in 1862. Surrounding the city are eastern Kentucky's coal, oil and gas fields. The urban area has transportation provided by bus and car. The city has hospitals, churches of all denominations, average shopping facilities, and good opportunities for part-time employment. Recreational facilities are available at a state park with boating, fishing, swimming, water skiing, horseback riding, and high lift. Locally are a public park, bowling alley, golf course, swimming pool and tennis courts. The Kentucky Highland Folk Festival, The Jenny Wiley Festival and Horse Show are annual events.

■ BLUEGRASS COMMUNITY AND TECHNICAL COLLEGE

470 Cooper Dr.
Lexington, KY 40506-0235
Tel: (859)246-0235; Free: 866-744-4872
E-mail: shelbie.hugle@kctcs.edu
Web Site: www.bluegrass.kctcs.edu/

Description: State-supported, 2-year, coed. Part of Kentucky Community and Technical College System. Awards certificates, diplomas, transfer associate, and terminal associate degrees. Founded 1965. Setting: 10-acre urban campus. Endowment: $967,117. Educational spending for the previous fiscal year: $6021 per student. Total enrollment: 11,596. Faculty: 846 (260 full-time, 586 part-time). Student-undergrad faculty ratio is 18:1. Full-time: 5,539 students, 57% women, 43% men. Part-time: 6,057 students,

56% women, 44% men. Students come from 16 states and territories, 26 other countries. 0.3% American Indian or Alaska Native, non-Hispanic/Latino; 3% Hispanic/Latino; 13% African American, non-Hispanic/Latino; 1% Asian, non-Hispanic/Latino; 0.1% Native Hawaiian or other Pacific Islander, non-Hispanic/Latino; 0.5% international. 3% live on campus, 4% transferred in. Core. Calendar: semesters. Academic remediation for entering students, ESL program, services for LD students, advanced placement, accelerated degree program, honors program, distance learning, double major, summer session for credit, part-time degree program, adult/continuing education programs, co-op programs. ROTC: Army (c), Air Force (c).

Entrance Requirements: Open admission. Options: electronic application, early admission. Recommended: high school transcript. Required for some: high school transcript. Entrance: noncompetitive. Application deadline: 8/2. Transfer credits accepted: Yes.

Costs Per Year: Application fee: $20. State resident tuition: $3360 full-time, $140 per credit part-time. Nonresident tuition: $11,760 full-time, $490 per credit part-time. Mandatory fees: $60 full-time, $30 per term part-time.

Collegiate Environment: Orientation program. Drama-theater group, choral group, student-run newspaper. Social organizations: 21 open to all. Most popular organizations: Student Nursing Association, intramural sports, Enlace (Latino Student Association), International Students' Association, Student American Dental Hygienists Association. Major annual events: Spring Fling, Fall Fest, Welcome Back Ice Cream Special. Student services: personal-psychological counseling. Campus security: 24-hour emergency response devices and patrols, late night transport-escort service. Bluegrass Community and Technical College Library with 27,000 books, 250 serials, an OPAC, and a Web page. Operations spending for the previous fiscal year: $185,767. 300 computers available on campus for general student use. A campuswide network can be accessed. Students can access the following: online class registration. Staffed computer lab on campus provides training in use of computers, software, and the Internet.

■ BRESCIA UNIVERSITY

717 Frederica St.
Owensboro, KY 42301-3023
Tel: (270)685-3131; Free: 877-273-7242
Fax: (270)686-6422
E-mail: admissions@brescia.edu
Web Site: www.brescia.edu/

Description: Independent Roman Catholic, comprehensive, coed. Awards associate, bachelor's, and master's degrees. Founded 1950. Setting: 9-acre urban campus. Endowment: $10.3 million. Total enrollment: 755. Faculty: 65 (37 full-time, 28 part-time). Student-undergrad faculty ratio is 13:1. 2,437 applied, 48% were admitted. Full-time: 546 students, 63% women, 37% men. Part-time: 187 students, 67% women, 33% men. Students come from 41 states and territories, 6 other countries, 37% from out-of-state. 0.3% American Indian or Alaska Native, non-Hispanic/Latino; 3% Hispanic/Latino; 11% African American, non-Hispanic/Latino; 0.1% Asian, non-Hispanic/Latino; 0% Native Hawaiian or other Pacific Islander, non-Hispanic/Latino; 2% international. 33% 25 or older, 41% live on campus, 15% transferred in. Retention: 57% of full-time freshmen returned the following year. Academic areas with the most degrees conferred: business/marketing; public administration and social services; health professions and related sciences. Core. Calendar: semesters. Academic remediation for entering students, services for LD students, advanced placement, self-designed majors, honors program, independent study, distance learning, double major, summer session for credit, part-time degree program, adult/continuing education programs, internships. Off campus study at Kentucky Wesleyan College, Owensboro Community and Technical College. Study abroad program.

Entrance Requirements: Options: electronic application, deferred admission. Required: high school transcript, GPA coincides with test scores, SAT or ACT. Required for some: essay, 1 recommendation, interview. Entrance: moderately difficult. Application deadlines: Rolling, Rolling for nonresidents. Notification: continuous, continuous for nonresidents. SAT Reasoning Test deadline: 8/23. SAT Subject Test deadline: 8/23. Transfer credits accepted: Yes.

Costs Per Year: Application fee: $25. One-time mandatory fee: $200. Comprehensive fee: $26,940 includes full-time tuition ($18,500), mandatory fees ($440), and college room and board ($8000). Full-time tuition and fees vary according to course load and degree level. Room and board charges vary according to board plan and housing facility. Part-time tuition: $540 per credit hour. Part-time tuition varies according to course load and degree level.

Collegiate Environment: Orientation program. Drama-theater group, choral

group, student-run newspaper. Social organizations: 15 open to all. Most popular organizations: Fellowship of Christian Athletes, Social Work Club, Ichabod Society, Habitat for Humanity, Spanish Club. Major annual events: Orientation, Brescia-Palooza, Founder's Day Convocation and Luncheon. Student services: personal-psychological counseling, women's center. Campus security: 24-hour emergency response devices, late night transport-escort service, controlled dormitory access. Fr. Leonard Alvey Library with 161,814 books, 69,015 microform titles, 26,045 serials, 3,635 audiovisual materials, an OPAC, and a Web page. Operations spending for the previous fiscal year: $356,000. 90 computers available on campus for general student use. Computer purchase/lease plans available. A campuswide network can be accessed from student residence rooms and from off campus. Staffed computer lab on campus provides training in use of computers, software, and the Internet.

Community Environment: Brescia University is located in Owensboro, Kentucky, on the Ohio River. With a metropolitan population of 55,500, Owensboro is easily accessible from any direction. The college campus is within walking distance of the revitalized downtown area, the performing arts center, public library, art museum, natural science and history museum, as well as numerous restaurants, churches, and parks. Many Owensboro industries and professional organizations cooperate with Brescia in providing enriching off-campus learning opportunities for students, particularly in the areas of business, education, psychology, social work, speech and hearing, and special education.

■ BROWN MACKIE COLLEGE–HOPKINSVILLE

4001 Fort Cambell Blvd.
Hopkinsville, KY 42240
Tel: (270)886-1302; Free: 800-359-4753
Fax: (270)886-3544
Web Site: www.brownmackie.edu/Hopkinsville/

Description: Proprietary, 2-year, coed. Part of Education Management Corporation. Awards diplomas, transfer associate, and terminal associate degrees. Setting: small town campus.

■ BROWN MACKIE COLLEGE–LOUISVILLE

3605 Fern Valley Rd.
Louisville, KY 40219
Tel: (502)968-7191; Free: 800-999-7387
Fax: (502)968-1727
Web Site: www.brownmackie.edu/louisville/

Description: Proprietary, primarily 2-year, coed. Part of Education Management Corporation. Awards certificates, diplomas, terminal associate, and bachelor's degrees. Founded 1972. Setting: suburban campus.

■ BROWN MACKIE COLLEGE–NORTHERN KENTUCKY

309 Buttermilk Pke.
Fort Mitchell, KY 41017-2191
Tel: (859)341-5627; Free: 800-888-1445
Fax: (859)341-6483
Web Site: www.brownmackie.edu/northernkentucky/

Description: Proprietary, primarily 2-year, coed. Part of Education Management Corporation. Awards certificates, diplomas, transfer associate, terminal associate, and bachelor's degrees. Founded 1927. Setting: suburban campus.

■ CAMPBELLSVILLE UNIVERSITY

1 University Dr.
Campbellsville, KY 42718-2799
Tel: (270)789-5000; Free: 800-264-6014
Fax: (270)789-5071
E-mail: admissions@campbellsville.edu
Web Site: www.campbellsville.edu/

Description: Independent, comprehensive, coed, affiliated with Kentucky Baptist Convention. Awards associate, bachelor's, and master's degrees. Founded 1906. Setting: 90-acre small town campus. Endowment: $910.2 million. Total enrollment: 3,664. Faculty: 311 (146 full-time, 165 part-time). Student-undergrad faculty ratio is 13:1. 2,477 applied, 67% were admitted. 17% from top 10% of their high school class, 38% from top quarter, 69% from top half. 15 valedictorians. Full-time: 1,967 students, 55% women, 45% men. Part-time: 1,165 students, 67% women, 33% men. Students come from 35 states and territories, 37 other countries, 12% from out-of-state. 0.2% American Indian or Alaska Native, non-Hispanic/Latino; 1% Hispanic/Latino; 11% African American, non-Hispanic/Latino; 0.4% Asian, non-

Hispanic/Latino; 0.1% Native Hawaiian or other Pacific Islander, non-Hispanic/Latino; 5% international. 19% 25 or older, 57% live on campus, 8% transferred in. Retention: 63% of full-time freshmen returned the following year. Academic areas with the most degrees conferred: education; business/marketing; theology and religious vocations. Core. Calendar: semesters. Academic remediation for entering students, ESL program, advanced placement, accelerated degree program, honors program, independent study, distance learning, double major, summer session for credit, part-time degree program, adult/continuing education programs, internships. Off campus study. Study abroad program. ROTC: Army (c).

Entrance Requirements: Options: electronic application, deferred admission. Required: high school transcript, minimum 2 high school GPA, SAT or ACT. Recommended: essay, minimum 3 high school GPA, interview. Entrance: moderately difficult. Application deadline: Rolling. Notification: continuous.

Costs Per Year: Application fee: $20. Comprehensive fee: $30,396 includes full-time tuition ($21,696), mandatory fees ($500), and college room and board ($8200). Room and board charges vary according to housing facility. Part-time tuition: $904 per credit hour.

Collegiate Environment: Orientation program. Drama-theater group, choral group, marching band, student-run newspaper, radio station. Social organizations: 48 open to all. Most popular organizations: Student Government Association, Baptist Student Union, Phi Beta Lambda, African-American Leadership League, Fellowship of Christian Athletes. Major annual events: Homecoming, Christmas celebration, Spring Formal. Student services: health clinic, personal-psychological counseling. Campus security: 24-hour emergency response devices and patrols, student patrols, late night transport-escort service, controlled dormitory access. 1,088 college housing spaces available; 1,028 were occupied in 2012-13. Freshmen guaranteed college housing. On-campus residence required through sophomore year. Options: men-only, women-only housing available. Montgomery Library plus 2 others with 370,163 books, 110,235 microform titles, 29,016 serials, an OPAC, and a Web page. Operations spending for the previous fiscal year: $420,228. 220 computers available on campus for general student use. A campuswide network can be accessed from student residence rooms and from off campus. Students can access the following: online class registration. Staffed computer lab on campus provides training in use of computers.

Community Environment: The 70-acre Campbellsville campus is situated precisely in the center of Kentucky, one-half mile from downtown Campbellsville (population 10,900), 40 minutes southeast of Elizabethtown, one and one-half hours from Louisville and Lexington, and just over two hours from Nashville. The college is located on KY55 and can be reached from the north by way of the Bluegrass Parkway and from the south by way of the Cumberland Parkway.

■ CENTRE COLLEGE

600 W Walnut St.
Danville, KY 40422-1394
Tel: (859)238-5200; Free: 800-423-6236
Fax: (859)238-5456
E-mail: admission@centre.edu
Web Site: www.centre.edu/

Description: Independent, 4-year, coed, affiliated with Presbyterian Church (U.S.A.). Awards bachelor's degrees. Founded 1819. Setting: 152-acre small town campus. Endowment: $182.2 million. Educational spending for the previous fiscal year: $12,307 per student. Total enrollment: 1,344. Faculty: 142 (117 full-time, 25 part-time). Student-undergrad faculty ratio is 11:1. 2,539 applied, 70% were admitted. 49% from top 10% of their high school class, 79% from top quarter, 5% from top half. Full-time: 1,343 students, 53% women, 47% men. Part-time: 1 student, 100% men. Students come from 44 states and territories, 10 other countries, 40% from out-of-state. 0% American Indian or Alaska Native, non-Hispanic/Latino; 2% Hispanic/Latino; 5% African American, non-Hispanic/Latino; 3% Asian, non-Hispanic/Latino; 0% Native Hawaiian or other Pacific Islander, non-Hispanic/Latino; 3% international. 0% 25 or older, 99% live on campus, 1% transferred in. Retention: 91% of full-time freshmen returned the following year. Academic areas with the most degrees conferred: social sciences; psychology; foreign languages and literature. Core. Calendar: 4-1-4. Services for LD students, advanced placement, self-designed majors, honors program, independent study, double major, co-op programs and internships. Off campus study at Associated Colleges of the South. Study abroad program. ROTC: Army (c), Air Force (c).

Entrance Requirements: Options: electronic application, early admission, early action, deferred admission, international baccalaureate accepted.

Required: essay, high school transcript, 1 recommendation, SAT or ACT. Recommended: interview. Entrance: very difficult. Application deadlines: 2/1, 12/1 for early action. Notification: 3/15, 1/15 for early action. SAT Reasoning Test deadline: 1/15. SAT Subject Test deadline: 1/15. Transfer credits accepted: Yes. Applicants placed on waiting list: 160. Wait-listed applicants offered admission: 22.

Costs Per Year: Application fee: $40. Comprehensive fee: $45,100 includes full-time tuition ($36,000) and college room and board ($9100). College room only: $4550. Room and board charges vary according to board plan. Part-time tuition: $1300 per credit.

Collegiate Environment: Orientation program. Drama-theater group, choral group, student-run newspaper, radio station. Social organizations: national fraternities, national sororities. Most popular organizations: Student Government Association, campus newspaper, admission tour guides and hosts, Christian fellowship group, Diversity Student Union. Major annual events: Homecoming, Spring Carnival, Family Weekend. Student services: health clinic, personal-psychological counseling. Campus security: 24-hour emergency response devices and patrols, late night transport-escort service, controlled dormitory access. 1,330 college housing spaces available; 1,265 were occupied in 2012-13. Freshmen guaranteed college housing. On-campus residence required through senior year. Options: coed, men-only housing available. Doherty Library with 294,086 books, 52,743 microform titles, 28,222 serials, 5,658 audiovisual materials, an OPAC, and a Web page. Operations spending for the previous fiscal year: $1.1 million. 425 computers available on campus for general student use. Computer purchase/lease plans available. A campuswide network can be accessed from student residence rooms and from off campus. Students can access the following: online class registration. Staffed computer lab on campus provides training in use of computers, software, and the Internet.

Community Environment: Danville is a prosperous community located on the southern edge of Kentucky's famous bluegrass region. The town has a rich historical heritage. It was the first seat of government west of the Alleghenies, and is also known for its early contributions in medicine, education, and government. Today, Danville is a model in Kentucky and the region as a center for light industry, with more than a dozen major employers. Midwinter days average 35 degrees; midsummer temperatures average 80 degrees. There is sunshine 60% of the time. Transportation is provided by a bus line and three main highways. Danville has fine horse farms, many churches, a library, a Regional Arts Center, bowling alley, fishing, boating, waterskiing, golf, and theaters. Part-time jobs are available.

■ **CLEAR CREEK BAPTIST BIBLE COLLEGE**
300 Clear Creek Rd.
Pineville, KY 40977-9754
Tel: (606)337-3196
E-mail: bhowell@ccbbc.edu
Web Site: www.ccbbc.edu/

Description: Independent Southern Baptist, 4-year, coed. Awards associate and bachelor's degrees. Founded 1926. Setting: 700-acre rural campus. Total enrollment: 172. Faculty: 16 (8 full-time, 8 part-time). Student-undergrad faculty ratio is 13:1. 52 applied, 88% were admitted. 72% 25 or older. Retention: 88% of full-time freshmen returned the following year. Core. Calendar: semesters. Summer session for credit, part-time degree program.

Entrance Requirements: Open admission. Options: electronic application, deferred admission. Required: essay, 4 recommendations. Recommended: high school transcript, interview. Entrance: noncompetitive. Application deadline: 7/15. Notification: continuous.

Costs Per Year: Application fee: $50. Comprehensive fee: $8840 includes full-time tuition ($5220), mandatory fees ($150), and college room and board ($3470). College room only: $1870.

Collegiate Environment: Orientation program. Choral group. Student services: health clinic, personal-psychological counseling. Campus security: 24-hour emergency response devices, student patrols. Carolyn Boatman Brooks Memorial Library with 38,000 books, 300 serials, and an OPAC. 15 computers available on campus for general student use. A campuswide network can be accessed. Staffed computer lab on campus.

Community Environment: The campus bounds Pine Mountain State Park. Pineville, founded in 1799, is located in a rural area 16 miles north of Cumberland Gap, and is served by the Greyhound bus line. Churches, a small shopping area and some part-time employment are available.

■ **DAYMAR COLLEGE (BELLEVUE)**
119 Fairfield Ave.
Bellevue, KY 41073

Tel: (859)291-0800; Free: 877-258-7796
Web Site: www.daymarcollege.edu/
Description: Proprietary, 2-year, coed. Awards certificates and terminal associate degrees. Total enrollment: 136. Student-undergrad faculty ratio is 9:1. 34% from out-of-state. 66% 25 or older.
Entrance Requirements: Open admission.

■ **DAYMAR COLLEGE (BOWLING GREEN)**
2421 Fitzgerald Industrial Dr.
Bowling Green, KY 42101
Tel: (270)843-6750; Free: 877-258-7796
Fax: (270)843-6976
E-mail: thenderson@daymarcollege.edu
Web Site: www.daymarcollege.edu/
Description: Proprietary, 2-year, coed. Awards diplomas and transfer associate degrees. Founded 1989. Setting: suburban campus with easy access to Nashville. Total enrollment: 499. Student-undergrad faculty ratio is 18:1. 6% from out-of-state. 67% 25 or older. Core. Calendar: semesters. Part-time degree program, adult/continuing education programs.
Entrance Requirements: Open admission. Required: high school transcript. Entrance: noncompetitive.
Collegiate Environment: Orientation program. Student-run newspaper. Student services: personal-psychological counseling. Campus security: 24-hour emergency response devices.

■ **DAYMAR COLLEGE (LOUISVILLE)**
4112 Fern Valley Rd.
Louisville, KY 40219
Tel: (502)495-1040; Free: 877-258-7796
Web Site: www.daymarcollege.edu/
Description: Proprietary, 2-year, coed. Awards diplomas and terminal associate degrees. Founded 2001. Total enrollment: 321. 70% 25 or older.
Entrance Requirements: Open admission. Required: high school transcript, interview.

■ **DAYMAR COLLEGE (OWENSBORO)**
3361 Buckland Sq.
Owensboro, KY 42301
Tel: (270)926-4040; Free: 877-258-7796
Fax: (270)685-4090
E-mail: info@daymarcollege.edu
Web Site: www.daymarcollege.edu/
Description: Proprietary, 2-year, coed. Awards certificates, diplomas, and transfer associate degrees. Founded 1963. Setting: 1-acre small town campus. Total enrollment: 257. 63% 25 or older. Core. Academic remediation for entering students, advanced placement, accelerated degree program, independent study, double major, summer session for credit, part-time degree program, adult/continuing education programs, co-op programs and internships.
Entrance Requirements: Open admission. Option: deferred admission. Required: high school transcript, interview, Wonderlic aptitude test. Required for some: SAT or ACT. Entrance: minimally difficult. Application deadline: Rolling.
Collegiate Environment: Orientation program. Student-run newspaper. Student services: personal-psychological counseling. Campus security: 24-hour emergency response devices. Learning Resource Center with 3,215 books, 67 serials, 77 audiovisual materials, and a Web page.

■ **DAYMAR COLLEGE (PADUCAH)**
509 S 30th St.
Paducah, KY 42001
Free: 877-258-7796
Web Site: www.daymarcollege.edu/
Description: Proprietary, primarily 2-year, coed. Awards certificates, terminal associate, and bachelor's degrees. Total enrollment: 225. Student-undergrad faculty ratio is 15:1. 0% from out-of-state. 69% 25 or older.
Entrance Requirements: Open admission.

■ **DEVRY UNIVERSITY**
10172 Linn Station Rd.
Ste. 300
Louisville, KY 40223
Free: 866-338-7941
Web Site: www.devry.edu/

Description: Proprietary, 4-year, coed. Awards associate and bachelor's degrees. Total enrollment: 89. Faculty: 21 (all part-time). Student-undergrad faculty ratio is 9:1. Full-time: 49 students, 35% women, 65% men. Part-time: 40 students, 53% women, 48% men. 15% from out-of-state. 74% 25 or older, 31% transferred in. Accelerated degree program, distance learning.
Entrance Requirements: Option: deferred admission. Application deadline: Rolling. Notification: continuous. SAT Reasoning Test deadline: 10/31.

■ **EASTERN KENTUCKY UNIVERSITY**
521 Lancaster Ave.
Richmond, KY 40475-3102
Tel: (859)622-1000; Free: 800-465-9191
Fax: (859)622-1020
E-mail: admissions@eku.edu
Web Site: www.eku.edu/
Description: State-supported, comprehensive, coed. Awards associate, bachelor's, master's, and doctoral degrees and post-master's certificates. Founded 1906. Setting: 500-acre small town campus with easy access to Lexington. Endowment: $55.6 million. Research spending for the previous fiscal year: $6.8 million. Educational spending for the previous fiscal year: $6253 per student. Total enrollment: 16,062. Faculty: 1,114 (680 full-time, 434 part-time). Student-undergrad faculty ratio is 15:1. 9,461 applied, 66% were admitted. Full-time: 11,288 students, 56% women, 44% men. Part-time: 2,614 students, 59% women, 41% men. Students come from 46 states and territories, 38 other countries, 13% from out-of-state. 0.4% American Indian or Alaska Native, non-Hispanic/Latino; 2% Hispanic/Latino; 6% African American, non-Hispanic/Latino; 1% Asian, non-Hispanic/Latino; 0.2% Native Hawaiian or other Pacific Islander, non-Hispanic/Latino; 1% international. 24% 25 or older, 9% transferred in. Retention: 62% of full-time freshmen returned the following year. Academic areas with the most degrees conferred: homeland security, law enforcement, firefighting, and protective services; health professions and related sciences; education. Core. Calendar: semesters. Academic remediation for entering students, ESL program, services for LD students, advanced placement, accelerated degree program, self-designed majors, honors program, independent study, distance learning, double major, summer session for credit, part-time degree program, external degree program, adult/continuing education programs, co-op programs and internships, graduate courses open to undergrads. Study abroad program. ROTC: Army, Air Force (c).
Entrance Requirements: Open admission for state residents. Options: electronic application, deferred admission. Required: high school transcript, minimum 2 high school GPA, SAT or ACT. Entrance: noncompetitive. Application deadline: 8/1. Notification: continuous.
Costs Per Year: Application fee: $30. State resident tuition: $7320 full-time, $305 per credit hour part-time. Nonresident tuition: $16,464 full-time, $686 per credit hour part-time. Part-time tuition varies according to course load. College room and board: $7316. Room and board charges vary according to board plan and housing facility.
Collegiate Environment: Orientation program. Drama-theater group, choral group, marching band, student-run newspaper, radio station. Social organizations: 160 open to all; national fraternities, national sororities; 8% of eligible men and 6% of eligible women are members. Most popular organizations: Honor Society, Regular Society. Major annual events: Homecoming, Fall Festival, Spring Fling. Student services: health clinic, personal-psychological counseling. Campus security: 24-hour emergency response devices and patrols, student patrols, late night transport-escort service, controlled dormitory access. John Grant Crabbe Library plus 2 others with 799,496 books, 344,753 microform titles, 2,901 serials, 14,021 audiovisual materials, an OPAC, and a Web page. Operations spending for the previous fiscal year: $3.5 million. 1,200 computers available on campus for general student use. A campuswide network can be accessed from student residence rooms and from off campus. Students can access the following: online class registration. Staffed computer lab on campus.
Community Environment: Local industries are a miniature lamp plant and tool and die manufacturing. Richmond is located in the famous Bluegrass Region, 26 miles southeast of Lexington, and 55 miles to the State Capital of Frankfort on the Kentucky River. Recreational facilities are available at nearby parks and lakes. There are part-time work opportunities available.

■ **ELIZABETHTOWN COMMUNITY AND TECHNICAL COLLEGE**
620 College St. Rd.
Elizabethtown, KY 42701
Tel: (270)769-2371; Free: 877-246-2322
Fax: (270)769-0736

E-mail: bryan.smith@kctcs.edu
Web Site: www.elizabethtown.kctcs.edu/
Description: State-supported, 2-year, coed. Part of Kentucky Community and Technical College System. Awards certificates, diplomas, transfer associate, and terminal associate degrees. Founded 1966. Setting: 80-acre small town campus. Endowment: $879,000. Educational spending for the previous fiscal year: $4155 per student. Total enrollment: 7,586. Faculty: 321 (141 full-time, 180 part-time). Student-undergrad faculty ratio is 23:1. Full-time: 3,221 students, 57% women, 43% men. Part-time: 4,365 students, 54% women, 46% men. Students come from 28 states and territories, 2 other countries, 1% from out-of-state. 0.4% American Indian or Alaska Native, non-Hispanic/Latino; 4% Hispanic/Latino; 8% African American, non-Hispanic/Latino; 1% Asian, non-Hispanic/Latino; 0.3% Native Hawaiian or other Pacific Islander, non-Hispanic/Latino; 0.01% international. 51% 25 or older, 5% transferred in. Retention: 56% of full-time freshmen returned the following year. Calendar: semesters. Academic remediation for entering students, services for LD students, advanced placement, distance learning, summer session for credit, part-time degree program, co-op programs and internships. Off campus study.
Entrance Requirements: Option: electronic application. Recommended: ACT. Required for some: high school transcript. Entrance: noncompetitive. Application deadline: Rolling. Notification: continuous.
Collegiate Environment: Orientation program. Student-run newspaper. Campus security: late night transport-escort service. College housing not available. Operations spending for the previous fiscal year: $100,600. 150 computers available on campus for general student use. A campuswide network can be accessed. Students can access the following: online class registration, online bill payment. Staffed computer lab on campus provides training in use of computers, software, and the Internet.

■ **GATEWAY COMMUNITY AND TECHNICAL COLLEGE**
500 Technology Way
Florence, KY 41042
Tel: (859)441-4500
Fax: (859)292-6415
E-mail: andre.washington@kctcs.edu
Web Site: www.gateway.kctcs.edu/
Description: State-supported, 2-year, coed. Part of Kentucky Community and Technical College System. Awards certificates, diplomas, and transfer associate degrees. Founded 1961. Setting: suburban campus with easy access to Cincinnati. Total enrollment: 4,648. Faculty: 291 (91 full-time, 200 part-time). Student-undergrad faculty ratio is 16:1. 0.3% American Indian or Alaska Native, non-Hispanic/Latino; 2% Hispanic/Latino; 10% African American, non-Hispanic/Latino; 1% Asian, non-Hispanic/Latino; 0.1% Native Hawaiian or other Pacific Islander, non-Hispanic/Latino; 0% international. Core. Calendar: semesters. Academic remediation for entering students, services for LD students, distance learning, summer session for credit, part-time degree program, co-op programs and internships.
Entrance Requirements: Open admission. Options: electronic application, early admission, deferred admission. Required: high school transcript, ACT or ACT COMPASS. Entrance: minimally difficult. Application deadlines: Rolling, Rolling for nonresidents. Notification: continuous, continuous for nonresidents.
Costs Per Year: State resident tuition: $3360 full-time, $140 per credit hour part-time. Nonresident tuition: $11,760 full-time, $490 per credit hour part-time. Mandatory fees: $40. Full-time tuition varies according to course load. Part-time tuition and fees vary according to course load.
Collegiate Environment: Orientation program. Social organizations: Phi Theta Kappa, National Technical Honor Society. Most popular organizations: Multi-Cultural Student Organization, Student Government Association, Speech Team, American Criminal Justice Association, Phi Theta Kappa. Student services: personal-psychological counseling. College housing not available. 881 computers available on campus for general student use. Students can access the following: online class registration.

■ **GEORGETOWN COLLEGE**
400 E College St.
Georgetown, KY 40324-1696
Tel: (502)863-8000; Free: 800-788-9985
Fax: (502)868-8891
E-mail: admissions@georgetowncollege.edu
Web Site: www.georgetowncollege.edu/
Description: Independent, comprehensive, coed, affiliated with Baptist Church. Awards bachelor's and master's degrees. Founded 1829. Setting:

104-acre suburban campus with easy access to Cincinnati. Endowment: $41.1 million. Educational spending for the previous fiscal year: $7007 per student. Total enrollment: 1,543. Faculty: 148 (115 full-time, 33 part-time). Student-undergrad faculty ratio is 9:1. 1,735 applied, 82% were admitted. 27% from top 10% of their high school class, 53% from top quarter, 80% from top half. 13 valedictorians. Full-time: 1,087 students, 55% women, 45% men. Part-time: 29 students, 52% women, 48% men. Students come from 25 states and territories, 12 other countries, 22% from out-of-state. 0.1% American Indian or Alaska Native, non-Hispanic/Latino; 3% Hispanic/Latino; 10% African American, non-Hispanic/Latino; 1% Asian, non-Hispanic/Latino; 0% Native Hawaiian or other Pacific Islander, non-Hispanic/Latino; 2% international. 1% 25 or older, 91% live on campus, 3% transferred in. Retention: 75% of full-time freshmen returned the following year. Academic areas with the most degrees conferred: health professions and related sciences; social sciences; business/marketing. Core. Calendar: semesters. ESL program, advanced placement, self-designed majors, honors program, independent study, distance learning, double major, summer session for credit, part-time degree program, co-op programs and internships. Off campus study at Central College Abroad, College Consortium for International Students, Kentucky Institute for International Studies, Cooperative Center for Study Abroad. Study abroad program. ROTC: Army (c), Air Force (c).

Entrance Requirements: Options: electronic application, early decision, early action, deferred admission. Required: high school transcript, minimum 2.5 high school GPA, SAT or ACT. Recommended: ACT. Required for some: essay, interview. Entrance: moderately difficult. Application deadline: 8/1. Notification: 10/1, continuous for nonresidents. SAT Reasoning Test deadline: 8/15. Transfer credits accepted: Yes.

Costs Per Year: Application fee: $30. Comprehensive fee: $38,690 includes full-time tuition ($30,770) and college room and board ($7920). College room only: $3820. Full-time tuition varies according to course load and degree level. Room and board charges vary according to board plan and housing facility. Part-time tuition: $1270 per credit hour. Part-time tuition varies according to degree level.

Collegiate Environment: Orientation program. Drama-theater group, choral group, student-run newspaper, radio station. Social organizations: 101 open to all; national fraternities, national sororities, local fraternities; 52% of eligible men and 44% of eligible women are members. Most popular organizations: Campus Ministries, Association of Georgetown Students, Harper-Gatton Leadership Center, President's Ambassadors, Phi Beta Lambda. Major annual events: Hanging of the Green, Homecoming/Festival of Song, Belle of the Blue. Student services: health clinic, personal-psychological counseling. Campus security: 24-hour patrols, late night transport-escort service. 1,331 college housing spaces available; 995 were occupied in 2012-13. Freshmen guaranteed college housing. On-campus residence required through senior year. Options: men-only, women-only housing available. Anna Ashcraft Ensor Learning Resource Center with 185,592 books, 189,600 microform titles, 42,015 serials, 10,465 audiovisual materials, an OPAC, and a Web page. Operations spending for the previous fiscal year: $783,030. 175 computers available on campus for general student use. Computer purchase/lease plans available. A campuswide network can be accessed from student residence rooms and from off campus. Students can access the following: online class registration. Staffed computer lab on campus provides training in use of computers, software, and the Internet.

Community Environment: This town was the site of McClelland's Fort, a log stockade that was completed about 1776. Today the city is a residential and educational community located 12 miles north of Lexington and 75 miles east of Louisville, and can be reached by several major highways. Recently identified as one of Kentucky's two"safest cities," Georgetown is also the site of the Toyota Corporation's manufacturing plant. The Kentucky State Horse Park is only 5 miles south of the campus.

■ **HAZARD COMMUNITY AND TECHNICAL COLLEGE**
1 Community College Dr.
Hazard, KY 41701-2403
Tel: (606)436-5721; Free: 800-246-7521
Fax: (606)439-2988
Web Site: www.hazard.kctcs.edu/
Description: State-supported, 2-year, coed. Part of Kentucky Community and Technical College System. Awards certificates, diplomas, transfer associate, and terminal associate degrees. Founded 1968. Setting: 34-acre rural campus. Total enrollment: 4,714. Faculty: 170 (80 full-time, 90 part-time). Student-undergrad faculty ratio is 25:1. 7% from top 10% of their high

school class, 26% from top quarter, 55% from top half. Full-time: 1,806 students, 62% women, 38% men. Part-time: 2,908 students, 37% women, 63% men. 2% from out-of-state. 43% 25 or older. Calendar: semesters. Honors program, independent study, distance learning, co-op programs.
Entrance Requirements: Open admission for state residents. Option: early admission. Required: high school transcript. Entrance: noncompetitive. Application deadline: Rolling. Notification: continuous.
Costs Per Year: Application fee: $0. State resident tuition: $4200 full-time, $140 per credit hour part-time. Nonresident tuition: $14,700 full-time, $490 per credit hour part-time.
Community Environment: Hazard, the County Seat of Perry County, is the retail and cultural center of southeastern Kentucky. The college serves an 8-county (Breathitt, Knott, Leslie, Letcher, Wolfe, Lee, Owsley, and Perry) all rural area. The College's service area is also in the heart of the state's coal country, in the Cumberland Mountains of Kentucky.

■ **HENDERSON COMMUNITY COLLEGE**
2660 S Green St.
Henderson, KY 42420-4623
Tel: (270)827-1867; Free: 800-696-9958
Web Site: www.henderson.kctcs.edu/
Description: State-supported, 2-year, coed. Part of Kentucky Community and Technical College System. Awards transfer associate and terminal associate degrees. Founded 1963. Setting: 120-acre small town campus. Total enrollment: 1,984. 61% 25 or older. Retention: 57% of full-time freshmen returned the following year. Core. Calendar: semesters. Academic remediation for entering students, ESL program, advanced placement, accelerated degree program, independent study, distance learning, double major, summer session for credit, part-time degree program, external degree program, adult/continuing education programs, co-op programs and internships. Off campus study.
Entrance Requirements: Open admission. Required: high school transcript. Required for some: essay, interview. Entrance: noncompetitive. Application deadline: 9/1.
Collegiate Environment: Orientation program. Drama-theater group, student-run radio station. Student services: personal-psychological counseling. Campus security: 24-hour emergency response devices. Hartfield Learning Resource Center plus 1 other with 30,206 books, 21,126 microform titles, 231 serials, 1,053 audiovisual materials, an OPAC, and a Web page.
Community Environment: An industrial city, Henderson is on the Ohio River in an important oil-producing and agricultural area. Principal crops are corn, soybeans and tobacco. Part-time employment is available. Transportation provided by rail and bus lines within the city and airlines located in Evansville, Indiana, nine miles away. Ellis Park Racetrack, three miles north, offers thoroughbred racing August through Labor Day and harness racing from in late May to late July. 95 organizations embrace all types of activities. There is a hospital and clinics, public library, YMCA, and 36 churches offering community service. This is the home of Audubon Museum which houses the world's finest collection of Audubon items. The city has one of the finest summer recreational programs in the state of Kentucky. the finest summer recreational programs in the state of Kentucky.

■ **HOPKINSVILLE COMMUNITY COLLEGE**
PO Box 2100
Hopkinsville, KY 42241-2100
Tel: (270)707-3700; Free: 866-534-2224
E-mail: janet.level@kctcs.edu
Web Site: hopkinsville.kctcs.edu/
Description: State-supported, 2-year, coed. Part of Kentucky Community and Technical College System. Awards certificates, diplomas, transfer associate, and terminal associate degrees. Founded 1965. Setting: 69-acre small town campus with easy access to Nashville. Educational spending for the previous fiscal year: $2841 per student. Total enrollment: 3,753. Faculty: 163 (65 full-time, 98 part-time). Student-undergrad faculty ratio is 25:1. 1,119 applied, 100% were admitted. Full-time: 1,771 students, 70% women, 30% men. Part-time: 1,982 students, 67% women, 33% men. Students come from 7 states and territories, 31% from out-of-state. 53% 25 or older, 8% transferred in. Retention: 55% of full-time freshmen returned the following year. Core. Calendar: semesters. Academic remediation for entering students, services for LD students, advanced placement, honors program, independent study, distance learning, summer session for credit, part-time degree program, co-op programs.
Entrance Requirements: Open admission except for nursing program. Options: electronic application, deferred admission. Recommended: high

school transcript. Entrance: noncompetitive. Application deadlines: Rolling, Rolling for nonresidents. Notification: continuous, continuous for nonresidents. Transfer credits accepted: Yes.

Costs Per Year: Application fee: $0. State resident tuition: $4200 full-time, $140 per credit hour part-time. Nonresident tuition: $14,700 full-time, $490 per credit hour part-time. Full-time tuition varies according to reciprocity agreements. Part-time tuition varies according to reciprocity agreements.

Collegiate Environment: Orientation program. Student-run newspaper. Social organizations: 25 open to all. Most popular organizations: Ag Tech, Amateur Radio, Ballroom Dance, Baptist Campus Ministries, Black Men United. Major annual events: Fun Day, Appreciation Day, Circle of Love. Campus security: 24-hour emergency response devices, late night transport-escort service, security provided by trained security personnel during hours of normal operation. Learning Resource Center with an OPAC and a Web page. 400 computers available on campus for general student use. Computer purchase/lease plans available. A campuswide network can be accessed from off-campus. Students can access the following: online class registration. Staffed computer lab on campus.

Community Environment: Hopkinsville is noted as an agricultural and industrial center with important livestock, grain, and dark tobacco markets, flour and feed production, and the manufacturing of shoes, clothing, hardwood flooring, lighting fixtures, industrial springs, and automotive products. The city is served by rail, bus, and air lines via nearby Clarksville and Nashville, Tennessee.

■ **ITT TECHNICAL INSTITUTE (LEXINGTON)**
2473 Fortune Dr., Ste. 180
Lexington, KY 40509
Tel: (859)246-3300; Free: 800-519-8151
Web Site: www.itt-tech.edu/
Description: Proprietary, 4-year, coed. Part of ITT Educational Services, Inc. Awards associate and bachelor's degrees. Founded 2006.
Entrance Requirements: Entrance: minimally difficult.

■ **ITT TECHNICAL INSTITUTE (LOUISVILLE)**
9500 Ormsby Station Rd.
Ste. 100
Louisville, KY 40223
Tel: (502)327-7424; Free: 888-790-7427
Web Site: www.itt-tech.edu/
Description: Proprietary, primarily 2-year, coed. Part of ITT Educational Services, Inc. Awards terminal associate and bachelor's degrees. Founded 1993. Setting: suburban campus.
Entrance Requirements: Entrance: minimally difficult.

■ **JEFFERSON COMMUNITY AND TECHNICAL COLLEGE**
109 E Broadway
Louisville, KY 40202-2005
Tel: (502)213-5333
Fax: (502)213-2115
Web Site: www.jefferson.kctcs.edu/
Description: State-supported, 2-year, coed. Part of Kentucky Community and Technical College System. Awards certificates, diplomas, transfer associate, and terminal associate degrees. Founded 1968. Setting: 10-acre urban campus. Endowment: $2.2 million. Educational spending for the previous fiscal year: $1982 per student. Total enrollment: 15,475. Faculty: 652 (292 full-time, 360 part-time). Student-undergrad faculty ratio is 19:1. Full-time: 4,879 students, 56% women, 44% men. Part-time: 10,596 students, 51% women, 49% men. Students come from 10 states and territories, 5% from out-of-state. 39% 25 or older, 14% transferred in. Core. Calendar: semesters. Academic remediation for entering students, ESL program, services for LD students, advanced placement, honors program, independent study, distance learning, summer session for credit, part-time degree program, external degree program, adult/continuing education programs, co-op programs and internships. Off campus study at members of the Kentuckiana Metroversity. ROTC: Army (c).
Entrance Requirements: Open admission except for high school students in early admissions programs. Option: early admission. Entrance: noncompetitive. Application deadline: Rolling. Notification: continuous.
Collegiate Environment: Drama-theater group, student-run newspaper. Student services: personal-psychological counseling. Campus security: 24-hour emergency response devices and patrols, late night transport-escort service. John T. Smith Learning Resource Center plus 3 others with 76,578 books, 156,316 microform titles, 391 serials, an OPAC, and a Web page.

Operations spending for the previous fiscal year: $282,102. 895 computers available on campus for general student use. A campuswide network can be accessed from off-campus. Students can access the following: online class registration. Staffed computer lab on campus provides training in use of computers and the Internet.
Community Environment: See University of Louisville.

■ **KENTUCKY CHRISTIAN UNIVERSITY**
100 Academic Pky.
Grayson, KY 41143-2205
Tel: (606)474-3000; Free: 800-522-3181
Fax: (606)474-3155
E-mail: sgreer@kcu.edu
Web Site: www.kcu.edu/
Description: Independent, comprehensive, coed, affiliated with Christian Churches and Churches of Christ. Awards bachelor's and master's degrees. Founded 1919. Setting: 121-acre small town campus. Endowment: $6.1 million. Educational spending for the previous fiscal year: $5222 per student. Total enrollment: 615. Faculty: 55 (37 full-time, 18 part-time). Student-undergrad faculty ratio is 13:1. 806 applied, 58% were admitted. 13% from top 10% of their high school class, 26% from top quarter, 56% from top half. 5 valedictorians. Full-time: 546 students, 42% women, 58% men. Part-time: 28 students, 96% women, 4% men. Students come from 30 states and territories, 4 other countries, 47% from out-of-state. 5% American Indian or Alaska Native, non-Hispanic/Latino; 1% Hispanic/Latino; 12% African American, non-Hispanic/Latino; 0.3% Asian, non-Hispanic/Latino; 0% Native Hawaiian or other Pacific Islander, non-Hispanic/Latino; 1% international. 7% 25 or older, 82% live on campus, 11% transferred in. Retention: 57% of full-time freshmen returned the following year. Academic areas with the most degrees conferred: interdisciplinary studies; education; theology and religious vocations. Core. Calendar: semesters. Academic remediation for entering students, advanced placement, accelerated degree program, independent study, double major, summer session for credit, part-time degree program, external degree program, adult/continuing education programs, co-op programs and internships, graduate courses open to undergrads. Off campus study.
Entrance Requirements: Options: electronic application, international baccalaureate accepted. Required: essay, high school transcript, 2 recommendations, SAT or ACT. Required for some: 3 recommendations, interview. Entrance: moderately difficult. Application deadline: Rolling. Notification: continuous. Preference given to students with a Christian background. SAT Reasoning Test deadline: 8/1. SAT Subject Test deadline: 8/1. Transfer credits accepted: Yes.
Costs Per Year: Application fee: $35. One-time mandatory fee: $100. Comprehensive fee: $24,318 includes full-time tuition ($17,088), mandatory fees ($330), and college room and board ($6900). Room and board charges vary according to housing facility. Part-time tuition: $534 per credit hour. Part-time mandatory fees: $534 per credit hour. Part-time tuition and fees vary according to class time, program, and reciprocity agreements.
Collegiate Environment: Orientation program. Drama-theater group, choral group, marching band. Student services: health clinic, personal-psychological counseling. Campus security: 24-hour emergency response devices, late night transport-escort service, controlled dormitory access. 588 college housing spaces available; 471 were occupied in 2012-13. Freshmen guaranteed college housing. On-campus residence required through sophomore year. Options: men-only, women-only housing available. Young Library with 201,843 books, 9,312 microform titles, 205 serials, 1,909 audiovisual materials, an OPAC, and a Web page. Operations spending for the previous fiscal year: $258,926. 55 computers available on campus for general student use. A campuswide network can be accessed from student residence rooms. Students can access the following: online class registration. Staffed computer lab on campus provides training in use of computers and software.
Community Environment: Grayson can be accessed via bus. It has many Protestant churches and several organizations, including the Creative Arts Club and Chamber of Commerce. Health services are provided by two clinic and two hospitals within 20 miles. Recreation available includes hunting, fishing, boating, bowling, swimming, horseback riding and miniature golf with three state parks in the area. Grayson is a friendly town with complete up-to-date modern stores comparable to a city twice its size.

■ **KENTUCKY MOUNTAIN BIBLE COLLEGE**
PO Box 10
Vancleve, KY 41385

Tel: (606)693-5000; Free: 800-879-KMBC
Fax: (606)693-7744
E-mail: kmbc@kmbc.edu
Web Site: www.kmbc.edu/

Description: Independent interdenominational, 4-year, coed. Awards associate and bachelor's degrees. Founded 1931. Setting: 400-acre rural campus with easy access to Lexington. Total enrollment: 73. Faculty: 16 (all part-time). Student-undergrad faculty ratio is 5:1. 56 applied, 54% were admitted. 7% from top 10% of their high school class, 15% from top quarter, 38% from top half. 2 valedictorians. Full-time: 65 students, 52% women, 48% men. Part-time: 8 students, 50% women, 50% men. Students come from 19 states and territories, 2 other countries, 58% from out-of-state. 1% American Indian or Alaska Native, non-Hispanic/Latino; 1% Hispanic/Latino; 1% African American, non-Hispanic/Latino; 0% Asian, non-Hispanic/Latino; 0% Native Hawaiian or other Pacific Islander, non-Hispanic/Latino; 4% international. 18% 25 or older, 95% live on campus, 10% transferred in. Retention: 53% of full-time freshmen returned the following year. Academic area with the most degrees conferred: theology and religious vocations. Core. Calendar: semesters. Academic remediation for entering students, independent study, distance learning, part-time degree program, co-op programs and internships.

Entrance Requirements: Required: essay, high school transcript, minimum 2 high school GPA, testimony of religious life, ACT. Recommended: interview. Entrance: minimally difficult. Application deadline: Rolling. Notification: continuous. Transfer credits accepted: Yes.

Costs Per Year: Application fee: $25. Comprehensive fee: $10,790 includes full-time tuition ($6000), mandatory fees ($690), and college room and board ($4100). College room only: $1400. Full-time tuition and fees vary according to program. Room and board charges vary according to board plan and housing facility. Part-time tuition: $200 per credit. Part-time mandatory fees: $585 per year. Part-time tuition and fees vary according to program.

Collegiate Environment: Orientation program. Drama-theater group, choral group, student-run newspaper. Social organizations: 1 open to all; Prayer groups, Missions Organizations; 45% of eligible men and 45% of eligible women are members. Most popular organization: Student Involvement. Major annual events: Convocation, Courage. Student services: personal-psychological counseling, women's center. Campus security: student patrols. Gibson Library plus 1 other with 24,336 books, 81 microform titles, 140 serials, 2,132 audiovisual materials, and an OPAC. 10 computers available on campus for general student use. A campuswide network can be accessed from student residence rooms. Staffed computer lab on campus.

Community Environment: Vancleve is a rural town located 7 miles northwest of Jackson just off State Highway 15. Radio Station WMTC is located here. Part-time employment found on campus.

■ **KENTUCKY STATE UNIVERSITY**
400 E Main St.
Frankfort, KY 40601
Tel: (502)597-6000
Fax: (502)597-6239
E-mail: juan.alexander@kysu.edu
Web Site: www.kysu.edu/

Description: State-related, comprehensive, coed. Awards associate, bachelor's, and master's degrees. Founded 1886. Setting: 915-acre small town campus with easy access to Louisville. Endowment: $28.6 million. Research spending for the previous fiscal year: $7.7 million. Educational spending for the previous fiscal year: $6829 per student. Total enrollment: 2,524. Faculty: 162 (134 full-time, 28 part-time). Student-undergrad faculty ratio is 14:1. 4,193 applied, 45% were admitted. Full-time: 1,782 students, 57% women, 43% men. Part-time: 514 students, 66% women, 34% men. Students come from 30 states and territories, 10 other countries, 43% from out-of-state. 0% American Indian or Alaska Native, non-Hispanic/Latino; 1% Hispanic/Latino; 57% African American, non-Hispanic/Latino; 0.3% Asian, non-Hispanic/Latino; 0.2% Native Hawaiian or other Pacific Islander, non-Hispanic/Latino; 1% international. 21% 25 or older, 37% live on campus, 8% transferred in. Retention: 46% of full-time freshmen returned the following year. Academic areas with the most degrees conferred: business/marketing; liberal arts/general studies; health professions and related sciences; psychology; education. Core. Calendar: semesters. Academic remediation for entering students, ESL program, services for LD students, advanced placement, self-designed majors, honors program, independent study, distance learning, double major, summer session for credit, part-time degree program, external degree program, adult/continuing education programs, co-op programs and internships. Off campus study. Study abroad program. ROTC: Army (c), Air Force (c).

Entrance Requirements: Options: electronic application, early admission, international baccalaureate accepted. Required: high school transcript, SAT or ACT. Recommended: minimum 2 high school GPA. Required for some: essay, 2 recommendations, interview. Entrance: minimally difficult. Application deadline: Rolling. Transfer credits accepted: Yes.

Costs Per Year: Application fee: $30. State resident tuition: $6108 full-time, $229 per credit hour part-time. Nonresident tuition: $15,708 full-time, $585 per credit hour part-time. Mandatory fees: $750 full-time, $25 per credit hour part-time. Full-time tuition and fees vary according to course load. Part-time tuition and fees vary according to course load. College room and board: $6580. College room only: $3340. Room and board charges vary according to board plan and housing facility.

Collegiate Environment: Orientation program. Drama-theater group, choral group, marching band, student-run newspaper. Social organizations: 55 open to all; national fraternities, national sororities, student, academic, religious, and non Greek-letter; 7% of eligible men and 9% of eligible women are members. Most popular organizations: Student Government Association, NAACP, Apostolic Lighthouse Organization, Whitney Young Council, Kentucky Education Association. Major annual events: Homecoming every Fall, Late Night Breakfast with the President, Men's/Women's Conferences. Student services: health clinic, personal-psychological counseling. Campus security: 24-hour emergency response devices and patrols, controlled dormitory access. 1,049 college housing spaces available; 850 were occupied in 2012-13. Freshmen given priority for college housing. On-campus residence required through sophomore year. Options: coed, men-only, women-only housing available. Paul G. Blazer Library with 326,821 books, 328,458 microform titles, 785 serials, 4,653 audiovisual materials, and an OPAC. Operations spending for the previous fiscal year: $1.8 million. 450 computers available on campus for general student use. A campuswide network can be accessed from student residence rooms and from off campus. Students can access the following: online class registration, accept financial aid awards. Staffed computer lab on campus.

Community Environment: Founded in 1786, Frankfort was selected as Kentucky's capital in 1792. Located at the western edge of the Bluegrass region, Frankfort, population 27,000, is home to several plants which manufacture electronic equipment, shoes, underwear, metal auto trim, precision parts and screws. There is access to rail and bus lines. The city has a public library, hospital, Y's, shopping facilities, theatres, and swimming. Organizations including major civic, fraternal, and veterans' are located in the area.

■ **KENTUCKY WESLEYAN COLLEGE**
3000 Frederica St.
Owensboro, KY 42301
Tel: (270)926-3111; Free: 800-990-0592
Fax: (270)926-3196
Web Site: www.kwc.edu/

Description: Independent Methodist, 4-year, coed. Awards bachelor's degrees. Founded 1858. Setting: 52-acre suburban campus. Endowment: $27.9 million. Educational spending for the previous fiscal year: $4740 per student. Total enrollment: 678. Faculty: 75 (48 full-time, 27 part-time). Student-undergrad faculty ratio is 12:1. 910 applied, 21% were admitted. 20% from top 10% of their high school class, 44% from top quarter, 68% from top half. Full-time: 641 students, 49% women, 51% men. Part-time: 37 students, 49% women, 51% men. Students come from 25 states and territories, 8 other countries, 28% from out-of-state. 1% American Indian or Alaska Native, non-Hispanic/Latino; 2% Hispanic/Latino; 10% African American, non-Hispanic/Latino; 0.3% Asian, non-Hispanic/Latino; 0% Native Hawaiian or other Pacific Islander, non-Hispanic/Latino; 1% international. 6% 25 or older, 45% live on campus, 8% transferred in. Retention: 54% of full-time freshmen returned the following year. Academic areas with the most degrees conferred: business/marketing; education; psychology; biological/life sciences; physical sciences. Core. Calendar: semesters. Academic remediation for entering students, services for LD students, advanced placement, accelerated degree program, self-designed majors, honors program, independent study, distance learning, double major, summer session for credit, part-time degree program, adult/continuing education programs, co-op programs and internships. Off campus study at Brescia University, Owensboro Community and Technical College. Study abroad program. ROTC: Army (c).

Entrance Requirements: Options: electronic application, early admission, deferred admission, international baccalaureate accepted. Required: high school transcript, SAT or ACT. Entrance: moderately difficult. Notification: continuous. SAT Reasoning Test deadline: 8/31. SAT Subject Test deadline: 8/31. Transfer credits accepted: Yes.

Costs Per Year: Application fee: $0. Comprehensive fee: $28,700 includes full-time tuition ($20,600), mandatory fees ($600), and college room and board ($7500). Full-time tuition and fees vary according to course load. Room and board charges vary according to board plan and housing facility. Part-time tuition: $585 per credit. Part-time tuition varies according to course load.

Collegiate Environment: Orientation program. Drama-theater group, choral group, marching band, student-run newspaper, radio station. Social organizations: 42 open to all; national fraternities, national sororities, local sororities; 8% of eligible men and 11% of eligible women are members. Most popular organizations: Student Government Association, Student Activities Programming Board, Campus Ministries, Pre Professional, St Jude Up 'Til Dawn Executive Board. Major annual events: Homecoming, Annual Thanksgiving Dinner/Lessons in Carols, K-Dub Idol. Student services: health clinic, personal-psychological counseling, women's center. Campus security: 24-hour emergency response devices, late night transport-escort service, controlled dormitory access, 12-hour patrols by trained security personnel. 520 college housing spaces available; 377 were occupied in 2012-13. Freshmen guaranteed college housing. On-campus residence required through senior year. Options: coed, men-only, women-only housing available. Library Learning Center with 135,688 books, 144,661 microform titles, 145 serials, 2,027 audiovisual materials, an OPAC, and a Web page. Operations spending for the previous fiscal year: $322,583. 125 computers available on campus for general student use. Computer purchase/lease plans available. A campuswide network can be accessed from student residence rooms and from off campus. Students can access the following: online class registration. Staffed computer lab on campus provides training in use of computers, software, and the Internet.

Community Environment: Owensboro, population 55,500, with sunshine 52-60 percent of the year is the largest city in western Kentucky. There are good commercial bus and air transportation facilities. The city has public libraries, many churches, a hospital, three medical centers and a public health center. Recreation facilities include theaters, drive-ins, bowling alleys, golf courses as well as fishing, boating, swimming, indoor athletics and other activities.

■ **LINCOLN COLLEGE OF TECHNOLOGY**
8095 Connector Dr.
Florence, KY 41042
Tel: (859)282-9999
Web Site: www.lincolnedu.com/
Description: Proprietary, 2-year, coed. Awards certificates, diplomas, and terminal associate degrees. Founded 1978. Setting: suburban campus with easy access to Cincinnati. Total enrollment: 234. Student-undergrad faculty ratio is 19:1. 123 applied. 17% from out-of-state. 51% 25 or older. Retention: 82% of full-time freshmen returned the following year.

■ **LINDSEY WILSON COLLEGE**
210 Lindsey Wilson St.
Columbia, KY 42728
Tel: (270)384-2126; Free: 800-264-0138
Fax: (270)384-8200
Web Site: www.lindsey.edu/.
Description: Independent United Methodist, comprehensive, coed. Awards associate, bachelor's, and master's degrees. Founded 1903. Setting: 225-acre rural campus. Endowment: $14.3 million. Educational spending for the previous fiscal year: $4218 per student. Total enrollment: 2,677. Faculty: 256 (110 full-time, 146 part-time). Student-undergrad faculty ratio is 14:1. 2,928 applied, 65% were admitted. 14% from top 10% of their high school class, 35% from top quarter, 70% from top half. 4 valedictorians. Full-time: 2,107 students, 59% women, 41% men. Part-time: 110 students, 73% women, 27% men. Students come from 30 states and territories, 27 other countries, 18% from out-of-state. 1% American Indian or Alaska Native, non-Hispanic/Latino; 1% Hispanic/Latino; 9% African American, non-Hispanic/Latino; 1% Asian, non-Hispanic/Latino; 0% Native Hawaiian or other Pacific Islander, non-Hispanic/Latino; 0.3% international. 23% 25 or older, 52% live on campus, 15% transferred in. Retention: 58% of full-time freshmen returned the following year. Academic areas with the most degrees conferred: public administration and social services; education; business/marketing. Core. Calendar: semesters. Academic remediation for entering students, ESL program, services for LD students, advanced placement, accelerated degree program, self-designed majors, independent study, double major, summer session for credit, part-time degree program, adult/continuing education programs, co-op programs and internships, graduate courses open to undergrads. Off campus study. Study abroad program.

Entrance Requirements: Open admission. Option: electronic application. Required: high school transcript. Recommended: interview. Required for some: SAT or ACT. Entrance: minimally difficult. Application deadline: Rolling. Notification: continuous.

Costs Per Year: Application fee: $0. Comprehensive fee: $30,470 includes full-time tuition ($21,840), mandatory fees ($230), and college room and board ($8400). College room only: $3100. Full-time tuition and fees vary according to location. Part-time tuition: $910 per credit hour. Part-time tuition varies according to location.

Collegiate Environment: Orientation program. Drama-theater group, choral group, marching band, student-run newspaper. Social organizations: 27 open to all. Major annual events: Homecoming, Founders' Day, Malvina Farkie Day. Student services: health clinic, personal-psychological counseling, women's center. Campus security: 24-hour emergency response devices and patrols. 1,150 college housing spaces available; 1,101 were occupied in 2012-13. Freshmen guaranteed college housing. On-campus residence required through senior year. Options: men-only, women-only housing available. Katie Murrell Library with 80,000 books, 1,500 serials, an OPAC, and a Web page. Operations spending for the previous fiscal year: $432,715. 120 computers available on campus for general student use. A campuswide network can be accessed from student residence rooms and from off campus. Students can access the following: online class registration. Staffed computer lab on campus.

Community Environment: Columbia is the seat of Adair County. The climate is moderate. The city is located 8 miles from Green River Lake State Park and 20 miles from Cumberland Lake State Park, both known for their boating, fishing, water skiing and other water activities. Community services include seven churches, a modern hospital, and adequate shopping. There are several service clubs, and an excellent relationship exists between the local population and the college.

■ **MADISONVILLE COMMUNITY COLLEGE**
2000 College Dr.
Madisonville, KY 42431-9185
Tel: (270)821-2250
Fax: (270)824-1866
Web Site: www.madcc.kctcs.edu/
Description: State-supported, 2-year, coed. Part of Kentucky Community and Technical College System. Awards certificates, diplomas, transfer associate, and terminal associate degrees. Founded 1968. Setting: 150-acre small town campus. Endowment: $2.4 million. Educational spending for the previous fiscal year: $4341 per student. Total enrollment: 3,500. Faculty: 184 (95 full-time, 89 part-time). 0.2% from out-of-state. 42% 25 or older. Core. Calendar: semesters. Academic remediation for entering students, services for LD students, advanced placement, independent study, distance learning, summer session for credit, part-time degree program, external degree program, adult/continuing education programs, co-op programs and internships. Off campus study.

Entrance Requirements: Open admission. Options: electronic application, early admission, deferred admission. Required: high school transcript. Entrance: noncompetitive. Application deadline: Rolling. Notification: continuous.

Collegiate Environment: Orientation program. Drama-theater group, choral group, student-run newspaper. Most popular organizations: student government, Baptist Student Union, Socratic Society, Student Ambassadors, Academic Team. Student services: personal-psychological counseling. Campus security: 24-hour emergency response devices, late night transport-escort service, evening patrols. Loman C. Trover Library plus 1 other with 26,793 books, 21,346 microform titles, 227 serials, 1,688 audiovisual materials, an OPAC, and a Web page. Operations spending for the previous fiscal year: $211,216. 35 computers available on campus for general student use. A campuswide network can be accessed from off-campus. Staffed computer lab on campus.

Community Environment: Centered on a plateau between the Pond and Tradewater Rivers, Madisonville is one of the principal loose leaf tobacco markets in western Kentucky. Underground coal mining operations are in the vicinity. Good shopping facilities are available. The city has several churches, a public library, and one theatre. The climate is moderate and part-time employment is available.

■ **MAYSVILLE COMMUNITY AND TECHNICAL COLLEGE (MAYSVILLE)**
1755 US 68
Maysville, KY 41056

Tel: (606)759-7141
E-mail: ccsmayrg@ukcc.uky.edu
Web Site: www.maysville.kctcs.edu/
Description: State-supported, 2-year, coed. Part of Kentucky Community and Technical College System. Awards certificates, diplomas, transfer associate, and terminal associate degrees. Founded 1967. Setting: 12-acre rural campus. Total enrollment: 3,630. 48% 25 or older. Core. Calendar: semesters. Academic remediation for entering students, ESL program, services for LD students, advanced placement, honors program, independent study, distance learning, summer session for credit, part-time degree program, external degree program, adult/continuing education programs, co-op programs and internships. Off campus study.
Entrance Requirements: Open admission except for nursing, early childhood education, respiratory care, surgical technologist programs. Option: early admission. Required: high school transcript. Entrance: noncompetitive. Application deadline: Rolling. Notification: continuous.
Collegiate Environment: Orientation program. Student services: personal-psychological counseling. Campus security: student patrols, evening parking lot security. Finch Library with 36,600 books, 7,700 microform titles, 288 serials, an OPAC, and a Web page.
Community Environment: From 1786 to 1789, Daniel Boone and his wife operated a tavern in Maysville, one of the first incorporated towns in Kentucky. Today this is a metropolitan city. The average temperature is 55.3 degrees with an average rainfall of 43.58 inches. Known as one of the largest burley tobacco markets in the world, the city has three large redrying plants and 18 loose-leaf sale warehouses. These warehouses are open daily from 10 to 2 during the tobacco sale and auction season. The manufacturer of power driven pulleys and bicycle parts are also among Maysville's chief industries. There is a hospital and clinic in town, and various civic, fraternal and veteran's organizations are represented. There are excellent shopping facilities. Cinema 4, boating, golf courses, and several private clubs are easily accessible for recreation. Part-time employment is available.

■ **MAYSVILLE COMMUNITY AND TECHNICAL COLLEGE (MOREHEAD)**
609 Viking Dr.
Morehead, KY 40351
Tel: (606)783-1538
Fax: (606)784-9876
Web Site: www.maysville.kctcs.edu/
Description: State-supported, 2-year, coed. Awards certificates, diplomas, and terminal associate degrees. Founded 1984. Calendar: semesters.

■ **MEDTECH COLLEGE**
1648 McGrathiana Pky.
Ste. 200
Lexington, KY 40511
Tel: (859)410-2100
Web Site: www.medtechcollege.edu/
Description: Proprietary, 2-year, coed. Founded 2009.

■ **MID-CONTINENT UNIVERSITY**
99 Powell Rd. E
Mayfield, KY 42066-9007
Tel: (270)247-8521; Free: 866-894-8878
Fax: (270)247-3115
E-mail: advantage@midcontinent.edu
Web Site: www.midcontinent.edu/
Description: Independent Southern Baptist, comprehensive, coed. Awards associate, bachelor's, and master's degrees. Founded 1949. Setting: 60-acre small town campus. Endowment: $3.4 million. Educational spending for the previous fiscal year: $2808 per student. Total enrollment: 2,264. Faculty: 199 (45 full-time, 154 part-time). Student-undergrad faculty ratio is 20:1. 419 applied, 87% were admitted. 5% from top 10% of their high school class, 18% from top quarter, 56% from top half. Full-time: 1,731 students, 63% women, 37% men. Part-time: 443 students, 60% women, 40% men. Students come from 21 states and territories, 10 other countries, 18% from out-of-state. 0.3% American Indian or Alaska Native, non-Hispanic/Latino; 2% Hispanic/Latino; 14% African American, non-Hispanic/Latino; 0.2% Asian, non-Hispanic/Latino; 0.1% Native Hawaiian or other Pacific Islander, non-Hispanic/Latino; 1% international. 5% live on campus, 18% transferred in. Retention: 60% of full-time freshmen returned the following year. Academic areas with the most degrees conferred: business/marketing; psychology; theology and religious vocations. Core. Calendar: semesters.

Academic remediation for entering students, ESL program, advanced placement, accelerated degree program, self-designed majors, independent study, distance learning, double major, summer session for credit, part-time degree program, adult/continuing education programs. Off campus study at Henderson Community College, Madisonville Community College, John A. Logan College, Rend Lake College, Shawnee Community College, and Southeastern Illinois College.
Entrance Requirements: Options: electronic application, early admission, deferred admission. Required: high school transcript, SAT or ACT. Required for some: essay, minimum 2 high school GPA, 1 recommendation, interview. Entrance: minimally difficult. Application deadlines: Rolling, Rolling for nonresidents. Notification: continuous, continuous for nonresidents. Transfer credits accepted: Yes.
Collegiate Environment: Orientation program. Drama-theater group, choral group, student-run newspaper. Social organizations: 5 open to all. Most popular organizations: Student Government Association, Baptist Student Union, Psychology Club, International Club, Ministry Association. Major annual events: Homecoming Spirit Week, Honor's Day Chapel, Athletic Awards Banquet. Student services: personal-psychological counseling. Campus security: 24-hour emergency response devices, late night transport-escort service, controlled dormitory access, night patrols by trained security personnel. 139 college housing spaces available; 114 were occupied in 2012-13. No special consideration for freshman housing applicants. On-campus residence required through sophomore year. Options: men-only, women-only housing available. Anne P. Markham Library with 38,053 books, 195 serials, 809 audiovisual materials, and an OPAC. Operations spending for the previous fiscal year: $165,911. 43 computers available on campus for general student use. A campuswide network can be accessed from student residence rooms and from off campus. Staffed computer lab on campus provides training in use of computers, software, and the Internet.
Community Environment: Mayfield is centrally located in the Mississippi River Valley. Transportation, commerce, industry and agriculture contribute to the prosperity of the area. Religious, medical and social facilities are available in the area.

■ **MIDWAY COLLEGE**
512 E Stephens St.
Midway, KY 40347-1120
Tel: (859)846-4421; Free: 800-755-0031
Fax: (859)846-5823
E-mail: jdean@midway.edu
Web Site: www.midway.edu/
Description: Independent, comprehensive, coed, affiliated with Christian Church (Disciples of Christ). Awards associate, bachelor's, master's, and doctoral degrees. Founded 1847. Setting: 110-acre small town campus with easy access to Louisville, Lexington. Total enrollment: 1,600. Faculty: 118 (57 full-time, 61 part-time). Student-undergrad faculty ratio is 16:1. 1,572 applied. 14% from top 10% of their high school class, 38% from top quarter, 68% from top half. 1 valedictorian, 32 student government officers. Full-time: 1,022 students, 88% women, 12% men. Part-time: 491 students, 78% women, 22% men. Students come from 27 states and territories, 2 other countries, 8% from out-of-state. 1% American Indian or Alaska Native, non-Hispanic/Latino; 1% Hispanic/Latino; 9% African American, non-Hispanic/Latino; 0.5% Asian, non-Hispanic/Latino; 1% Native Hawaiian or other Pacific Islander, non-Hispanic/Latino; 0.1% international. 40% 25 or older, 14% live on campus, 15% transferred in. Retention: 75% of full-time freshmen returned the following year. Academic areas with the most degrees conferred: business/marketing; education; agriculture. Core. Calendar: semesters. Academic remediation for entering students, services for LD students, advanced placement, honors program, independent study, distance learning, summer session for credit, part-time degree program, external degree program, adult/continuing education programs, internships. Off campus study at Kentucky Institute of International Studies. Study abroad program. ROTC: Army (c), Air Force (c).
Entrance Requirements: Options: electronic application, early admission, deferred admission. Required: high school transcript, SAT or ACT. Recommended: minimum 2.2 high school GPA. Required for some: essay, interview. Entrance: minimally difficult. Application deadline: Rolling. Notification: continuous.
Collegiate Environment: Orientation program. Choral group. Social organizations: 21 open to all. Most popular organizations: student government, Midway Chorale, Midway Association of Nursing Students, Kentucky Education Association-Student Program, Midway Horse Women's Association. Major annual events: Christmas Vespers, Last Supper, Night of Lights.

Student services: health clinic, personal-psychological counseling, women's center. Campus security: 24-hour emergency response devices and patrols, late night transport-escort service. Little Memorial Library with 96,236 books, 58,217 microform titles, 250 serials, an OPAC, and a Web page. 50 computers available on campus for general student use. A campuswide network can be accessed from student residence rooms and from off campus. Students can access the following: online class registration. Staffed computer lab on campus provides training in use of computers, software, and the Internet.
Community Environment: Appropriately named, Midway is located halfway between Lexington and Frankfort in Woodford County. The climate is moderate. Midway has seven churches of various denominations and several large horse farms.

■ MOREHEAD STATE UNIVERSITY

University Blvd.
Morehead, KY 40351
Tel: (606)783-2221; Free: 800-585-6781
Fax: (606)783-5038
E-mail: admissions@moreheadstate.edu
Web Site: www.moreheadstate.edu/
Description: State-supported, comprehensive, coed. Awards associate, bachelor's, master's, and doctoral degrees and post-master's certificates. Founded 1922. Setting: 1,016-acre small town campus. Research spending for the previous fiscal year: $2 million. Educational spending for the previous fiscal year: $6970 per student. Total enrollment: 11,172. Faculty: 479 (381 full-time, 98 part-time). Student-undergrad faculty ratio is 17:1. 5,230 applied, 84% were admitted. 20% from top 10% of their high school class, 47% from top quarter, 80% from top half. Full-time: 5,897 students, 60% women, 40% men. Part-time: 3,828 students, 64% women, 36% men. 14% from out-of-state. 0.2% American Indian or Alaska Native, non-Hispanic/Latino; 1% Hispanic/Latino; 3% African American, non-Hispanic/Latino; 0.4% Asian, non-Hispanic/Latino; 0.1% Native Hawaiian or other Pacific Islander, non-Hispanic/Latino; 1% international. 23% 25 or older, 35% live on campus, 5% transferred in. Retention: 66% of full-time freshmen returned the following year. Academic areas with the most degrees conferred: education; liberal arts/general studies; business/marketing. Core. Calendar: semesters. Academic remediation for entering students, services for LD students, advanced placement, accelerated degree program, self-designed majors, honors program, independent study, distance learning, double major, summer session for credit, part-time degree program, adult/continuing education programs, co-op programs and internships, graduate courses open to undergrads. Off campus study at Pikeville College. Study abroad program. ROTC: Army.
Entrance Requirements: Options: electronic application, early admission, deferred admission, international baccalaureate accepted. Required: high school transcript, SAT or ACT. Required for some: essay, 1 recommendation, interview. Entrance: minimally difficult. Application deadline: Rolling. Notification: continuous. Transfer credits accepted: Yes.
Costs Per Year: Application fee: $30. Area resident tuition: $276 per credit hour part-time. Nonresident tuition: $690 per credit hour part-time. Part-time tuition varies according to course load, degree level, location, reciprocity agreements, and student level.
Collegiate Environment: Orientation program. Drama-theater group, choral group, marching band, student-run newspaper, radio station. Social organizations: national fraternities, national sororities; 10% of eligible men and 10% of eligible women are members. Major annual events: Homecoming, Move-In Day/New Student Days. Student services: health clinic, personal-psychological counseling. Campus security: 24-hour emergency response devices and patrols, student patrols, late night transport-escort service, controlled dormitory access. 2,991 college housing spaces available. Freshmen given priority for college housing. On-campus residence required through sophomore year. Option: coed housing available. Camden Carroll Library with 591,287 books, 868,420 microform titles, 56,528 serials, 28,271 audiovisual materials, an OPAC, and a Web page. Operations spending for the previous fiscal year: $3.1 million. 1,000 computers available on campus for general student use. Computer purchase/lease plans available. A campuswide network can be accessed from student residence rooms and from off campus. Students can access the following: online class registration. Staffed computer lab on campus (open 24 hours a day) provides training in use of computers, software, and the Internet.
Community Environment: The city of Morehead is located between Lexington, KY, and Huntington, WV. Community services include a hospital, several churches, five motels, several restaurants and 2 shopping centers. Area recreation includes the Daniel Boone National Forest. The campus is a

1-hour drive from several state parks, and 20 minutes from swimming, boating, fishing, and water skiing. The campus also has Eagle Lake for recreation with a golf course and horseback riding. Several annual local festivals and university-sponsored Appalachia celebrations provide further entertainment.

■ MURRAY STATE UNIVERSITY

113 Sparks Hall
Murray, KY 42071
Tel: (270)762-3011; Free: 800-272-4678
Fax: (270)762-3413
E-mail: admissions@murraystate.edu
Web Site: www.murraystate.edu/
Description: State-supported, comprehensive, coed. Part of Kentucky Council on Post Secondary Education. Awards associate, bachelor's, master's, and doctoral degrees and post-master's certificates. Founded 1922. Setting: 238-acre small town campus. Endowment: $59 million. Research spending for the previous fiscal year: $3.3 million. Educational spending for the previous fiscal year: $7190 per student. Total enrollment: 10,832. Faculty: 611 (423 full-time, 188 part-time). Student-undergrad faculty ratio is 16:1. 4,573 applied, 82% were admitted. 17% from top 10% of their high school class, 41% from top quarter, 75% from top half. 55 valedictorians. Full-time: 7,090 students, 58% women, 42% men. Part-time: 1,801 students, 60% women, 40% men. Students come from 44 states and territories, 51 other countries, 29% from out-of-state. 0.2% American Indian or Alaska Native, non-Hispanic/Latino; 2% Hispanic/Latino; 7% African American, non-Hispanic/Latino; 1% Asian, non-Hispanic/Latino; 0.1% Native Hawaiian or other Pacific Islander, non-Hispanic/Latino; 5% international. 19% 25 or older, 36% live on campus, 8% transferred in. Retention: 70% of full-time freshmen returned the following year. Academic areas with the most degrees conferred: education; business/marketing; health professions and related sciences. Core. Calendar: semesters. Academic remediation for entering students, ESL program, services for LD students, advanced placement, freshman honors college, honors program, independent study, distance learning, double major, summer session for credit, part-time degree program, external degree program, adult/continuing education programs, co-op programs and internships, graduate courses open to undergrads. Off campus study at National Student Exchange. Study abroad program. ROTC: Army.
Entrance Requirements: Option: electronic application. Required: high school transcript, minimum 3 high school GPA, Pre-College Curricula, SAT or ACT. Recommended: ACT. Entrance: moderately difficult. Notification: continuous until 8/1, continuous until 1/8 for nonresidents. Transfer credits accepted: Yes.
Costs Per Year: Application fee: $30. State resident tuition: $5880 full-time, $285 per credit hour part-time. Nonresident tuition: $7942 full-time, $369 per credit hour part-time. Mandatory fees: $960 full-time. Full-time tuition and fees vary according to reciprocity agreements. Part-time tuition varies according to reciprocity agreements. College room and board: $7638. College room only: $4430. Room and board charges vary according to board plan and housing facility.
Collegiate Environment: Orientation program. Drama-theater group, choral group, marching band, student-run newspaper, radio station. Social organizations: 200 open to all; national fraternities, national sororities, local fraternities, local sororities; 15% of eligible men and 12% of eligible women are members. Most popular organizations: student government, Baptist Student Union, Christ Ambassadors, Residential Colleges, Greek Organizations. Major annual events: Homecoming, All Campus Sing. Student services: legal services, health clinic, personal-psychological counseling, women's center. Campus security: 24-hour emergency response devices and patrols, student patrols, late night transport-escort service, controlled dormitory access. 3,200 college housing spaces available; 280 were occupied in 2012-13. No special consideration for freshman housing applicants. On-campus residence required through sophomore year. Options: coed, women-only housing available. Waterfield Library plus 2 others with 934,637 books, 209,994 microform titles, 1,273 serials, 37,921 audiovisual materials, an OPAC, and a Web page. Operations spending for the previous fiscal year: $2.6 million. 1,800 computers available on campus for general student use. Computer purchase/lease plans available. A campuswide network can be accessed from student residence rooms and from off campus. Students can access the following: online class registration, billing accounts. Staffed computer lab on campus (open 24 hours a day) provides training in use of computers, software, and the Internet.
Community Environment: The area around Munas has a hospital and

several churches. Recreation is available at nearby Kentucky Lake, the largest lake created by the Tennessee Valley Authority, Lake Barkley, and Land Between Lakes, a recreation area of 177,000 acres. Part-time employment is available.

■ **NATIONAL COLLEGE (DANVILLE)**
115 E Lexington Ave.
Danville, KY 40422
Tel: (859)236-6991; Free: 888-9-JOBREADY
Web Site: www.national-college.edu/
Description: Proprietary, 2-year, coed. Part of National College of Business and Technology. Awards diplomas and terminal associate degrees. Founded 1962. Core. Services for LD students, advanced placement, honors program, double major, summer session for credit, part-time degree program, internships.
Entrance Requirements: Open admission. Option: electronic application. Required: high school transcript. Entrance: noncompetitive. Application deadline: Rolling. Notification: continuous.
Collegiate Environment: Orientation program.

■ **NATIONAL COLLEGE (FLORENCE)**
7627 Ewing Blvd.
Florence, KY 41042
Tel: (859)525-6510; Free: 888-9-JOBREADY
Fax: (859)525-8961
Web Site: www.national-college.edu/
Description: Proprietary, 2-year, coed. Part of National College of Business and Technology. Awards diplomas and terminal associate degrees. Founded 1941. Setting: suburban campus. Core. Services for LD students, advanced placement, honors program, double major, summer session for credit, part-time degree program, internships.
Entrance Requirements: Open admission. Option: electronic application. Recommended: interview. Required for some: high school transcript. Entrance: noncompetitive. Application deadline: Rolling. Notification: continuous.
Collegiate Environment: Orientation program. Campus security: 24-hour emergency response devices.

■ **NATIONAL COLLEGE (LEXINGTON)**
2376 Sir Barton Way
Lexington, KY 40509
Tel: (859)253-0621; Free: 888-9-JOBREADY
Web Site: www.national-college.edu/
Description: Proprietary, primarily 2-year, coed. Part of National College of Business and Technology. Awards diplomas, terminal associate, and bachelor's degrees. Founded 1947. Setting: urban campus. Core. Advanced placement, honors program, double major, summer session for credit, part-time degree program, internships.
Entrance Requirements: Open admission. Option: electronic application. Required: high school transcript. Entrance: noncompetitive. Application deadline: Rolling. Notification: continuous.
Collegiate Environment: Orientation program.

■ **NATIONAL COLLEGE (LOUISVILLE)**
4205 Dixie Hwy.
Louisville, KY 40216
Tel: (502)447-7634; Free: 888-9-JOBREADY
Web Site: www.national-college.edu/
Description: Proprietary, primarily 2-year, coed. Part of National College of Business and Technology. Awards diplomas, terminal associate, and bachelor's degrees. Founded 1990. Core. Services for LD students, advanced placement, honors program, double major, summer session for credit, part-time degree program, internships.
Entrance Requirements: Open admission. Option: electronic application. Recommended: interview. Required for some: high school transcript. Entrance: noncompetitive. Application deadline: Rolling. Notification: continuous.
Collegiate Environment: Orientation program.

■ **NATIONAL COLLEGE (PIKEVILLE)**
50 National College Blvd.
Pikeville, KY 41501
Tel: (606)478-7200; Free: 888-9-JOBREADY
Fax: (606)437-4952

Web Site: www.national-college.edu/
Description: Proprietary, 2-year, coed. Part of National College of Business and Technology. Awards diplomas and terminal associate degrees. Founded 1976. Setting: rural campus. Core. Services for LD students, advanced placement, honors program, double major, summer session for credit, part-time degree program, internships.
Entrance Requirements: Open admission. Recommended: interview. Required for some: high school transcript. Entrance: noncompetitive. Application deadline: Rolling. Notification: continuous.
Collegiate Environment: Orientation program.

■ **NATIONAL COLLEGE (RICHMOND)**
125 S Killarney Ln.
Richmond, KY 40475
Tel: (859)623-8956; Free: 888-9-JOBREADY
Fax: (859)624-5544
Web Site: www.national-college.edu/
Description: Proprietary, 2-year, coed. Part of National College of Business and Technology. Awards diplomas and terminal associate degrees. Founded 1951. Setting: suburban campus. Core. Advanced placement, honors program, double major, summer session for credit, part-time degree program, internships.
Entrance Requirements: Open admission. Option: electronic application. Recommended: interview. Required for some: high school transcript. Entrance: noncompetitive. Application deadline: Rolling. Notification: continuous.
Collegiate Environment: Orientation program.

■ **NORTHERN KENTUCKY UNIVERSITY**
Louie B Nunn Dr.
Highland Heights, KY 41099
Tel: (859)572-5100; Free: 800-637-9948
E-mail: admitnku@nku.edu
Web Site: www.nku.edu/
Description: State-supported, comprehensive, coed. Awards associate, bachelor's, master's, and doctoral degrees and post-master's certificates. Founded 1968. Setting: 398-acre suburban campus with easy access to Cincinnati. Endowment: $68.9 million. Research spending for the previous fiscal year: $185,600. Educational spending for the previous fiscal year: $5840 per student. Total enrollment: 15,634. Faculty: 1,060 (548 full-time, 512 part-time). Student-undergrad faculty ratio is 18:1. 7,064 applied, 47% were admitted. 9% from top 10% of their high school class, 29% from top quarter, 60% from top half. Full-time: 10,031 students, 54% women, 46% men. Part-time: 3,287 students, 57% women, 43% men. Students come from 43 states and territories, 51 other countries, 32% from out-of-state. 0.3% American Indian or Alaska Native, non-Hispanic/Latino; 2% Hispanic/Latino; 6% African American, non-Hispanic/Latino; 1% Asian, non-Hispanic/Latino; 0.1% Native Hawaiian or other Pacific Islander, non-Hispanic/Latino; 4% international. 27% 25 or older, 14% live on campus, 7% transferred in. Retention: 67% of full-time freshmen returned the following year. Academic areas with the most degrees conferred: business/marketing; health professions and related sciences; communication/journalism. Core. Calendar: semesters. Academic remediation for entering students, ESL program, services for LD students, advanced placement, accelerated degree program, self-designed majors, honors program, independent study, distance learning, double major, summer session for credit, part-time degree program, adult/continuing education programs, co-op programs and internships, graduate courses open to undergrads. Off campus study at all Kentucky state schools, members of the Greater Cincinnati Consortium of Colleges and Universities. Study abroad program. ROTC: Army (c), Air Force (c).
Entrance Requirements: Options: electronic application, early admission, deferred admission, international baccalaureate accepted. Required: high school transcript, SAT or ACT. Required for some: some programs require separate applications. Entrance: moderately difficult. Notification: continuous, continuous for nonresidents. Transfer credits accepted: Yes.
Costs Per Year: Application fee: $40. State resident tuition: $7872 full-time, $328 per credit hour part-time. Nonresident tuition: $15,744 full-time, $656 per credit hour part-time. Mandatory fees: $192 full-time. Full-time tuition and fees vary according to course load and reciprocity agreements. Part-time tuition varies according to course load and reciprocity agreements. College room and board: $7430. Room and board charges vary according to board plan and housing facility.
Collegiate Environment: Orientation program. Drama-theater group, choral group, student-run newspaper, radio station. Social organizations: 150 open

to all; national fraternities, national sororities; 8% of eligible men and 8% of eligible women are members. Most popular organizations: Sororities, Fraternities, Freshmen Service Leadership Committee, Student Alumni Association, Activities Programming Board. Major annual events: Freshfusion, Homecoming, Welcome Week. Student services: health clinic, personal-psychological counseling, women's center. Campus security: 24-hour emergency response devices and patrols, late night transport-escort service, controlled dormitory access. 1,822 college housing spaces available; 1,760 were occupied in 2012-13. Option: coed housing available. W. Frank Steely Library plus 1 other with 888,132 books, 620,179 microform titles, 46,140 serials, 11,004 audiovisual materials, an OPAC, and a Web page. Operations spending for the previous fiscal year: $6.6 million. 250 computers available on campus for general student use. Computer purchase/lease plans available. A campuswide network can be accessed from student residence rooms and from off campus. Students can access the following: online class registration. Staffed computer lab on campus provides training in use of computers, software, and the Internet.

Community Environment: Located in the largest metropolitan area of any state university in Kentucky, NKU is seven miles southeast of Cincinnati, Ohio.

■ OWENSBORO COMMUNITY AND TECHNICAL COLLEGE
4800 New Hartford Rd.
Owensboro, KY 42303-1899
Tel: (270)686-4400; Free: 866-755-6282
Fax: (270)686-4496
E-mail: barb.tipmore@kctcs.edu
Web Site: www.octc.kctcs.edu/

Description: State-supported, 2-year, coed. Part of Kentucky Community and Technical College System. Awards certificates, diplomas, transfer associate, and terminal associate degrees. Founded 1986. Setting: 102-acre suburban campus. Total enrollment: 4,768. Faculty: 206 (101 full-time, 105 part-time). Student-undergrad faculty ratio is 21:1. Full-time: 1,979 students, 60% women, 40% men. Part-time: 2,789 students, 55% women, 45% men. Students come from 11 states and territories, 4% from out-of-state. 0.2% American Indian or Alaska Native, non-Hispanic/Latino; 1% Hispanic/Latino; 3% African American, non-Hispanic/Latino; 0.2% Asian, non-Hispanic/Latino; 0.1% Native Hawaiian or other Pacific Islander, non-Hispanic/Latino; 0.04% international. 31% 25 or older. Retention: 59% of full-time freshmen returned the following year. Core. Calendar: semesters. Academic remediation for entering students, ESL program, services for LD students, advanced placement, self-designed majors, honors program, independent study, distance learning, double major, summer session for credit, part-time degree program, external degree program, adult/continuing education programs, co-op programs. Off campus study. Study abroad program.

Entrance Requirements: Open admission. Option: electronic application. Required: high school transcript. Recommended: SAT or ACT. Entrance: noncompetitive. Application deadline: Rolling. Notification: continuous. Transfer credits accepted: Yes.

Costs Per Year: Application fee: $0. State resident tuition: $4200 full-time, $140 per credit part-time. Nonresident tuition: $14,700 full-time, $490 per credit part-time. Full-time tuition varies according to course load and reciprocity agreements. Part-time tuition varies according to course load and reciprocity agreements.

Collegiate Environment: Orientation program. Drama-theater group, choral group. Social organizations: 5 open to all. Most popular organization: Student Government Association. Major annual events: Fall Fling, Spring Fling, Hanging of Greens. Campus security: 24-hour emergency response devices, late night transport-escort service. Learning Resource Center with 81,096 books, 2,463 audiovisual materials, an OPAC, and a Web page. 300 computers available on campus for general student use. A campuswide network can be accessed from off-campus. Students can access the following: online class registration. Staffed computer lab on campus provides training in use of computers and the Internet.

Community Environment: A myriad of items including bread, soybean oil, paper, plastics, and electronic components are made in the Owensboro area. Thirty manufacturers have forty or more employees, including such national firms as Baskin-Robbins, General Electric, and Kimberly Clark. Eight percent of the land is used for farming. The fifth largest city in the state, population 55,459, it is home to the International Barbecue Festival, the International Bluegrass Museum Association, and the world's largest sassafras tree.

■ ST. CATHARINE COLLEGE
2735 Bardstown Rd.
Saint Catharine, KY 40061-9499
Tel: (859)336-5082; Free: 800-599-2000
Fax: (859)336-5031
Web Site: www.sccky.edu/

Description: Independent Roman Catholic, comprehensive, coed. Awards associate and master's degrees. Founded 1931. Setting: 643-acre rural campus with easy access to Louisville. Endowment: $300,000. Total enrollment: 751. Faculty: 49 (35 full-time, 14 part-time). Student-undergrad faculty ratio is 15:1. 700 applied, 45% were admitted. Students come from 45 other countries. 32% 25 or older, 19% live on campus. Core. Calendar: semesters. Academic remediation for entering students, services for LD students, advanced placement, summer session for credit, part-time degree program, co-op programs and internships.

Entrance Requirements: Options: electronic application, early admission. Required for some: high school transcript. Entrance: minimally difficult. Application deadline: Rolling.

Collegiate Environment: Drama-theater group, choral group, student-run newspaper. Most popular organizations: African-American Club, International Club, student government, Phi Theta Kappa. Major annual events: Homecoming Weekend, Christmas Dance, Awards Banquet. Student services: personal-psychological counseling. Campus security: 24-hour emergency response devices, night security guard. St. Catharine College Library with 25,000 books, 110 serials, an OPAC, and a Web page. 60 computers available on campus for general student use. Staffed computer lab on campus.

■ SOMERSET COMMUNITY COLLEGE
808 Monticello St.
Somerset, KY 42501-2973
Tel: (606)679-8501; Free: 877-629-9722
E-mail: somerset-admissions@kctcs.edu
Web Site: www.somerset.kctcs.edu/

Description: State-supported, 2-year, coed. Part of Kentucky Community and Technical College System. Awards certificates, diplomas, transfer associate, and terminal associate degrees. Founded 1965. Setting: 70-acre small town campus. Total enrollment: 8,201. Student-undergrad faculty ratio is 23:1. 0% from out-of-state. 45% 25 or older. Retention: 59% of full-time freshmen returned the following year. Calendar: semesters. Academic remediation for entering students, advanced placement, distance learning, summer session for credit, part-time degree program, adult/continuing education programs.

Entrance Requirements: Open admission except for nursing, clinical laboratory technology, physical therapy assistant, surgical technology, radiography programs. Options: electronic application, early admission. Required: high school transcript. Entrance: noncompetitive. Application deadline: 8/14. Notification: continuous.

Costs Per Year: Application fee: $0. State resident tuition: $4200 full-time, $140 per credit hour part-time. Nonresident tuition: $14,700 full-time, $490 per credit hour part-time. Full-time tuition varies according to course load. Part-time tuition varies according to course load.

Collegiate Environment: Orientation program.

Community Environment: Located in an urban area in south central Kentucky, railroad and bus service are available to Somerset. It has a local YMCA, library, hospital and other health services and various organizations including Rotary, Kiwanis, Jaycees, and a Chamber of Commerce. Recreation is provided with 3 theatres, drive-ins, golf, tennis, and Lake Cumberland with 1,225 miles of shoreline.

■ SOUTHCENTRAL KENTUCKY COMMUNITY AND TECHNICAL COLLEGE
1845 Loop Dr.
Bowling Green, KY 42101
Tel: (270)901-1000; Free: 800-790-0990
Fax: (270)746-7466
Web Site: www.bowlinggreen.kctcs.edu/

Description: State-supported, 2-year, coed. Awards terminal associate degrees. Founded 1938. Total enrollment: 4,953. 54% 25 or older. Calendar: semesters.

Entrance Requirements: Open admission.

■ SOUTHEAST KENTUCKY COMMUNITY AND TECHNICAL COLLEGE
700 College Rd.
Cumberland, KY 40823-1099

Tel: (606)589-2145; Free: 888-274-SECC
Fax: (606)589-5423
E-mail: cookie.baldwin@kctcs.edu
Web Site: www.southeast.kctcs.edu/
Description: State-supported, 2-year, coed. Part of Kentucky Community and Technical College System. Awards certificates, diplomas, transfer associate, and terminal associate degrees. Founded 1960. Setting: 150-acre rural campus. Educational spending for the previous fiscal year: $5481 per student. Total enrollment: 4,959. Faculty: 214 (106 full-time, 108 part-time). Student-undergrad faculty ratio is 19:1. 650 applied, 98% were admitted. 20% from top 10% of their high school class, 30% from top quarter, 40% from top half. 4 valedictorians. Full-time: 1,943 students, 63% women, 37% men. Part-time: 3,016 students, 41% women, 59% men. Students come from 10 states and territories, 1 other country, 5% from out-of-state. 35% 25 or older, 1% transferred in. Retention: 65% of full-time freshmen returned the following year. Core. Calendar: semesters. Academic remediation for entering students, advanced placement, accelerated degree program, independent study, distance learning, summer session for credit, part-time degree program, adult/continuing education programs. Study abroad program.
Entrance Requirements: Open admission except for allied health programs that have selective admissions. Required: high school transcript. Recommended: ACT. Entrance: noncompetitive. Application deadline: 8/20. Notification: continuous until 9/3.
Collegiate Environment: Orientation program. Drama-theater group, choral group, student-run newspaper. Social organizations: 10 open to all. Most popular organizations: Professional Business Leaders, Student Government Association, Phi Theta Kappa, Black Student Union, Nursing Club. Major annual events: Octoberfest, Swappin' Meetin', Spring on Cloverlick. Gertrude Dale Library plus 4 others with 25,921 books, 200 serials, 924 audiovisual materials, an OPAC, and a Web page. 96 computers available on campus for general student use. A campuswide network can be accessed from off-campus. Students can access the following: online class registration, online admissions. Staffed computer lab on campus.
Community Environment: Cumberland is a rural town in Harlan County of southeastern Kentucky. The city has Protestant and Catholic churches, and a community hospital and other medical services. Recreation is provided by movie theaters, fishing at Kingdom Come State Park Lake, picnic areas, a lodge and trailer park and a city park. Local merchants employ college students since the town serves an area of approximately 20,000 persons. Various civic, service, fraternal and veteran's organizations, including a Chamber of Commerce, enhance the community spirit.

■ SOUTHERN BAPTIST THEOLOGICAL SEMINARY
2825 Lexington Rd.
Louisville, KY 40280-0004
Tel: (502)897-4011
Web Site: www.sbts.edu/
Description: Independent Southern Baptist, comprehensive, coed. Awards associate, bachelor's, master's, and doctoral degrees. Founded 1858. Total enrollment: 3,190. 110 applied, 71% were admitted. Full-time: 412 students, 28% women, 72% men. Part-time: 256 students, 31% women, 69% men. 63% 25 or older, 12% transferred in. Retention: 78% of full-time freshmen returned the following year. Core. Graduate courses open to undergrads.
Entrance Requirements: Open admission. Option: international baccalaureate accepted. Required: essay, high school transcript, minimum 2.0 high school GPA. Required for some: SAT or ACT. Application deadline: 7/15.
Collegiate Environment: Orientation program. Choral group. Student services: health clinic, personal-psychological counseling.
Community Environment: See University of Louisville.

■ SPALDING UNIVERSITY
845 S Third St.
Louisville, KY 40203-2188
Tel: (502)585-9911; Free: 800-896-8941
Fax: (502)585-7158
E-mail: admissions@spalding.edu
Web Site: www.spalding.edu/
Description: Independent, comprehensive, coed, affiliated with Roman Catholic Church. Awards associate, bachelor's, master's, and doctoral degrees and post-master's certificates. Founded 1814. Setting: 5-acre urban campus with easy access to Louisville. Endowment: $11.5 million. Research spending for the previous fiscal year: $72,986. Educational spending for the previous fiscal year: $6255 per student. Total enrollment: 2,432. Faculty: 169

(89 full-time, 80 part-time). Student-undergrad faculty ratio is 11:1. 790 applied, 43% were admitted. Full-time: 983 students, 73% women, 27% men. Part-time: 388 students, 75% women, 25% men. Students come from 13 states and territories, 7 other countries, 10% from out-of-state. 0.4% American Indian or Alaska Native, non-Hispanic/Latino; 3% Hispanic/Latino; 29% African American, non-Hispanic/Latino; 1% Asian, non-Hispanic/Latino; 0.1% Native Hawaiian or other Pacific Islander, non-Hispanic/Latino; 0.4% international. 52% 25 or older, 8% live on campus, 14% transferred in. Retention: 73% of full-time freshmen returned the following year. Academic areas with the most degrees conferred: health professions and related sciences; business/marketing; psychology. Core. Academic remediation for entering students, services for LD students, advanced placement, accelerated degree program, independent study, distance learning, double major, summer session for credit, part-time degree program, adult/continuing education programs, co-op programs and internships, graduate courses open to undergrads. Off campus study at other institutions in the Kentuckiana Metroversity (University of Louisville, Bellarmine University, Indiana University Southeast, Southern Baptist Theological Seminary, Louisville Presbyterian Theological Seminary, and Jefferson Community College) and the Regis Online Consortium. Study abroad program. ROTC: Army (c), Air Force (c).
Entrance Requirements: Options: electronic application, early admission, deferred admission, international baccalaureate accepted. Required: high school transcript, minimum 2.5 high school GPA, SAT or ACT. Recommended: interview. Required for some: essay. Entrance: moderately difficult. Application deadlines: Rolling, Rolling for nonresidents. Notification: continuous, continuous for nonresidents. Transfer credits accepted: Yes.
Costs Per Year: Application fee: $20. Comprehensive fee: $28,950 includes full-time tuition ($20,550) and college room and board ($8400). College room only: $5600. Full-time tuition varies according to course load and program. Room and board charges vary according to board plan.
Collegiate Environment: Orientation program. Social organizations: 18 open to all. Most popular organizations: Egan Service Learning Program, Student Government Association, Student Occupational Therapy Association, Residence Hall Advisory Council, Best Buddies. Major annual events: Rat Race - Run for the Rodents, Welcome Week, Pizza with the President. Student services: personal-psychological counseling. Campus security: 24-hour emergency response devices and patrols, late night transport-escort service, controlled dormitory access, outdoor emergency call stations located in various locations around campus. 342 college housing spaces available; 113 were occupied in 2012-13. No special consideration for freshman housing applicants. Option: coed housing available. Spalding Library with 101,988 books, 102 serials, 2,330 audiovisual materials, an OPAC, and a Web page. Operations spending for the previous fiscal year: $532,794. 250 computers available on campus for general student use. A campuswide network can be accessed from student residence rooms and from off campus. Students can access the following: online class registration. Staffed computer lab on campus provides training in use of computers, software, and the Internet.
Community Environment: See University of Louisville.

■ SPENCERIAN COLLEGE
4627 Dixie Hwy.
Louisville, KY 40216
Tel: (502)447-1000; Free: 800-264-1799
Fax: (502)447-4574
Web Site: www.spencerian.edu/
Description: Proprietary, 2-year, coed. Administratively affiliated with The Sullivan University System. Awards certificates, diplomas, and terminal associate degrees. Founded 1892. Setting: 10-acre urban campus. Total enrollment: 696. Faculty: 101 (47 full-time, 54 part-time). Student-undergrad faculty ratio is 11:1. Full-time: 429 students, 82% women, 18% men. Part-time: 267 students, 91% women, 9% men. 0.1% American Indian or Alaska Native, non-Hispanic/Latino; 2% Hispanic/Latino; 21% African American, non-Hispanic/Latino; 0.3% Asian, non-Hispanic/Latino; 0.1% Native Hawaiian or other Pacific Islander, non-Hispanic/Latino; 0% international. 1% live on campus. Distance learning, summer session for credit. Off campus study at Sullivan University System (general education courses for associate degree nursing students).
Entrance Requirements: Open admission selective admission to some programs. Required: high school transcript. Required for some: essay, interview, Some medical programs have specific selective admission criteria. Entrance: moderately difficult. Notification: continuous, continuous for nonresidents.

Collegiate Environment: Orientation program. Option: coed housing available. Spencerian College Learning Resource Center with 1,585 books, 300 audiovisual materials, an OPAC, and a Web page. 113 computers available on campus for general student use. A campuswide network can be accessed from off-campus.

■ **SPENCERIAN COLLEGE–LEXINGTON**
1575 Winchester Rd.
Lexington, KY 40505
Tel: (859)223-9608; Free: 800-456-3253
Fax: (859)224-7744
E-mail: dprofita@spencerian.edu
Web Site: www.spencerian.edu/
Description: Proprietary, 2-year, coed. Part of Sullivan Colleges System. Awards certificates, diplomas, and terminal associate degrees. Founded 1997. Setting: urban campus with easy access to Louisville. Total enrollment: 656. Faculty: 44 (24 full-time, 20 part-time). Student-undergrad faculty ratio is 11:1. 45% 25 or older. Academic remediation for entering students, services for LD students, independent study, summer session for credit, part-time degree program, co-op programs.
Entrance Requirements: Required: high school transcript, interview. Required for some: CPAt. Entrance: moderately difficult. Application deadline: Rolling.
Collegiate Environment: Orientation program. Student-run newspaper. Major annual events: golf tournament, school picnic, Student Appreciation Week. Campus security: 24-hour emergency response devices. Spencerian College Library with 450 books, 30 serials, and 25 audiovisual materials. 130 computers available on campus for general student use. A campuswide network can be accessed from off-campus. Staffed computer lab on campus.

■ **STRAYER UNIVERSITY - FLORENCE CAMPUS**
7300 Turfway Rd.
Ste. 250
Florence, KY 41042
Tel: (859)692-2800
Fax: (859)282-8078
Web Site: www.strayer.edu/campus/florence
Description: Proprietary, comprehensive, coed. Awards associate, bachelor's, and master's degrees.

■ **STRAYER UNIVERSITY - LEXINGTON CAMPUS**
220 Lexington Green Cir.
Ste. 550
Lexington, KY 40503
Tel: (859)971-4400
Fax: (859)971-4430
Web Site: www.strayer.edu/campus/lexington/
Description: Proprietary, comprehensive, coed. Awards associate, bachelor's, and master's degrees.

■ **STRAYER UNIVERSITY - LOUISVILLE CAMPUS**
2650 Eastpoint Pky.
Ste. 100
Louisville, KY 40223
Tel: (502)253-5000
Fax: (502)253-5030
Web Site: www.strayer.edu/campus/louisville/
Description: Proprietary, comprehensive, coed. Awards associate, bachelor's, and master's degrees.

■ **SULLIVAN COLLEGE OF TECHNOLOGY AND DESIGN**
3901 Atkinson Sq. Dr.
Louisville, KY 40218-4528
Tel: (502)456-6509; Free: 800-884-6528
Fax: (502)456-2341
E-mail: achauhdri@sctd.edu
Web Site: www.sctd.edu/
Description: Proprietary, primarily 2-year, coed. Part of The Sullivan University System, Inc. Awards transfer associate, terminal associate, and bachelor's degrees. Founded 1961. Setting: 10-acre suburban campus with easy access to Louisville. Total enrollment: 457. Faculty: 65 (30 full-time, 35 part-time). Student-undergrad faculty ratio is 12:1. Full-time: 316 students, 28% women, 72% men. Part-time: 141 students, 41% women, 59% men. Students come from 5 states and territories, 1 other country, 11% from out-of-state. 0.2% American Indian or Alaska Native, non-Hispanic/Latino; 5% Hispanic/Latino; 18% African American, non-Hispanic/Latino; 1% Asian, non-Hispanic/Latino; 0% Native Hawaiian or other Pacific Islander, non-Hispanic/Latino; 0% international. 45% 25 or older, 7% live on campus, 18% transferred in. Retention: 0% of full-time freshmen returned the following year. Academic areas with the most degrees conferred: visual and performing arts; computer and information sciences. Academic remediation for entering students, services for LD students, advanced placement, accelerated degree program, independent study, double major, summer session for credit, part-time degree program, adult/continuing education programs, internships.
Entrance Requirements: Options: electronic application, deferred admission. Required: high school transcript, interview, CPAT Exam or ACT/SAT Scores, Career Performance Assessment Test (CPAt) or ACT or SAT Language and Math scores in place of CPAt results. Recommended: SAT or ACT. Entrance: moderately difficult. Application deadlines: Rolling, Rolling for nonresidents. Notification: continuous, continuous for nonresidents. Transfer credits accepted: Yes.
Costs Per Year: Application fee: $100. One-time mandatory fee: $100. Comprehensive fee: $27,560 includes full-time tuition ($17,340), mandatory fees ($1400), and college room and board ($8820). Full-time tuition and fees vary according to course load, degree level, and program. Room and board charges vary according to board plan. Part-time tuition: $425 per quarter hour. Part-time tuition varies according to course load, degree level, and program. Tuition guaranteed not to increase for student's term of enrollment.
Collegiate Environment: Orientation program. Social organizations: 6 open to all; SCTD Honors Society. Most popular organizations: ASID, IIDA, ADDA, ADFED, Skills USA. Major annual events: School Picnic, Fall River Boat Cruise, Miscellaneous Events (Welcome Day, Halloween Costume Contest, Valentine's Day, Student Appreciation). Campus security: late night transport-escort service, controlled dormitory access, telephone alarm device during hours school is open; patrols by trained security personnel while classes are in session. 520 college housing spaces available; 31 were occupied in 2012-13. Freshmen given priority for college housing. Option: coed housing available. Sullivan College of Technology and Design Library plus 1 other with 3,035 books, 66 serials, 370 audiovisual materials, an OPAC, and a Web page. 232 computers available on campus for general student use. A campuswide network can be accessed from student residence rooms and from off campus. Students can access the following: wireless Internet. Staffed computer lab on campus provides training in use of computers, software, and the Internet.

■ **SULLIVAN UNIVERSITY**
3101 Bardstown Rd.
Louisville, KY 40205
Tel: (502)456-6504; Free: 800-844-1354
Fax: (502)456-0040
E-mail: admissions@sullivan.edu
Web Site: www.sullivan.edu/
Description: Proprietary, comprehensive, coed. Administratively affiliated with The Sullivan University System. Awards associate, bachelor's, master's, and doctoral degrees and post-master's certificates. Founded 1864. Setting: 15-acre urban campus. Educational spending for the previous fiscal year: $2669 per student. Total enrollment: 5,478. Faculty: 340 (152 full-time, 188 part-time). Student-undergrad faculty ratio is 18:1. 1,151 applied, 63% were admitted. Full-time: 2,182 students, 61% women, 39% men. Part-time: 1,817 students, 60% women, 40% men. Students come from 44 states and territories, 63 other countries, 15% from out-of-state. 1% American Indian or Alaska Native, non-Hispanic/Latino; 0.2% Hispanic/Latino; 21% African American, non-Hispanic/Latino; 1% Asian, non-Hispanic/Latino; 0.1% Native Hawaiian or other Pacific Islander, non-Hispanic/Latino; 0.2% international. 6% live on campus. Academic remediation for entering students, services for LD students, accelerated degree program, self-designed majors, independent study, distance learning, double major, summer session for credit, part-time degree program, adult/continuing education programs, co-op programs and internships.
Entrance Requirements: Options: electronic application, deferred admission. Required: high school transcript, interview, Acceptable SAT, ACT, Sullivan Admissions Placement Assessment Scores Required. Required for some: essay, 2 recommendations, Certain programs require criminal background checks and no felony convictions. Some drug and abuse related misdemeanors will exclude applicants from being accepted into several programs. Entrance: minimally difficult. Application deadline: Rolling. Notification: continuous. Transfer credits accepted: Yes.

Collegiate Environment: Orientation program. Choral group. Social organizations: 13 open to all; 2% of eligible men and 3% of eligible women are members. Most popular organizations: Student Activities Committee, Student Veterans Association, Sullivan Christian Fellowship, People 2 People Club, Glee Club. Major annual events: Luau, Summer Picnic/Festival, Haunted House. Student services: personal-psychological counseling. Campus security: 24-hour patrols, late night transport-escort service, controlled dormitory access. 520 college housing spaces available; 237 were occupied in 2012-13. Freshmen guaranteed college housing. Options: coed, men-only, women-only housing available. Sullivan University Library & Learning Resource Center with 38,889 books, 51,498 serials, 1,012 audiovisual materials, an OPAC, and a Web page. Operations spending for the previous fiscal year: $1 million. 92 computers available on campus for general student use. A campuswide network can be accessed from student residence rooms and from off campus. Staffed computer lab on campus provides training in use of computers, software, and the Internet.

■ **THOMAS MORE COLLEGE**
333 Thomas More Pky.
Crestview Hills, KY 41017-3495
Tel: (859)341-5800; Free: 800-825-4557
Fax: (859)344-3638
E-mail: admissions@thomasmore.edu
Web Site: www.thomasmore.edu/
Description: Independent Roman Catholic, comprehensive, coed. Awards associate, bachelor's, and master's degrees. Founded 1921. Setting: 100-acre suburban campus with easy access to Cincinnati. Endowment: $14 million. Educational spending for the previous fiscal year: $5420 per student. Total enrollment: 1,761. Faculty: 159 (76 full-time, 83 part-time). Student-undergrad faculty ratio is 14:1. 1,093 applied, 88% were admitted. 12% from top 10% of their high school class, 34% from top quarter, 62% from top half. 3 valedictorians. Full-time: 1,258 students, 50% women, 50% men. Part-time: 394 students, 60% women, 40% men. Students come from 16 states and territories, 3 other countries, 49% from out-of-state. 0.3% American Indian or Alaska Native, non-Hispanic/Latino; 2% Hispanic/Latino; 8% African American, non-Hispanic/Latino; 1% Asian, non-Hispanic/Latino; 0% Native Hawaiian or other Pacific Islander, non-Hispanic/Latino; 0.4% international. 31% 25 or older, 27% live on campus, 4% transferred in. Retention: 66% of full-time freshmen returned the following year. Academic areas with the most degrees conferred: business/marketing; health professions and related sciences; biological/life sciences; liberal arts/general studies. Core. Calendar: semesters. Academic remediation for entering students, services for LD students, advanced placement, accelerated degree program, self-designed majors, honors program, independent study, distance learning, double major, summer session for credit, part-time degree program, adult/continuing education programs, co-op programs and internships. Off campus study at members of the Greater Cincinnati Consortium of Colleges and Universities. Study abroad program. ROTC: Army (c), Air Force (c).
Entrance Requirements: Options: electronic application, deferred admission, international baccalaureate accepted. Required: high school transcript, minimum 2.5 high school GPA, SAT or ACT. Required for some: 2 recommendations. Entrance: moderately difficult. Application deadline: 8/1. Notification: continuous. SAT Reasoning Test deadline: 8/1. Transfer credits accepted: Yes.
Costs Per Year: Application fee: $25. Comprehensive fee: $34,720 includes full-time tuition ($26,500), mandatory fees ($720), and college room and board ($7500). College room only: $3500. Full-time tuition and fees vary according to student level. Room and board charges vary according to board plan and housing facility. Part-time tuition: $590 per credit. Part-time mandatory fees: $30 per hour, $15 per term. Part-time tuition and fees vary according to student level.
Collegiate Environment: Orientation program. Drama-theater group, choral group. Social organizations: 40 open to all; national fraternities, national sororities; 2% of eligible men and 4% of eligible women are members. Most popular organizations: Student Government Association, Student Activities Board, More Ministry, Outdoors Adventure Club, International Student Society. Major annual events: Pig Roast, Fall Carnival, Fall Day of Novelties. Student services: health clinic, personal-psychological counseling. Campus security: 24-hour emergency response devices and patrols, late night transport-escort service, controlled dormitory access. 400 college housing spaces available; 358 were occupied in 2012-13. No special consideration for freshman housing applicants. Options: coed, men-only, women-only housing available. Thomas More College Library with 113,904 books, 28,429 microform titles, 421 serials, 2,464 audiovisual materials, an OPAC, and a

Web page. Operations spending for the previous fiscal year: $452,582. 100 computers available on campus for general student use. A campuswide network can be accessed from student residence rooms and from off campus. Students can access the following: online class registration. Staffed computer lab on campus provides training in use of computers, software, and the Internet.
Community Environment: The campus is located just 10 minutes south of downtown Cincinnati. The Greater Cincinnati International Airport is a five-minute drive from campus. Numerous activities and faculties include the Cincinnati Symphony Orchestra, jazz clubs, restaurants, shops, live theater and ballet, the Cincinnati Zoo, the annual Riverfest, Oktoberfest and Taste of Cincinnati. Teams include the Cincinnati Reds and the Bengals.

■ **TRANSYLVANIA UNIVERSITY**
300 N Broadway
Lexington, KY 40508-1797
Tel: (859)233-8300; Free: 800-872-6798
Fax: (859)233-8797
E-mail: admissions@transy.edu
Web Site: www.transy.edu/
Description: Independent, 4-year, coed, affiliated with Christian Church (Disciples of Christ). Awards bachelor's degrees. Founded 1780. Setting: 40-acre urban campus with easy access to Cincinnati, Louisville. Educational spending for the previous fiscal year: $11,658 per student. Total enrollment: 1,074. Faculty: 108 (90 full-time, 18 part-time). Student-undergrad faculty ratio is 11:1. 1,569 applied, 85% were admitted. 40% from top 10% of their high school class, 72% from top quarter, 93% from top half. 4 National Merit Scholars, 15 valedictorians. Full-time: 1,060 students, 58% women, 42% men. Part-time: 14 students, 36% women, 64% men. Students come from 28 states and territories, 6 other countries, 18% from out-of-state. 0.1% American Indian or Alaska Native, non-Hispanic/Latino; 2% Hispanic/Latino; 3% African American, non-Hispanic/Latino; 2% Asian, non-Hispanic/Latino; 0% Native Hawaiian or other Pacific Islander, non-Hispanic/Latino; 1% international. 0.3% 25 or older, 76% live on campus, 2% transferred in. Retention: 88% of full-time freshmen returned the following year. Academic areas with the most degrees conferred: business/marketing; social sciences; visual and performing arts. Core. Calendar: 4-4-1. Services for LD students, advanced placement, self-designed majors, independent study, double major, summer session for credit, part-time degree program, internships. Off campus study at Washington Center for Internships and Academic Seminars, Kentucky Institute for International Studies. Study abroad program. ROTC: Army (c), Air Force (c).
Entrance Requirements: Options: electronic application, early admission, early action, deferred admission, international baccalaureate accepted. Required: essay, high school transcript, minimum 2.75 high school GPA, 2 recommendations, SAT or ACT. Recommended: interview. Required for some: interview. Entrance: very difficult. Application deadlines: 2/1, 12/1 for early action. Notification: 3/1, 1/15 for early action. SAT Reasoning Test deadline: 2/1. Transfer credits accepted: Yes.
Costs Per Year: Application fee: $0. Comprehensive fee: $38,615 includes full-time tuition ($28,645), mandatory fees ($1220), and college room and board ($8750). Room and board charges vary according to board plan, housing facility, and location. Part-time tuition: $3175 per course. Part-time tuition varies according to course load.
Collegiate Environment: Orientation program. Drama-theater group, choral group, student-run newspaper, radio station. Social organizations: 71 open to all; national fraternities, national sororities; 55% of eligible men and 57% of eligible women are members. Most popular organizations: Student Government Association, Delta Sigma Phi, Phi Mu, Delta Delta Delta, Chi Omega. Major annual events: Campus Sing, Crimson Affair, Transy's Got Talent. Student services: health clinic, personal-psychological counseling. Campus security: 24-hour emergency response devices and patrols, late night transport-escort service, controlled dormitory access. 972 college housing spaces available; 850 were occupied in 2012-13. Freshmen guaranteed college housing. On-campus residence required through junior year. Options: coed, men-only, women-only housing available. J. Douglas Gay Jr./Frances Carrick Thomas Library with 244,000 books, 13,571 microform titles, 18,000 serials, 4,483 audiovisual materials, an OPAC, and a Web page. Operations spending for the previous fiscal year: $643,393. 200 computers available on campus for general student use. A campuswide network can be accessed from student residence rooms and from off campus. Students can access the following: online class registration. Staffed computer lab on campus provides training in use of software.
Community Environment: See University of Kentucky.

■ UNION COLLEGE

310 College St.
Barbourville, KY 40906-1499
Tel: (606)546-4151; Free: 800-489-8646
Fax: (606)546-1667
E-mail: jjackson@unionky.edu
Web Site: www.unionky.edu/

Description: Independent United Methodist, comprehensive, coed. Awards bachelor's and master's degrees and post-master's certificates. Founded 1879. Setting: 100-acre small town campus. Total enrollment: 1,194. Faculty: 110 (66 full-time, 44 part-time). Student-undergrad faculty ratio is 12:1. 1,127 applied, 77% were admitted. Full-time: 720 students, 43% women, 57% men. Part-time: 61 students, 67% women, 33% men. Students come from 28 states and territories, 9 other countries; 29% from out-of-state. 0.4% American Indian or Alaska Native, non-Hispanic/Latino; 3% Hispanic/Latino; 12% African American, non-Hispanic/Latino; 0.1% Asian, non-Hispanic/Latino; 0.1% Native Hawaiian or other Pacific Islander, non-Hispanic/Latino; 4% international. 15% 25 or older, 39% live on campus, 9% transferred in. Retention: 53% of full-time freshmen returned the following year. Academic areas with the most degrees conferred: education; business/marketing; psychology. Core. Calendar: semesters. Academic remediation for entering students, ESL program, services for LD students, advanced placement, accelerated degree program, self-designed majors, honors program, independent study, double major, summer session for credit, part-time degree program, graduate courses open to undergrads. Off campus study. Study abroad program.

Entrance Requirements: Options: electronic application, deferred admission. Required: high school transcript, minimum 2 high school GPA, SAT or ACT. Required for some: interview. Entrance: moderately difficult. Application deadlines: Rolling, Rolling for nonresidents. Notification: continuous, continuous for nonresidents. Transfer credits accepted: Yes.

Costs Per Year: Application fee: $10. Comprehensive fee: $27,450 includes full-time tuition ($19,900), mandatory fees ($900), and college room and board ($6650). College room only: $3000. Full-time tuition and fees vary according to course load. Room and board charges vary according to board plan and housing facility. Part-time tuition: $325 per credit hour. Part-time tuition varies according to course load.

Collegiate Environment: Orientation program. Drama-theater group, choral group. Social organizations: 31 open to all. Most popular organizations: Special Performers, Off-campus Trips, Open Mic Night, Bingo Night, Movie Fest. Major annual events: Springfest, Co-curricular Awards, Christmas Dinner. Student services: health clinic, personal-psychological counseling. Campus security: 24-hour emergency response devices and patrols, late night transport-escort service, controlled dormitory access. 425 college housing spaces available; 337 were occupied in 2012-13. Freshmen guaranteed college housing. On-campus residence required through sophomore year. Options: men-only, women-only housing available. Weeks-Townsend Memorial Library with 116,825 books, 166,288 microform titles, 16,223 serials, 4,652 audiovisual materials, an OPAC, and a Web page. 230 computers available on campus for general student use. A campuswide network can be accessed from student residence rooms and from off campus. Students can access the following: online class registration. Staffed computer lab on campus provides training in use of computers, software, and the Internet.

■ UNIVERSITY OF THE CUMBERLANDS

6178 College Station Dr.
Williamsburg, KY 40769-1372
Tel: (606)549-2200; Free: 800-343-1609
Fax: (606)539-4303
E-mail: admiss@ucumberlands.edu
Web Site: www.ucumberlands.edu/

Description: Independent Kentucky Baptist, comprehensive, coed. Awards bachelor's, master's, and doctoral degrees and post-master's certificates. Founded 1889. Setting: 100-acre rural campus with easy access to Knoxville. Endowment: $70.5 million. Research spending for the previous fiscal year: $35,116. Educational spending for the previous fiscal year: $4023 per student. Total enrollment: 4,297. Faculty: 194 (112 full-time, 82 part-time). Student-undergrad faculty ratio is 13:1. 2,460 applied, 69% were admitted. 13% from top 10% of their high school class, 29% from top quarter, 71% from top half. 2 valedictorians. Full-time: 1,481 students, 47% women, 53% men. Part-time: 383 students, 54% women, 46% men. Students come from 45 states and territories, 31 other countries; 36% from out-of-state. 0.4% American Indian or Alaska Native, non-Hispanic/Latino; 2% Hispanic/

Latino; 6% African American, non-Hispanic/Latino; 0.4% Asian, non-Hispanic/Latino; 0.1% Native Hawaiian or other Pacific Islander, non-Hispanic/Latino; 6% international. 6% 25 or older, 77% live on campus, 4% transferred in. Retention: 63% of full-time freshmen returned the following year. Academic areas with the most degrees conferred: business/marketing; education; psychology; parks and recreation; biological/life sciences. Core. Calendar: semesters. Academic remediation for entering students, advanced placement, accelerated degree program, self-designed majors, honors program, independent study, distance learning, double major, summer session for credit, part-time degree program, adult/continuing education programs, co-op programs and internships, graduate courses open to undergrads. Study abroad program. ROTC: Army.

Entrance Requirements: Options: electronic application, deferred admission, international baccalaureate accepted. Required: high school transcript, minimum 2 high school GPA, SAT or ACT. Required for some: essay, interview. Entrance: moderately difficult. Application deadline: Rolling. Notification: continuous. SAT Reasoning Test deadline: 8/15. Transfer credits accepted: Yes.

Costs Per Year: Application fee: $30. Comprehensive fee: $27,140 includes full-time tuition ($19,640) and college room and board ($7500). Part-time tuition: $590 per credit. Part-time mandatory fees: $90 per term. Part-time tuition and fees vary according to course load.

Collegiate Environment: Orientation program. Drama-theater group, choral group, marching band, student-run newspaper, radio station. Social organizations: 45 open to all. Most popular organizations: Baptist Campus Ministries, Student Government Association, Campus Activity Board, Mountain Outreach, Fellowship of Christian Athletes. Major annual events: Homecoming, Hanging of the Green, Spring Fever. Student services: health clinic. Campus security: 24-hour emergency response devices and patrols, student patrols, late night transport-escort service. 1,213 college housing spaces available; 1,005 were occupied in 2012-13. Freshmen guaranteed college housing. On-campus residence required through senior year. Options: men-only, women-only housing available. Norma Perkins Hagan Memorial Library with 139,438 books, 822,853 microform titles, 52,316 serials, 3,723 audiovisual materials, an OPAC, and a Web page. Operations spending for the previous fiscal year: $503,960. 225 computers available on campus for general student use. A campuswide network can be accessed from student residence rooms and from off campus. Students can access the following: online class registration. Staffed computer lab on campus provides training in use of computers, software, and the Internet.

Community Environment: Located in the southeastern part of Kentucky, Williamsburg is accessible via bus service and interstate highway. The city offers facilities that include 14 churches of various denominations, 4 medical clinics, civic organizations and city parks. Recreation is found at Cumberland Falls State Park, Cumberland Lake, Laurel Lake, cinemas and theaters. There is adequate modern housing available and motels nearby. Part-time employment opportunities are available for students.

■ UNIVERSITY OF KENTUCKY

Lexington, KY 40506-0032
Tel: (859)257-9000; Free: 866-900-GO-UK
Fax: (859)257-4000
E-mail: admissio@uky.edu
Web Site: www.uky.edu/

Description: State-supported, university, coed. Awards bachelor's, master's, and doctoral degrees. Founded 1865. Setting: 685-acre urban campus with easy access to Cincinnati, Louisville. Total enrollment: 28,034. Faculty: 1,683 (1,365 full-time, 318 part-time). Student-undergrad faculty ratio is 18:1. 18,802 applied, 67% were admitted. 32% from top 10% of their high school class, 61% from top quarter, 88% from top half. 71 National Merit Scholars, 182 valedictorians. Full-time: 19,178 students, 51% women, 49% men. Part-time: 1,649 students, 47% women, 53% men. Students come from 53 states and territories, 71 other countries; 21% from out-of-state. 0.2% American Indian or Alaska Native, non-Hispanic/Latino; 3% Hispanic/Latino; 8% African American, non-Hispanic/Latino; 2% Asian, non-Hispanic/Latino; 0.1% Native Hawaiian or other Pacific Islander, non-Hispanic/Latino; 2% international. 9% 25 or older, 26% live on campus, 6% transferred in. Retention: 81% of full-time freshmen returned the following year. Academic areas with the most degrees conferred: business/marketing; education; communication/journalism. Core. Calendar: semesters. Academic remediation for entering students, ESL program, services for LD students, advanced placement, accelerated degree program, honors program, independent study, distance learning, double major, summer session for credit, part-time degree program, adult/continuing education programs, co-op programs and internships, graduate courses open to undergrads. Off campus study at Academic Common Market, University of Florida. Study abroad program. ROTC: Army, Air Force.

Entrance Requirements: Options: electronic application, deferred admission, international baccalaureate accepted. Required: high school transcript, minimum 2 high school GPA, SAT or ACT. Entrance: moderately difficult. Application deadline: 2/15. Notification: continuous. Preference given to state residents for certain programs. SAT Reasoning Test deadline: 2/15. Transfer credits accepted: Yes.

Costs Per Year: Application fee: $50. State resident tuition: $8610 full-time, $359.20 per credit hour part-time. Nonresident tuition: $18,798 full-time, $783.20 per credit hour part-time. Mandatory fees: $1066 full-time, $29.80 per credit hour part-time. Full-time tuition and fees vary according to degree level, program, reciprocity agreements, and student level. Part-time tuition and fees vary according to degree level, program, reciprocity agreements, and student level. College room and board: $10,192. College room only: $4510. Room and board charges vary according to board plan and housing facility.

Collegiate Environment: Orientation program. Drama-theater group, choral group, marching band, student-run newspaper, radio station. Social organizations: 481 open to all; national fraternities, national sororities; 16% of eligible men and 25% of eligible women are members. Most popular organizations: Student Activities Board, Student Government Association, Campus Progressive Coalition, Ski and Snowboard Club, Society of Women Engineers. Major annual events: Homecoming, Student Center Night, Cultural Diversity Festival. Student services: legal services, health clinic, personal-psychological counseling, women's center. Campus security: 24-hour emergency response devices and patrols, late night transport-escort service, controlled dormitory access. 5,310 college housing spaces available; 5,232 were occupied in 2012-13. No special consideration for freshman housing applicants. Options: coed, men-only, women-only housing available. William T. Young Library with an OPAC and a Web page.

Community Environment: Lexington is located in the famous Bluegrass area of Kentucky. It is centrally located with Louisville 80 miles to the west and Cincinnati 90 miles to the north. Travel is made easier with close access to Interstates 75 and 64. The Mountain Parkway connects the Bluegrass with eastern Kentucky, and the Bluegrass Parkway links the western part of the State and Interstate 65. Lexington, known throughout the world as the home of the thoroughbred, attracts thousands of horse fans and buyers each year. Keeneland, a thoroughbred race track, and the famous trotting track, the Red Mile draw racing fans. The thoroughbred is not Lexington's only equine citizen; the standardbred, the quarterhorse, the saddle horse, and the Arabian are some of the many other breeds that live on some of the world's most famous farms in the Bluegrass. Since 1974, Lexington has been governed by an urban county form of government. The Lexington-Fayette County population is approximately 268,000, and this second largest city in Kentucky has seen steady growth in population. Lexington is very proud of its quality of life which can be attributed to the rich history of the area, and this quality is carefully monitored so that expansion and growth will enhance rather than hinder that lifestyle. Its economy is diverse in its job opportunities with the University of Kentucky and LexMark being the major employers. Employment can also be found in equine related businesses, tobacco, medicine, and retail and service industries. Among the many products manufactured in this area are electric typewriters and computer printers, peanut butter, tobacco processing and by-products, paper goods, and various equine-related products. Lexington's climate includes a mean annual temperature of 55 degrees Fahrenheit, and annual precipitation is 44 inches. The Bluegrass area has four distinct seasons with no prolonged periods of extreme temperatures or precipitation.

■ **UNIVERSITY OF LOUISVILLE**
2301 S Third St.
Louisville, KY 40292-0001
Tel: (502)852-5555; Free: 800-334-8635
Fax: (502)852-4776
E-mail: admitme@louisville.edu
Web Site: www.louisville.edu/

Description: State-supported, university, coed. Awards associate, bachelor's, master's, and doctoral degrees and post-master's certificates. Founded 1798. Setting: 345-acre urban campus with easy access to Louisville. Endowment: $755.1 million. Research spending for the previous fiscal year: $184.3 million. Educational spending for the previous fiscal year: $20,678 per student. Total enrollment: 21,242. Faculty: 2,299 (1,668 full-time, 631 part-time). Student-undergrad faculty ratio is 17:1. 7,892 applied,

73% were admitted. 18 National Merit Scholars, 55 valedictorians. Full-time: 12,192 students, 52% women, 48% men. Part-time: 3,535 students, 50% women, 50% men. Students come from 47 states and territories, 58 other countries, 15% from out-of-state. 0.1% American Indian or Alaska Native, non-Hispanic/Latino; 3% Hispanic/Latino; 12% African American, non-Hispanic/Latino; 3% Asian, non-Hispanic/Latino; 0.1% Native Hawaiian or other Pacific Islander, non-Hispanic/Latino; 2% international. 21% 25 or older, 27% live on campus, 7% transferred in. Retention: 77% of full-time freshmen returned the following year. Academic areas with the most degrees conferred: business/marketing; engineering; parks and recreation. Core. Calendar: semesters. Academic remediation for entering students, ESL program, services for LD students, advanced placement, accelerated degree program, self-designed majors, honors program, independent study, distance learning, double major, summer session for credit, part-time degree program, adult/continuing education programs, co-op programs and internships, graduate courses open to undergrads. Off campus study at Consortium Name: Kentuckiana Metroversity. Institutions: Bellarmine University, Indiana University Southeast, Jefferson Community and Technical College, Louisville Presbyterian Theological Seminary, Southern Baptist Theological Seminary, Spalding University. Study abroad program. ROTC: Army, Air Force.

Entrance Requirements: Options: electronic application, deferred admission, international baccalaureate accepted. Required: high school transcript, minimum 2.5 high school GPA, SAT or ACT. Required for some: TOEFL for students whose primary language is not English. Entrance: moderately difficult. Application deadline: 2/15. Notification: continuous. Transfer credits accepted: Yes.

Costs Per Year: Application fee: $40. State resident tuition: $9466 full-time, $395 per credit hour part-time. Nonresident tuition: $22,950 full-time, $957 per credit hour part-time. Full-time tuition varies according to reciprocity agreements. Part-time tuition varies according to course load and reciprocity agreements. College room and board: $7570. College room only: $4650. Room and board charges vary according to board plan and housing facility.

Collegiate Environment: Orientation program. Drama-theater group, choral group, marching band, student-run newspaper, radio station. Social organizations: 324 open to all; national fraternities, national sororities; 15% of eligible men and 10% of eligible women are members. Most popular organizations: Baptist Campus Ministry, Society of Porter Scholars, Association of Black Students, commonGround, Phi Eta Sigma. Major annual events: Homecoming events, Fryberger Sing, Welcome Weekend. Student services: health clinic, personal-psychological counseling, women's center. Campus security: 24-hour emergency response devices and patrols, late night transport-escort service, controlled dormitory access, The University of Louisville Alert notification system. 5,089 college housing spaces available; 4,699 were occupied in 2012-13. Freshmen given priority for college housing. On-campus residence required in freshman year. Option: coed housing available. William F. Ekstrom Library plus 6 others with 2.4 million books, 224,637 microform titles, 60,047 audiovisual materials, an OPAC, and a Web page. Operations spending for the previous fiscal year: $17.6 million. 400 computers available on campus for general student use. Computer purchase/lease plans available. A campuswide network can be accessed from student residence rooms and from off campus. Students can access the following: online class registration. Staffed computer lab on campus provides training in use of computers, software, and the Internet.

Community Environment: Louisville is known as the Derby City for the annual running of the Kentucky Derby at Churchill Downs. The city was the base of supplies for Clark's expeditions, which culminated in the conquest of the northwest. U.S. river boats pass through the locks around 25-foot falls in the Ohio River. Louisville is an important distilling center and one of the largest tobacco product manufacturing centers in the world. There are many other local manufacturing firms in the area, and part-time employment is available. There is a community-wide fund for music, drama, and art, and the city has resident opera, ballet, orchestra, and theater companies.

■ **UNIVERSITY OF PHOENIX–LOUISVILLE CAMPUS**
10400 Linn Station Rd.
Louisville, KY 40223-3839
Tel: (502)423-0149; Free: 866-766-0766
Web Site: www.phoenix.edu/

Description: Proprietary, comprehensive, coed. Awards bachelor's, master's, and doctoral degrees.

■ **UNIVERSITY OF PIKEVILLE**
147 Sycamore St.
Pikeville, KY 41501

Tel: (606)218-5250; Free: 866-232-7700
Fax: (606)218-5269
E-mail: wewantyou@pc.edu
Web Site: www.upike.edu/
Description: Independent, comprehensive, coed, affiliated with Presbyterian Church (U.S.A.). Awards associate, bachelor's, master's, and doctoral degrees. Founded 1889. Setting: 25-acre small town campus. Endowment: $10.7 million. Educational spending for the previous fiscal year: $4904 per student. Total enrollment: 2,031. Faculty: 109 (68 full-time, 41 part-time). Student-undergrad faculty ratio is 16:1. 1,858 applied, 100% were admitted. 14% from top 10% of their high school class, 38% from top quarter, 67% from top half. Full-time: 1,219 students, 50% women, 50% men. Part-time: 401 students, 60% women, 40% men. Students come from 25 states and territories, 10 other countries, 20% from out-of-state. 0.1% American Indian or Alaska Native, non-Hispanic/Latino; 1% Hispanic/Latino; 8% African American, non-Hispanic/Latino; 1% Asian, non-Hispanic/Latino; 0% Native Hawaiian or other Pacific Islander, non-Hispanic/Latino; 1% international. 9% 25 or older, 60% live on campus, 9% transferred in. Retention: 52% of full-time freshmen returned the following year. Academic areas with the most degrees conferred: business/marketing; homeland security, law enforcement, firefighting, and protective services; biological/life sciences. Core. Calendar: semesters. Academic remediation for entering students, ESL program, services for LD students, advanced placement, self-designed majors, independent study, double major, summer session for credit, part-time degree program, internships. Study abroad program. ROTC: Army.
Entrance Requirements: Open admission except for nursing, education and social work programs. Options: electronic application, deferred admission. Required: high school transcript. Entrance: noncompetitive. Application deadlines: 8/15, 8/15 for nonresidents. Notification: continuous, continuous for nonresidents. SAT Reasoning Test deadline: 8/15. Transfer credits accepted: Yes.
Costs Per Year: Application fee: $0. Comprehensive fee: $23,750 includes full-time tuition ($17,050) and college room and board ($6700). Full-time tuition varies according to course load. Room and board charges vary according to housing facility. Part-time tuition: $710 per credit hour. Part-time tuition varies according to course load.
Collegiate Environment: Orientation program. Drama-theater group, choral group, student-run newspaper. Social organizations: 30 open to all; local fraternities, local sororities; 8% of eligible men and 9% of eligible women are members. Most popular organizations: student government, Phi Beta Lambda, Lambda Sigma, Concert Choir, Student Nurses at PC. Major annual events: Homecoming, Founders' Day. Student services: personal-psychological counseling. Campus security: 24-hour emergency response devices and patrols, controlled dormitory access. 827 college housing spaces available; 755 were occupied in 2012-13. No special consideration for freshman housing applicants. Options: coed, men-only, women-only housing available. Allara Library plus 1 other with 82,945 books, 44,536 microform titles, 38,849 serials, 2,127 audiovisual materials, an OPAC, and a Web page. Operations spending for the previous fiscal year: $680,437. 166 computers available on campus for general student use. A campuswide network can be accessed from student residence rooms and from off campus. Staffed computer lab on campus.
Community Environment: Located in the heart of Big Sandy Valley, Pikeville is an important mining and trade center in the midst of Elkhorn coalfield. Breaks Park, southeast of town and Jenny Wiley State Park north of town, provides recreational facilities. Part-time employment is available.

■ **WEST KENTUCKY COMMUNITY AND TECHNICAL COLLEGE**
4810 Alben Barkley Dr.
Paducah, KY 42002-7380
Tel: (270)554-9200
Fax: (270)554-6217
E-mail: Debbie.Smith@kctcs.edu
Web Site: www.westkentucky.kctcs.edu/
Description: State-supported, 2-year, coed. Part of Kentucky Community and Technical College System. Awards certificates, diplomas, transfer associate, and terminal associate degrees. Founded 1932. Setting: 117-acre small town campus. Total enrollment: 5,785. Full-time: 2,398 students, 59% women, 41% men. Part-time: 3,387 students, 58% women, 42% men. Students come from 26 states and territories, 1 other country, 8% from out-of-state. 0.3% American Indian or Alaska Native, non-Hispanic/Latino; 2% Hispanic/Latino; 7% African American, non-Hispanic/Latino; 0.4% Asian, non-Hispanic/Latino; 0.1% Native Hawaiian or other Pacific Islander, non-Hispanic/Latino; 0.1% international. 54% 25 or older, 4% transferred in.

Retention: 56% of full-time freshmen returned the following year. Core. Calendar: semesters. Academic remediation for entering students, ESL program, honors program, independent study, distance learning, part-time degree program, adult/continuing education programs, co-op programs and internships. Study abroad program.
Entrance Requirements: Open admission. Option: early admission. Required: SAT or ACT. Recommended: ACT. Required for some: high school transcript. Entrance: noncompetitive. Application deadline: Rolling.
Collegiate Environment: Orientation program. Drama-theater group, choral group. Campus security: late night transport-escort service, 14-hour patrols by trained security personnel. College housing not available. WKCTC Matheson Library with 74,676 books, 24,654 microform titles, 155 serials, 5,043 audiovisual materials, an OPAC, and a Web page. 160 computers available on campus for general student use. Staffed computer lab on campus.
Community Environment: A busy town with a leisurely atmosphere, Paducah was named for Indian Chief, Paduke, who is buried on the bank of the river. It is an important market for burley and dark tobacco. Diversified industries include boat and barge builders, electronics and chemicals plants. Part-time work is available. Located at the confluence of the Tennessee and Ohio Rivers, average winter temperature is 46.2 degrees, summer, 73.4 degrees. Highways, airlines, and bus lines serve the community. A public library, churches, two hospitals, hotels and motels and many civic organizations are available. Recreation areas include nearby Kentucky and Barkley Lakes and the"Land Between Lakes" area as well as three state parks, several public parks, a swimming pool, golf courses and theatres.

■ **WESTERN KENTUCKY UNIVERSITY**
1906 College Heights Blvd.
Bowling Green, KY 42101
Tel: (270)745-0111; Free: 800-495-8463
Fax: (270)745-6133
E-mail: admission@wku.edu
Web Site: www.wku.edu/
Description: State-supported, comprehensive, coed. Awards associate, bachelor's, master's, and doctoral degrees and post-master's certificates. Founded 1906. Setting: 235-acre suburban campus with easy access to Nashville. Endowment: $110,043. Research spending for the previous fiscal year: $10.3 million. Educational spending for the previous fiscal year: $6082 per student. Total enrollment: 21,110. Faculty: 1,131 (785 full-time, 346 part-time). Student-undergrad faculty ratio is 19:1. 8,526 applied, 92% were admitted. 22% from top 10% of their high school class, 44% from top quarter, 70% from top half. 2 National Merit Scholars, 80 valedictorians. Full-time: 13,868 students, 55% women, 45% men. Part-time: 4,233 students, 64% women, 36% men. Students come from 47 states and territories, 60 other countries, 16% from out-of-state. 0.3% American Indian or Alaska Native, non-Hispanic/Latino; 2% Hispanic/Latino; 11% African American, non-Hispanic/Latino; 1% Asian, non-Hispanic/Latino; 0.1% Native Hawaiian or other Pacific Islander, non-Hispanic/Latino; 3% international. 21% 25 or older, 29% live on campus, 6% transferred in. Retention: 71% of full-time freshmen returned the following year. Academic areas with the most degrees conferred: business/marketing; education; liberal arts/general studies. Core. Calendar: semesters. Academic remediation for entering students, ESL program, services for LD students, advanced placement, accelerated degree program, self-designed majors, freshman honors college, honors program, independent study, distance learning, double major, summer session for credit, part-time degree program, external degree program, adult/continuing education programs, co-op programs and internships, graduate courses open to undergrads. Off campus study at Space grant consortium, Service members Opportunity Colleges (SOC). Study abroad program. ROTC: Army, Air Force (c).
Entrance Requirements: Options: electronic application, international baccalaureate accepted. Required: high school transcript, minimum 2.5 high school GPA, SAT or ACT. Recommended: minimum 2.5 high school GPA. Required for some: minimum 2 high school GPA. Entrance: minimally difficult. Application deadline: 8/1. Notification: continuous. SAT Reasoning Test deadline: 8/1. SAT Subject Test deadline: 8/1. Transfer credits accepted: Yes.
Costs Per Year: Application fee: $40. State resident tuition: $8472 full-time, $353 per credit hour part-time. Nonresident tuition: $21,000 full-time, $875 per credit hour part-time. Full-time tuition varies according to course load, location, program, and reciprocity agreements. Part-time tuition varies according to course load, location, program, and reciprocity agreements. College room and board: $7320. College room only: $4170. Room and board charges vary according to board plan and housing facility.

Collegiate Environment: Orientation program. Drama-theater group, choral group, marching band, student-run newspaper, radio station. Social organizations: 246 open to all; national fraternities, national sororities; 11% of eligible men and 11% of eligible women are members. Most popular organizations: Student Government Association, Campus Activities Board, Campus Crusade for Christ, Campus Ministries, Residence Hall Association. Major annual events: Homecoming, Football tailgating, Step Show. Student services: health clinic, personal-psychological counseling, women's center. Campus security: 24-hour emergency response devices and patrols, student patrols, late night transport-escort service, controlled dormitory access. 5,043 college housing spaces available; 4,779 were occupied in 2012-13. Freshmen given priority for college housing. On-campus residence required through sophomore year. Options: coed, men-only, women-only housing available. Helm-Cravens Library plus 2 others with 1.9 million books, 2.3 million microform titles, 3,749 serials, 32,016 audiovisual materials, an OPAC, and a Web page. Operations spending for the previous fiscal year: $6 million. 542 computers available on campus for general student use. Computer purchase/lease plans available. A campuswide network can be accessed from student residence rooms and from off campus. Students can access the following: online class registration. Staffed computer lab on campus (open 24 hours a day) provides training in use of computers, software, and the Internet.

Community Environment: The city of Bowling Green is located on the Barrer River in Warren County in southern Kentucky. Situated 60 miles north of Nashville, and 103 miles south of Louisville, Bowling Green has about 80 churches of 26 denominations, a public library, and two hospitals. Recreation is provided by local theaters and parks, including nearby Mammoth Cave National Park.

■ BATON ROUGE COMMUNITY COLLEGE

5310 Florida Blvd.
Baton Rouge, LA 70806
Tel: (225)216-8000; Free: 800-601-4558
Fax: (225)216-8100
Web Site: www.mybrcc.edu/
Description: State-supported, 2-year, coed. Awards transfer associate and terminal associate degrees. Founded 1995. Total enrollment: 7,031. 24% 25 or older. Calendar: semesters.
Entrance Requirements: Open admission.

■ BATON ROUGE SCHOOL OF COMPUTERS

10425 Plz. Americana
Baton Rouge, LA 70816
Tel: (504)923-2525; Free: 888-920-BRSC
Fax: (504)923-2979
E-mail: admissions@brsc.net
Web Site: www.brsc.edu/
Description: Proprietary, 2-year, coed. Awards certificates and terminal associate degrees. Founded 1979. Total enrollment: 56. Student-undergrad faculty ratio is 25:1. 0% from out-of-state. 64% 25 or older.
Entrance Requirements: Required: interview, Wonderlic. Entrance: noncompetitive.

■ BLUE CLIFF COLLEGE–LAFAYETTE

100 Asma Blvd.
Ste. 350
Lafayette, LA 70508-3862
Tel: (337)269-0620; Free: 800-514-2609
Web Site: www.bluecliffcollege.com/
Description: Proprietary, 2-year, coed. Awards certificates and terminal associate degrees. Total enrollment: 116. 45% 25 or older.
Entrance Requirements: Open admission.

■ BLUE CLIFF COLLEGE–SHREVEPORT

8731 Park Plz. Dr.
Shreveport, LA 71105
Tel: (318)425-7941; Free: 800-516-6597
Web Site: www.bluecliffcollege.com/
Description: Proprietary, 2-year, coed. Awards certificates and terminal associate degrees. Setting: urban campus. Total enrollment: 237. Faculty: 21 (19 full-time, 2 part-time). Student-undergrad faculty ratio is 12:1. 58% 25 or older. Core. Summer session for credit, part-time degree program.
Entrance Requirements: Required: interview. Required for some: high school transcript. Entrance: noncompetitive. Transfer credits accepted: Yes.
Collegiate Environment: Orientation program. Student services: legal services, personal-psychological counseling.

■ BOSSIER PARISH COMMUNITY COLLEGE

6220 E Texas St.
Bossier City, LA 71111
Tel: (318)678-6000
Web Site: www.bpcc.edu/
Description: State-supported, 2-year, coed. Part of Louisiana Community and Technical College System. Awards certificates, diplomas, transfer as-

sociate, and terminal associate degrees. Founded 1967. Setting: 64-acre urban campus. Total enrollment: 7,917. Faculty: 322 (132 full-time, 190 part-time). Student-undergrad faculty ratio is 31:1. 3,205 applied, 97% were admitted. Full-time: 4,736 students, 62% women, 38% men. Part-time: 3,181 students, 68% women, 32% men. 3% from out-of-state. 1% American Indian or Alaska Native, non-Hispanic/Latino; 15% Hispanic/Latino; 32% African American, non-Hispanic/Latino; 1% Asian, non-Hispanic/Latino; 0.1% Native Hawaiian or other Pacific Islander, non-Hispanic/Latino; 0% international. 38% 25 or older, 14% transferred in. Retention: 49% of full-time freshmen returned the following year. Core. Calendar: semesters. Academic remediation for entering students, services for LD students, advanced placement, distance learning, double major, summer session for credit, part-time degree program, adult/continuing education programs.
Entrance Requirements: Open admission. Option: early admission. Required: high school transcript. Entrance: noncompetitive. Application deadline: 8/10.
Costs Per Year: Application fee: $15. State resident tuition: $2608 full-time, $159 per credit hour part-time. Nonresident tuition: $5834 full-time, $293 per credit hour part-time. Mandatory fees: $540 full-time. Full-time tuition and fees vary according to course load and program. Part-time tuition varies according to course load and program.
Collegiate Environment: Orientation program. Drama-theater group, choral group, student-run newspaper. Student services: personal-psychological counseling. Campus security: student patrols. College housing not available. Bossier Parish Community College Library with 29,600 books, 384 serials, and an OPAC.

■ CAMELOT COLLEGE

2618 Wooddale Blvd.
Ste. A
Baton Rouge, LA 70805
Tel: (225)928-3005; Free: 800-470-3320
Fax: (225)927-3794
Web Site: www.camelotcollege.com/
Description: Proprietary, 2-year, coed. Awards diplomas and terminal associate degrees. Founded 1986. Total enrollment: 188. Student-undergrad faculty ratio is 20:1. 3% from out-of-state. 29% 25 or older.
Entrance Requirements: Required: interview. Entrance: noncompetitive.

■ CAMERON COLLEGE

2740 Canal St.
New Orleans, LA 70119
Tel: (504)821-5881
Web Site: www.cameroncollege.com/
Description: Proprietary, 2-year, coed. Awards terminal associate degrees. Founded 1981. Total enrollment: 9. 29% 25 or older.
Entrance Requirements: Open admission.

■ CAPITAL AREA TECHNICAL COLLEGE–BATON ROUGE CAMPUS

3250 N Acadian Thruway, E
Baton Rouge, LA 70805
E-mail: aaguillard@ltc.edu
Web Site: region2.ltc.edu/
Description: State-supported, 2-year, coed. Part of Louisiana Community and Technical College System. Awards certificates, diplomas, and transfer

associate degrees. Founded 1930. Setting: urban campus. Endowment: $286,936. Educational spending for the previous fiscal year: $3121 per student. Total enrollment: 13,414. Faculty: 1,353 (780 full-time, 573 part-time). Student-undergrad faculty ratio is 10:1. 2,094 applied, 100% were admitted. Full-time: 7,264 students, 55% women, 45% men. Part-time: 6,150 students, 39% women, 61% men. 1% from out-of-state.
Entrance Requirements: Required: high school transcript, COMPASS. Entrance: noncompetitive.

■ **CAREER TECHNICAL COLLEGE**
2319 Louisville Ave.
Monroe, LA 71201
Tel: (318)323-2889; Free: 800-923-1947
Fax: (318)324-9883
E-mail: susan.boudreaux@careertc.edu
Web Site: www.careertc.edu/
Description: Proprietary, 2-year, coed. Part of Delta Career Education Corporation. Awards diplomas and terminal associate degrees. Founded 1985. Setting: 33,833 small town campus with easy access to Shreveport. Total enrollment: 558. Faculty: 35 (20 full-time, 15 part-time). Student-undergrad faculty ratio is 16:1. Full-time: 455 students, 80% women, 20% men. Part-time: 103 students, 78% women, 22% men. Students come from 2 states and territories, 1% from out-of-state. 0.2% American Indian or Alaska Native, non-Hispanic/Latino; 2% Hispanic/Latino; 64% African American, non-Hispanic/Latino; 0.4% Asian, non-Hispanic/Latino; 0.2% Native Hawaiian or other Pacific Islander, non-Hispanic/Latino; 0% international. 56% 25 or older. Retention: 90% of full-time freshmen returned the following year. Core. Academic remediation for entering students, advanced placement, independent study, double major, adult/continuing education programs, co-op programs and internships.
Entrance Requirements: Options: deferred admission, international baccalaureate accepted. Required: high school transcript, interview, SLE-Wonderlic Scholastic Level Exam; Math Proficiency Exam; English Proficiency Exam. Entrance: moderately difficult. Application deadlines: Rolling, Rolling for nonresidents. Notification: continuous, continuous for nonresidents. Transfer credits accepted: Yes.
Costs Per Year: Application fee: $40. One-time mandatory fee: $120. Tuition: $11,376 full-time. Mandatory fees: $1275 full-time. Full-time tuition and fees vary according to course load and program. Tuition guaranteed not to increase for student's term of enrollment.
Collegiate Environment: Orientation program. Social organizations: 10 open to all; Programmatic Clubs; 2% of eligible men and 20% of eligible women are members. Most popular organizations: Medical Assisting Club, Surgical Technology Club, Criminal Justice Club, Rad Tech Club, Management/Information Processing Club. Major annual events: Awards Day, Job Fair, Student Appreciation Day/Week. Campus security: 24-hour emergency response devices, late night transport-escort service, evening security guard. College housing not available. 78 computers available on campus for general student use. A campuswide network can be accessed. Staffed computer lab on campus provides training in use of computers, software, and the Internet.

■ **CENTENARY COLLEGE OF LOUISIANA**
2911 Centenary Blvd.
Shreveport, LA 71104
Tel: (318)869-5011; Free: 800-234-4448
Fax: (318)869-5005
Web Site: www.centenary.edu/
Description: Independent United Methodist, comprehensive, coed. Awards bachelor's and master's degrees. Founded 1825. Setting: 65-acre suburban campus with easy access to Shreveport. Total enrollment: 776. Faculty: 124 (58 full-time, 66 part-time). Student-undergrad faculty ratio is 9:1. 933 applied, 64% were admitted. 32% from top 10% of their high school class, 89% from top quarter, 97% from top half. Full-time: 673 students, 56% women, 44% men. Part-time: 25 students, 56% women, 44% men. 1% American Indian or Alaska Native, non-Hispanic/Latino; 5% Hispanic/Latino; 13% African American, non-Hispanic/Latino; 3% Asian, non-Hispanic/Latino; 0.3% Native Hawaiian or other Pacific Islander, non-Hispanic/Latino; 3% international. 56% live on campus. Retention: 69% of full-time freshmen returned the following year. Academic areas with the most degrees conferred: business/marketing; visual and performing arts; biological/life sciences. Core. Calendar: 4-4-1. Services for LD students, advanced placement, self-designed majors, honors program, independent study, double major, summer session for credit, part-time degree program, adult/continuing

education programs, internships, graduate courses open to undergrads. Off campus study at Associated Colleges of the South. Study abroad program.
Entrance Requirements: Options: electronic application, early admission, early action, deferred admission, international baccalaureate accepted. Required: essay, high school transcript, minimum 2 high school GPA, 1 recommendation, SAT or ACT. Recommended: interview, class rank. Entrance: moderately difficult. Application deadlines: 8/1, 8/1 for nonresidents, 12/15 for early action. Notification: continuous, continuous for nonresidents. Transfer credits accepted: Yes.
Costs Per Year: Application fee: $30. Comprehensive fee: $38,836 includes full-time tuition ($29,500) and college room and board ($9336). College room only: $4816. Full-time tuition varies according to degree level. Room and board charges vary according to board plan and housing facility. Part-time tuition: $880 per credit hour. Part-time tuition varies according to course load, degree level, and program.
Collegiate Environment: Orientation program. Drama-theater group, choral group, student-run newspaper, radio station. Social organizations: national fraternities, national sororities. Most popular organizations: intramural sports, Residence Life, FCA, Church Career/Campus Ministries, student media. Major annual events: Freak Week, Spring Fling, Homecoming. Student services: health clinic, personal-psychological counseling. Campus security: 24-hour emergency response devices and patrols, late night transport-escort service, controlled dormitory access. 372 undergraduates lived in college housing during 2012-13. Freshmen guaranteed college housing. On-campus residence required through senior year. Options: coed, women-only housing available. Magale Library plus 1 other with an OPAC and a Web page.
Community Environment: See Louisiana State University Shreveport.

■ **DELGADO COMMUNITY COLLEGE**
501 City Park Ave.
New Orleans, LA 70119-4399
Tel: (504)483-4400
Fax: (504)483-1986
E-mail: enroll@dcc.edu
Web Site: www.dcc.edu/
Description: State-supported, 2-year, coed. Part of Louisiana Community and Technical College System. Awards certificates, transfer associate, and terminal associate degrees. Founded 1921. Setting: 57-acre urban campus. Endowment: $1.9 million. Research spending for the previous fiscal year: $58,000. Total enrollment: 13,217. Faculty: 628 (389 full-time, 239 part-time). Student-undergrad faculty ratio is 20:1. 2,657 applied, 100% were admitted. Full-time: 6,068 students, 66% women, 34% men. Part-time: 7,149 students, 72% women, 28% men. Students come from 33 states and territories, 3 other countries, 0.3% from out-of-state. 56% 25 or older. Retention: 50% of full-time freshmen returned the following year. Core. Calendar: semesters. Academic remediation for entering students, ESL program, services for LD students, advanced placement, self-designed majors, honors program, distance learning, summer session for credit, part-time degree program, co-op programs. Off campus study at University of New Orleans, Southern University at New Orleans. ROTC: Army (c), Air Force (c).
Entrance Requirements: Open admission except for allied health, nursing, culinary arts programs. Recommended: high school transcript, proof of immunization. Required for some: high school transcript. Entrance: noncompetitive. Application deadline: Rolling.
Collegiate Environment: Orientation program. Drama-theater group, choral group, student-run newspaper. Social organizations: 50 open to all. Most popular organizations: student government, Circle K, International Club, Phi Theta Kappa, Lambda Phi Nu. Major annual events: Homecoming Week, Spring Fest, International Week. Student services: health clinic, personal-psychological counseling. Campus security: 24-hour patrols, student patrols. Moss Memorial Library with 110,000 books, 1,299 serials, an OPAC, and a Web page. Operations spending for the previous fiscal year: $1 million. 950 computers available on campus for general student use. A campuswide network can be accessed from off-campus. Staffed computer lab on campus.
Community Environment: See Tulane University.

■ **DELTA COLLEGE OF ARTS AND TECHNOLOGY**
7380 Exchange Pl.
Baton Rouge, LA 70806-3851
Tel: (504)928-7770
Fax: (504)927-9096
E-mail: bbrown@deltacollege.com
Web Site: www.deltacollege.com/
Description: Proprietary, 2-year, coed. Awards certificates, diplomas, and

terminal associate degrees. Setting: 3-acre urban campus. Total enrollment: 137. 56% 25 or older. Calendar: continuous (for most programs).

Entrance Requirements: Open admission.

■ DELTA SCHOOL OF BUSINESS & TECHNOLOGY

517 Broad St.
Lake Charles, LA 70601
Tel: (337)439-5765
Fax: (337)436-5151
Web Site: www.deltatech.edu/

Description: Private, 2-year, coed. Awards terminal associate degrees. Total enrollment: 345. Student-undergrad faculty ratio is 12:1. 1% from out-of-state. 58% 25 or older.

Entrance Requirements: Entrance: noncompetitive.

■ DILLARD UNIVERSITY

2601 Gentilly Blvd.
New Orleans, LA 70122-3097
Tel: (504)283-8822; Free: 800-216-8094
Fax: (504)286-4895
E-mail: acyprian@dillard.edu
Web Site: www.dillard.edu/

Description: Independent interdenominational, 4-year, coed. Awards bachelor's degrees. Founded 1869. Setting: 55-acre urban campus. Endowment: $54.8 million. Educational spending for the previous fiscal year: $13,990 per student. Total enrollment: 1,307. Student-undergrad faculty ratio is 14:1. 7,496 applied, 33% were admitted. 6% from top 10% of their high school class, 30% from top quarter, 70% from top half. Full-time: 1,222 students, 72% women, 28% men. Part-time: 85 students, 68% women, 32% men. Students come from 30 states and territories, 14 other countries, 35% from out-of-state. 0% American Indian or Alaska Native, non-Hispanic/Latino; 1% Hispanic/Latino; 93% African American, non-Hispanic/Latino; 0.2% Asian, non-Hispanic/Latino; 0% Native Hawaiian or other Pacific Islander, non-Hispanic/Latino; 2% international. 9% 25 or older, 43% live on campus, 7% transferred in. Retention: 68% of full-time freshmen returned the following year. Academic areas with the most degrees conferred: health professions and related sciences; business/marketing; social sciences. Core. Calendar: semesters. Academic remediation for entering students, ESL program, services for LD students, advanced placement, honors program, independent study, double major, summer session for credit, part-time degree program, external degree program, co-op programs and internships. Study abroad program. ROTC: Army (c), Air Force (c).

Entrance Requirements: Options: electronic application, early admission, international baccalaureate accepted. Required: high school transcript, minimum 2.5 high school GPA, 2 recommendations, SAT or ACT, minimum SAT score of 870 (math and verbal) or minimum ACT composite score of 18. Required for some: essay. Entrance: moderately difficult. Application deadlines: Rolling, Rolling for nonresidents. Notification: continuous, continuous for nonresidents. SAT Reasoning Test deadline: 8/15. SAT Subject Test deadline: 8/15. Transfer credits accepted: Yes.

Costs Per Year: Application fee: $30. Comprehensive fee: $23,536 includes full-time tuition ($13,650), mandatory fees ($1200), and college room and board ($8686). College room only: $5690. Room and board charges vary according to housing facility and student level.

Collegiate Environment: Orientation program. Drama-theater group, choral group, student-run newspaper, radio station. Social organizations: 45 open to all; national fraternities, national sororities; 25% of eligible men and 40% of eligible women are members. Most popular organizations: Student Government Association, Student Activities Board, National Pan-Hellenic Council, Collegiate 100, Class Councils. Major annual events: Coronation, Spring Fest, MLK Week for Peace and Justice. Student services: legal services, health clinic, personal-psychological counseling. Campus security: 24-hour emergency response devices and patrols, late night transport-escort service, controlled dormitory access. 683 college housing spaces available; 526 were occupied in 2012-13. Freshmen guaranteed college housing. On-campus residence required in freshman year. Options: coed, men-only, women-only housing available. Will W. Alexander Library plus 1 other with 105,286 books, 1,150 microform titles, 785 audiovisual materials, and an OPAC. 75 computers available on campus for general student use. A campuswide network can be accessed from student residence rooms and from off campus. Students can access the following: online class registration. Staffed computer lab on campus provides training in use of computers, software, and the Internet.

Community Environment: See Tulane University.

■ ELAINE P. NUNEZ COMMUNITY COLLEGE

3710 Paris Rd.
Chalmette, LA 70043-1249
Tel: (504)278-6200
Fax: (504)680-2243
E-mail: bmaillet@nunez.edu
Web Site: www.nunez.edu/

Description: State-supported, 2-year, coed. Part of Louisiana Community and Technical College System. Awards certificates, diplomas, transfer associate, and terminal associate degrees. Founded 1992. Setting: 20-acre suburban campus with easy access to New Orleans. Endowment: $1.2 million. Educational spending for the previous fiscal year: $3108 per student. Total enrollment: 2,294. Faculty: 79 (40 full-time, 39 part-time). Student-undergrad faculty ratio is 29:1. Full-time: 804 students, 67% women, 33% men. Part-time: 1,498 students, 66% women, 34% men. Students come from 2 states and territories. 49% 25 or older. Retention: 49% of full-time freshmen returned the following year. Core. Calendar: semesters. Academic remediation for entering students, services for LD students, advanced placement, self-designed majors, independent study, distance learning, double major, summer session for credit, part-time degree program, adult/continuing education programs, co-op programs and internships. Off campus study at University of New Orleans, Southeastern Louisiana University, Delgado Community College.

Entrance Requirements: Open admission. Options: electronic application, early admission, deferred admission, international baccalaureate accepted. Recommended: ACT. Required for some: high school transcript. Entrance: noncompetitive. Application deadline: Rolling. Transfer credits accepted: Yes.

Collegiate Environment: Orientation program. Drama-theater group, student-run newspaper. Social organizations: national fraternities. Most popular organization: Nunez Environmental Team. Major annual events: Spring Fling, Fall Fest, Job Fair. Student services: personal-psychological counseling. Campus security: 24-hour emergency response devices, late night transport-escort service, security cameras. College housing not available. Nunez Community College Library with 72,500 books, 81,267 microform titles, 2,500 serials, 3,128 audiovisual materials, an OPAC, and a Web page. Operations spending for the previous fiscal year: $306,147. 200 computers available on campus for general student use. A campuswide network can be accessed. Staffed computer lab on campus provides training in use of computers, software, and the Internet.

■ FLETCHER TECHNICAL COMMUNITY COLLEGE

1407 Hwy. 311
Schriever, LA 70395
Tel: (985)448-7900
Fax: (985)446-3308
Web Site: www.fletcher.edu/

Description: State-supported, 2-year, coed. Total enrollment: 788. Faculty: 61 (26 full-time, 35 part-time). Calendar: semesters.

■ FORTIS COLLEGE

9255 Interline Ave.
Baton Rouge, LA 70809
Tel: (225)248-1015
Fax: (225)248-9571
Web Site: www.fortis.edu/

Description: Proprietary, 2-year, coed. Awards diplomas and terminal associate degrees. Founded 1970. Setting: 4-acre urban campus. Total enrollment: 327. 198 applied. 51% 25 or older. Core. Internships.

Entrance Requirements: Required: high school transcript, interview, Wonderlic aptitude test. Recommended: minimum 2.0 high school GPA, 2 recommendations. Entrance: noncompetitive. Application deadline: Rolling. Notification: continuous.

■ GRAMBLING STATE UNIVERSITY

403 Main St.
Grambling, LA 71245
Tel: (318)247-3811; Free: 800-569-4714
Fax: (318)274-6172
E-mail: mossa@gram.edu
Web Site: www.gram.edu/

Description: State-supported, university, coed. Part of University of Louisiana System. Awards associate, bachelor's, master's, and doctoral degrees and post-master's certificates. Founded 1901. Setting: 433-acre small town campus with easy access to Shreveport. Endowment: $10.7 million. Research spending for the previous fiscal year: $455,747. Educational spending for the previous fiscal year: $4992 per student. Total enrollment: 5,277. Faculty: 239 (219 full-time, 20 part-time). Student-undergrad faculty ratio is 21:1. 5,154 applied, 42% were admitted. 7% from top 10% of their high school class, 23% from top quarter, 54% from top half. Full-time: 4,087 students, 59% women, 41% men. Part-time: 348 students, 68% women, 32% men. Students come from 40 states and territories, 26 other countries, 35% from out-of-state. 0.2% American Indian or Alaska Native, non-Hispanic/Latino; 1% Hispanic/Latino; 88% African American, non-Hispanic/Latino; 0.3% Asian, non-Hispanic/Latino; 0.05% Native Hawaiian or other Pacific Islander, non-Hispanic/Latino; 6% international. 16% 25 or older, 87% live on campus, 7% transferred in. Retention: 69% of full-time freshmen returned the following year. Academic areas with the most degrees conferred: business/marketing; homeland security, law enforcement, firefighting, and protective services; health professions and related sciences. Core. Calendar: semesters. Academic remediation for entering students, services for LD students, advanced placement, honors program, distance learning, double major, summer session for credit, part-time degree program, adult/continuing education programs, co-op programs and internships, graduate courses open to undergrads. Off campus study at Louisiana Tech University. ROTC: Army, Air Force (c).

Entrance Requirements: Options: electronic application, early admission. Required: high school transcript, minimum 2 high school GPA, 19 Units from Required Core 4 Curriculum; no more than one developmental course allowed; minimum test score of ACT English-18 and ACT Math-19 or SAT Critical Reading-450 and SAT Math-460 or COMPASS Writing-68 and COMPASS Algebra-40, SAT or ACT. Entrance: noncompetitive. Application deadline: 6/30. Notification: 8/1. SAT Reasoning Test deadline: 8/15. Transfer credits accepted: Yes.

Costs Per Year: Application fee: $20. State resident tuition: $3932 full-time, $164 per credit hour part-time. Nonresident tuition: $12,302 full-time, $164 per credit hour part-time. Mandatory fees: $1308 full-time, $164 per credit hour part-time, $349 per term part-time. Full-time tuition and fees vary according to course load, degree level, and student level. Part-time tuition and fees vary according to course load, degree level, and student level. College room and board: $9674. College room only: $5880. Room and board charges vary according to housing facility.

Collegiate Environment: Orientation program. Drama-theater group, choral group, marching band, student-run newspaper, radio station. Social organizations: 62 open to all; national fraternities, national sororities, local fraternities, local sororities. Most popular organizations: Tiger Marching Band, Black Dynasty Modeling Troupe, Academic and Professional Clubs, sororities, fraternities. Major annual events: Bayou Classic Football Game, Homecoming Festivities, Springfest. Student services: health clinic, personal-psychological counseling. Campus security: 24-hour patrols, student patrols, controlled dormitory access. College housing not available. A. C. Lewis Memorial Library plus 1 other with 234,524 books, 122,298 microform titles, 1.2 million serials, 6,394 audiovisual materials, an OPAC, and a Web page. Operations spending for the previous fiscal year: $1.2 million.

Community Environment: Grambling is in a suburban location five miles from Ruston, 35 miles from Monroe, and 70 miles from Shreveport. There is easy access to several major air and bus lines. The town has many fraternal, athletic, social, and civic organizations, and there are theatres in nearby Ruston. Excellent hunting, fishing, and boating facilities in the area. This is the home of the annual North Louisiana Broiler Show and Fair, and an annual Housing Clinic.

■ **HERZING UNIVERSITY**
2500 Williams Blvd.
Kenner, LA 70062
Tel: (504)733-0074; Free: 800-596-0724
Fax: (504)733-0020
Web Site: www.herzing.edu/
Description: Proprietary, 4-year, coed. Awards associate and bachelor's degrees. Founded 1996. Total enrollment: 166. 101 applied, 100% were admitted. 63% 25 or older. Calendar: semesters.
Entrance Requirements: Entrance: moderately difficult.

■ **ITI TECHNICAL COLLEGE**
13944 Airline Hwy.
Baton Rouge, LA 70817
Tel: (225)752-4233; Free: 888-211-7165

Fax: (225)756-0903
E-mail: mstevens@iticollege.edu
Web Site: www.iticollege.edu/
Description: Proprietary, 2-year, coed. Awards certificates and terminal associate degrees. Founded 1973. Setting: 10-acre suburban campus. Educational spending for the previous fiscal year: $2310 per student. Total enrollment: 585. Faculty: 51 (24 full-time, 27 part-time). Student-undergrad faculty ratio is 15:1. 174 applied, 99% were admitted. 0% from top 10% of their high school class, 0% from top quarter, 0% from top half. Full-time: 585 students, 15% women, 85% men. Students come from 3 states and territories, 1% from out-of-state. 1% American Indian or Alaska Native, non-Hispanic/Latino; 2% Hispanic/Latino; 38% African American, non-Hispanic/Latino; 1% Asian, non-Hispanic/Latino; 0% Native Hawaiian or other Pacific Islander, non-Hispanic/Latino; 0% international. 50% 25 or older, 0% transferred in. Retention: 81% of full-time freshmen returned the following year. Calendar: continuous. Internships.
Entrance Requirements: Open admission. Required: high school transcript, interview. Entrance: noncompetitive.
Collegiate Environment: Orientation program. Campus security: electronic alarm devices are activated during non-business hours and security cameras monitor campus 24 hours. College housing not available. ITI Technical College Library with 1,260 books. Operations spending for the previous fiscal year: $15,848. 8 computers available on campus for general student use. A campuswide network can be accessed. Staffed computer lab on campus provides training in use of computers, software, and the Internet.

■ **ITT TECHNICAL INSTITUTE (BATON ROUGE)**
14111 Airline Hwy.
Ste. 101
Baton Rouge, LA 70817
Tel: (225)754-5800; Free: 800-295-8485
Web Site: www.itt-tech.edu/
Description: Proprietary, primarily 2-year, coed. Awards terminal associate and bachelor's degrees.

■ **ITT TECHNICAL INSTITUTE (SAINT ROSE)**
140 James Dr. E
Saint Rose, LA 70087
Tel: (504)463-0338; Free: 866-463-0338
Web Site: www.itt-tech.edu/
Description: Proprietary, primarily 2-year, coed. Part of ITT Educational Services, Inc. Awards terminal associate and bachelor's degrees. Founded 1998.
Entrance Requirements: Entrance: minimally difficult.

■ **LOUISIANA COLLEGE**
1140 College Dr.
Pineville, LA 71359-0001
Tel: (318)487-7011; Free: 800-487-1906
Fax: (318)487-7550
E-mail: admissions@lacollege.edu
Web Site: www.lacollege.edu/
Description: Independent Southern Baptist, comprehensive, coed. Awards associate, bachelor's, and master's degrees. Founded 1906. Setting: 81-acre small town campus. Endowment: $29.3 million. Educational spending for the previous fiscal year: $6735 per student. Total enrollment: 1,557. Faculty: 115 (81 full-time, 34 part-time). Student-undergrad faculty ratio is 13:1. 820 applied, 74% were admitted. Full-time: 1,068 students, 49% women, 51% men. Part-time: 85 students, 51% women, 49% men. 1% American Indian or Alaska Native, non-Hispanic/Latino; 3% Hispanic/Latino; 18% African American, non-Hispanic/Latino; 1% Asian, non-Hispanic/Latino; 0.1% Native Hawaiian or other Pacific Islander, non-Hispanic/Latino; 1% international. 60% live on campus. Retention: 56% of full-time freshmen returned the following year. Academic areas with the most degrees conferred: health professions and related sciences; business/marketing; biological/life sciences. Core. Calendar: semesters. Academic remediation for entering students, services for LD students, advanced placement, accelerated degree program, self-designed majors, honors program, independent study, distance learning, double major, summer session for credit, part-time degree program, adult/continuing education programs, co-op programs and internships. Study abroad program. ROTC: Army.
Entrance Requirements: Options: electronic application, early admission. Required: high school transcript, minimum 2 high school GPA, class rank, SAT or ACT. Recommended: interview. Required for some: 3 recommenda-

tions. Entrance: moderately difficult. Application deadline: 8/15. Notification: continuous. Transfer credits accepted: Yes.

Costs Per Year: Application fee: $25. Comprehensive fee: $18,228 includes full-time tuition ($12,150), mandatory fees ($1630), and college room and board ($4448). Full-time tuition and fees vary according to course load. Room and board charges vary according to board plan and housing facility. Part-time tuition: $405 per credit hour. Part-time tuition varies according to course load.

Collegiate Environment: Orientation program. Drama-theater group, choral group, marching band, student-run newspaper, radio station. Social organizations: 40 open to all; local fraternities, local sororities; 20% of eligible men and 35% of eligible women are members. Most popular organizations: Baptist Student Union, Delta Xi Omega, Student Government Association, Union Board, Lambda Chi Beta. Major annual events: Gala Christmas, Homecoming, Cochon de Lait. Student services: health clinic, personal-psychological counseling. Campus security: 24-hour emergency response devices and patrols, student patrols, late night transport-escort service, controlled dormitory access. 703 college housing spaces available; 605 were occupied in 2012-13. Freshmen guaranteed college housing. On-campus residence required through junior year. Options: men-only, women-only housing available. Richard W. Norton Memorial Library with 357,313 books, 135,601 microform titles, 404 serials, 3,000 audiovisual materials, an OPAC, and a Web page. Operations spending for the previous fiscal year: $443,123. 233 computers available on campus for general student use. A campuswide network can be accessed from student residence rooms and from off campus. Students can access the following: online class registration. Staffed computer lab on campus provides training in use of computers, software, and the Internet.

Community Environment: Alexandria-Pineville is in the geographic heart of the state. The urban population of 64,000 has access to several major shopping malls, movie theaters, cultural attractions, fine restaurants, historical landmarks and churches representing nearly every denomination. The area is particularly noted for outdoor recreation opportunities, including year-round water sports and public hunting land. Part-time job opportunities in the community are numerous for college students.

■ **LOUISIANA DELTA COMMUNITY COLLEGE**
7500 Millhaven Rd.
Monroe, LA 71203
Tel: (318)345-9000; Free: 866-500-LDCC
Web Site: www.ladelta.edu/
Description: State-supported, 2-year, coed.

■ **LOUISIANA STATE UNIVERSITY AND AGRICULTURAL AND MECHANICAL COLLEGE**
Baton Rouge, LA 70803
Tel: (225)578-3202
Fax: (225)578-4433
E-mail: glamadrid@lsu.edu
Web Site: www.lsu.edu/
Description: State-supported, university, coed. Part of Louisiana State University System. Awards bachelor's, master's, and doctoral degrees and post-master's certificates. Founded 1860. Setting: 2,000-acre urban campus with easy access to New Orleans. Endowment: $348.8 million. Research spending for the previous fiscal year: $141.9 million. Educational spending for the previous fiscal year: $8218 per student. Total enrollment: 30,225. Faculty: 1,399 (1,230 full-time, 169 part-time). Student-undergrad faculty ratio is 23:1. 16,169 applied, 76% were admitted. 24% from top 10% of their high school class, 50% from top quarter, 80% from top half. 38 National Merit Scholars, 316 valedictorians. Full-time: 22,681 students, 51% women, 49% men. Part-time: 1,945 students, 52% women, 48% men. Students come from 51 states and territories, 80 other countries, 20% from out-of-state. 0.3% American Indian or Alaska Native, non-Hispanic/Latino; 5% Hispanic/Latino; 11% African American, non-Hispanic/Latino; 3% Asian, non-Hispanic/Latino; 0.1% Native Hawaiian or other Pacific Islander, non-Hispanic/Latino; 2% international. 6% 25 or older, 27% live on campus, 3% transferred in. Retention: 83% of full-time freshmen returned the following year. Academic areas with the most degrees conferred: business/marketing; engineering; education. Core. Calendar: semesters. ESL program, services for LD students, advanced placement, accelerated degree program, self-designed majors, freshman honors college, honors program, independent study, distance learning, double major, summer session for credit, part-time degree program, adult/continuing education programs, co-op programs and internships, graduate courses open to undergrads. Off campus study at Southern

University and Agricultural and Mechanical College, members of the National Student Exchange, Baton Rouge Community College. Study abroad program. ROTC: Army, Naval (c), Air Force.

Entrance Requirements: Options: electronic application, early admission, deferred admission, international baccalaureate accepted. Required: high school transcript, minimum 3 high school GPA, 22 ACT (1030 SAT) with a minimum critical reading score of 18 ACT (450 SAT), and a math score of 19 ACT (460 SAT), SAT or ACT. Required for some: essay. Entrance: moderately difficult. Application deadline: 4/15. Notification: continuous. SAT Reasoning Test deadline: 8/1. Transfer credits accepted: Yes.

Costs Per Year: Application fee: $40. State resident tuition: $5193 full-time. Nonresident tuition: $20,469 full-time. Mandatory fees: $1796 full-time. College room and board: $10,218. College room only: $6600. Room and board charges vary according to board plan and housing facility.

Collegiate Environment: Orientation program. Drama-theater group, choral group, marching band, student-run newspaper, radio station. Social organizations: 300 open to all; national fraternities, national sororities; 15% of eligible men and 24% of eligible women are members. Most popular organizations: intramural athletics, student political organizations, student professional organizations, religious organizations, cultural organizations. Major annual events: Fall Fest, Student Disability Week, Homecoming Week activities. Student services: legal services, health clinic, personal-psychological counseling, women's center. Campus security: 24-hour emergency response devices and patrols, late night transport-escort service, controlled dormitory access, self-defense education, crime prevention programs. 6,708 college housing spaces available; 6,556 were occupied in 2012-13. No special consideration for freshman housing applicants. Options: coed, men-only, women-only housing available. Troy H. Middleton Library plus 4 others with 4.5 million books, 2.3 million microform titles, 313,323 serials, 25,949 audiovisual materials, an OPAC, and a Web page. Operations spending for the previous fiscal year: $12.9 million. 1,400 computers available on campus for general student use. A campuswide network can be accessed from student residence rooms and from off campus. Students can access the following: online class registration, free software for download, personal Web sites, storage, discounts on hardware, virtual computer lab. Staffed computer lab on campus provides training in use of computers, software, and the Internet.

Community Environment: Baton Rouge, with a metropolitan-area population of more than 600,000, is the capital of Louisiana, the state's second largest port for ocean-going vessels, and the fifth largest inland port in the nation. A rich mixture of French, Spanish, and English cultures reflects Baton Rouge's history. Geographically, Baton Rouge is the center of South Louisiana's main cultural and recreational attractions. New Orleans is 80 miles to the southeast; the Feliciana parishes, noted for their antebellum homes, are less than an hour's drive to the north; and to the west lies the Acadian-French country of bayous, lakes, and marshes. Baton Rouge's industry is widely diversified. It is a major petrochemical center, as well as a center for banking and financial services and a major retail center. Cultural organizations include the Baton Rouge Symphony, the Baton Rouge Ballet, and community theater groups. Baton Rouge has many recreation centers, golf courses, and parks. Mild temperatures make outdoor activities possible and enjoyable throughout the year.

■ **LOUISIANA STATE UNIVERSITY AT ALEXANDRIA**
8100 Hwy. 71 S
Alexandria, LA 71302-9121
Tel: (318)445-3672; Free: 888-473-6417
Fax: (318)473-6418
E-mail: admissions@lsua.edu
Web Site: www.lsua.edu/
Description: State-supported, 4-year, coed. Part of Louisiana State University System. Awards associate and bachelor's degrees. Founded 1960. Setting: 3,114-acre rural campus. Endowment: $13.8 million. Educational spending for the previous fiscal year: $4537 per student. Total enrollment: 2,430. Faculty: 139 (86 full-time, 53 part-time). Student-undergrad faculty ratio is 15:1. 991 applied, 61% were admitted. 10% from top 10% of their high school class, 25% from top quarter, 50% from top half. Full-time: 1,196 students, 66% women, 34% men. Part-time: 1,211 students, 73% women, 27% men. Students come from 16 states and territories, 7 other countries, 2% from out-of-state. 1% American Indian or Alaska Native, non-Hispanic/Latino; 3% Hispanic/Latino; 18% African American, non-Hispanic/Latino; 1% Asian, non-Hispanic/Latino; 0% Native Hawaiian or other Pacific Islander, non-Hispanic/Latino; 0.1% international. 42% 25 or older, 8% live on campus, 7% transferred in. Retention: 49% of full-time

freshmen returned the following year. Academic areas with the most degrees conferred: business/marketing; liberal arts/general studies; psychology. Core. Calendar: semesters. Academic remediation for entering students, services for LD students, advanced placement, accelerated degree program, independent study, distance learning, double major, summer session for credit, part-time degree program, adult/continuing education programs, co-op programs and internships.

Entrance Requirements: Options: electronic application, early admission. Required: high school transcript, SAT or ACT. Required for some: minimum 2 high school GPA. Entrance: moderately difficult. Application deadline: Rolling. Notification: continuous. SAT Reasoning Test deadline: 8/15. SAT Subject Test deadline: 8/15. Transfer credits accepted: Yes.

Collegiate Environment: Orientation program. Drama-theater group, choral group, student-run newspaper. Most popular organization: Student Government Association. Major annual events: SGA Crawfish Boil, Trick or Treat Street, Mardi Gras Parade. Student services: personal-psychological counseling. Campus security: 24-hour emergency response devices and patrols. 252 college housing spaces available. Freshmen given priority for college housing. On-campus residence required in freshman year. Option: coed housing available. James C. Bolton Library with 166,340 books, 1,541 serials, an OPAC, and a Web page. 325 computers available on campus for general student use. A campuswide network can be accessed. Students can access the following: online class registration. Staffed computer lab on campus provides training in use of computers, software, and the Internet.

■ LOUISIANA STATE UNIVERSITY AT EUNICE

PO Box 1129
Eunice, LA 70535-1129
Tel: (337)457-7311
Fax: (337)457-7311
Web Site: www.lsue.edu/

Description: State-supported, 2-year, coed. Part of Louisiana State University System. Awards certificates, transfer associate, and terminal associate degrees. Founded 1967. Setting: 199-acre small town campus. Total enrollment: 2,833. Faculty: 131. 1,753 applied, 99% were admitted. Students come from 4 states and territories, 0.4% from out-of-state. 40% 25 or older. Core. Calendar: semesters. Academic remediation for entering students, services for LD students, advanced placement, honors program, distance learning, summer session for credit, part-time degree program, adult/continuing education programs, co-op programs.

Entrance Requirements: Open admission. Option: early admission. Required: high school transcript. Entrance: noncompetitive. Application deadline: 8/7.

Collegiate Environment: Orientation program. Student-run newspaper. Social organizations: 14 open to all; local fraternities, local sororities; 3% of eligible men and 3% of eligible women are members. Most popular organizations: Student Government Association, Students in Free Enterprise (SIFE), Criminal Justice Society, Student Nurses Association, Phi Theta Kappa. Major annual events: Festival of the Arts, Annual Blood Drive, End of Semester Bash. Student services: personal-psychological counseling. Campus security: 24-hour emergency response devices and patrols. Arnold LeDoux Library with 100,000 books, 253 serials, and an OPAC. 160 computers available on campus for general student use. A campuswide network can be accessed.

■ LOUISIANA STATE UNIVERSITY HEALTH SCIENCES CENTER

433 Bolivar St.
New Orleans, LA 70112-2223
Tel: (504)568-4808
Web Site: www.lsuhsc.edu/

Description: State-supported, university, coed. Part of Louisiana State University System. Awards associate, bachelor's, master's, and doctoral degrees and post-master's certificates. Founded 1931. Setting: 80-acre urban campus. Endowment: $68.5 million. Research spending for the previous fiscal year: $58.9 million. Educational spending for the previous fiscal year: $79,554 per student. Total enrollment: 2,644. Faculty: 893 (726 full-time, 167 part-time). Full-time: 644 students, 83% women, 17% men. Part-time: 186 students, 83% women, 17% men. Students come from 10 states and territories, 4 other countries, 1% from out-of-state. 28% 25 or older, 10% live on campus. Academic area with the most degrees conferred: health professions and related sciences. Calendar: varies by academic program. Services for LD students, advanced placement, accelerated degree program, independent study, distance learning, double major, summer session for credit, co-op programs and internships, graduate courses open to undergrads. ROTC: Army (c), Naval (c), Air Force (c).

Costs Per Year: Application fee: $50. State resident tuition: $3767 full-time, $241 per semester hour part-time. Nonresident tuition: $6897 full-time, $437 per semester hour part-time. Mandatory fees: $724 full-time, $39 per semester hour part-time. Full-time tuition and fees vary according to degree level, program, and reciprocity agreements. Part-time tuition and fees vary according to course load, degree level, program, and reciprocity agreements. College room only: $3708. Room charges vary according to housing facility.

Collegiate Environment: Orientation program. Student services: health clinic, personal-psychological counseling. Campus security: 24-hour emergency response devices and patrols, late night transport-escort service, controlled dormitory access. John P. Ische Library plus 1 other with 1,230 microform titles, 4,913 serials, 1,252 audiovisual materials, an OPAC, and a Web page. Operations spending for the previous fiscal year: $3.2 million. 120 computers available on campus for general student use. Computer purchase/lease plans available. A campuswide network can be accessed from student residence rooms and from off campus. Staffed computer lab on campus provides training in use of computers, software, and the Internet.

■ LOUISIANA STATE UNIVERSITY IN SHREVEPORT

1 University Pl.
Shreveport, LA 71115-2399
Tel: (318)797-5000; Free: 800-229-5957
Fax: (318)797-5286
E-mail: admissions@lsus.edu
Web Site: www.lsus.edu/

Description: State-supported, comprehensive, coed. Part of Louisiana State University System. Awards bachelor's and master's degrees and post-master's certificates. Founded 1965. Setting: 200-acre urban campus. Endowment: $16.3 million. Research spending for the previous fiscal year: $80,708. Educational spending for the previous fiscal year: $4392 per student. Total enrollment: 4,535. Faculty: 188 (127 full-time, 61 part-time). Student-undergrad faculty ratio is 21:1. 543 applied, 68% were admitted. Full-time: 2,306 students, 58% women, 42% men. Part-time: 1,818 students, 60% women, 40% men. Students come from 43 states and territories, 12 other countries, 6% from out-of-state. 1% American Indian or Alaska Native, non-Hispanic/Latino; 4% Hispanic/Latino; 23% African American, non-Hispanic/Latino; 2% Asian, non-Hispanic/Latino; 0.1% Native Hawaiian or other Pacific Islander, non-Hispanic/Latino; 2% international. 32% 25 or older, 9% transferred in. Retention: 65% of full-time freshmen returned the following year. Academic areas with the most degrees conferred: business/marketing; liberal arts/general studies; biological/life sciences; psychology. Core. Calendar: semesters plus 8-week and two 4-week summer terms. Academic remediation for entering students, ESL program, services for LD students, advanced placement, accelerated degree program, self-designed majors, honors program, independent study, distance learning, double major, summer session for credit, part-time degree program, adult/continuing education programs, co-op programs and internships, graduate courses open to undergrads. Off campus study. ROTC: Army.

Entrance Requirements: Options: electronic application, early admission, early decision, international baccalaureate accepted. Required: SAT or ACT. Required for some: high school transcript, minimum 2 high school GPA. Entrance: moderately difficult. Application deadline: Rolling. Transfer credits accepted: Yes.

Costs Per Year: Application fee: $10. State resident tuition: $3882 full-time, $161.77 per credit hour part-time. Nonresident tuition: $10,617 full-time, $442.42 per credit hour part-time. Mandatory fees: $1060 full-time, $44.20 per credit hour part-time.

Collegiate Environment: Orientation program. Drama-theater group, choral group, student-run newspaper. Social organizations: national fraternities, national sororities. Student services: personal-psychological counseling. Campus security: 24-hour emergency response devices and patrols, student patrols, controlled dormitory access. College housing not available. Noel Memorial Library with an OPAC and a Web page. Operations spending for the previous fiscal year: $1.5 million.

■ LOUISIANA TECH UNIVERSITY

PO Box 3168
Ruston, LA 71272
Tel: (318)257-0211; Free: 800-528-3241
E-mail: bulldog@latech.edu
Web Site: www.latech.edu/

Description: State-supported, university, coed. Part of University of Louisiana System. Awards associate, bachelor's, master's, and doctoral degrees and post-master's certificates. Founded 1894. Setting: 247-acre small town campus. Total enrollment: 11,304. Faculty: 406 (341 full-time, 65 part-time). Student-undergrad faculty ratio is 24:1. 4,580 applied, 71% were admitted. 18% from top 10% of their high school class, 45% from top quarter, 77% from top half. Full-time: 6,478 students, 44% women, 56% men. Part-time: 2,480 students, 57% women, 43% men. 10% from out-of-state. 0.4% American Indian or Alaska Native, non-Hispanic/Latino; 1% Hispanic/Latino; 13% African American, non-Hispanic/Latino; 1% Asian, non-Hispanic/Latino; 0.1% Native Hawaiian or other Pacific Islander, non-Hispanic/Latino; 4% international. 19% 25 or older, 15% live on campus, 4% transferred in. Retention: 77% of full-time freshmen returned the following year. Academic areas with the most degrees conferred: business/marketing; engineering; liberal arts/general studies. Core. Academic remediation for entering students, advanced placement, honors program, independent study, distance learning, double major, summer session for credit, part-time degree program, adult/continuing education programs, internships, graduate courses open to undergrads. Off campus study at Grambling State University. Study abroad program. ROTC: Army (c), Air Force.

Entrance Requirements: Option: early admission. Required: high school transcript, minimum 2.2 high school GPA, SAT or ACT. Recommended: ACT. Entrance: moderately difficult. Application deadline: 7/31. Notification: continuous. SAT Reasoning Test deadline: 7/1.

Collegiate Environment: Orientation program. Drama-theater group, choral group, marching band, student-run newspaper, radio station. Social organizations: national fraternities, national sororities. Most popular organizations: Student Government Association, Association of Women's Studies, Union Board. Major annual events: Homecoming, Spring Fling, Little Las Vegas Night. Student services: legal services, health clinic, personal-psychological counseling. Campus security: 24-hour emergency response devices and patrols, student patrols, late night transport-escort service, controlled dormitory access. On-campus residence required through sophomore year. Options: men-only, women-only housing available. Prescott Memorial Library with an OPAC and a Web page.

Community Environment: This is an urban area with bus service available. City has a public library, several churches, its own hospital, medical clinics, and good shopping facilities. Theatres, drive-in, golf, fishing, boating, and a campus olympic swimming pool provide recreation opportunities. There is also a concert association.

■ **LOYOLA UNIVERSITY NEW ORLEANS**
6363 Saint Charles Ave.
New Orleans, LA 70118-6195
Tel: (504)865-2011; Free: 800-4-LOYOLA
Fax: (504)865-3383
E-mail: admit@loyno.edu
Web Site: www.loyno.edu/

Description: Independent Roman Catholic (Jesuit), comprehensive, coed. Awards bachelor's, master's, and doctoral degrees and post-master's certificates. Founded 1912. Setting: 26-acre suburban campus with easy access to New Orleans. Endowment: $249 million. Research spending for the previous fiscal year: $1.1 million. Educational spending for the previous fiscal year: $11,843 per student. Total enrollment: 4,933. Faculty: 492 (316 full-time, 176 part-time). Student-undergrad faculty ratio is 10:1. 6,486 applied, 66% were admitted. 27% from top 10% of their high school class, 47% from top quarter, 77% from top half. 39 class presidents, 11 valedictorians, 212 student government officers. Full-time: 2,986 students, 58% women, 42% men. Part-time: 214 students, 57% women, 43% men. Students come from 53 states and territories, 48 other countries, 58% from out-of-state. 1% American Indian or Alaska Native, non-Hispanic/Latino; 15% Hispanic/Latino; 15% African American, non-Hispanic/Latino; 4% Asian, non-Hispanic/Latino; 0% Native Hawaiian or other Pacific Islander, non-Hispanic/Latino; 4% international. 8% 25 or older, 65% live on campus, 4% transferred in. Retention: 74% of full-time freshmen returned the following year. Academic areas with the most degrees conferred: business/marketing; visual and performing arts; social sciences. Core. Calendar: semesters. ESL program, services for LD students, advanced placement, accelerated degree program, self-designed majors, honors program, independent study, distance learning, double major, summer session for credit, part-time degree program, external degree program, adult/continuing education programs, co-op programs and internships, graduate courses open to undergrads. Off campus study at Tulane University, Xavier University of Louisiana, Notre Dame Seminary, University of New Orleans, Southern University at New Orleans. Study abroad program. ROTC: Army (c), Naval (c), Air Force (c).

Entrance Requirements: Options: electronic application, early admission,

international baccalaureate accepted. Required: essay, high school transcript, 1 recommendation, SAT or ACT. Recommended: interview. Required for some: interview. Entrance: moderately difficult. Application deadline: Rolling. Notification: continuous. SAT Reasoning Test deadline: 8/1. Transfer credits accepted: Yes.

Costs Per Year: Application fee: $20. Comprehensive fee: $48,795 includes full-time tuition ($35,504), mandatory fees ($1106), and college room and board ($12,185). College room only: $7250. Room and board charges vary according to board plan and housing facility. Part-time tuition: $1012 per credit.

Collegiate Environment: Orientation program. Drama-theater group, choral group, student-run newspaper, radio station. Social organizations: 85 open to all; national fraternities, national sororities, local fraternities; 6% of women are members. Most popular organizations: University Programming Board, Student Government Association, Black Student Union, Loyola University Community Action Program (LUCAP), Panhellenic Council. Major annual events: Loyola Week, Loyolapalooza Spring Music Festival, Wolves on the Prowl Community Service Day. Student services: health clinic, personal-psychological counseling, women's center. Campus security: 24-hour emergency response devices and patrols, student patrols, late night transport-escort service, controlled dormitory access, self-defense education, bicycle patrols, closed circuit TV monitors, door alarms, crime prevention programs, card access control. 1,350 college housing spaces available; all were occupied in 2012-13. Freshmen guaranteed college housing. On-campus residence required through sophomore year. Option: coed housing available. Monroe Library plus 1 other with 584,939 books, 1.4 million microform titles, 169,032 serials, 17,352 audiovisual materials, an OPAC, and a Web page. Operations spending for the previous fiscal year: $5.2 million. 525 computers available on campus for general student use. Computer purchase/lease plans available. A campuswide network can be accessed from student residence rooms and from off campus. Students can access the following: online class registration. Staffed computer lab on campus provides training in use of computers, software, and the Internet.

Community Environment: See Tulane University.

■ **MCNEESE STATE UNIVERSITY**
4205 Ryan St.
Lake Charles, LA 70609
Tel: (337)475-5000; Free: 800-622-3352
E-mail: ksmith2@mcneese.edu
Web Site: www.mcneese.edu/

Description: State-supported, comprehensive, coed. Part of University of Louisiana System. Awards associate, bachelor's, and master's degrees and post-master's certificates. Founded 1939. Setting: 766-acre suburban campus. Total enrollment: 8,588. Faculty: 428 (289 full-time, 139 part-time). Student-undergrad faculty ratio is 21:1. 3,547 applied, 61% were admitted. 20% from top 10% of their high school class, 43% from top quarter, 76% from top half. Full-time: 6,082 students, 60% women, 40% men. Part-time: 1,629 students, 66% women, 34% men. Students come from 38 states and territories, 47 other countries, 8% from out-of-state. 1% American Indian or Alaska Native, non-Hispanic/Latino; 1% Hispanic/Latino; 18% African American, non-Hispanic/Latino; 1% Asian, non-Hispanic/Latino; 0.1% Native Hawaiian or other Pacific Islander, non-Hispanic/Latino; 4% international. 23% 25 or older, 9% live on campus, 4% transferred in. Retention: 68% of full-time freshmen returned the following year. Academic areas with the most degrees conferred: liberal arts/general studies; health professions and related sciences; business/marketing. Core. Calendar: semesters. Academic remediation for entering students, ESL program, services for LD students, advanced placement, accelerated degree program, freshman honors college, honors program, independent study, distance learning, double major, summer session for credit, part-time degree program, co-op programs and internships, graduate courses open to undergrads. Off campus study at Council of Intercollegiate Nursing Consortium; Coushatta Project, Kinder, Louisiana. Study abroad program.

Entrance Requirements: Options: electronic application, early admission, deferred admission, international baccalaureate accepted. Required: high school transcript, minimum 2 high school GPA, Complete Louisiana Board of Regents high school core curriculum with 18 ACT English or 19 ACT math (450 SAT critical reading or 460 math) and minimum 2.5 GPA and meet one of the following: minimum high school core GPA of 2.0 or minimum ACT composite 20 (SAT critical reading/math combined scores 940), SAT or ACT. Entrance: moderately difficult. Application deadline: Rolling. Notification: continuous. Transfer credits accepted: Yes.

Costs Per Year: Application fee: $20. State resident tuition: $5120 full-time.

Nonresident tuition: $11,454 full-time. Full-time tuition varies according to course load. College room and board: $7468. Room and board charges vary according to board plan and housing facility.

Collegiate Environment: Orientation program. Drama-theater group, choral group, marching band, student-run newspaper. Social organizations: national fraternities, national sororities. Most popular organizations: Student Government Association, International Students Association, Resident Student Association. Major annual events: Homecoming, Spring Fling. Student services: health clinic, personal-psychological counseling, women's center. Campus security: 24-hour emergency response devices and patrols, late night transport-escort service, controlled dormitory access. 825 college housing spaces available; 789 were occupied in 2012-13. Option: coed housing available. 700 computers available on campus for general student use. A campuswide network can be accessed from student residence rooms and from off campus. Students can access the following: online class registration. Staffed computer lab on campus.

Community Environment: The city owes its development to the combination of Capt. J. B. Watkins, a variety of natural resources and a deepwater port. In 1887 Captain Watkins of New York moved his newspaper to Lake Charles and started an overwhelming advertising program, which, with the terminus of a railroad at New Orleans, resulted in the development of a 17-mill lumber industry. The discovery of oil in the early 1900s and a new process of mining sulfur further enriched the city. Forests are presently nearly depleted and the sulfur supply is no longer industrially profitable. This city with its vast oil companies in southwest Louisiana is a leader in the petrochemical industry. A deepwater port since 1926, it is currently the nation's leading rice port. Docks also handle general cargo, the output of chemical and petrochemical plants and products of the city's two large rice mills. Student employment is available. Transportation is provided by commercial passenger air lines, rail, and bus service. There are libraries, YMCA, a great number of churches, and three hospitals easily accessible. Recreation includes fishing, hunting, theatres, and an annual rodeo.

■ **NEW ORLEANS BAPTIST THEOLOGICAL SEMINARY**
3939 Gentilly Blvd.
New Orleans, LA 70126-4858
Tel: (504)282-4455; Free: 800-662-8701
Web Site: www.nobts.edu/

Description: Independent Southern Baptist, comprehensive, coed. Awards associate, bachelor's, master's, and doctoral degrees. Founded 1917. Setting: 81-acre suburban campus. Total enrollment: 2,036. Core. Calendar: semesters. Academic remediation for entering students, ESL program, independent study, summer session for credit, part-time degree program, adult/continuing education programs, internships. Off campus study.

Entrance Requirements: Open admission. Option: deferred admission. Recommended: minimum 2.0 high school GPA. Entrance: minimally difficult. Application deadline: 8/9. Notification: continuous.

Collegiate Environment: Orientation program. Choral group, student-run radio station. Student services: health clinic, personal-psychological counseling. Campus security: 24-hour emergency response devices and patrols. John Christian Library plus 1 other with 206,321 books.

Community Environment: See Tulane University.

■ **NICHOLLS STATE UNIVERSITY**
906 E First St.
Thibodaux, LA 70310
Tel: (985)446-8111; Free: 877-NICHOLLS
Fax: (985)448-4929
E-mail: nicholls@nicholls.edu
Web Site: www.nicholls.edu/

Description: State-supported, comprehensive, coed. Part of University of Louisiana System. Awards associate, bachelor's, and master's degrees and post-master's certificates. Founded 1948. Setting: 210-acre small town campus with easy access to New Orleans. Endowment: $15.2 million. Research spending for the previous fiscal year: $3.1 million. Educational spending for the previous fiscal year: $4206 per student. Total enrollment: 6,606. Faculty: 298 (263 full-time, 35 part-time). Student-undergrad faculty ratio is 20:1. 2,336 applied, 92% were admitted. 16% from top 10% of their high school class, 40% from top quarter, 73% from top half. 42 valedictorians. Full-time: 4,782 students, 62% women, 38% men. Part-time: 1,230 students, 63% women, 37% men. Students come from 18 states and territories, 42 other countries, 4% from out-of-state. 2% American Indian or Alaska Native, non-Hispanic/Latino; 3% Hispanic/Latino; 20% African American, non-Hispanic/Latino; 1% Asian, non-Hispanic/Latino; 0.1% Native

Hawaiian or other Pacific Islander, non-Hispanic/Latino; 2% international. 18% 25 or older, 26% live on campus, 4% transferred in. Retention: 69% of full-time freshmen returned the following year. Academic areas with the most degrees conferred: business/marketing; health professions and related sciences; liberal arts/general studies. Core. Calendar: semesters. Academic remediation for entering students, ESL program, services for LD students, advanced placement, accelerated degree program, honors program, independent study, distance learning, double major, summer session for credit, part-time degree program, adult/continuing education programs, co-op programs and internships, graduate courses open to undergrads. Off campus study. Study abroad program.

Entrance Requirements: Options: electronic application, early admission, deferred admission. Required: high school transcript, SAT or ACT. Entrance: noncompetitive. Application deadline: Rolling. Notification: 9/1.

Costs Per Year: Application fee: $20. State resident tuition: $3924 full-time. Nonresident tuition: $12,774 full-time. Mandatory fees: $1755 full-time. College room and board: $8560. College room only: $5670. Room and board charges vary according to board plan, housing facility, and location.

Collegiate Environment: Orientation program. Drama-theater group, choral group, marching band, student-run newspaper, radio station. Social organizations: 78 open to all; national fraternities, national sororities; 9% of eligible men and 8% of eligible women are members. Most popular organizations: Student Government Association, Student Programming Association, Residence Hall Association, Food Advisory Association. Major annual events: Homecoming, Spring Fest, Family Day. Student services: legal services, health clinic, personal-psychological counseling, women's center. Campus security: 24-hour emergency response devices and patrols, student patrols, late night transport-escort service. 1,470 college housing spaces available; 1,389 were occupied in 2012-13. Freshmen guaranteed college housing. On-campus residence required in freshman year. Options: coed, men-only, women-only housing available. Allen J. Ellender Memorial Library plus 3 others with 600,954 books, 354,164 microform titles, 11,149 serials, 15,395 audiovisual materials, an OPAC, and a Web page. Operations spending for the previous fiscal year: $2.3 million. 1,500 computers available on campus for general student use. A campuswide network can be accessed from student residence rooms and from off campus. Students can access the following: online class registration, course management system—Moodle. Staffed computer lab on campus.

Community Environment: The campus is located in a sugar-belt town on the banks of picturesque Bayou Lafourche. Incorporated in 1838, this was the first trading post established between New Orleans and the country along Bayou Teche in southeastern Louisiana. There are many beautiful plantations in the vicinity. Thibodaux presents a small town atmosphere. It is a quick 45 miles from historic New Orleans by rail or bus. The year-round climate is mild to moderate. The city has a public library, churches representing all denominations, and a hospital. Recreation includes movies, theater, hunting, boating, fishing, golf, bowling, swimming, and tennis. Student employment is available in the area and on campus.

■ **NORTHEAST LOUISIANA TECHNICAL COLLEGE–NORTHEAST CAMPUS**
1710 Warren St.
Winnsboro, LA 71295
Tel: (318)485-2163; Free: 877-842-6956
Web Site: www.ltc.edu/

Description: State-supported, 2-year, coed. Awards terminal associate degrees. Total enrollment: 310. Faculty: 18 (9 full-time, 9 part-time). Calendar: semesters.

■ **NORTHSHORE TECHNICAL COMMUNITY COLLEGE–FLORIDA PARISHES CAMPUS**
948 Hwy. 1042
Greensburg, LA 70441
Tel: (225)222-4251
Web Site: www.ltc.edu/

Description: State-supported, 2-year, coed. Part of Louisiana Community and Technical College System. Awards certificates, diplomas, and terminal associate degrees. Total enrollment: 618. 25% 25 or older. Calendar: semesters. Academic remediation for entering students, services for LD students, advanced placement, distance learning, adult/continuing education programs, co-op programs and internships.

Entrance Requirements: Open admission except when space is unavailable and student does not meet TABE and other program requirements. Option: early action. Required: high school transcript. Required for some: essay, interview. Notification: continuous.

Collegiate Environment: Orientation program. Student services: personal-psychological counseling. Campus security: 24-hour emergency response devices.

■ NORTHWESTERN STATE UNIVERSITY OF LOUISIANA

715 University Pky.
Natchitoches, LA 71497
Tel: (318)357-6361; Free: 800-327-1903
E-mail: recruiting@nsula.edu
Web Site: www.nsula.edu/

Description: State-supported, comprehensive, coed. Part of University of Louisiana System. Awards associate, bachelor's, and master's degrees and post-master's certificates. Founded 1884. Setting: 916-acre small town campus. Endowment: $10.9 million. Research spending for the previous fiscal year: $1.7 million. Educational spending for the previous fiscal year: $5326 per student. Total enrollment: 9,447. Faculty: 498 (267 full-time, 231 part-time). Student-undergrad faculty ratio is 20:1. 3,238 applied, 85% were admitted. 17% from top 10% of their high school class, 43% from top quarter, 76% from top half. 51 valedictorians. Full-time: 5,294 students, 65% women, 35% men. Part-time: 3,018 students, 74% women, 26% men. Students come from 48 states and territories, 21 other countries, 9% from out-of-state. 1% American Indian or Alaska Native, non-Hispanic/Latino; 4% Hispanic/Latino; 30% African American, non-Hispanic/Latino; 1% Asian, non-Hispanic/Latino; 0.1% Native Hawaiian or other Pacific Islander, non-Hispanic/Latino; 1% international. 35% 25 or older, 19% live on campus, 7% transferred in. Retention: 68% of full-time freshmen returned the following year. Academic areas with the most degrees conferred: health professions and related sciences; liberal arts/general studies; business/marketing. Core. Calendar: semesters. Academic remediation for entering students, services for LD students, advanced placement, freshman honors college, honors program, independent study, distance learning, double major, summer session for credit, part-time degree program, adult/continuing education programs, co-op programs and internships, graduate courses open to undergrads. Study abroad program. ROTC: Army, Air Force (c).

Entrance Requirements: Options: electronic application, deferred admission. Required: high school transcript, minimum 2 high school GPA, college preparatory curriculum, SAT or ACT. Entrance: moderately difficult. Application deadlines: 7/6, 7/6 for nonresidents. Notification: continuous, continuous for nonresidents. SAT Reasoning Test deadline: 7/27. Transfer credits accepted: Yes.

Costs Per Year: Application fee: $20. State resident tuition: $3938 full-time. Nonresident tuition: $13,304 full-time. Mandatory fees: $1542 full-time. Full-time tuition and fees vary according to course load and location. College room and board: $7826. College room only: $4896. Room and board charges vary according to board plan, housing facility, and location.

Collegiate Environment: Orientation program. Drama-theater group, choral group, marching band, student-run newspaper, radio station. Social organizations: 120 open to all; national fraternities, national sororities; 10% of eligible men and 6% of eligible women are members. Major annual events: Spring Fling Week, Homecoming Week, Welcome Week. Student services: health clinic, personal-psychological counseling. Campus security: 24-hour emergency response devices and patrols, student patrols, late night transport-escort service, controlled dormitory access. 1,517 college housing spaces available; 1,424 were occupied in 2012-13. Freshmen given priority for college housing. On-campus residence required through junior year. Option: coed housing available. Eugene P. Watson Memorial Library with 791,279 books, 632,689 microform titles, 700 serials, 5,514 audiovisual materials, an OPAC, and a Web page. Operations spending for the previous fiscal year: $1.9 million. 1,500 computers available on campus for general student use. A campuswide network can be accessed from student residence rooms and from off campus. Students can access the following: online class registration. Staffed computer lab on campus provides training in use of computers, software, and the Internet.

■ OUR LADY OF HOLY CROSS COLLEGE

4123 Woodland Dr.
New Orleans, LA 70131-7399
Tel: (504)394-7744; Free: 800-259-7744
Fax: (504)391-2421
E-mail: dkennedy@olhcc.edu
Web Site: www.olhcc.edu/

Description: Independent Roman Catholic, comprehensive, coed. Awards associate, bachelor's, and master's degrees. Founded 1916. Setting: 40-acre suburban campus. Total enrollment: 1,298. 42% 25 or older. Core.

Calendar: semesters plus summer sessions. Academic remediation for entering students, services for LD students, advanced placement, independent study, distance learning, double major, summer session for credit, part-time degree program, adult/continuing education programs, co-op programs and internships, graduate courses open to undergrads. Off campus study at Delgado Community College, St. Joseph Seminary College, Notre Dame Seminary, Ochsner Clinical Foundation, Louisiana Universities Marine Consortium, Gulf Coast Research Laboratories. Study abroad program. ROTC: Army (c), Air Force (c).

Entrance Requirements: Open admission. Options: electronic application, deferred admission, international baccalaureate accepted. Required: high school transcript. Recommended: minimum 2.0 high school GPA. Entrance: minimally difficult. Application deadline: 7/20. Notification: continuous.

Collegiate Environment: Orientation program. Drama-theater group, student-run newspaper. Student services: personal-psychological counseling. Campus security: 24-hour patrols. Blaine Kern Library with 83,631 books, 222,522 microform titles, 1,002 serials, 11,949 audiovisual materials, an OPAC, and a Web page.

Community Environment: See Tulane University.

■ OUR LADY OF THE LAKE COLLEGE

7434 Perkins Rd.
Baton Rouge, LA 70808
Tel: (225)768-1700
Fax: (225)768-1726
E-mail: admissions@ololcollege.edu
Web Site: www.ololcollege.edu/

Description: Independent Roman Catholic, comprehensive, coed. Awards associate, bachelor's, and master's degrees. Founded 1990. Setting: 5-acre suburban campus with easy access to New Orleans. Endowment: $8.6 million. Research spending for the previous fiscal year: $99,187. Total enrollment: 1,748. Faculty: 183 (97 full-time, 86 part-time). Student-undergrad faculty ratio is 18:1. Full-time: 524 students, 84% women, 16% men. Part-time: 1,096 students, 87% women, 13% men. Students come from 10 states and territories, 2% from out-of-state. 1% American Indian or Alaska Native, non-Hispanic/Latino; 1% Hispanic/Latino; 26% African American, non-Hispanic/Latino; 3% Asian, non-Hispanic/Latino; 0.4% Native Hawaiian or other Pacific Islander, non-Hispanic/Latino. 44% 25 or older, 9% transferred in. Retention: 63% of full-time freshmen returned the following year. Academic areas with the most degrees conferred: health professions and related sciences; liberal arts/general studies; homeland security, law enforcement, firefighting, and protective services. Core. Calendar: semesters. Academic remediation for entering students, services for LD students, advanced placement, accelerated degree program, summer session for credit, part-time degree program. Off campus study. ROTC: Army (c), Air Force (c).

Entrance Requirements: Open admission except for professional programs. Options: electronic application, early admission, deferred admission. Required: high school transcript, minimum 2 high school GPA, SAT or ACT, ACT ASSET. Entrance: minimally difficult. Application deadline: 8/15. Notification: continuous. SAT Reasoning Test deadline: 7/1. SAT Subject Test deadline: 7/1. Transfer credits accepted: Yes.

Collegiate Environment: Orientation program. Most popular organizations: Student Government Association, Cultural Arts Association, Christian Fellowship Association, Mathematics/Science Association. Major annual events: Welcoming Ceremony, Spring Student Social, Fall Festival. Student services: health clinic, personal-psychological counseling. Campus security: 24-hour patrols. Main library plus 1 other with 215 serials, 707 audiovisual materials, an OPAC, and a Web page. Operations spending for the previous fiscal year: $617,786. 150 computers available on campus for general student use. A campuswide network can be accessed. Students can access the following: online class registration.

■ REMINGTON COLLEGE–BATON ROUGE CAMPUS

10551 Coursey Blvd.
Baton Rouge, LA 70816
Tel: (225)922-3990
Fax: (225)922-6569
E-mail: monica.johnson@remingtoncollege.edu
Web Site: www.remingtoncollege.edu/

Description: Proprietary, 2-year, coed. Awards terminal associate degrees. Calendar: continuous.

■ REMINGTON COLLEGE–LAFAYETTE CAMPUS

303 Rue Louis XIV
Lafayette, LA 70508

Tel: (337)981-4010; Free: 800-560-6192
Fax: (337)983-7130
E-mail: shannon.williams@remingtoncollege.edu
Web Site: www.remingtoncollege.edu/
Description: Proprietary, 2-year, coed. Awards terminal associate degrees. Founded 1940. Setting: 4-acre urban campus. Calendar: continuous. Honors program, independent study.
Entrance Requirements: Entrance: noncompetitive.
Collegiate Environment: Campus security: 24-hour emergency response devices. Remington College Library with 15,435 books, 85 serials, 182 audiovisual materials, and an OPAC.

■ **REMINGTON COLLEGE–SHREVEPORT**
2106 Bert Kouns Industrial Loop
Shreveport, LA 71118
E-mail: marc.wright@remingtoncollege.edu
Web Site: www.remingtoncollege.edu/
Description: Proprietary, 2-year, coed. Awards terminal associate degrees.

■ **RIVER PARISHES COMMUNITY COLLEGE**
PO Box 310
Sorrento, LA 70778
Tel: (225)675-8270
Fax: (225)675-5478
E-mail: adauzat@rpcc.cc.la.us
Web Site: www.rpcc.edu/
Description: State-supported, 2-year, coed. Awards certificates, diplomas, and transfer associate degrees. Founded 1997. Total enrollment: 1,163. 28% 25 or older. Calendar: semesters.

■ **SAINT JOSEPH SEMINARY COLLEGE**
Saint Benedict, LA 70457
Tel: (985)867-2299
E-mail: registrar@sjasc.edu
Web Site: www.sjasc.edu/
Description: Independent Roman Catholic, 4-year, coed. Awards bachelor's degrees (Religious Studies Institute is coed). Founded 1891. Setting: 1,800-acre rural campus with easy access to New Orleans. Endowment: $1.1 million. Educational spending for the previous fiscal year: $6430 per student. Total enrollment: 107. Faculty: 22 (10 full-time, 12 part-time). Student-undergrad faculty ratio is 3:1. Full-time: 104 students, 100% men. Part-time: 3 students, 100% men. Students come from 8 states and territories, 5 other countries, 45% from out-of-state. 0% American Indian or Alaska Native, non-Hispanic/Latino; 19% Hispanic/Latino; 0% African American, non-Hispanic/Latino; 5% Asian, non-Hispanic/Latino; 0% Native Hawaiian or other Pacific Islander, non-Hispanic/Latino; 0% international. 28% 25 or older, 100% live on campus, 37% transferred in. Retention: 50% of full-time freshmen returned the following year. Core. Calendar: semesters. Academic remediation for entering students, ESL program, services for LD students, advanced placement, adult/continuing education programs.
Entrance Requirements: Options: early admission, deferred admission. Required: high school transcript, minimum 2 high school GPA, ACT. Entrance: minimally difficult. Application deadline: Rolling. Notification: continuous. Preference given to candidates for the priesthood. Transfer credits accepted: Yes.
Costs Per Year: Application fee: $0. One-time mandatory fee: $150. Comprehensive fee: $28,180 includes full-time tuition ($13,500), mandatory fees ($1640), and college room and board ($13,040). College room only: $6850. Part-time tuition: $175 per credit hour.
Collegiate Environment: Orientation program. Drama-theater group, choral group, student-run newspaper. Social organizations: 5 open to all. Most popular organizations: student government, yearbook. Major annual events: Annual Bonfire, Saint Joseph Day Celebration, Abbey Youth Festival. Student services: health clinic, personal-psychological counseling. Campus security: 24-hour emergency response devices, controlled dormitory access, entrance gate. 80 college housing spaces available; 74 were occupied in 2012-13. Freshmen guaranteed college housing. On-campus residence required through senior year. Option: men-only housing available. Pere Rouquette Library plus 1 other with 70,000 books, 137 serials, 1,500 audiovisual materials, an OPAC, and a Web page. Operations spending for the previous fiscal year: $65,900. 14 computers available on campus for general student use. A campuswide network can be accessed from student residence rooms and from off campus. Staffed computer lab on campus provides training in use of computers, software, and the Internet.

Community Environment: Saint Benedict is located four miles north of Covington and 50 miles north of New Orleans. There is bus service available to Covington from New Orleans, Baton Rouge, and Hammond.

■ **SOUTH CENTRAL LOUISIANA TECHNICAL COLLEGE–YOUNG MEMORIAL CAMPUS**
900 Youngs Rd.
Morgan City, LA 70381
Tel: (504)380-2436
Web Site: www.ltc.edu/
Description: State-supported, 2-year, coed. Awards certificates, diplomas, and terminal associate degrees. Total enrollment: 734. Faculty: 63 (39 full-time, 24 part-time). Calendar: semesters.

■ **SOUTH LOUISIANA COMMUNITY COLLEGE**
320 Devalcourt St.
Lafayette, LA 70506-2030
Tel: (337)521-8896
Web Site: www.southlouisiana.edu/
Description: State-supported, 2-year, coed. Awards certificates, transfer associate, and terminal associate degrees. Total enrollment: 4,084. Faculty: 192. Student-undergrad faculty ratio is 24:1. Calendar: semesters.

■ **SOUTHEASTERN LOUISIANA UNIVERSITY**
548 Ned McGehee Dr.
Hammond, LA 70402
Tel: (985)549-2000; Free: 800-222-7358
Fax: (985)549-5095
E-mail: admissions@selu.edu
Web Site: www.selu.edu/
Description: State-supported, comprehensive, coed. Part of University of Louisiana System. Awards associate, bachelor's, master's, and doctoral degrees. Founded 1925. Setting: 375-acre small town campus with easy access to New Orleans. Endowment: $28.4 million. Research spending for the previous fiscal year: $1.9 million. Educational spending for the previous fiscal year: $3651 per student. Total enrollment: 15,602. Faculty: 610 (489 full-time, 121 part-time). Student-undergrad faculty ratio is 23:1. 3,811 applied, 80% were admitted. 12% from top 10% of their high school class, 35% from top quarter, 68% from top half. Full-time: 10,474 students, 61% women, 39% men. Part-time: 3,766 students, 61% women, 39% men. Students come from 46 states and territories, 43 other countries, 3% from out-of-state. 0.4% American Indian or Alaska Native, non-Hispanic/Latino; 3% Hispanic/Latino; 15% African American, non-Hispanic/Latino; 1% Asian, non-Hispanic/Latino; 0.1% Native Hawaiian or other Pacific Islander, non-Hispanic/Latino; 2% international. 16% 25 or older, 18% live on campus, 5% transferred in. Retention: 69% of full-time freshmen returned the following year. Academic areas with the most degrees conferred: business/marketing; liberal arts/general studies; health professions and related sciences. Core. Calendar: semesters. ESL program, services for LD students, advanced placement, honors program, independent study, distance learning, double major, summer session for credit, part-time degree program, adult/continuing education programs, internships, graduate courses open to undergrads. Off campus study. Study abroad program. ROTC: Army (c).
Entrance Requirements: Options: electronic application, early admission, deferred admission, international baccalaureate accepted. Required: proof of immunization required for all, college transcripts and statement of good standing required for some, SAT or ACT. Required for some: high school transcript, minimum 2.5 high school GPA. Entrance: moderately difficult. Application deadlines: 8/1, 8/1 for nonresidents. Notification: continuous, continuous for nonresidents. SAT Reasoning Test deadline: 8/1. Transfer credits accepted: Yes.
Costs Per Year: Application fee: $20. State resident tuition: $5,426 full-time. Nonresident tuition: $16,285 full-time. Full-time tuition varies according to course load. College room and board: $6510. College room only: $4260. Room and board charges vary according to board plan and housing facility.
Collegiate Environment: Orientation program. Drama-theater group, choral group, marching band, student-run newspaper, radio station. Social organizations: 136 open to all; national fraternities, national sororities. Most popular organizations: Catholic Student Association, Gamma Beta Phi, National Society of Collegiate Scholars, Sigma Alpha Lambda, Student Nurses' Association. Major annual events: Homecoming, Gumbo Ya Ya, Strawberry Jubilee. Student services: health clinic, personal-psychological counseling. Campus security: 24-hour emergency response devices and patrols, student patrols, late night transport-escort service, controlled dormi-

tory access, video cameras, motorist assistance. 2,293 college housing spaces available; all were occupied in 2012-13. No special consideration for freshman housing applicants. On-campus residence required through sophomore year. Options: coed, women-only housing available. Sims Memorial Library with 790,197 books, 816,340 microform titles, 3,561 serials, 44,492 audiovisual materials, an OPAC, and a Web page. Operations spending for the previous fiscal year: $4 million. 1,622 computers available on campus for general student use. A campuswide network can be accessed from student residence rooms and from off campus. Students can access the following: online class registration, campus Webmail, student newspaper, transcripts, bookstore. Staffed computer lab on campus (open 24 hours a day) provides training in use of computers, software, and the Internet.

Community Environment: City is located in the Southeastern section of the state. Climate is subtropical. Transportation to and from city available via Illinois Central Railroad and Greyhound Bus Co. There are five libraries, six local theatres, golf, hunting, fishing, boating at Lake Ponchartrain for recreation. Two hospitals, six motels and numerous apartments are available. Part-time employment for students is limited. There are 35 civic, fraternal, and veteran's organizations in Hammond.

■ **SOUTHERN UNIVERSITY AND AGRICULTURAL AND MECHANICAL COLLEGE**
Baton Rouge, LA 70813
Tel: (225)771-4500
E-mail: velva_thomas@subr.edu
Web Site: www.subr.edu/
Description: State-supported, university, coed. Part of Southern University System. Awards associate, bachelor's, master's, and doctoral degrees and post-master's certificates. Founded 1880. Setting: 964-acre suburban campus. Endowment: $9.7 million. Research spending for the previous fiscal year: $8.9 million. Educational spending for the previous fiscal year: $3252 per student. Total enrollment: 7,699. Faculty: 546 (405 full-time, 141 part-time). Student-undergrad faculty ratio is 16:1. 2,943 applied, 57% were admitted. 3% from top 10% of their high school class, 9% from top quarter, 33% from top half. 12 valedictorians, 5 student government officers. Full-time: 5,763 students, 61% women, 39% men. Part-time: 696 students, 69% women, 31% men. Students come from 39 states and territories, 20 other countries, 18% from out-of-state. 20% 25 or older, 31% live on campus, 4% transferred in. Retention: 68% of full-time freshmen returned the following year. Academic areas with the most degrees conferred: health professions and related sciences; business/marketing; homeland security, law enforcement, firefighting, and protective services. Core. Calendar: semesters. Academic remediation for entering students, services for LD students, advanced placement, honors program, distance learning, summer session for credit, part-time degree program, adult/continuing education programs, co-op programs and internships, graduate courses open to undergrads. Off campus study at Louisiana State University and Agricultural and Mechanical College, Southeastern Louisiana University, Southern University at New Orleans, Baton Rouge Community College. Study abroad program. ROTC: Army, Naval, Air Force (c).
Entrance Requirements: Options: electronic application, early admission. Required: high school transcript, minimum 2 high school GPA, Louisiana Board of Regents Core curriculum of 16.5 units of selected courses, SAT or ACT. Entrance: moderately difficult. Application deadline: 7/1. Notification: continuous.
Collegiate Environment: Orientation program. Drama-theater group, choral group, marching band, student-run newspaper. Social organizations: 66 open to all; national fraternities, national sororities, local fraternities, local sororities; 2% of eligible men and 0.3% of eligible women are members. Most popular organizations: Student Government Association, Association for Women Students, Men's Federation, Collegiate 100 Black Men, Southern University Pan Hellenic Council. Major annual events: Homecoming, Founder's Day, Springfest. Student services: legal services, health clinic, personal-psychological counseling, women's center. Campus security: 24-hour emergency response devices and patrols, late night transport-escort service, controlled dormitory access. John B. Cade Library plus 2 others with 880,098 books, 744,000 microform titles, 8,882 serials, 21,677 audiovisual materials, an OPAC, and a Web page. Operations spending for the previous fiscal year: $2.3 million. 1,500 computers available on campus for general student use. A campuswide network can be accessed from student residence rooms and from off campus. Students can access the following: online class registration. Staffed computer lab on campus (open 24 hours a day) provides training in use of computers, software, and the Internet.

■ **SOUTHERN UNIVERSITY AT NEW ORLEANS**
6400 Press Dr.
New Orleans, LA 70126-1009
Tel: (504)286-5000
E-mail: llatimor@suno.edu
Web Site: www.suno.edu/
Description: State-supported, comprehensive, coed. Part of Southern University System. Awards associate, bachelor's, and master's degrees. Founded 1959. Setting: 66-acre urban campus with easy access to New Orleans. Endowment: $3.9 million. Research spending for the previous fiscal year: $365,398. Total enrollment: 3,141. Faculty: 102 (100 full-time, 2 part-time). 801 applied, 79% were admitted. Full-time: 2,048 students, 69% women, 31% men. Part-time: 542 students, 77% women, 23% men. Students come from 21 states and territories, 10 other countries, 3% from out-of-state. 49% 25 or older, 13% transferred in. Retention: 43% of full-time freshmen returned the following year. Academic areas with the most degrees conferred: liberal arts/general studies; business/marketing; homeland security, law enforcement, firefighting, and protective services; public administration and social services. Core. Calendar: semesters. Academic remediation for entering students, services for LD students, self-designed majors, distance learning, double major, summer session for credit, part-time degree program, adult/continuing education programs, co-op programs and internships, graduate courses open to undergrads. Off campus study at University of New Orleans, Delgado Community College. ROTC: Army (c), Air Force (c).
Entrance Requirements: Options: electronic application, early admission, early decision, early action, deferred admission. Required: high school transcript, health forms, SAT or ACT. Recommended: ACT. Entrance: noncompetitive. Application deadlines: 7/1, 7/1 for nonresidents. Transfer credits accepted: Yes.
Collegiate Environment: Social organizations: 4 open to all; national fraternities, national sororities, local fraternities, local sororities; 10% of eligible men and 10% of eligible women are members. Most popular organizations: Student Government Association, First 50 Knights, Psychology Club, Communication Club. Major annual events: International Week, Black History Month, Wellness Week. Student services: health clinic, personal-psychological counseling. Campus security: 24-hour emergency response devices and patrols, late night transport-escort service. Leonard Washington Library with an OPAC and a Web page. Operations spending for the previous fiscal year: $600,775. 100 computers available on campus for general student use. A campuswide network can be accessed. Students can access the following: online class registration. Staffed computer lab on campus provides training in use of computers, software, and the Internet.

■ **SOUTHERN UNIVERSITY AT SHREVEPORT**
3050 Martin Luther King, Jr. Dr.
Shreveport, LA 71107
Tel: (318)674-3300; Free: 800-458-1472
Fax: (318)674-3489
Web Site: www.susla.edu/
Description: State-supported, 2-year, coed. Part of Southern University System. Awards certificates, transfer associate, and terminal associate degrees. Founded 1964. Setting: 103-acre urban campus. Research spending for the previous fiscal year: $42,522. Educational spending for the previous fiscal year: $2521 per student. Total enrollment: 1,324. Faculty: 98 (49 full-time, 49 part-time). Student-undergrad faculty ratio is 16:1. 10% from top 10% of their high school class, 30% from top quarter. Full-time: 921 students, 69% women, 31% men. Part-time: 403 students, 74% women, 26% men. Students come from 5 states and territories, 45% from out-of-state. 41% 25 or older, 10% transferred in. Core. Calendar: semesters. Academic remediation for entering students, advanced placement, self-designed majors, honors program, summer session for credit, part-time degree program, adult/continuing education programs, co-op programs and internships. Off campus study at Louisiana State University in Shreveport.
Entrance Requirements: Open admission. Option: early admission. Required: high school transcript. Recommended: ACT. Entrance: noncompetitive. Application deadline: Rolling. Notification: continuous until 8/15.
Collegiate Environment: Orientation program. Choral group, student-run newspaper. Social organizations: 38 open to all. Most popular organizations: Afro-American Society, SUSBO Gospel Choir, Student Center Board, Allied Health, Engineering Club. Major annual events: Career Day, Homecoming, Crawfish Boil. Student services: personal-psychological counseling. Campus security: 24-hour patrols. Library/Learning Resources Center with 25,733 microform titles, 380 serials, 24,016 audiovisual materials, and an OPAC. Operations spending for the previous fiscal year: $308,227.

■ SOUTHWEST UNIVERSITY

2200 Veterans Memorial Blvd.
Kenner, LA 70062
Tel: (504)468-2900; Free: 800-433-5923
E-mail: admissions@southwest.edu
Web Site: www.southwest.edu/
Description: Proprietary, comprehensive, coed. Awards associate, bachelor's, and master's degrees. Total enrollment: 425. Core. Accelerated degree program, distance learning, double major.
Entrance Requirements: Required: high school transcript, resume.

■ SOWELA TECHNICAL COMMUNITY COLLEGE

3820 J. Bennett Johnston Ave.
Lake Charles, LA 70616-6950
Tel: (318)491-2698
Web Site: www.sowela.edu/
Description: State-supported, 2-year, coed. Founded 1938. Total enrollment: 1,479. Faculty: 165 (57 full-time, 108 part-time). Calendar: semesters.

■ STRAYER UNIVERSITY - METAIRIE CAMPUS

111 Veterans Memorial Blvd.
Ste. 420
Metairie, LA 70005
Tel: (504)799-1700
Fax: (504)849-9980
Web Site: www.strayer.edu/campus/metairie
Description: Proprietary, comprehensive, coed. Awards associate, bachelor's, and master's degrees.

■ TULANE UNIVERSITY

6823 St. Charles Ave.
New Orleans, LA 70118-5669
Tel: (504)865-5000; Free: 800-873-9283
Fax: (504)862-8715
E-mail: undergrad.admission@tulane.edu
Web Site: www.tulane.edu/
Description: Independent, university, coed. Awards associate, bachelor's, master's, and doctoral degrees. Founded 1834. Setting: 110-acre urban campus. Endowment: $121.1 million. Research spending for the previous fiscal year: $156.8 million. Educational spending for the previous fiscal year: $21,981 per student. Total enrollment: 13,486. Faculty: 1,179 (652 full-time, 527 part-time). Student-undergrad faculty ratio is 9:1. 30,080 applied, 27% were admitted. 52% from top 10% of their high school class, 83% from top quarter, 97% from top half. Full-time: 6,443 students, 57% women, 43% men. Part-time: 1,980 students, 59% women, 41% men. Students come from 53 states and territories, 79 other countries, 71% from out-of-state. 0.4% American Indian or Alaska Native, non-Hispanic/Latino; 6% Hispanic/Latino; 10% African American, non-Hispanic/Latino; 4% Asian, non-Hispanic/Latino; 0.05% Native Hawaiian or other Pacific Islander, non-Hispanic/Latino; 3% international. 15% 25 or older, 44% live on campus, 1% transferred in. Retention: 89% of full-time freshmen returned the following year. Academic areas with the most degrees conferred: business/marketing; social sciences; biological/life sciences. Core. Calendar: semesters plus 3 summer sessions. ESL program, services for LD students, advanced placement, accelerated degree program, self-designed majors, freshman honors college, honors program, independent study, distance learning, double major, summer session for credit, part-time degree program, adult/continuing education programs, co-op programs and internships, graduate courses open to undergrads. Off campus study at Xavier University of Louisiana, Loyola University New Orleans. Study abroad program. ROTC: Army, Naval, Air Force.
Entrance Requirements: Options: electronic application, early action, deferred admission, international baccalaureate accepted. Required: essay, high school transcript, 1 recommendation, SAT or ACT. Entrance: very difficult. Application deadline: 1/15. Notification: 4/1. SAT Reasoning Test deadline: 1/15. SAT Subject Test deadline: 1/15. Transfer credits accepted: No. Applicants placed on waiting list: 3,483. Wait-listed applicants offered admission: 0. Early action applicants: 16,167. Early action applicants admitted: 1,102.
Costs Per Year: Application fee: $0. Comprehensive fee: $56,787 includes full-time tuition ($41,500), mandatory fees ($3740), and college room and board ($11,547). College room only: $6597. Room and board charges vary according to board plan and housing facility.
Collegiate Environment: Orientation program. Drama-theater group, choral group, marching band, student-run newspaper, radio station. Social organizations: 250 open to all; national fraternities, national sororities; 26% of eligible men and 40% of eligible women are members. Most popular organizations: Community Action Council of Tulane Students (CACTUS), Associated Student Body, Tulane University Campus Programming (TUCP), Association of Club Sports (ACS), National Pan-Hellenic Council. Major annual events: Outreach Tulane (Community Service Day for Freshmen), Student Activities Expo, Homecoming. Student services: legal services, health clinic, personal-psychological counseling, women's center. Campus security: 24-hour emergency response devices and patrols, student patrols, late night transport-escort service, controlled dormitory access, on and off-campus shuttle service, crime prevention programs, lighted pathways. 3,772 college housing spaces available; 3,700 were occupied in 2012-13. Freshmen guaranteed college housing. On-campus residence required through sophomore year. Options: coed, women-only housing available. Howard Tilton Memorial Library plus 8 others with 4.3 million books, 2.5 million microform titles, 112,338 serials, 140,105 audiovisual materials, an OPAC, and a Web page. Operations spending for the previous fiscal year: $25.3 million. 556 computers available on campus for general student use. A campuswide network can be accessed from student residence rooms and from off campus. Students can access the following: online class registration. Staffed computer lab on campus (open 24 hours a day).
Community Environment: Year-round New Orleans offers festivals and jazz bands, symphonies and operas, Broadway shows and concerts. But the City that Care Forgot also blends its unique French and Spanish heritage to offer quiet entertainment in museums, galleries, quaint restaurants or strolls through the European ambiance of the French Quarter. The 1.3 million people living in the metropolitan area succeed as well in running Louisiana's business, banking, judicial and cultural capital. Many students find the city to be as much a place of learning and intellectual challenge as the classroom. Moderate temperatures can be enjoyed year-round. New Orleans is one of the greatest distributing points in the South, and one of the largest ports in the United States; it is a marketing center for cotton, oil, salt, sulfur, natural gas, agricultural and forest products. Good transportation facilities are available. This is a paradise for those who fish or hunt. Since the city is a tourist attraction, there are many recreational facilities and community services available. Work opportunities are available for students.

■ UNIVERSITY OF LOUISIANA AT LAFAYETTE

104 University Cir.
PO Drawer 41008
Lafayette, LA 70504
Tel: (337)482-1000; Free: 800-752-6553
Fax: (337)482-6195
E-mail: admissions@louisiana.edu
Web Site: www.louisiana.edu/
Description: State-supported, university, coed. Part of University of Louisiana System. Awards bachelor's, master's, and doctoral degrees and post-master's certificates. Founded 1898. Setting: 1,375-acre urban campus. Endowment: $112.3 million. Research spending for the previous fiscal year: $46.3 million. Educational spending for the previous fiscal year: $4670 per student. Total enrollment: 16,687. Faculty: 754 (596 full-time, 158 part-time). Student-undergrad faculty ratio is 22:1. 9,262 applied, 60% were admitted. 19% from top 10% of their high school class, 44% from top quarter, 76% from top half. Full-time: 12,542 students, 55% women, 45% men. Part-time: 2,601 students, 65% women, 35% men. Students come from 49 states and territories, 74 other countries, 5% from out-of-state. 0.5% American Indian or Alaska Native, non-Hispanic/Latino; 3% Hispanic/Latino; 21% African American, non-Hispanic/Latino; 2% Asian, non-Hispanic/Latino; 0.03% Native Hawaiian or other Pacific Islander, non-Hispanic/Latino; 2% international. 15% 25 or older, 17% live on campus, 4% transferred in. Retention: 74% of full-time freshmen returned the following year. Academic areas with the most degrees conferred: business/marketing; liberal arts/general studies; education. Core. Calendar: semesters. Academic remediation for entering students, services for LD students, advanced placement, accelerated degree program, self-designed majors, honors program, independent study, distance learning, double major, summer session for credit, part-time degree program, adult/continuing education programs, co-op programs and internships. Study abroad program. ROTC: Army.
Entrance Requirements: Options: electronic application, early admission, deferred admission, international baccalaureate accepted. Required: high school transcript, minimum 2 high school GPA, core requirements, no remedial courses, SAT or ACT. Entrance: moderately difficult. Application deadline: Rolling.

Costs Per Year: Application fee: $25. State resident tuition: $3,926 full-time, $163.60 per credit hour part-time. Nonresident tuition: $12,896 full-time, $537.35 per credit hour part-time. Mandatory fees: $1,448 full-time. Full-time tuition and fees vary according to course load. Part-time tuition varies according to course load. College room and board: $8102. Room and board charges vary according to board plan and housing facility.

Collegiate Environment: Orientation program. Drama-theater group, choral group, marching band, student-run newspaper, radio station. Social organizations: 200 open to all; national fraternities, national sororities; 9% of eligible men and 8% of eligible women are members. Most popular organizations: Union Program Council, Chi Alpha, Student Government Association, Greek Council, Newman Club. Major annual events: Homecoming, Lagniappe Day, Mardi Gras. Student services: legal services, health clinic, personal-psychological counseling, women's center. Campus security: 24-hour emergency response devices and patrols, late night transport-escort service, controlled dormitory access. 2,945 college housing spaces available; 2,446 were occupied in 2012-13. Freshmen guaranteed college housing. On-campus residence required in freshman year. Options: coed, men-only, women-only housing available. Edith Garland Dupre Library with 1.1 million books, 1.5 million microform titles, 1,965 serials, 20,981 audiovisual materials, an OPAC, and a Web page. Operations spending for the previous fiscal year: $4.6 million. 413 computers available on campus for general student use. A campuswide network can be accessed from off-campus. Students can access the following: online class registration. Staffed computer lab on campus provides training in use of computers, software, and the Internet.

■ **UNIVERSITY OF LOUISIANA AT MONROE**
700 University Ave.
Monroe, LA 71209-0001
Tel: (318)342-1000; Free: 800-372-5127
Fax: (318)342-1049
E-mail: admissions@ulm.edu
Web Site: www.ulm.edu/
Description: State-supported, university, coed. Part of University of Louisiana System. Awards associate, bachelor's, master's, and doctoral degrees and post-master's certificates. Founded 1931. Setting: 238-acre urban campus. Total enrollment: 8,545. Faculty: 407 (183 full-time, 224 part-time). Student-undergrad faculty ratio is 18:1. 2,641 applied, 49% were admitted. 22% from top 10% of their high school class, 48% from top quarter, 76% from top half. Full-time: 5,184 students, 64% women, 36% men. Part-time: 2,114 students, 61% women, 39% men. Students come from 46 states and territories, 58 other countries, 10% from out-of-state. 0.4% American Indian or Alaska Native, non-Hispanic/Latino; 2% Hispanic/Latino; 27% African American, non-Hispanic/Latino; 1% Asian, non-Hispanic/Latino; 0.1% Native Hawaiian or other Pacific Islander, non-Hispanic/Latino; 3% international. 16% 25 or older, 22% live on campus, 5% transferred in. Retention: 68% of full-time freshmen returned the following year. Academic areas with the most degrees conferred: liberal arts/general studies; health professions and related sciences; business/marketing. Core. Calendar: semesters. Academic remediation for entering students, ESL program, advanced placement, accelerated degree program, honors program, independent study, distance learning, double major, summer session for credit, external degree program, co-op programs and internships, graduate courses open to undergrads. Off campus study at University of Southern Mississippi, Louisiana Tech University, Grambling State University. Study abroad program. ROTC: Army (c), Air Force (c).
Entrance Requirements: Options: electronic application, early admission, deferred admission. Required: high school transcript, SAT or ACT. Entrance: moderately difficult. Application deadlines: Rolling, Rolling for nonresidents. Notification: continuous, continuous for nonresidents. Transfer credits accepted: Yes.
Costs Per Year: Application fee: $20. State resident tuition: $5443 full-time. Nonresident tuition: $14,263 full-time. Full-time tuition varies according to course load. College room and board: $6486. College room only: $3830. Room and board charges vary according to board plan and housing facility.
Collegiate Environment: Orientation program. Drama-theater group, marching band, student-run newspaper, radio station. Social organizations: 140 open to all; national fraternities, national sororities. Most popular organizations: Maroon Platoon, Alpha Lambda Delta, Louisiana Pharmacist Alliance, Association for Students in Kinesiology, Pre-Pharmacy Organization/Sound of Today. Major annual events: Homecoming, Spring Fever Week, Casino Night. Student services: health clinic, personal-psychological counseling. Campus security: 24-hour emergency response

devices and patrols, student patrols, late night transport-escort service. 1,839 college housing spaces available; 1,538 were occupied in 2012-13. Freshmen given priority for college housing. On-campus residence required through sophomore year. Options: coed, men-only, women-only housing available. University Library with 629,606 books, 622,994 microform titles, 95 serials, 61 audiovisual materials, and an OPAC. Operations spending for the previous fiscal year: $205,016.

■ **UNIVERSITY OF NEW ORLEANS**
2000 Lakeshore Dr.
New Orleans, LA 70148
Tel: (504)280-6000; Free: 800-256-5866
Fax: (504)280-5522
E-mail: admissions@uno.edu
Web Site: www.uno.edu/
Description: State-supported, university, coed. Part of University of Louisiana System. Awards bachelor's, master's, and doctoral degrees. Founded 1958. Setting: 345-acre urban campus. Endowment: $17.6 million. Research spending for the previous fiscal year: $24.9 million. Educational spending for the previous fiscal year: $5845 per student. Total enrollment: 10,071. Faculty: 519 (323 full-time, 196 part-time). Student-undergrad faculty ratio is 21:1. 3,237 applied, 49% were admitted. 13% from top 10% of their high school class, 34% from top quarter, 66% from top half. Full-time: 5,828 students, 50% women, 50% men. Part-time: 1,861 students, 50% women, 50% men. Students come from 48 states and territories, 59 other countries, 4% from out-of-state. 0.4% American Indian or Alaska Native, non-Hispanic/Latino; 9% Hispanic/Latino; 15% African American, non-Hispanic/Latino; 7% Asian, non-Hispanic/Latino; 0.1% Native Hawaiian or other Pacific Islander, non-Hispanic/Latino; 4% international. 31% 25 or older, 8% live on campus, 10% transferred in. Retention: 65% of full-time freshmen returned the following year. Academic areas with the most degrees conferred: business/marketing; interdisciplinary studies; visual and performing arts. Core. Calendar: semesters. ESL program, services for LD students, advanced placement, honors program, independent study, distance learning, double major, summer session for credit, part-time degree program, adult/continuing education programs, co-op programs and internships, graduate courses open to undergrads. Off campus study at Southern University at New Orleans, Delgado Community College, Nunez Community College. Study abroad program. ROTC: Army, Naval (c), Air Force (c).
Entrance Requirements: Options: electronic application, early admission, deferred admission, international baccalaureate accepted. Required: high school transcript, Core Requirements (19 units), SAT or ACT. Required for some: minimum 2.5 high school GPA. Entrance: moderately difficult. Application deadlines: 7/25, 6/1 for nonresidents. SAT Reasoning Test deadline: 7/25. Transfer credits accepted: Yes.
Costs Per Year: Application fee: $20. State resident tuition: $5164 full-time. Nonresident tuition: $17,176 full-time. Mandatory fees: $758 full-time. Full-time tuition and fees vary according to course load, location, and program. College room and board: $8310. Room and board charges vary according to board plan and housing facility.
Collegiate Environment: Orientation program. Drama-theater group, choral group, student-run newspaper. Social organizations: 131 open to all; national fraternities, national sororities; 1% of eligible men and 1% of eligible women are members. Most popular organizations: Student Activities Council, student government, International Student Organization, VASA, Greek Life. Major annual events: Annual Crawfish Boil, Annual International Night, Welcome Week Events. Student services: legal services, health clinic, personal-psychological counseling, women's center. Campus security: 24-hour emergency response devices and patrols, late night transport-escort service, controlled dormitory access. 1,604 college housing spaces available; 622 were occupied in 2012-13. No special consideration for freshman housing applicants. Option: coed housing available. Earl K. Long Library with 1 million books, 2.5 million microform titles, 83,687 serials, 42,067 audiovisual materials, an OPAC, and a Web page. Operations spending for the previous fiscal year: $3.7 million. 1,208 computers available on campus for general student use. A campuswide network can be accessed from student residence rooms and from off campus. Students can access the following: online class registration, classes in Moodle. Staffed computer lab on campus provides training in use of computers, software, and the Internet.
Community Environment: See Tulane University.

■ **UNIVERSITY OF PHOENIX–LOUISIANA CAMPUS**
1 Galleria Blvd.
Ste. 725

Metairie, LA 70001-2082
Tel: (504)461-8852; Free: 866-766-0766
Web Site: www.phoenix.edu/
Description: Proprietary, comprehensive, coed. Awards associate, bachelor's, and master's degrees. Founded 1976. Setting: urban campus. Total enrollment: 1,919. Faculty: 246 (18 full-time, 228 part-time). Full-time: 1,530 students, 75% women, 25% men. 83% 25 or older. Academic areas with the most degrees conferred: business/marketing; computer and information sciences; homeland security, law enforcement, firefighting, and protective services. Core. Calendar: continuous. Advanced placement, accelerated degree program, independent study, distance learning, external degree program, adult/continuing education programs, graduate courses open to undergrads.
Entrance Requirements: Open admission. Options: electronic application, deferred admission. Required: 1 recommendation. Required for some: high school transcript. Entrance: noncompetitive. Application deadline: Rolling.
Collegiate Environment: University Library with 16,781 serials, an OPAC, and a Web page. Operations spending for the previous fiscal year: $6.8 million.

■ VIRGINIA COLLEGE IN BATON ROUGE
9501 Cortana Pl.
Baton Rouge, LA 70815
Tel: (225)236-3900
Web Site: www.vc.edu/
Description: Proprietary, 2-year, coed. Founded 2010.

■ XAVIER UNIVERSITY OF LOUISIANA
1 Drexel Dr.
New Orleans, LA 70125-1098
Tel: (504)486-7411; Free: 877-XAVIERU
E-mail: apply@xula.edu
Web Site: www.xula.edu/
Description: Independent Roman Catholic, comprehensive, coed. Awards bachelor's, master's, and doctoral degrees. Founded 1925. Setting: 23-acre urban campus. Total enrollment: 3,178. Faculty: 261 (236 full-time, 25 part-time). Student-undergrad faculty ratio is 13:1. 3,987 applied, 64% were admitted. 33% from top 10% of their high school class, 60% from top quarter,

83% from top half. Full-time: 2,399 students, 71% women, 29% men. Part-time: 126 students, 71% women, 29% men. 48% from out-of-state. 0.2% American Indian or Alaska Native, non-Hispanic/Latino; 2% Hispanic/Latino; 78% African American, non-Hispanic/Latino; 10% Asian, non-Hispanic/Latino; 0% Native Hawaiian or other Pacific Islander, non-Hispanic/Latino; 2% international. 3% 25 or older, 47% live on campus, 5% transferred in. Retention: 65% of full-time freshmen returned the following year. Core. Calendar: semesters. Academic remediation for entering students, services for LD students, advanced placement, accelerated degree program, freshman honors college, honors program, independent study, double major, summer session for credit, part-time degree program, adult/continuing education programs, co-op programs and internships, graduate courses open to undergrads. Off campus study at 2 members of the New Orleans Consortium, St. Michael's College, University of Notre Dame. Study abroad program. ROTC: Army (c), Naval (c), Air Force (c).
Entrance Requirements: Options: electronic application, early action. Required: high school transcript, minimum 2 high school GPA, 1 recommendation, SAT or ACT. Required for some: interview. Entrance: moderately difficult. Application deadlines: 7/1, 1/15 for early action. Notification: continuous, 2/15 for early action. SAT Reasoning Test deadline: 4/15. Applicants placed on waiting list: 172. Wait-listed applicants offered admission: 8.
Costs Per Year: Application fee: $25. Comprehensive fee: $26,300 includes full-time tuition ($17,700), mandatory fees ($1000), and college room and board ($7600). Room and board charges vary according to housing facility. Part-time tuition: $775 per credit hour. Part-time tuition varies according to course load.
Collegiate Environment: Orientation program. Drama-theater group, choral group, student-run newspaper. Social organizations: 64 open to all; national fraternities, national sororities; 1% of eligible men and 1% of eligible women are members. Most popular organizations: Mobilization at Xavier, AWARE, NAACP, California Club, Beta Beta Beta (Biology Club). Major annual events: Homecoming, Spring Fest, Martin Luther King Week for Peace. Student services: health clinic, personal-psychological counseling. Campus security: 24-hour emergency response devices and patrols, student patrols, bicycle patrols. 1,433 college housing spaces available. Freshmen given priority for college housing. Options: coed, men-only, women-only housing available. Xavier Library plus 1 other with an OPAC and a Web page.
Community Environment: See Tulane University.

BATES COLLEGE

2 Andrews Rd.
Lewiston, ME 04240-6028
Tel: (207)786-6255
Fax: (207)786-6025
E-mail: admission@bates.edu
Web Site: www.bates.edu/

Description: Independent, 4-year, coed. Awards bachelor's degrees. Founded 1855. Setting: 109-acre small town campus. Endowment: $216.2 million. Research spending for the previous fiscal year: $1.8 million. Educational spending for the previous fiscal year: $20,252 per student. Total enrollment: 1,753. Faculty: 195 (168 full-time, 27 part-time). Student-undergrad faculty ratio is 10:1. 4,906 applied, 27% were admitted. 45% from top 10% of their high school class, 71% from top quarter, 94% from top half. Full-time: 1,753 students, 53% women, 47% men. Students come from 44 states and territories, 71 other countries, 89% from out-of-state. 0.4% American Indian or Alaska Native, non-Hispanic/Latino; 5% Hispanic/Latino; 4% African American, non-Hispanic/Latino; 4% Asian, non-Hispanic/Latino; 0% Native Hawaiian or other Pacific Islander, non-Hispanic/Latino; 6% international. 0% 25 or older, 92% live on campus, 1% transferred in. Retention: 95% of full-time freshmen returned the following year. Academic areas with the most degrees conferred: social sciences; psychology; biological/life sciences. Core. Calendar: 4-4-1. Services for LD students, advanced placement, accelerated degree program, self-designed majors, honors program, independent study, double major, internships. Off campus study at American University, Williams College (Mystic Seaport Program), Morehouse College, Spelman College. Study abroad program.

Entrance Requirements: Options: electronic application, early admission, early decision, deferred admission, international baccalaureate accepted. Required: essay, high school transcript, 3 recommendations. Recommended: interview. Entrance: most difficult. Application deadlines: 1/1, 11/15 for early decision plan 1, 1/1 for early decision plan 2. Notification: 4/1, 12/20 for early decision plan 1, 2/15 for early decision plan 2. SAT Reasoning Test deadline: 1/1. SAT Subject Test deadline: 1/1. Applicants placed on waiting list: 1,599. Wait-listed applicants offered admission: 72. Early decision applicants: 527. Early decision applicants admitted: 242.

Costs Per Year: Application fee: $60. Comprehensive fee: $57,235 includes full-time tuition ($44,040), mandatory fees ($260), and college room and board ($12,935).

Collegiate Environment: Orientation program. Drama-theater group, choral group, student-run newspaper, radio station. Social organizations: 110 open to all. Most popular organizations: Outing Club (outdoor recreation), International Club, Chase Hall Committee (student activities planning), Representative Assembly, WRBC (student radio station). Major annual events: All College Gala, Winter Carnival, Mount David Summit. Student services: health clinic, personal-psychological counseling, women's center. Campus security: 24-hour emergency response devices and patrols, student patrols, late night transport-escort service, controlled dormitory access. 1,640 college housing spaces available; 1,608 were occupied in 2012-13. Freshmen guaranteed college housing. On-campus residence required through senior year. Options: coed, men-only, women-only housing available. Ladd Library plus 1 other with 1 million books, 183,372 microform titles, 649 serials, 155,942 audiovisual materials, an OPAC, and a Web page. Operations spending for the previous fiscal year: $3.6 million. 175 computers available on campus for general student use. Computer purchase/lease plans available. A campuswide network can be accessed from student residence rooms and from off campus. Students can access the following: online class registration, course web pages, course evaluation, financial records. Staffed computer lab on campus provides training in use of computers, software, and the Internet.

Community Environment: The second largest city in state, Lewiston is Maine's leading textile center. It is located on the Androscoggin River at Twin Falls, directly opposite the city of Auburn. Minimum-maximum temperatures are 0-50 degrees in the winter and 50-90 degrees in the summer. Commercial transportation is available via air and bus. The city has several churches, Ys, a public library, two hospitals, several movie theaters, and hotels and motels.

BEAL COLLEGE

99 Farm Rd.
Bangor, ME 04401
Tel: (207)947-4591; Free: 800-660-7351
E-mail: admissions@bealcollege.edu
Web Site: www.bealcollege.edu/

Description: Proprietary, 2-year, coed. Awards certificates, diplomas, and terminal associate degrees. Founded 1891. Setting: 4-acre small town campus. Total enrollment: 411. Student-undergrad faculty ratio is 35:1. 0% from out-of-state. 52% 25 or older. Retention: 57% of full-time freshmen returned the following year. Core. Calendar: modular. Academic remediation for entering students, advanced placement, accelerated degree program, double major, summer session for credit, part-time degree program, adult/continuing education programs, internships.

Entrance Requirements: Open admission. Option: deferred admission. Required: high school transcript. Recommended: interview. Entrance: noncompetitive. Application deadline: Rolling.

Collegiate Environment: Orientation program. Student-run newspaper. Beal College Library with 9,351 books, 76 serials, and a Web page.

BOWDOIN COLLEGE

5000 College Station
Brunswick, ME 04011
Tel: (207)725-3000
Fax: (207)725-3003
E-mail: admissions@bowdoin.edu
Web Site: www.bowdoin.edu

Description: Independent, 4-year, coed. Awards bachelor's degrees (SAT or ACT considered if submitted. Test scores are required for home-schooled applicants). Founded 1794. Setting: 205-acre small town campus with easy access to Portland. Endowment: $902.4 million. Research spending for the previous fiscal year: $3.4 million. Educational spending for the previous fiscal year: $25,141 per student. Total enrollment: 1,839. Faculty: 228 (186 full-time, 42 part-time). Student-undergrad faculty ratio is 9:1. 6,716 applied, 16% were admitted. 86% from top 10% of their high school class, 98% from top quarter, 100% from top half. 32 National Merit Scholars, 45 valedictorians. Full-time: 1,831 students, 50% women, 50% men. Part-time: 8 students, 63% women, 38% men. Students come from 49 states and territories, 27 other countries, 87% from out-of-state. 0.1% American Indian or Alaska Native, non-Hispanic/Latino; 13% Hispanic/Latino; 5% African American, non-Hispanic/Latino; 7% Asian, non-Hispanic/Latino; 0.1% Native Hawaiian or other Pacific Islander, non-Hispanic/Latino; 4% international. 0% 25 or older, 92% live on campus, 0.1% transferred in. Retention: 97% of full-time freshmen returned the following year. Academic areas with the most degrees conferred: social sciences; biological/life sciences; foreign languages and literature. Core. Calendar: semesters. Services for LD students, advanced placement, accelerated degree program, self-designed majors, independent study, double major. Off campus study at Twelve College Exchange Program; American University, Washington Semester; Three Seas Program, East-West Marine Biology; Marine Biological Laboratory, Semester in Environmental Science, Woods Hole; SEA Semester, Woods Hole; Williams College Mystic Seaport Maritime Studies Program; National Theater Institute. Study abroad program.

Entrance Requirements: Options: electronic application, early admission, early decision, deferred admission, international baccalaureate accepted. Required: essay, high school transcript, 3 recommendations. Recommended: interview. Entrance: most difficult. Application deadlines: 1/1, 1/1 for nonresidents, 11/15 for early decision plan 1, 1/1 for early decision plan 2. Notification: 4/5, 4/5 for nonresidents, 12/15 for early decision plan 1, 2/15 for early decision plan 2. SAT Reasoning Test deadline: 1/1. SAT Subject Test deadline: 1/1. Early decision applicants: 887. Early decision applicants admitted: 259.

Costs Per Year: Application fee: $60. Comprehensive fee: $56,128 includes full-time tuition ($43,676), mandatory fees ($442), and college room and board ($12,010). College room only: $5620. Room and board charges vary according to board plan.

Collegiate Environment: Orientation program. Drama-theater group, choral group, student-run newspaper, radio station. Social organizations: 150 open to all. Most popular organizations: Outing Club, intramural sports, Community Service Volunteer Programs, WBOR 91.1 FM, Bowdoin Orient. Major annual events: Common Good Day, Spring Gala, Winter's Weekend. Student services: health clinic, personal-psychological counseling, women's center. Campus security: 24-hour emergency response devices and patrols, late night transport-escort service, controlled dormitory access, self-defense education, whistle program, safe ride service. 1,742 college housing spaces available; 1,691 were occupied in 2012-13. Freshmen guaranteed college housing. On-campus residence required through sophomore year. Option: coed housing available. Hawthorne-Longfellow Library plus 5 others with 1 million books, 109,273 microform titles, 49,007 serials, 29,444 audiovisual materials, an OPAC, and a Web page. Operations spending for the previous fiscal year: $5.4 million. 600 computers available on campus for general student use. Computer purchase/lease plans available. A campuswide network can be accessed from student residence rooms and from off campus. Students can access the following: training classes on variety of desktop and academic software, 24/7 software support, free equipment loaner pool: laptops, video and digital cameras, sound and lighting systems, iPads, iPods. Staffed computer lab on campus (open 24 hours a day) provides training in use of computers, software, and the Internet.

Community Environment: Brunswick, a community of 20,500, is located within brief driving distance of several fine beaches and summer resort areas; skiing is available in winter. There are excellent highways and airline service to Portland, only 26 miles away. The area has several excellent motels. The town has a public library, Maine State Music Theatre, which features Broadway musicals each summer, and churches of many denominations, shopping centers and movie theaters; good restaurants. Recreational facilities include golf, hunting, boating, fishing, skiing, biking, backpacking, and other sports.

■ **CENTRAL MAINE COMMUNITY COLLEGE**
1250 Turner St.
Auburn, ME 04210-6498
Tel: (207)755-5100; Free: 800-891-2002
Fax: (207)755-5491
E-mail: enroll@cmcc.edu
Web Site: www.cmcc.edu/
Description: State-supported, 2-year, coed. Part of Maine Community College System. Awards certificates, diplomas, transfer associate, and terminal associate degrees. Founded 1964. Setting: 135-acre small town campus. Endowment: $530,000. Educational spending for the previous fiscal year: $3684 per student. Total enrollment: 2,905. Faculty: 233 (50 full-time, 183 part-time). Student-undergrad faculty ratio is 13:1. 2,070 applied, 34% were admitted. Full-time: 1,351 students, 46% women, 54% men. Part-time: 1,454 students, 57% women, 43% men. Students come from 9 states and territories, 5 other countries, 8% from out-of-state. 1% American Indian or Alaska Native, non-Hispanic/Latino; 1% Hispanic/Latino; 2% African American, non-Hispanic/Latino; 1% Asian, non-Hispanic/Latino; 0.03% Native Hawaiian or other Pacific Islander, non-Hispanic/Latino; 0.3%

international. 41% 25 or older, 8% live on campus, 3% transferred in. Retention: 0% of full-time freshmen returned the following year. Core. Calendar: semesters. Academic remediation for entering students, ESL program, services for LD students, advanced placement, accelerated degree program, independent study, distance learning, summer session for credit, part-time degree program, adult/continuing education programs, co-op programs and internships.

Entrance Requirements: Options: electronic application, deferred admission. Required: high school transcript. Recommended: SAT. Entrance: minimally difficult. Application deadline: Rolling. Notification: continuous. Transfer credits accepted: Yes.

Collegiate Environment: Orientation program. Drama-theater group. Campus security: 24-hour emergency response devices, student patrols, controlled dormitory access, night patrols by police. 253 college housing spaces available; 250 were occupied in 2012-13. Freshmen given priority for college housing. Options: coed, men-only, women-only housing available. Central Maine Community College Library with 15,914 books, 160 microform titles, 200 serials, 2 audiovisual materials, an OPAC, and a Web page. Operations spending for the previous fiscal year: $294,371. 700 computers available on campus for general student use. A campuswide network can be accessed from student residence rooms and from off campus. Students can access the following: online class registration. Staffed computer lab on campus provides training in use of computers and the Internet.

Community Environment: See Bates College.

■ **CENTRAL MAINE MEDICAL CENTER COLLEGE OF NURSING AND HEALTH PROFESSIONS**
70 Middle St.
Lewiston, ME 04240-0305
Tel: (207)795-2840
Fax: (207)795-2849
E-mail: jenisod@cmhc.org
Web Site: www.cmmccollege.edu/
Description: Independent, 2-year, coed. Awards terminal associate degrees. Founded 1891. Setting: urban campus. Total enrollment: 217. Student-undergrad faculty ratio is 10:1. Full-time: 66 students, 74% women, 26% men. Part-time: 151 students, 80% women, 20% men. Students come from 2 states and territories, 1% from out-of-state. 76% 25 or older, 2% live on campus. Core. Calendar: semesters. Services for LD students, advanced placement, summer session for credit. Off campus study.

Entrance Requirements: Required: essay, high school transcript, Entrance exam, SAT or ACT, high school or college level algebra, second math, biology, chemistry, high school transcript or GED, SAT or ACT, ACCUPLACER Entrance Exam. Entrance: moderately difficult. Application deadline: 1/15. Notification: 3/15. SAT Reasoning Test deadline: 1/15. Transfer credits accepted: Yes.

Costs Per Year: Application fee: $40. Tuition: $7665 full-time. Mandatory fees: $1885 full-time. College room only: $2350.

Collegiate Environment: Orientation program. Social organizations: 3 open to all. Most popular organizations: Student Communication Council, student government, Student Nurses Association. Major annual events: Graduation Luncheon, Alumni Graduation Breakfast, Alumni Hosted Holiday Party. Student services: health clinic, personal-psychological counseling. Campus security: 24-hour emergency response devices and patrols, late night transport-escort service, controlled dormitory access. 13 college housing spaces available; 5 were occupied in 2012-13. No special consideration for freshman housing applicants. Option: coed housing available. Gerrish True Health Sciences Library plus 1 other with 1,975 books, 339 serials, an OPAC, and a Web page. 20 computers available on campus for general student use.

■ **COLBY COLLEGE**
Mayflower Hill
Waterville, ME 04901-8840
Tel: (207)872-3000; Free: 800-723-3032
Fax: (207)872-3474
E-mail: admissions@colby.edu
Web Site: www.colby.edu/
Description: Independent, 4-year, coed. Awards bachelor's degrees. Founded 1813. Setting: 714-acre small town campus. Endowment: $599.6 million. Research spending for the previous fiscal year: $2 million. Educational spending for the previous fiscal year: $21,570 per student. Total enrollment: 1,863. Faculty: 216 (166 full-time, 50 part-time). Student-undergrad faculty ratio is 10:1. 5,241 applied, 29% were admitted. 65% from

top 10% of their high school class, 85% from top quarter, 99% from top half. 5 National Merit Scholars, 16 valedictorians. Full-time: 1,863 students, 55% women, 45% men. Students come from 48 states and territories, 76 other countries, 87% from out-of-state. 0.1% American Indian or Alaska Native, non-Hispanic/Latino; 5% Hispanic/Latino; 3% African American, non-Hispanic/Latino; 6% Asian, non-Hispanic/Latino; 0.1% Native Hawaiian or other Pacific Islander, non-Hispanic/Latino; 6% international. 0% 25 or older, 93% live on campus, 0.3% transferred in. Retention: 95% of full-time freshmen returned the following year. Academic areas with the most degrees conferred: social sciences; interdisciplinary studies; English; biological/life sciences. Core. Calendar: 4-1-4. Services for LD students, advanced placement, self-designed majors, honors program, independent study, double major, internships. Off campus study at Pomona College, Pitzer College, Howard University, Claremont McKenna College, Scripps College, Boston University (SEA Semester), Williams College (Mystic Seaport Program), Clark Atlanta University, Semester in Environmental Science-Woods Hole, The Washington Center, Bigelow Laboratory for Ocean Sciences, Dartmouth Dual Degree program in Engineering, Columbia University Engineering program. Study abroad program. ROTC: Army (c).

Entrance Requirements: Options: electronic application, early admission, early decision, deferred admission, international baccalaureate accepted. Required: essay, high school transcript, 2 recommendations, Students must submit either (a) SAT, (b) ACT, or (c) three SAT Subject Tests of their choice. Recommended: interview. Entrance: most difficult. Application deadlines: 1/1, 1/1 for nonresidents, 11/15 for early decision plan 1, 1/1 for early decision plan 2. Notification: 4/1, 4/1 for nonresidents, 12/15 for early decision plan 1, 2/10 for early decision plan 2. SAT Reasoning Test deadline: 3/1. SAT Subject Test deadline: 3/1. Transfer credits accepted: Yes. Applicants placed on waiting list: 1,161. Wait-listed applicants offered admission: 11. Early decision applicants: 527. Early decision applicants admitted: 277.

Costs Per Year: Application fee: $0. Comprehensive fee: $55,700.

Collegiate Environment: Orientation program. Drama-theater group, choral group, student-run newspaper, radio station. Social organizations: 120 open to all. Most popular organizations: Outing Club, volunteer center, WMHB-FM (College Radio Station), student government, Powder and Wig (theater). Major annual events: Family Weekend, Junior/Senior Cotillion, Foss Arts Festival. Student services: health clinic, personal-psychological counseling, women's center. Campus security: 24-hour emergency response devices and patrols, late night transport-escort service, controlled dormitory access, campus lighting, student emergency response team, self-defense class, property id program, party monitors. College housing designed to accommodate 1,735 students; 1,743 undergraduates lived in college housing during 2012-13. Freshmen guaranteed college housing. On-campus residence required through senior year. Option: coed housing available. Miller Library plus 3 others with 1.2 million books, 300,500 microform titles, 19,877 serials, 24,768 audiovisual materials, an OPAC, and a Web page. Operations spending for the previous fiscal year: $6.6 million. 350 computers available on campus for general student use. A campuswide network can be accessed from student residence rooms and from off campus. Students can access the following: online class registration, portal. Staffed computer lab on campus (open 24 hours a day) provides training in use of computers, software, and the Internet.

Community Environment: Colby, located in the Kennebec River Valley, is one mile from downtown Waterville, a regional center for industry, professional, and retail trade. Major employers in the area include Maine General Medical Center, L.L. Bean, SAPPI Fine Paper, the Chinet Co., and The State of Maine. Transportation is available to Waterville by bus from Portland or Boston. Commercial airports serve Portland, Bangor, and Augusta.

■ **COLLEGE OF THE ATLANTIC**

105 Eden St.
Bar Harbor, ME 04609-1198
Tel: (207)288-5015; Free: 800-528-0025
Fax: (207)288-4126
E-mail: inquiry@coa.edu
Web Site: www.coa.edu/

Description: Independent, comprehensive, coed. Awards bachelor's and master's degrees. Founded 1969. Setting: 35-acre small town campus. Endowment: $29.3 million. Research spending for the previous fiscal year: $1.4 million. Educational spending for the previous fiscal year: $16,400 per student. Total enrollment: 340. Faculty: 44 (30 full-time, 14 part-time). Student-undergrad faculty ratio is 9:1. 378 applied, 71% were admitted. 52% from top 10% of their high school class, 70% from top quarter, 93% from top half. Full-time: 309 students, 71% women, 29% men. Part-time: 21 students,

76% women, 24% men. Students come from 38 states and territories, 34 other countries, 82% from out-of-state. 0.3% American Indian or Alaska Native, non-Hispanic/Latino; 3% Hispanic/Latino; 1% African American, non-Hispanic/Latino; 1% Asian, non-Hispanic/Latino; 0% Native Hawaiian or other Pacific Islander, non-Hispanic/Latino; 17% international. 4% 25 or older, 44% live on campus, 9% transferred in. Retention: 83% of full-time freshmen returned the following year. Academic area with the most degrees conferred: interdisciplinary studies. Core. Calendar: trimesters. Academic remediation for entering students, services for LD students, advanced placement, accelerated degree program, self-designed majors, independent study, summer session for credit, part-time degree program, co-op programs and internships, graduate courses open to undergrads. Off campus study at University of Maine; Ecoleague consortium: Alaska Pacific University, Green Mountain College, Northland College and Prescott College; SALT Institute for Documentary Studies. Study abroad program.

Entrance Requirements: Options: electronic application, early admission, early decision, deferred admission, international baccalaureate accepted. Required: essay, high school transcript, 3 recommendations. Recommended: minimum 3 high school GPA, interview, SAT or ACT. Required for some: interview. Entrance: very difficult. Application deadlines: 2/15, 12/1 for early decision plan 1, 1/10 for early decision plan 2. Notification: 4/1, 12/15 for early decision plan 1, 1/25 for early decision plan 2. Transfer credits accepted: Yes. Early decision applicants: 31. Early decision applicants admitted: 27.

Costs Per Year: Application fee: $50. Comprehensive fee: $48,210 includes full-time tuition ($38,403), mandatory fees ($549), and college room and board ($9258). College room only: $5952. Full-time tuition and fees vary according to course load. Room and board charges vary according to board plan. Part-time tuition: $4267 per credit. Part-time mandatory fees: $183 per term. Part-time tuition and fees vary according to course load.

Collegiate Environment: Orientation program. Drama-theater group, choral group, student-run newspaper. Social organizations: 12 open to all. Most popular organizations: All College Meeting, Open Mic, Outdoor Program, Campus Committee on Sustainability, Theater Club. Major annual events: Bar Island Swim (year-opening celebration with an ocean swim, Earth Day, Aurora Ball-ealis (midwinter elegant dance party with live band). Student services: health clinic, personal-psychological counseling. Campus security: 24-hour emergency response devices and patrols, late night transport-escort service. 152 college housing spaces available; 142 were occupied in 2012-13. Freshmen guaranteed college housing. On-campus residence required in freshman year. Option: coed housing available. Thorndike Library with 60,000 books, 37,000 microform titles, 30,000 serials, 3,259 audiovisual materials, an OPAC, and a Web page. Operations spending for the previous fiscal year: $490,000. 45 computers available on campus for general student use. A campuswide network can be accessed from student residence rooms. Students can access the following: online class registration, online billing, grades, transcript, financial aid and course management system. Staffed computer lab on campus provides training in use of computers, software, and the Internet.

Community Environment: Bar Harbor and Mount Desert Island's natural environment provide excellent opportunities for environmental studies. Cooperative resource sharing is available with the Jackson Laboratory, Mount Desert Island Biological Laboratory, Acadia National Park and the local school system. In the summer, Bar Harbor is supported by the tourist trade. Other businesses which provide for the local economy are boatbuilding, fishing, and lobstering. Bar Harbor is easily accessible by Bar Harbor Airlines, Greyhound Bus or automobile via State Routes 1 and 3.

■ **EASTERN MAINE COMMUNITY COLLEGE**

354 Hogan Rd.
Bangor, ME 04401-4206
Tel: (207)974-4600
Fax: (207)974-4683
E-mail: admissions@emcc.edu
Web Site: www.emcc.edu/

Description: State-supported, 2-year, coed. Part of Maine Community College System. Awards certificates, diplomas, transfer associate, and terminal associate degrees. Founded 1966. Setting: 72-acre small town campus. Total enrollment: 1,923. 1,823 applied. 33% 25 or older. Calendar: semesters. Academic remediation for entering students, advanced placement, summer session for credit, part-time degree program, adult/continuing education programs.

Entrance Requirements: Option: deferred admission. Required: essay, high school transcript, ACCUPLACER. Recommended: minimum 2.0 high school GPA. Required for some: interview, SAT. Entrance: minimally difficult. Application deadline: Rolling. Notification: continuous. Preference given to state residents.

Collegiate Environment: Orientation program. Student-run newspaper. Student services: health clinic, personal-psychological counseling. Campus security: late night transport-escort service, controlled dormitory access. Eastern Maine Technical College Library plus 1 other with 17,554 books, 159 serials, an OPAC, and a Web page.

■ **HUSSON UNIVERSITY**
One College Cir.
Bangor, ME 04401-2999
Tel: (207)941-7000; Free: 800-4-HUSSON
Fax: (207)941-7935
E-mail: beanc@husson.edu
Web Site: www.husson.edu/
Description: Independent, comprehensive, coed. Awards associate, bachelor's, master's, and doctoral degrees and post-master's certificates. Founded 1898. Setting: 208-acre suburban campus. Endowment: $9.2 million. Educational spending for the previous fiscal year: $4405 per student. Total enrollment: 3,077. Faculty: 320 (119 full-time, 201 part-time). Student-undergrad faculty ratio is 16:1. 1,509 applied, 77% were admitted. 13% from top 10% of their high school class, 44% from top quarter, 81% from top half. 18 class presidents, 25 student government officers. Full-time: 1,969 students, 57% women, 43% men. Part-time: 440 students, 64% women, 36% men. Students come from 35 states and territories, 11 other countries, 12% from out-of-state. 1% American Indian or Alaska Native, non-Hispanic/Latino; 1% Hispanic/Latino; 4% African American, non-Hispanic/Latino; 1% Asian, non-Hispanic/Latino; 0.2% Native Hawaiian or other Pacific Islander, non-Hispanic/Latino; 2% international. 19% 25 or older, 36% live on campus, 5% transferred in. Retention: 72% of full-time freshmen returned the following year. Academic areas with the most degrees conferred: business/marketing; health professions and related sciences; homeland security, law enforcement, firefighting, and protective services. Core. Calendar: semesters. Academic remediation for entering students, services for LD students, advanced placement, self-designed majors, independent study, distance learning, double major, summer session for credit, part-time degree program, adult/continuing education programs, co-op programs and internships, graduate courses open to undergrads. ROTC: Army, Naval (c).
Entrance Requirements: Options: electronic application, deferred admission, international baccalaureate accepted. Required: essay, high school transcript, 1 recommendation, SAT or ACT. Recommended: interview. Entrance: moderately difficult. Application deadline: 8/15. Notification: continuous. SAT Reasoning Test deadline: 8/1. SAT Subject Test deadline: 8/1. Transfer credits accepted: Yes.
Costs Per Year: Application fee: $40. Comprehensive fee: $23,386 includes full-time tuition ($14,760), mandatory fees ($370), and college room and board ($8256). College room only: $4102. Full-time tuition and fees vary according to class time. Room and board charges vary according to board plan and housing facility. Part-time tuition: $492 per credit. Part-time mandatory fees: $370 per year. Part-time tuition and fees vary according to class time and course load.
Collegiate Environment: Orientation program. Drama-theater group, student-run newspaper, radio station. Social organizations: 49 open to all; national fraternities, local fraternities, local sororities; 8% of eligible men and 12% of eligible women are members. Most popular organizations: student government, Organization of Student Nurses, Organization of Physical Therapy Students, Accounting Society, Criminal Justice Club. Major annual events: Chief Week, Spring Fling, Homecoming. Student services: health clinic, personal-psychological counseling. Campus security: 24-hour emergency response devices and patrols, late night transport-escort service, controlled dormitory access. 950 college housing spaces available; 711 were occupied in 2012-13. Freshmen guaranteed college housing. On-campus residence required through sophomore year. Option: coed housing available. Sawyer Library with 119,501 books, 14,947 microform titles, 114 serials, 469 audiovisual materials, an OPAC, and a Web page. Operations spending for the previous fiscal year: $361,477. 116 computers available on campus for general student use. A campuswide network can be accessed from student residence rooms and from off campus. Students can access the following: online class registration. Staffed computer lab on campus (open 24 hours a day) provides training in use of computers, software, and the Internet.

■ **KAPLAN UNIVERSITY (LEWISTON)**
475 Lisbon St.
Lewiston, ME 04240

Tel: (207)333-3300; Free: 800-527-5268
Web Site: lewiston.kaplanuniversity.edu/
Description: Proprietary, 2-year, coed. Awards certificates and terminal associate degrees.

■ **KAPLAN UNIVERSITY (SOUTH PORTLAND)**
265 Western Ave.
South Portland, ME 04106
Tel: (207)774-6126; Free: 800-527-5268
Fax: (207)774-1715
Web Site: portland.kaplanuniversity.edu/
Description: Proprietary, 2-year, coed. Awards certificates and terminal associate degrees. Founded 1966. Setting: urban campus. Calendar: modular.
Community Environment: Portland, located just two hours north of Boston, lies in the southern part of Maine. Southern Maine is home to some of the country's best-known companies including L.L. Bean, UNUM Insurance, J.J. Nissen Bakery, and Hannaford Brothers. These companies combine with the shipping and fishing industries to give Portland a vibrant and thriving economy. Portland also boasts some of the finest restaurants on the east coast and has a unique and charming shopping district in the old city. The city is home to a championship minor league hockey team, The Portland Pirates, an affiliate of the Washington Capitals, and one of the minor league's most successful baseball teams, The Portland Sea Dogs, an affiliate of the Florida Marlins. Portland also has a highly regarded art museum, professional stage and dance companies, public recreation facilities, and breathtaking views of the Atlantic Ocean. Portland is easily accessible by car, plane, or bus.

■ **KENNEBEC VALLEY COMMUNITY COLLEGE**
92 Western Ave.
Fairfield, ME 04937-1367
Tel: (207)453-5000; Free: 800-528-5882
E-mail: admissions@kvcc.me.edu
Web Site: www.kvcc.me.edu/
Description: State-supported, 2-year, coed. Part of Maine Community College System. Awards certificates, diplomas, transfer associate, and terminal associate degrees. Founded 1970. Setting: 61-acre small town campus. Total enrollment: 2,470. Faculty: 47 (all full-time). 1,851 applied, 45% were admitted. Full-time: 714 students, 58% women, 42% men. Part-time: 1,756 students, 71% women, 29% men. Students come from 9 states and territories, 1% from out-of-state. 1% American Indian or Alaska Native, non-Hispanic/Latino; 1% Hispanic/Latino; 1% African American, non-Hispanic/Latino; 1% Asian, non-Hispanic/Latino; 0.04% Native Hawaiian or other Pacific Islander, non-Hispanic/Latino; 0.1% international. 44% 25 or older, 8% transferred in. Core. Calendar: semesters. Academic remediation for entering students, services for LD students, advanced placement, accelerated degree program, independent study, distance learning, summer session for credit, part-time degree program, external degree program, adult/continuing education programs, internships.
Entrance Requirements: Open admission except for nursing, radiologic technology, physical therapist assistant, occupational therapist assistant, sonography, respiratory therapy programs. Options: electronic application, deferred admission. Required: essay, high school transcript. Recommended: SAT or ACT. Required for some: interview, HESI nursing exam, HOBET for Allied Health programs, ACCUPLACER. Entrance: noncompetitive. Application deadline: Rolling. Notification: continuous. Transfer credits accepted: Yes. Applicants placed on waiting list: 221. Wait-listed applicants offered admission: 75.
Costs Per Year: Application fee: $20. One-time mandatory fee: $30. State resident tuition: $2580 full-time, $86 per credit hour part-time. Nonresident tuition: $5160 full-time, $172 per credit hour part-time. Mandatory fees: $606 full-time, $3 per credit hour part-time.
Collegiate Environment: Orientation program. Choral group. Social organizations: 26 open to all. Most popular organizations: Phi Theta Kappa, National Society for Leadership & Success, Student Senate, Respiratory Therapy Club, KV Federal Nurses Association. Major annual events: Welcome Week Activities, Week of Eek, Valentine's Week. Student services: personal-psychological counseling. Campus security: evening security patrol. College housing not available. Lunder Library plus 1 other with 19,316 books, 188 serials, 2,955 audiovisual materials, an OPAC, and a Web page. 226 computers available on campus for general student use. A campuswide network can be accessed from off-campus. Students can access the following: online class registration. Staffed computer lab on campus provides training in use of computers, software, and the Internet.

Community Environment: See Colby College.

■ MAINE COLLEGE OF ART

522 Congress St.
Portland, ME 04101
Tel: (207)775-3052; Free: 800-699-1509
Fax: (207)772-5069
E-mail: scote@meca.edu
Web Site: www.meca.edu/

Description: Independent, comprehensive, coed. Awards bachelor's and master's degrees. Founded 1882. Setting: urban campus. Total enrollment: 405. Full-time: 353 students, 71% women, 29% men. Part-time: 16 students, 56% women, 44% men. Students come from 24 states and territories, 1 other country, 41% from out-of-state. 1% American Indian or Alaska Native, non-Hispanic/Latino; 3% Hispanic/Latino; 1% African American, non-Hispanic/Latino; 2% Asian, non-Hispanic/Latino; 0% Native Hawaiian or other Pacific Islander, non-Hispanic/Latino; 0% international. 10% 25 or older, 44% live on campus, 11% transferred in. Retention: 75% of full-time freshmen returned the following year. Core. Calendar: semesters. Services for LD students, advanced placement, double major, part-time degree program, co-op programs and internships. Off campus study at Association of Independent Colleges of Art and Design Mobility Program, Greater Portland Alliance of Colleges and Universities. Study abroad program.

Entrance Requirements: Required: essay, minimum 2 high school GPA, 2 recommendations, portfolio of 15-20 pieces of recent artwork. Recommended: interview. Required for some: high school transcript.

Costs Per Year: One-time mandatory fee: $300. Comprehensive fee: $41,870 includes full-time tuition ($30,260), mandatory fees ($1310), and college room and board ($10,300). Full-time tuition and fees vary according to program. Room and board charges vary according to housing facility. Part-time tuition: $1261 per credit hour. Part-time mandatory fees: $200 per term. Part-time tuition and fees vary according to program.

Collegiate Environment: Orientation program. Student services: personal-psychological counseling. Campus security: 24-hour emergency response devices and patrols, controlled dormitory access. 152 college housing spaces available; 143 were occupied in 2012-13. Freshmen guaranteed college housing. On-campus residence required in freshman year. Option: coed housing available. Joanne Waxman Library with 35,000 books, 150 serials, 450 audiovisual materials, an OPAC, and a Web page. 85 computers available on campus for general student use. A campuswide network can be accessed from student residence rooms and from off campus. Students can access the following: invoices, transcripts.

■ MAINE MARITIME ACADEMY

Castine, ME 04420
Tel: (207)326-4311; Free: 800-227-8465
Fax: (207)326-2515
E-mail: jeff.wright@mma.edu
Web Site: www.mainemaritime.edu/

Description: State-supported, comprehensive, coed. Awards associate, bachelor's, and master's degrees. Founded 1941. Setting: 35-acre small town campus. Endowment: $20 million. Total enrollment: 1,013. Faculty: 90 (69 full-time, 21 part-time). Student-undergrad faculty ratio is 15:1. 1,000 applied, 29% were admitted. 10% from top 10% of their high school class, 38% from top quarter, 50% from top half. Full-time: 993 students, 19% women, 81% men. Students come from 35 states and territories, 6 other countries, 30% from out-of-state. 0.1% American Indian or Alaska Native, non-Hispanic/Latino; 1% Hispanic/Latino; 1% African American, non-Hispanic/Latino; 1% Asian, non-Hispanic/Latino; 1% international. 12% 25 or older, 78% live on campus, 4% transferred in. Retention: 85% of full-time freshmen returned the following year. Academic areas with the most degrees conferred: engineering technologies; transportation and materials moving; engineering. Core. Calendar: semesters. Academic remediation for entering students, advanced placement, self-designed majors, honors program, independent study, double major, adult/continuing education programs, co-op programs and internships. Off campus study at International Association of Maritime Universities. Study abroad program. ROTC: Army (c), Naval.

Entrance Requirements: Options: electronic application, early admission, early decision, deferred admission, international baccalaureate accepted. Required: high school transcript, 1 recommendation, physical examination, SAT or ACT. Recommended: interview. Entrance: moderately difficult. Application deadlines: Rolling, 12/31 for early decision. Notification: 2/15 for early decision. Transfer credits accepted: Yes. Applicants placed on waiting list: 18. Wait-listed applicants offered admission: 8.

Costs Per Year: Application fee: $0. State resident tuition: $8800 full-time, $334 per credit part-time. Nonresident tuition: $18,800 full-time, $645 per credit part-time. Mandatory fees: $2725 full-time. Full-time tuition and fees vary according to course load and program. Part-time tuition varies according to course load and program. College room and board: $9548. College room only: $3628. Room and board charges vary according to board plan.

Collegiate Environment: Orientation program. Drama-theater group, choral group, marching band. Social organizations: 30 open to all. Most popular organizations: Rugby Club, yacht club, Alpha Phi Omega (community service), Chess Club, Drill Team. Major annual events: Parents & APO Weekends, Ring Dance, Ship jump. Student services: health clinic, personal-psychological counseling, women's center. Campus security: 24-hour emergency response devices and patrols, late night transport-escort service, controlled dormitory access. 750 college housing spaces available; all were occupied in 2012-13. Freshmen guaranteed college housing. On-campus residence required through junior year. Option: coed housing available. Nutting Memorial Library with 427,532 books, 1,661 microform titles, 240 serials, 2,161 audiovisual materials, an OPAC, and a Web page. 40 computers available on campus for general student use. Computer purchase/lease plans available. A computer is required for all students. A campuswide network can be accessed from student residence rooms and from off campus. Students can access the following: online class registration. Staffed computer lab on campus provides training in use of computers, software, and the Internet.

Community Environment: The French erected the first fort here in 1613, but the first permanent settlement was made by the English in 1760. Fort George, partially restored, is maintained as a memorial today. Castine is on south central coast of Maine, 35 miles south of Bangor.

■ NEW ENGLAND SCHOOL OF COMMUNICATIONS

1 College Cir.
Bangor, ME 04401-2999
Tel: (207)941-7176; Free: 888-877-1876
Fax: (207)947-3987
E-mail: info@nescom.edu
Web Site: www.nescom.edu/

Description: Independent, 4-year, coed. Administratively affiliated with Husson University. Awards bachelor's degrees. Founded 1981. Setting: 200-acre small town campus. Total enrollment: 499. Faculty: 73 (24 full-time, 49 part-time). Student-undergrad faculty ratio is 12:1. 325 applied, 61% were admitted. Full-time: 462 students, 21% women, 79% men. Part-time: 37 students, 22% women, 78% men. Students come from 18 states and territories, 1 other country, 33% from out-of-state. 0.4% American Indian or Alaska Native, non-Hispanic/Latino; 1% Hispanic/Latino; 2% African American, non-Hispanic/Latino; 1% Asian, non-Hispanic/Latino; 0.2% international. 9% 25 or older, 50% live on campus, 6% transferred in. Retention: 64% of full-time freshmen returned the following year. Academic area with the most degrees conferred: communication technologies. Core. Calendar: semesters. Services for LD students, advanced placement, summer session for credit, part-time degree program, adult/continuing education programs, co-op programs and internships. Off campus study at Husson University system. ROTC: Army (c).

Entrance Requirements: Options: electronic application, deferred admission, international baccalaureate accepted. Required: essay, high school transcript, minimum 2 high school GPA, 2 recommendations, interview, Wonderlic aptitude test. Recommended: SAT or ACT. Required for some: placement test. Entrance: minimally difficult. Application deadlines: Rolling, Rolling for nonresidents. Notification: continuous, continuous for nonresidents. Transfer credits accepted: Yes.

Costs Per Year: Application fee: $25. One-time mandatory fee: $100. Comprehensive fee: $22,410 includes full-time tuition ($13,034), mandatory fees ($1070), and college room and board ($8306). College room only: $4102.

Collegiate Environment: Orientation program. Drama-theater group, choral group, marching band, student-run newspaper, radio station. Social organizations: 32 open to all; national fraternities, national sororities, local fraternities, local sororities; 4% of eligible men and 4% of eligible women are members. Most popular organizations: Audio Engineering Society (AES), Society of Professional Journalists (SPJ), Public Relations Student Society of America (PRSSA), GAMERS club, Husson University Theatre. Major annual events: Winter Carnival, Greek Week. Student services: health clinic, personal-psychological counseling. Campus security: 24-hour emergency response devices and patrols, late night transport-escort service. 1,059 college housing spaces available; 252 were occupied in 2012-13. Freshmen given priority for college housing. On-campus residence required through sophomore year. Option: coed housing available. T. Tom and Bonnie Sawyer Library plus 1 other with 40,814 books, 14,148 microform titles, 500 serials, an OPAC, and a Web page. 195 computers available on campus for general student use. Computer purchase/lease plans available. A campuswide network can be accessed from student residence rooms and from off campus. Staffed computer lab on campus (open 24 hours a day) provides training in use of computers, software, and the Internet.

■ **NORTHERN MAINE COMMUNITY COLLEGE**
33 Edgemont Dr.
Presque Isle, ME 04769-2016
Tel: (207)768-2700; Free: 800-535-6682
Fax: (207)768-2831
E-mail: ngagnon@nmcc.edu
Web Site: www.nmcc.edu/
Description: State-related, 2-year, coed. Part of Maine Community College System. Awards certificates, transfer associate, and terminal associate degrees. Founded 1963. Setting: 86-acre small town campus. Educational spending for the previous fiscal year: $3456 per student. Total enrollment: 955. Faculty: 77 (45 full-time, 32 part-time). Student-undergrad faculty ratio is 18:1. 761 applied, 53% were admitted. Full-time: 573 students, 45% women, 55% men. Part-time: 177 students, 73% women, 27% men. Students come from 4 states and territories, 4% from out-of-state. 40% 25 or older, 63% live on campus, 9% transferred in. Retention: 57% of full-time freshmen returned the following year. Core. Calendar: semesters. Academic remediation for entering students, services for LD students, advanced placement, independent study, double major, summer session for credit, part-time degree program, adult/continuing education programs, co-op programs and internships. Off campus study at University of Maine at Presque Isle.
Entrance Requirements: Open admission. Options: electronic application, early admission, deferred admission. Required: high school transcript, interview, ACCUPLACER. Recommended: essay, minimum 2.0 high school GPA. Required for some: Net Test/RN. Entrance: minimally difficult. Application deadline: Rolling. Notification: continuous.
Collegiate Environment: Orientation program. Most popular organizations: Student Senate, Alpha Beta Gamma, Phi Theta Kappa, Student Nurses Association. Major annual events: Monte Carlo Night, Movie Night, Volleyball Tournament (fund raiser). Student services: health clinic. Campus security: 24-hour emergency response devices and patrols, controlled dormitory access. Northern Maine Technical College Library with 14,600 books, 125 serials, 200 audiovisual materials, an OPAC, and a Web page. Operations spending for the previous fiscal year: $163,430. 233 computers available on campus for general student use. Computer purchase/lease plans available. A campuswide network can be accessed from student residence rooms and from off campus. Students can access the following: online class registration. Staffed computer lab on campus provides training in use of computers, software, and the Internet.
Community Environment: See University of Maine - Presque Isle.

■ **SAINT JOSEPH'S COLLEGE OF MAINE**
278 Whites Bridge Rd.
Standish, ME 04084
Tel: (207)892-6766; Free: 800-338-7057
Fax: (207)893-7862
E-mail: admission@sjcme.edu
Web Site: www.sjcme.edu/
Description: Independent, comprehensive, coed, affiliated with Roman Catholic Church. Awards bachelor's and master's degrees and post-master's certificates (profile does not include enrollment in distance learning master's program). Founded 1912. Setting: 350-acre small town campus. Endowment: $9.2 million. Research spending for the previous fiscal year: $114,734. Total enrollment: 3,355. Faculty: 126 (68 full-time, 58 part-time). Student-undergrad faculty ratio is 14:1. 1,321 applied, 88% were admitted. 2 valedictorians. Full-time: 1,728 students, 69% women, 31% men. Part-time: 656 students, 79% women, 21% men. Students come from 15 states and territories, 1 other country, 45% from out-of-state. 0% American Indian or Alaska Native, non-Hispanic/Latino; 2% Hispanic/Latino; 3% African American, non-Hispanic/Latino; 1% Asian, non-Hispanic/Latino; 0% Native Hawaiian or other Pacific Islander, non-Hispanic/Latino. 38% 25 or older, 74% live on campus, 1% transferred in. Retention: 76% of full-time freshmen returned the following year. Academic areas with the most degrees conferred: health professions and related sciences; business/marketing; education. Core. Calendar: semesters. Services for LD students, advanced

placement, self-designed majors, honors program, independent study, distance learning, double major, summer session for credit, part-time degree program, adult/continuing education programs, co-op programs and internships. Off campus study at Greater Portland Alliance of Colleges and Universities, a consortium that includes University of Southern Maine, Maine College of Art, University of New England, Southern Maine Technical College, and Saint Joseph's College. Study abroad program. ROTC: Army (c).
Entrance Requirements: Options: electronic application, early action, deferred admission. Required: essay, high school transcript, minimum 2 high school GPA, 2 recommendations, SAT or ACT scores, SAT or ACT. Recommended: interview. Entrance: moderately difficult. Application deadlines: Rolling, 11/15 for early action. Notification: continuous, 12/17 for early action. Transfer credits accepted: Yes. Early action applicants: 464. Early action applicants admitted: 436.
Costs Per Year: Application fee: $0. Comprehensive fee: $40,400 includes full-time tuition ($29,000) and college room and board ($11,400). Room and board charges vary according to board plan.
Collegiate Environment: Orientation program. Drama-theater group, student-run newspaper. Social organizations: 25 open to all. Most popular organizations: Campus ministry, Superkids, Student Government Association and Senate, Business Club, Inter-Hall Council. Major annual events: Family Weekend, Spring Fling, Welcome Back Weekends. Student services: health clinic, personal-psychological counseling. Campus security: 24-hour emergency response devices and patrols, late night transport-escort service, controlled dormitory access. Wellehan Library with 85,000 books, 45,141 serials, 1,043 audiovisual materials, an OPAC, and a Web page. Operations spending for the previous fiscal year: $403,893. 102 computers available on campus for general student use. Computer purchase/lease plans available. A campuswide network can be accessed from student residence rooms. Students can access the following: online class registration. Staffed computer lab on campus provides training in use of computers, software, and the Internet.

■ **SOUTHERN MAINE COMMUNITY COLLEGE**
2 Fort Rd.
South Portland, ME 04106
Tel: (207)741-5500; Free: 877-282-2182
Fax: (207)741-5751
E-mail: alee@smccme.edu
Web Site: www.smccme.edu/
Description: State-supported, 2-year, coed. Part of Maine Community College System. Awards certificates, transfer associate, and terminal associate degrees. Founded 1946. Setting: 80-acre urban campus. Total enrollment: 7,574. Faculty: 482 (109 full-time, 373 part-time). Student-undergrad faculty ratio is 20:1. Full-time: 3,086 students, 46% women, 54% men. Part-time: 4,488 students, 49% women, 51% men. Students come from 24 states and territories, 41 other countries, 3% from out-of-state. 1% American Indian or Alaska Native, non-Hispanic/Latino; 2% Hispanic/Latino; 4% African American, non-Hispanic/Latino; 2% Asian, non-Hispanic/Latino; 0.1% Native Hawaiian or other Pacific Islander, non-Hispanic/Latino; 0.4% international. 41% 25 or older, 5% live on campus, 35% transferred in. Retention: 53% of full-time freshmen returned the following year. Calendar: semesters. Academic remediation for entering students, ESL program, services for LD students, advanced placement, honors program, independent study, distance learning, double major, summer session for credit, part-time degree program, internships. Off campus study at Great Portland Alliance of Colleges and Universities. Study abroad program.
Entrance Requirements: Open admission except for some health-related majors which are only open to Maine residents. Option: electronic application. Required: high school transcript or proof of high school graduation. Recommended: SAT or ACT, ACCUPLACER. Application deadlines: Rolling, Rolling for nonresidents. Notification: continuous, continuous for nonresidents. Transfer credits accepted: Yes.
Collegiate Environment: Orientation program. Drama-theater group, choral group, student-run newspaper. Most popular organization: Student Senate. Major annual events: Welcome Back Barbecue, Winter Carnival, Spring Fest. Student services: personal-psychological counseling. Campus security: 24-hour emergency response devices and patrols, student patrols, late night transport-escort service, controlled dormitory access. 400 college housing spaces available; all were occupied in 2012-13. Option: coed housing available. Southern Maine Community College Library with an OPAC and a Web page.

■ THOMAS COLLEGE

180 W River Rd.
Waterville, ME 04901-5097
Tel: (207)859-1111; Free: 800-339-7001
Fax: (207)859-1114
E-mail: admiss@thomas.edu
Web Site: www.thomas.edu/

Description: Independent, comprehensive, coed. Awards associate, bachelor's, and master's degrees (associate degree). Founded 1894. Setting: 70-acre small town campus. Endowment: $5.8 million. Educational spending for the previous fiscal year: $3199 per student. Total enrollment: 975. Faculty: 81 (21 full-time, 60 part-time). Student-undergrad faculty ratio is 18:1. 668 applied, 81% were admitted. 7% from top 10% of their high school class, 19% from top quarter, 54% from top half. Full-time: 633 students, 45% women, 55% men. Part-time: 132 students, 68% women, 32% men. Students come from 10 states and territories, 1 other country, 20% from out-of-state. 14% 25 or older, 64% live on campus, 1% transferred in. Retention: 64% of full-time freshmen returned the following year. Academic areas with the most degrees conferred: business/marketing; computer and information sciences; homeland security, law enforcement, firefighting, and protective services. Core. Calendar: semesters. Academic remediation for entering students, advanced placement, double major, summer session for credit, part-time degree program, adult/continuing education programs, co-op programs and internships, graduate courses open to undergrads. Off campus study at Colby College, Kennebec Valley Community College, Unity College. Study abroad program.

Entrance Requirements: Options: electronic application, early action, deferred admission, international baccalaureate accepted. Required: essay, high school transcript, 1 recommendation, SAT. Recommended: minimum 2.0 high school GPA, interview, rank in upper 50% of high school class. Entrance: minimally difficult. Application deadlines: Rolling, 12/15 for early action. Notification: continuous, 12/31 for early action.

Collegiate Environment: Orientation program. Drama-theater group, choral group, student-run newspaper. Social organizations: 17 open to all; national fraternities, national sororities, local fraternities, local sororities. Most popular organizations: Phi Beta Lambda, Students Club, GLOBE, Campus Activity Board, peer advisors. Major annual events: Homecoming, Parents' Day, Olympic Day. Student services: health clinic, personal-psychological counseling. Campus security: 24-hour emergency response devices and patrols, student patrols, controlled dormitory access. Marriner Library with 20,000 books, 5,000 serials, an OPAC, and a Web page. Operations spending for the previous fiscal year: $145,469. 120 computers available on campus for general student use. A campuswide network can be accessed from student residence rooms and from off campus. Students can access the following: online class registration. Staffed computer lab on campus provides training in use of computers, software, and the Internet.

■ UNITY COLLEGE

90 Quaker Hill Rd.
Unity, ME 04988
Tel: (207)948-3131
Fax: (207)948-6277
E-mail: jsalty@unity.edu
Web Site: www.unity.edu/

Description: Independent, 4-year, coed. Awards associate and bachelor's degrees. Founded 1965. Setting: 265-acre rural campus. Endowment: $13.2 million. Educational spending for the previous fiscal year: $6136 per student. Total enrollment: 537. Faculty: 65 (38 full-time, 27 part-time). Student-undergrad faculty ratio is 11:1. 402 applied, 87% were admitted. Full-time: 533 students, 54% women, 46% men. Part-time: 4 students, 25% women, 75% men. Students come from 35 states and territories, 77% from out-of-state. 1% American Indian or Alaska Native, non-Hispanic/Latino; 2% Hispanic/Latino; 1% African American, non-Hispanic/Latino; 1% Asian, non-Hispanic/Latino; 0.4% Native Hawaiian or other Pacific Islander, non-Hispanic/Latino; 0% international. 6% 25 or older, 65% live on campus, 6% transferred in. Retention: 75% of full-time freshmen returned the following year. Academic areas with the most degrees conferred: natural resources/environmental science; biological/life sciences; parks and recreation. Core. Calendar: semesters. Academic remediation for entering students, services for LD students, advanced placement, accelerated degree program, honors program, independent study, double major, part-time degree program, co-op programs and internships. Off campus study at The Washington Center. Study abroad program. ROTC: Army (c).

Entrance Requirements: Options: electronic application, early admission, early action, deferred admission, international baccalaureate accepted. Required: essay, high school transcript, 2 recommendations. Recommended: minimum 2 high school GPA, interview, SAT or ACT. Required for some: interview, SAT or ACT. Entrance: moderately difficult. Application deadline: Rolling. Transfer credits accepted: Yes. Applicants placed on waiting list: 0. Wait-listed applicants offered admission: 0.

Costs Per Year: Application fee: $25. Comprehensive fee: $32,814 includes full-time tuition ($23,000), mandatory fees ($1100), and college room and board ($8714). Room and board charges vary according to board plan and housing facility. Part-time tuition: $860 per credit hour. Part-time tuition varies according to course load.

Collegiate Environment: Orientation program. Drama-theater group. Social organizations: 35 open to all; 40% of eligible men and 48% of eligible women are members. Most popular organizations: Woodsmen Team, Ultimate Frisbee, Outing Club. Major annual events: Earth Day, Empty Bowls - community service, Roots Week. Student services: health clinic, personal-psychological counseling. Campus security: 24-hour emergency response devices and patrols. 360 college housing spaces available; 348 were occupied in 2012-13. Freshmen guaranteed college housing. On-campus residence required through sophomore year. Option: coed housing available. Dorothy Webb Quimby Library with 50,000 books, 62,713 serials, 5,076 audiovisual materials, an OPAC, and a Web page. Operations spending for the previous fiscal year: $250,236. 100 computers available on campus for general student use. A campuswide network can be accessed from student residence rooms and from off campus. Students can access the following: online class registration. Staffed computer lab on campus provides training in use of computers, software, and the Internet.

Community Environment: Located on Lake Winnecook, which is three miles long and has excellent fishing, canoeing, and sailing, Unity has several small businesses, two churches, a public library, and several fraternal organizations. Transportation is provided by air and bus lines. The climate is cool.

■ UNIVERSITY OF MAINE

Orono, ME 04469
Tel: (207)581-1110; Free: 877-486-2364
Fax: (207)581-1213
E-mail: um-admit@maine.edu
Web Site: www.umaine.edu/

Description: State-supported, university, coed. Part of University of Maine System. Awards bachelor's, master's, and doctoral degrees and post-master's certificates. Founded 1865. Setting: 3,300-acre small town campus. Endowment: $159.6 million. Research spending for the previous fiscal year: $51.9 million. Educational spending for the previous fiscal year: $9972 per student. Total enrollment: 11,168. Faculty: 789 (555 full-time, 234 part-time). Student-undergrad faculty ratio is 15:1. 8,093 applied, 78% were admitted. 21% from top 10% of their high school class, 51% from top quarter, 86% from top half. Full-time: 7,549 students, 48% women, 52% men. Part-time: 1,362 students, 52% women, 48% men. 16% from out-of-state. 1% American Indian or Alaska Native, non-Hispanic/Latino; 1% Hispanic/Latino; 2% African American, non-Hispanic/Latino; 1% Asian, non-Hispanic/Latino; 2% international. 13% 25 or older, 27% live on campus, 5% transferred in. Retention: 78% of full-time freshmen returned the following year. Academic areas with the most degrees conferred: business/marketing; engineering; education. Core. Calendar: semesters. ESL program, services for LD students, advanced placement, accelerated degree program, self-designed majors, freshman honors college, honors program, independent study, distance learning, double major, summer session for credit, part-time degree program, co-op programs and internships, graduate courses open to undergrads. Off campus study at Bangor Theological Seminary, other institutions of the University of Maine System. Study abroad program. ROTC: Army, Naval (c).

Entrance Requirements: Options: electronic application, early admission, early action, deferred admission, international baccalaureate accepted. Required: essay, high school transcript, 1 recommendation, SAT or ACT. Required for some: audition for music majors. Entrance: moderately difficult. Application deadlines: Rolling, Rolling for nonresidents, 12/15 for early action. Notification: continuous, continuous for nonresidents, 1/31 for early action. Transfer credits accepted: Yes.

Costs Per Year: Application fee: $40. State resident tuition: $8370 full-time, $279 per credit part-time. Nonresident tuition: $24,090 full-time, $803 per credit part-time. Mandatory fees: $2218 full-time. Full-time tuition and fees vary according to course load and program. Part-time tuition varies according to course load and program. College room and board: $8644. Room and board charges vary according to board plan and housing facility.

Collegiate Environment: Orientation program. Drama-theater group, choral group, marching band, student-run newspaper, radio station. Social organizations: 250 open to all; national fraternities, national sororities, local fraternities, local sororities. Most popular organizations: Alternative Spring Break, Circle K, Campus Crusade for Christ, Outing Club, Wilde Stein. Major annual events: Maine Day, Family and Friends Weekend, Homecoming. Student services: legal services, health clinic, personal-psychological counseling, women's center. Campus security: 24-hour emergency response devices and patrols, late night transport-escort service, controlled dormitory access, area emergency text and email message system. Fogler Library with 1.1 million books, 1.7 million microform titles, 16,988 serials, an OPAC, and a Web page. Operations spending for the previous fiscal year: $7.2 million. 500 computers available on campus for general student use. Computer purchase/lease plans available. A campuswide network can be accessed from student residence rooms and from off campus. Students can access the following: online class registration, online housing and financial aid information. Staffed computer lab on campus provides training in use of computers, software, and the Internet.

■ UNIVERSITY OF MAINE AT AUGUSTA

46 University Dr.
Augusta, ME 04330-9410
Tel: (207)621-3000; Free: 877-862-1234
Fax: (207)621-3116
E-mail: umaadm@maine.edu
Web Site: www.uma.maine.edu/
Description: State-supported, 4-year, coed. Part of University of Maine System. Awards associate and bachelor's degrees (also offers some graduate courses and continuing education programs with significant enrollment not reflected in profile). Founded 1965. Setting: 159-acre small town campus. Endowment: $5 million. Educational spending for the previous fiscal year: $4600 per student. Total enrollment: 4,974. Faculty: 290 (104 full-time, 186 part-time). Student-undergrad faculty ratio is 17:1. 948 applied, 96% were admitted. Full-time: 1,768 students, 66% women, 34% men. Part-time: 3,175 students, 76% women, 24% men. Students come from 37 states and territories, 10 other countries, 3% from out-of-state. 2% American Indian or Alaska Native, non-Hispanic/Latino; 1% Hispanic/Latino; 1% African American, non-Hispanic/Latino; 0.5% Asian, non-Hispanic/Latino; 0.02% Native Hawaiian or other Pacific Islander, non-Hispanic/Latino; 0.3% international. 69% 25 or older, 13% transferred in. Retention: 54% of full-time freshmen returned the following year. Academic areas with the most degrees conferred: health professions and related sciences; liberal arts/general studies; business/marketing. Core. Calendar: semesters. Academic remediation for entering students, services for LD students, advanced placement, self-designed majors, honors program, independent study, distance learning, double major, summer session for credit, part-time degree program, adult/continuing education programs, internships. Off campus study at other campuses of the University of Maine System. Study abroad program. ROTC: Army (c), Naval (c), Air Force (c).
Entrance Requirements: Options: electronic application, early admission, deferred admission. Required: high school transcript. Recommended: essay, SAT or ACT. Required for some: interview, music audition. Entrance: noncompetitive. Application deadlines: Rolling, Rolling for nonresidents. Notification: continuous, continuous for nonresidents. Transfer credits accepted: Yes.
Costs Per Year: Application fee: $40. State resident tuition: $6510 full-time, $217 per credit hour part-time. Nonresident tuition: $15,750 full-time, $525 per credit hour part-time. Mandatory fees: $938 full-time, $31.25 per credit hour part-time. Full-time tuition and fees vary according to course load, location, program, and reciprocity agreements. Part-time tuition and fees vary according to course load, location, program, and reciprocity agreements.
Collegiate Environment: Orientation program. Drama-theater group, student-run newspaper. Social organizations: 12 open to all. Most popular organizations: Honors Program Student Association, Arts and Architecture Students of UMA, Student Nurse Association, Student American Dental Hygiene Association, International Student Club. Major annual events: UMA Day, Jazz Week, Poetry Festival. Student services: personal-psychological counseling. Campus security: 24-hour emergency response devices, late night transport-escort service. The Bennett D. Katz Library plus 1 other with 85,245 books, 462 microform titles, 378 serials, 4,659 audiovisual materials, an OPAC, and a Web page. Operations spending for the previous fiscal year: $856,416. 315 computers available on campus for general student use. Computer purchase/lease plans available. A campuswide network can be accessed. Students can access the following: online class registration,

wireless internet available everywhere on campus. Staffed computer lab on campus provides training in use of computers, software, and the Internet.

■ UNIVERSITY OF MAINE AT FARMINGTON

224 Main St.
Farmington, ME 04938-1990
Tel: (207)778-7000
Fax: (207)778-8182
E-mail: umfadmit@maine.edu
Web Site: www.umf.maine.edu/
Description: State-supported, comprehensive, coed. Part of University of Maine System. Awards bachelor's and master's degrees. Founded 1863. Setting: 50-acre small town campus. Total enrollment: 2,180. Faculty: 171 (122 full-time, 49 part-time). Student-undergrad faculty ratio is 14:1. 1,488 applied, 86% were admitted. 11% from top 10% of their high school class, 38% from top quarter, 72% from top half. Full-time: 1,886 students, 64% women, 36% men. Part-time: 143 students, 68% women, 32% men. 16% from out-of-state. 0.1% American Indian or Alaska Native, non-Hispanic/Latino; 1% Hispanic/Latino; 0.4% African American, non-Hispanic/Latino; 2% Asian, non-Hispanic/Latino; 1% Native Hawaiian or other Pacific Islander, non-Hispanic/Latino; 0.3% international. 7% 25 or older, 50% live on campus, 6% transferred in. Retention: 71% of full-time freshmen returned the following year. Academic areas with the most degrees conferred: education; psychology; English. Core. Calendar: semesters plus May term and 2 5-week summer terms. Academic remediation for entering students, services for LD students, advanced placement, accelerated degree program, self-designed majors, honors program, independent study, distance learning, double major, summer session for credit, part-time degree program, internships. Off campus study at National Student Exchange, SALT Center for Documentary Field Studies, other institutions of the University of Maine System. Study abroad program.
Entrance Requirements: Options: electronic application, early admission, early action, deferred admission, international baccalaureate accepted. Required: essay, high school transcript, minimum 2 high school GPA, 1 recommendation, SAT or ACT. Recommended: interview. Required for some: minimum 2.5 high school GPA. Entrance: moderately difficult. Application deadlines: Rolling, 12/1 for early action. Notification: continuous, 1/8 for early action. Transfer credits accepted: Yes.
Costs Per Year: Application fee: $40. State resident tuition: $8352 full-time, $261 per credit hour part-time. Nonresident tuition: $17,440 full-time, $545 per credit hour part-time. Mandatory fees: $785 full-time. Full-time tuition and fees vary according to course load, reciprocity agreements, and student level. Part-time tuition varies according to course load, reciprocity agreements, and student level. College room and board: $8454. College room only: $4500. Room and board charges vary according to board plan and housing facility.
Collegiate Environment: Orientation program. Drama-theater group, choral group, student-run newspaper, radio station. Social organizations: 52 open to all. Most popular organizations: Program Board, Intramural Board, Campus Residence Council, campus radio station, Commuter Council. Major annual events: Intramural All Niter, Spring Fling, Campus Residence Council Semi-Formal. Student services: health clinic, personal-psychological counseling. Campus security: 24-hour emergency response devices and patrols, late night transport-escort service, controlled dormitory access, safety whistles. 1,124 college housing spaces available. Freshmen guaranteed college housing. Options: coed, women-only housing available. Mantor Library with an OPAC and a Web page.

■ UNIVERSITY OF MAINE AT FORT KENT

23 University Dr.
Fort Kent, ME 04743-1292
Tel: (207)834-7500; Free: 888-TRY-UMFK
Fax: (207)834-7609
E-mail: jillb@maine.edu
Web Site: www.umfk.maine.edu/
Description: State-supported, 4-year, coed. Part of University of Maine System. Awards associate and bachelor's degrees. Founded 1878. Setting: 52-acre rural campus. Endowment: $2 million. Research spending for the previous fiscal year: $150,000. Educational spending for the previous fiscal year: $5907 per student. Total enrollment: 1,169. Faculty: 74 (30 full-time, 44 part-time). Student-undergrad faculty ratio is 18:1. 561 applied, 57% were admitted. 2% from top 10% of their high school class, 15% from top quarter, 45% from top half. Full-time: 610 students, 64% women, 36% men. Part-time: 559 students, 62% women, 38% men. Students come from 22 states

and territories, 11 other countries, 6% from out-of-state. 1% American Indian or Alaska Native, non-Hispanic/Latino; 1% Hispanic/Latino; 2% African American, non-Hispanic/Latino; 0.3% Asian, non-Hispanic/Latino; 1% Native Hawaiian or other Pacific Islander, non-Hispanic/Latino; 7% international. 37% 25 or older, 25% live on campus, 11% transferred in. Retention: 64% of full-time freshmen returned the following year. Academic areas with the most degrees conferred: health professions and related sciences; education; business/marketing. Core. Calendar: semesters. Academic remediation for entering students, ESL program, services for LD students, advanced placement, accelerated degree program, self-designed majors, honors program, independent study, distance learning, double major, summer session for credit, part-time degree program, external degree program, co-op programs and internships.

Entrance Requirements: Options: electronic application, deferred admission. Required: essay, high school transcript. Recommended: SAT and SAT Subject Tests or ACT. Required for some: interview, SAT, SAT and SAT Subject Tests or ACT. Entrance: minimally difficult. Application deadlines: Rolling, Rolling for nonresidents. Notification: continuous, continuous for nonresidents. Transfer credits accepted: Yes.

Costs Per Year: Application fee: $40. State resident tuition: $6600 full-time, $220 per credit hour part-time. Nonresident tuition: $16,560 full-time, $552 per credit hour part-time. Mandatory fees: $975 full-time, $32.50 per credit hour part-time. Full-time tuition and fees vary according to course load and reciprocity agreements. Part-time tuition and fees vary according to reciprocity agreements. College room and board: $7400. College room only: $4000. Room and board charges vary according to board plan and housing facility.

Collegiate Environment: Orientation program. Drama-theater group, choral group. Social organizations: 9 open to all; national fraternities, national sororities; 3% of eligible men and 3% of eligible women are members. Most popular organizations: Student Nurses Organization, Student Teachers Educational Professional Society, Student Senate, Performing Arts Club, Dorm Council. Major annual events: Quebec City Carnival Field Trip, Scarecrow Festival, Spring Formal. Student services: health clinic, personal-psychological counseling. Campus security: controlled dormitory access, 8-hour night patrols by security personnel 11pm-7am. 225 college housing spaces available; 185 were occupied in 2012-13. Freshmen given priority for college housing. On-campus residence required in freshman year. Waneta Blake Library with 205,000 books, 17,000 microform titles, 44,000 serials, 2,500 audiovisual materials, an OPAC, and a Web page. Operations spending for the previous fiscal year: $284,057. 100 computers available on campus for general student use. A campuswide network can be accessed from student residence rooms and from off campus. Students can access the following: online class registration. Staffed computer lab on campus provides training in use of computers, software, and the Internet.

■ **UNIVERSITY OF MAINE AT MACHIAS**
9 O'Brien Ave.
Machias, ME 04654
Tel: (207)255-1200; Free: 888-468-6866
Fax: (207)255-1363
E-mail: ummadmissions@maine.edu
Web Site: umm.maine.edu/
Description: State-supported, 4-year, coed. Part of University of Maine System. Awards associate and bachelor's degrees. Founded 1909. Setting: 42-acre rural campus. Total enrollment: 925. Faculty: 89 (31 full-time, 58 part-time). Student-undergrad faculty ratio is 13:1. 442 applied, 83% were admitted. Full-time: 473 students, 66% women, 34% men. Part-time: 452 students, 77% women, 23% men. 21% from out-of-state. 3% American Indian or Alaska Native, non-Hispanic/Latino; 2% Hispanic/Latino; 3% African American, non-Hispanic/Latino; 0.1% Asian, non-Hispanic/Latino; 0% Native Hawaiian or other Pacific Islander, non-Hispanic/Latino; 1% international. 32% 25 or older, 41% live on campus, 6% transferred in. Retention: 67% of full-time freshmen returned the following year. Academic areas with the most degrees conferred: business/marketing; parks and recreation; biological/life sciences. Core. Calendar: semesters. Academic remediation for entering students, services for LD students, advanced placement, self-designed majors, independent study, distance learning, double major, summer session for credit, part-time degree program, co-op programs and internships. Off campus study. Study abroad program.
Entrance Requirements: Options: electronic application, early admission, early action, deferred admission. Required: essay, high school transcript, 1 recommendation, SAT or ACT. Recommended: minimum 2.5 high school GPA, 2 recommendations, interview. Required for some: minimum 2 high

school GPA, interview. Entrance: moderately difficult. Application deadlines: 8/15, 12/15 for early action. Notification: continuous. SAT Reasoning Test deadline: 8/1.
Costs Per Year: Application fee: $40. State resident tuition: $6600 full-time, $222 per credit hour part-time. Nonresident tuition: $18,480 full-time, $616 per credit hour part-time. Mandatory fees: $820 full-time. College room and board: $7900. College room only: $4000.
Collegiate Environment: Orientation program. No special consideration for freshman housing applicants. On-campus residence required through sophomore year. Option: coed housing available. Merrill Library with an OPAC and a Web page.

■ **UNIVERSITY OF MAINE AT PRESQUE ISLE**
181 Main St.
Presque Isle, ME 04769-2888
Tel: (207)768-9400
Fax: (207)768-9608
E-mail: erin.benson@umpi.edu
Web Site: www.umpi.edu/
Description: State-supported, 4-year, coed. Part of University of Maine System. Awards associate and bachelor's degrees. Founded 1903. Setting: 150-acre small town campus. Endowment: $6.1 million. Research spending for the previous fiscal year: $7820. Total enrollment: 1,453. Faculty: 103 (45 full-time, 58 part-time). Student-undergrad faculty ratio is 22:1. 504 applied, 82% were admitted. 8% from top 10% of their high school class, 23% from top quarter, 51% from top half. Full-time: 851 students, 56% women, 44% men. Part-time: 602 students, 73% women, 27% men. 5% American Indian or Alaska Native, non-Hispanic/Latino; 1% Hispanic/Latino; 1% African American, non-Hispanic/Latino; 0.1% Asian, non-Hispanic/Latino; 0% Native Hawaiian or other Pacific Islander, non-Hispanic/Latino; 11% international. 22% live on campus. Retention: 63% of full-time freshmen returned the following year. Academic areas with the most degrees conferred: education; liberal arts/general studies; business/marketing. Core. Calendar: semesters. Academic remediation for entering students, services for LD students, advanced placement, accelerated degree program, self-designed majors, honors program, independent study, distance learning, double major, summer session for credit, part-time degree program, adult/continuing education programs, co-op programs and internships. Off campus study at National Student Exchange. Study abroad program.
Entrance Requirements: Options: electronic application, early admission, early action, deferred admission, international baccalaureate accepted. Required: essay, high school transcript, minimum 2 high school GPA. Recommended: SAT or ACT. Required for some: 1 recommendation, interview. Entrance: minimally difficult. Application deadlines: Rolling, Rolling for nonresidents, 10/31 for early action. Notification: continuous, continuous for nonresidents, 4/1 for early action. Transfer credits accepted: Yes.
Costs Per Year: Application fee: $40. State resident tuition: $6600 full-time, $220 per credit part-time. Nonresident tuition: $16,560 full-time, $552 per credit part-time. Mandatory fees: $835 full-time, $18 per credit part-time, $51.25 per term part-time. Full-time tuition and fees vary according to course load, location, and reciprocity agreements. Part-time tuition and fees vary according to course load, location, and reciprocity agreements. College room and board: $7422. College room only: $4240. Room and board charges vary according to board plan and housing facility.
Collegiate Environment: Orientation program. Student-run newspaper, radio station. Social organizations: 38 open to all; national fraternities, national sororities, national honor societies; 20% of eligible men and 20% of eligible women are members. Most popular organizations: PE Majors Club, Student Senate, Athletic Training Student Club, Student Organization of Social Workers, Criminal Justice Club. Major annual events: Midnight Madness, University Day, Spring Ball. Student services: health clinic, personal-psychological counseling. Campus security: student patrols, controlled dormitory access, crime prevention programs, lighted pathways, security cameras. Library with an OPAC and a Web page. Operations spending for the previous fiscal year: $447,582. 85 computers available on campus for general student use. A campuswide network can be accessed from student residence rooms and from off campus. Students can access the following: online class registration. Staffed computer lab on campus provides training in use of software and the Internet.

■ **UNIVERSITY OF NEW ENGLAND**
11 Hills Beach Rd.
Biddeford, ME 04005-9526
Tel: (207)283-0171; Free: 800-477-4UNE

E-mail: admissions@une.edu
Web Site: www.une.edu/

Description: Independent, comprehensive, coed. Awards associate, bachelor's, master's, and doctoral degrees and post-master's certificates. Founded 1831. Setting: 540-acre small town campus. Endowment: $27.1 million. Research spending for the previous fiscal year: $6.1 million. Total enrollment: 5,666. Faculty: 437 (250 full-time, 187 part-time). Student-undergrad faculty ratio is 13:1. 3,885 applied, 86% were admitted. Full-time: 2,148 students, 70% women, 30% men. Part-time: 489 students, 66% women, 34% men. Students come from 49 states and territories, 8 other countries, 64% from out-of-state. 1% American Indian or Alaska Native, non-Hispanic/Latino; 0.2% Hispanic/Latino; 1% African American, non-Hispanic/Latino; 2% Asian, non-Hispanic/Latino; 0.2% Native Hawaiian or other Pacific Islander, non-Hispanic/Latino; 1% international. 4% 25 or older, 63% live on campus, 3% transferred in. Retention: 75% of full-time freshmen returned the following year. Academic areas with the most degrees conferred: biological/life sciences; health professions and related sciences; parks and recreation. Core. Calendar: semesters. Academic remediation for entering students, services for LD students, advanced placement, accelerated degree program, honors program, independent study, distance learning, double major, summer session for credit, part-time degree program, adult/continuing education programs, co-op programs and internships, graduate courses open to undergrads. Off campus study at Greater Portland Alliance of Colleges and Universities. Study abroad program. ROTC: Army (c).

Entrance Requirements: Options: electronic application, early admission, deferred admission, international baccalaureate accepted. Required: essay, high school transcript, SAT or ACT. Recommended: 1 recommendation. Entrance: moderately difficult. Application deadline: 2/15. Notification: continuous. Transfer credits accepted: Yes.

Costs Per Year: Application fee: $40. Comprehensive fee: $44,370 includes full-time tuition ($30,750), mandatory fees ($1120), and college room and board ($12,500). Room and board charges vary according to board plan, housing facility, and location. Part-time tuition: $1090 per credit hour.

Collegiate Environment: Orientation program. Drama-theater group, choral group, student-run newspaper. Most popular organizations: student government, Outing Club, Campus Programming Board, Earth's Eco, Dance Team. Major annual events: Homecoming, Jam Fest, Winter Fest. Student services: health clinic, personal-psychological counseling. Campus security: 24-hour emergency response devices and patrols, late night transport-escort service, controlled dormitory access. 1,619 college housing spaces available; 1,374 were occupied in 2012-13. On-campus residence required through junior year. Options: coed, women-only housing available. Jack S. Ketchum Library plus 1 other with 235,776 books, 536 microform titles, 67,970 serials, 10,220 audiovisual materials, an OPAC, and a Web page. Operations spending for the previous fiscal year: $2.8 million. 91 computers available on campus for general student use. Computer purchase/lease plans available. A campuswide network can be accessed from student residence rooms and from off campus. Students can access the following: online class registration. Staffed computer lab on campus (open 24 hours a day) provides training in use of software.

Community Environment: On the Saco River, the University of New England is located outside the small City of Biddeford (pop. 22,072) on the coast of Southern Maine, two hours from Boston and 25 minutes from Portland, Maine's largest city. Part-time work is available for students. Biddeford city services include hospital, churches, library, and Chamber of commerce. Recreational facilities good, with beaches of Biddeford Pool, Kennebunk, and Old Orchard; golf, fishing, swimming, skiing, are within easy reach.

■ **UNIVERSITY OF SOUTHERN MAINE**
96 Falmouth St.
Portland, ME 04104-9300
Tel: (207)780-4141; Free: 800-800-4USM
Fax: (207)780-5640
E-mail: usmadm@usm.maine.edu
Web Site: www.usm.maine.edu/

Description: State-supported, comprehensive, coed. Part of University of Maine System. Awards bachelor's, master's, and doctoral degrees and post-master's certificates. Founded 1878. Setting: 144-acre urban campus. System endowment: $121 million. Research spending for the previous fiscal year: $12.5 million. Total enrollment: 9,382. Faculty: 680 (357 full-time, 323 part-time). Student-undergrad faculty ratio is 15:1. 3,900 applied, 83% were admitted. 10% from top 10% of their high school class, 33% from top quarter,

69% from top half. Full-time: 4,551 students, 56% women, 44% men. Part-time: 2,856 students, 57% women, 43% men. Students come from 34 states and territories, 19 other countries, 19% from out-of-state. 1% American Indian or Alaska Native, non-Hispanic/Latino; 2% Hispanic/Latino; 3% African American, non-Hispanic/Latino; 2% Asian, non-Hispanic/Latino; 0.1% Native Hawaiian or other Pacific Islander, non-Hispanic/Latino; 1% international. 13% 25 or older, 14% live on campus, 13% transferred in. Retention: 64% of full-time freshmen returned the following year. Academic areas with the most degrees conferred: business/marketing; health professions and related sciences; social sciences. Core. Calendar: semesters. Academic remediation for entering students, ESL program, services for LD students, advanced placement, accelerated degree program, self-designed majors, honors program, independent study, distance learning, double major, summer session for credit, part-time degree program, adult/continuing education programs, co-op programs and internships, graduate courses open to undergrads. Off campus study at National Student Exchange. Study abroad program. ROTC: Army (c), Air Force (c).

Entrance Requirements: Options: electronic application, early admission, deferred admission, international baccalaureate accepted. Required: essay, high school transcript, SAT or ACT. Recommended: 1 recommendation, interview. Required for some: interview, auditions for music majors. Entrance: moderately difficult. Application deadline: 2/15. Notification: continuous, continuous for nonresidents. SAT Reasoning Test deadline: 8/2. Transfer credits accepted: Yes.

Costs Per Year: Application fee: $40. State resident tuition: $7590 full-time, $253 per credit hour part-time. Nonresident tuition: $19,950 full-time, $665 per credit hour part-time. Mandatory fees: $1330 full-time. Full-time tuition and fees vary according to course load, degree level, and reciprocity agreements. Part-time tuition varies according to course load, degree level, and reciprocity agreements. College room and board: $9130. College room only: $4978. Room and board charges vary according to board plan, housing facility, and location.

Collegiate Environment: Orientation program. Drama-theater group, choral group, student-run newspaper, radio station. Social organizations: national fraternities, national sororities, local fraternities, local sororities. Most popular organizations: Outing and Ski Clubs, Gorham Events Board, Commuter Student Group, Circle K. Major annual events: Spring Fling, Winter Weekend, theatre and music performers. Student services: legal services, health clinic, personal-psychological counseling, women's center. Campus security: 24-hour emergency response devices and patrols, late night transport-escort service, controlled dormitory access, security lighting, preventive programs within residence halls. 1,571 college housing spaces available; 1,149 were occupied in 2012-13. Freshmen given priority for college housing. Option: coed housing available. Glickman Library plus 3 others with 469,292 books, 733,581 microform titles, 1,177 serials, 13,328 audiovisual materials, and an OPAC. Operations spending for the previous fiscal year: $3.6 million. 219 computers available on campus for general student use. Computer purchase/lease plans available. A campuswide network can be accessed from student residence rooms and from off campus. Students can access the following: online class registration. Staffed computer lab on campus provides training in use of computers, software, and the Internet.

■ **WASHINGTON COUNTY COMMUNITY COLLEGE**
One College Dr.
Calais, ME 04619
Tel: (207)454-1000
Fax: (207)454-1026
Web Site: www.wccc.me.edu/

Description: State-supported, 2-year, coed. Part of Maine Technical College System. Awards certificates, diplomas, transfer associate, and terminal associate degrees. Founded 1969. Setting: 40-acre rural campus. Total enrollment: 374. Student-undergrad faculty ratio is 11:1. 0% from out-of-state. 40% 25 or older. Retention: 63% of full-time freshmen returned the following year. Calendar: semesters. Academic remediation for entering students, services for LD students, advanced placement, independent study, distance learning, double major, part-time degree program, external degree program, adult/continuing education programs, co-op programs and internships. Off campus study. Study abroad program.

Entrance Requirements: Open admission. Option: deferred admission. Required: essay, high school transcript, interview. Recommended: minimum 2.0 high school GPA. Entrance: noncompetitive. Application deadline: Rolling. Notification: continuous.

Collegiate Environment: Orientation program. Choral group. Student services: personal-psychological counseling. Campus security: 24-hour emergency response devices.

■ YORK COUNTY COMMUNITY COLLEGE

112 College Dr.
Wells, ME 04090
Tel: (207)646-9282; Free: 800-580-3820
Fax: (207)641-0837
Web Site: www.yccc.edu/

Description: State-supported, 2-year, coed. Part of Maine Community College System. Awards certificates, transfer associate, and terminal associate degrees. Founded 1994. Setting: 84-acre small town campus with easy access to Boston. Endowment: $804,057. Educational spending for the previous fiscal year: $3359 per student. Total enrollment: 1,524. Faculty: 136 (18 full-time, 118 part-time). Student-undergrad faculty ratio is 15:1. Full-time: 532 students, 61% women, 39% men. Part-time: 992 students, 67% women, 33% men. Students come from 7 states and territories, 1 other country, 2% from out-of-state. 1% American Indian or Alaska Native, non-Hispanic/Latino; 2% Hispanic/Latino; 1% African American, non-Hispanic/Latino; 1% Asian, non-Hispanic/Latino; 0% Native Hawaiian or other Pacific Islander, non-Hispanic/Latino; 0.3% international. 46% 25 or older, 5% transferred in.

Retention: 52% of full-time freshmen returned the following year. Calendar: semesters. Academic remediation for entering students, services for LD students, advanced placement, accelerated degree program, distance learning, summer session for credit, part-time degree program, adult/continuing education programs, co-op programs and internships.

Entrance Requirements: Open admission. Option: electronic application. Required: high school transcript, interview. Entrance: noncompetitive. Application deadline: Rolling.

Costs Per Year: Application fee: $0. State resident tuition: $2580 full-time, $86 per credit part-time. Nonresident tuition: $5160 full-time, $172 per credit part-time. Mandatory fees: $606 full-time.

Collegiate Environment: Orientation program. Most popular organizations: Student Senate, Phi Theta Kappa, Photography Club, Culinary Arts Club. Major annual events: Spring Fling, Halloween Dance, Welcome Back Cookout. Campus security: 24-hour emergency response devices, late night transport-escort service. College housing not available. Library and Learning Resource Center plus 1 other with 14,000 books, 93 serials, 1,926 audiovisual materials, an OPAC, and a Web page. Operations spending for the previous fiscal year: $213,902. 35 computers available on campus for general student use. A campuswide network can be accessed. Students can access the following: online class registration. Staffed computer lab on campus provides training in use of computers, software, and the Internet.

■ **ALLEGANY COLLEGE OF MARYLAND**
12401 Willowbrook Rd., SE
Cumberland, MD 21502-2596
Tel: (301)784-5000
Fax: (301)784-5024
E-mail: cnolan@allegany.edu
Web Site: www.allegany.edu/
Description: State and locally supported, 2-year, coed. Part of Maryland State Community Colleges System. Awards certificates, transfer associate, and terminal associate degrees. Founded 1961. Setting: 311-acre small town campus. Total enrollment: 4,913. Faculty: 232 (114 full-time, 118 part-time). Student-undergrad faculty ratio is 16:1. 7% live on campus. Calendar: semesters. Academic remediation for entering students, ESL program, advanced placement, honors program, independent study, distance learning, double major, summer session for credit, part-time degree program, adult/continuing education programs, internships. ROTC: Army (c).
Entrance Requirements: Open admission except for allied health programs. Options: electronic application, early admission. Required: high school transcript. Required for some: ACT. Entrance: noncompetitive. Application deadline: Rolling.
Collegiate Environment: Orientation program. Choral group. Social organizations: 24 open to all. Most popular organizations: SAHDA, Honors Club, EMT Club, Forestry Club. Major annual events: All College Awards Banquet, Welcome Back Picnic, Spring Fling Tension Breaker. Student services: personal-psychological counseling, women's center. Campus security: 24-hour emergency response devices and patrols, late night transport-escort service. Allegany College of Maryland Library with 86,636 books, 7,737 microform titles, 313 serials, an OPAC, and a Web page. 700 computers available on campus for general student use. A campuswide network can be accessed from off-campus. Students can access the following: online class registration. Staffed computer lab on campus.

■ **ANNE ARUNDEL COMMUNITY COLLEGE**
101 College Pky.
Arnold, MD 21012-1895
Tel: (410)647-7100
Fax: (410)541-2245
E-mail: 4info@aacc.edu
Web Site: www.aacc.edu/
Description: State and locally supported, 2-year, coed. Awards certificates, transfer associate, and terminal associate degrees. Founded 1961. Setting: 230-acre suburban campus with easy access to Baltimore and Washington, DC. Total enrollment: 17,650. Faculty: 1,194 (261 full-time, 933 part-time). Student-undergrad faculty ratio is 16:1. Full-time: 5,098 students, 52% women, 48% men. Part-time: 12,552 students, 64% women, 36% men. Students come from 34 states and territories. 1% American Indian or Alaska Native, non-Hispanic/Latino; 5% Hispanic/Latino; 18% African American, non-Hispanic/Latino; 4% Asian, non-Hispanic/Latino; 0.3% Native Hawaiian or other Pacific Islander, non-Hispanic/Latino; 1% international. 40% 25 or older. Core. Calendar: semesters. Academic remediation for entering students, ESL program, services for LD students, advanced placement, accelerated degree program, freshman honors college, honors program, independent study, distance learning, summer session for credit, part-time degree program, adult/continuing education programs, co-op programs and internships. ROTC: Army (c), Air Force (c).
Entrance Requirements: Open admission all except for certain allied health

programs. Options: electronic application, early admission, deferred admission, international baccalaureate accepted. Entrance: noncompetitive. Application deadlines: Rolling, Rolling for nonresidents. Notification: continuous, continuous for nonresidents. Transfer credits accepted: Yes.
Costs Per Year: Application fee: $0. Area resident tuition: $2700 full-time. State resident tuition: $5190 full-time. Nonresident tuition: $9180 full-time. Mandatory fees: $500 full-time. Full-time tuition and fees vary according to course load.
Collegiate Environment: Orientation program. Drama-theater group, choral group, student-run newspaper. Social organizations: 45 open to all. Most popular organizations: Drama Club, Student Association, Black Student Union, International Student Association, Chemistry Club. Major annual events: Activities Fair, family performances, dramatic/theatrical performances. Student services: health clinic, personal-psychological counseling. Campus security: 24-hour emergency response devices and patrols, student patrols, late night transport-escort service. College housing not available. Andrew G. Truxal Library plus 1 other with 175,000 books, 20 microform titles, 215 serials, 3,130 audiovisual materials, an OPAC, and a Web page. 1,000 computers available on campus for general student use. A campuswide network can be accessed from off-campus. Students can access the following: online class registration. Staffed computer lab on campus.

■ **BALTIMORE CITY COMMUNITY COLLEGE**
2901 Liberty Heights Ave.
Baltimore, MD 21215-7893
Tel: (410)462-8300
Fax: (410)462-7677
E-mail: dedangerfield@bccc.edu
Web Site: www.bccc.edu/
Description: State-supported, 2-year, coed. Awards certificates, transfer associate, and terminal associate degrees. Founded 1947. Setting: 19-acre urban campus. Total enrollment: 6,953. Student-undergrad faculty ratio is 18:1. 1% from out-of-state. 56% 25 or older. Core. Calendar: semesters. Academic remediation for entering students, ESL program, services for LD students, advanced placement, honors program, distance learning, double major, summer session for credit, part-time degree program, adult/continuing education programs, co-op programs and internships. Study abroad program.
Entrance Requirements: Open admission except for allied health programs. Options: early admission, deferred admission. Required: high school transcript. Recommended: interview. Entrance: noncompetitive. Application deadline: 8/9. Notification: continuous.
Collegiate Environment: Orientation program. Choral group, student-run newspaper, radio station. Student services: health clinic, personal-psychological counseling. Bard Library with an OPAC and a Web page.
Community Environment: See University of Baltimore.

■ **BOWIE STATE UNIVERSITY**
14000 Jericho Park Rd.
Bowie, MD 20715-9465
Tel: (301)860-4000; Free: 877-772-6943
Fax: (301)860-3510
E-mail: sholt@bowiestate.edu
Web Site: www.bowiestate.edu/
Description: State-supported, comprehensive, coed. Part of University

System of Maryland. Awards bachelor's, master's, and doctoral degrees. Founded 1865. Setting: 295-acre small town campus with easy access to Baltimore and Washington, DC. Endowment: $5.4 million. Total enrollment: 5,421. Faculty: 408 (216 full-time, 192 part-time). Student-undergrad faculty ratio is 16:1. 2,632 applied, 48% were admitted. 3% from top 10% of their high school class. Full-time: 3,493 students, 62% women, 38% men. Part-time: 790 students, 64% women, 36% men. Students come from 31 states and territories, 9% from out-of-state. 0.1% American Indian or Alaska Native, non-Hispanic/Latino; 3% Hispanic/Latino; 89% African American, non-Hispanic/Latino; 2% Asian, non-Hispanic/Latino; 0.1% Native Hawaiian or other Pacific Islander, non-Hispanic/Latino; 1% international. 25% 25 or older, 34% live on campus, 11% transferred in. Retention: 67% of full-time freshmen returned the following year. Academic areas with the most degrees conferred: business/marketing; social sciences; communication/journalism. Core. Calendar: semesters. Academic remediation for entering students, services for LD students, advanced placement, honors program, independent study, distance learning, double major, summer session for credit, part-time degree program, external degree program, adult/continuing education programs, co-op programs and internships, graduate courses open to undergrads. Off campus study at other units of the University System of Maryland. Study abroad program. ROTC: Army.

Entrance Requirements: Options: electronic application, international baccalaureate accepted. Required: high school transcript, minimum 2 high school GPA, SAT or ACT. Entrance: minimally difficult. Application deadline: 4/1. Notification: continuous. Preference given to state residents. Transfer credits accepted: Yes.

Costs Per Year: Application fee: $40. State resident tuition: $4683 full-time, $207 per credit hour part-time. Nonresident tuition: $15,239 full-time, $641 per credit hour part-time. Mandatory fees: $1956 full-time, $86.96 per credit hour part-time. Part-time tuition and fees vary according to course load. College room and board: $9597. Room and board charges vary according to board plan and housing facility.

Collegiate Environment: Orientation program. Drama-theater group, choral group, marching band, student-run newspaper, radio station. Social organizations: 52 open to all; national fraternities, national sororities; 3% of eligible men and 4% of eligible women are members. Most popular organizations: NSAP Student Leadership Institute, Honda Campus All-Star Challenge. Major annual events: Fall Convocation, Homecoming events, Honors Convocation. Student services: health clinic, personal-psychological counseling. Campus security: 24-hour emergency response devices and patrols, student patrols, late night transport-escort service, controlled dormitory access. 1,400 college housing spaces available; 1,367 were occupied in 2012-13. Freshmen given priority for college housing. Options: coed, men-only, women-only housing available. Thurgood Marshall Library with 285,815 books, 474,196 microform titles, 770 serials, 7,570 audiovisual materials, an OPAC, and a Web page. 3,144 computers available on campus for general student use. A campuswide network can be accessed from student residence rooms and from off campus. Students can access the following: online class registration. Staffed computer lab on campus.

Community Environment: A suburban community with good transportation facilities. Baltimore-Washington Airport at Baltimore is 14 miles. Student employment is available in many commercial establishments and private homes. Bowie is near beaches and many recreation centers.

■ **CAPITOL COLLEGE**
11301 Springfield Rd.
Laurel, MD 20708-9759
Tel: (301)369-2800; Free: 800-950-1992
E-mail: ghwalls@capitol-college.edu
Web Site: www.capitol-college.edu/
Description: Independent, comprehensive, coed. Awards associate, bachelor's, and master's degrees. Founded 1964. Setting: 52-acre suburban campus with easy access to Baltimore and Washington, DC. Total enrollment: 699. Student-undergrad faculty ratio is 12:1. 384 applied. Students come from 11 states and territories. 41% 25 or older. Core. Calendar: semesters. Academic remediation for entering students, ESL program, advanced placement, accelerated degree program, summer session for credit, part-time degree program, adult/continuing education programs, co-op programs. ROTC: Army (c).
Entrance Requirements: Options: electronic application, deferred admission, international baccalaureate accepted. Required: high school transcript, SAT or ACT. Recommended: minimum 2.2 high school GPA, interview. Required for some: essay, 2 recommendations, interview. Entrance: minimally difficult. Application deadline: Rolling.

Collegiate Environment: Orientation program. Student-run newspaper. Student services: personal-psychological counseling. Campus security: night security patrols.
Community Environment: The town is in Prince George's County, a suburban area within easy reach of Washington, DC, and Baltimore, MD. Much of Washington's electronic industry is located in this area. The Capital Beltway is only four minutes from the school, providing easy access to the metropolitan area.

■ **CARROLL COMMUNITY COLLEGE**
1601 Washington Rd.
Westminster, MD 21157
Tel: (410)386-8000; Free: 888-221-9748
Fax: (410)876-8855
E-mail: cedwards@carrollcc.edu
Web Site: www.carrollcc.edu/
Description: State and locally supported, 2-year, coed. Part of Maryland Higher Education Commission. Awards certificates, transfer associate, and terminal associate degrees. Founded 1993. Setting: 80-acre suburban campus with easy access to Baltimore. Endowment: $4.2 million. Total enrollment: 4,103. Faculty: 293 (77 full-time, 216 part-time). Student-undergrad faculty ratio is 16:1. 854 applied, 100% were admitted. Full-time: 1,614 students, 53% women, 47% men. Part-time: 2,489 students, 66% women, 34% men. Students come from 7 states and territories, 18 other countries, 2% from out-of-state. 0.2% American Indian or Alaska Native, non-Hispanic/Latino; 3% Hispanic/Latino; 3% African American, non-Hispanic/Latino; 1% Asian, non-Hispanic/Latino; 0.1% Native Hawaiian or other Pacific Islander, non-Hispanic/Latino; 0.2% international. 30% 25 or older, 8% transferred in. Core. Calendar: semesters plus winter session. Academic remediation for entering students, ESL program, services for LD students, advanced placement, honors program, independent study, distance learning, summer session for credit, part-time degree program, internships.
Entrance Requirements: Open admission Open Admission policy except for registered nurse track program; practical nursing track certificate program; physical therapist assistant program; Hill Scholars cohort program. Option: electronic application. Required: high school transcript. Entrance: noncompetitive. Application deadlines: Rolling, Rolling for nonresidents. Notification: continuous, continuous for nonresidents. Transfer credits accepted: Yes.
Costs Per Year: Application fee: $0. Area resident tuition: $3912 full-time, $130.40 per credit hour part-time. State resident tuition: $5676 full-time, $189.20 per credit hour part-time. Nonresident tuition: $7944 full-time, $264.80 per credit hour part-time.
Collegiate Environment: Orientation program. Drama-theater group, student-run newspaper. Most popular organizations: Student Government Organization, Carroll Student Art Society, Campus Activities Board, Service Learning Club, Academic Communities (Creativity, Education, Great Ideas, Health and Wellness). Major annual events: Crab Feast, Health Fair, Get out-of-town trips to New York City and Washington, D.C. Campus security: 24-hour emergency response devices, late night transport-escort service. College housing not available. Random House Learning Resources Center with 124,578 books, 965 microform titles, 181 serials, 3,878 audiovisual materials, an OPAC, and a Web page. 1,082 computers available on campus for general student use. A campuswide network can be accessed. Students can access the following: online class registration, total campus Wi-Fi, Blackboard. Staffed computer lab on campus provides training in use of computers, software, and the Internet.

■ **CECIL COLLEGE**
One Seahawk Dr.
North East, MD 21901-1999
Tel: (410)287-6060
Fax: (410)287-1026
E-mail: dlane@cecil.edu
Web Site: www.cecil.edu/
Description: County-supported, 2-year, coed. Awards certificates and transfer associate degrees. Founded 1968. Setting: 159-acre small town campus with easy access to Baltimore. Total enrollment: 2,641. Faculty: 251 (48 full-time, 203 part-time). Student-undergrad faculty ratio is 13:1. 672 applied, 100% were admitted. Full-time: 886 students, 54% women, 46% men. Part-time: 1,755 students, 66% women, 34% men. Students come from 13 states and territories, 16 other countries, 10% from out-of-state. 1% American Indian or Alaska Native, non-Hispanic/Latino; 4% Hispanic/Latino;

10% African American, non-Hispanic/Latino; 1% Asian, non-Hispanic/Latino; 0.1% Native Hawaiian or other Pacific Islander, non-Hispanic/Latino; 0.2% international. 32% 25 or older, 0.1% transferred in. Core. Calendar: semesters. Academic remediation for entering students, ESL program, services for LD students, advanced placement, accelerated degree program, independent study, distance learning, double major, summer session for credit, part-time degree program, adult/continuing education programs, co-op programs and internships. Off campus study.

Entrance Requirements: Open admission except for nursing program. Options: electronic application, early admission, deferred admission. Required: high school transcript. Entrance: noncompetitive. Application deadlines: Rolling, Rolling for nonresidents. Notification: continuous, continuous for nonresidents.

Costs Per Year: Area resident tuition: $2850 full-time, $95 per credit hour part-time. State resident tuition: $5550 full-time, $185 per credit hour part-time. Nonresident tuition: $6900 full-time, $230 per credit hour part-time. Mandatory fees: $362 full-time.

Collegiate Environment: Orientation program. Drama-theater group. Social organizations: 14 open to all; national fraternities; 6% of eligible men and 10% of eligible women are members. Most popular organizations: student government, Non-traditional Student Organization, Student Nurses Association. Major annual events: Welcome Back Event, Spring Fling, Chautaugua Festival. Student services: personal-psychological counseling, women's center. Campus security: 24-hour emergency response devices, late night transport-escort service. College housing not available. Cecil County Veterans Memorial Library with 57,776 books, 42 serials, 834 audiovisual materials, an OPAC, and a Web page. 95 computers available on campus for general student use. A campuswide network can be accessed from off-campus. Students can access the following: online class registration. Staffed computer lab on campus provides training in use of computers, software, and the Internet.

Community Environment: North East is approximately 5 miles west of Elkton, which is nestled in the valley where the Chesapeake Bay begins. It is within easy reach of the major cities on the East Coast with all forms of major commercial transportation available. Three interchanges on the John F. Kennedy Turnpike and super highways make New York or Washington, D.C., an easy two-hour drive. Elkton, rich in historical sites, has churches, health centers, and good shopping. The area offers hunting, fishing, camping, yachting, and racing and, with its beaches, parks, and marinas, is an ideal spot for vacationing.

■ **CHESAPEAKE COLLEGE**

PO Box 8
Wye Mills, MD 21679-0008
Tel: (410)822-5400
Fax: (410)827-9466
E-mail: rholliday@chesapeake.edu
Web Site: www.chesapeake.edu/

Description: State and locally supported, 2-year, coed. Awards certificates, transfer associate, and terminal associate degrees. Founded 1965. Setting: 170-acre rural campus with easy access to Baltimore and Washington, DC. Total enrollment: 2,856. Student-undergrad faculty ratio is 23:1. 2% from out-of-state. 35% 25 or older. Core. Calendar: semesters. Academic remediation for entering students, ESL program, services for LD students, advanced placement, self-designed majors, honors program, independent study, distance learning, summer session for credit, part-time degree program, adult/continuing education programs, co-op programs and internships.

Entrance Requirements: Open admission except for radiological technology, physical therapy assistant programs. Options: early admission, deferred admission. Required: high school transcript. Entrance: noncompetitive. Application deadline: Rolling. Notification: continuous.

Collegiate Environment: Orientation program. Drama-theater group, choral group. Student services: personal-psychological counseling, women's center. Campus security: 24-hour patrols. Learning Resource Center plus 1 other with an OPAC and a Web page.

■ **COLLEGE OF SOUTHERN MARYLAND**

8730 Mitchell Rd.
La Plata, MD 20646-0910
Tel: (301)934-2251; Free: 800-933-9177
Fax: (301)934-5255
E-mail: info@csmd.edu
Web Site: www.csmd.edu/

Description: State and locally supported, 2-year, coed. Awards certificates,

transfer associate, and terminal associate degrees. Founded 1958. Setting: 175-acre rural campus with easy access to Washington, DC. Total enrollment: 9,210. Faculty: 529 (129 full-time, 400 part-time). Student-undergrad faculty ratio is 20:1. Full-time: 3,405 students, 56% women, 44% men. Part-time: 5,805 students, 66% women, 34% men. 1% American Indian or Alaska Native, non-Hispanic/Latino; 5% Hispanic/Latino; 25% African American, non-Hispanic/Latino; 2% Asian, non-Hispanic/Latino; 0.5% Native Hawaiian or other Pacific Islander, non-Hispanic/Latino; 0.4% international. 35% 25 or older, 6% transferred in. Calendar: semesters. Academic remediation for entering students, services for LD students, advanced placement, accelerated degree program, honors program, distance learning, summer session for credit, part-time degree program, adult/continuing education programs, co-op programs and internships. Study abroad program.

Entrance Requirements: Open admission except for nursing program. Options: electronic application, early admission, deferred admission. Recommended: high school transcript. Entrance: noncompetitive. Application deadline: Rolling. Notification: continuous. Transfer credits accepted: Yes.

Costs Per Year: Application fee: $0. Area resident tuition: $4096 full-time, $111 per credit part-time. State resident tuition: $7085 full-time, $192 per credit part-time. Nonresident tuition: $9151 full-time, $248 per credit hour part-time. Full-time tuition varies according to course load. Part-time tuition varies according to course load.

Collegiate Environment: Orientation program. Drama-theater group, choral group, student-run newspaper. Social organizations: 20 open to all. Most popular organizations: Spanish Club, Nursing Student Association, Science Club, Black Student Union, BACCHUS. Major annual events: Spring Fling Week, Fall Picnic, Transfer Day. Student services: personal-psychological counseling, women's center. Campus security: 24-hour emergency response devices and patrols. College housing not available. College of Southern Maryland Library with 44,896 books, 2,214 microform titles, 166 serials, an OPAC, and a Web page. 130 computers available on campus for general student use. A campuswide network can be accessed from off-campus. Students can access the following: online class registration. Staffed computer lab on campus.

Community Environment: Southern Maryland is within a short distance of Washington, D.C. Community recreational activities include bowling, hunting, swimming, boating, camping, fishing, water sports, and fox hunting. Some of the special events are the annual county fair, and the Maryland Garden Tours.

■ **THE COMMUNITY COLLEGE OF BALTIMORE COUNTY**

7201 Rossville Blvd.
Baltimore, MD 21228
Tel: (443)840-2999
E-mail: ddrake@ccbcmd.edu
Web Site: www.ccbcmd.edu/

Description: County-supported, 2-year, coed. Awards certificates, transfer associate, and terminal associate degrees. Founded 1957. Setting: 350-acre suburban campus. Total enrollment: 25,188. Faculty: 1,379 (427 full-time, 952 part-time). Full-time: 8,373 students, 55% women, 45% men. Part-time: 16,815 students, 65% women, 35% men. 0.3% American Indian or Alaska Native, non-Hispanic/Latino; 4% Hispanic/Latino; 39% African American, non-Hispanic/Latino; 5% Asian, non-Hispanic/Latino; 0.2% Native Hawaiian or other Pacific Islander, non-Hispanic/Latino; 3% international. Calendar: semesters. Academic remediation for entering students, ESL program, services for LD students, advanced placement, honors program, independent study, distance learning, summer session for credit, co-op programs and internships. Off campus study. Study abroad program.

Entrance Requirements: Required: high school transcript. Recommended: SAT or ACT. Entrance: noncompetitive. Application deadlines: Rolling, Rolling for nonresidents.

Collegiate Environment: Orientation program. Campus security: 24-hour emergency response devices and patrols, late night transport-escort service. College housing not available.

■ **COPPIN STATE UNIVERSITY**

2500 W N Ave.
Baltimore, MD 21216-3698
Tel: (410)951-3000; Free: 800-635-3674
Fax: (410)523-7238
E-mail: mgross@coppin.edu
Web Site: www.coppin.edu/

Description: State-supported, comprehensive, coed. Part of University System of Maryland. Awards bachelor's and master's degrees. Founded

1900. Setting: 33-acre urban campus. Total enrollment: 3,800. Faculty: 312 (157 full-time, 155 part-time). Student-undergrad faculty ratio is 15:1. 3,767 applied, 54% were admitted. Full-time: 2,599 students, 75% women, 25% men. Part-time: 699 students, 80% women, 20% men. Students come from 25 states and territories, 7% from out-of-state. 41% 25 or older, 8% transferred in. Retention: 61% of full-time freshmen returned the following year. Academic areas with the most degrees conferred: health professions and related sciences; psychology; liberal arts/general studies. Core. Calendar: semesters. Academic remediation for entering students, ESL program, services for LD students, advanced placement, freshman honors college, honors program, double major, summer session for credit, part-time degree program, external degree program, adult/continuing education programs, co-op programs and internships, graduate courses open to undergrads. Off campus study at 6 members of the Cooperative Education Program. ROTC: Army.

Entrance Requirements: Options: electronic application, early admission, deferred admission. Required: high school transcript, SAT or ACT. Recommended: minimum 2.5 high school GPA, interview. Required for some: 2 recommendations. Entrance: moderately difficult. Application deadline: 7/15. Notification: continuous.

Collegiate Environment: Orientation program. Drama-theater group, choral group, student-run newspaper. Social organizations: national fraternities, national sororities, local fraternities, local sororities. Student services: health clinic, personal-psychological counseling. Campus security: 24-hour emergency response devices and patrols, late night transport-escort service, controlled dormitory access. Parlett L. Moore Library with 134,983 books, 665 serials, and an OPAC.

Community Environment: See University of Baltimore.

■ DEVRY UNIVERSITY

4550 Montgomery Ave., Ste. 100 N
Bethesda, MD 20814-3304
Tel: (301)652-8477; Free: 866-338-7941
Fax: (301)652-8577
Web Site: www.devry.edu/

Description: Proprietary, comprehensive, coed. Part of DeVry University. Awards bachelor's and master's degrees. Total enrollment: 142. Faculty: 21 (all part-time). Student-undergrad faculty ratio is 10:1. Full-time: 29 students, 48% women, 52% men. Part-time: 39 students, 54% women, 46% men. 10% from out-of-state. 74% 25 or older, 31% transferred in. Academic area with the most degrees conferred: business/marketing. Calendar: semesters. Academic remediation for entering students, services for LD students, advanced placement, accelerated degree program, distance learning, summer session for credit, part-time degree program, adult/continuing education programs.

Entrance Requirements: Options: electronic application, deferred admission, international baccalaureate accepted. Required: high school transcript, interview. Entrance: minimally difficult. Application deadline: Rolling. Notification: continuous. SAT Reasoning Test deadline: 10/31.

Collegiate Environment: Orientation program.

■ FAITH THEOLOGICAL SEMINARY

529 Walker Ave.
Baltimore, MD 21212
Tel: (410)323-6211
Fax: (410)323-6331
E-mail: sjwood@faiththeological.org
Web Site: www.faiththeological.org/

Description: Independent, comprehensive, coed, affiliated with Christian non-denominational. Awards bachelor's, master's, and doctoral degrees. Setting: urban campus. Academic area with the most degrees conferred: theology and religious vocations.

Entrance Requirements: Required: essay, high school transcript, 2 recommendations, photos. Recommended: interview. Required for some: interview.

Costs Per Year: Application fee: $50. Tuition: $4800 full-time, $200 per hour part-time. Mandatory fees: $280 full-time.

■ FREDERICK COMMUNITY COLLEGE

7932 Opossumtown Pke.
Frederick, MD 21702-2097
Tel: (301)846-2400
E-mail: admissions@frederick.edu
Web Site: www.frederick.edu/

Description: State and locally supported, 2-year, coed. Awards certificates, transfer associate, and terminal associate degrees. Founded 1957. Setting: 100-acre small town campus with easy access to Baltimore and Washington, DC. Endowment: $4 million. Total enrollment: 6,233. Faculty: 522 (97 full-time, 425 part-time). Student-undergrad faculty ratio is 12:1. Full-time: 2,359 students, 53% women, 47% men. Part-time: 3,874 students, 62% women, 38% men. 1% from out-of-state. 50% 25 or older. Retention: 45% of full-time freshmen returned the following year. Core. Calendar: semesters. Academic remediation for entering students, ESL program, services for LD students, advanced placement, freshman honors college, honors program, independent study, distance learning, summer session for credit, part-time degree program, adult/continuing education programs, co-op programs and internships. Off campus study at Hood College, Mount Saint Mary's College. Study abroad program. ROTC: Army (c).

Entrance Requirements: Open admission except for allied health program clinical portions. Option: electronic application. Recommended: high school transcript. Entrance: noncompetitive. Application deadline: Rolling. Notification: continuous. SAT Reasoning Test deadline: 9/1. SAT Subject Test deadline: 9/1. Transfer credits accepted: Yes.

Collegiate Environment: Orientation program. Drama-theater group, student-run newspaper. Social organizations: 30 open to all. Major annual events: Spring Fling, Welcome Back Lunch/Activities, free food events. Student services: personal-psychological counseling, women's center. Campus security: 24-hour emergency response devices and patrols, late night transport-escort service. FCC Library with 40,000 books, 2,400 microform titles, 5,150 serials, an OPAC, and a Web page. 230 computers available on campus for general student use. A campuswide network can be accessed from off-campus. Students can access the following: online class registration. Staffed computer lab on campus provides training in use of computers, software, and the Internet.

Community Environment: See Hood College.

■ FROSTBURG STATE UNIVERSITY

101 Braddock Rd.
Frostburg, MD 21532-1099
Tel: (301)687-4000
Fax: (301)687-7074
E-mail: fsuadmissions@frostburg.edu
Web Site: www.frostburg.edu/

Description: State-supported, comprehensive, coed. Part of University System of Maryland. Awards bachelor's, master's, and doctoral degrees and post-master's certificates. Founded 1898. Setting: 260-acre small town campus with easy access to Baltimore and Washington, DC. Endowment: $14.7 million. Educational spending for the previous fiscal year: $6165 per student. Total enrollment: 5,421. Faculty: 378 (245 full-time, 133 part-time). Student-undergrad faculty ratio is 17:1. 3,951 applied, 59% were admitted. 11% from top 10% of their high school class, 31% from top quarter, 66% from top half. Full-time: 4,253 students, 48% women, 52% men. Part-time: 378 students, 57% women, 43% men. Students come from 31 states and territories, 41 other countries, 8% from out-of-state. 0.1% American Indian or Alaska Native, non-Hispanic/Latino; 3% Hispanic/Latino; 25% African American, non-Hispanic/Latino; 1% Asian, non-Hispanic/Latino; 0.3% Native Hawaiian or other Pacific Islander, non-Hispanic/Latino; 1% international. 8% 25 or older, 32% live on campus, 10% transferred in. Retention: 72% of full-time freshmen returned the following year. Academic areas with the most degrees conferred: business/marketing; psychology; education. Core. Calendar: semesters. Services for LD students, advanced placement, freshman honors college, honors program, independent study, distance learning, double major, summer session for credit, part-time degree program, adult/continuing education programs, co-op programs and internships, graduate courses open to undergrads. Off campus study at Cooperative Education Program, Frostburg Programs at USM Hagerstown. Study abroad program.

Entrance Requirements: Options: electronic application, early admission. Required: high school transcript, minimum 2 high school GPA, SAT or ACT. Recommended: interview. Required for some: essay. Entrance: moderately difficult. Application deadlines: 2/15, 2/30 for nonresidents. Transfer credits accepted: Yes.

Costs Per Year: Application fee: $30. State resident tuition: $5630 full-time, $233 per credit part-time. Nonresident tuition: $16,278 full-time, $457 per credit part-time. Mandatory fees: $2098 full-time, $96 per credit part-time, $25 per term part-time. Full-time tuition and fees vary according to location. Part-time tuition and fees vary according to course load and location. College room and board: $7990. College room only: $3762. Room and board charges vary according to board plan and housing facility.

Collegiate Environment: Drama-theater group, choral group, marching band, student-run newspaper, radio station. Social organizations: 80 open to all; national fraternities, national sororities; 10% of eligible men and 10% of eligible women are members. Most popular organizations: Student Government Association, Black Student Association, Campus Activities Board, Residence Hall Association, University Programming Council. Major annual events: Homecoming, Parents' Weekend, Greek Week. Student services: health clinic, personal-psychological counseling, women's center. Campus security: 24-hour emergency response devices and patrols, student patrols, late night transport-escort service, controlled dormitory access, bicycle patrols. 1,700 college housing spaces available; 1,529 were occupied in 2012-13. No special consideration for freshman housing applicants. Options: coed, men-only, women-only housing available. Lewis J. Ort Library with 345,691 books, 450,771 microform titles, 3,899 serials, 29,331 audiovisual materials, an OPAC, and a Web page. Operations spending for the previous fiscal year: $728,961. 577 computers available on campus for general student use. Computer purchase/lease plans available. A campuswide network can be accessed from student residence rooms and from off campus. Students can access the following: online class registration. Staffed computer lab on campus (open 24 hours a day) provides training in use of computers, software, and the Internet.

Community Environment: The state university, in the City of Frostburg (population 7,958) is located in the mountains of western Maryland at an elevation of 2,200 feet. There are nearby state parks and winter sports activities including ice skating, skiing, and sleighing.

■ **GARRETT COLLEGE**
687 Mosser Rd.
McHenry, MD 21541
Tel: (301)387-3000; Free: 866-55-GARRETT
Fax: (301)387-3055
E-mail: admissions@garrettcollege.edu
Web Site: www.garrettcollege.edu/
Description: State and locally supported, 2-year, coed. Awards certificates, transfer associate, and terminal associate degrees. Founded 1966. Setting: 62-acre rural campus. Educational spending for the previous fiscal year: $6839 per student. Total enrollment: 873. Faculty: 81 (22 full-time, 59 part-time). Student-undergrad faculty ratio is 17:1. 1,463 applied, 90% were admitted. 3% from top 10% of their high school class, 24% from top quarter, 59% from top half. Full-time: 687 students, 51% women, 49% men. Part-time: 186 students, 56% women, 44% men. 0.2% American Indian or Alaska Native, non-Hispanic/Latino; 3% Hispanic/Latino; 23% African American, non-Hispanic/Latino; 0.3% Asian, non-Hispanic/Latino; 0.5% Native Hawaiian or other Pacific Islander, non-Hispanic/Latino; 2% international. 19% 25 or older, 19% live on campus, 6% transferred in. Core. Calendar: semesters. Academic remediation for entering students, services for LD students, advanced placement, honors program, independent study, distance learning, double major, summer session for credit, part-time degree program, external degree program, adult/continuing education programs, co-op programs and internships.
Entrance Requirements: Open admission. Options: early admission, deferred admission. Required: high school transcript. Recommended: SAT or ACT. Entrance: noncompetitive. Application deadlines: Rolling, Rolling for nonresidents. Notification: continuous, continuous for nonresidents. Transfer credits accepted: Yes.
Costs Per Year: Application fee: $0. Area resident tuition: $2632 full-time, $94 per credit hour part-time. State resident tuition: $6048 full-time, $216 per credit hour part-time. Nonresident tuition: $7140 full-time, $255 per credit hour part-time. Mandatory fees: $758 full-time, $26 per credit hour part-time, $15. Full-time tuition and fees vary according to reciprocity agreements. Part-time tuition and fees vary according to reciprocity agreements. College room and board: $7640. College room only: $5400. Room and board charges vary according to board plan and housing facility.
Collegiate Environment: Orientation program. Drama-theater group. Social organizations: 2 open to all. Most popular organizations: SGA, Theatre Club. Major annual events: Orientation, Halloween Costume Party/Dance, Spirit Week. Student services: health clinic, personal-psychological counseling. Campus security: 24-hour emergency response devices and patrols, controlled dormitory access. 177 college housing spaces available; all were occupied in 2012-13. No special consideration for freshman housing applicants. Option: coed housing available. Learning Resource Center with 56,588 books, 73 serials, 3,397 audiovisual materials, an OPAC, and a Web page. 48 computers available on campus for general student use. A campuswide network can be accessed from off-campus. Staffed computer lab on campus.

Community Environment: Garrett County is a rural area of approximately 30,000 year-round inhabitants, most of whom are employed in small business, education, agriculture and tourism. It is also a four-season resort area with seasonal swells in population. The natural resources of the region are conducive to the college's three signature programs: Adventure sports, Agricultural Management, and Natural Resources and Wildlife Technology.

■ **GOUCHER COLLEGE**
1021 Dulaney Valley Rd.
Baltimore, MD 21204-2794
Tel: (410)337-6000; Free: 800-468-2437
Fax: (410)337-6236
E-mail: admissions@goucher.edu
Web Site: www.goucher.edu/
Description: Independent, comprehensive, coed. Awards bachelor's and master's degrees. Founded 1885. Setting: 287-acre suburban campus with easy access to Baltimore and Washington, DC. Endowment: $183.7 million. Research spending for the previous fiscal year: $208,470. Educational spending for the previous fiscal year: $16,080 per student. Total enrollment: 2,254. Faculty: 218 (135 full-time, 83 part-time). Student-undergrad faculty ratio is 9:1. 3,615 applied, 72% were admitted. 26% from top 10% of their high school class, 57% from top quarter, 87% from top half. 2 valedictorians. Full-time: 1,446 students, 67% women, 33% men. Part-time: 38 students, 53% women, 47% men. Students come from 46 states and territories, 49 other countries, 73% from out-of-state. 0.3% American Indian or Alaska Native, non-Hispanic/Latino; 7% Hispanic/Latino; 9% African American, non-Hispanic/Latino; 3% Asian, non-Hispanic/Latino; 0.2% Native Hawaiian or other Pacific Islander, non-Hispanic/Latino; 3% international. 2% 25 or older, 86% live on campus, 3% transferred in. Retention: 84% of full-time freshmen returned the following year. Academic areas with the most degrees conferred: social sciences; psychology; visual and performing arts; communication/journalism; history. Core. Calendar: semesters. Services for LD students, advanced placement, self-designed majors, independent study, distance learning, double major, summer session for credit, part-time degree program, adult/continuing education programs, internships, graduate courses open to undergrads. Off campus study at Johns Hopkins University, Morgan State University, Maryland Institute, College of Art, Loyola College, Towson University, College of Notre Dame of Maryland University, Coppin State, Stevenson University, University of Maryland Baltimore County, University of Baltimore, Peabody Institute. Study abroad program. ROTC: Army (c), Air Force (c).
Entrance Requirements: Options: electronic application, early admission, early decision, early action, deferred admission, international baccalaureate accepted. Required: essay, high school transcript. Recommended: 3 recommendations, interview. Entrance: moderately difficult. Application deadlines: 2/1, 11/15 for early decision plan 1, 1/15 for early decision plan 2, 12/1 for early action. Notification: 4/1, 12/15 for early decision plan 1, 2/15 for early decision plan 2, 2/1 for early action. Transfer credits accepted: Yes. Applicants placed on waiting list: 201. Wait-listed applicants offered admission: 20. Early decision applicants: 83. Early decision applicants admitted: 54. Early action applicants: 1,635. Early action applicants admitted: 1,292.
Costs Per Year: Application fee: $55. Comprehensive fee: $50,252 includes full-time tuition ($38,462), mandatory fees ($622), and college room and board ($11,168). College room only: $6664. Room and board charges vary according to board plan and housing facility. Part-time tuition: $1282 per credit hour.
Collegiate Environment: Orientation program. Drama-theater group, choral group, student-run newspaper, radio station. Social organizations: 60 open to all. Most popular organizations: Student Government Association, The Quindecim, Earthworks / Ag Co-op / Gear (Environmental action clubs), Hillel, Umoja: The Black Student Union. Major annual events: Opening Celebration, GIG (Get Into Goucher Day), Gala. Student services: health clinic, personal-psychological counseling. Campus security: 24-hour emergency response devices and patrols, late night transport-escort service, controlled dormitory access, e2 campus alerts. 1,210 college housing spaces available; 1,201 were occupied in 2012-13. Freshmen guaranteed college housing. On-campus residence required through sophomore year. Options: coed, men-only, women-only housing available. Goucher College Library with 286,927 books, 22,078 microform titles, 32,638 serials, 6,967 audiovisual materials, an OPAC, and a Web page. Operations spending for the previous fiscal year: $2.3 million. 200 computers available on campus for general student use. Computer purchase/lease plans available. A campuswide network can be accessed from student residence rooms and from off campus. Students can access the following: online class registra-

tion, transcripts, financial aid information, billing, ePortfolios, academic progress reports, study abroad plan. Staffed computer lab on campus (open 24 hours a day) provides training in use of computers, software, and the Internet.

Community Environment: Goucher is located on 287 wooded acres in suburban Towson, seat of Baltimore County. The college is 20 minutes away from downtown Baltimore, an hour's drive from Washington, D.C., and 25 miles from the state capital of Annapolis, on the Chesapeake Bay. There are extensive walking, riding, and running trails that help create a small college atmosphere.

■ **HAGERSTOWN COMMUNITY COLLEGE**

11400 Robinwood Dr.
Hagerstown, MD 21742
Tel: (301)790-2800
Fax: (301)739-0737
E-mail: admissions@hagerstowncc.edu
Web Site: www.hagerstowncc.edu/

Description: State and locally supported, 2-year, coed. Awards certificates, transfer associate, and terminal associate degrees. Founded 1946. Setting: 319-acre suburban campus with easy access to Baltimore and Washington, DC. Total enrollment: 5,005. Faculty: 265 (80 full-time, 185 part-time). Student-undergrad faculty ratio is 18:1. Full-time: 1,382 students, 51% women, 49% men. Part-time: 3,623 students, 66% women, 34% men. Students come from 11 states and territories, 3 other countries, 20% from out-of-state. 0.4% American Indian or Alaska Native, non-Hispanic/Latino; 4% Hispanic/Latino; 10% African American, non-Hispanic/Latino; 2% Asian, non-Hispanic/Latino; 0.2% Native Hawaiian or other Pacific Islander, non-Hispanic/Latino; 0.3% international. 39% 25 or older, 7% transferred in. Retention: 62% of full-time freshmen returned the following year. Core. Calendar: semesters. Academic remediation for entering students, ESL program, services for LD students, advanced placement, accelerated degree program, honors program, independent study, distance learning, summer session for credit, part-time degree program, adult/continuing education programs, co-op programs and internships. Off campus study.

Entrance Requirements: Open admission open admission except for nursing (RN), radiological technology, paramedic emergency services (EMT) and practical nursing (LPN) programs. Options: electronic application, early admission, deferred admission. Required for some: high school transcript, selective admissions for RN, LPN, EMT, and radiography programs. Entrance: noncompetitive. Application deadlines: Rolling, Rolling for nonresidents. Notification: continuous, continuous for nonresidents. Transfer credits accepted: Yes.

Collegiate Environment: Orientation program. Drama-theater group, choral group, student-run newspaper. Social organizations: 34 open to all; Phi Theta Kappa. Most popular organizations: Phi Theta Kappa, Robinwood Players Theater Club, Association of Nursing Students, Radiography Club, Art and Design Club. Student services: personal-psychological counseling. Campus security: 24-hour patrols, student patrols. College housing not available. William Brish Library with an OPAC and a Web page. 650 computers available on campus for general student use. A campuswide network can be accessed from off-campus. Students can access the following: online class registration. Staffed computer lab on campus.

Community Environment: In the heart of Cumberland Valley, Hagerstown is manufacturing city nestled at an intersection of highway interstates and rail transportation. All forms of commercial transportation are available. Recreational facilities are numerous. Points of interest are Antietam Battlefield, Old Ft. Frederick State Park, Hager House, and Washington County Museum of Fine Arts. Special events include the annual Halloween Mummer's Parade.

■ **HARFORD COMMUNITY COLLEGE**

401 Thomas Run Rd.
Bel Air, MD 21015-1698
Tel: (443)412-2000
E-mail: sendinfo@harford.edu
Web Site: www.harford.edu/

Description: State and locally supported, 2-year, coed. Awards certificates, diplomas, transfer associate, and terminal associate degrees. Founded 1957. Setting: 331-acre small town campus with easy access to Baltimore. Total enrollment: 7,226. Faculty: 391 (106 full-time, 285 part-time). Student-undergrad faculty ratio is 22:1. Full-time: 2,830 students, 52% women, 48% men. Part-time: 4,396 students, 64% women, 36% men. 0.3% American Indian or Alaska Native, non-Hispanic/Latino; 4% Hispanic/Latino; 15%

African American, non-Hispanic/Latino; 2% Asian, non-Hispanic/Latino; 0.2% Native Hawaiian or other Pacific Islander, non-Hispanic/Latino; 1% international. 32% 25 or older. Core. Calendar: semesters. Academic remediation for entering students, ESL program, services for LD students, advanced placement, self-designed majors, honors program, independent study, distance learning, double major, summer session for credit, part-time degree program, adult/continuing education programs, co-op programs and internships. Study abroad program.

Entrance Requirements: Open admission. Options: electronic application, international baccalaureate accepted. Entrance: noncompetitive. Application deadline: Rolling. Transfer credits accepted: Yes.

Costs Per Year: Application fee: $0. Area resident tuition: $2610 full-time, $87 per credit hour part-time. State resident tuition: $5220 full-time, $174 per credit hour part-time. Nonresident tuition: $7830 full-time, $261 per credit hour part-time. Mandatory fees: $313 full-time.

Collegiate Environment: Orientation program. Drama-theater group, choral group, student-run newspaper, radio station. Social organizations: 32 open to all. Most popular organizations: Student Association, Paralegal Club, Multi-National Students Association, Student Nurses Association, Gamers Guild. Major annual events: Owlnet, Spring Welcome Back. Student services: personal-psychological counseling. Campus security: 24-hour patrols, late night transport-escort service. Harford Community College Library with 52,069 books, 309 microform titles, 129 serials, 4,224 audiovisual materials, an OPAC, and a Web page. 267 computers available on campus for general student use. A campuswide network can be accessed from off-campus. Students can access the following: online class registration. Staffed computer lab on campus.

■ **HOOD COLLEGE**

401 Rosemont Ave.
Frederick, MD 21701-8575
Tel: (301)663-3131; Free: 800-922-1599
E-mail: admissions@hood.edu
Web Site: www.hood.edu/

Description: Independent, comprehensive, coed. Awards bachelor's and master's degrees (also offers adult program with significant enrollment not reflected in profile). Founded 1893. Setting: 50-acre suburban campus with easy access to Baltimore and Washington, DC. Endowment: $62.1 million. Research spending for the previous fiscal year: $235,964. Educational spending for the previous fiscal year: $9316 per student. Total enrollment: 2,422. Faculty: 262 (88 full-time, 174 part-time). Student-undergrad faculty ratio is 12:1. 1,788 applied, 77% were admitted. 21% from top 10% of their high school class, 52% from top quarter, 82% from top half. 3 valedictorians. Full-time: 1,281 students, 66% women, 34% men. Part-time: 153 students, 69% women, 31% men. Students come from 32 states and territories, 23 other countries, 23% from out-of-state. 0.1% American Indian or Alaska Native, non-Hispanic/Latino; 7% Hispanic/Latino; 12% African American, non-Hispanic/Latino; 3% Asian, non-Hispanic/Latino; 0.1% Native Hawaiian or other Pacific Islander, non-Hispanic/Latino; 3% international. 11% 25 or older, 54% live on campus, 9% transferred in. Retention: 77% of full-time freshmen returned the following year. Academic areas with the most degrees conferred: education; business/marketing; visual and performing arts; biological/life sciences; social sciences. Core. Calendar: semesters. Academic remediation for entering students, ESL program, services for LD students, advanced placement, self-designed majors, honors program, independent study, double major, summer session for credit, part-time degree program, internships, graduate courses open to undergrads. Off campus study at Washington Semester Program, Public Leadership Education Network (PLEN), Council of International Education Exchange (CIEE), Duke University Marine Science Consort Education (MSEC). Study abroad program. ROTC: Army.

Entrance Requirements: Options: electronic application, early decision, early action, deferred admission, international baccalaureate accepted. Required: essay, high school transcript, minimum 2 high school GPA, 2 recommendations, SAT or ACT. Recommended: interview. Entrance: moderately difficult. Application deadlines: 8/15, 8/15 for nonresidents, 11/15 for early decision plan 1, 12/15 for early decision plan 2, 12/1 for early action. Notification: continuous, continuous for nonresidents, 12/1 for early decision plan 1, 1/1 for early decision plan 2, 12/15 for early action. SAT Reasoning Test deadline: 8/1. Transfer credits accepted: Yes. Applicants placed on waiting list: 7. Wait-listed applicants offered admission: 0. Early decision applicants: 31. Early decision applicants admitted: 12. Early action applicants: 1,119. Early action applicants admitted: 963.

Costs Per Year: Application fee: $35. Comprehensive fee: $43,210 includes

full-time tuition ($31,840), mandatory fees ($460), and college room and board ($10,910). College room only: $5700. Room and board charges vary according to board plan and housing facility. Part-time tuition: $920 per credit hour. Part-time mandatory fees: $150 per term.

Collegiate Environment: Orientation program. Drama-theater group, choral group, student-run newspaper, radio station. Social organizations: 59 open to all. Most popular organizations: Education Club, Black Student Union, Campus Activities Board, International Club, Hood Today (newspaper). Major annual events: Policies for Dollars, May Madness / Crabfest, Messiah Holiday Weekend. Student services: health clinic, personal-psychological counseling. Campus security: 24-hour emergency response devices and patrols, late night transport-escort service, controlled dormitory access. 828 college housing spaces available; 777 were occupied in 2012-13. Freshmen guaranteed college housing. On-campus residence required through sophomore year. Options: coed, women-only housing available. Beneficial-Hodson Library and Information Technology Center with 211,450 books, 734,811 microform titles, 56,500 serials, 6,459 audiovisual materials, an OPAC, and a Web page. Operations spending for the previous fiscal year: $809,417. 283 computers available on campus for general student use. Computer purchase/lease plans available. A campuswide network can be accessed from student residence rooms and from off campus. Students can access the following: online class registration. Staffed computer lab on campus provides training in use of computers, software, and the Internet.

Community Environment: Hood College is located on almost 50 acres near downtown Frederick, Maryland, a community of approximately 49,000. The campus is 45 miles west of Baltimore and an equal distance northwest of Washington D.C. The proximity of the Hood campus to these major metropolitan areas increases the opportunities open to students to participate in social and cultural activities, to complete internships, and to explore prominent research facilities.

■ HOWARD COMMUNITY COLLEGE

10901 Little Patuxent Pky.
Columbia, MD 21044-3197
Tel: (443)518-4800
E-mail: admissions@howardcc.edu
Web Site: www.howardcc.edu/

Description: State and locally supported, 2-year, coed. Awards certificates, transfer associate, and terminal associate degrees. Founded 1966. Setting: 122-acre suburban campus with easy access to Baltimore and Washington, DC. Total enrollment: 10,152. Faculty: 724 (173 full-time, 551 part-time). Student-undergrad faculty ratio is 19:1. 0.3% American Indian or Alaska Native, non-Hispanic/Latino; 9% Hispanic/Latino; 28% African American, non-Hispanic/Latino; 13% Asian, non-Hispanic/Latino; 0.3% Native Hawaiian or other Pacific Islander, non-Hispanic/Latino. Retention: 59% of full-time freshmen returned the following year. Core. Calendar: semesters. Academic remediation for entering students, ESL program, services for LD students, advanced placement, freshman honors college, honors program, distance learning, double major, summer session for credit, part-time degree program, external degree program, adult/continuing education programs, co-op programs. Off campus study. Study abroad program.

Entrance Requirements: Open admission except for nursing, cardiovascular technology, radiologic technology, Rouse scholars program, EMT-P. Options: electronic application, early admission, deferred admission, international baccalaureate accepted. Required for some: essay, high school transcript, 2 recommendations, SAT or ACT. Entrance: noncompetitive. Application deadlines: Rolling, Rolling for nonresidents. Notification: continuous, continuous for nonresidents. Transfer credits accepted: Yes.

Costs Per Year: Application fee: $25. Area resident tuition: $3690 full-time, $123 per credit hour part-time. State resident tuition: $6180 full-time, $206 per credit hour part-time. Nonresident tuition: $7530 full-time, $251 per credit hour part-time. Mandatory fees: $618 full-time, $20.60 per credit hour part-time.

Collegiate Environment: Orientation program. Drama-theater group, choral group, student-run newspaper, radio station. Social organizations: 25 open to all. Most popular organizations: Phi Theta Kappa, Nursing Club, Black Leadership Organization, student newspaper, Student Government Association. Major annual events: Fall Cookout, Spring Fling, Weekly Block Time. Student services: personal-psychological counseling. Campus security: 24-hour emergency response devices and patrols, late night transport-escort service. College housing not available. Howard Community College Library with 45,707 books, 39,910 serials, 2,636 audiovisual materials, an OPAC, and a Web page.

Community Environment: Columbia, a planned city of 100,000, was

designed as a community of village centers. Small lakes, parks, and bicycle paths add charm and access to the outdoors. Situated between two major cities, Baltimore and Washington, there is quick access to transportation facilities at airports and rail stations. The Columbia Mall provides major shopping facilities, and each village center complements the mall with supermarkets and convenience stores. The college serves as a cultural center in the county and hosts a variety of concerts, stage productions and cultural activities in its theatre.

■ ITT TECHNICAL INSTITUTE (HANOVER)

7030 Dorsey Rd.
Ste. 100
Hanover, MD 21076
Tel: (410)694-4700; Free: 877-243-6993
Web Site: www.itt-tech.edu/

Description: Proprietary, 4-year, coed. Awards associate and bachelor's degrees.

Entrance Requirements: Entrance: minimally difficult.

■ ITT TECHNICAL INSTITUTE (OWINGS MILLS)

11301 Red Run Blvd.
Owings Mills, MD 21117
Tel: (443)394-7115; Free: 877-411-6782
Web Site: www.itt-tech.edu/

Description: Proprietary, primarily 2-year, coed. Awards terminal associate and bachelor's degrees. Founded 2005.

Entrance Requirements: Entrance: minimally difficult.

■ THE JOHNS HOPKINS UNIVERSITY

3400 N Charles St.
Baltimore, MD 21218-2699
Tel: (410)516-8000
Fax: (410)516-6025
E-mail: gotojhu@jhu.edu
Web Site: www.jhu.edu/

Description: Independent, university, coed. Awards bachelor's, master's, and doctoral degrees and post-master's certificates. Founded 1876. Setting: 140-acre urban campus with easy access to Baltimore and Washington, DC. Endowment: $2.7 billion. Total enrollment: 7,221. Faculty: 609 (505 full-time, 104 part-time). Student-undergrad faculty ratio is 13:1. 20,502 applied, 18% were admitted. 84% from top 10% of their high school class, 99% from top quarter, 100% from top half. Full-time: 5,164 students, 48% women, 52% men. Part-time: 28 students, 32% women, 68% men. Students come from 53 states and territories, 71 other countries, 88% from out-of-state. 0.1% American Indian or Alaska Native, non-Hispanic/Latino; 10% Hispanic/Latino; 5% African American, non-Hispanic/Latino; 19% Asian, non-Hispanic/Latino; 0.1% Native Hawaiian or other Pacific Islander, non-Hispanic/Latino; 9% international. 1% 25 or older, 54% live on campus, 1% transferred in. Retention: 97% of full-time freshmen returned the following year. Academic areas with the most degrees conferred: health professions and related sciences; engineering; biological/life sciences. Core. Calendar: 4-1-4. Services for LD students, advanced placement, self-designed majors, honors program, independent study, double major, summer session for credit, part-time degree program, adult/continuing education programs, internships, graduate courses open to undergrads. Off campus study at Academic Cooperative Program: University of Maryland, Baltimore County; Loyola College; Towson University; Morgan State University; College of Notre Dame of Maryland; Stevenson University; Goucher College; and Maryland Institute College of Art. Study abroad program. ROTC: Army, Air Force (c).

Entrance Requirements: Options: electronic application, early admission, early decision, deferred admission, international baccalaureate accepted. Required: essay, high school transcript, 2 recommendations, SAT or ACT. Recommended: 3 recommendations, interview, SAT Subject Tests, Students applying to engineering are strongly encouraged to submit the SAT II Math 2. Entrance: most difficult. Application deadlines: 1/1, 11/1 for early decision. Notification: 4/1, 12/15 for early decision. SAT Reasoning Test deadline: 1/1. SAT Subject Test deadline: 1/1. Transfer credits accepted: Yes. Applicants placed on waiting list: 2,730. Wait-listed applicants offered admission: 1. Early decision applicants: 1,444. Early decision applicants admitted: 554.

Costs Per Year: Application fee: $70. Comprehensive fee: $59,802 includes full-time tuition ($45,470), mandatory fees ($500), and college room and board ($13,832). College room only: $7920. Room and board charges vary according to board plan and housing facility. Part-time tuition: $1515 per credit hour.

Collegiate Environment: Orientation program. Drama-theater group, choral group, student-run newspaper, radio station. Social organizations: 350 open to all; national fraternities, national sororities; 19% of eligible men and 22% of eligible women are members. Most popular organizations: The Outdoors Club, JHU Tutorial Project, The Barn Stormers (theater group), Inter-Asian Council, News-letter (student paper). Major annual events: Spring Fair, Homecoming, Family Weekend. Student services: health clinic, personal-psychological counseling. Campus security: 24-hour emergency response devices and patrols, student patrols, late night transport-escort service, controlled dormitory access, CCTV monitoring of public areas. 2,800 college housing spaces available; all were occupied in 2012-13. Freshmen guaranteed college housing. On-campus residence required through sophomore year. Option: coed housing available. Milton S. Eisenhower Library plus 6 others with 3.7 million books, 4.4 million microform titles, 171,000 serials, 44,164 audiovisual materials, an OPAC, and a Web page. 200 computers available on campus for general student use. Computer purchase/lease plans available. A campuswide network can be accessed from student residence rooms and from off campus. Students can access the following: online class registration. Staffed computer lab on campus (open 24 hours a day) provides training in use of computers, software, and the Internet.

Community Environment: See University of Baltimore.

■ **KAPLAN UNIVERSITY, HAGERSTOWN CAMPUS**
18618 Crestwood Dr.
Hagerstown, MD 21742-2797
Tel: (301)739-2670; Free: 800-527-5268
Fax: (301)791-7661
Web Site: www.ku-hagerstown.com/
Description: Proprietary, primarily 2-year, coed. Administratively affiliated with Kaplan Higher Education. Awards certificates, diplomas, terminal associate, and bachelor's degrees. Founded 1938. Setting: 8-acre small town campus. 3% live on campus.

■ **LOYOLA UNIVERSITY MARYLAND**
4501 N Charles St.
Baltimore, MD 21210-2699
Tel: (410)617-2000; Free: 800-221-9107
Fax: (410)323-2768
Web Site: www.loyola.edu/
Description: Independent Roman Catholic (Jesuit), university, coed. Awards bachelor's, master's, and doctoral degrees and post-master's certificates. Founded 1852. Setting: 89-acre urban campus with easy access to Washington, DC. Endowment: $159.3 million. Research spending for the previous fiscal year: $1.4 million. Educational spending for the previous fiscal year: $31,538 per student. Total enrollment: 5,978. Faculty: 556 (350 full-time, 206 part-time). Student-undergrad faculty ratio is 12:1. 12,664 applied, 65% were admitted. 25% from top 10% of their high school class, 59% from top quarter, 85% from top half. Full-time: 3,875 students, 61% women, 39% men. Part-time: 42 students, 55% women, 45% men. Students come from 38 states and territories, 61 other countries, 82% from out-of-state. 0.2% American Indian or Alaska Native, non-Hispanic/Latino; 8% Hispanic/Latino; 5% African American, non-Hispanic/Latino; 3% Asian, non-Hispanic/Latino; 0% Native Hawaiian or other Pacific Islander, non-Hispanic/Latino; 1% international. 1% 25 or older, 82% live on campus, 2% transferred in. Retention: 88% of full-time freshmen returned the following year. Academic areas with the most degrees conferred: business/marketing; communication/journalism; social sciences; psychology. Core. Calendar: semesters. Services for LD students, advanced placement, accelerated degree program, honors program, independent study, double major, summer session for credit, part-time degree program, co-op programs and internships, graduate courses open to undergrads. Off campus study at Johns Hopkins University; College of Notre Dame of Maryland; Goucher College; Towson State University; Morgan State University; Peabody Conservatory of Music of The Johns Hopkins University; Maryland Institute, College of Art. Study abroad program. ROTC: Army, Air Force (c).
Entrance Requirements: Options: electronic application, early admission, early action, deferred admission, international baccalaureate accepted. Required: essay, high school transcript. Entrance: moderately difficult. Application deadlines: 1/15, 1/15 for nonresidents, 11/1 for early action. Notification: 4/1, 4/1 for nonresidents, 1/15 for early action. Transfer credits accepted: Yes. Applicants placed on waiting list: 1,692. Wait-listed applicants offered admission: 177. Early action applicants: 5,131. Early action applicants admitted: 4,910.

Costs Per Year: Application fee: $50. One-time mandatory fee: $165. Comprehensive fee: $54,550 includes full-time tuition ($41,030), mandatory fees ($1400), and college room and board ($12,120). College room only: $9120. Full-time tuition and fees vary according to course load. Room and board charges vary according to housing facility. Part-time tuition: $665 per credit. Part-time mandatory fees: $25 per term. Part-time tuition and fees vary according to course load.
Collegiate Environment: Orientation program. Drama-theater group, choral group, student-run newspaper, radio station. Social organizations: 194 open to all. Most popular organizations: Student Government Association, Resident Affairs Council (RAC), Relay for Life, Resident Assistants (RA), The Evergreens. Major annual events: Loyolapalooza, Relay for Life, Athletics (Basketball, Soccer and Lacrosse). Student services: health clinic, personal-psychological counseling, women's center. Campus security: 24-hour emergency response devices and patrols, late night transport-escort service, controlled dormitory access. 3,281 college housing spaces available; 3,217 were occupied in 2012-13. Freshmen guaranteed college housing. Option: coed housing available. Loyola/Notre Dame Library plus 1 other with 1.1 million books, 691 microform titles, 56,888 serials, 19,086 audiovisual materials, an OPAC, and a Web page. Operations spending for the previous fiscal year: $2.9 million. 690 computers available on campus for general student use. Computer purchase/lease plans available. A campuswide network can be accessed from student residence rooms and from off campus. Students can access the following: online class registration, entire campus has unlimited wireless access. Staffed computer lab on campus provides training in use of computers, software, and the Internet.

■ **MAPLE SPRINGS BAPTIST BIBLE COLLEGE AND SEMINARY**
4130 Belt Rd.
Capitol Heights, MD 20743
Tel: (301)736-3631
Fax: (301)735-6507
Web Site: www.msbbcs.edu/
Description: Independent Baptist, comprehensive, coed. Awards associate, bachelor's, master's, and doctoral degrees. Founded 1986. Setting: 1-acre suburban campus with easy access to Washington, DC. Research spending for the previous fiscal year: $4370. Total enrollment: 99. Faculty: 23 (3 full-time, 20 part-time). 2 applied, 100% were admitted. Full-time: 3 students, 67% women, 33% men. Part-time: 71 students, 55% women, 45% men. Students come from 3 states and territories, 32% from out-of-state. 0% American Indian or Alaska Native, non-Hispanic/Latino; 4% Hispanic/Latino; 96% African American, non-Hispanic/Latino; 0% Asian, non-Hispanic/Latino; 0% Native Hawaiian or other Pacific Islander, non-Hispanic/Latino; 0% international. 100% 25 or older, 0% transferred in. Retention: 75% of full-time freshmen returned the following year. Core. Calendar: semesters. Academic remediation for entering students, accelerated degree program, independent study, part-time degree program, external degree program, adult/continuing education programs, internships, graduate courses open to undergrads.
Entrance Requirements: Open admission. Option: deferred admission. Required: essay, high school transcript, 2 recommendations, interview, math and English placement examination for all new students who do not have college English and math grades of C or above. Entrance: minimally difficult. Application deadline: Rolling. Notification: continuous. Transfer credits accepted: Yes.
Costs Per Year: Application fee: $50. Tuition: $4470 full-time, $2230 per term part-time. Mandatory fees: $120 full-time, $165 per credit part-time, $60 per term part-time. Full-time tuition and fees vary according to degree level. Part-time tuition and fees vary according to degree level.
Collegiate Environment: Orientation program. Student-run newspaper. Campus security: 24-hour emergency response devices, part-time security personnel. College housing not available. Maple Springs Baptist Bible College and Seminary Library plus 1 other with 1,781 books, 37 serials, and 35 audiovisual materials. Operations spending for the previous fiscal year: $45,900.

■ **MARYLAND INSTITUTE COLLEGE OF ART**
1300 Mount Royal Ave.
Baltimore, MD 21217
Tel: (410)669-9200
Fax: (410)225-2337
E-mail: cgyland@mica.edu
Web Site: www.mica.edu/
Description: Independent, comprehensive, coed. Awards bachelor's and

master's degrees. Founded 1826. Setting: 16-acre urban campus with easy access to Washington, DC. Endowment: $62.9 million. Educational spending for the previous fiscal year: $12,829 per student. Total enrollment: 2,168. Faculty: 363 (147 full-time, 216 part-time). Student-undergrad faculty ratio is 9:1. 3,139 applied, 52% were admitted. 37% from top 10% of their high school class, 69% from top quarter, 90% from top half. Full-time: 1,809 students, 71% women, 29% men. Part-time: 18 students, 56% women, 44% men. Students come from 49 states and territories, 49 other countries, 77% from out-of-state. 0.3% American Indian or Alaska Native, non-Hispanic/Latino; 4% Hispanic/Latino; 5% African American, non-Hispanic/Latino; 12% Asian, non-Hispanic/Latino; 0.1% Native Hawaiian or other Pacific Islander, non-Hispanic/Latino; 7% international. 3% 25 or older, 42% live on campus, 5% transferred in. Retention: 85% of full-time freshmen returned the following year. Academic areas with the most degrees conferred: visual and performing arts; education. Core. Calendar: semesters. ESL program, services for LD students, advanced placement, accelerated degree program, self-designed majors, independent study, distance learning, double major, summer session for credit, adult/continuing education programs, internships. Off campus study at Association of Independent Colleges of Art and Design, Johns Hopkins University, Goucher College, University of Baltimore, Loyola University, Notre Dame College, Peabody Conservatory of Music of the Johns Hopkins University, and Towson University. Study abroad program. ROTC: Army (c).

Entrance Requirements: Options: early admission, early decision, deferred admission, international baccalaureate accepted. Required: essay, high school transcript, 3 recommendations, art portfolio, SAT or ACT. Recommended: interview. Entrance: very difficult. Application deadlines: 2/1, 11/29 for early decision. Notification: 3/6, 12/14 for early decision. Transfer credits accepted: Yes. Applicants placed on waiting list: 35. Wait-listed applicants offered admission: 7. Early decision applicants: 50. Early decision applicants admitted: 39.

Costs Per Year: Application fee: $60. One-time mandatory fee: $160. Comprehensive fee: $50,220 includes full-time tuition ($37,900), mandatory fees ($1440), and college room and board ($10,880). College room only: $8200. Room and board charges vary according to board plan and housing facility. Part-time tuition: $1580 per credit. Part-time mandatory fees: $720 per term.

Collegiate Environment: Orientation program. Drama-theater group, choral group, student-run radio station. Social organizations: 63 open to all. Most popular organizations: Soccer Club, Urban Gaming Club, Black Student Union, Students of Sustainability, National Art Educators Association. Major annual events: Halloween Party, Fashion Show, Midnight Breakfast. Student services: health clinic, personal-psychological counseling. Campus security: 24-hour emergency response devices and patrols, student patrols, late night transport-escort service, controlled dormitory access, self-defense education, 24-hour building security, safety awareness programs, campus patrols by city police. 840 college housing spaces available; 729 were occupied in 2012-13. Freshmen guaranteed college housing. Option: coed housing available. Decker Library and Media Resources Collection with 98,963 books, 354 serials, 5,729 audiovisual materials, an OPAC, and a Web page. Operations spending for the previous fiscal year: $897,373. 650 computers available on campus for general student use. A campuswide network can be accessed from student residence rooms and from off campus. Students can access the following: online class registration, campus Portal, online gallery space, network storage space, personal Web sites, online software training tutorials (Lynda.com), and Learning management system (Moodle). Staffed computer lab on campus provides training in use of computers, software, and the Internet.

Community Environment: See University of Baltimore.

■ **MCDANIEL COLLEGE**
2 College Hill
Westminster, MD 21157-4390
Tel: (410)848-7000; Free: 800-638-5005
Fax: (410)857-2729
E-mail: admissions@mcdaniel.edu
Web Site: www.mcdaniel.edu/
Description: Independent, comprehensive, coed. Awards bachelor's and master's degrees. Founded 1867. Setting: 160-acre suburban campus with easy access to Baltimore and Washington, DC. Endowment: $88.4 million. Research spending for the previous fiscal year: $57,092. Educational spending for the previous fiscal year: $12,072 per student. Total enrollment: 3,284. Faculty: 380 (103 full-time, 277 part-time). Student-undergrad faculty ratio is 11:1. 3,560 applied, 64% were admitted. 29% from top 10% of their high

school class, 54% from top quarter, 87% from top half. 1 National Merit Scholar, 1 class president, 18 valedictorians, 5 student government officers. Full-time: 1,610 students, 54% women, 46% men. Part-time: 40 students, 58% women, 43% men. Students come from 33 states and territories, 21 other countries, 36% from out-of-state. 1% American Indian or Alaska Native, non-Hispanic/Latino; 5% Hispanic/Latino; 12% African American, non-Hispanic/Latino; 4% Asian, non-Hispanic/Latino; 0% Native Hawaiian or other Pacific Islander, non-Hispanic/Latino; 0% international. 2% 25 or older, 84% live on campus, 3% transferred in. Retention: 82% of full-time freshmen returned the following year. Academic areas with the most degrees conferred: social sciences; business/marketing; psychology. Core. Calendar: 4-1-4. Academic remediation for entering students, services for LD students, advanced placement, self-designed majors, honors program, independent study, distance learning, double major, summer session for credit, part-time degree program, adult/continuing education programs, internships, graduate courses open to undergrads. Off campus study at Gallaudet, Washington Semester, Washington Center, Washington Institute, Philadelphia Center. Study abroad program. ROTC: Army.

Entrance Requirements: Options: electronic application, early admission, early action, deferred admission, international baccalaureate accepted. Required: essay, high school transcript, minimum 2.5 high school GPA, 2 recommendations, SAT or ACT, SAT Optional Plan for students who are in the top 10% of their class if their HS ranks; otherwise, a cumulative GPA of a 3.5 or higher. SAT Subject Tests considered if submitted. Recommended: interview. Required for some: interview. Entrance: moderately difficult. Application deadlines: 2/15, 2/5 for nonresidents, 12/1 for early action. Notification: 3/9, 3/9 for nonresidents, 12/21 for early action. SAT Reasoning Test deadline: 2/15. Transfer credits accepted: Yes. Applicants placed on waiting list: 34. Wait-listed applicants offered admission: 0. Early action applicants: 2,154. Early action applicants admitted: 1,194.

Costs Per Year: Application fee: $50. Comprehensive fee: $45,600 includes full-time tuition ($36,960) and college room and board ($8640). Full-time tuition varies according to course load. Room and board charges vary according to board plan and housing facility. Part-time tuition: $1155 per credit hour. Part-time tuition varies according to course load and reciprocity agreements.

Collegiate Environment: Orientation program. Drama-theater group, choral group, student-run newspaper, radio station. Social organizations: 90 open to all; national fraternities, national sororities, local fraternities, local sororities; 15% of eligible men and 17% of eligible women are members. Most popular organizations: Student Government Association, Black Student Union, International Club, Maryland State Legislature, Up 'til Dawn. Major annual events: Homecoming, Up 'til Dawn Finale Event, Spring Fling. Student services: health clinic, personal-psychological counseling. Campus security: 24-hour emergency response devices and patrols, late night transport-escort service, About half patrol force sworn as campus police. All are certified to US DOT First Responder standards. 1,397 college housing spaces available; 1,362 were occupied in 2012-13. Freshmen guaranteed college housing. On-campus residence required through junior year. Options: coed, men-only, women-only housing available. Hoover Library with 222,268 books, 1.4 million microform titles, 717 serials, 24,477 audiovisual materials, an OPAC, and a Web page. Operations spending for the previous fiscal year: $1.6 million. 320 computers available on campus for general student use. A campuswide network can be accessed from student residence rooms and from off campus. Students can access the following: online class registration, online billing summaries, financial aid letter, tax information. Staffed computer lab on campus provides training in use of computers, software, and the Internet.

■ **MONTGOMERY COLLEGE**
51 Mannakee St.
Rockville, MD 20850
Tel: (240)567-5000
E-mail: melissa.gregory@montgomerycollege.edu
Web Site: www.montgomerycollege.edu/
Description: State and locally supported, 2-year, coed. Awards certificates, transfer associate, and terminal associate degrees. Founded 1946. Setting: 333-acre suburban campus with easy access to Washington, DC. Endowment: $17.8 million. Educational spending for the previous fiscal year: $7034 per student. Total enrollment: 27,453. Faculty: 1,569 (541 full-time, 1,028 part-time). Student-undergrad faculty ratio is 18:1. 10,756 applied, 100% were admitted. Full-time: 9,888 students, 49% women, 51% men. Part-time: 17,565 students, 55% women, 45% men. Students come from 26 states and territories, 162 other countries, 3% from out-of-state. 0.3% American Indian

or Alaska Native, non-Hispanic/Latino; 20% Hispanic/Latino; 25% African American, non-Hispanic/Latino; 12% Asian, non-Hispanic/Latino; 0.3% Native Hawaiian or other Pacific Islander, non-Hispanic/Latino; 10% international. 31% 25 or older, 5% transferred in. Core. Calendar: semesters. Academic remediation for entering students, ESL program, services for LD students, advanced placement, accelerated degree program, honors program, independent study, distance learning, double major, summer session for credit, part-time degree program, external degree program, adult/continuing education programs, co-op programs and internships. Off campus study. Study abroad program. ROTC: Air Force (c).

Entrance Requirements: Open admission. Options: electronic application, early admission, deferred admission, international baccalaureate accepted. Recommended: high school transcript, interview. Entrance: noncompetitive. Application deadlines: Rolling, Rolling for nonresidents. Notification: continuous, continuous for nonresidents. Transfer credits accepted: Yes.

Costs Per Year: Application fee: $25. One-time mandatory fee: $25. Area resident tuition: $2688 full-time, $112 per credit part-time. State resident tuition: $5496 full-time, $229 per credit part-time. Nonresident tuition: $7536 full-time, $314 per credit part-time. Mandatory fees: $874 full-time, $36.40 per credit part-time. Full-time tuition and fees vary according to course load. Part-time tuition and fees vary according to course load.

Collegiate Environment: Orientation program. Drama-theater group, choral group, student-run newspaper. Social organizations: 136 open to all; 32% of eligible men and 30% of eligible women are members. Most popular organizations: Math Club, International Club, Anime Society Club, Animation & Video Game Club, Soccer, basketball, Rugby, Cricket, Tennis, Lacrosse and Swim Clubs. Major annual events: Welcome Week for New and Return Students, Student Academic Excellence Awards, Club Rush (club fair recruit members); Student Jobs Fair (Job opportunities open by employer company or organization). Student services: personal-psychological counseling, women's center. Campus security: 24-hour emergency response devices and patrols, late night transport-escort service. Montgomery College Library plus 1 other with 402,499 books, 9,473 microform titles, 58,386 serials, 29,507 audiovisual materials, an OPAC, and a Web page. Operations spending for the previous fiscal year: $4.5 million. 5,633 computers available on campus for general student use. A campuswide network can be accessed. Students can access the following: online class registration. Staffed computer lab on campus provides training in use of computers and the Internet.

■ **MORGAN STATE UNIVERSITY**
1700 E Cold Spring Ln.
Baltimore, MD 21251
Tel: (443)885-3333; Free: 800-332-6674
E-mail: shantell.saunders@morgan.edu
Web Site: www.morgan.edu/

Description: State-supported, university, coed. Awards bachelor's, master's, and doctoral degrees. Founded 1867. Setting: 143-acre urban campus with easy access to Washington, DC. Total enrollment: 7,005. Faculty: 558 (436 full-time, 122 part-time). Student-undergrad faculty ratio is 13:1. 9,166 applied, 43% were admitted. Full-time: 5,472 students, 55% women, 45% men. Part-time: 642 students, 54% women, 46% men. Students come from 35 states and territories, 50 other countries, 24% from out-of-state. 12% 25 or older, 46% live on campus, 4% transferred in. Retention: 68% of full-time freshmen returned the following year. Academic areas with the most degrees conferred: family and consumer sciences; business/marketing; communication/journalism. Core. Calendar: semesters. Academic remediation for entering students, services for LD students, advanced placement, accelerated degree program, honors program, independent study, summer session for credit, part-time degree program, co-op programs and internships, graduate courses open to undergrads. Off campus study at Towson University, Coppin State College, University of Maryland. ROTC: Army.

Entrance Requirements: Options: electronic application, early admission, deferred admission, international baccalaureate accepted. Required: high school transcript, minimum 2.0 high school GPA, SAT or ACT. Recommended: essay. Required for some: 2 recommendations, interview, SAT Subject Tests. Entrance: moderately difficult. Application deadline: 4/15. Notification: 6/30. Preference given to state residents.

Collegiate Environment: Orientation program. Drama-theater group, choral group, marching band, student-run newspaper, radio station. Social organizations: 11 open to all; national fraternities, national sororities; 10% of eligible men and 10% of eligible women are members. Most popular organizations: Student Government Association, Greek Life, choir, band, cultural organizations. Major annual events: Homecoming, I Love Morgan

Day. Student services: health clinic, personal-psychological counseling. Campus security: 24-hour emergency response devices and patrols, late night transport-escort service, controlled dormitory access. 285 computers available on campus for general student use. A campuswide network can be accessed from student residence rooms and from off campus. Students can access the following: online class registration, engineering lab supercomputer. Staffed computer lab on campus.

Community Environment: See University of Baltimore.

■ **MOUNT ST. MARY'S UNIVERSITY**
16300 Old Emmitsburg Rd.
Emmitsburg, MD 21727-7799
Tel: (301)447-6122; Free: 800-448-4347
E-mail: admissions@msmary.edu
Web Site: www.msmary.edu/

Description: Independent Roman Catholic, comprehensive, coed. Awards bachelor's and master's degrees and post-master's certificates. Founded 1808. Setting: 1,400-acre rural campus with easy access to Baltimore and Washington, DC. Endowment: $41.5 million. Educational spending for the previous fiscal year: $8835 per student. Total enrollment: 2,350. Faculty: 193 (113 full-time, 80 part-time). Student-undergrad faculty ratio is 14:1. 5,283 applied, 55% were admitted. 17% from top 10% of their high school class, 40% from top quarter, 73% from top half. Full-time: 1,755 students, 55% women, 45% men. Part-time: 87 students, 51% women, 49% men. Students come from 36 states and territories, 16 other countries, 48% from out-of-state. 0.3% American Indian or Alaska Native, non-Hispanic/Latino; 9% Hispanic/Latino; 10% African American, non-Hispanic/Latino; 2% Asian, non-Hispanic/Latino; 0.2% Native Hawaiian or other Pacific Islander, non-Hispanic/Latino; 1% international. 3% 25 or older, 82% live on campus, 2% transferred in. Retention: 80% of full-time freshmen returned the following year. Academic areas with the most degrees conferred: business/marketing; social sciences; education. Core. Calendar: semesters. Academic remediation for entering students, services for LD students, advanced placement, accelerated degree program, self-designed majors, honors program, independent study, double major, summer session for credit, part-time degree program, adult/continuing education programs, internships, graduate courses open to undergrads. Off campus study at Frederick Community College. Study abroad program. ROTC: Army (c).

Entrance Requirements: Options: electronic application, early action, deferred admission, international baccalaureate accepted. Required: high school transcript, minimum 2 high school GPA, 1 recommendation, SAT or ACT. Recommended: essay, minimum 3 high school GPA, interview. Entrance: moderately difficult. Application deadlines: 3/1, 12/1 for early action. Notification: continuous, 12/25 for early action. SAT Reasoning Test deadline: 3/1. Transfer credits accepted: Yes. Applicants placed on waiting list: 120. Wait-listed applicants offered admission: 5. Early action applicants: 597. Early action applicants admitted: 386.

Costs Per Year: Application fee: $45. Comprehensive fee: $43,972 includes full-time tuition ($32,224), mandatory fees ($730), and college room and board ($11,018). College room only: $5392. Full-time tuition and fees vary according to location and program. Room and board charges vary according to board plan. Part-time tuition: $1076 per credit hour. Part-time tuition varies according to location and program.

Collegiate Environment: Orientation program. Drama-theater group, choral group, student-run newspaper, radio station. Social organizations: 70 open to all. Most popular organizations: Mount Students for Life, CRUX - Outdoor Adventures, Campus Ministry Student Organization, Circle K, Mount Chorale. Major annual events: Family Fest, Christmas Dance, Acoustic Battles. Student services: health clinic, personal-psychological counseling. Campus security: 24-hour emergency response devices and patrols, late night transport-escort service, controlled dormitory access. College housing designed to accommodate 1,371 students; 1,429 undergraduates lived in college housing during 2012-13. Freshmen guaranteed college housing. On-campus residence required in freshman year. Option: coed housing available. Phillips Library with 178,572 books, 390 serials, 2,938 audiovisual materials, an OPAC, and a Web page. Operations spending for the previous fiscal year: $873,090. 80 computers available on campus for general student use. A campuswide network can be accessed from student residence rooms. Students can access the following: online class registration, tuition payment, course management system.

■ **NATIONAL LABOR COLLEGE**
10000 New Hampshire Ave.
Silver Spring, MD 20903

Tel: (301)431-6400; Free: 888-427-8100
Fax: (301)431-5411
E-mail: crodgers@nlc.edu
Web Site: www.nlc.edu/
Description: Independent, upper-level, coed. Awards bachelor's degrees. Founded 1974. Total enrollment: 473. Student-undergrad faculty ratio is 9:1. 90% 25 or older. Distance learning.

■ **NER ISRAEL RABBINICAL COLLEGE**
400 Mount Wilson Ln.
Baltimore, MD 21208
Tel: (410)484-7200
Fax: (410)484-3060
Description: Independent Jewish, comprehensive, men only. Awards bachelor's, master's, and doctoral degrees. Founded 1933. Setting: 54-acre suburban campus. Total enrollment: 574. 67 applied. 7% 25 or older. Core. Calendar: semesters. Academic remediation for entering students, ESL program, honors program, summer session for credit, graduate courses open to undergrads. Study abroad program.
Entrance Requirements: Options: early admission, deferred admission. Required: high school transcript. Recommended: interview. Entrance: moderately difficult. Application deadline: Rolling.
Collegiate Environment: Student services: health clinic.
Community Environment: See University of Baltimore.

■ **NOTRE DAME OF MARYLAND UNIVERSITY**
4701 N Charles St.
Baltimore, MD 21210-2476
Tel: (410)435-0100; Free: 800-435-0200
Fax: (410)532-6287
E-mail: sbogdon@ndm.edu
Web Site: www.ndm.edu/
Description: Independent Roman Catholic, comprehensive, coed. Awards bachelor's, master's, and doctoral degrees and post-master's certificates (offers coed undergraduate program for adult students). Founded 1873. Setting: 58-acre urban campus with easy access to Baltimore and Washington, DC. Endowment: $26.3 million. Research spending for the previous fiscal year: $15,000. Educational spending for the previous fiscal year: $9387 per student. Total enrollment: 2,731. Faculty: 121 (104 full-time, 17 part-time). Student-undergrad faculty ratio is 12:1. 756 applied, 55% were admitted. 15% from top 10% of their high school class, 39% from top quarter, 80% from top half. Full-time: 510 students, 99% women, 1% men. Part-time: 786 students, 92% women, 8% men. Students come from 18 states and territories, 12 other countries, 16% from out-of-state. 11% 25 or older, 55% live on campus, 4% transferred in. Retention: 71% of full-time freshmen returned the following year. Academic areas with the most degrees conferred: liberal arts/general studies; biological/life sciences; English. Core. Calendar: 4-1-4. ESL program, services for LD students, advanced placement, accelerated degree program, self-designed majors, honors program, independent study, double major, summer session for credit, part-time degree program, adult/ continuing education programs, internships, graduate courses open to undergrads. Off campus study at Loyola College, Johns Hopkins University, Towson University, Goucher College, Morgan State University, Coppin State College, Maryland Institute College of Art. Study abroad program. ROTC: Army (c).
Entrance Requirements: Options: electronic application, early admission, early action, deferred admission, international baccalaureate accepted. Required: essay, high school transcript, minimum 2 high school GPA, 2 recommendations, SAT or ACT. Recommended: minimum 3 high school GPA, interview, resume. Entrance: moderately difficult. Application deadlines: 2/15, 12/3 for early action. Notification: continuous until 6/30, 1/1 for early action.
Costs Per Year: Application fee: $45. Comprehensive fee: $41,000 includes full-time tuition ($29,850), mandatory fees ($1000), and college room and board ($10,150). Room and board charges vary according to board plan.
Collegiate Environment: Orientation program. Drama-theater group, choral group, student-run newspaper, radio station. Social organizations: 40 open to all. Most popular organizations: Omega Phi Alpha Service Sorority, Maryland Student Legislature, Business and Economics Society, Sigma Tau Delta Honor Society, Residence Hall Council. Major annual events: Winterfest, Bachelor Ball, Family Weekend. Student services: health clinic, personal-psychological counseling, women's center. Campus security: 24-hour emergency response devices and patrols, late night transport-escort service, controlled dormitory access, emergency call boxes. Loyola/Notre

Dame Library with 999,295 books, 18,608 microform titles, 42,427 serials, 17,893 audiovisual materials, an OPAC, and a Web page. Operations spending for the previous fiscal year: $987,562. 60 computers available on campus for general student use. A campuswide network can be accessed from student residence rooms and from off campus. Students can access the following: online class registration, online classroom assignments and information. Staffed computer lab on campus provides training in use of computers, software, and the Internet.
Community Environment: Like Boston, Baltimore is a college town. There are nine nearby colleges and universities and over 60,000 students in the Baltimore metropolitan area which enhances academic and social opportunities. The Notre Dame campus is located 15 minutes from the nationally known Inner Harbor area where concerts, fairs and ethnic festivals are sponsored. Both mountains and ocean are only a few hours from Notre Dame, providing opportunities for skiing in the winter and relaxing on the beach in the summer. Annapolis, home of the U. S. Naval Academy, is about 45 minutes from Notre Dame, and Washington, D. C., with all of its resources, is less than an hour's drive from the college.

■ **PEABODY CONSERVATORY OF THE JOHNS HOPKINS UNIVERSITY**
1 E Mount Vernon Pl.
Baltimore, MD 21202-2397
Tel: (410)659-8150; Free: 800-368-2521
Web Site: www.peabody.jhu.edu/
Description: Independent, comprehensive, coed. Administratively affiliated with Johns Hopkins University. Awards bachelor's, master's, and doctoral degrees and post-master's certificates. Founded 1857. Setting: 1-acre urban campus with easy access to Washington, DC. Endowment: $84.2 million. Educational spending for the previous fiscal year: $17,886 per student. Total enrollment: 686. Faculty: 177 (81 full-time, 96 part-time). Student-undergrad faculty ratio is 6:1. 750 applied, 40% were admitted. Full-time: 300 students, 47% women, 53% men. Part-time: 12 students, 50% women, 50% men. Students come from 35 states and territories, 15 other countries, 73% from out-of-state. 4% Hispanic/Latino; 6% African American, non-Hispanic/Latino; 15% Asian, non-Hispanic/Latino; 1% Native Hawaiian or other Pacific Islander, non-Hispanic/Latino; 24% international. 2% 25 or older, 40% live on campus, 4% transferred in. Retention: 99% of full-time freshmen returned the following year. Academic areas with the most degrees conferred: visual and performing arts; education. Core. Calendar: semesters. Academic remediation for entering students, ESL program, services for LD students, advanced placement, accelerated degree program, honors program, independent study, double major, internships, graduate courses open to undergrads. Off campus study at Johns Hopkins University; Loyola College; Maryland Institute, College of Art.
Entrance Requirements: Required: essay, high school transcript, 3 recommendations, interview, audition. Recommended: minimum 3 high school GPA. Required for some: SAT or ACT. Entrance: very difficult. Application deadline: 12/1. Notification: 4/1. Transfer credits accepted: Yes.
Costs Per Year: Application fee: $100. One-time mandatory fee: $700. Comprehensive fee: $51,595 includes full-time tuition ($38,450), mandatory fees ($465), and college room and board ($12,680). Full-time tuition and fees vary according to program. Room and board charges vary according to board plan. Part-time tuition: $1097 per semester hour. Part-time tuition varies according to course load.
Collegiate Environment: Orientation program. Choral group. Social organizations: 84 open to all. Major annual events: beginning of the year events, Relaxation Day, End of Year Party. Student services: health clinic, personal-psychological counseling. Campus security: 24-hour emergency response devices and patrols, late night transport-escort service, controlled dormitory access. 188 college housing spaces available; 157 were occupied in 2012-13. Freshmen guaranteed college housing. On-campus residence required through sophomore year. Option: coed housing available. Arthur Friedheim Library plus 1 other with 103,898 books, 227 microform titles, 188 serials, 35,227 audiovisual materials, an OPAC, and a Web page. Operations spending for the previous fiscal year: $595,000. 40 computers available on campus for general student use. A campuswide network can be accessed from student residence rooms and from off campus. Students can access the following: online class registration, word processing, music processing. Staffed computer lab on campus provides training in use of computers, software, and the Internet.

■ **PRINCE GEORGE'S COMMUNITY COLLEGE**
301 Largo Rd.
Largo, MD 20774-2199

Tel: (301)336-6000

E-mail: enrollmentservices@pgcc.edu

Web Site: www.pgcc.edu/

Description: County-supported, 2-year, coed. Awards certificates, transfer associate, and terminal associate degrees. Founded 1958. Setting: 150-acre suburban campus with easy access to Washington, DC. Total enrollment: 11,861. Faculty: 695 (244 full-time, 451 part-time). Student-undergrad faculty ratio is 15:1. 4,178 applied, 100% were admitted. Full-time: 3,007 students, 55% women, 45% men. Part-time: 8,854 students, 67% women, 33% men. Students come from 20 states and territories, 98 other countries, 4% from out-of-state. 47% 25 or older, 8% transferred in. Retention: 58% of full-time freshmen returned the following year. Core. Calendar: semesters plus 2 summer sessions. Academic remediation for entering students, ESL program, services for LD students, advanced placement, honors program, distance learning, summer session for credit, part-time degree program, external degree program, adult/continuing education programs, co-op programs. ROTC: Army (c).

Entrance Requirements: Open admission. Option: early admission. Recommended: minimum 2.0 high school GPA. Required for some: high school transcript. Entrance: noncompetitive. Application deadline: Rolling. Notification: continuous.

Collegiate Environment: Orientation program. Drama-theater group, choral group, student-run newspaper. Social organizations: 40 open to all. Most popular organizations: Crusaders for Christ, Student Program Board, Union of Black Scholars, International Student Groups. Major annual events: International Festival, Bluebird Blues Jazz Festival, Jook Joint Saturday Night. Student services: health clinic, personal-psychological counseling. Campus security: 24-hour emergency response devices and patrols, late night transport-escort service. Accokeek Hall with 242,519 books, 226,390 microform titles, 750 serials, 16,645 audiovisual materials, and an OPAC. 450 computers available on campus for general student use. A campuswide network can be accessed from off-campus. Students can access the following: online class registration. Staffed computer lab on campus.

■ **ST. JOHN'S COLLEGE**

PO Box 2800

Annapolis, MD 21404

Tel: (410)263-2371; Free: 800-727-9238

E-mail: admissions@sjca.edu

Web Site: www.stjohnscollege.edu/

Description: Independent, comprehensive, coed. Awards bachelor's and master's degrees. Founded 1784. Setting: 36-acre small town campus with easy access to Baltimore and Washington, DC. Endowment: $86.3 million. Educational spending for the previous fiscal year: $20,372 per student. Total enrollment: 509. Faculty: 63 (58 full-time, 5 part-time). Student-undergrad faculty ratio is 8:1. 378 applied, 82% were admitted. 21% from top 10% of their high school class, 55% from top quarter, 82% from top half. 6 National Merit Scholars. Full-time: 447 students, 45% women, 55% men. Part-time: 2 students, 100% men. Students come from 42 states and territories, 15 other countries, 85% from out-of-state. 0.4% American Indian or Alaska Native, non-Hispanic/Latino; 7% Hispanic/Latino; 2% African American, non-Hispanic/Latino; 2% Asian, non-Hispanic/Latino; 0% Native Hawaiian or other Pacific Islander, non-Hispanic/Latino; 9% international. 6% 25 or older, 74% live on campus, 0% transferred in. Retention: 81% of full-time freshmen returned the following year. Academic area with the most degrees conferred: liberal arts/general studies. Core. Calendar: semesters. Off campus study at St. John's College (NM) is our second campus: students can transfer credits between the two.

Entrance Requirements: Options: electronic application, early admission, deferred admission, international baccalaureate accepted. Required: essay, high school transcript, 2 recommendations. Recommended: interview, SAT or ACT. Required for some: SAT or ACT. Entrance: moderately difficult. Application deadline: Rolling. Notification: continuous. Transfer credits accepted: No.

Costs Per Year: Application fee: $0. Comprehensive fee: $55,648 includes full-time tuition ($44,554), mandatory fees ($450), and college room and board ($10,644). Room and board charges vary according to board plan.

Collegiate Environment: Orientation program. Drama-theater group, choral group, student-run newspaper. Social organizations: 40 open to all. Most popular organizations: King William's Players (drama), Reality (social), Delegate Council (student government), Waltz (social), Student Committee on Instruction (advisory). Major annual events: Convocation, Annual croquet match against the USNA for the Annapolis Cup, Reality (year-end festival). Student services: health clinic, personal-psychological counseling. Campus

security: 24-hour emergency response devices and patrols, late night transport-escort service, controlled dormitory access. 360 college housing spaces available; 321 were occupied in 2012-13. Freshmen guaranteed college housing. On-campus residence required in freshman year. Option: coed housing available. Greenfield Library plus 1 other with 104,299 books, 439 microform titles, 144 serials, 2,660 audiovisual materials, an OPAC, and a Web page. Operations spending for the previous fiscal year: $378,221. 24 computers available on campus for general student use. A campuswide network can be accessed from student residence rooms. Staffed computer lab on campus provides training in use of computers, software, and the Internet.

■ **ST. MARY'S COLLEGE OF MARYLAND**

18952 E Fisher Rd.

Saint Mary's City, MD 20686-3001

Tel: (240)895-2000; Free: 800-492-7181

Fax: (240)895-5001

E-mail: admissions@smcm.edu

Web Site: www.smcm.edu/

Description: State-supported, comprehensive, coed. Awards bachelor's and master's degrees. Founded 1840. Setting: 361-acre rural campus. Endowment: $25.9 million. Research spending for the previous fiscal year: $410,946. Educational spending for the previous fiscal year: $9874 per student. Total enrollment: 1,933. Faculty: 225 (142 full-time, 83 part-time). Student-undergrad faculty ratio is 12:1. 1,985 applied, 72% were admitted. 32% from top 10% of their high school class, 67% from top quarter, 92% from top half. 4 valedictorians. Full-time: 1,837 students, 60% women, 40% men. Part-time: 64 students, 48% women, 52% men. Students come from 31 states and territories, 35 other countries, 11% from out-of-state. 0% American Indian or Alaska Native, non-Hispanic/Latino; 5% Hispanic/Latino; 7% African American, non-Hispanic/Latino; 2% Asian, non-Hispanic/Latino; 0.1% Native Hawaiian or other Pacific Islander, non-Hispanic/Latino; 2% international. 2% 25 or older, 86% live on campus, 4% transferred in. Retention: 87% of full-time freshmen returned the following year. Academic areas with the most degrees conferred: social sciences; psychology; biological/life sciences. Core. Calendar: semesters. Services for LD students, advanced placement, self-designed majors, freshman honors college, honors program, independent study, double major, summer session for credit, part-time degree program, co-op programs and internships. Off campus study at National Student Exchange. Study abroad program.

Entrance Requirements: Options: electronic application, early admission, early decision, deferred admission, international baccalaureate accepted. Required: essay, high school transcript, 2 recommendations, Prospective students should apply online through the Common Application, SAT or ACT. Recommended: interview. Entrance: very difficult. Application deadlines: 1/1, 11/1 for early decision plan 1, 1/1 for early decision plan 2. Notification: 4/1, 12/15 for early decision plan 1, 2/15 for early decision plan 2. SAT Reasoning Test deadline: 1/1. Transfer credits accepted: Yes. Applicants placed on waiting list: 172. Wait-listed applicants offered admission: 35. Early decision applicants: 228. Early decision applicants admitted: 143.

Costs Per Year: Application fee: $50. State resident tuition: $12,245 full-time, $195 per credit hour part-time. Nonresident tuition: $25,045 full-time, $195 per credit hour part-time. Mandatory fees: $2528 full-time. Full-time tuition and fees vary according to course load and degree level. Part-time tuition varies according to course load and degree level. College room and board: $11,305. College room only: $6385. Room and board charges vary according to board plan and housing facility.

Collegiate Environment: Orientation program. Drama-theater group, choral group, student-run newspaper, radio station. Social organizations: 82 open to all. Most popular organizations: Crew, Acappella groups, SEAC (Student Environmental Action Coalition), Dance Club, Outdoors Club. Major annual events: World Carnival, Dance Shows, Cardboard Boat Races. Student services: health clinic, personal-psychological counseling. Campus security: 24-hour emergency response devices and patrols, late night transport-escort service, controlled dormitory access. College housing designed to accommodate 1,571 students; 1,590 undergraduates lived in college housing during 2012-13. Freshmen guaranteed college housing. Options: coed, men-only, women-only housing available. The Library with 162,043 books, 39,782 microform titles, 21,103 serials, 16,927 audiovisual materials, an OPAC, and a Web page. Operations spending for the previous fiscal year: $2.2 million. 390 computers available on campus for general student use. Computer purchase/lease plans available. A campuswide network can be accessed from student residence rooms and from off campus. Students can access the following: online class registration, Blackboard. Staffed computer lab on campus provides training in use of computers, software, and the Internet.

■ **SALISBURY UNIVERSITY**
1101 Camden Ave.
Salisbury, MD 21801-6837
Tel: (410)543-6000; Free: 888-543-0148
Fax: (410)548-2587
E-mail: admissions@salisbury.edu
Web Site: www.salisbury.edu/
Description: State-supported, comprehensive, coed. Part of University System of Maryland. Awards bachelor's, master's, and doctoral degrees. Founded 1925. Setting: 161-acre small town campus. Endowment: $56.1 million. Research spending for the previous fiscal year: $746,734. Educational spending for the previous fiscal year: $5834 per student. Total enrollment: 8,657. Faculty: 661 (404 full-time, 257 part-time). Student-undergrad faculty ratio is 16:1. 8,866 applied, 53% were admitted. 24% from top 10% of their high school class, 60% from top quarter, 92% from top half. 1 National Merit Scholar, 4 class presidents, 1 valedictorian, 177 student government officers. Full-time: 7,323 students, 57% women, 43% men. Part-time: 646 students, 50% women, 50% men. Students come from 29 states and territories, 63 other countries, 99.9% from out-of-state. 0.2% American Indian or Alaska Native, non-Hispanic/Latino; 5% Hispanic/Latino; 11% African American, non-Hispanic/Latino; 2% Asian, non-Hispanic/Latino; 0.1% Native Hawaiian or other Pacific Islander, non-Hispanic/Latino; 1% international. 7% 25 or older, 38% live on campus, 12% transferred in. Retention: 84% of full-time freshmen returned the following year. Academic areas with the most degrees conferred: business/marketing; education; communication/journalism. Core. Calendar: 4-1-4. ESL program, services for LD students, advanced placement, accelerated degree program, self-designed majors, honors program, independent study, distance learning, double major, summer session for credit, part-time degree program, adult/continuing education programs, co-op programs and internships, graduate courses open to undergrads. Off campus study at other units of the University System of Maryland. Study abroad program. ROTC: Army, Air Force (c).
Entrance Requirements: Options: electronic application, early admission, early action, international baccalaureate accepted. Required: essay, high school transcript, minimum 2 high school GPA. Required for some: SAT or ACT, SAT/ACT not required for students who have been out of high school for more than 3 years or for whom TOEFL is required. Students earning a weighted grade point average of 3.5 or higher on a 4.0 scale may decide if they wish to submit standardized test scores. Entrance: moderately difficult. Application deadlines: 1/15, 12/1 for early action. Notification: 3/15, 1/15 for early action. SAT Reasoning Test deadline: 3/15. SAT Subject Test deadline: 3/15. Transfer credits accepted: Yes. Early action applicants: 4,410. Early action applicants admitted: 2,899.
Costs Per Year: Application fee: $50. State resident tuition: $5576 full-time, $231 per credit hour part-time. Nonresident tuition: $13,922 full-time, $578 per credit hour part-time. Mandatory fees: $2124 full-time, $77 per credit hour part-time. Full-time tuition and fees vary according to degree level. Part-time tuition and fees vary according to course load and degree level. College room and board: $9120. College room only: $5250. Room and board charges vary according to board plan and housing facility.
Collegiate Environment: Orientation program. Drama-theater group, choral group, student-run newspaper, radio station. Social organizations: 124 open to all; national fraternities, national sororities; 2% of eligible men and 4% of eligible women are members. Most popular organizations: Student Government Association, Radio (WXSU), Student Organization for Activity Planning (SOAP), Campus Crusade for Christ, Greek Council. Major annual events: Welcome Week, Family Weekend, Multicultural Festival. Student services: health clinic, personal-psychological counseling. Campus security: 24-hour emergency response devices and patrols, student patrols, late night transport-escort service, controlled dormitory access, lighted pathways, Sidewalks, 24-hour University Police protection. 2,060 college housing spaces available; 2,045 were occupied in 2012-13. Freshmen given priority for college housing. Option: coed housing available. Blackwell Library plus 1 other with 290,321 books, 755,883 microform titles, 980 serials, 1,695 audiovisual materials, an OPAC, and a Web page. Operations spending for the previous fiscal year: $2.6 million. 531 computers available on campus for general student use. Computer purchase/lease plans available. A campuswide network can be accessed from student residence rooms and from off campus. Students can access the following: online class registration, University accounts. Staffed computer lab on campus provides training in use of computers, software, and the Internet.

■ **SOJOURNER-DOUGLASS COLLEGE**
500 N Caroline St.
Baltimore, MD 21205-1814

Tel: (410)276-0306
Fax: (410)675-1810
E-mail: dsamuels@host.sdc.edu
Web Site: sdc.edu/
Description: Independent, comprehensive, coed. Awards bachelor's and master's degrees (offers only evening and weekend programs). Founded 1980. Setting: 15-acre urban campus with easy access to Baltimore. Educational spending for the previous fiscal year: $3144 per student. Total enrollment: 1,268. Faculty: 240 (104 full-time, 136 part-time). Student-undergrad faculty ratio is 5:1. Full-time: 826 students, 87% women, 13% men. Part-time: 381 students, 90% women, 10% men. Students come from 7 states and territories, 14 other countries, 4% from out-of-state. 0.2% Hispanic/Latino; 93% African American, non-Hispanic/Latino; 0.1% Asian, non-Hispanic/Latino; 0.1% Native Hawaiian or other Pacific Islander, non-Hispanic/Latino; 3% international. 86% 25 or older, 35% transferred in. Retention: 43% of full-time freshmen returned the following year. Academic areas with the most degrees conferred: health professions and related sciences; business/marketing; public administration and social services. Core. Calendar: trimesters. Academic remediation for entering students, services for LD students, accelerated degree program, self-designed majors, honors program, summer session for credit, part-time degree program, external degree program, adult/continuing education programs, internships, graduate courses open to undergrads.
Entrance Requirements: Open admission. Option: deferred admission. Required: essay, high school transcript, 2 recommendations, interview, resume. Entrance: noncompetitive. Application deadline: Rolling. Transfer credits accepted: Yes.
Costs Per Year: Application fee: $25. Tuition: $8650 full-time. Mandatory fees: $200 full-time.
Collegiate Environment: Social organizations: 3 open to all; national fraternities, national sororities; 10% of eligible men and 15% of eligible women are members. Most popular organizations: Student Government Association, Criminal Justice Club, Social Work Club. Major annual events: Ifetayo Celebration, Constitution Day, Judge Bell Day. Student services: personal-psychological counseling. 10,000 books and 25 serials 200 computers available on campus for general student use. A campuswide network can be accessed from off-campus. Students can access the following: online class registration. Staffed computer lab on campus provides training in use of computers, software, and the Internet.
Community Environment: The school is located in the heart of Baltimore, which is in the center of Maryland and accessible from every major state highway. The metropolitan area extends into five adjacent counties: Baltimore, Anne Arundel, Carroll, Harford, and Howard. The area has more than 1,000 different employers, primarily in the high technology and service industries. Recreational facilities are ample and can be found both on campus and in several public parks and indoor facilities.

■ **STEVENSON UNIVERSITY**
1525 Greenspring Valley Rd.
Stevenson, MD 21153
Tel: (410)486-7000; Free: 877-468-3852
E-mail: admissions@stevenson.edu
Web Site: www.stevenson.edu/
Description: Independent, comprehensive, coed. Awards bachelor's and master's degrees. Founded 1952. Setting: 168-acre suburban campus with easy access to Baltimore. Endowment: $44.8 million. Total enrollment: 4,418. Faculty: 502 (121 full-time, 381 part-time). Student-undergrad faculty ratio is 15:1. 5,735 applied, 59% were admitted. 22% from top 10% of their high school class, 47% from top quarter, 82% from top half. Full-time: 3,227 students, 63% women, 37% men. Part-time: 677 students, 76% women, 24% men. 15% from out-of-state. 0.3% American Indian or Alaska Native, non-Hispanic/Latino; 4% Hispanic/Latino; 27% African American, non-Hispanic/Latino; 3% Asian, non-Hispanic/Latino; 0.2% Native Hawaiian or other Pacific Islander, non-Hispanic/Latino; 0.4% international. 19% 25 or older, 47% live on campus, 10% transferred in. Retention: 69% of full-time freshmen returned the following year. Academic areas with the most degrees conferred: business/marketing; health professions and related sciences; computer and information sciences. Core. Calendar: semesters. Academic remediation for entering students, services for LD students, advanced placement, accelerated degree program, self-designed majors, honors program, independent study, distance learning, double major, summer session for credit, part-time degree program, adult/continuing education programs, co-op programs and internships, graduate courses open to undergrads. Off campus study at Chesapeake Community College, Anne Arundel Com-

munity College, Howard Community College, Carroll Community College, Prince George's Community College, BCCC. Study abroad program. ROTC: Army (c), Air Force (c).

Entrance Requirements: Options: electronic application, early admission, deferred admission, international baccalaureate accepted. Required: essay, high school transcript, 2 recommendations, SAT or ACT. Recommended: interview. Entrance: moderately difficult. Application deadline: Rolling. Notification: continuous. SAT Reasoning Test deadline: 3/1.

Costs Per Year: Application fee: $40. Comprehensive fee: $37,204 includes full-time tuition ($23,562), mandatory fees ($1748), and college room and board ($11,894). College room only: $7888. Full-time tuition and fees vary according to degree level. Room and board charges vary according to board plan and housing facility. Part-time tuition: $596 per credit hour. Part-time mandatory fees: $75 per term. Part-time tuition and fees vary according to course load and degree level.

Collegiate Environment: Orientation program. Drama-theater group, choral group, marching band, student-run newspaper, radio station. Social organizations: 50 open to all; national sororities; 2% of women are members. Most popular organizations: Student Government Association, MAP, Black Student Union, National Student Nurses Association, Phi Sigma. Major annual events: Welcome Picnic, Homecoming Weekend, Lacrosse Events. Student services: health clinic, personal-psychological counseling. Campus security: 24-hour emergency response devices and patrols, late night transport-escort service, controlled dormitory access, patrols by trained security personnel during campus hours. 1,800 college housing spaces available; 1,786 were occupied in 2012-13. Freshmen given priority for college housing. Stevenson University Learning Resource Center-Greenspring Campus plus 1 other with 81,802 books, 183,222 microform titles, 1,058 serials, 2,727 audiovisual materials, an OPAC, and a Web page. 300 computers available on campus for general student use. Computer purchase/lease plans available. A campuswide network can be accessed from student residence rooms and from off campus. Students can access the following: online class registration. Staffed computer lab on campus provides training in use of computers, software, and the Internet.

Community Environment: Located in the open countryside of Baltimore County, 20 minutes from the center of urban Baltimore, the college offers a country setting with city conveniences.

■ **STRATFORD UNIVERSITY**
210 S Central Ave.
Baltimore, MD 21202-3230
Tel: (410)752-4710; Free: 800-624-9926
Fax: (410)752-3730
E-mail: ngrasso@stratford.edu
Web Site: www.stratford.edu/
Description: Proprietary, comprehensive, coed. Awards associate, bachelor's, and master's degrees. Founded 1972. Setting: 6-acre urban campus with easy access to Baltimore and Washington, DC. Total enrollment: 353. Faculty: 31 (13 full-time, 18 part-time). Student-undergrad faculty ratio is 20:1. 162 applied, 71% were admitted. Full-time: 72 students, 50% women, 50% men. Part-time: 275 students, 55% women, 45% men. 12% from out-of-state. 0% American Indian or Alaska Native, non-Hispanic/Latino; 2% Hispanic/Latino; 70% African American, non-Hispanic/Latino; 1% Asian, non-Hispanic/Latino; 0% Native Hawaiian or other Pacific Islander, non-Hispanic/Latino; 0% international. 24% 25 or older, 14% transferred in. Retention: 87% of full-time freshmen returned the following year. Academic area with the most degrees conferred: personal and culinary services. Core. Calendar: semesters. Academic remediation for entering students, services for LD students, advanced placement, accelerated degree program, summer session for credit, part-time degree program, adult/continuing education programs, co-op programs and internships, graduate courses open to undergrads. Off campus study at Virginia Park Campus, County Cavan, Ireland.

Entrance Requirements: Open admission. Options: electronic application, early action, deferred admission. Required: essay, high school transcript, minimum 2 high school GPA, interview. Required for some: 1 recommendation. Entrance: minimally difficult. Application deadlines: Rolling, Rolling for nonresidents. Notification: continuous, continuous for nonresidents. Transfer credits accepted: Yes.

Costs Per Year: Application fee: $50. One-time mandatory fee: $850. Tuition: $14,986 full-time, $370 per quarter hour part-time. Mandatory fees: $2376 full-time, $176 per quarter hour part-time. Full-time tuition and fees vary according to course load and program. Part-time tuition and fees vary according to course load and program.

Collegiate Environment: Orientation program. Student-run newspaper. Social organizations: 9 open to all; local fraternities, local sororities; 8% of eligible men and 7% of eligible women are members. Most popular organizations: Chai Eta Psi / Eta Psi Xi, Gardening Club, Epicurean Club, Enactus, Event Planning Club. Major annual events: Candy Gram, Professional Development Conference, Career Fair. Student services: personal-psychological counseling. Campus security: late night transport-escort service, controlled dormitory access. College housing not available. Learning Resource Center with 3,000 books, 100 audiovisual materials, and an OPAC. 40 computers available on campus for general student use. A campuswide network can be accessed from off-campus. Staffed computer lab on campus provides training in use of computers, software, and the Internet.

■ **STRAYER UNIVERSITY - ANNE ARUNDEL CAMPUS**
1520 Jabez Run
Millersville, MD 21108
Tel: (410)923-4500
Fax: (410)923-4570
Web Site: www.strayer.edu/campus/anne-arundel
Description: Proprietary, comprehensive, coed. Awards associate, bachelor's, and master's degrees.

■ **STRAYER UNIVERSITY - OWINGS MILLS CAMPUS**
500 Redland Ct., Ste. 100
Owings Mills, MD 21117
Tel: (443)394-3339
Fax: (443)394-3394
Web Site: www.strayer.edu/campus/owings-mills
Description: Proprietary, comprehensive, coed. Awards associate, bachelor's, and master's degrees.

■ **STRAYER UNIVERSITY - PRINCE GEORGE'S CAMPUS**
4710 Auth Pl.
First Fl.
Suitland, MD 20746
Tel: (301)423-3600
Fax: (301)423-3999
Web Site: www.strayer.edu/campus/prince-georges
Description: Proprietary, comprehensive, coed. Awards associate, bachelor's, and master's degrees.

■ **STRAYER UNIVERSITY - ROCKVILLE CAMPUS**
4 Research Pl., Ste. 100
Rockville, MD 20850
Tel: (301)548-5500
Fax: (301)548-5530
Web Site: www.strayer.edu/campus/rockville
Description: Proprietary, comprehensive, coed. Awards associate, bachelor's, and master's degrees.

■ **STRAYER UNIVERSITY - WHITE MARSH CAMPUS**
9920 Franklin Sq. Dr.
Ste. 200
Baltimore, MD 21236
Tel: (410)238-9000
Fax: (410)238-9099
Web Site: www.strayer.edu/campus/white-marsh
Description: Proprietary, comprehensive, coed. Awards associate, bachelor's, and master's degrees. Founded 1892.

■ **TESST COLLEGE OF TECHNOLOGY (BALTIMORE)**
1520 S Caton Ave.
Baltimore, MD 21227
Tel: (410)644-6400; Free: 800-935-1857
Fax: (410)644-6481
Web Site: www.baltimore.tesst.com/
Description: Proprietary, 2-year, coed. Awards certificates and terminal associate degrees. Founded 1956.

■ **TESST COLLEGE OF TECHNOLOGY (BELTSVILLE)**
4600 Powder Mill Rd.
Beltsville, MD 20705
Tel: (301)937-8448; Free: 800-935-1857

Fax: (301)937-5327
Web Site: www.beltsville.tesst.com/
Description: Proprietary, 2-year, coed. Awards certificates and terminal associate degrees. Founded 1967.

■ **TESST COLLEGE OF TECHNOLOGY (TOWSON)**
803 Glen Eagles Ct.
Towson, MD 21286
Tel: (410)296-5350; Free: 800-935-1857
Fax: (410)296-5356
Web Site: www.towson.tesst.com/
Description: Proprietary, 2-year, coed. Awards certificates and terminal associate degrees. Founded 1992.

■ **TOWSON UNIVERSITY**
8000 York Rd.
Towson, MD 21252-0001
Tel: (410)704-2000
Fax: (410)704-3030
E-mail: admissions@towson.edu
Web Site: www.towson.edu/
Description: State-supported, university, coed. Part of University System of Maryland. Awards bachelor's, master's, and doctoral degrees and post-master's certificates. Founded 1866. Setting: 328-acre suburban campus with easy access to Baltimore and Washington, DC. System endowment: $52.9 million. Research spending for the previous fiscal year: $4.4 million. Educational spending for the previous fiscal year: $5689 per student. Total enrollment: 21,960. Faculty: 1,643 (848 full-time, 795 part-time). Student-undergrad faculty ratio is 17:1. 18,128 applied, 52% were admitted. 19% from top 10% of their high school class, 50% from top quarter, 89% from top half. Full-time: 15,852 students, 62% women, 38% men. Part-time: 2,136 students, 53% women, 47% men. Students come from 44 states and territories, 67 other countries, 16% from out-of-state. 0.2% American Indian or Alaska Native, non-Hispanic/Latino; 5% Hispanic/Latino; 14% African American, non-Hispanic/Latino; 4% Asian, non-Hispanic/Latino; 0.1% Native Hawaiian or other Pacific Islander, non-Hispanic/Latino; 2% international. 11% 25 or older, 25% live on campus, 12% transferred in. Retention: 86% of full-time freshmen returned the following year. Academic areas with the most degrees conferred: business/marketing; social sciences; education. Core. Calendar: semesters. Academic remediation for entering students, ESL program, services for LD students, advanced placement, accelerated degree program, self-designed majors, freshman honors college, honors program, independent study, distance learning, double major, summer session for credit, part-time degree program, adult/continuing education programs, co-op programs and internships, graduate courses open to undergrads. Off campus study at all state colleges in Maryland, other institutions of higher education in the Baltimore metropolitan area, members of the National Student Exchange. Study abroad program. ROTC: Army (c), Air Force (c).
Entrance Requirements: Options: electronic application, early admission, deferred admission, international baccalaureate accepted. Required: high school transcript, SAT or ACT. Recommended: minimum 3 high school GPA, 2 recommendations. Required for some: essay, interview. Entrance: moderately difficult. Application deadline: 2/15. Notification: continuous. SAT Reasoning Test deadline: 2/15. Transfer credits accepted: Yes. Applicants placed on waiting list: 4,050. Wait-listed applicants offered admission: 263.
Costs Per Year: Application fee: $45. State resident tuition: $5660 full-time, $246 per credit hour part-time. Nonresident tuition: $17,282 full-time, $723 per credit hour part-time. Mandatory fees: $2472 full-time, $103 per credit hour part-time. Full-time tuition and fees vary according to course load. Part-time tuition and fees vary according to course load. College room and board: $10,338. College room only: $5910. Room and board charges vary according to board plan and housing facility.
Collegiate Environment: Orientation program. Drama-theater group, choral group, marching band, student-run newspaper, radio station. Social organizations: 210 open to all; national fraternities, national sororities; 7% of eligible men and 8% of eligible women are members. Most popular organizations: University Residence Government, Queer Student Union, Black Student Union, Hillel, African Diaspora Club. Major annual events: Tiger Fest (spring festival), Homecoming Weekend, Welcome Week. Student services: health clinic, personal-psychological counseling, women's center. Campus security: 24-hour emergency response devices and patrols, late night transport-escort service, controlled dormitory access. College housing designed to accommodate 4,567 students; 4,642 undergraduates lived in college housing during 2012-13. Freshmen guaranteed college housing. Op-

tion: coed housing available. Cook Library with 719,299 books, 887,221 microform titles, 36,657 serials, 10,423 audiovisual materials, an OPAC, and a Web page. Operations spending for the previous fiscal year: $5.9 million. 3,047 computers available on campus for general student use. A campuswide network can be accessed from student residence rooms and from off campus. Students can access the following: online class registration. Staffed computer lab on campus provides training in use of computers, software, and the Internet.

■ **UNITED STATES NAVAL ACADEMY**
121 Blake Rd.
Annapolis, MD 21402-5000
Tel: (410)293-1000
Fax: (410)293-4348
E-mail: webmail@usna.edu
Web Site: www.usna.edu/
Description: Federally supported, 4-year, coed. Awards bachelor's degrees. Founded 1845. Setting: 338-acre small town campus with easy access to Baltimore and Washington, DC. Total enrollment: 4,536. Faculty: 528 (478 full-time, 50 part-time). Student-undergrad faculty ratio is 9:1. 20,601 applied, 6% were admitted. 53% from top 10% of their high school class, 80% from top quarter, 94% from top half. Full-time: 4,536 students, 21% women, 79% men. Students come from 54 states and territories, 31 other countries, 93% from out-of-state. 0.4% American Indian or Alaska Native, non-Hispanic/Latino; 12% Hispanic/Latino; 7% African American, non-Hispanic/Latino; 5% Asian, non-Hispanic/Latino; 1% Native Hawaiian or other Pacific Islander, non-Hispanic/Latino; 1% international. 1% 25 or older, 100% live on campus, 0% transferred in. Retention: 97% of full-time freshmen returned the following year. Academic areas with the most degrees conferred: engineering; social sciences; physical sciences. Core. Calendar: semesters. Academic remediation for entering students, advanced placement, honors program, independent study, double major, summer session for credit. Off campus study. Study abroad program.
Entrance Requirements: Options: electronic application, early action. Required: essay, high school transcript, 2 recommendations, interview, age 17-22, medical exam, authorized nomination, candidate fitness test, SAT or ACT. Entrance: very difficult. Application deadline: 1/31. Notification: continuous until 4/15. SAT Reasoning Test deadline: 1/31. Applicants placed on waiting list: 150. Wait-listed applicants offered admission: 15.
Costs Per Year: Application fee: $0. Comprehensive fee: $0. The Navy pays for the tuition, room and board, medical and dental care of Naval Academy midshipmen. Tuition guaranteed not to increase for student's term of enrollment.
Collegiate Environment: Orientation program. Drama-theater group, choral group, marching band, student-run radio station. Social organizations: 109 open to all. Most popular organizations: Mountaineering Club, Semper Fi, Black Studies Club, Midshipmen Action Club, Martial Arts Club. Major annual events: Parents' Weekend, Army-Navy football game, Commissioning Week. Student services: legal services, health clinic, personal-psychological counseling. Campus security: 24-hour emergency response devices and patrols, campus gate security. 4,700 college housing spaces available; 4,536 were occupied in 2012-13. Freshmen guaranteed college housing. On-campus residence required through senior year. Option: coed housing available. Nimitz Library with 1.1 million books, 204,701 microform titles, 1,194 serials, 7,439 audiovisual materials, an OPAC, and a Web page. 6,100 computers available on campus for general student use. Computer purchase/lease plans available. A computer is required for all students. A campuswide network can be accessed from student residence rooms and from off campus. Students can access the following: online class registration. Staffed computer lab on campus provides training in use of computers, software, and the Internet.

■ **UNIVERSITY OF BALTIMORE**
1420 N Charles St.
Baltimore, MD 21201-5779
Tel: (410)837-4200
Fax: (410)837-4793
E-mail: admissions@ubalt.edu
Web Site: www.ubalt.edu/
Description: State-supported, comprehensive, coed. Part of University System of Maryland. Awards bachelor's, master's, and doctoral degrees. Founded 1925. Setting: 49-acre urban campus. Total enrollment: 6,501. Faculty: 404 (182 full-time, 222 part-time). Student-undergrad faculty ratio is 19:1. 806 applied, 60% were admitted. Full-time: 1,924 students, 52%

women, 48% men. Part-time: 1,302 students, 62% women, 38% men. Students come from 14 states and territories, 62 other countries, 1% from out-of-state. 0.4% American Indian or Alaska Native, non-Hispanic/Latino; 3% Hispanic/Latino; 42% African American, non-Hispanic/Latino; 4% Asian, non-Hispanic/Latino; 0.1% Native Hawaiian or other Pacific Islander, non-Hispanic/Latino; 1% international. 50% 25 or older, 25% transferred in. Retention: 78% of full-time freshmen returned the following year. Core. Calendar: semesters. Academic remediation for entering students, services for LD students, advanced placement, accelerated degree program, freshman honors college, honors program, independent study, distance learning, summer session for credit, part-time degree program, adult/continuing education programs, co-op programs and internships, graduate courses open to undergrads. Off campus study at University of Maryland Baltimore County, Coppin State College, Morgan State University, Towson University, Bowie State College, Maryland Institute, College of Art. Study abroad program. ROTC: Army (c), Air Force (c).

Entrance Requirements: Options: electronic application, deferred admission, international baccalaureate accepted. Required: essay, high school transcript, SAT or ACT. Recommended: minimum 3 high school GPA, 2 recommendations, interview. Entrance: minimally difficult. Application deadline: Rolling. Notification: continuous. SAT Reasoning Test deadline: 7/31. Transfer credits accepted: Yes.

Collegiate Environment: Orientation program. Drama-theater group, choral group, student-run newspaper. Social organizations: 65 open to all; local fraternities, local sororities. Most popular organizations: Psi Chi, APALSA, International Student Association, African Student Association, Forensics Student Association. Major annual events: Semi-Annual Block Party, Speaker Series, Access UB. Student services: health clinic, personal-psychological counseling. Campus security: 24-hour emergency response devices and patrols, late night transport-escort service. Langsdale Library plus 1 other with 258,747 books, 368,607 microform titles, 10,738 serials, an OPAC, and a Web page. 135 computers available on campus for general student use. Computer purchase/lease plans available. A campuswide network can be accessed from off-campus. Students can access the following: online class registration. Staffed computer lab on campus (open 24 hours a day) provides training in use of computers, software, and the Internet.

Community Environment: Baltimore is an important industrial and educational center for the state of Maryland and the regional northeastern United States. The port has an active international market and foreign trade. Downtown Baltimore has become a popular tourist site; the Inner Harbor complex, including Harborplace and the National Aquarium, is recognized internationally. New stadiums to house the Baltimore Orioles and Baltimore Ravens have been completed at Camden Yards in downtown Baltimore. Pimlico Race Course is the home of the annual Preakness race. University of Baltimore is located in the cultural center of the city, adjacent to the Lyric Opera House, Meyerhoff Symphony Hall and the Maryland Institute of Art.

■ UNIVERSITY OF MARYLAND, BALTIMORE COUNTY

1000 Hilltop Cir.
Baltimore, MD 21250
Tel: (410)455-1000; Free: 800-862-2402
Fax: (410)455-1210
E-mail: admissions@umbc.edu
Web Site: www.umbc.edu/

Description: State-supported, university, coed. Part of University System of Maryland. Awards bachelor's, master's, and doctoral degrees. Founded 1963. Setting: 530-acre suburban campus with easy access to Washington, DC. Endowment: $59.7 million. Research spending for the previous fiscal year: $55.2 million. Educational spending for the previous fiscal year: $9020 per student. Total enrollment: 13,637. Faculty: 776 (497 full-time, 279 part-time). Student-undergrad faculty ratio is 20:1. 8,514 applied, 60% were admitted. 29% from top 10% of their high school class, 56% from top quarter, 85% from top half. Full-time: 9,371 students, 45% women, 55% men. Part-time: 1,582 students, 46% women, 54% men. Students come from 40 states and territories, 85 other countries, 6% from out-of-state. 0.2% American Indian or Alaska Native, non-Hispanic/Latino; 5% Hispanic/Latino; 16% African American, non-Hispanic/Latino; 20% Asian, non-Hispanic/Latino; 0.2% Native Hawaiian or other Pacific Islander, non-Hispanic/Latino; 4% international. 15% 25 or older, 34% live on campus, 12% transferred in. Retention: 85% of full-time freshmen returned the following year. Academic areas with the most degrees conferred: social sciences; biological/life sciences; psychology; computer and information sciences. Core. Calendar: 4-1-4. Academic remediation for entering students, ESL program, services

for LD students, advanced placement, self-designed majors, freshman honors college, honors program, independent study, distance learning, double major, summer session for credit, part-time degree program, external degree program, adult/continuing education programs, co-op programs and internships, graduate courses open to undergrads. Off campus study at Johns Hopkins University, University System of Maryland. Study abroad program. ROTC: Army (c), Air Force (c).

Entrance Requirements: Options: electronic application, early admission, early action, deferred admission, international baccalaureate accepted. Required: essay, high school transcript, SAT or ACT. Recommended: minimum 3 high school GPA, 2 recommendations. Entrance: moderately difficult. Application deadlines: 2/1, 11/1 for early action. Notification: continuous, 12/15 for early action. SAT Reasoning Test deadline: 2/1. Transfer credits accepted: Yes. Applicants placed on waiting list: 393. Wait-listed applicants offered admission: 160. Early action applicants: 4,843. Early action applicants admitted: 2,581.

Costs Per Year: Application fee: $50. One-time mandatory fee: $125. State resident tuition: $7085 full-time, $295 per credit hour part-time. Nonresident tuition: $18,146 full-time, $754 per credit hour part-time. Mandatory fees: $2679 full-time, $115 per credit hour part-time. Full-time tuition and fees vary according to location and program. Part-time tuition and fees vary according to location and program. College room and board: $10,142. College room only: $6126. Room and board charges vary according to board plan and housing facility.

Collegiate Environment: Orientation program. Drama-theater group, choral group, student-run newspaper, radio station. Social organizations: 230 open to all; national fraternities, national sororities; 4% of eligible men and 5% of eligible women are members. Most popular organizations: Student Government Association, Student Events Board, Retriever Weekly, Resident Student Association, Freedom Alliance. Major annual events: Quadmania-Spring Festival, Welcome Week/Involvement Fest (student organizations fair), Homecoming. Student services: legal services, health clinic, personal-psychological counseling, women's center. Campus security: 24-hour emergency response devices and patrols, late night transport-escort service. 3,855 college housing spaces available; 3,754 were occupied in 2012-13. Freshmen guaranteed college housing. Option: coed housing available. Albin O. Kuhn Library and Gallery with 1 million books, 1 million microform titles, 33,080 serials, 2.2 million audiovisual materials, an OPAC, and a Web page. Operations spending for the previous fiscal year: $8.4 million. 965 computers available on campus for general student use. A campuswide network can be accessed from student residence rooms and from off campus. Students can access the following: online class registration, student account information. Staffed computer lab on campus (open 24 hours a day).

Community Environment: The ultramodern 500-acre campus is in an open-country setting in Catonsville, only minutes from the heart of Baltimore and less than an hour from the nation's capital. Baltimore, just six miles from the campus, is a rich resource for university students. Opportunities for musical, athletic, theatrical, and cultural events abound. The dynamic and dramatic Inner Harbor area features a convention center, the Maryland Science Center, Pier 7 Performing Arts Pavilion, the National Aquarium, and the lively collection of shops and restaurants called Harborplace. The Morris Mechanic Theatre brings Broadway to Baltimore, while the Baltimore Symphony Orchestra and internationally acclaimed artists perform in the striking Meyerhoff Concert Hall. The Walters Art Gallery, the Enoch Pratt Library, and Oriole Park at Camden Yards are also part of the city's rich tradition. Washington, only 32 miles from the campus, offers the student a wealth of academic, cultural, political, and leisure activities.

■ UNIVERSITY OF MARYLAND, COLLEGE PARK

College Park, MD 20742
Tel: (301)405-1000; Free: 800-422-5867
Fax: (301)314-9693
Web Site: www.maryland.edu/

Description: State-supported, university, coed. Part of University System of Maryland. Awards bachelor's, master's, and doctoral degrees and post-master's certificates. Founded 1856. Setting: 1,500-acre suburban campus with easy access to Baltimore and Washington, DC. Endowment: $377.1 million. Research spending for the previous fiscal year: $468 million. Educational spending for the previous fiscal year: $13,305 per student. Total enrollment: 37,197. Faculty: 2,375 (1,677 full-time, 698 part-time). Student-undergrad faculty ratio is 18:1. 25,255 applied, 47% were admitted. 71% from top 10% of their high school class, 87% from top quarter, 98% from top half. Full-time: 24,448 students, 47% women, 53% men. Part-time: 2,039 students, 45% women, 55% men. Students come from 48 states and territories, 103 other countries, 23% from out-of-state. 0.1% American Indian or Alaska Native, non-Hispanic/Latino; 8% Hispanic/Latino; 12% African American, non-Hispanic/Latino; 15% Asian, non-Hispanic/Latino; 0.1% Native Hawaiian or other Pacific Islander, non-Hispanic/Latino; 3% international. 7% 25 or older, 47% live on campus, 7% transferred in. Retention: 94% of full-time freshmen returned the following year. Academic areas with the most degrees conferred: social sciences; business/marketing; engineering. Core. Calendar: semesters. Academic remediation for entering students, ESL program, services for LD students, advanced placement, accelerated degree program, self-designed majors, honors program, independent study, distance learning, double major, summer session for credit, part-time degree program, external degree program, adult/continuing education programs, co-op programs and internships, graduate courses open to undergrads. Off campus study at Consortium of Universities of the Washington, DC Area. Study abroad program. ROTC: Army, Naval (c), Air Force.

Entrance Requirements: Options: electronic application, early admission, early action, deferred admission, international baccalaureate accepted. Required: essay, high school transcript, SAT or ACT. Recommended: 2 recommendations. Required for some: Resume of activities; audition for music applicants; drawing requirement for architecture applicants. Entrance: moderately difficult. Application deadlines: 1/20, 11/1 for early action. Notification: 4/1, 1/31 for early action. Preference given to state residents. SAT Reasoning Test deadline: 11/1. Transfer credits accepted: Yes. Applicants placed on waiting list: 969. Wait-listed applicants offered admission: 0. Early action applicants: 18,870. Early action applicants admitted: 10,396.

Costs Per Year: Application fee: $65. State resident tuition: $7175 full-time, $299 per credit hour part-time. Nonresident tuition: $25,554 full-time, $1065 per credit hour part-time. Mandatory fees: $1,734 full-time, $399.81 per term part-time. Part-time tuition and fees vary according to course load. College room and board: $9893. College room only: $5918. Room and board charges vary according to board plan and housing facility.

Collegiate Environment: Orientation program. Drama-theater group, choral group, marching band, student-run newspaper, radio station. Social organizations: 815 open to all; national fraternities, national sororities; 15% of eligible men and 15% of eligible women are members. Most popular organizations: Student Government Association, Residence Hall Association, Black Student Union, Asian-American Student Union/Jewish Student Union, Commuter Students Association. Major annual events: First Look Fair, All-Niter, Art Attack. Student services: legal services, health clinic, personal-psychological counseling, women's center. Campus security: 24-hour emergency response devices and patrols, student patrols, late night transport-escort service, controlled dormitory access, campus police, video camera surveillance. 11,894 college housing spaces available; all were occupied in 2012-13. Freshmen guaranteed college housing. Options: coed, women-only housing available. McKeldin Library plus 6 others with 3.9 million books, 5.9 million microform titles, 150,889 serials, 396,467 audiovisual materials, an OPAC, and a Web page. Operations spending for the previous fiscal year: $27.6 million. 3,890 computers available on campus for general student use. Computer purchase/lease plans available. A campuswide network can be accessed from student residence rooms and from off campus. Students can access the following: online class registration, student account information, financial aid summary.

■ UNIVERSITY OF MARYLAND EASTERN SHORE

Princess Anne, MD 21853-1299
Tel: (410)651-2200
Fax: (410)651-7922
Web Site: www.umes.edu/

Description: State-supported, university, coed. Part of University System of Maryland. Awards bachelor's, master's, and doctoral degrees. Founded 1886. Setting: 744-acre rural campus. Total enrollment: 4,454. Faculty: 345 (217 full-time, 128 part-time). Student-undergrad faculty ratio is 16:1. 4,409 applied, 57% were admitted. Full-time: 3,449 students, 57% women, 43% men. Part-time: 309 students, 55% women, 45% men. 19% from out-of-state. 0.1% American Indian or Alaska Native, non-Hispanic/Latino; 2% Hispanic/Latino; 77% African American, non-Hispanic/Latino; 1% Asian, non-Hispanic/Latino; 0.1% Native Hawaiian or other Pacific Islander, non-Hispanic/Latino; 3% international. 11% 25 or older, 60% live on campus, 6% transferred in. Academic areas with the most degrees conferred: homeland security, law enforcement, firefighting, and protective services; health professions and related sciences; business/marketing. Calendar: semesters. Part-time degree program. ROTC: Army (c).

Entrance Requirements: Options: electronic application, deferred admission. Required: essay, high school transcript, minimum 2.5 high school GPA,

3 recommendations, SAT or ACT. Required for some: essay, interview. Entrance: moderately difficult. Application deadline: 7/15. SAT Reasoning Test deadline: 7/15. Transfer credits accepted: Yes.

Costs Per Year: Application fee: $25. State resident tuition: $4628 full-time, $193 per credit hour part-time. Nonresident tuition: $13,134 full-time, $484 per credit hour part-time. Mandatory fees: $2370 full-time. Full-time tuition and fees vary according to course load. Part-time tuition varies according to course load. College room and board: $8374. College room only: $4324. Room and board charges vary according to board plan and housing facility.

Collegiate Environment: Orientation program. Campus security: 24-hour emergency response devices and patrols, student patrols, late night transport-escort service, controlled dormitory access. Options: coed, men-only, women-only housing available.

■ UNIVERSITY OF MARYLAND UNIVERSITY COLLEGE

3501 University Blvd. E
Adelphi, MD 20783
Tel: (301)985-7000; Free: 800-888-8682
Fax: (301)985-7678
E-mail: enroll@umuc.edu
Web Site: www.umuc.edu/

Description: State-supported, comprehensive, coed. Part of University System of Maryland. Awards associate, bachelor's, master's, and doctoral degrees and post-master's certificates (offers primarily part-time evening and weekend degree programs at more than 30 off-campus locations in Maryland and the Washington, DC area, and more than 180 military communities in Europe and Asia with military enrollment not reflected in this profile; associate of arts program available to military students only). Founded 1947. Setting: suburban campus with easy access to Washington, DC. Total enrollment: 42,268. Faculty: 2,712 (218 full-time, 2,494 part-time). Student-undergrad faculty ratio is 18:1. 3,308 applied, 99.9% were admitted. Full-time: 6,144 students, 53% women, 47% men. Part-time: 22,129 students, 50% women, 50% men. Students come from 54 states and territories, 26 other countries, 44% from out-of-state. 1% American Indian or Alaska Native, non-Hispanic/Latino; 8% Hispanic/Latino; 31% African American, non-Hispanic/Latino; 4% Asian, non-Hispanic/Latino; 0.4% Native Hawaiian or other Pacific Islander, non-Hispanic/Latino; 1% international. 84% 25 or older, 13% transferred in. Academic areas with the most degrees conferred: business/marketing; computer and information sciences; psychology. Core. Calendar: semesters. Services for LD students, advanced placement, accelerated degree program, independent study, distance learning, double major, summer session for credit, part-time degree program, external degree program, co-op programs. Off campus study.

Entrance Requirements: Open admission. Options: electronic application, deferred admission. Required: high school transcript. Entrance: noncompetitive. Application deadline: Rolling. Notification: continuous.

Costs Per Year: Application fee: $50. State resident tuition: $6024 full-time, $251 per credit hour part-time. Nonresident tuition: $11,976 full-time, $499 per credit hour part-time. Mandatory fees: $360 full-time, $15 per credit hour part-time.

Collegiate Environment: Campus security: 24-hour emergency response devices and patrols, late night transport-escort service. College housing not available. Information and Library Services plus 1 other with 1,597 books, 136 microform titles, 117,788 serials, 33 audiovisual materials, an OPAC, and a Web page. 363 computers available on campus for general student use. Computer purchase/lease plans available. A campuswide network can be accessed from off-campus. Students can access the following: online class registration. Staffed computer lab on campus provides training in use of computers, software, and the Internet.

Community Environment: The administrative site is located at College Park, a small town of 25,000. Programs are offered at more than 30 locations throughout Maryland, Northern Virginia, and the Washington, D.C. area.

■ UNIVERSITY OF PHOENIX–MARYLAND CAMPUS

8830 Stanford Blvd.
Ste. 100
Columbia, MD 21045-5424
Tel: (410)872-9001; Free: 866-766-0766
Web Site: www.phoenix.edu/

Description: Proprietary, comprehensive, coed. Awards bachelor's and master's degrees. Setting: urban campus. Total enrollment: 755. Faculty: 159 (22 full-time, 137 part-time). Full-time: 615 students, 62% women, 38% men. 92% 25 or older. Academic areas with the most degrees conferred:

business/marketing; computer and information sciences; homeland security, law enforcement, firefighting, and protective services. Core. Calendar: continuous. Services for LD students, advanced placement, accelerated degree program, independent study, distance learning, external degree program, adult/continuing education programs, graduate courses open to undergrads.

Entrance Requirements: Open admission. Options: electronic application, deferred admission. Required: 1 recommendation. Required for some: high school transcript. Entrance: noncompetitive. Application deadline: Rolling.

Collegiate Environment: Campus security: late night transport-escort service. University Library with 16,781 serials, an OPAC, and a Web page. Operations spending for the previous fiscal year: $6.8 million.

■ WASHINGTON ADVENTIST UNIVERSITY

7600 Flower Ave.
Takoma Park, MD 20912
Tel: (301)891-4000; Free: 800-835-4212
Fax: (301)891-4230
E-mail: enroll@cuc.edu
Web Site: www.wau.edu/

Description: Independent Seventh-day Adventist, comprehensive, coed. Awards associate, bachelor's, and master's degrees. Founded 1904. Setting: suburban campus. Total enrollment: 1,493. Faculty: 134 (52 full-time, 82 part-time). Student-undergrad faculty ratio is 14:1. Full-time: 1,058 students, 68% women, 32% men. Part-time: 269 students, 67% women, 33% men. 34% from out-of-state. 0.5% American Indian or Alaska Native, non-Hispanic/Latino; 10% Hispanic/Latino; 60% African American, non-Hispanic/Latino; 7% Asian, non-Hispanic/Latino. 27% 25 or older, 0% transferred in. Retention: 69% of full-time freshmen returned the following year. Academic areas with the most degrees conferred: health professions and related sciences; business/marketing; psychology. Calendar: semesters. Part-time degree program, external degree program, adult/continuing education programs.

Entrance Requirements: Options: electronic application, early admission, deferred admission. Required: essay, high school transcript, minimum 2.5 high school GPA, 2 recommendations, SAT or ACT. Required for some: interview. Entrance: moderately difficult. Application deadline: 8/1. Notification: continuous. SAT Subject Test deadline: 8/1.

Costs Per Year: Application fee: $25. Comprehensive fee: $27,820 includes full-time tuition ($18,900), mandatory fees ($1320), and college room and board ($7600). Room and board charges vary according to housing facility. Part-time tuition: $760 per credit hour. Part-time mandatory fees: $432.50 per term. Part-time tuition and fees vary according to class time and course load.

Collegiate Environment: Orientation program. Campus security: 24-hour emergency response devices and patrols, late night transport-escort service.

Community Environment: A suburb of Washington, D.C., the residents of Takoma Park enjoy the cultural and recreational facilities of that city. There are many opportunities for part-time employment. Shopping facilities are excellent.

■ WASHINGTON COLLEGE

300 Washington Ave.
Chestertown, MD 21620-1197
Tel: (410)778-2800; Free: 800-422-1782
Fax: (410)778-7287
E-mail: admissions_office@washcoll.edu
Web Site: www.washcoll.edu/

Description: Independent, comprehensive, coed. Awards bachelor's and master's degrees. Founded 1782. Setting: 140-acre small town campus with easy access to Baltimore and Washington, DC. Endowment: $173 million. Educational spending for the previous fiscal year: $13,597 per student. Total enrollment: 1,607. Faculty: 172 (91 full-time, 81 part-time). Student-undergrad faculty ratio is 12:1. 4,484 applied, 66% were admitted. 35% from top 10% of their high school class, 65% from top quarter, 90% from top half. Full-time: 1,519 students, 60% women, 40% men. Part-time: 43 students, 56% women, 44% men. 49% from out-of-state. 0.1% American Indian or Alaska Native, non-Hispanic/Latino; 4% Hispanic/Latino; 3% African American, non-Hispanic/Latino; 2% Asian, non-Hispanic/Latino; 0% Native Hawaiian or other Pacific Islander, non-Hispanic/Latino; 5% international. 1% 25 or older, 85% live on campus, 2% transferred in. Retention: 85% of full-time freshmen returned the following year. Academic areas with the most degrees conferred: social sciences; business/marketing; biological/life sciences. Core. Calendar: semesters. ESL program, services for LD students,

advanced placement, self-designed majors, honors program, independent study, double major, part-time degree program, internships. Off campus study. Study abroad program.

Entrance Requirements: Options: electronic application, early admission, early decision, early action, deferred admission, international baccalaureate accepted. Required: essay, high school transcript, 1 recommendation, SAT or ACT. Recommended: interview. Required for some: interview. Entrance: moderately difficult. Application deadlines: Rolling, 11/1 for early decision, 12/1 for early action. Notification: continuous, 12/1 for early decision, 1/15 for early action. SAT Reasoning Test deadline: 2/15. Transfer credits accepted: Yes. Applicants placed on waiting list: 426. Wait-listed applicants offered admission: 22. Early decision applicants: 51. Early decision applicants admitted: 43.

Costs Per Year: Application fee: $50. Comprehensive fee: $48,768 includes full-time tuition ($39,208), mandatory fees ($736), and college room and board ($8824). College room only: $4482. Room and board charges vary according to board plan, housing facility, and location. Part-time tuition: $1578 per credit hour. Part-time tuition varies according to course load.

Collegiate Environment: Orientation program. Drama-theater group, choral group, student-run newspaper, radio station. Social organizations: 85 open to all; national fraternities, national sororities; 6% of eligible men and 9% of eligible women are members. Most popular organizations: Writers Union, Student Government Association, Hands Out, Omicron Delta Kappa, Dale Adams Society. Major annual events: Convocation, Fall Weekend, Birthday Ball. Student services: health clinic, personal-psychological counseling. Campus security: 24-hour emergency response devices and patrols, student patrols, late night transport-escort service, controlled dormitory access. 1,223 college housing spaces available. Freshmen guaranteed college housing. On-campus residence required through sophomore year. Options: coed, men-only, women-only housing available. Clifton M. Miller Library with 241,165 books, 100,635 microform titles, 27,953 serials, 8,736 audiovisual materials, an OPAC, and a Web page. 100 computers available on campus for general student use. Computer purchase/lease plans available. A campuswide network can be accessed from student residence rooms and from off campus. Students can access the following: online class registration, thousands of wireless addresses available for students. Staffed computer lab on campus provides training in use of computers, software, and the Internet.

Community Environment: Chestertown is on the eastern shore of Maryland, 40 miles from Chesapeake Bay Bridge. The community facilities include churches and numerous civic and service organizations. Boating, fishing and hunting are some of the outdoor sports of the area.

■ WOR-WIC COMMUNITY COLLEGE

32000 Campus Dr.
Salisbury, MD 21804
Tel: (410)334-2800
E-mail: admissions@worwic.edu
Web Site: www.worwic.edu/

Description: State and locally supported, 2-year, coed. Awards certificates, transfer associate, and terminal associate degrees. Founded 1976. Setting: 202-acre small town campus. Endowment: $5.5 million. Educational spending for the previous fiscal year: $3091 per student. Total enrollment: 4,045. Faculty: 181 (68 full-time, 113 part-time). Student-undergrad faculty ratio is 21:1. 1,005 applied, 100% were admitted. Full-time: 1,290 students, 59% women, 41% men. Part-time: 2,755 students, 68% women, 32% men. Students come from 11 states and territories, 2% from out-of-state. 45% 25 or older, 7% transferred in. Calendar: semesters. Academic remediation for entering students, ESL program, services for LD students, advanced placement, accelerated degree program, honors program, independent study, distance learning, double major, summer session for credit, part-time degree program, adult/continuing education programs, internships.

Entrance Requirements: Open admission except for emergency medical services, nursing and radiologic technology programs. Option: early admission. Recommended: high school transcript. Required for some: ACT. Entrance: noncompetitive. Application deadline: Rolling. Transfer credits accepted: Yes.

Collegiate Environment: Orientation program. Drama-theater group, choral group, student-run newspaper. Social organizations: 17 open to all. Most popular organizations: Student Government Association, Arts Club, Hotel-Motel-Restaurant Student Organization, Phi Beta Lambda, Nursing Student Organization. Major annual events: Welcome Week, Dolphin Daze, Wellness

Day. Student services: personal-psychological counseling. Campus security: 24-hour emergency response devices, late night transport-escort service, patrols by trained security personnel 9 am to midnight. Patricia M. Hazel Media Center plus 2 others with 44 serials, 272 audiovisual materials, and a Web page. Operations spending for the previous fiscal year: $350,272. 657 computers available on campus for general student use. A campuswide network can be accessed from off-campus. Students can access the following: online class registration. Staffed computer lab on campus provides training in use of computers, software, and the Internet.

■ **YESHIVA COLLEGE OF THE NATION'S CAPITAL**
1216 Arcola Ave.
Silver Spring, MD 20902
Tel: (301)593-2534
Fax: (301)949-7040
Web Site: www.yeshiva.edu/
Description: Independent Jewish, 4-year, men only. Awards bachelor's degrees. Founded 1963. Total enrollment: 43. 30% 25 or older.
Entrance Requirements: Open admission.

■ AMERICAN INTERNATIONAL COLLEGE
1000 State St.
Springfield, MA 01109-3189
Tel: (413)737-7000; Free: 800-242-3142
Fax: (413)737-2803
E-mail: kim.lablanc@aic.edu
Web Site: www.aic.edu/
Description: Independent, comprehensive, coed. Awards associate, bachelor's, master's, and doctoral degrees and post-master's certificates. Founded 1885. Setting: 58-acre urban campus. Endowment: $5.3 million. Educational spending for the previous fiscal year: $5259 per student. Total enrollment: 3,401. Faculty: 323 (89 full-time, 234 part-time). Student-undergrad faculty ratio is 15:1. 1,469 applied, 79% were admitted. 22% from top 10% of their high school class. Full-time: 1,581 students, 57% women, 43% men. Part-time: 148 students, 72% women, 28% men. Students come from 27 states and territories, 25 other countries, 35% from out-of-state. 23% 25 or older, 51% live on campus, 12% transferred in. Retention: 60% of full-time freshmen returned the following year. Academic areas with the most degrees conferred: health professions and related sciences; business/marketing; homeland security, law enforcement, firefighting, and protective services. Core. Calendar: semesters. Academic remediation for entering students, ESL program, services for LD students, advanced placement, accelerated degree program, honors program, independent study, double major, summer session for credit, part-time degree program, adult/continuing education programs, internships, graduate courses open to undergrads. Off campus study at Cooperating Colleges of Greater Springfield. Study abroad program. ROTC: Army (c), Air Force (c).
Entrance Requirements: Options: electronic application, early admission, deferred admission, international baccalaureate accepted. Required: high school transcript, minimum 2.5 high school GPA, 1 recommendation, SAT or ACT. Recommended: essay, interview. Required for some: interview. Entrance: moderately difficult. Application deadline: Rolling. Notification: continuous. SAT Reasoning Test deadline: 8/15. Transfer credits accepted: Yes.
Costs Per Year: Application fee: $25. Comprehensive fee: $40,868 includes full-time tuition ($29,158) and college room and board ($11,710). Full-time tuition varies according to program. Room and board charges vary according to board plan and housing facility. Part-time tuition: $601 per credit hour. Part-time mandatory fees: $30 per term. Part-time tuition and fees vary according to course load and program.
Collegiate Environment: Orientation program. Drama-theater group, choral group, student-run newspaper, radio station. Social organizations: 40 open to all; local fraternities, local sororities; 1% of eligible men and 11% of eligible women are members. Most popular organizations: Student Activities Committee, Best Buddies Program, PRIDE (Persons Ready in Defense of Ebony), student government, Partners Program. Major annual events: Homecoming, Model Congress, Press Forum. Student services: health clinic, personal-psychological counseling. Campus security: 24-hour emergency response devices and patrols, student patrols, late night transport-escort service, controlled dormitory access. James J. Shea Jr. Library with 70,741 books, 293 microform titles, 7,211 serials, 1,749 audiovisual materials, an OPAC, and a Web page. Operations spending for the previous fiscal year: $644,331. 175 computers available on campus for general student use. Computer purchase/lease plans available. A campuswide network can be accessed from student residence rooms and

from off campus. Students can access the following: online class registration. Staffed computer lab on campus provides training in use of computers, software, and the Internet.
Community Environment: Springfield is a city of 152,000 that offers a multitude of activities for college students, including a quadrangle of museums, the Stage West Theater Company, and the Springfield Civic Center.

■ AMHERST COLLEGE
PO Box 5000
Amherst, MA 01002-5000
Tel: (413)542-2000
Fax: (413)542-2040
E-mail: admission@amherst.edu
Web Site: www.amherst.edu/
Description: Independent, 4-year, coed. Awards bachelor's degrees. Founded 1821. Setting: 1,020-acre small town campus. Endowment: $1.6 billion. Total enrollment: 1,817. Faculty: 253 (211 full-time, 42 part-time). Student-undergrad faculty ratio is 8:1. 8,565 applied, 13% were admitted. 83% from top 10% of their high school class, 95% from top quarter, 100% from top half. Full-time: 1,817 students, 49% women, 51% men. Students come from 50 states and territories, 50 other countries, 86% from out-of-state. 0.1% American Indian or Alaska Native, non-Hispanic/Latino; 12% Hispanic/Latino; 11% African American, non-Hispanic/Latino; 12% Asian, non-Hispanic/Latino; 0% Native Hawaiian or other Pacific Islander, non-Hispanic/Latino; 10% international. 2% 25 or older, 99% live on campus, 1% transferred in. Retention: 98% of full-time freshmen returned the following year. Academic areas with the most degrees conferred: social sciences; English; foreign languages and literature. Calendar: semesters. Self-designed majors, honors program, independent study, double major. Off campus study at Five Colleges, Inc., Twelve College Exchange Program. Study abroad program. ROTC: Army (c), Air Force (c).
Entrance Requirements: Options: electronic application, early admission, early decision, deferred admission. Required: essay, high school transcript, 3 recommendations, Amherst College Supplement, SAT and SAT Subject Tests or ACT. Entrance: most difficult. Application deadlines: 1/1, 11/15 for early decision. Notification: 4/1, 12/15 for early decision. SAT Reasoning Test deadline: 1/1. SAT Subject Test deadline: 1/1. Applicants placed on waiting list: 1,430. Wait-listed applicants offered admission: 80. Early decision applicants: 490. Early decision applicants admitted: 183.
Costs Per Year: Application fee: $60. Comprehensive fee: $56,260 includes full-time tuition ($43,860), mandatory fees ($750), and college room and board ($11,650). College room only: $6310.
Collegiate Environment: Orientation program. Drama-theater group, choral group, student-run newspaper, radio station. Social organizations: 100 open to all. Most popular organizations: choral groups, WAMH (campus radio station), OUTREACH (community service), literary magazines, The Amherst Student (school newspaper). Major annual events: Homecoming, Casino Night, Newport Jazz. Student services: health clinic, personal-psychological counseling, women's center. Campus security: 24-hour emergency response devices and patrols, student patrols, late night transport-escort service, controlled dormitory access. Freshmen guaranteed college housing. On-campus residence required through senior year. Option: coed housing available. Robert Frost Library plus 5 others with 1 million books, 539,789 microform titles, 12,190 serials, 48,742 audiovisual materials, an OPAC, and a Web page. 182 computers available on campus for general student use.

Computer purchase/lease plans available. A campuswide network can be accessed from student residence rooms and from off campus. Staffed computer lab on campus provides training in use of computers, software, and the Internet.

Community Environment: Well-known American poets Emily Dickinson, Robert Frost and Eugene Field, and author Ray Stannard Baker (David Grayson) all lived in Amherst. Located on eastern edge of Connecticut Valley, the town has mean winter temperature of 25.2 degrees, and summer, 72 degrees. Annual rainfall is 43.8 inches. Rail and bus service is available. Free 5-college bus system connects all five institutions. Recreation provided at Mt. Sugarloaf and Mt. Tom Reservation nearby. Town has theatres, golf, tennis, fishing, and ice skating. Community opera performs annually. Nearby are the Pelham Hills, where Daniel Shays organized his rebellion; Deerfield, with its Bloody Brook, so named after a 17th-century clash between Indians and settlers; the Holyoke Range; and byways reminiscent of colonial days. Tobacco farms and apple orchards dot the Connecticut River valley, and throughout the neighboring hills are many opportunities for hiking, canoeing, and skiing amid the small villages, farms, and abandoned factories of another age. An exciting community lies in the midst of this bucolic setting. Amherst students and townspeople alike thrive on the contemporary vitality of a major academic center, since both Hampshire College and the University of Massachusetts are also located in Amherst, with Smith and Mount Holyoke Colleges nearby. The resulting concentration of students, teachers, practicing artists, and visiting speakers makes the area a hub of scholarship and creativity. It has even been said that, after Boston, the Pioneer Valley offers the richest array of cultural events in New England.

■ **ANNA MARIA COLLEGE**

50 Sunset Ln.
Paxton, MA 01612
Tel: (508)849-3300
E-mail: admissions@annamaria.edu
Web Site: www.annamaria.edu/

Description: Independent Roman Catholic, comprehensive, coed. Awards associate, bachelor's, and master's degrees and post-master's certificates. Founded 1946. Setting: 192-acre rural campus with easy access to Boston. System endowment: $4.7 million. Educational spending for the previous fiscal year: $6755 per student. Total enrollment: 1,456. Faculty: 200 (47 full-time, 153 part-time). Student-undergrad faculty ratio is 12:1. 2,394 applied, 60% were admitted. Full-time: 803 students, 49% women, 51% men. Part-time: 214 students, 55% women, 45% men. Students come from 28 states and territories, 22% from out-of-state. 1% American Indian or Alaska Native, non-Hispanic/Latino; 8% Hispanic/Latino; 8% African American, non-Hispanic/Latino; 1% Asian, non-Hispanic/Latino; 0% Native Hawaiian or other Pacific Islander, non-Hispanic/Latino; 0% international. 20% 25 or older, 46% live on campus, 4% transferred in. Core. Calendar: semesters. Academic remediation for entering students, services for LD students, advanced placement, accelerated degree program, self-designed majors, honors program, independent study, distance learning, double major, summer session for credit, part-time degree program, adult/continuing education programs, co-op programs and internships, graduate courses open to undergrads. Off campus study at Colleges of Worcester Consortium. Study abroad program. ROTC: Air Force (c).

Entrance Requirements: Options: electronic application, deferred admission, international baccalaureate accepted. Required: high school transcript, minimum 2 high school GPA, SAT or ACT. Recommended: 1 recommendation, interview. Required for some: essay, audition for music programs, portfolio for art programs. Entrance: minimally difficult. Application deadline: Rolling. Notification: continuous. Transfer credits accepted: Yes.

Costs Per Year: Application fee: $40. Comprehensive fee: $41,906 includes full-time tuition ($28,752), mandatory fees ($1704), and college room and board ($11,450). Full-time tuition and fees vary according to course load and program. Room and board charges vary according to board plan and housing facility.

Collegiate Environment: Orientation program. Drama-theater group, choral group, marching band. Social organizations: 15 open to all. Most popular organizations: Habitat for Humanity, Social Action Group, Chorus Club, Alana, Programming Board - AMCAB. Major annual events: President's Christmas Dinner, semi-formal, Spring Weekend. Student services: health clinic, personal-psychological counseling. Campus security: 24-hour emergency response devices and patrols, late night transport-escort service, controlled dormitory access. Mondor-Eagen Library with an OPAC. Operations spending for the previous fiscal year: $329,858. 85 computers available on campus for general student use. A campuswide network can be accessed

from student residence rooms. Students can access the following: online class registration, student account information.

Community Environment: Paxton is located in the geographical center of Massachusetts, eight miles northwest of Worcester and a one-hour drive from Boston or Providence. Summer and winter sports are available in the area. Excellent job opportunities are available in the immediate area.

■ **ASSUMPTION COLLEGE**

500 Salisbury St.
Worcester, MA 01609-1296
Tel: (508)767-7000; Free: 866-477-7776
Fax: (508)799-4412
E-mail: admiss@assumption.edu
Web Site: www.assumption.edu/

Description: Independent Roman Catholic, comprehensive, coed. Awards bachelor's and master's degrees and post-master's certificates. Founded 1904. Setting: 180-acre suburban campus with easy access to Boston. Endowment: $79.2 million. Educational spending for the previous fiscal year: $7924 per student. Total enrollment: 2,588. Faculty: 228 (145 full-time, 83 part-time). Student-undergrad faculty ratio is 12:1. 4,440 applied, 75% were admitted. 19% from top 10% of their high school class, 51% from top quarter, 84% from top half. Full-time: 2,031 students, 60% women, 40% men. Part-time: 25 students, 56% women, 44% men. Students come from 25 states and territories, 28 other countries, 37% from out-of-state. 0.1% American Indian or Alaska Native, non-Hispanic/Latino; 6% Hispanic/Latino; 4% African American, non-Hispanic/Latino; 2% Asian, non-Hispanic/Latino; 0% Native Hawaiian or other Pacific Islander, non-Hispanic/Latino; 1% international. 1% 25 or older, 92% live on campus, 2% transferred in. Retention: 81% of full-time freshmen returned the following year. Academic areas with the most degrees conferred: business/marketing; psychology; social sciences. Core. Calendar: semesters. Services for LD students, advanced placement, self-designed majors, honors program, independent study, double major, summer session for credit, part-time degree program, internships, graduate courses open to undergrads. Off campus study at Colleges of Worcester Consortium. Study abroad program. ROTC: Army (c), Air Force (c).

Entrance Requirements: Options: electronic application, early action, deferred admission, international baccalaureate accepted. Required: essay, high school transcript, 1 recommendation. Recommended: interview. Entrance: moderately difficult. Application deadlines: 2/15, 11/1 for early action. Notification: continuous, 12/15 for early action. SAT Reasoning Test deadline: 2/15. Transfer credits accepted: Yes. Applicants placed on waiting list: 387. Wait-listed applicants offered admission: 40. Early action applicants: 2,859. Early action applicants admitted: 2,394.

Costs Per Year: Application fee: $50. Comprehensive fee: $44,395 includes full-time tuition ($33,390), mandatory fees ($415), and college room and board ($10,590). College room only: $6660. Full-time tuition and fees vary according to course load and reciprocity agreements. Room and board charges vary according to housing facility. Part-time tuition: $1113 per credit hour. Part-time tuition varies according to course load.

Collegiate Environment: Orientation program. Drama-theater group, choral group, student-run newspaper. Social organizations: 60 open to all. Most popular organizations: Volunteer center, Campus Activities Board, student government, Campus Ministry, intramural sports. Major annual events: Family weekend, Spring Concert, Midnight Breakfast. Student services: health clinic, personal-psychological counseling. Campus security: 24-hour emergency response devices and patrols, student patrols, late night transport-escort service, controlled dormitory access, front gate security, well-lit pathways. 1,939 college housing spaces available; 1,781 were occupied in 2012-13. Freshmen guaranteed college housing. Options: coed, women-only housing available. Emmanuel d'Alzon Library with 219,558 books, 24,166 microform titles, 49,188 serials, 3,751 audiovisual materials, an OPAC, and a Web page. Operations spending for the previous fiscal year: $1.6 million. 361 computers available on campus for general student use. Computer purchase/lease plans available. A campuswide network can be accessed from student residence rooms and from off campus. Students can access the following: online class registration. Staffed computer lab on campus provides training in use of computers, software, and the Internet.

Community Environment: 175-acre park-like campus situated in residential section of city. See Clark University for area details.

■ **BABSON COLLEGE**

Babson Park, MA 02457-0310
Tel: (781)235-1200; Free: 800-488-3696

Fax: (781)239-5614
E-mail: ugradadmission@babson.edu
Web Site: www.babson.edu/

Description: Independent, comprehensive, coed. Awards bachelor's and master's degrees and post-master's certificates. Founded 1919. Setting: 370-acre suburban campus with easy access to Boston. Total enrollment: 3,250. Faculty: 261 (163 full-time, 98 part-time). Student-undergrad faculty ratio is 15:1. 5,512 applied, 30% were admitted. 53% from top 10% of their high school class, 84% from top quarter, 98% from top half. Full-time: 2,015 students, 44% women, 56% men. Students come from 41 states and territories, 70% from out-of-state. 0.2% American Indian or Alaska Native, non-Hispanic/Latino; 10% Hispanic/Latino; 4% African American, non-Hispanic/Latino; 12% Asian, non-Hispanic/Latino; 0% Native Hawaiian or other Pacific Islander, non-Hispanic/Latino; 27% international. 1% 25 or older, 85% live on campus, 2% transferred in. Retention: 94% of full-time freshmen returned the following year. Academic area with the most degrees conferred: business/marketing. Core. Calendar: semesters. Services for LD students, advanced placement, self-designed majors, freshman honors college, honors program, independent study, summer session for credit, internships. Off campus study at Pine Manor College, Regis College (MA), Brandeis University, Wellesley College, Olin College of Engineering. Study abroad program. ROTC: Army (c), Naval (c), Air Force (c).

Entrance Requirements: Options: electronic application, early decision, early action, deferred admission, international baccalaureate accepted. Required: essay, high school transcript, 2 recommendations, SAT or ACT. Recommended: interview, TOEFL or IELTS for non-native English speakers. Entrance: very difficult. Application deadlines: 1/1, 11/1 for early decision, 11/1 for early action. Notification: 4/1, 12/15 for early decision, 1/1 for early action. SAT Reasoning Test deadline: 1/1. Transfer credits accepted: Yes. Applicants placed on waiting list: 1,190. Wait-listed applicants offered admission: 25.

Costs Per Year: Application fee: $75. Comprehensive fee: $57,662 includes full-time tuition ($43,520) and college room and board ($14,142). College room only: $9126. Room and board charges vary according to board plan and housing facility.

Collegiate Environment: Orientation program. Drama-theater group, choral group, student-run newspaper, radio station. Social organizations: national fraternities, national sororities. Most popular organizations: Student Government Association, Free Press, Dance Ensemble, Asian Pacific Student Association, College Radio. Major annual events: Oktoberfest, Spring Weekend, Family Weekend. Student services: health clinic, personal-psychological counseling, women's center. Campus security: 24-hour emergency response devices and patrols, late night transport-escort service, controlled dormitory access. Freshmen guaranteed college housing. On-campus residence required in freshman year. Options: coed, men-only housing available. Horn Library plus 1 other with an OPAC and a Web page.

Community Environment: Breadth distinguishes Babson from other undergraduate management programs. The focus of the Babson education blends professional (50%) and liberal arts (50%) courses with campus and field experiences in a small college setting where both halves of the faculty work together to help students perform well and to grow in response to change. Babson is located 30 minutes by car from Boston.

■ BARD COLLEGE AT SIMON'S ROCK

84 Alford Rd.
Great Barrington, MA 01230-9702
Tel: (413)528-0771; Free: 800-235-7186
Fax: (413)528-7334
E-mail: admit@simons-rock.edu
Web Site: www.simons-rock.edu/

Description: Independent, 4-year, coed. Administratively affiliated with Bard College. Awards associate and bachelor's degrees. Founded 1964. Setting: 210-acre small town campus with easy access to Boston, New York City. Total enrollment: 350. Faculty: 71 (45 full-time, 26 part-time). Student-undergrad faculty ratio is 7:1. 290 applied, 87% were admitted. 53% from top 10% of their high school class, 84% from top quarter, 93% from top half. Full-time: 344 students, 66% women, 34% men. Part-time: 6 students, 33% women, 67% men. Students come from 36 states and territories, 13 other countries, 87% from out-of-state. 0.3% American Indian or Alaska Native, non-Hispanic/Latino; 5% Hispanic/Latino; 10% African American, non-Hispanic/Latino; 7% Asian, non-Hispanic/Latino; 0% Native Hawaiian or other Pacific Islander, non-Hispanic/Latino; 5% international. 0% 25 or older, 88% live on campus, 0.3% transferred in. Retention: 81% of full-time freshmen returned the following year. Academic areas with the most degrees

conferred: visual and performing arts; liberal arts/general studies; English; social sciences. Core. Calendar: semesters. Services for LD students, self-designed majors, independent study, double major, co-op programs and internships. Off campus study at Bard College, Columbia University, Dartmouth College, Bard Globalization and International Affairs Program. Study abroad program.

Entrance Requirements: Required: essay, high school transcript, 3 recommendations, interview, school report, parent supplement. Entrance: moderately difficult. Application deadlines: 5/31, 5/31 for nonresidents. Notification: continuous. Transfer credits accepted: Yes. Applicants placed on waiting list: 0. Wait-listed applicants offered admission: 0.

Collegiate Environment: Orientation program. Drama-theater group, choral group, student-run newspaper. Social organizations: 35 open to all. Most popular organizations: Black Student Union, QueerSA, Student Action Service Learning, U.S.O. (Untitled Student Organization), Boffing. Major annual events: MayFest, Prom, Dance Concert. Student services: health clinic, personal-psychological counseling, women's center. Campus security: 24-hour patrols, controlled dormitory access. Alumni Library with 71,702 books, 3,896 microform titles, 1,842 serials, 5,394 audiovisual materials, an OPAC, and a Web page. Operations spending for the previous fiscal year: $351,000. 80 computers available on campus for general student use. A campuswide network can be accessed from student residence rooms and from off campus. Staffed computer lab on campus provides training in use of computers, software, and the Internet.

■ BAY PATH COLLEGE

588 Longmeadow St.
Longmeadow, MA 01106-2292
Tel: (413)565-1000; Free: 800-782-7284
Fax: (413)567-0501
Web Site: www.baypath.edu/

Description: Independent, comprehensive. Awards associate, bachelor's, and master's degrees and post-master's certificates. Founded 1897. Setting: 48-acre suburban campus with easy access to Hartford, CT and Boston, MA. Endowment: $31.7 million. Educational spending for the previous fiscal year: $5566 per student. Total enrollment: 2,370. Faculty: 230 (55 full-time, 175 part-time). Student-undergrad faculty ratio is 12:1. 978 applied, 61% were admitted. 12% from top 10% of their high school class, 41% from top quarter, 78% from top half. Full-time: 1,259 students, 100% women. Part-time: 299 students, 100% women. Students come from 18 states and territories, 3 other countries, 37% from out-of-state. 0.4% American Indian or Alaska Native, non-Hispanic/Latino; 14% Hispanic/Latino; 12% African American, non-Hispanic/Latino; 1% Asian, non-Hispanic/Latino; 0.2% Native Hawaiian or other Pacific Islander, non-Hispanic/Latino; 0.4% international. 56% 25 or older, 63% live on campus, 19% transferred in. Retention: 74% of full-time freshmen returned the following year. Academic areas with the most degrees conferred: liberal arts/general studies; business/marketing; psychology. Core. Calendar: semesters. Academic remediation for entering students, ESL program, services for LD students, advanced placement, accelerated degree program, self-designed majors, honors program, independent study, distance learning, double major, summer session for credit, part-time degree program, adult/continuing education programs, co-op programs and internships, graduate courses open to undergrads. Off campus study at Cooperating Colleges of Greater Springfield. Study abroad program. ROTC: Army (c), Air Force (c).

Entrance Requirements: Options: electronic application, early admission, early action, deferred admission, international baccalaureate accepted. Required: high school transcript, SAT or ACT. Recommended: essay, minimum 2 high school GPA, interview. Required for some: interview. Entrance: moderately difficult. Application deadlines: Rolling, 12/15 for early action. Notification: continuous, 1/2 for early action. SAT Reasoning Test deadline: 7/1. Transfer credits accepted: Yes.

Costs Per Year: Application fee: $25. Comprehensive fee: $39,972 includes full-time tuition ($28,532) and college room and board ($11,440). Room and board charges vary according to board plan. Part-time tuition: $480 per credit. Part-time tuition varies according to course load.

Collegiate Environment: Orientation program. Drama-theater group, choral group. Social organizations: 33 open to all. Most popular organizations: student government, Black Student Association, Golden Z Service Club, Alliance, Women of Culture. Major annual events: Campus Day, Campus Awakening, Karaoke Unplugged. Student services: health clinic, personal-psychological counseling. Campus security: 24-hour emergency response devices and patrols, late night transport-escort service, controlled dormitory access. 410 college housing spaces available; 364 were occupied in 2012-

13. Freshmen guaranteed college housing. Option: women-only housing available. Hatch Library with 151,798 books, 4,410 microform titles, 308 serials, 17,522 audiovisual materials, an OPAC, and a Web page. Operations spending for the previous fiscal year: $778,361. 350 computers available on campus for general student use. A campuswide network can be accessed from student residence rooms and from off campus. Students can access the following: online class registration.

Community Environment: Longmeadow is a small, residential, historic town located on the Connecticut/Massachusetts border. Its location near two major cities provides cultural and social advantages.

■ BAY STATE COLLEGE
122 Commonwealth Ave.
Boston, MA 02116-2975
Tel: (617)236-8000; Free: 800-81-LEARN
Fax: (617)536-1735
E-mail: admissions@baystate.edu
Web Site: www.baystate.edu/

Description: Independent, primarily 2-year, coed. Awards diplomas, transfer associate, terminal associate, and bachelor's degrees. Founded 1946. Setting: urban campus. Total enrollment: 1,153. Student-undergrad faculty ratio is 16:1. 1,761 applied, 59% were admitted. 14% from out-of-state. 43% 25 or older. Retention: 76% of full-time freshmen returned the following year. Core. Calendar: semesters. Academic remediation for entering students, ESL program, advanced placement, independent study, part-time degree program, adult/continuing education programs, co-op programs and internships.

Entrance Requirements: Option: early admission. Required: high school transcript, minimum 2.3 high school GPA. Recommended: interview, SAT or ACT. Entrance: minimally difficult. Application deadline: Rolling.

Collegiate Environment: Orientation program. Student services: personal-psychological counseling. Campus security: late night transport-escort service, controlled dormitory access, 14-hour patrols by trained security personnel. Options: coed, women-only housing available. Bay State College Library with 6,000 books, 80 serials, and an OPAC.

Community Environment: See Boston University.

■ BECKER COLLEGE
61 Sever St.
Worcester, MA 01609
Tel: (508)791-9241; Free: 877-5BECKER
Fax: (508)831-7505
E-mail: admissions@becker.edu
Web Site: www.becker.edu/

Description: Independent, 4-year, coed. Awards associate and bachelor's degrees (also includes Leicester, MA small town campus). Founded 1784. Setting: 100-acre urban campus with easy access to Boston. Total enrollment: 1,826. Faculty: 193 (44 full-time, 149 part-time). Student-undergrad faculty ratio is 16:1. 3,350 applied, 62% were admitted. 4% from top 10% of their high school class, 27% from top quarter, 62% from top half. Full-time: 1,403 students, 52% women, 48% men. Part-time: 423 students, 77% women, 23% men. Students come from 33 states and territories, 19 other countries, 31% from out-of-state. 0.3% American Indian or Alaska Native, non-Hispanic/Latino; 8% Hispanic/Latino; 7% African American, non-Hispanic/Latino; 1% Asian, non-Hispanic/Latino; 0.1% Native Hawaiian or other Pacific Islander, non-Hispanic/Latino; 1% international. 27% 25 or older, 39% live on campus, 10% transferred in. Retention: 65% of full-time freshmen returned the following year. Academic areas with the most degrees conferred: business/marketing; psychology; education. Core. Calendar: semesters. Academic remediation for entering students, services for LD students, advanced placement, accelerated degree program, honors program, independent study, distance learning, part-time degree program, adult/continuing education programs, co-op programs and internships. Off campus study at Colleges of Worcester Consortium. Study abroad program. ROTC: Army (c).

Entrance Requirements: Options: electronic application, early admission, early action, deferred admission, international baccalaureate accepted. Required: high school transcript, minimum 2 high school GPA, 1 recommendation, SAT or ACT. Recommended: essay. Required for some: interview. Entrance: moderately difficult. Application deadlines: Rolling, 11/15 for early action. Notification: continuous, 12/15 for early action. SAT Reasoning Test deadline: 5/1. Transfer credits accepted: Yes.

Costs Per Year: Comprehensive fee: $41,390 includes full-time tuition ($28,900), mandatory fees ($1440), and college room and board ($11,050).

Full-time tuition and fees vary according to class time, course load, and program. Room and board charges vary according to board plan and housing facility. Part-time tuition: $1200 per credit hour. Part-time tuition varies according to class time, course load, and program.

Collegiate Environment: Orientation program. Drama-theater group, choral group, student-run newspaper. Social organizations: 30 open to all. Most popular organizations: student government, Student Activities Committee, Black Student Union, Animal Health Club, Drama Club. Major annual events: Family Weekend, Halloween Week, Spring Week. Student services: health clinic, personal-psychological counseling. Campus security: 24-hour emergency response devices and patrols, late night transport-escort service, controlled dormitory access. 679 college housing spaces available. Freshmen given priority for college housing. Options: coed, men-only, women-only housing available. Ruska Library plus 1 other with 75,000 books, 2,230 microform titles, 400 serials, and an OPAC. 155 computers available on campus for general student use. A campuswide network can be accessed from student residence rooms and from off campus. Students can access the following: online class registration. Staffed computer lab on campus provides training in use of computers, software, and the Internet.

■ BENJAMIN FRANKLIN INSTITUTE OF TECHNOLOGY
41 Berkeley St.
Boston, MA 02116-6296
Tel: (617)423-4630; Free: 877-400-BFIT
Fax: (617)482-3706
E-mail: bjohnson@bfit.edu
Web Site: www.bfit.edu/

Description: Independent, primarily 2-year, coed. Awards certificates, transfer associate, terminal associate, and bachelor's degrees. Founded 1908. Setting: 3-acre urban campus. Total enrollment: 536. Faculty: 70 (30 full-time, 40 part-time). Student-undergrad faculty ratio is 12:1. 964 applied, 66% were admitted. Full-time: 416 students, 10% women, 90% men. Part-time: 120 students, 14% women, 86% men. Students come from 7 states and territories, 5% from out-of-state, 19% 25 or older, 11% live on campus, 7% transferred in. Core. Calendar: semesters. Academic remediation for entering students, ESL program, services for LD students, advanced placement, summer session for credit, part-time degree program, adult/continuing education programs, co-op programs and internships. Off campus study at University of Massachusetts - Dartmouth, Boston Architectural College, Wentworth Institute of Technology.

Entrance Requirements: Open admission. Options: electronic application, deferred admission, international baccalaureate accepted. Required: high school transcript. Recommended: essay, minimum 2 high school GPA, interview. Entrance: minimally difficult. Application deadline: Rolling. Notification: continuous.

Costs Per Year: Application fee: $25. Tuition: $16,950 full-time, $707 per credit hour part-time. Full-time tuition varies according to course load and degree level. Part-time tuition varies according to course load and degree level. College room only: $10,200. Room charges vary according to housing facility.

Collegiate Environment: Orientation program. Social organizations: 25 open to all. Most popular organizations: Phi Theta Kappa, Student Government and Leadership, yearbook and video club, Green Technology Club, Women's Forum. Major annual events: Technology Olympics, Multicultural Feast, Spring Carnival. Student services: personal-psychological counseling. Campus security: 24-hour emergency response devices. Lufkin Memorial Library with 10,000 books, 90 serials, and an OPAC. 100 computers available on campus for general student use. Computer purchase/lease plans available. A campuswide network can be accessed from student residence rooms. Students can access the following: online payments. Staffed computer lab on campus provides training in use of computers, software, and the Internet.

■ BENTLEY UNIVERSITY
175 Forest St.
Waltham, MA 02452-4705
Tel: (781)891-2000; Free: 800-523-2354
Fax: (781)891-3414
E-mail: ugadmission@bentley.edu
Web Site: www.bentley.edu/

Description: Independent, comprehensive, coed. Awards associate, bachelor's, master's, and doctoral degrees and post-master's certificates. Founded 1917. Setting: 163-acre suburban campus with easy access to Boston. Endowment: $207.8 million. Research spending for the previous fiscal year: $3.5 million. Educational spending for the previous fiscal year: $12,869 per student. Total enrollment: 5,565. Faculty: 448 (280 full-time, 168 part-time). Student-undergrad faculty ratio is 14:1. 6,695 applied, 43% were admitted. 45% from top 10% of their high school class, 82% from top quarter, 98% from top half. Full-time: 4,066 students, 41% women, 59% men. Part-time: 162 students, 43% women, 57% men. Students come from 40 states and territories, 83 other countries, 52% from out-of-state. 0.1% American Indian or Alaska Native, non-Hispanic/Latino; 7% Hispanic/Latino; 3% African American, non-Hispanic/Latino; 7% Asian, non-Hispanic/Latino; 0% Native Hawaiian or other Pacific Islander, non-Hispanic/Latino; 13% international. 4% 25 or older, 79% live on campus, 3% transferred in. Retention: 94% of full-time freshmen returned the following year. Academic areas with the most degrees conferred: business/marketing; computer and information sciences; mathematics and statistics. Core. Calendar: semesters. Services for LD students, advanced placement, accelerated degree program, self-designed majors, honors program, independent study, double major, summer session for credit, adult/continuing education programs, internships, graduate courses open to undergrads. Off campus study. Study abroad program. ROTC: Army (c), Air Force (c).

Entrance Requirements: Options: electronic application, early admission, early action, deferred admission, international baccalaureate accepted. Required: essay, high school transcript, 2 recommendations, SAT or ACT. Required for some: interview, TOEFL (or IELTS) is required form non-native English speakers unless the student receives at least 577 (paper-based) or 90 (Internet-based) on the writing section of the SAT. Entrance: very difficult. Application deadlines: 1/15, 1/15 for nonresidents, 11/15 for early action. Notification: 4/1, 4/1 for nonresidents, 1/15 for early action. Transfer credits accepted: Yes. Applicants placed on waiting list: 1,400. Wait-listed applicants offered admission: 83. Early action applicants: 2,747. Early action applicants admitted: 1,610.

Costs Per Year: Application fee: $50. Comprehensive fee: $52,588 includes full-time tuition ($38,130), mandatory fees ($1498), and college room and board ($12,960). College room only: $7790. Room and board charges vary according to board plan and housing facility. Part-time tuition: $1932 per course. Part-time mandatory fees: $45 per term. Part-time tuition and fees vary according to class time and course load.

Collegiate Environment: Orientation program. Drama-theater group, choral group, student-run newspaper, radio station. Social organizations: 109 open to all; national fraternities, national sororities, local fraternities; 10% of eligible men and 14% of eligible women are members. Most popular organizations: Bentley Entrepreneurship Society, Campus Activities Board, Delta Sigma Pi, Bentley Investment Group, National Association of Black Accountants. Major annual events: Spring Day, Homecoming, Super Bingo. Student services: health clinic, personal-psychological counseling, women's center. Campus security: 24-hour emergency response devices and patrols, late night transport-escort service, controlled dormitory access, security cameras, Community Policing Team, self-defense classes, CPR and first-aid training. 3,350 undergraduates lived in college housing during 2012-13. Freshmen guaranteed college housing. Option: coed housing available. Bentley Library with 173,000 books, 4,000 microform titles, 55,700 serials, 9,900 audiovisual materials, an OPAC, and a Web page. Operations spending for the previous fiscal year: $2.7 million. 4,489 computers available on campus for general student use. Computer purchase/lease plans available. A computer is required for all students. A campuswide network can be accessed from student residence rooms and from off campus. Students can access the following: online class registration, Grade checking, online admission, Blackboard, resume review, student employment, interlibrary loan, free software. Staffed computer lab on campus provides training in use of computers, software, and the Internet.

Community Environment: The college represents the best of New England college campuses and provides an inviting atmosphere for study and socializing. Located in Waltham, Massachusetts, just 10 miles from Boston, Bentley's 163-acre suburban campus puts the city's many resources within easy reach. Boston is the country's ultimate college town. From theater to art exhibits, dance clubs to alternative rock concerts, championship sports to championship shopping, Boston has the proverbial "something for everyone." The college offers a shuttle service into Cambridge at Harvard Square, and from there, the entire city of Boston is accessible via public transportation.

■ **BERKLEE COLLEGE OF MUSIC**
1140 Boylston St.
Boston, MA 02215-3693
Tel: (617)266-1400; Free: 800-BERKLEE
Fax: (617)747-2047

E-mail: admissions@berklee.edu
Web Site: www.berklee.edu/

Description: Independent, comprehensive, coed. Awards bachelor's and master's degrees. Founded 1945. Setting: urban campus. Total enrollment: 4,521. Faculty: 569 (240 full-time, 329 part-time). Student-undergrad faculty ratio is 13:1. 5,538 applied, 19% were admitted. Full-time: 4,049 students, 29% women, 71% men. Part-time: 398 students, 36% women, 64% men. 84% from out-of-state. 0.1% American Indian or Alaska Native, non-Hispanic/Latino; 9% Hispanic/Latino; 6% African American, non-Hispanic/Latino; 3% Asian, non-Hispanic/Latino; 0.2% Native Hawaiian or other Pacific Islander, non-Hispanic/Latino; 29% international. 15% 25 or older, 17% live on campus, 3% transferred in. Retention: 82% of full-time freshmen returned the following year. Calendar: semesters.

Entrance Requirements: Options: electronic application, early action, deferred admission, international baccalaureate accepted. Required: essay, high school transcript, 2 recommendations, interview, 2 years of formal music study and audition. Entrance: moderately difficult. Application deadlines: 1/15, 11/1 for early action. Notification: 3/31, 1/31 for early action. Applicants placed on waiting list: 300. Wait-listed applicants offered admission: 148.

Costs Per Year: Application fee: $150. Comprehensive fee: $53,440 includes full-time tuition ($35,450), mandatory fees ($1040), and college room and board ($16,950). Part-time tuition: $1255 per credit hour.

Collegiate Environment: Orientation program. Campus security: 24-hour patrols. Freshmen given priority for college housing. Option: coed housing available. The Stan Getz Media Center and Library with an OPAC and a Web page.

Community Environment: See Boston University.

■ **BERKSHIRE COMMUNITY COLLEGE**
1350 W St.
Pittsfield, MA 01201-5786
Tel: (413)499-4660
Fax: (606)224-7744
E-mail: tschetti@berkshirecc.edu
Web Site: www.berkshirecc.edu/

Description: State-supported, 2-year, coed. Part of Massachusetts Public Higher Education System. Awards certificates, transfer associate, and terminal associate degrees. Founded 1960. Setting: 180-acre rural campus with easy access to Hartford, CT and Albany, NY. Endowment: $7.1 million. Educational spending for the previous fiscal year: $6710 per student. Total enrollment: 2,503. Faculty: 216 (52 full-time, 164 part-time). Student-undergrad faculty ratio is 15:1. 683 applied, 73% were admitted. Full-time: 922 students, 53% women, 47% men. Part-time: 1,581 students, 65% women, 35% men. Students come from 6 states and territories, 8 other countries, 3% from out-of-state. 0.4% American Indian or Alaska Native, non-Hispanic/Latino; 6% Hispanic/Latino; 6% African American, non-Hispanic/Latino; 2% Asian, non-Hispanic/Latino; 0.1% Native Hawaiian or other Pacific Islander, non-Hispanic/Latino; 0.3% international. 42% 25 or older, 46% transferred in. Retention: 35% of full-time freshmen returned the following year. Core. Calendar: semesters. Academic remediation for entering students, ESL program, services for LD students, advanced placement, accelerated degree program, honors program, independent study, distance learning, double major, summer session for credit, part-time degree program, adult/continuing education programs, co-op programs and internships. Off campus study at Massachusetts College of Liberal Arts, Williams College, Springfield Technical Community College, Greenfield Community College, Mount Wachusetts Community College.

Entrance Requirements: Open admission except for nursing and allied health programs. Option: deferred admission. Required: high school transcript. Recommended: interview. Entrance: noncompetitive. Application deadlines: Rolling, Rolling for nonresidents. Notification: continuous, continuous for nonresidents. Transfer credits accepted: Yes.

Costs Per Year: Application fee: $10. One-time mandatory fee: $10. State resident tuition: $624 full-time, $26 per credit part-time. Nonresident tuition: $6240 full-time, $260 per credit part-time. Mandatory fees: $4980 full-time, $166 per credit part-time. Full-time tuition and fees vary according to class time, course load, program, and reciprocity agreements. Part-time tuition and fees vary according to class time, course load, program, and reciprocity agreements.

Collegiate Environment: Orientation program. Drama-theater group, choral group, student-run newspaper. Social organizations: 17 open to all. Most popular organizations: Mass PIRG, Student Nurse Organization, Student Senate, Diversity Club, LPN Organization. Major annual events: concerts,

Speakers, film presentations. Student services: personal-psychological counseling. Campus security: 24-hour emergency response devices and patrols, late night transport-escort service. College housing not available. Jonathan Edwards Library plus 1 other with 76,918 books, 12,549 microform titles, 241 serials, 13,227 audiovisual materials, an OPAC, and a Web page. Operations spending for the previous fiscal year: $81,419. 247 computers available on campus for general student use. A campuswide network can be accessed from off-campus. Students can access the following: online class registration, web advisor. Staffed computer lab on campus provides training in use of computers, software, and the Internet.

Community Environment: Set in the cultural mecca of the rolling Berkshire hills, this attractive area is also the home to long established plastics and paper industries. The city has three libraries, numerous churches, two hospitals, a museum, YMCA, and good shopping facilities. Regular transportation is available by rail bus and air. Theatres, bowling, three golf courses, two large lakes, many parks, and closeness to area festivals and summer attractions make this city a favorite recreation spot. Part-time employment is available.

■ BOSTON ARCHITECTURAL COLLEGE
320 Newbury St.
Boston, MA 02115-2795
Tel: (617)262-5000; Free: 877-585-0100
Fax: (617)585-0111
E-mail: admissions@the-bac.edu
Web Site: www.the-bac.edu/

Description: Independent, comprehensive, coed. Awards bachelor's and master's degrees. Founded 1889. Setting: 1-acre urban campus. Endowment: $8.7 million. Educational spending for the previous fiscal year: $7042 per student. Total enrollment: 920. Faculty: 229 (11 full-time, 218 part-time). Student-undergrad faculty ratio is 4:1. 100 applied, 100% were admitted. 24% from top 10% of their high school class, 18% from top quarter, 24% from top half. Full-time: 455 students, 33% women, 67% men. Part-time: 11 students, 27% women, 73% men. Students come from 35 states and territories, 4 other countries, 51% from out-of-state. 1% American Indian or Alaska Native, non-Hispanic/Latino; 14% Hispanic/Latino; 6% African American, non-Hispanic/Latino; 8% Asian, non-Hispanic/Latino. 46% 25 or older, 9% transferred in. Retention: 62% of full-time freshmen returned the following year. Academic area with the most degrees conferred: architecture. Core. Calendar: semesters. Advanced placement, independent study, distance learning, summer session for credit, adult/continuing education programs, internships. Off campus study at Art Institute of Boston at Lesley College, ProArts Consortium.

Entrance Requirements: Open admission. Option: electronic application. Required: essay, high school transcript, resumes, creative exercise. Recommended: interview. Entrance: noncompetitive. Application deadlines: Rolling, Rolling for nonresidents. Notification: continuous, continuous for nonresidents. Transfer credits accepted: Yes.

Collegiate Environment: Orientation program. Social organizations: 12 open to all; professional organizations, GLBTIQA Organization. Most popular organizations: Atelier, Student Government, American Institute of Architectural Students, BAC Interior Design Society (IIDA and ASID), National Organization of Minority Architecture Students (NOMAS), Student American Society of Landscape Architects (SASLA). Major annual events: First Fridays, Midterm Midnight Munchies, Food for Finals and Extended Hours. Student services: personal-psychological counseling. Campus security: 24-hour emergency response devices and patrols, late night transport-escort service, electronically operated building access and CCTV systems. College housing not available. Shaw and Stone Library plus 1 other with 53,400 books, 1,945 microform titles, 26,353 serials, 326 audiovisual materials, an OPAC, and a Web page. Operations spending for the previous fiscal year: $665,424. 78 computers available on campus for general student use. Computer purchase/lease plans available. A campuswide network can be accessed from off-campus. Students can access the following: online class registration. Staffed computer lab on campus provides training in use of computers, software, and the Internet.

■ BOSTON BAPTIST COLLEGE
950 Metropolitan Ave.
Boston, MA 02136
Tel: (617)364-3510; Free: 888-235-2014
Fax: (617)364-0723
E-mail: kfox@boston.edu
Web Site: www.boston.edu/

Description: Independent Baptist, 4-year, coed. Awards associate and bachelor's degrees. Founded 1976. Setting: 8-acre suburban campus with easy access to Boston, Providence. Educational spending for the previous fiscal year: $17,100 per student. Total enrollment: 103. Faculty: 22 (3 full-time, 19 part-time). Student-undergrad faculty ratio is 9:1. 60 applied, 58% were admitted. Full-time: 85 students, 47% women, 53% men. Part-time: 18 students, 50% women, 50% men. Students come from 18 states and territories, 5 other countries, 63% from out-of-state. 4% Hispanic/Latino; 7% African American, non-Hispanic/Latino; 1% Asian, non-Hispanic/Latino; 3% international. 19% 25 or older, 65% live on campus, 3% transferred in. Retention: 72% of full-time freshmen returned the following year. Academic area with the most degrees conferred: theology and religious vocations. Core. Calendar: semesters. Academic remediation for entering students, advanced placement, honors program, distance learning, summer session for credit, part-time degree program, adult/continuing education programs. Off campus study.

Entrance Requirements: Option: deferred admission. Required: essay, high school transcript, 1 recommendation. Recommended: 1 recommendation. Required for some: SAT or ACT. Students who have been out of high school more than 3 years are no longer required to submit standardized test scores. Entrance: moderately difficult. Application deadlines: Rolling, Rolling for nonresidents. Transfer credits accepted: Yes.

Costs Per Year: Application fee: $50. Comprehensive fee: $22,750 includes full-time tuition ($13,500), mandatory fees ($1500), and college room and board ($7750). College room only: $4600. Room and board charges vary according to board plan. Part-time tuition: $391 per credit.

Collegiate Environment: Orientation program. Choral group. Social organizations: 3 open to all; local fraternities, local sororities; 90% of eligible men and 90% of eligible women are members. Most popular organizations: Community Service Organization, Recruitment, Campus Life. Student services: personal-psychological counseling. Campus security: 24-hour emergency response devices, student patrols, late night transport-escort service, controlled dormitory access. Boston Baptist College Library plus 1 other with an OPAC and a Web page. 10 computers available on campus for general student use. A campuswide network can be accessed from student residence rooms and from off campus. Staffed computer lab on campus provides training in use of computers, software, and the Internet.

■ BOSTON COLLEGE
140 Commonwealth Ave.
Chestnut Hill, MA 02467-3800
Tel: (617)552-8000; Free: 800-360-2522
Fax: (617)552-0798
Web Site: www.bc.edu/

Description: Independent Roman Catholic (Jesuit), university, coed. Awards bachelor's, master's, and doctoral degrees and post-master's certificates (also offers continuing education program with significant enrollment not reflected in profile). Founded 1863. Setting: 338-acre suburban campus with easy access to Boston. Endowment: $1.8 billion. Research spending for the previous fiscal year: $37.4 million. Total enrollment: 13,783. Faculty: 1,363 (752 full-time, 611 part-time). Student-undergrad faculty ratio is 14:1. 34,061 applied, 29% were admitted. 81% from top 10% of their high school class, 96% from top quarter, 99% from top half. 7 National Merit Scholars, 55 valedictorians, 333 student government officers. Full-time: 9,110 students, 53% women, 47% men. Students come from 53 states and territories, 59 other countries, 73% from out-of-state. 0.1% American Indian or Alaska Native, non-Hispanic/Latino; 11% Hispanic/Latino; 4% African American, non-Hispanic/Latino; 10% Asian, non-Hispanic/Latino; 0.02% Native Hawaiian or other Pacific Islander, non-Hispanic/Latino; 4% international. 85% live on campus, 1% transferred in. Retention: 95% of full-time freshmen returned the following year. Academic areas with the most degrees conferred: business/marketing; social sciences; psychology. Core. Calendar: semesters. Services for LD students, advanced placement, accelerated degree program, self-designed majors, honors program, independent study, double major, summer session for credit, part-time degree program, internships, graduate courses open to undergrads. Off campus study at Boston University, Brandeis University, Hebrew College, Pine Manor College, Regis College (MA), Tufts University. Study abroad program. ROTC: Army (c), Naval (c), Air Force (c).

Entrance Requirements: Options: electronic application, early admission, early action, deferred admission, international baccalaureate accepted. Required: essay, high school transcript, 2 recommendations, SAT and SAT Subject Tests or ACT. Entrance: very difficult. Application deadlines: 1/1, 11/1 for early action. Notification: 4/15, 12/25 for early action. SAT Reasoning

Test deadline: 1/1. SAT Subject Test deadline: 1/1. Transfer credits accepted: Yes. Applicants placed on waiting list: 6,220. Wait-listed applicants offered admission: 71. Early action applicants: 6,580. Early action applicants admitted: 2,646.

Costs Per Year: Application fee: $70. One-time mandatory fee: $458. Comprehensive fee: $56,486 includes full-time tuition ($43,140), mandatory fees ($738), and college room and board ($12,608). College room only: $7790. Room and board charges vary according to housing facility.

Collegiate Environment: Orientation program. Drama-theater group, choral group, marching band, student-run newspaper, radio station. Social organizations: 225 open to all. Most popular organizations: UGBC and individual School Senates, Asian Caucus, Appalachia Volunteers, Dance Marathon, 4Boston. Major annual events: Homecoming, Middlemarch Ball, sporting events. Student services: health clinic, personal-psychological counseling, women's center. Campus security: 24-hour emergency response devices and patrols, late night transport-escort service, controlled dormitory access. 7,403 college housing spaces available; all were occupied in 2012-13. Freshmen guaranteed college housing. Options: coed, women-only housing available. O'Neill Library plus 8 others with 2.8 million books, 4.3 million microform titles, 271,513 serials, 171,099 audiovisual materials, an OPAC, and a Web page. 1,000 computers available on campus for general student use. Computer purchase/lease plans available. A campuswide network can be accessed from student residence rooms and from off campus. Students can access the following: online class registration. Staffed computer lab on campus provides training in use of computers, software, and the Internet.

Community Environment: Boston College considers, and the students concur, that the suburban location of the campus six miles from Boston is the ideal setting for a University. The campus boasts superior academic, residential, and recreational facilities, and the dynamic Greater Boston area offers unlimited cultural, educational, and personal opportunities for individual development within a cosmopolitan atmosphere.

■ **THE BOSTON CONSERVATORY**
8 The Fenway
Boston, MA 02215
Tel: (617)536-6340
Fax: (617)536-3176
E-mail: mcadwallader@bostonconservatory.edu
Web Site: www.bostonconservatory.edu/

Description: Independent, comprehensive, coed. Awards bachelor's and master's degrees and post-master's certificates. Founded 1867. Setting: urban campus with easy access to Boston. Educational spending for the previous fiscal year: $30,000 per student. Total enrollment: 764. Faculty: 202 (88 full-time, 114 part-time). Student-undergrad faculty ratio is 4:1. 1,080 applied, 46% were admitted. Full-time: 533 students, 62% women, 38% men. Part-time: 11 students, 27% women, 73% men. Students come from 40 states and territories, 28 other countries, 88% from out-of-state. 0.01% 25 or older, 30% live on campus, 4% transferred in. Retention: 76% of full-time freshmen returned the following year. Academic area with the most degrees conferred: visual and performing arts. Core. Calendar: semesters. ESL program, advanced placement, independent study, double major, summer session for credit, co-op programs and internships, graduate courses open to undergrads. Off campus study at members of the Pro Arts Consortium.

Entrance Requirements: Options: electronic application, deferred admission, international baccalaureate accepted. Required: essay, high school transcript, minimum 2.7 high school GPA, 2 recommendations, audition, SAT or ACT. Required for some: interview. Entrance: moderately difficult. Application deadline: 12/1. Notification: 4/1. SAT Reasoning Test deadline: 2/1. Transfer credits accepted: Yes. Applicants placed on waiting list: 50. Wait-listed applicants offered admission: 0.

Costs Per Year: Application fee: $110. Comprehensive fee: $56,380 includes full-time tuition ($37,300), mandatory fees ($2000), and college room and board ($17,080). College room only: $10,700. Full-time tuition and fees vary according to course load, degree level, and program. Room and board charges vary according to board plan and housing facility. Part-time tuition: $1750 per credit hour. Part-time tuition varies according to course load, degree level, and program.

Collegiate Environment: Orientation program. Drama-theater group, choral group. Social organizations: national fraternities, national sororities; 25% of eligible men and 15% of eligible women are members. Most popular organizations: Student Government Association, BoCo Cares, The Tent, Sigma Alpha Iota, Phi Mu Alpha. Major annual event: BoCo Block Party. Student services: personal-psychological counseling. Campus security: 24-

hour emergency response devices and patrols, controlled dormitory access. 200 college housing spaces available; 181 were occupied in 2012-13. Freshmen guaranteed college housing. Option: coed housing available. The Albert Alphin Music Library plus 1 other with 30,522 books, 51 serials, 12,958 audiovisual materials, an OPAC, and a Web page. Operations spending for the previous fiscal year: $133,900. 20 computers available on campus for general student use. A campuswide network can be accessed from student residence rooms. Staffed computer lab on campus.

Community Environment: Located in an urban environment in central Boston near Symphony Hall and the Museum of Fine Arts. Public transportation, metropolitan shopping, artistic areas and fine dining are within walking distance.

■ **BOSTON UNIVERSITY**
Boston, MA 02215
Tel: (617)353-2000
Fax: (617)353-9695
E-mail: admissions@bu.edu
Web Site: www.bu.edu/

Description: Independent, university, coed. Awards bachelor's, master's, and doctoral degrees and post-master's certificates. Founded 1839. Setting: 132-acre urban campus. Endowment: $1.2 billion. Research spending for the previous fiscal year: $199 million. Educational spending for the previous fiscal year: $29,997 per student. Total enrollment: 32,603. Faculty: 2,630 (1,632 full-time, 998 part-time). Student-undergrad faculty ratio is 13:1. 44,005 applied, 46% were admitted. 57% from top 10% of their high school class, 87% from top quarter, 99% from top half. 29 National Merit Scholars, 67 valedictorians. Full-time: 16,634 students, 61% women, 39% men. Part-time: 1,672 students, 52% women, 48% men. Students come from 52 states and territories, 101 other countries, 77% from out-of-state. 0.1% American Indian or Alaska Native, non-Hispanic/Latino; 9% Hispanic/Latino; 3% African American, non-Hispanic/Latino; 14% Asian, non-Hispanic/Latino; 0.1% Native Hawaiian or other Pacific Islander, non-Hispanic/Latino; 13% international. 4% 25 or older, 77% live on campus, 2% transferred in. Retention: 92% of full-time freshmen returned the following year. Academic areas with the most degrees conferred: business/marketing; social sciences; communication/journalism. Core. Calendar: semesters. ESL program, services for LD students, advanced placement, accelerated degree program, self-designed majors, honors program, independent study, distance learning, double major, summer session for credit, part-time degree program, adult/continuing education programs, co-op programs and internships, graduate courses open to undergrads. Off campus study at Boston College, Brandeis University, Hebrew College, Tufts University. Study abroad program. ROTC: Army, Naval, Air Force.

Entrance Requirements: Options: electronic application, early admission, early decision, deferred admission, international baccalaureate accepted. Required: essay, high school transcript, 2 recommendations, SAT or ACT. Required for some: interview, audition, portfolio, SAT Subject Tests. Entrance: very difficult. Application deadlines: 1/1, 11/1 for early decision. Notification: 4/1, 12/15 for early decision. SAT Reasoning Test deadline: 1/1. SAT Subject Test deadline: 1/1. Transfer credits accepted: Yes. Applicants placed on waiting list: 2,649. Wait-listed applicants offered admission: 65. Early decision applicants: 1,069. Early decision applicants admitted: 501.

Costs Per Year: Application fee: $80. Comprehensive fee: $56,184 includes full-time tuition ($42,400), mandatory fees ($594), and college room and board ($13,190). College room only: $8600. Full-time tuition and fees vary according to class time. Room and board charges vary according to board plan and housing facility. Part-time tuition: $1325 per credit hour. Part-time mandatory fees: $40 per term. Part-time tuition and fees vary according to class time and course load.

Collegiate Environment: Orientation program. Drama-theater group, choral group, marching band, student-run newspaper, radio station. Social organizations: 483 open to all; national fraternities, national sororities; 3% of eligible men and 7% of eligible women are members. Most popular organizations: performing and acappella groups, cultural organizations, service organizations, student government, residence hall associations. Major annual events: Head of the Charles River Regatta, Beanpot Tournament, World Fair. Student services: health clinic, personal-psychological counseling, women's center. Campus security: 24-hour emergency response devices and patrols, late night transport-escort service, controlled dormitory access, security personnel at residence hall entrances, self-defense education, well-lit sidewalks. College housing designed to accommodate 11,364 students; 11,391 undergraduates lived in college housing during 2012-13. Freshmen guaranteed college housing. On-campus residence required in freshman year. Options: coed, women-only housing available. Mugar Memorial Library plus 18 others with 2.8 million books, an OPAC, and a Web page. Operations spending for the previous fiscal year: $23.5 million. 250 computers available on campus for general student use. Computer purchase/lease plans available. A campuswide network can be accessed from student residence rooms and from off campus. Students can access the following: online class registration, research and educational networks. Staffed computer lab on campus provides training in use of computers, software, and the Internet.

Community Environment: Historic capital of Massachusetts, Boston is a contrast of past and present with broad avenues disappearing into crooked, narrow streets of colonial Boston. Modern stores and buildings stand next to Revolutionary shrines. With one in every five residents a college student, Boston is America's ultimate college town.

■ **BRANDEIS UNIVERSITY**
415 S St.
Waltham, MA 02454-9110
Tel: (781)736-2000; Free: 800-622-0622
Fax: (781)736-3536
E-mail: admissions@brandeis.edu
Web Site: www.brandeis.edu/

Description: Independent, university, coed. Awards bachelor's, master's, and doctoral degrees. Founded 1948. Setting: 235-acre suburban campus with easy access to Boston. Endowment: $674.5 million. Research spending for the previous fiscal year: $46.5 million. Educational spending for the previous fiscal year: $24,195 per student. Total enrollment: 5,808. Faculty: 511 (361 full-time, 150 part-time). Student-undergrad faculty ratio is 10:1. 8,380 applied, 39% were admitted. 66% from top 10% of their high school class, 93% from top quarter, 98% from top half. Full-time: 3,563 students, 56% women, 44% men. Part-time: 25 students, 64% women, 36% men. Students come from 70 other countries, 72% from out-of-state. 0.1% American Indian or Alaska Native, non-Hispanic/Latino; 6% Hispanic/Latino; 4% African American, non-Hispanic/Latino; 13% Asian, non-Hispanic/Latino; 0% Native Hawaiian or other Pacific Islander, non-Hispanic/Latino; 14% international. 1% 25 or older, 82% live on campus, 2% transferred in. Retention: 95% of full-time freshmen returned the following year. Academic areas with the most degrees conferred: social sciences; area and ethnic studies; business/marketing. Core. Calendar: semesters. ESL program, services for LD students, advanced placement, self-designed majors, honors program, independent study, double major, summer session for credit, adult/continuing education programs, internships, graduate courses open to undergrads. Off campus study at Tufts University, Babson College, Bentley College, Boston University, Wellesley College, Boston College. Study abroad program. ROTC: Army (c), Air Force (c).

Entrance Requirements: Options: electronic application, early decision, deferred admission, international baccalaureate accepted. Required: essay, high school transcript, 2 recommendations, SAT or ACT. Recommended: interview. Entrance: most difficult. Application deadlines: 1/15, 11/15 for early decision plan 1, 1/1 for early decision plan 2. Notification: 4/1, 12/15 for early decision plan 1, 2/1 for early decision plan 2. SAT Reasoning Test deadline: 1/15. SAT Subject Test deadline: 1/15. Transfer credits accepted: Yes. Applicants placed on waiting list: 1,347. Wait-listed applicants offered admission: 117. Early decision applicants: 455. Early decision applicants admitted: 263.

Costs Per Year: Application fee: $65. Comprehensive fee: $56,550 includes full-time tuition ($42,682), mandatory fees ($1612), and college room and board ($12,256). College room only: $6812. Full-time tuition and fees vary according to student level. Room and board charges vary according to board plan and housing facility.

Collegiate Environment: Orientation program. Drama-theater group, choral group, student-run newspaper, radio station. Social organizations: 270 open to all. Most popular organizations: Waltham Group, Student Events, Student Environmental Action, Liquid Latex, Culinary Arts Club. Major annual events: Spring Fest, Culture X, Fall concert. Student services: health clinic, personal-psychological counseling. Campus security: 24-hour emergency response devices and patrols, late night transport-escort service, controlled dormitory access. 2,917 college housing spaces available; 2,903 were occupied in 2012-13. Freshmen guaranteed college housing. On-campus residence required in freshman year. Options: coed, men-only, women-only housing available. Goldfarb Library plus 2 others with 1.6 million books, 960,389 microform titles, 104,329 serials, 43,766 audiovisual materials, an OPAC, and a Web page. Operations spending for the previous fiscal year: $12.5 million. 156 computers available on campus for general student use.

Computer purchase/lease plans available. A campuswide network can be accessed from student residence rooms and from off campus. Students can access the following: online class registration, educational software. Staffed computer lab on campus provides training in use of computers, software, and the Internet.

Community Environment: Waltham is a city of 58,000, ten miles west of Boston on the Charles River. It is a traditional manufacturing community that now hosts extensive high-tech industries. The City is served by commuter railroad and excellent bus lines for easy access to Boston and Cambridge. The locale has two colleges, four hospitals, a wide range of religious institutions, public library, Federal Archives and Records Center, parks, and a variety of ethnic restaurants. Good job and community service opportunities for students are available.

■ **BRIDGEWATER STATE UNIVERSITY**
Bridgewater, MA 02325-0001
Tel: (508)531-1000
Fax: (508)531-1707
E-mail: admission@bridgew.edu
Web Site: www.bridgew.edu/

Description: State-supported, comprehensive, coed. Part of Massachusetts Department of Higher Education. Awards bachelor's and master's degrees and post-master's certificates. Founded 1840. Setting: 278-acre suburban campus with easy access to Boston. Endowment: $26.7 million. Educational spending for the previous fiscal year: $5638 per student. Total enrollment: 11,417. Faculty: 775 (321 full-time, 454 part-time). Student-undergrad faculty ratio is 20:1. 6,170 applied, 73% were admitted. Full-time: 8,032 students, 58% women, 42% men. Part-time: 1,652 students, 57% women, 43% men. Students come from 27 states and territories, 22 other countries, 4% from out-of-state. 0.3% American Indian or Alaska Native, non-Hispanic/Latino; 5% Hispanic/Latino; 7% African American, non-Hispanic/Latino; 2% Asian, non-Hispanic/Latino; 0.1% Native Hawaiian or other Pacific Islander, non-Hispanic/Latino; 1% international. 16% 25 or older, 35% live on campus, 11% transferred in. Retention: 81% of full-time freshmen returned the following year. Academic areas with the most degrees conferred: education; business/marketing; psychology. Core. Calendar: semesters. Academic remediation for entering students, ESL program, services for LD students, advanced placement, accelerated degree program, honors program, independent study, distance learning, double major, summer session for credit, part-time degree program, adult/continuing education programs, internships, graduate courses open to undergrads. Off campus study at Bridgewater State University is a member of the Southeastern Association for Cooperation in Higher Education in Massachusetts, the College Academic Program Sharing, and National Student Exchange. Study abroad program. ROTC: Army (c), Air Force (c).

Entrance Requirements: Options: electronic application, early action, deferred admission, international baccalaureate accepted. Required: high school transcript, minimum 2 high school GPA, SAT or ACT scores, SAT or ACT. Recommended: essay. Entrance: moderately difficult. Application deadlines: 2/15, 2/15 for nonresidents, 11/15 for early action. Notification: continuous until 4/15, continuous until 4/15 for nonresidents, 12/15 for early action. Transfer credits accepted: Yes. Applicants placed on waiting list: 673. Wait-listed applicants offered admission: 126. Early action applicants: 1,965. Early action applicants admitted: 594.

Costs Per Year: Application fee: $40. State resident tuition: $910 full-time, $38 per credit hour part-time. Nonresident tuition: $7050 full-time, $294 per credit hour part-time. Mandatory fees: $7142 full-time, $292.21 per credit hour part-time. Full-time tuition and fees vary according to class time. College room and board: $10,700. College room only: $7000. Room and board charges vary according to board plan and housing facility.

Collegiate Environment: Orientation program. Drama-theater group, choral group, student-run newspaper, radio station. Social organizations: 90 open to all; national fraternities, national sororities, Coed Fraternity; 7% of eligible men and 6% of eligible women are members. Most popular organizations: Dance Company, African American Society (Afro-Am), Program Committee, Panhellenic Association, Inter-Fraternity Council. Major annual events: Homecoming, Springfest, Campus Movie Fest. Student services: health clinic, personal-psychological counseling. Campus security: 24-hour emergency response devices and patrols, late night transport-escort service, controlled dormitory access, 24-Hour patrols by BSU Police. College housing designed to accommodate 2,781 students; 2,813 undergraduates lived in college housing during 2012-13. Freshmen given priority for college housing. Option: coed housing available. Clement C. Maxwell Library with 352,584 books, 715,736 microform titles, 55,658 serials, 7,613 audiovisual materials, an OPAC, and a Web page. Operations spending for the previous fiscal year: $2.6 million. 675 computers available on campus for general student use. A computer is required for all students. A campuswide network can be accessed from student residence rooms and from off campus. Students can access the following: online class registration, student account information, application software. Staffed computer lab on campus provides training in use of computers, software, and the Internet.

Community Environment: This largely residential, colonial town, 30 miles southeast of Boston, has among its manufactures, shoes, leatherboard, nails, and bricks. Extensive excavations by archaeologists have revealed the remains of two Indian civilizations in the area. Boston provides the area with all the cultural, and recreational advantages of a large city.

■ **BRISTOL COMMUNITY COLLEGE**
777 Elsbree St.
Fall River, MA 02720-7395
Tel: (508)678-2811
Fax: (508)674-8838
E-mail: Shilo.Henriques@bristolcc.edu
Web Site: www.bristolcc.edu/

Description: State-supported, 2-year, coed. Part of Massachusetts Community College System. Awards certificates, transfer associate, and terminal associate degrees. Founded 1965. Setting: 105-acre urban campus with easy access to Boston. Endowment: $4.1 million. Total enrollment: 9,022. Faculty: 710 (125 full-time, 585 part-time). Student-undergrad faculty ratio is 18:1. Full-time: 4,303 students, 57% women, 43% men. Part-time: 4,719 students, 65% women, 35% men. Students come from 15 other countries. 1% American Indian or Alaska Native, non-Hispanic/Latino; 7% Hispanic/Latino; 7% African American, non-Hispanic/Latino; 2% Asian, non-Hispanic/Latino; 0.1% Native Hawaiian or other Pacific Islander, non-Hispanic/Latino; 0.3% international. 36% 25 or older. Core. Calendar: semesters. Academic remediation for entering students, ESL program, services for LD students, self-designed majors, honors program, independent study, distance learning, summer session for credit, part-time degree program, adult/continuing education programs, co-op programs and internships. Off campus study at Southeastern Association for Cooperation in Higher Education in Massachusetts.

Entrance Requirements: Open admission Complementary Healthcare, Culinary Arts, Dental Hygiene, Clinical Laboratory Science, Healthcare Information, Histology, Medical Assisting, Nursing, Occupational Therapy Assistant, Pre-Radiology Technology, Phlebotomy, and Therapeutic Massage. Option: electronic application. Required: high school transcript. Entrance: noncompetitive. Notification: continuous.

Costs Per Year: Application fee: $10. State resident tuition: $24 per credit part-time. Nonresident tuition: $230 per credit part-time. Part-time tuition varies according to course load.

Collegiate Environment: Orientation program. Drama-theater group, student-run newspaper. Social organizations: 32 open to all. Most popular organizations: International Club, MASS/PIRG WaterWatch, Criminal Justice Society, Students in Free Enterprise (SIFE), Portuguese Club. Major annual events: Orientation, Student Awards Night, International Festival. Student services: health clinic, personal-psychological counseling, women's center. Campus security: 24-hour emergency response devices and patrols, late night transport-escort service. College housing not available. Learning Resources Center with 61,978 books, 256 serials, 18,109 audiovisual materials, an OPAC, and a Web page. 900 computers available on campus for general student use. A campuswide network can be accessed from off-campus. Students can access the following: online class registration. Staffed computer lab on campus provides training in use of computers, software, and the Internet.

Community Environment: Located approximately 50 miles south of Boston, Massachusetts and 18 miles southeast of Providence, Rhode Island on the New England Coast, the City is easily accessible by train, bus and air. Fall River's major industries include textiles, needlecrafts, and rubber and chemicals. The city, the factory outlet capital of New England, is experiencing a revitalization in its business and residential districts. Many opportunities exist for part-time and full-time work for students.

■ **BUNKER HILL COMMUNITY COLLEGE**
250 New Rutherford Ave.
Boston, MA 02129
Tel: (617)228-2000
Fax: (617)228-2120
Web Site: www.bhcc.mass.edu/

Description: State-supported, 2-year, coed. Awards certificates, transfer associate, and terminal associate degrees. Founded 1973. Setting: 21-acre urban campus. Endowment: $2.4 million. Educational spending for the previous fiscal year: $2912 per student. Total enrollment: 12,934. Faculty: 691 (142 full-time, 549 part-time). Student-undergrad faculty ratio is 19:1. 4,179 applied, 98% were admitted. Full-time: 4,486 students, 52% women, 48% men. Part-time: 8,448 students, 59% women, 41% men. Students come from 78 other countries. 1% American Indian or Alaska Native, non-Hispanic/Latino; 24% Hispanic/Latino; 19% African American, non-Hispanic/Latino; 10% Asian, non-Hispanic/Latino; 0% Native Hawaiian or other Pacific Islander, non-Hispanic/Latino; 6% international. 48% 25 or older, 7% transferred in. Core. Calendar: semesters. Academic remediation for entering students, ESL program, services for LD students, advanced placement, honors program, independent study, distance learning, summer session for credit, part-time degree program, external degree program, co-op programs and internships. Study abroad program.

Entrance Requirements: Open admission except for nursing, medical radiography, surgical technology, ultrasound, overhead electrical line worker programs. Option: deferred admission. Required: high school transcript. Entrance: noncompetitive. Application deadline: Rolling. Notification: continuous.

Costs Per Year: Application fee: $10. State resident tuition: $576 full-time, $24 per credit hour part-time. Nonresident tuition: $5520 full-time, $230 per credit hour part-time. Mandatory fees: $2808 full-time, $117 per credit hour part-time. Full-time tuition and fees vary according to course load, program, and reciprocity agreements. Part-time tuition and fees vary according to course load, program, and reciprocity agreements.

Collegiate Environment: Orientation program. Drama-theater group, choral group, student-run radio station. Social organizations: 29 open to all. Most popular organizations: Alpha Kappa Mu Honor Society, Asian-Pacific Students Association, African Students Club, Latinos Unidos Club, Haitian Students Club. Major annual events: Holiday Stroll, Family Day, Spring Day. Student services: health clinic, personal-psychological counseling. Campus security: 24-hour emergency response devices and patrols, late night transport-escort service. Bunker Hill Community College Library with 62,872 books, 5,745 microform titles, 211 serials, 11,475 audiovisual materials, an OPAC, and a Web page. Operations spending for the previous fiscal year: $453,186. 731 computers available on campus for general student use. A campuswide network can be accessed from off-campus. Students can access the following: online class registration, academic support services. Staffed computer lab on campus provides training in use of computers, software, and the Internet.

Community Environment: The college is located on a 21-acre site in the Charlestown District of Boston. The campus is very near the Bunker Hill Monument and the U.S.S. Constitution. The school is within immediate access to Boston's bus-streetcar-subway system.

■ **CAMBRIDGE COLLEGE**
1000 Massachusetts Ave.
Cambridge, MA 02138-5304
Tel: (617)868-1000; Free: 800-877-4723
Fax: (617)349-3545
E-mail: denise.haile@cambridgecollege.edu
Web Site: www.cambridgecollege.edu/

Description: Independent, comprehensive, coed. Awards bachelor's, master's, and doctoral degrees and post-master's certificates. Founded 1971. Setting: urban campus with easy access to Boston. Endowment: $11.4 million. Total enrollment: 3,757. Faculty: 453 (19 full-time, 434 part-time). Student-undergrad faculty ratio is 13:1. 107 applied, 64% were admitted. Full-time: 270 students, 71% women, 29% men. Part-time: 820 students, 66% women, 34% men. Students come from 7 states and territories, 13% from out-of-state. 0.3% American Indian or Alaska Native, non-Hispanic/Latino; 24% Hispanic/Latino; 32% African American, non-Hispanic/Latino; 3% Asian, non-Hispanic/Latino; 0.3% Native Hawaiian or other Pacific Islander, non-Hispanic/Latino; 5% international. 85% 25 or older, 7% transferred in. Retention: 41% of full-time freshmen returned the following year. Academic areas with the most degrees conferred: liberal arts/general studies; business/marketing; public administration and social services. Core. Calendar: trimesters. Services for LD students, advanced placement, accelerated degree program, independent study, distance learning, summer session for credit, part-time degree program, adult/continuing education programs, internships, graduate courses open to undergrads.

Entrance Requirements: Open admission. Options: electronic application, deferred admission, international baccalaureate accepted. Required: essay, high school transcript, 1 recommendation, resume, health insurance, immunizations form, application form. Recommended: interview. Entrance: noncompetitive. Application deadlines: Rolling, Rolling for nonresidents. Notification: continuous, continuous for nonresidents. Transfer credits accepted: Yes.

Collegiate Environment: Orientation program. College housing not available. Cambridge College Online Library with 75,331 books, 19,069 serials, and a Web page. Operations spending for the previous fiscal year: $246,380.

■ **CAPE COD COMMUNITY COLLEGE**
2240 Iyannough Rd.
West Barnstable, MA 02668-1599
Tel: (508)362-2131; Free: 877-846-3672
E-mail: admiss@capecod.edu
Web Site: www.capecod.edu/

Description: State-supported, 2-year, coed. Part of Massachusetts Public Higher Education System. Awards certificates, transfer associate, and terminal associate degrees. Founded 1961. Setting: 120-acre rural campus with easy access to Boston. Total enrollment: 4,657. Student-undergrad faculty ratio is 18:1. 1% from out-of-state. 39% 25 or older. Core. Calendar: semesters. Academic remediation for entering students, ESL program, services for LD students, advanced placement, freshman honors college, honors program, independent study, distance learning, summer session for credit, part-time degree program, adult/continuing education programs, co-op programs and internships. Off campus study at Bridgewater State College, Bristol Community College, Dean College, Massasoit Community College, Stonehill College, University of Massachusetts Dartmouth. Study abroad program.

Entrance Requirements: Open admission except for nursing, dental hygiene, physical therapy programs. Options: deferred admission, international baccalaureate accepted. Required: high school transcript. Required for some: essay. Entrance: noncompetitive. Application deadline: 8/10. Notification: continuous. Preference given to state residents.

Collegiate Environment: Orientation program. Drama-theater group, choral group, student-run newspaper, radio station. Student services: health clinic, personal-psychological counseling, women's center. Campus security: 24-hour patrols. Cape Cod Community College Learning Resource Center with an OPAC.

Community Environment: A rural village in the town of Barnstable on Cape Cod with several museums dedicated to early Americana in the area. The community has excellent facilities for all sports, yacht races and tournaments, and many historic celebrations. Part-time employment is available with exceptional opportunities in the summer. Transportation provided by air and bus. Shopping facilities are excellent.

■ **CLARK UNIVERSITY**
950 Main St.
Worcester, MA 01610-1477
Tel: (508)793-7711; Free: 800-GO-CLARK
Fax: (508)793-8821
E-mail: admissions@clarku.edu
Web Site: www.clarku.edu/

Description: Independent, university, coed. Awards bachelor's, master's, and doctoral degrees and post-master's certificates. Founded 1887. Setting: 50-acre urban campus with easy access to Boston. Endowment: $320.5 million. Research spending for the previous fiscal year: $8.5 million. Educational spending for the previous fiscal year: $11,081 per student. Total enrollment: 3,503. Faculty: 291 (197 full-time, 94 part-time). Student-undergrad faculty ratio is 10:1. 4,297 applied, 70% were admitted. 36% from top 10% of their high school class, 73% from top quarter, 94% from top half. Full-time: 2,253 students, 58% women, 42% men. Part-time: 99 students, 59% women, 41% men. Students come from 42 states and territories, 70 other countries, 60% from out-of-state. 0.1% American Indian or Alaska Native, non-Hispanic/Latino; 6% Hispanic/Latino; 4% African American, non-Hispanic/Latino; 5% Asian, non-Hispanic/Latino; 0% Native Hawaiian or other Pacific Islander, non-Hispanic/Latino; 11% international. 1% 25 or older, 71% live on campus, 2% transferred in. Retention: 92% of full-time freshmen returned the following year. Academic areas with the most degrees conferred: social sciences; psychology; visual and performing arts. Core. Calendar: semesters. Academic remediation for entering students, ESL program, services for LD students, advanced placement, accelerated degree program, self-designed majors, honors program, independent study, double major, summer session for credit, part-time degree program, adult/continuing

education programs, internships, graduate courses open to undergrads. Off campus study at Worcester Consortium for Higher Education, Howard University. Study abroad program. ROTC: Army (c), Naval (c), Air Force (c).

Entrance Requirements: Options: electronic application, early admission, early action, deferred admission, international baccalaureate accepted. Required: essay, high school transcript, 2 recommendations. Recommended: interview. Entrance: moderately difficult. Application deadlines: 1/15, 11/15 for early action. Notification: 4/1, 12/23 for early action. SAT Reasoning Test deadline: 1/15. Transfer credits accepted: Yes. Applicants placed on waiting list: 228. Wait-listed applicants offered admission: 4. Early action applicants: 1,111. Early action applicants admitted: 928.

Costs Per Year: Application fee: $55. Comprehensive fee: $47,020 includes full-time tuition ($39,200), mandatory fees ($350), and college room and board ($7470). College room only: $4170. Room and board charges vary according to board plan and housing facility. Part-time tuition: $1225 per credit hour. Part-time mandatory fees: $1225 per credit hour.

Collegiate Environment: Orientation program. Drama-theater group, choral group, marching band, student-run newspaper, radio station. Social organizations: 120 open to all. Most popular organizations: International Students Association, Outing Club, Science Fiction People of Clark, Ballroom Dance Team and Club, Hillel. Major annual events: International Gala, Euphoria Dance Parties, Annual Major Event Concert. Student services: health clinic, personal-psychological counseling, women's center. Campus security: 24-hour emergency response devices and patrols, student patrols, late night transport-escort service, controlled dormitory access. 1,634 college housing spaces available; 1,606 were occupied in 2012-13. Freshmen guaranteed college housing. On-campus residence required through sophomore year. Options: coed, women-only housing available. Robert Hutchings Goddard Library plus 4 others with 642,821 books, 61,149 microform titles, 2,153 serials, 2,302 audiovisual materials, an OPAC, and a Web page. Operations spending for the previous fiscal year: $2.9 million. 149 computers available on campus for general student use. A campuswide network can be accessed from student residence rooms and from off campus. Students can access the following: online class registration, online course support. Staffed computer lab on campus provides training in use of computers, software, and the Internet.

Community Environment: An industrial center and state center for biotechnology and related research, Worcester is the second largest city in all of New England. Good transportation facilities make area easily accessible. Located 38 miles west of Boston, city has several religious groups of all denominations, as well as significant libraries, museums, parks, theatre, and music facilities and municipal recreation opportunities and the Centrum (seating 13,000) houses concerts, sport events, and exhibits. Many students take advantage of the city's offerings through paid and unpaid internships with area corporations and institutions.

■ **COLLEGE OF THE HOLY CROSS**
1 College St.
Worcester, MA 01610-2395
Tel: (508)793-2011; Free: 800-442-2421
Fax: (508)793-3888
E-mail: admissions@holycross.edu
Web Site: www.holycross.edu/

Description: Independent Roman Catholic (Jesuit), 4-year, coed. Awards bachelor's degrees (standardized tests are optional for admission to the College of Holy Cross). Founded 1843. Setting: 174-acre suburban campus with easy access to Boston. Endowment: $589.8 million. Research spending for the previous fiscal year: $1.3 million. Educational spending for the previous fiscal year: $19,253 per student. Total enrollment: 2,926. Faculty: 316 (272 full-time, 44 part-time). Student-undergrad faculty ratio is 10:1. 7,228 applied, 34% were admitted. 60% from top 10% of their high school class, 95% from top quarter, 100% from top half. 1 National Merit Scholar, 7 valedictorians. Full-time: 2,891 students, 51% women, 49% men. Part-time: 35 students, 80% women, 20% men. Students come from 48 states and territories, 21 other countries, 63% from out-of-state. 0.2% American Indian or Alaska Native, non-Hispanic/Latino; 10% Hispanic/Latino; 5% African American, non-Hispanic/Latino; 5% Asian, non-Hispanic/Latino; 0.03% Native Hawaiian or other Pacific Islander, non-Hispanic/Latino; 1% international. 0% 25 or older, 91% live on campus, 0.5% transferred in. Retention: 95% of full-time freshmen returned the following year. Academic areas with the most degrees conferred: social sciences; psychology; English. Core. Calendar: semesters. Services for LD students, advanced placement, accelerated degree program, self-designed majors, honors program, independent study, double major, internships. Off campus study at Colleges of Worcester

Consortium of Higher Education, which includes the University of Massachusetts Medical School, Worcester Polytechnic Institute and Clark University. Study abroad program. ROTC: Army (c), Naval, Air Force (c).

Entrance Requirements: Options: electronic application, early admission, early decision, deferred admission, international baccalaureate accepted. Required: essay, high school transcript, 2 recommendations. Recommended: interview. Entrance: very difficult. Application deadlines: 1/15, 12/15 for early decision. Notification: 4/1, 1/15 for early decision. SAT Reasoning Test deadline: 1/15. SAT Subject Test deadline: 1/15. Transfer credits accepted: Yes. Applicants placed on waiting list: 1,540. Wait-listed applicants offered admission: 0. Early decision applicants: 481. Early decision applicants admitted: 325.

Costs Per Year: Application fee: $60. Comprehensive fee: $56,232 includes full-time tuition ($43,660), mandatory fees ($612), and college room and board ($11,960). College room only: $6450. Room and board charges vary according to housing facility.

Collegiate Environment: Orientation program. Drama-theater group, choral group, marching band, student-run newspaper, radio station. Social organizations: 100 open to all. Most popular organizations: SPUD (community service organization), choral and music groups, Campus Activities Board, Student Government Association, Purple Key Society. Major annual events: Homecoming, Family Weekend, Purple Pride Day. Student services: health clinic, personal-psychological counseling. Campus security: 24-hour emergency response devices and patrols, late night transport-escort service, controlled dormitory access. 2,503 college housing spaces available; 2,500 were occupied in 2012-13. Freshmen guaranteed college housing. On-campus residence required through sophomore year. Option: coed housing available. Dinand Library plus 5 others with 723,384 books, 16,554 microform titles, 6,224 serials, 34,595 audiovisual materials, an OPAC, and a Web page. Operations spending for the previous fiscal year: $4.3 million. 485 computers available on campus for general student use. Computer purchase/lease plans available. A campuswide network can be accessed from student residence rooms and from off campus. Students can access the following: online class registration. Staffed computer lab on campus provides training in use of computers, software, and the Internet.

Community Environment: See Clark University.

■ **CURRY COLLEGE**
1071 Blue Hill Ave.
Milton, MA 02186-9984
Tel: (617)333-0500; Free: 800-669-0686
Fax: (617)333-6860
E-mail: curryadm@curry.edu
Web Site: www.curry.edu/

Description: Independent, comprehensive, coed. Awards bachelor's and master's degrees. Founded 1879. Setting: 135-acre suburban campus with easy access to Boston. Total enrollment: 3,040. Faculty: 292 (125 full-time, 167 part-time). Student-undergrad faculty ratio is 12:1. 5,494 applied, 84% were admitted. 5% from top 10% of their high school class, 20% from top quarter, 52% from top half. Full-time: 1,995 students, 56% women, 44% men. Part-time: 774 students, 78% women, 22% men. Students come from 32 states and territories, 7 other countries, 21% from out-of-state. 0.4% American Indian or Alaska Native, non-Hispanic/Latino; 5% Hispanic/Latino; 8% African American, non-Hispanic/Latino; 2% Asian, non-Hispanic/Latino; 0.1% Native Hawaiian or other Pacific Islander, non-Hispanic/Latino; 1% international. 27% 25 or older, 50% live on campus, 3% transferred in. Retention: 69% of full-time freshmen returned the following year. Academic areas with the most degrees conferred: health professions and related sciences; business/marketing; communication/journalism; homeland security, law enforcement, firefighting, and protective services. Core. Calendar: semesters. Academic remediation for entering students, services for LD students, advanced placement, accelerated degree program, self-designed majors, honors program, independent study, double major, summer session for credit, part-time degree program, external degree program, adult/continuing education programs, internships. Off campus study. Study abroad program. ROTC: Army (c).

Entrance Requirements: Options: electronic application, early admission, early action, deferred admission, international baccalaureate accepted. Required: essay, high school transcript, minimum 2 high school GPA, 1 recommendation, supplemental form for Common Application subscribers and Program for Advancement of Learning. Recommended: interview. Required for some: interview, SAT or ACT, TOEFL for international applicants. The College's Program for the Advancement of Learning does not require nor does it consider SAT or ACT scores during the admissions

process. Entrance: moderately difficult. Application deadlines: 4/1, 12/1 for early action. Notification: continuous, 12/15 for early action. Transfer credits accepted: Yes.

Costs Per Year: Application fee: $50. One-time mandatory fee: $290. Comprehensive fee: $46,225 includes full-time tuition ($31,900), mandatory fees ($1565), and college room and board ($12,760). College room only: $7160. Full-time tuition and fees vary according to class time and location. Room and board charges vary according to board plan and housing facility. Part-time tuition: $1063 per credit hour. Part-time tuition varies according to class time, course load, and location.

Collegiate Environment: Orientation program. Drama-theater group, choral group, student-run newspaper, radio station. Most popular organizations: student radio station, student government, Campus Activities Board, student newspaper, Drama Club. Major annual events: Homecoming, Mr. Curry, Spring Fest. Student services: health clinic, personal-psychological counseling. Campus security: 24-hour emergency response devices and patrols, late night transport-escort service, controlled dormitory access. 1,385 college housing spaces available; 1,380 were occupied in 2012-13. No special consideration for freshman housing applicants. Options: coed, men-only, women-only housing available. Levin Library plus 1 other with 154,100 books, 47,600 serials, 3,950 audiovisual materials, an OPAC, and a Web page. 245 computers available on campus for general student use. A campuswide network can be accessed from student residence rooms and from off campus. Students can access the following: online class registration, library online catalog and research databases. Staffed computer lab on campus provides training in use of computers, software, and the Internet.

Community Environment: Suburban location about seven miles south of Boston near the Neponset River in the town of Milton. All forms of transportation easily accessible. Shuttle bus to Boston, rapid transit. Blue Hills Reservation, a summer and winter sports center with golf course, ice rink, ski slopes, is located nearby. Job opportunities, community services, and cultural advantages will be found in neighboring Boston, as well as on campus.

■ **DEAN COLLEGE**
99 Main St.
Franklin, MA 02038-1994
Tel: (508)541-1900; Free: 877-TRY-DEAN
Fax: (508)541-8726
E-mail: jfowler@dean.edu
Web Site: www.dean.edu/

Description: Independent, primarily 2-year, coed. Awards certificates, transfer associate, terminal associate, and bachelor's degrees. Founded 1865. Setting: 100-acre small town campus with easy access to Boston, Providence. Endowment: $22.8 million. Total enrollment: 1,106. Faculty: 112 (33 full-time, 79 part-time). Student-undergrad faculty ratio is 19:1. 1,910 applied, 73% were admitted. Full-time: 975 students, 45% women, 55% men. Part-time: 131 students, 69% women, 31% men. Students come from 23 states and territories, 131 other countries, 48% from out-of-state. 0% 25 or older, 88% live on campus, 4% transferred in. Retention: 62% of full-time freshmen returned the following year. Academic area with the most degrees conferred: visual and performing arts. Core. Calendar: semesters. Academic remediation for entering students, ESL program, services for LD students, advanced placement, accelerated degree program, self-designed majors, freshman honors college, honors program, independent study, summer session for credit, part-time degree program, adult/continuing education programs, internships. Off campus study at Washington Center for Internships and Academic Seminars.

Entrance Requirements: Options: electronic application, deferred admission, international baccalaureate accepted. Required: essay, high school transcript, SAT or ACT. Recommended: minimum 2 high school GPA, interview. Entrance: minimally difficult. Application deadline: Rolling. Notification: continuous.

Collegiate Environment: Orientation program. Drama-theater group, choral group, student-run radio station. Social organizations: 30 open to all. Most popular organizations: Emerging Leaders, College Success Staff, Student Ambassadors, student government, Phi Theta Kappa. Major annual events: Homecoming, Harvest Weekend, Leadership Conference. Student services: health clinic, personal-psychological counseling. Campus security: 24-hour emergency response devices and patrols, late night transport-escort service, controlled dormitory access. E. Ross Anderson Library with 45,565 books, 18,313 microform titles, 174 serials, and 1,203 audiovisual materials. 150 computers available on campus for general student use. A campuswide network can be accessed from student residence rooms. Staffed computer lab on campus.

Community Environment: Franklin is located 30 miles southwest of Boston and is the birthplace of Horace Mann. This is a rapidly growing area easily accessible by bus and rail. The community has swimming pools, tennis courts, ski facilities, riding, golf, movies, bowling, and dancing. There are many shopping centers nearby. Some part-time employment is available for students.

■ EASTERN NAZARENE COLLEGE

23 E Elm Ave.
Quincy, MA 02170
Tel: (617)745-3000; Free: 800-88-ENC88
Fax: (617)745-3907
E-mail: andrew.wright@enc.edu
Web Site: www.enc.edu/

Description: Independent, comprehensive, coed, affiliated with Church of the Nazarene. Awards associate, bachelor's, and master's degrees. Founded 1918. Setting: 17-acre urban campus with easy access to Boston. Endowment: $12.9 million. Educational spending for the previous fiscal year: $6039 per student. Total enrollment: 1,036. Faculty: 122 (48 full-time, 74 part-time). Student-undergrad faculty ratio is 17:1. 989 applied, 63% were admitted. 13% from top 10% of their high school class, 32% from top quarter, 65% from top half. Full-time: 850 students, 57% women, 43% men. Part-time: 12 students, 42% women, 58% men. Students come from 32 states and territories, 24 other countries, 35% from out-of-state. 0.1% American Indian or Alaska Native, non-Hispanic/Latino; 11% Hispanic/Latino; 15% African American, non-Hispanic/Latino; 4% Asian, non-Hispanic/Latino; 0.1% Native Hawaiian or other Pacific Islander, non-Hispanic/Latino; 1% international. 29% 25 or older, 52% live on campus, 10% transferred in. Retention: 69% of full-time freshmen returned the following year. Academic areas with the most degrees conferred: business/marketing; education; liberal arts/general studies. Core. Calendar: semesters. Academic remediation for entering students, services for LD students, advanced placement, accelerated degree program, honors program, independent study, double major, summer session for credit, part-time degree program, adult/continuing education programs, internships, graduate courses open to undergrads. Off campus study at Boston College, Boston University, Council for Christian Colleges and Universities, Massachusetts College of Pharmacy. Study abroad program. ROTC: Army (c), Naval (c), Air Force (c).

Entrance Requirements: Options: electronic application, early admission, deferred admission. Required: high school transcript, minimum 2 high school GPA, 1 recommendation, SAT or ACT. Recommended: essay, minimum 3 high school GPA, 2 recommendations, interview, SAT and SAT Subject Tests or ACT, SAT Subject Tests. Entrance: moderately difficult. Application deadlines: Rolling, Rolling for nonresidents. Notification: continuous, continuous for nonresidents. SAT Reasoning Test deadline: 9/1. SAT Subject Test deadline: 9/1. Transfer credits accepted: Yes.

Costs Per Year: Comprehensive fee: $35,184 includes full-time tuition ($25,944), mandatory fees ($940), and college room and board ($8300). Full-time tuition and fees vary according to class time, course load, degree level, location, program, and reciprocity agreements. Room and board charges vary according to board plan and housing facility. Part-time tuition: $1081 per credit, Part-time mandatory fees: $350 per term. Part-time tuition and fees vary according to class time, degree level, location, program, and reciprocity agreements.

Collegiate Environment: Orientation program. Drama-theater group, choral group, student-run newspaper. Social organizations: 50 open to all. Most popular organizations: Gospel Choir, Acappella Choir, Student Government Association, Open Hand, Open Heart, Kid's Club. Major annual events: Welcome Week, Homecoming, Heritage Day. Student services: health clinic, personal-psychological counseling. Campus security: 24-hour emergency response devices and patrols, student patrols, late night transport-escort service, controlled dormitory access. Nease Library with 117,540 books, 57,030 microform titles, 466 serials, an OPAC, and a Web page. Operations spending for the previous fiscal year: $572,181. 152 computers available on campus for general student use. Computer purchase/lease plans available. A campuswide network can be accessed from student residence rooms and from off campus. Students can access the following: online class registration. Staffed computer lab on campus provides training in use of computers, software, and the Internet.

Community Environment: See Quincy College.

■ ELMS COLLEGE

291 Springfield St.
Chicopee, MA 01013-2839

Tel: (413)594-2761; Free: 800-255-ELMS
Fax: (413)594-2781
E-mail: admissions@elms.edu
Web Site: www.elms.edu/

Description: Independent Roman Catholic, comprehensive, coed. Awards associate, bachelor's, and master's degrees. Founded 1928. Setting: 32-acre suburban campus. Total enrollment: 1,260. Student-undergrad faculty ratio is 11:1. 557 applied, 85% were admitted. 28% from out-of-state. 30% 25 or older. Retention: 85% of full-time freshmen returned the following year. Core. Calendar: semesters. Academic remediation for entering students, ESL program, advanced placement, accelerated degree program, self-designed majors, honors program, double major, summer session for credit, part-time degree program, adult/continuing education programs, internships, graduate courses open to undergrads. Off campus study at Cooperating Colleges of Greater Springfield, Sisters of Saint Joseph Colleges Consortium. Study abroad program. ROTC: Army (c), Air Force (c).

Entrance Requirements: Options: early admission, deferred admission, international baccalaureate accepted. Required: essay, high school transcript, 2 recommendations, SAT or ACT. Recommended: interview. Entrance: moderately difficult. Application deadline: Rolling. Notification: continuous.

Collegiate Environment: Orientation program. Drama-theater group, choral group, student-run newspaper, radio station. Student services: health clinic, personal-psychological counseling. Campus security: 24-hour emergency response devices and patrols, late night transport-escort service, controlled dormitory access. Alumnae Library with an OPAC.

Community Environment: Elms is located in western Massachusetts, two and one half miles from Springfield, near the junction of I-91 and I-90 (Mass. Turnpike). The climate is temperate. The community has several churches, museums, a library, theatre, sports center, cultural and social events at many of the nearby colleges, shopping, and major civic, fraternal, and veteran's organizations. Part-time employment is available.

■ EMERSON COLLEGE

120 Boylston St.
Boston, MA 02116-4624
Tel: (617)824-8500
Fax: (617)824-8609
E-mail: admission@emerson.edu
Web Site: www.emerson.edu/

Description: Independent, comprehensive, coed. Awards bachelor's, master's, and doctoral degrees. Founded 1880. Setting: urban campus. Endowment: $117.1 million. Total enrollment: 4,513. Faculty: 444 (186 full-time, 258 part-time). Student-undergrad faculty ratio is 13:1. 7,465 applied, 48% were admitted. 38% from top 10% of their high school class, 77% from top quarter, 93% from top half. Full-time: 3,586 students, 62% women, 38% men. Part-time: 89 students, 56% women, 44% men. Students come from 44 states and territories, 43 other countries, 77% from out-of-state. 0.1% American Indian or Alaska Native, non-Hispanic/Latino; 10% Hispanic/Latino; 3% African American, non-Hispanic/Latino; 4% Asian, non-Hispanic/Latino; 0.1% Native Hawaiian or other Pacific Islander, non-Hispanic/Latino; 4% international. 1% 25 or older, 57% live on campus, 5% transferred in. Retention: 88% of full-time freshmen returned the following year. Academic areas with the most degrees conferred: communication/journalism; visual and performing arts; English. Core. Calendar: semesters. Services for LD students, advanced placement, self-designed majors, honors program, independent study, double major, summer session for credit, part-time degree program, adult/continuing education programs, internships, graduate courses open to undergrads. Off campus study. Study abroad program.

Entrance Requirements: Options: electronic application, early admission, early action, deferred admission, international baccalaureate accepted. Required: essay, high school transcript, 1 recommendation, SAT or ACT. Required for some: interview. Entrance: very difficult. Application deadlines: 1/5, 11/1 for early action. Notification: 4/1, 12/15 for early action. SAT Reasoning Test deadline: 1/5. Applicants placed on waiting list: 1,229. Wait-listed applicants offered admission: 191. Early action applicants: 2,239. Early action applicants admitted: 1,389.

Costs Per Year: Application fee: $65. Comprehensive fee: $50,246 includes full-time tuition ($35,072), mandatory fees ($658), and college room and board ($14,516). Room and board charges vary according to board plan.

Collegiate Environment: Orientation program. Drama-theater group, choral group, student-run newspaper, radio station. Social organizations: 80 open to all; national fraternities, national sororities, local fraternities, local sororities; 3% of eligible men and 3% of eligible women are members. Most popular organizations: EIV (Emerson Independent Video), National Broadcasting Society (student chapter), EmComm (student marketing agency), Emerson Channel (campus television), Berkeley Beacon (student newspaper). Major annual events: EVVY's award show, Spring Musical, Emerson Recognition and Achievement (ERA) Awards (student government). Student services: health clinic, personal-psychological counseling. Campus security: 24-hour emergency response devices and patrols, late night transport-escort service, controlled dormitory access. 1,934 college housing spaces available; all were occupied in 2012-13. Freshmen guaranteed college housing. On-campus residence required through sophomore year. Option: coed housing available. Iwasaki Library plus 1 other with 223,336 books, 9,414 microform titles, 56,126 serials, 14,514 audiovisual materials, an OPAC, and a Web page. 480 computers available on campus for general student use. Computer purchase/lease plans available. A campuswide network can be accessed from student residence rooms and from off campus. Students can access the following: online class registration. Staffed computer lab on campus provides training in use of computers, software, and the Internet.

Community Environment: See Boston University.

■ **EMMANUEL COLLEGE**
400 The Fenway
Boston, MA 02115
Tel: (617)277-9340
Fax: (617)735-9801
E-mail: enroll@emmanuel.edu
Web Site: www.emmanuel.edu/
Description: Independent Roman Catholic, comprehensive, coed. Awards bachelor's and master's degrees and post-master's certificates. Founded 1919. Setting: 17-acre urban campus. Endowment: $64.7 million. Educational spending for the previous fiscal year: $5790 per student. Total enrollment: 2,488. Faculty: 242 (101 full-time, 141 part-time). Student-undergrad faculty ratio is 14:1. 7,851 applied, 50% were admitted. 20% from top 10% of their high school class, 46% from top quarter, 81% from top half. Full-time: 1,828 students, 70% women, 30% men. Part-time: 370 students, 85% women, 15% men. Students come from 33 states and territories, 35 other countries, 39% from out-of-state. 0.3% American Indian or Alaska Native, non-Hispanic/Latino; 6% Hispanic/Latino; 6% African American, non-Hispanic/Latino; 3% Asian, non-Hispanic/Latino; 1% international. 1% 25 or older, 74% live on campus, 2% transferred in. Retention: 81% of full-time freshmen returned the following year. Academic areas with the most degrees conferred: business/marketing; health professions and related sciences; psychology. Core. Calendar: semesters. Academic remediation for entering students, services for LD students, advanced placement, accelerated degree program, self-designed majors, honors program, independent study, distance learning, double major, summer session for credit, part-time degree program, adult/continuing education programs, internships, graduate courses open to undergrads. Off campus study at Colleges of the Fenway consortium. Study abroad program. ROTC: Army (c), Air Force (c).
Entrance Requirements: Options: electronic application, early admission, early decision, early action, deferred admission, international baccalaureate accepted. Required: essay, high school transcript, 2 recommendations, Official SAT or ACT report, SAT or ACT. Recommended: interview. Entrance: moderately difficult. Application deadlines: 2/15, 11/1 for early decision, 11/15 for early action. Notification: 12/1, 12/1 for early decision, 12/15 for early action. SAT Reasoning Test deadline: 2/15. SAT Subject Test deadline: 2/15. Transfer credits accepted: Yes. Applicants placed on waiting list: 0. Early decision applicants: 9. Early decision applicants admitted: 4. Early action applicants: 1,782. Early action applicants admitted: 1,372.
Costs Per Year: Application fee: $60. One-time mandatory fee: $225. Comprehensive fee: $46,640 includes full-time tuition ($33,450), mandatory fees ($200), and college room and board ($12,990). Full-time tuition and fees vary according to course load, degree level, and program. Room and board charges vary according to housing facility.
Collegiate Environment: Orientation program. Drama-theater group, choral group, student-run newspaper, radio station. Social organizations: 48 open to all. Most popular organizations: EC Superfans, Black Student Union, OUTSpoken (LGBTQ Club), Psychology Club, Campus Activities and Student Events. Major annual events: Moonlight Breakfast, Student Leadership Reception, International Hospitality Night. Student services: health clinic, personal-psychological counseling. Campus security: 24-hour emergency response devices and patrols, late night transport-escort service, controlled dormitory access, 24-hour staffed residence hall desks and security office, closed-circuit surveillance in public areas, off-campus

escorts, bike patrol. 1,290 college housing spaces available; all were occupied in 2012-13. Freshmen guaranteed college housing. Option: coed housing available. Cardinal Cushing Library with 150,000 books, 2,100 serials, 800 audiovisual materials, an OPAC, and a Web page. Operations spending for the previous fiscal year: $1 million. 117 computers available on campus for general student use. Computer purchase/lease plans available. A campuswide network can be accessed from student residence rooms and from off campus. Students can access the following: online class registration, software applications. Staffed computer lab on campus provides training in use of computers, software, and the Internet.

■ **ENDICOTT COLLEGE**
376 Hale St.
Beverly, MA 01915-2096
Tel: (978)927-0585; Free: 800-325-1114
Fax: (978)927-0084
E-mail: admissio@endicott.edu
Web Site: www.endicott.edu/
Description: Independent, comprehensive, coed. Awards associate, bachelor's, master's, and doctoral degrees. Founded 1939. Setting: 235-acre suburban campus with easy access to Boston. Endowment: $44.9 million. Educational spending for the previous fiscal year: $9377 per student. Total enrollment: 4,625. Faculty: 386 (93 full-time, 293 part-time). Student-undergrad faculty ratio is 14:1. 3,661 applied, 63% were admitted. 15% from top 10% of their high school class, 44% from top quarter, 80% from top half. Full-time: 2,498 students, 59% women, 41% men. Part-time: 264 students, 47% women, 53% men. Students come from 28 states and territories, 24 other countries, 51% from out-of-state. 0.3% American Indian or Alaska Native, non-Hispanic/Latino; 3% Hispanic/Latino; 2% African American, non-Hispanic/Latino; 1% Asian, non-Hispanic/Latino; 0.1% Native Hawaiian or other Pacific Islander, non-Hispanic/Latino; 2% international. 1% 25 or older, 83% live on campus, 2% transferred in. Retention: 83% of full-time freshmen returned the following year. Academic areas with the most degrees conferred: business/marketing; parks and recreation; visual and performing arts. Core. Calendar: semesters. Services for LD students, advanced placement, accelerated degree program, self-designed majors, honors program, independent study, distance learning, summer session for credit, part-time degree program, adult/continuing education programs, co-op programs and internships, graduate courses open to undergrads. Off campus study at 10 members of the Northeast Consortium of Colleges and Universities in Massachusetts. Study abroad program. ROTC: Army (c).
Entrance Requirements: Options: electronic application, international baccalaureate accepted. Required: essay, high school transcript, minimum 2.5 high school GPA, 1 recommendation, SAT or ACT. Recommended: interview. Required for some: interview. Entrance: moderately difficult. Application deadline: 2/15. Notification: continuous. SAT Reasoning Test deadline: 2/15. SAT Subject Test deadline: 2/15. Transfer credits accepted: Yes. Applicants placed on waiting list: 109. Wait-listed applicants offered admission: 0.
Costs Per Year: Application fee: $50. Comprehensive fee: $41,366 includes full-time tuition ($27,666), mandatory fees ($500), and college room and board ($13,200). College room only: $9100. Room and board charges vary according to board plan and housing facility.
Collegiate Environment: Orientation program. Drama-theater group, choral group, student-run newspaper, radio station. Social organizations: 58 open to all. Most popular organizations: Campus Activities Board, Student Senate, intramurals, Sailing Club, Shipmates. Major annual events: Homecoming/Family Weekend, Annual Regatta, Spring Week. Student services: health clinic, personal-psychological counseling. Campus security: 24-hour emergency response devices and patrols, student patrols, late night transport-escort service, controlled dormitory access, license plate recognition, crime prevention programs, rape awareness defense, property identification, security cameras, front gate. 2,006 college housing spaces available; 1,950 were occupied in 2012-13. Freshmen guaranteed college housing. Options: coed, women-only housing available. Diane M. Halle Library with 120,000 books, 6,987 microform titles, 82,037 serials, 2,113 audiovisual materials, an OPAC, and a Web page. Operations spending for the previous fiscal year: $702,304. 237 computers available on campus for general student use. Computer purchase/lease plans available. A campuswide network can be accessed from student residence rooms and from off campus. Students can access the following: online class registration. Staffed computer lab on campus provides training in use of computers, software, and the Internet.
Community Environment: Suburban.

■ FINE MORTUARY COLLEGE, LLC
150 Kerry Pl.
Norwood, MA 02062
Tel: (781)762-1211
Fax: (781)762-7177
E-mail: mwise@fine-ne.com
Web Site: www.fine-ne.com/
Description: Proprietary, 2-year, coed. Awards terminal associate degrees. Founded 1996. Setting: suburban campus. Total enrollment: 73. Faculty: 17 (2 full-time, 15 part-time). Student-undergrad faculty ratio is 5:1. 86% 25 or older. Core. Calendar: continuous. Academic remediation for entering students, distance learning, summer session for credit, internships. Off campus study.
Entrance Requirements: Required: essay, high school transcript, CPAt. Recommended: interview. Entrance: noncompetitive.
Collegiate Environment: Orientation program. Student services: personal-psychological counseling. 6 computers available on campus for general student use. A computer is required for all students. A campuswide network can be accessed. Staffed computer lab on campus provides training in use of computers, software, and the Internet.

■ FISHER COLLEGE
118 Beacon St.
Boston, MA 02116-1500
Tel: (617)236-8800
Fax: (617)236-8858
E-mail: admissions@fisher.edu
Web Site: www.fisher.edu/
Description: Independent, 4-year, coed. Awards associate and bachelor's degrees. Founded 1903. Setting: urban campus with easy access to Boston. Total enrollment: 1,751. Faculty: 155 (29 full-time, 126 part-time). Student-undergrad faculty ratio is 18:1. 2,460 applied, 64% were admitted. Full-time: 1,056 students, 65% women, 35% men. Part-time: 695 students, 89% women, 11% men. 34% from out-of-state. 0.4% American Indian or Alaska Native, non-Hispanic/Latino; 8% Hispanic/Latino; 12% African American, non-Hispanic/Latino; 2% Asian, non-Hispanic/Latino; 0% Native Hawaiian or other Pacific Islander, non-Hispanic/Latino; 8% international. 5% 25 or older, 47% live on campus, 2% transferred in. Retention: 65% of full-time freshmen returned the following year. Academic area with the most degrees conferred: business/marketing. Core. Calendar: semesters. Academic remediation for entering students, ESL program, services for LD students, advanced placement, honors program, independent study, distance learning, summer session for credit, part-time degree program, adult/continuing education programs, internships. Off campus study. Study abroad program. ROTC: Army (c).
Entrance Requirements: Options: electronic application, deferred admission. Required: high school transcript. Recommended: minimum 2 high school GPA. Required for some: essay, interview, SAT or ACT. Entrance: minimally difficult. Application deadline: Rolling. Notification: continuous. Transfer credits accepted: Yes.
Costs Per Year: Application fee: $50. Comprehensive fee: $40,699 includes full-time tuition ($25,780), mandatory fees ($995), and college room and board ($13,924). Room and board charges vary according to housing facility. Part-time tuition: $300 per credit.
Collegiate Environment: Orientation program. Drama-theater group, choral group. Student services: health clinic, personal-psychological counseling, women's center. Campus security: 24-hour emergency response devices and patrols, controlled dormitory access. 350 college housing spaces available; 330 were occupied in 2012-13. No special consideration for freshman housing applicants. Options: coed, women-only housing available. Fisher College Library plus 1 other with an OPAC. 137 computers available on campus for general student use. A campuswide network can be accessed from student residence rooms and from off campus. Students can access the following: online class registration. Staffed computer lab on campus provides training in use of computers, software, and the Internet.
Community Environment: See Boston University.

■ FITCHBURG STATE UNIVERSITY
160 Pearl St.
Fitchburg, MA 01420-2697
Tel: (978)345-2151; Free: 800-705-9692
Fax: (978)665-4540
E-mail: admissions@fitchburgstate.edu
Web Site: www.fitchburgstate.edu/
Description: State-supported, comprehensive, coed. Part of Massachusetts Public Higher Education System. Awards bachelor's and master's degrees and post-master's certificates. Founded 1894. Setting: 78-acre suburban campus with easy access to Boston. Endowment: $12.8 million. Total enrollment: 6,889. Faculty: 274 (184 full-time, 90 part-time). Student-undergrad faculty ratio is 16:1. 3,104 applied, 70% were admitted. Full-time: 3,329 students, 54% women, 46% men. Part-time: 834 students, 56% women, 44% men. Students come from 20 states and territories, 4 other countries, 8% from out-of-state. 0.2% American Indian or Alaska Native, non-Hispanic/Latino; 8% Hispanic/Latino; 5% African American, non-Hispanic/Latino; 2% Asian, non-Hispanic/Latino; 0.1% Native Hawaiian or other Pacific Islander, non-Hispanic/Latino; 0.2% international. 13% 25 or older, 40% live on campus, 8% transferred in. Retention: 73% of full-time freshmen returned the following year. Academic areas with the most degrees conferred: business/marketing; visual and performing arts; interdisciplinary studies. Core. Calendar: semesters. Academic remediation for entering students, services for LD students, advanced placement, accelerated degree program, self-designed majors, honors program, independent study, distance learning, double major, summer session for credit, part-time degree program, adult/continuing education programs, internships. Off campus study. Study abroad program. ROTC: Army.
Entrance Requirements: Options: electronic application, deferred admission. Required: essay, high school transcript, minimum 2 high school GPA, 16 core courses, SAT or ACT. Entrance: moderately difficult. Application deadlines: Rolling, Rolling for nonresidents. Notification: continuous, continuous for nonresidents. SAT Reasoning Test deadline: 5/1. Transfer credits accepted: Yes. Applicants placed on waiting list: 62. Wait-listed applicants offered admission: 10.
Costs Per Year: Application fee: $25. State resident tuition: $970 full-time. Nonresident tuition: $7050 full-time. Mandatory fees: $7740 full-time. Full-time tuition and fees vary according to class time and reciprocity agreements. College room and board: $8602. College room only: $5652. Room and board charges vary according to board plan and housing facility.
Collegiate Environment: Orientation program. Drama-theater group, choral group, student-run newspaper, radio station. Social organizations: 60 open to all; national fraternities, national sororities; 1% of eligible men and 3% of eligible women are members. Most popular organizations: Student Government Association, Dance Club, Activities Board, Greek Council, MASSPIRG. Major annual events: Rock the Block, Student Convocations, Family Weekend. Student services: health clinic, personal-psychological counseling. Campus security: 24-hour emergency response devices and patrols, student patrols, late night transport-escort service, controlled dormitory access. 1,559 college housing spaces available; 1,471 were occupied in 2012-13. Freshmen given priority for college housing. Option: coed housing available. Amelia V. Galucci-Cirio Library with 222,517 books, 95,999 microform titles, 3,050 serials, 3,001 audiovisual materials, an OPAC, and a Web page. 500 computers available on campus for general student use. Computer purchase/lease plans available. A computer is required for all students. A campuswide network can be accessed from student residence rooms and from off campus. Students can access the following: online class registration. Staffed computer lab on campus (open 24 hours a day).
Community Environment: The college is located in an urban setting, 50 miles from Boston.

■ FRAMINGHAM STATE UNIVERSITY
100 State St.
Framingham, MA 01701-9101
Tel: (508)620-1220
Fax: (508)626-4017
E-mail: admissions@framingham.edu
Web Site: www.framingham.edu/
Description: State-supported, 4-year, coed. Part of Massachusetts Public Higher Education System. Awards bachelor's and master's degrees. Founded 1839. Setting: 73-acre suburban campus with easy access to Boston. Endowment: $21.8 million. Educational spending for the previous fiscal year: $4048 per student. Total enrollment: 6,506. Faculty: 313 (176 full-time, 137 part-time). Student-undergrad faculty ratio is 16:1. 5,433 applied, 52% were admitted. 6% from top 10% of their high school class, 28% from top quarter, 70% from top half. Full-time: 3,804 students, 64% women, 36% men. Part-time: 686 students, 58% women, 42% men. 4% from out-of-state. 0.1% American Indian or Alaska Native, non-Hispanic/Latino; 8% Hispanic/Latino; 7% African American, non-Hispanic/Latino; 3% Asian, non-Hispanic/Latino; 0.04% Native Hawaiian or other Pacific Islander, non-Hispanic/Latino; 0.1% international. 14% 25 or older, 52% live on campus,

11% transferred in. Retention: 74% of full-time freshmen returned the following year. Academic areas with the most degrees conferred: business/marketing; family and consumer sciences; social sciences. Core. Calendar: semesters. ESL program, services for LD students, advanced placement, self-designed majors, honors program, independent study, distance learning, double major, summer session for credit, part-time degree program, co-op programs and internships. Off campus study at College Academic Program Sharing, 8 members of the other Massachusetts State colleges. Study abroad program.

Entrance Requirements: Options: electronic application, early action, deferred admission. Required: high school transcript, minimum 2 high school GPA, Minimum of 16 college preparatory courses in specified areas, SAT or ACT. Recommended: minimum 3 high school GPA. Entrance: moderately difficult. Application deadlines: 2/15, 11/15 for early action. Notification: continuous, 12/15 for early action. Preference given to state residents. SAT Reasoning Test deadline: 2/15. Transfer credits accepted: Yes. Early action applicants: 962. Early action applicants admitted: 658.

Costs Per Year: Application fee: $45. State resident tuition: $970 full-time, $162 per course part-time. Nonresident tuition: $7050 full-time, $1175 per course part-time. Mandatory fees: $7110 full-time, $1,250 per course part-time. Full-time tuition and fees vary according to class time. Part-time tuition and fees vary according to class time and course load. College room and board: $9540. College room only: $6380. Room and board charges vary according to board plan and housing facility.

Collegiate Environment: Orientation program. Drama-theater group, choral group, student-run newspaper, radio station. Social organizations: 50 open to all. Most popular organizations: Dance Club, Student Union Activities Board, Gatepost (student newspaper), Student Government Association, Hilltop Players (theater group). Major annual events: Homecoming, The Sandbox Festival, Semi-Formal. Student services: health clinic, personal-psychological counseling. Campus security: 24-hour emergency response devices and patrols, student patrols, late night transport-escort service, controlled dormitory access. 1,931 college housing spaces available; 1,832 were occupied in 2012-13. Freshmen given priority for college housing. Options: coed, women-only housing available. Henry Whittemore Library with 216,902 books, 163 serials, 4,288 audiovisual materials, an OPAC, and a Web page. Operations spending for the previous fiscal year: $1.6 million. 216 computers available on campus for general student use. Computer purchase/lease plans available. A computer is required for all students. A campuswide network can be accessed from student residence rooms and from off campus. Students can access the following: online class registration. Staffed computer lab on campus.

Community Environment: Area is located 20 miles west of Boston and has transportation facilities. Part-time job opportunities are available for students. This diversified community offers many opportunities in the areas of high technology, retailing, and manufacturing, as well as being a major residential center.

■ FRANKLIN W. OLIN COLLEGE OF ENGINEERING

Olin Way
Needham, MA 02492-1200
Tel: (781)292-2300
E-mail: info@olin.edu
Web Site: www.olin.edu/

Description: Independent, 4-year, coed. Awards bachelor's degrees. Founded 2002. Setting: 75-acre suburban campus with easy access to Boston. Endowment: $338.2 million. Research spending for the previous fiscal year: $2.5 million. Educational spending for the previous fiscal year: $31,247 per student. Total enrollment: 355. Faculty: 48 (35 full-time, 13 part-time). Student-undergrad faculty ratio is 9:1. 768 applied, 16% were admitted. 95% from top 10% of their high school class, 100% from top quarter, 100% from top half. 20 National Merit Scholars, 4 valedictorians, 18 student government officers. Full-time: 355 students, 47% women, 53% men. Students come from 38 states and territories, 10 other countries, 87% from out-of-state. 0% American Indian or Alaska Native, non-Hispanic/Latino; 1% Hispanic/Latino; 1% African American, non-Hispanic/Latino; 17% Asian, non-Hispanic/Latino; 0% Native Hawaiian or other Pacific Islander, non-Hispanic/Latino; 7% international. 0% 25 or older, 100% live on campus, 1% transferred in. Retention: 96% of full-time freshmen returned the following year. Academic area with the most degrees conferred: engineering. Core. Services for LD students, self-designed majors, independent study, internships. Off campus study at Babson College, Brandeis University and Wellesley College. Study abroad program.

Entrance Requirements: Options: electronic application, deferred admission, international baccalaureate accepted. Required: essay, high school transcript, 3 recommendations, interview, SAT or ACT, SAT Subject Tests. Entrance: most difficult. Application deadline: 1/1. Notification: 3/21. SAT Reasoning Test deadline: 12/31. Applicants placed on waiting list: 34. Wait-listed applicants offered admission: 5.

Costs Per Year: Application fee: $80. One-time mandatory fee: $2656. Comprehensive fee: $57,500 includes full-time tuition ($42,000), mandatory fees ($500), and college room and board ($15,000). College room only: $9000. Part-time tuition: $1400 per credit.

Collegiate Environment: Orientation program. Drama-theater group, choral group, student-run newspaper. Social organizations: 55 open to all. Most popular organizations: Greening Olin, Olin Fire Arts Club, Support, Encourage and Recognize Volunteerism (SERV), Olin Entrepreneurial Group, Open. Major annual events: Candidate's Weekend, ExpressO, SAC Carnival. Student services: health clinic, personal-psychological counseling. Campus security: 24-hour emergency response devices and patrols, controlled dormitory access. 350 college housing spaces available; all were occupied in 2012-13. Freshmen guaranteed college housing. On-campus residence required through senior year. Option: coed housing available. Franklin W.Olin Library with 318,252 books, 10 microform titles, 29,926 serials, 1,496 audiovisual materials, an OPAC, and a Web page. Operations spending for the previous fiscal year: $501,895. 410 computers available on campus for general student use. Computer purchase/lease plans available. A computer is required for all students. A campuswide network can be accessed from student residence rooms and from off campus. Students can access the following: online class registration. Staffed computer lab on campus (open 24 hours a day) provides training in use of computers, software, and the Internet.

■ GORDON COLLEGE

255 Grapevine Rd.
Wenham, MA 01984-1899
Tel: (978)927-2300; Free: 866-464-6736
Fax: (978)524-3704
E-mail: admissions@gordon.edu
Web Site: www.gordon.edu/

Description: Independent nondenominational, comprehensive, coed. Awards bachelor's and master's degrees. Founded 1889. Setting: 450-acre suburban campus with easy access to Boston. Endowment: $29 million. Research spending for the previous fiscal year: $121,300. Educational spending for the previous fiscal year: $11,298 per student. Total enrollment: 1,909. Faculty: 177 (92 full-time, 85 part-time). Student-undergrad faculty ratio is 13:1. 4,008 applied, 40% were admitted. 32% from top 10% of their high school class, 68% from top quarter, 91% from top half. 8 valedictorians. Full-time: 1,548 students, 62% women, 38% men. Part-time: 32 students, 53% women, 47% men. Students come from 41 states and territories, 69 other countries, 68% from out-of-state. 0% American Indian or Alaska Native, non-Hispanic/Latino; 7% Hispanic/Latino; 3% African American, non-Hispanic/Latino; 3% Asian, non-Hispanic/Latino; 0.4% Native Hawaiian or other Pacific Islander, non-Hispanic/Latino; 4% international. 2% 25 or older, 90% live on campus, 4% transferred in. Retention: 80% of full-time freshmen returned the following year. Academic areas with the most degrees conferred: psychology; business/marketing; visual and performing arts. Core. Calendar: semesters. Academic remediation for entering students, services for LD students, advanced placement, self-designed majors, honors program, independent study, double major, summer session for credit, part-time degree program, co-op programs and internships. Off campus study at members of the Christian College Consortium (CCC), Consortium of Christian Colleges and Universities (CCCU), Northeast Consortium of Colleges and Universities in Massachusetts (NECCUM). Study abroad program. ROTC: Army (c).

Entrance Requirements: Options: electronic application, early admission, early decision, early action, deferred admission, international baccalaureate accepted. Required: high school transcript, 2 recommendations, interview, Pastoral recommendation and statement of Christian faith, SAT or ACT. Recommended: essay, minimum 3 high school GPA, SAT Subject Tests. Entrance: moderately difficult. Application deadlines: Rolling, 11/1 for early decision, 11/15 for early action. Notification: continuous until 9/15, 12/1 for early decision, 12/15 for early action. SAT Reasoning Test deadline: 2/1. SAT Subject Test deadline: 2/1. Transfer credits accepted: Yes. Early decision applicants: 47. Early decision applicants admitted: 27. Early action applicants: 1,012. Early action applicants admitted: 289.

Costs Per Year: Application fee: $50. Comprehensive fee: $42,660 includes full-time tuition ($31,820), mandatory fees ($1410), and college room and

board ($9430). College room only: $6250. Full-time tuition and fees vary according to course load and program. Room and board charges vary according to board plan and housing facility. Part-time tuition: $1125 per credit. Part-time tuition varies according to course load and program.

Collegiate Environment: Orientation program. Drama-theater group, choral group, student-run newspaper, radio station. Social organizations: 35 open to all. Most popular organizations: Student Government Association, student ministries and volunteer programs, Diverse music ensembles, intramural sports, Short-term missions. Major annual events: Center for Christian Studies Spring Symposium, Homecoming, Golden Goose. Student services: health clinic, personal-psychological counseling. Campus security: 24-hour emergency response devices and patrols, late night transport-escort service, controlled dormitory access, video cameras. College housing designed to accommodate 1,350 students; 1,367 undergraduates lived in college housing during 2012-13. Freshmen guaranteed college housing. On-campus residence required through senior year. Options: coed, men-only, women-only housing available. Jenks Learning Resource Center with 154,045 books, 31,823 microform titles, 63,474 serials, 7,900 audiovisual materials, an OPAC, and a Web page. Operations spending for the previous fiscal year: $847,523. 100 computers available on campus for general student use. Computer purchase/lease plans available. A campuswide network can be accessed from student residence rooms and from off campus. Students can access the following: online class registration. Staffed computer lab on campus provides training in use of computers, software, and the Internet.

■ **GREENFIELD COMMUNITY COLLEGE**
1 College Dr.
Greenfield, MA 01301-9739
Tel: (413)775-1000
Fax: (413)773-5129
E-mail: admission@gcc.mass.edu
Web Site: www.gcc.mass.edu/

Description: State-supported, 2-year, coed. Part of Commonwealth of Massachusetts Department of Higher Education. Awards certificates, transfer associate, and terminal associate degrees. Founded 1962. Setting: 120-acre small town campus. Educational spending for the previous fiscal year: $6882 per student. Total enrollment: 2,437. Faculty: 183 (62 full-time, 121 part-time). Student-undergrad faculty ratio is 14:1. 944 applied, 100% were admitted. Full-time: 920 students, 54% women, 46% men. Part-time: 1,517 students, 61% women, 39% men. Students come from 14 states and territories, 11 other countries, 10% from out-of-state. 1% American Indian or Alaska Native, non-Hispanic/Latino; 5% Hispanic/Latino; 3% African American, non-Hispanic/Latino; 3% Asian, non-Hispanic/Latino; 0.1% Native Hawaiian or other Pacific Islander, non-Hispanic/Latino; 0% international. 42% 25 or older, 6% transferred in. Retention: 60% of full-time freshmen returned the following year. Core. Calendar: semesters. Academic remediation for entering students, ESL program, services for LD students, advanced placement, independent study, distance learning, double major, summer session for credit, part-time degree program, adult/continuing education programs, co-op programs and internships.

Entrance Requirements: Open admission except for allied health, outdoor leadership programs. Option: electronic application. Required for some: high school transcript, interview, Psychological Corporation Practical Nursing Entrance Examination. Entrance: noncompetitive. Application deadline: Rolling. Preference given to state residents.

Collegiate Environment: Orientation program. Drama-theater group, choral group. Social organizations: 19 open to all. Most popular organizations: Student Senate, Art Club, Permaculture Club, VetNet, International Students Club. Major annual event: Spring Weekend. Student services: personal-psychological counseling, women's center. Campus security: 24-hour emergency response devices and patrols, late night transport-escort service. College housing not available. Greenfield Community College Library with 69,974 books, 106 serials, 1,158 audiovisual materials, an OPAC, and a Web page. 130 computers available on campus for general student use. A campuswide network can be accessed from off-campus. Staffed computer lab on campus provides training in use of computers, software, and the Internet.

Community Environment: The world's largest producer of taps and dies, Greenfield is a center for winter sports, and hunting and fishing in season. This is a combined rural and suburban area with bus service and limited rail service available. Climate is temperate. Recreational facilities include excellent ski area, 13 movie theatres, and all water sports on Connecticut River. Limited part-time employment for students. County fair held annually in September; Winter Carnival in February; Spring Farmers' Market.

■ **HAMPSHIRE COLLEGE**
893 W St.
Amherst, MA 01002
Tel: (413)549-4600; Free: 877-937-4267
Fax: (413)582-5631
E-mail: admissions@hampshire.edu
Web Site: www.hampshire.edu/

Description: Independent, 4-year, coed. Awards bachelor's degrees. Founded 1965. Setting: 800-acre small town campus. Endowment: $28.9 million. Research spending for the previous fiscal year: $3.7 million. Educational spending for the previous fiscal year: $12,101 per student. Total enrollment: 1,461. Faculty: 145 (105 full-time, 40 part-time). Student-undergrad faculty ratio is 12:1. 2,856 applied, 64% were admitted. 0% from top 10% of their high school class, 0% from top quarter, 0% from top half. Full-time: 1,484 students, 58% women, 42% men. Students come from 47 states and territories, 19 other countries, 82% from out-of-state. 0.1% American Indian or Alaska Native, non-Hispanic/Latino; 9% Hispanic/Latino; 3% African American, non-Hispanic/Latino; 2% Asian, non-Hispanic/Latino; 0% Native Hawaiian or other Pacific Islander, non-Hispanic/Latino; 5% international. 2% 25 or older, 80% live on campus, 3% transferred in. Retention: 82% of full-time freshmen returned the following year. Academic areas with the most degrees conferred: visual and performing arts; social sciences; English. Core. Calendar: 4-1-4. Services for LD students, self-designed majors, independent study, internships. Off campus study at Hampshire is a member of Five Colleges, Inc. Students may take courses at any of the member institutions (Amherst, Mount Holyoke, Smith, and University of Massachusetts at Amherst) for no additional charge. Study abroad program. ROTC: Army (c).

Entrance Requirements: Options: electronic application, early admission, early decision, early action, deferred admission, international baccalaureate accepted. Required: essay, high school transcript, 1 recommendation. Recommended: interview, SAT and SAT Subject Tests or ACT. Entrance: moderately difficult. Application deadlines: 1/1, 11/15 for early decision plan 1, 1/1 for early decision plan 2, 12/1 for early action. Notification: 4/1, 12/15 for early decision plan 1, 2/1 for early decision plan 2, 2/1 for early action. SAT Reasoning Test deadline: 2/1. SAT Subject Test deadline: 2/1. Transfer credits accepted: Yes. Applicants placed on waiting list: 388. Wait-listed applicants offered admission: 47. Early decision applicants: 139. Early decision applicants admitted: 112.

Costs Per Year: Application fee: $60. Comprehensive fee: $58,655 includes full-time tuition ($45,100), mandatory fees ($1525), and college room and board ($12,030). College room only: $7680. Room and board charges vary according to board plan.

Collegiate Environment: Orientation program. Drama-theater group, choral group, student-run newspaper, radio station. Social organizations: 125 open to all. Most popular organizations: Red Scare Frisbee, Queer Community Alliance, Excalibur (fantasy/role playing), Sports Coop, Circus Folks Unite. Major annual events: Spring Jam, Hampshire Halloween, Family and Friends Weekend. Student services: health clinic, personal-psychological counseling, women's center. Campus security: 24-hour emergency response devices and patrols. College housing designed to accommodate 1,184 students; 1,193 undergraduates lived in college housing during 2012-13. Freshmen guaranteed college housing. On-campus residence required through senior year. Options: coed, men-only, women-only housing available. Harold F. Johnson Library with 199,013 books, 99 microform titles, 56,041 serials, 12,497 audiovisual materials, an OPAC, and a Web page. Operations spending for the previous fiscal year: $1.5 million. 215 computers available on campus for general student use. Computer purchase/lease plans available. A campuswide network can be accessed from student residence rooms and from off campus. Students can access the following: online class registration. Staffed computer lab on campus provides training in use of computers, software, and the Internet.

Community Environment: See Amherst College.

■ **HARVARD UNIVERSITY**
Cambridge, MA 02138
Tel: (617)495-1000
E-mail: college@harvard.edu
Web Site: www.harvard.edu/

Description: Independent, university, coed. Awards bachelor's, master's, and doctoral degrees. Founded 1636. Setting: 380-acre urban campus with easy access to Boston. Endowment: $32 billion. Total enrollment: 10,573. Faculty: 1,113 (928 full-time, 185 part-time). Student-undergrad faculty ratio is 7:1. 34,950 applied, 6% were admitted. 95% from top 10% of their high school class, 100% from top quarter, 100% from top half. Full-time: 6,671 students, 50% women, 50% men. Part-time: 5 students, 100% women. Students come from 55 states and territories, 111 other countries, 85% from out-of-state. 0.3% American Indian or Alaska Native, non-Hispanic/Latino; 9% Hispanic/Latino; 7% African American, non-Hispanic/Latino; 18% Asian, non-Hispanic/Latino; 0.03% Native Hawaiian or other Pacific Islander, non-Hispanic/Latino; 10% international. 1% 25 or older, 96% live on campus, 0.2% transferred in. Retention: 97% of full-time freshmen returned the following year. Academic areas with the most degrees conferred: social sciences; biological/life sciences; history. Core. Calendar: semesters. Services for LD students, advanced placement, accelerated degree program, self-designed majors, honors program, independent study, double major, summer session for credit, internships, graduate courses open to undergrads. Off campus study at Massachusetts Institute of Technology. Study abroad program. ROTC: Army (c), Naval, Air Force (c).

Entrance Requirements: Options: electronic application, early action, deferred admission, international baccalaureate accepted. Required: essay, high school transcript, SAT or ACT, SAT Subject Tests. Recommended: 2 recommendations, interview. Entrance: most difficult. Application deadline: 1/1. Notification: 4/1. SAT Reasoning Test deadline: 3/6. SAT Subject Test deadline: 2/23.

Costs Per Year: Application fee: $75. Comprehensive fee: $54,496 includes full-time tuition ($37,576), mandatory fees ($3290), and college room and board ($13,630). College room only: $8366.

Collegiate Environment: Orientation program. Drama-theater group, choral group, marching band, student-run newspaper, radio station. Social organizations: 447 open to all; house system. Most popular organizations: Phillips Brooks House Association, Asian-American Association, International Relations Council, Harvard Crimson (newspaper), Harvard/Radcliffe Chorus. Major annual events: Commencement, Welcome Back Event, Yardfest. Student services: health clinic, personal-psychological counseling, women's center. Campus security: 24-hour emergency response devices and patrols, late night transport-escort service, controlled dormitory access, required and optional safety courses. 6,570 college housing spaces available; 6,561 were occupied in 2012-13. Freshmen guaranteed college housing. On-campus residence required in freshman year. Option: coed housing available. Widener Library plus 73 others with 16.3 million books, 10 million microform titles, 121,791 serials, an OPAC, and a Web page. 605 computers available on campus for general student use. Computer purchase/lease plans available. A campuswide network can be accessed from student residence rooms and from off campus. Students can access the following: online class registration. Staffed computer lab on campus provides training in use of computers, software, and the Internet.

Community Environment: Settled in 1630, Cambridge has been the home of such famous writers as Henry Wadsworth Longfellow, James Russell Lowell, and Oliver Wendell Holmes. It is also the birthplace in Massachusetts of high technology industry. With a population of about 100,100 concentrated in 6.25 square miles, Cambridge today is the sixth largest city in the state. A vital university town, Cambridge is also a city of long-established neighborhoods with strong ethnic roots and traditions. Just across the Charles River and connected by an efficient transit system, Boston offers historical landmarks, professional sports, cosmopolitan shopping, world-famous hospitals and outstanding cultural opportunities.

■ **HELLENIC COLLEGE**
50 Goddard Ave.
Brookline, MA 02445-7496
Tel: (617)731-3500; Free: 866-424-2338
Fax: (617)232-7819
E-mail: admissions@hchc.edu
Web Site: www.hchc.edu/

Description: Independent Greek Orthodox, comprehensive, coed. Awards bachelor's and master's degrees (also offers graduate degree programs through Holy Cross Greek Orthodox School of Theology). Founded 1937. Setting: 52-acre suburban campus with easy access to Boston. Endowment: $25.9 million. Educational spending for the previous fiscal year: $14,295 per student. Total enrollment: 240. Faculty: 50 (18 full-time, 32 part-time). Student-undergrad faculty ratio is 9:1. 64 applied, 59% were admitted. Full-time: 99 students, 38% women, 62% men. Students come from 30 states and territories, 5 other countries, 80% from out-of-state. 0% American Indian or Alaska Native, non-Hispanic/Latino; 2% Asian, non-Hispanic/Latino; 0% Native Hawaiian or other Pacific Islander, non-Hispanic/Latino; 8% international. 10% 25 or older, 95% live on campus, 11% transferred in. Retention: 94% of full-time freshmen returned the following

year. Academic area with the most degrees conferred: liberal arts/general studies. Core. Calendar: semesters. Academic remediation for entering students, independent study, double major, summer session for credit, part-time degree program, internships, graduate courses open to undergrads. Off campus study at Boston Theological Institute, Boston College, Newbury College.

Entrance Requirements: Options: electronic application, early action, deferred admission. Required: essay, high school transcript, minimum 2 high school GPA, interview, health certificate, SAT or ACT Scores, SAT or ACT. Required for some: SAT Subject Tests. Entrance: minimally difficult. Application deadlines: Rolling, 12/1 for early action. Notification: continuous.

Collegiate Environment: Orientation program. Choral group, student-run newspaper. Student services: health clinic, personal-psychological counseling. Campus security: controlled dormitory access. Archbishop Iakovos Library with 63,374 books, 883 microform titles, 720 serials, 3,015 audiovisual materials, an OPAC, and a Web page. Operations spending for the previous fiscal year: $845,740. 35 computers available on campus for general student use. A campuswide network can be accessed from student residence rooms and from off campus. Students can access the following: online class registration. Staffed computer lab on campus provides training in use of computers, software, and the Internet.

■ **HOLYOKE COMMUNITY COLLEGE**
303 Homestead Ave.
Holyoke, MA 01040-1099
Tel: (413)538-7000
E-mail: admissions@hcc.edu
Web Site: www.hcc.edu/

Description: State-supported, 2-year, coed. Part of Massachusetts Public Higher Education System. Awards certificates, transfer associate, and terminal associate degrees. Founded 1946. Setting: 135-acre small town campus. System endowment: $9 million. Total enrollment: 7,164. Faculty: 531 (130 full-time, 401 part-time). Student-undergrad faculty ratio is 18:1. Full-time: 3,488 students, 57% women, 43% men. Part-time: 3,676 students, 67% women, 33% men. Students come from 16 states and territories, 1% from out-of-state. 1% American Indian or Alaska Native, non-Hispanic/Latino; 21% Hispanic/Latino; 7% African American, non-Hispanic/Latino; 2% Asian, non-Hispanic/Latino; 0.04% Native Hawaiian or other Pacific Islander, non-Hispanic/Latino; 0.3% international. 12% 25 or older, 8% transferred in. Core. Calendar: semesters. Academic remediation for entering students, ESL program, services for LD students, advanced placement, self-designed majors, honors program, independent study, distance learning, double major, summer session for credit, part-time degree program, external degree program, adult/continuing education programs, co-op programs and internships. Off campus study at the Cooperating Colleges of Greater Springfield. Study abroad program. ROTC: Army (c), Air Force (c).

Entrance Requirements: Open admission except for nursing, radiological science, ophthalmic technology programs. Options: electronic application, early admission, deferred admission. Required: high school transcript. Recommended: interview. Entrance: noncompetitive. Application deadline: Rolling. Notification: continuous.

Costs Per Year: Application fee: $0. State resident tuition: $576 full-time, $141 per credit part-time. Nonresident tuition: $5520 full-time, $347 per credit part-time. Mandatory fees: $2998 full-time, $95 per term part-time. Full-time tuition and fees vary according to course load. Part-time tuition and fees vary according to course load.

Collegiate Environment: Orientation program. Drama-theater group, student-run newspaper, radio station. Social organizations: 40 open to all. Most popular organizations: Drama Club, Japanese Anime Club, Student Senate, LISA Club, STRIVE. Major annual events: Spring Fling Week, Welcome Week, Black History Month. Student services: health clinic, personal-psychological counseling, women's center. Campus security: 24-hour emergency response devices and patrols, late night transport-escort service. College housing not available. Holyoke Community College Library plus 1 other with 98,569 books, 49,591 serials, 13,146 audiovisual materials, an OPAC, and a Web page. Operations spending for the previous fiscal year: $310,644. 900 computers available on campus for general student use. Computer purchase/lease plans available. A campuswide network can be accessed from off-campus. Students can access the following: online class registration. Staffed computer lab on campus provides training in use of computers, software, and the Internet.

Community Environment: Holyoke is located 87 miles west of Boston on the shores of the Connecticut River and was the first planned industrial center in the country. Industries include the production of fine writing paper and various mills. The game of volleyball, first known as minonette, was invented here in 1895. The city has historical points of interest, museums, three movie theatres, public beaches and marinas, a community concert series featuring nationally known artists, and Mt. Tom Ski area. Westover Air Force Base is five miles from town. Part-time employment is available.

■ **HULT INTERNATIONAL BUSINESS SCHOOL**
One Education St.
Cambridge, MA 02141
Tel: (617)746-1990
Fax: (617)746-1991
Web Site: www.hult.edu/
Description: Independent, comprehensive, coed. Awards bachelor's and master's degrees. Founded 1964. Calendar: trimesters.

■ **ITT TECHNICAL INSTITUTE (NORWOOD)**
333 Providence Hwy.
Norwood, MA 02062
Tel: (781)278-7200; Free: 800-879-8324
Web Site: www.itt-tech.edu/
Description: Proprietary, primarily 2-year, coed. Part of ITT Educational Services, Inc. Awards terminal associate and bachelor's degrees. Founded 1990. Setting: suburban campus.
Entrance Requirements: Entrance: minimally difficult.

■ **ITT TECHNICAL INSTITUTE (WILMINGTON)**
200 Ballardvale St.
Ste. 200
Wilmington, MA 01887
Tel: (978)658-2636; Free: 800-430-5097
Web Site: www.itt-tech.edu/
Description: Proprietary, primarily 2-year, coed. Part of ITT Educational Services, Inc. Awards terminal associate and bachelor's degrees. Founded 2000.
Entrance Requirements: Entrance: minimally difficult.

■ **LABOURÉ COLLEGE**
2120 Dorchester Ave.
Boston, MA 02124-5698
Tel: (617)296-8300
Web Site: www.laboure.edu/
Description: Independent Roman Catholic, 2-year, coed. Awards certificates, transfer associate, and terminal associate degrees. Founded 1971. Setting: urban campus. Total enrollment: 548. 119 applied. 73% 25 or older. Core. Calendar: semesters. Academic remediation for entering students, services for LD students, accelerated degree program, independent study, summer session for credit, part-time degree program, adult/continuing education programs.
Entrance Requirements: Option: deferred admission. Required: high school transcript. Entrance: minimally difficult. Application deadline: Rolling.
Collegiate Environment: Orientation program. Student-run newspaper. Student services: health clinic, personal-psychological counseling. Campus security: 24-hour emergency response devices. Helen Stubblefield Law Library with 10,975 books, 24 microform titles, 155 serials, 650 audiovisual materials, and an OPAC.

■ **LASELL COLLEGE**
1844 Commonwealth Ave.
Newton, MA 02466-2709
Tel: (617)243-2000; Free: 888-LASELL-4
Fax: (617)796-4343
E-mail: info@lasell.edu
Web Site: www.lasell.edu/
Description: Independent, comprehensive, coed. Awards bachelor's and master's degrees. Founded 1851. Setting: 50-acre suburban campus with easy access to Boston. Endowment: $30 million. Total enrollment: 325. Faculty: 229 (78 full-time, 151 part-time). Student-undergrad faculty ratio is 15:1. 3,998 applied, 70% were admitted. Full-time: 1,632 students, 64% women, 36% men. Part-time: 23 students, 65% women, 35% men. Students come from 36 states and territories, 21 other countries, 44% from out-of-state. 0.5% American Indian or Alaska Native, non-Hispanic/Latino; 7% Hispanic/Latino; 8% African American, non-Hispanic/Latino; 2% Asian, non-Hispanic/Latino; 0.4% Native Hawaiian or other Pacific Islander, non-Hispanic/Latino; 3% international. 2% 25 or older, 78% live on campus, 4%

transferred in. Retention: 72% of full-time freshmen returned the following year. Academic areas with the most degrees conferred: business/marketing; parks and recreation; visual and performing arts. Core. Calendar: semesters. ESL program, advanced placement, self-designed majors, honors program, independent study, double major, summer session for credit, part-time degree program, co-op programs and internships, graduate courses open to undergrads. Study abroad program.
Entrance Requirements: Options: electronic application, deferred admission, international baccalaureate accepted. Required: essay, high school transcript, 2 recommendations, college preparatory program, SAT or ACT. Recommended: interview. Entrance: moderately difficult. Application deadline: Rolling. Notification: continuous. SAT Reasoning Test deadline: 9/1. SAT Subject Test deadline: 9/1. Transfer credits accepted: Yes. Applicants placed on waiting list: 0. Wait-listed applicants offered admission: 0.
Costs Per Year: Application fee: $40. Comprehensive fee: $41,300 includes full-time tuition ($27,800), mandatory fees ($1200), and college room and board ($12,300). Full-time tuition and fees vary according to program. Room and board charges vary according to board plan. Part-time tuition: $940 per credit hour. Part-time mandatory fees: $300 per term. Part-time tuition and fees vary according to course load and program.
Collegiate Environment: Orientation program. Drama-theater group, choral group, student-run newspaper, radio station. Social organizations: 51 open to all. Most popular organizations: Campus Activities Board, Tennis Club, Lasell College Radio Station, Students Advocating for Equality, Lasell Environmental Action Force. Major annual events: River Day/Family and Friends Weekend, Torchlight Parade, Spring/Winter Ball. Student services: health clinic, personal-psychological counseling. Campus security: 24-hour emergency response devices and patrols, late night transport-escort service, controlled dormitory access. 1,275 undergraduates lived in college housing during 2012-13. Freshmen guaranteed college housing. Options: coed, women-only housing available. Brennan Library with 53,694 books, 224 serials, 2,736 audiovisual materials, an OPAC, and a Web page. 200 computers available on campus for general student use. Computer purchase/lease plans available. A campuswide network can be accessed from student residence rooms and from off campus. Students can access the following: online class registration, Online tutoring in various subjects. Staffed computer lab on campus provides training in use of computers, software, and the Internet.
Community Environment: See Boston University.

■ **LESLEY UNIVERSITY**
29 Everett St.
Cambridge, MA 02138-2790
Tel: (617)868-9600; Free: 800-999-1959
Fax: (617)349-8150
E-mail: lcadmissions@lesley.edu
Web Site: www.lesley.edu/
Description: Independent, comprehensive, coed. Awards associate, bachelor's, master's, and doctoral degrees and post-master's certificates. Founded 1909. Setting: urban campus with easy access to Boston. Total enrollment: 5,528. Faculty: 270 (71 full-time, 199 part-time). Student-undergrad faculty ratio is 28:1. 2,718 applied, 64% were admitted. 15% from top 10% of their high school class, 40% from top quarter, 82% from top half. Full-time: 1,451 students, 76% women, 24% men. Part-time: 117 students, 75% women, 25% men. 56% from out-of-state. 1% American Indian or Alaska Native, non-Hispanic/Latino; 6% Hispanic/Latino; 3% African American, non-Hispanic/Latino; 4% Asian, non-Hispanic/Latino; 0.1% Native Hawaiian or other Pacific Islander, non-Hispanic/Latino; 2% international. 3% 25 or older, 54% live on campus, 7% transferred in. Retention: 79% of full-time freshmen returned the following year. Academic areas with the most degrees conferred: liberal arts/general studies; visual and performing arts; psychology. Core. Calendar: semesters. Academic remediation for entering students, services for LD students, advanced placement, accelerated degree program, self-designed majors, freshman honors college, honors program, independent study, distance learning, double major, summer session for credit, part-time degree program, external degree program, adult/continuing education programs, internships, graduate courses open to undergrads. Off campus study. Study abroad program.
Entrance Requirements: Options: electronic application, early action, deferred admission, international baccalaureate accepted. Required: essay, high school transcript, SAT or ACT. Recommended: interview. Application deadline: Rolling. Notification: continuous. SAT Reasoning Test deadline: 3/1. SAT Subject Test deadline: 3/1. Applicants placed on waiting list: 2. Wait-listed applicants offered admission: 0.

Costs Per Year: Application fee: $50. Comprehensive fee: $46,250 includes full-time tuition ($32,000), mandatory fees ($250), and college room and board ($14,000). College room only: $8550. Full-time tuition and fees vary according to class time, course level, course load, degree level, location, program, reciprocity agreements, and student level. Room and board charges vary according to housing facility. Part-time tuition: $1310 per credit hour.

Collegiate Environment: Orientation program. Drama-theater group, choral group. Major annual event: Quad Fest. Student services: health clinic, personal-psychological counseling. Campus security: 24-hour emergency response devices and patrols, late night transport-escort service, controlled dormitory access. Freshmen given priority for college housing. Options: coed, women-only housing available. Sherrill Library with an OPAC.

■ MARIAN COURT COLLEGE

35 Little's Point Rd.
Swampscott, MA 01907-2840
Tel: (781)595-6768
Fax: (781)595-3560
Web Site: www.mariancourt.edu/

Description: Independent Roman Catholic, 2-year, coed. Awards certificates, transfer associate, and terminal associate degrees. Founded 1964. Setting: 6-acre suburban campus with easy access to Boston. Total enrollment: 250. Faculty: 22. Student-undergrad faculty ratio is 14:1. 226 applied, 74% were admitted. Students come from 5 other countries. 45% 25 or older. Calendar: semesters. Academic remediation for entering students, advanced placement, honors program, independent study, summer session for credit, part-time degree program, adult/continuing education programs, internships. Off campus study at members of the Northeast Consortium of Colleges and Universities in Massachusetts.

Entrance Requirements: Options: electronic application, deferred admission. Required: high school transcript, minimum 2.0 high school GPA, interview. Entrance: minimally difficult. Application deadline: Rolling.

Collegiate Environment: Orientation program. Most popular organizations: Travel Club, student government, community service. Major annual events: International Supper, Winter Dance, Luau. Student services: personal-psychological counseling. Campus security: well-lit parking lots. Lindsay Library with 5,006 books, 40 serials, and an OPAC. 43 computers available on campus for general student use. Staffed computer lab on campus.

■ MASSACHUSETTS BAY COMMUNITY COLLEGE

50 Oakland St.
Wellesley Hills, MA 02481
Tel: (781)239-3000
Fax: (781)239-1047
E-mail: info@massbay.edu
Web Site: www.massbay.edu/

Description: State-supported, 2-year, coed. Awards certificates, transfer associate, and terminal associate degrees. Founded 1961. Setting: 84-acre suburban campus with easy access to Boston. Total enrollment: 5,427. Faculty: 382 (87 full-time, 295 part-time). Student-undergrad faculty ratio is 17:1. 2,017 applied, 99.9% were admitted. Full-time: 2,058 students, 45% women, 55% men. Part-time: 3,369 students, 61% women, 39% men. Students come from 12 states and territories, 100 other countries, 2% from out-of-state. 1% American Indian or Alaska Native, non-Hispanic/Latino; 13% Hispanic/Latino; 17% African American, non-Hispanic/Latino; 4% Asian, non-Hispanic/Latino; 0.1% Native Hawaiian or other Pacific Islander, non-Hispanic/Latino; 2% international. 39% 25 or older, 5% transferred in. Retention: 55% of full-time freshmen returned the following year. Core. Calendar: semesters. Academic remediation for entering students, services for LD students, advanced placement, honors program, distance learning, summer session for credit, part-time degree program, adult/continuing education programs, co-op programs and internships.

Entrance Requirements: Open admission except for nursing program. Options: electronic application, deferred admission. Entrance: noncompetitive. Application deadline: Rolling. Notification: continuous. Transfer credits accepted: Yes.

Costs Per Year: Application fee: $20. State resident tuition: $576 full-time, $24 per credit part-time. Nonresident tuition: $5520 full-time, $230 per credit part-time. Mandatory fees: $3680 full-time, $130 per credit part-time, $20 per term part-time. Full-time tuition and fees vary according to program and reciprocity agreements. Part-time tuition and fees vary according to program and reciprocity agreements.

Collegiate Environment: Drama-theater group, student-run newspaper.

Social organizations: 18 open to all. Most popular organizations: Student Government Association, Latino Student Organization, New World Society Club, Mass Bay Players, Student Occupational Therapy Association. Major annual events: Spring Barbeque, Health Fair, Career Fair. Student services: health clinic, personal-psychological counseling. Campus security: 24-hour emergency response devices and patrols. College housing not available. Perkins Library with 51,429 books, 10,210 microform titles, 280 serials, 4,780 audiovisual materials, an OPAC, and a Web page. Operations spending for the previous fiscal year: $427,680. 400 computers available on campus for general student use. A campuswide network can be accessed from off-campus. Staffed computer lab on campus.

Community Environment: See Wellesley College.

■ MASSACHUSETTS COLLEGE OF ART AND DESIGN

621 Huntington Ave.
Boston, MA 02115-5882
Tel: (617)879-7000
Fax: (617)879-7250
E-mail: admissions@massart.edu
Web Site: www.massart.edu/

Description: State-supported, comprehensive, coed. Part of Massachusetts Public Higher Education System. Awards bachelor's and master's degrees. Founded 1873. Setting: 5-acre urban campus. Endowment: $13.6 million. Educational spending for the previous fiscal year: $28,511 per student. Total enrollment: 2,326. Faculty: 277 (106 full-time, 171 part-time). Student-undergrad faculty ratio is 10:1. 1,381 applied, 70% were admitted. Full-time: 1,637 students, 68% women, 32% men. Part-time: 535 students, 67% women, 33% men. Students come from 26 states and territories, 49 other countries, 29% from out-of-state. 0.3% American Indian or Alaska Native, non-Hispanic/Latino; 5% Hispanic/Latino; 3% African American, non-Hispanic/Latino; 6% Asian, non-Hispanic/Latino; 0.1% Native Hawaiian or other Pacific Islander, non-Hispanic/Latino; 2% international. 8% 25 or older, 38% live on campus, 6% transferred in. Retention: 88% of full-time freshmen returned the following year. Academic areas with the most degrees conferred: visual and performing arts; education. Core. Calendar: semesters. Self-designed majors, independent study, double major, summer session for credit, part-time degree program, internships, graduate courses open to undergrads. Off campus study at members of the Pro Arts Consortium, Association of Independent Colleges of Art and Design, CAPS, Colleges of the Fenway. Study abroad program.

Entrance Requirements: Options: electronic application, early action, deferred admission. Required: essay, high school transcript, 2 recommendations, portfolio required; for GPA between 2.0 and 2.9, SAT/ACT scores considered with GPA on sliding scale, SAT or ACT. Recommended: minimum 3 high school GPA. Entrance: very difficult. Application deadlines: 2/1, 12/1 for early action. Notification: 1/5 for early action. Preference given to state residents. Applicants placed on waiting list: 2. Wait-listed applicants offered admission: 2. Early action applicants: 191. Early action applicants admitted: 146.

Costs Per Year: Application fee: $50. State resident tuition: $10,400 full-time. Nonresident tuition: $27,500 full-time. College room and board: $12,150. Room and board charges vary according to board plan and housing facility.

Collegiate Environment: Orientation program. Drama-theater group, student-run newspaper, radio station. Social organizations: 30 open to all. Most popular organizations: International Students' Club, Design Research Unit, Spectrum, film society, Event Works. Major annual events: All School Show, Annual Holiday Sale, Service Learning Day. Student services: health clinic, personal-psychological counseling, women's center. Campus security: 24-hour emergency response devices and patrols, late night transport-escort service, security lighting, self-defense workshops. 658 undergraduates lived in college housing during 2012-13. Freshmen guaranteed college housing. Option: coed housing available. Morton R. Godine Library with 258,675 books, 1,117 microform titles, 557 serials, an OPAC, and a Web page. Operations spending for the previous fiscal year: $238,663. 370 computers available on campus for general student use. Computer purchase/lease plans available. A campuswide network can be accessed from student residence rooms and from off campus. Students can access the following: online class registration. Staffed computer lab on campus provides training in use of computers, software, and the Internet.

Community Environment: See Boston University.

■ MASSACHUSETTS COLLEGE OF LIBERAL ARTS

375 Church St.
North Adams, MA 01247-4100

Tel: (413)662-5000; Free: 800-989-MCLA

Fax: (413)662-5179

E-mail: annette.jeffes@mcla.edu

Web Site: www.mcla.edu/

Description: State-supported, comprehensive, coed. Part of Massachusetts State University System. Awards bachelor's and master's degrees and post-master's certificates. Founded 1894. Setting: 105-acre small town campus with easy access to Albany-Schenectady-Troy New York Metro Area. Total enrollment: 1,799. Faculty: 174 (86 full-time, 88 part-time). Student-undergrad faculty ratio is 13:1. 1,689 applied, 67% were admitted. 15% from top 10% of their high school class, 30% from top quarter, 80% from top half. Full-time: 1,408 students, 59% women, 41% men. Part-time: 192 students, 62% women, 38% men. Students come from 15 states and territories, 1 other country, 23% from out-of-state. 0.2% American Indian or Alaska Native, non-Hispanic/Latino; 6% Hispanic/Latino; 9% African American, non-Hispanic/Latino; 1% Asian, non-Hispanic/Latino; 0.1% Native Hawaiian or other Pacific Islander, non-Hispanic/Latino. 13% 25 or older, 63% live on campus, 9% transferred in. Retention: 75% of full-time freshmen returned the following year. Academic areas with the most degrees conferred: business/marketing; English; social sciences. Core. Calendar: semesters. Academic remediation for entering students, services for LD students, advanced placement, accelerated degree program, self-designed majors, honors program, independent study, distance learning, double major, summer session for credit, part-time degree program, adult/continuing education programs, co-op programs and internships, graduate courses open to undergrads. Off campus study at College Academic Program Sharing, Williams College, Berkshire Community College. Study abroad program.

Entrance Requirements: Options: electronic application, early admission, early action, deferred admission, international baccalaureate accepted. Required: essay, high school transcript, minimum 3 high school GPA, 1 recommendation, SAT or ACT. Required for some: interview, sliding scale applies (GPA and SAT) if below 3.0. Entrance: moderately difficult. Application deadlines: Rolling, 12/1 for early action. Notification: continuous, 12/15 for early action. SAT Reasoning Test deadline: 6/30. Transfer credits accepted: Yes. Early action applicants: 395. Early action applicants admitted: 323.

Costs Per Year: Application fee: $40. State resident tuition: $1030 full-time, $42.92 per credit part-time. Nonresident tuition: $9975 full-time, $415.63 per credit part-time. Mandatory fees: $7495 full-time, $253.42 per credit part-time. Part-time tuition and fees vary according to course load. College room and board: $9102. Room and board charges vary according to board plan and housing facility.

Collegiate Environment: Orientation program. Drama-theater group, choral group, student-run newspaper, radio station. Social organizations: 40 open to all; national fraternities, national sororities, local fraternities, local sororities. Most popular organizations: Student Activities Council, Student Government Association, The Beacon (Student Newspaper), Harlequin-Musical Theatre Company, Dance Company. Major annual events: Summer Reading Program, Midnight Madness, Midnight Breakfast. Student services: health clinic, personal-psychological counseling, women's center. Campus security: 24-hour emergency response devices and patrols, late night transport-escort service, controlled dormitory access, escort service. 1,021 college housing spaces available; 974 were occupied in 2012-13. Freshmen guaranteed college housing. On-campus residence required through junior year. Option: coed housing available. Eugene L. Freel Library with 170,000 books, 290,000 microform titles, 70 serials, 6,300 audiovisual materials, an OPAC, and a Web page. 140 computers available on campus for general student use. Computer purchase/lease plans available. A computer is required for all students. A campuswide network can be accessed from student residence rooms and from off campus. Students can access the following: online class registration. Staffed computer lab on campus provides training in use of computers, software, and the Internet.

Community Environment: In the northwestern corner of state, this Berkshire town produces a diversity of small business establishments and cultural activities. Bus lines are accessible. A regional hospital, Sterling and Francine Clark Art Institute, Massachusetts Museum of Contemporary Art, and numerous civic and service organizations are found here. There are 6 major ski areas within 25 miles and Mohawk and Taconic Trails. Part-time employment is seasonal for students. The city has an annual Fall Festival.

■ MASSACHUSETTS COLLEGE OF PHARMACY AND HEALTH SCIENCES

179 Longwood Ave.

Boston, MA 02115-5896

Tel: (617)732-2800

Fax: (617)732-2801

E-mail: admissions@mcphs.edu

Web Site: www.mcphs.edu/

Description: Independent, university, coed. Awards bachelor's, master's, and doctoral degrees and post-master's certificates. Founded 1823. Setting: 3-acre urban campus. Endowment: $258 million. Total enrollment: 6,010. Faculty: 259 (258 full-time, 1 part-time). Student-undergrad faculty ratio is 23:1. 4,939 applied, 90% were admitted. Full-time: 3,439 students, 67% women, 33% men. Part-time: 188 students, 77% women, 23% men. Students come from 48 states and territories, 35 other countries, 37% from out-of-state. 0.1% American Indian or Alaska Native, non-Hispanic/Latino; 2% Hispanic/Latino; 4% African American, non-Hispanic/Latino; 25% Asian, non-Hispanic/Latino; 0.1% Native Hawaiian or other Pacific Islander, non-Hispanic/Latino; 9% international. 11% 25 or older, 20% live on campus, 13% transferred in. Retention: 85% of full-time freshmen returned the following year. Core. Calendar: semesters. Services for LD students, advanced placement, accelerated degree program, independent study, distance learning, double major, summer session for credit, part-time degree program, adult/continuing education programs, internships, graduate courses open to undergrads. Off campus study at Colleges of the Fenway. Study abroad program.

Entrance Requirements: Open admission selective admission to some programs. Options: electronic application, early action, deferred admission, international baccalaureate accepted. Required: essay, 2 recommendations, SAT or ACT. Required for some: high school transcript, interview. Application deadlines: Rolling, 11/15 for early action. Notification: continuous until 2/15, 12/19 for early action.

Costs Per Year: Application fee: $0. Comprehensive fee: $40,888 includes full-time tuition ($26,600), mandatory fees ($840), and college room and board ($13,448). College room only: $10,400. Full-time tuition and fees vary according to course load, degree level, location, program, and student level. Room and board charges vary according to board plan, housing facility, and location. Part-time tuition: $980 per credit. Part-time mandatory fees: $220 per term.

Collegiate Environment: Orientation program. Drama-theater group, choral group, student-run newspaper. Social organizations: 97 open to all; national fraternities. Most popular organizations: Residence Hall Council, Vietnamese Student Association, Student Government Association, Campus Activities Board, Student Indian Organization. Major annual events: Fall Harvest Ball, Culture Fest, Activities Fair. Student services: health clinic, personal-psychological counseling. Campus security: 24-hour emergency response devices and patrols, late night transport-escort service, controlled dormitory access, electronically operated academic area entrances, security guards at entrance. 667 college housing spaces available; 650 were occupied in 2012-13. Freshmen guaranteed college housing. Option: coed housing available. Henrietta DeBenedictis Library plus 2 others with an OPAC and a Web page. 507 computers available on campus for general student use. A campuswide network can be accessed from student residence rooms and from off campus. Students can access the following: online class registration. Staffed computer lab on campus.

■ MASSACHUSETTS INSTITUTE OF TECHNOLOGY

77 Massachusetts Ave.

Cambridge, MA 02139-4307

Tel: (617)253-1000

Fax: (617)258-8304

E-mail: admissions@mit.edu

Web Site: web.mit.edu/

Description: Independent, university, coed. Awards bachelor's, master's, and doctoral degrees. Founded 1861. Setting: 168-acre urban campus with easy access to Boston. Endowment: $10.1 billion. Research spending for the previous fiscal year: $681.1 million. Educational spending for the previous fiscal year: $64,300 per student. Total enrollment: 11,189. Faculty: 1,447 (1,193 full-time, 254 part-time). Student-undergrad faculty ratio is 8:1. 18,109 applied, 9% were admitted. 98% from top 10% of their high school class, 100% from top quarter, 100% from top half. 203 valedictorians. Full-time: 4,480 students, 45% women, 55% men. Part-time: 23 students, 30% women, 70% men. Students come from 54 states and territories, 92 other countries, 91% from out-of-state. 0.3% American Indian or Alaska Native, non-Hispanic/Latino; 15% Hispanic/Latino; 6% African American, non-Hispanic/Latino; 24% Asian, non-Hispanic/Latino; 0% Native Hawaiian or other Pacific Islander, non-Hispanic/Latino; 10% international. 1% 25 or older, 90% live on campus, 1% transferred in. Retention: 97% of full-time freshmen returned the following year. Academic areas with the most degrees conferred: engineering; computer and information sciences; physical sciences. Core. Calendar: 4-1-4. ESL program, services for LD students, advanced placement, independent study, double major, co-op programs and internships, graduate courses open to undergrads. Off campus study at Wellesley College, Harvard University, Massachusetts College of Art and Design, and the School of the Museum of Fine Arts. Study abroad program. ROTC: Army, Naval, Air Force.

Entrance Requirements: Options: electronic application, early action, deferred admission, international baccalaureate accepted. Required: essay, high school transcript, 2 recommendations, SAT, ACT or TOEFL. Two SAT II Subject tests: one in math and one in science, SAT or ACT, SAT Subject Tests. Recommended: interview. Entrance: most difficult. Application deadlines: 1/1, 11/1 for early action. Notification: 3/20, 12/20 for early action. SAT Reasoning Test deadline: 2/15. SAT Subject Test deadline: 2/15. Transfer credits accepted: Yes. Applicants placed on waiting list: 849. Wait-listed applicants offered admission: 0. Early action applicants: 6,008. Early action applicants admitted: 680.

Costs Per Year: Application fee: $75. Comprehensive fee: $54,238 includes full-time tuition ($41,770), mandatory fees ($280), and college room and board ($12,188). College room only: $7554. Room and board charges vary according to board plan and housing facility. Part-time tuition: $650 per unit. Part-time tuition varies according to course load.

Collegiate Environment: Orientation program. Drama-theater group, choral group, marching band, student-run newspaper, radio station. Social organizations: 400 open to all; national fraternities, national sororities, local fraternities, over 400 student organizations. Most popular organizations: Educational Studies Program, Dance Troupe, Science Fiction Society, The Tech (student newspaper), Anime Club. Major annual events: Independent Activities Period (IAP), Brass Rat (Class Ring) Premiere, Campus Preview Weekend. Student services: health clinic, personal-psychological counseling. Campus security: 24-hour emergency response devices and patrols, late night transport-escort service, controlled dormitory access. 3,571 college housing spaces available; 3,395 were occupied in 2012-13. Freshmen guaranteed college housing. On-campus residence required in freshman year. Options: coed, women-only housing available. MIT Libraries plus 5 others with 3.6 million books, 2.4 million microform titles, 47,457 audiovisual materials, an OPAC, and a Web page. Operations spending for the previous fiscal year: $22.4 million. 1,100 computers available on campus for general student use. Computer purchase/lease plans available. A campuswide network can be accessed from student residence rooms and from off campus. Students can access the following: online class registration. Staffed computer lab on campus (open 24 hours a day) provides training in use of computers, software, and the Internet.

Community Environment: See Harvard University.

■ **MASSACHUSETTS MARITIME ACADEMY**
101 Academy Dr.
Buzzards Bay, MA 02532-1803
Tel: (508)830-5000; Free: 800-544-3411
Fax: (508)830-5077
E-mail: jmclaughlin@maritime.edu
Web Site: www.maritime.edu/

Description: State-supported, comprehensive, coed. Part of Massachusetts State University System. Awards bachelor's and master's degrees. Founded 1891. Setting: 55-acre small town campus with easy access to Boston, Providence. Endowment: $7.4 million. Educational spending for the previous fiscal year: $7750 per student. Total enrollment: 1,415. Faculty: 137 (71 full-time, 66 part-time). Student-undergrad faculty ratio is 13:1. 787 applied, 77% were admitted. Full-time: 1,269 students, 10% women, 90% men. Part-time: 43 students, 14% women, 86% men. Students come from 29 states and territories, 4 other countries, 23% from out-of-state. 1% American Indian or Alaska Native, non-Hispanic/Latino; 2% Hispanic/Latino; 2% African American, non-Hispanic/Latino; 2% Asian, non-Hispanic/Latino; 0% Native Hawaiian or other Pacific Islander, non-Hispanic/Latino; 1% international. 4% 25 or older, 95% live on campus, 3% transferred in. Retention: 89% of full-time freshmen returned the following year. Academic areas with the most degrees conferred: engineering; transportation and materials moving; homeland security, law enforcement, firefighting, and protective services. Core. Calendar: semesters plus sea term. Academic remediation for entering students, services for LD students, advanced placement, distance learning, double major, summer session for credit, part-time degree program, co-op programs and internships, graduate courses open to undergrads. Off campus study. Study abroad program. ROTC: Army (c), Naval.

Entrance Requirements: Options: electronic application, early action, deferred admission. Required: essay, high school transcript, minimum 2 high school GPA, 2 recommendations, for students transferring between 12 and 23 credits minimum college GPA 2.5; for less than 23 transferable credits minimum college GPA 2.0 and meet admission standards for freshman applicants; for more than 24 transferable credits minimum college GPA 2.0, SAT and SAT Subject Tests or ACT. Recommended: interview. Entrance: moderately difficult. Application deadlines: Rolling, Rolling for nonresidents, 11/1 for early action. Notification: continuous, continuous for nonresidents. SAT Reasoning Test deadline: 5/1. SAT Subject Test deadline: 5/1. Transfer credits accepted: Yes. Applicants placed on waiting list: 114. Wait-listed applicants offered admission: 20.

Collegiate Environment: Orientation program. Drama-theater group, choral group, marching band, student-run newspaper. Social organizations: 20 open to all. Most popular organizations: club hockey, water sports, sailing/crew, rugby club, scuba club. Major annual events: Emery Rice Day, Homecoming/Ring Dance, winter sea term cruise. Student services: health clinic, personal-psychological counseling, women's center. Campus security: 24-hour emergency response devices and patrols, student patrols, late night transport-escort service, controlled dormitory access. 1,200 college housing spaces available; 1,177 were occupied in 2012-13. Freshmen guaranteed college housing. On-campus residence required in freshman year. Option: coed housing available. American Bureau of Shipping Information Commons plus 1 other with 93,499 books, 97 serials, 1,221 audiovisual materials, an OPAC, and a Web page. Operations spending for the previous fiscal year: $342,116. 150 computers available on campus for general student use. Computer purchase/lease plans available. A computer is required for all students. A campuswide network can be accessed from student residence rooms and from off campus. Students can access the following: online class registration, course-supported e-learning, wireless available campus wide. Staffed computer lab on campus provides training in use of computers, software, and the Internet.

Community Environment: Bourne is the second largest town on Cape Cod and has a New England climate. It is located 60 miles from Boston, and bus service and air service from Hyannis are available. The Trading Post, located here, is a replica of the trading post built in 1627. Bourne Scenic Park is a good area for picnics and camping. Boating, fishing, swimming and golf are available for recreation in this resort community.

■ **MASSASOIT COMMUNITY COLLEGE**
1 Massasoit Blvd.
Brockton, MA 02302-3996
Tel: (508)588-9100; Free: 800-CAREERS
Fax: (508)427-1220
Web Site: www.massasoit.mass.edu/

Description: State-supported, 2-year, coed. Awards certificates, transfer associate, and terminal associate degrees. Founded 1966. Setting: 100-acre suburban campus with easy access to Boston. Total enrollment: 7,941. Faculty: 503 (119 full-time, 384 part-time). Full-time: 3,631 students, 49% women, 51% men. Part-time: 4,310 students, 62% women, 38% men. Students come from 13 states and territories, 6 other countries, 1% from out-of-state. 38% 25 or older, 6% transferred in. Core. Calendar: semesters. Academic remediation for entering students, ESL program, services for LD students, accelerated degree program, independent study, distance learning, summer session for credit, part-time degree program, adult/continuing education programs, co-op programs and internships. Off campus study at 9 members of the Southeastern Association for Cooperation in Higher Education in Massachusetts.

Entrance Requirements: Open admission except for allied health programs. Entrance: noncompetitive. Application deadline: Rolling. Notification: continuous. Preference given to state residents.

Collegiate Environment: Drama-theater group, student-run newspaper, radio station. Social organizations: 32 open to all. Most popular organizations: Drama Club, student newspaper, Phi Theta Kappa, International Student Association, Student Senate. Student services: health clinic, personal-psychological counseling, women's center. Campus security: 24-hour patrols. 75,000 books, 396 serials, and a Web page.

Community Environment: Brockton is located 20 miles south of downtown Boston and the center of the second fastest growing area of the State. The college service area encompasses one million people in 51 cities and towns south of Boston and includes the city of Quincy.

■ **MERRIMACK COLLEGE**
315 Tpke. St.
North Andover, MA 01845-5800

Tel: (978)837-5000
Fax: (978)837-5222
E-mail: admission@merrimack.edu
Web Site: www.merrimack.edu/
Description: Independent Roman Catholic, comprehensive, coed. Awards bachelor's and master's degrees and post-master's certificates. Founded 1947. Setting: 220-acre suburban campus with easy access to Boston. Endowment: $35.1 million. Educational spending for the previous fiscal year: $9267 per student. Total enrollment: 2,657. Faculty: 315 (138 full-time, 177 part-time). Student-undergrad faculty ratio is 12:1. 5,661 applied, 77% were admitted. Full-time: 2,309 students, 49% women, 51% men. Part-time: 120 students, 43% women, 58% men. Students come from 20 states and territories, 18 other countries, 27% from out-of-state. 0.1% American Indian or Alaska Native, non-Hispanic/Latino; 7% Hispanic/Latino; 3% African American, non-Hispanic/Latino; 2% Asian, non-Hispanic/Latino; 0.04% Native Hawaiian or other Pacific Islander, non-Hispanic/Latino; 6% international. 5% 25 or older, 71% live on campus, 3% transferred in. Retention: 80% of full-time freshmen returned the following year. Academic areas with the most degrees conferred: business/marketing; biological/life sciences; psychology. Core. Calendar: semesters. Academic remediation for entering students, ESL program, services for LD students, advanced placement, self-designed majors, honors program, independent study, double major, summer session for credit, part-time degree program, adult/continuing education programs, co-op programs and internships. Off campus study at Northeast Consortium of Colleges and Universities in Massachusetts, American University Washington Semester, Massachusetts Bay Marine Studies Consortium. Study abroad program. ROTC: Air Force (c).
Entrance Requirements: Options: electronic application, early admission, early decision, early action, deferred admission, international baccalaureate accepted. Required: essay, high school transcript, 1 recommendation, first quarter senior grades. Recommended: interview. Required for some: interview. Entrance: moderately difficult. Application deadlines: 2/15, 11/15 for early decision, 11/15 for early action. Notification: continuous until 3/15, 12/15 for early decision, 12/25 for early action. SAT Reasoning Test deadline: 2/15. Transfer credits accepted: Yes. Applicants placed on waiting list: 608. Wait-listed applicants offered admission: 41. Early decision applicants: 27. Early decision applicants admitted: 26. Early action applicants: 1,917. Early action applicants admitted: 1,815.
Costs Per Year: Application fee: $0. Comprehensive fee: $45,610 includes full-time tuition ($32,720), mandatory fees ($1200), and college room and board ($11,690). Room and board charges vary according to board plan and housing facility.
Collegiate Environment: Orientation program. Drama-theater group, choral group, student-run newspaper. Social organizations: 55 open to all; national fraternities, national sororities, local fraternities, local sororities; 3% of eligible men and 10% of eligible women are members. Most popular organizations: Programming Board, Student Government; Class Councils, Greek Life, A.L.A.N.A. Major annual events: Relay for Life, Spring Weekend, Mr. Merrimack. Student services: health clinic, personal-psychological counseling. Campus security: 24-hour emergency response devices and patrols, student patrols, late night transport-escort service, controlled dormitory access, staffed dorm entrances. Freshmen given priority for college housing. Option: coed housing available. McQuade Library with an OPAC and a Web page.
Community Environment: North Andover is approximately 25 miles north of Boston and has rail and bus service to the city. Andover is used extensively for relaxation, shopping and eating. The local area is rich in cultural and historic attractions.

■ **MIDDLESEX COMMUNITY COLLEGE**
Springs Rd.
Bedford, MA 01730-1655
Tel: (781)280-3200; Free: 800-818-3434
Fax: (978)656-3322
E-mail: orellanad@middlesex.cc.ma.us
Web Site: www.middlesex.mass.edu/
Description: State-supported, 2-year, coed. Part of Massachusetts Public Higher Education System. Awards certificates, transfer associate, and terminal associate degrees. Founded 1970. Setting: 200-acre suburban campus with easy access to Boston. Total enrollment: 9,664. 35% 25 or older. Core. Calendar: semesters. Academic remediation for entering students, ESL program, services for LD students, advanced placement, accelerated degree program, honors program, independent study, distance learning, summer session for credit, part-time degree program, adult/

continuing education programs, co-op programs and internships. Off campus study at members of the Northeast Consortium of Colleges and Universities in Massachusetts. Study abroad program. ROTC: Air Force (c).
Entrance Requirements: Open admission for most programs. Options: electronic application, early admission. Required for some: essay, high school transcript, 3 recommendations, interview, CPT. Entrance: noncompetitive. Application deadline: Rolling. Notification: continuous. Preference given to state residents.
Costs Per Year: Application fee: $0. State resident tuition: $4224 full-time. Nonresident tuition: $9168 full-time. Mandatory fees: $50 full-time. Full-time tuition and fees vary according to course load and reciprocity agreements.
Collegiate Environment: Orientation program. Drama-theater group, student-run newspaper. Student services: legal services, health clinic, personal-psychological counseling. Campus security: 24-hour emergency response devices and patrols. College housing not available. Main library plus 1 other with 52,960 books, 538 serials, an OPAC, and a Web page.

■ **MONTSERRAT COLLEGE OF ART**
23 Essex St.
Beverly, MA 01915
Tel: (978)922-8222; Free: 800-836-0487
Fax: (978)922-4268
E-mail: jeffrey.newell@montserrat.edu
Web Site: www.montserrat.edu/
Description: Independent, 4-year, coed. Awards bachelor's degrees. Founded 1970. Setting: 10-acre suburban campus with easy access to Boston. Endowment: $670,985. Research spending for the previous fiscal year: $4452. Educational spending for the previous fiscal year: $6389 per student. Total enrollment: 397. Faculty: 77 (19 full-time, 58 part-time). Student-undergrad faculty ratio is 12:1. 404 applied, 79% were admitted. Full-time: 389 students, 73% women, 27% men. Part-time: 8 students, 75% women, 25% men. Students come from 23 states and territories, 1 other country, 52% from out-of-state. 0.3% American Indian or Alaska Native, non-Hispanic/Latino; 4% Hispanic/Latino; 2% African American, non-Hispanic/Latino; 2% Native Hawaiian or other Pacific Islander, non-Hispanic/Latino; 1% international. 5% 25 or older, 63% live on campus, 5% transferred in. Retention: 79% of full-time freshmen returned the following year. Academic area with the most degrees conferred: visual and performing arts. Core. Calendar: semesters. Academic remediation for entering students, services for LD students, advanced placement, self-designed majors, independent study, double major, part-time degree program, adult/continuing education programs, co-op programs and internships. Off campus study at Northeast Consortium of Colleges and Universities in Massachusetts, Association of Independent Colleges of Art and Design. Study abroad program.
Entrance Requirements: Options: electronic application, early action, deferred admission, international baccalaureate accepted. Required: essay, high school transcript, minimum 2 high school GPA, 2 recommendations, portfolio. Recommended: minimum 2 high school GPA, interview. Required for some: SAT or ACT. Entrance: moderately difficult. Application deadlines: 8/15, 8/15 for nonresidents, 12/1 for early action. Notification: continuous until 12/15, continuous until 12/15 for nonresidents, 12/15 for early action. Transfer credits accepted: Yes. Applicants placed on waiting list: 10. Wait-listed applicants offered admission: 1. Early action applicants: 125. Early action applicants admitted: 50.
Costs Per Year: Application fee: $50. Tuition: $25,500 full-time, $1065 per credit part-time. Mandatory fees: $1100 full-time, $50 per credit part-time. College room only: $7300.
Collegiate Environment: Orientation program. Drama-theater group, student-run newspaper. Most popular organizations: Student Voice, Theatre Club, Bear Gallery, Dance Club, InterVarsity. Major annual events: Kwanahunakmas, Halloween Party, Drag Show. Student services: health clinic, personal-psychological counseling. Campus security: 24-hour emergency response devices and patrols, student patrols, late night transport-escort service, controlled dormitory access. Paul Scott Library plus 1 other with 12,025 books, 76 serials, 50,031 audiovisual materials, and an OPAC. Operations spending for the previous fiscal year: $115,583. 98 computers available on campus for general student use. A campuswide network can be accessed from student residence rooms and from off campus. Staffed computer lab on campus provides training in use of computers, software, and the Internet.
Community Environment: Just 30 minutes north of Boston, Beverly is a residential city with a population of 39,800. The historic rocky coast of the north shore of Boston offers a contemplative setting with its harborside parks and beaches, access to the nearby fishing and yachting harbors of

Gloucester, Marblehead and Rockport, and to the historic city of Salem, immediately adjacent to Beverly. The environment of the north shore is offset by the accessibility to a large metropolitan city with galleries, museums, cultural events, and nightlife.

■ MOUNT HOLYOKE COLLEGE

50 College St.
South Hadley, MA 01075
Tel: (413)538-2000
Fax: (413)538-2409
E-mail: admission@mtholyoke.edu
Web Site: www.mtholyoke.edu/

Description: Independent, comprehensive, women only. Awards bachelor's and master's degrees. Founded 1837. Setting: 800-acre small town campus with easy access to Springfield. Endowment: $594 million. Research spending for the previous fiscal year: $2.9 million. Educational spending for the previous fiscal year: $21,773 per student. Total enrollment: 2,344. Faculty: 268 (224 full-time, 44 part-time). Student-undergrad faculty ratio is 10:1. 3,876 applied, 42% were admitted. 56% from top 10% of their high school class, 82% from top quarter, 97% from top half. 17 valedictorians. Full-time: 2,287 students. Part-time: 35 students. Students come from 45 states and territories, 78 other countries, 77% from out-of-state. 0.04% American Indian or Alaska Native, non-Hispanic/Latino; 8% Hispanic/Latino; 6% African American, non-Hispanic/Latino; 7% Asian, non-Hispanic/Latino; 0.04% Native Hawaiian or other Pacific Islander, non-Hispanic/Latino; 23% international. 4% 25 or older, 95% live on campus, 2% transferred in. Retention: 92% of full-time freshmen returned the following year. Academic areas with the most degrees conferred: social sciences; biological/life sciences; visual and performing arts. Core. Calendar: semesters. ESL program, services for LD students, advanced placement, self-designed majors, independent study, double major, part-time degree program, adult/continuing education programs, co-op programs and internships. Off campus study at members of the Twelve College Exchange Program, Five Colleges, Inc., Spelman College, Mills College. Study abroad program. ROTC: Army (c), Air Force (c).

Entrance Requirements: Options: electronic application, early admission, early decision, deferred admission, international baccalaureate accepted. Required: essay, high school transcript, 2 recommendations. Recommended: interview. Required for some: SAT Subject Tests. Entrance: very difficult. Application deadlines: 1/15, 11/15 for early decision plan 1, 1/1 for early decision plan 2. Notification: 4/1, 1/1 for early decision plan 1, 2/1 for early decision plan 2. SAT Subject Test deadline: 1/15. Transfer credits accepted: Yes. Applicants placed on waiting list: 974. Wait-listed applicants offered admission: 30.

Costs Per Year: Application fee: $60. Comprehensive fee: $53,596 includes full-time tuition ($41,270), mandatory fees ($186), and college room and board ($12,140). College room only: $5940. Part-time tuition: $1290 per credit hour.

Collegiate Environment: Orientation program. Drama-theater group, choral group, student-run newspaper, radio station. Social organizations: 100 open to all. Most popular organizations: Student Government Association, Model UN, Mount Holyoke African and Caribbean Student Association (MHCASA), Ice Hockey, Rugby. Major annual events: Acappella Jams, Pangy Day (Pangynaskeia), Las Vegas Night. Student services: health clinic, personal-psychological counseling. Campus security: 24-hour emergency response devices and patrols, student patrols, late night transport-escort service, controlled dormitory access, police officers on-campus. 2,233 college housing spaces available; 2,196 were occupied in 2012-13. Freshmen guaranteed college housing. On-campus residence required through senior year. Option: women-only housing available. Williston Memorial Library plus 2 others with 1.3 million books, 24,362 microform titles, 8,052 serials, 11,202 audiovisual materials, an OPAC, and a Web page. Operations spending for the previous fiscal year: $8.3 million. 447 computers available on campus for general student use. Computer purchase/lease plans available. A campuswide network can be accessed from student residence rooms and from off campus. Students can access the following: online class registration, personal Web pages. Staffed computer lab on campus provides training in use of computers, software, and the Internet.

Community Environment: Across from campus in South Hadley Center is the Village Commons, apartments, movie theaters, a restaurant, an ice cream shop, a pub, a video rental shop, clothing stores, and offices, all attract people from across the five college areas. South Hadley is approximately 3 hours from the city of New York and only an hour and 30 minutes away from Boston. The Bradley International Airport is 40 minutes away and serves the Hartford and Springfield areas. Springfield, only 12

miles away, is accessible by Amtrak. There are buses running from Boston, Hartford, and Springfield to the campus gates. A free bus runs every half hour, taking students to the four other schools (Smith, Amherst, Hampshire, and The University of Massachusetts at Amherst).

■ MOUNT IDA COLLEGE

777 Dedham St.
Newton, MA 02459-3310
Tel: (617)928-4500
Fax: (617)928-4507
E-mail: admissions@mountida.edu
Web Site: www.mountida.edu/

Description: Independent, comprehensive, coed. Awards associate, bachelor's, and master's degrees. Founded 1899. Setting: 72-acre suburban campus with easy access to Boston. Total enrollment: 1,481. Faculty: 189 (66 full-time, 123 part-time). Student-undergrad faculty ratio is 14:1. 1,730 applied, 75% were admitted. Full-time: 1,365 students, 66% women, 34% men. Part-time: 96 students, 68% women, 32% men. Students come from 32 states and territories, 22 other countries, 41% from out-of-state. 0.4% American Indian or Alaska Native, non-Hispanic/Latino; 8% Hispanic/Latino; 15% African American, non-Hispanic/Latino; 2% Asian, non-Hispanic/Latino; 0% Native Hawaiian or other Pacific Islander, non-Hispanic/Latino; 4% international. 9% 25 or older, 63% live on campus, 7% transferred in. Retention: 64% of full-time freshmen returned the following year. Academic areas with the most degrees conferred: business/marketing; visual and performing arts; health professions and related sciences. Core. Calendar: semesters. Academic remediation for entering students, ESL program, services for LD students, advanced placement, honors program, independent study, distance learning, double major, summer session for credit, part-time degree program, co-op programs and internships, graduate courses open to undergrads. Study abroad program.

Entrance Requirements: Options: electronic application, deferred admission, international baccalaureate accepted. Required: high school transcript, 1 recommendation, SAT or ACT scores, SAT or ACT. Recommended: essay, minimum 2 high school GPA. Required for some: interview. Entrance: moderately difficult. Application deadline: Rolling. Notification: continuous. SAT Reasoning Test deadline: 8/15. SAT Subject Test deadline: 8/15. Transfer credits accepted: Yes.

Costs Per Year: Application fee: $45. Comprehensive fee: $39,429 includes full-time tuition ($26,664), mandatory fees ($265), and college room and board ($12,500). Part-time tuition: $705 per credit. Part-time tuition varies according to course load.

Collegiate Environment: Orientation program. Drama-theater group, choral group, student-run newspaper, radio station. Social organizations: 25 open to all. Most popular organizations: Student Government Association, Campus Activities Team, Balfour Peer Leaders, Black Student Achievement Coalition, Alpha Chi. Major annual events: Homecoming/Parents' Weekend, Welcome Weeks, Spring Weekend. Student services: health clinic, personal-psychological counseling. Campus security: 24-hour emergency response devices and patrols, student patrols, late night transport-escort service, controlled dormitory access, secured campus entrance. Wadsworth Learning Resource Center plus 1 other with 94,464 books, 3,735 serials, 3,655 audiovisual materials, an OPAC, and a Web page. 82 computers available on campus for general student use. A campuswide network can be accessed from student residence rooms. Staffed computer lab on campus provides training in use of computers, software, and the Internet.

■ MOUNT WACHUSETT COMMUNITY COLLEGE

444 Green St.
Gardner, MA 01440-1000
Tel: (978)632-6600
Fax: (978)632-8925
E-mail: admissions@mwcc.mass.edu
Web Site: www.mwcc.mass.edu/

Description: State-supported, 2-year, coed. Part of Massachusetts Public Higher Education System. Awards certificates, transfer associate, and terminal associate degrees. Founded 1963. Setting: 270-acre small town campus with easy access to Boston. Endowment: $3.4 million. Total enrollment: 4,755. Faculty: 237 (73 full-time, 164 part-time). Student-undergrad faculty ratio is 23:1. 1,922 applied, 100% were admitted. Full-time: 2,016 students, 60% women, 40% men. Part-time: 2,739 students, 69% women, 31% men. Students come from 10 states and territories, 4% from out-of-state. 0.4% American Indian or Alaska Native, non-Hispanic/Latino; 13% Hispanic/Latino; 7% African American, non-Hispanic/Latino; 2% Asian, non-

Hispanic/Latino; 0.1% Native Hawaiian or other Pacific Islander, non-Hispanic/Latino; 1% international. 46% 25 or older, 6% transferred in. Retention: 54% of full-time freshmen returned the following year. Core. Calendar: semesters. Academic remediation for entering students, ESL program, services for LD students, advanced placement, accelerated degree program, honors program, independent study, distance learning, double major, summer session for credit, part-time degree program, adult/continuing education programs, co-op programs and internships. Study abroad program.

Entrance Requirements: Open admission except for nursing, physical therapy assistant, dental hygiene, clinical lab science, complementary health care, massage therapy, and accelerated business administration programs. Options: electronic application, early admission. Required: high school transcript. Recommended: interview, SAT, ACT, SAT or ACT, SAT and SAT Subject Tests or ACT, SAT Subject Tests. Required for some: 2 recommendations, SAT. Entrance: noncompetitive. Application deadline: Rolling. Notification: continuous. Preference given to state residents. SAT Reasoning Test deadline: 3/10. SAT Subject Test deadline: 10/10.

Collegiate Environment: Orientation program. Drama-theater group, choral group, student-run newspaper. Social organizations: 22 open to all. Most popular organizations: Art Club, Dental Hygienist Club, International Club, Student Government Association, Student Nurses Association. Major annual events: Orientation, Fall Fest, Commencement Dinner/Awards Ceremony. Student services: health clinic, personal-psychological counseling. Campus security: 24-hour emergency response devices and patrols. LaChance Library with 53,763 books, 3,884 microform titles, 2,495 audiovisual materials, an OPAC, and a Web page. Operations spending for the previous fiscal year: $510,472. 455 computers available on campus for general student use. A campuswide network can be accessed. Students can access the following: online class registration.

Community Environment: City has airport and bus service. Community services include three libraries, many churches of most denominations, the Henry Heywood Memorial Hospital, and a downtown shopping center. Recreational facilities are swimming pool, golf course, lakes, bowling and theatre. Excellent opportunities for part-time employment.

■ NEW ENGLAND COLLEGE OF BUSINESS AND FINANCE

10 High St.
Ste. 204
Boston, MA 02111-2645
Tel: (617)951-2350; Free: 800-997-1673
Fax: (617)951-2533
E-mail: Mina.Goldman@necb.edu
Web Site: necb.edu/

Description: Independent, comprehensive, coed. Part of Whitney International University. Awards associate, bachelor's, and master's degrees (offers primarily part-time evening degree programs; bachelor's degree offered jointly with Bentley College, Assumption College, Providence College, University of Hartford, and University System College for Lifelong Learning). Founded 1909. Setting: urban campus. Total enrollment: 412. Faculty: 29 (1 full-time, 28 part-time). Student-undergrad faculty ratio is 38:1. Students come from 8 states and territories, 39% from out-of-state. 78% 25 or older. Retention: 79% of full-time freshmen returned the following year. Core. Calendar: 8 week terms (6 per academic year). Academic remediation for entering students, independent study, distance learning, summer session for credit, part-time degree program, adult/continuing education programs, internships.

Entrance Requirements: Open admission. Option: electronic application. Required: essay, high school transcript, interview. Entrance: noncompetitive. Application deadline: Rolling. Notification: continuous. Transfer credits accepted: Yes.

Collegiate Environment: Campus security: reception desk in lobby of building. 5 computers available on campus for general student use. A computer is required for all students. Students can access the following: online class registration.

■ NEW ENGLAND CONSERVATORY OF MUSIC

290 Huntington Ave.
Boston, MA 02115-5000
Tel: (617)585-1100
Fax: (617)585-1115
E-mail: christina.daly@necmusic.edu
Web Site: necmusic.edu/

Description: Independent, comprehensive, coed. Awards bachelor's, master's, and doctoral degrees and post-master's certificates. Founded

1867. Setting: 2-acre urban campus. Endowment: $112.1 million. Educational spending for the previous fiscal year: $26,702 per student. Total enrollment: 814. Faculty: 234 (94 full-time, 140 part-time). Student-undergrad faculty ratio is 6:1. 1,098 applied, 33% were admitted. Full-time: 406 students, 43% women, 57% men. Part-time: 30 students, 53% women, 47% men. Students come from 37 states and territories, 25 other countries, 86% from out-of-state. 0% American Indian or Alaska Native, non-Hispanic/Latino; 5% Hispanic/Latino; 2% African American, non-Hispanic/Latino; 10% Asian, non-Hispanic/Latino; 0% Native Hawaiian or other Pacific Islander, non-Hispanic/Latino; 32% international. 3% 25 or older, 30% live on campus, 5% transferred in. Retention: 93% of full-time freshmen returned the following year. Academic area with the most degrees conferred: visual and performing arts. Core. Calendar: semesters. ESL program, services for LD students, advanced placement, independent study, double major, summer session for credit, internships, graduate courses open to undergrads. Off campus study at Simmons College, Tufts University, Northeastern University. Study abroad program.

Entrance Requirements: Options: electronic application, deferred admission. Required: essay, high school transcript, minimum 2.75 high school GPA, 2 recommendations, audition recording, repertoire list. Entrance: very difficult. Application deadline: 12/1. Notification: 4/1. Transfer credits accepted: Yes. Applicants placed on waiting list: 144. Wait-listed applicants offered admission: 5.

Costs Per Year: Application fee: $115. Comprehensive fee: $50,805 includes full-time tuition ($38,000), mandatory fees ($455), and college room and board ($12,350). Room and board charges vary according to board plan. Part-time tuition: $1210 per credit.

Collegiate Environment: Orientation program. Drama-theater group, choral group, student-run newspaper. Social organizations: 15 open to all. Most popular organizations: Fellowship with Christ, Hillel, The Penguin (newspaper), Rockin' Rangers Theatre Improv. Major annual events: spring and fall barbecues, Prom at the Colonnade, Commencement. Student services: health clinic, personal-psychological counseling. Campus security: 24-hour patrols, late night transport-escort service. 157 college housing spaces available; 130 were occupied in 2012-13. Freshmen guaranteed college housing. On-campus residence required in freshman year. Option: coed housing available. Spaulding Library plus 3 others with 973,930 books, 351 microform titles, 295 serials, 67,785 audiovisual materials, an OPAC, and a Web page. Operations spending for the previous fiscal year: $735,005. 70 computers available on campus for general student use. A campuswide network can be accessed. Students can access the following: online class registration, online activity effective Fall 2010. Staffed computer lab on campus provides training in use of computers, software, and the Internet.

Community Environment: See Boston University.

■ THE NEW ENGLAND INSTITUTE OF ART

10 Brookline Pl. W
Brookline, MA 02445
Tel: (617)267-7910; Free: 800-903-4425
Fax: (617)236-7883
Web Site: www.artinstitutes.edu/boston/

Description: Proprietary, 4-year, coed. Part of Education Management Corporation. Awards associate and bachelor's degrees. Setting: urban campus. Calendar: semesters.

■ NEWBURY COLLEGE

129 Fisher Ave.
Brookline, MA 02445
Tel: (617)730-7000; Free: 800-NEWBURY
Fax: (617)731-9618
E-mail: admissions@newbury.edu
Web Site: www.newbury.edu/

Description: Independent, 4-year, coed. Awards associate and bachelor's degrees. Founded 1962. Setting: 10-acre suburban campus with easy access to Boston. Endowment: $1.6 million. Educational spending for the previous fiscal year: $5626 per student. Total enrollment: 1,003. Faculty: 107 (35 full-time, 72 part-time). Student-undergrad faculty ratio is 16:1. 5,543 applied, 62% were admitted. Full-time: 883 students, 58% women, 42% men. Part-time: 120 students, 56% women, 44% men. Students come from 28 states and territories, 13 other countries, 29% from out-of-state. 0% American Indian or Alaska Native, non-Hispanic/Latino; 16% Hispanic/Latino; 32% African American, non-Hispanic/Latino; 7% Asian, non-Hispanic/Latino; 0% Native Hawaiian or other Pacific Islander, non-Hispanic/Latino; 3% international. 4% 25 or older, 35% live on campus, 4% transferred in.

Retention: 61% of full-time freshmen returned the following year. Academic areas with the most degrees conferred: business/marketing; homeland security, law enforcement, firefighting, and protective services; psychology; personal and culinary services; visual and performing arts. Core. Calendar: semesters. Academic remediation for entering students, services for LD students, advanced placement, accelerated degree program, self-designed majors, honors program, independent study, distance learning, double major, summer session for credit, part-time degree program, adult/continuing education programs, co-op programs and internships. Off campus study. Study abroad program.

Entrance Requirements: Options: electronic application, international baccalaureate accepted. Required: essay, high school transcript, 2 recommendations. Recommended: minimum 2 high school GPA. Required for some: interview. Entrance: minimally difficult. Application deadline: 9/1. Notification: continuous. Transfer credits accepted: Yes.

Costs Per Year: Application fee: $25. One-time mandatory fee: $175. Comprehensive fee: $41,850 includes full-time tuition ($27,850), mandatory fees ($1100), and college room and board ($12,900). Full-time tuition and fees vary according to program and reciprocity agreements. Room and board charges vary according to housing facility.

Collegiate Environment: Orientation program. Drama-theater group, choral group, student-run radio station. Social organizations: 16 open to all; 25% of eligible men and 35% of eligible women are members. Most popular organizations: Innkeeper's Club, Campus Activities Board, Step Team, Fashion Forward Club, Commuter Council/Residence Hall Council. Major annual events: Spring Carnival, Halloween Dance, Newbury Olympics. Student services: personal-psychological counseling. Campus security: 24-hour emergency response devices and patrols, late night transport-escort service. 358 college housing spaces available; 309 were occupied in 2012-13. Freshmen given priority for college housing. Option: coed housing available. Newbury College Library with 51,146 books, 26,899 serials, 311 audiovisual materials, an OPAC, and a Web page. Operations spending for the previous fiscal year: $805,688. 122 computers available on campus for general student use. A campuswide network can be accessed from student residence rooms and from off campus. Students can access the following: online class registration, Online software and document storage. Staffed computer lab on campus provides training in use of computers, software, and the Internet.

Community Environment: The main campus of Newbury College is nestled in a beautiful residential section of Brookline, Massachusetts, just 4 miles from downtown Boston, and easily accessible by public transportation.

■ **NICHOLS COLLEGE**
PO Box 5000
Dudley, MA 01571-5000
Tel: (508)213-1560; Free: 800-470-3379
Fax: (508)213-9885
E-mail: admissions@nichols.edu
Web Site: www.nichols.edu/

Description: Independent, comprehensive, coed. Awards associate, bachelor's, and master's degrees. Founded 1815. Setting: 210-acre suburban campus with easy access to Boston. Endowment: $11.9 million. Educational spending for the previous fiscal year: $2073 per student. Total enrollment: 1,547. Faculty: 80 (36 full-time, 44 part-time). Student-undergrad faculty ratio is 18:1. 1,983 applied, 74% were admitted. Full-time: 1,159 students, 37% women, 63% men. Part-time: 178 students, 66% women, 34% men. Students come from 25 states and territories, 4 other countries, 39% from out-of-state. 80% live on campus, 3% transferred in. Retention: 66% of full-time freshmen returned the following year. Academic areas with the most degrees conferred: business/marketing; psychology; mathematics and statistics; English; history. Core. Calendar: semesters. Academic remediation for entering students, services for LD students, advanced placement, accelerated degree program, honors program, independent study, distance learning, double major, summer session for credit, part-time degree program, adult/continuing education programs, co-op programs and internships, graduate courses open to undergrads. Off campus study. Study abroad program. ROTC: Army (c).

Entrance Requirements: Options: electronic application, deferred admission. Required: essay, high school transcript, 1 recommendation, SAT or ACT. Required for some: interview. Entrance: moderately difficult. Application deadline: Rolling. Notification: continuous. Transfer credits accepted: Yes.

Costs Per Year: Application fee: $25. Comprehensive fee: $42,440 includes full-time tuition ($31,440), mandatory fees ($300), and college room and board ($10,700). College room only: $5800. Room and board charges vary according to housing facility.

Collegiate Environment: Orientation program. Drama-theater group, student-run newspaper, radio station. Social organizations: 30 open to all. Most popular organizations: Rugby Club, Accounting Club, Racquetball Club, student publications, Theater Club. Major annual events: Homecoming, Spring Weekend, Commencement. Student services: health clinic, personal-psychological counseling. Campus security: 24-hour emergency response devices and patrols, student patrols, late night transport-escort service. Conant Library plus 1 other with 80,000 books, 2,936 microform titles, 152 serials, 905 audiovisual materials, an OPAC, and a Web page. Operations spending for the previous fiscal year: $387,455. 69 computers available on campus for general student use. Computer purchase/lease plans available. A campuswide network can be accessed from student residence rooms and from off campus. Students can access the following: online class registration. Staffed computer lab on campus provides training in use of computers, software, and the Internet.

■ **NORTH SHORE COMMUNITY COLLEGE**
1 Ferncroft Rd.
Danvers, MA 01923-4093
Tel: (978)762-4000
Fax: (978)762-4021
E-mail: lbarrett@northshore.edu
Web Site: www.northshore.edu/

Description: State-supported, 2-year, coed. Awards certificates, transfer associate, and terminal associate degrees. Founded 1965. Setting: suburban campus with easy access to Boston. Endowment: $5.5 million. Educational spending for the previous fiscal year: $4991 per student. Total enrollment: 7,912. Faculty: 486 (135 full-time, 351 part-time). Student-undergrad faculty ratio is 17:1. 4,760 applied, 84% were admitted. Full-time: 3,064 students, 55% women, 45% men. Part-time: 4,848 students, 65% women, 35% men. Students come from 9 states and territories, 8 other countries, 2% from out-of-state. 0.3% American Indian or Alaska Native, non-Hispanic/Latino; 19% Hispanic/Latino; 9% African American, non-Hispanic/Latino; 4% Asian, non-Hispanic/Latino; 0.1% Native Hawaiian or other Pacific Islander, non-Hispanic/Latino; 0.2% international. 41% 25 or older, 8% transferred in. Core. Calendar: semesters. Academic remediation for entering students, ESL program, services for LD students, advanced placement, accelerated degree program, honors program, independent study, distance learning, summer session for credit, part-time degree program, adult/continuing education programs, co-op programs and internships.

Entrance Requirements: Open admission except for nursing, engineering, health-related programs. Options: electronic application, early admission, deferred admission. Required for some: essay, high school transcript, interview. Entrance: noncompetitive. Application deadline: Rolling. Notification: continuous. Preference given to state residents.

Costs Per Year: Application fee: $0. State resident tuition: $600 full-time, $25 per credit hour part-time. Nonresident tuition: $6168 full-time, $257 per credit hour part-time. Mandatory fees: $3456 full-time, $144 per credit hour part-time.

Collegiate Environment: Orientation program. Drama-theater group, student-run newspaper. Social organizations: 23 open to all; national fraternities. Most popular organizations: Program Council, student government, performing arts, student newspaper, Phi Theta Kappa. Major annual events: Multicultural Fair, Spring Fling, Alcohol Awareness Week. Student services: health clinic, personal-psychological counseling, women's center. Campus security: 24-hour emergency response devices and patrols, late night transport-escort service. College housing not available. Learning Resource Center plus 2 others with 68,035 books, 257 serials, 4,213 audiovisual materials, an OPAC, and a Web page. 160 computers available on campus for general student use. A campuswide network can be accessed from off-campus. Students can access the following: online class registration, online bill pay, full compliment of Google apps, shared network storage, online advising, personal web space, mobile printing from personally owned devices, emergency notification services. Staffed computer lab on campus provides training in use of computers, software, and the Internet.

Community Environment: Suburban.

■ **NORTHEASTERN UNIVERSITY**
360 Huntington Ave.
Boston, MA 02115-5096
Tel: (617)373-2000
Fax: (617)373-8780
E-mail: admissions@neu.edu
Web Site: www.northeastern.edu/

Description: Independent, university, coed. Awards bachelor's, master's, and doctoral degrees and post-master's certificates. Founded 1898. Setting: 73-acre urban campus. Endowment: $578.3 million. Research spending for the previous fiscal year: $90.6 million. Total enrollment: 24,540. Faculty: 1,536 (1,100 full-time, 436 part-time). Student-undergrad faculty ratio is 14:1. 44,208 applied, 32% were admitted. 63% from top 10% of their high school class, 88% from top quarter, 99% from top half. 99 National Merit Scholars. Full-time: 16,685 students, 50% women, 50% men. Students come from 52 states and territories, 122 other countries, 71% from out-of-state. 0.1% American Indian or Alaska Native, non-Hispanic/Latino; 6% Hispanic/Latino; 3% African American, non-Hispanic/Latino; 9% Asian, non-Hispanic/Latino; 0.02% Native Hawaiian or other Pacific Islander, non-Hispanic/Latino; 15% international. 1% 25 or older, 54% live on campus, 4% transferred in. Retention: 96% of full-time freshmen returned the following year. Academic areas with the most degrees conferred: business/marketing; engineering; health professions and related sciences. Core. Calendar: semesters. Academic remediation for entering students, ESL program, services for LD students, advanced placement, accelerated degree program, self-designed majors, honors program, independent study, distance learning, double major, summer session for credit, part-time degree program, adult/continuing education programs, co-op programs and internships, graduate courses open to undergrads. Off campus study at New England Conservatory of Music, Hebrew College, Roxbury Community College, School of the Museum of Fine Arts. Study abroad program. ROTC: Army, Naval (c), Air Force (c).
Entrance Requirements: Options: electronic application, early admission, early action, deferred admission, international baccalaureate accepted. Required: essay, high school transcript, 2 recommendations, SAT or ACT. Entrance: very difficult. Application deadlines: 1/15, 11/1 for early action. Notification: continuous until 4/1, 12/31 for early action. SAT Reasoning Test deadline: 1/15. SAT Subject Test deadline: 1/15. Transfer credits accepted: Yes.
Costs Per Year: Application fee: $75. Comprehensive fee: $53,356 includes full-time tuition ($39,320), mandatory fees ($416), and college room and board ($13,620). College room only: $7240. Room and board charges vary according to board plan and housing facility.
Collegiate Environment: Orientation program. Drama-theater group, choral group, student-run newspaper, radio station. Social organizations: 325 open to all; national fraternities, national sororities, local fraternities, local sororities; 3% of eligible men and 5% of eligible women are members. Most popular organizations: Student Government Association, Council for University Programs, Resident Student Association, Society of Collegiate Scholars, No Limits Dance Crew. Major annual events: Homecoming Week, Springfest, Mardi Gras. Student services: health clinic, personal-psychological counseling. Campus security: 24-hour emergency response devices and patrols, student patrols, late night transport-escort service, controlled dormitory access, public safety website. 8,375 college housing spaces available; all were occupied in 2012-13. Freshmen guaranteed college housing. On-campus residence required through sophomore year. Option: coed housing available. Snell Library plus 3 others with 1.5 million books, 1.3 million microform titles, 128,027 serials, 18,210 audiovisual materials, an OPAC, and a Web page. Operations spending for the previous fiscal year: $19.6 million. 1,993 computers available on campus for general student use. Computer purchase/lease plans available. A campuswide network can be accessed from student residence rooms and from off campus. Students can access the following: online class registration. Staffed computer lab on campus (open 24 hours a day) provides training in use of computers, software, and the Internet.
Community Environment: Students at Northeastern University have access to the full range of cultural, educational, historical, and recreational offerings of Boston, the higher education capital of the world. The cultural opportunities include the Museum of Fine Arts, Symphony Hall, and the Boston Public Library. The University is adjacent to the Fenway, a spacious park that includes a beautiful rose garden and paths.

■ **NORTHERN ESSEX COMMUNITY COLLEGE**
100 Elliott St.
Haverhill, MA 01830
Tel: (978)556-3000
Web Site: www.necc.mass.edu/
Description: State-supported, 2-year, coed. Awards certificates, transfer associate, and terminal associate degrees. Founded 1960. Setting: 106-acre suburban campus with easy access to Boston. Endowment: $4.5 million. Educational spending for the previous fiscal year: $5650 per student. Total enrollment: 7,312. Faculty: 657 (108 full-time, 549 part-time). Student-

undergrad faculty ratio is 22:1. 3,000 applied, 93% were admitted. Full-time: 2,596 students, 54% women, 46% men. Part-time: 4,716 students, 66% women, 34% men. Students come from 6 states and territories, 17% from out-of-state. 0.2% American Indian or Alaska Native, non-Hispanic/Latino; 34% Hispanic/Latino; 4% African American, non-Hispanic/Latino; 2% Asian, non-Hispanic/Latino; 1% Native Hawaiian or other Pacific Islander, non-Hispanic/Latino; 0.5% international. 51% 25 or older, 5% transferred in. Retention: 61% of full-time freshmen returned the following year. Core. Calendar: semesters. Academic remediation for entering students, ESL program, services for LD students, advanced placement, freshman honors college, honors program, independent study, distance learning, double major, summer session for credit, part-time degree program, adult/continuing education programs, co-op programs and internships. Off campus study at Bradford College, members of the Northeast Consortium of Colleges and Universities in Massachusetts. Study abroad program. ROTC: Air Force (c).
Entrance Requirements: Open admission except for health, human services, technology programs. Option: early admission. Required: high school transcript, Psychological Corporation Aptitude Test for Practical Nursing. Entrance: noncompetitive. Application deadline: Rolling. Notification: continuous. Preference given to state residents.
Collegiate Environment: Drama-theater group, student-run newspaper. Student services: health clinic, personal-psychological counseling, women's center. Campus security: 24-hour emergency response devices and patrols. College housing not available. Bentley Library with 61,120 books, 598 serials, and an OPAC. Operations spending for the previous fiscal year: $702,044. 300 computers available on campus for general student use. A campuswide network can be accessed from off-campus. Students can access the following: online class registration. Staffed computer lab on campus (open 24 hours a day) provides training in use of computers.

■ **NORTHPOINT BIBLE COLLEGE**
320 S Main St.
Haverhill, MA 01835
Tel: (978)478-3400; Free: 800-356-4014
E-mail: admissions@zbc.edu
Web Site: northpoint.edu/
Description: Independent, 4-year, coed, affiliated with Assembly of God Church. Awards bachelor's degrees. Founded 1924. Total enrollment: 265. 35% 25 or older. Calendar: semesters.
Entrance Requirements: Open admission.

■ **PINE MANOR COLLEGE**
400 Heath St.
Chestnut Hill, MA 02467
Tel: (617)731-7000; Free: 800-762-1357
Fax: (617)731-7199
E-mail: slyons@pmc.edu
Web Site: www.pmc.edu/
Description: Independent, 4-year, women only. Awards associate, bachelor's, and master's degrees. Founded 1911. Setting: 55-acre suburban campus. Endowment: $8.6 million. Educational spending for the previous fiscal year: $9778 per student. Total enrollment: 28. Faculty: 70. Student-undergrad faculty ratio is 10:1. 392 applied, 64% were admitted. Full-time: 306 students. Part-time: 11 students. Students come from 18 states and territories, 15 other countries, 28% from out-of-state. 0.3% American Indian or Alaska Native, non-Hispanic/Latino; 17% Hispanic/Latino; 27% African American, non-Hispanic/Latino; 6% Asian, non-Hispanic/Latino; 0% Native Hawaiian or other Pacific Islander, non-Hispanic/Latino; 11% international. 5% 25 or older, 5% transferred in. Retention: 50% of full-time freshmen returned the following year. Academic areas with the most degrees conferred: psychology; biological/life sciences; business/marketing. Core. Calendar: semesters. Academic remediation for entering students, ESL program, services for LD students, advanced placement, self-designed majors, honors program, independent study, double major, summer session for credit, part-time degree program, external degree program, adult/continuing education programs, internships. Off campus study. Study abroad program.
Entrance Requirements: Options: electronic application, deferred admission, international baccalaureate accepted. Required: essay, high school transcript, SAT or ACT scores, SAT or ACT. Recommended: minimum 2 high school GPA, interview. Entrance: moderately difficult. Application deadline: Rolling. Notification: continuous. SAT Reasoning Test deadline: 8/1. Transfer credits accepted: Yes.
Costs Per Year: Application fee: $25. Comprehensive fee: $37,051 includes

full-time tuition ($24,301) and college room and board ($12,750). Full-time tuition varies according to course load. Room and board charges vary according to housing facility. Part-time tuition: $725 per credit. Part-time tuition varies according to course load.

Collegiate Environment: Orientation program. Drama-theater group, choral group, student-run newspaper, radio station. Most popular organizations: African American, Latina, Asian, Native American and All (ALANA), Community Service Committee, International Student Club, The Model UN, Student Government Association (SGA). Major annual event: Community Learning Day. Student services: health clinic, personal-psychological counseling, women's center. Campus security: 24-hour emergency response devices and patrols, student patrols, late night transport-escort service, controlled dormitory access. 495 college housing spaces available; 165 were occupied in 2012-13. Option: coed housing available. Annenberg Library with 65,000 books, an OPAC, and a Web page. Operations spending for the previous fiscal year: $360,368. 85 computers available on campus for general student use. A campuswide network can be accessed from student residence rooms and from off campus.

■ **QUINCY COLLEGE**
34 Coddington St.
Quincy, MA 02169-4522
Tel: (617)984-1700; Free: 800-698-1700
Fax: (617)984-1669
E-mail: psmith@quincycollege.edu
Web Site: www.quincycollege.edu/

Description: City-supported, 2-year, coed. Awards certificates, transfer associate, and terminal associate degrees. Founded 1958. Setting: 2-acre suburban campus with easy access to Boston. Endowment: $112,021. Total enrollment: 4,000. Faculty: 404 (20 full-time, 384 part-time). Students come from 11 states and territories, 92 other countries. 45% 25 or older. Core. Calendar: semesters. Academic remediation for entering students, ESL program, advanced placement, summer session for credit, part-time degree program, adult/continuing education programs, internships.

Entrance Requirements: Open admission except for nursing, surgical technology programs. Options: early admission, deferred admission. Required: high school transcript. Entrance: noncompetitive. Application deadline: Rolling. Notification: continuous.

Costs Per Year: Application fee: $20. State resident tuition: $4296 full-time, $179 per credit part-time. Nonresident tuition: $4296 full-time, $179 per credit part-time. Mandatory fees: $25 per term part-time. Full-time tuition varies according to course load and program. Part-time tuition and fees vary according to course load and program.

Collegiate Environment: Orientation program. Most popular organizations: Student Government Association, Phi Theta Kappa, campus newspaper. Campus security: 24-hour emergency response devices and patrols. Anselmo Library plus 1 other with 32,000 books and 125 serials. 130 computers available on campus for general student use. A campuswide network can be accessed. Staffed computer lab on campus.

Community Environment: An important business and industrial city today, Quincy has given the nation some of its most important patriots. Quincy was the birthplace of two presidents, John Adams and his son, John Quincy Adams. This South Shore suburb is located about seven miles from downtown Boston, a 15-minute ride by public transportation. There is easy access to all Boston facilities.

■ **QUINSIGAMOND COMMUNITY COLLEGE**
670 W Boylston St.
Worcester, MA 01606-2092
Tel: (508)853-2300
Fax: (508)852-6943
E-mail: qccadm@qcc.mass.edu
Web Site: www.qcc.edu/

Description: State-supported, 2-year, coed. Part of Massachusetts System of Higher Education. Awards certificates, transfer associate, and terminal associate degrees. Founded 1963. Setting: 57-acre urban campus with easy access to Boston. Endowment: $390,167. Educational spending for the previous fiscal year: $5816 per student. Total enrollment: 8,991. Faculty: 580 (136 full-time, 444 part-time). Student-undergrad faculty ratio is 20:1. 4,327 applied, 54% were admitted. Full-time: 3,943 students, 52% women, 48% men. Part-time: 5,048 students, 62% women, 38% men. Students come from 11 states and territories, 34 other countries, 1% from out-of-state. 0.4% American Indian or Alaska Native, non-Hispanic/Latino; 15% Hispanic/Latino; 12% African American, non-Hispanic/Latino; 4% Asian, non-Hispanic/

Latino; 0.1% Native Hawaiian or other Pacific Islander, non-Hispanic/Latino; 0.3% international. 40% 25 or older, 0% transferred in. Retention: 0% of full-time freshmen returned the following year. Core. Calendar: semesters. Academic remediation for entering students, ESL program, services for LD students, advanced placement, accelerated degree program, honors program, independent study, distance learning, double major, summer session for credit, part-time degree program, co-op programs and internships. Off campus study at member of the Colleges of Worcester Consortium. ROTC: Army (c).

Entrance Requirements: Open admission. Option: electronic application. Required: high school transcript. Required for some: interview. Entrance: noncompetitive. Application deadlines: Rolling, Rolling for nonresidents. Notification: continuous, continuous for nonresidents. Transfer credits accepted: Yes. Applicants placed on waiting list: 52. Wait-listed applicants offered admission: 0.

Costs Per Year: Application fee: $20. State resident tuition: $576 full-time, $24 per credit hour part-time. Nonresident tuition: $5520 full-time, $230 per credit hour part-time. Mandatory fees: $4518 full-time, $157 per credit hour part-time, $280 per term part-time. Full-time tuition and fees vary according to course load and program. Part-time tuition and fees vary according to course load and program.

Collegiate Environment: Orientation program. Drama-theater group, student-run newspaper. Social organizations: 15 open to all. Most popular organizations: Phi Theta Kappa, academic-related clubs, Student Senate, Chess Club, Business Club. Major annual events: Welcome Week, Spring Fling, Honors and Awards Banquet. Student services: personal-psychological counseling. Campus security: 24-hour emergency response devices and patrols, late night transport-escort service. College housing not available. Alden Library with 95,000 books, 5,200 microform titles, 140 serials, 1,500 audiovisual materials, an OPAC, and a Web page. Operations spending for the previous fiscal year: $912,481. 500 computers available on campus for general student use. A campuswide network can be accessed from off-campus. Students can access the following: online class registration, Portal. Staffed computer lab on campus provides training in use of computers, software, and the Internet.

Community Environment: See Clark University.

■ **REGIS COLLEGE**
235 Wellesley St.
Weston, MA 02493
Tel: (781)768-7000; Free: 866-438-7344
Fax: (781)768-8339
E-mail: admission@regiscollege.edu
Web Site: www.regiscollege.edu/

Description: Independent Roman Catholic, comprehensive, coed. Awards associate, bachelor's, master's, and doctoral degrees and post-master's certificates. Founded 1927. Setting: 131-acre small town campus with easy access to Boston. Endowment: $15.4 million. Educational spending for the previous fiscal year: $8504 per student. Total enrollment: 1,991. Faculty: 177 (73 full-time, 104 part-time). Student-undergrad faculty ratio is 13:1. 2,041 applied, 73% were admitted. 10% from top 10% of their high school class, 32% from top quarter, 64% from top half. Full-time: 902 students, 75% women, 25% men. Part-time: 247 students, 87% women, 13% men. Students come from 21 states and territories, 11 other countries, 13% from out-of-state. 0.3% American Indian or Alaska Native, non-Hispanic/Latino; 12% Hispanic/Latino; 21% African American, non-Hispanic/Latino; 4% Asian, non-Hispanic/Latino; 0% Native Hawaiian or other Pacific Islander, non-Hispanic/Latino; 1% international. 17% 25 or older, 57% live on campus, 2% transferred in. Retention: 77% of full-time freshmen returned the following year. Academic areas with the most degrees conferred: health professions and related sciences; biological/life sciences; business/marketing. Core. Calendar: semesters. Academic remediation for entering students, ESL program, services for LD students, advanced placement, accelerated degree program, self-designed majors, honors program, independent study, double major, summer session for credit, part-time degree program, adult/continuing education programs, internships, graduate courses open to undergrads. Off campus study at Babson College, Bentley College, Boston College, American University, National Federation of Carondolet Colleges. Study abroad program. ROTC: Army (c).

Entrance Requirements: Options: electronic application, early admission, early action, deferred admission, international baccalaureate accepted. Required: essay, high school transcript, minimum 2 high school GPA, 2 recommendations, SAT or ACT. Recommended: minimum 3 high school GPA, interview, rank in upper 50% of high school class. Required for some:

interview. Entrance: moderately difficult. Application deadlines: Rolling, 12/1 for early action. Notification: 12/23 for early action. SAT Reasoning Test deadline: 8/1. Transfer credits accepted: Yes. Early action applicants: 456. Early action applicants admitted: 446.

Costs Per Year: Application fee: $50. One-time mandatory fee: $200. Comprehensive fee: $45,860 includes full-time tuition ($33,060) and college room and board ($12,800). Full-time tuition varies according to course load.

Collegiate Environment: Orientation program. Drama-theater group, choral group, student-run newspaper, radio station. Social organizations: 27 open to all. Most popular organizations: Campus Ministry, SGA-Student Government Association, Asian American Student Organization, Dynasty Step Club, Black Student Organization. Major annual events: Spring Weekend/Week, AAA Fear Factor, Christmas Tree Lighting. Student services: health clinic, personal-psychological counseling. Campus security: 24-hour emergency response devices and patrols, late night transport-escort service, controlled dormitory access. 675 college housing spaces available; 593 were occupied in 2012-13. Freshmen guaranteed college housing. Options: coed, women-only housing available. Regis College Library with 134,706 books, 10,826 microform titles, 397 serials, 5,833 audiovisual materials, an OPAC, and a Web page. Operations spending for the previous fiscal year: $785,919. 196 computers available on campus for general student use. A campuswide network can be accessed from student residence rooms and from off campus. Students can access the following: online class registration, online bills, financial aid award letters and check-in requirements. Staffed computer lab on campus provides training in use of computers and software.

Community Environment: Regis College is in a suburban community located approximately 12 miles west of Boston. Community services, cultural, and recreational facilities are located in Boston.

■ **ROXBURY COMMUNITY COLLEGE**
1234 Columbus Ave.
Roxbury Crossing, MA 02120-3400
Tel: (617)427-0060
Web Site: www.rcc.mass.edu/
Description: State-supported, 2-year, coed. Part of Massachusetts Public Higher Education System. Awards certificates, transfer associate, and terminal associate degrees. Founded 1973. Setting: 12-acre urban campus with easy access to Boston. Total enrollment: 2,382. Faculty: 120 (65 full-time, 55 part-time). Student-undergrad faculty ratio is 16:1. 1,290 applied, 83% were admitted. Full-time: 1,124 students, 62% women, 38% men. Part-time: 1,258 students, 65% women, 35% men. Students come from 14 states and territories. 61% 25 or older, 1% transferred in. Core. Calendar: semesters. Academic remediation for entering students, ESL program, services for LD students, self-designed majors, honors program, summer session for credit, part-time degree program, adult/continuing education programs, internships. Off campus study.

Entrance Requirements: Open admission except for nursing program. Option: deferred admission. Required: high school transcript. Entrance: noncompetitive. Application deadline: Rolling. Notification: continuous. Preference given to local residents.

Collegiate Environment: Drama-theater group, choral group, student-run newspaper. Student services: personal-psychological counseling. Campus security: 24-hour emergency response devices and patrols, late night transport-escort service. Roxbury Community College Library with 12,800 books. 100 computers available on campus for general student use. A campuswide network can be accessed from off-campus. Staffed computer lab on campus.

■ **SALEM STATE UNIVERSITY**
352 Lafayette St.
Salem, MA 01970-5353
Tel: (978)542-6000
Fax: (978)542-6126
E-mail: admissions@salemstate.edu
Web Site: www.salemstate.edu/
Description: State-supported, comprehensive, coed. Part of Massachusetts Public Higher Education System. Awards bachelor's and master's degrees and post-master's certificates. Founded 1854. Setting: 62-acre urban campus with easy access to Boston. Total enrollment: 9,456. Faculty: 783 (344 full-time, 439 part-time). 4,855 applied, 69% were admitted. Full-time: 5,862 students, 60% women, 40% men. Part-time: 1,879 students, 62% women, 38% men. Students come from 50 other countries, 3% from out-of-state. 24% 25 or older, 28% live on campus, 11% transferred in. Retention: 74% of full-time freshmen returned the following year. Academic areas with

the most degrees conferred: business/marketing; health professions and related sciences; education. Core. Calendar: semesters. Academic remediation for entering students, ESL program, services for LD students, advanced placement, accelerated degree program, self-designed majors, honors program, independent study, distance learning, double major, summer session for credit, part-time degree program, adult/continuing education programs, internships, graduate courses open to undergrads. Off campus study at other Massachusetts state colleges, Northeast Consortium of Colleges and Universities in Massachusetts. Study abroad program. ROTC: Army (c), Air Force (c).

Entrance Requirements: Options: electronic application, early action, deferred admission, international baccalaureate accepted. Required: high school transcript, minimum 2 high school GPA, SAT or ACT. Required for some: interview. Entrance: minimally difficult. Application deadline: 5/1. Notification: continuous. SAT Reasoning Test deadline: 4/15. Transfer credits accepted: Yes.

Costs Per Year: Application fee: $40. State resident tuition: $910 full-time, $37.92 per credit hour part-time. Nonresident tuition: $7050 full-time, $293.75 per credit hour part-time. Mandatory fees: $7140 full-time, $297.50 per credit hour part-time. Full-time tuition and fees vary according to class time and course load. Part-time tuition and fees vary according to class time and course load. College room only: $8292. Room charges vary according to housing facility.

Collegiate Environment: Orientation program. Drama-theater group, choral group, student-run newspaper, radio station. Social organizations: 62 open to all; national fraternities, national sororities. Most popular organizations: Student Government Association, Program Council, Residence Hall Association, Multicultural Student Association, Hispanic- American Society. Major annual events: Big Name Comedy Concert, Senior Diner/Dance Cruise on Boston Harbor, NCAA Athletic Events. Student services: legal services, health clinic, personal-psychological counseling, women's center. Campus security: 24-hour emergency response devices and patrols, late night transport-escort service, controlled dormitory access. 2,000 college housing spaces available; all were occupied in 2012-13. Freshmen given priority for college housing. Option: coed housing available. Salem State University Library with 308,252 books, 584,273 microform titles, 71,269 serials, 7,222 audiovisual materials, an OPAC, and a Web page. 255 computers available on campus for general student use. Computer purchase/lease plans available. A computer is required for all students. A campuswide network can be accessed from student residence rooms and from off campus. Students can access the following: online class registration. Staffed computer lab on campus provides training in use of computers, software, and the Internet.

Community Environment: Salem State College is located in Salem, Massachusetts. Salem was founded in 1626, and is one of the oldest cities in the country. It was one of the most active seaports in the New World, and was the capital of the Massachusetts Bay Colony until 1630. Salem was the site of the witchcraft trials in which the accusations of group of children and women caused 19 people to be hanged and one pressed to death. Many handsome old houses reminiscent of the days when sea captains and China merchants grew rich from importing are still to be seen. Marblehead harbor, one of the yachting capitals of the world, is only three miles away. The city is located approximately 14 miles north of Boston, is suburban in nature and has good bus and train service.

■ **SALTER COLLEGE**
645 Shawinigan Dr.
Chicopee, MA 01020
Tel: (413)206-0300
Web Site: www.saltercollege.com/
Description: Proprietary, 2-year, coed.

■ **SCHOOL OF THE MUSEUM OF FINE ARTS, BOSTON**
230 The Fenway
Boston, MA 02115
Tel: (617)267-6100
Fax: (617)369-3679
E-mail: admissions@smfa.edu
Web Site: www.smfa.edu/
Description: Independent, comprehensive, coed. Administratively affiliated with Museum of Fine Arts, Boston; Tufts University. Awards bachelor's and master's degrees. Founded 1876. Setting: 14-acre urban campus with easy access to Boston. Endowment: $22.7 million. Total enrollment: 775. Faculty: 147 (49 full-time, 98 part-time). Student-undergrad faculty ratio is 9:1. 701 applied, 82% were admitted. Full-time: 422 students, 69% women, 31%

men. Part-time: 172 students, 73% women, 27% men. Students come from 36 states and territories, 37 other countries, 65% from out-of-state. 1% American Indian or Alaska Native, non-Hispanic/Latino; 8% Hispanic/Latino; 3% African American, non-Hispanic/Latino; 4% Asian, non-Hispanic/Latino; 0% Native Hawaiian or other Pacific Islander, non-Hispanic/Latino; 8% international. 8% 25 or older, 10% live on campus, 7% transferred in. Retention: 68% of full-time freshmen returned the following year. Academic area with the most degrees conferred: visual and performing arts. Core. Calendar: semesters. Services for LD students, self-designed majors, independent study, double major, summer session for credit, part-time degree program, adult/continuing education programs, internships. Off campus study at Pro Arts Consortium, Association of Independent Colleges of Art and Design Mobility, Massachusetts Institute of Technology. Study abroad program.

Entrance Requirements: Options: electronic application, deferred admission. Required: essay, high school transcript, 2 recommendations, portfolio. Recommended: interview, Test scores are considered if submitted. Entrance: moderately difficult. Application deadlines: Rolling, Rolling for nonresidents. Notification: continuous, continuous for nonresidents. Transfer credits accepted: Yes.

Costs Per Year: Application fee: $65. Comprehensive fee: $50,018 includes full-time tuition ($36,828), mandatory fees ($1200), and college room and board ($11,990). Full-time tuition and fees vary according to course load, degree level, program, and student level. Room and board charges vary according to board plan and housing facility. Part-time tuition: $1370 per unit. Part-time tuition varies according to class time, course load, program, and student level.

Collegiate Environment: Orientation program. Most popular organizations: GLBT Group, Student Body, Inc and Student Voice, Library Sounds, SMFARM (garden group - smfa farm), CRU @ SMFA. Major annual events: juried and unjuried art exhibitions, All-School lunches (especially Thanksgiving), Film and Movie Screenings. Student services: health clinic, personal-psychological counseling. Campus security: 24-hour emergency response devices and patrols, late night taxis service between buildings. 60 college housing spaces available; all were occupied in 2012-13. Freshmen given priority for college housing. Option: coed housing available. W. Van Alan Clark, Jr. Library plus 1 other with 25,162 books, 9 microform titles, 67 serials, 889 audiovisual materials, an OPAC, and a Web page. Operations spending for the previous fiscal year: $205,561. 100 computers available on campus for general student use. Computer purchase/lease plans available. A campuswide network can be accessed. Students can access the following: online class registration. Staffed computer lab on campus provides training in use of computers and software.

Community Environment: See Boston University.

■ **SIMMONS COLLEGE**
300 The Fenway
Boston, MA 02115
Tel: (617)521-2000; Free: 800-345-8468
Fax: (617)521-3199
E-mail: ugadm@simmons.edu
Web Site: www.simmons.edu/

Description: Independent, university. Awards bachelor's, master's, and doctoral degrees and post-master's certificates. Founded 1899. Setting: 12-acre urban campus with easy access to Boston. Total enrollment: 4,830. Faculty: 623 (218 full-time, 405 part-time). Student-undergrad faculty ratio is 11:1. 4,440 applied, 48% were admitted. 25% from top 10% of their high school class, 57% from top quarter, 87% from top half. Full-time: 1,647 students, 100% women. Part-time: 145 students, 99% women, 1% men. 37% from out-of-state. 0.2% American Indian or Alaska Native, non-Hispanic/Latino; 6% Hispanic/Latino; 7% African American, non-Hispanic/Latino; 8% Asian, non-Hispanic/Latino; 0.1% Native Hawaiian or other Pacific Islander, non-Hispanic/Latino; 3% international. 15% 25 or older, 55% live on campus, 3% transferred in. Retention: 85% of full-time freshmen returned the following year. Academic areas with the most degrees conferred: health professions and related sciences; social sciences; business/marketing. Core. Calendar: semesters. Academic remediation for entering students, services for LD students, advanced placement, accelerated degree program, self-designed majors, honors program, independent study, distance learning, double major, summer session for credit, part-time degree program, adult/continuing education programs, co-op programs and internships, graduate courses open to undergrads. Off campus study at Exchange programs with Mills College, Spelman College, Colleges of the Fenway; double degree programs with the Massachusetts College of Pharmacy & Health Sciences. Study abroad program. ROTC: Army (c), Naval (c).

Entrance Requirements: Options: electronic application, early action, deferred admission, international baccalaureate accepted. Required: essay, high school transcript, 2 recommendations, Test scores. SAT or ACT. Recommended: minimum 3 high school GPA, interview. Entrance: moderately difficult. Application deadlines: 2/1, 2/1 for nonresidents, 12/1 for early action. Notification: 3/15, 3/15 for nonresidents, 1/15 for early action. SAT Reasoning Test deadline: 2/1. SAT Subject Test deadline: 2/1. Transfer credits accepted: Yes. Applicants placed on waiting list: 143. Wait-listed applicants offered admission: 17.

Costs Per Year: Application fee: $55. Comprehensive fee: $48,770 includes full-time tuition ($34,350), mandatory fees ($1020), and college room and board ($13,400). Full-time tuition and fees vary according to course load and program. Room and board charges vary according to board plan. Part-time tuition: $1178 per credit hour. Part-time tuition varies according to course load and program.

Collegiate Environment: Orientation program. Drama-theater group, choral group, student-run newspaper, radio station. Social organizations: 91 open to all. Most popular organizations: Student Government Association, Black Students Organization, Campus Activities Board, Asian Students Association, Simmons Voice. Major annual events: Winter Wonderland Dinner, Spring Spree Weekend, Simmons Cup. Student services: health clinic, personal-psychological counseling, women's center. Campus security: 24-hour emergency response devices and patrols, late night transport-escort service, controlled dormitory access. 1,039 college housing spaces available; 975 were occupied in 2012-13. Freshmen given priority for college housing. On-campus residence required in freshman year. Options: coed, women-only housing available. Beatley Library with 277,169 books, 13,580 microform titles, 59,134 serials, 7,122 audiovisual materials, an OPAC, and a Web page. 350 computers available on campus for general student use. A campuswide network can be accessed from student residence rooms and from off campus. Students can access the following: online class registration. Staffed computer lab on campus provides training in use of computers, software, and the Internet.

Community Environment: Simmons College is next door to the Isabella Stewart Gardner Museum and two blocks away from the Museum of Fine Arts. Other nearby attractions are Fenway Park, the Charles River, Beacon Hill, Back Bay, Cambridge and the North End. Complete intercity transportation is available.

■ **SMITH COLLEGE**
Northampton, MA 01063
Tel: (413)584-2700; Free: 800-383-3232
Fax: (413)585-2123
E-mail: admission@smith.edu
Web Site: www.smith.edu/

Description: Independent, comprehensive. Awards bachelor's, master's, and doctoral degrees and post-master's certificates. Founded 1871. Setting: 147-acre small town campus with easy access to Hartford. Total enrollment: 3,212. Faculty: 299 (275 full-time, 24 part-time). Student-undergrad faculty ratio is 9:1. 4,341 applied, 42% were admitted. 66% from top 10% of their high school class, 90% from top quarter, 99% from top half. Full-time: 2,643 students, 99.9% women, 0.04% men. Part-time: 21 students, 100% women. 78% from out-of-state. 0.2% American Indian or Alaska Native, non-Hispanic/Latino; 9% Hispanic/Latino; 5% African American, non-Hispanic/Latino; 12% Asian, non-Hispanic/Latino; 0.1% Native Hawaiian or other Pacific Islander, non-Hispanic/Latino; 12% international. 4% 25 or older, 95% live on campus, 2% transferred in. Retention: 93% of full-time freshmen returned the following year. Academic areas with the most degrees conferred: social sciences; foreign languages and literature; visual and performing arts; biological/life sciences; psychology. Calendar: semesters. Part-time degree program, adult/continuing education programs. ROTC: Army (c), Air Force (c).

Entrance Requirements: Options: electronic application, early admission, early decision, deferred admission, international baccalaureate accepted. Required: essay, high school transcript, 3 recommendations. Recommended: interview. Entrance: very difficult. Application deadlines: 1/15, 11/15 for early decision plan 1, 1/2 for early decision plan 2. Notification: 4/1, 12/15 for early decision plan 1, 2/2 for early decision plan 2. SAT Subject Test deadline: 2/1. Applicants placed on waiting list: 562. Wait-listed applicants offered admission: 118. Early decision applicants: 371. Early decision applicants admitted: 180.

Costs Per Year: Application fee: $60. Comprehensive fee: $55,320 includes full-time tuition ($41,190), mandatory fees ($270), and college room and board ($13,860). College room only: $6940. Part-time tuition: $1290 per credit hour.

Collegiate Environment: Campus security: 24-hour emergency response devices and patrols, late night transport-escort service, self-defense workshops, emergency telephones, programs in crime and sexual assault prevention. Freshmen guaranteed college housing. On-campus residence required through senior year. Option: women-only housing available. Neilson Library with an OPAC and a Web page.

Community Environment: The early frontier town of Northampton, settled in 1654, has been transformed over the intervening three-and-one-half centuries into a lively and sophisticated center of culture, commerce, and entertainment. Northampton has been named the Number 1 small town for the arts in the country by writer John Villani. Today there is a population of over 28,000. Located in the western-central part of state, about 18 miles north of Springfield, the area is easily accessible to good recreational sites. The city has a community hospital, theatres, art galleries, parks, and several hotels and motels. Part-time work is available for students.

■ **SPRINGFIELD COLLEGE**
263 Alden St.
Springfield, MA 01109-3797
Tel: (413)748-3000; Free: 800-343-1257
Fax: (413)748-3764
E-mail: admissions@spfldcol.edu
Web Site: www.spfldcol.edu/

Description: Independent, comprehensive, coed. Awards bachelor's, master's, and doctoral degrees. Founded 1885. Setting: 150-acre suburban campus. Total enrollment: 5,000. Faculty: 342. Student-undergrad faculty ratio is 13:1. Core. Calendar: semesters. ESL program, services for LD students, advanced placement, accelerated degree program, independent study, double major, summer session for credit, part-time degree program, adult/continuing education programs, co-op programs and internships, graduate courses open to undergrads. Off campus study. Study abroad program. ROTC: Army (c), Air Force (c).

Entrance Requirements: Options: electronic application, early admission, early decision, deferred admission. Required: high school transcript, 1 recommendation, SAT or ACT. Recommended: interview. Required for some: portfolio. Entrance: moderately difficult. Application deadlines: 4/1, 12/1 for early decision. Notification: continuous until 4/15, 2/1 for early decision. Preference given to children of alumni.

Costs Per Year: Application fee: $50. Comprehensive fee: $42,320 includes full-time tuition ($31,690) and college room and board ($10,630). College room only: $5780. Room and board charges vary according to board plan and housing facility. Part-time tuition: $884 per credit hour.

Collegiate Environment: Orientation program. Drama-theater group, choral group, student-run newspaper, radio station. Student services: health clinic, personal-psychological counseling.

Community Environment: Established as a trading post in 1636, Springfield is located on the Connecticut River in Southwestern part of the state. City is noted today for its diversified industries including the manufacture of firearms, plastics, chemicals, radio equipment, tires, paper, and electrical equipment. Ample part-time job opportunities available. Several movie theatres, municipal auditorium, drive-ins, summer theatre, two municipal golf courses, 150 parks, civic center, and playgrounds, swimming, skating, quadrangle of museums, public libraries, provide excellent recreational and cultural opportunities. Easy access to commercial, bus and rail service.

■ **SPRINGFIELD TECHNICAL COMMUNITY COLLEGE**
1 Armory Sq., Ste. One
Springfield, MA 01105
Tel: (413)781-7822
Fax: (413)781-5805
E-mail: rblair@stcc.edu
Web Site: www.stcc.edu/

Description: State-supported, 2-year, coed. Awards certificates, transfer associate, and terminal associate degrees. Founded 1967. Setting: 34-acre urban campus. Educational spending for the previous fiscal year: $5229 per student. Total enrollment: 7,011. Faculty: 398 (148 full-time, 250 part-time). Student-undergrad faculty ratio is 19:1. 3,279 applied, 88% were admitted. Full-time: 3,104 students, 52% women, 48% men. Part-time: 3,907 students, 62% women, 38% men. Students come from 12 states and territories, 15 other countries, 3% from out-of-state. 1% American Indian or Alaska Native, non-Hispanic/Latino; 24% Hispanic/Latino; 16% African American, non-Hispanic/Latino; 3% Asian, non-Hispanic/Latino; 0.1% Native Hawaiian or other Pacific Islander, non-Hispanic/Latino; 1% international. 45% 25 or

older, 9% transferred in. Calendar: semesters. Academic remediation for entering students, ESL program, services for LD students, advanced placement, honors program, independent study, distance learning, summer session for credit, part-time degree program, adult/continuing education programs, co-op programs and internships. Off campus study at the Cooperating Colleges of Greater Springfield.

Entrance Requirements: Open admission except for certain vocational programs. Option: electronic application. Required: high school transcript. Required for some: interview, SAT. Entrance: noncompetitive. Application deadline: Rolling. Transfer credits accepted: Yes.

Costs Per Year: Application fee: $10. State resident tuition: $750 full-time, $25 per credit part-time. Nonresident tuition: $7260 full-time, $242 per credit part-time. Mandatory fees: $4356 full-time, $138 per credit part-time, $108 per term part-time. Full-time tuition and fees vary according to course load and reciprocity agreements. Part-time tuition and fees vary according to course load and reciprocity agreements. Tuition guaranteed not to increase for student's term of enrollment.

Collegiate Environment: Orientation program. Social organizations: 31 open to all. Most popular organizations: Phi Theta Kappa, Campus Civitian Club, Tech Times (student newspaper), Dental Hygiene Club, Landscape Design Club. Major annual events: Multicultural Luncheon, Spring Fling, Opening Picnic. Student services: health clinic, personal-psychological counseling. Campus security: 24-hour emergency response devices and patrols, late night transport-escort service. College housing not available. Springfield Technical Community College Library with 58,950 books, 323 serials, 15,031 audiovisual materials, an OPAC, and a Web page. 1,673 computers available on campus for general student use. A campuswide network can be accessed from off-campus. Students can access the following: online class registration. Staffed computer lab on campus.

Community Environment: See Springfield College.

■ **STONEHILL COLLEGE**
320 Washington St.
Easton, MA 02357
Tel: (508)565-1000
Fax: (508)565-1500
E-mail: admission@stonehill.edu
Web Site: www.stonehill.edu/

Description: Independent Roman Catholic, 4-year, coed. Awards bachelor's degrees. Founded 1948. Setting: 384-acre suburban campus with easy access to Boston. Endowment: $146.7 million. Research spending for the previous fiscal year: $288,445. Educational spending for the previous fiscal year: $10,713 per student. Total enrollment: 2,599. Faculty: 278 (168 full-time, 110 part-time). Student-undergrad faculty ratio is 13:1. 6,117 applied, 80% were admitted. 35% from top 10% of their high school class, 65% from top quarter, 90% from top half. Full-time: 2,590 students, 61% women, 39% men. Part-time: 9 students, 67% women, 33% men. Students come from 31 states and territories, 8 other countries, 55% from out-of-state. 0% American Indian or Alaska Native, non-Hispanic/Latino; 4% Hispanic/Latino; 3% African American, non-Hispanic/Latino; 2% Asian, non-Hispanic/Latino; 0.04% Native Hawaiian or other Pacific Islander, non-Hispanic/Latino; 1% international. 1% 25 or older, 93% live on campus, 1% transferred in. Retention: 86% of full-time freshmen returned the following year. Academic areas with the most degrees conferred: business/marketing; social sciences; psychology. Core. Calendar: semesters. Services for LD students, advanced placement, self-designed majors, honors program, independent study, double major, summer session for credit, part-time degree program, internships. Off campus study at Eight members of the Southeastern Association for Cooperation of Higher Education in Massachusetts (SACHEM): Bridgewater State University, Bristol Community College, Cape Cod Community College, Dean College, Massasoit Community College, University of Massachusetts at Dartmouth, Wheaton college, Massachusetts Maritime Academy. Study abroad program. ROTC: Army.

Entrance Requirements: Options: electronic application, early decision, early action, deferred admission, international baccalaureate accepted. Required: essay, high school transcript, 2 recommendations. Recommended: campus visit. Required for some: interview. Entrance: very difficult. Application deadlines: 1/15, 11/1 for early decision, 11/1 for early action. Notification: 3/15, 12/25 for early decision, 1/15 for early action. SAT Reasoning Test deadline: 1/15. Transfer credits accepted: Yes. Applicants placed on waiting list: 207. Wait-listed applicants offered admission: 8. Early decision applicants: 51. Early decision applicants admitted: 48. Early action applicants: 2,573. Early action applicants admitted: 2,176.

Costs Per Year: Application fee: $60. Comprehensive fee: $49,970 includes

full-time tuition ($36,160) and college room and board ($13,810). Room and board charges vary according to board plan. Part-time tuition: $1205 per credit. Part-time tuition varies according to course load.

Collegiate Environment: Orientation program. Drama-theater group, choral group, student-run newspaper, radio station. Social organizations: 75 open to all. Most popular organizations: Into the Streets, Recreation/Intramural Sports Teams, Dance Club, Student Government Association, Education Society. Major annual events: Spring Weekend, Mr. Stonehill, Midnight Madness. Student services: health clinic, personal-psychological counseling, women's center. Campus security: 24-hour emergency response devices and patrols, late night transport-escort service, controlled dormitory access. 2,199 college housing spaces available; 2,109 were occupied in 2012-13. No special consideration for freshman housing applicants. Options: coed, women-only housing available. MacPhaidin Library plus 2 others with 341,757 books, 376,809 microform titles, 39,653 serials, 10,651 audiovisual materials, an OPAC, and a Web page. Operations spending for the previous fiscal year: $1.8 million. 403 computers available on campus for general student use. A campuswide network can be accessed from student residence rooms and from off campus. Students can access the following: online class registration, Learning Management System; online degree evaluation and planning; add funds to ID online and use at off campus locations; online housing contracts and room lottery; online financial aid awards; online time sheets and payments for campus jobs; and ebill. Staffed computer lab on campus (open 24 hours a day) provides training in use of computers, software, and the Internet.

Community Environment: The College is in Easton, adjoining Brockton and 20 miles south of Boston. Transportation is available to Brockton, and the Boston subway system. Cultural, recreational and community services are all quite accessible.

■ **SUFFOLK UNIVERSITY**

8 Ashburton Pl.

Boston, MA 02108-2770

Tel: (617)573-8000; Free: 800-6-SUFFOLK

Fax: (617)742-4291

E-mail: admission@suffolk.edu

Web Site: www.suffolk.edu/

Description: Independent, comprehensive, coed. Awards associate, bachelor's, master's, and doctoral degrees and post-master's certificates (doctoral degree in law). Founded 1906. Setting: 2-acre urban campus. Endowment: $130 million. Research spending for the previous fiscal year: $1.6 million. Educational spending for the previous fiscal year: $8281 per student. Total enrollment: 9,044. Faculty: 863 (392 full-time, 471 part-time). Student-undergrad faculty ratio is 12:1. 9,418 applied, 78% were admitted. 14% from top 10% of their high school class, 41% from top quarter, 78% from top half. Full-time: 5,364 students, 56% women, 44% men. Part-time: 406 students, 56% women, 44% men. Students come from 43 states and territories, 105 other countries, 33% from out-of-state. 0.2% American Indian or Alaska Native, non-Hispanic/Latino; 10% Hispanic/Latino; 5% African American, non-Hispanic/Latino; 7% Asian, non-Hispanic/Latino; 0% Native Hawaiian or other Pacific Islander, non-Hispanic/Latino; 17% international. 6% 25 or older; 22% live on campus, 8% transferred in. Retention: 76% of full-time freshmen returned the following year. Academic areas with the most degrees conferred: history; communication/journalism; social sciences. Core. Calendar: semesters. Academic remediation for entering students, ESL program, services for LD students, advanced placement, accelerated degree program, freshman honors college, honors program, independent study, distance learning, double major, summer session for credit, part-time degree program, adult/continuing education programs, co-op programs and internships, graduate courses open to undergrads. Off campus study. Study abroad program. ROTC: Army (c).

Entrance Requirements: Options: electronic application, early action, deferred admission, international baccalaureate accepted. Required: essay, high school transcript, 2 recommendations, SAT or ACT. Recommended: minimum 2.5 high school GPA. Required for some: interview. Entrance: moderately difficult. Application deadlines: 2/15, 11/15 for early action. Notification: 3/20, 12/20 for early action. SAT Subject Test deadline: 6/6. Applicants placed on waiting list: 735. Wait-listed applicants offered admission: 29. Early action applicants: 2,175. Early action applicants admitted: 1,701.

Costs Per Year: Application fee: $50. One-time mandatory fee: $200. Comprehensive fee: $45,522 includes full-time tuition ($30,672), mandatory fees ($120), and college room and board ($14,730). College room only: $12,124. Room and board charges vary according to board plan and housing facility.

Collegiate Environment: Orientation program. Drama-theater group, choral group, student-run newspaper, radio station. Social organizations: 75 open to all; national fraternities, local sororities; 1% of eligible men and 1% of eligible women are members. Most popular organizations: Student Government Association, Program Committee, Suffolk Free Radio, Black Student Union, Journey Leadership Program. Major annual events: Temple Street Fair, Unity Week, Winter/Spring Ball. Student services: health clinic, personal-psychological counseling, women's center. Campus security: 24-hour emergency response devices, late night transport-escort service, controlled dormitory access. 1,249 college housing spaces available; 1,241 were occupied in 2012-13. Freshmen given priority for college housing. Option: coed housing available. Mildred Sawyer Library plus 2 others with 256,033 books, 145,121 microform titles, 59,990 serials, 832 audiovisual materials, an OPAC, and a Web page. Operations spending for the previous fiscal year: $7.5 million. 539 computers available on campus for general student use. Computer purchase/lease plans available. A campuswide network can be accessed from student residence rooms and from off campus. Students can access the following: online class registration. Staffed computer lab on campus provides training in use of computers, software, and the Internet.

Community Environment: Suffolk University is located in the heart of Boston, a city rich in history and culture. In addition to being an international center for high-technology, finance, architecture, and medicine, Boston boasts over 50 of the finest colleges and universities in the nation. Founded in 1630, ten years after the Pilgrims landed at Plymouth, Boston is the capital of the Commonwealth of Massachusetts and is the largest city in New England. The city of Boston has a population of over 559,000 people whose heritage is drawn worldwide. The Freedom Trail includes 16 landmarks significant to our nation's history, including Faneuil Hall, the Old North Church, Paul Revere's house, Old Ironsides and the Bunker Hill Monument. Hidden throughout Boston are treasures such as the Isabella Stewart Gardner Museum and the African Meeting House, which is the oldest African American church building still standing in this country. There is various entertainment such as the Boston Ballet, the Boston Symphony Orchestra, and the theatre, as well as comedy clubs and clubs featuring many different types of music. In addition, Boston offers some of the finest shopping and dining facilities in the country. Boston is also the home of four professional sports teams — the Boston Bruins, the Boston Celtics, the Boston Red Sox, and the New England Patriots. The city is accessible by public transportation, commuter rail, bus service, air service, and taxi service. Due to its size, Boston is also an excellent walking city. At the hub of the transportation system is Suffolk University, on the edge of Beacon Hill, a maze of brick sidewalks and cobblestone streets, 18th and 19th century townhouses and mansions. The area was settled by the Boston Brahmins and is still one of the most desirable addresses.

■ **TUFTS UNIVERSITY**

Medford, MA 02155

Tel: (617)628-5000

Fax: (617)627-3860

E-mail: admissions.inquiry@ase.tufts.edu

Web Site: www.tufts.edu/

Description: Independent, university, coed. Awards bachelor's, master's, and doctoral degrees and post-master's certificates. Founded 1852. Setting: 150-acre suburban campus with easy access to Boston. Endowment: $1.4 billion. Total enrollment: 10,837. Faculty: 1,045 (699 full-time, 346 part-time). Student-undergrad faculty ratio is 9:1. 16,369 applied, 21% were admitted. 90% from top 10% of their high school class, 99% from top quarter, 100% from top half. 58 National Merit Scholars. Full-time: 5,167 students, 51% women, 49% men. Part-time: 88 students, 58% women, 42% men. Students come from 52 states and territories, 60 other countries, 77% from out-of-state. 0.1% American Indian or Alaska Native, non-Hispanic/Latino; 7% Hispanic/Latino; 4% African American, non-Hispanic/Latino; 10% Asian, non-Hispanic/Latino; 0.04% Native Hawaiian or other Pacific Islander, non-Hispanic/Latino; 7% international. 1% 25 or older, 64% live on campus, 2% transferred in. Retention: 97% of full-time freshmen returned the following year. Academic areas with the most degrees conferred: social sciences; engineering; visual and performing arts. Core. Calendar: semesters. Services for LD students, advanced placement, self-designed majors, independent study, double major, summer session for credit, adult/continuing education programs, internships, graduate courses open to undergrads. Off campus study at Boston College, Boston University, Brandeis University, Swarthmore College, American University, Lincoln University. Study abroad program. ROTC: Army (c), Naval (c), Air Force (c).

Entrance Requirements: Options: electronic application, early decision, deferred admission, international baccalaureate accepted. Required: essay, high school transcript, 2 recommendations, Common Application, the Tufts Supplement, and standardized testing, SAT and SAT Subject Tests or ACT. Recommended: interview. Entrance: most difficult. Application deadlines: 1/1, 11/1 for early decision plan 1, 1/1 for early decision plan 2. Notification: 4/1, 12/15 for early decision plan 1, 2/1 for early decision plan 2. SAT Reasoning Test deadline: 2/1. SAT Subject Test deadline: 2/1. Transfer credits accepted: Yes. Early decision applicants: 1,384. Early decision applicants admitted: 546.

Costs Per Year: Application fee: $70. Comprehensive fee: $58,780 includes full-time tuition ($45,590), mandatory fees ($1008), and college room and board ($12,182). College room only: $6630. Room and board charges vary according to board plan.

Collegiate Environment: Orientation program. Drama-theater group, choral group, marching band, student-run newspaper, radio station. Social organizations: 285 open to all; national fraternities, national sororities; 19% of eligible men and 11% of eligible women are members. Most popular organizations: Leonard Carmichael Society (community service), Tufts Mountain Club, intramural sports, Tufts Daily (newspaper), Pen, Paint, and Pretzels (student directed theater umbrella organization). Major annual events: Homecoming, Spring Fling, Supershow. Student services: legal services, health clinic, personal-psychological counseling, women's center. Campus security: 24-hour emergency response devices and patrols, late night transport-escort service, controlled dormitory access, security lighting, call boxes to campus police. 3,363 college housing spaces available. Freshmen guaranteed college housing. On-campus residence required through sophomore year. Options: coed, women-only housing available. Tisch Library plus 3 others with 1.1 million books, 1.2 million microform titles, 62,359 serials, 60,413 audiovisual materials, an OPAC, and a Web page. Operations spending for the previous fiscal year: $16.8 million. 300 computers available on campus for general student use. Computer purchase/lease plans available. A campuswide network can be accessed from student residence rooms and from off campus. Students can access the following: online class registration, Cloud storage for all students, staff, and faculty. Staffed computer lab on campus provides training in use of computers.

Community Environment: Medford is a residential suburb of Boston, located approximately five miles northwest of the city. One of the oldest settlements in the Commonwealth and in the United States, Medford was founded in 1630 and has many historical points of interest. Beautiful Mystic Lakes are located on the northwest border of the city, and further recreational opportunities are provided by the Middlesex Fells, a mountainous reservation of approximately 4,000 acres. Part-time employment is available in Boston.

■ **UNIVERSITY OF MASSACHUSETTS AMHERST**
Amherst, MA 01003
Tel: (413)545-0111
Fax: (413)545-4312
E-mail: mail@admissions.umass.edu
Web Site: www.umass.edu/

Description: State-supported, university, coed. Part of University of Massachusetts. Awards associate, bachelor's, master's, and doctoral degrees and post-master's certificates. Founded 1863. Setting: 1,463-acre small town campus with easy access to Hartford. Endowment: $230.6 million. Research spending for the previous fiscal year: $194.8 million. Educational spending for the previous fiscal year: $12,764 per student. Total enrollment: 28,236. Faculty: 1,361 (1,217 full-time, 144 part-time). Student-undergrad faculty ratio is 18:1. 34,326 applied, 63% were admitted. 27% from top 10% of their high school class, 66% from top quarter, 95% from top half. Full-time: 20,306 students, 48% women, 52% men. Part-time: 1,622 students, 59% women, 41% men. Students come from 51 states and territories, 69 other countries, 21% from out-of-state. 0.1% American Indian or Alaska Native, non-Hispanic/Latino; 5% Hispanic/Latino; 4% African American, non-Hispanic/Latino; 7% Asian, non-Hispanic/Latino; 0.1% Native Hawaiian or other Pacific Islander, non-Hispanic/Latino; 2% international. 7% 25 or older, 61% live on campus, 5% transferred in. Retention: 88% of full-time freshmen returned the following year. Academic areas with the most degrees conferred: business/marketing; social sciences; psychology. Core. Calendar: semesters. Academic remediation for entering students, ESL program, services for LD students, advanced placement, accelerated degree program, self-designed majors, freshman honors college, honors program, independent study, distance learning, double major, summer session for credit, part-time degree program, adult/continuing education programs, co-op programs

and internships, graduate courses open to undergrads. Off campus study at members of the National Student Exchange, Five Colleges, Inc., other units of the University of Massachusetts System. Study abroad program. ROTC: Army, Air Force.

Entrance Requirements: Options: electronic application, early action, deferred admission, international baccalaureate accepted. Required: essay, high school transcript, SAT or ACT, SAT or ACT. Recommended: minimum 3 high school GPA. Entrance: moderately difficult. Application deadlines: 1/15, 1/15 for nonresidents, 11/1 for early action. Notification: continuous, continuous for nonresidents, 12/15 for early action. SAT Reasoning Test deadline: 2/1. Transfer credits accepted: Yes. Applicants placed on waiting list: 3,808. Wait-listed applicants offered admission: 566. Early action applicants: 11,723. Early action applicants admitted: 9,105.

Costs Per Year: Application fee: $75. One-time mandatory fee: $185. State resident tuition: $1714 full-time, $71.50 per credit part-time. Nonresident tuition: $9937 full-time, $414 per credit part-time. Mandatory fees: $11,701 full-time, $671.83 per credit part-time. Full-time tuition and fees vary according to class time, course load, location, program, reciprocity agreements, and student level. Part-time tuition and fees vary according to class time, course load, location, program, reciprocity agreements, and student level. College room and board: $10,767. College room only: $5563. Room and board charges vary according to board plan and housing facility.

Collegiate Environment: Orientation program. Drama-theater group, choral group, marching band, student-run newspaper, radio station. Social organizations: 356 open to all; national fraternities, national sororities, local fraternities, local sororities; 6% of eligible men and 6% of eligible women are members. Most popular organizations: Minutemen Marching Band, Theater Guild, Ski Club, Outing Club, student newspaper. Major annual events: First Week, Family Weekend, Homecoming Week. Student services: legal services, health clinic, personal-psychological counseling, women's center. Campus security: 24-hour emergency response devices and patrols, student patrols, late night transport-escort service, controlled dormitory access. 12,866 college housing spaces available; 12,420 were occupied in 2012-13. Freshmen guaranteed college housing. On-campus residence required in freshman year. Options: coed, men-only, women-only housing available. W. E. B. Du Bois Library plus 1 other with 4.1 million books, 177,732 serials, 31,595 audiovisual materials, an OPAC, and a Web page. 419 computers available on campus for general student use. A campuswide network can be accessed from student residence rooms and from off campus. Students can access the following: online class registration, online housing assignments, bill payment, Learning Management System, file storage, web hosting, blogs. Staffed computer lab on campus (open 24 hours a day) provides training in use of computers, software, and the Internet.

Community Environment: See Amherst College.

■ **UNIVERSITY OF MASSACHUSETTS BOSTON**
100 Morrissey Blvd.
Boston, MA 02125-3393
Tel: (617)287-5000
E-mail: enrollment.info@umb.edu
Web Site: www.umb.edu/

Description: State-supported, university, coed. Part of University of Massachusetts. Awards bachelor's, master's, and doctoral degrees and post-master's certificates. Founded 1964. Setting: 187-acre urban campus. Endowment: $51.9 million. Research spending for the previous fiscal year: $30.9 million. Educational spending for the previous fiscal year: $10,605 per student. Total enrollment: 15,874. Faculty: 1,193 (587 full-time, 606 part-time). Student-undergrad faculty ratio is 15:1. 7,876 applied, 61% were admitted. Full-time: 8,426 students, 55% women, 45% men. Part-time: 3,698 students, 58% women, 42% men. Students come from 39 states and territories, 143 other countries, 5% from out-of-state. 0.2% American Indian or Alaska Native, non-Hispanic/Latino; 11% Hispanic/Latino; 15% African American, non-Hispanic/Latino; 11% Asian, non-Hispanic/Latino; 0.05% Native Hawaiian or other Pacific Islander, non-Hispanic/Latino; 8% international. 36% 25 or older, 15% transferred in. Retention: 79% of full-time freshmen returned the following year. Academic areas with the most degrees conferred: business/marketing; health professions and related sciences; psychology. Core. Calendar: semesters. Academic remediation for entering students, ESL program, services for LD students, advanced placement, accelerated degree program, self-designed majors, freshman honors college, honors program, independent study, distance learning, double major, summer session for credit, part-time degree program, adult/continuing education programs, co-op programs and internships, graduate courses open to undergrads. Off campus study at members of the National Student

Exchange, New England Regional Student Exchange, Boston Five Course Exchange Program. Study abroad program. ROTC: Army (c), Naval (c), Air Force (c).

Entrance Requirements: Options: electronic application, deferred admission, international baccalaureate accepted. Required: high school transcript, minimum 2.5 high school GPA, SAT, ACT, SAT or ACT. Recommended: essay, SAT and SAT Subject Tests or ACT, SAT Subject Tests. Required for some: essay, minimum 2.75 high school GPA, interview. Entrance: moderately difficult. Application deadline: 4/1. Notification: continuous. SAT Reasoning Test deadline: 4/1. Transfer credits accepted: Yes.

Costs Per Year: Application fee: $40. State resident tuition: $11,320 full-time. Nonresident tuition: $25,504 full-time. Mandatory fees: $646 full-time. Full-time tuition and fees vary according to program.

Collegiate Environment: Orientation program. Drama-theater group, choral group, student-run newspaper, radio station. Social organizations: 80 open to all. Most popular organizations: Student Arts & Events Council, Haitian Student Association, Golden Key Honor Society, Campus Kitchens, Mass Media. Major annual events: Convocation, Commencement, fall and spring festivals. Student services: legal services, health clinic, personal-psychological counseling, women's center. Campus security: 24-hour emergency response devices and patrols, late night transport-escort service, crime prevention program, bicycle patrols. College housing not available. Joseph P. Healey Library with 600,000 books, 75,000 serials, an OPAC, and a Web page. Operations spending for the previous fiscal year: $4.9 million. 350 computers available on campus for general student use. A campuswide network can be accessed from off-campus. Students can access the following: online class registration. Staffed computer lab on campus provides training in use of computers, software, and the Internet.

Community Environment: See Boston University.

■ UNIVERSITY OF MASSACHUSETTS DARTMOUTH

285 Old Westport Rd.
North Dartmouth, MA 02747-2300
Tel: (508)999-8000
Fax: (508)999-8755
E-mail: admissions@umassd.edu
Web Site: www.umassd.edu/

Description: State-supported, university, coed. Part of University of Massachusetts. Awards bachelor's, master's, and doctoral degrees and post-master's certificates. Founded 1895. Setting: 710-acre suburban campus with easy access to Boston, Providence. Endowment: $39 million. Research spending for the previous fiscal year: $18.9 million. Educational spending for the previous fiscal year: $8092 per student. Total enrollment: 9,210. Faculty: 660 (375 full-time, 285 part-time). Student-undergrad faculty ratio is 18:1. 8,063 applied, 72% were admitted. 17% from top 10% of their high school class, 40% from top quarter, 78% from top half. Full-time: 6,580 students, 46% women, 54% men. Part-time: 982 students, 60% women, 40% men. Students come from 32 states and territories, 38 other countries, 4% from out-of-state. 0.2% American Indian or Alaska Native, non-Hispanic/Latino; 6% Hispanic/Latino; 11% African American, non-Hispanic/Latino; 3% Asian, non-Hispanic/Latino; 0.03% Native Hawaiian or other Pacific Islander, non-Hispanic/Latino; 2% international. 14% 25 or older, 55% live on campus, 6% transferred in. Retention: 74% of full-time freshmen returned the following year. Academic areas with the most degrees conferred: business/marketing; health professions and related sciences; engineering. Core. Calendar: semesters. Academic remediation for entering students, services for LD students, advanced placement, self-designed majors, honors program, independent study, distance learning, double major, summer session for credit, part-time degree program, co-op programs and internships, graduate courses open to undergrads. Off campus study at members of the Southeastern Association for Cooperation in Higher Education in Massachusetts. Study abroad program. ROTC: Army (c).

Entrance Requirements: Options: electronic application, early admission, early action, deferred admission. Required: essay, high school transcript, minimum 3 high school GPA, SAT or ACT. Recommended: essay, 1 recommendation. Entrance: moderately difficult. Application deadlines: Rolling, 11/15 for early action. Notification: continuous, 12/15 for early action. SAT Reasoning Test deadline: 8/20. Transfer credits accepted: Yes. Early action applicants: 0. Early action applicants admitted: 0.

Costs Per Year: Application fee: $40. State resident tuition: $1417 full-time. Nonresident tuition: $8099 full-time. Mandatory fees: $10,264 full-time. Full-time tuition and fees vary according to class time, program, and reciprocity agreements.

Collegiate Environment: Orientation program. Drama-theater group, choral

group, student-run newspaper, radio station. Social organizations: 114 open to all; national fraternities, national sororities; 1% of eligible men and 1% of eligible women are members. Most popular organizations: Student Activities Board, Ski & Snowboard Club, Phi Sigma Sigma, American Red Cross Club, Pride Alliance. Major annual events: Senior Week, Welcome Back Week, Spring Semi-Formal. Student services: legal services, health clinic, personal-psychological counseling, women's center. Campus security: 24-hour emergency response devices and patrols, student patrols, late night transport-escort service, controlled dormitory access. 4,500 college housing spaces available; 4,156 were occupied in 2012-13. No special consideration for freshman housing applicants. Option: coed housing available. University of Massachusetts Dartmouth Claire T. Carney Library plus 1 other with 438,887 books, 69,407 microform titles, 2,017 serials, 7,913 audiovisual materials, an OPAC, and a Web page. Operations spending for the previous fiscal year: $4.7 million. 368 computers available on campus for general student use. A campuswide network can be accessed from student residence rooms and from off campus. Students can access the following: online class registration. Staffed computer lab on campus provides training in use of computers, software, and the Internet.

Community Environment: North Dartmouth is located near the larger city of New Bedford, MA. This city, on Buzzard's Bay, was once the greatest whaling port in the world. Fishing fleets and allied industries contribute one-fifth of New Bedford's income. The city is also known for the manufacture of fine textile goods, plastics, tire fabrics, boats, golf balls, cut glass, and other products. The area is easily accessible by rail, bus, and air. The city has a library and whaling museum. Major community services are located in the immediate area. Part-time jobs opportunities are available.

■ UNIVERSITY OF MASSACHUSETTS LOWELL

1 University Ave.
Lowell, MA 01854-2881
Tel: (978)934-4000
Fax: (978)934-3000
E-mail: admissions@umi.edu
Web Site: www.uml.edu/

Description: State-supported, university, coed. Part of University of Massachusetts. Awards associate, bachelor's, master's, and doctoral degrees and post-master's certificates. Founded 1894. Setting: 100-acre urban campus with easy access to Boston. Endowment: $49.5 million. Research spending for the previous fiscal year: $35.3 million. Educational spending for the previous fiscal year: $7669 per student. Total enrollment: 15,431. Student-undergrad faculty ratio is 14:1. 7,720 applied, 65% were admitted. 17% from top 10% of their high school class, 43% from top quarter, 82% from top half. Full-time: 8,424 students, 39% women, 61% men. Part-time: 3,305 students, 42% women, 58% men. Students come from 32 other countries, 14% from out-of-state. 0.1% American Indian or Alaska Native, non-Hispanic/Latino; 9% Hispanic/Latino; 7% African American, non-Hispanic/Latino; 9% Asian, non-Hispanic/Latino; 0.02% Native Hawaiian or other Pacific Islander, non-Hispanic/Latino; 1% international. 27% 25 or older, 39% live on campus, 9% transferred in. Retention: 79% of full-time freshmen returned the following year. Academic areas with the most degrees conferred: business/marketing; engineering; homeland security, law enforcement, firefighting, and protective services. Core. Calendar: semesters. Services for LD students, advanced placement, accelerated degree program, honors program, independent study, distance learning, double major, summer session for credit, part-time degree program, adult/continuing education programs, co-op programs and internships, graduate courses open to undergrads. Off campus study at Northeast Consortium of Colleges and Universities in Massachusetts. Study abroad program. ROTC: Army (c), Air Force.

Entrance Requirements: Options: electronic application, early action, deferred admission, international baccalaureate accepted. Required: essay, high school transcript, minimum 3 high school GPA, 1 recommendation, Audition for music students, SAT or ACT. Entrance: moderately difficult. Application deadlines: 2/15, 2/15 for nonresidents, 12/1 for early action. Notification: continuous, continuous for nonresidents, 1/20 for early action. SAT Reasoning Test deadline: 3/1. Transfer credits accepted: Yes. Applicants placed on waiting list: 318. Wait-listed applicants offered admission: 14.

Costs Per Year: Application fee: $60. One-time mandatory fee: $200. State resident tuition: $1454 full-time, $61 per credit part-time. Nonresident tuition: $8567 full-time, $357 per credit part-time. Mandatory fees: $10,398 full-time, $433.05 per credit part-time. Part-time tuition and fees vary according to course load. College room and board: $10,282. College room only: $6854. Room and board charges vary according to board plan and housing facility.

Collegiate Environment: Orientation program. Drama-theater group, choral group, marching band, student-run newspaper, radio station. Social organizations: 167 open to all; national fraternities, national sororities, local fraternities, local sororities. Most popular organizations: Student Government Association, Recreational Sports Club, Association of Students of African Origin, WUML (radio station), Campus Activities Programming Association. Major annual events: Spring Carnival, Family Day, Culture Shock. Student services: health clinic, personal-psychological counseling. Campus security: 24-hour emergency response devices and patrols, late night transport-escort service, controlled dormitory access. O'Leary Library and Learning Commons plus 2 others with 298,756 books, 70,009 microform titles, 45,105 serials, 12,249 audiovisual materials, an OPAC, and a Web page. Operations spending for the previous fiscal year: $4.6 million. 3,125 computers available on campus for general student use. Computer purchase/lease plans available. A campuswide network can be accessed from student residence rooms and from off campus. Students can access the following: online class registration. Staffed computer lab on campus provides training in use of computers, software, and the Internet.

Community Environment: in the metropolitan area, the cotton and woolen plants once caused city to be known as"the spindle city." Today, textile manufacture has been de-emphasized and industry is diversified with electronics paramount. Lowell is the home of the only federal Urban National Park. Part-time employment available for students. Commercial air, rail, and bus service is easily accessible. Community has public library, churches of all denominations, YMCA, YWCA, art gallery, and hospitals. All sports facilities are available as well as beaches, theatres, and famous ski area within a short distance.

■ **UNIVERSITY OF PHOENIX–BOSTON CAMPUS**
100 Grossman Dr.
Braintree, MA 02184-4949
Tel: (781)843-0844; Free: 866-766-0766
Web Site: www.phoenix.edu/
Description: Proprietary, comprehensive, coed. Awards bachelor's and master's degrees. Founded 2001. Setting: urban campus. Total enrollment: 361. Faculty: 107 (9 full-time, 98 part-time). Full-time: 265 students, 54% women, 46% men. 79% 25 or older. Academic areas with the most degrees conferred: business/marketing; computer and information sciences. Core. Calendar: continuous. Services for LD students, advanced placement, accelerated degree program, independent study, distance learning, external degree program, adult/continuing education programs, graduate courses open to undergrads.
Entrance Requirements: Open admission. Options: electronic application, deferred admission. Required: 1 recommendation. Required for some: high school transcript. Entrance: noncompetitive. Application deadline: Rolling.
Collegiate Environment: Campus security: late night transport-escort service. University Library with 16,781 serials, an OPAC, and a Web page. Operations spending for the previous fiscal year: $6.8 million.

■ **UNIVERSITY OF PHOENIX–CENTRAL MASSACHUSETTS CAMPUS**
One Research Dr.
Westborough, MA 01581-3906
Tel: (508)614-4100; Free: 866-766-0766
Web Site: www.phoenix.edu/
Description: Proprietary, comprehensive, coed. Awards bachelor's and master's degrees. Founded 2003. Setting: urban campus. Total enrollment: 148. Faculty: 80 (5 full-time, 75 part-time). Full-time: 117 students, 52% women, 48% men. 83% 25 or older. Retention: 38% of full-time freshmen returned the following year. Academic areas with the most degrees conferred: computer and information sciences; business/marketing. Core. Calendar: continuous. Services for LD students, advanced placement, accelerated degree program, independent study, distance learning, graduate courses open to undergrads.
Entrance Requirements: Open admission. Options: electronic application, deferred admission. Required: 1 recommendation. Required for some: high school transcript. Entrance: noncompetitive. Application deadline: Rolling.
Collegiate Environment: Campus security: late night transport-escort service. University Library with 16,781 microform titles, 3,000 audiovisual materials, and an OPAC. Operations spending for the previous fiscal year: $6.8 million.

■ **URBAN COLLEGE OF BOSTON**
178 Tremont St.
Boston, MA 02111

Tel: (617)292-4723
Fax: (617)423-4758
Web Site: www.urbancollege.edu/
Description: Independent, 2-year, coed. Awards certificates and terminal associate degrees. Founded 1993. Setting: urban campus. Total enrollment: 634. Student-undergrad faculty ratio is 13:1. 0% from out-of-state. 90% 25 or older. Retention: 50% of full-time freshmen returned the following year. Calendar: semesters. Part-time degree program.
Entrance Requirements: Open admission.

■ **WELLESLEY COLLEGE**
106 Central St.
Wellesley, MA 02481
Tel: (781)283-1000
Fax: (781)283-3678
E-mail: admission@wellesley.edu
Web Site: www.wellesley.edu/
Description: Independent, 4-year, women only. Awards bachelor's degrees (double bachelor's degree with Massachusetts Institute of Technology). Founded 1870. Setting: 500-acre suburban campus with easy access to Boston. Endowment: $1.5 billion. Research spending for the previous fiscal year: $10.5 million. Educational spending for the previous fiscal year: $93,554 per student. Total enrollment: 2,481. Faculty: 346 (287 full-time, 59 part-time). Student-undergrad faculty ratio is 7:1. 4,478 applied, 30% were admitted. Full-time: 2,366 students. Part-time: 117 students. Students come from 49 states and territories, 80 other countries, 84% from out-of-state. 0.04% American Indian or Alaska Native, non-Hispanic/Latino; 10% Hispanic/Latino; 6% African American, non-Hispanic/Latino; 21% Asian, non-Hispanic/Latino; 0.04% Native Hawaiian or other Pacific Islander, non-Hispanic/Latino; 12% international. 2% 25 or older, 93% live on campus, 1% transferred in. Retention: 97% of full-time freshmen returned the following year. Academic areas with the most degrees conferred: social sciences; biological/life sciences; foreign languages and literature. Core. Calendar: semesters. Services for LD students, advanced placement, self-designed majors, honors program, independent study, double major, summer session for credit, part-time degree program, adult/continuing education programs, internships. Off campus study at Brandeis University, Babson College, Massachusetts Institute of Technology, members of the Twelve College Exchange Program, Spelman College, Mills College. Study abroad program. ROTC: Army (c), Air Force (c).
Entrance Requirements: Options: electronic application, early admission, early decision, deferred admission, international baccalaureate accepted. Required: essay, high school transcript, 3 recommendations, first senior marking period grades and mid-year report, SAT and SAT Subject Tests or ACT. Recommended: interview. Required for some: interview. Entrance: most difficult. Application deadlines: 1/15, 1/15 for nonresidents, 11/1 for early decision. Notification: 4/1, 4/1 for nonresidents, 12/15 for early decision. SAT Reasoning Test deadline: 12/31. SAT Subject Test deadline: 12/31. Transfer credits accepted: Yes. Early decision applicants: 304. Early decision applicants admitted: 165.
Costs Per Year: Application fee: $50. Comprehensive fee: $57,042 includes full-time tuition ($43,288), mandatory fees ($266), and college room and board ($13,488). College room only: $6846. Part-time tuition: $1352 per credit hour. Part-time tuition varies according to course load.
Collegiate Environment: Orientation program. Drama-theater group, choral group, student-run newspaper, radio station. Social organizations: 160 open to all. Most popular organizations: student government, radio station, cultural clubs, rugby club, theater groups. Major annual events: Spring Weekend, Acappella Concerts, Cultural Shows. Student services: health clinic, personal-psychological counseling, women's center. Campus security: 24-hour emergency response devices and patrols, late night transport-escort service, controlled dormitory access. 2,211 college housing spaces available; all were occupied in 2012-13. Freshmen guaranteed college housing. Option: women-only housing available. Margaret Clapp Library plus 4 others with 1.5 million books, 536,499 microform titles, 100,754 serials, 36,660 audiovisual materials, an OPAC, and a Web page. Operations spending for the previous fiscal year: $5.7 million. 200 computers available on campus for general student use. Computer purchase/lease plans available. A campuswide network can be accessed from student residence rooms and from off campus. Students can access the following: online class registration. Staffed computer lab on campus (open 24 hours a day) provides training in use of computers, software, and the Internet.
Community Environment: The campus is located in a suburb of Boston 15

miles from the heart of the city. Railroad and bus transportation is available. Community services, and cultural and recreational facilities are found in adjacent Boston.

■ **WENTWORTH INSTITUTE OF TECHNOLOGY**
550 Huntington Ave.
Boston, MA 02115-5998
Tel: (617)989-4590; Free: 800-556-0610
Fax: (617)989-4010
E-mail: dufoura@wit.edu
Web Site: www.wit.edu/

Description: Independent, comprehensive, coed. Awards associate, bachelor's, and master's degrees. Founded 1904. Setting: 31-acre urban campus. Endowment: $74.4 million. Research spending for the previous fiscal year: $19,880. Educational spending for the previous fiscal year: $7741 per student. Total enrollment: 4,155. Faculty: 310 (145 full-time, 165 part-time). Student-undergrad faculty ratio is 16:1. 5,650 applied, 61% were admitted. 12% from top 10% of their high school class, 40% from top quarter, 76% from top half. Full-time: 3,592 students, 19% women, 81% men. Part-time: 411 students, 14% women, 86% men. Students come from 36 states and territories, 49 other countries, 36% from out-of-state. 0.3% American Indian or Alaska Native, non-Hispanic/Latino; 4% Hispanic/Latino; 5% African American, non-Hispanic/Latino; 6% Asian, non-Hispanic/Latino; 0% Native Hawaiian or other Pacific Islander, non-Hispanic/Latino; 4% international. 5% 25 or older, 49% live on campus, 3% transferred in. Retention: 82% of full-time freshmen returned the following year. Academic areas with the most degrees conferred: business/marketing; engineering technologies; architecture. Calendar: semesters for freshmen and sophomores, trimesters for juniors and seniors. Academic remediation for entering students, services for LD students, advanced placement, summer session for credit, part-time degree program, co-op programs and internships. Off campus study at Emmanuel College (MA), Massachusetts College of Pharmacy and Allied Health Sciences, Simmons College, Wheelock College. Study abroad program. ROTC: Army (c), Air Force (c).

Entrance Requirements: Options: electronic application, deferred admission, international baccalaureate accepted. Required: essay, high school transcript, 1 recommendation, SAT or ACT. Recommended: minimum 2 high school GPA, interview. Entrance: moderately difficult. Application deadlines: 5/1, 5/1 for nonresidents. Notification: continuous. SAT Reasoning Test deadline: 7/1. SAT Subject Test deadline: 7/1.

Costs Per Year: Application fee: $50. Comprehensive fee: $40,476 includes full-time tuition ($27,950) and college room and board ($12,526). College room only: $11,384. Room and board charges vary according to board plan and housing facility. Part-time tuition: $875 per credit hour. Part-time mandatory fees: $440 per credit hour. Part-time tuition and fees vary according to course load and degree level.

Collegiate Environment: Orientation program. Student-run radio station. Social organizations: 40 open to all. Most popular organizations: Intramural Sports, Wentworth Events Board, Multicultural Student Association, Phi Sigma Pi, Major Particular Professional Student Associations. Major annual events: Beaux Arts Ball, Family Weekend, Design Lecture Series. Student services: health clinic, personal-psychological counseling, women's center. Campus security: 24-hour emergency response devices and patrols, student patrols, late night transport-escort service, controlled dormitory access. 1,992 college housing spaces available; 1,817 were occupied in 2012-13. Freshmen guaranteed college housing. On-campus residence required through sophomore year. Option: coed housing available. Wentworth Alumni Library with 154,959 books, 43,324 serials, 2,873 audiovisual materials, an OPAC, and a Web page. Operations spending for the previous fiscal year: $1.2 million. 320 computers available on campus for general student use. Computer purchase/lease plans available. A computer is required for all students. A campuswide network can be accessed from student residence rooms and from off campus. Students can access the following: online class registration. Staffed computer lab on campus provides training in use of computers.

Community Environment: See Boston University.

■ **WESTERN NEW ENGLAND UNIVERSITY**
1215 Wilbraham Rd.
Springfield, MA 01119
Tel: (413)782-3111; Free: 800-325-1122
Fax: (413)782-1777
E-mail: learn@wne.edu
Web Site: www.wne.edu/

Description: Independent, comprehensive, coed. Awards associate, bachelor's, master's, and doctoral degrees. Founded 1919. Setting: 215-acre suburban campus. Endowment: $34.1 million. Total enrollment: 3,729. Faculty: 337 (205 full-time, 132 part-time). Student-undergrad faculty ratio is 14:1. 5,752 applied, 80% were admitted. 15% from top 10% of their high school class, 41% from top quarter, 75% from top half. Full-time: 2,472 students, 39% women, 61% men. Part-time: 201 students, 49% women, 51% men. 54% from out-of-state. 0.2% American Indian or Alaska Native, non-Hispanic/Latino; 6% Hispanic/Latino; 5% African American, non-Hispanic/Latino; 3% Asian, non-Hispanic/Latino; 0% Native Hawaiian or other Pacific Islander, non-Hispanic/Latino; 1% international. 72% live on campus, 4% transferred in. Retention: 73% of full-time freshmen returned the following year. Academic areas with the most degrees conferred: business/marketing; engineering; psychology. Core. Calendar: semesters. Services for LD students, advanced placement, accelerated degree program, self-designed majors, honors program, independent study, distance learning, double major, summer session for credit, part-time degree program, adult/continuing education programs, internships, graduate courses open to undergrads. Off campus study at Cooperating Colleges of Greater Springfield. Study abroad program. ROTC: Army, Air Force (c).

Entrance Requirements: Options: electronic application, international baccalaureate accepted. Required: high school transcript, 1 recommendation, SAT or ACT. Recommended: essay, interview. Entrance: moderately difficult. Application deadline: Rolling. Notification: continuous.

Costs Per Year: Application fee: $40. Comprehensive fee: $44,056 includes full-time tuition ($29,738), mandatory fees ($2174), and college room and board ($12,144). Full-time tuition and fees vary according to program. Room and board charges vary according to board plan and housing facility. Part-time tuition: $560 per credit hour. Part-time tuition varies according to location and program.

Collegiate Environment: Orientation program. Drama-theater group, choral group, student-run newspaper, radio station. Social organizations: 60 open to all. Most popular organizations: Student Senate, Residence Hall Association, Campus Activities Board, student radio station, The Westerner (student newspaper). Major annual events: Homecoming, Family Weekend, spring concert. Student services: health clinic, personal-psychological counseling. Campus security: 24-hour emergency response devices and patrols, student patrols, late night transport-escort service, controlled dormitory access, security cameras. D'Amour Library plus 1 other with 130,900 books, 194,268 microform titles, 208 serials, 5,200 audiovisual materials, an OPAC, and a Web page. 400 computers available on campus for general student use. Computer purchase/lease plans available. A campuswide network can be accessed from student residence rooms and from off campus. Students can access the following: online class registration. Staffed computer lab on campus.

Community Environment: The College is located in a residential section of Springfield, Massachusetts, about four miles from the city's downtown area. Because Springfield is a city of 157,000 people, there are a variety of social, cultural, and athletic activities from which to choose. Some of the city's special features are live theater ant City Stage; the Springfield Symphony; the Quadrangle, a complex of museums; the Basketball Hall of Fame; the Springfield Falcons hockey team; Six Flags New England Amusement Park; the Eastern States Exposition fairgrounds; and many activities, shows, and concerts held in the Springfield Civic Center. Public transportation is available to locations throughout the greater Springfield area. The College is also a member of the Cooperating Colleges of Greater Springfield, a group of 8 private and public colleges in the immediate area.

■ **WESTFIELD STATE UNIVERSITY**
577 Western Ave.
Westfield, MA 01086
Tel: (413)572-5300
E-mail: admission@westfield.ma.edu
Web Site: www.wsc.ma.edu/

Description: State-supported, comprehensive, coed. Part of Massachusetts Public Higher Education System. Awards bachelor's and master's degrees and post-master's certificates. Founded 1838. Setting: 256-acre suburban campus. Total enrollment: 6,079. Faculty: 469 (223 full-time, 246 part-time). Student-undergrad faculty ratio is 17:1. 4,941 applied, 64% were admitted. 6% from top 10% of their high school class, 27% from top quarter, 72% from top half. Full-time: 4,712 students, 53% women, 47% men. Part-time: 656 students, 53% women, 47% men. Students come from 17 states and territories, 14 other countries, 7% from out-of-state. 0.2% American Indian or Alaska Native, non-Hispanic/Latino; 6% Hispanic/Latino; 4% African

American, non-Hispanic/Latino; 1% Asian, non-Hispanic/Latino; 0.1% Native Hawaiian or other Pacific Islander, non-Hispanic/Latino; 1% international. 12% 25 or older, 54% live on campus, 7% transferred in. Retention: 81% of full-time freshmen returned the following year. Academic areas with the most degrees conferred: education; homeland security, law enforcement, firefighting, and protective services; business/marketing. Core. Calendar: semesters. Services for LD students, advanced placement, self-designed majors, honors program, independent study, distance learning, double major, summer session for credit, part-time degree program, adult/continuing education programs, co-op programs and internships, graduate courses open to undergrads. Off campus study at National Student Exchange, College Academic Program Sharing (MA State Colleges), Cooperating Colleges of Greater Springfield. Study abroad program. ROTC: Army (c), Air Force (c).

Entrance Requirements: Options: electronic application, deferred admission. Required: high school transcript, minimum 3 high school GPA, SAT or ACT. Required for some: interview, audition for music major, portfolio for art major, also sliding scale minimum high school GPA using SAT/ACT scores for GPAs between 2.0 and 3.0. Entrance: moderately difficult. Application deadlines: 3/1, 3/1 for nonresidents. Notification: continuous until 3/15, continuous until 3/15 for nonresidents. SAT Reasoning Test deadline: 3/1. Transfer credits accepted: Yes.

Costs Per Year: Application fee: $50. State resident tuition: $970 full-time, $260 per credit hour part-time. Nonresident tuition: $7050 full-time, $260 per credit hour part-time. Mandatory fees: $7327 full-time, $75 per term part-time. Full-time tuition and fees vary according to program and reciprocity agreements. Part-time tuition and fees vary according to course load. College room and board: $9233. Room and board charges vary according to board plan and housing facility.

Collegiate Environment: Orientation program. Drama-theater group, choral group, student-run newspaper, radio station. Social organizations: 78 open to all. Most popular organizations: Student National Education Association, Student Government Association, Campus Activities Board, The Dance Company, Multicultural Student Association. Major annual events: Spring Weekend, Opening Day Picnic, Homecoming Weekend. Student services: legal services, health clinic, personal-psychological counseling. Campus security: 24-hour emergency response devices and patrols, student patrols, late night transport-escort service, controlled dormitory access. College housing designed to accommodate 2,767 students; 2,814 undergraduates lived in college housing during 2012-13. Freshmen given priority for college housing. Option: coed housing available. Governor Joseph B. Ely Library with 157,062 books, 481,151 microform titles, 1,967 serials, 5,453 audiovisual materials, an OPAC, and a Web page. Operations spending for the previous fiscal year: $632,793. 640 computers available on campus for general student use. A campuswide network can be accessed from student residence rooms and from off campus. Students can access the following: online class registration, online transcripts and billing information, web portal.

Community Environment: Founded in 1669, city is located in southwestern part of state approximately nine miles northwest of Springfield. This is an industrial city manufacturing paper, machinery, and toys. Part-time employment is available for students. Several historical sites are found in the immediate area, including Grandmother's Garden, a municipally owned garden of old-fashioned flowers and herbs. Nearby Stanley Park offers 85 acres of floral gardens, arboretum, concerts, 96-foot high Carillon, covered bridge, old mill, blacksmith shop, and multicolored fountain. Adjacent cities offer many community services.

■ **WHEATON COLLEGE**
26 E Main St.
Norton, MA 02766
Tel: (508)285-7722; Free: 800-394-6003
Fax: (508)285-8271
E-mail: admission@wheatoncollege.edu
Web Site: www.wheatoncollege.edu/

Description: Independent, 4-year, coed. Awards bachelor's degrees. Founded 1834. Setting: 400-acre suburban campus with easy access to Boston. Endowment: $159.5 million. Research spending for the previous fiscal year: $618,329. Educational spending for the previous fiscal year: $17,922 per student. Total enrollment: 1,616. Faculty: 171 (132 full-time, 39 part-time). Student-undergrad faculty ratio is 11:1. 4,046 applied, 64% were admitted. 38% from top 10% of their high school class, 78% from top quarter, 98% from top half. Full-time: 1,613 students, 64% women, 36% men. Part-time: 6 students, 67% women, 33% men. Students come from 42 states and territories, 38 other countries, 64% from out-of-state. 0.1% American Indian

or Alaska Native, non-Hispanic/Latino; 7% Hispanic/Latino; 5% African American, non-Hispanic/Latino; 3% Asian, non-Hispanic/Latino; 0% Native Hawaiian or other Pacific Islander, non-Hispanic/Latino; 8% international. 0.3% 25 or older, 95% live on campus, 1% transferred in. Retention: 86% of full-time freshmen returned the following year. Academic areas with the most degrees conferred: social sciences; psychology; area and ethnic studies. Core. Calendar: semesters. Advanced placement, accelerated degree program, self-designed majors, honors program, independent study, double major, part-time degree program, internships. Off campus study at members of the Twelve College Exchange Program, American University, Williams College, Brown University, members of the Southeastern Association for Cooperation in Higher Education in Massachusetts, Connecticut College (National Theatre Institute), SALT Center for Documentary Field Studies, Marine Biological Laboratory (Woods Hole, MA). Study abroad program. ROTC: Army (c).

Entrance Requirements: Options: electronic application, early admission, early decision, early action, deferred admission, international baccalaureate accepted. Required: essay, high school transcript, 2 recommendations. Recommended: interview. Entrance: very difficult. Application deadlines: 1/15, 11/15 for early decision, 11/15 for early action. Notification: 4/1, 12/15 for early decision, 1/15 for early action. SAT Reasoning Test deadline: 1/15. SAT Subject Test deadline: 1/15. Transfer credits accepted: Yes. Applicants placed on waiting list: 377. Wait-listed applicants offered admission: 16. Early decision applicants: 124. Early decision applicants admitted: 112. Early action applicants: 1,130. Early action applicants admitted: 854.

Costs Per Year: Application fee: $50. One-time mandatory fee: $50. Comprehensive fee: $56,574 includes full-time tuition ($44,780), mandatory fees ($294), and college room and board ($11,500). College room only: $6140.

Collegiate Environment: Orientation program. Drama-theater group, choral group, student-run newspaper, radio station. Social organizations: 103 open to all; 40% of eligible men and 60% of eligible women are members. Most popular organizations: Student Government Association, Community Service Council, Amnesty International, acappella singing groups, Programming Council. Major annual events: Spring Weekend's Head of the Peacock, Norton Community Day, Wheaton Homecoming. Student services: health clinic, personal-psychological counseling, women's center. Campus security: 24-hour emergency response devices and patrols, student patrols, late night transport-escort service, controlled dormitory access. 1,525 college housing spaces available; all were occupied in 2012-13. Freshmen guaranteed college housing. On-campus residence required through senior year. Options: coed, men-only, women-only housing available. Madeleine Clark Wallace Library with 365,467 books, 55,780 microform titles, 29,832 serials, 18,069 audiovisual materials, an OPAC, and a Web page. Operations spending for the previous fiscal year: $3.4 million. 356 computers available on campus for general student use. Computer purchase/lease plans available. A campuswide network can be accessed from student residence rooms and from off campus. Students can access the following: online class registration. Staffed computer lab on campus provides training in use of computers, software, and the Internet.

■ **WHEELOCK COLLEGE**
200 The Riverway
Boston, MA 02215-4176
Tel: (617)879-2000; Free: 800-734-5212
Fax: (617)566-7531
E-mail: kharrington@wheelock.edu
Web Site: www.wheelock.edu/

Description: Independent, comprehensive, coed. Awards bachelor's and master's degrees and post-master's certificates. Founded 1888. Setting: 6-acre urban campus. Endowment: $43.7 million. Educational spending for the previous fiscal year: $7374 per student. Total enrollment: 1,308. Faculty: 167 (65 full-time, 102 part-time). Student-undergrad faculty ratio is 9:1. 1,537 applied, 71% were admitted. 7% from top 10% of their high school class, 36% from top quarter, 63% from top half. 6 class presidents, 3 valedictorians, 15 student government officers. Full-time: 837 students, 90% women, 10% men. Part-time: 79 students, 81% women, 19% men. Students come from 15 states and territories, 8 other countries, 35% from out-of-state. 0% American Indian or Alaska Native, non-Hispanic/Latino; 11% Hispanic/Latino; 12% African American, non-Hispanic/Latino; 2% Asian, non-Hispanic/Latino; 0% Native Hawaiian or other Pacific Islander, non-Hispanic/Latino; 0.5% international. 70% live on campus, 15% transferred in. Retention: 80% of full-time freshmen returned the following year. Academic areas with the most degrees conferred: family and consumer sciences; education; public administration and social services. Core. Calendar: semesters. Services for LD students, advanced placement, freshman honors college, honors program, independent study, double major, summer session for credit, part-time degree program, internships, graduate courses open to undergrads. Off campus study. Study abroad program.

Entrance Requirements: Options: electronic application, early admission, early action, deferred admission, international baccalaureate accepted. Required: essay, high school transcript, minimum 2 high school GPA, 1 recommendation, SAT or ACT. Recommended: interview. Entrance: minimally difficult. Application deadlines: 3/1, 12/1 for early action. Notification: continuous. SAT Reasoning Test deadline: 3/1. Transfer credits accepted: Yes. Early action applicants: 350. Early action applicants admitted: 325.

Costs Per Year: Application fee: $15. Comprehensive fee: $43,755 includes full-time tuition ($29,860), mandatory fees ($1095), and college room and board ($12,800). Full-time tuition and fees vary according to course load. Part-time tuition: $935 per credit hour. Part-time mandatory fees: $62 per credit. Part-time tuition and fees vary according to course load.

Collegiate Environment: Orientation program. Drama-theater group, choral group. Student services: health clinic, personal-psychological counseling, women's center. Campus security: 24-hour patrols, late night transport-escort service, controlled dormitory access. Wheelock College Library plus 1 other with 81,642 books, 168,576 microform titles, 59,203 serials, 2,891 audiovisual materials, an OPAC, and a Web page. Operations spending for the previous fiscal year: $896,000. 100 computers available on campus for general student use. Computer purchase/lease plans available. A campuswide network can be accessed from student residence rooms and from off campus. Students can access the following: online class registration.

Community Environment: See Boston University.

■ WILLIAMS COLLEGE

880 Main St.
Williamstown, MA 01267
Tel: (413)597-3131
Fax: (413)597-4018
E-mail: admission@williams.edu
Web Site: www.williams.edu/

Description: Independent, 4-year, coed. Awards bachelor's and master's degrees. Founded 1793. Setting: 450-acre small town campus with easy access to Albany, NY. Endowment: $1.8 billion. Total enrollment: 2,106. Faculty: 334 (273 full-time, 61 part-time). Student-undergrad faculty ratio is 7:1. 7,069 applied, 17% were admitted. 92% from top 10% of their high school class, 97% from top quarter, 100% from top half. Full-time: 2,013 students, 52% women, 48% men. Part-time: 39 students, 56% women, 44% men. Students come from 50 states and territories, 63 other countries, 86% from out-of-state. 0.3% American Indian or Alaska Native, non-Hispanic/Latino; 12% Hispanic/Latino; 8% African American, non-Hispanic/Latino; 11% Asian, non-Hispanic/Latino; 0% Native Hawaiian or other Pacific Islander, non-Hispanic/Latino; 6% international. 0% 25 or older, 94% live on campus, 0.3% transferred in. Retention: 96% of full-time freshmen returned the following year. Academic areas with the most degrees conferred: social sciences; history; psychology; English; visual and performing arts. Core. Calendar: 4-1-4. Self-designed majors, independent study, double major, internships. Off campus study. Study abroad program. ROTC: Air Force (c).

Entrance Requirements: Options: electronic application, early admission, early decision, deferred admission. Required: essay, high school transcript, 2 recommendations, SAT and SAT Subject Tests or ACT. Entrance: most difficult. Application deadlines: 1/1, 1/1 for nonresidents, 11/10 for early decision. Notification: 4/7, 4/7 for nonresidents, 12/15 for early decision. Transfer credits accepted: Yes. Applicants placed on waiting list: 1,308. Wait-listed applicants offered admission: 21. Early decision applicants: 569. Early decision applicants admitted: 239.

Costs Per Year: Application fee: $65. Comprehensive fee: $54,560 includes full-time tuition ($42,938), mandatory fees ($252), and college room and board ($11,370). College room only: $5780. Room and board charges vary according to board plan.

Collegiate Environment: Orientation program. Drama-theater group, choral group, marching band, student-run newspaper, radio station. Social organizations: 147 open to all. Major annual events: Mountain Day, Winter Carnival, Claiming Williams. Student services: health clinic, personal-psychological counseling. 2,020 college housing spaces available. On-campus residence required in freshman year. Option: coed housing available. Sawyer Library plus 10 others with 945,691 books, 480,233 microform

titles, 29,200 serials, 41,691 audiovisual materials, an OPAC, and a Web page. 252 computers available on campus for general student use. A campuswide network can be accessed from student residence rooms and from off campus. Students can access the following: online class registration. Staffed computer lab on campus.

Community Environment: This pleasant colonial town was named for its founder, Col. Ephraim Williams. It is located in the Berkshire Mountains within easy commuting distance of Albany, Boston, and New York. Heavy tourist trade is found here, and the area is known as"Village Beautiful." Excellent facilities are available for skiing, horseback riding, hunting in season, fishing, hiking, and golf. The town has several art museum and its own symphony orchestra. The Tanglewood Music Festival is held nearby annually.

■ WORCESTER POLYTECHNIC INSTITUTE

100 Institute Rd.
Worcester, MA 01609-2280
Tel: (508)831-5000
Fax: (508)831-5875
E-mail: admissions@wpi.edu
Web Site: www.wpi.edu/

Description: Independent, university, coed. Awards bachelor's, master's, and doctoral degrees. Founded 1865. Setting: 80-acre suburban campus with easy access to Boston. Endowment: $358.6 million. Research spending for the previous fiscal year: $19.2 million. Educational spending for the previous fiscal year: $19,749 per student. Total enrollment: 5,957. Faculty: 460 (302 full-time, 158 part-time). Student-undergrad faculty ratio is 14:1. 7,585 applied, 53% were admitted. 66% from top 10% of their high school class, 92% from top quarter, 99% from top half. 6 National Merit Scholars, 46 valedictorians. Full-time: 3,787 students, 32% women, 68% men. Part-time: 165 students, 28% women, 72% men. Students come from 49 states and territories, 70 other countries, 53% from out-of-state. 0.2% American Indian or Alaska Native, non-Hispanic/Latino; 7% Hispanic/Latino; 3% African American, non-Hispanic/Latino; 5% Asian, non-Hispanic/Latino; 0% Native Hawaiian or other Pacific Islander, non-Hispanic/Latino; 12% international. 1% 25 or older, 45% live on campus, 1% transferred in. Retention: 96% of full-time freshmen returned the following year. Academic areas with the most degrees conferred: engineering; biological/life sciences; computer and information sciences. Core. Calendar: 4 7-week terms. ESL program, services for LD students, advanced placement, accelerated degree program, self-designed majors, independent study, distance learning, double major, summer session for credit, part-time degree program, co-op programs and internships, graduate courses open to undergrads. Off campus study at Colleges of Worcester Consortium. Study abroad program. ROTC: Army, Naval (c), Air Force.

Entrance Requirements: Options: electronic application, early admission, early action, deferred admission, international baccalaureate accepted. Required: essay, high school transcript, 2 recommendations. Required for some: interview, SAT or ACT, IELTS or TOEFL. Entrance: very difficult. Application deadlines: 2/1, 11/10 for early action. Notification: 4/1, 12/20 for early action. SAT Reasoning Test deadline: 3/1. SAT Subject Test deadline: 3/1. Transfer credits accepted: Yes. Applicants placed on waiting list: 2,033. Wait-listed applicants offered admission: 73. Early action applicants: 4,310. Early action applicants admitted: 2,807.

Costs Per Year: Application fee: $60. One-time mandatory fee: $200. Comprehensive fee: $55,860 includes full-time tuition ($42,178), mandatory fees ($600), and college room and board ($13,082). College room only: $7466. Room and board charges vary according to board plan and housing facility. Part-time tuition: $1172 per credit hour. Part-time tuition varies according to course load.

Collegiate Environment: Orientation program. Drama-theater group, choral group, marching band, student-run newspaper, radio station. Social organizations: 204 open to all; national fraternities, national sororities; 30% of eligible men and 35% of eligible women are members. Most popular organizations: Student Government Association, Social Committee (Student Events Programming Board), Music Association (all music-performing groups), intramural and club sports, International Student Council. Major annual events: Homecoming/Parents' Weekend, Traditions Day, Quadfest. Student services: health clinic, personal-psychological counseling. Campus security: 24-hour emergency response devices and patrols, student patrols, late night transport-escort service, controlled dormitory access. 1,685 college housing spaces available; 1,676 were occupied in 2012-13. Freshmen guaranteed college housing. Options: coed, men-only, women-only housing available. George C. Gordon Library with 764,633 books, 189,960 microform titles, 80,510 serials, 3,593 audiovisual materials, an OPAC, and a Web page. Operations spending for the previous fiscal year: $3.9 million. 500 computers available on campus for general student use. Computer purchase/lease plans available. A campuswide network can be accessed from student residence rooms and from off campus. Students can access the following: online class registration, online course content. Staffed computer lab on campus provides training in use of computers, software, and the Internet.

Community Environment: See Clark University.

■ WORCESTER STATE UNIVERSITY

486 Chandler St.
Worcester, MA 01602-2597
Tel: (508)929-8000; Free: 866-WSC-CALL
Fax: (508)929-8131
E-mail: admissions@worcester.edu
Web Site: www.worcester.edu/

Description: State-supported, comprehensive, coed. Part of Massachusetts Public Higher Education System. Awards bachelor's and master's degrees and post-master's certificates. Founded 1874. Setting: 58-acre urban campus with easy access to Boston. Endowment: $10.6 million. Educational spending for the previous fiscal year: $6742 per student. Total enrollment: 6,221. Faculty: 422 (196 full-time, 226 part-time). Student-undergrad faculty ratio is 18:1. 3,434 applied, 68% were admitted. Full-time: 3,973 students, 59% women, 41% men. Part-time: 1,334 students, 63% women, 37% men. Students come from 21 states and territories, 13 other countries, 3% from out-of-state. 0.4% American Indian or Alaska Native, non-Hispanic/Latino; 7% Hispanic/Latino; 6% African American, non-Hispanic/Latino; 3% Asian, non-Hispanic/Latino; 0.1% Native Hawaiian or other Pacific Islander, non-Hispanic/Latino; 1% international. 18% 25 or older, 31% live on campus, 10% transferred in. Retention: 78% of full-time freshmen returned the following year. Academic areas with the most degrees conferred: business/marketing; health professions and related sciences; psychology. Core. Calendar: semesters. Academic remediation for entering students, ESL program, services for LD students, advanced placement, accelerated degree program, honors program, independent study, distance learning, double major, summer session for credit, part-time degree program, adult/continuing education programs, internships, graduate courses open to undergrads. Off campus study at Colleges of Worcester Consortium, Inc. Study abroad program. ROTC: Army (c), Naval (c), Air Force (c).

Entrance Requirements: Options: electronic application, deferred admission. Required: high school transcript, minimum 2 high school GPA, SAT or

ACT. Required for some: essay. Entrance: moderately difficult. Application deadline: 5/1. Notification: continuous. Transfer credits accepted: Yes.

Costs Per Year: Application fee: $40. State resident tuition: $970 full-time, $40.42 per credit part-time. Nonresident tuition: $7050 full-time, $293.75 per credit part-time. Mandatory fees: $7187 full-time, $278.45 per credit part-time. Full-time tuition and fees vary according to class time, course load, degree level, and reciprocity agreements. Part-time tuition and fees vary according to class time, course load, degree level, and reciprocity agreements. College room and board: $10,500. College room only: $7380. Room and board charges vary according to board plan and housing facility.

Collegiate Environment: Orientation program. Drama-theater group, choral group, student-run newspaper, radio station. Social organizations: 33 open to all. Most popular organizations: Senate, SEC (Student Events Committee), TWA (Third World Alliance), WSCW (radio station), Dance Company/Club. Major annual events: Multicultural Festival, Homecoming, SGA Auction to Benefit the Homeless. Student services: health clinic, personal-psychological counseling. Campus security: 24-hour emergency response devices and patrols, late night transport-escort service, controlled dormitory access, well-lit campus and limited access to campus at night. College housing designed to accommodate 1,177 students; 1,230 undergraduates lived in college housing during 2012-13. No special consideration for freshman housing applicants. Options: coed, men-only, women-only housing available. Worcester State University Library with 204,971 books, 16,459 microform titles, 496 serials, 4,267 audiovisual materials, an OPAC, and a Web page. Operations spending for the previous fiscal year: $356,401. 500 computers available on campus for general student use. Computer purchase/lease plans available. A computer is required for all students. A campuswide network can be accessed from student residence rooms and from off campus. Students can access the following: online class registration. Staffed computer lab on campus provides training in use of computers, software, and the Internet.

Community Environment: The Worcester State College location has the advantages of a suburban setting in the west side of Worcester, while less than two miles from downtown Worcester. A shuttle service provides free student transportation to the other nine college in the Colleges of Worcester Consortium and to City Hall, the Worcester Public Library, and several cultural centers. Worcester, the"Heart of New England," is about 40 miles from Boston, 45 miles from Providence, Rhode Island and 60 miles from Hartford, Connecticut. More than 700,000 people live within an hour's drive. The Worcester Centrum and Convention Center, with a seating capacity of 15,500, hosts a variety of sports and entertainment events. Lakes, rivers, city parks and beaches make fishing and boating, and a variety of activities, available. Hiking and skiing are available in nearby Mt. Wachusett.

■ ADRIAN COLLEGE
110 S Madison St.
Adrian, MI 49221-2575
Tel: (517)265-5161; Free: 800-877-2246
Fax: (517)265-3331
E-mail: admissions@adrian.edu
Web Site: www.adrian.edu/
Description: Independent, comprehensive, coed, affiliated with United Methodist Church. Awards associate, bachelor's, and master's degrees. Founded 1859. Setting: 100-acre small town campus with easy access to Detroit, Toledo. Total enrollment: 1,678. Faculty: 176 (89 full-time, 87 part-time). Student-undergrad faculty ratio is 14:1. 3,263 applied, 64% were admitted. Full-time: 461 students, 47% women, 53% men. Students come from 28 states and territories, 4 other countries, 22% from out-of-state. 0.2% American Indian or Alaska Native, non-Hispanic/Latino; 3% Hispanic/Latino; 8% African American, non-Hispanic/Latino; 0.3% Asian, non-Hispanic/Latino; 0.1% Native Hawaiian or other Pacific Islander, non-Hispanic/Latino; 5% international. 3% 25 or older, 15% transferred in. Retention: 75% of full-time freshmen returned the following year. Academic areas with the most degrees conferred: business/marketing; visual and performing arts; parks and recreation. Core. Calendar: semesters. Academic remediation for entering students, ESL program, services for LD students, advanced placement, self-designed majors, honors program, independent study, double major, summer session for credit, part-time degree program, adult/continuing education programs, internships. Off campus study at Urban Life Center (Chicago), The Washington Center. Study abroad program. ROTC: Army (c).
Entrance Requirements: Options: electronic application, deferred admission, international baccalaureate accepted. Required: high school transcript, SAT or ACT. Recommended: interview, ACT. Required for some: essay. Entrance: moderately difficult. Application deadline: 3/15. Notification: continuous. Transfer credits accepted: Yes.
Costs Per Year: Application fee: $0. Comprehensive fee: $37,952 includes full-time tuition ($28,606), mandatory fees ($550), and college room and board ($8796). College room only: $4226. Room and board charges vary according to board plan and housing facility.
Collegiate Environment: Orientation program. Drama-theater group, choral group, marching band, student-run newspaper, radio station. Social organizations: 80 open to all; national fraternities, national sororities. Most popular organizations: Student Government Association, Adrian College Premedical Chapter of the American Medical Association, Adrian College Kinesiology Club, Campus Activities Network. Major annual events: Homecoming, International Week, Dance Marathon. Student services: health clinic, personal-psychological counseling. Campus security: 24-hour patrols, student patrols, late night transport-escort service. Shipman Library with 145,742 books, 50,865 microform titles, 567 serials, 3,069 audiovisual materials, an OPAC, and a Web page.
Community Environment: Adrian is 35 miles southwest of Ann Arbor and 35 miles northwest of Toledo, Ohio, located in the center of a large industrial, agricultural and recreational area. Leading manufactured products include aircraft, automobile, and refrigerator parts, paper, wood cabinetry, plastics, tools, and chemicals. Water sports and fishing are easily accessible with many lakes within a 25-mile radius. Part-time job opportunities are available.

■ ALBION COLLEGE
611 E Porter St.
Albion, MI 49224-1831
Tel: (517)629-1000; Free: 800-858-6770
Fax: (517)629-0569
E-mail: plittlefield@albion.edu
Web Site: www.albion.edu/
Description: Independent Methodist, 4-year, coed. Awards bachelor's degrees. Founded 1835. Setting: 565-acre small town campus with easy access to Detroit. System endowment: $161.2 million. Research spending for the previous fiscal year: $318,554. Educational spending for the previous fiscal year: $14,333 per student. Total enrollment: 1,382. Faculty: 151 (105 full-time, 46 part-time). Student-undergrad faculty ratio is 11:1. 2,383 applied, 70% were admitted. Full-time: 1,353 students, 49% women, 51% men. Part-time: 29 students, 66% women, 34% men. Students come from 20 states and territories, 23 other countries, 9% from out-of-state. 0.2% American Indian or Alaska Native, non-Hispanic/Latino; 3% Hispanic/Latino; 4% African American, non-Hispanic/Latino; 1% Asian, non-Hispanic/Latino; 0% Native Hawaiian or other Pacific Islander, non-Hispanic/Latino; 4% international. 0% 25 or older, 90% live on campus, 3% transferred in. Retention: 73% of full-time freshmen returned the following year. Academic areas with the most degrees conferred: social sciences; biological/life sciences; physical sciences. Core. Calendar: semesters. Services for LD students, advanced placement, self-designed majors, honors program, independent study, double major, summer session for credit, part-time degree program, internships. Off campus study at Great Lakes Colleges Association. Study abroad program.
Entrance Requirements: Options: electronic application, early action, deferred admission, international baccalaureate accepted. Required: essay, high school transcript, minimum 3 high school GPA, 1 recommendation, SAT or ACT. Recommended: interview. Entrance: moderately difficult. Application deadlines: Rolling, 12/1 for early action. Notification: continuous, 11/1 for early action. SAT Reasoning Test deadline: 6/1. Transfer credits accepted: Yes. Early action applicants: 1,218. Early action applicants admitted: 972.
Costs Per Year: One-time mandatory fee: $185. Comprehensive fee: $43,884 includes full-time tuition ($33,600), mandatory fees ($594), and college room and board ($9690). College room only: $4740. Full-time tuition and fees vary according to course load. Room and board charges vary according to board plan and housing facility. Part-time tuition: $1430 per credit hour. Part-time mandatory fees: $297 per term. Part-time tuition and fees vary according to course load.
Collegiate Environment: Orientation program. Drama-theater group, choral group, marching band, student-run newspaper, radio station. Social organizations: 110 open to all; national fraternities, national sororities; 51% of eligible men and 43% of eligible women are members. Most popular organizations: Greek Life (Fraternities and Sororities), Student Senate (Student Government), Umbrella (Diversity Groups), Union Board (Programming Board), Spiritual Life (Religious Centered groups). Major annual events: Briton Bash, Party on Perry, Day of Woden. Student services: health clinic, personal-psychological counseling, women's center. Campus security: 24-hour emergency response devices and patrols, student patrols, late night transport-escort service, controlled dormitory access. 1,784 college housing spaces available; 1,170 were occupied in 2012-13. Freshmen guaranteed college housing. Options: coed, men-only, women-only housing available. Stockwell Mudd Libraries with 356,176 books, 49,107 microform titles, 88,631 serials, 12,851 audiovisual materials, an OPAC, and a Web page. Operations spending for the previous fiscal year: $1.3 million. 120 computers available on campus for general student use. A campuswide network can be accessed from student residence rooms and from off campus. Students can

access the following: online class registration, online student account and financial aid. Staffed computer lab on campus (open 24 hours a day) provides training in use of computers, software, and the Internet.

Community Environment: Located one and one-half hours west of Detroit and three hours east of Chicago, the city of Albion combines small town life, a strong industrial base, and the amenities of a college town to form a unique community for its citizens. Albion boasts a rich history of educational and industrial accomplishment and prides itself on its ethnic and cultural diversity. Part-time employment is available. The area is served by Greyhound Bus and Amtrak and has a library, hospital, parks, and several civic and service organizations. Facilities are provided for tennis, golf, skating, and water sports.

■ ALMA COLLEGE

614 W Superior St.
Alma, MI 48801-1599
Tel: (989)463-7111; Free: 800-321-ALMA
Fax: (989)463-7057
E-mail: admissions@alma.edu
Web Site: www.alma.edu/

Description: Independent Presbyterian, 4-year, coed. Awards bachelor's degrees. Founded 1886. Setting: 125-acre small town campus. Endowment: $96.5 million. Research spending for the previous fiscal year: $76,017. Educational spending for the previous fiscal year: $7517 per student. Total enrollment: 1,464. Faculty: 174 (95 full-time, 79 part-time). Student-undergrad faculty ratio is 12:1. 2,232 applied, 72% were admitted. 23% from top 10% of their high school class, 54% from top quarter, 84% from top half. 16 valedictorians. Full-time: 1,414 students, 55% women, 45% men. Part-time: 50 students, 52% women, 48% men. Students come from 28 states and territories, 14 other countries, 8% from out-of-state. 1% American Indian or Alaska Native, non-Hispanic/Latino; 2% Hispanic/Latino; 3% African American, non-Hispanic/Latino; 1% Asian, non-Hispanic/Latino; 0% Native Hawaiian or other Pacific Islander, non-Hispanic/Latino; 1% international. 1% 25 or older, 90% live on campus, 4% transferred in. Retention: 80% of full-time freshmen returned the following year. Academic areas with the most degrees conferred: biological/life sciences; business/marketing; English. Core. Calendar: 4-4-1. Academic remediation for entering students, services for LD students, advanced placement, self-designed majors, honors program, independent study, double major, summer session for credit, internships. Off campus study at New York Arts program, Philadelphia Center Internship, Urban Life Center, Washington Semester. Study abroad program. ROTC: Army (c).

Entrance Requirements: Options: electronic application, deferred admission, international baccalaureate accepted. Required: essay, high school transcript, minimum 3 high school GPA, SAT or ACT. Recommended: interview. Required for some: 3 recommendations. Entrance: moderately difficult. Application deadlines: Rolling, Rolling for nonresidents. Notification: continuous, continuous for nonresidents. SAT Reasoning Test deadline: 3/1. SAT Subject Test deadline: 3/1.

Costs Per Year: Application fee: $25. Comprehensive fee: $40,050 includes full-time tuition ($30,700), mandatory fees ($360), and college room and board ($8990). College room only: $4495. Room and board charges vary according to board plan and housing facility. Part-time tuition: $1000 per credit hour. Part-time tuition varies according to course load.

Collegiate Environment: Orientation program. Drama-theater group, choral group, marching band, student-run newspaper, radio station. Social organizations: 75 open to all; national fraternities, national sororities, local fraternities, local sororities; 21% of eligible men and 27% of eligible women are members. Most popular organizations: Ambassadors, Alma College Union Board, New Life Campus Ministries, Student Congress, Alpha Phi Omega. Major annual events: Homecoming, Songfest, Orientation Hypnotist. Student services: health clinic, personal-psychological counseling. Campus security: 24-hour emergency response devices and patrols, controlled dormitory access. 1,426 college housing spaces available; all were occupied in 2012-13. Freshmen guaranteed college housing. On-campus residence required through senior year. Option: coed housing available. Kerhl Building-Monteith Library with 284,164 books, 246,853 microform titles, 1,500 serials, 12,151 audiovisual materials, an OPAC, and a Web page. Operations spending for the previous fiscal year: $1.1 million. 298 computers available on campus for general student use. A campuswide network can be accessed from student residence rooms and from off campus. Students can access the following: online class registration. Staffed computer lab on campus provides training in use of computers, software, and the Internet.

Community Environment: Alma is located in a rural area in the center of Michigan's lower peninsula. Major industries include manufacturing of automotive parts, plastic extrusions, drainage and metal products. Some part-time work available for students. Area has access to rail service and airport. Alma has its own public library, hospital and motels. Recreation facilities include golf, Community Center, swimming pool, parks and the Pine River for boating and fishing. Alma College is within two hours of Michigan's beaches and ski resorts.

■ ALPENA COMMUNITY COLLEGE

665 Johnson St.
Alpena, MI 49707-1495
Tel: (989)356-9021
Fax: (989)358-7553
E-mail: kollienm@alpenacc.edu
Web Site: www.alpenacc.edu/

Description: State and locally supported, 2-year, coed. Awards certificates, transfer associate, and terminal associate degrees. Founded 1952. Setting: 700-acre small town campus. Endowment: $3.3 million. Educational spending for the previous fiscal year: $7628 per student. Total enrollment: 1,950. Faculty: 125 (55 full-time, 70 part-time). Student-undergrad faculty ratio is 17:1. 1,050 applied, 100% were admitted. 10% from top 10% of their high school class, 25% from top quarter, 50% from top half. Students come from 4 states and territories, 0.01% from out-of-state. 40% 25 or older, 2% live on campus. Retention: 55% of full-time freshmen returned the following year. Core. Calendar: semesters. Academic remediation for entering students, services for LD students, advanced placement, distance learning, double major, summer session for credit, part-time degree program, internships.

Entrance Requirements: Open admission except for nursing, utility technician programs. Options: electronic application, early admission, deferred admission. Recommended: high school transcript. Entrance: noncompetitive. Application deadline: Rolling. Notification: continuous.

Costs Per Year: Application fee: $0. Area resident tuition: $3180 full-time, $106 per contact hour part-time. State resident tuition: $3660 full-time, $122 per contact hour part-time. Nonresident tuition: $3660 full-time, $122 per contact hour part-time. Mandatory fees: $600 full-time, $16 per hour part-time, $30 per term part-time. College room and board: $3500.

Collegiate Environment: Orientation program. Drama-theater group, choral group. Social organizations: 8 open to all. Most popular organizations: Nursing Association, Student Senate, Phi Theta Kappa, Law Enforcement Club. Major annual events: Awards Night, Spring Fling. Student services: personal-psychological counseling. Campus security: 24-hour emergency response devices. 64 college housing spaces available; all were occupied in 2012-13. No special consideration for freshman housing applicants. Options: coed, men-only, women-only housing available. Stephen Fletcher Library with 29,000 books, 183 serials, an OPAC, and a Web page. Operations spending for the previous fiscal year: $324,807. 75 computers available on campus for general student use. A campuswide network can be accessed from off-campus. Staffed computer lab on campus.

Community Environment: Located on Thunder Bay, 94 miles south of the Straits of Mackinac and 235 miles north of Detroit, Alpena is the largest port on northern Lake Huron. Industries include a cement plant, paper mill, and shale quarry. The mean annual temperature is 42.2 degrees. Air and bus service are available. The community has several churches, theatres, a hospital, museum, and planetarium. Alpena is well known for fine fishing, hunting, and winter sports. There are five city parks and over 240,000 acres of public land within a one-hour drive. Recreation facilities include golf, sailboat racing, tennis, and skating. Part-time employment is available for students.

■ ANDREWS UNIVERSITY

Berrien Springs, MI 49104
Tel: (269)471-7771; Free: 800-253-2874
Fax: (269)471-3228
E-mail: enroll@andrews.edu
Web Site: www.andrews.edu/

Description: Independent Seventh-day Adventist, university, coed. Awards associate, bachelor's, master's, and doctoral degrees and post-master's certificates. Founded 1874. Setting: 1,650-acre small town campus. Endowment: $37.7 million. Research spending for the previous fiscal year: $1.2 million. Educational spending for the previous fiscal year: $11,733 per student. Total enrollment: 1,634. Faculty: 292 (229 full-time, 63 part-time). Student-undergrad faculty ratio is 10:1. 2,551 applied, 38% were admitted. 23% from top 10% of their high school class, 45% from top quarter, 76%

from top half. 24 National Merit Scholars. Full-time: 1,704 students, 55% women, 45% men. Part-time: 213 students, 59% women, 41% men. Students come from 50 states and territories, 55 other countries, 72% from out-of-state. 0.2% American Indian or Alaska Native, non-Hispanic/Latino; 15% Hispanic/Latino; 24% African American, non-Hispanic/Latino; 11% Asian, non-Hispanic/Latino; 1% Native Hawaiian or other Pacific Islander, non-Hispanic/Latino; 14% international. 12% 25 or older, 69% live on campus, 7% transferred in. Retention: 79% of full-time freshmen returned the following year. Academic areas with the most degrees conferred: education; visual and performing arts; transportation and materials moving; business/marketing. Core. Calendar: semesters. Academic remediation for entering students, ESL program, advanced placement, accelerated degree program, self-designed majors, freshman honors college, honors program, distance learning, double major, summer session for credit, part-time degree program, adult/continuing education programs, co-op programs and internships, graduate courses open to undergrads. Off campus study. Study abroad program.

Entrance Requirements: Options: electronic application, deferred admission, international baccalaureate accepted. Required: high school transcript, minimum 2.25 high school GPA, 2 recommendations, SAT or ACT. Entrance: moderately difficult. Application deadline: Rolling. Notification: continuous.

Costs Per Year: Application fee: $30. Comprehensive fee: $32,006 includes full-time tuition ($23,700), mandatory fees ($778), and college room and board ($7528). College room only: $4008. Full-time tuition and fees vary according to course load. Room and board charges vary according to board plan. Part-time tuition: $988 per credit hour. Part-time tuition varies according to course load.

Collegiate Environment: Orientation program. Drama-theater group, choral group, student-run newspaper, radio station. Social organizations: 30 open to all. Major annual events: College Days, Feast of Lights, homecoming. Student services: health clinic, personal-psychological counseling. Campus security: 24-hour emergency response devices and patrols, controlled dormitory access. 1,227 college housing spaces available; 1,200 were occupied in 2012-13. Freshmen guaranteed college housing. On-campus residence required through senior year. Options: men-only, women-only housing available. James White Library plus 2 others with 678,734 books, 96,228 microform titles, 94,000 serials, 29,430 audiovisual materials, an OPAC, and a Web page. Operations spending for the previous fiscal year: $2.8 million. 130 computers available on campus for general student use. Computer purchase/lease plans available. A campuswide network can be accessed from student residence rooms and from off campus. Students can access the following: online class registration, degree audit. Staffed computer lab on campus.

Community Environment: Andrews is located in a small town in the southwest part of Michigan. The area is accessible by bus, airplane, or Amtrak. Shopping and cultural activities are located in South Bend, Indiana, which is 25 miles away, and St. Joseph/Benton Harbor, Michigan, which is 10 miles away, and are approximately 30 minutes away. Lake Michigan, with its 200-foot high sand dunes and water activities, is less than 30 minutes distant. Chicago is less than two hours distant.

■ **AQUINAS COLLEGE**
1607 Robinson Rd., SE
Grand Rapids, MI 49506-1799
Tel: (616)459-8281; Free: 800-678-9593
Fax: (616)459-2563
E-mail: admissions@aquinas.edu
Web Site: www.aquinas.edu/
Description: Independent Roman Catholic, comprehensive, coed. Awards associate, bachelor's, and master's degrees. Founded 1886. Setting: 107-acre suburban campus with easy access to Detroit, Chicago, Grand Rapids. Endowment: $32.2 million. Educational spending for the previous fiscal year: $6433 per student. Total enrollment: 2,327. Faculty: 251 (90 full-time, 161 part-time). Student-undergrad faculty ratio is 13:1. 2,637 applied, 89% were admitted. 20% from top 10% of their high school class, 48% from top quarter, 60% from top half. Full-time: 1,847 students, 65% women, 35% men. Part-time: 267 students, 60% women, 40% men. Students come from 25 states and territories, 8 other countries, 6% from out-of-state. 0.4% American Indian or Alaska Native, non-Hispanic/Latino; 5% Hispanic/Latino; 3% African American, non-Hispanic/Latino; 1% Asian, non-Hispanic/Latino; 0.04% Native Hawaiian or other Pacific Islander, non-Hispanic/Latino; 0.2% international. 1% 25 or older, 46% live on campus, 4% transferred in. Retention: 75% of full-time freshmen returned the following year. Academic areas with the most degrees conferred: business/marketing; social sciences;

education. Core. Calendar: semesters. Academic remediation for entering students, services for LD students, advanced placement, accelerated degree program, self-designed majors, honors program, independent study, distance learning, double major, summer session for credit, part-time degree program, external degree program, adult/continuing education programs, co-op programs and internships, graduate courses open to undergrads. Off campus study at members of the Dominican College Interchange. Study abroad program. ROTC: Army (c).

Entrance Requirements: Options: electronic application, early admission, deferred admission, international baccalaureate accepted. Required: high school transcript, minimum 2.5 high school GPA, SAT or ACT. Required for some: essay, interview. Entrance: moderately difficult. Application deadline: Rolling. SAT Reasoning Test deadline: 8/1. Transfer credits accepted: Yes.

Costs Per Year: Application fee: $0. Comprehensive fee: $33,060 includes full-time tuition ($25,070), mandatory fees ($180), and college room and board ($7810). College room only: $3644. Full-time tuition and fees vary according to course load. Room and board charges vary according to board plan and housing facility. Part-time tuition: $498 per credit hour. Part-time tuition varies according to course load.

Collegiate Environment: Orientation program. Drama-theater group, choral group, student-run newspaper, radio station. Social organizations: 63 open to all. Most popular organizations: Community Senate Programming Board, The Saint (newspaper), Insignis Honors Group, Community Action Volunteers of Aquinas (CAVA), RHC. Major annual events: Homecoming, St. Thomas Aquinas Celebration Week, Spring Fling. Student services: health clinic, personal-psychological counseling, women's center. Campus security: 24-hour emergency response devices and patrols, student patrols, late night transport-escort service, controlled dormitory access. Grace Hauenstein Library plus 1 other with 100,540 books, 223,804 microform titles, 409 serials, an OPAC, and a Web page. Operations spending for the previous fiscal year: $1.1 million. 210 computers available on campus for general student use. Computer purchase/lease plans available. A campuswide network can be accessed from student residence rooms and from off campus. Students can access the following: online class registration. Staffed computer lab on campus provides training in use of computers, software, and the Internet.

Community Environment: Grand Rapids is an urban setting. The greater Grand Rapids area has a population of over 1,000,000, and is one of the fastest growing areas in the nation. It is the commercial, medical and cultural center of west Michigan.

■ **THE ART INSTITUTE OF MICHIGAN**
28125 Cabot Dr.
Ste. 120
Novi, MI 48377
Tel: (248)675-3800; Free: 800-479-0087
Fax: (248)675-3830
Web Site: www.artinstitutes.edu/detroit/
Description: Proprietary, 4-year, coed. Part of Education Management Corporation. Awards associate and bachelor's degrees.

■ **THE ART INSTITUTE OF MICHIGAN–TROY**
1414 E Maple Ave.
Ste. 150
Troy, MI 48083
Tel: (248)837-3200; Free: 877-320-3275
Fax: (248)837-3300
Web Site: www.artinstitutes.edu/troy
Description: Proprietary, 4-year, coed. Awards associate and bachelor's degrees.

■ **BAKER COLLEGE OF ALLEN PARK**
4500 Enterprise Dr.
Allen Park, MI 48101
Tel: (313)425-3700; Free: 800-767-4120
E-mail: steve.peterson@baker.edu
Web Site: www.baker.edu/
Description: Independent, 4-year, coed. Part of Baker College System. Awards associate and bachelor's degrees. Founded 2003. Setting: 13-acre suburban campus with easy access to Detroit. Total enrollment: 3,954. Faculty: 88 (2 full-time, 86 part-time). Student-undergrad faculty ratio is 34:1. 1,582 applied, 100% were admitted. 1% American Indian or Alaska Native, non-Hispanic/Latino; 5% Hispanic/Latino; 36% African American, non-Hispanic/Latino; 0.5% Asian, non-Hispanic/Latino; 0% Native Hawaiian or other Pacific Islander, non-Hispanic/Latino; 0% international. Academic

remediation for entering students, services for LD students, advanced placement, accelerated degree program, independent study, distance learning, double major, summer session for credit, part-time degree program, external degree program, co-op programs and internships. Off campus study.

Entrance Requirements: Options: electronic application, deferred admission. Required: high school transcript, interview. Recommended: SAT or ACT. Entrance: minimally difficult. Application deadline: 9/24. Transfer credits accepted: Yes.

Costs Per Year: Application fee: $0. Tuition: $7740 full-time, $215 per quarter hour part-time. Full-time tuition varies according to program. Part-time tuition varies according to program.

Collegiate Environment: Orientation program. Student services: personal-psychological counseling. Campus security: 24-hour patrols. 150 computers available on campus for general student use. A campuswide network can be accessed. Students can access the following: online class registration. Staffed computer lab on campus provides training in use of computers, software, and the Internet.

■ **BAKER COLLEGE OF AUBURN HILLS**
1500 University Dr.
Auburn Hills, MI 48326-1586
Tel: (248)340-0600; Free: 888-429-0410
Web Site: www.baker.edu/

Description: Independent, 4-year, coed. Part of Baker College System. Awards associate and bachelor's degrees. Founded 1911. Setting: 10-acre urban campus with easy access to Detroit. Total enrollment: 3,803. Faculty: 155 (11 full-time, 144 part-time). Student-undergrad faculty ratio is 41:1. 1,358 applied, 100% were admitted. 0% from out-of-state. 1% American Indian or Alaska Native, non-Hispanic/Latino; 3% Hispanic/Latino; 18% African American, non-Hispanic/Latino; 2% Asian, non-Hispanic/Latino; 0% Native Hawaiian or other Pacific Islander, non-Hispanic/Latino; 0% international. 41% 25 or older. Core. Academic remediation for entering students, services for LD students, advanced placement, accelerated degree program, independent study, distance learning, double major, summer session for credit, part-time degree program, external degree program, co-op programs and internships.

Entrance Requirements: Open admission. Options: early admission, deferred admission. Required: high school transcript. Recommended: SAT or ACT. Entrance: minimally difficult. Application deadline: Rolling.

Costs Per Year: Application fee: $20. Tuition: $7740 full-time, $215 per quarter hour part-time. Full-time tuition varies according to program. Part-time tuition varies according to program.

Collegiate Environment: Most popular organizations: Baker Business Club, Interior Design Society, Students Action in Engineering, Marketing Club. Major annual events: Fall Kick Day, Spring Spirit Day. Campus security: 24-hour emergency response devices. Baker College of Auburn Hills Library with 5,400 books, 95 serials, an OPAC, and a Web page. 110 computers available on campus for general student use. A campuswide network can be accessed from off-campus. Students can access the following: online class registration. Staffed computer lab on campus provides training in use of computers, software, and the Internet.

■ **BAKER COLLEGE OF CADILLAC**
9600 E 13th St.
Cadillac, MI 49601
Tel: (231)876-3100; Free: 888-313-3463
Fax: (231)775-8505
E-mail: audrey.charmoli@baker.edu
Web Site: www.baker.edu/

Description: Independent, 4-year, coed. Part of Baker College System. Awards associate and bachelor's degrees. Founded 1986. Setting: 40-acre small town campus. Total enrollment: 1,639. Faculty: 105 (4 full-time, 101 part-time). Student-undergrad faculty ratio is 42:1. 580 applied, 100% were admitted. Students come from 4 states and territories, 0% from out-of-state. 0.1% American Indian or Alaska Native, non-Hispanic/Latino; 0.3% Hispanic/Latino; 0.2% African American, non-Hispanic/Latino; 0.1% Asian, non-Hispanic/Latino; 0% Native Hawaiian or other Pacific Islander, non-Hispanic/Latino; 0% international. 56% 25 or older. Retention: 69% of full-time freshmen returned the following year. Core. Academic remediation for entering students, services for LD students, advanced placement, independent study, distance learning, double major, summer session for credit, part-time degree program, external degree program, co-op programs and internships.

Entrance Requirements: Open admission. Options: early admission,

deferred admission. Required: high school transcript. Recommended: interview, SAT or ACT. Entrance: minimally difficult. Application deadline: 9/24.

Costs Per Year: Application fee: $20. Tuition: $7740 full-time, $215 per quarter hour part-time. Full-time tuition varies according to program. Part-time tuition varies according to program.

Collegiate Environment: Campus security: 24-hour emergency response devices. Baker College of Cadillac Library with 4,000 books, 78 serials, an OPAC, and a Web page. 100 computers available on campus for general student use. A campuswide network can be accessed from off-campus. Students can access the following: online class registration. Staffed computer lab on campus provides training in use of computers, software, and the Internet.

■ **BAKER COLLEGE OF CLINTON TOWNSHIP**
34950 Little Mack Ave.
Clinton Township, MI 48035-4701
Tel: (586)791-6610; Free: 888-272-2842
Fax: (586)791-6611
E-mail: annette.looser@baker.edu
Web Site: www.baker.edu/

Description: Independent, 4-year, coed. Part of Baker College System. Awards associate and bachelor's degrees. Founded 1990. Setting: 30-acre urban campus with easy access to Detroit. Total enrollment: 5,138. Faculty: 208 (17 full-time, 191 part-time). Student-undergrad faculty ratio is 45:1. 2,010 applied, 100% were admitted. Students come from 2 states and territories. 1% American Indian or Alaska Native, non-Hispanic/Latino; 2% Hispanic/Latino; 27% African American, non-Hispanic/Latino; 1% Asian, non-Hispanic/Latino; 0% Native Hawaiian or other Pacific Islander, non-Hispanic/Latino; 0% international. 42% 25 or older. Core. Academic remediation for entering students, services for LD students, advanced placement, summer session for credit, part-time degree program, external degree program, co-op programs and internships.

Entrance Requirements: Open admission. Options: electronic application, early admission, deferred admission, international baccalaureate accepted. Required: high school transcript. Required for some: SAT or ACT. Entrance: minimally difficult. Application deadline: Rolling. Transfer credits accepted: Yes.

Costs Per Year: Application fee: $20. Tuition: $7920 full-time, $220 per quarter hour part-time. Full-time tuition varies according to program. Part-time tuition varies according to program.

Collegiate Environment: Student services: personal-psychological counseling. Campus security: 24-hour emergency response devices and patrols, evening security guard. College housing not available. Baker College of Mt. Clemens Library with 8,000 books, 97 serials, an OPAC, and a Web page. 127 computers available on campus for general student use. A campuswide network can be accessed from off-campus. Staffed computer lab on campus provides training in use of computers, software, and the Internet.

■ **BAKER COLLEGE OF FLINT**
1050 W Bristol Rd.
Flint, MI 48507-5508
Tel: (810)767-7600; Free: 800-964-4299
Fax: (810)766-4049
Web Site: www.baker.edu/

Description: Independent, 4-year, coed. Part of Baker College System. Awards associate and bachelor's degrees. Founded 1911. Setting: 53-acre urban campus with easy access to Detroit. Total enrollment: 6,329. Faculty: 315 (40 full-time, 275 part-time). Student-undergrad faculty ratio is 31:1. 2,507 applied, 100% were admitted. Students come from 5 states and territories, 1% from out-of-state. 1% American Indian or Alaska Native, non-Hispanic/Latino; 3% Hispanic/Latino; 21% African American, non-Hispanic/Latino; 0.3% Asian, non-Hispanic/Latino; 0% Native Hawaiian or other Pacific Islander, non-Hispanic/Latino; 0% international. 2% live on campus. Core. Academic remediation for entering students, services for LD students, advanced placement, accelerated degree program, independent study, distance learning, double major, summer session for credit, part-time degree program, external degree program, co-op programs and internships.

Entrance Requirements: Open admission. Options: early admission, deferred admission, international baccalaureate accepted. Required: high school transcript. Recommended: SAT or ACT. Entrance: minimally difficult. Application deadline: 9/20.

Costs Per Year: Application fee: $20. Tuition: $7740 full-time, $215 per quarter hour part-time. Full-time tuition varies according to program. Part-time tuition varies according to program. College room only: $3000. Room charges vary according to housing facility.

Collegiate Environment: Most popular organizations: Occupational Therapy Club, Interior Design Society, Medical Assistants Student Organization, Physical Therapist Assistant Club, Cyber Defense Team. Major annual events: Campus Spirit Day, Student Club Day. Student services: personal-psychological counseling. Campus security: 24-hour patrols, late night transport-escort service, controlled dormitory access, video monitoring of high traffic areas. Marianne Jewell Library with 168,700 books, an OPAC, and a Web page. 412 computers available on campus for general student use. A campuswide network can be accessed from off-campus. Staffed computer lab on campus provides training in use of computers, software, and the Internet.

■ BAKER COLLEGE OF JACKSON
2800 Springport Rd.
Jackson, MI 49202
Tel: (517)789-6123; Free: 888-343-3683
E-mail: kevin.pnacek@baker.edu
Web Site: www.baker.edu/

Description: Independent, 4-year, coed. Part of Baker College System. Awards associate and bachelor's degrees. Founded 1994. Setting: 42-acre suburban campus with easy access to Lansing. Total enrollment: 2,730. Faculty: 85 (5 full-time, 80 part-time). Student-undergrad faculty ratio is 36:1. 891 applied, 100% were admitted. Students come from 2 states and territories, 1% from out-of-state. 1% American Indian or Alaska Native, non-Hispanic/Latino; 3% Hispanic/Latino; 9% African American, non-Hispanic/Latino; 0.4% Asian, non-Hispanic/Latino; 0% Native Hawaiian or other Pacific Islander, non-Hispanic/Latino; 0% international. 56% 25 or older. Core. Academic remediation for entering students, services for LD students, advanced placement, accelerated degree program, independent study, distance learning, double major, summer session for credit, part-time degree program, external degree program, co-op programs and internships.

Entrance Requirements: Open admission. Options: electronic application, early admission, deferred admission, international baccalaureate accepted. Required: high school transcript. Recommended: SAT or ACT. Entrance: minimally difficult. Application deadline: 9/19. Notification: continuous.

Costs Per Year: Application fee: $20. Tuition: $7740 full-time, $215 per quarter hour part-time. Full-time tuition varies according to program. Part-time tuition varies according to program.

Collegiate Environment: Student services: personal-psychological counseling. Campus security: 24-hour emergency response devices. Baker College of Jackson Library with 7,000 books, 150 serials, an OPAC, and a Web page. 150 computers available on campus for general student use. A campuswide network can be accessed from off-campus. Students can access the following: online class registration. Staffed computer lab on campus.

■ BAKER COLLEGE OF MUSKEGON
1903 Marquette Ave.
Muskegon, MI 49442-3497
Tel: (231)777-5200; Free: 800-937-0337
Fax: (231)777-5201
E-mail: kathy.jacobson@baker.edu
Web Site: www.baker.edu/

Description: Independent, 4-year, coed. Part of Baker College System. Awards associate and bachelor's degrees. Founded 1888. Setting: 45-acre suburban campus with easy access to Grand Rapids. Total enrollment: 4,994. Faculty: 177 (17 full-time, 160 part-time). Student-undergrad faculty ratio is 55:1. 1,942 applied, 100% were admitted. Students come from 17 states and territories, 1% from out-of-state. 1% American Indian or Alaska Native, non-Hispanic/Latino; 5% Hispanic/Latino; 12% African American, non-Hispanic/Latino; 1% Asian, non-Hispanic/Latino; 0% Native Hawaiian or other Pacific Islander, non-Hispanic/Latino; 0% international. 45% 25 or older, 11% live on campus. Core. Academic remediation for entering students, services for LD students, advanced placement, accelerated degree program, independent study, distance learning, double major, summer session for credit, part-time degree program, external degree program, adult/continuing education programs, co-op programs and internships.

Entrance Requirements: Open admission. Options: electronic application, early admission, deferred admission, international baccalaureate accepted. Required: high school transcript. Recommended: SAT or ACT. Entrance: minimally difficult. Application deadline: 9/24. Notification: continuous.

Costs Per Year: Application fee: $20. Tuition: $7740 full-time, $215 per quarter hour part-time. Full-time tuition varies according to program. Part-time tuition varies according to program.

Collegiate Environment: Orientation program. Social organizations: 4 open to all. Most popular organizations: Accounting Club, Rehab Club, Travel Club, Culinary Club. Major annual event: Career/Job Fair. Student services: personal-psychological counseling. Campus security: 24-hour emergency response devices and patrols, late night transport-escort service, controlled dormitory access, 24-hour security camera surveillance. Marianne Jewell Library with 32,000 books, 90 microform titles, 140 serials, an OPAC, and a Web page. 165 computers available on campus for general student use. A campuswide network can be accessed from student residence rooms and from off campus. Staffed computer lab on campus provides training in use of computers, software, and the Internet.

■ BAKER COLLEGE OF OWOSSO
1020 S Washington St.
Owosso, MI 48867-4400
Tel: (989)729-3300; Free: 800-879-3797
Fax: (989)729-3411
E-mail: mike.konopacke@baker.edu
Web Site: www.baker.edu/

Description: Independent, 4-year, coed. Part of Baker College System. Awards associate and bachelor's degrees. Founded 1984. Setting: 52-acre small town campus. Total enrollment: 3,078. Faculty: 144 (8 full-time, 136 part-time). Student-undergrad faculty ratio is 40:1. 1,231 applied, 100% were admitted. Students come from 4 states and territories, 0% from out-of-state. 1% American Indian or Alaska Native, non-Hispanic/Latino; 2% Hispanic/Latino; 93% African American, non-Hispanic/Latino; 0.2% Asian, non-Hispanic/Latino; 0% Native Hawaiian or other Pacific Islander, non-Hispanic/Latino; 0% international. 41% 25 or older, 15% live on campus. Core. Academic remediation for entering students, services for LD students, advanced placement, accelerated degree program, summer session for credit, part-time degree program, external degree program, adult/continuing education programs, co-op programs and internships.

Entrance Requirements: Open admission. Options: early admission, deferred admission, international baccalaureate accepted. Required: high school transcript. Recommended: SAT or ACT. Entrance: minimally difficult. Application deadline: Rolling. Transfer credits accepted: Yes.

Costs Per Year: Application fee: $20. Tuition: $7740 full-time, $215 per quarter hour part-time. Full-time tuition varies according to program. Part-time tuition varies according to program. College room only: $3000. Room charges vary according to housing facility.

Collegiate Environment: Orientation program. Student-run newspaper. Most popular organizations: Accounting Club, Travel Club, Management Club, Baker Health Information Management Club, RAD Club. Major annual event: Spirit Day. Student services: personal-psychological counseling. Campus security: 24-hour emergency response devices and patrols, late night transport-escort service, controlled dormitory access. Baker College of Owosso Library with 35,424 books, 71 microform titles, and 215 serials. Operations spending for the previous fiscal year: $244,284. 210 computers available on campus for general student use. A campuswide network can be accessed from off-campus. Staffed computer lab on campus provides training in use of computers, software, and the Internet.

■ BAKER COLLEGE OF PORT HURON
3403 Lapeer Rd.
Port Huron, MI 48060-2597
Tel: (810)985-7000; Free: 888-262-2442
Fax: (810)985-7066
E-mail: kenny_d@porthuron.baker.edu
Web Site: www.baker.edu/

Description: Independent, 4-year, coed. Part of Baker College System. Awards associate and bachelor's degrees. Founded 1990. Setting: 10-acre urban campus with easy access to Detroit. Total enrollment: 1,177. Faculty: 126 (12 full-time, 114 part-time). Student-undergrad faculty ratio is 28:1. 334 applied, 100% were admitted. 0% from out-of-state. 0.1% American Indian or Alaska Native, non-Hispanic/Latino; 2% Hispanic/Latino; 3% African American, non-Hispanic/Latino; 0.2% Asian, non-Hispanic/Latino; 0% Native Hawaiian or other Pacific Islander, non-Hispanic/Latino; 0% international. 51% 25 or older. Core. Academic remediation for entering students, services for LD students, advanced placement, accelerated degree program, independent study, distance learning, double major, summer session for credit, part-time degree program, external degree program, co-op programs and internships.

Entrance Requirements: Open admission. Options: early admission, deferred admission, international baccalaureate accepted. Required: high school transcript, interview. Recommended: SAT or ACT. Entrance: minimally difficult. Application deadline: 9/24. Notification: continuous. Transfer credits accepted: Yes.

Costs Per Year: Application fee: $20. Tuition: $7920 full-time, $220 per quarter hour part-time. Full-time tuition varies according to program. Part-time tuition varies according to program.

Collegiate Environment: Orientation program. Most popular organizations: Travel Club, Student Association Dental Hygienists of America. Major annual events: Spirit Days, collections for the underprivileged. Student services: personal-psychological counseling. Campus security: 24-hour emergency response devices, late night transport-escort service. College housing not available. Baker College of Port Huron Library with 16,823 books, 181 serials, an OPAC, and a Web page. Operations spending for the previous fiscal year: $99,399. 165 computers available on campus for general student use. A campuswide network can be accessed from off-campus. Students can access the following: online class registration, software. Staffed computer lab on campus provides training in use of computers, software, and the Internet.

■ **BAY MILLS COMMUNITY COLLEGE**
12214 W Lakeshore Dr.
Brimley, MI 49715
Tel: (906)248-3354; Free: 800-844-BMCC
Fax: (906)248-3351
Web Site: www.bmcc.edu/
Description: District-supported, 2-year, coed. Awards certificates, diplomas, and transfer associate degrees. Founded 1984. Setting: rural campus. Total enrollment: 427. 67% 25 or older. Calendar: semesters. Academic remediation for entering students, part-time degree program, internships.
Entrance Requirements: Open admission. Option: early admission. Required: high school transcript. Entrance: noncompetitive. Application deadline: Rolling.
Collegiate Environment: Student services: personal-psychological counseling. Campus security: 24-hour emergency response devices.

■ **BAY DE NOC COMMUNITY COLLEGE**
2001 N Lincoln Rd.
Escanaba, MI 49829-2511
Tel: (906)786-5802; Free: 800-221-2001
Fax: (906)786-6555
E-mail: carterc@baycollege.edu
Web Site: www.baycollege.edu/
Description: County-supported, 2-year, coed. Part of Michigan Department of Education. Awards certificates, transfer associate, and terminal associate degrees. Founded 1963. Setting: 150-acre rural campus. Endowment: $8.3 million. Educational spending for the previous fiscal year: $3875 per student. Total enrollment: 2,414. Faculty: 163 (46 full-time, 117 part-time). Student-undergrad faculty ratio is 20:1. Full-time: 1,400 students, 57% women, 43% men. Part-time: 1,014 students, 65% women, 35% men. Students come from 3 states and territories, 6% from out-of-state. 34% 25 or older, 4% live on campus, 19% transferred in. Retention: 56% of full-time freshmen returned the following year. Core. Calendar: semesters. Academic remediation for entering students, advanced placement, distance learning, double major, summer session for credit, part-time degree program, adult/continuing education programs, co-op programs and internships.
Entrance Requirements: Open admission. Options: electronic application, early admission. Required: high school transcript. Entrance: noncompetitive. Application deadline: 8/15. Notification: continuous.
Costs Per Year: Application fee: $25. Area resident tuition: $2970 full-time, $99 per contact hour part-time. State resident tuition: $5310 full-time, $177 per contact hour part-time. Nonresident tuition: $8910 full-time, $297 per contact hour part-time. Mandatory fees: $498 full-time, $17 per contact hour part-time. Full-time tuition and fees vary according to course load, location, and reciprocity agreements. Part-time tuition and fees vary according to course load, location, and reciprocity agreements. College room only: $3000.
Collegiate Environment: Orientation program. Drama-theater group, student-run newspaper. Social organizations: 12 open to all. Most popular organizations: Phi Theta Kappa, Dramaddicts, Model UN, Student Government/Activities Board, Circle K. Major annual events: Welcome Week Cookout, Student Organization Fair, Hypnotist. Student services: personal-psychological counseling. Campus security: resident assistants in housing. Library/Learning Resources Center with 63,643 books, 613 microform titles,

200 serials, 6,420 audiovisual materials, an OPAC, and a Web page. Operations spending for the previous fiscal year: $248,528. 535 computers available on campus for general student use. A campuswide network can be accessed from student residence rooms and from off campus. Students can access the following: online class registration. Staffed computer lab on campus.

Community Environment: An industrial city, Escanaba has an excellent deepwater harbor and mammoth ore docks from which about six million tons of iron ore are shipped annually. Local manufactures include paper, welding machines and lumber products. Part-time employment is available for students. City services include a library, hospital, and major transportation facilities. Recreation includes swimming, boating, golf, tennis, fishing and winter sports.

■ **CALVIN COLLEGE**
3201 Burton St., SE
Grand Rapids, MI 49546-4388
Tel: (616)526-6000; Free: 800-688-0122
Fax: (616)526-8551
E-mail: admissions@calvin.edu
Web Site: www.calvin.edu/
Description: Independent Christian Reformed, comprehensive, coed. Awards bachelor's and master's degrees. Founded 1876. Setting: 400-acre suburban campus with easy access to Grand Rapids. Endowment: $107.8 million. Research spending for the previous fiscal year: $3 million. Educational spending for the previous fiscal year: $14,446 per student. Total enrollment: 4,008. Faculty: 394 (302 full-time, 92 part-time). Student-undergrad faculty ratio is 12:1. 3,284 applied, 75% were admitted. 34% from top 10% of their high school class, 60% from top quarter, 85% from top half. 23 National Merit Scholars, 42 valedictorians. Full-time: 3,763 students, 54% women, 46% men. Part-time: 167 students, 45% women, 55% men. Students come from 48 states and territories, 56 other countries, 45% from out-of-state. 0.3% American Indian or Alaska Native, non-Hispanic/Latino; 3% Hispanic/Latino; 3% African American, non-Hispanic/Latino; 4% Asian, non-Hispanic/Latino; 0% Native Hawaiian or other Pacific Islander, non-Hispanic/Latino; 10% international. 2% 25 or older, 61% live on campus, 3% transferred in. Retention: 86% of full-time freshmen returned the following year. Academic areas with the most degrees conferred: education; business/marketing; social sciences. Core. Calendar: 4-1-4. Academic remediation for entering students, services for LD students, advanced placement, accelerated degree program, self-designed majors, honors program, independent study, distance learning, double major, summer session for credit, part-time degree program, internships, graduate courses open to undergrads. Off campus study at Council for Christian Colleges and Universities, Central College, Trinity Christian College, Au Sable Institute. Study abroad program. ROTC: Army (c).
Entrance Requirements: Options: electronic application, deferred admission, international baccalaureate accepted. Required: essay, high school transcript, minimum 2.5 high school GPA, 1 recommendation. Recommended: interview. Required for some: SAT or ACT. Entrance: moderately difficult. Application deadline: 8/15. Notification: continuous. SAT Reasoning Test deadline: 8/15. Transfer credits accepted: Yes.
Costs Per Year: Application fee: $35. Comprehensive fee: $37,585 includes full-time tuition ($28,025), mandatory fees ($225), and college room and board ($9335). Full-time tuition and fees vary according to degree level and program. Room and board charges vary according to board plan and housing facility. Part-time tuition: $670 per credit hour. Part-time tuition varies according to course load and degree level.
Collegiate Environment: Orientation program. Drama-theater group, choral group, student-run newspaper. Social organizations: 75 open to all. Most popular organizations: Dance Guild, Airband (Lip-syncing contest), Chimes (Student Newspaper), International Reconciliation Organization, Knight Investment Management Organization. Major annual events: Rangeela (international student talent showcase), Fall and Spring Music and Arts Festivals, Chaos Day. Student services: health clinic, personal-psychological counseling. Campus security: 24-hour emergency response devices and patrols, student patrols, late night transport-escort service, controlled dormitory access, crime prevention programs, crime alert bulletins. 2,400 college housing spaces available; 2,330 were occupied in 2012-13. Freshmen guaranteed college housing. On-campus residence required through sophomore year. Options: men-only, women-only housing available. Hekman Library with 1.3 million books, 809,327 microform titles, 37,307 serials, 25,936 audiovisual materials, an OPAC, and a Web page. Operations spending for the previous fiscal year: $2.4 million. 1,025 computers available

on campus for general student use. Computer purchase/lease plans available. A campuswide network can be accessed from student residence rooms and from off campus. Students can access the following: online class registration. Staffed computer lab on campus provides training in use of computers, software, and the Internet.

Community Environment: The city of Grand Rapids provides additional service, internship, recreational, and employment opportunities for students in the area's six colleges. It has a lively interest in the arts, as evidenced by an active symphony orchestra, civic theatre, ballet association, and art museum. Recreational opportunities abound with professional hockey, basketball, baseball, and arena football or concerts at DeVos Hall or Van Andel Arena.

■ **CENTRAL MICHIGAN UNIVERSITY**
Mount Pleasant, MI 48859
Tel: (989)774-4000; Free: 888-292-5366
Fax: (989)774-3537
E-mail: johns1s@cmich.edu
Web Site: www.cmich.edu/
Description: State-supported, university, coed. Awards bachelor's, master's, and doctoral degrees and post-master's certificates. Founded 1892. Setting: 854-acre small town campus. Endowment: $81.2 million. Research spending for the previous fiscal year: $11.9 million. Educational spending for the previous fiscal year: $7981 per student. Total enrollment: 27,626. Faculty: 1,113 (764 full-time, 349 part-time). Student-undergrad faculty ratio is 22:1. 17,769 applied, 64% were admitted. 14% from top 10% of their high school class, 40% from top quarter, 76% from top half. Full-time: 18,564 students, 56% women, 44% men. Part-time: 2,768 students, 58% women, 42% men. Students come from 50 states and territories, 55 other countries, 3% from out-of-state. 1% American Indian or Alaska Native, non-Hispanic/Latino; 3% Hispanic/Latino; 7% African American, non-Hispanic/Latino; 1% Asian, non-Hispanic/Latino; 0.05% Native Hawaiian or other Pacific Islander, non-Hispanic/Latino; 2% international. 5% 25 or older, 31% live on campus, 6% transferred in. Retention: 75% of full-time freshmen returned the following year. Academic areas with the most degrees conferred: business/marketing; education; parks and recreation. Core. Calendar: semesters. Academic remediation for entering students, ESL program, services for LD students, advanced placement, accelerated degree program, self-designed majors, freshman honors college, honors program, independent study, distance learning, double major, summer session for credit, part-time degree program, adult/continuing education programs, internships, graduate courses open to undergrads. Off campus study. Study abroad program. ROTC: Army, Air Force (c).
Entrance Requirements: Options: electronic application, early admission, early action, deferred admission, international baccalaureate accepted. Required: high school transcript, SAT or ACT. Recommended: ACT. Required for some: essay, interview. Entrance: moderately difficult. Application deadline: Rolling. Notification: continuous. SAT Reasoning Test deadline: 7/1. Transfer credits accepted: Yes.
Costs Per Year: Application fee: $35. State resident tuition: $10,950 full-time, $365 per credit hour part-time. Nonresident tuition: $23,670 full-time, $789 per credit hour part-time. Full-time tuition varies according to location. Part-time tuition varies according to location. College room and board: $8368. College room only: $4184. Room and board charges vary according to board plan, housing facility, location, and student level.
Collegiate Environment: Orientation program. Drama-theater group, choral group, marching band, student-run newspaper, radio station. Social organizations: 285 open to all; national fraternities, national sororities; 5% of eligible men and 7% of eligible women are members. Most popular organizations: Residence Hall Assembly, Student Government Association, High Adventure Club, Fellowship of Christian Athletes, College Republicans. Major annual events: Homecoming, Siblings' Weekend, Mainstage. Student services: legal services, health clinic, personal-psychological counseling, women's center. Campus security: 24-hour emergency response devices and patrols, student patrols, late night transport-escort service, controlled dormitory access. 6,441 college housing spaces available; 5,926 were occupied in 2012-13. Freshmen guaranteed college housing. On-campus residence required in freshman year. Options: coed, men-only, women-only housing available. Charles V. Park Library plus 1 other with 1.4 million books, 1.4 million microform titles, 57,780 serials, 105,992 audiovisual materials, an OPAC, and a Web page. Operations spending for the previous fiscal year: $9.1 million. 3,000 computers available on campus for general student use. Computer purchase/lease plans available. A campuswide network can be accessed from student residence rooms and from off

campus. Students can access the following: online class registration, Blackboard. Staffed computer lab on campus (open 24 hours a day) provides training in use of computers, software, and the Internet.

Community Environment: Located in the approximate center of the state, Mount Pleasant is the largest city in the county. Average temperature is 45.6 degrees; rainfall, 26.14; snowfall, 45.7 inches. The area has a hospital, auditoriums, theatres, motels, a public stadium, and its own airport. Ten lakes and a ski range nearby offer excellent recreational facilities. An Indian reservation is located four miles east of the city.

■ **CLEARY UNIVERSITY**
3601 Plymouth Rd.
Ann Arbor, MI 48105-2659
Tel: (517)548-3670; Free: 800-686-1883
E-mail: admissions@cleary.edu
Web Site: www.cleary.edu/
Description: Independent, comprehensive, coed. Awards associate, bachelor's, and master's degrees. Founded 1883. Setting: 32-acre suburban campus with easy access to Detroit, Ann Arbor. Endowment: $998,704. Educational spending for the previous fiscal year: $3309 per student. Total enrollment: 704. Faculty: 78 (all part-time). Student-undergrad faculty ratio is 15:1. 81 applied, 48% were admitted. Full-time: 268 students, 60% women, 40% men. Part-time: 350 students, 55% women, 45% men. Students come from 11 states and territories, 2% from out-of-state. 0.2% American Indian or Alaska Native, non-Hispanic/Latino; 1% Hispanic/Latino; 7% African American, non-Hispanic/Latino; 1% Asian, non-Hispanic/Latino; 0% Native Hawaiian or other Pacific Islander, non-Hispanic/Latino; 0% international. 78% 25 or older, 14% transferred in. Retention: 75% of full-time freshmen returned the following year. Academic area with the most degrees conferred: business/marketing. Core. Advanced placement, accelerated degree program, honors program, independent study, distance learning, double major, summer session for credit, part-time degree program, adult/continuing education programs, co-op programs and internships. Off campus study at Consortium agreements with Mott Community College (Flint), Henry Ford Community College, Montcalm Community College, and Concordia University (Ann Arbor).
Entrance Requirements: Options: electronic application, early admission, deferred admission, international baccalaureate accepted. Required: high school transcript, minimum 2.5 high school GPA, SAT or ACT. Recommended: interview. Required for some: essay, First-Time/First Year Students: minimum ACT score of 19. Minimum high school GPA of 2.0 required for non-traditional and transfer students, SAT Subject Tests. Entrance: moderately difficult. Application deadlines: 7/15, 7/15 for nonresidents. Transfer credits accepted: Yes.
Collegiate Environment: Orientation program. Social organizations: 6 open to all; Student Veterans Association, Computer Club; 1% of eligible men and 1% of eligible women are members. Most popular organizations: Cleary Professional Accounting Associates, Human Resources & Organizational Leadership Association, Event and Meeting Planning Student Association, Veterans Club, Accounting/Fraud Examiners Club. Major annual events: Cleary University Auction, Cleary Classic Alumni and Friends Gold Outing, Livingston Economic Club Speaker Series. Student services: personal-psychological counseling. Campus security: 24-hour emergency response devices, access to facilities limited to authorized persons. College housing not available. Cleary Online Library with a Web page. Operations spending for the previous fiscal year: $34,496. 26 computers available on campus for general student use. A computer is required for all students. A campuswide network can be accessed from off-campus. Staffed computer lab on campus.

■ **COLLEGE FOR CREATIVE STUDIES**
201 E Kirby
Detroit, MI 48202-4034
Tel: (313)664-7400; Free: 800-952-ARTS
Fax: (313)872-2739
E-mail: admissions@collegeforcreativestudies.edu
Web Site: www.collegeforcreativestudies.edu/
Description: Independent, comprehensive, coed. Awards bachelor's and master's degrees. Founded 1926. Setting: 11-acre urban campus. Total enrollment: 1,441. Faculty: 252 (47 full-time, 205 part-time). Student-undergrad faculty ratio is 11:1. 1,615 applied, 45% were admitted. Full-time: 1,109 students, 50% women, 50% men. Part-time: 277 students, 52% women, 48% men. 17% from out-of-state. 0.4% American Indian or Alaska Native, non-Hispanic/Latino; 5% Hispanic/Latino; 8% African American, non-Hispanic/Latino; 5% Asian, non-Hispanic/Latino; 0.1% Native Hawaiian or

other Pacific Islander, non-Hispanic/Latino; 6% international. 16% 25 or older, 29% live on campus, 11% transferred in. Retention: 76% of full-time freshmen returned the following year. Academic area with the most degrees conferred: visual and performing arts. Calendar: semesters. Part-time degree program.

Entrance Requirements: Options: electronic application, deferred admission. Required: essay, high school transcript, portfolio, SAT or ACT. Recommended: minimum 2.5 high school GPA. Required for some: interview. Entrance: moderately difficult. Application deadline: 7/1. Notification: continuous.

Costs Per Year: Application fee: $35. Comprehensive fee: $43,760 includes full-time tuition ($34,320), mandatory fees ($1390), and college room and board ($8050). College room only: $5150. Part-time tuition: $1144 per credit hour.

Collegiate Environment: Orientation program. Campus security: 24-hour patrols, late night transport-escort service, controlled dormitory access. Option: coed housing available.

■ CONCORDIA UNIVERSITY ANN ARBOR

4090 Geddes Rd.
Ann Arbor, MI 48105-2797
Tel: (734)995-7300; Free: 877-955-7520
Fax: (734)995-4610
E-mail: admissions@cuaa.edu
Web Site: www.cuaa.edu/

Description: Independent, comprehensive, coed, affiliated with Lutheran Church-Missouri Synod. Part of Concordia University System. Awards associate, bachelor's, and master's degrees. Founded 1963. Setting: 187-acre suburban campus with easy access to Detroit. Endowment: $7.6 million. Educational spending for the previous fiscal year: $6014 per student. Total enrollment: 711. Faculty: 124 (28 full-time, 96 part-time). Student-undergrad faculty ratio is 11:1. 837 applied, 56% were admitted. Full-time: 474 students, 43% women, 57% men. Part-time: 35 students, 46% women, 54% men. 0% American Indian or Alaska Native, non-Hispanic/Latino; 4% Hispanic/Latino; 10% African American, non-Hispanic/Latino; 1% Asian, non-Hispanic/Latino; 0% Native Hawaiian or other Pacific Islander, non-Hispanic/Latino; 2% international. 9% 25 or older, 79% live on campus, 9% transferred in. Retention: 58% of full-time freshmen returned the following year. Academic areas with the most degrees conferred: education; business/marketing; family and consumer sciences. Core. Calendar: semesters. Academic remediation for entering students, ESL program, services for LD students, advanced placement, accelerated degree program, self-designed majors, independent study, distance learning, double major, summer session for credit, part-time degree program, co-op programs and internships, graduate courses open to undergrads. Off campus study at Concordia University System. Study abroad program. ROTC: Army (c), Air Force (c).

Entrance Requirements: Options: electronic application, deferred admission, international baccalaureate accepted. Required: high school transcript, SAT or ACT. Recommended: minimum 2.5 high school GPA, ACT. Required for some: essay, 1 recommendation, interview. Entrance: moderately difficult. Application deadline: Rolling. SAT Reasoning Test deadline: 8/15. SAT Subject Test deadline: 8/15.

Costs Per Year: Application fee: $25. Comprehensive fee: $30,762 includes full-time tuition ($22,464) and college room and board ($8298). Full-time tuition varies according to location and program. Room and board charges vary according to housing facility. Part-time tuition: $936 per credit hour. Part-time tuition varies according to course load, location, and program.

Collegiate Environment: Orientation program. Drama-theater group, choral group. Social organizations: 16 open to all. Most popular organizations: Student Activities Committee, Athletes in Action, Student Senate, Spiritual Life Committee, Off-campus ministries. Major annual events: Boar's Head Christmas Festival, Homecoming, Spring Formal. Student services: personal-psychological counseling. Campus security: 24-hour emergency response devices and patrols, late night transport-escort service, controlled dormitory access. Zimmerman Library with an OPAC. Operations spending for the previous fiscal year: $266,548. 60 computers available on campus for general student use. A campuswide network can be accessed from student residence rooms and from off campus. Students can access the following: online class registration, online billing information. Staffed computer lab on campus provides training in use of computers, software, and the Internet.

■ CORNERSTONE UNIVERSITY

1001 E Beltline Ave., NE
Grand Rapids, MI 49525-5897

Tel: (616)949-5300; Free: 800-787-9778
Fax: (616)222-1540
E-mail: admissions@cornerstone.edu
Web Site: www.cornerstone.edu/

Description: Independent nondenominational, comprehensive, coed. Awards associate, bachelor's, and master's degrees. Founded 1941. Setting: 132-acre suburban campus. Endowment: $6.6 million. Educational spending for the previous fiscal year: $3727 per student. Total enrollment: 2,747. Faculty: 114 (53 full-time, 61 part-time). Student-undergrad faculty ratio is 24:1. 2,062 applied, 63% were admitted. 17% from top 10% of their high school class, 44% from top quarter, 78% from top half. Full-time: 1,693 students, 61% women, 39% men. Part-time: 432 students, 64% women, 36% men. Students come from 34 states and territories, 12 other countries, 22% from out-of-state. 1% American Indian or Alaska Native, non-Hispanic/Latino; 4% Hispanic/Latino; 10% African American, non-Hispanic/Latino; 0.3% Asian, non-Hispanic/Latino; 1% international. 4% 25 or older, 62% live on campus, 3% transferred in. Retention: 74% of full-time freshmen returned the following year. Academic areas with the most degrees conferred: business/marketing; education; theology and religious vocations. Core. Calendar: semesters. Academic remediation for entering students, ESL program, services for LD students, advanced placement, accelerated degree program, honors program, independent study, distance learning, double major, summer session for credit, part-time degree program, adult/continuing education programs, internships, graduate courses open to undergrads. Off campus study at Kuyper College, Grace Bible College, Kendall College of Ferris State University, Hong Dong University of South Korea, EDE University of the Netherlands. Study abroad program. ROTC: Army (c).

Entrance Requirements: Options: electronic application, deferred admission. Required: essay, high school transcript, minimum 2.5 high school GPA, 1 recommendation, pastoral letter, SAT or ACT. Recommended: interview. Entrance: minimally difficult. Application deadline: Rolling. Notification: continuous. Transfer credits accepted: Yes.

Costs Per Year: Application fee: $25. Comprehensive fee: $32,078 includes full-time tuition ($23,598), mandatory fees ($570), and college room and board ($7910). Full-time tuition and fees vary according to course load and reciprocity agreements. Room and board charges vary according to board plan and housing facility. Part-time tuition: $905 per credit. Part-time mandatory fees: $185 per term. Part-time tuition and fees vary according to course load.

Collegiate Environment: Orientation program. Drama-theater group, choral group, student-run newspaper. Social organizations: 8 open to all. Most popular organizations: student government, Student Education Association, Breakpoint, Student Activities Council, International Justice Mission. Major annual events: Homecoming, Winter Banquet, Spring Splash. Student services: health clinic, personal-psychological counseling. Campus security: 24-hour emergency response devices and patrols, student patrols, late night transport-escort service, controlled dormitory access. 817 college housing spaces available; 772 were occupied in 2012-13. Freshmen guaranteed college housing. On-campus residence required through sophomore year. Options: men-only, women-only housing available. Miller Library with 160,815 books, 276,107 microform titles, 2,587 serials, 43,820 audiovisual materials, an OPAC, and a Web page. Operations spending for the previous fiscal year: $865,751. 1,300 computers available on campus for general student use. A campuswide network can be accessed from student residence rooms and from off campus. Students can access the following: online class registration. Staffed computer lab on campus provides training in use of computers, software, and the Internet.

■ DAVENPORT UNIVERSITY

6191 Kraft Ave. SE
Grand Rapids, MI 49512
Tel: (616)451-3511; Free: 866-925-3884
Fax: (616)732-1142
E-mail: daryl.kingrey@davenport.edu
Web Site: www.davenport.edu/

Description: Independent, comprehensive, coed. Awards associate, bachelor's, and master's degrees and post-master's certificates. Founded 1866. Setting: suburban campus. Endowment: $16.2 million. Total enrollment: 11,304. Faculty: 982 (155 full-time, 827 part-time). Student-undergrad faculty ratio is 14:1. 1,324 applied, 95% were admitted. Full-time: 2,425 students, 48% women, 52% men. Part-time: 6,457 students, 68% women, 32% men. Students come from 53 states and territories, 32 other countries, 2% from out-of-state. 0.4% American Indian or Alaska Native, non-Hispanic/Latino; 2% Hispanic/Latino; 19% African American, non-Hispanic/Latino; 2%

Asian, non-Hispanic/Latino; 0.1% Native Hawaiian or other Pacific Islander, non-Hispanic/Latino; 2% international. 61% 25 or older, 4% live on campus, 11% transferred in. Retention: 69% of full-time freshmen returned the following year. Academic areas with the most degrees conferred: business/marketing; computer and information sciences; health professions and related sciences. Core. Calendar: semesters. Academic remediation for entering students, ESL program, services for LD students, advanced placement, accelerated degree program, independent study, distance learning, summer session for credit, part-time degree program, adult/continuing education programs, co-op programs and internships. Study abroad program.

Entrance Requirements: Options: electronic application, deferred admission. Required: high school transcript. Recommended: interview, SAT or ACT. Entrance: minimally difficult. Application deadlines: Rolling, Rolling for nonresidents. Notification: continuous, continuous for nonresidents.

Costs Per Year: Application fee: $25. Comprehensive fee: $21,456 includes full-time tuition ($12,672), mandatory fees ($350), and college room and board ($8434). Full-time tuition and fees vary according to location and program. Room and board charges vary according to board plan and housing facility. Part-time tuition: $528 per credit hour. Part-time tuition varies according to location and program.

Collegiate Environment: Orientation program. Student-run newspaper. Social organizations: 31 open to all. Most popular organizations: Business Professionals of America, Delta Epsilon Chi, student government, Health Occupations Students of America, Connect. Major annual events: Pantherpalooza, Homecoming, MLK Volunteer Day. Student services: personal-psychological counseling. Campus security: 24-hour emergency response devices and patrols, late night transport-escort service, controlled dormitory access. 500 college housing spaces available; 451 were occupied in 2012-13. Freshmen given priority for college housing. Option: coed housing available. Margaret D. Sneden Library Information Commons with 74,714 books, 219 serials, and an OPAC. 3,098 computers available on campus for general student use. Computer purchase/lease plans available. A campuswide network can be accessed from student residence rooms. Students can access the following: online class registration. Staffed computer lab on campus provides training in use of computers.

■ **DELTA COLLEGE**
1961 Delta Rd.
University Center, MI 48710
Tel: (989)686-9000
Fax: (989)686-8736
E-mail: admit@delta.edu
Web Site: www.delta.edu/

Description: District-supported, 2-year, coed. Awards certificates, transfer associate, and terminal associate degrees. Founded 1961. Setting: 640-acre rural campus. Endowment: $12 million. Educational spending for the previous fiscal year: $4092 per student. Total enrollment: 10,899. Faculty: 527 (219 full-time, 308 part-time). Student-undergrad faculty ratio is 20:1. 3,344 applied, 100% were admitted. Full-time: 4,499 students, 51% women, 49% men. Part-time: 6,400 students, 58% women, 42% men. Students come from 2 states and territories, 22 other countries, 0% from out-of-state. 35% 25 or older, 4% transferred in. Core. Calendar: semesters. Academic remediation for entering students, services for LD students, advanced placement, self-designed majors, freshman honors college, honors program, independent study, distance learning, double major, summer session for credit, part-time degree program, external degree program, adult/continuing education programs, co-op programs and internships. Off campus study. Study abroad program.

Entrance Requirements: Open admission except for international applicants. Options: electronic application, early admission, deferred admission. Recommended: high school transcript. Required for some: essay. Entrance: noncompetitive. Application deadline: Rolling.

Collegiate Environment: Orientation program. Student-run newspaper. Social organizations: 10 open to all. Most popular organizations: intramural activities, Student Senate, Phi Theta Kappa, Inter-Varsity Christian Fellowship, DECA. Major annual events: Earth Day, Job Fair, Global Awareness Week. Student services: personal-psychological counseling. Campus security: 24-hour emergency response devices and patrols, student patrols, late night transport-escort service. Library Learning Information Center with 110,985 books, 24,000 microform titles, 267 serials, 4,500 audiovisual materials, an OPAC, and a Web page. Operations spending for the previous fiscal year: $703,547. 550 computers available on campus for general student use. A campuswide network can be accessed from off-campus.

Students can access the following: online class registration. Staffed computer lab on campus provides training in use of computers, software, and the Internet.

Community Environment: University Center encompasses the tri-county area of Bay, Midland and Saginaw counties. The area has good shopping, commuter bus service and very active churches. Saginaw Arts Council promotes and encourages the area's cultural and educational organizations. There are excellent part-time employment opportunities for students. Summer and winter sports resort areas are located nearby. Some areas are highly industrialized.

■ **DEVRY UNIVERSITY**
26999 Central Park Blvd., Ste. 125
Southfield, MI 48076
Tel: (248)213-1610; Free: 866-338-7941
Fax: (248)353-1804
Web Site: www.devry.edu/

Description: Proprietary, 4-year, coed. Awards associate and bachelor's degrees. Founded 2008. Total enrollment: 88. Faculty: 14 (all part-time). Student-undergrad faculty ratio is 10:1. Full-time: 28 students, 61% women, 39% men. Part-time: 60 students, 35% women, 65% men. 1% from out-of-state. 70% 25 or older, 27% transferred in. Academic area with the most degrees conferred: business/marketing. Calendar: semesters. Accelerated degree program, distance learning.

Entrance Requirements: Option: deferred admission. Application deadline: Rolling. Notification: continuous. SAT Reasoning Test deadline: 10/31.

■ **EASTERN MICHIGAN UNIVERSITY**
Ypsilanti, MI 48197
Tel: (734)487-1849; Free: 800-GO TO EMU
Fax: (734)487-1484
Web Site: www.emich.edu/

Description: State-supported, comprehensive, coed. Awards bachelor's, master's, and doctoral degrees and post-master's certificates. Founded 1849. Setting: 460-acre suburban campus with easy access to Detroit. Endowment: $51.4 million. Research spending for the previous fiscal year: $5 million. Educational spending for the previous fiscal year: $7210 per student. Total enrollment: 23,502. Faculty: 1,226 (759 full-time, 467 part-time). Student-undergrad faculty ratio is 19:1. 11,538 applied, 65% were admitted. 14% from top 10% of their high school class, 39% from top quarter, 74% from top half. Full-time: 13,178 students, 57% women, 43% men. Part-time: 5,736 students, 59% women, 41% men. Students come from 45 states and territories, 26 other countries, 8% from out-of-state. 0.4% American Indian or Alaska Native, non-Hispanic/Latino; 3% Hispanic/Latino; 22% African American, non-Hispanic/Latino; 2% Asian, non-Hispanic/Latino; 0.1% Native Hawaiian or other Pacific Islander, non-Hispanic/Latino; 2% international. 28% 25 or older, 22% live on campus, 11% transferred in. Retention: 75% of full-time freshmen returned the following year. Academic areas with the most degrees conferred: business/marketing; education; health professions and related sciences. Core. Calendar: semesters. Academic remediation for entering students, ESL program, services for LD students, advanced placement, accelerated degree program, self-designed majors, honors program, independent study, distance learning, double major, summer session for credit, part-time degree program, external degree program, co-op programs and internships, graduate courses open to undergrads. Study abroad program. ROTC: Army, Naval (c), Air Force (c).

Entrance Requirements: Options: electronic application, deferred admission, international baccalaureate accepted. Required: high school transcript, minimum 2 high school GPA, SAT or ACT. Required for some: 1 recommendation, interview. Entrance: moderately difficult. Application deadlines: Rolling, Rolling for nonresidents. Notification: continuous, continuous for nonresidents. Transfer credits accepted: Yes.

Costs Per Year: Application fee: $30. One-time mandatory fee: $300. State resident tuition: $7701 full-time, $256.70 per credit hour part-time. Nonresident tuition: $22,683 full-time, $756.10 per credit hour part-time. Mandatory fees: $1,325 full-time, $40.90 per credit hour part-time, $48.20 per term part-time. Full-time tuition and fees vary according to course level and reciprocity agreements. Part-time tuition and fees vary according to course level and reciprocity agreements. College room and board: $8286. College room only: $3952. Room and board charges vary according to board plan, housing facility, and location.

Collegiate Environment: Orientation program. Drama-theater group, choral group, marching band, student-run newspaper, radio station. Social organizations: 277 open to all; national fraternities, national sororities, local fraternities, local sororities; 4% of eligible men and 4% of eligible women are members. Most popular organizations: International Student Association, Golden Key International Honor Society, Psychology Club, Indian Student Association, GREEN (Gathering Resources to Educate about our Environment and Nature). Major annual events: Homecoming, Family Weekend, campus-wide picnic. Student services: legal services, health clinic, personal-psychological counseling, women's center. Campus security: 24-hour emergency response devices and patrols, student patrols, late night transport-escort service, controlled dormitory access, bicycle patrols, local police in dormitories, self-defense education, lighted pathways, bike lock lease program. College housing designed to accommodate 3,110 students; 3,296 undergraduates lived in college housing during 2012-13. No special consideration for freshman housing applicants. On-campus residence required through sophomore year. Option: coed housing available. Bruce T. Halle Library with 1 million books, 993,322 microform titles, 28,120 serials, 19,232 audiovisual materials, an OPAC, and a Web page. Operations spending for the previous fiscal year: $7.7 million. 1,600 computers available on campus for general student use. A campuswide network can be accessed from student residence rooms. Students can access the following: online class registration, Wireless internet connections are available for all students. Staffed computer lab on campus (open 24 hours a day) provides training in use of computers, software, and the Internet.

Community Environment: Named for the Greek general of the 1820s Demetrius Ypsilanti, the community became a city in 1858. Ypsilanti is located in southeastern Michigan, approximately 40 miles west of Detroit and 7 miles from Ann Arbor. In addition to the extensive cultural opportunities at Eastern, the resources of the University of Michigan are 15 minutes away and downtown Detroit is a 45 minute drive. Regular bus service is available. Ypsilanti has an impressive historic district (Depot Town) and hosts a Heritage Festival annually in late August.

■ FERRIS STATE UNIVERSITY

1201 S State St.
Big Rapids, MI 49307
Tel: (231)591-2000; Free: 800-433-7747
Fax: (231)591-2978
E-mail: dadayja@ferris.edu
Web Site: www.ferris.edu/

Description: State-supported, comprehensive, coed. Awards associate, bachelor's, master's, and doctoral degrees (associate degree). Founded 1884. Setting: 941-acre small town campus with easy access to Grand Rapids. Endowment: $35.2 million. Research spending for the previous fiscal year: $304,272. Educational spending for the previous fiscal year: $7012 per student. Total enrollment: 14,533. Faculty: 969 (567 full-time, 402 part-time). Student-undergrad faculty ratio is 16:1. 9,457 applied, 71% were admitted. Full-time: 9,366 students, 48% women, 52% men. Part-time: 3,895 students, 59% women, 41% men. Students come from 48 states and territories, 30 other countries, 5% from out-of-state. 1% American Indian or Alaska Native, non-Hispanic/Latino; 3% Hispanic/Latino; 7% African American, non-Hispanic/Latino; 2% Asian, non-Hispanic/Latino; 0.1% Native Hawaiian or other Pacific Islander, non-Hispanic/Latino; 2% international. 25% 25 or older, 28% live on campus, 10% transferred in. Retention: 70% of full-time freshmen returned the following year. Academic areas with the most degrees conferred: business/marketing; health professions and related sciences; engineering technologies; homeland security, law enforcement, firefighting, and protective services. Core. Calendar: semesters. Academic remediation for entering students, ESL program, services for LD students, advanced placement, accelerated degree program, self-designed majors, freshman honors college, honors program, independent study, distance learning, double major, summer session for credit, part-time degree program, external degree program, adult/continuing education programs, co-op programs and internships, graduate courses open to undergrads. Off campus study at Delta College, Henry Ford Community College (CC), Lansing CC, Mott CC, Macomb CC, Macomb CC, St. Clair County CC, North Central Michigan College, Northwestern Michigan College, University Center, Gaylord, Westshore Community College, Muskegon CC, Southwestern Michigan College, Alpena CC, Bay Mills CC, Bay College, Grand Rapids CC, Mid-Michigan CC, Montcalm CC, Oakland CC, Schoolcraft College, Wayne CC District, Kirtland CC. Study abroad program. ROTC: Army (c).

Entrance Requirements: Open admission. Options: electronic application, international baccalaureate accepted. Required: high school transcript, minimum 2.5 high school GPA, SAT or ACT, SAT or ACT. Entrance: minimally difficult. Application deadline: 8/1. Notification: continuous. SAT Reasoning Test deadline: 8/1. Transfer credits accepted: Yes.

Costs Per Year: Application fee: $30. One-time mandatory fee: $162. State resident tuition: $10,710 full-time, $357 per credit hour part-time. Nonresident tuition: $16,080 full-time, $536 per credit hour part-time. Full-time tuition varies according to location and program. Part-time tuition varies according to location. College room and board: $8744. Room and board charges vary according to board plan and housing facility.

Collegiate Environment: Orientation program. Drama-theater group, choral group, student-run newspaper, radio station. Social organizations: 220 open to all; national fraternities, national sororities, local fraternities, local sororities; 4% of eligible men and 5% of eligible women are members. Most popular organizations: Panhellenic Council, Interfraternal Council, Music Industry Management Association, Pre-Pharmacy Organization, Crafter's Anonymous. Major annual events: Homecoming, Ferris Fest, The Big Event. Student services: health clinic, personal-psychological counseling. Campus security: 24-hour emergency response devices, student patrols, late night transport-escort service, controlled dormitory access. 3,680 college housing spaces available; 3,191 were occupied in 2012-13. Freshmen guaranteed college housing. On-campus residence required through sophomore year. Option: coed housing available. Ferris Library for Information, Technology and Education (FLITE) with 430,018 books, 3.7 million microform titles, 74,121 serials, 5,097 audiovisual materials, an OPAC, and a Web page. Operations spending for the previous fiscal year: $4.1 million. 1,930 computers available on campus for general student use. A campuswide network can be accessed from student residence rooms and from off campus. Students can access the following: online class registration. Staffed computer lab on campus provides training in use of computers.

Community Environment: Home for Ferris is Big Rapids, a city of approximately 15,000 residents. The county seat of Mecosta County, Big Rapids is at the junction of U.S. 131 and M-20, 54 miles north of Michigan's second-largest city, Grand Rapids, and within approximately 200 miles of Detroit and Chicago. As one might guess from its name, Big Rapids' primary natural feature is a river, the Muskegon, whose wooded banks wind through town and form the eastern border of the Ferris campus. The former logging community is located in the heart of an extensive recreation area of which Mecosta County, with its 101 lakes and four county parks is a significant part. The city is served by a daily newspaper, one AM and two FM radio stations, a cable television system, a movie theater, roller skating and ice skating rinks, 18-hole college golf course, community pool, diverse commercial districts, four banks, three motels, Holiday Inn Hotel and Conference center, bus lines, 24 churches, a 74-bed hospital, and a community library holding nearly 50,000 volumes.

■ FINLANDIA UNIVERSITY

601 Quincy St.
Hancock, MI 49930-1882
Tel: (906)482-5300; Free: 877-202-5491
Fax: (906)487-7300
E-mail: admissions@finlandia.edu
Web Site: www.finlandia.edu/

Description: Independent, 4-year, coed, affiliated with Evangelical Lutheran Church in America. Awards associate and bachelor's degrees. Founded 1896. Setting: 25-acre small town campus. Endowment: $2.5 million. Educational spending for the previous fiscal year: $7441 per student. Total enrollment: 545. Faculty: 70 (42 full-time, 28 part-time). Student-undergrad faculty ratio is 10:1. 646 applied, 67% were admitted. 3 class presidents, 6 valedictorians, 3 student government officers. Full-time: 485 students, 63% women, 37% men. Part-time: 60 students, 80% women, 20% men. Students come from 13 states and territories, 3 other countries, 10% from out-of-state. 26% 25 or older, 24% live on campus, 10% transferred in. Retention: 61% of full-time freshmen returned the following year. Academic areas with the most degrees conferred: business/marketing; health professions and related sciences; visual and performing arts. Core. Calendar: semesters. Academic remediation for entering students, ESL program, services for LD students, advanced placement, accelerated degree program, independent study, distance learning, summer session for credit, part-time degree program, adult/continuing education programs, co-op programs and internships. Off campus study. Study abroad program. ROTC: Army (c), Air Force (c).

Entrance Requirements: Options: electronic application, early admission, international baccalaureate accepted. Required: essay, high school transcript, minimum 2.0 high school GPA. Recommended: SAT or ACT. Required for some: interview. Entrance: minimally difficult. Application deadlines: 8/25, 8/25 for nonresidents. Notification: continuous, continuous for nonresidents.

Collegiate Environment: Orientation program. Drama-theater group, choral

group, student-run newspaper. Social organizations: 12 open to all. Most popular organizations: Student Senate, Campus Ministry, student newspaper, International Club, Artists Coalition. Major annual events: Homecoming, Arts and Music Festival, Campus Play. Campus security: 24-hour emergency response devices, student patrols. Sulo and Aileen Maki Library with 68,803 books, 1,867 microform titles, 997 serials, 2,865 audiovisual materials, an OPAC, and a Web page. Operations spending for the previous fiscal year: $169,206. 80 computers available on campus for general student use. A campuswide network can be accessed from student residence rooms and from off campus. Students can access the following: online class registration, home directory/network. Staffed computer lab on campus provides training in use of computers.

Community Environment: The campus is located near downtown Hancock, within a day's drive of Detroit, Chicago, Milwaukee, Duluth, and Minneapolis. The city, in "Copper County" sprang up amid the region's copper mining industry at the turn of the century. The area still has historical remnants of the mining but it is also know for its autumn when the expansive forests are ablaze with color. Community services include two hospitals, four theaters, and all major civic, fraternal, and service organizations. Recreational activities include fishing, camping, skiing, hunting, golf, hockey, and basketball, as well as the cold water and clean beaches of Lake Superior. Limited off-campus employment is available.

■ GLEN OAKS COMMUNITY COLLEGE

62249 Shimmel Rd.
Centreville, MI 49032-9719
Tel: (269)467-9945; Free: 888-994-7818
Fax: (269)467-9068
Web Site: www.glenoaks.edu/

Description: State and locally supported, 2-year, coed. Part of Michigan Department of Career Development. Awards certificates, transfer associate, and terminal associate degrees. Founded 1965. Setting: 300-acre rural campus. Total enrollment: 1,383. 35% 25 or older. Core. Calendar: semesters. Academic remediation for entering students, services for LD students, advanced placement, distance learning, summer session for credit, part-time degree program, adult/continuing education programs, internships.

Entrance Requirements: Open admission. Required: high school transcript. Entrance: noncompetitive. Application deadline: Rolling.

Collegiate Environment: Student services: personal-psychological counseling. Campus security: 24-hour emergency response devices. E. J. Shaheen Library with 37,087 books, 347 serials, and an OPAC.

Community Environment: Glen Oaks is located in the center of St. Joseph County, almost equidistant between Three Rivers and Sturgis, the county's two largest cities. Nestled in the hills of Sherman Township, it has a population of approximately 1,180 people. The area is primarily agricultural, with heavy-to-light industry focused in Sturgis and Three Rivers. Located midway between Chicago and Detroit on the"Chicago Trail," it has the potential for vast economic and population growth. The area also abounds in lakes and rolling hills, affording many opportunities for a variety of recreational activities throughout the year. The citizens are fortunate to be served by modern medical facilities and by well-supported public educational facilities. An energetic civic outreach program provides support for the educational, cultural, civil and economic community and assures its growth and progress.

■ GOGEBIC COMMUNITY COLLEGE

E-4946 Jackson Rd.
Ironwood, MI 49938
Tel: (906)932-4231; Free: 800-682-5910
Fax: (906)932-5541
E-mail: jeanneg@gogebic.edu
Web Site: www.gogebic.edu/

Description: State and locally supported, 2-year, coed. Part of Michigan Department of Education. Awards certificates, transfer associate, and terminal associate degrees. Founded 1932. Setting: 195-acre small town campus. Total enrollment: 975. 40% 25 or older. Core. Calendar: semesters. Academic remediation for entering students, services for LD students, advanced placement, honors program, distance learning, summer session for credit, part-time degree program, adult/continuing education programs, co-op programs and internships.

Entrance Requirements: Open admission except for nursing program. Options: electronic application, early admission, deferred admission. Required: high school transcript. Entrance: noncompetitive. Application deadlines: Rolling, 8/15 for nonresidents. Notification: continuous.

Costs Per Year: Application fee: $10. Area resident tuition: $3069 full-time,

$99 per credit hour part-time. State resident tuition: $4154 full-time, $134 per credit hour part-time. Nonresident tuition: $5115 full-time, $165 per credit hour part-time. Mandatory fees: $934 full-time, $6 per credit hour part-time. Full-time tuition and fees vary according to course load and reciprocity agreements. Part-time tuition and fees vary according to course load and reciprocity agreements. College room and board: $6704. College room only: $4004.

Collegiate Environment: Orientation program. Drama-theater group, choral group. Student services: personal-psychological counseling. Alex D. Chisholm Learning Resources Center with 22,000 books, 220 serials, an OPAC, and a Web page.

Community Environment: On the Michigan-Wisconsin border, in the heart of the Midwest ski area, Ironwood is the trading center and lumbering headquarters of the Gogebic Range. The area has refreshing summers and snowy invigorating winters. The city has a library, churches, a hospital, and passenger transportation via air and bus lines. The community has two theatres, hunting, boating, fishing, and excellent skiing for recreation.

■ GRACE BIBLE COLLEGE

1011 Aldon St. SW
Grand Rapids, MI 49509-0910
Tel: (616)538-2330; Free: 800-968-1887
Fax: (616)538-0599
E-mail: gbc@gbcol.edu
Web Site: www.gbcol.edu/

Description: Independent, 4-year, coed, affiliated with Grace Gospel Fellowship. Awards associate and bachelor's degrees. Founded 1945. Setting: 21-acre suburban campus. Endowment: $319,000. Educational spending for the previous fiscal year: $5262 per student. Total enrollment: 207. Faculty: 21 (7 full-time, 14 part-time). Student-undergrad faculty ratio is 17:1. 158 applied, 34% were admitted. 17% from top 10% of their high school class, 27% from top quarter, 47% from top half. Full-time: 192 students, 42% women, 58% men. Part-time: 15 students, 47% women, 53% men. Students come from 15 states and territories, 3 other countries, 19% from out-of-state. 0% American Indian or Alaska Native, non-Hispanic/Latino; 2% Hispanic/Latino; 4% African American, non-Hispanic/Latino; 1% Asian, non-Hispanic/Latino; 0.5% Native Hawaiian or other Pacific Islander, non-Hispanic/Latino; 0.5% international. 8% 25 or older, 53% live on campus, 11% transferred in. Retention: 80% of full-time freshmen returned the following year. Academic areas with the most degrees conferred: theology and religious vocations; public administration and social services; interdisciplinary studies. Core. Calendar: semesters. Academic remediation for entering students, advanced placement, independent study, internships. Off campus study at Grand Rapids Community College, Davenport University, Cornerstone University. ROTC: Army (c).

Entrance Requirements: Options: electronic application, early admission, deferred admission. Required: high school transcript, 2 recommendations, SAT and SAT Subject Tests or ACT. Recommended: minimum 2.5 high school GPA. Required for some: interview. Entrance: minimally difficult. Application deadline: 7/15. Notification: 8/1.

Costs Per Year: Application fee: $0. Comprehensive fee: $22,300 includes full-time tuition ($15,300) and college room and board ($7000). Room and board charges vary according to board plan and housing facility.

Collegiate Environment: Orientation program. Choral group. Social organizations: 4 open to all. Most popular organizations: Student Missionary Fellowship, Student Activities Committee, Student Council, Campus Ministry Team. Major annual events: Campus Clean-Up Days, Fridays at Grace, Winter Formal. Student services: personal-psychological counseling. Campus security: student patrols, controlled dormitory access. Bultema Memorial Library with 42,867 books, 53 microform titles, 110 serials, 933 audiovisual materials, and an OPAC. Operations spending for the previous fiscal year: $69,656. 27 computers available on campus for general student use. A campuswide network can be accessed from student residence rooms. Students can access the following: library catalog search. Staffed computer lab on campus provides training in use of computers, software, and the Internet.

■ GRAND RAPIDS COMMUNITY COLLEGE

143 Bostwick Ave., NE
Grand Rapids, MI 49503-3201
Tel: (616)234-4000
Fax: (616)234-4005
E-mail: dpatrick@grcc.edu
Web Site: www.grcc.edu/

Description: District-supported, 2-year, coed. Part of Michigan Department of Education. Awards certificates, transfer associate, and terminal associate degrees. Founded 1914. Setting: 35-acre urban campus. Endowment: $30.5 million. Educational spending for the previous fiscal year: $4926 per student. Total enrollment: 17,448. Faculty: 847 (257 full-time, 590 part-time). Student-undergrad faculty ratio is 22:1. 11,571 applied. Full-time: 6,264 students, 49% women, 51% men. Part-time: 11,184 students, 55% women, 45% men. Students come from 8 states and territories, 23 other countries, 1% from out-of-state. 1% American Indian or Alaska Native, non-Hispanic/Latino; 8% Hispanic/Latino; 12% African American, non-Hispanic/Latino; 3% Asian, non-Hispanic/Latino; 0.01% Native Hawaiian or other Pacific Islander, non-Hispanic/Latino; 0.1% international. 35% 25 or older, 9% transferred in. Retention: 55% of full-time freshmen returned the following year. Core. Calendar: semesters. Academic remediation for entering students, ESL program, services for LD students, advanced placement, honors program, independent study, distance learning, summer session for credit, part-time degree program, adult/continuing education programs, co-op programs and internships. Off campus study. Study abroad program.

Entrance Requirements: Open admission except for international applicants or allied health programs. Options: electronic application, early admission, deferred admission. Required: high school transcript. Recommended: SAT or ACT. Entrance: noncompetitive. Application deadline: 8/30. Notification: continuous. Transfer credits accepted: Yes.

Costs Per Year: Application fee: $0. Area resident tuition: $2940 full-time, $98 per contact hour part-time. State resident tuition: $6450 full-time, $215 per contact hour part-time. Nonresident tuition: $9660 full-time, $322 per contact hour part-time. Mandatory fees: $459 full-time, $5.50 per contact hour part-time, $125 per term part-time. Full-time tuition and fees vary according to course load. Part-time tuition and fees vary according to course load.

Collegiate Environment: Orientation program. Drama-theater group, choral group, student-run newspaper. Social organizations: 45 open to all. Most popular organizations: Student Congress, Phi Theta Kappa, Hispanic Student Organization, Student Gamers Association, Foreign Affairs Club. Major annual events: Finals Relaxer, Orientation Week, Entertainment Series. Student services: personal-psychological counseling. Campus security: 24-hour emergency response devices, late night transport-escort service. College housing not available. Arthur Andrews Memorial Library with 161,263 books, 151,398 microform titles, 33,064 serials, 3,200 audiovisual materials, an OPAC, and a Web page. Operations spending for the previous fiscal year: $2 million. 1,500 computers available on campus for general student use. A campuswide network can be accessed from off-campus. Students can access the following: online class registration. Staffed computer lab on campus provides training in use of computers, software, and the Internet.

Community Environment: See Calvin College.

■ **GRAND VALLEY STATE UNIVERSITY**
1 Campus Dr.
Allendale, MI 49401-9403
Tel: (616)331-5000; Free: 800-748-0246
Fax: (616)331-2000
E-mail: go2gvsu@gvsu.edu
Web Site: www.gvsu.edu/
Description: State-supported, comprehensive, coed. Awards bachelor's, master's, and doctoral degrees and post-master's certificates. Founded 1960. Setting: 1,337-acre small town campus with easy access to Grand Rapids. Endowment: $75.3 million. Research spending for the previous fiscal year: $7.9 million. Total enrollment: 24,654. Faculty: 1,678 (1,097 full-time, 581 part-time). Student-undergrad faculty ratio is 17:1. 17,880 applied, 82% were admitted. 19% from top 10% of their high school class, 50% from top quarter, 88% from top half. Full-time: 18,663 students, 59% women, 41% men. Part-time: 2,654 students, 56% women, 44% men. Students come from 39 states and territories, 73 other countries, 5% from out-of-state. 0.4% American Indian or Alaska Native, non-Hispanic/Latino; 4% Hispanic/Latino; 5% African American, non-Hispanic/Latino; 2% Asian, non-Hispanic/Latino; 0.1% Native Hawaiian or other Pacific Islander, non-Hispanic/Latino; 1% international. 11% 25 or older, 27% live on campus, 8% transferred in. Retention: 82% of full-time freshmen returned the following year. Academic areas with the most degrees conferred: business/marketing; health professions and related sciences; social sciences. Core. Calendar: semesters. Academic remediation for entering students, ESL program, services for LD students, advanced placement, accelerated degree program, freshman honors program, honors program, independent study, distance learning,

double major, summer session for credit, part-time degree program, adult/continuing education programs, co-op programs and internships, graduate courses open to undergrads. Study abroad program.

Entrance Requirements: Option: electronic application. Required: high school transcript, SAT or ACT. Required for some: essay, interview. Entrance: moderately difficult. Application deadline: 5/1. Notification: 5/1.

Costs Per Year: Application fee: $30. State resident tuition: $10,078 full-time, $420 per credit hour part-time. Nonresident tuition: $14,568 full-time, $607 per credit hour part-time. Full-time tuition varies according to course level, degree level, program, and student level. Part-time tuition varies according to course level, course load, degree level, program, and student level. College room and board: $7920. College room only: $5400. Room and board charges vary according to board plan, housing facility, and location.

Collegiate Environment: Orientation program. Drama-theater group, choral group, marching band, student-run newspaper, radio station. Social organizations: 315 open to all; national fraternities, national sororities, local fraternities, local sororities. Most popular organizations: Habitat for Humanity, Alternative Breaks, Hospitality and tourism Management Club, Dance Troupe, Colleges Against Cancer. Major annual events: Campus Life Night, Homecoming, President's Ball. Student services: health clinic, personal-psychological counseling, women's center. Campus security: 24-hour emergency response devices and patrols, student patrols, late night transport-escort service, controlled dormitory access. 5,820 college housing spaces available; all were occupied in 2012-13. Freshmen guaranteed college housing. Option: coed housing available. James H. Zumberge Library plus 2 others with an OPAC. Operations spending for the previous fiscal year: $10.3 million. 2,600 computers available on campus for general student use. A campuswide network can be accessed from student residence rooms and from off campus. Students can access the following: online class registration, transcript, degree audit, credit card payments. Staffed computer lab on campus provides training in use of computers, software, and the Internet.

Community Environment: This is a rural community that has Protestant and Catholic churches and a small library. Many part-time job opportunities are available for students. Allendale has facilities for bowling, water sports, and winter sports. The area features an annual winter carnival and spring arts festival.

■ **GREAT LAKES CHRISTIAN COLLEGE**
6211 W Willow Hwy.
Lansing, MI 48917-1299
Tel: (517)321-0242; Free: 800-YES-GLCC
Fax: (517)321-5902
E-mail: jcarter@glcc.edu
Web Site: www.glcc.edu/
Description: Independent, 4-year, coed, affiliated with Christian Churches and Churches of Christ. Awards associate and bachelor's degrees. Founded 1949. Setting: 47-acre suburban campus. Endowment: $442,503. Educational spending for the previous fiscal year: $5258 per student. Total enrollment: 225. Faculty: 23 (10 full-time, 13 part-time). Student-undergrad faculty ratio is 14:1. Students come from 4 states and territories, 3 other countries, 2% from out-of-state. Retention: 53% of full-time freshmen returned the following year. Academic area with the most degrees conferred: theology and religious vocations. Core. Calendar: semesters. Academic remediation for entering students, services for LD students, advanced placement, independent study, double major, part-time degree program, internships. Off campus study.

Entrance Requirements: Option: electronic application. Required: essay, high school transcript, minimum 2.25 high school GPA, 3 recommendations, SAT or ACT. Entrance: moderately difficult. Application deadline: 8/1. Notification: 8/15. Transfer credits accepted: Yes.

Costs Per Year: Application fee: $30. One-time mandatory fee: $200. Comprehensive fee: $22,642 includes full-time tuition ($13,312), mandatory fees ($1330), and college room and board ($8000). Room and board charges vary according to board plan and housing facility. Part-time tuition: $416 per credit hour.

Collegiate Environment: Orientation program. Drama-theater group, choral group, student-run newspaper. Major annual events: Madrigal Dinner Theater, concerts. Student services: personal-psychological counseling. Campus security: controlled dormitory access, evening security patrols. Louis M. Detro Memorial Library with 48,790 books, 11,926 serials, 1,368 audiovisual materials, an OPAC, and a Web page. Operations spending for the previous fiscal year: $122,477. 24 computers available on campus for general student use. A campuswide network can be accessed from student

residence rooms and from off campus. Staffed computer lab on campus provides training in use of computers, software, and the Internet.
Community Environment: See Lansing Community College.

■ GRIGGS UNIVERSITY

8903 U.S. Hwy. 31
Berrien Springs, MI 49014
Tel: (269)471-6570; Free: 800-782-4769
Fax: (269)471-2804
E-mail: LLundberg@griggs.edu
Web Site: www.griggs.edu/college.html

Description: Independent Seventh-day Adventist, 4-year, coed. Part of Seventh-day Adventist Parochial School System. Awards associate and bachelor's degrees (offers only external degree programs). Founded 1990. Setting: suburban campus with easy access to Washington, DC. Total enrollment: 865. Faculty: 38 (all part-time). 28 applied, 100% were admitted. Students come from 11 other countries, 6% from out-of-state. Retention: 73% of full-time freshmen returned the following year. Core. Calendar: continuous. Advanced placement, accelerated degree program, independent study, distance learning, double major, summer session for credit, part-time degree program, external degree program, adult/continuing education programs.

Entrance Requirements: Options: early admission, deferred admission. Required: essay, high school transcript, minimum 2 high school GPA. Entrance: minimally difficult. Application deadline: Rolling.

■ HENRY FORD COMMUNITY COLLEGE

5101 Evergreen Rd.
Dearborn, MI 48128-1495
Tel: (313)845-9615; Free: 800-585-HFCC
Fax: (313)845-9658
E-mail: enroll@hfcc.edu
Web Site: www.hfcc.edu/

Description: District-supported, 2-year, coed. Awards certificates, transfer associate, and terminal associate degrees. Founded 1938. Setting: 75-acre suburban campus with easy access to Detroit. Total enrollment: 17,542. Student-undergrad faculty ratio is 24:1. 0% from out-of-state. 39% 25 or older. Core. Calendar: semesters. Academic remediation for entering students, ESL program, advanced placement, freshman honors college, honors program, independent study, distance learning, summer session for credit, part-time degree program, adult/continuing education programs, co-op programs and internships. Study abroad program.

Entrance Requirements: Open admission except for nursing, allied health, honors programs. Options: early admission, deferred admission. Recommended: high school transcript. Entrance: noncompetitive. Application deadline: Rolling. Notification: continuous.

Collegiate Environment: Drama-theater group, choral group, student-run newspaper, radio station. Student services: personal-psychological counseling, women's center. Campus security: 24-hour emergency response devices and patrols, late night transport-escort service. Eshleman Library with an OPAC and a Web page.

Community Environment: Dearborn's boundaries have been extended to join those of Detroit, and it is difficult to discern where one city ends and the other begins. Dearborn is a distinct entity with history, government and industries of its own. The area is called the city with no slums. There are limited job opportunities within the immediate area, though Detroit offers good part-time employment. Camp Dearborn 35 miles northwest offers 6 lakes, a trout stream, picnic groves, a 1/2 mile beach, and camping facilities. Community services include two general hospitals, five public libraries, and limited access to all major forms of public transportation. The city has outstanding public recreation facilities.

■ HILLSDALE COLLEGE

33 E College St.
Hillsdale, MI 49242-1298
Tel: (517)437-7341
Fax: (517)437-0190
E-mail: admissions@hillsdale.edu
Web Site: www.hillsdale.edu/

Description: Independent, comprehensive, coed. Awards bachelor's, master's, and doctoral degrees. Founded 1844. Setting: 250-acre small town campus. Endowment: $350 million. Educational spending for the previous fiscal year: $16,000 per student. Total enrollment: 1,447. Faculty: 163 (118 full-time, 45 part-time). Student-undergrad faculty ratio is 10:1. 2,018 ap-

plied, 49% were admitted. 54% from top 10% of their high school class, 82% from top quarter, 99% from top half. 17 National Merit Scholars, 53 class presidents, 63 valedictorians, 188 student government officers. Full-time: 1,399 students, 53% women, 47% men. Part-time: 35 students, 49% women, 51% men. Students come from 47 states and territories, 8 other countries, 64% from out-of-state. 1% 25 or older, 75% live on campus, 2% transferred in. Retention: 98% of full-time freshmen returned the following year. Academic areas with the most degrees conferred: business/marketing; social sciences; education. Core. Calendar: semesters. Advanced placement, accelerated degree program, honors program, independent study, double major, summer session for credit, part-time degree program, internships. Off campus study. Study abroad program.

Entrance Requirements: Options: electronic application, early admission, early decision, early action, international baccalaureate accepted. Required: essay, high school transcript, 2 recommendations, SAT or ACT. Recommended: minimum 3.5 high school GPA, interview, SAT Subject Tests. Required for some: minimum 3.5 high school GPA, interview. Entrance: very difficult. Application deadlines: 2/15, 2/15 for nonresidents, 11/15 for early decision, 12/15 for early action. Notification: 4/1, 4/1 for nonresidents, 12/1 for early decision, 2/15 for early action. SAT Reasoning Test deadline: 2/15. SAT Subject Test deadline: 2/15. Applicants placed on waiting list: 55. Wait-listed applicants offered admission: 6. Early decision applicants: 145. Early decision applicants admitted: 70. Early action applicants: 1,180. Early action applicants admitted: 600.

Costs Per Year: Application fee: $0. Comprehensive fee: $31,890 includes full-time tuition ($22,250), mandatory fees ($640), and college room and board ($9000). College room only: $4460. Room and board charges vary according to board plan. Part-time tuition: $880 per credit.

Collegiate Environment: Orientation program. Drama-theater group, choral group, student-run newspaper. Social organizations: 45 open to all; national fraternities, national sororities; 35% of eligible men and 45% of eligible women are members. Most popular organizations: Inter-Varsity Christian Fellowship, Varsity H-Club, Student Federation, Young Life, College Republicans. Major annual events: Homecoming, Parents' Weekend, Centralhallapalooza. Student services: health clinic, personal-psychological counseling. Campus security: 24-hour emergency response devices and patrols, late night transport-escort service, controlled dormitory access. 900 college housing spaces available; all were occupied in 2012-13. Freshmen guaranteed college housing. On-campus residence required through sophomore year. Options: men-only, women-only housing available. Mossey Learning Center plus 3 others with 240,000 books, 61,400 microform titles, 1,650 serials, 8,000 audiovisual materials, an OPAC, and a Web page. Operations spending for the previous fiscal year: $1.1 million. 220 computers available on campus for general student use. A campuswide network can be accessed from student residence rooms and from off campus. Students can access the following: online class registration. Staffed computer lab on campus provides training in use of computers, software, and the Internet.

Community Environment: Hillsdale is a county seat located in the south central part of the lower peninsula. In an agricultural region, it is a resort and industrial community, manufacturing automobile parts and accessories, and tool and die products. The area has bus service and a municipal airport.

■ HOPE COLLEGE

141 E 12th St.
Holland, MI 49422-9000
Tel: (616)395-7000; Free: 800-968-7850
Fax: (616)395-7130
E-mail: admissions@hope.edu
Web Site: www.hope.edu/

Description: Independent, 4-year, coed, affiliated with Reformed Church in America. Awards bachelor's degrees. Founded 1866. Setting: 45-acre suburban campus with easy access to Grand Rapids. Endowment: $150.9 million. Research spending for the previous fiscal year: $6 million. Educational spending for the previous fiscal year: $9895 per student. Total enrollment: 3,343. Faculty: 329 (226 full-time, 103 part-time). Student-undergrad faculty ratio is 12:1. 3,491 applied, 85% were admitted. 37% from top 10% of their high school class, 64% from top quarter, 94% from top half. 8 National Merit Scholars. Full-time: 3,205 students, 60% women, 40% men. Part-time: 138 students, 54% women, 46% men. Students come from 44 states and territories, 35 other countries, 31% from out-of-state. 0.1% American Indian or Alaska Native, non-Hispanic/Latino; 6% Hispanic/Latino; 2% African American, non-Hispanic/Latino; 2% Asian, non-Hispanic/Latino; 0.03% Native Hawaiian or other Pacific Islander, non-Hispanic/Latino; 2% international. 1% 25 or older, 81% live on campus, 2% transferred in. Retention: 90% of full-time freshmen returned the following year. Academic areas with the most degrees conferred: education; business/marketing; psychology. Core. Calendar: semesters. ESL program, services for LD students, advanced placement, self-designed majors, independent study, double major, summer session for credit, part-time degree program, internships. Off campus study at members of the Great Lakes Colleges Association, Associated Colleges of the Midwest, Institute of European Studies, Council for International Educational Exchange. Study abroad program. ROTC: Army (c).

Entrance Requirements: Options: electronic application, early admission, deferred admission, international baccalaureate accepted. Required: essay, high school transcript, SAT or ACT. Recommended: interview. Required for some: 1 recommendation. Entrance: moderately difficult. Application deadline: Rolling. Notification: continuous. SAT Reasoning Test deadline: 3/31. Transfer credits accepted: Yes. Applicants placed on waiting list: 0. Wait-listed applicants offered admission: 0.

Costs Per Year: Application fee: $50. Comprehensive fee: $37,530 includes full-time tuition ($28,550), mandatory fees ($170), and college room and board ($8810). College room only: $4040. Room and board charges vary according to board plan.

Collegiate Environment: Orientation program. Drama-theater group, choral group, student-run newspaper, radio station. Social organizations: 78 open to all; national fraternities, national sororities, local fraternities, local sororities; 10% of eligible men and 12% of eligible women are members. Most popular organizations: Social Activities Committee, Greek Life, Dance Marathon, Hockey Club, Relay for Life. Major annual events: Homecoming Weekend Events, Nykerk Cup Competition, Spring Fling. Student services: health clinic, personal-psychological counseling. Campus security: 24-hour emergency response devices and patrols, late night transport-escort service, controlled dormitory access. 2,474 college housing spaces available; all were occupied in 2012-13. Freshmen guaranteed college housing. On-campus residence required through junior year. Options: coed, men-only, women-only housing available. Van Wylen Library plus 2 others with 375,564 books, 385,797 microform titles, 6,873 serials, 20,296 audiovisual materials, an OPAC, and a Web page. Operations spending for the previous fiscal year: $2.5 million. 300 computers available on campus for general student use. A campuswide network can be accessed from student residence rooms and from off campus. Students can access the following: online class registration. Staffed computer lab on campus provides training in use of computers, software, and the Internet.

Community Environment: Settled by the Dutch in 1847, the city still has many of the characteristics of a Dutch town. This is the tulip center of America, and millions of these flowers bloom in the parks and residential sections during May. Located on Lake Macatawa and Lake Michigan, the area offers many opportunities for water and other outdoor sports activities. Holland is surrounded by a large fruit-growing and farming area, and is also an industrial and resort town. The city has bus and train service, two airports, a public library, several churches, a hospital and several parks. Holland has a population of approximately 34,400; it is a very friendly, safe and clean community.

■ ITT TECHNICAL INSTITUTE (CANTON)
1905 S Haggerty Rd.
Canton, MI 48188-2025
Tel: (734)397-7800; Free: 800-247-4477
Fax: (734)397-1945
Web Site: www.itt-tech.edu/
Description: Proprietary, primarily 2-year, coed. Part of ITT Educational Services, Inc. Awards terminal associate and bachelor's degrees. Founded 2002.
Entrance Requirements: Entrance: minimally difficult.

■ ITT TECHNICAL INSTITUTE (DEARBORN)
19855 W Outer Dr.
Ste. L10W
Dearborn, MI 48124
Tel: (313)278-5208; Free: 800-605-0801
Web Site: www.itt-tech.edu/
Description: Proprietary, primarily 2-year, coed. Part of ITT Educational Services, Inc. Awards terminal associate and bachelor's degrees.

■ ITT TECHNICAL INSTITUTE (GRAND RAPIDS)
3518 Plainfield Ave. NE
Grand Rapids, MI 49525

Tel: (616)365-4800; Free: 877-264-1715
Web Site: www.itt-tech.edu/
Description: Proprietary, 4-year, coed. Awards associate and bachelor's degrees.
Entrance Requirements: Entrance: minimally difficult.

■ ITT TECHNICAL INSTITUTE (SOUTHFIELD)
26700 Lahser Rd.
Ste. 100
Southfield, MI 48033
Tel: (248)603-6100; Free: 877-363-3221
Web Site: www.itt-tech.edu/
Description: Proprietary, 4-year, coed. Awards associate and bachelor's degrees.
Entrance Requirements: Entrance: minimally difficult.

■ ITT TECHNICAL INSTITUTE (SWARTZ CREEK)
6359 Miller Rd.
Swartz Creek, MI 48473
Tel: (810)628-2500; Free: 800-514-6564
Web Site: www.itt-tech.edu/
Description: Proprietary, primarily 2-year, coed. Part of ITT Educational Services, Inc. Awards transfer associate and bachelor's degrees. Founded 2005.
Entrance Requirements: Entrance: minimally difficult.

■ ITT TECHNICAL INSTITUTE (TROY)
1522 E Big Beaver Rd.
Troy, MI 48083-1905
Tel: (248)524-1800; Free: 800-832-6817
Web Site: www.itt-tech.edu/
Description: Proprietary, primarily 2-year, coed. Part of ITT Educational Services, Inc. Awards terminal associate and bachelor's degrees. Founded 1987.
Entrance Requirements: Entrance: minimally difficult.

■ ITT TECHNICAL INSTITUTE (WYOMING)
1980 Metro Ct. SW
Wyoming, MI 49519
Tel: (616)406-1200; Free: 800-632-4676
Web Site: www.itt-tech.edu/
Description: Proprietary, primarily 2-year, coed. Part of ITT Educational Services, Inc. Awards terminal associate and bachelor's degrees.
Entrance Requirements: Entrance: minimally difficult.

■ JACKSON COLLEGE
2111 Emmons Rd.
Jackson, MI 49201-8399
Tel: (517)787-0800; Free: 888-522-7344
E-mail: admissions@jccmi.edu
Web Site: www.jccmi.edu/
Description: County-supported, 2-year, coed. Awards certificates, transfer associate, and terminal associate degrees. Founded 1928. Setting: 580-acre suburban campus with easy access to Detroit. Total enrollment: 6,328. Faculty: 488 (89 full-time, 399 part-time). Student-undergrad faculty ratio is 17:1. Full-time: 2,598 students, 58% women, 42% men. Part-time: 3,739 students, 63% women, 37% men. 0.1% from out-of-state. 1% American Indian or Alaska Native, non-Hispanic/Latino; 4% Hispanic/Latino; 8% African American, non-Hispanic/Latino; 1% Asian, non-Hispanic/Latino; 0% Native Hawaiian or other Pacific Islander, non-Hispanic/Latino; 0.1% international. 56% 25 or older, 2% live on campus. Core. Calendar: semesters. Academic remediation for entering students, ESL program, services for LD students, advanced placement, accelerated degree program, freshman honors college, honors program, independent study, distance learning, double major, summer session for credit, part-time degree program, adult/continuing education programs, co-op programs and internships.
Entrance Requirements: Open admission Nursing and allied health programs have a secondary admission process. Options: electronic application, international baccalaureate accepted. Required: Minimum ACT of 16 is required for housing admission. Recommended: ACT. Required for some: minimum 16 high school GPA, ACT. Entrance: noncompetitive. Application deadlines: Rolling, Rolling for nonresidents. Notification: continuous, continuous for nonresidents. Transfer credits accepted: Yes.

Costs Per Year: Application fee: $0. Area resident tuition: $2544 full-time, $106 per contact hour part-time. State resident tuition: $3816 full-time, $159 per contact hour part-time. Nonresident tuition: $5088 full-time, $212 per contact hour part-time. Mandatory fees: $768 full-time, $32 per contact hour part-time, $32. Full-time tuition and fees vary according to location. Part-time tuition and fees vary according to location. College room only: $5150.

Collegiate Environment: Orientation program. Drama-theater group, choral group. Student services: health clinic. Campus security: 24-hour emergency response devices and patrols, student patrols, late night transport-escort service, controlled dormitory access. 192 college housing spaces available; 190 were occupied in 2012-13. No special consideration for freshman housing applicants. Option: coed housing available.

Community Environment: The college is located seven miles south of Jackson, an important industrial city that manufactures mainly automobile and airplane parts and supplies. Major highways provide access to Chicago and Detroit. The county has numerous lakes, golf courses and parks. Cultural activities include a symphony orchestra, music, and dance and theater groups. Also located in the area are the Illuminated Cascades, the Ella Sharp Museum and the Michigan Space and Science Center.

■ **KALAMAZOO COLLEGE**
1200 Academy St.
Kalamazoo, MI 49006-3295
Tel: (269)337-7000; Free: 800-253-3602
Fax: (269)337-7251
E-mail: admission.records@kzoo.edu
Web Site: www.kzoo.edu/

Description: Independent, 4-year, coed, affiliated with American Baptist Churches in the U.S.A. Awards bachelor's degrees. Founded 1833. Setting: 60-acre suburban campus with easy access to Grand Rapids. Endowment: $169.5 million. Total enrollment: 1,379. Faculty: 114 (96 full-time, 18 part-time). Student-undergrad faculty ratio is 12:1. 2,294 applied, 69% were admitted. 46% from top 10% of their high school class, 87% from top quarter, 96% from top half. 8 National Merit Scholars, 15 class presidents, 10 valedictorians, 64 student government officers. Full-time: 1,366 students, 58% women, 42% men. Part-time: 13 students, 54% women, 46% men. Students come from 38 states and territories, 32 other countries, 38% from out-of-state. 0.4% American Indian or Alaska Native, non-Hispanic/Latino; 9% Hispanic/Latino; 4% African American, non-Hispanic/Latino; 5% Asian, non-Hispanic/Latino; 0.1% Native Hawaiian or other Pacific Islander, non-Hispanic/Latino; 7% international. 1% 25 or older, 70% live on campus, 1% transferred in. Retention: 94% of full-time freshmen returned the following year. Academic areas with the most degrees conferred: social sciences; biological/life sciences; physical sciences. Core. Services for LD students, advanced placement, self-designed majors, independent study, double major, internships. Off campus study at Western Michigan University. Study abroad program. ROTC: Army (c).

Entrance Requirements: Options: electronic application, early decision, early action, deferred admission, international baccalaureate accepted. Required: essay, high school transcript, 2 recommendations, Common Application Supplement, SAT or ACT. Recommended: minimum 3 high school GPA, interview. Entrance: very difficult. Application deadlines: 2/1, 11/10 for early decision, 11/20 for early action. Notification: 4/1, 11/20 for early decision, 12/20 for early action. SAT Reasoning Test deadline: 2/1. Transfer credits accepted: Yes. Applicants placed on waiting list: 206. Wait-listed applicants offered admission: 44. Early decision applicants: 24. Early decision applicants admitted: 23. Early action applicants: 883. Early action applicants admitted: 818.

Costs Per Year: Application fee: $40. Comprehensive fee: $45,984 includes full-time tuition ($37,392), mandatory fees ($318), and college room and board ($8274). College room only: $4035. Room and board charges vary according to board plan.

Collegiate Environment: Orientation program. Drama-theater group, choral group, student-run newspaper, radio station. Social organizations: 70 open to all. Most popular organizations: Frelon Dance Company, Acappella groups, Environmental Student Organization, Kaleidoscope, Student Commission. Major annual events: Monte Carlo Night, Crystal Ball, K Fest. Student services: health clinic, personal-psychological counseling. Campus security: 24-hour emergency response devices and patrols, late night transport-escort service, controlled dormitory access. 876 college housing spaces available; 840 were occupied in 2012-13. Freshmen guaranteed college housing. On-campus residence required through junior year. Option: coed housing available. Upjohn Library Commons with 344,258 books, 14,587 microform titles, 73,180 serials, 7,067 audiovisual materials, an

OPAC, and a Web page. 250 computers available on campus for general student use. A campuswide network can be accessed from student residence rooms and from off campus. Students can access the following: online class registration, RCC - Residential computer consultant. Staffed computer lab on campus (open 24 hours a day) provides training in use of computers, software, and the Internet.

Community Environment: Kalamazoo is a college-centered community, 130 miles from Detroit and Chicago. The airport serves nine major airlines. Locally, many companies, hospitals and local governments make internships available to students.

■ **KALAMAZOO VALLEY COMMUNITY COLLEGE**
PO Box 4070
Kalamazoo, MI 49003-4070
Tel: (269)488-4400
Fax: (269)448-4555
Web Site: www.kvcc.edu/

Description: State and locally supported, 2-year, coed. Awards certificates, transfer associate, and terminal associate degrees. Founded 1966. Setting: 187-acre suburban campus. Educational spending for the previous fiscal year: $311 per student. Total enrollment: 11,113. 1% from out-of-state. 37% 25 or older. Core. Calendar: semesters. Academic remediation for entering students, ESL program, services for LD students, advanced placement, self-designed majors, honors program, independent study, distance learning, summer session for credit, part-time degree program, co-op programs and internships. Off campus study at 5 members of the Kalamazoo Consortium. ROTC: Army (c).

Entrance Requirements: Open admission. Required: high school transcript, ACT. Entrance: noncompetitive. Application deadline: Rolling. Notification: continuous. Transfer credits accepted: Yes.

Collegiate Environment: Orientation program. Choral group. Student services: personal-psychological counseling. Campus security: 24-hour emergency response devices and patrols. Kalamazoo Valley Community College Library with 88,791 books, 420 serials, an OPAC, and a Web page.

Community Environment: See Western Michigan University.

■ **KELLOGG COMMUNITY COLLEGE**
450 N Ave.
Battle Creek, MI 49017-3397
Tel: (616)965-3931
Fax: (616)965-4133
E-mail: harriss@kellogg.edu
Web Site: www.kellogg.edu/

Description: State and locally supported, 2-year, coed. Part of Michigan Department of Education. Awards certificates, transfer associate, and terminal associate degrees. Founded 1956. Setting: 120-acre urban campus. Total enrollment: 5,976. Faculty: 385 (92 full-time, 293 part-time). Student-undergrad faculty ratio is 23:1. 2,623 applied, 100% were admitted. Full-time: 2,053 students, 60% women, 40% men. Part-time: 3,923 students, 68% women, 32% men. 46% 25 or older. Core. Calendar: semesters. Academic remediation for entering students, ESL program, services for LD students, advanced placement, accelerated degree program, freshman honors college, honors program, independent study, distance learning, double major, summer session for credit, part-time degree program, adult/continuing education programs, co-op programs and internships. Off campus study.

Entrance Requirements: Open admission except for allied health and nursing programs. Options: electronic application, early admission. Required for some: high school transcript, minimum 2 high school GPA, ACT, SAT or ACT. Entrance: noncompetitive. Application deadline: Rolling. Notification: continuous. Transfer credits accepted: Yes.

Collegiate Environment: Orientation program. Drama-theater group, choral group, student-run newspaper. Social organizations: 23 open to all. Most popular organizations: Tech Club, Phi Theta Kappa, Student Nurses Association, Crude Arts Club, Art League. Major annual events: KCC Bruin Boost and KCC Bruin Blast, Leadership Conference, Blood Drive. Campus security: 24-hour emergency response devices and patrols, late night transport-escort service. Emory W. Morris Learning Resource Center with 42,131 books, 78,179 microform titles, 172 serials, an OPAC, and a Web page. 550 computers available on campus for general student use. A campuswide network can be accessed from off-campus. Students can access the following: online class registration. Staffed computer lab on campus provides training in use of computers and software.

Community Environment: This is the home of cereal manufacturers. Other manufacturers produce packaging machines and auto parts. Commercial passenger facilities include bus, rail, and air. Some part-time employment is available for students. The city has good recreational areas for picnicking, golf, camping, tobogganing and skiing. All are easily accessible. The American Amateur Baseball Series is held here annually.

■ KETTERING UNIVERSITY

1700 University Ave.

Flint, MI 48504

Tel: (810)762-9500; Free: 800-955-4464

Fax: (810)762-9837

E-mail: admissions@kettering.edu

Web Site: www.kettering.edu/

Description: Independent, comprehensive, coed. Awards bachelor's and master's degrees. Founded 1919. Setting: 85-acre urban campus with easy access to Detroit. Endowment: $65.9 million. Research spending for the previous fiscal year: $6.8 million. Educational spending for the previous fiscal year: $10,555 per student. Total enrollment: 2,079. Faculty: 154 (122 full-time, 32 part-time). Student-undergrad faculty ratio is 13:1. 1,770 applied, 62% were admitted. 36% from top 10% of their high school class, 71% from top quarter, 94% from top half. 9 valedictorians. Full-time: 1,706 students, 19% women, 81% men. Part-time: 39 students, 21% women, 79% men. Students come from 44 states and territories, 11 other countries, 29% from out-of-state. 0.3% American Indian or Alaska Native, non-Hispanic/Latino; 3% Hispanic/Latino; 4% African American, non-Hispanic/Latino; 2% Asian, non-Hispanic/Latino; 0.1% Native Hawaiian or other Pacific Islander, non-Hispanic/Latino; 3% international. 2% 25 or older, 34% live on campus, 2% transferred in. Retention: 89% of full-time freshmen returned the following year. Academic areas with the most degrees conferred: engineering; computer and information sciences; business/marketing. Core. Calendar: semesters (11 weeks of full-time study plus 12 weeks of paid co-op experience per semester). Services for LD students, advanced placement, independent study, distance learning, double major, summer session for credit, co-op programs and internships, graduate courses open to undergrads. Study abroad program.

Entrance Requirements: Options: electronic application, deferred admission, international baccalaureate accepted. Required: high school transcript, SAT or ACT. Recommended: minimum 3 high school GPA, interview. Required for some: essay. Entrance: very difficult. Application deadlines: Rolling, Rolling for nonresidents. Notification: continuous, continuous for nonresidents. SAT Reasoning Test deadline: 9/1. SAT Subject Test deadline: 9/1. Transfer credits accepted: Yes.

Costs Per Year: Application fee: $35. Comprehensive fee: $40,606 includes full-time tuition ($33,946) and college room and board ($6660). College room only: $4150. Part-time tuition: $1132 per credit. Tuition guaranteed not to increase for student's term of enrollment.

Collegiate Environment: Orientation program. Choral group, student-run newspaper, radio station. Social organizations: 41 open to all; national fraternities, national sororities, local sororities; 36% of eligible men and 39% of eligible women are members. Most popular organizations: student government, Society of Automotive Engineers, Firebirds, Outdoors Club, International Club. Major annual events: Greek Week, Relay for Life, Midnight Breakfast. Student services: health clinic, personal-psychological counseling, women's center. Campus security: 24-hour emergency response devices and patrols, late night transport-escort service, controlled dormitory access, security card access to all campus buildings 24/7 except the campus center main entrance which is secure 11pm-7am. Kettering University Library plus 1 other with 164,180 books, 36,000 microform titles, 400 serials, 2,000 audiovisual materials, an OPAC, and a Web page. Operations spending for the previous fiscal year: $941,340. 450 computers available on campus for general student use. A campuswide network can be accessed from student residence rooms and from off campus. Students can access the following: online class registration. Staffed computer lab on campus provides training in use of computers, software, and the Internet.

Community Environment: A pioneer in the early days of the automobile industry, Flint is located about one hour north of Detroit and within an hour of Ann Arbor and East Lansing. Commercial transportation is provided by air, bus, and rail lines. The Flint area has several hospitals, churches of most faiths, the Flint Cultural Center with museums and institutes of arts and music, and shopping. Recreational facilities are abundant, from the university Recreation Center and playing fields, to nearby golf courses, ski slopes, lakes, theatres, and more.

■ KEWEENAW BAY OJIBWA COMMUNITY COLLEGE

111 Beartown Rd.

Baraga, MI 49908

Tel: (906)353-4600

E-mail: megan@kbocc.org

Web Site: www.kbocc.org/

Description: County-supported, 2-year, coed. Awards transfer associate and terminal associate degrees.

Entrance Requirements: Required: high school transcript.

■ KIRTLAND COMMUNITY COLLEGE

10775 N St. Helen Rd.

Roscommon, MI 48653-9699

Tel: (989)275-5000

Fax: (989)275-8210

E-mail: registrar@kirtland.edu

Web Site: www.kirtland.edu/

Description: District-supported, 2-year, coed. Awards certificates, transfer associate, and terminal associate degrees. Founded 1966. Setting: 180-acre rural campus. Educational spending for the previous fiscal year: $4940 per student. Total enrollment: 1,807. Faculty: 124 (38 full-time, 86 part-time). Student-undergrad faculty ratio is 18:1. 414 applied, 100% were admitted. Full-time: 690 students, 61% women, 39% men. Part-time: 1,117 students, 66% women, 34% men. Students come from 4 states and territories, 4 other countries. 1% American Indian or Alaska Native, non-Hispanic/Latino; 2% Hispanic/Latino; 1% African American, non-Hispanic/Latino; 0.3% Asian, non-Hispanic/Latino; 0.1% Native Hawaiian or other Pacific Islander, non-Hispanic/Latino; 0.4% international. 45% 25 or older. Core. Calendar: semesters. Academic remediation for entering students, ESL program, services for LD students, advanced placement, honors program, independent study, distance learning, summer session for credit, part-time degree program, adult/continuing education programs, co-op programs and internships.

Entrance Requirements: Open admission. Option: electronic application. Recommended: ACT. Entrance: noncompetitive. Application deadline: Rolling. Notification: continuous until 8/22. Transfer credits accepted: Yes.

Costs Per Year: Application fee: $0. Area resident tuition: $2760 full-time, $92 per contact hour part-time. State resident tuition: $3840 full-time, $128 per contact hour part-time. Nonresident tuition: $6360 full-time, $212 per contact hour part-time. Mandatory fees: $475 full-time, $13.50 per contact hour part-time, $35 per term part-time.

Collegiate Environment: Orientation program. Social organizations: CJ Club, Student Senate, Phi Theta Kappa. Campus security: 24-hour emergency response devices, student patrols, late night transport-escort service, campus warning siren, uniformed armed police officers, RAVE alert system (text, email, voice). College housing not available. Kirtland Community College Library with 33,000 books, 321 serials, and an OPAC. 180 computers available on campus for general student use. A campuswide network can be accessed from off-campus. Students can access the following: online class registration. Staffed computer lab on campus provides training in use of software and the Internet.

Community Environment: The college is located in the heart of Michigan's four-season vacationland amidst excellent hunting, fishing, swimming, boating, skiing and snowmobiling lands and lakes. Interstate Route I-75 provides the most direct means of approach to within twelve miles of the campus, which is located at the juncture of Roscommon, Ogemaw, Oscoda and Crawford counties on County Road F-97.

■ KUYPER COLLEGE

3333 E Beltline, NE

Grand Rapids, MI 49525-9749

Tel: (616)222-3000

Fax: (616)222-3045

E-mail: admissions@kuyper.edu

Web Site: www.kuyper.edu/

Description: Independent Christian, 4-year, coed. Awards associate and bachelor's degrees. Founded 1939. Setting: 34-acre suburban campus with easy access to Grand Rapids. Endowment: $7.4 million. Educational spending for the previous fiscal year: $10,533 per student. Total enrollment: 314. Faculty: 37 (13 full-time, 24 part-time). Student-undergrad faculty ratio is 15:1. 17% from top 10% of their high school class, 22% from top quarter, 52% from top half. Full-time: 276 students, 53% women, 47% men. Part-time: 36 students, 64% women, 36% men. 12% from out-of-state. 1% American Indian or Alaska Native, non-Hispanic/Latino; 1% Hispanic/Latino;

3% African American, non-Hispanic/Latino; 2% Asian, non-Hispanic/Latino; 0% Native Hawaiian or other Pacific Islander, non-Hispanic/Latino; 4% international. 16% 25 or older, 51% live on campus, 0% transferred in. Retention: 69% of full-time freshmen returned the following year. Academic areas with the most degrees conferred: theology and religious vocations; public administration and social services; liberal arts/general studies. Core. Calendar: semesters. Academic remediation for entering students, services for LD students, advanced placement, independent study, distance learning; double major, summer session for credit, part-time degree program, co-op programs and internships. Off campus study at Grand Rapids Community College, Cornerstone University, Calvin College. Study abroad program. ROTC: Army (c).

Entrance Requirements: Options: electronic application, deferred admission, international baccalaureate accepted. Required: essay, high school transcript, minimum 2.5 high school GPA. Recommended: interview. Entrance: moderately difficult. Application deadline: Rolling. Notification: continuous. Transfer credits accepted: Yes.

Collegiate Environment: Orientation program. Drama-theater group, choral group. Social organizations: 10 open to all. Most popular organizations: intramurals, Student Activities Club, Helping and Nurturing During Service, yearbook, Roots. Major annual events: Christmas Banquet, Variety Show, All Campus Retreat. Student services: health clinic, personal-psychological counseling. Campus security: 24-hour emergency response devices, student patrols, late night transport-escort service, controlled dormitory access. 160 college housing spaces available. Freshmen guaranteed college housing. On-campus residence required through sophomore year. Option: coed housing available. Zondervan Library with 56,590 books, 4,752 microform titles, 204 serials, 3,515 audiovisual materials, an OPAC, and a Web page. Operations spending for the previous fiscal year: $345,123. 70 computers available on campus for general student use. A campuswide network can be accessed from student residence rooms and from off campus. Students can access the following: online class registration. Staffed computer lab on campus provides training in use of computers, software, and the Internet.

Community Environment: See Calvin College.

■ **LAKE MICHIGAN COLLEGE**
2755 E Napier Ave.
Benton Harbor, MI 49022-1899
Tel: (269)927-8100; Free: 800-252-1LMC
E-mail: thomas@lakemichigancollege.edu
Web Site: www.lakemichigancollege.edu/

Description: District-supported, 2-year, coed. Part of Michigan Department of Education. Awards certificates, transfer associate, and terminal associate degrees. Founded 1946. Setting: 260-acre small town campus. Endowment: $6.4 million. Educational spending for the previous fiscal year: $4368 per student. Total enrollment: 4,548. Faculty: 327 (58 full-time, 269 part-time). Student-undergrad faculty ratio is 17:1. 1,580 applied, 94% were admitted. 5% from top 10% of their high school class, 18% from top quarter, 47% from top half. Full-time: 1,508 students, 57% women, 43% men. Part-time: 3,040 students, 61% women, 39% men. Students come from 5 states and territories, 50 other countries, 2% from out-of-state. 1% American Indian or Alaska Native, non-Hispanic/Latino; 6% Hispanic/Latino; 21% African American, non-Hispanic/Latino; 1% Asian, non-Hispanic/Latino; 0.4% Native Hawaiian or other Pacific Islander, non-Hispanic/Latino; 0% international. 37% 25 or older, 6% transferred in. Retention: 42% of full-time freshmen returned the following year. Core. Calendar: semesters. Academic remediation for entering students, ESL program, services for LD students, self-designed majors, honors program, independent study, distance learning, summer session for credit, part-time degree program, adult/continuing education programs, co-op programs. Off campus study at Western Michigan University.

Entrance Requirements: Open admission. Option: electronic application. Required: high school transcript. Required for some: interview. Entrance: noncompetitive. Application deadline: Rolling. Notification: continuous. Transfer credits accepted: Yes.

Costs Per Year: Application fee: $0. Area resident tuition: $2490 full-time, $83 per contact hour part-time. State resident tuition: $3840 full-time, $128 per contact hour part-time. Nonresident tuition: $5070 full-time, $169 per contact hour part-time. Mandatory fees: $1170 full-time, $39 per contact hour part-time.

Collegiate Environment: Orientation program. Drama-theater group, choral group. Social organizations: 20 open to all. Most popular organizations: Cheer Team, Phi Theta Kappa, Student Senate, Movie Club, LMC Sky Kings (Sky Diving Club). Major annual events: Welcome Week, Spring Fling,

Honors Convocation. Campus security: 24-hour emergency response devices, contracted campus security force. College housing not available. William Hessel Library with 98,682 books, 294 microform titles, 23,943 serials, 3,837 audiovisual materials, an OPAC, and a Web page. Operations spending for the previous fiscal year: $348,404. 120 computers available on campus for general student use. A campuswide network can be accessed. Students can access the following: online class registration, online financial aid information. Staffed computer lab on campus provides training in use of computers, software, and the Internet.

■ **LAKE SUPERIOR STATE UNIVERSITY**
650 W Easterday Ave.
Sault Sainte Marie, MI 49783
Tel: (906)632-6841; Free: 888-800-LSSU
Fax: (906)635-6669
E-mail: admissions@lssu.edu
Web Site: www.lssu.edu/

Description: State-supported, comprehensive, coed. Awards associate, bachelor's, and master's degrees. Founded 1946. Setting: 115-acre small town campus. Endowment: $8.2 million. Research spending for the previous fiscal year: $369,014. Educational spending for the previous fiscal year: $5982 per student. Total enrollment: 2,530. Faculty: 184 (115 full-time, 69 part-time). Student-undergrad faculty ratio is 17:1. 1,425 applied, 90% were admitted. 14% from top 10% of their high school class, 35% from top quarter, 67% from top half. Full-time: 2,105 students, 49% women, 51% men. Part-time: 418 students, 57% women, 43% men. Students come from 36 states and territories, 15 other countries, 8% from out-of-state. 8% American Indian or Alaska Native, non-Hispanic/Latino; 2% Hispanic/Latino; 2% African American, non-Hispanic/Latino; 1% Asian, non-Hispanic/Latino; 0% Native Hawaiian or other Pacific Islander, non-Hispanic/Latino; 7% international. 20% 25 or older, 34% live on campus, 7% transferred in. Retention: 70% of full-time freshmen returned the following year. Academic areas with the most degrees conferred: health professions and related sciences; business/marketing; homeland security, law enforcement, firefighting, and protective services. Core. Calendar: semesters. Services for LD students, advanced placement, self-designed majors, freshman honors college, honors program, independent study, distance learning, double major, summer session for credit, part-time degree program, co-op programs and internships, graduate courses open to undergrads. Off campus study at Regional campus locations in Dearborn, MI; Gaylord, MI; Petosky, MI; and Escanaba, MI. Study abroad program.

Entrance Requirements: Options: electronic application, deferred admission, international baccalaureate accepted. Required: high school transcript, SAT or ACT. Required for some: SAT or ACT for students out of high school for less than 26 months or have less than 19 transferable credits. Entrance: moderately difficult. Application deadline: Rolling. Notification: continuous. Transfer credits accepted: Yes.

Costs Per Year: Application fee: $25. One-time mandatory fee: $125. State resident tuition: $9540 full-time, $397.50 per credit hour part-time. Nonresident tuition: $14,310 full-time, $596.25 per credit hour part-time. Mandatory fees: $175 full-time. Full-time tuition and fees vary according to program and reciprocity agreements. Part-time tuition varies according to course load, location, program, and reciprocity agreements. College room and board: $8481. Room and board charges vary according to board plan and housing facility.

Collegiate Environment: Orientation program. Drama-theater group, choral group, student-run newspaper, radio station. Social organizations: 65 open to all; national fraternities, national sororities, local fraternities, local sororities; 1% of women are members. Most popular organizations: Enactus (Formally known as SIFE), SAILS - Student Alumni Involved in Lake State, Fisheries and Wildlife, Harry Potter Club, Dance Company. Major annual events: Winter Carnival, Laker Week, Lakerpalooza. Student services: health clinic, personal-psychological counseling. Campus security: 24-hour emergency response devices and patrols, student patrols, late night transport-escort service. 1,031 college housing spaces available; 909 were occupied in 2012-13. Freshmen guaranteed college housing. On-campus residence required through sophomore year. Options: coed, men-only, women-only housing available. Kenneth Shouldice Library with 200,449 books, 139,742 microform titles, 850 serials, 592 audiovisual materials, and an OPAC. Operations spending for the previous fiscal year: $938,563. 350 computers available on campus for general student use. A campuswide network can be accessed from student residence rooms and from off campus. Students can access the following: online class registration. Staffed computer lab on campus provides training in use of software.

■ LANSING COMMUNITY COLLEGE

PO Box 40010
Lansing, MI 48901-7210
Tel: (517)483-1957; Free: 800-644-4LCC
Fax: (517)483-9668
E-mail: grossbt@lcc.edu
Web Site: www.lcc.edu/

Description: State and locally supported, 2-year, coed. Part of Michigan Department of Education. Awards certificates, transfer associate, and terminal associate degrees. Founded 1957. Setting: 28-acre urban campus. Endowment: $7.3 million. Educational spending for the previous fiscal year: $3542 per student. Total enrollment: 19,123. Faculty: 2,047 (215 full-time, 1,832 part-time). Student-undergrad faculty ratio is 13:1. Full-time: 7,133 students, 52% women, 48% men. Part-time: 11,990 students, 57% women, 43% men. Students come from 17 states and territories, 37 other countries, 0.2% from out-of-state. 1% American Indian or Alaska Native, non-Hispanic/Latino; 2% Hispanic/Latino; 11% African American, non-Hispanic/Latino; 3% Asian, non-Hispanic/Latino; 0.3% Native Hawaiian or other Pacific Islander, non-Hispanic/Latino; 2% international. 40% 25 or older, 2% transferred in. Core. Calendar: semesters. Academic remediation for entering students, ESL program, services for LD students, advanced placement, honors program, independent study, distance learning, double major, summer session for credit, part-time degree program, external degree program, adult/continuing education programs, co-op programs and internships. Study abroad program. ROTC: Army (c), Air Force (c).

Entrance Requirements: Open admission except for international students or allied health, fire science, automotive technologies, law enforcement programs. Options: electronic application, early admission, deferred admission, international baccalaureate accepted. Required for some: essay, high school transcript, 2 recommendations, interview, Special requirements for health, aviation, music, police academy, and fire academy program admissions. Entrance: noncompetitive. Application deadline: 8/7. Preference given to district residents. Transfer credits accepted: Yes.

Costs Per Year: Application fee: $0. Area resident tuition: $2430 full-time, $81 per credit hour part-time. State resident tuition: $4860 full-time, $162 per credit hour part-time. Nonresident tuition: $7290 full-time, $243 per credit hour part-time. Mandatory fees: $200 full-time, $5 per credit hour part-time, $25 per term part-time. College room and board: $7100.

Collegiate Environment: Orientation program. Drama-theater group, choral group, student-run newspaper. Social organizations: 200 open to all; national fraternities, national sororities. Most popular organizations: American Marketing Association, Phi Theta Kappa, Future Teachers' Club, Health Career Related Clubs (Dental Hygiene, Nurses), Gay-Straight Alliance. Major annual events: Graduation, Student Recognition Banquet, Welcome Week/Spring Fling. Student services: personal-psychological counseling, women's center. Campus security: 24-hour emergency response devices and patrols, student patrols, late night transport-escort service. College housing not available. Lansing Community College Library with 340,420 books, 164 serials, 7,455 audiovisual materials, an OPAC, and a Web page. Operations spending for the previous fiscal year: $499,174. 2,600 computers available on campus for general student use. A campuswide network can be accessed from off-campus. Students can access the following: online class registration. Staffed computer lab on campus provides training in use of computers, software, and the Internet.

Community Environment: Named capital of the state in 1847, Lansing is well-known for its automotive industries. Over two-thirds of its products are gas engines, automobile parts, drop forgings and castings. The State Historical Museum is located here. The area has golf courses, theatres, a baseball team, museums, parks, and a riverfront walk. Excellent part-time employment is available for students.

■ LAWRENCE TECHNOLOGICAL UNIVERSITY

21000 W Ten Mile Rd.
Southfield, MI 48075-1058
Tel: (248)204-4000; Free: 800-225-5588
Fax: (248)204-3727
E-mail: admissions@ltu.edu
Web Site: www.ltu.edu/

Description: Independent, university, coed. Awards associate, bachelor's, master's, and doctoral degrees. Founded 1932. Setting: 102-acre suburban campus with easy access to Detroit. Endowment: $50 million. Research spending for the previous fiscal year: $1.8 million. Educational spending for the previous fiscal year: $8693 per student. Total enrollment: 4,154. Faculty: 398 (114 full-time, 284 part-time). Student-undergrad faculty ratio is 11:1.

1,819 applied, 44% were admitted. 26% from top 10% of their high school class, 57% from top quarter, 88% from top half. Full-time: 1,382 students, 27% women, 73% men. Part-time: 1,683 students, 24% women, 76% men. Students come from 21 states and territories, 29 other countries, 3% from out-of-state. 0.4% American Indian or Alaska Native, non-Hispanic/Latino; 2% Hispanic/Latino; 9% African American, non-Hispanic/Latino; 30% Asian, non-Hispanic/Latino; 0% Native Hawaiian or other Pacific Islander, non-Hispanic/Latino; 5% international. 17% 25 or older, 18% live on campus, 6% transferred in. Retention: 74% of full-time freshmen returned the following year. Academic areas with the most degrees conferred: architecture; engineering; computer and information sciences. Core. Calendar: semesters. Academic remediation for entering students, ESL program, services for LD students, advanced placement, accelerated degree program, honors program, independent study, distance learning, double major, summer session for credit, part-time degree program, adult/continuing education programs, co-op programs and internships, graduate courses open to undergrads. Off campus study at Lansing Community College. Study abroad program. ROTC: Air Force (c).

Entrance Requirements: Options: electronic application, early admission, deferred admission, international baccalaureate accepted. Required: high school transcript, minimum 2.5 high school GPA, ACT (preferred). Required for some: essay, minimum 2.75 high school GPA, 1 recommendation, interview, SAT or ACT. Entrance: moderately difficult. Application deadline: 8/15. Notification: continuous until 8/26. SAT Reasoning Test deadline: 6/30. SAT Subject Test deadline: 6/30. Transfer credits accepted: Yes.

Costs Per Year: Application fee: $30. Comprehensive fee: $36,857 includes full-time tuition ($27,300), mandatory fees ($570), and college room and board ($8987). College room only: $4959. Full-time tuition and fees vary according to course level, degree level, location, program, and student level. Room and board charges vary according to board plan and housing facility. Part-time tuition: $910 per credit hour. Part-time mandatory fees: $285 per term. Part-time tuition and fees vary according to course level, degree level, location, program, and student level.

Collegiate Environment: Orientation program. Drama-theater group, student-run newspaper. Social organizations: 48 open to all; national fraternities, national sororities, local fraternities, local sororities; 6% of eligible men and 6% of eligible women are members. Most popular organizations: American Institute of Architecture Students, American Society of Mechanical Engineers, Institute of Electric and Electronic Engineers, American Society of Civil Engineers, student government. Major annual events: Discovery Days, New Student Convocation, Welcome Back Picnic. Student services: personal-psychological counseling. Campus security: 24-hour emergency response devices and patrols, late night transport-escort service, controlled dormitory access. 545 college housing spaces available; 538 were occupied in 2012-13. Freshmen given priority for college housing. Option: coed housing available. Lawrence Technological University Library plus 1 other with 213,260 books, 30,260 microform titles, 110,387 serials, 768 audiovisual materials, an OPAC, and a Web page. Operations spending for the previous fiscal year: $962,632. 126 computers available on campus for general student use. Computer purchase/lease plans available. A computer is required for all students. A campuswide network can be accessed from student residence rooms and from off campus. Students can access the following: online class registration, degree audit, Blackboard, SCT Banner (student information), Personal websites, Document collection. Staffed computer lab on campus (open 24 hours a day) provides training in use of computers, software, and the Internet.

Community Environment: The city is a northern suburb of Detroit, with excellent full-time and part-time employment opportunities for students. Good recreational facilities are nearby. Southfield has excellent shopping areas and a Civic Center that includes a 166-acre park. Transportation and other facilities of Detroit are easily accessible.

■ MACOMB COMMUNITY COLLEGE

14500 E Twelve Mile Rd.
Warren, MI 48088-3896
Tel: (586)445-7999; Free: 866-MACOMB1
Fax: (586)445-7140
E-mail: stevensr@macomb.edu
Web Site: www.macomb.edu/

Description: District-supported, 2-year, coed. Part of Michigan Public Community College System. Awards certificates, transfer associate, and terminal associate degrees. Founded 1954. Setting: 384-acre suburban campus with easy access to Detroit. Endowment: $16.4 million. Educational spending for the previous fiscal year: $4490 per student. Total enrollment: 23,729.

Faculty: 1,102 (226 full-time, 857 part-time). Student-undergrad faculty ratio is 27:1. Full-time: 7,624 students, 51% women, 49% men. Part-time: 16,105 students, 54% women, 46% men. Students come from 4 states and territories, 0% from out-of-state. 1% American Indian or Alaska Native, non-Hispanic/Latino; 2% Hispanic/Latino; 11% African American, non-Hispanic/Latino; 3% Asian, non-Hispanic/Latino; 0.1% Native Hawaiian or other Pacific Islander, non-Hispanic/Latino; 1% international. 36% 25 or older. Retention: 56% of full-time freshmen returned the following year. Calendar: semesters. Academic remediation for entering students, ESL program, services for LD students, advanced placement, self-designed majors, honors program, summer session for credit, part-time degree program, adult/continuing education programs, co-op programs and internships. Off campus study at Wayne State University, Wayne County Community College, Benjamin Davis Vocational Technical Center, Oakland Community College.

Entrance Requirements: Open admission except for nursing, occupational therapy, respiratory therapy, veterinary technician, physical therapy programs. Options: early admission, deferred admission. Entrance: noncompetitive. Application deadline: Rolling.

Costs Per Year: Application fee: $0. Area resident tuition: $2666 full-time, $86 per credit hour part-time. State resident tuition: $4061 full-time, $131 per credit hour part-time. Nonresident tuition: $5270 full-time, $170 per credit hour part-time. Mandatory fees: $100 full-time, $50 per term part-time. Full-time tuition and fees vary according to course load. Part-time tuition and fees vary according to course load.

Collegiate Environment: Orientation program. Drama-theater group. Social organizations: 20 open to all. Most popular organizations: Phi Beta Kappa, Adventure Unlimited, Alpha Rho Rho, SADD. Major annual events: Welcome Back Picnic, Spring Fling, Bandemonium. Student services: health clinic, personal-psychological counseling. Campus security: 24-hour emergency response devices and patrols, late night transport-escort service, security phones in parking lots, surveillance cameras. College housing not available. Library of South Campus, Library of Center Campus with 159,226 books, 4,240 serials, and an OPAC. Operations spending for the previous fiscal year: $1.7 million. 2,000 computers available on campus for general student use. A campuswide network can be accessed from off-campus. Staffed computer lab on campus.

Community Environment: Community has many libraries, churches of various denominations, hospitals, and excellent shopping facilities. Some part-time work is available for students. City has major recreational facilities, and borders Lake St. Clair.

■ **MADONNA UNIVERSITY**
36600 Schoolcraft Rd.
Livonia, MI 48150-1173
Tel: (734)432-5300; Free: 800-852-4951
Fax: (734)432-5393
E-mail: admissions@madonna.edu
Web Site: www.madonna.edu/

Description: Independent Roman Catholic, comprehensive, coed. Awards associate, bachelor's, master's, and doctoral degrees and post-master's certificates. Founded 1947. Setting: 49-acre suburban campus with easy access to Detroit. Endowment: $29 million. Educational spending for the previous fiscal year: $7602 per student. Total enrollment: 4,429. Faculty: 415 (129 full-time, 286 part-time). Student-undergrad faculty ratio is 10:1. 537 applied, 70% were admitted. 14% from top 10% of their high school class, 43% from top quarter, 76% from top half. Full-time: 1,625 students, 73% women, 27% men. Part-time: 1,580 students, 70% women, 30% men. Students come from 7 states and territories, 26 other countries, 1% from out-of-state. 0.5% American Indian or Alaska Native, non-Hispanic/Latino; 4% Hispanic/Latino; 14% African American, non-Hispanic/Latino; 1% Asian, non-Hispanic/Latino; 0.1% Native Hawaiian or other Pacific Islander, non-Hispanic/Latino; 9% international. 44% 25 or older, 7% live on campus, 16% transferred in. Retention: 83% of full-time freshmen returned the following year. Academic areas with the most degrees conferred: health professions and related sciences; homeland security, law enforcement, firefighting, and protective services; business/marketing. Core. Calendar: semesters. Academic remediation for entering students, ESL program, services for LD students, advanced placement, accelerated degree program, self-designed majors, independent study, distance learning, double major, summer session for credit, part-time degree program, adult/continuing education programs, co-op programs and internships, graduate courses open to undergrads. Off campus study at 5 members of the Detroit Area Consortium of Catholic Colleges. Study abroad program. ROTC: Army (c).

Entrance Requirements: Options: electronic application, deferred admis-

sion, international baccalaureate accepted. Required: essay, high school transcript, minimum 2.75 high school GPA, SAT or ACT. Recommended: interview. Required for some: 2 recommendations. Entrance: moderately difficult. Application deadline: Rolling. Notification: continuous. SAT Reasoning Test deadline: 9/1. SAT Subject Test deadline: 9/1. Transfer credits accepted: Yes.

Costs Per Year: Application fee: $25. Comprehensive fee: $22,994 includes full-time tuition ($15,180), mandatory fees ($120), and college room and board ($7694). College room only: $4178. Full-time tuition and fees vary according to course load. Room and board charges vary according to board plan. Part-time tuition: $506 per credit hour. Part-time mandatory fees: $60 per term. Part-time tuition and fees vary according to course load.

Collegiate Environment: Orientation program. Drama-theater group, choral group, student-run newspaper, radio station. Social organizations: 45 open to all. Most popular organizations: Campus Ministry, Red Cross Club, Madonna University Nursing Student Association, Broadcast & Film Club, Society of Future Teachers. Major annual events: Welcome Week and Winter Welcome Back, Spirit Week/Founder's Day Activities, American Red Cross Blood Drives. Student services: personal-psychological counseling. Campus security: 24-hour emergency response devices and patrols, late night transport-escort service, controlled dormitory access. 245 college housing spaces available; all were occupied in 2012-13. Freshmen guaranteed college housing. Options: men-only, women-only housing available. Madonna University Library with 191,242 books, 453,260 microform titles, 515 serials, 938 audiovisual materials, an OPAC, and a Web page. Operations spending for the previous fiscal year: $1.8 million. 243 computers available on campus for general student use. Computer purchase/lease plans available. A campuswide network can be accessed from student residence rooms and from off campus. Students can access the following: online class registration, online payments, online statements, online Unofficial Transcripts. Staffed computer lab on campus provides training in use of computers, software, and the Internet.

Community Environment: See Schoolcraft College.

■ **MARYGROVE COLLEGE**
8425 W McNichols Rd.
Detroit, MI 48221-2599
Tel: (313)927-1200; Free: 866-313-1297
Fax: (313)927-1345
E-mail: info@marygrove.edu
Web Site: www.marygrove.edu/

Description: Independent Roman Catholic, comprehensive, coed. Awards associate, bachelor's, and master's degrees. Founded 1905. Setting: 50-acre urban campus. Endowment: $10.4 million. Educational spending for the previous fiscal year: $4877 per student. Total enrollment: 2,953. Faculty: 64 (56 full-time, 8 part-time). Student-undergrad faculty ratio is 22:1. 548 applied, 42% were admitted. Full-time: 455 students, 75% women, 25% men. Part-time: 325 students, 85% women, 15% men. Students come from 3 states and territories, 9 other countries, 0.4% from out-of-state. 61% 25 or older, 12% live on campus, 17% transferred in. Retention: 54% of full-time freshmen returned the following year. Academic areas with the most degrees conferred: social sciences; visual and performing arts; business/marketing. Core. Calendar: semesters. Academic remediation for entering students, advanced placement, self-designed majors, distance learning, double major, summer session for credit, part-time degree program, co-op programs and internships, graduate courses open to undergrads. Off campus study at Detroit Area Consortium of Catholic Colleges.

Entrance Requirements: Options: early admission, deferred admission. Required: high school transcript, minimum 2.7 high school GPA, ACT. Required for some: interview. Entrance: moderately difficult. Application deadline: 8/15. Notification: continuous until 9/1.

Collegiate Environment: Orientation program. Choral group. Social organizations: 16 open to all. Most popular organizations: Association of Black Social Workers, Council of Student Organization, Political Science Club, United Brotherhood, Marygrove Business Association. Major annual events: Fall Fest, Welcome Picnic and New Student Welcome, Martin Luther King, Jr. Celebration. Student services: personal-psychological counseling. Campus security: 24-hour emergency response devices and patrols, late night transport-escort service. Marygrove College Library plus 1 other with 86,268 books, 71,601 microform titles, 72,048 serials, an OPAC, and a Web page. Operations spending for the previous fiscal year: $772,455. 115 computers available on campus for general student use. Computer purchase/lease plans available. A campuswide network can be accessed from student residence rooms. Staffed computer lab on campus.

Community Environment: Located 15 minutes from downtown Detroit, Marygrove offers considerable cultural and social opportunities. Theater, symphony, ballet, opera, and the nationally famous Detroit Institute of Arts are within easy commuting distance. Shopping centers, art galleries, sports arenas, and recreation centers are nearby.

■ **MICHIGAN JEWISH INSTITUTE**
6890 Maple Rd.
West Bloomfield, MI 48322
Tel: (248)414-6900; Free: 888-INFO-MJI
Fax: (248)414-6907
E-mail: dstein@mji.edu
Web Site: www.mji.edu/
Description: Independent, 4-year, coed. Awards associate and bachelor's degrees. Founded 1994. Total enrollment: 256. Faculty: 24 (6 full-time, 18 part-time). Retention: 63% of full-time freshmen returned the following year. Academic areas with the most degrees conferred: computer and information sciences; business/marketing. Core. Calendar: semesters. Academic remediation for entering students, ESL program, services for LD students, advanced placement, accelerated degree program, independent study, double major, summer session for credit, adult/continuing education programs, co-op programs and internships. Study abroad program.
Entrance Requirements: Open admission. Options: electronic application, early admission, deferred admission, international baccalaureate accepted. Required: high school transcript, minimum 2.0 high school GPA. Entrance: minimally difficult. Application deadline: Rolling. Notification: continuous.
Collegiate Environment: Orientation program. Major annual event: weekend retreats. Michigan Jewish Institute Library plus 1 other with an OPAC. 11 computers available on campus for general student use. A computer is required for all students. A campuswide network can be accessed. Students can access the following: online class registration. Staffed computer lab on campus provides training in use of computers, software, and the Internet.

■ **MICHIGAN STATE UNIVERSITY**
East Lansing, MI 48824
Tel: (517)355-1855
E-mail: admis@msu.edu
Web Site: www.msu.edu/
Description: State-supported, university, coed. Awards bachelor's, master's, and doctoral degrees and post-master's certificates. Founded 1855. Setting: 5,192-acre suburban campus with easy access to Detroit. Endowment: $1.4 billion. Research spending for the previous fiscal year: $348 million. Educational spending for the previous fiscal year: $13,390 per student. Total enrollment: 48,906. Faculty: 2,789 (2,384 full-time, 405 part-time). Student-undergrad faculty ratio is 16:1. 30,224 applied, 71% were admitted. 27% from top 10% of their high school class, 64% from top quarter, 94% from top half. 38 National Merit Scholars. Full-time: 34,296 students, 51% women, 49% men. Part-time: 3,158 students, 45% women, 55% men. Students come from 55 states and territories, 96 other countries, 9% from out-of-state. 0.3% American Indian or Alaska Native, non-Hispanic/Latino; 4% Hispanic/Latino; 7% African American, non-Hispanic/Latino; 4% Asian, non-Hispanic/Latino; 0.1% Native Hawaiian or other Pacific Islander, non-Hispanic/Latino; 11% international. 5% 25 or older, 42% live on campus, 4% transferred in. Retention: 91% of full-time freshmen returned the following year. Academic areas with the most degrees conferred: business/marketing; social sciences; biological/life sciences. Core. Calendar: semesters. Academic remediation for entering students, ESL program, services for LD students, advanced placement, accelerated degree program, self-designed majors, freshman honors college, honors program, independent study, distance learning, double major, summer session for credit, part-time degree program, adult/continuing education programs, co-op programs and internships, graduate courses open to undergrads. Off campus study at Committee on Institutional Cooperation, Great Plains Interactive Distance Education Alliance. Study abroad program. ROTC: Army, Air Force.
Entrance Requirements: Options: electronic application, early action, international baccalaureate accepted. Required: essay, high school transcript, SAT or ACT. Entrance: moderately difficult. Application deadlines: Rolling, Rolling for nonresidents. Notification: continuous, continuous for nonresidents. Transfer credits accepted: Yes.
Costs Per Year: Application fee: $50. State resident tuition: $13,800 full-time, $420.75 per credit hour part-time. Nonresident tuition: $33,608 full-time, $1086 per credit hour part-time. Full-time tuition varies according to course load, program, and student level. Part-time tuition varies according to

course load, program, and student level. College room and board: $8476. College room only: $3500. Room and board charges vary according to board plan and housing facility.
Collegiate Environment: Orientation program. Drama-theater group, choral group, marching band, student-run newspaper, radio station. Social organizations: 550 open to all; national fraternities, national sororities; 8% of eligible men and 7% of eligible women are members. Major annual events: football games in Spartan Stadium, basketball games in Breslin Center, Homecoming festivities. Student services: legal services, health clinic, personal-psychological counseling, women's center. Campus security: 24-hour emergency response devices and patrols, late night transport-escort service, controlled dormitory access, self-defense workshops. 16,620 college housing spaces available; 15,229 were occupied in 2012-13. Freshmen guaranteed college housing. On-campus residence required in freshman year. Options: coed, women-only housing available. Main Library plus 14 others with 6.7 million books, 5.9 million microform titles, 172,144 serials, 81,463 audiovisual materials, an OPAC, and a Web page. Operations spending for the previous fiscal year: $27 million.
Community Environment: Located in a metropolitan area adjacent to Lansing, the state capital of Michigan. There are four hospitals, access to houses of worship, various entertainment venues, and good shopping facilities within the immediate area.

■ **MICHIGAN TECHNOLOGICAL UNIVERSITY**
1400 Townsend Dr.
Houghton, MI 49931
Tel: (906)487-1885; Free: 888-MTU-1885
Fax: (906)487-3343
E-mail: mtu4u@mtu.edu
Web Site: www.mtu.edu/
Description: State-supported, university, coed. Awards associate, bachelor's, master's, and doctoral degrees. Founded 1885. Setting: 925-acre small town campus. Total enrollment: 7,034. Faculty: 469 (406 full-time, 63 part-time). Student-undergrad faculty ratio is 13:1. 4,573 applied, 75% were admitted. 30% from top 10% of their high school class, 61% from top quarter, 89% from top half. Full-time: 5,318 students, 25% women, 75% men. Part-time: 413 students, 28% women, 72% men. 22% from out-of-state. 1% American Indian or Alaska Native, non-Hispanic/Latino; 2% Hispanic/Latino; 1% African American, non-Hispanic/Latino; 1% Asian, non-Hispanic/Latino; 0.1% Native Hawaiian or other Pacific Islander, non-Hispanic/Latino; 7% international. 5% 25 or older, 45% live on campus, 4% transferred in. Retention: 83% of full-time freshmen returned the following year. Academic areas with the most degrees conferred: engineering; business/marketing; computer and information sciences. Core. Calendar: semesters. ESL program, services for LD students, advanced placement, honors program, independent study, distance learning, double major, summer session for credit, part-time degree program, co-op programs and internships, graduate courses open to undergrads. Off campus study at National Student Exchange. Study abroad program. ROTC: Army, Air Force.
Entrance Requirements: Options: electronic application, deferred admission. Required: high school transcript, SAT or ACT. Recommended: minimum 2.75 high school GPA, interview. Entrance: moderately difficult. Application deadline: Rolling. Notification: continuous. SAT Reasoning Test deadline: 8/15.
Costs Per Year: Application fee: $0. State resident tuition: $13,095 full-time, $436.50 per credit hour part-time. Nonresident tuition: $27,000 full-time, $900 per credit hour part-time. Mandatory fees: $258 full-time, $129 per term part-time. Full-time tuition and fees vary according to course load and program. Part-time tuition and fees vary according to course load and program. College room and board: $8865. College room only: $4742. Room and board charges vary according to board plan and housing facility.
Collegiate Environment: Orientation program. Drama-theater group, choral group, student-run newspaper, radio station. Social organizations: national fraternities, national sororities, local fraternities, local sororities. Student services: health clinic, personal-psychological counseling. Campus security: 24-hour emergency response devices and patrols, late night transport-escort service, controlled dormitory access. J. R. Van Pelt Library with an OPAC and a Web page.
Community Environment: The main campus is located in Houghton, at the heart of the colorful Keweenaw Peninsula in Upper Michigan. Houghton is part of the Houghton-Hancock twin-city center of approximately 12,000. Numerous water and winter sports are available. The community has public libraries, churches for all major religions, a hospital, and opportunities for a variety of recreational and cultural activities. Part-time employment is available.

■ MID MICHIGAN COMMUNITY COLLEGE

1375 S Clare Ave.
Harrison, MI 48625-9447
Tel: (989)386-6622
Fax: (989)386-9088
E-mail: apply@midmich.edu
Web Site: www.midmich.edu/

Description: State and locally supported, 2-year, coed. Part of Michigan Department of Education. Awards certificates, transfer associate, and terminal associate degrees. Founded 1965. Setting: 560-acre rural campus. Educational spending for the previous fiscal year: $903 per student. Total enrollment: 4,885. Faculty: 264 (46 full-time, 218 part-time). Student-undergrad faculty ratio is 26:1. 785 applied, 100% were admitted. Full-time: 2,193 students, 53% women, 47% men. Part-time: 2,692 students, 63% women, 37% men. 1% from out-of-state. 2% American Indian or Alaska Native, non-Hispanic/Latino; 3% Hispanic/Latino; 3% African American, non-Hispanic/Latino; 0.2% Asian, non-Hispanic/Latino; 0.4% Native Hawaiian or other Pacific Islander, non-Hispanic/Latino; 1% international. 29% 25 or older, 4% transferred in. Retention: 43% of full-time freshmen returned the following year. Core. Calendar: semesters. Academic remediation for entering students, services for LD students, advanced placement, honors program, independent study, distance learning, summer session for credit, part-time degree program, adult/continuing education programs, co-op programs and internships.

Entrance Requirements: Open admission except for allied health programs. Options: electronic application, early admission. Recommended: high school transcript. Entrance: noncompetitive. Application deadline: Rolling. Notification: continuous. Transfer credits accepted: Yes.

Costs Per Year: Application fee: $0. Area resident tuition: $2600 full-time, $92.50 per contact hour part-time. State resident tuition: $4748 full-time, $182 per contact hour part-time. Nonresident tuition: $8396 full-time, $334 per contact hour part-time. Mandatory fees: $10 per contact hour part-time, $45 per term part-time. Full-time tuition varies according to course load. Part-time tuition and fees vary according to course load.

Collegiate Environment: Orientation program. Drama-theater group. Social organizations: 35 open to all. Most popular organizations: MC2, Phi Theta Kappa, Art Club, ECHO, Japan Culture Club. Major annual events: Spring Picnic, Fall Festival, Christmas canned food drive and coats for kids programs. Student services: personal-psychological counseling. Campus security: 24-hour emergency response devices. Charles A. Amble Library with 29,450 books and 200 serials. 175 computers available on campus for general student use. Computer purchase/lease plans available. A campuswide network can be accessed from off-campus. Students can access the following: online class registration. Staffed computer lab on campus provides training in use of computers.

■ MONROE COUNTY COMMUNITY COLLEGE

1555 S Raisinville Rd.
Monroe, MI 48161-9047
Tel: (734)242-7300
Fax: (734)242-9711
E-mail: mhall@monroeccc.edu
Web Site: www.monroeccc.edu/

Description: County-supported, 2-year, coed. Part of Michigan Department of Education. Awards certificates, transfer associate, and terminal associate degrees. Founded 1964. Setting: 150-acre small town campus with easy access to Detroit, Toledo. Faculty: 196 (54 full-time, 142 part-time). 1,700 applied, 99% were admitted. Students come from 3 other countries, 4% from out-of-state. 45% 25 or older. Core. Calendar: semesters. Academic remediation for entering students, services for LD students, advanced placement, independent study, distance learning, summer session for credit, part-time degree program.

Entrance Requirements: Open admission except for allied health, culinary arts programs. Options: early admission, deferred admission. Required: high school transcript, Baseline cut scores on ACT or COMPASS, ACT, ACT COMPASS. Recommended: ACT. Required for some: ACT. Entrance: noncompetitive. Notification: continuous.

Costs Per Year: Application fee: $0. Area resident tuition: $2316 full-time. State resident tuition: $3726 full-time. Nonresident tuition: $4110 full-time.

Collegiate Environment: Orientation program. Drama-theater group, choral group, student-run newspaper. Most popular organizations: student government, Society of Auto Engineers, Oasis, Nursing Students Organization. Major annual events: Family Fun Night, Santa's Winter Wonderland, Honors Reception. Campus security: police patrols during open hours. College

housing not available. Campbell Learning Resource Center with 47,352 books, 321 serials, and an OPAC. 210 computers available on campus for general student use. A campuswide network can be accessed from off-campus. Students can access the following: online class registration. Staffed computer lab on campus.

Community Environment: The third oldest community in the state, Monroe was founded in 1780 by the French. This early settlement, called Frenchtown, was the scene of the River Raisin Massacre in 1813. The only Michigan port on Lake Erie, Monroe includes among its industries large nurseries, paper mills, a limestone quarry, recreation, and a branch automotive factory. It is a suburban city with a community airport and bus lines easily accessible. There are many civic, fraternal and veteran's organizations in this area. Community has a library, YMCA, museum, hospital, theater, 9 golf courses, many public parks and 6 shopping centers.

■ MONTCALM COMMUNITY COLLEGE

2800 College Dr.
Sidney, MI 48885
Tel: (989)328-2111; Free: 877-328-2111
Fax: (989)328-2950
E-mail: admissions@montcalm.edu
Web Site: www.montcalm.edu/

Description: State and locally supported, 2-year, coed. Part of Michigan Department of Education. Awards certificates, transfer associate, and terminal associate degrees. Founded 1965. Setting: 240-acre rural campus with easy access to Grand Rapids. Endowment: $4.7 million. Total enrollment: 2,011. Faculty: 114 (28 full-time, 86 part-time). 244 applied, 100% were admitted. Full-time: 680 students, 65% women, 35% men. Part-time: 1,331 students, 65% women, 35% men. 0.2% American Indian or Alaska Native, non-Hispanic/Latino; 2% Hispanic/Latino; 0.2% African American, non-Hispanic/Latino; 0.2% Asian, non-Hispanic/Latino. 56% 25 or older, 19% transferred in. Core. Calendar: semesters. Academic remediation for entering students, services for LD students, advanced placement, independent study, distance learning, double major, summer session for credit, part-time degree program, adult/continuing education programs, co-op programs and internships. Off campus study. Study abroad program.

Entrance Requirements: Open admission except for nursing program. Options: electronic application, early admission, deferred admission. Recommended: high school transcript. Entrance: noncompetitive. Application deadline: Rolling. Notification: continuous.

Costs Per Year: Application fee: $0. Area resident tuition: $87 per credit hour part-time. State resident tuition: $164 per credit hour part-time. Nonresident tuition: $244 per credit hour part-time.

Collegiate Environment: Orientation program. Drama-theater group, choral group. Social organizations: 12 open to all. Most popular organizations: Nursing Club, Native American Club, Phi Theta Kappa, Business Club, Judo Club. Student services: personal-psychological counseling. College housing not available. Montcalm Community College Library with 29,848 books, 3,670 serials, an OPAC, and a Web page. Operations spending for the previous fiscal year: $235,862. 450 computers available on campus for general student use. A campuswide network can be accessed from off-campus. Students can access the following: online class registration. Staffed computer lab on campus.

Community Environment: Located in a rural area, air transportation is accessible within a one-hour drive. A neighboring city has theatres, libraries and hospitals. There are 104 lakes in the county providing excellent recreational opportunities. Some part-time employment is available for students.

■ MOTT COMMUNITY COLLEGE

1401 E Ct. St.
Flint, MI 48503-2089
Tel: (810)762-0200; Free: 800-852-8614
Fax: (810)762-0292
E-mail: regina.broomfield@mcc.edu
Web Site: www.mcc.edu/

Description: District-supported, 2-year, coed. Part of Michigan Workforce Programs/Postsecondary Services/Community College Services. Awards certificates, transfer associate, and terminal associate degrees. Founded 1923. Setting: 32-acre urban campus with easy access to Detroit. Endowment: $35.3 million. Educational spending for the previous fiscal year: $4099 per student. Total enrollment: 9,968. Faculty: 517 (145 full-time, 372 part-time). Student-undergrad faculty ratio is 20:1. Full-time: 3,140 students, 56% women, 44% men. Part-time: 6,828 students, 60% women, 40% men.

Students come from 15 states and territories. 1% American Indian or Alaska Native, non-Hispanic/Latino; 4% Hispanic/Latino; 19% African American, non-Hispanic/Latino; 0.4% Asian, non-Hispanic/Latino; 0.1% Native Hawaiian or other Pacific Islander, non-Hispanic/Latino; 0.2% international. 47% 25 or older, 2% transferred in. Core. Calendar: semesters. Academic remediation for entering students, ESL program, services for LD students, advanced placement, accelerated degree program, honors program, independent study, distance learning, double major, summer session for credit, part-time degree program, adult/continuing education programs, co-op programs and internships.

Entrance Requirements: Open admission. Options: electronic application, early admission, deferred admission. Required: high school transcript. Entrance: noncompetitive. Application deadline: 8/31. Transfer credits accepted: Yes.

Costs Per Year: Application fee: $0. Area resident tuition: $2813 full-time, $117.23 per contact hour part-time. State resident tuition: $4102 full-time, $170.93 per contact hour part-time. Nonresident tuition: $5832 full-time, $243 per contact hour part-time. Mandatory fees: $396 full-time, $6.72 per contact hour part-time, $117.23 per term part-time. Full-time tuition and fees vary according to course load. Part-time tuition and fees vary according to course load.

Collegiate Environment: Orientation program. Choral group, student-run newspaper. Social organizations: 25 open to all. Most popular organizations: Otaku Club, Gay, Straight Alliance (GSA), Student Veteran's Services (SVA), American Sign Language (ASL), Dental Hygiene Club. Major annual events: Fall Rally, College Night, Annual Tree Lighting. Student services: health clinic, personal-psychological counseling. Campus security: 24-hour emergency response devices and patrols, student patrols, late night transport-escort service. College housing not available. Charles Stewart Mott Library with 66,741 books, 6,189 microform titles, 165 serials, 89 audiovisual materials, an OPAC, and a Web page. Operations spending for the previous fiscal year: $902,232. 1,350 computers available on campus for general student use. A campuswide network can be accessed from off-campus. Students can access the following: online class registration. Staffed computer lab on campus.

■ **MUSKEGON COMMUNITY COLLEGE**
221 S Quarterline Rd.
Muskegon, MI 49442-1493
Tel: (231)773-9131; Free: 866-711-4622
Fax: (231)777-0255
E-mail: Dalene.Peklar@muskegoncc.edu
Web Site: www.muskegoncc.edu/

Description: State and locally supported, 2-year, coed. Part of Michigan Department of Education. Awards transfer associate and terminal associate degrees. Founded 1926. Setting: 112-acre small town campus with easy access to Grand Rapids. Total enrollment: 5,579. Faculty: 318 (100 full-time, 218 part-time). Student-undergrad faculty ratio is 20:1. 524 applied, 97% were admitted. Full-time: 1,886 students, 52% women, 48% men. Part-time: 3,693 students, 62% women, 38% men. 1% American Indian or Alaska Native, non-Hispanic/Latino; 4% Hispanic/Latino; 9% African American, non-Hispanic/Latino; 1% Asian, non-Hispanic/Latino; 0.1% Native Hawaiian or other Pacific Islander, non-Hispanic/Latino; 0.1% international. Core. Calendar: semesters. Academic remediation for entering students, self-designed majors, honors program, summer session for credit, part-time degree program, adult/continuing education programs, co-op programs.

Entrance Requirements: Open admission. Options: electronic application, early admission, deferred admission. Required: high school transcript. Entrance: noncompetitive. Application deadline: Rolling. Notification: continuous. Transfer credits accepted: Yes.

Costs Per Year: Application fee: $0. Area resident tuition: $1980 full-time, $85.50 per credit hour part-time. State resident tuition: $3432 full-time, $153 per credit hour part-time. Nonresident tuition: $4704 full-time, $210 per credit hour part-time. Mandatory fees: $10 per contact hour part-time.

Collegiate Environment: Orientation program. Drama-theater group, choral group, student-run newspaper. Social organizations: 30 open to all. Most popular organizations: Respiratory Therapy, Hispanic Student Organization, Black Student Alliance, International Club, Rotaract. Major annual events: Taste Of Tomorrow, College Open House, Welcome Days for new and returning students. Student services: personal-psychological counseling. Campus security: 24-hour emergency response devices, on-campus security officer. Hendrik Meijer and Technology Center with 48,597 books and 450 serials. 135 computers available on campus for general student use. A campuswide network can be accessed. Students can access the fol-

lowing: online class registration. Staffed computer lab on campus provides training in use of computers, software, and the Internet.

Community Environment: Formerly known as the Lumber Queen of the World, cutting 800 million board feet of lumber in 1888, Muskegon is the largest city on the east bank of Lake Michigan. Today it is an important lake port and a manufacturing and resort center. Numerous industries produce automotive parts, foundry products, paper, oil, chemicals and recreational equipment. Area has an international airport and a seaway-depth port. There are art galleries, museums, and historical sites located within the immediate vicinity. The nearby Muskegon River offers excellent fishing, boating, and canoeing.

■ **NORTH CENTRAL MICHIGAN COLLEGE**
1515 Howard St.
Petoskey, MI 49770-8717
Tel: (231)348-6600; Free: 888-298-6605
E-mail: jtobin@ncmich.edu
Web Site: www.ncmich.edu/

Description: County-supported, 2-year, coed. Awards certificates, transfer associate, and terminal associate degrees. Founded 1958. Setting: 270-acre small town campus. Total enrollment: 2,770. Faculty: 133 (31 full-time, 102 part-time). Student-undergrad faculty ratio is 17:1. 55% 25 or older. Calendar: semesters. Academic remediation for entering students, services for LD students, advanced placement, independent study, distance learning, double major, summer session for credit, part-time degree program, co-op programs and internships.

Entrance Requirements: Open admission except for nursing program. Required: high school transcript, ACT. Entrance: noncompetitive. Application deadline: Rolling. Notification: continuous.

Collegiate Environment: Orientation program. Student services: personal-psychological counseling. Campus security: 24-hour emergency response devices. North Central Michigan College Library with 29,249 books, 325 serials, an OPAC, and a Web page. 133 computers available on campus for general student use. A campuswide network can be accessed. Students can access the following: online class registration. Staffed computer lab on campus.

Community Environment: A resort and health center, the city is located on Little Traverse Bay. Within a 30-minute drive are 6 major ski resorts. Other recreational facilities include water sports on Lake Michigan, summer concerts, golf and tennis. The area has good transportation provided by air and bus service. There is some part-time employment available for students. Community services include a library, an arts center, many churches, 2 hospitals, and a clinic.

■ **NORTHERN MICHIGAN UNIVERSITY**
1401 Presque Isle Ave.
Marquette, MI 49855-5301
Tel: (906)227-1000; Free: 800-682-9797
Fax: (906)227-1747
E-mail: admiss@nmu.edu
Web Site: www.nmu.edu/

Description: State-supported, comprehensive, coed. Awards associate, bachelor's, and master's degrees and post-master's certificates. Founded 1899. Setting: 300-acre small town campus. Total enrollment: 9,089. Student-undergrad faculty ratio is 22:1. 6,841 applied, 68% were admitted. Full-time: 7,587 students, 53% women, 47% men. Part-time: 864 students, 56% women, 44% men. 19% from out-of-state. 1% American Indian or Alaska Native, non-Hispanic/Latino; 2% Hispanic/Latino; 3% African American, non-Hispanic/Latino; 0.4% Asian, non-Hispanic/Latino; 0% Native Hawaiian or other Pacific Islander, non-Hispanic/Latino; 1% international. 16% 25 or older, 38% live on campus, 7% transferred in. Retention: 72% of full-time freshmen returned the following year. Academic areas with the most degrees conferred: business/marketing; education; health professions and related sciences. Calendar: semesters. Part-time degree program, adult/continuing education programs. ROTC: Army.

Entrance Requirements: Options: electronic application, deferred admission, international baccalaureate accepted. Required: high school transcript, SAT or ACT. Required for some: minimum 2.25 high school GPA. Entrance: minimally difficult. Application deadline: Rolling. Notification: continuous. SAT Reasoning Test deadline: 8/1. SAT Subject Test deadline: 8/1.

Costs Per Year: Application fee: $30. One-time mandatory fee: $225. State resident tuition: $8646 full-time, $324 per credit hour part-time. Nonresident tuition: $13,542 full-time, $521 per credit hour part-time. Mandatory fees: $64 full-time. Full-time tuition and fees vary according to program. Part-time tuition varies according to program. College room and board: $8404. College room only: $4208. Room and board charges vary according to board plan and housing facility.

Collegiate Environment: Orientation program. Campus security: 24-hour emergency response devices and patrols, student patrols, late night transport-escort service. Freshmen guaranteed college housing. On-campus residence required through sophomore year. Option: coed housing available. Lydia Olson Library with an OPAC and a Web page.

Community Environment: Located on Lake Superior, Marquette is a day's driving distance from Chicago, Minneapolis, Duluth and Milwaukee. It is an important service and distribution center.

■ **NORTHWESTERN MICHIGAN COLLEGE**

1701 E Front St.
Traverse City, MI 49686-3061
Tel: (231)995-1000; Free: 800-748-0566
Fax: (231)995-1680
E-mail: welcome@nmc.edu
Web Site: www.nmc.edu/

Description: State and locally supported, 2-year, coed. Awards certificates, transfer associate, and terminal associate degrees. Founded 1951. Setting: 180-acre small town campus. Educational spending for the previous fiscal year: $5559 per student. Total enrollment: 4,609. Faculty: 280 (91 full-time, 189 part-time). Student-undergrad faculty ratio is 18:1. 1,645 applied, 89% were admitted. Full-time: 2,011 students, 53% women, 47% men. Part-time: 2,598 students, 64% women, 36% men. Students come from 19 states and territories, 21 other countries, 2% from out-of-state. 37% 25 or older, 5% live on campus, 11% transferred in. Retention: 61% of full-time freshmen returned the following year. Core. Calendar: semesters. Academic remediation for entering students, services for LD students, advanced placement, honors program, independent study, distance learning, summer session for credit, part-time degree program, adult/continuing education programs, co-op programs and internships.

Entrance Requirements: Open admission for residents of sponsoring counties. Options: electronic application, early admission, deferred admission. Recommended: minimum 2.0 high school GPA. Required for some: high school transcript. Entrance: noncompetitive. Application deadline: Rolling. Notification: continuous until 8/22.

Costs Per Year: Application fee: $15. Area resident tuition: $2706 full-time, $84.60 per contact hour part-time. State resident tuition: $5308 full-time, $165.90 per contact hour part-time. Nonresident tuition: $6798 full-time, $212.45 per contact hour part-time. Mandatory fees: $814 full-time, $23 per contact hour part-time, $25 per term part-time. Full-time tuition and fees vary according to course load and program. Part-time tuition and fees vary according to course load, program, and reciprocity agreements. College room and board: $8500. College room only: $6400. Room and board charges vary according to board plan, housing facility, and student level.

Collegiate Environment: Orientation program. Drama-theater group, choral group, student-run newspaper, radio station. Social organizations: 17 open to all. Most popular organizations: Residence Hall Council, Honors fraternity, student newspaper, student magazine, student radio station. Major annual events: Campus Clean-Up Day, Annual Barbecue, graduation. Student services: health clinic, personal-psychological counseling. Campus security: 24-hour emergency response devices and patrols, student patrols, late night transport-escort service, controlled dormitory access, well-lit campus. Mark and Helen Osterlin Library plus 1 other with 97,458 books, 155,643 microform titles, 9,820 serials, 3,000 audiovisual materials, an OPAC, and a Web page. Operations spending for the previous fiscal year: $572,868. 625 computers available on campus for general student use. A campuswide network can be accessed from student residence rooms and from off campus. Students can access the following: online class registration. Staffed computer lab on campus provides training in use of computers, software, and the Internet.

Community Environment: The Grand Traverse region is the center of Michigan's cherry-growing belt, with Traverse City marketing more cherries than any other city in the country. This is also an important year-round resort area. The temperature averages about 70 degrees in summer. Bus and air transportation are easily accessible. There are many churches, 2 hospitals, 2 libraries, 2 museums, and other major community services. Recreational activities include sailing, golf, hunting, tennis, swimming, water skiing, fishing, bowling, skating, and all winter sports. Concerts and travel lectures are given here, and the National Cherry Festival is an annual event.

■ **NORTHWOOD UNIVERSITY, MICHIGAN CAMPUS**

4000 Whiting Dr.
Midland, MI 48640-2398
Tel: (989)837-4200; Free: 800-457-7878
Fax: (989)837-4490
E-mail: miadmit@northwood.edu
Web Site: www.northwood.edu/

Description: Independent, comprehensive, coed. Awards associate, bachelor's, and master's degrees. Founded 1959. Setting: 434-acre small town campus. Endowment: $31.1 million. Educational spending for the previous fiscal year: $5339 per student. Total enrollment: 1,787. Faculty: 130 (53 full-time, 77 part-time). Student-undergrad faculty ratio is 21:1. 1,258 applied, 68% were admitted. 12% from top 10% of their high school class, 40% from top quarter, 71% from top half. Full-time: 1,456 students, 38% women, 62% men. Part-time: 80 students, 41% women, 59% men. Students come from 21 states and territories, 24 other countries, 11% from out-of-state. 0.4% American Indian or Alaska Native, non-Hispanic/Latino; 3% Hispanic/Latino; 8% African American, non-Hispanic/Latino; 1% Asian, non-Hispanic/Latino; 0% Native Hawaiian or other Pacific Islander, non-Hispanic/Latino; 9% international. 3% 25 or older, 41% live on campus, 13% transferred in. Retention: 77% of full-time freshmen returned the following year. Academic areas with the most degrees conferred: business/marketing; parks and recreation; computer and information sciences. Core. Academic remediation for entering students, services for LD students, advanced placement, accelerated degree program, honors program, distance learning, double major, summer session for credit, part-time degree program, external degree program, adult/continuing education programs, co-op programs and internships. Off campus study. Study abroad program.

Entrance Requirements: Options: electronic application, early admission, deferred admission, international baccalaureate accepted. Required: essay, high school transcript, SAT or ACT. Recommended: 1 recommendation, interview. Entrance: moderately difficult. Application deadlines: 8/1, 8/1 for nonresidents. Notification: continuous, continuous for nonresidents. SAT Reasoning Test deadline: 8/1. Transfer credits accepted: Yes.

Costs Per Year: Application fee: $25. Comprehensive fee: $29,766 includes full-time tuition ($20,040), mandatory fees ($956), and college room and board ($8770). College room only: $4570. Room and board charges vary according to board plan. Part-time tuition: $776 per credit hour.

Collegiate Environment: Orientation program. Drama-theater group, student-run newspaper. Social organizations: 52 open to all; national fraternities, national sororities, local fraternities, local sororities; 30% of eligible men and 20% of eligible women are members. Most popular organizations: Student Senate, intramural sports/club sports, campus art, Northwood University International Auto Show (NUTAS). Major annual events: Auto Show/Homecoming, Values Emphasis Week, Basketball Homecoming. Student services: health clinic, personal-psychological counseling. Campus security: 24-hour emergency response devices and patrols, late night transport-escort service, controlled dormitory access. 868 college housing spaces available; 586 were occupied in 2012-13. Freshmen guaranteed college housing. On-campus residence required in freshman year. Options: men-only, women-only housing available. Strosacker Library with 40,063 books, 47,200 microform titles, 335 serials, an OPAC, and a Web page. 215 computers available on campus for general student use. A campuswide network can be accessed from student residence rooms and from off campus. Students can access the following: online class registration. Staffed computer lab on campus.

■ **OAKLAND COMMUNITY COLLEGE**

2480 Opdyke Rd.
Bloomfield Hills, MI 48304-2266
Tel: (248)341-2000
Fax: (248)341-2099
E-mail: smlinden@oaklandcc.edu
Web Site: www.oaklandcc.edu/

Description: State and locally supported, 2-year, coed. Awards certificates, transfer associate, and terminal associate degrees. Founded 1964. Setting: 540-acre suburban campus with easy access to Detroit. Endowment: $1.2 million. Research spending for the previous fiscal year: $1. Educational spending for the previous fiscal year: $3242 per student. Total enrollment: 27,296. Faculty: 986 (251 full-time, 735 part-time). Student-undergrad faculty ratio is 30:1. 10,336 applied, 100% were admitted. Full-time: 8,662 students, 52% women, 48% men. Part-time: 18,634 students, 59% women, 41% men. Students come from 11 states and territories, 47 other countries, 0.1% from out-of-state. 1% American Indian or Alaska Native, non-Hispanic/Latino; 3%

Hispanic/Latino; 29% African American, non-Hispanic/Latino; 2% Asian, non-Hispanic/Latino; 0.1% Native Hawaiian or other Pacific Islander, non-Hispanic/Latino; 4% international. 49% 25 or older, 0% live on campus, 0.01% transferred in. Retention: 44% of full-time freshmen returned the following year. Core. Calendar: semesters. Academic remediation for entering students, ESL program, services for LD students, advanced placement, distance learning, summer session for credit, part-time degree program, adult/continuing education programs, co-op programs and internships. Off campus study at Macomb Community College. Study abroad program.

Entrance Requirements: Open admission. Options: electronic application, deferred admission. Recommended: high school transcript, interview. Entrance: noncompetitive. Application deadline: Rolling. Notification: continuous. Transfer credits accepted: Yes.

Costs Per Year: Application fee: $0. Area resident tuition: $2142 full-time, $71.40 per credit hour part-time. State resident tuition: $3,760 full-time, $125.32 per credit hour part-time. Nonresident tuition: $5,275 full-time, $175.82 per credit hour part-time. Mandatory fees: $70 full-time, $35 per term part-time. Full-time tuition and fees vary according to course load and reciprocity agreements. Part-time tuition and fees vary according to course load and reciprocity agreements.

Collegiate Environment: Orientation program. Drama-theater group, choral group. Social organizations: 42 open to all. Most popular organizations: Phi Theta Kappa, Gamers Guild, BELIEVERS, Criminal Justice Student Organization, student government. Major annual events: Welcome Week Resource Fair, Welcome Week Student Organization Fair, Student Life Speaker Series. Student services: personal-psychological counseling, women's center. Campus security: 24-hour emergency response devices, late night transport-escort service. College housing not available. Main library plus 5 others with 263,563 books, 266,842 microform titles, 1,159 serials, 8,835 audiovisual materials, an OPAC, and a Web page. Operations spending for the previous fiscal year: $4.1 million. 2,501 computers available on campus for general student use. A campuswide network can be accessed from off-campus. Students can access the following: online class registration. Staffed computer lab on campus provides training in use of computers, software, and the Internet.

Community Environment: Oakland County is composed of both rural and urban towns and has all types of public transportation. Average temperature in winter is 20 degrees, with 70 degrees in summer. The average precipitation is 30 inches. There are good summer and winter sports facilities within the immediate area, with more than 400 lakes nearby. Extensive health services are available.

■ **OAKLAND UNIVERSITY**
Rochester, MI 48309-4401
Tel: (248)370-2100; Free: 800-OAK-UNIV
Fax: (248)370-4462
E-mail: ouinfo@oakland.edu
Web Site: www.oakland.edu/
Description: State-supported, university, coed. Awards bachelor's, master's, and doctoral degrees and post-master's certificates. Founded 1957. Setting: 1,444-acre suburban campus with easy access to Detroit. Endowment: $50.9 million. Research spending for the previous fiscal year: $10.1 million. Educational spending for the previous fiscal year: $5622 per student. Total enrollment: 19,740. Faculty: (560 full-time). 12,152 applied, 62% were admitted. 18% from top 10% of their high school class, 47% from top quarter, 82% from top half. Full-time: 11,880 students, 60% women, 40% men. Part-time: 4,310 students, 60% women, 40% men. 19% from out-of-state. 0.3% American Indian or Alaska Native, non-Hispanic/Latino; 2% Hispanic/Latino; 8% African American, non-Hispanic/Latino; 4% Asian, non-Hispanic/Latino; 0.1% Native Hawaiian or other Pacific Islander, non-Hispanic/Latino; 1% international. 22% 25 or older, 14% live on campus, 12% transferred in. Retention: 70% of full-time freshmen returned the following year. Academic areas with the most degrees conferred: health professions and related sciences; business/marketing; communication/journalism. Core. Calendar: semesters. Academic remediation for entering students, ESL program, services for LD students, advanced placement, accelerated degree program, self-designed majors, honors program, independent study, distance learning, double major, summer session for credit, part-time degree program, co-op programs and internships, graduate courses open to undergrads. Off campus study at Macomb Community College, Beaumont Hospital-Troy. Study abroad program. ROTC: Air Force (c).
Entrance Requirements: Options: electronic application, deferred admission, international baccalaureate accepted. Required: high school transcript, minimum 2.5 high school GPA. Recommended: SAT or ACT. Required for

some: minimum 3 high school GPA, interview, audition, ACT. Entrance: moderately difficult. Application deadline: Rolling. Notification: continuous. Transfer credits accepted: Yes.

Costs Per Year: Application fee: $0. State resident tuition: $11,183 full-time, $341 per credit hour part-time. Nonresident tuition: $25,598 full-time, $795.75 per credit hour part-time. Full-time tuition varies according to program and student level. Part-time tuition varies according to program and student level. College room and board: $8208. Room and board charges vary according to housing facility.

Collegiate Environment: Orientation program. Drama-theater group, choral group, student-run newspaper, radio station. Social organizations: 283 open to all; national fraternities, national sororities, local sororities; 1% of eligible men and 2% of eligible women are members. Most popular organizations: Beta Alpha Psi, OASIS, AMA, InterVarsity Christian Fellowship, Alternative Spring Break & Global Brigades, Oakland University Student Congress, Greek Life (Sororities & Fraternities). Major annual events: Welcome Week at Oakland University, Weekend of Champions @Oakland University, OU Homecoming Celebration. Student services: health clinic, personal-psychological counseling. Campus security: 24-hour emergency response devices and patrols, student patrols, late night transport-escort service, controlled dormitory access, state certified police officers, security lighting, extensive camera system, self-defense/alcohol abuse classes. 2,192 college housing spaces available; all were occupied in 2012-13. Freshmen given priority for college housing. Option: coed housing available. Kresge Library plus 1 other with 826,421 books, 1.2 million microform titles, 20,610 serials, 21,039 audiovisual materials, an OPAC, and a Web page. Operations spending for the previous fiscal year: $4.3 million.

Community Environment: This is a suburban community with access to nearby Detroit via Interstate 75, and Michigan Highway 59. The immediate area has a hospital, shopping facilities, Oakland Technology Park, and several churches. Recreation is extensive both on and off campus. On campus cultural opportunities include Meadow Brook Theater, Meadow Brook Music Festival, Meadow Brook Art Gallery, and the Oakland University Center for Performing Arts. In addition, roller rinks, bowling centers, golf courses, Silverdome, the Palace (Home of the Detroit Pistons), theatres, and the local Avon Players offer recreational and cultural activities off campus. There is seasonal part-time employment for students. Special events held annually include Meadowbrook Music Festival in summer and the Christmas Parade; the annual Arts and Apples Festival is in September.

■ **OLIVET COLLEGE**
320 S Main St.
Olivet, MI 49076-9701
Tel: (269)749-7000; Free: 800-456-7189
Fax: (616)749-3821
Web Site: www.olivetcollege.edu/
Description: Independent, 4-year, coed, affiliated with Congregational Christian Church. Awards bachelor's and master's degrees. Founded 1844. Setting: 92-acre small town campus with easy access to Lansing, Battle Creek. Total enrollment: 1,206. Faculty: 90 (46 full-time, 44 part-time). Student-undergrad faculty ratio is 17:1. 2,379 applied, 53% were admitted. Full-time: 1,057 students, 45% women, 55% men. Part-time: 107 students, 52% women, 48% men. Students come from 10 states and territories, 2 other countries. 0.3% American Indian or Alaska Native, non-Hispanic/Latino; 3% Hispanic/Latino; 8% African American, non-Hispanic/Latino; 0.3% Asian, non-Hispanic/Latino; 0.3% Native Hawaiian or other Pacific Islander, non-Hispanic/Latino; 0% international. 7% 25 or older, 49% live on campus. Retention: 71% of full-time freshmen returned the following year. Academic areas with the most degrees conferred: business/marketing; homeland security, law enforcement, firefighting, and protective services; education. Core. Calendar: 4-4-1. Advanced placement, self-designed majors, honors program, independent study, double major, summer session for credit, part-time degree program, co-op programs and internships. ROTC: Air Force (c).
Entrance Requirements: Options: electronic application, deferred admission. Required: high school transcript, SAT or ACT. Recommended: minimum 2.6 high school GPA. Required for some: essay, interview. Entrance: minimally difficult. Application deadline: Rolling. Notification: continuous. Transfer credits accepted: Yes.
Collegiate Environment: Orientation program. Drama-theater group, choral group, marching band, student-run newspaper, radio station. Social organizations: 16 open to all; local fraternities, local sororities, Theme houses. Most popular organizations: Mathletes math club, Common Ground service club, Student Athletes club, Psych Club, Olivet College Vets. Major annual events: Lecture and Symposium speakers series, Founder's Day

observance, Midnight breakfast. Student services: health clinic, personal-psychological counseling, women's center. Campus security: 24-hour emergency response devices and patrols, student patrols, late night transport-escort service, security cameras in all dorms and campus surveillance. 613 college housing spaces available; 573 were occupied in 2012-13. Freshmen guaranteed college housing. On-campus residence required through junior year. Options: coed, men-only, women-only housing available. Burrage Library with 68,464 books, 3 microform titles, 123 serials, 92 audiovisual materials, and an OPAC. 118 computers available on campus for general student use. A campuswide network can be accessed from student residence rooms and from off campus. Students can access the following: online class registration. Staffed computer lab on campus.

Community Environment: Olivet, population 1,789, is located 30 miles south of Lansing and 125 miles west of Detroit.

■ THE ROBERT B. MILLER COLLEGE
450 N Ave.
Battle Creek, MI 49017
Tel: (269)660-8021
Web Site: www.millercollege.edu/
Description: Independent, 4-year, coed.

■ ROCHESTER COLLEGE
800 W Avon Rd.
Rochester Hills, MI 48307-2764
Tel: (248)218-2000; Free: 800-521-6010
Fax: (248)218-2005
E-mail: admissions@rc.edu
Web Site: www.rc.edu/
Description: Independent, comprehensive, coed, affiliated with Church of Christ. Awards associate, bachelor's, and master's degrees. Founded 1959. Setting: 83-acre suburban campus with easy access to Detroit. Endowment: $1.5 million. Educational spending for the previous fiscal year: $2650 per student. Total enrollment: 980. Faculty: 159 (46 full-time, 113 part-time). Student-undergrad faculty ratio is 6:1. 210 applied, 80% were admitted. 14% from top 10% of their high school class, 28% from top quarter, 60% from top half. 1 valedictorian, 10 student government officers. Full-time: 636 students, 56% women, 44% men. Part-time: 334 students, 73% women, 27% men. Students come from 20 states and territories, 6 other countries, 14% from out-of-state. 47% 25 or older, 25% live on campus, 17% transferred in. Retention: 55% of full-time freshmen returned the following year. Academic areas with the most degrees conferred: business/marketing; psychology; family and consumer sciences. Core. Calendar: semesters. Academic remediation for entering students, advanced placement, accelerated degree program, independent study, distance learning, double major, summer session for credit, part-time degree program, external degree program, adult/continuing education programs, internships. Off campus study at Madonna University, Macomb Community College, Oakland Community College, Mott Community College, Specs Howard School of Broadcasters. Study abroad program.
Entrance Requirements: Options: electronic application, early admission, deferred admission. Required: high school transcript, minimum 2.25 high school GPA, SAT or ACT. Recommended: essay, 2 recommendations. Required for some: interview. Entrance: minimally difficult. Application deadline: Rolling. Notification: continuous.
Collegiate Environment: Orientation program. Drama-theater group, choral group, student-run newspaper. Social organizations: 3 open to all; local fraternities, local sororities; 10% of eligible men and 10% of eligible women are members. Most popular organizations: Image, student government, American Marketing Association. Major annual event: Celebration. Student services: personal-psychological counseling. Campus security: 24-hour emergency response devices, late night transport-escort service, controlled dormitory access, evening security guards. Ennis and Nancy Ham Library with 55,000 books, 17,500 microform titles, 200 serials, an OPAC, and a Web page. Operations spending for the previous fiscal year: $275,567. 61 computers available on campus for general student use. A campuswide network can be accessed from student residence rooms and from off campus. Staffed computer lab on campus.
Community Environment: See Oakland University.

■ SACRED HEART MAJOR SEMINARY
2701 Chicago Blvd.
Detroit, MI 48206-1799
Tel: (313)883-8500

Web Site: www.shms.edu/
Description: Independent Roman Catholic, comprehensive, coed. Awards associate, bachelor's, and master's degrees. Founded 1919. Setting: 24-acre urban campus. Total enrollment: 466. Faculty: 75 (29 full-time, 46 part-time). Student-undergrad faculty ratio is 6:1. 4 applied, 100% were admitted. 33% from top quarter of their high school class. Full-time: 57 students, 4% women, 96% men. Part-time: 207 students, 53% women, 47% men. 4% from out-of-state. 1% American Indian or Alaska Native, non-Hispanic/Latino; 5% Hispanic/Latino; 4% African American, non-Hispanic/Latino; 0% Asian, non-Hispanic/Latino; 0% Native Hawaiian or other Pacific Islander, non-Hispanic/Latino; 3% international. 82% 25 or older, 17% live on campus, 10% transferred in. Retention: 100% of full-time freshmen returned the following year. Academic areas with the most degrees conferred: liberal arts/general studies; theology and religious vocations. Calendar: semesters. Part-time degree program.
Entrance Requirements: Options: early admission, deferred admission. Required: essay, high school transcript, minimum 2 high school GPA, 1 recommendation, interview, SAT or ACT. Entrance: moderately difficult. Application deadline: 8/15. Notification: 8/22. Preference given to candidates for the priesthood. SAT Reasoning Test deadline: 8/15. SAT Subject Test deadline: 8/15.
Costs Per Year: Application fee: $30. Comprehensive fee: $25,445 includes full-time tuition ($16,405), mandatory fees ($100), and college room and board ($8940). Part-time tuition: $385 per credit hour. Part-time mandatory fees: $50 per term.
Collegiate Environment: Orientation program. Choral group. Student services: personal-psychological counseling.
Community Environment: At the turn of the 20th century, Detroit was a quiet, tree-shaded community brewing beer and producing comfortable carriages and comforting stoves. The serenity was broken by Henry Ford's creation, a vehicle "propelled by power generated from within itself." Today it is the greatest automobile-manufacturing city in the world. It is also rapidly becoming a steel center and a leader in the manufacturing of pharmaceuticals, office equipment, rubber products, salt, television components, synthetic resins and paints, meat products, marine engines, and more than half the garden seed used throughout the country. Annual mean temperature is 49.3 degrees, and annual rainfall is 31.03 inches. Definitely an industrial city, Detroit has a civic center complex on the riverfront, an excellent park system, and numerous museums and art galleries.

■ SAGINAW CHIPPEWA TRIBAL COLLEGE
2274 Enterprise Dr.
Mount Pleasant, MI 48858
Tel: (989)775-4123
Fax: (989)775-4528
E-mail: treed@sagchip.org
Web Site: www.sagchip.edu/
Description: Independent, 2-year, coed. Awards transfer associate and terminal associate degrees. Founded 1998. Educational spending for the previous fiscal year: $3380 per student. Total enrollment: 123. Faculty: 17 (4 full-time, 13 part-time). Student-undergrad faculty ratio is 9:1. 36 applied, 100% were admitted. Full-time: 43 students, 70% women, 30% men. Part-time: 80 students, 78% women, 23% men. 0% from out-of-state. 74% 25 or older. Calendar: semesters.
Entrance Requirements: Required: high school transcript. Entrance: noncompetitive.
Collegiate Environment: Student-run newspaper.

■ SAGINAW VALLEY STATE UNIVERSITY
7400 Bay Rd.
University Center, MI 48710
Tel: (989)964-4000; Free: 800-968-9500
Fax: (989)964-0180
E-mail: admissions@svsu.edu
Web Site: www.svsu.edu/
Description: State-supported, comprehensive, coed. Awards bachelor's and master's degrees and post-master's certificates. Founded 1963. Setting: 782-acre small town campus. Endowment: $44.2 million. Research spending for the previous fiscal year: $826,235. Educational spending for the previous fiscal year: $4537 per student. Total enrollment: 10,552. Faculty: 767 (296 full-time, 471 part-time). Student-undergrad faculty ratio is 20:1. 6,262 applied, 85% were admitted. 17% from top 10% of their high school class, 38% from top quarter, 70% from top half. Full-time: 7,784 students, 57% women, 43% men. Part-time: 1,268 students, 55% women, 45% men. Students

come from 17 states and territories, 26 other countries, 1% from out-of-state. 0.3% American Indian or Alaska Native, non-Hispanic/Latino; 3% Hispanic/Latino; 11% African American, non-Hispanic/Latino; 1% Asian, non-Hispanic/Latino; 0.1% Native Hawaiian or other Pacific Islander, non-Hispanic/Latino; 6% international. 16% 25 or older, 30% live on campus, 6% transferred in. Retention: 70% of full-time freshmen returned the following year. Academic areas with the most degrees conferred: education; business/marketing; health professions and related sciences. Core. Calendar: semesters plus summer session. Academic remediation for entering students, ESL program, services for LD students, advanced placement, accelerated degree program, self-designed majors, honors program, independent study, distance learning, double major, summer session for credit, part-time degree program, adult/continuing education programs, co-op programs and internships, graduate courses open to undergrads. Study abroad program.

Entrance Requirements: Options: electronic application, deferred admission, international baccalaureate accepted. Required: high school transcript, ACT. Recommended: minimum 2.5 high school GPA. Entrance: moderately difficult. Application deadline: Rolling. Notification: continuous. Transfer credits accepted: Yes.

Costs Per Year: Application fee: $30. State resident tuition: $7682 full-time, $256.05 per credit hour part-time. Nonresident tuition: $18,626 full-time, $620.85 per credit hour part-time. Mandatory fees: $438 full-time, $14.60 per credit hour part-time. Full-time tuition and fees vary according to course level, course load, location, and program. Part-time tuition and fees vary according to course level, course load, location, and program. College room and board: $8190. College room only: $5560. Room and board charges vary according to board plan, housing facility, and student level.

Collegiate Environment: Orientation program. Drama-theater group, choral group, marching band, student-run newspaper. Social organizations: 120 open to all; national fraternities, national sororities; 3% of eligible men and 3% of eligible women are members. Most popular organizations: His House Christian Fellowship, Criminal Justice Society, Delta Sigma Pi, Alpha Phi Omega, International Students Club. Major annual events: Card's Party, Homecoming Week, Battle of the Valleys. Student services: health clinic, personal-psychological counseling. Campus security: 24-hour emergency response devices and patrols, student patrols, late night transport-escort service, controlled dormitory access, rape prevention program. 2,750 college housing spaces available; 2,695 were occupied in 2012-13. Freshmen guaranteed college housing. Options: men-only, women-only housing available. Zahnow Library plus 1 other with 333,201 books, 370,628 microform titles, 41,964 serials, 27,023 audiovisual materials, an OPAC, and a Web page. Operations spending for the previous fiscal year: $820,959. 1,033 computers available on campus for general student use. A campuswide network can be accessed from student residence rooms and from off campus. Students can access the following: online class registration. Staffed computer lab on campus.

Community Environment: The college has a 782-acre campus located 3 miles south of I-75 on M-84. Combined with this rural atmosphere are urban advantages available in neighboring Saginaw, Bay City and Midland, where tri-county populations total 325,000.

■ ST. CLAIR COUNTY COMMUNITY COLLEGE

323 Erie St.
Port Huron, MI 48061-5015
Tel: (810)984-3881; Free: 800-553-2427
Fax: (810)984-4730
Web Site: www.sc4.edu/

Description: State and locally supported, 2-year, coed. Part of Michigan Department of Education. Awards certificates, transfer associate, and terminal associate degrees. Founded 1923. Setting: 25-acre small town campus with easy access to Detroit. Total enrollment: 4,547. Faculty: 251 (74 full-time, 177 part-time). Student-undergrad faculty ratio is 20:1. Full-time: 1,853 students, 56% women, 44% men. Part-time: 2,694 students, 61% women, 39% men. 0% from out-of-state. 1% American Indian or Alaska Native, non-Hispanic/Latino; 3% Hispanic/Latino; 4% African American, non-Hispanic/Latino; 0.5% Asian, non-Hispanic/Latino; 0.1% Native Hawaiian or other Pacific Islander, non-Hispanic/Latino; 0.3% international. 32% 25 or older, 21% transferred in. Retention: 60% of full-time freshmen returned the following year. Core. Calendar: semesters. Academic remediation for entering students, advanced placement, honors program, independent study, distance learning, summer session for credit, part-time degree program, adult/continuing education programs, co-op programs.

Entrance Requirements: Open admission nursing, radiologic technology and health information technology programs require a secondary application

and competitive admissions. Options: electronic application, early admission. Required: high school transcript. Entrance: noncompetitive. Application deadline: Rolling. Transfer credits accepted: Yes.

Costs Per Year: Application fee: $0. Area resident tuition: $2835 full-time, $94.50 per contact hour part-time. State resident tuition: $5520 full-time, $184 per contact hour part-time. Nonresident tuition: $8040 full-time, $268 per contact hour part-time. Mandatory fees: $418 full-time, $10 per contact hour part-time. Full-time tuition and fees vary according to course load and location. Part-time tuition and fees vary according to course load and location.

Collegiate Environment: Orientation program. Drama-theater group, student-run newspaper, radio station. Social organizations: 18 open to all; Phi Theta Kappa, International Honor Society. Most popular organizations: Phi Theta Kappa, Zombie Defense Council, Marketing and Management Club, Gay- Straight Alliance, Criminal Justice Club. Major annual events: StressBreaker, Club Awareness Day, Paczki Day. Student services: personal-psychological counseling. Campus security: 24-hour emergency response devices, late night transport-escort service, patrols by security until 10 pm. College housing not available. Library plus 1 other with an OPAC and a Web page.

■ SCHOOLCRAFT COLLEGE

18600 Haggerty Rd.
Livonia, MI 48152-2696
Tel: (734)462-4400
Fax: (734)462-4553
E-mail: admissions@schoolcraft.edu
Web Site: www.schoolcraft.edu/

Description: District-supported, 2-year, coed. Part of Michigan Department of Education. Awards certificates, transfer associate, and terminal associate degrees. Founded 1961. Setting: 183-acre suburban campus with easy access to Detroit. Research spending for the previous fiscal year: $781,774. Total enrollment: 12,522. Faculty: 514 (93 full-time, 421 part-time). Student-undergrad faculty ratio is 29:1. Full-time: 4,654 students, 54% women, 46% men. Part-time: 7,868 students, 58% women, 42% men. 1% American Indian or Alaska Native, non-Hispanic/Latino; 3% Hispanic/Latino; 15% African American, non-Hispanic/Latino; 3% Asian, non-Hispanic/Latino; 0.2% Native Hawaiian or other Pacific Islander, non-Hispanic/Latino; 1% international. Retention: 57% of full-time freshmen returned the following year. Core. Calendar: semesters. Academic remediation for entering students, ESL program, services for LD students, advanced placement, honors program, distance learning, summer session for credit, part-time degree program, adult/continuing education programs, internships. Study abroad program.

Entrance Requirements: Open admission. Options: early admission, deferred admission. Recommended: high school transcript. Required for some: high school transcript. Entrance: noncompetitive. Application deadline: Rolling.

Collegiate Environment: Orientation program. Drama-theater group, choral group, student-run newspaper. Social organizations: national fraternities. Most popular organizations: Student Activities Board, Ski Club, student newspaper, Music Club, Phi Theta Kappa. Major annual event: School Daze. Student services: legal services, health clinic, personal-psychological counseling, women's center. Campus security: 24-hour emergency response devices and patrols, late night transport-escort service. College housing not available. Bradner Library with an OPAC.

Community Environment: Livonia is in a suburban area, population 97,977, located 20 miles west of Detroit and is convenient to airports. Good part-time employment opportunities are available for students.

■ SIENA HEIGHTS UNIVERSITY

1247 E Siena Heights Dr.
Adrian, MI 49221-1796
Tel: (517)263-0731; Free: 800-521-0009
Fax: (517)264-7745
E-mail: sjohnson@sienaheights.edu
Web Site: www.sienaheights.edu/

Description: Independent Roman Catholic, comprehensive, coed. Awards associate, bachelor's, and master's degrees. Founded 1919. Setting: 140-acre small town campus with easy access to Detroit, Toledo. Total enrollment: 2,629. Student-undergrad faculty ratio is 17:1. 1,815 applied, 60% were admitted. Full-time: 1,173 students, 50% women, 50% men. Part-time: 1,149 students, 62% women, 38% men. Students come from 5 other countries. 1% American Indian or Alaska Native, non-Hispanic/Latino; 4% Hispanic/Latino; 13% African American, non-Hispanic/Latino; 1% Asian, non-

Hispanic/Latino; 0.1% Native Hawaiian or other Pacific Islander, non-Hispanic/Latino; 0.3% international. 21% transferred in. Retention: 63% of full-time freshmen returned the following year. Core. Calendar: semesters. Academic remediation for entering students, ESL program, services for LD students, advanced placement, accelerated degree program, self-designed majors, independent study, distance learning, double major, summer session for credit, part-time degree program, adult/continuing education programs, co-op programs and internships. Off campus study. Study abroad program.

Entrance Requirements: Options: electronic application, deferred admission, international baccalaureate accepted. Required: high school transcript, SAT or ACT. Required for some: essay, interview. Entrance: moderately difficult. Application deadlines: Rolling, Rolling for nonresidents. Transfer credits accepted: Yes.

Costs Per Year: Application fee: $0. Comprehensive fee: $30,280 includes full-time tuition ($21,250), mandatory fees ($320), and college room and board ($8710). Full-time tuition and fees vary according to course load, location, and program. Room and board charges vary according to board plan, housing facility, and location.

Collegiate Environment: Orientation program. Drama-theater group, choral group, marching band, student-run newspaper. Social organizations: national fraternities, national sororities. Major annual events: Football Games, Mid-night breakfast during exam weeks, Theatre Productions. Student services: health clinic, personal-psychological counseling. Campus security: 24-hour emergency response devices and patrols, student patrols, late night transport-escort service. 400 college housing spaces available; all were occupied in 2012-13. Freshmen guaranteed college housing. On-campus residence required through junior year. Option: coed housing available. Siena Heights University Library with an OPAC and a Web page.

Community Environment: See Adrian College.

■ **SOUTH UNIVERSITY**

41555 Twelve Mile Rd.
Novi, MI 48377
Free: 877-693-2085
Fax: (248)675-0190
Web Site: www.southuniversity.edu/novi.aspx

Description: Proprietary, comprehensive, coed. Part of Education Management Corporation. Awards associate, bachelor's, and master's degrees.

■ **SOUTHWESTERN MICHIGAN COLLEGE**

58900 Cherry Grove Rd.
Dowagiac, MI 49047-9793
Tel: (269)782-1000; Free: 800-456-8675
Fax: (269)782-8414
E-mail: apalsak@swmich.edu
Web Site: www.swmich.edu/

Description: State and locally supported, 2-year, coed. Awards certificates, transfer associate, and terminal associate degrees. Founded 1964. Setting: 240-acre rural campus. Total enrollment: 2,639. Faculty: 171 (51 full-time, 120 part-time). Student-undergrad faculty ratio is 19:1. 2,029 applied, 99% were admitted. Full-time: 1,312 students, 59% women, 41% men. Part-time: 1,327 students, 64% women, 36% men. Students come from 9 states and territories, 12 other countries, 11% from out-of-state. 1% American Indian or Alaska Native, non-Hispanic/Latino; 3% Hispanic/Latino; 10% African American, non-Hispanic/Latino; 1% Asian, non-Hispanic/Latino; 1% international. 34% 25 or older, 10% live on campus, 35% transferred in. Retention: 52% of full-time freshmen returned the following year. Core. Calendar: semesters. Academic remediation for entering students, ESL program, services for LD students, advanced placement, accelerated degree program, independent study, distance learning, double major, summer session for credit, part-time degree program, adult/continuing education programs, co-op programs and internships.

Entrance Requirements: Open admission Students who test below a specific score on the College's basic assessment tests in reading, writing and math will be admitted as provisional students. Students may be exempted based upon ACT/SAT scores. Special requirements for nursing programs. Options: electronic application, deferred admission. Required: high school transcript. Required for some: interview. Entrance: noncompetitive. Application deadline: Rolling. Notification: continuous. Transfer credits accepted: Yes.

Costs Per Year: Application fee: $0. Area resident tuition: $2711 full-time, $104.25 per contact hour part-time. State resident tuition: $3504 full-time, $134.75 per contact hour part-time. Nonresident tuition: $3816 full-time,

$146.75 per contact hour part-time. Mandatory fees: $1034 full-time, $39.75 per contact hour part-time. College room and board: $7715. College room only: $5465.

Collegiate Environment: Orientation program. Drama-theater group, choral group. Social organizations: 12 open to all. Most popular organizations: Dionysus Drama Club, Rock Climbing Club, SMC Community of Veterans, Alpha Kappa Omega, SMC Green Club. Major annual events: Campus Bash (Fall and Spring), Intramural Football and Basketball, Off Campus Student Activities/Trips. Campus security: 24-hour emergency response devices and patrols, controlled dormitory access, day and evening police patrols. 260 college housing spaces available; all were occupied in 2012-13. No special consideration for freshman housing applicants. Option: coed housing available. Fred L. Mathews Library with 29,157 books, 19,757 serials, 3,001 audiovisual materials, an OPAC, and a Web page. 416 computers available on campus for general student use. Computer purchase/lease plans available. A campuswide network can be accessed from student residence rooms and from off campus. Students can access the following: online class registration. Staffed computer lab on campus provides training in use of computers, software, and the Internet.

■ **SPRING ARBOR UNIVERSITY**

106 E Main St.
Spring Arbor, MI 49283-9799
Tel: (517)750-1200; Free: 800-968-0011
Fax: (517)750-1604
E-mail: admissions@arbor.edu
Web Site: www.arbor.edu/

Description: Independent Free Methodist, comprehensive, coed. Awards associate, bachelor's, and master's degrees. Founded 1873. Setting: 100-acre rural campus. Endowment: $9.8 million. Educational spending for the previous fiscal year: $5902 per student. Total enrollment: 4,125. Faculty: 143 (81 full-time, 62 part-time). Student-undergrad faculty ratio is 15:1. 2,674 applied, 70% were admitted. 22% from top 10% of their high school class, 48% from top quarter, 75% from top half. 1 National Merit Scholar, 8 valedictorians, 6 student government officers. Full-time: 2,137 students, 66% women, 34% men. Part-time: 921 students, 76% women, 24% men. Students come from 24 states and territories, 11 other countries, 12% from out-of-state. 0.5% American Indian or Alaska Native, non-Hispanic/Latino; 3% Hispanic/Latino; 13% African American, non-Hispanic/Latino; 1% Asian, non-Hispanic/Latino; 0% Native Hawaiian or other Pacific Islander, non-Hispanic/Latino; 1% international. 7% 25 or older, 73% live on campus, 3% transferred in. Retention: 77% of full-time freshmen returned the following year. Academic areas with the most degrees conferred: business/marketing; family and consumer sciences; health professions and related sciences. Core. Calendar: 4-1-4. Academic remediation for entering students, ESL program, services for LD students, advanced placement, accelerated degree program, self-designed majors, honors program, independent study, distance learning, double major, summer session for credit, part-time degree program, adult/continuing education programs, internships, graduate courses open to undergrads. Off campus study at Christian College Consortium. Study abroad program. ROTC: Army, Air Force (c).

Entrance Requirements: Options: electronic application, early admission, deferred admission. Required: high school transcript, SAT or ACT. Recommended: minimum 2.6 high school GPA, Guidance counselor's form and ACT score of 20 or SAT score of 930 recommended, ACT. Required for some: essay, interview. Entrance: moderately difficult. Application deadlines: 8/1, 8/1 for nonresidents. Notification: continuous, continuous for nonresidents. SAT Reasoning Test deadline: 8/1. Transfer credits accepted: Yes.

Costs Per Year: Application fee: $30. Comprehensive fee: $30,438 includes full-time tuition ($21,998), mandatory fees ($540), and college room and board ($7900). College room only: $3710. Full-time tuition and fees vary according to course load, degree level, and program. Room and board charges vary according to board plan and housing facility. Part-time tuition: $535 per credit hour. Part-time mandatory fees: $255 per term. Part-time tuition and fees vary according to course load, degree level, program, and reciprocity agreements.

Collegiate Environment: Orientation program. Drama-theater group, choral group, student-run newspaper, radio station. Social organizations: 50 open to all. Most popular organizations: Inter-faith Shelter Ministries, Band of Brothers, Action Jackson, Circle of Sisters, Heartside Homeless. Major annual events: Arbor Games, Porchfest, Midnight Breakfast. Student services: health clinic, personal-psychological counseling. Campus security: 24-hour emergency response devices and patrols, student patrols, late night transport-escort service, controlled dormitory access. 1,309 college housing spaces available; 1,162 were occupied in 2012-13. Freshmen guaranteed college housing. On-campus residence required through senior year. Options: men-only, women-only housing available. Hugh A. White Library with 115,987 books, 709,935 microform titles, 523 serials, 3,999 audiovisual materials, an OPAC, and a Web page. Operations spending for the previous fiscal year: $265,904. 251 computers available on campus for general student use. A campuswide network can be accessed from student residence rooms and from off campus. Students can access the following: online class registration. Staffed computer lab on campus provides training in use of computers, software, and the Internet.

■ **UNIVERSITY OF DETROIT MERCY**

4001 W McNichols Rd.

Detroit, MI 48221

Tel: (313)993-1000; Free: 800-635-5020

Fax: (313)993-3326

E-mail: admissions@udmercy.edu

Web Site: www.udmercy.edu/

Description: Independent Roman Catholic (Jesuit), university, coed. Awards associate, bachelor's, master's, and doctoral degrees and post-master's certificates. Founded 1877. Setting: 70-acre urban campus. Total enrollment: 5,725. Student-undergrad faculty ratio is 7:1. 3,173 applied. 6% from out-of-state. 34% 25 or older. Retention: 77% of full-time freshmen returned the following year. Calendar: semesters. Summer session for credit. Off campus study at 4 members of the Detroit Area Consortium of Catholic Colleges.

Entrance Requirements: Option: deferred admission. Required: high school transcript, minimum 2.5 high school GPA, SAT or ACT. Recommended: essay, interview. Required for some: 1 recommendation, interview. Entrance: moderately difficult. Application deadline: Rolling. Notification: continuous.

Costs Per Year: Application fee: $25. Comprehensive fee: $44,000 includes full-time tuition ($34,530) and college room and board ($9470). College room only: $5450. Full-time tuition varies according to program. Room and board charges vary according to board plan and housing facility.

Collegiate Environment: Orientation program. Campus security: 24-hour emergency response devices and patrols, student patrols, late night transport-escort service.

Community Environment: See Wayne State University.

■ **UNIVERSITY OF MICHIGAN**

Ann Arbor, MI 48109

Tel: (734)764-1817

Fax: (734)936-0740

Web Site: www.umich.edu/

Description: State-supported, university, coed. Awards bachelor's, master's, and doctoral degrees and post-master's certificates. Founded 1817. Setting: 3,177-acre small town campus. Endowment: $7.7 billion. Research spending for the previous fiscal year: $1.2 billion. Educational spending for the previous fiscal year: $18,770 per student. Total enrollment: 42,716. Faculty: 3,139 (2,547 full-time, 592 part-time). Student-undergrad faculty ratio is 16:1. 39,584 applied, 41% were admitted. Full-time: 26,538 students, 49% women, 51% men. Part-time: 869 students, 42% women, 58% men. Students come from 56 states and territories, 93 other countries, 36% from out-of-state. 0.2% American Indian or Alaska Native, non-Hispanic/Latino; 4% Hispanic/Latino; 4% African American, non-Hispanic/Latino; 12% Asian, non-Hispanic/Latino; 0.04% Native Hawaiian or other Pacific Islander, non-Hispanic/Latino; 6% international. 2% 25 or older, 37% live on campus, 3% transferred in. Retention: 96% of full-time freshmen returned the following year. Academic areas with the most degrees conferred: social sciences; engineering; psychology. Core. Calendar: trimesters. ESL program, services for LD students, advanced placement, accelerated degree program, self-designed majors, honors program, independent study, distance learning, double major, summer session for credit, part-time degree program, external degree program, adult/continuing education programs, co-op programs and internships, graduate courses open to undergrads. Off campus study. Study abroad program. ROTC: Army, Naval, Air Force.

Entrance Requirements: Options: electronic application, early action, deferred admission, international baccalaureate accepted. Required: essay, high school transcript, SAT or ACT. Required for some: interview, audition for School of Music, Theatre and Dance; portfolio for School of Art and Design, SAT Subject Tests. Entrance: very difficult. Application deadlines: 2/1, 2/1 for nonresidents, 10/31 for early action. Notification: continuous, continuous for nonresidents, 12/22 for early action. SAT Reasoning Test deadline: 2/1. SAT

Subject Test deadline: 2/1. Transfer credits accepted: Yes. Applicants placed on waiting list: 14,659. Wait-listed applicants offered admission: 42.

Costs Per Year: Application fee: $65. State resident tuition: $13,625 full-time, $504 per credit hour part-time. Nonresident tuition: $40,302 full-time, $1592 per credit hour part-time. Mandatory fees: $194 full-time, $97 per term part-time. Full-time tuition and fees vary according to course load, program, and student level. Part-time tuition and fees vary according to course load, program, and student level. College room and board: $9752. Room and board charges vary according to board plan and housing facility.

Collegiate Environment: Orientation program. Drama-theater group, choral group, marching band, student-run newspaper, radio station. Social organizations: 1,310 open to all; national fraternities, national sororities; 16% of eligible men and 20% of eligible women are members. Most popular organizations: Hillel Society, K-Grams (Kids' Program), M-Powered Entrepreneurial Club, Dance Marathon, Alternative Spring Break. Major annual events: Martin Luther King Day Symposium, FestiFall. Student services: legal services, health clinic, personal-psychological counseling, women's center. Campus security: 24-hour emergency response devices and patrols, student patrols, late night transport-escort service, controlled dormitory access, Safewalk, Night Owl ride service. 9,996 college housing spaces available; 9,924 were occupied in 2012-13. Freshmen guaranteed college housing. Options: coed, women-only housing available. Shapiro Undergraduate Library plus 27 others with 12.4 million books, 10,643 microform titles, 151,854 serials, 709 audiovisual materials, an OPAC, and a Web page. Operations spending for the previous fiscal year: $56.8 million. 2,529 computers available on campus for general student use. Computer purchase/lease plans available. A campuswide network can be accessed from student residence rooms and from off campus. Students can access the following: online class registration, file storage. Staffed computer lab on campus (open 24 hours a day) provides training in use of computers, software, and the Internet.

Community Environment: Predominantly a college community, Ann Arbor also serves as a center for scientific and industrial research and development. Products manufactured in the area include precision instruments, automotive parts, ball bearings, computer components and machine tools. Part-time employment is available for students. Average summer temperature is 79 degrees; winter, 27.8 degrees; average rainfall is 30.7 inches. Average snowfall is 35.3 inches. City has excellent transportation facilities including rail, bus, air service, and expressways out of Detroit. Area offers many cultural and recreational advantages usually found only in a large metropolis. For instance, the Ann Arbor Musical Society provides classical concerts of major world orchestras, chamber music groups and soloists. The Ann Arbor May Festival is an additional musical attraction each year.

■ **UNIVERSITY OF MICHIGAN–DEARBORN**

4901 Evergreen Rd.

Dearborn, MI 48128-1491

Tel: (313)593-5000

E-mail: admissions@umd.umich.edu

Web Site: www.umd.umich.edu/

Description: State-supported, comprehensive, coed. Part of University of Michigan System. Awards bachelor's, master's, and doctoral degrees. Founded 1959. Setting: 210-acre suburban campus with easy access to Detroit. Total enrollment: 8,790. Faculty: 571 (315 full-time, 256 part-time). 4,807 applied, 60% were admitted. Full-time: 4,869 students, 50% women, 50% men. Part-time: 2,459 students, 53% women, 47% men. 1% American Indian or Alaska Native, non-Hispanic/Latino; 5% Hispanic/Latino; 12% African American, non-Hispanic/Latino; 6% Asian, non-Hispanic/Latino; 0.04% Native Hawaiian or other Pacific Islander, non-Hispanic/Latino; 3% international. 12% transferred in. Academic areas with the most degrees conferred: psychology; business/marketing; communication/journalism. Calendar: semesters. Part-time degree program, adult/continuing education programs. ROTC: Army.

Entrance Requirements: Options: electronic application, deferred admission, international baccalaureate accepted. Required: high school transcript, minimum 3 high school GPA, SAT or ACT. Required for some: interview. Entrance: moderately difficult. Application deadline: Rolling. Notification: continuous. Transfer credits accepted: Yes.

Costs Per Year: Application fee: $30. State resident tuition: $9876 full-time, $391 per credit hour part-time. Nonresident tuition: $22,290 full-time, $887 per credit hour part-time. Mandatory fees: $606 full-time, $245. Full-time tuition and fees vary according to course level, course load, degree level, program, and student level. Part-time tuition and fees vary according to course level, course load, degree level, program, and student level.

Collegiate Environment: Orientation program. Campus security: 24-hour emergency response devices and patrols, late night transport-escort service. College housing not available.

Community Environment: The university is situated in the middle of a rapidly expanding industrial, residential and social area. Nearby is the Ford Motor Company World Headquarters Complex, the Fairlane Town Center, the Hyatt Regency Hotel and several new apartment and townhouse complexes. Within one hour's driving distance are the cultural opportunities available in Ann Arbor, Meadow Brook Theatre in Rochester, the Michigan Opera Theatre and the Fisher Theatre of Detroit and the various social and cultural events in the city of Dearborn.

■ **UNIVERSITY OF MICHIGAN–FLINT**
303 E Kearsley St.
Flint, MI 48502-1950
Tel: (810)762-3000; Free: 800-942-5636
E-mail: admissions@umflint.edu
Web Site: www.umflint.edu/

Description: State-supported, comprehensive, coed. Part of University of Michigan System. Awards bachelor's, master's, and doctoral degrees and post-master's certificates. Founded 1956. Setting: 72-acre urban campus with easy access to Detroit, Lansing. Endowment: $77.4 million. Research spending for the previous fiscal year: $697,000. Educational spending for the previous fiscal year: $7928 per student. Total enrollment: 8,289. Faculty: 549 (287 full-time, 262 part-time). Student-undergrad faculty ratio is 16:1. 2,638 applied, 74% were admitted. 19% from top 10% of their high school class, 44% from top quarter, 79% from top half. 10 valedictorians. Full-time: 4,379 students, 58% women, 42% men. Part-time: 2,605 students, 66% women, 34% men. Students come from 42 states and territories, 35 other countries, 1% from out-of-state. 1% American Indian or Alaska Native, non-Hispanic/Latino; 4% Hispanic/Latino; 12% African American, non-Hispanic/Latino; 2% Asian, non-Hispanic/Latino; 0.1% Native Hawaiian or other Pacific Islander, non-Hispanic/Latino; 4% international. 40% 25 or older, 4% live on campus, 12% transferred in. Retention: 74% of full-time freshmen returned the following year. Academic areas with the most degrees conferred: health professions and related sciences; business/marketing; education. Core. Calendar: semesters. Academic remediation for entering students, ESL program, services for LD students, advanced placement, accelerated degree program, self-designed majors, honors program, independent study, distance learning, double major, summer session for credit, part-time degree program, adult/continuing education programs, co-op programs and internships, graduate courses open to undergrads. Off campus study. Study abroad program. ROTC: Army (c), Naval (c), Air Force (c).

Entrance Requirements: Options: electronic application, deferred admission. Required: high school transcript, SAT or ACT. Entrance: moderately difficult. Application deadlines: 8/20, Rolling for nonresidents. Notification: continuous, continuous for nonresidents. SAT Reasoning Test deadline: 6/30. SAT Subject Test deadline: 6/30. Transfer credits accepted: Yes.

Costs Per Year: Application fee: $30. State resident tuition: $9102 full-time, $359 per credit hour part-time. Nonresident tuition: $17,754 full-time, $717.25 per credit hour part-time. Mandatory fees: $412 full-time, $157 per term part-time. Full-time tuition and fees vary according to course level, course load, degree level, program, and student level. Part-time tuition and fees vary according to course level, course load, degree level, program, and student level. College room and board: $7506. College room only: $4692. Room and board charges vary according to housing facility.

Collegiate Environment: Orientation program. Drama-theater group, choral group, student-run newspaper. Social organizations: 103 open to all; national fraternities, national sororities, local fraternities, local sororities; 5% of eligible men and 3% of eligible women are members. Most popular organizations: International Student Organization, Muslim Student Association, Kappa Sigma Fraternity, Inter-Varsity Christian Fellowship. Major annual events: Welcome Back Picnic, President's Ball. Student services: health clinic, personal-psychological counseling, women's center. Campus security: 24-hour emergency response devices and patrols, student patrols, late night transport-escort service, controlled dormitory access. 310 college housing spaces available; all were occupied in 2012-13. No special consideration for freshman housing applicants. Option: coed housing available. Frances Willson Thompson Library with 353,617 books, 600,610 microform titles, 559 serials, 10,581 audiovisual materials, an OPAC, and a Web page. Operations spending for the previous fiscal year: $1.7 million. 507 computers available on campus for general student use. Computer purchase/lease plans available. A campuswide network can be accessed from student residence rooms and from off campus. Students can access the following: online class

registration. Staffed computer lab on campus provides training in use of computers, software, and the Internet.
Community Environment: See Kettering University.

■ **UNIVERSITY OF PHOENIX–DETROIT CAMPUS**
26999 Central Park Blvd., Ste. 100
Southfield, MI 48076
Tel: (248)262-3003; Free: 866-766-0766
Web Site: www.phoenix.edu/
Description: Proprietary, comprehensive, coed. Awards bachelor's, master's, and doctoral degrees.

■ **UNIVERSITY OF PHOENIX–METRO DETROIT CAMPUS**
5480 Corporate Dr.
Ste. 240
Troy, MI 48098-2623
Tel: (248)925-4100; Free: 866-766-0766
Fax: (248)267-0147
Web Site: www.phoenix.edu/
Description: Proprietary, comprehensive, coed. Awards bachelor's and master's degrees. Setting: urban campus. Total enrollment: 2,547. Faculty: 329 (39 full-time, 290 part-time). Full-time: 2,018 students, 67% women, 33% men. 83% 25 or older. Academic areas with the most degrees conferred: business/marketing; computer and information sciences; homeland security, law enforcement, firefighting, and protective services. Core. Calendar: continuous. Services for LD students, advanced placement, accelerated degree program, independent study, distance learning, external degree program, adult/continuing education programs, graduate courses open to undergrads.
Entrance Requirements: Open admission. Options: electronic application, deferred admission. Required: 1 recommendation. Required for some: high school transcript. Entrance: noncompetitive. Application deadline: Rolling.
Collegiate Environment: Campus security: late night transport-escort service. University Library with 1,759 books, 692 serials, an OPAC, and a Web page. Operations spending for the previous fiscal year: $6.8 million.

■ **UNIVERSITY OF PHOENIX–WEST MICHIGAN CAMPUS**
318 River Ridge Dr. NW
Walker, MI 49544
Tel: (616)647-5100; Free: 866-766-0766
Web Site: www.phoenix.edu/
Description: Proprietary, comprehensive, coed. Awards bachelor's and master's degrees. Founded 2000. Setting: urban campus. Total enrollment: 524. Faculty: 149 (13 full-time, 136 part-time). Full-time: 456 students, 65% women, 35% men. 85% 25 or older. Academic areas with the most degrees conferred: business/marketing; computer and information sciences; public administration and social services. Core. Calendar: continuous. Services for LD students, advanced placement, accelerated degree program, independent study, distance learning, external degree program, adult/continuing education programs, graduate courses open to undergrads.
Entrance Requirements: Open admission. Options: electronic application, deferred admission, international baccalaureate accepted. Required: 1 recommendation. Required for some: high school transcript. Entrance: noncompetitive. Application deadline: Rolling.
Collegiate Environment: Campus security: late night transport-escort service. University Library with 16,781 serials, an OPAC, and a Web page. Operations spending for the previous fiscal year: $6.8 million.

■ **WALSH COLLEGE OF ACCOUNTANCY AND BUSINESS ADMINISTRATION**
3838 Livernois Rd.
Troy, MI 48007-7006
Tel: (248)689-8282; Free: 800-925-7401
Fax: (248)524-2520
E-mail: jguc@walshcollege.edu
Web Site: www.walshcollege.edu/
Description: Independent, upper-level, coed. Awards bachelor's and master's degrees. Founded 1922. Setting: 29-acre suburban campus with easy access to Detroit. Endowment: $5.1 million. Educational spending for the previous fiscal year: $4004 per student. Total enrollment: 3,106. Faculty: 178 (18 full-time, 160 part-time). Student-undergrad faculty ratio is 17:1. Full-time: 149 students, 46% women, 54% men. Part-time: 876 students, 57% women, 43% men. Students come from 6 states and territories, 37 other countries, 1% from out-of-state. 67% 25 or older, 96% transferred in.

Academic areas with the most degrees conferred: business/marketing; computer and information sciences. Calendar: 4-11week terms. Services for LD students, advanced placement, independent study, distance learning, double major, summer session for credit, part-time degree program, adult/continuing education programs, internships. Off campus study.

Collegiate Environment: Orientation program. Social organizations: 7 open to all. Most popular organizations: student government, American Marketing Association, Economics/Finance Club, Accounting Club, National Association of Black Accountants. Campus security: 24-hour emergency response devices. Vollbrecht Library plus 1 other with 26,300 books, 123,000 microform titles, 8,210 serials, 121 audiovisual materials, an OPAC, and a Web page. Operations spending for the previous fiscal year: $763,800. 300 computers available on campus for general student use. Computer purchase/lease plans available. A campuswide network can be accessed from off-campus. Students can access the following: online class registration. Staffed computer lab on campus provides training in use of computers, software, and the Internet.

Community Environment: The college is located north of Detroit in the city of Troy, population 81,168. The city serves as headquarters for many large corporations.

■ **WASHTENAW COMMUNITY COLLEGE**
4800 E Huron River Dr.
Ann Arbor, MI 48106
Tel: (734)973-3300
Fax: (734)677-5408
Web Site: www.wccnet.edu/

Description: State and locally supported, 2-year, coed. Awards certificates, transfer associate, and terminal associate degrees. Founded 1965. Setting: 235-acre suburban campus with easy access to Detroit. Total enrollment: 12,912. Student-undergrad faculty ratio is 16:1. 1% from out-of-state. 45% 25 or older. Retention: 65% of full-time freshmen returned the following year. Core. Calendar: semesters. Academic remediation for entering students, advanced placement, distance learning, summer session for credit, part-time degree program, external degree program, adult/continuing education programs, internships. Study abroad program. ROTC: Army (c), Naval (c), Air Force (c).

Entrance Requirements: Open admission except for health occupations programs. Options: electronic application, early admission, deferred admission, international baccalaureate accepted. Recommended: SAT or ACT. Required for some: high school transcript. Entrance: noncompetitive. Application deadline: Rolling. Notification: continuous. Preference given to county residents for over-subscribed programs.

Collegiate Environment: Orientation program. Campus security: 24-hour emergency response devices and patrols, late night transport-escort service.

Community Environment: See University of Michigan.

■ **WAYNE COUNTY COMMUNITY COLLEGE DISTRICT**
801 W Fort St.
Detroit, MI 48226-3010
Tel: (313)496-2600
Fax: (313)961-2791
E-mail: caafjh@wccc.edu
Web Site: www.wcccd.edu/

Description: State and locally supported, 2-year, coed. Awards certificates, transfer associate, and terminal associate degrees. Founded 1967. Setting: urban campus. Total enrollment: 21,540. Student-undergrad faculty ratio is 21:1. 0% from out-of-state. 48% 25 or older. Retention: 62% of full-time freshmen returned the following year. Calendar: semesters. Academic remediation for entering students, advanced placement, distance learning, summer session for credit, part-time degree program, adult/continuing education programs. Study abroad program.

Entrance Requirements: Open admission. Options: early admission, deferred admission. Required: high school transcript. Entrance: noncompetitive. Application deadline: Rolling.

Collegiate Environment: Orientation program. Campus security: 24-hour emergency response devices.

■ **WAYNE STATE UNIVERSITY**
656 W Kirby St.
Detroit, MI 48202
Tel: (313)577-2424; Free: 877-WSU-INFO
Fax: (313)577-7536
E-mail: admissions@wayne.edu

Web Site: www.wayne.edu/

Description: State-supported, university, coed. Awards bachelor's, master's, and doctoral degrees and post-master's certificates. Founded 1868. Setting: 200-acre urban campus with easy access to Detroit. Endowment: $260.8 million. Research spending for the previous fiscal year: $153.5 million. Educational spending for the previous fiscal year: $5385 per student. Total enrollment: 28,938. Faculty: 1,873 (1,047 full-time, 826 part-time). Student-undergrad faculty ratio is 16:1. 10,249 applied, 81% were admitted. 24% from top 10% of their high school class, 53% from top quarter, 81% from top half. 15 National Merit Scholars. Full-time: 12,471 students, 56% women, 44% men. Part-time: 6,871 students, 58% women, 42% men. Students come from 43 states and territories, 50 other countries, 2% from out-of-state. 0.4% American Indian or Alaska Native, non-Hispanic/Latino; 3% Hispanic/Latino; 23% African American, non-Hispanic/Latino; 8% Asian, non-Hispanic/Latino; 0.05% Native Hawaiian or other Pacific Islander, non-Hispanic/Latino; 2% international. 28% 25 or older, 11% live on campus, 11% transferred in. Retention: 75% of full-time freshmen returned the following year. Academic areas with the most degrees conferred: business/marketing; psychology; education. Core. Calendar: semesters. Academic remediation for entering students, ESL program, services for LD students, advanced placement, accelerated degree program, freshman honors college, honors program, independent study, distance learning, double major, summer session for credit, part-time degree program, adult/continuing education programs, co-op programs and internships, graduate courses open to undergrads. Off campus study. Study abroad program. ROTC: Army, Naval (c), Air Force (c).

Entrance Requirements: Options: electronic application, deferred admission, international baccalaureate accepted. Required: minimum 2 high school GPA, SAT or ACT. Required for some: ACT. Entrance: minimally difficult. Application deadlines: 8/26, 8/26 for nonresidents. Notification: continuous until 8/26, continuous until 8/26 for nonresidents. Transfer credits accepted: Yes.

Costs Per Year: Application fee: $0. State resident tuition: $324.90 per credit hour part-time. Nonresident tuition: $745.75 per credit hour part-time. Part-time tuition varies according to course load, program, reciprocity agreements, and student level. College room and board: $8504. College room only: $5384. Room and board charges vary according to board plan and housing facility.

Collegiate Environment: Orientation program. Choral group, marching band, student-run newspaper. Social organizations: 395 open to all; national fraternities, national sororities, local fraternities, local sororities; 3% of eligible men and 3% of eligible women are members. Most popular organizations: Muslim Students Association, Honors Students Association, Indian Students Association, American Medical Students Association-Pre-Med Chapter. Major annual events: Welcome Back Week, Late Night Breakfast, International Fair. Student services: legal services, health clinic, personal-psychological counseling. Campus security: 24-hour emergency response devices and patrols, late night transport-escort service, controlled dormitory access. 2,070 undergraduates lived in college housing during 2012-13. Freshmen given priority for college housing. Options: coed, women-only housing available. David Adamany Undergraduate Library plus 6 others with 3.4 million books, 4.4 million microform titles, 71,737 serials, 101,322 audiovisual materials, an OPAC, and a Web page. Operations spending for the previous fiscal year: $18.2 million. 2,877 computers available on campus for general student use. A campuswide network can be accessed from student residence rooms and from off campus. Students can access the following: online class registration. Staffed computer lab on campus provides training in use of software and the Internet.

Community Environment: At the turn of the 20th Century, Detroit was a quiet, tree-shaded community brewing beer and producing comfortable carriages and comforting stoves. The serenity was broken by Henry Ford's creation, a vehicle "propelled by power generated from within itself." Today, it is the greatest automobile-manufacturing city in the world. It is also rapidly becoming a steel center and a leader in the manufacturing of pharmaceuticals, office equipment, rubber products, salt, television components, synthetic resins and paints, meat products, marine engines and more than half the garden seed used throughout the country. Annual mean temperature is 49.3 degrees, and annual rainfall is 31.03 inches. Definitely an industrial city, Detroit has a civic center complex on the riverfront, an excellent park system and numerous museums and art galleries.

■ **WEST SHORE COMMUNITY COLLEGE**
PO Box 277, 3000 N Stiles Rd.
Scottville, MI 49454-0277
Tel: (231)845-6211

Fax: (231)845-0207

E-mail: admissions@westshore.edu

Web Site: www.westshore.edu/

Description: District-supported, 2-year, coed. Part of Michigan Department of Education. Awards certificates, transfer associate, and terminal associate degrees. Founded 1967. Setting: 375-acre rural campus. Total enrollment: 1,372. Faculty: 100 (28 full-time, 72 part-time). 245 applied, 100% were admitted. Full-time: 658 students, 56% women, 44% men. Part-time: 895 students, 67% women, 33% men. 0% from out-of-state. 39% 25 or older, 3% transferred in. Core. Calendar: semesters. Academic remediation for entering students, services for LD students, advanced placement, self-designed majors, independent study, distance learning, summer session for credit, part-time degree program, adult/continuing education programs, co-op programs and internships. Off campus study.

Entrance Requirements: Open admission except for applicants under 18 or nursing program. Options: early admission, deferred admission. Required: high school transcript. Entrance: noncompetitive. Application deadline: Rolling. Notification: continuous.

Collegiate Environment: Orientation program. Drama-theater group, choral group, student-run newspaper. Social organizations: 13 open to all. Most popular organizations: Art Club, Student Senate, Phi Theta Kappa, Science Club, Law Enforcement Club. Student services: personal-psychological counseling. Campus security: 24-hour emergency response devices and patrols. West Shore Library plus 1 other with 2,500 books, 910 microform titles, 150 serials, 1,100 audiovisual materials, an OPAC, and a Web page. 185 computers available on campus for general student use. A campuswide network can be accessed from off-campus. Students can access the following: e-mail. Staffed computer lab on campus.

Community Environment: Scottville is a rural city located 80 miles northwest of Grand Rapids. Agriculture is the main economic feature of the city with a Stokley canning factory second. Recreation is provided by local Riverside Park, with camping, boating and fishing. In addition, duck and small game hunting is available in the surrounding area. Community services include a library, and five churches. Bus, rail and air transportation are easily accessible.

■ **WESTERN MICHIGAN UNIVERSITY**

1903 W Michigan Ave.

Kalamazoo, MI 49008

Tel: (269)387-1000

Fax: (269)387-2096

E-mail: ask-wmu@wmich.edu

Web Site: www.wmich.edu/

Description: State-supported, university, coed. Awards bachelor's, master's, and doctoral degrees and post-master's certificates. Founded 1903. Setting: 1,200-acre urban campus. Endowment: $204.1 million. Research spending for the previous fiscal year: $23 million. Educational spending for the previous fiscal year: $7257 per student. Total enrollment: 24,598. Faculty: 1,456 (913 full-time, 543 part-time). Student-undergrad faculty ratio is 18:1. 13,985 applied, 83% were admitted. 10% from top 10% of their high school class, 31% from top quarter, 70% from top half. Full-time: 16,303 students, 50% women, 50% men. Part-time: 3,175 students, 49% women, 51% men. Students come from 40 states and territories, 65 other countries, 7% from out-of-state. 0.4% American Indian or Alaska Native, non-Hispanic/Latino; 4% Hispanic/Latino; 11% African American, non-Hispanic/Latino; 1% Asian, non-Hispanic/Latino; 0.2% Native Hawaiian or other Pacific Islander, non-Hispanic/Latino; 3% international. 14% 25 or older, 27% live on campus, 9% transferred in. Retention: 73% of full-time freshmen returned the following year. Academic areas with the most degrees conferred: business/marketing; education; health professions and related sciences. Core. Calendar:

semesters. Academic remediation for entering students, ESL program, services for LD students, advanced placement, accelerated degree program, self-designed majors, freshman honors college, honors program, independent study, distance learning, double major, summer session for credit, part-time degree program, adult/continuing education programs, co-op programs and internships, graduate courses open to undergrads. Off campus study at Kalamazoo College and Kalamazoo Valley Community College. Study abroad program. ROTC: Army.

Entrance Requirements: Options: electronic application, international baccalaureate accepted. Required: high school transcript, SAT or ACT. Required for some: interview. Entrance: moderately difficult. Application deadline: Rolling. Notification: continuous. SAT Reasoning Test deadline: 9/1. SAT Subject Test deadline: 9/1. Transfer credits accepted: Yes.

Costs Per Year: Application fee: $35. One-time mandatory fee: $300. State resident tuition: $9138 full-time, $316.03 per credit hour part-time. Nonresident tuition: $22,418 full-time, $775.28 per credit hour part-time. Mandatory fees: $844 full-time, $228.25 per term part-time. Full-time tuition and fees vary according to course load, location, program, and student level. Part-time tuition and fees vary according to course load, location, program, and student level. College room and board: $8414. College room only: $4340. Room and board charges vary according to board plan.

Collegiate Environment: Orientation program. Drama-theater group, choral group, marching band, student-run newspaper, radio station. Social organizations: 361 open to all; national fraternities, national sororities, local fraternities, local sororities; 5% of eligible men and 7% of eligible women are members. Most popular organizations: Campus Activities Board, Western Student Association, Young Black Male Support Network, Drive Safe Kalamazoo, Alternative Spring Break. Major annual events: Homecoming, Bronco Bash, Finals Finish. Student services: legal services, health clinic, personal-psychological counseling, women's center. Campus security: 24-hour emergency response devices and patrols, student patrols, late night transport-escort service, controlled dormitory access. 6,205 college housing spaces available; 5,053 were occupied in 2012-13. Freshmen guaranteed college housing. Options: coed, men-only, women-only housing available. Waldo Library plus 4 others with 2 million books, 2.1 million microform titles, 67,458 serials, 29,690 audiovisual materials, an OPAC, and a Web page. Operations spending for the previous fiscal year: $15.3 million. 2,309 computers available on campus for general student use. Computer purchase/lease plans available. A campuswide network can be accessed from student residence rooms and from off campus. Students can access the following: online class registration. Staffed computer lab on campus provides training in use of computers, software, and the Internet.

Community Environment: At one time a gathering place of the Potawatomies, the city received its name from the Indian word meaning"place where the water boils." Today the city is an important paper-manufacturing center with an annual production of over three million tons. The city is also prominent in the manufacture of pharmaceutical drugs. Part-time work is available for students. The largest city in southwest Michigan, Kalamazoo has many parks and picnic areas, 9 golf courses, ski areas, sandy beaches, and good hunting in season. Community service is provided by several churches, 2 hospitals, and shopping malls. The municipal library, art center, civic players, and symphony orchestra provide cultural outlets.

■ **YESHIVA GEDOLAH OF GREATER DETROIT**

24600 Greenfield

Oak Park, MI 48237-1544

Tel: (810)968-3360

Description: Independent Jewish, comprehensive, men only. Awards bachelor's and master's degrees. Founded 1985. Setting: 1-acre campus with easy access to Detroit. Total enrollment: 64. 27 applied, 100% were admitted. 2% 25 or older.

■ **ACADEMY COLLEGE**
1101 E 78th St.
Bloomington, MN 55420
Tel: (952)851-0066; Free: 800-292-9149
Fax: (952)851-0094
E-mail: admissions@academycollege.edu
Web Site: www.academycollege.edu/
Description: Proprietary, 4-year, coed. Awards associate and bachelor's degrees. Founded 1936. Setting: urban campus. Total enrollment: 150. Faculty: 54 (4 full-time, 50 part-time). Student-undergrad faculty ratio is 7:1. Full-time: 141 students, 41% women, 59% men. Part-time: 9 students, 44% women, 56% men. Students come from 3 states and territories, 1 other country, 2% from out-of-state. 65% 25 or older, 10% transferred in. Retention: 100% of full-time freshmen returned the following year. Academic areas with the most degrees conferred: business/marketing; visual and performing arts; computer and information sciences. Core. Academic remediation for entering students, ESL program, services for LD students, advanced placement, accelerated degree program, honors program, distance learning, double major, summer session for credit, part-time degree program, adult/continuing education programs, co-op programs and internships.
Entrance Requirements: Open admission. Options: electronic application, early admission, deferred admission, international baccalaureate accepted. Required: high school transcript, interview. Entrance: minimally difficult. Notification: continuous.
Collegiate Environment: Orientation program. Learning Resource Center plus 1 other with 1,309 books, 22 serials, an OPAC, and a Web page. 75 computers available on campus for general student use. A campuswide network can be accessed. Students can access the following: online class registration. Staffed computer lab on campus.

■ **ALEXANDRIA TECHNICAL AND COMMUNITY COLLEGE**
1601 Jefferson St.
Alexandria, MN 56308-3707
Tel: (320)762-0221; Free: 888-234-1222
Fax: (320)762-4430
E-mail: admissionsrep@alextech.edu
Web Site: www.alextech.edu/
Description: State-supported, 2-year, coed. Part of Minnesota State Colleges and Universities System. Awards certificates, diplomas, transfer associate, and terminal associate degrees. Founded 1961. Setting: 98-acre small town campus. Total enrollment: 2,877. Faculty: 108 (67 full-time, 41 part-time). Student-undergrad faculty ratio is 24:1. Students come from 22 states and territories, 1 other country, 3% from out-of-state. 1% American Indian or Alaska Native, non-Hispanic/Latino; 1% Hispanic/Latino; 1% African American, non-Hispanic/Latino; 1% Asian, non-Hispanic/Latino. 24% 25 or older. Calendar: semesters. Academic remediation for entering students, services for LD students, advanced placement, self-designed majors, independent study, distance learning, double major, summer session for credit, part-time degree program, internships.
Entrance Requirements: Open admission. Options: electronic application, early admission, deferred admission. Required: high school transcript. Required for some: interview. Entrance: minimally difficult. Application deadlines: Rolling, Rolling for nonresidents. Notification: continuous, continuous for nonresidents. Transfer credits accepted: Yes.
Collegiate Environment: Orientation program. Choral group. Social organizations: 3 open to all. Most popular organizations: Skills USA, Busi-

ness Professionals of America, Delta Epsilon Chi, Student Senate, Phi Theta Kappa. Major annual events: Open House, College for a Day, Sno-Daze. Student services: personal-psychological counseling. Campus security: student patrols, late night transport-escort service, security cameras inside and outside. College housing not available. Learning Resource Center with 23,886 books, 1,995 serials, 1,378 audiovisual materials, an OPAC, and a Web page. 1,576 computers available on campus for general student use. Computer purchase/lease plans available. A campuswide network can be accessed from off-campus. Students can access the following: online class registration. Staffed computer lab on campus provides training in use of computers, software, and the Internet.

■ **ANOKA-RAMSEY COMMUNITY COLLEGE**
11200 Mississippi Blvd. NW
Coon Rapids, MN 55433-3470
Tel: (763)433-1100
Fax: (763)576-5944
E-mail: admissions@anokaramsey.edu
Web Site: www.anokaramsey.edu/
Description: State-supported, 2-year, coed. Part of Minnesota State Colleges and Universities System. Awards certificates, transfer associate, and terminal associate degrees. Founded 1965. Setting: 100-acre suburban campus with easy access to Minneapolis-St. Paul. Total enrollment: 7,773. Faculty: 227 (111 full-time, 116 part-time). Student-undergrad faculty ratio is 39:1. 2,884 applied, 53% were admitted. 4% from out-of-state. 0.5% American Indian or Alaska Native, non-Hispanic/Latino; 5% Hispanic/Latino; 8% African American, non-Hispanic/Latino; 4% Asian, non-Hispanic/Latino; 0.1% Native Hawaiian or other Pacific Islander, non-Hispanic/Latino; 0.3% international. 27% 25 or older. Retention: 52% of full-time freshmen returned the following year. Core. Calendar: semesters. Academic remediation for entering students, services for LD students, advanced placement, accelerated degree program, honors program, independent study, distance learning, double major, summer session for credit, part-time degree program, co-op programs and internships. Off campus study at other colleges in the Minnesota State Colleges and Universities System; evening courses at area community centers and high schools. Study abroad program. ROTC: Air Force (c).
Entrance Requirements: Open admission for state residents only; the nursing program and some technical programs have additional admission requirements. Options: electronic application, early admission, deferred admission. Required for some: high school transcript. Entrance: noncompetitive. Application deadlines: Rolling, Rolling for nonresidents. Notification: continuous, continuous for nonresidents. Transfer credits accepted: Yes.
Costs Per Year: Application fee: $20. State resident tuition: $4,349 full-time, $144.96 per credit part-time. Nonresident tuition: $4,349 full-time, $144.96 per credit part-time. Mandatory fees: $639 full-time, $21.31 per credit part-time. Full-time tuition and fees vary according to course load and program. Part-time tuition and fees vary according to course load and program.
Collegiate Environment: Orientation program. Drama-theater group, choral group, student-run newspaper. Social organizations: 37 open to all. Most popular organizations: student government, Phi Theta Kappa, Multicultural Club, CRU (Campus Christian group), Salmagundi (student newspaper). Major annual events: Fall Picnic, Spring Picnic. Student services: personal-psychological counseling. Campus security: 24-hour emergency response devices, late night transport-escort service. College housing not available. Coon Rapids Campus Library with 41,992 books, 26,106 microform titles,

157 serials, 2,003 audiovisual materials, an OPAC, and a Web page. 728 computers available on campus for general student use. A campuswide network can be accessed from off-campus. Students can access the following: online class registration. Staffed computer lab on campus.

Community Environment: A suburban area with a temperate climate, Coon Rapids (population 53,000) enjoys all the recreational, social and cultural advantages of the Twin Cities. All forms of commercial transportation are available. Community facilities include churches, a public library and a community hospital nearby.

■ **ANOKA-RAMSEY COMMUNITY COLLEGE, CAMBRIDGE CAMPUS**
300 Spirit River Dr. S
Cambridge, MN 55008-5706
Tel: (763)433-1110
Fax: (763)689-7050
E-mail: admissions@anokaramsey.edu
Web Site: www.anokaramsey.edu/
Description: State-supported, 2-year, coed. Part of Minnesota State Colleges and Universities System. Awards certificates, transfer associate, and terminal associate degrees. Founded 1965. Setting: small town campus. Total enrollment: 2,545. Faculty: 60 (30 full-time, 30 part-time). Student-undergrad faculty ratio is 36:1. 695 applied, 51% were admitted. 4% from out-of-state. 1% American Indian or Alaska Native, non-Hispanic/Latino; 3% Hispanic/Latino; 1% African American, non-Hispanic/Latino; 1% Asian, non-Hispanic/Latino; 0.2% Native Hawaiian or other Pacific Islander, non-Hispanic/Latino; 0.1% international. 30% 25 or older. Retention: 47% of full-time freshmen returned the following year. Core. Calendar: semesters. Academic remediation for entering students, services for LD students, advanced placement, accelerated degree program, honors program, independent study, distance learning, double major, summer session for credit, part-time degree program, co-op programs and internships. Off campus study at other colleges in the Minnesota State College and Universities System. Study abroad program. ROTC: Air Force (c).
Entrance Requirements: Open admission for state residents only; the nursing program and some technical programs have additional admission requirements. Options: electronic application, early admission, deferred admission. Required for some: high school transcript. Entrance: noncompetitive. Application deadlines: Rolling, Rolling for nonresidents. Notification: continuous, continuous for nonresidents. Transfer credits accepted: Yes.
Costs Per Year: Application fee: $20. State resident tuition: $4,349 full-time, $144.96 per credit part-time. Nonresident tuition: $4,349 full-time, $144.96 per credit part-time. Mandatory fees: $632 full-time, $21.06 per credit part-time. Full-time tuition and fees vary according to course load and program. Part-time tuition and fees vary according to course load and program.
Collegiate Environment: Orientation program. Drama-theater group, choral group, student-run newspaper. Social organizations: 14 open to all. Student services: personal-psychological counseling. Campus security: 24-hour emergency response devices, late night transport-escort service. College housing not available. Cambridge Campus Library with 17,406 books, 7,876 microform titles, 131 serials, 1,240 audiovisual materials, an OPAC, and a Web page. 261 computers available on campus for general student use. A campuswide network can be accessed from off-campus. Students can access the following: online class registration. Staffed computer lab on campus.

■ **ANOKA TECHNICAL COLLEGE**
1355 W Hwy. 10
Anoka, MN 55303
Tel: (763)576-4700
E-mail: lbrown@anokatech.edu
Web Site: www.anokatech.edu/
Description: State-supported, 2-year, coed. Part of Minnesota State Colleges and Universities System. Awards certificates, diplomas, transfer associate, and terminal associate degrees. Founded 1967. Setting: small town campus with easy access to Minneapolis-St. Paul. Total enrollment: 2,141. 40% 25 or older. Calendar: semesters. Academic remediation for entering students, ESL program, services for LD students, advanced placement, distance learning, double major, part-time degree program, co-op programs and internships.
Entrance Requirements: Open admission. Options: electronic application, deferred admission. Required: high school transcript. Required for some: interview. Entrance: noncompetitive. Application deadline: 8/1.
Collegiate Environment: Orientation program. Student services: personal-psychological counseling. Campus security: late night transport-escort service.

■ **ANTHEM COLLEGE–ST. LOUIS PARK**
5100 Gamble Dr.
Saint Louis Park, MN 55416
Tel: (952)417-2200; Free: 855-331-7769
Fax: (952)545-6149
Web Site: anthem.edu/minneapolis-minnesota/
Description: Proprietary, 2-year, coed. Awards terminal associate degrees. Founded 1996. Total enrollment: 795. Calendar: semesters.
Entrance Requirements: Entrance: noncompetitive.

■ **ARGOSY UNIVERSITY, TWIN CITIES**
1515 Central Pky.
Eagan, MN 55121
Tel: (651)846-2882; Free: 888-844-2004
Fax: (952)844-0472
Web Site: www.argosy.edu/twincities/
Description: Proprietary, university, coed. Part of Education Management Corporation. Awards associate, bachelor's, master's, and doctoral degrees and post-master's certificates. Founded 1961. Setting: suburban campus. Calendar: semesters.

■ **THE ART INSTITUTES INTERNATIONAL MINNESOTA**
15 S 9th St.
Minneapolis, MN 55402
Tel: (612)332-3361; Free: 800-777-3643
Fax: (612)332-3934
Web Site: www.artinstitutes.edu/minneapolis/
Description: Proprietary, 4-year, coed. Part of Education Management Corporation. Awards associate and bachelor's degrees. Founded 1964. Setting: urban campus.

■ **AUGSBURG COLLEGE**
2211 Riverside Ave.
Minneapolis, MN 55454-1351
Tel: (612)330-1000; Free: 800-788-5678
Fax: (612)330-1649
E-mail: admissions@augsburg.edu
Web Site: www.augsburg.edu/
Description: Independent Lutheran, comprehensive, coed. Awards bachelor's, master's, and doctoral degrees and post-master's certificates. Founded 1869. Setting: 23-acre urban campus with easy access to Minneapolis-St. Paul. Endowment: $29.8 million. Educational spending for the previous fiscal year: $18,165 per student. Total enrollment: 3,841. Faculty: 400 (192 full-time, 208 part-time). Student-undergrad faculty ratio is 14:1. 1,853 applied, 69% were admitted. 9% from top 10% of their high school class, 28% from top quarter, 44% from top half. Full-time: 2,357 students, 53% women, 47% men. Part-time: 641 students, 70% women, 30% men. Students come from 35 states and territories, 30 other countries, 9% from out-of-state. 2% American Indian or Alaska Native, non-Hispanic/Latino; 5% Hispanic/Latino; 10% African American, non-Hispanic/Latino; 8% Asian, non-Hispanic/Latino; 0.3% Native Hawaiian or other Pacific Islander, non-Hispanic/Latino; 2% international. 30% 25 or older, 51% live on campus, 10% transferred in. Retention: 79% of full-time freshmen returned the following year. Academic areas with the most degrees conferred: business/marketing; education; social sciences. Core. Calendar: semesters for undergraduate programs; trimesters for graduate programs and weekend college. Academic remediation for entering students, ESL program, services for LD students, advanced placement, self-designed majors, freshman honors college, honors program, independent study, double major, summer session for credit, part-time degree program, adult/continuing education programs, co-op programs and internships. Off campus study at Associated Colleges of the Twin Cities. Study abroad program. ROTC: Army (c), Naval (c), Air Force (c).
Entrance Requirements: Options: electronic application, deferred admission, international baccalaureate accepted. Required: essay, high school transcript, minimum 2.5 high school GPA, interview. Recommended: SAT or ACT. Required for some: 2 recommendations. Entrance: moderately difficult. Application deadline: 8/15. Notification: continuous. SAT Reasoning Test deadline: 8/15. SAT Subject Test deadline: 8/15.
Collegiate Environment: Orientation program. Drama-theater group, choral group, student-run newspaper, radio station. Social organizations: 60 open to all. Most popular organizations: Student Activities Council, student government, newspaper/yearbook, campus ministry, intramurals. Major annual events: Days in May, Advent Vespers/Velkommen Jul, Spring Affair. Student

services: health clinic, personal-psychological counseling, women's center. Campus security: 24-hour emergency response devices and patrols, student patrols, late night transport-escort service, controlled dormitory access. 1,050 college housing spaces available; 1,043 were occupied in 2012-13. Freshmen given priority for college housing. Options: coed, men-only, women-only housing available. James G. Lindell Library with 146,433 books, 19,819 microform titles, 754 serials, an OPAC, and a Web page. Operations spending for the previous fiscal year: $1 million. 260 computers available on campus for general student use. A campuswide network can be accessed from student residence rooms and from off campus. Students can access the following: online class registration. Staffed computer lab on campus.

Community Environment: Augsburg's campus is located in the heart of the Twin Cities, surrounding Murphy Square, the first of 155 parks in the"City of Lakes." The University of Minnesota West Bank campus and two of the city's largest hospitals, Fairview and St. Mary's, are adjacent to the campus. Downtown Minneapolis and St. Paul are minutes west and east via Interstate 94 which forms the southern border of the campus, or on bus routes that also connect with the suburbs.

■ **BEMIDJI STATE UNIVERSITY**
1500 Birchmont Dr., NE
Bemidji, MN 56601-2699
Tel: (218)755-2000; Free: 800-475-2001
Fax: (218)755-2074
E-mail: LMorris@bemidjistate.edu
Web Site: www.bemidjistate.edu/
Description: State-supported, comprehensive, coed. Part of Minnesota State Colleges and Universities System. Awards associate, bachelor's, and master's degrees. Founded 1919. Setting: 89-acre small town campus. Total enrollment: 5,017. Faculty: 260 (153 full-time, 107 part-time). Student-undergrad faculty ratio is 21:1. 3,121 applied, 42% were admitted. 8% from top 10% of their high school class, 22% from top quarter, 55% from top half. Full-time: 3,524 students, 52% women, 48% men. Part-time: 1,220 students, 66% women, 34% men. 12% from out-of-state. 3% American Indian or Alaska Native, non-Hispanic/Latino; 1% Hispanic/Latino; 1% African American, non-Hispanic/Latino; 1% Asian, non-Hispanic/Latino; 0.04% Native Hawaiian or other Pacific Islander, non-Hispanic/Latino; 3% international. 25% 25 or older, 30% live on campus, 7% transferred in. Retention: 69% of full-time freshmen returned the following year. Academic areas with the most degrees conferred: business/marketing; education; health professions and related sciences. Calendar: semesters. Part-time degree program, adult/continuing education programs.
Entrance Requirements: Options: electronic application, deferred admission, international baccalaureate accepted. Required: high school transcript, SAT or ACT. Required for some: essay, interview. Entrance: moderately difficult. Application deadline: Rolling. Notification: continuous.
Costs Per Year: Application fee: $20. State resident tuition: $7146 full-time. Nonresident tuition: $7146 full-time. Mandatory fees: $960 full-time. Full-time tuition and fees vary according to course load, location, program, and reciprocity agreements. College room and board: $6970. Room and board charges vary according to board plan and housing facility.
Collegiate Environment: Orientation program. Campus security: 24-hour emergency response devices and patrols, late night transport-escort service, controlled dormitory access. Freshmen given priority for college housing. Option: coed housing available.
Community Environment: A regional home for outdoor sports and cultural arts activities, Bemidji (population 13,000) lies in Minnesota North Country on the shores of Lake Bemidji. This area is noted for its scenic forests and lakes that are enjoyed by recreational enthusiasts during all seasons. From excellent fishing in the summer to cross-country and downhill skiing in the winter, residents and visitors alike have found Bemidji to be a community that satisfies a great diversity of interests.

■ **BETHANY LUTHERAN COLLEGE**
700 Luther Dr.
Mankato, MN 56001-6163
Tel: (507)344-7000; Free: 800-944-3066
Fax: (507)344-7376
E-mail: dwestpha@blc.edu
Web Site: www.blc.edu/
Description: Independent Lutheran, 4-year, coed. Awards bachelor's degrees. Founded 1927. Setting: 50-acre small town campus with easy access to Minneapolis-St. Paul. Endowment: $37.4 million. Educational spending for the previous fiscal year: $24,874 per student. Total enrollment: 600.

Faculty: 79 (41 full-time, 38 part-time). Student-undergrad faculty ratio is 10:1. 441 applied, 78% were admitted. 17% from top 10% of their high school class, 42% from top quarter, 72% from top half. Full-time: 570 students, 52% women, 48% men. Part-time: 30 students, 57% women, 43% men. Students come from 24 states and territories, 9 other countries, 26% from out-of-state. 0% American Indian or Alaska Native, non-Hispanic/Latino; 3% Hispanic/Latino; 2% African American, non-Hispanic/Latino; 1% Asian, non-Hispanic/Latino; 0% Native Hawaiian or other Pacific Islander, non-Hispanic/Latino; 1% international. 4% 25 or older, 65% live on campus, 6% transferred in. Retention: 72% of full-time freshmen returned the following year. Academic areas with the most degrees conferred: business/marketing; communication/journalism; visual and performing arts. Core. Calendar: semesters. Academic remediation for entering students, services for LD students, advanced placement, self-designed majors, independent study, double major, co-op programs and internships. Study abroad program. ROTC: Army (c).
Entrance Requirements: Options: electronic application, international baccalaureate accepted. Required: essay, high school transcript, minimum 2.4 high school GPA, SAT or ACT. Recommended: minimum 3.2 high school GPA, interview. Required for some: interview. Entrance: moderately difficult. Application deadline: 7/1. Transfer credits accepted: Yes.
Costs Per Year: Application fee: $0. One-time mandatory fee: $130. Comprehensive fee: $30,250 includes full-time tuition ($22,810), mandatory fees ($330), and college room and board ($7110). College room only: $3310. Room and board charges vary according to board plan and housing facility. Part-time tuition: $960 per credit. Part-time mandatory fees: $165 per term. Part-time tuition and fees vary according to course load.
Collegiate Environment: Orientation program. Drama-theater group, choral group, student-run newspaper. Social organizations: 19 open to all. Most popular organizations: Bethany Activities Committee, Student Senate, Scholastic Leadership Society, PAMA (Promoting Awareness, spurring Motivation, and encouraging Action), Bethany Society of Royal Scientists. Major annual events: Spring Formal, Fall Festival, Luthapalooza. Student services: personal-psychological counseling. Campus security: 24-hour emergency response devices and patrols, late night transport-escort service, controlled dormitory access. 513 college housing spaces available; 375 were occupied in 2012-13. Freshmen guaranteed college housing. On-campus residence required through sophomore year. Options: men-only, women-only housing available. Memorial Library plus 1 other with 67,550 books, 289 serials, 3,338 audiovisual materials, an OPAC, and a Web page. Operations spending for the previous fiscal year: $354,952. 100 computers available on campus for general student use. A campuswide network can be accessed from student residence rooms and from off campus. Students can access the following: online class registration. Staffed computer lab on campus provides training in use of computers, software, and the Internet.
Community Environment: See Minnesota State University-Mankato.

■ **BETHEL UNIVERSITY**
3900 Bethel Dr.
Saint Paul, MN 55112-6999
Tel: (651)638-6400; Free: 800-255-8706
E-mail: buadmissions-cas@bethel.edu
Web Site: www.bethel.edu/
Description: Independent, comprehensive, coed, affiliated with Baptist General Conference. Awards associate, bachelor's, master's, and doctoral degrees and post-master's certificates. Founded 1871. Setting: 247-acre suburban campus with easy access to Minneapolis-St. Paul. Endowment: $25.9 million. Educational spending for the previous fiscal year: $8286 per student. Total enrollment: 5,326. Faculty: 306 (182 full-time, 124 part-time). Student-undergrad faculty ratio is 12:1. 2,684 applied, 71% were admitted. 32% from top 10% of their high school class, 61% from top quarter, 84% from top half. Full-time: 2,743 students, 61% women, 39% men. Part-time: 724 students, 70% women, 30% men. Students come from 40 states and territories, 8 other countries, 22% from out-of-state. 0.1% American Indian or Alaska Native, non-Hispanic/Latino; 2% Hispanic/Latino; 5% African American, non-Hispanic/Latino; 3% Asian, non-Hispanic/Latino; 0.1% Native Hawaiian or other Pacific Islander, non-Hispanic/Latino; 0.1% international. 4% 25 or older, 60% live on campus, 4% transferred in. Retention: 83% of full-time freshmen returned the following year. Academic areas with the most degrees conferred: health professions and related sciences; business/marketing; education. Core. Calendar: 4-1-4. Academic remediation for entering students, services for LD students, advanced placement, accelerated degree program, self-designed majors, honors program, independent study, double major, summer session for credit, part-time degree program,

adult/continuing education programs, internships. Off campus study at Council for Christian Colleges and Universities. Study abroad program. ROTC: Army (c), Air Force (c).

Entrance Requirements: Options: electronic application, early admission, deferred admission, international baccalaureate accepted. Required: essay, high school transcript, rank in upper 50% of high school class, SAT or ACT. Recommended: minimum 2.5 high school GPA, interview. Required for some: 2 recommendations. Entrance: moderately difficult. Application deadlines: Rolling, Rolling for nonresidents. Notification: continuous, continuous for nonresidents. Transfer credits accepted: Yes. Applicants placed on waiting list: 36. Wait-listed applicants offered admission: 12.

Costs Per Year: Application fee: $0. Comprehensive fee: $39,740 includes full-time tuition ($30,700), mandatory fees ($140), and college room and board ($8900). College room only: $5100. Room and board charges vary according to board plan. Part-time tuition: $1280 per credit. Part-time tuition varies according to course load.

Collegiate Environment: Orientation program. Drama-theater group, choral group, student-run newspaper, radio station. Social organizations: 55 open to all. Major annual events: Christmas Formal and Dance, Homecoming week events, Airband Competition (annual lip sync competition). Student services: health clinic, personal-psychological counseling. Campus security: 24-hour emergency response devices and patrols, student patrols, late night transport-escort service, controlled dormitory access, video surveillance for residence halls, academic buildings, and parking lots. 2,025 college housing spaces available; 1,675 were occupied in 2012-13. Freshmen guaranteed college housing. On-campus residence required through sophomore year. Option: coed housing available. Bethel University Library plus 1 other with 198,836 books, 165,200 microform titles, 44,016 serials, 13,799 audiovisual materials, an OPAC, and a Web page. Operations spending for the previous fiscal year: $2.4 million. 420 computers available on campus for general student use. Computer purchase/lease plans available. A campuswide network can be accessed from student residence rooms and from off campus. Students can access the following: online class registration. Staffed computer lab on campus provides training in use of computers, software, and the Internet.

■ BROWN COLLEGE

1440 Northland Dr.
Mendota Heights, MN 55120
Tel: (651)905-3400; Free: 866-551-0049
Fax: (651)905-3550
Web Site: www.browncollege.edu/

Description: Proprietary, primarily 2-year, coed. Part of Career Education Corporation. Awards transfer associate, terminal associate, and bachelor's degrees. Founded 1946. Setting: 20-acre suburban campus with easy access to Minneapolis-St. Paul. Total enrollment: 1,233. Faculty: 122 (78 full-time, 44 part-time). Student-undergrad faculty ratio is 11:1. 239 applied, 100% were admitted. Full-time: 1,106 students, 30% women, 70% men. Part-time: 127 students, 35% women, 65% men. Students come from 12 states and territories, 2 other countries, 5% from out-of-state. 35% 25 or older, 5% transferred in. Core. Academic remediation for entering students, summer session for credit, part-time degree program, internships.

Entrance Requirements: Open admission. Options: electronic application, early decision, early action, deferred admission, international baccalaureate accepted. Required: high school transcript, interview. Recommended: essay. Required for some: minimum 2.0 high school GPA. Entrance: minimally difficult. Application deadline: Rolling.

Collegiate Environment: Orientation program. Student-run radio station. Most popular organization: Student Senate. Major annual events: Summer Fling, Portfolio Preview, Cultural Diversity Week. Campus security: 24-hour emergency response devices, student patrols, late night transport-escort service. Career Resource Center with 768 books and 33 serials. 60 computers available on campus for general student use. Computer purchase/lease plans available. A computer is required for all students. A campuswide network can be accessed from student residence rooms and from off campus. Students can access the following: online class registration. Staffed computer lab on campus provides training in use of computers, software, and the Internet.

■ CAPELLA UNIVERSITY

225 S 6th St., 9th Fl.
Minneapolis, MN 55402
Tel: (612)252-4200; Free: 866-283-7921
Fax: (612)337-5396

E-mail: info@capella.edu
Web Site: www.capella.edu/

Description: Proprietary, upper-level, coed. Awards bachelor's, master's, and doctoral degrees and post-master's certificates (offers only distance learning degree programs). Founded 1993. Setting: urban campus. Total enrollment: 36,375. Full-time: 1,156 students, 57% women, 43% men. Part-time: 6,331 students, 67% women, 33% men. 1% American Indian or Alaska Native, non-Hispanic/Latino; 5% Hispanic/Latino; 28% African American, non-Hispanic/Latino; 1% Asian, non-Hispanic/Latino; 0.4% Native Hawaiian or other Pacific Islander, non-Hispanic/Latino; 0.2% international. Academic areas with the most degrees conferred: business/marketing; computer and information sciences; homeland security, law enforcement, firefighting, and protective services. Core. Services for LD students, advanced placement, accelerated degree program, independent study, distance learning, double major, summer session for credit, part-time degree program, adult/continuing education programs, internships. Off campus study.

Entrance Requirements: Transfer credits accepted: Yes.

Collegiate Environment: Orientation program.

■ CARLETON COLLEGE

One N College St.
Northfield, MN 55057-4001
Tel: (507)646-4000; Free: 800-995-2275
Fax: (507)646-4526
E-mail: admissions@carleton.edu
Web Site: www.carleton.edu/

Description: Independent, 4-year, coed. Awards bachelor's degrees. Founded 1866. Setting: 955-acre small town campus with easy access to Minneapolis-St. Paul. Endowment: $653.5 million. Research spending for the previous fiscal year: $2.4 million. Educational spending for the previous fiscal year: $25,960 per student. Total enrollment: 2,055. Faculty: 243 (211 full-time, 32 part-time). Student-undergrad faculty ratio is 9:1. 5,856 applied, 26% were admitted. 80% from top 10% of their high school class, 98% from top quarter, 100% from top half. 77 National Merit Scholars. Full-time: 2,037 students, 53% women, 47% men. Part-time: 18 students, 72% women, 28% men. Students come from 52 states and territories, 38 other countries, 78% from out-of-state. 0.05% American Indian or Alaska Native, non-Hispanic/Latino; 6% Hispanic/Latino; 3% African American, non-Hispanic/Latino; 8% Asian, non-Hispanic/Latino; 0.05% Native Hawaiian or other Pacific Islander, non-Hispanic/Latino; 8% international. 0% 25 or older, 94% live on campus, 0.3% transferred in. Retention: 98% of full-time freshmen returned the following year. Academic areas with the most degrees conferred: social sciences; physical sciences; visual and performing arts. Core. Calendar: three courses for each of three terms. Services for LD students, advanced placement, accelerated degree program, self-designed majors, independent study, double major, internships. Off campus study at Cooperative programs/St. Olaf College, memberships in Associated Colleges of the Midwest, Higher Education Consortium for Urban Affairs. Study abroad program.

Entrance Requirements: Options: electronic application, early admission, early decision, deferred admission, international baccalaureate accepted. Required: essay, high school transcript, 2 recommendations, common application supplement, SAT or ACT. Recommended: interview, SAT Subject Tests. Entrance: very difficult. Application deadlines: 1/15, 11/15 for early decision plan 1, 1/15 for early decision plan 2. Notification: 4/15, 12/15 for early decision plan 1, 2/15 for early decision plan 2. SAT Reasoning Test deadline: 2/1. SAT Subject Test deadline: 2/1. Transfer credits accepted: Yes. Applicants placed on waiting list: 1,618. Wait-listed applicants offered admission: 0. Early decision applicants: 556. Early decision applicants admitted: 216.

Costs Per Year: Application fee: $30. Comprehensive fee: $55,998 includes full-time tuition ($44,184), mandatory fees ($261), and college room and board ($11,553). College room only: $6069. Room and board charges vary according to board plan.

Collegiate Environment: Orientation program. Drama-theater group, choral group, student-run newspaper, radio station. Social organizations: 132 open to all. Most popular organizations: CANOE (Carleton Association of Nature and Outdoor Enthusiasts), Farm Club, Ebony II, WHIMS (Women in Math and Science), Amnesty International. Major annual events: Halloween Concert and Masquerade Ball, spring concert, Mid-Winter Ball. Student services: health clinic, personal-psychological counseling, women's center. Campus security: 24-hour emergency response devices and patrols, student patrols, late night transport-escort service, controlled dormitory access, Emergency Notification Service (cell phone text and email alerts). 1,850 college housing spaces available; 1,767 were occupied in 2012-13. Freshmen guaranteed college housing. On-campus residence required through senior year. Option: coed housing available. Laurence McKinley Gould Library plus 1 other with 1.1 million books, 278,138 microform titles, 520,661 serials, 12,061 audiovisual materials, an OPAC, and a Web page. Operations spending for the previous fiscal year: $6.1 million. 388 computers available on campus for general student use. Computer purchase/lease plans available. A campuswide network can be accessed from student residence rooms and from off campus. Students can access the following: online class registration. Staffed computer lab on campus (open 24 hours a day) provides training in use of computers, software, and the Internet.

Community Environment: Northfield (population 18,671), a two-college town, located 40 miles south of Minneapolis and St. Paul, is the home of several major industries that contribute to the prosperity of the community. Part-time employment is limited. Good shopping facilities, library, churches, a hospital and an arts guild are a part of the community. A Carleton - St. Olaf bus also makes round trips daily to the Twin Cities. The Defeat of Jesse James Days in September is a special annual event.

■ **CENTRAL LAKES COLLEGE**
501 W College Dr.
Brainerd, MN 56401-3904
Tel: (218)855-8000; Free: 800-933-0346
Fax: (218)855-8220
E-mail: cdaniels@clcmn.edu
Web Site: www.clcmn.edu/

Description: State-supported, 2-year, coed. Part of Minnesota State Colleges and Universities System. Awards certificates, diplomas, transfer associate, and terminal associate degrees. Founded 1938. Setting: small town campus. Endowment: $3.4 million. Educational spending for the previous fiscal year: $3616 per student. Total enrollment: 4,378. Faculty: 155 (90 full-time, 65 part-time). Student-undergrad faculty ratio is 20:1. Students come from 12 states and territories, 0.3% from out-of-state. 3% American Indian or Alaska Native, non-Hispanic/Latino; 1% Hispanic/Latino; 2% African American, non-Hispanic/Latino; 1% Asian, non-Hispanic/Latino; 0.1% Native Hawaiian or other Pacific Islander, non-Hispanic/Latino. 32% 25 or older. Core. Calendar: semesters. Academic remediation for entering students, ESL program, services for LD students, advanced placement, independent study, distance learning, summer session for credit, part-time degree program, external degree program, internships. Off campus study at other colleges in the Minnesota State Colleges and Universities System.

Entrance Requirements: Open admission except for nonresidents. Options: electronic application, deferred admission. Required: high school transcript. Entrance: noncompetitive. Application deadlines: Rolling, Rolling for nonresidents. Transfer credits accepted: Yes.

Collegiate Environment: Orientation program. Drama-theater group, choral group, student-run newspaper. Major annual events: Homecoming, Snow Daze Festival. Student services: personal-psychological counseling. Campus security: 24-hour emergency response devices and patrols, student patrols, late night transport-escort service. Learning Resource Center with 16,052 books, 286 serials, an OPAC, and a Web page. 100 computers available on campus for general student use. A campuswide network can be accessed. Students can access the following: online class registration. Staffed computer lab on campus provides training in use of computers, software, and the Internet.

Community Environment: One of the state's best developed vacation areas, Brainerd (population 13,684) is on the Mississippi River near the center of the state. The town is the supply point for resorts along 464 lakes within a 25-mile radius of the town. There are opportunities for varied types of sports activities such as fishing, golfing, skiing, snowmobiling and water sports. Other activities include summer theatre, yacht club regatta, antique shows and concerts. Shopping areas, churches, a public library, a hospital and a YMCA are available. Transportation is provided by bus, railway and airlines.

■ **CENTURY COLLEGE**
3300 Century Ave. N
White Bear Lake, MN 55110
Tel: (651)779-3200; Free: 800-228-1978
Fax: (651)779-5810
E-mail: admissions@century.edu
Web Site: www.century.edu/

Description: State-supported, 2-year, coed. Part of Minnesota State Colleges and Universities System. Awards certificates, diplomas, transfer associate, and terminal associate degrees. Founded 1970. Setting: 170-acre

suburban campus with easy access to Minneapolis-St. Paul. Total enrollment: 10,422. Faculty: 389 (225 full-time, 164 part-time). Student-undergrad faculty ratio is 23:1. 3,310 applied, 100% were admitted. Full-time: 4,490 students, 48% women, 52% men. Part-time: 5,932 students, 61% women, 39% men. Students come from 35 states and territories, 50 other countries, 6% from out-of-state. 0.5% American Indian or Alaska Native, non-Hispanic/Latino; 6% Hispanic/Latino; 11% African American, non-Hispanic/Latino; 16% Asian, non-Hispanic/Latino; 0.2% Native Hawaiian or other Pacific Islander, non-Hispanic/Latino; 1% international. 44% 25 or older, 44% transferred in. Calendar: semesters. Academic remediation for entering students, ESL program, services for LD students, advanced placement, honors program, distance learning, double major, summer session for credit, part-time degree program, internships. ROTC: Air Force (c).

Entrance Requirements: Open admission. Options: electronic application, deferred admission, international baccalaureate accepted. Required: high school transcript. Entrance: noncompetitive. Application deadline: Rolling.

Costs Per Year: Application fee: $20. State resident tuition: $4818 full-time, $160.60 per semester hour part-time. Nonresident tuition: $4818 full-time, $160.60 per semester hour part-time. Mandatory fees: $539 full-time, $17.96 per credit hour part-time. Full-time tuition and fees vary according to class time, program, and reciprocity agreements. Part-time tuition and fees vary according to class time, program, and reciprocity agreements.

Collegiate Environment: Orientation program. Drama-theater group, choral group, student-run newspaper. Social organizations: 35 open to all. Most popular organizations: Asian Student Association, Intercultural Club, Student Senate, Phi Theta Kappa, Planning Activities Committee. Major annual events: Student Success Day (Fall/Spring), All Campus (Student and Staff) Conference. Student services: personal-psychological counseling. Campus security: late night transport-escort service, day patrols. College housing not available. Century College Library with 105,530 books, 19,123 microform titles, 289 serials, 13,992 audiovisual materials, and an OPAC. Operations spending for the previous fiscal year: $1 million. 1,590 computers available on campus for general student use. A campuswide network can be accessed from off-campus. Students can access the following: online class registration. Staffed computer lab on campus provides training in use of computers, software, and the Internet.

■ **COLLEGE OF SAINT BENEDICT**
37 S College Ave.
Saint Joseph, MN 56374
Tel: (320)363-5011; Free: 800-544-1489
Fax: (320)363-5010
E-mail: admissions@csbsju.edu
Web Site: www.csbsju.edu/

Description: Independent Roman Catholic, 4-year, women only. Awards bachelor's degrees (coordinate with Saint John's University for men). Founded 1887. Setting: 3,500-acre small town campus with easy access to Minneapolis-St. Paul. Endowment: $43.2 million. Research spending for the previous fiscal year: $1.1 million. Educational spending for the previous fiscal year: $10,493 per student. Total enrollment: 2,070. Faculty: 189 (151 full-time, 38 part-time). Student-undergrad faculty ratio is 12:1. 1,938 applied, 77% were admitted. 37% from top 10% of their high school class, 76% from top quarter, 95% from top half. 2 National Merit Scholars. Full-time: 2,037 students. Part-time: 33 students. Students come from 30 states and territories, 22 other countries, 17% from out-of-state. 1% American Indian or Alaska Native, non-Hispanic/Latino; 4% Hispanic/Latino; 2% African American, non-Hispanic/Latino; 6% Asian, non-Hispanic/Latino; 0.05% Native Hawaiian or other Pacific Islander, non-Hispanic/Latino; 6% international. 1% 25 or older, 85% live on campus, 1% transferred in. Retention: 89% of full-time freshmen returned the following year. Academic areas with the most degrees conferred: biological/life sciences; English; psychology. Core. Calendar: semesters. ESL program, services for LD students, advanced placement, self-designed majors, honors program, independent study, double major, internships. Off campus study at Tri-College Exchange Program (MN), Saint John's University (MN). Study abroad program. ROTC: Army (c).

Entrance Requirements: Options: electronic application, early action, deferred admission, international baccalaureate accepted. Required: essay, high school transcript, 1 recommendation, SAT or ACT. Recommended: minimum 3 high school GPA, interview. Entrance: moderately difficult. Application deadlines: Rolling, 11/15 for early action. Notification: continuous, 12/15 for early action. Transfer credits accepted: Yes. Applicants placed on waiting list: 25. Wait-listed applicants offered admission: 10. Early action applicants: 1,560. Early action applicants admitted: 1,278.

Costs Per Year: Application fee: $0. Comprehensive fee: $45,489 includes full-time tuition ($35,298), mandatory fees ($920), and college room and board ($9271). College room only: $4463. Room and board charges vary according to board plan and housing facility. Part-time tuition: $1471 per semester hour. Part-time tuition varies according to course load.

Collegiate Environment: Orientation program. Drama-theater group, choral group, student-run newspaper, radio station. Social organizations: 94 open to all. Most popular organizations: China Cross Cultural Communications Club, Outskirts Snow Crew, Buddhist Meditation Club, Dance Team, AKS Sorority. Major annual events: Community BBQ, Pines(spring concert and festival), Festival of Cultures. Student services: health clinic, personal-psychological counseling, women's center. Campus security: 24-hour emergency response devices and patrols, student patrols, late night transport-escort service, controlled dormitory access, well-lit pathways, closed circuit TV monitors. 1,682 college housing spaces available; 1,633 were occupied in 2012-13. Freshmen guaranteed college housing. On-campus residence required through senior year. Option: women-only housing available. Clemens Library plus 2 others with 647,908 books, 121,406 microform titles, 43,129 serials, 40,623 audiovisual materials, an OPAC, and a Web page. Operations spending for the previous fiscal year: $1.5 million. 980 computers available on campus for general student use. A campuswide network can be accessed from student residence rooms and from off campus. Students can access the following: online class registration, online student accounts. Staffed computer lab on campus provides training in use of computers, software, and the Internet.

■ **THE COLLEGE OF ST. SCHOLASTICA**
1200 Kenwood Ave.
Duluth, MN 55811-4199
Tel: (218)723-6000; Free: 800-249-6412
Fax: (218)723-6290
E-mail: admissions@css.edu
Web Site: www.css.edu/

Description: Independent, comprehensive, coed, affiliated with Roman Catholic Church. Awards bachelor's, master's, and doctoral degrees and post-master's certificates. Founded 1912. Setting: 186-acre suburban campus. Endowment: $48.8 million. Educational spending for the previous fiscal year: $7035 per student. Total enrollment: 4,144. Faculty: 383 (172 full-time, 211 part-time). Student-undergrad faculty ratio is 13:1. 1,833 applied, 78% were admitted. 20% from top 10% of their high school class, 42% from top quarter, 86% from top half. 14 valedictorians, 58 student government officers. Full-time: 2,464 students, 66% women, 34% men. Part-time: 413 students, 78% women, 22% men. Students come from 35 states and territories, 36 other countries, 14% from out-of-state. 2% American Indian or Alaska Native, non-Hispanic/Latino; 2% Hispanic/Latino; 2% African American, non-Hispanic/Latino; 1% Asian, non-Hispanic/Latino; 0.1% Native Hawaiian or other Pacific Islander, non-Hispanic/Latino; 3% international. 27% 25 or older, 52% live on campus, 15% transferred in. Retention: 81% of full-time freshmen returned the following year. Academic areas with the most degrees conferred: health professions and related sciences; business/marketing; biological/life sciences. Core. Calendar: semesters. Services for LD students, advanced placement, accelerated degree program, self-designed majors, honors program, independent study, distance learning, double major, summer session for credit, part-time degree program, external degree program, adult/continuing education programs, internships, graduate courses open to undergrads. Off campus study at University of Wisconsin-Superior, University of Minnesota, Duluth. Study abroad program. ROTC: Air Force (c).

Entrance Requirements: Options: electronic application, deferred admission, international baccalaureate accepted. Required: high school transcript, SAT or ACT. Recommended: interview. Required for some: minimum 2 high school GPA, interview. Entrance: moderately difficult. Application deadline: Rolling. Notification: continuous. SAT Reasoning Test deadline: 9/1. Transfer credits accepted: Yes.

Costs Per Year: Application fee: $0. Comprehensive fee: $39,960 includes full-time tuition ($31,416), mandatory fees ($196), and college room and board ($8348). College room only: $4644. Full-time tuition and fees vary according to class time and program. Room and board charges vary according to board plan and housing facility. Part-time tuition: $981 per credit. Part-time tuition varies according to class time, course load, and program.

Collegiate Environment: Orientation program. Drama-theater group, choral group, student-run newspaper. Social organizations: 68 open to all. Most popular organizations: Campus Activity Board, Inter-Varsity, Habitat for Humanity, SHIMA, Volunteers Involved Through Action. Major annual

events: Mayfest, Fallfest, Homecoming. Student services: health clinic, personal-psychological counseling. Campus security: 24-hour emergency response devices and patrols, late night transport-escort service, controlled dormitory access, student door monitor at night. College housing designed to accommodate 1,025 students; 1,058 undergraduates lived in college housing during 2012-13. Freshmen guaranteed college housing. On-campus residence required through sophomore year. Option: coed housing available. College of St. Scholastica Library with 124,652 books, 1,905 microform titles, 54,961 serials, 14,193 audiovisual materials, an OPAC, and a Web page. Operations spending for the previous fiscal year: $1.3 million. 488 computers available on campus for general student use. A campuswide network can be accessed from student residence rooms and from off campus. Students can access the following: online class registration, student account information and transcripts online. Staffed computer lab on campus provides training in use of computers, software, and the Internet.

■ **CONCORDIA COLLEGE**
901 S 8th St.
Moorhead, MN 56562
Tel: (218)299-4000; Free: 800-699-9897
Fax: (218)299-3947
E-mail: sellings@cord.edu
Web Site: www.concordiacollege.edu/

Description: Independent, comprehensive, coed, affiliated with Evangelical Lutheran Church in America. Awards bachelor's and master's degrees. Founded 1891. Setting: 113-acre suburban campus. Endowment: $78.7 million. Research spending for the previous fiscal year: $26,142. Educational spending for the previous fiscal year: $10,256 per student. Total enrollment: 2,631. Faculty: 252 (180 full-time, 72 part-time). Student-undergrad faculty ratio is 13:1. 2,350 applied, 78% were admitted. 32% from top 10% of their high school class, 64% from top quarter, 91% from top half. 4 National Merit Scholars. Full-time: 2,554 students, 62% women, 38% men. Part-time: 49 students, 65% women, 35% men. Students come from 34 states and territories, 35 other countries, 32% from out-of-state. 0.4% American Indian or Alaska Native, non-Hispanic/Latino; 1% Hispanic/Latino; 1% African American, non-Hispanic/Latino; 2% Asian, non-Hispanic/Latino; 0.04% Native Hawaiian or other Pacific Islander, non-Hispanic/Latino; 4% international. 1% 25 or older, 63% live on campus, 3% transferred in. Retention: 80% of full-time freshmen returned the following year. Academic areas with the most degrees conferred: business/marketing; education; biological/life sciences; communication/journalism. Core. Calendar: semesters. Services for LD students, advanced placement, self-designed majors, honors program, independent study, double major, summer session for credit, part-time degree program, co-op programs and internships, graduate courses open to undergrads. Off campus study at Tri-College University; Superior Studies Consortium. Study abroad program. ROTC: Army (c), Air Force (c).

Entrance Requirements: Options: electronic application, early admission, deferred admission, international baccalaureate accepted. Required: high school transcript, 2 recommendations, SAT or ACT. Entrance: moderately difficult. Application deadline: Rolling. Notification: continuous. SAT Reasoning Test deadline: 8/1. Transfer credits accepted: Yes.

Costs Per Year: Application fee: $20. Comprehensive fee: $39,974 includes full-time tuition ($32,600), mandatory fees ($214), and college room and board ($7160). College room only: $3090. Full-time tuition and fees vary according to course load and degree level. Room and board charges vary according to board plan and housing facility. Part-time tuition: $1280 per contact hour. Part-time tuition varies according to course load and degree level.

Collegiate Environment: Orientation program. Drama-theater group, choral group, student-run newspaper, radio station. Social organizations: 111 open to all. Most popular organizations: Campus Service Commission, Habitat for Humanity, Lead Now, Colleges Against Cancer (Relay for Life), Campus Ministry Commission. Major annual events: Family Weekend, Homecoming, Faith, Reason and World Affairs Symposium. Student services: health clinic, personal-psychological counseling, women's center. Campus security: 24-hour emergency response devices and patrols, late night transport-escort service, controlled dormitory access, well-lighted campus. 1,790 college housing spaces available; 1,629 were occupied in 2012-13. Freshmen given priority for college housing. On-campus residence required through sophomore year. Options: coed, women-only housing available. Carl B. Ylvisaker Library with 337,352 books, 44,055 microform titles, 3,907 serials, 22,918 audiovisual materials, an OPAC, and a Web page. Operations spending for the previous fiscal year: $1.2 million. 570 computers available on campus for general student use. A campuswide network can be accessed from student residence rooms and from off campus. Students can access the following: online class registration, online degree audit. Staffed computer lab on campus provides training in use of software.

■ **CONCORDIA UNIVERSITY, ST. PAUL**
275 Syndicate St., N
Saint Paul, MN 55104-5494
Tel: (651)641-8278; Free: 800-333-4705
Fax: (651)659-0207
E-mail: admission@csp.edu
Web Site: www.csp.edu/
Description: Independent, comprehensive, coed, affiliated with Lutheran Church-Missouri Synod. Awards associate, bachelor's, and master's degrees and post-master's certificates. Founded 1893. Setting: 37-acre urban campus with easy access to Minneapolis/St. Paul. Endowment: $26.9 million. Educational spending for the previous fiscal year: $5406 per student. Total enrollment: 3,013. Faculty: 325 (82 full-time, 243 part-time). Student-undergrad faculty ratio is 15:1. 935 applied, 65% were admitted. 14% from top 10% of their high school class, 35% from top quarter, 67% from top half. Full-time: 988 students, 57% women, 43% men. Part-time: 836 students, 62% women, 38% men. Students come from 43 states and territories, 4 other countries, 16% from out-of-state. 1% American Indian or Alaska Native, non-Hispanic/Latino; 5% Hispanic/Latino; 11% African American, non-Hispanic/Latino; 6% Asian, non-Hispanic/Latino; 0.5% Native Hawaiian or other Pacific Islander, non-Hispanic/Latino; 0.5% international. 39% 25 or older, 26% live on campus, 16% transferred in. Retention: 71% of full-time freshmen returned the following year. Academic areas with the most degrees conferred: business/marketing; family and consumer sciences; education; homeland security, law enforcement, firefighting, and protective services. Core. Calendar: semesters. Academic remediation for entering students, services for LD students, advanced placement, accelerated degree program, self-designed majors, honors program, independent study, distance learning, double major, summer session for credit, part-time degree program, adult/continuing education programs, internships, graduate courses open to undergrads. Off campus study at University of Minnesota-Twin Cities Campus. Study abroad program. ROTC: Army (c), Air Force (c).
Entrance Requirements: Options: electronic application, early admission, deferred admission, international baccalaureate accepted. Required: high school transcript, 2 recommendations, ACT. Recommended: minimum 2 high school GPA. Required for some: essay. Entrance: minimally difficult. Application deadline: 8/1. Notification: continuous. Transfer credits accepted: Yes.
Costs Per Year: Application fee: $30. Comprehensive fee: $27,450 includes full-time tuition ($19,700) and college room and board ($7750). Full-time tuition varies according to program. Room and board charges vary according to board plan and housing facility. Part-time tuition: $635 per credit. Part-time tuition varies according to course load and program.
Collegiate Environment: Orientation program. Drama-theater group, choral group, student-run newspaper. Social organizations: 40 open to all. Major annual events: Homecoming, Festival of Beginnings, Honors Convocation. Student services: health clinic, personal-psychological counseling. Campus security: 24-hour emergency response devices and patrols, student patrols, late night transport-escort service, controlled dormitory access. 500 college housing spaces available; 436 were occupied in 2012-13. Freshmen guaranteed college housing. On-campus residence required in freshman year. Options: coed, men-only, women-only housing available. Library Technology Center with 178,388 books, 11,474 microform titles, 380 serials, 3,553 audiovisual materials, an OPAC, and a Web page. Operations spending for the previous fiscal year: $795,130.

■ **CROSSROADS COLLEGE**
920 Mayowood Rd., SW
Rochester, MN 55902-2382
Tel: (507)288-4563; Free: 800-456-7651
Fax: (507)288-9046
E-mail: admissions@crossroadscollege.edu
Web Site: www.crossroadscollege.edu/
Description: Independent, 4-year, coed, affiliated with Christian Churches and Churches of Christ. Awards associate and bachelor's degrees. Founded 1913. Setting: 40-acre urban campus with easy access to Minneapolis-St. Paul. Endowment: $934,902. Educational spending for the previous fiscal year: $20,343 per student. Total enrollment: 154. Faculty: 28 (7 full-time, 21 part-time). Student-undergrad faculty ratio is 10:1. 85 applied, 29% were admitted. 0% from top 10% of their high school class, 7% from top quarter, 29% from top half. Full-time: 134 students, 56% women, 44% men. Part-

time: 20 students, 75% women, 25% men. Students come from 7 states and territories, 1 other country, 27% from out-of-state. 1% American Indian or Alaska Native, non-Hispanic/Latino; 3% Hispanic/Latino; 6% African American, non-Hispanic/Latino; 3% Asian, non-Hispanic/Latino; 1% Native Hawaiian or other Pacific Islander, non-Hispanic/Latino; 1% international. 32% 25 or older, 16% transferred in. Retention: 67% of full-time freshmen returned the following year. Academic areas with the most degrees conferred: theology and religious vocations; business/marketing; psychology. Core. Calendar: semesters. Academic remediation for entering students, advanced placement, self-designed majors, independent study, distance learning, double major, summer session for credit, external degree program, adult/continuing education programs, co-op programs and internships.
Entrance Requirements: Options: electronic application, deferred admission. Required: essay, high school transcript, minimum 2 high school GPA, 3 recommendations, SAT or ACT. Recommended: interview. Entrance: noncompetitive. Application deadline: 8/15. Notification: continuous until 9/1. Transfer credits accepted: Yes.
Collegiate Environment: Orientation program. Drama-theater group, choral group. Social organizations: 5 open to all. Most popular organizations: Musical Outreach Concert Choir, Adoration, Ambassadors Mission Group, Staged Reactions (drama group). Major annual events: Spiritual Emphasis Week, Missions Emphasis Week, Fall Conference/Homecoming Weekend. Student services: personal-psychological counseling. Campus security: student patrols, late night transport-escort service. 100 college housing spaces available; 76 were occupied in 2012-13. Freshmen guaranteed college housing. On-campus residence required through sophomore year. Options: men-only, women-only housing available. G. H. Cachiaras Memorial Library with 30,815 books, 547 serials, 1,363 audiovisual materials, an OPAC, and a Web page. Operations spending for the previous fiscal year: $77,169. 15 computers available on campus for general student use. A campuswide network can be accessed from student residence rooms and from off campus. Students can access the following: online class registration. Staffed computer lab on campus provides training in use of computers.
Community Environment: See Rochester Community and Technical College.

■ **CROWN COLLEGE**
8700 College View Dr.
Saint Bonifacius, MN 55375-9001
Tel: (952)446-4100; Free: 800-68-CROWN
Fax: (952)446-4149
E-mail: admissions@crown.edu
Web Site: www.crown.edu/
Description: Independent, comprehensive, coed, affiliated with The Christian and Missionary Alliance. Awards associate, bachelor's, and master's degrees. Founded 1916. Setting: 215-acre small town campus with easy access to Minneapolis-St. Paul. Endowment: $6.5 million. Educational spending for the previous fiscal year: $3444 per student. Total enrollment: 1,269. Faculty: 160 (33 full-time, 127 part-time). Student-undergrad faculty ratio is 15:1. 838 applied, 56% were admitted. 0% from top 10% of their high school class, 0% from top quarter, 0% from top half. Full-time: 885 students, 55% women, 45% men. Part-time: 203 students, 64% women, 36% men. Students come from 34 states and territories, 11 other countries, 39% from out-of-state. 1% American Indian or Alaska Native, non-Hispanic/Latino; 4% Hispanic/Latino; 3% African American, non-Hispanic/Latino; 7% Asian, non-Hispanic/Latino; 0% Native Hawaiian or other Pacific Islander, non-Hispanic/Latino; 3% international. 6% 25 or older, 79% live on campus, 5% transferred in. Retention: 79% of full-time freshmen returned the following year. Academic areas with the most degrees conferred: theology and religious vocations; business/marketing; health professions and related sciences. Core. Calendar: semesters. Academic remediation for entering students, ESL program, services for LD students, advanced placement, accelerated degree program, honors program, independent study, distance learning, double major, summer session for credit, part-time degree program, external degree program, adult/continuing education programs, internships, graduate courses open to undergrads. Study abroad program. ROTC: Army (c).
Entrance Requirements: Options: electronic application, early admission, deferred admission, international baccalaureate accepted. Required: essay, high school transcript, minimum 2 high school GPA, SAT or ACT. Required for some: interview. Entrance: minimally difficult. Application deadlines: Rolling, Rolling for nonresidents. Notification: continuous, continuous for nonresidents. SAT Reasoning Test deadline: 8/15. SAT Subject Test deadline: 8/15. Transfer credits accepted: Yes.

Costs Per Year: Application fee: $20. Comprehensive fee: $29,910 includes full-time tuition ($22,430) and college room and board ($7480). College room only: $3890. Full-time tuition varies according to course load and program. Room and board charges vary according to board plan and housing facility. Part-time tuition: $950 per credit. Part-time tuition varies according to course load and program.

Collegiate Environment: Orientation program. Drama-theater group, choral group, student-run newspaper, radio station. Social organizations: Hmong Student Fellowship; Umojo; Vida; MuKappa. Most popular organizations: Hmong Student Fellowship, Global Impact Team, Student Activities Board, Student Senate, Storm Chaser Newspaper. Major annual events: Homecoming and following Regatta, Christmas Dinner/Advent service, Spring Banquet. Student services: health clinic, personal-psychological counseling. Campus security: 24-hour emergency response devices, student patrols, late night transport-escort service, controlled dormitory access. 514 college housing spaces available; 487 were occupied in 2012-13. Freshmen guaranteed college housing. On-campus residence required through senior year. Options: men-only, women-only housing available. Peter Watne Memorial Library with 148,561 books, 70,000 microform titles, 29,308 serials, 1,706 audiovisual materials, an OPAC, and a Web page. Operations spending for the previous fiscal year: $362,834. 95 computers available on campus for general student use. A campuswide network can be accessed from student residence rooms and from off campus. Students can access the following: online class registration. Staffed computer lab on campus provides training in use of the Internet.

Community Environment: The College is located in a small community about 20 miles west of Minneapolis.

■ DAKOTA COUNTY TECHNICAL COLLEGE
1300 E 145th St.
Rosemount, MN 55068
Tel: (651)423-8000; Free: 877-YES-DCTC
E-mail: admissions@dctc.mnscu.edu
Web Site: www.dctc.edu/
Description: State-supported, 2-year, coed. Part of Minnesota State Colleges and Universities System. Awards certificates, diplomas, transfer associate, and terminal associate degrees. Founded 1970. Setting: 100-acre suburban campus with easy access to Minneapolis-St. Paul. Endowment: $3.2 million. Research spending for the previous fiscal year: $193,000. Educational spending for the previous fiscal year: $2670 per student. Total enrollment: 3,672. Faculty: 141 (93 full-time, 48 part-time). Student-undergrad faculty ratio is 30:1. Full-time: 1,690 students, 40% women, 60% men. Part-time: 1,982 students, 40% women, 60% men. Students come from 8 states and territories, 28 other countries, 3% from out-of-state. 1% American Indian or Alaska Native, non-Hispanic/Latino; 3% Hispanic/Latino; 7% African American, non-Hispanic/Latino; 3% Asian, non-Hispanic/Latino; 0% Native Hawaiian or other Pacific Islander, non-Hispanic/Latino; 1% international. 46% 25 or older, 17% transferred in. Core. Calendar: semesters. Academic remediation for entering students, ESL program, services for LD students, self-designed majors, independent study, distance learning, double major, summer session for credit, part-time degree program, co-op programs and internships.
Entrance Requirements: Open admission. Option: electronic application. Required for some: high school transcript. Entrance: noncompetitive. Application deadlines: Rolling, Rolling for nonresidents. Transfer credits accepted: Yes. Applicants placed on waiting list: 250. Wait-listed applicants offered admission: 113.
Collegiate Environment: Orientation program. Social organizations: 16 open to all. Most popular organizations: Phi Theta Kappa International Honor Society, SkillsUSA Minnesota, Multicultural Student Leadership Association, Veterans Club, Automotive Club. Major annual events: Multicultural Day, Spring Fling, College Showcase. Student services: personal-psychological counseling. Campus security: 24-hour emergency response devices, late night transport-escort service. DCTC Library with 27,292 books, 130 serials, 1,097 audiovisual materials, an OPAC, and a Web page. Operations spending for the previous fiscal year: $427,000. 600 computers available on campus for general student use. A campuswide network can be accessed. Students can access the following: online class registration. Staffed computer lab on campus provides training in use of the Internet.

■ DEVRY UNIVERSITY
7700 France Ave. S
Ste. 575
Edina, MN 55435

Tel: (952)838-1860; Free: 866-338-7941
Fax: (952)838-3737
Web Site: www.devry.edu/
Description: Proprietary, comprehensive, coed. Awards associate, bachelor's, and master's degrees. Total enrollment: 207. Full-time: 56 students, 43% women, 57% men. Part-time: 72 students, 38% women, 63% men. 5% from out-of-state. 77% 25 or older, 30% transferred in. Academic areas with the most degrees conferred: business/marketing; computer and information sciences. Accelerated degree program, distance learning.
Entrance Requirements: Options: electronic application, deferred admission. Required: high school transcript, interview. Application deadline: Rolling. Notification: continuous. SAT Reasoning Test deadline: 10/31.

■ DULUTH BUSINESS UNIVERSITY
4724 Mike Colalillo Dr.
Duluth, MN 55807
Tel: (218)722-4000; Free: 800-777-8406
E-mail: markt@dbumn.edu
Web Site: www.dbumn.edu/
Description: Proprietary, 2-year, coed. Awards diplomas and terminal associate degrees. Founded 1891. Setting: 2-acre urban campus. Total enrollment: 367. 278 applied. 53% 25 or older.

■ DUNWOODY COLLEGE OF TECHNOLOGY
818 Dunwoody Blvd.
Minneapolis, MN 55403
Tel: (612)374-5800; Free: 800-292-4625
Fax: (612)374-4128
Web Site: www.dunwoody.edu/
Description: Independent, primarily 2-year, coed. Awards diplomas, terminal associate, and bachelor's degrees. Founded 1914. Setting: 12-acre urban campus with easy access to Minneapolis, Minnesota. Total enrollment: 1,131. Faculty: 130 (78 full-time, 52 part-time). Student-undergrad faculty ratio is 10:1. 494 applied, 58% were admitted. 12% from top 10% of their high school class, 36% from top quarter, 56% from top half. Full-time: 881 students, 12% women, 88% men. Part-time: 250 students, 19% women, 81% men. 3% from out-of-state. 1% American Indian or Alaska Native, non-Hispanic/Latino; 2% Hispanic/Latino; 6% African American, non-Hispanic/Latino; 5% Asian, non-Hispanic/Latino; 0.2% Native Hawaiian or other Pacific Islander, non-Hispanic/Latino; 0% international. 51% 25 or older. Retention: 67% of full-time freshmen returned the following year. Academic areas with the most degrees conferred: business/marketing; visual and performing arts. Core. Academic remediation for entering students, independent study, distance learning, summer session for credit, internships. Study abroad program.
Entrance Requirements: Option: electronic application. Required: essay, high school transcript, minimum 2.5 high school GPA, interview. Recommended: SAT or ACT. Required for some: minimum 3 high school GPA. Entrance: minimally difficult. Application deadline: Rolling. Notification: continuous. Transfer credits accepted: Yes. Applicants placed on waiting list: 26. Wait-listed applicants offered admission: 13.
Costs Per Year: Application fee: $50. Tuition: $17,077 full-time. Mandatory fees: $1437 full-time.
Collegiate Environment: Orientation program. Most popular organizations: student government, Historic Green. Major annual events: Fall Fling, Spring Picnic. Student services: personal-psychological counseling, women's center. Campus security: 24-hour emergency response devices, late night transport-escort service. College housing not available. Learning Resource Center with 8,000 books, 115 serials, 250 audiovisual materials, an OPAC, and a Web page. 300 computers available on campus for general student use. Computer purchase/lease plans available. A campuswide network can be accessed from off-campus. Staffed computer lab on campus provides training in use of computers, software, and the Internet.

■ FOND DU LAC TRIBAL AND COMMUNITY COLLEGE
2101 14th St.
Cloquet, MN 55720
Tel: (218)879-0800; Free: 800-657-3712
Fax: (218)879-0814
E-mail: admissions@fdltcc.edu
Web Site: www.fdltcc.edu/
Description: State-supported, 2-year, coed. Part of Minnesota State Colleges and Universities System. Awards certificates, transfer associate, and terminal associate degrees. Founded 1987. Setting: 31-acre rural campus.

Total enrollment: 2,305. Student-undergrad faculty ratio is 29:1. 9% from out-of-state. 21% 25 or older. Core. Calendar: semesters. Academic remediation for entering students, services for LD students, advanced placement, independent study, distance learning, double major, summer session for credit, part-time degree program, external degree program, adult/continuing education programs, co-op programs and internships. Off campus study.
Entrance Requirements: Open admission. Options: electronic application, early admission, deferred admission. Required for some: high school transcript. Entrance: noncompetitive. Notification: continuous until 8/20.
Collegiate Environment: Orientation program. Drama-theater group, choral group, student-run newspaper. Student services: personal-psychological counseling. Campus security: 24-hour emergency response devices, late night transport-escort service, controlled dormitory access, video surveillance system. Ruth Meyers Library with an OPAC.

■ **GLOBE UNIVERSITY–MINNEAPOLIS**
80 S 8th St.
Ste. 51
Minneapolis, MN 55402
Tel: (612)455-3000
E-mail: aschefers@msbcollege.edu
Web Site: www.globeuniversity.edu/
Description: Proprietary, comprehensive, coed. Part of Globe Education Network (GEN) which is composed of Globe University, Minnesota School of Business, Broadview University, The Institute of Production and Recording and Minnesota School of Cosmetology. Awards associate, bachelor's, master's, and doctoral degrees. Setting: 4 urban campus. Total enrollment: 247. Faculty: 30 (8 full-time, 22 part-time). Student-undergrad faculty ratio is 14:1. Full-time: 59 students, 47% women, 53% men. Part-time: 129 students, 55% women, 45% men. 0% from out-of-state. 2% American Indian or Alaska Native, non-Hispanic/Latino; 4% Hispanic/Latino; 26% African American, non-Hispanic/Latino; 2% Asian, non-Hispanic/Latino; 0% Native Hawaiian or other Pacific Islander, non-Hispanic/Latino; 14% international. 28% 25 or older, 28% transferred in. Retention: 25% of full-time freshmen returned the following year. Academic area with the most degrees conferred: business/marketing. Core. Academic remediation for entering students, services for LD students, advanced placement, accelerated degree program, summer session for credit, part-time degree program, adult/continuing education programs, internships.
Entrance Requirements: Option: electronic application. Required: high school transcript, interview, ACCUPLACER is required of all applicants unless documentation of a minimum ACT composite score of 21 or documentation of a minimum composite score of 1485 on the SAT is presented. Required for some: essay, 2 recommendations, GED certificate in lieu of high school transcript. Application deadlines: Rolling, Rolling for nonresidents. Notification: continuous, continuous for nonresidents. Transfer credits accepted: Yes.
Costs Per Year: Application fee: $50. Tuition: $15,300 full-time, $460 per credit part-time. Mandatory fees: $1548 full-time, $43 per credit part-time. Full-time tuition and fees vary according to course load, degree level, location, and program. Part-time tuition and fees vary according to course load, degree level, location, and program.
Collegiate Environment: Orientation program. Social organizations: Program specific student led organizations. Major annual events: Service Learning Projects, Applied Learning Projects, Student Appreciation Events. Campus security: 24-hour emergency response devices, late night transport-escort service. Minneapolis Campus Library with 1,526 books, 53,123 serials, 42 audiovisual materials, an OPAC, and a Web page. 46 computers available on campus for general student use. A campuswide network can be accessed. Students can access the following: online class registration. Staffed computer lab on campus provides training in use of computers, software, and the Internet.

■ **GLOBE UNIVERSITY–WOODBURY**
8089 Globe Dr.
Woodbury, MN 55125
Tel: (651)730-5100; Free: 800-231-0660
Fax: (651)730-5151
E-mail: jmccabe@globeuniversity.edu
Web Site: www.globeuniversity.edu/
Description: Proprietary, comprehensive, coed. Part of Globe Education Network (GEN) which is composed of Globe University, Minnesota School of Business, Broadview University, The Institute of Production and Recording and Minnesota School of Cosmetology. Awards associate, bachelor's,

master's, and doctoral degrees. Founded 1885. Setting: 5-acre suburban campus with easy access to Minneapolis-St. Paul. Total enrollment: 1,542. Faculty: 159 (23 full-time, 136 part-time). Student-undergrad faculty ratio is 15:1. Full-time: 518 students, 70% women, 30% men. Part-time: 981 students, 72% women, 28% men. Students come from 12 states and territories, 6% from out-of-state. 1% American Indian or Alaska Native, non-Hispanic/Latino; 3% Hispanic/Latino; 7% African American, non-Hispanic/Latino; 5% Asian, non-Hispanic/Latino; 0.3% Native Hawaiian or other Pacific Islander, non-Hispanic/Latino; 1% international. 36% 25 or older, 22% transferred in. Retention: 38% of full-time freshmen returned the following year. Academic areas with the most degrees conferred: business/marketing; computer and information sciences; law/legal studies. Core. Academic remediation for entering students, services for LD students, advanced placement, accelerated degree program, summer session for credit, part-time degree program, adult/continuing education programs, internships.
Entrance Requirements: Option: electronic application. Required: high school transcript, interview, ACCUPLACER is required of all applicants unless documentation of a minimum ACT composite score of 21 or documentation of a minimum composite score of 1485 on the SAT is presented. Required for some: essay, 2 recommendations, GED certificate in lieu of high school transcript. Application deadlines: Rolling, Rolling for nonresidents. Notification: continuous, continuous for nonresidents. Transfer credits accepted: Yes.
Costs Per Year: Application fee: $50. Tuition: $15,300 full-time, $460 per credit part-time. Mandatory fees: $1548 full-time, $43 per credit part-time. Full-time tuition and fees vary according to course level, course load, degree level, location, and program. Part-time tuition and fees vary according to course level, course load, degree level, location, and program.
Collegiate Environment: Orientation program. Social organizations: Program specific student led organizations. Major annual events: Service Learning Projects, Applied Learning Projects, Student Appreciation Events. Campus security: 24-hour emergency response devices, late night transport-escort service. Woodbury Campus Library with 8,069 books, 63,753 serials, 2,129 audiovisual materials, an OPAC, and a Web page. 95 computers available on campus for general student use. A campuswide network can be accessed. Students can access the following: online class registration. Staffed computer lab on campus provides training in use of computers, software, and the Internet.

■ **GUSTAVUS ADOLPHUS COLLEGE**
800 W College Ave.
Saint Peter, MN 56082-1498
Tel: (507)933-8000; Free: 800-GUSTAVU(S)
E-mail: admission@gac.edu
Web Site: www.gustavus.edu/
Description: Independent, 4-year, coed, affiliated with Evangelical Lutheran Church in America. Awards bachelor's degrees. Founded 1862. Setting: 340-acre small town campus with easy access to Minneapolis-St. Paul. Endowment: $108.3 million. Research spending for the previous fiscal year: $81,824. Educational spending for the previous fiscal year: $13,832 per student. Total enrollment: 2,524. Faculty: 230 (191 full-time, 39 part-time). Student-undergrad faculty ratio is 12:1. 4,881 applied, 63% were admitted. 37% from top 10% of their high school class, 74% from top quarter, 96% from top half. Full-time: 2,482 students, 56% women, 44% men. Part-time: 42 students, 50% women, 50% men. Students come from 41 states and territories, 20 other countries, 18% from out-of-state. 1% American Indian or Alaska Native, non-Hispanic/Latino; 3% Hispanic/Latino; 3% African American, non-Hispanic/Latino; 4% Asian, non-Hispanic/Latino; 2% international. 1% 25 or older, 95% live on campus, 2% transferred in. Retention: 90% of full-time freshmen returned the following year. Academic areas with the most degrees conferred: biological/life sciences; social sciences; business/marketing. Core. Calendar: 4-1-4. Services for LD students, advanced placement, accelerated degree program, self-designed majors, honors program, independent study, double major, summer session for credit, co-op programs and internships. Off campus study at Minnesota State University, Mankato. Study abroad program. ROTC: Army (c).
Entrance Requirements: Options: electronic application, early admission, early action, deferred admission, international baccalaureate accepted. Required: essay, high school transcript, 1 recommendation. Recommended: interview, SAT or ACT. Entrance: very difficult. Application deadlines: 4/1, 11/1 for early action. Notification: continuous, 11/20 for early action. Applicants placed on waiting list: 10. Wait-listed applicants offered admission: 0.
Costs Per Year: Application fee: $0. One-time mandatory fee: $450.

Comprehensive fee: $46,486 includes full-time tuition ($37,210), mandatory fees ($396), and college room and board ($8880). College room only: $5710. Room and board charges vary according to board plan and housing facility. Part-time tuition: $5080 per course.

Collegiate Environment: Orientation program. Drama-theater group, choral group, student-run newspaper, radio station. Social organizations: 100 open to all; national fraternities, national sororities, local fraternities, local sororities; 14% of eligible men and 16% of eligible women are members. Most popular organizations: Proclaim, Big Partner/Little Partner, Study Buddies, I am...We are, Pound Pals. Major annual events: Nobel Conference, Christmas in Christ Chapel, Mayday. Student services: health clinic, personal-psychological counseling, women's center. Campus security: 24-hour emergency response devices and patrols, late night transport-escort service, controlled dormitory access. 2,060 college housing spaces available; 1,970 were occupied in 2012-13. Freshmen guaranteed college housing. On-campus residence required through senior year. Option: coed housing available. Folke Bernadotte Memorial Library plus 1 other with 357,186 books, 37,395 microform titles, 23,619 serials, 18,874 audiovisual materials, an OPAC, and a Web page. 440 computers available on campus for general student use. A campuswide network can be accessed from student residence rooms and from off campus. Students can access the following: online class registration. Staffed computer lab on campus provides training in use of computers and software.

Community Environment: St. Peter is located 68 miles south of Minneapolis with the usual community facilities. Bus transportation is convenient.

■ **HAMLINE UNIVERSITY**
1536 Hewitt Ave.
Saint Paul, MN 55104-1284
Tel: (651)523-2800; Free: 800-753-9753
Fax: (651)523-2458
E-mail: admission@hamline.edu
Web Site: www.hamline.edu/

Description: Independent, comprehensive, coed, affiliated with United Methodist Church. Awards bachelor's, master's, and doctoral degrees and post-master's certificates. Founded 1854. Setting: 60-acre urban campus with easy access to Minneapolis-St. Paul. Total enrollment: 4,683. Faculty: 448 (195 full-time, 253 part-time). Student-undergrad faculty ratio is 12:1. 3,282 applied, 70% were admitted. 23% from top 10% of their high school class, 46% from top quarter, 85% from top half. 5 National Merit Scholars, 14 valedictorians. Full-time: 1,998 students, 59% women, 41% men. Part-time: 142 students, 63% women, 37% men. Students come from 40 states and territories, 39 other countries, 18% from out-of-state. 1% American Indian or Alaska Native, non-Hispanic/Latino; 5% Hispanic/Latino; 6% African American, non-Hispanic/Latino; 6% Asian, non-Hispanic/Latino; 0.1% Native Hawaiian or other Pacific Islander, non-Hispanic/Latino; 2% international. 7% 25 or older, 41% live on campus, 7% transferred in. Retention: 81% of full-time freshmen returned the following year. Academic areas with the most degrees conferred: social sciences; business/marketing; psychology. Core. Calendar: 4-1-4. Academic remediation for entering students, ESL program, services for LD students, advanced placement, self-designed majors, honors program, independent study, distance learning, double major, summer session for credit, part-time degree program, internships, graduate courses open to undergrads. Off campus study at members of the Associated Colleges of the Twin Cities, American University, Higher Education Consortium for Urban Affairs, and New American Colleges and Universities. Study abroad program. ROTC: Army (c), Air Force (c).

Entrance Requirements: Options: electronic application, early admission, early action, deferred admission, international baccalaureate accepted. Required: essay, high school transcript, 1 recommendation, ACT or SAT, SAT or ACT. Recommended: interview. Entrance: moderately difficult. Application deadlines: Rolling, Rolling for nonresidents, 12/1 for early action. Notification: continuous, continuous for nonresidents, 12/20 for early action. SAT Reasoning Test deadline: 6/30. SAT Subject Test deadline: 6/30. Transfer credits accepted: Yes. Applicants placed on waiting list: 69. Waitlisted applicants offered admission: 7. Early action applicants: 1,960. Early action applicants admitted: 1,437.

Costs Per Year: Application fee: $0. Comprehensive fee: $42,452 includes full-time tuition ($33,236), mandatory fees ($516), and college room and board ($8700). College room only: $4500. Room and board charges vary according to board plan and housing facility. Part-time tuition: $1040 per credit. Part-time mandatory fees: $444 per year. Part-time tuition and fees vary according to course load.

Collegiate Environment: Orientation program. Drama-theater group, choral group, student-run newspaper, radio station. Social organizations: 88 open to all; national fraternities, local sororities; 5% of eligible men and 5% of eligible women are members. Most popular organizations: Student Congress (HUSC), Hand in Hand (elementary school mentoring program), Residence Hall Association, PRIDE, Hamline Oracle (student newspaper). Major annual events: Homecoming events, End of the Year Party, Up All Night. Student services: health clinic, personal-psychological counseling, women's center. Campus security: 24-hour emergency response devices and patrols, late night transport-escort service, controlled dormitory access, security cameras on campus and in residence halls. Security officers are trained as first responders. 944 college housing spaces available; 866 were occupied in 2012-13. Freshmen guaranteed college housing. Option: coed housing available. Bush Library with an OPAC and a Web page. 300 computers available on campus for general student use. A campuswide network can be accessed from student residence rooms and from off campus. Students can access the following: online class registration. Staffed computer lab on campus provides training in use of computers, software, and the Internet.

■ **HENNEPIN TECHNICAL COLLEGE**
9000 Brooklyn Blvd.
Brooklyn Park, MN 55445
Tel: (952)995-1300; Free: 800-645-4655
Fax: (763)488-2944
Web Site: www.hennepintech.edu/

Description: State-supported, 2-year, coed. Part of Minnesota State Colleges and Universities System. Awards certificates, diplomas, transfer associate, and terminal associate degrees. Founded 1972. Setting: 100-acre suburban campus with easy access to Minneapolis-St. Paul. Total enrollment: 13,832. Faculty: 172. Student-undergrad faculty ratio is 25:1. 7,690 applied, 100% were admitted. 51% 25 or older. Core. Calendar: semesters. Academic remediation for entering students, ESL program, services for LD students, advanced placement, self-designed majors, honors program, independent study, distance learning, double major, summer session for credit, adult/continuing education programs, co-op programs and internships.

Entrance Requirements: Open admission. Options: electronic application, international baccalaureate accepted. Recommended: high school transcript. Entrance: minimally difficult. Application deadline: Rolling. Notification: continuous. Transfer credits accepted: Yes.

Collegiate Environment: Orientation program. Most popular organizations: Student Senate, Pangea, Images, Skills USA. Major annual event: International Festival. Student services: personal-psychological counseling. Campus security: late night transport-escort service, security service. 100 computers available on campus for general student use. A campuswide network can be accessed. Students can access the following: online class registration. Staffed computer lab on campus provides training in use of software and the Internet.

■ **HERZING UNIVERSITY**
5700 W Broadway
Minneapolis, MN 55428
Tel: (763)535-3000; Free: 800-596-0724
Fax: (763)535-9205
E-mail: info@mpls.herzing.edu
Web Site: www.herzing.edu/minneapolis

Description: Proprietary, primarily 2-year, coed. Part of Herzing College. Awards certificates, diplomas, terminal associate, and bachelor's degrees. Founded 1961. Setting: 1-acre suburban campus. Total enrollment: 270. Faculty: 32 (21 full-time, 11 part-time). Student-undergrad faculty ratio is 14:1. 128 applied, 75% were admitted. Full-time: 242 students, 93% women, 7% men. Part-time: 28 students, 89% women, 11% men. Students come from 3 states and territories, 1% from out-of-state. 43% 25 or older. Core. Calendar: semesters. Distance learning, part-time degree program, adult/continuing education programs, internships.

Entrance Requirements: Open admission. Required: high school transcript, interview, ACCUPLACER.

Collegiate Environment: Orientation program. Major annual event: Dental Assistants State Convention. Student services: personal-psychological counseling. Campus security: 24-hour emergency response devices. Operations spending for the previous fiscal year: $53,173. 50 computers available on campus for general student use. Staffed computer lab on campus.

■ **HIBBING COMMUNITY COLLEGE**
1515 E 25th St.
Hibbing, MN 55746-3300

Tel: (218)262-7200; Free: 800-224-4HCC
E-mail: admissions@hibbing.edu
Web Site: www.hcc.mnscu.edu/

Description: State-supported, 2-year, coed. Part of Minnesota State Colleges and Universities System. Awards certificates, diplomas, transfer associate, and terminal associate degrees. Founded 1916. Setting: 100-acre small town campus. Total enrollment: 1,596. Student-undergrad faculty ratio is 17:1. 3% from out-of-state. 44% 25 or older. Core. Calendar: semesters. Academic remediation for entering students, services for LD students, advanced placement, distance learning, summer session for credit, part-time degree program, adult/continuing education programs, co-op programs and internships. Off campus study at other colleges in the Minnesota State Colleges and Universities System. Study abroad program.

Entrance Requirements: Open admission except for nursing, law enforcement programs. Options: early admission, deferred admission. Required: high school transcript. Entrance: noncompetitive. Application deadline: Rolling. Notification: continuous.

Collegiate Environment: Orientation program. Drama-theater group, choral group, marching band. Student services: personal-psychological counseling. Campus security: late night transport-escort service. Hibbing Community College Library with 43,104 books, 186 serials, and a Web page.

Community Environment: Hibbing (population 16,500) is the largest of the Mesabi Range towns where there are many open pits for mining ore. Located 70 miles from Duluth, plants in the area mine taconite, an ore-bearing rock that yields a rich iron ore concentrate when processed. The community facilities include a library, churches of major denominations, a hospital, 3 clinics, and shopping areas. Some part-time employment is available. Recreational activities include bowling, hunting, skiing, snowmobiling, fishing, tennis, water sports and curling. Points of interest are the Hibbing-Chisholm Pit Crossing Route and the Hull-Rust-Mahoning Mine. The Last Chance International Curling Bonspeil and the Winter Carnival are annual events.

■ **THE INSTITUTE OF PRODUCTION AND RECORDING**
312 Washington Ave. N
Minneapolis, MN 55401
Tel: (612)375-1900
E-mail: sferkingstad@ipr.edu
Web Site: www.ipr.edu/

Description: Proprietary, 2-year, coed. Part of Globe Education Network (GEN) which is composed of Globe University, Minnesota School of Business, Broadview University, The Institute of Production and Recording and Minnesota School of Cosmetology. Awards transfer associate and terminal associate degrees. Setting: 4-acre urban campus with easy access to Minneapolis-St. Paul. Total enrollment: 456. Faculty: 38. Student-undergrad faculty ratio is 10:1. Full-time: 389 students, 12% women, 88% men. Part-time: 67 students, 25% women, 75% men. Students come from 28 states and territories, 6% from out-of-state. 1% American Indian or Alaska Native, non-Hispanic/Latino; 5% Hispanic/Latino; 8% African American, non-Hispanic/Latino; 2% Asian, non-Hispanic/Latino; 0.2% Native Hawaiian or other Pacific Islander, non-Hispanic/Latino; 0% international. 16% transferred in. Core. Academic remediation for entering students, services for LD students, advanced placement, accelerated degree program, summer session for credit, part-time degree program, adult/continuing education programs, internships.

Entrance Requirements: Option: electronic application. Required: high school transcript, interview, high school transcript or GED, ACCUPLACER is required of all applicants unless documentation of a minimum ACT composite score of 21 or documentation of a minimum composite score of 1485 on the SAT is presented. Required for some: essay, 2 recommendations. Application deadlines: Rolling, Rolling for nonresidents. Notification: continuous, continuous for nonresidents. Transfer credits accepted: Yes.

Costs Per Year: Application fee: $50. Tuition: $16,560 full-time, $460 per credit part-time. Mandatory fees: $1548 full-time, $43 per credit part-time. Full-time tuition and fees vary according to course load, degree level, and program. Part-time tuition and fees vary according to course load, degree level, and program.

Collegiate Environment: Orientation program. Social organizations: Program specific student led organizations. Major annual events: Service Learning Projects, Applied Learning Projects, Student Appreciation Events. Campus security: 24-hour emergency response devices, late night transport-escort service. Institute of Production and Recording Campus Library with 1,640 books, 53,111 serials, 2,079 audiovisual materials, an OPAC, and a Web page. 119 computers available on campus for general student use. A campuswide network can be accessed. Students can access the following: online class registration. Staffed computer lab on campus provides training in use of computers, software, and the Internet.

■ **INVER HILLS COMMUNITY COLLEGE**
2500 E 80th St.
Inver Grove Heights, MN 55076-3224
Tel: (651)450-8500
Fax: (651)450-8677
E-mail: admissions@inverhills.edu
Web Site: www.inverhills.edu/

Description: State-supported, 2-year, coed. Part of Minnesota State Colleges and Universities System. Awards certificates, transfer associate, and terminal associate degrees. Founded 1969. Setting: 100-acre suburban campus with easy access to Minneapolis-St. Paul. Total enrollment: 6,342. Faculty: 226 (105 full-time, 121 part-time). 1,000 applied, 98% were admitted. Full-time: 2,502 students, 53% women, 47% men. Part-time: 3,840 students, 64% women, 36% men. Students come from 19 states and territories, 2% from out-of-state. 1% American Indian or Alaska Native, non-Hispanic/Latino; 5% Hispanic/Latino; 11% African American, non-Hispanic/Latino; 6% Asian, non-Hispanic/Latino; 0.3% Native Hawaiian or other Pacific Islander, non-Hispanic/Latino; 1% international. 43% 25 or older, 5% transferred in. Core. Calendar: semesters. Academic remediation for entering students, ESL program, services for LD students, advanced placement, accelerated degree program, honors program, independent study, distance learning, summer session for credit, part-time degree program, external degree program, co-op programs and internships. Off campus study at other colleges in the Minnesota State Colleges and Universities System. ROTC: Army (c), Air Force (c).

Entrance Requirements: Open admission except for nursing, emergency medical technology programs. Options: electronic application, international baccalaureate accepted. Recommended: high school transcript. Required for some: high school transcript. Entrance: noncompetitive. Application deadline: 8/15. Notification: continuous. Transfer credits accepted: Yes.

Collegiate Environment: Orientation program. Drama-theater group, choral group. Most popular organizations: VIBE, Student Senate, Health Service Student Association, Phi Theta Kappa, Nursing Club. Major annual events: Student Success Day, Spring Fling, Kick-Off day. Student services: health clinic, personal-psychological counseling. Campus security: late night transport-escort service, evening police patrol. 42,073 books, 300 serials, an OPAC, and a Web page 1,400 computers available on campus for general student use. A campuswide network can be accessed. Students can access the following: online class registration. Staffed computer lab on campus (open 24 hours a day) provides training in use of computers, software, and the Internet.

Community Environment: See Bethel College.

■ **ITASCA COMMUNITY COLLEGE**
1851 Hwy. 169 E
Grand Rapids, MN 55744
Tel: (218)322-2300; Free: 800-996-6422
Fax: (218)327-4350
E-mail: iccinfo@itascacc.edu
Web Site: www.itascacc.edu/

Description: State-supported, 2-year, coed. Part of Minnesota State Colleges and Universities System, Northeastern Higher Education District. Awards certificates, diplomas, transfer associate, and terminal associate degrees. Founded 1922. Setting: 24-acre rural campus. Endowment: $4 million. Total enrollment: 1,299. Faculty: 77 (43 full-time, 34 part-time). Student-undergrad faculty ratio is 17:1. 946 applied, 100% were admitted. Students come from 2 other countries, 4% from out-of-state. 4% American Indian or Alaska Native, non-Hispanic/Latino; 0.4% Hispanic/Latino; 3% African American, non-Hispanic/Latino; 0.5% Asian, non-Hispanic/Latino; 0.2% Native Hawaiian or other Pacific Islander, non-Hispanic/Latino; 0% international. 28% 25 or older, 10% live on campus. Retention: 53% of full-time freshmen returned the following year. Core. Calendar: semesters. Academic remediation for entering students, services for LD students, advanced placement, independent study, double major, summer session for credit, part-time degree program, adult/continuing education programs, co-op programs and internships. Off campus study. Study abroad program.

Entrance Requirements: Open admission. Options: electronic application, international baccalaureate accepted. Required: high school transcript. Entrance: noncompetitive. Application deadline: 8/20. Notification: continuous.

Costs Per Year: Application fee: $0. State resident tuition: $4,729 full-time. Nonresident tuition: $5,911 full-time. Mandatory fees: $578 full-time. College room only: $3480.

Collegiate Environment: Orientation program. Social organizations: 20 open to all. Most popular organizations: Student Association, Circle K, Student Ambassadors, Minority Student Club, Psychology Club. Major annual events: Free Christmas Dinner, Marker Dance, Rock and Bowl. Campus security: student patrols, late night transport-escort service, controlled dormitory access, evening patrols by trained security personnel. Itasca Community College Library with 28,790 books, 16,900 microform titles, 280 serials, an OPAC, and a Web page. 250 computers available on campus for general student use. A campuswide network can be accessed from student residence rooms and from off campus. Students can access the following: online class registration. Staffed computer lab on campus.

Community Environment: A rural community beautifully situated on the Mississippi River and 5 lakes, Grand Rapids (population 8,000) is the county seat of Itasca County, a bustling community with a strong tourist trade. Over 1,000 lakes in the county provide the facilities for all water sports; fishing, hunting, bowling and golf are some of the other recreational activities available. Quadna Mt. ski resort is nearby. Part-time employment opportunities are good.

■ ITT TECHNICAL INSTITUTE (BROOKLYN CENTER)

6120 Earle Brown Dr.
Ste. 100
Brooklyn Center, MN 55430
Tel: (763)549-5900; Free: 800-216-8883
Web Site: www.itt-tech.edu/

Description: Proprietary, primarily 2-year, coed. Part of ITT Educational Services, Inc. Awards terminal associate and bachelor's degrees.

■ ITT TECHNICAL INSTITUTE (EDEN PRAIRIE)

8911 Columbine Rd.
Eden Prairie, MN 55347
Tel: (952)914-5300; Free: 888-488-9646
Web Site: www.itt-tech.edu/

Description: Proprietary, primarily 2-year, coed. Part of ITT Educational Services, Inc. Awards terminal associate and bachelor's degrees. Founded 2003.

Entrance Requirements: Entrance: minimally difficult.

■ LAKE SUPERIOR COLLEGE

2101 Trinity Rd.
Duluth, MN 55811
Tel: (218)733-7600; Free: 800-432-2884
E-mail: enroll@lsc.edu
Web Site: www.lsc.edu/

Description: State-supported, 2-year, coed. Part of Minnesota State Colleges and Universities System. Awards certificates, diplomas, transfer associate, and terminal associate degrees. Founded 1995. Setting: 105-acre urban campus. Total enrollment: 4,627. Faculty: 235 (104 full-time, 131 part-time). Student-undergrad faculty ratio is 22:1. 990 applied, 100% were admitted. Full-time: 2,122 students, 50% women, 50% men. Part-time: 2,505 students, 63% women, 37% men. Students come from 29 states and territories, 3 other countries, 12% from out-of-state. 2% American Indian or Alaska Native, non-Hispanic/Latino; 2% Hispanic/Latino; 4% African American, non-Hispanic/Latino; 1% Asian, non-Hispanic/Latino; 0.2% Native Hawaiian or other Pacific Islander, non-Hispanic/Latino; 0.1% international. 36% 25 or older, 41% transferred in. Retention: 48% of full-time freshmen returned the following year. Calendar: semesters. Academic remediation for entering students, services for LD students, advanced placement, independent study, distance learning, double major, summer session for credit, part-time degree program, internships. Study abroad program.

Entrance Requirements: Open admission. Option: electronic application. Required: Transcripts from high school, GED, or HSED and official transcripts from all previous post-secondary institutions attended. Required for some: high school transcript. Entrance: noncompetitive. Application deadline: Rolling. Notification: continuous. Transfer credits accepted: Yes.

Collegiate Environment: Orientation program. Choral group. Social organizations: 30 open to all. Student services: personal-psychological counseling. Campus security: late night transport-escort service. College housing not available. Harold P. Erickson Library with an OPAC and a Web page.

■ LE CORDON BLEU COLLEGE OF CULINARY ARTS

1315 Mendota Heights Rd.
Saint Paul, MN 55120
Free: 888-348-5222
Web Site: www.chefs.edu/Minneapolis-St-Paul/

Description: Proprietary, 2-year, coed. Awards certificates and terminal associate degrees. Total enrollment: 835. Student-undergrad faculty ratio is 33:1. 24% from out-of-state. 37% 25 or older.

Entrance Requirements: Open admission.

■ LEECH LAKE TRIBAL COLLEGE

6945 Littlewolf Rd. NW
Cass Lake, MN 56633
Tel: (218)335-4200
Fax: (218)335-4282
E-mail: shelly.braford@lltc.edu
Web Site: www.lltc.edu/

Description: Public, 2-year, coed. Awards certificates, diplomas, transfer associate, and terminal associate degrees. Founded 1992. Setting: rural campus. Total enrollment: 243. Faculty: 28 (9 full-time, 19 part-time). Student-undergrad faculty ratio is 16:1. Full-time: 190 students, 46% women, 54% men. Part-time: 53 students, 79% women, 21% men. 0% from out-of-state. 20% 25 or older. Core. Calendar: semesters. Academic remediation for entering students, services for LD students, advanced placement, independent study, double major, summer session for credit, part-time degree program, internships.

Entrance Requirements: Open admission. Required: high school transcript. Notification: continuous until 8/22. Transfer credits accepted: Yes.

Collegiate Environment: Orientation program. Student services: personal-psychological counseling. 50 computers available on campus for general student use. A campuswide network can be accessed. Staffed computer lab on campus provides training in use of computers, software, and the Internet.

■ MACALESTER COLLEGE

1600 Grand Ave.
Saint Paul, MN 55105-1899
Tel: (651)696-6000; Free: 800-231-7974
Fax: (651)696-6500
E-mail: admissions@macalester.edu
Web Site: www.macalester.edu/

Description: Independent Presbyterian, 4-year, coed. Awards bachelor's degrees. Founded 1874. Setting: 53-acre urban campus. Endowment: $654.2 million. Research spending for the previous fiscal year: $1.5 million. Educational spending for the previous fiscal year: $16,370 per student. Total enrollment: 2,070. Faculty: 237 (174 full-time, 63 part-time). Student-undergrad faculty ratio is 10:1. 6,030 applied, 37% were admitted. 65% from top 10% of their high school class, 93% from top quarter, 99% from top half. 33 National Merit Scholars, 35 valedictorians. Full-time: 2,035 students, 60% women, 40% men. Part-time: 35 students, 51% women, 49% men. Students come from 94 other countries, 81% from out-of-state. 0.2% American Indian or Alaska Native, non-Hispanic/Latino; 6% Hispanic/Latino; 3% African American, non-Hispanic/Latino; 7% Asian, non-Hispanic/Latino; 0% Native Hawaiian or other Pacific Islander, non-Hispanic/Latino; 13% international. 0% 25 or older, 62% live on campus, 1% transferred in. Retention: 94% of full-time freshmen returned the following year. Academic areas with the most degrees conferred: social sciences; biological/life sciences; English. Core. Calendar: semesters. Services for LD students, advanced placement, self-designed majors, honors program, independent study, double major, summer session for credit, part-time degree program, internships. Off campus study at St. Catherine University, University of St. Thomas, Augsburg College, Hamline University, Minneapolis College of Art and Design. Study abroad program. ROTC: Army (c), Naval (c), Air Force (c).

Entrance Requirements: Options: electronic application, early admission, early decision, deferred admission, international baccalaureate accepted. Required: essay, high school transcript, 2 recommendations, SAT or ACT. Recommended: interview. Entrance: very difficult. Application deadlines: 1/15, 11/15 for early decision plan 1, 1/2 for early decision plan 2. Notification: 3/30, 12/15 for early decision plan 1, 2/7 for early decision plan 2. SAT Reasoning Test deadline: 1/15. SAT Subject Test deadline: 1/15. Transfer credits accepted: Yes. Applicants placed on waiting list: 469. Wait-listed applicants offered admission: 116. Early decision applicants: 245. Early decision applicants admitted: 118.

Costs Per Year: Application fee: $40. Comprehensive fee: $55,456 includes full-time tuition ($45,167), mandatory fees ($221), and college room and

board ($10,068). College room only: $5412. Full-time tuition and fees vary according to course load. Room and board charges vary according to board plan and housing facility. Part-time tuition: $1411 per credit. Part-time tuition varies according to course load.

Collegiate Environment: Orientation program. Drama-theater group, choral group, student-run newspaper, radio station. Social organizations: 110 open to all. Most popular organizations: Community Service Organization, Outing Club (outdoor recreation), Multicultural Organization, International Organization, campus publications. Major annual events: Founders' Day, Springfest, Engagement Fair/Welcome Week. Student services: health clinic, personal-psychological counseling. Campus security: 24-hour emergency response devices and patrols, late night transport-escort service. 1,320 college housing spaces available; 1,270 were occupied in 2012-13. Freshmen guaranteed college housing. On-campus residence required through sophomore year. Options: coed, men-only, women-only housing available. DeWitt Wallace Library with 435,851 books, 87,004 microform titles, 5,492 serials, 31,409 audiovisual materials, an OPAC, and a Web page. Operations spending for the previous fiscal year: $2.3 million. 500 computers available on campus for general student use. Computer purchase/lease plans available. A campuswide network can be accessed from student residence rooms and from off campus. Students can access the following: online class registration, Web space, online course management (LMS), shared calendars, Room and Board transactions. Staffed computer lab on campus (open 24 hours a day) provides training in use of computers, software, and the Internet.

Community Environment: The Twin Cities, Minneapolis and St. Paul, with their suburbs, comprise a metropolitan area with a population of 3 million people. The area is the cultural and economic gateway to the northwest and it abounds in cultural advantages of every sort for students. Great art galleries, theaters for the performing arts, notable choral and instrumental music organizations as well as parks, lakes, and professional sports enrich community life.

■ MARTIN LUTHER COLLEGE

1995 Luther Ct.
New Ulm, MN 56073
Tel: (507)354-8221; Free: 877-MLC-1995
Fax: (507)354-8225
E-mail: brutlaro@mlc-wels.edu
Web Site: www.mlc-wels.edu/

Description: Independent, comprehensive, coed, affiliated with Wisconsin Evangelical Lutheran Synod. Awards bachelor's and master's degrees. Founded 1995. Setting: 50-acre small town campus. Total enrollment: 799. Faculty: 73 (46 full-time, 27 part-time). Student-undergrad faculty ratio is 13:1. 223 applied, 97% were admitted. 18% from top 10% of their high school class, 37% from top quarter, 66% from top half. Full-time: 694 students, 50% women, 50% men. Part-time: 48 students, 46% women, 54% men. 83% from out-of-state. 0.3% American Indian or Alaska Native, non-Hispanic/Latino; 0.4% Hispanic/Latino; 0.4% African American, non-Hispanic/Latino; 1% Asian, non-Hispanic/Latino; 0% Native Hawaiian or other Pacific Islander, non-Hispanic/Latino; 2% international. 7% 25 or older, 89% live on campus, 4% transferred in. Retention: 84% of full-time freshmen returned the following year. Academic areas with the most degrees conferred: education; theology and religious vocations. Calendar: semesters.

Entrance Requirements: Option: deferred admission. Required: high school transcript, minimum 2 high school GPA, ACT. Entrance: moderately difficult. Application deadline: 5/1. Notification: continuous. SAT Reasoning Test deadline: 6/30.

Costs Per Year: Comprehensive fee: $17,160 includes full-time tuition ($12,300) and college room and board ($4860).

Collegiate Environment: Orientation program. Drama-theater group, choral group. Student services: health clinic, personal-psychological counseling. On-campus residence required through junior year. Options: men-only, women-only housing available.

Community Environment: New Ulm (population 13,600), a rural area 100 miles from Minneapolis and St. Paul, is a city where German immigrants carefully planned wide streets and numerous park areas in such a way that it has not been necessary to change the original plan. Part-time employment opportunities are good. Historical points of interest include the Brown County Historical Museum, Hermann's Monument, and Glockenspiel.

■ MCNALLY SMITH COLLEGE OF MUSIC

19 Exchange St. E
Saint Paul, MN 55101
Tel: (651)291-0177; Free: 800-594-9500
Fax: (651)291-0366
E-mail: katie.marshall@mcnallysmith.edu
Web Site: www.mcnallysmith.edu/

Description: Proprietary, comprehensive, coed. Awards associate, bachelor's, and master's degrees. Founded 1985. Setting: 1-acre urban campus with easy access to Minneapolis-St. Paul. Educational spending for the previous fiscal year: $6242 per student. Total enrollment: 644. Faculty: 126 (59 full-time, 67 part-time). Student-undergrad faculty ratio is 8:1. 521 applied, 65% were admitted. Full-time: 498 students, 24% women, 76% men. Part-time: 131 students, 22% women, 78% men. Students come from 36 states and territories, 12 other countries, 42% from out-of-state. 0.3% American Indian or Alaska Native, non-Hispanic/Latino; 4% Hispanic/Latino; 11% African American, non-Hispanic/Latino; 3% Asian, non-Hispanic/Latino; 0% Native Hawaiian or other Pacific Islander, non-Hispanic/Latino; 3% international. 15% 25 or older, 15% live on campus, 7% transferred in. Retention: 80% of full-time freshmen returned the following year. Academic area with the most degrees conferred: visual and performing arts. Core. Calendar: semesters. Academic remediation for entering students, services for LD students, advanced placement, independent study, distance learning, double major, summer session for credit, part-time degree program, co-op programs and internships. Off campus study. Study abroad program.

Entrance Requirements: Options: electronic application, international baccalaureate accepted. Required: essay, high school transcript, minimum 2 high school GPA, interview. Recommended: minimum 2.5 high school GPA, ACT, SAT or ACT. Required for some: audition or demo recording, ACT, SAT or ACT. Entrance: moderately difficult. Application deadline: 8/1. Notification: continuous until 8/1. Transfer credits accepted: Yes.

Costs Per Year: Application fee: $75. Comprehensive fee: $31,090 includes full-time tuition ($23,790), mandatory fees ($2200), and college room and board ($5100). Full-time tuition and fees vary according to course load and degree level. Room and board charges vary according to board plan and housing facility. Part-time tuition: $915 per credit hour. Part-time mandatory fees: $450 per term. Part-time tuition and fees vary according to course load and degree level. Tuition guaranteed not to increase for student's term of enrollment.

Collegiate Environment: Orientation program. Choral group, student-run newspaper. Social organizations: 5 open to all. Most popular organizations: Student Advisory Board, Audio Engineering Society, Minnesota Songwriters Association, Jazz Club, intramural sports. Student services: personal-psychological counseling. Campus security: 24-hour emergency response devices and patrols, late night transport-escort service. 88 college housing spaces available; all were occupied in 2012-13. Freshmen given priority for college housing. Option: coed housing available. McNally Smith College Library plus 1 other with 6,000 books, 50 serials, 4,000 audiovisual materials, and an OPAC. Operations spending for the previous fiscal year: $158,655. 40 computers available on campus for general student use. Computer purchase/lease plans available. A campuswide network can be accessed. Students can access the following: online class registration. Staffed computer lab on campus provides training in use of computers, software, and the Internet.

■ MESABI RANGE COMMUNITY AND TECHNICAL COLLEGE

1001 W Chestnut St.
Virginia, MN 55792-3448
Tel: (218)741-3095; Free: 800-657-3860
E-mail: b.kochevar@mr.mnscu.edu
Web Site: www.mesabirange.edu/

Description: State-supported, 2-year, coed. Part of Minnesota State Colleges and Universities System. Awards certificates, diplomas, transfer associate, and terminal associate degrees. Founded 1918. Setting: 30-acre small town campus. Total enrollment: 1,467. Faculty: 89. Student-undergrad faculty ratio is 24:1. Students come from 6 states and territories, 2 other countries, 4% from out-of-state. 37% 25 or older, 10% live on campus. Core. Calendar: semesters. Academic remediation for entering students, services for LD students, advanced placement, self-designed majors, independent study, summer session for credit, part-time degree program, adult/continuing education programs, co-op programs and internships. Off campus study at other colleges in the Minnesota State Colleges and Universities System. Study abroad program.

Entrance Requirements: Open admission. Options: early admission, deferred admission. Required: high school transcript. Entrance: noncompetitive. Application deadline: Rolling. Notification: continuous.

Collegiate Environment: Orientation program. Drama-theater group, choral

group, student-run newspaper. Social organizations: 20 open to all. Most popular organizations: Student Senate, Human Services Club, Native American Club, Student Life Club, Black Awareness Club. Student services: personal-psychological counseling. Campus security: late night transport-escort service. Mesabi Library with 23,000 books and 167 serials. 120 computers available on campus for general student use. Staffed computer lab on campus.

Community Environment: The hub of Minnesota Arrowhead country and Taconite capital of the world, Virginia offers ready access to countless waterways and forestland, including Voyageurs National Park and the Boundary Waters Canoe Area. The Giants Ridge Ski Area features excellent alpine and cross country skiing. The city also has 2 municipal parks, 2 lakes and an 18-hole golf course. Part-time employment is available.

■ **METROPOLITAN STATE UNIVERSITY**
700 E 7th St.
Saint Paul, MN 55106-5000
Tel: (651)793-1212
Fax: (651)772-7632
E-mail: daryl.johnson@metrostate.edu
Web Site: www.metrostate.edu/

Description: State-supported, comprehensive, coed. Part of Minnesota State Colleges and Universities System. Awards bachelor's, master's, and doctoral degrees (offers primarily part-time evening degree programs). Founded 1971. Setting: urban campus with easy access to Minneapolis-St. Paul. Endowment: $2.4 million. Research spending for the previous fiscal year: $1.1 million. Educational spending for the previous fiscal year: $4288 per student. Total enrollment: 8,474. Student-undergrad faculty ratio is 16:1. Full-time: 2,804 students, 53% women, 47% men. Part-time: 4,777 students, 57% women, 43% men. 1% American Indian or Alaska Native, non-Hispanic/Latino; 5% Hispanic/Latino; 15% African American, non-Hispanic/Latino; 10% Asian, non-Hispanic/Latino; 0.1% Native Hawaiian or other Pacific Islander, non-Hispanic/Latino; 1% international. Retention: 70% of full-time freshmen returned the following year. Academic areas with the most degrees conferred: business/marketing; interdisciplinary studies; health professions and related sciences. Core. Calendar: semesters. ESL program, advanced placement, self-designed majors, independent study, distance learning, double major, summer session for credit, part-time degree program, external degree program, adult/continuing education programs, internships. Off campus study at other colleges in the Minnesota State College and University System. Study abroad program.

Entrance Requirements: Options: electronic application, deferred admission, international baccalaureate accepted. Required: high school transcript, minimum 2 high school GPA. Recommended: SAT or ACT. Entrance: minimally difficult. Application deadline: 6/15.

Costs Per Year: Application fee: $20. State resident tuition: $6,329 full-time, $210.97 part-time. Nonresident tuition: $12,914 full-time, $430.45 part-time. Mandatory fees: $313 full-time, $10.43 part-time. Full-time tuition and fees vary according to degree level, program, and reciprocity agreements. Part-time tuition and fees vary according to degree level, program, and reciprocity agreements.

Collegiate Environment: Orientation program. Drama-theater group, student-run newspaper. Social organizations: 33 open to all. Student services: personal-psychological counseling. Campus security: 24-hour emergency response devices, late night transport-escort service. College housing not available. Library and Learning Center with an OPAC and a Web page.

Community Environment: See Bethel College.

■ **MINNEAPOLIS BUSINESS COLLEGE**
1711 W County Rd. B
Roseville, MN 55113
Tel: (612)636-7406; Free: 800-279-5200
Fax: (612)636-8185
Web Site: www.minneapolisbusinesscollege.edu/

Description: Private, 2-year, coed. Awards diplomas and terminal associate degrees. Founded 1874. Setting: suburban campus with easy access to Minneapolis-St. Paul. Total enrollment: 373. 565 applied, 88% were admitted. Accelerated degree program, internships.

■ **MINNEAPOLIS COLLEGE OF ART AND DESIGN**
2501 Stevens Ave.
Minneapolis, MN 55404-4347
Tel: (612)874-3700; Free: 800-874-6223

Fax: (612)874-3704
E-mail: wmullen@mcad.edu
Web Site: www.mcad.edu/

Description: Independent, comprehensive, coed. Awards bachelor's and master's degrees. Founded 1886. Setting: 7-acre urban campus. Endowment: $25.9 million. Educational spending for the previous fiscal year: $14,422 per student. Total enrollment: 734. Faculty: 111 (42 full-time, 69 part-time). Student-undergrad faculty ratio is 13:1. 427 applied, 70% were admitted. Full-time: 632 students, 60% women, 40% men. Part-time: 70 students, 56% women, 44% men. Students come from 39 states and territories, 36% from out-of-state. 2% American Indian or Alaska Native, non-Hispanic/Latino; 6% Hispanic/Latino; 2% African American, non-Hispanic/Latino; 5% Asian, non-Hispanic/Latino; 0% Native Hawaiian or other Pacific Islander, non-Hispanic/Latino; 1% international. 5% 25 or older, 45% live on campus, 9% transferred in. Retention: 70% of full-time freshmen returned the following year. Academic area with the most degrees conferred: visual and performing arts. Core. Calendar: semesters. Services for LD students, advanced placement, independent study, distance learning, summer session for credit, part-time degree program, adult/continuing education programs, co-op programs and internships. Off campus study at members of the Association of Independent Colleges of Art and Design, Macalester College. Study abroad program.

Entrance Requirements: Options: electronic application, international baccalaureate accepted. Required: essay, high school transcript, 1 recommendation, SAT or ACT. Recommended: minimum 2.75 high school GPA, interview. Required for some: portfolio of visual artwork. Entrance: moderately difficult. Application deadlines: 5/1, 5/1 for nonresidents. Notification: continuous, continuous for nonresidents. SAT Reasoning Test deadline: 5/1. Transfer credits accepted: Yes.

Collegiate Environment: Orientation program. Student-run radio station. Social organizations: 36 open to all. Major annual events: art sale, Thanksgiving Dinner, Black and White Ball. Student services: personal-psychological counseling. Campus security: 24-hour emergency response devices and patrols, late night transport-escort service, controlled dormitory access. Minneapolis College of Art and Design Library with 47,166 books, 1,193 microform titles, 196 serials, 139,245 audiovisual materials, and a Web page. Operations spending for the previous fiscal year: $368,687. 110 computers available on campus for general student use. Computer purchase/lease plans available. A computer is required for all students. A campuswide network can be accessed from student residence rooms and from off campus. Staffed computer lab on campus provides training in use of computers, software, and the Internet.

Community Environment: See University of Minnesota - Twin Cities.

■ **MINNEAPOLIS COMMUNITY AND TECHNICAL COLLEGE**
1501 Hennepin Ave.
Minneapolis, MN 55403-1779
Tel: (612)659-6000; Free: 800-247-0911
Fax: (612)659-6210
E-mail: admissions.office@minneapolis.edu
Web Site: www.minneapolis.edu/

Description: State-supported, 2-year, coed. Part of Minnesota State Colleges and Universities System. Awards certificates, diplomas, transfer associate, and terminal associate degrees. Founded 1965. Setting: 22-acre urban campus. Total enrollment: 9,991. Faculty: 477 (158 full-time, 319 part-time). Student-undergrad faculty ratio is 27:1. Full-time: 3,758 students, 48% women, 52% men. Part-time: 6,233 students, 56% women, 44% men. Students come from 31 states and territories. 2% American Indian or Alaska Native, non-Hispanic/Latino; 8% Hispanic/Latino; 31% African American, non-Hispanic/Latino; 5% Asian, non-Hispanic/Latino; 0.1% Native Hawaiian or other Pacific Islander, non-Hispanic/Latino; 2% international. 53% 25 or older, 12% transferred in. Core. Calendar: semesters. Academic remediation for entering students, ESL program, services for LD students, advanced placement, accelerated degree program, honors program, independent study, distance learning, summer session for credit, part-time degree program, adult/continuing education programs, internships. Off campus study at other colleges in the Minnesota State Colleges and Universities System. Study abroad program.

Entrance Requirements: Open admission except for students in the Cinema Division; students in the air traffic control, law enforcement and nursing programs; and international students. Options: electronic application, early admission, deferred admission. Required: high school transcript. Entrance: noncompetitive. Application deadline: Rolling. Notification: continuous.

Costs Per Year: Application fee: $20. State resident tuition: $4523 full-time. Nonresident tuition: $4523 full-time. Mandatory fees: $669 full-time.

Collegiate Environment: Orientation program. Drama-theater group, choral group, student-run newspaper. Social organizations: 44 open to all. Most popular organizations: Student Senate, College Choirs, Student African American Brotherhood /B2B, Science Club, Phi Theta Kappa. Major annual events: Sustainability Fair (annual), Science, Technology, Engineering, and Math Fair (annual), MCTC College Transfer Fairs (semi-annual). Student services: legal services, health clinic, personal-psychological counseling, women's center. Campus security: 24-hour emergency response devices and patrols, late night transport-escort service. 279 computers available on campus for general student use. A campuswide network can be accessed from off-campus. Students can access the following: online class registration. Staffed computer lab on campus provides training in use of computers, software, and the Internet.

Community Environment: Minneapolis Community College's beautiful campus borders a city park and is within walking distance of cultural centers (Guthrie Theatre, Walker Art Center) and downtown Minneapolis.

■ MINNEAPOLIS MEDIA INSTITUTE
4100 W 76th St.
Edina, MN 55435
Tel: (866)701-1310; Free: 800-236-4997
Web Site: www.mediainstitute.edu/
Description: Proprietary, 2-year, coed. Calendar: semesters.

■ MINNESOTA SCHOOL OF BUSINESS–BLAINE
3680 Pheasant Ridge Dr. NE
Blaine, MN 55449
Tel: (763)225-8000
Fax: (763)225-8001
E-mail: kswanson@msbcollege.edu
Web Site: www.msbcollege.edu/
Description: Proprietary, 4-year, coed. Part of Globe Education Network (GEN) which is composed of Globe University, Minnesota School of Business, Broadview University, The Institute of Production and Recording and Minnesota School of Cosmetology. Awards associate and bachelor's degrees. Setting: 7-acre suburban campus with easy access to Minneapolis-St. Paul. Total enrollment: 1,012. Faculty: 132 (16 full-time, 116 part-time). Student-undergrad faculty ratio is 11:1. Full-time: 290 students, 65% women, 35% men. Part-time: 722 students, 77% women, 23% men. Students come from 3 states and territories, 0.1% from out-of-state. 1% American Indian or Alaska Native, non-Hispanic/Latino; 2% Hispanic/Latino; 1% African American, non-Hispanic/Latino; 3% Asian, non-Hispanic/Latino; 0.1% Native Hawaiian or other Pacific Islander, non-Hispanic/Latino; 0% international. 37% 25 or older, 14% transferred in. Retention: 48% of full-time freshmen returned the following year. Academic areas with the most degrees conferred: business/marketing; computer and information sciences; law/legal studies. Core. Academic remediation for entering students, services for LD students, advanced placement, accelerated degree program, summer session for credit, part-time degree program, adult/continuing education programs, internships.

Entrance Requirements: Option: electronic application. Required: high school transcript, interview. Required for some: essay, 2 recommendations, GED certificate in lieu of high school transcript. Application deadlines: Rolling, Rolling for nonresidents. Notification: continuous, continuous for nonresidents. Transfer credits accepted: Yes.

Costs Per Year: Application fee: $50. Tuition: $15,300 full-time, $460 per credit part-time. Mandatory fees: $1548 full-time, $43 per credit part-time. Full-time tuition and fees vary according to course load, degree level, location, and program. Part-time tuition and fees vary according to course load, degree level, location, and program.

Collegiate Environment: Orientation program. Social organizations: Program specific student led organizations. Major annual events: Service Learning Projects, Applied Learning Projects, Student Appreciation Events. Campus security: 24-hour emergency response devices, late night transport-escort service. Blaine Campus Library with 2,389 books, 53,136 serials, 64 audiovisual materials, an OPAC, and a Web page. 104 computers available on campus for general student use. A campuswide network can be accessed. Students can access the following: online class registration. Staffed computer lab on campus provides training in use of computers, software, and the Internet.

■ MINNESOTA SCHOOL OF BUSINESS–BROOKLYN CENTER
5910 Shingle Creek Pky.
Brooklyn Center, MN 55430

Tel: (763)566-7777
Fax: (763)566-7030
E-mail: kellyobrien@msbcollege.edu
Web Site: www.msbcollege.edu/
Description: Proprietary, primarily 2-year, coed. Part of Globe Education Network (GEN) which is composed of Globe University, Minnesota School of Business, Broadview University, The Institute of Production and Recording and Minnesota School of Cosmetology. Awards diplomas, transfer associate, terminal associate, and bachelor's degrees. Founded 1989. Setting: 4-acre suburban campus with easy access to Minneapolis-St. Paul. Total enrollment: 620. Faculty: 100 (15 full-time, 85 part-time). Student-undergrad faculty ratio is 10:1. 675 applied, 68% were admitted. Full-time: 145 students, 64% women, 36% men. Part-time: 475 students, 70% women, 30% men. Students come from 2 states and territories, 0.2% from out-of-state. 1% American Indian or Alaska Native, non-Hispanic/Latino; 1% Hispanic/Latino; 22% African American, non-Hispanic/Latino; 7% Asian, non-Hispanic/Latino; 0% Native Hawaiian or other Pacific Islander, non-Hispanic/Latino; 0% international. 43% 25 or older, 14% transferred in. Retention: 38% of full-time freshmen returned the following year. Academic areas with the most degrees conferred: business/marketing; computer and information sciences; law/legal studies. Core. Academic remediation for entering students, services for LD students, advanced placement, accelerated degree program, summer session for credit, part-time degree program, adult/continuing education programs, internships.

Entrance Requirements: Option: electronic application. Required: high school transcript, interview, High school transcript or GED, ACCUPLACER is required of all applicants unless documentation of a minimum ACT composite score of 21 or documentation of a minimum composite score of 1485 on the SAT is presented. Required for some: essay, 2 recommendations. Application deadlines: Rolling, Rolling for nonresidents. Notification: continuous, continuous for nonresidents. Transfer credits accepted: Yes.

Costs Per Year: Application fee: $50. Tuition: $15,300 full-time, $460 per credit part-time. Mandatory fees: $1548 full-time, $43 per credit part-time. Full-time tuition and fees vary according to course load, degree level, location, and program. Part-time tuition and fees vary according to course load, degree level, location, and program.

Collegiate Environment: Orientation program. Social organizations: Program specific student led organizations. Major annual events: Service Learning Projects, Applied Learning Projects, Student Appreciation Projects. Campus security: 24-hour emergency response devices, late night transport-escort service. Brooklyn Center Campus Library with 3,076 books, 53,133 serials, 132 audiovisual materials, an OPAC, and a Web page. 97 computers available on campus for general student use. A campuswide network can be accessed. Students can access the following: online class registration. Staffed computer lab on campus provides training in use of computers, software, and the Internet.

■ MINNESOTA SCHOOL OF BUSINESS–ELK RIVER
11500 193rd Ave. NW
Elk River, MN 55330
Tel: (763)367-7000
E-mail: telliott@msbcollege.edu
Web Site: www.msbcollege.edu/
Description: Proprietary, 4-year, coed. Part of Globe Education Network (GEN) which is composed of Globe University, Minnesota School of Business, Broadview University, The Institute of Production and Recording and Minnesota School of Cosmetology. Awards associate and bachelor's degrees. Setting: 4-acre suburban campus with easy access to Minneapolis-St. Paul. Total enrollment: 545. Faculty: 48 (10 full-time, 38 part-time). Student-undergrad faculty ratio is 16:1. Full-time: 175 students, 66% women, 34% men. Part-time: 370 students, 78% women, 22% men. 0% from out-of-state. 1% American Indian or Alaska Native, non-Hispanic/Latino; 1% Hispanic/Latino; 1% African American, non-Hispanic/Latino; 1% Asian, non-Hispanic/Latino; 0% Native Hawaiian or other Pacific Islander, non-Hispanic/Latino; 0% international. 44% 25 or older, 22% transferred in. Retention: 57% of full-time freshmen returned the following year. Academic area with the most degrees conferred: business/marketing. Core. Academic remediation for entering students, services for LD students, advanced placement, accelerated degree program, summer session for credit, part-time degree program, adult/continuing education programs, internships.

Entrance Requirements: Option: electronic application. Required: high school transcript, interview, High school transcript or GED, ACCUPLACER is required of all applicants unless documentation of a minimum ACT composite score of 21 or documentation of a minimum composite score of

1485 on the SAT is presented. Required for some: essay, 2 recommendations. Application deadlines: Rolling, Rolling for nonresidents. Notification: continuous, continuous for nonresidents. Transfer credits accepted: Yes.

Costs Per Year: Application fee: $50. Tuition: $15,300 full-time, $460 per credit part-time. Mandatory fees: $1548 full-time, $43 per credit part-time. Full-time tuition and fees vary according to course load, degree level, location, and program. Part-time tuition and fees vary according to course load, degree level, location, and program.

Collegiate Environment: Orientation program. Social organizations: Program specific student led organizations. Major annual events: Service Learning Projects, Applied Learning Projects, Student Appreciation Events. Campus security: 24-hour emergency response devices, late night transport-escort service. Elk River Campus Library with 1,872 books, 53,146 serials, 48 audiovisual materials, an OPAC, and a Web page. 65 computers available on campus for general student use. A campuswide network can be accessed. Students can access the following: online class registration. Staffed computer lab on campus provides training in use of computers, software, and the Internet.

■ **MINNESOTA SCHOOL OF BUSINESS–LAKEVILLE**
17685 Juniper Path
Lakeville, MN 55044
Tel: (952)892-9000
E-mail: bsaintey@msbcollege.edu
Web Site: www.msbcollege.edu/

Description: Proprietary, 4-year, coed. Part of Globe Education Network (GEN) which is composed of Globe University, Minnesota School of Business, Broadview University, The Institute of Production and Recording and Minnesota School of Cosmetology. Awards associate and bachelor's degrees. Setting: 3-acre small town campus with easy access to Minneapolis-St. Paul. Total enrollment: 255. Faculty: 36 (9 full-time, 27 part-time). Student-undergrad faculty ratio is 11:1. Full-time: 114 students, 64% women, 36% men. Part-time: 141 students, 67% women, 33% men. 0% from out-of-state. 0% American Indian or Alaska Native, non-Hispanic/Latino; 4% Hispanic/Latino; 2% African American, non-Hispanic/Latino; 4% Asian, non-Hispanic/Latino; 0% Native Hawaiian or other Pacific Islander, non-Hispanic/Latino; 0.4% international. 36% 25 or older, 29% transferred in. Retention: 86% of full-time freshmen returned the following year. Academic area with the most degrees conferred: business/marketing. Core. Academic remediation for entering students, services for LD students, advanced placement, accelerated degree program, summer session for credit, part-time degree program, adult/continuing education programs, internships.

Entrance Requirements: Option: electronic application. Required: high school transcript, interview, ACCUPLACER is required of all applicants unless documentation of a minimum ACT composite score of 21 or documentation of a minimum composite score of 1485 on the SAT is presented. Required for some: essay, 2 recommendations, GED certificate in lieu of high school transcript. Application deadlines: Rolling, Rolling for nonresidents. Notification: continuous, continuous for nonresidents. Transfer credits accepted: Yes.

Costs Per Year: Application fee: $50. Tuition: $15,300 full-time, $460 per credit part-time. Mandatory fees: $1548 full-time, $43 per credit part-time. Full-time tuition and fees vary according to course load, degree level, location, and program. Part-time tuition and fees vary according to course load, degree level, location, and program.

Collegiate Environment: Orientation program. Social organizations: Program specific student led organizations. Major annual events: Service Learning Projects, Applied Learning Projects, Student Appreciation Events. Campus security: 24-hour emergency response devices, late night transport-escort service. Lakeville Campus Library with 1,900 books, 53,140 serials, 14 audiovisual materials, an OPAC, and a Web page. 49 computers available on campus for general student use. A campuswide network can be accessed. Students can access the following: online class registration. Staffed computer lab on campus provides training in use of computers, software, and the Internet.

■ **MINNESOTA SCHOOL OF BUSINESS–MOORHEAD**
2777 34th St. S
Moorhead, MN 56560
Tel: (218)422-1000
E-mail: agoulet@mbscollege.edu
Web Site: www.msbcollege.edu/

Description: Proprietary, 4-year, coed. Part of Globe Education Network (GEN) which is composed of Globe University, Minnesota School of Business, Broadview University, The Institute of Production and Recording and Minnesota School of Cosmetology. Awards associate and bachelor's degrees. Setting: 5-acre small town campus. Total enrollment: 318. Faculty: 40 (9 full-time, 31 part-time). Student-undergrad faculty ratio is 12:1. Full-time: 180 students, 78% women, 22% men. Part-time: 138 students, 79% women, 21% men. Students come from 3 states and territories, 6% from out-of-state. 2% American Indian or Alaska Native, non-Hispanic/Latino; 2% Hispanic/Latino; 1% African American, non-Hispanic/Latino; 0.3% Asian, non-Hispanic/Latino; 0% Native Hawaiian or other Pacific Islander, non-Hispanic/Latino; 0% international. 31% 25 or older, 16% transferred in. Retention: 46% of full-time freshmen returned the following year. Academic areas with the most degrees conferred: business/marketing; law/legal studies. Core. Academic remediation for entering students, services for LD students, advanced placement, accelerated degree program, summer session for credit, part-time degree program, adult/continuing education programs, internships.

Entrance Requirements: Option: electronic application. Required: high school transcript, interview, High school transcript or GED, ACCUPLACER is required of all applicants unless documentation of a minimum ACT composite score of 21 or documentation of a minimum composite score of 1485 on the SAT is presented. Required for some: essay, 2 recommendations. Application deadlines: Rolling, Rolling for nonresidents. Notification: continuous, continuous for nonresidents. Transfer credits accepted: Yes.

Collegiate Environment: Orientation program. Social organizations: Program specific student led organizations. Major annual events: Service Learning Projects, Applied Learning Projects, Student Appreciation Events. Campus security: 24-hour emergency response devices, late night transport-escort service. Moorhead Campus Library with 1,799 books, 53,140 serials, 17 audiovisual materials, an OPAC, and a Web page. 59 computers available on campus for general student use. A campuswide network can be accessed. Students can access the following: online class registration. Staffed computer lab on campus provides training in use of computers, software, and the Internet.

■ **MINNESOTA SCHOOL OF BUSINESS–PLYMOUTH**
1455 Country Rd. 101 N
Minneapolis, MN 55447
Tel: (763)476-2000
Web Site: www.msbcollege.edu/

Description: Proprietary, primarily 2-year, coed. Part of Globe Education Network (GEN) which is composed of Globe University, Minnesota School of Business, Broadview University, The Institute of Production and Recording and Minnesota School of Cosmetology. Awards diplomas, transfer associate, terminal associate, and bachelor's degrees. Founded 2002. Setting: 7-acre suburban campus with easy access to Minneapolis-St. Paul. Total enrollment: 487. Faculty: 36 (8 full-time, 28 part-time). Student-undergrad faculty ratio is 21:1. Full-time: 114 students, 61% women, 39% men. Part-time: 373 students, 78% women, 22% men. 0% from out-of-state. 1% American Indian or Alaska Native, non-Hispanic/Latino; 2% Hispanic/Latino; 6% African American, non-Hispanic/Latino; 1% Asian, non-Hispanic/Latino; 0.2% Native Hawaiian or other Pacific Islander, non-Hispanic/Latino; 0% international. 43% 25 or older, 14% transferred in. Retention: 44% of full-time freshmen returned the following year. Academic areas with the most degrees conferred: business/marketing; law/legal studies; parks and recreation. Core. Academic remediation for entering students, services for LD students, advanced placement, accelerated degree program, summer session for credit, part-time degree program, adult/continuing education programs, internships.

Entrance Requirements: Option: electronic application. Required: high school transcript, interview, High school transcript or GED, ACCUPLACER is required of all applicants unless documentation of a minimum ACT composite score of 21 or documentation of a minimum composite score of 1485 on the SAT is presented. Required for some: essay, 2 recommendations. Application deadlines: Rolling, Rolling for nonresidents. Notification: continuous, continuous for nonresidents. Transfer credits accepted: Yes.

Costs Per Year: Application fee: $50. Tuition: $15,300 full-time, $460 per credit part-time. Mandatory fees: $1548 full-time, $43 per credit part-time. Full-time tuition and fees vary according to course load, degree level, location, and program. Part-time tuition and fees vary according to course load, degree level, location, and program.

Collegiate Environment: Orientation program. Social organizations: Program specific student led organizations. Major annual events: Service Learning Projects, Applied Learning Projects, Student Appreciation Events. Campus security: 24-hour emergency response devices, late night transport-escort service. Plymouth Campus Library with 2,773 books, 53,143 serials, 52 audiovisual materials, an OPAC, and a Web page. 39 computers available on campus for general student use. A campuswide network can be accessed. Students can access the following: online class registration. Staffed computer lab on campus provides training in use of computers, software, and the Internet.

■ MINNESOTA SCHOOL OF BUSINESS–RICHFIELD

1401 W 76th St.
Ste. 500
Richfield, MN 55423
Tel: (612)861-2000; Free: 800-752-4223
Fax: (612)861-5548
E-mail: cpeterson@msbcollege.edu
Web Site: www.msbcollege.edu/

Description: Proprietary, primarily 2-year, coed. Part of Globe Education Network (GEN) which is composed of Globe University, Minnesota School of Business, Broadview University, The Institute of Production and Recording and Minnesota School of Cosmetology. Awards diplomas, terminal associate, and bachelor's degrees. Founded 1877. Setting: 3-acre urban campus with easy access to Minneapolis-St. Paul. Total enrollment: 1,840. Faculty: 177 (22 full-time, 155 part-time). Student-undergrad faculty ratio is 16:1. Full-time: 524 students, 57% women, 43% men. Part-time: 1,214 students, 67% women, 33% men. Students come from 9 states and territories, 1% from out-of-state. 1% American Indian or Alaska Native, non-Hispanic/Latino; 2% Hispanic/Latino; 9% African American, non-Hispanic/Latino; 3% Asian, non-Hispanic/Latino; 0.1% Native Hawaiian or other Pacific Islander, non-Hispanic/Latino; 0.2% international. 46% 25 or older, 18% transferred in. Retention: 28% of full-time freshmen returned the following year. Academic areas with the most degrees conferred: business/marketing; health professions and related sciences; computer and information sciences. Core. Academic remediation for entering students, services for LD students, advanced placement, accelerated degree program, summer session for credit, part-time degree program, adult/continuing education programs, internships.

Entrance Requirements: Option: electronic application. Required: high school transcript, interview, High school transcript or GED, ACCUPLACER is required of all applicants unless documentation of a minimum ACT composite score of 21 or documentation of a minimum composite score of 1485 on the SAT is presented. Required for some: essay, 2 recommendations. Application deadlines: Rolling, Rolling for nonresidents. Notification: continuous, continuous for nonresidents. Transfer credits accepted: Yes.

Costs Per Year: Application fee: $50. Tuition: $15,300 full-time, $460 per credit part-time. Mandatory fees: $1548 full-time, $43 per credit part-time. Full-time tuition and fees vary according to course load, degree level, location, and program. Part-time tuition and fees vary according to course load, degree level, location, and program.

Collegiate Environment: Orientation program. Social organizations: Program specific student led organizations. Major annual events: Service Learning Projects, Applied Learning Projects, Student Appreciation Events. Campus security: 24-hour emergency response devices, late night transport-escort service. Richfield Campus Library with 20,058 books, 85,016 serials, 4,265 audiovisual materials, an OPAC, and a Web page. 73 computers available on campus for general student use. A campuswide network can be accessed. Students can access the following: online class registration. Staffed computer lab on campus provides training in use of computers, software, and the Internet.

■ MINNESOTA SCHOOL OF BUSINESS–ROCHESTER

2521 Pennington Dr., NW
Rochester, MN 55901
Tel: (507)536-9500; Free: 888-662-8772
Fax: (507)535-8011
E-mail: ahelm@msbcollege.edu
Web Site: www.msbcollege.edu/

Description: Proprietary, comprehensive, coed. Part of Globe Education Network (GEN) which is composed of Globe University, Minnesota School of Business, Broadview University, The Institute of Production and Recording and Minnesota School of Cosmetology. Administratively affiliated with Minnesota School of Business. Awards associate, bachelor's, and master's degrees. Setting: 5-acre small town campus. Total enrollment: 650. Faculty: 39 (12 full-time, 27 part-time). Student-undergrad faculty ratio is 23:1. Full-time: 316 students, 69% women, 31% men. Part-time: 334 students, 75% women, 25% men. Students come from 2 states and territories, 1% from

out-of-state. 0.3% American Indian or Alaska Native, non-Hispanic/Latino; 2% Hispanic/Latino; 1% African American, non-Hispanic/Latino; 2% Asian, non-Hispanic/Latino; 0% Native Hawaiian or other Pacific Islander, non-Hispanic/Latino; 0.2% international. 47% 25 or older, 14% transferred in. Retention: 50% of full-time freshmen returned the following year. Academic areas with the most degrees conferred: business/marketing; parks and recreation; health professions and related sciences. Core. Academic remediation for entering students, services for LD students, advanced placement, accelerated degree program, summer session for credit, part-time degree program, adult/continuing education programs, internships.

Entrance Requirements: Option: electronic application. Required: high school transcript, interview, High school transcript or GED, ACCUPLACER is required of all applicants unless documentation of a minimum ACT composite score of 21 or documentation of a minimum composite score of 1485 on the SAT is presented. Required for some: essay, 2 recommendations. Application deadlines: Rolling, Rolling for nonresidents. Notification: continuous, continuous for nonresidents. Transfer credits accepted: Yes.

Costs Per Year: Application fee: $50. Tuition: $15,300 full-time, $460 per credit part-time. Mandatory fees: $1548 full-time, $43 per credit part-time. Full-time tuition and fees vary according to course level, course load, degree level, location, and program. Part-time tuition and fees vary according to course level, course load, degree level, location, and program.

Collegiate Environment: Orientation program. Social organizations: Program specific student led organizations. Major annual events: Service Learning Projects, Applied Learning Projects, Student Appreciation Events. Campus security: 24-hour emergency response devices, late night transport-escort service. Rochester Campus Library with 3,549 books, 53,143 serials, 199 audiovisual materials, an OPAC, and a Web page. 97 computers available on campus for general student use. A campuswide network can be accessed. Students can access the following: online class registration. Staffed computer lab on campus provides training in use of computers, software, and the Internet.

■ MINNESOTA SCHOOL OF BUSINESS–ST. CLOUD

1201 2nd St. S
Waite Park, MN 56387
Tel: (320)257-2000; Free: 866-403-3333
E-mail: kplombon@msbcollege.edu
Web Site: www.msbcollege.edu/

Description: Proprietary, primarily 2-year, coed. Part of Globe Education Network (GEN) which is composed of Globe University, Minnesota School of Business, Broadview University, The Institute of Production and Recording and Minnesota School of Cosmetology. Awards diplomas, transfer associate, terminal associate, and bachelor's degrees. Founded 2004. Setting: 2-acre small town campus. Total enrollment: 921. Faculty: 61 (18 full-time, 43 part-time). Student-undergrad faculty ratio is 22:1. Full-time: 468 students, 65% women, 35% men. Part-time: 453 students, 79% women, 21% men. 0% from out-of-state. 1% American Indian or Alaska Native, non-Hispanic/Latino; 1% Hispanic/Latino; 2% African American, non-Hispanic/Latino; 1% Asian, non-Hispanic/Latino; 0% Native Hawaiian or other Pacific Islander, non-Hispanic/Latino; 0.1% international. 37% 25 or older, 16% transferred in. Retention: 47% of full-time freshmen returned the following year. Academic areas with the most degrees conferred: business/marketing; law/legal studies; health professions and related sciences. Core. Academic remediation for entering students, services for LD students, advanced placement, accelerated degree program, summer session for credit, part-time degree program, adult/continuing education programs, internships.

Entrance Requirements: Option: electronic application. Required: high school transcript, interview, High school transcript or GED, ACCUPLACER is required of all applicants unless documentation of a minimum ACT composite score of 21 or documentation of a minimum composite score of 1485 on the SAT is presented. Required for some: essay, 2 recommendations. Application deadlines: Rolling, Rolling for nonresidents. Notification: continuous, continuous for nonresidents. Transfer credits accepted: Yes.

Costs Per Year: Application fee: $50. Tuition: $15,300 full-time, $460 per credit part-time. Mandatory fees: $1548 full-time, $43 per credit part-time. Full-time tuition and fees vary according to course level, course load, degree level, location, and program. Part-time tuition and fees vary according to course level, course load, degree level, location, and program.

Collegiate Environment: Orientation program. Social organizations: Program specific student led organizations. Major annual events: Service Learning Projects, Applied Learning Projects, Student Appreciation Events. Campus security: 24-hour emergency response devices, late night transport-escort service. St. Cloud Campus Library with 3,549 books, 53,154 serials,

199 audiovisual materials, an OPAC, and a Web page. 116 computers available on campus for general student use. A campuswide network can be accessed. Students can access the following: online class registration. Staffed computer lab on campus provides training in use of computers, software, and the Internet.

■ MINNESOTA SCHOOL OF BUSINESS–SHAKOPEE

1200 Shakopee Town Sq.
Shakopee, MN 55379
Tel: (952)345-1200; Free: 866-766-1200
Fax: (952)345-1201
E-mail: gseifert@msbcollege.edu
Web Site: www.msbcollege.edu/
Description: Proprietary, primarily 2-year, coed. Part of Globe Education Network (GEN) which is composed of Globe University, Minnesota School of Business, Broadview University, The Institute of Production and Recording and Minnesota School of Cosmetology. Awards diplomas, transfer associate, terminal associate, and bachelor's degrees. Founded 2004. Setting: 1-acre suburban campus. Total enrollment: 390. Faculty: 36 (13 full-time, 23 part-time). Student-undergrad faculty ratio is 15:1. Full-time: 154 students, 80% women, 20% men. Part-time: 236 students, 82% women, 18% men. 0% from out-of-state. 1% American Indian or Alaska Native, non-Hispanic/Latino; 3% Hispanic/Latino; 2% African American, non-Hispanic/Latino; 4% Asian, non-Hispanic/Latino; 0% Native Hawaiian or other Pacific Islander, non-Hispanic/Latino; 1% international. 41% 25 or older, 14% transferred in. Retention: 20% of full-time freshmen returned the following year. Academic areas with the most degrees conferred: business/marketing; law/legal studies; health professions and related sciences. Core. Academic remediation for entering students, services for LD students, advanced placement, accelerated degree program, summer session for credit, part-time degree program, adult/continuing education programs, internships.
Entrance Requirements: Option: electronic application. Required: high school transcript, interview, High school transcript or GED, ACCUPLACER is required of all applicants unless documentation of a minimum ACT composite score of 21 or documentation of a minimum composite score of 1485 on the SAT is presented. Required for some: essay, 2 recommendations. Application deadlines: Rolling, Rolling for nonresidents. Notification: continuous, continuous for nonresidents. Transfer credits accepted: Yes.
Collegiate Environment: Orientation program. Social organizations: Program specific student led organizations. Major annual events: Service Learning Projects, Applied Learning Projects, Student Appreciation Events. Campus security: 24-hour emergency response devices, late night transport-escort service. Shakopee Campus Library with 2,987 books, 53,132 serials, 28 audiovisual materials, an OPAC, and a Web page. 53 computers available on campus for general student use. A campuswide network can be accessed. Students can access the following: online class registration. Staffed computer lab on campus provides training in use of computers, software, and the Internet.

■ MINNESOTA STATE COLLEGE–SOUTHEAST TECHNICAL

1250 Homer Rd.
Winona, MN 55987
Tel: (507)453-2700; Free: 800-372-8164
Fax: (507)453-2715
E-mail: enrollmentservices@southeastmn.edu
Web Site: www.southeastmn.edu/
Description: State-supported, 2-year, coed. Part of Minnesota State Colleges and Universities System. Awards certificates, diplomas, transfer associate, and terminal associate degrees. Founded 1992. Setting: 132-acre small town campus with easy access to Minneapolis-St. Paul. Total enrollment: 2,237. Faculty: 183 (67 full-time, 116 part-time). Student-undergrad faculty ratio is 19:1. 11% from top 10% of their high school class, 37% from top quarter, 74% from top half. Full-time: 1,350 students, 55% women, 45% men. Part-time: 887 students, 70% women, 30% men. 27% from out-of-state. 1% American Indian or Alaska Native, non-Hispanic/Latino; 1% Hispanic/Latino; 4% African American, non-Hispanic/Latino; 2% Asian, non-Hispanic/Latino; 0.1% Native Hawaiian or other Pacific Islander, non-Hispanic/Latino; 0.4% international. 47% 25 or older, 49% transferred in. Calendar: semesters. Distance learning, double major, internships.
Entrance Requirements: Open admission except for nursing, radiography, and truck driving programs. Option: electronic application. Required: high school transcript. Recommended: interview. Entrance: noncompetitive. Application deadlines: Rolling, Rolling for nonresidents. Notification: continuous, continuous for nonresidents.

Collegiate Environment: Orientation program. Campus security: 24-hour emergency response devices, late night transport-escort service.

■ MINNESOTA STATE COMMUNITY AND TECHNICAL COLLEGE

1414 College Way
Fergus Falls, MN 56537-1009
Tel: (218)736-1500; Free: 877-450-3322
Fax: (218)739-7475
E-mail: carrie.brimhall@minnesota.edu
Web Site: www.minnesota.edu/
Description: State-supported, 2-year, coed. Part of Minnesota State Colleges and Universities System. Awards certificates, diplomas, transfer associate, and terminal associate degrees. Founded 1960. Setting: rural campus. Total enrollment: 6,925. Faculty: 456 (193 full-time, 263 part-time). Student-undergrad faculty ratio is 18:1. 3% American Indian or Alaska Native, non-Hispanic/Latino; 1% Hispanic/Latino; 4% African American, non-Hispanic/Latino; 1% Asian, non-Hispanic/Latino; 0.2% Native Hawaiian or other Pacific Islander, non-Hispanic/Latino. 34% 25 or older, 2% live on campus. Core. Calendar: semesters. Academic remediation for entering students, ESL program, services for LD students, advanced placement, accelerated degree program, freshman honors college, honors program, independent study, distance learning, double major, summer session for credit, part-time degree program, co-op programs and internships. Off campus study at other online courses from colleges in the Minnesota State Colleges and Universities System. Study abroad program.
Entrance Requirements: Open admission except for heath care programs. Options: electronic application, early admission, deferred admission. Required: high school transcript. Entrance: noncompetitive. Application deadlines: Rolling, Rolling for nonresidents. Notification: continuous, continuous for nonresidents. Transfer credits accepted: Yes.
Collegiate Environment: Orientation program. Drama-theater group, choral group. Most popular organizations: Student Senate, Students In Free Enterprise (SIFE), Phi Theta Kappa, Business Professionals of America, Skills USA - VICA. Major annual events: Homecoming, Minnesota Meltdown, Health Awareness Week. Student services: personal-psychological counseling, women's center. Campus security: 24-hour emergency response devices, late night transport-escort service, security for special events. Minnesota State Community and Technical College - Fergus Falls Library plus 4 others with an OPAC.
Community Environment: One of the largest dairy products and poultry shipping points in the northwest, Fergus Falls (population 13,722) also has the largest cooperative creamery in this region. Trains and buses are convenient for transportation. There are 1,000 lakes in the area which are within a 10 minute drive to an hour's drive. A fine park system, public golf course, municipal swimming beach, trap-shooting facilities, tennis courts, archery range, ice skating rinks, skiing facilities and rope tows provide the recreational activities. The hunting and fishing opportunities are unsurpassed.

■ MINNESOTA STATE COMMUNITY AND TECHNICAL COLLEGE–DETROIT LAKES

900 Hwy. 34, E
Detroit Lakes, MN 56501
Tel: (218)846-7444; Free: 800-492-4836
Fax: (218)847-7170
Web Site: www.minnesota.edu/
Description: State-supported, 2-year, coed. Awards certificates, transfer associate, and terminal associate degrees. Founded 1966. Total enrollment: 650. Calendar: semesters.
Entrance Requirements: Required: high school transcript, immunization record.

■ MINNESOTA STATE COMMUNITY AND TECHNICAL COLLEGE–MOORHEAD

1900 28th Ave., S
Moorhead, MN 56560
Tel: (218)236-6277; Free: 800-426-5603
Fax: (218)299-6584
Web Site: www.minnesota.edu/
Description: State-supported, 2-year, coed. Awards certificates and transfer associate degrees. Total enrollment: 2,300. Calendar: semesters.
Entrance Requirements: Required: high school transcript, immunization record.

■ MINNESOTA STATE COMMUNITY AND TECHNICAL COLLEGE–WADENA

405 Colfax Ave., SW
Wadena, MN 56482
Tel: (218)631-7800; Free: 800-247-2007
Fax: (218)631-7901
Web Site: www.minnesota.edu/
Description: State-supported, 2-year, coed. Awards certificates, transfer associate, and terminal associate degrees. Total enrollment: 635. Calendar: semesters.
Entrance Requirements: Required: high school transcript, immunization record.

■ MINNESOTA STATE UNIVERSITY MANKATO

228 Wiecking Ctr.
Mankato, MN 56001
Tel: (507)389-2463; Free: 800-722-0544
E-mail: admissions@mnsu.edu
Web Site: www.mnsu.edu/
Description: State-supported, university, coed. Part of Minnesota State Colleges and Universities System. Awards associate, bachelor's, master's, and doctoral degrees and post-master's certificates. Founded 1868. Setting: 303-acre small town campus with easy access to Minneapolis-St. Paul. Research spending for the previous fiscal year: $928,730. Educational spending for the previous fiscal year: $3712 per student. Total enrollment: 15,195. Faculty: 762 (470 full-time, 292 part-time). Student-undergrad faculty ratio is 27:1. 7,787 applied, 61% were admitted. 7% from top 10% of their high school class, 25% from top quarter, 67% from top half. Full-time: 11,468 students, 50% women, 50% men. Part-time: 1,817 students, 60% women, 40% men. Students come from 45 states and territories, 76 other countries, 17% from out-of-state. 0.2% American Indian or Alaska Native, non-Hispanic/Latino; 3% Hispanic/Latino; 4% African American, non-Hispanic/Latino; 3% Asian, non-Hispanic/Latino; 0.1% Native Hawaiian or other Pacific Islander, non-Hispanic/Latino; 5% international. 12% 25 or older, 25% live on campus, 8% transferred in. Retention: 70% of full-time freshmen returned the following year. Academic areas with the most degrees conferred: business/marketing; education; health professions and related sciences. Core. Calendar: semesters. Academic remediation for entering students, ESL program, services for LD students, advanced placement, accelerated degree program, self-designed majors, honors program, independent study, distance learning, double major, summer session for credit, part-time degree program, external degree program, adult/continuing education programs, co-op programs and internships, graduate courses open to undergrads. Off campus study at other colleges in the Minnesota State College and University System. Study abroad program. ROTC: Army.
Entrance Requirements: Options: electronic application, early admission, deferred admission, international baccalaureate accepted. Required: high school transcript, SAT or ACT. Required for some: essay, 3 recommendations, personal statement, SAT or ACT. Entrance: moderately difficult. Application deadline: Rolling. Notification: continuous. Transfer credits accepted: Yes.
Costs Per Year: Application fee: $20. State resident tuition: $7532 full-time, $262.33 per credit hour part-time. Nonresident tuition: $15,010 full-time, $564.04 per credit hour part-time. Mandatory fees: $864 full-time, $35.91 per credit hour part-time. Full-time tuition and fees vary according to course load, location, and reciprocity agreements. Part-time tuition and fees vary according to course load, location, and reciprocity agreements. College room and board: $7053. Room and board charges vary according to board plan and housing facility.
Collegiate Environment: Orientation program. Drama-theater group, choral group, student-run newspaper, radio station. Social organizations: 200 open to all; national fraternities, national sororities, local fraternities, local sororities. Major annual events: Homecoming events, Welcome Week activities, Mavericks After Dark. Student services: legal services, health clinic, personal-psychological counseling, women's center. Campus security: 24-hour emergency response devices and patrols, student patrols, late night transport-escort service, Night Owl security program in residence halls, closed circuit cameras in parking lots. 3,508 college housing spaces available. Freshmen given priority for college housing. Option: coed housing available. Memorial Library with 1.2 million books, 280,000 microform titles, 20,000 serials, an OPAC, and a Web page. Operations spending for the previous fiscal year: $4.6 million. 900 computers available on campus for general student use. Computer purchase/lease plans available. A campuswide network can be accessed from student residence rooms and

from off campus. Students can access the following: online class registration. Staffed computer lab on campus provides training in use of computers, software, and the Internet.
Community Environment: Mankato (population 35,000), on a great bend in the Minnesota River, is the trade and distributing center for agricultural southwestern Minnesota. Bus and air service is available. Community facilities include a number of churches, hospitals, and the usual civic and service organizations. About 30 lakes within a 25-mile area provide facilities for all water sports and fishing; other activities include golf, hunting and skiing. Points of interest are the Blue Earth County Historical Society Museum, Minneopa State Park and Sibley Park.

■ MINNESOTA STATE UNIVERSITY MOORHEAD

1104 7th Ave. S
Moorhead, MN 56563-0002
Tel: (218)236-2011; Free: 800-593-7246
Fax: (218)236-2168
E-mail: dragon@mnstate.edu
Web Site: www.mnstate.edu/
Description: State-supported, comprehensive, coed. Part of Minnesota State Colleges and Universities System. Awards associate, bachelor's, master's, and doctoral degrees and post-master's certificates. Founded 1885. Setting: 119-acre urban campus. Endowment: $7.8 million. Research spending for the previous fiscal year: $98,000. Total enrollment: 6,904. Faculty: 469 (198 full-time, 271 part-time). Student-undergrad faculty ratio is 21:1. 3,748 applied, 84% were admitted. 11% from top 10% of their high school class, 28% from top quarter, 62% from top half. Full-time: 5,276 students, 59% women, 41% men. Part-time: 1,150 students, 61% women, 39% men. Students come from 39 states and territories, 57 other countries, 36% from out-of-state. 1% American Indian or Alaska Native, non-Hispanic/Latino; 1% Hispanic/Latino; 2% African American, non-Hispanic/Latino; 1% Asian, non-Hispanic/Latino; 7% international. 20% 25 or older, 26% live on campus, 11% transferred in. Retention: 68% of full-time freshmen returned the following year. Academic areas with the most degrees conferred: education; business/marketing; health professions and related sciences. Core. Calendar: semesters. Academic remediation for entering students, ESL program, services for LD students, advanced placement, self-designed majors, honors program, independent study, distance learning, double major, summer session for credit, part-time degree program, adult/continuing education programs, internships, graduate courses open to undergrads. Off campus study at North Dakota State University, Concordia College (Moorhead, MN), other colleges of the Minnesota State Colleges and Universities System. Study abroad program. ROTC: Army (c), Air Force (c).
Entrance Requirements: Options: electronic application, early admission, deferred admission, international baccalaureate accepted. Required: high school transcript, SAT or ACT. Entrance: moderately difficult. Application deadlines: 8/1, 8/1 for nonresidents. SAT Reasoning Test deadline: 8/1. Transfer credits accepted: Yes.
Costs Per Year: Application fee: $20. State resident tuition: $6898 full-time, $222.43 per credit hour part-time. Nonresident tuition: $13,796 full-time, $444.86 per credit hour part-time. Mandatory fees: $936 full-time, $41.74 per credit hour part-time. Full-time tuition and fees vary according to course load, degree level, program, and reciprocity agreements. Part-time tuition and fees vary according to course load, degree level, program, and reciprocity agreements. College room and board: $6984. College room only: $4310. Room and board charges vary according to board plan and housing facility.
Collegiate Environment: Orientation program. Drama-theater group, choral group, student-run newspaper, radio station. Social organizations: 120 open to all; national fraternities, national sororities. Most popular organizations: Chi Alpha, International Student Organization, Student Orientation Counselor & Friends, Education Minnesota Student Program, Student Senate. Major annual events: Homecoming, Sidewalk Cafe, DragonFest. Student services: health clinic, personal-psychological counseling, women's center. Campus security: 24-hour emergency response devices and patrols, student patrols, late night transport-escort service, controlled dormitory access. 1,857 college housing spaces available. Options: coed, men-only, women-only housing available. Livingston Lord Library plus 1 other with 600,891 books, 835,465 microform titles, 8,585 serials, 7,671 audiovisual materials, an OPAC, and a Web page. 2,200 computers available on campus for general student use. Computer purchase/lease plans available. A campuswide network can be accessed from student residence rooms and from off campus. Students can access the following: online class registration. Staffed computer lab on campus (open 24 hours a day) provides training in use of computers, software, and the Internet.

Community Environment: Consistently ranked as one of the best places to live in the country by leading publications, the cities of Moorhead, Minn., and Fargo, N.D. boast a high quality of life based on excellent schools and hospitals, booming business and job growth, superior educational, professional and recreational opportunities, and a safe, clean environment. In 2000 Fargo/Moorhead was awarded The prestigious All-American City Award. More than 20,000 students attend six educational institutions in Fargo-Moorhead. With a metro population of 157,000, the community is a regional center for education, business, communication, finance, health care and entertainment. MSU is just 4 hours from Minneapolis-St. Paul, 3 1/2 hours from Winnipeg, 3 hours from Bismarck, N.D., and 45 minutes from some of the best lake country in Minnesota.

■ **MINNESOTA WEST COMMUNITY AND TECHNICAL COLLEGE**

1314 N Hiawatha Ave.
Pipestone, MN 56164
Tel: (507)825-6800; Free: 800-658-2330
Fax: (507)825-4656
E-mail: crystal.strouth@mnwest.edu
Web Site: www.mnwest.edu/

Description: State-supported, 2-year, coed. Part of Minnesota State Colleges and Universities System. Awards certificates, diplomas, transfer associate, and terminal associate degrees (profile contains information from Canby, Granite Falls, Jackson, and Worthington campuses). Founded 1967. Setting: rural campus. Total enrollment: 3,467. Faculty: 95 (84 full-time, 11 part-time). Student-undergrad faculty ratio is 13:1. 3,301 applied. Full-time: 1,316 students, 56% women, 44% men. Part-time: 2,151 students, 57% women, 43% men. Students come from 30 states and territories, 3 other countries, 11% from out-of-state. 1% American Indian or Alaska Native, non-Hispanic/Latino; 5% Hispanic/Latino; 4% African American, non-Hispanic/Latino; 2% Asian, non-Hispanic/Latino; 0.1% Native Hawaiian or other Pacific Islander, non-Hispanic/Latino; 0.2% international. 1% transferred in. Retention: 54% of full-time freshmen returned the following year. Core. Calendar: semesters. Academic remediation for entering students, services for LD students, advanced placement, honors program, independent study, distance learning, double major, summer session for credit, part-time degree program, external degree program, co-op programs and internships.

Entrance Requirements: Open admission. Option: electronic application. Required: high school transcript, ACCUPLACER. Entrance: noncompetitive. Application deadline: Rolling. Transfer credits accepted: Yes.

Costs Per Year: Application fee: $20. State resident tuition: $171.55 per credit part-time. Mandatory fees: $17.13 per credit hour part-time. Part-time tuition and fees vary according to course load, program, and reciprocity agreements.

Collegiate Environment: Orientation program. Choral group. Library and Academic Resource Center plus 4 others with 44,078 books, 213 serials, 4,253 audiovisual materials, an OPAC, and a Web page.

■ **NATIONAL AMERICAN UNIVERSITY (BLOOMINGTON)**

112 W Market
Bloomington, MN 55425
Tel: (605)394-4800; Free: 866-628-6387
E-mail: jmichaelson@national.edu
Web Site: www.national.edu/

Description: Proprietary, 2-year, coed. Awards terminal associate degrees. Setting: urban campus. Total enrollment: 474. Faculty: 46 (15 full-time, 31 part-time). Student-undergrad faculty ratio is 19:1. 36 applied, 100% were admitted. Full-time: 311 students, 64% women, 36% men. Part-time: 163 students, 61% women, 39% men. Students come from 25 states and territories, 7 other countries, 24% from out-of-state. 51% 25 or older, 18% live on campus, 4% transferred in. Retention: 46% of full-time freshmen returned the following year. ESL program, services for LD students, advanced placement, honors program, independent study, distance learning, double major, summer session for credit, part-time degree program, external degree program, adult/continuing education programs, co-op programs and internships. ROTC: Air Force.

Entrance Requirements: Recommended: high school transcript, interview. Required for some: high school transcript.

■ **NATIONAL AMERICAN UNIVERSITY (BROOKLYN CENTER)**

6200 Shingle Creek Pky.
Ste. 130
Brooklyn Center, MN 55430
Tel: (763)852-7500

Fax: (763)549-9955
Web Site: www.national.edu/
Description: Proprietary, 2-year, coed. Awards terminal associate degrees.

■ **NATIONAL AMERICAN UNIVERSITY (ROSEVILLE)**

1500 W Hwy. 36
Roseville, MN 55113
Tel: (651)644-1265
Fax: (651)644-0690
Web Site: www.national.edu/

Description: Proprietary, 4-year, coed. Part of National American University. Awards associate and bachelor's degrees. Setting: 1-acre urban campus. Faculty: 32 (5 full-time, 27 part-time). Student-undergrad faculty ratio is 10:1. 259 applied, 100% were admitted. Students come from 5 states and territories. 50% 25 or older. Retention: 52% of full-time freshmen returned the following year.

Entrance Requirements: Required: high school transcript. Recommended: minimum 2.0 high school GPA, interview. Required for some: essay. Application deadline: Rolling. Notification: continuous.

Collegiate Environment: Student-run newspaper. Social organizations: 3 open to all. Most popular organizations: Southeast Asian Student Organization, Phi Beta Lambda/Lambda Beta Omicron, Student Government Association, International Student Organization. Major annual event: Grad Fest. Campus security: late night transport-escort service.

■ **NORMANDALE COMMUNITY COLLEGE**

9700 France Ave. S
Bloomington, MN 55431-4399
Tel: (952)487-8200; Free: 866-880-8740
Fax: (612)487-8101
E-mail: information@normandale.edu
Web Site: www.normandale.edu/

Description: State-supported, 2-year, coed. Part of Minnesota State Colleges and Universities System. Awards certificates, transfer associate, and terminal associate degrees. Founded 1968. Setting: 90-acre suburban campus with easy access to Minneapolis-St. Paul. Total enrollment: 9,790. Faculty: 358 (193 full-time, 165 part-time). 1,544 applied, 100% were admitted. Full-time: 4,279 students, 50% women, 50% men. Part-time: 5,511 students, 59% women, 41% men. 1% American Indian or Alaska Native, non-Hispanic/Latino; 4% Hispanic/Latino; 17% African American, non-Hispanic/Latino; 9% Asian, non-Hispanic/Latino; 0.3% Native Hawaiian or other Pacific Islander, non-Hispanic/Latino; 0% international. 0% live on campus. Retention: 53% of full-time freshmen returned the following year. Core. Calendar: semesters. Academic remediation for entering students, ESL program, services for LD students, advanced placement, self-designed majors, independent study, distance learning, summer session for credit, part-time degree program, external degree program, adult/continuing education programs, co-op programs and internships. Off campus study at other colleges in the Minnesota State Colleges and Universities System. Study abroad program.

Entrance Requirements: Open admission applies to all for admission to the institution, additional requirements for participation in specific health science degree programs. Options: electronic application, deferred admission, international baccalaureate accepted. Required for some: high school transcript, GED is also accepted for admission. Entrance: noncompetitive. Application deadline: Rolling. Notification: continuous. Transfer credits accepted: Yes.

Costs Per Year: Application fee: $20. State resident tuition: $161.49 per credit hour part-time. Nonresident tuition: $161.49 per credit hour part-time. Mandatory fees: $28.31 per credit hour part-time. Part-time tuition and fees vary according to program and reciprocity agreements.

Collegiate Environment: Orientation program. Drama-theater group, choral group, student-run newspaper. Social organizations: 30 open to all. Most popular organizations: Program Board (NPB), Student Senate, Phi Theta Kappa, Inter-Varsity Christian Fellowship, Latino Student Club. Major annual events: Spring Fling, Winter Festival Breakfast, CultureFest. Student services: personal-psychological counseling. Campus security: 24-hour emergency response devices, student patrols, late night transport-escort service. College housing not available. Library plus 1 other with 93,000 books, 4,800 microform titles, 600 serials, 40,000 audiovisual materials, an OPAC, and a Web page. 846 computers available on campus for general student use. Computer purchase/lease plans available. A campuswide network can be accessed from off-campus. Students can access the following: online class registration, online school catalog. Staffed computer lab on campus provides training in use of computers, software, and the Internet.

Community Environment: The college is located in Bloomington, a suburb of 85,000 people located 10 miles south of Minneapolis and 7 miles west of the Minneapolis/St. Paul Airport.

■ NORTH CENTRAL UNIVERSITY

910 Elliot Ave.
Minneapolis, MN 55404-1322
Tel: (612)332-3491; Free: 800-289-6222
Fax: (612)343-4778
E-mail: admissions@northcentral.edu
Web Site: www.northcentral.edu/

Description: Independent, 4-year, coed, affiliated with Assemblies of God. Awards associate and bachelor's degrees. Founded 1930. Setting: 9-acre urban campus. Total enrollment: 1,125. Faculty: 102 (40 full-time, 62 part-time). Student-undergrad faculty ratio is 19:1. 450 applied. Students come from 42 states and territories, 6 other countries, 55% from out-of-state. 10% 25 or older, 80% live on campus. Core. Calendar: semesters plus January and May terms. Academic remediation for entering students, services for LD students, advanced placement, self-designed majors, independent study, double major, summer session for credit, part-time degree program, co-op programs and internships. Off campus study. ROTC: Army (c), Air Force (c).

Entrance Requirements: Open admission. Options: electronic application, deferred admission, international baccalaureate accepted. Required: essay, high school transcript, minimum 2.2 high school GPA, Christian testimony, SAT or ACT. Required for some: interview. Entrance: noncompetitive. Application deadline: 6/1. Notification: 6/15.

Costs Per Year: Application fee: $25. One-time mandatory fee: $125. Comprehensive fee: $24,952 includes full-time tuition ($18,610), mandatory fees ($456), and college room and board ($5886). College room only: $3206. Full-time tuition and fees vary according to course load. Room and board charges vary according to board plan and housing facility. Part-time tuition: $775 per credit hour. Part-time mandatory fees: $10 per credit hour, $59 per term. Part-time tuition and fees vary according to course load.

Collegiate Environment: Orientation program. Drama-theater group, choral group, student-run newspaper, radio station. Most popular organizations: Residence Life, Discipleship Leaders, Orientation Leaders, Student Ministries Board, Student Activities Committee. Major annual events: The Week, Battle of the Floors, Holy Convocation. Student services: personal-psychological counseling. Campus security: 24-hour emergency response devices and patrols, late night transport-escort service, controlled dormitory access. T. J. Jones Information Resource Center with 80,000 books, 915 audiovisual materials, and an OPAC. 40 computers available on campus for general student use. A campuswide network can be accessed from student residence rooms. Students can access the following: online class registration. Staffed computer lab on campus.

Community Environment: See University of Minnesota - Twin Cities.

■ NORTH HENNEPIN COMMUNITY COLLEGE

7411 85th Ave. N
Brooklyn Park, MN 55445-2231
Tel: (763)488-0391; Free: 800-818-0395
Fax: (763)424-0929
E-mail: aleintz@nhcc.edu
Web Site: www.nhcc.edu/

Description: State-supported, 2-year, coed. Part of Minnesota State Colleges and Universities System. Awards certificates, transfer associate, and terminal associate degrees. Founded 1966. Setting: 80-acre suburban campus. Endowment: $697,321. Research spending for the previous fiscal year: $201,000. Educational spending for the previous fiscal year: $4191 per student. Total enrollment: 7,657. Faculty: 248 (105 full-time, 143 part-time). Student-undergrad faculty ratio is 31:1. 3,192 applied, 66% were admitted. Full-time: 2,260 students, 50% women, 50% men. Part-time: 5,397 students, 59% women, 41% men. Students come from 18 states and territories, 47 other countries, 0.3% from out-of-state. 0.4% American Indian or Alaska Native, non-Hispanic/Latino; 5% Hispanic/Latino; 20% African American, non-Hispanic/Latino; 11% Asian, non-Hispanic/Latino; 0.04% Native Hawaiian or other Pacific Islander, non-Hispanic/Latino; 1% international. 49% 25 or older, 14% transferred in. Retention: 56% of full-time freshmen returned the following year. Core. Calendar: semesters. Academic remediation for entering students, ESL program, services for LD students, advanced placement, accelerated degree program, self-designed majors, honors program, independent study, distance learning, double major, summer session for

credit, part-time degree program, external degree program, adult/continuing education programs, internships. Off campus study. Study abroad program. ROTC: Army (c), Naval (c), Air Force (c).

Entrance Requirements: Open admission except for nursing program, nonresident aliens, graphic design, medical laboratory technology, and histologic technology. Options: electronic application, early admission, deferred admission, international baccalaureate accepted. Recommended: high school transcript. Entrance: noncompetitive. Application deadline: Rolling. Notification: continuous. Transfer credits accepted: Yes.

Costs Per Year: Application fee: $20. State resident tuition: $4952 full-time, $206.30 per credit part-time. Nonresident tuition: $4952 full-time, $20.60 per credit part-time. Mandatory fees: $495 full-time. Full-time tuition and fees vary according to course load, location, and program. Part-time tuition varies according to course load, location, and program.

Collegiate Environment: Orientation program. Drama-theater group, choral group. Social organizations: 4 open to all; Phi Theta Kappa and Delta Epsilon Chi Will; 50% of eligible men and 50% of eligible women are members. Most popular organizations: Muslim Student Association, Phi Theta Kappa, Student Anime Game Club, Multicultural Club. Major annual events: We Love Our Students, Welcome Back Fall Picnic, Welcome to Spring Picnic. Student services: personal-psychological counseling. Campus security: 24-hour emergency response devices, student patrols, late night transport-escort service. College housing not available. Learning Resource Center with 52,849 books, 7,595 microform titles, 8,000 serials, 3,244 audiovisual materials, an OPAC, and a Web page. Operations spending for the previous fiscal year: $570,112. 800 computers available on campus for general student use. A campuswide network can be accessed from off-campus. Students can access the following: online class registration. Staffed computer lab on campus provides training in use of computers, software, and the Internet.

■ NORTHLAND COMMUNITY AND TECHNICAL COLLEGE–THIEF RIVER FALLS & EAST GRAND FORKS

1101 Hwy. One E
Thief River Falls, MN 56701
Tel: (218)681-0701; Free: 800-959-6282
Fax: (218)681-6405
E-mail: eugene.klinke@northlandcollege.edu
Web Site: www.northlandcollege.edu/

Description: State-supported, 2-year, coed. Part of Minnesota State Colleges and Universities System. Awards certificates, diplomas, transfer associate, and terminal associate degrees. Founded 1965. Setting: 239-acre small town campus. Educational spending for the previous fiscal year: $6144 per student. Total enrollment: 4,135. Faculty: 233 (126 full-time, 107 part-time). Student-undergrad faculty ratio is 21:1. 1,569 applied, 100% were admitted. Full-time: 1,946 students, 55% women, 45% men. Part-time: 2,189 students, 59% women, 41% men. Students come from 19 states and territories, 1 other country, 45% from out-of-state. 10% transferred in. Calendar: semesters. Academic remediation for entering students, services for LD students, advanced placement, distance learning, double major, summer session for credit, part-time degree program, adult/continuing education programs, internships. Off campus study at other colleges in the Minnesota State Colleges and Universities System.

Entrance Requirements: Open admission. Options: electronic application, early admission, deferred admission, international baccalaureate accepted. Required: high school transcript. Entrance: noncompetitive. Application deadlines: 8/26, 8/26 for nonresidents. Notification: continuous, continuous for nonresidents.

Costs Per Year: Application fee: $20. State resident tuition: $4950 full-time, $165 per credit part-time. Nonresident tuition: $4950 full-time, $165 per credit part-time. Mandatory fees: $552 full-time, $18.41 per credit part-time. Full-time tuition and fees vary according to course load and program. Part-time tuition and fees vary according to course load and program.

Collegiate Environment: Orientation program. Choral group, student-run radio station. Social organizations: Phi Theta Kappa. Most popular organizations: Student Senate, Nursing, African Student Association, Martial Arts, PAMA. Major annual events: Homecoming, Snow-Fest, Illusionist/Magician. Student services: personal-psychological counseling, women's center. Campus security: student patrols, late night transport-escort service. Northland Comm & Tech College Library plus 1 other with 42,588 books, 166 serials, 3,411 audiovisual materials, an OPAC, and a Web page. 800 computers available on campus for general student use. A campuswide network can be accessed from off-campus. Students can access the following: online class registration. Staffed computer lab on campus provides training in use of computers, software, and the Internet.

Community Environment: Thief River Falls (population 8,300) is in northwest Minnesota. The facilities for outdoor recreation are numerous. Commercial transportation is available. The community provides a complete downtown shopping center, a public library, hospitals and an employment office.

■ **NORTHWEST TECHNICAL COLLEGE**
905 Grant Ave., SE
Bemidji, MN 56601
Tel: (218)333-6600; Free: 800-942-8324
E-mail: kari.kantack@ntcmn.edu
Web Site: www.ntcmn.edu/
Description: State-supported, 2-year, coed. Part of Minnesota State Colleges and Universities System. Administratively affiliated with Bemidji State University. Awards certificates, diplomas, and terminal associate degrees. Founded 1993. Setting: small town campus. Total enrollment: 1,168. Faculty: 67 (31 full-time, 36 part-time). Student-undergrad faculty ratio is 16:1. Full-time: 435 students, 57% women, 43% men. Part-time: 733 students, 76% women, 24% men. 7% from out-of-state. 11% American Indian or Alaska Native, non-Hispanic/Latino; 2% Hispanic/Latino; 4% African American, non-Hispanic/Latino; 1% Asian, non-Hispanic/Latino; 0.1% Native Hawaiian or other Pacific Islander, non-Hispanic/Latino; 0.1% international. 53% 25 or older, 3% live on campus, 19% transferred in. Retention: 39% of full-time freshmen returned the following year. Calendar: semesters. Part-time degree program.
Entrance Requirements: Option: electronic application. Required: high school transcript. Entrance: noncompetitive. Application deadline: Rolling. Notification: continuous.
Costs Per Year: Application fee: $20. State resident tuition: $5190 full-time, $173 per credit part-time. Nonresident tuition: $5190 full-time, $173 per credit part-time. Mandatory fees: $292 full-time, $9.64 per credit part-time. Full-time tuition and fees vary according to program. Part-time tuition and fees vary according to program. College room and board: $6970. College room only: $4380. Room and board charges vary according to board plan and housing facility.
Collegiate Environment: Orientation program. Option: coed housing available.

■ **NORTHWEST TECHNICAL INSTITUTE**
950 Blue Gentian Rd.
Ste. 500
Eagan, MN 55121
Tel: (952)944-0080; Free: 800-443-4223
Fax: (952)944-9274
Web Site: www.nti.edu/
Description: Proprietary, 2-year, coed. Awards transfer associate and terminal associate degrees. Founded 1957. Setting: 2-acre suburban campus with easy access to Minneapolis-St. Paul. Total enrollment: 72. 4% 25 or older. Core. Calendar: semesters. Honors program, independent study.
Entrance Requirements: Open admission. Required: high school transcript, interview. Entrance: noncompetitive. Application deadline: Rolling. Notification: continuous.
Collegiate Environment: Orientation program. Campus security: 24-hour emergency response devices and patrols, late night transport-escort service. 565 books and 4 serials.

■ **NORTHWESTERN COLLEGE**
3003 Snelling Ave. N
Saint Paul, MN 55113-1598
Tel: (651)631-5100; Free: 800-827-6827
Fax: (651)631-5680
E-mail: admissions@nwc.edu
Web Site: www.nwc.edu/
Description: Independent nondenominational, comprehensive, coed. Awards associate, bachelor's, and master's degrees. Founded 1902. Setting: 107-acre suburban campus with easy access to Minneapolis-St. Paul. Total enrollment: 3,267. Faculty: 159 (97 full-time, 62 part-time). Student-undergrad faculty ratio is 17:1. 2,253 applied, 59% were admitted. 21% from top 10% of their high school class, 51% from top quarter, 80% from top half. 18 valedictorians. Full-time: 2,012 students, 59% women, 41% men. Part-time: 1,074 students, 59% women, 41% men. Students come from 34 states and territories, 12 other countries, 27% from out-of-state. 0.5% American Indian or Alaska Native, non-Hispanic/Latino; 1% Hispanic/Latino; 3% African American, non-Hispanic/Latino; 4% Asian, non-Hispanic/Latino; 0%

Native Hawaiian or other Pacific Islander, non-Hispanic/Latino; 1% international. 11% 25 or older, 67% live on campus, 5% transferred in. Retention: 80% of full-time freshmen returned the following year. Academic areas with the most degrees conferred: business/marketing; theology and religious vocations; psychology. Core. Calendar: semesters. Academic remediation for entering students, services for LD students, advanced placement, self-designed majors, honors program, independent study, distance learning, double major, summer session for credit, part-time degree program, adult/continuing education programs, internships. Off campus study at Council for Christian Colleges and Universities, EduVenture, Focus on the Family Institute, William Mitchell College of Law, Jerusalem University College, Au Sable Institute. Study abroad program. ROTC: Army (c), Air Force (c).
Entrance Requirements: Options: electronic application, early admission, deferred admission, international baccalaureate accepted. Required: essay, high school transcript, minimum 2 high school GPA, 2 recommendations, lifestyle agreement, statement of Christian faith, SAT or ACT. Recommended: minimum 3 high school GPA. Required for some: interview. Entrance: moderately difficult. Application deadlines: 8/1, 8/1 for nonresidents. Notification: continuous, continuous for nonresidents. SAT Reasoning Test deadline: 8/1. SAT Subject Test deadline: 8/1. Transfer credits accepted: Yes.
Costs Per Year: Application fee: $25. Comprehensive fee: $35,170 includes full-time tuition ($26,740), mandatory fees ($220), and college room and board ($8210). College room only: $4820. Full-time tuition and fees vary according to course load. Room and board charges vary according to board plan and student level. Part-time tuition: $1140 per semester hour. Part-time mandatory fees: $65 per term. Part-time tuition and fees vary according to course load.
Collegiate Environment: Orientation program. Drama-theater group, choral group, student-run newspaper, radio station. Social organizations: 30 open to all. Most popular organizations: Northwestern Student Association (student government), The Gathering (religious group), Student Missions Fellowship, Guardian Angels, Outreach Ministries. Major annual events: Variety Shows, Christmas at Northwestern, Day of Prayer and Service. Student services: health clinic, personal-psychological counseling. Campus security: 24-hour emergency response devices and patrols, late night transport-escort service, controlled dormitory access, gated access to main campus, emergency notification system. 1,072 college housing spaces available; 1,041 were occupied in 2012-13. Freshmen guaranteed college housing. On-campus residence required through junior year. Options: men-only, women-only housing available. Berntsen Library with 124,574 books, 70,350 microform titles, 1,263 serials, 6,270 audiovisual materials, an OPAC, and a Web page. 200 computers available on campus for general student use. Computer purchase/lease plans available. A computer is required for all students. A campuswide network can be accessed from student residence rooms and from off campus. Students can access the following: online class registration, network file space, personal web site, integrated student portal, b/w and color printing, virtual labs. Staffed computer lab on campus provides training in use of computers, software, and the Internet.

■ **OAK HILLS CHRISTIAN COLLEGE**
1600 Oak Hills Rd., SW
Bemidji, MN 56601-8832
Tel: (218)751-8670; Free: 888-751-8670
Fax: (218)751-8825
E-mail: admissions@oakhills.edu
Web Site: www.oakhills.edu/
Description: Independent interdenominational, 4-year, coed. Awards associate and bachelor's degrees. Founded 1946. Setting: 180-acre rural campus. Endowment: $371,108. Educational spending for the previous fiscal year: $2700 per student. Total enrollment: 140. Faculty: 19 (6 full-time, 13 part-time). Student-undergrad faculty ratio is 13:1. 70 applied, 56% were admitted. 5% from top 10% of their high school class, 5% from top quarter, 47% from top half. Full-time: 134 students, 51% women, 49% men. Part-time: 6 students, 67% women, 33% men. Students come from 16 states and territories, 1 other country, 33% from out-of-state. 1% American Indian or Alaska Native, non-Hispanic/Latino; 1% Hispanic/Latino; 4% African American, non-Hispanic/Latino; 1% Asian, non-Hispanic/Latino; 1% international. 14% 25 or older, 85% live on campus, 11% transferred in. Retention: 55% of full-time freshmen returned the following year. Academic areas with the most degrees conferred: theology and religious vocations; liberal arts/general studies. Core. Calendar: semesters. Academic

remediation for entering students, services for LD students, advanced placement, independent study, double major, part-time degree program, internships. Off campus study.

Entrance Requirements: Options: electronic application, deferred admission. Required: essay, high school transcript, minimum 2 high school GPA, 2 recommendations, SAT or ACT. Required for some: interview. Entrance: minimally difficult. Application deadlines: Rolling, Rolling for nonresidents. Notification: continuous, continuous for nonresidents. SAT Reasoning Test deadline: 9/1. SAT Subject Test deadline: 9/1. Transfer credits accepted: Yes.

Collegiate Environment: Choral group. Most popular organizations: Student Council (SALT), Students Older Than Average, Student Activity Team, Outreach Program. Major annual events: Spring Banquet, Christmas Festival, Spiritual Enrichment Days and Campus Clean-Up. Student services: health clinic, personal-psychological counseling. Campus security: controlled dormitory access, evening patrols by trained security personnel. Cummings Library with 27,325 books, 34 serials, 781 audiovisual materials, an OPAC, and a Web page. Operations spending for the previous fiscal year: $56,924. 8 computers available on campus for general student use. A campuswide network can be accessed from student residence rooms. Students can access the following: online class registration. Staffed computer lab on campus.

■ PINE TECHNICAL COLLEGE
900 4th St. SE
Pine City, MN 55063
Tel: (320)629-5100; Free: 800-521-7463
Fax: (320)629-5101
Web Site: www.pinetech.edu/

Description: State-supported, 2-year, coed. Part of Minnesota State Colleges and Universities System. Awards certificates, diplomas, transfer associate, and terminal associate degrees. Founded 1965. Setting: 6-acre small town campus with easy access to Minneapolis-St. Paul. Total enrollment: 812. Faculty: 39 (18 full-time, 21 part-time). Student-undergrad faculty ratio is 18:1. Full-time: 296 students, 60% women, 40% men. Part-time: 516 students, 72% women, 28% men. Students come from 5 states and territories, 10% from out-of-state. 45% 25 or older, 11% transferred in. Core. Calendar: semesters. Academic remediation for entering students, services for LD students, advanced placement, independent study, distance learning, double major, summer session for credit, part-time degree program, internships.

Entrance Requirements: Open admission except for gunsmithing. Option: early admission. Required: high school transcript. Entrance: noncompetitive. Application deadline: Rolling.

Collegiate Environment: Orientation program. Student services: personal-psychological counseling, women's center. Campus security: late night transport-escort service. Learning Resource Technololgy Center plus 1 other with 6,000 books, 30 serials, an OPAC, and a Web page. 150 computers available on campus for general student use. A campuswide network can be accessed from off-campus. Students can access the following: online class registration. Staffed computer lab on campus.

■ RAINY RIVER COMMUNITY COLLEGE
1501 Hwy. 71
International Falls, MN 56649
Tel: (218)285-7722; Free: 800-456-3996
Fax: (218)285-2239
E-mail: bhagen@rrcc.mnscu.edu
Web Site: www.rrcc.mnscu.edu/

Description: State-supported, 2-year, coed. Part of Minnesota State Colleges and Universities System. Awards certificates, diplomas, transfer associate, and terminal associate degrees. Founded 1967. Setting: 80-acre small town campus. Total enrollment: 344. Faculty: 25 (10 full-time, 15 part-time). Student-undergrad faculty ratio is 15:1. 5% American Indian or Alaska Native, non-Hispanic/Latino; 1% Hispanic/Latino; 13% African American, non-Hispanic/Latino; 1% Asian, non-Hispanic/Latino; 8% international. 54% 25 or older. Core. Calendar: semesters. Academic remediation for entering students, services for LD students, advanced placement, honors program, independent study, summer session for credit, part-time degree program, adult/continuing education programs, co-op programs and internships.

Entrance Requirements: Open admission. Options: electronic application, early admission, deferred admission. Recommended: high school transcript. Entrance: noncompetitive. Application deadlines: Rolling, Rolling for nonresidents. Notification: continuous, continuous for nonresidents. Transfer credits accepted: Yes.

Costs Per Year: Application fee: $20. State resident tuition: $4729 full-time. Nonresident tuition: $5911 full-time. Mandatory fees: $594 full-time. Full-time tuition and fees vary according to program and reciprocity agreements. College room only: $2950. Room charges vary according to housing facility.

Collegiate Environment: Orientation program. Drama-theater group. Social organizations: 3 open to all. Most popular organizations: Anishinaabe Student Coalition, Student Senate, Black Student Association. Major annual events: Awareness Week, Diversity Week. Student services: personal-psychological counseling. Campus security: 24-hour emergency response devices, late night transport-escort service, controlled dormitory access. Rainy River Community College Library with 20,000 books and an OPAC. 70 computers available on campus for general student use. A campuswide network can be accessed. Students can access the following: online class registration. Staffed computer lab on campus provides training in use of computers, software, and the Internet.

Community Environment: Located on the Rainy River, which is the Minnesota-Ontario border. International Falls (population 6,332) is the supply point for an immense wilderness region famous for hunting, fishing and canoe trips. It is also an important port of entry from Ontario vacation country. Community facilities include complete church representation, good medical services, downtown and mall shopping areas, and numerous service organizations. Because of the great influx of summer tourists, many part-time jobs are available. Millions of acres are in the wilderness including Voyageurs National Park, which is close to International Falls. Rainy Lake, the biggest tourist attraction in the area, is 3 miles from town and features year-round good fishing. Other sports are swimming, water skiing, camping, hunting, boating and winter sports.

■ RASMUSSEN COLLEGE BLAINE
3629 95th Ave. NE
Blaine, MN 55014
Tel: (763)795-4720; Free: 888-549-6755
E-mail: susan.hammerstrom@rasmussen.edu
Web Site: www.rasmussen.edu/

Description: Proprietary, 4-year, coed. Part of Rasmussen College System. Awards associate and bachelor's degrees. Setting: suburban campus. Total enrollment: 500. Student-undergrad faculty ratio is 22:1. 84% 25 or older. Core. Academic remediation for entering students, accelerated degree program, distance learning, double major, summer session for credit, part-time degree program, adult/continuing education programs, internships.

Entrance Requirements: Options: electronic application, early admission, deferred admission. Required: high school transcript, minimum 2 high school GPA, Internal Exam. Required for some: interview. Entrance: minimally difficult. Application deadline: Rolling. Transfer credits accepted: Yes.

Costs Per Year: Tuition: $14,220 full-time. Mandatory fees: $1800 full-time. Full-time tuition and fees vary according to course level, course load, degree level, location, and program.

Collegiate Environment: Orientation program. College housing not available. Rasmussen College Library - Blaine with 1,617 books, 19 serials, 9 audiovisual materials, an OPAC, and a Web page. 81 computers available on campus for general student use. A campuswide network can be accessed from off-campus.

■ RASMUSSEN COLLEGE BLOOMINGTON
4400 W 78th St.
Bloomington, MN 55305
Tel: (952)545-2000; Free: 888-549-6755
Web Site: www.rasmussen.edu/

Description: Proprietary, primarily 2-year, coed. Part of Rasmussen College System. Awards certificates, diplomas, transfer associate, terminal associate, and bachelor's degrees. Founded 1904. Setting: suburban campus with easy access to Minneapolis/St. Paul. Total enrollment: 546. Student-undergrad faculty ratio is 22:1. 88% 25 or older. Core. Academic remediation for entering students, accelerated degree program, distance learning, double major, summer session for credit, part-time degree program, adult/continuing education programs, internships.

Entrance Requirements: Options: electronic application, early admission, deferred admission. Required: high school transcript, minimum 2 high school GPA, Internal Exam. Required for some: interview. Entrance: minimally difficult. Application deadline: Rolling. Transfer credits accepted: Yes.

Costs Per Year: Tuition: $14,220 full-time. Mandatory fees: $1800 full-time. Full-time tuition and fees vary according to course level, course load, degree level, location, and program.

Collegiate Environment: Orientation program. College housing not available. Rasmussen College Library - Bloomington with 2,259 books, 29 serials, 296 audiovisual materials, an OPAC, and a Web page. 68 computers available on campus for general student use. A campuswide network can be accessed from off-campus. Staffed computer lab on campus.

■ **RASMUSSEN COLLEGE BROOKLYN PARK**
8301 93rd Ave. N
Brooklyn Park, MN 55445-1512
Tel: (763)493-4500; Free: 888-549-6755
Fax: (763)425-4344
E-mail: susan.hammerstrom@rasmussen.edu
Web Site: www.rasmussen.edu/
Description: Proprietary, primarily 2-year, coed. Part of Rasmussen College System. Awards certificates, diplomas, transfer associate, terminal associate, and bachelor's degrees. Setting: suburban campus. Total enrollment: 892. Student-undergrad faculty ratio is 22:1. 89% 25 or older. Core. Academic remediation for entering students, accelerated degree program, distance learning, double major, summer session for credit, part-time degree program, adult/continuing education programs, internships.
Entrance Requirements: Options: electronic application, early admission, deferred admission. Required: high school transcript, minimum 2 high school GPA, Internal Exam. Required for some: interview. Entrance: minimally difficult. Application deadline: Rolling. Transfer credits accepted: Yes.
Costs Per Year: Tuition: $14,220 full-time. Mandatory fees: $1800 full-time. Full-time tuition and fees vary according to course level, course load, degree level, location, and program.
Collegiate Environment: Orientation program. College housing not available. Rasmussen College Library - Brooklyn Park with 2,563 books, 22 serials, 387 audiovisual materials, an OPAC, and a Web page. 80 computers available on campus for general student use. A campuswide network can be accessed from off-campus.

■ **RASMUSSEN COLLEGE EAGAN**
3500 Federal Dr.
Eagan, MN 55122-1346
Tel: (651)687-9000; Free: 888-549-6755
Fax: (651)687-0507
E-mail: susan.hammerstrom@rasmussen.edu
Web Site: www.rasmussen.edu/
Description: Proprietary, primarily 2-year, coed. Part of Rasmussen College System. Awards certificates, diplomas, transfer associate, terminal associate, and bachelor's degrees. Founded 1904. Setting: suburban campus with easy access to Minneapolis/St. Paul. Total enrollment: 883. Student-undergrad faculty ratio is 22:1. 88% 25 or older. Core. Academic remediation for entering students, accelerated degree program, distance learning, double major, summer session for credit, part-time degree program, adult/continuing education programs, internships.
Entrance Requirements: Options: electronic application, early admission, deferred admission. Required: high school transcript, minimum 2 high school GPA, Internal Exam. Required for some: interview. Entrance: minimally difficult. Application deadline: Rolling. Transfer credits accepted: Yes.
Costs Per Year: Tuition: $14,220 full-time. Mandatory fees: $1800 full-time. Full-time tuition and fees vary according to course level, course load, degree level, location, and program.
Collegiate Environment: Orientation program. College housing not available. Rasmussen College Library - Eagan with 2,542 books, 19 serials, 207 audiovisual materials, an OPAC, and a Web page. 93 computers available on campus for general student use. A campuswide network can be accessed from off-campus.

■ **RASMUSSEN COLLEGE LAKE ELMO/WOODBURY**
8565 Eagle Point Cir.
Lake Elmo, MN 55042
Tel: (651)259-6600; Free: 888-549-6755
Fax: (651)259-6601
E-mail: susan.hammerstrom@rasmussen.edu
Web Site: www.rasmussen.edu/
Description: Proprietary, primarily 2-year, coed. Part of Rasmussen College System. Awards certificates, diplomas, transfer associate, terminal associate, and bachelor's degrees. Setting: suburban campus. Total enrollment: 682. Student-undergrad faculty ratio is 22:1. 87% 25 or older. Core. Academic remediation for entering students, accelerated degree program, distance learning, double major, summer session for credit, part-time degree program, adult/continuing education programs, internships.

Entrance Requirements: Options: electronic application, early admission, deferred admission. Required: high school transcript, minimum 2 high school GPA, Internal Exam. Required for some: interview. Entrance: minimally difficult. Application deadline: Rolling. Transfer credits accepted: Yes.
Costs Per Year: Tuition: $14,220 full-time. Mandatory fees: $1800 full-time. Full-time tuition and fees vary according to course level, course load, degree level, location, and program.
Collegiate Environment: Orientation program. College housing not available. Rasmussen College Library - Lake Elmo with 2,981 books, 22 serials, 90 audiovisual materials, an OPAC, and a Web page. 85 computers available on campus for general student use. A campuswide network can be accessed from off-campus.

■ **RASMUSSEN COLLEGE MANKATO**
130 Saint Andrews Dr.
Mankato, MN 56001
Tel: (507)625-6556; Free: 888-549-6755
Fax: (507)625-6557
E-mail: susan.hammerstrom@rasmussen.edu
Web Site: www.rasmussen.edu/
Description: Proprietary, primarily 2-year, coed. Part of Rasmussen College System. Awards certificates, diplomas, transfer associate, terminal associate, and bachelor's degrees. Founded 1904. Setting: suburban campus. Total enrollment: 745. Student-undergrad faculty ratio is 22:1. 84% 25 or older. Core. Academic remediation for entering students, accelerated degree program, distance learning, double major, summer session for credit, part-time degree program, adult/continuing education programs, internships.
Entrance Requirements: Options: electronic application, early admission, deferred admission. Required: high school transcript, minimum 2 high school GPA, Internal Exam. Required for some: interview. Entrance: minimally difficult. Application deadline: Rolling. Transfer credits accepted: Yes.
Costs Per Year: Tuition: $14,220 full-time. Mandatory fees: $1800 full-time. Full-time tuition and fees vary according to course level, course load, degree level, location, and program.
Collegiate Environment: Orientation program. College housing not available. Rasmussen College Library - Mankato with 2,838 books, 24 serials, 261 audiovisual materials, an OPAC, and a Web page. 116 computers available on campus for general student use. A campuswide network can be accessed from off-campus.

■ **RASMUSSEN COLLEGE MOORHEAD**
1250 29th Ave. S
Moorhead, MN 56560
Tel: (218)304-6200; Free: 888-549-6755
Fax: (218)304-2601
E-mail: susan.hammerstrom@rasmussen.edu
Web Site: www.rasmussen.edu/
Description: Proprietary, primarily 2-year, coed. Part of Rasmussen College System. Awards certificates, diplomas, transfer associate, terminal associate, and bachelor's degrees. Setting: suburban campus. Total enrollment: 420. Student-undergrad faculty ratio is 22:1. 83% 25 or older. Core. Academic remediation for entering students, accelerated degree program, distance learning, double major, summer session for credit, part-time degree program, adult/continuing education programs, internships.
Entrance Requirements: Options: electronic application, early admission, deferred admission. Required: high school transcript, minimum 2 high school GPA, Internal Exam. Required for some: interview. Entrance: minimally difficult. Application deadline: Rolling. Transfer credits accepted: Yes.
Costs Per Year: Tuition: $14,220 full-time. Mandatory fees: $1800 full-time. Full-time tuition and fees vary according to course level, course load, degree level, location, and program.
Collegiate Environment: Orientation program. College housing not available. Rasmussen College Library - Moorhead with 624 books, 12 serials, 112 audiovisual materials, an OPAC, and a Web page. 31 computers available on campus for general student use. A campuswide network can be accessed from off-campus.

■ **RASMUSSEN COLLEGE ST. CLOUD**
226 Park Ave. S
Saint Cloud, MN 56301-3713
Tel: (320)251-5600; Free: 888-549-6755
Fax: (320)251-3702
E-mail: susan.hammerstrom@rasmussen.edu
Web Site: www.rasmussen.edu/

Description: Proprietary, primarily 2-year, coed. Part of Rasmussen College System. Awards certificates, diplomas, transfer associate, terminal associate, and bachelor's degrees. Founded 1904. Setting: suburban campus. Total enrollment: 845. Student-undergrad faculty ratio is 22:1. 86% 25 or older. Core. Academic remediation for entering students, accelerated degree program, distance learning, double major, summer session for credit, part-time degree program, adult/continuing education programs, internships.
Entrance Requirements: Options: electronic application, early admission, deferred admission. Required: high school transcript, minimum 2 high school GPA, Internal Exam. Required for some: interview. Entrance: minimally difficult. Application deadline: Rolling. Transfer credits accepted: Yes.
Costs Per Year: Tuition: $14,220 full-time. Mandatory fees: $1800 full-time. Full-time tuition and fees vary according to course level, course load, degree level, location, and program.
Collegiate Environment: Orientation program. College housing not available. Rasmussen College Library - St. Cloud with 2,423 books, 6 serials, 397 audiovisual materials, an OPAC, and a Web page. 91 computers available on campus for general student use. A campuswide network can be accessed from off-campus.

■ **RIDGEWATER COLLEGE**
PO Box 1097
Willmar, MN 56201-1097
Tel: (320)235-5114; Free: 800-722-1151
Fax: (320)231-6602
E-mail: linda.barron@ridgewater.edu
Web Site: www.ridgewater.edu/
Description: State-supported, 2-year, coed. Part of Minnesota State Colleges and Universities System. Awards certificates, diplomas, transfer associate, and terminal associate degrees. Founded 1961. Setting: 83-acre small town campus. Total enrollment: 4,177. Faculty: 239 (122 full-time, 117 part-time). Full-time: 2,576 students, 52% women, 48% men. Part-time: 1,601 students, 59% women, 41% men. 35% 25 or older. Calendar: semesters. Academic remediation for entering students, services for LD students, advanced placement, self-designed majors, distance learning, summer session for credit, part-time degree program, co-op programs and internships. Off campus study at other colleges in the Minnesota State Colleges and Universities System.
Entrance Requirements: Open admission except for nursing, chemical dependency practitioner, radiological technology, veterinary technology programs. Required: high school transcript. Required for some: interview. Entrance: noncompetitive.
Collegiate Environment: Orientation program. Student services: personal-psychological counseling. Campus security: 24-hour emergency response devices. 30,000 books, 401 serials, an OPAC, and a Web page 267 computers available on campus for general student use. A campuswide network can be accessed from off-campus. Students can access the following: online class registration. Staffed computer lab on campus provides training in use of computers, software, and the Internet.
Community Environment: Greater Willmar, with a population of approximately 18,000, is the largest city within a 60-mile radius. It is an important shipping point for grain and livestock. The division headquarters of the Burlington Northern Railway and a large Hormel turkey-processing plant are located here. Other products manufactured here are plastics, furniture, sheet metal, concrete, clothing, machinery, cookies, and dairy products. The many lakes in the area provide good fishing and recreation. The campus is located in prime hunting country. The community offers a semirural setting with many cultural opportunities and, at the same time, is two hours from the Twin Cities of Minneapolis and St. Paul. The city of Hutchinson is a population center of approximately 13,700 and is located 60 miles west of the Twin Cities on Highway 7. Hutchinson has the second oldest park system in the United States and takes pride in its adaptation to the local environment, such as the Crow River, which flows through the community. In addition, there are a dozen lakes within 15 minutes which are ideal for boating and fishing. Major employers in Hutchinson include 3M Company, Hutchinson Technology, Inc., Hutchinson Manufacturing, and Mid-America Dairymen, Inc. A small town atmosphere with a high-tech future.

■ **RIVERLAND COMMUNITY COLLEGE**
1900 8th Ave., NW
Austin, MN 55912
Tel: (507)433-0600; Free: 800-247-5039
Fax: (507)433-0515
E-mail: admissions@riverland.edu

Web Site: www.riverland.edu/
Description: State-supported, 2-year, coed. Part of Minnesota State Colleges and Universities System. Awards certificates, diplomas, transfer associate, and terminal associate degrees. Founded 1940. Setting: 187-acre small town campus with easy access to Minneapolis-St. Paul. Educational spending for the previous fiscal year: $5636 per student. Total enrollment: 3,686. Faculty: 200. Student-undergrad faculty ratio is 18:1. 3,485 applied, 62% were admitted. Students come from 5 states and territories, 8 other countries, 3% from out-of-state. 45% 25 or older, 2% live on campus. Core. Calendar: semesters. Academic remediation for entering students, ESL program, services for LD students, advanced placement, independent study, distance learning, double major, summer session for credit, part-time degree program, adult/continuing education programs, internships. Off campus study at other colleges in the Minnesota State Colleges and Universities System. Study abroad program.
Entrance Requirements: Open admission except for nursing, human services, occupational therapy assistant, physical therapy assistant, law enforcement programs. Option: early admission. Required: high school transcript. Entrance: noncompetitive. Application deadline: Rolling.
Collegiate Environment: Orientation program. Drama-theater group, choral group, student-run newspaper. Social organizations: 8 open to all. Most popular organizations: College Choir, student newspaper, Student Activities Board, Phi Theta Kappa, Theater Club. Major annual events: Multicultural Week, College Fair, Technology Day. Student services: personal-psychological counseling, women's center. Campus security: late night transport-escort service. Riverland Community College Library plus 2 others with 33,500 books, 278 serials, and an OPAC. Operations spending for the previous fiscal year: $114,000. 175 computers available on campus for general student use. A campuswide network can be accessed from student residence rooms. Students can access the following: online class registration. Staffed computer lab on campus provides training in use of computers, software, and the Internet.

■ **ROCHESTER COMMUNITY AND TECHNICAL COLLEGE**
851 30th Ave., SE
Rochester, MN 55904-4999
Tel: (507)285-7210
Fax: (507)285-7496
Web Site: www.rctc.edu/
Description: State-supported, primarily 2-year, coed. Part of Minnesota State Colleges and Universities System. Awards certificates, diplomas, transfer associate, terminal associate, and bachelor's degrees (also offers 13 programs that lead to a bachelor's degree with Winona State University or University of Minnesota). Founded 1915. Setting: 460-acre small town campus. Total enrollment: 5,898. 34% 25 or older. Core. Calendar: semesters. Academic remediation for entering students, ESL program, services for LD students, advanced placement, honors program, independent study, distance learning, summer session for credit, part-time degree program, internships. Off campus study at other colleges in the Minnesota State Colleges and Universities System, Winona State University-Rochester Center.
Entrance Requirements: Open admission except for allied health, technology programs. Option: early admission. Required: high school transcript. Entrance: noncompetitive. Application deadline: 8/24. Notification: continuous.
Collegiate Environment: Orientation program. Drama-theater group, choral group, student-run newspaper. Student services: health clinic, personal-psychological counseling. Campus security: student patrols, late night transport-escort service. Goddard Library plus 1 other with 62,000 books and 600 serials.
Community Environment: The Mayo Clinic, founded by Drs. William and Charles Mayo, has made Rochester (population 94,950) world famous. The transient population is estimated at 8,000 to 10,000 at any given time. Visitors are estimated at 550,000 annually. All forms of commercial transportation are available. Community cultural facilities include the Rochester Symphony Orchestra, Rochester Municipal Band, Oratorio Society, summer open-air concerts, Carillon concerts 3 times a week, and a civic theater with a full-time director.

■ **ST. CATHERINE UNIVERSITY**
2004 Randolph Ave.
Saint Paul, MN 55105
Tel: (651)690-6000; Free: 800-945-4599
Fax: (651)690-6042

E-mail: stkate@stkate.edu

Web Site: www.stkate.edu/

Description: Independent Roman Catholic, comprehensive. Awards associate, bachelor's, master's, and doctoral degrees and post-master's certificates. Founded 1905. Setting: 110-acre urban campus with easy access to Minneapolis. Total enrollment: 5,075. Faculty: 330 (267 full-time, 63 part-time). Student-undergrad faculty ratio is 13:1. 2,892 applied, 59% were admitted. 27% from top 10% of their high school class, 63% from top quarter, 93% from top half. Full-time: 2,403 students, 99% women, 1% men. Part-time: 1,260 students, 92% women, 8% men. 11% from out-of-state. 1% American Indian or Alaska Native, non-Hispanic/Latino; 5% Hispanic/Latino; 10% African American, non-Hispanic/Latino; 10% Asian, non-Hispanic/Latino; 0.1% Native Hawaiian or other Pacific Islander, non-Hispanic/Latino; 1% international. 12% 25 or older, 41% live on campus, 18% transferred in. Retention: 83% of full-time freshmen returned the following year. Academic areas with the most degrees conferred: health professions and related sciences; business/marketing; public administration and social services; education. Calendar: 4-1-4. Part-time degree program, adult/continuing education programs. ROTC: Army (c), Air Force (c).

Entrance Requirements: Options: deferred admission, international baccalaureate accepted. Required: high school transcript, 1 recommendation, SAT or ACT. Recommended: interview. Required for some: essay, interview. Entrance: moderately difficult. Application deadline: Rolling. Notification: continuous. SAT Reasoning Test deadline: 8/15.

Costs Per Year: Application fee: $0. Comprehensive fee: $41,258 includes full-time tuition ($32,310), mandatory fees ($380), and college room and board ($8568). College room only: $4860. Full-time tuition and fees vary according to class time and degree level. Room and board charges vary according to board plan and housing facility. Part-time tuition: $1077 per credit hour. Part-time tuition varies according to class time and degree level.

Collegiate Environment: Orientation program. Campus security: 24-hour emergency response devices and patrols, student patrols, late night transport-escort service, controlled dormitory access. Freshmen guaranteed college housing. Option: women-only housing available. St. Catherine Library plus 1 other with an OPAC and a Web page.

■ **ST. CLOUD STATE UNIVERSITY**

720 4th Ave. S

Saint Cloud, MN 56301-4498

Tel: (320)308-0121; Free: 877-654-7278

E-mail: scsu4u@stcloudstate.edu

Web Site: www.stcloudstate.edu/

Description: State-supported, comprehensive, coed. Part of Minnesota State Colleges and Universities System. Awards associate, bachelor's, master's, and doctoral degrees and post-master's certificates. Founded 1869. Setting: 922-acre suburban campus with easy access to Minneapolis-St. Paul. Endowment: $15.6 million. Research spending for the previous fiscal year: $2.6 million. Educational spending for the previous fiscal year: $5572 per student. Total enrollment: 17,231. Faculty: 872 (557 full-time, 315 part-time). Student-undergrad faculty ratio is 21:1. 5,256 applied, 90% were admitted. 7% from top 10% of their high school class, 22% from top quarter, 58% from top half. Full-time: 11,224 students, 50% women, 50% men. Part-time: 4,312 students, 55% women, 45% men. Students come from 49 states and territories, 75 other countries, 8% from out-of-state. 0.4% American Indian or Alaska Native, non-Hispanic/Latino; 3% Hispanic/Latino; 5% African American, non-Hispanic/Latino; 3% Asian, non-Hispanic/Latino; 0.1% Native Hawaiian or other Pacific Islander, non-Hispanic/Latino; 6% international. 16% 25 or older, 19% live on campus, 8% transferred in. Retention: 69% of full-time freshmen returned the following year. Academic areas with the most degrees conferred: business/marketing; education; communication/journalism. Core. Calendar: semesters. Academic remediation for entering students, ESL program, services for LD students, advanced placement, accelerated degree program, self-designed majors, honors program, independent study, distance learning, double major, summer session for credit, part-time degree program, adult/continuing education programs, internships, graduate courses open to undergrads. Off campus study at members of the Tri-College Exchange Program, other colleges in the Minnesota State Colleges and University System. Study abroad program. ROTC: Army.

Entrance Requirements: Options: electronic application, deferred admission, international baccalaureate accepted. Required: high school transcript, SAT or ACT. Required for some: ACT/SAT score. Entrance: moderately difficult. Application deadlines: 8/1, 8/1 for nonresidents. Notification: continuous, continuous for nonresidents. SAT Reasoning Test deadline: 8/1. SAT

Subject Test deadline: 8/1. Transfer credits accepted: Yes. Applicants placed on waiting list: 0. Wait-listed applicants offered admission: 0.

Costs Per Year: Application fee: $20. State resident tuition: $6,584 full-time. Nonresident tuition: $14,226 full-time. Mandatory fees: $855 full-time. Full-time tuition and fees vary according to course load and reciprocity agreements. College room and board: $6994. Room and board charges vary according to board plan and housing facility.

Collegiate Environment: Orientation program. Drama-theater group, choral group, student-run newspaper, radio station. Social organizations: 240 open to all; national fraternities, national sororities, local sororities. Major annual events: Mississippi Music Fest, Mainstreet, Kick-Off. Student services: legal services, health clinic, personal-psychological counseling, women's center. Campus security: 24-hour emergency response devices and patrols, student patrols, late night transport-escort service. James W. Miller Learning Resources Center with 947,787 books, 1.9 million microform titles, 955 serials, 26,927 audiovisual materials, an OPAC, and a Web page. Operations spending for the previous fiscal year: $12.8 million. 1,465 computers available on campus for general student use. Computer purchase/lease plans available. A campuswide network can be accessed from student residence rooms and from off campus. Students can access the following: online class registration. Staffed computer lab on campus provides training in use of computers, software, and the Internet.

■ **ST. CLOUD TECHNICAL & COMMUNITY COLLEGE**

1540 Northway Dr.

Saint Cloud, MN 56303-1240

Tel: (320)654-5000; Free: 800-222-1009

Fax: (320)654-5981

E-mail: jelness@sctcc.edu

Web Site: www.sctcc.edu/

Description: State-supported, 2-year, coed. Part of Minnesota State Colleges and Universities System. Awards certificates, diplomas, transfer associate, and terminal associate degrees. Founded 1948. Setting: 35-acre urban campus with easy access to Minneapolis-St. Paul. Research spending for the previous fiscal year: $5476. Educational spending for the previous fiscal year: $4900 per student. Total enrollment: 4,751. Faculty: 259 (96 full-time, 163 part-time). Student-undergrad faculty ratio is 22:1. 1,866 applied, 98% were admitted. Full-time: 2,230 students, 49% women, 51% men. Part-time: 2,521 students, 58% women, 42% men. Students come from 7 states and territories, 1 other country, 3% from out-of-state. 0.5% American Indian or Alaska Native, non-Hispanic/Latino; 3% Hispanic/Latino; 6% African American, non-Hispanic/Latino; 1% Asian, non-Hispanic/Latino; 0.02% Native Hawaiian or other Pacific Islander, non-Hispanic/Latino; 0.3% international. 35% 25 or older, 37% transferred in. Retention: 49% of full-time freshmen returned the following year. Calendar: semesters. Academic remediation for entering students, ESL program, services for LD students, advanced placement, independent study, distance learning, summer session for credit, part-time degree program, adult/continuing education programs, co-op programs and internships.

Entrance Requirements: Open admission except for dental hygiene, echocardiography, sonography, nursing, invasive cardiovascular technology. Options: electronic application, early admission, deferred admission. Required: high school transcript. Required for some: essay, interview. Entrance: noncompetitive. Application deadline: Rolling. Notification: continuous until 8/1. Transfer credits accepted: Yes.

Costs Per Year: Application fee: $20. State resident tuition: $4767 full-time, $159 per credit part-time. Nonresident tuition: $4767 full-time, $159 per credit part-time. Mandatory fees: $534 full-time, $18 per credit part-time. Full-time tuition and fees vary according to location and program. Part-time tuition and fees vary according to course load, location, and program.

Collegiate Environment: Orientation program. Drama-theater group. Social organizations: 18 open to all. Most popular organizations: Student Senate, Distributive Education Club of America, Phi Theta Kappa Honor Society, Skills USA, Central Minnesota Builders Association. Major annual events: Graduation, Annual Job Fair, Fall Welcome Back Activities. Student services: personal-psychological counseling. Campus security: late night transport-escort service. College housing not available. Learning Resource Center plus 1 other with 103,766 books, 53 serials, 620 audiovisual materials, an OPAC, and a Web page. Operations spending for the previous fiscal year: $240,130. 690 computers available on campus for general student use. Computer purchase/lease plans available. A computer is required for all students. A campuswide network can be accessed. Students can access the following: online class registration. Staffed computer lab on campus provides training in use of computers, software, and the Internet.

■ **SAINT JOHN'S UNIVERSITY**

PO Box 2000

Collegeville, MN 56321

Tel: (320)363-2011; Free: 800-544-1489

Fax: (320)363-3206

E-mail: admissions@csbsju.edu

Web Site: www.csbsju.edu/

Description: Independent Roman Catholic, comprehensive, men only. Awards bachelor's and master's degrees (coordinate with College of Saint Benedict for women). Founded 1857. Setting: 3,500-acre rural campus with easy access to Minneapolis-St. Paul. Endowment: $141.5 million. Research spending for the previous fiscal year: $1.1 million. Educational spending for the previous fiscal year: $12,347 per student. Total enrollment: 1,983. Faculty: 167 (133 full-time, 34 part-time). Student-undergrad faculty ratio is 12:1. 1,595 applied, 75% were admitted. 22% from top 10% of their high school class, 51% from top quarter, 86% from top half. 3 National Merit Scholars. Full-time: 1,823 students. Part-time: 31 students. Students come from 36 states and territories, 26 other countries, 18% from out-of-state. 1% American Indian or Alaska Native, non-Hispanic/Latino; 4% Hispanic/Latino; 3% African American, non-Hispanic/Latino; 3% Asian, non-Hispanic/Latino; 0.3% Native Hawaiian or other Pacific Islander, non-Hispanic/Latino; 6% international. 1% 25 or older, 84% live on campus, 1% transferred in. Retention: 89% of full-time freshmen returned the following year. Academic areas with the most degrees conferred: business/marketing; social sciences; biological/life sciences. Core. Calendar: semesters. ESL program, services for LD students, advanced placement, self-designed majors, honors program, independent study, double major, internships, graduate courses open to undergrads. Off campus study at College of Saint Benedict, Tri-College Exchange Program. Study abroad program. ROTC: Army.

Entrance Requirements: Options: electronic application, early action, deferred admission, international baccalaureate accepted. Required: essay, high school transcript, 1 recommendation, SAT or ACT. Recommended: minimum 3 high school GPA, interview. Entrance: moderately difficult. Application deadlines: Rolling, 11/15 for early action. Notification: continuous, 12/15 for early action. Transfer credits accepted: Yes. Applicants placed on waiting list: 0. Early action applicants: 1,156. Early action applicants admitted: 947.

Costs Per Year: Application fee: $0. Comprehensive fee: $44,125 includes full-time tuition ($34,838), mandatory fees ($648), and college room and board ($8639). College room only: $4350. Room and board charges vary according to board plan and housing facility. Part-time tuition: $1452 per credit hour. Part-time tuition varies according to course load.

Collegiate Environment: Orientation program. Drama-theater group, choral group, student-run newspaper, radio station. Social organizations: 94 open to all. Most popular organizations: China Cross Cultural Communications Club, Outskirts Snow Crew, Buddhist Meditation Club, Magis, Johnball club. Major annual events: Community Barbecue, Pines(spring concert and festival), Festival of Cultures. Student services: health clinic, personal-psychological counseling. Campus security: 24-hour emergency response devices and patrols, student patrols, late night transport-escort service, controlled dormitory access, well-lit pathways, 911 center on campus, closed circuit TV monitors. 1,540 college housing spaces available; 1,467 were occupied in 2012-13. Freshmen guaranteed college housing. On-campus residence required through senior year. Option: men-only housing available. Alcuin Library plus 2 others with 647,908 books, 121,406 microform titles, 43,129 serials, 40,623 audiovisual materials, an OPAC, and a Web page. Operations spending for the previous fiscal year: $1.8 million. 980 computers available on campus for general student use. A campuswide network can be accessed from student residence rooms and from off campus. Students can access the following: online class registration, online student accounts. Staffed computer lab on campus provides training in use of computers, software, and the Internet.

■ **SAINT MARY'S UNIVERSITY OF MINNESOTA**

700 Ter. Heights

Winona, MN 55987-1399

Tel: (507)452-4430; Free: 800-635-5987

Fax: (507)457-1722

E-mail: admission@smumn.edu

Web Site: www.smumn.edu/

Description: Independent Roman Catholic, comprehensive, coed. Awards bachelor's, master's, and doctoral degrees and post-master's certificates. Founded 1912. Setting: 350-acre small town campus. Endowment: $44 million. Research spending for the previous fiscal year: $80,308. Educational

spending for the previous fiscal year: $5905 per student. Total enrollment: 5,574. Faculty: 555 (103 full-time, 452 part-time). Student-undergrad faculty ratio is 16:1. 1,704 applied, 79% were admitted. 16% from top 10% of their high school class, 43% from top quarter, 69% from top half. 5 valedictorians, 37 student government officers. Full-time: 1,332 students, 51% women, 49% men. Part-time: 653 students, 57% women, 43% men. Students come from 30 states and territories, 18 other countries, 42% from out-of-state. 0.1% American Indian or Alaska Native, non-Hispanic/Latino; 5% Hispanic/Latino; 5% African American, non-Hispanic/Latino; 2% Asian, non-Hispanic/Latino; 0.1% Native Hawaiian or other Pacific Islander, non-Hispanic/Latino; 2% international. 3% 25 or older, 88% live on campus, 8% transferred in. Retention: 75% of full-time freshmen returned the following year. Academic areas with the most degrees conferred: business/marketing; visual and performing arts; homeland security, law enforcement, firefighting, and protective services. Core. Calendar: semesters. Academic remediation for entering students, ESL program, services for LD students, advanced placement, accelerated degree program, self-designed majors, honors program, independent study, distance learning, double major, summer session for credit, part-time degree program, adult/continuing education programs, co-op programs and internships, graduate courses open to undergrads. Off campus study at Winona State University, Lasallian International Programs Consortium. Study abroad program. ROTC: Army (c).

Entrance Requirements: Options: electronic application, early admission, deferred admission, international baccalaureate accepted. Required: essay, high school transcript, minimum 2.5 high school GPA, SAT or ACT. Recommended: 2 recommendations. Required for some: interview. Entrance: moderately difficult. Application deadline: 5/1. Notification: continuous. SAT Reasoning Test deadline: 5/1. Transfer credits accepted: Yes.

Costs Per Year: Application fee: $25. Comprehensive fee: $37,015 includes full-time tuition ($28,790), mandatory fees ($525), and college room and board ($7700). College room only: $4310. Full-time tuition and fees vary according to course load. Room and board charges vary according to board plan and housing facility. Part-time tuition: $960 per credit. Part-time mandatory fees: $525 per year. Part-time tuition and fees vary according to course load.

Collegiate Environment: Orientation program. Drama-theater group, choral group, student-run newspaper, radio station. Social organizations: 80 open to all; national fraternities, national sororities; 4% of eligible men and 3% of eligible women are members. Most popular organizations: Student Activity Committee, PR Business Club, Serving Others United in Love (Soul) - Mission Trips, Colleges Against Cancer, Club Hockey. Major annual events: BLUE Angel, Gaslight, Taylor Richmond Benefit Dance. Student services: health clinic, personal-psychological counseling. Campus security: 24-hour emergency response devices and patrols, late night transport-escort service, controlled dormitory access. 1,288 college housing spaces available; 1,119 were occupied in 2012-13. Freshmen guaranteed college housing. On-campus residence required through sophomore year. Options: coed, men-only, women-only housing available. Fitzgerald Library plus 1 other with 209,807 books, 200,692 microform titles, 40,015 serials, 9,789 audiovisual materials, an OPAC, and a Web page. Operations spending for the previous fiscal year: $1.2 million. 200 computers available on campus for general student use. A campuswide network can be accessed from student residence rooms and from off campus. Students can access the following: online class registration. Staffed computer lab on campus provides training in use of computers, software, and the Internet.

■ **ST. OLAF COLLEGE**

1520 St. Olaf Ave.

Northfield, MN 55057-1098

Tel: (507)646-2222; Free: 800-800-3025

Fax: (507)646-3832

E-mail: admissions@stolaf.edu

Web Site: www.stolaf.edu/

Description: Independent Lutheran, 4-year, coed. Awards bachelor's degrees. Founded 1874. Setting: 300-acre small town campus with easy access to Minneapolis-St. Paul. Endowment: $333.5 million. Research spending for the previous fiscal year: $1.5 million. Educational spending for the previous fiscal year: $15,391 per student. Total enrollment: 3,176. Faculty: 340 (223 full-time, 117 part-time). Student-undergrad faculty ratio is 12:1. 3,937 applied, 60% were admitted. 50% from top 10% of their high school class, 80% from top quarter, 97% from top half. 35 National Merit Scholars. Full-time: 3,128 students, 56% women, 44% men. Part-time: 48 students, 46% women, 54% men. Students come from 50 states and territories, 63 other countries, 49% from out-of-state. 0.2% American Indian or Alaska Native, non-Hispanic/Latino; 4% Hispanic/Latino; 2% African American, non-Hispanic/Latino; 5% Asian, non-Hispanic/Latino; 0.1% Native Hawaiian or other Pacific Islander, non-Hispanic/Latino; 5% international. 0% 25 or older, 91% live on campus, 1% transferred in. Retention: 93% of full-time freshmen returned the following year. Academic areas with the most degrees conferred: social sciences; biological/life sciences; physical sciences. Core. Calendar: 4-1-4. ESL program, services for LD students, advanced placement, self-designed majors, independent study, double major, summer session for credit, part-time degree program, internships. Off campus study at Minnesota Intercollegiate Nursing Consortium, Oak Ridge Science semester, HECUA programs, ACM programs, Washington Semester — American University, Oregon Extension, Art Semester (various independent Colleges of Art). Study abroad program.

Entrance Requirements: Options: electronic application, early decision, deferred admission, international baccalaureate accepted. Required: essay, high school transcript, 1 recommendation, SAT or ACT. Recommended: interview. Entrance: very difficult. Application deadlines: 1/15, 11/15 for early decision plan 1, 1/15 for early decision plan 2. Notification: 3/15, 12/15 for early decision plan 1, 2/15 for early decision plan 2. SAT Reasoning Test deadline: 1/15. Transfer credits accepted: Yes. Applicants placed on waiting list: 627. Wait-listed applicants offered admission: 1. Early decision applicants: 344. Early decision applicants admitted: 273.

Costs Per Year: Application fee: $40. Comprehensive fee: $48,650 includes full-time tuition ($39,560) and college room and board ($9090). College room only: $4260. Full-time tuition varies according to course load. Room and board charges vary according to board plan and housing facility. Part-time tuition: $4945 per course. Part-time tuition varies according to course load.

Collegiate Environment: Orientation program. Drama-theater group, choral group, student-run newspaper, radio station. Social organizations: 205 open to all. Most popular organizations: Student Government Association, Ultimate Frisbee Teams, Ole Spring Relief, Taiko Drumming, SELAH. Major annual events: Homecoming/Family Weekend, Christmas Festival, Cocurricular Extravaganza. Student services: health clinic, personal-psychological counseling. Campus security: 24-hour emergency response devices and patrols, late night transport-escort service, controlled dormitory access, lighted pathways and sidewalks, first-year only dorms, quiet halls. 2,885 college housing spaces available; 2,790 were occupied in 2012-13. Freshmen guaranteed college housing. On-campus residence required through senior year. Option: coed housing available. Rolvaag Memorial Library plus 2 others with 742,064 books, 19,106 microform titles, 53,758 serials, 160,861 audiovisual materials, an OPAC, and a Web page. Operations spending for the previous fiscal year: $3.3 million. 1,154 computers available on campus for general student use. A campuswide network can be accessed from student residence rooms and from off campus. Students can access the following: online class registration. Staffed computer lab on campus provides training in use of computers, software, and the Internet.

■ SAINT PAUL COLLEGE–A COMMUNITY & TECHNICAL COLLEGE
235 Marshall Ave.
Saint Paul, MN 55102-1800
Tel: (651)846-1600; Free: 800-227-6029
Fax: (651)221-1416
E-mail: admissions@saintpaul.edu
Web Site: www.saintpaul.edu/

Description: State-related, 2-year, coed. Part of Minnesota State Colleges and Universities System. Awards certificates, diplomas, transfer associate, and terminal associate degrees. Founded 1919. Setting: urban campus. Research spending for the previous fiscal year: $200,000. Total enrollment: 5,928. Faculty: 316 (107 full-time, 209 part-time). Student-undergrad faculty ratio is 18:1. 4,454 applied, 100% were admitted. Full-time: 2,454 students, 50% women, 50% men. Part-time: 3,474 students, 54% women, 46% men. 8% from out-of-state. 54% 25 or older, 13% transferred in. Calendar: semesters. Academic remediation for entering students, ESL program, honors program, distance learning, summer session for credit, part-time degree program, adult/continuing education programs, internships. Off campus study.

Entrance Requirements: Open admission. Options: electronic application, early admission. Required: ACCUPLACER. Required for some: high school transcript, interview. Entrance: noncompetitive. Application deadline: Rolling.

Collegiate Environment: Most popular organization: Student Senate. Student services: personal-psychological counseling, women's center. Campus security: late night transport-escort service. Saint Paul College Library with 12,000 books, 47 microform titles, 110 serials, an OPAC, and a Web page. Operations spending for the previous fiscal year: $200,000.

■ SOUTH CENTRAL COLLEGE
1920 Lee Blvd.
North Mankato, MN 56003
Tel: (507)389-7200
Web Site: southcentral.edu/

Description: State-supported, 2-year, coed. Part of Minnesota State Colleges and Universities System. Awards certificates, diplomas, transfer associate, and terminal associate degrees. Founded 1946. Setting: urban campus. Total enrollment: 3,839. Student-undergrad faculty ratio is 12:1. 1% from out-of-state. 42% 25 or older. Retention: 60% of full-time freshmen returned the following year. Calendar: semesters. Academic remediation for entering students, advanced placement, distance learning, part-time degree program.

Entrance Requirements: Open admission. Required: high school transcript. Application deadline: 8/1. Notification: continuous.

Collegiate Environment: Orientation program.

■ SOUTHWEST MINNESOTA STATE UNIVERSITY
1501 State St.
Marshall, MN 56258
Tel: (507)537-7021; Free: 800-642-0684
Fax: (507)537-7154
E-mail: andrew.hlubek@smsu.edu
Web Site: www.smsu.edu/

Description: State-supported, comprehensive, coed. Part of Minnesota State Colleges and Universities System. Awards associate, bachelor's, and master's degrees. Founded 1963. Setting: 216-acre small town campus. Research spending for the previous fiscal year: $251. Educational spending for the previous fiscal year: $4176 per student. Total enrollment: 6,588. Faculty: 180 (118 full-time, 62 part-time). Student-undergrad faculty ratio is 18:1. 1,455 applied, 80% were admitted. 9% from top 10% of their high school class, 27% from top quarter, 65% from top half. Full-time: 2,107 students, 55% women, 45% men. Part-time: 4,053 students, 60% women, 40% men. Students come from 26 states and territories, 25 other countries, 20% from out-of-state. 1% American Indian or Alaska Native, non-Hispanic/Latino; 2% Hispanic/Latino; 4% African American, non-Hispanic/Latino; 2% Asian, non-Hispanic/Latino; 0.04% Native Hawaiian or other Pacific Islander, non-Hispanic/Latino; 4% international. 19% 25 or older, 40% live on campus, 3% transferred in. Retention: 70% of full-time freshmen returned the following year. Academic areas with the most degrees conferred: business/marketing; education; parks and recreation. Core. Calendar: semesters. Academic remediation for entering students, ESL program, services for LD students, advanced placement, accelerated degree program, self-designed majors, freshman honors college, honors program, independent study, distance learning, double major, summer session for credit, part-time degree program, external degree program, adult/continuing education programs, internships, graduate courses open to undergrads. Off campus study at other colleges in the Minnesota State College and University System. Study abroad program.

Entrance Requirements: Options: electronic application, early admission, deferred admission. Required: high school transcript, minimum 3 high school GPA, top half of graduating class or 21 ACT, SAT or ACT. Recommended: ACT. Required for some: interview. Entrance: minimally difficult. Application deadlines: 9/1, 9/1 for nonresidents. SAT Reasoning Test deadline: 8/23. SAT Subject Test deadline: 8/23. Transfer credits accepted: Yes.

Collegiate Environment: Orientation program. Drama-theater group, choral group, marching band, student-run newspaper, radio station. Social organizations: 100 open to all. Most popular organizations: Students in Free Enterprise (SIFE), Society of Leadership & Success, Family and Child Educators (FACE), Habitat for Humanity, Education Minnesota Student Program. Major annual events: Red Cross Blood Drive, Fall Fest (Homecoming), Hawaiian Night. Student services: health clinic, personal-psychological counseling, women's center. Campus security: 24-hour emergency response devices and patrols, student patrols, late night transport-escort service, controlled dormitory access. Southwest Minnesota State University with 404,784 books, 105,382 microform titles, 45,569 serials, 12,465 audiovisual materials, an OPAC, and a Web page. Operations spending for the previous fiscal year: $922,260. 420 computers available on campus for general student use. A campuswide network can be accessed from student residence rooms and from off campus. Students can access the following: online class registration. Staffed computer lab on campus provides training in use of computers, software, and the Internet.

Community Environment: Marshall (population 12,200) is in the heart of rural, southwestern Minnesota. Air service, bus service and major highways make it accessible to parks, Minneapolis-St. Paul, Duluth and Sioux Falls, S.D. Marshall is a "college town" with restaurants, a shopping mall, churches, 3 movie theaters and a modern downtown area. It is also an expanding commercial center with a large industrial park and is the headquarters for several national agribusinesses and related firms. Marshall has a new, multimillion dollar hospital and health care facility. 5 city parks, a county park and 2 state parks are within a short drive. The community and university combine to offer concerts, theater and art/craft exhibits. Part-time job opportunities are available for students.

■ **UNIVERSITY OF MINNESOTA, CROOKSTON**

2900 University Ave.
Crookston, MN 56716-5001
Tel: (218)281-6510; Free: 800-862-6466
Fax: (218)281-8050
E-mail: phaiah@umn.edu
Web Site: www.umcrookston.edu/

Description: State-supported, 4-year, coed. Part of University of Minnesota System. Awards bachelor's degrees. Founded 1966. Setting: 237-acre rural campus. Endowment: $11.4 million. Research spending for the previous fiscal year: $415,228. Educational spending for the previous fiscal year: $5537 per student. Total enrollment: 2,764. Faculty: 90 (73 full-time, 17 part-time). Student-undergrad faculty ratio is 19:1. 650 applied, 73% were admitted. 11% from top 10% of their high school class, 37% from top quarter, 71% from top half. Full-time: 1,393 students, 48% women, 52% men. Part-time: 1,371 students, 57% women, 43% men. Students come from 40 states and territories, 17 other countries, 27% from out-of-state. 1% American Indian or Alaska Native, non-Hispanic/Latino; 2% Hispanic/Latino; 7% African American, non-Hispanic/Latino; 2% Asian, non-Hispanic/Latino; 0.2% Native Hawaiian or other Pacific Islander, non-Hispanic/Latino; 7% international. 37% 25 or older, 39% live on campus, 9% transferred in. Retention: 73% of full-time freshmen returned the following year. Academic areas with the most degrees conferred: business/marketing; agriculture; natural resources/environmental science. Core. Calendar: semesters. Academic remediation for entering students, ESL program, services for LD students, advanced placement, self-designed majors, honors program, independent study, distance learning, double major, summer session for credit, part-time degree program, external degree program, internships. Off campus study at the five campuses of the University of Minnesota. Study abroad program. ROTC: Air Force (c).

Entrance Requirements: Options: electronic application, deferred admission, international baccalaureate accepted. Required: high school transcript, minimum 2 high school GPA, ACT composite 21 or SAT 980, SAT or ACT. Recommended: ACT. Entrance: moderately difficult. Application deadlines: Rolling, Rolling for nonresidents. Notification: continuous, continuous for nonresidents. SAT Reasoning Test deadline: 8/1. Transfer credits accepted: Yes.

Costs Per Year: Application fee: $30. State resident tuition: $10,030 full-time, $385.77 per semester hour part-time. Nonresident tuition: $10,030 full-time, $385.77 per semester hour part-time. Mandatory fees: $1425 full-time. Full-time tuition and fees vary according to course load and reciprocity agreements. Part-time tuition varies according to course load and reciprocity agreements. College room and board: $7018. College room only: $3170. Room and board charges vary according to board plan and housing facility.

Collegiate Environment: Orientation program. Drama-theater group, choral group. Social organizations: 42 open to all; national fraternities, local fraternities; 2% of eligible men and 1% of eligible women are members. Most popular organizations: Students in Free Enterprise (SIFE), Natural Resources Club, Horseman's Association, Multicultural and International Club, Ag-Arama Planning Club. Major annual events: Homecoming, Sno-Daze, Ag Arama. Student services: health clinic, personal-psychological counseling, women's center. Campus security: 24-hour emergency response devices, student patrols, controlled dormitory access. 591 college housing spaces available; all were occupied in 2012-13. Freshmen given priority for college housing. Option: coed housing available. UMC Library with 197,960 books, 26,204 microform titles, 90,411 serials, 2,222 audiovisual materials, an OPAC, and a Web page. Operations spending for the previous fiscal year: $150,000. 25 computers available on campus for general student use. Computer purchase/lease plans available. A campuswide network can be accessed from student residence rooms and from off campus. Students can access the following: online class registration, personal Web pages. Staffed computer lab on campus provides training in use of computers, software, and the Internet.

Community Environment: Crookston (population 7,929) is the county seat

of Polk County, one of the largest rural counties in the state. It is an agricultural processing center for the Red River Valley that produces wheat, barley, and sugar beets. Trains and buses are convenient for transportation. Recreational activities include swimming, camping, roller skating, ice skating, golf and bowling. The Old Crossing Treaty State Historic Park and the Polk County Pioneer Museum are some of the points of interest.

■ **UNIVERSITY OF MINNESOTA, DULUTH**

1049 University Dr.
Duluth, MN 55812-2496
Tel: (218)726-8000; Free: 800-232-1339
Fax: (218)726-6394
E-mail: umdadmis@d.umn.edu
Web Site: www.d.umn.edu/

Description: State-supported, comprehensive, coed. Part of University of Minnesota System. Awards bachelor's, master's, and doctoral degrees. Founded 1947. Setting: 250-acre suburban campus. Endowment: $66.5 million. Research spending for the previous fiscal year: $22.3 million. Educational spending for the previous fiscal year: $5875 per student. Total enrollment: 11,491. Faculty: 596 (477 full-time, 119 part-time). Student-undergrad faculty ratio is 20:1. 6,763 applied, 78% were admitted. 17% from top 10% of their high school class, 42% from top quarter, 87% from top half. Full-time: 9,176 students, 46% women, 54% men. Part-time: 1,170 students, 55% women, 45% men. Students come from 34 states and territories, 29 other countries, 11% from out-of-state. 1% American Indian or Alaska Native, non-Hispanic/Latino; 2% Hispanic/Latino; 2% African American, non-Hispanic/Latino; 4% Asian, non-Hispanic/Latino; 0.2% Native Hawaiian or other Pacific Islander, non-Hispanic/Latino; 2% international. 5% 25 or older, 26% live on campus, 5% transferred in. Retention: 79% of full-time freshmen returned the following year. Academic areas with the most degrees conferred: business/marketing; social sciences; education. Core. Calendar: semesters. Academic remediation for entering students, ESL program, services for LD students, advanced placement, self-designed majors, honors program, independent study, distance learning, double major, summer session for credit, part-time degree program, external degree program, adult/continuing education programs, co-op programs and internships, graduate courses open to undergrads. Off campus study at University of Wisconsin-Superior, College of St. Scholastica, Mesabi Range Community and Technical College, Rochester Community and Technical College. Study abroad program. ROTC: Air Force.

Entrance Requirements: Options: electronic application, international baccalaureate accepted. Required: high school transcript, SAT or ACT. Entrance: moderately difficult. Application deadline: 12/15. Notification: continuous. SAT Reasoning Test deadline: 8/1. Transfer credits accepted: Yes.

Costs Per Year: Application fee: $35. State resident tuition: $11,720 full-time, $450.76 per credit part-time. Nonresident tuition: $14,385 full-time, $553.26 per credit part-time. Mandatory fees: $1,028 full-time, $108.83 per term part-time. Full-time tuition and fees vary according to course load, program, and reciprocity agreements. Part-time tuition and fees vary according to course load, program, and reciprocity agreements. College room and board: $6732. Room and board charges vary according to board plan and housing facility.

Collegiate Environment: Orientation program. Drama-theater group, choral group, marching band, student-run newspaper, radio station. Social organizations: 240 open to all; national fraternities, national sororities, local fraternities, local sororities; 1% of eligible men and 1% of eligible women are members. Major annual events: Out Cold Winter Festival, Homecoming, UMD vs. UMTC Hockey weekend. Student services: health clinic, personal-psychological counseling, women's center. Campus security: 24-hour emergency response devices and patrols, late night transport-escort service. 3,173 college housing spaces available; 2,714 were occupied in 2012-13. Freshmen given priority for college housing. Options: coed, men-only, women-only housing available. University of Minnesota Duluth Library with 760,885 books, 756,339 microform titles, 669 serials, 19,317 audiovisual materials, an OPAC, and a Web page. Operations spending for the previous fiscal year: $3.6 million. 590 computers available on campus for general student use. Computer purchase/lease plans available. A campuswide network can be accessed from student residence rooms and from off campus. Students can access the following: online class registration. Staffed computer lab on campus provides training in use of computers, software, and the Internet.

Community Environment: On picturesque slopes, Duluth (population

84,800) commands splendid views of the St. Louis River, the harbor and Lake Superior. The city is headquarters for the Superior National Forest, which is the largest in the nation.

■ UNIVERSITY OF MINNESOTA, MORRIS
600 E 4th St.
Morris, MN 56267-2134
Tel: (320)589-2211; Free: 800-992-8863
Fax: (320)589-6399
E-mail: admissions@morris.umn.edu
Web Site: www.mrs.umn.edu/

Description: State-supported, 4-year, coed. Part of University of Minnesota System. Awards bachelor's degrees. Founded 1959. Setting: 130-acre small town campus. Endowment: $8.8 million. Research spending for the previous fiscal year: $64,915. Educational spending for the previous fiscal year: $6044 per student. Total enrollment: 1,607. Faculty: 153 (105 full-time, 48 part-time). Student-undergrad faculty ratio is 13:1. 1,504 applied, 71% were admitted. 28% from top 10% of their high school class, 56% from top quarter, 87% from top half. 27 class presidents, 36 valedictorians, 99 student government officers. Full-time: 1,489 students, 57% women, 43% men. Part-time: 118 students, 73% women, 27% men. Students come from 30 states and territories, 11 other countries, 12% from out-of-state. 5% 25 or older, 7% transferred in. Retention: 88% of full-time freshmen returned the following year. Academic areas with the most degrees conferred: social sciences; English; biological/life sciences; education. Core. Calendar: semesters. ESL program, services for LD students, advanced placement, accelerated degree program, self-designed majors, freshman honors college, honors program, independent study, distance learning, double major, summer session for credit, part-time degree program, internships. Off campus study at other units of the University of Minnesota System, National Student Exchange.

Entrance Requirements: Options: electronic application, early admission, early action, deferred admission, international baccalaureate accepted. Required: high school transcript, SAT or ACT. Recommended: minimum 3.0 high school GPA. Required for some: essay, 1 recommendation, interview. Entrance: moderately difficult. Application deadline: 3/15. Notification: continuous.

Costs Per Year: Application fee: $35. State resident tuition: $11,720 full-time. Nonresident tuition: $11,720 full-time. Mandatory fees: $830 full-time. Full-time tuition and fees vary according to reciprocity agreements. College room and board: $7324. College room only: $3460. Room and board charges vary according to board plan and housing facility.

Collegiate Environment: Orientation program. Drama-theater group, choral group, student-run newspaper, radio station. Social organizations: 85 open to all. Most popular organizations: student radio station, Inter-Varsity Christian Fellowship, jazz ensemble/concert choir, Big Friend, Little Friend, student newspaper. Major annual events: Homecoming, Jazz Fest, The Great Finals Pancake Break. Student services: legal services, health clinic, personal-psychological counseling, women's center. Campus security: 24-hour emergency response devices and patrols, late night transport-escort service, controlled dormitory access. 124 computers available on campus for general student use. Computer purchase/lease plans available. A campuswide network can be accessed from student residence rooms and from off campus. Students can access the following: online class registration. Staffed computer lab on campus.

Community Environment: The rural setting of Morris (population 5,091) is ideal for outdoor activities year round. Students participate in the community through the many churches, the library, hospital and ambulance service, nursing home, community education, and parks. Employment is available for students that seek work.

■ UNIVERSITY OF MINNESOTA, TWIN CITIES CAMPUS
100 Church St., SE
Minneapolis, MN 55455-0213
Tel: (612)625-5000; Free: 800-752-1000
Fax: (612)626-1693
E-mail: admissions@tc.umn.edu
Web Site: www.umn.edu/tc/

Description: State-supported, comprehensive, coed. Part of University of Minnesota System. Awards bachelor's, master's, and doctoral degrees and post-master's certificates. Founded 1851. Setting: 2,000-acre urban campus. Research spending for the previous fiscal year: $633.2 million. Total enrollment: 51,853. Faculty: 2,837 (1,906 full-time, 931 part-time). Student-undergrad faculty ratio is 21:1. 38,174 applied, 50% were admitted. 44% from top 10% of their high school class, 80% from top quarter, 100%

from top half. Full-time: 29,125 students, 51% women, 49% men. Part-time: 5,344 students, 53% women, 47% men. Students come from 51 states and territories, 88 other countries, 26% from out-of-state. 0.3% American Indian or Alaska Native, non-Hispanic/Latino; 3% Hispanic/Latino; 4% African American, non-Hispanic/Latino; 8% Asian, non-Hispanic/Latino; 0.1% Native Hawaiian or other Pacific Islander, non-Hispanic/Latino; 8% international. 10% 25 or older, 21% live on campus, 6% transferred in. Retention: 91% of full-time freshmen returned the following year. Academic areas with the most degrees conferred: social sciences; engineering; biological/life sciences. Core. Calendar: semesters. Academic remediation for entering students, ESL program, services for LD students, advanced placement, accelerated degree program, self-designed majors, freshman honors college, honors program, independent study, distance learning, double major, summer session for credit, part-time degree program, external degree program, adult/continuing education programs, co-op programs and internships, graduate courses open to undergrads. Off campus study at National Student Exchange, Minnesota Community College System. Study abroad program. ROTC: Army, Naval, Air Force.

Entrance Requirements: Options: electronic application, early admission, deferred admission. Required: high school transcript, SAT or ACT. Recommended: minimum 2 high school GPA. Entrance: moderately difficult. Application deadline: Rolling. Notification: continuous. SAT Reasoning Test deadline: 12/15. SAT Subject Test deadline: 12/15. Transfer credits accepted: Yes.

Costs Per Year: Application fee: $45. State resident tuition: $12,060 full-time, $463.85 per credit part-time. Nonresident tuition: $17,310 full-time, $665.77 per credit part-time. Mandatory fees: $1399 full-time. Full-time tuition and fees vary according to program and reciprocity agreements. Part-time tuition varies according to course load, program, and reciprocity agreements. College room and board: $8000. College room only: $4548. Room and board charges vary according to board plan, housing facility, and location.

Collegiate Environment: Orientation program. Drama-theater group, choral group, marching band, student-run newspaper, radio station. Social organizations: 350 open to all; national fraternities, national sororities, local sororities; 3% of eligible men and 3% of eligible women are members. Most popular organization: student government. Major annual event: Homecoming. Student services: legal services, health clinic, personal-psychological counseling, women's center. Campus security: 24-hour emergency response devices and patrols, student patrols, late night transport-escort service, controlled dormitory access, safety/security orientation, security lighting. 6,346 college housing spaces available. Freshmen guaranteed college housing. Option: coed housing available. Wilson Library plus 17 others with 5.7 million books, 5.7 million microform titles, 45,000 serials, 1.2 million audiovisual materials, an OPAC, and a Web page.

■ UNIVERSITY OF PHOENIX–MINNEAPOLIS/ST. LOUIS PARK CAMPUS
435 Ford Rd. Ste. No.1000
Saint Louis Park, MN 55426
Tel: (952)487-7226; Free: 866-766-0766
Web Site: www.phoenix.edu/

Description: Proprietary, comprehensive, coed. Awards bachelor's, master's, and doctoral degrees.

■ UNIVERSITY OF ST. THOMAS
2115 Summit Ave.
Saint Paul, MN 55105-1096
Tel: (651)962-5000; Free: 800-328-6819
Fax: (651)962-6160
E-mail: admissions@stthomas.edu
Web Site: www.stthomas.edu/

Description: Independent Roman Catholic, university, coed. Awards bachelor's, master's, and doctoral degrees and post-master's certificates. Founded 1885. Setting: 78-acre urban campus with easy access to Minneapolis. Total enrollment: 10,316. Student-undergrad faculty ratio is 14:1. 5,362 applied, 27% were admitted. 24% from top 10% of their high school class, 54% from top quarter, 88% from top half. Full-time: 6,073 students, 46% women, 54% men. Part-time: 263 students, 49% women, 51% men. Students come from 43 states and territories, 60 other countries, 19% from out-of-state. 0.1% American Indian or Alaska Native, non-Hispanic/Latino; 4% Hispanic/Latino; 3% African American, non-Hispanic/Latino; 4% Asian, non-Hispanic/Latino; 0% Native Hawaiian or other Pacific Islander, non-Hispanic/Latino; 3% international. 4% 25 or older, 42% live on campus, 4%

transferred in. Retention: 88% of full-time freshmen returned the following year. Academic areas with the most degrees conferred: business/marketing; social sciences; communication/journalism. Core. Calendar: 4-1-4. ESL program, services for LD students, advanced placement, self-designed majors, honors program, independent study, double major, summer session for credit, part-time degree program, internships, graduate courses open to undergrads. Off campus study at 5 members of the Associated Colleges of the Twin Cities. Study abroad program. ROTC: Army (c), Naval (c), Air Force.

Entrance Requirements: Options: electronic application, deferred admission, international baccalaureate accepted. Required: essay, high school transcript, SAT or ACT. Recommended: interview. Entrance: moderately difficult. Application deadline: Rolling. Notification: continuous.

Costs Per Year: Application fee: $0. Comprehensive fee: $42,565 includes full-time tuition ($33,040), mandatory fees ($747), and college room and board ($8778). College room only: $5546. Full-time tuition and fees vary according to course load, degree level, and program. Room and board charges vary according to board plan and housing facility. Part-time tuition: $1032 per credit hour. Part-time tuition varies according to course load, degree level, and program.

Collegiate Environment: Orientation program. Drama-theater group, choral group, student-run newspaper, radio station. Student services: legal services, health clinic, personal-psychological counseling, women's center. Campus security: 24-hour emergency response devices and patrols, late night transport-escort service, controlled dormitory access. 2,720 college housing spaces available; 2,612 were occupied in 2012-13. Freshmen given priority for college housing. Options: men-only, women-only housing available. O'Shaughnessy-Frey Library with 828,677 books, 1.1 million microform titles, 60,228 serials, 34,935 audiovisual materials, an OPAC, and a Web page.

■ VERMILION COMMUNITY COLLEGE

1900 E Camp St.
Ely, MN 55731-1996
Tel: (218)365-7200; Free: 800-657-3608
Web Site: www.vcc.edu/

Description: State-supported, 2-year, coed. Part of Minnesota State Colleges and Universities System. Awards certificates, diplomas, transfer associate, and terminal associate degrees. Founded 1922. Setting: 5-acre rural campus. Total enrollment: 745. Faculty: 85 (25 full-time, 60 part-time). Student-undergrad faculty ratio is 13:1. 595 applied, 57% were admitted. Students come from 42 states and territories, 3 other countries. 10% 25 or older, 50% live on campus. Core. Calendar: semesters. Academic remediation for entering students, services for LD students, advanced placement, honors program, summer session for credit, part-time degree program, adult/continuing education programs, co-op programs and internships. Off campus study at other colleges in the Minnesota State Colleges and Universities System.

Entrance Requirements: Open admission. Options: electronic application, early admission, deferred admission. Required: high school transcript. Entrance: noncompetitive. Application deadline: Rolling. Notification: continuous.

Collegiate Environment: Orientation program. Most popular organizations: Student Life Committee, student government, Drama Club. Major annual events: New Student Week, New Year's Dance, Karaoke Night. Student services: personal-psychological counseling, women's center. Campus security: student patrols, late night transport-escort service, controlled dormitory access. Vermilion Community College Library with 19,500 books, 100 serials, and an OPAC. 60 computers available on campus for general student use. A campuswide network can be accessed from student residence rooms and from off campus. Staffed computer lab on campus.

Community Environment: Located on the edge of the Boundary Waters Canoe Area, Vermilion offers its students one of the most beautiful wilderness areas in America for a college setting. The town of Ely, with a population of about 3,600, provides nearby shopping facilities, churches, a golf course, tennis courts, restaurants and an excellent hospital. Limited part-time work is available in the community. The area provides exceptional opportunities for camping, canoeing, fishing, hunting, snowmobiling, cross-country skiing, downhill skiing, and even dog sledding.

■ WALDEN UNIVERSITY

100 Washington S
Minneapolis, MN 55401
Tel: (612)338-7224; Free: 866-492-5336

E-mail: Devon.Loetz@waldenu.edu
Web Site: www.waldenu.edu/

Description: Proprietary, upper-level, coed. Part of Laureate. Awards bachelor's, master's, and doctoral degrees and post-master's certificates. Founded 1970. Total enrollment: 50,208. Faculty: 2,705 (265 full-time, 2,440 part-time). 520 applied, 96% were admitted. Full-time: 886 students, 80% women, 20% men. Part-time: 7,809 students, 75% women, 25% men. Students come from 55 states and territories, 48 other countries, 98% from out-of-state. 0.5% American Indian or Alaska Native, non-Hispanic/Latino; 6% Hispanic/Latino; 37% African American, non-Hispanic/Latino; 1% Asian, non-Hispanic/Latino; 0.2% Native Hawaiian or other Pacific Islander, non-Hispanic/Latino; 1% international. 89% 25 or older, 24% transferred in. Academic areas with the most degrees conferred: health professions and related sciences; business/marketing; psychology. Core. Calendar: quarter/semester depending on program. Academic remediation for entering students, services for LD students, accelerated degree program, self-designed majors, distance learning, summer session for credit, part-time degree program, internships, graduate courses open to undergrads. Off campus study. Study abroad program.

Entrance Requirements: Transfer credits accepted: Yes.

Costs Per Year: Application fee: $50. Tuition: $13,050 full-time, $290 per credit hour part-time. Mandatory fees: $285 full-time, $95 per term part-time. Full-time tuition and fees vary according to course level, course load, and program. Part-time tuition and fees vary according to course level, course load, and program.

Collegiate Environment: Orientation program. Major annual events: Social Change Conference, National Day of Service. Student services: legal services, personal-psychological counseling. Walden University Library with 2.9 million books, 56,087 serials, an OPAC, and a Web page.

■ WINONA STATE UNIVERSITY

170 W Sanborn
Winona, MN 55987
Tel: (507)457-5000; Free: 800-DIAL WSU
Fax: (507)457-5620
E-mail: admissions@winona.edu
Web Site: www.winona.edu/

Description: State-supported, comprehensive, coed. Part of Minnesota State Colleges and Universities System. Awards associate, bachelor's, master's, and doctoral degrees and post-master's certificates. Founded 1858. Setting: 40-acre small town campus. Total enrollment: 8,890. Faculty: 556 (293 full-time, 263 part-time). Student-undergrad faculty ratio is 22:1. 6,528 applied, 69% were admitted. 10% from top 10% of their high school class, 33% from top quarter, 71% from top half. Full-time: 7,594 students, 61% women, 39% men. Part-time: 775 students, 61% women, 39% men. 33% from out-of-state. 0.1% American Indian or Alaska Native, non-Hispanic/Latino; 2% Hispanic/Latino; 2% African American, non-Hispanic/Latino; 2% Asian, non-Hispanic/Latino; 0.1% Native Hawaiian or other Pacific Islander, non-Hispanic/Latino; 3% international. 14% 25 or older, 92% live on campus, 8% transferred in. Retention: 78% of full-time freshmen returned the following year. Academic areas with the most degrees conferred: business/marketing; education; health professions and related sciences. Core. Calendar: semesters. Academic remediation for entering students, ESL program, services for LD students, advanced placement, accelerated degree program, self-designed majors, honors program, independent study, distance learning, double major, summer session for credit, part-time degree program, external degree program, adult/continuing education programs, internships, graduate courses open to undergrads. Off campus study at Saint Mary's University of Minnesota, other colleges in the Minnesota State Colleges and Universities System. Study abroad program. ROTC: Army (c).

Entrance Requirements: Options: electronic application, early admission, early action, deferred admission, international baccalaureate accepted. Required: high school transcript, class rank, SAT or ACT. Required for some: essay, minimum 3 high school GPA, interview. Entrance: moderately difficult. Application deadline: 3/5. Notification: continuous. SAT Reasoning Test deadline: 3/1. SAT Subject Test deadline: 2/1. Transfer credits accepted: Yes.

Costs Per Year: Application fee: $20. State resident tuition: $7080 full-time, $236 per credit part-time. Nonresident tuition: $12,740 full-time, $425 per credit part-time. Mandatory fees: $1850 full-time. Full-time tuition and fees vary according to location and reciprocity agreements. Part-time tuition varies according to course load, location, and reciprocity agreements. College room and board: $7800. Room and board charges vary according to board plan, housing facility, and location.

Collegiate Environment: Orientation program. Drama-theater group, choral group, marching band, student-run newspaper, radio station. Social organizations: 180 open to all; national fraternities, national sororities, local fraternities, local sororities; 3% of eligible men and 3% of eligible women are members. Most popular organizations: University Program Activities Committee, Student Senate, Residence Hall Association, Inter Varsity. Major annual events: Homecoming, Family Weekend, Club Fair. Student services: legal services, health clinic, personal-psychological counseling, women's center. Campus security: 24-hour emergency response devices and patrols, student patrols, late night transport-escort service, controlled dormitory access, security cameras. 2,500 college housing spaces available; all were occupied in 2012-13. Freshmen guaranteed college housing. Options: coed, men-only, women-only housing available. Darrel W. Krueger with 320,353 books, 120,000 microform titles, 36,660 serials, 8,304 audiovisual materials,

an OPAC, and a Web page. 8,500 computers available on campus for general student use. Computer purchase/lease plans available. A computer is required for all students. A campuswide network can be accessed from student residence rooms and from off campus. Students can access the following: online class registration. Staffed computer lab on campus provides training in use of computers, software, and the Internet.

Community Environment: Winona (population 26,500) is a large town in southeastern Minnesota, in a sector known as Hiawatha Valley. Limestone from the quarries here is comparable to much of Italy's finest travertine. Winona is headquarters for the Upper Mississippi River Wildlife and Fish Refuge. Trains and buses provide commercial transportation. Community facilities include many churches, a public library, a hospital, hotels and motels. Part-time employment is available. Recreational activities include fishing, golf, swimming, hunting, boating and skiing.

■ ALCORN STATE UNIVERSITY

1000 ASU Dr.
Alcorn State, MS 39096-7500
Tel: (601)877-6100; Free: 800-222-6790
Fax: (601)877-6347
E-mail: ebarnes@alcorn.edu
Web Site: www.alcorn.edu/
Description: State-supported, comprehensive, coed. Part of Mississippi Institutions of Higher Learning. Awards associate, bachelor's, and master's degrees and post-master's certificates. Founded 1871. Setting: 1,756-acre rural campus. Endowment: $10.2 million. Research spending for the previous fiscal year: $8.2 million. Educational spending for the previous fiscal year: $4955 per student. Total enrollment: 3,950. Faculty: 214 (169 full-time, 45 part-time). Student-undergrad faculty ratio is 18:1. 3,663 applied, 47% were admitted. 66% from top half of their high school class. Full-time: 2,831 students, 64% women, 36% men. Part-time: 377 students, 74% women, 26% men. Students come from 38 states and territories, 16 other countries, 13% from out-of-state. 0.1% American Indian or Alaska Native, non-Hispanic/Latino; 1% Hispanic/Latino; 93% African American, non-Hispanic/Latino; 0.4% Asian, non-Hispanic/Latino; 1% international. 25% 25 or older, 52% live on campus, 5% transferred in. Retention: 69% of full-time freshmen returned the following year. Academic areas with the most degrees conferred: health professions and related sciences; liberal arts/general studies; biological/life sciences. Core. Calendar: semesters. Academic remediation for entering students, advanced placement, accelerated degree program, honors program, independent study, distance learning, double major, summer session for credit, part-time degree program, adult/continuing education programs, co-op programs and internships, graduate courses open to undergrads. Off campus study. Study abroad program. ROTC: Army.
Entrance Requirements: Options: electronic application, deferred admission, international baccalaureate accepted. Required: high school transcript, minimum 2 high school GPA, SAT or ACT. Entrance: moderately difficult. Application deadline: Rolling. Notification: continuous. Transfer credits accepted: Yes.
Costs Per Year: Application fee: $0. State resident tuition: $5724 full-time, $238 per credit hour part-time. Nonresident tuition: $14,162 full-time, $586 per credit hour part-time. Full-time tuition varies according to course load. Part-time tuition varies according to course load. College room and board: $7999. Room and board charges vary according to housing facility.
Collegiate Environment: Orientation program. Drama-theater group, choral group, marching band, student-run newspaper, radio station. Social organizations: national fraternities, national sororities. Most popular organizations: marching band, Gospel Choir, inter-faith choir. Major annual events: Greek Step Show, concerts, Homecoming. Student services: health clinic, personal-psychological counseling. Campus security: 24-hour emergency response devices and patrols, late night transport-escort service. 1,726 college housing spaces available; 1,654 were occupied in 2012-13. Freshmen guaranteed college housing. Options: men-only, women-only housing available. John Dewey Boyd Library plus 1 other with 390,419 books, 385,629 microform titles, 82,054 serials, 34,704 audiovisual materials, and an OPAC. Operations spending for the previous fiscal year: $758,843. 500 computers available on campus for general student use. A campuswide network can be accessed from student residence rooms and from off campus. Students can access the following: online class registration. Staffed computer lab on campus provides training in use of computers, software, and the Internet.

Community Environment: This rural community has a population of less than 3,900. Multidenominational churches serve the area. It is an ideal place for hiking, camping and other outdoor recreational activities. The university is located in Claiborne County, seven miles west of Lorman, seventeen miles southwest of Poet Gibson, and forty-five miles south of Vicksburg.

■ ANTONELLI COLLEGE (HATTIESBURG)

1500 N 31st Ave.
Hattiesburg, MS 39401
Tel: (601)583-4100
Fax: (601)583-0839
E-mail: admissionsh@antonellicollege.edu
Web Site: www.antonellicollege.edu/
Description: Proprietary, 2-year, coed. Awards certificates and transfer associate degrees. Total enrollment: 354.
Entrance Requirements: Entrance: noncompetitive.

■ ANTONELLI COLLEGE (JACKSON)

2323 Lakeland Dr.
Jackson, MS 39232
Tel: (601)362-9991
Fax: (601)362-2333
E-mail: admissions.jackson@antonellicollege.edu
Web Site: www.antonellicollege.edu/
Description: Proprietary, 2-year, coed. Awards diplomas, transfer associate, and terminal associate degrees. Total enrollment: 240. 67% 25 or older.
Entrance Requirements: Open admission.

■ BELHAVEN UNIVERSITY

1500 Peachtree St.
Jackson, MS 39202-1789
Tel: (601)968-5928; Free: 800-960-5940
Fax: (601)968-9998
E-mail: admission@belhaven.edu
Web Site: www.belhaven.edu/
Description: Independent Presbyterian, comprehensive, coed. Awards associate, bachelor's, and master's degrees. Founded 1883. Setting: 42-acre urban campus. Endowment: $5 million. Educational spending for the previous fiscal year: $4501 per student. Total enrollment: 3,519. Faculty: 335 (102 full-time, 233 part-time). Student-undergrad faculty ratio is 11:1. 1,301 applied, 66% were admitted. 15% from top 10% of their high school class, 38% from top quarter, 67% from top half. Full-time: 1,206 students, 58% women, 42% men. Part-time: 1,339 students, 70% women, 30% men. Students come from 42 states and territories, 27 other countries, 51% from out-of-state. 1% American Indian or Alaska Native, non-Hispanic/Latino; 6% Hispanic/Latino; 46% African American, non-Hispanic/Latino; 1% Asian, non-Hispanic/Latino; 1% Native Hawaiian or other Pacific Islander, non-Hispanic/Latino; 3% international. 58% 25 or older, 20% live on campus, 51% transferred in. Retention: 72% of full-time freshmen returned the following year. Academic areas with the most degrees conferred: business/marketing; education; social sciences. Core. Calendar: semesters. Academic remediation for entering students, ESL program, advanced placement, accelerated degree program, self-designed majors, honors program, independent study, distance learning, double major, summer session for credit, part-time degree program, adult/continuing education programs,

internships. Off campus study at Coalition for Christian Colleges and Universities. Study abroad program. ROTC: Army (c), Air Force (c).

Entrance Requirements: Options: electronic application, early admission, deferred admission, international baccalaureate accepted. Required: high school transcript, minimum 2 high school GPA, 1 recommendation, SAT or ACT. Required for some: essay, interview. Entrance: moderately difficult. Application deadlines: Rolling, Rolling for nonresidents. Notification: continuous, continuous for nonresidents. Transfer credits accepted: Yes.

Costs Per Year: Application fee: $25. Comprehensive fee: $26,090 includes full-time tuition ($19,200) and college room and board ($6890). Room and board charges vary according to housing facility. Part-time tuition: $375 per credit. Part-time tuition varies according to course load.

Collegiate Environment: Orientation program. Drama-theater group, choral group, marching band, student-run newspaper. Social organizations: 26 open to all. Most popular organizations: Belhaven Activities Team, intramurals, Reformed University Fellowship, Quartertone, Sports Medicine: Exercise Science Club. Major annual events: Martin Luther King Jr. Service Day, Luau, Singing Christmas Tree. Student services: health clinic, personal-psychological counseling. Campus security: 24-hour emergency response devices and patrols, late night transport-escort service, controlled dormitory access. 556 college housing spaces available; 496 were occupied in 2012-13. Freshmen guaranteed college housing. On-campus residence required through sophomore year. Options: men-only, women-only housing available. Warren A. Hood Library with 137,028 books, 1,501 microform titles, 677 serials, 2,365 audiovisual materials, an OPAC, and a Web page. Operations spending for the previous fiscal year: $448,594. 36 computers available on campus for general student use. A campuswide network can be accessed from student residence rooms and from off campus. Students can access the following: online class registration. Staffed computer lab on campus provides training in use of computers.

Community Environment: See Jackson State University.

■ BLUE MOUNTAIN COLLEGE

201 W Main St.
Blue Mountain, MS 38610-9509
Tel: (662)685-4771; Free: 800-235-0136
Fax: (662)685-4776
E-mail: mteel@bmc.edu
Web Site: www.bmc.edu/

Description: Independent Southern Baptist, comprehensive, coed. Awards bachelor's and master's degrees. Founded 1873. Setting: 44-acre rural campus with easy access to Memphis. Endowment: $11.2 million. Educational spending for the previous fiscal year: $3504 per student. Total enrollment: 513. Faculty: 44 (32 full-time, 12 part-time). Student-undergrad faculty ratio is 13:1. 416 applied, 31% were admitted. 18% from top 10% of their high school class, 43% from top quarter, 80% from top half. 3 valedictorians. Full-time: 459 students, 59% women, 41% men. Part-time: 43 students, 72% women, 28% men. Students come from 18 states and territories, 4 other countries, 21% from out-of-state. 0.2% American Indian or Alaska Native, non-Hispanic/Latino; 1% Hispanic/Latino; 11% African American, non-Hispanic/Latino; 0% Asian, non-Hispanic/Latino; 0% Native Hawaiian or other Pacific Islander, non-Hispanic/Latino; 1% international. 18% 25 or older, 52% live on campus, 14% transferred in. Retention: 85% of full-time freshmen returned the following year. Academic areas with the most degrees conferred: education; psychology; theology and religious vocations. Core. Calendar: semesters. Academic remediation for entering students, advanced placement, accelerated degree program, honors program, distance learning, double major, summer session for credit, part-time degree program, internships, graduate courses open to undergrads.

Entrance Requirements: Options: electronic application, deferred admission. Required: SAT or ACT. Recommended: minimum 2 high school GPA. Required for some: high school transcript. Entrance: moderately difficult. Application deadlines: Rolling, Rolling for nonresidents. Notification: continuous, continuous for nonresidents. SAT Reasoning Test deadline: 8/15. SAT Subject Test deadline: 8/15. Transfer credits accepted: Yes.

Costs Per Year: Application fee: $10. Comprehensive fee: $13,230 includes full-time tuition ($8250), mandatory fees ($980), and college room and board ($4000). Full-time tuition and fees vary according to course load and degree level. Room and board charges vary according to board plan. Part-time tuition: $275 per semester hour. Part-time mandatory fees: $365 per term. Part-time tuition and fees vary according to course load and degree level.

Collegiate Environment: Orientation program. Drama-theater group, choral group. Social organizations: 10 open to all; societies for men and women; 70% of eligible men and 60% of eligible women are members. Most popular

organizations: Baptist Student Union, Student Body Association, Intramural Association, Ministerial Association, Mississippi Association of Educators/ Student Program. Major annual events: BSU/SGA Welcome Back Parties, Society Rush, Track Meet. Campus security: 24-hour emergency response devices and patrols. 273 college housing spaces available; 270 were occupied in 2012-13. No special consideration for freshman housing applicants. On-campus residence required through junior year. Options: men-only, women-only housing available. Guyton Library plus 1 other with 76,831 books, 111 serials, 1,320 audiovisual materials, an OPAC, and a Web page. Operations spending for the previous fiscal year: $143,884. 41 computers available on campus for general student use. A campuswide network can be accessed from student residence rooms. Students can access the following: online class registration. Staffed computer lab on campus provides training in use of computers, software, and the Internet.

Community Environment: A rural community, Blue Mountain has a warm and pleasant climate with an average temperature of 68 degrees. Blue Mountain is about 70 miles from Memphis. Recreational facilities include a swimming pool, golf course, athletic field, physical education center, tennis courts, student center and 2 auditoriums for productions.

■ COAHOMA COMMUNITY COLLEGE

3240 Friars Point Rd.
Clarksdale, MS 38614-9799
Tel: (662)627-2571; Free: 866-470-1CCC
Web Site: www.ccc.cc.ms.us/

Description: State and locally supported, 2-year, coed. Part of Mississippi State Board for Community and Junior Colleges. Awards certificates, transfer associate, and terminal associate degrees. Founded 1949. Setting: 29-acre rural campus with easy access to Memphis. Total enrollment: 2,216. Faculty: 117 (53 full-time, 64 part-time). Student-undergrad faculty ratio is 19:1. Full-time: 1,962 students, 69% women, 31% men. Part-time: 254 students, 80% women, 20% men. 41% 25 or older, 22% live on campus. Retention: 58% of full-time freshmen returned the following year. Core. Calendar: semesters. Academic remediation for entering students, advanced placement, accelerated degree program, self-designed majors, distance learning, part-time degree program, adult/continuing education programs, co-op programs. Off campus study.

Entrance Requirements: Open admission. Required: high school transcript. Required for some: interview. Entrance: noncompetitive. Application deadline: Rolling. Notification: continuous.

Collegiate Environment: Orientation program. Drama-theater group, choral group, marching band, student-run newspaper. Most popular organizations: Student Government Association, VICA (Vocational Industrial Clubs of America), Phi Theta Kappa Honor Society. Major annual events: High School Day, Coronation of Miss Coahoma Community College, graduation. Student services: health clinic, personal-psychological counseling. Campus security: 24-hour patrols, controlled dormitory access. Dickerson-Johnson Library with a Web page. 25 computers available on campus for general student use. A campuswide network can be accessed from student residence rooms. Students can access the following: online class registration. Staffed computer lab on campus provides training in use of computers and the Internet.

Community Environment: Clarksdale, an important distributing outlet in an agricultural region, is a prime example of the state's"Balance Agriculture with Industry" program. The city gins large amounts of cotton and manufactures conveyor equipment, corrugated boxes, farm machinery, tire tubes, agricultural chemicals and fertilizers, builder's hardware, electronic equipment and furniture. The Greyhound Bus line serves the city. The area has a public library, hospital, churches of all major denominations and movie theatres.

■ COPIAH-LINCOLN COMMUNITY COLLEGE

PO Box 649
Wesson, MS 39191
Tel: (601)643-5101
Fax: (601)643-8212
E-mail: gay.langham@colin.edu
Web Site: www.colin.edu/

Description: State and locally supported, 2-year, coed. Part of Mississippi Community College Board. Awards certificates, transfer associate, and terminal associate degrees. Founded 1928. Setting: 525-acre rural campus with easy access to Jackson. Endowment: $2.5 million. Total enrollment: 3,436. Faculty: 138. Full-time: 2,754 students, 63% women, 37% men. Part-time: 682 students, 68% women, 32% men. Students come from 10 states and territories, 1 other country. 0.1% American Indian or Alaska Native, non-Hispanic/Latino; 1% Hispanic/Latino; 43% African American, non-Hispanic/Latino; 0.2% Asian, non-Hispanic/Latino; 0% Native Hawaiian or other Pacific Islander, non-Hispanic/Latino; 0% international. 20% 25 or older, 30% live on campus. Calendar: semesters. Academic remediation for entering students, advanced placement, self-designed majors, honors program, summer session for credit, part-time degree program, adult/continuing education programs.

Entrance Requirements: Open admission. Option: early admission. Required: high school transcript. Entrance: noncompetitive. Application deadline: Rolling. Preference given to state residents.

Costs Per Year: Application fee: $0. State resident tuition: $2100 full-time. Nonresident tuition: $3900 full-time.

Collegiate Environment: Orientation program. Drama-theater group, choral group, marching band, student-run newspaper, radio station. Student services: health clinic, personal-psychological counseling. Campus security: 24-hour patrols. 591 college housing spaces available; all were occupied in 2012-13. Oswalt Memorial Library with 34,357 books and 166 serials. Operations spending for the previous fiscal year: $396,208. 300 computers available on campus for general student use. A campuswide network can be accessed from student residence rooms. Students can access the following: online class registration. Staffed computer lab on campus provides training in use of computers and software.

Community Environment: Wesson is located on U.S. Highway 51, approximately 150 miles north of New Orleans. The climate is pleasant. Transportation is provided by the Illinois Central railroad. Some part-time employment is available for students.

■ **COPIAH-LINCOLN COMMUNITY COLLEGE–NATCHEZ CAMPUS**
11 Co-Lin Cir.
Natchez, MS 39120-8446
Tel: (601)442-9111
Fax: (601)446-9967
E-mail: gwen.mccalip@colin.edu
Web Site: www.colin.edu/

Description: State and locally supported, 2-year, coed. Part of Mississippi State Board for Community and Junior Colleges. Awards certificates, transfer associate, and terminal associate degrees. Founded 1972. Setting: 24-acre small town campus. Total enrollment: 850. Faculty: 57 (24 full-time, 33 part-time). Student-undergrad faculty ratio is 22:1. Full-time: 663 students, 69% women, 31% men. Part-time: 187 students, 76% women, 24% men. Students come from 4 states and territories. 33% 25 or older. Core. Calendar: semesters. Academic remediation for entering students, advanced placement, self-designed majors, distance learning, summer session for credit, part-time degree program, adult/continuing education programs, internships.

Entrance Requirements: Open admission. Option: early admission. Required: high school transcript. Entrance: noncompetitive. Application deadline: Rolling. Notification: continuous.

Collegiate Environment: Orientation program. Student-run newspaper. Most popular organization: student newspaper. Student services: personal-psychological counseling. Campus security: 24-hour patrols. Willie Mae Dunn Library with 19,000 books, 112 serials, 700 audiovisual materials, an OPAC, and a Web page. 175 computers available on campus for general student use. A campuswide network can be accessed from off-campus. Students can access the following: online class registration. Staffed computer lab on campus provides training in use of computers, software, and the Internet.

■ **DELTA STATE UNIVERSITY**
Hwy. 8 W
Cleveland, MS 38733-0001
Tel: (662)846-3000; Free: 800-468-6378
Fax: (662)846-4016
E-mail: dheslep@deltastate.edu
Web Site: www.deltastate.edu/

Description: State-supported, comprehensive, coed. Part of Mississippi Institutions of Higher Learning. Awards bachelor's, master's, and doctoral degrees and post-master's certificates. Founded 1924. Setting: 274-acre small town campus. Research spending for the previous fiscal year: $14,192. Educational spending for the previous fiscal year: $5879 per student. Total enrollment: 4,763. Faculty: 257 (184 full-time, 73 part-time). Student-undergrad faculty ratio is 20:1. 510 applied, 89% were admitted. 12% from top 10% of their high school class, 35% from top quarter, 79%

from top half. Full-time: 2,253 students, 59% women, 41% men. Part-time: 503 students, 61% women, 39% men. Students come from 30 states and territories, 19 other countries, 9% from out-of-state. 0.2% American Indian or Alaska Native, non-Hispanic/Latino; 1% Hispanic/Latino; 36% African American, non-Hispanic/Latino; 1% Asian, non-Hispanic/Latino; 0% Native Hawaiian or other Pacific Islander, non-Hispanic/Latino; 2% international. 23% 25 or older, 24% live on campus, 15% transferred in. Retention: 61% of full-time freshmen returned the following year. Academic areas with the most degrees conferred: business/marketing; education; health professions and related sciences. Core. Calendar: semesters. Academic remediation for entering students, services for LD students, advanced placement, freshman honors college, honors program, independent study, distance learning, double major, summer session for credit, part-time degree program, adult/continuing education programs, co-op programs and internships. ROTC: Army.

Entrance Requirements: Options: electronic application, deferred admission. Required: high school transcript, minimum 2 high school GPA, ACT. Recommended: SAT or ACT. Required for some: interview for art, music majors. Entrance: noncompetitive. Application deadlines: Rolling, Rolling for nonresidents. Notification: continuous, continuous for nonresidents. Transfer credits accepted: Yes.

Costs Per Year: Application fee: $25. State resident tuition: $5724 full-time. Nonresident tuition: $5724 full-time. College room and board: $7100. College room only: $4508. Room and board charges vary according to housing facility.

Collegiate Environment: Orientation program. Drama-theater group, choral group, marching band, student-run newspaper. Social organizations: 49 open to all; national fraternities, national sororities; 16% of eligible men and 13% of eligible women are members. Most popular organizations: Student Government Association, Student Alumni Association, Baptist Student Union, Union Program Council, Delta Volunteers. Major annual events: Homecoming, Pig Pickin, Springfest. Student services: health clinic, personal-psychological counseling. Campus security: 24-hour emergency response devices and patrols, late night transport-escort service, controlled dormitory access. 1,249 college housing spaces available; 774 were occupied in 2012-13. Freshmen guaranteed college housing. On-campus residence required in freshman year. Options: men-only, women-only housing available. Roberts-LaForge Library with 445,626 books, 832,822 microform titles, 24,101 serials, 20,028 audiovisual materials, an OPAC, and a Web page. Operations spending for the previous fiscal year: $925,829. 533 computers available on campus for general student use. Computer purchase/lease plans available. A campuswide network can be accessed from student residence rooms. Students can access the following: online class registration. Staffed computer lab on campus.

Community Environment: Located midway between Memphis, Tennessee and Vicksburg, Mississippi, the city has a public library, several churches representing the major denominations, and a hospital. Bus lines are accessible to the area and a regional airport is located 30 miles from campus in Greenville. Recreation is provided in the community through a local Little Theatre, movies, swimming pools, 4 municipal parks, a nine-hole golf course, bowling, and fishing and hunting in the nearby lake region. Average living facilities are provided by a hotel, motel, several apartments, rooming houses and dormitories. The city has over 35 civic, fraternal and business organizations. Some part-time employment is available for students.

■ **EAST CENTRAL COMMUNITY COLLEGE**
PO Box 129
Decatur, MS 39327-0129
Tel: (601)635-2111; Free: 877-462-3222
Fax: (601)635-2150
Web Site: www.eccc.edu/

Description: State and locally supported, 2-year, coed. Part of Mississippi State Board for Community and Junior Colleges. Awards certificates, transfer associate, and terminal associate degrees. Founded 1928. Setting: 200-acre rural campus. Total enrollment: 2,281. 31% 25 or older. Core. Calendar: semesters. Academic remediation for entering students, services for LD students, advanced placement, honors program, summer session for credit, part-time degree program, adult/continuing education programs.

Entrance Requirements: Open admission. Option: early admission. Required: high school transcript. Entrance: noncompetitive. Application deadline: Rolling. Notification: continuous.

Collegiate Environment: Orientation program. Drama-theater group, choral group, marching band, student-run newspaper. Student services: health clinic, personal-psychological counseling. Campus security: 24-hour patrols.

Community Environment: Located in a rural area with a healthful atmosphere, Decatur has 2 churches and very active civic, fraternal and veteran's organizations. Hunting in the local area, fishing and swimming provide recreation for the city.

■ EAST MISSISSIPPI COMMUNITY COLLEGE
PO Box 158
Scooba, MS 39358-0158
Tel: (662)476-8442
Web Site: www.eastms.edu/

Description: State and locally supported, 2-year, coed. Part of Mississippi State Board for Community and Junior Colleges. Awards certificates, transfer associate, and terminal associate degrees. Founded 1927. Setting: 25-acre rural campus. Total enrollment: 4,012. 36% 25 or older. Core. Calendar: semesters. Academic remediation for entering students, services for LD students, advanced placement, honors program, distance learning, double major, summer session for credit, part-time degree program, adult/continuing education programs, co-op programs.

Entrance Requirements: Open admission. Options: electronic application, deferred admission. Required: high school transcript. Entrance: noncompetitive. Application deadline: Rolling.

Collegiate Environment: Orientation program. Drama-theater group, choral group, marching band, student-run newspaper. Social organizations: local fraternities. Student services: personal-psychological counseling. Campus security: 24-hour emergency response devices and patrols. Tubb-May Library with 27,840 books, 116 serials, 3,478 audiovisual materials, an OPAC, and a Web page.

Community Environment: Scooba is located in the east central part of Mississippi, 35 miles north of Meridian. The area is accessible by railroad and U.S. Highway 45. There are excellent bus, train and air facilities in nearby Meridian.

■ HINDS COMMUNITY COLLEGE
PO Box 1100
Raymond, MS 39154-1100
Tel: (601)857-5261; Free: 800-HINDSCC
E-mail: randall.harris@hindscc.edu
Web Site: www.hindscc.edu/

Description: State and locally supported, 2-year, coed. Part of Mississippi Community College Board. Awards certificates, diplomas, transfer associate, and terminal associate degrees (reported data includes Raymond, Jackson Academic and Technical Center, Jackson Nursing-Allied Health Center, Rankin, Utica, and Vicksburg campus locations). Founded 1917. Setting: 671-acre small town campus. Endowment: $46,120. Educational spending for the previous fiscal year: $13,250 per student. Total enrollment: 11,667. Faculty: 731 (407 full-time, 324 part-time). Student-undergrad faculty ratio is 18:1. Full-time: 8,017 students, 62% women, 38% men. Part-time: 3,650 students, 69% women, 31% men. Students come from 24 states and territories, 14 other countries, 1% from out-of-state. 0.4% American Indian or Alaska Native, non-Hispanic/Latino; 1% Hispanic/Latino; 58% African American, non-Hispanic/Latino; 1% Asian, non-Hispanic/Latino; 0.2% Native Hawaiian or other Pacific Islander, non-Hispanic/Latino; 0.02% international. 35% 25 or older, 12% live on campus, 7% transferred in. Retention: 60% of full-time freshmen returned the following year. Core. Calendar: semesters. Academic remediation for entering students, services for LD students, advanced placement, accelerated degree program, freshman honors college, honors program, independent study, distance learning, double major, summer session for credit, part-time degree program, adult/continuing education programs, co-op programs and internships. Study abroad program. ROTC: Army (c).

Entrance Requirements: Open admission Special requirements for allied health programs. ACT not required for placement in vocational programs. Interview required for allied health and some vocational programs. Options: electronic application, early admission. Required: high school transcript. Required for some: SAT and SAT Subject Tests or ACT. Entrance: noncompetitive. Application deadline: Rolling. Notification: continuous. Transfer credits accepted: Yes.

Costs Per Year: Application fee: $0. Area resident tuition: $2160 full-time, $100 per semester hour part-time. State resident tuition: $2160 full-time, $100 per semester hour part-time. Nonresident tuition: $4760 full-time, $200 per semester hour part-time. Mandatory fees: $100 full-time, $50 per term part-time. Part-time tuition and fees vary according to course load. College room and board: $3900. Room and board charges vary according to board plan and housing facility.

Collegiate Environment: Drama-theater group, choral group, marching band, student-run newspaper. Student services: legal services, personal-psychological counseling. Campus security: 24-hour emergency response devices and patrols, controlled dormitory access. College housing designed to accommodate 1,889 students; 1,958 undergraduates lived in college housing during 2012-13. Options: coed, men-only, women-only housing available. McLendon Library plus 5 others with an OPAC. 214 computers available on campus for general student use. A campuswide network can be accessed from student residence rooms. Students can access the following: online class registration, independent study modules. Staffed computer lab on campus provides training in use of computers, software, and the Internet.

Community Environment: Raymond is a suburban area 15 miles east of Jackson. The community has a regional library and a general hospital 8 miles east. There are several churches of various denominations in the immediate area. Local clubs include Lions, Business & Professional Women, and the Jaycees. Hinds Community College has a part-time employment agreement with a local industry.

■ HOLMES COMMUNITY COLLEGE
PO Box 369
Goodman, MS 39079-0369
Tel: (662)472-2312; Free: 800-HOLMES-4
Fax: (662)472-9156
Web Site: www.holmescc.edu/

Description: State and locally supported, 2-year, coed. Part of Mississippi State Board for Community and Junior Colleges. Awards certificates, transfer associate, and terminal associate degrees. Founded 1928. Setting: 196-acre small town campus. Total enrollment: 5,107. 34% 25 or older. Core. Calendar: semesters. Academic remediation for entering students, services for LD students, advanced placement, distance learning, summer session for credit, adult/continuing education programs, co-op programs.

Entrance Requirements: Open admission. Option: early admission. Required: high school transcript. Entrance: noncompetitive. Application deadline: Rolling. Notification: continuous.

Collegiate Environment: Drama-theater group, choral group, marching band, student-run newspaper. Student services: personal-psychological counseling. Campus security: 24-hour emergency response devices and patrols. McMorrough Library plus 2 others with 53,000 books, 550 serials, and an OPAC.

Community Environment: Located in a rural area, there is bus service to Goodman. The climate is mild and humid. Railroad service is available in nearby Durant, Mississippi. Several churches of various denominations are located here. Many cultural, recreational and community services available in Jackson, the State Capital, 48 miles away. There is some work available for students requiring financial assistance.

■ ITAWAMBA COMMUNITY COLLEGE
602 W Hill St.
Fulton, MS 38843
Tel: (662)862-8000
Fax: (662)862-8036
E-mail: laboggs@iccms.edu
Web Site: www.iccms.edu/

Description: State and locally supported, 2-year, coed. Part of Mississippi State Board for Community and Junior Colleges. Awards transfer associate and terminal associate degrees. Founded 1947. Setting: 300-acre small town campus. Total enrollment: 5,213. Faculty: 210 (85 full-time, 125 part-time). Student-undergrad faculty ratio is 24:1. Full-time: 3,649 students, 62% women, 38% men. Part-time: 1,564 students, 68% women, 32% men. 18% 25 or older. Core. Calendar: semesters. Academic remediation for entering students, services for LD students, honors program, summer session for credit, part-time degree program, adult/continuing education programs. ROTC: Army.

Entrance Requirements: Open admission except for allied health programs. Option: early admission. Required: high school transcript. Entrance: noncompetitive. Application deadline: Rolling. Notification: continuous.

Collegiate Environment: Orientation program. 36,816 books and 231 serials 200 computers available on campus for general student use. A campuswide network can be accessed from student residence rooms and from off campus. Students can access the following: online class registration. Staffed computer lab on campus provides training in use of computers, software, and the Internet.

Community Environment: Fulton is a rural community in northeast Mississippi. The climate is moderate to warm. The area is accessible to bus and rail lines and has several churches of various denominations. Recreation is provided by local theatres, boating water skiing, fishing, and golf. Community services include the County Health Department, a hospital, and fine shopping facilities. There are many active civic and fraternal organizations within the immediate area.

■ ITT TECHNICAL INSTITUTE
382 Galleria Pky.
Ste. 100
Madison, MS 39110
Tel: (601)607-4500; Free: 800-209-2521
Web Site: www.itt-tech.edu/
Description: Proprietary, 4-year, coed. Part of ITT Educational Services, Inc. Awards associate and bachelor's degrees.
Entrance Requirements: Entrance: minimally difficult.

■ JACKSON STATE UNIVERSITY
1400 John R Lynch St.
Jackson, MS 39217
Tel: (601)979-2121; Free: 800-848-6817
Fax: (601)979-2358
E-mail: schatman@ccaix.jsums.edu
Web Site: www.jsums.edu/
Description: State-supported, university, coed. Part of Mississippi Institutions of Higher Learning. Awards bachelor's, master's, and doctoral degrees and post-master's certificates. Founded 1877. Setting: 250-acre urban campus. Research spending for the previous fiscal year: $1.1 million. Educational spending for the previous fiscal year: $5397 per student. Total enrollment: 8,783. Faculty: 525 (406 full-time, 119 part-time). Student-undergrad faculty ratio is 16:1. 8,002 applied, 54% were admitted. Full-time: 5,835 students, 61% women, 39% men. Part-time: 970 students, 71% women, 29% men. Students come from 38 states and territories, 42 other countries, 16% from out-of-state. 33% 25 or older, 25% live on campus, 7% transferred in. Retention: 76% of full-time freshmen returned the following year. Academic areas with the most degrees conferred: business/marketing; education; interdisciplinary studies. Core. Calendar: semesters. Academic remediation for entering students, ESL program, services for LD students, advanced placement, honors program, distance learning, double major, summer session for credit, part-time degree program, adult/continuing education programs, co-op programs and internships, graduate courses open to undergrads. Off campus study at Mississippi State University, Auburn University, Southern Illinois University, National Student Exchange. Study abroad program. ROTC: Army, Air Force.
Entrance Requirements: Options: electronic application, early admission, deferred admission, international baccalaureate accepted. Required: high school transcript, minimum 2 high school GPA, SAT or ACT. Required for some: 3 recommendations. Entrance: minimally difficult. Application deadline: 8/1. Notification: continuous. SAT Reasoning Test deadline: 8/1.
Costs Per Year: Application fee: $0. State resident tuition: $5988 full-time. Nonresident tuition: $14,676 full-time. Full-time tuition varies according to course load. College room and board: $6996. College room only: $4214. Room and board charges vary according to board plan and housing facility.
Collegiate Environment: Orientation program. Drama-theater group, choral group, marching band, student-run newspaper. Social organizations: 129 open to all; national fraternities, national sororities; 11% of eligible men and 19% of eligible women are members. Most popular organizations: Tiger Pride Connection, Sonic Boom of the South, Students in Free Enterprise (SIFE), Interfaith, NAACP. Major annual events: Homecoming, Founders' Day, Capital City Classic. Student services: health clinic, personal-psychological counseling. Campus security: 24-hour emergency response devices and patrols, late night transport-escort service, controlled dormitory access. H. T. Sampson Library plus 5 others with 749,089 books, 653,962 microform titles, 78,830 serials, 2,354 audiovisual materials, an OPAC, and a Web page. Operations spending for the previous fiscal year: $2.1 million. 300 computers available on campus for general student use. A campuswide network can be accessed from off-campus. Students can access the following: online class registration. Staffed computer lab on campus provides training in use of computers, software, and the Internet.
Community Environment: On the Pearl River, Jackson is the capital and largest city of Mississippi. It was first established as a trading post by the French. In the early days, many Virginians and Carolinians passed through here as they followed the Old Natchez Trace to the Southwest. The area enjoys year-round pleasant weather. Being a major city, there are good facili-

ties for rail and air transportation. Community associations sponsoring cultural pursuits include Jackson Music Association, Little Theatre, Municipal Art Gallery and Symphony Orchestra. Local services are supplied by 5 hospitals, libraries and many churches. Recreation facilities include 12 parks, 4 municipal swimming pools, a zoo, golf courses, tennis courts, and fishing and hunting nearby.

■ JONES COUNTY JUNIOR COLLEGE
900 S Ct. St.
Ellisville, MS 39437-3901
Tel: (601)477-4000
Fax: (601)477-4017
Web Site: www.jcjc.edu/
Description: State and locally supported, 2-year, coed. Part of Mississippi State Board for Community and Junior Colleges. Awards certificates, transfer associate, and terminal associate degrees. Founded 1928. Setting: 360-acre small town campus. Total enrollment: 5,640. Faculty: 175 (170 full-time, 5 part-time). Student-undergrad faculty ratio is 25:1. Students come from 9 states and territories. 22% 25 or older, 20% live on campus. Core. Calendar: semesters. Academic remediation for entering students, advanced placement, honors program, distance learning, summer session for credit, part-time degree program, co-op programs. ROTC: Army (c), Air Force (c).
Entrance Requirements: Open admission. Option: early admission. Required: high school transcript, SAT or ACT. Entrance: noncompetitive. Application deadline: 8/26. Notification: continuous. Preference given to district residents.
Collegiate Environment: Drama-theater group, choral group, marching band, student-run newspaper. Most popular organization: student government. Major annual events: Homecoming, Spring Fever Week. Student services: health clinic, personal-psychological counseling. Campus security: 24-hour patrols. Memorial Library with 62,349 books and 654 serials. 600 computers available on campus for general student use. Staffed computer lab on campus.
Community Environment: The city is located 7 miles from Laurel. The climate is mild. Churches, libraries and museums all contribute to the pleasant living of the area. Transportation is provided by rail and air lines, and the town is easily accessible by highway. Fishing, hunting, and golf are the major recreational pastimes. There are some part-time job opportunities for students.

■ MERIDIAN COMMUNITY COLLEGE
910 Hwy. 19 N
Meridian, MS 39307
Tel: (601)483-8241; Free: 800-MCC-THE-1
E-mail: apayne@meridiancc.edu
Web Site: www.meridiancc.edu/
Description: State and locally supported, 2-year, coed. Part of Mississippi State Board for Community and Junior Colleges. Awards certificates, transfer associate, and terminal associate degrees. Founded 1937. Setting: 62-acre small town campus. Endowment: $6.3 million. Educational spending for the previous fiscal year: $3162 per student. Total enrollment: 3,614. Faculty: 209 (154 full-time, 55 part-time). Student-undergrad faculty ratio is 18:1. Students come from 16 states and territories, 3% from out-of-state. 30% 25 or older, 12% live on campus. Retention: 51% of full-time freshmen returned the following year. Core. Calendar: semesters. Academic remediation for entering students, ESL program, services for LD students, advanced placement, independent study, distance learning, summer session for credit, part-time degree program, external degree program, adult/continuing education programs, co-op programs.
Entrance Requirements: Open admission. Option: early admission. Required: high school transcript, minimum 2 high school GPA. Recommended: ACT. Required for some: essay. Entrance: noncompetitive. Application deadline: Rolling.
Collegiate Environment: Orientation program. Drama-theater group, choral group, student-run newspaper, radio station. Social organizations: 22 open to all. Most popular organizations: Phi Theta Kappa, VICA (Vocational Industrial Clubs of America), Health Occupations Students of America, Organization of Student Nurses, Distributive Education Clubs of America. Major annual events: Spring Fest, Octoberfest, Fall Picnic. Student services: health clinic, personal-psychological counseling. Campus security: 24-hour patrols, student patrols. L. O. Todd Library with 50,000 books and 600 serials. Operations spending for the previous fiscal year: $702,517. 148 computers available on campus for general student use. A campuswide network can be accessed from student residence rooms and from off campus. Students

can access the following: online class registration. Staffed computer lab on campus provides training in use of computers, software, and the Internet.

Community Environment: Neither destruction by fire during the Civil War, a riot in 1871, a yellow fever epidemic in 1878, nor a cyclone in 1906 could keep Meridian down. It survived these disasters to become the state's leading industrial city. In an area providing abundant raw agricultural and industrial materials, local industries produce wood products, clothing, clay pipes, metal windows, asphalt roofing, fabricated steel and dairy and meat products. The region also produces timber, corn, cotton and cattle. Passenger air, rail and bus service is available. The city has private hospitals. Cultural activities include Little Theatre, Symphony Orchestra, Meridian Chorale and Art Association. The economic base is evenly divided between agriculture, industry and military payrolls.

■ **MILLSAPS COLLEGE**
1701 N State St.
Jackson, MS 39210-0001
Tel: (601)974-1000; Free: 800-352-1050
Fax: (601)974-1059
E-mail: admissions@millsaps.edu
Web Site: www.millsaps.edu/

Description: Independent United Methodist, comprehensive, coed. Awards bachelor's and master's degrees. Founded 1890. Setting: 100-acre urban campus. Endowment: $92.1 million. Educational spending for the previous fiscal year: $13,600 per student. Total enrollment: 915. Faculty: 120 (94 full-time, 26 part-time). Student-undergrad faculty ratio is 8:1. 2,255 applied, 55% were admitted. 35% from top 10% of their high school class, 60% from top quarter, 85% from top half. Full-time: 833 students, 49% women, 51% men. Part-time: 16 students, 56% women, 44% men. Students come from 25 states and territories, 18 other countries, 56% from out-of-state. 1% American Indian or Alaska Native, non-Hispanic/Latino; 2% Hispanic/Latino; 11% African American, non-Hispanic/Latino; 5% Asian, non-Hispanic/Latino; 0.1% Native Hawaiian or other Pacific Islander, non-Hispanic/Latino; 2% international. 3% 25 or older, 84% live on campus, 4% transferred in. Retention: 78% of full-time freshmen returned the following year. Academic areas with the most degrees conferred: biological/life sciences; business/marketing; psychology. Core. Calendar: semesters. Services for LD students, advanced placement, accelerated degree program, self-designed majors, honors program, independent study, double major, summer session for credit, part-time degree program, internships, graduate courses open to undergrads. Off campus study at AIFS (American Institute for Foreign Study), AustraLearn, AsiaLearn, EuroLearn (educational programs of GlobalLinks Learning Abroad), CIEE (Council on International Educational Exchange). Millsaps is a member institution of ISEP (International Student Exchange Programs) and IES Abroad Consortium. Millsaps also encourages students to participate in several other programs, including The Alliance for Global Education, Arcadia University, IFSA-Butler, GSE, ISA, Semester at Sea. Study abroad program. ROTC: Army (c), Air Force (c).

Entrance Requirements: Options: electronic application, early admission, early action, deferred admission, international baccalaureate accepted. Required: essay, high school transcript, minimum 2.5 high school GPA, 1 recommendation, secondary school report, SAT or ACT. Required for some: interview. Entrance: moderately difficult. Application deadlines: 2/1, 2/1 for nonresidents, 12/1 for early action. Notification: continuous until 3/15, continuous until 3/15 for nonresidents, 1/15 for early action. SAT Reasoning Test deadline: 7/1. Transfer credits accepted: Yes.

Costs Per Year: Application fee: $0. Comprehensive fee: $41,800 includes full-time tuition ($29,052), mandatory fees ($1922), and college room and board ($10,826). College room only: $6110. Room and board charges vary according to housing facility.

Collegiate Environment: Orientation program. Drama-theater group, choral group, student-run newspaper. Social organizations: 80 open to all; national fraternities, national sororities; 57% of eligible men and 59% of eligible women are members. Most popular organizations: Campus Ministry Team, Student Body Association, SAPS (Campus Programming Board), Interfraternity/Panhellenic Councils, intramural sports. Major annual events: Major Madness, Homecoming, Project Midtown. Student services: health clinic, personal-psychological counseling. Campus security: 24-hour emergency response devices and patrols, student patrols, late night transport-escort service, controlled dormitory access, self-defense education, lighted pathways. 881 college housing spaces available; 707 were occupied in 2012-13. Freshmen guaranteed college housing. On-campus residence required through sophomore year. Options: coed, men-only, women-only housing available. Millsaps-Wilson Library with 200,396 books,

35,525 microform titles, 38,588 serials, 8,984 audiovisual materials, an OPAC, and a Web page. Operations spending for the previous fiscal year: $653,731. 150 computers available on campus for general student use. Computer purchase/lease plans available. A campuswide network can be accessed from student residence rooms and from off campus. Students can access the following: online class registration, online transcripts. Staffed computer lab on campus provides training in use of computers, software, and the Internet.

Community Environment: See Jackson State University.

■ **MISSISSIPPI COLLEGE**
200 S Capitol St.
Clinton, MS 39058
Tel: (601)925-3000; Free: 800-738-1236
Fax: (601)925-3804
E-mail: enrollment-services@mc.edu
Web Site: www.mc.edu/

Description: Independent Southern Baptist, comprehensive, coed. Part of Mississippi Baptist Convention. Awards bachelor's, master's, and doctoral degrees and post-master's certificates. Founded 1826. Setting: 474-acre suburban campus with easy access to Jackson. Endowment: $61.1 million. Research spending for the previous fiscal year: $166,074. Educational spending for the previous fiscal year: $7139 per student. Total enrollment: 5,070. Faculty: 461 (205 full-time, 256 part-time). Student-undergrad faculty ratio is 15:1. 2,178 applied, 58% were admitted. 33% from top 10% of their high school class, 54% from top quarter, 74% from top half. 45 National Merit Scholars. Full-time: 2,623 students, 60% women, 40% men. Part-time: 419 students, 66% women, 34% men. Students come from 36 states and territories, 10 other countries, 24% from out-of-state. 1% American Indian or Alaska Native, non-Hispanic/Latino; 2% Hispanic/Latino; 24% African American, non-Hispanic/Latino; 1% Asian, non-Hispanic/Latino; 0% Native Hawaiian or other Pacific Islander, non-Hispanic/Latino; 3% international. 20% 25 or older, 49% live on campus, 10% transferred in. Retention: 73% of full-time freshmen returned the following year. Academic areas with the most degrees conferred: business/marketing; education; health professions and related sciences. Core. Calendar: semesters. Academic remediation for entering students, ESL program, services for LD students, advanced placement, accelerated degree program, honors program, independent study, distance learning, double major, summer session for credit, part-time degree program, adult/continuing education programs, co-op programs and internships, graduate courses open to undergrads. Study abroad program. ROTC: Army, Air Force.

Entrance Requirements: Options: electronic application, early admission, early decision, deferred admission, international baccalaureate accepted. Required: high school transcript, SAT or ACT. Recommended: minimum 2 high school GPA, interview. Required for some: 2 recommendations. Entrance: moderately difficult. Application deadlines: Rolling, Rolling for nonresidents, 12/1 for early decision. Notification: continuous, continuous for nonresidents, 12/15 for early decision. Transfer credits accepted: Yes.

Costs Per Year: Application fee: $25. Comprehensive fee: $22,018 includes full-time tuition ($14,120), mandatory fees ($748), and college room and board ($7150). Full-time tuition and fees vary according to course load. Room and board charges vary according to housing facility. Part-time tuition: $442 per credit hour. Part-time mandatory fees: $188 per term. Part-time tuition and fees vary according to course load.

Collegiate Environment: Orientation program. Drama-theater group, choral group, marching band, student-run newspaper, radio station. Social organizations: 74 open to all; local fraternities, local sororities; 13% of eligible men and 24% of eligible women are members. Most popular organizations: Baptist Student Union, Nenamoosha Social Tribe, Laguna Social Tribe, Civitan Service Club, Shawreth Service Club. Major annual events: Welcome Week, Homecoming, Spring Fever Week. Student services: health clinic, personal-psychological counseling. Campus security: 24-hour emergency response devices and patrols, late night transport-escort service, controlled dormitory access. 1,734 college housing spaces available; 1,489 were occupied in 2012-13. Freshmen given priority for college housing. On-campus residence required through junior year. Options: men-only, women-only housing available. Leland Speed Library plus 1 other with 247,916 books, 332,108 microform titles, 79,074 serials, 13,487 audiovisual materials, an OPAC, and a Web page. Operations spending for the previous fiscal year: $1.2 million. 492 computers available on campus for general student use. A campuswide network can be accessed from student residence rooms and from off campus. Students can access the following: online class registration. Staffed computer lab on campus provides training in use of computers, software, and the Internet.

Community Environment: This is a suburban community located adjacent to Jackson's city limits. The climate is warm. The area has a shopping center, and rapid expansion of businesses and residential areas is anticipated. Clinton has excellent highway, air, and rail connections.

■ **MISSISSIPPI DELTA COMMUNITY COLLEGE**
Hwy. 3 and Cherry St.
Moorhead, MS 38761-0668
Tel: (662)246-6322
Web Site: www.msdelta.edu/
Description: District-supported, 2-year, coed. Part of Mississippi State Board for Community and Junior Colleges. Awards certificates, diplomas, transfer associate, and terminal associate degrees. Founded 1926. Setting: 425-acre small town campus. Educational spending for the previous fiscal year: $2372 per student. Total enrollment: 4,000. Faculty: 125. 909 applied, 100% were admitted. Students come from 6 states and territories. 19% 25 or older, 25% live on campus. Calendar: semesters. Academic remediation for entering students, advanced placement, summer session for credit, part-time degree program, adult/continuing education programs.
Entrance Requirements: Option: deferred admission. Required: high school transcript. Required for some: ACT. Entrance: noncompetitive. Application deadline: 7/27. Preference given to district residents.
Collegiate Environment: Drama-theater group, choral group, marching band, student-run newspaper. Social organizations: 16 open to all. Student services: personal-psychological counseling. Campus security: 24-hour emergency response devices and patrols, late night transport-escort service. Stanny Sanders Library with 33,020 books, 250 serials, and an OPAC. Operations spending for the previous fiscal year: $443,719. 80 computers available on campus for general student use. Staffed computer lab on campus.
Community Environment: This is a rural area with bus and air transportation 8 miles distant. The immediate area supports a clinic and small stores. There is some part-time employment for men over 18. Better employment opportunities for students are available in the neighboring community. The city has a theater, swimming pool and tennis courts. 5 local lakes provide hunting and fishing within the area.

■ **MISSISSIPPI GULF COAST COMMUNITY COLLEGE**
PO Box 609
Perkinston, MS 39573
Tel: (601)928-5211
Fax: (601)928-6299
E-mail: ladd.taylor@mgccc.edu
Web Site: www.mgccc.edu/
Description: District-supported, 2-year, coed. Part of Mississippi State Board for Community and Junior Colleges. Awards certificates, diplomas, transfer associate, and terminal associate degrees. Founded 1911. Setting: 600-acre small town campus with easy access to New Orleans. Endowment: $3 million. Total enrollment: 8,822. Faculty: 624 (387 full-time, 237 part-time). Student-undergrad faculty ratio is 26:1. 1,974 applied, 100% were admitted. Full-time: 5,551 students, 62% women, 38% men. Part-time: 3,271 students, 62% women, 38% men. Students come from 15 states and territories, 4% from out-of-state. 7% live on campus. Retention: 62% of full-time freshmen returned the following year. Core. Calendar: semesters. Academic remediation for entering students, ESL program, advanced placement, honors program, independent study, distance learning, summer session for credit, part-time degree program, adult/continuing education programs, co-op programs and internships. Study abroad program.
Entrance Requirements: Open admission except for allied health programs. Options: electronic application, early admission. Required: high school transcript. Entrance: noncompetitive. Application deadline: Rolling. Notification: continuous. Preference given to district residents.
Collegiate Environment: Orientation program. Drama-theater group, choral group, marching band, student-run newspaper. Social organizations: 33 open to all. Most popular organizations: VICA (Vocational Industrial Clubs of America), Students in Free Enterprise (SIFE), Student Government Association. Major annual events: Homecoming, Vocational Awareness Week, Drug/Alcohol Awareness Week. Student services: personal-psychological counseling, women's center. Campus security: 24-hour emergency response devices and patrols. Main library plus 3 others with 100,472 books, 933 serials, and an OPAC. Operations spending for the previous fiscal year: $949,826. 435 computers available on campus for general student use. A campuswide network can be accessed from student residence rooms. Staffed computer lab on campus.

Community Environment: The city lies 25 miles north of Gulfport. Area is reached by Interstate 10 and Highway 49. Air service is available.

■ **MISSISSIPPI STATE UNIVERSITY**
Mississippi State, MS 39762
Tel: (662)325-2323
Fax: (662)325-3299
E-mail: admit@msstate.edu
Web Site: www.msstate.edu/
Description: State-supported, university, coed. Part of Mississippi Institutions of Higher Learning. Awards associate, bachelor's, master's, and doctoral degrees and post-master's certificates. Founded 1878. Setting: 4,200-acre small town campus. Endowment: $320.5 million. Research spending for the previous fiscal year: $154.9 million. Educational spending for the previous fiscal year: $6198 per student. Total enrollment: 20,365. Faculty: 1,005 (882 full-time, 123 part-time). Student-undergrad faculty ratio is 19:1. 10,449 applied, 69% were admitted. 27% from top 10% of their high school class, 28% from top quarter, 83% from top half. 17 National Merit Scholars. Full-time: 15,004 students, 48% women, 52% men. Part-time: 1,386 students, 50% women, 50% men. Students come from 52 states and territories, 58 other countries, 22% from out-of-state. 1% American Indian or Alaska Native, non-Hispanic/Latino; 2% Hispanic/Latino; 22% African American, non-Hispanic/Latino; 1% Asian, non-Hispanic/Latino; 0.1% Native Hawaiian or other Pacific Islander, non-Hispanic/Latino; 2% international. 12% 25 or older, 27% live on campus, 10% transferred in. Retention: 81% of full-time freshmen returned the following year. Academic areas with the most degrees conferred: business/marketing; education; engineering. Core. Calendar: semesters. Academic remediation for entering students, ESL program, services for LD students, advanced placement, accelerated degree program, self-designed majors, freshman honors college, honors program, independent study, distance learning, double major, summer session for credit, part-time degree program, adult/continuing education programs, co-op programs and internships, graduate courses open to undergrads. Off campus study at Meridian Campus, Stennis Center (Hancock County). Study abroad program. ROTC: Army, Air Force.
Entrance Requirements: Options: electronic application, international baccalaureate accepted. Required: high school transcript, minimum 2 high school GPA, SAT or ACT. Entrance: moderately difficult. Application deadline: 8/1. Notification: continuous. Transfer credits accepted: Yes.
Costs Per Year: Application fee: $40. State resident tuition: $6264 full-time, $261 per credit hour part-time. Nonresident tuition: $15,828 full-time, $659.50 per credit hour part-time. Part-time tuition varies according to course load. College room and board: $8486. College room only: $4936. Room and board charges vary according to board plan, housing facility, and student level.
Collegiate Environment: Orientation program. Drama-theater group, choral group, marching band, student-run newspaper, radio station. Social organizations: 370 open to all; national fraternities, national sororities; 16% of eligible men and 21% of eligible women are members. Most popular organizations: Student Association, Black Student Alliance, Residence Hall Association, Fashion Board, Campus Activities Board. Major annual events: Bulldog Bash, Homecoming, athletic events. Student services: health clinic, personal-psychological counseling. Campus security: 24-hour emergency response devices and patrols, late night transport-escort service, controlled dormitory access, bicycle patrols, crime prevention program, RAD program, general law enforcement services. 4,615 college housing spaces available; 4,506 were occupied in 2012-13. On-campus residence required in freshman year. Options: coed, men-only, women-only housing available. Mitchell Memorial Library plus 2 others with 2.4 million books, 3.5 million microform titles, 117,097 serials, 15,069 audiovisual materials, an OPAC, and a Web page. Operations spending for the previous fiscal year: $11.7 million. 1,000 computers available on campus for general student use. A campuswide network can be accessed from student residence rooms and from off campus. Students can access the following: online class registration, campus-wide wireless Internet access. Staffed computer lab on campus provides training in use of computers and the Internet.

■ **MISSISSIPPI UNIVERSITY FOR WOMEN**
1100 College St., MUW-1600
Columbus, MS 39701-9998
Tel: (662)329-4750; Free: 877-GO 2 THE W
Fax: (662)329-7297
E-mail: cderden@admissions.muw.edu
Web Site: www.muw.edu/

Description: State-supported, comprehensive, coed. Part of Mississippi Institutions of Higher Learning. Awards associate, bachelor's, master's, and doctoral degrees and post-master's certificates. Founded 1884. Setting: 110-acre small town campus. Endowment: $39.8 million. Research spending for the previous fiscal year: $1.2 million. Educational spending for the previous fiscal year: $4440 per student. Total enrollment: 2,650. Faculty: 214 (130 full-time, 84 part-time). Student-undergrad faculty ratio is 15:1. 1,542 applied, 44% were admitted. 25% from top 10% of their high school class, 59% from top quarter, 93% from top half. 8 valedictorians. Full-time: 2,009 students, 85% women, 15% men. Part-time: 494 students, 74% women, 26% men. Students come from 26 states and territories, 10 other countries, 9% from out-of-state. 0.1% American Indian or Alaska Native, non-Hispanic/Latino; 1% Hispanic/Latino; 38% African American, non-Hispanic/Latino; 2% Asian, non-Hispanic/Latino; 0.04% Native Hawaiian or other Pacific Islander, non-Hispanic/Latino; 1% international. 40% 25 or older, 28% live on campus, 22% transferred in. Retention: 74% of full-time freshmen returned the following year. Academic areas with the most degrees conferred: health professions and related sciences; business/marketing; education. Core. Calendar: semesters. Academic remediation for entering students, services for LD students, advanced placement, freshman honors college, honors program, independent study, distance learning, double major, summer session for credit, part-time degree program, adult/continuing education programs, internships, graduate courses open to undergrads. Off campus study at Mississippi State University. Study abroad program. ROTC: Army (c), Air Force (c).

Entrance Requirements: Options: electronic application, early admission, international baccalaureate accepted. Required: high school transcript. Recommended: SAT or ACT. Required for some: minimum 2 high school GPA, interview, rank in upper 50% of high school class, SAT or ACT. Entrance: moderately difficult. Application deadlines: Rolling, Rolling for nonresidents. Notification: continuous, continuous for nonresidents. SAT Reasoning Test deadline: 8/21. SAT Subject Test deadline: 8/21. Transfer credits accepted: Yes.

Costs Per Year: Application fee: $0. State resident tuition: $5316 full-time, $221.50 per credit hour part-time. Nonresident tuition: $14,484 full-time, $603.50 per credit hour part-time. Part-time tuition varies according to course load. College room and board: $5991. College room only: $3454. Room and board charges vary according to housing facility.

Collegiate Environment: Orientation program. Drama-theater group, choral group, student-run newspaper, radio station. Social organizations: 15 open to all; national fraternities, national sororities, local fraternities, local sororities; 9% of eligible men and 12% of eligible women are members. Most popular organizations: Student Government Association, Toastmasters, Wesley Foundation, Modeling Squad. Major annual events: Welcome Week, Late Night Exam Breakfast, intramurals. Student services: health clinic, personal-psychological counseling, women's center. Campus security: 24-hour emergency response devices and patrols, controlled dormitory access. 625 college housing spaces available; 566 were occupied in 2012-13. Freshmen guaranteed college housing. Options: men-only, women-only housing available. John Clayton Fant Memorial Library with 31,682 books, 29,787 microform titles, 4,347 serials, 690 audiovisual materials, an OPAC, and a Web page. Operations spending for the previous fiscal year: $913,229. 352 computers available on campus for general student use. A campuswide network can be accessed from student residence rooms and from off campus. Students can access the following: online class registration. Staffed computer lab on campus provides training in use of computers, software, and the Internet.

■ **MISSISSIPPI VALLEY STATE UNIVERSITY**
14000 Hwy. 82 W
Itta Bena, MS 38941-1400
Tel: (662)254-9041
Fax: (662)254-7900
E-mail: jawill@mvsu.edu
Web Site: www.mvsu.edu/
Description: State-supported, comprehensive, coed. Part of Mississippi Institutions of Higher Learning. Awards bachelor's and master's degrees. Founded 1946. Setting: 450-acre small town campus. Endowment: $1.7 million. Educational spending for the previous fiscal year: $6885 per student. Total enrollment: 2,479. Faculty: 165 (134 full-time, 31 part-time). Student-undergrad faculty ratio is 15:1. 4,740 applied, 24% were admitted. Full-time: 1,826 students, 58% women, 42% men. Part-time: 342 students, 76% women, 24% men. Students come from 28 states and territories, 6 other countries, 13% from out-of-state. 0.05% American Indian or Alaska Native,

non-Hispanic/Latino; 1% Hispanic/Latino; 90% African American, non-Hispanic/Latino; 0% Asian, non-Hispanic/Latino. 24% 25 or older, 38% live on campus, 10% transferred in. Retention: 61% of full-time freshmen returned the following year. Academic areas with the most degrees conferred: education; public administration and social services; business/marketing. Core. Calendar: semesters. Academic remediation for entering students, freshman honors college, honors program, distance learning, double major, summer session for credit, part-time degree program, co-op programs and internships, graduate courses open to undergrads. ROTC: Army.

Entrance Requirements: Option: deferred admission. Required: high school transcript, SAT or ACT. Recommended: interview. Required for some: 2.5 recommendations. Entrance: minimally difficult. Application deadline: Rolling. Notification: continuous.

Costs Per Year: Application fee: $0. State resident tuition: $5628 full-time, $235 per hour part-time. Nonresident tuition: $14,076 full-time, $352 per hour part-time. Mandatory fees: $150 full-time. College room and board: $6510.

Collegiate Environment: Orientation program. Drama-theater group, choral group, marching band, student-run newspaper, radio station. Social organizations: 52 open to all; national fraternities, national sororities, local fraternities, local sororities; 20% of eligible men and 15% of eligible women are members. Most popular organizations: Student Government Association, Baptist Student Union, Black Student Fellowship, National Education Association. Major annual events: Homecoming, Black History Month, Founders' Day. Student services: health clinic, personal-psychological counseling. Campus security: 24-hour emergency response devices and patrols, controlled dormitory access. 1,509 college housing spaces available; 815 were occupied in 2012-13. Options: men-only, women-only housing available. James Herbert White Library with 147,172 books, 423,630 serials, 1,425 audiovisual materials, and an OPAC. Operations spending for the previous fiscal year: $823,498. 285 computers available on campus for general student use. A campuswide network can be accessed from student residence rooms and from off campus. Students can access the following: online class registration. Staffed computer lab on campus.

Community Environment: This is a rural community with a mild, temperate climate. Bus service provides transportation for the city and adjacent areas. Community services within the immediate area include churches of major denominations and a clinic. Shopping facilities are available within the surrounding communities. There is no part-time employment available for students.

■ **NORTHEAST MISSISSIPPI COMMUNITY COLLEGE**
101 Cunningham Blvd.
Booneville, MS 38829
Tel: (662)728-7751; Free: 800-555-2154
Fax: (662)728-1165
E-mail: admitme@nemcc.edu
Web Site: www.nemcc.edu/
Description: State-supported, 2-year, coed. Part of Mississippi State Board for Community and Junior Colleges. Awards certificates, transfer associate, and terminal associate degrees. Founded 1948. Setting: 100-acre small town campus. Total enrollment: 3,339. 24% 25 or older. Core. Calendar: semesters. Academic remediation for entering students, services for LD students, advanced placement, self-designed majors, summer session for credit, part-time degree program, adult/continuing education programs, co-op programs.

Entrance Requirements: Open admission. Option: early admission. Required for some: SAT or ACT. Entrance: noncompetitive. Application deadline: Rolling. Notification: continuous.

Collegiate Environment: Orientation program. Drama-theater group, choral group, marching band, student-run newspaper. Student services: personal-psychological counseling. Campus security: 24-hour patrols, student patrols, controlled dormitory access. Eula Dees Library with 29,879 books and 378 serials.

Community Environment: The city is located in the northeast corner of Mississippi, 100 miles southeast of Memphis, Tennessee. It has a warm and pleasant climate.

■ **NORTHWEST MISSISSIPPI COMMUNITY COLLEGE**
4975 Hwy. 51 N
Senatobia, MS 38668-1701
Tel: (662)562-3200
Fax: (662)562-3911

Web Site: www.northwestms.edu/

Description: State and locally supported, 2-year, coed. Part of Mississippi State Board for Community and Junior Colleges. Awards transfer associate and terminal associate degrees. Founded 1927. Setting: 75-acre rural campus with easy access to Memphis. Total enrollment: 6,300. Faculty: 200. Student-undergrad faculty ratio is 20:1. 2,000 applied, 100% were admitted. Core. Calendar: semesters. Academic remediation for entering students, services for LD students, honors program, summer session for credit, part-time degree program, adult/continuing education programs. ROTC: Air Force.

Entrance Requirements: Open admission. Options: early admission, deferred admission. Required: high school transcript. Entrance: noncompetitive. Application deadline: 9/7. Notification: continuous.

Collegiate Environment: Drama-theater group, choral group, marching band, student-run newspaper, radio station. Major annual events: Homecoming, Career Week, Senior Round-Ups. Student services: health clinic. Campus security: 24-hour emergency response devices, late night transport-escort service, controlled dormitory access. R. C. Pugh Library with 38,000 books and 325 serials. 50 computers available on campus for general student use.

Community Environment: Senatobia is the seat of Tate County, lying 40 miles south of Memphis, Tennessee. The area is served by Illinois Central Railroad. The city itself is located off Interstate Highway 55. Nearby is Arkabutla Reservoir and Dam, a well-known recreation facility.

■ **PEARL RIVER COMMUNITY COLLEGE**

101 Hwy. 11 N
Poplarville, MS 39470
Tel: (601)403-1000
Fax: (601)403-1135
E-mail: dford@prcc.edu
Web Site: www.prcc.edu/

Description: State and locally supported, 2-year, coed. Part of Mississippi State Board for Community and Junior Colleges. Awards certificates, transfer associate, and terminal associate degrees. Founded 1909. Setting: 240-acre rural campus with easy access to New Orleans. Total enrollment: 3,700. Faculty: 225 (160 full-time, 65 part-time). Students come from 11 states and territories. 27% 25 or older, 20% live on campus. Core. Calendar: semesters. Academic remediation for entering students, advanced placement, self-designed majors, summer session for credit, part-time degree program, adult/continuing education programs, co-op programs.

Entrance Requirements: Open admission except for nursing, data processing programs. Options: early admission, deferred admission. Required: high school transcript. Entrance: minimally difficult. Application deadline: Rolling. Notification: continuous until 8/15. Preference given to state residents.

Collegiate Environment: Drama-theater group, choral group, marching band, student-run newspaper. Social organizations: 4 open to all. Major annual events: Homecoming, Fall Fest, Spring Fest. Student services: health clinic, personal-psychological counseling, women's center. Campus security: 24-hour patrols. Pearl River Community College Library with 40,000 books and 340 serials. 90 computers available on campus for general student use. Staffed computer lab on campus.

Community Environment: Poplarville is located in the southern portion of the state and has a temperate climate. New Orleans may be reached 70 miles southwest via Interstate Highway 59. Poplarville has its own hospital.

■ **RUST COLLEGE**

150 Rust Ave.
Holly Springs, MS 38635-2328
Tel: (662)252-8000; Free: 888-886-8492
Fax: (662)252-6107
E-mail: admissions@rustcollege.edu
Web Site: www.rustcollege.edu/

Description: Independent United Methodist, 4-year, coed. Awards associate and bachelor's degrees. Founded 1866. Setting: 126-acre rural campus with easy access to Memphis. Endowment: $21.4 million. Educational spending for the previous fiscal year: $3592 per student. Total enrollment: 922. Faculty: 50 (48 full-time, 2 part-time). Student-undergrad faculty ratio is 17:1. 3,983 applied, 7% were admitted. Full-time: 810 students, 63% women, 37% men. Part-time: 112 students, 56% women, 44% men. Students come from 27 states and territories, 8 other countries, 50% from out-of-state. 0% American Indian or Alaska Native, non-Hispanic/Latino; 0% Hispanic/Latino; 93% African American, non-Hispanic/Latino; 0.2% Asian, non-Hispanic/Latino; 0% Native Hawaiian or other Pacific Islander, non-Hispanic/Latino;

5% international. 20% 25 or older, 67% live on campus, 4% transferred in. Retention: 53% of full-time freshmen returned the following year. Academic areas with the most degrees conferred: biological/life sciences; business/marketing; communication/journalism. Core. Calendar: semesters. Academic remediation for entering students, advanced placement, accelerated degree program, honors program, independent study, distance learning, double major, summer session for credit, part-time degree program, adult/continuing education programs, internships. Study abroad program.

Entrance Requirements: Required: high school transcript, minimum 2.2 high school GPA, 2 recommendations, ACT. Entrance: minimally difficult. Application deadlines: Rolling, Rolling for nonresidents. Notification: continuous, continuous for nonresidents. Transfer credits accepted: Yes.

Costs Per Year: Application fee: $10. Comprehensive fee: $12,150 includes full-time tuition ($8300) and college room and board ($3850). Full-time tuition varies according to course load.

Collegiate Environment: Orientation program. Drama-theater group, choral group, marching band, student-run newspaper, radio station. Social organizations: 31 open to all; national fraternities, national sororities; 11% of eligible men and 2% of eligible women are members. Most popular organizations: Acappella Choir, BSU (Baptist Student Union), DOBSAC (Division of Business Students' Advisory Council), MAE (Mississippi Association for Educators), Pre-Alumni Council. Major annual events: Founders' Day/Homecoming, Job Fair, Religious Emphasis Week. Student services: health clinic, personal-psychological counseling. Campus security: 24-hour emergency response devices and patrols, late night transport-escort service, controlled dormitory access. Leontyne Price Library with 123,055 books, 340 serials, and an OPAC. Operations spending for the previous fiscal year: $582,372. 220 computers available on campus for general student use. A campuswide network can be accessed from student residence rooms and from off campus. Staffed computer lab on campus.

Community Environment: A typical antebellum town, Holly Springs grew up during the great cotton boom before the Civil War. The fine old mansions and churches of the town reflect the prosperity of the cotton era. There are shopping areas in nearby Memphis. No part-time employment is available for students.

■ **SOUTHEASTERN BAPTIST COLLEGE**

4229 Hwy. 15 N
Laurel, MS 39440-1096
Tel: (601)426-6346
Web Site: www.southeasternbaptist.edu/

Description: Independent Baptist, 4-year, coed. Awards associate and bachelor's degrees. Founded 1949. Setting: 23-acre small town campus. Total enrollment: 79. 20% from out-of-state. 51% 25 or older, 31% live on campus. Core. Calendar: semesters. Academic remediation for entering students, advanced placement, summer session for credit, part-time degree program, adult/continuing education programs.

Entrance Requirements: Open admission. Options: early admission, deferred admission. Required: high school transcript, 2 recommendations. Required for some: interview. Entrance: noncompetitive. Application deadline: Rolling.

Collegiate Environment: Choral group.

Community Environment: Laurel's growth from a small village in 1900 to its present metropolitan size has been due to its pine forests and oil development. Lumber represents an important industry, but other firms manufacture clothing, machines, doors, furniture, agricultural implements, distribution transformers, oil well drilling equipment, walk-in refrigerators, condiments and janitorial supplies. There is a complete recreation program in the city, and it is close to resorts and state parks. Railroad, bus and air transportation is available in the immediate area. Laurel is considered the medical center of the surrounding area.

■ **SOUTHWEST MISSISSIPPI COMMUNITY COLLEGE**

1156 College Dr.
Summit, MS 39666
Tel: (601)276-2000
Fax: (601)276-3888
E-mail: mattc@smcc.edu
Web Site: www.smcc.cc.ms.us/

Description: State and locally supported, 2-year, coed. Part of Mississippi State Board for Community and Junior Colleges. Awards certificates, transfer associate, and terminal associate degrees. Founded 1918. Setting: 701-acre rural campus. Total enrollment: 2,053. Faculty: 90 (71 full-time, 19 part-time). Student-undergrad faculty ratio is 24:1. Full-time: 1,785 students,

63% women, 37% men. Part-time: 268 students, 75% women, 25% men. Students come from 8 states and territories, 1 other country, 6% from out-of-state. 0.4% American Indian or Alaska Native, non-Hispanic/Latino; 0.3% Hispanic/Latino; 43% African American, non-Hispanic/Latino; 0.5% Asian, non-Hispanic/Latino; 0.05% Native Hawaiian or other Pacific Islander, non-Hispanic/Latino; 0.05% international. 29% 25 or older, 35% live on campus, 45% transferred in. Retention: 50% of full-time freshmen returned the following year. Core. Calendar: semesters. Academic remediation for entering students, advanced placement, distance learning, summer session for credit, part-time degree program, adult/continuing education programs.

Entrance Requirements: Open admission. Required: high school transcript. Entrance: noncompetitive. Application deadlines: 8/1, 8/1 for nonresidents. Transfer credits accepted: Yes.

Collegiate Environment: Orientation program. Choral group, marching band, student-run newspaper. Campus security: 24-hour patrols. Library Learning Resources Center (LLRC) with 34,000 books, 150 serials, and an OPAC. 300 computers available on campus for general student use. A campuswide network can be accessed from student residence rooms. Students can access the following: online class registration. Staffed computer lab on campus provides training in use of computers, software, and the Internet.

Community Environment: Summit is a suburban area near McComb, Mississippi. The city is served by bus and rail. Health services, a library, and churches, are to be found in the neighboring city. There are shopping facilities in the immediate area. Some part-time employment is available. Recreation in the area includes boating, fishing and camping.

■ STRAYER UNIVERSITY - JACKSON CAMPUS

460 Briarwood Dr.
Ste. 200
Jackson, MS 39206
Tel: (601)718-5900
Fax: (601)206-5788
Web Site: www.strayer.edu/campus/jackson
Description: Proprietary, comprehensive, coed. Awards associate, bachelor's, and master's degrees.

■ TOUGALOO COLLEGE

500 W County Line Rd.
Tougaloo, MS 39174
Tel: (601)977-7700; Free: 888-42GALOO
Fax: (601)977-7739
E-mail: jjacobs@tougaloo.edu
Web Site: www.tougaloo.edu/
Description: Independent, 4-year, coed, affiliated with United Church of Christ. Awards associate and bachelor's degrees. Founded 1869. Setting: 500-acre suburban campus. Endowment: $4.7 million. Research spending for the previous fiscal year: $236,232. Total enrollment: 856. Faculty: 103 (70 full-time, 33 part-time). Student-undergrad faculty ratio is 13:1. 627 applied, 99% were admitted. 14% from top 10% of their high school class, 34% from top quarter, 55% from top half. Full-time: 816 students, 68% women, 32% men. Part-time: 40 students, 65% women, 35% men. Students come from 26 states and territories, 2 other countries, 18% from out-of-state. 4% 25 or older, 4% transferred in. Retention: 71% of full-time freshmen returned the following year. Academic areas with the most degrees conferred: social sciences; English; psychology. Core. Calendar: semesters. Academic remediation for entering students, accelerated degree program, self-designed majors, honors program, part-time degree program, adult/continuing education programs, co-op programs and internships. Off campus study at Brown University, New York University, Boston University. Study abroad program. ROTC: Army.

Entrance Requirements: Options: early admission, international baccalaureate accepted. Required: high school transcript, minimum 2.0 high school GPA, SAT or ACT. Entrance: minimally difficult. Application deadline: Rolling. Notification: continuous.

Collegiate Environment: Orientation program. Drama-theater group, choral group, student-run newspaper. Social organizations: 8 open to all; national fraternities, national sororities; 30% of eligible men and 35% of eligible women are members. Most popular organizations: concert choir, Student Government Association, gospel choir, NAACP, Pre-Alumni Club. Major annual events: Founders' Weekend, Humanities Festival, Faculty Recognition Day. Student services: health clinic, personal-psychological counseling. Campus security: 24-hour emergency response devices and patrols. L. Zenobiz Coleman Library with 231,106 books, 7,371 microform titles, 432

serials, and 1,651 audiovisual materials. 100 computers available on campus for general student use. A campuswide network can be accessed from student residence rooms and from off campus. Students can access the following: online class registration. Staffed computer lab on campus provides training in use of computers, software, and the Internet.

Community Environment: See Jackson State University.

■ UNIVERSITY OF MISSISSIPPI

University, MS 38677
Tel: (662)915-7211
Fax: (662)915-5869
E-mail: admissions@olemiss.edu
Web Site: www.olemiss.edu/
Description: State-supported, university, coed. Part of Mississippi Institutions of Higher Learning. Awards bachelor's, master's, and doctoral degrees and post-master's certificates. Founded 1844. Setting: 3,350-acre small town campus with easy access to Memphis. Endowment: $461.9 million. Research spending for the previous fiscal year: $50.2 million. Educational spending for the previous fiscal year: $9035 per student. Total enrollment: 18,794. Faculty: 875 (798 full-time, 77 part-time). Student-undergrad faculty ratio is 19:1. 13,934 applied, 61% were admitted. 17% from top 10% of their high school class, 47% from top quarter, 77% from top half. Full-time: 14,933 students, 55% women, 45% men. Part-time: 1,127 students, 54% women, 46% men. Students come from 50 states and territories, 70 other countries, 37% from out-of-state. 0.3% American Indian or Alaska Native, non-Hispanic/Latino; 3% Hispanic/Latino; 17% African American, non-Hispanic/Latino; 2% Asian, non-Hispanic/Latino; 0.1% Native Hawaiian or other Pacific Islander, non-Hispanic/Latino; 1% international. 11% 25 or older, 10% transferred in. Retention: 81% of full-time freshmen returned the following year. Academic areas with the most degrees conferred: business/marketing; education; psychology. Core. Calendar: semesters. Academic remediation for entering students, ESL program, services for LD students, advanced placement, accelerated degree program, self-designed majors, freshman honors college, honors program, independent study, distance learning, double major, summer session for credit, part-time degree program, adult/continuing education programs, co-op programs and internships, graduate courses open to undergrads. Study abroad program. ROTC: Army, Naval, Air Force.

Entrance Requirements: Options: electronic application, international baccalaureate accepted. Required: high school transcript, minimum 2 high school GPA, SAT or ACT. Entrance: moderately difficult. Application deadlines: Rolling, Rolling for nonresidents. Notification: continuous, continuous for nonresidents. SAT Reasoning Test deadline: 8/1. SAT Subject Test deadline: 8/1. Transfer credits accepted: Yes.

Costs Per Year: Application fee: $35. State resident tuition: $6282 full-time, $261.75 per credit hour part-time. Nonresident tuition: $16,266 full-time, $677.75 per credit hour part-time. Full-time tuition varies according to course load and program. Part-time tuition varies according to course load and program. College room and board: $9200. Room and board charges vary according to board plan and housing facility.

Collegiate Environment: Orientation program. Drama-theater group, choral group, marching band, student-run newspaper, radio station. Social organizations: 275 open to all; national fraternities, national sororities. Most popular organizations: Associated Student Body, Gospel Choir, sport clubs, Black Student Union, Student Programming Board. Major annual events: Welcome Week, Grove Bowl Week/Grove Bowl Game/Spring Concert, Awards of Distinction. Student services: health clinic, personal-psychological counseling, women's center. Campus security: 24-hour emergency response devices and patrols, late night transport-escort service, controlled dormitory access, crime prevention programs. 5,010 college housing spaces available; 30 were occupied in 2012-13. Freshmen guaranteed college housing. On-campus residence required in freshman year. Options: men-only, women-only housing available. J. D. Williams Library plus 1 other with 1.9 million books, 1.1 million microform titles, 1.7 million serials, 118,668 audiovisual materials, an OPAC, and a Web page. Operations spending for the previous fiscal year: $10.5 million. 50 computers available on campus for general student use. A campuswide network can be accessed from student residence rooms and from off campus. Students can access the following: online class registration, application for admission, registration for orientation. Staffed computer lab on campus (open 24 hours a day) provides training in use of computers, software, and the Internet.

Community Environment: University is a part of Oxford. Located in a cotton, corn and cattle region, Oxford is the seat of Lafayette County. Annual average temperature is 80 degrees in July and 40 degrees in January, with average rainfall 54.55 inches. Total snowfall yearly averages 1.2 inches. Bus service and shuttle service from Memphis Airport are available to the city. Area has 3 recreational parks, swimming pools, movie theaters, bowling and golf facilities. Oxford is near Holly Springs National Forest which encompasses over 90,000 acres and numerous lakes. The lakes provide excellent hunting, swimming, boating and vacation facilities.

■ UNIVERSITY OF MISSISSIPPI MEDICAL CENTER

2500 N State St.

Jackson, MS 39216-4505

Tel: (601)984-1000

Fax: (601)984-1080

Web Site: www.umc.edu/

Description: State-supported, upper-level, coed. Administratively affiliated with University of Mississippi. Awards bachelor's, master's, and doctoral degrees. Founded 1955. Setting: 164-acre urban campus. Endowment: $33.5 million. Research spending for the previous fiscal year: $35.3 million. Educational spending for the previous fiscal year: $6579 per student. Total enrollment: 2,092. Faculty: 836 (698 full-time, 138 part-time). Student-undergrad faculty ratio is 2:1. Full-time: 383 students, 81% women, 19% men. Part-time: 129 students, 75% women, 25% men. 0% from out-of-state. 64% transferred in. Academic area with the most degrees conferred: health professions and related sciences. Calendar: semesters. Services for LD students, distance learning, internships. Study abroad program.

Collegiate Environment: Orientation program. Student-run newspaper. Student services: health clinic, personal-psychological counseling. Campus security: 24-hour emergency response devices and patrols, late night transport-escort service, controlled dormitory access. Rowland Medical Library with 310,016 books, 62,134 microform titles, 2,732 serials, an OPAC, and a Web page. Operations spending for the previous fiscal year: $3.3 million. 90 computers available on campus for general student use. Computer purchase/lease plans available. A campuswide network can be accessed from off-campus. Staffed computer lab on campus.

Community Environment: See Jackson State University.

■ UNIVERSITY OF SOUTHERN MISSISSIPPI

118 College Dr.

Hattiesburg, MS 39406-0001

Tel: (601)266-7011

E-mail: admissions@usm.edu

Web Site: www.usm.edu/

Description: State-supported, university, coed. Part of Mississippi Institutions of Higher Learning. Awards bachelor's, master's, and doctoral degrees and post-master's certificates. Founded 1910. Setting: 1,090-acre suburban campus. Endowment: $64.7 million. Research spending for the previous fiscal year: $52.8 million. Educational spending for the previous fiscal year: $7758 per student. Total enrollment: 16,468. Faculty: 903 (687 full-time, 216 part-time). Student-undergrad faculty ratio is 18:1. 7,076 applied, 65% were admitted. 29% from top 10% of their high school class, 43% from top quarter, 79% from top half. Full-time: 11,393 students, 63% women, 37% men. Part-time: 2,265 students, 57% women, 43% men. Students come from 47 states and territories, 33 other countries, 12% from out-of-state. 0.3% American Indian or Alaska Native, non-Hispanic/Latino; 3% Hispanic/Latino; 31% African American, non-Hispanic/Latino; 1% Asian, non-Hispanic/Latino; 0.1% Native Hawaiian or other Pacific Islander, non-Hispanic/Latino; 1% international. 22% 25 or older, 45% live on campus, 13% transferred in. Retention: 75% of full-time freshmen returned the following year. Academic areas with the most degrees conferred: business/marketing; health professions and related sciences; education. Core. Calendar: semesters. Academic remediation for entering students, ESL program, services for LD students, advanced placement, accelerated degree program, honors program, independent study, distance learning, double major, summer session for credit, part-time degree program, co-op programs and internships, graduate courses open to undergrads. Off campus study at Gulf Coast Research Laboratory, Marine Science Laboratory, Stennis Space Center. Study abroad program. ROTC: Army (c), Air Force.

Entrance Requirements: Options: electronic application, early admission. Required: high school transcript, minimum 2 high school GPA, SAT or ACT. Entrance: moderately difficult. Application deadline: 7/1. SAT Subject Test deadline: 8/1.

Costs Per Year: Application fee: $35. State resident tuition: $6336 full-time, $264 per credit hour part-time. Nonresident tuition: $14,448 full-time, $602 per credit hour part-time. Part-time tuition varies according to course load

and degree level. College room and board: $6907. Room and board charges vary according to board plan and housing facility.

Collegiate Environment: Orientation program. Drama-theater group, choral group, marching band, student-run newspaper, radio station. Social organizations: 291 open to all; national fraternities, national sororities, local fraternities, local sororities; 20% of eligible men and 25% of eligible women are members. Most popular organizations: Southern Miss Activities Council, Residence Halls Associations, Student Government Association, Baptist Student Union, African American Student Organization. Major annual events: Crawfish Festival, Friday Night at the Fountain Pep Rally, Homecoming. Student services: legal services, health clinic, personal-psychological counseling, women's center. Campus security: 24-hour emergency response devices and patrols, late night transport-escort service, controlled dormitory access. 3,609 college housing spaces available; 3,352 were occupied in 2012-13. Freshmen given priority for college housing. Options: men-only, women-only housing available. Cook Memorial Library plus 4 others with 1.2 million books, 5 million microform titles, 33,307 serials, 32,975 audiovisual materials, an OPAC, and a Web page. Operations spending for the previous fiscal year: $3753. 500 computers available on campus for general student use. Computer purchase/lease plans available. A campuswide network can be accessed from student residence rooms and from off campus. Students can access the following: online class registration. Staffed computer lab on campus provides training in use of computers, software, and the Internet.

Community Environment: Primarily a thriving industrial city, Hattiesburg produces chemicals, clothing, concrete and corrugated containers, and has food processing plants, lumber mills and an oil refinery. Passenger bus, rail and air service is accessible. The city is a well-rounded community with a splendid balance among agriculture, commerce and industry. There are a public library and two hospitals located within the city limits. Each year, the Hattiesburg Concert Association brings concerts, symphonies and choral groups to the city. A full-time recreation department is operated, with both indoor and outdoor programs year-round. There is good hunting and fishing in the general area.

■ VIRGINIA COLLEGE IN JACKSON

4795 Interstate 55 N

Jackson, MS 39206

Tel: (601)977-0960

Fax: (601)956-4325

Web Site: www.vc.edu/

Description: Proprietary, 2-year, coed. Awards diplomas and terminal associate degrees. Founded 2000. Setting: 3-acre urban campus. Total enrollment: 932. Student-undergrad faculty ratio is 24:1. 1,422 applied. 0% from out-of-state. 65% 25 or older. Retention: 86% of full-time freshmen returned the following year.

Entrance Requirements: Required: high school transcript, interview, CPAt.

Collegiate Environment: Campus security: 24-hour emergency response devices and patrols.

■ WILLIAM CAREY UNIVERSITY

498 Tuscan Ave.

Hattiesburg, MS 39401-5499

Tel: (601)318-6051; Free: 800-962-5991

Fax: (601)318-6454

E-mail: admissions@wmcarey.edu

Web Site: www.wmcarey.edu/

Description: Independent Southern Baptist, comprehensive, coed. Awards bachelor's and master's degrees. Founded 1906. Setting: 110-acre small town campus with easy access to New Orleans. Total enrollment: 3,248. Student-undergrad faculty ratio is 19:1. 465 applied, 93% were admitted. 11% from out-of-state. 45% 25 or older. Retention: 74% of full-time freshmen returned the following year. Core. Calendar: trimesters. Academic remediation for entering students, services for LD students, advanced placement, accelerated degree program, honors program, independent study, distance learning, double major, summer session for credit, part-time degree program, adult/continuing education programs, internships, graduate courses open to undergrads. Off campus study. ROTC: Army (c), Air Force (c).

Entrance Requirements: Options: early admission, deferred admission, international baccalaureate accepted. Required: high school transcript, SAT or ACT. Recommended: minimum 2.0 high school GPA. Entrance: moderately difficult. Application deadline: Rolling. Notification: continuous until 8/15.

Costs Per Year: Application fee: $30. Comprehensive fee: $14,250 includes full-time tuition ($9750), mandatory fees ($600), and college room and board ($3900). Full-time tuition and fees vary according to degree level and location. Room and board charges vary according to board plan, housing facility, and location. Part-time tuition: $325 per credit hour. Part-time tuition and fees vary according to degree level and location.

Collegiate Environment: Orientation program. Drama-theater group, choral group, student-run newspaper. Social organizations: local fraternities, local sororities. Student services: personal-psychological counseling. Campus security: 24-hour patrols, controlled dormitory access. Smith-Rouse Library with an OPAC and a Web page.

Community Environment: See University of Southern Mississippi.

Missouri

■ **AMERICAN COLLEGE OF TECHNOLOGY**

2300 Frederick Ave.
Saint Joseph, MO 64506
Free: 800-908-9329
Fax: (888)890-8190
E-mail: ricahrd@acot.edu
Web Site: www.acot.edu/
Description: Proprietary, 2-year, coed. Awards terminal associate degrees. Founded 2001.

■ **ANTHEM COLLEGE–KANSAS CITY**

9001 State Line Rd.
Kansas City, MO 64114
Tel: (816)444-4300; Free: 855-464-2684
Fax: (816)444-4494
Web Site: anthem.edu/kansas-city-missouri/
Description: Proprietary, 2-year, coed. Awards terminal associate degrees. Founded 2003. Total enrollment: 687. Calendar: semesters.
Entrance Requirements: Entrance: noncompetitive.

■ **ANTHEM COLLEGE–MARYLAND HEIGHTS**

13723 Riverport Dr.
Ste. 103
Maryland Heights, MO 63043
Tel: (314)595-3400; Free: 855-526-8436
Fax: (314)739-5133
Web Site: anthem.edu/maryland-heights-missouri/
Description: Proprietary, 2-year, coed. Administratively affiliated with Anthem Education. Awards certificates and terminal associate degrees. Setting: 1-acre urban campus with easy access to St. Louis. Total enrollment: 281. Faculty: 24 (10 full-time, 14 part-time). Student-undergrad faculty ratio is 21:1. 34 applied, 100% were admitted. Full-time: 281 students, 85% women, 15% men. Students come from 1 other country, 0.03% from out-of-state. 0% American Indian or Alaska Native, non-Hispanic/Latino; 2% Hispanic/Latino; 43% African American, non-Hispanic/Latino; 1% Asian, non-Hispanic/Latino; 0% Native Hawaiian or other Pacific Islander, non-Hispanic/Latino; 0.4% international. 70% 25 or older, 0% transferred in. Retention: 0% of full-time freshmen returned the following year. Core. Academic remediation for entering students, internships.
Entrance Requirements: Open admission. Required: high school transcript, interview, Entrance Assessment Tests. Entrance: noncompetitive. Application deadlines: Rolling, Rolling for nonresidents. Transfer credits accepted: Yes.
Collegiate Environment: Orientation program. Campus security: 24-hour emergency response devices and patrols. Anthem College Library - consists of Library Word and Ebrary with 69,000 books, 25 serials, 75 audiovisual materials, and an OPAC. 100 computers available on campus for general student use. Computer purchase/lease plans available. A campuswide network can be accessed. Staffed computer lab on campus provides training in use of computers and software.

■ **THE ART INSTITUTE OF ST. LOUIS**

1520 S Fifth St.
Saint Charles, MO 63303
Tel: (636)688-3010
Web Site: www.artinstitutes.edu/st-louis/

Description: Proprietary, 4-year, coed.

■ **AVIATION INSTITUTE OF MAINTENANCE–KANSAS CITY**

4100 Raytown Rd.
Kansas City, MO 64129
Tel: (816)753-9920; Free: 888-349-5387
Fax: (816)753-9941
Web Site: www.aviationmaintenance.edu/
Description: Proprietary, 2-year, coed. Awards certificates and terminal associate degrees. Total enrollment: 117. Student-undergrad faculty ratio is 11:1. 21% from out-of-state. 61% 25 or older. Retention: 37% of full-time freshmen returned the following year.
Entrance Requirements: Required: high school diploma or GED.

■ **AVILA UNIVERSITY**

11901 Wornall Rd.
Kansas City, MO 64145-1698
Tel: (816)942-8400; Free: 800-GO-AVILA
Fax: (816)942-3362
E-mail: bethany.bauer@avila.edu
Web Site: www.avila.edu/
Description: Independent Roman Catholic, comprehensive, coed. Administratively affiliated with The Sisters of Saint Joseph of Carondelet, St. Louis Province. Awards bachelor's and master's degrees. Founded 1916. Setting: 50-acre suburban campus. Total enrollment: 1,818. Faculty: 209 (65 full-time, 144 part-time). Student-undergrad faculty ratio is 14:1. 1,170 applied, 53% were admitted. 13% from top 10% of their high school class, 38% from top quarter, 69% from top half. Full-time: 988 students, 61% women, 39% men. Part-time: 231 students, 76% women, 24% men. Students come from 23 states and territories, 16 other countries, 32% from out-of-state. 1% American Indian or Alaska Native, non-Hispanic/Latino; 6% Hispanic/Latino; 18% African American, non-Hispanic/Latino; 1% Asian, non-Hispanic/Latino; 0.4% Native Hawaiian or other Pacific Islander, non-Hispanic/Latino; 4% international. 37% 25 or older, 28% live on campus, 13% transferred in. Retention: 65% of full-time freshmen returned the following year. Academic areas with the most degrees conferred: health professions and related sciences; business/marketing; psychology. Core. Calendar: semesters. Academic remediation for entering students, ESL program, services for LD students, advanced placement, accelerated degree program, independent study, distance learning, double major, summer session for credit, part-time degree program, adult/continuing education programs, co-op programs and internships. Off campus study at Sisters of St. Joseph Consortium, Council of Independent Colleges Exchange Program. Study abroad program. ROTC: Army (c).
Entrance Requirements: Options: electronic application, early admission, international baccalaureate accepted. Required: high school transcript, minimum 2.5 high school GPA, secondary school report, SAT or ACT. Recommended: interview. Required for some: essay. Entrance: minimally difficult. Application deadline: 8/15. Notification: 8/15.
Costs Per Year: Comprehensive fee: $31,650 includes full-time tuition ($24,000), mandatory fees ($850), and college room and board ($6800). College room only: $3400. Full-time tuition and fees vary according to course load and program. Room and board charges vary according to board plan and housing facility. Part-time tuition: $600 per credit hour. Part-time mandatory fees: $30 per credit hour. Part-time tuition and fees vary according to course load and program. Tuition guaranteed not to increase for student's term of enrollment.

Collegiate Environment: Orientation program. Drama-theater group, choral group, student-run newspaper. Social organizations: 40 open to all. Most popular organizations: Avila Ambassadors, Avila Student Nurses Association, Campus Ministries, Saudi Arabian Student Association, Avila University Theatre Company. Major annual events: Homecoming Week, Spring Fling Week, AU Kick Off Celebration. Student services: health clinic, personal-psychological counseling. Campus security: 24-hour emergency response devices, student patrols, late night transport-escort service, controlled dormitory access. 380 college housing spaces available; 370 were occupied in 2012-13. Freshmen guaranteed college housing. On-campus residence required through sophomore year. Options: coed, men-only, women-only housing available. Hooley Bundshu Library with 80,845 books, 460,130 microform titles, 22,464 serials, an OPAC, and a Web page. 180 computers available on campus for general student use. A campuswide network can be accessed from student residence rooms and from off campus. Students can access the following: online class registration. Staffed computer lab on campus (open 24 hours a day) provides training in use of computers, software, and the Internet.

Community Environment: See University of Missouri - Kansas City.

■ **BAPTIST BIBLE COLLEGE**

628 E Kearney St.
Springfield, MO 65803-3498
Tel: (417)268-6000; Free: 800-228-5754
Fax: (417)831-8029
Web Site: www.gobbc.edu/

Description: Independent Baptist, comprehensive, coed. Awards associate, bachelor's, master's, and doctoral degrees. Founded 1950. Setting: 38-acre suburban campus. Total enrollment: 636. Faculty: 53 (26 full-time, 27 part-time). 264 applied, 76% were admitted. Full-time: 444 students, 50% women, 50% men. Part-time: 100 students, 34% women, 66% men. Students come from 36 states and territories, 6 other countries, 57% from out-of-state. 17% 25 or older, 61% live on campus, 6% transferred in. Retention: 57% of full-time freshmen returned the following year. Core. Calendar: semesters. Academic remediation for entering students, summer session for credit, part-time degree program, internships, graduate courses open to undergrads. ROTC: Army (c).

Entrance Requirements: Options: electronic application, early admission, deferred admission. Required: high school transcript, 1 recommendation, SAT or ACT. Entrance: noncompetitive. Application deadline: Rolling. Notification: continuous. Preference given to members of supporting churches.

Collegiate Environment: Orientation program. Drama-theater group, choral group, student-run radio station. Student services: health clinic, personal-psychological counseling. G. B. Vick Memorial Library plus 1 other with 64,236 books, 17,536 microform titles, 335 serials, and 3,311 audiovisual materials. 50 computers available on campus for general student use. Staffed computer lab on campus.

Community Environment: See Southwest Missouri State University.

■ **BROWN MACKIE COLLEGE–ST. LOUIS**

No.2 Soccer Park Rd.
Fenton, MO 63026
Web Site: www.brownmackie.edu/st-louis/

Description: Proprietary, primarily 2-year, coed. Part of Education Management Corporation. Awards diplomas, terminal associate, and bachelor's degrees.

■ **CALVARY BIBLE COLLEGE AND THEOLOGICAL SEMINARY**

15800 Calvary Rd.
Kansas City, MO 64147-1341
Tel: (816)322-0110; Free: 800-326-3960
E-mail: admissions@calvary.edu
Web Site: www.calvary.edu/

Description: Independent nondenominational, comprehensive, coed. Awards associate, bachelor's, and master's degrees. Founded 1932. Setting: 55-acre suburban campus. Total enrollment: 337. 52 applied, 83% were admitted. Full-time: 175 students, 49% women, 51% men. Part-time: 108 students, 44% women, 56% men. 56% from out-of-state. 1% American Indian or Alaska Native, non-Hispanic/Latino; 4% Hispanic/Latino; 10% African American, non-Hispanic/Latino; 1% Asian, non-Hispanic/Latino; 0% Native Hawaiian or other Pacific Islander, non-Hispanic/Latino; 1% international. 34% 25 or older, 20% transferred in. Retention: 70% of full-time freshmen returned the following year. Academic areas with the most

degrees conferred: theology and religious vocations; interdisciplinary studies; business/marketing. Core. Calendar: semesters. Academic remediation for entering students, services for LD students, advanced placement, self-designed majors, independent study, distance learning, double major, summer session for credit, part-time degree program, external degree program, adult/continuing education programs, internships, graduate courses open to undergrads. ROTC: Army (c).

Entrance Requirements: Option: electronic application. Required: essay, high school transcript, 2 recommendations, statement of faith, SAT or ACT. Entrance: minimally difficult. Application deadline: 7/15. Transfer credits accepted: Yes.

Costs Per Year: Application fee: $25. Comprehensive fee: $15,116 includes full-time tuition ($9300), mandatory fees ($816), and college room and board ($5000). Room and board charges vary according to housing facility. Part-time tuition: $310 per credit. Part-time mandatory fees: $29 per credit, $120 per term. Tuition guaranteed not to increase for student's term of enrollment.

Collegiate Environment: Orientation program. Drama-theater group, choral group, student-run radio station. Social organizations: 2 open to all. Most popular organizations: Missions Encounter, Masterworks (Fine Arts). Major annual events: Day of Prayer, Missions Emphasis Week, All-Calvary Workday. Student services: personal-psychological counseling. Campus security: late night transport-escort service, night patrols by trained security personnel. Hilda Kroeker Library plus 1 other with an OPAC and a Web page. 23 computers available on campus for general student use. Students can access the following: online class registration. Staffed computer lab on campus provides training in use of computers, software, and the Internet.

Community Environment: See University of Missouri Kansas City.

■ **CENTRAL BIBLE COLLEGE**

3000 N Grant Ave.
Springfield, MO 65803-1096
Tel: (417)833-2551; Free: 800-831-4222
Fax: (417)833-5141
E-mail: jbell@cbcag.edu
Web Site: www.cbcag.edu/

Description: Independent Assemblies of God, 4-year, coed. Awards associate and bachelor's degrees. Founded 1922. Setting: 108-acre suburban campus. Total enrollment: 673. 255 applied. 19% 25 or older. Core. Calendar: semesters. Academic remediation for entering students, services for LD students, advanced placement, independent study, distance learning, double major, summer session for credit, part-time degree program, internships.

Entrance Requirements: Options: early admission, deferred admission. Required: essay, high school transcript, 3 recommendations. Recommended: minimum 2.0 high school GPA. Required for some: interview. Entrance: moderately difficult. Application deadline: Rolling. Preference given to Christians.

Collegiate Environment: Orientation program. Campus security: 24-hour emergency response devices and patrols, student patrols, controlled dormitory access. Meyer Pearlman Library with 107,023 books, 38,341 microform titles, 1,074 serials, 6,894 audiovisual materials, an OPAC, and a Web page.

Community Environment: See Southwest Missouri State University.

■ **CENTRAL CHRISTIAN COLLEGE OF THE BIBLE**

911 Urbandale Dr. E
Moberly, MO 65270-1997
Tel: (660)263-3900; Free: 888-263-3900
Fax: (660)263-3936
E-mail: admissions@cccb.edu
Web Site: www.cccb.edu/

Description: Independent, 4-year, coed, affiliated with Christian Churches and Churches of Christ. Awards associate and bachelor's degrees. Founded 1957. Setting: 40-acre small town campus. Total enrollment: 417. Student-undergrad faculty ratio is 19:1. 354 applied, 65% were admitted. 56% from out-of-state. 18% 25 or older. Retention: 57% of full-time freshmen returned the following year. Core. Calendar: semesters. Academic remediation for entering students, self-designed majors, part-time degree program, internships. Off campus study at Fort Hays State University, Tabor College, Johnson Bible College, Moberly Area Community College.

Entrance Requirements: Options: early admission, deferred admission. Required: high school transcript, 3 recommendations, SAT or ACT. Entrance: noncompetitive. Application deadline: Rolling. Preference given to Christians.

Collegiate Environment: Orientation program. Choral group. Student services: personal-psychological counseling. 75,460 books and 320 serials.

■ CENTRAL METHODIST UNIVERSITY

411 Central Methodist Sq.
Fayette, MO 65248-1198
Tel: (660)248-3391; Free: 877-CMU-1854
Fax: (660)248-2287
E-mail: admissions@centralmethodist.edu
Web Site: www.centralmethodist.edu/

Description: Independent Methodist, comprehensive, coed. Awards associate and bachelor's degrees. Founded 1854. Setting: 80-acre small town campus. Total enrollment: 1,173. Faculty: 123 (63 full-time, 60 part-time). Student-undergrad faculty ratio is 14:1. 1,344 applied, 67% were admitted. 13% from top 10% of their high school class, 37% from top quarter, 78% from top half. Full-time: 1,158 students, 50% women, 50% men. Part-time: 15 students, 67% women, 33% men. 10% from out-of-state. 1% American Indian or Alaska Native, non-Hispanic/Latino; 2% Hispanic/Latino; 6% African American, non-Hispanic/Latino; 1% Asian, non-Hispanic/Latino; 1% Native Hawaiian or other Pacific Islander, non-Hispanic/Latino; 3% international. 8% 25 or older, 85% live on campus, 9% transferred in. Retention: 72% of full-time freshmen returned the following year. Academic areas with the most degrees conferred: education; health professions and related sciences; business/marketing. Core. Calendar: semesters. Services for LD students, accelerated degree program, honors program, independent study, distance learning, double major, summer session for credit, part-time degree program, adult/continuing education programs, internships. Off campus study at Mineral Area College, East Central College, State Fair Community College, Linn Technical. Study abroad program. ROTC: Army (c), Air Force (c).

Entrance Requirements: Options: electronic application, deferred admission. Required: high school transcript, minimum 2.5 high school GPA, SAT or ACT. Required for some: 2 recommendations. Entrance: moderately difficult. Application deadline: Rolling. Notification: continuous. SAT Reasoning Test deadline: 8/1. SAT Subject Test deadline: 8/1. Transfer credits accepted: Yes.

Costs Per Year: Application fee: $20. Tuition: $20,590 full-time, $190 per credit hour part-time. Full-time tuition varies according to location. Part-time tuition varies according to course load and location.

Collegiate Environment: Orientation program. Drama-theater group, choral group, marching band, student-run newspaper, radio station. Social organizations: 37 open to all; national fraternities, local fraternities, local sororities; 25% of eligible men and 25% of eligible women are members. Most popular organizations: Student Government Association, Students in Free Enterprise (SIFE), Alpha Phi Omega, Beta Beta Beta, Campus Ministries. Major annual events: Family Day, Homecoming, Service Day. Student services: health clinic, personal-psychological counseling. Campus security: 24-hour emergency response devices, late night transport-escort service, controlled dormitory access. Freshmen given priority for college housing. On-campus residence required through senior year. Options: coed, men-only, women-only housing available. Smiley Library plus 1 other with 97,793 books, 140,742 microform titles, 316 serials, 379 audiovisual materials, an OPAC, and a Web page. 72 computers available on campus for general student use. A campuswide network can be accessed from student residence rooms and from off campus. Staffed computer lab on campus (open 24 hours a day) provides training in use of software.

Community Environment: Fayette (population 2,700) is the county seat of Howard County and is in an area that is noted for the production of purebred cattle. Both Kansas City and St. Louis are about a two-hour drive away. The cultural facilities of both large cities are available and add charm to the community.

■ CHAMBERLAIN COLLEGE OF NURSING

11830 Westline Industrial Dr.
Ste. 106
Saint Louis, MO 63146
Tel: (314)991-6200; Free: 888-556-8CCN
Fax: (314)768-5673
Web Site: www.chamberlain.edu/

Description: Proprietary, 4-year, coed. Part of DeVry University. Awards bachelor's degrees. Founded 1889. Setting: urban campus. Total enrollment: 540. Faculty: 246 (47 full-time, 199 part-time). Student-undergrad faculty ratio is 31:1. Full-time: 368 students, 93% women, 7% men. Part-time: 172 students, 90% women, 10% men. 22% from out-of-state. 0.2% American

Indian or Alaska Native, non-Hispanic/Latino; 1% Hispanic/Latino; 12% African American, non-Hispanic/Latino; 2% Asian, non-Hispanic/Latino; 0.2% Native Hawaiian or other Pacific Islander, non-Hispanic/Latino; 0.2% international. 50% 25 or older, 0% live on campus, 37% transferred in. Academic area with the most degrees conferred: health professions and related sciences. Calendar: semesters. Part-time degree program.

Entrance Requirements: Required: essay, high school transcript, SAT or ACT. Required for some: interview. Entrance: moderately difficult. Application deadline: Rolling. Notification: continuous.

Costs Per Year: Application fee: $95. Tuition: $16,360 full-time, $665 per credit hour part-time. Mandatory fees: $600 full-time.

Collegiate Environment: Orientation program. Campus security: 24-hour patrols, late night transport-escort service, controlled dormitory access.

■ CITY VISION COLLEGE

PO Box 413188
Kansas City, MO 64141-3188
Tel: (816)960-2008
Fax: (816)569-0223
E-mail: mliimatta@cityvision.edu
Web Site: www.cityvision.edu/

Description: Independent Christian, upper-level, coed. Awards bachelor's degrees. Total enrollment: 63. Faculty: 19 (all part-time). Student-undergrad faculty ratio is 3:1. Full-time: 36 students, 61% women, 39% men. Part-time: 27 students, 48% women, 52% men. Students come from 23 states and territories, 1 other country, 93% from out-of-state. 2% American Indian or Alaska Native, non-Hispanic/Latino; 3% Hispanic/Latino; 32% African American, non-Hispanic/Latino; 0% Asian, non-Hispanic/Latino; 0% Native Hawaiian or other Pacific Islander, non-Hispanic/Latino; 0% international. 77% 25 or older, 46% transferred in. Retention: 31% of full-time entering class returned the following year. Academic areas with the most degrees conferred: health professions and related sciences; theology and religious vocations; business/marketing. Distance learning, double major, summer session for credit, part-time degree program, adult/continuing education programs, internships.

Entrance Requirements: Transfer credits accepted: Yes.

Costs Per Year: Application fee: $25. One-time mandatory fee: $25. Tuition: $6000 full-time, $3000 per year part-time. Full-time tuition varies according to course load. Part-time tuition varies according to course load.

Collegiate Environment: Orientation program.

■ COLLEGE OF THE OZARKS

PO Box 17
Point Lookout, MO 65726
Tel: (417)334-6411; Free: 800-222-0525
Fax: (417)335-2618
E-mail: admiss4@cofo.edu
Web Site: www.cofo.edu/

Description: Independent Presbyterian, 4-year, coed. Awards bachelor's degrees. Founded 1906. Setting: 1,000-acre small town campus. Endowment: $298.2 million. Educational spending for the previous fiscal year: $11,400 per student. Total enrollment: 1,379. Faculty: 129 (83 full-time, 46 part-time). Student-undergrad faculty ratio is 14:1. 3,048 applied, 9% were admitted. 19% from top 10% of their high school class, 50% from top quarter, 87% from top half. 13 valedictorians. Full-time: 1,361 students, 57% women, 43% men. Part-time: 18 students, 50% women, 50% men. Students come from 25 states and territories, 22 other countries, 21% from out-of-state. 0.4% American Indian or Alaska Native, non-Hispanic/Latino; 2% Hispanic/Latino; 1% African American, non-Hispanic/Latino; 0.3% Asian, non-Hispanic/Latino; 0.1% Native Hawaiian or other Pacific Islander, non-Hispanic/Latino; 2% international. 2% 25 or older, 80% live on campus, 3% transferred in. Retention: 87% of full-time freshmen returned the following year. Academic areas with the most degrees conferred: education; business/marketing; agriculture. Core. Calendar: semesters. Academic remediation for entering students, services for LD students, advanced placement, self-designed majors, independent study, double major, internships. Off campus study at Focus on the Family. ROTC: Army.

Entrance Requirements: Option: electronic application. Required: high school transcript, 2 recommendations, interview, medical history, financial statement, SAT or ACT. Recommended: minimum 3 high school GPA. Entrance: moderately difficult. Application deadline: 2/15. Notification: continuous. Preference given to financially needy students. SAT Reasoning Test deadline: 2/15. SAT Subject Test deadline: 2/15. Transfer credits accepted: Yes. Applicants placed on waiting list: 896. Wait-listed applicants offered admission: 7.

Costs Per Year: Application fee: $0. Comprehensive fee: $6330 includes full-time tuition ($0), mandatory fees ($430), and college room and board ($5900). College room only: $2900. Part-time tuition: $295 per credit. Part-time tuition varies according to course load. Each student participates in the on-campus work program for 15 hours per week and two forty-hour work weeks. Earnings from participation in the work program, plus any federal and/or state aid for which students qualify, plus a College of the Ozarks Cost of Education Scholarship combine to meet each student's full tuition charge.

Collegiate Environment: Orientation program. Drama-theater group, choral group, student-run newspaper, radio station. Social organizations: 30 open to all. Most popular organizations: Students in Free Enterprise (SIFE), Student Senate, Baptist Student Union, Aggie Club, Business Undergraduate Society. Major annual events: Homecoming, Mud Fest, Spring Formal. Student services: health clinic, personal-psychological counseling. Campus security: 24-hour emergency response devices and patrols, controlled dormitory access, front gate closed 6 p.m. to 5 a.m., Security checks cars for proper credentials for entry. 1,054 college housing spaces available; all were occupied in 2012-13. No special consideration for freshman housing applicants. On-campus residence required through senior year. Options: men-only, women-only housing available. Lyons Memorial Library plus 2 others with 108,128 books, 30,713 microform titles, 370 serials, 5,572 audiovisual materials, and an OPAC. Operations spending for the previous fiscal year: $602,700. 164 computers available on campus for general student use. A campuswide network can be accessed from student residence rooms and from off campus. Students can access the following: online class registration. Staffed computer lab on campus provides training in use of computers, software, and the Internet.

Community Environment: Point Lookout is a rural area near Branson, 38 miles south of Springfield. Bus service is available and air travel is a little more than 60 minutes away. Shopping areas, a library, and churches of major denominations are part of the community. A great deal of part-time employment is available especially during the April-December tourist season. All recreational facilities are available in the summer resort area.

■ **COLORADO TECHNICAL UNIVERSITY NORTH KANSAS CITY**
520 E 19th Ave.
North Kansas City, MO 64116
Tel: (816)472-7400
Fax: (816)472-0688
E-mail: avietti@kc.coloradotech.edu
Web Site: kc.coloradotech.edu/
Description: Proprietary, 4-year, coed. Administratively affiliated with Colorado Technical University. Awards associate and bachelor's degrees. Founded 1992. Setting: suburban campus. Total enrollment: 679. Faculty: 110. Full-time: 338 students, 77% women, 23% men. Part-time: 341 students, 80% women, 20% men. 2% from out-of-state. 30% 25 or older, 14% transferred in. Academic areas with the most degrees conferred: business/marketing; homeland security, law enforcement, firefighting, and protective services; health professions and related sciences. Core. Advanced placement, accelerated degree program, distance learning, double major, part-time degree program, adult/continuing education programs, co-op programs and internships.
Entrance Requirements: Options: electronic application, deferred admission, international baccalaureate accepted. Required: high school transcript, interview. Entrance: minimally difficult. Application deadline: Rolling. Notification: continuous.
Collegiate Environment: Orientation program. Campus security: 24-hour patrols. 145 computers available on campus for general student use. A campuswide network can be accessed. Staffed computer lab on campus.

■ **COLUMBIA COLLEGE**
1001 Rogers St.
Columbia, MO 65216-0002
Tel: (573)875-8700; Free: 800-231-2391
Fax: (573)875-7506
E-mail: admissions@ccis.edu
Web Site: www.ccis.edu/
Description: Independent, comprehensive, coed, affiliated with Christian Church (Disciples of Christ). Awards associate, bachelor's, and master's degrees (offers continuing education program with significant enrollment not reflected in profile). Founded 1851. Setting: 33-acre urban campus. Endowment: $93.5 million. Educational spending for the previous fiscal year: $3609 per student. Total enrollment: 1,193. Faculty: 118 (68 full-time, 50 part-time). Student-undergrad faculty ratio is 11:1. 571 applied, 69% were admitted.

20% from top 10% of their high school class, 23% from top quarter, 78% from top half. Full-time: 793 students, 59% women, 41% men. Part-time: 160 students, 56% women, 44% men. Students come from 19 states and territories, 30 other countries, 11% from out-of-state. 1% American Indian or Alaska Native, non-Hispanic/Latino; 3% Hispanic/Latino; 5% African American, non-Hispanic/Latino; 1% Asian, non-Hispanic/Latino; 0.1% Native Hawaiian or other Pacific Islander, non-Hispanic/Latino; 9% international. 19% 25 or older, 34% live on campus, 14% transferred in. Retention: 67% of full-time freshmen returned the following year. Academic areas with the most degrees conferred: business/marketing; visual and performing arts; psychology. Core. Calendar: semesters. ESL program, services for LD students, advanced placement, self-designed majors, honors program, independent study, distance learning, double major, summer session for credit, part-time degree program, adult/continuing education programs, co-op programs and internships, graduate courses open to undergrads. Off campus study at cooperative cross-enrollment with the University of Missouri-Columbia and Stephens College (MO) and a study abroad consortium with Central College (IA). Study abroad program. ROTC: Army (c), Naval (c), Air Force (c).
Entrance Requirements: Options: electronic application, deferred admission, international baccalaureate accepted. Required: high school transcript, minimum 2.5 high school GPA, SAT or ACT. Required for some: essay, interview. Entrance: moderately difficult. Application deadline: 8/13. Notification: continuous. SAT Reasoning Test deadline: 8/15. SAT Subject Test deadline: 8/15. Transfer credits accepted: Yes.
Costs Per Year: Application fee: $35. Tuition: $19,386 full-time, $417 per credit hour part-time. Full-time tuition varies according to class time, course load, degree level, and program. Part-time tuition varies according to class time, course load, degree level, and location. Tuition guaranteed not to increase for student's term of enrollment.
Collegiate Environment: Orientation program. Drama-theater group, choral group. Social organizations: 33 open to all. Most popular organizations: Elysium Players, Student Government Association, International Club, Chi Alpha Christian Fellowship, The Pride. Major annual events: Cougar Fest, Family Day, intramurals. Student services: health clinic, personal-psychological counseling. Campus security: 24-hour emergency response devices and patrols, late night transport-escort service, controlled dormitory access. 395 college housing spaces available; 330 were occupied in 2012-13. Freshmen guaranteed college housing. On-campus residence required through sophomore year. Options: coed, women-only housing available. J.W. and Lois Stafford Library with 63,273 books, 199 serials, 1,761 audiovisual materials, an OPAC, and a Web page. Operations spending for the previous fiscal year: $826,145. 121 computers available on campus for general student use. Computer purchase/lease plans available. A campuswide network can be accessed from student residence rooms and from off campus. Students can access the following: online class registration. Staffed computer lab on campus provides training in use of computers and software.

■ **CONCEPTION SEMINARY COLLEGE**
PO Box 502
Conception, MO 64433-0502
Tel: (660)944-3105
Fax: (660)944-2829
E-mail: vocations@conception.edu
Web Site: www.conception.edu/
Description: Independent Roman Catholic, 4-year, men only. Awards bachelor's degrees. Founded 1886. Setting: 30-acre rural campus. Total enrollment: 108. Student-undergrad faculty ratio is 4:1. 40 applied, 95% were admitted. 58% from out-of-state. 19% 25 or older. Retention: 75% of full-time freshmen returned the following year. Core. Calendar: semesters. Academic remediation for entering students, ESL program, advanced placement, independent study, double major. Off campus study at Northwest Missouri State University.
Entrance Requirements: Option: electronic application. Required: essay, high school transcript, minimum 2.0 high school GPA, 2 recommendations, church certificate, medical history, ACT. Entrance: noncompetitive. Application deadline: 7/31. Notification: continuous until 8/15. Preference given to Catholic seminarians.
Collegiate Environment: Orientation program. Drama-theater group, choral group, student-run newspaper. Student services: health clinic, personal-psychological counseling. Campus security: 24-hour emergency response devices. Conception Seminary College Library with an OPAC and a Web page.
Community Environment: Conception is located in northwest Missouri, 85

miles north of Kansas City. The Abbey contains a collection of rare manuscripts dating back to the 10th century. See also Missouri Western State College for information about St. Joseph, the nearest large city.

■ CONCORDE CAREER COLLEGE

3239 Broadway
Kansas City, MO 64111-2407
Tel: (816)531-5223
Fax: (816)756-3231
E-mail: dcrow@concorde.edu
Web Site: www.concorde.edu/
Description: Proprietary, 2-year, coed. Awards terminal associate degrees. Founded 1983. Total enrollment: 821. Student-undergrad faculty ratio is 29:1. 261 applied, 100% were admitted. 20% from out-of-state. 62% 25 or older.
Entrance Requirements: Required: high school transcript.

■ COTTEY COLLEGE

1000 W Austin
Nevada, MO 64772
Tel: (417)667-8181; Free: 888-526-8839
Fax: (417)667-8103
E-mail: enrollmgt@cottey.edu
Web Site: www.cottey.edu/
Description: Independent, 2-year, women only. Awards transfer associate degrees. Founded 1884. Setting: 51-acre small town campus. Endowment: $95,497. Educational spending for the previous fiscal year: $15,741 per student. Total enrollment: 331. Faculty: 42 (34 full-time, 8 part-time). Student-undergrad faculty ratio is 9:1. 535 applied, 63% were admitted. 13% from top 10% of their high school class, 46% from top quarter, 83% from top half. 2 class presidents, 3 valedictorians, 20 student government officers. Full-time: 331 students. Students come from 40 states and territories, 21 other countries, 80% from out-of-state. 1% 25 or older, 98% live on campus, 1% transferred in. Retention: 78% of full-time freshmen returned the following year. Core. Calendar: semesters. Services for LD students, advanced placement, independent study, distance learning, part-time degree program, internships. Study abroad program.
Entrance Requirements: Options: electronic application, early admission, deferred admission, international baccalaureate accepted. Required: essay, high school transcript, 1 recommendation, SAT or ACT. Recommended: minimum 2.6 high school GPA, interview. Entrance: moderately difficult. Application deadlines: Rolling, Rolling for nonresidents. Notification: continuous, continuous for nonresidents.
Collegiate Environment: Orientation program. Drama-theater group, choral group, student-run newspaper. Social organizations: 30 open to all. Most popular organizations: International Friendship Circle, Cottey Intramural Association, Ozarks Explorers Club, Inter-Varsity Club, Golden Keys. Major annual events: Hanging of the Greens, Quad C Week, Humanities Film Festival. Student services: health clinic, personal-psychological counseling. Campus security: 24-hour emergency response devices and patrols, late night transport-escort service, controlled dormitory access. Blanche Skiff Ross Memorial Library with 54,200 books, 246 serials, and an OPAC. Operations spending for the previous fiscal year: $194,423. 50 computers available on campus for general student use. A campuswide network can be accessed from student residence rooms and from off campus. Staffed computer lab on campus provides training in use of computers, software, and the Internet.
Community Environment: Located 100 miles south of Kansas City, 60 miles north of Joplin, and 90 miles north of Springfield, Nevada has a population of 8,500 and is the county seat of Vernon County. Although historically an agricultural community, Nevada has a diverse economic base. The Jefferson Bus Lines connect Nevada to the International Airport in Kansas City and the municipal airport in Joplin. The community facilities include 27 churches, a number of civic, fraternal, and veterans' organizations, a municipal hospital, and a community center. Part-time employment for students is available. Recreational activities are hunting, fishing, golf, and bowling. The Chamber of Commerce holds a number of special events during the year.

■ COX COLLEGE

1423 N Jefferson
Springfield, MO 65802
Tel: (417)269-3401
E-mail: admissions@coxcollege.edu

Web Site: www.coxcollege.edu/
Description: Independent, comprehensive, coed. Administratively affiliated with Cox Health Systems. Awards associate, bachelor's, and master's degrees. Founded 1994. Setting: urban campus. Total enrollment: 497. Student-undergrad faculty ratio is 9:1. 274 applied, 86% were admitted. 0% from out-of-state. 51% 25 or older. Core. Calendar: semesters. Academic remediation for entering students, accelerated degree program, summer session for credit, part-time degree program.
Entrance Requirements: Option: early decision. Required: high school transcript, minimum 2.5 high school GPA. Recommended: SAT or ACT. Application deadlines: 1/15, 11/1 for early decision. Notification: 3/1, 12/1 for early decision.
Collegiate Environment: Orientation program. Student services: personal-psychological counseling. Campus security: 24-hour patrols, late night transport-escort service. The Cox Health Systems Libraries with 29,750 books and 249 serials.

■ CROWDER COLLEGE

601 Laclede Ave.
Neosho, MO 64850-9160
Tel: (417)451-3223; Free: 866-238-7788
Fax: (417)451-4280
E-mail: jimriggs@crowder.edu
Web Site: www.crowder.edu/
Description: State and locally supported, 2-year, coed. Part of Missouri Coordinating Board for Higher Education. Awards certificates, transfer associate, and terminal associate degrees. Founded 1963. Setting: 608-acre rural campus. Total enrollment: 5,576. Faculty: 436 (85 full-time, 351 part-time). Student-undergrad faculty ratio is 12:1. Full-time: 2,516 students, 62% women, 38% men. Part-time: 3,060 students, 65% women, 35% men. Students come from 19 states and territories, 25 other countries, 4% from out-of-state. 2% American Indian or Alaska Native, non-Hispanic/Latino; 7% Hispanic/Latino; 2% African American, non-Hispanic/Latino; 1% Asian, non-Hispanic/Latino; 0.5% Native Hawaiian or other Pacific Islander, non-Hispanic/Latino; 0.2% international. 12% 25 or older, 10% live on campus, 1% transferred in. Core. Calendar: semesters. Academic remediation for entering students, ESL program, advanced placement, self-designed majors, freshman honors college, honors program, independent study, summer session for credit, part-time degree program, adult/continuing education programs, co-op programs. Study abroad program.
Entrance Requirements: Open admission except for nursing program. Required: high school transcript. Entrance: noncompetitive. Application deadline: Rolling. Notification: continuous.
Collegiate Environment: Orientation program. Drama-theater group, choral group, student-run newspaper. Social organizations: 15 open to all. Most popular organizations: Phi Theta Kappa, Students in Free Enterprise (SIFE), Baptist Student Union, Student Senate, Student Ambassadors. Major annual events: Homecoming, Spring Fling, Spirit Week. Student services: personal-psychological counseling. Campus security: 24-hour patrols. 240 college housing spaces available; 200 were occupied in 2012-13. No special consideration for freshman housing applicants. Options: men-only, women-only housing available. Bill & Margot Lee Library with 42,996 books, 191,052 microform titles, 183 serials, 6,499 audiovisual materials, an OPAC, and a Web page. 970 computers available on campus for general student use. A campuswide network can be accessed. Staffed computer lab on campus provides training in use of computers, software, and the Internet.
Community Environment: Neosho (population 11,000) is the birthplace of Thomas Hart Benton, 18 miles from Joplin. All forms of commercial transportation are available. Churches of most of the major denominations, two libraries, a museum, two hospitals and numerous civic and fraternal organizations are represented. Part time jobs are available in Neosho and the two county districts. Neosho provides the area with a full time recreation director and planned activities for the community. The Government Fish Hatchery is nearby.

■ CULINARY INSTITUTE OF ST. LOUIS AT HICKEY COLLEGE

2700 N Lindbergh Blvd.
Saint Louis, MO 63114
Tel: (314)434-2212
Web Site: www.ci-stl.com/
Description: Private, 2-year, coed. Awards terminal associate degrees. Founded 2009. Setting: suburban campus. Total enrollment: 103.
Entrance Requirements: Early decision applicants: 237. Early decision applicants admitted: 189.

■ **CULVER-STOCKTON COLLEGE**
1 College Hill
Canton, MO 63435-1299
Tel: (217)231-6000; Free: 800-537-1883
Fax: (217)231-6611
E-mail: admissions@culver.edu
Web Site: www.culver.edu/
Description: Independent, 4-year, coed, affiliated with Christian Church (Disciples of Christ). Awards bachelor's degrees. Founded 1853. Setting: 143-acre rural campus. Endowment: $20.1 million. Educational spending for the previous fiscal year: $5231 per student. Total enrollment: 769. Faculty: 89 (49 full-time, 40 part-time). Student-undergrad faculty ratio is 12:1. 1,162 applied, 62% were admitted. 10% from top 10% of their high school class, 29% from top quarter, 66% from top half. 6 valedictorians. Full-time: 710 students, 46% women, 54% men. Part-time: 59 students, 63% women, 37% men. Students come from 27 states and territories, 13 other countries, 47% from out-of-state. 1% American Indian or Alaska Native, non-Hispanic/Latino; 4% Hispanic/Latino; 12% African American, non-Hispanic/Latino; 0.3% Asian, non-Hispanic/Latino; 0.3% Native Hawaiian or other Pacific Islander, non-Hispanic/Latino; 2% international. 3% 25 or older, 83% live on campus, 10% transferred in. Retention: 68% of full-time freshmen returned the following year. Academic areas with the most degrees conferred: business/marketing; health professions and related sciences; education. Core. Calendar: semesters. Academic remediation for entering students, services for LD students, advanced placement, self-designed majors, honors program, independent study, distance learning, double major, summer session for credit, part-time degree program, adult/continuing education programs, internships. Off campus study at Central College in Pella, IA and the Missouri Consortium for International Programs and Studies and Internship Program in London, England. Study abroad program.
Entrance Requirements: Options: electronic application, deferred admission, international baccalaureate accepted. Required: high school transcript, minimum 2 high school GPA, SAT or ACT. Recommended: essay, 1 recommendation, interview. Entrance: moderately difficult. Application deadline: Rolling. Notification: continuous. SAT Reasoning Test deadline: 8/20. Transfer credits accepted: Yes.
Costs Per Year: Application fee: $0. One-time mandatory fee: $200. Comprehensive fee: $30,900 includes full-time tuition ($23,000), mandatory fees ($300), and college room and board ($7600). College room only: $3400. Room and board charges vary according to board plan and housing facility. Part-time tuition: $540 per credit hour. Part-time mandatory fees: $12.50 per credit hour.
Collegiate Environment: Orientation program. Drama-theater group, choral group, student-run newspaper, radio station. Social organizations: 32 open to all; national fraternities, national sororities; 38% of eligible men and 42% of eligible women are members. Most popular organizations: Up 'til Dawn (benefiting St. Jude's Hospital), Interfraternity Council/Panhellenic Council, Student Government Association, Students in Free Enterprise (SIFE), Campus Programming Council. Major annual events: Hillstock, Wildcat Welcome, Greek Week. Student services: personal-psychological counseling. Campus security: 24-hour emergency response devices and patrols, late night transport-escort service, controlled dormitory access, lighted pathways/sidewalks; self defense education is currently offered on campus. 651 college housing spaces available; 589 were occupied in 2012-13. Freshmen guaranteed college housing. On-campus residence required through senior year. Option: coed housing available. Carl Johann Memorial Library with 193,789 books, 155 microform titles, 25,561 serials, 5,537 audiovisual materials, an OPAC, and a Web page. Operations spending for the previous fiscal year: $286,767. 100 computers available on campus for general student use. A campuswide network can be accessed from student residence rooms and from off campus. Students can access the following: online class registration. Staffed computer lab on campus provides training in use of computers, software, and the Internet.
Community Environment: Canton, population 2,502, is 20 miles north of Quincy, IL, 30 miles south of Keokuk, IA, and approximately two hours north of St. Louis, MO. On the Mississippi River, it is the site of the U.S. Lock and Dam No. 20, which is one of the series of navigation dams built between Minneapolis and St. Louis. Libraries, museums, many churches, and good shopping facilities all provide service to the community. A state park is nearby for recreational and outdoor play. The college homecoming is a community affair. Part-time employment is available.

■ **DEVRY UNIVERSITY (KANSAS CITY)**
11224 Holmes Rd.
Kansas City, MO 64131

Tel: (816)943-7300; Free: 866-338-7941
Web Site: www.devry.edu/
Description: Proprietary, comprehensive, coed. Part of DeVry University. Awards associate, bachelor's, and master's degrees. Founded 1931. Setting: urban campus. Total enrollment: 893. Faculty: 76 (24 full-time, 52 part-time). Student-undergrad faculty ratio is 13:1. Full-time: 306 students, 30% women, 70% men. Part-time: 389 students, 36% women, 64% men. 40% from out-of-state. 1% American Indian or Alaska Native, non-Hispanic/Latino; 4% Hispanic/Latino; 16% African American, non-Hispanic/Latino; 2% Asian, non-Hispanic/Latino; 0.4% Native Hawaiian or other Pacific Islander, non-Hispanic/Latino; 0.3% international. 61% 25 or older, 18% transferred in. Academic areas with the most degrees conferred: computer and information sciences; business/marketing; engineering technologies. Calendar: semesters. Part-time degree program, adult/continuing education programs.
Entrance Requirements: Required: high school transcript, interview. Entrance: minimally difficult. Application deadline: Rolling. Notification: continuous.
Costs Per Year: Application fee: $40. Tuition: $16,076 full-time, $609 per credit hour part-time. Mandatory fees: $80 full-time.
Collegiate Environment: Orientation program. College housing not available.

■ **DEVRY UNIVERSITY - KANSAS CITY DOWNTOWN CENTER (KANSAS CITY)**
City Ctr. Sq.
1100 Main St., Ste. 118
Kansas City, MO 64105-2112
Tel: (816)221-1300; Free: 866-338-7941
Fax: (816)474-0318
Web Site: www.devry.edu/
Description: Proprietary, comprehensive, coed. Awards bachelor's and master's degrees. Calendar: semesters.

■ **DEVRY UNIVERSITY (SAINT LOUIS)**
1801 Park 270 Dr., Ste. 260
Saint Louis, MO 63146-4020
Tel: (314)542-4222; Free: 866-338-7941
Fax: (314)542-4004
Web Site: www.devry.edu/
Description: Proprietary, comprehensive, coed. Awards bachelor's and master's degrees. Calendar: semesters.

■ **DRURY UNIVERSITY**
900 N Benton Ave.
Springfield, MO 65802
Tel: (417)873-7879; Free: 800-922-2274
Fax: (417)873-7529
E-mail: druryad@drury.edu
Web Site: www.drury.edu/
Description: Independent, comprehensive, coed. Awards bachelor's and master's degrees (also offers evening program with significant enrollment not reflected in profile). Founded 1873. Setting: 80-acre urban campus. Endowment: $56.2 million. Research spending for the previous fiscal year: $208,689. Educational spending for the previous fiscal year: $10,221 per student. Total enrollment: 2,060. Faculty: 169 (135 full-time, 34 part-time). Student-undergrad faculty ratio is 12:1. 1,043 applied, 82% were admitted. 34% from top 10% of their high school class, 59% from top quarter, 93% from top half. Full-time: 1,575 students, 54% women, 46% men. Part-time: 32 students, 50% women, 50% men. Students come from 30 states and territories, 38 other countries, 19% from out-of-state. 0.5% American Indian or Alaska Native, non-Hispanic/Latino; 3% Hispanic/Latino; 3% African American, non-Hispanic/Latino; 2% Asian, non-Hispanic/Latino; 0% Native Hawaiian or other Pacific Islander, non-Hispanic/Latino; 9% international. 4% 25 or older, 54% live on campus, 6% transferred in. Retention: 83% of full-time freshmen returned the following year. Academic areas with the most degrees conferred: psychology; business/marketing; social sciences. Core. Calendar: semesters. Academic remediation for entering students, ESL program, services for LD students, advanced placement, accelerated degree program, self-designed majors, honors program, independent study, distance learning, double major, summer session for credit, part-time degree program, adult/continuing education programs, co-op programs and internships, graduate courses open to undergrads. Off campus study. Study abroad program. ROTC: Army (c).
Entrance Requirements: Options: electronic application, deferred admis-

sion, international baccalaureate accepted. Required: essay, high school transcript, minimum 2.7 high school GPA, 1 recommendation, SAT or ACT. Recommended: interview. Entrance: moderately difficult. Application deadline: 8/1. Notification: continuous. SAT Reasoning Test deadline: 8/1. SAT Subject Test deadline: 8/1. Transfer credits accepted: Yes.

Costs Per Year: Application fee: $25. One-time mandatory fee: $150. Comprehensive fee: $30,615 includes full-time tuition ($21,700), mandatory fees ($715), and college room and board ($8200). Full-time tuition and fees vary according to class time. Room and board charges vary according to board plan and housing facility.

Collegiate Environment: Orientation program. Drama-theater group, choral group, student-run newspaper, radio station. Social organizations: 94 open to all; national fraternities, national sororities, Honor societies and clubs; 22% of eligible men and 28% of eligible women are members. Most popular organizations: Drury Volunteer Corps (DVC), International Student Association, Lambda Chi Alpha, Zeta Tau Alpha, Kappa Delta. Major annual events: Fall Homecoming, Late Night Breakfast, Fireworks on Sunderland Field. Student services: health clinic, personal-psychological counseling. Campus security: 24-hour emergency response devices and patrols, student patrols, late night transport-escort service, controlled dormitory access, security cameras in parking areas, police substation on campus, well-lit campus. 1,022 college housing spaces available; 878 were occupied in 2012-13. Freshmen guaranteed college housing. On-campus residence required through junior year. Options: coed, men-only, women-only housing available. F. W. Olin Library plus 1 other with 194,988 books, 13,565 microform titles, 469 serials, 5,344 audiovisual materials, an OPAC, and a Web page. Operations spending for the previous fiscal year: $1.1 million. 389 computers available on campus for general student use. A campuswide network can be accessed from student residence rooms and from off campus. Students can access the following: online class registration, digital imaging lab, online bill payment/student information. Staffed computer lab on campus (open 24 hours a day) provides training in use of computers, software, and the Internet.

Community Environment: See Southwest Missouri State University.

■ **EAST CENTRAL COLLEGE**

1964 Prairie Dell Rd.
Union, MO 63084
Tel: (636)583-5193
Fax: (636)583-1897
E-mail: poynterm@eastcentral.edu
Web Site: www.eastcentral.edu/

Description: District-supported, 2-year, coed. Awards certificates, transfer associate, and terminal associate degrees. Founded 1959. Setting: 207-acre rural campus with easy access to St. Louis. Endowment: $2.5 million. Educational spending for the previous fiscal year: $3197 per student. Total enrollment: 4,203. Faculty: 241 (72 full-time, 169 part-time). Student-undergrad faculty ratio is 22:1. 51% from top half of their high school class. Full-time: 2,137 students, 58% women, 42% men. Part-time: 2,066 students, 60% women, 40% men. Students come from 6 states and territories, 2 other countries. Retention: 61% of full-time freshmen returned the following year. Core. Calendar: semesters. Academic remediation for entering students, ESL program, services for LD students, advanced placement, honors program, independent study, distance learning, summer session for credit, part-time degree program, adult/continuing education programs, internships. Off campus study at Occupational Therapy Assistant Program - University of Missouri Columbia. Study abroad program.

Entrance Requirements: Open admission. Options: early admission, deferred admission. Required: high school transcript. Entrance: noncompetitive. Application deadline: Rolling. Transfer credits accepted: Yes.

Collegiate Environment: Orientation program. Drama-theater group, choral group, student-run newspaper. Social organizations: 22 open to all. Most popular organizations: ECC Student Senate, Phi Theta Kappa, Student Nurses Association, Sigma Alpha Pi, S-MSTA. Major annual events: All Campus Day-Fall, All Campus Day-Spring, ECC Cash Auction (Reward Point System). Student services: personal-psychological counseling. Campus security: 24-hour emergency response devices, late night transport-escort service. East Central College Library with an OPAC and a Web page. Operations spending for the previous fiscal year: $334,047. 475 computers available on campus for general student use. A campuswide network can be accessed from off-campus. Students can access the following: online class registration. Staffed computer lab on campus provides training in use of computers, software, and the Internet.

Community Environment: Union (population 9,000) is the county seat of

Franklin County, and is located 40 miles west of St. Louis; see Washington University for information about St. Louis.

■ **EVANGEL UNIVERSITY**

1111 N Glenstone
Springfield, MO 65802
Tel: (417)865-2811; Free: 800-382-6435
Fax: (417)865-9599
E-mail: admissions@evangel.edu
Web Site: www.evangel.edu/

Description: Independent, comprehensive, coed, affiliated with Assemblies of God. Awards associate, bachelor's, and master's degrees. Founded 1955. Setting: 80-acre urban campus. Total enrollment: 2,079. Faculty: 154 (108 full-time, 46 part-time). 1,260 applied, 67% were admitted. 18% from top 10% of their high school class, 40% from top quarter, 72% from top half. Full-time: 1,704 students, 57% women, 43% men. Part-time: 175 students, 49% women, 51% men. 47% from out-of-state. 1% American Indian or Alaska Native, non-Hispanic/Latino; 5% Hispanic/Latino; 5% African American, non-Hispanic/Latino; 1% Asian, non-Hispanic/Latino; 1% international. 7% transferred in. Academic areas with the most degrees conferred: business/marketing; education; communication/journalism. Calendar: semesters. ROTC: Army (c).

Entrance Requirements: Options: electronic application, deferred admission, international baccalaureate accepted. Required: essay, high school transcript, interview, SAT or ACT. Recommended: minimum 2 high school GPA. Entrance: moderately difficult. Application deadline: Rolling. Notification: continuous.

Costs Per Year: Application fee: $25. Comprehensive fee: $25,690 includes full-time tuition ($17,930), mandatory fees ($1120), and college room and board ($6640). College room only: $3430. Full-time tuition and fees vary according to course load. Room and board charges vary according to board plan. Part-time tuition: $747 per credit hour. Part-time tuition varies according to course load.

Collegiate Environment: Orientation program. Drama-theater group, choral group, marching band, student-run newspaper, radio station. Most popular organizations: Activities Board, student government, CrossWalk Student Ministries, Honor Societies, Music Ensembles. Student services: health clinic, personal-psychological counseling. Campus security: 24-hour emergency response devices and patrols, student patrols, late night transport-escort service, controlled dormitory access. On-campus residence required through senior year. Options: coed, men-only, women-only housing available.

Community Environment: See Southwest Missouri State University.

■ **EVEREST COLLEGE**

1010 W Sunshine
Springfield, MO 65807-2488
Tel: (417)864-7220; Free: 888-741-4270
Fax: (417)865-5697
Web Site: www.everest.edu/

Description: Proprietary, primarily 2-year, coed. Part of Corinthian Colleges, Inc. Awards certificates, terminal associate, and bachelor's degrees. Founded 1976. Setting: 2-acre urban campus. Total enrollment: 584. 226 applied. 0% from out-of-state. 66% 25 or older. Retention: 100% of full-time freshmen returned the following year. Summer session for credit, part-time degree program.

Entrance Requirements: Required: high school transcript, interview, CPAt. Entrance: noncompetitive. Application deadline: Rolling.

Collegiate Environment: Orientation program. Social organizations: local fraternities.

Community Environment: Established as a trading post in 1636, Springfield is located on the Connecticut River in Southwestern part of the state. City is noted today for its diversified industries including the manufacture of firearms, plastics, chemicals, radio equipment, tires, paper, and electrical equipment. Ample part-time job opportunities available. Several movie theatres, municipal auditorium, drive-ins, summer theatre, two municipal golf courses, 150 parks, civic center, and playgrounds, swimming, skating, quadrangle of museums, public libraries, provide excellent recreational and cultural opportunities. Easy access to commercial, bus and rail service.

■ **FONTBONNE UNIVERSITY**

6800 Wydown Blvd.
Saint Louis, MO 63105-3098

Tel: (314)862-3456; Free: 800-205-5862

Fax: (314)719-8021

E-mail: gtaylor@fontbonne.edu

Web Site: www.fontbonne.edu/

Description: Independent Roman Catholic, comprehensive, coed. Awards bachelor's and master's degrees. Founded 1917. Setting: 13-acre suburban campus with easy access to St. Louis. Endowment: $20.3 million. Educational spending for the previous fiscal year: $9927 per student. Total enrollment: 2,293. Faculty: 276 (81 full-time, 195 part-time). Student-undergrad faculty ratio is 11:1. 632 applied, 63% were admitted. 14% from top 10% of their high school class, 42% from top half. Full-time: 1,116 students, 64% women, 36% men. Part-time: 384 students, 78% women, 22% men. Students come from 21 states and territories, 16 other countries, 15% from out-of-state. 0.1% American Indian or Alaska Native, non-Hispanic/Latino; 2% Hispanic/Latino; 24% African American, non-Hispanic/Latino; 1% Asian, non-Hispanic/Latino; 0% Native Hawaiian or other Pacific Islander, non-Hispanic/Latino; 5% international. 43% 25 or older, 23% live on campus, 13% transferred in. Retention: 70% of full-time freshmen returned the following year. Academic areas with the most degrees conferred: business/marketing; education; communication/journalism. Core. Calendar: semesters. Academic remediation for entering students, ESL program, services for LD students, advanced placement, accelerated degree program, self-designed majors, honors program, independent study, distance learning, double major, summer session for credit, part-time degree program, adult/continuing education programs, co-op programs and internships, graduate courses open to undergrads. Off campus study at Webster University, Maryville College, Lindenwood College, Missouri Baptist College. Study abroad program. ROTC: Army (c), Air Force (c).

Entrance Requirements: Options: electronic application, early admission, deferred admission. Required: high school transcript, minimum 2.5 high school GPA, SAT or ACT. Recommended: 2 recommendations, interview. Required for some: essay. Entrance: moderately difficult. Application deadline: Rolling. Notification: continuous. SAT Reasoning Test deadline: 5/1.

Costs Per Year: Application fee: $25. Comprehensive fee: $30,654 includes full-time tuition ($22,054) and college room and board ($8600). Full-time tuition varies according to program. Room and board charges vary according to board plan and housing facility.

Collegiate Environment: Orientation program. Drama-theater group, choral group, student-run newspaper. Social organizations: 28 open to all. Most popular organizations: Future Teachers Association, Students for the Enhancement of Black Awareness, Fontbonne Athletic Association, Fontbonne in Service and Humility, Student Government Association. Major annual events: Late Night with Lee McKinney, Christmas Ball, Springfest. Student services: health clinic, personal-psychological counseling. Campus security: 24-hour patrols, late night transport-escort service, controlled dormitory access. The Jack C. Taylor Library at Fontbonne University with 96,421 books, 46,277 serials, 4,787 audiovisual materials, an OPAC, and a Web page. Operations spending for the previous fiscal year: $747,914. 285 computers available on campus for general student use. Computer purchase/lease plans available. A campuswide network can be accessed from student residence rooms and from off campus. Students can access the following: online class registration. Staffed computer lab on campus provides training in use of computers, software, and the Internet.

■ **GLOBAL UNIVERSITY**

1211 S Glenstone Ave.

Springfield, MO 65804

Tel: (417)862-9533; Free: 800-443-1083

Fax: (417)862-5318

E-mail: twaggoner@globaluniversity.edu

Web Site: www.globaluniversity.edu/

Description: Independent, comprehensive, coed, affiliated with Assemblies of God. Awards associate, bachelor's, master's, and doctoral degrees (offers only external degree programs). Founded 1948. Setting: small town campus. Total enrollment: 4,551. Faculty: 633 (81 full-time, 552 part-time). Student-undergrad faculty ratio is 11:1. Students come from 50 states and territories, 127 other countries, 98% from out-of-state. 91% 25 or older. Academic area with the most degrees conferred: theology and religious vocations. Core. Calendar: continuous. Independent study, distance learning, double major, part-time degree program, external degree program, adult/continuing education programs, graduate courses open to undergrads. Off campus study.

Entrance Requirements: Open admission. Option: international bac-

calaureate accepted. Required: high school transcript. Recommended: essay. Required for some: 1 recommendation. Entrance: noncompetitive. Application deadline: Rolling.

Costs Per Year: Application fee: $40. Tuition: $3870 full-time, $129 per credit part-time.

Collegiate Environment: Campus security: 24-hour emergency response devices. Global University Library with 180 serials and a Web page.

■ **GOLDFARB SCHOOL OF NURSING AT BARNES-JEWISH COLLEGE**

4483 Duncan Ave.

Saint Louis, MO 63110

Tel: (314)454-7055; Free: 800-832-9009

Fax: (314)454-5239

E-mail: mward@bjc.org

Web Site: www.barnesjewishcollege.edu/

Description: Independent, comprehensive, coed. Administratively affiliated with Barnes Jewish Hospital. Awards bachelor's, master's, and doctoral degrees and post-master's certificates. Founded 1902. Setting: urban campus. Endowment: $20 million. Total enrollment: 838. Faculty: 50 (43 full-time, 7 part-time). Student-undergrad faculty ratio is 8:1. Full-time: 631 students, 90% women, 10% men. Part-time: 6 students, 67% women, 33% men. Students come from 15 states and territories, 10 other countries, 25% from out-of-state. 0.2% American Indian or Alaska Native, non-Hispanic/Latino; 2% Hispanic/Latino; 6% African American, non-Hispanic/Latino; 3% Asian, non-Hispanic/Latino; 0.3% Native Hawaiian or other Pacific Islander, non-Hispanic/Latino; 0% international. 55% 25 or older, 100% transferred in. Retention: 0% of full-time freshmen returned the following year. Academic area with the most degrees conferred: health professions and related sciences. Core. Calendar: trimesters. Services for LD students, advanced placement, accelerated degree program, independent study, summer session for credit, graduate courses open to undergrads. Off campus study.

Entrance Requirements: Options: deferred admission, international baccalaureate accepted. Entrance: moderately difficult. Applicants placed on waiting list: 266. Wait-listed applicants offered admission: 163.

Costs Per Year: Application fee: $50. Tuition: $25,768 full-time. Mandatory fees: $1565 full-time. Full-time tuition and fees vary according to course load and degree level.

Collegiate Environment: Orientation program. Student-run newspaper. Most popular organization: Student Nurses Association. Major annual events: Fall Ice Cream Social, Spring Barbeque, Holiday Event. Student services: health clinic, personal-psychological counseling. Campus security: 24-hour patrols, late night transport-escort service. College housing not available. Main library plus 2 others with 1,125 books, 47 serials, 125 audiovisual materials, an OPAC, and a Web page. Operations spending for the previous fiscal year: $313,600. 160 computers available on campus for general student use. A campuswide network can be accessed from off-campus. Students can access the following: software, research databases. Staffed computer lab on campus provides training in use of computers, software, and the Internet.

■ **GRACELAND UNIVERSITY**

1401 W Truman Rd.

Independence, MO 64050-3434

Tel: (816)833-0524; Free: 866-GRACELAND

E-mail: gic@graceland.edu

Web Site: www.graceland.edu/

Description: Independent Community of Christ, comprehensive, coed. Awards bachelor's and master's degrees and post-master's certificates. Calendar: 4-1-4.

■ **GRANTHAM UNIVERSITY**

7200 NW 86th St., Ste. M

Kansas City, MO 64153

Free: 800-955-2527

Fax: (816)595-5757

E-mail: admissions@grantham.edu

Web Site: www.grantham.edu/

Description: Proprietary, comprehensive, coed. Awards associate, bachelor's, and master's degrees (offers only external degree programs). Founded 1951. Setting: urban campus with easy access to Kansas City. Total enrollment: 9,463. Faculty: 10 (all full-time). Student-undergrad faculty ratio is 17:1. Core. Calendar: continuous. Academic remediation for entering students, advanced placement, accelerated degree program, self-designed majors, independent study, distance learning, part-time degree program, external degree program, adult/continuing education programs.

Entrance Requirements: Open admission. Options: electronic application, international baccalaureate accepted. Entrance: noncompetitive. Application deadlines: Rolling, Rolling for nonresidents. Notification: continuous, continuous for nonresidents. Transfer credits accepted: Yes.

Costs Per Year: Application fee: $30. One-time mandatory fee: $30. Tuition: $6360 full-time, $265 per credit hour part-time. Mandatory fees: $120 full-time, $30 per term part-time.

Collegiate Environment: Orientation program. College housing not available. Grantham Online Library with 1,639 books and 12,260 serials. Operations spending for the previous fiscal year: $106,602.

■ **HANNIBAL-LAGRANGE UNIVERSITY**
2800 Palmyra Rd.
Hannibal, MO 63401-1999
Tel: (573)221-3675; Free: 800-HLG-1119
Fax: (573)221-6594
E-mail: admissio@hlg.edu
Web Site: www.hlg.edu/

Description: Independent Southern Baptist, comprehensive, coed. Awards associate, bachelor's, and master's degrees. Founded 1858. Setting: 110-acre small town campus. Total enrollment: 1,128. Faculty: 146 (60 full-time, 86 part-time). Student-undergrad faculty ratio is 13:1. Full-time: 895 students, 62% women, 38% men. Part-time: 212 students, 69% women, 31% men. Students come from 26 states and territories, 26 other countries, 29% from out-of-state. 0.3% American Indian or Alaska Native, non-Hispanic/Latino; 3% Hispanic/Latino; 5% African American, non-Hispanic/Latino; 0.2% Asian, non-Hispanic/Latino; 0.3% Native Hawaiian or other Pacific Islander, non-Hispanic/Latino; 6% international. 44% live on campus, 18% transferred in. Retention: 62% of full-time freshmen returned the following year. Academic areas with the most degrees conferred: business/marketing; education; homeland security, law enforcement, firefighting, and protective services. Core. Calendar: semesters. Academic remediation for entering students, ESL program, services for LD students, advanced placement, accelerated degree program, self-designed majors, honors program, independent study, distance learning, double major, summer session for credit, part-time degree program, adult/continuing education programs, internships. Off campus study. Study abroad program.

Entrance Requirements: Options: electronic application, early admission, deferred admission. Required: high school transcript, minimum 2 high school GPA, SAT or ACT. Required for some: GED. Entrance: minimally difficult. Application deadlines: 9/10, 8/10 for nonresidents. Notification: continuous until 9/10, 9/10 for nonresidents. SAT Reasoning Test deadline: 9/10. SAT Subject Test deadline: 9/10. Transfer credits accepted: Yes.

Costs Per Year: Application fee: $25. Comprehensive fee: $24,370 includes full-time tuition ($17,150), mandatory fees ($650), and college room and board ($6570). Full-time tuition and fees vary according to course load, degree level, program, and reciprocity agreements. Room and board charges vary according to housing facility. Part-time tuition: $571 per credit. Part-time tuition varies according to course load, degree level, program, and reciprocity agreements.

Collegiate Environment: Orientation program. Drama-theater group, choral group, student-run newspaper. Social organizations: 27 open to all; national fraternities, national sororities; 50% of eligible men and 50% of eligible women are members. Most popular organizations: Phi Beta Lambda, student government, Student Teachers Organization, Phi Beta Delta, Alpha Tau Beta. Major annual events: Homecoming, Booster Banquet, Parents' Day. Student services: health clinic. Campus security: 24-hour emergency response devices and patrols, controlled dormitory access. L. A. Foster Library with 145,985 books, 21,831 microform titles, 395 serials, 6,026 audiovisual materials, an OPAC, and a Web page. 90 computers available on campus for general student use. A campuswide network can be accessed from student residence rooms and from off campus. Students can access the following: online class registration. Staffed computer lab on campus provides training in use of computers.

Community Environment: The boyhood home of Mark Twain, Hannibal (population 17,649), is located on the west bank of the Mississippi River, 120 miles north of St. Louis. Buses and trains are the principal forms of transportation as well as a municipal airport that serves the area. A public library, YMCA, churches, a music association, and numerous civic and service organizations are a part of the community. Some recreational activities include swimming, bowling, and fishing.

■ **HARRIS-STOWE STATE UNIVERSITY**
3026 Laclede Ave.
Saint Louis, MO 63103-2136
Tel: (314)340-3366
Fax: (314)340-3322
E-mail: admissions@hssu.edu
Web Site: www.hssu.edu/

Description: State-supported, 4-year, coed. Part of Missouri Coordinating Board for Higher Education. Awards bachelor's degrees. Founded 1857. Setting: 22-acre urban campus. Total enrollment: 1,484. Faculty: 203 (55 full-time, 148 part-time). Student-undergrad faculty ratio is 12:1. 884 applied, 100% were admitted. 6% from top 10% of their high school class, 21% from top quarter, 45% from top half. Full-time: 1,096 students, 63% women, 37% men. Part-time: 388 students, 69% women, 31% men. Students come from 15 states and territories, 5 other countries, 11% from out-of-state. 0.1% American Indian or Alaska Native, non-Hispanic/Latino; 2% Hispanic/Latino; 84% African American, non-Hispanic/Latino; 0.3% Asian, non-Hispanic/Latino; 0% Native Hawaiian or other Pacific Islander, non-Hispanic/Latino; 0.2% international. 31% 25 or older, 15% live on campus, 11% transferred in. Retention: 44% of full-time freshmen returned the following year. Academic areas with the most degrees conferred: business/marketing; education; homeland security, law enforcement, firefighting, and protective services. Core. Calendar: semesters. Academic remediation for entering students, services for LD students, advanced placement, self-designed majors, summer session for credit, part-time degree program, co-op programs and internships. Off campus study at Saint Louis University, University of Missouri-St. Louis. ROTC: Army (c), Air Force (c).

Entrance Requirements: Open admission. Options: electronic application, early admission, deferred admission. Required: high school transcript. Recommended: SAT or ACT. Required for some: institutional placement test. Entrance: noncompetitive. Application deadline: Rolling. Notification: continuous. Transfer credits accepted: Yes.

Collegiate Environment: Orientation program. Drama-theater group, choral group. Social organizations: 43 open to all; national fraternities, national sororities; 1% of eligible men and 1% of eligible women are members. Most popular organizations: Drama Club, Concert chorale, Student Government Association, Multicultural Council, Student Ambassadors. Major annual events: Homecoming, Commencement, Organization Day. Student services: health clinic, personal-psychological counseling. Campus security: 24-hour emergency response devices and patrols, late night transport-escort service, controlled dormitory access. 428 college housing spaces available; 218 were occupied in 2012-13. Freshmen given priority for college housing. Option: coed housing available. AT&T Library and Technology Center plus 1 other with 60,000 books, 8,700 microform titles, 340 serials, and an OPAC. 333 computers available on campus for general student use. A campuswide network can be accessed from off-campus. Students can access the following: online class registration. Staffed computer lab on campus provides training in use of computers and the Internet.

■ **HERITAGE COLLEGE**
1200 E 104th St.
Ste. 300
Kansas City, MO 64131
Tel: (816)942-5474; Free: 888-334-7339
Fax: (816)942-5405
E-mail: info@heritage-education.com
Web Site: www.heritage-education.com/

Description: Proprietary, 2-year, coed. Awards terminal associate degrees. Total enrollment: 702. Student-undergrad faculty ratio is 31:1. 2% from out-of-state. 49% 25 or older. Retention: 84% of full-time freshmen returned the following year.

Entrance Requirements: Open admission. Entrance: noncompetitive.

■ **HICKEY COLLEGE**
940 W Port Plz.
Ste. 101
Saint Louis, MO 63146
Tel: (314)434-2212; Free: 800-777-1544
Fax: (314)434-1974
Web Site: www.hickeycollege.edu/

Description: Private, 4-year, coed. Awards associate and bachelor's degrees. Founded 1933. Setting: suburban campus with easy access to St. Louis. Total enrollment: 500. 916 applied, 71% were admitted. Calendar: semesters. Accelerated degree program, internships.

■ IHM ACADEMY OF EMS

2500 Abbott Pl.
Saint Louis, MO 63143
Tel: (314)768-1234
Fax: (314)768-1595
E-mail: info@ihmhealthstudies.edu
Web Site: www.ihmacademyofems.net/
Description: Independent, 2-year, coed. Awards certificates and terminal associate degrees. Founded 1977. Setting: suburban campus. Calendar: trimesters.

■ ITT TECHNICAL INSTITUTE (ARNOLD)

1930 Meyer Drury Dr.
Arnold, MO 63010
Tel: (636)464-6600; Free: 888-488-1082
Web Site: www.itt-tech.edu/
Description: Proprietary, primarily 2-year, coed. Part of ITT Educational Services, Inc. Awards terminal associate and bachelor's degrees. Founded 1997.
Entrance Requirements: Entrance: minimally difficult.

■ ITT TECHNICAL INSTITUTE (EARTH CITY)

3640 Corporate Trl. Dr.
Earth City, MO 63045
Tel: (314)298-7800; Free: 800-235-5488
Fax: (314)298-0559
Web Site: www.itt-tech.edu/
Description: Proprietary, primarily 2-year, coed. Part of ITT Educational Services, Inc. Awards terminal associate and bachelor's degrees. Founded 1936. Setting: suburban campus.
Entrance Requirements: Entrance: minimally difficult.

■ ITT TECHNICAL INSTITUTE (KANSAS CITY)

9150 E 41st Ter.
Kansas City, MO 64133
Tel: (816)276-1400; Free: 877-488-1442
Web Site: www.itt-tech.edu/
Description: Proprietary, primarily 2-year, coed. Part of ITT Educational Services, Inc. Awards terminal associate and bachelor's degrees. Founded 2004.
Entrance Requirements: Entrance: minimally difficult.

■ ITT TECHNICAL INSTITUTE (SPRINGFIELD)

3216 S National Ave.
Springfield, MO 65807
Tel: (417)877-4800; Free: 877-219-4387
Web Site: www.itt-tech.edu/
Description: Proprietary, 4-year, coed. Part of ITT Educational Services, Inc. Awards associate and bachelor's degrees.
Entrance Requirements: Entrance: minimally difficult.

■ JEFFERSON COLLEGE

1000 Viking Dr.
Hillsboro, MO 63050-2441
Tel: (636)797-3000
Fax: (636)789-4012
E-mail: admissions@jeffco.edu
Web Site: www.jeffco.edu/
Description: District-supported, 2-year, coed. Awards certificates, diplomas, transfer associate, and terminal associate degrees. Founded 1963. Setting: 455-acre rural campus with easy access to St. Louis. System endowment: $681,575. Educational spending for the previous fiscal year: $3254 per student. Total enrollment: 5,494. Faculty: 360 (93 full-time, 267 part-time). Full-time: 2,944 students, 55% women, 45% men. Part-time: 2,550 students, 62% women, 38% men. 12% from out-of-state. 1% American Indian or Alaska Native, non-Hispanic/Latino; 1% Hispanic/Latino; 2% African American, non-Hispanic/Latino; 1% Asian, non-Hispanic/Latino; 0.1% Native Hawaiian or other Pacific Islander, non-Hispanic/Latino; 0.2% international. 25% 25 or older. Core. Calendar: semesters. Academic remediation for entering students, ESL program, services for LD students, advanced placement, freshman honors college, honors program, distance learning, summer session for credit, part-time degree program, adult/continuing education programs, internships. Off campus study.
Entrance Requirements: Open admission except for veterinary technology, nursing, emergency medical technician programs and law enforcement academy. Options: electronic application, early admission. Required: high school transcript. Entrance: noncompetitive. Application deadline: Rolling. Transfer credits accepted: Yes.
Costs Per Year: Application fee: $25. One-time mandatory fee: $25. Area resident tuition: $2910 full-time. State resident tuition: $4260 full-time. Nonresident tuition: $5610 full-time. Mandatory fees: $90 full-time. College room and board: $5121. College room only: $3240. Room and board charges vary according to housing facility.
Collegiate Environment: Orientation program. Drama-theater group, choral group, student-run newspaper. Social organizations: 15 open to all; national sororities. Most popular organizations: Student Senate, Nursing associations, Baptist Student Unit, Phi Beta Lambda, Phi Theta Kappa. Major annual events: Special Olympics, Shocktober Night, Spring Fling. Student services: personal-psychological counseling. Campus security: 24-hour patrols. Option: coed housing available. Jefferson College Library plus 1 other with 71,576 books, 9,448 microform titles, 60 serials, 2,713 audiovisual materials, an OPAC, and a Web page. 187 computers available on campus for general student use. A campuswide network can be accessed from student residence rooms and from off campus. Students can access the following: online class registration. Staffed computer lab on campus.
Community Environment: Hillsboro (population 1,784) is a rural community with a temperate climate. It is located within a 30-minute drive of metropolitan St. Louis. The town is situated near several small lakes, which are excellent for fishing and boating. Hillsboro is the headquarters for the county health unit. The community facilities include civic clubs, a shopping center, churches of major denominations, and a college library. The recreational, social and cultural facilities of St. Louis are accessible. Opportunities for part-time employment are good. See also Washington University for information on St. Louis.

■ KANSAS CITY ART INSTITUTE

4415 Warwick Blvd.
Kansas City, MO 64111-1874
Tel: (816)472-4852; Free: 800-522-5224
Fax: (816)531-6296
E-mail: admiss@kcai.edu
Web Site: www.kcai.edu/
Description: Independent, 4-year, coed. Awards bachelor's degrees. Founded 1885. Setting: 18-acre urban campus. Endowment: $43.7 million. Educational spending for the previous fiscal year: $5305 per student. Total enrollment: 777. Faculty: 104 (51 full-time, 53 part-time). 650 applied, 67% were admitted. 2% from top 10% of their high school class, 34% from top quarter, 67% from top half. Full-time: 771 students, 60% women, 40% men. Part-time: 6 students, 50% women, 50% men. Students come from 37 states and territories, 2 other countries, 60% from out-of-state. 1% American Indian or Alaska Native, non-Hispanic/Latino; 7% Hispanic/Latino; 4% African American, non-Hispanic/Latino; 3% Asian, non-Hispanic/Latino; 0% Native Hawaiian or other Pacific Islander, non-Hispanic/Latino; 1% international. 6% 25 or older, 25% live on campus, 1% transferred in. Retention: 78% of full-time freshmen returned the following year. Academic area with the most degrees conferred: visual and performing arts. Core. Calendar: semesters. Academic remediation for entering students, ESL program, services for LD students, advanced placement, independent study, double major, summer session for credit, co-op programs and internships. Off campus study at New York Studio Program, AICAD School Exchange.
Entrance Requirements: Options: electronic application, deferred admission. Required: essay, high school transcript, minimum 2.5 high school GPA, 2 recommendations, portfolio, statement of purpose, SAT or ACT. Recommended: interview. Entrance: moderately difficult. Application deadline: Rolling. Notification: 8/1.
Costs Per Year: Application fee: $35. Comprehensive fee: $41,364 includes full-time tuition ($31,992) and college room and board ($9372).
Collegiate Environment: Orientation program. Most popular organizations: Student Assembly (council), Ethnic Student Association. Major annual events: Department Openings, Visiting Artist Series, Student Film Series. Student services: personal-psychological counseling. Campus security: 24-hour emergency response devices and patrols, late night transport-escort service, controlled dormitory access. Jannes Library with 40,362 books, 88 serials, 332 audiovisual materials, an OPAC, and a Web page. Operations spending for the previous fiscal year: $257,683. 145 computers available on campus for general student use. Computer purchase/lease plans available. A computer is required for all students. A campuswide network can be accessed from student residence rooms and from off campus. Students can

access the following: online class registration. Staffed computer lab on campus provides training in use of computers and the Internet.
Community Environment: See University of Missouri - Kansas City.

■ **LINCOLN UNIVERSITY**
820 Chestnut St.
Jefferson City, MO 65102
Tel: (573)681-5000; Free: 800-521-5052
Fax: (573)681-6074
E-mail: enroll@lincolnu.edu
Web Site: www.lincolnu.edu/
Description: State-supported, comprehensive, coed. Part of Missouri Coordinating Board for Higher Education. Awards associate, bachelor's, and master's degrees and post-master's certificates. Founded 1866. Setting: 171-acre small town campus. Endowment: $1.5 million. Research spending for the previous fiscal year: $6.7 million. Educational spending for the previous fiscal year: $4727 per student. Total enrollment: 3,205. Faculty: 214 (132 full-time, 82 part-time). Student-undergrad faculty ratio is 15:1. 2,487 applied, 43% were admitted. 4% from top 10% of their high school class, 15% from top quarter, 46% from top half. Full-time: 1,927 students, 54% women, 46% men. Part-time: 1,086 students, 66% women, 34% men. Students come from 36 states and territories, 16 other countries, 16% from out-of-state. 0.4% American Indian or Alaska Native, non-Hispanic/Latino; 2% Hispanic/Latino; 44% African American, non-Hispanic/Latino; 0.3% Asian, non-Hispanic/Latino; 0.04% Native Hawaiian or other Pacific Islander, non-Hispanic/Latino; 2% international. 22% 25 or older, 22% live on campus, 7% transferred in. Retention: 36% of full-time freshmen returned the following year. Academic areas with the most degrees conferred: business/marketing; education; homeland security, law enforcement, firefighting, and protective services. Core. Calendar: semesters. Academic remediation for entering students, services for LD students, advanced placement, accelerated degree program, honors program, independent study, distance learning, double major, summer session for credit, part-time degree program, adult/continuing education programs, internships, graduate courses open to undergrads. Off campus study at Mid-Missouri Associated Colleges and Universities (MMACU) consortium. Study abroad program. ROTC: Army, Naval (c), Air Force (c).
Entrance Requirements: Open admission for first-time freshmen who are Missouri residents. Options: electronic application, deferred admission, international baccalaureate accepted. Required: high school transcript, SAT or ACT. Required for some: minimum 2 high school GPA, audition for sacred music and music education. Entrance: noncompetitive. Application deadlines: 7/15, 7/15 for nonresidents. Notification: continuous, continuous for nonresidents. SAT Reasoning Test deadline: 7/15. Transfer credits accepted: Yes.
Costs Per Year: Application fee: $20. State resident tuition: $6150 full-time, $205 per credit hour part-time. Nonresident tuition: $12,150 full-time, $405 per credit hour part-time. Mandatory fees: $474 full-time, $16.75 per credit hour part-time, $36. Full-time tuition and fees vary according to location and reciprocity agreements. Part-time tuition and fees vary according to location and reciprocity agreements. College room and board: $4750. College room only: $2626. Room and board charges vary according to board plan and housing facility.
Collegiate Environment: Orientation program. Drama-theater group, choral group, marching band, student-run newspaper, radio station. Social organizations: 17 open to all; national fraternities, national sororities, local fraternities, local sororities. Most popular organizations: Student Government Association (SGA), Lincoln University Band, Alpha Kappa Mu, Army ROTC, International Students Association. Major annual events: Homecoming, Springfest, Founders' Day. Student services: health clinic, personal-psychological counseling. Campus security: 24-hour emergency response devices and patrols, student patrols, late night transport-escort service, controlled dormitory access, security-related training upon request, Operation ID-ent, Timely Warnings, text message safety alerts, webpage with helpful tips. 923 college housing spaces available; 650 were occupied in 2012-13. No special consideration for freshman housing applicants. On-campus residence required through sophomore year. Options: coed, men-only, women-only housing available. Inman E. Page Library with 151,643 books, 127,131 microform titles, 96 serials, 7,512 audiovisual materials, an OPAC, and a Web page. Operations spending for the previous fiscal year: $953,383. 250 computers available on campus for general student use. Computer purchase/lease plans available. A campuswide network can be accessed from student residence rooms. Students can access the following: online class registrations. Staffed computer lab on campus.

■ **LINDENWOOD UNIVERSITY**
209 S Kingshighway
Saint Charles, MO 63301-1695
Tel: (636)949-2000
Fax: (636)949-4910
E-mail: jparisi@lindenwood.edu
Web Site: www.lindenwood.edu/
Description: Independent Presbyterian, comprehensive, coed. Awards bachelor's, master's, and doctoral degrees and post-master's certificates. Founded 1827. Setting: 500-acre suburban campus with easy access to St. Louis. Endowment: $108.9 million. Educational spending for the previous fiscal year: $4939 per student. Total enrollment: 11,903. Faculty: 920 (234 full-time, 686 part-time). Student-undergrad faculty ratio is 17:1. 2,807 applied, 66% were admitted. 11% from top 10% of their high school class, 29% from top quarter, 64% from top half. Full-time: 7,399 students, 53% women, 47% men. Part-time: 897 students, 62% women, 38% men. Students come from 47 states and territories, 88 other countries, 27% from out-of-state. 0.4% American Indian or Alaska Native, non-Hispanic/Latino; 4% Hispanic/Latino; 14% African American, non-Hispanic/Latino; 1% Asian, non-Hispanic/Latino; 0.2% Native Hawaiian or other Pacific Islander, non-Hispanic/Latino; 10% international. 31% 25 or older, 52% live on campus, 7% transferred in. Retention: 72% of full-time freshmen returned the following year. Academic areas with the most degrees conferred: business/marketing; education; communication/journalism. Core. Calendar: 4-1-4 for daytime programs; quarters and trimesters for evening programs. Academic remediation for entering students, ESL program, services for LD students, advanced placement, accelerated degree program, self-designed majors, freshman honors college, honors program, independent study, distance learning, double major, summer session for credit, part-time degree program, external degree program, adult/continuing education programs, internships, graduate courses open to undergrads. Off campus study at St. Louis Private College Consortium, Washington University in St. Louis, University of Missouri-Columbia. Study abroad program. ROTC: Army.
Entrance Requirements: Options: electronic application, deferred admission, international baccalaureate accepted. Required: high school transcript, minimum 2.5 high school GPA, Personal resume indicating community service, youth leadership, clubs, organizations, and non-academic experience, SAT or ACT. Recommended: essay, 3 recommendations, interview. Entrance: moderately difficult. Application deadline: Rolling. Notification: continuous. SAT Reasoning Test deadline: 8/27. SAT Subject Test deadline: 8/27. Transfer credits accepted: Yes. Applicants placed on waiting list: 95. Wait-listed applicants offered admission: 95.
Costs Per Year: Application fee: $30. Comprehensive fee: $22,180 includes full-time tuition ($14,250), mandatory fees ($350), and college room and board ($7580). College room only: $4180. Full-time tuition and fees vary according to program. Part-time tuition: $412 per credit hour. Part-time tuition varies according to course load.
Collegiate Environment: Orientation program. Drama-theater group, choral group, marching band, student-run newspaper, radio station. Social organizations: 70 open to all; national fraternities, national sororities, local fraternities, local sororities; 1% of eligible men and 1% of eligible women are members. Most popular organizations: Social Work Student Association, Kappa Delta Pi, International Student Fellowship, Cru, Delta Zeta. Major annual events: Homecoming, Dark Carnival, Sibley Day. Student services: health clinic, personal-psychological counseling. Campus security: 24-hour emergency response devices and patrols, late night transport-escort service, controlled dormitory access. 4,299 college housing spaces available; 4,265 were occupied in 2012-13. Freshmen given priority for college housing. Options: men-only, women-only housing available. Butler Library with 91,393 books, 313 serials, 3,044 audiovisual materials, an OPAC, and a Web page. Operations spending for the previous fiscal year: $1.6 million. 240 computers available on campus for general student use. A campuswide network can be accessed from student residence rooms and from off campus. Students can access the following: online class registration, Blackboard. Staffed computer lab on campus provides training in use of computers and the Internet.
Community Environment: St. Charles was one of the first settlements on the Missouri River. It is located 20 miles from St. Louis. An airport is located ten miles away. Community facilities include restaurants, shopping, churches, hospital, hotels, motels, and recreation centers. Swimming, boating, and skating are some of the recreational activities found in St. Charles County.

■ **LINN STATE TECHNICAL COLLEGE**
One Technology Dr.
Linn, MO 65051-9606

Tel: (573)897-5000; Free: 800-743-TECH
E-mail: kathy.scheulen@linnstate.edu
Web Site: www.linnstate.edu/
Description: State-supported, 2-year, coed. Awards certificates and terminal associate degrees. Founded 1961. Setting: 249-acre rural campus. Total enrollment: 1,168. Faculty: 96 (84 full-time, 12 part-time). Student-undergrad faculty ratio is 12:1. 1,024 applied, 63% were admitted. Full-time: 1,001 students, 10% women, 90% men. Part-time: 167 students, 29% women, 71% men. Students come from 7 states and territories, 4% from out-of-state. 1% American Indian or Alaska Native, non-Hispanic/Latino; 0.3% Hispanic/ Latino; 2% African American, non-Hispanic/Latino; 0.3% Asian, non-Hispanic/Latino; 0% Native Hawaiian or other Pacific Islander, non-Hispanic/ Latino; 0% international. 14% 25 or older, 15% live on campus, 14% transferred in. Retention: 77% of full-time freshmen returned the following year. Core. Calendar: semesters. Academic remediation for entering students, services for LD students, independent study, distance learning, double major, summer session for credit, part-time degree program, adult/ continuing education programs, co-op programs and internships. Off campus study at Students in Nuclear Technology and Automation and Robotics Technology at our Mexico, MO campus take general education classes from Moberly Area Community College. Students in the Physical Therapy Assistant program may take general education classes from Linn State Technical College or other colleges in the Missouri Health Professions Consortium including North Central Missouri College, Three Rivers Community College, East Central College, Moberly Area Community College, and State Fair Community College. ROTC: Army (c).
Entrance Requirements: Open admission some programs are filled on first-come, first-served basis and others are filled on a competitive basis. Option: electronic application. Required: high school transcript, COMPASS. Required for some: essay, 1 recommendation, interview, some require high school attendance, mechanical test, ACT. Application deadlines: Rolling, Rolling for nonresidents. Notification: continuous, continuous for nonresidents. Transfer credits accepted: Yes. Applicants placed on waiting list: 87. Wait-listed applicants offered admission: 42.
Collegiate Environment: Orientation program. Social organizations: 16 open to all. Most popular organizations: Skills USA, Phi Theta Kappa, Student Government Association, Aviation Club, Electricity Club. Major annual events: Power Up, Casino Night, Family Day. Student services: personal-psychological counseling. Campus security: 24-hour emergency response devices, student patrols, controlled dormitory access, indoor and outdoor surveillance cameras. Linn State Technical College Library with 18,725 books, 130 serials, 2,040 audiovisual materials, an OPAC, and a Web page. 35 computers available on campus for general student use. A campuswide network can be accessed from student residence rooms. Staffed computer lab on campus provides training in use of computers, software, and the Internet.

■ **LOGAN UNIVERSITY–COLLEGE OF CHIROPRACTIC**
1851 Schoettler Rd., Box 1065
Chesterfield, MO 63006-1065
Tel: (636)227-2100; Free: 800-533-9210
Fax: (636)227-9338
E-mail: loganadm@logan.edu
Web Site: www.logan.edu/
Description: Independent, upper-level, coed. Awards bachelor's, master's, and doctoral degrees. Founded 1935. Setting: 111-acre suburban campus with easy access to St. Louis. Endowment: $13.9 million. Research spending for the previous fiscal year: $1.1 million. Educational spending for the previous fiscal year: $7015 per student. Total enrollment: 1,015. Faculty: 102 (49 full-time, 53 part-time). Student-undergrad faculty ratio is 12:1. 108 applied, 72% were admitted. Full-time: 46 students, 43% women, 57% men. Part-time: 50 students, 46% women, 54% men. 0% American Indian or Alaska Native, non-Hispanic/Latino; 0% Hispanic/Latino; 2% African American, non-Hispanic/Latino; 1% Asian, non-Hispanic/Latino; 0% Native Hawaiian or other Pacific Islander, non-Hispanic/Latino; 1% international. 38% 25 or older. Academic area with the most degrees conferred: biological/ life sciences. Core. Calendar: trimesters. Services for LD students, advanced placement, independent study, distance learning, part-time degree program, adult/continuing education programs, internships, graduate courses open to undergrads.
Entrance Requirements: Transfer credits accepted: Yes.
Costs Per Year: Application fee: $50. Tuition: $4800 full-time, $200 per credit hour part-time. Mandatory fees: $420 full-time, $140 per term part-time.

Collegiate Environment: Orientation program. Social organizations: 24 open to all; national fraternities, national sororities; 16% of eligible men and 28% of eligible women are members. Most popular organizations: Pi Kappa Chi, Lambda Kappa Chi, Chiro Sigma, Student American Chiropractic Association, Omega Sigma Pi. Major annual events: Field Day, Homecoming, Graduation celebrations. Student services: health clinic, personal-psychological counseling. Campus security: 24-hour patrols, late night transport-escort service. College housing not available. Learning Resources Center with 45,361 books, 26,951 serials, 1,576 audiovisual materials, an OPAC, and a Web page. Operations spending for the previous fiscal year: $411,298. 95 computers available on campus for general student use. A campuswide network can be accessed. Students can access the following: online class registration, online classes, course homepages, wireless technologies, Academic Software Solutions for teaching and learning, library resources, academic records access. Staffed computer lab on campus provides training in use of computers, software, and the Internet.

■ **MARYVILLE UNIVERSITY OF SAINT LOUIS**
650 Maryville University Dr.
Saint Louis, MO 63141-7299
Tel: (314)529-9300; Free: 800-627-9855
Fax: (314)529-9927
E-mail: admissions@maryville.edu
Web Site: www.maryville.edu/
Description: Independent, comprehensive, coed. Awards bachelor's, master's, and doctoral degrees. Founded 1872. Setting: 130-acre suburban campus with easy access to St. Louis. Endowment: $34.1 million. Educational spending for the previous fiscal year: $8671 per student. Total enrollment: 4,203. Faculty: 433 (114 full-time, 319 part-time). Student-undergrad faculty ratio is 12:1. 1,281 applied, 71% were admitted. 26% from top 10% of their high school class, 56% from top quarter, 86% from top half. 7 valedictorians. Full-time: 1,725 students, 68% women, 32% men. Part-time: 1,255 students, 81% women, 19% men. Students come from 34 states and territories, 30 other countries, 17% from out-of-state. 0.3% American Indian or Alaska Native, non-Hispanic/Latino; 2% Hispanic/Latino; 9% African American, non-Hispanic/Latino; 1% Asian, non-Hispanic/Latino; 0.2% Native Hawaiian or other Pacific Islander, non-Hispanic/Latino; 2% international. 40% 25 or older, 22% live on campus, 13% transferred in. Retention: 87% of full-time freshmen returned the following year. Academic areas with the most degrees conferred: health professions and related sciences; business/marketing; psychology. Core. Calendar: semesters. ESL program, services for LD students, advanced placement, accelerated degree program, honors program, independent study, distance learning, double major, summer session for credit, part-time degree program, adult/continuing education programs, co-op programs and internships, graduate courses open to undergrads. Off campus study at Fontbonne University, Lindenwood University, Webster University, Missouri Baptist University. Study abroad program. ROTC: Army (c).
Entrance Requirements: Options: electronic application, deferred admission, international baccalaureate accepted. Required: high school transcript, minimum 2.5 high school GPA, SAT or ACT. Required for some: essay, interview, audition, portfolio. Entrance: moderately difficult. Application deadline: 8/15. Notification: continuous. Transfer credits accepted: Yes.
Costs Per Year: Application fee: $30. Comprehensive fee: $32,988 includes full-time tuition ($22,786), mandatory fees ($960), and college room and board ($9242). Full-time tuition and fees vary according to course load. Room and board charges vary according to board plan and housing facility. Part-time tuition: $683 per credit hour. Part-time mandatory fees: $240 per term. Part-time tuition and fees vary according to class time.
Collegiate Environment: Orientation program. Drama-theater group, choral group, student-run newspaper. Social organizations: 50 open to all. Most popular organizations: Campus Activities Board, Physical Therapy Club, Student Nurses Association, Community Service Club. Major annual events: Fall Festival, End of the Year Bash, Involvement Fair. Student services: health clinic, personal-psychological counseling. Campus security: 24-hour emergency response devices and patrols, late night transport-escort service, controlled dormitory access, video security system in residence halls, self-defense and education programs. 711 college housing spaces available; 658 were occupied in 2012-13. No special consideration for freshman housing applicants. Option: coed housing available. Maryville University Library with 128,952 books, 491,724 microform titles, 84,817 serials, 3,519 audiovisual materials, an OPAC, and a Web page. Operations spending for the previous fiscal year: $1 million. 530 computers available on campus for general student use. Computer purchase/lease plans available. A campuswide

network can be accessed from student residence rooms and from off campus. Students can access the following: online class registration, specialized software, university catalog. Staffed computer lab on campus (open 24 hours a day) provides training in use of computers, software, and the Internet.

Community Environment: The campus is located at Highway 40/I-64 and Woods Mill Road, 2 miles west of I-270 in West St. Louis County. The campus is nestled on 130 acres of rolling hills, with wooded areas, creeks, and two lakes. It is within 20 minutes of downtown St. Louis which provides many social, cultural, athletic, and entertainment facilities including, the St. Louis Art Museum, St. Louis Symphony Orchestra, St. Louis Science Center, Missouri Botanical Garden, Municipal Opera, ballet, rock performances, theaters, restaurants, a world renown zoo, a large park system, as well as professional baseball, hockey, soccer, and football, and an International airport.

■ **METRO BUSINESS COLLEGE (CAPE GIRARDEAU)**
1732 N Kingshighway
Cape Girardeau, MO 63701
Tel: (573)334-9181; Free: 888-206-4545
Fax: (573)334-0617
Web Site: www.metrobusinesscollege.edu/
Description: Proprietary, primarily 2-year, coed. Awards certificates, diplomas, terminal associate, and bachelor's degrees. Total enrollment: 396. 57% 25 or older.
Entrance Requirements: Entrance: minimally difficult.

■ **METRO BUSINESS COLLEGE (JEFFERSON CITY)**
1407 SW Blvd.
Jefferson City, MO 65109
Tel: (573)635-6600; Free: 888-206-4545
Fax: (573)635-6999
E-mail: cheri@metrobusinesscollege.edu
Web Site: www.metrobusinesscollege.edu/
Description: Proprietary, 2-year, coed. Awards certificates, diplomas, and terminal associate degrees. Founded 1979.
Entrance Requirements: Required: essay, high school transcript, interview, Wonderlic aptitude test. Application deadline: Rolling. Notification: continuous.
Collegiate Environment: Student-run newspaper. Student services: personal-psychological counseling.

■ **METRO BUSINESS COLLEGE (ROLLA)**
1202 E Hwy. 72
Rolla, MO 65401
Tel: (573)364-8464; Free: 888-206-4545
Fax: (573)364-8077
E-mail: inforolla@metrobusinesscollege.edu
Web Site: www.metrobusinesscollege.edu/
Description: Proprietary, 2-year, coed. Awards certificates and terminal associate degrees. Founded 1979.
Entrance Requirements: Required: interview.

■ **METROPOLITAN COMMUNITY COLLEGE–KANSAS CITY**
3200 Broadway
Lee's Summit, MO 64111
Tel: (816)604-1000
E-mail: tuesday.stanley@mcckc.edu
Web Site: www.mcckc.edu/
Description: State and locally supported, 2-year, coed. Part of Metropolitan Community Colleges System. Awards certificates, transfer associate, and terminal associate degrees. Founded 1969. Setting: 420-acre suburban campus with easy access to Kansas City. System endowment: $3.4 million. Total enrollment: 20,141. Faculty: 1,147 (274 full-time, 873 part-time). Student-undergrad faculty ratio is 35:1. 4,468 applied, 100% were admitted. Full-time: 7,736 students, 54% women, 46% men. Part-time: 12,405 students, 60% women, 40% men. Students come from 18 states and territories, 80 other countries, 1% from out-of-state. 0.4% American Indian or Alaska Native, non-Hispanic/Latino; 7% Hispanic/Latino; 18% African American, non-Hispanic/Latino; 2% Asian, non-Hispanic/Latino; 0.4% Native Hawaiian or other Pacific Islander, non-Hispanic/Latino; 0.1% international. 39% 25 or older, 4% transferred in. Retention: 53% of full-time freshmen returned the following year. Core. Calendar: semesters. Academic remediation for entering students, ESL program, services for LD students,

advanced placement, accelerated degree program, honors program, independent study, distance learning, summer session for credit, part-time degree program, adult/continuing education programs, co-op programs and internships. Off campus study at Johnson County Community College.
Entrance Requirements: Open admission except for Automotive, Veterinary Technology, and the Allied Health fields. Options: electronic application, early admission, deferred admission. Recommended: ACT, Placement Testing for first-time freshman. Entrance: noncompetitive. Application deadline: Rolling. Notification: continuous.
Collegiate Environment: Orientation program. Drama-theater group, choral group, student-run newspaper. Social organizations: national fraternities. Most popular organizations: student newspaper, student government, Phi Theta Kappa, Metropolitan Chorale of KC, Student Ambassadors. Major annual events: Panache Fashion Show, Flights of Fancy, Day of Service. Student services: personal-psychological counseling. Campus security: 24-hour emergency response devices and patrols, late night transport-escort service. College housing not available. College Library with 10,098 books, 5,584 microform titles, 288 serials, 103 audiovisual materials, and an OPAC. Operations spending for the previous fiscal year: $1.9 million. 2,778 computers available on campus for general student use. A campuswide network can be accessed from off-campus. Students can access the following: online class registration. Staffed computer lab on campus provides training in use of computers, software, and the Internet.
Community Environment: See University of Missouri Kansas City.

■ **MIDWEST INSTITUTE (FENTON)**
964 S Hwy. Dr.
Fenton, MO 63026
Tel: (314)965-8363; Free: 800-695-5550
Fax: (314)965-1558
Web Site: www.midwestinstitute.com/
Description: Proprietary, 2-year, coed. Awards terminal associate degrees. Founded 1963. Total enrollment: 162. 150 applied, 99% were admitted.
Entrance Requirements: Recommended: high school transcript.

■ **MIDWEST INSTITUTE (SAINT LOUIS)**
4260 Shoreline Dr.
Saint Louis, MO 63045
Tel: (314)344-4440; Free: 800-695-5550
Fax: (314)344-0495
Web Site: www.midwestinstitute.com/
Description: Proprietary, 2-year, coed. Awards terminal associate degrees.

■ **MINERAL AREA COLLEGE**
PO Box 1000
Park Hills, MO 63601-1000
Tel: (573)431-4593
E-mail: lhuffman@mineralarea.edu
Web Site: www.mineralarea.edu/
Description: District-supported, 2-year, coed. Part of Missouri Coordinating Board for Higher Education. Awards certificates, transfer associate, and terminal associate degrees. Founded 1922. Setting: 240-acre rural campus with easy access to St. Louis. Total enrollment: 3,784. Faculty: 335 (74 full-time, 261 part-time). Student-undergrad faculty ratio is 11:1. Full-time: 2,342 students, 61% women, 39% men. Part-time: 1,442 students, 65% women, 35% men. Students come from 13 states and territories, 7 other countries, 1% from out-of-state. 1% American Indian or Alaska Native, non-Hispanic/Latino; 1% Hispanic/Latino; 2% African American, non-Hispanic/Latino; 0.3% Asian, non-Hispanic/Latino; 0.03% Native Hawaiian or other Pacific Islander, non-Hispanic/Latino; 0.2% international. 34% 25 or older, 5% transferred in. Retention: 66% of full-time freshmen returned the following year. Core. Calendar: semesters. Academic remediation for entering students, services for LD students, advanced placement, honors program, distance learning, summer session for credit, part-time degree program, internships. Off campus study at East Central College, Jefferson College.
Entrance Requirements: Open admission except for allied health and law enforcement programs. Options: electronic application, early admission. Required: high school transcript. Entrance: noncompetitive. Application deadline: Rolling. Notification: continuous.
Costs Per Year: Application fee: $15. Area resident tuition: $2760 full-time, $92 per semester hour part-time. State resident tuition: $3660 full-time, $122 per semester hour part-time. Nonresident tuition: $4650 full-time, $155 per semester hour part-time. College room only: $3555. Room charges vary according to housing facility.

Collegiate Environment: Orientation program. Drama-theater group, choral group. Student services: personal-psychological counseling. Campus security: 24-hour patrols. 212 college housing spaces available. No special consideration for freshman housing applicants. Option: coed housing available. C. H. Cozen Learning Resource Center with 32,228 books, 3,068 microform titles, 214 serials, 4,859 audiovisual materials, an OPAC, and a Web page. 125 computers available on campus for general student use. A campuswide network can be accessed from student residence rooms and from off campus. Students can access the following: online class registration. Staffed computer lab on campus provides training in use of computers and software.

Community Environment: Park Hills (population 8,525) is located in east-central Missouri, 60 miles south of St. Louis. Kentucky, Illinois and Arkansas are not too distant. District facilities include most denominations of churches, four newspapers, four radio station and parks. Outdoor activities are hunting and fishing, tennis, golf.

■ MISSOURI BAPTIST UNIVERSITY
One College Park Dr.
Saint Louis, MO 63141-8660
Tel: (314)434-1115; Free: 877-434-1115
Fax: (314)434-7596
E-mail: admissions@mobap.edu
Web Site: www.mobap.edu/

Description: Independent Southern Baptist, comprehensive, coed. Awards associate, bachelor's, master's, and doctoral degrees and post-master's certificates. Founded 1964. Setting: 65-acre suburban campus with easy access to Saint Louis. Endowment: $3.6 million. Educational spending for the previous fiscal year: $4009 per student. Total enrollment: 5,212. Faculty: 309 (75 full-time, 234 part-time). Student-undergrad faculty ratio is 12:1. 900 applied, 58% were admitted. Full-time: 1,429 students, 55% women, 45% men. Part-time: 2,421 students, 61% women, 39% men. Students come from 34 states and territories, 13 other countries, 19% from out-of-state. 0.4% American Indian or Alaska Native, non-Hispanic/Latino; 3% Hispanic/Latino; 11% African American, non-Hispanic/Latino; 1% Asian, non-Hispanic/Latino; 0% Native Hawaiian or other Pacific Islander, non-Hispanic/Latino; 2% international. 14% live on campus, 9% transferred in. Retention: 60% of full-time freshmen returned the following year. Core. Calendar: semesters. Academic remediation for entering students, services for LD students, advanced placement, accelerated degree program, self-designed majors, honors program, independent study, distance learning, double major, summer session for credit, part-time degree program, adult/continuing education programs, internships, graduate courses open to undergrads. Off campus study at Maryville University of Saint Louis, Lindenwood University, Fontbonne University, Webster University. Study abroad program. ROTC: Army (c).

Entrance Requirements: Option: electronic application. Required: high school transcript, minimum 2 high school GPA, 1 recommendation. Required for some: SAT or ACT. Entrance: moderately difficult. Application deadlines: Rolling, Rolling for nonresidents. Notification: continuous, continuous for nonresidents. SAT Reasoning Test deadline: 8/12. SAT Subject Test deadline: 8/12. Transfer credits accepted: Yes.

Costs Per Year: Application fee: $30. Comprehensive fee: $28,884 includes full-time tuition ($19,730), mandatory fees ($924), and college room and board ($8230). Full-time tuition and fees vary according to course load and location. Room and board charges vary according to board plan and housing facility. Part-time tuition: $680 per credit. Part-time mandatory fees: $22 per credit, $30 per term. Part-time tuition and fees vary according to course load and location.

Collegiate Environment: Orientation program. Drama-theater group, choral group, student-run radio station. Social organizations: 21 open to all. Most popular organizations: Baptist Collegiate Ministry, Students in Free Enterprise (SIFE), Missouri State Teacher's Association, Fellowship of Christian Athletes, Ministerial Alliance. Major annual events: Homecoming, The Perk - the event, Welcome Weekend. Student services: personal-psychological counseling. Campus security: 24-hour emergency response devices and patrols, late night transport-escort service, controlled dormitory access, self-defense classes. 250 college housing spaces available; all were occupied in 2012-13. No special consideration for freshman housing applicants. Options: men-only, women-only housing available. Jung-Kellogg Library with 70,315 books, 3,708 microform titles, 200 serials, 2,631 audiovisual materials, an OPAC, and a Web page. Operations spending for the previous fiscal year: $418,402. 100 computers available on campus for general student use. A campuswide network can be accessed from student

residence rooms. Students can access the following: online class registration. Staffed computer lab on campus provides training in use of computers, software, and the Internet.

Community Environment: See Washington University.

■ MISSOURI COLLEGE
1405 S Hanley Rd.
Brentwood, MO 63117
Tel: (314)821-7700; Free: 800-216-6732
Web Site: www.missouricollege.edu/

Description: Proprietary, primarily 2-year, coed. Awards diplomas, terminal associate, and bachelor's degrees. Founded 1963. Total enrollment: 508. 43% 25 or older.

Entrance Requirements: Open admission. Required: essay, interview. Application deadline: Rolling.

■ MISSOURI SOUTHERN STATE UNIVERSITY
3950 E Newman Rd.
Joplin, MO 64801-1595
Tel: (417)625-9300; Free: 866-818-MSSU
Fax: (417)659-4429
E-mail: admissions@mssu.edu
Web Site: www.mssu.edu/

Description: State-supported, comprehensive, coed. Awards associate, bachelor's, and master's degrees. Founded 1937. Setting: 350-acre small town campus. Total enrollment: 5,591. Faculty: 306 (206 full-time, 100 part-time). Student-undergrad faculty ratio is 18:1. 1,691 applied, 97% were admitted. Full-time: 4,039 students, 57% women, 43% men. Part-time: 1,497 students, 59% women, 41% men. 3% American Indian or Alaska Native, non-Hispanic/Latino; 3% Hispanic/Latino; 4% African American, non-Hispanic/Latino; 1% Asian, non-Hispanic/Latino; 0.1% Native Hawaiian or other Pacific Islander, non-Hispanic/Latino; 2% international. 8% transferred in. Retention: 60% of full-time freshmen returned the following year. Academic areas with the most degrees conferred: business/marketing; education; English. Core. Calendar: semesters. Academic remediation for entering students, ESL program, services for LD students, advanced placement, accelerated degree program, honors program, independent study, distance learning, double major, summer session for credit, part-time degree program, adult/continuing education programs, co-op programs and internships. Off campus study at Nevada Consortium. Study abroad program.

Entrance Requirements: Options: electronic application, deferred admission, international baccalaureate accepted. Required: high school transcript, class rank, SAT or ACT, SAT and SAT Subject Tests or ACT. Recommended: ACT. Required for some: 2 recommendations, Michigan Test of English Language Proficiency. Entrance: moderately difficult. Application deadline: 8/1. Notification: continuous. SAT Reasoning Test deadline: 8/1.

Costs Per Year: Application fee: $25. State resident tuition: $4564 full-time, $143 per credit hour part-time. Nonresident tuition: $9128 full-time, $297.20 per credit hour part-time. Mandatory fees: $526 full-time. Full-time tuition and fees vary according to course load. College room and board: $5976. Room and board charges vary according to board plan and housing facility.

Collegiate Environment: Orientation program. Drama-theater group, choral group, marching band, student-run newspaper, radio station. Social organizations: national fraternities, national sororities, local fraternities. Student services: health clinic, personal-psychological counseling. Campus security: 24-hour emergency response devices and patrols, late night transport-escort service, controlled dormitory access, security at campus events, emergency vehicle assistance, safety awareness information to students. Spiva Library with an OPAC and a Web page.

Community Environment: Located in southwest Missouri at the northern gateway of the Ozark Resort area, Joplin (population 47,000) is surrounded by numerous spring fed fishing streams in scenic hill country. The city has many manufacturing and wholesale firms as well as industry involving the mining and processing of zinc ore. All forms of commercial transportation are available. Part-time employment is available. There are over 100 churches, 14 elementary schools, 1 junior high school, 1 high school, 2 four-year colleges, and 2 hospitals.

■ MISSOURI STATE UNIVERSITY
901 S National
Springfield, MO 65897
Tel: (417)836-5000; Free: 800-492-7900
Fax: (417)836-6334
E-mail: info@missouristate.edu

Web Site: www.missouristate.edu/

Description: State-supported, comprehensive, coed. Awards bachelor's, master's, and doctoral degrees and post-master's certificates. Founded 1905. Setting: 225-acre suburban campus. Endowment: $63 million. Research spending for the previous fiscal year: $12.9 million. Educational spending for the previous fiscal year: $5424 per student. Total enrollment: 20,629. Faculty: 1,056 (695 full-time, 361 part-time). Student-undergrad faculty ratio is 20:1. 7,342 applied, 83% were admitted. 24% from top 10% of their high school class, 53% from top quarter, 83% from top half. Full-time: 13,465 students, 57% women, 43% men. Part-time: 3,969 students, 55% women, 45% men. Students come from 50 states and territories, 83 other countries, 8% from out-of-state. 1% American Indian or Alaska Native, non-Hispanic/Latino; 3% Hispanic/Latino; 4% African American, non-Hispanic/Latino; 1% Asian, non-Hispanic/Latino; 0.2% Native Hawaiian or other Pacific Islander, non-Hispanic/Latino; 4% international. 16% 25 or older, 23% live on campus, 9% transferred in. Retention: 75% of full-time freshmen returned the following year. Academic areas with the most degrees conferred: business/marketing; education; social sciences. Core. Calendar: semesters. ESL program, services for LD students, advanced placement, accelerated degree program, self-designed majors, freshman honors college, honors program, independent study, distance learning, double major, summer session for credit, part-time degree program, co-op programs and internships, graduate courses open to undergrads. Off campus study at National Student Exchange. Study abroad program. ROTC: Army.

Entrance Requirements: Options: electronic application, international baccalaureate accepted. Required: high school transcript, SAT or ACT. Required for some: essay, interview. Entrance: moderately difficult. Application deadline: 7/20. Notification: continuous. SAT Reasoning Test deadline: 7/20. Transfer credits accepted: Yes.

Costs Per Year: Application fee: $35. State resident tuition: $6014 full-time, $200.48 per credit hour part-time. Nonresident tuition: $12,360 full-time, $412 per credit hour part-time. Mandatory fees: $778 full-time. Full-time tuition and fees vary according to course level, course load, and program. Part-time tuition varies according to course level, course load, and program. College room and board: $6844. Room and board charges vary according to board plan, housing facility, and location.

Collegiate Environment: Orientation program. Drama-theater group, choral group, marching band, student-run newspaper, radio station. Social organizations: 348 open to all; national fraternities, national sororities. Most popular organizations: Residence Hall Association, Campus Ministries, Fraternity and Sorority Life, Student Government Association, Student Activities Council. Major annual events: New Student Festival, Homecoming, Bear Bash. Student services: legal services, health clinic, personal-psychological counseling. Campus security: 24-hour emergency response devices and patrols, late night transport-escort service, controlled dormitory access, on-campus police substation. 4,000 college housing spaces available; all were occupied in 2012-13. Freshmen guaranteed college housing. On-campus residence required in freshman year. Option: coed housing available. Meyer Library plus 3 others with 1.7 million books, 1.1 million microform titles, 4,206 serials, 20,050 audiovisual materials, an OPAC, and a Web page. Operations spending for the previous fiscal year: $6.1 million. 1,940 computers available on campus for general student use. A campuswide network can be accessed from student residence rooms and from off campus. Students can access the following: online class registration. Staffed computer lab on campus (open 24 hours a day) provides training in use of computers, software, and the Internet.

Community Environment: Springfield (population 150,290) is Missouri's third largest city and is within one hour's drive from many of the popular resort and vacation areas of the southwest Missouri Ozark region. Springfield has become a major health care center for the region and is home to several major businesses and industries including Bass Pro Shops, General Electric, Kraft, and Associated Wholesale Grocers.

■ MISSOURI STATE UNIVERSITY–WEST PLAINS

128 Garfield

West Plains, MO 65775

Tel: (417)255-7255; Free: 888-466-7897

E-mail: melissajett@missouristate.edu

Web Site: wp.missouristate.edu/

Description: State-supported, 2-year, coed. Part of Missouri State University. Awards certificates, transfer associate, and terminal associate degrees. Founded 1963. Setting: 20-acre small town campus. Endowment: $6.4 million. Educational spending for the previous fiscal year: $1041 per student. Total enrollment: 2,102. Faculty: 110 (33 full-time, 77 part-time).

Student-undergrad faculty ratio is 25:1. 1,027 applied, 76% were admitted. 8% from top 10% of their high school class, 26% from top quarter, 54% from top half. Full-time: 1,260 students, 57% women, 43% men. Part-time: 842 students, 62% women, 38% men. Students come from 27 states and territories, 3 other countries, 3% from out-of-state. 1% American Indian or Alaska Native, non-Hispanic/Latino; 1% Hispanic/Latino; 2% African American, non-Hispanic/Latino; 1% Asian, non-Hispanic/Latino; 1% international. 37% 25 or older, 4% live on campus, 4% transferred in. Retention: 45% of full-time freshmen returned the following year. Core. Calendar: semesters. Academic remediation for entering students, services for LD students, advanced placement, honors program, distance learning, summer session for credit, part-time degree program, adult/continuing education programs, co-op programs and internships. Off campus study at Missouri State University - Mountain Grove. Study abroad program.

Entrance Requirements: Open admission except for the nursing program which requires a separate application with a March 1 deadline. Admission eligibility requirements include a ranking score computation based on GPA and ACT or COMPASS scores. Option: electronic application. Required for some: high school transcript. Entrance: noncompetitive. Application deadlines: 8/20, 8/20 for nonresidents. Notification: continuous, continuous for nonresidents. Transfer credits accepted: Yes.

Costs Per Year: Application fee: $15. State resident tuition: $3624 full-time, $111 per quarter hour part-time. Nonresident tuition: $6954 full-time, $222 per quarter hour part-time. Mandatory fees: $294 full-time, $5 per quarter hour part-time, $72 per year part-time. Full-time tuition and fees vary according to course load, location, and program. Part-time tuition and fees vary according to course load and location. College room and board: $5300. Room and board charges vary according to board plan.

Collegiate Environment: Orientation program. Social organizations: 27 open to all. Most popular organizations: Student Government Association, Chi Alpha, Adult Students in Higher Education, Lambda Lambda Lambda, Programming Board. Major annual events: Homecoming, University Life Talent Show, Welcome Week. Student services: legal services, personal-psychological counseling. Campus security: access only with key. 60 college housing spaces available; all were occupied in 2012-13. No special consideration for freshman housing applicants. Options: men-only, women-only housing available. Garnett Library with 40,233 books, 8,347 microform titles, 149 serials, 1,280 audiovisual materials, an OPAC, and a Web page. 120 computers available on campus for general student use. A campuswide network can be accessed from student residence rooms and from off campus. Students can access the following: online class registration, Portal, LMS, File Storage, Internet Access, On-line account review and billpay. Staffed computer lab on campus provides training in use of computers, software, and the Internet.

■ MISSOURI TECH

1690 Country Club Plz. Dr.

Saint Charles, MO 63303

Tel: (636)573-9300; Free: 800-960-TECH

Fax: (636)573-9398

Description: Proprietary, 4-year, coed. Awards associate and bachelor's degrees. Founded 1932. Setting: suburban campus. Total enrollment: 114. 21 applied. 63% 25 or older. Calendar: semesters. Advanced placement, accelerated degree program, summer session for credit, part-time degree program, adult/continuing education programs, internships.

Entrance Requirements: Option: electronic application. Required: high school transcript. Recommended: ACT. Required for some: interview. Entrance: moderately difficult. Application deadline: Rolling.

Collegiate Environment: Campus security: 24-hour emergency response devices.

■ MISSOURI UNIVERSITY OF SCIENCE AND TECHNOLOGY

1870 Miner Cir.

Rolla, MO 65409

Tel: (573)341-4111; Free: 800-522-0938

E-mail: admissions@mst.edu

Web Site: www.mst.edu/

Description: State-supported, university, coed. Part of University of Missouri System. Awards bachelor's, master's, and doctoral degrees. Founded 1870. Setting: 284-acre small town campus. Endowment: $138 million. Total enrollment: 7,647. Faculty: 493 (343 full-time, 150 part-time). Student-undergrad faculty ratio is 17:1. 2,842 applied, 90% were admitted. 35% from top 10% of their high school class, 70% from top quarter, 92% from top half. Full-time: 5,260 students, 23% women, 77% men. Part-time: 583 students, 29%

women, 71% men. 16% from out-of-state. 0.4% American Indian or Alaska Native, non-Hispanic/Latino; 2% Hispanic/Latino; 4% African American, non-Hispanic/Latino; 2% Asian, non-Hispanic/Latino; 0.2% Native Hawaiian or other Pacific Islander, non-Hispanic/Latino; 5% international. 7% 25 or older, 51% live on campus, 6% transferred in. Retention: 85% of full-time freshmen returned the following year. Academic areas with the most degrees conferred: engineering; computer and information sciences; physical sciences. Core. Calendar: semesters. Academic remediation for entering students, ESL program, services for LD students, advanced placement, accelerated degree program, freshman honors program, honors program, independent study, distance learning, double major, summer session for credit, part-time degree program, adult/continuing education programs, co-op programs and internships, graduate courses open to undergrads. Off campus study at University of Missouri-Columbia. Study abroad program. ROTC: Army, Naval (c), Air Force.

Entrance Requirements: Options: electronic application, early admission, deferred admission, international baccalaureate accepted. Required: high school transcript, SAT or ACT. Recommended: essay, ACT. Entrance: very difficult. Application deadline: 7/1. Notification: continuous. SAT Reasoning Test deadline: 7/1. Transfer credits accepted: Yes.

Costs Per Year: Application fee: $50. State resident tuition: $8082 full-time, $269.40 per credit hour part-time. Nonresident tuition: $22,398 full-time, $746.60 per credit hour part-time. Mandatory fees: $1268 full-time, $269.40 per credit hour part-time. Full-time tuition and fees vary according to course load, degree level, and program. Part-time tuition and fees vary according to course load, degree level, and program. College room and board: $8900. College room only: $5610. Room and board charges vary according to board plan, housing facility, and location.

Collegiate Environment: Orientation program. Drama-theater group, choral group, marching band, student-run newspaper, radio station. Social organizations: 200 open to all; national fraternities, national sororities, local sororities; 22% of eligible men and 20% of eligible women are members. Most popular organizations: student government, Student Union Board, Residence Hall Association, academic organizations, service organizations. Major annual events: Homecoming, St. Patrick's celebration, Parents' Day. Student services: health clinic, personal-psychological counseling. Campus security: 24-hour emergency response devices and patrols, student patrols, late night transport-escort service, controlled dormitory access, crime prevention programs. 1,758 college housing spaces available; 1,711 were occupied in 2012-13. Freshmen guaranteed college housing. On-campus residence required through sophomore year. Options: coed, men-only, women-only housing available. Curtis Laws Wilson Library with 470,990 books, 570,970 microform titles, 5,920 serials, 7,590 audiovisual materials, an OPAC, and a Web page. 980 computers available on campus for general student use. Computer purchase/lease plans available. A campuswide network can be accessed from student residence rooms and from off campus. Students can access the following: online class registration. Staffed computer lab on campus (open 24 hours a day) provides training in use of computers, software, and the Internet.

Community Environment: Rolla, population 17,717, is one of the most scenic sections of the Ozarks, where excellent fishing and hunting are available. Situated in the center of Missouri, on Interstate 44. A number of churches of most denominations, a hospital, clinics, a library and civic organizations are all a part of the community services. Lake and river recreation available, caves to explore, tennis courts, baseball diamonds, golf courses, and bowling alleys provide recreation. Part time employment for students is available. Rolla originally was an Ozarks farm trade center. After the establishment of the university campus, several large and important federal and state government agencies located here. Today the community is unusual in its concentration of about 1,000 professional engineers, geologists, cartographers, mathematicians, and technicians who are employed by these offices.

■ **MISSOURI VALLEY COLLEGE**
500 E College
Marshall, MO 65340-3197
Tel: (660)831-4000
Fax: (660)831-4039
E-mail: admissions@moval.edu
Web Site: www.moval.edu/
Description: Independent, 4-year, coed, affiliated with Presbyterian Church. Awards associate and bachelor's degrees. Founded 1889. Setting: 140-acre small town campus with easy access to Kansas City. Endowment: $3.4 million. Total enrollment: 1,639. Faculty: 90 (59 full-time, 31 part-time). Student-

undergrad faculty ratio is 18:1. 1,543 applied, 57% were admitted. 4% from top 10% of their high school class, 18% from top quarter, 46% from top half. Full-time: 1,394 students, 40% women, 60% men. Part-time: 245 students, 61% women, 39% men. Students come from 42 states and territories, 29 other countries, 28% from out-of-state. 9% 25 or older, 73% live on campus, 8% transferred in. Retention: 55% of full-time freshmen returned the following year. Academic areas with the most degrees conferred: business/marketing; homeland security, law enforcement, firefighting, and protective services; health professions and related sciences. Core. Calendar: semesters plus 2 summer sessions. Academic remediation for entering students, ESL program, services for LD students, advanced placement, self-designed majors, independent study, distance learning, double major, summer session for credit, part-time degree program, adult/continuing education programs, co-op programs and internships. Study abroad program. ROTC: Army.

Entrance Requirements: Options: electronic application, early admission, deferred admission. Required: high school transcript, SAT or ACT. Recommended: minimum 2.0 high school GPA, interview. Required for some: essay, 3 recommendations, interview. Entrance: minimally difficult. Application deadline: Rolling. Notification: continuous.

Collegiate Environment: Orientation program. Drama-theater group, choral group, student-run newspaper, radio station. Social organizations: 33 open to all; national fraternities, national sororities; 20% of eligible men and 15% of eligible women are members. Most popular organizations: student government, Valley players, American Humanics. Major annual events: Homecoming, Family Weekend, Spring Fest. Student services: health clinic, personal-psychological counseling. Campus security: 24-hour emergency response devices, student patrols, late night transport-escort service, controlled dormitory access, evening patrol by trained security personnel. Murrell Memorial Library plus 1 other with 71,203 books, 26,373 microform titles, 338 serials, 2,456 audiovisual materials, an OPAC, and a Web page. Operations spending for the previous fiscal year: $141,566. 250 computers available on campus for general student use. A campuswide network can be accessed from student residence rooms and from off campus. Students can access the following: online class registration. Staffed computer lab on campus provides training in use of computers, software, and the Internet.

Community Environment: Marshall, population 12,400, is located 80 miles east of Kansas City and bus transportation is available. Community recreational facilities include a bowling alley, skating rink, and a philharmonic orchestra. The Indian Foothills Park, at the eastern city limits, provides tennis courts, ball fields, a golf course, swimming, fishing, and picnic grounds.

■ **MISSOURI WESTERN STATE UNIVERSITY**
4525 Downs Dr.
Saint Joseph, MO 64507-2294
Tel: (816)271-4200; Free: 800-662-7041
Fax: (816)271-5833
E-mail: admission@missouriwestern.edu
Web Site: www.missouriwestern.edu/
Description: State-supported, comprehensive, coed. Awards associate, bachelor's, and master's degrees. Founded 1915. Setting: 744-acre suburban campus with easy access to Kansas City. Total enrollment: 6,056. Faculty: 393 (185 full-time, 208 part-time). Student-undergrad faculty ratio is 19:1. 3,472 applied, 100% were admitted. 10% from top 10% of their high school class, 27% from top quarter, 58% from top half. Full-time: 4,077 students, 57% women, 43% men. Part-time: 1,808 students, 55% women, 45% men. Students come from 32 states and territories, 21 other countries, 8% from out-of-state. 1% American Indian or Alaska Native, non-Hispanic/Latino; 1% Hispanic/Latino; 11% African American, non-Hispanic/Latino; 1% Asian, non-Hispanic/Latino; 0.3% Native Hawaiian or other Pacific Islander, non-Hispanic/Latino; 1% international. 27% 25 or older, 21% live on campus, 6% transferred in. Retention: 58% of full-time freshmen returned the following year. Academic areas with the most degrees conferred: business/marketing; health professions and related sciences; education. Core. Calendar: semesters. Academic remediation for entering students, ESL program, services for LD students, advanced placement, accelerated degree program, self-designed majors, freshman honors college, honors program, independent study, distance learning, double major, summer session for credit, part-time degree program, adult/continuing education programs, internships, graduate courses open to undergrads. Off campus study. Study abroad program. ROTC: Army.

Entrance Requirements: Open admission. Options: electronic application, early admission, international baccalaureate accepted. Required: high school transcript, SAT or ACT. Entrance: noncompetitive. Application deadline: 5/1. Notification: continuous. Transfer credits accepted: Yes.

Costs Per Year: Application fee: $15. State resident tuition: $5,667 full-time, $188.91 per credit hour part-time. Nonresident tuition: $11,171 full-time, $372.36 per credit hour part-time. Mandatory fees: $718 full-time. Full-time tuition and fees vary according to location and program. Part-time tuition varies according to location and program. College room and board: $6918. Room and board charges vary according to board plan and housing facility.

Collegiate Environment: Orientation program. Drama-theater group, choral group, marching band, student-run newspaper. Social organizations: 77 open to all; national fraternities, national sororities; 3% of eligible men and 4% of eligible women are members. Major annual events: Homecoming, Family Day, Springfest. Student services: health clinic, personal-psychological counseling, women's center. Campus security: 24-hour emergency response devices and patrols, student patrols, late night transport-escort service, controlled dormitory access. 1,336 college housing spaces available; 1,247 were occupied in 2012-13. No special consideration for freshman housing applicants. On-campus residence required in freshman year. Option: coed housing available. Missouri Western State University Library with 224,131 books, 110,502 microform titles, 3,214 serials, 18,317 audiovisual materials, an OPAC, and a Web page. 618 computers available on campus for general student use. Computer purchase/lease plans available. A campuswide network can be accessed from student residence rooms and from off campus. Students can access the following: online class registration, Personal online storage. Staffed computer lab on campus provides training in use of computers, software, and the Internet.

Community Environment: Located in America's heartland, St. Joseph was one of only 10 cities nationwide to receive the prestigious 1997 All-America City Award. A thriving business community has seen St. Joseph grow from a booming frontier town to the market place for the four-state area of Missouri, Iowa, Kansas, and Nebraska. With a population of 72,600, St. Joseph boasts metropolitan advantages blended with small town flavor. The city offers 26-miles of parkway system, Olympic-size ice rink, YMCA and YWCA, St. Joseph Symphony, Performing Arts Association Arts Association, Robidoux Resident Theatre, and 13 museums, including the Albrecht-Kemper Museum of Art; Jesse James House; Pony Express Stables and the St. Joseph Museum.

■ MOBERLY AREA COMMUNITY COLLEGE

101 College Ave.
Moberly, MO 65270-1304
Tel: (660)263-4110; Free: 800-622-2070
Fax: (660)263-6252
E-mail: info@macc.edu
Web Site: www.macc.edu/

Description: State and locally supported, 2-year, coed. Awards certificates, transfer associate, and terminal associate degrees. Founded 1927. Setting: 32-acre small town campus. Total enrollment: 4,009. Faculty: 233 (67 full-time, 166 part-time). Student-undergrad faculty ratio is 21:1. 25% from top quarter of their high school class, 60% from top half. Full-time: 2,023 students, 57% women, 43% men. Part-time: 1,986 students, 63% women, 37% men. Students come from 21 states and territories, 9 other countries, 1% from out-of-state. 23% 25 or older, 1% live on campus, 5% transferred in. Retention: 44% of full-time freshmen returned the following year. Core. Calendar: semesters. Academic remediation for entering students, services for LD students, advanced placement, honors program, distance learning, summer session for credit, part-time degree program, adult/continuing education programs, co-op programs and internships. Study abroad program.

Entrance Requirements: Open admission except for nursing, law enforcement, and medical laboratory technician programs. Options: electronic application, international baccalaureate accepted. Required: high school transcript. Recommended: ACT. Required for some: ACT. Entrance: noncompetitive. Application deadline: Rolling. Notification: continuous until 9/1.

Collegiate Environment: Orientation program. Drama-theater group, choral group, student-run newspaper. Social organizations: 9 open to all; local fraternities, local sororities; 10% of eligible men and 10% of eligible women are members. Most popular organizations: Phi Theta Kappa, Student Nurses Association, Affiliate of the Missouri Association for the Education of Young Children, Delta Epsilon Chi, Multicultural Club. Major annual events: Theatrical production, Fall Picnic, Spring Picnic. Campus security: student patrols, controlled dormitory access, extensive surveillance. Kate Stamper Wilhite Library with 23,027 books, 80 microform titles, 88 serials, an OPAC, and a Web page. 750 computers available on campus for general student use. A campuswide network can be accessed from student residence rooms and

from off campus. Students can access the following: online class registration. Staffed computer lab on campus provides training in use of computers, software, and the Internet.

Community Environment: Moberly (population 13,900) is the county seat of Randolph County, in central Missouri. The town is served by one major railroad and the Omar Bradley Airport. Community facilities include churches of all denominations, a regional hospital, and Little Dixie Regional Library. A moderately large shopping district is available. Student employment is available in retail, restaurants, filling stations, and warehouses. Housing may be found in hotels, motels, and apartments. Outdoor activities are golf, boating, fishing, hunting, baseball, and tennis.

■ NATIONAL AMERICAN UNIVERSITY

7490 NW 87th St.
Kansas City, MO 64153
Tel: (816)412-5500
E-mail: zradmissions@national.edu
Web Site: www.national.edu/

Description: Proprietary, 4-year, coed. Part of National College. Awards associate and bachelor's degrees. Founded 1941. Setting: 1-acre urban campus. Total enrollment: 315. 77% 25 or older. Independent study, distance learning, summer session for credit, part-time degree program, external degree program, co-op programs. Study abroad program.

Entrance Requirements: Open admission. Options: early admission, deferred admission, international baccalaureate accepted. Required: high school transcript, interview. Entrance: noncompetitive. Application deadline: Rolling. Notification: continuous until 9/12.

Collegiate Environment: Campus security: 24-hour patrols. Learning Resource Center plus 1 other with 1,500 books and 60 serials.

■ NORTH CENTRAL MISSOURI COLLEGE

1301 Main St.
Trenton, MO 64683-1824
Tel: (660)359-3948
E-mail: megoodin@mail.ncmissouri.edu
Web Site: www.ncmissouri.edu/

Description: District-supported, 2-year, coed. Awards certificates, transfer associate, and terminal associate degrees. Founded 1925. Setting: 2-acre small town campus. Endowment: $443,875. Total enrollment: 1,505. Faculty: 94 (33 full-time, 61 part-time). Student-undergrad faculty ratio is 16:1. 708 applied, 88% were admitted. Full-time: 796 students, 72% women, 28% men. Part-time: 709 students, 70% women, 30% men. Students come from 10 states and territories, 1% from out-of-state. 28% 25 or older, 6% transferred in. Retention: 69% of full-time freshmen returned the following year. Calendar: semesters. Academic remediation for entering students, services for LD students, advanced placement, accelerated degree program, distance learning, summer session for credit, part-time degree program, adult/continuing education programs, co-op programs and internships.

Entrance Requirements: Open admission except for health occupations programs. Required: high school transcript. Recommended: SAT or ACT. Entrance: noncompetitive. Application deadline: Rolling.

Costs Per Year: Application fee: $15. Area resident tuition: $2100 full-time, $70 per credit hour part-time. State resident tuition: $3060 full-time, $102 per credit hour part-time. Nonresident tuition: $4200 full-time, $140 per credit hour part-time. Mandatory fees: $600 full-time, $20 per credit hour part-time. Full-time tuition and fees vary according to location and program. Part-time tuition and fees vary according to location and program. College room and board: $5008. Room and board charges vary according to board plan.

Collegiate Environment: Orientation program. Drama-theater group. Social organizations: local fraternities, local sororities. Most popular organizations: Student Nurses Association for AND, Student Practical Nurses Association, Delta Epsilon Chi (business), Pre-med Club, Postsecondary Agriculture Students. Student services: personal-psychological counseling. Campus security: controlled dormitory access. North Central Missouri College Library with 34,748 books, 1,886 microform titles, 6,122 serials, 1,326 audiovisual materials, an OPAC, and a Web page. 159 computers available on campus for general student use. A campuswide network can be accessed. Students can access the following: online class registration. Staffed computer lab on campus provides training in use of computers, software, and the Internet.

Community Environment: A rural location in central north Missouri, Trenton (population 6,001) has 11 churches, libraries, a hospital, and numerous civic, fraternal, and veteran's organizations. Several lakes are nearby offering excellent fishing, swimming, and boating. City parks also provide facilities for recreation. Part-time employment is available.

■ NORTHWEST MISSOURI STATE UNIVERSITY

800 University Dr.

Maryville, MO 64468-6001

Tel: (660)562-1212; Free: 800-633-1175

Fax: (660)562-1121

E-mail: admissions@nwmissouri.edu

Web Site: www.nwmissouri.edu/

Description: State-supported, comprehensive, coed. Part of Missouri Coordinating Board for Higher Education. Awards bachelor's and master's degrees and post-master's certificates. Founded 1905. Setting: 370-acre small town campus with easy access to Kansas City. Research spending for the previous fiscal year: $441,089. Educational spending for the previous fiscal year: $7811 per student. Total enrollment: 6,831. Faculty: 300 (245 full-time, 55 part-time). Student-undergrad faculty ratio is 23:1. 4,412 applied, 88% were admitted. 14% from top 10% of their high school class, 39% from top quarter, 75% from top half. Full-time: 5,335 students, 56% women, 44% men. Part-time: 679 students, 55% women, 45% men. Students come from 48 states and territories, 27 other countries, 26% from out-of-state. 0.3% American Indian or Alaska Native, non-Hispanic/Latino; 3% Hispanic/Latino; 6% African American, non-Hispanic/Latino; 1% Asian, non-Hispanic/Latino; 0.2% Native Hawaiian or other Pacific Islander, non-Hispanic/Latino; 2% international. 5% 25 or older, 38% live on campus, 5% transferred in. Retention: 67% of full-time freshmen returned the following year. Academic areas with the most degrees conferred: business/marketing; education; psychology. Core. Calendar: trimesters. Academic remediation for entering students, ESL program, services for LD students, advanced placement, honors program, independent study, distance learning, double major, summer session for credit, part-time degree program, internships, graduate courses open to undergrads. Off campus study at Black Hawk Community College, Byuksung College, Capital University of Economics and Business- China, Central Community College, Colby Community College, Colorado Online Community College, Cottey College, Crowder College, Des Moines Area Community College, East Central College, Eastern Iowa Community College, Hawkeye Community College, Highland Community College - Freeport, IL, Highland Community College - Highland, KS, Indian Hills Community College, Iowa Central Community College. Study abroad program. ROTC: Army.

Entrance Requirements: Options: electronic application, deferred admission, international baccalaureate accepted. Required: high school transcript, minimum 2 high school GPA, SAT or ACT. Required for some: interview. Entrance: moderately difficult. Application deadlines: Rolling, Rolling for nonresidents. Notification: continuous, continuous for nonresidents. Preference given to state residents. SAT Reasoning Test deadline: 8/1. SAT Subject Test deadline: 8/1. Transfer credits accepted: Yes.

Costs Per Year: Application fee: $25. One-time mandatory fee: $140. State resident tuition: $5237 full-time, $174.56 per credit hour part-time. Nonresident tuition: $11,345 full-time, $378.18 per credit hour part-time. Mandatory fees: $2,482 full-time, $82.75 per credit hour part-time. Full-time tuition and fees vary according to course load, location, and reciprocity agreements. Part-time tuition and fees vary according to course load and location. College room and board: $8614. College room only: $5538. Room and board charges vary according to board plan and housing facility.

Collegiate Environment: Orientation program. Drama-theater group, choral group, marching band, student-run newspaper, radio station. Social organizations: 180 open to all; national fraternities, national sororities, local sororities; 18% of eligible men and 15% of eligible women are members. Most popular organizations: student government, Residence Hall Association, Greek Life. Major annual events: Homecoming, Family Day, Greek Week. Student services: health clinic, personal-psychological counseling, women's center. Campus security: 24-hour emergency response devices and patrols, student patrols, late night transport-escort service, controlled dormitory access, security personnel are all police officers. 2,942 college housing spaces available; 2,285 were occupied in 2012-13. Freshmen guaranteed college housing. On-campus residence required in freshman year. Option: coed housing available. Owens Library with 359,371 books, 807,678 microform titles, 26,629 serials, 5,972 audiovisual materials, an OPAC, and a Web page. Operations spending for the previous fiscal year: $1.7 million. 7,000 computers available on campus for general student use. Computer purchase/lease plans available. A campuswide network can be accessed from student residence rooms and from off campus. Students can access the following: online class registration, online courses with library and databases. Staffed computer lab on campus provides training in use of computers, software, and the Internet.

Community Environment: Maryville (population 10,500) is a rural area in northwest Missouri. Dormitories, fraternity houses, and private homes provide housing. Community facilities include a library, 13 churches, a hospital, and several civic, national, and international branches of clubs and organizations are represented. Train and bus transportation is available. 90 miles from Kansas City, 45 from St. Joseph, 110 from Omaha and 125 from Des Moines.

■ OZARK CHRISTIAN COLLEGE

1111 N Main St.

Joplin, MO 64801-4804

Tel: (417)624-2518; Free: 800-299-4622

Fax: (417)624-0090

E-mail: occadmin@occ.edu

Web Site: www.occ.edu/

Description: Independent Christian, 4-year, coed. Awards associate and bachelor's degrees. Founded 1942. Setting: 110-acre small town campus. Faculty: 60 (30 full-time, 30 part-time). Student-undergrad faculty ratio is 19:1. 63% live on campus. Calendar: semesters. Academic remediation for entering students, ESL program, services for LD students, distance learning, double major, summer session for credit, part-time degree program, adult/continuing education programs, internships.

Entrance Requirements: Option: electronic application. Required: essay, high school transcript, 2 recommendations, SAT or ACT. Required for some: interview. Entrance: noncompetitive. Application deadline: 8/5.

Collegiate Environment: Orientation program. Drama-theater group, choral group, student-run radio station. Social organizations: 3 open to all. Most popular organizations: Family Outreach Group, God's Spokesman, Imagine. Major annual events: Parents' Day, Living Christmas Tree, preaching/teaching convention. Student services: health clinic, personal-psychological counseling. Campus security: 24-hour emergency response devices, controlled dormitory access, 12-hour patrols by trained security personnel. Seth Wilson Library with 59,808 books, 182 microform titles, 362 serials, an OPAC, and a Web page. 28 computers available on campus for general student use. Staffed computer lab on campus.

■ OZARKS TECHNICAL COMMUNITY COLLEGE

1001 E Chestnut Expy.

Springfield, MO 65802

Tel: (417)447-7500

Fax: (417)895-7161

Web Site: www.otc.edu/

Description: District-supported, 2-year, coed. Part of Missouri Coordinating Board for Higher Education. Awards certificates, diplomas, transfer associate, and terminal associate degrees. Founded 1990. Setting: urban campus. Total enrollment: 15,179. Faculty: 667 (188 full-time, 479 part-time). Student-undergrad faculty ratio is 25:1. Full-time: 7,447 students, 56% women, 44% men. Part-time: 7,732 students, 60% women, 40% men. Students come from 31 states and territories, 2% from out-of-state. 1% American Indian or Alaska Native, non-Hispanic/Latino; 2% Hispanic/Latino; 3% African American, non-Hispanic/Latino; 1% Asian, non-Hispanic/Latino; 0.2% Native Hawaiian or other Pacific Islander, non-Hispanic/Latino; 0.03% international. 39% 25 or older, 6% transferred in. Retention: 59% of full-time freshmen returned the following year. Core. Calendar: semesters. Academic remediation for entering students, ESL program, services for LD students, honors program, distance learning, double major, summer session for credit, part-time degree program, adult/continuing education programs, co-op programs and internships. Off campus study at Missouri State University.

Entrance Requirements: Open admission OTC is an open admission college. Some programs within the College have selective admission. (Example: Allied Health programs). Option: electronic application. Required: high school transcript. Entrance: noncompetitive. Application deadlines: Rolling, Rolling for nonresidents. Notification: continuous, continuous for nonresidents. Transfer credits accepted: Yes.

Costs Per Year: Application fee: $0. Area resident tuition: $2184 full-time, $91 per credit hour part-time. State resident tuition: $3084 full-time, $128.50 per credit hour part-time. Nonresident tuition: $4056 full-time, $169 per credit hour part-time. Mandatory fees: $500 full-time.

Collegiate Environment: Orientation program. Student-run newspaper. Most popular organization: Phi Theta Kappa. Major annual event: Annual Student Picnic. Student services: personal-psychological counseling. Campus security: 24-hour emergency response devices. College housing not available. Library plus 1 other with 6,000 books, 190 serials, an OPAC, and a Web page. 150 computers available on campus for general student use. A campuswide network can be accessed. Students can access the following: online class registration. Staffed computer lab on campus.

■ **PARK UNIVERSITY**
8700 NW River Park Dr.
Parkville, MO 64152-3795
Tel: (816)741-2000; Free: 800-745-7275
Fax: (816)741-4462
E-mail: admissions@mail.park.edu
Web Site: www.park.edu/
Description: Independent, comprehensive, coed. Awards associate, bachelor's, and master's degrees. Founded 1875. Setting: 800-acre suburban campus with easy access to Kansas City. Endowment: $42.5 million. Total enrollment: 2,458. Faculty: 174 (94 full-time, 80 part-time). Student-undergrad faculty ratio is 11:1. 778 applied, 69% were admitted. 31% from top 10% of their high school class, 53% from top quarter, 77% from top half. 2 class presidents, 1 valedictorian, 20 student government officers. Full-time: 1,204 students, 55% women, 45% men. Part-time: 470 students, 61% women, 39% men. Students come from 49 states and territories, 96 other countries, 20% from out-of-state. 1% American Indian or Alaska Native, non-Hispanic/Latino; 5% Hispanic/Latino; 10% African American, non-Hispanic/Latino; 0.4% Asian, non-Hispanic/Latino; 0.1% Native Hawaiian or other Pacific Islander, non-Hispanic/Latino; 19% international. 30% 25 or older, 20% live on campus, 16% transferred in. Retention: 61% of full-time freshmen returned the following year. Academic areas with the most degrees conferred: business/marketing; education; visual and performing arts. Core. Calendar: semesters. Academic remediation for entering students, ESL program, services for LD students, advanced placement, self-designed majors, honors program, independent study, distance learning, double major, summer session for credit, part-time degree program, external degree program, adult/continuing education programs, internships, graduate courses open to undergrads. Off campus study at members of the Kansas City Professional Development Council. ROTC: Army.
Entrance Requirements: Options: electronic application, early admission, deferred admission, international baccalaureate accepted. Required: high school transcript, minimum 2 high school GPA, SAT or ACT. Recommended: essay. Required for some: 2 recommendations, interview. Entrance: moderately difficult. Application deadline: 8/1. Notification: continuous.
Costs Per Year: Application fee: $25. Comprehensive fee: $17,051 includes full-time tuition ($9800), mandatory fees ($100), and college room and board ($7151). College room only: $3525. Full-time tuition and fees vary according to course load. Room and board charges vary according to housing facility. Part-time tuition: $350 per credit. Part-time tuition varies according to course load.
Collegiate Environment: Orientation program. Drama-theater group, choral group, student-run newspaper, radio station. Social organizations: 15 open to all. Most popular organizations: World Student Union, Student Senate, Radio Club, Latin American Student Organization, marketing club. Major annual events: Harvest Fest, Spring Fling, Christmas on the River. Student services: health clinic, personal-psychological counseling. Campus security: 24-hour patrols, student patrols, late night transport-escort service. 410 college housing spaces available; 334 were occupied in 2012-13. Freshmen guaranteed college housing. On-campus residence required through junior year. Option: coed housing available. McAfee Memorial Library with 150,503 books, 90,000 microform titles, 591 serials, and an OPAC. Operations spending for the previous fiscal year: $672,867. 143 computers available on campus for general student use. A campuswide network can be accessed from student residence rooms. Students can access the following: online class registration. Staffed computer lab on campus.
Community Environment: See University of Missouri - Kansas City.

■ **PINNACLE CAREER INSTITUTE**
1001 E 101st Ter.
Ste. 325
Kansas City, MO 64131
Tel: (816)331-5700; Free: 877-241-3097
Web Site: www.pcitraining.edu/
Description: Proprietary, 2-year, coed. Awards certificates and transfer associate degrees. Founded 1953. Total enrollment: 437. 167 applied. 44% 25 or older.
Entrance Requirements: Application deadline: 6/1.

■ **RANKEN TECHNICAL COLLEGE**
4431 Finney Ave.
Saint Louis, MO 63113

Tel: (314)371-0233; Free: 866-4-RANKEN
Fax: (314)371-0241
Web Site: www.ranken.edu/
Description: Independent, primarily 2-year, coed. Awards certificates, transfer associate, terminal associate, and bachelor's degrees. Founded 1907. Setting: 10-acre urban campus. Total enrollment: 1,743. 34% 25 or older. Calendar: semesters. Academic remediation for entering students, services for LD students, advanced placement, independent study, distance learning, summer session for credit, part-time degree program, adult/continuing education programs, co-op programs and internships.
Entrance Requirements: Option: electronic application. Required: essay, high school transcript, interview. Entrance: moderately difficult. Application deadline: Rolling.
Collegiate Environment: Orientation program. Student-run newspaper. Student services: personal-psychological counseling, women's center. Campus security: 24-hour emergency response devices and patrols. Ashley Gray, Jr. Learning Center with 11,000 books, 182 serials, an OPAC, and a Web page.

■ **RESEARCH COLLEGE OF NURSING**
2252 E Meyer Blvd.
Kansas City, MO 64132
Tel: (816)995-2800
Fax: (816)276-3526
E-mail: lane.ramey@rockhurst.edu
Web Site: www.researchcollege.edu/
Description: Independent, comprehensive, coed. Part of Rockhurst University. Awards bachelor's and master's degrees (bachelor's degree offered jointly with Rockhurst College). Founded 1980. Setting: 66-acre urban campus with easy access to Kansas City. Total enrollment: 441. Faculty: 29 (26 full-time, 3 part-time). Student-undergrad faculty ratio is 7:1. 339 applied, 73% were admitted. 24% from top 10% of their high school class, 67% from top quarter, 95% from top half. Full-time: 300 students, 93% women, 7% men. Part-time: 6 students, 100% women. Students come from 7 states and territories. 0.3% American Indian or Alaska Native, non-Hispanic/Latino; 3% Hispanic/Latino; 6% African American, non-Hispanic/Latino; 1% Asian, non-Hispanic/Latino; 0.3% Native Hawaiian or other Pacific Islander, non-Hispanic/Latino; 0% international. 30% 25 or older, 2% transferred in. Academic area with the most degrees conferred: health professions and related sciences. Core. Calendar: semesters. Services for LD students, advanced placement, accelerated degree program, honors program, independent study, double major, summer session for credit, graduate courses open to undergrads. Study abroad program. ROTC: Army (c).
Entrance Requirements: Options: electronic application, deferred admission, international baccalaureate accepted. Required: high school transcript, 1 recommendation, ACT or SAT, SAT or ACT. Recommended: minimum 2.8 high school GPA, interview. Entrance: moderately difficult. Application deadline: 6/30. Notification: 8/15, 6/20 for nonresidents.
Costs Per Year: Application fee: $0. Comprehensive fee: $38,300 includes full-time tuition ($29,100), mandatory fees ($740), and college room and board ($8460). College room only: $5060. Room and board charges vary according to board plan, housing facility, and location. Part-time tuition: $970 per credit hour. Part-time tuition varies according to class time.
Collegiate Environment: Orientation program. Drama-theater group, choral group, student-run newspaper, radio station. Social organizations: 40 open to all; national fraternities, national sororities, local sororities; 75% of eligible men and 75% of eligible women are members. Major annual events: Mass of the Holy Spirit, Polar Walk, homecoming. Student services: health clinic, personal-psychological counseling. Campus security: 24-hour emergency response devices and patrols, late night transport-escort service, controlled dormitory access. 1,800 college housing spaces available. Freshmen guaranteed college housing. Options: coed, men-only, women-only housing available. Greenlease Library with 150,000 books, 675 serials, an OPAC, and a Web page. 125 computers available on campus for general student use. A campuswide network can be accessed from student residence rooms and from off campus. Students can access the following: online class registration. Staffed computer lab on campus.

■ **ROCKHURST UNIVERSITY**
1100 Rockhurst Rd.
Kansas City, MO 64110-2561
Tel: (816)501-4000; Free: 800-842-6776
Fax: (816)501-4241
E-mail: admission@rockhurst.edu

Web Site: www.rockhurst.edu/

Description: Independent Roman Catholic (Jesuit), comprehensive, coed. Awards bachelor's, master's, and doctoral degrees. Founded 1910. Setting: 35-acre urban campus. Endowment: $32.7 million. Research spending for the previous fiscal year: $58,463. Educational spending for the previous fiscal year: $6562 per student. Total enrollment: 2,808. Faculty: 253 (123 full-time, 130 part-time). Student-undergrad faculty ratio is 13:1. 2,184 applied, 78% were admitted. 25% from top 10% of their high school class, 56% from top quarter, 86% from top half. Full-time: 1,486 students, 58% women, 42% men. Part-time: 674 students, 65% women, 35% men. Students come from 26 states and territories, 18 other countries, 29% from out-of-state. 1% American Indian or Alaska Native, non-Hispanic/Latino; 5% Hispanic/Latino; 6% African American, non-Hispanic/Latino; 3% Asian, non-Hispanic/Latino; 0.2% Native Hawaiian or other Pacific Islander, non-Hispanic/Latino; 1% international. 7% 25 or older, 52% live on campus, 3% transferred in. Retention: 86% of full-time freshmen returned the following year. Academic areas with the most degrees conferred: health professions and related sciences; business/marketing; psychology. Core. Calendar: semesters. Academic remediation for entering students, services for LD students, advanced placement, accelerated degree program, freshman honors college, honors program, independent study, distance learning, double major, summer session for credit, part-time degree program, co-op programs and internships, graduate courses open to undergrads. Off campus study at Kansas City Area Student Exchange. Study abroad program. ROTC: Army (c).

Entrance Requirements: Options: electronic application, deferred admission, international baccalaureate accepted. Required: high school transcript, minimum 2 high school GPA, 1 recommendation, SAT or ACT. Required for some: essay, interview. Entrance: moderately difficult. Application deadline: 6/30. Notification: continuous. SAT Reasoning Test deadline: 8/1. SAT Subject Test deadline: 8/1. Transfer credits accepted: Yes.

Costs Per Year: Application fee: $25. Comprehensive fee: $37,900 includes full-time tuition ($29,100), mandatory fees ($740), and college room and board ($8060). College room only: $5060. Full-time tuition and fees vary according to class time and course load. Room and board charges vary according to board plan and housing facility.

Collegiate Environment: Orientation program. Drama-theater group, choral group, student-run newspaper. Social organizations: national fraternities, national sororities, local sororities; 25% of eligible men and 25% of eligible women are members. Most popular organizations: Student Activities Board, Student Senate, Delta Sigma Pi Business Fraternity, Student Organization of Latinos, Rockhurst University Players (theatre troupe). Major annual events: Homecoming, Greek Week, Family Weekend. Student services: health clinic, personal-psychological counseling. Campus security: 24-hour emergency response devices and patrols, late night transport-escort service, controlled dormitory access, closed-circuit TV monitors. 939 college housing spaces available; 832 were occupied in 2012-13. Freshmen guaranteed college housing. On-campus residence required through sophomore year. Options: coed, men-only, women-only housing available. Greenlease Library plus 1 other with 166,042 books, 40,888 microform titles, 82,738 serials, 1,103 audiovisual materials, an OPAC, and a Web page. Operations spending for the previous fiscal year: $710,467. 240 computers available on campus for general student use. Computer purchase/lease plans available. A campuswide network can be accessed from student residence rooms and from off campus. Students can access the following: online class registration.

Community Environment: See University of Missouri - Kansas City.

■ SAINT CHARLES COMMUNITY COLLEGE

4601 Mid Rivers Mall Dr.
Cottleville, MO 63376
Tel: (636)922-8000
Fax: (636)922-8236
E-mail: regist@stchas.edu
Web Site: www.stchas.edu/

Description: State-supported, 2-year, coed. Part of Missouri Coordinating Board for Higher Education. Awards certificates, transfer associate, and terminal associate degrees. Founded 1986. Setting: 234-acre suburban campus with easy access to St. Louis. Educational spending for the previous fiscal year: $4263 per student. Total enrollment: 8,202. Faculty: 420 (95 full-time, 325 part-time). Student-undergrad faculty ratio is 25:1. 2,874 applied, 98% were admitted. Full-time: 4,313 students, 52% women, 48% men. Part-time: 3,889 students, 63% women, 37% men. Students come from 11 states and territories, 20 other countries. 31% 25 or older, 5% transferred in. Retention: 64% of full-time freshmen returned the following year. Core. Calendar:

semesters. Academic remediation for entering students, ESL program, services for LD students, advanced placement, independent study, distance learning, double major, summer session for credit, part-time degree program, adult/continuing education programs, co-op programs and internships. Study abroad program.

Entrance Requirements: Open admission except for nursing and allied health programs. Options: electronic application, early admission, deferred admission. Recommended: high school transcript. Required for some: high school transcript, minimum 2.5 high school GPA. Entrance: noncompetitive. Application deadlines: Rolling, Rolling for nonresidents. Notification: continuous, continuous for nonresidents. Transfer credits accepted: Yes.

Collegiate Environment: Orientation program. Drama-theater group, choral group, student-run newspaper. Social organizations: 34 open to all. Most popular organizations: Phi Theta Kappa, Student Nurse Organization, Student Ambassadors, Outdoors Crew, Roller Hockey. Major annual events: Spring Fling, Fall Fun Blitz, Student Awards Banquet. Student services: personal-psychological counseling. Campus security: 24-hour emergency response devices and patrols, late night transport-escort service, campus police officers on duty during normal operating hours. Paul and Helen Schnare Library with 94,931 books, 7,171 microform titles, 278 serials, 8,108 audiovisual materials, an OPAC, and a Web page. Operations spending for the previous fiscal year: $889,240. 250 computers available on campus for general student use. Computer purchase/lease plans available. A campuswide network can be accessed from off-campus. Students can access the following: online class registration, WebCT/Blackboard. Staffed computer lab on campus provides training in use of computers, software, and the Internet.

■ SAINT LOUIS CHRISTIAN COLLEGE

1360 Grandview Dr.
Florissant, MO 63033-6499
Tel: (314)837-6777; Free: 800-887-SLCC
Fax: (314)837-8291
E-mail: losborn@slcconline.edu
Web Site: www.slcconline.edu/

Description: Independent Christian, 4-year, coed. Awards associate and bachelor's degrees. Founded 1956. Setting: 20-acre suburban campus with easy access to St. Louis. Endowment: $1 million. Educational spending for the previous fiscal year: $4733 per student. Total enrollment: 246. Faculty: 27 (11 full-time, 16 part-time). Student-undergrad faculty ratio is 13:1. 124 applied, 27% were admitted. 3% from top 10% of their high school class, 10% from top quarter, 37% from top half. Full-time: 192 students, 40% women, 60% men. Part-time: 54 students, 39% women, 61% men. Students come from 15 states and territories, 1 other country, 37% from out-of-state. 0.4% American Indian or Alaska Native, non-Hispanic/Latino; 3% Hispanic/Latino; 35% African American, non-Hispanic/Latino; 1% Asian, non-Hispanic/Latino; 0% Native Hawaiian or other Pacific Islander, non-Hispanic/Latino; 2% international. 45% 25 or older, 53% live on campus. Retention: 48% of full-time freshmen returned the following year. Academic area with the most degrees conferred: theology and religious vocations. Core. Calendar: semesters. Academic remediation for entering students, ESL program, services for LD students, advanced placement, accelerated degree program, double major, summer session for credit, part-time degree program, adult/continuing education programs, internships. Study abroad program.

Entrance Requirements: Options: electronic application, early admission. Required: essay, high school transcript, 2 recommendations, 18+ on ACT, SAT or ACT. Recommended: minimum 2 high school GPA. Required for some: interview. Entrance: minimally difficult. Application deadline: 8/7. Notification: continuous. SAT Reasoning Test deadline: 8/7. SAT Subject Test deadline: 8/7. Transfer credits accepted: Yes.

Costs Per Year: Application fee: $0. Comprehensive fee: $12,215 includes full-time tuition ($8215) and college room and board ($4000). Room and board charges vary according to housing facility.

Collegiate Environment: Orientation program. Drama-theater group, choral group. Social organizations: 3 open to all. Most popular organizations: World Christians Unlimited, Drama Club, pep band. Major annual events: Jam Fest, Jesus Encounter, Junior High Winterfest. Student services: personal-psychological counseling. Campus security: 24-hour emergency response devices and patrols, controlled dormitory access, night security. 215 college housing spaces available; 131 were occupied in 2012-13. No special consideration for freshman housing applicants. On-campus residence required through senior year. Options: men-only, women-only housing available. St. Louis Christian College Library with 39,728 books, 144 serials, 255 audiovisual materials, and a Web page. Operations spending for the previous fiscal year: $80,626. 11 computers available on campus for general student use. A campuswide network can be accessed from off-campus. Staffed computer lab on campus provides training in use of computers, software, and the Internet.

■ ST. LOUIS COLLEGE OF HEALTH CAREERS
909 S Taylor Ave.
Saint Louis, MO 63110-1511
Tel: (314)652-0300; Free: 888-789-4820
Fax: (314)652-4825
Web Site: www.slchc.com/
Description: Proprietary, 2-year, coed. Awards certificates and terminal associate degrees. Founded 1981. Total enrollment: 340. Student-undergrad faculty ratio is 12:1. 30% from out-of-state. 45% 25 or older.
Entrance Requirements: Required: high school transcript, interview.

■ ST. LOUIS COLLEGE OF PHARMACY
4588 Parkview Pl.
Saint Louis, MO 63110-1088
Tel: (314)367-8700; Free: 800-278-267
Fax: (314)367-2784
E-mail: chorrall@stlcop.edu
Web Site: www.stlcop.edu/
Description: Independent, comprehensive, coed. Awards doctoral degrees. Founded 1864. Setting: 5-acre urban campus with easy access to St. Louis. Endowment: $113.6 million. Research spending for the previous fiscal year: $692,052. Educational spending for the previous fiscal year: $13,489 per student. Total enrollment: 1,299. Faculty: 134 (83 full-time, 51 part-time). Student-undergrad faculty ratio is 18:1. 528 applied, 70% were admitted. 44% from top 10% of their high school class, 31% from top quarter, 25% from top half. 12 valedictorians. Full-time: 707 students, 59% women, 41% men. Part-time: 7 students, 43% women, 57% men. Students come from 29 states and territories, 2 other countries, 51% from out-of-state. 1% American Indian or Alaska Native, non-Hispanic/Latino; 1% Hispanic/Latino; 5% African American, non-Hispanic/Latino; 22% Asian, non-Hispanic/Latino; 0.3% Native Hawaiian or other Pacific Islander, non-Hispanic/Latino; 1% international. 0% 25 or older, 40% live on campus, 6% transferred in. Retention: 92% of full-time freshmen returned the following year. Core. Calendar: semesters. Academic remediation for entering students, advanced placement, summer session for credit, internships. ROTC: Army (c), Naval (c), Air Force (c).
Entrance Requirements: Options: electronic application, early decision. Required: essay, high school transcript, minimum 3 high school GPA, 2 recommendations, letter of reference from science teacher, SAT or ACT. Required for some: interview. Entrance: moderately difficult. Application deadlines: 2/1, 12/15 for early decision. Notification: 3/1, 1/15 for early decision. SAT Reasoning Test deadline: 2/1. SAT Subject Test deadline: 2/1. Transfer credits accepted: Yes. Early decision applicants: 248. Early decision applicants admitted: 198.
Costs Per Year: Application fee: $50. Comprehensive fee: $35,405 includes full-time tuition ($25,800), mandatory fees ($325), and college room and board ($9280). College room only: $5475. Full-time tuition and fees vary according to student level. Room and board charges vary according to housing facility. Part-time tuition: $845 per credit.
Collegiate Environment: Orientation program. Drama-theater group, choral group, student-run newspaper. Social organizations: 50 open to all; national fraternities, national sororities, professional fraternities; 70% of eligible men and 65% of eligible women are members. Most popular organizations: Outdoor Club, Student Body Union, International Student Organization, Student ambassadors, Student Organization for Drug and Alcohol Awareness. Major annual events: Homecoming, Organization Fair (Welcome Week), Spring Fling. Student services: personal-psychological counseling. Campus security: 24-hour emergency response devices and patrols, late night transport-escort service, controlled dormitory access. 300 college housing spaces available; 282 were occupied in 2012-13. Freshmen given priority for college housing. Option: coed housing available. O. J. Cloughly Alumni Library with 72,616 books, 5,259 microform titles, 200 serials, 1,961 audiovisual materials, an OPAC, and a Web page. Operations spending for the previous fiscal year: $382,041. 6 computers available on campus for general student use. Computer purchase/lease plans available. A computer is required for all students. A campuswide network can be accessed from student residence rooms and from off campus. Students can access the following: online class registration.

■ ST. LOUIS COMMUNITY COLLEGE AT FLORISSANT VALLEY
3400 Pershall Rd.
Saint Louis, MO 63135-1499
Tel: (314)513-4200
Fax: (314)513-2224
Web Site: www.stlcc.edu/
Description: District-supported, 2-year, coed. Part of St. Louis Community College System. Awards certificates, transfer associate, and terminal associate degrees. Founded 1963. Setting: 108-acre suburban campus. Students come from 31 other countries. 53% 25 or older. Core. Calendar: semesters. Academic remediation for entering students, ESL program, services for LD students, advanced placement, honors program, summer session for credit, part-time degree program, adult/continuing education programs, co-op programs. Study abroad program. ROTC: Army (c).
Entrance Requirements: Open admission. Options: electronic application, early admission. Required: high school transcript. Entrance: noncompetitive. Application deadline: 8/19. Notification: continuous.
Collegiate Environment: Orientation program. Drama-theater group, student-run newspaper, radio station. Social organizations: 20 open to all; national fraternities, national sororities; 20% of eligible men and 15% of eligible women are members. Most popular organizations: Phi Theta Kappa, Student Nurses Association, Women in New Goals, Florissant Valley Association of the Deaf, Student Government Association. Major annual events: awareness days, school spirit days, Children's Christmas Party. Student services: health clinic, personal-psychological counseling. Campus security: 24-hour emergency response devices and patrols, late night transport-escort service. 90,021 books and 655 serials 470 computers available on campus for general student use. A campuswide network can be accessed. Staffed computer lab on campus.

■ ST. LOUIS COMMUNITY COLLEGE AT FOREST PARK
5600 Oakland Ave.
Saint Louis, MO 63110-1316
Tel: (314)644-9100
E-mail: fp-admissions@stlcc.edu
Web Site: www.stlcc.edu/
Description: District-supported, 2-year, coed. Part of St. Louis Community College System. Awards certificates, transfer associate, and terminal associate degrees. Founded 1962. Setting: 34-acre suburban campus. System endowment: $1.3 million. Total enrollment: 7,991. Faculty: 452 (144 full-time, 308 part-time). Student-undergrad faculty ratio is 19:1. Full-time: 2,765 students, 58% women, 42% men. Part-time: 5,226 students, 65% women, 35% men. Students come from 17 states and territories, 75 other countries, 3% from out-of-state. 0.4% American Indian or Alaska Native, non-Hispanic/Latino; 3% Hispanic/Latino; 56% African American, non-Hispanic/Latino; 3% Asian, non-Hispanic/Latino; 0.2% Native Hawaiian or other Pacific Islander, non-Hispanic/Latino; 1% international. 61% 25 or older, 10% transferred in. Retention: 40% of full-time freshmen returned the following year. Core. Calendar: semesters. Academic remediation for entering students, ESL program, services for LD students, advanced placement, accelerated degree program, honors program, independent study, distance learning, summer session for credit, part-time degree program, adult/continuing education programs, internships. Study abroad program.
Entrance Requirements: Open admission except for nursing, paramedic, occupational therapy, physical therapy programs. Option: electronic application. Recommended: SAT or ACT. Required for some: high school transcript, interview. Entrance: noncompetitive. Application deadlines: Rolling, Rolling for nonresidents. Notification: continuous, continuous for nonresidents. Transfer credits accepted: Yes.
Costs Per Year: Application fee: $0. Area resident tuition: $2232 full-time, $93 per credit part-time. State resident tuition: $3336 full-time, $139 per credit part-time. Nonresident tuition: $4536 full-time, $189 per credit part-time. Full-time tuition varies according to course load. Part-time tuition varies according to course load.
Collegiate Environment: Orientation program. Student-run newspaper. Social organizations: 18 open to all. Most popular organizations: Programming Board, Phi Theta Kappa, Radiology Club, Forest Park Business Club, Human Services Club. Major annual events: Annual meet the college president event that is held in the fall of each academic year, International Festival, 2nd Annual 'Commit To Complete' Event. Student services: personal-psychological counseling. Campus security: 24-hour emergency response devices, late night transport-escort service. College housing not available. Forest Park Library with 74,861 books, 333,928 microform titles, 284 serials, 1,778 audiovisual materials, an OPAC, and a Web page. 140

computers available on campus for general student use. A campuswide network can be accessed from off-campus. Students can access the following: online class registration.

ST. LOUIS COMMUNITY COLLEGE AT MERAMEC

11333 Big Bend Blvd.
Kirkwood, MO 63122-5720
Tel: (314)984-7500
Fax: (314)984-7117
E-mail: mc-admissions@stlcc.edu
Web Site: www.stlcc.edu/

Description: District-supported, 2-year, coed. Part of St. Louis Community College System. Awards certificates, transfer associate, and terminal associate degrees. Founded 1963. Setting: 80-acre suburban campus with easy access to St. Louis. System endowment: $1.3 million. Total enrollment: 10,432. Faculty: 554 (190 full-time, 364 part-time). Student-undergrad faculty ratio is 22:1. Full-time: 4,717 students, 51% women, 49% men. Part-time: 5,715 students, 61% women, 39% men. Students come from 17 states and territories, 74 other countries, 1% from out-of-state. 0.3% American Indian or Alaska Native, non-Hispanic/Latino; 3% Hispanic/Latino; 10% African American, non-Hispanic/Latino; 3% Asian, non-Hispanic/Latino; 0.1% Native Hawaiian or other Pacific Islander, non-Hispanic/Latino; 1% international. 40% 25 or older, 8% transferred in. Retention: 62% of full-time freshmen returned the following year. Core. Calendar: semesters. Academic remediation for entering students, ESL program, services for LD students, advanced placement, accelerated degree program, honors program, independent study, distance learning, summer session for credit, part-time degree program, adult/continuing education programs, internships. Off campus study. Study abroad program.

Entrance Requirements: Open admission except for nursing, paramedic, occupational therapy, physical therapy programs. Option: electronic application. Recommended: SAT or ACT. Required for some: high school transcript, interview. Entrance: noncompetitive. Application deadlines: Rolling, Rolling for nonresidents. Notification: continuous, continuous for nonresidents. Transfer credits accepted: Yes.

Costs Per Year: Application fee: $0. Area resident tuition: $2232 full-time, $93 per credit part-time. State resident tuition: $3336 full-time, $139 per credit part-time. Nonresident tuition: $4536 full-time, $189 per credit part-time. Full-time tuition varies according to course load. Part-time tuition varies according to course load.

Collegiate Environment: Orientation program. Drama-theater group, student-run newspaper. Student services: personal-psychological counseling. Campus security: 24-hour emergency response devices, late night transport-escort service. College housing not available. Meramec Library with 122,988 books, 333,928 microform titles, 496 serials, 11,538 audiovisual materials, an OPAC, and a Web page. 192 computers available on campus for general student use. A campuswide network can be accessed from off-campus. Students can access the following: online class registration.

SAINT LOUIS UNIVERSITY

One Grand Blvd.
Saint Louis, MO 63103-2097
Tel: (314)977-2222; Free: 800-758-3678
Fax: (314)977-7136
E-mail: admitme@slu.edu
Web Site: www.slu.edu/

Description: Independent Roman Catholic (Jesuit), university, coed. Awards bachelor's, master's, and doctoral degrees and post-master's certificates. Founded 1818. Setting: 269-acre urban campus. System endowment: $852.8 million. Research spending for the previous fiscal year: $33.7 million. Educational spending for the previous fiscal year: $13,583 per student. Total enrollment: 13,981. Faculty: 1,340 (740 full-time, 600 part-time). Student-undergrad faculty ratio is 12:1. 13,060 applied, 64% were admitted. 38% from top 10% of their high school class, 68% from top quarter, 90% from top half. 12 National Merit Scholars. Full-time: 7,914 students, 58% women, 42% men. Part-time: 892 students, 69% women, 31% men. Students come from 48 states and territories, 49 other countries, 61% from out-of-state. 0.2% American Indian or Alaska Native, non-Hispanic/Latino; 4% Hispanic/Latino; 7% African American, non-Hispanic/Latino; 8% Asian, non-Hispanic/Latino; 0% Native Hawaiian or other Pacific Islander, non-Hispanic/Latino; 8% international. 5% 25 or older, 52% live on campus, 5% transferred in. Retention: 88% of full-time freshmen returned the following year. Academic areas with the most degrees conferred: business/marketing; health profes-

sions and related sciences; social sciences. Core. Calendar: semesters. Academic remediation for entering students, ESL program, services for LD students, advanced placement, accelerated degree program, self-designed majors, honors program, independent study, distance learning, double major, summer session for credit, part-time degree program, adult/continuing education programs, co-op programs and internships, graduate courses open to undergrads. Off campus study. Study abroad program. ROTC: Army (c), Air Force.

Entrance Requirements: Options: electronic application, deferred admission, international baccalaureate accepted. Required: essay, high school transcript, minimum 2.5 high school GPA, SAT or ACT. Recommended: 2 recommendations, interview, secondary school report form and health examination. Entrance: moderately difficult. Application deadlines: 8/20, 8/20 for nonresidents. Notification: 9/15, 9/15 for nonresidents. SAT Reasoning Test deadline: 12/1. Transfer credits accepted: Yes. Applicants placed on waiting list: 211. Wait-listed applicants offered admission: 190.

Costs Per Year: Application fee: $0. Comprehensive fee: $44,878 includes full-time tuition ($34,740), mandatory fees ($526), and college room and board ($9612). College room only: $5444. Full-time tuition and fees vary according to location and program. Room and board charges vary according to board plan, housing facility, and location. Part-time tuition: $1215 per credit hour. Part-time mandatory fees: $153 per term. Part-time tuition and fees vary according to location and program.

Collegiate Environment: Orientation program. Drama-theater group, choral group, student-run newspaper, radio station. Social organizations: 120 open to all; national fraternities, national sororities; 14% of eligible men and 18% of eligible women are members. Most popular organizations: Alpha Phi Omega, Oriflamme, Student Activities Board, Interfraternity Council, Panhellenic Council. Major annual events: Student Activities Fair, Welcome Week, Billiken World Festival. Student services: health clinic, personal-psychological counseling, women's center. Campus security: 24-hour emergency response devices and patrols, late night transport-escort service, controlled dormitory access, crime prevention program, bicycle patrols, pamphlets, posters, films, identification of valuables, video cameras. 3,842 college housing spaces available; 3,757 were occupied in 2012-13. Freshmen guaranteed college housing. On-campus residence required through sophomore year. Options: coed, men-only, women-only housing available. Pius XII Memorial Library plus 2 others with 1.9 million books, 2.7 million microform titles, 13,049 serials, 77,699 audiovisual materials, an OPAC, and a Web page. Operations spending for the previous fiscal year: $11 million. 581 computers available on campus for general student use. A campuswide network can be accessed from student residence rooms and from off campus. Students can access the following: online class registration. Staffed computer lab on campus (open 24 hours a day) provides training in use of computers, software, and the Internet.

Community Environment: See Washington University.

SAINT LUKE'S COLLEGE OF HEALTH SCIENCES

8320 Ward Pky., Ste. 300
Kansas City, MO 64114
Tel: (816)932-6700
Web Site: www.saintlukescollege.edu/

Description: Independent Episcopal, upper-level, coed. Administratively affiliated with Saint Luke's Hospital. Awards bachelor's degrees. Founded 1903. Setting: 3-acre urban campus. Endowment: $2.8 million. Total enrollment: 113. Faculty: 15 (all full-time). Student-undergrad faculty ratio is 8:1. Full-time: 101 students, 91% women, 9% men. Part-time: 12 students, 83% women, 17% men. Students come from 5 states and territories. 51% 25 or older, 46% transferred in. Core. Calendar: semesters. Summer session for credit, part-time degree program, co-op programs.

Entrance Requirements: Transfer credits accepted: Yes.

Collegiate Environment: Orientation program. Social organizations: 1 open to all. Most popular organization: Saint Luke's Student Nurse Association. Major annual events: College Picnic, College Spring Banquet. Student services: health clinic, personal-psychological counseling. Campus security: 24-hour emergency response devices and patrols. Health Sciences Library with a Web page. 20 computers available on campus for general student use. Students can access the following: Evolve. Staffed computer lab on campus provides training in use of computers.

SOUTHEAST MISSOURI HOSPITAL COLLEGE OF NURSING AND HEALTH SCIENCES

2001 William St.
Cape Girardeau, MO 63701

Tel: (573)334-6825
Fax: (573)339-7805
E-mail: tbuttry@sehosp.org
Web Site: www.southeastmissourihospitalcollege.edu/

Description: Independent, 2-year, coed. Awards certificates, transfer associate, and terminal associate degrees. Founded 1928. Setting: 1-acre rural campus. Total enrollment: 196. Faculty: 31 (22 full-time, 9 part-time). Student-undergrad faculty ratio is 5:1. 215 applied, 80% were admitted. Full-time: 25 students, 80% women, 20% men. Part-time: 171 students, 80% women, 20% men. Students come from 3 states and territories, 5% from out-of-state. 0% American Indian or Alaska Native, non-Hispanic/Latino; 1% Hispanic/Latino; 3% African American, non-Hispanic/Latino; 1% Asian, non-Hispanic/Latino; 1% Native Hawaiian or other Pacific Islander, non-Hispanic/Latino; 0% international. 66% 25 or older, 96% transferred in. Retention: 100% of full-time freshmen returned the following year. Core. Calendar: six 7-week terms per year. Advanced placement.

Entrance Requirements: Required: high school transcript, minimum 2 high school GPA, 1 recommendation, Bridge Program requirement is a minimum score of 75 on NLN exam. COMPASS exam minimum scores are required for the associate degree programs of 75 in writing, 85 in reading, and 46 in Pre-Algebra, SAT or ACT, COMPASS and NLN also used for various programs and tracks. Entrance: moderately difficult. Application deadlines: Rolling, Rolling for nonresidents. Notification: continuous, continuous for nonresidents.

Costs Per Year: Application fee: $50. Tuition: $300 per credit part-time. Mandatory fees: $21 per hour part-time. Part-time tuition and fees vary according to course load and program.

Collegiate Environment: Orientation program. Major annual events: Political Barbeque, Christmas Party, Professional Development Seminar. Campus security: 24-hour emergency response devices and patrols, late night transport-escort service, electronic campus access. 27 computers available on campus for general student use. A campuswide network can be accessed from off-campus.

■ **SOUTHEAST MISSOURI STATE UNIVERSITY**
One University Plz.
Cape Girardeau, MO 63701-4799
Tel: (573)651-2000
E-mail: lhahn@semo.edu
Web Site: www.semo.edu/

Description: State-supported, comprehensive, coed. Part of Missouri Coordinating Board for Higher Education. Awards associate, bachelor's, and master's degrees and post-master's certificates. Founded 1873. Setting: 400-acre small town campus. Endowment: $57.2 million. Research spending for the previous fiscal year: $490,739. Educational spending for the previous fiscal year: $5014 per student. Total enrollment: 11,729. Faculty: 598 (395 full-time, 203 part-time). Student-undergrad faculty ratio is 22:1. 4,161 applied, 97% were admitted. 17% from top 10% of their high school class, 42% from top quarter, 72% from top half. 54 valedictorians. Full-time: 8,206 students, 56% women, 44% men. Part-time: 2,335 students, 58% women, 42% men. Students come from 39 states and territories, 46 other countries, 15% from out-of-state. 0.4% American Indian or Alaska Native, non-Hispanic/Latino; 1% Hispanic/Latino; 9% African American, non-Hispanic/Latino; 1% Asian, non-Hispanic/Latino; 0.03% Native Hawaiian or other Pacific Islander, non-Hispanic/Latino; 6% international. 18% 25 or older, 30% live on campus, 6% transferred in. Retention: 74% of full-time freshmen returned the following year. Academic areas with the most degrees conferred: education; business/marketing; liberal arts/general studies. Core. Calendar: semesters. Academic remediation for entering students, ESL program, services for LD students, advanced placement, accelerated degree program, self-designed majors, honors program, independent study, distance learning, double major, summer session for credit, part-time degree program, adult/continuing education programs, internships, graduate courses open to undergrads. Study abroad program. ROTC: Air Force.

Entrance Requirements: Options: electronic application, deferred admission, international baccalaureate accepted. Required: high school transcript, minimum 2 high school GPA, SAT or ACT. Entrance: moderately difficult. Application deadlines: 7/1, 7/1 for nonresidents. Notification: 9/1, 9/1 for nonresidents. SAT Reasoning Test deadline: 8/20. Transfer credits accepted: Yes.

Costs Per Year: Application fee: $30. State resident tuition: $5814 full-time, $193.80 per credit hour part-time. Nonresident tuition: $11,049 full-time, $368.30 per credit hour part-time. Mandatory fees: $936 full-time, $31.20 per credit hour part-time. Full-time tuition and fees vary according to course load

and location. Part-time tuition and fees vary according to course load and location. College room and board: $8110. College room only: $5420. Room and board charges vary according to board plan and housing facility.

Collegiate Environment: Orientation program. Drama-theater group, choral group, marching band, student-run newspaper, radio station. Social organizations: 152 open to all; national fraternities, national sororities; 14% of eligible men and 11% of eligible women are members. Most popular organizations: student government, Panhellenic Council, Interfraternity Council, Residence Hall Association, Student Activities Council. Major annual events: Ice Cream Pigout, Homecoming Parade, Late Night Breakfast. Student services: health clinic, personal-psychological counseling. Campus security: 24-hour emergency response devices and patrols, late night transport-escort service, controlled dormitory access. 3,140 college housing spaces available; 3,006 were occupied in 2012-13. On-campus residence required through sophomore year. Options: coed, men-only, women-only housing available. Kent Library with 438,795 books, 1.2 million microform titles, 67,885 serials, 13,967 audiovisual materials, an OPAC, and a Web page. Operations spending for the previous fiscal year: $4 million. 1,550 computers available on campus for general student use. A campuswide network can be accessed from student residence rooms. Students can access the following: online class registration. Staffed computer lab on campus (open 24 hours a day) provides training in use of computers, software, and the Internet.

Community Environment: Cape Girardeau (population 36,200) was founded in 1793 as an Indian trading post. It is now a progressive industrial city. Commercial transportation is convenient; other community facilities include many churches, hospitals, shopping areas and a library. Part time employment is available.

■ **SOUTHWEST BAPTIST UNIVERSITY**
1600 University Ave.
Bolivar, MO 65613-2597
Tel: (417)326-5281; Free: 800-526-5859
Fax: (417)328-1514
E-mail: dcrowder@sbuniv.edu
Web Site: www.sbuniv.edu/

Description: Independent Southern Baptist, comprehensive, coed. Awards associate, bachelor's, master's, and doctoral degrees and post-master's certificates. Founded 1878. Setting: 152-acre small town campus. Endowment: $20.7 million. Educational spending for the previous fiscal year: $5357 per student. Total enrollment: 3,864. Faculty: 304 (128 full-time, 176 part-time). Student-undergrad faculty ratio is 14:1. 1,912 applied, 59% were admitted. 27% from top 10% of their high school class, 51% from top quarter, 75% from top half. Full-time: 2,065 students, 60% women, 40% men. Part-time: 944 students, 74% women, 26% men. Students come from 40 states and territories, 19 other countries, 29% from out-of-state. 1% American Indian or Alaska Native, non-Hispanic/Latino; 1% Hispanic/Latino; 4% African American, non-Hispanic/Latino; 1% Asian, non-Hispanic/Latino; 1% international. 5% 25 or older, 63% live on campus, 3% transferred in. Retention: 67% of full-time freshmen returned the following year. Academic areas with the most degrees conferred: education; health professions and related sciences; business/marketing. Core. Calendar: 4-1-4. Academic remediation for entering students, services for LD students, advanced placement, self-designed majors, honors program, independent study, distance learning, double major, summer session for credit, part-time degree program, co-op programs and internships, graduate courses open to undergrads. Off campus study at Mountain View Center, Salem Center, Springfield Center. Study abroad program. ROTC: Army (c).

Entrance Requirements: Options: electronic application, international baccalaureate accepted. Required: high school transcript, minimum 2.5 high school GPA, SAT or ACT. Recommended: essay, interview. Required for some: 3 recommendations. Entrance: moderately difficult. Application deadline: Rolling. Notification: continuous. SAT Reasoning Test deadline: 8/25. SAT Subject Test deadline: 8/25. Transfer credits accepted: Yes.

Costs Per Year: Application fee: $30. Comprehensive fee: $25,500 includes full-time tuition ($18,360), mandatory fees ($790), and college room and board ($6350). College room only: $3150. Full-time tuition and fees vary according to course load and location. Room and board charges vary according to board plan and housing facility.

Collegiate Environment: Orientation program. Drama-theater group, choral group, student-run newspaper. Social organizations: 27 open to all. Most popular organizations: Enactus, Student Government Association, Fellowship of Christian Athletes, Student Missouri State Teachers Association, PSY CHI. Major annual events: Homecoming, Bye Bash, Concerts. Student services: health clinic, personal-psychological counseling. Campus security: 24-hour emergency response devices and patrols, controlled dormitory access. 1,104 college housing spaces available; 1,003 were occupied in 2012-13. Freshmen guaranteed college housing. On-campus residence required through junior year. Options: men-only, women-only housing available. Harriett K. Hutchens Library with 222,145 books, 482,341 microform titles, 32,160 serials, 12,565 audiovisual materials, an OPAC, and a Web page. Operations spending for the previous fiscal year: $1.8 million. 321 computers available on campus for general student use. A campuswide network can be accessed from student residence rooms and from off campus. Students can access the following: online class registration. Staffed computer lab on campus provides training in use of computers, software, and the Internet.

Community Environment: The county seat of Polk County, Bolivar (population 10,100) is in the midst of a recreational area and is the center of a developing lake region. There is bus transportation to Springfield and Kansas City from Bolivar. A community concert association, allied with Columbia Artists Management of New York, brings quality musical attractions to Bolivar each season. The Southwest Regional Library which serves three counties is located here.

■ STATE FAIR COMMUNITY COLLEGE

3201 W 16th St.
Sedalia, MO 65301-2199
Tel: (660)530-5800; Free: 877-311-7322
Fax: (660)530-5820
E-mail: mcarter@sfccmo.edu
Web Site: www.sfccmo.edu/

Description: District-supported, 2-year, coed. Part of Missouri Coordinating Board for Higher Education. Awards certificates, transfer associate, and terminal associate degrees. Founded 1966. Setting: 128-acre small town campus. Endowment: $6.5 million. Educational spending for the previous fiscal year: $3636 per student. Total enrollment: 4,263. Faculty: 302 (67 full-time, 235 part-time). Student-undergrad faculty ratio is 21:1. 3% from top 10% of their high school class, 17% from top quarter, 47% from top half. Full-time: 2,455 students, 62% women, 38% men. Part-time: 1,808 students, 63% women, 37% men. Students come from 19 states and territories, 1% from out-of-state. 39% 25 or older, 3% live on campus, 5% transferred in. Retention: 61% of full-time freshmen returned the following year. Core. Calendar: semesters. Academic remediation for entering students, ESL program, services for LD students, advanced placement, distance learning, summer session for credit, part-time degree program, adult/continuing education programs, internships. Off campus study. ROTC: Army.

Entrance Requirements: Open admission except for allied health programs. Option: electronic application. Required: high school transcript. Application deadline: Rolling. Transfer credits accepted: Yes.

Collegiate Environment: Orientation program. Drama-theater group, choral group. Campus security: controlled dormitory access, security during evening class hours. Donald C. Proctor Library with 41,258 books, 10,227 serials, 1,633 audiovisual materials, an OPAC, and a Web page. Operations spending for the previous fiscal year: $238,889. 520 computers available on campus for general student use. A campuswide network can be accessed from student residence rooms and from off campus. Students can access the following: online class registration. Staffed computer lab on campus provides training in use of computers, software, and the Internet.

Community Environment: Sedalia (population 20,430) is a rural community, and is the home of the Missouri State Fair. It is also an industrial area that produces truck bodies, brooms, mops, wheels, toolboxes, restaurant equipment, and fans. All forms of commercial transportation are available. Good shopping facilities, many churches, and various service clubs are a part of the community's facilities. Many part-time employment opportunities are available. Parks provide opportunities for recreation.

■ STEPHENS COLLEGE

1200 E Broadway
Columbia, MO 65215-0002
Tel: (573)442-2211; Free: 800-876-7207
Fax: (573)876-7237
E-mail: apply@stephens.edu
Web Site: www.stephens.edu/

Description: Independent, comprehensive, coed. Awards associate, bachelor's, and master's degrees and post-master's certificates. Founded 1833. Setting: 86-acre urban campus. Endowment: $34.7 million. Educational spending for the previous fiscal year: $7221 per student. Total enrollment: 881. Faculty: 104 (52 full-time, 52 part-time). Student-undergrad

faculty ratio is 11:1. 683 applied, 63% were admitted. 0% from top 10% of their high school class, 8% from top quarter, 66% from top half. Full-time: 553 students, 99% women, 1% men. Part-time: 120 students, 92% women, 8% men. Students come from 44 states and territories, 1 other country, 47% from out-of-state. 1% American Indian or Alaska Native, non-Hispanic/Latino; 2% Hispanic/Latino; 15% African American, non-Hispanic/Latino; 1% Asian, non-Hispanic/Latino; 0.3% Native Hawaiian or other Pacific Islander, non-Hispanic/Latino; 0% international. 23% 25 or older, 67% live on campus, 9% transferred in. Retention: 74% of full-time freshmen returned the following year. Academic areas with the most degrees conferred: visual and performing arts; business/marketing; health professions and related sciences. Core. Calendar: semesters. Academic remediation for entering students, services for LD students, advanced placement, accelerated degree program, self-designed majors, freshman honors college, honors program, independent study, distance learning, double major, summer session for credit, part-time degree program, external degree program, adult/continuing education programs, co-op programs and internships, graduate courses open to undergrads. Off campus study at University of Missouri, Washington University, Chatham University, Lincoln University, William Woods University, Westminster College, and Columbia College. Study abroad program. ROTC: Army (c), Naval (c), Air Force (c).

Entrance Requirements: Options: electronic application, deferred admission, international baccalaureate accepted. Required: essay, high school transcript, minimum 2 high school GPA, SAT or ACT. Recommended: minimum 2.5 high school GPA, interview. Required for some: 1 recommendation, audition mandatory for dance, recommended for theater. Entrance: moderately difficult. Notification: continuous until 9/15. SAT Reasoning Test deadline: 8/1. SAT Subject Test deadline: 8/1. Transfer credits accepted: Yes.

Costs Per Year: Application fee: $25. One-time mandatory fee: $200. Comprehensive fee: $37,510 includes full-time tuition ($27,210) and college room and board ($10,300). College room only: $6900. Full-time tuition varies according to course load, degree level, program, and reciprocity agreements. Room and board charges vary according to board plan and housing facility. Part-time tuition: $700 per credit hour. Part-time tuition varies according to course load, degree level, and program.

Collegiate Environment: Orientation program. Drama-theater group, choral group, student-run newspaper, radio station. Social organizations: 15 open to all; national sororities; 7% of women are members. Most popular organizations: IFA, Warehouse Theatre, student government, American Marketing Association (AMA). Major annual events: Opening Convocation, Midnight Breakfast, Honors Convocation. Student services: health clinic, personal-psychological counseling. Campus security: 24-hour emergency response devices and patrols, student patrols, late night transport-escort service, controlled dormitory access. 817 college housing spaces available; 456 were occupied in 2012-13. Freshmen guaranteed college housing. On-campus residence required through senior year. Option: women-only housing available. Hugh Stephens Library with 137,565 books, 10,870 microform titles, 29,593 serials, 2,839 audiovisual materials, an OPAC, and a Web page. Operations spending for the previous fiscal year: $319,658. 107 computers available on campus for general student use. Computer purchase/lease plans available. A campuswide network can be accessed from student residence rooms and from off campus. Staffed computer lab on campus provides training in use of computers, software, and the Internet.

Community Environment: Stephens College is located in Columbia, Missouri. Situated between Kansas City and St. Louis, Columbia is the cultural, medical, and business center of mid-Missouri. Often called "College Town, USA", Columbia is also the home of Columbia College and the University of Missouri. Stephens students have easy access to Columbia's shopping, dining, and entertainment offerings.

■ STEVENS INSTITUTE OF BUSINESS & ARTS

1521 Washington Ave.
Saint Louis, MO 63102
Tel: (314)421-0949; Free: 800-871-0949
Fax: (314)421-0304
E-mail: admission@siba.edu
Web Site: www.siba.edu/

Description: Proprietary, 4-year, coed. Awards associate and bachelor's degrees. Founded 1947. Setting: urban campus. Educational spending for the previous fiscal year: $3700 per student. Total enrollment: 187. Faculty: 22 (7 full-time, 15 part-time). Student-undergrad faculty ratio is 10:1. 22 applied, 86% were admitted. Students come from 2 states and territories, 25% from out-of-state. 48% 25 or older. Retention: 100% of full-time freshmen returned the following year. Academic areas with the most degrees conferred: law/legal studies; business/marketing. Core. Academic remediation for entering students, advanced placement, accelerated degree program, honors program, independent study, summer session for credit, part-time degree program, adult/continuing education programs, co-op programs and internships.

Entrance Requirements: Required: essay, high school transcript, interview. Required for some: minimum 2.75 high school GPA, SAT or ACT. Entrance: moderately difficult. Application deadlines: Rolling, Rolling for nonresidents. Notification: continuous, continuous for nonresidents. Transfer credits accepted: Yes.

Costs Per Year: Application fee: $15. Tuition: $225 per quarter hour part-time. Tuition guaranteed not to increase for student's term of enrollment.

Collegiate Environment: Orientation program. Student services: personal-psychological counseling. Campus security: 24-hour emergency response devices, late night transport-escort service. Stevens Institute of Business & Arts Library with 7 audiovisual materials. Operations spending for the previous fiscal year: $16,500. 45 computers available on campus for general student use. A campuswide network can be accessed from student residence rooms and from off campus. Students can access the following: wireless Internet. Staffed computer lab on campus provides training in use of computers, software, and the Internet.

■ **THREE RIVERS COMMUNITY COLLEGE**
2080 Three Rivers Blvd.
Poplar Bluff, MO 63901-2393
Tel: (573)840-9600; Free: 877-TRY-TRCC
E-mail: trytrcc@trcc.edu
Web Site: www.trcc.edu/

Description: State and locally supported, 2-year, coed. Part of Missouri Coordinating Board for Higher Education. Awards certificates, transfer associate, and terminal associate degrees. Founded 1966. Setting: 70-acre rural campus. Endowment: $678,633. Educational spending for the previous fiscal year: $2341 per student. Total enrollment: 3,185. Faculty: 189 (60 full-time, 129 part-time). Student-undergrad faculty ratio is 23:1. 691 applied, 100% were admitted. 7% from top 10% of their high school class, 25% from top quarter, 58% from top half. 8 valedictorians. Full-time: 1,942 students, 64% women, 36% men. Part-time: 1,243 students, 72% women, 28% men. Students come from 13 states and territories, 4% from out-of-state. 44% 25 or older, 5% live on campus, 0.1% transferred in. Core. Calendar: semesters. Academic remediation for entering students, ESL program, services for LD students, advanced placement, accelerated degree program, honors program, independent study, distance learning, double major, summer session for credit, part-time degree program, external degree program, adult/continuing education programs, internships.

Entrance Requirements: Open admission. Option: early admission. Required: high school transcript. Entrance: noncompetitive.

Collegiate Environment: Orientation program. Social organizations: 14 open to all. Most popular organizations: Marketing Management Association, Phi Theta Kappa, Phi Beta Lambda, Alpha Beta Gamma, TRCC Aggies. Campus security: 24-hour patrols. Rutland Library with 33,289 books, 15,654 microform titles, 177 serials, 1,200 audiovisual materials, an OPAC, and a Web page. 200 computers available on campus for general student use. A campuswide network can be accessed from student residence rooms. Students can access the following: online class registration. Staffed computer lab on campus provides training in use of computers, software, and the Internet.

Community Environment: Poplar Bluff, population 16,900, is a metropolitan area in southeast Missouri where the climate is temperate and living is pleasant. The community has two private general hospitals, one veteran's hospital, many churches, a library, and numerous civic organizations. Many natural streams and lakes within driving distance of the city provide excellent facilities for all outdoor sports. Part-time jobs are available.

■ **TRUMAN STATE UNIVERSITY**
100 E Normal St.
Kirksville, MO 63501-4221
Tel: (660)785-4000; Free: 800-892-7792
Fax: (660)785-7456
E-mail: mchamber@truman.edu
Web Site: www.truman.edu/

Description: State-supported, comprehensive, coed. Awards bachelor's and master's degrees. Founded 1867. Setting: 140-acre small town campus. Endowment: $29.3 million. Research spending for the previous fiscal year:

$938,367. Educational spending for the previous fiscal year: $8397 per student. Total enrollment: 6,237. Faculty: 373 (316 full-time, 57 part-time). Student-undergrad faculty ratio is 17:1. 4,445 applied, 74% were admitted. 46% from top 10% of their high school class, 79% from top quarter, 97% from top half. 18 National Merit Scholars, 132 valedictorians. Full-time: 5,357 students, 59% women, 41% men. Part-time: 515 students, 58% women, 42% men. Students come from 39 states and territories, 54 other countries, 17% from out-of-state. 0.3% American Indian or Alaska Native, non-Hispanic/Latino; 3% Hispanic/Latino; 4% African American, non-Hispanic/Latino; 2% Asian, non-Hispanic/Latino; 0.1% Native Hawaiian or other Pacific Islander, non-Hispanic/Latino; 6% international. 1% 25 or older, 45% live on campus, 3% transferred in. Retention: 89% of full-time freshmen returned the following year. Academic areas with the most degrees conferred: business/marketing; parks and recreation; English. Core. Calendar: semesters. Services for LD students, advanced placement, accelerated degree program, self-designed majors, honors program, independent study, double major, summer session for credit, part-time degree program, co-op programs and internships, graduate courses open to undergrads. Off campus study. Study abroad program. ROTC: Army.

Entrance Requirements: Options: electronic application, deferred admission, international baccalaureate accepted. Required: essay, high school transcript, official college entrance exam scores required, activities list/resume recommended, SAT or ACT. Recommended: minimum 3 high school GPA, interview. Entrance: moderately difficult. Application deadlines: Rolling, Rolling for nonresidents. Notification: continuous until 9/15, continuous until 9/15 for nonresidents. Transfer credits accepted: Yes.

Costs Per Year: Application fee: $0. One-time mandatory fee: $315. State resident tuition: $6978 full-time, $291 per credit hour part-time. Nonresident tuition: $12,714 full-time, $530 per credit hour part-time. Mandatory fees: $238 full-time. Full-time tuition and fees vary according to course load and program. Part-time tuition varies according to course load and program. College room and board: $7504. Room and board charges vary according to housing facility.

Collegiate Environment: Orientation program. Drama-theater group, choral group, marching band, student-run newspaper, radio station. Social organizations: 190 open to all; national fraternities, national sororities, local sororities; 25% of eligible men and 17% of eligible women are members. Most popular organizations: Nursing Students' Association (NSA), Beta Beta Beta (Biology Honors), Alpha Phi Omega (co-ed service fraternity), Communication Disorders Association, American Medical Student Association (AMSA). Major annual events: Homecoming, Final Blowout (spring carnival), BIG Event (one-day community service event). Student services: health clinic, personal-psychological counseling, women's center. Campus security: 24-hour emergency response devices and patrols, student patrols, late night transport-escort service, controlled dormitory access, patrols by commissioned officers, perimeter access system, dual 911 call center for campus & community, emergency text messaging system. 2,900 college housing spaces available; 2,688 were occupied in 2012-13. Freshmen guaranteed college housing. On-campus residence required in freshman year. Option: coed housing available. Pickler Memorial Library with 512,535 books, 1.5 million microform titles, 3,315 serials, 37,645 audiovisual materials, an OPAC, and a Web page. Operations spending for the previous fiscal year: $2.8 million. 738 computers available on campus for general student use. A campuswide network can be accessed from student residence rooms and from off campus. Students can access the following: online class registration. Staffed computer lab on campus provides training in use of computers, software, and the Internet.

Community Environment: Kirksville, Missouri, is located in the northeastern part of the state, a 3 to 4-hour drive from Kansas City, St. Louis, and Des Moines, Iowa, and 80 miles west of historic Hannibal, Missouri, and Quincy, Illinois. The town is served by a direct Amtrak connection from Chicago and Quincy, IL. A municipal airport provides daily flights to and from Kansas City. Kirksville offers an environment for serious study in a community where higher education is the focal point. Besides University students, the community is home to 17,000 townspeople and nearly 250 medical students at the Kirksville College of Osteopathic Medicine.

■ **UNIVERSITY OF CENTRAL MISSOURI**
Warrensburg, MO 64093
Tel: (660)543-4111; Free: 800-729-8266
Fax: (660)543-8517
E-mail: admit@ucmo.edu
Web Site: www.ucmo.edu/

Description: State-supported, comprehensive, coed. Awards associate, bachelor's, and master's degrees and post-master's certificates. Founded 1871. Setting: 1,561-acre small town campus with easy access to Kansas City. System endowment: $27.8 million. Research spending for the previous fiscal year: $423,886. Educational spending for the previous fiscal year: $7699 per student. Total enrollment: 11,637. Faculty: (459 full-time). Student-undergrad faculty ratio is 17:1. 4,410 applied, 80% were admitted. 11% from top 10% of their high school class, 33% from top quarter, 66% from top half. Full-time: 8,009 students, 54% women, 46% men. Part-time: 1,457 students, 56% women, 44% men. Students come from 42 states and territories, 47 other countries, 6% from out-of-state. 0.4% American Indian or Alaska Native, non-Hispanic/Latino; 2% Hispanic/Latino; 8% African American, non-Hispanic/Latino; 0.3% Asian, non-Hispanic/Latino; 0.2% Native Hawaiian or other Pacific Islander, non-Hispanic/Latino; 3% international. 17% 25 or older, 33% live on campus,' 10% transferred in. Retention: 72% of full-time freshmen returned the following year. Academic areas with the most degrees conferred: education; business/marketing; homeland security, law enforcement, firefighting, and protective services; engineering technologies. Core. Calendar: semesters. Academic remediation for entering students, ESL program, services for LD students, advanced placement, self-designed majors, honors program, distance learning, double major, summer session for credit, part-time degree program, adult/continuing education programs, co-op programs and internships, graduate courses open to undergrads. Off campus study. Study abroad program. ROTC: Army, Air Force (c).

Entrance Requirements: Options: electronic application, deferred admission, international baccalaureate accepted. Required: high school transcript, rank in upper two-thirds of high school class, SAT or ACT. Entrance: moderately difficult. Application deadline: Rolling. Notification: continuous.

Collegiate Environment: Orientation program. Drama-theater group, choral group, marching band, student-run newspaper, radio station. Social organizations: 225 open to all; national fraternities, national sororities; 8% of eligible men and 9% of eligible women are members. Most popular organizations: Roaring Red (Student Booster Club), Greek Organization, Campus Christian House, BSU (Baptist Student Union), International Student Organization. Major annual events: Homecoming, Greek Week activities, Welcome Week. Student services: health clinic, personal-psychological counseling, women's center. Campus security: 24-hour emergency response devices and patrols, student patrols, late night transport-escort service, controlled dormitory access, canine patrol. James C. Kirkpatrick Library with 1.3 million books, 815,885 microform titles, 835 serials, 21,598 audiovisual materials, an OPAC, and a Web page. Operations spending for the previous fiscal year: $4.8 million. 6,395 computers available on campus for general student use. A campuswide network can be accessed from student residence rooms and from off campus. Students can access the following: online class registration. Staffed computer lab on campus provides training in use of computers, software, and the Internet.

Community Environment: Surrounded by rolling prairie and scenic woodlands, Warrensburg is located just south of Interstate 70 at the junction of highways 50 and 13. An hour's drive southeast of Kansas City, it is directly en route to a number of popular Missouri attractions, including the Lake of the Ozarks and Branson. Warrensburg's 18,500 residents are in the enviable position of being close to a metropolitan area while able to enjoy the safety and advantages of small-town life. Bus and train lines serve the town. Employment and housing are available both on and off campus.

■ **UNIVERSITY OF MISSOURI**
Columbia, MO 65211
Tel: (573)882-2121
Fax: (573)882-7887
E-mail: mu4u@missouri.edu
Web Site: www.missouri.edu/
Description: State-supported, university, coed. Part of University of Missouri System. Awards bachelor's, master's, and doctoral degrees and post-master's certificates. Founded 1839. Setting: 1,262-acre suburban campus. Endowment: $620 million. Research spending for the previous fiscal year: $165.5 million. Total enrollment: 34,748. Faculty: 1,489 (1,369 full-time, 120 part-time). Student-undergrad faculty ratio is 20:1. 20,564 applied, 81% were admitted. 26% from top 10% of their high school class, 56% from top quarter, 86% from top half. 29 National Merit Scholars. Full-time: 25,178 students, 52% women, 48% men. Part-time: 1,818 students, 49% women, 51% men. Students come from 53 states and territories, 84 other countries, 21% from out-of-state. 0.3% American Indian or Alaska Native, non-Hispanic/Latino; 3% Hispanic/Latino; 8% African American, non-Hispanic/Latino; 2% Asian, non-Hispanic/Latino; 0.05% Native Hawaiian or other Pacific Islander, non-Hispanic/Latino; 3% international. 4% 25 or older, 27% live on campus, 5%

transferred in. Retention: 84% of full-time freshmen returned the following year. Academic areas with the most degrees conferred: business/marketing; communication/journalism; health professions and related sciences. Core. Calendar: semesters. ESL program, services for LD students, advanced placement, accelerated degree program, self-designed majors, freshman honors college, honors program, independent study, distance learning, double major, summer session for credit, part-time degree program, external degree program, adult/continuing education programs, co-op programs and internships, graduate courses open to undergrads. Off campus study at Mid-Missouri Associated Colleges and Universities, National Student Exchange. Study abroad program. ROTC: Army, Naval, Air Force.

Entrance Requirements: Options: electronic application, deferred admission. Required: high school transcript, specific high school curriculum, SAT or ACT. Recommended: ACT. Entrance: moderately difficult. Application deadline: Rolling. Notification: continuous. SAT Reasoning Test deadline: 5/1. SAT Subject Test deadline: 5/1.

Costs Per Year: Application fee: $50. State resident tuition: $8082 full-time. Nonresident tuition: $22,191 full-time. Mandatory fees: $1175 full-time. Full-time tuition and fees vary according to course load, program, and reciprocity agreements. College room and board: $8944. College room only: $5564. Room and board charges vary according to board plan and housing facility.

Collegiate Environment: Orientation program. Drama-theater group, choral group, marching band, student-run newspaper, radio station. Social organizations: 650 open to all; national fraternities, national sororities; 20% of eligible men and 26% of eligible women are members. Most popular organizations: Academic organizations, Greek organizations, religious organizations, sports clubs, Student Governance. Major annual events: Homecoming, Student Activities Mart, Fall Welcome. Student services: legal services, health clinic, personal-psychological counseling, women's center. Campus security: 24-hour emergency response devices and patrols, late night transport-escort service, controlled dormitory access. 6,967 college housing spaces available; 6,812 were occupied in 2012-13. Freshmen guaranteed college housing. On-campus residence required in freshman year. Options: coed, men-only, women-only housing available. Ellis Library plus 10 others with 2.7 million books, 8.1 million microform titles, 35,711 audiovisual materials, an OPAC, and a Web page. Operations spending for the previous fiscal year: $18.1 million. 1,242 computers available on campus for general student use. Computer purchase/lease plans available. A campuswide network can be accessed from student residence rooms and from off campus. Students can access the following: online class registration. Staffed computer lab on campus (open 24 hours a day) provides training in use of computers, software, and the Internet.

Community Environment: The University rests in the heart of Columbia, a growing city of more than 76,000. Cited for its excellent educational opportunities and quality of life, Columbia has ranked among the top most livable cities in the United States for more than a decade, according to Money Magazine. Columbia combines the benefits of a large city - a wide selection of lodging, dining, shopping, cultural and sporting opportunities - with the friendly atmosphere and convenience of a small town. All forms of public transportation are available. Situated midway between St. Louis and Kansas City (each about two hours away), Columbia also is within a two-hour drive for the Lake of the Ozarks recreation area, which provides opportunities for many outdoor sports.

■ **UNIVERSITY OF MISSOURI–KANSAS CITY**
5100 Rockhill Rd.
Kansas City, MO 64110-2499
Tel: (816)235-1000; Free: 800-775-8652
Fax: (816)235-1717
E-mail: admit@umkc.edu
Web Site: www.umkc.edu/
Description: State-supported, university, coed. Part of University of Missouri System. Awards bachelor's, master's, and doctoral degrees and post-master's certificates. Founded 1929. Setting: 191-acre urban campus with easy access to Kansas City. Endowment: $235.5 million. Total enrollment: 16,019. Faculty: 1,187 (759 full-time, 428 part-time). Student-undergrad faculty ratio is 13:1. 4,452 applied, 68% were admitted. 28% from top 10% of their high school class, 54% from top quarter, 81% from top half. 5 National Merit Scholars. Full-time: 6,894 students, 57% women, 43% men. Part-time: 3,732 students, 61% women, 39% men. Students come from 43 states and territories, 38 other countries, 22% from out-of-state. 0.4% American Indian or Alaska Native, non-Hispanic/Latino; 6% Hispanic/Latino; 14% African American, non-Hispanic/Latino; 5% Asian, non-Hispanic/Latino; 0.2% Native Hawaiian or other Pacific Islander, non-Hispanic/Latino; 4% international. 1%

25 or older, 8% live on campus, 14% transferred in. Retention: 69% of full-time freshmen returned the following year. Academic areas with the most degrees conferred: liberal arts/general studies; health professions and related sciences; business/marketing. Core. Calendar: semesters. ESL program, services for LD students, advanced placement, accelerated degree program, self-designed majors, honors program, independent study, distance learning, double major, summer session for credit, part-time degree program, adult/continuing education programs, co-op programs and internships, graduate courses open to undergrads. Off campus study at other campuses of the University of Missouri System. Study abroad program. ROTC: Army, Air Force (c).

Entrance Requirements: Options: electronic application, deferred admission, international baccalaureate accepted. Required: high school transcript, SAT or ACT. Required for some: essay, interview. Entrance: moderately difficult. Application deadline: Rolling. Notification: continuous. SAT Reasoning Test deadline: 8/15.

Costs Per Year: Application fee: $45. State resident tuition: $7968 full-time, $265.60 per credit hour part-time. Nonresident tuition: $20,502 full-time, $683.40 per credit hour part-time. Mandatory fees: $1252 full-time, $63.51 per credit hour part-time. Full-time tuition and fees vary according to course load and program. Part-time tuition and fees vary according to course load and program. College room and board: $11,428. Room and board charges vary according to board plan and housing facility.

Collegiate Environment: Orientation program. Drama-theater group, choral group, student-run newspaper, radio station. Social organizations: 250 open to all; national fraternities, national sororities, local fraternities, local sororities; 5% of eligible men and 7% of eligible women are members. Most popular organizations: Activities and Programs Council, International Student Council, Alpha Phi Omega, Omicron Delta Kappa, Greek Organizations. Major annual events: Activity and Program Council's Big Event, Activity and Program Council Talent Show, Roos Give Back Community Service Day. Student services: legal services, health clinic, personal-psychological counseling, women's center. Campus security: 24-hour emergency response devices and patrols, late night transport-escort service, controlled dormitory access. 1,399 college housing spaces available; 852 were occupied in 2012-13. No special consideration for freshman housing applicants. Option: coed housing available. Miller-Nichols Library plus 3 others with 1.5 million books, 1.3 million microform titles, 53,976 serials, 403,176 audiovisual materials, an OPAC, and a Web page. 400 computers available on campus for general student use. Computer purchase/lease plans available. A campuswide network can be accessed from student residence rooms and from off campus. Students can access the following: online class registration. Staffed computer lab on campus provides training in use of computers, software, and the Internet.

Community Environment: One of the country's largest railroad centers, Kansas City is also a great manufacturing city and an important distributing point located at the confluence of the Kansas and Missouri Rivers. All forms of commercial transportation are convenient. Extensive cultural activities are available. Recreational facilities are numerous. Swope Park is one the largest municipal playgrounds in the country that contains 1,705 acres, two golf courses, tennis courts, picnic grounds, a zoo, swimming pool and a lagoon for boating. Kansas City is the home of the Chiefs of the National Football League and Royals baseball team of the American League. The Country Club district in the southern part of the city has gained international attention as a model for city planning. Each home in this district is planned to harmonize with its surroundings, and careful selection of European art objects beautify street corners.

■ **UNIVERSITY OF MISSOURI–ST. LOUIS**

One University Blvd.
Saint Louis, MO 63121
Tel: (314)516-5000; Free: 888-GO2-USML
Fax: (314)516-5310
E-mail: askdrew@umsl.edu
Web Site: www.umsl.edu/

Description: State-supported, university, coed. Part of University of Missouri System. Awards bachelor's, master's, and doctoral degrees and post-master's certificates. Founded 1963. Setting: 350-acre suburban campus. Endowment: $55.3 million. Research spending for the previous fiscal year: $13.3 million. Educational spending for the previous fiscal year: $7845 per student. Total enrollment: 16,719. Faculty: 1,005 (483 full-time, 522 part-time). Student-undergrad faculty ratio is 16:1. 1,936 applied, 69% were admitted. 31% from top 10% of their high school class, 56% from top quarter, 83% from top half. 20 valedictorians. Full-time: 6,069 students, 57% women,

43% men. Part-time: 7,280 students, 59% women, 41% men. Students come from 36 states and territories, 48 other countries, 10% from out-of-state. 0.3% American Indian or Alaska Native, non-Hispanic/Latino; 2% Hispanic/Latino; 20% African American, non-Hispanic/Latino; 4% Asian, non-Hispanic/Latino; 0.1% Native Hawaiian or other Pacific Islander, non-Hispanic/Latino; 4% international. 40% 25 or older, 8% live on campus, 14% transferred in. Retention: 78% of full-time freshmen returned the following year. Academic areas with the most degrees conferred: business/marketing; education; health professions and related sciences; social sciences. Core. Calendar: semesters. ESL program, services for LD students, advanced placement, accelerated degree program, self-designed majors, freshman honors college, honors program, independent study, distance learning, double major, summer session for credit, part-time degree program, adult/continuing education programs, co-op programs and internships, graduate courses open to undergrads. Off campus study at Southern Illinois University, Saint Louis University, Washington University in St. Louis, St. Charles Community College, Mineral Area Community College, East Central Community College, Jefferson Community College, St. Louis Community College. Study abroad program. ROTC: Army (c), Air Force (c).

Entrance Requirements: Options: electronic application, international baccalaureate accepted. Required: high school transcript, minimum 2 high school GPA, CBHE core requirements, SAT or ACT. Required for some: essay, 2 recommendations, interview. Entrance: moderately difficult. Application deadlines: 8/23, 8/23 for nonresidents. Notification: continuous until 10/1, continuous until 10/1 for nonresidents. SAT Reasoning Test deadline: 8/23. SAT Subject Test deadline: 8/23. Transfer credits accepted: Yes.

Costs Per Year: Application fee: $35. State resident tuition: $9474 full-time, $315.80 per credit hour part-time. Nonresident tuition: $24,429 full-time, $814.30 per credit hour part-time. Full-time tuition varies according to course load, program, and reciprocity agreements. Part-time tuition varies according to course load, program, and reciprocity agreements. College room and board: $8830. College room only: $5200. Room and board charges vary according to board plan and housing facility.

Collegiate Environment: Orientation program. Drama-theater group, choral group, student-run newspaper, radio station. Social organizations: 125 open to all; national fraternities, national sororities; 1% of eligible men and 1% of eligible women are members. Most popular organizations: Student Government Association, Associated Black Collegians, Pierre laclede Honors College Student Association, Residence Hall Association, UMSL Radio Station. Major annual events: Pack the Stands, Mirthday (Spring Carnival), Homecoming. Student services: health clinic, personal-psychological counseling, women's center. Campus security: 24-hour emergency response devices and patrols, late night transport-escort service, controlled dormitory access. 1,205 college housing spaces available; 1,003 were occupied in 2012-13. No special consideration for freshman housing applicants. Options: coed, men-only, women-only housing available. Thomas Jefferson Library plus 2 others with 1.3 million books, 2.2 million microform titles, 2,631 serials, 4,030 audiovisual materials, an OPAC, and a Web page. Operations spending for the previous fiscal year: $4.9 million. 1,280 computers available on campus for general student use. Computer purchase/lease plans available. A campuswide network can be accessed from student residence rooms and from off campus. Students can access the following: online class registration. Staffed computer lab on campus provides training in use of computers, software, and the Internet.

■ **UNIVERSITY OF PHOENIX–KANSAS CITY CAMPUS**

901 E 104th St., Ste. 200
Kansas City, MO 64131-4517
Tel: (816)943-9600; Free: 866-766-0766
Fax: (816)943-6675
Web Site: www.phoenix.edu/

Description: Proprietary, comprehensive, coed. Awards bachelor's and master's degrees. Founded 2002. Setting: urban campus. Total enrollment: 770. Faculty: 124 (8 full-time, 116 part-time). Full-time: 617 students, 65% women, 35% men. 82% 25 or older. Academic areas with the most degrees conferred: business/marketing; computer and information sciences; homeland security, law enforcement, firefighting, and protective services. Core. Calendar: continuous. Services for LD students, advanced placement, accelerated degree program, independent study, distance learning, external degree program, adult/continuing education programs, graduate courses open to undergrads.

Entrance Requirements: Open admission. Options: electronic application, deferred admission. Required: 1 recommendation. Required for some: high school transcript. Entrance: noncompetitive. Application deadline: Rolling.

Collegiate Environment: Campus security: late night transport-escort service. University Library with 16,781 serials, an OPAC, and a Web page. Operations spending for the previous fiscal year: $6.8 million.

■ **UNIVERSITY OF PHOENIX–ST. LOUIS CAMPUS**
Riverport Lakes W
13801 Riverport Dr., Ste. 102
Saint Louis, MO 63043-4828
Tel: (314)298-9755; Free: 866-766-0766
Fax: (314)291-2901
Web Site: www.phoenix.edu/
Description: Proprietary, comprehensive, coed. Awards associate, bachelor's, and master's degrees. Founded 2000. Setting: urban campus. Total enrollment: 445. Faculty: 104 (7 full-time, 97 part-time). Full-time: 401 students, 65% women, 35% men. 80% 25 or older. Academic areas with the most degrees conferred: business/marketing; computer and information sciences; homeland security, law enforcement, firefighting, and protective services. Core. Calendar: continuous. Services for LD students, advanced placement, accelerated degree program, independent study, distance learning, external degree program, adult/continuing education programs, graduate courses open to undergrads.
Entrance Requirements: Open admission. Options: electronic application, deferred admission. Required: 1 recommendation. Required for some: high school transcript. Entrance: noncompetitive. Application deadline: Rolling.
Collegiate Environment: Campus security: late night transport-escort service. University Library with 16,781 serials, an OPAC, and a Web page. Operations spending for the previous fiscal year: $6.8 million.

■ **UNIVERSITY OF PHOENIX–SPRINGFIELD CAMPUS**
1343 E Kingsley St.
Springfield, MO 65804-7211
Free: 866-766-0766
Web Site: www.phoenix.edu/
Description: Proprietary, comprehensive, coed. Awards associate, bachelor's, and master's degrees. Setting: urban campus. Total enrollment: 119. Faculty: 39 (5 full-time, 34 part-time). Student-undergrad faculty ratio is 9:1. Full-time: 104 students, 60% women, 40% men. 76% 25 or older. Academic areas with the most degrees conferred: business/marketing; computer and information sciences; homeland security, law enforcement, firefighting, and protective services. Core. Services for LD students, advanced placement, accelerated degree program, independent study, distance learning, graduate courses open to undergrads.
Entrance Requirements: Open admission. Options: electronic application, deferred admission. Required: 1 recommendation. Required for some: high school transcript. Entrance: noncompetitive. Application deadline: Rolling.
Collegiate Environment: Campus security: late night transport-escort service. University Library with 16,781 serials and an OPAC. Operations spending for the previous fiscal year: $6.8 million.

■ **VATTEROTT COLLEGE (BERKELEY)**
8580 Evans Ave.
Berkeley, MO 63134
Tel: (314)264-1000; Free: 888-553-6627
Web Site: www.vatterott.edu/
Description: Proprietary, primarily 2-year, coed. Awards certificates, diplomas, terminal associate, and bachelor's degrees. Founded 1969. Setting: 5-acre suburban campus with easy access to St. Louis. Total enrollment: 755. 6% from out-of-state. 61% 25 or older. Retention: 77% of full-time freshmen returned the following year. Calendar: continuous.
Collegiate Environment: Orientation program.

■ **VATTEROTT COLLEGE (KANSAS CITY)**
4131 N Corrington Ave.
Kansas City, MO 64117
Tel: (816)861-1000; Free: 888-553-6627
Fax: (816)861-1400
Web Site: www.vatterott.edu/
Description: Proprietary, 2-year, coed. Awards terminal associate degrees. Total enrollment: 702. 171 applied, 84% were admitted. Calendar: semesters.

■ **VATTEROTT COLLEGE (SAINT CHARLES)**
3550 W Clay St.
Saint Charles, MO 63301

Tel: (636)940-4100; Free: 888-553-6627
E-mail: ofallon@vatterott-college.edu
Web Site: www.vatterott.edu/
Description: Proprietary, 2-year, coed. Awards diplomas and terminal associate degrees. Total enrollment: 392. 1% from out-of-state. 69% 25 or older.

■ **VATTEROTT COLLEGE (SAINT JOSEPH)**
3131 Frederick Ave.
Saint Joseph, MO 64506
Tel: (816)364-5399; Free: 888-553-6627
Fax: (816)364-1593
Web Site: www.vatterott.edu/
Description: Proprietary, 2-year, coed. Awards diplomas and terminal associate degrees. Setting: urban campus. Total enrollment: 200. Student-undergrad faculty ratio is 22:1. 7% from out-of-state. 49% 25 or older. Retention: 67% of full-time freshmen returned the following year. Calendar: semesters.
Entrance Requirements: Open admission.

■ **VATTEROTT COLLEGE (SPRINGFIELD)**
3850 S Campbell Ave.
Springfield, MO 65807
Tel: (417)831-8116; Free: 888-553-6627
Fax: (417)831-5099
E-mail: springfield@vatterott-college.edu
Web Site: www.vatterott.edu/
Description: Proprietary, 2-year, coed. Awards diplomas and terminal associate degrees. Setting: 2-acre urban campus. Faculty: 23 (14 full-time, 9 part-time). Student-undergrad faculty ratio is 30:1. Core. Internships.
Entrance Requirements: Required: high school transcript, interview.
Collegiate Environment: Orientation program. Social organizations: 1 open to all. Major annual events: Fall Student Appreciation, Student Appreciation. Campus security: alarm devices and personnel during open hours; security alarms during closed hours. 200 computers available on campus for general student use. A campuswide network can be accessed. Staffed computer lab on campus provides training in use of computers, software, and the Internet.

■ **VATTEROTT COLLEGE (SUNSET HILLS)**
12900 Maurer Industrial Dr.
Sunset Hills, MO 63127
Tel: (314)843-4200; Free: 888-553-6627
Fax: (314)843-1709
Web Site: www.vatterott.edu/
Description: Proprietary, primarily 2-year, coed. Awards diplomas, terminal associate, and bachelor's degrees. Total enrollment: 494. Student-undergrad faculty ratio is 21:1. 10% from out-of-state. 56% 25 or older. Retention: 82% of full-time freshmen returned the following year. Calendar: semesters.
Entrance Requirements: Open admission.

■ **VET TECH INSTITUTE AT HICKEY COLLEGE**
2780 N Lindbergh Blvd.
Saint Louis, MO 63114
Tel: (314)434-2212; Free: 888-884-1459
Web Site: www.vettechinstitute.edu/
Description: Private, 2-year, coed. Awards terminal associate degrees. Founded 2007. Setting: suburban campus. Total enrollment: 134. 420 applied, 59% were admitted. Accelerated degree program, internships.

■ **WASHINGTON UNIVERSITY IN ST. LOUIS**
One Brookings Dr.
Saint Louis, MO 63130-4899
Tel: (314)935-5000; Free: 800-638-0700
Fax: (314)935-4290
E-mail: admissions@wustl.edu
Web Site: www.wustl.edu/
Description: Independent, university, coed. Awards bachelor's, master's, and doctoral degrees and post-master's certificates. Founded 1853. Setting: 169-acre suburban campus. Endowment: $5.3 billion. Research spending for the previous fiscal year: $494.7 million. Total enrollment: 13,952. Faculty: 1,102 (953 full-time, 149 part-time). Student-undergrad faculty ratio is 7:1. 27,265 applied, 18% were admitted. 96% from top 10% of their high school class, 100% from top quarter, 100% from top half. Full-time: 6,455 students, 50% women, 50% men. Part-time: 804 students, 64% women, 36% men.

Students come from 54 states and territories, 55 other countries, 93% from out-of-state. 0.1% American Indian or Alaska Native, non-Hispanic/Latino; 5% Hispanic/Latino; 6% African American, non-Hispanic/Latino; 17% Asian, non-Hispanic/Latino; 0% Native Hawaiian or other Pacific Islander, non-Hispanic/Latino; 8% international. 4% 25 or older, 79% live on campus, 1% transferred in. Retention: 96% of full-time freshmen returned the following year. Academic areas with the most degrees conferred: social sciences; engineering; business/marketing. Core. Calendar: semesters. ESL program, services for LD students, advanced placement, accelerated degree program, self-designed majors, independent study, distance learning, double major, summer session for credit, part-time degree program, adult/continuing education programs, co-op programs and internships, graduate courses open to undergrads. Off campus study at Consortium on Financing Higher Education. Study abroad program. ROTC: Army, Air Force (c).

Entrance Requirements: Options: electronic application, early admission, early decision, deferred admission, international baccalaureate accepted. Required: essay, high school transcript, 2 recommendations, SAT or ACT. Recommended: minimum 3 high school GPA, Portfolios are required for students applying to the College of Art. Portfolios are strongly encouraged for students applying to the College of Architecture. Entrance: most difficult. Application deadlines: 1/15, 11/15 for early decision. Notification: 4/1, 12/15 for early decision. SAT Reasoning Test deadline: 1/15. SAT Subject Test deadline: 1/15.

Costs Per Year: Application fee: $75. Comprehensive fee: $58,818 includes full-time tuition ($44,100), mandatory fees ($741), and college room and board ($13,977). College room only: $9437. Room and board charges vary according to board plan and housing facility.

Collegiate Environment: Orientation program. Drama-theater group, choral group, student-run newspaper, radio station. Social organizations: 300 open to all; national fraternities, national sororities; 25% of eligible men and 25% of eligible women are members. Major annual events: Thurtene Carnival, W.I.L.D. (concert festival), Homecoming. Student services: health clinic, personal-psychological counseling, women's center. Campus security: 24-hour emergency response devices and patrols, student patrols, late night transport-escort service, controlled dormitory access. 5,168 college housing spaces available; 5,041 were occupied in 2012-13. Freshmen guaranteed college housing. On-campus residence required in freshman year. Options: coed, men-only, women-only housing available. John M. Olin Library plus 12 others with 3.4 million books, 3.5 million microform titles, 89,622 serials, 70,765 audiovisual materials, an OPAC, and a Web page. Operations spending for the previous fiscal year: $35.9 million. 2,500 computers available on campus for general student use. Computer purchase/lease plans available. A campuswide network can be accessed from student residence rooms and from off campus. Students can access the following: online class registration. Staffed computer lab on campus.

■ **WEBSTER UNIVERSITY**

470 E Lockwood Ave.
Saint Louis, MO 63119-3194
Tel: (314)968-6900; Free: 800-75-ENROL
Fax: (314)968-7115
E-mail: lauear@webster.edu
Web Site: www.webster.edu/

Description: Independent, comprehensive, coed. Awards bachelor's, master's, and doctoral degrees and post-master's certificates. Founded 1915. Setting: 47-acre suburban campus with easy access to St. Louis. Endowment: $86.5 million. Educational spending for the previous fiscal year: $6745 per student. Total enrollment: 5,119. Faculty: 641 (194 full-time, 447 part-time). Student-undergrad faculty ratio is 11:1. 1,706 applied, 59% were admitted. 20% from top 10% of their high school class, 45% from top quarter, 79% from top half. Full-time: 2,449 students, 56% women, 44% men. Part-time: 546 students, 58% women, 42% men. Students come from 40 states and territories, 37 other countries, 23% from out-of-state. 0.3% American Indian or Alaska Native, non-Hispanic/Latino; 3% Hispanic/Latino; 11% African American, non-Hispanic/Latino; 2% Asian, non-Hispanic/Latino; 0.03% Native Hawaiian or other Pacific Islander, non-Hispanic/Latino; 2% international. 19% 25 or older, 25% live on campus, 11% transferred in. Retention: 79% of full-time freshmen returned the following year. Academic areas with the most degrees conferred: business/marketing; visual and performing arts; communication/journalism. Core. Calendar: semesters. Academic remediation for entering students, ESL program, services for LD students, advanced placement, accelerated degree program, self-designed majors, independent study, distance learning, double major, summer session for credit, part-time degree program, adult/continuing education programs,

co-op programs and internships, graduate courses open to undergrads. Off campus study at Fontbonne University, Lindenwood University, Maryville University of Saint Louis, Eden Theological Seminary, Missouri Baptist University. Study abroad program. ROTC: Army (c), Air Force (c).

Entrance Requirements: Options: electronic application, early admission, deferred admission, international baccalaureate accepted. Required: essay, high school transcript, minimum 2.5 high school GPA, 1 recommendation, SAT or ACT. Recommended: minimum 3 high school GPA, interview. Required for some: minimum 3 high school GPA, audition for dance, music, theatre, and musical theatre students; portfolio for art and film students. Entrance: moderately difficult. Application deadlines: 8/1, 8/1 for nonresidents. Notification: continuous, continuous for nonresidents. SAT Reasoning Test deadline: 8/1. Transfer credits accepted: Yes.

Costs Per Year: Application fee: $35. Comprehensive fee: $32,960 includes full-time tuition ($23,010) and college room and board ($9950). College room only: $5520. Full-time tuition varies according to program. Room and board charges vary according to board plan, housing facility, and location. Part-time tuition: $590 per credit hour. Part-time tuition varies according to location.

Collegiate Environment: Orientation program. Drama-theater group, choral group, student-run newspaper, radio station. Social organizations: 66 open to all; national sororities; 2% of women are members. Most popular organizations: Student Government Association, Association for African American Collegians, International Student Association, Commuter Council, Residential Housing Association. Major annual events: Webster Works Worldwide Community Service Day, Springfest, Homecoming. Student services: health clinic, personal-psychological counseling, women's center. Campus security: 24-hour emergency response devices and patrols, student patrols, late night transport-escort service, controlled dormitory access. 725 college housing spaces available; all were occupied in 2012-13. Freshmen given priority for college housing. On-campus residence required in freshman year. Option: coed housing available. Emerson Library with 289,523 books, 137,400 microform titles, 1,702 serials, 21,558 audiovisual materials, an OPAC, and a Web page. Operations spending for the previous fiscal year: $3.1 million. 661 computers available on campus for general student use. Computer purchase/lease plans available. A campuswide network can be accessed from student residence rooms and from off campus. Students can access the following: online class registration. Staffed computer lab on campus provides training in use of computers, software, and the Internet.

Community Environment: A suburban area 10 miles from St. Louis, Webster Groves (population 22,896) has the convenience of all major forms of transportation. The shopping facilities here are excellent, numerous civic and service organizations are active. Webster Groves also enjoys the recreational and cultural advantages of St. Louis. Other facilities include a library, and churches of major denominations. Some part-time employment is available.

■ **WENTWORTH MILITARY ACADEMY AND COLLEGE**

1880 Washington Ave.
Lexington, MO 64067
Tel: (660)259-2221
Fax: (660)259-2677
E-mail: admissions@wma.edu
Web Site: www.wma.edu/

Description: Independent, 2-year, coed. Awards diplomas, transfer associate, and terminal associate degrees. Founded 1880. Setting: 130-acre small town campus with easy access to Kansas City. Total enrollment: 941. Faculty: 63 (19 full-time, 44 part-time). Student-undergrad faculty ratio is 10:1. 456 applied, 100% were admitted. 2% from top 10% of their high school class, 5% from top quarter, 4% from top half. Full-time: 84 students, 36% women, 64% men. Part-time: 857 students, 50% women, 50% men. Students come from 22 states and territories, 4 other countries, 43% from out-of-state. 0.4% American Indian or Alaska Native, non-Hispanic/Latino; 2% Hispanic/Latino; 2% African American, non-Hispanic/Latino; 1% Asian, non-Hispanic/Latino; 1% Native Hawaiian or other Pacific Islander, non-Hispanic/Latino; 2% international. 10% 25 or older, 0.1% transferred in. Retention: 88% of full-time freshmen returned the following year. Core. Calendar: semesters. Academic remediation for entering students, ESL program, advanced placement, self-designed majors, distance learning, summer session for credit, part-time degree program, adult/continuing education programs. ROTC: Army.

Entrance Requirements: Option: international baccalaureate accepted. Required: high school transcript. Recommended: SAT or ACT. Required for some: SAT or ACT. Entrance: minimally difficult. Application deadlines: 9/1,

9/1 for nonresidents. Notification: continuous until 9/1, continuous until 9/1 for nonresidents. SAT Reasoning Test deadline: 9/2. Transfer credits accepted: Yes.

Collegiate Environment: Orientation program. Choral group, marching band. Major annual events: Kansas City Symphony concert, Artist Series, Field Days. Student services: health clinic, personal-psychological counseling. Campus security: 24-hour emergency response devices and patrols. Sellers-Coombs Library with 18,890 books, 6,655 microform titles, 49 serials, 919 audiovisual materials, and a Web page. 35 computers available on campus for general student use. Staffed computer lab on campus provides training in use of the Internet.

■ WESTMINSTER COLLEGE

501 Westminster Ave.
Fulton, MO 65251-1299
Tel: (573)642-3361; Free: 800-475-3361
Fax: (573)592-5227
E-mail: admissions@westminster-mo.edu
Web Site: www.westminster-mo.edu/

Description: Independent, 4-year, coed, affiliated with Presbyterian Church. Awards bachelor's degrees. Founded 1851. Setting: 80-acre small town campus. Endowment: $46.2 million. Educational spending for the previous fiscal year: $6532 per student. Total enrollment: 1,084. Faculty: 97 (64 full-time, 33 part-time). Student-undergrad faculty ratio is 14:1. 1,420 applied, 72% were admitted. 23% from top 10% of their high school class, 43% from top quarter, 75% from top half. Full-time: 1,074 students, 44% women, 56% men. Part-time: 10 students, 60% women, 40% men. Students come from 32 states and territories, 66 other countries, 20% from out-of-state. 2% American Indian or Alaska Native, non-Hispanic/Latino; 4% Hispanic/Latino; 6% African American, non-Hispanic/Latino; 1% Asian, non-Hispanic/Latino; 0.1% Native Hawaiian or other Pacific Islander, non-Hispanic/Latino; 15% international. 3% 25 or older, 85% live on campus, 5% transferred in. Retention: 83% of full-time freshmen returned the following year. Academic areas with the most degrees conferred: business/marketing; biological/life sciences; education. Core. Calendar: semesters. Academic remediation for entering students, ESL program, services for LD students, advanced placement, self-designed majors, honors program, independent study, double major, summer session for credit, part-time degree program, co-op programs and internships. Off campus study at Chicago Urban Studies Semester, American University. Study abroad program. ROTC: Army (c), Air Force (c).

Entrance Requirements: Options: electronic application, early admission, deferred admission, international baccalaureate accepted. Required: high school transcript, 1 recommendation, SAT or ACT. Recommended: essay, minimum 2.5 high school GPA. Required for some: interview. Entrance: moderately difficult. Notification: 8/1.

Costs Per Year: Application fee: $0. Comprehensive fee: $29,300 includes full-time tuition ($19,750), mandatory fees ($1100), and college room and board ($8450). College room only: $4500. Room and board charges vary according to board plan and housing facility. Part-time tuition: $800 per credit hour.

Collegiate Environment: Orientation program. Drama-theater group, choral group, student-run newspaper. Social organizations: 54 open to all; national fraternities, national sororities; 50% of eligible men and 34% of eligible women are members. Most popular organizations: Student Government Association, Environmentally Concerned Students, International Student Club, Habitat for Humanity, Little Brother/Little Sister. Major annual events: Leadership Challenge, Take Back the Night, Wellness Week. Student services: health clinic, personal-psychological counseling, women's center. Campus security: 24-hour emergency response devices and patrols, late night transport-escort service, controlled dormitory access, well-lit campus. 636 college housing spaces available; 601 were occupied in 2012-13. Freshmen guaranteed college housing. On-campus residence required through junior year. Options: coed, men-only, women-only housing available. Reeves Memorial Library plus 1 other with 131,992 books, 6,912 microform titles, 30,201 serials, 2,171 audiovisual materials, an OPAC, and a Web page. 188 computers available on campus for general student use. A campuswide network can be accessed from student residence rooms and from off campus. Students can access the following: online class registration. Staffed computer lab on campus provides training in use of computers, software, and the Internet.

■ WILLIAM JEWELL COLLEGE

500 College Hill
Liberty, MO 64068-1843

Tel: (816)781-7700; Free: 888-2JEWELL
Fax: (816)415-5027
E-mail: chapmanc@william.jewell.edu
Web Site: www.jewell.edu/

Description: Independent, 4-year, coed. Awards bachelor's degrees (also offers evening program with significant enrollment not reflected in profile). Founded 1849. Setting: 200-acre suburban campus with easy access to Kansas City. Endowment: $62.5 million. Educational spending for the previous fiscal year: $9010 per student. Total enrollment: 1,052. Faculty: 141 (74 full-time, 67 part-time). Student-undergrad faculty ratio is 11:1. 3,006 applied, 61% were admitted. 25% from top 10% of their high school class, 61% from top quarter, 89% from top half. 9 valedictorians. Full-time: 1,011 students, 57% women, 43% men. Part-time: 41 students, 76% women, 24% men. Students come from 31 states and territories, 17 other countries, 37% from out-of-state. 1% American Indian or Alaska Native, non-Hispanic/Latino; 3% Hispanic/Latino; 5% African American, non-Hispanic/Latino; 1% Asian, non-Hispanic/Latino; 0.1% Native Hawaiian or other Pacific Islander, non-Hispanic/Latino; 3% international. 85% live on campus, 3% transferred in. Retention: 73% of full-time freshmen returned the following year. Academic areas with the most degrees conferred: health professions and related sciences; business/marketing; education; psychology. Core. Calendar: semesters. Services for LD students, advanced placement, accelerated degree program, self-designed majors, honors program, independent study, distance learning, double major, summer session for credit, co-op programs and internships. Off campus study. Study abroad program. ROTC: Army (c).

Entrance Requirements: Options: electronic application, deferred admission, international baccalaureate accepted. Required: essay, high school transcript. Recommended: interview, SAT or ACT. Required for some: interview. Entrance: moderately difficult. Application deadline: 8/15. SAT Reasoning Test deadline: 8/1. SAT Subject Test deadline: 8/1. Transfer credits accepted: Yes.

Costs Per Year: Application fee: $25. Comprehensive fee: $39,120 includes full-time tuition ($30,800), mandatory fees ($300), and college room and board ($8020). Full-time tuition and fees vary according to class time, course load, program, and student level. Room and board charges vary according to board plan and housing facility. Part-time tuition: $890 per credit.

Collegiate Environment: Orientation program. Drama-theater group, choral group, student-run newspaper, radio station. Social organizations: 60 open to all; national fraternities, national sororities; 42% of eligible men and 43% of eligible women are members. Most popular organizations: College Union Activities, intramurals, Mosaic, Student Senate, Black Student Association. Major annual events: Homecoming, Hanging of the Green/Lighting of the Quad, Undergraduate Research Colloquium. Student services: health clinic, personal-psychological counseling. Campus security: 24-hour emergency response devices and patrols, late night transport-escort service, controlled dormitory access. 1,012 college housing spaces available; 861 were occupied in 2012-13. Freshmen guaranteed college housing. On-campus residence required through senior year. Options: coed, men-only, women-only housing available. Charles F. Curry Library with 143,567 books, 847 microform titles, 83,352 serials, 9,508 audiovisual materials, an OPAC, and a Web page. Operations spending for the previous fiscal year: $955,054. 220 computers available on campus for general student use. A computer is required for all students. A campuswide network can be accessed from student residence rooms and from off campus. Students can access the following: online class registration. Staffed computer lab on campus provides training in use of computers, software, and the Internet.

Community Environment: A suburban community, Liberty is 13 miles northeast of Kansas City and enjoys all of the cultural and recreational advantages afforded by its proximity to a major metropolitan area of 1.5 million people. Several points of interest are the State Ballet of Missouri, the Kansas city Symphony, and the Nelson-Atkins Museum of Art. Kansas City also offers professional football and baseball. The Harriman Fine Arts Program provides great performances from such artists as Itzhak Perlman, Paul Taylor Dance Company, and Yo Yo Ma.

■ WILLIAM WOODS UNIVERSITY

One University Ave.
Fulton, MO 65251-1098
Tel: (573)642-2251; Free: 800-995-3159
Fax: (573)592-1146
E-mail: admissions@williamwoods.edu
Web Site: www.williamwoods.edu/

Description: Independent, comprehensive, coed, affiliated with Christian Church (Disciples of Christ). Awards associate, bachelor's, and master's degrees and post-master's certificates. Founded 1870. Setting: rural campus with easy access to St. Louis. Total enrollment: 2,020. Faculty: 357 (73 full-time, 284 part-time). Student-undergrad faculty ratio is 12:1. 753 applied, 80% were admitted. 17% from top 10% of their high school class, 40% from top quarter, 74% from top half. Full-time: 872 students, 74% women, 26% men. Part-time: 164 students, 69% women, 31% men. 34% from out-of-state. 0.5% American Indian or Alaska Native, non-Hispanic/Latino; 1% Hispanic/Latino; 4% African American, non-Hispanic/Latino; 1% Asian, non-Hispanic/Latino; 0% Native Hawaiian or other Pacific Islander, non-Hispanic/Latino; 0.1% international. 4% 25 or older, 75% live on campus, 11% transferred in. Retention: 74% of full-time freshmen returned the following year. Academic areas with the most degrees conferred: business/marketing; education; agriculture. Calendar: semesters. Academic remediation for entering students, advanced placement, accelerated degree program, self-designed majors, honors program, independent study, double major, summer session for credit, part-time degree program, adult/continuing education programs, internships. Off campus study at University of Missouri-Columbia, Westminster College (MO), Stephens College, Lincoln University (MO). Study abroad program. ROTC: Army (c), Naval (c), Air Force (c).

Entrance Requirements: Options: deferred admission, international baccalaureate accepted. Required: high school transcript, minimum 2.5 high school GPA, 16 hours college preparatory units, SAT or ACT. Recommended: interview. Required for some: essay, 2 recommendations. Entrance: moderately difficult. Application deadline: 8/15. Notification: continuous. SAT Reasoning Test deadline: 8/15. SAT Subject Test deadline: 8/15.

Costs Per Year: Application fee: $25. Comprehensive fee: $27,100 includes full-time tuition ($19,200) and college room and board ($7900). College room only: $4000. Full-time tuition varies according to degree level and program. Room and board charges vary according to board plan and housing facility.

Collegiate Environment: Orientation program. Campus security: 24-hour emergency response devices and patrols, late night transport-escort service, controlled dormitory access.

Community Environment: The wooded Missouri landscape provides a scenic setting for residents of the area. Colleges, state educational and health facilities and professional industries are primary employers. Part-time employment is available. The regional area provides major medical centers, churches, libraries, restaurants, and recreational and entertainment facilities.

AANIIIH NAKODA COLLEGE

PO Box 159
Harlem, MT 59526-0159
Tel: (406)353-2607
Fax: (406)353-2898
E-mail: dbrockie@mail.fbcc.edu
Web Site: www.fbcc.edu/
Description: Federally supported, 2-year, coed. Awards certificates, transfer associate, and terminal associate degrees. Founded 1984. Setting: 3-acre rural campus. Total enrollment: 236. Student-undergrad faculty ratio is 11:1. 0% from out-of-state. 66% 25 or older. Core. Academic remediation for entering students, part-time degree program, co-op programs.
Entrance Requirements: Open admission. Options: early admission, deferred admission. Required: high school transcript. Entrance: noncompetitive. Application deadline: Rolling. Notification: continuous.
Collegiate Environment: Orientation program. Student-run radio station. Campus security: 24-hour patrols. Fort Belknap College Library with an OPAC and a Web page.

BLACKFEET COMMUNITY COLLEGE

PO Box 819
Browning, MT 59417-0819
Tel: (406)338-5441; Free: 800-549-7457
Fax: (406)338-3272
Web Site: www.bfcc.edu/
Description: Independent, 2-year, coed. Awards certificates, diplomas, transfer associate, and terminal associate degrees. Founded 1974. Setting: 5-acre small town campus. Total enrollment: 471. 55% 25 or older. Core. Calendar: semesters. Academic remediation for entering students, part-time degree program, adult/continuing education programs. Off campus study at members of the American Indian Higher Education Consortium.
Entrance Requirements: Open admission. Option: early admission. Required: high school transcript, immunization with second MMR; certificate of Indian blood. Entrance: noncompetitive. Application deadline: 8/29. Notification: continuous.
Collegiate Environment: Orientation program. Campus security: 16 hour patrols by security personnel. 10,000 books and 175 serials.

CARROLL COLLEGE

1601 N Benton Ave.
Helena, MT 59625-0002
Tel: (406)447-4300; Free: 800-992-3648
Fax: (406)447-4533
E-mail: admission@carroll.edu
Web Site: www.carroll.edu/
Description: Independent Roman Catholic, 4-year, coed. Awards associate and bachelor's degrees. Founded 1909. Setting: 61-acre small town campus. Endowment: $27.3 million. Total enrollment: 1,464. Faculty: 170 (91 full-time, 79 part-time). Student-undergrad faculty ratio is 12:1. 2,529 applied, 62% were admitted. 25% from top 10% of their high school class, 60% from top quarter, 91% from top half. Full-time: 1,364 students, 58% women, 42% men. Part-time: 100 students, 53% women, 47% men. Students come from 33 states and territories, 7 other countries, 50% from out-of-state. 1% American Indian or Alaska Native, non-Hispanic/Latino; 3% Hispanic/Latino; 1% African American, non-Hispanic/Latino; 1% Asian, non-Hispanic/Latino;

0.3% Native Hawaiian or other Pacific Islander, non-Hispanic/Latino; 1% international. 7% 25 or older, 3% transferred in. Retention: 86% of full-time freshmen returned the following year. Academic areas with the most degrees conferred: health professions and related sciences; business/marketing; biological/life sciences. Core. Calendar: semesters. ESL program, advanced placement, accelerated degree program, self-designed majors, freshman honors college, honors program, independent study, double major, summer session for credit, part-time degree program, adult/continuing education programs, co-op programs and internships. Study abroad program. ROTC: Army.
Entrance Requirements: Options: electronic application, deferred admission, international baccalaureate accepted. Required: essay, high school transcript, SAT or ACT. Recommended: interview. Required for some: interview, SAT Subject Tests. Entrance: moderately difficult. Application deadlines: 2/15, 2/15 for nonresidents. Notification: continuous, continuous for nonresidents. SAT Reasoning Test deadline: 6/15. SAT Subject Test deadline: 6/15. Transfer credits accepted: Yes.
Costs Per Year: Application fee: $35. Comprehensive fee: $34,616 includes full-time tuition ($26,004), mandatory fees ($550), and college room and board ($8062). College room only: $4292. Full-time tuition and fees vary according to course load. Room and board charges vary according to board plan and housing facility. Part-time tuition: $1094 per credit hour. Part-time mandatory fees: $137.50 per term. Part-time tuition and fees vary according to course load.
Collegiate Environment: Orientation program. Drama-theater group, choral group, student-run newspaper, radio station. Most popular organizations: student government, Carroll Outreach Team, Carroll Adventure and Mountaineering Program, Up 'Til Dawn, Engineers Without Borders. Major annual events: Homecoming, Casino Night, Spring Softball Tournament. Student services: health clinic, personal-psychological counseling. Campus security: 24-hour emergency response devices, late night transport-escort service, controlled dormitory access. 875 college housing spaces available; 827 were occupied in 2012-13. Freshmen guaranteed college housing. On-campus residence required through sophomore year. Option: coed housing available. Corette Library plus 1 other with 320,000 books, 10,000 microform titles, 35,980 serials, 2,111 audiovisual materials, an OPAC, and a Web page.

CHIEF DULL KNIFE COLLEGE

1 College Dr.
Lame Deer, MT 59043-0098
Tel: (406)477-6215
Fax: (406)477-6219
Web Site: www.cdkc.edu/
Description: Independent, 2-year, coed. Awards certificates, transfer associate, and terminal associate degrees. Founded 1975. Setting: 3-acre rural campus. Total enrollment: 472. Student-undergrad faculty ratio is 13:1. 0% from out-of-state. 40% 25 or older. Core. Calendar: semesters. Academic remediation for entering students, services for LD students, summer session for credit, part-time degree program, adult/continuing education programs, co-op programs and internships. Off campus study at members of the American Indian Higher Education Consortium.
Entrance Requirements: Open admission. Option: early admission. Required: high school transcript. Entrance: noncompetitive. Application deadline: Rolling. Notification: continuous.
Costs Per Year: Application fee: $0. Comprehensive fee: $2540 includes

full-time tuition ($1680), mandatory fees ($260), and college room and board ($600). Full-time tuition and fees vary according to course level and course load. Part-time tuition: $70 per credit. Part-time mandatory fees: $20 per credit. Part-time tuition and fees vary according to course level and course load.

Collegiate Environment: Student-run newspaper. Student services: personal-psychological counseling.

■ DAWSON COMMUNITY COLLEGE

300 College Dr.
Glendive, MT 59330-0421
Tel: (406)377-3396; Free: 800-821-8320
Fax: (406)377-8132
E-mail: myers@dawson.edu
Web Site: www.dawson.edu/

Description: State and locally supported, 2-year, coed. Part of Montana University System. Awards certificates, transfer associate, and terminal associate degrees. Founded 1940. Setting: 300-acre rural campus. Endowment: $344,944. Research spending for the previous fiscal year: $3000. Educational spending for the previous fiscal year: $3897 per student. Total enrollment: 603. Faculty: 26 (23 full-time, 3 part-time). Student-undergrad faculty ratio is 26:1. Full-time: 284 students, 53% women, 47% men. Part-time: 319 students, 63% women, 37% men. 21% 25 or older. Core. Calendar: semesters. Academic remediation for entering students, services for LD students, independent study, distance learning, summer session for credit, part-time degree program, adult/continuing education programs, internships.

Entrance Requirements: Open admission. Option: deferred admission. Required: high school transcript. Entrance: noncompetitive. Application deadline: Rolling. Notification: continuous. Transfer credits accepted: Yes.

Collegiate Environment: Orientation program. Drama-theater group, choral group. Social organizations: 18 open to all. Most popular organizations: Phi Theta Kappa, Associated Student Body, Rodeo Club, Law Enforcement Club, Campus Corp. Major annual events: Homecoming, Taste of Dawson, Awards Ceremony. Campus security: 24-hour emergency response devices. Jane Carey Memorial Library with 17,182 books, 90 serials, 1,127 audiovisual materials, an OPAC, and a Web page. Operations spending for the previous fiscal year: $169,351. 2,010 computers available on campus for general student use. A campuswide network can be accessed from student residence rooms and from off campus. Students can access the following: online class registration. Staffed computer lab on campus provides training in use of computers, software, and the Internet.

Community Environment: Dawson is located in Glendive, the county seat of Dawson County. It is a transportation, agricultural and energy resource center located on the Yellowstone River on I-94. The city has a library, Frontier Gateway Museum, several churches, a hospital, and most major civic, fraternal and veteran's organizations within the immediate area. Recreation facilities include indoor and outdoor theaters, good hunting, limited boating and fishing, golf, and other outdoor sports. Some part-time work is available for students.

■ FLATHEAD VALLEY COMMUNITY COLLEGE

777 Grandview Dr.
Kalispell, MT 59901-2622
Tel: (406)756-3822; Free: 800-313-3822
Fax: (406)756-3815
E-mail: mstoltz@fvcc.cc.mt.us
Web Site: www.fvcc.edu/

Description: State and locally supported, 2-year, coed. Part of Montana University System. Awards certificates, transfer associate, and terminal associate degrees. Founded 1967. Setting: 209-acre small town campus. Endowment: $5.4 million. Educational spending for the previous fiscal year: $4133 per student. Total enrollment: 2,395. Faculty: 197 (53 full-time, 144 part-time). Student-undergrad faculty ratio is 16:1. Full-time: 1,170 students, 57% women, 43% men. Part-time: 1,225 students, 67% women, 33% men. Students come from 14 states and territories, 3% from out-of-state. 4% American Indian or Alaska Native, non-Hispanic/Latino; 2% Hispanic/Latino; 0.3% African American, non-Hispanic/Latino; 1% Asian, non-Hispanic/Latino; 0.3% Native Hawaiian or other Pacific Islander, non-Hispanic/Latino; 0% international. 49% 25 or older, 1% live on campus, 7% transferred in. Retention: 52% of full-time freshmen returned the following year. Core. Calendar: semesters. Academic remediation for entering students, ESL program, services for LD students, advanced placement, honors program, independent study, distance learning, double major, summer session for credit, part-

time degree program, adult/continuing education programs, co-op programs and internships. Study abroad program.

Entrance Requirements: Open admission. Options: early admission, deferred admission. Required: high school transcript, COMPASS Placement Test. Entrance: noncompetitive. Application deadline: Rolling. Transfer credits accepted: Yes.

Costs Per Year: Application fee: $15. Area resident tuition: $2761 full-time, $99 per credit hour part-time. State resident tuition: $4133 full-time, $148 per credit hour part-time. Nonresident tuition: $9901 full-time, $354 per credit hour part-time. Mandatory fees: $969 full-time, $35 per credit hour part-time. Full-time tuition and fees vary according to course load. Part-time tuition and fees vary according to course load.

Collegiate Environment: Orientation program. Drama-theater group, choral group, student-run newspaper. Social organizations: 23 open to all. Most popular organizations: Forestry Club, Phi Theta Kappa. Student services: health clinic, personal-psychological counseling. 30 college housing spaces available; all were occupied in 2012-13. No special consideration for freshman housing applicants. Option: coed housing available. Flathead Valley Community College Library with 35,000 books, 495 microform titles, 125 serials, 514 audiovisual materials, an OPAC, and a Web page. Operations spending for the previous fiscal year: $238,002. 230 computers available on campus for general student use. A campuswide network can be accessed. Students can access the following: online class registration. Staffed computer lab on campus.

Community Environment: The campus is located 3 miles north of Kalispell city center in the beautiful Flathead Valley, a region noted for the production of seed potatoes, wheat, cattle, Christmas trees, plywood, lumber and sweet cherries. The city is circled by dense forests, lakes, and mountains, with more than 2,000 miles of good fishing streams. Transportation for the area is provided by air, rail, and bus lines. There are 28 churches, one library, a hospital and a medical center. Convenient shopping is easily accessible. Although Kalispell is a resort area, the local industries include plywood production, camper and camp trailer manufacturing, log-skidding machinery, and chemical and concrete products. Part-time employment is available for students.

■ FORT PECK COMMUNITY COLLEGE

PO Box 398
Poplar, MT 59255-0398
Tel: (406)768-5551
Web Site: www.fpcc.edu/

Description: District-supported, 2-year, coed. Awards certificates, transfer associate, and terminal associate degrees. Founded 1978. Setting: small town campus. Total enrollment: 422. 63% 25 or older. Core. Calendar: semesters. Summer session for credit, part-time degree program. Off campus study at members of the American Indian Higher Education Consortium.

Entrance Requirements: Open admission. Options: electronic application, early admission. Entrance: noncompetitive. Application deadline: Rolling.

■ GREAT FALLS COLLEGE MONTANA STATE UNIVERSITY

2100 16th Ave., S
Great Falls, MT 59405
Tel: (406)771-4300; Free: 800-446-2698
Fax: (406)771-4317
E-mail: brittany.budeski@gfcmsu.edu
Web Site: www.gfcmsu.edu/

Description: State-supported, 2-year, coed. Part of Montana University System. Awards certificates, transfer associate, and terminal associate degrees. Founded 1969. Setting: 40-acre small town campus. Endowment: $11,300. Educational spending for the previous fiscal year: $4405 per student. Total enrollment: 1,835. Faculty: 145 (46 full-time, 99 part-time). Student-undergrad faculty ratio is 15:1. 477 applied, 96% were admitted. 3% from top 10% of their high school class, 15% from top quarter, 43% from top half. Full-time: 909 students, 66% women, 34% men. Part-time: 926 students, 75% women, 25% men. Students come from 27 states and territories, 1 other country, 2% from out-of-state. 6% American Indian or Alaska Native, non-Hispanic/Latino; 4% Hispanic/Latino; 1% African American, non-Hispanic/Latino; 1% Asian, non-Hispanic/Latino; 0.2% Native Hawaiian or other Pacific Islander, non-Hispanic/Latino; 0% international. 50% 25 or older, 8% transferred in. Calendar: semesters. Academic remediation for entering students, services for LD students, advanced placement, independent study, distance learning, double major, summer session for credit, part-time degree program, internships. Off campus study.

Entrance Requirements: Open admission special admission requirements for some programs, including dental assistant and hygiene, radiologic technology, practical nurse, surgical technology, respiratory care, pharmacy technician, sustainable energy, physical therapist assistant programs. Option: early admission. Required: high school transcript, proof of immunization. Entrance: noncompetitive. Application deadlines: Rolling, Rolling for nonresidents. Notification: continuous, continuous for nonresidents. Transfer credits accepted: Yes.

Costs Per Year: Application fee: $30. State resident tuition: $2496 full-time, $104 per credit hour part-time. Nonresident tuition: $8748 full-time, $364.48 per credit hour part-time. Mandatory fees: $581 full-time, $20.07 per semester hour part-time, $49.74 per term part-time. Full-time tuition and fees vary according to course load and program. Part-time tuition and fees vary according to course load and program.

Collegiate Environment: Orientation program. Social organizations: 6 open to all. Most popular organizations: The Associated Students of Great Falls College Montana State University, Native American Students, Veteran's Club. Campus security: 24-hour emergency response devices. Weaver Library with 50,470 books, 50,274 serials, 1,294 audiovisual materials, an OPAC, and a Web page. Operations spending for the previous fiscal year: $294,440. 495 computers available on campus for general student use. A campuswide network can be accessed from off-campus. Students can access the following: online class registration. Staffed computer lab on campus.

■ **LITTLE BIG HORN COLLEGE**

Box 370
1 Forest Ln.
Crow Agency, MT 59022-0370
Tel: (406)638-3104
Web Site: www.lbhc.edu/

Description: Independent, 2-year, coed. Awards certificates, transfer associate, and terminal associate degrees. Founded 1980. Setting: 5-acre rural campus. Total enrollment: 317. Faculty: 12 (11 full-time, 1 part-time). Student-undergrad faculty ratio is 25:1. 50% 25 or older. Core. Part-time degree program. Off campus study at members of the American Indian Higher Education Consortium.

Entrance Requirements: Open admission. Required: high school transcript. Entrance: noncompetitive. Application deadline: Rolling. Notification: continuous.

Collegiate Environment: Student-run newspaper. 30 computers available on campus for general student use. Staffed computer lab on campus.

■ **MILES COMMUNITY COLLEGE**

2715 Dickinson
Miles City, MT 59301-4799
Tel: (406)874-6100; Free: 800-541-9281
Fax: (406)874-6282
E-mail: andersonh@milescc.edu
Web Site: www.milescc.edu/

Description: State and locally supported, 2-year, coed. Part of Montana University System. Awards certificates, transfer associate, and terminal associate degrees. Founded 1939. Setting: 8-acre small town campus. Total enrollment: 441. Faculty: 50 (24 full-time, 26 part-time). Student-undergrad faculty ratio is 10:1. 319 applied, 100% were admitted. Full-time: 280 students, 50% women, 50% men. Part-time: 161 students, 81% women, 19% men. Students come from 24 states and territories, 4 other countries, 14% from out-of-state. 4% American Indian or Alaska Native, non-Hispanic/Latino; 2% Hispanic/Latino; 2% African American, non-Hispanic/Latino; 1% Asian, non-Hispanic/Latino; 0% Native Hawaiian or other Pacific Islander, non-Hispanic/Latino; 2% international. 0% 25 or older, 32% live on campus, 11% transferred in. Core. Calendar: semesters. Academic remediation for entering students, ESL program, services for LD students, advanced placement, accelerated degree program, honors program, independent study, distance learning, double major, summer session for credit, part-time degree program, adult/continuing education programs, co-op programs and internships.

Entrance Requirements: Open admission except for nursing program, heavy equipment operator program. Options: electronic application, early admission, deferred admission. Required: high school transcript. Entrance: noncompetitive. Application deadline: Rolling. Transfer credits accepted: Yes. Applicants placed on waiting list: 0. Wait-listed applicants offered admission: 0.

Collegiate Environment: Orientation program. Drama-theater group.

Student services: personal-psychological counseling. Campus security: 24-hour emergency response devices, Manual dormitory entrances locked all the time, only accessible with key. 160 college housing spaces available; 139 were occupied in 2012-13. On-campus residence required in freshman year. Option: coed housing available. Library Resource Center with 17,563 books, 36 microform titles, 310 serials, 174 audiovisual materials, an OPAC, and a Web page. 165 computers available on campus for general student use. A campuswide network can be accessed from student residence rooms and from off campus. Staffed computer lab on campus.

Community Environment: Vast livestock ranches around Miles City raise more than one-fourth of the cattle and sheep produced in Montana. Wheat is the primary crop grown in the dryland area. The city itself is a pleasant residential town with a mean annual temperature of 44.4 degrees, and an average rainfall of 13.79 inches. Local area is served by airlines and bus lines. The community has 17 churches, tennis courts, two theaters, bowling alley, golf course, radio and TV station and various civic and fraternal organizations. Local homes, apartments and rooms provide student housing in addition to dormitories. There are limited part-time work opportunities for students.

■ **MONTANA STATE UNIVERSITY**

Bozeman, MT 59717
Tel: (406)994-0211; Free: 888-MSU-CATS
E-mail: admissions@montana.edu
Web Site: www.montana.edu/

Description: State-supported, university, coed. Part of Montana University System. Awards associate, bachelor's, master's, and doctoral degrees and post-master's certificates. Founded 1893. Setting: 1,781-acre small town campus. Endowment: $92.9 million. Research spending for the previous fiscal year: $112.3 million. Educational spending for the previous fiscal year: $5345 per student. Total enrollment: 14,660. Faculty: 917 (580 full-time, 337 part-time). Student-undergrad faculty ratio is 18:1. 12,081 applied, 58% were admitted. 18% from top 10% of their high school class, 43% from top quarter, 73% from top half. 9 National Merit Scholars, 97 valedictorians. Full-time: 10,598 students, 45% women, 55% men. Part-time: 2,174 students, 49% women, 51% men. Students come from 50 states and territories, 66 other countries, 34% from out-of-state. 2% American Indian or Alaska Native, non-Hispanic/Latino; 3% Hispanic/Latino; 1% African American, non-Hispanic/Latino; 1% Asian, non-Hispanic/Latino; 0.04% Native Hawaiian or other Pacific Islander, non-Hispanic/Latino; 3% international. 18% 25 or older, 25% live on campus, 7% transferred in. Retention: 74% of full-time freshmen returned the following year. Academic areas with the most degrees conferred: business/marketing; engineering; health professions and related sciences; family and consumer sciences. Core. Calendar: semesters. Academic remediation for entering students, ESL program, services for LD students, advanced placement, self-designed majors, honors program, independent study, distance learning, double major, summer session for credit, part-time degree program, adult/continuing education programs, internships, graduate courses open to undergrads. Off campus study at members of the National Student Exchange. Study abroad program. ROTC: Army, Air Force.

Entrance Requirements: Options: electronic application, early admission, deferred admission, international baccalaureate accepted. Required: high school transcript, minimum 2.5 high school GPA, SAT or ACT. Entrance: moderately difficult. Application deadlines: Rolling, Rolling for nonresidents. Notification: continuous, continuous for nonresidents.

Costs Per Year: Application fee: $30. State resident tuition: $5330 full-time, $222 per credit part-time. Nonresident tuition: $18,599 full-time, $779 per credit part-time. Mandatory fees: $1419 full-time, $106 per credit part-time. Full-time tuition and fees vary according to course load, degree level, and program. Part-time tuition and fees vary according to course load, degree level, and program. College room and board: $8070. Room and board charges vary according to board plan and housing facility.

Collegiate Environment: Orientation program. Drama-theater group, choral group, marching band, student-run newspaper, radio station. Social organizations: 150 open to all; national fraternities, national sororities; 2% of eligible men and 2% of eligible women are members. Most popular organizations: Spurs, Inter-Varsity Christian Fellowship, Campus Crusade for Christ, Fangs, Mortar Board. Major annual events: International Food Bazaar, Native American Pow-wow, Day of Student Recognition. Student services: legal services, health clinic, personal-psychological counseling, women's center. Campus security: 24-hour emergency response devices and patrols, student patrols, late night transport-escort service, 24-hour residence hall monitoring. 3,260 college housing spaces available; 2,683 were occupied in 2012-

13. Freshmen guaranteed college housing. On-campus residence required in freshman year. Options: coed, men-only, women-only housing available. Renne Library plus 2 others with 868,041 books, 2.2 million microform titles, 15,615 serials, 16,380 audiovisual materials, an OPAC, and a Web page. Operations spending for the previous fiscal year: $7.7 million. 850 computers available on campus for general student use. A campuswide network can be accessed from student residence rooms and from off campus. Students can access the following: online class registration. Staffed computer lab on campus provides training in use of computers, software, and the Internet.

Community Environment: At the heart of the Gallatin Valley, known for its scenic beauty, the city is headquarters for Gallatin National Forest. The Bridger Bowl Ski Area, 18 miles northwest, and Big Sky, Inc. 33 miles south offer skiing from mid-November to mid-March. Immediately south of Bozeman, Highway 191 follows Gallatin River through the forest to Yellowstone National Park 90 miles away. The Gallatin Field airport is 8 miles from Bozeman and is served by Delta and Northwest. Community services include many churches, public library, one hospital, and many hotels and motels. Various service clubs, veteran's clubs, and many fraternal organizations are represented within the immediate area. Recreation other than skiing is provided by local picnic areas, swimming pools, five parks, tennis courts, dude ranches, golf courses, hunting, boating, and fishing. Bozeman is known for its year-round outdoor recreational opportunities.

■ MONTANA STATE UNIVERSITY BILLINGS

1500 University Dr.
Billings, MT 59101-0298
Tel: (406)657-2011; Free: 800-565-6782
Fax: (406)657-2302
E-mail: tammi.watson@msubillings.edu
Web Site: www.msubillings.edu/

Description: State-supported, comprehensive, coed. Part of Montana University System. Awards associate, bachelor's, and master's degrees. Founded 1927. Setting: 92-acre urban campus. Endowment: $15.6 million. Research spending for the previous fiscal year: $888,959. Educational spending for the previous fiscal year: $5643 per student. Total enrollment: 5,081. Faculty: 343 (154 full-time, 189 part-time). Student-undergrad faculty ratio is 18:1. 1,565 applied, 97% were admitted. 8% from top 10% of their high school class, 26% from top quarter, 66% from top half. 10 valedictorians. Full-time: 3,262 students, 58% women, 42% men. Part-time: 1,275 students, 69% women, 31% men. Students come from 40 states and territories, 21 other countries, 9% from out-of-state. 4% American Indian or Alaska Native, non-Hispanic/Latino; 4% Hispanic/Latino; 1% African American, non-Hispanic/Latino; 1% Asian, non-Hispanic/Latino; 0.2% Native Hawaiian or other Pacific Islander, non-Hispanic/Latino; 3% international. 36% 25 or older, 18% live on campus, 10% transferred in. Retention: 56% of full-time freshmen returned the following year. Academic areas with the most degrees conferred: education; business/marketing; liberal arts/general studies. Core. Calendar: semesters. Academic remediation for entering students, ESL program, services for LD students, advanced placement, accelerated degree program, honors program, independent study, distance learning, double major, summer session for credit, part-time degree program, external degree program, adult/continuing education programs, co-op programs and internships, graduate courses open to undergrads. Off campus study. Study abroad program. ROTC: Army.

Entrance Requirements: Options: electronic application, early admission, deferred admission. Required: high school transcript, minimum 2.5 high school GPA, SAT or ACT. Entrance: minimally difficult. Application deadline: 7/1. Notification: continuous. Transfer credits accepted: Yes.

Costs Per Year: Application fee: $30. State resident tuition: $4397 full-time, $158 per credit hour part-time. Nonresident tuition: $16,726 full-time, $522 per credit hour part-time. Mandatory fees: $1314 full-time. Full-time tuition and fees vary according to course load, degree level, and location. Part-time tuition varies according to course load, degree level, and location. College room and board: $6320. Room and board charges vary according to board plan and housing facility.

Collegiate Environment: Orientation program. Drama-theater group, choral group, student-run newspaper, radio station. Social organizations: 53 open to all; local fraternities, local sororities; 5% of eligible men and 10% of eligible women are members. Most popular organizations: Art Student League, Band Club, Inter-Varsity Christian Fellowship, Residence Hall Association, Student Council for Exceptional Children. Major annual events: Homecoming, Welcome Week events, Summerfest. Student services: legal services, health clinic, personal-psychological counseling, women's center. Campus security: 24-hour emergency response devices and patrols, late

night transport-escort service, controlled dormitory access. 550 college housing spaces available; 525 were occupied in 2012-13. Freshmen given priority for college housing. On-campus residence required in freshman year. Options: coed, men-only, women-only housing available. Montana State University-Billings Library plus 2 others with 228,225 books, 549,194 microform titles, 60,540 serials, 2,275 audiovisual materials, an OPAC, and a Web page. Operations spending for the previous fiscal year: $1 million. 1,500 computers available on campus for general student use. Computer purchase/lease plans available. A campuswide network can be accessed from student residence rooms and from off campus. Students can access the following: online class registration, online degree programs. Staffed computer lab on campus provides training in use of computers, software, and the Internet.

Community Environment: Billings is an expanding city located in the Yellowstone River Valley between rugged mountains and sweeping plains. The city is the largest in Montana, and has a population of approximately 98,700 people living in the metropolitan area. The "Magic City" is a transportation, medical, agricultural, wholesale, and retail trade center. It is served by major air, bus, and rail lines, and excellent interstate highways. Community services include many churches representing most denominations, a city library, theatres, museums, art galleries, two hospitals, YMCA, YWCA, and various civic and fraternal organizations. Recreational sites are numerous and include opportunities for fishing, hunting, boating, bowling, golf, skiing, and hiking.

■ MONTANA STATE UNIVERSITY–NORTHERN

PO Box 7751
Havre, MT 59501-7751
Tel: (406)265-3700; Free: 800-662-6132
Fax: (406)265-3777
Web Site: www.msun.edu/

Description: State-supported, comprehensive, coed. Part of Montana University System. Awards associate, bachelor's, and master's degrees. Founded 1929. Setting: small town campus. Total enrollment: 1,273. Faculty: 96 (62 full-time, 34 part-time). Student-undergrad faculty ratio is 15:1. 378 applied, 64% were admitted. 4% from top 10% of their high school class, 14% from top quarter, 43% from top half. Full-time: 923 students, 43% women, 57% men. Part-time: 285 students, 74% women, 26% men. 89% from out-of-state. 13% American Indian or Alaska Native, non-Hispanic/Latino; 2% Hispanic/Latino; 1% African American, non-Hispanic/Latino; 1% Asian, non-Hispanic/Latino; 0% Native Hawaiian or other Pacific Islander, non-Hispanic/Latino; 1% international. 34% 25 or older, 22% live on campus, 15% transferred in. Retention: 58% of full-time freshmen returned the following year. Academic areas with the most degrees conferred: education; mechanic and repair technologies; health professions and related sciences. Calendar: semesters. Part-time degree program, adult/continuing education programs.

Entrance Requirements: Options: early admission, deferred admission. Required: high school transcript, SAT or ACT. Required for some: minimum 2 high school GPA. Entrance: moderately difficult. Application deadline: Rolling. Notification: continuous.

Costs Per Year: Application fee: $30. State resident tuition: $3765 full-time, $232 per credit hour part-time. Nonresident tuition: $14,943 full-time, $635 per credit hour part-time. Mandatory fees: $1305 full-time. Full-time tuition and fees vary according to course level, course load, degree level, location, reciprocity agreements, and student level. Part-time tuition varies according to course level, course load, degree level, location, reciprocity agreements, and student level. College room and board: $6275. College room only: $2147. Room and board charges vary according to board plan.

Collegiate Environment: Orientation program.

Community Environment: Havre is the transportation hub of the Northern Great Plains, America's agricultural heartland. Montana's panoramic Big Sky meets a horizon of rolling foothills and abundant lakes and reservoirs. The community is easily accessible from all directions by highway, Amtrak, and a commuter airline with links to major international airports. Rugged environments such as Glacier National Park, the Cypress Hills of Canada, the Bears Paw Mountains and the Little Rockies, are only a few hours away. Picnicking, camping, abundant wildlife, lakes with great fishing, boating, and water skiing, and numerous winter and summer sports offer recreation for outdoor enthusiasts.

■ MONTANA TECH OF THE UNIVERSITY OF MONTANA

1300 W Park St.
Butte, MT 59701-8997

Tel: (406)496-4101; Free: 800-445-TECH
Fax: (406)496-4710
E-mail: scrowe@mtech.edu
Web Site: www.mtech.edu/

Description: State-supported, comprehensive, coed. Part of Montana University System. Awards associate, bachelor's, and master's degrees. Founded 1895. Setting: 56-acre small town campus. Endowment: $26.3 million. Research spending for the previous fiscal year: $12.5 million. Educational spending for the previous fiscal year: $9910 per student. Total enrollment: 2,816. Faculty: 213 (135 full-time, 78 part-time). Student-undergrad faculty ratio is 15:1. 822 applied, 90% were admitted. 22% from top 10% of their high school class, 47% from top quarter, 79% from top half. Full-time: 2,186 students, 36% women, 64% men. Part-time: 460 students, 60% women, 40% men. Students come from 31 states and territories, 9 other countries, 13% from out-of-state. 2% American Indian or Alaska Native, non-Hispanic/Latino; 2% Hispanic/Latino; 0.5% African American, non-Hispanic/Latino; 1% Asian, non-Hispanic/Latino; 0% Native Hawaiian or other Pacific Islander, non-Hispanic/Latino; 6% international. 30% 25 or older, 12% live on campus, 8% transferred in. Retention: 66% of full-time freshmen returned the following year. Academic areas with the most degrees conferred: engineering; business/marketing; health professions and related sciences. Core. Calendar: semesters. Academic remediation for entering students, services for LD students, advanced placement, self-designed majors, honors program, independent study, distance learning, double major, summer session for credit, part-time degree program, external degree program, adult/continuing education programs, co-op programs and internships, graduate courses open to undergrads.

Entrance Requirements: Open admission for Highlands College students. Options: electronic application, deferred admission, international baccalaureate accepted. Required: high school transcript, proof of immunization, SAT or ACT. Required for some: minimum 2.5 high school GPA. Entrance: moderately difficult. Application deadline: Rolling. Notification: continuous.

Costs Per Year: Application fee: $30. State resident tuition: $5177 full-time, $215 per credit part-time. Nonresident tuition: $17,432 full-time, $726 per credit part-time. Mandatory fees: $1516 full-time, $69 per credit four part-time. Full-time tuition and fees vary according to course load, degree level, location, program, and student level. Part-time tuition and fees vary according to course load, degree level, location, program, and student level. College room and board: $7626. College room only: $3392. Room and board charges vary according to board plan.

Collegiate Environment: Orientation program. Choral group, student-run newspaper, radio station. Social organizations: 30 open to all. Most popular organizations: Circle K, Ski/Snowboard Club, BSU, Hockey Club, Dance Club. Major annual events: Homecoming, Mulletfest, Holiday Stroll. Student services: health clinic, personal-psychological counseling. Campus security: 24-hour patrols, controlled dormitory access. 283 college housing spaces available; all were occupied in 2012-13. Freshmen guaranteed college housing. On-campus residence required in freshman year. Option: coed housing available. Montana Tech Library with 140,851 books, 60,390 microform titles, 126,580 serials, 5,329 audiovisual materials, an OPAC, and a Web page. Operations spending for the previous fiscal year: $778,644. 585 computers available on campus for general student use. A campuswide network can be accessed from student residence rooms and from off campus. Students can access the following: online class registration.

Community Environment: Known as the "richest hill on earth," Butte has the reputation of being the world's greatest mining city. Mine workings consist of more than 10,000 miles of underground excavation. They produce a substantial percentage of the total amount of copper mined in the United States and a quantity of zinc ore. The Butte mining district is on the edge of one of the broad, faulted valleys characteristic of western Montana. During the more than 100 years of its active existence, this district has yielded manganese, copper, zinc, silver, lead, gold, and minor amounts of other metals. Three mountain ranges surround the city from the Continental Divide. The area is served by two transcontinental railroads, airlines, and bus lines. Butte community service facilities include many churches, two hospitals, five radio stations, and two TV stations. The city has a wholesale and retail shopping center. Many civic, fraternal, and professional organizations meet regularly in the immediate area. Recreation in the forms of skiing, hiking, fishing, hunting, boating, and golf are within minutes of the city.

■ **ROCKY MOUNTAIN COLLEGE**
1511 Poly Dr.
Billings, MT 59102-1796
Tel: (406)657-1000; Free: 800-877-6259

Fax: (406)259-9751
E-mail: admissions@rocky.edu
Web Site: www.rocky.edu/

Description: Independent interdenominational, comprehensive, coed. Awards associate, bachelor's, and master's degrees. Founded 1878. Setting: 60-acre urban campus. Endowment: $22.2 million. Educational spending for the previous fiscal year: $6725 per student. Total enrollment: 1,087. Faculty: 127 (65 full-time, 62 part-time). Student-undergrad faculty ratio is 12:1. 1,347 applied, 64% were admitted. 10% from top 10% of their high school class, 36% from top quarter, 70% from top half. Full-time: 969 students, 49% women, 51% men. Part-time: 38 students, 32% women, 68% men. Students come from 48 states and territories, 20 other countries, 44% from out-of-state. 2% American Indian or Alaska Native, non-Hispanic/Latino; 4% Hispanic/Latino; 3% African American, non-Hispanic/Latino; 1% Asian, non-Hispanic/Latino; 0.5% Native Hawaiian or other Pacific Islander, non-Hispanic/Latino; 4% international. 9% 25 or older, 49% live on campus, 8% transferred in. Retention: 67% of full-time freshmen returned the following year. Academic areas with the most degrees conferred: business/marketing; parks and recreation; agriculture. Core. Calendar: semesters. Academic remediation for entering students, ESL program, services for LD students, advanced placement, accelerated degree program, self-designed majors, honors program, independent study, distance learning, double major, summer session for credit, part-time degree program, adult/continuing education programs, internships. Off campus study. Study abroad program. ROTC: Army.

Entrance Requirements: Options: electronic application, early admission, early action, deferred admission, international baccalaureate accepted. Required: high school transcript, minimum 2.5 high school GPA, SAT or ACT. Required for some: essay, 2 recommendations, interview. Entrance: moderately difficult. Application deadline: Rolling. Notification: continuous. Transfer credits accepted: Yes.

Costs Per Year: Application fee: $35. Comprehensive fee: $31,148 includes full-time tuition ($23,228), mandatory fees ($490), and college room and board ($7430). College room only: $3462. Full-time tuition and fees vary according to course load, degree level, and program. Room and board charges vary according to board plan and housing facility. Part-time tuition: $968 per credit. Part-time tuition varies according to course load, degree level, and program.

Collegiate Environment: Orientation program. Drama-theater group, choral group, student-run newspaper. Social organizations: 20 open to all. Most popular organizations: Outdoor Recreation/Climbing Club, Students in Free Enterprise (SIFE), Flight Team/Club, Residence Hall Association, OISTERS, Organization of Interested Students Toward Environmentally Responsible Solutions. Major annual events: Homecoming, Yule Log Dinner, Academic Awards Banquet. Student services: health clinic, personal-psychological counseling. Campus security: 24-hour emergency response devices, student patrols, late night transport-escort service, controlled dormitory access, security cameras. 525 college housing spaces available; 483 were occupied in 2012-13. Freshmen guaranteed college housing. On-campus residence required through sophomore year. Option: coed housing available. Paul M. Adams Memorial Library with 102,531 books, 1,268 microform titles, 26,959 serials, 1,615 audiovisual materials, an OPAC, and a Web page. Operations spending for the previous fiscal year: $248,544. 129 computers available on campus for general student use. A campuswide network can be accessed from student residence rooms and from off campus. Students can access the following: online class registration. Staffed computer lab on campus (open 24 hours a day) provides training in use of computers, software, and the Internet.

■ **SALISH KOOTENAI COLLEGE**
PO Box 70
Pablo, MT 59855-0117
Tel: (406)275-4800
Fax: (406)275-4801
E-mail: jackie_moran@skc.edu
Web Site: www.skc.edu/

Description: Independent, primarily 2-year, coed. Awards certificates, transfer associate, terminal associate, and bachelor's degrees. Founded 1977. Setting: 4-acre rural campus. Total enrollment: 1,088. Faculty: 80 (45 full-time, 35 part-time). 344 applied, 64% were admitted. 50% from top half of their high school class. Full-time: 585 students, 63% women, 37% men. Part-time: 503 students, 58% women, 42% men. Students come from 3 states and territories. 48% 25 or older. Core. Academic remediation for entering students, services for LD students, summer session for credit, part-time degree program, adult/continuing education programs, co-op programs. Off campus study at members of the American Indian Higher Education Consortium.

Entrance Requirements: Open admission. Option: deferred admission. Required: high school transcript, proof of immunization, tribal enrollment. Entrance: noncompetitive. Application deadline: Rolling. Notification: continuous. Preference given to Native Americans.

Collegiate Environment: Drama-theater group. Student services: personal-psychological counseling. 24,000 books and 200 serials 30 computers available on campus for general student use.

■ STONE CHILD COLLEGE

RR1, Box 1082

Box Elder, MT 59521

Tel: (406)395-4313

Fax: (406)395-4836

E-mail: uanet337@quest.ocsc.montana.edu

Web Site: www.stonechild.edu/

Description: Independent, 2-year, coed. Awards certificates, transfer associate, and terminal associate degrees. Founded 1984. Setting: rural campus. Total enrollment: 240. Faculty: 22 (10 full-time, 12 part-time). 11 applied, 100% were admitted. Calendar: semesters.

Entrance Requirements: Open admission. Required: high school transcript. Entrance: noncompetitive.

Collegiate Environment: 42 computers available on campus for general student use. Staffed computer lab on campus.

■ UNIVERSITY OF GREAT FALLS

1301 Twentieth St. S

Great Falls, MT 59405

Tel: (406)761-8210; Free: 800-856-9544

Fax: (406)791-5209

E-mail: enroll@ugf.edu

Web Site: www.ugf.edu/

Description: Independent Roman Catholic, comprehensive, coed. Awards associate, bachelor's, and master's degrees. Founded 1932. Setting: 40-acre urban campus. Total enrollment: 1,058. Faculty: 116 (44 full-time, 72 part-time). Student-undergrad faculty ratio is 13:1. 828 applied, 84% were admitted. Full-time: 667 students, 61% women, 39% men. Part-time: 307 students, 73% women, 27% men. 47% from out-of-state. 4% American Indian or Alaska Native, non-Hispanic/Latino; 5% Hispanic/Latino; 3% African American, non-Hispanic/Latino; 1% Asian, non-Hispanic/Latino; 2% Native Hawaiian or other Pacific Islander, non-Hispanic/Latino; 1% international. 40% 25 or older, 34% live on campus, 13% transferred in. Retention: 66% of full-time freshmen returned the following year. Academic areas with the most degrees conferred: health professions and related sciences; education; psychology. Calendar: semesters. Part-time degree program, adult/continuing education programs.

Entrance Requirements: Options: electronic application, early admission, deferred admission, international baccalaureate accepted. Required: high school transcript, SAT or ACT. Recommended: essay, interview, SAT and SAT Subject Tests or ACT, SAT Subject Tests. Entrance: noncompetitive. Application deadline: 9/1. Notification: continuous. SAT Reasoning Test deadline: 8/1. SAT Subject Test deadline: 8/1.

Costs Per Year: Application fee: $35. Comprehensive fee: $27,760 includes full-time tuition ($19,860), mandatory fees ($1100), and college room and board ($6800). College room only: $3900. Full-time tuition and fees vary according to course load. Room and board charges vary according to housing facility. Part-time tuition: $607 per credit hour. Part-time tuition varies according to course load, location, and program.

Collegiate Environment: Orientation program. Campus security: 24-hour emergency response devices and patrols, late night transport-escort service, controlled dormitory access. Freshmen guaranteed college housing. On-campus residence required through sophomore year. Option: coed housing available.

Community Environment: Montana's second largest city, Great Falls is an industrial, financial, wholesale and distributing center. Major agricultural pursuits in the area are livestock farming and wood production. Known as the city "between the parks," Great Falls is almost equidistant to Yellowstone and Glacier National Parks. The winters are moderate. Summer evenings are cool. The area is served by air, rail, and bus lines. Local attractions include dude and guest ranches, fishing, hunting, and skiing. Some employment opportunities are available in the area.

■ THE UNIVERSITY OF MONTANA

Missoula, MT 59812-0002

Tel: (406)243-0211; Free: 800-462-8636

Fax: (406)243-5711

E-mail: admiss@umontana.edu

Web Site: www.umt.edu/

Description: State-supported, university, coed. Part of Montana University System. Awards associate, bachelor's, master's, and doctoral degrees and post-master's certificates. Founded 1893. Setting: 220-acre urban campus. Endowment: $122.6 million. Research spending for the previous fiscal year: $65 million. Educational spending for the previous fiscal year: $5906 per student. Total enrollment: 14,207. Faculty: 800 (564 full-time, 236 part-time). Student-undergrad faculty ratio is 19:1. 5,342 applied, 96% were admitted. 19% from top 10% of their high school class, 39% from top quarter, 71% from top half. 18 National Merit Scholars, 52 valedictorians. Full-time: 10,136 students, 52% women, 48% men. Part-time: 2,060 students, 59% women, 41% men. Students come from 52 states and territories, 65 other countries, 25% from out-of-state. 19% 25 or older, 29% live on campus, 7% transferred in. Retention: 72% of full-time freshmen returned the following year. Academic areas with the most degrees conferred: business/marketing; social sciences; natural resources/environmental science. Core. Calendar: semesters. Academic remediation for entering students, ESL program, services for LD students, advanced placement, freshman honors college, honors program, independent study, distance learning, double major, summer session for credit, part-time degree program, co-op programs and internships, graduate courses open to undergrads. Off campus study at members of the National Student Exchange. ROTC: Army.

Entrance Requirements: Options: electronic application, early admission, deferred admission, international baccalaureate accepted. Required: high school transcript, minimum 2.5 high school GPA, SAT or ACT. Entrance: moderately difficult. Application deadline: Rolling. Notification: continuous.

Costs Per Year: Application fee: $30. State resident tuition: $4604 full-time, $192 per credit hour part-time. Nonresident tuition: $20,194 full-time, $841 per credit hour part-time. Mandatory fees: $1612 full-time, $50 per credit hour part-time. Full-time tuition and fees vary according to degree level, location, program, reciprocity agreements, and student level. Part-time tuition and fees vary according to course load, degree level, location, and student level. College room and board: $7262. College room only: $3170. Room and board charges vary according to board plan and housing facility.

Collegiate Environment: Orientation program. Drama-theater group, choral group, marching band, student-run newspaper, radio station. Social organizations: national fraternities, national sororities; 6% of eligible men and 6% of eligible women are members. Most popular organizations: Forestry Club, Honors Student Association, Campus Outdoor Program, International Organization, Kyi-Yo Native American Student Association. Major annual events: Aber Day (clean earth day), Foresters' Ball, Homecoming (FB). Student services: legal services, health clinic, personal-psychological counseling, women's center. Campus security: 24-hour emergency response devices and patrols, student patrols, late night transport-escort service, controlled dormitory access. Maureen Library (Maureen and Mike Mansfield Library) plus 1 other with 1.1 million books, 321,801 microform titles, 31,614 serials, 64,880 audiovisual materials, and an OPAC. Operations spending for the previous fiscal year: $7.8 million. 545 computers available on campus for general student use. A campuswide network can be accessed from student residence rooms and from off campus. Students can access the following: online class registration. Staffed computer lab on campus.

■ THE UNIVERSITY OF MONTANA WESTERN

710 S Atlantic

Dillon, MT 59725-3598

Tel: (406)683-7011; Free: 877-683-7331

Fax: (406)683-7493

E-mail: j_jones@umwestern.edu

Web Site: www.umwestern.edu/

Description: State-supported, 4-year, coed. Part of Montana University System. Awards associate and bachelor's degrees. Founded 1893. Setting: 30-acre small town campus. Endowment: $3.4 million. Research spending for the previous fiscal year: $274,808. Educational spending for the previous fiscal year: $6873 per student. Total enrollment: 1,483. Faculty: 108 (64 full-time, 44 part-time). Student-undergrad faculty ratio is 17:1. 602 applied, 75% were admitted. 5% from top 10% of their high school class, 16% from top quarter, 45% from top half. Full-time: 1,233 students, 53% women, 47% men. Part-time: 250 students, 80% women, 20% men. Students come from

40 states and territories, 3 other countries, 22% from out-of-state. 2% American Indian or Alaska Native, non-Hispanic/Latino; 2% Hispanic/Latino; 1% African American, non-Hispanic/Latino; 1% Asian, non-Hispanic/Latino; 2% Native Hawaiian or other Pacific Islander, non-Hispanic/Latino; 0.2% international. 22% 25 or older, 25% live on campus, 11% transferred in. Retention: 77% of full-time freshmen returned the following year. Academic areas with the most degrees conferred: education; liberal arts/general studies; business/marketing. Core. Calendar: semesters. Academic remediation for entering students, services for LD students, advanced placement, honors program, independent study, distance learning, double major, summer session for credit, part-time degree program, co-op programs and internships. Off campus study. Study abroad program.

Entrance Requirements: Options: electronic application, early admission, deferred admission. Required: high school transcript, MMR, ACT or SAT, high school self report form, SAT or ACT. Entrance: minimally difficult. Application deadline: Rolling. Notification: continuous. SAT Reasoning Test deadline: 8/29. SAT Subject Test deadline: 8/29. Transfer credits accepted: Yes.

Costs Per Year: Application fee: $30. State resident tuition: $3699 full-time, $153 per credit part-time. Nonresident tuition: $13,532 full-time, $562 per credit part-time. Mandatory fees: $1020 full-time, $134 per credit part-time. Full-time tuition and fees vary according to course load, location, program, reciprocity agreements, and student level. Part-time tuition and fees vary according to course load, location, program, reciprocity agreements, and student level. College room and board: $6180. College room only: $2310. Room and board charges vary according to housing facility.

Collegiate Environment: Orientation program. Drama-theater group, choral group, student-run radio station. Social organizations: 34 open to all. Most popular organizations: Chi Alpha, Drama Club, Humans in Performance, Western Gaming Alliance, Rodeo Club. Major annual events: Athletic Events, Welcome Fair, Student Senate and Radio Station Concerts. Student services: health clinic, personal-psychological counseling. Campus security: 24-hour emergency response devices and patrols, student patrols, late night transport-escort service. 440 college housing spaces available; 25 were occupied in 2012-13. Freshmen guaranteed college housing. On-campus residence required in freshman year. Options: coed, men-only, women-only housing available. Lucy Carson Memorial Library with 140,117 books, 8,895 microform titles, 9,052 serials, 4,234 audiovisual materials, an OPAC, and a Web page. Operations spending for the previous fiscal year: $560,177. 140 computers available on campus for general student use. A campuswide network can be accessed from student residence rooms and from off campus. Students can access the following: online class registration. Staffed computer lab on campus provides training in use of computers, software, and the Internet.

■ THE UNIVERSITY OF MONTANA–HELENA COLLEGE OF TECHNOLOGY

1115 N Roberts St.
Helena, MT 59601
Tel: (406)444-6800; Free: 800-241-4882
Fax: (406)444-6892
Web Site: www.umhelena.edu/

Description: State-supported, 2-year, coed. Part of Montana University System. Administratively affiliated with The University of Montana. Awards certificates, transfer associate, and terminal associate degrees. Founded 1939. Setting: small town campus. Educational spending for the previous fiscal year: $6795 per student. Total enrollment: 1,679. Faculty: 140 (37 full-time, 103 part-time). Student-undergrad faculty ratio is 15:1. 414 applied, 87% were admitted. Full-time: 813 students, 49% women, 51% men. Part-time: 866 students, 63% women, 37% men. Students come from 10 states and territories, 2% from out-of-state. 5% American Indian or Alaska Native, non-Hispanic/Latino; 3% Hispanic/Latino; 0.5% African American, non-Hispanic/Latino; 1% Asian, non-Hispanic/Latino. 55% 25 or older, 7% transferred in. Retention: 61% of full-time freshmen returned the following year. Calendar: semesters. Academic remediation for entering students, services for LD students, distance learning, double major, summer session for credit, part-time degree program, adult/continuing education programs, internships.

Entrance Requirements: Open admission. Options: early admission, deferred admission, international baccalaureate accepted. Required for some: high school transcript. Entrance: noncompetitive. Application deadline: Rolling. Transfer credits accepted: Yes.

Costs Per Year: Application fee: $30. State resident tuition: $3030 full-time. Nonresident tuition: $8326 full-time. Mandatory fees: $672 full-time. Full-time tuition and fees vary according to course load and reciprocity agreements.

Collegiate Environment: Orientation program. Social organizations: 3 open to all. Most popular organizations: Student Senate, Circle K, College Christian Fellowship, Phi Theta Kappa. Major annual events: Fall and Spring BBQs, Community Fairs, ASUMH Christmas Party. Student services: personal-psychological counseling. Campus security: late night transport-escort service. UM-Helena Library with 95,845 books, 38,794 serials, 6,219 audiovisual materials, an OPAC, and a Web page. 200 computers available on campus for general student use. A campuswide network can be accessed. Students can access the following: online class registration. Staffed computer lab on campus provides training in use of computers, software, and the Internet.

■ BELLEVUE UNIVERSITY

1000 Galvin Rd. S
Bellevue, NE 68005-3098
Tel: (402)291-8100; Free: 800-756-7920
Fax: (402)293-2020
E-mail: nick.baker@bellevue.edu
Web Site: www.bellevue.edu/

Description: Independent, comprehensive, coed. Awards bachelor's, master's, and doctoral degrees. Founded 1965. Setting: 50-acre suburban campus with easy access to Omaha. Endowment: $43.6 million. Research spending for the previous fiscal year: $1.2 million. Educational spending for the previous fiscal year: $2696 per student. Total enrollment: 10,304. Faculty: 411 (89 full-time, 322 part-time). Student-undergrad faculty ratio is 40:1. Full-time: 4,978 students, 49% women, 51% men. Part-time: 1,850 students, 48% women, 52% men. Students come from 53 states and territories, 34 other countries, 50% from out-of-state. 1% American Indian or Alaska Native, non-Hispanic/Latino; 7% Hispanic/Latino; 13% African American, non-Hispanic/Latino; 2% Asian, non-Hispanic/Latino; 0.4% Native Hawaiian or other Pacific Islander, non-Hispanic/Latino; 2% international. 80% 25 or older. Retention: 50% of full-time freshmen returned the following year. Academic areas with the most degrees conferred: business/marketing; social sciences; health professions and related sciences; computer and information sciences. Core. Calendar: semesters for day division, trimesters for evening division. Academic remediation for entering students, ESL program, services for LD students, advanced placement, accelerated degree program, independent study, distance learning, double major, summer session for credit, part-time degree program, external degree program, adult/continuing education programs, internships. Off campus study. Study abroad program. ROTC: Army (c), Air Force (c).

Entrance Requirements: Open admission. Options: electronic application, deferred admission. Required: high school transcript. Entrance: noncompetitive. Application deadline: Rolling. Transfer credits accepted: Yes.

Costs Per Year: Application fee: $50. Tuition: $7500 full-time, $250 per credit hour part-time. Mandatory fees: $200 full-time, $100 per term part-time. Full-time tuition and fees vary according to course load. Part-time tuition and fees vary according to course load.

Collegiate Environment: Orientation program. Social organizations: 5 open to all. Most popular organizations: International Student Organization, Multicultural Club, Student Advisory Council, Student Veterans Organization, Institute of Management Accountants. Major annual events: Student Appreciation Day, BRUIN Week, Bowling Night. Campus security: 24-hour emergency response devices. Freeman/Lozier Library plus 1 other with 118,581 books, 17,357 microform titles, 46,566 serials, 6,442 audiovisual materials, an OPAC, and a Web page. Operations spending for the previous fiscal year: $1.3 million. 470 computers available on campus for general student use. A campuswide network can be accessed from off-campus. Students can access the following: online class registration. Staffed computer lab on campus provides training in use of computers, software, and the Internet.

Community Environment: The oldest continuous settlement in Nebraska, Bellevue is located on the bluffs of the Missouri River, just south of Omaha and adjoining Offutt Air Force Base, the headquarters of the Strategic Air Command. The Fontenelle Forest Nature Center between Bellevue and the Missouri River contains displays of regional habitats.

■ CENTRAL COMMUNITY COLLEGE–COLUMBUS CAMPUS

4500 63rd St.
Columbus, NE 68602-1027
Tel: (402)564-7132; Free: 877-CCC-0780
Fax: (402)562-1201
E-mail: eleffler@cccneb.edu
Web Site: www.cccneb.edu/

Description: State and locally supported, 2-year, coed. Part of Central Community College. Awards certificates, diplomas, transfer associate, and terminal associate degrees. Founded 1968. Setting: 90-acre small town campus. Total enrollment: 2,872. Faculty: 99 (46 full-time, 53 part-time). Full-time: 523 students, 53% women, 47% men. Part-time: 2,349 students, 61% women, 39% men. Students come from 38 states and territories, 24 other countries. 0.2% American Indian or Alaska Native, non-Hispanic/Latino; 13% Hispanic/Latino; 2% African American, non-Hispanic/Latino; 1% Asian, non-Hispanic/Latino; 0.2% Native Hawaiian or other Pacific Islander, non-Hispanic/Latino; 0% international. 39% 25 or older, 17% live on campus, 4% transferred in. Core. Calendar: semesters plus six-week summer session. Academic remediation for entering students, ESL program, services for LD students, advanced placement, accelerated degree program, self-designed majors, independent study, distance learning, summer session for credit, part-time degree program, external degree program, adult/continuing education programs, co-op programs and internships. Off campus study.

Entrance Requirements: Open admission. Options: electronic application, early admission. Required: high school transcript. Required for some: 3 recommendations, interview. Entrance: noncompetitive. Application deadlines: Rolling, Rolling for nonresidents. Notification: continuous, continuous for nonresidents. Transfer credits accepted: Yes.

Collegiate Environment: Orientation program. Drama-theater group, choral group. Social organizations: 12 open to all. Most popular organizations: Phi Theta Kappa, Drama Club, Art Club, Cantari, Chorale. Major annual events: East Central Nebraska College Fair, Ethnic Festival, Christmas Party. Student services: personal-psychological counseling, women's center. Campus security: 24-hour emergency response devices and patrols, controlled dormitory access, night security. Learning Resources Center with 14,047 books, 66 serials, 12 audiovisual materials, and an OPAC.

Community Environment: Columbus was originally an agricultural area, but in the late 1940s, as the town was dying from the loss of young people to the larger cities, a concerted effort was begun to introduce industry to the community. This effort has been very successful, and to date the area has more industrial workers per capita than any other city in the Midwest. Products range from agricultural equipment to medical equipment. Commercial transportation is available. Pawnee Park offers swimming, tennis, picnic grounds, and athletic fields. Lake North offers swimming, water skiing, and boating. Lake Babcock offers fishing and boating, plus free camp grounds equipped with electrical outlets and tables. Columbus is 85 miles from Omaha and 80 miles from Lincoln. The community facilities include 22 churches and one library.

■ CENTRAL COMMUNITY COLLEGE–GRAND ISLAND CAMPUS

PO Box 4903
Grand Island, NE 68802-4903
Tel: (308)398-4222; Free: 877-CCC-0780
Fax: (308)398-7398
E-mail: mlubken@cccneb.edu
Web Site: www.cccneb.edu/

Description: State and locally supported, 2-year, coed. Part of Central Community College. Awards certificates, diplomas, transfer associate, and terminal associate degrees. Founded 1976. Setting: 80-acre small town campus. Total enrollment: 3,469. Faculty: 112. Student-undergrad faculty ratio is 15:1. Full-time: 423 students, 57% women, 43% men. Part-time: 3,046 students, 68% women, 32% men. Students come from 24 other countries. 0.5% American Indian or Alaska Native, non-Hispanic/Latino; 13% Hispanic/Latino; 2% African American, non-Hispanic/Latino; 1% Asian, non-Hispanic/Latino; 0.2% Native Hawaiian or other Pacific Islander, non-Hispanic/Latino; 0% international. 46% 25 or older, 10% live on campus, 3% transferred in. Core. Calendar: semesters plus six-week summer session. Academic remediation for entering students, ESL program, services for LD students, advanced placement, accelerated degree program, self-designed majors, independent study, distance learning, summer session for credit, part-time degree program, external degree program, adult/continuing education programs, co-op programs and internships. Off campus study.

Entrance Requirements: Open admission. Options: electronic application, early admission. Required: high school transcript. Required for some: 3 recommendations, interview. Entrance: noncompetitive. Application deadlines: Rolling, Rolling for nonresidents. Notification: continuous, continuous for nonresidents. Transfer credits accepted: Yes.

Collegiate Environment: Orientation program. Social organizations: 7 open to all. Most popular organizations: Mid-Nebraska Users of Computers, Student Activities Organization, intramurals, TRIO, Phi Theta Kappa. Major annual events: Christmas Party, Spring Picnic, Halloween Party. Student services: personal-psychological counseling. Central Community College-Grand Island Campus Library with 8,023 books, 144 serials, 142 audiovisual materials, an OPAC, and a Web page.

Community Environment: Grand Island is located in Central Nebraska and is a leading agricultural center for retailing and industry. Due to agricultural production, industry has quickly expanded, with a resulting rapid population growth. There are many recreational opportunities available to residents and visitors, including swimming, golfing, horse racing, bowling, hunting, and a variety of health-related activities. A large museum complex is located at Grand Island and reflects the Old West tradition. More than 40 churches, two hospitals, a children's zoo and a major library are available.

■ CENTRAL COMMUNITY COLLEGE–HASTINGS CAMPUS

PO Box 1024
Hastings, NE 68902-1024
Tel: (402)463-9811; Free: 877-CCC-0780
E-mail: rglenn@ccneb.edu
Web Site: www.cccneb.edu/

Description: State and locally supported, 2-year, coed. Part of Central Community College. Awards certificates, diplomas, transfer associate, and terminal associate degrees. Founded 1966. Setting: 644-acre small town campus. Total enrollment: 2,966. Faculty: 109 (49 full-time, 60 part-time). Student-undergrad faculty ratio is 15:1. Full-time: 1,001 students, 46% women, 54% men. Part-time: 1,965 students, 63% women, 37% men. Students come from 38 states and territories, 24 other countries. 0.4% American Indian or Alaska Native, non-Hispanic/Latino; 7% Hispanic/Latino; 1% African American, non-Hispanic/Latino; 1% Asian, non-Hispanic/Latino; 0.1% Native Hawaiian or other Pacific Islander, non-Hispanic/Latino; 0% international. 36% 25 or older, 5% transferred in. Core. Calendar: semesters plus six-week summer session. Academic remediation for entering students, ESL program, services for LD students, advanced placement, accelerated degree program, self-designed majors, independent study, distance learning, summer session for credit, part-time degree program, external degree program, adult/continuing education programs, co-op programs and internships. Off campus study.

Entrance Requirements: Open admission. Options: electronic application, early admission. Required: high school transcript. Required for some: 3 recommendations, interview. Entrance: noncompetitive. Application deadlines: Rolling, Rolling for nonresidents. Notification: continuous, continuous for nonresidents. Transfer credits accepted: Yes.

Collegiate Environment: Orientation program. Student-run radio station. Social organizations: 13 open to all. Most popular organizations: Student Senate, Central Dormitory Council, Judicial Board, Seeds and Soils, Young Farmers and Ranchers. Major annual events: Back-to-school week, Christmas Party. Student services: personal-psychological counseling, women's center. Campus security: 24-hour emergency response devices and patrols, controlled dormitory access. Nuckolls Library with 7,201 books, 44 serials, 11 audiovisual materials, and an OPAC.

Community Environment: See Hastings College.

■ CHADRON STATE COLLEGE

1000 Main St.
Chadron, NE 69337
Tel: (308)432-6000; Free: 800-242-3766
Fax: (308)432-6229
E-mail: inquire@csc.edu
Web Site: www.csc.edu/

Description: State-supported, comprehensive, coed. Part of Nebraska State College System. Awards bachelor's and master's degrees. Founded 1911. Setting: 281-acre small town campus. Total enrollment: 2,649. Student-undergrad faculty ratio is 19:1. 31% from out-of-state. 24% 25 or older. Retention: 64% of full-time freshmen returned the following year. Core. Calendar: semesters. Services for LD students, advanced placement, self-designed majors, honors program, independent study, distance learning, double major, summer session for credit, part-time degree program, external degree program, adult/continuing education programs, co-op programs and internships, graduate courses open to undergrads. Off campus study. Study abroad program.

Entrance Requirements: Open admission. Options: electronic application, early admission. Required: high school transcript, health forms. Entrance: noncompetitive. Application deadline: Rolling. Notification: continuous.

Collegiate Environment: Orientation program. Drama-theater group, choral group, student-run newspaper, radio station. Student services: health clinic, personal-psychological counseling. Campus security: 24-hour emergency response devices and patrols, student patrols, late night transport-escort service. Reta King Library with an OPAC and a Web page.

Community Environment: Chadron, located in northwestern Nebraska, is near the Nebraska National Forest where hunting is popular as well as trout fishing. Chadron is also a short drive from snow skiing, water skiing, and the Black Hills of South Dakota. The community facilities include a public library, hospital, churches, and numerous civic organizations.

■ CLARKSON COLLEGE

101 S 42nd St.
Omaha, NE 68131-2739
Tel: (402)552-3100; Free: 800-647-5500
Fax: (402)552-6057
E-mail: workdenise@clarksoncollege.edu
Web Site: www.clarksoncollege.edu/

Description: Independent, comprehensive, coed. Awards associate, bachelor's, and master's degrees and post-master's certificates. Founded 1888. Setting: 3-acre urban campus. Endowment: $937,115. Educational spending for the previous fiscal year: $8259 per student. Total enrollment: 820. Faculty: 101 (48 full-time, 53 part-time). Student-undergrad faculty ratio is 8:1. 87 applied, 55% were admitted. 15% from top 10% of their high school class, 30% from top quarter, 85% from top half. Full-time: 39 students, 95% women, 5% men. Students come from 33 states and territories, 33% from out-of-state. 42% 25 or older, 14% live on campus, 99.9% transferred in. Retention: 85% of full-time freshmen returned the following year. Academic area with the most degrees conferred: health professions and related sciences. Core. Calendar: semesters. Advanced placement, accelerated degree program, independent study, distance learning, double major, summer session for credit, part-time degree program, external degree program, adult/continuing education programs, co-op programs and internships, graduate courses open to undergrads. Study abroad program. ROTC: Army (c), Air Force (c).

Entrance Requirements: Options: electronic application, deferred admission. Required: essay, high school transcript, minimum 2.5 high school GPA. Recommended: minimum 3 high school GPA. Required for some: minimum 3 high school GPA, 2 recommendations, SAT or ACT. Entrance: moderately difficult. Application deadlines: Rolling, Rolling for nonresidents. Notification: continuous, continuous for nonresidents.

Collegiate Environment: Orientation program. Student-run newspaper. Social organizations: 10 open to all. Most popular organizations: Student Nurses Association, Radiology Student Association, Student Government Association, Student Ambassadors, Physical Therapist Assistant Student Association. Major annual events: Welcome Week, talent show, Casino Night. Student services: health clinic, personal-psychological counseling. Campus security: 24-hour emergency response devices and patrols, student patrols, late night transport-escort service, controlled dormitory access. Clarkson College Library with 8,807 books, 25,000 microform titles, 262 serials, 530 audiovisual materials, an OPAC, and a Web page. Operations spending for the previous fiscal year: $242,150. 40 computers available on campus for general student use. A campuswide network can be accessed from off-campus. Students can access the following: online class registration. Staffed computer lab on campus provides training in use of computers, software, and the Internet.

■ COLLEGE OF SAINT MARY

7000 Mercy Rd.
Omaha, NE 68106
Tel: (402)399-2400; Free: 800-926-5534
Fax: (402)399-2412
E-mail: enroll@csm.edu
Web Site: www.csm.edu/

Description: Independent Roman Catholic, comprehensive, women only. Awards associate, bachelor's, master's, and doctoral degrees. Founded 1923. Setting: 25-acre urban campus. Endowment: $7.9 million. Research spending for the previous fiscal year: $44,283. Educational spending for the previous fiscal year: $5607 per student. Total enrollment: 1,037. Faculty: 158 (58 full-time, 100 part-time). Student-undergrad faculty ratio is 9:1. 402 applied, 52% were admitted. 19% from top 10% of their high school class, 45% from top quarter, 78% from top half. Full-time: 632 students. Part-time: 150 students. Students come from 18 states and territories, 7 other countries, 15% from out-of-state. 0.4% American Indian or Alaska Native, non-Hispanic/Latino; 11% Hispanic/Latino; 7% African American, non-Hispanic/Latino; 1% Asian, non-Hispanic/Latino; 0.3% Native Hawaiian or other Pacific Islander, non-Hispanic/Latino; 0.1% international. 34% 25 or older, 34% live on campus, 14% transferred in. Retention: 69% of full-time freshmen returned the following year. Academic areas with the most degrees conferred: health professions and related sciences; education; business/marketing; biological/life sciences; law/legal studies. Core. Calendar: semesters. Academic remediation for entering students, services for LD students, advanced placement, accelerated degree program, honors program, independent study, distance learning, double major, summer session for credit, part-time degree program, internships, graduate courses open to undergrads. Study abroad program. ROTC: Army (c), Air Force (c).

Entrance Requirements: Options: electronic application, international baccalaureate accepted. Required: high school transcript, minimum 2 high school GPA, Students graduating high school within the past five years with less than 12 transfer credits are required to submit ACT scores. The minimum ACT score for admission is 18. Required for some: essay, 3 recommendations, interview. Entrance: minimally difficult. Application deadline: Rolling. Notification: continuous. Transfer credits accepted: Yes. Applicants placed on waiting list: 25. Wait-listed applicants offered admission: 17.

Costs Per Year: Application fee: $30. Comprehensive fee: $32,110 includes full-time tuition ($24,830), mandatory fees ($480), and college room and board ($6800). Full-time tuition and fees vary according to location and program. Part-time tuition: $825 per credit. Part-time mandatory fees: $16 per credit. Part-time tuition and fees vary according to class time, course load, location, and program.

Collegiate Environment: Orientation program. Drama-theater group, choral group. Social organizations: 19 open to all. Most popular organizations: Students Against Violence (SAV), Campus Activities Board, Student Education Association of Nebraska, Student Occupational Therapy Club, Student Nurses Association. Major annual events: Senate Casino Night, Hypnotist/Mentalist, Queen of Hearts Celebration. Student services: health clinic, personal-psychological counseling. Campus security: 24-hour emergency response devices and patrols, late night transport-escort service, controlled dormitory access, surveillance cameras at residence hall entrances; CSM Alert Text Message System. 275 college housing spaces available; 241 were occupied in 2012-13. Freshmen guaranteed college housing. On-campus residence required through sophomore year. Option: women-only housing available. College of Saint Mary Library with 88,503 books, 178 serials, 1,999 audiovisual materials, an OPAC, and a Web page. Operations spending for the previous fiscal year: $396,444. 170 computers available on campus for general student use. A campuswide network can be accessed from student residence rooms. Students can access the following: online class registration. Staffed computer lab on campus provides training in use of computers, software, and the Internet.

■ CONCORDIA UNIVERSITY, NEBRASKA

800 N Columbia Ave.
Seward, NE 68434-1599
Tel: (402)643-3651; Free: 800-535-5494
Fax: (402)643-4073
E-mail: admiss@cune.edu
Web Site: www.cune.edu/

Description: Independent, comprehensive, coed, affiliated with Lutheran Church-Missouri Synod. Awards bachelor's and master's degrees. Founded 1894. Setting: 120-acre small town campus with easy access to Omaha. Endowment: $36.8 million. Educational spending for the previous fiscal year: $4509 per student. Total enrollment: 2,091. Faculty: 161 (60 full-time, 101 part-time). Student-undergrad faculty ratio is 14:1. 1,288 applied, 76% were admitted. 18% from top 10% of their high school class, 42% from top quarter, 71% from top half. Full-time: 1,159 students, 51% women, 49% men. Part-time: 322 students, 59% women, 41% men. Students come from 40 states and territories, 10 other countries, 52% from out-of-state. 0.1% American Indian or Alaska Native, non-Hispanic/Latino; 3% Hispanic/Latino; 3% African American, non-Hispanic/Latino; 0.4% Asian, non-Hispanic/Latino; 0.2% Native Hawaiian or other Pacific Islander, non-Hispanic/Latino; 1% international. 4% 25 or older, 73% live on campus, 4% transferred in. Retention: 79% of full-time freshmen returned the following year. Academic areas with the most degrees conferred: education; business/marketing; visual and performing arts. Core. Calendar: 4-4-1. Academic remediation for entering students, ESL program, services for LD students, advanced placement, accelerated degree program, independent study, distance learning, double major, summer session for credit, part-time degree program, adult/continuing education programs, internships, graduate courses open to undergrads. Off campus study at University of Nebraska-Lincoln. Study abroad program. ROTC: Army (c), Air Force (c).

Entrance Requirements: Options: deferred admission, international baccalaureate accepted. Required: high school transcript, SAT or ACT. Recommended: interview. Entrance: moderately difficult. Application deadline: 8/1. Notification: continuous. SAT Reasoning Test deadline: 8/1. Transfer credits accepted: Yes.

Costs Per Year: Application fee: $0. Comprehensive fee: $31,450 includes full-time tuition ($24,500), mandatory fees ($250), and college room and board ($6700). College room only: $2750. Room and board charges vary according to board plan and housing facility. Part-time tuition: $765 per credit hour.

Collegiate Environment: Orientation program. Drama-theater group, choral group, student-run newspaper. Social organizations: 35 open to all. Most popular organizations: Student Activities Council, Musical Groups, Curtain/Drama Club, Student Senate, Concordia Youth Ministry. Major annual events: Homecoming weekend events, Spring weekend events, Concordia Christmas. Student services: health clinic, personal-psychological counseling. Campus security: 24-hour emergency response devices and patrols, controlled dormitory access. 979 college housing spaces available; 846 were occupied in 2012-13. Freshmen guaranteed college housing. On-campus residence required through junior year. Options: men-only, women-only housing available. Link Library with 150,000 books, 319 serials, 5,450 audiovisual materials, an OPAC, and a Web page. 220 computers available on campus for general student use. A campuswide network can be accessed from student residence rooms and from off campus. Students can access the following: online class registration, academic plans, human resource data. Staffed computer lab on campus provides training in use of computers, software, and the Internet.

■ CREATIVE CENTER

10850 Emmet St.
Omaha, NE 68164
Tel: (402)898-1000; Free: 888-898-1789
Fax: (402)898-1301
E-mail: rich_c@creativecenter.edu
Web Site: www.creativecenter.edu/

Description: Proprietary, 4-year, coed. Awards associate and bachelor's degrees. Founded 1993. Setting: 2-acre urban campus with easy access to Omaha. Total enrollment: 102. Faculty: 16 (5 full-time, 11 part-time). Student-undergrad faculty ratio is 13:1. Retention: 82% of full-time freshmen returned the following year. Academic area with the most degrees conferred: visual and performing arts. Core. Calendar: semesters. Services for LD students, accelerated degree program, part-time degree program.

Entrance Requirements: Required: essay, high school transcript, 1 recommendation, interview, portfolio. Recommended: minimum 2 high school GPA.

Costs Per Year: Tuition: $27,600 full-time. Mandatory fees: $3555 full-time.

Collegiate Environment: Orientation program. College housing not available. 8 computers available on campus for general student use. Computer purchase/lease plans available. A computer is required for all students. A campuswide network can be accessed. Students can access the following: All students receive a laptop computer and software- included in tuition and fees.

■ CREIGHTON UNIVERSITY

2500 California Plz.
Omaha, NE 68178-0001
Tel: (402)280-2700; Free: 800-282-5835
Fax: (402)280-2685
E-mail: williampierce@creighton.edu
Web Site: www.creighton.edu/

Description: Independent Roman Catholic (Jesuit), university, coed. Awards associate, bachelor's, master's, and doctoral degrees and post-master's certificates. Founded 1878. Setting: 130-acre urban campus with easy access to Omaha. Endowment: $299.9 million. Research spending for the previous fiscal year: $25.4 million. Educational spending for the previous fiscal year: $16,586 per student. Total enrollment: 7,736. Faculty: 764 (534 full-time, 230 part-time). Student-undergrad faculty ratio is 12:1. 5,361 applied, 78% were admitted. 40% from top 10% of their high school class, 72% from top quarter, 93% from top half. 8 National Merit Scholars, 36 class presidents, 41 valedictorians, 292 student government officers. Full-time: 3,813 students, 59% women, 41% men. Part-time: 219 students, 68% women, 32% men. Students come from 51 states and territories, 42 other countries, 68% from out-of-state. 0.5% American Indian or Alaska Native, non-Hispanic/Latino; 6% Hispanic/Latino; 3% African American, non-Hispanic/Latino; 10% Asian, non-Hispanic/Latino; 0.3% Native Hawaiian or other Pacific Islander, non-Hispanic/Latino; 2% international. 7% 25 or older, 49% live on campus, 1% transferred in. Retention: 90% of full-time freshmen returned the following year. Academic areas with the most degrees conferred: health professions and related sciences; business/marketing; biological/life sciences. Core. Calendar: semesters. Academic remediation for entering students, ESL program, services for LD students, advanced placement, accelerated degree program, freshman honors college, honors program, independent study, distance learning, double major, summer session for credit, part-time degree program, external degree program, adult/continuing education programs, internships, graduate courses open to undergrads. Off campus study at Cooperative Engineering program with The University of Detroit Mercy. Study abroad program. ROTC: Army, Air Force (c).

Entrance Requirements: Options: electronic application, deferred admission, international baccalaureate accepted. Required: essay, high school transcript, minimum 2.75 high school GPA, 1 recommendation, SAT or ACT. Entrance: moderately difficult. Application deadline: 2/15. Notification: continuous. SAT Reasoning Test deadline: 3/1. Transfer credits accepted: Yes. Applicants placed on waiting list: 0. Wait-listed applicants offered admission: 0.

Costs Per Year: Application fee: $40. Comprehensive fee: $42,776 includes full-time tuition ($31,856), mandatory fees ($1474), and college room and board ($9446). College room only: $5350. Full-time tuition and fees vary according to course load and degree level. Room and board charges vary according to board plan and housing facility. Part-time tuition: $996 per credit hour. Part-time tuition and fees vary according to course load and degree level.

Collegiate Environment: Orientation program. Drama-theater group, choral group, student-run newspaper. Social organizations: 210 open to all; national fraternities, national sororities, local fraternities, local sororities; 32% of eligible men and 40% of eligible women are members. Most popular organizations: Birdcage (Athletic Boosters), Pre-Medical Society, Student Nurses Association, Alpha Kappa Psi (business majors), Omicron Delta Kappa (Greek Leadership). Major annual events: Spring Fling, J Jam, Fallapalooza. Student services: health clinic, personal-psychological counseling, women's center. Campus security: 24-hour emergency response devices and patrols, student patrols, late night transport-escort service, controlled dormitory access. 2,447 college housing spaces available; 2,378 were occupied in 2012-13. Freshmen guaranteed college housing. On-campus residence required through sophomore year. Options: coed, women-only housing available. Reinert Alumni Memorial Library plus 2 others with 722,682 books, 2 million microform titles, 59,602 serials, 15,679 audiovisual materials, an OPAC, and a Web page. Operations spending for the previous fiscal year: $10.2 million. 550 computers available on campus for general student use. Computer purchase/lease plans available. A campuswide network can be accessed from student residence rooms and from off campus. Students can access the following: online class registration, financial aid information.

Community Environment: Metropolitan Omaha has a population of over 414,000 and serves as a communication and cultural center for the Plains States. Urban Omaha is in a period of rapid renewal through publicly and privately supported programs. It is a major insurance center of the nation,

other industries such as railroads, telecommunications, creative enterprises, and health care institutions are well represented. It is best known, however, as a food processing center because of its location in the area known as the "bread basket of America". Cultural attractions include the Omaha Symphony Orchestra, Ballet and Opera Company, Community Playhouse, the Joslyn Art Museum, and the Henry Dvorly Zoo, rated the no. 1 family attraction in America by Family Life Magazine.

■ DOANE COLLEGE

1014 Boswell Ave.
Crete, NE 68333-2430
Tel: (402)826-2161; Free: 800-333-6263
Fax: (402)826-8600
E-mail: joel.weyand@doane.edu
Web Site: www.doane.edu/

Description: Independent, comprehensive, coed, affiliated with United Church of Christ. Awards bachelor's and master's degrees and post-master's certificates (non-traditional undergraduate programs and graduate programs offered at Lincoln campus). Founded 1872. Setting: 300-acre small town campus with easy access to Omaha. Endowment: $77.8 million. Educational spending for the previous fiscal year: $8514 per student. Total enrollment: 1,149. Faculty: 123 (78 full-time, 45 part-time). Student-undergrad faculty ratio is 12:1. 1,733 applied, 76% were admitted. 17% from top 10% of their high school class, 46% from top quarter, 81% from top half. Full-time: 1,138 students, 51% women, 49% men. Part-time: 11 students, 36% women, 64% men. Students come from 29 states and territories, 7 other countries, 17% from out-of-state. 0.3% American Indian or Alaska Native, non-Hispanic/Latino; 5% Hispanic/Latino; 3% African American, non-Hispanic/Latino; 1% Asian, non-Hispanic/Latino; 0.2% Native Hawaiian or other Pacific Islander, non-Hispanic/Latino; 1% international. 1% 25 or older, 82% live on campus, 5% transferred in. Retention: 76% of full-time freshmen returned the following year. Academic areas with the most degrees conferred: education; business/marketing; social sciences. Core. Calendar: 4-1-4. ESL program, advanced placement, self-designed majors, honors program, independent study, double major, summer session for credit, co-op programs and internships, graduate courses open to undergrads. Off campus study at Association of Nebraska Interterm Colleges. Study abroad program. ROTC: Army (c), Air Force (c).

Entrance Requirements: Options: electronic application, early admission, deferred admission, international baccalaureate accepted. Required: high school transcript, 2 recommendations, SAT or ACT. Recommended: minimum 2 high school GPA. Required for some: interview. Entrance: moderately difficult. Application deadline: Rolling. Notification: continuous.

Costs Per Year: Application fee: $0. Comprehensive fee: $32,220 includes full-time tuition ($24,460), mandatory fees ($620), and college room and board ($7140). Full-time tuition and fees vary according to location. Room and board charges vary according to board plan, housing facility, and location. Part-time tuition: $815 per credit hour. Part-time tuition varies according to course load and location.

Collegiate Environment: Orientation program. Drama-theater group, choral group, marching band, student-run newspaper, radio station. Social organizations: 60 open to all; local fraternities, local sororities; 20% of eligible men and 23% of eligible women are members. Most popular organizations: Student Activities Council, Hansen Leadership Program, band/choir, Doane Ambassadors, Doane Art League. Major annual events: Homecoming, Big Event, Stop Day. Student services: health clinic, personal-psychological counseling. Campus security: 24-hour emergency response devices and patrols, student patrols, late night transport-escort service, controlled dormitory access, evening patrols by trained security personnel. 825 college housing spaces available; 789 were occupied in 2012-13. Freshmen guaranteed college housing. On-campus residence required through senior year. Options: coed, women-only housing available. Perkins Library plus 1 other with 352,896 books, 10,295 microform titles, 54,528 serials, 7,417 audiovisual materials, an OPAC, and a Web page. Operations spending for the previous fiscal year: $639,949. 250 computers available on campus for general student use. Computer purchase/lease plans available. A campuswide network can be accessed from student residence rooms and from off campus. Students can access the following: online class registration. Staffed computer lab on campus provides training in use of computers, software, and the Internet.

Community Environment: Crete, a community of 5,000 persons, is located 25 miles southwest of Lincoln. The community includes nine churches of different denominations, a hospital, library, and numerous civic, fraternal and veterans' organizations. Recreation includes bowling, fishing, hunting, golf, and numerous other activities.

■ GRACE UNIVERSITY
1311 S Ninth St.
Omaha, NE 68108
Tel: (402)449-2800; Free: 800-383-1422
Fax: (402)341-9587
E-mail: admissions@graceuniversity.com
Web Site: www.graceuniversity.edu/
Description: Independent interdenominational, comprehensive, coed. Awards associate, bachelor's, and master's degrees. Founded 1943. Setting: 15-acre urban campus with easy access to Omaha. Endowment: $890,668. Educational spending for the previous fiscal year: $3885 per student. Total enrollment: 434. Faculty: 50 (25 full-time, 25 part-time). Student-undergrad faculty ratio is 18:1. 228 applied, 64% were admitted. 19% from top 10% of their high school class, 42% from top quarter, 72% from top half. Full-time: 287 students, 60% women, 40% men. Part-time: 79 students, 46% women, 54% men. Students come from 26 states and territories, 6 other countries, 39% from out-of-state. 0.3% American Indian or Alaska Native, non-Hispanic/Latino; 8% Hispanic/Latino; 7% African American, non-Hispanic/Latino; 2% Asian, non-Hispanic/Latino; 1% Native Hawaiian or other Pacific Islander, non-Hispanic/Latino; 0.3% international. 34% 25 or older, 60% live on campus, 10% transferred in. Retention: 70% of full-time freshmen returned the following year. Core. Calendar: semesters. Academic remediation for entering students, services for LD students, advanced placement, accelerated degree program, self-designed majors, independent study, distance learning, double major, summer session for credit, part-time degree program, external degree program, adult/continuing education programs, co-op programs and internships, graduate courses open to undergrads. Off campus study at Iowa Western Community College, Metropolitan Community College (NE), University of Nebraska at Omaha, Bellevue University, Clarkson College. Study abroad program. ROTC: Army (c), Air Force (c).
Entrance Requirements: Options: electronic application, early admission, deferred admission, international baccalaureate accepted. Required: essay, high school transcript, minimum 2.75 high school GPA, SAT or ACT. Required for some: interview. Entrance: moderately difficult. Application deadline: Rolling.
Costs Per Year: Application fee: $20. Comprehensive fee: $23,320 includes full-time tuition ($16,816), mandatory fees ($550), and college room and board ($5954). College room only: $2800. Room and board charges vary according to board plan and student level. Part-time tuition: $473 per credit hour. Part-time tuition varies according to course load.
Collegiate Environment: Orientation program. Drama-theater group, choral group, student-run radio station. Most popular organizations: band, yearbook. Major annual events: Spiritual Orientation (Welcome Week), Bible Conference, World Christian Conference. Student services: health clinic, personal-psychological counseling. Campus security: student patrols, late night transport-escort service, controlled dormitory access. 322 college housing spaces available; 176 were occupied in 2012-13. Freshmen given priority for college housing. On-campus residence required through junior year. Options: men-only, women-only housing available. Grace University Library with 46,736 books, 623 microform titles, 3,721 serials, 3,882 audiovisual materials, an OPAC, and a Web page. Operations spending for the previous fiscal year: $116,023. 45 computers available on campus for general student use. A campuswide network can be accessed from student residence rooms and from off campus. Students can access the following: online class registration. Staffed computer lab on campus provides training in use of computers, software, and the Internet.
Community Environment: Grace University adheres to four values that revolve around community living: honesty, integrity, responsibility, and accountability.

■ HASTINGS COLLEGE
800 N Turner Ave.
Hastings, NE 68901-7696
Tel: (402)463-2402; Free: 800-532-7642
Fax: (402)463-3002
E-mail: mmolliconi@hastings.edu
Web Site: www.hastings.edu/
Description: Independent Presbyterian, comprehensive, coed. Awards bachelor's and master's degrees. Founded 1882. Setting: 109-acre small town campus. Endowment: $66 million. Educational spending for the previous fiscal year: $7262 per student. Total enrollment: 1,138. Faculty: 123 (87 full-time, 36 part-time). Student-undergrad faculty ratio is 12:1. 1,564 applied, 78% were admitted. 16% from top 10% of their high school class, 40% from top quarter, 65% from top half. 21 valedictorians. Full-time: 1,068 students, 46% women, 54% men. Part-time: 23 students, 48% women, 52% men. Students come from 27 states and territories, 4 other countries, 27% from out-of-state. 3% 25 or older, 67% live on campus, 6% transferred in. Retention: 76% of full-time freshmen returned the following year. Academic areas with the most degrees conferred: business/marketing; visual and performing arts; education. Core. Calendar: 4-1-4. Services for LD students, advanced placement, self-designed majors, independent study, double major, summer session for credit, part-time degree program, adult/continuing education programs, internships, graduate courses open to undergrads. Off campus study. Study abroad program.
Entrance Requirements: Option: international baccalaureate accepted. Required: high school transcript, minimum 2.0 high school GPA, counselor's recommendation, SAT or ACT. Required for some: essay, 2 recommendations, interview. Entrance: moderately difficult. Application deadline: 8/1. Notification: continuous.
Collegiate Environment: Orientation program. Drama-theater group, choral group, marching band, student-run newspaper, radio station. Social organizations: 60 open to all; local fraternities, local sororities; 20% of eligible men and 30% of eligible women are members. Most popular organizations: Student Association, Student Alumni Ambassadors, Fellowship of Christian Athletes, Phi Mu Alpha Sinfonia, Hastings College Singers. Major annual events: Homecoming, Boar's Head Dinner, Greek Dinner Dance. Student services: health clinic, personal-psychological counseling. Campus security: 24-hour emergency response devices, student patrols, late night transport-escort service, controlled dormitory access, security cameras at entrances and parking lots. Perkins Library with 113,318 books, 120,500 microform titles, 636 serials, an OPAC, and a Web page. Operations spending for the previous fiscal year: $608,000. 181 computers available on campus for general student use. A campuswide network can be accessed from student residence rooms and from off campus. Students can access the following: e-mail. Staffed computer lab on campus.
Community Environment: Located in the south central section of the state, Hastings is in the heart of an important irrigated agricultural and stock-raising area. All commercial transportation is available. Part-time jobs are available for students. Community facilities include a library, churches of all denominations and numerous fraternal organizations. Prospect Park contains the Aquacourt, an ultramodern swimming pool, fishing and skiing. A municipal pool is in Libs Park. Lake Hastings, one mile north, offers water sports and fishing. Points of interest are the Fisher Rainbow Fountain, the Hastings Museum, which includes the J.M. McDonald Planetarium, and the Imax theater.

■ ITT TECHNICAL INSTITUTE
1120 N 103rd Plz.
Ste. 200
Omaha, NE 68114
Tel: (402)331-2900; Free: 800-677-9260
Fax: (402)331-9495
Web Site: www.itt-tech.edu/
Description: Proprietary, primarily 2-year, coed. Part of ITT Educational Services, Inc. Awards terminal associate and bachelor's degrees. Founded 1991. Setting: urban campus.
Entrance Requirements: Entrance: minimally difficult.

■ KAPLAN UNIVERSITY, LINCOLN
1821 K St.
Lincoln, NE 68501-2826
Tel: (402)474-5315; Free: 800-527-5268
Fax: (402)474-5302
Web Site: www.lincoln.kaplanuniversity.edu/
Description: Proprietary, primarily 2-year, coed. Awards certificates, diplomas, transfer associate, terminal associate, and bachelor's degrees. Founded 1884. Setting: urban campus.

■ KAPLAN UNIVERSITY, OMAHA
5425 N 103rd St.
Omaha, NE 68134
Tel: (402)572-8500; Free: 800-527-5268
Fax: (402)573-1341
Web Site: www.omaha.kaplanuniversity.edu/
Description: Proprietary, primarily 2-year, coed. Awards certificates, diplomas, transfer associate, terminal associate, and bachelor's degrees. Founded 1891. Setting: urban campus.

■ **LITTLE PRIEST TRIBAL COLLEGE**
PO Box 270
Winnebago, NE 68071
Tel: (402)878-2380
Fax: (402)878-2355
E-mail: yattym@littlepriest.edu
Web Site: www.littlepriest.edu/
Description: Independent, 2-year, coed. Awards transfer associate degrees. Founded 1996. Setting: 10-acre rural campus with easy access to Sioux City, Iowa. Endowment: $1.5 million. Total enrollment: 122. Faculty: 34 (11 full-time, 23 part-time). Student-undergrad faculty ratio is 6:1. Full-time: 80 students, 64% women, 36% men. Part-time: 42 students, 83% women, 17% men. Students come from 10 states and territories, 10% from out-of-state. 93% American Indian or Alaska Native, non-Hispanic/Latino. 62% 25 or older. Core.
Entrance Requirements: Open admission. Options: electronic application, early admission. Required: high school transcript. Transfer credits accepted: Yes.
Costs Per Year: Application fee: $10. State resident tuition: $2400 full-time, $100 per credit hour part-time. Nonresident tuition: $2400 full-time, $100 per credit hour part-time. Mandatory fees: $176 full-time, $88 per term part-time.
Collegiate Environment: Orientation program. Social organizations: Student Senate. Major annual event: 2 Beginning of semester kick off pow wows. Campus security: 24-hour emergency response devices. College housing not available. Little Priest Tribal College Library with 21,735 books, 154 microform titles, 100 serials, 3,439 audiovisual materials, and an OPAC. Operations spending for the previous fiscal year: $171,500. 72 computers available on campus for general student use. Computer purchase/lease plans available. A campuswide network can be accessed. Students can access the following: online class registration. Staffed computer lab on campus provides training in use of computers, software, and the Internet.

■ **METROPOLITAN COMMUNITY COLLEGE**
PO Box 3777
Omaha, NE 68103-0777
Tel: (402)457-2400; Free: 800-228-9553
Fax: (402)457-2564
E-mail: mvazquez@mccneb.edu
Web Site: www.mccneb.edu/
Description: State and locally supported, 2-year, coed. Part of Nebraska Coordinating Commission for Postsecondary Education. Awards certificates, diplomas, transfer associate, and terminal associate degrees. Founded 1974. Setting: 172-acre urban campus. Endowment: $1.4 million. Educational spending for the previous fiscal year: $2790 per student. Total enrollment: 17,003. Faculty: 877 (198 full-time, 679 part-time). Student-undergrad faculty ratio is 16:1. 4,141 applied, 100% were admitted. Full-time: 7,095 students, 55% women, 45% men. Part-time: 9,908 students, 58% women, 42% men. Students come from 31 states and territories, 3% from out-of-state. 44% 25 or older, 0.2% live on campus, 17% transferred in. Retention: 50% of full-time freshmen returned the following year. Core. Academic remediation for entering students, ESL program, services for LD students, advanced placement, independent study, distance learning, summer session for credit, part-time degree program, adult/continuing education programs, co-op programs and internships. ROTC: Army (c).
Entrance Requirements: Open admission. Option: early admission. Recommended: high school transcript. Entrance: noncompetitive. Application deadline: Rolling. Notification: continuous.
Collegiate Environment: Orientation program. Student services: personal-psychological counseling. Campus security: 24-hour emergency response devices and patrols, late night transport-escort service, controlled dormitory access, security on duty 9 pm to 6 am. Metropolitan Community College plus 2 others with 43,788 books, 824 microform titles, 453 serials, 8,008 audiovisual materials, an OPAC, and a Web page. Operations spending for the previous fiscal year: $891,473. 1,700 computers available on campus for general student use. A campuswide network can be accessed from student residence rooms and from off campus. Students can access the following: online class registration, online classes, e-mail. Staffed computer lab on campus provides training in use of computers and software.
Community Environment: See Creighton University.

■ **MID-PLAINS COMMUNITY COLLEGE**
1101 Halligan Dr.
North Platte, NE 69101
Tel: (308)535-3600; Free: 800-658-4348

Fax: (308)532-8590
E-mail: driskellm@mpcc.edu
Web Site: www.mpcc.edu/
Description: District-supported, 2-year, coed. Awards certificates, diplomas, transfer associate, and terminal associate degrees. Founded 1973. Setting: small town campus. Endowment: $5.9 million. Educational spending for the previous fiscal year: $4079 per student. Total enrollment: 2,591. Faculty: 311 (67 full-time, 244 part-time). Student-undergrad faculty ratio is 10:1. 426 applied, 100% were admitted. Full-time: 980 students, 53% women, 47% men. Part-time: 1,611 students, 62% women, 38% men. Students come from 39 states and territories, 13 other countries, 7% from out-of-state. 1% American Indian or Alaska Native, non-Hispanic/Latino; 8% Hispanic/Latino; 4% African American, non-Hispanic/Latino; 0.3% Asian, non-Hispanic/Latino; 0% Native Hawaiian or other Pacific Islander, non-Hispanic/Latino; 1% international. 36% 25 or older, 8% live on campus, 3% transferred in. Retention: 0% of full-time freshmen returned the following year. Core. Calendar: semesters. Academic remediation for entering students, ESL program, services for LD students, advanced placement, accelerated degree program, independent study, distance learning, double major, summer session for credit, part-time degree program, external degree program, adult/continuing education programs, co-op programs and internships.
Entrance Requirements: Open admission. Options: electronic application, deferred admission. Required: high school transcript. Recommended: ACT. Required for some: 2 recommendations, interview, COMPASS. Entrance: minimally difficult. Application deadline: Rolling. Notification: continuous. Transfer credits accepted: Yes.
Costs Per Year: Application fee: $0. State resident tuition: $2310 full-time, $77 per credit hour part-time. Nonresident tuition: $3450 full-time, $115 per credit hour part-time. Mandatory fees: $450 full-time, $15 per credit hour part-time. Full-time tuition and fees vary according to reciprocity agreements. Part-time tuition and fees vary according to reciprocity agreements. College room and board: $5460. Room and board charges vary according to board plan, housing facility, and location.
Collegiate Environment: Orientation program. Drama-theater group, choral group, student-run newspaper. Social organizations: 10 open to all; national fraternities, national sororities, Non-Traditional Student Group, SMAC. Most popular organizations: Student Senate, Phi Theta Kappa, Phi Beta Lambda, Intercollegiate Athletics, MPCC Student Nurses Association. Major annual events: Annual Welcome Week Hypnotist Entertainment, Annual Homecoming Week, Annual Chili Feed. Campus security: controlled dormitory access, patrols by trained security personnel. 344 college housing spaces available; 286 were occupied in 2012-13. No special consideration for freshman housing applicants. Option: coed housing available. McDonald-Belton Learning Resource Center (LRC) plus 1 other with 79,334 books, 124 serials, 1,803 audiovisual materials, an OPAC, and a Web page. Operations spending for the previous fiscal year: $237,600. 400 computers available on campus for general student use. A campuswide network can be accessed from student residence rooms and from off campus. Students can access the following: online class registration. Staffed computer lab on campus.
Community Environment: A rural and agricultural community, North Platte is a railroad division point with extensive railroad shops. Important crops raised are corn, wheat, and alfalfa. Maloney Reservoir, six miles south of North Platte, offers boating, fishing and hunting. Community facilities include many churches, a regional medical center, shopping areas, a community playhouse, civic music association and numerous social and service organizations. Part-time employment opportunities are good.

■ **MIDLAND UNIVERSITY**
900 N Clarkson St.
Fremont, NE 68025-4200
Tel: (402)721-5480; Free: 800-642-8382
Fax: (402)721-0250
E-mail: oliver@midlandu.edu
Web Site: www.midlandu.edu/
Description: Independent Lutheran, 4-year, coed. Awards associate and bachelor's degrees. Founded 1883. Setting: 27-acre small town campus with easy access to Omaha. Endowment: $21 million. Educational spending for the previous fiscal year: $5371 per student. Total enrollment: 827. Faculty: 81 (54 full-time, 27 part-time). Student-undergrad faculty ratio is 14:1. 920 applied, 88% were admitted. 9% from top 10% of their high school class, 26% from top quarter, 57% from top half. 1 class president, 17 valedictorians, 5 student government officers. Full-time: 808 students, 56% women, 44% men. Part-time: 19 students, 58% women, 42% men. Students come from 18 states and territories, 1 other country, 26% from out-of-state. 5% 25 or

older, 62% live on campus, 5% transferred in. Retention: 80% of full-time freshmen returned the following year. Core. Calendar: 4-1-4. Academic remediation for entering students, ESL program, services for LD students, advanced placement, accelerated degree program, self-designed majors, honors program, independent study, double major, summer session for credit, part-time degree program, co-op programs and internships. Off campus study at Concordia University, Doane College, Dana College, Hastings College, Central College. Study abroad program.

Entrance Requirements: Options: electronic application, early admission, international baccalaureate accepted. Required: high school transcript, SAT or ACT. Recommended: essay, minimum 3.0 high school GPA. Required for some: interview. Entrance: moderately difficult. Application deadline: Rolling. Notification: continuous until 9/1.

Collegiate Environment: Orientation program. Drama-theater group, choral group, marching band, student-run newspaper. Social organizations: 48 open to all; local fraternities, local sororities; 40% of eligible men and 40% of eligible women are members. Most popular organizations: Student Nurses Association, Student Education Association, Phi Beta Lambda, Fellowship of Christian Athletes, Circle K. Major annual events: Homecoming, Snow Days, Spring Fling. Student services: health clinic, personal-psychological counseling. Campus security: 24-hour emergency response devices, student patrols, late night transport-escort service, controlled dormitory access. Luther Library with 110,000 books, 900 serials, an OPAC, and a Web page. Operations spending for the previous fiscal year: $276,356. 190 computers available on campus for general student use. A campuswide network can be accessed from student residence rooms and from off campus. Students can access the following: online class registration. Staffed computer lab on campus provides training in use of computers, software, and the Internet.

Community Environment: Situated near the Platte River, Fremont, the trading center of a dairying and livestock area, is located 35 miles northwest of Omaha and 51 miles north of Lincoln, Nebraska. Fremont is also recognized as the hybrid seed corn center of the state. Some of the products of industry are poultry, butter, flour, soybeans, and animal food. Some nationally known manufacturers such as Campbell Soup, Fel-Tex Ammonia, Magnus Metal, and Hormel Meats have plants in the area. Part-time employment is available. Boating, fishing and hunting are some of the outdoor sports available.

■ MYOTHERAPY INSTITUTE
6020 S 58th St.
Lincoln, NE 68516
Tel: (402)421-7410
Fax: (402)421-6736
Web Site: www.myotherapy.edu/
Description: Proprietary, 2-year, coed. Awards terminal associate degrees. Total enrollment: 52.
Entrance Requirements: Entrance: noncompetitive.

■ NEBRASKA CHRISTIAN COLLEGE
12550 S 114th Steet
Papillion, NE 68046
Tel: (402)379-5000
Web Site: www.nechristian.edu/
Description: Independent, 4-year, coed, affiliated with Christian Churches and Churches of Christ. Awards associate and bachelor's degrees. Founded 1944. Setting: 85-acre small town campus. Endowment: $324,000. Total enrollment: 146. Faculty: 20. Student-undergrad faculty ratio is 7:1. 154 applied. 10% from top 10% of their high school class, 30% from top quarter, 52% from top half. Full-time: 140 students, 44% women, 56% men. Part-time: 6 students, 33% women, 67% men. Students come from 12 states and territories, 4 other countries, 42% from out-of-state. 3% 25 or older, 90% live on campus, 8% transferred in. Retention: 30% of full-time freshmen returned the following year. Core. Calendar: semesters. Part-time degree program, internships. Off campus study at Northeast Community College, Wayne State College, York College (NE), Fort Hays State University.
Entrance Requirements: Option: electronic application. Required: high school transcript, 2 recommendations, ACT. Required for some: interview. Entrance: minimally difficult. Application deadline: Rolling. Notification: continuous until 9/1.
Collegiate Environment: Orientation program. Choral group. Social organizations: 4 open to all. Major annual events: Fall Formal, Challenge Week, Spring Formal. Swedberg Library with 250,000 books and 149 serials. 12 computers available on campus for general student use. A

campuswide network can be accessed from student residence rooms and from off campus. Staffed computer lab on campus.
Community Environment: Primarily a rural community, Norfolk depends very heavily on agriculture and the raising of beef as its primary industries. The livestock business is valued at almost a $40 million industry. Community facilities include a public library, 20 churches representing 16 denominations, a YMCA and civic organizations such as Rotary, Kiwanis and the Lions Club. Part-time employment is available. Lewis and Clark Lake and other facilities provide swimming, boating, fishing and golf. The Norfolk Historical Museum exhibits a collection of local historical relics.

■ NEBRASKA COLLEGE OF TECHNICAL AGRICULTURE
RR3, Box 23A
Curtis, NE 69025-9205
Tel: (308)367-4124; Free: 800-3CURTIS
Fax: (308)367-5203
Web Site: www.ncta.unl.edu/
Description: State-supported, 2-year, coed. Part of University of Nebraska System. Administratively affiliated with Institute of Agriculture and Natural Resources - University of Nebraska. Awards certificates, transfer associate, and terminal associate degrees. Founded 1965. Setting: 634-acre rural campus. Research spending for the previous fiscal year: $2360. Total enrollment: 425. Faculty: 21 (13 full-time, 8 part-time). Student-undergrad faculty ratio is 13:1. Full-time: 246 students, 52% women, 48% men. Part-time: 179 students, 49% women, 51% men. Students come from 10 states and territories. 0.02% 25 or older, 45% live on campus. Retention: 64% of full-time freshmen returned the following year. Core. Calendar: 8-week modular system. Academic remediation for entering students, independent study, distance learning, double major, part-time degree program, external degree program, adult/continuing education programs, internships. Study abroad program.
Entrance Requirements: Open admission. Option: early admission. Required: high school transcript, ACT. Recommended: interview. Entrance: noncompetitive. Application deadline: Rolling. Transfer credits accepted: Yes.
Collegiate Environment: Orientation program. Student-run newspaper. Social organizations: 13 open to all. Most popular organizations: Aggie Livestock Association, Student Technicians Veterinary Medicine Association, Business Club, Phi Theta Kappa, Rodeo Club. Major annual events: Annual Open House, Step Ahead Days, Orientation. Student services: health clinic, personal-psychological counseling. Campus security: 24-hour emergency response devices, controlled dormitory access, night security. Nebraska College of Technical Agriculture Library with 6,000 books, 230 serials, an OPAC, and a Web page. Operations spending for the previous fiscal year: $55,223. 45 computers available on campus for general student use. Computer purchase/lease plans available. A campuswide network can be accessed from student residence rooms and from off campus. Students can access the following: online class registration. Staffed computer lab on campus.

■ NEBRASKA INDIAN COMMUNITY COLLEGE
PO Box 428
Macy, NE 68039-0428
Tel: (402)837-5078
Fax: (402)878-2522
Web Site: www.thenicc.edu/
Description: Federally supported, 2-year, coed. Awards certificates, transfer associate, and terminal associate degrees. Founded 1979. Setting: 2-acre rural campus with easy access to Omaha. Endowment: $68,020. Educational spending for the previous fiscal year: $4385 per student. Total enrollment: 115. Faculty: 12 (5 full-time, 7 part-time). Full-time: 55 students, 51% women, 49% men. Part-time: 60 students, 62% women, 38% men. Students come from 2 states and territories, 7% from out-of-state. 75% 25 or older. Core. Calendar: semesters. Academic remediation for entering students, double major, part-time degree program, adult/continuing education programs. Study abroad program.
Entrance Requirements: Open admission. Options: early admission, deferred admission. Required: high school transcript, certificate of tribal enrollment if applicable. Entrance: noncompetitive. Application deadline: Rolling. Notification: continuous.
Collegiate Environment: Orientation program. 10 computers available on campus for general student use. Staffed computer lab on campus.

■ NEBRASKA METHODIST COLLEGE
720 N 87th St.
Omaha, NE 68114

Tel: (402)354-7000; Free: 800-335-5510
Fax: (402)354-4819
E-mail: sara.hanson@methodistcollege.edu
Web Site: www.methodistcollege.edu/

Description: Independent, comprehensive, coed, affiliated with United Methodist Church. Awards associate, bachelor's, and master's degrees and post-master's certificates. Founded 1891. Setting: 7-acre urban campus. Total enrollment: 891. Faculty: 61 (50 full-time, 11 part-time). Student-undergrad faculty ratio is 12:1. 109 applied, 51% were admitted. 11% from top 10% of their high school class, 32% from top quarter, 75% from top half. Full-time: 454 students, 90% women, 10% men. Part-time: 284 students, 89% women, 11% men. Students come from 10 states and territories, 15% from out-of-state. 1% American Indian or Alaska Native, non-Hispanic/Latino; 3% Hispanic/Latino; 3% African American, non-Hispanic/Latino; 2% Asian, non-Hispanic/Latino; 0.3% Native Hawaiian or other Pacific Islander, non-Hispanic/Latino; 0.4% international. 25% 25 or older, 11% live on campus, 9% transferred in. Retention: 72% of full-time freshmen returned the following year. Academic area with the most degrees conferred: health professions and related sciences. Core. Calendar: semesters. Academic remediation for entering students, services for LD students, advanced placement, accelerated degree program, independent study, distance learning, summer session for credit, external degree program, adult/continuing education programs, internships. ROTC: Army (c), Air Force (c).

Entrance Requirements: Options: electronic application, deferred admission. Required: essay, high school transcript, minimum 2.5 high school GPA, SAT or ACT. Entrance: moderately difficult. Application deadlines: Rolling, Rolling for nonresidents. Transfer credits accepted: Yes.

Costs Per Year: Application fee: $25. Tuition: $15,840 full-time, $528 per credit hour part-time. Mandatory fees: $1227 full-time. Full-time tuition and fees vary according to degree level and program. Part-time tuition varies according to degree level and program. College room only: $6160. Room charges vary according to housing facility.

Collegiate Environment: Orientation program. Social organizations: 12 open to all; Nursing sorority. Most popular organizations: Student Senate, Student Nurses Association, Methodist Allied Health Student Association, Student Ambassadors, Residence Hall Council. Major annual events: Campus Casino night for Autism, Welcome Week, Carnival. Student services: health clinic, personal-psychological counseling. Campus security: 24-hour emergency response devices and patrols, late night transport-escort service, controlled dormitory access. 101 college housing spaces available; 65 were occupied in 2012-13. Freshmen given priority for college housing. Option: coed housing available. John Moritz Library with 10,300 books, 640 serials, and an OPAC. 47 computers available on campus for general student use. A campuswide network can be accessed. Students can access the following: online class registration. Staffed computer lab on campus provides training in use of computers, software, and the Internet.

■ **NEBRASKA WESLEYAN UNIVERSITY**
5000 Saint Paul Ave.
Lincoln, NE 68504-2796
Tel: (402)466-2371; Free: 800-541-3818
Fax: (402)465-2179
E-mail: admissions@nebrwesleyan.edu
Web Site: www.nebrwesleyan.edu/

Description: Independent United Methodist, comprehensive, coed. Awards bachelor's and master's degrees and post-master's certificates. Founded 1887. Setting: 50-acre suburban campus with easy access to Omaha. Endowment: $45.8 million. Educational spending for the previous fiscal year: $8323 per student. Total enrollment: 2,071. Faculty: 156 (98 full-time, 58 part-time). Student-undergrad faculty ratio is 12:1. 2,106 applied, 79% were admitted. 25% from top 10% of their high school class, 56% from top quarter, 85% from top half. Full-time: 1,544 students, 58% women, 42% men. Part-time: 270 students, 76% women, 24% men. Students come from 26 states and territories, 16 other countries, 11% from out-of-state. 1% American Indian or Alaska Native, non-Hispanic/Latino; 3% Hispanic/Latino; 2% African American, non-Hispanic/Latino; 2% Asian, non-Hispanic/Latino; 0.1% Native Hawaiian or other Pacific Islander, non-Hispanic/Latino; 0% international. 0% 25 or older, 63% live on campus, 4% transferred in. Retention: 79% of full-time freshmen returned the following year. Academic areas with the most degrees conferred: business/marketing; education; biological/life sciences. Core. Calendar: semesters. Services for LD students, advanced placement, accelerated degree program, self-designed majors, independent study, double major, summer session for credit, part-time

degree program, adult/continuing education programs, internships, graduate courses open to undergrads. Off campus study. Study abroad program. ROTC: Army (c), Air Force (c).

Entrance Requirements: Options: electronic application, deferred admission, international baccalaureate accepted. Required: high school transcript, SAT or ACT. Recommended: interview. Required for some: essay. Entrance: moderately difficult. Application deadline: 8/15. Notification: continuous. Transfer credits accepted: Yes.

Costs Per Year: Application fee: $20. One-time mandatory fee: $120. Comprehensive fee: $34,790 includes full-time tuition ($26,740), mandatory fees ($500), and college room and board ($7550). Room and board charges vary according to board plan and housing facility. Part-time tuition: $1005 per credit hour. Part-time tuition varies according to class time and location.

Collegiate Environment: Orientation program. Drama-theater group, choral group, student-run newspaper. Social organizations: 80 open to all; national fraternities, national sororities, local fraternities, local sororities. Major annual events: Jim Wand hypnotist show, Visions and Ventures Symposium, Homecoming. Student services: health clinic, personal-psychological counseling, women's center. Campus security: 24-hour emergency response devices, late night transport-escort service, controlled dormitory access. 755 undergraduates lived in college housing during 2012-13. Freshmen guaranteed college housing. On-campus residence required through junior year. Options: coed, women-only housing available. Cochrane Woods Library with 225,771 books, 4,952 microform titles, 1,551 serials, 9,651 audiovisual materials, an OPAC, and a Web page. 360 computers available on campus for general student use. A campuswide network can be accessed from student residence rooms and from off campus. Students can access the following: online class registration. Staffed computer lab on campus (open 24 hours a day).

Community Environment: The capital, Lincoln, in southeastern Nebraska, is in a vast agricultural area where irrigation is an important factor. Many insurance firms have their home offices here. Major forms of transportation are available. Pershing Municipal Auditorium and the Bob Devaney Sports Center is used for conventions, concerts and athletic activities. Recreational facilities and sporting events are numerous. Some of the points of interest are Antelope Park, the Sunken Garden, Fairview, a home occupied by the William Jennings Bryan family for 15 years, Pioneer Park, Holmes Lake with bike trails, Sheldon Memorial Art Gallery, the University of Nebraska State Museum, and the Haymarket District. Part-time jobs are available on and off campus.

■ **NORTHEAST COMMUNITY COLLEGE**
801 E Benjamin Ave.
Norfolk, NE 68702-0469
Tel: (402)371-2020
Fax: (402)644-0650
E-mail: admission@northeast.edu
Web Site: www.northeast.edu/

Description: State and locally supported, 2-year, coed. Part of Nebraska Coordinating Commission for Postsecondary Education. Awards certificates, diplomas, transfer associate, and terminal associate degrees. Founded 1973. Setting: 205-acre small town campus. Total enrollment: 5,161. Faculty: 381 (114 full-time, 267 part-time). Student-undergrad faculty ratio is 16:1. 1,644 applied, 100% were admitted. Full-time: 2,169 students, 48% women, 52% men. Part-time: 2,992 students, 45% women, 55% men. 6% from out-of-state. 1% American Indian or Alaska Native, non-Hispanic/Latino; 6% Hispanic/Latino; 1% African American, non-Hispanic/Latino; 0.3% Asian, non-Hispanic/Latino; 0.04% Native Hawaiian or other Pacific Islander, non-Hispanic/Latino; 1% international. 57% 25 or older, 6% live on campus, 5% transferred in. Retention: 65% of full-time freshmen returned the following year. Core. Calendar: semesters. Academic remediation for entering students, ESL program, services for LD students, advanced placement, distance learning, double major, summer session for credit, part-time degree program, adult/continuing education programs, co-op programs and internships. Off campus study.

Entrance Requirements: Open admission. Options: electronic application, early admission. Recommended: high school transcript. Required for some: high school transcript, minimum 2 high school GPA, 3 recommendations, interview. Entrance: noncompetitive. Application deadlines: Rolling, Rolling for nonresidents. Notification: continuous, continuous for nonresidents. Transfer credits accepted: Yes. Applicants placed on waiting list: 283. Wait-listed applicants offered admission: 116.

Collegiate Environment: Orientation program. Drama-theater group, choral group, student-run newspaper, radio station. Student services: personal-psychological counseling. Campus security: 24-hour patrols, controlled dormitory access. Library Resource Center plus 1 other with an OPAC and a Web page.

Community Environment: See Nebraska Christian College.

■ OMAHA SCHOOL OF MASSAGE THERAPY AND HEALTHCARE OF HERZING UNIVERSITY

9748 Park Dr.
Omaha, NE 68127
Tel: (402)331-3694
Fax: (402)331-0280
Web Site: www.osmhc.com/

Description: Proprietary, 2-year, coed. Awards diplomas and terminal associate degrees. Founded 1991.

■ PERU STATE COLLEGE

PO Box 10
Peru, NE 68421
Tel: (402)872-3815; Free: 800-741-4412
E-mail: mwillis@peru.edu
Web Site: www.peru.edu/

Description: State-supported, comprehensive, coed. Part of Nebraska State College System. Awards bachelor's and master's degrees. Founded 1867. Setting: 104-acre rural campus. Total enrollment: 2,358. Faculty: 109 (47 full-time, 62 part-time). Student-undergrad faculty ratio is 24:1. 869 applied, 49% were admitted. 13% from top quarter of their high school class, 46% from top half. Full-time: 1,192 students, 58% women, 42% men. Part-time: 902 students, 60% women, 40% men. 1% American Indian or Alaska Native, non-Hispanic/Latino; 4% Hispanic/Latino; 5% African American, non-Hispanic/Latino; 1% Asian, non-Hispanic/Latino; 0.1% Native Hawaiian or other Pacific Islander, non-Hispanic/Latino; 0% international. 33% live on campus, 9% transferred in. Academic areas with the most degrees conferred: business/marketing; education; homeland security, law enforcement, firefighting, and protective services. Core. Calendar: semesters. Academic remediation for entering students, services for LD students, advanced placement, accelerated degree program, freshman honors college, honors program, distance learning, double major, summer session for credit, part-time degree program, external degree program, adult/continuing education programs, co-op programs and internships, graduate courses open to undergrads. Off campus study. ROTC: Army (c), Air Force (c).

Entrance Requirements: Open admission. Options: electronic application, international baccalaureate accepted. Required: high school transcript. Required for some: SAT or ACT. Entrance: noncompetitive. Application deadlines: Rolling, Rolling for nonresidents. Notification: continuous, continuous for nonresidents. Transfer credits accepted: Yes.

Costs Per Year: Application fee: $0. State resident tuition: $4200 full-time. Nonresident tuition: $4200 full-time. Full-time tuition varies according to course level, course load, and location. College room and board: $5970. College room only: $3162. Room and board charges vary according to board plan and housing facility.

Collegiate Environment: Orientation program. Drama-theater group, choral group, marching band, student-run newspaper. Social organizations: 20 open to all. Most popular organizations: Campus Activities Board, Black Student Union, Peru Student Education Association (PSEA), Phi Beta Lambda (PBL), Pilot Club. Major annual events: Homecoming, Spring Fling, Oakstock. Student services: health clinic. Campus security: 24-hour emergency response devices and patrols, late night transport-escort service. Peru State College Library with 230,636 books, 599,601 microform titles, 30,000 serials, 7,737 audiovisual materials, an OPAC, and a Web page. Operations spending for the previous fiscal year: $144,370. 125 computers available on campus for general student use. A campuswide network can be accessed from student residence rooms. Students can access the following: online class registration. Staffed computer lab on campus.

Community Environment: Peru is situated in an agricultural region of southeast Nebraska on bluffs overlooking the Missouri River. Corn, wheat, apples, and many other crops are raised in the area. The town is 65 miles from Omaha and 75 miles from Lincoln.

■ ST. GREGORY THE GREAT SEMINARY

800 Fletcher Rd.
Seward, NE 67434
Tel: (402)643-4052
Fax: (402)643-6964
E-mail: sggs@stgregoryseminary.edu

Web Site: www.stgregoryseminary.edu/

Description: Independent Roman Catholic, 4-year, men only. Awards bachelor's degrees. Setting: 60-acre small town campus. Total enrollment: 44. Faculty: 13 (7 full-time, 6 part-time). 6 applied, 100% were admitted. Full-time: 44 students. Students come from 6 states and territories, 4 other countries, 45% from out-of-state. 9% Hispanic/Latino; 5% international. 9% 25 or older, 100% live on campus, 18% transferred in. Retention: 88% of full-time freshmen returned the following year. Core.

Entrance Requirements: Required: essay, high school transcript, 3 recommendations, interview, Church documents, letter of sponsorship from diocese, SAT or ACT. Transfer credits accepted: Yes.

Collegiate Environment: Orientation program. Our Lady Seat of Wisdom Library with 41,000 books, 37 serials, and an OPAC.

■ SOUTHEAST COMMUNITY COLLEGE, BEATRICE CAMPUS

4771 W Scott Rd.
Beatrice, NE 68310
Tel: (402)228-3468; Free: 800-233-5027
Fax: (402)228-2218
Web Site: www.southeast.edu/

Description: District-supported, 2-year, coed. Part of Southeast Community College System. Awards certificates, diplomas, transfer associate, and terminal associate degrees. Founded 1976. Setting: 640-acre small town campus. Core. Calendar: semesters. Academic remediation for entering students, services for LD students, advanced placement, distance learning, summer session for credit, part-time degree program, adult/continuing education programs, co-op programs and internships. Off campus study at Peru State College.

Entrance Requirements: Open admission. Options: electronic application, early admission, deferred admission. Required: high school transcript. Recommended: minimum 2.0 high school GPA, SAT or ACT, ACT ASSET, ACT COMPASS. Required for some: ACT ASSET, ACT COMPASS. Entrance: noncompetitive. Application deadline: Rolling.

Collegiate Environment: Orientation program. Drama-theater group, choral group, student-run newspaper, radio station. Student services: personal-psychological counseling. Campus security: controlled dormitory access, evening security. Learning Resource Center with an OPAC.

■ SOUTHEAST COMMUNITY COLLEGE, LINCOLN CAMPUS

8800 O St.
Lincoln, NE 68520-1299
Tel: (402)471-3333; Free: 800-642-4075
Web Site: www.southeast.edu/

Description: District-supported, 2-year, coed. Part of Southeast Community College System. Awards certificates, diplomas, transfer associate, and terminal associate degrees. Founded 1973. Setting: 115-acre suburban campus with easy access to Omaha. Core. Academic remediation for entering students, ESL program, services for LD students, advanced placement, independent study, distance learning, summer session for credit, part-time degree program, adult/continuing education programs, co-op programs and internships. Off campus study at University of Nebraska-Lincoln.

Entrance Requirements: Open admission. Options: electronic application, early admission, deferred admission. Required: high school transcript. Entrance: noncompetitive. Application deadline: Rolling.

Collegiate Environment: Orientation program. Campus security: late night transport-escort service.

■ SOUTHEAST COMMUNITY COLLEGE, MILFORD CAMPUS

600 State St.
Milford, NE 68405
Tel: (402)761-2131; Free: 800-933-7223
Web Site: www.southeast.edu/

Description: District-supported, 2-year, coed. Part of Southeast Community College System. Awards diplomas and terminal associate degrees. Founded 1941. Setting: 50-acre small town campus with easy access to Omaha. Academic remediation for entering students, services for LD students, distance learning, co-op programs and internships.

Entrance Requirements: Open admission. Required: high school transcript. Recommended: SAT, ACT. Entrance: noncompetitive. Application deadline: Rolling. Notification: continuous.

Collegiate Environment: Campus security: 24-hour patrols, late night transport-escort service.

■ UNION COLLEGE

3800 S 48th St.
Lincoln, NE 68506-4300

Tel: (402)486-2600; Free: 800-228-4600
Fax: (402)486-2895
E-mail: ucenroll@ucollege.edu
Web Site: www.ucollege.edu/
Description: Independent Seventh-day Adventist, comprehensive, coed. Awards associate, bachelor's, and master's degrees. Founded 1891. Setting: 26-acre suburban campus with easy access to Omaha. Endowment: $14 million. Educational spending for the previous fiscal year: $9740 per student. Total enrollment: 881. Faculty: 118 (56 full-time, 62 part-time). Student-undergrad faculty ratio is 10:1. 1,251 applied, 45% were admitted. 8% from top 10% of their high school class, 21% from top quarter, 58% from top half. Full-time: 673 students, 58% women, 42% men. Part-time: 122 students, 66% women, 34% men. Students come from 48 states and territories, 32 other countries, 76% from out-of-state. 1% American Indian or Alaska Native, non-Hispanic/Latino; 13% Hispanic/Latino; 4% African American, non-Hispanic/Latino; 4% Asian, non-Hispanic/Latino; 1% Native Hawaiian or other Pacific Islander, non-Hispanic/Latino; 7% international. 15% 25 or older, 62% live on campus, 9% transferred in. Retention: 72% of full-time freshmen returned the following year. Academic areas with the most degrees conferred: health professions and related sciences; education; business/marketing. Core. Calendar: semesters. ESL program, services for LD students, advanced placement, accelerated degree program, self-designed majors, honors program, independent study, double major, summer session for credit, part-time degree program, adult/continuing education programs, co-op programs and internships. Off campus study at University of Nebraska, Southeast Community College. Study abroad program.
Entrance Requirements: Option: electronic application. Required: high school transcript, minimum 2.5 high school GPA, 3 recommendations, SAT or ACT. Required for some: essay, interview. Entrance: moderately difficult. Application deadline: Rolling. Notification: continuous. SAT Reasoning Test deadline: 8/31. SAT Subject Test deadline: 8/31.
Costs Per Year: Application fee: $0. Comprehensive fee: $26,840 includes full-time tuition ($19,550), mandatory fees ($920), and college room and board ($6370). College room only: $3620. Full-time tuition and fees vary according to course load, degree level, and program. Room and board charges vary according to housing facility. Part-time tuition: $815 per credit hour. Part-time tuition varies according to program.
Collegiate Environment: Orientation program. Drama-theater group, choral group, student-run newspaper. Student services: health clinic, personal-psychological counseling. Campus security: 24-hour emergency response devices, student patrols, late night transport-escort service. 778 college housing spaces available; 492 were occupied in 2012-13. Freshmen guaranteed college housing. On-campus residence required through junior year. Options: men-only, women-only housing available. Ella Johnson Crandall Library plus 1 other with 176,653 books, 1,941 microform titles, 32,990 serials, 3,359 audiovisual materials, an OPAC, and a Web page. Operations spending for the previous fiscal year: $610,235. 85 computers available on campus for general student use. A campuswide network can be accessed from student residence rooms and from off campus. Students can access the following: online class registration. Staffed computer lab on campus.

■ **UNIVERSITY OF NEBRASKA AT KEARNEY**
905 W 25th St.
Kearney, NE 68849-0001
Tel: (308)865-8441; Free: 800-532-7639
Fax: (308)865-8987
E-mail: admissionsug@unk.edu
Web Site: www.unk.edu/
Description: State-supported, comprehensive, coed. Part of University of Nebraska System. Awards bachelor's and master's degrees and post-master's certificates. Founded 1903. Setting: 235-acre small town campus. Research spending for the previous fiscal year: $1.5 million. Educational spending for the previous fiscal year: $7322 per student. Total enrollment: 7,199. Faculty: 406 (305 full-time, 101 part-time). Student-undergrad faculty ratio is 16:1. 2,895 applied, 77% were admitted. 17% from top 10% of their high school class, 43% from top quarter, 76% from top half. Full-time: 4,964 students, 56% women, 44% men. Part-time: 684 students, 54% women, 46% men. 9% from out-of-state. 0.2% American Indian or Alaska Native, non-Hispanic/Latino; 8% Hispanic/Latino; 1% African American, non-Hispanic/Latino; 1% Asian, non-Hispanic/Latino; 0% Native Hawaiian or other Pacific Islander, non-Hispanic/Latino; 9% international. 11% 25 or older, 50% live on campus, 6% transferred in. Retention: 79% of full-time freshmen returned the following year. Academic areas with the most degrees

conferred: business/marketing; education; parks and recreation. Calendar: semesters. Part-time degree program. ROTC: Army.
Entrance Requirements: Option: electronic application. Required: high school transcript, rank in upper 50% of high school class, SAT and SAT Subject Tests or ACT. Entrance: moderately difficult. Application deadline: 9/1. Notification: continuous. SAT Reasoning Test deadline: 8/1.
Costs Per Year: Application fee: $45. State resident tuition: $5235 full-time, $174.50 per credit hour part-time. Nonresident tuition: $10,740 full-time, $358 per credit hour part-time. Mandatory fees: $1271 full-time, $25 per credit hour part-time, $263.50 per term part-time. Full-time tuition and fees vary according to course level, course load, degree level, and location. Part-time tuition and fees vary according to course level, course load, degree level, and location. College room and board: $8038. College room only: $4114. Room and board charges vary according to board plan and housing facility.
Collegiate Environment: Orientation program. Drama-theater group, marching band, student-run newspaper, radio station. Social organizations: national fraternities, national sororities. Student services: health clinic. Campus security: 24-hour emergency response devices and patrols, late night transport-escort service. Freshmen guaranteed college housing. On-campus residence required in freshman year. Option: coed housing available. 600 computers available on campus for general student use. A campuswide network can be accessed from student residence rooms and from off campus. Students can access the following: online class registration, online degree audit, online personal information update, online bill viewing and payment, online financial aid awards and acceptance. Staffed computer lab on campus (open 24 hours a day).

■ **UNIVERSITY OF NEBRASKA MEDICAL CENTER**
Nebraska Medical Ctr.
Omaha, NE 68198
Tel: (402)559-4000; Free: 800-626-8431
Fax: (402)559-6796
Web Site: www.unmc.edu/
Description: State-supported, upper-level, coed. Part of University of Nebraska System. Awards bachelor's, master's, and doctoral degrees and post-master's certificates. Founded 1869. Setting: 16-acre urban campus. Endowment: $11.9 million. Research spending for the previous fiscal year: $101.5 million. Educational spending for the previous fiscal year: $42,076 per student. Total enrollment: 3,625. Faculty: 1,232 (1,023 full-time, 209 part-time). Student-undergrad faculty ratio is 3:1. Full-time: 895 students, 88% women, 12% men. Part-time: 118 students, 77% women, 23% men. Students come from 20 states and territories, 10 other countries, 10% from out-of-state. 1% American Indian or Alaska Native, non-Hispanic/Latino; 3% Hispanic/Latino; 1% African American, non-Hispanic/Latino; 2% Asian, non-Hispanic/Latino; 0.1% Native Hawaiian or other Pacific Islander, non-Hispanic/Latino; 1% international. 38% 25 or older, 42% transferred in. Academic area with the most degrees conferred: health professions and related sciences. Calendar: semesters. Services for LD students, accelerated degree program, honors program, distance learning, summer session for credit, part-time degree program, graduate courses open to undergrads. Off campus study at University of Nebraska-Lincoln, University of Nebraska at Omaha, University of Nebraska at Kearney. ROTC: Army (c), Air Force (c).
Entrance Requirements: Transfer credits accepted: Yes.
Collegiate Environment: Orientation program. Social organizations: 5 open to all; national fraternities, national sororities. Most popular organizations: student government, Toastmasters, Student Alliance for Global Health, Christian Medical Society, Student Research Group. Major annual event: Spring Dance. Student services: health clinic, personal-psychological counseling. Campus security: 24-hour emergency response devices and patrols, late night transport-escort service. McGoogan Library of Medicine with 251,347 books, 9 microform titles, 7,603 serials, an OPAC, and a Web page. Operations spending for the previous fiscal year: $2.9 million. 120 computers available on campus for general student use. A campuswide network can be accessed from off-campus. Students can access the following: online class registration.
Community Environment: See Creighton University.

■ **UNIVERSITY OF NEBRASKA AT OMAHA**
6001 Dodge St.
Omaha, NE 68182
Tel: (402)554-2200
Fax: (402)554-3472
E-mail: jadams@unomaha.edu

Web Site: www.unomaha.edu/

Description: State-supported, university, coed. Part of University of Nebraska System. Awards bachelor's, master's, and doctoral degrees and post-master's certificates. Founded 1908. Setting: 503-acre urban campus. Research spending for the previous fiscal year: $9.1 million. Educational spending for the previous fiscal year: $7490 per student. Total enrollment: 14,786. Faculty: 984 (505 full-time, 479 part-time). Student-undergrad faculty ratio is 17:1. 4,536 applied, 80% were admitted. 15% from top 10% of their high school class, 39% from top quarter, 73% from top half. Full-time: 9,147 students, 53% women, 47% men. Part-time: 2,989 students, 48% women, 52% men. Students come from 47 states and territories, 79 other countries, 7% from out-of-state. 0.4% American Indian or Alaska Native, non-Hispanic/ Latino; 7% Hispanic/Latino; 7% African American, non-Hispanic/Latino; 3% Asian, non-Hispanic/Latino; 0.1% Native Hawaiian or other Pacific Islander, non-Hispanic/Latino; 3% international. 23% 25 or older, 11% live on campus, 10% transferred in. Retention: 72% of full-time freshmen returned the following year. Academic areas with the most degrees conferred: business/ marketing; education; homeland security, law enforcement, firefighting, and protective services. Core. Calendar: semesters. ESL program, services for LD students, advanced placement, self-designed majors, honors program, independent study, distance learning, double major, summer session for credit, part-time degree program, adult/continuing education programs, co-op programs and internships, graduate courses open to undergrads. Off campus study at other units of the University of Nebraska System. Study abroad program. ROTC: Army (c), Air Force.

Entrance Requirements: Options: electronic application, deferred admission. Required: high school transcript, SAT or ACT. Entrance: minimally difficult. Application deadline: 8/1. Notification: continuous.

Costs Per Year: Application fee: $45. State resident tuition: $5180 full-time, $196.75 per credit part-time. Nonresident tuition: $15,520 full-time, $598 per credit part-time. Mandatory fees: $1370 full-time. College room and board: $8090.

Collegiate Environment: Orientation program. Drama-theater group, choral group, marching band, student-run newspaper, radio station. Social organizations: 167 open to all; national fraternities, national sororities; 2% of eligible men and 2% of eligible women are members. Most popular organizations: Student Programming Board-Maverick Productions, student government, Greek Life, Emerging Leaders, PRSSA - Public Relations student society of America. Major annual events: Homecoming, International Banquet, Welcome Week. Student services: legal services, health clinic, personal-psychological counseling, women's center. Campus security: 24-hour emergency response devices and patrols, late night transport-escort service, controlled dormitory access. 2,032 college housing spaces available; 1,989 were occupied in 2012-13. No special consideration for freshman housing applicants. Option: coed housing available. Criss Library with 1.5 million books, 2.1 million microform titles, 65,790 serials, 14,341 audiovisual materials, an OPAC, and a Web page. Operations spending for the previous fiscal year: $5.9 million. 2,450 computers available on campus for general student use. Computer purchase/lease plans available. A campuswide network can be accessed from student residence rooms and from off campus. Students can access the following: online class registration. Staffed computer lab on campus (open 24 hours a day) provides training in use of the Internet.

■ **UNIVERSITY OF NEBRASKA–LINCOLN**

14th and R Sts.

Lincoln, NE 68588

Tel: (402)472-7211; Free: 800-742-8800

Fax: (402)472-0670

E-mail: admissions@unl.edu

Web Site: www.unl.edu/

Description: State-supported, university, coed. Part of University of Nebraska System. Awards associate, bachelor's, master's, and doctoral degrees and post-master's certificates. Founded 1869. Setting: 622-acre urban campus with easy access to Omaha. System endowment: $1.2 billion. Research spending for the previous fiscal year: $171.9 million. Educational spending for the previous fiscal year: $8420 per student. Total enrollment: 24,207. Faculty: 1,089 (1,071 full-time, 18 part-time). Student-undergrad faculty ratio is 20:1. 10,350 applied, 64% were admitted. 26% from top 10% of their high school class, 54% from top quarter, 83% from top half. 45 National Merit Scholars. Full-time: 17,766 students, 46% women, 54% men. Part-time: 1,337 students, 44% women, 56% men. Students come from 51 states and territories, 89 other countries, 16% from out-of-state. 0.3% American Indian or Alaska Native, non-Hispanic/Latino; 4% Hispanic/Latino;

2% African American, non-Hispanic/Latino; 2% Asian, non-Hispanic/Latino; 0.1% Native Hawaiian or other Pacific Islander, non-Hispanic/Latino; 5% international. 7% 25 or older, 41% live on campus, 5% transferred in. Retention: 84% of full-time freshmen returned the following year. Academic areas with the most degrees conferred: business/marketing; engineering; family and consumer sciences. Core. Calendar: semesters. ESL program, services for LD students, advanced placement, accelerated degree program, self-designed majors, honors program, independent study, distance learning, double major, summer session for credit, part-time degree program, adult/ continuing education programs, co-op programs and internships, graduate courses open to undergrads. Off campus study at Iowa State University. Study abroad program. ROTC: Army, Naval, Air Force.

Entrance Requirements: Options: electronic application, international baccalaureate accepted. Required: high school transcript, SAT or ACT. Recommended: ACT. Required for some: rank in upper 50% of high school class. Entrance: moderately difficult. Application deadline: 5/1. Notification: continuous. SAT Reasoning Test deadline: 5/1. Transfer credits accepted: Yes.

Costs Per Year: Application fee: $45. State resident tuition: $6480 full-time, $216 per credit hour part-time. Nonresident tuition: $19,230 full-time, $641 per credit hour part-time. Mandatory fees: $1,416 full-time, $11.35 per credit hour part-time, $299 per term part-time. Full-time tuition and fees vary according to course load, program, and reciprocity agreements. Part-time tuition and fees vary according to course load, program, and reciprocity agreements. College room and board: $9122. Room and board charges vary according to board plan and housing facility.

Collegiate Environment: Orientation program. Drama-theater group, choral group, marching band, student-run newspaper, radio station. Social organizations: 249 open to all; national fraternities, national sororities, local fraternities, local sororities; 17% of eligible men and 21% of eligible women are members. Most popular organizations: Student Alumni Association, University Ambassadors, University Program Council, Golden Key Honor Society, ASUN (Association of Students of the University of Nebraska, student body government). Major annual events: Homecoming, Big Red Welcome, The Big Event. Student services: legal services, health clinic, personal-psychological counseling, women's center. Campus security: 24-hour emergency response devices and patrols, late night transport-escort service, controlled dormitory access. 8,999 college housing spaces available; 7,826 were occupied in 2012-13. Freshmen guaranteed college housing. On-campus residence required in freshman year. Options: coed, women-only housing available. Love Memorial Library plus 7 others with 3.9 million books, 3.8 million microform titles, 62,471 serials, 317,124 audiovisual materials, an OPAC, and a Web page. Operations spending for the previous fiscal year: $17.6 million. 600 computers available on campus for general student use. A campuswide network can be accessed from student residence rooms and from off campus. Students can access the following: online class registration. Staffed computer lab on campus (open 24 hours a day) provides training in use of computers, software, and the Internet.

Community Environment: UNL is located in the capital city of Lincoln, a community of more than 209,000 that combines a college-town atmosphere with the entertainment and nightlife of a larger city. Lincoln boasts a thriving arts community with dozens of art galleries and the Lied Center for Performing Arts, which hosts major productions such as Les Miserables, Cats, and performances by the Russian Ballet, Celine Dion, and cellist Yo-yo Ma. Lincoln has more parks per capita than any other U.S. city and a growing network of bike paths that extend far beyond the city limits. There are 16 golf courses, hundreds of restaurants, more than 30 movie screens, major shopping malls, and a restored downtown historic district complete with specialty shops, coffeehouses, and a dinner theater. Major metropolitan cities like Omaha, Kansas City, Chicago, and Denver are within a day's driving distance, and Lincoln is easily accessible by plane, train, and bus.

■ **UNIVERSITY OF PHOENIX–OMAHA CAMPUS**

13321 California St., Ste. 200

Omaha, NE 68154-5240

Tel: (402)334-4936; Free: 866-766-0766

Web Site: www.phoenix.edu/

Description: Proprietary, comprehensive, coed. Awards bachelor's, master's, and doctoral degrees.

■ **VATTEROTT COLLEGE**

11818 I St.

Omaha, NE 68137

Tel: (402)891-9411; Free: 888-553-6627

Fax: (402)891-9413

Web Site: www.vatterott.edu/

Description: Proprietary, 2-year, coed. Awards terminal associate degrees. Total enrollment: 276. Student-undergrad faculty ratio is 12:1. 7% from out-of-state. 54% 25 or older. Retention: 64% of full-time freshmen returned the following year. Calendar: semesters.

Entrance Requirements: Open admission.

■ **WAYNE STATE COLLEGE**

1111 Main St.

Wayne, NE 68787

Tel: (402)375-7000; Free: 866-WSC-CATS

Fax: (402)375-7204

E-mail: admit1@wsc.edu

Web Site: www.wsc.edu/

Description: State-supported, comprehensive, coed. Part of Nebraska State College System. Awards bachelor's and master's degrees and post-master's certificates. Founded 1910. Setting: 128-acre small town campus. Endowment: $12.2 million. Total enrollment: 3,555. Faculty: 216 (123 full-time, 93 part-time). Student-undergrad faculty ratio is 20:1. 2,278 applied, 100% were admitted. 9% from top 10% of their high school class, 24% from top quarter, 57% from top half. Full-time: 2,779 students, 56% women, 44% men. Part-time: 241 students, 67% women, 33% men. Students come from 29 states and territories, 18 other countries, 14% from out-of-state. 1% American Indian or Alaska Native, non-Hispanic/Latino; 6% Hispanic/Latino; 3% African American, non-Hispanic/Latino; 0.4% Asian, non-Hispanic/Latino; 0.1% Native Hawaiian or other Pacific Islander, non-Hispanic/Latino; 0.5% international. 9% 25 or older, 47% live on campus, 7% transferred in. Retention: 70% of full-time freshmen returned the following year. Academic areas with the most degrees conferred: education; business/marketing; psychology. Core. Calendar: semesters. Services for LD students, advanced placement, self-designed majors, honors program, independent study, distance learning, double major, summer session for credit, part-time degree program, adult/continuing education programs, co-op programs and internships, graduate courses open to undergrads. Off campus study at Northeast Community College, Central Community College. Study abroad program. ROTC: Army.

Entrance Requirements: Open admission Certain programs (RHOP, Neihardt Scholar, etc.) have higher guidelines for acceptance. Options: electronic application, deferred admission. Required: high school transcript. Recommended: SAT or ACT. Entrance: noncompetitive. Application deadlines: Rolling, Rolling for nonresidents. Notification: continuous, continuous for nonresidents. Transfer credits accepted: Yes.

Costs Per Year: State resident tuition: $4200 full-time, $140 per credit hour part-time. Nonresident tuition: $8400 full-time, $280 per credit hour part-time. Mandatory fees: $1320 full-time, $52.25 per credit hour part-time. Full-time tuition and fees vary according to course level and course load. Part-time tuition and fees vary according to course level and course load. College room and board: $5960. College room only: $2880. Room and board charges vary according to board plan and housing facility.

Collegiate Environment: Orientation program. Drama-theater group, choral group, marching band, student-run newspaper, radio station. Social organizations: 110 open to all; national fraternities, national sororities, local fraternities, local sororities. Student services: health clinic, personal-psychological counseling. Campus security: 24-hour emergency response devices and patrols, student patrols, late night transport-escort service, controlled dormitory access. 1,571 college housing spaces available; 1,386 were occupied in 2012-13. Freshmen guaranteed college housing. On-campus residence required in freshman year. Option: coed housing available. U. S. Conn Library with 348,951 books, 620,128 microform titles, 45,026 serials, 19,820 audiovisual materials, an OPAC, and a Web page. 365 computers available on campus for general student use. Computer purchase/lease plans available. A campuswide network can be accessed from student residence rooms and from off campus. Students can access the following: online class registration. Staffed computer lab on campus provides training in use of computers, software, and the Internet.

Community Environment: Located 45 miles southwest of Sioux City, Iowa, Wayne is the county seat. Bus transportation and chartered air service are available. Dormitories, motels, and rooming houses provide housing for students. Community facilities include churches of most denominations and a hospital. Hunting, swimming and golf are some of the outdoor activities available.

■ **WESTERN NEBRASKA COMMUNITY COLLEGE**

371 College Dr.

Sidney, NE 69162

Tel: (308)254-5450; Free: 800-222-9682

Fax: (308)254-7444

E-mail: rhovey@wncc.net

Web Site: www.wncc.net/

Description: State and locally supported, 2-year, coed. Part of Western Community College Area System. Awards certificates, diplomas, transfer associate, and terminal associate degrees. Founded 1926. Setting: 20-acre rural campus. Total enrollment: 2,304. Student-undergrad faculty ratio is 11:1. 17% from out-of-state. 39% 25 or older. Retention: 56% of full-time freshmen returned the following year. Core. Calendar: semesters. Academic remediation for entering students, services for LD students, advanced placement, accelerated degree program, independent study, distance learning, summer session for credit, part-time degree program, adult/continuing education programs, co-op programs and internships.

Entrance Requirements: Open admission. Option: electronic application. Recommended: high school transcript. Entrance: noncompetitive. Application deadline: Rolling. Notification: continuous until 8/21.

Collegiate Environment: Orientation program. Drama-theater group, choral group, student-run newspaper. Social organizations: national sororities. Student services: personal-psychological counseling. Campus security: 24-hour emergency response devices and patrols, late night transport-escort service, controlled dormitory access, patrols by trained security personnel from 12:30 am to 6 am. Western Nebraska Community College Library with an OPAC.

Community Environment: In the valley of the North Platte River, Scottsbluff is an agriculture center. It is also called the Capital of America's Valley of the Nile. This is the location of the largest continuous area of irrigated land in the country. Recreational activities include hunting, fishing, golf, swimming and winter sports nearby.

■ **YORK COLLEGE**

1125 E 8th St.

York, NE 68467

Tel: (402)363-5600; Free: 800-950-9675

Fax: (402)363-5666

E-mail: enroll@york.edu

Web Site: www.york.edu/

Description: Independent, 4-year, coed, affiliated with Church of Christ. Awards associate and bachelor's degrees. Founded 1890. Setting: 44-acre small town campus. Endowment: $5.9 million. Educational spending for the previous fiscal year: $4440 per student. Total enrollment: 430. Faculty: 38 (22 full-time, 16 part-time). Student-undergrad faculty ratio is 11:1. 485 applied, 60% were admitted. 9% from top 10% of their high school class, 24% from top quarter, 47% from top half. 2 valedictorians. Full-time: 416 students, 44% women, 56% men. Part-time: 14 students, 64% women, 36% men. Students come from 23 states and territories, 4 other countries, 70% from out-of-state. 5% 25 or older, 80% live on campus, 14% transferred in. Retention: 58% of full-time freshmen returned the following year. Academic areas with the most degrees conferred: education; psychology; business/marketing. Core. Calendar: semesters. Academic remediation for entering students, services for LD students, advanced placement, honors program, independent study, double major, summer session for credit, part-time degree program, co-op programs and internships. Study abroad program. ROTC: Army (c), Naval (c), Air Force (c).

Entrance Requirements: Options: electronic application, early admission, deferred admission, international baccalaureate accepted. Required: high school transcript, minimum 2 high school GPA, SAT or ACT. Required for some; 1 recommendation. Entrance: moderately difficult. Application deadline: Rolling. Notification: continuous. SAT Reasoning Test deadline: 8/1. Transfer credits accepted: Yes.

Costs Per Year: Application fee: $20. Comprehensive fee: $21,800 includes full-time tuition ($13,760), mandatory fees ($1840), and college room and board ($6200). Full-time tuition and fees vary according to course load. Room and board charges vary according to board plan and housing facility. Part-time tuition: $550 per credit hour. Part-time mandatory fees: $60 per credit hour. Part-time tuition and fees vary according to course load.

Collegiate Environment: Orientation program. Drama-theater group, choral group, student-run newspaper. Social organizations: 8 open to all; local fraternities, local sororities; 46% of eligible men and 64% of eligible women are members. Most popular organizations: concert choir, Student Association, Promethians, Marksmen. Major annual events: Homecoming, Songfest, All-School Banquet. Student services: personal-psychological counseling. Campus security: 24-hour patrols, student patrols, controlled dormitory access. Levitt Library with 134,738 books, 292 serials, 2,566 audiovisual materials, an OPAC, and a Web page. Operations spending for the previous fiscal year: $240,236. 57 computers available on campus for general student use. A campuswide network can be accessed from student residence rooms and from off campus. Staffed computer lab on campus provides training in use of computers, software, and the Internet.

Community Environment: York is located about 50 miles from Lincoln, where all forms of commercial transportation are available. Various civic and service organizations are active here as well as churches of many denominations. Recreational facilities include parks, playgrounds, a swimming pool, baseball park, basketball courts, and a community center.

■ ANTHEM INSTITUTE–LAS VEGAS

2320 S Rancho Dr.

Las Vegas, NV 89102

Tel: (702)385-6700; Free: 855-331-7762

Fax: (702)388-4463

Web Site: anthem.edu/las-vegas-nevada/

Description: Proprietary, 2-year, coed. Awards terminal associate degrees. Founded 2002. Total enrollment: 589. Calendar: semesters.

Entrance Requirements: Entrance: noncompetitive.

■ THE ART INSTITUTE OF LAS VEGAS

2350 Corporate Cir. Dr.

Henderson, NV 89074

Tel: (702)369-9944; Free: 800-833-2678

Fax: (702)992-8558

Web Site: www.artinstitutes.edu/lasvegas/

Description: Proprietary, 4-year, coed. Part of Education Management Corporation. Awards associate and bachelor's degrees. Founded 2002. Setting: suburban campus.

■ CAREER COLLEGE OF NORTHERN NEVADA

1421 Pullman Dr.

Sparks, NV 89434

Tel: (775)856-2266

E-mail: lgoldhammer@ccnn4u.com

Web Site: www.ccnn.edu/

Description: Proprietary, 2-year, coed. Awards diplomas and terminal associate degrees. Founded 1984. Setting: 1-acre urban campus. Total enrollment: 363. Faculty: 23 (11 full-time, 12 part-time). Student-undergrad faculty ratio is 20:1. 419 applied, 100% were admitted. Students come from 3 states and territories, 2 other countries, 3% from out-of-state. 70% 25 or older. Retention: 51% of full-time freshmen returned the following year. Core. Calendar: six-week terms. Academic remediation for entering students, accelerated degree program, double major, summer session for credit, co-op programs and internships.

Entrance Requirements: Open admission. Required: essay, high school transcript, interview. Entrance: noncompetitive. Application deadline: Rolling. Notification: continuous.

Collegiate Environment: Orientation program. Student-run newspaper. Major annual events: Annual School Picnic, Christmas Party. Campus security: 24-hour emergency response devices. 380 books and 7 serialsOperations spending for the previous fiscal year: $7000. 120 computers available on campus for general student use. A campuswide network can be accessed. Staffed computer lab on campus.

■ CARRINGTON COLLEGE–LAS VEGAS

5740 S Eastern Ave.

Las Vegas, NV 89119

Tel: (702)688-4300

Web Site: carrington.edu/

Description: Proprietary, 2-year, coed. Part of Carrington Colleges Group, Inc. Awards certificates and terminal associate degrees. Total enrollment: 182. Faculty: 15 (6 full-time, 9 part-time). Student-undergrad faculty ratio is 20:1. Full-time: 182 students, 61% women, 39% men. 1% American Indian or Alaska Native, non-Hispanic/Latino; 13% Hispanic/Latino; 15% African American, non-Hispanic/Latino; 21% Asian, non-Hispanic/Latino; 8% Native Hawaiian or other Pacific Islander, non-Hispanic/Latino; 0% international. 68% 25 or older.

Entrance Requirements: Required: essay, high school transcript, interview, Entrance test administered by Carrington College.

Collegiate Environment: College housing not available.

■ CARRINGTON COLLEGE–RENO

5580 Kietzke Ln.

Reno, NV 89511

Tel: (775)335-2900

E-mail: mcomo@carrington.edu

Web Site: carrington.edu/

Description: Proprietary, 2-year, coed. Part of Carrington Colleges Group, Inc. Awards terminal associate degrees. Total enrollment: 315. Faculty: 32 (18 full-time, 14 part-time). Student-undergrad faculty ratio is 14:1. Full-time: 315 students, 84% women, 16% men. 1% American Indian or Alaska Native, non-Hispanic/Latino; 12% Hispanic/Latino; 2% African American, non-Hispanic/Latino; 3% Asian, non-Hispanic/Latino; 1% Native Hawaiian or other Pacific Islander, non-Hispanic/Latino; 0% international. 69% 25 or older.

Entrance Requirements: Required: essay, high school transcript, interview, Entrance test administered by Carrington College.

Collegiate Environment: College housing not available.

■ COLLEGE OF SOUTHERN NEVADA

3200 E Cheyenne Ave.

North Las Vegas, NV 89030-4296

Tel: (702)651-4000

Fax: (702)643-6243

Web Site: www.csn.edu/

Description: State-supported, primarily 2-year, coed. Part of University and Community College System of Nevada. Awards certificates, transfer associate, and bachelor's degrees. Founded 1971. Setting: 89-acre suburban campus with easy access to Las Vegas. Core. Calendar: semesters. Academic remediation for entering students, ESL program, services for LD students, advanced placement, accelerated degree program, honors program, independent study, distance learning, double major, summer session for credit, part-time degree program, adult/continuing education programs, co-op programs and internships. ROTC: Army.

Entrance Requirements: Open admission except for allied health programs. Option: early admission. Required: student data form. Entrance: noncompetitive. Application deadline: Rolling.

Collegiate Environment: Orientation program. Drama-theater group, choral group, student-run newspaper. Student services: legal services, health clinic, personal-psychological counseling, women's center. Campus security: 24-hour emergency response devices and patrols. Learning Assistance Center with an OPAC and a Web page.

Community Environment: See University of Nevada - Las Vegas.

■ DEVRY UNIVERSITY

2490 Paseo Verde Pky.

Henderson, NV 89074-7120

Tel: (702)933-9700; Free: 866-338-7941

Fax: (702)933-9717

Web Site: www.devry.edu/

Description: Proprietary, comprehensive, coed. Part of DeVry University. Awards associate, bachelor's, and master's degrees. Total enrollment: 373. Faculty: 29 (2 full-time, 27 part-time). Student-undergrad faculty ratio is 20:1. Full-time: 139 students, 37% women, 63% men. Part-time: 144 students, 46% women, 54% men. 3% from out-of-state. 70% 25 or older, 27% transferred in. Academic area with the most degrees conferred: business/marketing. Calendar: semesters. Academic remediation for entering students, services for LD students, advanced placement, accelerated degree program, distance learning, summer session for credit, part-time degree program, adult/continuing education programs.

Entrance Requirements: Options: electronic application, deferred admission, international baccalaureate accepted. Required: high school transcript, interview. Entrance: minimally difficult. Application deadline: Rolling. Notification: continuous. SAT Reasoning Test deadline: 10/31.

Collegiate Environment: Orientation program.

■ **EVEREST COLLEGE**

170 N Stephanie St., 1st Fl.
Henderson, NV 89074
Tel: (702)567-1920; Free: 888-741-4270
Web Site: www.everest.edu/

Description: Proprietary, 2-year, coed. Awards terminal associate degrees. Total enrollment: 639. 212 applied. 59% 25 or older.

■ **GREAT BASIN COLLEGE**

1500 College Pky.
Elko, NV 89801-3348
Tel: (775)738-8493
E-mail: janicek@gwmail.gbcnv.edu
Web Site: www.gbcnv.edu/

Description: State-supported, primarily 2-year, coed. Part of University and Community College System of Nevada. Awards certificates, transfer associate, terminal associate, and bachelor's degrees. Founded 1967. Setting: 45-acre small town campus. Endowment: $187,761. Educational spending for the previous fiscal year: $6483 per student. Total enrollment: 3,691. Faculty: 241 (64 full-time, 177 part-time). Student-undergrad faculty ratio is 15:1. Full-time: 1,141 students, 64% women, 36% men. Part-time: 2,550 students, 67% women, 33% men. Students come from 13 states and territories, 3% from out-of-state. 54% 25 or older, 5% live on campus. Retention: 77% of full-time freshmen returned the following year. Academic areas with the most degrees conferred: education; business/marketing; health professions and related sciences. Core. Calendar: semesters. Academic remediation for entering students, ESL program, services for LD students, accelerated degree program, independent study, distance learning, double major, summer session for credit, part-time degree program, external degree program, adult/continuing education programs, co-op programs. Off campus study at UNR/GBC Social Work Program.

Entrance Requirements: Open admission except for nursing program. Options: electronic application, early admission, deferred admission. Entrance: noncompetitive. Application deadlines: Rolling, Rolling for nonresidents. Notification: continuous, continuous for nonresidents. Transfer credits accepted: Yes.

Collegiate Environment: Orientation program. Social organizations: 21 open to all. Most popular organizations: Student Nurses Organization, Housing Central, Skills USA, Agriculture Student Organization, Colleges Against Cancer. Major annual events: Red Ribbon Week- Drug and Alcohol Awareness Week, Love your Body Week- Wellness Week, Halloween Costume Party. Student services: personal-psychological counseling. Campus security: late night transport-escort service, evening patrols by trained security personnel. Learning Resource Center with 113,341 books, 3,714 microform titles, 142 serials, 1,852 audiovisual materials, and an OPAC. Operations spending for the previous fiscal year: $349,787. 95 computers available on campus for general student use. A campuswide network can be accessed from student residence rooms and from off campus. Students can access the following: online class registration. Staffed computer lab on campus provides training in use of computers, software, and the Internet.

Community Environment: Primarily involved in mining, ranching, and government business, Elko is the largest city in Elko County and is at the heart of the nation's finest hunting and fishing areas, along with such historic landmarks as old ghost towns and deserted mining camps. Located at the base of the Ruby Mountains, Elko is also near Jarbidge Wilderness area and Great Basin National Park.

■ **ITT TECHNICAL INSTITUTE (HENDERSON)**

168 N Gibson Rd.
Henderson, NV 89014
Tel: (702)558-5404; Free: 800-488-8459
Web Site: www.itt-tech.edu/

Description: Proprietary, primarily 2-year, coed. Part of ITT Educational Services, Inc. Awards terminal associate and bachelor's degrees. Founded 1997.

Entrance Requirements: Entrance: minimally difficult.

■ **ITT TECHNICAL INSTITUTE (NORTH LAS VEGAS)**

3825 W Cheyenne Ave.
Ste. 600
North Las Vegas, NV 89032
Tel: (702)240-0967; Free: 877-832-8442
Web Site: www.itt-tech.edu/

Description: Proprietary, primarily 2-year, coed. Part of ITT Educational Services, Inc. Awards terminal associate and bachelor's degrees.

■ **KAPLAN COLLEGE, LAS VEGAS CAMPUS**

3535 W Sahara Ave.
Las Vegas, NV 89102
Tel: (702)368-2338; Free: 800-935-1857
Fax: (702)638-3853
Web Site: las-vegas.kaplancollege.com/

Description: Proprietary, 2-year, coed. Awards diplomas and terminal associate degrees. Founded 1990.

■ **LE CORDON BLEU COLLEGE OF CULINARY ARTS, LAS VEGAS**

1451 Ctr. Crossing Rd.
Las Vegas, NV 89144
Tel: (702)365-7690; Free: 888-551-8222
Fax: (702)365-7911
Web Site: www.vegasculinary.com/

Description: Proprietary, 2-year, coed. Awards terminal associate degrees. Founded 2003. Total enrollment: 892.

Entrance Requirements: Entrance: noncompetitive.

■ **MORRISON UNIVERSITY**

10315 Professional Cir.
Reno, NV 89521
Tel: (775)850-0700; Free: 866-381-6050
Fax: (775)850-0711
E-mail: ctiminsky@morrison.neumont.edu
Web Site: anthem.edu/morrison/

Description: Proprietary, comprehensive, coed. Awards associate, bachelor's, and master's degrees. Founded 1902. Setting: 2-acre urban campus. Total enrollment: 136. Faculty: 25 (15 full-time, 10 part-time). 10% from top 10% of their high school class, 60% from top quarter, 90% from top half. Full-time: 52 students, 56% women, 44% men. Part-time: 62 students, 50% women, 50% men. Students come from 8 states and territories, 5 other countries. 74% 25 or older, 61% transferred in. Retention: 73% of full-time freshmen returned the following year. Core. Calendar: 5 sessions per year. Academic remediation for entering students, ESL program, accelerated degree program, summer session for credit, part-time degree program, adult/continuing education programs, internships.

Entrance Requirements: Open admission. Options: early admission, deferred admission. Required: high school transcript, interview. Recommended: CPAt of 160 for paralegal program. Required for some: essay. Entrance: noncompetitive. Notification: continuous.

Collegiate Environment: Student-run newspaper. Social organizations: 1 open to all; national fraternities, national sororities; 25% of eligible men and 35% of eligible women are members. Most popular organization: Phi Beta Lambda. Major annual events: Summer Picnic, Christmas Party, Holiday Potlucks. Student services: personal-psychological counseling. Campus security: 24-hour emergency response devices, late night transport-escort service, evening patrols by security. Morrison College Library with 6,000 books and 20 serials. 50 computers available on campus for general student use. A campuswide network can be accessed. Staffed computer lab on campus.

■ **NEVADA STATE COLLEGE AT HENDERSON**

1125 Nevada State Dr.
Henderson, NV 89015

Tel: (702)992-2000
Fax: (702)992-2226
E-mail: admissions@nsc.nevada.edu
Web Site: www.nsc.nevada.edu/
Description: State-supported, 4-year, coed. Part of Nevada System of Higher Education. Awards bachelor's degrees. Founded 2002. Setting: 520-acre suburban campus with easy access to Las Vegas. Educational spending for the previous fiscal year: $2000 per student. Total enrollment: 2,988. Faculty: 94 (46 full-time, 48 part-time). Student-undergrad faculty ratio is 28:1. 652 applied, 82% were admitted. 8% from top 10% of their high school class, 30% from top quarter, 63% from top half. Full-time: 1,131 students, 76% women, 24% men. Part-time: 1,857 students, 75% women, 25% men. Students come from 14 states and territories, 1 other country, 7% from out-of-state. 1% American Indian or Alaska Native, non-Hispanic/Latino; 20% Hispanic/Latino; 12% African American, non-Hispanic/Latino; 11% Asian, non-Hispanic/Latino; 2% Native Hawaiian or other Pacific Islander, non-Hispanic/Latino; 0.3% international. 48% 25 or older, 19% transferred in. Retention: 65% of full-time freshmen returned the following year. Academic areas with the most degrees conferred: health professions and related sciences; education; business/marketing. Core. Calendar: semesters. Academic remediation for entering students, services for LD students, advanced placement, accelerated degree program, self-designed majors, independent study, distance learning, double major, summer session for credit, part-time degree program, adult/continuing education programs, co-op programs and internships. ROTC: Army (c).
Entrance Requirements: Option: electronic application. Required: high school transcript, minimum 2 high school GPA. Entrance: minimally difficult. Application deadline: Rolling. Notification: continuous. Transfer credits accepted: Yes.
Collegiate Environment: Orientation program. Student-run newspaper. Social organizations: 10 open to all. Most popular organizations: Nevada State Student Alliance (Student Government), Pre-Professional Club, American Sign Language Club, Student Nurses Association, Circle K International. Major annual events: Welcome Back Events, Halloween Event, Annual Spring Luau. Campus security: private contracted security patrols. Nevada State College Library plus 1 other with 16,016 books, 47 serials, 525 audiovisual materials, an OPAC, and a Web page. Operations spending for the previous fiscal year: $524,703. 136 computers available on campus for general student use. A campuswide network can be accessed from off-campus. Students can access the following: online class registration. Staffed computer lab on campus provides training in use of computers, software, and the Internet.

■ **PIMA MEDICAL INSTITUTE**
3333 E Flamingo Rd.
Las Vegas, NV 89121
Tel: (702)458-9650; Free: 800-477-PIMA
Web Site: www.pmi.edu/
Description: Proprietary, primarily 2-year, coed. Part of Vocational Training Institutes, Inc. Awards certificates, terminal associate, and bachelor's degrees. Founded 2003. Setting: urban campus. Total enrollment: 820. 57% 25 or older. Core. Calendar: modular. Advanced placement, distance learning, internships.
Entrance Requirements: Required: interview, Wonderlic Scholastic Level Exam (SLE). Required for some: essay, high school transcript. Entrance: moderately difficult.
Collegiate Environment: Orientation program.

■ **SIERRA NEVADA COLLEGE**
999 Tahoe Blvd.
Incline Village, NV 89451
Tel: (775)831-1314
Fax: (775)831-1347
E-mail: admissions@sierranevada.edu
Web Site: www.sierranevada.edu/
Description: Independent, comprehensive, coed. Awards bachelor's and master's degrees. Founded 1969. Setting: 20-acre small town campus with easy access to Reno. Endowment: $4.1 million. Educational spending for the previous fiscal year: $10,295 per student. Total enrollment: 925. Faculty: 127 (34 full-time, 93 part-time). Student-undergrad faculty ratio is 11:1. 709 applied, 69% were admitted. Full-time: 515 students, 42% women, 58% men. Part-time: 21 students, 38% women, 62% men. Students come from 34 states and territories, 12 other countries, 84% from out-of-state. 2% American Indian or Alaska Native, non-Hispanic/Latino; 2% Hispanic/Latino;

2% African American, non-Hispanic/Latino; 2% Asian, non-Hispanic/Latino; 0.4% Native Hawaiian or other Pacific Islander, non-Hispanic/Latino; 9% international. 15% 25 or older, 52% live on campus, 14% transferred in. Retention: 79% of full-time freshmen returned the following year. Academic areas with the most degrees conferred: business/marketing; interdisciplinary studies; visual and performing arts. Core. Calendar: semesters. Academic remediation for entering students, ESL program, services for LD students, advanced placement, accelerated degree program, self-designed majors, honors program, independent study, double major, summer session for credit, part-time degree program, external degree program, adult/continuing education programs, co-op programs and internships, graduate courses open to undergrads. Study abroad program.
Entrance Requirements: Options: electronic application, deferred admission, international baccalaureate accepted. Required: essay, high school transcript, minimum 2.6 high school GPA, SAT or ACT. Recommended: interview. Required for some: 1 recommendation. Entrance: moderately difficult. Application deadline: Rolling. Notification: continuous. SAT Reasoning Test deadline: 8/19. Transfer credits accepted: Yes.
Costs Per Year: Application fee: $0. Comprehensive fee: $40,255 includes full-time tuition ($27,753), mandatory fees ($730), and college room and board ($11,772). College room only: $5900. Full-time tuition and fees vary according to degree level and location. Room and board charges vary according to board plan. Part-time tuition: $1180 per credit. Part-time tuition varies according to degree level and location.
Collegiate Environment: Orientation program. Choral group, student-run newspaper. Social organizations: 15 open to all; 15% of eligible men and 21% of eligible women are members. Most popular organizations: Film Club, International Club, Sustainability Club, Rock Climbing Club, First Generation Club. Major annual events: Spring Formal, Bohemia Night, Casino Night. Campus security: 24-hour emergency response devices and patrols, controlled dormitory access. 168 college housing spaces available; all were occupied in 2012-13. Freshmen guaranteed college housing. On-campus residence required through sophomore year. Option: coed housing available. Prim Library with 40,845 books, 224 serials, an OPAC, and a Web page. Operations spending for the previous fiscal year: $292,006. 50 computers available on campus for general student use. A computer is required for all students. A campuswide network can be accessed from student residence rooms and from off campus. Staffed computer lab on campus provides training in use of computers, software, and the Internet.

■ **TRUCKEE MEADOWS COMMUNITY COLLEGE**
7000 Dandini Blvd.
Reno, NV 89512-3901
Tel: (775)673-7000
Fax: (775)673-7028
E-mail: mbuckheart@tmcc.edu
Web Site: www.tmcc.edu/
Description: State-supported, 2-year, coed. Part of Nevada System of Higher Education. Awards certificates, transfer associate, and terminal associate degrees. Founded 1971. Setting: 63-acre suburban campus. Endowment: $9 million. Educational spending for the previous fiscal year: $3895 per student. Total enrollment: 12,587. Faculty: 593 (179 full-time, 414 part-time). Student-undergrad faculty ratio is 22:1. 3,666 applied, 100% were admitted. Full-time: 3,530 students, 54% women, 46% men. Part-time: 9,057 students, 57% women, 43% men. Students come from 18 states and territories, 7% from out-of-state. 2% American Indian or Alaska Native, non-Hispanic/Latino; 19% Hispanic/Latino; 3% African American, non-Hispanic/Latino; 5% Asian, non-Hispanic/Latino; 1% Native Hawaiian or other Pacific Islander, non-Hispanic/Latino; 1% international. 43% 25 or older, 5% transferred in. Retention: 62% of full-time freshmen returned the following year. Calendar: semesters. Academic remediation for entering students, ESL program, services for LD students, advanced placement, accelerated degree program, distance learning, summer session for credit, part-time degree program, adult/continuing education programs. ROTC: Army (c).
Entrance Requirements: Open admission except for allied health programs. Options: early admission, deferred admission. Entrance: noncompetitive. Application deadlines: 8/3, 8/3 for nonresidents. Notification: 3/1, 3/1 for nonresidents. Transfer credits accepted: Yes.
Costs Per Year: Application fee: $10. State resident tuition: $2265 full-time, $75.50 per credit part-time. Nonresident tuition: $8910 full-time, $158.50 per credit part-time. Mandatory fees: $445 full-time, $14.50 per credit part-time. Full-time tuition and fees vary according to course load and program. Part-time tuition and fees vary according to course load and program.
Collegiate Environment: Orientation program. Drama-theater group. Social

organizations: 3 open to all. Major annual events: Commencement, Welcome Back Fair, Spring Fling. Student services: personal-psychological counseling. Campus security: 24-hour emergency response devices and patrols, late night transport-escort service. Elizabeth Storm Library with an OPAC and a Web page. Operations spending for the previous fiscal year: $971,000.

Community Environment: Reno/Sparks, cities of approximately 240,000, are bounded on the west by the majestic Sierra Nevada, and on the east by the rolling basin and range province. The climate is cool and dry, and is marked by the full pageant of the seasons. A mixture of metropolitan and quietly provincial, the area is noted on the one hand for its fashionable hotels and tourist attractions, and on the other for its beautiful parks, which line the Truckee River, and its modern residential areas. Recreational activities abound, both in Reno and its environs. Within a one-hour drive of the campus are the Lake Tahoe resort area in the high Sierra, and the unique prehistoric desert sea, Pyramid Lake. The adjoining Sierra is also the site of a number of nationally famed ski areas, including Squaw Valley, site of the 1960 Winter Olympics. Other scenic attractions include Virginia City, setting for one of the West's richest mining bonanzas, and Genoa, the state's first pioneer settlement.

■ **UNIVERSITY OF NEVADA, LAS VEGAS**

4505 S Maryland Pky.
Las Vegas, NV 89154
Tel: (702)895-3011
Fax: (702)895-1118
E-mail: admissions@unlv.edu
Web Site: www.unlv.edu/

Description: State-supported, university, coed. Part of Nevada System of Higher Education. Awards bachelor's, master's, and doctoral degrees and post-master's certificates. Founded 1957. Setting: urban campus. Total enrollment: 27,402. Student-undergrad faculty ratio is 21:1. 6,366 applied, 81% were admitted. 23% from top 10% of their high school class, 54% from top quarter, 86% from top half. Full-time: 15,885 students, 55% women, 45% men. Part-time: 6,547 students, 55% women, 45% men. 14% from out-of-state. 0.4% American Indian or Alaska Native, non-Hispanic/Latino; 21% Hispanic/Latino; 8% African American, non-Hispanic/Latino; 16% Asian, non-Hispanic/Latino; 2% Native Hawaiian or other Pacific Islander, non-Hispanic/Latino; 4% international. 24% 25 or older, 5% live on campus, 10% transferred in. Retention: 76% of full-time freshmen returned the following year. Academic areas with the most degrees conferred: business/marketing; psychology; social sciences. Core. Calendar: semesters. Academic remediation for entering students, ESL program, services for LD students, advanced placement, honors program, independent study, distance learning, double major, summer session for credit, part-time degree program, adult/continuing education programs, co-op programs and internships, graduate courses open to undergrads. Study abroad program. ROTC: Army, Air Force.

Entrance Requirements: Options: electronic application, early admission, deferred admission, international baccalaureate accepted. Required: high school transcript, minimum 3 high school GPA, SAT or ACT. Required for some: 2 recommendations. Entrance: moderately difficult. Application deadline: 7/1. Notification: continuous.

Costs Per Year: Application fee: $60. State resident tuition: $6,089 full-time, $191.50 per credit hour part-time. Nonresident tuition: $19,999 full-time, $402.25 per credit hour part-time. Mandatory fees: $496 full-time. Full-time tuition and fees vary according to course level, program, and reciprocity agreements. Part-time tuition varies according to course level, program, and reciprocity agreements. College room and board: $10,524. College room only: $5880. Room and board charges vary according to board plan.

Collegiate Environment: Orientation program. Drama-theater group, choral group, marching band, student-run newspaper, radio station. Social organizations: national fraternities, national sororities, local fraternities, local sororities. Student services: legal services, health clinic, personal-psychological counseling, women's center. Campus security: 24-hour emergency response devices and patrols, late night transport-escort service, controlled dormitory access. Freshmen given priority for college housing. Option: coed housing available.

Community Environment: Situated in southeast Nevada, Las Vegas is a great vacation and convention center located near Lake Mead and the mountains. Las Vegas is one of the fastest growing cities in the United States; some 1.3 million people live in southern Nevada. Community facilities include churches of most denominations, hospitals and clinics, and good shopping centers. The hotels feature some of the best entertainers in America. Nearby Charleston Peak provides expert ski runs and other snow sports facilities.

■ **UNIVERSITY OF NEVADA, RENO**

Reno, NV 89557
Tel: (775)784-1110; Free: 866-263-8232
E-mail: asknevada@unr.edu
Web Site: www.unr.edu/

Description: State-supported, university, coed. Part of Nevada System of Higher Education. Awards associate, bachelor's, master's, and doctoral degrees and post-master's certificates. Founded 1874. Setting: 200-acre urban campus. Total enrollment: 18,227. Faculty: 566 (546 full-time, 20 part-time). Student-undergrad faculty ratio is 29:1. 7,753 applied, 83% were admitted. 27% from top 10% of their high school class, 54% from top quarter, 82% from top half. Full-time: 12,415 students, 53% women, 47% men. Part-time: 2,667 students, 52% women, 48% men. Students come from 46 states and territories, 39 other countries, 21% from out-of-state. 1% American Indian or Alaska Native, non-Hispanic/Latino; 15% Hispanic/Latino; 4% African American, non-Hispanic/Latino; 6% Asian, non-Hispanic/Latino; 0.4% Native Hawaiian or other Pacific Islander, non-Hispanic/Latino; 2% international. 16% 25 or older, 14% live on campus, 7% transferred in. Retention: 79% of full-time freshmen returned the following year. Academic areas with the most degrees conferred: health professions and related sciences; social sciences; business/marketing. Core. Calendar: semesters. Academic remediation for entering students, ESL program, services for LD students, advanced placement, honors program, independent study, distance learning, double major, summer session for credit, part-time degree program, adult/continuing education programs, internships, graduate courses open to undergrads. Off campus study at National Student Exchange. Study abroad program. ROTC: Army.

Entrance Requirements: Options: electronic application, early admission, deferred admission, international baccalaureate accepted. Required: high school transcript, minimum 3 high school GPA, SAT or ACT. Entrance: moderately difficult. Application deadline: 5/31. Notification: continuous. SAT Reasoning Test deadline: 5/31.

Costs Per Year: Application fee: $60. State resident tuition: $5745 full-time, $191.50 per credit hour part-time. Nonresident tuition: $19,655 full-time, $402.50 per credit hour part-time. Mandatory fees: $620 full-time. Full-time tuition and fees vary according to course level, course load, degree level, and program. Part-time tuition varies according to course level, course load, degree level, and program. College room and board: $9518. Room and board charges vary according to board plan and housing facility.

Collegiate Environment: Orientation program. Drama-theater group, choral group, marching band, student-run newspaper, radio station. Social organizations: national fraternities, national sororities; 7% of eligible men and 8% of eligible women are members. Most popular organizations: Intervarsity Christian Fellowship, Student Ambassadors, Young Democrats, Asian American Association, Blue Crew. Major annual events: Homecoming, MacKay Days, Night of All Nations. Student services: legal services, health clinic, personal-psychological counseling, women's center. Campus security: 24-hour emergency response devices and patrols, late night transport-escort service, controlled dormitory access. 2,162 college housing spaces available; all were occupied in 2012-13. Freshmen given priority for college housing. Options: coed, men-only, women-only housing available. Mathewson-IGT Knowledge Center plus 2 others with 1.2 million books, 1.1 million microform titles, 25,360 serials, 20,814 audiovisual materials, an OPAC, and a Web page. 725 computers available on campus for general student use. Computer purchase/lease plans available. A campuswide network can be accessed from student residence rooms and from off campus. Students can access the following: online class registration. Staffed computer lab on campus provides training in use of computers, software, and the Internet.

Community Environment: When Reno was laid out as a townsite in 1868, it was named in honor of Major General Jesse L. Reno, who died in the Battle of the South Mountain during the Civil War. Reno is situated on the Truckee River near the base of the Sierra Nevada and has a cool, dry climate. Mining, livestock raising, lumber products, agriculture and tourism are the important industries of the area. Part-time employment is available. The city has a number of parks with facilities for swimming, tennis and picnicking; within a 25 to 90 minute drive from Reno, winter sports are available at a number of major resorts. Annual events are the Reno Rodeo, Reno Balloon Race, Air Races, and Holiday Festival of Trees.

■ **UNIVERSITY OF PHOENIX–LAS VEGAS CAMPUS**

7455 Washington Ave.
Ste. 317
Las Vegas, NV 89128
Tel: (702)638-7279; Free: 866-766-0766

Fax: (702)638-8035
Web Site: www.phoenix.edu/
Description: Proprietary, comprehensive, coed. Awards associate, bachelor's, and master's degrees and post-master's certificates. Founded 1994. Setting: urban campus. Total enrollment: 3,162. Faculty: 279 (35 full-time, 244 part-time). Full-time: 2,301 students, 67% women, 33% men. 83% 25 or older. Retention: 38% of full-time freshmen returned the following year. Academic areas with the most degrees conferred: business/marketing; computer and information sciences; homeland security, law enforcement, firefighting, and protective services. Core. Calendar: continuous. Services for LD students, advanced placement, accelerated degree program, independent study, distance learning, external degree program, adult/continuing education programs, graduate courses open to undergrads.
Entrance Requirements: Open admission. Options: electronic application, deferred admission. Required: 1 recommendation. Required for some: high school transcript. Entrance: noncompetitive. Application deadline: Rolling.
Collegiate Environment: Campus security: late night transport-escort service. University Library with 16,781 serials, an OPAC, and a Web page. Operations spending for the previous fiscal year: $6.8 million.

■ **UNIVERSITY OF PHOENIX–NORTHERN NEVADA CAMPUS**
10345 Professional Cir.
Ste. 200
Reno, NV 89521-5862
Tel: (775)828-7999; Free: 866-766-0766
Web Site: www.phoenix.edu/
Description: Proprietary, comprehensive, coed. Awards associate, bachelor's, and master's degrees. Total enrollment: 605. Faculty: 130 (24 full-time, 106 part-time). Full-time: 401 students, 63% women, 37% men. 87% 25 or older. Academic areas with the most degrees conferred: business/marketing; computer and information sciences; interdisciplinary studies. Core. Graduate courses open to undergrads.

Entrance Requirements: Open admission. Options: electronic application, international baccalaureate accepted. Required: 1 recommendation. Required for some: high school transcript. Entrance: noncompetitive.
Collegiate Environment: University Library with 16,781 serials and an OPAC. Operations spending for the previous fiscal year: $6.8 million.

■ **WESTERN NEVADA COLLEGE**
2201 W College Pky.
Carson City, NV 89703-7316
Tel: (775)445-3000
Fax: (775)887-3141
E-mail: wncc_aro@wncc.edu
Web Site: www.wnc.edu/
Description: State-supported, primarily 2-year, coed. Part of Nevada System of Higher Education. Awards certificates, diplomas, transfer associate, terminal associate, and bachelor's degrees. Founded 1971. Setting: 200-acre small town campus. Total enrollment: 5,229. Student-undergrad faculty ratio is 18:1. 5% from out-of-state. 52% 25 or older. Core. Calendar: semesters. Academic remediation for entering students, ESL program, services for LD students, advanced placement, honors program, independent study, distance learning, summer session for credit, part-time degree program, adult/continuing education programs, co-op programs and internships.
Entrance Requirements: Open admission. Option: early admission. Required for some: high school transcript. Entrance: noncompetitive. Application deadline: Rolling.
Collegiate Environment: Orientation program. Drama-theater group, choral group. Student services: personal-psychological counseling. Campus security: late night transport-escort service. Western Nevada Community College Library and Media Services with an OPAC and a Web page.
Community Environment: Carson City (pop. 56,062), the Capital of Nevada, is located near scenic Lake Tahoe and the Carson River. It is an agricultural region formerly important for silver production.

■ COLBY-SAWYER COLLEGE

541 Main St.
New London, NH 03257
Tel: (603)526-3000; Free: 800-272-1015
Fax: (603)526-3452
E-mail: admissions@colby-sawyer.edu
Web Site: www.colby-sawyer.edu/
Description: Independent, 4-year, coed. Awards associate and bachelor's degrees. Founded 1837. Setting: 200-acre small town campus. Endowment: $28.2 million. Educational spending for the previous fiscal year: $7279 per student. Total enrollment: 948. Faculty: 127 (60 full-time, 67 part-time). Student-undergrad faculty ratio is 11:1. 1,672 applied, 87% were admitted. Full-time: 928 students, 66% women, 34% men. Part-time: 20 students, 45% women, 55% men. Students come from 25 states and territories, 11 other countries, 68% from out-of-state. 2% 25 or older, 90% live on campus, 3% transferred in. Retention: 71% of full-time freshmen returned the following year. Academic areas with the most degrees conferred: psychology; health professions and related sciences; education; visual and performing arts; business/marketing. Core. Calendar: semesters. ESL program, services for LD students, advanced placement, accelerated degree program, honors program, independent study, double major, part-time degree program, internships. Off campus study at The New Hampshire College and University Council, American University. Study abroad program. ROTC: Army (c), Air Force (c).
Entrance Requirements: Options: electronic application, early admission, early decision, deferred admission, international baccalaureate accepted. Required: essay, high school transcript, minimum 2.0 high school GPA, 2 recommendations, minimum of 15 units of college preparatory work, SAT or ACT. Recommended: interview. Entrance: moderately difficult. Application deadlines: 4/1, 12/1 for early decision. Notification: continuous until 1/1, 12/15 for early decision.
Costs Per Year: Application fee: $45. Comprehensive fee: $47,870 includes full-time tuition ($35,810) and college room and board ($12,060).
Collegiate Environment: Orientation program. Drama-theater group, choral group, student-run newspaper, radio station. Social organizations: 40 open to all. Most popular organizations: Student Government Association, campus radio station, Alpha Chi Honor Society, Outing Club. Major annual events: Mountain Day, Spring Weekend, Hogan Games. Student services: health clinic, personal-psychological counseling. Campus security: 24-hour emergency response devices and patrols, late night transport-escort service, controlled dormitory access, awareness seminars. Susan Colgate Cleveland Library Learning Center with 93,696 books, 204,109 microform titles, 27,072 serials, 2,315 audiovisual materials, an OPAC, and a Web page. Operations spending for the previous fiscal year: $492,570. 150 computers available on campus for general student use. A campuswide network can be accessed from student residence rooms. Staffed computer lab on campus (open 24 hours a day) provides training in use of computers, software, and the Internet.
Community Environment: Located in west central New Hampshire, New London enjoys a very agreeable climate and is a summer and winter tourist haven. Lake Sunapee is ten minutes west of New London and Mount Sunapee Ski Area is approximately twenty minutes away. There are excellent stores and specialty shops along with hotels, inns and lodges that are found in a resort area. Recreation includes winter skiing, hiking, biking, and seasonal fishing in lakes and streams.

■ COLLEGE OF SAINT MARY MAGDALEN

511 Kearsarge Mountain Rd.
Warner, NH 03278
Tel: (603)456-2656; Free: 877-498-1723
Fax: (603)456-2660
E-mail: admissions@magdalen.edu
Web Site: www.magdalen.edu/
Description: Independent Roman Catholic, 4-year, coed. Awards associate and bachelor's degrees. Founded 1973. Setting: 135-acre small town campus. Total enrollment: 68. Student-undergrad faculty ratio is 11:1. 95% from out-of-state. 4% 25 or older, 100% live on campus. Retention: 86% of full-time freshmen returned the following year. Academic area with the most degrees conferred: liberal arts/general studies. Core. Calendar: semesters. Academic remediation for entering students, part-time degree program, co-op programs.
Entrance Requirements: Option: early decision. Required: essay, high school transcript, 2 recommendations, interview, medical examination form, SAT or ACT. Entrance: moderately difficult. Application deadline: Rolling.
Collegiate Environment: Orientation program. Choral group. Student services: personal-psychological counseling. Campus security: 24-hour emergency response devices, student patrols.

■ DANIEL WEBSTER COLLEGE

20 University Dr.
Nashua, NH 03063-1300
Tel: (603)577-6000; Free: 800-325-6876
Fax: (603)577-6001
E-mail: nilsson@dwc.edu
Web Site: www.dwc.edu/
Description: Independent, comprehensive, coed. Awards bachelor's and master's degrees. Founded 1965. Setting: 59-acre suburban campus with easy access to Boston. Total enrollment: 621. Faculty: 85 (23 full-time, 62 part-time). Student-undergrad faculty ratio is 13:1. 656 applied, 64% were admitted. Full-time: 544 students, 19% women, 81% men. Part-time: 59 students, 36% women, 64% men. Students come from 19 states and territories, 15 other countries, 54% from out-of-state. 0.2% American Indian or Alaska Native, non-Hispanic/Latino; 2% Hispanic/Latino; 3% African American, non-Hispanic/Latino; 1% Asian, non-Hispanic/Latino; 0.2% Native Hawaiian or other Pacific Islander, non-Hispanic/Latino; 0% international. 14% 25 or older, 51% live on campus, 10% transferred in. Retention: 58% of full-time freshmen returned the following year. Academic areas with the most degrees conferred: transportation and materials moving; business/marketing; parks and recreation; homeland security, law enforcement, firefighting, and protective services. Core. Calendar: semesters. Academic remediation for entering students, advanced placement, accelerated degree program, independent study, distance learning, double major, summer session for credit, part-time degree program, internships, graduate courses open to undergrads. Off campus study. ROTC: Army (c), Air Force (c).
Entrance Requirements: Options: electronic application, early admission, deferred admission, international baccalaureate accepted. Required: high school transcript, SAT or ACT. Recommended: interview. Entrance: moderately difficult. Application deadlines: Rolling, Rolling for nonresidents. Notification: continuous, continuous for nonresidents. Transfer credits accepted: Yes.
Costs Per Year: Application fee: $0. Comprehensive fee: $25,380 includes full-time tuition ($15,090) and college room and board ($10,290). College

room only: $5050. Full-time tuition varies according to course load. Room and board charges vary according to board plan and housing facility. Part-time tuition: $503 per credit. Part-time tuition varies according to course load.

Collegiate Environment: Orientation program. Drama-theater group. Social organizations: 15 open to all. Most popular organizations: Student Activity Board, Gaming Guild, SATCA (Student Air Traffic Controllers Association), AIAA (American Institute of Aeronautics and Astronautics), Culinary Club. Major annual events: Quest (Scavenger Hunt Game Show), Block Party, Casino Night. Student services: health clinic, personal-psychological counseling. Campus security: 24-hour emergency response devices and patrols, controlled dormitory access. 487 college housing spaces available; 294 were occupied in 2012-13. Freshmen guaranteed college housing. On-campus residence required through sophomore year. Options: coed, men-only housing available. Veterans Memorial Library with 127,324 books, 4,025 microform titles, 40,820 serials, 2,256 audiovisual materials, an OPAC, and a Web page. 50 computers available on campus for general student use. A campuswide network can be accessed from student residence rooms and from off campus. Students can access the following: online class registration. Staffed computer lab on campus provides training in use of computers, software, and the Internet.

Community Environment: See Rivier College.

■ **DARTMOUTH COLLEGE**
Hanover, NH 03755
Tel: (603)646-1110
Fax: (603)646-1216
E-mail: admissions.reply@dartmouth.edu
Web Site: www.dartmouth.edu/

Description: Independent, university, coed. Awards bachelor's, master's, and doctoral degrees. Founded 1769. Setting: 269-acre small town campus. Endowment: $3.5 billion. Research spending for the previous fiscal year: $202.7 million. Total enrollment: 6,277. Faculty: 702 (553 full-time, 149 part-time). Student-undergrad faculty ratio is 8:1. 23,110 applied, 10% were admitted. 90% from top 10% of their high school class, 100% from top half. Full-time: 4,139 students, 49% women, 51% men. Part-time: 54 students, 56% women, 44% men. Students come from 54 states and territories, 69 other countries, 96% from out-of-state. 2% American Indian or Alaska Native, non-Hispanic/Latino; 8% Hispanic/Latino; 7% African American, non-Hispanic/Latino; 14% Asian, non-Hispanic/Latino; 0.1% Native Hawaiian or other Pacific Islander, non-Hispanic/Latino; 8% international. 0% 25 or older, 85% live on campus, 0.4% transferred in. Retention: 97% of full-time freshmen returned the following year. Academic areas with the most degrees conferred: social sciences; biological/life sciences; area and ethnic studies; history. Core. Services for LD students, advanced placement, self-designed majors, honors program, independent study, double major, summer session for credit, internships, graduate courses open to undergrads. Off campus study at members of the Twelve College Exchange Program, University of California, San Diego, McGill University, Morehouse College, Spelman College, Stanford University. Study abroad program. ROTC: Army (c).

Entrance Requirements: Options: electronic application, early admission, early decision, deferred admission, international baccalaureate accepted. Required: essay, high school transcript, 2 recommendations, peer evaluation, SAT or ACT, SAT Subject Tests. Recommended: interview. Entrance: most difficult. Application deadlines: 1/1, 11/1 for early decision. Notification: 4/1, 12/15 for early decision. SAT Reasoning Test deadline: 1/1. SAT Subject Test deadline: 1/1. Applicants placed on waiting list: 1,736. Wait-listed applicants offered admission: 82. Early decision applicants: 1,801. Early decision applicants admitted: 465.

Costs Per Year: Application fee: $80. Comprehensive fee: $58,166 includes full-time tuition ($43,782), mandatory fees ($1430), and college room and board ($12,954). College room only: $7755. Full-time tuition and fees vary according to student level. Room and board charges vary according to board plan.

Collegiate Environment: Orientation program. Drama-theater group, choral group, marching band, student-run newspaper, radio station. Social organizations: 250 open to all; national fraternities, national sororities, local fraternities, local sororities; 66% of eligible men and 64% of eligible women are members. Most popular organizations: Dartmouth Student Assembly, Dartmouth Outing Club. Major annual events: Dartmouth Night/Homecoming, Winter Carnival, Green Key Weekend. Student services: health clinic, personal-psychological counseling, women's center. Campus security: 24-hour emergency response devices and patrols, student patrols, late night transport-escort service, controlled dormitory access. Freshmen guaranteed

college housing. On-campus residence required in freshman year. Option: coed housing available. Baker-Berry Library plus 9 others with 2.6 million books, 2.6 million microform titles, 6.8 million serials, an OPAC, and a Web page. Operations spending for the previous fiscal year: $9.5 million. 200 computers available on campus for general student use. Computer purchase/lease plans available. A computer is required for all students. A campuswide network can be accessed from student residence rooms and from off campus. Students can access the following: online class registration. Staffed computer lab on campus.

Community Environment: The northern New England surroundings and the small town pleasantness of Hanover are very much a part of undergraduate life. Located in the central western part of New Hampshire, Hanover is bordered by the Connecticut River dividing New Hampshire and Vermont. The rural location provides unsurpassed facilities and opportunities for all forms of outdoor recreation. Hanover provides convenient student shopping facilities, and is easily accessible to all major transportation centers in New England and New York by interstate highway, bus and commuter airline service. Boston, two hours away by car, is the nearest large metropolitan area.

■ **FRANKLIN PIERCE UNIVERSITY**
40 University Dr.
Rindge, NH 03461-0060
Tel: (603)899-4000; Free: 800-437-0048
Fax: (603)899-4372
E-mail: admissions@franklinpierce.edu
Web Site: www.franklinpierce.edu/

Description: Independent, university, coed. Awards associate, bachelor's, master's, and doctoral degrees and post-master's certificates (profile does not reflect significant enrollment at 6 continuing education sites; master's degree is only offered at these sites). Founded 1962. Setting: 1,000-acre rural campus. Endowment: $7.7 million. Educational spending for the previous fiscal year: $15,217 per student. Total enrollment: 2,267. Faculty: 315 (96 full-time, 219 part-time). Student-undergrad faculty ratio is 14:1. 3,544 applied, 85% were admitted. 8% from top 10% of their high school class, 47% from top half. 30 National Merit Scholars, 2 class presidents, 16 student government officers. Full-time: 1,497 students, 51% women, 49% men. Part-time: 240 students, 76% women, 24% men. 79% from out-of-state. 0.4% American Indian or Alaska Native, non-Hispanic/Latino; 5% Hispanic/Latino; 3% African American, non-Hispanic/Latino; 0.4% Asian, non-Hispanic/Latino; 0.1% Native Hawaiian or other Pacific Islander, non-Hispanic/Latino; 2% international. 2% 25 or older, 86% live on campus, 3% transferred in. Retention: 63% of full-time freshmen returned the following year. Academic areas with the most degrees conferred: business/marketing; health professions and related sciences; communication/journalism. Core. Calendar: differs by branch and program. Academic remediation for entering students, ESL program, services for LD students, advanced placement, accelerated degree program, self-designed majors, freshman honors college, honors program, independent study, distance learning, double major, summer session for credit, part-time degree program, external degree program, adult/continuing education programs, internships, graduate courses open to undergrads. Off campus study. Study abroad program. ROTC: Army (c), Air Force (c).

Entrance Requirements: Options: electronic application, early admission, deferred admission, international baccalaureate accepted. Required: essay, high school transcript, 1 recommendation, SAT or ACT. Recommended: minimum 2.2 high school GPA, interview. Required for some: minimum 2 high school GPA. Entrance: minimally difficult. Application deadlines: Rolling, Rolling for nonresidents. Notification: continuous, continuous for nonresidents. SAT Reasoning Test deadline: 8/31. Transfer credits accepted: Yes.

Costs Per Year: Application fee: $40. Comprehensive fee: $41,210 includes full-time tuition ($28,250), mandatory fees ($1700), and college room and board ($11,260). College room only: $6634. Full-time tuition and fees vary according to course load, degree level, location, and program. Room and board charges vary according to board plan, housing facility, and student level. Part-time tuition: $945 per credit hour. Part-time tuition varies according to course load, degree level, location, and program.

Collegiate Environment: Orientation program. Drama-theater group, choral group, student-run newspaper, radio station. Social organizations: 32 open to all. Most popular organizations: Outing Club, WFPR Radio, Student Senate, Law Club, Business Club. Major annual events: Fall Weekend, Crimson and Grey Cultural Series, Alternative Spring Break. Student services: health clinic, personal-psychological counseling. Campus security: 24-hour emergency response devices and patrols, student patrols, late night transport-escort service, controlled dormitory access. 1,443 college housing spaces available. Freshmen guaranteed college housing. On-campus residence required through senior year. Option: coed housing available. Frank S. DiPietro Library plus 1 other with 144,770 books, 26,182 microform titles, 30,093 serials, 10,312 audiovisual materials, an OPAC, and a Web page. Operations spending for the previous fiscal year: $1.1 million. 60 computers available on campus for general student use. Computer purchase/lease plans available. A campuswide network can be accessed from student residence rooms. Students can access the following: online class registration. Staffed computer lab on campus.

Community Environment: Rindge is a rural community with a temperate climate. Cathedral of the Pines, an outdoor international shrine for people of all faiths, is located here. Numerous lakes in the area provide facilities for boating and fishing. There is limited part-time work for students off campus.

■ **GRANITE STATE COLLEGE**
25 Hall St.
Concord, NH 03301
Tel: (603)228-3000; Free: 888-228-3000
Fax: (603)229-0964
E-mail: gsc.admissions@granite.edu
Web Site: www.granite.edu/
Description: State and locally supported, comprehensive, coed. Part of University System of New Hampshire. Awards associate, bachelor's, and master's degrees (offers primarily part-time degree programs; courses offered at 50 locations in New Hampshire). Founded 1972. Setting: suburban campus. Endowment: $2 million. Research spending for the previous fiscal year: $379,369. Educational spending for the previous fiscal year: $3285 per student. Total enrollment: 2,018. Faculty: 189 (5 full-time, 184 part-time). Student-undergrad faculty ratio is 11:1. 354 applied, 100% were admitted. Full-time: 879 students, 67% women, 33% men. Part-time: 858 students, 74% women, 26% men. Students come from 24 states and territories, 11% from out-of-state. 1% American Indian or Alaska Native, non-Hispanic/Latino; 2% Hispanic/Latino; 1% African American, non-Hispanic/Latino; 0.4% Asian, non-Hispanic/Latino; 0.1% international. 71% 25 or older, 16% transferred in. Retention: 75% of full-time freshmen returned the following year. Academic areas with the most degrees conferred: interdisciplinary studies; liberal arts/general studies; business/marketing. Core. Calendar: trimesters. Academic remediation for entering students, services for LD students, advanced placement, accelerated degree program, self-designed majors, independent study, distance learning, double major, summer session for credit, part-time degree program, adult/continuing education programs, co-op programs and internships, graduate courses open to undergrads. Off campus study at other units of the University System of New Hampshire and the New Hampshire College and University Council. ROTC: Army (c), Air Force (c).
Entrance Requirements: Open admission. Option: electronic application. Required for some: high school transcript, self-certify high school graduate or GED. Entrance: noncompetitive. Application deadlines: Rolling, Rolling for nonresidents. Notification: continuous, continuous for nonresidents. Transfer credits accepted: Yes.
Costs Per Year: Application fee: $0. State resident tuition: $6840 full-time, $285 per credit part-time. Nonresident tuition: $7080 full-time, $295 per credit part-time. Mandatory fees: $75 per term part-time.
Collegiate Environment: Orientation program. Social organizations: 2 open to all. Most popular organizations: Alumni Learner Association, Green Team. Campus security: UNH Alert, a system that provides emergency notifications via text and voice messages. College housing not available. GSC Library & Research Commons with 128,000 books, 40 serials, an OPAC, and a Web page. Operations spending for the previous fiscal year: $79,435. 139 computers available on campus for general student use. A campuswide network can be accessed from off-campus. Students can access the following: online class registration. Staffed computer lab on campus provides training in use of computers and the Internet.

■ **GREAT BAY COMMUNITY COLLEGE**
320 Corporate Dr.
Portsmouth, NH 03801
Tel: (603)427-7600
E-mail: askgreatbay@ccsnh.edu
Web Site: www.greatbay.edu/
Description: State-supported, 2-year, coed. Awards certificates, diplomas, transfer associate, and terminal associate degrees. Total enrollment: 1,850. Student-undergrad faculty ratio is 10:1. 4% from out-of-state. 36% 25 or older.
Entrance Requirements: Open admission. Required: high school transcript.

■ **HESSER COLLEGE, CONCORD**
16 Foundry St.
Concord, NH 03301
Tel: (603)225-9200; Free: 800-935-1824
Web Site: www.hesser.edu/
Description: Proprietary, primarily 2-year, coed. Awards diplomas, terminal associate, and bachelor's degrees.

■ **HESSER COLLEGE, MANCHESTER**
3 Sundial Ave.
Manchester, NH 03103
Tel: (603)668-6660; Free: 800-935-1824
Web Site: www.hesser.edu/
Description: Proprietary, primarily 2-year, coed. Awards diplomas, terminal associate, and bachelor's degrees. Founded 1900. Setting: urban campus. Calendar: semesters.
Community Environment: See Saint Anselm College.

■ **HESSER COLLEGE, NASHUA**
410 Amherst St.
Nashua, NH 03063
Tel: (603)883-0404; Free: 800-935-1824
Web Site: www.hesser.edu/
Description: Proprietary, primarily 2-year, coed. Awards diplomas, terminal associate, and bachelor's degrees.

■ **HESSER COLLEGE, PORTSMOUTH**
170 Commerce Way
Portsmouth, NH 03801
Tel: (603)436-5300; Free: 800-935-1824
Web Site: www.hesser.edu/
Description: Proprietary, primarily 2-year, coed. Awards diplomas, terminal associate, and bachelor's degrees.

■ **HESSER COLLEGE, SALEM**
11 Manor Pky.
Salem, NH 03079
Tel: (603)898-3480; Free: 800-935-1824
Web Site: www.hesser.edu/
Description: Proprietary, primarily 2-year, coed. Awards diplomas, terminal associate, and bachelor's degrees.

■ **KEENE STATE COLLEGE**
229 Main St.
Keene, NH 03435
Tel: (603)352-1909; Free: 800-KSC-1909
Fax: (603)358-2767
E-mail: mrichmon@keene.edu
Web Site: www.keene.edu/
Description: State-supported, comprehensive, coed. Part of University System of New Hampshire. Awards bachelor's and master's degrees and post-master's certificates. Founded 1909. Setting: 160-acre small town campus. Total enrollment: 5,060. Faculty: 464 (206 full-time, 258 part-time). Student-undergrad faculty ratio is 17:1. 6,315 applied, 78% were admitted. 5% from top 10% of their high school class, 21% from top quarter, 60% from top half. Full-time: 4,657 students, 57% women, 43% men. Part-time: 276 students, 53% women, 47% men. Students come from 29 states and territories, 4 other countries, 50% from out-of-state. 0.2% American Indian or Alaska Native, non-Hispanic/Latino; 3% Hispanic/Latino; 1% African American, non-Hispanic/Latino; 1% Asian, non-Hispanic/Latino; 0.02% Native Hawaiian or other Pacific Islander, non-Hispanic/Latino; 0.02% international. 1% 25 or older, 54% live on campus, 4% transferred in. Retention: 76% of full-time freshmen returned the following year. Academic areas with the most degrees conferred: education; psychology; social sciences. Core. Calendar: semesters. ESL program, services for LD students, advanced placement, self-designed majors, freshman honors college, honors program, independent study, double major, summer session for credit, part-time degree program, co-op programs and internships, graduate courses open to undergrads. Off campus study. Study abroad program. ROTC: Army (c), Air Force (c).
Entrance Requirements: Options: electronic application, deferred admission. Required: essay, high school transcript, 1 recommendation, SAT or

ACT. Entrance: moderately difficult. Application deadline: 4/1. Notification: continuous. SAT Reasoning Test deadline: 4/1. Transfer credits accepted: Yes.

Costs Per Year: Application fee: $50. State resident tuition: $10,410 full-time, $440 per credit hour part-time. Nonresident tuition: $17,310 full-time, $720 per credit hour part-time. Mandatory fees: $2366 full-time, $94 per credit hour part-time. Part-time tuition and fees vary according to course load. College room and board: $8762. Room and board charges vary according to board plan and housing facility.

Collegiate Environment: Orientation program. Drama-theater group, choral group, student-run newspaper, radio station. Social organizations: 100 open to all; national fraternities, national sororities, local fraternities, local sororities; 3% of eligible men and 3% of eligible women are members. Most popular organizations: Social Activities Council, Humans vs. Zobies, student government, Phi Sigma Sigma Sorority, Delta Phi Epsilon Sorority. Major annual events: Pumpkin Festival, Parent and Family Weekend, Academic Excellence Conference. Student services: health clinic, personal-psychological counseling, women's center. Campus security: 24-hour emergency response devices and patrols, late night transport-escort service, controlled dormitory access. 2,726 college housing spaces available; 2,589 were occupied in 2012-13. Freshmen guaranteed college housing. On-campus residence required through sophomore year. Options: coed, women-only housing available. Mason Library with 334,204 books, 230,800 microform titles, 55,271 serials, 15,585 audiovisual materials, an OPAC, and a Web page. 600 computers available on campus for general student use. Computer purchase/lease plans available. A campuswide network can be accessed from student residence rooms. Students can access the following: online class registration, Student web pages. Staffed computer lab on campus provides training in use of computers, software, and the Internet.

Community Environment: Keene, population 22,700, is located in the southwest corner of New Hampshire, 90 miles from Boston. All forms of commercial transportation are available. Keene is a city of diversified industry with metal and machine industries the most important. There are a number of churches, a community hospital and library serving the area. One of the most popular resorts in the state, Keene has many lakes and ponds within a 20-mile radius as well as golf courses and facilities for winter sports. A number of covered bridges may be seen on side roads off State Highway 10 between Keene and Winchester.

■ **LAKES REGION COMMUNITY COLLEGE**
379 Belmont Rd.
Laconia, NH 03246
Tel: (603)524-3207
Fax: (603)524-8084
E-mail: wfraser@ccsnh.edu
Web Site: www.lrcc.edu/
Description: State-supported, 2-year, coed. Awards transfer associate and terminal associate degrees. Total enrollment: 1,171. Student-undergrad faculty ratio is 9:1. 8% from out-of-state. 37% 25 or older.
Entrance Requirements: Required: high school transcript.

■ **MANCHESTER COMMUNITY COLLEGE**
1066 Front St.
Manchester, NH 03102-8518
Tel: (603)668-6706
E-mail: jpoirier@nhctc.edu
Web Site: www.mccnh.edu/
Description: State-supported, 2-year, coed. Part of New Hampshire Community Technical College System. Awards certificates, diplomas, transfer associate, and terminal associate degrees. Founded 1945. Setting: 60-acre urban campus with easy access to Boston. Research spending for the previous fiscal year: $35,000. Total enrollment: 3,122. Faculty: 202 (52 full-time, 150 part-time). Student-undergrad faculty ratio is 14:1. Students come from 5 states and territories, 7% from out-of-state. 40% 25 or older. Core. Calendar: semesters. Academic remediation for entering students, ESL program, services for LD students, advanced placement, independent study, distance learning, double major, summer session for credit, part-time degree program, external degree program, adult/continuing education programs, co-op programs and internships.
Entrance Requirements: Options: early admission, deferred admission. Required: high school transcript. Required for some: interview. Entrance: minimally difficult. Application deadline: Rolling. Notification: continuous.
Collegiate Environment: Orientation program. Social organizations: 4 open to all. Most popular organizations: Student Senate, Phi Theta Kappa,

American Society of Welders, Student Nurses Association. Major annual events: Spring Formal, Graduation. Student services: personal-psychological counseling. Campus security: trained security personnel. New Hampshire Community Technical College Library plus 1 other with 18,000 books, 160 serials, and an OPAC. Operations spending for the previous fiscal year: $66,600. 210 computers available on campus for general student use. A campuswide network can be accessed. Students can access the following: online class registration. Staffed computer lab on campus.

■ **NASHUA COMMUNITY COLLEGE**
505 Amherst St.
Nashua, NH 03063-1026
Tel: (603)882-6923
Fax: (603)882-8690
E-mail: pgoodman@ccsnh.edu
Web Site: www.nashuacc.edu/
Description: State-supported, 2-year, coed. Part of Community College System of New Hampshire. Awards certificates, transfer associate, and terminal associate degrees. Founded 1967. Setting: 66-acre urban campus with easy access to Boston. Total enrollment: 2,100. Faculty: 108 (42 full-time, 66 part-time). 1 valedictorian. Core. Calendar: semesters. Academic remediation for entering students, ESL program, services for LD students, self-designed majors, distance learning, summer session for credit, part-time degree program, adult/continuing education programs, co-op programs and internships.
Entrance Requirements: Open admission. Option: deferred admission. Required: high school transcript, interview. Required for some: TEAS testing for pre-nursing. Entrance: noncompetitive. Application deadline: Rolling. Notification: continuous. Transfer credits accepted: Yes.
Costs Per Year: Application fee: $20. State resident tuition: $6780 full-time, $226 per credit hour part-time. Nonresident tuition: $14,340 full-time, $478 per credit hour part-time. Mandatory fees: $480 full-time, $16 per credit hour part-time. Full-time tuition and fees vary according to class time. Part-time tuition and fees vary according to class time.
Collegiate Environment: Orientation program. Drama-theater group, student-run newspaper. Social organizations: 11 open to all. Most popular organizations: Student Senate, Phi Theta Kappa, AmeriCorp, Paralegal Club, Athletics. Major annual event: Orientation. Student services: personal-psychological counseling. Campus security: 24-hour emergency response devices, late night transport-escort service. Walter B. Peterson Library and Media Center with 22,000 books, 250 serials, and an OPAC. 150 computers available on campus for general student use. A campuswide network can be accessed. Staffed computer lab on campus.

■ **NEW ENGLAND COLLEGE**
15 Main St.
Henniker, NH 03242-3293
Tel: (603)428-2211; Free: 800-521-7642
E-mail: vsalyer@nec.edu
Web Site: www.nec.edu/
Description: Independent, comprehensive, coed. Awards associate, bachelor's, master's, and doctoral degrees. Founded 1946. Setting: 225-acre small town campus with easy access to Boston. Endowment: $8.1 million. Research spending for the previous fiscal year: $48,825. Educational spending for the previous fiscal year: $5686 per student. Total enrollment: 2,016. Faculty: 180 (68 full-time, 112 part-time). Student-undergrad faculty ratio is 11:1. 3,723 applied, 65% were admitted. 2% from top 10% of their high school class, 7% from top quarter, 40% from top half. 4 class presidents, 26 student government officers. Full-time: 1,041 students, 50% women, 50% men. Part-time: 85 students, 38% women, 62% men. Students come from 51 states and territories, 17 other countries, 67% from out-of-state. 1% American Indian or Alaska Native, non-Hispanic/Latino; 4% Hispanic/Latino; 12% African American, non-Hispanic/Latino; 2% Asian, non-Hispanic/Latino; 0.2% Native Hawaiian or other Pacific Islander, non-Hispanic/Latino; 4% international. 21% 25 or older, 47% live on campus, 13% transferred in. Retention: 63% of full-time freshmen returned the following year. Academic areas with the most degrees conferred: business/marketing; education; parks and recreation. Core. Calendar: semesters. Academic remediation for entering students, ESL program, services for LD students, advanced placement, accelerated degree program, self-designed majors, honors program, independent study, distance learning, double major, summer session for credit, part-time degree program, adult/continuing education programs, internships, graduate courses open to undergrads. Off

campus study at members of the New Hampshire College and University Council. Study abroad program. ROTC: Army (c), Air Force (c).

Entrance Requirements: Options: electronic application, deferred admission, international baccalaureate accepted. Required: essay, high school transcript, 3 recommendations. Recommended: interview. Entrance: minimally difficult. Application deadlines: 9/7, 9/7 for nonresidents. Notification: continuous, continuous for nonresidents. Transfer credits accepted: Yes.

Costs Per Year: Application fee: $35. Comprehensive fee: $44,178 includes full-time tuition ($31,394), mandatory fees ($350), and college room and board ($12,434). College room only: $5750. Full-time tuition and fees vary according to class time, course load, degree level, location, program, and reciprocity agreements. Room and board charges vary according to board plan and housing facility. Part-time tuition: $385 per credit. Part-time tuition varies according to class time, course load, degree level, location, and program.

Collegiate Environment: Orientation program. Drama-theater group, student-run newspaper, radio station. Social organizations: 32 open to all; national fraternities, national sororities, local fraternities, local sororities, Honors Coed Greek Organization; 6% of eligible men and 11% of eligible women are members. Most popular organizations: Student Senate, Campus Activities Board, Role Playing Association, International Student Association, Political Science Club. Major annual events: Midnight Madness, Winter Carnival, River Day. Student services: health clinic, personal-psychological counseling, women's center. Campus security: 24-hour emergency response devices and patrols, student patrols, late night transport-escort service, controlled dormitory access, Emergency Text System. 661 college housing spaces available; 510 were occupied in 2012-13. Freshmen guaranteed college housing. On-campus residence required through sophomore year. Option: coed housing available. Danforth Library with 110,000 books, 275 serials, 1,600 audiovisual materials, an OPAC, and a Web page. Operations spending for the previous fiscal year: $177,990. 191 computers available on campus for general student use. Computer purchase/lease plans available. A campuswide network can be accessed from student residence rooms and from off campus. Students can access the following: online class registration. Staffed computer lab on campus (open 24 hours a day) provides training in use of computers, software, and the Internet.

Community Environment: The campus is situated in an area abounding in natural beauty. Henniker, a village of 3,200, is located on the Contoocook River in a mountainous area of New Hampshire 85 miles from Boston and 15 miles from Concord, the capital. The campus facilities are located throughout Henniker allowing students easy walking access to stores and restaurants. Alpine skiing and snowboarding are available at Pat's Peak two miles from Henniker. Other outdoor recreational facilities abound in the surrounding area.

■ NEW HAMPSHIRE INSTITUTE OF ART

148 Concord St.
Manchester, NH 03104
Tel: (603)623-0313; Free: 866-241-4918
Fax: (603)641-1832
E-mail: aabbott@nhia.edu
Web Site: www.nhia.edu/

Description: Proprietary, 4-year, coed. Awards bachelor's degrees. Founded 1898. Setting: urban campus with easy access to Boston. Endowment: $220.1 million. Total enrollment: 566. Faculty: 79 (17 full-time, 62 part-time). Student-undergrad faculty ratio is 12:1. 775 applied, 52% were admitted. Full-time: 510 students, 67% women, 33% men. Part-time: 56 students, 80% women, 20% men. Students come from 16 states and territories, 28% from out-of-state. 1% American Indian or Alaska Native, non-Hispanic/Latino; 4% Hispanic/Latino; 1% African American, non-Hispanic/Latino; 1% Asian, non-Hispanic/Latino; 0% Native Hawaiian or other Pacific Islander, non-Hispanic/Latino. 4% 25 or older, 53% live on campus, 2% transferred in. Retention: 74% of full-time freshmen returned the following year. Academic area with the most degrees conferred: visual and performing arts. Core. Calendar: semesters. Advanced placement, independent study, double major, summer session for credit, part-time degree program, adult/continuing education programs, co-op programs. Study abroad program.

Entrance Requirements: Options: electronic application, early action, deferred admission. Required: essay, high school transcript, 2 recommendations, interview, portfolio review. Recommended: interview, SAT and SAT Subject Tests or ACT. Entrance: moderately difficult. Application deadlines: Rolling, Rolling for nonresidents, 12/6 for early action. Notification: continu-

ous, continuous for nonresidents, 12/23 for early action. Transfer credits accepted: Yes. Early action applicants: 109. Early action applicants admitted: 109.

Collegiate Environment: Orientation program. Choral group. Social organizations: 6 open to all. Most popular organizations: Student Council, Comic Club, Neo-Victorian Club, Crit Club, Gay/Straight Alliance. Major annual events: Student Art Exhibitions, Halloween Ball, Vernal Equi-Rocks. Student services: personal-psychological counseling. Campus security: late night transport-escort service, controlled dormitory access. Teti Library with 14,526 books, 125 serials, 988 audiovisual materials, an OPAC, and a Web page. Operations spending for the previous fiscal year: $193,850. 100 computers available on campus for general student use. A campuswide network can be accessed from student residence rooms and from off campus. Students can access the following: online class registration. Staffed computer lab on campus provides training in use of computers, software, and the Internet.

■ NHTI, CONCORD'S COMMUNITY COLLEGE

31 College Dr.
Concord, NH 03301-7412
Tel: (603)271-6484; Free: 800-247-0179
Fax: (603)271-7734
E-mail: fmeyer@ccsnh.edu
Web Site: www.nhti.edu/

Description: State-supported, 2-year, coed. Part of Community College System of New Hampshire. Awards certificates, diplomas, and transfer associate degrees. Founded 1964. Setting: 225-acre small town campus with easy access to Boston. Total enrollment: 3,700. Faculty: 109. Student-undergrad faculty ratio is 15:1. 50% 25 or older, 23% live on campus. Calendar: semesters. Academic remediation for entering students, ESL program, services for LD students, advanced placement, distance learning, double major, summer session for credit, part-time degree program, external degree program, adult/continuing education programs.

Entrance Requirements: Option: electronic application. Required: high school transcript. Recommended: minimum 2 high school GPA, SAT or ACT. Required for some: essay, interview, National League of Nursing Exam. Entrance: moderately difficult. Application deadline: Rolling. Notification: continuous. Preference given to state residents. Transfer credits accepted: Yes.

Collegiate Environment: Orientation program. Drama-theater group. Most popular organizations: Phi Theta Kappa, Student Senate, Student Nurses Association, Criminal Justice Club, Outing Club. Major annual events: Convocation, International Student Day, Awards Day. Student services: health clinic, personal-psychological counseling. Campus security: 24-hour emergency response devices and patrols, late night transport-escort service, controlled dormitory access, cameras in vital locations. 350 college housing spaces available. No special consideration for freshman housing applicants. Option: coed housing available. Farnum Library plus 1 other with 32,000 books, 12,000 microform titles, 500 serials, 1,000 audiovisual materials, an OPAC, and a Web page. 160 computers available on campus for general student use. Students can access the following: online class registration, electronic application. Staffed computer lab on campus.

Community Environment: Bisected by the Merrimack River, Concord is the capital of New Hampshire, and is the economic and political center of the state. It is a key city on the interstate highway system. Community facilities include three libraries, numerous churches, a YMCA, hospitals, and good shopping. Job opportunities are good.

■ PLYMOUTH STATE UNIVERSITY

17 High St.
Plymouth, NH 03264-1595
Tel: (603)535-5000; Free: 800-842-6900
Fax: (603)535-2714
E-mail: plymouthadmit@plymouth.edu
Web Site: www.plymouth.edu/

Description: State-supported, comprehensive, coed. Part of University System of New Hampshire. Awards bachelor's, master's, and doctoral degrees and post-master's certificates. Founded 1871. Setting: 170-acre small town campus with easy access to Manchester, NH. Endowment: $9.1 million. Research spending for the previous fiscal year: $2.3 million. Educational spending for the previous fiscal year: $6790 per student. Total enrollment: 5,431. Faculty: 418 (187 full-time, 231 part-time). Student-undergrad faculty ratio is 17:1. 4,940 applied, 76% were admitted. 3% from top 10% of their high school class, 17% from top quarter, 55% from top half.

Full-time: 3,926 students, 48% women, 52% men. Part-time: 312 students, 42% women, 58% men. Students come from 29 states and territories, 23 other countries, 41% from out-of-state. 0.2% American Indian or Alaska Native, non-Hispanic/Latino; 2% Hispanic/Latino; 1% African American, non-Hispanic/Latino; 1% Asian, non-Hispanic/Latino; 1% international. 4% 25 or older, 53% live on campus, 5% transferred in. Retention: 74% of full-time freshmen returned the following year. Academic areas with the most degrees conferred: business/marketing; education; parks and recreation; communication/journalism; homeland security, law enforcement, firefighting, and protective services. Core. Calendar: semesters. ESL program, services for LD students, advanced placement, self-designed majors, honors program, independent study, distance learning, double major, summer session for credit, part-time degree program, adult/continuing education programs, internships, graduate courses open to undergrads. Off campus study at members of the New Hampshire College and University Council, National Student Exchange. Study abroad program. ROTC: Army (c), Air Force (c).

Entrance Requirements: Options: electronic application, deferred admission. Required: essay, high school transcript, 1 recommendation, SAT or ACT. Required for some: interview. Entrance: moderately difficult. Application deadline: 4/1. Notification: continuous until 11/1. SAT Reasoning Test deadline: 4/1. SAT Subject Test deadline: 4/1. Transfer credits accepted: Yes.

Costs Per Year: Application fee: $50. One-time mandatory fee: $198. State resident tuition: $10,410 full-time, $435 per credit hour part-time. Nonresident tuition: $17,310 full-time, $720 per credit hour part-time. Mandatory fees: $2150 full-time, $92 per credit hour part-time. Full-time tuition and fees vary according to reciprocity agreements. Part-time tuition and fees vary according to reciprocity agreements. College room and board: $9440. College room only: $6370. Room and board charges vary according to board plan and housing facility.

Collegiate Environment: Orientation program. Drama-theater group, choral group, student-run newspaper, radio station. Social organizations: 100 open to all; national sororities, local sororities; 1% of women are members. Most popular organizations: Programming Activities in College Environment, Student Senate, Marketing Association of Plymouth State, CommonGround - Environmental and Social Justice Organization, PSU Pep Band. Major annual events: Spring Fling, Family Weekend, Homecoming Weekend. Student services: health clinic, personal-psychological counseling, women's center. Campus security: 24-hour emergency response devices and patrols, student patrols, late night transport-escort service, controlled dormitory access, shuttle bus service, crime prevention programs, self-defense education. 2,475 college housing spaces available; 2,167 were occupied in 2012-13. Freshmen given priority for college housing. On-campus residence required in freshman year. Option: coed housing available. Lamson Library with 349,390 books, 325,000 microform titles, 1,600 serials, 10,000 audiovisual materials, an OPAC, and a Web page. Operations spending for the previous fiscal year: $2.3 million. 900 computers available on campus for general student use. Computer purchase/lease plans available. A campuswide network can be accessed from student residence rooms and from off campus. Students can access the following: online class registration, degree audit, academic history, account status. Staffed computer lab on campus provides training in use of computers, software, and the Internet.

Community Environment: With the White Mountains to the north, the Lakes Region to the south, and the Pemigewasset Rivers bordering the town to the east, Plymouth, NH is home to some of the country's most spectacular wilderness. PSU students step outside every morning into a natural landscape that provides four seasons of recreational and educational adventure. Here, the outdoors offer a natural laboratory, a classroom, and a playground. The campus is nestled in the town of Plymouth, which has been ranked seventh in The 100 Best Small Towns in America. Plymouth is less than 2 hours' drive from Boston. Portland, Maine is 2 hours east; Burlington, Vermont, is 2 hours to the northwest; and Montreal, Canada is only 3 1/2 hours to the north. Recreational activities include skiing and other winter sports, hiking, fishing, boating, and hunting.

■ RIVER VALLEY COMMUNITY COLLEGE

1 College Dr.
Claremont, NH 03743
Tel: (603)542-7744
Fax: (603)543-1844
E-mail: ckusselow@ccsnh.edu
Web Site: www.rivervalley.edu/

Description: State-supported, 2-year, coed. Awards certificates, diplomas,

transfer associate, and terminal associate degrees. Total enrollment: 1,012. Student-undergrad faculty ratio is 5:1. 6% from out-of-state. 53% 25 or older.

Entrance Requirements: Open admission.

■ RIVIER UNIVERSITY

420 S Main St.
Nashua, NH 03060
Tel: (603)888-1311; Free: 800-44RIVIER
Fax: (603)891-1799
E-mail: rivadmit@rivier.edu
Web Site: www.rivier.edu/

Description: Independent Roman Catholic, comprehensive, coed. Awards associate, bachelor's, master's, and doctoral degrees and post-master's certificates. Founded 1933. Setting: 68-acre suburban campus with easy access to Boston. Endowment: $39.3 million. Total enrollment: 2,316. Faculty: 200 (71 full-time, 129 part-time). Student-undergrad faculty ratio is 17:1. 776 applied, 83% were admitted. 8% from top 10% of their high school class, 20% from top quarter, 58% from top half. Full-time: 912 students, 78% women, 22% men. Part-time: 647 students, 86% women, 14% men. Students come from 15 states and territories, 1 other country, 39% from out-of-state. 0.1% American Indian or Alaska Native, non-Hispanic/Latino; 4% Hispanic/Latino; 2% African American, non-Hispanic/Latino; 3% Asian, non-Hispanic/Latino; 0.1% Native Hawaiian or other Pacific Islander, non-Hispanic/Latino; 0% international. 35% 25 or older, 49% live on campus, 10% transferred in. Retention: 78% of full-time freshmen returned the following year. Academic areas with the most degrees conferred: health professions and related sciences; business/marketing; education; social sciences. Core. Calendar: semesters. Services for LD students, advanced placement, independent study, distance learning, double major, summer session for credit, part-time degree program, internships, graduate courses open to undergrads. Off campus study at members of the New Hampshire College and University Council. Study abroad program. ROTC: Air Force (c).

Entrance Requirements: Options: electronic application, deferred admission. Required: essay, high school transcript, 1 recommendation, SAT or ACT. Recommended: minimum 2.3 high school GPA, interview. Required for some: interview, nursing exam. Entrance: moderately difficult. Application deadline: Rolling. Notification: continuous. Transfer credits accepted: Yes.

Costs Per Year: Application fee: $25. One-time mandatory fee: $275. Comprehensive fee: $36,873 includes full-time tuition ($26,430), mandatory fees ($325), and college room and board ($10,118). College room only: $5500. Full-time tuition and fees vary according to program and reciprocity agreements. Room and board charges vary according to board plan and housing facility. Part-time tuition: $881 per credit. Part-time mandatory fees: $25 per year. Part-time tuition and fees vary according to class time, course load, program, and reciprocity agreements.

Collegiate Environment: Orientation program. Drama-theater group, choral group. Social organizations: 13 open to all. Most popular organizations: Student Government Association, Student Program Board, Outdoor Club, Student Nurses Association, Habitat for Humanity. Major annual events: Family Weekend, Spring Carnival, Halloween Extravaganza. Student services: health clinic, personal-psychological counseling. Campus security: 24-hour emergency response devices and patrols, late night transport-escort service, controlled dormitory access. 423 college housing spaces available; 404 were occupied in 2012-13. Freshmen guaranteed college housing. Option: coed housing available. Regina Library plus 1 other with 177,535 books, 135,000 microform titles, 317 serials, 4,150 audiovisual materials, an OPAC, and a Web page. Operations spending for the previous fiscal year: $1.1 million. 175 computers available on campus for general student use. A campuswide network can be accessed from student residence rooms and from off campus. Students can access the following: online class registration. Staffed computer lab on campus provides training in use of computers, software, and the Internet.

Community Environment: Nashua is the second largest city in New Hampshire. It is conveniently located within an hour's drive of Boston, the White Mountains, and the seacoast, and is home to a large technology industry. Buses provide ample transportation to shopping malls, libraries, banking facilities, and many other services within just a few miles of the campus.

■ SAINT ANSELM COLLEGE

100 Saint Anselm Dr.
Manchester, NH 03102-1310
Tel: (603)641-7000; Free: 888-4ANSELM
Fax: (603)641-7550

E-mail: admission@anselm.edu
Web Site: www.anselm.edu/
Description: Independent Roman Catholic, 4-year, coed. Awards bachelor's degrees. Founded 1889. Setting: 450-acre suburban campus with easy access to Boston. Endowment: $85.3 million. Total enrollment: 1,954. Faculty: 217 (144 full-time, 73 part-time). Student-undergrad faculty ratio is 11:1. 4,089 applied, 75% were admitted. 20% from top 10% of their high school class, 54% from top quarter, 89% from top half. Full-time: 1,900 students, 58% women, 42% men. Part-time: 54 students, 72% women, 28% men. Students come from 24 states and territories, 3 other countries, 77% from out-of-state. 0.3% American Indian or Alaska Native, non-Hispanic/Latino; 3% Hispanic/Latino; 1% African American, non-Hispanic/Latino; 1% Asian, non-Hispanic/Latino; 0.1% Native Hawaiian or other Pacific Islander, non-Hispanic/Latino; 0.5% international. 1% 25 or older, 90% live on campus, 1% transferred in. Retention: 88% of full-time freshmen returned the following year. Academic areas with the most degrees conferred: social sciences; business/marketing; health professions and related sciences. Core. Calendar: semesters. Services for LD students, advanced placement, honors program, independent study, double major, summer session for credit, part-time degree program, internships. Off campus study at member institutions of the New Hampshire College and University Council. Study abroad program. ROTC: Army (c), Air Force (c).
Entrance Requirements: Options: electronic application, early admission, early action, deferred admission, international baccalaureate accepted. Required: essay, high school transcript, 2 recommendations. Recommended: interview. Required for some: SAT or ACT. Entrance: moderately difficult. Application deadlines: 2/1, 11/15 for early action. Notification: continuous, 1/15 for early action. SAT Reasoning Test deadline: 2/15. SAT Subject Test deadline: 2/15. Transfer credits accepted: Yes. Applicants placed on waiting list: 577. Wait-listed applicants offered admission: 51. Early action applicants: 2,165. Early action applicants admitted: 1,669.
Costs Per Year: Application fee: $55. Comprehensive fee: $48,324 includes full-time tuition ($34,084), mandatory fees ($1550), and college room and board ($12,690). College room only: $7636. Room and board charges vary according to housing facility.
Collegiate Environment: Orientation program. Drama-theater group, choral group, student-run newspaper, radio station. Social organizations: 65 open to all. Most popular organizations: Center for Volunteers, Anselmian Abbey Players, Knights of Columbus, spring break alternative, International Relations Club. Major annual events: Homecoming, Spring Weekend, Family Weekend. Student services: health clinic, personal-psychological counseling. Campus security: 24-hour emergency response devices and patrols, late night transport-escort service, controlled dormitory access. College housing designed to accommodate 1,643 students; 1,692 undergraduates lived in college housing during 2012-13. Freshmen guaranteed college housing. Options: coed, men-only, women-only housing available. Geisel Library with 222,000 books, 66,000 microform titles, 1,900 serials, 8,000 audiovisual materials, an OPAC, and a Web page. 400 computers available on campus for general student use. Computer purchase/lease plans available. A campuswide network can be accessed from student residence rooms and from off campus. Students can access the following: online class registration. Staffed computer lab on campus.
Community Environment: On the banks of Merrimack River, Manchester is the largest city in the state. The city is a retail, industrial, distribution and financial center. All means of commercial transportation are available. Community facilities include 54 churches, 8 hospitals, a public library, hotels and motels. The recreational activities are numerous. They include golf, swimming, bowling, tennis, roller skating, fishing, sailing, skiing, ice skating, and tobogganing. Points of interest are the Currier Gallery of Art, Manchester Historic Association and the Old Blodgett Canal.

■ **SOUTHERN NEW HAMPSHIRE UNIVERSITY**
2500 N River Rd.
Manchester, NH 03106-1045
Tel: (603)668-2211; Free: 888-327-7648
Fax: (603)645-9693
E-mail: s.soba@snhu.edu
Web Site: www.snhu.edu/
Description: Independent, university, coed. Awards associate, bachelor's, master's, and doctoral degrees and post-master's certificates. Founded 1932. Setting: 317-acre suburban campus with easy access to Boston. Total enrollment: 17,534. Faculty: 1,167 (124 full-time, 1,043 part-time). Student-undergrad faculty ratio is 24:1. 4,386 applied, 81% were admitted. 10% from top 10% of their high school class, 27% from top quarter, 63% from top half.

Full-time: 5,805 students, 55% women, 45% men. Part-time: 5,448 students, 61% women, 39% men. 0.1% American Indian or Alaska Native, non-Hispanic/Latino; 1% Hispanic/Latino; 1% African American, non-Hispanic/Latino; 0.4% Asian, non-Hispanic/Latino; 0% Native Hawaiian or other Pacific Islander, non-Hispanic/Latino; 2% international. 73% live on campus. Retention: 73% of full-time freshmen returned the following year. Academic areas with the most degrees conferred: business/marketing; psychology; English. Core. Calendar: semesters. Academic remediation for entering students, ESL program, services for LD students, advanced placement, accelerated degree program, honors program, independent study, distance learning, double major, summer session for credit, part-time degree program, adult/continuing education programs, co-op programs and internships, graduate courses open to undergrads. Off campus study at members of the New Hampshire College and University Council. Study abroad program. ROTC: Army (c), Air Force (c).
Entrance Requirements: Options: electronic application, early action, deferred admission, international baccalaureate accepted. Required: essay, high school transcript, minimum 2 high school GPA, 1 recommendation. Recommended: interview, SAT or ACT. Entrance: moderately difficult. Application deadlines: Rolling, 11/15 for early action. Notification: continuous, 12/15 for early action. Transfer credits accepted: Yes.
Costs Per Year: Application fee: $40. Comprehensive fee: $40,504 includes full-time tuition ($28,554), mandatory fees ($330), and college room and board ($11,620). College room only: $7720. Full-time tuition and fees vary according to class time and course load. Room and board charges vary according to board plan and housing facility. Part-time tuition: $1190 per credit. Part-time tuition varies according to class time, location, and program.
Collegiate Environment: Orientation program. Drama-theater group, choral group, student-run newspaper, radio station. Social organizations: 62 open to all; national fraternities, national sororities, local fraternities, local sororities. Most popular organizations: Coordinators of Activities and Programming Events (CAPE), International Student Association, Radio SNHU, Outing Club, Outreach Association. Major annual events: Family Weekend, New Student Fall Orientation, Fall/Spring Weekend. Student services: health clinic, personal-psychological counseling. Campus security: 24-hour emergency response devices and patrols, student patrols, late night transport-escort service, controlled dormitory access. 1,997 college housing spaces available. No special consideration for freshman housing applicants. Option: coed housing available. Harry A. B. and Gertrude C. Shapiro Library with 104,507 books, 347,425 microform titles, 53,649 serials, 2,729 audiovisual materials, an OPAC, and a Web page. 557 computers available on campus for general student use. Computer purchase/lease plans available. A computer is required for all students. A campuswide network can be accessed from student residence rooms and from off campus. Students can access the following: online class registration. Staffed computer lab on campus provides training in use of computers, software, and the Internet.
Community Environment: Combining the tradition of the past with the sophistication of the future, Manchester has everything to be expected in a city with a population of more than 100,000, offering a thriving business environment as well as numerous cultural facilities. It is also within an hour of Boston, many ski resorts, and beaches that provide opportunities for jobs and recreation.

■ **THOMAS MORE COLLEGE OF LIBERAL ARTS**
6 Manchester St.
Merrimack, NH 03054-4818
Tel: (603)880-8308; Free: 800-880-8308
Fax: (603)880-9280
E-mail: admissions@thomasmorecollege.edu
Web Site: www.thomasmorecollege.edu/
Description: Independent, 4-year, coed, affiliated with Roman Catholic Church. Awards bachelor's degrees. Founded 1978. Setting: 14-acre small town campus with easy access to Boston. Educational spending for the previous fiscal year: $4044 per student. Total enrollment: 99. Faculty: 13. Student-undergrad faculty ratio is 12:1. 100 applied, 70% were admitted. 2 National Merit Scholars. Full-time: 99 students, 49% women, 51% men. Students come from 24 states and territories, 4 other countries, 84% from out-of-state. 3% 25 or older, 97% live on campus, 9% transferred in. Retention: 85% of full-time freshmen returned the following year. Academic areas with the most degrees conferred: English; social sciences; biological/life sciences. Core. Calendar: semesters. Independent study. Study abroad program.
Entrance Requirements: Option: electronic application. Required: essay, high school transcript, 2 recommendations. Recommended: SAT or ACT.

Required for some: interview. Entrance: moderately difficult. Application deadline: Rolling. Notification: continuous.

Collegiate Environment: Orientation program. Drama-theater group, choral group. Major annual events: Graduation, Convocation, visiting lectures. Student services: personal-psychological counseling. Campus security: student patrols, late night transport-escort service. Warren Memorial Library plus 1 other with 45,000 books, 20 serials, and 1,000 audiovisual materials. Operations spending for the previous fiscal year: $16,806. 6 computers available on campus for general student use. Staffed computer lab on campus.

■ **UNIVERSITY OF NEW HAMPSHIRE**
Durham, NH 03824
Tel: (603)862-1234
E-mail: admissions@unh.edu
Web Site: www.unh.edu/

Description: State-supported, university, coed. Part of University System of New Hampshire. Awards associate, bachelor's, master's, and doctoral degrees and post-master's certificates. Founded 1866. Setting: 2,600-acre small town campus with easy access to Boston. Endowment: $177.6 million. Research spending for the previous fiscal year: $147.3 million. Total enrollment: 15,301. Faculty: 987 (596 full-time, 391 part-time). Student-undergrad faculty ratio is 20:1. 17,234 applied, 78% were admitted. 18% from top 10% of their high school class, 50% from top quarter, 90% from top half. 69 valedictorians. Full-time: 12,335 students, 54% women, 46% men. Part-time: 476 students, 49% women, 51% men. Students come from 45 states and territories, 30 other countries, 40% from out-of-state. 0.3% American Indian or Alaska Native, non-Hispanic/Latino; 2% Hispanic/Latino; 1% African American, non-Hispanic/Latino; 2% Asian, non-Hispanic/Latino; 0.02% Native Hawaiian or other Pacific Islander, non-Hispanic/Latino; 1% international. 1% 25 or older, 57% live on campus, 4% transferred in. Retention: 86% of full-time freshmen returned the following year. Academic areas with the most degrees conferred: business/marketing; social sciences; health professions and related sciences. Core. Calendar: semesters. ESL program, services for LD students, advanced placement, accelerated degree program, self-designed majors, honors program, independent study, distance learning, double major, summer session for credit, part-time degree program, co-op programs and internships, graduate courses open to undergrads. Off campus study at National Student Exchange, New Hampshire College and University Council Exchange, New England Land Grant Universities Exchange, University of California, Santa Cruz Exchange, The Washington (D.C.) Center Internship. Study abroad program. ROTC: Army, Air Force.

Entrance Requirements: Options: electronic application, early action, deferred admission, international baccalaureate accepted. Required: essay, high school transcript, 1 recommendation, SAT or ACT. Recommended: minimum 3 high school GPA. Entrance: moderately difficult. Application deadlines: 2/1, 2/1 for nonresidents, 11/15 for early action. Notification: 4/15, 4/15 for nonresidents, 1/15 for early action. Preference given to state residents. SAT Reasoning Test deadline: 2/1. Transfer credits accepted: Yes. Early action applicants: 7,860. Early action applicants admitted: 6,941.

Costs Per Year: Application fee: $50. State resident tuition: $13,670 full-time, $570 per credit hour part-time. Nonresident tuition: $26,130 full-time, $1089 per credit hour part-time. Mandatory fees: $2752 full-time, $688 per term part-time. Full-time tuition and fees vary according to degree level and program. Part-time tuition and fees vary according to course load, degree level, and program. College room and board: $9764. College room only: $6090. Room and board charges vary according to board plan and housing facility.

Collegiate Environment: Orientation program. Drama-theater group, choral group, marching band, student-run newspaper, radio station. Social organizations: 235 open to all; national fraternities, national sororities; 8% of eligible men and 10% of eligible women are members. Most popular organizations: Campus Activity Board, The Outing Club, Resident Hall Association, Best Buddies, Memorial Union Student Organization. Major annual events: Student Activities Fair (in conjunction with University Day), Jukebox, May Day Carnival. Student services: legal services, health clinic, personal-psychological counseling, women's center. Campus security: 24-hour emergency response devices and patrols, student patrols, late night transport-escort service, controlled dormitory access, lighted pathways and sidewalks. 7,500 college housing spaces available; 7,115 were occupied in 2012-13. Freshmen guaranteed college housing. Option: coed housing available. Dimond Library plus 4 others with 1.8 million books, 3 million microform titles, 58,875 serials, 369,109 audiovisual materials, an OPAC, and a Web page. Operations spending for the previous fiscal year: $16.7 million. 464

computers available on campus for general student use. Computer purchase/lease plans available. A campuswide network can be accessed from student residence rooms and from off campus. Students can access the following: online class registration. Staffed computer lab on campus (open 24 hours a day) provides training in use of computers, software, and the Internet.

Community Environment: Situated in southeastern New Hampshire, Durham is a quiet college town with many small restaurants, shops, and pubs located near the university. The cultural and recreational advantages of Portland to the northeast and nearby Boston to the south are both within one hour's drive. The University is 10 miles from the Atlantic coastline and historic Portsmouth. The White Mountains and ski areas are 60 miles to the northwest.

■ **UNIVERSITY OF NEW HAMPSHIRE AT MANCHESTER**
400 Commercial St.
Manchester, NH 03101-1113
Tel: (603)641-4321
Fax: (603)641-4125
E-mail: unhm@unh.edu
Web Site: www.unhm.unh.edu/

Description: State-supported, comprehensive, coed. Part of University System of New Hampshire. Awards associate, bachelor's, and master's degrees. Founded 1967. Setting: urban campus with easy access to Boston. Total enrollment: 777. Faculty: 109 (38 full-time, 71 part-time). Student-undergrad faculty ratio is 13:1. 157 applied, 48% were admitted. Full-time: 586 students, 51% women, 49% men. Part-time: 191 students, 46% women, 54% men. 0.1% American Indian or Alaska Native, non-Hispanic/Latino; 4% Hispanic/Latino; 2% African American, non-Hispanic/Latino; 2% Asian, non-Hispanic/Latino; 0.1% Native Hawaiian or other Pacific Islander, non-Hispanic/Latino; 0.1% international. Core. Calendar: semesters. Academic remediation for entering students, services for LD students, advanced placement, self-designed majors, independent study, double major, summer session for credit, part-time degree program, adult/continuing education programs, internships. Off campus study at 12 members of the New Hampshire College and University Council. Study abroad program. ROTC: Army (c), Air Force (c).

Entrance Requirements: Options: electronic application, deferred admission. Required: essay, high school transcript, 1 recommendation, SAT or ACT. Recommended: interview. Entrance: moderately difficult. Application deadline: 6/15. Notification: continuous. Transfer credits accepted: Yes.

Costs Per Year: Application fee: $45. State resident tuition: $13,350 full-time, $556 per credit hour part-time. Nonresident tuition: $25,810 full-time, $1075 per credit hour part-time. Mandatory fees: $407 full-time. Full-time tuition and fees vary according to course load and program. Part-time tuition varies according to course load and program.

Collegiate Environment: Orientation program. Student-run radio station. Most popular organization: Student Council. Major annual events: Jazz in the Mills Series, Cultural Connections, New England Voices poetry series. Campus security: 24-hour emergency response devices, late night transport-escort service. College housing not available. UNH Manchester Library plus 1 other with 37,147 books, 12,345 microform titles, 150 serials, 4,921 audiovisual materials, an OPAC, and a Web page. 108 computers available on campus for general student use. A campuswide network can be accessed from off-campus. Students can access the following: online class registration. Staffed computer lab on campus (open 24 hours a day) provides training in use of computers, software, and the Internet.

■ **WHITE MOUNTAINS COMMUNITY COLLEGE**
2020 Riverside Dr.
Berlin, NH 03570
Tel: (603)752-1113; Free: 800-445-4525
Fax: (603)752-6335
E-mail: jrivard@ccsnh.edu
Web Site: www.wmcc.edu/

Description: State-supported, 2-year, coed. Part of Community College System of New Hampshire. Awards certificates, diplomas, transfer associate, and terminal associate degrees. Founded 1966. Setting: 325-acre rural campus. Total enrollment: 922. Faculty: 253 (29 full-time, 224 part-time). Full-time: 348 students, 51% women, 49% men. Part-time: 574 students, 74% women, 26% men. Core. Calendar: semesters. Academic remediation for entering students, services for LD students, advanced placement, independent study, distance learning, double major, summer session for credit, part-time degree program, external degree program, adult/continuing education programs, internships.

Entrance Requirements: Open admission. Options: electronic application, deferred admission. Required: high school transcript, placement test, ACCUPLACER Placement Test, Pre National League of Nursing entrance exam (Nursing AS Degree). Required for some: essay. Entrance: minimally difficult. Application deadline: Rolling. Notification: continuous.

Costs Per Year: Application fee: $20. State resident tuition: $6300 full-time, $210 per credit part-time. Nonresident tuition: $14,340 full-time, $478 per credit part-time. Mandatory fees: $540 full-time, $18 per credit part-time.

Collegiate Environment: Orientation program. Most popular organization: Student Senate. Fortier Library with 18,000 books, 15 microform titles, 85 serials, 350 audiovisual materials, and an OPAC. 153 computers available on campus for general student use. A campuswide network can be accessed. Students can access the following: online class registration. Staffed computer lab on campus.

■ **ASSUMPTION COLLEGE FOR SISTERS**
350 Bernardsville Rd.
Mendham, NJ 07945-0800
Tel: (973)543-6528
Fax: (973)543-9459
E-mail: deanregistrar@acs350.org
Web Site: www.acs350.org/
Description: Independent Roman Catholic, 2-year, women only. Awards certificates and transfer associate degrees. Founded 1953. Setting: 112-acre rural campus with easy access to New York City. Total enrollment: 33. Student-undergrad faculty ratio is 7:1. 91% 25 or older. Retention: 100% of full-time freshmen returned the following year. Core. Calendar: semesters. Academic remediation for entering students, ESL program, services for LD students, advanced placement, summer session for credit, part-time degree program.
Entrance Requirements: Required: high school transcript, 1 recommendation, women religious or women in religious formation. Entrance: noncompetitive.
Collegiate Environment: Orientation program. Choral group. Campus security: 24-hour emergency response devices. Assumption College for Sisters Library with an OPAC.

■ **ATLANTIC CAPE COMMUNITY COLLEGE**
5100 Black Horse Pke.
Mays Landing, NJ 08330-2699
Tel: (609)625-1111
Fax: (609)343-4921
E-mail: accadmit@atlantic.edu
Web Site: www.atlantic.edu/
Description: County-supported, 2-year, coed. Awards certificates, diplomas, transfer associate, and terminal associate degrees. Founded 1964. Setting: 537-acre small town campus with easy access to Philadelphia. Total enrollment: 7,007. Student-undergrad faculty ratio is 21:1. 1% from out-of-state. 36% 25 or older. Retention: 60% of full-time freshmen returned the following year. Core. Calendar: semesters. Academic remediation for entering students, ESL program, services for LD students, advanced placement, independent study, distance learning, double major, summer session for credit, part-time degree program, adult/continuing education programs, co-op programs and internships.
Entrance Requirements: Open admission except for culinary arts, nursing, allied health, occupation therapy, physical therapy, respiratory therapy assistant programs. Options: electronic application, early admission, deferred admission. Recommended: high school transcript. Entrance: noncompetitive. Application deadline: 7/1.
Collegiate Environment: Orientation program. Drama-theater group, student-run newspaper, radio station. Student services: personal-psychological counseling. Campus security: 24-hour emergency response devices and patrols. William Spangler Library with 80,551 books, 130 serials, an OPAC, and a Web page.
Community Environment: Population 2,321. Mays Landing is the county seat of Atlantic County, 18 miles from Atlantic City.

■ **BERGEN COMMUNITY COLLEGE**
400 Paramus Rd.
Paramus, NJ 07652-1595
Tel: (201)447-7100
Fax: (201)444-7036
E-mail: admsoffice@bergen.edu
Web Site: www.bergen.edu/
Description: County-supported, 2-year, coed. Awards certificates, transfer associate, and terminal associate degrees. Founded 1965. Setting: 167-acre suburban campus with easy access to New York City. Total enrollment: 16,469. Student-undergrad faculty ratio is 22:1. 1% from out-of-state. 30% 25 or older. Core. Calendar: semesters. Academic remediation for entering students, ESL program, services for LD students, honors program, distance learning, summer session for credit, part-time degree program, adult/continuing education programs, co-op programs and internships. Study abroad program.
Entrance Requirements: Open admission except for allied health programs. Entrance: noncompetitive. Notification: continuous. Preference given to county residents for nursing and dental hygiene programs.
Collegiate Environment: Orientation program. Drama-theater group, choral group, student-run newspaper. Student services: health clinic, personal-psychological counseling. Campus security: 24-hour patrols. Sidney Silverman Library and Learning Resources Center plus 1 other with an OPAC.
Community Environment: Bergen Community College is located in Paramus, which is the geographic center of Bergen County in northern New Jersey. With more than 300,000 households and nearly 1 million residents, Bergen County is one of the largest counties in the state. The college is located on a 167-acre campus that is bordered by two golf courses and a county park. There is convenient transportation to New York City by bus, train, and ferry. The college is approximately 20 minutes from the George Washington Bridge.

■ **BERKELEY COLLEGE**
44 Rifle Camp Rd.
Woodland Park, NJ 07424-3353
Tel: (973)278-5400; Free: 800-446-5400
Fax: (973)278-2242
E-mail: info@berkeleycollege.edu
Web Site: www.berkeleycollege.edu/
Description: Proprietary, 4-year, coed. Awards associate and bachelor's degrees. Founded 1931. Setting: 25-acre suburban campus with easy access to New York City. Total enrollment: 3,709. Student-undergrad faculty ratio is 28:1. 2,453 applied, 77% were admitted. 2% from out-of-state. 33% 25 or older. Retention: 52% of full-time freshmen returned the following year. Core. Academic remediation for entering students, ESL program, advanced placement, accelerated degree program, independent study, distance learning, summer session for credit, part-time degree program, adult/continuing education programs, co-op programs and internships. Off campus study at Berkeley College, New York; Berkeley College, White Plains.
Entrance Requirements: Options: electronic application, deferred admission. Required: high school transcript. Recommended: interview. Entrance: minimally difficult. Application deadline: Rolling.
Collegiate Environment: Student-run newspaper. Social organizations: local fraternities, local sororities. Student services: personal-psychological counseling. Campus security: 24-hour emergency response devices, controlled dormitory access, security patrols. Walter A. Brower Library with an OPAC and a Web page.

■ BETH MEDRASH GOVOHA

617 Sixth St.
Lakewood, NJ 08701-2797
Tel: (732)367-1060
Description: Independent Jewish, comprehensive, men only. Awards bachelor's and master's degrees. Founded 1943. Setting: small town campus with easy access to New York City, Philadelphia. Total enrollment: 5,639. 37% 25 or older. Calendar: semesters.
Entrance Requirements: Entrance: moderately difficult.
Community Environment: See Georgian Court College.

■ BLOOMFIELD COLLEGE

467 Franklin St.
Bloomfield, NJ 07003-9981
Tel: (973)748-9000; Free: 800-848-4555
Fax: (973)748-0916
E-mail: nicole_cibelli@bloomfield.edu
Web Site: www.bloomfield.edu/
Description: Independent, comprehensive, coed, affiliated with Presbyterian Church (U.S.A.). Awards bachelor's and master's degrees. Founded 1868. Setting: 12-acre suburban campus with easy access to New York City. Endowment: $9.5 million. Educational spending for the previous fiscal year: $7068 per student. Total enrollment: 2,045. Faculty: 226 (70 full-time, 156 part-time). Student-undergrad faculty ratio is 15:1. 3,115 applied, 55% were admitted. 6% from top 10% of their high school class, 22% from top quarter, 59% from top half. Full-time: 1,810 students, 63% women, 37% men. Part-time: 226 students, 70% women, 30% men. Students come from 18 states and territories, 29 other countries, 5% from out-of-state. 0.3% American Indian or Alaska Native, non-Hispanic/Latino; 20% Hispanic/Latino; 51% African American, non-Hispanic/Latino; 3% Asian, non-Hispanic/Latino; 0% Native Hawaiian or other Pacific Islander, non-Hispanic/Latino; 3% international. 23% 25 or older, 24% live on campus, 11% transferred in. Retention: 64% of full-time freshmen returned the following year. Academic areas with the most degrees conferred: social sciences; visual and performing arts; business/marketing. Core. Calendar: semesters. Academic remediation for entering students, services for LD students, advanced placement, accelerated degree program, self-designed majors, honors program, independent study, distance learning, double major, summer session for credit, part-time degree program, internships, graduate courses open to undergrads. Off campus study at BS/MS in Computer Information Systems program offered with New Jersey Institute of Technology, BS-AHT in Allied Health Technologies offered with University of Medicine and Dentistry of New Jersey. Study abroad program. ROTC: Army (c).
Entrance Requirements: Options: electronic application, early action, deferred admission. Required: essay, high school transcript, minimum 2.5 high school GPA, 2 recommendations, graded essay/term paper or personal essay, SAT or ACT. Recommended: interview. Entrance: moderately difficult. Application deadlines: 8/1, 8/1 for nonresidents, 12/1 for early action. Notification: continuous until 10/1, continuous until 10/1 for nonresidents, 12/23 for early action. SAT Reasoning Test deadline: 8/1. Transfer credits accepted: Yes. Applicants placed on waiting list: 142. Wait-listed applicants offered admission: 51. Early action applicants: 660. Early action applicants admitted: 467.
Costs Per Year: Application fee: $40. Comprehensive fee: $35,750 includes full-time tuition ($23,850), mandatory fees ($1200), and college room and board ($10,700). College room only: $5350. Room and board charges vary according to housing facility. Part-time tuition: $2980 per course. Part-time tuition varies according to course load.
Collegiate Environment: Orientation program. Drama-theater group, student-run radio station. Social organizations: 43 open to all; national fraternities, national sororities, local fraternities, local sororities; 13% of eligible men and 11% of eligible women are members. Most popular organizations: First Ladies, Team Infinite, Lambda Theta Alpha, Gentlemen's Club, Iota Phi Theta/ Chi Phi Sigma/Zeta Phi Beta. Major annual events: Welcome Back BBQ, Midnight Fever, Spring Formal. Student services: health clinic, personal-psychological counseling. Campus security: 24-hour emergency response devices and patrols, late night transport-escort service, security cameras in high-traffic areas. 531 college housing spaces available; all were occupied in 2012-13. No special consideration for freshman housing applicants. Option: coed housing available. Bloomfield College Library plus 1 other with 64,000 books, 460 serials, 3,359 audiovisual materials, an OPAC, and a Web page. Operations spending for the previous fiscal year: $862,588. 363 computers available on campus for general student use. A campuswide network can be accessed from student residence rooms and from off campus. Staffed computer lab on campus provides training in use of computers, software, and the Internet.
Community Environment: Located between Newark and Montclair, Bloomfield, population 55,000, is a suburban, residential city. Excellent shopping facilities, libraries, churches, numerous civic and service organizations and hospitals are a part of the community. Part-time employment is available. Commercial transportation is convenient.

■ BROOKDALE COMMUNITY COLLEGE

765 Newman Springs Rd.
Lincroft, NJ 07738-1597
Tel: (732)842-1900
Fax: (732)576-1643
Web Site: www.brookdalecc.edu/
Description: County-supported, 2-year, coed. Part of New Jersey Commission on Higher Education. Awards certificates, transfer associate, and terminal associate degrees. Founded 1967. Setting: 221-acre small town campus with easy access to New York City. Total enrollment: 14,025. 29% 25 or older. Core. Calendar: semesters plus 1 ten-week and 2 six-week summer terms. Academic remediation for entering students, ESL program, services for LD students, advanced placement, honors program, independent study, distance learning, summer session for credit, part-time degree program, adult/continuing education programs, co-op programs and internships. Study abroad program. ROTC: Army (c), Air Force (c).
Entrance Requirements: Open admission. Options: early admission, deferred admission. Required: high school transcript. Entrance: noncompetitive. Application deadline: Rolling. Notification: continuous. Preference given to county residents.
Collegiate Environment: Orientation program. Drama-theater group, student-run newspaper, radio station. Student services: personal-psychological counseling, women's center. Campus security: 24-hour emergency response devices and patrols. Brookdale Community College Library with 150,000 books, 17,987 microform titles, 709 serials, 33,000 audiovisual materials, and an OPAC.
Community Environment: Bounded by Sandy Hook Bay and the Navesink River, the Lincroft countryside area is located along the eastern shore of central New Jersey. The area abounds in orchards and horse farms. Community facilities include a library, churches of various faiths, above-average shopping facilities and many civic and service organizations. Railroads and buses furnish public transportation. Recreational facilities are very good including 7 miles of seashore for bay fishing, swimming and water sports.

■ BURLINGTON COUNTY COLLEGE

601 Pemberton Browns Mills Rd.
Pemberton, NJ 08068
Tel: (609)894-9311
Fax: (609)894-0183
E-mail: kgasioro@bcc.edu
Web Site: www.bcc.edu/
Description: County-supported, 2-year, coed. Awards certificates, transfer associate, and terminal associate degrees. Founded 1966. Setting: 225-acre suburban campus with easy access to Philadelphia. Total enrollment: 10,071. Faculty: 657 (56 full-time, 601 part-time). Student-undergrad faculty ratio is 26:1. 5,521 applied, 100% were admitted. Full-time: 5,129 students, 55% women, 45% men. Part-time: 4,942 students, 61% women, 39% men. Students come from 17 states and territories, 1% from out-of-state. 0.2% American Indian or Alaska Native, non-Hispanic/Latino; 9% Hispanic/Latino; 19% African American, non-Hispanic/Latino; 3% Asian, non-Hispanic/Latino; 0.2% Native Hawaiian or other Pacific Islander, non-Hispanic/Latino; 2% international. 35% 25 or older, 7% transferred in. Retention: 60% of full-time freshmen returned the following year. Core. Calendar: semesters plus 2 summer terms. Academic remediation for entering students, ESL program, services for LD students, advanced placement, accelerated degree program, honors program, independent study, distance learning, double major, summer session for credit, part-time degree program, adult/continuing education programs, co-op programs and internships. Study abroad program.
Entrance Requirements: Open admission except for allied health program. Options: electronic application, early admission, deferred admission. Recommended: high school transcript. Entrance: noncompetitive. Application deadlines: Rolling, Rolling for nonresidents. Notification: continuous, continuous for nonresidents. Transfer credits accepted: Yes.
Costs Per Year: Application fee: $20. Area resident tuition: $2760 full-time, $92 per credit hour part-time. State resident tuition: $3240 full-time, $108 per credit hour part-time. Nonresident tuition: $5190 full-time, $173 per credit

hour part-time. Mandatory fees: $855 full-time, $92 per credit hour part-time. Full-time tuition and fees vary according to course load and program. Part-time tuition and fees vary according to course load and program.

Collegiate Environment: Orientation program. Drama-theater group, choral group, student-run radio station. Social organizations: 29 open to all. Most popular organizations: Student Government Association, Phi Theta Kappa, Creative Writing Guild. Major annual events: National Make a Difference Day, African American History Month Events, Drugs/Alcohol Awareness Week. Student services: health clinic, personal-psychological counseling. Campus security: 24-hour emergency response devices and patrols, late night transport-escort service, electronic entrances to buildings and rooms, surveillance cameras. College housing not available. Burlington County College Library plus 1 other with 92,400 books, 15,400 microform titles, 1,750 serials, an OPAC, and a Web page. Operations spending for the previous fiscal year: $528,314. 1,198 computers available on campus for general student use. A campuswide network can be accessed from off-campus. Students can access the following: online class registration. Staffed computer lab on campus provides training in use of computers, software, and the Internet.

Community Environment: The main campus is located in a rural setting where the principal agricultural pursuit is the raising of berries. Bus transportation is available. The campus is located 35 minutes from Center City Philadelphia and 90 minutes from New York City. Fort Dix and McGuire Air Force Base are nearby. Burlington County, the largest of New Jersey's 21 counties, has numerous churches and synagogues and excellent health care and recreational facilities.

■ **CALDWELL COLLEGE**
120 Bloomfield Ave.
Caldwell, NJ 07006-6195
Tel: (973)618-3000
E-mail: squinn@caldwell.edu
Web Site: www.caldwell.edu/

Description: Independent Roman Catholic, comprehensive, coed. Awards bachelor's, master's, and doctoral degrees and post-master's certificates. Founded 1939. Setting: 70-acre suburban campus with easy access to New York City. Endowment: $5.8 million. Educational spending for the previous fiscal year: $7122 per student. Total enrollment: 2,213. Faculty: 227 (88 full-time, 139 part-time). Student-undergrad faculty ratio is 12:1. 2,598 applied, 61% were admitted. 10% from top 10% of their high school class, 25% from top quarter, 62% from top half. Full-time: 1,260 students, 67% women, 33% men. Part-time: 331 students, 68% women, 32% men. Students come from 19 states and territories, 24 other countries, 8% from out-of-state. 0.2% American Indian or Alaska Native, non-Hispanic/Latino; 15% Hispanic/Latino; 16% African American, non-Hispanic/Latino; 3% Asian, non-Hispanic/Latino; 0.2% Native Hawaiian or other Pacific Islander, non-Hispanic/Latino; 4% international. 24% 25 or older, 31% live on campus, 3% transferred in. Retention: 82% of full-time freshmen returned the following year. Academic areas with the most degrees conferred: business/marketing; psychology; social sciences. Core. Calendar: semesters. Academic remediation for entering students, ESL program, services for LD students, advanced placement, accelerated degree program, self-designed majors, honors program, independent study, distance learning, double major, summer session for credit, part-time degree program, external degree program, adult/continuing education programs, co-op programs and internships, graduate courses open to undergrads. Off campus study. Study abroad program. ROTC: Army (c).

Entrance Requirements: Options: electronic application, early admission, early action, deferred admission, international baccalaureate accepted. Required: essay, high school transcript, 2 recommendations, SAT or ACT scores, SAT or ACT. Recommended: minimum 3 high school GPA, interview. Required for some: interview. Entrance: moderately difficult. Application deadlines: Rolling, Rolling for nonresidents, 12/1 for early action. Notification: continuous, continuous for nonresidents, 12/31 for early action. SAT Reasoning Test deadline: 5/1. SAT Subject Test deadline: 5/1. Transfer credits accepted: Yes. Early action applicants: 373. Early action applicants admitted: 337.

Costs Per Year: Application fee: $40. Comprehensive fee: $40,000 includes full-time tuition ($27,900), mandatory fees ($1100), and college room and board ($11,000). Full-time tuition and fees vary according to course load and location. Room and board charges vary according to housing facility. Part-time tuition: $738 per credit hour. Part-time tuition and fees vary according to course load and location.

Collegiate Environment: Orientation program. Drama-theater group, choral

group, student-run newspaper. Social organizations: 30 open to all; national fraternities, national sororities. Most popular organizations: Black Student Union, Latino American Student Organization, Autism Awareness Club, Martial Arts Club, Marketing Club. Major annual events: Spring Formal, Halloween Dance, Mr. Caldwell Pageant. Student services: health clinic, personal-psychological counseling. Campus security: 24-hour patrols, late night transport-escort service, controlled dormitory access, dusk-to-dawn patrols by trained security personnel. 546 college housing spaces available; 504 were occupied in 2012-13. Freshmen given priority for college housing. Option: coed housing available. Jennings Library plus 1 other with 151,293 books, 8,864 microform titles, 422 serials, 3,188 audiovisual materials, an OPAC, and a Web page. Operations spending for the previous fiscal year: $870,449. 286 computers available on campus for general student use. A campuswide network can be accessed from student residence rooms and from off campus. Students can access the following: online class registration. Staffed computer lab on campus.

Community Environment: The birthplace of President Grover Cleveland, Caldwell is situated in Western Essex County with bus lines serving the area, and New York City only 20 miles away. Community services include a number of churches, a public library, hospitals and various civic organizations. The Grover Cleveland County Park, golf courses and tennis courts provide facilities for recreation. Skiing and ice skating are available during the winter season.

■ **CAMDEN COUNTY COLLEGE**
PO Box 200
Blackwood, NJ 08012-0200
Tel: (856)227-7200
E-mail: ddelaney@camdencc.edu
Web Site: www.camdencc.edu/

Description: State and locally supported, 2-year, coed. Part of New Jersey Commission on Higher Education. Awards certificates, transfer associate, and terminal associate degrees. Founded 1967. Setting: 320-acre suburban campus with easy access to Philadelphia. Total enrollment: 15,670. Faculty: 729 (139 full-time, 590 part-time). 7,889 applied. Full-time: 8,529 students, 56% women, 44% men. Part-time: 7,141 students, 66% women, 34% men. Students come from 9 states and territories. 39% 25 or older. Retention: 67% of full-time freshmen returned the following year. Core. Calendar: semesters. Academic remediation for entering students, ESL program, services for LD students, freshman honors college, honors program, independent study, distance learning, double major, summer session for credit, part-time degree program, external degree program, adult/continuing education programs, co-op programs and internships. Off campus study. Study abroad program.

Entrance Requirements: Open admission. Option: early admission. Required for some: high school transcript. Entrance: noncompetitive. Application deadline: Rolling.

Collegiate Environment: Drama-theater group, choral group, student-run radio station. Campus security: 24-hour emergency response devices. Learning Resource Center with 91,366 books, 19,970 microform titles, 449 serials, 2,038 audiovisual materials, and an OPAC.

Community Environment: Blackwood is located in Gloucester Township (population 66,539), near Philadelphia, PA.

■ **CENTENARY COLLEGE**
400 Jefferson St.
Hackettstown, NJ 07840-2100
Tel: (908)852-1400; Free: 800-236-8679
Fax: (908)852-3454
Web Site: www.centenarycollege.edu/

Description: Independent, comprehensive, coed, affiliated with United Methodist Church. Awards associate, bachelor's, and master's degrees. Founded 1867. Setting: suburban campus. Total enrollment: 2,644. Faculty: 222 (75 full-time, 147 part-time). Student-undergrad faculty ratio is 19:1. 1,060 applied, 88% were admitted. 11% from top 10% of their high school class, 28% from top quarter, 55% from top half. Full-time: 1,800 students, 62% women, 38% men. Part-time: 115 students, 64% women, 36% men. 16% from out-of-state. 0.1% American Indian or Alaska Native, non-Hispanic/Latino; 6% Hispanic/Latino; 9% African American, non-Hispanic/Latino; 2% Asian, non-Hispanic/Latino; 0% Native Hawaiian or other Pacific Islander, non-Hispanic/Latino; 3% international. 46% 25 or older, 56% live on campus, 9% transferred in. Retention: 76% of full-time freshmen returned the following year. Academic areas with the most degrees conferred: business/marketing; visual and performing arts; homeland security, law enforcement, firefighting, and protective services. Calendar: semesters. Part-time degree program, adult/continuing education programs.

Entrance Requirements: Options: electronic application, deferred admission, international baccalaureate accepted. Required: essay, high school transcript, SAT or ACT. Recommended: interview. Required for some: interview. Entrance: moderately difficult. Application deadline: Rolling. Notification: continuous. SAT Reasoning Test deadline: 8/1.

Costs Per Year: Application fee: $30. Comprehensive fee: $38,616 includes full-time tuition ($28,500) and college room and board ($10,116). Full-time tuition varies according to program. Room and board charges vary according to board plan.

Collegiate Environment: Orientation program. Campus security: 24-hour emergency response devices and patrols, late night transport-escort service, controlled dormitory access.

Community Environment: Population 9,375, Hackettstown is a suburban and residential community. The area industry has not destroyed the natural surroundings. There is easy access to New York City by bus and train. The ski resorts of the Pocono Mountains are only 30 minutes via Route 80 West. State parks maintained by New Jersey are minutes away.

■ THE COLLEGE OF NEW JERSEY

PO Box 7718
Ewing, NJ 08628
Tel: (609)771-1855
E-mail: admiss@tcnj.edu
Web Site: www.tcnj.edu/

Description: State-supported, comprehensive, coed. Awards bachelor's and master's degrees and post-master's certificates. Founded 1855. Setting: 255-acre suburban campus with easy access to Philadelphia. Total enrollment: 7,270. Faculty: 754 (351 full-time, 403 part-time). Student-undergrad faculty ratio is 13:1. 10,295 applied, 46% were admitted. 58% from top 10% of their high school class, 93% from top quarter, 99% from top half. Full-time: 6,340 students, 56% women, 44% men. Part-time: 205 students, 62% women, 38% men. Students come from 19 states and territories, 9 other countries, 6% from out-of-state. 0.1% American Indian or Alaska Native, non-Hispanic/Latino; 10% Hispanic/Latino; 6% African American, non-Hispanic/Latino; 9% Asian, non-Hispanic/Latino; 0.4% Native Hawaiian or other Pacific Islander, non-Hispanic/Latino; 0.2% international. 2% 25 or older, 60% live on campus, 4% transferred in. Retention: 94% of full-time freshmen returned the following year. Academic areas with the most degrees conferred: education; business/marketing; psychology; biological/life sciences. Core. Calendar: semesters. Academic remediation for entering students, services for LD students, advanced placement, accelerated degree program, self-designed majors, honors program, independent study, double major, summer session for credit, part-time degree program, internships, graduate courses open to undergrads. Off campus study at members of the National Student Exchange, Philadelphia College of Pharmacy and Science, New Jersey Marine Sciences Consortium (Sandy Hook and Sea Isle City). Study abroad program. ROTC: Army (c), Air Force (c).

Entrance Requirements: Options: electronic application, early decision, deferred admission, international baccalaureate accepted. Required: essay, high school transcript, SAT or ACT. Recommended: minimum 2.5 high school GPA, 3 recommendations. Required for some: interview, art portfolio or music audition. Entrance: very difficult. Application deadlines: 1/15, 11/15 for early decision. Notification: continuous until 1/15, 12/15 for early decision. SAT Reasoning Test deadline: 1/15. Applicants placed on waiting list: 1,437. Wait-listed applicants offered admission: 9. Early decision applicants: 524. Early decision applicants admitted: 313.

Costs Per Year: Application fee: $75. State resident tuition: $10,102 full-time, $358 per credit hour part-time. Nonresident tuition: $20,254 full-time, $716.87 per credit hour part-time. Mandatory fees: $4276 full-time, $170.29 per credit hour part-time. Part-time tuition and fees vary according to course load. College room and board: $10,998. College room only: $8006. Room and board charges vary according to board plan.

Collegiate Environment: Orientation program. Drama-theater group, choral group, student-run newspaper, radio station. Social organizations: 205 open to all; national fraternities, national sororities, local fraternities, local sororities; 16% of eligible men and 13% of eligible women are members. Most popular organizations: Student Government Association, College Union Board, Inter-Greek Council, The Signal. Major annual events: Homecoming Spirit Week, Multicultural STEP Show, TCNJ Late Nighter. Student services: legal services, health clinic, personal-psychological counseling, women's center. Campus security: 24-hour emergency response devices and patrols, student patrols, late night transport-escort service, controlled dormitory ac-

cess. 3,921 college housing spaces available; all were occupied in 2012-13. Freshmen guaranteed college housing. On-campus residence required in freshman year. Option: coed housing available. New Library with 694,144 books, 426,253 microform titles, 73,733 serials, 40,127 audiovisual materials, an OPAC, and a Web page. 631 computers available on campus for general student use. Computer purchase/lease plans available. A campuswide network can be accessed from student residence rooms and from off campus. Students can access the following: online class registration. Staffed computer lab on campus provides training in use of computers, software, and the Internet.

Community Environment: See Rider University.

■ COLLEGE OF SAINT ELIZABETH

2 Convent Rd.
Morristown, NJ 07960-6989
Tel: (973)290-4000; Free: 800-210-7900
Fax: (973)290-4710
E-mail: apply@csa.edu
Web Site: www.cse.edu/

Description: Independent Roman Catholic, comprehensive, coed. Awards bachelor's, master's, and doctoral degrees (also offers coed adult undergraduate degree program and coed graduate programs). Founded 1899. Setting: 188-acre suburban campus with easy access to New York City. Endowment: $19.4 million. Educational spending for the previous fiscal year: $1169 per student. Total enrollment: 1,687. Faculty: 289 (69 full-time, 220 part-time). Student-undergrad faculty ratio is 7:1. 1,386 applied, 58% were admitted. 7% from top 10% of their high school class, 23% from top quarter, 58% from top half. Full-time: 583 students, 98% women, 2% men. Part-time: 496 students, 87% women, 13% men. Students come from 8 states and territories, 25 other countries, 3% from out-of-state. 0.3% American Indian or Alaska Native, non-Hispanic/Latino; 15% Hispanic/Latino; 21% African American, non-Hispanic/Latino; 3% Asian, non-Hispanic/Latino; 0.2% Native Hawaiian or other Pacific Islander, non-Hispanic/Latino; 4% international. 50% 25 or older, 63% live on campus, 2% transferred in. Retention: 70% of full-time freshmen returned the following year. Academic areas with the most degrees conferred: health professions and related sciences; psychology; business/marketing; education. Core. Calendar: semesters. Academic remediation for entering students, ESL program, services for LD students, advanced placement, accelerated degree program, self-designed majors, honors program, independent study, distance learning, double major, summer session for credit, part-time degree program, internships, graduate courses open to undergrads. Off campus study at 4 members of the Seton Colleges, Drew University, Fairleigh Dickinson University. Study abroad program.

Entrance Requirements: Options: electronic application, deferred admission, international baccalaureate accepted. Required: high school transcript, minimum 2 high school GPA, 2 recommendations, SAT or ACT. Recommended: essay, interview. Entrance: moderately difficult. Application deadline: 8/15. Notification: 11/15. SAT Reasoning Test deadline: 8/15.

Costs Per Year: Application fee: $35. Comprehensive fee: $42,161 includes full-time tuition ($28,026), mandatory fees ($1881), and college room and board ($12,254). Full-time tuition and fees vary according to class time and location. Room and board charges vary according to board plan. Part-time tuition: $806 per credit hour. Part-time tuition varies according to class time, course load, location, program, and reciprocity agreements.

Collegiate Environment: Orientation program. Drama-theater group, choral group, student-run newspaper. Social organizations: 20 open to all. Most popular organizations: Student Government Association, Students Take Action Committee, International/Intercultural Club, College Activities Board, Campus Ministry. Major annual events: Oktoberfest/Parents' Day, International Night, Christmas Celebration. Student services: health clinic, personal-psychological counseling. Campus security: 24-hour emergency response devices and patrols, late night transport-escort service, controlled dormitory access. 411 college housing spaces available; 386 were occupied in 2012-13. Freshmen guaranteed college housing. Option: women-only housing available. Mahoney Library with 119,438 books, 142,451 microform titles, 1,048 serials, 1,744 audiovisual materials, an OPAC, and a Web page. Operations spending for the previous fiscal year: $2.3 million. 127 computers available on campus for general student use. A campuswide network can be accessed from student residence rooms and from off campus. Students can access the following: online class registration. Staffed computer lab on campus provides training in use of computers, software, and the Internet.

Community Environment: Situated in northern New Jersey, two miles east of Morristown (population 18,851), the college is near enough to New York to enjoy the educational, cultural and social advantages of that city. All forms of commercial transportation are convenient.

■ **COUNTY COLLEGE OF MORRIS**
214 Ctr. Grove Rd.
Randolph, NJ 07869-2086
Tel: (973)328-5000
Fax: (973)328-1282
E-mail: admiss@ccm.edu
Web Site: www.ccm.edu/
Description: County-supported, 2-year, coed. Part of New Jersey Commission on Higher Education. Awards certificates, transfer associate, and terminal associate degrees. Founded 1966. Setting: 218-acre suburban campus with easy access to New York City. Total enrollment: 8,679. Faculty: 885 (447 full-time, 438 part-time). Student-undergrad faculty ratio is 10:1. Students come from 3 states and territories, 0% from out-of-state. 0.3% American Indian or Alaska Native, non-Hispanic/Latino; 18% Hispanic/Latino; 5% African American, non-Hispanic/Latino; 5% Asian, non-Hispanic/Latino; 0.1% Native Hawaiian or other Pacific Islander, non-Hispanic/Latino. 23% 25 or older. Calendar: semesters.
Entrance Requirements: Open admission. Required: high school transcript. Entrance: noncompetitive. Notification: continuous.
Costs Per Year: Application fee: $30. Area resident tuition: $3580 full-time, $117 per credit hour part-time. State resident tuition: $7160 full-time, $234 per credit hour part-time. Nonresident tuition: $10,740 full-time, $251 per credit hour part-time. Mandatory fees: $525 full-time, $17.50 per credit hour part-time. Full-time tuition and fees vary according to location and program. Part-time tuition and fees vary according to course load, location, and program.
Collegiate Environment: College housing not available.
Community Environment: Morristown, population 18,851 is a suburban area 27 miles west of New York City, and was the winter encampment of General Washington's army during the winter of 1777 and 1779-80. Many historical events took place in Morristown. The sites have been restored and are incorporated in the Morristown National Historical Park. Commercial transportation is available. Excellent shopping and recreational facilities are available, including all water sports. Part-time employment opportunities are good.

■ **CUMBERLAND COUNTY COLLEGE**
PO Box 1500, College Dr.
Vineland, NJ 08362
Tel: (856)691-8600
Fax: (856)691-6157
Web Site: www.cccnj.edu/
Description: State and locally supported, 2-year, coed. Part of New Jersey Commission on Higher Education. Awards certificates, transfer associate, and terminal associate degrees. Founded 1963. Setting: 100-acre small town campus with easy access to Philadelphia. Total enrollment: 4,014. Faculty: 290 (47 full-time, 243 part-time). Student-undergrad faculty ratio is 14:1. 37% 25 or older. Core. Calendar: semesters. Academic remediation for entering students, ESL program, services for LD students, advanced placement, honors program, distance learning, double major, summer session for credit, part-time degree program, co-op programs.
Entrance Requirements: Open admission except for nursing, radiography programs. Options: electronic application, early admission, deferred admission. Required: high school transcript. Entrance: noncompetitive. Application deadline: Rolling. Notification: continuous.
Collegiate Environment: Orientation program. Drama-theater group, choral group, student-run newspaper. Student services: personal-psychological counseling. Campus security: 24-hour emergency response devices, late night transport-escort service. Cumberland County College Library with 51,000 books, 3,900 microform titles, 213 serials, 480 audiovisual materials, an OPAC, and a Web page.
Community Environment: Cumberland County's population lies mainly in the tri-city area of Vineland, Bridgeton, and Millville. Industries include glass production, clothing manufacturing, and food processing and canning. Most church denominations are represented, and a hospital, shopping facilities, and numerous service and civic groups all contribute to the general well-being of the Cumberland area. Golf, tennis, and water sports are the main recreational activities in the county.

■ **DEVRY UNIVERSITY (NORTH BRUNSWICK)**
630 US Hwy. 1
North Brunswick, NJ 08902-3362

Tel: (732)729-3532; Free: 866-338-7941
Web Site: www.devry.edu/
Description: Proprietary, comprehensive, coed. Part of DeVry University. Awards associate, bachelor's, and master's degrees. Founded 1969. Setting: urban campus. Total enrollment: 1,414. Faculty: 159 (34 full-time, 125 part-time). Student-undergrad faculty ratio is 12:1. Full-time: 556 students, 26% women, 74% men. Part-time: 657 students, 29% women, 71% men. 9% from out-of-state. 0.4% American Indian or Alaska Native, non-Hispanic/Latino; 20% Hispanic/Latino; 16% African American, non-Hispanic/Latino; 5% Asian, non-Hispanic/Latino; 0.4% Native Hawaiian or other Pacific Islander, non-Hispanic/Latino; 2% international. 55% 25 or older, 14% transferred in. Academic areas with the most degrees conferred: business/marketing; computer and information sciences; engineering technologies. Calendar: semesters. Part-time degree program, adult/continuing education programs.
Entrance Requirements: Required: high school transcript, interview. Entrance: minimally difficult. Application deadline: Rolling. Notification: continuous.
Costs Per Year: Application fee: $40. Tuition: $16,076 full-time, $609 per credit hour part-time. Mandatory fees: $80 full-time.
Collegiate Environment: College housing not available.
Community Environment: North Brunswick is a suburban community within easy access to New York City, and Philadelphia and all their cultural and recreational resources. In addition, the 125-mile New Jersey Seacoast provides all forms of water sports.

■ **DEVRY UNIVERSITY (PARAMUS)**
35 Plz., 81 E State Rte. 4
Ste. 102
Paramus, NJ 07652
Tel: (201)556-2840; Free: 866-338-7941
Web Site: www.devry.edu/
Description: Proprietary, comprehensive, coed. Awards associate, bachelor's, and master's degrees.

■ **DREW UNIVERSITY**
36 Madison Ave.
Madison, NJ 07940-1493
Tel: (973)408-3000
Fax: (973)408-3939
E-mail: cadm@drew.edu
Web Site: www.drew.edu/
Description: Independent, university, coed, affiliated with United Methodist Church. Awards bachelor's, master's, and doctoral degrees and post-master's certificates. Founded 1867. Setting: 186-acre suburban campus with easy access to New York City. Endowment: $210 million. Total enrollment: 2,447. Faculty: 300 (160 full-time, 140 part-time). Student-undergrad faculty ratio is 10:1. 3,872 applied, 85% were admitted. 31% from top 10% of their high school class, 58% from top quarter, 85% from top half. Full-time: 1,568 students, 60% women, 40% men. Part-time: 72 students, 58% women, 42% men. Students come from 35 states and territories, 24 other countries, 35% from out-of-state. 0.1% American Indian or Alaska Native, non-Hispanic/Latino; 14% Hispanic/Latino; 10% African American, non-Hispanic/Latino; 5% Asian, non-Hispanic/Latino; 0% Native Hawaiian or other Pacific Islander, non-Hispanic/Latino; 2% international. 2% 25 or older, 82% live on campus, 3% transferred in. Retention: 75% of full-time freshmen returned the following year. Academic areas with the most degrees conferred: social sciences; visual and performing arts; biological/life sciences. Core. Calendar: semesters. Academic remediation for entering students, services for LD students, advanced placement, accelerated degree program, self-designed majors, honors program, independent study, double major, summer session for credit, part-time degree program, external degree program, adult/continuing education programs, internships, graduate courses open to undergrads. Off campus study at College of Saint Elizabeth, Fairleigh Dickinson University. Study abroad program.
Entrance Requirements: Options: electronic application, early admission, early decision, early action, deferred admission. Required: essay, high school transcript, 1 recommendation. Recommended: interview, SAT and ACT scores are optional and are considered if submitted. SAT subject tests are not used. Entrance: moderately difficult. Application deadlines: 2/1, 11/1 for early decision plan 1, 1/15 for early decision plan 2, 1/15 for early action. Notification: continuous until 11/15, 1/15 for early decision plan 1, 2/15 for early decision plan 2. Transfer credits accepted: Yes. Early decision applicants: 237. Early decision applicants admitted: 163.

Costs Per Year: Application fee: $60. Comprehensive fee: $56,012 includes full-time tuition ($42,936), mandatory fees ($1132), and college room and board ($11,944). College room only: $7684. Full-time tuition and fees vary according to course load. Room and board charges vary according to board plan and housing facility. Part-time tuition: $1789 per credit hour. Part-time tuition varies according to course load.

Collegiate Environment: Orientation program. Drama-theater group, choral group, student-run newspaper, radio station. Social organizations: 50 open to all. Most popular organizations: New Social Engine, Student Government Association, D.U.D.S.-Drew University Dramatic Society, University Program Board, Kuumba Pan African Student Association. Major annual events: First Annual Picnic, Holiday Ball, Drewtopia. Student services: health clinic, personal-psychological counseling. Campus security: 24-hour emergency response devices and patrols, late night transport-escort service, controlled dormitory access. Freshmen guaranteed college housing. Option: coed housing available. Drew University/Rose Library plus 1 other with an OPAC and a Web page.

Community Environment: Madison, population approximately 16,000, is a suburban community in historical surroundings. Bordering a rural area that features numerous horse farms and a 6,000-acre national wildlife preserve, Madison is on a commuter rail line, just 30 miles from Manhattan. Some part-time employment is available.

■ **ESSEX COUNTY COLLEGE**
303 University Ave.
Newark, NJ 07102-1798
Tel: (973)877-3000
Fax: (973)623-6449
Web Site: www.essex.edu/

Description: County-supported, 2-year, coed. Part of New Jersey Commission on Higher Education. Awards certificates, transfer associate, and terminal associate degrees. Founded 1966. Setting: 22-acre urban campus with easy access to New York City. Total enrollment: 11,979. Faculty: 601 (118 full-time, 483 part-time). Student-undergrad faculty ratio is 29:1. 7,757 applied, 100% were admitted. Full-time: 6,569 students, 57% women, 43% men. Part-time: 5,410 students, 59% women, 41% men. Students come from 9 states and territories, 49 other countries, 1% from out-of-state. 0.2% American Indian or Alaska Native, non-Hispanic/Latino; 24% Hispanic/Latino; 48% African American, non-Hispanic/Latino; 4% Asian, non-Hispanic/Latino; 0.1% Native Hawaiian or other Pacific Islander, non-Hispanic/Latino; 8% international. 41% 25 or older, 2% transferred in. Retention: 50% of full-time freshmen returned the following year. Core. Calendar: semesters. Academic remediation for entering students, ESL program, services for LD students, advanced placement, accelerated degree program, independent study, distance learning, double major, summer session for credit, part-time degree program, adult/continuing education programs, co-op programs and internships. Off campus study at New Jersey Institute of Technology; Rutgers, The State University of New Jersey; University of Medicine and Dentistry of New Jersey. ROTC: Army (c).

Entrance Requirements: Open admission except for allied health programs. Options: electronic application, deferred admission. Required: high school transcript. Entrance: noncompetitive. Application deadline: 8/15. Notification: continuous, continuous for nonresidents.

Costs Per Year: Application fee: $25. Area resident tuition: $3255 full-time, $108.50 per credit hour part-time. State resident tuition: $6510 full-time, $217 per credit hour part-time. Nonresident tuition: $6510 full-time, $217 per credit hour part-time. Mandatory fees: $975 full-time, $32.50 per credit hour part-time.

Collegiate Environment: Orientation program. Drama-theater group, choral group, student-run newspaper. Social organizations: 20 open to all. Most popular organizations: Fashion Entertainment Board, Phi Theta Kappa, Latin Student Union, DECA, Black Student Association. Student services: personal-psychological counseling, women's center. Campus security: 24-hour emergency response devices and patrols. College housing not available. Martin Luther King, Jr. Library with 91,000 books, 29,607 microform titles, 639 serials, an OPAC, and a Web page. 750 computers available on campus for general student use. A campuswide network can be accessed from off-campus. Staffed computer lab on campus.

Community Environment: See New Jersey Institute of Technology.

■ **FAIRLEIGH DICKINSON UNIVERSITY, COLLEGE AT FLORHAM**
285 Madison Ave.
Madison, NJ 07940-1099
Tel: (973)443-8500; Free: 800-338-8803

E-mail: globaleducation@fdu.edu
Web Site: www.fdu.edu/

Description: Independent, comprehensive, coed. Awards bachelor's, master's, and doctoral degrees and post-master's certificates. Founded 1942. Setting: 178-acre suburban campus with easy access to New York City. Total enrollment: 3,067. Faculty: 378 (141 full-time, 237 part-time). Student-undergrad faculty ratio is 12:1. 3,647 applied, 78% were admitted. 14% from top 10% of their high school class, 36% from top quarter, 75% from top half. Full-time: 2,213 students, 56% women, 44% men. Part-time: 183 students, 51% women, 49% men. Students come from 26 states and territories, 11 other countries, 16% from out-of-state. 1% American Indian or Alaska Native, non-Hispanic/Latino; 13% Hispanic/Latino; 11% African American, non-Hispanic/Latino; 4% Asian, non-Hispanic/Latino; 0% Native Hawaiian or other Pacific Islander, non-Hispanic/Latino; 1% international. 5% 25 or older, 63% live on campus, 5% transferred in. Retention: 76% of full-time freshmen returned the following year. Academic areas with the most degrees conferred: business/marketing; psychology; communication/journalism. Core. Calendar: semesters. Academic remediation for entering students, services for LD students, advanced placement, accelerated degree program, self-designed majors, honors program, independent study, distance learning, double major, summer session for credit, part-time degree program, adult/continuing education programs, co-op programs and internships, graduate courses open to undergrads. Off campus study at College of Saint Elizabeth, Drew University. Study abroad program. ROTC: Army (c), Air Force (c).

Entrance Requirements: Options: electronic application, international baccalaureate accepted. Required: high school transcript, 2 recommendations, SAT or ACT. Entrance: moderately difficult. Application deadline: Rolling. Notification: continuous. Transfer credits accepted: Yes.

Costs Per Year: Application fee: $40. Comprehensive fee: $48,324 includes full-time tuition ($35,412), mandatory fees ($940), and college room and board ($11,972). College room only: $7902. Room and board charges vary according to board plan and housing facility. Part-time tuition: $1054 per credit hour.

Collegiate Environment: Orientation program. Drama-theater group, choral group, student-run newspaper. Social organizations: 60 open to all; national fraternities, national sororities. Most popular organizations: College Panhellenic Council, Association of Black Collegians, Latin American Student Organization, Florham Programming Committee, InterFraternity Council. Major annual events: Homecoming, Greek Week, Black History Month. Student services: health clinic, personal-psychological counseling. Campus security: 24-hour emergency response devices and patrols, late night transport-escort service, controlled dormitory access, trained law enforcement personnel on staff. 1,534 college housing spaces available; 1,474 were occupied in 2012-13. Freshmen given priority for college housing. Option: coed housing available. College of Florham Library with 149,376 books, 19,626 microform titles, 144 serials, 1,417 audiovisual materials, and an OPAC. 150 computers available on campus for general student use. Computer purchase/lease plans available. A campuswide network can be accessed from student residence rooms and from off campus. Students can access the following: online class registration. Staffed computer lab on campus.

■ **FAIRLEIGH DICKINSON UNIVERSITY, METROPOLITAN CAMPUS**
1000 River Rd.
Teaneck, NJ 07666-1914
Tel: (201)692-2000; Free: 800-338-8803
E-mail: globaleducation@fdu.edu
Web Site: www.fdu.edu/

Description: Independent, comprehensive, coed. Awards associate, bachelor's, master's, and doctoral degrees and post-master's certificates. Founded 1942. Setting: 88-acre suburban campus with easy access to New York City. Total enrollment: 9,130. Faculty: 753 (190 full-time, 563 part-time). Student-undergrad faculty ratio is 15:1. 5,193 applied, 73% were admitted. 18% from top 10% of their high school class, 45% from top quarter, 83% from top half. Full-time: 2,882 students, 59% women, 41% men. Part-time: 3,893 students, 60% women, 40% men. Students come from 30 states and territories, 45 other countries, 14% from out-of-state. 0.2% American Indian or Alaska Native, non-Hispanic/Latino; 34% Hispanic/Latino; 14% African American, non-Hispanic/Latino; 5% Asian, non-Hispanic/Latino; 0.1% Native Hawaiian or other Pacific Islander, non-Hispanic/Latino; 7% international. 34% 25 or older, 19% live on campus, 6% transferred in. Retention: 70% of full-time freshmen returned the following year. Academic areas with the most degrees conferred: liberal arts/general studies; health professions and related sciences; business/marketing. Core. Calendar: semesters. Academic remediation for entering students, ESL program, services for LD students, advanced placement, accelerated degree program, self-designed majors, honors program, independent study, distance learning, double major, summer session for credit, part-time degree program, adult/continuing education programs, co-op programs and internships, graduate courses open to undergrads. Off campus study at College of St. Elizabeth, Drew University. Study abroad program. ROTC: Army (c), Air Force (c).

Entrance Requirements: Options: electronic application, early admission. Required: high school transcript, 2 recommendations, SAT or ACT. Required for some: interview. Entrance: moderately difficult. Application deadline: Rolling. Notification: continuous. Transfer credits accepted: Yes.

Costs Per Year: Application fee: $40. Comprehensive fee: $46,198 includes full-time tuition ($32,852), mandatory fees ($940), and college room and board ($12,406). College room only: $8336. Room and board charges vary according to board plan and housing facility. Part-time tuition: $1054 per credit hour.

Collegiate Environment: Orientation program. Drama-theater group, choral group, student-run newspaper, radio station. Social organizations: 70 open to all; national fraternities, national sororities. Most popular organizations: Student Programming Board, Student Government Association, Greek Life, Residence Hall Association, Spectrum (LGBT). Major annual events: Welcome Week, Springfest, Metro Knights. Student services: health clinic, personal-psychological counseling, women's center. Campus security: 24-hour emergency response devices and patrols, late night transport-escort service, controlled dormitory access, trained law enforcement personnel on staff. 991 college housing spaces available; 788 were occupied in 2012-13. Options: coed, men-only, women-only housing available. Giovatto Library plus 1 other with 155,753 books, 17,000 microform titles, 2,105 audiovisual materials, and an OPAC. 225 computers available on campus for general student use. Computer purchase/lease plans available. A campuswide network can be accessed from student residence rooms and from off campus. Students can access the following: online class registration. Staffed computer lab on campus.

■ FELICIAN COLLEGE
262 S Main St.
Lodi, NJ 07644-2117
Tel: (201)559-6000
Fax: (973)778-4111
E-mail: admissions@felician.edu
Web Site: www.felician.edu/

Description: Independent Roman Catholic, comprehensive, coed. Awards associate, bachelor's, master's, and doctoral degrees and post-master's certificates. Founded 1942. Setting: 37-acre suburban campus with easy access to New York City. Endowment: $4.8 million. Educational spending for the previous fiscal year: $8033 per student. Total enrollment: 2,109. Faculty: 241 (116 full-time, 125 part-time). Student-undergrad faculty ratio is 12:1. 2,206 applied, 90% were admitted. 8% from top 10% of their high school class, 35% from top quarter, 65% from top half. Full-time: 1,485 students, 73% women, 27% men. Part-time: 290 students, 78% women, 22% men. Students come from 12 states and territories, 20 other countries, 6% from out-of-state. 1% American Indian or Alaska Native, non-Hispanic/Latino; 22% Hispanic/Latino; 15% African American, non-Hispanic/Latino; 7% Asian, non-Hispanic/Latino; 0.4% Native Hawaiian or other Pacific Islander, non-Hispanic/Latino; 2% international. 36% 25 or older, 18% live on campus, 5% transferred in. Retention: 73% of full-time freshmen returned the following year. Academic areas with the most degrees conferred: health professions and related sciences; business/marketing; education. Core. Calendar: semesters. Academic remediation for entering students, ESL program, services for LD students, advanced placement, accelerated degree program, self-designed majors, honors program, independent study, distance learning, double major, summer session for credit, part-time degree program, adult/continuing education programs, co-op programs and internships, graduate courses open to undergrads. Off campus study at University of Medicine and Dentistry of New Jersey. Study abroad program.

Entrance Requirements: Option: deferred admission. Required: high school transcript, minimum 2 high school GPA, SAT or ACT. Required for some: essay, interview, ACT, SAT Subject Tests. Entrance: moderately difficult. Application deadline: Rolling. Notification: continuous. SAT Reasoning Test deadline: 6/10. Transfer credits accepted: Yes.

Costs Per Year: Application fee: $30. Comprehensive fee: $41,640 includes full-time tuition ($28,360), mandatory fees ($1630), and college room and board ($11,650). Full-time tuition and fees vary according to program. Room

and board charges vary according to housing facility. Part-time tuition: $935 per credit hour. Part-time tuition varies according to course load and program.

Collegiate Environment: Orientation program. Drama-theater group, choral group, student-run radio station. Social organizations: 37 open to all; local fraternities, local sororities. Most popular organizations: Student Nurses Association, Zeta Alpha Zeta teaching sorority, Campus Activity Board, Students In Free Enterprise (SIFE), Student Government Association. Major annual events: Homecoming/College Festival, Midnight Madness, Springfest. Student services: health clinic, personal-psychological counseling. Campus security: 24-hour patrols, student patrols, late night transport-escort service. 500 college housing spaces available; 321 were occupied in 2012-13. Freshmen given priority for college housing. Options: coed, men-only, women-only housing available. Felician College Library plus 2 others with 158,728 books, 89,191 microform titles, 22,575 serials, 1,575 audiovisual materials, an OPAC, and a Web page. Operations spending for the previous fiscal year: $655,849. 100 computers available on campus for general student use. A campuswide network can be accessed from student residence rooms and from off campus. Students can access the following: online class registration. Staffed computer lab on campus provides training in use of computers and the Internet.

Community Environment: Felician is located on two campuses, in Lodi and in Rutherford, in Bergen County, New Jersey, 12 miles from New York City and 10 minutes from the Meadowlands Sports Complex.

■ GEORGIAN COURT UNIVERSITY
900 Lakewood Ave.
Lakewood, NJ 08701-2697
Tel: (732)987-2760; Free: 800-458-8422
Fax: (732)987-2000
E-mail: admissions@georgian.edu
Web Site: www.georgian.edu/

Description: Independent Roman Catholic, comprehensive, coed. Awards bachelor's and master's degrees and post-master's certificates. Founded 1908. Setting: 156-acre suburban campus with easy access to New York City, Philadelphia. Total enrollment: 2,555. Faculty: 272 (105 full-time, 167 part-time). Student-undergrad faculty ratio is 13:1. 1,134 applied, 66% were admitted. 9% from top 10% of their high school class, 29% from top quarter, 68% from top half. Full-time: 1,393 students, 95% women, 5% men. Part-time: 379 students, 76% women, 24% men. 4% from out-of-state. 0.3% American Indian or Alaska Native, non-Hispanic/Latino; 10% Hispanic/Latino; 14% African American, non-Hispanic/Latino; 2% Asian, non-Hispanic/Latino; 0.1% Native Hawaiian or other Pacific Islander, non-Hispanic/Latino; 0.3% international. 22% 25 or older, 25% live on campus, 13% transferred in. Retention: 65% of full-time freshmen returned the following year. Academic areas with the most degrees conferred: education; psychology; business/marketing. Calendar: semesters. Part-time degree program, adult/continuing education programs.

Entrance Requirements: Options: electronic application, early action, deferred admission. Required: high school transcript, minimum 2.5 high school GPA, 2 recommendations, SAT or ACT. Recommended: essay, interview. Entrance: moderately difficult. Application deadlines: 8/1, 11/15 for early action. Notification: 12/30 for early action. Transfer credits accepted: Yes.

Costs Per Year: Application fee: $40. Comprehensive fee: $39,600 includes full-time tuition ($26,740) and college room and board ($12,860).

Collegiate Environment: Orientation program. Campus security: 24-hour emergency response devices and patrols, late night transport-escort service, controlled dormitory access. The Sister Mary Joseph Cunningham Library with an OPAC and a Web page.

Community Environment: Lakewood, population 36,000, is located in the central part of New Jersey and is convenient to the Route 9 corridor, Garden State Parkway, and Interstate 95. New York City, Philadelphia, and Atlantic City are each less than one and one-half hours from the college. Lakewood offers the services of a public library, hospital, various houses of worship, and numerous major civic and service organizations. The famous New Jersey shore is less than one-half hour away. Nearby are also the Naval Air Engineering Center, a sport parachuting center, and shopping centers.

■ GLOUCESTER COUNTY COLLEGE
1400 Tanyard Rd.
Sewell, NJ 08080
Tel: (856)468-5000
Fax: (856)468-8498

E-mail: jatkinso@gccnj.edu

Web Site: www.gccnj.edu/

Description: County-supported, 2-year, coed. Part of New Jersey Commission on Higher Education. Awards certificates, transfer associate, and terminal associate degrees. Founded 1967. Setting: 270-acre rural campus with easy access to Philadelphia. Total enrollment: 6,490. Student-undergrad faculty ratio is 28:1. 1% from out-of-state. 28% 25 or older. Core. Calendar: semesters. Academic remediation for entering students, services for LD students, advanced placement, distance learning, summer session for credit, part-time degree program, co-op programs.

Entrance Requirements: Open admission except for nursing, respiratory therapy, nuclear medicine, ultrasound, auto technology programs. Options: electronic application, deferred admission. Required: high school transcript. Required for some: SAT or ACT. Entrance: noncompetitive. Application deadline: Rolling.

Collegiate Environment: Drama-theater group, choral group, student-run newspaper, radio station. Student services: health clinic, personal-psychological counseling, women's center. Campus security: 24-hour emergency response devices and patrols, late night transport-escort service. Gloucester County College Library with an OPAC.

Community Environment: See Rutgers, The State University of New Jersey - Camden College of Arts and Sciences.

■ **HUDSON COUNTY COMMUNITY COLLEGE**

25 Journal Sq.

Jersey City, NJ 07306

Tel: (201)656-2020

Fax: (201)714-2136

E-mail: martin@hccc.edu

Web Site: www.hccc.edu/

Description: State and locally supported, 2-year, coed. Part of New Jersey Commission on Higher Education. Awards diplomas, transfer associate, and terminal associate degrees. Founded 1974. Setting: urban campus with easy access to New York City. Total enrollment: 7,019. 38% 25 or older. Core. Calendar: semesters. Academic remediation for entering students, ESL program, services for LD students, advanced placement, honors program, independent study, double major, summer session for credit, part-time degree program, adult/continuing education programs, internships.

Entrance Requirements: Open admission. Required: high school transcript. Entrance: noncompetitive. Application deadline: 9/1. Notification: continuous until 9/1. Preference given to county residents.

Collegiate Environment: Drama-theater group, choral group, student-run newspaper. Student services: personal-psychological counseling. Campus security: 24-hour emergency response devices. Hudson County Community College Library/Learning Resources Center with 32,000 books, 11,000 microform titles, 251 serials, 1,690 audiovisual materials, an OPAC, and a Web page.

■ **ITT TECHNICAL INSTITUTE**

9000 Lincoln Dr. E

Ste. 100

Marlton, NJ 08053

Tel: (856)396-3500; Free: 877-209-5410

Web Site: www.itt-tech.edu/

Description: Proprietary, 2-year, coed. Awards terminal associate degrees.

Entrance Requirements: Entrance: minimally difficult.

■ **KEAN UNIVERSITY**

1000 Morris Ave.

Union, NJ 07083

Tel: (908)737-KEAN

Fax: (908)737-3415

E-mail: admitme@kean.edu

Web Site: www.kean.edu/

Description: State-supported, comprehensive, coed. Part of New Jersey State College System. Awards bachelor's, master's, and doctoral degrees and post-master's certificates. Founded 1855. Setting: 186-acre suburban campus with easy access to New York City. Endowment: $13.1 million. Research spending for the previous fiscal year: $1.4 million. Educational spending for the previous fiscal year: $7638 per student. Total enrollment: 15,391. Faculty: 1,481 (344 full-time, 1,137 part-time). Student-undergrad faculty ratio is 17:1. 6,015 applied, 68% were admitted. 8% from top 10% of their high school class, 31% from top quarter, 70% from top half. Full-time: 9,899 students, 60% women, 40% men. Part-time: 2,996 students, 65%

women, 35% men. Students come from 21 states and territories, 50 other countries, 2% from out-of-state. 0.1% American Indian or Alaska Native, non-Hispanic/Latino; 22% Hispanic/Latino; 17% African American, non-Hispanic/Latino; 5% Asian, non-Hispanic/Latino; 0.4% Native Hawaiian or other Pacific Islander, non-Hispanic/Latino; 1% international. 27% 25 or older, 14% live on campus, 12% transferred in. Retention: 72% of full-time freshmen returned the following year. Academic areas with the most degrees conferred: business/marketing; education; psychology. Core. Calendar: semesters. Academic remediation for entering students, ESL program, services for LD students, advanced placement, accelerated degree program, honors program, independent study, distance learning, double major, summer session for credit, part-time degree program, adult/continuing education programs, co-op programs and internships, graduate courses open to undergrads. Off campus study. Study abroad program. ROTC: Army (c), Air Force (c).

Entrance Requirements: Options: electronic application, international baccalaureate accepted. Required: essay, high school transcript, minimum 2.8 high school GPA, 2 recommendations, SAT or ACT, SAT or ACT. Required for some: interview. Entrance: moderately difficult. Application deadline: 5/31. Notification: continuous. SAT Reasoning Test deadline: 5/31. Transfer credits accepted: Yes.

Costs Per Year: Application fee: $75. State resident tuition: $6925 full-time, $270 per credit part-time. Nonresident tuition: $12,967 full-time, $457 per credit part-time. Mandatory fees: $3,676 full-time, $135 per credit part-time. Part-time tuition and fees vary according to course load. College room and board: $13,934. College room only: $10,804. Room and board charges vary according to board plan, housing facility, and student level.

Collegiate Environment: Orientation program. Drama-theater group, choral group, student-run newspaper, radio station. Social organizations: 143 open to all; national fraternities, national sororities, local fraternities, local sororities. Most popular organizations: Association for Computing Machinery, Student Occupational Therapy Association, Accounting Club, American Sign Language, Association of Latin American Students. Major annual events: Homecoming, Unity Week, Campus Awareness Festival. Student services: health clinic, personal-psychological counseling. Campus security: 24-hour emergency response devices and patrols, student patrols, late night transport-escort service, controlled dormitory access, 24-hour patrols by campus police. 2,045 college housing spaces available; 1,725 were occupied in 2012-13. Freshmen given priority for college housing. Option: coed housing available. Nancy Thompson Library with 357,020 books, 2,500 microform titles, 43,593 serials, an OPAC, and a Web page. Operations spending for the previous fiscal year: $4 million. 1,700 computers available on campus for general student use. A campuswide network can be accessed from student residence rooms and from off campus. Students can access the following: online class registration. Staffed computer lab on campus (open 24 hours a day) provides training in use of computers and the Internet.

Community Environment: The township of Union, population 55,326, and its proximity to major automobile, bus, rail, and air transportation networks makes access to the university excellent. This provides continuous cultural, intellectual and social interchange between the cities and the university. Community facilities include library, numerous churches, hospitals and clinics, major civic and service organizations. A recreation center provides facilities for special activities.

■ **MERCER COUNTY COMMUNITY COLLEGE**

1200 Old Trenton Rd.

Trenton, NJ 08690-1004

Tel: (609)586-4800; Free: 800-392-MCCC

Fax: (609)586-6944

E-mail: admiss@mccc.edu

Web Site: www.mccc.edu/

Description: State and locally supported, 2-year, coed. Awards certificates, transfer associate, and terminal associate degrees. Founded 1966. Setting: 292-acre suburban campus with easy access to New York City, Philadelphia. Educational spending for the previous fiscal year: $6061 per student. Total enrollment: 9,621. Faculty: 583 (131 full-time, 452 part-time). Student-undergrad faculty ratio is 22:1. Full-time: 4,372 students, 55% women, 45% men. Part-time: 5,249 students, 56% women, 44% men. Students come from 5 states and territories, 91 other countries, 7% from out-of-state. 39% 25 or older, 3% transferred in. Retention: 68% of full-time freshmen returned the following year. Core. Calendar: semesters. Academic remediation for entering students, ESL program, services for LD students, advanced placement, accelerated degree program, self-designed majors, independent study, distance learning, double major, summer session for credit, part-time degree program, external degree program, adult/continuing education programs, co-op programs and internships. ROTC: Army (c), Air Force (c).

Entrance Requirements: Open admission. Options: electronic application, deferred admission. Required: high school transcript. Recommended: interview. Entrance: noncompetitive. Application deadline: Rolling. Notification: continuous. Preference given to county residents.

Collegiate Environment: Orientation program. Drama-theater group, choral group, student-run newspaper, radio station. Social organizations: 38 open to all. Most popular organizations: Student Government Association, student radio station, African-American Student Organization, Student Activities Board, Phi Theta Kappa. Major annual events: NJCAA National Soccer Tournament, Club Day, Spring Day. Student services: personal-psychological counseling. Campus security: 24-hour emergency response devices and patrols. Mercer County Community College Library plus 1 other with 57,317 books, 251,470 microform titles, 8,934 audiovisual materials, an OPAC, and a Web page. Operations spending for the previous fiscal year: $555,239.

Community Environment: See Rider University.

■ **MIDDLESEX COUNTY COLLEGE**
2600 Woodbridge Ave.
Edison, NJ 08818-3050
Tel: (732)548-6000
Web Site: www.middlesexcc.edu/

Description: County-supported, 2-year, coed. Awards certificates, transfer associate, and terminal associate degrees. Founded 1964. Setting: 200-acre suburban campus with easy access to New York City. Total enrollment: 13,356. Student-undergrad faculty ratio is 26:1. 1% from out-of-state. 25% 25 or older. Calendar: semesters. Academic remediation for entering students, ESL program, services for LD students, advanced placement, independent study, distance learning, summer session for credit, part-time degree program, adult/continuing education programs, co-op programs and internships. Off campus study. Study abroad program. ROTC: Army (c).

Entrance Requirements: Open admission except for dental hygiene, nursing, radiography, medical laboratory technology, psychosocial rehabilitation, respiratory care and automotive technology programs. Options: early admission, deferred admission. Required: high school transcript. Required for some: National League of Nursing Exam for most health-related programs. Entrance: noncompetitive. Application deadline: Rolling. Notification: continuous. Preference given to county residents.

Collegiate Environment: Orientation program. Drama-theater group, choral group, student-run newspaper, radio station. Student services: health clinic, personal-psychological counseling. Campus security: 24-hour emergency response devices and patrols. Middlesex County College Library plus 1 other with 89,950 books, 302 serials, an OPAC, and a Web page.

Community Environment: Edison (population, 97,687) is located in a major metropolitan area, and is both a residential and industrial city with train and bus service available. It is located 45 minutes from New York City. Community facilities include a library, churches of all denominations, several hospitals, museums and various civic and service organizations. Edison offers fine shopping facilities. Part-time jobs are available. Parks and the Raritan River provide for boating and swimming, etc.

■ **MONMOUTH UNIVERSITY**
400 Cedar Ave.
West Long Branch, NJ 07764-1898
Tel: (732)571-3400; Free: 800-543-9671
Fax: (732)263-5166
E-mail: admission@monmouth.edu
Web Site: www.monmouth.edu/

Description: Independent, comprehensive, coed. Awards associate, bachelor's, master's, and doctoral degrees and post-master's certificates. Founded 1933. Setting: 156-acre suburban campus with easy access to New York City, Philadelphia. Endowment: $61.6 million. Research spending for the previous fiscal year: $2.9 million. Educational spending for the previous fiscal year: $8316 per student. Total enrollment: 6,472. Faculty: 597 (266 full-time, 331 part-time). Student-undergrad faculty ratio is 15:1. 6,127 applied, 71% were admitted. 21% from top 10% of their high school class, 50% from top quarter, 84% from top half. Full-time: 4,437 students, 59% women, 41% men. Part-time: 301 students, 61% women, 39% men. Students come from 29 states and territories, 23 other countries, 12% from out-of-state. 0.1% American Indian or Alaska Native, non-Hispanic/Latino; 9% Hispanic/Latino; 4% African American, non-Hispanic/Latino; 2% Asian, non-Hispanic/Latino; 0.1% Native Hawaiian or other Pacific Islander, non-Hispanic/Latino; 1% international. 6% 25 or older, 46% live on campus, 7% transferred in.

Retention: 79% of full-time freshmen returned the following year. Academic areas with the most degrees conferred: business/marketing; communication/journalism; education. Core. Calendar: semesters. Academic remediation for entering students, services for LD students, advanced placement, accelerated degree program, self-designed majors, honors program, independent study, distance learning, double major, summer session for credit, part-time degree program, co-op programs and internships, graduate courses open to undergrads. Study abroad program. ROTC: Army (c), Air Force (c).

Entrance Requirements: Options: electronic application, early action, deferred admission, international baccalaureate accepted. Required: essay, high school transcript, 1 recommendation, SAT or ACT. Recommended: resume of activities including community involvement and leadership positions. Required for some: essay, interview. Entrance: moderately difficult. Application deadlines: 3/1, 12/1 for early action. Notification: 4/1, 1/15 for early action. SAT Reasoning Test deadline: 3/1. Transfer credits accepted: Yes. Early action applicants: 2,870. Early action applicants admitted: 2,177.

Costs Per Year: Application fee: $50. One-time mandatory fee: $200. Comprehensive fee: $40,512 includes full-time tuition ($29,082), mandatory fees ($628), and college room and board ($10,802). College room only: $6169. Room and board charges vary according to board plan and housing facility. Part-time tuition: $842 per credit hour. Part-time mandatory fees: $157 per term. Part-time tuition and fees vary according to course load.

Collegiate Environment: Orientation program. Drama-theater group, choral group, student-run newspaper, radio station. Social organizations: 76 open to all; national fraternities, national sororities; 11% of eligible men and 12% of eligible women are members. Most popular organizations: radio station WMCX 88.9 FM, Student Government Association, student newspaper (Outlook), Student Activities Board, Shadows (yearbook). Major annual events: Homecoming, The Big Event, Spring Fest. Student services: legal services, health clinic, personal-psychological counseling, women's center. Campus security: 24-hour emergency response devices and patrols, late night transport-escort service, controlled dormitory access. 2,004 college housing spaces available; all were occupied in 2012-13. Freshmen guaranteed college housing. Option: coed housing available. Monmouth University Library with 286,000 books, 43,200 serials, 800 audiovisual materials, an OPAC, and a Web page. Operations spending for the previous fiscal year: $2.2 million. 423 computers available on campus for general student use. Computer purchase/lease plans available. A campuswide network can be accessed from student residence rooms and from off campus. Students can access the following: online class registration. Staffed computer lab on campus (open 24 hours a day) provides training in use of computers, software, and the Internet.

Community Environment: The university is located in West Long Branch, a suburban community of 7,700 people. The campus is located just one mile from the Atlantic Ocean. Both New York and Philadelphia are about a one and a half hour trip away. Newark airport is 45 miles distant. Train and bus service are available 2 miles from campus.

■ **MONTCLAIR STATE UNIVERSITY**
1 Normal Ave.
Montclair, NJ 07043-1624
Tel: (973)655-4000
Fax: (973)893-5455
E-mail: undergraduate.admissions@montclair.edu
Web Site: www.montclair.edu/

Description: State-supported, comprehensive, coed. Awards bachelor's, master's, and doctoral degrees. Founded 1908. Setting: 275-acre suburban campus with easy access to New York City. Endowment: $53.2 million. Research spending for the previous fiscal year: $4 million. Educational spending for the previous fiscal year: $8356 per student. Total enrollment: 18,382. Faculty: 1,589 (579 full-time, 1,010 part-time). Student-undergrad faculty ratio is 17:1. 12,319 applied, 55% were admitted. 16% from top 10% of their high school class, 42% from top quarter, 82% from top half. Full-time: 12,380 students, 61% women, 39% men. Part-time: 2,052 students, 60% women, 40% men. Students come from 33 states and territories, 70 other countries, 3% from out-of-state. 0.1% American Indian or Alaska Native, non-Hispanic/Latino; 22% Hispanic/Latino; 9% African American, non-Hispanic/Latino; 5% Asian, non-Hispanic/Latino; 0.1% Native Hawaiian or other Pacific Islander, non-Hispanic/Latino; 2% international. 15% 25 or older, 26% live on campus, 10% transferred in. Retention: 82% of full-time freshmen returned the following year. Academic areas with the most degrees conferred: family and consumer sciences; business/marketing; visual and performing arts. Core. Calendar: semesters. Academic remediation for entering students, ESL program, services for LD students, advanced placement, accelerated degree program, freshman honors college, honors program, independent study, double major, summer session for credit, part-time degree program, adult/continuing education programs, co-op programs and internships, graduate courses open to undergrads. Off campus study at New Jersey School of Conservation, New Jersey Marine Science Consortium. Study abroad program. ROTC: Army, Naval, Air Force.

Entrance Requirements: Options: electronic application, deferred admission, international baccalaureate accepted. Required: essay, high school transcript, SAT or ACT. Required for some: interview. Entrance: moderately difficult. Application deadline: 3/1. Notification: continuous.

Costs Per Year: Application fee: $65. State resident tuition: $7982 full-time, $266.07 per credit part-time. Nonresident tuition: $17,060 full-time, $568.65 per credit part-time. Mandatory fees: $3076 full-time, $102.52 per credit part-time. College room and board: $13,443. College room only: $9543. Room and board charges vary according to board plan, housing facility, and student level.

Collegiate Environment: Orientation program. Drama-theater group, choral group, student-run newspaper, radio station. Social organizations: 80 open to all; national fraternities, national sororities, local fraternities, local sororities. Most popular organizations: Latin American Student Organization, Campus Recreation, MSU Gamers, Unified Asian American Student Organization, Human Relations and Leadership Association. Major annual events: Homecoming, Welcome Week, World's Fair. Student services: health clinic, personal-psychological counseling, women's center. Campus security: 24-hour emergency response devices and patrols, late night transport-escort service, controlled dormitory access, video surveillance, student escorts. 5,200 college housing spaces available; 4,300 were occupied in 2012-13. Freshmen guaranteed college housing. Options: coed, women-only housing available. Sprague Library with 521,826 books, 1.1 million microform titles, 35,000 serials, 27,007 audiovisual materials, an OPAC, and a Web page. Operations spending for the previous fiscal year: $5.2 million. 300 computers available on campus for general student use. Computer purchase/lease plans available. A campuswide network can be accessed from student residence rooms and from off campus. Students can access the following: online class registration. Staffed computer lab on campus (open 24 hours a day) provides training in use of computers, software, and the Internet.

Community Environment: Population about 37,700, the township of Montclair is a residential suburb about 14 miles west of New York City and about six miles northwest of Newark. Residents can commute to Manhattan by bus or railroad. An art museum, theater groups, music societies, and a library are provided by the community as well as two hospitals, several shopping areas and numerous active civic and social organizations.

■ NEW JERSEY CITY UNIVERSITY

2039 Kennedy Blvd.
Jersey City, NJ 07305-1597
Tel: (201)200-2000; Free: 888-441-NJCU
Fax: (201)200-2044
E-mail: admissions@nicu.edu
Web Site: www.njcu.edu/

Description: State-supported, comprehensive, coed. Awards bachelor's and master's degrees and post-master's certificates. Founded 1927. Setting: 51-acre urban campus with easy access to New York City. Endowment: $3.3 million. Research spending for the previous fiscal year: $131.4 million. Total enrollment: 8,493. Faculty: 752 (240 full-time, 512 part-time). Student-undergrad faculty ratio is 16:1. 4,971 applied, 44% were admitted. 14% from top 10% of their high school class, 34% from top quarter, 71% from top half. Full-time: 4,831 students, 59% women, 41% men. Part-time: 1,753 students, 63% women, 37% men. Students come from 13 states and territories, 23 other countries, 1% from out-of-state. 0.2% American Indian or Alaska Native, non-Hispanic/Latino; 35% Hispanic/Latino; 20% African American, non-Hispanic/Latino; 8% Asian, non-Hispanic/Latino; 0% Native Hawaiian or other Pacific Islander, non-Hispanic/Latino; 1% international. 41% 25 or older, 4% live on campus, 15% transferred in. Retention: 64% of full-time freshmen returned the following year. Academic areas with the most degrees conferred: business/marketing; homeland security, law enforcement, firefighting, and protective services; health professions and related sciences. Core. Calendar: semesters. Academic remediation for entering students, ESL program, services for LD students, advanced placement, accelerated degree program, honors program, independent study, distance learning, double major, summer session for credit, part-time degree program, adult/continuing education programs, co-op programs and internships, graduate courses open to undergrads. Off campus study at Hudson County Consortium. Study abroad program.

Entrance Requirements: Options: electronic application, early admission, deferred admission. Required: essay, high school transcript, minimum 2 high school GPA, SAT. Recommended: 1 recommendation. Required for some: interview. Entrance: moderately difficult. Application deadline: 4/1. Notification: continuous.

Costs Per Year: Application fee: $50. State resident tuition: $245.25 per credit hour part-time. Nonresident tuition: $518.20 per credit hour part-time. Part-time tuition varies according to course load.

Collegiate Environment: Orientation program. Drama-theater group, choral group, student-run newspaper, radio station. Social organizations: 40 open to all; national fraternities, local fraternities, local sororities; 2% of eligible men and 2% of eligible women are members. Most popular organizations: International Student Association, Black Freedom Society, Latin Power Association. Major annual events: Unity Banquet, Spring and Fall Formals, Club and Greek Day. Student services: legal services, health clinic, personal-psychological counseling, women's center. Campus security: 24-hour emergency response devices and patrols, late night transport-escort service. 265 college housing spaces available. No special consideration for freshman housing applicants. Option: coed housing available. Congressman Frank J. Guarini Library with 319,360 books, 1.8 million microform titles, 25,214 serials, 3,618 audiovisual materials, an OPAC, and a Web page. 704 computers available on campus for general student use. Computer purchase/lease plans available. A campuswide network can be accessed from student residence rooms and from off campus. Students can access the following: online class registration. Staffed computer lab on campus provides training in use of computers, software, and the Internet.

Community Environment: Jersey City, the second largest in the state with a population of 239,614, is just across the Hudson River (via the Holland Tunnel or PATH trains) from New York City. A manufacturing center, Jersey City is home to roughly 600 industrial plants. It is a major shipping port and the terminus for some of the nation's largest railroads and transcontinental motor freight lines. Transportation is convenient for all the entertainment, recreational, cultural, and historical offerings to be had in either New Jersey or throughout the tri-state area.

■ NEW JERSEY INSTITUTE OF TECHNOLOGY

University Heights
Newark, NJ 07102
Tel: (973)596-3000; Free: 800-925-NJIT
Fax: (973)802-1854
E-mail: admissions@njit.edu
Web Site: www.njit.edu/

Description: State-supported, university, coed. Awards bachelor's, master's, and doctoral degrees. Founded 1881. Setting: 48-acre urban campus with easy access to New York City. Endowment: $67.5 million. Research spending for the previous fiscal year: $92.3 million. Educational spending for the previous fiscal year: $9376 per student. Total enrollment: 9,944. Faculty: 691 (418 full-time, 273 part-time). Student-undergrad faculty ratio is 16:1. 4,216 applied, 64% were admitted. 20% from top 10% of their high school class, 52% from top quarter, 85% from top half. Full-time: 5,529 students, 21% women, 79% men. Part-time: 1,582 students, 32% women, 68% men. Students come from 23 states and territories, 86 other countries, 9% from out-of-state. 0.1% American Indian or Alaska Native, non-Hispanic/Latino; 15% Hispanic/Latino; 9% African American, non-Hispanic/Latino; 21% Asian, non-Hispanic/Latino; 0.1% Native Hawaiian or other Pacific Islander, non-Hispanic/Latino; 5% international. 18% 25 or older, 26% live on campus, 9% transferred in. Retention: 82% of full-time freshmen returned the following year. Academic areas with the most degrees conferred: engineering; computer and information sciences; engineering technologies. Core. Calendar: semesters. Academic remediation for entering students, ESL program, services for LD students, advanced placement, accelerated degree program, freshman honors college, honors program, independent study, distance learning, double major, summer session for credit, part-time degree program, adult/continuing education programs, co-op programs and internships, graduate courses open to undergrads. Off campus study at Essex County College, Rutgers, The State University of New Jersey, University of Medicine and Dentistry of New Jersey; Camden County College. Study abroad program. ROTC: Army (c), Air Force.

Entrance Requirements: Options: electronic application, early admission, deferred admission, international baccalaureate accepted. Required: high school transcript, SAT or ACT. Recommended: 1 recommendation, Standardized test scores recommended for some. Required for some: essay, interview. Entrance: moderately difficult. Application deadline: 3/1. Notification: continuous. Preference given to state residents. SAT Reasoning Test deadline: 7/1. Transfer credits accepted: Yes.

Costs Per Year: Application fee: $70. State resident tuition: $12,400 full-time, $472 per credit part-time. Nonresident tuition: $24,800 full-time, $1060 per credit part-time. Mandatory fees: $2340 full-time, $116 per credit part-time. Full-time tuition and fees vary according to course load and degree level. Part-time tuition and fees vary according to course load and degree level. College room and board: $11,750. Room and board charges vary according to board plan and housing facility.

Collegiate Environment: Orientation program. Drama-theater group, marching band, student-run newspaper, radio station. Social organizations: 70 open to all; national fraternities, national sororities, local fraternities, local sororities; 5% of eligible men and 3% of eligible women are members. Most popular organizations: Student Senate, Student Activities Council, Vector, Institute of Industrial Engineers, WJTB Geek Radio. Major annual events: NJIT Day, World Week, Miniversity. Student services: health clinic, personal-psychological counseling, women's center. Campus security: 24-hour emergency response devices and patrols, late night transport-escort service, controlled dormitory access, bicycle patrols. College housing designed to accommodate 1,500 students; 2,000 undergraduates lived in college housing during 2012-13. No special consideration for freshman housing applicants. Option: coed housing available. Van Houten Library plus 1 other with 160,000 books, 1,100 serials, an OPAC, and a Web page. Operations spending for the previous fiscal year: $3.2 million. 1,938 computers available on campus for general student use. Computer purchase/lease plans available. A campuswide network can be accessed from student residence rooms and from off campus. Students can access the following: online class registration. Staffed computer lab on campus provides training in use of computers, software, and the Internet.

Community Environment: Newark is the largest metropolis of New Jersey and contains some of the state's greatest cultural institutions: the Newark Museum, the Newark Public Library, and Symphony Hall. Construction has begun on the 12.5 acre New Jersey Center for the Performing Arts. Part-time employment opportunities are good.

■ **OCEAN COUNTY COLLEGE**
College Dr.
Toms River, NJ 08754-2001
Tel: (732)255-0400
E-mail: eclements@ocean.edu
Web Site: www.ocean.edu/

Description: County-supported, 2-year, coed. Part of New Jersey Commission on Higher Education. Awards certificates, diplomas, transfer associate, and terminal associate degrees. Founded 1964. Setting: 275-acre suburban campus with easy access to Philadelphia. Educational spending for the previous fiscal year: $2540 per student. Total enrollment: 10,048. Faculty: 536 (108 full-time, 385 part-time). Student-undergrad faculty ratio is 29:1. 3,922 applied, 100% were admitted. Full-time: 5,232 students, 53% women, 47% men. Part-time: 4,816 students, 62% women, 38% men. Students come from 23 states and territories, 13 other countries, 2% from out-of-state. 1% American Indian or Alaska Native, non-Hispanic/Latino; 9% Hispanic/Latino; 5% African American, non-Hispanic/Latino; 2% Asian, non-Hispanic/Latino; 0.1% Native Hawaiian or other Pacific Islander, non-Hispanic/Latino; 1% international. 28% 25 or older, 3% transferred in. Retention: 71% of full-time freshmen returned the following year. Core. Calendar: semesters. Academic remediation for entering students, ESL program, services for LD students, advanced placement, accelerated degree program, honors program, independent study, distance learning, summer session for credit, part-time degree program, adult/continuing education programs, co-op programs and internships. Study abroad program.

Entrance Requirements: Open admission except for nursing program. Option: electronic application. Required for some: high school transcript, Accuplacer testing required for degree seeking students not meeting minimum ACT or SAT institutional requirements. Selective admissions for nursing students. Please see our website for details, ACCUPLACER is required for degree seeking students. Waiver may be obtained by meeting institution's minimum ACT or SAT scores, or English and math transfer credits. Entrance: noncompetitive. Application deadlines: Rolling, Rolling for nonresidents. Notification: continuous, continuous for nonresidents. Preference given to county residents for nursing program. Transfer credits accepted: Yes.

Costs Per Year: Application fee: $0. Area resident tuition: $3030 full-time, $101 per credit part-time. State resident tuition: $3990 full-time, $133 per credit part-time. Nonresident tuition: $6450 full-time, $215 per credit part-time. Mandatory fees: $960 full-time, $30 per credit part-time, $20 per term part-time. Full-time tuition and fees vary according to course load and program. Part-time tuition and fees vary according to program.

Collegiate Environment: Orientation program. Drama-theater group, choral group, student-run newspaper, radio station. Social organizations: 90 open to all; academic, cultural, community service. Most popular organizations: Student Activities Board, student government, OCC Vikings Cheerleaders, Speech and Theater Club, Veterans' Club. Major annual events: Spring Dinner Dance, Welcome Back Picnic, Spring Day. Student services: personal-psychological counseling. Campus security: 24-hour emergency response devices and patrols, late night transport-escort service, security cameras in hallways and parking lots. College housing not available. Ocean County College Library with 75,809 books, 287 serials, 1,434 audiovisual materials, an OPAC, and a Web page. Operations spending for the previous fiscal year: $1.3 million. 1,200 computers available on campus for general student use. Computer purchase/lease plans available. A campuswide network can be accessed from off-campus. Students can access the following: online class registration. Staffed computer lab on campus provides training in use of computers, software, and the Internet.

Community Environment: A principality in Dover Township, Toms River is the business, vacation, financial, and industrial hub of Ocean County. The city is located four miles inland from the New Jersey shoreline where buses and trains are convenient. An airport is within 20 miles. Community facilities include churches of the major denominations, hospitals, libraries, and civic and service organizations. Recreational activities offered are swimming, picnicking, hiking, camping and canoeing. Some part-time work is available.

■ **PASSAIC COUNTY COMMUNITY COLLEGE**
One College Blvd.
Paterson, NJ 07505-1179
Tel: (973)684-6800
Web Site: www.pccc.cc.nj.us/

Description: County-supported, 2-year, coed. Awards certificates, transfer associate, and terminal associate degrees. Founded 1968. Setting: 6-acre urban campus with easy access to New York City. Endowment: $78,695. Research spending for the previous fiscal year: $97,474. Educational spending for the previous fiscal year: $3777 per student. Total enrollment: 6,308. Faculty: 357 (78 full-time, 279 part-time). 2,076 applied, 100% were admitted. 1% from out-of-state. 41% 25 or older. Calendar: semesters. Academic remediation for entering students, ESL program, advanced placement, honors program, independent study, distance learning, double major, summer session for credit, part-time degree program, co-op programs and internships. Study abroad program. ROTC: Army (c).

Entrance Requirements: Open admission except for nursing, respiratory therapy, radiological technology programs. Options: early admission, deferred admission. Entrance: noncompetitive. Application deadline: Rolling. Preference given to county residents.

Collegiate Environment: Choral group, student-run newspaper. Most popular organizations: Latin American Club, Christian Club, International Club, Soccer Club, Volleyball Club. Student services: personal-psychological counseling. Campus security: late night transport-escort service. Passaic County Community College Learning Resource Center plus 1 other with 90,000 books, 250 microform titles, 263 serials, and 2,000 audiovisual materials. Operations spending for the previous fiscal year: $482,542. 150 computers available on campus for general student use. Staffed computer lab on campus.

Community Environment: See Bergen Community College.

■ **PILLAR COLLEGE**
10 College Way
Zarephath, NJ 08890-9035
Tel: (732)356-1595; Free: 800-234-9305
Fax: (732)356-4846
E-mail: info@somerset.edu
Web Site: www.somerset.edu/

Description: Independent Pillar of Fire International, 4-year, coed. Awards associate and bachelor's degrees. Founded 1908. Setting: rural campus with easy access to New York City. Total enrollment: 240. Faculty: 8. Student-undergrad faculty ratio is 15:1. 126 applied, 48% were admitted. Full-time: 174 students, 55% women, 45% men. Part-time: 66 students, 62% women, 38% men. Students come from 3 states and territories, 0% from out-of-state. 75% 25 or older, 12% transferred in. Retention: 70% of full-time freshmen returned the following year. Core. Calendar: semesters plus 'FastTrack' semesters. Academic remediation for entering students, services for LD students, advanced placement, accelerated degree program, distance learning, double major, summer session for credit, part-time degree program, adult/continuing education programs, co-op programs and internships.

Entrance Requirements: Options: electronic application, deferred admission, international baccalaureate accepted. Required: essay. Required for some: high school transcript, minimum 2.5 high school GPA, interview, SAT or ACT. Entrance: minimally difficult. Application deadline: Rolling. Notification: continuous. Transfer credits accepted: Yes.

Collegiate Environment: Orientation program. Social organizations: 3 open to all. Most popular organizations: Student Government Association, FYI (For Your Inspiration art club), LYF (Life Your Faith Community Service). Major annual events: chapels, Convocation, picnics. Student services: health clinic, personal-psychological counseling. Arthur K. White Library with 60,000 books, 95 serials, 150 audiovisual materials, an OPAC, and a Web page. 20 computers available on campus for general student use. A campuswide network can be accessed. Students can access the following: online class registration. Staffed computer lab on campus provides training in use of computers, software, and the Internet.

■ **PRINCETON UNIVERSITY**
Princeton, NJ 08544-1019
Tel: (609)258-3000
E-mail: uaoffice@princeton.edu
Web Site: www.princeton.edu/
Description: Independent, university, coed. Awards bachelor's, master's, and doctoral degrees. Founded 1746. Setting: 600-acre suburban campus with easy access to New York City, Philadelphia. Endowment: $17 billion. Research spending for the previous fiscal year: $272.7 million. Educational spending for the previous fiscal year: $47,865 per student. Total enrollment: 8,010. Faculty: 1,098 (868 full-time, 230 part-time). Student-undergrad faculty ratio is 6:1. 26,664 applied, 8% were admitted. 96% from top 10% of their high school class, 99% from top quarter, 100% from top half. Full-time: 5,264 students, 49% women, 51% men. Part-time: 72 students, 31% women, 69% men. Students come from 52 states and territories, 91 other countries, 83% from out-of-state. 0.2% American Indian or Alaska Native, non-Hispanic/Latino; 7% Hispanic/Latino; 7% African American, non-Hispanic/Latino; 19% Asian, non-Hispanic/Latino; 0.1% Native Hawaiian or other Pacific Islander, non-Hispanic/Latino; 11% international. 0.2% 25 or older, 97% live on campus, 0% transferred in. Retention: 98% of full-time freshmen returned the following year. Academic areas with the most degrees conferred: social sciences; engineering; biological/life sciences. Core. Calendar: semesters. Services for LD students, advanced placement, self-designed majors, independent study, adult/continuing education programs, graduate courses open to undergrads. Off campus study at Rutgers, The State University of New Jersey, Westminster Choir College of Rider University, Princeton Theological Seminary. Study abroad program. ROTC: Army, Naval (c).
Entrance Requirements: Options: electronic application, early action, deferred admission, international baccalaureate accepted. Required: essay, high school transcript, 3 recommendations, SAT or ACT. Recommended: interview. Entrance: most difficult. Application deadlines: 1/1, 11/1 for early action. Notification: 3/31. SAT Reasoning Test deadline: 1/1. SAT Subject Test deadline: 1/1. Transfer credits accepted: Yes. Applicants placed on waiting list: 1,472. Wait-listed applicants offered admission: 0.
Costs Per Year: Application fee: $65. Comprehensive fee: $53,795 includes full-time tuition ($40,170), mandatory fees ($545), and college room and board ($13,080). College room only: $7220. Room and board charges vary according to board plan.
Collegiate Environment: Orientation program. Drama-theater group, choral group, marching band, student-run newspaper, radio station. Social organizations: 250 open to all. Student services: legal services, health clinic, personal-psychological counseling, women's center. Campus security: 24-hour emergency response devices and patrols, student patrols, late night transport-escort service, controlled dormitory access. 5,142 college housing spaces available; 5,100 were occupied in 2012-13. Freshmen guaranteed college housing. On-campus residence required through sophomore year. Options: coed, men-only, women-only housing available. Harvey S. Firestone Memorial Library plus 10 others with 7.4 million books, 6.7 million microform titles, 84,283 serials, 115,356 audiovisual materials, an OPAC, and a Web page. Operations spending for the previous fiscal year: $73.9 million. 500 computers available on campus for general student use. Computer purchase/lease plans available. A campuswide network can be accessed from student residence rooms and from off campus. Students can access the following: online class registration, academic applications and courseware, printing, network file space, Web site hosting, media lab, broadcast center. Staffed computer lab on campus (open 24 hours a day) provides training in use of computers, software, and the Internet.

Community Environment: Numerous historical events have taken place at Princeton since the time of its founding in 1746. The first state legislature met here in 1776, as well as in 1873; the Continental Congress Sessions were held here. Princeton is 50 miles southwest of New York City and 45 miles northeast of Philadelphia. All forms of commercial transportation are available. Community facilities are excellent, housing is available for students. The James Forrestal Campus which adjoins Princeton University's campus is an integral part of the University's advanced training and research in the basic and engineering sciences. The largest single project at Forrestal is the Plasma Physics Laboratory, a long range effort to develop a controlled thermonuclear reactor which would provide an infinite energy source. Many of the facilities of the Department of Aerospace and Mechanical Sciences for the Aerospace Propulsion Sciences and the Gas Dynamics Laboratories are here. Rockingham, five miles north is also known as the Berrien Mansion which was used as General Washington's headquarters during 1783. His"Farewell Address to the Armies" was delivered here.

■ **RABBI JACOB JOSEPH SCHOOL**
One Plainfield Ave.
Edison, NJ 08817
Tel: (908)985-6533
Description: Independent Jewish, 4-year, men only. Awards bachelor's degrees. Total enrollment: 41. 17 applied, 100% were admitted.
Entrance Requirements: Recommended: high school transcript.

■ **RABBINICAL COLLEGE OF AMERICA**
226 Sussex Ave.
Morristown, NJ 07962-1996
Tel: (973)267-9404
Fax: (973)267-5208
E-mail: rca079@aol.com
Web Site: www.rca.edu/
Description: Independent Jewish, 4-year, men only. Awards bachelor's degrees. Founded 1956. Setting: 81-acre small town campus with easy access to New York City. Total enrollment: 259. Faculty: 16 (all full-time). Student-undergrad faculty ratio is 12:1. 60 applied, 100% were admitted. Students come from 24 states and territories, 10 other countries. Core. Calendar: semesters. Academic remediation for entering students, accelerated degree program, summer session for credit, internships. Off campus study at Yeshivah Gedolah of New England, Yeshivah Gedolah of Miami. Study abroad program.
Entrance Requirements: Required: interview. Entrance: minimally difficult. Application deadline: Rolling.
Collegiate Environment: Student services: health clinic, personal-psychological counseling. 10,000 books.

■ **RAMAPO COLLEGE OF NEW JERSEY**
505 Ramapo Valley Rd.
Mahwah, NJ 07430-1680
Tel: (201)684-7500; Free: 800-9RAMAPO
Fax: (201)684-7508
E-mail: admissions@ramapo.edu
Web Site: www.ramapo.edu/
Description: State-supported, comprehensive, coed. Part of New Jersey State College System. Awards bachelor's and master's degrees and post-master's certificates. Founded 1969. Setting: 300-acre suburban campus with easy access to New York City. Total enrollment: 5,817. Faculty: 503 (218 full-time, 285 part-time). Student-undergrad faculty ratio is 17:1. 6,299 applied, 47% were admitted. 28% from top 10% of their high school class, 61% from top quarter, 90% from top half. Full-time: 5,052 students, 58% women, 42% men. Part-time: 572 students, 62% women, 38% men. 5% from out-of-state. 0.2% American Indian or Alaska Native, non-Hispanic/Latino; 12% Hispanic/Latino; 4% African American, non-Hispanic/Latino; 5% Asian, non-Hispanic/Latino; 0.4% Native Hawaiian or other Pacific Islander, non-Hispanic/Latino; 1% international. 10% 25 or older, 51% live on campus, 11% transferred in. Retention: 88% of full-time freshmen returned the following year. Academic areas with the most degrees conferred: business/marketing; psychology; communication/journalism. Core. Calendar: semesters. Academic remediation for entering students, services for LD students, advanced placement, accelerated degree program, self-designed majors, freshman honors college, honors program, independent study, distance learning, double major, summer session for credit, part-time degree program, external degree program, adult/continuing education programs, co-op programs and internships, graduate courses open to undergrads. Off

campus study at New Jersey Institute of Technology; SUNY State College of Optometry; University of Medical and Dentistry of NJ; NY Chiropractic College. Study abroad program. ROTC: Air Force (c).

Entrance Requirements: Options: electronic application, early admission, early action, deferred admission. Required: essay, high school transcript, SAT. Recommended: minimum 3 high school GPA. Entrance: moderately difficult. Application deadline: 3/1. Notification: continuous until 3/15. SAT Reasoning Test deadline: 2/28. Applicants placed on waiting list: 877. Wait-listed applicants offered admission: 197.

Costs Per Year: Application fee: $60. State resident tuition: $8480 full-time, $265 per credit hour part-time. Nonresident tuition: $16,960 full-time, $530 per credit hour part-time. Mandatory fees: $4664 full-time. College room and board: $11,370. College room only: $1940.

Collegiate Environment: Orientation program. Drama-theater group, choral group, student-run newspaper, radio station. Social organizations: 112 open to all; national fraternities, national sororities, Fraternities, Sororities, Honor Societies, clubs. Most popular organizations: NORML, 1 Step, Biology & Biochemistry Club, Campus Crusade for Christ, Culture Club. Major annual events: Relay For Life, major concerts (one each semester), Octoberfest and LollanoBooza. Student services: health clinic, personal-psychological counseling, women's center. Campus security: 24-hour emergency response devices and patrols, late night transport-escort service, controlled dormitory access, surveillance cameras, patrols by trained security personnel. 3,060 college housing spaces available. Freshmen guaranteed college housing. Option: coed housing available. George T. Potter Library with an OPAC and a Web page.

Community Environment: Mahwah, population 24,600, is a suburban community near the foothills of the Ramapo Mountains on the New York-New Jersey border. Darlington County Park offers two lakes for swimming and a third for boating. Sports facilities, skiing, nature trails and picnic areas exist at nearby Campgaw Mountain.

■ RARITAN VALLEY COMMUNITY COLLEGE

118 Lamington Rd.
Branchburg, NJ 08876
Tel: (908)526-1200
Fax: (908)704-3442
E-mail: dpalubni@raritanval.edu
Web Site: www.raritanval.edu/

Description: State and locally supported, 2-year, coed. Awards certificates, transfer associate, and terminal associate degrees. Founded 1965. Setting: 225-acre suburban campus with easy access to New York City, Philadelphia. Endowment: $871,383. Educational spending for the previous fiscal year: $1292 per student. Total enrollment: 8,398. Faculty: 470 (117 full-time, 353 part-time). Student-undergrad faculty ratio is 22:1. 2,581 applied, 99% were admitted. 9% from top 10% of their high school class, 20% from top quarter, 52% from top half. Full-time: 3,712 students, 45% women, 55% men. Part-time: 4,686 students, 59% women, 41% men. Students come from 13 states and territories, 1% from out-of-state. 0.2% American Indian or Alaska Native, non-Hispanic/Latino; 15% Hispanic/Latino; 9% African American, non-Hispanic/Latino; 6% Asian, non-Hispanic/Latino; 0.3% Native Hawaiian or other Pacific Islander, non-Hispanic/Latino; 2% international. 27% 25 or older, 6% transferred in. Core. Calendar: semesters. Academic remediation for entering students, ESL program, services for LD students, advanced placement, honors program, independent study, distance learning, double major, summer session for credit, part-time degree program, adult/continuing education programs, co-op programs and internships. Off campus study at Somerset County Technical Institute. ROTC: Army (c), Air Force (c).

Entrance Requirements: Open admission except for applicants to programs in Nursing, Respiratory Care, Dental Hygiene and Dental Assisting programs. Options: electronic application, international baccalaureate accepted. Required: high school transcript. Entrance: noncompetitive. Application deadline: Rolling. Transfer credits accepted: Yes.

Collegiate Environment: Orientation program. Drama-theater group, choral group, student-run radio station. Social organizations: International Student Assoc., Non-Traditional SA; 40% of eligible men and 60% of eligible women are members. Most popular organizations: Phi Theta Kappa, Orgullo Latino, Student Nurses Association, Business Club/SIFE, Environmental club. Major annual events: Fall Picnic, Spring Picnic, Student Awards Banquet. Student services: personal-psychological counseling. Campus security: 24-hour emergency response devices and patrols, late night transport-escort service, 24-hour outdoor and indoor surveillance cameras; 24-hr mobile patrols; 24-hr communication center. College housing not available. Evelyn S. Field Library with 143,559 books, 26,810 serials, 2,712 audiovisual materials, an

OPAC, and a Web page. Operations spending for the previous fiscal year: $269,745. 1,270 computers available on campus for general student use. A campuswide network can be accessed from off-campus. Students can access the following: online class registration, library services, degree audits, grades, class schedules. Staffed computer lab on campus provides training in use of computers, software, and the Internet.

Community Environment: Somerville is the county seat for Somerset County. It is a suburban community located ten miles west of Plainfield and ten miles northwest of New Brunswick.

■ THE RICHARD STOCKTON COLLEGE OF NEW JERSEY

101 Vera King Farris Dr.
Galloway, NJ 08205-9441
Tel: (609)652-1776
Fax: (609)748-5541
E-mail: admissions@stockton.edu
Web Site: www.stockton.edu/

Description: State-supported, comprehensive, coed. Part of New Jersey State College System. Awards bachelor's, master's, and doctoral degrees. Founded 1969. Setting: 2,000-acre suburban campus with easy access to Philadelphia. Endowment: $21 million. Research spending for the previous fiscal year: $920,656. Educational spending for the previous fiscal year: $7818 per student. Total enrollment: 8,400. Faculty: 626 (284 full-time, 342 part-time). Student-undergrad faculty ratio is 18:1. 6,195 applied, 57% were admitted. 24% from top 10% of their high school class, 60% from top quarter, 97% from top half. 23 class presidents, 4 valedictorians, 180 student government officers. Full-time: 6,820 students, 58% women, 42% men. Part-time: 696 students, 56% women, 44% men. Students come from 13 states and territories, 6 other countries, 1% from out-of-state. 0.2% American Indian or Alaska Native, non-Hispanic/Latino; 9% Hispanic/Latino; 7% African American, non-Hispanic/Latino; 5% Asian, non-Hispanic/Latino; 0.2% Native Hawaiian or other Pacific Islander, non-Hispanic/Latino; 0.2% international. 16% 25 or older, 35% live on campus, 14% transferred in. Retention: 84% of full-time freshmen returned the following year. Academic areas with the most degrees conferred: business/marketing; social sciences; psychology. Core. Calendar: semesters. Academic remediation for entering students, services for LD students, advanced placement, accelerated degree program, self-designed majors, honors program, independent study, distance learning, summer session for credit, part-time degree program, adult/continuing education programs, internships, graduate courses open to undergrads. Off campus study at Washington Center for Internships and Academic Seminars. Study abroad program. ROTC: Army (c).

Entrance Requirements: Options: electronic application, early admission, international baccalaureate accepted. Required: high school transcript, minimum 2 high school GPA, SAT or ACT. Recommended: essay, minimum 3 high school GPA, 3 recommendations. Entrance: very difficult. Application deadline: 5/1. Notification: 5/15. SAT Reasoning Test deadline: 5/1. Applicants placed on waiting list: 955. Wait-listed applicants offered admission: 123.

Costs Per Year: Application fee: $50. State resident tuition: $7948 full-time, $306 per credit hour part-time. Nonresident tuition: $14,341 full-time, $552 per credit hour part-time. Mandatory fees: $4374 full-time, $168 per credit hour part-time, $70 per term part-time. Part-time tuition and fees vary according to course load. College room and board: $10,796. College room only: $7381. Room and board charges vary according to board plan and housing facility.

Collegiate Environment: Orientation program. Drama-theater group, choral group, student-run newspaper, radio station. Social organizations: 111 open to all; national fraternities, national sororities; 3% of eligible men and 3% of eligible women are members. Most popular organizations: Multi-Cultural Connection, Stockton Entertainment Team, Los Latinos Unidos, Unified Black Student Society, Stockton Action Volunteers for the Environment. Major annual events: Osprey Ball, Multi-Cultural Dinner, Student, Faculty and Staff Dinner. Student services: health clinic, personal-psychological counseling, women's center. Campus security: 24-hour emergency response devices and patrols, late night transport-escort service, controlled dormitory access, on-campus sworn/commissioned police force. 2,744 college housing spaces available; 2,629 were occupied in 2012-13. Freshmen guaranteed college housing. Option: coed housing available. Richard E. Bjork Library with 308,800 books, 1.2 million microform titles, 47,250 serials, 14,600 audiovisual materials, an OPAC, and a Web page. Operations spending for the previous fiscal year: $4.6 million. 930 computers available on campus for general student use. A campuswide network can be accessed from student residence rooms and from off campus. Students can access the following:

online class registration. Staffed computer lab on campus (open 24 hours a day) provides training in use of computers, software, and the Internet.

Community Environment: Pomona is located about 12 miles northwest of Atlantic City in an undeveloped forest area.

■ RIDER UNIVERSITY

2083 Lawrenceville Rd.
Lawrenceville, NJ 08648-3001
Tel: (609)896-5000; Free: 800-257-9026
Fax: (609)895-6645
E-mail: wlarrousse@rider.edu
Web Site: www.rider.edu/

Description: Independent, comprehensive, coed. Awards associate, bachelor's, and master's degrees and post-master's certificates. Founded 1865. Setting: 280-acre suburban campus with easy access to New York City, Philadelphia. Endowment: $50.3 million. Research spending for the previous fiscal year: $1.9 million. Educational spending for the previous fiscal year: $14,610 per student. Total enrollment: 5,485. Faculty: 626 (257 full-time, 369 part-time). Student-undergrad faculty ratio is 12:1. 7,903 applied, 72% were admitted. 20% from top 10% of their high school class, 52% from top quarter, 86% from top half. Full-time: 3,928 students, 58% women, 42% men. Part-time: 621 students, 60% women, 40% men. Students come from 44 states and territories, 64 other countries, 22% from out-of-state. 0.2% American Indian or Alaska Native, non-Hispanic/Latino; 9% Hispanic/Latino; 10% African American, non-Hispanic/Latino; 4% Asian, non-Hispanic/Latino; 0.2% Native Hawaiian or other Pacific Islander, non-Hispanic/Latino; 2% international. 21% 25 or older, 57% live on campus, 5% transferred in. Retention: 77% of full-time freshmen returned the following year. Academic areas with the most degrees conferred: business/marketing; education; English. Core. Calendar: semesters. Academic remediation for entering students, ESL program, services for LD students, advanced placement, honors program, independent study, distance learning, double major, summer session for credit, part-time degree program, adult/continuing education programs, co-op programs and internships, graduate courses open to undergrads. Study abroad program. ROTC: Army (c).

Entrance Requirements: Options: electronic application, early admission, early action, deferred admission, international baccalaureate accepted. Required: essay, high school transcript, 2 recommendations, SAT or ACT. Required for some: interview. Entrance: moderately difficult. Application deadlines: Rolling, 11/15 for early action. Notification: continuous, 12/15 for early action. Applicants placed on waiting list: 70. Wait-listed applicants offered admission: 49. Early action applicants: 2,519. Early action applicants admitted: 1,655.

Costs Per Year: Application fee: $50. Comprehensive fee: $45,760 includes full-time tuition ($32,820), mandatory fees ($600), and college room and board ($12,340). College room only: $7770. Full-time tuition and fees vary according to course load and program. Room and board charges vary according to board plan, housing facility, and location. Part-time tuition: $596.87 per credit. Part-time mandatory fees: $35 per course. Part-time tuition and fees vary according to course load and program.

Collegiate Environment: Orientation program. Drama-theater group, choral group, student-run newspaper, radio station. Social organizations: 110 open to all; national fraternities, national sororities; 5% of eligible men and 9% of eligible women are members. Most popular organizations: Student Government Association, Greek Council, Association of Commuter Students, Black Student Union, Residence Hall Association. Major annual events: Cranberry Fest, Homecoming, Family Day/Weekend. Student services: health clinic, personal-psychological counseling. Campus security: 24-hour emergency response devices and patrols, student patrols, late night transport-escort service, controlled dormitory access. 2,726 college housing spaces available; 2,567 were occupied in 2012-13. Freshmen given priority for college housing. Options: coed, women-only housing available. Franklin F. Moore Library plus 1 other with 448,025 books, 657,600 microform titles, 50,594 serials, 5,444 audiovisual materials, an OPAC, and a Web page. Operations spending for the previous fiscal year: $4.6 million. 300 computers available on campus for general student use. Computer purchase/lease plans available. A campuswide network can be accessed from student residence rooms and from off campus. Students can access the following: online class registration. Staffed computer lab on campus (open 24 hours a day).

Community Environment: The capital of the state, Trenton's slogan is"Trenton Makes-the World Takes" and more than 400 industries support this claim. Products include pottery, wire, rope, rubber and cigars. Situated midway between New York City and Philadelphia, all forms of commercial transportation are available. Along with the usual community facilities,

Trenton supports a symphony orchestra and provides community concerts. There are many part-time job opportunities in the New York to Philadelphia corridor. The mountains and seashore are a short distance, providing excellent recreational facilities. Some of the numerous points of interest are the Friends Meetinghouse, New Jersey State Museum, Old Barracks, Trent House and Washington Crossing State Park.

■ ROWAN UNIVERSITY

201 Mullica Hill Rd.
Glassboro, NJ 08028-1701
Tel: (856)256-4500; Free: 800-447-1165N
E-mail: admissions@rowan.edu
Web Site: www.rowan.edu/

Description: State-supported, comprehensive, coed. Part of New Jersey State College System. Awards bachelor's, master's, and doctoral degrees. Founded 1923. Setting: 800-acre suburban campus with easy access to Philadelphia. Endowment: $140.5 million. Research spending for the previous fiscal year: $3.4 million. Total enrollment: 12,133. Faculty: 1,125 (385 full-time, 740 part-time). Student-undergrad faculty ratio is 16:1. 7,346 applied, 62% were admitted. 0% from top 10% of their high school class, 2% from top quarter, 14% from top half. Full-time: 9,254 students, 48% women, 52% men. Part-time: 1,496 students, 64% women, 36% men. 4% from out-of-state. 1% American Indian or Alaska Native, non-Hispanic/Latino; 9% Hispanic/Latino; 9% African American, non-Hispanic/Latino; 4% Asian, non-Hispanic/Latino; 0.2% Native Hawaiian or other Pacific Islander, non-Hispanic/Latino. 13% 25 or older, 35% live on campus, 12% transferred in. Retention: 85% of full-time freshmen returned the following year. Academic areas with the most degrees conferred: education; business/marketing; communication/journalism. Core. Calendar: semesters. Academic remediation for entering students, ESL program, services for LD students, advanced placement, freshman honors college, honors program, independent study, distance learning, double major, summer session for credit, part-time degree program, adult/continuing education programs, co-op programs and internships, graduate courses open to undergrads. Off campus study at Camden County College, Cumberland County College. Study abroad program. ROTC: Army (c).

Entrance Requirements: Options: electronic application, early admission, deferred admission. Required: high school transcript, SAT or ACT. Recommended: minimum 2 high school GPA. Required for some: interview. Entrance: moderately difficult. Application deadline: 3/1. Notification: continuous. Transfer credits accepted: Yes.

Costs Per Year: Application fee: $65. State resident tuition: $8906 full-time, $342 per credit hour part-time. Nonresident tuition: $16,712 full-time, $644 per credit hour part-time. Mandatory fees: $3474 full-time. Full-time tuition and fees vary according to course load, degree level, and program. Part-time tuition varies according to course load, degree level, and program. College room and board: $10,972. College room only: $6892. Room and board charges vary according to board plan and housing facility.

Collegiate Environment: Orientation program. Drama-theater group, choral group, student-run newspaper, radio station. Social organizations: 140 open to all; national fraternities, national sororities. Most popular organizations: Kappa Delta Pi, Public Relations Student Society of America, Student University Programmes, Rowan Television Network, Elementary Education Club. Major annual events: Profstock (spring concert), Homecoming Week, Spring Festival Weekend. Student services: legal services, health clinic, personal-psychological counseling. Campus security: 24-hour emergency response devices and patrols, student patrols, late night transport-escort service, controlled dormitory access, EMS Service including 2 ambulances, Security and Campus Police trained as Police Officers in NJ. 3,927 college housing spaces available. Freshmen guaranteed college housing. On-campus residence required through sophomore year. Option: coed housing available. Keith and Shirley Campbell Library plus 1 other with 438,135 books, 519,060 microform titles, 50,883 serials, 13,584 audiovisual materials, an OPAC, and a Web page. Operations spending for the previous fiscal year: $4.8 million. 1,200 computers available on campus for general student use. A campuswide network can be accessed from student residence rooms and from off campus. Students can access the following: online class registration, online library. Staffed computer lab on campus provides training in use of computers, software, and the Internet.

Community Environment: Glassboro was established in 1775 when a German widow and her seven sons organized Stanger & Co., the first successful glass factory in North America. Hollybush, a mansion of a glass manufacturer, which formed part of the original campus, was the site of a summit conference between President Lyndon Johnson and Russian

Premier Alexei Kosygin in 1967. Glassboro is near enough to large cities that all forms of commercial transportation are available. Philadelphia Airport is 35 minutes away. Part-time employment is available. Nearby lakes and beaches provide recreational facilities.

■ RUTGERS, THE STATE UNIVERSITY OF NEW JERSEY, CAMDEN

406 Penn St.
Camden, NJ 08102-1401
Tel: (856)225-1766
E-mail: bowles@ugadm.rutgers.edu
Web Site: www.rutgers.edu/

Description: State-supported, university, coed. Part of Rutgers, The State University of New Jersey. Awards bachelor's, master's, and doctoral degrees. Founded 1927. Setting: 34-acre urban campus with easy access to Philadelphia. System endowment: $508.8 million. Research spending for the previous fiscal year: $301.5 million. Educational spending for the previous fiscal year: $14,621 per student. Total enrollment: 6,343. Faculty: 537 (285 full-time, 252 part-time). Student-undergrad faculty ratio is 11:1. 5,686 applied, 62% were admitted. 14% from top 10% of their high school class, 40% from top quarter, 77% from top half. Full-time: 3,833 students, 54% women, 46% men. Part-time: 875 students, 59% women, 41% men. Students come from 18 states and territories, 12 other countries, 2% from out-of-state. 0.1% American Indian or Alaska Native, non-Hispanic/Latino; 10% Hispanic/Latino; 17% African American, non-Hispanic/Latino; 8% Asian, non-Hispanic/Latino; 0.2% Native Hawaiian or other Pacific Islander, non-Hispanic/Latino; 1% international. 30% 25 or older, 20% live on campus, 18% transferred in. Retention: 82% of full-time freshmen returned the following year. Academic areas with the most degrees conferred: business/marketing; psychology; social sciences. Core. Calendar: semesters. Academic remediation for entering students, ESL program, services for LD students, advanced placement, accelerated degree program, self-designed majors, freshman honors college, honors program, independent study, distance learning, double major, summer session for credit, part-time degree program, co-op programs and internships. Study abroad program. ROTC: Army (c), Air Force (c).

Entrance Requirements: Option: electronic application. Required: high school transcript, SAT or ACT. Entrance: moderately difficult. Application deadline: 12/1. Notification: 2/28. Preference given to state residents.

Costs Per Year: Application fee: $65. State resident tuition: $10,356 full-time, $333 per credit part-time. Nonresident tuition: $23,232 full-time, $754 per credit part-time. Mandatory fees: $2567 full-time, $1004 per year part-time. Part-time tuition and fees vary according to course load. College room and board: $11,206. College room only: $7906. Room and board charges vary according to board plan and housing facility.

Collegiate Environment: Orientation program. Drama-theater group, student-run radio station. Social organizations: 75 open to all. Campus security: 24-hour emergency response devices and patrols, student patrols, late night transport-escort service, controlled dormitory access. 772 college housing spaces available; 566 were occupied in 2012-13. Option: coed housing available. Paul Robeson Library plus 2 others with 729,987 books, 974,491 microform titles, 15,013 serials, and 591 audiovisual materials. 184 computers available on campus for general student use. Computer purchase/lease plans available. A campuswide network can be accessed from student residence rooms and from off campus. Students can access the following: online class registration, online grade reports. Staffed computer lab on campus.

■ RUTGERS, THE STATE UNIVERSITY OF NEW JERSEY, NEW BRUNSWICK

65 Davidson Rd.
Rm. 202
Piscataway, NJ 08854-8097
Tel: (732)932-4636
Web Site: www.rutgers.edu/

Description: State-supported, university, coed. Part of Rutgers, The State University of New Jersey. Awards bachelor's, master's, and doctoral degrees and post-master's certificates. Founded 1766. Setting: 2,683-acre urban campus with easy access to New York City. System endowment: $508.8 million. Research spending for the previous fiscal year: $301.5 million. Educational spending for the previous fiscal year: $14,621 per student. Total enrollment: 40,434. Faculty: 2,890 (1,762 full-time, 1,128 part-time). Student-undergrad faculty ratio is 14:1. 28,635 applied, 61% were admitted. 41% from top 10% of their high school class, 77% from top quarter, 98% from top half. Full-time: 30,038 students, 49% women, 51% men. Part-time: 1,555 students, 50% women, 50% men. Students come from 52 states and ter-

ritories, 72 other countries, 6% from out-of-state. 0.1% American Indian or Alaska Native, non-Hispanic/Latino; 12% Hispanic/Latino; 8% African American, non-Hispanic/Latino; 25% Asian, non-Hispanic/Latino; 0.3% Native Hawaiian or other Pacific Islander, non-Hispanic/Latino; 3% international. 6% 25 or older, 53% live on campus, 7% transferred in. Retention: 92% of full-time freshmen returned the following year. Academic areas with the most degrees conferred: social sciences; engineering; psychology. Core. Calendar: semesters. Academic remediation for entering students, ESL program, advanced placement, accelerated degree program, self-designed majors, honors program, independent study, distance learning, double major, part-time degree program, co-op programs and internships, graduate courses open to undergrads. Study abroad program. ROTC: Army, Air Force.

Entrance Requirements: Option: electronic application. Required: high school transcript, SAT or ACT. Recommended: essay. Required for some: interview. Entrance: moderately difficult. Application deadline: 12/1. Notification: 2/28. Preference given to state residents. Transfer credits accepted: Yes.

Costs Per Year: Application fee: $65. State resident tuition: $10,356 full-time, $333 per credit part-time. Nonresident tuition: $23,676 full-time, $768 per credit part-time. Mandatory fees: $2717 full-time, $658 per year part-time. College room and board: $11,412. College room only: $7042. Room and board charges vary according to board plan and housing facility.

Collegiate Environment: Orientation program. Drama-theater group, choral group, marching band, student-run newspaper, radio station. Social organizations: 400 open to all; national fraternities, national sororities. Major annual events: Rutgers Day, Dance Marathon. Student services: health clinic, personal-psychological counseling, women's center. Campus security: 24-hour emergency response devices and patrols, student patrols, late night transport-escort service, controlled dormitory access. 15,102 college housing spaces available; 14,660 were occupied in 2012-13. Options: coed, men-only, women-only housing available. Archibald S. Alexander Library plus 11 others with 5.1 million books, 3.5 million microform titles, 87,902 serials, 112,656 audiovisual materials, an OPAC, and a Web page. 1,450 computers available on campus for general student use. Computer purchase/lease plans available. A campuswide network can be accessed from student residence rooms and from off campus. Students can access the following: online class registration, online grade reports. Staffed computer lab on campus (open 24 hours a day) provides training in use of computers, software, and the Internet.

■ RUTGERS, THE STATE UNIVERSITY OF NEW JERSEY, NEWARK

249 University Ave.
Newark, NJ 07102
Tel: (973)353-1766
Fax: (973)353-1048
E-mail: admissions@ugadm.rutgers.edu
Web Site: www.rutgers.edu/

Description: State-supported, university, coed. Part of Rutgers, The State University of New Jersey. Awards bachelor's, master's, and doctoral degrees. Founded 1892. Setting: 38-acre urban campus. System endowment: $508.8 million. Research spending for the previous fiscal year: $301.5 million. Educational spending for the previous fiscal year: $14,621 per student. Total enrollment: 12,011. Faculty: 819 (493 full-time, 326 part-time). Student-undergrad faculty ratio is 11:1. 11,863 applied, 58% were admitted. 24% from top 10% of their high school class, 57% from top quarter, 88% from top half. Full-time: 6,220 students, 53% women, 47% men. Part-time: 1,446 students, 57% women, 43% men. Students come from 25 states and territories, 45 other countries, 16% from out-of-state. 0.1% American Indian or Alaska Native, non-Hispanic/Latino; 22% Hispanic/Latino; 18% African American, non-Hispanic/Latino; 23% Asian, non-Hispanic/Latino; 1% Native Hawaiian or other Pacific Islander, non-Hispanic/Latino; 3% international. 24% 25 or older, 20% live on campus, 12% transferred in. Retention: 89% of full-time freshmen returned the following year. Academic areas with the most degrees conferred: business/marketing; homeland security, law enforcement, firefighting, and protective services; health professions and related sciences. Core. Calendar: semesters. Academic remediation for entering students, ESL program, services for LD students, advanced placement, accelerated degree program, self-designed majors, freshman honors college, honors program, independent study, distance learning, double major, summer session for credit, part-time degree program, adult/continuing education programs, co-op programs and internships. Off campus study at New Jersey Institute of Technology. Study abroad program. ROTC: Army, Naval, Air Force.

Entrance Requirements: Option: electronic application. Required: high school transcript, SAT or ACT. Entrance: moderately difficult. Application deadline: 12/1. Notification: 2/28. Preference given to state residents.

Costs Per Year: Application fee: $65. State resident tuition: $10,356 full-time, $333 per credit part-time. Nonresident tuition: $23,676 full-time, $768 per credit part-time. Mandatory fees: $2234 full-time, $632 per year part-time. Part-time tuition and fees vary according to course load. College room and board: $12,285. College room only: $7613. Room and board charges vary according to board plan and housing facility.

Collegiate Environment: Orientation program. Drama-theater group, choral group, student-run newspaper, radio station. Social organizations: 85 open to all. Campus security: 24-hour emergency response devices and patrols, student patrols, late night transport-escort service, controlled dormitory access. 1,268 college housing spaces available; 1,262 were occupied in 2012-13. Option: coed housing available. John Cotton Dana Library plus 4 others with 1.1 million books, 1.6 million microform titles, 14,321 serials, and 43,210 audiovisual materials. Operations spending for the previous fiscal year: $38.4 million. 708 computers available on campus for general student use. Computer purchase/lease plans available. A campuswide network can be accessed from student residence rooms and from off campus. Students can access the following: online grade reports. Staffed computer lab on campus.

■ **SAINT PETER'S UNIVERSITY**
2641 Kennedy Blvd.
Jersey City, NJ 07306-5997
Tel: (201)761-6000; Free: 888-SPC-9933
Fax: (201)432-5860
E-mail: admissions@spc.edu
Web Site: www.spcollege.edu/

Description: Independent Roman Catholic (Jesuit), comprehensive, coed. Awards associate, bachelor's, master's, and doctoral degrees and post-master's certificates. Founded 1872. Setting: 15-acre urban campus with easy access to New York City. Total enrollment: 3,045. Faculty: 279 (115 full-time, 164 part-time). Student-undergrad faculty ratio is 12:1. 3,256 applied, 61% were admitted. 12% from top 10% of their high school class, 28% from top quarter, 61% from top half. Full-time: 1,902 students, 57% women, 43% men. Part-time: 415 students, 76% women, 24% men. 15% from out-of-state. 1% American Indian or Alaska Native, non-Hispanic/Latino; 27% Hispanic/Latino; 29% African American, non-Hispanic/Latino; 10% Asian, non-Hispanic/Latino; 0.3% Native Hawaiian or other Pacific Islander, non-Hispanic/Latino; 3% international. 22% 25 or older, 36% live on campus, 7% transferred in. Retention: 76% of full-time freshmen returned the following year. Academic areas with the most degrees conferred: business/marketing; biological/life sciences; health professions and related sciences. Core. Calendar: semesters. Academic remediation for entering students, services for LD students, advanced placement, accelerated degree program, self-designed majors, honors program, independent study, distance learning, double major, summer session for credit, part-time degree program, adult/continuing education programs, co-op programs and internships, graduate courses open to undergrads. Off campus study at members of the Jesuit Student Exchange. Study abroad program. ROTC: Army (c), Air Force (c).

Entrance Requirements: Options: early admission, early action, deferred admission, international baccalaureate accepted. Required: essay, high school transcript, minimum 2 high school GPA, 2 recommendations, SAT or ACT. Recommended: interview. Required for some: interview. Entrance: moderately difficult. Application deadline: Rolling. Notification: continuous. Applicants placed on waiting list: 299.

Costs Per Year: Application fee: $0. Comprehensive fee: $45,688 includes full-time tuition ($31,230), mandatory fees ($1000), and college room and board ($13,458). College room only: $8542. Full-time tuition and fees vary according to class time and course load. Room and board charges vary according to board plan, housing facility, and student level. Part-time tuition: $990 per credit hour. Part-time tuition varies according to class time and course load.

Collegiate Environment: Orientation program. Drama-theater group, choral group, student-run newspaper, radio station. Most popular organizations: Caribbean Culture Club, Black Action Committee, Asian American Student Union, Argus Eyes Dramatic Society, Voices of Praise Gospel Choir. Major annual events: Spring Fest, Winter Fest, All-Nighter. Student services: health clinic, personal-psychological counseling. Campus security: 24-hour emergency response devices and patrols, late night transport-escort service, controlled dormitory access, ID checks at residence halls and library. Freshmen guaranteed college housing. Option: coed housing available. Theresa and Edward O'Toole Library plus 1 other with an OPAC and a Web page. 150 computers available on campus for general student use. A campuswide

network can be accessed from student residence rooms and from off campus. Staffed computer lab on campus provides training in use of computers, software, and the Internet.

■ **SALEM COMMUNITY COLLEGE**
460 Hollywood Ave.
Carneys Point, NJ 08069-2799
Tel: (856)299-2100
Fax: (856)299-9193
E-mail: info@salemcc.edu
Web Site: www.salemcc.edu/

Description: County-supported, 2-year, coed. Awards certificates, transfer associate, and terminal associate degrees. Founded 1972. Setting: small town campus with easy access to Philadelphia. Total enrollment: 1,321. Faculty: 112 (22 full-time, 90 part-time). Student-undergrad faculty ratio is 20:1. 17% from out-of-state. 0.1% American Indian or Alaska Native, non-Hispanic/Latino; 3% Hispanic/Latino; 22% African American, non-Hispanic/Latino; 1% Asian, non-Hispanic/Latino; 0% Native Hawaiian or other Pacific Islander, non-Hispanic/Latino; 0% international. 33% 25 or older. Core. Calendar: semesters. Academic remediation for entering students, ESL program, services for LD students, advanced placement, independent study, distance learning, double major, summer session for credit, part-time degree program, adult/continuing education programs, co-op programs. Off campus study.

Entrance Requirements: Open admission Nursing is not open admission. Nuclear Energy Technology is capped and requires a pre-enrollment test. Options: electronic application, early admission, deferred admission. Required: high school transcript, Basic Skills test or minimum SAT scores. Students with a minimum score of 530 in math and 540 in English on the SAT are exempt from placement testing. Required for some: essay. Entrance: noncompetitive. Application deadlines: Rolling, Rolling for nonresidents. Notification: continuous. Transfer credits accepted: Yes.

Collegiate Environment: Orientation program. Choral group. Student services: personal-psychological counseling, women's center. Campus security: 24-hour emergency response devices and patrols, late night transport-escort service. Michael S. Cettei Memorial Library plus 1 other with an OPAC.

■ **SETON HALL UNIVERSITY**
400 S Orange Ave.
South Orange, NJ 07079-2697
Tel: (973)761-9000; Free: 800-THE HALL
Fax: (973)761-9452
E-mail: thehall@shu.edu
Web Site: www.shu.edu/

Description: Independent Roman Catholic, university, coed. Awards bachelor's, master's, and doctoral degrees and post-master's certificates. Founded 1856. Setting: 58-acre suburban campus with easy access to New York City. Endowment: $178.7 million. Research spending for the previous fiscal year: $2.5 million. Total enrollment: 9,616. Faculty: 879 (460 full-time, 419 part-time). Student-undergrad faculty ratio is 14:1. 10,851 applied, 79% were admitted. 22% from top 10% of their high school class, 50% from top quarter, 83% from top half. Full-time: 4,671 students, 58% women, 42% men. Part-time: 542 students, 63% women, 37% men. Students come from 48 states and territories, 36 other countries, 25% from out-of-state. 7% 25 or older, 43% live on campus, 6% transferred in. Retention: 82% of full-time freshmen returned the following year. Academic areas with the most degrees conferred: business/marketing; health professions and related sciences; social sciences. Core. Calendar: semesters. Academic remediation for entering students, ESL program, services for LD students, advanced placement, accelerated degree program, honors program, independent study, distance learning, double major, summer session for credit, part-time degree program, co-op programs and internships, graduate courses open to undergrads. Study abroad program. ROTC: Army.

Entrance Requirements: Options: electronic application, early action, deferred admission, international baccalaureate accepted. Required: essay, high school transcript, counselor report, SAT or ACT. Recommended: minimum 3 high school GPA, interview. Required for some: minimum 3 high school GPA, interview. Entrance: moderately difficult. Application deadlines: Rolling, 11/15 for early action. Notification: continuous until 12/1, 12/30 for early action. SAT Reasoning Test deadline: 6/1. Transfer credits accepted: Yes.

Costs Per Year: Application fee: $55. One-time mandatory fee: $300. Comprehensive fee: $47,702 includes full-time tuition ($32,700), mandatory fees ($2050), and college room and board ($12,952). College room only: $8248. Full-time tuition and fees vary according to course load. Room and board charges vary according to board plan and housing facility.

Collegiate Environment: Orientation program. Drama-theater group, choral group, student-run newspaper, radio station. Social organizations: 116 open to all; national fraternities, national sororities, local fraternities, local sororities. Most popular organizations: Martin Luther King Jr. Scholars Association, Adelante/Caribe, Black Student Union, National Council of Negro Women. Major annual events: University Day, Deck The Hall, Career Day. Student services: health clinic, personal-psychological counseling, women's center. Campus security: 24-hour emergency response devices and patrols, late night transport-escort service, controlled dormitory access. Walsh Library plus 1 other with 506,042 books, 530,000 microform titles, 1,475 serials, 2,225 audiovisual materials, an OPAC, and a Web page. 300 computers available on campus for general student use. Computer purchase/lease plans available. A computer is required for all students. A campuswide network can be accessed from student residence rooms and from off campus. Students can access the following: online class registration. Staffed computer lab on campus provides training in use of computers, software, and the Internet.

Community Environment: A upper middle class suburb, South Orange enjoys the cultural and recreational advantages of New York City and Newark. Mass transportation is available. Community facilities include a public library, two hospitals in nearby Livingston and Summit, and Catholic, Methodist, Episcopal and Presbyterian churches.

■ **STEVENS INSTITUTE OF TECHNOLOGY**
Castle Point on Hudson
Hoboken, NJ 07030
Tel: (201)216-5000; Free: 800-458-5323
Fax: (201)216-8348
E-mail: admissions@stevens.edu
Web Site: www.stevens.edu/

Description: Independent, university, coed. Awards bachelor's, master's, and doctoral degrees. Founded 1870. Setting: 55-acre urban campus with easy access to New York City. Endowment: $144 million. Research spending for the previous fiscal year: $25.7 million. Total enrollment: 5,541. Faculty: 406 (235 full-time, 171 part-time). Student-undergrad faculty ratio is 8:1. 3,600 applied, 42% were admitted. 56% from top 10% of their high school class, 88% from top quarter, 99% from top half. Full-time: 2,421 students, 25% women, 75% men. Part-time: 6 students, 33% women, 67% men. Students come from 47 states and territories, 60 other countries, 35% from out-of-state. 0.1% American Indian or Alaska Native, non-Hispanic/Latino; 9% Hispanic/Latino; 3% African American, non-Hispanic/Latino; 10% Asian, non-Hispanic/Latino; 0% Native Hawaiian or other Pacific Islander, non-Hispanic/Latino; 7% international. 0% 25 or older, 85% live on campus, 3% transferred in. Retention: 92% of full-time freshmen returned the following year. Academic areas with the most degrees conferred: engineering; business/marketing; computer and information sciences; engineering technologies. Core. Calendar: semesters. Services for LD students, advanced placement, accelerated degree program, honors program, independent study, double major, summer session for credit, co-op programs and internships, graduate courses open to undergrads. Off campus study at New York University Dual-degree program; Parsons School of Design. ROTC: Army (c), Air Force (c).

Entrance Requirements: Options: electronic application, early admission, early decision, deferred admission, international baccalaureate accepted. Required: essay, high school transcript, 2 recommendations, interview, SAT or ACT. Required for some: SAT Subject Tests. Entrance: very difficult. Application deadlines: 2/1, 11/15 for early decision plan 1, 1/15 for early decision plan 2. Notification: 3/15, 12/15 for early decision plan 1, 2/15 for early decision plan 2. SAT Reasoning Test deadline: 3/1. Transfer credits accepted: Yes. Early decision applicants: 515. Early decision applicants admitted: 322.

Costs Per Year: Application fee: $55. Comprehensive fee: $55,742 includes full-time tuition ($41,670), mandatory fees ($272), and college room and board ($13,800). Room and board charges vary according to board plan and housing facility.

Collegiate Environment: Orientation program. Drama-theater group, choral group, student-run newspaper, radio station. Social organizations: 120 open to all; national fraternities, national sororities, local sororities; 20% of eligible men and 20% of eligible women are members. Most popular organizations: Drama Society, Student Council, APO Service Fraternity, Jazz Band, Ethnic Student Association. Major annual events: Boken, Techfest, Midnight

Breakfast. Student services: health clinic, personal-psychological counseling, women's center. Campus security: 24-hour emergency response devices and patrols, late night transport-escort service, controlled dormitory access. Samuel Williams plus 1 other with 123,063 books, 11,274 microform titles, 39,500 serials, an OPAC, and a Web page. Operations spending for the previous fiscal year: $1.5 million. 500 computers available on campus for general student use. A computer is required for all students. A campuswide network can be accessed from student residence rooms and from off campus. Students can access the following: online class registration, online account information, debit dining program, laundry status. Staffed computer lab on campus (open 24 hours a day) provides training in use of computers, software, and the Internet.

Community Environment: Hoboken, a quaint, park-like community, is just one mile square and easily accessible to Manhattan. Recently it has become a residential center for young professionals. Many new shops, restaurants, and clubs have opened in the past ten years. The recreational and cultural advantages of New York are convenient for Hoboken, as well as many job opportunities. Stevens takes advantage of its location and has a popular cooperative education program, in addition to providing internships and research opportunities with leading companies.

■ **STRAYER UNIVERSITY - CHERRY HILL CAMPUS**
2201 Rte. 38
Ste. 100
Cherry Hill, NJ 08002
Tel: (856)482-4200
Fax: (856)482-4230
Web Site: www.strayer.edu/campus/cherry-hill/
Description: Proprietary, comprehensive, coed. Awards bachelor's and master's degrees.

■ **STRAYER UNIVERSITY - LAWRENCEVILLE CAMPUS**
3150 Brunswick Pke.
Ste. 100
Lawrenceville, NJ 08648
Tel: (609)406-7600
Fax: (609)771-8636
Web Site: www.strayer.edu/campus/lawrenceville
Description: Proprietary, comprehensive, coed. Awards bachelor's and master's degrees.

■ **STRAYER UNIVERSITY - PISCATAWAY CAMPUS**
242 Old New Brunswick Rd.
Ste. 220
Piscataway, NJ 08854
Tel: (732)743-3800
Fax: (732)562-1780
Web Site: www.strayer.edu/campus/piscataway
Description: Proprietary, comprehensive, coed. Awards bachelor's and master's degrees.

■ **STRAYER UNIVERSITY - WILLINGBORO CAMPUS**
300 Willingboro Pky.
Willingboro Town Ctr., Ste. 125
Willingboro, NJ 08046
Tel: (609)835-6000
Fax: (609)835-6030
Web Site: www.strayer.edu/campus/willingboro
Description: Proprietary, comprehensive, coed. Awards bachelor's and master's degrees.

■ **SUSSEX COUNTY COMMUNITY COLLEGE**
1 College Hill
Newton, NJ 07860
Tel: (973)300-2100
E-mail: jdonohue@sussex.edu
Web Site: www.sussex.edu/
Description: State and locally supported, 2-year, coed. Part of New Jersey Commission on Higher Education. Awards certificates, transfer associate, and terminal associate degrees. Founded 1981. Setting: 160-acre small town campus with easy access to New York City. Total enrollment: 3,732. Faculty: 276 (43 full-time, 233 part-time). Student-undergrad faculty ratio is 21:1. Full-time: 2,059 students, 50% women, 50% men. Part-time: 1,673 students, 64% women, 36% men. Students come from 3 states and ter-

ritories, 12% from out-of-state. 60% 25 or older, 5% transferred in. Retention: 66% of full-time freshmen returned the following year. Core. Calendar: 4-1-4. Academic remediation for entering students, ESL program, services for LD students, advanced placement, distance learning, double major, summer session for credit, part-time degree program, internships.

Entrance Requirements: Open admission. Required: high school transcript. Entrance: noncompetitive. Application deadline: Rolling. Notification: continuous.

Collegiate Environment: Drama-theater group, choral group, student-run newspaper. Social organizations: 23 open to all. Most popular organizations: Student Government Association, The College Hill (newspaper), Human Services Club, Arts Club, Returning Adult Support Group. Major annual events: Fall Festival, Talent Show, International Festival. Student services: personal-psychological counseling, women's center. Campus security: late night transport-escort service, trained security personnel. Sussex County Community College Library with 34,346 books, 173 microform titles, 266 serials, 602 audiovisual materials, an OPAC, and a Web page. 302 computers available on campus for general student use. A campuswide network can be accessed. Students can access the following: online class registration. Staffed computer lab on campus.

■ **TALMUDICAL ACADEMY OF NEW JERSEY**
868 Rte. 524
Adelphia, NJ 07710
Tel: (732)431-1600
Description: Independent Jewish, comprehensive, men only. Awards bachelor's and master's degrees. Founded 1967. Setting: small town campus. Total enrollment: 48. 15 applied, 100% were admitted. 8% 25 or older. Calendar: semesters.

■ **THOMAS EDISON STATE COLLEGE**
101 W State St.
Trenton, NJ 08608-1176
Tel: (609)984-1100; Free: 888-442-8372
Fax: (609)292-9000
E-mail: admissions@tesc.edu
Web Site: www.tesc.edu/
Description: State-supported, comprehensive, coed. Awards associate, bachelor's, and master's degrees and post-master's certificates (offers only distance learning degree programs). Founded 1972. Setting: 2-acre urban campus with easy access to Philadelphia. Total enrollment: 20,606. Part-time: 19,406 students, 45% women, 55% men. Students come from 56 states and territories, 68 other countries, 60% from out-of-state. 1% American Indian or Alaska Native, non-Hispanic/Latino; 8% Hispanic/Latino; 16% African American, non-Hispanic/Latino; 4% Asian, non-Hispanic/Latino; 1% Native Hawaiian or other Pacific Islander, non-Hispanic/Latino; 1% international. 87% 25 or older. Academic areas with the most degrees conferred: liberal arts/general studies; business/marketing; health professions and related sciences. Core. Calendar: continuous. Services for LD students, advanced placement, accelerated degree program, self-designed majors, independent study, distance learning, double major, summer session for credit, part-time degree program, external degree program, adult/continuing education programs, graduate courses open to undergrads.
Entrance Requirements: Open admission. Option: electronic application. Required: age 21 or older and a high school graduate. Entrance: noncompetitive. Application deadlines: Rolling, Rolling for nonresidents. Transfer credits accepted: Yes.
Costs Per Year: Application fee: $75. State resident tuition: $5508 full-time, $164 per credit hour part-time. Nonresident tuition: $8111 full-time, $221 per credit hour part-time. Mandatory fees: $117 per year part-time. Part-time tuition and fees vary according to program and student level. There are two tuition plans available. Students may choose either the Comprehensive Plan: $5322 per year (state residents and military personnel), $7837 (non-resident), which covers up to 36 credits per year for all credit-earning options, or the Enrolled Options Plan: $1533 per year (state residents and military personnel), $2858 (non-resident) and $4011 (international) for annual enrollment tuition and a technology services fee($113); tests, portfolios, courses and other fees at additional cost.
Collegiate Environment: Campus security: 24-hour emergency response devices and patrols, late night transport-escort service, security officer from 7 am to 11 pm, local police patrol. College housing not available.

■ **UNION COUNTY COLLEGE**
1033 Springfield Ave.
Cranford, NJ 07016

Tel: (908)709-7000
Fax: (908)709-0527
E-mail: hernandez@ucc.edu
Web Site: www.ucc.edu/
Description: State and locally supported, 2-year, coed. Part of New Jersey Commission on Higher Education. Awards certificates, transfer associate, and terminal associate degrees. Founded 1933. Setting: 49-acre urban campus with easy access to New York City. Endowment: $9 million. Educational spending for the previous fiscal year: $4701 per student. Total enrollment: 12,146. Faculty: 519 (173 full-time, 346 part-time). Student-undergrad faculty ratio is 27:1. 8,515 applied, 41% were admitted. Full-time: 5,886 students, 59% women, 41% men. Part-time: 6,260 students, 67% women, 33% men. Students come from 10 states and territories, 77 other countries, 3% from out-of-state. 1% American Indian or Alaska Native, non-Hispanic/Latino; 31% Hispanic/Latino; 27% African American, non-Hispanic/Latino; 4% Asian, non-Hispanic/Latino; 0.4% Native Hawaiian or other Pacific Islander, non-Hispanic/Latino; 3% international. 43% 25 or older, 2% transferred in. Retention: 60% of full-time freshmen returned the following year. Core. Calendar: semesters. Academic remediation for entering students, ESL program, services for LD students, advanced placement, accelerated degree program, self-designed majors, honors program, independent study, distance learning, summer session for credit, part-time degree program, adult/continuing education programs, internships. Off campus study. ROTC: Air Force (c).
Entrance Requirements: Open admission except for allied health programs. Options: electronic application, early admission, deferred admission. Required: high school transcript. Required for some: interview. Entrance: noncompetitive. Application deadline: Rolling. Notification: continuous.
Costs Per Year: Application fee: $0. Area resident tuition: $2688 full-time, $112 per credit part-time. State resident tuition: $5376 full-time, $224 per credit part-time. Nonresident tuition: $5376 full-time, $224 per credit part-time. Mandatory fees: $918 full-time, $38.25 per credit part-time. Full-time tuition and fees vary according to course load. Part-time tuition and fees vary according to course load.
Collegiate Environment: Orientation program. Drama-theater group, student-run newspaper, radio station. Social organizations: 30 open to all. Most popular organizations: SIGN, Business Management Club, Art Society, La Sociedad Hispanica de UCC, Architecture Club. Major annual events: new student mixers/orientation, Overcoming Hatred, Job Fair. Student services: personal-psychological counseling. Campus security: 24-hour emergency response devices and patrols, late night transport-escort service. College housing not available. MacKay Library plus 2 others with 137,731 books, 8,665 microform titles, 20,938 serials, 3,610 audiovisual materials, an OPAC, and a Web page. Operations spending for the previous fiscal year: $1.5 million. 1,021 computers available on campus for general student use. A campuswide network can be accessed from off-campus. Students can access the following: online class registration. Staffed computer lab on campus (open 24 hours a day).
Community Environment: A suburban area, 10 miles southwest of Newark, Cranford enjoys all the cultural and recreational advantages of nearby New York. Major forms of commercial transportation are available.

■ **UNIVERSITY OF MEDICINE AND DENTISTRY OF NEW JERSEY**
65 Bergen St.
Newark, NJ 07107-1709
Tel: (973)972-4300
Fax: (973)972-4429
Web Site: www.umdnj.edu/
Description: State-supported, comprehensive, coed. Part of The School of Health Related Professions is one of 8 schools within the University of Medicine and Dentistry of New Jersey. Awards associate, bachelor's, master's, and doctoral degrees and post-master's certificates. Founded 1970. Setting: rural campus with easy access to New York City, Philadelphia, Newark. Total enrollment: 1,568. Faculty: 448 (152 full-time, 296 part-time). Student-undergrad faculty ratio is 10:1. Students come from 29 states and territories, 10 other countries, 17% from out-of-state. 0.2% American Indian or Alaska Native, non-Hispanic/Latino; 13% Hispanic/Latino; 18% African American, non-Hispanic/Latino; 12% Asian, non-Hispanic/Latino; 1% Native Hawaiian or other Pacific Islander, non-Hispanic/Latino; 2% international. 72% 25 or older. Academic area with the most degrees conferred: health professions and related sciences. Calendar: semesters. Academic remediation for entering students, services for LD students, accelerated degree program, honors program, independent study, distance learning,

summer session for credit, part-time degree program, external degree program, internships, graduate courses open to undergrads. Off campus study at numerous community colleges and 4 year institutions throughout NJ.

Entrance Requirements: Required for some: essay, interview.

Costs Per Year: State resident tuition: $7658 full-time, $319 per credit hour part-time. Nonresident tuition: $11,844 full-time, $493.50 per credit hour part-time. Full-time tuition varies according to class time, course load, location, and program. Part-time tuition varies according to class time, course load, location, and program.

Collegiate Environment: Orientation program. Most popular organizations: Student Leadership Council, Student Senate. Major annual events: Allied Health Week/Month, Annual Convocation, Annual Graduation Ceremony. Student services: health clinic, personal-psychological counseling. Campus security: 24-hour emergency response devices and patrols, late night transport-escort service, controlled dormitory access. 461 college housing spaces available; 14 were occupied in 2012-13. Option: coed housing available. UMDNJ University Libraries plus 3 others with 249,841 books, 4,784 serials, 7,159 audiovisual materials, an OPAC, and a Web page. 120 computers available on campus for general student use. A campuswide network can be accessed from student residence rooms and from off campus. Students can access the following: online class registration. Staffed computer lab on campus.

■ **UNIVERSITY OF PHOENIX–JERSEY CITY CAMPUS**

100 Town Sq. Pl.
Jersey City, NJ 07310
Tel: (201)610-1408; Free: 866-766-0766
Web Site: www.phoenix.edu/

Description: Proprietary, comprehensive, coed. Awards associate, bachelor's, and master's degrees.

■ **WARREN COUNTY COMMUNITY COLLEGE**

475 Rte. 57 W
Washington, NJ 07882-4343
Tel: (908)835-9222
E-mail: shorwath@warren.edu
Web Site: www.warren.edu/

Description: State and locally supported, 2-year, coed. Part of New Jersey Commission on Higher Education. Awards certificates, transfer associate, and terminal associate degrees. Founded 1981. Setting: 77-acre rural campus. Total enrollment: 2,180. Student-undergrad faculty ratio is 22:1. 0% from out-of-state. 26% 25 or older. Retention: 62% of full-time freshmen returned the following year. Core. Calendar: semesters. Academic remediation for entering students, ESL program, services for LD students, advanced placement, independent study, distance learning, double major, summer session for credit, part-time degree program, co-op programs and internships. Off campus study at Raritan Valley Community College, Union County College, Northampton County Area Community College.

Entrance Requirements: Open admission. Options: early admission, deferred admission. Entrance: noncompetitive. Application deadline: Rolling.

Collegiate Environment: Drama-theater group, student-run newspaper. Social organizations: national fraternities. Campus security: evening and weekend security.

■ **WILLIAM PATERSON UNIVERSITY OF NEW JERSEY**

300 Pompton Rd.
Wayne, NJ 07470-8420
Tel: (973)720-2000; Free: 877-WPU-EXCEL
Fax: (973)720-2910
E-mail: leckeya@wpunj.edu
Web Site: www.wpunj.edu/

Description: State-supported, comprehensive, coed. Part of New Jersey State College System. Awards bachelor's, master's, and doctoral degrees and post-master's certificates. Founded 1855. Setting: 370-acre suburban campus with easy access to New York City. Endowment: $6.2 million. Research spending for the previous fiscal year: $133,041. Educational spending for the previous fiscal year: $8774 per student. Total enrollment: 11,423. Faculty: 1,060 (400 full-time, 660 part-time). Student-undergrad faculty ratio is 16:1. 6,941 applied, 61% were admitted. Full-time: 8,381 students, 54% women, 46% men. Part-time: 1,708 students, 55% women, 45% men. Students come from 41 states and territories, 41 other countries, 2% from out-of-state. 0.2% American Indian or Alaska Native, non-Hispanic/Latino; 23% Hispanic/Latino; 14% African American, non-Hispanic/Latino; 7% Asian, non-Hispanic/Latino; 1% international. 18% 25 or older, 23% live on campus, 14% transferred in. Retention: 77% of full-time freshmen returned the following year. Academic areas with the most degrees conferred: business/marketing; education; social sciences. Core. Calendar: semesters. Academic remediation for entering students, ESL program, services for LD students, advanced placement, accelerated degree program, freshman honors college, honors program, independent study, distance learning, double major, summer session for credit, part-time degree program, adult/continuing education programs, internships, graduate courses open to undergrads. Off campus study at members of the National Student Exchange. Study abroad program. ROTC: Air Force (c).

Entrance Requirements: Options: electronic application, early admission, deferred admission. Required: high school transcript, SAT or ACT. Recommended: minimum 2 high school GPA. Required for some: essay, interview, portfolio for art, audition for music. Entrance: moderately difficult. Application deadline: 6/1. Notification: continuous. Transfer credits accepted: Yes.

Costs Per Year: Application fee: $50. State resident tuition: $7,197 full-time, $230.19 per credit hour part-time. Nonresident tuition: $14,597 full-time, $473.19 per credit hour part-time. Mandatory fees: $4,497 full-time, $144.81 per credit hour part-time. Full-time tuition and fees vary according to course load and location. Part-time tuition and fees vary according to course load and location. College room and board: $10,540. College room only: $6700. Room and board charges vary according to board plan and housing facility.

Collegiate Environment: Orientation program. Drama-theater group, choral group, student-run newspaper, radio station. Social organizations: 90 open to all; national fraternities, national sororities; 2% of eligible men and 2% of eligible women are members. Most popular organizations: 720 Modeling Group, Organization of Latin American Students (OLAS), Young Democratic Socialists, WPBN (TV Club), Honors College Club. Major annual events: Welcome Week, Music Fest, Greek Welcome Back BBQ. Student services: legal services, health clinic, personal-psychological counseling, women's center. Campus security: 24-hour emergency response devices and patrols, student patrols, controlled dormitory access. 2,299 college housing spaces available; 2,284 were occupied in 2012-13. No special consideration for freshman housing applicants. Option: coed housing available. David and Lorraine Cheng Library with 338,573 books, 568,839 microform titles, 6,569 serials, 17,511 audiovisual materials, an OPAC, and a Web page. Operations spending for the previous fiscal year: $4.5 million. 700 computers available on campus for general student use. Computer purchase/lease plans available. A campuswide network can be accessed from student residence rooms and from off campus. Students can access the following: online class registration. Staffed computer lab on campus provides training in use of computers, software, and the Internet.

Community Environment: Population 54,000, Wayne is a suburban community located in the center of Passaic County's Wayne Township. The University lies twenty miles west of New York City and is easily accessed by all major New Jersey arteries and nearby Newark Airport. Community facilities include excellent shopping, hospitals, churches of all denominations and numerous clubs and organizations. The University is located within an hour of New York City, the Jersey shore, the Delaware Water Gap and the Meadowlands all of which offer facilities for recreation.

■ BROOKLINE COLLEGE

4201 Central Ave. NW
Ste. J
Albuquerque, NM 87105-1649
Tel: (505)880-2877; Free: 888-660-2428
Fax: (505)352-0199
E-mail: awebb@brooklinecollege.edu
Web Site: brooklinecollege.edu/
Description: Proprietary, 4-year, coed. Awards associate and bachelor's degrees. Setting: urban campus with easy access to Albuquerque. Total enrollment: 522. Faculty: 28 (13 full-time, 15 part-time). Student-undergrad faculty ratio is 18:1. 52% 25 or older. Core. Calendar: continuous. Accelerated degree program, part-time degree program.
Entrance Requirements: Open admission. Option: electronic application. Required: interview. Entrance: noncompetitive. Application deadlines: Rolling, Rolling for nonresidents. Notification: continuous, continuous for nonresidents. Transfer credits accepted: Yes.
Collegiate Environment: Orientation program. Campus security: 24-hour emergency response devices. Learning Resource Center with an OPAC and a Web page. 20 computers available on campus for general student use. A campuswide network can be accessed from off-campus. Staffed computer lab on campus provides training in use of computers, software, and the Internet.

■ BROWN MACKIE COLLEGE–ALBUQUERQUE

10500 Copper Ave. NE
Albuquerque, NM 87123
Tel: (505)559-5200; Free: 877-271-3488
Fax: (505)559-5222
Web Site: www.brownmackie.edu/albuquerque/
Description: Proprietary, primarily 2-year, coed. Part of Education Management Corporation. Awards terminal associate and bachelor's degrees.

■ CARRINGTON COLLEGE–ALBUQUERQUE

1001 Menaul Blvd. NE
Albuquerque, NM 87107
Tel: (505)254-7777
Web Site: carrington.edu/
Description: Proprietary, 2-year, coed. Part of Carrington Colleges Group, Inc. Awards certificates and terminal associate degrees. Total enrollment: 628. Faculty: 54 (16 full-time, 38 part-time). Student-undergrad faculty ratio is 22:1. Full-time: 628 students, 82% women, 18% men. 13% American Indian or Alaska Native, non-Hispanic/Latino; 53% Hispanic/Latino; 3% African American, non-Hispanic/Latino; 2% Asian, non-Hispanic/Latino; 0% Native Hawaiian or other Pacific Islander, non-Hispanic/Latino; 0% international. 61% 25 or older.
Entrance Requirements: Required: essay, high school transcript, interview. Entrance test administered by Carrington College.

■ CENTRAL NEW MEXICO COMMUNITY COLLEGE

525 Buena Vista, SE
Albuquerque, NM 87106-4096
Tel: (505)224-3000
Fax: (505)224-4740
Web Site: www.cnm.edu/

Description: State-supported, 2-year, coed. Awards certificates, transfer associate, and terminal associate degrees. Founded 1965. Setting: 312-acre urban campus. Endowment: $1.6 million. Total enrollment: 28,323. Faculty: 1,035 (316 full-time, 719 part-time). Student-undergrad faculty ratio is 28:1. 6,818 applied, 100% were admitted. Full-time: 9,324 students, 54% women, 46% men. Part-time: 18,999 students, 58% women, 42% men. Students come from 29 states and territories, 0.4% from out-of-state. 7% American Indian or Alaska Native, non-Hispanic/Latino; 45% Hispanic/Latino; 3% African American, non-Hispanic/Latino; 2% Asian, non-Hispanic/Latino; 0.3% Native Hawaiian or other Pacific Islander, non-Hispanic/Latino; 3% international. 48% 25 or older, 5% transferred in. Retention: 58% of full-time freshmen returned the following year. Core. Calendar: trimesters. Academic remediation for entering students, ESL program, services for LD students, advanced placement, honors program, independent study, distance learning, summer session for credit, part-time degree program, adult/continuing education programs, co-op programs and internships. ROTC: Army (c), Naval (c), Air Force (c).
Entrance Requirements: Open admission. Option: electronic application. Entrance: noncompetitive. Application deadlines: Rolling, Rolling for nonresidents. Notification: continuous, continuous for nonresidents.
Collegiate Environment: Orientation program. Student-run newspaper. Social organizations: 20 open to all. Student services: health clinic, personal-psychological counseling. Campus security: 24-hour emergency response devices and patrols, late night transport-escort service. College housing not available. Main Campus Library with 58,855 books, 16,304 serials, an OPAC, and a Web page. Operations spending for the previous fiscal year: $1.2 million.

■ CLOVIS COMMUNITY COLLEGE

417 Schepps Blvd.
Clovis, NM 88101-8381
Tel: (505)769-2811; Free: 800-769-1409
E-mail: admissions@clovis.edu
Web Site: www.clovis.edu/
Description: State-supported, 2-year, coed. Awards certificates, transfer associate, and terminal associate degrees. Founded 1990. Setting: 25-acre small town campus. Endowment: $740,423. Educational spending for the previous fiscal year: $2260 per student. Total enrollment: 4,175. Faculty: 182 (52 full-time, 130 part-time). Student-undergrad faculty ratio is 21:1. 513 applied, 100% were admitted. Full-time: 995 students, 66% women, 34% men. Part-time: 3,180 students, 64% women, 36% men. Students come from 37 states and territories, 14% from out-of-state. 56% 25 or older, 8% transferred in. Retention: 43% of full-time freshmen returned the following year. Core. Calendar: semesters. Academic remediation for entering students, ESL program, services for LD students, advanced placement, independent study, distance learning, double major, summer session for credit, part-time degree program, adult/continuing education programs, co-op programs and internships.
Entrance Requirements: Open admission except for nursing, radiological technician, cosmetology, construction programs. Required: high school transcript. Required for some: interview. Entrance: noncompetitive. Application deadline: Rolling. Notification: continuous. Transfer credits accepted: Yes.
Collegiate Environment: Orientation program. Drama-theater group, choral group. Social organizations: 10 open to all. Most popular organizations: Student Senate, Student Nursing Association, Black Advisory Council,

Hispanic Advisory Council, student ambassadors. Major annual events: Graduation, Transfer Day, concert series. Student services: personal-psychological counseling. Campus security: student patrols, late night transport-escort service. Clovis Community College Library and Learning Resources Center with 52,000 books, 138,000 microform titles, 370 serials, and an OPAC. Operations spending for the previous fiscal year: $274,400. 305 computers available on campus for general student use. A campuswide network can be accessed. Students can access the following: online class registration. Staffed computer lab on campus provides training in use of computers, software, and the Internet.

■ DOÑA ANA COMMUNITY COLLEGE
MSC-3DA, Box 30001
3400 S Espina St.
Las Cruces, NM 88003-8001
Tel: (505)527-7500; Free: 800-903-7503
Fax: (505)527-7515
Web Site: dabcc-www.nmsu.edu/
Description: State and locally supported, 2-year, coed. Part of New Mexico State University System. Awards certificates, transfer associate, and terminal associate degrees. Founded 1973. Setting: 15-acre urban campus with easy access to El Paso. Endowment: $18,682. Total enrollment: 8,891. Faculty: 344. Student-undergrad faculty ratio is 21:1. 556 applied. Full-time: 4,037 students, 56% women, 44% men. Part-time: 4,854 students, 57% women, 43% men. Students come from 14 states and territories, 1 other country, 12% from out-of-state. 2% American Indian or Alaska Native, non-Hispanic/Latino; 65% Hispanic/Latino; 3% African American, non-Hispanic/Latino; 1% Asian, non-Hispanic/Latino; 2% international. 38% 25 or older, 2% transferred in. Retention: 85% of full-time freshmen returned the following year. Core. Calendar: semesters. Academic remediation for entering students, ESL program, services for LD students, advanced placement, freshman honors college, honors program, distance learning, summer session for credit, part-time degree program, adult/continuing education programs, co-op programs and internships. ROTC: Army (c), Air Force (c).
Entrance Requirements: Open admission except for radiological technology, nursing, respiratory care, paramedic, electrical apprenticeship, area vocational school programs. Options: electronic application, deferred admission. Required: high school transcript. Recommended: ACT, ACT ASSET, or ACT COMPASS. Entrance: noncompetitive. Application deadline: Rolling.
Collegiate Environment: Orientation program. Drama-theater group, choral group, marching band, student-run newspaper, radio station. Social organizations: 21 open to all; national fraternities, national sororities, local fraternities, local sororities. Major annual events: Homecoming, Spring Fling, Return to Campus. Student services: legal services, health clinic, personal-psychological counseling, women's center. Campus security: 24-hour emergency response devices and patrols, late night transport-escort service, controlled dormitory access. Library/Media Center with 17,140 books, 213 serials, and an OPAC. Operations spending for the previous fiscal year: $570,144. 210 computers available on campus for general student use. Computer purchase/lease plans available. A campuswide network can be accessed from off-campus. Students can access the following: online class registration. Staffed computer lab on campus provides training in use of computers, software, and the Internet.

■ EASTERN NEW MEXICO UNIVERSITY
1200 W University
Portales, NM 88130
Tel: (575)562-1011; Free: 800-367-3668
Fax: (575)562-2118
E-mail: cody.spitz@enmu.edu
Web Site: www.enmu.edu/
Description: State-supported, comprehensive, coed. Administratively affiliated with Eastern New Mexico University-Ruidoso; Eastern New Mexico University-Roswell. Awards associate, bachelor's, and master's degrees. Founded 1934. Setting: 400-acre rural campus. Endowment: $7.3 million. Research spending for the previous fiscal year: $46,882. Educational spending for the previous fiscal year: $4677 per student. Total enrollment: 5,814. Faculty: 378 (151 full-time, 227 part-time). Student-undergrad faculty ratio is 17:1. 2,291 applied, 66% were admitted. 12% from top 10% of their high school class, 36% from top quarter, 68% from top half. Full-time: 2,845 students, 56% women, 44% men. Part-time: 1,741 students, 58% women, 42% men. Students come from 49 states and territories, 20 other countries, 24% from out-of-state. 2% American Indian or Alaska Native, non-Hispanic/Latino; 34% Hispanic/Latino; 0.5% African American, non-Hispanic/Latino;

1% Asian, non-Hispanic/Latino; 0.3% Native Hawaiian or other Pacific Islander, non-Hispanic/Latino; 3% international. 36% 25 or older, 26% live on campus, 11% transferred in. Retention: 63% of full-time freshmen returned the following year. Academic areas with the most degrees conferred: liberal arts/general studies; education; business/marketing. Core. Calendar: semesters. Academic remediation for entering students, ESL program, services for LD students, advanced placement, accelerated degree program, self-designed majors, independent study, distance learning, double major, summer session for credit, part-time degree program, adult/continuing education programs, co-op programs and internships, graduate courses open to undergrads.
Entrance Requirements: Options: electronic application, international baccalaureate accepted. Required: Official transcripts from any post-secondary institution attended - must be in good standing with all institutions. Required for some: high school transcript, minimum 2.5 high school GPA, SAT or ACT. Entrance: noncompetitive. Application deadlines: 8/24, 8/24 for nonresidents. Notification: continuous until 8/1, continuous until 8/1 for nonresidents. SAT Reasoning Test deadline: 8/1. SAT Subject Test deadline: 8/1. Transfer credits accepted: Yes.
Costs Per Year: Application fee: $0. One-time mandatory fee: $120. State resident tuition: $4350 full-time, $121.85 per credit hour part-time. Nonresident tuition: $9860 full-time, $351.45 per credit hour part-time. Mandatory fees: $1426 full-time, $59.40 per credit hour part-time. Full-time tuition and fees vary according to course load and reciprocity agreements. Part-time tuition and fees vary according to course load. College room and board: $6090. College room only: $2930. Room and board charges vary according to gender, housing facility, location, and student level.
Collegiate Environment: Orientation program. Drama-theater group, choral group, marching band, student-run newspaper, radio station. Social organizations: 55 open to all; national fraternities, national sororities. Most popular organizations: student government, Student Activities Board, Residence Hall Association, IFC (Inter-Fraternity Council)£anhellenic Council. Major annual events: Homecoming Weekend, Wagon Wheel Football Game - ENMU v. WTAMU, Dawg Days - Freshmen Move-in. Student services: health clinic, personal-psychological counseling. Campus security: 24-hour emergency response devices and patrols, late night transport-escort service, controlled dormitory access, University Emergency Notification System; security cameras; security lights. 1,084 college housing spaces available; 1,030 were occupied in 2012-13. Freshmen guaranteed college housing. On-campus residence required in freshman year. Options: coed, women-only housing available. Golden Library plus 2 others with 8 million books, 467,071 microform titles, 62,670 serials, 22,128 audiovisual materials, an OPAC, and a Web page. Operations spending for the previous fiscal year: $1.3 million. 208 computers available on campus for general student use. A campuswide network can be accessed from student residence rooms and from off campus. Students can access the following: online class registration, WIFI in most buildings. Staffed computer lab on campus provides training in use of computers, software, and the Internet.

■ EASTERN NEW MEXICO UNIVERSITY–ROSWELL
PO Box 6000
Roswell, NM 88202-6000
Tel: (505)624-7000; Free: 800-624-7000
Fax: (505)624-7119
E-mail: lily.quezada@roswell.enmu.edu
Web Site: www.roswell.enmu.edu/
Description: State-supported, 2-year, coed. Part of Eastern New Mexico University System. Awards certificates, transfer associate, and terminal associate degrees. Founded 1958. Setting: 241-acre small town campus. Total enrollment: 4,347. Student-undergrad faculty ratio is 20:1. 10% from out-of-state. 54% 25 or older. Core. Calendar: semesters. Academic remediation for entering students, ESL program, services for LD students, advanced placement, independent study, distance learning, summer session for credit, part-time degree program, adult/continuing education programs, co-op programs and internships. Off campus study at other units of the Eastern New Mexico University System. ROTC: Army (c), Naval (c), Air Force (c).
Entrance Requirements: Open admission except for nursing, occupational therapy programs. Option: early admission. Required: high school transcript. Recommended: ACT. Entrance: noncompetitive. Application deadline: Rolling.
Collegiate Environment: Orientation program. Drama-theater group, choral group, student-run newspaper. Campus security: 24-hour emergency response devices, student patrols, late night transport-escort service. Learning Resource Center with an OPAC.

■ **INSTITUTE OF AMERICAN INDIAN ARTS**
83 Avan Nu Po Rd.
Santa Fe, NM 87508
Tel: (505)424-2300
Fax: (505)424-0505
E-mail: uperson@iaia.edu
Web Site: www.iaia.edu/
Description: Federally supported, comprehensive, coed. Awards associate, bachelor's, and master's degrees. Founded 1962. Setting: 140-acre urban campus. Total enrollment: 414. Student-undergrad faculty ratio is 15:1. 53% 25 or older. Core. Calendar: semesters. Academic remediation for entering students, services for LD students, independent study, distance learning, double major, summer session for credit, internships. Off campus study at Santa Fe Community College.
Entrance Requirements: Required: high school transcript, 2 recommendations, SAT or ACT, ACCUPLACER, Compass, ASSET. Recommended: interview. Required for some: essay, interview.
Collegiate Environment: Orientation program. Drama-theater group, student-run newspaper. Student services: personal-psychological counseling. Campus security: 24-hour patrols, late night transport-escort service. Option: coed housing available. Fogelson Library plus 1 other with 38,000 books and 60 serials.

■ **ITT TECHNICAL INSTITUTE**
5100 Masthead St., NE
Albuquerque, NM 87109-4366
Tel: (505)828-1114; Free: 800-636-1114
Fax: (505)828-1849
Web Site: www.itt-tech.edu/
Description: Proprietary, primarily 2-year, coed. Part of ITT Educational Services, Inc. Awards terminal associate and bachelor's degrees. Founded 1989.
Entrance Requirements: Entrance: minimally difficult.

■ **LUNA COMMUNITY COLLEGE**
PO Box 1510
Las Vegas, NM 87701
Tel: (505)454-2500; Free: 800-5888-7232
E-mail: hgriego@luna.cc.nm.us
Web Site: www.luna.edu/
Description: State-supported, 2-year, coed. Awards certificates, diplomas, transfer associate, and terminal associate degrees. Setting: 25-acre small town campus. Total enrollment: 1,789. Full-time: 544 students, 56% women, 44% men. Part-time: 1,245 students, 56% women, 44% men. Students come from 6 states and territories, 1% from out-of-state. 25% 25 or older, 1% transferred in. Retention: 38% of full-time freshmen returned the following year. Core. Calendar: semesters. Academic remediation for entering students, honors program, independent study, distance learning, part-time degree program, co-op programs.
Entrance Requirements: Open admission. Option: electronic application. Required: high school transcript. Entrance: noncompetitive.
Collegiate Environment: Orientation program. Samuel F. Vigil Learning Resource Center plus 1 other with 37,343 books, 178 serials, 5,000 audiovisual materials, and an OPAC.

■ **MESALANDS COMMUNITY COLLEGE**
911 S Tenth St.
Tucumcari, NM 88401
Tel: (505)461-4413
Fax: (505)461-1901
Web Site: www.mesalands.edu/
Description: State-supported, 2-year, coed. Awards certificates, transfer associate, and terminal associate degrees. Founded 1979. Setting: small town campus. Total enrollment: 635. 64% 25 or older. Calendar: semesters.
Entrance Requirements: Required: high school transcript. Entrance: minimally difficult. Application deadline: Rolling.
Collegiate Environment: Campus security: 24-hour emergency response devices.

■ **NATIONAL AMERICAN UNIVERSITY (ALBUQUERQUE)**
4775 Indian School, NE, Ste. 200
Albuquerque, NM 87110
Tel: (505)265-7517; Free: 800-895-9904
Fax: (505)265-7542

E-mail: albadmissions@national.edu
Web Site: www.national.edu/
Description: Proprietary, 4-year, coed. Awards associate and bachelor's degrees. Founded 1941. Setting: 5-acre suburban campus. Total enrollment: 336. 90% 25 or older. Core. Accelerated degree program, independent study, distance learning, double major, summer session for credit, part-time degree program, external degree program, adult/continuing education programs, co-op programs and internships. Off campus study.
Entrance Requirements: Open admission. Required: high school transcript. Entrance: noncompetitive. Application deadline: Rolling.
Collegiate Environment: Orientation program. Campus security: 24-hour patrols, late night transport-escort service.

■ **NATIONAL AMERICAN UNIVERSITY - ALBUQUERQUE WEST (ALBUQUERQUE)**
10131 Coors Blvd. NW
Ste. I-01
Albuquerque, NM 87114
Tel: (505)348-3750
Web Site: www.national.edu/
Description: Proprietary, 2-year, coed. Awards terminal associate degrees. Total enrollment: 231.
Entrance Requirements: Entrance: noncompetitive.

■ **NATIONAL COLLEGE OF MIDWIFERY**
209 State Rd. 240
Taos, NM 87571
Tel: (505)758-8914
Fax: (505)758-0302
E-mail: info@midwiferycollege.org
Web Site: www.midwiferycollege.org/
Description: Independent, comprehensive, women only. Awards associate, bachelor's, and master's degrees. Founded 1989. Calendar: trimesters.

■ **NAVAJO TECHNICAL COLLEGE**
PO Box 849
Crownpoint, NM 87313
Tel: (505)786-4100
Fax: (505)786-5644
Web Site: www.navajotech.edu/
Description: Independent, 2-year, coed. Awards certificates and terminal associate degrees. Founded 1979. Total enrollment: 751. Student-undergrad faculty ratio is 18:1. 49% from out-of-state. 37% 25 or older. Calendar: semesters.
Entrance Requirements: Open admission.
Costs Per Year: Tuition: $1200 full-time, $50 per credit hour part-time. Mandatory fees: $190 full-time, $190 per term part-time. Full-time tuition and fees vary according to course level, course load, location, and program. Part-time tuition and fees vary according to course level, course load, location, and program. College room only: $2280. Room charges vary according to housing facility and location.

■ **NEW MEXICO HIGHLANDS UNIVERSITY**
PO Box 9000
Las Vegas, NM 87701
Tel: (505)454-3000; Free: 800-338-6648
Fax: (505)454-3311
E-mail: judycordova@nmhu.edu
Web Site: www.nmhu.edu/
Description: State-supported, comprehensive, coed. Awards bachelor's and master's degrees and post-master's certificates. Founded 1893. Setting: small town campus. Endowment: $1.8 million. Research spending for the previous fiscal year: $1.7 million. Educational spending for the previous fiscal year: $3080 per student. Total enrollment: 3,738. Faculty: 331 (141 full-time, 190 part-time). Student-undergrad faculty ratio is 14:1. 2,649 applied, 100% were admitted. 4% from top 10% of their high school class, 14% from top quarter, 43% from top half. Full-time: 1,724 students, 53% women, 47% men. Part-time: 692 students, 74% women, 26% men. 23% from out-of-state. 7% American Indian or Alaska Native, non-Hispanic/Latino; 57% Hispanic/Latino; 6% African American, non-Hispanic/Latino; 0.4% Asian, non-Hispanic/Latino; 0.5% Native Hawaiian or other Pacific Islander, non-Hispanic/Latino; 7% international. 35% 25 or older, 29% live on campus, 16% transferred in. Retention: 55% of full-time freshmen returned the following year. Academic areas with the most degrees conferred: education; health

professions and related sciences; business/marketing. Core. Calendar: semesters. Academic remediation for entering students, services for LD students, advanced placement, accelerated degree program, honors program, independent study, distance learning, double major, summer session for credit, part-time degree program, co-op programs and internships, graduate courses open to undergrads. Off campus study at San Juan Community College, Santa Fe Community College, NMHU Center at Roswell; NMHU Center at Rio Rancho.

Entrance Requirements: Open admission. Options: electronic application, early admission, deferred admission, international baccalaureate accepted. Required: high school transcript, minimum 2 high school GPA. Recommended: SAT or ACT, COMPASS. Required for some: 2 recommendations, interview. Entrance: minimally difficult. Application deadlines: Rolling, Rolling for nonresidents. Notification: continuous, continuous for nonresidents.

Costs Per Year: State resident tuition: $2653 full-time, $221.22 per credit hour part-time. Nonresident tuition: $5671 full-time, $401.72 per credit hour part-time. Mandatory fees: $851 full-time. Full-time tuition and fees vary according to course load and location. Part-time tuition varies according to course load and location. College room and board: $5920. Room and board charges vary according to board plan and housing facility.

Collegiate Environment: Orientation program. Drama-theater group, choral group, marching band, student-run radio station. Social organizations: 59 open to all; national fraternities, national sororities, local fraternities, local sororities; 10% of eligible men and 12% of eligible women are members. Most popular organizations: Vatos Rugby, Fire Escape Club, MeChA, NMHU Cheerleaders, NMHU Student Ambassadors. Major annual events: Homecoming Pageant, Welcome Back Week, Campus Wide Thanksgiving Dinner. Student services: health clinic, personal-psychological counseling, women's center. Campus security: 24-hour emergency response devices and patrols, late night transport-escort service, controlled dormitory access. 690 college housing spaces available. No special consideration for freshman housing applicants. Options: coed, men-only, women-only housing available. Thomas C. Donnelly Library with 437,323 books, 168,607 microform titles, 43,235 serials, 1,442 audiovisual materials, an OPAC, and a Web page. Operations spending for the previous fiscal year: $1.5 million. 500 computers available on campus for general student use. A campuswide network can be accessed from student residence rooms and from off campus. Students can access the following: online class registration. Staffed computer lab on campus.

Community Environment: Las Vegas has grown considerably since its days as a Mormon outpost on the Santa Fe Trail. The city is in the foothills of the Sangre de Cristo Mountains and produces lumber, dairy and wool products. The area has a stimulating, dry climate with winters that are bracing but sunny. Recreational facilities nearby include hunting, fishing and skiing. Some part-time employment is available for students.

■ **NEW MEXICO INSTITUTE OF MINING AND TECHNOLOGY**

801 Leroy Pl.
Socorro, NM 87801
Tel: (505)835-5011; Free: 800-428-TECH
Fax: (505)835-5989
E-mail: admission@admin.nmt.edu
Web Site: www.nmt.edu/

Description: State-supported, university, coed. Awards associate, bachelor's, master's, and doctoral degrees. Founded 1889. Setting: 320-acre small town campus with easy access to Albuquerque. Endowment: $25.3 million. Research spending for the previous fiscal year: $81.7 million. Educational spending for the previous fiscal year: $10,610 per student. Total enrollment: 2,105. Faculty: 162 (124 full-time, 38 part-time). Student-undergrad faculty ratio is 12:1. 1,188 applied, 31% were admitted. 35% from top 10% of their high school class, 63% from top quarter, 91% from top half. Full-time: 1,359 students, 27% women, 73% men. Part-time: 206 students, 53% women, 47% men. Students come from 38 states and territories, 10 other countries, 17% from out-of-state. 3% American Indian or Alaska Native, non-Hispanic/Latino; 26% Hispanic/Latino; 2% African American, non-Hispanic/Latino; 2% Asian, non-Hispanic/Latino; 0.1% Native Hawaiian or other Pacific Islander, non-Hispanic/Latino; 3% international. 12% 25 or older, 48% live on campus, 7% transferred in. Retention: 74% of full-time freshmen returned the following year. Academic areas with the most degrees conferred: engineering; physical sciences; biological/life sciences. Core. Calendar: semesters. Services for LD students, advanced placement, accelerated degree program, self-designed majors, independent study, distance learning, double major, summer session for credit, co-op programs and internships, graduate courses open to undergrads.

Entrance Requirements: Options: electronic application, deferred admission. Required: high school transcript, minimum 2.5 high school GPA, SAT or ACT. Recommended: interview, ACT. Required for some: 2 recommendations. Entrance: moderately difficult. Application deadline: 8/1. Notification: continuous. SAT Reasoning Test deadline: 8/1. Transfer credits accepted: No.

Costs Per Year: Application fee: $15. State resident tuition: $4,828 full-time, $201.18 per credit hour part-time. Nonresident tuition: $15,699 full-time, $654.12 per credit hour part-time. Mandatory fees: $668 full-time, $18 per credit hour part-time, $71.50 per term part-time. Full-time tuition and fees vary according to reciprocity agreements. Part-time tuition and fees vary according to course load. College room and board: $6304. Room and board charges vary according to board plan and housing facility.

Collegiate Environment: Orientation program. Drama-theater group, choral group, student-run newspaper, radio station. Major annual events: 49'ers, Spring Fling, International Fair. Student services: health clinic, personal-psychological counseling. Campus security: 24-hour emergency response devices and patrols, late night transport-escort service. 710 college housing spaces available; 686 were occupied in 2012-13. No special consideration for freshman housing applicants. Options: coed, men-only, women-only housing available. The Skeen Library plus 1 other with 385,987 books, 79,926 microform titles, 50,000 serials, 2,899 audiovisual materials, an OPAC, and a Web page. 225 computers available on campus for general student use. A campuswide network can be accessed from student residence rooms and from off campus. Students can access the following: online class registration. Staffed computer lab on campus.

Community Environment: Located 75 miles south of Albuquerque, Socorro (Spanish meaning"help") is in the valley of the Rio Grande. Socorro is the county seat of Socorro County and relies primarily on a service economy and serves a trade territory encompassing both Socorro and Catron Counties. The town draws trade and population from those who work at Stallion Site on the northern end of the White Sands Missile Range, and at the Very Large Array (VLA), the largest radio telescope complex in the world, located on the San Augustin Plains, about 50 miles west of Socorro. The Tech campus provides facilities for golf, tennis, and swimming. The surrounding area provides mountain biking, hiking, and fishing. The town also supports an improving public school system, a general hospital, and 14 churches. Opportunities for part-time employment on the Tech campus are excellent.

■ **NEW MEXICO JUNIOR COLLEGE**

5317 Lovington Hwy.
Hobbs, NM 88240-9123
Tel: (505)392-4510; Free: 800-657-6260
Fax: (505)392-2527
Web Site: www.nmjc.edu/

Description: State and locally supported, 2-year, coed. Part of New Mexico Commission on Higher Education. Awards certificates, transfer associate, and terminal associate degrees. Founded 1965. Setting: 185-acre small town campus. Research spending for the previous fiscal year: $21,370. Total enrollment: 3,222. Faculty: 120 (65 full-time, 55 part-time). Student-undergrad faculty ratio is 19:1. 9% from top 10% of their high school class, 24% from top quarter, 72% from top half. 5 valedictorians. Students come from 17 states and territories, 7 other countries, 10% from out-of-state. 52% 25 or older, 15% live on campus. Core. Calendar: semesters. Academic remediation for entering students, services for LD students, advanced placement, distance learning, summer session for credit, part-time degree program, adult/continuing education programs, co-op programs and internships.

Entrance Requirements: Open admission. Options: early admission, deferred admission. Entrance: noncompetitive. Application deadline: Rolling.

Collegiate Environment: Drama-theater group, choral group. Most popular organizations: Student Nurses Association, Phi Theta Kappa, Fellowship of Christian Athletes. Major annual events: Cowboy Roundup Days, Southwest Poets' Conference, New Mexico Junior College Rodeo. Student services: health clinic, personal-psychological counseling. Campus security: 24-hour emergency response devices and patrols, late night transport-escort service, controlled dormitory access. Pannell Library with 118,500 books, 45 serials, an OPAC, and a Web page. 275 computers available on campus for general student use. A campuswide network can be accessed from off-campus. Staffed computer lab on campus.

Community Environment: A tent city sprang up in this once little-known ranchland corner of New Mexico when oil was discovered in 1927. The settlement soon became the terminal point for oil companies, producing 90% of the state's petroleum. Farmlands in the surrounding area are irrigated by artesian wells and produce alfalfa, cotton and grain sorghums. The city has an airport and bus service for transportation. Community facilities include churches representing major denominations, a library, a hospital, and various civic and fraternal organizations. Recreational areas within reasonable distance provide hunting, fishing, golf, boating and other water sports. Part-time employment is available for students.

■ NEW MEXICO MILITARY INSTITUTE

101 W College Blvd.
Roswell, NM 88201-5173
Tel: (505)622-6250; Free: 800-421-5376
Fax: (505)624-8067
E-mail: admissions@nmmi.edu
Web Site: www.nmmi.edu/

Description: State-supported, 2-year, coed. Part of New Mexico Commission on Higher Education. Awards transfer associate degrees. Founded 1891. Setting: 42-acre small town campus. Endowment: $370.9 million. Total enrollment: 480. Faculty: 65 (all full-time). Student-undergrad faculty ratio is 17:1. 601 applied, 62% were admitted. Students come from 43 states and territories, 9 other countries, 59% from out-of-state. 0% 25 or older, 100% live on campus. Retention: 93% of full-time freshmen returned the following year. Core. Calendar: semesters. Academic remediation for entering students, ESL program, summer session for credit. ROTC: Army.

Entrance Requirements: Options: early admission, deferred admission. Required: high school transcript, minimum 2.0 high school GPA, SAT or ACT. Entrance: moderately difficult. Application deadline: 8/1. Notification: continuous. Preference given to state residents.

Collegiate Environment: Orientation program. Drama-theater group, choral group, marching band, student-run newspaper. Social organizations: 30 open to all. Most popular organizations: band, chorus, drill teams, Officer's Club. Major annual events: Parents' Weekend, Homecoming, Open House. Student services: health clinic, personal-psychological counseling. Campus security: 24-hour emergency response devices and patrols, controlled dormitory access. Paul Horgan Library plus 2 others with 65,000 books, 200 serials, and an OPAC. Operations spending for the previous fiscal year: $165,220. 700 computers available on campus for general student use. Computer purchase/lease plans available. A campuswide network can be accessed from student residence rooms and from off campus. Staffed computer lab on campus.

Community Environment: With a population of approximately 45,000, Roswell, a Pecos Valley City, noted for its fine climate, is the distributing and supply point for a great agricultural, stockraising and oil producing territory. The summer mean temperature is 77.5 degrees, and the winter mean temperature is 41.2 degrees. The area is reached by bus, rail and air lines. Community services include several churches, a public library, a community museum and art center, a community concert association and 2 hospitals. A local park offers a swimming pool, tennis courts and golf courses.

■ NEW MEXICO STATE UNIVERSITY

PO Box 30001
Las Cruces, NM 88003-8001
Tel: (575)646-0111; Free: 800-662-6678
E-mail: admssions@nmsu.edu
Web Site: www.nmsu.edu/

Description: State-supported, university, coed. Part of New Mexico State University System. Awards associate, bachelor's, master's, and doctoral degrees and post-master's certificates. Founded 1888. Setting: 900-acre suburban campus with easy access to El Paso. Endowment: $77.9 million. Research spending for the previous fiscal year: $134.1 million. Educational spending for the previous fiscal year: $6713 per student. Total enrollment: 17,651. Faculty: 833 (619 full-time, 214 part-time). Student-undergrad faculty ratio is 22:1. 5,928 applied, 80% were admitted. 20% from top 10% of their high school class, 48% from top quarter, 81% from top half. Full-time: 11,673 students, 53% women, 47% men. Part-time: 2,603 students, 56% women, 44% men. Students come from 50 states and territories, 62 other countries, 21% from out-of-state. 2% American Indian or Alaska Native, non-Hispanic/Latino; 51% Hispanic/Latino; 3% African American, non-Hispanic/Latino; 1% Asian, non-Hispanic/Latino; 0.2% Native Hawaiian or other Pacific Islander, non-Hispanic/Latino; 4% international. 24% 25 or older, 18% live on campus, 5% transferred in. Retention: 72% of full-time freshmen returned the following year. Academic areas with the most degrees conferred: business/marketing; engineering; education. Core. Calendar: semesters. Academic remediation for entering students, ESL program, services for LD students, advanced placement, accelerated degree program, self-designed majors,

honors program, independent study, distance learning, double major, summer session for credit, part-time degree program, adult/continuing education programs, co-op programs and internships, graduate courses open to undergrads. Off campus study at members of the National Student Exchange, other units of the New Mexico State University System. Study abroad program. ROTC: Army, Air Force.

Entrance Requirements: Options: electronic application, early admission, deferred admission. Required: high school transcript, minimum 2 high school GPA, Applicants must score 20 on the ACT or may take the SAT (accepted, but not recommended) and submit a composite score of 780. The GED is accepted. Minimum high school participation includes 4 units of English, 3 of math, 2 beyond general science, and 1 foreign language/fine arts, SAT or ACT. Entrance: moderately difficult. Application deadline: 8/19. Notification: continuous. SAT Reasoning Test deadline: 8/15. Transfer credits accepted: Yes.

Costs Per Year: Application fee: $20. One-time mandatory fee: $40. State resident tuition: $4766 full-time, $199 per credit hour part-time. Nonresident tuition: $17,794 full-time, $741 per credit hour part-time. Mandatory fees: $1274 full-time, $53.10 per credit hour part-time. College room and board: $7182. College room only: $3946. Room and board charges vary according to board plan and housing facility.

Collegiate Environment: Orientation program. Drama-theater group, choral group, marching band, student-run newspaper, radio station. Social organizations: 244 open to all; national fraternities, national sororities; 4% of eligible men and 4% of eligible women are members. Most popular organizations: Pride Marching Band, Kappa Sigma (Social Fraternity), Blue Wings, Gamma Beta Phi, Chi Omega (social sorority). Major annual events: Fiestas Latinas, Aggie Welcome Week, Greek Week. Student services: legal services, health clinic, personal-psychological counseling. Campus security: 24-hour emergency response devices and patrols, late night transport-escort service, controlled dormitory access. 3,806 college housing spaces available; 2,982 were occupied in 2012-13. No special consideration for freshman housing applicants. Option: coed housing available. New Mexico State University Library plus 1 other with 1.8 million books, 1.5 million microform titles, 61,113 serials, 17,008 audiovisual materials, an OPAC, and a Web page. Operations spending for the previous fiscal year: $7.5 million. 369 computers available on campus for general student use. Computer purchase/lease plans available. A campuswide network can be accessed from student residence rooms and from off campus. Students can access the following: online class registration, dialup internet, antivirus software, student portal online (Microsoft products, file share/storage space, student employee clock-in, payments system, emergency notification signup) PC/laptop/equipment rentals, short-term iPad checkout, software discounts. Staffed computer lab on campus provides training in use of computers, software, and the Internet.

■ NEW MEXICO STATE UNIVERSITY–ALAMOGORDO

2400 N Scenic Dr.
Alamogordo, NM 88311-0477
Tel: (505)439-3600
E-mail: advisor@nmsua.nmsu.edu
Web Site: nmsua.edu/

Description: State-supported, 2-year, coed. Part of New Mexico State University System. Awards certificates, transfer associate, and terminal associate degrees. Founded 1958. Setting: 540-acre small town campus. Endowment: $147,086. Educational spending for the previous fiscal year: $3856 per student. Total enrollment: 3,371. Faculty: 158 (54 full-time, 104 part-time). Student-undergrad faculty ratio is 20:1. 423 applied, 100% were admitted. 6% from top 10% of their high school class, 19% from top quarter, 48% from top half. Full-time: 1,005 students, 61% women, 39% men. Part-time: 2,366 students, 65% women, 35% men. Students come from 26 states and territories, 15% from out-of-state. 3% American Indian or Alaska Native, non-Hispanic/Latino; 38% Hispanic/Latino; 4% African American, non-Hispanic/Latino; 2% Asian, non-Hispanic/Latino; 0.1% Native Hawaiian or other Pacific Islander, non-Hispanic/Latino; 2% international. 47% 25 or older, 6% transferred in. Retention: 50% of full-time freshmen returned the following year. Core. Calendar: semesters. Academic remediation for entering students, services for LD students, advanced placement, honors program, independent study, distance learning, double major, summer session for credit, part-time degree program, adult/continuing education programs, internships. Off campus study at other branches of New Mexico State University. Study abroad program.

Entrance Requirements: Open admission except for medical laboratory technology, nursing programs. Options: electronic application, early admission, deferred admission. Required: high school transcript, minimum 2 high school GPA. Entrance: noncompetitive. Application deadlines: Rolling, Rolling for nonresidents. Notification: continuous, continuous for nonresidents. Transfer credits accepted: Yes.

Costs Per Year: Application fee: $20. Area resident tuition: $1824 full-time, $76 per credit hour part-time. State resident tuition: $2160 full-time, $90 per credit hour part-time. Nonresident tuition: $4872 full-time, $203 per credit hour part-time. Mandatory fees: $96 full-time, $4 per credit hour part-time. Full-time tuition and fees vary according to course load.

Collegiate Environment: Orientation program. Drama-theater group, choral group. Social organizations: 7 open to all. Most popular organizations: student government, advocates for Children in Education, Phi Theta Kappa, Social Science Club, Student Veterans of America-Alamogordo. Major annual events: Crimson Day, Earth Day, Take Back the Night. Campus security: 24-hour emergency response devices. David H. Townsend Library with 50,000 books, 350 serials, an OPAC, and a Web page. Operations spending for the previous fiscal year: $275,732. 70 computers available on campus for general student use. A campuswide network can be accessed from off-campus. Students can access the following: online class registration. Staffed computer lab on campus provides training in use of computers, software, and the Internet.

■ NEW MEXICO STATE UNIVERSITY–CARLSBAD

1500 University Dr.
Carlsbad, NM 88220-3509
Tel: (575)234-9200
E-mail: eshannon@nmsu.edu
Web Site: www.cavern.nmsu.edu/

Description: State-supported, 2-year, coed. Part of New Mexico State University System. Awards certificates, diplomas, transfer associate, and terminal associate degrees. Founded 1950. Setting: 40-acre small town campus. Educational spending for the previous fiscal year: $2380 per student. Total enrollment: 1,998. Faculty: 91 (41 full-time, 50 part-time). 306 applied, 100% were admitted. Full-time: 583 students, 65% women, 35% men. Part-time: 1,415 students, 63% women, 37% men. Students come from 20 states and territories, 1% from out-of-state. 28% 25 or older, 5% transferred in. Retention: 41% of full-time freshmen returned the following year. Core. Calendar: semesters. Academic remediation for entering students, ESL program, services for LD students, advanced placement, self-designed majors, honors program, independent study, distance learning, double major, summer session for credit, part-time degree program, adult/continuing education programs, co-op programs and internships.

Entrance Requirements: Open admission except for nursing program. Options: electronic application, early admission. Required for some: high school transcript. Entrance: noncompetitive. Application deadlines: Rolling, Rolling for nonresidents. Notification: continuous, continuous for nonresidents. Transfer credits accepted: Yes.

Collegiate Environment: Orientation program. Social organizations: 4 open to all. Most popular organizations: Student Nurses Association, Alpha Sigma Phi Criminal Justice Association, Phi Theta Kappa International Honors Society, Associated Students Student Government Association. Major annual events: Career Expo, Halloween Carnival, Welcome Week. Student services: health clinic, personal-psychological counseling. Campus security: 24-hour emergency response devices, late night transport-escort service. Library/Media Center with 25,890 books, 370 microform titles, 194 serials, 1,632 audiovisual materials, an OPAC, and a Web page. Operations spending for the previous fiscal year: $222,072. 300 computers available on campus for general student use. A campuswide network can be accessed. Students can access the following: online class registration. Staffed computer lab on campus provides training in use of computers, software, and the Internet.

■ NEW MEXICO STATE UNIVERSITY–GRANTS

1500 3rd St.
Grants, NM 87020-2025
Tel: (505)287-7981
Web Site: grants.nmsu.edu/

Description: State-supported, 2-year, coed. Part of New Mexico State University System. Awards certificates, transfer associate, and terminal associate degrees. Founded 1968. Setting: small town campus. Total enrollment: 798. 49% 25 or older. Core. Calendar: semesters. Summer session for credit, part-time degree program.

Entrance Requirements: Open admission. Option: early admission. Required: high school transcript, CPT. Entrance: noncompetitive. Application deadline: 7/30.

Collegiate Environment: 30,000 books and 20 serials 150 computers available on campus for general student use. A campuswide network can be accessed. Staffed computer lab on campus.

■ NORTHERN NEW MEXICO COLLEGE

921 Paseo de Oñate
Española, NM 87532
Tel: (505)747-2100
E-mail: dms@nnmc.edu
Web Site: www.nnmc.edu/

Description: State-supported, primarily 2-year, coed. Awards certificates, transfer associate, terminal associate, and bachelor's degrees. Founded 1909. Setting: 35-acre rural campus. Endowment: $829,791. Total enrollment: 2,272. Faculty: 253 (45 full-time, 208 part-time). 320 applied, 100% were admitted. 5% from top 10% of their high school class, 23% from top quarter, 52% from top half. Students come from 5 states and territories, 1% from out-of-state. 60% 25 or older, 1% live on campus. Core. Calendar: semesters. Academic remediation for entering students, services for LD students, advanced placement, distance learning, summer session for credit, part-time degree program.

Entrance Requirements: Open admission. Options: early admission, deferred admission. Required: high school transcript. Entrance: noncompetitive. Application deadline: Rolling.

Collegiate Environment: Social organizations: 9 open to all. Most popular organizations: nursing organization, radiography organization, AISES, Aikido Club, Phi Theta Kappa. Campus security: 24-hour emergency response devices and patrols. Northern New Mexico Community College Library with 18,065 books and 222 serials. Operations spending for the previous fiscal year: $112,638. 12 computers available on campus for general student use. A campuswide network can be accessed from off-campus. Staffed computer lab on campus.

■ PIMA MEDICAL INSTITUTE (ALBUQUERQUE)

RMTS 32, 8601 Golf Course Rd., NW
Albuquerque, NM 87114
Tel: (505)881-1234
E-mail: kmcgrath@pmi.edu
Web Site: www.pmi.edu/

Description: Proprietary, 2-year, coed. Setting: urban campus. Core. Distance learning, co-op programs and internships.

Entrance Requirements: Required: high school transcript, interview, Wonderlic Scholastic Level Exam (SLE).

Collegiate Environment: Orientation program.

■ PIMA MEDICAL INSTITUTE (ALBUQUERQUE)

4400 Cutler Ave. NE
Albuquerque, NM 87110
Tel: (505)881-1234; Free: 888-477-PIMA
Fax: (505)884-8371
Web Site: www.pmi.edu/

Description: Proprietary, primarily 2-year, coed. Part of Vocational Training Institutes, Inc. Awards certificates, terminal associate, and bachelor's degrees. Founded 1985. Setting: urban campus. Total enrollment: 716. 47% 25 or older. Calendar: modular. Academic remediation for entering students, services for LD students, distance learning, co-op programs and internships.

Entrance Requirements: Option: early admission. Required: interview, Wonderlic Scholastic Level Exam (SLE). Required for some: high school transcript. Entrance: minimally difficult.

Collegiate Environment: Orientation program.

■ ST. JOHN'S COLLEGE

1160 Camino Cruz Blanca
Santa Fe, NM 87505
Tel: (505)984-6000; Free: 800-331-5232
E-mail: admissions@sjcsf.edu
Web Site: www.stjohnscollege.edu/

Description: Independent, comprehensive, coed. Administratively affiliated with St. John's College (MD). Awards bachelor's and master's degrees. Founded 1964. Setting: 250-acre suburban campus with easy access to Albuquerque. System endowment: $129.9 million. Educational spending for the previous fiscal year: $18,828 per student. Total enrollment: 430. Faculty: 60 (58 full-time, 2 part-time). Student-undergrad faculty ratio is 7:1. 251 applied, 84% were admitted. 16% from top 10% of their high school class, 41% from top quarter, 70% from top half. Full-time: 345 students, 43% women,

57% men. Part-time: 4 students, 75% women, 25% men. Students come from 18 states and territories, 24 other countries, 79% from out-of-state. 1% American Indian or Alaska Native, non-Hispanic/Latino; 11% Hispanic/Latino; 1% African American, non-Hispanic/Latino; 3% Asian, non-Hispanic/Latino; 0% Native Hawaiian or other Pacific Islander, non-Hispanic/Latino; 14% international. 8% 25 or older, 82% live on campus, 6% transferred in. Retention: 70% of full-time freshmen returned the following year. Academic area with the most degrees conferred: liberal arts/general studies. Core. Calendar: semesters. Summer session for credit, internships. Off campus study at St. John's College (MD).

Entrance Requirements: Options: electronic application, early action. Required: essay, high school transcript, 2 recommendations. Recommended: 3 recommendations, interview. Required for some: interview, SAT. Entrance: very difficult. Application deadline: 11/15 for early action. Notification: 12/15 for early action. Applicants placed on waiting list: 0.

Costs Per Year: Application fee: $0. Comprehensive fee: $54,998 includes full-time tuition ($44,554), mandatory fees ($450), and college room and board ($9994). College room only: $4997. Room and board charges vary according to board plan. Part-time tuition: $1311 per credit hour.

Collegiate Environment: Orientation program. Drama-theater group, student-run newspaper. Social organizations: 60 open to all. Most popular organizations: Iron Bookworm Workout, Chrysostomos (Theater), Jazz Dance, Student Government/Student Committee on Instruction, intramural sports. Major annual events: Dean's Opening Lecture, All-College Seminar, Reality. Student services: health clinic, personal-psychological counseling. Campus security: 24-hour emergency response devices and patrols, late night transport-escort service, controlled dormitory access. 357 college housing spaces available; 287 were occupied in 2012-13. Freshmen guaranteed college housing. On-campus residence required through senior year. Options: coed, men-only, women-only housing available. Meem Library with 68,197 books, 95 serials, 4,501 audiovisual materials, an OPAC, and a Web page. Operations spending for the previous fiscal year: $404,704. 21 computers available on campus for general student use. A campuswide network can be accessed from student residence rooms and from off campus. Staffed computer lab on campus provides training in use of computers, software, and the Internet.

■ **SAN JUAN COLLEGE**
4601 College Blvd.
Farmington, NM 87402-4699
Tel: (505)326-3311
Fax: (505)599-3385
E-mail: mastons@sanjuancollege.edu
Web Site: www.sanjuancollege.edu/

Description: State-supported, 2-year, coed. Part of New Mexico Higher Education Department. Awards certificates, diplomas, transfer associate, and terminal associate degrees. Founded 1958. Setting: 698-acre small town campus. Endowment: $10.5 million. Educational spending for the previous fiscal year: $4799 per student. Total enrollment: 9,463. Faculty: 406 (160 full-time, 246 part-time). Student-undergrad faculty ratio is 25:1. 1,013 applied, 100% were admitted. Full-time: 3,085 students, 60% women, 40% men. Part-time: 6,378 students, 47% women, 53% men. Students come from 50 states and territories, 32 other countries, 23% from out-of-state. 35% American Indian or Alaska Native, non-Hispanic/Latino; 14% Hispanic/Latino; 1% African American, non-Hispanic/Latino; 1% Asian, non-Hispanic/Latino; 0.2% Native Hawaiian or other Pacific Islander, non-Hispanic/Latino; 1% international. 58% 25 or older, 5% transferred in. Retention: 50% of full-time freshmen returned the following year. Core. Calendar: semesters. Academic remediation for entering students, ESL program, services for LD students, advanced placement, honors program, independent study, distance learning, summer session for credit, part-time degree program, adult/continuing education programs, co-op programs and internships.

Entrance Requirements: Open admission. Options: electronic application, early admission, deferred admission. Required: high school transcript. Entrance: noncompetitive. Application deadline: Rolling. Notification: continuous. Transfer credits accepted: Yes.

Costs Per Year: Application fee: $0. State resident tuition: $984 full-time, $41 per credit hour part-time. Nonresident tuition: $2520 full-time, $105 per credit hour part-time. Mandatory fees: $288 full-time, $12 per credit hour part-time. Full-time tuition and fees vary according to reciprocity agreements.

Collegiate Environment: Orientation program. Drama-theater group, choral group, student-run newspaper, radio station. Social organizations: national fraternities, national sororities. Student services: personal-psychological counseling. Campus security: 24-hour emergency response devices and

patrols, late night transport-escort service. College housing not available. San Juan College Library with 98,621 books, 78,524 microform titles, 261 serials, 5,021 audiovisual materials, an OPAC, and a Web page. Operations spending for the previous fiscal year: $846,538. 1,032 computers available on campus for general student use. A campuswide network can be accessed from off-campus. Students can access the following: online class registration. Staffed computer lab on campus provides training in use of computers, software, and the Internet.

Community Environment: At the junction of the San Juan, Las Animas and La Plata Rivers, Farmington is a producer of gas and oil. This is the starting point for two large natural gas pipelines, one leading to Los Angeles, San Diego and San Francisco, the other to the Pacific Northwest. Irrigated lands surrounding the general locale produce farm crops and grazing for livestock. The region is also noted for apple and peach raising. Some part-time employment is available for students.

■ **SANTA FE COMMUNITY COLLEGE**
6401 Richards Ave.
Santa Fe, NM 87508
Tel: (505)428-1000
Fax: (505)428-1237
E-mail: rebecca.estrada@sfcc.edu
Web Site: www.sfcc.edu/

Description: State and locally supported, 2-year, coed. Awards certificates, transfer associate, and terminal associate degrees. Founded 1983. Setting: 366-acre suburban campus with easy access to Albuquerque. Educational spending for the previous fiscal year: $3044 per student. Total enrollment: 4,856. Faculty: 338 (68 full-time, 270 part-time). Student-undergrad faculty ratio is 17:1. Full-time: 1,668 students, 60% women, 40% men. Part-time: 3,188 students, 63% women, 37% men. Students come from 50 states and territories, 17 other countries, 11% from out-of-state. 32% 25 or older. Retention: 56% of full-time freshmen returned the following year. Core. Calendar: semesters. Academic remediation for entering students, ESL program, services for LD students, advanced placement, honors program, independent study, distance learning, double major, summer session for credit, part-time degree program, external degree program, adult/continuing education programs, co-op programs and internships.

Entrance Requirements: Open admission except for nursing and early childhood education programs. Options: electronic application, early admission, deferred admission, international baccalaureate accepted. Recommended: high school transcript. Entrance: noncompetitive. Application deadline: Rolling. Notification: continuous. Transfer credits accepted: Yes.

Collegiate Environment: Orientation program. Drama-theater group, choral group. Social organizations: 9 open to all. Most popular organizations: Student Ambassadors, Student Government Association, The Clay Club, The Ping-Pong Club, Phi Theta Kappa. Major annual events: Graduation, Welcome Back Week, Halloween: costume contest, decoration contest, masquerade ball, and safe trick or treat for students and community. Student services: personal-psychological counseling. Campus security: 24-hour emergency response devices and patrols, late night transport-escort service. Learning Resource Center with 155,000 books, 11,000 microform titles, 7,820 serials, 4,350 audiovisual materials, an OPAC, and a Web page. Operations spending for the previous fiscal year: $135,000. 454 computers available on campus for general student use. A campuswide network can be accessed from off-campus. Students can access the following: online class registration, wireless network campus wide. Staffed computer lab on campus provides training in use of computers and the Internet.

■ **SANTA FE UNIVERSITY OF ART AND DESIGN**
1600 Saint Michael's Dr.
Santa Fe, NM 87505-7634
Tel: (505)473-6011; Free: 800-456-2673
Fax: (505)473-6127
E-mail: christine.guevara@santafeuniversity.edu
Web Site: www.santafeuniversity.edu/

Description: Independent, 4-year, coed. Administratively affiliated with Laureate International Universities. Awards bachelor's degrees. Founded 1947. Setting: 100-acre suburban campus with easy access to Albuquerque. Total enrollment: 544. Faculty: 99 (27 full-time, 72 part-time). Student-undergrad faculty ratio is 10:1. 347 applied, 100% were admitted. Full-time: 541 students, 53% women, 47% men. Part-time: 3 students, 33% women, 67% men. Students come from 40 states and territories, 12 other countries, 66% from out-of-state. 3% American Indian or Alaska Native, non-Hispanic/Latino; 22% Hispanic/Latino; 7% African American, non-Hispanic/Latino; 1%

Asian, non-Hispanic/Latino; 1% Native Hawaiian or other Pacific Islander, non-Hispanic/Latino; 12% international. 11% 25 or older, 66% live on campus, 12% transferred in. Retention: 55% of full-time freshmen returned the following year. Academic areas with the most degrees conferred: visual and performing arts; English; business/marketing. Core. Calendar: semesters. Academic remediation for entering students, ESL program, services for LD students, advanced placement, accelerated degree program, self-designed majors, independent study, double major, summer session for credit, co-op programs and internships. Off campus study at Great Lakes Colleges Association, New York City Arts Program. Study abroad program.

Entrance Requirements: Options: electronic application, deferred admission, international baccalaureate accepted. Required: essay, high school transcript, SAT or ACT. Recommended: minimum 2 high school GPA. Required for some: portfolio or audition for visual and performing arts programs. Entrance: moderately difficult. Application deadlines: Rolling, Rolling for nonresidents. Notification: continuous, continuous for nonresidents. Transfer credits accepted: Yes.

Costs Per Year: Application fee: $50. Tuition: $28,836 full-time, $1081 per credit hour part-time.

Collegiate Environment: Orientation program. Drama-theater group, choral group, student-run newspaper. Social organizations: 18 open to all. Most popular organizations: Student Writer's Association, Performing Arts Collective, Colors: Queer Identity Group, Cluster, Film Clubs. Major annual events: Annual Day of Service, Quadstock (music festival), Vampire Ball. Student services: health clinic, personal-psychological counseling. Campus security: 24-hour patrols, late night transport-escort service, controlled dormitory access. 812 college housing spaces available; 381 were occupied in 2012-13. No special consideration for freshman housing applicants. On-campus residence required through sophomore year. Option: coed housing available. Fogelson Library Center plus 2 others with 170,662 books, 90,465 microform titles, 19,517 audiovisual materials, an OPAC, and a Web page. 84 computers available on campus for general student use. A campuswide network can be accessed from student residence rooms and from off campus. Students can access the following: online class registration. Staffed computer lab on campus provides training in use of computers, software, and the Internet.

Community Environment: Santa Fe, the oldest state capital in the United States, is one of the country's top art markets and cultural centers. According to Conde Nast Traveler magazine, Santa Fe is one of the top tourist destinations in the world. The charm of narrow, winding streets and fascinating architecture, combined with such exciting annual events as the Indian Market and Fiestas, make Santa Fe a fun place to visit and a great place in which to live and study. Outdoors, Santa Fe has an ideal four-season climate. Recreation includes world-class skiing, white water rafting on the Rio Grande, biking, and hiking. Any time of the year, Sante Fe's sunsets are notoriously beautiful.

■ **SOUTHWESTERN INDIAN POLYTECHNIC INSTITUTE**
9169 Coors, NW, Box 10146
Albuquerque, NM 87184-0146
Tel: (505)346-2347; Free: 800-586-7474
Fax: (505)346-2343
E-mail: jcarpio@sipi.bia.edu
Web Site: www.sipi.edu/

Description: Federally supported, 2-year, coed. Awards certificates, transfer associate, and terminal associate degrees. Founded 1971. Setting: 144-acre suburban campus. Research spending for the previous fiscal year: $72,958. Total enrollment: 480. Faculty: 48 (14 full-time, 34 part-time). Student-undergrad faculty ratio is 15:1. 247 applied, 55% were admitted. 3% from top 10% of their high school class, 11% from top quarter, 32% from top half. Full-time: 406 students, 50% women, 50% men. Part-time: 74 students, 70% women, 30% men. Students come from 21 states and territories. 38% 25 or older, 60% live on campus. Core. Calendar: trimesters. Academic remediation for entering students, services for LD students, advanced placement, distance learning, double major, summer session for credit, part-time degree program, co-op programs and internships.

Entrance Requirements: Required: high school transcript, Certificate of Indian Blood. Entrance: noncompetitive. Application deadline: 7/30. Notification: continuous. Preference given to Native Americans who are enrolled members of federally recognized tribes. Transfer credits accepted: Yes.

Costs Per Year: Application fee: $0. State resident tuition: $675 full-time, $150 per term part-time. Nonresident tuition: $675 full-time, $150 per term part-time. College room and board: $165.

Collegiate Environment: Social organizations: Phi Theta Kappa; 20% of eligible men and 24% of eligible women are members. Most popular

organizations: Dance club, Student Senate, rodeo club, Natural Resources, Pow-wow club. Major annual events: SIPI Pow-wow, Veterans Pow-wow. Student services: personal-psychological counseling. Campus security: 24-hour emergency response devices and patrols, late night transport-escort service. Southwester Indian Polytechnic Institute Library with 27,000 books and 715 serials. 350 computers available on campus for general student use. A campuswide network can be accessed from student residence rooms.

■ **UNIVERSITY OF NEW MEXICO**
Albuquerque, NM 87131-2039
Tel: (505)277-0111; Free: 800-CALL-UNM
Fax: (505)277-6686
E-mail: apply@unm.edu
Web Site: www.unm.edu/

Description: State-supported, university, coed. Awards associate, bachelor's, master's, and doctoral degrees and post-master's certificates. Founded 1889. Setting: 769-acre urban campus with easy access to Albuquerque. Endowment: $336 million. Research spending for the previous fiscal year: $89 million. Faculty: 1,548 (1,014 full-time, 534 part-time). Student-undergrad faculty ratio is 23:1. 11,467 applied, 65% were admitted. Students come from 52 states and territories, 63 other countries. Retention: 77% of full-time freshmen returned the following year. Academic areas with the most degrees conferred: business/marketing; education; psychology. Core. Calendar: semesters. Academic remediation for entering students, ESL program, services for LD students, advanced placement, accelerated degree program, self-designed majors, freshman honors college, honors program, independent study, distance learning, double major, summer session for credit, part-time degree program, adult/continuing education programs, co-op programs and internships, graduate courses open to undergrads. Off campus study at National Student Exchange, Western Undergraduate Exchange, Western Interstate Commission for Higher Education, International Student Exchange. Study abroad program. ROTC: Army, Naval, Air Force.

Entrance Requirements: Options: electronic application, early admission, deferred admission, international baccalaureate accepted. Required: high school transcript, minimum 2.5 high school GPA, SAT or ACT. Required for some: essay, interview. Entrance: moderately difficult. Application deadline: Rolling. Notification: continuous. SAT Reasoning Test deadline: 6/1. SAT Subject Test deadline: 6/1. Transfer credits accepted: Yes.

Costs Per Year: Application fee: $20. State resident tuition: $6,049 full-time. Nonresident tuition: $20,688 full-time. Mandatory fees: $612 full-time. Full-time tuition and fees vary according to program.

Collegiate Environment: Orientation program. Drama-theater group, choral group, marching band, student-run newspaper, radio station. Social organizations: 425 open to all; national fraternities, national sororities, local sororities. Most popular organizations: Associated Students of UNM, Graduate and Professional Students Association, Golden Key National Honor Society. Major annual events: Spring Fiestas, Welcome Back Days, Homecoming. Student services: health clinic, personal-psychological counseling, women's center. Campus security: 24-hour emergency response devices and patrols, student patrols, late night transport-escort service, controlled dormitory access. Option: coed housing available. The University of New Mexico University Libraries plus 7 others with 4.3 million books, 4 million microform titles, 71,932 serials, 54,238 audiovisual materials, an OPAC, and a Web page. Operations spending for the previous fiscal year: $21.7 million. 766 computers available on campus for general student use. A campuswide network can be accessed from student residence rooms and from off campus. Students can access the following: online class registration. Staffed computer lab on campus provides training in use of computers, software, and the Internet.

■ **UNIVERSITY OF NEW MEXICO–GALLUP**
200 College Rd.
Gallup, NM 87301-5603
Tel: (505)863-7500
Fax: (505)863-7532
Web Site: www.gallup.unm.edu/

Description: State-supported, primarily 2-year, coed. Part of New Mexico Commission on Higher Education. Awards certificates, diplomas, transfer associate, terminal associate, and bachelor's degrees. Founded 1968. Setting: 80-acre small town campus. Total enrollment: 2,839. Student-undergrad faculty ratio is 20:1. 11% from out-of-state. 41% 25 or older. Retention: 56% of full-time freshmen returned the following year. Core. Calendar: semesters. Academic remediation for entering students, services for LD students, advanced placement, self-designed majors, honors program, summer session for credit, part-time degree program, adult/continuing education programs, co-op programs and internships.

Entrance Requirements: Open admission. Option: early admission. Required for some: high school transcript, SAT, ACT. Entrance: noncompetitive. Application deadline: Rolling. Notification: continuous.

Costs Per Year: Application fee: $15. State resident tuition: $852 full-time, $71 per credit hour part-time. Nonresident tuition: $1,607 full-time, $133.90 per credit hour part-time. Full-time tuition varies according to course load and degree level. Part-time tuition varies according to course load and degree level.

Collegiate Environment: Orientation program. Student-run newspaper. Campus security: late night transport-escort service.

■ UNIVERSITY OF NEW MEXICO–LOS ALAMOS BRANCH

4000 University Dr.
Los Alamos, NM 87544-2233
Tel: (505)662-5919
E-mail: L65130@unm.edu
Web Site: www.la.unm.edu/

Description: State-supported, 2-year, coed. Part of New Mexico Commission on Higher Education. Awards certificates, transfer associate, and terminal associate degrees. Founded 1980. Setting: 5-acre small town campus. Total enrollment: 683. Student-undergrad faculty ratio is 13:1. 1% from out-of-state. 48% 25 or older. Core. Calendar: semesters. Academic remediation for entering students, ESL program, services for LD students, advanced placement, summer session for credit, part-time degree program, adult/continuing education programs, co-op programs and internships. Off campus study at University of New Mexico, Northern New Mexico Community College, Santa Fe Community College.

Entrance Requirements: Open admission. Options: early admission, deferred admission. Entrance: noncompetitive. Application deadline: 8/12. Notification: continuous.

Collegiate Environment: Orientation program. Choral group, student-run newspaper.

■ UNIVERSITY OF NEW MEXICO–TAOS

115 Civic Plz. Dr.
Taos, NM 87571
Tel: (575)737-6200
E-mail: valvarez@unm.edu
Web Site: taos.unm.edu/

Description: State-supported, 2-year, coed. Awards terminal associate degrees. Founded 1923. Total enrollment: 1,429. Student-undergrad faculty ratio is 19:1. 1% from out-of-state. 52% 25 or older. Calendar: semesters.

Entrance Requirements: Required: high school transcript.

■ UNIVERSITY OF NEW MEXICO–VALENCIA CAMPUS

280 La Entrada
Los Lunas, NM 87031-7633
Tel: (505)925-8580
Fax: (505)925-8563
E-mail: mhulett@unm.edu
Web Site: www.unm.edu/~unmvc/

Description: State-supported, 2-year, coed. Part of New Mexico Commission on Higher Education. Awards certificates, transfer associate, and terminal associate degrees. Founded 1981. Setting: small town campus with easy access to Albuquerque. Total enrollment: 2,170. Student-undergrad faculty ratio is 25:1. 0% from out-of-state. 36% 25 or older. Core. Calendar: semesters. Academic remediation for entering students, ESL program, services for LD students, honors program, summer session for credit, part-time degree program, adult/continuing education programs.

Entrance Requirements: Open admission. Options: early admission, deferred admission. Recommended: high school transcript. Required for some: minimum 2.0 high school GPA. Entrance: noncompetitive. Application deadline: Rolling. Notification: continuous until 8/25.

Collegiate Environment: Student services: personal-psychological counseling. Campus security: 24-hour emergency response devices and patrols, late night transport-escort service. 65 computers available on campus for general student use. A campuswide network can be accessed from off-campus. Staffed computer lab on campus.

■ UNIVERSITY OF PHOENIX–NEW MEXICO CAMPUS

5700 Pasadena NE
Albuquerque, NM 87113-1570

Tel: (505)821-4800; Free: 866-766-0766
Web Site: www.phoenix.edu/

Description: Proprietary, comprehensive, coed. Awards bachelor's and master's degrees. Setting: urban campus. Total enrollment: 4,170. Faculty: 427 (45 full-time, 382 part-time). Full-time: 3,452 students, 64% women, 36% men. 80% 25 or older. Academic areas with the most degrees conferred: business/marketing; computer and information sciences; public administration and social services. Core. Calendar: continuous. Services for LD students, advanced placement, accelerated degree program, independent study, distance learning, external degree program, adult/continuing education programs, graduate courses open to undergrads.

Entrance Requirements: Open admission. Options: electronic application, deferred admission. Required: 1 recommendation. Required for some: high school transcript. Entrance: noncompetitive. Application deadline: Rolling.

Collegiate Environment: Campus security: late night transport-escort service. University Library with 16,781 serials, an OPAC, and a Web page. Operations spending for the previous fiscal year: $6.8 million.

■ UNIVERSITY OF THE SOUTHWEST

6610 Lovington Hwy.
Hobbs, NM 88240-9129
Tel: (575)392-6561; Free: 800-530-4400
E-mail: ataylor@usw.edu
Web Site: www.usw.edu/

Description: Independent Christian, comprehensive, coed. Awards bachelor's and master's degrees. Founded 1962. Setting: 162-acre small town campus. Endowment: $4.5 million. Educational spending for the previous fiscal year: $3521 per student. Total enrollment: 627. Faculty: 43 (14 full-time, 29 part-time). Student-undergrad faculty ratio is 15:1. 171 applied, 50% were admitted. 14% from top 10% of their high school class, 37% from top quarter, 75% from top half. Full-time: 266 students, 47% women, 53% men. Part-time: 56 students, 70% women, 30% men. Students come from 16 states and territories, 2 other countries, 53% from out-of-state. 1% American Indian or Alaska Native, non-Hispanic/Latino; 43% Hispanic/Latino; 14% African American, non-Hispanic/Latino; 1% Asian, non-Hispanic/Latino; 1% Native Hawaiian or other Pacific Islander, non-Hispanic/Latino; 1% international. 29% 25 or older, 55% live on campus, 29% transferred in. Retention: 45% of full-time freshmen returned the following year. Academic areas with the most degrees conferred: business/marketing; education; psychology. Core. Calendar: semesters. Services for LD students, advanced placement, distance learning, double major, summer session for credit, part-time degree program, internships, graduate courses open to undergrads.

Entrance Requirements: Options: electronic application, early admission, deferred admission. Required: high school transcript, minimum 2 high school GPA, SAT or ACT. Entrance: moderately difficult. Application deadline: Rolling. Notification: continuous. Transfer credits accepted: Yes.

Costs Per Year: Application fee: $25. One-time mandatory fee: $300. Comprehensive fee: $18,905 includes full-time tuition ($12,240), mandatory fees ($25), and college room and board ($6640). College room only: $3720. Full-time tuition and fees vary according to course load. Room and board charges vary according to board plan and housing facility. Part-time tuition: $510 per semester hour. Part-time tuition varies according to course load.

Collegiate Environment: Orientation program. Social organizations: 7 open to all. Most popular organizations: Student Government Association (SGA), Students in Free Enterprise (SIFE), Southwest Association of Future Educators, Fellowship of Christian Athletes, BEST. Major annual events: Homecoming, Mustang Stampede, Annual Distinguished Lecture Series. Student services: personal-psychological counseling. Campus security: student patrols, controlled dormitory access, night Security. Scarborough Memorial Library with 54,349 books, 25,750 microform titles, 202 serials, 576 audiovisual materials, an OPAC, and a Web page. Operations spending for the previous fiscal year: $159,601. 65 computers available on campus for general student use. A campuswide network can be accessed from student residence rooms. Students can access the following: online class registration. Staffed computer lab on campus provides training in use of computers, software, and the Internet.

Community Environment: See New Mexico Junior College.

■ WESTERN NEW MEXICO UNIVERSITY

PO Box 680
Silver City, NM 88062-0680
Tel: (505)538-6336; Free: 800-872-WNMU
Fax: (505)538-6155
E-mail: tresslerd@wnmu.edu

Web Site: www.wnmu.edu/

Description: State-supported, comprehensive, coed. Awards associate, bachelor's, and master's degrees. Founded 1893. Setting: 83-acre rural campus. Endowment: $5 million. Research spending for the previous fiscal year: $38,500. Total enrollment: 2,697. Faculty: 259 (128 full-time, 131 part-time). Student-undergrad faculty ratio is 17:1. 788 applied, 100% were admitted. 8% from top 10% of their high school class, 21% from top quarter, 40% from top half. Full-time: 1,363 students, 62% women, 38% men. Part-time: 856 students, 64% women, 36% men. Students come from 33 states and territories, 14 other countries. 46% 25 or older. Retention: 48% of full-time freshmen returned the following year. Academic areas with the most degrees conferred: business/marketing; education; liberal arts/general studies. Core. Calendar: semesters. Academic remediation for entering students, services for LD students, advanced placement, accelerated degree program, self-designed majors, summer session for credit, part-time degree program, adult/continuing education programs, co-op programs and internships, graduate courses open to undergrads.

Entrance Requirements: Open admission. Options: electronic application, early admission, deferred admission, international baccalaureate accepted.

Required: high school transcript. Recommended: ACT. Entrance: noncompetitive. Application deadline: 8/1. Notification: continuous.

Collegiate Environment: Orientation program. Drama-theater group, choral group, student-run newspaper. Student services: personal-psychological counseling, women's center. Campus security: 24-hour emergency response devices and patrols, student patrols, late night transport-escort service. Miller Library plus 2 others with 245,146 books, 236 serials, an OPAC, and a Web page. Operations spending for the previous fiscal year: $707,000. 85 computers available on campus for general student use. A campuswide network can be accessed from student residence rooms. Students can access the following: online class registration, online classes in Spanish. Staffed computer lab on campus.

Community Environment: Once an Apache Indian campsite and later a booming gold, silver, and zinc mining town, Silver City is a trading center for the cattle ranching and copper-mining area today. The city, located in the foothills of the mountains, has various active civic, fraternal, and veteran's organizations, and is served by commuter airline. Recreational activities include football, hunting, fishing, camping, and picnicking.

■ ADELPHI UNIVERSITY

One S Ave.
Garden City, NY 11530-0701
Tel: (516)877-3000; Free: 800-ADELPHI
Fax: (516)877-3039
E-mail: admissions@adelphi.edu
Web Site: www.adelphi.edu/

Description: Independent, university, coed. Awards associate, bachelor's, master's, and doctoral degrees and post-master's certificates. Founded 1896. Setting: 75-acre suburban campus with easy access to New York City. Endowment: $131.3 million. Research spending for the previous fiscal year: $900,000. Educational spending for the previous fiscal year: $12,449 per student. Total enrollment: 7,859. Faculty: 999 (322 full-time, 677 part-time). Student-undergrad faculty ratio is 12:1. 9,184 applied, 66% were admitted. 23% from top 10% of their high school class, 55% from top quarter, 85% from top half. Full-time: 4,525 students, 69% women, 31% men. Part-time: 578 students, 72% women, 28% men. Students come from 36 states and territories, 39 other countries, 8% from out-of-state. 0.2% American Indian or Alaska Native, non-Hispanic/Latino; 13% Hispanic/Latino; 10% African American, non-Hispanic/Latino; 7% Asian, non-Hispanic/Latino; 0.3% Native Hawaiian or other Pacific Islander, non-Hispanic/Latino; 3% international. 15% 25 or older, 24% live on campus, 11% transferred in. Retention: 82% of full-time freshmen returned the following year. Academic areas with the most degrees conferred: health professions and related sciences; business/marketing; social sciences. Core. Calendar: semesters. ESL program, services for LD students, advanced placement, accelerated degree program, self-designed majors, freshman honors college, honors program, independent study, distance learning, double major, summer session for credit, part-time degree program, co-op programs and internships, graduate courses open to undergrads. Study abroad program. ROTC: Army (c), Air Force (c).

Entrance Requirements: Options: electronic application, early action, deferred admission, international baccalaureate accepted. Required: essay, high school transcript. Recommended: minimum 3.36 high school GPA. Required for some: 2 recommendations, interview, auditions/portfolios for performing and fine arts, SAT or ACT. Entrance: moderately difficult. Application deadlines: Rolling, 12/1 for early action. Notification: continuous, 12/31 for early action. Transfer credits accepted: Yes. Early action applicants: 2,502. Early action applicants admitted: 2,014.

Costs Per Year: Application fee: $40. Comprehensive fee: $41,220 includes full-time tuition ($27,870), mandatory fees ($1450), and college room and board ($11,900). College room only: $8420. Full-time tuition and fees vary according to course level, course load, location, program, and student level. Room and board charges vary according to board plan and housing facility. Part-time tuition: $860 per credit hour. Part-time tuition varies according to course level, course load, location, program, and student level.

Collegiate Environment: Orientation program. Choral group, student-run newspaper, radio station. Social organizations: 80 open to all; national fraternities, national sororities, Social fellowship; 3% of eligible men and 7% of eligible women are members. Most popular organizations: Student Activities Board, C. A. L. I. B. E. R. (Cause to Achieve Leadership, Intelligence, Brotherhood, Excellence, and Respect), Circle K International, Commuter Student Organization, S.N.A.P. Student Nurses Acting for Progress. Major annual events: Family Weekend/Midnight Madness, Spring-In Festival/Spike It Volleyball Tournament, Spring Concert. Student services: health clinic, personal-psychological counseling. Campus security: 24-hour emergency response devices and patrols, late night transport-escort service, controlled dormitory access. 1,280 college housing spaces available; 1,212 were occupied in 2012-13. Freshmen given priority for college housing. Option: coed housing available. Swirbul Library plus 1 other with 605,791 books, 785,962 microform titles, 77,060 serials, 26,472 audiovisual materials, an OPAC, and a Web page. Operations spending for the previous fiscal year: $6.3 million. 880 computers available on campus for general student use. Computer purchase/lease plans available. A campuswide network can be accessed from student residence rooms and from off campus. Students can access the following: online class registration, payment, drop/add classes, check application status. Staffed computer lab on campus provides training in use of computers, software, and the Internet.

Community Environment: Garden City, Long Island, was one of the first planned residential communities in the country. The settlement was established around the Cathedral of the Incarnation. The climate is temperate. Located near New York City, the area has good transportation connections with the adjoining metropolis. A library, churches of major denominations, and hospitals nearby all serve the city. There is some part-time employment in the immediate area. The locale has good shopping facilities and active civic, fraternal, and veteran's organizations.

■ ADIRONDACK COMMUNITY COLLEGE

640 Bay Rd.
Queensbury, NY 12804
Tel: (518)743-2200; Free: 888-SUNY-ADK
Fax: (518)745-1433
Web Site: www.sunyacc.edu/

Description: State and locally supported, 2-year, coed. Part of State University of New York System. Awards certificates, transfer associate, and terminal associate degrees. Founded 1960. Setting: 141-acre small town campus. Endowment: $2.9 million. Total enrollment: 3,987. Faculty: 276 (89 full-time, 187 part-time). Student-undergrad faculty ratio is 14:1. 1,236 applied, 99% were admitted. Full-time: 2,263 students, 56% women, 44% men. Part-time: 1,724 students, 66% women, 34% men. Students come from 10 states and territories, 9 other countries, 1% from out-of-state. 0.3% American Indian or Alaska Native, non-Hispanic/Latino; 2% Hispanic/Latino; 1% African American, non-Hispanic/Latino; 1% Asian, non-Hispanic/Latino; 0.03% Native Hawaiian or other Pacific Islander, non-Hispanic/Latino; 0.4% international. 31% 25 or older, 5% transferred in. Retention: 59% of full-time freshmen returned the following year. Calendar: semesters. Academic remediation for entering students, services for LD students, advanced placement, accelerated degree program, independent study, distance learning, double major, summer session for credit, part-time degree program, adult/continuing education programs, co-op programs and internships. Study abroad program.

Entrance Requirements: Open admission The open admission policy applies to all programs except the Nursing AAS degree program. Students must have minimum GPA of 2.8 and be eligible to take college level math, English, and human anatomy and physiology to be considered for the nursing program. Option: electronic application. Entrance: minimally difficult. Transfer credits accepted: Yes.

Costs Per Year: Application fee: $35. One-time mandatory fee: $75. State resident tuition: $3664 full-time, $153 per credit hour part-time. Nonresident tuition: $7328 full-time, $306 per credit hour part-time. Mandatory fees: $309 full-time, $11 per credit hour part-time, $5 per term part-time. Full-time tuition and fees vary according to course load and program. Part-time tuition and fees vary according to course load and program.

Collegiate Environment: Orientation program. Drama-theater group, choral group, student-run radio station. Student services: personal-psychological counseling. Campus security: late night transport-escort service, patrols by trained security personnel 8 am to 10 pm. 400 college housing spaces available. Option: coed housing available. SUNY Adirondack Library with 65,000 books, 391 serials, an OPAC, and a Web page.

■ **ALBANY COLLEGE OF PHARMACY AND HEALTH SCIENCES**

106 New Scotland Ave.
Albany, NY 12208
Tel: (518)445-7200; Free: 888-203-8010
Fax: (518)445-7202
E-mail: admissions@acphs.edu
Web Site: www.acphs.edu/

Description: Independent, comprehensive, coed. Awards bachelor's, master's, and doctoral degrees. Founded 1881. Setting: 28-acre urban campus. Total enrollment: 1,701. Faculty: 142 (108 full-time, 34 part-time). Student-undergrad faculty ratio is 13:1. 1,507 applied, 67% were admitted. 37% from top 10% of their high school class, 72% from top quarter, 94% from top half. Full-time: 1,060 students, 58% women, 42% men. Part-time: 12 students, 58% women, 42% men. Students come from 18 other countries. 0.4% American Indian or Alaska Native, non-Hispanic/Latino; 4% Hispanic/Latino; 4% African American, non-Hispanic/Latino; 15% Asian, non-Hispanic/Latino; 0.2% Native Hawaiian or other Pacific Islander, non-Hispanic/Latino; 5% international. 65% live on campus, 10% transferred in. Retention: 86% of full-time freshmen returned the following year. Academic area with the most degrees conferred: health professions and related sciences. Core. Calendar: semesters. Services for LD students, advanced placement, double major, summer session for credit. Off campus study at Hudson-Mohawk Association of Colleges and Universities.

Entrance Requirements: Options: electronic application, early decision. Required: essay, high school transcript, 2 recommendations, SAT or ACT. Recommended: minimum 3 high school GPA. Required for some: interview. Entrance: moderately difficult. Application deadlines: 2/1, 11/1 for early decision. Notification: 3/15, 12/16 for early decision. SAT Reasoning Test deadline: 2/1. Transfer credits accepted: Yes. Applicants placed on waiting list: 49. Wait-listed applicants offered admission: 21. Early decision applicants: 104. Early decision applicants admitted: 86.

Costs Per Year: Application fee: $75. Comprehensive fee: $37,390 includes full-time tuition ($26,900), mandatory fees ($730), and college room and board ($9760). College room only: $6400. Full-time tuition and fees vary according to degree level, program, and student level. Room and board charges vary according to board plan, housing facility, and location. Part-time tuition: $900 per credit hour. Part-time tuition varies according to degree level, program, and student level.

Collegiate Environment: Orientation program. Student-run newspaper. Social organizations: 26 open to all; national fraternities, national sororities. Most popular organizations: American Pharmacy Association-Student Chapter, Orthodox Christian Student Association, Student Government Association, Colleges Against Cancer. Major annual events: Parents' Weekend, Orientation, Springfest. Student services: health clinic, personal-psychological counseling. Campus security: 24-hour emergency response devices and patrols, controlled dormitory access. 740 college housing spaces available; 700 were occupied in 2012-13. Freshmen guaranteed college housing. On-campus residence required through sophomore year. Option: coed housing available. George and Leona Lewis Library with 13,418 books, 28,388 microform titles, 3,731 serials, 950 audiovisual materials, and an OPAC. 30 computers available on campus for general student use. Computer purchase/lease plans available. A computer is required for all students. A campuswide network can be accessed from student residence rooms and from off campus. Students can access the following: online class registration. Staffed computer lab on campus.

■ **ALFRED UNIVERSITY**

One Saxon Dr.
Alfred, NY 14802-1205
Tel: (607)871-2111; Free: 800-541-9229
Fax: (607)871-2198
E-mail: admissions@alfred.edu
Web Site: www.alfred.edu/

Description: Independent, university, coed. Awards bachelor's, master's, and doctoral degrees and post-master's certificates. Founded 1836. Setting: 232-acre rural campus with easy access to Rochester, NY. Endowment: $85.9 million. Research spending for the previous fiscal year: $3.9 million.

Educational spending for the previous fiscal year: $12,048 per student. Total enrollment: 2,362. Faculty: 190 (155 full-time, 35 part-time). Student-undergrad faculty ratio is 13:1. 3,332 applied, 70% were admitted. 17% from top 10% of their high school class, 51% from top quarter, 80% from top half. 4 valedictorians. Full-time: 1,884 students, 51% women, 49% men. Part-time: 51 students, 57% women, 43% men. Students come from 37 states and territories, 16 other countries, 25% from out-of-state. 0.1% American Indian or Alaska Native, non-Hispanic/Latino; 6% Hispanic/Latino; 7% African American, non-Hispanic/Latino; 2% Asian, non-Hispanic/Latino; 0% Native Hawaiian or other Pacific Islander, non-Hispanic/Latino; 3% international. 3% 25 or older, 77% live on campus, 4% transferred in. Retention: 68% of full-time freshmen returned the following year. Academic areas with the most degrees conferred: visual and performing arts; engineering; business/marketing. Calendar: semesters. ESL program, services for LD students, advanced placement, self-designed majors, honors program, independent study, double major, summer session for credit, part-time degree program, co-op programs and internships, graduate courses open to undergrads. Off campus study. Study abroad program. ROTC: Army (c).

Entrance Requirements: Options: electronic application, early admission, early decision, deferred admission, international baccalaureate accepted. Required: essay, high school transcript, 1 recommendation, SAT or ACT. Recommended: interview. Required for some: interview, portfolio for applicants to the School of Art & Design. Entrance: moderately difficult. Application deadlines: 8/1, 12/1 for early decision. Notification: continuous, 12/15 for early decision. SAT Reasoning Test deadline: 8/1. SAT Subject Test deadline: 8/1. Transfer credits accepted: Yes. Applicants placed on waiting list: 49. Wait-listed applicants offered admission: 7. Early decision applicants: 54. Early decision applicants admitted: 54.

Costs Per Year: Application fee: $50. Comprehensive fee: $40,272 includes full-time tuition ($27,824), mandatory fees ($950), and college room and board ($11,498). Full-time tuition and fees vary according to program. Room and board charges vary according to board plan and housing facility. Part-time tuition: $902 per credit hour. Part-time mandatory fees: $160 per year.

Collegiate Environment: Orientation program. Drama-theater group, choral group, student-run newspaper, radio station. Social organizations: 90 open to all. Most popular organizations: Student Senate, Habitat for Humanity, Drawn to Diversity, Student Activities Board. Major annual events: Hot Dog Day, Homecoming, Family Weekend. Student services: health clinic, personal-psychological counseling, women's center. Campus security: 24-hour emergency response devices, student patrols, late night transport-escort service, all dormitories are key-only access, but not electronic. 1,461 college housing spaces available; 1,446 were occupied in 2012-13. Freshmen guaranteed college housing. On-campus residence required through junior year. Option: coed housing available. Herrick Memorial Library plus 1 other with 286,995 books, 79,676 microform titles, 86,783 serials, 5,800 audiovisual materials, an OPAC, and a Web page. Operations spending for the previous fiscal year: $1.6 million.

Community Environment: Alfred is a small residential community situated among the foothills of the Allegheny Mountains near the Finger Lakes Region of New York. It is served by air service in nearby cities (Rochester/Elmira), and also bus service. It is the home of the Davis Memorial Carillon, which contains the oldest carillon bells in the western hemisphere. Outdoor activities including hiking, white water rafting, downhill and cross-country skiing, and horseback riding are located a short distance from campus. Numerous groups sponsor appearances by visiting professors, speakers, and artists. Student groups sponsor a number of popular entertainers and rock and folk concerts. Both a current movie series and a classics series provide weekly films. The Fosdick Nelson Gallery shows exhibits of sculpture, glass, ceramics, paintings, lithographs and photographs. Additionally, student theatre and dance productions, as well as performances by musical ensembles, are scheduled throughout the year.

■ **AMERICAN ACADEMY OF DRAMATIC ARTS-NEW YORK**

120 Madison Ave.
New York, NY 10016-7004
Tel: (212)686-9244; Free: 800-463-8990
E-mail: shong@aada.edu
Web Site: www.aada.org/

Description: Independent, 2-year, coed. Part of AADA-New York has a branch campus: American Academy of Dramatic Arts - Los Angeles. Awards certificates and terminal associate degrees. Founded 1884. Setting: urban campus. System endowment: $6 million. Educational spending for the previous fiscal year: $4289 per student. Total enrollment: 258. Faculty: 29 (8 full-time, 21 part-time). Student-undergrad faculty ratio is 9:1. 468 applied, 81%

were admitted. 13% from top 10% of their high school class, 24% from top quarter, 79% from top half. Students come from 34 states and territories, 20 other countries, 86% from out-of-state. 0% American Indian or Alaska Native, non-Hispanic/Latino; 7% Hispanic/Latino; 8% African American, non-Hispanic/Latino; 2% Asian, non-Hispanic/Latino; 0% Native Hawaiian or other Pacific Islander, non-Hispanic/Latino; 38% international. 7% 25 or older, 40% live on campus. Core. Calendar: continuous. Academic remediation for entering students, honors program.

Entrance Requirements: Options: electronic application, deferred admission. Required: essay, high school transcript, minimum 2 high school GPA, 2 recommendations, interview, audition. Entrance: moderately difficult. Application deadline: Rolling. Notification: continuous. Transfer credits accepted: No.

Costs Per Year: Application fee: $50. Tuition: $29,900 full-time. Mandatory fees: $750 full-time.

Collegiate Environment: Orientation program. Social organizations: 1 open to all; Student Council. Major annual events: Christmas Party hosted by Academy Theatre Company, Graduation at Broadway Theatre/Reception at AADA, Seminars and Q&A's by guest lecturers. Student services: personal-psychological counseling. Campus security: 24-hour emergency response devices and patrols, controlled dormitory access, trained security guard during hours of operation and campus housing. 131 college housing spaces available; 104 were occupied in 2012-13. Freshmen given priority for college housing. On-campus residence required in freshman year. Option: coed housing available. Academy/CBS Library with 10,000 books, 24 serials, 670 audiovisual materials, and an OPAC. Operations spending for the previous fiscal year: $49,000. 5 computers available on campus for general student use. A campuswide network can be accessed from student residence rooms.

■ **AMERICAN ACADEMY MCALLISTER INSTITUTE OF FUNERAL SERVICE**
619 W 54th St.
New York, NY 10019-3602
Tel: (212)757-1190; Free: 866-932-2264
Fax: (212)765-5923
Web Site: www.funeraleducation.org/
Description: Independent, 2-year, coed. Awards diplomas and terminal associate degrees. Founded 1926. Setting: urban campus. Total enrollment: 317. Student-undergrad faculty ratio is 18:1. 30% from out-of-state. 68% 25 or older. Core. Calendar: semesters.
Entrance Requirements: Open admission. Options: early admission, deferred admission. Required: high school transcript, 2 recommendations. Recommended: interview. Entrance: noncompetitive. Application deadline: Rolling. Notification: continuous until 8/15.

■ **THE ART INSTITUTE OF NEW YORK CITY**
11 Beach St.
New York, NY 10013
Tel: (212)226-5500; Free: 800-654-2433
Fax: (212)226-5644
Web Site: www.artinstitutes.edu/newyork/
Description: Proprietary, 2-year, coed. Part of Education Management Corporation. Awards transfer associate and terminal associate degrees. Founded 1980. Setting: urban campus.

■ **ASA THE COLLEGE FOR EXCELLENCE**
81 Willoughby St.
Brooklyn, NY 11201
Tel: (718)522-9073; Free: 877-679-8772
Fax: (718)834-0835
Web Site: www.asa.edu/
Description: Proprietary, 2-year, coed. Awards certificates and terminal associate degrees. Founded 1985. Setting: urban campus with easy access to New York City. Total enrollment: 6,475. 3,368 applied. Calendar: semesters. Academic remediation for entering students, ESL program, advanced placement, accelerated degree program, distance learning, part-time degree program, co-op programs and internships.
Entrance Requirements: Option: electronic application. Required: high school transcript, interview. Transfer credits accepted: Yes.
Collegiate Environment: Orientation program.

■ **BARD COLLEGE**
PO Box 5000
Annandale-on-Hudson, NY 12504

Tel: (845)758-6822
E-mail: admission@bard.edu
Web Site: www.bard.edu/
Description: Independent, comprehensive, coed. Awards bachelor's, master's, and doctoral degrees. Founded 1860. Setting: 600-acre rural campus. Total enrollment: 2,322. Faculty: 265 (149 full-time, 116 part-time). Student-undergrad faculty ratio is 10:1. 5,410 applied, 35% were admitted. 60% from top 10% of their high school class, 95% from top quarter, 97% from top half. Full-time: 1,958 students, 57% women, 43% men. Part-time: 93 students, 51% women, 49% men. Students come from 48 states and territories, 65 other countries, 57% from out-of-state. 1% American Indian or Alaska Native, non-Hispanic/Latino; 3% Hispanic/Latino; 5% African American, non-Hispanic/Latino; 3% Asian, non-Hispanic/Latino; 0% Native Hawaiian or other Pacific Islander, non-Hispanic/Latino; 12% international. 1% 25 or older, 73% live on campus, 3% transferred in. Retention: 86% of full-time freshmen returned the following year. Academic areas with the most degrees conferred: visual and performing arts; social sciences; English. Core. Calendar: semesters. Services for LD students, advanced placement, self-designed majors, independent study, double major, part-time degree program, adult/continuing education programs, internships, graduate courses open to undergrads. Off campus study at Vassar College, State University of New York at New Paltz. Study abroad program.
Entrance Requirements: Options: electronic application, early admission, early action, deferred admission, international baccalaureate accepted. Required: essay, high school transcript, minimum 3 high school GPA, 3 recommendations. Entrance: very difficult. Application deadlines: 1/1, 11/1 for early action. Notification: 4/1, 1/1 for early action. Transfer credits accepted: Yes. Applicants placed on waiting list: 313. Wait-listed applicants offered admission: 10. Early action applicants: 657. Early action applicants admitted: 462.
Costs Per Year: Application fee: $50. One-time mandatory fee: $1574. Comprehensive fee: $59,872 includes full-time tuition ($45,730), mandatory fees ($640), and college room and board ($13,502). Full-time tuition and fees vary according to degree level. Part-time tuition: $1429 per credit hour. Part-time tuition varies according to degree level.
Collegiate Environment: Orientation program. Drama-theater group, choral group, student-run newspaper, radio station. Social organizations: 150 open to all. Most popular organizations: student government, Debate Team, Queer-Straight Alliance, International Student Organization / Black Student Organization, Free Press (student newspaper). Major annual events: Surrealist Circus, Spring Fling, International Student Organization Cultural Show. Student services: legal services, health clinic, personal-psychological counseling. Campus security: 24-hour emergency response devices and patrols, student patrols, late night transport-escort service, controlled dormitory access. 1,464 college housing spaces available; all were occupied in 2012-13. Freshmen guaranteed college housing. On-campus residence required through sophomore year. Options: coed, women-only housing available. Stevenson Library plus 3 others with 375,709 books, 8,002 microform titles, 37,766 serials, 5,268 audiovisual materials, an OPAC, and a Web page. 425 computers available on campus for general student use. A campuswide network can be accessed from student residence rooms and from off campus. Students can access the following: online class registration. Staffed computer lab on campus (open 24 hours a day) provides training in use of computers, software, and the Internet.
Community Environment: The town is situated on the Hudson River in eastern New York. The area is accessible via Metro North and Amtrak Railroad nearby, the Taconic State Parkway, or the New York Thruway, using Exit 19 and the Kingston-Rhinecliff Bridge.

■ **BARNARD COLLEGE**
3009 Broadway
New York, NY 10027-6598
Tel: (212)854-5262
Fax: (212)854-6220
E-mail: admissions@barnard.edu
Web Site: www.barnard.edu/
Description: Independent, 4-year, women only. Part of Columbia University. Awards bachelor's degrees. Founded 1889. Setting: 4-acre urban campus. Total enrollment: 2,445. Faculty: 335 (206 full-time, 129 part-time). Student-undergrad faculty ratio is 10:1. 5,153 applied, 25% were admitted. 81% from top 10% of their high school class, 99% from top quarter, 99% from top half. Full-time: 2,389 students. Part-time: 56 students. 66% from out-of-state. 0.1% American Indian or Alaska Native, non-Hispanic/Latino; 9% Hispanic/Latino; 5% African American, non-Hispanic/Latino; 17% Asian, non-Hispanic/

Latino; 0.2% Native Hawaiian or other Pacific Islander, non-Hispanic/Latino; 6% international. 89% live on campus, 1% transferred in. Retention: 94% of full-time freshmen returned the following year. Academic areas with the most degrees conferred: social sciences; English; visual and performing arts; psychology. Calendar: semesters. ROTC: Air Force (c).

Entrance Requirements: Options: early admission, early decision, deferred admission, international baccalaureate accepted. Required: essay, high school transcript, 3 recommendations, Common Application with Barnard supplement, SAT with writing and two subject tests or ACT with writing. Recommended: interview. Entrance: most difficult. Application deadlines: 1/1, 11/15 for early decision. Notification: 4/1, 12/15 for early decision. SAT Reasoning Test deadline: 1/1. SAT Subject Test deadline: 1/1. Applicants placed on waiting list: 896. Wait-listed applicants offered admission: 7. Early decision applicants: 550. Early decision applicants admitted: 240.

Costs Per Year: Application fee: $55. Comprehensive fee: $57,312 includes full-time tuition ($41,850), mandatory fees ($1652), and college room and board ($13,810). College room only: $8240. Room and board charges vary according to board plan and housing facility.

Collegiate Environment: Orientation program. Campus security: 24-hour emergency response devices and patrols, late night transport-escort service, gated campus with permanent security posts.

Community Environment: See Columbia University.

■ **BARUCH COLLEGE OF THE CITY UNIVERSITY OF NEW YORK**
1 Bernard Baruch Way
New York, NY 10010-5585
Tel: (646)312-1000
E-mail: marisa.delacruz@baruch.cuny.edu
Web Site: www.baruch.cuny.edu/
Description: State and locally supported, comprehensive, coed. Part of City University of New York System. Awards bachelor's and master's degrees. Founded 1919. Setting: urban campus. Total enrollment: 17,373. Faculty: 1,070 (472 full-time, 598 part-time). Student-undergrad faculty ratio is 18:1. 19,863 applied, 25% were admitted. 41% from top 10% of their high school class, 71% from top quarter, 89% from top half. Full-time: 10,365 students, 47% women, 53% men. Part-time: 3,412 students, 48% women, 48% men. 4% from out-of-state. 0.1% American Indian or Alaska Native, non-Hispanic/Latino; 13% Hispanic/Latino; 10% African American, non-Hispanic/Latino; 34% Asian, non-Hispanic/Latino; 0.2% Native Hawaiian or other Pacific Islander, non-Hispanic/Latino; 12% international. 26% 25 or older, 1% live on campus, 15% transferred in. Retention: 92% of full-time freshmen returned the following year. Academic areas with the most degrees conferred: business/marketing; communication/journalism; social sciences. Core. Calendar: semesters. ESL program, services for LD students, advanced placement, accelerated degree program, self-designed majors, freshman honors college, honors program, independent study, distance learning, double major, summer session for credit, part-time degree program, adult/continuing education programs, internships, graduate courses open to undergrads. Study abroad program. ROTC: Army (c).
Entrance Requirements: Options: electronic application, early admission, early decision, deferred admission, international baccalaureate accepted. Required: high school transcript, minimum 2.5 high school GPA, 16 academic units, SAT or ACT. Required for some: interview. Entrance: very difficult. Application deadline: 2/1. Notification: 5/15. SAT Reasoning Test deadline: 4/1. Transfer credits accepted: Yes.
Costs Per Year: Application fee: $65. State resident tuition: $5430 full-time. Nonresident tuition: $14,550 full-time. Full-time tuition varies according to course load. College room only: $11,590. Room charges vary according to housing facility.
Collegiate Environment: Orientation program. Drama-theater group, choral group, student-run newspaper, radio station. Social organizations: 172 open to all; national fraternities, national sororities, local fraternities, local sororities. Most popular organizations: Accounting Society, Caribbean Students Association, Association of Latino Professionals in Finance and Accounting, Golden Key International Honor Society, Helpline. Major annual events: Street Fair, Club Fair, Caribbean Cultural Festival. Student services: legal services, health clinic, personal-psychological counseling. Campus security: 24-hour emergency response devices and patrols, late night transport-escort service, controlled access by ID card. 163 college housing spaces available; all were occupied in 2012-13. Option: coed housing available. The William and Anita Newman Library with 626,753 books, 2.1 million microform titles, 52,020 audiovisual materials, an OPAC, and a Web page. 1,300 computers available on campus for general student use. A campuswide network can be

accessed. Students can access the following: online class registration. Staffed computer lab on campus provides training in use of computers, software, and the Internet.

■ **BEIS MEDRASH HEICHAL DOVID**
257 Beach 17th St.
Far Rockaway, NY 11691
Tel: (718)868-2300
Fax: (718)868-0517
Description: Proprietary, comprehensive, men only. Awards bachelor's and master's degrees. Total enrollment: 111. 37 applied.
Entrance Requirements: Recommended: high school transcript.

■ **BERKELEY COLLEGE–NEW YORK CITY CAMPUS**
3 E 43rd St.
New York, NY 10017-4604
Tel: (212)986-4343; Free: 800-446-5400
Fax: (212)697-3371
E-mail: info@berkeleycollege.edu
Web Site: www.berkeleycollege.edu/
Description: Proprietary, 4-year, coed. Administratively affiliated with Berkeley College. Awards associate and bachelor's degrees. Founded 1936. Setting: urban campus. Total enrollment: 4,430. Student-undergrad faculty ratio is 32:1. 2,308 applied, 72% were admitted. 10% from out-of-state. 34% 25 or older. Retention: 46% of full-time freshmen returned the following year. Core. Academic remediation for entering students, ESL program, advanced placement, accelerated degree program, self-designed majors, independent study, distance learning, summer session for credit, part-time degree program, adult/continuing education programs, co-op programs and internships. Off campus study at Berkeley College, White Plains; Berkeley College, West Paterson. Study abroad program.
Entrance Requirements: Options: electronic application, deferred admission. Required: high school transcript. Recommended: interview. Entrance: minimally difficult. Application deadline: Rolling.
Collegiate Environment: Student-run newspaper. Social organizations: local fraternities, local sororities. Student services: personal-psychological counseling. Campus security: 24-hour emergency response devices.

■ **BERKELEY COLLEGE–WESTCHESTER CAMPUS**
99 Church St.
White Plains, NY 10601
Tel: (914)694-1122; Free: 800-446-5400
Fax: (914)694-5832
E-mail: info@berkeleycollege.edu
Web Site: www.berkeleycollege.edu/
Description: Proprietary, primarily 2-year, coed. Awards certificates, transfer associate, terminal associate, and bachelor's degrees. Founded 1945. Setting: suburban campus with easy access to New York City. Core. Academic remediation for entering students, ESL program, advanced placement, accelerated degree program, self-designed majors, independent study, distance learning, summer session for credit, part-time degree program, adult/continuing education programs, co-op programs and internships. Off campus study at Berkeley College, West Paterson; Berkeley College, New York. Study abroad program.
Entrance Requirements: Options: electronic application, deferred admission. Required: high school transcript. Recommended: interview. Entrance: minimally difficult. Application deadline: Rolling.
Collegiate Environment: Student-run newspaper. Social organizations: local sororities. Student services: personal-psychological counseling. Campus security: 24-hour emergency response devices, controlled dormitory access, monitored entrance with front desk security guard.

■ **BETH HAMEDRASH SHAAREI YOSHER INSTITUTE**
4102-10 Sixteenth Ave.
Brooklyn, NY 11204
Tel: (718)854-2290
Description: Independent Jewish, comprehensive, men only. Awards bachelor's and master's degrees. Founded 1962. Total enrollment: 82. 17 applied, 100% were admitted. Calendar: semesters.

■ **BETH HATALMUD RABBINICAL COLLEGE**
2127 Eighty-second St.
Brooklyn, NY 11214
Tel: (718)259-2525

Description: Independent Jewish, comprehensive, men only. Awards bachelor's and master's degrees. Founded 1950. Total enrollment: 75. 28 applied, 100% were admitted. Calendar: semesters.

■ **BINGHAMTON UNIVERSITY, STATE UNIVERSITY OF NEW YORK**
PO Box 6000
Binghamton, NY 13902-6000
Tel: (607)777-2000
E-mail: admit@binghamton.edu
Web Site: www.binghamton.edu/
Description: State-supported, university, coed. Part of State University of New York System. Awards bachelor's, master's, and doctoral degrees and post-master's certificates. Founded 1946. Setting: 930-acre suburban campus. Endowment: $62 million. Research spending for the previous fiscal year: $34.1 million. Educational spending for the previous fiscal year: $11,464 per student. Total enrollment: 15,308. Faculty: 866 (604 full-time, 262 part-time). Student-undergrad faculty ratio is 20:1. 28,232 applied, 43% were admitted. 55% from top 10% of their high school class, 88% from top quarter, 99% from top half. Full-time: 11,904 students, 47% women, 53% men. Part-time: 452 students, 39% women, 61% men. Students come from 46 states and territories, 102 other countries, 12% from out-of-state. 0.1% American Indian or Alaska Native, non-Hispanic/Latino; 9% Hispanic/Latino; 5% African American, non-Hispanic/Latino; 13% Asian, non-Hispanic/Latino; 0.1% Native Hawaiian or other Pacific Islander, non-Hispanic/Latino; 12% international. 4% 25 or older, 61% live on campus, 9% transferred in. Retention: 91% of full-time freshmen returned the following year. Academic areas with the most degrees conferred: social sciences; business/marketing; psychology. Core. Calendar: semesters. ESL program, services for LD students, advanced placement, accelerated degree program, self-designed majors, honors program, independent study, distance learning, double major, summer session for credit, part-time degree program, adult/continuing education programs, internships, graduate courses open to undergrads. Off campus study at National Student Exchange, New York State Visiting Student Program. Study abroad program. ROTC: Army (c), Air Force (c).
Entrance Requirements: Options: electronic application, early admission, early action, deferred admission, international baccalaureate accepted. Required: essay, high school transcript, 1 recommendation, SAT or ACT. Required for some: portfolio, audition. Entrance: very difficult. Application deadlines: 1/15, 1/15 for nonresidents, 11/15 for early action. Notification: 4/1, 4/1 for nonresidents, 1/15 for early action. Transfer credits accepted: Yes. Applicants placed on waiting list: 1,588. Wait-listed applicants offered admission: 44. Early action applicants: 8,328. Early action applicants admitted: 4,726.
Costs Per Year: Application fee: $50. State resident tuition: $5570 full-time, $232 per credit hour part-time. Nonresident tuition: $14,720 full-time, $613 per credit hour part-time. Mandatory fees: $2075 full-time, $84.42 per credit hour part-time, $24.50 per term part-time. Full-time tuition and fees vary according to program. Part-time tuition and fees vary according to course load and program. College room and board: $12,446. Room and board charges vary according to board plan and housing facility.
Collegiate Environment: Orientation program. Drama-theater group, choral group, student-run newspaper, radio station. Social organizations: 366 open to all; national fraternities, national sororities, local fraternities, local sororities; 12% of eligible men and 10% of eligible women are members. Most popular organizations: intramurals, club sports, Student Association, cultural organizations, Peer Counseling/Mentoring/Volunteering Program. Major annual events: Spring Fling, University Fest, Homecoming. Student services: legal services, health clinic, personal-psychological counseling, women's center. Campus security: 24-hour emergency response devices and patrols, student patrols, late night transport-escort service, controlled dormitory access, well-lit campus, self-defense/safety education, secured entrances 12 am-5 am, emergency phones, emergency text messages, safety escorts. 7,330 college housing spaces available; 7,280 were occupied in 2012-13. Freshmen guaranteed college housing. On-campus residence required in freshman year. Option: coed housing available. Glenn G. Bartle Library plus 2 others with 2.5 million books, 1.9 million microform titles, 87,696 serials, 126,483 audiovisual materials, an OPAC, and a Web page. Operations spending for the previous fiscal year: $11.7 million. 1,300 computers available on campus for general student use. A campuswide network can be accessed from student residence rooms and from off campus. Students can access the following: online class registration, course management system, personal Web space, wiki, virtual desktop. Staffed computer lab on campus (open 24 hours a day) provides training in use of computers, software, and the Internet.

■ **BORICUA COLLEGE**
3755 Broadway
New York, NY 10032-1560
Tel: (212)694-1000
E-mail: mpfeffer@boricuacollege.edu
Web Site: www.boricuacollege.edu/
Description: Independent, comprehensive, coed. Awards associate, bachelor's, and master's degrees. Founded 1974. Setting: urban campus. Endowment: $626,808. Educational spending for the previous fiscal year: $2599 per student. Total enrollment: 1,058. Faculty: 133 (57 full-time, 76 part-time). Student-undergrad faculty ratio is 20:1. 924 applied, 40% were admitted. Full-time: 1,004 students, 79% women, 21% men. Students come from 2 states and territories, 0% from out-of-state. 89% 25 or older. Retention: 53% of full-time freshmen returned the following year. Core. Calendar: 15-15-8. Accelerated degree program, honors program, summer session for credit, adult/continuing education programs, internships. Study abroad program.
Entrance Requirements: Option: deferred admission. Required: essay, high school transcript, 2 recommendations, interview, proficiency in English, Boricua College Exam. Entrance: moderately difficult. Application deadline: Rolling.
Costs Per Year: Application fee: $25. One-time mandatory fee: $25. Tuition: $10,000 full-time.
Collegiate Environment: Choral group. Campus security: 24-hour emergency response devices. Boricua College Library plus 1 other with 112,600 books and 780 serials. Operations spending for the previous fiscal year: $192,471. 120 computers available on campus for general student use. Staffed computer lab on campus provides training in use of computers, software, and the Internet.

■ **BOROUGH OF MANHATTAN COMMUNITY COLLEGE OF THE CITY UNIVERSITY OF NEW YORK**
199 Chambers St.
New York, NY 10007-1097
Tel: (212)346-8000; Free: 866-593-5729
Fax: (212)346-8816
E-mail: admissions@bmcc.cuny.edu
Web Site: www.bmcc.cuny.edu/
Description: State and locally supported, 2-year, coed. Part of City University of New York System. Awards certificates, transfer associate, and terminal associate degrees. Founded 1963. Setting: 5-acre urban campus. Total enrollment: 24,537. Faculty: 1,559 (429 full-time, 1,130 part-time). Student-undergrad faculty ratio is 24:1. Full-time: 16,151 students, 56% women, 44% men. Part-time: 8,386 students, 60% women, 40% men. 2% from out-of-state. 0.2% American Indian or Alaska Native, non-Hispanic/Latino; 40% Hispanic/Latino; 31% African American, non-Hispanic/Latino; 12% Asian, non-Hispanic/Latino; 7% international. 24% 25 or older, 4% transferred in. Core. Calendar: semesters. Academic remediation for entering students, ESL program, services for LD students, advanced placement, honors program, independent study, distance learning, summer session for credit, part-time degree program, adult/continuing education programs, co-op programs and internships. Off campus study at other units of the City University of New York System. Study abroad program.
Entrance Requirements: Open admission. Options: electronic application, deferred admission. Required: high school transcript. Recommended: SAT or ACT. Entrance: noncompetitive. Application deadline: Rolling. Notification: continuous. Preference given to city residents.
Collegiate Environment: Orientation program. Drama-theater group, choral group, student-run newspaper. Student services: health clinic, personal-psychological counseling, women's center. Campus security: 24-hour patrols. College housing not available. A. Philip Randolph Library with 342,000 books, 250 serials, an OPAC, and a Web page.

■ **BRAMSON ORT COLLEGE**
69-30 Austin St.
Forest Hills, NY 11375-4239
Tel: (718)261-5800
E-mail: admissions@bramsonort.edu
Web Site: www.bramsonort.edu/
Description: Independent, 2-year, coed. Awards certificates and terminal associate degrees. Founded 1977. Total enrollment: 789. Student-undergrad faculty ratio is 22:1. 0% from out-of-state. 49% 25 or older. Calendar: semesters. Academic remediation for entering students, ESL program, advanced placement, summer session for credit, part-time degree program, internships.

Entrance Requirements: Open admission. Options: early admission, deferred admission. Required: high school transcript. Entrance: noncompetitive. Application deadline: Rolling.

Costs Per Year: Application fee: $50. One-time mandatory fee: $50. Tuition: $10,440 full-time, $435 per credit part-time. Mandatory fees: $530 full-time, $530 per year part-time. Full-time tuition and fees vary according to course load. Part-time tuition and fees vary according to course load. Tuition guaranteed not to increase for student's term of enrollment.

Collegiate Environment: Student-run newspaper. Student services: personal-psychological counseling, women's center.

■ BRIARCLIFFE COLLEGE

1055 Stewart Ave.
Bethpage, NY 11714
Tel: (516)918-3600; Free: 888-348-4999
Fax: (516)470-6020
Web Site: www.briarcliffe.edu/

Description: Proprietary, 4-year, coed. Part of Career Education Corporation. Awards associate and bachelor's degrees. Founded 1966. Setting: suburban campus with easy access to New York City. Total enrollment: 1,779. Student-undergrad faculty ratio is 21:1. 3% from out-of-state. 32% 25 or older. Core. Calendar: semesters. Academic remediation for entering students, services for LD students, advanced placement, accelerated degree program, independent study, distance learning, summer session for credit, part-time degree program, co-op programs and internships.

Entrance Requirements: Options: electronic application, deferred admission. Required: high school transcript, interview. Recommended: SAT or ACT. Entrance: noncompetitive. Application deadlines: Rolling, Rolling for nonresidents. Notification: continuous, continuous for nonresidents.

Collegiate Environment: Orientation program. Student-run newspaper, radio station. Social organizations: national fraternities. Campus security: late night transport-escort service.

■ BRONX COMMUNITY COLLEGE OF THE CITY UNIVERSITY OF NEW YORK

2155 University Ave.
Bronx, NY 10453
Tel: (718)289-5100
E-mail: admission@bcc.cuny.edu
Web Site: www.bcc.cuny.edu/

Description: State and locally supported, 2-year, coed. Part of City University of New York System. Awards certificates, transfer associate, and terminal associate degrees. Founded 1959. Setting: 50-acre urban campus with easy access to New York City. Endowment: $469,572. Educational spending for the previous fiscal year: $4597 per student. Total enrollment: 10,131. Faculty: 363 (260 full-time, 103 part-time). Student-undergrad faculty ratio is 28:1. Full-time: 6,013 students, 59% women, 41% men. Part-time: 4,118 students, 63% women, 37% men. Students come from 119 other countries, 8% from out-of-state. 35% 25 or older, 10% transferred in. Retention: 65% of full-time freshmen returned the following year. Core. Calendar: semesters. Academic remediation for entering students, ESL program, services for LD students, advanced placement, accelerated degree program, honors program, independent study, distance learning, double major, summer session for credit, part-time degree program, adult/continuing education programs, co-op programs and internships. Off campus study. Study abroad program.

Entrance Requirements: Open admission. Option: early admission. Required: high school transcript, copy of accredited high school diploma or GED scores. Recommended: SAT or ACT. Entrance: noncompetitive. Application deadline: 7/1. Notification: 8/15. Transfer credits accepted: Yes.

Collegiate Environment: Orientation program. Drama-theater group, choral group, student-run newspaper. Social organizations: 31 open to all. Most popular organizations: Muslim Students Association, Top Models Club, Anime/Manga Gaming Club, Business Club, Media Technology and Film Society. Major annual events: Freshman Convocation, Commencement and Commencement related programs, New Student Orientation. Student services: health clinic, personal-psychological counseling. Campus security: 24-hour emergency response devices and patrols, late night transport-escort service. A free shuttle bus service provides evening students with transportation from campus to several subway and bus lines between 5pm-11pm. Library & Gerald S. Lieblich Learning Resources Center with 75,000 books, 30,667 microform titles, 800 serials, 4,501 audiovisual materials, an OPAC, and a Web page. Operations spending for the previous fiscal year: $1.5 million. 1,425 computers available on campus for general student use. A campuswide network can be accessed from off-campus. Students can access the following: online class registration. Staffed computer lab on campus provides training in use of computers, software, and the Internet.

■ BROOKLYN COLLEGE OF THE CITY UNIVERSITY OF NEW YORK

2900 Bedford Ave.
Brooklyn, NY 11210-2889
Tel: (718)951-5000
E-mail: adminqry@brooklyn.cuny.edu
Web Site: www.brooklyn.cuny.edu/

Description: State and locally supported, comprehensive, coed. Part of City University of New York System. Awards bachelor's, master's, and doctoral degrees and post-master's certificates. Founded 1930. Setting: 26-acre urban campus with easy access to Manhattan. Total enrollment: 17,094. Faculty: 1,401 (557 full-time, 844 part-time). Student-undergrad faculty ratio is 15:1. 17,497 applied, 28% were admitted. 19% from top 10% of their high school class, 56% from top quarter, 85% from top half. Full-time: 9,268 students, 59% women, 41% men. Part-time: 3,801 students, 62% women, 38% men. Students come from 25 states and territories, 75 other countries, 1% from out-of-state. 29% 25 or older, 11% transferred in. Retention: 78% of full-time freshmen returned the following year. Academic areas with the most degrees conferred: business/marketing; education; psychology. Core. Calendar: semesters. ESL program, services for LD students, advanced placement, freshman honors college, honors program, independent study, distance learning, double major, summer session for credit, part-time degree program, adult/continuing education programs, internships, graduate courses open to undergrads. Off campus study at other units of the City University of New York System. Study abroad program.

Entrance Requirements: Options: early admission, international baccalaureate accepted. Required: high school transcript, minimum 3.1 high school GPA, combined SAT or ACT scores of 1000, SAT or ACT. Entrance: moderately difficult. Application deadlines: 2/1, 2/1 for nonresidents. Notification: continuous. Transfer credits accepted: Yes.

Costs Per Year: Application fee: $65. State resident tuition: $5430 full-time. Nonresident tuition: $14,550 full-time. Mandatory fees: $454 full-time.

Collegiate Environment: Orientation program. Drama-theater group, choral group, student-run newspaper, radio station. Social organizations: 150 open to all; national fraternities, national sororities, local fraternities, local sororities; 3% of eligible men and 3% of eligible women are members. Most popular organizations: Academic Club Association, Kingsman and Excelsior Newspaper, NY Public Interest Group (NYPIRG), Student Government CIAS, SGS, and GSO, Student Forensics. Major annual events: Presidential Convocation, Graduation Ceremony, student government elections. Student services: health clinic, personal-psychological counseling, women's center. Campus security: 24-hour emergency response devices and patrols, late night transport-escort service. Brooklyn College Library plus 1 other with 1.3 million books, 1.6 million microform titles, 13,500 serials, 21,731 audiovisual materials, an OPAC, and a Web page. 1,000 computers available on campus for general student use. A campuswide network can be accessed from off-campus. Students can access the following: online class registration. Staffed computer lab on campus provides training in use of computers, software, and the Internet.

■ BROOME COMMUNITY COLLEGE

PO Box 1017
Binghamton, NY 13902-1017
Tel: (607)778-5000
E-mail: admissions@sunybroome.edu
Web Site: www.sunybroome.edu/

■ BRYANT & STRATTON COLLEGE - ALBANY CAMPUS

1259 Central Ave.
Albany, NY 12205-5230
Tel: (518)437-1802
Fax: (518)437-1048
Web Site: www.bryantstratton.edu/

Description: Proprietary, 2-year, coed. Part of Bryant and Stratton College, Inc. Awards terminal associate degrees. Founded 1857. Setting: suburban campus. Total enrollment: 470. Faculty: 45 (12 full-time, 33 part-time). Full-time: 354 students, 79% women, 21% men. Part-time: 116 students, 74% women, 26% men. 0% from out-of-state. 51% 25 or older. Retention: 45% of full-time freshmen returned the following year. Core. Calendar: semesters. Academic remediation for entering students, services for LD students, independent study, distance learning, double major, summer session for credit, part-time degree program, internships.

Entrance Requirements: Option: deferred admission. Required: high school transcript, interview, entrance and placement evaluations, CPAt, ACCUPLACER. Recommended: SAT or ACT. Entrance: minimally difficult. Application deadline: Rolling.

Collegiate Environment: Orientation program. Student-run newspaper. Campus security: 24-hour emergency response devices. Library with 3,500 books, 5 serials, 136 audiovisual materials, an OPAC, and a Web page. 110 computers available on campus for general student use. A campuswide network can be accessed. Staffed computer lab on campus.

■ **BRYANT & STRATTON COLLEGE - AMHERST CAMPUS**
3650 Millersport Hwy.
Getzville, NY 14068
Tel: (716)625-6300
E-mail: bkdioguardi@bryantstratton.edu
Web Site: www.bryantstratton.edu/
Description: Proprietary, primarily 2-year, coed. Awards terminal associate and bachelor's degrees. Founded 1977. Setting: 5-acre suburban campus with easy access to Buffalo. Total enrollment: 474. Faculty: 67 (9 full-time, 58 part-time). Full-time: 277 students, 73% women, 27% men. Part-time: 197 students, 78% women, 22% men. 0% from out-of-state. 56% 25 or older, 9% transferred in. Core. Calendar: trimesters. Academic remediation for entering students, services for LD students, advanced placement, distance learning, summer session for credit, part-time degree program, adult/continuing education programs, internships.

Entrance Requirements: Options: electronic application, early admission. Required: high school transcript, interview, entrance evaluation and placement evaluation, TABE, CPAt or ACCUPLACER. Recommended: SAT or ACT. Required for some: essay. Application deadline: Rolling.

Collegiate Environment: Orientation program. Most popular organizations: Phi Beta Lambda, Student Government Association, Information Technology Club, Ambassadors Club, National Technical Honor Society. Major annual events: Career Fair, Bring a Friend Day, Health Fair. Library Resource Center with 4,500 books, 25 serials, 150 audiovisual materials, an OPAC, and a Web page. 100 computers available on campus for general student use. A campuswide network can be accessed from student residence rooms and from off campus. Staffed computer lab on campus provides training in use of computers, software, and the Internet.

■ **BRYANT & STRATTON COLLEGE - BUFFALO CAMPUS**
465 Main St.
Ste. 400
Buffalo, NY 14203
Tel: (716)884-9120
E-mail: pjstruebel@bryantstratton.edu
Web Site: www.bryantstratton.edu/
Description: Proprietary, primarily 2-year, coed. Awards terminal associate and bachelor's degrees. Founded 1854. Setting: urban campus. Total enrollment: 693. Faculty: 53 (11 full-time, 42 part-time). 305 applied, 75% were admitted. Full-time: 473 students, 73% women, 27% men. Part-time: 220 students, 82% women, 18% men. 0% from out-of-state. 46% 25 or older, 7% transferred in. Core. Calendar: trimesters. Academic remediation for entering students, services for LD students, advanced placement, distance learning, summer session for credit, part-time degree program, adult/continuing education programs, internships.

Entrance Requirements: Options: electronic application, early admission. Required: high school transcript, interview, entrance and placement evaluation, TABE, CPAt or ACCUPLACER. Recommended: SAT or ACT. Required for some: essay. Application deadline: Rolling.

Collegiate Environment: Orientation program. Most popular organizations: Medical Assisting Club, Criminal Justice Club, SHRM, National Technical Honor Society, Phi Beta Lambda. Major annual events: Bring A Friend Day, Career Fair, Health Fair. Library Resource Center plus 2 others with 30,000 books, 28,217 serials, 252 audiovisual materials, and an OPAC. 150 computers available on campus for general student use.

Community Environment: See Canisius College.

■ **BRYANT & STRATTON COLLEGE - GREECE CAMPUS**
150 Bellwood Dr.
Rochester, NY 14606
Tel: (585)720-0660
Fax: (585)720-9226

Web Site: www.bryantstratton.edu/
Description: Proprietary, 2-year, coed. Part of Bryant and Stratton College, Inc. Awards terminal associate degrees. Founded 1973. Setting: suburban campus. Educational spending for the previous fiscal year: $2734 per student. Total enrollment: 279. Faculty: 49 (8 full-time, 41 part-time). Student-undergrad faculty ratio is 10:1. Full-time: 192 students, 81% women, 19% men. Part-time: 87 students, 87% women, 13% men. 0% from out-of-state. 73% 25 or older, 4% transferred in. Core. Calendar: semesters. Academic remediation for entering students, services for LD students, advanced placement, independent study, distance learning, summer session for credit, part-time degree program, adult/continuing education programs, internships.

Entrance Requirements: Options: electronic application, deferred admission. Required: high school transcript, interview, entrance evaluation and placement evaluation, CPAt. Recommended: SAT or ACT. Entrance: minimally difficult. Application deadline: Rolling.

Collegiate Environment: Orientation program. Social organizations: 3 open to all; 10% of eligible men and 90% of eligible women are members. Most popular organizations: Bryant and Stratton Student Association (BASSA), Student Ambassadors, Criminal Justice Club. Major annual events: Holiday Party, Backyard Bar-B-Cue, Spring Fling. Campus security: 24-hour emergency response devices, late night transport-escort service. Greece Campus Library with 2,824 books, 28 serials, 104 audiovisual materials, and an OPAC. Operations spending for the previous fiscal year: $19,925. 88 computers available on campus for general student use. A campuswide network can be accessed.

■ **BRYANT & STRATTON COLLEGE - HENRIETTA CAMPUS**
1225 Jefferson Rd.
Rochester, NY 14623-3136
Tel: (585)292-5627
Fax: (585)292-6015
E-mail: djprofita@bryantstratton.edu
Web Site: www.bryantstratton.edu/
Description: Proprietary, 2-year, coed. Part of Bryant and Stratton College, Inc. Awards terminal associate degrees. Founded 1985. Setting: 1-acre urban campus. Educational spending for the previous fiscal year: $3525 per student. Total enrollment: 407. Faculty: 64 (17 full-time, 47 part-time). Student-undergrad faculty ratio is 10:1. 181 applied, 78% were admitted. Full-time: 288 students, 77% women, 23% men. Part-time: 119 students, 82% women, 18% men. 0% from out-of-state. 47% 25 or older, 7% transferred in. Core. Calendar: semesters. Academic remediation for entering students, services for LD students, advanced placement, independent study, distance learning, summer session for credit, part-time degree program, adult/continuing education programs, internships.

Entrance Requirements: Options: electronic application, deferred admission. Required: high school transcript, interview, entrance evaluation and placement evaluation, CPAt. Recommended: minimum 2 high school GPA, SAT or ACT. Entrance: minimally difficult. Application deadline: Rolling.

Collegiate Environment: Orientation program. Social organizations: 4 open to all; Bryant and Stratton Student Association (BASSA); 15% of eligible men and 85% of eligible women are members. Most popular organizations: BASSA, Student Ambassadors, Paralegal Club, Graphic Design Club. Major annual events: student Christmas parties, Spring Fling, Picnic in the Park. Campus security: late night transport-escort service. Henrietta Campus Library with 4,056 books, 43 serials, 72 audiovisual materials, and an OPAC. Operations spending for the previous fiscal year: $44,201. 160 computers available on campus for general student use. A campuswide network can be accessed.

■ **BRYANT & STRATTON COLLEGE - NORTH CAMPUS**
8687 Carling Rd.
Liverpool, NY 13090-1315
Tel: (315)652-6500
Web Site: www.bryantstratton.edu/
Description: Proprietary, 2-year, coed. Part of Bryant and Stratton Business Institute, Inc. Awards diplomas and terminal associate degrees. Founded 1983. Setting: 1-acre suburban campus with easy access to Syracuse. Total enrollment: 497. Faculty: 57 (16 full-time, 41 part-time). Student-undergrad faculty ratio is 9:1. Full-time: 333 students, 70% women, 30% men. Part-time: 164 students, 80% women, 20% men. 0% from out-of-state. 52% 25 or older, 0% transferred in. Core. Calendar: semesters. Academic remediation for entering students, services for LD students, advanced placement,

independent study, distance learning, double major, summer session for credit, part-time degree program, adult/continuing education programs, co-op programs and internships.

Entrance Requirements: Open admission. Option: deferred admission. Required: high school transcript, interview, entrance evaluation and placement evaluation, TABE, CPAt. Recommended: minimum 2 high school GPA. Entrance: minimally difficult. Application deadline: Rolling. Notification: continuous.

Collegiate Environment: Orientation program. Social organizations: 7 open to all; national fraternities. Student services: personal-psychological counseling. Campus security: 24-hour emergency response devices. Resource Center plus 1 other with 1,936 books, 13 serials, 85 audiovisual materials, and an OPAC.

■ **BRYANT & STRATTON COLLEGE - SOUTHTOWNS CAMPUS**
200 Redtail
Orchard Park, NY 14127
Tel: (716)821-9331
E-mail: tdominiak@bryantstratton.edu
Web Site: www.bryantstratton.edu/

Description: Proprietary, primarily 2-year, coed. Awards terminal associate and bachelor's degrees. Founded 1989. Setting: suburban campus with easy access to Buffalo. Total enrollment: 1,206. Faculty: 75 (23 full-time, 52 part-time). Full-time: 663 students, 80% women, 20% men. Part-time: 543 students, 79% women, 21% men. Students come from 27 states and territories, 1 other country, 60% from out-of-state. 49% 25 or older, 11% transferred in. Core. Calendar: trimesters. Academic remediation for entering students, services for LD students, advanced placement, distance learning, summer session for credit, part-time degree program, adult/continuing education programs, internships.

Entrance Requirements: Options: electronic application, early admission. Required: high school transcript, interview, entrance and placement evaluations, TABE, CPAt or ACCUPLACER. Recommended: SAT or ACT. Required for some: essay. Application deadline: Rolling.

Collegiate Environment: Orientation program. Most popular organizations: Accounting/Business Club, Administrative Professionals Club, Phi Beta Lambda, National Technical Honor Society, student newsletter. Major annual events: Career Fair, Health Fair, Fall Festival. Library Resource Center with 1,402 books, 42 serials, 128 audiovisual materials, an OPAC, and a Web page. 125 computers available on campus for general student use.

■ **BRYANT & STRATTON COLLEGE - SYRACUSE CAMPUS**
953 James St.
Syracuse, NY 13203-2502
Tel: (315)472-6603
Fax: (315)474-4383
Web Site: www.bryantstratton.edu/

Description: Proprietary, 2-year, coed. Part of Bryant and Stratton Business Institute, Inc. Awards terminal associate degrees. Founded 1854. Setting: 1-acre urban campus. Total enrollment: 715. Faculty: 55 (21 full-time, 34 part-time). Student-undergrad faculty ratio is 13:1. 254 applied, 94% were admitted. Full-time: 494 students, 74% women, 26% men. Part-time: 221 students, 77% women, 23% men. Students come from 2 states and territories, 2 other countries, 1% from out-of-state. 48% 25 or older, 12% live on campus, 6% transferred in. Retention: 38% of full-time freshmen returned the following year. Core. Calendar: semesters. Academic remediation for entering students, services for LD students, distance learning, double major, summer session for credit, part-time degree program, co-op programs and internships.

Entrance Requirements: Required: high school transcript, interview, entrance, placement evaluations, CPAt. Recommended: SAT or ACT. Entrance: noncompetitive. Application deadline: Rolling.

Collegiate Environment: Orientation program. Student-run newspaper. Social organizations: 10 open to all. Most popular organizations: Management Club, Travel Club, Medical Club, Computer Club, Veterans Club. Major annual events: Summer Picnic, Fall Pep Rally, Career Day. Campus security: 24-hour emergency response devices and patrols, controlled dormitory access. Bryant and Stratton, Syracuse Campus Library with 1,325 books, 40 serials, and 40 audiovisual materials. 190 computers available on campus for general student use. Staffed computer lab on campus provides training in use of computers, software, and the Internet.

■ **BUFFALO STATE COLLEGE, STATE UNIVERSITY OF NEW YORK**
1300 Elmwood Ave.
Buffalo, NY 14222-1095

Tel: (716)878-4000
Fax: (716)878-6100
E-mail: admissions@buffalostate.edu
Web Site: www.buffalostate.edu/

Description: State-supported, comprehensive, coed. Part of State University of New York System. Awards bachelor's and master's degrees and post-master's certificates. Founded 1867. Setting: 115-acre urban campus. Endowment: $24.1 million. Research spending for the previous fiscal year: $2.9 million. Educational spending for the previous fiscal year: $17,657 per student. Total enrollment: 11,214. Faculty: 842 (412 full-time, 430 part-time). Student-undergrad faculty ratio is 17:1. 11,856 applied, 46% were admitted. 8% from top 10% of their high school class, 31% from top quarter, 69% from top half. Students come from 27 states and territories, 18 other countries, 1% from out-of-state. 0.4% American Indian or Alaska Native, non-Hispanic/Latino; 8% Hispanic/Latino; 18% African American, non-Hispanic/Latino; 2% Asian, non-Hispanic/Latino; 0.1% Native Hawaiian or other Pacific Islander, non-Hispanic/Latino; 1% international. 19% 25 or older, 26% live on campus. Retention: 74% of full-time freshmen returned the following year. Academic areas with the most degrees conferred: education; business/marketing; homeland security, law enforcement, firefighting, and protective services. Core. Calendar: semesters. Academic remediation for entering students, ESL program, services for LD students, advanced placement, freshman honors college, honors program, independent study, distance learning, double major, summer session for credit, part-time degree program, adult/continuing education programs, co-op programs and internships, graduate courses open to undergrads. Off campus study at Western New York Consortium, National Student Exchange. Study abroad program. ROTC: Army (c).

Entrance Requirements: Options: electronic application, early admission, early decision, deferred admission, international baccalaureate accepted. Required: high school transcript, minimum 3 high school GPA, SAT and SAT Subject Tests or ACT. Recommended: SAT. Required for some: essay, interview. Entrance: moderately difficult. Application deadlines: Rolling, 11/15 for early decision. Notification: continuous, 12/15 for early decision. Early decision applicants: 93. Early decision applicants admitted: 60.

Costs Per Year: Application fee: $40. State resident tuition: $5570 full-time. Nonresident tuition: $14,820 full-time. Mandatory fees: $1124 full-time. College room and board: $11,192. College room only: $6592. Room and board charges vary according to board plan, housing facility, and student level.

Collegiate Environment: Orientation program. Drama-theater group, choral group, student-run newspaper, radio station. Social organizations: 75 open to all; national fraternities, national sororities, local fraternities, local sororities; 1% of eligible men and 1% of eligible women are members. Most popular organizations: United Student Government, African-American Student Organization, Caribbean Student Organization, The Record, WBNY radio. Major annual events: Homecoming, Commuter Daze. Student services: legal services, health clinic, personal-psychological counseling, women's center. Campus security: 24-hour emergency response devices and patrols, student patrols, late night transport-escort service, controlled dormitory access. 2,529 undergraduates lived in college housing during 2012-13. Freshmen guaranteed college housing. On-campus residence required through sophomore year. Option: coed housing available. E. H. Butler Library plus 1 other with 676,636 books, 409,227 microform titles, 64,012 serials, 9,483 audiovisual materials, an OPAC, and a Web page. Operations spending for the previous fiscal year: $3.5 million. 1,700 computers available on campus for general student use. A campuswide network can be accessed from student residence rooms and from off campus. Students can access the following: online class registration. Staffed computer lab on campus.

■ **BUSINESS INFORMATICS CENTER, INC.**
134 S Central Ave.
Valley Stream, NY 11580-5431
Tel: (516)561-0050
Fax: (516)561-0074
E-mail: info@thecollegeforbusiness.com
Web Site: www.thecollegeforbusiness.com/

Description: Proprietary, 2-year, coed. Awards terminal associate degrees. Founded 1982. Total enrollment: 142. Student-undergrad faculty ratio is 12:1. 8 applied, 50% were admitted. 0% from out-of-state. 58% 25 or older. Retention: 67% of full-time freshmen returned the following year.

Entrance Requirements: Required: high school transcript, interview.

■ CANISIUS COLLEGE

2001 Main St.
Buffalo, NY 14208-1098
Tel: (716)883-7000; Free: 800-843-1517
Fax: (716)888-2377
E-mail: admissions@canisius.edu
Web Site: www.canisius.edu/
Description: Independent Roman Catholic (Jesuit), comprehensive, coed. Awards associate, bachelor's, and master's degrees and post-master's certificates. Founded 1870. Setting: 72-acre urban campus. Endowment: $86.7 million. Educational spending for the previous fiscal year: $8998 per student. Total enrollment: 4,908. Faculty: 519 (225 full-time, 294 part-time). Student-undergrad faculty ratio is 11:1. 4,361 applied, 74% were admitted. 25% from top 10% of their high school class, 55% from top quarter, 86% from top half. 6 valedictorians. Full-time: 2,954 students, 53% women, 47% men. Part-time: 326 students, 19% women, 81% men. Students come from 32 states and territories, 27 other countries, 8% from out-of-state. 0.3% American Indian or Alaska Native, non-Hispanic/Latino; 3% Hispanic/Latino; 7% African American, non-Hispanic/Latino; 2% Asian, non-Hispanic/Latino; 0.03% Native Hawaiian or other Pacific Islander, non-Hispanic/Latino; 4% international. 4% 25 or older, 49% live on campus, 5% transferred in. Retention: 82% of full-time freshmen returned the following year. Academic areas with the most degrees conferred: business/marketing; education; communication/journalism. Core. Calendar: semesters. Academic remediation for entering students, ESL program, services for LD students, advanced placement, honors program, independent study, distance learning, double major, summer session for credit, part-time degree program, adult/continuing education programs, co-op programs and internships, graduate courses open to undergrads. Off campus study at members of the Western New York Consortium. Study abroad program. ROTC: Army.
Entrance Requirements: Options: electronic application, early admission, deferred admission, international baccalaureate accepted. Required: high school transcript, minimum 2 high school GPA, SAT or ACT. Recommended: essay, 1 recommendation, interview. Required for some: interview. Entrance: moderately difficult. Application deadline: 5/1. Notification: continuous. SAT Reasoning Test deadline: 4/1. Transfer credits accepted: Yes.
Costs Per Year: Application fee: $40. Comprehensive fee: $43,850 includes full-time tuition ($30,780), mandatory fees ($1250), and college room and board ($11,820). College room only: $6940. Full-time tuition and fees vary according to course load and degree level. Room and board charges vary according to board plan and housing facility. Part-time tuition: $879 per credit. Part-time mandatory fees: $20.50 per credit hour. Part-time tuition and fees vary according to course load and degree level.
Collegiate Environment: Orientation program. Drama-theater group, choral group, student-run newspaper, radio station. Social organizations: 140 open to all; national fraternities, national sororities; 1% of eligible men and 1% of eligible women are members. Most popular organizations: Campus Programming Board, Undergraduate Student Association, Afro-American Society, Residence Hall Association, Student Association. Major annual events: Parents' Weekend, Spring Fest (End of School Year Celebration), International Fest Week. Student services: health clinic, personal-psychological counseling. Campus security: 24-hour emergency response devices and patrols, late night transport-escort service, controlled dormitory access, crime prevention programs, closed-circuit television monitors, emergency call boxes across campus. 1,596 college housing spaces available; 1,450 were occupied in 2012-13. Freshmen given priority for college housing. On-campus residence required through sophomore year. Option: coed housing available. Andrew L. Bouwhuis Library plus 1 other with 426,340 books, 599,947 microform titles, 47,740 serials, 14,058 audiovisual materials, an OPAC, and a Web page. Operations spending for the previous fiscal year: $949,576. 700 computers available on campus for general student use. Computer purchase/lease plans available. A campuswide network can be accessed from student residence rooms and from off campus. Students can access the following: online class registration, online accounts. Staffed computer lab on campus provides training in use of computers, software, and the Internet.
Community Environment: The Buffalo metropolitan area of over 1.2 million people offers varied cultural, athletic, and entertainment facilities. Among them are the world-famous Albright-Knox Art Gallery, renowned for its modern and contemporary collection; the Buffalo Philharmonic Orchestra, among the top ranked orchestras in North America, which makes its home in the acoustically excellent Kleinhans Music Hall; the Studio Arena, which offers legitimate theater; and the Buffalo Zoo, one of the leading zoos in the United States. For sports fans, there are the Buffalo Bills football team, the Buffalo Sabres hockey team, and the Buffalo Bisons baseball team. Niagara Falls, the ski areas of western New York, and many attractions in Canada are within easy driving distance of the College. The central location of the College also provides many opportunities for students interested in community service, internships, and employment.

■ CAYUGA COUNTY COMMUNITY COLLEGE

197 Franklin St.
Auburn, NY 13021-3099
Tel: (315)255-1743; Free: 866-598-8883
Web Site: www.cayuga-cc.edu/
Description: State and locally supported, 2-year, coed. Part of State University of New York System. Awards certificates, transfer associate, and terminal associate degrees. Founded 1953. Setting: 50-acre small town campus with easy access to Rochester, Syracuse. Endowment: $6.3 million. Educational spending for the previous fiscal year: $4058 per student. Total enrollment: 4,619. Faculty: 275 (55 full-time, 220 part-time). Student-undergrad faculty ratio is 24:1. 2,304 applied, 70% were admitted. Full-time: 2,314 students, 61% women, 39% men. Part-time: 2,305 students, 64% women, 36% men. 1% American Indian or Alaska Native, non-Hispanic/Latino; 2% Hispanic/Latino; 4% African American, non-Hispanic/Latino; 1% Asian, non-Hispanic/Latino; 0% Native Hawaiian or other Pacific Islander, non-Hispanic/Latino; 0% international. 34% 25 or older, 7% transferred in. Retention: 51% of full-time freshmen returned the following year. Core. Calendar: semesters. Academic remediation for entering students, services for LD students, advanced placement, accelerated degree program, honors program, independent study, distance learning, double major, summer session for credit, part-time degree program, adult/continuing education programs, co-op programs and internships. Off campus study. Study abroad program. ROTC: Air Force (c).
Entrance Requirements: Open admission except for RN Degree. Options: electronic application, deferred admission. Required: high school transcript. Required for some: interview, SAT or ACT. Entrance: noncompetitive. Application deadline: Rolling. Notification: continuous. Transfer credits accepted: Yes.
Costs Per Year: Application fee: $0. State resident tuition: $3950 full-time, $160 per credit hour part-time. Nonresident tuition: $7990 full-time, $300 per credit hour part-time. Mandatory fees: $376 full-time, $19 per credit part-time. Full-time tuition and fees vary according to course load. Part-time tuition and fees vary according to course load. College room only: $6500.
Collegiate Environment: Orientation program. Drama-theater group, choral group, student-run newspaper, radio station. Most popular organizations: Student Activity Board, student government, Criminal Justice Club, Tutor Club, Early Childhood Club. Major annual events: Graduation, Orientation, Holiday Craft Festival. Student services: health clinic. Campus security: security from 8 am to 9 pm. 97 college housing spaces available; all were occupied in 2012-13. Option: coed housing available. Norman F. Bourke Memorial Library plus 2 others with 92,156 books, 9,713 microform titles, 187 serials, 5,240 audiovisual materials, an OPAC, and a Web page. Operations spending for the previous fiscal year: $1.1 million. 450 computers available on campus for general student use. A campuswide network can be accessed. Students can access the following: online class registration. Staffed computer lab on campus provides training in use of computers, software, and the Internet.

■ CAZENOVIA COLLEGE

22 Sullivan St.
Cazenovia, NY 13035-1084
Tel: (315)655-7000; Free: 800-654-3210
Fax: (315)655-2190
E-mail: admission@cazenovia.edu
Web Site: www.cazenovia.edu/
Description: Independent, 4-year, coed. Awards associate and bachelor's degrees. Founded 1824. Setting: 40-acre small town campus with easy access to Syracuse. Endowment: $30 million. Total enrollment: 1,092. Faculty: 129 (57 full-time, 72 part-time). Student-undergrad faculty ratio is 12:1. 2,279 applied, 70% were admitted. 11% from top 10% of their high school class, 35% from top quarter, 66% from top half. Full-time: 955 students, 74% women, 26% men. Part-time: 137 students, 72% women, 28% men. Students come from 19 states and territories, 3 other countries, 22% from out-of-state. 2% 25 or older, 90% live on campus, 4% transferred in. Retention: 70% of full-time freshmen returned the following year. Academic areas with the most degrees conferred: visual and performing arts; business/marketing; homeland security, law enforcement, firefighting, and protective

services. Core. Calendar: semesters. Academic remediation for entering students, services for LD students, advanced placement, accelerated degree program, freshman honors college, honors program, independent study, distance learning, double major, summer session for credit, part-time degree program, adult/continuing education programs, internships. Off campus study. Study abroad program. ROTC: Army (c), Air Force (c).

Entrance Requirements: Options: electronic application, deferred admission, international baccalaureate accepted. Required: high school transcript, 1 recommendation. Recommended: essay, minimum 2 high school GPA, interview, portfolio for art and design students, SAT or ACT. Entrance: minimally difficult. Application deadlines: Rolling, Rolling for nonresidents. Notification: continuous, continuous for nonresidents. Transfer credits accepted: Yes.

Costs Per Year: Application fee: $30. Comprehensive fee: $39,420 includes full-time tuition ($27,550), mandatory fees ($472), and college room and board ($11,398). Full-time tuition and fees vary according to class time, course load, and program. Room and board charges vary according to board plan and housing facility. Part-time tuition: $585 per credit hour. Part-time tuition varies according to class time and course load.

Collegiate Environment: Orientation program. Drama-theater group, choral group, student-run newspaper, radio station. Social organizations: 54 open to all. Most popular organizations: Activities Board, Multicultural Student Group, performing arts, student radio station, yearbook. Major annual events: Spring Day, Parents' Weekend, Quad Day. Student services: health clinic, personal-psychological counseling. Campus security: 24-hour emergency response devices and patrols, late night transport-escort service, controlled dormitory access. Witheral Library with 87,465 books, 15,282 microform titles, 61,297 serials, 4,482 audiovisual materials, an OPAC, and a Web page. 350 computers available on campus for general student use. A campuswide network can be accessed from student residence rooms and from off campus. Staffed computer lab on campus provides training in use of computers, software, and the Internet.

Community Environment: The village of Cazenovia is a rural community near Syracuse with a population of 2,700. The climate is temperate with 4 definite seasons. Cazenovia has a local library, churches of many denominations, motels, inns, and restaurants, and various civic, fraternal, and veteran's organizations. Recreational activities include water sports, summer and winter mountain sports including hiking and skiing, as well as local and regional sports teams and cultural events.

■ CENTRAL YESHIVA TOMCHEI TMIMIM-LUBAVITCH

841-853 Ocean Pky.
Brooklyn, NY 11230
Tel: (718)434-0784

Description: Independent Jewish, comprehensive, men only. Awards bachelor's and master's degrees. Founded 1941. Total enrollment: 664. 260 applied, 100% were admitted. 2% 25 or older. Calendar: semesters.

■ CITY COLLEGE OF THE CITY UNIVERSITY OF NEW YORK

160 Convent Ave.
New York, NY 10031-9198
Tel: (212)650-7000
Fax: (212)650-6417
E-mail: admissions@ccny.cuny.edu
Web Site: www.ccny.cuny.edu/

Description: State and locally supported, comprehensive, coed. Part of City University of New York System. Awards bachelor's, master's, and doctoral degrees and post-master's certificates. Founded 1847. Setting: 35-acre urban campus with easy access to New York City. Research spending for the previous fiscal year: $60 million. Total enrollment: 16,161. Faculty: 1,922 (520 full-time, 1,402 part-time). Student-undergrad faculty ratio is 13:1. 28,183 applied, 33% were admitted. Full-time: 9,524 students, 52% women, 48% men. Part-time: 3,589 students, 51% women, 49% men. Students come from 140 other countries, 4% from out-of-state. 0.1% American Indian or Alaska Native, non-Hispanic/Latino; 32% Hispanic/Latino; 20% African American, non-Hispanic/Latino; 22% Asian, non-Hispanic/Latino; 8% international. 25% 25 or older, 1% live on campus, 11% transferred in. Retention: 83% of full-time freshmen returned the following year. Academic areas with the most degrees conferred: engineering; psychology; social sciences. Core. Calendar: semesters. ESL program, services for LD students, advanced placement, accelerated degree program, self-designed majors, freshman honors college, honors program, independent study, summer session for credit, part-time degree program, adult/continuing education

programs, internships, graduate courses open to undergrads. Off campus study at other units of the City University of New York System. Study abroad program. ROTC: Army.

Entrance Requirements: Options: early admission, deferred admission, international baccalaureate accepted. Required: high school transcript, SAT or ACT. Required for some: essay, creative challenge for Architecture, supplemental application for Engineering. Entrance: moderately difficult. Application deadline: 2/1. Notification: continuous until 2/1.

Costs Per Year: Application fee: $65. State resident tuition: $5131 full-time. Nonresident tuition: $13,800 full-time. Full-time tuition varies according to course load and program.

Collegiate Environment: Orientation program. Drama-theater group, choral group, student-run newspaper, radio station. Social organizations: 140 open to all; national fraternities, local fraternities. Most popular organizations: LAESA-SHPE, NSBE, BSA, Salsa-Mambo, IVCF. Major annual events: Fashion Show-FIC, Harlemween-USG. Student services: health clinic, personal-psychological counseling. Campus security: 24-hour patrols, late night transport-escort service, controlled dormitory access. 580 college housing spaces available. Option: coed housing available. Morris Raphael Cohen Library plus 8 others with 1.4 million books, 901,638 microform titles, 77,000 serials, 257,712 audiovisual materials, an OPAC, and a Web page. Operations spending for the previous fiscal year: $4.6 million. 3,000 computers available on campus for general student use. Computer purchase/lease plans available. A campuswide network can be accessed from off-campus. Students can access the following: online class registration. Staffed computer lab on campus provides training in use of software and the Internet.

■ CLARKSON UNIVERSITY

Potsdam, NY 13699
Tel: (315)268-6400; Free: 800-527-6577
Fax: (315)268-7647
E-mail: admission@clarkson.edu
Web Site: www.clarkson.edu/

Description: Independent, university, coed. Awards bachelor's, master's, and doctoral degrees. Founded 1896. Setting: 640-acre small town campus. Endowment: $158.3 million. Research spending for the previous fiscal year: $14.3 million. Educational spending for the previous fiscal year: $12,700 per student. Total enrollment: 3,604. Faculty: 273 (220 full-time, 53 part-time). Student-undergrad faculty ratio is 15:1. 4,199 applied, 76% were admitted. 38% from top 10% of their high school class, 74% from top quarter, 93% from top half. 23 valedictorians. Full-time: 3,050 students, 28% women, 72% men. Part-time: 22 students, 50% women, 50% men. Students come from 38 states and territories, 29 other countries, 26% from out-of-state. 0.2% American Indian or Alaska Native, non-Hispanic/Latino; 4% Hispanic/Latino; 3% African American, non-Hispanic/Latino; 3% Asian, non-Hispanic/Latino; 0% Native Hawaiian or other Pacific Islander, non-Hispanic/Latino; 3% international. 1% 25 or older, 83% live on campus, 3% transferred in. Retention: 86% of full-time freshmen returned the following year. Academic areas with the most degrees conferred: engineering; business/marketing; engineering technologies. Core. Calendar: semesters. ESL program, services for LD students, advanced placement, accelerated degree program, self-designed majors, honors program, independent study, distance learning, double major, summer session for credit, part-time degree program, co-op programs, graduate courses open to undergrads. Off campus study at Associated Colleges of the St. Lawrence Valley; Semester at Sea; American University Washington Semester Program. Study abroad program. ROTC: Army, Air Force.

Entrance Requirements: Options: electronic application, early admission, early decision, deferred admission, international baccalaureate accepted. Required: essay, high school transcript, 2 recommendations, SAT or ACT, SAT or ACT. Recommended: interview, SAT Subject Tests. Entrance: very difficult. Application deadlines: 1/15, 12/1 for early decision. Notification: continuous, 1/1 for early decision. SAT Reasoning Test deadline: 1/15. SAT Subject Test deadline: 1/15. Transfer credits accepted: Yes. Applicants placed on waiting list: 131. Wait-listed applicants offered admission: 0. Early decision applicants: 153. Early decision applicants admitted: 100.

Costs Per Year: Application fee: $50. Comprehensive fee: $53,608 includes full-time tuition ($39,770), mandatory fees ($840), and college room and board ($12,998). College room only: $6886. Full-time tuition and fees vary according to course load. Room and board charges vary according to board plan and housing facility. Part-time tuition: $1324 per credit. Part-time tuition varies according to course load.

Collegiate Environment: Orientation program. Drama-theater group, choral

group, student-run newspaper, radio station. Social organizations: 148 open to all; national fraternities, national sororities, local fraternities; 12% of eligible men and 14% of eligible women are members. Most popular organizations: Ski Club, Outing Club, Pep Band, Ultimate Frisbee Club, Sports Car Club. Major annual events: Springfest and Winterfest, World in Potsdam Diversity Festival, NCAA Division I Championship Hockey Games. Student services: legal services, health clinic, personal-psychological counseling. Campus security: 24-hour emergency response devices and patrols, late night transport-escort service, controlled dormitory access. 2,453 college housing spaces available; 2,423 were occupied in 2012-13. Freshmen guaranteed college housing. On-campus residence required through senior year. Options: coed, men-only, women-only housing available. Harriet Call Burnap Memorial Library plus 1 other with 367,825 books, 256,647 microform titles, 22,717 serials, 424 audiovisual materials, an OPAC, and a Web page. Operations spending for the previous fiscal year: $1.6 million. 350 computers available on campus for general student use. Computer purchase/lease plans available. A campuswide network can be accessed from student residence rooms and from off campus. Students can access the following: online class registration.

Community Environment: This is a college community with a population of 9,700. Bus and air lines serve the area. Local community services include a library, a museum, a hospital, churches of major denominations, and several civic, fraternal, and veterans' organizations. There are part-time jobs available at the campus and with businesses in the area. Recreational activities include bowling, canoeing, fishing, hiking, golfing, mountain biking, swimming, skiing, and theater.

■ **CLINTON COMMUNITY COLLEGE**

136 Clinton Point Dr.
Plattsburgh, NY 12901-9573
Tel: (518)562-4200; Free: 800-552-1160
Fax: (518)562-8621
E-mail: tobi.hay@clinton.edu
Web Site: clintoncc.suny.edu/

Description: State and locally supported, 2-year, coed. Part of State University of New York System. Awards certificates, transfer associate, and terminal associate degrees. Founded 1969. Setting: 100-acre small town campus. Educational spending for the previous fiscal year: $5618 per student. Total enrollment: 2,240. Faculty: 163 (53 full-time, 110 part-time). Student-undergrad faculty ratio is 9:1. Students come from 7 states and territories, 19 other countries, 2% from out-of-state. 25% 25 or older, 10% live on campus. Retention: 52% of full-time freshmen returned the following year. Core. Calendar: semesters. Academic remediation for entering students, ESL program, services for LD students, advanced placement, self-designed majors, independent study, distance learning, summer session for credit, part-time degree program, external degree program, adult/continuing education programs, co-op programs and internships. Off campus study at State University of New York College at Plattsburgh.

Entrance Requirements: Open admission except for nursing, electronics technology and wind engine and turbine technology. Options: electronic application, deferred admission. Required: high school transcript. Required for some: essay, 3 recommendations, interview. Entrance: noncompetitive. Application deadline: 8/26. Notification: continuous, continuous for nonresidents. Preference given to Clinton County residents. Transfer credits accepted: Yes.

Costs Per Year: Application fee: $0. State resident tuition: $3620 full-time, $151 per credit part-time. Nonresident tuition: $8500 full-time, $350 per credit part-time. Mandatory fees: $464 full-time, $16 per credit part-time, $10. Full-time tuition and fees vary according to program. Part-time tuition and fees vary according to course load and program. College room and board: $8250. College room only: $4300. Room and board charges vary according to board plan.

Collegiate Environment: Orientation program. Drama-theater group, choral group, student-run newspaper. Social organizations: 30 open to all. Most popular organizations: Athletics, Future Human Services Professionals, PTK (Honor Society), Drama Club, Criminal Justice Club. Major annual events: Fall Carnival, Spring Club Fair, Drama Club Performances. Student services: health clinic, personal-psychological counseling. Campus security: 24-hour emergency response devices and patrols, late night transport-escort service, controlled dormitory access. 265 college housing spaces available; all were occupied in 2012-13. Freshmen guaranteed college housing. Option: coed housing available. Clinton Community College Learning Resource Center plus 1 other with 40,665 books, 59,765 serials, 1,687 audiovisual materials, an OPAC, and a Web page. Operations spending for the previous fiscal

year: $434,980. 300 computers available on campus for general student use. A campuswide network can be accessed from student residence rooms and from off campus. Staffed computer lab on campus provides training in use of computers and the Internet.

■ **COCHRAN SCHOOL OF NURSING**

967 N Broadway
Yonkers, NY 10701
Tel: (914)964-4283
E-mail: kvitola@riversidehealth.org
Web Site: www.cochranschoolofnursing.us/

Description: Independent, 2-year, coed. Administratively affiliated with Mercy College, International Academic Alliance (NIT). Awards terminal associate degrees. Founded 1894. Setting: urban campus with easy access to New York City. Total enrollment: 328. Faculty: 24 (all full-time). Student-undergrad faculty ratio is 10:1. 81% 25 or older. Core. Calendar: semesters. Advanced placement, part-time degree program.

Entrance Requirements: Option: deferred admission. Required: essay, high school transcript, interview, ATI-entrance exam. Required for some: SAT. Entrance: moderately difficult. Application deadline: 4/15. Notification: 4/15.

Costs Per Year: Application fee: $35. Tuition: $9571 full-time, $563 per credit part-time. Mandatory fees: $1,937 full-time, $1,937.43 per term part-time. Full-time tuition and fees vary according to course load and student level. Part-time tuition and fees vary according to course load and student level.

Collegiate Environment: Major annual events: Spring Fling Dance, Boat Trip, Holiday Luncheon. Student services: health clinic, personal-psychological counseling. Campus security: 24-hour emergency response devices and patrols, late night transport-escort service. Cochran School of Nursing Library with 4,314 books, 115 serials, 500 audiovisual materials, and an OPAC. 47 computers available on campus for general student use. Staffed computer lab on campus provides training in use of computers, software, and the Internet.

■ **COLGATE UNIVERSITY**

13 Oak Dr.
Hamilton, NY 13346-1386
Tel: (315)228-1000
Fax: (315)228-7798
E-mail: admission@colgate.edu
Web Site: www.colgate.edu/

Description: Independent, comprehensive, coed. Awards bachelor's and master's degrees. Founded 1819. Setting: 515-acre rural campus with easy access to Syracuse, Utica. Endowment: $693.4 million. Research spending for the previous fiscal year: $584,217. Educational spending for the previous fiscal year: $16,062 per student. Total enrollment: 2,865. Faculty: 349 (294 full-time, 55 part-time). Student-undergrad faculty ratio is 9:1. 7,798 applied, 29% were admitted. 68% from top 10% of their high school class. Full-time: 2,850 students, 54% women, 46% men. Students come from 48 states and territories, 45 other countries, 75% from out-of-state. 0.3% American Indian or Alaska Native, non-Hispanic/Latino; 8% Hispanic/Latino; 4% African American, non-Hispanic/Latino; 4% Asian, non-Hispanic/Latino; 0.1% Native Hawaiian or other Pacific Islander, non-Hispanic/Latino; 8% international. 0% 25 or older, 92% live on campus, 0.3% transferred in. Retention: 95% of full-time freshmen returned the following year. Academic areas with the most degrees conferred: social sciences; biological/life sciences; English. Core. Calendar: semesters. Services for LD students, advanced placement, self-designed majors, honors program, independent study, double major, internships, graduate courses open to undergrads. Off campus study at New York State Visiting Student Program. Study abroad program. ROTC: Army (c).

Entrance Requirements: Options: electronic application, early decision, deferred admission, international baccalaureate accepted. Required: essay, high school transcript, 3 recommendations, Colgate supplement, SAT or ACT. Entrance: most difficult. Application deadlines: 1/15, 1/15 for nonresidents, 11/15 for early decision plan 1, 1/15 for early decision plan 2. Notification: 4/1, 4/1 for nonresidents, 12/15 for early decision plan 1, Rolling for early decision plan 2. SAT Reasoning Test deadline: 1/15. SAT Subject Test deadline: 1/15. Transfer credits accepted: Yes. Applicants placed on waiting list: 1,422. Wait-listed applicants offered admission: 36. Early decision applicants: 650. Early decision applicants admitted: 335.

Costs Per Year: Application fee: $60. One-time mandatory fee: $50. Comprehensive fee: $55,715 includes full-time tuition ($44,330), mandatory fees ($310), and college room and board ($11,075). College room only:

$5345. Full-time tuition and fees vary according to course load. Room and board charges vary according to board plan and housing facility. Part-time tuition: $5,541.25 per course. Part-time tuition varies according to course load.

Collegiate Environment: Orientation program. Drama-theater group, choral group, student-run newspaper, radio station. Social organizations: 180 open to all; national fraternities, national sororities, local fraternities; 19% of eligible men and 23% of eligible women are members. Most popular organizations: COVE, student government, cultural/ethnic interest groups, student publications, Outdoor Education. Major annual events: Dancefest, Spring Party Weekend, Real World. Student services: legal services, health clinic, personal-psychological counseling, women's center. Campus security: 24-hour emergency response devices and patrols, student patrols, late night transport-escort service, controlled dormitory access. 2,385 college housing spaces available; 2,107 were occupied in 2012-13. Freshmen guaranteed college housing. On-campus residence required through junior year. Option: coed housing available. Case Library and Geyer Center for Information Technology plus 1 other with 1.2 million books, 679,135 microform titles, 29,632 serials, 16,184 audiovisual materials, an OPAC, and a Web page. Operations spending for the previous fiscal year: $5.4 million. 780 computers available on campus for general student use. Computer purchase/lease plans available. A campuswide network can be accessed from student residence rooms and from off campus. Students can access the following: online class registration, software applications. Staffed computer lab on campus provides training in use of computers, software, and the Internet.

Community Environment: Hamilton (population 3,550) lies 25 miles south of Utica and 38 miles southeast of Syracuse, New York. Bus and airline connections are to be found in the neighboring cities. The climate is moderate. Part-time employment is available for students. The village has a library, a small museum with library, a movie theater, coffee house, restaurants, hospital, and numerous civic, fraternal and veterans' organizations. Local recreational facilities include hunting, fishing, boating, skiing, and golf.

■ THE COLLEGE AT BROCKPORT, STATE UNIVERSITY OF NEW YORK

350 New Campus Dr.
Brockport, NY 14420-2997
Tel: (585)395-2211
Fax: (585)395-5452
E-mail: admit@brockport.edu
Web Site: www.brockport.edu/

Description: State-supported, comprehensive, coed. Part of State University of New York System. Awards bachelor's and master's degrees and post-master's certificates. Founded 1867. Setting: 454-acre small town campus with easy access to Rochester. Total enrollment: 8,271. Faculty: 604 (327 full-time, 277 part-time). Student-undergrad faculty ratio is 18:1. 8,570 applied, 48% were admitted. 15% from top 10% of their high school class, 48% from top quarter, 86% from top half. Full-time: 6,444 students, 54% women, 46% men. Part-time: 689 students, 59% women, 41% men. 2% from out-of-state. 0.3% American Indian or Alaska Native, non-Hispanic/Latino; 5% Hispanic/Latino; 7% African American, non-Hispanic/Latino; 1% Asian, non-Hispanic/Latino; 0.1% Native Hawaiian or other Pacific Islander, non-Hispanic/Latino. 15% 25 or older, 38% live on campus, 14% transferred in. Retention: 81% of full-time freshmen returned the following year. Academic areas with the most degrees conferred: business/marketing; health professions and related sciences; education. Core. Calendar: semesters. Academic remediation for entering students, ESL program, services for LD students, advanced placement, accelerated degree program, self-designed majors, freshman honors college, honors program, independent study, distance learning, double major, summer session for credit, part-time degree program, co-op programs and internships, graduate courses open to undergrads. Off campus study at Rochester Area Colleges, New York State Visiting Student Program. Study abroad program. ROTC: Army, Naval (c), Air Force (c).

Entrance Requirements: Options: electronic application, deferred admission, international baccalaureate accepted. Required: essay, high school transcript, 1 recommendation, SAT or ACT, SAT or ACT. Recommended: minimum 3.1 high school GPA. Required for some: interview. Entrance: moderately difficult. Application deadline: Rolling. Notification: continuous. Preference given to exceptional talent in arts, dance, and athletics. Transfer credits accepted: Yes. Applicants placed on waiting list: 362. Wait-listed applicants offered admission: 87.

Costs Per Year: Application fee: $50. State resident tuition: $5870 full-time.

Nonresident tuition: $14,820 full-time. Mandatory fees: $1340 full-time. College room and board: $11,386. Room and board charges vary according to board plan and housing facility.

Collegiate Environment: Orientation program. Drama-theater group, choral group, student-run newspaper, radio station. Social organizations: national fraternities, national sororities; 1% of eligible men and 2% of eligible women are members. Most popular organizations: fine arts clubs, Organization for Students of African Descent, Communication Club, student radio station, sports clubs. Major annual events: Homecoming/Family Weekend, Scholars' Day, Brock the Port. Student services: legal services, health clinic, personal-psychological counseling, women's center. Campus security: 24-hour emergency response devices and patrols, student patrols, late night transport-escort service, controlled dormitory access. Freshmen guaranteed college housing. On-campus residence required through sophomore year. Option: coed housing available.

■ COLLEGE OF MOUNT SAINT VINCENT

6301 Riverdale Ave.
Riverdale, NY 10471-1093
Tel: (718)405-3200; Free: 800-665-CMSV
Fax: (718)549-7945
E-mail: brenda.nelson@mountsaintvincent.edu
Web Site: www.mountsaintvincent.edu/

Description: Independent, comprehensive, coed. Awards bachelor's and master's degrees and post-master's certificates. Founded 1911. Setting: 70-acre suburban campus with easy access to New York City. Endowment: $8.6 million. Total enrollment: 1,925. Faculty: 232 (77 full-time, 155 part-time). Student-undergrad faculty ratio is 13:1. 2,637 applied, 92% were admitted. 3% from top 10% of their high school class, 17% from top quarter, 44% from top half. Full-time: 1,455 students, 70% women, 30% men. Part-time: 236 students, 86% women, 14% men. Students come from 24 states and territories, 7 other countries, 9% from out-of-state. 0.2% American Indian or Alaska Native, non-Hispanic/Latino; 36% Hispanic/Latino; 16% African American, non-Hispanic/Latino; 8% Asian, non-Hispanic/Latino; 0.1% Native Hawaiian or other Pacific Islander, non-Hispanic/Latino; 1% international. 12% 25 or older, 43% live on campus, 6% transferred in. Retention: 71% of full-time freshmen returned the following year. Academic areas with the most degrees conferred: health professions and related sciences; business/marketing; communication/journalism; liberal arts/general studies. Core. Calendar: semesters. Academic remediation for entering students, services for LD students, advanced placement, accelerated degree program, honors program, independent study, double major, summer session for credit, part-time degree program, adult/continuing education programs, internships, graduate courses open to undergrads. Study abroad program. ROTC: Air Force (c).

Entrance Requirements: Options: electronic application, early admission, early action, deferred admission, international baccalaureate accepted. Required: essay, high school transcript, minimum 2 high school GPA, SAT or ACT. Recommended: 2 recommendations, interview. Required for some: interview. Entrance: moderately difficult. Application deadlines: Rolling, 11/15 for early action. Notification: continuous, 12/1 for early action. SAT Reasoning Test deadline: 3/15. Transfer credits accepted: Yes. Early action applicants: 383. Early action applicants admitted: 362.

Costs Per Year: Application fee: $35. Comprehensive fee: $42,350 includes full-time tuition ($28,980), mandatory fees ($1310), and college room and board ($12,060). Part-time tuition: $900 per credit. Part-time mandatory fees: $250 per term.

Collegiate Environment: Orientation program. Drama-theater group, choral group, student-run newspaper, radio station. Social organizations: 36 open to all. Most popular organizations: Casa Latina, Players, Dance Club, Student Nurse Association. Major annual events: Midnight Madness, Block Party, Talent Show. Student services: health clinic, personal-psychological counseling. Campus security: 24-hour emergency response devices and patrols, late night transport-escort service, controlled dormitory access, emergency call boxes. 774 college housing spaces available; 712 were occupied in 2012-13. Freshmen guaranteed college housing. Option: coed housing available. Elizabeth Seton Library with 102,479 books, 3,672 audiovisual materials, an OPAC, and a Web page. Operations spending for the previous fiscal year: $404,955. 249 computers available on campus for general student use. A campuswide network can be accessed from student residence rooms and from off campus. Students can access the following: online class registration. Staffed computer lab on campus provides training in use of computers, software, and the Internet.

Community Environment: See Fordham University.

■ **THE COLLEGE OF NEW ROCHELLE**
29 Castle Pl.
New Rochelle, NY 10805-2308
Tel: (914)654-5000; Free: 800-933-5923
Fax: (914)654-5554
E-mail: admission@cnr.edu
Web Site: www.cnr.edu/
Description: Independent, comprehensive, coed. Awards bachelor's and master's degrees and post-master's certificates (also offers a non-traditional adult program with significant enrollment not reflected in profile). Founded 1904. Setting: 20-acre suburban campus with easy access to New York City. Total enrollment: 1,670. Student-undergrad faculty ratio is 10:1. 1,114 applied, 37% were admitted. 15% from top 10% of their high school class, 33% from top quarter, 78% from top half. Full-time: 526 students, 94% women, 6% men. Part-time: 314 students, 87% women, 13% men. Students come from 16 states and territories, 10% from out-of-state. 0.2% American Indian or Alaska Native, non-Hispanic/Latino; 19% Hispanic/Latino; 33% African American, non-Hispanic/Latino; 6% Asian, non-Hispanic/Latino; 0.2% Native Hawaiian or other Pacific Islander, non-Hispanic/Latino; 1% international. 22% 25 or older, 23% live on campus, 13% transferred in. Retention: 80% of full-time freshmen returned the following year. Academic areas with the most degrees conferred: health professions and related sciences; psychology; biological/life sciences. Core. Calendar: semesters. Academic remediation for entering students, services for LD students, advanced placement, accelerated degree program, self-designed majors, honors program, independent study, double major, summer session for credit, part-time degree program, adult/continuing education programs, co-op programs and internships, graduate courses open to undergrads. Off campus study at Iona College, Concordia College (NY), Marymount College, Dominican College of San Rafael. Study abroad program.
Entrance Requirements: Options: electronic application, early admission, early decision, deferred admission. Required: high school transcript, SAT or ACT. Recommended: essay, 1 recommendation, interview. Entrance: moderately difficult. Application deadlines: Rolling, 11/1 for early decision. Notification: continuous, 12/15 for early decision. Transfer credits accepted: Yes.
Costs Per Year: Application fee: $35. Comprehensive fee: $42,950 includes full-time tuition ($30,210), mandatory fees ($1050), and college room and board ($11,690). Full-time tuition and fees vary according to course load, location, and program. Room and board charges vary according to housing facility. Part-time tuition: $896 per credit. Part-time mandatory fees: $450 per term. Part-time tuition and fees vary according to course load, location, and program.
Collegiate Environment: Orientation program. Drama-theater group, choral group, student-run newspaper. Social organizations: 23 open to all. Most popular organizations: Drama Club, CNR Model United Nations, Student Nurses Association. Major annual events: Strawberry Festival, Family Weekend, Spirit Competition. Student services: health clinic, personal-psychological counseling, women's center. Campus security: 24-hour emergency response devices and patrols, late night transport-escort service, controlled dormitory access, 24-hour monitored security cameras at residence hall entrances. 341 college housing spaces available; 206 were occupied in 2012-13. Freshmen guaranteed college housing. Option: women-only housing available. Gill Library with 220,000 books, 284 microform titles, 1,450 serials, and an OPAC. 120 computers available on campus for general student use. Computer purchase/lease plans available. A campuswide network can be accessed from student residence rooms and from off campus. Students can access the following: online class registration. Staffed computer lab on campus provides training in use of computers, software, and the Internet.
Community Environment: See Iona College.

■ **THE COLLEGE OF SAINT ROSE**
432 Western Ave.
Albany, NY 12203-1419
Tel: (518)454-5111; Free: 800-637-8556
Fax: (518)451-2013
E-mail: admit@strose.edu
Web Site: www.strose.edu/
Description: Independent, comprehensive, coed. Awards bachelor's and master's degrees and post-master's certificates. Founded 1920. Setting: 46-acre urban campus. Endowment: $31.7 million. Educational spending for the previous fiscal year: $15,669 per student. Total enrollment: 4,698. Faculty: 426 (206 full-time, 220 part-time). Student-undergrad faculty ratio is 14:1.

5,353 applied, 66% were admitted. 14% from top 10% of their high school class, 44% from top quarter, 76% from top half. Full-time: 2,721 students, 67% women, 33% men. Part-time: 160 students, 59% women, 41% men. Students come from 24 states and territories, 27 other countries, 10% from out-of-state. 1% American Indian or Alaska Native, non-Hispanic/Latino; 5% Hispanic/Latino; 6% African American, non-Hispanic/Latino; 2% Asian, non-Hispanic/Latino; 0.1% Native Hawaiian or other Pacific Islander, non-Hispanic/Latino; 1% international. 7% 25 or older, 47% live on campus, 9% transferred in. Retention: 81% of full-time freshmen returned the following year. Academic areas with the most degrees conferred: education; business/marketing; visual and performing arts. Core. Calendar: semesters. Academic remediation for entering students, services for LD students, advanced placement, accelerated degree program, self-designed majors, independent study, double major, summer session for credit, part-time degree program, external degree program, internships, graduate courses open to undergrads. Off campus study at the Association of Colleges of Sisters of Saint Joseph (ACSSJ) Student Exchange Program offers students the opportunity to enrich their educational experience by studying for a semester or a year at a member campus: Avila University, Kansas City, MO; Chestnut Hill College, Philadelphia, PA; Elms College, Chicopee, MA; Fontbonne University, St. Louis, MO; Mount Saint Mary's College, Los Angeles, CA; Regis College, Weston, MA; St. Catherine University, St. Paul, MN and St. Joseph's College, New York, NY. Study abroad program. ROTC: Army (c), Naval (c), Air Force (c).
Entrance Requirements: Options: electronic application, early admission, early action, deferred admission, international baccalaureate accepted. Required: essay, high school transcript, 1 recommendation. Recommended: minimum 3 high school GPA. Required for some: interview, SAT or ACT. Entrance: moderately difficult. Application deadlines: 2/1, 12/1 for early action. Notification: continuous, 12/15 for early action. Transfer credits accepted: Yes. Early action applicants: 2,665. Early action applicants admitted: 2,060.
Costs Per Year: Application fee: $40. Comprehensive fee: $38,934 includes full-time tuition ($26,750), mandatory fees ($934), and college room and board ($11,250). College room only: $5630. Full-time tuition and fees vary according to class time and course load. Room and board charges vary according to board plan and housing facility. Part-time tuition: $894 per credit hour. Part-time mandatory fees: $30 per credit hour. Part-time tuition and fees vary according to class time and course load.
Collegiate Environment: Orientation program. Drama-theater group, choral group, student-run newspaper, radio station. Social organizations: 33 open to all. Most popular organizations: Student Association, Student Events Board, Spectrum-ALANA Student Union, Colleges Against Cancer, Music & Entertainment Industry Student Association. Major annual events: Midnight Madness, Rose Rock, Harvest Fest. Student services: health clinic, personal-psychological counseling. Campus security: 24-hour emergency response devices and patrols, late night transport-escort service, controlled dormitory access. 1,385 college housing spaces available; 1,329 were occupied in 2012-13. Freshmen given priority for college housing. Options: coed, men-only, women-only housing available. Neil Hellman Library plus 2 others with 223,091 books, 313,339 microform titles, 562 serials, 5,626 audiovisual materials, an OPAC, and a Web page. Operations spending for the previous fiscal year: $1.8 million. 733 computers available on campus for general student use. A campuswide network can be accessed from student residence rooms and from off campus. Students can access the following: online class registration. Staffed computer lab on campus (open 24 hours a day) provides training in use of computers, software, and the Internet.
Community Environment: See State University of New York at Albany.

■ **COLLEGE OF STATEN ISLAND OF THE CITY UNIVERSITY OF NEW YORK**
2800 Victory Blvd.
Staten Island, NY 10314-6600
Tel: (718)982-2000
Fax: (718)982-2500
E-mail: admissions@cuny.csi.edu
Web Site: www.csi.cuny.edu/
Description: State and locally supported, comprehensive, coed. Part of City University of New York. Awards associate, bachelor's, master's, and doctoral degrees and post-master's certificates. Founded 1955. Setting: 204-acre urban campus with easy access to New York City. Endowment: $5 million. Educational spending for the previous fiscal year: $5025 per student. Total enrollment: 14,321. Faculty: 1,219 (331 full-time, 888 part-time). Student-undergrad faculty ratio is 19:1. 11,630 applied, 100% were admitted. Full-

time: 9,917 students, 54% women, 46% men. Part-time: 3,447 students, 60% women, 40% men. Students come from 11 states and territories, 67 other countries, 1% from out-of-state. 0.2% American Indian or Alaska Native, non-Hispanic/Latino; 15% Hispanic/Latino; 9% African American, non-Hispanic/Latino; 9% Asian, non-Hispanic/Latino; 0.2% Native Hawaiian or other Pacific Islander, non-Hispanic/Latino; 3% international. 22% 25 or older, 5% transferred in. Retention: 84% of full-time freshmen returned the following year. Academic areas with the most degrees conferred: business/marketing; social sciences; psychology. Calendar: semesters. Academic remediation for entering students, ESL program, services for LD students, advanced placement, accelerated degree program, self-designed majors, freshman honors college, honors program, independent study, distance learning, double major, summer session for credit, adult/continuing education programs, co-op programs and internships. Off campus study at other units of the City University of New York. Study abroad program.

Entrance Requirements: Options: electronic application, deferred admission, international baccalaureate accepted. Required: high school transcript, SAT or ACT. Required for some: essay, 1 recommendation, interview. Entrance: noncompetitive. Application deadline: Rolling. Notification: continuous. SAT Reasoning Test deadline: 5/1. Transfer credits accepted: Yes.

Costs Per Year: Application fee: $65. State resident tuition: $5430 full-time, $230 per credit part-time. Nonresident tuition: $14,550 full-time, $485 per credit part-time. Mandatory fees: $428 full-time, $128 per term part-time.

Collegiate Environment: Orientation program. Drama-theater group, choral group, student-run newspaper, radio station. Social organizations: 45 open to all. Most popular organizations: Japanese Visual Culture Club, Hillel Club, International Business Society, Psychology Club, Love Your Neighbor Club. Major annual events: Spring Carnival, CSI's Got Talent, Relay for Life. Student services: health clinic, personal-psychological counseling, women's center. College of Staten Island Library with 606,427 microform titles, 58,025 serials, an OPAC, and a Web page. Operations spending for the previous fiscal year: $2.5 million. 1,408 computers available on campus for general student use. A campuswide network can be accessed. Students can access the following: online class registration, zero balance confirmation. Staffed computer lab on campus provides training in use of computers, software, and the Internet.

■ **THE COLLEGE OF WESTCHESTER**
325 Central Ave.
White Plains, NY 10602
Tel: (914)948-4442; Free: 800-660-7093
Fax: (914)948-5441
E-mail: admissions@cw.edu
Web Site: www.cw.edu/
Description: Proprietary, 2-year, coed. Awards certificates, transfer associate, and terminal associate degrees. Founded 1915. Setting: suburban campus with easy access to New York City. Total enrollment: 1,363. Faculty: 82 (25 full-time, 57 part-time). Student-undergrad faculty ratio is 15:1. 947 applied, 74% were admitted. 4% from top 10% of their high school class, 19% from top quarter, 55% from top half. 1 National Merit Scholar. 4% from out-of-state. 41% 25 or older. Core. Calendar: for day division, semesters for evening and weekend divisions. Academic remediation for entering students, accelerated degree program, honors program, double major, summer session for credit, part-time degree program, adult/continuing education programs, co-op programs and internships.
Entrance Requirements: Options: electronic application, deferred admission. Required: high school transcript, interview. Recommended: SAT. Required for some: essay. Entrance: minimally difficult. Application deadline: Rolling.
Costs Per Year: Application fee: $40. Tuition: $21,900 full-time, $730 per credit hour part-time. Mandatory fees: $1000 full-time, $200 per term part-time. Full-time tuition and fees vary according to course load. Part-time tuition and fees vary according to course load.
Collegiate Environment: Orientation program. Student-run newspaper. Student services: personal-psychological counseling. 214 computers available on campus for general student use. A campuswide network can be accessed. Staffed computer lab on campus.

■ **COLUMBIA-GREENE COMMUNITY COLLEGE**
4400 Rte. 23
Hudson, NY 12534-0327
Tel: (518)828-4181
Fax: (518)828-8543

Web Site: www.sunycgcc.edu/
Description: State and locally supported, 2-year, coed. Part of State University of New York System. Awards certificates, transfer associate, and terminal associate degrees. Founded 1969. Setting: 143-acre rural campus. Total enrollment: 2,048. Student-undergrad faculty ratio is 19:1. 0% from out-of-state. 28% 25 or older. Core. Calendar: semesters. Academic remediation for entering students, services for LD students, advanced placement, honors program, independent study, distance learning, double major, summer session for credit, part-time degree program, adult/continuing education programs, internships.
Entrance Requirements: Open admission except for nursing, automotive technology, massage therapy programs. Options: early admission, deferred admission. Required: high school transcript. Required for some: interview. Entrance: noncompetitive. Application deadline: Rolling. Notification: continuous. Preference given to residents of sponsoring counties.
Collegiate Environment: Orientation program. Drama-theater group, choral group, student-run radio station. Campus security: 24-hour patrols, late night transport-escort service. CGCC Library with an OPAC and a Web page.

■ **COLUMBIA UNIVERSITY**
116th St. and Broadway
New York, NY 10027
Tel: (212)854-1754
Web Site: www.columbia.edu/
Description: Independent, university, coed. Awards bachelor's, master's, and doctoral degrees. Founded 1754. Setting: 36-acre urban campus. Endowment: $7.8 billion. Total enrollment: 6,068. Faculty: 1,965 (1,485 full-time, 480 part-time). Student-undergrad faculty ratio is 6:1. 31,851 applied, 7% were admitted. Full-time: 6,068 students, 47% women, 53% men. 73% from out-of-state. 2% American Indian or Alaska Native, non-Hispanic/Latino; 15% Hispanic/Latino; 12% African American, non-Hispanic/Latino; 20% Asian, non-Hispanic/Latino; 12% international. 0% 25 or older, 94% live on campus, 2% transferred in. Retention: 99% of full-time freshmen returned the following year. Academic areas with the most degrees conferred: social sciences; engineering; biological/life sciences. Core. Calendar: semesters. Services for LD students, advanced placement, accelerated degree program, self-designed majors, independent study, double major, summer session for credit, internships, graduate courses open to undergrads. Off campus study. Study abroad program. ROTC: Army (c), Naval, Air Force (c).
Entrance Requirements: Options: electronic application, early admission, early decision, deferred admission, international baccalaureate accepted. Required: essay, high school transcript, 3 recommendations, SAT and 2 SAT Subject Tests or ACT, SAT and SAT Subject Tests or ACT. Entrance: most difficult. Application deadlines: 1/1, 11/1 for early decision. Notification: 4/1, 12/15 for early decision. SAT Reasoning Test deadline: 2/1. SAT Subject Test deadline: 2/1. Transfer credits accepted: Yes. Early decision applicants: 3,086. Early decision applicants admitted: 630.
Costs Per Year: Application fee: $80. One-time mandatory fee: $511. Comprehensive fee: $58,842 includes full-time tuition ($45,028), mandatory fees ($2318), and college room and board ($11,496).
Collegiate Environment: Orientation program. Drama-theater group, choral group, marching band, student-run newspaper, radio station. Social organizations: 500 open to all; national fraternities, national sororities; 10% of eligible men and 10% of eligible women are members. Most popular organizations: community service, cultural organizations, performing arts, athletics, publications. Major annual events: Bacchanal (Spring Fest), Tree Lighting/Yule Log Ceremony, Columbia Community Outreach. Student services: health clinic, personal-psychological counseling, women's center. Campus security: 24-hour emergency response devices and patrols, late night transport-escort service, controlled dormitory access. 5,580 college housing spaces available; all were occupied in 2012-13. Freshmen guaranteed college housing. On-campus residence required in freshman year. Options: coed, men-only, women-only housing available. Butler plus 25 others with 9.5 million books, 117,264 serials, an OPAC, and a Web page. 400 computers available on campus for general student use. Computer purchase/lease plans available. A campuswide network can be accessed from student residence rooms and from off campus. Students can access the following: online class registration. Staffed computer lab on campus.

■ **COLUMBIA UNIVERSITY, SCHOOL OF GENERAL STUDIES**
2970 Broadway
408 Lewisohn Hall, MC 4101
New York, NY 10027-6939
Tel: (212)854-2772; Free: 800-895-1169

E-mail: gsdegree@columbia.edu

Web Site: www.gs.columbia.edu/

Description: Independent, 4-year, coed. Part of Columbia University. Awards bachelor's degrees. Founded 1754. Setting: 36-acre urban campus. System endowment: $6.5 billion. Total enrollment: 1,632. 601 applied, 34% were admitted. Full-time: 1,108 students, 41% women, 59% men. Part-time: 524 students, 48% women, 52% men. 45% from out-of-state. 0.2% American Indian or Alaska Native, non-Hispanic/Latino; 10% Hispanic/Latino; 5% African American, non-Hispanic/Latino; 7% Asian, non-Hispanic/Latino; 1% Native Hawaiian or other Pacific Islander, non-Hispanic/Latino; 16% international. 71% 25 or older, 24% live on campus, 28% transferred in. Academic areas with the most degrees conferred: social sciences; liberal arts/general studies; physical sciences. Core. Calendar: semesters. Services for LD students, advanced placement, self-designed majors, independent study, double major, summer session for credit, part-time degree program, external degree program, adult/continuing education programs, internships. Off campus study. Study abroad program. ROTC: Army (c), Naval, Air Force (c).

Entrance Requirements: Options: electronic application, early action, deferred admission. Required: essay, high school transcript, 2 recommendations, SAT or ACT. Required for some: interview. Entrance: most difficult. Application deadlines: 6/1, 3/1 for early action. Notification: continuous, 5/1 for early action. SAT Reasoning Test deadline: 6/1. SAT Subject Test deadline: 6/1. Transfer credits accepted: Yes.

Costs Per Year: Application fee: $80. Comprehensive fee: $55,932 includes full-time tuition ($43,620), mandatory fees ($2079), and college room and board ($10,233). College room only: $5823. Full-time tuition and fees vary according to course load, program, and student level. Room and board charges vary according to board plan and housing facility. Part-time tuition: $1454 per credit hour. Part-time tuition varies according to course load, program, and student level.

Collegiate Environment: Orientation program. Drama-theater group, choral group, marching band, student-run newspaper, radio station. Social organizations: national fraternities, national sororities. Most popular organization: General Studies Student Council. Major annual event: Commencement. Student services: health clinic, personal-psychological counseling, women's center. Campus security: 24-hour emergency response devices and patrols, late night transport-escort service. Option: coed housing available. Butler Library plus 22 others with 10.4 million books, 6.4 million microform titles, 144,787 serials, 156,717 audiovisual materials, an OPAC, and a Web page. 768 computers available on campus for general student use. Computer purchase/lease plans available. A campuswide network can be accessed from student residence rooms and from off campus. Students can access the following: online class registration. Staffed computer lab on campus provides training in use of computers, software, and the Internet.

■ **CONCORDIA COLLEGE–NEW YORK**

171 White Plains Rd.

Bronxville, NY 10708-1998

Tel: (914)337-9300; Free: 800-YES-COLLEGE

Fax: (914)395-4500

E-mail: admission@concordia-ny.edu

Web Site: www.concordia-ny.edu/

Description: Independent Lutheran, 4-year, coed. Part of Concordia University System. Awards associate, bachelor's, and master's degrees. Founded 1881. Setting: 33-acre suburban campus with easy access to New York City. Endowment: $6.4 million. Educational spending for the previous fiscal year: $6410 per student. Total enrollment: 721. Faculty: 77 (33 full-time, 44 part-time). Student-undergrad faculty ratio is 12:1. 1,206 applied, 71% were admitted. 13% from top 10% of their high school class, 27% from top quarter, 64% from top half. 8 class presidents, 3 valedictorians, 30 student government officers. Full-time: 587 students, 61% women, 39% men. Part-time: 128 students, 79% women, 21% men. Students come from 46 states and territories, 35 other countries, 29% from out-of-state. 1% American Indian or Alaska Native, non-Hispanic/Latino; 16% Hispanic/Latino; 16% African American, non-Hispanic/Latino; 1% Asian, non-Hispanic/Latino; 0.4% Native Hawaiian or other Pacific Islander, non-Hispanic/Latino; 11% international. 13% 25 or older, 68% live on campus, 6% transferred in. Retention: 73% of full-time freshmen returned the following year. Academic areas with the most degrees conferred: business/marketing; social sciences; liberal arts/general studies. Core. Calendar: semesters. Academic remediation for entering students, ESL program, services for LD students, advanced placement, accelerated degree program, self-designed majors, honors program, independent study, distance learning, double major, part-

time degree program, adult/continuing education programs, internships. Off campus study at Concordia University System. Study abroad program. ROTC: Army (c), Air Force (c).

Entrance Requirements: Options: electronic application, early admission, early action, deferred admission, international baccalaureate accepted. Required: essay, high school transcript, 1 recommendation, Common Application Supplement, SAT or ACT, TOEFL or IELTS are required for students who's first language is not English. Recommended: minimum 2.7 high school GPA. Required for some: interview. Entrance: moderately difficult. Application deadlines: 3/15, 11/15 for early action. Notification: continuous until 4/15, 12/1 for early action. Transfer credits accepted: Yes. Early action applicants: 114. Early action applicants admitted: 103.

Costs Per Year: Application fee: $50. Comprehensive fee: $38,280 includes full-time tuition ($27,000), mandatory fees ($1000), and college room and board ($10,280). College room only: $5500. Full-time tuition and fees vary according to course load and program. Room and board charges vary according to board plan. Part-time tuition: $775 per credit. Part-time tuition varies according to course load and program.

Collegiate Environment: Orientation program. Drama-theater group, choral group, student-run newspaper. Social organizations: 22 open to all; local fraternities, local sororities; 12% of eligible men and 15% of eligible women are members. Most popular organizations: Campus Christian Ministries, Drama Club, Student Government Association, International and Afro/Latin American Club, Yearbook and newspaper. Major annual events: Homecoming events, Accepted Student Weekend, Band Bash. Student services: health clinic, personal-psychological counseling. Campus security: 24-hour emergency response devices and patrols, late night transport-escort service, controlled dormitory access. 450 college housing spaces available; 315 were occupied in 2012-13. Freshmen guaranteed college housing. On-campus residence required in freshman year. Options: men-only, women-only housing available. Scheele Memorial Library with 71,500 books, 20,850 microform titles, 467 serials, an OPAC, and a Web page. Operations spending for the previous fiscal year: $276,825. 50 computers available on campus for general student use. A campuswide network can be accessed from student residence rooms and from off campus. Students can access the following: online class registration. Staffed computer lab on campus provides training in use of computers, software, and the Internet.

■ **COOPER UNION FOR THE ADVANCEMENT OF SCIENCE AND ART**

30 Cooper Sq.

New York, NY 10003-7120

Tel: (212)353-4100

Fax: (212)353-4343

E-mail: admissions@cooper.edu

Web Site: www.cooper.edu/

Description: Independent, comprehensive, coed. Awards bachelor's and master's degrees (also offers master's program primarily made up of currently-enrolled students). Founded 1859. Setting: urban campus with easy access to New York City. Endowment: $640.5 million. Research spending for the previous fiscal year: $580,175. Educational spending for the previous fiscal year: $27,684 per student. Total enrollment: 991. Faculty: 229 (52 full-time, 177 part-time). Student-undergrad faculty ratio is 9:1. 3,415 applied, 8% were admitted. 93% from top 10% of their high school class, 98% from top quarter, 99% from top half. 25 National Merit Scholars, 15 class presidents, 24 valedictorians, 48 student government officers. Full-time: 902 students, 38% women, 62% men. Part-time: 25 students, 52% women, 48% men. Students come from 38 states and territories, 30 other countries, 46% from out-of-state. 1% American Indian or Alaska Native, non-Hispanic/Latino; 9% Hispanic/Latino; 6% African American, non-Hispanic/Latino; 18% Asian, non-Hispanic/Latino; 0.2% Native Hawaiian or other Pacific Islander, non-Hispanic/Latino; 15% international. 10% 25 or older, 20% live on campus, 4% transferred in. Retention: 96% of full-time freshmen returned the following year. Academic areas with the most degrees conferred: engineering; visual and performing arts; architecture. Core. Calendar: semesters. Services for LD students, advanced placement, self-designed majors, honors program, independent study, summer session for credit, internships, graduate courses open to undergrads. Off campus study at East Coast members of the National Association of Schools of Art and Design, New York University, Eugene Lang College (New School), Members of Association of Independent Colleges of Art and Design Mobility Program. Study abroad program.

Entrance Requirements: Options: electronic application, early admission, early decision, deferred admission. Required: essay, high school transcript, minimum 2 high school GPA, SAT or ACT. Recommended: minimum 3 high school GPA. Required for some: minimum 3.5 high school GPA, 3 recommendations, interview, portfolio, home examination for art and architecture applicants, SAT Subject Tests. Entrance: most difficult. Application deadlines: 1/1, 12/1 for early decision plan 1, 12/1 for early decision plan 2. Notification: 4/1, 12/24 for early decision plan 1, 2/1 for early decision plan 2. SAT Reasoning Test deadline: 2/28. SAT Subject Test deadline: 2/28. Transfer credits accepted: Yes. Applicants placed on waiting list: 70. Wait-listed applicants offered admission: 10. Early decision applicants: 719. Early decision applicants admitted: 70.

Costs Per Year: Application fee: $65. Comprehensive fee: $54,220 includes full-time tuition ($38,550), mandatory fees ($1700), and college room and board ($13,970). College room only: $9970. Room and board charges vary according to board plan and housing facility. All international students are assessed a fee of $ 1,910/year. Please note: All of our undergraduate students (including international) specifically for the 2012-2013 school year are offered a full-tuition scholarship valued at $38,550.

Collegiate Environment: Orientation program. Drama-theater group, choral group, student-run newspaper. Social organizations: 90 open to all; national fraternities, national sororities; 20% of eligible men and 15% of eligible women are members. Most popular organizations: South Asian Society, Pro Musica, Chinese Student Association, Drama Society, Outdoors Club; Intervarsity Christian Fellowship. Major annual events: Fall Festival, Pro Musica Jam, Cultural Show and Food Festival. Student services: personal-psychological counseling. Campus security: 24-hour emergency response devices and patrols, controlled dormitory access, security guards. 183 college housing spaces available; all were occupied in 2012-13. Freshmen given priority for college housing. Option: coed housing available. Cooper Union Library with 136,711 books, 24,207 microform titles, 3,427 serials, 1,837 audiovisual materials, an OPAC, and a Web page. Operations spending for the previous fiscal year: $1.1 million. 100 computers available on campus for general student use. Computer purchase/lease plans available. A campuswide network can be accessed from student residence rooms and from off campus. Staffed computer lab on campus provides training in use of computers, software, and the Internet.

■ **CORNELL UNIVERSITY**
Ithaca, NY 14853-0001
Tel: (607)255-2000
Fax: (607) 255-0659
E-mail: admissions@cornell.edu
Web Site: www.cornell.edu/

Description: Independent, university, coed. Awards bachelor's, master's, and doctoral degrees. Founded 1865. Setting: 745-acre small town campus with easy access to Syracuse. Endowment: $5.1 million. Research spending for the previous fiscal year: $386.6 million. Educational spending for the previous fiscal year: $20,779 per student. Total enrollment: 21,131. Faculty: 1,827 (1,646 full-time, 181 part-time). Student-undergrad faculty ratio is 9:1. 36,387 applied, 18% were admitted. 89% from top 10% of their high school class, 98% from top quarter, 99% from top half. Full-time: 14,167 students, 50% women, 50% men. Students come from 54 states and territories, 82 other countries, 65% from out-of-state. 0.3% American Indian or Alaska Native, non-Hispanic/Latino; 9% Hispanic/Latino; 6% African American, non-Hispanic/Latino; 16% Asian, non-Hispanic/Latino; 0.1% Native Hawaiian or other Pacific Islander, non-Hispanic/Latino; 9% international. 1% 25 or older, 57% live on campus, 4% transferred in. Retention: 97% of full-time freshmen returned the following year. Academic areas with the most degrees conferred: engineering; business/marketing; agriculture. Calendar: semesters. Academic remediation for entering students, ESL program, services for LD students, advanced placement, accelerated degree program, self-designed majors, honors program, independent study, distance learning, double major, summer session for credit, co-op programs and internships, graduate courses open to undergrads. Off campus study at Ithaca College, Wells College. Study abroad program. ROTC: Army, Naval, Air Force.

Entrance Requirements: Options: electronic application; early decision, deferred admission, international baccalaureate accepted. Required: essay, high school transcript, 2 recommendations, SAT or ACT. Required for some: interview, SAT Subject Tests. Entrance: most difficult. Application deadlines: 1/2, 11/1 for early decision. Notification: 3/31, 12/15 for early decision. Transfer credits accepted: Yes. Applicants placed on waiting list: 2,982. Wait-listed applicants offered admission: 0. Early decision applicants: 3,479. Early decision applicants admitted: 1,227.

Costs Per Year: Application fee: $75. Comprehensive fee: $57,091 includes full-time tuition ($43,185), mandatory fees ($228), and college room and board ($13,678). College room only: $8112. Full-time tuition and fees vary according to degree level. Room and board charges vary according to board plan and housing facility.

Collegiate Environment: Orientation program. Drama-theater group, choral group, marching band, student-run newspaper, radio station. Social organizations: 865 open to all; national fraternities, national sororities, local fraternities. Major annual events: Undergraduate Research Forum, Dragon Day, Cornell ice hockey games. Student services: health clinic, personal-psychological counseling, women's center. Campus security: 24-hour emergency response devices and patrols, late night transport-escort service, controlled dormitory access, indoor and outdoor emergency phones. 8.3 million books, 8.5 million microform titles, 100,000 serials, 150,272 audiovisual materials, an OPAC, and a Web page. Operations spending for the previous fiscal year: $30.6 million. 2,650 computers available on campus for general student use. Computer purchase/lease plans available. A campuswide network can be accessed from student residence rooms and from off campus. Students can access the following: online class registration. Staffed computer lab on campus (open 24 hours a day) provides training in use of computers, software, and the Internet.

Community Environment: Population 30,000. Located at the southern tip of Cayuga Lake, the city encompasses scenic, deep gorges through which flow Six Mile, Fall and Cascadilla Creeks. Ithaca is in the heart of central New York's Finger Lakes region. Good transportation is provided by bus and airlines, as well as state highways. Ithaca has various fraternal, civic and veteran's organizations, and over 30 churches representative of most major denominations. Part-time employment is available for students. Recreational facilities within the vicinity include YMCA, theatres, 3 state parks, indoor ice rink, fishing, boating, swimming, hunting, horseback riding, bowling, a pistol range, archery, museums, golf courses, and 14 public parks.

■ **CORNING COMMUNITY COLLEGE**
One Academic Dr.
Corning, NY 14830-3297
Tel: (607)962-9CCC
Fax: (607)962-9456
E-mail: admissions@corning-cc.edu
Web Site: www.corning-cc.edu/

Description: State and locally supported, 2-year, coed. Part of State University of New York System. Awards certificates, transfer associate, and terminal associate degrees. Founded 1956. Setting: 500-acre rural campus. Endowment: $535,490. Educational spending for the previous fiscal year: $5150 per student. Total enrollment: 4,957. Faculty: 245 (92 full-time, 153 part-time). Student-undergrad faculty ratio is 22:1. 2,088 applied, 99% were admitted. Full-time: 2,298 students, 55% women, 45% men. Part-time: 2,659 students, 60% women, 40% men. Students come from 7 states and territories, 19 other countries, 5% from out-of-state. 0.3% American Indian or Alaska Native, non-Hispanic/Latino; 5% Hispanic/Latino; 4% African American, non-Hispanic/Latino; 1% Asian, non-Hispanic/Latino; 0.04% Native Hawaiian or other Pacific Islander, non-Hispanic/Latino; 0.1% international. 35% 25 or older, 4% transferred in. Retention: 56% of full-time freshmen returned the following year. Core. Calendar: semesters. Academic remediation for entering students, ESL program, services for LD students, advanced placement, accelerated degree program, self-designed majors, honors program, independent study, distance learning, double major, summer session for credit, part-time degree program, adult/continuing education programs, co-op programs and internships. Off campus study at ACE (Accelerated College Education): concurrent enrollment in regional high schools. Study abroad program.

Entrance Requirements: Open admission. Options: electronic application, early admission. Required: high school transcript. Required for some: interview. Entrance: noncompetitive. Application deadline: Rolling. Notification: continuous. Preference given to residents of sponsoring counties. Transfer credits accepted: Yes.

Costs Per Year: Application fee: $25. State resident tuition: $3950 full-time, $165 per credit hour part-time. Nonresident tuition: $7900 full-time, $330 per credit hour part-time. Mandatory fees: $442 full-time, $8.55 per credit hour part-time. Part-time tuition and fees vary according to course load. College room and board: $4250.

Collegiate Environment: Orientation program. Drama-theater group, choral group, student-run newspaper, radio station. Social organizations: 20 open to all. Most popular organizations: Student Association, EQUAL, Nursing Society, Muse of Fire theatre group, WCEB radio station. Major annual events: WoW (Welcome on Wednesday: Student Services fair), SPRINGfest, CLUBfest (Student Clubs/Organizations fair). Student services: health clinic, personal-psychological counseling. Campus security: 24-hour emergency response devices and patrols, late night transport-escort service, controlled dormitory access. 320 college housing spaces available. No special consideration for freshman housing applicants. Options: coed, men-only, women-only housing available. Arthur A. Houghton, Jr. Library with 46,427 books, 44,819 serials, 1,107 audiovisual materials, an OPAC, and a Web page. Operations spending for the previous fiscal year: $855,970. 350 computers available on campus for general student use. Computer purchase/lease plans available. A campuswide network can be accessed from off-campus. Students can access the following: online class registration. Staffed computer lab on campus provides training in use of computers, software, and the Internet.

■ **CROUSE HOSPITAL SCHOOL OF NURSING**

736 Irving Ave.
Syracuse, NY 13210
Tel: (315)470-7481
E-mail: amygraham@crouse.org
Web Site: www.crouse.org/nursing/

Description: Independent, 2-year, coed. Awards transfer associate and terminal associate degrees. Founded 1913. Setting: urban campus. Total enrollment: 285. 253 applied. Students come from 2 states and territories, 1% from out-of-state. 52% 25 or older. Core. Calendar: semesters. Academic remediation for entering students, services for LD students, advanced placement, part-time degree program.

Entrance Requirements: Option: deferred admission. Required: high school transcript, minimum 2.5 high school GPA, 2 recommendations. Recommended: SAT or ACT. Required for some: SAT or ACT. Entrance: moderately difficult. Application deadline: 2/1. Transfer credits accepted: Yes.

Collegiate Environment: Orientation program. Social organizations: 1 open to all. Most popular organization: NSNA. Student services: health clinic, personal-psychological counseling. Campus security: 24-hour emergency response devices and patrols, late night transport-escort service, controlled dormitory access. Crouse Hospital Library with 5,000 books, 913 serials, 250 audiovisual materials, an OPAC, and a Web page. 20 computers available on campus for general student use. A campuswide network can be accessed. Students can access the following: online class registration. Staffed computer lab on campus provides training in use of computers, software, and the Internet.

■ **THE CULINARY INSTITUTE OF AMERICA**

1946 Campus Dr.
Hyde Park, NY 12538-1499
Tel: (845)452-9600; Free: 800-CULINARY
Fax: (845)452-8629
E-mail: admissions@culinary.edu
Web Site: www.ciachef.edu/

Description: Independent, 4-year, coed. Awards associate and bachelor's degrees. Founded 1946. Setting: 170-acre suburban campus. Endowment: $101.1 million. Research spending for the previous fiscal year: $171,817. Educational spending for the previous fiscal year: $19,121 per student. Total enrollment: 2,827. Faculty: 192 (151 full-time, 41 part-time). Student-undergrad faculty ratio is 17:1. 951 applied, 84% were admitted. 10% from top 10% of their high school class, 31% from top quarter, 68% from top half. Full-time: 2,827 students, 47% women, 53% men. Students come from 55 states and territories, 39 other countries, 77% from out-of-state. 1% American Indian or Alaska Native, non-Hispanic/Latino; 11% Hispanic/Latino; 4% African American, non-Hispanic/Latino; 7% Asian, non-Hispanic/Latino; 1% Native Hawaiian or other Pacific Islander, non-Hispanic/Latino; 8% international. 21% 25 or older, 79% live on campus. Academic area with the most degrees conferred: business/marketing. Core. Calendar: semesters plus 18 or 21 week externship program. Academic remediation for entering students, services for LD students, honors program, internships. Off campus study at Associated Colleges of the Mid-Hudson Area.

Entrance Requirements: Options: electronic application, deferred admission. Required: essay, high school transcript, 1 recommendation. Recommended: SAT or ACT. Required for some: Affidavit of Support. Entrance: moderately difficult. Application deadline: Rolling. Preference given to candidates with 6 months of prior food service experience.

Costs Per Year: Application fee: $50. Comprehensive fee: $35,710 includes full-time tuition ($25,900), mandatory fees ($1230), and college room and board ($8580). College room only: $5920. Full-time tuition and fees according to degree level. Room and board charges vary according to board plan and housing facility.

Collegiate Environment: Orientation program. Choral group, student-run newspaper. Social organizations: 20 open to all; Eta Sigma Phi National Honor Society; 10% of eligible men and 12% of eligible women are members. Most popular organizations: Alliance, Baking and Pastry Society, Global Culinary Society, Eta Sigma Delta Honor Society, Chips Supporting Agriculture. Major annual events: Fall Festival, Chili Cook-off, Chowder Cook-Off. Student services: health clinic, personal-psychological counseling. Campus security: 24-hour emergency response devices and patrols, late night transport-escort service, controlled dormitory access. 1,698 college housing spaces available; 1,529 were occupied in 2012-13. Freshmen guaranteed college housing. Option: coed housing available. Conrad N. Hilton Library with 86,000 books, 280 serials, 4,500 audiovisual materials, and an OPAC. Operations spending for the previous fiscal year: $654,060. 218 computers available on campus for general student use. A campuswide network can be accessed from student residence rooms and from off campus. Students can access the following: online class registration, online course guides. Staffed computer lab on campus provides training in use of computers, software, and the Internet.

■ **DAEMEN COLLEGE**

4380 Main St.
Amherst, NY 14226-3592
Tel: (716)839-3600; Free: 800-462-7652
Fax: (716)839-8516
E-mail: admissions@daemen.edu
Web Site: www.daemen.edu/

Description: Independent, comprehensive, coed. Awards bachelor's, master's, and doctoral degrees and post-master's certificates. Founded 1947. Setting: 35-acre suburban campus with easy access to Buffalo. Endowment: $7.1 million. Educational spending for the previous fiscal year: $6001 per student. Total enrollment: 3,005. Faculty: 291 (119 full-time, 172 part-time). Student-undergrad faculty ratio is 14:1. 2,372 applied, 59% were admitted. 15% from top 10% of their high school class, 51% from top quarter, 85% from top half. Full-time: 1,654 students, 70% women, 30% men. Part-time: 502 students, 77% women, 23% men. Students come from 9 other countries. 0.2% American Indian or Alaska Native, non-Hispanic/Latino; 4% Hispanic/Latino; 10% African American, non-Hispanic/Latino; 2% Asian, non-Hispanic/Latino; 0.1% Native Hawaiian or other Pacific Islander, non-Hispanic/Latino; 3% international. 23% 25 or older, 14% transferred in. Retention: 81% of full-time freshmen returned the following year. Academic areas with the most degrees conferred: health professions and related sciences; interdisciplinary studies; business/marketing. Core. Calendar: semesters. Academic remediation for entering students, services for LD students, advanced placement, accelerated degree program, self-designed majors, honors program, independent study, double major, summer session for credit, part-time degree program, adult/continuing education programs, internships, graduate courses open to undergrads. Off campus study at Western New York Consortium; Consortium for Innovative Environments in Learning (CIEL). Study abroad program. ROTC: Army (c).

Entrance Requirements: Options: electronic application, early admission, deferred admission, international baccalaureate accepted. Required: essay, high school transcript, minimum 2 high school GPA, 1 recommendation. Recommended: SAT or ACT. Required for some: 3 recommendations, interview, high school transcript, class rank, writing sample-test optional. Entrance: moderately difficult. Application deadlines: Rolling, Rolling for nonresidents. Notification: continuous, continuous for nonresidents. Transfer credits accepted: Yes. Applicants placed on waiting list: 0.

Costs Per Year: Application fee: $25. Comprehensive fee: $33,830 includes full-time tuition ($22,620), mandatory fees ($510), and college room and board ($10,700). Full-time tuition and fees vary according to location and reciprocity agreements. Room and board charges vary according to board plan and housing facility. Part-time tuition: $750 per credit hour. Part-time mandatory fees: $6 per credit hour, $80 per term. Part-time tuition and fees vary according to course load, location, and reciprocity agreements.

Collegiate Environment: Orientation program. Student-run newspaper. Social organizations: 15 open to all; local fraternities, local sororities. Most popular organizations: Students Without Borders, Step Team, Ski Club, Multi-Cultural Association. Major annual events: Homecoming and Family Weekend, Midnight Madness, Springfest. Student services: personal-psychological counseling. Campus security: 24-hour emergency response devices and patrols, late night transport-escort service, 24-hour security cameras. Research and Information Commons with 181,410 books, 28,415 microform titles, 53,175 serials, 2,276 audiovisual materials, an OPAC, and a Web page. Operations spending for the previous fiscal year: $466,072.

146 computers available on campus for general student use. A campuswide network can be accessed from student residence rooms and from off campus. Students can access the following: online class registration. Staffed computer lab on campus provides training in use of computers and software. **Community Environment:** The college is located in a quiet suburban environment accessible to the City of Buffalo and the international boundary with Canada. Transportation hubs-plane, train, and bus-are located a short distance from the campus.

■ DARKEI NOAM RABBINICAL COLLEGE

2822 Ave. J
Brooklyn, NY 11210
Tel: (718)338-6464

Description: Independent Jewish, comprehensive, men only. Awards bachelor's and master's degrees. Founded 1977. Setting: urban campus. Total enrollment: 16. 1 applied, 100% were admitted. Core. Calendar: semesters.

Entrance Requirements: Required: interview. Entrance: minimally difficult.

Collegiate Environment: Kat Lowitz Library with 53,000 books and 2 serials.

■ DAVIS COLLEGE

400 Riverside Dr.
Johnson City, NY 13790
Tel: (607)729-1581; Free: 877-949-3248
Fax: (607)729-2962
E-mail: admissions@davisny.edu
Web Site: www.davisny.edu/

Description: Independent nondenominational, 4-year, coed. Awards associate and bachelor's degrees. Founded 1900. Setting: 22-acre suburban campus with easy access to Syracuse. Educational spending for the previous fiscal year: $16,000 per student. Total enrollment: 323. Faculty: 24 (7 full-time, 17 part-time). Student-undergrad faculty ratio is 14:1. 60 applied, 68% were admitted. 1% from top 10% of their high school class, 28% from top quarter, 62% from top half. Students come from 9 states and territories, 5 other countries, 24% from out-of-state. 29% 25 or older, 61% live on campus. Retention: 84% of full-time freshmen returned the following year. Academic area with the most degrees conferred: theology and religious vocations. Core. Calendar: semesters. Academic remediation for entering students, ESL program, services for LD students, advanced placement, independent study, summer session for credit, part-time degree program, adult/continuing education programs, co-op programs and internships.

Entrance Requirements: Options: electronic application, deferred admission, international baccalaureate accepted. Required: high school transcript, 2 recommendations, references, SAT or ACT. Recommended: minimum 2 high school GPA, interview. Required for some: essay. Entrance: minimally difficult. Application deadline: Rolling. Notification: continuous. Transfer credits accepted: Yes.

Collegiate Environment: Orientation program. Drama-theater group, choral group, student-run newspaper. Social organizations: 4 open to all. Most popular organizations: Student Missionary Fellowship, Student Wives Fellowship, Student Life Committee, Married Couples Fellowship. Major annual events: Annual Missions Conference, Fall Bible Conference, Prayer Days. Student services: health clinic, personal-psychological counseling. Campus security: 24-hour emergency response devices and patrols, student patrols, late night transport-escort service. Alice E. Chatlos Library with 77,000 books, 8,494 microform titles, 644 serials, an OPAC, and a Web page. Operations spending for the previous fiscal year: $125,317. 12 computers available on campus for general student use. A campuswide network can be accessed from student residence rooms. Staffed computer lab on campus.

■ DEVRY COLLEGE OF NEW YORK

180 Madison Ave., Ste. 900
New York, NY 10016-5267
Tel: (212)312-4300; Free: 866-338-7941
Web Site: www.devry.edu/

Description: Proprietary, comprehensive, coed. Part of DeVry University. Awards associate, bachelor's, and master's degrees. Founded 1998. Setting: urban campus. Total enrollment: 1,953. Faculty: 68 (27 full-time, 41 part-time). Student-undergrad faculty ratio is 31:1. Full-time: 711 students, 28% women, 72% men. Part-time: 528 students, 28% women, 72% men. 15% from out-of-state. 0.2% American Indian or Alaska Native, non-Hispanic/Latino; 28% Hispanic/Latino; 27% African American, non-Hispanic/Latino; 6% Asian, non-Hispanic/Latino; 0.5% Native Hawaiian or other

Pacific Islander, non-Hispanic/Latino; 3% international. 66% 25 or older, 21% transferred in. Academic areas with the most degrees conferred: business/marketing; computer and information sciences; engineering technologies. Calendar: semesters. Part-time degree program, adult/continuing education programs.

Entrance Requirements: Required: high school transcript, interview. Entrance: minimally difficult. Application deadline: Rolling. Notification: continuous.

Costs Per Year: Application fee: $40. Tuition: $16,076 full-time, $609 per credit hour part-time. Mandatory fees: $80 full-time.

Collegiate Environment: Orientation program. College housing not available.

■ DOMINICAN COLLEGE

470 Western Hwy.
Orangeburg, NY 10962-1210
Tel: (845)359-7800; Free: 866-432-4636
Fax: (845)359-2313
E-mail: admissions@dc.edu
Web Site: www.dc.edu/

Description: Independent, comprehensive, coed. Awards associate, bachelor's, master's, and doctoral degrees. Founded 1952. Setting: 70-acre suburban campus with easy access to New York City. Endowment: $3.2 million. Educational spending for the previous fiscal year: $8665 per student. Total enrollment: 2,051. Faculty: 237 (75 full-time, 162 part-time). Student-undergrad faculty ratio is 15:1. 1,850 applied, 69% were admitted. Full-time: 1,357 students, 65% women, 35% men. Part-time: 238 students, 80% women, 20% men. Students come from 23 states and territories, 13 other countries, 24% from out-of-state. 0.3% American Indian or Alaska Native, non-Hispanic/Latino; 24% Hispanic/Latino; 16% African American, non-Hispanic/Latino; 8% Asian, non-Hispanic/Latino; 1% international. 20% 25 or older, 51% live on campus, 13% transferred in. Retention: 64% of full-time freshmen returned the following year. Academic areas with the most degrees conferred: health professions and related sciences; business/marketing; social sciences. Core. Calendar: semesters. Academic remediation for entering students, services for LD students, advanced placement, accelerated degree program, freshman honors college, honors program, independent study, distance learning, double major, summer session for credit, part-time degree program, adult/continuing education programs, co-op programs and internships. Off campus study.

Entrance Requirements: Options: electronic application, deferred admission, international baccalaureate accepted. Required: high school transcript, SAT or ACT. Recommended: interview. Required for some: essay, interview. Entrance: noncompetitive. Application deadline: Rolling. Notification: continuous. SAT Reasoning Test deadline: 8/15. Applicants placed on waiting list: 0. Wait-listed applicants offered admission: 0.

Costs Per Year: Application fee: $35. Comprehensive fee: $35,950 includes full-time tuition ($23,200), mandatory fees ($770), and college room and board ($11,980). Full-time tuition and fees vary according to degree level. Room and board charges vary according to board plan and housing facility. Part-time tuition: $700 per credit hour. Part-time tuition varies according to degree level and program.

Collegiate Environment: Orientation program. Drama-theater group, choral group, student-run newspaper, radio station. Social organizations: 31 open to all. Most popular organizations: Student Government Association, Business Club, Aquin Players, school newspaper, Nursing Association. Major annual events: Fire in the Sky, Fall Festival, Spring Festival, Family Day. Student services: health clinic, personal-psychological counseling. Campus security: 24-hour emergency response devices and patrols, student patrols, late night transport-escort service, controlled dormitory access. 653 college housing spaces available; 627 were occupied in 2012-13. Freshmen guaranteed college housing. Option: coed housing available. Sullivan Library plus 1 other with 120,000 books, 450 serials, 24,000 audiovisual materials, an OPAC, and a Web page. Operations spending for the previous fiscal year: $596,011. 150 computers available on campus for general student use. A campuswide network can be accessed from student residence rooms and from off campus. Students can access the following: online class registration, Web portal, Black Board. Staffed computer lab on campus provides training in use of computers, software, and the Internet.

Community Environment: Orangeburg, population 3,400, is located in southeast New York, located 3 miles southwest of Nyack on the northern border of New Jersey. The area may be reached by the New York State Thruway, Exit 12, or Palisades Parkway, Exit 6E.

■ **DOROTHEA HOPFER SCHOOL OF NURSING AT THE MOUNT VERNON HOSPITAL**
53 Valentine St.
Mount Vernon, NY 10550
Tel: (914)664-8000
Fax: (914)665-7047
E-mail: hopferadmissions@sshsw.org
Web Site: www.ssmc.org/
Description: Independent, 2-year, coed. Awards terminal associate degrees. Total enrollment: 134. Student-undergrad faculty ratio is 5:1. 10 applied, 10% were admitted. 87% 25 or older.
Entrance Requirements: Required: high school transcript, TEAS Exam.

■ **DOWLING COLLEGE**
150 Idle Hour Blvd.
Oakdale, NY 11769-1999
Tel: (631)244-3000; Free: 800-DOWLING
Fax: (631)563-3827
Web Site: www.dowling.edu/
Description: Independent, comprehensive, coed. Awards bachelor's, master's, and doctoral degrees and post-master's certificates. Founded 1955. Setting: 157-acre suburban campus with easy access to New York City. Educational spending for the previous fiscal year: $10,112 per student. Total enrollment: 4,416. Faculty: 431 (115 full-time, 316 part-time). Student-undergrad faculty ratio is 15:1. 2,495 applied, 79% were admitted. Full-time: 1,910 students, 53% women, 47% men. Part-time: 973 students, 58% women, 42% men. 6% from out-of-state. 0.1% American Indian or Alaska Native, non-Hispanic/Latino; 7% Hispanic/Latino; 8% African American, non-Hispanic/Latino; 1% Asian, non-Hispanic/Latino; 0.03% Native Hawaiian or other Pacific Islander, non-Hispanic/Latino; 3% international. 18% 25 or older, 13% live on campus, 9% transferred in. Retention: 65% of full-time freshmen returned the following year. Academic areas with the most degrees conferred: business/marketing; education; social sciences. Core. Calendar: semesters. Academic remediation for entering students, ESL program, services for LD students, advanced placement, accelerated degree program, self-designed majors, honors program, independent study, distance learning, double major, summer session for credit, part-time degree program, co-op programs and internships, graduate courses open to undergrads. Off campus study at Long Island Regional Advisory Council for Higher Education. Study abroad program. ROTC: Army (c), Air Force (c).
Entrance Requirements: Options: electronic application, early action, deferred admission, international baccalaureate accepted. Required: essay, high school transcript, minimum 2 high school GPA, 1 recommendation. Recommended: minimum 2.5 high school GPA, SAT or ACT. Entrance: moderately difficult. Application deadlines: Rolling, Rolling for nonresidents, 12/31 for early action. Notification: continuous, continuous for nonresidents, 1/31 for early action. SAT Reasoning Test deadline: 6/1. SAT Subject Test deadline: 6/1. Transfer credits accepted: Yes.
Costs Per Year: Application fee: $35. Comprehensive fee: $37,714 includes full-time tuition ($25,324), mandatory fees ($1800), and college room and board ($10,590). Full-time tuition and fees vary according to course load and degree level. Room and board charges vary according to housing facility and location. Part-time tuition: $849 per credit. Part-time mandatory fees: $566 per term. Part-time tuition and fees vary according to course load and degree level.
Collegiate Environment: Orientation program. Drama-theater group, choral group, student-run newspaper, radio station. Social organizations: 35 open to all. Most popular organizations: Student Government Association, Dormitory Councils, Aviation Organization, student newspaper. Major annual events: Welcome Back BBQ and Club Fair, Spring Cotillion, Holiday Children's Fund. Student services: health clinic, personal-psychological counseling. Campus security: 24-hour emergency response devices and patrols, late night transport-escort service, controlled dormitory access. Dowling College Library plus 2 others with 142,195 books, 483,026 microform titles, 1,249 serials, 2,498 audiovisual materials, an OPAC, and a Web page. Operations spending for the previous fiscal year: $1.9 million. 317 computers available on campus for general student use. A campuswide network can be accessed from student residence rooms and from off campus. Students can access the following: online class registration. Staffed computer lab on campus provides training in use of computers, software, and the Internet.
Community Environment: Population 8,000. Oakdale is a suburban community west of Sayville with temperate climate. The area is served by the Long Island Railroad, and a main bus route to Patchogue and Freeport.

There are 3 hospitals within 20 miles and a college health service. Adjoining cities furnish community services as well as recreational and cultural opportunities. Some part-time employment is available for students.

■ **DUTCHESS COMMUNITY COLLEGE**
53 Pendell Rd.
Poughkeepsie, NY 12601-1595
Tel: (845)431-8000
E-mail: michael.roe@sunydutchess.edu
Web Site: www.sunydutchess.edu/
Description: State and locally supported, 2-year, coed. Part of State University of New York System. Awards certificates, transfer associate, and terminal associate degrees. Founded 1957. Setting: 130-acre suburban campus with easy access to New York City. Total enrollment: 10,316. Faculty: 551 (127 full-time, 424 part-time). Full-time: 5,095 students, 50% women, 50% men. Part-time: 5,221 students, 59% women, 41% men. 0.2% American Indian or Alaska Native, non-Hispanic/Latino; 13% Hispanic/Latino; 10% African American, non-Hispanic/Latino; 3% Asian, non-Hispanic/Latino; 0.1% Native Hawaiian or other Pacific Islander, non-Hispanic/Latino; 0.5% international. 23% 25 or older, 5% live on campus, 4% transferred in. Calendar: semesters. Academic remediation for entering students, ESL program, services for LD students, advanced placement, freshman honors college, honors program, distance learning, summer session for credit, part-time degree program, adult/continuing education programs, internships. Off campus study at Marist College, Vassar College, State University of New York College at New Paltz, Culinary Institute of America, Bard College.
Entrance Requirements: Open admission for most programs. Options: early admission, deferred admission. Required: high school transcript. Entrance: noncompetitive. Application deadline: Rolling. Notification: continuous. Preference given to county residents.
Costs Per Year: State resident tuition: $3100 full-time, $129 per hour part-time. Nonresident tuition: $6200 full-time, $258 per hour part-time. Mandatory fees: $420 full-time, $10 per hour part-time, $13 per term part-time. College room and board: $8690.
Collegiate Environment: Orientation program. Drama-theater group, choral group, student-run newspaper, radio station. Social organizations: 36 open to all. Most popular organizations: Rap, Poetry & Music, Outdoor Adventure, Gamers Guild, Masquers Guild, Christian Fellowship. Major annual events: Fall Freshmen Day, Family Festival, Lyceum Series of Speakers. Student services: health clinic, personal-psychological counseling. Campus security: 24-hour emergency response devices and patrols, late night transport-escort service. 465 college housing spaces available; 455 were occupied in 2012-13. Option: coed housing available. Dutchess Library with 173,128 books, 2,519 microform titles, 255 serials, 2,149 audiovisual materials, an OPAC, and a Web page. 1,500 computers available on campus for general student use. A campuswide network can be accessed from student residence rooms and from off campus. Students can access the following: online class registration. Staffed computer lab on campus provides training in use of computers.

■ **D'YOUVILLE COLLEGE**
320 Porter Ave.
Buffalo, NY 14201-1084
Tel: (716)829-8000; Free: 800-777-3921
Fax: (716)829-7790
Web Site: www.dyc.edu/
Description: Independent, comprehensive, coed. Awards bachelor's, master's, and doctoral degrees and post-master's certificates. Founded 1908. Setting: 7-acre urban campus. Endowment: $25.2 million. Educational spending for the previous fiscal year: $7538 per student. Total enrollment: 2,971. Faculty: 322 (144 full-time, 178 part-time). Student-undergrad faculty ratio is 12:1. 949 applied, 83% were admitted. Full-time: 1,467 students, 72% women, 28% men. Part-time: 399 students, 81% women, 19% men. Students come from 21 states and territories, 48 other countries, 5% from out-of-state. 25% 25 or older, 13% live on campus, 13% transferred in. Retention: 73% of full-time freshmen returned the following year. Academic areas with the most degrees conferred: health professions and related sciences; business/marketing; interdisciplinary studies. Core. Calendar: semesters plus summer session. Academic remediation for entering students, services for LD students, accelerated degree program, independent study, distance learning, double major, summer session for credit, part-time degree program, adult/continuing education programs, internships, graduate courses open to undergrads. Off campus study at Western New York Consortium. Study abroad program. ROTC: Army (c).

Entrance Requirements: Options: electronic application, deferred admission, international baccalaureate accepted. Required: high school transcript, minimum 2 high school GPA, SAT or ACT. Required for some: essay, minimum 3 high school GPA, interview. Entrance: moderately difficult. Application deadline: Rolling. Notification: continuous.

Costs Per Year: Application fee: $25. Comprehensive fee: $32,490 includes full-time tuition ($21,930), mandatory fees ($310), and college room and board ($10,250). Full-time tuition and fees vary according to course load, degree level, and program. Room and board charges vary according to board plan and housing facility. Part-time tuition: $680 per credit hour. Part-time mandatory fees: $3 per credit hour, $55 per term. Part-time tuition and fees vary according to course load, degree level, and program. Tuition guaranteed not to increase for student's term of enrollment.

Collegiate Environment: Orientation program. Drama-theater group, choral group, student-run newspaper. Social organizations: 35 open to all. Most popular organizations: Student Association, Occupational Therapy Student Association, Physical Therapy Student Association, Student Nurses Association, Black Student Union. Major annual events: Family and Friends Weekend, Honors Convocation, Moving Up Days. Student services: health clinic, personal-psychological counseling. Campus security: 24-hour emergency response devices and patrols, late night transport-escort service, controlled dormitory access. Montante Family Library with 116,237 books, 212,191 microform titles, 725 serials, 3,668 audiovisual materials, an OPAC, and a Web page. Operations spending for the previous fiscal year: $866,995. 72 computers available on campus for general student use. A campuswide network can be accessed from student residence rooms and from off campus. Students can access the following: online class registration. Staffed computer lab on campus provides training in use of computers, software, and the Internet.

■ ELLIS SCHOOL OF NURSING
1101 Nott St.
Schenectady, NY 12308
Tel: (518)243-4471
E-mail: lansingc@ellismedicine.org
Web Site: www.ellismedicine.org/AboutEllis/SchoolofNursing.aspx
Description: Independent, 2-year, coed. Awards transfer associate and terminal associate degrees. Founded 1906. Setting: urban campus. Total enrollment: 132. Student-undergrad faculty ratio is 6:1. 100% from top 10% of their high school class. Full-time: 45 students, 80% women, 20% men. Part-time: 87 students, 85% women, 15% men. Students come from 3 states and territories, 0% from out-of-state. 2% American Indian or Alaska Native, non-Hispanic/Latino; 8% Hispanic/Latino; 7% African American, non-Hispanic/Latino; 3% Asian, non-Hispanic/Latino; 0% Native Hawaiian or other Pacific Islander, non-Hispanic/Latino. 65% 25 or older, 0% transferred in. Core.
Entrance Requirements: Required: essay, high school transcript, minimum 3 high school GPA, 2 recommendations. Recommended: SAT or ACT.
Costs Per Year: Tuition: $7863 full-time, $5181 per year part-time. Mandatory fees: $903 full-time, $483 per year part-time.
Collegiate Environment: Orientation program.

■ ELMIRA BUSINESS INSTITUTE
303 N Main St.
Elmira, NY 14901
Tel: (607)733-7177; Free: 800-843-1812
Fax: (607)733-7178
E-mail: info@ebi-college.com
Web Site: www.ebi-college.com/
Description: Private, 2-year, coed. Awards certificates, transfer associate, and terminal associate degrees. Founded 1858. Setting: urban campus. Total enrollment: 235. Student-undergrad faculty ratio is 9:1. Full-time: 192 students, 89% women, 11% men. Part-time: 43 students, 81% women, 19% men. 10% from out-of-state. 70% 25 or older, 0% transferred in. Calendar: semesters. Academic remediation for entering students, advanced placement, part-time degree program, internships.
Entrance Requirements: Open admission. Option: electronic application. Required: high school transcript, interview. Required for some: essay. Application deadline: Rolling. Transfer credits accepted: Yes.
Costs Per Year: Application fee: $0. Tuition: $12,000 full-time, $400 per credit part-time. Mandatory fees: $700 full-time. Full-time tuition and fees vary according to program. Part-time tuition varies according to program. Tuition guaranteed not to increase for student's term of enrollment.
Collegiate Environment: Orientation program. Campus security: 24-hour

emergency response devices. College housing not available. 90 computers available on campus for general student use. A campuswide network can be accessed.

■ ELMIRA COLLEGE
One Park Pl.
Elmira, NY 14901
Tel: (607)735-1800; Free: 800-935-6472
Fax: (607)735-1718
E-mail: admissions@elmira.edu
Web Site: www.elmira.edu/
Description: Independent, comprehensive, coed. Awards associate, bachelor's, and master's degrees. Founded 1855. Setting: 55-acre suburban campus. Total enrollment: 1,533. Faculty: 192 (95 full-time, 97 part-time). Student-undergrad faculty ratio is 10:1. 2,056 applied, 89% were admitted. 35% from top 10% of their high school class, 57% from top quarter, 86% from top half. 52 valedictorians. Full-time: 1,199 students, 69% women, 31% men. Part-time: 187 students, 83% women, 17% men. Students come from 35 states and territories, 31 other countries, 50% from out-of-state. 0.2% American Indian or Alaska Native, non-Hispanic/Latino; 3% Hispanic/Latino; 3% African American, non-Hispanic/Latino; 1% Asian, non-Hispanic/Latino; 0% Native Hawaiian or other Pacific Islander, non-Hispanic/Latino; 6% international. 3% 25 or older, 94% live on campus, 3% transferred in. Retention: 75% of full-time freshmen returned the following year. Academic areas with the most degrees conferred: education; business/marketing; health professions and related sciences. Core. Calendar: 4-4-1. ESL program, services for LD students, advanced placement, accelerated degree program, self-designed majors, independent study, distance learning, double major, summer session for credit, part-time degree program, adult/continuing education programs, internships, graduate courses open to undergrads. Off campus study. Study abroad program. ROTC: Army, Air Force (c).
Entrance Requirements: Options: electronic application, early decision, deferred admission, international baccalaureate accepted. Required: essay, high school transcript, minimum 2 high school GPA, 1 recommendation, SAT or ACT. Recommended: interview. Required for some: interview. Entrance: moderately difficult. Application deadlines: 3/31, 11/15 for early decision plan 1, 1/15 for early decision plan 2. Notification: continuous until 4/30, 12/15 for early decision plan 1, 1/31 for early decision plan 2. Transfer credits accepted: Yes. Applicants placed on waiting list: 42. Wait-listed applicants offered admission: 10. Early decision applicants: 80. Early decision applicants admitted: 56.
Costs Per Year: Application fee: $50. Comprehensive fee: $49,950 includes full-time tuition ($36,600), mandatory fees ($1550), and college room and board ($11,800). College room only: $6300. Room and board charges vary according to housing facility.
Collegiate Environment: Orientation program. Drama-theater group, choral group, student-run newspaper, radio station. Social organizations: 105 open to all. Most popular organizations: student radio station, Student Activities Board, College Republicans and Democrats, Ski Club, Habitat for Humanity. Major annual events: Octagon Fair, Holiday Banquet and Ball, May Days. Student services: health clinic, personal-psychological counseling. Campus security: 24-hour patrols, late night transport-escort service, 24-hour locked residence hall entrances. 1,238 college housing spaces available; 1,193 were occupied in 2012-13. Freshmen guaranteed college housing. On-campus residence required through senior year. Options: coed, women-only housing available. Gannett-Tripp Library with 203,343 books, 591,429 microform titles, 337 serials, 5,897 audiovisual materials, an OPAC, and a Web page. 173 computers available on campus for general student use. Computer purchase/lease plans available. A campuswide network can be accessed from student residence rooms and from off campus. Staffed computer lab on campus provides training in use of computers, software, and the Internet.
Community Environment: Founded as a commercial and transportation center, Elmira, population 30,000, dominates south-central New York State and nearby Pennsylvania as the trade, industrial, financial, and transportation hub of the southern Finger Lakes region. Light industrial activity remains as the economic base for the county, though a large portion of Chemung County is still rural in activity and atmosphere. Transportation is available with the Elmira-Corning Airport, buses, and car via Routes 13, 14, and 17. There are two hospitals, approximately 60 churches, a public library, theatres, good shopping centers, and more than 200 fraternal, service, and social organizations. Recreational facilities include parks, playgrounds, golf, swimming, bowling, tennis, horseback riding, picnic areas, fishing, ice skating, and skiing nearby. Located within walking distance of the campus is the Samuel Clemens Performing Arts Center.

ERIE COMMUNITY COLLEGE

121 Ellicott St.
Buffalo, NY 14203-2698
Tel: (716)851-1001
Fax: (716)842-1972
Web Site: www.ecc.edu/
Description: State and locally supported, 2-year, coed. Part of State University of New York System. Awards certificates, diplomas, transfer associate, and terminal associate degrees. Founded 1971. Setting: 1-acre urban campus. Total enrollment: 3,333. Faculty: 219 (76 full-time, 143 part-time). Student-undergrad faculty ratio is 18:1. 3,540 applied, 67% were admitted. Full-time: 2,483 students, 61% women, 39% men. Part-time: 850 students, 60% women, 40% men. Students come from 14 states and territories, 6 other countries, 1% from out-of-state. 0.5% American Indian or Alaska Native, non-Hispanic/Latino; 10% Hispanic/Latino; 31% African American, non-Hispanic/Latino; 1% Asian, non-Hispanic/Latino; 0.1% Native Hawaiian or other Pacific Islander, non-Hispanic/Latino; 7% international. 41% 25 or older, 7% transferred in. Core. Calendar: semesters. Academic remediation for entering students, ESL program, services for LD students, advanced placement, self-designed majors, honors program, independent study, distance learning, double major, summer session for credit, part-time degree program, adult/continuing education programs, co-op programs and internships. Study abroad program. ROTC: Army (c).
Entrance Requirements: Open admission except for nursing and radiologic technology programs. Option: electronic application. Required: high school transcript. Required for some: interview. Entrance: noncompetitive. Application deadline: Rolling. Notification: continuous. Transfer credits accepted: Yes.
Costs Per Year: Application fee: $25. One-time mandatory fee: $75. Area resident tuition: $3900 full-time, $163 per credit hour part-time. State resident tuition: $7800 full-time, $326 per credit hour part-time. Nonresident tuition: $7800 full-time, $326 per credit hour part-time. Mandatory fees: $580 full-time, $15 per credit hour part-time, $60 per term part-time.
Collegiate Environment: Orientation program. Drama-theater group, choral group, student-run newspaper, radio station. Social organizations: 5 open to all. Major annual events: Chicken Fest, School Spirit Day, Holiday Social. Student services: health clinic, personal-psychological counseling, women's center. Campus security: 24-hour emergency response devices and patrols, late night transport-escort service. College housing not available. Leon E. Butler Library with 22,876 books, 95 serials, 1,483 audiovisual materials, an OPAC, and a Web page. 341 computers available on campus for general student use. A campuswide network can be accessed from off-campus. Students can access the following: online class registration. Staffed computer lab on campus provides training in use of computers, software, and the Internet.

ERIE COMMUNITY COLLEGE, NORTH CAMPUS

6205 Main St.
Williamsville, NY 14221-7095
Tel: (716)851-1002
Fax: (716)634-3802
Web Site: www.ecc.edu/
Description: State and locally supported, 2-year, coed. Part of State University of New York System. Awards certificates, diplomas, transfer associate, and terminal associate degrees. Founded 1946. Setting: 120-acre suburban campus with easy access to Buffalo. Total enrollment: 6,561. Faculty: 374 (151 full-time, 223 part-time). Student-undergrad faculty ratio is 18:1. 5,675 applied, 73% were admitted. Full-time: 4,269 students, 48% women, 52% men. Part-time: 2,292 students, 51% women, 49% men. Students come from 15 states and territories, 23 other countries, 0.5% from out-of-state. 1% American Indian or Alaska Native, non-Hispanic/Latino; 5% Hispanic/Latino; 13% African American, non-Hispanic/Latino; 2% Asian, non-Hispanic/Latino; 0.04% Native Hawaiian or other Pacific Islander, non-Hispanic/Latino; 4% international. 36% 25 or older, 10% transferred in. Core. Calendar: semesters plus summer sessions, winter intersession. Academic remediation for entering students, ESL program, services for LD students, advanced placement, self-designed majors, honors program, independent study, distance learning, double major, summer session for credit, part-time degree program, adult/continuing education programs, co-op programs and internships. Study abroad program. ROTC: Army (c).
Entrance Requirements: Open admission except for nursing, dental hygiene and respiratory care. Option: electronic application. Required: high school transcript. Required for some: interview. Entrance: noncompetitive. Application deadline: Rolling. Notification: continuous. Transfer credits accepted: Yes.

Costs Per Year: Application fee: $25. One-time mandatory fee: $75. Area resident tuition: $3900 full-time, $163 per credit hour part-time. State resident tuition: $7800 full-time, $326 per credit hour part-time. Nonresident tuition: $7800 full-time, $326 per credit hour part-time. Mandatory fees: $580 full-time, $15 per credit hour part-time, $60 per term part-time.
Collegiate Environment: Orientation program. Drama-theater group, choral group, student-run newspaper, radio station. Social organizations: 7 open to all. Major annual events: Homecoming Bash, Dan Sperry, Magician, Solo Circus. Student services: health clinic, personal-psychological counseling, women's center. Campus security: 24-hour emergency response devices and patrols, late night transport-escort service. College housing not available. Richard R. Dry Memorial Library with 52,846 books, 285 serials, 4,743 audiovisual materials, an OPAC, and a Web page. 457 computers available on campus for general student use. A campuswide network can be accessed from off-campus. Students can access the following: online class registration. Staffed computer lab on campus provides training in use of computers, software, and the Internet.

ERIE COMMUNITY COLLEGE, SOUTH CAMPUS

4041 Southwestern Blvd.
Orchard Park, NY 14127-2199
Tel: (716)851-1003
Fax: (716)648-9953
Web Site: www.ecc.edu/
Description: State and locally supported, 2-year, coed. Part of State University of New York System. Awards certificates, diplomas, transfer associate, and terminal associate degrees. Founded 1974. Setting: 110-acre suburban campus with easy access to Buffalo. Total enrollment: 4,096. Faculty: 321 (96 full-time, 225 part-time). Student-undergrad faculty ratio is 18:1. 2,427 applied, 80% were admitted. Full-time: 2,441 students, 41% women, 59% men. Part-time: 1,655 students, 50% women, 50% men. Students come from 16 states and territories, 5 other countries, 1% from out-of-state. 1% American Indian or Alaska Native, non-Hispanic/Latino; 5% Hispanic/Latino; 6% African American, non-Hispanic/Latino; 1% Asian, non-Hispanic/Latino; 0.1% Native Hawaiian or other Pacific Islander, non-Hispanic/Latino; 1% international. 25% 25 or older, 6% transferred in. Core. Calendar: semesters plus summer sessions, winter intersession. Academic remediation for entering students, ESL program, services for LD students, advanced placement, self-designed majors, honors program, independent study, distance learning, double major, summer session for credit, part-time degree program, adult/continuing education programs, co-op programs and internships. Study abroad program. ROTC: Army (c).
Entrance Requirements: Open admission. Option: electronic application. Required: high school transcript. Required for some: interview. Entrance: noncompetitive. Application deadline: Rolling. Notification: continuous. Transfer credits accepted: Yes.
Costs Per Year: Application fee: $25. One-time mandatory fee: $75. Area resident tuition: $3900 full-time, $163 per credit hour part-time. State resident tuition: $7800 full-time, $326 per credit hour part-time. Nonresident tuition: $7800 full-time, $326 per credit hour part-time. Mandatory fees: $580 full-time, $15 per credit hour part-time, $60 per term part-time.
Collegiate Environment: Orientation program. Drama-theater group, choral group, student-run newspaper, radio station. Social organizations: 4 open to all. Major annual events: Chicken Fest, Meet the Kats, Homecoming Cookout. Student services: health clinic, personal-psychological counseling, women's center. Campus security: 24-hour emergency response devices and patrols, late night transport-escort service. College housing not available. 47,316 books, 192 serials, 1,368 audiovisual materials, an OPAC, and a Web page 434 computers available on campus for general student use. A campuswide network can be accessed from off-campus. Students can access the following: online class registration. Staffed computer lab on campus provides training in use of computers, software, and the Internet.

EUGENE LANG COLLEGE THE NEW SCHOOL FOR LIBERAL ARTS

65 W 11th St.
New York, NY 10011-8601
Tel: (212)229-5600; Free: 800-292-3040
Fax: (212)229-5355
E-mail: lang@newschool.edu
Web Site: www.newschool.edu/lang
Description: Independent, 4-year, coed. Part of The New School. Awards bachelor's degrees. Founded 1978. Setting: 5-acre urban campus with easy access to New York City. Total enrollment: 1,457. Faculty: 149 (64 full-time,

85 part-time). Student-undergrad faculty ratio is 15:1. 1,543 applied, 73% were admitted. 27% from top 10% of their high school class, 57% from top quarter, 88% from top half. Full-time: 288 students, 72% women, 28% men. Part-time: 2 students, 50% women, 50% men. 70% from out-of-state. 0.1% American Indian or Alaska Native, non-Hispanic/Latino; 13% Hispanic/Latino; 6% African American, non-Hispanic/Latino; 5% Asian, non-Hispanic/Latino; 0.1% Native Hawaiian or other Pacific Islander, non-Hispanic/Latino; 5% international. 4% 25 or older, 27% live on campus, 50% transferred in. Retention: 80% of full-time freshmen returned the following year. Academic areas with the most degrees conferred: English; visual and performing arts; social sciences. Core. Calendar: semesters. ESL program, services for LD students, advanced placement, accelerated degree program, self-designed majors, independent study, distance learning, double major, summer session for credit, internships. Off campus study at Cooper Union for the Advancement of Science and Art, Bank Street College of Education, Sarah Lawrence College. Study abroad program.

Entrance Requirements: Options: electronic application, early decision, deferred admission, international baccalaureate accepted. Required: essay, high school transcript, interview, counselor evaluation, teacher evaluation. Recommended: minimum 3 high school GPA. Entrance: very difficult. Application deadlines: 1/5, 11/1 for early decision. Notification: 4/1, 12/1 for early decision. SAT Reasoning Test deadline: 1/6. Transfer credits accepted: Yes.

Costs Per Year: Application fee: $50. Comprehensive fee: $55,870 includes full-time tuition ($37,710), mandatory fees ($860), and college room and board ($17,300). College room only: $13,900. Part-time tuition: $1280 per credit hour.

Collegiate Environment: Orientation program. Drama-theater group, choral group, student-run newspaper, radio station. Student services: health clinic, personal-psychological counseling. Campus security: 24-hour emergency response devices, controlled dormitory access, 24-hour desk attendants in residence halls. Freshmen given priority for college housing. Option: coed housing available. Raymond Fogelman Library plus 2 others with an OPAC and a Web page.

■ EUGENIO MARÍA DE HOSTOS COMMUNITY COLLEGE OF THE CITY UNIVERSITY OF NEW YORK
500 Grand Concourse
Bronx, NY 10451
Tel: (718)518-4444
Fax: (718)518-4256
E-mail: admissions@hostos.cuny.edu
Web Site: www.hostos.cuny.edu/

Description: State and locally supported, 2-year, coed. Part of City University of New York System. Awards certificates, transfer associate, and terminal associate degrees. Founded 1968. Setting: 8-acre urban campus. Total enrollment: 6,187. Student-undergrad faculty ratio is 19:1. 0% from out-of-state. 38% 25 or older. Core. Calendar: semesters. Academic remediation for entering students, ESL program, services for LD students, distance learning, double major, summer session for credit, part-time degree program, adult/continuing education programs, internships. Study abroad program.

Entrance Requirements: Open admission. Required: high school transcript. Entrance: noncompetitive. Application deadline: Rolling. Notification: continuous until 8/15.

Collegiate Environment: Orientation program. Student-run newspaper. Student services: legal services, health clinic, personal-psychological counseling, women's center. Campus security: 24-hour emergency response devices and patrols, late night transport-escort service. Hostos Community College Library with an OPAC and a Web page.

■ EVEREST INSTITUTE
1630 Portland Ave.
Rochester, NY 14621
Tel: (585)266-0430
Web Site: www.everest.edu/campus/rochester/

Description: Proprietary, 2-year, coed. Part of Corinthian Colleges, Inc. Awards certificates, diplomas, and terminal associate degrees. Founded 1863. Setting: 2-acre suburban campus. Total enrollment: 1,150. Student-undergrad faculty ratio is 16:1. 59% 25 or older. Retention: 64% of full-time freshmen returned the following year. Advanced placement, distance learning, summer session for credit, part-time degree program, adult/continuing education programs, co-op programs.

Entrance Requirements: Options: early admission, deferred admission. Required: high school transcript, interview. Required for some: CPAt for

those with High School Diploma or GED; COMPASS or Asset for applicants without a High School Diploma or GED. Entrance: minimally difficult. Application deadlines: Rolling, Rolling for nonresidents. Notification: continuous, continuous for nonresidents.

Collegiate Environment: Orientation program.

■ EXCELSIOR COLLEGE
7 Columbia Cir.
Albany, NY 12203-5159
Tel: (518)464-8500; Free: 888-647-2388
Fax: (518)464-8777
E-mail: admissions@excelsior.edu
Web Site: www.excelsior.edu/

Description: Independent, comprehensive; coed. Awards associate, bachelor's, and master's degrees and post-master's certificates (offers only external degree programs). Founded 1970. Setting: suburban campus with easy access to Albany, NY. Total enrollment: 37,194. Faculty: (1,463 part-time). Student-undergrad faculty ratio is 8:1. Part-time: 35,302 students, 59% women, 41% men. Students come from 52 states and territories, 20 other countries, 86% from out-of-state. 1% American Indian or Alaska Native, non-Hispanic/Latino; 8% Hispanic/Latino; 23% African American, non-Hispanic/Latino; 3% Asian, non-Hispanic/Latino; 1% Native Hawaiian or other Pacific Islander, non-Hispanic/Latino; 1% international. 94% 25 or older, 29% transferred in. Academic areas with the most degrees conferred: liberal arts/general studies; business/marketing; health professions and related sciences. Core. Calendar: continuous. ESL program, services for LD students, advanced placement, accelerated degree program, self-designed majors, honors program, independent study, distance learning, part-time degree program, external degree program, adult/continuing education programs, graduate courses open to undergrads. Off campus study.

Entrance Requirements: Open admission Admission to the associate degree in nursing program is limited to individuals with specific health care experience. Admission to the bachelor's degree program in nursing is limited to students with a valid RN license. Options: electronic application, international baccalaureate accepted. Required for some: college transcripts. Application deadline: Rolling. Notification: continuous. Transfer credits accepted: Yes.

Costs Per Year: Application fee: $80. Tuition: $390 per credit hour part-time.

Collegiate Environment: Orientation program. Social organizations: Nursing and Engineering Honor Societies. Major annual event: Commencement. Excelsior College Virtual Library via Johns Hopkins University with a Web page.

■ FARMINGDALE STATE COLLEGE
2350 Broadhollow Rd.
Farmingdale, NY 11735
Tel: (631)420-2000; Free: 877-4-FARMINGDALE
Fax: (631)420-2633
E-mail: admissions@farmingdale.edu
Web Site: www.farmingdale.edu/

Description: State-supported, 4-year, coed. Part of State University of New York System. Awards associate and bachelor's degrees. Founded 1912. Setting: 380-acre small town campus with easy access to New York City. Endowment: $6.5 million. Research spending for the previous fiscal year: $408,401. Educational spending for the previous fiscal year: $9986 per student. Total enrollment: 7,889. Faculty: 592 (201 full-time, 391 part-time). Student-undergrad faculty ratio is 20:1. 5,398 applied, 58% were admitted. Full-time: 5,787 students, 38% women, 62% men. Part-time: 2,102 students, 52% women, 48% men. Students come from 13 states and territories, 38 other countries, 1% from out-of-state. 0.2% American Indian or Alaska Native, non-Hispanic/Latino; 14% Hispanic/Latino; 11% African American, non-Hispanic/Latino; 7% Asian, non-Hispanic/Latino; 1% Native Hawaiian or other Pacific Islander, non-Hispanic/Latino; 3% international. 27% 25 or older, 8% live on campus, 14% transferred in. Retention: 80% of full-time freshmen returned the following year. Academic areas with the most degrees conferred: business/marketing; engineering technologies; communication/journalism. Core. Calendar: semesters. Academic remediation for entering students, ESL program, services for LD students, advanced placement, accelerated degree program, self-designed majors, independent study, distance learning, double major, summer session for credit, part-time degree program, internships. Study abroad program. ROTC: Army (c), Naval (c), Air Force (c).

Entrance Requirements: Options: electronic application, early admission, deferred admission. Required: high school transcript, minimum 2.5 high school GPA, SAT or ACT. Required for some: interview. Requirements are vary by program. Entrance: moderately difficult. Application deadline: Rolling. Notification: continuous. SAT Reasoning Test deadline: 7/1. Transfer credits accepted: Yes.

Costs Per Year: Application fee: $50. State resident tuition: $5870 full-time, $245 per credit part-time. Nonresident tuition: $15,320 full-time, $638 per credit part-time. Mandatory fees: $1255 full-time. Part-time tuition varies according to course load. College room and board: $11,860. College room only: $7260. Room and board charges vary according to board plan and housing facility.

Collegiate Environment: Orientation program. Drama-theater group, student-run newspaper, radio station. Social organizations: 57 open to all; national fraternities, national sororities. Most popular organizations: Campus Activities Board, Farmingdale Student Government, student radio station, Rambler Newspaper. Major annual events: Farewell to Farmingdale, Spring Fling, Homecoming. Student services: health clinic, personal-psychological counseling. Campus security: 24-hour emergency response devices and patrols, controlled dormitory access. 650 college housing spaces available; 615 were occupied in 2012-13. No special consideration for freshman housing applicants. Option: coed housing available. Greenley Hall with 180,000 books, 27,000 microform titles, 706 serials, 1,446 audiovisual materials, an OPAC, and a Web page. 926 computers available on campus for general student use. A campuswide network can be accessed from student residence rooms and from off campus. Students can access the following: online class registration. Staffed computer lab on campus provides training in use of computers, software, and the Internet.

■ FASHION INSTITUTE OF TECHNOLOGY

Seventh Ave. at 27th St.
New York, NY 10001-5992
Tel: (212)217-7999
Fax: (212)217-7481
E-mail: fitinfo@fitnyc.edu
Web Site: www.fitnyc.edu/

Description: State and locally supported, comprehensive, coed. Part of State University of New York System. Awards associate, bachelor's, and master's degrees. Founded 1944. Setting: 5-acre urban campus with easy access to New York City. Endowment: $25.9 million. Educational spending for the previous fiscal year: $9298 per student. Total enrollment: 10,052. Faculty: 977 (239 full-time, 738 part-time). Student-undergrad faculty ratio is 17:1. 4,449 applied, 45% were admitted. Full-time: 7,154 students, 86% women, 14% men. Part-time: 2,694 students, 82% women, 18% men. 35% from out-of-state. 0.1% American Indian or Alaska Native, non-Hispanic/Latino; 15% Hispanic/Latino; 9% African American, non-Hispanic/Latino; 10% Asian, non-Hispanic/Latino; 0.4% Native Hawaiian or other Pacific Islander, non-Hispanic/Latino; 13% international. 22% 25 or older, 28% live on campus, 10% transferred in. Retention: 85% of full-time freshmen returned the following year. Academic areas with the most degrees conferred: visual and performing arts; business/marketing; communication/journalism. Core. Calendar: semesters. Academic remediation for entering students, ESL program, services for LD students, advanced placement, honors program, distance learning, summer session for credit, part-time degree program, adult/continuing education programs, internships. Study abroad program.

Entrance Requirements: Options: electronic application, international baccalaureate accepted. Required: essay, high school transcript. Recommended: SAT or ACT. Required for some: portfolio for art and design programs. Entrance: moderately difficult. Application deadline: 1/1. Notification: 4/1. Transfer credits accepted: Yes.

Costs Per Year: Application fee: $50. State resident tuition: $5768 full-time, $240 per credit hour part-time. Nonresident tuition: $15,430 full-time, $643 per credit hour part-time. Mandatory fees: $590 full-time, $7.50 per credit hour part-time, $170 per term part-time. Full-time tuition and fees vary according to degree level. Part-time tuition and fees vary according to degree level. College room and board: $12,598. Room and board charges vary according to board plan and housing facility.

Collegiate Environment: Orientation program. Drama-theater group, choral group, student-run newspaper, radio station. Social organizations: 70 open to all. Most popular organizations: Asian Student Network, Fashion Show Club, Black Student Union, Phi Theta Kappa, Gospel Choir. Major annual events: FIT Dance-a-thon Charity Fundraiser, Homecoming, Spring Block Party. Student services: health clinic, personal-psychological counseling. Campus security: 24-hour emergency response devices and patrols, late night transport-escort service, controlled dormitory access. 2,300 college

housing spaces available; all were occupied in 2012-13. Freshmen given priority for college housing. Options: coed, women-only housing available. 1,700 computers available on campus for general student use. Computer purchase/lease plans available. A campuswide network can be accessed from student residence rooms and from off campus. Students can access the following: online class registration. Staffed computer lab on campus provides training in use of computers, software, and the Internet.

■ FINGER LAKES COMMUNITY COLLEGE

3325 Marvin Sands Dr.
Canandaigua, NY 14424-8395
Tel: (585)394-3500
Fax: (585)394-5005
E-mail: admissions@flcc.edu
Web Site: www.flcc.edu/

Description: State and locally supported, 2-year, coed. Part of State University of New York System. Awards certificates, transfer associate, and terminal associate degrees. Founded 1965. Setting: 300-acre small town campus with easy access to Rochester. Total enrollment: 6,539. Faculty: 383 (118 full-time, 265 part-time). Student-undergrad faculty ratio is 22:1. Full-time: 3,610 students, 52% women, 48% men. Part-time: 2,929 students, 62% women, 38% men. Students come from 25 states and territories, 4 other countries, 1% from out-of-state. 0.4% American Indian or Alaska Native, non-Hispanic/Latino; 5% Hispanic/Latino; 8% African American, non-Hispanic/Latino; 1% Asian, non-Hispanic/Latino; 0.04% Native Hawaiian or other Pacific Islander, non-Hispanic/Latino; 0.1% international. 32% 25 or older, 5% transferred in. Core. Calendar: semesters. Academic remediation for entering students, services for LD students, advanced placement, honors program, distance learning, summer session for credit, part-time degree program, internships. Off campus study at the Rochester Area Colleges. ROTC: Air Force (c).

Entrance Requirements: Open admission except for nursing, therapeutic massage and integrative health care programs. Options: electronic application, early admission, deferred admission, international baccalaureate accepted. Required: high school transcript. Entrance: noncompetitive. Application deadline: 8/23. Notification: continuous. Preference given to state residents. Transfer credits accepted: Yes.

Costs Per Year: Application fee: $20. State resident tuition: $3654 full-time, $151 per credit hour part-time. Nonresident tuition: $7308 full-time, $303 per credit hour part-time. Mandatory fees: $414 full-time, $13 per credit hour part-time. Full-time tuition and fees vary according to course load. Part-time tuition and fees vary according to course load.

Collegiate Environment: Orientation program. Drama-theater group, choral group, student-run radio station. Social organizations: 45 open to all. Student services: legal services, health clinic, personal-psychological counseling. Campus security: 24-hour emergency response devices and patrols, late night transport-escort service. College housing not available. Charles Meder Library with 75,610 books, 5,927 microform titles, 464 serials, 6,954 audiovisual materials, and an OPAC. 425 computers available on campus for general student use. A campuswide network can be accessed from off-campus. Staffed computer lab on campus.

■ FIORELLO H. LAGUARDIA COMMUNITY COLLEGE OF THE CITY UNIVERSITY OF NEW YORK

31-10 Thomson Ave.
Long Island City, NY 11101-3071
Tel: (718)482-7200
Fax: (718)482-5599
E-mail: admissions@lagcc.cuny.edu
Web Site: www.lagcc.cuny.edu/

Description: State and locally supported, 2-year, coed. Part of City University of New York System. Awards certificates, transfer associate, and terminal associate degrees. Founded 1970. Setting: 6-acre urban campus with easy access to New York City. Total enrollment: 17,468. Faculty: 1,121 (325 full-time, 796 part-time). Student-undergrad faculty ratio is 21:1. 6,624 applied, 100% were admitted. Full-time: 9,752 students, 57% women, 43% men. Part-time: 7,716 students, 60% women, 40% men. Students come from 15 states and territories, 160 other countries, 2% from out-of-state. 0.3% American Indian or Alaska Native, non-Hispanic/Latino; 37% Hispanic/Latino; 16% African American, non-Hispanic/Latino; 13% Asian, non-Hispanic/Latino; 0.4% Native Hawaiian or other Pacific Islander, non-Hispanic/Latino; 10% international. 29% 25 or older, 8% transferred in. Core. Calendar: enhanced semester. Academic remediation for entering students, ESL program, services for LD students, advanced placement, accelerated degree program, self-designed majors, honors program, independent study, distance learning, double major, summer session for credit, part-time degree program, adult/continuing education programs, co-op programs and internships. Off campus study at Summer program with Vassar College, other units of the City University of New York System. Study abroad program.

Entrance Requirements: Open admission. Options: electronic application, early admission, deferred admission. Required: high school transcript. Entrance: noncompetitive. Application deadline: Rolling. Notification: continuous. Transfer credits accepted: Yes.

Costs Per Year: Application fee: $65. State resident tuition: $3900 full-time, $165 per credit part-time. Nonresident tuition: $7800 full-time, $260 per credit part-time. Mandatory fees: $366 full-time, $91.85 per term part-time.

Collegiate Environment: Orientation program. Drama-theater group, student-run newspaper, radio station. Social organizations: 30 open to all. Most popular organizations: Bangladesh Student Association, Christian Club, Chinese Club, Web Radio, Black Student Union. Major annual events: Spring Night: Bangladesh Student Association, Black Expo: Black Student Union, Halloween Havoc: Rock Musicians Society, Gamer's Club, SGA, Japanese Club and Web Radio. Student services: legal services, health clinic, personal-psychological counseling, women's center. Campus security: 24-hour emergency response devices and patrols, late night transport-escort service. College housing not available. Fiorello H. LaGuardia Community College Library Media Resources Center plus 1 other with 342,977 books, 10,542 microform titles, 531 serials, 3,577 audiovisual materials, an OPAC, and a Web page. 1,585 computers available on campus for general student use. Computer purchase/lease plans available. A campuswide network can be accessed from off-campus. Students can access the following: online class registration. Staffed computer lab on campus provides training in use of computers, software, and the Internet.

■ FIVE TOWNS COLLEGE

305 N Service Rd.
Dix Hills, NY 11746-6055
Tel: (631)424-7000
Fax: (631)656-2172
E-mail: jerry.cohen@ftc.edu
Web Site: www.ftc.edu/

Description: Independent, comprehensive, coed. Awards associate, bachelor's, master's, and doctoral degrees. Founded 1972. Setting: 35-acre suburban campus with easy access to New York City. Total enrollment: 899. Faculty: 94 (38 full-time, 56 part-time). Student-undergrad faculty ratio is 9:1. 745 applied, 41% were admitted. 15% from top 10% of their high school class, 40% from top quarter, 55% from top half. Full-time: 835 students, 31% women, 69% men. Part-time: 34 students, 12% women, 88% men. Students come from 12 states and territories, 2 other countries, 12% from out-of-state. 0.3% American Indian or Alaska Native, non-Hispanic/Latino; 20% Hispanic/Latino; 26% African American, non-Hispanic/Latino; 5% Asian, non-Hispanic/Latino; 0% Native Hawaiian or other Pacific Islander, non-Hispanic/Latino; 0.1% international. 8% 25 or older, 20% live on campus, 11% transferred in. Retention: 55% of full-time freshmen returned the following year. Academic areas with the most degrees conferred: visual and performing arts; business/marketing; education. Core. Calendar: semesters. Academic remediation for entering students, services for LD students, advanced placement, independent study, summer session for credit, part-time degree program, adult/continuing education programs, internships, graduate courses open to undergrads. Off campus study at Nassau BOCES, Western Suffolk BOCES, Eastern Suffolk BOCES, Nassau Community College, Suffolk County Community College.

Entrance Requirements: Options: electronic application, early decision, deferred admission, international baccalaureate accepted. Required: essay, high school transcript, minimum 2.3 high school GPA, 2 recommendations, Immunization records and an audition for Music or Theatre students, SAT or ACT. Required for some: interview. Entrance: moderately difficult. Application deadlines: Rolling, Rolling for nonresidents, 12/1 for early decision. Notification: continuous, continuous for nonresidents, 12/15 for early decision. Transfer credits accepted: Yes. Early decision applicants: 5. Early decision applicants admitted: 4.

Costs Per Year: Application fee: $35. One-time mandatory fee: $110. Comprehensive fee: $33,740 includes full-time tuition ($19,900), mandatory fees ($370), and college room and board ($13,470). College room only: $8100. Full-time tuition and fees vary according to course level, degree level, program, and student level. Part-time tuition: $825 per credit hour. Part-time mandatory fees: $120 per term, $70 per year. Part-time tuition and fees vary according to course level, course load, degree level, program, and student level.

Collegiate Environment: Orientation program. Drama-theater group, choral group, student-run newspaper, radio station. Social organizations: 10 open to all. Most popular organizations: Film Video Club, Audio Club, Music Business Club, Hip Hop Club, yearbook. Major annual events: Long Island Music Industry Conference, College Senior Picnic, L.I. Media Art Show. Student services: personal-psychological counseling. Campus security: 24-hour emergency response devices and patrols, late night transport-escort service, controlled dormitory access. 200 college housing spaces available; 196 were occupied in 2012-13. No special consideration for freshman housing applicants. Option: coed housing available. Five Towns College Library with 40,000 books, 600 serials, 1,000 audiovisual materials, and an OPAC. 110 computers available on campus for general student use. A campuswide network can be accessed from student residence rooms. Staffed computer lab on campus provides training in use of computers and the Internet.

Community Environment: See Adelphi University.

■ FORDHAM UNIVERSITY

441 E Fordham Rd.
New York, NY 10458
Tel: (718)817-1000; Free: 800-FORDHAM
Fax: (718)367-9404
E-mail: enroll@fordham.edu
Web Site: www.fordham.edu/

Description: Independent Roman Catholic (Jesuit), university, coed. Awards bachelor's, master's, and doctoral degrees and post-master's certificates (branch locations at Rose Hill and Lincoln Center). Founded 1841. Setting: 85-acre urban campus with easy access to New York City. Endowment: $491.6 million. Research spending for the previous fiscal year: $14.4 million. Total enrollment: 15,170. Faculty: 1,510 (699 full-time, 811 part-time). Student-undergrad faculty ratio is 13:1. 34,069 applied, 43% were admitted. 50% from top 10% of their high school class, 87% from top quarter, 99% from top half. Full-time: 7,710 students, 53% women, 47% men. Part-time: 615 students, 59% women, 41% men. Students come from 44 states and territories, 69 other countries, 48% from out-of-state. 0.1% American Indian or Alaska Native, non-Hispanic/Latino; 14% Hispanic/Latino; 5% African American, non-Hispanic/Latino; 9% Asian, non-Hispanic/Latino; 0.1% Native Hawaiian or other Pacific Islander, non-Hispanic/Latino; 5% international. 8% 25 or older, 56% live on campus, 4% transferred in. Retention: 88% of full-time freshmen returned the following year. Academic areas with the most degrees conferred: business/marketing; social sciences; communication/journalism. Core. Calendar: semesters. ESL program, services for LD students, advanced placement, accelerated degree program, self-designed majors, honors program, independent study, double major, summer session for credit, part-time degree program, adult/continuing education programs, internships, graduate courses open to undergrads. Off campus study at University of San Francisco. Study abroad program. ROTC: Army, Naval (c), Air Force (c).

Entrance Requirements: Options: electronic application, early admission, early action, deferred admission, international baccalaureate accepted. Required: essay, high school transcript, 1 recommendation, SAT or ACT. Recommended: SAT Subject Tests. Entrance: very difficult. Application deadlines: 1/15, 11/1 for early action. Notification: 4/1, 12/25 for early action. SAT Reasoning Test deadline: 2/1. SAT Subject Test deadline: 2/1. Transfer credits accepted: Yes. Applicants placed on waiting list: 5,749. Wait-listed applicants offered admission: 748. Early action applicants: 11,278. Early action applicants admitted: 5,177.

Costs Per Year: Application fee: $70. Comprehensive fee: $57,102 includes full-time tuition ($41,000), mandatory fees ($732), and college room and board ($15,370). College room only: $10,205. Full-time tuition and fees vary according to student level. Room and board charges vary according to board plan, housing facility, and location.

Collegiate Environment: Orientation program. Drama-theater group, choral group, marching band, student-run newspaper, radio station. Social organizations: 143 open to all. Most popular organizations: United Student Government, Commuting Student Association, Residence Hall Association, Ambassador Program (Admission Department Student Tour Guides), Campus Activities Board. Major annual events: Under the Tent Dance, President's Ball, Spring Weekend. Student services: health clinic, personal-psychological counseling. Campus security: 24-hour emergency response devices and patrols, student patrols, late night transport-escort service, controlled dormitory access, security at each campus entrance and at residence halls. 3,907 college housing spaces available. Option: coed housing available. Walsh Library plus 3 others with 2.2 million books, 3.2 million microform titles, 49,914 serials, 47,800 audiovisual materials, an OPAC, and a Web page. Operations spending for the previous fiscal year: $15.8 million. 1,400 computers available on campus for general student use. Computer purchase/lease plans available. A campuswide network can be accessed from student residence rooms and from off campus. Students can access the following: online class registration. Staffed computer lab on campus provides training in use of computers, software, and the Internet.

■ FULTON-MONTGOMERY COMMUNITY COLLEGE

2805 State Hwy. 67
Johnstown, NY 12095-3790
Tel: (518)762-4651
Fax: (518)762-6518
E-mail: llaporte@fmcc.suny.edu
Web Site: www.fmcc.suny.edu/

Description: State and locally supported, 2-year, coed. Part of State University of New York System. Awards certificates, transfer associate, and terminal associate degrees. Founded 1964. Setting: 195-acre rural campus. Endowment: $1.7 million. Total enrollment: 2,833. Faculty: 145 (54 full-time, 91 part-time). Student-undergrad faculty ratio is 24:1. Full-time: 1,863 students, 54% women, 46% men. Part-time: 970 students, 65% women, 35% men. Students come from 6 states and territories, 18 other countries, 1% from out-of-state. 29% 25 or older, 4% transferred in. Retention: 56% of full-time freshmen returned the following year. Core. Calendar: semesters plus winter session. Academic remediation for entering students, ESL program, services for LD students, advanced placement, accelerated degree program, self-designed majors, honors program, independent study, distance learning, double major, summer session for credit, part-time degree program, external degree program, adult/continuing education programs, co-op programs and internships. Off campus study at State University of New York College of Technology at Canton, State University of New York College of Agriculture and Technology at Cobleskill. Study abroad program.

Entrance Requirements: Open admission except for nursing program, radiological technology. Options: electronic application, early admission, deferred admission. Required: high school transcript. Entrance: noncompetitive. Application deadline: 9/10. Notification: continuous.

Collegiate Environment: Orientation program. Drama-theater group, choral group, student-run newspaper. Social organizations: 30 open to all. Major annual events: Spring Fling, Orientation. Student services: personal-psychological counseling. Campus security: weekend and night security. Evans Library with an OPAC and a Web page. Operations spending for the previous fiscal year: $406,724. 400 computers available on campus for general student use. A campuswide network can be accessed from off-campus. Staffed computer lab on campus.

■ GENESEE COMMUNITY COLLEGE

1 College Rd.
Batavia, NY 14020-9704
Tel: (585)343-0055; Free: 800-CALL GCC
Fax: (585)345-4541
E-mail: tmlanemartin@genesee.edu
Web Site: www.genesee.edu/

Description: State and locally supported, 2-year, coed. Part of State University of New York System. Awards certificates, transfer associate, and terminal associate degrees. Founded 1966. Setting: 256-acre small town campus with easy access to Buffalo, Rochester. Endowment: $3 million. Educational spending for the previous fiscal year: $3146 per student. Total enrollment: 6,965. Faculty: 369 (87 full-time, 282 part-time). Student-undergrad faculty ratio is 18:1. 2,796 applied, 100% were admitted. Full-time: 3,469 students, 64% women, 36% men. Part-time: 3,496 students, 63% women, 37% men. Students come from 25 states and territories, 27 other countries, 4% from out-of-state. 1% American Indian or Alaska Native, non-Hispanic/Latino; 3% Hispanic/Latino; 9% African American, non-Hispanic/Latino; 1% Asian, non-Hispanic/Latino; 0.1% Native Hawaiian or other Pacific Islander, non-Hispanic/Latino; 3% international. 36% 25 or older, 6% transferred in. Core. Calendar: semesters. Academic remediation for entering students, ESL program, services for LD students, advanced placement, honors program, independent study, distance learning, double major, summer session for credit, part-time degree program, adult/continuing education programs, co-op programs and internships. Study abroad program.

Entrance Requirements: Open admission except for nursing, physical therapy assistant, paralegal, respiratory care, veterinary technology, engineering science, and polysomnographic technology programs. Option: electronic application. Required: high school transcript. Recommended: ACT.

Required for some: 1 recommendation. Entrance: noncompetitive. Application deadlines: Rolling, Rolling for nonresidents. Notification: continuous, continuous for nonresidents. Transfer credits accepted: Yes.

Costs Per Year: Application fee: $0. State resident tuition: $3550 full-time, $145 per credit hour part-time. Nonresident tuition: $4150 full-time, $165 per credit hour part-time. Mandatory fees: $350 full-time, $2 per credit hour part-time, $42 per term part-time. Full-time tuition and fees vary according to course load. Part-time tuition and fees vary according to course load. College room only: $5800. Room charges vary according to housing facility.

Collegiate Environment: Orientation program. Drama-theater group, choral group, student-run newspaper, radio station. Social organizations: 40 open to all. Most popular organizations: Student Government Association, Phi Theta Kappa, DECA, Student Activities Council, Forum Players. Major annual events: Outdoor Festivals, Fashion Show, Up All Night. Student services: health clinic, personal-psychological counseling. Campus security: 24-hour emergency response devices and patrols, student patrols, late night transport-escort service, controlled dormitory access. 387 college housing spaces available; all were occupied in 2012-13. No special consideration for freshman housing applicants. Alfred C. OConnell Library with 81,811 books, 5,000 microform titles, 180 serials, 6,789 audiovisual materials, an OPAC, and a Web page. Operations spending for the previous fiscal year: $867,273. 408 computers available on campus for general student use. A campuswide network can be accessed from off-campus. Students can access the following: online class registration, applications software. Staffed computer lab on campus provides training in use of computers, software, and the Internet.

■ GLOBE INSTITUTE OF TECHNOLOGY

500 7th Ave.
New York, NY 10018
Tel: (212)349-4330; Free: 800-51-GLOBE
Fax: (212)227-5920
E-mail: admissions@globe.edu
Web Site: www.globe.edu/

Description: Proprietary, 4-year, coed. Awards associate and bachelor's degrees. Setting: urban campus with easy access to New York City. Students come from 7 states and territories, 3% from out-of-state. 63% 25 or older. Core. Calendar: semesters. Academic remediation for entering students, ESL program, services for LD students, advanced placement, accelerated degree program, freshman honors college, independent study, summer session for credit, part-time degree program, internships. Off campus study.

Entrance Requirements: Open admission. Option: electronic application. Required: high school transcript, interview. Recommended: SAT or ACT. Entrance: minimally difficult. Application deadline: Rolling. Notification: continuous.

Collegiate Environment: Orientation program. Drama-theater group. Student services: personal-psychological counseling. Globe Institute of Technology's Library with 20,000 books, 1,237 serials, and a Web page. 140 computers available on campus for general student use. A campuswide network can be accessed from off-campus. Staffed computer lab on campus.

■ HAMILTON COLLEGE

198 College Hill Rd.
Clinton, NY 13323-1296
Tel: (315)859-4011; Free: 800-843-2655
Fax: (315)859-4124
E-mail: admission@hamilton.edu
Web Site: www.hamilton.edu/

Description: Independent, 4-year, coed. Awards bachelor's degrees. Founded 1812. Setting: 1,300-acre small town campus. Endowment: $635.2 million. Research spending for the previous fiscal year: $1.5 million. Educational spending for the previous fiscal year: $28,129 per student. Total enrollment: 1,884. Faculty: 223 (188 full-time, 35 part-time). Student-undergrad faculty ratio is 9:1. 5,107 applied, 27% were admitted. 79% from top 10% of their high school class, 97% from top quarter, 100% from top half. 13 class presidents, 20 valedictorians, 57 student government officers. Full-time: 1,868 students, 51% women, 49% men. Part-time: 16 students, 56% women, 44% men. Students come from 47 states and territories, 39 other countries, 67% from out-of-state. 0.3% American Indian or Alaska Native, non-Hispanic/Latino; 7% Hispanic/Latino; 4% African American, non-Hispanic/Latino; 8% Asian, non-Hispanic/Latino; 0% Native Hawaiian or other Pacific Islander, non-Hispanic/Latino; 5% international. 1% 25 or older, 98% live on campus, 1% transferred in. Retention: 96% of full-time freshmen returned the following year. Academic areas with the most degrees conferred: social sciences; biological/life sciences; foreign languages and literature. Calendar: semesters. ESL program, services for LD students, advanced placement, accelerated degree program, self-designed majors, independent study, double major, part-time degree program, adult/continuing education programs, internships. Off campus study at Colgate University, Utica College. Study abroad program. ROTC: Army (c), Air Force (c).

Entrance Requirements: Options: electronic application, early decision, deferred admission, international baccalaureate accepted. Required: essay, high school transcript, 1 recommendation, SAT and SAT Subject Tests or ACT. Recommended: interview. Entrance: very difficult. Application deadlines: 1/1, 11/15 for early decision plan 1, 1/1 for early decision plan 2. Notification: 4/1, 12/15 for early decision plan 1, 2/15 for early decision plan 2. SAT Reasoning Test deadline: 2/1. SAT Subject Test deadline: 2/1. Transfer credits accepted: Yes. Applicants placed on waiting list: 1,016. Wait-listed applicants offered admission: 3. Early decision applicants: 641. Early decision applicants admitted: 251.

Costs Per Year: Application fee: $60. Comprehensive fee: $55,620 includes full-time tuition ($43,910), mandatory fees ($440), and college room and board ($11,270). College room only: $6160. Room and board charges vary according to board plan. Part-time tuition: $5,488.75 per course.

Collegiate Environment: Orientation program. Drama-theater group, choral group, student-run newspaper, radio station. Social organizations: 189 open to all; national fraternities, national sororities, local sororities; 26% of eligible men and 17% of eligible women are members. Most popular organizations: WHCL (Hamilton College Radio), Culinary Society, AHI Undergraduate Fellows, Operation Smile, Slow Food. Major annual events: Class & Charter Day, Diwali (Indian Holiday Celebration), Campus Activity Board late night events (ex. Electronic Late Nite). Student services: health clinic, personal-psychological counseling, women's center. Campus security: 24-hour emergency response devices and patrols, late night transport-escort service, controlled dormitory access, student safety program. 1,835 college housing spaces available; 1,805 were occupied in 2012-13. Freshmen guaranteed college housing. On-campus residence required through senior year. Option: coed housing available. Burke Library plus 1 other with 625,376 books, 293,834 microform titles, 4,546 serials, 35,217 audiovisual materials, an OPAC, and a Web page. Operations spending for the previous fiscal year: $3.2 million. 811 computers available on campus for general student use. Computer purchase/lease plans available. A campuswide network can be accessed from student residence rooms and from off campus. Students can access the following: online class registration. Staffed computer lab on campus provides training in use of computers, software, and the Internet.

Community Environment: Clinton, population 1,918, is a suburban community 10 miles southwest of Utica, population 59,336. The climate is temperate. Access via bus, rail, and air lines are through Utica. Nearby Kirkland has a library, five churches, an art center, a Chamber of Commerce, and civic, fraternal, and veteran's organizations. Hockey, skiing, camping, and ice skating are popular recreational activities in the area.

■ **HARTWICK COLLEGE**
One Hartwick Dr.
Oneonta, NY 13820-4020
Tel: (607)431-4200; Free: 888-HARTWICK
Fax: (607)431-4138
E-mail: admissions@hartwick.edu
Web Site: www.hartwick.edu/

Description: Independent, 4-year, coed. Awards bachelor's degrees. Founded 1797. Setting: 425-acre small town campus with easy access to Albany, NY. Endowment: $57.8 million. Research spending for the previous fiscal year: $179,611. Educational spending for the previous fiscal year: $11,546 per student. Total enrollment: 1,558. Faculty: 183 (105 full-time, 78 part-time). Student-undergrad faculty ratio is 11:1. 4,897 applied, 77% were admitted. 22% from top 10% of their high school class, 54% from top quarter, 84% from top half. 10 student government officers. Full-time: 1,503 students, 59% women, 41% men. Part-time: 55 students, 65% women, 35% men. Students come from 32 states and territories, 18 other countries, 26% from out-of-state. 1% American Indian or Alaska Native, non-Hispanic/Latino; 6% Hispanic/Latino; 5% African American, non-Hispanic/Latino; 1% Asian, non-Hispanic/Latino; 0.1% Native Hawaiian or other Pacific Islander, non-Hispanic/Latino; 3% international. 4% 25 or older, 78% live on campus, 3% transferred in. Retention: 73% of full-time freshmen returned the following year. Academic areas with the most degrees conferred: social sciences; business/marketing; health professions and related sciences; visual and performing arts. Core. Calendar: 4-1-4. Services for LD students, advanced

placement, accelerated degree program, self-designed majors, honors program, independent study, double major, summer session for credit, part-time degree program, internships. Off campus study at State University of New York College at Oneonta, American University, Central University of Iowa, Syracuse University, The School for International Training. Study abroad program.

Entrance Requirements: Options: electronic application, early admission, early decision, deferred admission, international baccalaureate accepted. Required: high school transcript. Recommended: minimum 2.5 high school GPA. Required for some: audition for music program; portfolio for Art majors; SAT scores for Nursing majors, SAT or ACT. Entrance: moderately difficult. Application deadlines: Rolling, 11/1 for early decision. Notification: continuous, 12/1 for early decision plan 1, Rolling for early decision plan 2. Transfer credits accepted: Yes. Applicants placed on waiting list: 487. Wait-listed applicants offered admission: 89. Early decision applicants: 63. Early decision applicants admitted: 55.

Costs Per Year: Application fee: $0. One-time mandatory fee: $400. Comprehensive fee: $49,415 includes full-time tuition ($38,120), mandatory fees ($810), and college room and board ($10,485). College room only: $5515. Room and board charges vary according to board plan and housing facility. Part-time tuition: $1217 per credit.

Collegiate Environment: Orientation program. Drama-theater group, choral group, student-run newspaper, radio station. Social organizations: 5 open to all; national fraternities, national sororities, local fraternities, local sororities; 3% of eligible men and 5% of eligible women are members. Most popular organizations: Student Union, student radio station, Student Senate, Hilltops campus newspaper, Cardboard Alley Players. Major annual events: Alumni Weekend, OH Fest (State College at Oneonta & Hartwick spring weekend events and concerts), Midnight Madness. Student services: health clinic, personal-psychological counseling, women's center. Campus security: 24-hour emergency response devices and patrols, late night transport-escort service, controlled dormitory access. 1,200 college housing spaces available; all were occupied in 2012-13. Freshmen guaranteed college housing. On-campus residence required through junior year. Option: coed housing available. Stevens-German Library with 299,336 books, 29,708 microform titles, 12,204 serials, 4,790 audiovisual materials, an OPAC, and a Web page. 80 computers available on campus for general student use. Computer purchase/lease plans available. A campuswide network can be accessed from student residence rooms and from off campus. Students can access the following: online class registration.

Community Environment: Oneonta, population 13,200, is large enough to support industries and two colleges, and serves as a regional commerce center. Cooperstown is 20 miles away and attracts many people annually who discover Oneonta (home of the National Soccer Hall of Fame) and its restaurants, motels, bed and breakfasts, and who use its local parks and facilities for swimming, golf, fishing, skiing, and boating. Public transportation is available in town. Oneonta is on Interstate 88, a freeway that connects Albany, New York, and central-eastern Pennsylvania.

■ **HELENE FULD COLLEGE OF NURSING OF NORTH GENERAL HOSPITAL**
24 E 120th St.
New York, NY 10035
Tel: (212)423-2700
Web Site: www.helenefuld.edu/

Description: Independent, 2-year, coed. Awards transfer associate and terminal associate degrees (program only open to licensed practical nurses). Founded 1945. Setting: urban campus. Total enrollment: 354. Student-undergrad faculty ratio is 11:1. 32 applied, 100% were admitted. 8% from out-of-state. 90% 25 or older. Core. Accelerated degree program, summer session for credit, part-time degree program.

Entrance Requirements: Option: deferred admission. Required: essay, high school transcript, 3 recommendations, interview, must be Licensed Practical Nurse, nursing exam, Nelson Denny Reading Test, math exam. Entrance: moderately difficult. Application deadline: Rolling.

Collegiate Environment: Orientation program. Student services: personal-psychological counseling. Campus security: security guard during open hours.

■ **HERKIMER COUNTY COMMUNITY COLLEGE**
Reservoir Rd.
Herkimer, NY 13350
Tel: (315)866-0300
Fax: (315)866-7253

Web Site: www.herkimer.edu/

Description: State and locally supported, 2-year, coed. Part of State University of New York System. Awards certificates, transfer associate, and terminal associate degrees. Founded 1966. Setting: 500-acre small town campus with easy access to Syracuse. Total enrollment: 3,328. 24% 25 or older. Calendar: semesters. Academic remediation for entering students, ESL program, services for LD students, advanced placement, honors program, summer session for credit, part-time degree program, adult/continuing education programs, internships.

Entrance Requirements: Open admission except for occupational therapy assistant, physical therapy assistant programs. Option: early admission. Required: high school transcript. Entrance: noncompetitive. Application deadline: 8/20. Notification: continuous. Preference given to county residents.

Collegiate Environment: Orientation program. Drama-theater group, student-run newspaper, radio station. Student services: personal-psychological counseling. Campus security: 24-hour emergency response devices and patrols. Herkimer County Community College Library with 70,000 books, 220 serials, and an OPAC.

■ HILBERT COLLEGE

5200 S Park Ave.
Hamburg, NY 14075-1597
Tel: (716)649-7900; Free: 800-649-8003
Fax: (716)649-0702
E-mail: jrogers@hilbert.edu
Web Site: www.hilbert.edu/

Description: Independent, comprehensive, coed. Awards associate, bachelor's, and master's degrees. Founded 1957. Setting: 40-acre suburban campus with easy access to Buffalo. Endowment: $5.1 million. Educational spending for the previous fiscal year: $5246 per student. Total enrollment: 1,075. Faculty: 122 (53 full-time, 69 part-time). Student-undergrad faculty ratio is 12:1. 1,035 applied, 77% were admitted. 6% from top 10% of their high school class, 28% from top quarter, 61% from top half. Full-time: 878 students, 55% women, 45% men. Part-time: 155 students, 63% women, 37% men. Students come from 13 states and territories, 2 other countries, 3% from out-of-state. 2% American Indian or Alaska Native, non-Hispanic/Latino; 2% Hispanic/Latino; 11% African American, non-Hispanic/Latino; 0.4% Asian, non-Hispanic/Latino; 0.2% Native Hawaiian or other Pacific Islander, non-Hispanic/Latino; 1% international. 18% 25 or older, 28% live on campus, 10% transferred in. Retention: 67% of full-time freshmen returned the following year. Academic areas with the most degrees conferred: homeland security, law enforcement, firefighting, and protective services; business/marketing; public administration and social services. Core. Calendar: semesters. Academic remediation for entering students, services for LD students, advanced placement, honors program, independent study, distance learning, summer session for credit, part-time degree program, co-op programs and internships. Study abroad program. ROTC: Army (c).

Entrance Requirements: Options: electronic application, deferred admission, international baccalaureate accepted. Required: high school transcript. Recommended: essay, interview, SAT or ACT. Required for some: interview. Entrance: minimally difficult. Application deadline: Rolling. Notification: continuous. Transfer credits accepted: Yes.

Costs Per Year: Application fee: $25. One-time mandatory fee: $50. Comprehensive fee: $29,150 includes full-time tuition ($19,900), mandatory fees ($600), and college room and board ($8650). College room only: $4450. Full-time tuition and fees vary according to course load. Room and board charges vary according to board plan and housing facility. Part-time tuition: $485 per credit. Part-time mandatory fees: $13 per credit, $55 per term. Part-time tuition and fees vary according to course load.

Collegiate Environment: Orientation program. Drama-theater group, student-run newspaper, radio station. Social organizations: 20 open to all. Most popular organizations: Student Government Association, Student Business and Accounting Association, SADD, Students in Free Enterprise (SIFE), Criminal Justice Association. Major annual events: Quad Party, Fall Fest, Student Life Awards. Student services: health clinic, personal-psychological counseling. Campus security: 24-hour emergency response devices and patrols, student patrols, late night transport-escort service, controlled dormitory access. 304 college housing spaces available; 286 were occupied in 2012-13. Freshmen given priority for college housing. Option: coed housing available. McGrath Library with 41,684 books, 1,000 microform titles, 56,513 serials, 1,636 audiovisual materials, an OPAC, and a Web page. Operations spending for the previous fiscal year: $460,360. 146 computers available on campus for general student use. A campuswide

network can be accessed from student residence rooms. Students can access the following: online class registration. Staffed computer lab on campus provides training in use of software and the Internet.

Community Environment: Hamburg, population 9,600, is a suburban area adjacent to Buffalo. Within the immediate vicinity there are 18 churches, a theater, shopping center, and major civic, fraternal, and veteran's organizations. Some part-time employment is available for students in the immediate area. The Buffalo Raceway and annual Erie County Fair are here. Rich Stadium, home of the Buffalo Bills, is 5 minutes away and area ski resorts are nearby. All the cultural, community service, and recreational facilities of Buffalo are easily accessible.

■ HOBART AND WILLIAM SMITH COLLEGES

Geneva, NY 14456-3397
Tel: (315)781-3000; Free: 800-852-2256
Fax: (315)781-5471
E-mail: murphy@hws.edu
Web Site: www.hws.edu/

Description: Independent, comprehensive, coed. Awards bachelor's and master's degrees. Founded 1822. Setting: 200-acre small town campus with easy access to Rochester, Syracuse. Endowment: $161.2 million. Research spending for the previous fiscal year: $2.7 million. Educational spending for the previous fiscal year: $14,243 per student. Total enrollment: 2,300. Faculty: 231 (216 full-time, 15 part-time). Student-undergrad faculty ratio is 11:1. 4,465 applied, 53% were admitted. 34% from top 10% of their high school class, 63% from top quarter, 90% from top half. 16 valedictorians. Full-time: 2,267 students, 55% women, 45% men. Part-time: 25 students, 12% women, 88% men. Students come from 45 states and territories, 27 other countries, 57% from out-of-state. 0.4% American Indian or Alaska Native, non-Hispanic/Latino; 3% Hispanic/Latino; 4% African American, non-Hispanic/Latino; 2% Asian, non-Hispanic/Latino; 0% Native Hawaiian or other Pacific Islander, non-Hispanic/Latino; 4% international. 0% 25 or older, 90% live on campus, 1% transferred in. Retention: 88% of full-time freshmen returned the following year. Academic areas with the most degrees conferred: social sciences; area and ethnic studies; communication/journalism; English. Core. Calendar: semesters. ESL program, services for LD students, advanced placement, accelerated degree program, self-designed majors, honors program, independent study, double major, adult/continuing education programs, internships. Off campus study at New York State Visiting Student Program. Study abroad program. ROTC: Army (c), Air Force (c).

Entrance Requirements: Options: electronic application, early admission, early decision, deferred admission, international baccalaureate accepted. Required: essay, high school transcript, 1 recommendation. Recommended: interview. Required for some: SAT or ACT. Entrance: very difficult. Application deadlines: 2/1, 11/15 for early decision plan 1, 1/1 for early decision plan 2. Notification: 4/1, 12/15 for early decision plan 1, 2/1 for early decision plan 2. SAT Reasoning Test deadline: 2/1. Applicants placed on waiting list: 517. Wait-listed applicants offered admission: 25. Early decision applicants: 369. Early decision applicants admitted: 312.

Costs Per Year: Application fee: $45. Comprehensive fee: $55,699 includes full-time tuition ($43,484), mandatory fees ($954), and college room and board ($11,261). Room and board charges vary according to board plan.

Collegiate Environment: Orientation program. Drama-theater group, choral group, student-run newspaper, radio station. Social organizations: 80 open to all; national fraternities; 15% of men are members. Most popular organizations: Student Life and Leadership, student government, campus publications, Service Network, sports clubs. Major annual events: Day of Service, President's Forum, Charter Day/Moving Up Day. Student services: legal services, health clinic, personal-psychological counseling, women's center. Campus security: 24-hour emergency response devices and patrols, late night transport-escort service, controlled dormitory access. 1,885 college housing spaces available; all were occupied in 2012-13. Freshmen guaranteed college housing. On-campus residence required through junior year. Options: coed, men-only, women-only housing available. Warren Hunting Smith Library plus 1 other with 483,408 books, 47,701 microform titles, 3,256 serials, 15,044 audiovisual materials, an OPAC, and a Web page. Operations spending for the previous fiscal year: $2.1 million. 167 computers available on campus for general student use. Computer purchase/lease plans available. A campuswide network can be accessed from student residence rooms and from off campus. Students can access the following: online class registration. Staffed computer lab on campus provides training in use of computers, software, and the Internet.

Community Environment: Geneva, population 13,500, is on Seneca Lake, the largest of the Finger Lakes. It is the center of a rich agricultural and nursery region with a number of diversified industries adding to the city's economy. There are several churches of major denominations, a public library, historical museum, YMCA, and many service and fraternal organizations within the town. Seneca lake offers excellent facilities for fishing, boating, and other water sports. Some part-time employment is available.

■ HOFSTRA UNIVERSITY

100 Hofstra University
Hempstead, NY 11549
Tel: (516)463-6600; Free: 800-HOFSTRA
Fax: (516)560-7660
E-mail: admission@hofstra.edu
Web Site: www.hofstra.edu/

Description: Independent, university, coed. Awards bachelor's, master's, and doctoral degrees and post-master's certificates. Founded 1935. Setting: 240-acre suburban campus with easy access to New York City. Endowment: $311 million. Research spending for the previous fiscal year: $3.4 million. Educational spending for the previous fiscal year: $15,750 per student. Total enrollment: 11,023. Faculty: 1,135 (517 full-time, 618 part-time). Student-undergrad faculty ratio is 14:1. 22,733 applied, 59% were admitted. 28% from top 10% of their high school class, 61% from top quarter, 87% from top half. 7 valedictorians. Full-time: 6,374 students, 54% women, 46% men. Part-time: 519 students, 44% women, 56% men. Students come from 46 states and territories, 50 other countries, 35% from out-of-state. 0.3% American Indian or Alaska Native, non-Hispanic/Latino; 11% Hispanic/Latino; 9% African American, non-Hispanic/Latino; 7% Asian, non-Hispanic/Latino; 1% Native Hawaiian or other Pacific Islander, non-Hispanic/Latino; 2% international. 5% 25 or older, 49% live on campus, 7% transferred in. Retention: 78% of full-time freshmen returned the following year. Academic areas with the most degrees conferred: business/marketing; communication/journalism; social sciences. Core. Calendar: 4-1-4. ESL program, services for LD students, advanced placement, accelerated degree program, self-designed majors, freshman honors college, honors program, independent study, distance learning, double major, summer session for credit, part-time degree program, external degree program, internships, graduate courses open to undergrads. Off campus study at Hofstra University, St. John's University, and Adelphi University. Study abroad program. ROTC: Army.

Entrance Requirements: Options: electronic application, early admission, early action, deferred admission, international baccalaureate accepted. Required: essay, high school transcript, 2 recommendations, Proof of degree required for all; TOEFL required for international students. Recommended: minimum 2.5 high school GPA, SAT Subject Tests. Required for some: interview, SAT or ACT. Entrance: moderately difficult. Application deadlines: Rolling, 12/15 for early action. Notification: 2/1, 1/15 for early action. Transfer credits accepted: Yes. Applicants placed on waiting list: 407. Wait-listed applicants offered admission: 31. Early action applicants: 11,337. Early action applicants admitted: 6,756.

Costs Per Year: Application fee: $70. Comprehensive fee: $48,320 includes full-time tuition ($34,900), mandatory fees ($1050), and college room and board ($12,370). College room only: $8450. Full-time tuition and fees vary according to course load and program. Room and board charges vary according to board plan and housing facility. Part-time tuition: $1100 per credit hour. Part-time mandatory fees: $145 per term. Part-time tuition and fees vary according to course load and program. Tuition guaranteed not to increase for student's term of enrollment.

Collegiate Environment: Orientation program. Drama-theater group, choral group, student-run newspaper, radio station. Social organizations: 216 open to all; national fraternities, national sororities, local sororities; 11% of eligible men and 9% of eligible women are members. Most popular organizations: Chinese Student Association (Graduate Club), Inter Fraternal and Sororal Council, Danceworks, Phi Eta Sigma Honor Society, Hofstra vs. Zombies. Major annual events: Club Carnival, Fall Festival, Musicfest. Student services: legal services, health clinic, personal-psychological counseling. Campus security: 24-hour emergency response devices and patrols, student patrols, late night transport-escort service, controlled dormitory access, residence halls - security cameras/card access to entry (monitored 24/7); bike patrol; and motorist assistance program. 3,800 college housing spaces available; 3,138 were occupied in 2012-13. Freshmen given priority for college housing. Option: coed housing available. Axinn Library plus 2 others with 1 million books, 3.5 million microform titles, 16,752 serials, 16,730 audiovisual materials, an OPAC, and a Web page. Operations spending for the previous fiscal year: $12.8 million. 1,628 computers available on campus for general student use. Computer purchase/lease plans available. A

campuswide network can be accessed from student residence rooms and from off campus. Students can access the following: online class registration, Gmail/Google Apps for students; Emergency Notification System; Online course management system; online card services balance update; online e-portfolio. Staffed computer lab on campus (open 24 hours a day) provides training in use of computers, software, and the Internet.

Community Environment: Population 52,800. A residential community and retail shopping center, Hempstead is particularly interesting for its 3 historic churches. A suburban area, it is situated 25 miles east of New York City. The immediate vicinity has a public library, the Nassau Coliseum, shopping mall, YMCA, YWCA, a hospital, churches and synagogues. There are theaters, water sports, and several civic, fraternal and veterans organizations in the city. Kennedy and La Guardia airports are within 30 minutes of the campus.

■ HOLY TRINITY ORTHODOX SEMINARY

PO Box 36
Jordanville, NY 13361
Tel: (315)858-0945
Fax: (315)858-0945
E-mail: ejwillmarth@hts.edu
Web Site: www.hts.edu/

Description: Independent Russian Orthodox, 5-year, men only. Awards bachelor's degrees. Founded 1948. Setting: 900-acre rural campus. Total enrollment: 29. Faculty: 15. Student-undergrad faculty ratio is 2:1. 12 applied, 100% were admitted. Full-time: 29 students. 95% live on campus. Academic area with the most degrees conferred: theology and religious vocations. Core. Calendar: semesters. ESL program, accelerated degree program, distance learning.

Entrance Requirements: Option: deferred admission. Required: essay, high school transcript, 1 recommendation, interview, Orthodoxy/Orthodox baptism, entrance exam required. Recommendation from spiritual father or parish priest necessary. Entrance: noncompetitive. Application deadlines: 5/1, 5/1 for nonresidents. Transfer credits accepted: Yes.

Costs Per Year: Application fee: $0. Comprehensive fee: $8000 includes full-time tuition ($5500) and college room and board ($2500).

Collegiate Environment: Orientation program. Choral group, student-run newspaper. Social organizations: 1 open to all. Most popular organization: Student Union. Major annual events: Holy Trinity Seminary Colloquium, Seminary Feast Day, Graduation. Student services: health clinic, personal-psychological counseling. Campus security: 24-hour emergency response devices. 40 college housing spaces available; 29 were occupied in 2012-13. Option: men-only housing available. Holy Trinity Orthodox Seminary Library with 40,000 books, 50 serials, an OPAC, and a Web page. 8 computers available on campus for general student use. A campuswide network can be accessed.

■ HOUGHTON COLLEGE

One Willard Ave.
Houghton, NY 14744
Tel: (585)567-9200; Free: 800-777-2556
Fax: (585)567-9522
E-mail: admission@houghton.edu
Web Site: www.houghton.edu/

Description: Independent Wesleyan, comprehensive, coed. Awards associate, bachelor's, and master's degrees. Founded 1883. Setting: 1,300-acre rural campus with easy access to Buffalo, Rochester. Endowment: $38.1 million. Research spending for the previous fiscal year: $22,200. Educational spending for the previous fiscal year: $11,494 per student. Total enrollment: 1,165. Faculty: 125 (71 full-time, 54 part-time). Student-undergrad faculty ratio is 12:1. 830 applied, 73% were admitted. 30% from top 10% of their high school class, 65% from top quarter, 91% from top half. 1 National Merit Scholar, 13 valedictorians. Full-time: 1,086 students, 66% women, 34% men. Part-time: 61 students, 59% women, 41% men. Students come from 35 states and territories, 30 other countries, 39% from out-of-state. 0.5% American Indian or Alaska Native, non-Hispanic/Latino; 2% Hispanic/Latino; 3% African American, non-Hispanic/Latino; 1% Asian, non-Hispanic/Latino; 0% Native Hawaiian or other Pacific Islander, non-Hispanic/Latino; 5% international. 1% 25 or older, 87% live on campus, 4% transferred in. Retention: 88% of full-time freshmen returned the following year. Academic areas with the most degrees conferred: business/marketing; education; English. Core. Calendar: semesters. Services for LD students, advanced placement, accelerated degree program, self-designed majors, honors program, independent study, distance learning, double major, summer session for credit, adult/continuing education programs, internships, graduate courses open to undergrads. Off campus study at members of the Western New York Higher Education Consortium, Rochester Area Colleges, Council for Christian Colleges and Universities, Five College Committee, and the Christian College Consortium. Study abroad program. ROTC: Army (c).

Entrance Requirements: Options: electronic application, early action, deferred admission, international baccalaureate accepted. Required: high school transcript, 1 recommendation, SAT or ACT. Recommended: essay, minimum 3 high school GPA, interview. Required for some: essay. Entrance: moderately difficult. Application deadline: Rolling. Notification: continuous. Transfer credits accepted: Yes.

Costs Per Year: Application fee: $40. Comprehensive fee: $35,740 includes full-time tuition ($27,578), mandatory fees ($150), and college room and board ($8012). College room only: $4298. Room and board charges vary according to board plan, gender, housing facility, and student level. Part-time tuition: $1159 per credit hour.

Collegiate Environment: Orientation program. Drama-theater group, choral group, student-run newspaper. Social organizations: 27 open to all. Most popular organizations: Student Government Association, Global Christian Fellowship, Allegany County Outreach, Drama Clubs, Intercultural Student Association. Major annual events: SPOT (variety/talent/comedy, etc.), Midnight Breakfast, Homecoming. Student services: health clinic, personal-psychological counseling. Campus security: 24-hour emergency response devices and patrols, late night transport-escort service, controlled dormitory access, emergency phone number rings directly to cell phone carried by officer on duty 24/7, automatic fire alarms throughout campus. 1,126 college housing spaces available; 950 were occupied in 2012-13. Freshmen guaranteed college housing. On-campus residence required through sophomore year. Options: men-only, women-only housing available. Willard J. Houghton Library plus 1 other with 295,983 books, 47,023 microform titles, 48,277 serials, 26,146 audiovisual materials, an OPAC, and a Web page. Operations spending for the previous fiscal year: $819,312. 30 computers available on campus for general student use. A campuswide network can be accessed from student residence rooms and from off campus. Students can access the following: online class registration. Staffed computer lab on campus provides training in use of computers, software, and the Internet.

Community Environment: Houghton is a small rural community in southwestern New York, just south of Letchworth State Park. Nearby state park makes available good fishing, hunting, and skiing in season. The college also has its own ski slopes with rope-tow, an initiatives rope course, an equestrian riding program and miles of cross-country ski trails.

■ **HUDSON VALLEY COMMUNITY COLLEGE**
80 Vandenburgh Ave.
Troy, NY 12180-6096
Tel: (518)629-4822; Free: 877-325-HVCC
Web Site: www.hvcc.edu/

Description: State and locally supported, 2-year, coed. Part of State University of New York System. Awards certificates, transfer associate, and terminal associate degrees. Founded 1953. Setting: 135-acre suburban campus. Total enrollment: 13,320. Student-undergrad faculty ratio is 20:1. 2% from out-of-state. 27% 25 or older. Calendar: semesters. Academic remediation for entering students, services for LD students, advanced placement, self-designed majors, summer session for credit, part-time degree program, external degree program, adult/continuing education programs, co-op programs and internships. Off campus study at 14 members of the Hudson-Mohawk Association of Colleges and Universities. ROTC: Army, Air Force (c).

Entrance Requirements: Open admission for individual studies program. Options: early admission, deferred admission. Required: high school transcript. Entrance: minimally difficult. Application deadline: Rolling. Notification: continuous.

Collegiate Environment: Drama-theater group, student-run newspaper, radio station. Student services: legal services, health clinic, personal-psychological counseling, women's center. Campus security: 24-hour emergency response devices and patrols, late night transport-escort service.

■ **HUNTER COLLEGE OF THE CITY UNIVERSITY OF NEW YORK**
695 Park Ave.
New York, NY 10021-5085
Tel: (212)772-4000
E-mail: bill.zlata@hunter.cuny.edu
Web Site: www.hunter.cuny.edu/

Description: State and locally supported, comprehensive, coed. Part of City University of New York System. Awards bachelor's, master's, and doctoral degrees and post-master's certificates. Founded 1870. Setting: urban campus. System endowment: $65.7 million. Research spending for the previous fiscal year: $30.5 million. Total enrollment: 23,007. Faculty: 1,908 (710 full-time, 1,198 part-time). Student-undergrad faculty ratio is 15:1. 30,758 applied, 30% were admitted. 21% from top 10% of their high school class, 45% from top quarter, 80% from top half. Full-time: 11,956 students, 65% women, 35% men. Part-time: 4,752 students, 67% women, 33% men. Students come from 37 states and territories, 140 other countries, 4% from out-of-state. 0.2% American Indian or Alaska Native, non-Hispanic/Latino; 19% Hispanic/Latino; 11% African American, non-Hispanic/Latino; 25% Asian, non-Hispanic/Latino; 0% Native Hawaiian or other Pacific Islander, non-Hispanic/Latino; 7% international. 27% 25 or older, 1% live on campus, 11% transferred in. Retention: 85% of full-time freshmen returned the following year. Academic areas with the most degrees conferred: psychology; social sciences; English. Core. Calendar: semesters. ESL program, services for LD students, advanced placement, self-designed majors, freshman honors college, honors program, independent study, distance learning, double major, summer session for credit, part-time degree program, internships, graduate courses open to undergrads. Off campus study at Marymount Manhattan College, New School for Social Research, YIVD Institute, other units of the City University of New York System. Study abroad program.

Entrance Requirements: Options: early admission, international baccalaureate accepted. Required: high school transcript, SAT or ACT. Entrance: moderately difficult. Application deadline: 3/15. Notification: continuous.

Costs Per Year: Application fee: $65. State resident tuition: $5430 full-time, $230 per credit part-time. Nonresident tuition: $14,550 full-time, $485 per credit part-time. Mandatory fees: $399 full-time, $183.50 part-time. Full-time tuition and fees vary according to degree level and program. Part-time tuition and fees vary according to degree level and program. College room only: $5500.

Collegiate Environment: Orientation program. Drama-theater group, choral group, student-run newspaper, radio station. Social organizations: local fraternities, local sororities. Student services: personal-psychological counseling, women's center. Campus security: 24-hour emergency response devices and patrols. 662 college housing spaces available. Option: coed housing available. Hunter College Library plus 1 other with 885,246 books, 650,500 microform titles, 93,547 serials, 70,000 audiovisual materials, an OPAC, and a Web page. Operations spending for the previous fiscal year: $4.4 million. 1,280 computers available on campus for general student use. A campuswide network can be accessed. Students can access the following: online class registration. Staffed computer lab on campus.

■ **INSTITUTE OF DESIGN AND CONSTRUCTION**
141 Willoughby St.
Brooklyn, NY 11201-5317
Tel: (718)855-3661
Fax: (718)852-5889
E-mail: ebattista@idc.edu
Web Site: www.idcbrooklyn.org/

Description: Independent, 2-year, coed. Awards transfer associate and terminal associate degrees. Founded 1947. Setting: urban campus. Total enrollment: 127. Faculty: 22 (all part-time). Student-undergrad faculty ratio is 10:1. 30 applied, 100% were admitted. Full-time: 55 students, 18% women, 82% men. Part-time: 72 students, 14% women, 86% men. Students come from 3 states and territories, 2 other countries, 3% from out-of-state. 0% American Indian or Alaska Native, non-Hispanic/Latino; 17% Hispanic/Latino; 39% African American, non-Hispanic/Latino; 9% Asian, non-Hispanic/Latino; 0% Native Hawaiian or other Pacific Islander, non-Hispanic/Latino; 2% international. 42% 25 or older, 7% transferred in. Retention: 40% of full-time freshmen returned the following year. Core. Calendar: semesters. Academic remediation for entering students, advanced placement, summer session for credit, part-time degree program, adult/continuing education programs, co-op programs.

Entrance Requirements: Open admission. Options: electronic application, deferred admission, international baccalaureate accepted. Required: high school transcript. Recommended: interview. Entrance: noncompetitive. Application deadline: Rolling. Notification: continuous until 9/3. Transfer credits accepted: Yes.

Costs Per Year: Application fee: $30. One-time mandatory fee: $30. Tuition: $7800 full-time, $325 per credit part-time. Mandatory fees: $280 full-time, $140 per term part-time.

Collegiate Environment: Orientation program. Student services: personal-psychological counseling. College housing not available. Vito P. Battista Library plus 1 other with an OPAC. 18 computers available on campus for general student use.

■ IONA COLLEGE
715 N Ave.
New Rochelle, NY 10801-1890
Tel: (914)633-2000; Free: 800-231-IONA
Fax: (914)633-2096
E-mail: admissions@iona.edu
Web Site: www.iona.edu/

Description: Independent, comprehensive, coed, affiliated with Roman Catholic Church. Awards bachelor's and master's degrees and post-master's certificates. Founded 1940. Setting: 35-acre suburban campus with easy access to New York City. Endowment: $52.5 million. Research spending for the previous fiscal year: $288,000. Educational spending for the previous fiscal year: $7738 per student. Total enrollment: 4,241. Faculty: 353 (176 full-time, 177 part-time). Student-undergrad faculty ratio is 15:1. 8,741 applied, 86% were admitted. 17% from top 10% of their high school class, 44% from top quarter, 76% from top half. 2 National Merit Scholars. Full-time: 2,927 students, 57% women, 43% men. Part-time: 535 students, 54% women, 46% men. Students come from 33 states and territories, 32 other countries, 24% from out-of-state. 0.2% American Indian or Alaska Native, non-Hispanic/Latino; 18% Hispanic/Latino; 6% African American, non-Hispanic/Latino; 2% Asian, non-Hispanic/Latino; 0.1% Native Hawaiian or other Pacific Islander, non-Hispanic/Latino; 2% international. 1% 25 or older, 43% live on campus, 3% transferred in. Retention: 81% of full-time freshmen returned the following year. Academic areas with the most degrees conferred: business/marketing; communication/journalism; education. Core. Calendar: semesters. Services for LD students, advanced placement, accelerated degree program, honors program, independent study, distance learning, double major, summer session for credit, part-time degree program, external degree program, adult/continuing education programs, internships, graduate courses open to undergrads. Off campus study. Study abroad program. ROTC: Army (c), Air Force (c).

Entrance Requirements: Options: electronic application, early action, deferred admission, international baccalaureate accepted. Required: essay, high school transcript, 2 recommendations, SAT or ACT scores, SAT or ACT. Required for some: interview. Entrance: moderately difficult. Application deadlines: 2/15, 12/1 for early action. Notification: continuous, 12/21 for early action. SAT Reasoning Test deadline: 2/15. Transfer credits accepted: Yes. Applicants placed on waiting list: 1,184. Wait-listed applicants offered admission: 1,120. Early action applicants: 3,913. Early action applicants admitted: 3,648.

Costs Per Year: Application fee: $50. Comprehensive fee: $45,945 includes full-time tuition ($30,670), mandatory fees ($2100), and college room and board ($13,175). Room and board charges vary according to housing facility. Part-time tuition: $1020 per credit. Part-time mandatory fees: $520 per term. Part-time tuition and fees vary according to course load.

Collegiate Environment: Orientation program. Drama-theater group, choral group, marching band, student-run newspaper, radio station. Social organizations: 70 open to all; national fraternities, national sororities, local fraternities, local sororities; 6% of eligible men and 9% of eligible women are members. Most popular organizations: Student Government Association, Gales Activities Board, Council for Greek Governance, Council of Multicultural Leaders, The Ionian - Student Newspaper. Major annual events: Involvement Fair/Club Day Activities, Homecoming, Spring Weekend. Student services: health clinic, personal-psychological counseling. Campus security: 24-hour emergency response devices and patrols, controlled dormitory access. 1,358 college housing spaces available; 1,296 were occupied in 2012-13. Freshmen given priority for college housing. Option: coed housing available. Ryan Library plus 3 others with 268,476 books, 510,213 microform titles, 1,143 serials, 4,176 audiovisual materials, an OPAC, and a Web page. Operations spending for the previous fiscal year: $1.4 million. 745 computers available on campus for general student use. Computer purchase/lease plans available. A campuswide network can be accessed from student residence rooms and from off campus. Students can access the following: online class registration, bill payment. Staffed computer lab on campus provides training in use of computers, software, and the Internet.

Community Environment: Population 73,000. An attractive residential suburb is 35 minutes from the center of Manhattan. Located on Long Island Sound, New Rochelle was settled by the Huguenots in 1688. Many houses date from the days of Dutch and English occupancy. Easy access to New York City is provided by rail and bus lines. There are many churches, a YMCA, hospital, public library, and various fraternal, civic, and veteran's organizations. Recreation in the area is provided by 8 miles of Long Island Sound frontage, inland lakes, and public parks as well as facilities for golf, tennis, canoeing, fishing, skating, and hockey. Part-time employment is available.

■ ISLAND DRAFTING AND TECHNICAL INSTITUTE
128 Broadway
Amityville, NY 11701
Tel: (631)691-8733
Fax: (631)691-8738
E-mail: info@idti.edu
Web Site: www.idti.edu/

Description: Proprietary, 2-year, coed. Awards certificates, diplomas, transfer associate, and terminal associate degrees. Founded 1957. Setting: suburban campus with easy access to New York City. Total enrollment: 116. Faculty: 11 (5 full-time, 6 part-time). Student-undergrad faculty ratio is 15:1. 67 applied, 81% were admitted. 5% from top 10% of their high school class, 25% from top quarter, 80% from top half. Full-time: 116 students, 14% women, 86% men. 21% Hispanic/Latino; 18% African American, non-Hispanic/Latino; 1% Asian, non-Hispanic/Latino. 45% 25 or older. Retention: 80% of full-time freshmen returned the following year. Core. Calendar: semesters. Accelerated degree program, summer session for credit, adult/continuing education programs.

Entrance Requirements: Open admission. Options: early admission, international baccalaureate accepted. Required: interview. Recommended: high school transcript. Entrance: noncompetitive. Notification: continuous.

Costs Per Year: Application fee: $25. Tuition: $15,300 full-time, $510 per credit hour part-time. Mandatory fees: $350 full-time. Tuition guaranteed not to increase for student's term of enrollment.

■ ITHACA COLLEGE
953 Danby Rd.
Ithaca, NY 14850
Tel: (607)274-3011; Free: 800-429-4274
Fax: (607)274-1900
E-mail: admission@ithaca.edu
Web Site: www.ithaca.edu/

Description: Independent, comprehensive, coed. Awards bachelor's, master's, and doctoral degrees. Founded 1892. Setting: 669-acre small town campus with easy access to Syracuse. Endowment: $205.3 million. Research spending for the previous fiscal year: $1.1 million. Educational spending for the previous fiscal year: $12,725 per student. Total enrollment: 6,760. Faculty: 701 (478 full-time, 223 part-time). Student-undergrad faculty ratio is 12:1. 13,436 applied, 68% were admitted. 31% from top 10% of their high school class, 68% from top quarter, 92% from top half. 8 National Merit Scholars, 14 valedictorians. Full-time: 6,173 students, 57% women, 43% men. Part-time: 103 students, 55% women, 45% men. Students come from 52 states and territories, 67 other countries, 56% from out-of-state. 0.2% American Indian or Alaska Native, non-Hispanic/Latino; 6% Hispanic/Latino; 4% African American, non-Hispanic/Latino; 3% Asian, non-Hispanic/Latino; 0.1% Native Hawaiian or other Pacific Islander, non-Hispanic/Latino; 2% international. 1% 25 or older, 69% live on campus, 2% transferred in. Retention: 83% of full-time freshmen returned the following year. Academic areas with the most degrees conferred: communication/journalism; visual and performing arts; health professions and related sciences. Core. Calendar: semesters. Services for LD students, advanced placement, accelerated degree program, self-designed majors, freshman honors college, honors program, independent study, distance learning, double major, summer session for credit, part-time degree program, adult/continuing education programs, internships, graduate courses open to undergrads. Off campus study at Cornell University, Wells College. Study abroad program. ROTC: Army (c), Air Force (c).

Entrance Requirements: Options: electronic application, early admission, early decision, early action, deferred admission, international baccalaureate accepted. Required: essay, high school transcript, 1 recommendation. Recommended: minimum 3 high school GPA. Required for some: audition for some programs, SAT or ACT. Entrance: moderately difficult. Application deadlines: 2/1, 11/1 for early decision, 12/1 for early action. Notification: 4/15, 12/15 for early decision, 2/1 for early action. SAT Reasoning Test deadline: 2/1. SAT Subject Test deadline: 2/1. Applicants placed on waiting list: 1,633. Wait-listed applicants offered admission: 95. Early decision applicants: 242. Early decision applicants admitted: 223.

Costs Per Year: Application fee: $60. Comprehensive fee: $50,400 includes full-time tuition ($37,000) and college room and board ($13,400). College room only: $7200. Room and board charges vary according to board plan and housing facility. Part-time tuition: $1232 per credit hour.

Collegiate Environment: Orientation program. Drama-theater group, choral group, student-run newspaper, radio station. Social organizations: 180 open to all; national fraternities, national sororities; 1% of eligible men and 1% of eligible women are members. Most popular organizations: Student Government Association, African-Latino Society, Residence Hall Association, Habitat for Humanity, Senior Class. Major annual events: major concerts/speakers on campus, Dr. Martin Luther King Week, Cortaca Jug: annual football game. Student services: health clinic, personal-psychological counseling. Campus security: 24-hour emergency response devices and patrols, student patrols, late night transport-escort service, controlled dormitory access. 4,401 college housing spaces available; 4,273 were occupied in 2012-13. Freshmen guaranteed college housing. On-campus residence required through junior year. Options: coed, women-only housing available. Ithaca College Library with 352,500 books, 36,000 microform titles, 46,350 serials, 37,500 audiovisual materials, an OPAC, and a Web page. Operations spending for the previous fiscal year: $3.8 million. 640 computers available on campus for general student use. Computer purchase/lease plans available. A campuswide network can be accessed from student residence rooms and from off campus. Students can access the following: online class registration. Staffed computer lab on campus (open 24 hours a day) provides training in use of computers, software, and the Internet.

Community Environment: See Cornell University.

■ ITT TECHNICAL INSTITUTE (ALBANY)

13 Airline Dr.
Albany, NY 12205
Tel: (518)452-9300; Free: 800-489-1191
Web Site: www.itt-tech.edu/
Description: Proprietary, 2-year, coed. Part of ITT Educational Services, Inc. Awards terminal associate degrees. Founded 1998.
Entrance Requirements: Entrance: minimally difficult.

■ ITT TECHNICAL INSTITUTE (GETZVILLE)

2295 Millersport Hwy.
Getzville, NY 14068
Tel: (716)689-2200; Free: 800-469-7593
Web Site: www.itt-tech.edu/
Description: Proprietary, 2-year, coed. Part of ITT Educational Services, Inc. Awards terminal associate degrees.
Entrance Requirements: Entrance: minimally difficult.

■ ITT TECHNICAL INSTITUTE (LIVERPOOL)

235 Greenfield Pky.
Liverpool, NY 13088
Tel: (315)461-8000; Free: 877-488-0011
Web Site: www.itt-tech.edu/
Description: Proprietary, 2-year, coed. Part of ITT Educational Services, Inc. Awards terminal associate degrees. Founded 1998. Calendar: semesters.
Entrance Requirements: Entrance: minimally difficult.

■ JAMESTOWN BUSINESS COLLEGE

7 Fairmount Ave., Box 429
Jamestown, NY 14702-0429
Tel: (716)664-5100
Fax: (716)664-3144
E-mail: brendasalemme@jamestownbusinesscollege.edu
Web Site: www.jbcny.org/
Description: Proprietary, primarily 2-year, coed. Awards certificates, terminal associate, and bachelor's degrees. Founded 1886. Setting: 1-acre small town campus. Total enrollment: 294. Faculty: 24 (7 full-time, 17 part-time). Student-undergrad faculty ratio is 25:1. 98 applied, 93% were admitted. 2% from top 10% of their high school class, 22% from top quarter, 47% from top half. Full-time: 288 students, 73% women, 27% men. Part-time: 6 students, 67% women, 33% men. Students come from 2 states and territories, 11% from out-of-state. 2% American Indian or Alaska Native, non-Hispanic/Latino; 3% Hispanic/Latino; 2% African American, non-Hispanic/Latino; 1% Asian, non-Hispanic/Latino; 0.3% Native Hawaiian or other Pacific Islander, non-Hispanic/Latino; 0% international. 47% 25 or older, 10% transferred in. Core. Advanced placement, double major, summer session

for credit, part-time degree program, internships. Off campus study at SUNY Empire State College, Niagara University, Hilbert College, and Gannon University.

Entrance Requirements: Required: essay, high school transcript, interview. Entrance: minimally difficult. Application deadline: Rolling.

Costs Per Year: Application fee: $25. One-time mandatory fee: $25. Tuition: $10,500 full-time, $291.66 per credit hour part-time. Mandatory fees: $900 full-time, $150 per term part-time.

Collegiate Environment: Orientation program. Major annual events: School Picnics (Summer, Fall, and Spring), The Battle of the Programs (Fall Term), Student Activities. Campus security: 24-hour emergency response devices. College housing not available. James Prendergast Library with 279,270 books, 372 serials, an OPAC, and a Web page. 100 computers available on campus for general student use. A campuswide network can be accessed from off-campus. Staffed computer lab on campus provides training in use of computers, software, and the Internet.

■ JAMESTOWN COMMUNITY COLLEGE

525 Falconer St.
Jamestown, NY 14701-1999
Tel: (716)338-1000; Free: 800-388-8557
E-mail: admissions@mail.sunyjcc.edu
Web Site: www.sunyjcc.edu/
Description: State and locally supported, 2-year, coed. Part of State University of New York System. Awards certificates, transfer associate, and terminal associate degrees. Founded 1950. Setting: 107-acre small town campus. Endowment: $8.1 million. Educational spending for the previous fiscal year: $4114 per student. Total enrollment: 3,582. Faculty: 340 (72 full-time, 268 part-time). Student-undergrad faculty ratio is 16:1. 2,065 applied, 96% were admitted. 7% from top 10% of their high school class, 21% from top quarter, 50% from top half. Full-time: 2,533 students, 56% women, 44% men. Part-time: 1,049 students, 65% women, 35% men. Students come from 16 states and territories, 5 other countries, 9% from out-of-state. 1% American Indian or Alaska Native, non-Hispanic/Latino; 6% Hispanic/Latino; 4% African American, non-Hispanic/Latino; 0.5% Asian, non-Hispanic/Latino; 0.1% Native Hawaiian or other Pacific Islander, non-Hispanic/Latino; 0.1% international. 30% 25 or older, 9% live on campus, 7% transferred in. Core. Calendar: semesters. Academic remediation for entering students, services for LD students, advanced placement, honors program, independent study, distance learning, summer session for credit, part-time degree program, adult/continuing education programs, internships. Off campus study. Study abroad program.

Entrance Requirements: Open admission Nursing and Occupational Therapy Assistant programs have selective admissions, all other programs are open admissions. Options: electronic application, deferred admission. Required: high school transcript. Required for some: standardized test scores used for placement, GEDs accepted. TOEFL (or equivalent) for international students. Entrance: noncompetitive. Application deadlines: Rolling, Rolling for nonresidents. Notification: continuous, continuous for nonresidents. Transfer credits accepted: Yes.

Costs Per Year: Application fee: $0. State resident tuition: $4050 full-time, $170 per credit hour part-time. Nonresident tuition: $8100 full-time, $305 per credit hour part-time. Mandatory fees: $445 full-time. Full-time tuition and fees vary according to course load and program. Part-time tuition varies according to course load and program. College room and board: $9600. College room only: $6600. Room and board charges vary according to board plan.

Collegiate Environment: Drama-theater group, choral group, student-run radio station. Social organizations: 28 open to all; Phi Theta Kappa. Most popular organizations: Nursing Club, InterVarsity Christian Fellowship, Anime Club, Student Occupational Therapy Assistant (SOTA) Club, InterWeave Gay-Straight Alliance. Major annual events: Fall Picnic, Spring Picnic/Spring Fling, Orientation. Student services: health clinic, personal-psychological counseling. 340 college housing spaces available; 306 were occupied in 2012-13. No special consideration for freshman housing applicants. Option: coed housing available. Hultquist Library with 88,767 books, 51,659 microform titles, 334 serials, 6,373 audiovisual materials, an OPAC, and a Web page. Operations spending for the previous fiscal year: $932,976. 671 computers available on campus for general student use. A campuswide network can be accessed from student residence rooms and from off campus. Students can access the following: online class registration. Staffed computer lab on campus.

■ JEFFERSON COMMUNITY COLLEGE
1220 Coffeen St.
Watertown, NY 13601
Tel: (315)786-2200; Free: 888-435-6522
Fax: (315)786-0158
E-mail: admissions@sunyjefferson.edu
Web Site: www.sunyjefferson.edu/
Description: State and locally supported, 2-year, coed. Part of State University of New York System. Awards certificates, transfer associate, and terminal associate degrees. Founded 1961. Setting: 90-acre small town campus with easy access to Syracuse. Total enrollment: 4,143. Faculty: 230 (80 full-time, 150 part-time). Student-undergrad faculty ratio is 18:1. Full-time: 2,204 students, 61% women, 39% men. Part-time: 1,939 students, 61% women, 39% men. 1% American Indian or Alaska Native, non-Hispanic/Latino; 8% Hispanic/Latino; 5% African American, non-Hispanic/Latino; 1% Asian, non-Hispanic/Latino; 0.5% Native Hawaiian or other Pacific Islander, non-Hispanic/Latino; 0.02% international. Calendar: semesters. Academic remediation for entering students, services for LD students, advanced placement, self-designed majors, honors program, independent study, distance learning, double major, summer session for credit, part-time degree program, co-op programs and internships.
Entrance Requirements: Options: electronic application, early admission, deferred admission. Required: high school transcript. Recommended: SAT or ACT. Required for some: interview. Entrance: minimally difficult. Application deadline: 9/6. Notification: continuous. Preference given to county residents.
Costs Per Year: Application fee: $0. State resident tuition: $3744 full-time, $156 per credit hour part-time. Nonresident tuition: $5394 full-time, $225 per credit hour part-time. Mandatory fees: $533 full-time. Full-time tuition and fees vary according to course load, location, program, and reciprocity agreements. Part-time tuition varies according to course load, location, program, and reciprocity agreements.
Collegiate Environment: Orientation program. Student-run newspaper. Social organizations: 30 open to all. Major annual events: Fall Fest/Spring Fest, Stage/Theater Production. Student services: health clinic, personal-psychological counseling. Campus security: 24-hour emergency response devices and patrols. College housing not available. Melvil Dewey Library with 172,262 books, 2,269 microform titles, 144 serials, 5,761 audiovisual materials, an OPAC, and a Web page. 354 computers available on campus for general student use. A campuswide network can be accessed. Students can access the following: online class registration. Staffed computer lab on campus.

■ THE JEWISH THEOLOGICAL SEMINARY
3080 Broadway
New York, NY 10027-4649
Tel: (212)678-8000
Fax: (212)678-8947
E-mail: lcadmissions@jtsa.edu
Web Site: www.jtsa.edu/
Description: Independent Jewish, university, coed. Awards bachelor's, master's, and doctoral degrees (double bachelor's degree with Barnard College, Columbia University, joint bachelor's degree with Columbia University). Founded 1886. Setting: 1-acre urban campus. Endowment: $105.7 million. Educational spending for the previous fiscal year: $13,909 per student. Total enrollment: 566. Faculty: 130 (63 full-time, 67 part-time). Student-undergrad faculty ratio is 5:1. 124 applied, 60% were admitted. Full-time: 182 students, 55% women, 45% men. Part-time: 8 students, 88% women, 13% men. Students come from 24 states and territories, 3 other countries, 81% from out-of-state. 0% 25 or older, 75% live on campus, 0% transferred in. Retention: 100% of full-time freshmen returned the following year. Core. Calendar: semesters. Academic remediation for entering students, services for LD students, advanced placement, self-designed majors, freshman honors college, honors program, distance learning, double major, summer session for credit, part-time degree program, adult/continuing education programs, internships, graduate courses open to undergrads. Off campus study at Barnard College, Columbia University. Study abroad program. ROTC: Army (c), Naval (c), Air Force (c).
Entrance Requirements: Options: early admission, early decision, deferred admission, international baccalaureate accepted. Required: essay, high school transcript, 2 recommendations, SAT or ACT. Recommended: minimum 3.0 high school GPA, interview. Entrance: very difficult. Application deadlines: 2/15, 11/15 for early decision plan 1, 1/15 for early decision plan 2. Notification: 4/15, 12/15 for early decision plan 1, 2/15 for early decision plan 2.

Collegiate Environment: Orientation program. Drama-theater group, choral group, student-run newspaper, radio station. Student services: health clinic, personal-psychological counseling, women's center. Campus security: 24-hour emergency response devices and patrols, late night transport-escort service, controlled dormitory access. Library of the Jewish Theological Seminary with 380,000 books, 9,100 microform titles, 720 serials, 5,250 audiovisual materials, an OPAC, and a Web page. Operations spending for the previous fiscal year: $2.7 million. 50 computers available on campus for general student use. A campuswide network can be accessed from student residence rooms and from off campus. Students can access the following: online class registration. Staffed computer lab on campus provides training in use of computers, software, and the Internet.
Community Environment: See Columbia University.

■ JOHN JAY COLLEGE OF CRIMINAL JUSTICE OF THE CITY UNIVERSITY OF NEW YORK
899 Tenth Ave.
New York, NY 10019-1093
Tel: (212)237-8000; Free: 877-JOHNJAY
E-mail: mmarrero@jjay.cuny.edu
Web Site: www.jjay.cuny.edu/
Description: State and locally supported, comprehensive, coed. Part of City University of New York System. Awards associate, bachelor's, and master's degrees. Founded 1964. Setting: urban campus with easy access to New York City. Research spending for the previous fiscal year: $6249. Total enrollment: 14,996. 13,753 applied, 48% were admitted. 0% from top 10% of their high school class, 0% from top quarter, 0% from top half. Full-time: 10,286 students, 56% women, 44% men. Part-time: 2,881 students, 55% women, 45% men. Students come from 23 states and territories, 67 other countries, 3% from out-of-state. 0.3% American Indian or Alaska Native, non-Hispanic/Latino; 39% Hispanic/Latino; 22% African American, non-Hispanic/Latino; 11% Asian, non-Hispanic/Latino; 0% Native Hawaiian or other Pacific Islander, non-Hispanic/Latino; 3% international. 21% 25 or older, 0% live on campus, 12% transferred in. Retention: 78% of full-time freshmen returned the following year. Academic areas with the most degrees conferred: homeland security, law enforcement, firefighting, and protective services; psychology; social sciences. Core. Calendar: semesters. Academic remediation for entering students, ESL program, services for LD students, advanced placement, self-designed majors, honors program, independent study, distance learning, double major, summer session for credit, part-time degree program, co-op programs and internships, graduate courses open to undergrads. Off campus study at other units of the City University of New York System. Study abroad program.
Entrance Requirements: Required: high school transcript, minimum 2 high school GPA, high school diploma and minimum SAT score of 1100, SAT or ACT. Entrance: moderately difficult. Application deadline: 5/31. Notification: continuous until 1/15. SAT Reasoning Test deadline: 2/1. Transfer credits accepted: Yes.
Costs Per Year: Application fee: $65. State resident tuition: $5430 full-time. Nonresident tuition: $14,550 full-time. Mandatory fees: $330 full-time. Full-time tuition and fees vary according to course load and program.
Collegiate Environment: Orientation program. Drama-theater group, choral group, student-run newspaper, radio station. Social organizations: 40 open to all. Most popular organizations: JJC Debate Team, Universal Image Dance Group, Environmental Club, Justice in Action Club, Artist United. Student services: legal services, health clinic, personal-psychological counseling, women's center. Campus security: 24-hour emergency response devices and patrols. College housing not available. Lloyd George Sealy Library with 335,000 books, 1,800 serials, an OPAC, and a Web page. 1,900 computers available on campus for general student use. A campuswide network can be accessed from off-campus. Students can access the following: online class registration. Staffed computer lab on campus provides training in use of computers, software, and the Internet.

■ THE JUILLIARD SCHOOL
60 Lincoln Ctr. Plz.
New York, NY 10023-6588
Tel: (212)799-5000
Fax: (212)724-0263
E-mail: admissions@juilliard.edu
Web Site: www.juilliard.edu/
Description: Independent, comprehensive, coed. Awards bachelor's, master's, and doctoral degrees and post-master's certificates. Founded 1905. Setting: urban campus. Total enrollment: 1,009. Faculty: 307 (124 full-

time, 183 part-time). Student-undergrad faculty ratio is 4:1. 2,566 applied, 6% were admitted. Full-time: 521 students, 45% women, 55% men. Part-time: 163 students, 50% women, 50% men. 85% from out-of-state. 0% American Indian or Alaska Native, non-Hispanic/Latino; 6% Hispanic/Latino; 6% African American, non-Hispanic/Latino; 12% Asian, non-Hispanic/Latino; 0% Native Hawaiian or other Pacific Islander, non-Hispanic/Latino; 23% international. 7% 25 or older, 55% live on campus, 4% transferred in. Academic area with the most degrees conferred: visual and performing arts. Calendar: semesters. Adult/continuing education programs.

Entrance Requirements: Option: electronic application. Required: essay, high school transcript, audition. Entrance: most difficult. Application deadline: 12/1. Notification: 4/1. Applicants placed on waiting list: 44. Wait-listed applicants offered admission: 12.

Costs Per Year: Application fee: $110. Comprehensive fee: $46,400 includes full-time tuition ($33,630) and college room and board ($12,770).

Collegiate Environment: Orientation program. Campus security: 24-hour emergency response devices and patrols, controlled dormitory access, electronically operated main building entrances. Freshmen guaranteed college housing. On-campus residence required in freshman year. Option: coed housing available.

Community Environment: See New York University.

■ KEHILATH YAKOV RABBINICAL SEMINARY

340 Illington Rd.
Ossining, NY 10562
Tel: (718)963-1212
Fax: (718)387-8586

Description: Independent Jewish, comprehensive, men only. Awards bachelor's and master's degrees. Founded 1950. Total enrollment: 88. Calendar: semesters.

■ KEUKA COLLEGE

Keuka Park, NY 14478-0098
Tel: (315)279-5000; Free: 800-33-KEUKA
Fax: (315)279-5216
E-mail: admissions@mail.keuka.edu
Web Site: www.keuka.edu/

Description: Independent, comprehensive, coed, affiliated with American Baptist Churches in the U.S.A. Awards bachelor's and master's degrees. Founded 1890. Setting: 173-acre rural campus with easy access to Rochester. Endowment: $8.2 million. Educational spending for the previous fiscal year: $6572 per student. Total enrollment: 2,083. Faculty: 153 (84 full-time, 69 part-time). Student-undergrad faculty ratio is 14:1. 840 applied, 76% were admitted. 9% from top 10% of their high school class, 33% from top quarter, 69% from top half. Full-time: 1,551 students, 73% women, 27% men. Part-time: 323 students, 83% women, 17% men. Students come from 22 states and territories, 4 other countries, 6% from out-of-state. 1% American Indian or Alaska Native, non-Hispanic/Latino; 1% Hispanic/Latino; 7% African American, non-Hispanic/Latino; 2% Asian, non-Hispanic/Latino; 0.2% Native Hawaiian or other Pacific Islander, non-Hispanic/Latino; 0% international. 34% 25 or older, 81% live on campus, 4% transferred in. Retention: 70% of full-time freshmen returned the following year. Academic areas with the most degrees conferred: health professions and related sciences; business/marketing; education. Core. Calendar: 4-1-4. Academic remediation for entering students, services for LD students, advanced placement, accelerated degree program, self-designed majors, independent study, double major, summer session for credit, part-time degree program, adult/continuing education programs, co-op programs and internships. Off campus study at Rochester Area Colleges. Study abroad program.

Entrance Requirements: Options: electronic application, early admission, deferred admission. Required: essay, high school transcript, 1 recommendation. Recommended: minimum 2.75 high school GPA, interview, SAT or ACT. Required for some: interview. Entrance: moderately difficult. Application deadline: Rolling.

Costs Per Year: Application fee: $30. Comprehensive fee: $36,600 includes full-time tuition ($25,530), mandatory fees ($790), and college room and board ($10,280). College room only: $4880. Full-time tuition and fees vary according to degree level and program. Room and board charges vary according to board plan and housing facility. Part-time tuition: $850 per credit hour. Part-time mandatory fees: $700 per year. Part-time tuition and fees vary according to program.

Collegiate Environment: Orientation program. Drama-theater group, choral group, student-run newspaper, radio station. Social organizations: 42 open to all. Most popular organizations: Student Senate, Campus Activities Board,

OTTERS (occupational therapy club), Education Club, BAKU. Major annual events: May Day Weekend, Homecoming, Spring Weekend. Student services: health clinic, personal-psychological counseling. Campus security: 24-hour emergency response devices and patrols, late night transport-escort service. Freshmen guaranteed college housing. Options: coed, women-only housing available. Lightner Library plus 1 other with 112,541 books, 4,023 microform titles, 384 serials, 3,551 audiovisual materials, and an OPAC. Operations spending for the previous fiscal year: $432,000. 256 computers available on campus for general student use. A campuswide network can be accessed from student residence rooms and from off campus. Staffed computer lab on campus.

Community Environment: The college is located on the western shore of Keuka Lake near Penn Yan, population 5,170. This pleasant rural setting is accessible by major roadways. The area provides boating, fishing, water sports, hunting, and winter sports.

■ THE KING'S COLLEGE

52 Broadway 5th Fl.
New York, NY 10004
Tel: (212)659-7200; Free: 888-969-7200
E-mail: bparker@tkc.edu
Web Site: www.tkc.edu/

Description: Independent nondenominational, 4-year, coed. Awards bachelor's degrees. Founded 1939. Setting: urban campus. Endowment: $755,106. Educational spending for the previous fiscal year: $13,470 per student. Total enrollment: 582. Faculty: 43 (24 full-time, 19 part-time). Student-undergrad faculty ratio is 18:1. 3,388 applied, 67% were admitted. 24% from top 10% of their high school class, 52% from top quarter, 79% from top half. Full-time: 565 students, 60% women, 40% men. Part-time: 16 students, 50% women, 50% men. Students come from 37 states and territories, 6 other countries, 93% from out-of-state. 1% American Indian or Alaska Native, non-Hispanic/Latino; 8% Hispanic/Latino; 4% African American, non-Hispanic/Latino; 4% Asian, non-Hispanic/Latino; 0% Native Hawaiian or other Pacific Islander, non-Hispanic/Latino; 2% international. 0% 25 or older, 76% live on campus, 6% transferred in. Retention: 68% of full-time freshmen returned the following year. Academic areas with the most degrees conferred: liberal arts/general studies; business/marketing. Core. Calendar: semesters. Advanced placement, independent study, distance learning, summer session for credit, internships.

Entrance Requirements: Options: electronic application, early action, deferred admission, international baccalaureate accepted. Required: high school transcript, SAT or ACT. Recommended: high school transcript, minimum 3 high school GPA, interview. Entrance: moderately difficult. Application deadlines: Rolling, Rolling for nonresidents, 11/15 for early action. Notification: continuous, continuous for nonresidents, 12/15 for early action. Transfer credits accepted: Yes.

Costs Per Year: Application fee: $30. Tuition: $28,890 full-time, $1,203.75 per credit hour part-time. Mandatory fees: $350 full-time, $175 per term part-time. Full-time tuition and fees vary according to course load. Part-time tuition and fees vary according to course load. College room only: $11,600. Room charges vary according to location.

Collegiate Environment: Orientation program. Drama-theater group, choral group, student-run newspaper. Social organizations: house system. Most popular organizations: King's Debate Society, King's Theater, sports clubs, King's Dancers, The Tent. Major annual events: Spring Formal, Homecoming, Interregnum. Student services: personal-psychological counseling. Campus security: 24-hour emergency response devices. 358 college housing spaces available; 350 were occupied in 2012-13. Freshmen guaranteed college housing. Options: men-only, women-only housing available. Battles Library with 14,000 books, 85 serials, 14 audiovisual materials, an OPAC, and a Web page. Operations spending for the previous fiscal year: $120,531. 14 computers available on campus for general student use. A computer is required for all students. A campuswide network can be accessed from student residence rooms and from off campus. Students can access the following: online class registration. Staffed computer lab on campus provides training in use of computers, software, and the Internet.

■ KINGSBOROUGH COMMUNITY COLLEGE OF THE CITY UNIVERSITY OF NEW YORK

2001 Oriental Blvd., Manhattan Beach
Brooklyn, NY 11235
Tel: (718)368-5000
E-mail: info@kbcc.cuny.edu
Web Site: www.kbcc.cuny.edu/

Description: State and locally supported, 2-year, coed. Part of City University of New York System. Awards transfer associate and terminal associate degrees. Founded 1963. Setting: 72-acre urban campus with easy access to New York City. Total enrollment: 19,261. Faculty: 944 (354 full-time, 590 part-time). Student-undergrad faculty ratio is 23:1. Full-time: 11,205 students, 55% women, 45% men. Part-time: 8,056 students, 58% women, 42% men. Students come from 10 states and territories, 136 other countries, 1% from out-of-state. 0.2% American Indian or Alaska Native, non-Hispanic/Latino; 16% Hispanic/Latino; 33% African American, non-Hispanic/Latino; 13% Asian, non-Hispanic/Latino; 3% international. 27% 25 or older, 9% transferred in. Retention: 66% of full-time freshmen returned the following year. Core. Calendar: semesters. Academic remediation for entering students, ESL program, services for LD students, advanced placement, honors program, independent study, distance learning, summer session for credit, part-time degree program, adult/continuing education programs, internships. Off campus study at other units of the City University of New York System.

Entrance Requirements: Open admission. Required: high school transcript. Entrance: noncompetitive. Application deadline: 8/15.

Costs Per Year: Application fee: $65. State resident tuition: $3610 full-time, $150 per credit part-time. Nonresident tuition: $7200 full-time, $240 per credit part-time. Mandatory fees: $350 full-time, $92 per term part-time.

Collegiate Environment: Orientation program. Drama-theater group, choral group, student-run newspaper, radio station. Social organizations: 80 open to all. Most popular organizations: Peer Advisors, Caribbean Club, DECA. Major annual events: Club Fair, Family Day. Student services: health clinic, personal-psychological counseling, women's center. Campus security: 24-hour emergency response devices and patrols. Robert J. Kibbee Library with 198,343 books, 10,496 microform titles, 335 serials, 2,145 audiovisual materials, and an OPAC. 900 computers available on campus for general student use. A campuswide network can be accessed. Staffed computer lab on campus.

■ **LE MOYNE COLLEGE**
1419 Salt Springs Rd.
Syracuse, NY 13214
Tel: (315)445-4100; Free: 800-333-4733
Fax: (315)445-4711
E-mail: admission@lemoyne.edu
Web Site: www.lemoyne.edu/

Description: Independent Roman Catholic (Jesuit), comprehensive, coed. Awards bachelor's and master's degrees and post-master's certificates. Founded 1946. Setting: 161-acre suburban campus. Endowment: $114.7 million. Research spending for the previous fiscal year: $87,126. Educational spending for the previous fiscal year: $9728 per student. Total enrollment: 3,339. Faculty: 326 (150 full-time, 176 part-time). Student-undergrad faculty ratio is 13:1. 4,304 applied, 70% were admitted. 21% from top 10% of their high school class, 55% from top quarter, 90% from top half. 9 valedictorians. Full-time: 2,338 students, 58% women, 42% men. Part-time: 411 students, 75% women, 25% men. Students come from 27 states and territories, 34 other countries, 6% from out-of-state. 1% American Indian or Alaska Native, non-Hispanic/Latino; 5% Hispanic/Latino; 5% African American, non-Hispanic/Latino; 2% Asian, non-Hispanic/Latino; 0% Native Hawaiian or other Pacific Islander, non-Hispanic/Latino; 1% international. 8% 25 or older, 59% live on campus, 7% transferred in. Retention: 85% of full-time freshmen returned the following year. Academic areas with the most degrees conferred: business/marketing; psychology; social sciences; biological/life sciences. Core. Calendar: semesters. Academic remediation for entering students, services for LD students, advanced placement, accelerated degree program, honors program, independent study, double major, summer session for credit, part-time degree program, adult/continuing education programs, internships, graduate courses open to undergrads. Off campus study at The Syracuse Consortium for Culture and Medicine. Study abroad program. ROTC: Army (c), Air Force (c).

Entrance Requirements: Options: electronic application, early admission, deferred admission, international baccalaureate accepted. Required: essay, high school transcript, 2 recommendations, SAT or ACT. Recommended: interview. Entrance: moderately difficult. Application deadline: 2/1. Notification: continuous until 12/1. SAT Reasoning Test deadline: 2/1. Transfer credits accepted: Yes.

Costs Per Year: Application fee: $35. Comprehensive fee: $42,200 includes full-time tuition ($29,470), mandatory fees ($990), and college room and board ($11,740). College room only: $7430. Room and board charges vary according to board plan and housing facility. Part-time tuition: $618 per credit hour. Part-time tuition varies according to class time and course load.

Collegiate Environment: Orientation program. Drama-theater group, choral group, student-run newspaper, radio station. Social organizations: 80 open to all. Most popular organizations: Student Programming Board, Outing Club, performing arts groups, Student Dancers, New Student Orientation Committee. Major annual events: Winter/Spring Formals, Spring Olympics, Halloween Dance. Student services: health clinic, personal-psychological counseling. Campus security: 24-hour emergency response devices and patrols, late night transport-escort service, controlled dormitory access, lighted pathways, closed-circuit security cameras, and emergency code blue phones. 1,575 college housing spaces available; 1,519 were occupied in 2012-13. Freshmen guaranteed college housing. On-campus residence required through senior year. Options: coed, women-only housing available. Noreen Reale Falcone Library with 283,814 books, 282,785 microform titles, 131,112 serials, 13,302 audiovisual materials, an OPAC, and a Web page. Operations spending for the previous fiscal year: $765,263. 330 computers available on campus for general student use. A campuswide network can be accessed from student residence rooms and from off campus. Students can access the following: online class registration, ECHO (campus-wide portal), some virtual access from off campus. Staffed computer lab on campus provides training in use of computers, software, and the Internet.

Community Environment: See Syracuse University.

■ **LEHMAN COLLEGE OF THE CITY UNIVERSITY OF NEW YORK**
250 Bedford Park Blvd. W
Bronx, NY 10468-1589
Tel: (718)960-8000; Free: 877-LEHMAN1
Fax: (718)960-8712
E-mail: enroll@lehman.cuny.edu
Web Site: www.lehman.cuny.edu/

Description: State and locally supported, comprehensive, coed. Part of City University of New York System. Awards bachelor's and master's degrees and post-master's certificates. Founded 1931. Setting: 37-acre urban campus. Endowment: $7.1 million. Research spending for the previous fiscal year: $214,000. Educational spending for the previous fiscal year: $11,595 per student. Total enrollment: 11,862. Faculty: 912 (368 full-time, 544 part-time). Student-undergrad faculty ratio is 13:1. 15,518 applied, 23% were admitted. Full-time: 5,344 students, 67% women, 33% men. Part-time: 4,233 students, 69% women, 31% men. Students come from 15 states and territories, 99 other countries, 1% from out-of-state. 0.1% American Indian or Alaska Native, non-Hispanic/Latino; 50% Hispanic/Latino; 30% African American, non-Hispanic/Latino; 6% Asian, non-Hispanic/Latino; 4% international. 49% 25 or older, 13% transferred in. Retention: 82% of full-time freshmen returned the following year. Academic areas with the most degrees conferred: business/marketing; health professions and related sciences; social sciences. Core. Calendar: semesters. ESL program, services for LD students, advanced placement, self-designed majors, freshman honors college, honors program, independent study, distance learning, double major, summer session for credit, part-time degree program, adult/continuing education programs, co-op programs and internships, graduate courses open to undergrads. Off campus study at other units of the City University of New York System. Study abroad program. ROTC: Army (c).

Entrance Requirements: Options: deferred admission, international baccalaureate accepted. Required: high school transcript, minimum 3 high school GPA, SAT or ACT. Required for some: essay, interview. Entrance: moderately difficult. Application deadline: Rolling. Notification: continuous.

Costs Per Year: Application fee: $65. State resident tuition: $5430 full-time, $230 per credit part-time. Nonresident tuition: $11,640 full-time, $485 per credit part-time. Mandatory fees: $378 full-time. College room only: $8085.

Collegiate Environment: Orientation program. Drama-theater group, choral group, student-run newspaper, radio station. Social organizations: 33 open to all. Most popular organizations: Club Mac, African Students Association, Dominican Student Association, The Sociology Club, Club Live. Major annual events: Multicultural Festival, Student Life Fair, Student Organization Open House. Student services: health clinic, personal-psychological counseling, women's center. Campus security: 24-hour emergency response devices and patrols, student patrols, late night transport-escort service. Leonard Lief Library plus 1 other with 660,616 books, 713,912 microform titles, 9,370 serials, 6,735 audiovisual materials, an OPAC, and a Web page. Operations spending for the previous fiscal year: $1.5 million. 800 computers available on campus for general student use. A campuswide network can be accessed from student residence rooms. Students can access the following: online class registration. Staffed computer lab on campus.

■ LIM COLLEGE

12 E 53rd St.
New York, NY 10022-5268
Tel: (212)752-1530; Free: 800-677-1323
Fax: (212)832-6708
E-mail: admissions@limcollege.edu
Web Site: www.limcollege.edu/

Description: Proprietary, comprehensive, coed. Awards associate, bachelor's, and master's degrees. Founded 1939. Setting: urban campus with easy access to New York City. Total enrollment: 1,552. Faculty: 202 (29 full-time, 173 part-time). Student-undergrad faculty ratio is 16:1. 1,253 applied, 73% were admitted. Full-time: 1,391 students, 94% women, 6% men. Part-time: 86 students, 85% women, 15% men. Students come from 40 states and territories, 9 other countries, 58% from out-of-state. 0.3% American Indian or Alaska Native, non-Hispanic/Latino; 15% Hispanic/Latino; 15% African American, non-Hispanic/Latino; 5% Asian, non-Hispanic/Latino; 1% Native Hawaiian or other Pacific Islander, non-Hispanic/Latino; 1% international. 1% 25 or older, 24% live on campus, 11% transferred in. Retention: 60% of full-time freshmen returned the following year. Academic areas with the most degrees conferred: business/marketing; visual and performing arts. Core. Calendar: semesters. Academic remediation for entering students, advanced placement, accelerated degree program, honors program, distance learning, summer session for credit, part-time degree program, external degree program, co-op programs and internships. Off campus study. Study abroad program.

Entrance Requirements: Options: electronic application, early action, deferred admission. Required: essay, high school transcript, 2 recommendations, interview, SAT or ACT. Recommended: minimum 2.5 high school GPA. Entrance: moderately difficult. Application deadlines: Rolling, Rolling for nonresidents, 11/15 for early action. Notification: continuous, continuous for nonresidents, 12/15 for early action. Transfer credits accepted: Yes.

Costs Per Year: Application fee: $40. Tuition: $23,070 full-time, $770 per credit part-time. Mandatory fees: $575 full-time, $338 per term part-time. College room only: $15,850.

Collegiate Environment: Orientation program. Social organizations: 16 open to all. Most popular organizations: Fashion Club, Fashion Styling Club, Student Life Activities Board, Dance Team, Black Retail Action Group. Major annual events: student-run fashion show, ski trip, holiday parties. Student services: personal-psychological counseling. Campus security: controlled dormitory access. 350 college housing spaces available; all were occupied in 2012-13. No special consideration for freshman housing applicants. Option: coed housing available. Adrian G. Marcuse Library with 25,000 books, 150 serials, 800 audiovisual materials, and an OPAC. 335 computers available on campus for general student use. Computer purchase/lease plans available. A campuswide network can be accessed from student residence rooms and from off campus. Students can access the following: online class registration. Staffed computer lab on campus provides training in use of computers and software.

Community Environment: LIM's location right in the center of the greatest fashion city, New York, gives its students the best of all possible worlds. Within a block of the school are internationally known department stores, French and Italian designers' boutiques, retailing establishments of every kind, with goods imported from every continent of the world. Only a few blocks away is the heart of the garment district, Seventh Avenue. Merchandising creativity originates here and finds its way into the shopping centers of America, Europe, and the Far East.

■ LIU GLOBAL

9 Hanover Pl., 4th Fl.
Brooklyn, NY 11201
Tel: (631)287-8474; Free: 800-LIU-PLAN
Fax: (631)287-8463
E-mail: amy.greenstein@liu.edu
Web Site: www.liu.edu/globalcollege/

Description: Independent, 4-year, coed. Part of Long Island University. Awards bachelor's degrees. Founded 1965. Setting: urban campus. Total enrollment: 98. Faculty: 20. Student-undergrad faculty ratio is 4:1. 88 applied, 73% were admitted. Full-time: 98 students, 68% women, 32% men. Students come from 20 states and territories, 76% from out-of-state. 10% 25 or older, 15% transferred in. Retention: 59% of full-time freshmen returned the following year. Core. Calendar: semesters. Advanced placement, independent study, external degree program, internships. Off campus study at Long Island University (C.W. Post campus, Brooklyn campus). Study abroad program.

Entrance Requirements: Open admission. Options: electronic application, early admission, deferred admission, international baccalaureate accepted. Required: essay, high school transcript, interview. Recommended: minimum 3.0 high school GPA. Entrance: minimally difficult. Application deadline: Rolling. Notification: continuous.

Collegiate Environment: Orientation program. Most popular organizations: Activist Club, P.E.A.C.E, LaFuenza Latina, Caribbean Student Association, Women's Issues Collective. Major annual events: Ingathering, World Conference, Graduation/Senior Recognition ceremony. Student services: health clinic, personal-psychological counseling. LIU Brooklyn Campus Library with 115,380 books, 140,000 microform titles, 665 serials, and a Web page.

■ LONG ISLAND BUSINESS INSTITUTE

136-18 39th Ave., 5th Fl.
Flushing, NY 11354
Tel: (718)939-5100
Fax: (718)939-9235
E-mail: czang@libi.edu
Web Site: www.libi.edu/

Description: Proprietary, 2-year, coed. Awards certificates and transfer associate degrees (information provided for Commack and Flushing campuses). Founded 1968. Setting: urban campus with easy access to New York City. Total enrollment: 513. Faculty: 90 (15 full-time, 75 part-time). Student-undergrad faculty ratio is 10:1. 286 applied, 40% were admitted. Full-time: 380 students, 68% women, 32% men. Part-time: 133 students, 93% women, 7% men. Students come from 2 states and territories, 23 other countries, 1% from out-of-state. 0% American Indian or Alaska Native, non-Hispanic/Latino; 23% Hispanic/Latino; 10% African American, non-Hispanic/Latino; 43% Asian, non-Hispanic/Latino; 0% Native Hawaiian or other Pacific Islander, non-Hispanic/Latino; 5% international. 66% 25 or older, 8% transferred in. Calendar: semesters. Academic remediation for entering students, ESL program, advanced placement, honors program, independent study, summer session for credit, part-time degree program, adult/continuing education programs, co-op programs.

Entrance Requirements: Open admission. Required: essay, high school transcript, interview, COMPASS, CELSA. Entrance: noncompetitive. Application deadline: Rolling. Transfer credits accepted: Yes.

Costs Per Year: Application fee: $55. Tuition: $13,299 full-time, $375 per credit part-time. Mandatory fees: $600 full-time, $200 per term part-time.

Collegiate Environment: Orientation program. Most popular organizations: Small Business Club, Web Design Club, Investment Club, Court Reporting Alumni Association. Major annual events: Sneaker Day, Holiday Fundraiser, International Food Day. Campus security: 24-hour emergency response devices. College housing not available. Flushing Main Campus Library, Commack Campus Library with 7,314 books, 77 serials, 1,209 audiovisual materials, an OPAC, and a Web page. 308 computers available on campus for general student use. Staffed computer lab on campus provides training in use of computers, software, and the Internet.

■ LONG ISLAND COLLEGE HOSPITAL SCHOOL OF NURSING

350 Henry St.
7th Fl.
Brooklyn, NY 11201
Tel: (718)780-1953
Fax: (718)780-1936
E-mail: bevans@chpnet.org
Web Site: www.futurenurselich.org/

Description: Independent, 2-year, coed. Awards certificates, transfer associate, and terminal associate degrees. Founded 1883. Setting: urban campus. Total enrollment: 173. Faculty: 18 (7 full-time, 11 part-time). Student-undergrad faculty ratio is 18:1. 21 applied, 14% were admitted. Full-time: 70 students, 84% women, 16% men. Part-time: 103 students, 83% women, 17% men. 0% from out-of-state. 72% 25 or older, 47% transferred in. Core. Calendar: semesters. Advanced placement, independent study, summer session for credit, co-op programs and internships.

Entrance Requirements: Required: essay, high school transcript, minimum 2.0 high school GPA, 2 recommendations, interview, NLN test. Entrance: moderately difficult. Application deadline: 4/21. Notification: continuous.

Collegiate Environment: Social organizations: 1 open to all. Most popular organization: Student Government Association. Major annual events: Open House, Atlantic Antic Street Fair, Awards and Recognition Ceremony. Student services: health clinic, personal-psychological counseling. Campus security: 24-hour emergency response devices. E. King Morgan M.D. Health Sciences Library plus 1 other with 16,000 books and 400 serials. 4 computers available on campus for general student use. A computer is required for all students. A campuswide network can be accessed from student residence rooms and from off campus.

■ **LONG ISLAND UNIVERSITY–BRENTWOOD CAMPUS**
100 Second Ave.
Brentwood, NY 11717
Tel: (631)273-5112
Fax: (631)952-0809
Web Site: www.liu.edu/
Description: Independent, upper-level, coed. Part of Long Island University. Awards bachelor's and master's degrees and post-master's certificates. Founded 1959. Setting: 172-acre suburban campus with easy access to Manhattan. Endowment: $74 million. Total enrollment: 430. Faculty: 75 (20 full-time, 55 part-time). Student-undergrad faculty ratio is 6:1. Full-time: 12 students, 42% women, 58% men. Part-time: 17 students, 59% women, 41% men. 0% from out-of-state. 0% American Indian or Alaska Native, non-Hispanic/Latino; 10% Hispanic/Latino; 21% African American, non-Hispanic/Latino; 0% Asian, non-Hispanic/Latino; 0% Native Hawaiian or other Pacific Islander, non-Hispanic/Latino; 0% international. 66% 25 or older, 17% transferred in. Retention: 66% of full-time entering class returned the following year. Academic area with the most degrees conferred: law/legal studies. Core. Calendar: semesters. Services for LD students, advanced placement, independent study, summer session for credit, part-time degree program, internships, graduate courses open to undergrads.
Entrance Requirements: Transfer credits accepted: Yes.
Collegiate Environment: Campus security: evening security guards. 50 computers available on campus for general student use. Computer purchase/lease plans available. A campuswide network can be accessed from off-campus. Students can access the following: online class registration. Staffed computer lab on campus provides training in use of computers.

■ **LONG ISLAND UNIVERSITY–BROOKLYN CAMPUS**
One University Plz.
Brooklyn, NY 11201-8423
Tel: (718)488-1000; Free: 800-LIU-PLAN
E-mail: admissions@brooklyn.liu.edu
Web Site: www.liu.edu/
Description: Independent, university, coed. Awards associate, bachelor's, master's, and doctoral degrees and post-master's certificates. Founded 1926. Setting: 10-acre urban campus. Total enrollment: 8,567. Faculty: 863 (300 full-time, 563 part-time). Student-undergrad faculty ratio is 15:1. 5,071 applied, 83% were admitted. Full-time: 4,307 students, 69% women, 31% men. Part-time: 802 students, 78% women, 22% men. Students come from 42 states and territories, 41 other countries, 14% from out-of-state. 0.4% American Indian or Alaska Native, non-Hispanic/Latino; 15% Hispanic/Latino; 33% African American, non-Hispanic/Latino; 15% Asian, non-Hispanic/Latino; 0.1% Native Hawaiian or other Pacific Islander, non-Hispanic/Latino; 2% international. 27% 25 or older, 15% live on campus, 13% transferred in. Retention: 65% of full-time freshmen returned the following year. Academic areas with the most degrees conferred: health professions and related sciences; business/marketing; biological/life sciences. Core. Calendar: semesters. Academic remediation for entering students, ESL program, services for LD students, advanced placement, accelerated degree program, self-designed majors, honors program, independent study, distance learning, double major, summer session for credit, part-time degree program, co-op programs and internships, graduate courses open to undergrads. Study abroad program.
Entrance Requirements: Options: electronic application, deferred admission, international baccalaureate accepted. Required: essay, high school transcript, minimum 2 high school GPA, 3 recommendations, SAT or ACT. Recommended: minimum 2.5 high school GPA, interview. Required for some: minimum 3 high school GPA. Entrance: moderately difficult. Application deadline: Rolling. Notification: continuous. Transfer credits accepted: Yes.
Costs Per Year: Application fee: $40. Comprehensive fee: $46,184 includes full-time tuition ($32,370), mandatory fees ($1750), and college room and board ($12,064). Full-time tuition and fees vary according to program. Room and board charges vary according to board plan and housing facility. Part-time tuition: $1010 per credit hour. Part-time tuition varies according to program.
Collegiate Environment: Orientation program. Drama-theater group, choral group, student-run newspaper, radio station. Social organizations: 40 open to all; national fraternities, national sororities. Most popular organizations:

The Student Government Association, The American Pharmacists Association - Academy of Student Pharmacists, Hillel Jewish Students Organization, Student Activities Board, The Society of Health Systems Pharmacists. Major annual events: Homecoming, Spring Day, Orientation Day. Student services: health clinic, personal-psychological counseling. Campus security: 24-hour emergency response devices and patrols, controlled dormitory access, lighted pathways/sidewalks. 1,000 college housing spaces available; 761 were occupied in 2012-13. Freshmen given priority for college housing. Option: coed housing available. Salena Library plus 1 other with 431,179 books, 114,312 microform titles, 129,613 serials, 7,344 audiovisual materials, an OPAC, and a Web page. 300 computers available on campus for general student use. A campuswide network can be accessed from student residence rooms and from off campus. Students can access the following: online class registration. Staffed computer lab on campus provides training in use of computers.
Community Environment: The campus in downtown Brooklyn, at Flatbush and DeKalb Avenues, within easy distance of the Brooklyn Academy of Music, Prospect Park, the Brooklyn Museum, and midtown Manhattan.

■ **LONG ISLAND UNIVERSITY–C. W. POST CAMPUS**
720 Northern Blvd.
Brookville, NY 11548-1300
Tel: (516)299-2000; Free: 800-LIU-PLAN
E-mail: post-enroll@liu.edu
Web Site: www.liu.edu/
Description: Independent, comprehensive, coed. Awards associate, bachelor's, master's, and doctoral degrees and post-master's certificates. Founded 1954. Setting: 308-acre suburban campus with easy access to New York City. Total enrollment: 11,012. Faculty: 798 (302 full-time, 496 part-time). Student-undergrad faculty ratio is 13:1. 7,215 applied, 79% were admitted. Full-time: 3,978 students, 64% women, 36% men. Part-time: 4,337 students, 85% women, 15% men. Students come from 31 states and territories, 38 other countries, 7% from out-of-state. 0.2% American Indian or Alaska Native, non-Hispanic/Latino; 12% Hispanic/Latino; 10% African American, non-Hispanic/Latino; 4% Asian, non-Hispanic/Latino; 0% Native Hawaiian or other Pacific Islander, non-Hispanic/Latino; 10% international. 13% 25 or older, 36% live on campus, 6% transferred in. Retention: 68% of full-time freshmen returned the following year. Academic areas with the most degrees conferred: education; health professions and related sciences; business/marketing. Core. Calendar: semesters. Academic remediation for entering students, ESL program, services for LD students, advanced placement, accelerated degree program, self-designed majors, honors program, independent study, distance learning, double major, summer session for credit, part-time degree program, adult/continuing education programs, co-op programs and internships, graduate courses open to undergrads. Study abroad program. ROTC: Army (c).
Entrance Requirements: Options: electronic application, deferred admission. Required: essay, high school transcript, minimum 3 high school GPA, 1 recommendation, SAT or ACT. Required for some: interview. Entrance: moderately difficult. Application deadline: Rolling. Notification: continuous. Transfer credits accepted: Yes.
Costs Per Year: Application fee: $40. Comprehensive fee: $46,604 includes full-time tuition ($32,370), mandatory fees ($1700), and college room and board ($12,534). Room and board charges vary according to board plan and housing facility. Part-time tuition: $1010 per credit hour.
Collegiate Environment: Orientation program. Drama-theater group, choral group, student-run newspaper, radio station. Social organizations: 80 open to all; national fraternities, national sororities. Most popular organizations: Student Government Association, Association for Campus Programming, African People's Organization, Resident Student Association, Post TV and Newman. Major annual events: Homecoming, Spring Fling, Orientation Day. Student services: health clinic, personal-psychological counseling. Campus security: 24-hour emergency response devices and patrols, late night transport-escort service, controlled dormitory access, lighted pathways/sidewalks. 1,800 college housing spaces available; 1,137 were occupied in 2012-13. Freshmen guaranteed college housing. Option: coed housing available. B. Davis Schwartz Memorial Library plus 1 other with 506,198 books, 442,224 microform titles, 3,660 audiovisual materials, an OPAC, and a Web page. 500 computers available on campus for general student use. A campuswide network can be accessed from student residence rooms and from off campus. Students can access the following: online class registration. Staffed computer lab on campus provides training in use of computers and software.

■ **MACHZIKEI HADATH RABBINICAL COLLEGE**

5407 Sixteenth Ave.

Brooklyn, NY 11204-1805

Tel: (718)854-8777

Description: Independent Jewish, comprehensive, men only. Awards bachelor's and master's degrees. Founded 1956. Total enrollment: 112. 123 applied. 2% 25 or older. Core. Calendar: semesters. Academic remediation for entering students. Study abroad program.

Entrance Requirements: Required: interview. Entrance: moderately difficult. Application deadline: Rolling. Notification: continuous.

Collegiate Environment: Abraham Koppel Library plus 1 other with 20,000 books.

■ **MANHATTAN COLLEGE**

4513 Manhattan College Pky.

Riverdale, NY 10471

Tel: (718)862-8000; Free: 800-622-9235

Fax: (718)862-8019

E-mail: admit@manhattan.edu

Web Site: www.manhattan.edu/

Description: Independent, comprehensive, coed, affiliated with Roman Catholic Church. Awards bachelor's and master's degrees and post-master's certificates. Founded 1853. Setting: 31-acre urban campus with easy access to New York City. Endowment: $56.9 million. Research spending for the previous fiscal year: $568,000. Educational spending for the previous fiscal year: $9712 per student. Total enrollment: 3,800. Faculty: 408 (210 full-time, 198 part-time). Student-undergrad faculty ratio is 12:1. 6,545 applied, 70% were admitted. 25% from top 10% of their high school class, 54% from top quarter, 84% from top half. Full-time: 3,141 students, 45% women, 55% men. Part-time: 210 students, 28% women, 72% men. Students come from 36 states and territories, 46 other countries, 28% from out-of-state. 0.1% American Indian or Alaska Native, non-Hispanic/Latino; 17% Hispanic/Latino; 4% African American, non-Hispanic/Latino; 3% Asian, non-Hispanic/Latino; 0% Native Hawaiian or other Pacific Islander, non-Hispanic/Latino; 2% international. 3% 25 or older, 67% live on campus, 4% transferred in. Retention: 88% of full-time freshmen returned the following year. Academic areas with the most degrees conferred: engineering; business/marketing; education. Core. Calendar: semesters. ESL program, services for LD students, advanced placement, accelerated degree program, self-designed majors, honors program, independent study, distance learning, double major, summer session for credit, part-time degree program, adult/continuing education programs, co-op programs and internships, graduate courses open to undergrads. Off campus study. Study abroad program. ROTC: Army (c), Air Force.

Entrance Requirements: Options: electronic application, early admission, early decision, deferred admission, international baccalaureate accepted. Required: essay, high school transcript, minimum 2.5 high school GPA, 1 recommendation, SAT or ACT scores, SAT or ACT. Recommended: minimum 3 high school GPA, interview. Required for some: interview. Entrance: moderately difficult. Application deadlines: 4/15, 11/15 for early decision. Notification: continuous until 4/15, 12/1 for early decision. SAT Reasoning Test deadline: 3/1. Transfer credits accepted: Yes. Applicants placed on waiting list: 272. Wait-listed applicants offered admission: 52. Early decision applicants: 47. Early decision applicants admitted: 46.

Costs Per Year: Application fee: $60. Comprehensive fee: $48,805 includes full-time tuition ($33,000), mandatory fees ($2725), and college room and board ($13,080). Full-time tuition and fees vary according to course load, program, and student level. Room and board charges vary according to board plan.

Collegiate Environment: Orientation program. Drama-theater group, choral group, marching band, student-run newspaper, radio station. Social organizations: 64 open to all; national fraternities, national sororities, local fraternities; 33% of eligible men and 33% of eligible women are members. Most popular organizations: Society of Hispanic Professional Engineers, Gaelic Society, student government, LaSallian Collegians (Community Service Group), Manhattan College Players (Theater/Drama group). Major annual events: Springfest (concert and carnival), Manhattan Madness (basketball pep rally to start the season), Relay for Life. Student services: health clinic, personal-psychological counseling. Campus security: 24-hour emergency response devices and patrols, late night transport-escort service, controlled dormitory access. 2,095 college housing spaces available; 2,015 were occupied in 2012-13. Freshmen guaranteed college housing. Option: coed housing available. O'Malley Library with 427,073 books, 675,489 microform titles, 555 serials, 2,676 audiovisual materials, an OPAC, and a

Web page. Operations spending for the previous fiscal year: $3 million. 350 computers available on campus for general student use. A campuswide network can be accessed from student residence rooms and from off campus. Students can access the following: online class registration, course management system. Staffed computer lab on campus (open 24 hours a day) provides training in use of computers and the Internet.

Community Environment: See Fordham University.

■ **MANHATTAN SCHOOL OF MUSIC**

120 Claremont Ave.

New York, NY 10027-4698

Tel: (212)749-2802

Fax: (212)749-5471

E-mail: admission@msmnyc.edu

Web Site: www.msmnyc.edu/

Description: Independent, comprehensive, coed. Awards bachelor's, master's, and doctoral degrees and post-master's certificates. Founded 1917. Setting: 1-acre urban campus. Endowment: $15.5 million. Educational spending for the previous fiscal year: $15,225 per student. Total enrollment: 930. Faculty: 369 (84 full-time, 285 part-time). Student-undergrad faculty ratio is 6:1. 990 applied, 35% were admitted. Full-time: 388 students, 48% women, 52% men. Part-time: 4 students, 25% women, 75% men. Students come from 30 states and territories, 27 other countries, 80% from out-of-state. 4% 25 or older, 68% live on campus, 5% transferred in. Retention: 89% of full-time freshmen returned the following year. Academic area with the most degrees conferred: visual and performing arts. Core. Calendar: semesters. Academic remediation for entering students, ESL program, services for LD students, advanced placement, graduate courses open to undergrads. Off campus study at Barnard College.

Entrance Requirements: Options: electronic application, deferred admission, international baccalaureate accepted. Required: essay, high school transcript, minimum 2.8 high school GPA, 1 recommendation, audition. Recommended: minimum 3 high school GPA, interview, SAT or ACT. Entrance: very difficult. Application deadline: 12/1. Notification: 4/1. Applicants placed on waiting list: 48. Wait-listed applicants offered admission: 17.

Costs Per Year: Application fee: $100. Comprehensive fee: $46,716 includes full-time tuition ($34,640), mandatory fees ($500), and college room and board ($11,576). College room only: $9150. Full-time tuition and fees vary according to course load. Room and board charges vary according to housing facility. Part-time tuition: $1400 per credit hour. Part-time tuition varies according to course load.

Collegiate Environment: Orientation program. Choral group. Most popular organizations: Pan-African Student Union, International Student Association, Student Council, Resident Community Council, Gay/Lesbian/Bisexual Students Association. Major annual events: Winter Formal, Cafe Jazz, Rite of Spring. Student services: personal-psychological counseling. Campus security: 24-hour patrols, controlled dormitory access. Peter J. Sharp Library plus 1 other with 13,189 books, 164 serials, an OPAC, and a Web page. Operations spending for the previous fiscal year: $515,730. 20 computers available on campus for general student use. A campuswide network can be accessed from student residence rooms and from off campus. Students can access the following: online class registration. Staffed computer lab on campus.

Community Environment: See Columbia University.

■ **MANHATTANVILLE COLLEGE**

2900 Purchase St.

Purchase, NY 10577-2132

Tel: (914)694-2200; Free: 800-328-4553

Fax: (914)694-1732

E-mail: admissions@mville.edu

Web Site: www.manhattanville.edu/

Description: Independent, comprehensive, coed. Awards bachelor's, master's, and doctoral degrees and post-master's certificates. Founded 1841. Setting: 100-acre suburban campus with easy access to New York City. Endowment: $10.9 million. Educational spending for the previous fiscal year: $8906 per student. Total enrollment: 3,019. Faculty: 352 (104 full-time, 248 part-time). Student-undergrad faculty ratio is 12:1. 4,148 applied, 69% were admitted. 22% from top 10% of their high school class, 47% from top quarter, 80% from top half. Full-time: 1,659 students, 64% women, 36% men. Part-time: 108 students, 50% women, 50% men. Students come from 39 states and territories, 53 other countries, 39% from out-of-state. 0.5% American Indian or Alaska Native, non-Hispanic/Latino; 17% Hispanic/

Latino; 10% African American, non-Hispanic/Latino; 3% Asian, non-Hispanic/Latino; 11% international. 1% 25 or older, 78% live on campus, 3% transferred in. Retention: 73% of full-time freshmen returned the following year. Academic areas with the most degrees conferred: business/marketing; visual and performing arts; social sciences; communication/journalism; psychology. Core. Calendar: semesters. Academic remediation for entering students, ESL program, services for LD students, advanced placement, accelerated degree program, self-designed majors, honors program, independent study, distance learning, double major, summer session for credit, part-time degree program, adult/continuing education programs, internships, graduate courses open to undergrads. Off campus study at Purchase College, State University of New York, Mills College, American University (Washington Semester), New York State Visiting Student Program. Study abroad program.

Entrance Requirements: Options: electronic application, early admission, early decision, deferred admission, international baccalaureate accepted. Required: essay, high school transcript, minimum 2 high school GPA, 2 recommendations. Recommended: minimum 3 high school GPA, interview. Entrance: moderately difficult. Application deadline: 3/1. Notification: continuous. Transfer credits accepted: Yes.

Costs Per Year: Application fee: $75. Comprehensive fee: $49,710 includes full-time tuition ($34,020), mandatory fees ($1350), and college room and board ($14,340). College room only: $8680. Room and board charges vary according to board plan. Part-time tuition: $790 per credit. Part-time mandatory fees: $60 per term. Part-time tuition and fees vary according to program.

Collegiate Environment: Orientation program. Drama-theater group, choral group, student-run newspaper, radio station. Social organizations: 50 open to all. Most popular organizations: Latin American Student Organization, International Student Organization, Black Student Union, WMVL (radio station), Connie Hogarth Center. Major annual events: Quad Jam, 200 Nights, International Bazaar. Student services: health clinic, personal-psychological counseling, women's center. Campus security: 24-hour emergency response devices and patrols, late night transport-escort service, controlled dormitory access. 1,114 college housing spaces available; all were occupied in 2012-13. Freshmen guaranteed college housing. Option: coed housing available. Manhattanville College Library with 250,209 books, 259,230 microform titles, 36,923 serials, 5,312 audiovisual materials, an OPAC, and a Web page. Operations spending for the previous fiscal year: $1.7 million. 240 computers available on campus for general student use. Computer purchase/lease plans available. A campuswide network can be accessed from student residence rooms and from off campus. Students can access the following: online class registration. Staffed computer lab on campus.

Community Environment: Located approximately 25 miles from New York City, Purchase enjoys the cultural, civic, educational, and recreational facilities of its neighbor. There are railroad connections at nearby White Plains and Rye. Job opportunities are available within the immediate area.

■ MANNES COLLEGE THE NEW SCHOOL FOR MUSIC

150 W 85th St.
New York, NY 10024-4402
Tel: (212)580-0210; Free: 800-292-3040
Fax: (212)580-1738
E-mail: mannesadmissions@newschool.edu
Web Site: www.mannes.edu/

Description: Independent, comprehensive, coed. Part of The New School. Awards bachelor's and master's degrees and post-master's certificates. Founded 1916. Setting: urban campus with easy access to Manhattan. Total enrollment: 381. Faculty: 233 (18 full-time, 215 part-time). Student-undergrad faculty ratio is 4:1. 393 applied, 41% were admitted. Full-time: 38 students, 63% women, 37% men. Part-time: 1 student, 100% women. 64% from out-of-state. 5% Hispanic/Latino; 1% African American, non-Hispanic/Latino; 8% Asian, non-Hispanic/Latino; 44% international. 19% 25 or older, 10% live on campus, 87% transferred in. Retention: 83% of full-time freshmen returned the following year. Academic area with the most degrees conferred: visual and performing arts. Calendar: semesters. Academic remediation for entering students, ESL program, services for LD students, advanced placement, independent study, summer session for credit, internships, graduate courses open to undergrads.

Entrance Requirements: Options: electronic application, international baccalaureate accepted. Required: essay, high school transcript, 1 recommendation, interview, audition, written test. Entrance: very difficult. Application deadline: 12/1. Notification: 4/1.

Costs Per Year: Application fee: $100. Comprehensive fee: $54,820

includes full-time tuition ($36,660), mandatory fees ($860), and college room and board ($17,300). College room only: $13,900. Part-time tuition: $1200 per credit hour.

Collegiate Environment: Orientation program. Drama-theater group, choral group, student-run newspaper, radio station. Student services: health clinic, personal-psychological counseling. Campus security: 24-hour emergency response devices, controlled dormitory access. Freshmen given priority for college housing. Option: coed housing available. Harry Scherman Music Library plus 2 others with an OPAC and a Web page.

■ MARIA COLLEGE

700 New Scotland Ave.
Albany, NY 12208-1798
Tel: (518)438-3111
E-mail: admissions@mariacollege.edu
Web Site: www.mariacollege.edu/

Description: Independent, 4-year, coed. Awards associate and bachelor's degrees. Founded 1958. Setting: 9-acre urban campus. Total enrollment: 905. Faculty: 89 (30 full-time, 59 part-time). Student-undergrad faculty ratio is 12:1. 341 applied, 21% were admitted. Full-time: 242 students, 83% women, 17% men. Part-time: 663 students, 87% women, 13% men. 3% from out-of-state. 0.4% American Indian or Alaska Native, non-Hispanic/Latino; 3% Hispanic/Latino; 16% African American, non-Hispanic/Latino; 3% Asian, non-Hispanic/Latino; 0.2% Native Hawaiian or other Pacific Islander, non-Hispanic/Latino; 0% international. 29% 25 or older. Retention: 54% of full-time freshmen returned the following year. Core. Calendar: semesters. Academic remediation for entering students, services for LD students, advanced placement, independent study, distance learning, summer session for credit, part-time degree program, adult/continuing education programs. Off campus study. ROTC: Air Force (c).

Entrance Requirements: Options: electronic application, early admission. Required: essay, high school transcript, minimum 2 high school GPA, 1 recommendation, interview, SAT or ACT. Entrance: minimally difficult. Application deadline: 8/25. Transfer credits accepted: Yes. Applicants placed on waiting list: 30. Wait-listed applicants offered admission: 10.

Costs Per Year: Application fee: $35. Tuition: $9400 full-time, $390 per credit hour part-time. Mandatory fees: $350 full-time.

Collegiate Environment: Orientation program. Social organizations: Phi Theta Kappa. Student services: personal-psychological counseling. Campus security: late night transport-escort service. College housing not available. Maria College Library with 59,245 books, 160 serials, an OPAC, and a Web page. 78 computers available on campus for general student use. A campuswide network can be accessed. Students can access the following: online class registration. Staffed computer lab on campus provides training in use of computers, software, and the Internet.

Community Environment: See State University of New York at Albany.

■ MARIST COLLEGE

3399 N Rd.
Poughkeepsie, NY 12601-1387
Tel: (845)575-3000; Free: 800-436-5483
Fax: (845)471-6213
E-mail: admission@marist.edu
Web Site: www.marist.edu/

Description: Independent, comprehensive, coed. Administratively affiliated with Istituto Lorenzo de'Medici in Florence Italy. Awards bachelor's and master's degrees. Founded 1929. Setting: 210-acre suburban campus with easy access to Albany, New York City. Endowment: $147.1 million. Research spending for the previous fiscal year: $533,457. Educational spending for the previous fiscal year: $8521 per student. Total enrollment: 6,377. Faculty: 558 (220 full-time, 338 part-time). Student-undergrad faculty ratio is 16:1. 11,466 applied, 31% were admitted. 25% from top 10% of their high school class, 69% from top quarter, 90% from top half. 2 valedictorians. Full-time: 4,768 students, 59% women, 41% men. Part-time: 792 students, 53% women, 47% men. 45% from out-of-state. 0.2% American Indian or Alaska Native, non-Hispanic/Latino; 8% Hispanic/Latino; 4% African American, non-Hispanic/Latino; 2% Asian, non-Hispanic/Latino; 0.2% Native Hawaiian or other Pacific Islander, non-Hispanic/Latino; 1% international. 7% 25 or older, 67% live on campus, 6% transferred in. Retention: 89% of full-time freshmen returned the following year. Academic areas with the most degrees conferred: business/marketing; communication/journalism; psychology. Core. Calendar: semesters. Academic remediation for entering students, ESL program, services for LD students, advanced placement, accelerated degree program, honors program, independent study, distance learning, double major, summer session for credit, part-time degree program, external degree program, adult/continuing education programs, co-op programs and internships, graduate courses open to undergrads. Off campus study at Associated Colleges of the Mid-Hudson Area. Study abroad program. ROTC: Army.

Entrance Requirements: Options: electronic application, early admission, early decision, early action, deferred admission, international baccalaureate accepted. Required: essay, high school transcript, 2 recommendations. Entrance: very difficult. Application deadlines: 2/1, 11/1 for early decision, 11/15 for early action. Notification: 3/30, 12/15 for early decision, 1/30 for early action. SAT Reasoning Test deadline: 2/1. SAT Subject Test deadline: 2/1. Transfer credits accepted: Yes. Applicants placed on waiting list: 5,113. Wait-listed applicants offered admission: 144. Early decision applicants: 245. Early decision applicants admitted: 198. Early action applicants: 5,663. Early action applicants admitted: 2,015.

Costs Per Year: Application fee: $50. One-time mandatory fee: $90. Comprehensive fee: $42,600 includes full-time tuition ($29,500), mandatory fees ($500), and college room and board ($12,600). College room only: $8100. Full-time tuition and fees vary according to course load and location. Room and board charges vary according to board plan, housing facility, and location. Part-time tuition: $634 per credit hour. Part-time mandatory fees: $40 per term. Part-time tuition and fees vary according to course load.

Collegiate Environment: Orientation program. Drama-theater group, choral group, marching band, student-run newspaper, radio station. Social organizations: 81 open to all; national fraternities, local fraternities, local sororities; 1% of eligible men and 1% of eligible women are members. Most popular organizations: Marist Singers, Dance Club, student government, Theater Club, Community Service and Campus Ministry. Major annual events: Giving Tree, St. Jude's Children's Research Hospital Up till Dawn, Relay for Life. Student services: health clinic, personal-psychological counseling. Campus security: 24-hour emergency response devices and patrols, student patrols, late night transport-escort service, controlled dormitory access, night residence hall monitors. College housing designed to accommodate 3,045 students; 3,168 undergraduates lived in college housing during 2012-13. Freshmen guaranteed college housing. Option: coed housing available. James A. Cannavino Library with 275,298 books, 36,320 serials, 3,933 audiovisual materials, an OPAC, and a Web page. Operations spending for the previous fiscal year: $2 million. 804 computers available on campus for general student use. Computer purchase/lease plans available. A campuswide network can be accessed from student residence rooms and from off campus. Students can access the following: online class registration, Admissions, Billing, Transcript, Degree Audit, Financial Aid Application, Financial Aid Award Review, Student Account Summary, Payment, Library Database Search, Campus OneCard Account. Staffed computer lab on campus (open 24 hours a day) provides training in use of computers, software, and the Internet.

Community Environment: See Vassar College.

■ **MARYMOUNT MANHATTAN COLLEGE**
221 E 71st St.
New York, NY 10021-4597
Tel: (212)517-0400; Free: 800-MARYMOUNT
E-mail: admissions@mmm.edu
Web Site: www.mmm.edu/

Description: Independent, 4-year, coed. Awards associate and bachelor's degrees and post-master's certificates. Founded 1936. Setting: 3-acre urban campus. Endowment: $14 million. Educational spending for the previous fiscal year: $8314 per student. Total enrollment: 1,908. Faculty: 293 (103 full-time, 190 part-time). Student-undergrad faculty ratio is 11:1. 4,174 applied, 72% were admitted. Full-time: 1,563 students, 83% women, 17% men. Part-time: 345 students, 90% women, 10% men. 57% from out-of-state. 1% American Indian or Alaska Native, non-Hispanic/Latino; 17% Hispanic/Latino; 10% African American, non-Hispanic/Latino; 5% Asian, non-Hispanic/Latino; 0.2% Native Hawaiian or other Pacific Islander, non-Hispanic/Latino; 3% international. 8% 25 or older, 39% live on campus, 7% transferred in. Retention: 68% of full-time freshmen returned the following year. Academic areas with the most degrees conferred: visual and performing arts; communication/journalism; business/marketing. Core. Calendar: semesters plus summer and January mini-semesters. Academic remediation for entering students, services for LD students, advanced placement, accelerated degree program, honors program, independent study, distance learning, double major, summer session for credit, part-time degree program, adult/continuing education programs, internships. Off campus study at Hunter College of the City University of New York. Study abroad program.

Entrance Requirements: Options: electronic application, deferred admission, international baccalaureate accepted. Required: essay, high school transcript, minimum 2 high school GPA, 2 recommendations, SAT or ACT. Recommended: interview. Required for some: audition for dance and theater programs. Entrance: moderately difficult. Application deadline: Rolling. Notification: continuous.

Costs Per Year: Application fee: $60. Comprehensive fee: $40,118 includes full-time tuition ($24,482), mandatory fees ($1206), and college room and board ($14,430). College room only: $11,930. Part-time tuition: $816 per credit hour.

Collegiate Environment: Orientation program. Drama-theater group, choral group, student-run newspaper, radio station. Social organizations: 38 open to all; local sororities; 2% of women are members. Most popular organizations: Education Club, African-American Heritage Club, Asian-American Heritage Club, Latino Heritage Club, Business Club. Major annual event: Strawberry Festival. Student services: personal-psychological counseling. Campus security: 24-hour emergency response devices and patrols, student patrols, 24-hour security in residence halls. 775 college housing spaces available; 760 were occupied in 2012-13. Freshmen given priority for college housing. Option: coed housing available. Shanahan Library with 111,227 books, 129,792 microform titles, 23,572 serials, 4,454 audiovisual materials, an OPAC, and a Web page. Operations spending for the previous fiscal year: $975,734. 152 computers available on campus for general student use. A campuswide network can be accessed from student residence rooms and from off campus. Students can access the following: online class registration. Staffed computer lab on campus provides training in use of computers, software, and the Internet.

Community Environment: See New York University.

■ **MEDAILLE COLLEGE**
18 Agassiz Cir.
Buffalo, NY 14214-2695
Tel: (716)884-3281; Free: 800-292-1582
Fax: (716)884-0291
E-mail: admissionsug@medaille.edu
Web Site: www.medaille.edu/

Description: Independent, comprehensive, coed. Awards associate, bachelor's, master's, and doctoral degrees and post-master's certificates. Founded 1875. Setting: 13-acre urban campus. Total enrollment: 2,634. Faculty: 281 (81 full-time, 200 part-time). Student-undergrad faculty ratio is 16:1. 1,497 applied, 60% were admitted. Full-time: 1,650 students, 65% women, 35% men. Part-time: 194 students, 78% women, 22% men. Students come from 19 states and territories, 4 other countries, 3% from out-of-state. 1% American Indian or Alaska Native, non-Hispanic/Latino; 5% Hispanic/Latino; 18% African American, non-Hispanic/Latino; 3% Asian, non-Hispanic/Latino; 2% Native Hawaiian or other Pacific Islander, non-Hispanic/Latino; 0.1% international. 27% 25 or older, 23% live on campus, 11% transferred in. Academic areas with the most degrees conferred: business/marketing; health professions and related sciences; parks and recreation; education. Core. Calendar: semesters (modular courses available for evening studies and weekend college program). Academic remediation for entering students, services for LD students, advanced placement, accelerated degree program, self-designed majors, honors program, independent study, double major, summer session for credit, part-time degree program, adult/continuing education programs, internships, graduate courses open to undergrads. Off campus study at 16 members of the Western New York Consortium. ROTC: Army (c).

Entrance Requirements: Options: electronic application, early admission, deferred admission. Required: high school transcript, interview, SAT or ACT. Recommended: essay, minimum 2 high school GPA, 1 recommendation, SAT. Required for some: essay, 2.5 high school GPA for veterinary technology and elementary teacher education majors. Entrance: moderately difficult. Application deadline: 8/1. Notification: continuous.

Costs Per Year: Application fee: $25. Comprehensive fee: $33,438 includes full-time tuition ($22,678) and college room and board ($10,760). Full-time tuition varies according to location. Room and board charges vary according to housing facility. Part-time tuition: $799 per credit hour. Part-time tuition varies according to course load.

Collegiate Environment: Orientation program. Drama-theater group, student-run newspaper, radio station. Social organizations: 27 open to all. Most popular organizations: student government, Club Green, Dance Team, WMCB The Lizard (college radio station), ice hockey club. Major annual events: Holiday Party, Reindeer Run, Music Feast. Student services: health clinic, personal-psychological counseling. Campus security: 24-hour emergency response devices and patrols, late night transport-escort service, controlled dormitory access. 526 college housing spaces available; 370 were occupied in 2012-13. No special consideration for freshman housing applicants. Options: coed, men-only, women-only housing available. Medaille College Library with 50,497 books, 183 serials, 1,319 audiovisual materials, an OPAC, and a Web page. 120 computers available on campus for general student use. A campuswide network can be accessed from student residence rooms and from off campus. Students can access the following: online class registration. Staffed computer lab on campus provides training in use of computers, software, and the Internet.

Community Environment: See Canisius College.

■ **MEDGAR EVERS COLLEGE OF THE CITY UNIVERSITY OF NEW YORK**
1650 Bedford St.
Brooklyn, NY 11225-2298
Tel: (718)270-4900
E-mail: jaugustin@mec.cuny.edu
Web Site: www.mec.cuny.edu/

Description: State and locally supported, 4-year, coed. Part of City University of New York System. Awards associate and bachelor's degrees. Founded 1969. Setting: 8-acre urban campus. Endowment: $515,142. Research spending for the previous fiscal year: $1.8 million. Educational spending for the previous fiscal year: $18,121 per student. Total enrollment: 6,540. Faculty: 536 (165 full-time, 371 part-time). Student-undergrad faculty ratio is 18:1. 8,474 applied, 100% were admitted. Full-time: 4,154 students, 72% women, 28% men. Part-time: 2,386 students, 76% women, 24% men. Students come from 7 states and territories, 77 other countries, 1% from out-of-state. 0.03% American Indian or Alaska Native, non-Hispanic/Latino; 9% Hispanic/Latino; 85% African American, non-Hispanic/Latino; 1% Asian, non-Hispanic/Latino; 0% Native Hawaiian or other Pacific Islander, non-Hispanic/Latino; 0.4% international. 45% 25 or older, 9% transferred in. Retention: 66% of full-time freshmen returned the following year. Academic areas with the most degrees conferred: business/marketing; biological/life sciences; psychology; public administration and social services. Core. Calendar: semesters. Academic remediation for entering students, ESL program, services for LD students, advanced placement, honors program, independent study, double major, summer session for credit, part-time degree program, external degree program, adult/continuing education programs, co-op programs and internships. Off campus study at other units of the City University of New York System. Study abroad program.

Entrance Requirements: Open admission except for nursing program. Options: electronic application, deferred admission. Required: high school transcript. Recommended: SAT and SAT Subject Tests or ACT. Entrance: noncompetitive. Application deadline: Rolling. Notification: continuous. Preference given to city residents.

Costs Per Year: Application fee: $65. State resident tuition: $5800 full-time. Nonresident tuition: $20,770 full-time. Full-time tuition varies according to course load.

Collegiate Environment: Drama-theater group, choral group, student-run newspaper, radio station. Social organizations: 32 open to all. Most popular organizations: American Marketing Association, Drama Students Association, Rising Stars, Medgar Evers College Society of Public Administrators, National Society of Black Accountants. Major annual events: Presidential Lecture Series, Black Solidarity Day, Club Fair. Student services: legal services, women's center. Campus security: 24-hour patrols. College housing not available. Charles Evans Inniss Memorial Library plus 1 other with 120,000 books, 42,225 microform titles, 24,410 serials, an OPAC, and a Web page. 120 computers available on campus for general student use. Computer purchase/lease plans available. A campuswide network can be accessed from off-campus. Students can access the following: online class registration. Staffed computer lab on campus provides training in use of computers, software, and the Internet.

■ **MEMORIAL HOSPITAL SCHOOL OF NURSING**
600 Northern Blvd.
Albany, NY 12204
Tel: (518)471-3260
Fax: (518)447-3559
Web Site: www.nehealth.com/son/

Description: Independent, 2-year, coed. Awards terminal associate degrees. Total enrollment: 113. Calendar: semesters.

Entrance Requirements: Recommended: high school transcript.

■ **MERCY COLLEGE**
555 Broadway
Dobbs Ferry, NY 10522-1189
Tel: (914)693-4500; Free: 800-MERCY-NY
Fax: (914)674-7382
E-mail: admissions@mercy.edu
Web Site: www.mercy.edu/

Description: Independent, comprehensive, coed. Awards bachelor's, master's, and doctoral degrees and post-master's certificates. Founded 1951. Setting: 45-acre suburban campus with easy access to New York City. Research spending for the previous fiscal year: $1. Total enrollment: 11,454. Faculty: 893 (188 full-time, 705 part-time). Student-undergrad faculty ratio is 18:1. 5,766 applied, 65% were admitted. Full-time: 5,505 students, 68% women, 32% men. Part-time: 2,524 students, 67% women, 33% men. Students come from 19 states and territories, 43 other countries, 7% from out-of-state. 0.3% American Indian or Alaska Native, non-Hispanic/Latino; 30% Hispanic/Latino; 25% African American, non-Hispanic/Latino; 3% Asian, non-Hispanic/Latino; 0.2% Native Hawaiian or other Pacific Islander, non-Hispanic/Latino; 1% international. 35% 25 or older, 8% live on campus, 14% transferred in. Retention: 69% of full-time freshmen returned the following year. Academic areas with the most degrees conferred: social sciences; health professions and related sciences; business/marketing. Core. Calendar: semesters. Academic remediation for entering students, services for LD students, advanced placement, accelerated degree program, honors program, independent study, distance learning, double major, summer session for credit, part-time degree program, adult/continuing education programs, co-op programs and internships, graduate courses open to undergrads. Off campus study at Westchester Conservatory of Music, New York Medical College. Study abroad program. ROTC: Army (c), Air Force (c).

Entrance Requirements: Options: electronic application, deferred admission, international baccalaureate accepted. Required: high school transcript, minimum 2.5 high school GPA. Recommended: SAT, ACT, SAT or ACT, SAT and SAT Subject Tests or ACT, SAT Subject Tests. Required for some: essay, interview. Entrance: moderately difficult. Application deadlines: Rolling, Rolling for nonresidents. Notification: continuous, continuous for nonresidents. Transfer credits accepted: Yes.

Costs Per Year: Application fee: $40. Comprehensive fee: $29,740 includes full-time tuition ($16,996), mandatory fees ($560), and college room and board ($12,184). College room only: $8734. Full-time tuition and fees vary according to course load. Room and board charges vary according to board plan and housing facility. Part-time tuition: $715 per credit. Part-time mandatory fees: $140 per term. Part-time tuition and fees vary according to course load.

Collegiate Environment: Orientation program. Student-run newspaper. Social organizations: 20 open to all. Most popular organizations: PACT, Honors, Mercy Gives Back, Model United Nations. Major annual events: New York Blood Center Blood Drive, Holiday Food and Clothing Drives, Grad Salutes. Student services: health clinic, personal-psychological counseling. Campus security: 24-hour emergency response devices and patrols, late night transport-escort service, controlled dormitory access. 713 college housing spaces available; all were occupied in 2012-13. Freshmen given priority for college housing. Option: coed housing available. Mercy College Library with 249,571 books, 126,178 microform titles, 736 serials, 7,421 audiovisual materials, an OPAC, and a Web page. 186 computers available on campus for general student use. Computer purchase/lease plans available. A campuswide network can be accessed from student residence rooms and from off campus. Students can access the following: online class registration. Staffed computer lab on campus provides training in use of computers, software, and the Internet.

Community Environment: Population 11,070. Primarily a residential community, Dobbs Ferry is located on the banks of the Hudson River and is 15 miles from New York City.

■ **MESIVTA OF EASTERN PARKWAY–YESHIVA ZICHRON MEILECH**
510 Dahill Rd.
Brooklyn, NY 11218-5559
Tel: (718)438-1002

Description: Independent Jewish, comprehensive, men only. Awards bachelor's and master's degrees. Founded 1947. Setting: 1-acre campus. Total enrollment: 40. 19 applied, 100% were admitted. Core. Calendar: semesters. Academic remediation for entering students, honors program, graduate courses open to undergrads.

Entrance Requirements: Required: high school transcript, 1 recommendation, interview, Orthodox Jewish commitment. Entrance: moderately difficult. Application deadline: Rolling.

Collegiate Environment: 7,500 books and 15 serials.

■ MESIVTA TIFERETH JERUSALEM OF AMERICA

145 E Broadway
New York, NY 10002-6301
Tel: (212)964-2830
Description: Independent Jewish, comprehensive, men only. Awards bachelor's and master's degrees. Founded 1907. Total enrollment: 72. 15 applied, 100% were admitted. Calendar: semesters.

■ MESIVTA TORAH VODAATH RABBINICAL SEMINARY

425 E Ninth St.
Brooklyn, NY 11218-5299
Tel: (718)941-8000
Fax: (718)941-8032
Web Site: www.torahvodaath.org/
Description: Independent Jewish, comprehensive, men only. Awards bachelor's and master's degrees. Founded 1918. Total enrollment: 354. 66 applied. 35% 25 or older. Core. Calendar: semesters. Summer session for credit, part-time degree program. Study abroad program.
Entrance Requirements: Options: early admission, deferred admission. Required: high school transcript, 2 recommendations. Entrance: moderately difficult. Application deadline: Rolling. Notification: continuous. Preference given to Orthodox Jews.
Collegiate Environment: Student services: personal-psychological counseling. 40,000 books and 12 serials.

■ METROPOLITAN COLLEGE OF NEW YORK

431 Canal St.
New York, NY 10013
Tel: (212)343-1234; Free: 800-33-THINK
Fax: (212)343-8470
Web Site: www.metropolitan.edu/
Description: Independent, comprehensive, coed. Awards associate, bachelor's, and master's degrees. Founded 1964. Setting: urban campus. Endowment: $9 million. Educational spending for the previous fiscal year: $25,983 per student. Total enrollment: 1,084. Faculty: 183 (26 full-time, 157 part-time). Student-undergrad faculty ratio is 11:1. 653 applied, 51% were admitted. Students come from 2 states and territories, 2% from out-of-state. 76% 25 or older. Retention: 54% of full-time freshmen returned the following year. Academic areas with the most degrees conferred: liberal arts/general studies; business/marketing. Core. Calendar: 3 15-week semesters. Academic remediation for entering students, ESL program, services for LD students, accelerated degree program, honors program, independent study, distance learning, summer session for credit, part-time degree program, adult/continuing education programs, co-op programs and internships. Study abroad program.
Entrance Requirements: Options: electronic application, deferred admission, international baccalaureate accepted. Required: essay, high school transcript, 2 recommendations, interview. Recommended: minimum 3 high school GPA, SAT or ACT. Required for some: ACCUPLACER. Entrance: moderately difficult. Application deadline: 8/15. Notification: 8/31.
Collegiate Environment: Orientation program. Student-run newspaper. Social organizations: 10 open to all. Most popular organizations: student government, student newsletter, Networking Club, yearbook committee. Major annual events: Graduation Ceremony, New Student Orientation. Student services: personal-psychological counseling. Campus security: 24-hour patrols. Main Library with 39,217 books, 110 audiovisual materials, an OPAC, and a Web page. Operations spending for the previous fiscal year: $789,823. 150 computers available on campus for general student use. A campuswide network can be accessed from off-campus. Staffed computer lab on campus provides training in use of computers and software.

■ MILDRED ELLEY SCHOOL

855 Central Ave.
Albany, NY 12206
Tel: (518)786-0855; Free: 800-622-6327
Fax: (518)786-0898
Web Site: www.mildred-elley.edu/
Description: Proprietary, 2-year, coed. Awards certificates, diplomas, transfer associate, and terminal associate degrees. Founded 1917. Setting: suburban campus. Total enrollment: 396. 130 applied. 65% 25 or older.
Entrance Requirements: Required: CPAt.
Collegiate Environment: Student services: legal services.

■ MILDRED ELLEY–NEW YORK CITY

25 Broadway, 16th Fl.
New York, NY 10004-1010
Tel: (212)380-9004
Web Site: www.mildred-elley.edu/
Description: Proprietary, 2-year, coed.

■ MIRRER YESHIVA

1795 Ocean Pky.
Brooklyn, NY 11223-2010
Tel: (718)645-0536
Description: Independent Jewish, comprehensive, men only. Awards bachelor's and master's degrees. Founded 1926. Total enrollment: 307. 66 applied, 100% were admitted. 4% 25 or older. Calendar: semesters.

■ MOHAWK VALLEY COMMUNITY COLLEGE

1101 Sherman Dr.
Utica, NY 13501-5394
Tel: (315)792-5400; Free: 800-SEE-MVCC
Fax: (315)792-5527
E-mail: sfiebiger@mvcc.edu
Web Site: www.mvcc.edu/
Description: State and locally supported, 2-year, coed. Part of State University of New York System. Awards certificates, transfer associate, and terminal associate degrees. Founded 1946. Setting: 80-acre suburban campus. Endowment: $3.8 million. Educational spending for the previous fiscal year: $4140 per student. Total enrollment: 7,445. Faculty: 488 (136 full-time, 352 part-time). Student-undergrad faculty ratio is 23:1. 4,760 applied, 76% were admitted. 3% from top 10% of their high school class, 12% from top quarter, 41% from top half. 1 valedictorian. Full-time: 4,601 students, 52% women, 48% men. Part-time: 2,844 students, 60% women, 40% men. Students come from 13 states and territories, 19 other countries. 1% American Indian or Alaska Native, non-Hispanic/Latino; 7% Hispanic/Latino; 8% African American, non-Hispanic/Latino; 3% Asian, non-Hispanic/Latino; 0.1% Native Hawaiian or other Pacific Islander, non-Hispanic/Latino; 1% international. 34% 25 or older, 7% live on campus, 5% transferred in. Core. Calendar: semesters. Academic remediation for entering students, ESL program, services for LD students, advanced placement, self-designed majors, honors program, independent study, distance learning, double major, summer session for credit, part-time degree program, internships. Off campus study at Mohawk Valley College Consortium. ROTC: Army (c), Air Force (c).
Entrance Requirements: Open admission. Options: electronic application, deferred admission, international baccalaureate accepted. Recommended: interview. Required for some: high school transcript. Entrance: noncompetitive. Application deadlines: Rolling, Rolling for nonresidents. Notification: continuous, continuous for nonresidents. Transfer credits accepted: Yes.
Costs Per Year: Application fee: $0. State resident tuition: $3580 full-time, $130 per credit hour part-time. Nonresident tuition: $7160 full-time, $260 per credit hour part-time. Mandatory fees: $550 full-time, $7 per credit hour part-time, $40 per term part-time. College room and board: $9150. College room only: $5500. Room and board charges vary according to board plan.
Collegiate Environment: Orientation program. Drama-theater group, student-run newspaper. Social organizations: 40 open to all. Most popular organizations: Student Congress, Student Nurses Organization (SNO), Photography Club, Recreation Club, Phi Theta Kappa. Student services: health clinic, personal-psychological counseling. Campus security: 24-hour emergency response devices and patrols, late night transport-escort service, controlled dormitory access. 506 college housing spaces available; 499 were occupied in 2012-13. Freshmen given priority for college housing. Options: coed, men-only, women-only housing available. Mohawk Valley Community College Library plus 1 other with 127,254 books, 3,265 microform titles, 32,838 serials, 9,039 audiovisual materials, an OPAC, and a Web page. Operations spending for the previous fiscal year: $930,091. 145 computers available on campus for general student use. A campuswide network can be accessed from student residence rooms and from off campus. Students can access the following: online class registration. Staffed computer lab on campus provides training in use of computers, software, and the Internet.

■ MOLLOY COLLEGE

1000 Hempstead Ave.
Rockville Centre, NY 11571-5002
Tel: (516)678-5000; Free: 888-4MOLLOY
E-mail: admissions@molloy.edu

Web Site: www.molloy.edu/

Description: Independent, comprehensive, coed. Awards associate, bachelor's, master's, and doctoral degrees and post-master's certificates. Founded 1955. Setting: 30-acre suburban campus with easy access to New York City. Endowment: $28 million. Educational spending for the previous fiscal year: $13,049 per student. Total enrollment: 4,482. Faculty: 674 (179 full-time, 495 part-time). Student-undergrad faculty ratio is 10:1. 2,304 applied, 74% were admitted. 34% from top 10% of their high school class, 57% from top quarter, 89% from top half. Full-time: 2,642 students, 74% women, 26% men. Part-time: 802 students, 81% women, 19% men. Students come from 13 states and territories, 6 other countries, 1% from out-of-state. 0.2% American Indian or Alaska Native, non-Hispanic/Latino; 14% Hispanic/Latino; 13% African American, non-Hispanic/Latino; 7% Asian, non-Hispanic/Latino; 1% Native Hawaiian or other Pacific Islander, non-Hispanic/Latino; 0.1% international. 28% 25 or older, 5% live on campus, 11% transferred in. Retention: 88% of full-time freshmen returned the following year. Academic areas with the most degrees conferred: public administration and social services; health professions and related sciences; education. Core. Calendar: 4-1-4. Academic remediation for entering students, ESL program, services for LD students, advanced placement, self-designed majors, honors program, independent study, double major, summer session for credit, part-time degree program, adult/continuing education programs, internships. Study abroad program. ROTC: Army (c), Naval (c).

Entrance Requirements: Options: electronic application, early admission, early action, deferred admission, international baccalaureate accepted. Required: SAT or ACT. Recommended: interview. Required for some: essay, high school transcript, 1 recommendation. Entrance: moderately difficult. Application deadline: Rolling. Notification: continuous. SAT Reasoning Test deadline: 8/30. Transfer credits accepted: Yes. Early action applicants: 956. Early action applicants admitted: 378.

Costs Per Year: Application fee: $30. Comprehensive fee: $36,500 includes full-time tuition ($23,410), mandatory fees ($1010), and college room and board ($12,080). College room only: $9090. Full-time tuition and fees vary according to degree level. Room and board charges vary according to board plan. Part-time tuition: $770 per credit hour. Part-time tuition varies according to degree level.

Collegiate Environment: Orientation program. Drama-theater group, choral group, student-run newspaper. Social organizations: 46 open to all; 11% of eligible men and 17% of eligible women are members. Most popular organizations: Men's Rugby, Women's Rugby, Molloy Student Government, Molloy Nursing Student Association, Student Media. Major annual events: Halloween Party, Scavenger Hunt, Gala. Student services: legal services, health clinic, personal-psychological counseling, women's center. Campus security: 24-hour emergency response devices and patrols, late night transport-escort service. 158 college housing spaces available; all were occupied in 2012-13. Freshmen given priority for college housing. Option: coed housing available. James Edward Tobin Library plus 1 other with 190,629 books, 70 microform titles, 108,090 serials, 3,680 audiovisual materials, an OPAC, and a Web page. Operations spending for the previous fiscal year: $2.7 million. 457 computers available on campus for general student use. A campuswide network can be accessed from student residence rooms and from off campus. Students can access the following: online class registration. Staffed computer lab on campus provides training in use of computers.

Community Environment: Rockville Centre, population 24,200, is a suburb of New York City on Long Island. Good transportation facilities make all the cultural, recreational, civic services, and employment opportunities of New York easily accessible. Within the immediate area there are a public library, churches of major denominations, and a hospital. Some part-time work is available in the local area.

■ MONROE COLLEGE (BRONX)

Monroe College Way
Bronx, NY 10468-5407
Tel: (718)933-6700; Free: 800-55MONROE
Web Site: www.monroecollege.edu/

Description: Proprietary, comprehensive, coed. Awards associate, bachelor's, and master's degrees. Founded 1933. Setting: urban campus. Total enrollment: 5,068. Faculty: 251 (61 full-time, 190 part-time). Student-undergrad faculty ratio is 32:1. 1,426 applied, 61% were admitted. Full-time: 3,471 students, 72% women, 28% men. Part-time: 1,334 students, 76% women, 24% men. Students come from 8 states and territories, 14 other countries, 1% from out-of-state. 56% 25 or older, 1% live on campus, 13% transferred in. Retention: 70% of full-time freshmen returned the following year. Academic areas with the most degrees conferred: business/marketing;

health professions and related sciences; homeland security, law enforcement, firefighting, and protective services. Core. Calendar: trimesters. Academic remediation for entering students, ESL program, distance learning, summer session for credit, part-time degree program, adult/continuing education programs, co-op programs and internships.

Entrance Requirements: Options: electronic application, early admission, early decision, early action, deferred admission. Required: essay, high school transcript, interview. Recommended: SAT or ACT. Required for some: 2 recommendations. Entrance: moderately difficult. Application deadline: 8/26. Notification: continuous until 9/3.

Collegiate Environment: Orientation program. Drama-theater group, choral group, student-run newspaper. Social organizations: 18 open to all. Most popular organizations: Students in Free Enterprise (SIFE), Creative Campus Club, Multicultural Student Association, Criminal Justice Club, Poetry is Truth. Major annual events: Homecoming, Athletics Playoffs, Spirit Day. Student services: personal-psychological counseling. Campus security: late night transport-escort service. Main library plus 1 other with 28,000 books, 301 serials, an OPAC, and a Web page. 541 computers available on campus for general student use. A campuswide network can be accessed from student residence rooms and from off campus. Students can access the following: online class registration. Staffed computer lab on campus (open 24 hours a day) provides training in use of computers, software, and the Internet.

■ MONROE COLLEGE (NEW ROCHELLE)

434 Main St.
New Rochelle, NY 10801
Tel: (914)632-5400; Free: 800-55MONROE
Fax: (914)632-5462
E-mail: lscorca@monroecollege.edu
Web Site: www.monroecollege.edu/

Description: Proprietary, comprehensive, coed. Awards associate, bachelor's, and master's degrees. Founded 1983. Setting: suburban campus with easy access to New York City. Total enrollment: 2,222. Faculty: 93 (24 full-time, 69 part-time). Student-undergrad faculty ratio is 38:1. 1,186 applied, 60% were admitted. Students come from 9 states and territories, 16 other countries, 2% from out-of-state. 31% 25 or older, 20% live on campus. Retention: 72% of full-time freshmen returned the following year. Academic areas with the most degrees conferred: business/marketing; computer and information sciences; homeland security, law enforcement, firefighting, and protective services. Core. Calendar: trimesters. Academic remediation for entering students, ESL program, distance learning, summer session for credit, part-time degree program, external degree program, adult/continuing education programs, co-op programs and internships.

Entrance Requirements: Options: electronic application, early admission, deferred admission. Required: high school transcript, interview. Entrance: moderately difficult. Application deadline: 8/26. Notification: 9/3.

Collegiate Environment: Drama-theater group, student-run newspaper. Social organizations: 5 open to all. Student services: personal-psychological counseling. Campus security: late night transport-escort service. Main library plus 1 other with 8,400 books and 211 serials. 370 computers available on campus for general student use. A campuswide network can be accessed from student residence rooms. Students can access the following: online class registration. Staffed computer lab on campus.

■ MONROE COMMUNITY COLLEGE

1000 E Henrietta Rd.
Rochester, NY 14623-5780
Tel: (585)292-2000
Fax: (585)427-2749
E-mail: admissions@monroecc.edu
Web Site: www.monroecc.edu/

Description: State and locally supported, 2-year, coed. Part of State University of New York System. Awards certificates, transfer associate, and terminal associate degrees. Founded 1961. Setting: 314-acre suburban campus with easy access to Buffalo. Total enrollment: 17,296. Faculty: 895 (323 full-time, 572 part-time). Student-undergrad faculty ratio is 25:1. Full-time: 10,554 students, 51% women, 49% men. Part-time: 6,742 students, 58% women, 42% men. 0.3% American Indian or Alaska Native, non-Hispanic/Latino; 8% Hispanic/Latino; 19% African American, non-Hispanic/Latino; 3% Asian, non-Hispanic/Latino; 0.1% Native Hawaiian or other Pacific Islander, non-Hispanic/Latino; 1% international. 41% 25 or older. Retention: 61% of full-time freshmen returned the following year. Calendar: semesters. Academic remediation for entering students, ESL program, services for LD students, advanced placement, accelerated degree program, honors program, summer session for credit, part-time degree program, adult/continuing education programs, co-op programs and internships. Off campus study at the Rochester Area Colleges. ROTC: Army (c), Air Force (c).

Entrance Requirements: Open admission except for allied health, business, computer science, engineering science programs. Options: electronic application, early admission. Required: high school transcript. Entrance: noncompetitive. Application deadline: Rolling. Notification: continuous. Preference given to county residents. Transfer credits accepted: Yes.

Costs Per Year: Application fee: $20. State resident tuition: $3140 full-time, $131 per credit hour part-time. Nonresident tuition: $6280 full-time, $262 per credit hour part-time. Mandatory fees: $13 full-time, $18 per year part-time. Full-time tuition and fees vary according to program. Part-time tuition and fees vary according to course load and program. College room and board: $5800. Room and board charges vary according to housing facility.

Collegiate Environment: Orientation program. Drama-theater group, choral group, student-run newspaper, radio station. Social organizations: 52 open to all. Most popular organizations: student newspaper, Phi Theta Kappa, student government. Student services: health clinic, personal-psychological counseling. Campus security: 24-hour emergency response devices, late night transport-escort service. LeRoy V. Good Library plus 1 other with 110,748 books, 12,975 microform titles, 745 serials, 4,100 audiovisual materials, and an OPAC. 150 computers available on campus for general student use. A campuswide network can be accessed from off-campus. Students can access the following: online class registration. Staffed computer lab on campus.

■ **MORRISVILLE STATE COLLEGE**

PO Box 901
Morrisville, NY 13408-0901
Tel: (315)684-6000; Free: 800-258-0111
Fax: (315)684-6116
E-mail: admissions@morrisville.edu
Web Site: www.morrisville.edu/

Description: State-supported, 4-year, coed. Part of State University of New York System. Awards associate and bachelor's degrees. Founded 1908. Setting: 185-acre rural campus with easy access to Syracuse. Total enrollment: 3,095. Faculty: 252 (143 full-time, 109 part-time). Student-undergrad faculty ratio is 17:1. 4,251 applied, 64% were admitted. 0% from top 10% of their high school class, 0% from top quarter, 0% from top half. Full-time: 2,708 students, 48% women, 52% men. Part-time: 387 students, 48% women, 52% men. Students come from 18 states and territories, 8 other countries, 5% from out-of-state. 1% American Indian or Alaska Native, non-Hispanic/Latino; 0.5% Hispanic/Latino; 21% African American, non-Hispanic/Latino; 1% Asian, non-Hispanic/Latino; 0.1% Native Hawaiian or other Pacific Islander, non-Hispanic/Latino; 0% international. 17% 25 or older, 66% live on campus, 8% transferred in. Retention: 57% of full-time freshmen returned the following year. Academic areas with the most degrees conferred: agriculture; computer and information sciences; business/marketing. Core. Calendar: semesters. Academic remediation for entering students, services for LD students, advanced placement, self-designed majors, independent study, distance learning, double major, summer session for credit, part-time degree program, co-op programs and internships. Off campus study at other units of the State University of New York System. ROTC: Army (c), Air Force (c).

Entrance Requirements: Options: electronic application, deferred admission. Required: essay, high school transcript, 1 recommendation. Recommended: minimum 2 high school GPA, interview. Required for some: SAT, ACT, SAT or ACT. Entrance: moderately difficult. Application deadlines: Rolling, Rolling for nonresidents. Notification: continuous, continuous for nonresidents. Transfer credits accepted: Yes.

Costs Per Year: Application fee: $50. State resident tuition: $5570 full-time, $232 per credit hour part-time. Nonresident tuition: $9740 full-time, $406 per credit hour part-time. Mandatory fees: $2222 full-time, $175.05 per credit hour part-time. Full-time tuition and fees vary according to degree level. Part-time tuition and fees vary according to course load and degree level. College room and board: $10,720. College room only: $6160. Room and board charges vary according to board plan and housing facility.

Collegiate Environment: Orientation program. Drama-theater group, choral group, student-run newspaper, radio station. Social organizations: 60 open to all; local fraternities, local sororities; 15% of eligible men and 15% of eligible women are members. Most popular organizations: African Student Union Black Alliance, Student Government Organization, Agriculture Club, Latino-American Student Association, WCVM (student radio station). Major

annual events: Mustang Weekend College/Community Picnic, Parents' Weekend, College/Community Picnic. Student services: legal services, health clinic, personal-psychological counseling. Campus security: 24-hour emergency response devices and patrols, student patrols, late night transport-escort service, controlled dormitory access. 2,800 college housing spaces available; 1,900 were occupied in 2012-13. Freshmen guaranteed college housing. On-campus residence required through sophomore year. Option: coed housing available. Morrisville State Library (Butcher Library) plus 1 other with 120,098 books, 6,755 microform titles, 98,344 serials, 3,801 audiovisual materials, an OPAC, and a Web page. 150 computers available on campus for general student use. Computer purchase/lease plans available. A campuswide network can be accessed from student residence rooms and from off campus. Students can access the following: online class registration. Staffed computer lab on campus provides training in use of computers, software, and the Internet.

■ **MOUNT SAINT MARY COLLEGE**

330 Powell Ave.
Newburgh, NY 12550-3494
Tel: (845)561-0800; Free: 888-937-6762
Fax: (845)562-6762
E-mail: admissions@msmc.edu
Web Site: www.msmc.edu/

Description: Independent, comprehensive, coed. Awards bachelor's and master's degrees and post-master's certificates. Founded 1960. Setting: 86-acre suburban campus with easy access to New York City. Endowment: $4.8 million. Educational spending for the previous fiscal year: $7003 per student. Total enrollment: 2,581. Faculty: 279 (88 full-time, 191 part-time). Student-undergrad faculty ratio is 14:1. 3,472 applied, 81% were admitted. 8% from top 10% of their high school class, 30% from top quarter, 69% from top half. Full-time: 1,863 students, 70% women, 30% men. Part-time: 423 students, 77% women, 23% men. Students come from 13 states and territories, 11% from out-of-state. 1% American Indian or Alaska Native, non-Hispanic/Latino; 11% Hispanic/Latino; 6% African American, non-Hispanic/Latino; 3% Asian, non-Hispanic/Latino; 0.2% Native Hawaiian or other Pacific Islander, non-Hispanic/Latino; 0.1% international. 21% 25 or older, 44% live on campus, 8% transferred in. Retention: 70% of full-time freshmen returned the following year. Academic areas with the most degrees conferred: health professions and related sciences; business/marketing; history. Core. Calendar: semesters. Academic remediation for entering students, services for LD students, advanced placement, accelerated degree program, self-designed majors, freshman honors college, honors program, independent study, distance learning, double major, summer session for credit, part-time degree program, adult/continuing education programs, co-op programs and internships, graduate courses open to undergrads. Off campus study at Associated Colleges of the Mid-Hudson Area. Study abroad program. ROTC: Army (c).

Entrance Requirements: Options: electronic application, early admission, deferred admission. Required: essay, high school transcript, SAT or ACT. Recommended: minimum 3 high school GPA, 2 recommendations. Required for some: 2 recommendations, interview. Entrance: moderately difficult. Application deadline: 8/15. Notification: continuous. SAT Reasoning Test deadline: 8/1. SAT Subject Test deadline: 8/1. Transfer credits accepted: Yes.

Costs Per Year: Application fee: $45. Comprehensive fee: $39,540 includes full-time tuition ($25,300), mandatory fees ($950), and college room and board ($13,290). College room only: $7698. Full-time tuition and fees vary according to class time, location, and program. Room and board charges vary according to board plan and housing facility. Part-time tuition: $843 per credit hour. Part-time tuition varies according to class time, location, and program.

Collegiate Environment: Orientation program. Drama-theater group, choral group, student-run newspaper, radio station. Social organizations: 33 open to all. Most popular organizations: Student Government Association, Different Stages, Big Brothers/Big Sisters, Dance Team and Cheerleading, Habitat for Humanity. Major annual events: Siblings' Week, Parents' Weekend, Spring Weekend. Student services: health clinic, personal-psychological counseling. Campus security: 24-hour emergency response devices and patrols, student patrols, late night transport-escort service, controlled dormitory access, monitored surveillance cameras in all residence halls. 1,083 college housing spaces available; 998 were occupied in 2012-13. Freshmen given priority for college housing. On-campus residence required through junior year. Options: coed, men-only, women-only housing available. Curtin Memorial Library plus 1 other with 80,568 books, 69,503 serials, 6,950 audiovisual materials, an OPAC, and a Web page. Operations spending for the previous fiscal year: $948,628. 576 computers available on campus for general student use. Computer purchase/lease plans available. A campuswide network can be accessed from student residence rooms and from off campus. Students can access the following: online class registration, Intranet. Staffed computer lab on campus provides training in use of computers, software, and the Internet.

Community Environment: Mount Saint Mary College is located in the historic Hudson Valley Region, at the foothills of the Catskill Mountains, 60 miles north of New York City. Cultural, historical, and outdoor activities abound.

■ **NASSAU COMMUNITY COLLEGE**

1 Education Dr.

Garden City, NY 11530-6793

Tel: (516)572-7500

E-mail: admissions@sunynassau.edu

Web Site: www.ncc.edu/

Description: State and locally supported, 2-year, coed. Part of State University of New York System. Awards certificates, transfer associate, and terminal associate degrees. Founded 1959. Setting: 225-acre suburban campus with easy access to New York City. Total enrollment: 23,079. Faculty: 1,474 (479 full-time, 995 part-time). Student-undergrad faculty ratio is 22:1. Full-time: 14,306 students, 48% women, 52% men. Part-time: 8,684 students, 53% women, 47% men. Students come from 19 states and territories, 69 other countries, 0.3% from out-of-state. 0.3% American Indian or Alaska Native, non-Hispanic/Latino; 20% Hispanic/Latino; 22% African American, non-Hispanic/Latino; 6% Asian, non-Hispanic/Latino; 0.4% Native Hawaiian or other Pacific Islander, non-Hispanic/Latino; 1% international. 23% 25 or older, 6% transferred in. Retention: 32% of full-time freshmen returned the following year. Calendar: semesters. Academic remediation for entering students, ESL program, services for LD students, advanced placement, honors program, distance learning, summer session for credit, part-time degree program, adult/continuing education programs, co-op programs and internships. Off campus study at members of the Long Island Regional Advisory Council for Higher Education.

Entrance Requirements: Open admission for liberal arts students and some non-competitive programs. Options: electronic application, deferred admission, international baccalaureate accepted. Required: high school transcript. Recommended: minimum 2 high school GPA, SAT or ACT. Required for some: minimum 3 high school GPA, interview. Entrance: noncompetitive. Application deadline: 8/7. Notification: continuous.

Costs Per Year: Application fee: $40. Area resident tuition: $3990 full-time. State resident tuition: $7980 full-time. Mandatory fees: $340 full-time.

Collegiate Environment: Orientation program. Drama-theater group, choral group, student-run newspaper, radio station. Social organizations: 110 open to all. Most popular organizations: Muslim Student Association, Make a Difference Club, Interact Club, Political Science Club, Investment Club. Major annual events: Spring Festival, Multicultural Fair, Student Government Association Pep Rally. Student services: personal-psychological counseling, women's center. Campus security: 24-hour emergency response devices and patrols, late night transport-escort service. College housing not available. A. Holly Patterson Library with 186,782 books, 11,314 microform titles, 401 serials, 18,903 audiovisual materials, an OPAC, and a Web page. 1,250 computers available on campus for general student use. A campuswide network can be accessed from off-campus. Students can access the following: online class registration. Staffed computer lab on campus provides training in use of computers, software, and the Internet.

■ **NAZARETH COLLEGE OF ROCHESTER**

4245 E Ave.

Rochester, NY 14618-3790

Tel: (585)389-2525; Free: 800-462-3944

Fax: (585)389-2826

E-mail: admissions@naz.edu

Web Site: www.naz.edu/

Description: Independent, comprehensive, coed. Awards bachelor's, master's, and doctoral degrees and post-master's certificates. Founded 1924. Setting: 150-acre suburban campus. Endowment: $53.9 million. Educational spending for the previous fiscal year: $10,775 per student. Total enrollment: 2,910. Faculty: 461 (175 full-time, 286 part-time). Student-undergrad faculty ratio is 10:1. 3,109 applied, 71% were admitted. 25% from top 10% of their high school class, 58% from top quarter, 82% from top half. 1 valedictorian. Full-time: 2,321 students, 77% women, 23% men. Part-time:

135 students, 76% women, 24% men. Students come from 28 states and territories, 21 other countries, 7% from out-of-state. 1% American Indian or Alaska Native, non-Hispanic/Latino; 4% Hispanic/Latino; 5% African American, non-Hispanic/Latino; 2% Asian, non-Hispanic/Latino; 0% Native Hawaiian or other Pacific Islander, non-Hispanic/Latino; 2% international. 6% 25 or older, 56% live on campus, 6% transferred in. Retention: 82% of full-time freshmen returned the following year. Academic areas with the most degrees conferred: health professions and related sciences; education; business/marketing. Core. Calendar: semesters. Academic remediation for entering students, ESL program, services for LD students, advanced placement, honors program, independent study, double major, summer session for credit, part-time degree program, adult/continuing education programs, co-op programs and internships. Off campus study. Study abroad program. ROTC: Army (c), Air Force (c).

Entrance Requirements: Options: electronic application, early admission, early decision, early action, deferred admission, international baccalaureate accepted. Required: essay, high school transcript, 1 recommendation. Recommended: interview. Required for some: audition/portfolio review. Entrance: moderately difficult. Application deadlines: 2/15, 11/1 for early decision, 12/1 for early action. Notification: continuous until 3/1, 12/1 for early decision, 1/15 for early action. SAT Reasoning Test deadline: 2/1. SAT Subject Test deadline: 2/1. Transfer credits accepted: Yes. Applicants placed on waiting list: 139. Wait-listed applicants offered admission: 6. Early decision applicants: 83. Early decision applicants admitted: 73. Early action applicants: 1,193. Early action applicants admitted: 974.

Costs Per Year: Application fee: $45. Comprehensive fee: $38,366 includes full-time tuition ($26,048), mandatory fees ($1174), and college room and board ($11,144). Full-time tuition and fees vary according to course load and program. Room and board charges vary according to board plan and housing facility. Part-time tuition: $621 per credit hour. Part-time mandatory fees: $25 per term.

Collegiate Environment: Orientation program. Drama-theater group, choral group, student-run newspaper, radio station. Social organizations: 50 open to all. Most popular organizations: Student Activities Council, intramurals and recreation, Theater League, Center for Spirituality Council, NAZ Ultimate Frisbee. Major annual events: Spring Fest, Siblings' Weekend, Parents' Weekend. Student services: health clinic, personal-psychological counseling, women's center. Campus security: 24-hour emergency response devices and patrols, student patrols, late night transport-escort service, controlled dormitory access, alarm system, security beeper, lighted pathways. 1,224 college housing spaces available; 1,100 were occupied in 2012-13. Freshmen guaranteed college housing. On-campus residence required through sophomore year. Option: coed housing available. Lorette Wilmot Library with 283,248 books, 16,102 serials, an OPAC, and a Web page. Operations spending for the previous fiscal year: $1.9 million. 240 computers available on campus for general student use. A campuswide network can be accessed from student residence rooms and from off campus. Students can access the following: online class registration. Staffed computer lab on campus (open 24 hours a day) provides training in use of computers, software, and the Internet.

Community Environment: See University of Rochester.

■ **THE NEW SCHOOL FOR JAZZ AND CONTEMPORARY MUSIC**

55 W 13th St., 5th Fl.

New York, NY 10011

Tel: (212)229-5896; Free: 800-292-3040

E-mail: jazzadm@newschool.edu

Web Site: www.jazz.newschool.edu/

Description: Independent, 4-year, coed. Part of The New School. Awards bachelor's degrees. Founded 1986. Setting: urban campus with easy access to Manhattan. Total enrollment: 269. Faculty: 59 (3 full-time, 56 part-time). Student-undergrad faculty ratio is 11:1. 416 applied, 73% were admitted. Full-time: 257 students, 19% women, 81% men. Part-time: 12 students, 100% men. 51% from out-of-state. 0% American Indian or Alaska Native, non-Hispanic/Latino; 7% Hispanic/Latino; 9% African American, non-Hispanic/Latino; 3% Asian, non-Hispanic/Latino; 0% Native Hawaiian or other Pacific Islander, non-Hispanic/Latino; 33% international. 20% 25 or older, 27% live on campus, 14% transferred in. Retention: 80% of full-time freshmen returned the following year. Academic area with the most degrees conferred: visual and performing arts. Core. Calendar: semesters. Academic remediation for entering students, ESL program, services for LD students, advanced placement, independent study, double major, internships.

Entrance Requirements: Options: electronic application, deferred admission, international baccalaureate accepted. Required: essay, high school

transcript, 1 recommendation, audition, pre-screen tape/CD. Entrance: very difficult. Application deadline: 1/1. Notification: continuous. Transfer credits accepted: Yes.

Costs Per Year: Application fee: $100. Comprehensive fee: $55,526 includes full-time tuition ($37,950), mandatory fees ($276), and college room and board ($17,300). Part-time tuition: $1245 per credit.

Collegiate Environment: Orientation program. Drama-theater group, choral group, student-run newspaper, radio station. Student services: health clinic, personal-psychological counseling. Campus security: 24-hour emergency response devices, controlled dormitory access. Freshmen given priority for college housing. Option: coed housing available. Harry Scherman Music Library and Raymond Fogelman Library plus 1 other with an OPAC and a Web page.

■ THE NEW SCHOOL FOR PUBLIC ENGAGEMENT

66 W 12th St.
New York, NY 10011-8603
Tel: (212)229-5600; Free: 800-292-3040
Fax: (212)645-0661
E-mail: nsadmissions@newschool.edu
Web Site: www.newschool.edu/public-engagement/

Description: Independent, comprehensive, coed. Part of The New School. Awards bachelor's and master's degrees. Founded 1919. Setting: urban campus with easy access to Manhattan. Total enrollment: 1,634. Faculty: 385 (64 full-time, 321 part-time). 11 applied, 91% were admitted. Full-time: 275 students, 61% women, 39% men. Part-time: 319 students, 61% women, 39% men. Students come from 91 other countries, 36% from out-of-state. 0.3% American Indian or Alaska Native, non-Hispanic/Latino; 12% Hispanic/Latino; 10% African American, non-Hispanic/Latino; 4% Asian, non-Hispanic/Latino; 0.2% Native Hawaiian or other Pacific Islander, non-Hispanic/Latino; 8% international. 20% transferred in. Retention: 67% of full-time freshmen returned the following year. Academic areas with the most degrees conferred: liberal arts/general studies; visual and performing arts. Calendar: semesters. ESL program, services for LD students, advanced placement, self-designed majors, independent study, distance learning, summer session for credit, part-time degree program, adult/continuing education programs, internships, graduate courses open to undergrads. Study abroad program.

Entrance Requirements: Options: electronic application, deferred admission. Required: essay, resume and college transcripts. Required for some: high school transcript, interview. Entrance: moderately difficult. Transfer credits accepted: Yes.

Collegiate Environment: Orientation program. Drama-theater group, choral group, student-run newspaper, radio station. Student services: health clinic, personal-psychological counseling. Campus security: 24-hour emergency response devices, controlled dormitory access, trained security personnel in central buildings. Option: coed housing available. Raymond Fogelman Library plus 2 others with an OPAC and a Web page.

■ NEW YORK CAREER INSTITUTE

11 Park Place- 4th Fl.
New York, NY 10007
Tel: (212)962-0002
Fax: (212)385-7574
E-mail: lstieglitz@nyci.edu
Web Site: www.nyci.com/

Description: Proprietary, 2-year, coed. Awards certificates and terminal associate degrees. Founded 1942. Setting: urban campus. Total enrollment: 702. Faculty: 42 (9 full-time, 33 part-time). 1% American Indian or Alaska Native, non-Hispanic/Latino; 17% Hispanic/Latino; 25% African American, non-Hispanic/Latino; 2% Asian, non-Hispanic/Latino; 0% Native Hawaiian or other Pacific Islander, non-Hispanic/Latino. Calendar: trimesters (semesters for evening division). Academic remediation for entering students, advanced placement, summer session for credit, part-time degree program, internships.

Entrance Requirements: Required: high school transcript, interview. Entrance: noncompetitive. Application deadline: 9/7. Notification: continuous. Transfer credits accepted: Yes.

Costs Per Year: Application fee: $50. Tuition: $12,750 full-time, $400 per credit hour part-time. Mandatory fees: $150 full-time, $50 per term part-time. Full-time tuition and fees vary according to class time. Part-time tuition and fees vary according to class time.

Collegiate Environment: Orientation program. College housing not available. 5,010 books and 23 serials 50 computers available on campus for general student use. Students can access the following: online class registration.

■ NEW YORK CITY COLLEGE OF TECHNOLOGY OF THE CITY UNIVERSITY OF NEW YORK

300 Jay St.
Brooklyn, NY 11201-2983
Tel: (718)260-5000
Fax: (718)260-5198
E-mail: achaconis@citytech.cuny.edu
Web Site: www.citytech.cuny.edu/

Description: State and locally supported, 4-year, coed. Part of City University of New York System. Awards associate and bachelor's degrees. Founded 1946. Setting: urban campus. Total enrollment: 16,207. Faculty: 1,350 (433 full-time, 917 part-time). Student-undergrad faculty ratio is 16:1. 16,870 applied, 77% were admitted. Full-time: 10,018 students, 41% women, 59% men. Part-time: 6,189 students, 52% women, 48% men. Students come from 14 states and territories, 138 other countries. 0.4% American Indian or Alaska Native, non-Hispanic/Latino; 29% Hispanic/Latino; 34% African American, non-Hispanic/Latino; 17% Asian, non-Hispanic/Latino; 0.4% Native Hawaiian or other Pacific Islander, non-Hispanic/Latino; 5% international. 31% 25 or older, 8% transferred in. Retention: 77% of full-time freshmen returned the following year. Academic areas with the most degrees conferred: business/marketing; visual and performing arts; health professions and related sciences. Core. Calendar: semesters. Academic remediation for entering students, ESL program, services for LD students, advanced placement, accelerated degree program, self-designed majors, freshman honors college, honors program, independent study, distance learning, summer session for credit, part-time degree program, adult/continuing education programs, internships. Off campus study. Study abroad program.

Entrance Requirements: Open admission except for upper-level bachelor's degree programs. Options: electronic application, deferred admission, international baccalaureate accepted. Required: high school transcript. Required for some: SAT or ACT. Entrance: noncompetitive. Application deadline: 2/1. Notification: continuous until 2/1. SAT Reasoning Test deadline: 8/1. Transfer credits accepted: Yes.

Costs Per Year: Application fee: $65. State resident tuition: $5430 full-time, $230 per credit part-time. Nonresident tuition: $14,550 full-time, $485 per credit part-time. Mandatory fees: $339 full-time, $85.20 per term part-time.

Collegiate Environment: Orientation program. Drama-theater group, choral group, student-run newspaper. Social organizations: 60 open to all. Most popular organizations: International Business Organization (IBO), NYCCT - Mock Trial Club, Chess Club, Women in Islam, ASCE-Student Chapter of American Society of Civil Engineering. Major annual events: Club Fair, Welcome Back Bash/Event, Applefest (fall) and Strawberryfest (spring). Student services: health clinic, personal-psychological counseling, women's center. Campus security: 24-hour emergency response devices and patrols. College housing not available. Ursula C. Schwerin Library with 355,770 books, 14,007 microform titles, 107,900 serials, 88,527 audiovisual materials, an OPAC, and a Web page. 340 computers available on campus for general student use. A campuswide network can be accessed from off-campus. Students can access the following: online class registration. Staffed computer lab on campus provides training in use of computers, software, and the Internet.

■ NEW YORK COLLEGE OF HEALTH PROFESSIONS

6801 Jericho Tpke.
Syosset, NY 11791-4413
Tel: (516)364-0808; Free: 800-922-7337
Fax: (516)364-0989
E-mail: rdodas@nycollege.edu
Web Site: www.nycollege.edu/

Description: Independent, comprehensive, coed. Awards associate, incidental bachelor's, and master's degrees. Founded 1981. Setting: suburban campus with easy access to New York City. Total enrollment: 879. Faculty: 93 (17 full-time, 76 part-time). Student-undergrad faculty ratio is 19:1. Full-time: 332 students, 77% women, 23% men. Part-time: 469 students, 75% women, 25% men. Academic area with the most degrees conferred: health professions and related sciences. Core. Calendar: trimesters. Academic remediation for entering students, services for LD students, advanced placement, accelerated degree program, double major, summer session for credit, part-time degree program, adult/continuing education programs, co-op programs and internships, graduate courses open to undergrads.

Entrance Requirements: Options: electronic application, deferred admis-

sion. Required: essay, high school transcript, minimum 2.0 high school GPA, interview. Entrance: moderately difficult. Application deadline: Rolling. Notification: continuous.

Collegiate Environment: Orientation program. Student services: health clinic. Campus security: 24-hour emergency response devices and patrols, security guard evening and weekend hours. James and Lenore Jacobson Library at the Syosset Campus with 5,500 books, 40 serials, 200 audiovisual materials, an OPAC, and a Web page. 3 computers available on campus for general student use. Staffed computer lab on campus.

■ **NEW YORK INSTITUTE OF TECHNOLOGY**

PO Box 8000

Old Westbury, NY 11568-8000

Tel: (516)686-7516; Free: 800-345-NYIT

Fax: (516)686-7613

E-mail: admissions@nyit.edu

Web Site: www.nyit.edu/

Description: Independent, university, coed. Awards associate, bachelor's, master's, and doctoral degrees and post-master's certificates. Founded 1955. Setting: 1,050-acre suburban campus with easy access to New York City. Endowment: $54.8 million. Research spending for the previous fiscal year: $8.8 million. Total enrollment: 7,883. Faculty: 1,248 (283 full-time, 965 part-time). Student-undergrad faculty ratio is 11:1. 6,546 applied, 66% were admitted. 12% from top 10% of their high school class, 39% from top quarter, 67% from top half. Full-time: 4,017 students, 38% women, 62% men. Part-time: 779 students, 43% women, 57% men. Students come from 32 states and territories, 86 other countries, 11% from out-of-state. 0.3% American Indian or Alaska Native, non-Hispanic/Latino; 12% Hispanic/Latino; 8% African American, non-Hispanic/Latino; 14% Asian, non-Hispanic/Latino; 0.1% Native Hawaiian or other Pacific Islander, non-Hispanic/Latino; 12% international. 18% 25 or older, 15% live on campus, 10% transferred in. Retention: 70% of full-time freshmen returned the following year. Academic areas with the most degrees conferred: business/marketing; architecture; biological/life sciences. Core. Calendar: semesters. Academic remediation for entering students, ESL program, services for LD students, advanced placement, accelerated degree program, self-designed majors, honors program, independent study, distance learning, double major, summer session for credit, part-time degree program, external degree program, adult/continuing education programs, co-op programs and internships, graduate courses open to undergrads. Off campus study at New York State Teachers' Centers. Study abroad program. ROTC: Army, Air Force.

Entrance Requirements: Options: electronic application, early admission, early decision, deferred admission, international baccalaureate accepted. Required: essay, high school transcript, 2 recommendations, SAT or ACT. Recommended: minimum 3 high school GPA. Required for some: interview, Occupational Therapy and Physical Therapy requires 100 volunteer hours. Entrance: moderately difficult. Application deadlines: Rolling, Rolling for nonresidents. Notification: continuous, continuous for nonresidents. SAT Reasoning Test deadline: 7/1. Transfer credits accepted: Yes. Early decision applicants: 1,603. Early decision applicants admitted: 1,017.

Costs Per Year: Application fee: $50. Comprehensive fee: $40,590 includes full-time tuition ($28,020), mandatory fees ($920), and college room and board ($11,650). College room only: $7320. Full-time tuition and fees vary according to course load and program. Room and board charges vary according to board plan, housing facility, and location. Part-time tuition: $950 per credit hour. Part-time mandatory fees: $400 per term. Part-time tuition and fees vary according to course load.

Collegiate Environment: Orientation program. Drama-theater group, choral group, student-run newspaper, radio station. Social organizations: 145 open to all; national fraternities, national sororities, local fraternities, local sororities; 3% of eligible men and 4% of eligible women are members. Student services: health clinic, personal-psychological counseling, women's center. Campus security: 24-hour emergency response devices and patrols, late night transport-escort service, controlled dormitory access. 671 college housing spaces available. Freshmen guaranteed college housing. Option: coed housing available. George and Gertrude Wisser Memorial Library plus 4 others with 135,630 books, 699,846 microform titles, 2,308 serials, 242 audiovisual materials, an OPAC, and a Web page. Operations spending for the previous fiscal year: $4.4 million. 1,386 computers available on campus for general student use. A campuswide network can be accessed from student residence rooms and from off campus. Students can access the following: e-mail. Staffed computer lab on campus.

■ **NEW YORK SCHOOL OF INTERIOR DESIGN**

170 E 70th St.

New York, NY 10021-5110

Tel: (212)472-1500; Free: 800-336-9743

Fax: (212)472-1867

E-mail: admissions@nysid.edu

Web Site: www.nysid.edu/

Description: Independent, comprehensive, coed. Awards associate, bachelor's, and master's degrees. Founded 1916. Setting: 1-acre urban campus. Endowment: $3.1 million. Total enrollment: 710. Faculty: 109 (8 full-time, 101 part-time). Student-undergrad faculty ratio is 6:1. 156 applied, 38% were admitted. 0% from top 10% of their high school class, 9% from top quarter, 55% from top half. Full-time: 166 students, 84% women, 16% men. Part-time: 390 students, 89% women, 11% men. Students come from 24 states and territories, 28 other countries, 33% from out-of-state. 0% American Indian or Alaska Native, non-Hispanic/Latino; 8% Hispanic/Latino; 3% African American, non-Hispanic/Latino; 7% Asian, non-Hispanic/Latino; 0% Native Hawaiian or other Pacific Islander, non-Hispanic/Latino; 16% international. 59% 25 or older, 1% live on campus, 8% transferred in. Retention: 75% of full-time freshmen returned the following year. Core. Calendar: semesters. ESL program, services for LD students, advanced placement, independent study, summer session for credit, part-time degree program, external degree program, adult/continuing education programs, internships.

Entrance Requirements: Options: electronic application, deferred admission, international baccalaureate accepted. Required: essay, high school transcript, minimum 2.8 high school GPA, 2 recommendations, portfolio. Required for some: SAT or ACT. Entrance: moderately difficult. Application deadline: 2/1. Notification: 4/1. Transfer credits accepted: Yes.

Costs Per Year: Application fee: $60. Tuition: $27,324 full-time, $828 per credit part-time. Mandatory fees: $570 full-time, $570 per term part-time. Full-time tuition and fees vary according to course load. Part-time tuition and fees vary according to course load. College room only: $14,400.

Collegiate Environment: Orientation program. Social organizations: 3 open to all. Most popular organizations: American Society of Interior Designers, Contract Club, Student Council. Major annual events: lecture series, ASID student auction, gallery exhibition openings. Campus security: security during school hours. 30 college housing spaces available; 18 were occupied in 2012-13. No special consideration for freshman housing applicants. Option: coed housing available. 135 computers available on campus for general student use. A campuswide network can be accessed from student residence rooms and from off campus. Students can access the following: online class registration. Staffed computer lab on campus provides training in use of computers and software.

■ **NEW YORK UNIVERSITY**

70 Washington Sq. S

New York, NY 10012-1019

Tel: (212)998-1212

Fax: (212)995-4902

E-mail: admissions@nyu.edu

Web Site: www.nyu.edu/

Description: Independent, university, coed. Awards associate, bachelor's, master's, and doctoral degrees and post-master's certificates. Founded 1831. Setting: urban campus. Endowment: $2.8 billion. Research spending for the previous fiscal year: $644 million. Educational spending for the previous fiscal year: $38,609 per student. Total enrollment: 44,516. Faculty: 6,574 (2,525 full-time, 4,049 part-time). Student-undergrad faculty ratio is 10:1. 42,807 applied, 35% were admitted. Full-time: 21,247 students, 60% women, 40% men. Part-time: 1,251 students, 59% women, 41% men. Students come from 52 states and territories, 94 other countries, 65% from out-of-state. 0.3% American Indian or Alaska Native, non-Hispanic/Latino; 10% Hispanic/Latino; 5% African American, non-Hispanic/Latino; 19% Asian, non-Hispanic/Latino; 0.05% Native Hawaiian or other Pacific Islander, non-Hispanic/Latino; 12% international. 6% 25 or older, 50% live on campus, 3% transferred in. Retention: 92% of full-time freshmen returned the following year. Academic areas with the most degrees conferred: visual and performing arts; social sciences; business/marketing. Core. Calendar: semesters. Services for LD students, advanced placement, accelerated degree program, self-designed majors, honors program, independent study, double major, summer session for credit, part-time degree program, adult/continuing education programs, internships, graduate courses open to undergrads. Off campus study at Spelman College, Morehouse College, Xavier University of New Orleans. Study abroad program. ROTC: Army (c), Air Force (c).

Entrance Requirements: Options: electronic application, early decision, deferred admission, international baccalaureate accepted. Required: essay, high school transcript, 1 recommendation, SAT and SAT Subject Tests or ACT, Three SAT subject tests or three Advanced Placement Exam scores. These scores must be submitted in the form of: one in literature or the humanities; one in math or science; and one test of the student's choice in any subject. Required for some: audition or a portfolio for some specific programs. Entrance: most difficult. Application deadlines: 1/1, 1/1 for nonresidents, 11/1 for early decision plan 1, 1/1 for early decision plan 2. Notification: 4/1, 4/1 for nonresidents, 12/15 for early decision plan 1, 2/15 for early decision plan 2. SAT Reasoning Test deadline: 1/1. SAT Subject Test deadline: 1/1. Transfer credits accepted: Yes. Early decision applicants: 5,778. Early decision applicants admitted: 1,890.

Costs Per Year: Application fee: $70. Comprehensive fee: $59,337 includes full-time tuition ($40,878), mandatory fees ($2326), and college room and board ($16,133). Full-time tuition and fees vary according to course load and program. Room and board charges vary according to board plan and housing facility. Part-time tuition: $1204 per credit. Part-time mandatory fees: $63 per credit, $434 per term. Part-time tuition and fees vary according to program.

Collegiate Environment: Orientation program. Drama-theater group, choral group, student-run newspaper, radio station. Social organizations: 454 open to all; national fraternities, national sororities, local sororities; 5% of eligible men and 4% of eligible women are members. Most popular organizations: Inter-Varsity Christian Fellowship, Asian Cultural Union, Hillel, Latinos Unidos Con Honor y Amistad (LUCHA), South Asian Student Association (SHRUTI). Major annual events: Career Services Fair, Strawberry Festival, Community Service Week. Student services: health clinic, personal-psychological counseling, women's center. Campus security: 24-hour emergency response devices and patrols, student patrols, late night transport-escort service, controlled dormitory access, 24-hour security in residence halls. Freshmen guaranteed college housing. Option: coed housing available. Elmer H. Bobst Library plus 12 others with an OPAC and a Web page. Operations spending for the previous fiscal year: $69.1 million. 4,500 computers available on campus for general student use. A campuswide network can be accessed from student residence rooms and from off campus. Students can access the following: online class registration. Staffed computer lab on campus provides training in use of computers, software, and the Internet.

Community Environment: New York City, the largest city in the nation, is also its business, entertainment, and artistic capital. This teeming city is considered the greatest center of higher education in the country, and claims the largest library outside the Library of Congress. Its intellectual and cultural opportunities are limitless and virtually impossible to duplicate elsewhere. Broadway, one of the great theatre districts of the world, Lincoln Center for the Performing Arts, more than 60 museums, and many historic sites dating from the pre-Revolutionary period are among New York's cultural attractions. More than one-sixth of the city is park land, offering facilities for many sports and activities in beautifully planned areas such as Central Park and Riverside Park. The financial district, with famous Wall Street, houses the complex mechanism of banking and security markets. A vast system of subways, roadways and buses span the areas of New York's 5 boroughs, connecting richly diverse communities and people from virtually all walks of life. Points of interest on Manhattan island include: the United Nations complex, Rockefeller Center, the"tremendous city within a city," and skyscrapers like the renowned Empire State Building. New York City, with a population of over 8 million and limitless activity, provides a unique campus.

■ NIAGARA COUNTY COMMUNITY COLLEGE

3111 Saunders Settlement Rd.
Sanborn, NY 14132-9460
Tel: (716)614-6222
Fax: (716)731-4053
E-mail: admissions@niagaracc.suny.edu
Web Site: www.niagaracc.suny.edu/
Description: State and locally supported, 2-year, coed. Part of State University of New York System. Awards certificates, transfer associate, and terminal associate degrees. Founded 1962. Setting: 287-acre rural campus with easy access to Buffalo. Endowment: $3.7 million. Educational spending for the previous fiscal year: $5532 per student. Total enrollment: 6,743. Faculty: 382 (111 full-time, 271 part-time). Student-undergrad faculty ratio is 17:1. 2,455 applied, 100% were admitted. 6% from top 10% of their high school class, 26% from top quarter, 63% from top half. Full-time: 4,202 students, 55% women, 45% men. Part-time: 2,541 students, 60% women, 40% men. Students come from 11 states and territories, 5 other countries,

1% from out-of-state. 2% American Indian or Alaska Native, non-Hispanic/Latino; 2% Hispanic/Latino; 9% African American, non-Hispanic/Latino; 1% Asian, non-Hispanic/Latino; 0.4% international. 27% 25 or older, 4% live on campus, 4% transferred in. Calendar: semesters. Academic remediation for entering students, services for LD students, advanced placement, self-designed majors, honors program, independent study, distance learning, double major, summer session for credit, part-time degree program, adult/continuing education programs, co-op programs and internships. Off campus study at 17 members of the Western New York Consortium. Study abroad program. ROTC: Army (c).
Entrance Requirements: Open admission. Options: electronic application, early admission. Required: high school transcript. Required for some: minimum 2 high school GPA. Entrance: noncompetitive. Notification: continuous until 8/31.
Costs Per Year: Application fee: $0. State resident tuition: $3696 full-time, $154 per credit hour part-time. Nonresident tuition: $9240 full-time, $385 per credit hour part-time. Mandatory fees: $344 full-time, $169 per term part-time. Full-time tuition and fees vary according to course load and program. Part-time tuition and fees vary according to course load and program. College room and board: $10,860. College room only: $8360. Room and board charges vary according to housing facility.
Collegiate Environment: Orientation program. Drama-theater group, choral group, student-run newspaper, radio station. Social organizations: 40 open to all. Most popular organizations: student radio station, Student Nurses Association, Phi Theta Kappa, Alpha Beta Gamma, Physical Education Club. Major annual events: All College Picnics, Orientation, Theatrical/musical events. Student services: health clinic, personal-psychological counseling. Campus security: 24-hour emergency response devices and patrols, student patrols, late night transport-escort service. Option: coed housing available. Henrietta G. Lewis Library with 99,210 books, 135,059 microform titles, 345 serials, 7,861 audiovisual materials, an OPAC, and a Web page. Operations spending for the previous fiscal year: $1 million. 414 computers available on campus for general student use. A campuswide network can be accessed. Students can access the following: online class registration. Staffed computer lab on campus provides training in use of computers and software.

■ NIAGARA UNIVERSITY

Niagara University, NY 14109
Tel: (716)285-1212; Free: 800-462-2111
Fax: (716)286-8355
E-mail: admissions@niagara.edu
Web Site: www.niagara.edu/
Description: Independent, comprehensive, coed, affiliated with Roman Catholic Church. Awards associate, bachelor's, master's, and doctoral degrees and post-master's certificates. Founded 1856. Setting: 160-acre suburban campus with easy access to Buffalo, Toronto. Endowment: $72.2 million. Educational spending for the previous fiscal year: $7293 per student. Total enrollment: 4,045. Faculty: 333 (157 full-time, 176 part-time). Student-undergrad faculty ratio is 11:1. 3,703 applied, 69% were admitted. 13% from top 10% of their high school class, 41% from top quarter, 78% from top half. Full-time: 2,810 students, 59% women, 41% men. Part-time: 365 students, 70% women, 30% men. Students come from 31 states and territories, 12 other countries, 8% from out-of-state. 1% American Indian or Alaska Native, non-Hispanic/Latino; 3% Hispanic/Latino; 5% African American, non-Hispanic/Latino; 1% Asian, non-Hispanic/Latino; 0.03% Native Hawaiian or other Pacific Islander, non-Hispanic/Latino; 16% international. 13% 25 or older, 51% live on campus, 6% transferred in. Retention: 81% of full-time freshmen returned the following year. Academic areas with the most degrees conferred: business/marketing; education; homeland security, law enforcement, firefighting, and protective services; social sciences. Core. Calendar: semesters. Academic remediation for entering students, ESL program, services for LD students, advanced placement, accelerated degree program, freshman honors college, honors program, independent study, double major, summer session for credit, part-time degree program, co-op programs and internships, graduate courses open to undergrads. Off campus study at members of the New York State Visiting Student Program, the Western New York Consortium. Study abroad program. ROTC: Army.
Entrance Requirements: Options: electronic application, early admission, deferred admission. Required: high school transcript, SAT or ACT. Recommended: minimum 3 high school GPA, 3 recommendations, interview. Entrance: moderately difficult. Application deadline: 8/1. Transfer credits accepted: Yes.
Costs Per Year: Application fee: $30. Comprehensive fee: $38,530 includes full-time tuition ($26,100), mandatory fees ($1130), and college room and board ($11,300). Part-time tuition: $870 per credit hour.

Collegiate Environment: Orientation program. Drama-theater group, choral group, student-run newspaper, radio station. Social organizations: 70 open to all; national fraternities. Most popular organizations: Niagara University Community Action Program, student government, Programming Board. Major annual events: Family Weekend, Fall Weekend, Spring Weekend. Student services: health clinic, personal-psychological counseling. Campus security: 24-hour emergency response devices and patrols, late night transport-escort service, controlled dormitory access, 24-hour escort service. 1,535 college housing spaces available; 1,348 were occupied in 2012-13. Freshmen guaranteed college housing. On-campus residence required through sophomore year. Option: coed housing available. Our Lady of Angels plus 1 other with 198,622 books, 6,436 microform titles, 22,000 serials, and an OPAC. Operations spending for the previous fiscal year: $1.5 million. 175 computers available on campus for general student use. A campuswide network can be accessed from student residence rooms. Students can access the following: online class registration. Staffed computer lab on campus (open 24 hours a day) provides training in use of computers, software, and the Internet.

■ **NORTH COUNTRY COMMUNITY COLLEGE**
23 Santanoni Ave.
Saranac Lake, NY 12983-0089
Tel: (518)891-2915; Free: 888-TRY-NCCC
Fax: (518)891-2915
E-mail: info@nccc.edu
Web Site: www.nccc.edu/
Description: State and locally supported, 2-year, coed. Part of State University of New York System. Awards certificates, transfer associate, and terminal associate degrees. Founded 1967. Setting: 100-acre rural campus. Total enrollment: 1,751. Faculty: 151 (46 full-time, 105 part-time). Student-undergrad faculty ratio is 15:1. 8% from top 10% of their high school class, 25% from top quarter, 64% from top half. Full-time: 956 students, 64% women, 36% men. Part-time: 795 students, 59% women, 41% men. 31% 25 or older, 7% live on campus. Core. Calendar: semesters. Academic remediation for entering students, services for LD students, advanced placement, self-designed majors, distance learning, double major, summer session for credit, part-time degree program, internships.
Entrance Requirements: Open admission except for radiologic technology, nursing, massage therapy programs. Options: electronic application, early admission, early decision, deferred admission. Required: high school transcript. Recommended: essay, interview, SAT or ACT. Entrance: minimally difficult. Application deadline: Rolling. Notification: continuous. Preference given to residents of sponsoring counties.
Collegiate Environment: Drama-theater group, student-run newspaper. Most popular organizations: Student Government Association, Wilderness Recreation Club, Nursing Club, Radiology Club, Criminal Justice Club. Major annual events: Winter Carnival, Winter Fest, May Fest. Student services: personal-psychological counseling. Campus security: controlled dormitory access. North Country Community College Library plus 1 other with 58,556 books, 12,475 microform titles, 177 serials, and a Web page. 140 computers available on campus for general student use. A campuswide network can be accessed. Students can access the following: online class registration. Staffed computer lab on campus (open 24 hours a day).

■ **NYACK COLLEGE**
One S Blvd.
Nyack, NY 10960-3698
Tel: (845)358-1710; Free: 800-33-NYACK
Fax: (845)358-3047
E-mail: admissions@nyack.edu
Web Site: www.nyack.edu/
Description: Independent, comprehensive, coed, affiliated with The Christian and Missionary Alliance. Awards associate, bachelor's, master's, and doctoral degrees. Founded 1882. Setting: 125-acre suburban campus with easy access to New York City. Total enrollment: 3,318. Faculty: 315 (115 full-time, 200 part-time). Student-undergrad faculty ratio is 13:1. 638 applied, 93% were admitted. 10% from top 10% of their high school class, 24% from top quarter, 50% from top half. Full-time: 1,693 students, 60% women, 40% men. Part-time: 347 students, 65% women, 35% men. Students come from 36 states and territories, 44 other countries, 31% from out-of-state. 0.3% American Indian or Alaska Native, non-Hispanic/Latino; 25% Hispanic/Latino; 33% African American, non-Hispanic/Latino; 10% Asian, non-Hispanic/Latino; 0.4% Native Hawaiian or other Pacific Islander, non-Hispanic/Latino; 5% international. 29% 25 or older, 70% live on campus,

11% transferred in. Retention: 66% of full-time freshmen returned the following year. Academic areas with the most degrees conferred: business/marketing; theology and religious vocations; interdisciplinary studies. Core. Calendar: semesters. Academic remediation for entering students, ESL program, services for LD students, advanced placement, accelerated degree program, honors program, independent study, distance learning, double major, summer session for credit, part-time degree program, adult/continuing education programs, internships, graduate courses open to undergrads. Off campus study at Council for Christian Colleges and Universities. Study abroad program.
Entrance Requirements: Options: electronic application, deferred admission, international baccalaureate accepted. Required: essay, high school transcript, minimum 2 high school GPA, 1 recommendation, Signed statement of faith and community life form. Required for some: interview, SAT or ACT. Entrance: minimally difficult. Application deadlines: Rolling, Rolling for nonresidents. Notification: continuous, continuous for nonresidents. SAT Reasoning Test deadline: 8/30. Transfer credits accepted: Yes.
Costs Per Year: Application fee: $25. One-time mandatory fee: $100. Comprehensive fee: $31,900 includes full-time tuition ($23,000), mandatory fees ($250), and college room and board ($8650). Room and board charges vary according to board plan and housing facility. Part-time tuition: $960 per credit hour. Part-time mandatory fees: $75 per term.
Collegiate Environment: Orientation program. Drama-theater group, choral group, student-run newspaper, radio station. Social organizations: 50 open to all. Student services: health clinic, personal-psychological counseling. Campus security: 24-hour emergency response devices and patrols, late night transport-escort service. 754 college housing spaces available; 691 were occupied in 2012-13. Freshmen guaranteed college housing. On-campus residence required through sophomore year. Options: men-only, women-only housing available. Bailey Library plus 3 others with 169,062 books, 34,744 microform titles, 428 serials, 7,876 audiovisual materials, an OPAC, and a Web page. 130 computers available on campus for general student use. A campuswide network can be accessed from student residence rooms and from off campus. Students can access the following: online class registration. Staffed computer lab on campus provides training in use of computers, software, and the Internet.
Community Environment: Suburban village setting about 20 miles from New York City, Nyack is on the west bank of the Hudson River where it widens out to lake proportions. Early Dutch settlers called it the Tappan Zee. It has a local hospital, library, YMCA, and churches of all major denominations. The area has motels, hotels and shopping centers. Recreational facilities include bowling alleys, swimming pools, tennis, field sports, boating, lakes, ice skating, hunting, and fishing. There is ample part-time employment available for students.

■ **OHR HAMEIR THEOLOGICAL SEMINARY**
141 Furnace Woods Rd.
Cortlandt Manor, NY 10567
Tel: (914)736-1500
Description: Independent Jewish, comprehensive, men only. Awards bachelor's and master's degrees. Founded 1962. Total enrollment: 86. 4 applied, 100% were admitted. Calendar: semesters.

■ **OHR SOMAYACH/JOSEPH TANENBAUM EDUCATIONAL CENTER**
PO Box 334, 244 Rte. 306
Monsey, NY 10952-0334
Tel: (845)425-1370
E-mail: ohr@os.edu
Web Site: ohr.edu/
Description: Independent Jewish, comprehensive, men only. Awards bachelor's and doctoral degrees. Founded 1979. Setting: 7-acre small town campus with easy access to New York City. Research spending for the previous fiscal year: $23,000. Total enrollment: 77. Faculty: 16 (8 full-time, 8 part-time). 100 applied, 65% were admitted. Full-time: 65 students. Students come from 10 states and territories, 6 other countries, 39% from out-of-state. 75% 25 or older, 6% transferred in. Core. Calendar: semesters. Academic remediation for entering students, services for LD students, honors program, summer session for credit, part-time degree program, adult/continuing education programs, internships.
Entrance Requirements: Option: early admission. Required: interview. Recommended: high school transcript. Required for some: essay. Entrance: moderately difficult. Application deadline: Rolling.
Collegiate Environment: Student services: personal-psychological counseling. Campus security: 24-hour emergency response devices and patrols, controlled dormitory access. Finer Library with 2,300 books.

■ OLEAN BUSINESS INSTITUTE
301 N Union St.
Olean, NY 14760-2691
Tel: (716)372-7978
Fax: (716)372-2120
Web Site: www.obi.edu/
Description: Proprietary, 2-year, coed. Awards diplomas and terminal associate degrees. Founded 1961. Setting: small town campus. Total enrollment: 87. 66% 25 or older. Calendar: semesters. Double major, summer session for credit, part-time degree program, internships.
Entrance Requirements: Required: high school transcript. Required for some: essay, interview. Entrance: noncompetitive. Application deadline: 8/31. Notification: continuous until 9/1.
Collegiate Environment: Orientation program. Student services: personal-psychological counseling. Campus security: 24-hour emergency response devices, late night transport-escort service. 1,800 books, 25 serials, and an OPAC.

■ ONONDAGA COMMUNITY COLLEGE
4585 W Seneca Tpke.
Syracuse, NY 13215
Tel: (315)498-2622
Fax: (315)469-2107
E-mail: admissions@sunyocc.edu
Web Site: www.sunyocc.edu/
Description: State and locally supported, 2-year, coed. Part of State University of New York System. Awards certificates, diplomas, transfer associate, and terminal associate degrees. Founded 1962. Setting: 280-acre suburban campus. Endowment: $6 million. Educational spending for the previous fiscal year: $4958 per student. Total enrollment: 12,991. Faculty: 660 (175 full-time, 485 part-time). Student-undergrad faculty ratio is 27:1. 8,099 applied, 70% were admitted. Full-time: 6,704 students, 48% women, 52% men. Part-time: 6,287 students, 56% women, 44% men. Students come from 22 states and territories, 23 other countries, 1% from out-of-state. 2% American Indian or Alaska Native, non-Hispanic/Latino; 4% Hispanic/Latino; 12% African American, non-Hispanic/Latino; 2% Asian, non-Hispanic/Latino; 0.1% Native Hawaiian or other Pacific Islander, non-Hispanic/Latino; 0.5% international. 29% 25 or older, 6% live on campus, 49% transferred in. Calendar: semesters. Academic remediation for entering students, ESL program, services for LD students, advanced placement, accelerated degree program, honors program, distance learning, double major, summer session for credit, part-time degree program, external degree program, adult/continuing education programs, co-op programs and internships. Study abroad program. ROTC: Air Force (c).
Entrance Requirements: Open admission except for allied health, engineering, computer science, technology, art, music programs. Option: electronic application. Required: high school transcript, some programs require specific prerequisite courses and/or tests to be admitted directly to the program; an alternate program is offered. Required for some: minimum 2 high school GPA, interview. Entrance: noncompetitive. Application deadline: 8/12. Notification: continuous. Preference given to county residents, members of the Armed Forces. Transfer credits accepted: Yes.
Costs Per Year: Application fee: $0. State resident tuition: $4050 full-time, $161 per credit hour part-time. Nonresident tuition: $8100 full-time, $322 per credit hour part-time. Mandatory fees: $554 full-time, $115 per term part-time. Full-time tuition and fees vary according to program. Part-time tuition and fees vary according to course load and program. College room only: $6200.
Collegiate Environment: Orientation program. Drama-theater group, choral group, student-run newspaper, radio station. Student services: personal-psychological counseling. Campus security: 24-hour emergency response devices and patrols, controlled dormitory access. 779 college housing spaces available; all were occupied in 2012-13. No special consideration for freshman housing applicants. Option: coed housing available. Sidney B. Coulter Library with 114,481 books, 86,576 microform titles, 277 serials, 14,874 audiovisual materials, an OPAC, and a Web page. Operations spending for the previous fiscal year: $1.5 million. 1,100 computers available on campus for general student use. A campuswide network can be accessed from student residence rooms and from off campus. Students can access the following: online class registration. Staffed computer lab on campus provides training in use of computers, software, and the Internet.

■ ORANGE COUNTY COMMUNITY COLLEGE
115 S St.
Middletown, NY 10940-6437

Tel: (845)344-6222
Fax: (845)343-1228
E-mail: apply@sunyorange.edu
Web Site: www.sunyorange.edu/
Description: State and locally supported, 2-year, coed. Part of State University of New York System. Awards certificates, transfer associate, and terminal associate degrees. Founded 1950. Setting: 37-acre suburban campus with easy access to New York City. Total enrollment: 6,876. Student-undergrad faculty ratio is 17:1. 1% from out-of-state. 24% 25 or older. Core. Calendar: semesters. Academic remediation for entering students, ESL program, services for LD students, accelerated degree program, honors program, summer session for credit, part-time degree program, external degree program, adult/continuing education programs, internships.
Entrance Requirements: Open admission except for dental hygiene, engineering, occupational therapy, physical therapy, computer science programs. Options: early admission, deferred admission. Required: high school transcript. Entrance: noncompetitive. Application deadline: 8/1. Notification: continuous. Preference given to county residents.
Collegiate Environment: Orientation program. Drama-theater group, choral group, student-run newspaper, radio station. Social organizations: local sororities. Student services: health clinic, personal-psychological counseling. Campus security: 24-hour emergency response devices, late night transport-escort service. Learning Resource Center with an OPAC and a Web page.

■ PACE UNIVERSITY
One Pace Plz.
New York, NY 10038
Tel: (212)346-1200; Free: 800-874-7223
Fax: (212)346-1040
E-mail: dgrandpre@pace.edu
Web Site: www.pace.edu/
Description: Independent, university, coed. Awards associate, bachelor's, master's, and doctoral degrees and post-master's certificates. Founded 1906. Setting: urban campus with easy access to New York City. Endowment: $121.8 million. Research spending for the previous fiscal year: $4.2 million. Educational spending for the previous fiscal year: $11,658 per student. Total enrollment: 12,772. Faculty: 1,324 (466 full-time, 858 part-time). Student-undergrad faculty ratio is 14:1. 12,885 applied, 77% were admitted. 19% from top 10% of their high school class, 51% from top quarter, 86% from top half. Full-time: 7,107 students, 61% women, 39% men. Part-time: 1,229 students, 48% women, 52% men. Students come from 50 states and territories, 103 other countries, 37% from out-of-state. 0.3% American Indian or Alaska Native, non-Hispanic/Latino; 16% Hispanic/Latino; 11% African American, non-Hispanic/Latino; 9% Asian, non-Hispanic/Latino; 0.2% Native Hawaiian or other Pacific Islander, non-Hispanic/Latino; 7% international. 13% 25 or older, 45% live on campus, 8% transferred in. Retention: 76% of full-time freshmen returned the following year. Academic areas with the most degrees conferred: business/marketing; communication/journalism; health professions and related sciences; psychology. Core. Calendar: semesters. ESL program, advanced placement, accelerated degree program, freshman honors college, honors program, independent study, distance learning, double major, summer session for credit, part-time degree program, adult/continuing education programs, co-op programs and internships, graduate courses open to undergrads. Study abroad program. ROTC: Army (c), Air Force (c).
Entrance Requirements: Options: electronic application, early action, deferred admission, international baccalaureate accepted. Required: essay, high school transcript, 2 recommendations, SAT or ACT. Recommended: minimum 3 high school GPA, interview. Entrance: moderately difficult. Application deadlines: 2/15, 11/30 for early action. Notification: continuous, 1/1 for early action. SAT Reasoning Test deadline: 2/28. Transfer credits accepted: Yes. Early action applicants: 4,843. Early action applicants admitted: 4,064.
Costs Per Year: Application fee: $50. Comprehensive fee: $49,154 includes full-time tuition ($35,320), mandatory fees ($1244), and college room and board ($12,590). Room and board charges vary according to board plan, housing facility, location, and student level. Part-time tuition: $1013 per credit. Part-time tuition varies according to course load.
Collegiate Environment: Orientation program. Drama-theater group, choral group, student-run newspaper, radio station. Social organizations: 110 open to all; national fraternities, national sororities, local fraternities, local sororities, Accounting Society, Environmental Club; 5% of eligible men and 5% of eligible women are members. Most popular organizations: Black Student Union, Beta Alpha Psi, OLAS (Organization of Latin American Students),

Pace Board, Lubin Business Association. Major annual events: Homecoming (Octoberfest, Homecoming Concert, Dean's Brunch), Club Fair, national trips and conferences sponsored by student organizations. Student services: health clinic, personal-psychological counseling. Campus security: 24-hour emergency response devices and patrols, late night transport-escort service, controlled dormitory access. 3,285 college housing spaces available; 3,213 were occupied in 2012-13. No special consideration for freshman housing applicants. Option: coed housing available. Henry Birnbaum Library plus 3 others with 809,911 books, 53,688 microform titles, 147,624 serials, 4,390 audiovisual materials, an OPAC, and a Web page. Operations spending for the previous fiscal year: $7.8 million. 268 computers available on campus for general student use. Computer purchase/lease plans available. A campuswide network can be accessed from student residence rooms and from off campus. Students can access the following: online class registration, administrative functions - pay tuition, view student records, update personal information, view financial aid and complete health insurance waiver. Staffed computer lab on campus provides training in use of computers, software, and the Internet.

Community Environment: The New York City campus is just a short walk from Wall Street and the South Street Seaport. Lincoln Center, the theater district, the Metropolitan Museum, and other world-famous centers of the arts are just a few minutes away by subway or cab. The Pleasantville/Briarcliff campus is in a suburban setting in Westchester County, with access to twenty-three international corporate headquarters and excellent shopping nearby. The campus offers an environmental center, riding stables, and a variety of recreational facilities. The White Plains campus is adjacent to the train station.

■ **PARSONS THE NEW SCHOOL FOR DESIGN**

65 Fifth Ave.
New York, NY 10011-8878
Tel: (212)229-8900; Free: 800-292-3040
Fax: (212)229-8975
E-mail: thinkparsons@newschool.edu
Web Site: www.parsons.edu/

Description: Independent, comprehensive, coed. Part of The New School. Awards associate, bachelor's, and master's degrees. Founded 1896. Setting: 2-acre urban campus with easy access to Manhattan. Total enrollment: 4,916. Faculty: 1,046 (158 full-time, 888 part-time). Student-undergrad faculty ratio is 10:1. 2,634 applied, 63% were admitted. 12% from top 10% of their high school class, 42% from top quarter, 76% from top half. Full-time: 712 students, 77% women, 23% men. Part-time: 5 students, 100% women. 73% from out-of-state. 0.1% American Indian or Alaska Native, non-Hispanic/Latino; 9% Hispanic/Latino; 4% African American, non-Hispanic/Latino; 15% Asian, non-Hispanic/Latino; 0.2% Native Hawaiian or other Pacific Islander, non-Hispanic/Latino; 39% international. 20% 25 or older, 21% live on campus, 73% transferred in. Retention: 85% of full-time freshmen returned the following year. Academic areas with the most degrees conferred: visual and performing arts; architecture; natural resources/environmental science. Core. Calendar: semesters. ESL program, services for LD students, advanced placement, self-designed majors, independent study, distance learning, summer session for credit, co-op programs and internships, graduate courses open to undergrads. Off campus study at Association of Independent Colleges of Art and Design. Study abroad program.

Entrance Requirements: Options: electronic application, early action, deferred admission, international baccalaureate accepted. Required: high school transcript, portfolio, home examination, SAT or ACT. Recommended: minimum 3 high school GPA. Required for some: essay, interview. Entrance: very difficult. Application deadline: Rolling. Notification: continuous. SAT Reasoning Test deadline: 2/1. SAT Subject Test deadline: 2/1. Transfer credits accepted: Yes.

Costs Per Year: Application fee: $50. Comprehensive fee: $55,240 includes full-time tuition ($39,280), mandatory fees ($860), and college room and board ($15,100). Part-time tuition: $1335 per credit hour.

Collegiate Environment: Orientation program. Drama-theater group, choral group, student-run newspaper, radio station. Student services: health clinic, personal-psychological counseling. Campus security: 24-hour emergency response devices, controlled dormitory access. Freshmen given priority for college housing. Option: coed housing available. Adam and Sophie Gimbel Design Library plus 3 others with an OPAC and a Web page.

■ **PAUL SMITH'S COLLEGE**

PO Box 265
Paul Smiths, NY 12970-0265

Tel: (518)327-6000; Free: 800-421-2605
Fax: (518)327-6060
E-mail: admissions@paulsmiths.edu
Web Site: www.paulsmiths.edu/

Description: Independent, 4-year, coed. Awards associate and bachelor's degrees. Founded 1937. Setting: 14,200-acre rural campus. Endowment: $18.7 million. Research spending for the previous fiscal year: $80,900. Educational spending for the previous fiscal year: $6400 per student. Total enrollment: 910. Faculty: 83 (57 full-time, 26 part-time). Student-undergrad faculty ratio is 14:1. 831 applied, 86% were admitted. 5% from top 10% of their high school class, 17% from top quarter, 44% from top half. 85% live on campus. Core. Calendar: semesters. Academic remediation for entering students, services for LD students, advanced placement, honors program, double major, summer session for credit, adult/continuing education programs, co-op programs and internships. Study abroad program.

Entrance Requirements: Options: electronic application, deferred admission. Required: high school transcript. Recommended: essay, 2 recommendations, interview, SAT or ACT. Required for some: interview, SAT or ACT. Entrance: minimally difficult. Application deadline: Rolling.

Collegiate Environment: Orientation program. Student-run newspaper, radio station. Social organizations: 30 open to all. Most popular organizations: Forestry Club, Junior American Culinary, Wildlife Society, Fish and Game Club, Koinonia. Major annual events: Parents Weekend, Winter Carnival, Winter Weekend. Student services: health clinic, personal-psychological counseling. Campus security: 24-hour emergency response devices and patrols, controlled dormitory access. Joan Weill Adirondack Library with 56,000 books, 406 serials, an OPAC, and a Web page. Operations spending for the previous fiscal year: $1 million. 300 computers available on campus for general student use. A campuswide network can be accessed from student residence rooms and from off campus. Students can access the following: online class registration.

■ **PHILLIPS BETH ISRAEL SCHOOL OF NURSING**

776 6th Ave.
Ste. 4
New York, NY 10001
Tel: (212)614-6110
Fax: (212)614-6109
E-mail: bstern@chpnet.org
Web Site: www.futurenursebi.org/

Description: Independent, 2-year, coed. Awards transfer associate and terminal associate degrees. Founded 1904. Setting: urban campus. Endowment: $1.2 million. Educational spending for the previous fiscal year: $5400 per student. Total enrollment: 251. Faculty: 25 (10 full-time, 15 part-time). Student-undergrad faculty ratio is 10:1. 145 applied, 8% were admitted. 20% from top 10% of their high school class, 80% from top quarter, 100% from top half. Full-time: 17 students, 76% women, 24% men. Part-time: 234 students, 77% women, 23% men. Students come from 9 states and territories, 6 other countries, 15% from out-of-state. 0% American Indian or Alaska Native, non-Hispanic/Latino; 9% Hispanic/Latino; 23% African American, non-Hispanic/Latino; 14% Asian, non-Hispanic/Latino; 4% Native Hawaiian or other Pacific Islander, non-Hispanic/Latino; 0% international. 65% 25 or older, 40% transferred in. Retention: 84% of full-time freshmen returned the following year. Core. Calendar: semesters. Academic remediation for entering students, services for LD students, advanced placement, honors program, distance learning, summer session for credit, part-time degree program, co-op programs. Off campus study at Pace University.

Entrance Requirements: Options: deferred admission, international baccalaureate accepted. Required: essay, high school transcript, minimum 2.5 high school GPA, 2 recommendations, interview, nursing exam. Recommended: SAT. Entrance: moderately difficult. Application deadline: 4/1. Notification: continuous. Transfer credits accepted: Yes.

Collegiate Environment: Orientation program. Choral group, student-run newspaper. Social organizations: 2 open to all. Most popular organizations: Student Government Organization, National Student Nurses Association. Major annual events: Holiday Party, Senior Luncheon, Senior Gala. Student services: health clinic, personal-psychological counseling. Campus security: 24-hour emergency response devices. Phillips Health Science Library with 12,000 books, 950 serials, and an OPAC. Operations spending for the previous fiscal year: $150,000. 40 computers available on campus for general student use. A computer is required for all students. Students can access the following: online class registration. Staffed computer lab on campus provides training in use of computers, software, and the Internet.

■ PLAZA COLLEGE

7409 37th Ave.
Jackson Heights, NY 11372-6300
Tel: (718)779-1430
Fax: (718)779-1456
E-mail: info@plazacollege.edu
Web Site: www.plazacollege.edu/

Description: Proprietary, primarily 2-year, coed. Awards transfer associate, terminal associate, and bachelor's degrees. Founded 1916. Setting: urban campus with easy access to New York City. Total enrollment: 776. 1,138 applied. 56% 25 or older. Core. Calendar: semesters. Academic remediation for entering students, ESL program, services for LD students, summer session for credit, internships.

Entrance Requirements: Option: electronic application. Required: essay, interview, placement test, CPAt. Entrance: moderately difficult. Application deadline: Rolling. Transfer credits accepted: Yes.

Costs Per Year: Application fee: $100. One-time mandatory fee: $200. Tuition: $9900 full-time, $440 per credit hour part-time. Mandatory fees: $1450 full-time, $440 per credit hour part-time, $725 per term part-time. Full-time tuition and fees vary according to program. Part-time tuition and fees vary according to course load and program.

Collegiate Environment: Orientation program. Campus security: 24-hour emergency response devices.

■ POLYTECHNIC INSTITUTE OF NEW YORK UNIVERSITY

Six Metrotech Ctr.
Brooklyn, NY 11201-2990
Tel: (718)260-3600; Free: 800-POLYTECH
Fax: (718)260-3136
E-mail: uadmit@poly.edu
Web Site: www.poly.edu/

Description: Independent, university, coed. Administratively affiliated with New York University. Awards bachelor's, master's, and doctoral degrees. Founded 1854. Setting: 3-acre urban campus. Endowment: $107 million. Research spending for the previous fiscal year: $11.8 million. Educational spending for the previous fiscal year: $10,512 per student. Total enrollment: 4,652. Faculty: 396 (157 full-time, 239 part-time). Student-undergrad faculty ratio is 14:1. 3,284 applied, 75% were admitted. 46% from top 10% of their high school class, 81% from top quarter, 95% from top half. 25 National Merit Scholars, 2 valedictorians, 15 student government officers. Full-time: 1,952 students, 22% women, 78% men. Part-time: 119 students, 26% women, 74% men. Students come from 38 states and territories, 33 other countries, 19% from out-of-state. 0.2% American Indian or Alaska Native, non-Hispanic/Latino; 10% Hispanic/Latino; 6% African American, non-Hispanic/Latino; 35% Asian, non-Hispanic/Latino; 0% Native Hawaiian or other Pacific Islander, non-Hispanic/Latino; 10% international. 6% 25 or older, 24% live on campus, 4% transferred in. Retention: 85% of full-time freshmen returned the following year. Academic areas with the most degrees conferred: engineering; business/marketing; computer and information sciences. Core. Calendar: semesters. Academic remediation for entering students, advanced placement, accelerated degree program, honors program, distance learning, double major, summer session for credit, part-time degree program, co-op programs and internships, graduate courses open to undergrads. Study abroad program. ROTC: Army (c), Air Force (c).

Entrance Requirements: Options: electronic application, early admission, deferred admission. Required: essay, high school transcript, 2 recommendations, SAT or ACT. Recommended: interview, SAT Subject Tests. Entrance: very difficult. Application deadline: 2/1. Transfer credits accepted: Yes.

Collegiate Environment: Orientation program. Student-run newspaper. Social organizations: 39 open to all; national fraternities, national sororities, local fraternities, local sororities, coed fraternity; 2% of eligible men and 1% of eligible women are members. Most popular organizations: National Society of Black Engineers, Society of Hispanic Professional Engineers, Association for Computing Machinery, Alpha Phi Omega, Chinese Student Society. Major annual events: Club Day/Club Rush, Career Fair, Poly Pride Day Mini-Fair. Student services: health clinic, personal-psychological counseling, women's center. Campus security: 24-hour patrols, controlled dormitory access. College housing designed to accommodate 400 students; 465 undergraduates lived in college housing during 2012-13. Freshmen given priority for college housing. Option: coed housing available. Bern Dibner Library plus 1 other with 140,000 books, 20,000 microform titles, 43,500 serials, an OPAC, and a Web page. Operations spending for the previous fiscal year: $1.1 million. 1,334 computers available on campus for general student use. Computer purchase/lease plans available. A computer

is required for all students. A campuswide network can be accessed from student residence rooms and from off campus. Students can access the following: online class registration. Staffed computer lab on campus provides training in use of computers, software, and the Internet.

■ PRATT INSTITUTE

200 Willoughby Ave.
Brooklyn, NY 11205-3899
Tel: (718)636-3600; Free: 800-331-0834
Fax: (718)636-3670
E-mail: visit@pratt.edu
Web Site: www.pratt.edu/

Description: Independent, comprehensive, coed. Awards associate, bachelor's, and master's degrees and post-master's certificates. Founded 1887. Setting: 25-acre urban campus. Total enrollment: 4,722. Faculty: 1,005 (130 full-time, 875 part-time). Student-undergrad faculty ratio is 11:1. 4,247 applied, 60% were admitted. Full-time: 2,873 students, 64% women, 36% men. Part-time: 148 students, 54% women, 46% men. 69% from out-of-state. 0.1% American Indian or Alaska Native, non-Hispanic/Latino; 9% Hispanic/Latino; 4% African American, non-Hispanic/Latino; 18% Asian, non-Hispanic/Latino; 0.1% Native Hawaiian or other Pacific Islander, non-Hispanic/Latino; 17% international. 7% 25 or older, 53% live on campus, 5% transferred in. Retention: 83% of full-time freshmen returned the following year. Academic areas with the most degrees conferred: visual and performing arts; architecture; liberal arts/general studies. Calendar: semesters plus optional May term and summer session. Part-time degree program.

Entrance Requirements: Options: electronic application, early action, deferred admission, international baccalaureate accepted. Required: essay, high school transcript, 1 recommendation, SAT or ACT. Recommended: minimum 3 high school GPA. Required for some: portfolio, SAT Subject Tests. Entrance: very difficult. Application deadlines: 1/5, 11/1 for early action. Notification: 4/1, 12/22 for early action. SAT Reasoning Test deadline: 2/1. SAT Subject Test deadline: 2/1. Applicants placed on waiting list: 580. Wait-listed applicants offered admission: 30.

Costs Per Year: Application fee: $50. Comprehensive fee: $51,598 includes full-time tuition ($39,282), mandatory fees ($1810), and college room and board ($10,506). College room only: $6726. Full-time tuition and fees vary according to program. Room and board charges vary according to board plan and housing facility. Part-time tuition: $1267 per credit. Part-time tuition varies according to program.

Collegiate Environment: Orientation program. Campus security: 24-hour emergency response devices and patrols, late night transport-escort service. Freshmen guaranteed college housing. Option: coed housing available. Pratt Institute Library with an OPAC and a Web page.

■ PURCHASE COLLEGE, STATE UNIVERSITY OF NEW YORK

735 Anderson Hill Rd.
Purchase, NY 10577-1400
Tel: (914)251-6000
E-mail: admission@purchase.edu
Web Site: www.purchase.edu/

Description: State-supported, comprehensive, coed. Part of State University of New York System. Awards bachelor's and master's degrees and post-master's certificates. Founded 1967. Setting: 500-acre small town campus with easy access to New York City. Total enrollment: 4,267. Faculty: 403 (159 full-time, 244 part-time). Student-undergrad faculty ratio is 16:1. 8,907 applied, 33% were admitted. 10% from top 10% of their high school class, 39% from top quarter, 71% from top half. Full-time: 3,740 students, 56% women, 44% men. Part-time: 415 students, 55% women, 45% men. Students come from 43 states and territories, 31 other countries, 17% from out-of-state. 0.1% American Indian or Alaska Native, non-Hispanic/Latino; 16% Hispanic/Latino; 7% African American, non-Hispanic/Latino; 2% Asian, non-Hispanic/Latino; 0% Native Hawaiian or other Pacific Islander, non-Hispanic/Latino; 2% international. 9% 25 or older, 67% live on campus, 11% transferred in. Retention: 83% of full-time freshmen returned the following year. Academic areas with the most degrees conferred: visual and performing arts; liberal arts/general studies; social sciences. Core. Calendar: semesters. Academic remediation for entering students, ESL program, services for LD students, advanced placement, self-designed majors, independent study, double major, summer session for credit, part-time degree program, adult/continuing education programs, internships. Off campus study at Manhattanville College. Study abroad program.

Entrance Requirements: Options: electronic application, early admission, early action, deferred admission. Required: high school transcript, minimum

3 high school GPA, SAT or ACT. Recommended: SAT. Required for some: essay, 1 recommendation, interview, audition, portfolio. Entrance: moderately difficult. Application deadlines: 7/15, 11/15 for early action. Notification: continuous until 5/1, 12/15 for early action. SAT Reasoning Test deadline: 7/1. Transfer credits accepted: Yes.

Costs Per Year: Application fee: $40. One-time mandatory fee: $200. State resident tuition: $5570 full-time, $232 per credit part-time. Nonresident tuition: $14,820 full-time, $618 per credit part-time. Mandatory fees: $1660 full-time, $68 per credit part-time. Full-time tuition and fees vary according to program. Part-time tuition and fees vary according to course load and program. College room and board: $11,566. College room only: $7378. Room and board charges vary according to board plan and housing facility.

Collegiate Environment: Orientation program. Drama-theater group, choral group, student-run newspaper, radio station. Social organizations: 40 open to all. Most popular organizations: Student Union, WPUR radio station, Latinos Unidos, Gay/Lesbian/Bisexual/Transgender Union, Organization of African People in America. Major annual events: Culture Shock, Fall Ball, Pancake Madness. Student services: legal services, health clinic, personal-psychological counseling, women's center. Campus security: 24-hour emergency response devices and patrols, late night transport-escort service, controlled dormitory access, 24-hour patrols by police officers. 2,620 college housing spaces available. Freshmen given priority for college housing. Option: coed housing available. Purchase College Library with 238,695 books, 64,633 serials, 20,567 audiovisual materials, an OPAC, and a Web page. 600 computers available on campus for general student use. A campuswide network can be accessed from student residence rooms and from off campus. Students can access the following: online class registration. Staffed computer lab on campus provides training in use of computers, software, and the Internet.

■ QUEENS COLLEGE OF THE CITY UNIVERSITY OF NEW YORK

65-30 Kissena Blvd.
Flushing, NY 11367-1597
Tel: (718)997-5000
Fax: (718)997-5617
E-mail: vincent.angrisani@qc.cuny.edu
Web Site: www.qc.cuny.edu/

Description: State and locally supported, comprehensive, coed. Part of City University of New York System. Awards bachelor's and master's degrees and post-master's certificates. Founded 1937. Setting: 79-acre urban campus with easy access to New York City. Endowment: $38.3 million. Research spending for the previous fiscal year: $21 million. Educational spending for the previous fiscal year: $7554 per student. Total enrollment: 20,100. Faculty: 1,508 (609 full-time, 899 part-time). Student-undergrad faculty ratio is 9:1. 19,032 applied, 37% were admitted. Full-time: 11,300 students, 57% women, 43% men. Part-time: 4,887 students, 59% women, 41% men. Students come from 15 states and territories, 170 other countries, 1% from out-of-state. 0.1% American Indian or Alaska Native, non-Hispanic/Latino; 18% Hispanic/Latino; 8% African American, non-Hispanic/Latino; 24% Asian, non-Hispanic/Latino; 5% international. 3% live on campus, 14% transferred in. Retention: 87% of full-time freshmen returned the following year. Academic areas with the most degrees conferred: social sciences; business/marketing; psychology. Core. Calendar: semesters. ESL program, services for LD students, advanced placement, accelerated degree program, self-designed majors, honors program, independent study, double major, summer session for credit, part-time degree program, adult/continuing education programs, internships, graduate courses open to undergrads. Off campus study at other units of the City University of New York System. Study abroad program. ROTC: Army (c), Naval (c).

Entrance Requirements: Options: electronic application, deferred admission. Required: high school transcript, minimum 3 high school GPA, SAT or ACT. Recommended: SAT Subject Tests. Required for some: SAT Subject Tests. Entrance: very difficult. Application deadline: 2/1. Notification: 2/15. SAT Reasoning Test deadline: 1/1. Transfer credits accepted: Yes.

Costs Per Year: Application fee: $65. State resident tuition: $5730 full-time, $245 per credit part-time. Nonresident tuition: $15,300 full-time, $510 per credit part-time.

Collegiate Environment: Orientation program. Drama-theater group, choral group, student-run newspaper, radio station. Social organizations: 81 open to all; national fraternities, national sororities; 1% of eligible men and 1% of eligible women are members. Most popular organizations: Alliance of Latin American Students, Black Student Union, Caribbean Student Association, Hillel-Jewish Student Organization, India Cultural Exchange. Major annual events: Fall Campus Fest (Carnival theme), Spring Campus Fest (multi-

cultural theme), Career Week. Student services: health clinic, personal-psychological counseling. Campus security: 24-hour emergency response devices and patrols. 494 college housing spaces available. No special consideration for freshman housing applicants. Option: coed housing available. The Benjamin S. Rosenthal Library plus 1 other with 1.1 million books, 978,608 microform titles, 42,000 serials, 41,563 audiovisual materials, an OPAC, and a Web page. Operations spending for the previous fiscal year: $3.7 million. 2,500 computers available on campus for general student use. Computer purchase/lease plans available. A campuswide network can be accessed from student residence rooms and from off campus. Students can access the following: online class registration. Staffed computer lab on campus provides training in use of computers, software, and the Internet.

■ QUEENSBOROUGH COMMUNITY COLLEGE OF THE CITY UNIVERSITY OF NEW YORK

222-05 56th Ave.
Bayside, NY 11364
Tel: (718)631-6262
Fax: (718)281-5189
Web Site: www.qcc.cuny.edu/

Description: State and locally supported, 2-year, coed. Part of City University of New York System. Awards certificates, transfer associate, and terminal associate degrees. Founded 1958. Setting: 34-acre urban campus with easy access to New York City. Endowment: $1 million. Educational spending for the previous fiscal year: $3000 per student. Total enrollment: 13,008. Faculty: 736 (291 full-time, 445 part-time). Student-undergrad faculty ratio is 21:1. 3,485 applied, 100% were admitted. Students come from 2 states and territories, 132 other countries, 1% from out-of-state. 32% 25 or older. Core. Calendar: semesters. Academic remediation for entering students, ESL program, services for LD students, advanced placement, self-designed majors, honors program, summer session for credit, part-time degree program, adult/continuing education programs, co-op programs and internships. ROTC: Army (c).

Entrance Requirements: Open admission. Options: electronic application, deferred admission. Required: high school transcript. Entrance: noncompetitive. Application deadline: Rolling. Notification: continuous.

Collegiate Environment: Drama-theater group, choral group, student-run newspaper, radio station. Social organizations: 42 open to all. Most popular organizations: Student Orientation Leaders, Student Nurses Association, Newman Club, Accounting Club, Flip Culture Society. Major annual events: Multicultural Festival, Transfer Day, Job Fair. Student services: health clinic, personal-psychological counseling. Campus security: 24-hour patrols, late night transport-escort service. The Kurt R. Schmeller with 140,000 books and 600 serials. Operations spending for the previous fiscal year: $1.3 million. 1,001 computers available on campus for general student use. Students can access the following: online class registration. Staffed computer lab on campus.

■ RABBINICAL ACADEMY MESIVTA RABBI CHAIM BERLIN

1605 Coney Island Ave.
Brooklyn, NY 11230-4715
Tel: (718)377-0777

Description: Independent Jewish, comprehensive, men only. Awards bachelor's and master's degrees. Founded 1939. Total enrollment: 243. 20 applied, 100% were admitted. 10% 25 or older. Core. Calendar: semesters. Academic remediation for entering students, services for LD students.

Entrance Requirements: Entrance: moderately difficult.

Collegiate Environment: Student services: personal-psychological counseling.

■ RABBINICAL COLLEGE BETH SHRAGA

28 Saddle River Rd.
Monsey, NY 10952-3035
Tel: (914)356-1980

Description: Independent Jewish, comprehensive, men only. Awards bachelor's and master's degrees. Founded 1965. Setting: small town campus. Total enrollment: 42. 10 applied, 100% were admitted. Calendar: semesters.

■ RABBINICAL COLLEGE BOBOVER YESHIVA B'NEI ZION

1577 Forty-eighth St.
Brooklyn, NY 11219
Tel: (718)438-2018

Description: Independent Jewish, comprehensive, men only. Awards bachelor's and master's degrees. Founded 1947. Total enrollment: 235. Core. Calendar: semesters.
Entrance Requirements: Entrance: moderately difficult.

■ **RABBINICAL COLLEGE CH'SAN SOFER**
1876 Fiftieth St.
Brooklyn, NY 11204
Tel: (718)236-1171
Description: Independent Jewish, comprehensive, men only. Awards bachelor's and master's degrees. Founded 1940. Total enrollment: 56. 29 applied. Calendar: semesters.

■ **RABBINICAL COLLEGE OF LONG ISLAND**
205 W Beech St.
Long Beach, NY 11561-3305
Tel: (516)431-7414
Description: Independent Jewish, comprehensive, men only. Awards bachelor's and master's degrees. Founded 1965. Setting: small town campus. Total enrollment: 145. 40 applied, 100% were admitted. Calendar: semesters.

■ **RABBINICAL COLLEGE OF OHR SHIMON YISROEL**
215-217 Hewes St.
Brooklyn, NY 11211
Tel: (718)855-4092
Description: Independent Jewish, 4-year, men only. Awards bachelor's degrees. Total enrollment: 186. 175 applied. 6% 25 or older.

■ **RABBINICAL SEMINARY ADAS YEREIM**
185 Wilson St.
Brooklyn, NY 11211-7206
Tel: (718)388-1751
Description: Independent Jewish, comprehensive, men only. Awards bachelor's and master's degrees. Founded 1961. Total enrollment: 58. 57 applied. Calendar: semesters.

■ **RABBINICAL SEMINARY OF AMERICA**
76-01 147th St.
Flushing, NY 11367
Tel: (718)268-4700
Description: Independent Jewish, comprehensive, men only. Awards bachelor's, master's, and doctoral degrees. Founded 1933. Setting: urban campus with easy access to New York City. Total enrollment: 516. 105 applied. 3% 25 or older, 90% live on campus. Core. Calendar: semesters. Academic remediation for entering students, honors program, adult/continuing education programs. Study abroad program.
Entrance Requirements: Option: early admission. Required: high school transcript, interview. Entrance: very difficult. Application deadline: 12/1. Notification: continuous.
Collegiate Environment: Student services: personal-psychological counseling. Rabbinical Seminary of America Otzar HaSeforim Library plus 3 others with 30,000 books and 50 serials.
Community Environment: See Queens College of the City University of New York.

■ **RABBINICAL SEMINARY M'KOR CHAIM**
1571 Fifty-fifth St.
Brooklyn, NY 11219
Tel: (718)851-0183
Description: Independent Jewish, comprehensive, men only. Awards bachelor's and doctoral degrees. Founded 1965. Total enrollment: 53. 8 applied, 100% were admitted. Calendar: semesters.

■ **RENSSELAER POLYTECHNIC INSTITUTE**
110 8th St.
Troy, NY 12180-3590
Tel: (518)276-6000
Fax: (518)276-4072
E-mail: admissions@rpi.edu
Web Site: www.rpi.edu/
Description: Independent, university, coed. Awards bachelor's, master's, and doctoral degrees. Founded 1824. Setting: 284-acre suburban campus with easy access to Albany, NY. Endowment: $583.4 million. Research

spending for the previous fiscal year: $130.1 million. Educational spending for the previous fiscal year: $20,775 per student. Total enrollment: 6,999. Faculty: 500 (380 full-time, 120 part-time). Student-undergrad faculty ratio is 15:1. 15,222 applied, 44% were admitted. 66% from top 10% of their high school class, 95% from top quarter, 99% from top half. 21 National Merit Scholars, 60 valedictorians. Full-time: 5,371 students, 29% women, 71% men. Part-time: 20 students, 30% women, 70% men. Students come from 50 states and territories, 31 other countries, 66% from out-of-state. 0.2% American Indian or Alaska Native, non-Hispanic/Latino; 6% Hispanic/Latino; 2% African American, non-Hispanic/Latino; 10% Asian, non-Hispanic/Latino; 0.1% Native Hawaiian or other Pacific Islander, non-Hispanic/Latino; 6% international. 2% 25 or older, 57% live on campus, 3% transferred in. Retention: 94% of full-time freshmen returned the following year. Academic areas with the most degrees conferred: engineering; computer and information sciences; biological/life sciences; business/marketing. Core. Calendar: semesters. ESL program, services for LD students, advanced placement, accelerated degree program, self-designed majors, honors program, independent study, double major, summer session for credit, part-time degree program, adult/continuing education programs, co-op programs and internships, graduate courses open to undergrads. Off campus study at Williams College, Harvey Mudd College. Study abroad program. ROTC: Army, Naval, Air Force.
Entrance Requirements: Options: electronic application, early admission, early decision, deferred admission, international baccalaureate accepted. Required: high school transcript, SAT or ACT. Recommended: 1 recommendation. Required for some: essay, portfolio for Electronic Arts, SAT and SAT Subject Tests or ACT. Entrance: very difficult. Application deadlines: 1/15, 11/15 for early decision plan 1, 12/15 for early decision plan 2. Notification: 3/9, 12/4 for early decision plan 1, 1/18 for early decision plan 2. SAT Reasoning Test deadline: 12/31. Applicants placed on waiting list: 2,690. Wait-listed applicants offered admission: 63. Early decision applicants: 956. Early decision applicants admitted: 332.
Costs Per Year: Application fee: $70. Comprehensive fee: $56,925 includes full-time tuition ($43,350), mandatory fees ($1125), and college room and board ($12,450). College room only: $7110. Room and board charges vary according to board plan and location. Part-time tuition: $1805 per credit hour.
Collegiate Environment: Orientation program. Drama-theater group, choral group, student-run newspaper, radio station. Social organizations: 205 open to all; national fraternities, national sororities, local fraternities, local sororities; 21% of eligible men and 16% of eligible women are members. Most popular organizations: Red Army Spirit Club, Outing Club, Indian Student Association, Chinese American Student Association, pep band. Major annual events: Grand Marshal Week, Big Red Freakout, Fall Fest Weekend. Student services: legal services, health clinic, personal-psychological counseling, women's center. Campus security: 24-hour emergency response devices and patrols, late night transport-escort service, controlled dormitory access, campus foot patrols at night. 3,400 college housing spaces available; 3,118 were occupied in 2012-13. Freshmen guaranteed college housing. On-campus residence required through sophomore year. Option: coed housing available. Folsom Library plus 2 others with 374,742 books, 134,280 microform titles, 21,056 serials, 5,163 audiovisual materials, an OPAC, and a Web page. Operations spending for the previous fiscal year: $3.6 million.
Community Environment: Troy, a city of 55,000, located at the head of navigation on the Hudson River, is an important industrial city and the eastern terminus of the New York State Barge Canal. The city, within 15 miles of Albany and Schenectady, is served by air, bus, and rail lines, houses of worship, 3 hospitals, and various civic, fraternal, and veteran's organizations. There are numerous opportunities for part-time student employment.

■ **ROBERTS WESLEYAN COLLEGE**
2301 Westside Dr.
Rochester, NY 14624-1997
Tel: (585)594-6000; Free: 800-777-4RWC
Fax: (585)594-6371
E-mail: admissions@roberts.edu
Web Site: www.roberts.edu/
Description: Independent, comprehensive, coed, affiliated with Free Methodist Church of North America. Awards associate, bachelor's, and master's degrees. Founded 1866. Setting: 188-acre suburban campus. Endowment: $16.4 million. Educational spending for the previous fiscal year: $11,253 per student. Total enrollment: 1,752. Faculty: 259 (92 full-time, 167 part-time). Student-undergrad faculty ratio is 11:1. 1,928 applied, 47% were admitted. 24% from top 10% of their high school class, 49% from top quarter, 85% from top half. 3 valedictorians. Full-time: 1,177 students, 70% women,

30% men. Part-time: 146 students, 66% women, 34% men. Students come from 28 states and territories, 33 other countries, 8% from out-of-state. 0.3% American Indian or Alaska Native, non-Hispanic/Latino; 5% Hispanic/Latino; 12% African American, non-Hispanic/Latino; 1% Asian, non-Hispanic/Latino; 0.1% Native Hawaiian or other Pacific Islander, non-Hispanic/Latino; 4% international. 26% 25 or older, 63% live on campus, 7% transferred in. Retention: 80% of full-time freshmen returned the following year. Academic areas with the most degrees conferred: health professions and related sciences; business/marketing; education. Core. Calendar: semesters. Academic remediation for entering students, ESL program, services for LD students, advanced placement, accelerated degree program, self-designed majors, honors program, independent study, double major, summer session for credit, co-op programs and internships, graduate courses open to undergrads. Off campus study at Rochester Area Colleges, Council of Christian Colleges and Universities. Study abroad program. ROTC: Army, Air Force (c).

Entrance Requirements: Options: electronic application, early admission, deferred admission, international baccalaureate accepted. Required: essay, high school transcript, 1 recommendation, SAT or ACT. Recommended: minimum 2.7 high school GPA, 2 recommendations, interview. Entrance: moderately difficult. Application deadline: 2/1. SAT Reasoning Test deadline: 8/15.

Costs Per Year: Application fee: $35. One-time mandatory fee: $375. Comprehensive fee: $37,094 includes full-time tuition ($26,352), mandatory fees ($1112), and college room and board ($9630). College room only: $6166. Room and board charges vary according to board plan and housing facility.

Collegiate Environment: Orientation program. Drama-theater group, choral group, student-run newspaper. Social organizations: 43 open to all. Most popular organizations: Intramurals, Foot of the Cross, Fellowship of Christian Athletes, Nursing Club, Drama Club. Major annual events: Spring Formal, LIVE-Student Variety Show, Homecoming/Parents & Friends Weekend. Student services: health clinic, personal-psychological counseling. Campus security: 24-hour emergency response devices and patrols, student patrols, late night transport-escort service, controlled dormitory access, 24-hour Resident Life staff on-call. 759 college housing spaces available; 618 were occupied in 2012-13. Freshmen guaranteed college housing. On-campus residence required through senior year. Options: men-only, women-only housing available. B. Thomas Golisano Library with 139,427 books, 170,262 microform titles, 2,148 serials, 4,352 audiovisual materials, an OPAC, and a Web page. Operations spending for the previous fiscal year: $1 million. 250 computers available on campus for general student use. A campuswide network can be accessed from student residence rooms and from off campus. Students can access the following: online class registration. Staffed computer lab on campus (open 24 hours a day) provides training in use of computers, software, and the Internet.

Community Environment: North Chili is a suburb of Rochester, New York. A municipal airport and bus service and railroad provide transportation to Rochester which has all major transportation facilities, as well as community services, public library, museums, art gallery, and hospitals. Part-time employment is available for students. Local recreational facilities include skiing, skating, tennis, swimming and golf.

■ ROCHESTER INSTITUTE OF TECHNOLOGY

One Lomb Memorial Dr.
Rochester, NY 14623-5603
Tel: (585)475-2411
Fax: (585)475-7424
E-mail: admissions@rit.edu
Web Site: www.rit.edu/

Description: Independent, comprehensive, coed. Awards associate, bachelor's, master's, and doctoral degrees and post-master's certificates. Founded 1829. Setting: 1,300-acre suburban campus with easy access to Rochester. Endowment: $628.1 million. Total enrollment: 16,362. Faculty: 1,475 (975 full-time, 500 part-time). Student-undergrad faculty ratio is 13:1. 16,353 applied, 58% were admitted. 35% from top 10% of their high school class, 66% from top quarter, 93% from top half. 57 valedictorians. Full-time: 12,393 students, 33% women, 67% men. Part-time: 1,318 students, 29% women, 71% men. Students come from 52 states and territories, 102 other countries, 45% from out-of-state. 0.2% American Indian or Alaska Native, non-Hispanic/Latino; 6% Hispanic/Latino; 5% African American, non-Hispanic/Latino; 5% Asian, non-Hispanic/Latino; 0.1% Native Hawaiian or other Pacific Islander, non-Hispanic/Latino; 5% international. 10% 25 or older, 68% live on campus, 5% transferred in. Retention: 89% of full-time

freshmen returned the following year. Academic areas with the most degrees conferred: computer and information sciences; visual and performing arts; engineering technologies. Core. ESL program, services for LD students, advanced placement, accelerated degree program, self-designed majors, freshman honors college, honors program, independent study, distance learning, double major, summer session for credit, part-time degree program, adult/continuing education programs, co-op programs and internships, graduate courses open to undergrads. Off campus study at members of the Rochester Area Colleges. Study abroad program. ROTC: Army, Naval (c), Air Force.

Entrance Requirements: Options: electronic application, early admission, early decision, deferred admission, international baccalaureate accepted. Required: essay, high school transcript, SAT or ACT. Recommended: minimum 3.3 high school GPA, 1 recommendation, interview. Required for some: portfolio of original artwork for applicants to the School of Art and the School of Design. Entrance: moderately difficult. Application deadlines: 2/1, 12/1 for early decision. Notification: 3/15, 1/15 for early decision. Transfer credits accepted: Yes.

Costs Per Year: Application fee: $60. Comprehensive fee: $46,164 includes full-time tuition ($33,932), mandatory fees ($492), and college room and board ($11,740). College room only: $6530. Full-time tuition and fees vary according to course load. Room and board charges vary according to board plan and housing facility. Part-time tuition: $1191 per credit. Part-time tuition varies according to class time and course load.

Collegiate Environment: Orientation program. Drama-theater group, choral group, student-run newspaper, radio station. Social organizations: 205 open to all; national fraternities, national sororities, local fraternities, local sororities; 5% of eligible men and 5% of eligible women are members. Major annual events: Brick City Festival (Fall Weekend/Parents' Weekend), New Student Convocation, Creativity and Innovation Festival/Spring Weekend. Student services: legal services, health clinic, personal-psychological counseling, women's center. Campus security: 24-hour emergency response devices and patrols, student patrols, late night transport-escort service. 7,144 college housing spaces available. Freshmen guaranteed college housing. On-campus residence required in freshman year. Options: coed, men-only, women-only housing available. Wallace Memorial Library with 452,355 books, 509,294 microform titles, 23,325 serials, 9,719 audiovisual materials, an OPAC, and a Web page. 2,500 computers available on campus for general student use. Computer purchase/lease plans available. A campuswide network can be accessed from student residence rooms and from off campus. Students can access the following: online class registration, student account information. Staffed computer lab on campus provides training in use of computers, software, and the Internet.

Community Environment: The Greater Rochester area - the city and its immediate suburbs - has a population of about 1,100,000. Per capital income is among the highest for metropolitan areas in the nation. The area's many internationally known industries employ a high proportion of scientists, technologists and skilled workers. Rochester is the world center of photography, the largest producer of optical goods in the United States, and among the leaders in graphic arts and reproduction and in production of electronic equipment and precision instruments. Rochester's industries have always been closely associated with RIT's programs and progress to the mutual benefit of all.

■ ROCKLAND COMMUNITY COLLEGE

145 College Rd.
Suffern, NY 10901-3699
Tel: (845)574-4000; Free: 800-722-7666
E-mail: lglynn@sunyrockland.edu
Web Site: www.sunyrockland.edu/

Description: State and locally supported, 2-year, coed. Part of State University of New York System. Awards certificates, transfer associate, and terminal associate degrees. Founded 1959. Setting: 150-acre suburban campus with easy access to New York City. Total enrollment: 7,986. Faculty: 707 (120 full-time, 587 part-time). Student-undergrad faculty ratio is 20:1. 1,610 applied, 100% were admitted. Full-time: 4,752 students, 48% women, 52% men. Part-time: 3,234 students, 64% women, 36% men. 0.4% American Indian or Alaska Native, non-Hispanic/Latino; 19% Hispanic/Latino; 20% African American, non-Hispanic/Latino; 5% Asian, non-Hispanic/Latino; 0% Native Hawaiian or other Pacific Islander, non-Hispanic/Latino; 2% international. 8% transferred in. Retention: 64% of full-time freshmen returned the following year. Calendar: semesters. Part-time degree program, external degree program, adult/continuing education programs.

Entrance Requirements: Open admission. Options: early admission, deferred admission. Required: high school transcript. Entrance: noncompetitive. Application deadline: Rolling.

Collegiate Environment: Orientation program. Campus security: 24-hour emergency response devices and patrols, student patrols, late night transport-escort service.

■ RUSSELL SAGE COLLEGE

65 1st St.
Troy, NY 12180-4115
Tel: (518)244-2000; Free: 888-VERY SAGE
Fax: (518)244-6880
E-mail: breent@sage.edu
Web Site: www.sage.edu/rsc/

Description: Independent, 4-year, women only. Part of The Sage Colleges. Awards bachelor's degrees. Founded 1916. Setting: 8-acre urban campus. System endowment: $24.8 million. Research spending for the previous fiscal year: $345,099. Educational spending for the previous fiscal year: $7570 per student. Total enrollment: 827. Faculty: 114 (73 full-time, 41 part-time). Student-undergrad faculty ratio is 9:1. 851 applied, 59% were admitted. 19% from top 10% of their high school class, 58% from top quarter, 90% from top half. Full-time: 780 students. Part-time: 47 students. Students come from 17 states and territories, 1 other country, 8% from out-of-state. 0.4% American Indian or Alaska Native, non-Hispanic/Latino; 6% Hispanic/Latino; 10% African American, non-Hispanic/Latino; 4% Asian, non-Hispanic/Latino; 0.3% Native Hawaiian or other Pacific Islander, non-Hispanic/Latino; 1% international. 15% 25 or older, 48% live on campus, 13% transferred in. Retention: 73% of full-time freshmen returned the following year. Academic areas with the most degrees conferred: health professions and related sciences; education; liberal arts/general studies. Core. Calendar: semesters. Academic remediation for entering students, services for LD students, advanced placement, accelerated degree program, self-designed majors, honors program, independent study, distance learning, double major, summer session for credit, co-op programs and internships. Off campus study at Hudson-Mohawk Association of Colleges and Universities. Study abroad program. ROTC: Army (c), Air Force (c).

Entrance Requirements: Options: electronic application, early admission, early action, deferred admission. Required: essay, high school transcript, minimum 2.5 high school GPA, 2 recommendations. Recommended: interview. Required for some: SAT or ACT. Entrance: moderately difficult. Application deadline: Rolling. Notification: continuous. Transfer credits accepted: Yes. Early action applicants: 307. Early action applicants admitted: 222.

Costs Per Year: Application fee: $30. Comprehensive fee: $38,995 includes full-time tuition ($27,000), mandatory fees ($1000), and college room and board ($10,995). College room only: $5795. Room and board charges vary according to board plan. Part-time tuition: $900 per credit hour.

Collegiate Environment: Orientation program. Drama-theater group, choral group, student-run newspaper. Social organizations: 23 open to all. Most popular organizations: student government, Sage Recreation Association, Physical Therapy Club, Crew Club, Black-Latin Student Alliance. Major annual events: Rally Day, Founder's Day, Sage Fest. Student services: health clinic, personal-psychological counseling, women's center. Campus security: 24-hour emergency response devices and patrols, late night transport-escort service, controlled dormitory access. 520 college housing spaces available; 374 were occupied in 2012-13. Freshmen guaranteed college housing. Option: women-only housing available. James Wheelock Clark Library plus 1 other with 403,058 books, 18,514 microform titles, 63,939 serials, 7,960 audiovisual materials, and an OPAC. Operations spending for the previous fiscal year: $1.3 million. 165 computers available on campus for general student use. Computer purchase/lease plans available. A campuswide network can be accessed from student residence rooms and from off campus. Students can access the following: online class registration. Staffed computer lab on campus provides training in use of computers, software, and the Internet.

Community Environment: The campus is located in the heart of New York State's Capital Region overlooking the Hudson River in historic Troy, New York, a regional center for music, art, and theatre with a rapidly developing artists' district. Troy is within easy driving distance of recreation opportunities in the nearby Adirondack, Berkshire, Catskill, and Green Mountains. There is also easy access to major Northeastern cities, including Boston, New York, Providence, and Montreal. Fourteen colleges and universities are within a 30-mile radius of Albany, the state capital and center of government, including two research universities that are lending strong development to the technology industry.

■ SAGE COLLEGE OF ALBANY

140 New Scotland Ave.
Albany, NY 12208-3425
Tel: (518)292-1730; Free: 888-VERY-SAGE
Fax: (518)292-1912
E-mail: scaadm@sage.edu
Web Site: www.sage.edu/

Description: Independent, 4-year, coed. Part of The Sage Colleges. Awards bachelor's degrees. Founded 1957. Setting: 15-acre urban campus. System endowment: $24.8 million. Research spending for the previous fiscal year: $345,099. Educational spending for the previous fiscal year: $7570 per student. Total enrollment: 911. Faculty: 69 (42 full-time, 27 part-time). Student-undergrad faculty ratio is 16:1. 1,241 applied, 51% were admitted. 19% from top 10% of their high school class, 56% from top quarter, 84% from top half. Full-time: 678 students, 58% women, 42% men. Part-time: 233 students, 75% women, 25% men. Students come from 16 states and territories, 2 other countries, 5% from out-of-state. 0.2% American Indian or Alaska Native, non-Hispanic/Latino; 9% Hispanic/Latino; 17% African American, non-Hispanic/Latino; 2% Asian, non-Hispanic/Latino; 0.3% Native Hawaiian or other Pacific Islander, non-Hispanic/Latino; 1% international. 32% 25 or older, 51% live on campus, 17% transferred in. Retention: 75% of full-time freshmen returned the following year. Academic areas with the most degrees conferred: business/marketing; visual and performing arts; health professions and related sciences. Core. Calendar: semesters. Academic remediation for entering students, services for LD students, advanced placement, accelerated degree program, self-designed majors, honors program, independent study, distance learning, summer session for credit, part-time degree program, adult/continuing education programs, co-op programs and internships. Off campus study at members of the Hudson-Mohawk Association of Colleges and Universities. Study abroad program. ROTC: Army (c), Air Force (c).

Entrance Requirements: Options: electronic application, deferred admission. Required: essay, high school transcript, minimum 2.5 high school GPA, 2 recommendations, portfolio for fine arts program. Recommended: interview. Required for some: SAT or ACT. Entrance: minimally difficult. Application deadline: Rolling. Notification: 8/15.

Costs Per Year: Application fee: $30. Comprehensive fee: $38,995 includes full-time tuition ($27,000), mandatory fees ($1000), and college room and board ($10,995). College room only: $5795. Room and board charges vary according to board plan. Part-time tuition: $900 per credit hour.

Collegiate Environment: Orientation program. Social organizations: 15 open to all. Most popular organizations: Sage African, Latino, Asian, and Native American, VIBE, College Republicans, Love Your College Experience, Sage GEMS. Major annual events: Spirit of Sage River Cruise, Sage GEMS: Fall Dance Party, Sneak Peek Movie Night. Student services: health clinic, personal-psychological counseling. Campus security: 24-hour emergency response devices and patrols, late night transport-escort service, controlled dormitory access, 24-hour security cameras. 452 college housing spaces available; 333 were occupied in 2012-13. Freshmen given priority for college housing. Options: coed, women-only housing available. Troy and Albany Campus Libraries with 403,058 books, 18,514 microform titles, 63,939 serials, 7,960 audiovisual materials, and an OPAC. Operations spending for the previous fiscal year: $1.3 million. 205 computers available on campus for general student use. Computer purchase/lease plans available. A campuswide network can be accessed from student residence rooms and from off campus. Students can access the following: online class registration. Staffed computer lab on campus provides training in use of computers, software, and the Internet.

■ ST. BONAVENTURE UNIVERSITY

3261 W State Rd.
Saint Bonaventure, NY 14778-2284
Tel: (716)375-2000; Free: 800-462-5050
Fax: (716)375-2005
E-mail: memery@sbu.edu
Web Site: www.sbu.edu/

Description: Independent, comprehensive, coed, affiliated with Roman Catholic Church. Awards bachelor's and master's degrees and post-master's certificates. Founded 1858. Setting: 500-acre small town campus. Endowment: $50.6 million. Research spending for the previous fiscal year: $1.1 million. Educational spending for the previous fiscal year: $7651 per student. Total enrollment: 2,329. Faculty: 220 (154 full-time, 66 part-time). Student-undergrad faculty ratio is 12:1. 2,456 applied, 79% were admitted. 18% from top 10% of their high school class, 42% from top quarter, 72% from top half.

Full-time: 1,839 students, 52% women, 48% men. Part-time: 69 students, 51% women, 49% men. Students come from 33 states and territories, 32 other countries, 76% from out-of-state. 1% American Indian or Alaska Native, non-Hispanic/Latino; 5% Hispanic/Latino; 5% African American, non-Hispanic/Latino; 3% Asian, non-Hispanic/Latino; 1% Native Hawaiian or other Pacific Islander, non-Hispanic/Latino; 2% international. 2% 25 or older, 76% live on campus, 4% transferred in. Retention: 81% of full-time freshmen returned the following year. Academic areas with the most degrees conferred: business/marketing; education; communication/journalism. Core. Calendar: semesters. Services for LD students, advanced placement, accelerated degree program, self-designed majors, honors program, independent study, distance learning, double major, summer session for credit, part-time degree program, internships, graduate courses open to undergrads. Off campus study at American University. Study abroad program. ROTC: Army.

Entrance Requirements: Options: electronic application, deferred admission, international baccalaureate accepted. Required: high school transcript, 1 recommendation, SAT or ACT. Recommended: essay, minimum 3 high school GPA, 3 recommendations, interview. Required for some: essay, SAT Subject Tests. Entrance: moderately difficult. Application deadline: 7/1. Notification: continuous until 10/15. SAT Reasoning Test deadline: 8/15. SAT Subject Test deadline: 12/15. Transfer credits accepted: Yes.

Costs Per Year: Application fee: $0. Comprehensive fee: $39,431 includes full-time tuition ($27,762), mandatory fees ($965), and college room and board ($10,704). College room only: $5294. Room and board charges vary according to board plan and housing facility. Part-time tuition: $830 per credit hour. Part-time tuition varies according to course load.

Collegiate Environment: Orientation program. Drama-theater group, choral group, student-run newspaper, radio station. Social organizations: 65 open to all. Most popular organizations: Student Government Association, Bona Responds, BV newspaper, Students for the Mountain, Student Ambassadors. Major annual events: Family Weekend, Spring Weekend, Junior Prom. Student services: health clinic, personal-psychological counseling. Campus security: 24-hour emergency response devices and patrols, late night transport-escort service, controlled dormitory access. 1,661 college housing spaces available; 1,428 were occupied in 2012-13. Freshmen guaranteed college housing. On-campus residence required in freshman year. Option: coed housing available. Friedsam Library with 355,521 books, 16,950 microform titles, 36,061 serials, 15,987 audiovisual materials, an OPAC, and a Web page. Operations spending for the previous fiscal year: $963,521. 220 computers available on campus for general student use. A campuswide network can be accessed from student residence rooms and from off campus. Students can access the following: online class registration. Staffed computer lab on campus provides training in use of computers, software, and the Internet.

Community Environment: Allegany (population 1,831) is a rural community located in southwest New York a short distance from Allegany State Park. The area is accessible by bus and the Southern Tier Expressway. Climate is temperate with 4 definite seasons. Allegany has 1 library, several churches of different denominations. Various civic and fraternal organizations are active here. Part-time work for students is available. Olean (population 14,799) is a manufacturing and regional commercial center where part-time employment is available for students. Transportation is provided by bus or airlines. Nearby"Enchanted Mountains" resort area provides hunting, fishing, skiing, and other sports. The city has a hospital, numerous restaurants, movie theaters, shopping areas, and most of the major service clubs found in larger cities.

■ ST. ELIZABETH COLLEGE OF NURSING

2215 Genesee St.
Utica, NY 13501
Tel: (315)798-8144
E-mail: dernst@secon.edu
Web Site: www.secon.edu/

Description: Independent, 2-year, coed. Administratively affiliated with St. Elizabeth Medical Center. Awards terminal associate degrees. Founded 1904. Setting: 1-acre small town campus with easy access to Syracuse. Total enrollment: 217. Faculty: 17. Student-undergrad faculty ratio is 10:1. 42 applied, 60% were admitted. Full-time: 145 students, 88% women, 12% men. Part-time: 72 students, 86% women, 14% men. Students come from 4 states and territories, 1 other country, 1% from out-of-state. 1% American Indian or Alaska Native, non-Hispanic/Latino; 1% Hispanic/Latino; 1% African American, non-Hispanic/Latino; 2% Asian, non-Hispanic/Latino; 0% Native Hawaiian or other Pacific Islander, non-Hispanic/Latino; 2%

international. 46% 25 or older, 42% transferred in. Retention: 75% of full-time freshmen returned the following year. Core. Calendar: semesters. Academic remediation for entering students, services for LD students, advanced placement, part-time degree program. Off campus study at SUNY IT - Utica; Mohawk Valley Community College - Utica; Herkimer County Community College - Herkimer.

Entrance Requirements: Option: electronic application. Required: high school transcript, 2 recommendations, SAT or ACT. Recommended: minimum 3 high school GPA, SAT or ACT. Application deadline: Rolling. Notification: continuous. SAT Reasoning Test deadline: 4/30. SAT Subject Test deadline: 4/30. Transfer credits accepted: Yes.

Costs Per Year: Application fee: $65. Tuition: $12,750 full-time, $375 per credit hour part-time. Mandatory fees: $1000 full-time, $500 per term part-time. Full-time tuition and fees vary according to course load, location, program, and student level. Part-time tuition and fees vary according to course load, location, program, and student level.

Collegiate Environment: Orientation program. Major annual events: Freshmen Pinning Ceremony, Moving Up Day Ceremony, Graduation Mass, Breakfast, and Ceremony. Student services: health clinic, personal-psychological counseling. Campus security: 24-hour emergency response devices and patrols. 30 computers available on campus for general student use. A campuswide network can be accessed from off-campus. Staffed computer lab on campus provides training in use of computers, software, and the Internet.

■ ST. FRANCIS COLLEGE

180 Remsen St.
Brooklyn Heights, NY 11201-4398
Tel: (718)522-2300
Fax: (718)522-1274
E-mail: lrandazzo@sfc.edu
Web Site: www.sfc.edu/

Description: Independent Roman Catholic, comprehensive, coed. Awards associate, bachelor's, and master's degrees. Founded 1884. Setting: 1-acre urban campus with easy access to New York City. Total enrollment: 2,903. Faculty: 281 (85 full-time, 196 part-time). Student-undergrad faculty ratio is 18:1. 2,577 applied, 74% were admitted. 3 valedictorians. Full-time: 2,541 students, 56% women, 44% men. Part-time: 296 students, 63% women, 38% men. Students come from 20 states and territories, 53 other countries, 3% from out-of-state. 0.2% American Indian or Alaska Native, non-Hispanic/Latino; 21% Hispanic/Latino; 20% African American, non-Hispanic/Latino; 4% Asian, non-Hispanic/Latino; 0.3% Native Hawaiian or other Pacific Islander, non-Hispanic/Latino; 5% international. 12% 25 or older, 5% live on campus, 6% transferred in. Retention: 78% of full-time freshmen returned the following year. Academic areas with the most degrees conferred: business/marketing; health professions and related sciences; education. Core. Calendar: semesters. Academic remediation for entering students, ESL program, advanced placement, accelerated degree program, self-designed majors, honors program, independent study, double major, summer session for credit, part-time degree program, co-op programs and internships. Study abroad program. ROTC: Army (c), Air Force (c).

Entrance Requirements: Options: electronic application, deferred admission, international baccalaureate accepted. Required: essay, high school transcript, minimum 2 high school GPA, 1 recommendation, SAT. Recommended: interview. Entrance: moderately difficult. Application deadline: Rolling. Notification: continuous. Transfer credits accepted: Yes.

Costs Per Year: Application fee: $35. Tuition: $18,500 full-time, $620 per credit part-time. Mandatory fees: $700 full-time, $175 per term part-time. Full-time tuition and fees vary according to course level, course load, degree level, and program. Part-time tuition and fees vary according to course level, course load, and degree level. College room only: $13,000. Room charges vary according to housing facility.

Collegiate Environment: Orientation program. Drama-theater group, choral group, student-run newspaper, radio station. Social organizations: 50 open to all; national fraternities, national sororities, local fraternities, local sororities. Most popular organizations: Latin American Society, Fine Arts Society, Power Lifting Club, Games Club, Haitian American Students Alliance. Major annual events: International Night, Franciscan Spirit Week, Community Day. Student services: personal-psychological counseling. Campus security: ID checks, crime awareness workshops, pamphlets, posters, films, emergency notification system. 144 college housing spaces available; all were occupied in 2012-13. No special consideration for freshman housing applicants. McCardle Student Library with 116,716 books, 10,856 microform titles, 31,391 serials, 2,568 audiovisual materials, and an OPAC. 354 computers available on campus for general student use. A campuswide network can be accessed from off-campus. Students can access the following: online class registration, wireless zones. Staffed computer lab on campus provides training in use of computers, software, and the Internet.

■ **ST. JOHN FISHER COLLEGE**

3690 E Ave.
Rochester, NY 14618-3597
Tel: (585)385-8000; Free: 800-444-4640
Fax: (585)385-8129
E-mail: admissions@sjfc.edu
Web Site: www.sjfc.edu/

Description: Independent, comprehensive, coed, affiliated with Roman Catholic Church. Awards bachelor's, master's, and doctoral degrees and post-master's certificates. Founded 1948. Setting: 154-acre suburban campus. Endowment: $50.5 million. Educational spending for the previous fiscal year: $8725 per student. Total enrollment: 4,008. Faculty: 415 (223 full-time, 192 part-time). Student-undergrad faculty ratio is 13:1. 3,769 applied, 64% were admitted. 21% from top 10% of their high school class, 52% from top quarter, 87% from top half. Full-time: 2,753 students, 60% women, 40% men. Part-time: 207 students, 58% women, 42% men. Students come from 25 states and territories, 2 other countries, 3% from out-of-state. 0.3% American Indian or Alaska Native, non-Hispanic/Latino; 4% Hispanic/Latino; 4% African American, non-Hispanic/Latino; 3% Asian, non-Hispanic/Latino; 0.1% Native Hawaiian or other Pacific Islander, non-Hispanic/Latino; 0.1% international. 10% 25 or older, 49% live on campus, 10% transferred in. Retention: 84% of full-time freshmen returned the following year. Academic areas with the most degrees conferred: business/marketing; education; health professions and related sciences. Core. Calendar: semesters. Academic remediation for entering students, services for LD students, advanced placement, accelerated degree program, self-designed majors, honors program, independent study, distance learning, double major, summer session for credit, part-time degree program, adult/continuing education programs, internships, graduate courses open to undergrads. Off campus study at Members of the Rochester Area Colleges. Study abroad program. ROTC: Army (c), Naval (c), Air Force (c).
Entrance Requirements: Options: electronic application, early decision, deferred admission, international baccalaureate accepted. Required: essay, high school transcript, minimum 3 high school GPA, 1 recommendation, SAT or ACT. Recommended: interview. Entrance: moderately difficult. Application deadlines: Rolling, 12/1 for early decision. Notification: continuous until 12/1, 12/15 for early decision. SAT Reasoning Test deadline: 4/1. Transfer credits accepted: Yes. Early decision applicants: 172. Early decision applicants admitted: 113.
Costs Per Year: Application fee: $30. Comprehensive fee: $39,370 includes full-time tuition ($27,870), mandatory fees ($560), and college room and board ($10,940). College room only: $7090. Room and board charges vary according to board plan. Part-time tuition: $730 per credit hour. Part-time tuition varies according to course load.
Collegiate Environment: Orientation program. Drama-theater group, choral group, student-run newspaper. Social organizations: 75 open to all. Most popular organizations: student government, Student Activities Board, Commuter Council, Resident Student Association, Teddi Dance for Love. Major annual events: Teddi Project Dance Marathon, Family Weekend, Spring Event. Student services: health clinic, personal-psychological counseling. Campus security: 24-hour emergency response devices and patrols, late night transport-escort service, controlled dormitory access. College housing designed to accommodate 1,400 students; 1,440 undergraduates lived in college housing during 2012-13. Freshmen guaranteed college housing. Options: coed, women-only housing available. Charles J. Lavery Library with 229,031 books, 197,464 microform titles, 48,558 serials, 7,641 audiovisual materials, an OPAC, and a Web page. Operations spending for the previous fiscal year: $1.8 million. 550 computers available on campus for general student use. A campuswide network can be accessed from student residence rooms and from off campus. Students can access the following: online class registration. Staffed computer lab on campus (open 24 hours a day) provides training in use of computers, software, and the Internet.

■ **ST. JOHN'S UNIVERSITY**

8000 Utopia Pky.
Queens, NY 11439
Tel: (718)990-6161; Free: 888-9STJOHNS
E-mail: admhelp@stjohns.edu
Web Site: www.stjohns.edu/

Description: Independent, university, coed, affiliated with Roman Catholic Church. Awards associate, bachelor's, master's, and doctoral degrees and post-master's certificates. Founded 1870. Setting: 105-acre urban campus with easy access to New York City. Endowment: $350.5 million. Research spending for the previous fiscal year: $7.3 million. Educational spending for the previous fiscal year: $9877 per student. Total enrollment: 21,087. Faculty: 1,467 (643 full-time, 824 part-time). Student-undergrad faculty ratio is 17:1. 51,634 applied, 53% were admitted. 17% from top 10% of their high school class, 40% from top quarter, 71% from top half. Full-time: 10,956 students, 52% women, 48% men. Part-time: 4,884 students, 59% women, 41% men. Students come from 48 states and territories, 92 other countries, 29% from out-of-state. 0.2% American Indian or Alaska Native, non-Hispanic/Latino; 16% Hispanic/Latino; 19% African American, non-Hispanic/Latino; 18% Asian, non-Hispanic/Latino; 0.3% Native Hawaiian or other Pacific Islander, non-Hispanic/Latino; 5% international. 5% 25 or older, 31% live on campus, 3% transferred in. Retention: 76% of full-time freshmen returned the following year. Academic areas with the most degrees conferred: business/marketing; communication/journalism; health professions and related sciences. Core. Calendar: semesters. ESL program, services for LD students, advanced placement, accelerated degree program, honors program, independent study, distance learning, double major, summer session for credit, part-time degree program, adult/continuing education programs, internships, graduate courses open to undergrads. Off campus study at American Academy McAllister Institute of Funeral Service; The American Academy of Dramatic Arts. Study abroad program. ROTC: Army.
Entrance Requirements: Options: electronic application, early admission, deferred admission, international baccalaureate accepted. Required: high school transcript, SAT or ACT. Recommended: essay, minimum 3 high school GPA. Required for some: essay, 2 recommendations, interview. Entrance: moderately difficult. Application deadlines: Rolling, Rolling for nonresidents. Notification: continuous, continuous for nonresidents. Transfer credits accepted: Yes.
Costs Per Year: Application fee: $50. Comprehensive fee: $50,790 includes full-time tuition ($34,750), mandatory fees ($770), and college room and board ($15,270). College room only: $9550. Full-time tuition and fees vary according to course load, program, and student level. Room and board charges vary according to board plan, housing facility, and location. Part-time tuition: $1158 per credit. Part-time mandatory fees: $287.50 per term. Part-time tuition and fees vary according to course load, program, and student level.
Collegiate Environment: Orientation program. Drama-theater group, choral group, student-run newspaper, radio station. Social organizations: 180 open to all; national fraternities, national sororities, local fraternities, local sororities; 8% of eligible men and 8% of eligible women are members. Most popular organizations: Student Government, Incorporated, Student Programming Board, Haraya (Pan-African Students Coalition), American Pharmaceutical Association, Muslim Student Organization. Major annual events: Spring Fling, I Heart STJ, Fall Activities Fair. Student services: health clinic, personal-psychological counseling. Campus security: 24-hour emergency response devices and patrols, student patrols, late night transport-escort service, controlled dormitory access, Emergency Notification System. 3,800 college housing spaces available; 3,600 were occupied in 2012-13. Freshmen given priority for college housing. Option: coed housing available. St. John's University Library plus 4 others with 995,651 books, 358,925 microform titles, 57,144 serials, 11,007 audiovisual materials, an OPAC, and a Web page. Operations spending for the previous fiscal year: $11.8 million. 13,025 computers available on campus for general student use. Computer purchase/lease plans available. A computer is required for all students. A campuswide network can be accessed from student residence rooms and from off campus. Students can access the following: online class registration. Staffed computer lab on campus provides training in use of computers, software, and the Internet.

■ **ST. JOSEPH'S COLLEGE, LONG ISLAND CAMPUS**

155 W Roe Blvd.
Patchogue, NY 11772-2399
Tel: (631)447-3200
Fax: (631)447-1734
E-mail: glamens@sjcny.edu
Web Site: www.sjcny.edu/

Description: Independent, comprehensive, coed. Awards bachelor's and master's degrees. Founded 1916. Setting: 51-acre suburban campus with easy access to New York City. Endowment: $25.5 million. Educational spending for the previous fiscal year: $6368 per student. Total enrollment:

4,113. Faculty: 453 (118 full-time, 335 part-time). Student-undergrad faculty ratio is 14:1. 1,609 applied, 72% were admitted. Full-time: 2,847 students, 70% women, 30% men. Part-time: 675 students, 74% women, 26% men. Students come from 13 states and territories, 35 other countries, 1% from out-of-state. 0.4% American Indian or Alaska Native, non-Hispanic/Latino; 7% Hispanic/Latino; 5% African American, non-Hispanic/Latino; 2% Asian, non-Hispanic/Latino; 0.2% Native Hawaiian or other Pacific Islander, non-Hispanic/Latino. 24% 25 or older, 13% transferred in. Retention: 85% of full-time freshmen returned the following year. Academic areas with the most degrees conferred: education; business/marketing; psychology; English. Core. Calendar: 4-1-4. Services for LD students, advanced placement, accelerated degree program, honors program, independent study, distance learning, double major, summer session for credit, part-time degree program, adult/continuing education programs, co-op programs and internships, graduate courses open to undergrads. Off campus study at Long Island Regional Advisory Council for Higher Education. Study abroad program.

Entrance Requirements: Options: electronic application, early admission, deferred admission, international baccalaureate accepted. Required: essay, high school transcript, minimum 2.75 high school GPA, Standardized test scores required for most. Mid-year grades required for some, SAT or ACT. Recommended: 2 recommendations, interview, SAT Subject Tests. Entrance: moderately difficult. Application deadline: 8/15. Notification: continuous until 11/1. SAT Reasoning Test deadline: 8/15. Transfer credits accepted: Yes.

Costs Per Year: Application fee: $25. Tuition: $19,500 full-time, $635 per credit hour part-time. Mandatory fees: $625 full-time. Full-time tuition and fees vary according to course load, degree level, and program. Part-time tuition varies according to course load, degree level, and program.

Collegiate Environment: Orientation program. Drama-theater group, choral group, student-run newspaper. Social organizations: 47 open to all; national fraternities, national sororities, local sororities; 15% of eligible men and 30% of eligible women are members. Most popular organizations: Student Leadership Experience, Biology Club, Diversity Union, Child Study Club, Stars. Major annual events: Annual Concert, Student Leadership Experience, Club Fair. Student services: health clinic, personal-psychological counseling. Campus security: 24-hour emergency response devices and patrols, late night transport-escort service, Emergency Notification System via cell phones. College housing not available. Callahan Library with 178,727 books, 1,375 microform titles, 37,523 serials, 2,519 audiovisual materials, an OPAC, and a Web page. Operations spending for the previous fiscal year: $1.2 million. 269 computers available on campus for general student use. A campuswide network can be accessed. Students can access the following: online class registration. Staffed computer lab on campus provides training in use of computers.

■ ST. JOSEPH'S COLLEGE, NEW YORK

245 Clinton Ave.
Brooklyn, NY 11205-3688
Tel: (718)636-6800
Fax: (718)636-7242
E-mail: mlearmond@sjcny.edu
Web Site: www.sjcny.edu/

Description: Independent, comprehensive, coed. Awards bachelor's and master's degrees. Founded 1916. Setting: 5-acre urban campus. Endowment: $7.6 million. Educational spending for the previous fiscal year: $5873 per student. Total enrollment: 1,519. Faculty: 189 (60 full-time, 129 part-time). Student-undergrad faculty ratio is 11:1. 1,572 applied, 69% were admitted. Full-time: 970 students, 71% women, 29% men. Part-time: 329 students, 76% women, 24% men. Students come from 14 states and territories, 35 other countries, 3% from out-of-state. 0.2% American Indian or Alaska Native, non-Hispanic/Latino; 16% Hispanic/Latino; 30% African American, non-Hispanic/Latino; 7% Asian, non-Hispanic/Latino; 0.2% Native Hawaiian or other Pacific Islander, non-Hispanic/Latino; 0.2% international. 32% 25 or older, 1% live on campus, 8% transferred in. Retention: 84% of full-time freshmen returned the following year. Academic areas with the most degrees conferred: health professions and related sciences; business/marketing; education. Core. Calendar: semesters. Advanced placement, honors program, independent study, distance learning, double major, summer session for credit, part-time degree program, adult/continuing education programs, co-op programs and internships, graduate courses open to undergrads. Study abroad program.

Entrance Requirements: Options: electronic application, early admission, deferred admission, international baccalaureate accepted. Required: high

school transcript, minimum 2.5 high school GPA, SAT or ACT. Recommended: essay, 2 recommendations. Required for some: interview. Entrance: moderately difficult. Application deadline: 8/15. SAT Reasoning Test deadline: 8/15. Transfer credits accepted: Yes.

Costs Per Year: Application fee: $25. Tuition: $19,500 full-time, $635 per credit hour part-time. Mandatory fees: $615 full-time. Full-time tuition and fees vary according to course load, degree level, and program. Part-time tuition varies according to course load, degree level, and program.

Collegiate Environment: Orientation program. Drama-theater group, choral group, student-run newspaper. Social organizations: 38 open to all; national sororities, local fraternities, local sororities; 15% of eligible men and 30% of eligible women are members. Most popular organizations: Black Student Association, Student Leadership Experience, Chapel Players, Child Study Club, Dance Team. Major annual events: Student Leadership Experience, Fashion Show, Multicultural Fair. Student services: health clinic, personal-psychological counseling. Campus security: 24-hour emergency response devices and patrols, late night transport-escort service, Emergency Notification System via cell phones. College housing not available. McEntegart Hall Library with 156,232 books, 367 microform titles, 28,299 serials, 2,895 audiovisual materials, an OPAC, and a Web page. Operations spending for the previous fiscal year: $933,000. 214 computers available on campus for general student use. A campuswide network can be accessed. Students can access the following: online class registration.

■ ST. JOSEPH'S COLLEGE OF NURSING

206 Prospect Ave.
Syracuse, NY 13203
Tel: (315)448-5040
Fax: (315)448-5745
E-mail: collegeofnursing@sjhsyr.org
Web Site: www.sjhsyr.org/nursing/

Description: Independent Roman Catholic, 2-year, coed. Awards terminal associate degrees. Founded 1898. Setting: urban campus. Educational spending for the previous fiscal year: $10,000 per student. Total enrollment: 273. Faculty: 29 (16 full-time, 13 part-time). Student-undergrad faculty ratio is 9:1. 42 applied, 55% were admitted. 100% from top half of their high school class. Full-time: 166 students, 90% women, 10% men. Part-time: 107 students, 93% women, 7% men. Students come from 2 states and territories, 0.01% from out-of-state. 20% live on campus. Core. Calendar: semesters. Academic remediation for entering students, services for LD students, advanced placement, part-time degree program, adult/continuing education programs, co-op programs and internships.

Entrance Requirements: Options: electronic application, deferred admission. Required: essay, high school transcript, minimum 3 high school GPA, 2 recommendations, interview, SAT or ACT. Entrance: moderately difficult. Application deadlines: Rolling, Rolling for nonresidents. Notification: continuous, continuous for nonresidents. Transfer credits accepted: Yes.

Costs Per Year: Application fee: $50. Tuition: $16,592 full-time, $488 per credit hour part-time. Mandatory fees: $200 full-time. Full-time tuition and fees vary according to course load. Part-time tuition varies according to course load. College room only: $4400.

Collegiate Environment: Orientation program. Social organizations: 10 open to all. Most popular organizations: New York State Student Nurse's Association, Syracuse Area Black Nurses Association, Student Body Organization. Major annual events: holiday parties, WalkRun Charity Events, Commitment to Nursing Ceremony. Student services: legal services, health clinic, personal-psychological counseling. Campus security: 24-hour patrols. St. Joseph's Hospital Health Center School of Nursing Library with 4,500 books, 900 microform titles, 230 serials, 500 audiovisual materials, and an OPAC. Operations spending for the previous fiscal year: $27,000. 30 computers available on campus for general student use. A campuswide network can be accessed from student residence rooms and from off campus. Staffed computer lab on campus (open 24 hours a day) provides training in use of computers, software, and the Internet.

■ ST. LAWRENCE UNIVERSITY

Canton, NY 13617-1455
Tel: (315)229-5011; Free: 800-285-1856
Fax: (315)229-5502
E-mail: jrickey@stlawu.edu
Web Site: www.stlawu.edu/

Description: Independent, comprehensive, coed. Awards bachelor's and master's degrees and post-master's certificates. Founded 1856. Setting: 1,000-acre small town campus. Endowment: $230.3 million. Total enrollment: 2,488. Faculty: 201 (168 full-time, 33 part-time). Student-undergrad faculty ratio is 12:1. 4,067 applied, 48% were admitted. 44% from top 10% of their high school class, 76% from top quarter, 94% from top half. 8 valedictorians. Full-time: 2,374 students, 55% women, 45% men. Part-time: 24 students, 63% women, 38% men. Students come from 42 states and territories, 50 other countries, 53% from out-of-state. 0.3% American Indian or Alaska Native, non-Hispanic/Latino; 4% Hispanic/Latino; 3% African American, non-Hispanic/Latino; 2% Asian, non-Hispanic/Latino; 0.1% Native Hawaiian or other Pacific Islander, non-Hispanic/Latino; 7% international. 0% 25 or older, 97% live on campus, 1% transferred in. Retention: 93% of full-time freshmen returned the following year. Academic areas with the most degrees conferred: social sciences; biological/life sciences; psychology. Core. Calendar: semesters. Services for LD students, advanced placement, self-designed majors, independent study, double major, summer session for credit, part-time degree program, internships, graduate courses open to undergrads. Off campus study at Clarkson University, State University of New York College of Technology at Canton, State University of New York College at Potsdam, Fisk University, American University. Study abroad program. ROTC: Army (c), Air Force (c).

Entrance Requirements: Options: electronic application, early admission, early decision, deferred admission, international baccalaureate accepted. Required: essay, high school transcript, 2 recommendations. Recommended: minimum 2 high school GPA, interview. Entrance: very difficult. Application deadlines: 2/1, 11/1 for early decision plan 1, 2/1 for early decision plan 2. Notification: 3/31, 12/15 for early decision. SAT Reasoning Test deadline: 2/1. SAT Subject Test deadline: 2/1. Transfer credits accepted: Yes. Applicants placed on waiting list: 203. Wait-listed applicants offered admission: 20. Early decision applicants: 285. Early decision applicants admitted: 248.

Costs Per Year: Application fee: $60. Comprehensive fee: $55,825 includes full-time tuition ($44,075), mandatory fees ($315), and college room and board ($11,435). College room only: $6155. Room and board charges vary according to board plan.

Collegiate Environment: Orientation program. Drama-theater group, choral group, student-run newspaper, radio station. Social organizations: 100 open to all; national fraternities, national sororities, local sororities; 12% of eligible men and 23% of eligible women are members. Most popular organizations: Outing Club, student newspaper, student government, Circle K, Habitat for Humanity. Major annual events: Moving-Up Day, Peak Weekend, Holiday Candlelight Service. Student services: health clinic, personal-psychological counseling, women's center. Campus security: 24-hour emergency response devices and patrols, student patrols, late night transport-escort service, controlled dormitory access. 2,222 college housing spaces available; 2,164 were occupied in 2012-13. Freshmen guaranteed college housing. On-campus residence required through senior year. Options: coed, women-only housing,available. Owen D. Young Library plus 1 other with 622,455 books, 594,395 microform titles, 8,702 serials, 8,234 audiovisual materials, an OPAC, and a Web page. 681 computers available on campus for general student use. Computer purchase/lease plans available. A campuswide network can be accessed from student residence rooms and from off campus. Students can access the following: online class registration. Staffed computer lab on campus provides training in use of computers, software, and the Internet.

■ **ST. PAUL'S SCHOOL OF NURSING**

97-77 Queens Blvd.
Rego Park, NY 11374
Tel: (718)357-0500
Fax: (718)357-4683
E-mail: nwolinski@svcmcny.org
Web Site: www.stpaulsschoolofnursing.com/

Description: Independent, 2-year, coed. Awards terminal associate degrees. Founded 1969. Setting: 2-acre suburban campus. Total enrollment: 106. Faculty: 10 (8 full-time, 2 part-time). Student-undergrad faculty ratio is 10:1. 737 applied, 9% were admitted. 25% from top 10% of their high school class, 75% from top quarter. Students come from 2 states and territories. 50% 25 or older. Core. Calendar: semesters. Part-time degree program.

Entrance Requirements: Option: deferred admission. Required: essay, high school transcript, entrance exam, college transcript, nursing exam. Entrance: moderately difficult. Application deadline: 4/1. Notification: continuous.

Collegiate Environment: Orientation program. 6 computers available on campus for general student use.

■ **ST. THOMAS AQUINAS COLLEGE**

125 Rte. 340
Sparkill, NY 10976
Tel: (845)398-4000; Free: 800-999-STAC
E-mail: dmackay@stac.edu
Web Site: www.stac.edu/

Description: Independent, comprehensive, coed. Awards associate, bachelor's, and master's degrees and post-master's certificates. Founded 1952. Setting: 46-acre suburban campus with easy access to New York City. Endowment: $23.1 million. Educational spending for the previous fiscal year: $7120 per student. Total enrollment: 1,957. Faculty: 143 (63 full-time, 80 part-time). Student-undergrad faculty ratio is 14:1. 1,723 applied, 78% were admitted. 0% from top 10% of their high school class, 0% from top quarter, 0% from top half. Full-time: 1,241 students, 53% women, 47% men. Part-time: 555 students, 53% women, 47% men. Students come from 10 other countries, 21% from out-of-state. 0.3% American Indian or Alaska Native, non-Hispanic/Latino; 15% Hispanic/Latino; 6% African American, non-Hispanic/Latino; 2% Asian, non-Hispanic/Latino; 0% Native Hawaiian or other Pacific Islander, non-Hispanic/Latino; 1% international. 5% 25 or older, 33% live on campus, 6% transferred in. Retention: 75% of full-time freshmen returned the following year. Academic areas with the most degrees conferred: business/marketing; education; law/legal studies. Core. Calendar: semesters. Academic remediation for entering students, services for LD students, advanced placement, accelerated degree program, freshman honors college, honors program, independent study, double major, summer session for credit, part-time degree program, adult/continuing education programs, internships, graduate courses open to undergrads. Off campus study at New York University. Study abroad program. ROTC: Air Force (c).

Entrance Requirements: Options: electronic application, early decision, early action, deferred admission. Required: high school transcript, minimum 2 high school GPA, SAT or ACT. Recommended: essay, 2 recommendations, interview. Required for some: 3 recommendations. Entrance: moderately difficult. Application deadlines: Rolling, 12/1 for early decision, 12/15 for early action. Notification: 10/1, 1/15 for early decision, 1/15 for early action. Early decision applicants: 0. Early decision applicants admitted: 0.

Costs Per Year: Application fee: $30. Comprehensive fee: $38,140 includes full-time tuition ($25,840), mandatory fees ($1000), and college room and board ($11,300). College room only: $6090. Room and board charges vary according to board plan and housing facility. Part-time tuition: $825 per credit.

Collegiate Environment: Orientation program. Drama-theater group, choral group, student-run newspaper, radio station. Social organizations: 26 open to all; national fraternities, local fraternities, local sororities. Most popular organizations: Spartan Volunteers, Campus Activities Board, WSTK campus radio, Bowling Club, Laetare Players. Major annual events: Spring Fest, Oktoberfest, Holiday Semi-Formal. Student services: health clinic, personal-psychological counseling. Campus security: 24-hour emergency response devices and patrols, student patrols, late night transport-escort service, controlled dormitory access. 622 college housing spaces available; 591 were occupied in 2012-13. Freshmen guaranteed college housing. Options: men-only, women-only housing available. Lougheed Library plus 1 other with 97,000 books, 135,354 microform titles, 63,317 serials, 2,175 audiovisual materials, an OPAC, and a Web page. Operations spending for the previous fiscal year: $889,000. 200 computers available on campus for general student use. Computer purchase/lease plans available. A campuswide network can be accessed from student residence rooms and from off campus. Students can access the following: online class registration. Staffed computer lab on campus provides training in use of computers, software, and the Internet.

■ **SAMARITAN HOSPITAL SCHOOL OF NURSING**

2215 Burdett Ave.
Troy, NY 12180
Tel: (518)271-3285
Fax: (518)271-3303
E-mail: marronej@nehealth.com
Web Site: www.nehealth.com/

Description: Independent, 2-year, coed. Administratively affiliated with Samaritan Hospital (Troy, NY). Awards diplomas, transfer associate, and terminal associate degrees. Total enrollment: 119. Faculty: 9 (5 full-time, 4 part-time). Full-time: 36 students, 94% women, 6% men. Part-time: 83 students, 89% women, 11% men. 57% 25 or older.

Entrance Requirements: Required: essay, high school transcript, TEAS. Recommended: SAT or ACT. Application deadline: Rolling. Notification: continuous.

Collegiate Environment: Orientation program. Student services: health clinic, personal-psychological counseling, women's center. 8 computers available on campus for general student use. Staffed computer lab on campus provides training in use of computers, software, and the Internet.

■ SARAH LAWRENCE COLLEGE

1 Mead Way
Bronxville, NY 10708-5999
Tel: (914)337-0700; Free: 800-888-2858
Fax: (914)395-2668
E-mail: slcadmit@sarahlawrence.edu
Web Site: www.sarahlawrence.edu/

Description: Independent, comprehensive, coed. Awards bachelor's and master's degrees and post-master's certificates. Founded 1926. Setting: 44-acre suburban campus with easy access to New York City. Total enrollment: 1,744. Faculty: 311 (110 full-time, 201 part-time). Student-undergrad faculty ratio is 9:1. 2,012 applied, 61% were admitted. 37% from top 10% of their high school class, 59% from top quarter, 91% from top half. Full-time: 1,369 students, 72% women, 28% men. Part-time: 44 students, 75% women, 25% men. 78% from out-of-state. 1% American Indian or Alaska Native, non-Hispanic/Latino; 8% Hispanic/Latino; 4% African American, non-Hispanic/Latino; 7% Asian, non-Hispanic/Latino; 1% Native Hawaiian or other Pacific Islander, non-Hispanic/Latino; 6% international. 85% live on campus, 3% transferred in. Retention: 89% of full-time freshmen returned the following year. Academic area with the most degrees conferred: liberal arts/general studies. Calendar: semesters. Part-time degree program, adult/continuing education programs.

Entrance Requirements: Options: early admission, early decision, deferred admission, international baccalaureate accepted. Required: essay, high school transcript, 3 recommendations. Recommended: minimum 3 high school GPA, interview. Entrance: very difficult. Application deadlines: 1/1, 11/1 for early decision plan 1, 1/1 for early decision plan 2. Notification: 4/1, 12/15 for early decision plan 1, 2/15 for early decision plan 2. Transfer credits accepted: Yes. Early decision applicants admitted: 0.

Costs Per Year: Tuition: $45,900 full-time. Mandatory fees: $1024 full-time. Full-time tuition and fees vary according to course load. College room only: $9324.

Collegiate Environment: Campus security: 24-hour emergency response devices and patrols, late night transport-escort service, controlled dormitory access.

Community Environment: Population 6,455, Bronxville is a residential suburb in Westchester County. Public transportation in the area and to New York City is very accessible. Grand Central Station is only a 30 minute trip on the Metro North train.

■ SBI CAMPUS–AN AFFILIATE OF SANFORD-BROWN

320 S Service Rd.
Melville, NY 11747-3785
Tel: (631)370-3300
Fax: (631)293-1276
Web Site: www.sbmelville.edu/

Description: Proprietary, 2-year, coed. Part of Career Education Corporation. Awards certificates, transfer associate, and terminal associate degrees. Founded 1971. Setting: suburban campus with easy access to New York City. Total enrollment: 546. 625 applied, 100% were admitted. Internships. ROTC: Army (c).

Entrance Requirements: Option: deferred admission. Required: high school transcript, interview. Recommended: 1 recommendation, SAT. Required for some: CPAt. Entrance: minimally difficult. Application deadline: Rolling. Notification: continuous.

Collegiate Environment: Student-run newspaper. Student services: personal-psychological counseling. Campus security: security guard.

■ SCHENECTADY COUNTY COMMUNITY COLLEGE

78 Washington Ave.
Schenectady, NY 12305-2294
Tel: (518)381-1200
E-mail: sampsodg@gw.sunysccc.edu
Web Site: www.sunysccc.edu/

Description: State and locally supported, 2-year, coed. Part of State University of New York System. Awards certificates, transfer associate, and terminal associate degrees. Founded 1969. Setting: 50-acre urban campus. 30% 25 or older. Core. Calendar: semesters. Academic remediation for entering students, ESL program, services for LD students, advanced place-

ment, honors program, distance learning, double major, summer session for credit, part-time degree program, adult/continuing education programs, internships. Off campus study at 14 members of the Hudson-Mohawk Association of Colleges and Universities.

Entrance Requirements: Open admission. Options: electronic application, early admission, deferred admission. Required: high school transcript. Entrance: noncompetitive. Application deadline: Rolling. Notification: continuous. Preference given to county residents.

Collegiate Environment: Orientation program. Drama-theater group, choral group. Social organizations: local fraternities, local sororities. Student services: personal-psychological counseling. Campus security: 24-hour emergency response devices and patrols, late night transport-escort service. Begley Library with 85,000 books, 75,000 microform titles, 640 serials, 2,600 audiovisual materials, an OPAC, and a Web page.

■ SCHOOL OF VISUAL ARTS

209 E 23rd St.
New York, NY 10010-3994
Tel: (212)592-2000; Free: 800-436-4204
Fax: (212)592-2116
E-mail: admissions@sva.edu
Web Site: www.sva.edu/

Description: Proprietary, comprehensive, coed. Awards bachelor's and master's degrees. Founded 1947. Setting: 1-acre urban campus. Total enrollment: 4,214. Faculty: 929 (142 full-time, 787 part-time). Student-undergrad faculty ratio is 10:1. 3,219 applied, 74% were admitted. Full-time: 3,394 students, 59% women, 41% men. Part-time: 256 students, 57% women, 43% men. 55% from out-of-state. 0.5% American Indian or Alaska Native, non-Hispanic/Latino; 11% Hispanic/Latino; 4% African American, non-Hispanic/Latino; 13% Asian, non-Hispanic/Latino; 0% Native Hawaiian or other Pacific Islander, non-Hispanic/Latino; 19% international. 11% 25 or older, 29% live on campus, 9% transferred in. Retention: 84% of full-time freshmen returned the following year. Academic areas with the most degrees conferred: visual and performing arts; computer and information sciences; communication technologies. Core. Calendar: semesters. Academic remediation for entering students, ESL program, services for LD students, advanced placement, freshman honors college, honors program, independent study, summer session for credit, adult/continuing education programs, internships. Study abroad program.

Entrance Requirements: Options: electronic application, deferred admission. Required: essay, high school transcript, minimum 2.5 high school GPA, portfolio, SAT or ACT. Recommended: interview. Entrance: moderately difficult. Application deadline: Rolling. Notification: continuous. SAT Reasoning Test deadline: 5/1. SAT Subject Test deadline: 5/1.

Costs Per Year: Application fee: $50. Comprehensive fee: $47,230 includes full-time tuition ($31,030) and college room and board ($16,200). College room only: $13,200. Room and board charges vary according to housing facility. Part-time tuition: $1034 per credit hour.

Collegiate Environment: Orientation program. Student-run newspaper, radio station. Student services: health clinic, personal-psychological counseling. Campus security: 24-hour patrols. School of Visual Arts Library with an OPAC.

■ SH'OR YOSHUV RABBINICAL COLLEGE

1 Cedarlawn Ave.
Lawrence, NY 11559-1714
Tel: (718)327-2048
E-mail: mrubin@shoryoshuv.org
Web Site: www.shoryoshuv.org/

Description: Independent Jewish, comprehensive, men only. Awards bachelor's and master's degrees. Founded 1963. Total enrollment: 257. Faculty: (17 full-time). Student-undergrad faculty ratio is 15:1. 83 applied. Full-time: 217 students. Students come from 10 states and territories, 5 other countries, 30% from out-of-state. 13% 25 or older, 84% live on campus, 12% transferred in. Retention: 85% of full-time freshmen returned the following year. Core. Calendar: semesters. Academic remediation for entering students, self-designed majors, independent study, summer session for credit, part-time degree program, external degree program, adult/continuing education programs, co-op programs and internships.

Entrance Requirements: Options: electronic application, international baccalaureate accepted. Required: interview. Required for some: essay, high school transcript. Entrance: noncompetitive. Application deadline: 9/20. Notification: 9/22.

Collegiate Environment: Major annual events: Purim Festivities, High

Holiday Prayer, Winter Retreat. Student services: legal services, personal-psychological counseling. Operations spending for the previous fiscal year: $50,000. 10 computers available on campus for general student use. Staffed computer lab on campus.

■ **SIENA COLLEGE**
515 Loudon Rd.
Loudonville, NY 12211-1462
Tel: (518)783-2300; Free: 888-AT-SIENA
Fax: (518)783-4293
E-mail: admit@siena.edu
Web Site: www.siena.edu/

Description: Independent Roman Catholic, comprehensive, coed. Awards bachelor's and master's degrees. Founded 1937. Setting: 175-acre suburban campus. Endowment: $120.7 million. Research spending for the previous fiscal year: $1.6 million. Educational spending for the previous fiscal year: $12,444 per student. Total enrollment: 3,289. Faculty: 354 (210 full-time, 144 part-time). Student-undergrad faculty ratio is 12:1. 9,577 applied, 57% were admitted. 22% from top 10% of their high school class, 57% from top quarter, 89% from top half. Full-time: 3,047 students, 53% women, 47% men. Part-time: 189 students, 38% women, 62% men. Students come from 33 states and territories, 13 other countries, 19% from out-of-state. 0.3% American Indian or Alaska Native, non-Hispanic/Latino; 6% Hispanic/Latino; 3% African American, non-Hispanic/Latino; 4% Asian, non-Hispanic/Latino; 0.1% Native Hawaiian or other Pacific Islander, non-Hispanic/Latino; 2% international. 4% 25 or older, 77% live on campus, 4% transferred in. Retention: 89% of full-time freshmen returned the following year. Academic areas with the most degrees conferred: business/marketing; psychology; biological/life sciences. Core. Calendar: semesters. ESL program, services for LD students, advanced placement, accelerated degree program, honors program, independent study, double major, summer session for credit, part-time degree program, internships, graduate courses open to undergrads. Off campus study at member of the Hudson-Mohawk Association of Colleges and Universities. Study abroad program. ROTC: Army, Naval (c), Air Force (c).

Entrance Requirements: Options: electronic application, early admission, early decision, early action, deferred admission, international baccalaureate accepted. Required: essay, high school transcript, 1 recommendation, SAT or ACT. Recommended: interview. Required for some: interview. Entrance: moderately difficult. Application deadlines: 2/15, 12/1 for early decision, 12/1 for early action. Notification: 3/15, 12/15 for early decision, 1/1 for early action. SAT Reasoning Test deadline: 2/15. Transfer credits accepted: Yes. Applicants placed on waiting list: 873. Wait-listed applicants offered admission: 34. Early decision applicants: 469. Early decision applicants admitted: 51. Early action applicants: 5,744. Early action applicants admitted: 4,136.

Costs Per Year: Application fee: $50. One-time mandatory fee: $250. Comprehensive fee: $43,863 includes full-time tuition ($31,118), mandatory fees ($250), and college room and board ($12,495). College room only: $7365. Full-time tuition and fees vary according to course load and student level. Room and board charges vary according to board plan and housing facility. Part-time tuition: $500 per credit. Part-time tuition varies according to course load and student level.

Collegiate Environment: Orientation program. Drama-theater group, choral group, student-run newspaper, radio station. Social organizations: 70 open to all; national fraternities, national sororities. Most popular organizations: Dog Pound (sports spirit group), Mentoring Program, Outing Club, READ for the Stars, Accounting student Association. Major annual events: Musical Mayhem (Battle of the Bands), SienaFest (Spring Weekend) Carnival, Mr. Siena (fundraiser for Habitat for Humanity). Student services: legal services, health clinic, personal-psychological counseling, women's center. Campus security: 24-hour emergency response devices and patrols, late night transport-escort service, controlled dormitory access, call boxes in parking lots and on roadways. 2,502 college housing spaces available; 2,456 were occupied in 2012-13. Freshmen given priority for college housing. On-campus residence required through senior year. Option: coed housing available. J. Spencer and Patricia Standish Library with 364,698 books, 27,735 microform titles, 24,567 serials, 5,922 audiovisual materials, an OPAC, and a Web page. Operations spending for the previous fiscal year: $1.9 million. 361 computers available on campus for general student use. Computer purchase/lease plans available. A campuswide network can be accessed from student residence rooms and from off campus. Students can access the following: online class registration. Staffed computer lab on campus provides training in use of computers, software, and the Internet.

Community Environment: Population 11,000, Loudonville is a suburban

community of Albany easily reached by bus, railroad, all major airlines, and interstate highways. The community provides a local church, hospital, and shopping facilities. Part-time employment is available for students. The Saratoga Performing Arts Center and Lake George are nearby.

■ **SIMMONS INSTITUTE OF FUNERAL SERVICE**
1828 S Ave.
Syracuse, NY 13207
Tel: (315)475-5142; Free: 800-727-3536
Fax: (315)477-3817
E-mail: admissions@simmonsinstitute.com
Web Site: www.simmonsinstitute.com/

Description: Proprietary, 2-year, coed. Awards transfer associate and terminal associate degrees. Founded 1900. Setting: 1-acre urban campus. Total enrollment: 42. Student-undergrad faculty ratio is 11:1. 0% from out-of-state. 23% 25 or older. Retention: 24% of full-time freshmen returned the following year. Calendar: semesters. Part-time degree program.

Entrance Requirements: Open admission. Required: essay, high school transcript, interview. Entrance: minimally difficult. Application deadline: 6/30. Notification: 7/30.

Collegiate Environment: Orientation program. Campus security: 24-hour emergency response devices.

■ **SKIDMORE COLLEGE**
815 N Broadway
Saratoga Springs, NY 12866
Tel: (518)580-5000; Free: 800-867-6007
Fax: (518)581-7462
E-mail: admissions@skidmore.edu
Web Site: www.skidmore.edu/

Description: Independent, 4-year, coed. Awards bachelor's and master's degrees. Founded 1903. Setting: 800-acre small town campus with easy access to Albany, NY. Endowment: $283.1 million. Total enrollment: 2,689. Faculty: 335 (245 full-time, 90 part-time). Student-undergrad faculty ratio is 9:1. 5,702 applied, 42% were admitted. 43% from top 10% of their high school class, 78% from top quarter, 95% from top half. Full-time: 2,624 students, 61% women, 39% men. Part-time: 39 students, 49% women, 51% men. Students come from 46 states and territories, 51 other countries, 67% from out-of-state. 0.04% American Indian or Alaska Native, non-Hispanic/Latino; 8% Hispanic/Latino; 4% African American, non-Hispanic/Latino; 6% Asian, non-Hispanic/Latino; 0.3% Native Hawaiian or other Pacific Islander, non-Hispanic/Latino; 6% international. 0.3% 25 or older, 86% live on campus, 1% transferred in. Retention: 92% of full-time freshmen returned the following year. Academic areas with the most degrees conferred: social sciences; visual and performing arts; business/marketing. Core. Calendar: semesters plus optional 6-week internship period. Services for LD students, advanced placement, accelerated degree program, self-designed majors, honors program, independent study, double major, summer session for credit, adult/continuing education programs, internships. Off campus study at members of the Hudson-Mohawk Association of Colleges and Universities. Study abroad program. ROTC: Army (c), Air Force (c).

Entrance Requirements: Options: electronic application, early admission, early decision, deferred admission, international baccalaureate accepted. Required: essay, high school transcript, 2 recommendations, SAT or ACT. Recommended: interview, SAT Subject Tests. Entrance: very difficult. Application deadlines: 1/15, 11/15 for early decision plan 1, 1/15 for early decision plan 2. Notification: 4/1, 12/15 for early decision plan 1, 2/15 for early decision plan 2. SAT Reasoning Test deadline: 2/1. SAT Subject Test deadline: 2/1. Transfer credits accepted: Yes. Applicants placed on waiting list: 1,396. Wait-listed applicants offered admission: 41. Early decision applicants: 377. Early decision applicants admitted: 284.

Costs Per Year: Application fee: $65. Comprehensive fee: $55,764 includes full-time tuition ($43,138), mandatory fees ($882), and college room and board ($11,744). College room only: $6944. Full-time tuition and fees vary according to course load. Room and board charges vary according to board plan and housing facility. Part-time tuition: $1438 per credit. Part-time mandatory fees: $25 per term. Part-time tuition and fees vary according to course load.

Collegiate Environment: Orientation program. Drama-theater group, choral group, student-run newspaper, radio station. Social organizations: 77 open to all. Most popular organizations: Student Government Association, student radio station, Student Volunteer Bureau, Outing Club, Skidmore News. Major annual events: Fall Convocation, Spring Convocation, Homecoming/Oktoberfest. Student services: health clinic, personal-psychological counseling. Campus security: 24-hour emergency response devices and patrols, late night transport-escort service, controlled dormitory access, well-lit campus. College housing designed to accommodate 1,947 students; 2,087 undergraduates lived in college housing during 2012-13. Freshmen guaranteed college housing. On-campus residence required through sophomore year. Options: coed, women-only housing available. Scribner Library with an OPAC and a Web page. 600 computers available on campus for general student use. Computer purchase/lease plans available. A campuswide network can be accessed from student residence rooms and from off campus. Students can access the following: online class registration. Staffed computer lab on campus (open 24 hours a day) provides training in use of computers, software, and the Internet.

Community Environment: This resort is famous for the beauty of its setting, the reputed health-giving properties of its water and the gaiety of its summer life. It is also gaining popularity as a winter sport center with downhill and cross-country skiing available nearby. The area has rail, bus, and airline service. Activities to be found within the area include Saratoga Performing Arts Center (summer home of the New York Ballet, Philadelphia Orchestra, and the Acting Company), thoroughbred racing, night harness racing, Yaddo Artist's Colony, Congress Park, Newport Jazz Festival, Petrified Sea Gardens, State Tree Nursery, Grant's Cottage on Mount McGregor, and the Saratoga Historical Museum in the Canfield Casino. Saratoga has churches representing the major denominations. Part-time employment is available.

■ **STATE UNIVERSITY OF NEW YORK COLLEGE OF AGRICULTURE AND TECHNOLOGY AT COBLESKILL**
Cobleskill, NY 12043
Tel: (518)255-5011; Free: 800-295-8988
Fax: (518)255-5333
E-mail: admissions@cobleskill.edu
Web Site: www.cobleskill.edu/

Description: State-supported, 4-year, coed. Part of State University of New York System. Awards associate and bachelor's degrees. Founded 1916. Setting: 75,775-acre rural campus with easy access to Albany, NY. Endowment: $2.1 million. Research spending for the previous fiscal year: $765,735. Educational spending for the previous fiscal year: $6629 per student. Total enrollment: 2,519. Faculty: 150 (113 full-time, 37 part-time). Student-undergrad faculty ratio is 19:1. 2,635 applied, 74% were admitted. 6% from top 10% of their high school class, 22% from top quarter, 56% from top half. Full-time: 2,318 students, 51% women, 49% men. Part-time: 174 students, 57% women, 43% men. Students come from 16 states and territories, 13 other countries, 7% from out-of-state. 0.4% American Indian or Alaska Native, non-Hispanic/Latino; 5% Hispanic/Latino; 10% African American, non-Hispanic/Latino; 1% Asian, non-Hispanic/Latino; 0% Native Hawaiian or other Pacific Islander, non-Hispanic/Latino; 2% international. 9% 25 or older, 76% live on campus, 8% transferred in. Retention: 74% of full-time freshmen returned the following year. Academic areas with the most degrees conferred: natural resources/environmental science; agriculture; business/marketing. Core. Calendar: semesters. Academic remediation for entering students, services for LD students, advanced placement, honors program, independent study, distance learning, summer session for credit, part-time degree program, co-op programs and internships. Off campus study at other units of the State University of New York System. Study abroad program.

Entrance Requirements: Options: electronic application, early admission, deferred admission. Required: high school transcript. Recommended: minimum 1.8 high school GPA. Required for some: essay, minimum 2 high school GPA, 3 recommendations, interview, SAT or ACT. Entrance: minimally difficult. Application deadline: Rolling. Notification: continuous. SAT Reasoning Test deadline: 8/1. SAT Subject Test deadline: 8/1. Transfer credits accepted: Yes.

Costs Per Year: Application fee: $50. One-time mandatory fee: $55. State resident tuition: $5570 full-time, $232 per credit hour part-time. Nonresident tuition: $14,820 full-time, $618 per credit hour part-time. Mandatory fees: $2692 full-time, $73.32 per credit hour part-time. College room and board: $10,866. College room only: $6600. Room and board charges vary according to board plan.

Collegiate Environment: Orientation program. Drama-theater group, choral group, student-run newspaper. Social organizations: 39 open to all; 40% of eligible men and 40% of eligible women are members. Most popular organizations: Post-Secondary Agricultural Students, Woodsmen's Team, Society for Agricultural Engineers, Council for Student Activities. Major annual events: Block Party, Snowball, Spring Fling. Student services: health clinic, personal-psychological counseling. Campus security: 24-hour

emergency response devices and patrols, student patrols, late night transport-escort service, controlled dormitory access, bicycle patrols, horse-mounted patrols. 1,890 college housing spaces available; all were occupied in 2012-13. Freshmen guaranteed college housing. On-campus residence required through sophomore year. Options: coed, men-only, women-only housing available. Jared van Wagenen Library with 75,155 books, 31,173 microform titles, 34,514 serials, 3,631 audiovisual materials, an OPAC, and a Web page. Operations spending for the previous fiscal year: $1 million. 360 computers available on campus for general student use. A campuswide network can be accessed from student residence rooms and from off campus. Students can access the following: online class registration. Staffed computer lab on campus provides training in use of computers.

■ **STATE UNIVERSITY OF NEW YORK COLLEGE AT CORTLAND**
PO Box 2000
Cortland, NY 13045
Tel: (607)753-2011
Fax: (607)753-5999
E-mail: admissions@cortland.edu
Web Site: www.cortland.edu/

Description: State-supported, comprehensive, coed. Part of State University of New York System. Awards bachelor's and master's degrees and post-master's certificates. Founded 1868. Setting: 191-acre small town campus with easy access to Syracuse. Total enrollment: 7,098. Faculty: 641 (278 full-time, 363 part-time). Student-undergrad faculty ratio is 17:1. 11,687 applied, 44% were admitted. 22% from top 10% of their high school class, 61% from top quarter, 100% from top half. Full-time: 6,228 students, 57% women, 43% men. Part-time: 117 students, 51% women, 49% men. 0.2% American Indian or Alaska Native, non-Hispanic/Latino; 9% Hispanic/Latino; 4% African American, non-Hispanic/Latino; 1% Asian, non-Hispanic/Latino; 0.05% Native Hawaiian or other Pacific Islander, non-Hispanic/Latino; 0.4% international. 10% transferred in. Retention: 85% of full-time freshmen returned the following year. Academic areas with the most degrees conferred: education; parks and recreation; social sciences. Calendar: semesters. Adult/continuing education programs. Off campus study at other units of the State University of New York System. ROTC: Army (c), Air Force (c).

Entrance Requirements: Options: early admission, early action, deferred admission, international baccalaureate accepted. Required: essay, high school transcript, minimum 2.3 high school GPA, 1 recommendation, SAT or ACT. Recommended: minimum 3 high school GPA, 3 recommendations, interview. Entrance: moderately difficult. Application deadlines: Rolling, 11/15 for early action. Notification: continuous, 1/1 for early action. Applicants placed on waiting list: 245. Wait-listed applicants offered admission: 31.

Costs Per Year: Application fee: $50. State resident tuition: $5570 full-time, $232 per credit hour part-time. Nonresident tuition: $14,820 full-time, $618 per credit hour part-time. Mandatory fees: $1372 full-time. Full-time tuition and fees vary according to degree level. Part-time tuition varies according to degree level. College room and board: $11,430. College room only: $7070. Room and board charges vary according to board plan and housing facility.

Collegiate Environment: Orientation program. Campus security: 24-hour emergency response devices and patrols, late night transport-escort service. Option: coed housing available.

■ **STATE UNIVERSITY OF NEW YORK COLLEGE OF ENVIRONMENTAL SCIENCE AND FORESTRY**
1 Forestry Dr.
Syracuse, NY 13210-2779
Tel: (315)470-6500
Fax: (315)470-6933
E-mail: esfinfo@esf.edu
Web Site: www.esf.edu/

Description: State-supported, university, coed. Part of State University of New York System. Awards associate, bachelor's, master's, and doctoral degrees. Founded 1911. Setting: 17-acre urban campus. Endowment: $19.5 million. Research spending for the previous fiscal year: $18.5 million. Total enrollment: 2,401. Faculty: 183 (145 full-time, 38 part-time). Student-undergrad faculty ratio is 14:1. 1,619 applied, 51% were admitted. 38% from top 10% of their high school class, 72% from top quarter, 95% from top half. Full-time: 10,020 students, 91% women, 9% men. Part-time: 157 students, 49% women, 51% men. Students come from 36 states and territories, 13 other countries, 19% from out-of-state. 0.2% American Indian or Alaska Native, non-Hispanic/Latino; 3% Hispanic/Latino; 1% African American, non-Hispanic/Latino; 3% Asian, non-Hispanic/Latino; 2% international. 5% 25 or older, 40% live on campus, 2% transferred in. Retention: 87% of full-time freshmen returned the following year. Academic areas with the most degrees conferred: biological/life sciences; natural resources/environmental science; engineering. Core. Calendar: semesters. ESL program, services for LD students, advanced placement, accelerated degree program, freshman honors college, honors program, independent study, distance learning, double major, summer session for credit, part-time degree program, adult/continuing education programs, co-op programs and internships, graduate courses open to undergrads. Off campus study at Syracuse University. Study abroad program. ROTC: Army (c), Air Force (c).

Entrance Requirements: Options: electronic application, early admission, early decision, deferred admission, international baccalaureate accepted. Required: essay, high school transcript, minimum 3 high school GPA, supplemental application, SAT or ACT. Recommended: 1 recommendation, interview, SAT Subject Tests. Entrance: very difficult. Application deadlines: 2/1, 2/1 for nonresidents, 12/1 for early decision. Notification: continuous, continuous for nonresidents, Rolling for early decision. SAT Reasoning Test deadline: 3/1. SAT Subject Test deadline: 3/1. Transfer credits accepted: Yes. Applicants placed on waiting list: 95. Wait-listed applicants offered admission: 11. Early decision applicants: 130. Early decision applicants admitted: 89.

Costs Per Year: Application fee: $50. State resident tuition: $5570 full-time, $232 per credit hour part-time. Nonresident tuition: $14,820 full-time, $618 per credit hour part-time. Mandatory fees: $1023 full-time, $43.10 per credit hour part-time. Full-time tuition and fees vary according to location. Part-time tuition and fees vary according to course load and location. College room and board: $14,400. Room and board charges vary according to board plan, housing facility, and location.

Collegiate Environment: Orientation program. Drama-theater group, choral group, marching band, student-run newspaper. Social organizations: 300 open to all; national fraternities, national sororities; 33% of eligible men and 33% of eligible women are members. Most popular organizations: Bob Marshall/Outing Club, Forestry Club, Student Environmental Action Coalition, Student Green Campus Initiative, Recycling Club. Major annual events: Earth Day, Family and Friends Fall Barbecue, Awards Banquet. Student services: legal services, health clinic, personal-psychological counseling, women's center. Campus security: 24-hour emergency response devices and patrols, late night transport-escort service, controlled dormitory access. 460 college housing spaces available. Freshmen guaranteed college housing. On-campus residence required in freshman year. Option: coed housing available. F. Franklin Moon Library plus 1 other with 137,367 books, 2,634 microform titles, 1,587 serials, 535 audiovisual materials, an OPAC, and a Web page. Operations spending for the previous fiscal year: $608,116. 350 computers available on campus for general student use. Computer purchase/lease plans available. A campuswide network can be accessed from student residence rooms and from off campus. Students can access the following: online class registration. Staffed computer lab on campus.

Community Environment: See Syracuse University.

■ **STATE UNIVERSITY OF NEW YORK COLLEGE OF ENVIRONMENTAL SCIENCE AND FORESTRY, RANGER SCHOOL**
PO Box 48, 257 Ranger School Rd.
Wanakena, NY 13695
Tel: (315)848-2566
Fax: (315)470-6933
E-mail: esfinfo@esf.edu
Web Site: www.esf.edu/rangerschool/default.asp
Description: State-supported, 2-year, coed. Part of State University of New York. Administratively affiliated with State University of New York College of Environmental Science and Forestry. Awards transfer associate and terminal associate degrees (The associate degrees offered at The Ranger School campus of SUNY-ESF are 1 + 1 programs enrolling students for the second year of study after they complete their first-year requirements at SUNY-ESF's Syracuse campus or the college of their choice). Founded 1912. Setting: 2,800-acre rural campus. Research spending for the previous fiscal year: $16.9 million. Total enrollment: 58. Faculty: 6 (all full-time). Student-undergrad faculty ratio is 9:1. Full-time: 58 students, 17% women, 83% men. 0% from out-of-state. 2% Hispanic/Latino; 2% Asian, non-Hispanic/Latino. 15% 25 or older, 100% live on campus, 60% transferred in. Core. Calendar: semesters. Advanced placement.

Entrance Requirements: Options: electronic application, deferred admission. Required: essay, high school transcript, minimum 2.5 high school GPA, SAT or ACT. Recommended: essay, high school transcript, minimum 2.5 high school GPA, interview. Entrance: minimally difficult. Transfer credits accepted: Yes.

Costs Per Year: Application fee: $50. State resident tuition: $5570 full-time, $220 per credit hour part-time. Nonresident tuition: $15,180 full-time, $597 per credit hour part-time. Mandatory fees: $1260 full-time. Full-time tuition and fees vary according to course load and location. Part-time tuition varies according to course load and location. College room and board: $10,020. College room only: $2720. Room and board charges vary according to housing facility.

Collegiate Environment: Orientation program. Most popular organizations: Hockey Club, Outing Club. Major annual events: Winter Weekend, Open House. Student services: legal services, health clinic, personal-psychological counseling. Campus security: 24-hour emergency response devices. Ranger School Library with 1,500 books, 60 serials, and an OPAC. Operations spending for the previous fiscal year: $598,859. 50 computers available on campus for general student use. Computer purchase/lease plans available. A campuswide network can be accessed from student residence rooms and from off campus.

■ **STATE UNIVERSITY OF NEW YORK COLLEGE AT GENESEO**
1 College Cir.
Geneseo, NY 14454-1401
Tel: (585)245-5211; Free: 866-245-5211
Fax: (585)245-5005
E-mail: admissions@geneseo.edu
Web Site: www.geneseo.edu/
Description: State-supported, comprehensive, coed. Part of State University of New York System. Awards bachelor's and master's degrees. Founded 1871. Setting: 220-acre small town campus with easy access to Rochester. Endowment: $18.2 million. Research spending for the previous fiscal year: $3.6 million. Total enrollment: 5,557. Faculty: 359 (255 full-time, 104 part-time). Student-undergrad faculty ratio is 19:1. 9,164 applied, 46% were admitted. 54% from top 10% of their high school class, 85% from top quarter, 98% from top half. Full-time: 5,277 students, 58% women, 42% men. Part-time: 111 students, 54% women, 46% men. Students come from 34 states and territories, 42 other countries, 2% from out-of-state. 0.2% American Indian or Alaska Native, non-Hispanic/Latino; 6% Hispanic/Latino; 2% African American, non-Hispanic/Latino; 7% Asian, non-Hispanic/Latino; 0.04% Native Hawaiian or other Pacific Islander, non-Hispanic/Latino; 3% international. 3% 25 or older, 54% live on campus, 7% transferred in. Retention: 90% of full-time freshmen returned the following year. Academic areas with the most degrees conferred: education; social sciences; business/marketing. Core. Calendar: semesters. ESL program, services for LD students, advanced placement, honors program, independent study, distance learning, double major, summer session for credit, part-time degree program, internships, graduate courses open to undergrads. Off campus study at Rochester Area Colleges. Study abroad program. ROTC: Army (c), Air Force (c).

Entrance Requirements: Options: electronic application, early admission, early decision, deferred admission, international baccalaureate accepted. Required: essay, high school transcript, SAT or ACT. Recommended: 1 recommendation. Entrance: very difficult. Application deadlines: 1/1, 11/15 for early decision. Notification: 3/1, 12/15 for early decision. SAT Reasoning Test deadline: 1/1. Transfer credits accepted: Yes. Applicants placed on waiting list: 1,350. Wait-listed applicants offered admission: 47. Early decision applicants: 270. Early decision applicants admitted: 133.

Costs Per Year: Application fee: $50. State resident tuition: $5570 full-time. Nonresident tuition: $14,820 full-time. Mandatory fees: $1525 full-time. College room and board: $10,960. College room only: $6950. Room and board charges vary according to board plan and housing facility.

Collegiate Environment: Orientation program. Drama-theater group, choral group, student-run newspaper, radio station. Social organizations: 191 open to all; national fraternities, national sororities, local fraternities, local sororities; 12% of eligible men and 14% of eligible women are members. Most popular organizations: Alpha Phi Omega, Inter-Varsity Christian Fellowship, Inter-Residence Council, Colleges Against Cancer, Geneseo Area Gaming Group. Major annual events: Weeks of Welcome, Student Organization Expo, Great Day. Student services: legal services, health clinic, personal-psychological counseling. Campus security: 24-hour emergency response devices and patrols, student patrols, late night transport-escort service, controlled dormitory access. 3,293 college housing spaces available; 2,909 were occupied in 2012-13. Freshmen guaranteed college housing. On-campus residence required through sophomore year. Option: coed housing available. Milne Library with 595,325 books, 842,015 microform titles, 191,137 serials, 22,567 audiovisual materials, an OPAC, and a Web page. Operations spending for the previous fiscal year: $2.3 million. 503 computers available on campus for general student use. Computer purchase/lease plans available. A computer is required for all students. A campuswide network can be accessed from student residence rooms and from off campus. Students can access the following: online class registration. Staffed computer lab on campus provides training in use of computers, software, and the Internet.

■ **STATE UNIVERSITY OF NEW YORK COLLEGE AT OLD WESTBURY**
PO Box 210
Old Westbury, NY 11568-0210
Tel: (516)876-3000
Fax: (516)876-3307
E-mail: enroll@oldwestbury.edu
Web Site: www.oldwestbury.edu/
Description: State-supported, comprehensive, coed. Part of State University of New York System. Awards bachelor's and master's degrees and post-master's certificates. Founded 1965. Setting: 604-acre suburban campus with easy access to New York City. Total enrollment: 4,422. Faculty: 311 (148 full-time, 163 part-time). Student-undergrad faculty ratio is 18:1. 3,855 applied, 52% were admitted. 12% from top 10% of their high school class, 45% from top quarter, 80% from top half. Full-time: 3,609 students, 59% women, 41% men. Part-time: 608 students, 59% women, 41% men. Students come from 13 states and territories, 58 other countries, 1% from out-of-state. 1% American Indian or Alaska Native, non-Hispanic/Latino; 21% Hispanic/Latino; 30% African American, non-Hispanic/Latino; 9% Asian, non-Hispanic/Latino; 0.4% Native Hawaiian or other Pacific Islander, non-Hispanic/Latino; 1% international. 20% 25 or older, 22% live on campus, 17% transferred in. Retention: 80% of full-time freshmen returned the following year. Academic areas with the most degrees conferred: business/marketing; social sciences; psychology. Core. Calendar: semesters. Academic remediation for entering students, ESL program, services for LD students, advanced placement, freshman honors college, honors program, independent study, distance learning, double major, summer session for credit, part-time degree program, internships. Off campus study at other units of the State University of New York System, Long Island University, C.W. Post Campus, New York Institute of Technology. Study abroad program. ROTC: Army (c), Air Force (c).
Entrance Requirements: Options: electronic application, early admission, early decision, deferred admission. Required: essay, high school transcript, 2 recommendations, SAT or ACT. Required for some: interview. Entrance: moderately difficult. Application deadlines: Rolling, 11/1 for early decision. Notification: continuous, 12/15 for early decision. SAT Reasoning Test deadline: 6/1. SAT Subject Test deadline: 6/1.
Costs Per Year: Application fee: $50. State resident tuition: $5570 full-time, $232 per credit part-time. Nonresident tuition: $14,820 full-time, $618 per credit part-time. Mandatory fees: $1054 full-time, $20.85 per credit part-time, $148 per term part-time. Part-time tuition and fees vary according to course load. College room and board: $9700. College room only: $6600. Room and board charges vary according to board plan.
Collegiate Environment: Orientation program. Drama-theater group, choral group, student-run newspaper, radio station. Social organizations: 55 open to all; national fraternities, national sororities, local fraternities, local sororities; 2% of eligible men and 2% of eligible women are members. Most popular organizations: Student Government Association, Alianza Latina, PRIDE, Step Tunes, Anime Magna Games Club. Major annual events: Midnight Madness, Meet the Greeks, Step & Stroll Exhibition. Student services: health clinic, personal-psychological counseling, women's center. Campus security: 24-hour emergency response devices and patrols, student patrols, late night transport-escort service, controlled dormitory access. 1,000 college housing spaces available; 921 were occupied in 2012-13. Freshmen guaranteed college housing. Option: coed housing available. SUNY College at Old Westbury Library plus 1 other with 251,930 books, 18,864 microform titles, 2,532 serials, 1,634 audiovisual materials, an OPAC, and a Web page. 640 computers available on campus for general student use. A campuswide network can be accessed from student residence rooms and from off campus. Students can access the following: online class registration, financial aid, billing information, grades. Staffed computer lab on campus provides training in use of computers, software, and the Internet.

■ **STATE UNIVERSITY OF NEW YORK COLLEGE AT ONEONTA**
Ravine Pky.
Oneonta, NY 13820-4015

Tel: (607)436-3500; Free: 800-SUNY-123
Fax: (607)436-3074
E-mail: admissions@oneonta.edu
Web Site: www.oneonta.edu/
Description: State-supported, comprehensive, coed. Part of State University of New York. Awards bachelor's and master's degrees and post-master's certificates. Founded 1889. Setting: 250-acre small town campus. Endowment: $37.8 million. Research spending for the previous fiscal year: $5.9 million. Educational spending for the previous fiscal year: $5889 per student. Total enrollment: 6,023. Faculty: 483 (253 full-time, 230 part-time). Student-undergrad faculty ratio is 18:1. 12,338 applied, 43% were admitted. Full-time: 5,738 students, 59% women, 41% men. Part-time: 114 students, 45% women, 55% men. Students come from 11 states and territories, 17 other countries, 1% from out-of-state. 0.2% American Indian or Alaska Native, non-Hispanic/Latino; 4% Hispanic/Latino; 3% African American, non-Hispanic/Latino; 2% Asian, non-Hispanic/Latino; 0% Native Hawaiian or other Pacific Islander, non-Hispanic/Latino; 2% international. 3% 25 or older, 59% live on campus, 8% transferred in. Retention: 84% of full-time freshmen returned the following year. Academic areas with the most degrees conferred: education; visual and performing arts; communication/journalism. Core. Calendar: semesters. Academic remediation for entering students, ESL program, services for LD students, advanced placement, honors program, independent study, distance learning, double major, summer session for credit, part-time degree program, adult/continuing education programs, internships, graduate courses open to undergrads. Off campus study at Hartwick College. Study abroad program.
Entrance Requirements: Options: electronic application, early admission, early action, deferred admission, international baccalaureate accepted. Required: essay, high school transcript, SAT or ACT. Recommended: minimum 3 high school GPA, 3 recommendations. Entrance: very difficult. Application deadlines: Rolling, 11/15 for early action. Notification: continuous, 12/15 for early action. SAT Reasoning Test deadline: 2/15. Early action applicants: 3,695. Early action applicants admitted: 2,326.
Costs Per Year: Application fee: $50. State resident tuition: $5570 full-time, $232 per semester hour part-time. Nonresident tuition: $14,820 full-time, $618 per semester hour part-time. Mandatory fees: $1317 full-time, $37 per semester hour part-time. Part-time tuition and fees vary according to course load. College room and board: $10,540. College room only: $6740. Room and board charges vary according to housing facility.
Collegiate Environment: Orientation program. Drama-theater group, choral group, student-run newspaper, radio station. Social organizations: 115 open to all; national fraternities, national sororities, local fraternities, local sororities; 6% of eligible men and 7% of eligible women are members. Most popular organizations: Center for Social Responsibility and Community, Music Industry Club, Terpsichorean Dance Company, student government, Zombie Defense Corps. Major annual events: Homecoming and Family Weekend, Club Expo, Spring Weekend. Student services: health clinic, personal-psychological counseling, women's center. Campus security: 24-hour emergency response devices and patrols, late night transport-escort service, controlled dormitory access, Oneonta Emergency Squad: an organization of student volunteers with first responder credentials, e.g., EMT training, CPR certification. Milne Library with 490,112 books, 1.2 million microform titles, 64,031 serials, 13,410 audiovisual materials, an OPAC, and a Web page. Operations spending for the previous fiscal year: $2.5 million. 700 computers available on campus for general student use. Computer purchase/lease plans available. A campuswide network can be accessed from student residence rooms and from off campus. Students can access the following: online class registration, Digital video/audio editing suites, presentation rehearsal room using lecture capture software, large format printing, network file storage space. Staffed computer lab on campus (open 24 hours a day) provides training in use of computers, software, and the Internet.

■ **STATE UNIVERSITY OF NEW YORK COLLEGE AT POTSDAM**
44 Pierrepont Ave.
Potsdam, NY 13676
Tel: (315)267-2000; Free: 877-POTSDAM
Fax: (315)267-2163
E-mail: admissions@potsdam.edu
Web Site: www.potsdam.edu/
Description: State-supported, comprehensive, coed. Part of State University of New York System. Awards bachelor's and master's degrees. Founded 1816. Setting: 240-acre small town campus. Endowment: $18.5 million. Research spending for the previous fiscal year: $217,094.

Educational spending for the previous fiscal year: $10,775 per student. Total enrollment: 4,224. Faculty: 362 (261 full-time, 101 part-time). Student-undergrad faculty ratio is 14:1. 5,022 applied, 65% were admitted. 9% from top 10% of their high school class, 31% from top quarter, 74% from top half. Full-time: 3,762 students, 58% women, 42% men. Part-time: 106 students, 53% women, 47% men. Students come from 54 states and territories, 20 other countries, 3% from out-of-state. 1% American Indian or Alaska Native, non-Hispanic/Latino; 7% Hispanic/Latino; 5% African American, non-Hispanic/Latino; 1% Asian, non-Hispanic/Latino; 0.1% Native Hawaiian or other Pacific Islander, non-Hispanic/Latino; 1% international. 6% 25 or older, 97% live on campus, 9% transferred in. Retention: 75% of full-time freshmen returned the following year. Academic areas with the most degrees conferred: education; visual and performing arts; social sciences; English. Core. Calendar: semesters. Services for LD students, advanced placement, self-designed majors, honors program, independent study, distance learning, double major, summer session for credit, part-time degree program, internships, graduate courses open to undergrads. Off campus study at Associated Colleges of the St. Lawrence Valley, National Student Exchange. Study abroad program. ROTC: Army (c), Air Force (c).

Entrance Requirements: Options: electronic application, early admission, deferred admission, international baccalaureate accepted. Required: high school transcript, minimum 2.5 high school GPA, audition for music program. Required for some: essay, minimum 2 high school GPA, interview, SAT or ACT. Entrance: moderately difficult. Application deadline: Rolling. Notification: continuous. Transfer credits accepted: Yes.

Costs Per Year: Application fee: $50. State resident tuition: $5570 full-time, $232 per credit hour part-time. Nonresident tuition: $14,820 full-time, $618 per credit hour part-time. Mandatory fees: $1272 full-time. College room and board: $10,180. College room only: $5970. Room and board charges vary according to board plan and housing facility.

Collegiate Environment: Orientation program. Drama-theater group, choral group, student-run newspaper, radio station. Social organizations: 100 open to all; national fraternities, national sororities, local fraternities, local sororities; 5% of eligible men and 7% of eligible women are members. Most popular organizations: Student Government Association, Crane Student Association, Student Entertainment Services (Programming Board), WALH Radio, The Racquette Student Newspaper. Major annual events: Springfest, Welcome Weekend, Crane Candlelight Concert. Student services: legal services, health clinic, personal-psychological counseling, women's center. Campus security: 24-hour emergency response devices and patrols, late night transport-escort service, controlled dormitory access, educational programs, campus rescue squad, portable jump start packets, vehicle lock outs and parking management. 2,763 college housing spaces available; 2,442 were occupied in 2012-13. Freshmen guaranteed college housing. On-campus residence required through sophomore year. Option: coed housing available. F. W. Crumb Memorial Library plus 1 other with 441,519 books, 772,929 microform titles, 58,997 serials, 13,719 audiovisual materials, an OPAC, and a Web page. 608 computers available on campus for general student use. Computer purchase/lease plans available. A campuswide network can be accessed from student residence rooms and from off campus. Students can access the following: online class registration, online access to financial aid status, unofficial transcripts, billing, meal plan and housing sign ups,225 wireless hot spots with 95 on campus and 130 in the residence halls. Staffed computer lab on campus provides training in use of computers, software, and the Internet.

■ **STATE UNIVERSITY OF NEW YORK COLLEGE OF TECHNOLOGY AT ALFRED**

10 Upper College Dr.
Alfred, NY 14802
Tel: (607)587-4111; Free: 800-4-ALFRED
Fax: (607)587-4299
E-mail: admissions@alfredstate.edu
Web Site: www.alfredstate.edu/

Description: State-supported, primarily 2-year, coed. Part of The State University of New York System. Awards certificates, transfer associate, terminal associate, and bachelor's degrees. Founded 1908. Setting: 1,084-acre rural campus with easy access to Rochester, Buffalo. Endowment: $3.6 million. Research spending for the previous fiscal year: $33,166. Educational spending for the previous fiscal year: $8760 per student. Total enrollment: 3,527. Faculty: 219 (181 full-time, 38 part-time). Student-undergrad faculty ratio is 18:1. 3,890 applied, 55% were admitted. Full-time: 3,211 students, 35% women, 65% men. Part-time: 316 students, 77% women, 23% men. Students come from 35 states and territories, 19 other countries, 7% from

out-of-state. 0.3% American Indian or Alaska Native, non-Hispanic/Latino; 6% Hispanic/Latino; 9% African American, non-Hispanic/Latino; 2% Asian, non-Hispanic/Latino; 0.1% Native Hawaiian or other Pacific Islander, non-Hispanic/Latino. 15% 25 or older, 74% live on campus, 7% transferred in. Retention: 81% of full-time freshmen returned the following year. Academic areas with the most degrees conferred: engineering technologies; business/marketing; computer and information sciences. Calendar: semesters. Academic remediation for entering students, ESL program, services for LD students, advanced placement, self-designed majors, honors program, independent study, distance learning, double major, summer session for credit, part-time degree program, adult/continuing education programs, co-op programs and internships. Off campus study at Cross registration available at Alfred University, Rochester Area Colleges, and Consortium of Western New York Colleges; ROTC with St. Bonaventure University. Study abroad program. ROTC: Army (c).

Entrance Requirements: Options: electronic application, international baccalaureate accepted. Required: high school transcript, minimum 2 high school GPA. Recommended: essay, interview, SAT or ACT. Required for some: SAT or ACT. Entrance: moderately difficult. Application deadlines: Rolling, Rolling for nonresidents. Notification: continuous, continuous for nonresidents. Transfer credits accepted: Yes. Applicants placed on waiting list: 270. Wait-listed applicants offered admission: 36.

Costs Per Year: Application fee: $50. One-time mandatory fee: $100. State resident tuition: $5570 full-time, $232 per credit hour part-time. Nonresident tuition: $9740 full-time, $406 per credit hour part-time. Mandatory fees: $1304 full-time, $53.45 per credit hour part-time, $10. Full-time tuition and fees vary according to course load and degree level. Part-time tuition and fees vary according to course load and degree level. College room and board: $11,160. College room only: $6650. Room and board charges vary according to board plan and housing facility.

Collegiate Environment: Orientation program. Drama-theater group, choral group, student-run newspaper, radio station. Social organizations: 60 open to all; local fraternities, local sororities; 3% of eligible men and 2% of eligible women are members. Most popular organizations: Outdoor Recreation Club, International Club, intramural sports, Pioneer Woodsmen Team, Black Student Union. Major annual events: Hot Dog Day, Homecoming, Freshman Carnival. Student services: health clinic, personal-psychological counseling. Campus security: 24-hour emergency response devices and patrols, late night transport-escort service, controlled dormitory access, residence hall entrance guards. 2,650 college housing spaces available; 2,404 were occupied in 2012-13. Freshmen guaranteed college housing. Options: coed, men-only, women-only housing available. Walter C. Hinkle Memorial Library plus 1 other with 61,639 books, 52,125 microform titles, 68,689 serials, 4,478 audiovisual materials, an OPAC, and a Web page. Operations spending for the previous fiscal year: $480,863. 100 computers available on campus for general student use. Computer purchase/lease plans available. A campuswide network can be accessed from student residence rooms and from off campus. Students can access the following: online class registration. Staffed computer lab on campus provides training in use of computers, software, and the Internet.

■ **STATE UNIVERSITY OF NEW YORK COLLEGE OF TECHNOLOGY AT CANTON**

Cornell Dr.
Canton, NY 13617
Tel: (315)386-7011; Free: 800-388-7123
Fax: (315)386-7930
E-mail: admissions@canton.edu
Web Site: www.canton.edu/

Description: State-supported, comprehensive, coed. Part of State University of New York System. Awards associate, bachelor's, and master's degrees. Founded 1906. Setting: 555-acre small town campus. Endowment: $8.1 million. Total enrollment: 3,780. Faculty: 220 (118 full-time, 102 part-time). Student-undergrad faculty ratio is 22:1. 4,884 applied, 67% were admitted. 3% from top 10% of their high school class, 17% from top quarter, 50% from top half. Full-time: 3,087 students, 53% women, 47% men. Part-time: 693 students, 63% women, 37% men. Students come from 33 states and territories, 9 other countries, 3% from out-of-state. 2% American Indian or Alaska Native, non-Hispanic/Latino; 9% Hispanic/Latino; 18% African American, non-Hispanic/Latino; 1% Asian, non-Hispanic/Latino; 0.1% Native Hawaiian or other Pacific Islander, non-Hispanic/Latino; 1% international. 25% 25 or older, 35% live on campus, 9% transferred in. Retention: 75% of full-time freshmen returned the following year. Academic areas with the most degrees conferred: business/marketing; homeland security, law enforcement, firefighting, and protective services; law/legal studies. Core. Calendar: semesters. Academic remediation for entering students, services for LD students, advanced placement, self-designed majors, honors program, independent study, distance learning, summer session for credit, internships. Off campus study at the Associated Colleges of the St. Lawrence Valley. Study abroad program. ROTC: Army (c), Air Force (c).

Entrance Requirements: Options: electronic application, early admission, deferred admission, international baccalaureate accepted. Required: high school transcript. Recommended: minimum 2 high school GPA. Required for some: essay, interview, SAT or ACT. Entrance: minimally difficult. Application deadlines: Rolling, Rolling for nonresidents. Notification: continuous, continuous for nonresidents. Transfer credits accepted: Yes.

Costs Per Year: Application fee: $40. One-time mandatory fee: $90. State resident tuition: $5570 full-time, $220 per credit hour part-time. Nonresident tuition: $10,324 full-time, $597 per credit hour part-time. Mandatory fees: $1400 full-time, $58 per credit hour part-time, $5 per term part-time. Full-time tuition and fees vary according to degree level, location, and program. Part-time tuition and fees vary according to degree level, location, and program. College room and board: $10,952. College room only: $6510. Room and board charges vary according to board plan and housing facility.

Collegiate Environment: Orientation program. Drama-theater group, choral group. Social organizations: 72 open to all; national fraternities, national sororities, local fraternities, local sororities; 4% of eligible men and 4% of eligible women are members. Most popular organizations: Criminal Justice, Student Cooperative Alliance, Automotive Club, Gaming Club, African Student Union. Major annual events: Family Weekend, Springfest. Student services: health clinic, personal-psychological counseling. Campus security: 24-hour emergency response devices and patrols, late night transport-escort service, controlled dormitory access. 1,300 college housing spaces available; all were occupied in 2012-13. Freshmen guaranteed college housing. On-campus residence required through junior year. Option: coed housing available. Southworth Library plus 1 other with 56,481 books, 3,828 microform titles, 120 serials, 1,473 audiovisual materials, an OPAC, and a Web page. 635 computers available on campus for general student use. A campuswide network can be accessed. Students can access the following: online class registration, bill payment. Staffed computer lab on campus.

■ STATE UNIVERSITY OF NEW YORK COLLEGE OF TECHNOLOGY AT DELHI

2 Main St.
Delhi, NY 13753
Tel: (607)746-4000; Free: 800-96-DELHI
Fax: (607)746-4104
E-mail: enroll@delhi.edu
Web Site: www.delhi.edu/

Description: State-supported, 4-year, coed. Part of State University of New York System. Awards associate and bachelor's degrees. Founded 1913. Setting: 405-acre rural campus. Endowment: $3.5 million. Research spending for the previous fiscal year: $135,000. Educational spending for the previous fiscal year: $8776 per student. Total enrollment: 3,151. Faculty: 227 (129 full-time, 98 part-time). Student-undergrad faculty ratio is 17:1. 5,012 applied, 57% were admitted. 3% from top 10% of their high school class, 11% from top quarter, 42% from top half. Full-time: 2,605 students, 46% women, 54% men. Part-time: 546 students, 81% women, 19% men. Students come from 22 states and territories, 6 other countries, 4% from out-of-state. 0.2% American Indian or Alaska Native, non-Hispanic/Latino; 11% Hispanic/Latino; 14% African American, non-Hispanic/Latino; 2% Asian, non-Hispanic/Latino; 0.1% Native Hawaiian or other Pacific Islander, non-Hispanic/Latino; 1% international. 25% 25 or older, 48% live on campus, 17% transferred in. Retention: 72% of full-time freshmen returned the following year. Academic areas with the most degrees conferred: business/marketing; health professions and related sciences; computer and information sciences. Core. Calendar: semesters. Academic remediation for entering students, ESL program, services for LD students, advanced placement, self-designed majors, honors program, distance learning, summer session for credit, part-time degree program, internships. Off campus study at Bachelor degree programs offered at Monroe Community College, Nassau Community College, Onondaga Community College, Schenectady County Community College, Suffolk Community College, and Tompkins Cortland Community College.

Entrance Requirements: Options: electronic application, early admission, deferred admission. Required: high school transcript. Recommended: interview, SAT or ACT. Required for some: minimum 2 high school GPA, some Bachelor degree programs require Associate degree for admission;

BSN program requires RN license. Entrance: moderately difficult. Application deadline: Rolling. Notification: continuous. SAT Reasoning Test deadline: 8/1. SAT Subject Test deadline: 8/1. Transfer credits accepted: Yes. Applicants placed on waiting list: 403. Wait-listed applicants offered admission: 10.

Costs Per Year: Application fee: $50. State resident tuition: $5570 full-time, $232 per credit hour part-time. Nonresident tuition: $9740 full-time, $406 per credit hour part-time. Mandatory fees: $1520 full-time, $76.24 per credit hour part-time, $76.24. Full-time tuition and fees vary according to degree level. Part-time tuition and fees vary according to degree level. College room and board: $10,346. College room only: $5936. Room and board charges vary according to board plan and housing facility.

Collegiate Environment: Orientation program. Drama-theater group, student-run newspaper, radio station. Social organizations: 60 open to all; national fraternities, local fraternities, local sororities; 10% of eligible men and 8% of eligible women are members. Most popular organizations: Latin American Student Organization, Hotel Sales Management Association, student radio station, Phi Theta Kappa, Student Programming Board. Major annual events: Fall Weekend, Winter Weekend, Spring Weekend. Student services: health clinic, personal-psychological counseling. Campus security: 24-hour emergency response devices and patrols, late night transport-escort service, controlled dormitory access. College housing designed to accommodate 1,578 students; 1,740 undergraduates lived in college housing during 2012-13. On-campus residence required through sophomore year. Options: coed, women-only housing available. Resnick Library plus 1 other with 47,659 books, 304 microform titles, 248 serials, 2,873 audiovisual materials, and an OPAC. Operations spending for the previous fiscal year: $553,837. 350 computers available on campus for general student use. A campuswide network can be accessed from student residence rooms and from off campus. Students can access the following: online class registration. Staffed computer lab on campus provides training in use of computers, software, and the Internet.

■ STATE UNIVERSITY OF NEW YORK DOWNSTATE MEDICAL CENTER

450 Clarkson Ave.
Brooklyn, NY 11203-2098
Tel: (718)270-1000
Fax: (718)270-7592
E-mail: admissions@downstate.edu
Web Site: www.downstate.edu/

Description: State-supported, upper-level, coed. Part of State University of New York System. Awards bachelor's, master's, and doctoral degrees and post-master's certificates. Founded 1858. Setting: urban campus. Total enrollment: 1,694. Faculty: 981 (838 full-time, 143 part-time). 1,005 applied, 14% were admitted. Full-time: 193 students, 78% women, 22% men. Part-time: 150 students, 90% women, 10% men. 1% from out-of-state. 0% American Indian or Alaska Native, non-Hispanic/Latino; 6% Hispanic/Latino; 39% African American, non-Hispanic/Latino; 14% Asian, non-Hispanic/Latino; 1% international. Academic area with the most degrees conferred: health professions and related sciences. Core. Calendar: semesters. Services for LD students, advanced placement, accelerated degree program, independent study, summer session for credit, part-time degree program, internships. Off campus study.

Collegiate Environment: Orientation program. Student services: health clinic, personal-psychological counseling. Campus security: late night transport-escort service. 183 computers available on campus for general student use. A campuswide network can be accessed from student residence rooms and from off campus. Staffed computer lab on campus.

■ STATE UNIVERSITY OF NEW YORK EMPIRE STATE COLLEGE

2 Union Ave.
Saratoga Springs, NY 12866-4391
Tel: (518)587-2100; Free: 800-847-3000
Fax: (518)587-2100
E-mail: Jennifer.D'Agostino@esc.edu
Web Site: www.esc.edu/

Description: State-supported, comprehensive, coed. Part of State University of New York System. Awards associate, bachelor's, and master's degrees (branch locations at 7 regional centers with 35 auxiliary units). Founded 1971. Setting: small town campus. Endowment: $13.8 million. Research spending for the previous fiscal year: $58,870. Educational spending for the previous fiscal year: $8709 per student. Total enrollment: 12,091. Faculty: 1,400 (202 full-time, 1,198 part-time). Student-undergrad faculty ratio is 8:1. 1,536 applied, 79% were admitted. Full-time: 4,352 students, 69% women, 31% men. Part-time: 6,769 students, 57% women, 43% men. Students come from 52 states and territories, 13 other countries, 8% from out-of-state. 1% American Indian or Alaska Native, non-Hispanic/Latino; 5% Hispanic/Latino; 18% African American, non-Hispanic/Latino; 2% Asian, non-Hispanic/Latino; 1% Native Hawaiian or other Pacific Islander, non-Hispanic/Latino. 83% 25 or older, 16% transferred in. Academic areas with the most degrees conferred: business/marketing; public administration and social services; psychology. Core. Calendar: continuous. Services for LD students, advanced placement, self-designed majors, independent study, distance learning, summer session for credit, part-time degree program, external degree program, adult/continuing education programs, co-op programs. Off campus study at New York State Visiting Student Program.

Entrance Requirements: Options: electronic application, early admission. Required: essay, high school transcript. Required for some: interview. Entrance: minimally difficult. Application deadline: Rolling. Transfer credits accepted: Yes.

Costs Per Year: Application fee: $0. State resident tuition: $5570 full-time, $232 per credit hour part-time. Nonresident tuition: $14,820 full-time, $618 per credit hour part-time. Mandatory fees: $345 full-time, $7.10 per credit hour part-time, $115 per term part-time. Full-time tuition and fees vary according to course level, course load, location, and program. Part-time tuition and fees vary according to course level, location, and program.

Collegiate Environment: Orientation program. College housing not available. 70,000 books, 57,000 serials, and a Web pageOperations spending for the previous fiscal year: $379,166. 100 computers available on campus for general student use. A campuswide network can be accessed from off-campus. Students can access the following: online class registration. Staffed computer lab on campus.

■ **STATE UNIVERSITY OF NEW YORK AT FREDONIA**
Fredonia, NY 14063-1136
Tel: (716)673-3111; Free: 800-252-1212
Fax: (716)673-3249
E-mail: admissions@fredonia.edu
Web Site: www.fredonia.edu/

Description: State-supported, comprehensive, coed. Part of State University of New York System. Awards bachelor's and master's degrees and post-master's certificates. Founded 1826. Setting: 249-acre small town campus with easy access to Buffalo. Endowment: $24.5 million. Research spending for the previous fiscal year: $201,789. Educational spending for the previous fiscal year: $9542 per student. Total enrollment: 5,523. Faculty: 482 (253 full-time, 229 part-time). Student-undergrad faculty ratio is 16:1. 5,883 applied, 52% were admitted. 12% from top 10% of their high school class, 37% from top quarter, 80% from top half. Full-time: 5,068 students, 56% women, 44% men. Part-time: 160 students, 55% women, 45% men. Students come from 26 states and territories, 12 other countries, 2% from out-of-state. 0.4% American Indian or Alaska Native, non-Hispanic/Latino; 4% Hispanic/Latino; 4% African American, non-Hispanic/Latino; 1% Asian, non-Hispanic/Latino; 0.1% Native Hawaiian or other Pacific Islander, non-Hispanic/Latino; 3% international. 4% 25 or older, 53% live on campus, 8% transferred in. Retention: 78% of full-time freshmen returned the following year. Academic areas with the most degrees conferred: education; business/marketing; visual and performing arts. Core. Calendar: semesters. Services for LD students, advanced placement, accelerated degree program, self-designed majors, honors program, independent study, distance learning, double major, summer session for credit, part-time degree program, adult/continuing education programs, internships, graduate courses open to undergrads. Off campus study at Western New York Consortium. Study abroad program.

Entrance Requirements: Options: electronic application, early admission, early decision, deferred admission, international baccalaureate accepted. Required: essay, high school transcript, 1 recommendation, SAT or ACT. Required for some: interview, Audition for music, dance and theater programs; portfolio for visual arts and technical theatre programs. Entrance: moderately difficult. Application deadlines: Rolling, 11/1 for early decision. Notification: continuous, 12/1 for early decision. Transfer credits accepted: Yes. Early decision applicants: 55. Early decision applicants admitted: 45.

Costs Per Year: Application fee: $50. State resident tuition: $5570 full-time, $232 per credit hour part-time. Nonresident tuition: $14,820 full-time, $618 per credit hour part-time. Mandatory fees: $1488 full-time, $61.85 per credit part-time. College room and board: $11,100. College room only: $6550. Room and board charges vary according to board plan and housing facility.

Collegiate Environment: Orientation program. Drama-theater group, choral group, student-run newspaper, radio station. Social organizations: 149 open to all; national fraternities, national sororities; 4% of eligible men and 4% of eligible women are members. Most popular organizations: Student Association, Undergraduate Alumni Council, Communication Club, ethnic organizations, spectrum entertainment board. Major annual events: Homecoming, Fredoniafest, Family Weekend. Student services: legal services, health clinic, personal-psychological counseling. Campus security: 24-hour emergency response devices and patrols, late night transport-escort service, controlled dormitory access. 2,773 college housing spaces available; 2,709 were occupied in 2012-13. Freshmen guaranteed college housing. On-campus residence required through sophomore year. Options: coed, men-only, women-only housing available. Daniel A. Reed Library with 571,880 books, 1.1 million microform titles, 66,032 serials, 27,346 audiovisual materials, an OPAC, and a Web page. Operations spending for the previous fiscal year: $1.6 million. 500 computers available on campus for general student use. Computer purchase/lease plans available. A campuswide network can be accessed from student residence rooms and from off campus. Students can access the following: online class registration. Staffed computer lab on campus provides training in use of computers, software, and the Internet.

■ **STATE UNIVERSITY OF NEW YORK INSTITUTE OF TECHNOLOGY**
100 Seymour Rd.
Utica, NY 13504-3050
Tel: (315)792-7100; Free: 866-2-SUNYIT
Fax: (315)792-7837
E-mail: admissions@sunyit.edu
Web Site: www.sunyit.edu/

Description: State-supported, comprehensive, coed. Part of State University of New York System. Awards bachelor's and master's degrees and post-master's certificates. Founded 1966. Setting: 850-acre suburban campus. Endowment: $2.4 million. Research spending for the previous fiscal year: $261,144. Educational spending for the previous fiscal year: $5135 per student. Total enrollment: 2,377. Faculty: 180 (73 full-time, 107 part-time). Student-undergrad faculty ratio is 18:1. 1,884 applied, 39% were admitted. 15% from top 10% of their high school class, 55% from top quarter, 90% from top half. Full-time: 1,272 students, 37% women, 63% men. Part-time: 421 students, 72% women, 28% men. Students come from 22 states and territories, 12 other countries, 1% from out-of-state. 0.2% American Indian or Alaska Native, non-Hispanic/Latino; 5% Hispanic/Latino; 8% African American, non-Hispanic/Latino; 2% Asian, non-Hispanic/Latino; 0% Native Hawaiian or other Pacific Islander, non-Hispanic/Latino; 1% international. 33% 25 or older, 30% live on campus, 18% transferred in. Retention: 70% of full-time freshmen returned the following year. Academic areas with the most degrees conferred: business/marketing; health professions and related sciences; engineering technologies. Core. Calendar: semesters. ESL program, services for LD students, advanced placement, accelerated degree program, independent study, distance learning, double major, summer session for credit, part-time degree program, co-op programs and internships, graduate courses open to undergrads. Off campus study at Mohawk Valley Consortium. Study abroad program. ROTC: Army (c), Air Force (c).

Entrance Requirements: Options: electronic application, early admission, early action, deferred admission, international baccalaureate accepted. Required: essay, high school transcript, minimum 3 high school GPA, 2 recommendations, SAT or ACT. Recommended: interview, SAT Subject Tests. Entrance: moderately difficult. Application deadlines: Rolling, Rolling for nonresidents, 11/1 for early action. Notification: continuous until 1/15, continuous until 1/15 for nonresidents, 12/15 for early action. SAT Reasoning Test deadline: 8/15. SAT Subject Test deadline: 8/15. Transfer credits accepted: Yes. Early action applicants: 139. Early action applicants admitted: 112.

Costs Per Year: Application fee: $50. State resident tuition: $5570 full-time, $232 per credit hour part-time. Nonresident tuition: $14,820 full-time, $618 per credit hour part-time. Mandatory fees: $1194 full-time, $49.63 per credit hour part-time, $49.63. Part-time tuition and fees vary according to course load. College room and board: $10,290. Room and board charges vary according to board plan.

Collegiate Environment: Orientation program. Student-run newspaper, radio station. Social organizations: 35 open to all. Most popular organizations: SUNYIT Gamers Club, Soccer Club, Black and Latino Student Union, Psychology and Sociology Club, Anime Club. Major annual events: Fall Fest, Apocalypse, Carnival Day. Student services: legal services, health clinic, personal-psychological counseling. Campus security: 24-hour emergency response devices and patrols, student patrols, late night transport-escort service, controlled dormitory access, closed-circuit TV monitors, 24 hour police department. 824 college housing spaces available; 500 were occupied in 2012-13. Freshmen guaranteed college housing. On-campus residence required through sophomore year. Option: coed housing available. Peter J. Cayan Library with 148,670 books, 2,682 microform titles, 322 serials, 1,502 audiovisual materials, an OPAC, and a Web page. Operations spending for the previous fiscal year: $354,600. 244 computers available on campus for general student use. A campuswide network can be accessed from student residence rooms and from off campus. Students can access the following: online class registration.

■ STATE UNIVERSITY OF NEW YORK MARITIME COLLEGE

6 Pennyfield Ave.
Throggs Neck, NY 10465-4198
Tel: (718)409-7200
Fax: (718)409-7392
E-mail: ysaintvil@sunymaritime.edu
Web Site: www.sunymaritime.edu/

Description: State-supported, comprehensive, coed. Part of State University of New York System. Awards associate, bachelor's, and master's degrees. Founded 1874. Setting: 56-acre suburban campus with easy access to New York City. Endowment: $5 million. Research spending for the previous fiscal year: $91,650. Educational spending for the previous fiscal year: $7229 per student. Total enrollment: 1,761. Faculty: 149 (97 full-time, 52 part-time). Student-undergrad faculty ratio is 14:1. 1,317 applied, 58% were admitted. Full-time: 1,553 students, 9% women, 91% men. Part-time: 61 students, 16% women, 84% men. Students come from 32 states and territories, 21 other countries, 27% from out-of-state. 0.1% American Indian or Alaska Native, non-Hispanic/Latino; 8% Hispanic/Latino; 3% African American, non-Hispanic/Latino; 3% Asian, non-Hispanic/Latino; 0% Native Hawaiian or other Pacific Islander, non-Hispanic/Latino; 3% international. 7% 25 or older, 78% live on campus, 5% transferred in. Retention: 81% of full-time freshmen returned the following year. Academic areas with the most degrees conferred: business/marketing; engineering; liberal arts/general studies; physical sciences. Core. Calendar: semesters plus 2-month summer sea term. Academic remediation for entering students, ESL program, services for LD students, advanced placement, honors program, independent study, distance learning, double major, summer session for credit, adult/continuing education programs, co-op programs and internships, graduate courses open to undergrads. ROTC: Army (c), Naval.
Entrance Requirements: Options: electronic application, early decision, deferred admission, international baccalaureate accepted. Required: essay, SAT or ACT. Recommended: high school transcript, interview. Entrance: very difficult. Application deadline: Rolling. Notification: continuous. SAT Reasoning Test deadline: 3/15. SAT Subject Test deadline: 3/15. Transfer credits accepted: Yes.
Costs Per Year: Application fee: $50. State resident tuition: $5570 full-time, $232 per credit hour part-time. Nonresident tuition: $14,820 full-time, $618 per credit hour part-time. Mandatory fees: $1212 full-time, $50.50 per credit hour part-time. Full-time tuition and fees vary according to degree level and program. Part-time tuition and fees vary according to course load, degree level, and program. College room and board: $10,444. College room only: $6594. Room and board charges vary according to board plan, gender, and housing facility.
Collegiate Environment: Orientation program. Choral group, marching band. Social organizations: 25 open to all. Most popular organizations: student government, Maritime Activities and Programs, Campus Crusade for Christ, The Propeller Club, Chorale. Major annual events: Ring Dance, Training Ship Departure and Return, Homecoming. Student services: health clinic, personal-psychological counseling. Campus security: 24-hour emergency response devices and patrols, student patrols, late night transport-escort service, controlled dormitory access. 1,365 college housing spaces available; all were occupied in 2012-13. On-campus residence required through senior year. Option: coed housing available. Stephen Luce Library plus 1 other with 85,000 books, 4,000 microform titles, 47,317 serials, 350 audiovisual materials, an OPAC, and a Web page. Operations spending for the previous fiscal year: $636,301. 110 computers available on campus for general student use. A campuswide network can be accessed from student residence rooms and from off campus. Students can access the following: online class registration. Staffed computer lab on campus.
Community Environment: The College is located on the Throgs Neck Peninsula, a small waterfront community within New York City.

■ STATE UNIVERSITY OF NEW YORK AT NEW PALTZ

1 Hawk Dr.
New Paltz, NY 12561

Tel: (845)257-2121
Fax: (845)257-3209
E-mail: admissions@newpaltz.edu
Web Site: www.newpaltz.edu/

Description: State-supported, comprehensive, coed. Part of State University of New York System. Awards bachelor's and master's degrees and post-master's certificates. Founded 1828. Setting: 216-acre small town campus. Endowment: $13.5 million. Research spending for the previous fiscal year: $4 million. Educational spending for the previous fiscal year: $9741 per student. Total enrollment: 1,082. Faculty: 634 (337 full-time, 297 part-time). Student-undergrad faculty ratio is 16:1. 12,892 applied, 44% were admitted. 29% from top 10% of their high school class, 62% from top quarter, 88% from top half. Full-time: 6,194 students, 63% women, 37% men. Part-time: 491 students, 62% women, 38% men. Students come from 74 other countries, 4% from out-of-state. 0.1% American Indian or Alaska Native, non-Hispanic/Latino; 12% Hispanic/Latino; 5% African American, non-Hispanic/Latino; 4% Asian, non-Hispanic/Latino; 0.1% Native Hawaiian or other Pacific Islander, non-Hispanic/Latino; 3% international. 9% 25 or older, 42% live on campus, 10% transferred in. Retention: 88% of full-time freshmen returned the following year. Core. Calendar: semesters. Academic remediation for entering students, ESL program, services for LD students, advanced placement, self-designed majors, honors program, independent study, distance learning, double major, summer session for credit, part-time degree program, adult/continuing education programs, co-op programs and internships, graduate courses open to undergrads. Off campus study at Associated Colleges of the Mid-Hudson Area. Study abroad program.
Entrance Requirements: Options: electronic application, early admission, early action, international baccalaureate accepted. Required: essay, high school transcript, 1 recommendation, SAT or ACT. Required for some: portfolio for art program, audition for music and theater programs. Entrance: very difficult. Application deadlines: 4/1, 11/15 for early action. Notification: continuous, 12/15 for early action. SAT Reasoning Test deadline: 1/31. Transfer credits accepted: Yes. Applicants placed on waiting list: 482. Waitlisted applicants offered admission: 62.
Collegiate Environment: Orientation program. Drama-theater group, choral group, student-run newspaper, radio station. Social organizations: national fraternities, national sororities, local fraternities, local sororities. Most popular organizations: Student Association, Residence Hall Student Association, intramurals and club sports, Outing Club. Major annual events: Rock Against Racism, Take Back the Night, Battle of the Bands. Student services: legal services, health clinic, personal-psychological counseling. Campus security: 24-hour emergency response devices and patrols, late night transport-escort service, controlled dormitory access, safety seminars, RAD Women's Self Defense. 2,980 college housing spaces available; 2,721 were occupied in 2012-13. Freshmen guaranteed college housing. On-campus residence required in freshman year. Options: coed, men-only, women-only housing available. Sojourner Truth Library with 490,782 books, 573 microform titles, 573 serials, 4,033 audiovisual materials, an OPAC, and a Web page.

■ STATE UNIVERSITY OF NEW YORK AT OSWEGO

7060 Rte. 104
Oswego, NY 13126
Tel: (315)312-2500
Fax: (315)312-5799
E-mail: admiss@oswego.edu
Web Site: www.oswego.edu/

Description: State-supported, comprehensive, coed. Part of State University of New York System. Awards bachelor's and master's degrees and post-master's certificates. Founded 1861. Setting: 696-acre small town campus with easy access to Syracuse. Endowment: $12.1 million. Research spending for the previous fiscal year: $2.1 million. Educational spending for the previous fiscal year: $9559 per student. Total enrollment: 7,921. Faculty: 576 (338 full-time, 238 part-time). Student-undergrad faculty ratio is 18:1. 9,746 applied, 48% were admitted. 16% from top 10% of their high school class, 55% from top quarter, 87% from top half. Full-time: 6,815 students, 52% women, 48% men. Part-time: 336 students, 52% women, 48% men. Students come from 26 states and territories, 17 other countries, 2% from out-of-state. 0.2% American Indian or Alaska Native, non-Hispanic/Latino; 8% Hispanic/Latino; 5% African American, non-Hispanic/Latino; 2% Asian, non-Hispanic/Latino; 0.1% Native Hawaiian or other Pacific Islander, non-Hispanic/Latino; 1% international. 8% 25 or older, 56% live on campus, 11% transferred in. Retention: 80% of full-time freshmen returned the following year. Academic areas with the most degrees conferred: business/marketing; education; communication/journalism. Core. Calendar: semesters. ESL program, services for LD students, advanced placement, accelerated degree program, freshman honors college, honors program, independent study, distance learning, double major, summer session for credit, part-time degree program, adult/continuing education programs, co-op programs and internships, graduate courses open to undergrads. Off campus study at Bryant and Stratton North Campus, Finger Lakes Community College, Jefferson-Lewis Board of Cooperative Educational Services, Onondage-Cortland-Madison Board of Cooperative Educational Services. Study abroad program. ROTC: Army (c).

Entrance Requirements: Options: electronic application, early admission, early decision, deferred admission, international baccalaureate accepted. Required: high school transcript, SAT or ACT. Recommended: essay, interview. Entrance: moderately difficult. Application deadlines: Rolling, 11/15 for early decision. Notification: 1/15, 12/15 for early decision. Early decision applicants: 175. Early decision applicants admitted: 90.

Costs Per Year: Application fee: $50. State resident tuition: $5570 full-time, $232 per credit hour part-time. Nonresident tuition: $14,820 full-time, $618 per credit hour part-time. Mandatory fees: $1271 full-time, $52.96 per credit hour part-time. Full-time tuition and fees vary according to degree level. Part-time tuition and fees vary according to course load and degree level. College room and board: $12,510. Room and board charges vary according to board plan and housing facility.

Collegiate Environment: Orientation program. Drama-theater group, choral group, student-run newspaper, radio station. Social organizations: 160 open to all; national fraternities, national sororities, local fraternities, local sororities; 7% of eligible men and 6% of eligible women are members. Most popular organizations: club/intramural sports, student radio/television stations (WNYO and WTOP), Outing/Recreation Club, Dance Organization (Del Sarte), Financial Management Association. Major annual events: Quest, May Day/Spring Fling, Family and Friends Weekend. Student services: legal services, health clinic, personal-psychological counseling, women's center. Campus security: 24-hour emergency response devices and patrols, controlled dormitory access. 4,400 college housing spaces available; 4,030 were occupied in 2012-13. Freshmen guaranteed college housing. On-campus residence required through sophomore year. Option: coed housing available. Penfield Library with 554,986 books, 1.6 million microform titles, 2,830 serials, 31,384 audiovisual materials, an OPAC, and a Web page. Operations spending for the previous fiscal year: $2.2 million. 1,050 computers available on campus for general student use. Computer purchase/lease plans available. A campuswide network can be accessed from student residence rooms and from off campus. Students can access the following: online class registration. Staffed computer lab on campus provides training in use of computers, software, and the Internet.

■ STATE UNIVERSITY OF NEW YORK AT PLATTSBURGH

101 Broad St.
Plattsburgh, NY 12901-2681
Tel: (518)564-2000; Free: 888-673-0012
Fax: (518)564-2045
E-mail: carrie.woodward@plattsburgh.edu
Web Site: www.plattsburgh.edu/

Description: State-supported, comprehensive, coed. Part of State University of New York System. Awards bachelor's and master's degrees and post-master's certificates. Founded 1889. Setting: 265-acre small town campus with easy access to Montreal. Endowment: $13.8 million. Research spending for the previous fiscal year: $1 million. Educational spending for the previous fiscal year: $10,038 per student. Total enrollment: 6,167. Faculty: 519 (285 full-time, 234 part-time). Student-undergrad faculty ratio is 16:1. 7,939 applied, 46% were admitted. 12% from top 10% of their high school class, 42% from top quarter, 82% from top half. Full-time: 5,318 students, 55% women, 45% men. Part-time: 388 students, 64% women, 36% men. Students come from 29 states and territories, 65 other countries, 4% from out-of-state. 0.3% American Indian or Alaska Native, non-Hispanic/Latino; 8% Hispanic/Latino; 6% African American, non-Hispanic/Latino; 2% Asian, non-Hispanic/Latino; 0.1% Native Hawaiian or other Pacific Islander, non-Hispanic/Latino; 6% international. 10% 25 or older, 46% live on campus, 12% transferred in. Retention: 78% of full-time freshmen returned the following year. Academic areas with the most degrees conferred: business/marketing; health professions and related sciences; education. Core. Calendar: semesters plus 2 5-week summer sessions and 1 winter session. Academic remediation for entering students, ESL program, services for LD students, advanced placement, accelerated degree program, self-designed majors, honors program, independent study, distance learning, double major, summer session for credit, part-time degree program, adult/continuing

education programs, co-op programs and internships, graduate courses open to undergrads. Off campus study. Study abroad program. ROTC: Army.

Entrance Requirements: Options: electronic application, early admission, early decision, deferred admission, international baccalaureate accepted. Required: essay, high school transcript, minimum 2.5 high school GPA, 1 recommendation, SAT or ACT. Recommended: minimum 3 high school GPA, interview. Required for some: minimum 3.4 high school GPA. Entrance: moderately difficult. Notification: continuous. Transfer credits accepted: Yes. Applicants placed on waiting list: 289. Wait-listed applicants offered admission: 69. Early decision applicants: 68. Early decision applicants admitted: 39.

Costs Per Year: Application fee: $50. State resident tuition: $5570 full-time, $232 per credit hour part-time. Nonresident tuition: $14,820 full-time, $618 per credit hour part-time. Mandatory fees: $1238 full-time, $51.40 per credit hour part-time. Part-time tuition and fees vary according to course load. College room and board: $10,582. College room only: $6682. Room and board charges vary according to board plan and housing facility.

Collegiate Environment: Orientation program. Drama-theater group, choral group, student-run newspaper, radio station. Social organizations: 120 open to all; national fraternities, national sororities, local fraternities, local sororities; 11% of eligible men and 9% of eligible women are members. Most popular organizations: Student Association, Honor Societies, Student Media Organizations, service/leadership organizations, intramural and recreational sports. Major annual events: President's Gala, Volunteer Opportunities (Relay For Life, Up 'Till Dawn, etc), Plattsburgh's Best Dance Crew and Plattsburgh's Got Talent Competitions. Student services: legal services, health clinic, personal-psychological counseling, women's center. Campus security: 24-hour emergency response devices and patrols, late night transport-escort service, controlled dormitory access. 2,772 college housing spaces available; 2,586 were occupied in 2012-13. Freshmen guaranteed college housing. On-campus residence required through sophomore year. Option: coed housing available. Feinberg Library with 541,609 books, 723,474 microform titles, 5,222 serials, 25,698 audiovisual materials, an OPAC, and a Web page. Operations spending for the previous fiscal year: $2.7 million. 450 computers available on campus for general student use. Computer purchase/lease plans available. A campuswide network can be accessed from student residence rooms and from off campus. Students can access the following: online class registration. Staffed computer lab on campus provides training in use of computers, software, and the Internet.

■ STATE UNIVERSITY OF NEW YORK UPSTATE MEDICAL UNIVERSITY

766 Irving Ave.
Syracuse, NY 13210-2334
Tel: (315)464-5540; Free: 800-736-2171
Fax: (315)464-8823
E-mail: admiss@upstate.edu
Web Site: www.upstate.edu/

Description: Independent Mennonite, 4-year, coed. Awards bachelor's degrees. Founded 1936. Setting: 16-acre urban campus with easy access to Winnipeg. Total enrollment: 148. Faculty: 14 (4 full-time, 10 part-time). Student-undergrad faculty ratio is 18:1. 59 applied, 81% were admitted. Retention: 55% of full-time freshmen returned the following year. Calendar: semesters.

Entrance Requirements: Option: electronic application. Entrance: minimally difficult. Transfer credits accepted: Yes.

Collegiate Environment: Orientation program. Health Sciences Library with 220,160 books, 3,200 serials, 4,331 audiovisual materials, an OPAC, and a Web page. Operations spending for the previous fiscal year: $2.6 million. 150 computers available on campus for general student use. A campuswide network can be accessed from student residence rooms and from off campus. Students can access the following: online class registration. Staffed computer lab on campus provides training in use of computers, software, and the Internet.

Community Environment: See Syracuse University.

■ STONY BROOK UNIVERSITY, STATE UNIVERSITY OF NEW YORK

Nicolls Rd.
Stony Brook, NY 11794
Tel: (631)632-6000
E-mail: enroll@stonybrook.edu
Web Site: www.sunysb.edu/

Description: State-supported, university, coed. Part of State University of New York. Awards bachelor's, master's, and doctoral degrees and post-master's certificates. Founded 1957. Setting: 1,450-acre suburban campus with easy access to New York City. Endowment: $125.4 million. Research spending for the previous fiscal year: $225.1 million. Educational spending for the previous fiscal year: $18,589 per student. Total enrollment: 24,149. Faculty: 1,467 (957 full-time, 510 part-time). Student-undergrad faculty ratio is 18:1. 27,513 applied, 40% were admitted. 42% from top 10% of their high school class, 75% from top quarter, 95% from top half. 64 National Merit Scholars, 70 valedictorians. Full-time: 14,689 students, 47% women, 53% men. Part-time: 1,314 students, 52% women, 48% men. Students come from 48 states and territories, 110 other countries, 8% from out-of-state. 0.1% American Indian or Alaska Native, non-Hispanic/Latino; 10% Hispanic/Latino; 6% African American, non-Hispanic/Latino; 25% Asian, non-Hispanic/Latino; 0.1% Native Hawaiian or other Pacific Islander, non-Hispanic/Latino; 9% international. 9% 25 or older, 61% live on campus, 9% transferred in. Retention: 90% of full-time freshmen returned the following year. Academic areas with the most degrees conferred: health professions and related sciences; biological/life sciences; social sciences. Core. Calendar: semesters. Academic remediation for entering students, ESL program, services for LD students, advanced placement, self-designed majors, freshman honors college, honors program, independent study, distance learning, double major, summer session for credit, part-time degree program, adult/continuing education programs, co-op programs and internships, graduate courses open to undergrads. Off campus study at 17 members of the Long Island Regional Advisory Council for Higher Education and The National Student Exchange. Study abroad program. ROTC: Army, Naval (c), Air Force (c).

Entrance Requirements: Options: electronic application, deferred admission, international baccalaureate accepted. Required: essay, high school transcript, minimum 3 high school GPA, 1 recommendation, SAT or ACT. Recommended: interview. Required for some: audition. Entrance: very difficult. Application deadline: 1/15. Notification: 4/1. Transfer credits accepted: Yes. Applicants placed on waiting list: 2,884. Wait-listed applicants offered admission: 169.

Costs Per Year: Application fee: $50. State resident tuition: $5570 full-time, $232 per credit hour part-time. Nonresident tuition: $16,190 full-time, $675 per credit hour part-time. Mandatory fees: $1,990 full-time, $97.55 per credit hour part-time. Full-time tuition and fees vary according to course load. Part-time tuition and fees vary according to course load. College room and board: $10,934. College room only: $6968. Room and board charges vary according to board plan and housing facility.

Collegiate Environment: Orientation program. Drama-theater group, choral group, marching band, student-run newspaper, radio station. Social organizations: 328 open to all; national fraternities, national sororities, local fraternities, local sororities; 1% of eligible men and 2% of eligible women are members. Most popular organizations: Inter Fraternity and Sorority Council, Residence Hall Association, Commuter Student Association, Undergraduate Student Government - Student Activities Board, Chinese Association at Stony Brook. Major annual events: Roth Pond Regatta, Opening of School - First Night Out, Diversity Day/Strawberry Festival. Student services: legal services, health clinic, personal-psychological counseling, women's center. Campus security: 24-hour emergency response devices and patrols, late night transport-escort service, controlled dormitory access. College housing designed to accommodate 8,330 students; 8,517 undergraduates lived in college housing during 2012-13. Freshmen guaranteed college housing. Option: coed housing available. Frank Melville, Jr. Memorial Library plus 6 others with 2.3 million books, 3.9 million microform titles, 55,500 serials, 58,525 audiovisual materials, an OPAC, and a Web page. Operations spending for the previous fiscal year: $13.7 million. 2,600 computers available on campus for general student use. Computer purchase/lease plans available. A campuswide network can be accessed from student residence rooms and from off campus. Students can access the following: online class registration. Staffed computer lab on campus provides training in use of computers, software, and the Internet.

■ SUFFOLK COUNTY COMMUNITY COLLEGE

533 College Rd.
Selden, NY 11784-2899
Tel: (631)451-4110
Web Site: www.sunysuffolk.edu/

Description: State and locally supported, 2-year, coed. Part of State University of New York System. Awards certificates, diplomas, transfer associate, and terminal associate degrees. Founded 1959. Setting: 500-acre small town campus with easy access to New York City. Total enrollment: 28,294. Student-undergrad faculty ratio is 18:1. 2% from top 10% of their high school class, 19% from top quarter, 43% from top half. Students come

from 14 states and territories, 1% from out-of-state. 33% 25 or older. Core. Calendar: semesters. Academic remediation for entering students, ESL program, services for LD students, advanced placement, freshman honors college, honors program, independent study, distance learning, summer session for credit, part-time degree program, adult/continuing education programs, co-op programs and internships. Off campus study at members of the Long Island Regional Advisory Council for Higher Education. Study abroad program. ROTC: Army (c).

Entrance Requirements: Open admission except for some programs. Options: electronic application, deferred admission, international baccalaureate accepted. Required: high school transcript. Required for some: interview. Entrance: noncompetitive. Application deadline: Rolling. Notification: continuous. Preference given to county residents. Transfer credits accepted: Yes.

Collegiate Environment: Orientation program. Drama-theater group, choral group, student-run newspaper. Student services: personal-psychological counseling. Campus security: 24-hour emergency response devices and patrols.

■ SULLIVAN COUNTY COMMUNITY COLLEGE

112 College Rd.
Loch Sheldrake, NY 12759
Tel: (845)434-5750; Free: 800-577-5243
Fax: (845)434-4806
E-mail: sarir@sunysullivan.edu
Web Site: www.sullivan.suny.edu/

Description: State and locally supported, 2-year, coed. Part of State University of New York System. Awards certificates, transfer associate, and terminal associate degrees. Founded 1962. Setting: 405-acre rural campus. Endowment: $956,148. Educational spending for the previous fiscal year: $4112 per student. Total enrollment: 1,614. Faculty: 109 (48 full-time, 61 part-time). Student-undergrad faculty ratio is 18:1. 1,775 applied, 97% were admitted. Full-time: 1,040 students, 55% women, 45% men. Part-time: 574 students, 62% women, 38% men. Students come from 8 states and territories, 6 other countries, 3% from out-of-state. 0.4% American Indian or Alaska Native, non-Hispanic/Latino; 15% Hispanic/Latino; 21% African American, non-Hispanic/Latino; 1% Asian, non-Hispanic/Latino; 0.4% international. 25% 25 or older, 22% live on campus, 5% transferred in. Core. Calendar: 4-1-4. Academic remediation for entering students, services for LD students, advanced placement, honors program, independent study, distance learning, double major, summer session for credit, part-time degree program, adult/continuing education programs, internships. Off campus study at Hudson Valley Educational Consortium (HVEC), a collaborative effort between SUNY Sullivan, SUNY Orange, SUNY Ulster and SUNY Rockland.

Entrance Requirements: Open admission. Options: electronic application, early admission, deferred admission. Required: high school transcript. Entrance: noncompetitive. Application deadlines: Rolling, Rolling for nonresidents. Notification: continuous, continuous for nonresidents. Transfer credits accepted: Yes.

Costs Per Year: Application fee: $20. State resident tuition: $4474 full-time, $174 per credit hour part-time. Nonresident tuition: $8948 full-time, $230 per credit hour part-time. Mandatory fees: $642 full-time, $67 per credit hour part-time. Full-time tuition and fees vary according to program and student level. Part-time tuition and fees vary according to program and student level. College room and board: $8620. College room only: $5600. Room and board charges vary according to board plan and housing facility.

Collegiate Environment: Orientation program. Student-run newspaper, radio station. Social organizations: 14 open to all. Most popular organizations: Science Alliance, Black Student Union, Gay Straight Alliance, Dance Club, Honor Society. Major annual events: Talent Show, Kite Day, Completion Day. Student services: legal services, health clinic, personal-psychological counseling. Campus security: 24-hour emergency response devices and patrols, student patrols, controlled dormitory access. 375 college housing spaces available; 350 were occupied in 2012-13. Freshmen given priority for college housing. Option: coed housing available. Hermann Memorial Library plus 1 other with 62,500 books, 215 serials, 8,275 audiovisual materials, an OPAC, and a Web page. Operations spending for the previous fiscal year: $491,208. 205 computers available on campus for general student use. A campuswide network can be accessed. Students can access the following: online class registration. Staffed computer lab on campus provides training in use of computers, software, and the Internet.

■ SWEDISH INSTITUTE, COLLEGE OF HEALTH SCIENCES

226 W 26th St.
New York, NY 10001-6700
Tel: (212)924-5900
Fax: (212)924-7600
E-mail: admissions@swedishinstitute.edu
Web Site: www.swedishinstitute.org/

Description: Proprietary, comprehensive, coed. Awards associate, bachelor's, master's, and doctoral degrees. Founded 1916. Setting: urban campus. Total enrollment: 480. Faculty: 50 (17 full-time, 33 part-time). Student-undergrad faculty ratio is 11:1. 202 applied, 95% were admitted. Students come from 6 states and territories, 4 other countries, 4% from out-of-state. 72% 25 or older. Calendar: trimesters. Services for LD students, advanced placement, part-time degree program, adult/continuing education programs, co-op programs.

Entrance Requirements: Required: essay, 2 recommendations, interview, Nelson-Denny. Required for some: high school transcript. Entrance: moderately difficult. Application deadline: 11/9.

Collegiate Environment: Campus security: 24-hour emergency response devices and patrols. The Lillian F. Phillips Library with 2,700 books, 30 serials, 250 audiovisual materials, and an OPAC.

■ SYRACUSE UNIVERSITY

Syracuse, NY 13244
Tel: (315)443-1870
E-mail: orange@syr.edu
Web Site: www.syr.edu/

Description: Independent, university, coed. Awards bachelor's, master's, and doctoral degrees and post-master's certificates. Founded 1870. Setting: 200-acre urban campus with easy access to Syracuse. Endowment: $940.1 million. Total enrollment: 21,029. Faculty: 1,563 (1,019 full-time, 544 part-time). Student-undergrad faculty ratio is 16:1. 25,790 applied, 51% were admitted. 38% from top 10% of their high school class, 72% from top quarter, 95% from top half. Full-time: 14,169 students, 56% women, 44% men. Part-time: 629 students, 56% women, 44% men. Students come from 49 states and territories, 82 other countries, 55% from out-of-state. 1% American Indian or Alaska Native, non-Hispanic/Latino; 10% Hispanic/Latino; 9% African American, non-Hispanic/Latino; 8% Asian, non-Hispanic/Latino; 0.1% Native Hawaiian or other Pacific Islander, non-Hispanic/Latino; 8% international. 4% 25 or older, 75% live on campus, 3% transferred in. Retention: 92% of full-time freshmen returned the following year. Academic areas with the most degrees conferred: business/marketing; communication/journalism; visual and performing arts. Calendar: semesters. Academic remediation for entering students, ESL program, services for LD students, advanced placement, accelerated degree program, self-designed majors, freshman honors college, honors program, independent study, distance learning, double major, summer session for credit, part-time degree program, adult/continuing education programs, co-op programs and internships, graduate courses open to undergrads. Off campus study. Study abroad program. ROTC: Army, Air Force.

Entrance Requirements: Options: electronic application, early admission, early decision, deferred admission, international baccalaureate accepted. Required: essay, high school transcript, 2 recommendations, SAT or ACT. Entrance: very difficult. Application deadlines: 1/1, 11/15 for early decision. Transfer credits accepted: Yes. Applicants placed on waiting list: 3,661. Wait-listed applicants offered admission: 319. Early decision applicants: 1,064. Early decision applicants admitted: 773.

Costs Per Year: Application fee: $70. Comprehensive fee: $52,696 includes full-time tuition ($37,610), mandatory fees ($1394), and college room and board ($13,692). College room only: $7212. Full-time tuition and fees vary according to course load. Room and board charges vary according to board plan and housing facility. Part-time tuition: $1637 per credit hour. Part-time tuition varies according to course load.

Collegiate Environment: Orientation program. Drama-theater group, choral group, marching band, student-run newspaper, radio station. Social organizations: 350 open to all; national fraternities, national sororities. Most popular organizations: University Union, Student Association, Student Leadership Conference, Habitat for Humanity. Major annual events: Orange Central, Senior Celebration, Winter Carnival. Student services: legal services, health clinic, personal-psychological counseling, women's center. Campus security: 24-hour emergency response devices and patrols, student patrols, late night transport-escort service, controlled dormitory access, crisis alert notification system, outdoor emergency sirens, off-campus patrols in student rental neighborhoods. 8,201 college housing spaces available; 8,194

were occupied in 2012-13. Freshmen guaranteed college housing. On-campus residence required through sophomore year. Option: coed housing available. E. S. Bird Library plus 5 others with 3.8 million books, 7.6 million microform titles, 57,452 serials, 1.2 million audiovisual materials, an OPAC, and a Web page. 3,500 computers available on campus for general student use. Computer purchase/lease plans available. A campuswide network can be accessed from student residence rooms and from off campus. Students can access the following: online class registration, Library; web conferencing; learning management system (Blackboard); blogging service; personal websites; Advising Reports; digital asset management system (Collage). Staffed computer lab on campus provides training in use of computers, software, and the Internet.

Community Environment: The city of Syracuse (metropolitan area population of 732,000) is the business, educational, and cultural hub of central New York. The city offers professional theater, symphony, opera, and visiting artists and performers. Highlights of the downtown area are the Everson Museum of Art, designed by I.M. Pei, the impressive Civic Center, and the popular Carousel Center shopping Mall. Central New York offers lakes, parks, mountains, and outstanding recreational opportunities. Syracuse is serviced by most major airlines, Amtrak, and Greyhound. Hancock International Airport is only a few miles from downtown and the University, and is served by taxis. The famous Finger Lakes region, offering excellent summer and winter activities, is easily accessible. Diversified industry includes medicine, education, manufacturing, banking, insurance, communications, engineering, and retailing. Part-time employment opportunities are available for students. A transportation network includes bus lines, airlines, and excellent highways and thruways. Parking is excellent in the downtown shopping and theatrical districts. Syracuse is home to 40 museums and galleries, 40 golf courses (more than any other area in the northeast), and has more than 50 parks and several nature centers in the Syracuse area.

■ TALMUDICAL INSTITUTE OF UPSTATE NEW YORK

769 Park Ave.
Rochester, NY 14607-3046
Tel: (716)473-2810
Fax: (716)442-0417
E-mail: yeshiva@tiuny.org
Web Site: www.tiuny.org/

Description: Independent Jewish, 5-year, men only. Awards bachelor's degrees (also offers some graduate courses). Founded 1974. Setting: 1-acre urban campus. Total enrollment: 26. 13 applied, 100% were admitted. Calendar: semesters. Self-designed majors.

Entrance Requirements: Option: early admission. Required: high school transcript. Required for some: interview. Entrance: noncompetitive. Application deadline: Rolling. Notification: continuous.

Collegiate Environment: Campus security: student patrols. Talmudical Library with 3,000 books and 5 serials.

■ TALMUDICAL SEMINARY OHOLEI TORAH

667 Eastern Pky.
Brooklyn, NY 11213-3310
Tel: (718)774-5050
E-mail: info@oholeitorah.com

Description: Independent Jewish, 4-year, men only. Awards bachelor's degrees. Founded 1956. Setting: urban campus. Total enrollment: 337. 65 applied, 100% were admitted. Core. Calendar: semesters. Honors program.

Entrance Requirements: Option: deferred admission. Required: high school transcript, interview, Talmudic examination. Application deadline: 9/1. Notification: continuous.

Collegiate Environment: Student services: personal-psychological counseling. Campus security: late night transport-escort service.

■ TCI—THE COLLEGE OF TECHNOLOGY

320 W 31st St.
New York, NY 10001-2705
Tel: (212)594-4000; Free: 800-878-8246
Fax: (212)629-3937
E-mail: admissions@tcicollege.edu
Web Site: www.tcicollege.edu/

Description: Proprietary, 2-year, coed. Awards certificates, transfer associate, and terminal associate degrees. Founded 1909. Setting: urban campus. Total enrollment: 4,064. Student-undergrad faculty ratio is 34:1. 2% from out-of-state. 47% 25 or older. Retention: 40% of full-time freshmen returned the

following year. Calendar: semesters. Academic remediation for entering students, ESL program, advanced placement, double major, summer session for credit, part-time degree program, adult/continuing education programs.
Entrance Requirements: Open admission. Required: essay, high school transcript, interview. Entrance: minimally difficult. Application deadline: Rolling. Notification: continuous.
Collegiate Environment: Orientation program. Social organizations: international social clubs. Campus security: 24-hour patrols. Technical Career Institutes Library with an OPAC.

■ **TOMPKINS CORTLAND COMMUNITY COLLEGE**
170 N St.
Dryden, NY 13053-0139
Tel: (607)844-8211; Free: 888-567-8211
Fax: (607)844-6538
E-mail: admissions@tc3.edu
Web Site: www.TC3.edu/
Description: State and locally supported, 2-year, coed. Part of State University of New York System. Awards certificates, transfer associate, and terminal associate degrees. Founded 1968. Setting: 250-acre rural campus with easy access to Syracuse. Total enrollment: 5,663. Faculty: 347 (68 full-time, 279 part-time). Student-undergrad faculty ratio is 19:1. Full-time: 2,930 students, 52% women, 48% men. Part-time: 2,732 students, 58% women, 42% men. 0.4% American Indian or Alaska Native, non-Hispanic/Latino; 7% Hispanic/Latino; 7% African American, non-Hispanic/Latino; 1% Asian, non-Hispanic/Latino; 0.1% Native Hawaiian or other Pacific Islander, non-Hispanic/Latino; 2% international. 23% live on campus. Core. Calendar: semesters. Academic remediation for entering students, ESL program, services for LD students, advanced placement, honors program, independent study, distance learning, double major, summer session for credit, part-time degree program, adult/continuing education programs, co-op programs and internships. Off campus study at State University of New York College at Cortland. Study abroad program.
Entrance Requirements: Open admission except for nursing program. Options: electronic application, early admission, deferred admission. Required: high school transcript. Required for some: essay, interview. Entrance: noncompetitive. Application deadlines: Rolling, Rolling for nonresidents. Notification: continuous, continuous for nonresidents. Transfer credits accepted: Yes.
Costs Per Year: Application fee: $15. State resident tuition: $4150 full-time, $147 per credit hour part-time. Nonresident tuition: $8600 full-time, $304 per credit hour part-time. Mandatory fees: $721 full-time, $24.80 per credit hour part-time, $12 per year part-time. Part-time tuition and fees vary according to course load. College room and board: $9290. Room and board charges vary according to board plan and housing facility.
Collegiate Environment: Orientation program. Drama-theater group. Social organizations: 22 open to all. Most popular organizations: College Entertainment Board, Sport Management Club, Nursing Club, Media Club, Writer's Guild. Major annual events: Attendance at College Entertainment Board programs, Registration Day, Voter registration drives. Student services: health clinic, personal-psychological counseling. Campus security: 24-hour patrols, late night transport-escort service, controlled dormitory access, Armed peace officers. 814 college housing spaces available; all were occupied in 2012-13. Option: coed housing available. Gerald A. Barry Memorial Library plus 1 other with 65,386 books, 5,765 microform titles, 200 serials, 3,445 audiovisual materials, an OPAC, and a Web page. 400 computers available on campus for general student use. A campuswide network can be accessed from student residence rooms. Students can access the following: online class registration. Staffed computer lab on campus.

■ **TORAH TEMIMAH TALMUDICAL SEMINARY**
507 Ocean Pky.
Brooklyn, NY 11218-5913
Tel: (718)853-8500
Description: Independent Jewish, 4-year, men only. Awards bachelor's degrees. Founded 1978. Total enrollment: 170. 55 applied, 100% were admitted. Calendar: semesters.

■ **TOURO COLLEGE**
27-33 W 23rd St.
New York, NY 10010
Tel: (212)463-0400
Fax: (212)779-2344

E-mail: david.luk@touro.edu
Web Site: www.touro.edu/
Description: Independent, comprehensive, coed. Awards associate, bachelor's, master's, and doctoral degrees and post-master's certificates. Founded 1971. Setting: urban campus. Total enrollment: 17,544. 2,576 applied, 57% were admitted. 40% 25 or older. Core. Calendar: semesters. Academic remediation for entering students, ESL program, services for LD students, advanced placement, accelerated degree program, self-designed majors, freshman honors college, honors program, independent study, distance learning, double major, summer session for credit, part-time degree program, external degree program, internships, graduate courses open to undergrads. Study abroad program.
Entrance Requirements: Open admission for associate degree programs. Options: early admission, deferred admission. Required: high school transcript. Recommended: essay, 1 recommendation, SAT or ACT. Required for some: minimum 3 high school GPA, 2 recommendations, interview. Entrance: moderately difficult. Application deadlines: Rolling, Rolling for nonresidents. Notification: continuous, continuous for nonresidents. Transfer credits accepted: Yes.
Costs Per Year: Application fee: $50. Comprehensive fee: $25,770 includes full-time tuition ($14,800), mandatory fees ($570), and college room and board ($10,400). College room only: $7300. Full-time tuition and fees vary according to course load, degree level, location, and program. Room and board charges vary according to housing facility and location. Part-time tuition: $610 per credit hour. Part-time tuition varies according to course load, degree level, location, and program.
Collegiate Environment: Orientation program. Student-run newspaper. Student services: personal-psychological counseling. Campus security: 24-hour emergency response devices and patrols. Touro College Library plus 14 others with 302,700 books, 14,470 microform titles, 6,950 serials, 735 audiovisual materials, an OPAC, and a Web page.
Community Environment: See New York University.

■ **TROCAIRE COLLEGE**
360 Choate Ave.
Buffalo, NY 14220-2094
Tel: (716)826-1200
Fax: (716)826-4704
E-mail: info@trocaire.edu
Web Site: www.trocaire.edu/
Description: Independent, 2-year, coed. Awards certificates, transfer associate, and terminal associate degrees. Founded 1958. Setting: 1-acre urban campus. Total enrollment: 1,153. Student-undergrad faculty ratio is 10:1. 1% from out-of-state. 56% 25 or older. Core. Calendar: semesters. Academic remediation for entering students, services for LD students, advanced placement, independent study, summer session for credit, part-time degree program, external degree program, adult/continuing education programs, internships. Off campus study at members of the Western New York Consortium.
Entrance Requirements: Option: deferred admission. Required: high school transcript. Recommended: interview. Required for some: SAT or ACT. Entrance: minimally difficult. Application deadline: Rolling.
Collegiate Environment: Orientation program. Student-run newspaper. Social organizations: national fraternities. Student services: health clinic, personal-psychological counseling. Campus security: 24-hour emergency response devices and patrols, late night transport-escort service. The Rachel R. Savarino Library with an OPAC and a Web page.
Community Environment: Trocaire is located in a residential area of South Buffalo, adjacent to Mercy Hospital and Cazenovia Park, a quiet corner of the city. Three bus lines serve the city and within a short distance is the New York State Thruway and the Buffalo Skyway.

■ **ULSTER COUNTY COMMUNITY COLLEGE**
491 Cottekill Rd.
Stone Ridge, NY 12484
Tel: (845)687-5000; Free: 800-724-0833
E-mail: admissionsoffice@sunyulster.edu
Web Site: www.sunyulster.edu/
Description: State and locally supported, 2-year, coed. Part of State University of New York System. Awards certificates, diplomas, transfer associate, and terminal associate degrees. Founded 1961. Setting: 165-acre rural campus. Endowment: $4.9 million. Educational spending for the previous fiscal year: $5961 per student. Total enrollment: 3,540. Faculty: 189 (66 full-time, 123 part-time). Student-undergrad faculty ratio is 19:1. 618 applied,

100% were admitted. 4% from top 10% of their high school class, 14% from top quarter, 41% from top half. Full-time: 1,759 students, 53% women, 47% men. Part-time: 1,781 students, 65% women, 35% men. Students come from 10 states and territories, 8 other countries. 23% 25 or older, 6% transferred in. Core. Calendar: semesters. Academic remediation for entering students, ESL program, services for LD students, advanced placement, self-designed majors, honors program, independent study, distance learning, double major, summer session for credit, part-time degree program, adult/continuing education programs, co-op programs and internships. Off campus study at Cross registration agreements with SUNY New Paltz and Dutchess Community College; Study abroad opportunities with State University of New York Colleges-Hudson Valley Educational Consortium which includes: Ulster County Community College - Emergency Mgt; Orange County Community College - Cyber Security; Sullivan County Community College - Green Building; Rockland County Community College -Fire Protection Tech; Jointly Registered program with Marist College for Individual Studies/Paralegal Degree/Certificate program. Study abroad program.

Entrance Requirements: Open admission except for nursing program. Options: electronic application, early admission, deferred admission, international baccalaureate accepted. Required: high school transcript. Entrance: noncompetitive. Application deadline: Rolling. Notification: continuous. Transfer credits accepted: Yes.

Costs Per Year: Application fee: $0. State resident tuition: $4130 full-time, $149 per credit hour part-time. Nonresident tuition: $8260 full-time, $298 per credit hour part-time. Mandatory fees: $670 full-time, $50 per course part-time, $35 per term part-time.

Collegiate Environment: Orientation program. Drama-theater group, choral group. Social organizations: 15 open to all. Most popular organizations: Vet Tech, Biology Club, Nursing Club, Business Club, Visual Arts Club. Major annual events: Earth Day BBQ, Veterans Day Luncheon, Welcome Back BBQ. Student services: personal-psychological counseling. Campus security: 24-hour emergency response devices and patrols. McDonald Dewitt Library with 86,597 books, 27,637 microform titles, 202 serials, 4,828 audiovisual materials, an OPAC, and a Web page. Operations spending for the previous fiscal year: $665,724. 85 computers available on campus for general student use. A campuswide network can be accessed. Students can access the following: online class registration. Staffed computer lab on campus provides training in use of computers, software, and the Internet.

■ UNION COLLEGE

807 Union St.
Schenectady, NY 12308-2311
Tel: (518)388-6000; Free: 888-843-6688
Fax: (518)388-6986
E-mail: admissions@union.edu
Web Site: www.union.edu/

Description: Independent, 4-year, coed. Awards bachelor's degrees. Founded 1795. Setting: 100-acre urban campus. Endowment: $322 million. Research spending for the previous fiscal year: $914,064. Educational spending for the previous fiscal year: $18,804 per student. Total enrollment: 2,241. Faculty: 236 (202 full-time, 34 part-time). Student-undergrad faculty ratio is 10:1. 5,565 applied, 38% were admitted. 58% from top 10% of their high school class, 79% from top quarter, 97% from top half. 9 valedictorians. Full-time: 2,209 students, 46% women, 54% men. Part-time: 32 students, 44% women, 56% men. Students come from 37 states and territories, 37 other countries, 60% from out-of-state. 0.2% American Indian or Alaska Native, non-Hispanic/Latino; 7% Hispanic/Latino; 4% African American, non-Hispanic/Latino; 6% Asian, non-Hispanic/Latino; 0.05% Native Hawaiian or other Pacific Islander, non-Hispanic/Latino; 5% international. 0% 25 or older, 89% live on campus, 1% transferred in. Retention: 94% of full-time freshmen returned the following year. Academic areas with the most degrees conferred: social sciences; biological/life sciences; psychology. Core. Calendar: trimesters. Advanced placement, accelerated degree program, self-designed majors, honors program, independent study, double major, summer session for credit, internships. Off campus study at Hudson-Mohawk Association of Colleges and Universities. Study abroad program. ROTC: Army (c), Naval (c), Air Force (c).

Entrance Requirements: Options: electronic application, early admission, early decision, deferred admission, international baccalaureate accepted. Required: essay, high school transcript, 2 recommendations. Recommended: interview. Required for some: SAT or ACT, SAT and SAT Subject Tests or ACT, Testing is optional except for combined programs. International students are required to submit the SAT or ACT. Entrance: very difficult. Application deadlines: 1/15, 11/15 for early decision plan 1, 1/15 for early deci-

sion plan 2. Notification: 4/1, 12/15 for early decision plan 1, 2/1 for early decision plan 2. SAT Reasoning Test deadline: 2/15. SAT Subject Test deadline: 2/15. Transfer credits accepted: Yes. Applicants placed on waiting list: 851. Wait-listed applicants offered admission: 18. Early decision applicants: 403. Early decision applicants admitted: 259.

Costs Per Year: Application fee: $50. Comprehensive fee: $58,248 includes full-time tuition ($46,314), mandatory fees ($471), and college room and board ($11,463). College room only: $6285.

Collegiate Environment: Orientation program. Drama-theater group, choral group, student-run newspaper, radio station. Social organizations: 101 open to all; national fraternities, national sororities, local fraternities, local sororities, theme houses. Most popular organizations: U-Program (Programming Board), speaker's forum, student newspaper, Concert Committee, ski club. Major annual events: Spring Fest, large scale lectures, large concerts. Student services: health clinic, personal-psychological counseling, women's center. Campus security: 24-hour emergency response devices and patrols, late night transport-escort service, controlled dormitory access, awareness programs, bicycle patrol, shuttle service. 1,975 college housing spaces available; 1,861 were occupied in 2012-13. Freshmen guaranteed college housing. On-campus residence required through senior year. Option: coed housing available. Schaffer Library with 617,945 books, 803,952 microform titles, 11,333 serials, 14,366 audiovisual materials, an OPAC, and a Web page. Operations spending for the previous fiscal year: $4.6 million. 541 computers available on campus for general student use. Computer purchase/lease plans available. A campuswide network can be accessed from student residence rooms and from off campus. Students can access the following: online class registration, multimedia lab. Staffed computer lab on campus (open 24 hours a day) provides training in use of computers, software, and the Internet.

■ UNITED STATES MERCHANT MARINE ACADEMY

300 Steamboat Rd.
Kings Point, NY 11024-1699
Tel: (516)773-5000; Free: 866-546-4778
Fax: (516)773-5390
E-mail: admissions@usmma.edu
Web Site: www.usmma.edu/

Description: Federally supported, comprehensive, coed. Awards bachelor's and master's degrees. Founded 1943. Setting: 82-acre suburban campus with easy access to New York City. Total enrollment: 1,012. Faculty: (79 full-time). 2,211 applied, 12% were admitted. 28% from top 10% of their high school class, 66% from top quarter, 95% from top half. 19 National Merit Scholars, 34 class presidents, 5 valedictorians, 101 student government officers. Full-time: 987 students, 14% women, 86% men. Students come from 59 states and territories, 2 other countries, 88% from out-of-state. 1% American Indian or Alaska Native, non-Hispanic/Latino; 7% Hispanic/Latino; 2% African American, non-Hispanic/Latino; 5% Asian, non-Hispanic/Latino; 0% Native Hawaiian or other Pacific Islander, non-Hispanic/Latino; 2% international. 0.01% 25 or older, 100% live on campus, 3% transferred in. Retention: 85% of full-time freshmen returned the following year. Academic area with the most degrees conferred: engineering. Core. Calendar: trimesters. Honors program, internships.

Entrance Requirements: Option: electronic application. Required: essay, high school transcript, 3 recommendations, SAT or ACT, SAT or ACT. Recommended: interview. Entrance: very difficult. Application deadline: 3/1. Notification: continuous until 4/1. SAT Reasoning Test deadline: 3/1. Transfer credits accepted: Yes. Applicants placed on waiting list: 235.

Costs Per Year: Application fee: $0.

Collegiate Environment: Orientation program. Drama-theater group, choral group, marching band, student-run newspaper. Most popular organizations: Regimental Band, CFC, Neuman Club, Honor Guard. Major annual events: Homecoming, Parent's/Acceptance Weekend, Graduation/Commencement. Student services: health clinic, personal-psychological counseling. Campus security: 24-hour emergency response devices and patrols. Freshmen guaranteed college housing. On-campus residence required through senior year. Option: coed housing available. Schuyler Otis Bland Memorial Library with 207,377 books, 20,904 microform titles, 912 serials, 5,157 audiovisual materials, an OPAC, and a Web page.

■ UNITED STATES MILITARY ACADEMY

600 Thayer Rd.
West Point, NY 10996
Tel: (845)938-4011
Fax: (845)938-3021

E-mail: 8dad@sunams.usma.army.mil

Web Site: www.usma.edu/

Description: Federally supported, 4-year, coed. Awards bachelor's degrees. Founded 1802. Setting: 16,080-acre small town campus with easy access to New York City. Endowment: $201.1 million. Total enrollment: 4,592. Faculty: 617 (all full-time). Student-undergrad faculty ratio is 7:1. 15,171 applied, 9% were admitted. 50% from top 10% of their high school class, 76% from top quarter, 95% from top half. 219 National Merit Scholars, 213 class presidents, 100 valedictorians, 196 student government officers. Full-time: 4,592 students, 16% women, 84% men. Students come from 55 states and territories, 35 other countries, 93% from out-of-state. 1% American Indian or Alaska Native, non-Hispanic/Latino; 9% Hispanic/Latino; 7% African American, non-Hispanic/Latino; 5% Asian, non-Hispanic/Latino; 1% Native Hawaiian or other Pacific Islander, non-Hispanic/Latino; 1% international. 1% 25 or older, 100% live on campus, 0% transferred in. Retention: 96% of full-time freshmen returned the following year. Academic areas with the most degrees conferred: computer and information sciences; engineering; social sciences. Core. Calendar: semesters. Academic remediation for entering students, advanced placement, honors program, independent study, double major, summer session for credit. Off campus study at United States Naval Academy, United States Air Force Academy, United States Coast Guard Academy. Study abroad program.

Entrance Requirements: Option: electronic application. Required: essay, high school transcript, 4 recommendations, You must obtain nominations from an approved source, pass a Department of Defense qualifying medical examination, must be at least 17 but not yet 23 years of age by July 1 of year of entry, and be an unmarried U.S. citizen (foreign nationals with approval) with no parental obligations, SAT or ACT. Recommended: interview. Entrance: most difficult. Application deadline: 2/28. Notification: 5/1.

Costs Per Year: Comprehensive fee: $0. All students receive a full scholarship, including room and board, and medical and dental-care are provided by the US Army. Cadets are on Active Duty Status as members of the US Army and receive an annual salary. A portion of the cadet pay is deposited into a personal checking account. Another portion of cadet pay is deposited to a Cadet Account that is used to help a cadet pay for expenses such as uniforms, books, a computer, activity fees, etc. The only cost for students is a one-time deposit upon admission to defray the initial costs of uniforms, books, supplies, and equipment. If needed, loans for the deposit are available from $100-2,000.

Collegiate Environment: Orientation program. Drama-theater group, choral group, student-run radio station. Social organizations: 116 open to all; 80% of eligible men and 80% of eligible women are members. Most popular organizations: Asian-Pacific Club, Big Brothers and Big Sisters, Spirit Support Group, Film Forum, Philosophy Forum. Major annual events: Graduation Week, Homecoming/Ring Weekend, Army-Navy Football Week. Student services: legal services, health clinic, personal-psychological counseling. Campus security: 24-hour emergency response devices and patrols, late night transport-escort service. 4,592 college housing spaces available; all were occupied in 2012-13. Freshmen guaranteed college housing. On-campus residence required through senior year. Option: coed housing available. United States Military Academy Library at West Point with 426,298 books, 76,358 microform titles, 376 serials, 11,601 audiovisual materials, an OPAC, and a Web page. Operations spending for the previous fiscal year: $4.5 million.

■ **UNITED TALMUDICAL SEMINARY**

191 Rodney St.

Brooklyn, NY 11211

Tel: (718)963-9260

Description: Independent Jewish, comprehensive, men only. Awards bachelor's and master's degrees. Founded 1949. Total enrollment: 1,500. 4% 25 or older. Calendar: semesters.

Entrance Requirements: Open admission.

■ **UNIVERSITY AT ALBANY, STATE UNIVERSITY OF NEW YORK**

1400 Washington Ave.

Albany, NY 12222-0001

Tel: (518)442-3300

E-mail: ugadmissions@albany.edu

Web Site: www.albany.edu/

Description: State-supported, university, coed. Part of State University of New York System. Awards bachelor's, master's, and doctoral degrees and post-master's certificates. Founded 1844. Setting: 560-acre suburban campus. Endowment: $35.2 million. Research spending for the previous fis-

cal year: $231.3 million. Educational spending for the previous fiscal year: $12,906 per student. Total enrollment: 17,316. Faculty: 1,198 (589 full-time, 609 part-time). Student-undergrad faculty ratio is 20:1. 21,178 applied, 55% were admitted. 19% from top 10% of their high school class, 53% from top quarter, 88% from top half. Full-time: 12,068 students, 48% women, 52% men. Part-time: 807 students, 45% women, 55% men. Students come from 38 states and territories, 53 other countries, 5% from out-of-state. 0.3% American Indian or Alaska Native, non-Hispanic/Latino; 12% Hispanic/Latino; 13% African American, non-Hispanic/Latino; 7% Asian, non-Hispanic/Latino; 0.2% Native Hawaiian or other Pacific Islander, non-Hispanic/Latino; 4% international. 7% 25 or older, 57% live on campus, 11% transferred in. Retention: 83% of full-time freshmen returned the following year. Academic areas with the most degrees conferred: social sciences; English; psychology. Core. Calendar: semesters. ESL program, services for LD students, advanced placement, accelerated degree program, self-designed majors, freshman honors college, honors program, independent study, distance learning, double major, summer session for credit, part-time degree program, internships, graduate courses open to undergrads. Off campus study at New York State Visiting Student Program, Hudson-Mohawk Association of Colleges and Universities. Study abroad program. ROTC: Army, Air Force (c).

Entrance Requirements: Options: electronic application, early admission, early action, deferred admission, international baccalaureate accepted. Required: essay, high school transcript, 1 recommendation, SAT or ACT. Required for some: portfolio, audition. Entrance: very difficult. Application deadlines: 3/1, 3/1 for nonresidents, 11/15 for early action. Notification: continuous, 1/15 for early action. SAT Reasoning Test deadline: 3/1. Transfer credits accepted: Yes.

Costs Per Year: Application fee: $50. State resident tuition: $5570 full-time, $232 per credit hour part-time. Nonresident tuition: $14,050 full-time, $613 per credit hour part-time. Mandatory fees: $1993 full-time. Part-time tuition varies according to course load. College room and board: $11,276. College room only: $6976. Room and board charges vary according to board plan and housing facility.

Collegiate Environment: Orientation program. Drama-theater group, choral group, student-run newspaper, radio station. Social organizations: 200 open to all; national fraternities, national sororities, local fraternities, local sororities; 2% of eligible men and 4% of eligible women are members. Most popular organizations: intramural athletics, cultural organizations, political organizations, community service, honor societies. Major annual events: Purple Growl, Relay for Life. Student services: legal services, health clinic, personal-psychological counseling. Campus security: 24-hour emergency response devices and patrols, late night transport-escort service, controlled dormitory access, Five Quad Ambulance Service; On-Campus Dead Car Battery Assistance. 7,700 college housing spaces available; 7,600 were occupied in 2012-13. Freshmen guaranteed college housing. On-campus residence required through sophomore year. Option: coed housing available. University Library plus 2 others with 2.5 million books, 2.9 million microform titles, 525,782 serials, 13,360 audiovisual materials, an OPAC, and a Web page. Operations spending for the previous fiscal year: $11.7 million. 500 computers available on campus for general student use. Computer purchase/lease plans available. A campuswide network can be accessed from student residence rooms and from off campus. Students can access the following: online class registration. Staffed computer lab on campus provides training in use of computers, software, and the Internet.

■ **UNIVERSITY AT BUFFALO, THE STATE UNIVERSITY OF NEW YORK**

Capen Hall

Buffalo, NY 14260

Tel: (716)645-2000; Free: 888-UB-ADMIT

Fax: (716)645-6411

E-mail: ub-admissions@buffalo.edu

Web Site: www.buffalo.edu/

Description: State-supported, university, coed. Part of State University of New York System. Awards bachelor's, master's, and doctoral degrees and post-master's certificates. Founded 1846. Setting: 1,350-acre suburban campus. Endowment: $511 million. Research spending for the previous fiscal year: $340 million. Educational spending for the previous fiscal year: $14,405 per student. Total enrollment: 28,952. Faculty: 1,719 (1,170 full-time, 549 part-time). Student-undergrad faculty ratio is 14:1. 22,009 applied, 57% were admitted. 30% from top 10% of their high school class, 63% from top quarter, 94% from top half. 23 valedictorians. Full-time: 17,903 students, 45% women, 55% men. Part-time: 1,602 students, 51% women, 49% men.

Students come from 46 states and territories, 80 other countries, 4% from out-of-state. 0.3% American Indian or Alaska Native, non-Hispanic/Latino; 7% Hispanic/Latino; 7% African American, non-Hispanic/Latino; 11% Asian, non-Hispanic/Latino; 0.1% Native Hawaiian or other Pacific Islander, non-Hispanic/Latino; 16% international. 8% 25 or older, 35% live on campus, 10% transferred in. Retention: 87% of full-time freshmen returned the following year. Academic areas with the most degrees conferred: business/marketing; social sciences; psychology. Core. Calendar: semesters. Academic remediation for entering students, ESL program, services for LD students, advanced placement, accelerated degree program, self-designed majors, freshman honors college, honors program, independent study, distance learning, double major, summer session for credit, part-time degree program, co-op programs and internships, graduate courses open to undergrads. Off campus study at WNY Consortium. Study abroad program. ROTC: Army (c).

Entrance Requirements: Options: electronic application, early admission, early decision, international baccalaureate accepted. Required: essay, high school transcript, 1 recommendation, SAT or ACT. Required for some: Architecture requires a portfolio and Dance, Music Theatre, Theatre and Music require an audition. Entrance: moderately difficult. Application deadline: 11/1 for early decision. Notification: continuous, 12/15 for early decision. Transfer credits accepted: Yes. Applicants placed on waiting list: 55. Wait-listed applicants offered admission: 25. Early decision applicants: 480. Early decision applicants admitted: 319.

Costs Per Year: Application fee: $50. State resident tuition: $5570 full-time, $232 per credit hour part-time. Nonresident tuition: $16,190 full-time, $675 per credit hour part-time. Mandatory fees: $2419 full-time, $94 per credit hour part-time. Part-time tuition and fees vary according to course load. College room and board: $11,310. College room only: $6540. Room and board charges vary according to board plan and housing facility.

Collegiate Environment: Orientation program. Drama-theater group, choral group, marching band, student-run newspaper, radio station. Social organizations: 285 open to all; national fraternities, national sororities, local fraternities, local sororities; 2% of eligible men and 2% of eligible women are members. Major annual events: Opening Weekend, Fallfest/Springfest, Homecoming/Parents' Weekend. Student services: legal services, health clinic, personal-psychological counseling. Campus security: 24-hour emergency response devices and patrols, student patrols, late night transport-escort service, controlled dormitory access, self-defense and awareness programs, security cameras. 6,954 college housing spaces available; 6,859 were occupied in 2012-13. Freshmen guaranteed college housing. Option: coed housing available. Lockwood Memorial Library plus 11 others with 4.1 million books, 6.2 million microform titles, 101,758 serials, 284,796 audiovisual materials, an OPAC, and a Web page. Operations spending for the previous fiscal year: $22.9 million. 2,700 computers available on campus for general student use. A campuswide network can be accessed from student residence rooms and from off campus. Students can access the following: online class registration. Staffed computer lab on campus (open 24 hours a day).

■ **UNIVERSITY OF ROCHESTER**
Wilson Blvd.
Rochester, NY 14627
Tel: (585)275-2121; Free: 888-822-2256
Fax: (585)273-1118
E-mail: admit@admissions.rochester.edu
Web Site: www.rochester.edu/

Description: Independent, university, coed. Awards bachelor's, master's, and doctoral degrees and post-master's certificates. Founded 1850. Setting: 655-acre suburban campus. Endowment: $1.6 billion. Research spending for the previous fiscal year: $315.5 million. Educational spending for the previous fiscal year: $35,200 per student. Total enrollment: 10,510. Faculty: 762 (567 full-time, 195 part-time). Student-undergrad faculty ratio is 10:1. 14,987 applied, 36% were admitted. 77% from top 10% of their high school class, 93% from top quarter, 100% from top half. 25 National Merit Scholars, 8 valedictorians. Full-time: 5,512 students, 50% women, 50% men. Part-time: 273 students, 76% women, 24% men. Students come from 52 states and territories, 94 other countries, 64% from out-of-state. 0.3% American Indian or Alaska Native, non-Hispanic/Latino; 6% Hispanic/Latino; 5% African American, non-Hispanic/Latino; 11% Asian, non-Hispanic/Latino; 0.1% Native Hawaiian or other Pacific Islander, non-Hispanic/Latino; 13% international. 6% 25 or older, 83% live on campus, 2% transferred in. Retention: 96% of full-time freshmen returned the following year. Academic areas with the most degrees conferred: social sciences; biological/life sciences; health

professions and related sciences. Calendar: semesters plus optional summer term. ESL program, services for LD students, advanced placement, accelerated degree program, self-designed majors, honors program, independent study, double major, summer session for credit, part-time degree program, co-op programs and internships, graduate courses open to undergrads. Off campus study at Rochester area colleges. Study abroad program. ROTC: Army (c), Naval, Air Force (c).

Entrance Requirements: Options: electronic application, early admission, early decision, deferred admission, international baccalaureate accepted. Required: essay, high school transcript. Recommended: 2 recommendations, interview, SAT or ACT, SAT Subject Tests. Required for some: Audition is required for music programs at Eastman School of Music, SAT and SAT Subject Tests or ACT. Entrance: very difficult. Application deadlines: 1/1, 1/1 for nonresidents, 11/1 for early decision. Notification: 4/1, 4/1 for nonresidents, 12/15 for early decision. SAT Reasoning Test deadline: 1/1. SAT Subject Test deadline: 1/1. Transfer credits accepted: Yes. Applicants placed on waiting list: 2,029. Wait-listed applicants offered admission: 56. Early decision applicants: 718. Early decision applicants admitted: 272.

Costs Per Year: Application fee: $70. Comprehensive fee: $56,284 includes full-time tuition ($42,890), mandatory fees ($776), and college room and board ($12,618). College room only: $7682. Full-time tuition and fees vary according to student level. Room and board charges vary according to board plan. Part-time tuition: $1340 per credit hour. Part-time tuition varies according to course load.

Collegiate Environment: Orientation program. Drama-theater group, choral group, marching band, student-run newspaper, radio station. Social organizations: 250 open to all; national fraternities, national sororities; 16% of eligible men and 15% of eligible women are members. Most popular organizations: Campus Activities Board, Black Students' Union, Grassroots (environmental group), Women's Caucus, American Sign Language Club. Major annual events: Boar's Head Dinner, Mela, Meliora Weekend. Student services: legal services, health clinic, personal-psychological counseling, women's center. Campus security: 24-hour emergency response devices and patrols, student patrols, late night transport-escort service, controlled dormitory access. 3,709 college housing spaces available; 3,600 were occupied in 2012-13. Freshmen guaranteed college housing. On-campus residence required through sophomore year. Option: coed housing available. Rush Rhees Library plus 7 others with 4.1 million books, 4.7 million microform titles, 40,879 serials, 137,751 audiovisual materials, an OPAC, and a Web page. Operations spending for the previous fiscal year: $59.4 million. 512 computers available on campus for general student use. Computer purchase/lease plans available. A campuswide network can be accessed from student residence rooms and from off campus. Students can access the following: online class registration. Staffed computer lab on campus (open 24 hours a day) provides training in use of computers, software, and the Internet.

Community Environment: With Lake Ontario on its northern border and the scenic Finger Lakes on the south, the Rochester community of about one million people is located in an attractive setting. It offers a wide range of cultural and recreational opportunities-from concerts by the Rochester Philharmonic Orchestra and Eastman School ensembles, performances by resident professional theater companies, and an unusual concentration of first-class museums (including the University's own Memorial Art Gallery), to professional baseball and ice hockey and nearby opportunities for recreational canoeing, sculling, ice-skating, and skiing.

■ **U.T.A. MESIVTA OF KIRYAS JOEL**
9 Nickelsburg Rd., Unit 312
Monroe, NY 10950
Tel: (845)873-9901
Fax: (845)782-3620
Description: Independent Jewish, 4-year, men only. Awards bachelor's degrees. Total enrollment: 989. 1% 25 or older.
Entrance Requirements: Open admission.

■ **UTICA COLLEGE**
1600 Burrstone Rd.
Utica, NY 13502-4892
Tel: (315)792-3111; Free: 800-782-8884
Fax: (315)792-3003
Web Site: www.utica.edu/
Description: Independent, comprehensive, coed. Awards bachelor's, master's, and doctoral degrees. Founded 1946. Setting: 128-acre suburban campus. Endowment: $20.1 million. Total enrollment: 3,839. Faculty: 378

(143 full-time, 235 part-time). Student-undergrad faculty ratio is 11:1. 3,260 applied, 81% were admitted. 9% from top 10% of their high school class, 29% from top quarter, 65% from top half. Full-time: 2,126 students, 55% women, 45% men. Part-time: 642 students, 75% women, 25% men. Students come from 42 states and territories, 27 other countries, 16% from out-of-state. 0.4% American Indian or Alaska Native, non-Hispanic/Latino; 8% Hispanic/Latino; 10% African American, non-Hispanic/Latino; 2% Asian, non-Hispanic/Latino; 0.2% Native Hawaiian or other Pacific Islander, non-Hispanic/Latino; 3% international. 26% 25 or older, 47% live on campus, 6% transferred in. Retention: 67% of full-time freshmen returned the following year. Academic areas with the most degrees conferred: health professions and related sciences; homeland security, law enforcement, firefighting, and protective services; business/marketing. Core. Calendar: semesters. Academic remediation for entering students, services for LD students, advanced placement, accelerated degree program, honors program, independent study, distance learning, double major, summer session for credit, part-time degree program, adult/continuing education programs, internships, graduate courses open to undergrads. Off campus study at members of the New York State Visiting Student Program. Study abroad program. ROTC: Army, Air Force (c).

Entrance Requirements: Options: electronic application, deferred admission, international baccalaureate accepted. Required: essay, high school transcript, minimum 2 high school GPA, 1 recommendation. Recommended: interview. Required for some: minimum 3 high school GPA, SAT or ACT. Entrance: moderately difficult. Application deadline: Rolling. Notification: 9/1.

Collegiate Environment: Orientation program. Drama-theater group, choral group, student-run newspaper, radio station. Social organizations: 81 open to all; national fraternities, national sororities, local fraternities, local sororities; 1% of eligible men and 1% of eligible women are members. Most popular organizations: Physical Therapy Society, Student Nurses Association, Kappa Delta Pi, Student Senate, Utica College Honor Association. Major annual events: Homecoming Weekend, Annual Faculty-served Dinner, Air Band Competition. Student services: health clinic, personal-psychological counseling, women's center. Campus security: 24-hour emergency response devices and patrols, late night transport-escort service, controlled dormitory access. 1,046 college housing spaces available; 974 were occupied in 2012-13. Freshmen guaranteed college housing. On-campus residence required through sophomore year. Option: coed housing available. Frank E. Gannett Memorial Library with 145,412 books, 34,282 microform titles, 657 serials, 10,260 audiovisual materials, an OPAC, and a Web page. 430 computers available on campus for general student use. A campuswide network can be accessed from student residence rooms. Students can access the following: online class registration. Staffed computer lab on campus provides training in use of computers, software, and the Internet.

Community Environment: Utica is an area rich in the history of the Iroquois Confederacy, the French and Indian Wars, the American Revolution, the great migration to the Midwest and the western expansion of American commerce via the Erie Canal. Historic treasures in the area include the Oriskany Battlefield, Revolutionary Fort Stanwix (restored as a national monument) in Rome, and the homes of Revolutionary War heroes General Nicholas Herkimer and Major General Friedrich Wilhelm Baron von Steuben. Within an hour's drive of Utica are Johnson Hall, home of Sir William Johnson, colonial superintendent of Indian Affairs, in Johnstown; the Mansion House of the Oneida Community in Oneida; and Cooperstown, birthplace of James Fenimore Cooper, site of the Baseball Museum and Hall of Fame, the Farmer's Museum, and the headquarters of the New York State Historical Association. Utica's cultural assets include Munson-Williams-Proctor Institute and School of Art, one of the finest small art institutions in the country; the Oneida Historical Society; the Utica Civic Symphony; the Broadway Theatre League; the Players Theater Company; the Great Artists Concert series; the Utica Public Library and the Oneida County Junior Museum. These are greatly enhanced by the libraries, art galleries and cultural programs of the colleges in the area. The Utica area abounds in outdoor recreational resources. The city's park system includes the Val Bialas municipal ski slopes and ice skating rink just a mile from campus, an outstanding small zoo, 3 large public swimming pools, an 18-hole public golf course, public tennis courts, picnic grounds, and an abundance of public athletic fields. Excellent golfing, swimming, boating, fishing, hiking, and camping facilities surround the city. Nearby lakes include Otsego at Cooperstown, Oneida at Verona, Delta north of Rome, and the famous Fulton Chain of Lakes in the Adirondacks at Old Forge. Fine ski facilities near Utica include Snow Ridge at Turin, and Woods Valley near Rome.

■ UTICA SCHOOL OF COMMERCE
201 Bleecker St.
Utica, NY 13501-2280
Tel: (315)733-2307; Free: 800-321-4USC
Fax: (315)733-9281
Web Site: www.uscny.edu/
Description: Proprietary, 2-year, coed. Awards certificates, diplomas, transfer associate, and terminal associate degrees. Founded 1896. Setting: 2-acre urban campus. Total enrollment: 414. Student-undergrad faculty ratio is 14:1. 99 applied, 100% were admitted. 0% from out-of-state. 55% 25 or older. Retention: 81% of full-time freshmen returned the following year. Academic remediation for entering students, advanced placement, summer session for credit, part-time degree program, adult/continuing education programs.
Entrance Requirements: Required: high school transcript, interview. Recommended: essay. Entrance: noncompetitive. Application deadline: Rolling.
Collegiate Environment: Orientation program. Campus security: security during class hours. Utica School of Commerce Library with an OPAC and a Web page.

■ VASSAR COLLEGE
124 Raymond Ave.
Poughkeepsie, NY 12604
Tel: (845)437-7000; Free: 800-827-7270
Fax: (845)437-7063
E-mail: admissions@vassar.edu
Web Site: www.vassar.edu/
Description: Independent, 4-year, coed. Awards bachelor's and master's degrees. Founded 1861. Setting: 1,000-acre suburban campus with easy access to New York City. Endowment: $804.9 million. Research spending for the previous fiscal year: $4.1 million. Educational spending for the previous fiscal year: $29,672 per student. Total enrollment: 2,406. Faculty: 320 (277 full-time, 43 part-time). Student-undergrad faculty ratio is 8:1. 7,908 applied, 23% were admitted. 70% from top 10% of their high school class, 95% from top quarter, 100% from top half. 31 valedictorians. Full-time: 2,370 students, 56% women, 44% men. Part-time: 36 students, 53% women, 47% men. Students come from 52 states and territories, 60 other countries, 73% from out-of-state. 0% American Indian or Alaska Native, non-Hispanic/Latino; 11% Hispanic/Latino; 6% African American, non-Hispanic/Latino; 9% Asian, non-Hispanic/Latino; 0% Native Hawaiian or other Pacific Islander; non-Hispanic/Latino; 7% international. 1% 25 or older, 94% live on campus, 0.4% transferred in. Retention: 96% of full-time freshmen returned the following year. Academic areas with the most degrees conferred: social sciences; visual and performing arts; biological/life sciences. Calendar: semesters. Services for LD students, advanced placement, self-designed majors, independent study, double major, part-time degree program, co-op programs and internships. Off campus study at Howard University, Fisk University, Hampton University, Spelman College, Morehouse College, members of the Twelve College Exchange Program, Bard College. Study abroad program.
Entrance Requirements: Options: electronic application, early decision, deferred admission, international baccalaureate accepted. Required: essay, high school transcript, 2 recommendations, SAT and SAT Subject Tests or ACT. Entrance: very difficult. Application deadlines: 1/1, 11/15 for early decision. Notification: 4/1, 12/15 for early decision. SAT Reasoning Test deadline: 2/15. SAT Subject Test deadline: 2/15. Transfer credits accepted: Yes. Applicants placed on waiting list: 1,340. Wait-listed applicants offered admission: 29. Early decision applicants: 600. Early decision applicants admitted: 259.
Costs Per Year: Application fee: $70. One-time mandatory fee: $75. Comprehensive fee: $57,070 includes full-time tuition ($45,580), mandatory fees ($690), and college room and board ($10,800). College room only: $5860. Room and board charges vary according to board plan and housing facility. Part-time tuition: $5410 per unit. Part-time tuition varies according to course load.
Collegiate Environment: Orientation program. Drama-theater group, choral group, student-run newspaper, radio station. Social organizations: 120 open to all. Most popular organizations: Student Association, WVKR radio station, VICE (programming social events), Vassar Greens, Ultimate Frisbee. Major annual events: Fall Convocation, Founders' Day, All-Parents' Weekend. Student services: health clinic, personal-psychological counseling, women's center. Campus security: 24-hour emergency response devices and patrols, student patrols, late night transport-escort service, controlled dormitory access. 2,384 college housing spaces available; 2,298 were occupied in 2012-

13. Freshmen guaranteed college housing. On-campus residence required through senior year. Options: coed, women-only housing available. Vassar College Libraries plus 4 others with 1 million books, 762,899 microform titles, 8,257 serials, 31,054 audiovisual materials, an OPAC, and a Web page. Operations spending for the previous fiscal year: $7.2 million. 509 computers available on campus for general student use. Computer purchase/lease plans available. A campuswide network can be accessed from student residence rooms and from off campus. Students can access the following: online class registration, Ethernet. Staffed computer lab on campus provides training in use of computers, software, and the Internet.

Community Environment: Poughkeepsie, population 30,355, originally settled by the Dutch, was the capital of New York from 1778 to 1783. Situated on a plateau above the Hudson River, Poughkeepsie is about 75 miles north of New York City and is easily accessible by car, train, bus, and air. Community services include a library, YMCA, YWCA, churches, art galleries, the Mid-Hudson Civic Center (with an ice-skating rink), the Bardavon Opera House (1869), and a Jewish Community Center. The area offers facilities for recreation and places of historic interest such as the Franklin D. Roosevelt National Historic Site in Hyde Park, and the Vanderbilt Mansion. Industries within the area include IBM and the Fairchild Corporation.

■ **VAUGHN COLLEGE OF AERONAUTICS AND TECHNOLOGY**
86-01 23rd Ave.
Flushing, NY 11369
Tel: (718)429-6600; Free: 866-6VAUGHN
Fax: (718)429-0256
E-mail: David.griffey@vaughn.edu
Web Site: www.vaughn.edu/

Description: Independent, comprehensive, coed. Awards associate, bachelor's, and master's degrees. Founded 1932. Setting: 6-acre urban campus with easy access to New York City. Endowment: $21.5 million. Educational spending for the previous fiscal year: $7740 per student. Total enrollment: 1,812. Faculty: 216 (41 full-time, 175 part-time). Student-undergrad faculty ratio is 15:1. 723 applied, 85% were admitted. Full-time: 1,362 students, 13% women, 87% men. Part-time: 437 students, 14% women, 86% men. Students come from 31 states and territories, 10 other countries, 11% from out-of-state. 1% American Indian or Alaska Native, non-Hispanic/Latino; 38% Hispanic/Latino; 19% African American, non-Hispanic/Latino; 8% Asian, non-Hispanic/Latino; 5% Native Hawaiian or other Pacific Islander, non-Hispanic/Latino; 2% international. 30% 25 or older, 10% live on campus, 14% transferred in. Retention: 80% of full-time freshmen returned the following year. Academic areas with the most degrees conferred: transportation and materials moving; engineering technologies; business/marketing. Core. Calendar: semesters. Academic remediation for entering students, advanced placement, independent study, distance learning, double major, summer session for credit, part-time degree program, co-op programs and internships. ROTC: Army (c), Air Force (c).

Entrance Requirements: Open admission for students in the Aviation Training Institute. Options: electronic application, international baccalaureate accepted. Required: high school transcript. Recommended: essay, 2 recommendations, interview. Required for some: SAT and SAT Subject Tests or ACT. Entrance: moderately difficult. Application deadlines: Rolling, Rolling for nonresidents. Notification: continuous, continuous for nonresidents. Transfer credits accepted: Yes.

Costs Per Year: Application fee: $40. One-time mandatory fee: $160. Comprehensive fee: $32,330 includes full-time tuition ($19,850), mandatory fees ($600), and college room and board ($11,880). College room only: $9480. Full-time tuition and fees vary according to course load and program. Room and board charges vary according to board plan. Part-time tuition: $665 per credit. Part-time tuition varies according to course load and program.

Collegiate Environment: Orientation program. Social organizations: 20 open to all; academic fraternal organizations; 5% of eligible men and 5% of eligible women are members. Most popular organizations: American Association of Airport Executives, Women in Aviation-International, Institute of Electrical and Electronics Engineers, Robotics Club, Red Tail Pilots Club. Major annual events: Career Fair, Academic Honor Society, Springfest. Student services: personal-psychological counseling. Campus security: 24-hour emergency response devices and patrols, student patrols, late night transport-escort service, controlled dormitory access. 200 college housing spaces available; 172 were occupied in 2012-13. Freshmen given priority for college housing. Option: coed housing available. George A. Vaughn Memorial Library with 117,455 books, 23,000 serials, 4,252 audiovisual materials, and an OPAC. Operations spending for the previous fiscal year: $486,948.

50 computers available on campus for general student use. A campuswide network can be accessed from student residence rooms and from off campus. Students can access the following: online class registration, Vaughn Student Portal. Staffed computer lab on campus provides training in use of computers, software, and the Internet.

Community Environment: See Queens College of the City University of New York.

■ **VILLA MARIA COLLEGE OF BUFFALO**
240 Pine Ridge Rd.
Buffalo, NY 14225-3999
Tel: (716)896-0700
Fax: (716)896-0705
E-mail: admissions@villa.edu
Web Site: www.villa.edu/

Description: Independent, 4-year, coed, affiliated with Roman Catholic Church. Awards associate and bachelor's degrees. Founded 1960. Setting: 15-acre suburban campus. Endowment: $1.2 million. Educational spending for the previous fiscal year: $15,710 per student. Total enrollment: 411. Faculty: 74 (30 full-time, 44 part-time). Student-undergrad faculty ratio is 8:1. 243 applied, 81% were admitted. 5% from top 10% of their high school class, 11% from top quarter, 41% from top half. Full-time: 364 students, 61% women, 39% men. Part-time: 106 students, 69% women, 31% men. Students come from 6 states and territories, 1 other country, 2% from out-of-state. 0.2% American Indian or Alaska Native, non-Hispanic/Latino; 5% Hispanic/Latino; 17% African American, non-Hispanic/Latino; 1% Asian, non-Hispanic/Latino; 0% Native Hawaiian or other Pacific Islander, non-Hispanic/Latino; 0% international. 25% 25 or older, 7% live on campus, 10% transferred in. Retention: 70% of full-time freshmen returned the following year. Academic areas with the most degrees conferred: visual and performing arts; architecture. Core. Calendar: semesters. Academic remediation for entering students, services for LD students, advanced placement, independent study, summer session for credit, part-time degree program, co-op programs and internships. Off campus study at members of the Western New York Consortium.

Entrance Requirements: Options: electronic application, deferred admission. Required: essay, high school transcript, interview, Admission to music programs require audition; Arts programs require portfolio review. Required for some: Admission to music programs require audition; Arts programs require portfolio review. Entrance: minimally difficult. Application deadlines: Rolling, Rolling for nonresidents. Notification: continuous, continuous for nonresidents. Transfer credits accepted: Yes.

Costs Per Year: Tuition: $17,640 full-time. Mandatory fees: $370 full-time. Full-time tuition and fees vary according to program. Part-time fees vary according to course load and program.

Collegiate Environment: Orientation program. Choral group. Social organizations: 19 open to all. Most popular organizations: Design and Beyond, Teachers Love Children, Multicultural Club, Phi Theta Kappa, Helping Adults New Dreams Succeed. Major annual events: Spring Arts Festival, Music Series, Fall/Spring Fest. Student services: health clinic, personal-psychological counseling. Campus security: late night transport-escort service, security guard during hours of operation. College housing not available. Villa Maria College Library with 37,000 books, 17,300 microform titles, 130 serials, an OPAC, and a Web page. Operations spending for the previous fiscal year: $319,290. 250 computers available on campus for general student use. Computer purchase/lease plans available. A campuswide network can be accessed. Students can access the following: online class registration. Staffed computer lab on campus provides training in use of computers, software, and the Internet.

Community Environment: See Canisius College.

■ **WAGNER COLLEGE**
1 Campus Rd.
Staten Island, NY 10301-4495
Tel: (718)390-3100; Free: 800-221-1010
Fax: (718)390-3105
E-mail: robert.herr@wagner.edu
Web Site: www.wagner.edu/

Description: Independent, comprehensive, coed. Awards bachelor's and master's degrees and post-master's certificates. Founded 1883. Setting: 105-acre urban campus with easy access to New York City. Endowment: $64.4 million. Educational spending for the previous fiscal year: $10,202 per student. Total enrollment: 2,208. Faculty: 275 (102 full-time, 173 part-time). Student-undergrad faculty ratio is 13:1. 16% from top 10% of their high school class, 72% from top quarter, 91% from top half. Full-time: 1,744 students, 65% women, 35% men. Part-time: 77 students, 70% women, 30% men. Students come from 40 states and territories, 30 other countries, 48% from out-of-state. 0.1% American Indian or Alaska Native, non-Hispanic/Latino; 9% Hispanic/Latino; 6% African American, non-Hispanic/Latino; 2% Asian, non-Hispanic/Latino; 0.2% Native Hawaiian or other Pacific Islander, non-Hispanic/Latino; 2% international. 7% 25 or older, 67% live on campus, 5% transferred in. Retention: 83% of full-time freshmen returned the following year. Academic areas with the most degrees conferred: visual and performing arts; health professions and related sciences; business/marketing. Core. Calendar: semesters. Services for LD students, advanced placement, self-designed majors, honors program, independent study, double major, summer session for credit, part-time degree program, adult/continuing education programs, internships, graduate courses open to undergrads. Off campus study at California Lutheran University. Study abroad program. ROTC: Army (c).

Entrance Requirements: Required: essay, high school transcript, minimum 2.5 high school GPA, 2 recommendations. Recommended: minimum 3 high school GPA, interview. Required for some: interview, SAT or ACT, SAT Subject Tests.

Costs Per Year: Comprehensive fee: $50,880 includes full-time tuition ($38,920), mandatory fees ($300), and college room and board ($11,660). Part-time tuition: $4865 per unit.

Collegiate Environment: Orientation program. Drama-theater group, choral group, student-run newspaper, radio station. Social organizations: 66 open to all; national fraternities, national sororities, local fraternities, local sororities; 15% of eligible men and 13% of eligible women are members. Most popular organizations: Student Government Association, Student Activities Board, Wagner College Theatre, Wagner College Choir, student newspaper. Major annual events: Homecoming, Songfest, Spring Fling. Student services: health clinic, personal-psychological counseling. Campus security: 24-hour emergency response devices and patrols, late night transport-escort service, controlled dormitory access. 1,500 college housing spaces available; 1,279 were occupied in 2012-13. Freshmen guaranteed college housing. Option: coed housing available. August Horrmann Library with 158,160 books, 218 microform titles, 56,399 serials, 2,453 audiovisual materials, an OPAC, and a Web page. Operations spending for the previous fiscal year: $1.1 million. 230 computers available on campus for general student use. A campuswide network can be accessed from student residence rooms and from off campus. Students can access the following: online class registration. Staffed computer lab on campus provides training in use of computers, software, and the Internet.

■ **WEBB INSTITUTE**
Crescent Beach Rd.
Glen Cove, NY 11542-1398
Tel: (516)671-2213
Fax: (516)674-9838
E-mail: admissions@webb-institute.edu
Web Site: www.webb-institute.edu/

Description: Independent, 4-year, coed. Awards bachelor's degrees. Founded 1889. Setting: 26-acre suburban campus with easy access to New York City. Endowment: $50.2 million. Research spending for the previous fiscal year: $53,211. Educational spending for the previous fiscal year: $71,297 per student. Total enrollment: 79. Faculty: 14 (11 full-time, 3 part-time). Student-undergrad faculty ratio is 7:1. 82 applied, 38% were admitted. 80% from top 10% of their high school class, 20% from top quarter, 100% from top half. Full-time: 79 students, 19% women, 81% men. Students come from 20 states and territories, 3 other countries, 70% from out-of-state. 0% American Indian or Alaska Native, non-Hispanic/Latino; 4% Hispanic/Latino; 0% African American, non-Hispanic/Latino; 6% Asian, non-Hispanic/Latino; 0% Native Hawaiian or other Pacific Islander, non-Hispanic/Latino; 0% international. 1% 25 or older, 100% live on campus, 3% transferred in. Retention: 83% of full-time freshmen returned the following year. Academic area with the most degrees conferred: engineering. Core. Calendar: semesters. Services for LD students, independent study, double major, co-op programs and internships. Study abroad program.

Entrance Requirements: Options: early decision, international baccalaureate accepted. Required: high school transcript, minimum 3.5 high school GPA, 2 recommendations, interview, proof of U.S. citizenship or permanent residency status, SAT, SAT Subject Tests. Entrance: most difficult. Application deadlines: 2/15, 10/15 for early decision. Notification: 4/30, 12/15 for early decision. SAT Reasoning Test deadline: 2/15. SAT Subject Test deadline: 2/15. Transfer credits accepted: No. Early decision applicants: 10. Early decision applicants admitted: 3.

Costs Per Year: Application fee: $25. Comprehensive fee: $13,750 includes full-time tuition ($0) and college room and board ($13,750). Full-tuition scholarship covering all four years are awarded to all accepted students who are U.S. citizens or Green Card holders.

Collegiate Environment: Orientation program. Choral group. Social organizations: The Webb Women; 100% of women are members. Most popular organizations: Student Organization, Society of Naval Architects and Marine Engineers, American Society of Naval Engineers, Society of Women Engineers, Marine Technology Society. Major annual events: Family Weekend, Webbstock, Founders Day. Student services: personal-psychological counseling. Campus security: 24-hour emergency response devices and patrols, controlled dormitory access. 110 college housing spaces available; 79 were occupied in 2012-13. Freshmen guaranteed college housing. On-campus residence required through senior year. Options: coed, men-only, women-only housing available. Livingston Library with 53,319 books, 1,656 microform titles, 270 serials, an OPAC, and a Web page. 25 computers available on campus for general student use. Computer purchase/lease plans available. A computer is required for all students. A campuswide network can be accessed from student residence rooms and from off campus. Staffed computer lab on campus (open 24 hours a day) provides training in use of computers, software, and the Internet.

Community Environment: Population 26,600, Glen Cove lies 22 miles from New York City on Long Island's historic North Shore. The Long Island Railroad furnishes commuter service to New York City. The area has excellent boating, swimming, horseback riding, and fishing facilities. Part-time employment is available.

■ **WELLS COLLEGE**
170 Main St.
Aurora, NY 13026
Tel: (315)364-3266; Free: 800-952-9355
Fax: (315)364-3227
E-mail: admissions@wells.edu
Web Site: www.wells.edu/

Description: Independent, 4-year, coed. Awards bachelor's degrees. Founded 1868. Setting: 365-acre rural campus with easy access to Syracuse. Endowment: $23.5 million. Research spending for the previous fiscal year: $35,000. Total enrollment: 532. Faculty: 68 (39 full-time, 29 part-time). Student-undergrad faculty ratio is 10:1. 1,803 applied, 45% were admitted. 34% from top 10% of their high school class, 63% from top quarter, 90% from top half. 4 valedictorians, 20 student government officers. Full-time: 523 students, 68% women, 32% men. Part-time: 9 students, 44% women, 56% men. Students come from 30 states and territories, 6 other countries, 27% from out-of-state. 1% American Indian or Alaska Native, non-Hispanic/Latino; 5% Hispanic/Latino; 11% African American, non-Hispanic/Latino; 2% Asian, non-Hispanic/Latino; 0.4% Native Hawaiian or other Pacific Islander, non-Hispanic/Latino; 2% international. 4% 25 or older, 84% live on campus, 4% transferred in. Retention: 70% of full-time freshmen returned the following year. Academic areas with the most degrees conferred: English; biological/life sciences; social sciences. Core. Calendar: semesters. ESL program, services for LD students, advanced placement, accelerated degree program, self-designed majors, independent study, double major, part-time degree program, adult/continuing education programs, internships. Off campus study at members of the Association of Colleges and Universities of the State of New York, Cornell University, American University, Ithaca College. Study abroad program. ROTC: Army (c), Air Force (c).

Entrance Requirements: Options: electronic application, early admission, early decision, early action, deferred admission, international baccalaureate accepted. Required: essay, high school transcript, 2 recommendations, SAT or ACT. Recommended: minimum 3 high school GPA, interview. Entrance: moderately difficult. Application deadlines: 3/1, 12/15 for early decision, 12/15 for early action. Notification: 4/1, 1/15 for early decision, 2/1 for early action. SAT Reasoning Test deadline: 3/1. Transfer credits accepted: Yes. Early decision applicants: 64. Early decision applicants admitted: 13. Early action applicants: 770. Early action applicants admitted: 428.

Costs Per Year: Application fee: $40. Comprehensive fee: $46,600 includes full-time tuition ($33,200), mandatory fees ($1500), and college room and board ($11,900).

Collegiate Environment: Orientation program. Drama-theater group, choral group, student-run newspaper. Social organizations: 44 open to all. Most popular organizations: Praising Our Work Ethnicity and Race (POWER), Women's Resource Center (WRC), Dance Collective, Model UN, Red Cross Club. Major annual events: Spring Weekend, Fall Semi-Formal, Odd-Even

Game/Weekend. Student services: health clinic, personal-psychological counseling, women's center. Campus security: 24-hour emergency response devices and patrols, late night transport-escort service, controlled dormitory access. 475 college housing spaces available; 435 were occupied in 2012-13. Freshmen guaranteed college housing. On-campus residence required through senior year. Options: coed, women-only housing available. Louis Jefferson Long Library with 213,140 books, 20,128 microform titles, 399 serials, 1,007 audiovisual materials, an OPAC, and a Web page. Operations spending for the previous fiscal year: $440,000. 96 computers available on campus for general student use. A campuswide network can be accessed from student residence rooms and from off campus. Students can access the following: online class registration. Staffed computer lab on campus provides training in use of computers, software, and the Internet.

Community Environment: The college has always shared a close relationship with the small, picturesque village of Aurora, New York; which is noted on the National Historic Registry. Aurora is also home to the highly acclaimed Aurora Inn and the nationally known company Mackenzie-Childs.

■ WESTCHESTER COMMUNITY COLLEGE
75 Grasslands Rd.
Valhalla, NY 10595-1698
Tel: (914)785-6600
E-mail: admissions@sunywcc.edu
Web Site: www.sunywcc.edu/

Description: State and locally supported, 2-year, coed. Part of State University of New York System. Awards certificates, transfer associate, and terminal associate degrees. Founded 1946. Setting: 218-acre suburban campus with easy access to New York City. Educational spending for the previous fiscal year: $5531 per student. Total enrollment: 13,997. Faculty: 1,069 (161 full-time, 908 part-time). Student-undergrad faculty ratio is 18:1. 5,606 applied, 96% were admitted. Full-time: 7,618 students, 50% women, 50% men. Part-time: 6,379 students, 58% women, 42% men. Students come from 13 states and territories, 40 other countries, 0.5% from out-of-state. 1% American Indian or Alaska Native, non-Hispanic/Latino; 28% Hispanic/Latino; 21% African American, non-Hispanic/Latino; 5% Asian, non-Hispanic/Latino; 0.2% Native Hawaiian or other Pacific Islander, non-Hispanic/Latino. 28% 25 or older, 7% transferred in. Core. Calendar: semesters. Academic remediation for entering students, ESL program, services for LD students, advanced placement, self-designed majors, honors program, independent study, distance learning, double major, summer session for credit, part-time degree program, adult/continuing education programs, co-op programs and internships. Off campus study. Study abroad program.

Entrance Requirements: Open admission except for nursing, radiological technology, respiratory care programs. Option: early admission. Required: high school transcript. Recommended: interview. Entrance: noncompetitive. Application deadline: Rolling. Notification: continuous until 2/2. Transfer credits accepted: Yes.

Costs Per Year: Application fee: $35. State resident tuition: $4280 full-time, $179 per credit part-time. Nonresident tuition: $11,770 full-time, $493 per credit part-time. Mandatory fees: $423 full-time, $98 per term part-time.

Collegiate Environment: Orientation program. Drama-theater group, choral group, student-run newspaper, radio station. Social organizations: 90 open to all. Most popular organizations: Deca Fashion Retail, Future Educators, Respiratory Club, Black Student Union, Diversity Action. Major annual events: Solidarity Day, Club Day, Talent Day. Student services: health clinic, personal-psychological counseling, women's center. Campus security: 24-hour emergency response devices and patrols, late night transport-escort service. College housing not available. Harold L. Drimmer Library plus 1 other with 225,654 books, 6,830 microform titles, 253 serials, 4,877 audiovisual materials, an OPAC, and a Web page. Operations spending for the previous fiscal year: $4 million. 3,118 computers available on campus for general student use. A campuswide network can be accessed from off-campus. Students can access the following: online class registration. Staffed computer lab on campus.

■ WOOD TOBE–COBURN SCHOOL
8 E 40th St.
New York, NY 10016
Tel: (212)686-9040; Free: 800-394-9663
Fax: (212)686-9171
Web Site: www.woodtobecoburn.edu/

Description: Private, 2-year, coed. Awards diplomas and terminal associate

degrees. Founded 1879. Setting: urban campus. Total enrollment: 617. 967 applied, 84% were admitted. Calendar: semesters. Accelerated degree program, internships.

Collegiate Environment: College housing not available.

■ YESHIVA DERECH CHAIM
1573 39th St.
Brooklyn, NY 11218
Tel: (718)438-3070

Description: Independent Jewish, comprehensive, men only. Awards bachelor's and master's degrees. Founded 1975. Total enrollment: 162. 31 applied, 100% were admitted. 3% 25 or older. Calendar: semesters.

■ YESHIVA D'MONSEY RABBINICAL COLLEGE
2 Roman Blvd.
Monsey, NY 10952
Tel: (914)352-5852
Fax: (914)362-3453

Description: Independent Jewish, 4-year, men only. Awards bachelor's degrees. Total enrollment: 72. 26 applied, 100% were admitted.

■ YESHIVA GEDOLAH IMREI YOSEF D'SPINKA
1466 56th St.
Brooklyn, NY 11219
Tel: (718)851-8721

Description: Independent Jewish, 4-year, men only. Awards bachelor's degrees. Total enrollment: 153. 5% 25 or older.

Entrance Requirements: Open admission.

■ YESHIVA KARLIN STOLIN RABBINICAL INSTITUTE
1818 Fifty-fourth St.
Brooklyn, NY 11204
Tel: (718)232-7800
Fax: (718)331-4833

Description: Independent Jewish, comprehensive, men only. Awards bachelor's and master's degrees. Founded 1948. Setting: urban campus. Total enrollment: 69. 30 applied, 100% were admitted. 7% 25 or older. Core. Calendar: semesters. Independent study, co-op programs. Study abroad program.

Entrance Requirements: Required: high school transcript, interview. Entrance: very difficult. Application deadline: Rolling. Preference given to students from Mesivta Karlin Stolin.

Collegiate Environment: Student services: personal-psychological counseling. Campus security: 24-hour emergency response devices. 6,000 books.

■ YESHIVA AND KOLEL BAIS MEDRASH ELYON
73 Main St.
Monsey, NY 10952
Tel: (845)356-7064

Description: Independent Jewish, 4-year, men only. Awards bachelor's degrees. Total enrollment: 24. 13 applied, 100% were admitted.

■ YESHIVA AND KOLLEL HARBOTZAS TORAH
1049 E 15th St.
Brooklyn, NY 11230
Tel: (718)692-0208

Description: Independent Jewish, 4-year, men only. Awards bachelor's degrees. Total enrollment: 31.

■ YESHIVA OF NITRA RABBINICAL COLLEGE
Pines Bridge Rd.
Mount Kisco, NY 10549
Tel: (718)384-5460

Description: Independent Jewish, comprehensive, men only. Awards bachelor's and master's degrees. Founded 1946. Setting: small town campus with easy access to New York City. Total enrollment: 214. 252 applied. Calendar: semesters.

■ YESHIVA SHAAR HATORAH TALMUDIC RESEARCH INSTITUTE
117-06 84th Ave.
Kew Gardens, NY 11418-1469
Tel: (718)846-1940

Description: Independent Jewish, comprehensive, men only. Awards bachelor's and master's degrees. Founded 1976. Total enrollment: 141. 43 applied. Calendar: semesters.

■ **YESHIVA SHAAREI TORAH OF ROCKLAND**
91 W Carlton Rd.
Suffern, NY 10901
Tel: (845)352-3431
Description: Independent Jewish, 4-year, men only. Awards bachelor's degrees. Total enrollment: 46. 42 applied.

■ **YESHIVA OF THE TELSHE ALUMNI**
4904 Independence Ave.
Riverdale, NY 10471
Tel: (718)601-3523
Description: Independent Jewish, 4-year, men only. Awards bachelor's degrees. Total enrollment: 112. 26 applied, 100% were admitted.
Entrance Requirements: Recommended: high school transcript.

■ **YESHIVA UNIVERSITY**
500 W 185th St.
New York, NY 10033-3201
Tel: (212)960-5400
Fax: (212)960-0086
Web Site: www.yu.edu/
Description: Independent, university, coed. Awards associate, bachelor's, master's, and doctoral degrees and post-master's certificates (Yeshiva College and Stern College for Women are coordinate undergraduate colleges of arts and sciences for men and women, respectively. Sy Syms School of Business offers programs at both campuses). Founded 1886. Setting: urban campus. Total enrollment: 6,753. Faculty: 1,477 (986 full-time, 491 part-time). Student-undergrad faculty ratio is 6:1. 1,622 applied, 84% were admitted. 47% from top 10% of their high school class, 75% from top quarter, 96% from top half. Full-time: 2,817 students, 49% women, 51% men. Part-time: 52 students, 31% women, 69% men. 65% from out-of-state. 0.1% American Indian or Alaska Native, non-Hispanic/Latino; 1% Hispanic/Latino; 0.1% African American, non-Hispanic/Latino; 0.1% Asian, non-Hispanic/Latino; 0% Native Hawaiian or other Pacific Islander, non-Hispanic/Latino; 6% international. 1% 25 or older, 78% live on campus, 1% transferred in. Retention: 92% of full-time freshmen returned the following year. Academic areas with the most degrees conferred: business/marketing; psychology; biological/life sciences. Calendar: semesters. Advanced placement, self-designed majors, honors program, independent study, double major, summer session for credit, internships. Off campus study at Fashion Institute of Technology (Stern College students only). Study abroad program.
Entrance Requirements: Options: early admission, deferred admission. Required: essay, high school transcript, 2 recommendations, interview, SAT or ACT. Entrance: moderately difficult. Application deadline: 2/1. Notification: 4/1.
Costs Per Year: Application fee: $65. Comprehensive fee: $48,750 includes full-time tuition ($36,600), mandatory fees ($1000), and college room and board ($11,150). Full-time tuition and fees vary according to student level. Part-time tuition: $1240 per credit hour.
Collegiate Environment: Orientation program. Drama-theater group, choral group, student-run newspaper, radio station. Campus security: 24-hour emergency response devices and patrols, late night transport-escort service. Options: men-only, women-only housing available.
Community Environment: See New York University.

■ **YESHIVAS NOVOMINSK**
1569 47th St.
Brooklyn, NY 11219
Tel: (718)438-2727
Description: Independent Jewish, 4-year, men only. Awards bachelor's degrees. Total enrollment: 100. 25 applied, 100% were admitted.

■ **YESHIVAT MIKDASH MELECH**
1326 Ocean Pky.
Brooklyn, NY 11230-5601
Tel: (718)339-1090
E-mail: mikdashmelech@verizon.net
Description: Independent Jewish, 4-year, men only. Awards bachelor's degrees. Founded 1972. Total enrollment: 78. 50 applied, 100% were admitted. 17% 25 or older. Calendar: continuous.

Entrance Requirements: Recommended: high school transcript. Application deadline: Rolling. Notification: continuous.

■ **YESHIVATH VIZNITZ**
25 Phyllis Ter.
Monsey, NY 10952
Tel: (914)356-1010
Description: Independent Jewish, comprehensive, men only. Awards bachelor's and master's degrees. Founded 1946. Setting: small town campus with easy access to New York City. Total enrollment: 420. 70 applied, 100% were admitted. 0% 25 or older. Calendar: semesters.

■ **YESHIVATH ZICHRON MOSHE**
Laurel Park Rd.
South Fallsburg, NY 12779
Tel: (914)434-5240
Description: Independent Jewish, comprehensive, men only. Awards bachelor's and master's degrees. Founded 1969. Setting: 70-acre small town campus. Total enrollment: 222. 74 applied, 100% were admitted. Core. Calendar: semesters.
Collegiate Environment: Student services: personal-psychological counseling.

■ **YORK COLLEGE OF THE CITY UNIVERSITY OF NEW YORK**
94-20 Guy R Brewer Blvd.
Jamaica, NY 11451-0001
Tel: (718)262-2000
E-mail: lbruno@york.cuny.edu
Web Site: www.york.cuny.edu/
Description: State and locally supported, comprehensive, coed. Part of City University of New York System. Awards bachelor's and master's degrees. Founded 1967. Setting: 50-acre urban campus with easy access to New York City. Total enrollment: 8,389. Faculty: 553 (201 full-time, 352 part-time). Student-undergrad faculty ratio is 19:1. 13,319 applied, 60% were admitted. Full-time: 5,327 students, 66% women, 34% men. Part-time: 3,023 students, 67% women, 33% men. Students come from 4 states and territories, 131 other countries, 0.1% from out-of-state. 1% American Indian or Alaska Native, non-Hispanic/Latino; 18% Hispanic/Latino; 34% African American, non-Hispanic/Latino; 16% Asian, non-Hispanic/Latino; 0% Native Hawaiian or other Pacific Islander, non-Hispanic/Latino; 0% international. 30% 25 or older, 9% transferred in. Retention: 77% of full-time freshmen returned the following year. Academic areas with the most degrees conferred: business/marketing; psychology; health professions and related sciences. Core. Calendar: semesters. ESL program, services for LD students, advanced placement, honors program, independent study, double major, summer session for credit, part-time degree program, adult/continuing education programs, co-op programs and internships. Off campus study at other units of the City University of New York System. Study abroad program. ROTC: Army.
Entrance Requirements: Options: electronic application, early admission, deferred admission, international baccalaureate accepted. Required: high school transcript, minimum 2.5 high school GPA, SAT or ACT. Recommended: minimum 3 high school GPA. Required for some: minimum 2.8 high school GPA. Entrance: moderately difficult. Application deadlines: Rolling, Rolling for nonresidents. Notification: continuous, continuous for nonresidents. Transfer credits accepted: Yes.
Costs Per Year: Application fee: $65. State resident tuition: $5730 full-time, $245 per credit part-time. Nonresident tuition: $12,240 full-time, $510 per credit part-time. Mandatory fees: $366 full-time, $113 per term part-time. Full-time tuition and fees vary according to degree level and student level. Part-time tuition and fees vary according to degree level and student level.
Collegiate Environment: Orientation program. Drama-theater group, choral group, student-run newspaper. Most popular organizations: Haitian Students Association, Caribbean Students Association, Haitian Cultural Association, Latin Caucus, Muslim Student Association. Major annual events: Club Fairs, talent shows, ethnic fairs. Student services: health clinic, personal-psychological counseling, women's center. Campus security: 24-hour emergency response devices and patrols, late night transport-escort service. College housing not available. Main library plus 1 other with 575,480 books, 149,394 microform titles, 71,713 serials, an OPAC, and a Web page. 650 computers available on campus for general student use. A campuswide network can be accessed from off-campus. Students can access the following: online class registration. Staffed computer lab on campus provides training in use of computers, software, and the Internet.

■ **ALAMANCE COMMUNITY COLLEGE**
PO Box 8000
Graham, NC 27253-8000
Tel: (336)578-2002
Fax: (336)578-1987
E-mail: brehlere@alamancecc.edu
Web Site: www.alamancecc.edu/
Description: State-supported, 2-year, coed. Part of North Carolina Community College System. Awards certificates, diplomas, transfer associate, and terminal associate degrees. Founded 1959. Setting: 48-acre small town campus. Endowment: $2.9 million. Total enrollment: 4,739. Faculty: 435 (115 full-time, 320 part-time). Student-undergrad faculty ratio is 12:1. 646 applied, 100% were admitted. Students come from 6 states and territories, 1% from out-of-state. 1% American Indian or Alaska Native, non-Hispanic/Latino; 4% Hispanic/Latino; 21% African American, non-Hispanic/Latino; 2% Asian, non-Hispanic/Latino; 0.02% international. 44% 25 or older. Calendar: semesters. Academic remediation for entering students, ESL program, services for LD students, independent study, distance learning, double major, summer session for credit, part-time degree program, adult/continuing education programs, co-op programs. Off campus study at University of North Carolina at Greensboro.
Entrance Requirements: Open admission except for nursing, allied health programs. Option: electronic application. Required: high school transcript. Entrance: noncompetitive. Application deadline: Rolling. Notification: continuous.
Costs Per Year: Application fee: $0. State resident tuition: $2070 full-time. Nonresident tuition: $7830 full-time. Mandatory fees: $30 full-time. Full-time tuition and fees vary according to course load.
Collegiate Environment: Orientation program. Social organizations: 5 open to all. Student services: personal-psychological counseling. Campus security: 24-hour emergency response devices and patrols, student patrols, late night transport-escort service. College housing not available. Learning Resources Center with 22,114 books, 25,837 microform titles, 185 serials, an OPAC, and a Web page. Operations spending for the previous fiscal year: $406,075. 56 computers available on campus for general student use. A campuswide network can be accessed. Staffed computer lab on campus provides training in use of computers, software, and the Internet.
Community Environment: The industrialized economy of Alamance County depends primarily upon textiles, hosiery, electronics, metal cutting and fabricating, packaging and plastics. The bulk of the industries are located here. Planes and buses serve the area. A library, museum, YMCA, hospitals and various civic and service organizations are a part of the community. Some part-time employment is available for students. Recreational facilities include a supervised city recreational program, and many lakes are available for winter sports and outdoor living.

■ **APEX SCHOOL OF THEOLOGY**
2945 S Miami Blvd., Ste. 114
Durham, NC 27703
Tel: (919)572-1625
Fax: (919)572-1762
E-mail: registrar@apexsot.edu
Web Site: www.apexsot.edu/
Description: Independent interdenominational, comprehensive, coed. Awards associate, bachelor's, master's, and doctoral degrees. Founded 1995. Setting: suburban campus. Total enrollment: 721. Faculty: 41 (14 full-

time, 27 part-time). Student-undergrad faculty ratio is 17:1. 362 applied, 83% were admitted. 0% from out-of-state. 2% Hispanic/Latino; 95% African American, non-Hispanic/Latino. 100% 25 or older. Retention: 92% of full-time freshmen returned the following year. Core. Calendar: semesters. Independent study, distance learning, double major, internships.
Entrance Requirements: Option: electronic application. Required: essay, high school transcript, 1 recommendation. Entrance: moderately difficult. Transfer credits accepted: Yes.
Costs Per Year: Application fee: $25. Tuition: $4800 full-time, $200 per credit hour part-time. Mandatory fees: $200 full-time. Tuition guaranteed not to increase for student's term of enrollment.
Collegiate Environment: Choral group, student-run newspaper.

■ **APPALACHIAN STATE UNIVERSITY**
Boone, NC 28608
Tel: (828)262-2000
Fax: (828)262-3296
E-mail: admissions@appstate.edu
Web Site: www.appstate.edu/
Description: State-supported, comprehensive, coed. Part of University of North Carolina System. Awards bachelor's, master's, and doctoral degrees and post-master's certificates. Founded 1899. Setting: 411-acre small town campus. Endowment: $72.2 million. Research spending for the previous fiscal year: $3.1 million. Educational spending for the previous fiscal year: $6896 per student. Total enrollment: 17,589. Faculty: 1,256 (897 full-time, 359 part-time). Student-undergrad faculty ratio is 16:1. 12,248 applied, 63% were admitted. 21% from top 10% of their high school class, 56% from top quarter, 90% from top half. Full-time: 14,837 students, 52% women, 48% men. Part-time: 875 students, 60% women, 40% men. Students come from 44 states and territories, 60 other countries, 8% from out-of-state. 0.2% American Indian or Alaska Native, non-Hispanic/Latino; 4% Hispanic/Latino; 3% African American, non-Hispanic/Latino; 1% Asian, non-Hispanic/Latino; 0.1% Native Hawaiian or other Pacific Islander, non-Hispanic/Latino; 1% international. 7% 25 or older, 37% live on campus, 7% transferred in. Retention: 88% of full-time freshmen returned the following year. Academic areas with the most degrees conferred: business/marketing; education; social sciences. Core. Calendar: semesters. Academic remediation for entering students, ESL program, services for LD students, advanced placement, self-designed majors, honors program, independent study, distance learning, double major, summer session for credit, part-time degree program, adult/continuing education programs, internships, graduate courses open to undergrads. Off campus study at Appalachian Learning Alliance (consortium of 10 community colleges including: Caldwell Community College & Technical Institute, Catawba Valley Community College, Cleveland Community College, Forsyth Technical Community College, Isothermal Community College, Mayland Community College, McDowell Technical Community College, Surry Community College, Western Piedmont Community College and Wilkes Community College). Study abroad program. ROTC: Army.
Entrance Requirements: Options: electronic application, deferred admission, international baccalaureate accepted. Required: high school transcript, SAT or ACT. Entrance: moderately difficult. Application deadlines: 11/15, 11/15 for nonresidents. Notification: 3/1, 3/1 for nonresidents. Transfer credits accepted: Yes. Applicants placed on waiting list: 1,782. Wait-listed applicants offered admission: 200.
Costs Per Year: Application fee: $55. State resident tuition: $3542 full-time, $106.50 per credit hour part-time. Nonresident tuition: $15,590 full-time,

$513.50 per credit hour part-time. Mandatory fees: $2317 full-time, $13 per credit hour part-time. Part-time tuition and fees vary according to course load. College room and board: $7060. College room only: $3900. Room and board charges vary according to board plan and housing facility.

Collegiate Environment: Orientation program. Drama-theater group, choral group, marching band, student-run newspaper, radio station. Social organizations: 219 open to all; national fraternities, national sororities; 7% of eligible men and 11% of eligible women are members. Most popular organizations: Appalachian Intramural Recreation Sports Association, Appalachian State Fly-Fishing Club, Health Professions Club, Invisible Children at Appalachian State, APPS Special Events. Major annual events: Homecoming, Annual Diversity Celebration, Fall Club EXPO. Student services: legal services, health clinic, personal-psychological counseling, women's center. Campus security: 24-hour emergency response devices and patrols, late night transport-escort service, controlled dormitory access. 5,938 college housing spaces available; 5,775 were occupied in 2012-13. Freshmen guaranteed college housing. On-campus residence required in freshman year. Options: coed, men-only, women-only housing available. Carol Grotnes Belk Library plus 1 other with 937,956 books, 1.5 million microform titles, 23,861 serials, 72,813 audiovisual materials, an OPAC, and a Web page. Operations spending for the previous fiscal year: $8.9 million. 2,422 computers available on campus for general student use. Computer purchase/lease plans available. A campuswide network can be accessed from student residence rooms and from off campus. Students can access the following: online class registration. Staffed computer lab on campus provides training in use of computers, software, and the Internet.

Community Environment: Located in Boone, North Carolina, Appalachian State University is in the middle of one of the most popular year-round recreation areas in the East. The campus is only a few miles from several major ski resorts, and Pisgah National Forest and the Appalachian Trail are easily accessible from Boone. Grandfather Mountain and"Tweetsie" railroad are famous tourist attractions."Horn in the West" is a historical drama portraying with music and dance the story of Daniel Boone and the struggle to establish freedom in the southern Appalachian Highlands. This is performed in an outdoor amphitheater in a lovely mountain setting during July and August. The climate in the area is temperate. The average summer temperature rarely climbs above 80 degrees, and when it does a brief, refreshing shower usually cools things off. Fall brings clear, brisk and color-splashed days and cool evenings. Winter means picturesque snowfalls and fireside nights. Besides skiing, the area offers ample opportunities for other outdoor recreation, including river canoeing, hiking and camping. Three highways, U.S. 421, reaching from the Great Lakes to the North Carolina coast, and U.S. 321 and 221, all come through Boone, providing easy travel in all directions. The scenic Blue Ridge Parkway is only six miles from campus. The area, both urban and rural, is rich in contrasts between a growing university town and traditional southern Appalachian folkways. The university offers a wide variety of cultural events throughout the academic year, ranging from symphony orchestras to bluegrass concerts and from student talent shows to Broadway plays.

■ **THE ART INSTITUTE OF CHARLOTTE**
Three LakePointe Plz.
2110 Water Ridge Pky.
Charlotte, NC 28217
Tel: (704)357-8020; Free: 800-872-4417
Fax: (704)357-1133
Web Site: www.artinstitutes.edu/charlotte/
Description: Proprietary, 4-year, coed. Part of Education Management Corporation. Awards associate and bachelor's degrees. Founded 1973. Setting: suburban campus. Summer session for credit.

■ **THE ART INSTITUTE OF RALEIGH-DURHAM**
410 Blackwell St.
Ste. 200
Durham, NC 27701
Free: 888-245-9593
Web Site: www.artinstitutes.edu/raleigh-durham
Description: Proprietary, 4-year, coed. Part of Education Management Corporation. Awards associate and bachelor's degrees. Founded 2008.

■ **ASHEVILLE-BUNCOMBE TECHNICAL COMMUNITY COLLEGE**
340 Victoria Rd.
Asheville, NC 28801-4897
Tel: (828)254-1921

Fax: (828)251-6355
E-mail: admissions@abtech.edu
Web Site: www.abtech.edu/
Description: State-supported, 2-year, coed. Part of North Carolina Community College System. Awards certificates, diplomas, transfer associate, and terminal associate degrees. Founded 1959. Setting: 126-acre urban campus. Total enrollment: 7,542. Student-undergrad faculty ratio is 15:1. 1% from out-of-state. 43% 25 or older. Core. Calendar: semesters. Academic remediation for entering students, services for LD students, advanced placement, independent study, distance learning, double major, summer session for credit, part-time degree program, adult/continuing education programs, co-op programs and internships.

Entrance Requirements: Open admission except for allied health programs. Option: deferred admission. Required: high school transcript. Required for some: interview. Entrance: noncompetitive. Application deadline: Rolling. Notification: continuous.

Collegiate Environment: Orientation program. Drama-theater group, student-run newspaper. Student services: personal-psychological counseling. Campus security: 24-hour emergency response devices and patrols. Holly Learning Resources Center with an OPAC.

Community Environment: The main campus is located on Victoria Road in Asheville, NC, a city repeatedly named as one of the most livable in America. Nestled between the Blue Ride and Great Smoky mountains, Asheville offers beautiful mountain scenery and an excellent quality of life. Recognized as an entrepreneurial hotspot, Asheville also enjoys a thriving business climate.

■ **BARTON COLLEGE**
PO Box 5000
Wilson, NC 27893-7000
Tel: (252)399-6300; Free: 800-345-4973
Fax: (252)237-4957
E-mail: ahmetts@barton.edu
Web Site: www.barton.edu/
Description: Independent, comprehensive, coed, affiliated with Christian Church (Disciples of Christ). Awards bachelor's and master's degrees. Founded 1902. Setting: 76-acre small town campus with easy access to Raleigh-Durham. Total enrollment: 1,106. Faculty: 111 (69 full-time, 42 part-time). Student-undergrad faculty ratio is 12:1. 3,017 applied, 44% were admitted. 12% from top 10% of their high school class, 35% from top quarter, 73% from top half. Full-time: 879 students, 65% women, 35% men. Part-time: 215 students, 88% women, 12% men. Students come from 26 states and territories, 9 other countries, 14% from out-of-state. 1% American Indian or Alaska Native, non-Hispanic/Latino; 3% Hispanic/Latino; 27% African American, non-Hispanic/Latino; 1% Asian, non-Hispanic/Latino; 0.5% Native Hawaiian or other Pacific Islander, non-Hispanic/Latino; 3% international. 30% 25 or older. Retention: 71% of full-time freshmen returned the following year. Academic areas with the most degrees conferred: business/marketing; public administration and social services; education. Core. Calendar: 4-1-4. Academic remediation for entering students, ESL program, services for LD students, advanced placement, honors program, independent study, double major, summer session for credit, part-time degree program, adult/continuing education programs, co-op programs and internships.

Entrance Requirements: Options: electronic application, deferred admission, international baccalaureate accepted. Required: high school transcript, SAT or ACT. Recommended: minimum 2.3 high school GPA, interview. Entrance: minimally difficult. Application deadline: Rolling. Notification: continuous.

Costs Per Year: Application fee: $25. Comprehensive fee: $32,120 includes full-time tuition ($22,278), mandatory fees ($1902), and college room and board ($7940). College room only: $3600. Full-time tuition and fees vary according to class time, course load, and program. Room and board charges vary according to board plan and housing facility. Part-time tuition: $941 per credit hour. Part-time tuition varies according to class time, course load, and program.

Collegiate Environment: Orientation program. Drama-theater group, choral group, student-run newspaper. Social organizations: 52 open to all; national fraternities, national sororities; 16% of eligible men and 14% of eligible women are members. Most popular organizations: Barton College Association of Nurses, Students in Free Enterprise (SIFE), Stage and Script, Campus Activities Board, College Habitat for Humanity. Major annual events: Welcome Week, Lighting of the Luminaries and Christmas Celebration, Pre-Exam Jam. Student services: health clinic, personal-psychological counseling. Campus security: 24-hour emergency response devices, late night transport-escort service, controlled dormitory access, city police substation on campus. 690 college housing spaces available. Freshmen guaranteed college housing. On-campus residence required through sophomore year. Options: coed, women-only housing available. Willis N. Hackney Library plus 1 other with an OPAC and a Web page. 125 computers available on campus for general student use. A campuswide network can be accessed from student residence rooms and from off campus. Students can access the following: student picture directory. Staffed computer lab on campus provides training in use of computers, software, and the Internet.

Community Environment: Bus and train transportation are available. Community facilities include churches of all denominations, a hospital, library, shopping centers, numerous civic and service organizations, and a drama theater. Recreational parks with swimming pools, golf courses, and a large stadium are located here. Part-time jobs are available.

■ **BEAUFORT COUNTY COMMUNITY COLLEGE**
PO Box 1069
Washington, NC 27889-1069
Tel: (252)946-6194
Fax: (252)946-0271
E-mail: garyb@beaufortccc.edu
Web Site: www.beaufortccc.edu/
Description: State-supported, 2-year, coed. Part of North Carolina Community College System. Awards certificates, diplomas, transfer associate, and terminal associate degrees. Founded 1967. Setting: 67-acre rural campus. Total enrollment: 1,933. 856 applied, 100% were admitted. 1% American Indian or Alaska Native, non-Hispanic/Latino; 2% Hispanic/Latino; 32% African American, non-Hispanic/Latino; 0.2% Asian, non-Hispanic/Latino. Calendar: semesters. Academic remediation for entering students, ESL program, services for LD students, advanced placement, distance learning, summer session for credit, part-time degree program, co-op programs.
Entrance Requirements: Open admission allied health programs (ADN, PN, MLT) and Basic Law Enforcement Training (BLET). Option: electronic application. Required: ACCUPLACER, COMPASS, ASSET. Recommended: SAT or ACT. Required for some: high school transcript. Entrance: noncompetitive. Application deadlines: Rolling, Rolling for nonresidents. Transfer credits accepted: Yes.
Collegiate Environment: Orientation program. Most popular organizations: Student Government Association, Gamma Beta Phi, BECANS-Nursing. Major annual events: Christmas, Thanksgiving, Fall and Spring Fling. Student services: personal-psychological counseling. Campus security: 24-hour emergency response devices and patrols, late night transport-escort service. College housing not available. Beaufort Community College Library with 25,734 books, 214 serials, an OPAC, and a Web page. 60 computers available on campus for general student use. A campuswide network can be accessed from off-campus. Staffed computer lab on campus provides training in use of computers, software, and the Internet.
Community Environment: Washington, NC is located on the Pamlico River, which affords excellent fishing, boating, and water skiing. North Carolina's finest beach areas are only a short distance away. Year-round golf courses and tennis courts are also easily accessible. Other points of interest include the NC Estuarium, the Beaufort County Arts Council (located in the old Atlantic Coastal Railroad Depot), and the newly renovated Turnage Theater.

■ **BELMONT ABBEY COLLEGE**
100 Belmont-Mt. Holly Rd.
Belmont, NC 28012-1802
Tel: (704)825-6700; Free: 888-BAC-0110
Fax: (704)825-6670
E-mail: rogerjones@bac.edu
Web Site: www.belmontabbeycollege.edu/
Description: Independent Roman Catholic, 4-year, coed. Awards bachelor's degrees. Founded 1876. Setting: 650-acre small town campus with easy access to Charlotte. Endowment: $8.4 million. Educational spending for the previous fiscal year: $4392 per student. Total enrollment: 1,706. Faculty: 157 (76 full-time, 81 part-time). Student-undergrad faculty ratio is 16:1. 1,842 applied, 64% were admitted. 12% from top 10% of their high school class, 85% from top quarter, 65% from top half. Full-time: 1,590 students, 58% women, 42% men. Part-time: 116 students, 72% women, 28% men. Students come from 45 states and territories, 24 other countries, 28% from out-of-state. 0.2% American Indian or Alaska Native, non-Hispanic/Latino; 2% Hispanic/Latino; 27% African American, non-Hispanic/Latino; 1% Asian, non-Hispanic/Latino; 0.1% Native Hawaiian or other Pacific Islander, non-Hispanic/Latino; 3% international. 44% 25 or older, 43% live on campus, 11% transferred in.

Retention: 63% of full-time freshmen returned the following year. Academic areas with the most degrees conferred: business/marketing; education; psychology. Core. Calendar: semesters. Services for LD students, advanced placement, accelerated degree program, freshman honors college, honors program, independent study, double major, summer session for credit, part-time degree program, external degree program, adult/continuing education programs, co-op programs and internships. Off campus study at Charlotte Area Educational Consortium. Study abroad program. ROTC: Army (c), Air Force (c).
Entrance Requirements: Options: electronic application, deferred admission, international baccalaureate accepted. Required: high school transcript, minimum 2.25 high school GPA. Recommended: interview. Required for some: essay, 2 recommendations, SAT or ACT. Entrance: moderately difficult. Application deadline: 8/1. Notification: continuous. SAT Reasoning Test deadline: 8/1. Transfer credits accepted: Yes.
Costs Per Year: Application fee: $35. One-time mandatory fee: $400. Comprehensive fee: $38,025 includes full-time tuition ($27,622) and college room and board ($10,403). College room only: $6137. Full-time tuition varies according to class time, course load, location, program, and reciprocity agreements. Room and board charges vary according to board plan, housing facility, and location. Part-time tuition: $921 per credit hour. Part-time tuition varies according to class time, course load, location, and reciprocity agreements.
Collegiate Environment: Orientation program. Drama-theater group, choral group, student-run newspaper, radio station. Social organizations: 21 open to all; national fraternities, national sororities, local fraternities, local sororities; 6% of eligible men and 5% of eligible women are members. Most popular organizations: Abbey Ambassadors, Abbey Players, The Crusader, Greek Life (fraternities and sororities). Major annual events: Homecoming, President's Ball, Love the Abbey Day. Student services: health clinic, personal-psychological counseling. Campus security: 24-hour emergency response devices and patrols, late night transport-escort service. 747 college housing spaces available; 736 were occupied in 2012-13. Freshmen guaranteed college housing. On-campus residence required through senior year. Options: coed, men-only, women-only housing available. Abbot Vincent Taylor Library plus 1 other with 118,827 books, 116,173 microform titles, 275 serials, 7,418 audiovisual materials, and an OPAC. Operations spending for the previous fiscal year: $515,063. 125 computers available on campus for general student use. A campuswide network can be accessed from student residence rooms and from off campus. Staffed computer lab on campus provides training in use of computers and software.
Community Environment: In the southern Piedmont section of the state, Belmont is a growing textile center. Commercial transportation is available. The community facilities include churches of all denominations, hospitals and health services, a library, YMCA, and shopping centers. Numerous civic and service organizations are active. Hunting and fishing are popular sports in the area as well as all water sports, enjoyed at Lake Wylie. The Belmont Abbey, located here, was the first Cathedral Abbey in the United States, and is listed in the National Register of Historical Places.

■ **BENNETT COLLEGE**
900 E Washington St.
Greensboro, NC 27401-3239
Tel: (336)273-4431; Free: 800-413-5323
E-mail: tmonroe@bennett.edu
Web Site: www.bennett.edu/
Description: Independent United Methodist, 4-year, women only. Awards bachelor's degrees. Founded 1873. Setting: 55-acre urban campus. Endowment: $12.3 million. Educational spending for the previous fiscal year: $9115 per student. Total enrollment: 736. Faculty: 89 (61 full-time, 28 part-time). Student-undergrad faculty ratio is 10:1. 1,433 applied, 63% were admitted. 8% from top 10% of their high school class, 12% from top quarter, 50% from top half. Full-time: 672 students. Part-time: 64 students. Students come from 31 states and territories, 2 other countries, 61% from out-of-state. 0.3% American Indian or Alaska Native, non-Hispanic/Latino; 3% Hispanic/Latino; 93% African American, non-Hispanic/Latino; 0.3% Asian, non-Hispanic/Latino; 0.3% international. 2% 25 or older, 65% live on campus, 2% transferred in. Retention: 73% of full-time freshmen returned the following year. Academic areas with the most degrees conferred: communication/journalism; biological/life sciences; psychology. Core. Calendar: semesters. Academic remediation for entering students, services for LD students, advanced placement, honors program, independent study, double major, part-time degree program, co-op programs and internships. Off campus study at members of the Greensboro Regional Consortium, Piedmont

Independent College Association of North Carolina, Howard University (chemistry/pharmacy and nursing), Life University (biology), St. John's University of NY (law). Study abroad program. ROTC: Army (c), Air Force (c).

Entrance Requirements: Options: electronic application, deferred admission, international baccalaureate accepted. Required: essay, high school transcript, minimum 2 high school GPA, 2 recommendations. Recommended: SAT or ACT. Required for some: interview. Entrance: moderately difficult. Application deadlines: Rolling, Rolling for nonresidents. Notification: continuous, continuous for nonresidents. Transfer credits accepted: Yes.

Costs Per Year: Application fee: $35. One-time mandatory fee: $225. Comprehensive fee: $24,222 includes full-time tuition ($14,614), mandatory fees ($2180), and college room and board ($7428). College room only: $3698. Part-time tuition: $609 per credit hour. Part-time mandatory fees: $900 per term. Part-time tuition and fees vary according to course load.

Collegiate Environment: Orientation program. Drama-theater group, choral group, student-run newspaper. Social organizations: 49 open to all; national sororities; 6% of eligible undergrads are members. Most popular organizations: Christian Fellowship, Pre-Alumnae Council, Belles of Harmony, NAACP, National Council of Negro Women. Major annual events: Convocatum Est, Founder's Day, Spring Festival. Student services: legal services, health clinic, personal-psychological counseling, women's center. Campus security: 24-hour patrols, late night transport-escort service, controlled dormitory access. Holgate Library plus 1 other with 95,614 books, 51 serials, 1,951 audiovisual materials, an OPAC, and a Web page. Operations spending for the previous fiscal year: $272,858.

Community Environment: See Greensboro College.

▪ BLADEN COMMUNITY COLLEGE

PO Box 266
Dublin, NC 28332-0266
Tel: (910)879-5500
Fax: (910)879-5508
E-mail: acarterfisher@bladencc.edu
Web Site: www.bladen.cc.nc.us/

Description: State and locally supported, 2-year, coed. Part of North Carolina Community College System. Awards certificates, diplomas, transfer associate, and terminal associate degrees. Founded 1967. Setting: 45-acre rural campus. Endowment: $72,151. Educational spending for the previous fiscal year: $2997 per student. Total enrollment: 1,736. Faculty: 85 (35 full-time, 50 part-time). 10% from top 10% of their high school class, 20% from top quarter, 78% from top half. 2 class presidents, 6 student government officers. Students come from 3 states and territories, 0% from out-of-state. 62% 25 or older. Retention: 35% of full-time freshmen returned the following year. Core. Calendar: semesters. Academic remediation for entering students, services for LD students, advanced placement, independent study, distance learning, double major, summer session for credit, part-time degree program, adult/continuing education programs.

Entrance Requirements: Open admission. Options: electronic application, deferred admission. Required: high school transcript, ACT COMPASS. Recommended: SAT or ACT. Entrance: noncompetitive. Application deadline: 8/1. Notification: continuous until 8/15.

Collegiate Environment: Orientation program. Most popular organizations: Student Government Association, National Honors English Society, History Club, Criminal Justice Club, Bladen Community College Gospel Choir. Major annual events: Spring Field Day, Christmas Dinner, Fall Convocation. Student services: personal-psychological counseling. Campus security: 14-hour patrols. Learning Resource Center with 19,881 books, 36,052 microform titles, 52 serials, 2,364 audiovisual materials, an OPAC, and a Web page. Operations spending for the previous fiscal year: $160,321. 150 computers available on campus for general student use. A campuswide network can be accessed from off-campus. Staffed computer lab on campus.

Community Environment: Dublin is located 30 miles south of Fayetteville. The principal business is agriculture. Community facilities include 15 churches of various denominations and a public library. Bladen Arts Council frequently sponsors cultural activities in the campus's 1,000-seat auditorium. A golf course, parks, state forest and several lakes provide facilities for excellent fishing and water sports.

▪ BLUE RIDGE COMMUNITY COLLEGE

180 W Campus Dr.
Flat Rock, NC 28731
Tel: (828)694-1700
Fax: (828)694-1690
E-mail: kirstenb@blueridge.edu
Web Site: www.blueridge.edu/

Description: State and locally supported, 2-year, coed. Part of North Carolina Community College System. Awards certificates, diplomas, and transfer associate degrees. Founded 1969. Setting: 109-acre small town campus. Total enrollment: 2,488. Full-time: 766 students, 51% women, 49% men. Part-time: 1,722 students, 60% women, 40% men. Students come from 6 states and territories, 1% from out-of-state. 38% 25 or older. Core. Calendar: semesters. Academic remediation for entering students, ESL program, services for LD students, advanced placement, distance learning, double major, summer session for credit, part-time degree program, adult/continuing education programs, co-op programs and internships.

Entrance Requirements: Open admission except for nursing, surgical technology, pharmacy technology programs. Option: early admission. Required: high school transcript. Entrance: noncompetitive. Application deadline: Rolling. Notification: continuous.

Collegiate Environment: Orientation program. Drama-theater group, student-run newspaper. Student services: personal-psychological counseling. Campus security: sheriff's deputy during class hours. Blue Ridge Community College Library plus 1 other with 47,655 books, 19,025 microform titles, 3,875 serials, 1,692 audiovisual materials, and an OPAC.

▪ BREVARD COLLEGE

1 Brevard College Dr.
Brevard, NC 28712-3306
Tel: (828)883-8292; Free: 800-527-9090
Fax: (828)884-3790
E-mail: admissions@brevard.edu
Web Site: www.brevard.edu/

Description: Independent United Methodist, 4-year, coed. Awards bachelor's degrees. Founded 1853. Setting: 120-acre small town campus. Endowment: $21.8 million. Educational spending for the previous fiscal year: $8590 per student. Total enrollment: 633. Faculty: 84 (52 full-time, 32 part-time). Student-undergrad faculty ratio is 10:1. 1,591 applied, 54% were admitted. 9% from top 10% of their high school class, 28% from top quarter, 60% from top half. Full-time: 621 students, 41% women, 59% men. Part-time: 12 students, 58% women, 42% men. Students come from 30 states and territories, 17 other countries, 42% from out-of-state. 1% American Indian or Alaska Native, non-Hispanic/Latino; 0.2% Hispanic/Latino; 11% African American, non-Hispanic/Latino; 1% Asian, non-Hispanic/Latino; 0% Native Hawaiian or other Pacific Islander, non-Hispanic/Latino; 5% international. 7% 25 or older, 76% live on campus, 7% transferred in. Retention: 52% of full-time freshmen returned the following year. Academic areas with the most degrees conferred: parks and recreation; business/marketing; visual and performing arts. Core. Calendar: semesters. Academic remediation for entering students, services for LD students, advanced placement, self-designed majors, honors program, independent study, double major, part-time degree program, internships. Study abroad program.

Entrance Requirements: Options: electronic application, deferred admission, international baccalaureate accepted. Required: essay, high school transcript, minimum 2 high school GPA, SAT or ACT. Required for some: interview, students in music require auditions, music tests; students in art require portfolio. Entrance: minimally difficult. Application deadlines: Rolling, Rolling for nonresidents. Notification: continuous, continuous for nonresidents. SAT Reasoning Test deadline: 8/1. Transfer credits accepted: Yes.

Costs Per Year: Application fee: $30. Comprehensive fee: $32,100 includes full-time tuition ($23,900) and college room and board ($8200). Full-time tuition varies according to course load. Room and board charges vary according to board plan and housing facility. Part-time tuition: $850 per credit hour. Part-time tuition varies according to course load.

Collegiate Environment: Orientation program. Drama-theater group, choral group, student-run newspaper. Social organizations: 27 open to all. Most popular organizations: Fine Arts organizations, Omicron Delta Kappa, Fellowship of Christian Athletes, BC Greens, Business Club. Major annual events: Earth Week Service and Celebration/EarthFest, Move-a-Mountain Day, Martin Luther King, Jr. Community Celebration. Student services: health clinic, personal-psychological counseling, women's center. Campus security: 24-hour emergency response devices and patrols. 558 college housing spaces available; 479 were occupied in 2012-13. Freshmen guaranteed college housing. On-campus residence required through senior year. Options: coed, men-only, women-only housing available. Jones Library with 195,515 books, 3,274 microform titles, 24,242 serials, 36,478 audiovisual materials, an OPAC, and a Web page. Operations spending for the previous fiscal year: $314,821. 100 computers available on campus for general student use. A campuswide network can be accessed from student residence rooms.

Community Environment: Brevard, known as the "Land of Waterfalls" is 33 miles southwest of Asheville, NC. The area is the location of the Carl Sandburg home, the Thomas Wolfe Home, and the Brevard Music Center. This popular summer resort is at the entrance of Pisgah National Forest. Community facilities include churches of most major denominations, hospital and many civic and service organizations. Part-time employment is available on and off campus. Recreational activities include camping, biking, backpacking, canoeing, snowskiing, kayaking, and mountain climbing.

■ BRUNSWICK COMMUNITY COLLEGE
50 College Rd.
Supply, NC 28462-0030
Tel: (910)755-7300; Free: 800-754-1050
Fax: (910)754-9609
E-mail: admissions@brunswickcc.edu
Web Site: www.brunswickcc.edu/

Description: State-supported, 2-year, coed. Part of North Carolina Community College System. Awards certificates, diplomas, transfer associate, and terminal associate degrees. Founded 1979. Setting: 266-acre rural campus. Total enrollment: 1,558. Student-undergrad faculty ratio is 12:1. 4% from out-of-state. 37% 25 or older. Core. Calendar: semesters. Academic remediation for entering students, ESL program, services for LD students, advanced placement, independent study, distance learning, summer session for credit, part-time degree program, co-op programs and internships.

Entrance Requirements: Open admission except for allied health programs. Option: electronic application. Required: high school transcript. Required for some: interview. Entrance: noncompetitive. Application deadline: Rolling. Notification: continuous.

Collegiate Environment: Student services: personal-psychological counseling. Campus security: late night transport-escort service, campus police. Brunswick Community College Library plus 1 other with an OPAC.

■ CABARRUS COLLEGE OF HEALTH SCIENCES
401 Medical Park Dr.
Concord, NC 28025
Tel: (704)783-1555
Fax: (704)783-1764
E-mail: mellison@cabarruscollege.edu
Web Site: www.cabarruscollege.edu/

Description: Independent, 4-year, coed. Awards associate and bachelor's degrees. Founded 1942. Setting: 5-acre suburban campus with easy access to Charlotte. Endowment: $356,000. Educational spending for the previous fiscal year: $6085 per student. Total enrollment: 372. Faculty: 51 (25 full-time, 26 part-time). Student-undergrad faculty ratio is 7:1. 134 applied, 43% were admitted. 9% from top 10% of their high school class, 32% from top quarter, 73% from top half. Full-time: 226 students, 90% women, 10% men. Part-time: 146 students, 90% women, 10% men. Students come from 3 states and territories, 1% from out-of-state. 42% 25 or older, 21% transferred in. Academic area with the most degrees conferred: health professions and related sciences. Core. Calendar: semesters. Advanced placement, independent study, distance learning, double major, part-time degree program.

Entrance Requirements: Option: electronic application. Required: essay, high school transcript, minimum 2.0 high school GPA, 2 recommendations, SAT or ACT. Recommended: minimum 3.0 high school GPA. Required for some: interview. Entrance: moderately difficult. Application deadline: 3/1. Notification: 4/15.

Collegiate Environment: Orientation program. Most popular organizations: Student Nurse Association, Christian Student Union, student government, honor society, Allied Health Student Association. Major annual events: Welcome Picnic Convocation, Spring Family Day. Student services: health clinic, personal-psychological counseling. Campus security: 24-hour emergency response devices and patrols. Cabarrus Health Sciences Library with 800 audiovisual materials, an OPAC, and a Web page. Operations spending for the previous fiscal year: $100,000. 46 computers available on campus for general student use. A campuswide network can be accessed from off-campus. Students can access the following: online class registration, degree audits. Staffed computer lab on campus.

■ CALDWELL COMMUNITY COLLEGE AND TECHNICAL INSTITUTE
2855 Hickory Blvd.
Hudson, NC 28638-2397

Tel: (828)726-2200
Fax: (828)726-2490
E-mail: cwoodard@cccti.edu
Web Site: www.cccti.edu/

Description: State-supported, 2-year, coed. Part of North Carolina Community College System. Awards certificates, diplomas, transfer associate, and terminal associate degrees. Founded 1964. Setting: 50-acre small town campus. Total enrollment: 3,728. Faculty: 420 (130 full-time, 290 part-time). Full-time: 1,388 students, 58% women, 42% men. Part-time: 2,340 students, 53% women, 47% men. 62% 25 or older. Core. Calendar: semesters. Academic remediation for entering students, services for LD students, advanced placement, independent study, distance learning, double major, summer session for credit, part-time degree program, adult/continuing education programs, co-op programs.

Entrance Requirements: Open admission except for allied health programs. Option: early admission. Required: high school transcript. Entrance: noncompetitive. Application deadline: Rolling. Notification: continuous.

Collegiate Environment: Orientation program. Drama-theater group, choral group. Student services: personal-psychological counseling. Campus security: trained security personnel during open hours. Broyhill Center for Learning Resources with 50,770 books, 251 serials, an OPAC, and a Web page. 850 computers available on campus for general student use. Computer purchase/lease plans available. A campuswide network can be accessed from off-campus. Students can access the following: online class registration. Staffed computer lab on campus provides training in use of computers, software, and the Internet.

Community Environment: Since more wood furniture is manufactured here than any other place in the South, Lenoir is known as "furniture land." Numerous parks and two recreation centers provide the facilities for relaxation. A number of churches are represented in the community.

■ CAMPBELL UNIVERSITY
450 Leslie Campbell Ave.
Buies Creek, NC 27506
Tel: (910)893-1200; Free: 800-334-4111
Fax: (910)893-1288
E-mail: adm@mailcenter.campbell.edu
Web Site: www.campbell.edu/

Description: Independent, university, coed, affiliated with North Carolina Baptist State Convention. Awards associate, bachelor's, master's, and doctoral degrees. Founded 1887. Setting: 850-acre rural campus with easy access to Raleigh. Endowment: $104.7 million. Educational spending for the previous fiscal year: $11,437 per student. Total enrollment: 4,743. Faculty: 305 (196 full-time, 109 part-time). Student-undergrad faculty ratio is 14:1. 3,348 applied, 60% were admitted. 38% from top 10% of their high school class, 80% from top quarter, 92% from top half. 5 National Merit Scholars, 5 class presidents, 34 valedictorians, 94 student government officers. Full-time: 2,731 students, 53% women, 47% men. Part-time: 203 students, 36% women, 64% men. Students come from 50 states and territories, 42 other countries, 22% from out-of-state. 12% 25 or older, 62% live on campus, 16% transferred in. Retention: 71% of full-time freshmen returned the following year. Academic areas with the most degrees conferred: business/marketing; liberal arts/general studies; psychology. Core. Calendar: semesters. Advanced placement, accelerated degree program, freshman honors college, honors program, independent study, distance learning, double major, summer session for credit, part-time degree program, adult/continuing education programs, co-op programs and internships, graduate courses open to undergrads. Study abroad program. ROTC: Army.

Entrance Requirements: Options: electronic application, early admission, deferred admission, international baccalaureate accepted. Required: high school transcript, SAT or ACT. Recommended: essay, interview. Required for some: 3 recommendations. Entrance: moderately difficult. Application deadline: Rolling. Notification: continuous.

Collegiate Environment: Orientation program. Drama-theater group, choral group, student-run newspaper. Social organizations: 44 open to all. Most popular organizations: Student Government Association, Baptist Student Union, Campbell Catholic Community, Presidential Scholars Club, Pre-Pharmacy Club. Major annual events: Homecoming, Spring Fling, Parents' Day. Student services: health clinic, personal-psychological counseling. Campus security: 24-hour emergency response devices and patrols, late night transport-escort service, controlled dormitory access. Carrie Rich Memorial Library plus 2 others with 231,298 books, 1.3 million microform titles, 17,268 serials, an OPAC, and a Web page. Operations spending for the previous fiscal year: $3.4 million. 256 computers available on campus for general student use. A campuswide network can be accessed from student residence rooms and from off campus. Students can access the following: online class registration. Staffed computer lab on campus provides training in use of computers, software, and the Internet.

Community Environment: Located 30 miles south of Raleigh where the climate is mild, and 30 miles north of Fayetteville, the community is served by Baptist and United Methodist churches, a community civic club and a full-time campus infirmary. There is a hospital seven miles away. Part-time employment for students is available.

■ CAPE FEAR COMMUNITY COLLEGE

411 N Front St.
Wilmington, NC 28401-3993
Tel: (910)362-7000; Free: 877-799-2322
E-mail: admissions@cfcc.edu
Web Site: www.cfcc.edu/

Description: State-supported, 2-year, coed. Part of North Carolina Community College System. Awards certificates, diplomas, transfer associate, and terminal associate degrees. Founded 1959. Setting: 150-acre urban campus. Endowment: $5.3 million. Educational spending for the previous fiscal year: $4176 per student. Total enrollment: 9,559. Faculty: 1,017 (296 full-time, 721 part-time). Student-undergrad faculty ratio is 8:1. 4,924 applied, 49% were admitted. Full-time: 4,771 students, 50% women, 50% men. Part-time: 4,788 students, 58% women, 42% men. Students come from 36 states and territories, 5 other countries, 4% from out-of-state. 1% American Indian or Alaska Native, non-Hispanic/Latino; 4% Hispanic/Latino; 16% African American, non-Hispanic/Latino; 1% Asian, non-Hispanic/Latino. 31% 25 or older, 8% transferred in. Core. Calendar: semesters. Academic remediation for entering students, ESL program, services for LD students, advanced placement, independent study, distance learning, double major, summer session for credit, part-time degree program, adult/continuing education programs, co-op programs. Off campus study.

Entrance Requirements: Open admission except for nursing, allied health programs. Options: electronic application, early admission. Required for some: high school transcript, interview, placement testing. Entrance: noncompetitive. Application deadline: 8/20. Notification: continuous. Transfer credits accepted: Yes.

Costs Per Year: Application fee: $0. State resident tuition: $2204 full-time, $69 per credit hour part-time. Nonresident tuition: $8352 full-time, $261 per credit hour part-time. Mandatory fees: $137 full-time. Full-time tuition and fees vary according to course load. Part-time tuition varies according to course load.

Collegiate Environment: Orientation program. Choral group, student-run newspaper. Social organizations: 35 open to all. Most popular organizations: Nursing Club, Dental Hygiene Club, Pineapple Guild, Phi Theta Kappa, Occupational Therapy. Major annual events: Spring Fling, Fall Fest, Harvest Health and Wellness Fair. Student services: personal-psychological counseling. Campus security: 24-hour emergency response devices and patrols, late night transport-escort service, armed police officer. College housing not available. Cape Fear Community College Library with 31,324 microform titles, 7,951 serials, 16,682 audiovisual materials, an OPAC, and a Web page. Operations spending for the previous fiscal year: $1.6 million. 1,703 computers available on campus for general student use. A campuswide network can be accessed from off-campus. Students can access the following: online class registration. Staffed computer lab on campus provides training in use of computers, software, and the Internet.

Community Environment: See University of North Carolina - Wilmington.

■ CAROLINA CHRISTIAN COLLEGE

4209 Indiana Ave.
Winston-Salem, NC 27102-0777
Tel: (336)744-0900
Fax: (336)744-0901
E-mail: latanya@carolina.edu
Web Site: www.carolina.edu/

Description: Independent nondenominational, comprehensive, coed. Awards associate, bachelor's, and master's degrees. Founded 1949. Setting: 2-acre small town campus. Endowment: $250,000. Educational spending for the previous fiscal year: $315 per student. Total enrollment: 78. Faculty: 12 (2 full-time, 10 part-time). Student-undergrad faculty ratio is 13:1. 22 applied, 68% were admitted. 0% from top 10% of their high school class, 0% from top quarter, 0% from top half. Full-time: 67 students, 51% women, 49% men. Part-time: 3 students, 67% women, 33% men. 0% from out-of-

state. 0% American Indian or Alaska Native, non-Hispanic/Latino; 4% Hispanic/Latino; 92% African American, non-Hispanic/Latino; 1% Asian, non-Hispanic/Latino; 0% Native Hawaiian or other Pacific Islander, non-Hispanic/Latino; 0% international. 95% 25 or older, 0% live on campus, 0% transferred in. Retention: 90% of full-time freshmen returned the following year. Core. Calendar: semesters. Accelerated degree program, part-time degree program, external degree program, adult/continuing education programs, graduate courses open to undergrads.

Entrance Requirements: Open admission. Option: electronic application. Required: essay, high school transcript, 2 recommendations, interview. Entrance: noncompetitive. Application deadlines: Rolling, Rolling for nonresidents. Notification: continuous, continuous for nonresidents. Transfer credits accepted: Yes.

Costs Per Year: Application fee: $50. Tuition: $7500 full-time, $937.50 per course part-time. Mandatory fees: $200 full-time.

Collegiate Environment: Social organizations: 2% of women are members. Student services: personal-psychological counseling. Campus security: 24-hour emergency response devices. Aubrey Payne with 30,000 books, 5,000 serials, 200 audiovisual materials, and an OPAC. Operations spending for the previous fiscal year: $6000. 8 computers available on campus for general student use. Staffed computer lab on campus provides training in use of computers, software, and the Internet.

■ CAROLINA COLLEGE OF BIBLICAL STUDIES

817 S McPherson Church Rd.
Fayetteville, NC 28303
Tel: (910)323-5614
Web Site: carolinabiblecollege.org/

Description: Independent religious, 4-year, coed. Founded 1973.

■ CAROLINAS COLLEGE OF HEALTH SCIENCES

PO Box 32861, 1200 Blythe Blvd.
Charlotte, NC 28232-2861
Tel: (704)355-5043
Fax: (704)355-5967
E-mail: cchsinformation@carolinashealthcare.org
Web Site: www.carolinascollege.edu/

Description: Public, 2-year, coed. Awards certificates, diplomas, and terminal associate degrees. Founded 1990. Setting: 3-acre urban campus with easy access to Charlotte. Endowment: $1.8 million. Educational spending for the previous fiscal year: $6223 per student. Total enrollment: 438. Faculty: 71 (26 full-time, 45 part-time). Student-undergrad faculty ratio is 11:1. Full-time: 58 students, 84% women, 16% men. Part-time: 380 students, 86% women, 14% men. Students come from 4 states and territories, 6% from out-of-state. 0.5% American Indian or Alaska Native, non-Hispanic/Latino; 4% Hispanic/Latino; 9% African American, non-Hispanic/Latino; 2% Asian, non-Hispanic/Latino; 1% Native Hawaiian or other Pacific Islander, non-Hispanic/Latino; 0% international. 61% 25 or older, 0% transferred in. Calendar: semesters. Services for LD students, advanced placement, honors program, independent study, distance learning, double major, summer session for credit.

Entrance Requirements: Option: electronic application. Required: minimum 2.5 high school GPA. Required for some: high school transcript, 1 recommendation, interview, SAT or ACT scores, SAT or ACT. Entrance: very difficult. Preference given to county residents. Transfer credits accepted: Yes.

Costs Per Year: Application fee: $50. State resident tuition: $11,760 full-time, $308 per credit hour part-time. Nonresident tuition: $11,760 full-time, $308 per credit hour part-time. Mandatory fees: $1215 full-time, $125 per term part-time. Full-time tuition and fees vary according to course load and program. Part-time tuition and fees vary according to course load and program.

Collegiate Environment: Orientation program. Major annual events: Thanksgiving Luncheon, Fall Festival, Spring Fling. Student services: health clinic, personal-psychological counseling. Campus security: 24-hour emergency response devices and patrols, late night transport-escort service. 45 college housing spaces available; all were occupied in 2012-13. No special consideration for freshman housing applicants. AHEC Library with 9,810 books, 503 serials, an OPAC, and a Web page. Operations spending for the previous fiscal year: $86,520. 30 computers available on campus for general student use. A campuswide network can be accessed from off-campus. Students can access the following: online class registration, online billing. Staffed computer lab on campus provides training in use of computers, software, and the Internet.

■ CARTERET COMMUNITY COLLEGE

3505 Arendell St.
Morehead City, NC 28557-2989
Tel: (252)222-6000
Fax: (252)222-6274
E-mail: admissions@carteret.edu
Web Site: www.carteret.edu/

Description: State-supported, 2-year, coed. Part of North Carolina Community College System. Awards certificates, diplomas, transfer associate, and terminal associate degrees. Founded 1963. Setting: 25-acre small town campus. Total enrollment: 1,872. Faculty: 253 (66 full-time, 187 part-time). Student-undergrad faculty ratio is 9:1. 2,156 applied, 91% were admitted. Full-time: 804 students, 66% women, 34% men. Part-time: 1,068 students, 72% women, 28% men. Students come from 27 states and territories, 2 other countries. 53% 25 or older, 8% transferred in. Retention: 52% of full-time freshmen returned the following year. Core. Calendar: semesters. Academic remediation for entering students, services for LD students, distance learning, double major, summer session for credit, part-time degree program, adult/continuing education programs, co-op programs and internships.

Entrance Requirements: Open admission except for health sciences, cosmetic arts, basic law enforcement training, and lateral entry. Options: electronic application, international baccalaureate accepted. Required: high school transcript. Recommended: SAT or ACT. Required for some: interview. Entrance: noncompetitive. Application deadlines: Rolling, Rolling for nonresidents. Notification: continuous, continuous for nonresidents. Transfer credits accepted: Yes.

Collegiate Environment: Orientation program. Drama-theater group, student-run newspaper. Social organizations: 25 open to all; local fraternities; 15% of eligible men and 35% of eligible women are members. Most popular organizations: Student Government Association, Medical Assisting Club, Respiratory Therapy Club, Radiography Club, Chess Club. Major annual event: Springfest. Campus security: late night transport-escort service, security service from 7 am until 11:30 pm. Michael J. Smith Learning Resource Center with 22,000 books, 168 serials, an OPAC, and a Web page. Operations spending for the previous fiscal year: $308,559. 610 computers available on campus for general student use. A campuswide network can be accessed from off-campus. Students can access the following: online class registration. Staffed computer lab on campus provides training in use of computers, software, and the Internet.

Community Environment: Morehead City is one of the most popular coastal resorts in the state. The $4 million Port Terminal with its 2,600-foot pier affords excellent facilities for oceangoing vessels. Fishing, particularly for menhaden, is an important industry. The Atlantic Beach across Bogue Sound is an excellent 24-mile beach. Recreational facilities are numerous for all kinds of ocean fishing, and for hunting wild ducks and geese.

■ CATAWBA COLLEGE

2300 W Innes St.
Salisbury, NC 28144-2488
Tel: (704)637-4111; Free: 800-CATAWBA
E-mail: admissions@catawba.edu
Web Site: www.catawba.edu/

Description: Independent, comprehensive, coed, affiliated with United Church of Christ. Awards bachelor's and master's degrees. Founded 1851. Setting: 210-acre small town campus with easy access to Charlotte. Research spending for the previous fiscal year: $18,221. Educational spending for the previous fiscal year: $6010 per student. Total enrollment: 1,293. Faculty: 129 (65 full-time, 64 part-time). Student-undergrad faculty ratio is 15:1. 3,448 applied, 45% were admitted. 9% from top 10% of their high school class, 29% from top quarter, 63% from top half. Full-time: 1,202 students, 51% women, 49% men. Part-time: 77 students, 68% women, 32% men. Students come from 29 states and territories, 13 other countries, 30% from out-of-state. 1% American Indian or Alaska Native, non-Hispanic/Latino; 3% Hispanic/Latino; 19% African American, non-Hispanic/Latino; 1% Asian, non-Hispanic/Latino; 0% Native Hawaiian or other Pacific Islander, non-Hispanic/Latino; 3% international. 22% 25 or older, 50% live on campus, 9% transferred in. Retention: 67% of full-time freshmen returned the following year. Academic areas with the most degrees conferred: business/marketing; education; visual and performing arts. Core. Calendar: semesters. Services for LD students, advanced placement, self-designed majors, honors program, independent study, double major, summer session for credit, part-time degree program, internships. Study abroad program. ROTC: Army (c), Air Force (c).

Entrance Requirements: Options: electronic application, early admission, deferred admission, international baccalaureate accepted. Required: essay, high school transcript, minimum 2 high school GPA, 2 recommendations, SAT or ACT. Recommended: interview. Entrance: moderately difficult. Application deadline: Rolling. Notification: continuous. SAT Reasoning Test deadline: 8/1. SAT Subject Test deadline: 8/1. Transfer credits accepted: Yes.

Costs Per Year: Application fee: $25. Comprehensive fee: $36,230 includes full-time tuition ($26,820) and college room and board ($9410). Full-time tuition varies according to class time and course load. Part-time tuition: $680 per credit hour. Part-time mandatory fees: $50 per term. Part-time tuition and fees vary according to class time and course load.

Collegiate Environment: Orientation program. Drama-theater group, choral group, marching band, student-run newspaper, radio station. Social organizations: 47 open to all. Most popular organizations: Volunteer Catawba, Catawba Ambassadors (admissions guides), Blue Masque (drama), Fellowship of Christian Athletes, Wigwam Productions (student activities board). Major annual events: Homecoming, Family Weekend, Catawbapalooza. Student services: health clinic, personal-psychological counseling. Campus security: 24-hour emergency response devices and patrols, late night transport-escort service, controlled dormitory access. 762 college housing spaces available; 659 were occupied in 2012-13. Freshmen guaranteed college housing. On-campus residence required through senior year. Options: coed, men-only, women-only housing available. Corriher-Linn-Black Memorial Library plus 1 other with 169,872 books, 635,100 microform titles, 185 serials, 2,174 audiovisual materials, an OPAC, and a Web page. Operations spending for the previous fiscal year: $642,524. 97 computers available on campus for general student use. A campuswide network can be accessed from student residence rooms and from off campus. Students can access the following: online class registration. Staffed computer lab on campus provides training in use of computers, software, and the Internet.

Community Environment: Salisbury was founded in 1753 and during the year 1781 the city served, at different times, as headquarters for both Cornwallis and Greene, British and patriot generals. Community facilities include numerous churches, a public library, hospitals, and various civic and service organizations. Recreational activities include golf, swimming, fishing, and other sports. Part-time employment is available.

■ CATAWBA VALLEY COMMUNITY COLLEGE

2550 Hwy. 70 SE
Hickory, NC 28602-9699
Tel: (828)327-7000
Fax: (828)327-7000
E-mail: lwegner@cvcc.edu
Web Site: www.cvcc.edu/

Description: State and locally supported, 2-year, coed. Part of North Carolina Community College System. Awards certificates, diplomas, transfer associate, and terminal associate degrees. Founded 1960. Setting: 50-acre small town campus with easy access to Charlotte. Endowment: $1.3 million. Educational spending for the previous fiscal year: $310,369 per student. Total enrollment: 5,099. Faculty: 542 (157 full-time, 385 part-time). Student-undergrad faculty ratio is 10:1. 1,867 applied, 99% were admitted. Full-time: 1,910 students, 56% women, 44% men. Part-time: 3,189 students, 60% women, 40% men. Students come from 9 states and territories. 1% American Indian or Alaska Native, non-Hispanic/Latino; 6% Hispanic/Latino; 9% African American, non-Hispanic/Latino; 8% Asian, non-Hispanic/Latino; 0.1% Native Hawaiian or other Pacific Islander, non-Hispanic/Latino; 0.1% international. 42% 25 or older, 25% transferred in. Core. Calendar: semesters. Academic remediation for entering students, ESL program, services for LD students, advanced placement, self-designed majors, independent study, distance learning, double major, summer session for credit, part-time degree program, adult/continuing education programs, co-op programs.

Entrance Requirements: Open admission except for allied health programs. Option: electronic application. Required: high school transcript, COMPASS test series. Required for some: 1 recommendation. Entrance: noncompetitive. Application deadlines: Rolling, Rolling for nonresidents. Notification: continuous, continuous for nonresidents. Transfer credits accepted: Yes.

Costs Per Year: Application fee: $0. State resident tuition: $1656 full-time, $69 per credit hour part-time. Nonresident tuition: $6264 full-time, $261 per credit part-time. Mandatory fees: $87 full-time, $5 per credit hour part-time, $11.25 per term part-time. Part-time tuition and fees vary according to course load.

Collegiate Environment: Orientation program. Drama-theater group, choral group. Social organizations: 15 open to all; Phi Theta Kappa organization. Most popular organizations: Campus Crusade for Christ, Emerging Entrepreneur, Rotaract, Circle K, Skills USA. Major annual events: Fall Fling, Have a 'Dog' with the 'Big Dawg', Red Cross Bloodmobile. Student services: personal-psychological counseling. Campus security: 24-hour patrols. College housing not available. Learning Resource Center with 27,000 books, 1,250 serials, 700 audiovisual materials, an OPAC, and a Web page. Operations spending for the previous fiscal year: $353,700. 1,144 computers available on campus for general student use. A campuswide network can be accessed from off-campus. Students can access the following: online class registration. Staffed computer lab on campus provides training in use of computers, software, and the Internet.
Community Environment: See Lenoir-Rhyne College.

■ **CENTRAL CAROLINA COMMUNITY COLLEGE**
1105 Kelly Dr.
Sanford, NC 27330-9000
Tel: (919)775-5401; Free: 800-682-8353
Fax: (919)775-1221
Web Site: www.cccc.edu/
Description: State and locally supported, 2-year, coed. Part of North Carolina Community College System. Awards certificates, diplomas, transfer associate, and terminal associate degrees. Founded 1962. Setting: 41-acre small town campus. Endowment: $3 million. Educational spending for the previous fiscal year: $3589 per student. Total enrollment: 4,900. Faculty: 1,050 (370 full-time, 680 part-time). Full-time: 2,138 students, 64% women, 36% men. Part-time: 2,762 students, 68% women, 32% men. Students come from 36 states and territories, 6% from out-of-state. 1% American Indian or Alaska Native, non-Hispanic/Latino; 9% Hispanic/Latino; 23% African American, non-Hispanic/Latino; 1% Asian, non-Hispanic/Latino; 0.1% Native Hawaiian or other Pacific Islander, non-Hispanic/Latino; 0.4% international. 53% 25 or older. Core. Calendar: semesters. Academic remediation for entering students, ESL program, services for LD students, advanced placement, independent study, distance learning, double major, summer session for credit, part-time degree program, adult/continuing education programs, internships.
Entrance Requirements: Open admission except for nursing, veterinary medical assistant programs. Options: electronic application, early admission, deferred admission. Required: high school transcript. Entrance: noncompetitive. Application deadline: Rolling. Notification: continuous. Preference given to residents of sponsoring counties.
Collegiate Environment: Orientation program. Student-run radio station. Major annual event: Activity Day. Student services: personal-psychological counseling. Campus security: 24-hour emergency response devices and patrols, student patrols, patrols by trained security personnel during operating hours. College housing not available. Library/Learning Resources Center plus 2 others with 50,479 books, 240 serials, 5,946 audiovisual materials, an OPAC, and a Web page. Operations spending for the previous fiscal year: $886,647. 100 computers available on campus for general student use. A campuswide network can be accessed from off-campus. Staffed computer lab on campus.
Community Environment: Sanford, known as the brick capital of the nation, is nearly the exact center of North Carolina with all forms of commercial transportation available. Over 50 manufacturing and processing firms are located here. Modern shopping facilities and the privately owned hospital serve the community. Recreational opportunities are unparalleled at nearby Cape Fear and the resort areas of Pinehurst and Southern Pines.

■ **CENTRAL PIEDMONT COMMUNITY COLLEGE**
PO Box 35009
Charlotte, NC 28235-5009
Tel: (704)330-2722
Web Site: www.cpcc.edu/
Description: State and locally supported, 2-year, coed. Part of North Carolina Community College System. Awards certificates, diplomas, transfer associate, and terminal associate degrees. Founded 1963. Setting: 37-acre urban campus. Endowment: $16.7 million. Educational spending for the previous fiscal year: $2896 per student. Total enrollment: 19,364. Faculty: 1,741 (337 full-time, 1,404 part-time). 2,243 applied, 100% were admitted. Full-time: 7,630 students, 54% women, 46% men. Part-time: 11,734 students, 57% women, 43% men. Students come from 13 states and territories, 117 other countries, 3% from out-of-state. 47% 25 or older, 11% transferred in. Core. Calendar: semesters. Academic remediation for enter-

ing students, ESL program, services for LD students, advanced placement, accelerated degree program, self-designed majors, honors program, distance learning, summer session for credit, part-time degree program, co-op programs. Off campus study at members of the Charlotte Area Educational Consortium.
Entrance Requirements: Open admission. Required: high school transcript. Entrance: noncompetitive. Application deadlines: Rolling, Rolling for nonresidents. Notification: continuous, continuous for nonresidents.
Collegiate Environment: Orientation program. Drama-theater group, choral group, student-run newspaper. Social organizations: 22 open to all; local fraternities. Most popular organizations: Phi Theta Kappa, Black Students Organization, Students for Environmental Sanity, Sierra Club, Nursing Club. Major annual events: Fall Fest, Spring Fling, World Games. Student services: personal-psychological counseling, women's center. Campus security: 24-hour emergency response devices and patrols. Hagemeyer Learning Center plus 5 others with 102,649 books, 125,462 microform titles, 750 serials, 17,802 audiovisual materials, an OPAC, and a Web page. Operations spending for the previous fiscal year: $1.5 million.
Community Environment: See Queens College.

■ **CHOWAN UNIVERSITY**
One University Pl.
Murfreesboro, NC 27855
Tel: (252)398-6500; Free: 888-4-CHOWAN
Fax: (252)398-1190
E-mail: shermk@chowan.edu
Web Site: www.chowan.edu/
Description: Independent Baptist, comprehensive, coed. Awards associate, bachelor's, and master's degrees. Founded 1848. Setting: 300-acre small town campus with easy access to Norfolk. Total enrollment: 1,316. Faculty: 105 (63 full-time, 42 part-time). Student-undergrad faculty ratio is 16:1. 4,330 applied, 58% were admitted. 6% from top 10% of their high school class, 25% from top quarter, 78% from top half. Full-time: 1,239 students, 53% women, 47% men. Part-time: 69 students, 71% women, 29% men. Students come from 21 states and territories, 12 other countries, 52% from out-of-state. 1% American Indian or Alaska Native, non-Hispanic/Latino; 3% Hispanic/Latino; 67% African American, non-Hispanic/Latino; 0.1% Asian, non-Hispanic/Latino; 0% Native Hawaiian or other Pacific Islander, non-Hispanic/Latino; 1% international. 7% 25 or older, 80% live on campus, 6% transferred in. Retention: 43% of full-time freshmen returned the following year. Academic areas with the most degrees conferred: business/marketing; education; social sciences. Core. Calendar: semesters. Services for LD students, advanced placement, self-designed majors, freshman honors college, honors program, independent study, double major, summer session for credit, part-time degree program, co-op programs and internships. Study abroad program.
Entrance Requirements: Options: electronic application, international baccalaureate accepted. Required: high school transcript, SAT or ACT. Recommended: minimum 2 high school GPA, 2 recommendations. Required for some: essay, interview. Entrance: minimally difficult. Application deadlines: Rolling, Rolling for nonresidents. Notification: continuous, continuous for nonresidents. SAT Reasoning Test deadline: 8/23. SAT Subject Test deadline: 8/23. Transfer credits accepted: Yes.
Costs Per Year: Application fee: $20. Comprehensive fee: $30,030 includes full-time tuition ($22,160) and college room and board ($7870). College room only: $3900. Full-time tuition varies according to class time, course load, and program. Room and board charges vary according to board plan and housing facility.
Collegiate Environment: Orientation program. Drama-theater group, choral group, student-run newspaper. Social organizations: national fraternities, national sororities, local fraternities, local sororities. Major annual events: Relay For Life, Homecoming, Health Fair. Student services: health clinic, personal-psychological counseling. Campus security: 24-hour emergency response devices and patrols, late night transport-escort service, controlled dormitory access. 1,212 college housing spaces available; 937 were occupied in 2012-13. Freshmen guaranteed college housing. On-campus residence required through sophomore year. Options: men-only, women-only housing available. Whitaker Library plus 1 other with 352,000 books, 32,000 microform titles, 38,000 serials, 69,000 audiovisual materials, an OPAC, and a Web page. 215 computers available on campus for general student use. Computer purchase/lease plans available. A campuswide network can be accessed from student residence rooms. Students can access the following: online class registration. Staffed computer lab on campus provides training in use of computers, software, and the Internet.

Community Environment: In the northeastern section of North Carolina, Murfreesboro is the location of several historical sites. Community facilities include several churches, museums and a library. A hospital and commercial transportation are available in nearby towns. Hunting, fishing, boating, jet skiing, and water skiing are some of the recreational activities.

■ **CLEVELAND COMMUNITY COLLEGE**
137 S Post Rd.
Shelby, NC 28152
Tel: (704)484-4000
E-mail: areye@clevelandcc.edu
Web Site: www.clevelandcc.edu/
Description: State-supported, 2-year, coed. Part of North Carolina Community College System. Awards certificates, diplomas, transfer associate, and terminal associate degrees. Founded 1965. Setting: 43-acre small town campus with easy access to Charlotte. Total enrollment: 3,398. Student-undergrad faculty ratio is 10:1. 4,355 applied, 99% were admitted. Full-time: 1,736 students, 64% women, 36% men. Part-time: 1,662 students, 63% women, 37% men. 0.4% American Indian or Alaska Native, non-Hispanic/Latino; 2% Hispanic/Latino; 24% African American, non-Hispanic/Latino; 0.4% Asian, non-Hispanic/Latino; 0% Native Hawaiian or other Pacific Islander, non-Hispanic/Latino; 1% international. Core. Calendar: semesters. Academic remediation for entering students, ESL program, advanced placement, independent study, distance learning, double major, summer session for credit, part-time degree program, adult/continuing education programs, co-op programs. Off campus study at Foothills Nursing Consortium.
Entrance Requirements: Open admission except for allied health programs. Options: electronic application, deferred admission. Required: high school transcript. Entrance: noncompetitive. Application deadline: Rolling. Notification: continuous. Transfer credits accepted: Yes.
Costs Per Year: Application fee: $0. State resident tuition: $2128 full-time. Nonresident tuition: $8272 full-time. Mandatory fees: $94 full-time.
Collegiate Environment: Orientation program. Drama-theater group. Student services: personal-psychological counseling. Campus security: security personnel during open hours. College housing not available. Jim & Patsy Rose Library with an OPAC and a Web page.
Community Environment: Shelby is the county seat for Cleveland County and is a diversified manufacturing area. The principal businesses are mercantile, textiles, and machine parts. A city park and a large lake provide the area with recreation facilities.

■ **COASTAL CAROLINA COMMUNITY COLLEGE**
444 Western Blvd.
Jacksonville, NC 28546-6899
Tel: (910)455-1221
Fax: (910)455-2767
E-mail: calihanh@coastal.cc.nc.us
Web Site: www.coastalcarolina.edu/
Description: State and locally supported, 2-year, coed. Part of North Carolina Community College System. Awards certificates, diplomas, transfer associate, and terminal associate degrees. Founded 1964. Setting: 98-acre small town campus. Endowment: $2.2 million. Educational spending for the previous fiscal year: $2880 per student. Total enrollment: 4,349. Faculty: 469 (140 full-time, 329 part-time). Student-undergrad faculty ratio is 17:1. 4,513 applied, 62% were admitted. Full-time: 1,476 students, 67% women, 33% men. Part-time: 2,873 students, 64% women, 36% men. Students come from 16 states and territories, 3% from out-of-state. 45% 25 or older, 9% transferred in. Retention: 61% of full-time freshmen returned the following year. Core. Calendar: semesters. Academic remediation for entering students, ESL program, services for LD students, advanced placement, independent study, distance learning, double major, summer session for credit, part-time degree program, adult/continuing education programs, internships.
Entrance Requirements: Open admission. Options: deferred admission, international baccalaureate accepted. Required: high school transcript. Required for some: 2 recommendations, interview. Entrance: noncompetitive. Application deadline: Rolling. Notification: continuous.
Costs Per Year: Application fee: $0. State resident tuition: $2208 full-time, $69 per credit hour part-time. Nonresident tuition: $8352 full-time, $261 per credit hour part-time. Mandatory fees: $30 full-time, $5 per term part-time.
Collegiate Environment: Orientation program. Drama-theater group. Social organizations: 7 open to all. Most popular organizations: Phi Theta Kappa, SPYS (social sciences group), student government, Star of Life, Association of Nursing Students. Major annual events: Spring Fling, Winter Meltdown,

Fall Festival. Student services: personal-psychological counseling. Campus security: 24-hour emergency response devices and patrols, late night transport-escort service. C. Louis Shields Learning Resources Center with 44,062 books, 738 microform titles, 266 serials, and an OPAC. Operations spending for the previous fiscal year: $418,421. 936 computers available on campus for general student use. A campuswide network can be accessed from off-campus. Staffed computer lab on campus.
Community Environment: The principal business of Jacksonville are marine-related industries, military support services, and wood products. Railroads serve the area. Thirty churches of various faiths, one library and numerous historical sites are within the community. Hunting and fishing are excellent, and there are also parks are in the area for other recreational activities.

■ **COLLEGE OF THE ALBEMARLE**
PO Box 2327
Elizabeth City, NC 27906-2327
Tel: (252)335-0821
Fax: (252)335-2011
E-mail: kkrentz@albemarle.edu
Web Site: www.albemarle.edu/
Description: State-supported, 2-year, coed. Part of North Carolina Community College System. Awards certificates, diplomas, transfer associate, and terminal associate degrees. Founded 1960. Setting: 40-acre small town campus. Total enrollment: 2,071. Faculty: 122 (60 full-time, 62 part-time). Full-time: 854 students, 63% women, 37% men. Part-time: 1,217 students, 68% women, 32% men. Students come from 17 states and territories, 4 other countries. 56% 25 or older. Calendar: semesters. Academic remediation for entering students, ESL program, services for LD students, advanced placement, summer session for credit, part-time degree program, adult/continuing education programs, co-op programs.
Entrance Requirements: Open admission except for nursing, allied health programs. Options: early admission, deferred admission. Required: high school transcript. Entrance: noncompetitive. Application deadline: Rolling. Notification: continuous.
Collegiate Environment: Drama-theater group, choral group. Social organizations: 18 open to all. Most popular organizations: Phi Beta Lambda, Phi Theta Kappa. Major annual events: Welcome Back Day, Spring Fling, Career Day. Student services: personal-psychological counseling. Campus security: 24-hour patrols. Learning Resources Center with 48,400 books, 280 serials, an OPAC, and a Web page. 85 computers available on campus for general student use. Staffed computer lab on campus.
Community Environment: Elizabeth City is the home of a variety of manufacturing firms and serves as a shipping center for a large agricultural area producing corn, soybeans, potatoes, small grains, cabbage and other vegetables. All forms of commercial transportation are available. The Pasquotant River and nearby waterways provide for water sports, and deep sea and surf fishing on the Atlantic Ocean 40 miles away. The Dismal Swamp is a paradise for hunters, fishermen and naturalists. Big and small game include black bears, deer, foxes and many small mammals. Some of the historic points of interest are the Shiloh Baptist Church, the Old Brick House, Hall Creek Church, Winslow and Bayfield Home, the site of Culpepper's Rebellion in 1677-the first open rebellion against the king. Kitty Hawk, site of the Wright brothers' first powered flight, and Manteo, location of the first attempted English Colony, are nearby.

■ **CRAVEN COMMUNITY COLLEGE**
800 College Ct.
New Bern, NC 28562-4984
Tel: (252)638-4131
Fax: (252)638-4649
Web Site: www.cravencc.edu/
Description: State-supported, 2-year, coed. Part of North Carolina Community College System. Awards certificates, diplomas, transfer associate, and terminal associate degrees. Founded 1965. Setting: 100-acre suburban campus. Total enrollment: 3,032. 45% 25 or older. Core. Calendar: semesters. Academic remediation for entering students, services for LD students, advanced placement, self-designed majors, independent study, distance learning, double major, summer session for credit, part-time degree program, adult/continuing education programs, co-op programs and internships.
Entrance Requirements: Open admission except for nursing program. Required: high school transcript, interview. Entrance: noncompetitive. Application deadline: Rolling.

Collegiate Environment: Orientation program. Drama-theater group, choral group. Student services: personal-psychological counseling. Campus security: 24-hour patrols. R. C. Godwin Memorial Library with 21,000 books, 301 serials, and an OPAC.

Community Environment: New Bern, one of the oldest towns in the state, is interesting for its old buildings and many historical sites and markers. The first Provincial Congresses met here in 1774 and 1775. Some points of interest are the Christ Church, Federal Building, First Presbyterian Church and the Tryon Palace Restoration.

■ **DAVIDSON COLLEGE**

Davidson, NC 28035

Tel: (704)894-2000; Free: 800-768-0380

Fax: (704)894-2016

E-mail: admission@davidson.edu

Web Site: www.davidson.edu/

Description: Independent Presbyterian, 4-year, coed. Awards bachelor's degrees. Founded 1837. Setting: 665-acre small town campus with easy access to Charlotte. Endowment: $511.4 million. Research spending for the previous fiscal year: $1.1 million. Educational spending for the previous fiscal year: $17,326 per student. Total enrollment: 1,790. Faculty: 176 (169 full-time, 7 part-time). Student-undergrad faculty ratio is 10:1. 4,770 applied, 25% were admitted. 79% from top 10% of their high school class, 97% from top quarter, 100% from top half. Full-time: 1,790 students, 50% women, 50% men. Students come from 47 states and territories, 39 other countries, 76% from out-of-state. 1% American Indian or Alaska Native, non-Hispanic/Latino; 6% Hispanic/Latino; 7% African American, non-Hispanic/Latino; 5% Asian, non-Hispanic/Latino; 0.1% Native Hawaiian or other Pacific Islander, non-Hispanic/Latino; 5% international. 0% 25 or older, 92% live on campus, 0.4% transferred in. Retention: 97% of full-time freshmen returned the following year. Academic areas with the most degrees conferred: social sciences; psychology; English. Core. Calendar: semesters. Services for LD students, advanced placement, self-designed majors, honors program, independent study, double major, internships. Off campus study at 19 members of the Charlotte Area Educational Consortium. Study abroad program. ROTC: Army, Air Force (c).

Entrance Requirements: Options: electronic application, early admission, early decision, deferred admission, international baccalaureate accepted. Required: essay, high school transcript, 3 recommendations, SAT or ACT. Recommended: interview, SAT and SAT Subject Tests or ACT. Entrance: very difficult. Application deadlines: 1/2, 11/15 for early decision plan 1, 1/2 for early decision plan 2. Notification: 4/1, 12/15 for early decision plan 1, 2/1 for early decision plan 2. SAT Reasoning Test deadline: 1/2. SAT Subject Test deadline: 1/2. Transfer credits accepted: Yes. Early decision applicants: 565. Early decision applicants admitted: 280.

Costs Per Year: Application fee: $50. Comprehensive fee: $54,683 includes full-time tuition ($42,425), mandatory fees ($424), and college room and board ($11,834). College room only: $6249. Room and board charges vary according to board plan.

Collegiate Environment: Orientation program. Drama-theater group, choral group, student-run newspaper, radio station. Social organizations: 200 open to all; national fraternities, national sororities; 36% of eligible men and 3% of eligible women are members. Most popular organizations: Inter-Varsity Christian Fellowship, Dean Rusk Program Student Advisory Council, music organizations, Community Service Council, Student Government Association. Major annual events: Homecoming, fall concert, spring concert. Student services: health clinic, personal-psychological counseling, women's center. Campus security: 24-hour emergency response devices and patrols, late night transport-escort service, controlled dormitory access. 1,670 college housing spaces available; 1,628 were occupied in 2012-13. Freshmen guaranteed college housing. On-campus residence required through senior year. Option: coed housing available. E. H. Little Library plus 1 other with 556,462 books, 602,026 microform titles, 96,529 serials, 15,698 audiovisual materials, an OPAC, and a Web page. Operations spending for the previous fiscal year: $3.3 million. 180 computers available on campus for general student use. A campuswide network can be accessed from student residence rooms and from off campus. Students can access the following: online class registration. Staffed computer lab on campus provides training in use of computers, software, and the Internet.

Community Environment: The town of Davidson has grown around Davidson College. The cultural, social and religious life of the community revolves around the college. Davidson is twenty minutes north of Charlotte, NC, and offers students the advantages of that city's services, amenities, and recreational opportunities.

■ **DAVIDSON COUNTY COMMUNITY COLLEGE**

PO Box 1287

Lexington, NC 27293-1287

Tel: (336)249-8186

Fax: (336)249-0379

E-mail: admissions@davidsonccc.edu

Web Site: www.davidsonccc.edu/

Description: State and locally supported, 2-year, coed. Part of North Carolina Community College System. Awards certificates, diplomas, transfer associate, and terminal associate degrees. Founded 1958. Setting: 83-acre rural campus. Total enrollment: 4,101. Student-undergrad faculty ratio is 20:1. 0% from out-of-state. 53% 25 or older. Core. Calendar: semesters. Academic remediation for entering students, services for LD students, advanced placement, double major, summer session for credit, part-time degree program, adult/continuing education programs, co-op programs and internships. Off campus study at Rowan-Cabarrus Community College, Forsyth Technical Community College, Guilford Technical Community College, Rockingham Community College.

Entrance Requirements: Open admission except for nursing, allied health programs. Options: early admission, deferred admission. Required: high school transcript. Required for some: interview. Entrance: noncompetitive. Application deadline: Rolling. Notification: continuous.

Costs Per Year: Application fee: $0. State resident tuition: $1656 full-time, $69 per credit hour part-time. Nonresident tuition: $6264 full-time, $261 per credit hour part-time. Mandatory fees: $130 full-time, $3 per credit hour part-time, $17.50 per term part-time. Full-time tuition and fees vary according to course load. Part-time tuition and fees vary according to course load.

Collegiate Environment: Orientation program. Drama-theater group. Campus security: 24-hour patrols, late night transport-escort service, security guards. Grady E. Love Learning Resource Center with an OPAC and a Web page.

Community Environment: Lexington is a suburban community located approximately 25 miles south of Greensboro, N.C. Industry here includes furniture, textiles, apparel, electronics, and food processing. Bus and train transportation are available. A YMCA, churches of all major denominations, a library, hospital, and numerous civic and service organizations serve the community. For recreation, High Rock Lake, about 12 miles south of Lexington, offers boating, fishing, swimming and picnicking. There are job opportunities for students.

■ **DEVRY UNIVERSITY**

2015 Ayrsley Town Blvd., Ste. 109

Charlotte, NC 28273-4068

Tel: (704)362-2345; Free: 866-338-7941

Fax: (704)362-2668

Web Site: www.devry.edu/

Description: Proprietary, comprehensive, coed. Part of DeVry University. Awards associate, bachelor's, and master's degrees. Total enrollment: 393. Faculty: 7 (2 full-time, 5 part-time). Student-undergrad faculty ratio is 64:1. Full-time: 144 students, 49% women, 51% men. Part-time: 106 students, 49% women, 51% men. 8% from out-of-state. 76% 25 or older, 24% transferred in. Academic areas with the most degrees conferred: business/marketing; computer and information sciences. Calendar: semesters. Academic remediation for entering students, advanced placement, accelerated degree program, distance learning, summer session for credit, part-time degree program, adult/continuing education programs.

Entrance Requirements: Options: electronic application, deferred admission, international baccalaureate accepted. Required: high school transcript, interview. Entrance: minimally difficult. Application deadline: Rolling. Notification: continuous. SAT Reasoning Test deadline: 10/31.

Collegiate Environment: Orientation program.

■ **DUKE UNIVERSITY**

Durham, NC 27708-0586

Tel: (919)684-8111

Fax: (919)681-8941

E-mail: askduke@admiss.duke.edu

Web Site: www.duke.edu/

Description: Independent, university, coed, affiliated with United Methodist Church. Awards bachelor's, master's, and doctoral degrees and post-master's certificates. Founded 1838. Setting: 8,500-acre suburban campus. Endowment: $4.4 billion. Research spending for the previous fiscal year: $758.6 million. Educational spending for the previous fiscal year: $57,112 per student. Total enrollment: 14,350. Faculty: 1,155 (1,038 full-time, 117 part-time). Student-undergrad faculty ratio is 8:1. 22,280 applied, 19% were admitted. 90% from top 10% of their high school class, 97% from top quarter, 100% from top half. 105 National Merit Scholars. Full-time: 6,550 students, 49% women, 51% men. Part-time: 28 students, 46% women, 54% men. Students come from 53 states and territories, 89 other countries, 84% from out-of-state. 0% 25 or older, 84% live on campus, 0.2% transferred in. Retention: 97% of full-time freshmen returned the following year. Academic areas with the most degrees conferred: social sciences; engineering; psychology. Core. Calendar: semesters. ESL program, services for LD students, advanced placement, accelerated degree program, self-designed majors, honors program, independent study, distance learning, double major, summer session for credit, part-time degree program, adult/continuing education programs, internships, graduate courses open to undergrads. Off campus study at University of North Carolina at Chapel Hill, North Carolina Central University, North Carolina State University, Howard University. Study abroad program. ROTC: Army, Naval, Air Force.

Entrance Requirements: Options: electronic application, early admission, early decision, deferred admission, international baccalaureate accepted. Required: essay, high school transcript, SAT and SAT Subject Tests or ACT. Recommended: interview. Required for some: audition tape for dance, drama, or music; slides of work for art. Entrance: most difficult. Application deadlines: 1/2, 11/1 for early decision. Notification: 4/1, 12/15 for early decision. Preference given to children of alumni, minorities, state residents. SAT Reasoning Test deadline: 1/2. SAT Subject Test deadline: 1/2. Transfer credits accepted: Yes. Early decision applicants: 1,537. Early decision applicants admitted: 550.

Collegiate Environment: Orientation program. Drama-theater group, choral group, marching band, student-run newspaper, radio station. Social organizations: 400 open to all; national fraternities, national sororities; 29% of eligible men and 42% of eligible women are members. Major annual events: Homecoming, Parents' Weekend, Oktoberfest. Student services: legal services, health clinic, personal-psychological counseling, women's center. Campus security: 24-hour emergency response devices and patrols, late night transport-escort service, controlled dormitory access. Perkins Library plus 14 others with 6 million books, 4.3 million microform titles, 62,639 serials, 137,868 audiovisual materials, an OPAC, and a Web page. Operations spending for the previous fiscal year: $42.1 million. 500 computers available on campus for general student use. Computer purchase/lease plans available. A campuswide network can be accessed from student residence rooms and from off campus. Students can access the following: online class registration. Staffed computer lab on campus (open 24 hours a day).

Community Environment: Durham, North Carolina, a city of about 200,000 people, is approximately 250 miles south of Washington, D.C. Durham and nearby Raleigh and Chapel Hill constitute the three points of what is known as the Research Triangle, one of the nation's foremost centers for research-oriented industries and government, research, and regulatory agencies. The combined population of the Raleigh, Durham, and Chapel Hill area is one million. Two major interstates and the Raleigh-Durham International Airport (a 20-minute drive from campus) make Durham easily accessible from almost anywhere in the United States. Nationally known hospitals and clinics, including the Duke University Medical Center, make Durham a center for medicine. Other community facilities include numerous churches, museums, parks, shopping areas, an arts center, and major civic and service organizations. Both beaches and mountains are within a three-hour drive.

■ DURHAM TECHNICAL COMMUNITY COLLEGE
1637 Lawson St.
Durham, NC 27703-5023
Tel: (919)686-3300
Web Site: www.durhamtech.edu/
Description: State-supported, 2-year, coed. Part of North Carolina Community College System. Awards certificates, diplomas, transfer associate, and terminal associate degrees. Founded 1961. Setting: urban campus. Total enrollment: 5,170. 61% 25 or older. Core. Calendar: semesters. Academic remediation for entering students, ESL program, services for LD students, advanced placement, accelerated degree program, self-designed majors, distance learning, summer session for credit, part-time degree program, adult/continuing education programs, co-op programs and internships. Off campus study at University of North Carolina at Chapel Hill, University of North Carolina at Greensboro, Wake Technical Community College, Asheville-Buncombe Community College, Central Piedmont Community College, Guilford Technical Community College, Piedmont Community College.

Entrance Requirements: Open admission. Option: deferred admission. Required: high school transcript. Recommended: interview. Entrance: noncompetitive. Application deadline: Rolling. Notification: continuous.
Collegiate Environment: Orientation program. Drama-theater group. Student services: personal-psychological counseling. Campus security: 24-hour patrols, late night transport-escort service. Educational Resource Center with 36,388 books, 123,657 microform titles, 1,348 audiovisual materials, and an OPAC.
Community Environment: See Duke University.

■ EAST CAROLINA UNIVERSITY
E 5th St.
Greenville, NC 27858-4353
Tel: (252)328-6131
Fax: (252)328-6495
E-mail: admis@ecu.edu
Web Site: www.ecu.edu/
Description: State-supported, university, coed. Part of University of North Carolina System. Awards bachelor's, master's, and doctoral degrees and post-master's certificates. Founded 1907. Setting: 1,401-acre urban campus. Endowment: $128.7 million. Research spending for the previous fiscal year: $26.9 million. Educational spending for the previous fiscal year: $11,058 per student. Total enrollment: 26,947. Faculty: 1,491 (1,166 full-time, 325 part-time). Student-undergrad faculty ratio is 18:1. 15,535 applied, 62% were admitted. 15% from top 10% of their high school class, 44% from top quarter, 82% from top half. Full-time: 18,317 students, 58% women, 42% men. Part-time: 2,981 students, 63% women, 37% men. Students come from 42 states and territories, 54 other countries, 12% from out-of-state. 1% American Indian or Alaska Native, non-Hispanic/Latino; 3% Hispanic/Latino; 15% African American, non-Hispanic/Latino; 2% Asian, non-Hispanic/Latino; 0.1% Native Hawaiian or other Pacific Islander, non-Hispanic/Latino; 1% international. 14% 25 or older, 24% live on campus, 7% transferred in. Retention: 78% of full-time freshmen returned the following year. Academic areas with the most degrees conferred: business/marketing; health professions and related sciences; education. Core. Calendar: semesters. Services for LD students, advanced placement, accelerated degree program, self-designed majors, honors program, independent study, distance learning, double major, summer session for credit, part-time degree program, adult/continuing education programs, co-op programs and internships, graduate courses open to undergrads. Off campus study. Study abroad program. ROTC: Army, Air Force.

Entrance Requirements: Options: electronic application, early admission, deferred admission, international baccalaureate accepted. Required: high school transcript, minimum 2 high school GPA, SAT or ACT. Entrance: moderately difficult. Application deadlines: 3/15, 3/15 for nonresidents. Notification: continuous, continuous for nonresidents. Preference given to state residents. SAT Reasoning Test deadline: 3/15. SAT Subject Test deadline: 3/15. Transfer credits accepted: Yes.
Costs Per Year: Application fee: $70. State resident tuition: $3758 full-time, $469.75 per course part-time. Nonresident tuition: $17,572 full-time, $2,197 per course part-time. Mandatory fees: $2111 full-time, $263.88 per course part-time. Full-time tuition and fees vary according to location. Part-time tuition and fees vary according to course load and location. College room and board: $8300. College room only: $4774. Room and board charges vary according to board plan and housing facility.
Collegiate Environment: Orientation program. Drama-theater group, choral group, marching band, student-run newspaper, radio station. Social organizations: 337 open to all; national fraternities, national sororities. Most popular organizations: Student Government Association, Student Union, Residence Hall Association, Student Pirate Club, Black Student Union. Major annual events: Midnight Madness, Pirate Palooza, Barefoot on the Mall. Student services: legal services, health clinic, personal-psychological counseling. Campus security: 24-hour emergency response devices and patrols, student patrols, late night transport-escort service, controlled dormitory access, Operation ID, Staff and Faculty Eyes, Campus Community Watch program. 5,424 college housing spaces available; 5,106 were occupied in 2012-13. No special consideration for freshman housing applicants. Options: coed, women-only housing available. Joyner Library plus 1 other with 2.4 million books, 1.2 million microform titles, 73,498 serials, 69,251 audiovisual materials, an OPAC, and a Web page. Operations spending for the previous fiscal year: $17.1 million. 2,625 computers available on campus for general student use. Computer purchase/lease plans available. A campuswide network can be accessed from student residence rooms and from off campus. Students can access the following: online class

registration. Staffed computer lab on campus (open 24 hours a day) provides training in use of computers, software, and the Internet.

Community Environment: Greenville (population 69,500) is the largest medical, cultural and retailing center on eastern North Carolina. The climate is mild, the mean annual temperature being 61 degrees. There are churches of all major denominations, a major hospital, a community art center, one library, and various civic and service organizations in the community. Employment opportunities are good.

■ ECPI COLLEGE OF TECHNOLOGY (CHARLOTTE)

4800 Airport Ctr. Pky.
Charlotte, NC 28208
Tel: (704)399-1010; Free: 866-708-6167
Web Site: www.ecpi.edu/
Description: Proprietary, primarily 2-year, coed. Awards diplomas, terminal associate, and bachelor's degrees.

■ ECPI COLLEGE OF TECHNOLOGY (GREENSBORO)

7802 Airport Ctr. Dr.
Greensboro, NC 27409
Tel: (336)665-1400; Free: 866-708-6170
Web Site: www.ecpi.edu/
Description: Proprietary, primarily 2-year, coed. Awards diplomas, terminal associate, and bachelor's degrees.

■ ECPI COLLEGE OF TECHNOLOGY (RALEIGH)

4101 Doie Cope Rd.
Raleigh, NC 27613
Tel: (919)571-0057; Free: 800-986-1200
Fax: (919)571-0780
E-mail: swells@ecpi.edu
Web Site: www.ecpi.edu/
Description: Proprietary, 4-year, coed. Awards associate and bachelor's degrees. Founded 1990. Total enrollment: 550. Student-undergrad faculty ratio is 13:1. 0% from out-of-state. 51% 25 or older. Core. Calendar: trimesters. Academic remediation for entering students, accelerated degree program, independent study, distance learning, adult/continuing education programs, co-op programs and internships. Study abroad program.
Entrance Requirements: Option: electronic application. Required: high school transcript, interview. Recommended: SAT, SAT or ACT, SAT Subject Tests. Entrance: moderately difficult. Application deadline: Rolling. Notification: continuous.
Collegiate Environment: Orientation program. Student-run newspaper. Social organizations: national fraternities, national sororities, local fraternities, local sororities; 25% of eligible men and 20% of eligible women are members. Student services: personal-psychological counseling. 200 computers available on campus for general student use. A campuswide network can be accessed from off-campus. Staffed computer lab on campus.

■ EDGECOMBE COMMUNITY COLLEGE

2009 W Wilson St.
Tarboro, NC 27886-9399
Tel: (252)823-5166
Fax: (252)823-6817
Web Site: www.edgecombe.edu/
Description: State and locally supported, 2-year, coed. Part of North Carolina Community College System. Awards certificates, diplomas, transfer associate, and terminal associate degrees. Founded 1968. Setting: 90-acre small town campus. Total enrollment: 1,687. 57% 25 or older. Calendar: semesters. Academic remediation for entering students, ESL program, services for LD students; advanced placement, independent study, distance learning, double major, summer session for credit, part-time degree program, adult/continuing education programs, co-op programs. Off campus study.
Entrance Requirements: Open admission except for radiological technology, nursing, respiratory therapy, surgical technology, networking technology programs. Option: electronic application. Required: high school transcript, minimum 2.0 high school GPA. Entrance: noncompetitive. Application deadline: Rolling. Notification: continuous.
Collegiate Environment: Orientation program. 42,460 books, 54,841 microform titles, 239 serials, 2,527 audiovisual materials, an OPAC, and a Web page.
Community Environment: See North Carolina Wesleyan College.

■ ELIZABETH CITY STATE UNIVERSITY

1704 Weeksville Rd.
Elizabeth City, NC 27909-7806
Tel: (252)335-3400; Free: 800-347-3278
Fax: (252)335-3731
Web Site: www.ecsu.edu/
Description: State-supported, comprehensive, coed. Part of University of North Carolina System. Awards bachelor's and master's degrees. Founded 1891. Setting: 200-acre small town campus with easy access to Norfolk. Total enrollment: 2,878. Faculty: 218 (167 full-time, 51 part-time). Student-undergrad faculty ratio is 14:1. 3,925 applied, 57% were admitted. 1% from top 10% of their high school class, 6% from top quarter, 33% from top half. Full-time: 2,509 students, 59% women, 41% men. Part-time: 251 students, 73% women, 27% men. 13% from out-of-state. 0.5% American Indian or Alaska Native, non-Hispanic/Latino; 1% Hispanic/Latino; 73% African American, non-Hispanic/Latino; 0.4% Asian, non-Hispanic/Latino; 0.04% Native Hawaiian or other Pacific Islander, non-Hispanic/Latino; 0% international. 21% 25 or older, 52% live on campus, 7% transferred in. Retention: 79% of full-time freshmen returned the following year. Academic areas with the most degrees conferred: business/marketing; education; homeland security, law enforcement, firefighting, and protective services. Core. Calendar: semesters. Academic remediation for entering students, services for LD students, advanced placement, honors program, independent study, distance learning, double major, summer session for credit, part-time degree program, adult/continuing education programs, co-op programs and internships, graduate courses open to undergrads. Off campus study at North Carolina Model Teacher Education Consortium. Study abroad program. ROTC: Army.
Entrance Requirements: Options: electronic application, deferred admission. Required: high school transcript, minimum 2.3 high school GPA, SAT or ACT. Entrance: moderately difficult. Application deadline: Rolling. Notification: continuous. Preference given to state residents. SAT Reasoning Test deadline: 8/15.
Costs Per Year: Application fee: $30. Area resident tuition: $347 per credit hour part-time. State resident tuition: $2,776 full-time. Nonresident tuition: $13,633 full-time, $1,704.11 per credit hour part-time. Mandatory fees: $1,652 full-time. College room and board: $7,213. College room only: $4,440. Room and board charges vary according to housing facility.
Collegiate Environment: Orientation program. Drama-theater group, choral group, marching band, student-run newspaper. Social organizations: 60 open to all; national fraternities, national sororities, local fraternities, local sororities; 70% of eligible men and 80% of eligible women are members. Most popular organizations: Vans (Vikings Assisting New Students), Student Activities Committee, Vike Nu' Fashion Troupe, Pep Squad, Essence of Praise. Major annual events: Homecoming, Viking Fast, Student and Body Meetings. Student services: health clinic, personal-psychological counseling. Campus security: 24-hour emergency response devices and patrols. 1,785 college housing spaces available. Freshmen guaranteed college housing. Options: coed, men-only, women-only housing available. G. R. Little Library with 207,495 books, 488,671 microform titles, 2,997 serials, 488,899 audiovisual materials, an OPAC, and a Web page. 1,035 computers available on campus for general student use. Computer purchase/lease plans available. A campuswide network can be accessed from student residence rooms and from off campus. Students can access the following: online class registration. Staffed computer lab on campus provides training in use of computers, software, and the Internet.
Community Environment: See College of the Albemarle.

■ ELON UNIVERSITY

2700 Campus Box
Elon, NC 27244-2010
Tel: (336)278-2000; Free: 800-334-8448
Fax: (336)538-3986
E-mail: admissions@elon.edu
Web Site: www.elon.edu/
Description: Independent, comprehensive, coed, affiliated with United Church of Christ. Awards bachelor's, master's, and doctoral degrees. Founded 1889. Setting: 620-acre suburban campus with easy access to Raleigh. Endowment: $132 million. Total enrollment: 6,029. Faculty: 535 (385 full-time, 150 part-time). Student-undergrad faculty ratio is 13:1. 10,241 applied, 52% were admitted. 26% from top 10% of their high school class, 65% from top quarter, 91% from top half. Full-time: 5,209 students, 59% women, 41% men. Part-time: 148 students, 56% women, 44% men. Students come from 48 states and territories, 48 other countries, 75% from

out-of-state. 0.3% American Indian or Alaska Native, non-Hispanic/Latino; 4% Hispanic/Latino; 6% African American, non-Hispanic/Latino; 2% Asian, non-Hispanic/Latino; 0.1% Native Hawaiian or other Pacific Islander, non-Hispanic/Latino; 2% international. 1% 25 or older, 60% live on campus, 2% transferred in. Retention: 90% of full-time freshmen returned the following year. Academic areas with the most degrees conferred: business/marketing; communication/journalism; social sciences. Core. Calendar: semesters 3-week winter term. ESL program, services for LD students, advanced placement, accelerated degree program, self-designed majors, honors program, independent study, double major, summer session for credit, part-time degree program, internships. Off campus study at University of North Carolina-Wilmington, Arcadia University, Curtin University (Australia), American University in Cairo, University of Sussex (England), University of Heidelbery (Germany), University of Haifa (Israel), University of St. Andrews (Scotland). In affiliation with: Council on International Educational Exchange (CIEE), Foundation for International Education (FIE), Alliance for Global Education, Foundation for International Education (FIE), School for Field Studies (SFS), Organization for Tropical Studies (OTS). Study abroad program. ROTC: Army, Air Force (c).

Entrance Requirements: Options: electronic application, early admission, early decision, early action, deferred admission, international baccalaureate accepted. Required: essay, high school transcript, SAT or ACT. Required for some: interview. Entrance: moderately difficult. Application deadlines: 1/10, 11/1 for early decision, 11/10 for early action. Notification: 3/15, 12/1 for early decision, 12/20 for early action. Transfer credits accepted: Yes. Applicants placed on waiting list: 3,297. Wait-listed applicants offered admission: 41. Early decision applicants: 399. Early decision applicants admitted: 342. Early action applicants: 6,331. Early action applicants admitted: 3,143.

Costs Per Year: Application fee: $50. Comprehensive fee: $38,460 includes full-time tuition ($28,633), mandatory fees ($347), and college room and board ($9480). College room only: $4690. Room and board charges vary according to board plan and housing facility. Part-time tuition: $898 per hour. Part-time tuition varies according to course load.

Collegiate Environment: Orientation program. Drama-theater group, choral group, marching band, student-run newspaper, radio station. Social organizations: 200 open to all; national fraternities, national sororities; 22% of eligible men and 38% of eligible women are members. Most popular organizations: Elon volunteers, student media, intramural athletics, religious life, Habitat for Humanity. Major annual events: Homecoming, Family Weekend, Fall Convocation. Student services: health clinic, personal-psychological counseling, women's center. Campus security: 24-hour emergency response devices and patrols, late night transport-escort service, controlled dormitory access. 3,400 college housing spaces available; all were occupied in 2012-13. Freshmen guaranteed college housing. On-campus residence required through sophomore year. Options: coed, men-only, women-only housing available. Carol Grotnes Belk with 373,934 books, 460,447 microform titles, 18,644 serials, 23,572 audiovisual materials, an OPAC, and a Web page. Operations spending for the previous fiscal year: $3.2 million. 1,169 computers available on campus for general student use. Computer purchase/lease plans available. A campuswide network can be accessed from student residence rooms and from off campus. Students can access the following: online class registration. Staffed computer lab on campus (open 24 hours a day) provides training in use of computers, software, and the Internet.

Community Environment: See Alamance Community College.

■ FAYETTEVILLE STATE UNIVERSITY

1200 Murchison Rd.
Fayetteville, NC 28301-4298
Tel: (910)672-1111; Free: 800-222-2594
Fax: (910)672-1769
E-mail: admissions@uncfsu.edu
Web Site: www.uncfsu.edu/

Description: State-supported, comprehensive, coed. Part of University of North Carolina System. Awards bachelor's, master's, and doctoral degrees. Founded 1867. Setting: 156-acre urban campus with easy access to Raleigh. Endowment: $13.6 million. Research spending for the previous fiscal year: $885,149. Total enrollment: 6,060. Faculty: 334 (276 full-time, 58 part-time). Student-undergrad faculty ratio is 16:1. 4,010 applied, 55% were admitted. 5% from top 10% of their high school class, 19% from top quarter, 57% from top half. Full-time: 3,916 students, 67% women, 33% men. Part-time: 1,371 students, 76% women, 24% men. Students come from 30 states and territories, 7 other countries, 5% from out-of-state. 2% American Indian or Alaska Native, non-Hispanic/Latino; 6% Hispanic/Latino; 68% African

American, non-Hispanic/Latino; 1% Asian, non-Hispanic/Latino; 0.1% Native Hawaiian or other Pacific Islander, non-Hispanic/Latino; 1% international. 43% 25 or older, 29% live on campus, 14% transferred in. Retention: 76% of full-time freshmen returned the following year. Academic areas with the most degrees conferred: business/marketing; homeland security, law enforcement, firefighting, and protective services; psychology. Core. Calendar: semesters. Academic remediation for entering students, services for LD students, advanced placement, accelerated degree program, honors program, independent study, distance learning, double major, summer session for credit, part-time degree program, adult/continuing education programs, co-op programs and internships, graduate courses open to undergrads. Study abroad program. ROTC: Army (c), Air Force.

Entrance Requirements: Options: electronic application, early admission, early decision, early action, deferred admission. Required: high school transcript, minimum 2 high school GPA, SAT or ACT. Recommended: essay. Entrance: minimally difficult. Application deadline: 6/30. Notification: continuous. SAT Reasoning Test deadline: 7/1.

Costs Per Year: Application fee: $35. State resident tuition: $2585 full-time. Nonresident tuition: $13,289 full-time. Mandatory fees: $3086 full-time. Full-time tuition and fees vary according to course level, course load, degree level, location, and program. College room and board: $6142. College room only: $3392. Room and board charges vary according to board plan and housing facility.

Collegiate Environment: Orientation program. Drama-theater group, choral group, marching band, student-run newspaper, radio station. Social organizations: 30 open to all; national fraternities, national sororities, local fraternities, local sororities; 1% of eligible men and 1% of eligible women are members. Most popular organizations: Student Government Association, Student Activities Council, Pan-Hellenic Council, Residence-Hall Association, Illusions and Black Millennium Modeling Clubs. Major annual events: Homecoming Week Activities, Rodeo Week Activities, National Pan Hellenic Council Campus Presentation. Student services: health clinic, personal-psychological counseling. Campus security: 24-hour emergency response devices and patrols, late night transport-escort service, controlled dormitory access. 1,298 college housing spaces available; 1,204 were occupied in 2012-13. Freshmen given priority for college housing. Options: coed, men-only, women-only housing available. Charles W. Chestnut Library with 335,922 books, 1 million microform titles, 4,732 serials, 20,676 audiovisual materials, an OPAC, and a Web page. 600 computers available on campus for general student use. Computer purchase/lease plans available. A campuswide network can be accessed from student residence rooms and from off campus. Students can access the following: online class registration. Staffed computer lab on campus provides training in use of computers, software, and the Internet.

Community Environment: The"All-America City" of Fayetteville is located in Cumberland County with a metropolitan population of 299,060. It is near three of the most heavily traveled North-South Highways: US 301, US 401 and I-95. Fayetteville is the home of Pope Air Force Base and Fort Bragg, one of America's largest and most important military installations. It is the fourth largest urban population center in the state and one of the ten fastest growing counties in the southern states. Agriculture has contributed significantly to the area's economic growth and development.

■ FAYETTEVILLE TECHNICAL COMMUNITY COLLEGE

2201 Hull Rd.
Fayetteville, NC 28303-0236
Tel: (910)678-8400
Fax: (910)678-8407
E-mail: jonesma@faytechcc.edu
Web Site: www.faytechcc.edu/

Description: State-supported, 2-year, coed. Part of North Carolina Community College System. Awards certificates, diplomas, transfer associate, and terminal associate degrees. Founded 1961. Setting: 209-acre suburban campus with easy access to Raleigh. Endowment: $39,050. Educational spending for the previous fiscal year: $3581 per student. Total enrollment: 12,594. Faculty: 496 (266 full-time, 230 part-time). Student-undergrad faculty ratio is 16:1. 4,263 applied, 100% were admitted. 0% from top 10% of their high school class, 18% from top quarter, 41% from top half. Full-time: 5,197 students, 64% women, 36% men. Part-time: 7,397 students, 59% women, 41% men. Students come from 45 states and territories, 43 other countries, 21% from out-of-state. 3% American Indian or Alaska Native, non-Hispanic/Latino; 9% Hispanic/Latino; 44% African American, non-Hispanic/Latino; 1% Asian, non-Hispanic/Latino; 0.4% Native Hawaiian or other Pacific Islander, non-Hispanic/Latino; 1% international. 74% 25 or older, 21% transferred in.

Core. Calendar: semesters. Academic remediation for entering students, ESL program, services for LD students, advanced placement, accelerated degree program, independent study, distance learning, double major, summer session for credit, part-time degree program, adult/continuing education programs, co-op programs and internships. Off campus study at North Carolina University System, Methodist University, Campbell University, High Point College, Mars Hill College, Meredith College, Montreat-Anderson College, Mount Olive College, North Carolina Wesleyan College, Shaw University, Southeastern Baptist Theological College, St. Andrews University, Wingate University, Fayetteville State University, Kaplan University.

Entrance Requirements: Open admission Open admission except for allied health programs. Options: electronic application, international baccalaureate accepted. Required: ACCUPLACER is required or ACT and SAT scores in lieu of ACCUPLACER if the scores are no more than 5 years old or ASSET and COMPASS scores are also accepted if they are no more than 3 years old. Required for some: essay, high school transcript, interview. Entrance: noncompetitive. Application deadlines: Rolling, Rolling for nonresidents. Notification: continuous, continuous for nonresidents. Transfer credits accepted: Yes.

Costs Per Year: Application fee: $0. One-time mandatory fee: $25. State resident tuition: $2208 full-time, $69 per credit hour part-time. Nonresident tuition: $8352 full-time, $261 per credit hour part-time. Mandatory fees: $180 full-time, $90 per term part-time. Full-time tuition and fees vary according to course load. Part-time tuition and fees vary according to course load.

Collegiate Environment: Orientation program. Social organizations: 35 open to all. Most popular organizations: Parents for Higher Education, Early Childhood Club, Phi Beta Lambda, Association of Nursing Students, African/American Heritage Club. Major annual events: Fall Fling, Spring Fling, On-Campus Job Fairs. Student services: personal-psychological counseling. Campus security: 24-hour emergency response devices and patrols, late night transport-escort service, campus-wide emergency notification system. College housing not available. Paul H. Thompson Library plus 1 other with 67,997 books, 3,488 microform titles, 329 serials, 594 audiovisual materials, an OPAC, and a Web page. Operations spending for the previous fiscal year: $1.8 million. 1,450 computers available on campus for general student use. A campuswide network can be accessed from off-campus. Students can access the following: online class registration, In Web Advisor (currently enrolled students can access their admissions status, retrieve documents and notices, application processes, test scores, along with program evaluation, financial aid status, pre-registration, and tuition payment). Staffed computer lab on campus provides training in use of computers, software, and the Internet.

Community Environment: See Fayetteville State University.

■ **FORSYTH TECHNICAL COMMUNITY COLLEGE**
2100 Silas Creek Pky.
Winston-Salem, NC 27103-5197
Tel: (336)723-0371
Fax: (336)761-2098
E-mail: admissions@forsythtech.edu
Web Site: www.forsythtech.edu/

Description: State-supported, 2-year, coed. Part of North Carolina Community College System. Awards certificates, diplomas, transfer associate, and terminal associate degrees. Founded 1964. Setting: 38-acre suburban campus. Total enrollment: 9,941. Faculty: 729 (217 full-time, 512 part-time). Student-undergrad faculty ratio is 17:1. Full-time: 4,639 students, 57% women, 43% men. Part-time: 5,302 students, 65% women, 35% men. 1% from out-of-state. 46% 25 or older, 26% transferred in. Calendar: semesters. Academic remediation for entering students, ESL program, services for LD students, advanced placement, independent study, distance learning, double major, summer session for credit, part-time degree program, adult/continuing education programs, co-op programs and internships. Off campus study at Dual Enrollment with Winston-Salem State University.

Entrance Requirements: Required: high school transcript, COMPASS.

Costs Per Year: State resident tuition: $2208 full-time, $69 per credit hour part-time. Nonresident tuition: $7952 full-time, $261 per credit hour part-time. Mandatory fees: $30 full-time, $30 per term part-time. Full-time tuition and fees vary according to course load. Part-time tuition and fees vary according to course load.

Collegiate Environment: Orientation program. Student-run newspaper. Major annual events: Fall Festival, Spring Fling. Student services: personal-psychological counseling, women's center. Campus security: 24-hour emergency response devices and patrols, late night transport-escort service.

College housing not available. Forsyth Technical Community College Library plus 1 other with an OPAC and a Web page.

Community Environment: See Wake Forest University.

■ **GARDNER-WEBB UNIVERSITY**
110 S Main St.
Boiling Springs, NC 28017
Tel: (704)406-2361; Free: 800-253-6472
Fax: (704)434-4488
E-mail: admissions@gardner-webb.edu
Web Site: www.gardner-webb.edu/

Description: Independent Baptist, university, coed. Awards associate, bachelor's, master's, and doctoral degrees. Founded 1905. Setting: 250-acre small town campus with easy access to Charlotte, NC. Endowment: $51.1 million. Educational spending for the previous fiscal year: $5707 per student. Total enrollment: 4,854. Faculty: 258 (123 full-time, 135 part-time). Student-undergrad faculty ratio is 13:1. 5,232 applied, 54% were admitted. 19% from top 10% of their high school class, 47% from top quarter, 80% from top half. Full-time: 2,192 students, 62% women, 38% men. Part-time: 485 students, 78% women, 22% men. Students come from 43 states and territories, 13 other countries, 22% from out-of-state. 1% American Indian or Alaska Native, non-Hispanic/Latino; 2% Hispanic/Latino; 19% African American, non-Hispanic/Latino; 1% Asian, non-Hispanic/Latino; 2% international. 35% 25 or older, 51% live on campus, 17% transferred in. Retention: 67% of full-time freshmen returned the following year. Academic areas with the most degrees conferred: social sciences; business/marketing; health professions and related sciences. Core. Calendar: semesters. Academic remediation for entering students, ESL program, services for LD students, advanced placement, accelerated degree program, honors program, independent study, distance learning, double major, summer session for credit, part-time degree program, adult/continuing education programs, co-op programs and internships, graduate courses open to undergrads. Off campus study. Study abroad program. ROTC: Army, Air Force (c).

Entrance Requirements: Options: electronic application, international baccalaureate accepted. Required: high school transcript, minimum 2.5 high school GPA, SAT or ACT, SAT or ACT. Recommended: essay, 2 recommendations. Required for some: 2 recommendations, interview. Entrance: moderately difficult. Application deadlines: Rolling, Rolling for nonresidents. Notification: continuous, continuous for nonresidents. SAT Reasoning Test deadline: 8/15. Transfer credits accepted: Yes.

Costs Per Year: Application fee: $40. One-time mandatory fee: $100. Comprehensive fee: $32,580 includes full-time tuition ($24,250), mandatory fees ($390), and college room and board ($7940). College room only: $4080. Full-time tuition and fees vary according to degree level. Room and board charges vary according to board plan and housing facility. Part-time tuition: $387 per credit hour. Part-time tuition varies according to course load.

Collegiate Environment: Orientation program. Drama-theater group, choral group, marching band, student-run newspaper, radio station. Social organizations: 65 open to all. Most popular organizations: Campus Ministries United, Student Government Association, Dawg Pound, Honors Student Association, International Club. Major annual events: Homecoming, Parents' Weekend, Welcome Back events. Student services: personal-psychological counseling. Campus security: 24-hour emergency response devices and patrols, student patrols, late night transport-escort service, controlled dormitory access. 1,376 college housing spaces available; 1,176 were occupied in 2012-13. Freshmen guaranteed college housing. On-campus residence required through junior year. Options: men-only, women-only housing available. Dover Memorial Library plus 1 other with 297,291 books, 655,188 microform titles, 230,143 serials, 13,060 audiovisual materials, an OPAC, and a Web page. Operations spending for the previous fiscal year: $402,312. 121 computers available on campus for general student use. Computer purchase/lease plans available. A campuswide network can be accessed from student residence rooms and from off campus. Students can access the following: online class registration. Staffed computer lab on campus provides training in use of computers and the Internet.

Community Environment: Boiling Springs is located within the noted thermal belt; bus transportation is within five miles; three major railroad lines are within 10 miles; nearest airport is Charlotte, N.C., 50 miles. The community has access to the indoor swimming pool at the college, observatory, theatre, football stadium, gymnasium and the many cultural arts and entertainment programs at the college. Shopping facilities are good, other community facilities include United Methodist and Baptist churches, and in nearby Shelby, churches of most major denominations, plus numerous civic and service organizations. Part-time employment opportunities are good.

■ GASTON COLLEGE

201 Hwy. 321 S
Dallas, NC 28034-1499
Tel: (704)922-6200
Web Site: www.gaston.edu/

Description: State and locally supported, 2-year, coed. Part of North Carolina Community College System. Awards certificates, diplomas, transfer associate, and terminal associate degrees. Founded 1963. Setting: 166-acre small town campus with easy access to Charlotte. Total enrollment: 6,507. Student-undergrad faculty ratio is 15:1. 0% from out-of-state. 50% 25 or older. Core. Calendar: semesters. Academic remediation for entering students, ESL program, services for LD students, advanced placement, summer session for credit, part-time degree program, co-op programs. Off campus study at 10 members of the Charlotte Area Educational Consortium.

Entrance Requirements: Open admission except for nursing, allied health programs. Required: high school transcript, ACT COMPASS. Required for some: SAT and SAT Subject Tests or ACT. Entrance: noncompetitive. Application deadline: Rolling. Notification: continuous.

Collegiate Environment: Orientation program. Student-run radio station. Campus security: 24-hour patrols, late night transport-escort service. Gaston College Library with an OPAC.

Community Environment: The 140 textile plants of Gaston County, 59 of which are in Gastonia, manufacture more than 80 percent of the fine combed cotton yarn made in the United States. Gastonia is an important industrial city of the South. Railroads serve the area with the Charlotte Airport 15 miles away. Community facilities include numerous churches, hospitals, a public library, and a number of civic and service organizations. Rankin Lake is the city's natural reservoir. Adjoining it is a public park that provides a museum and planetarium as well as facilities for golfing, swimming, boating, fishing, and tennis. The Atlantic Coast is within a five-hour drive.

■ GRACE COLLEGE OF DIVINITY

5117 Cliffdale Rd.
Fayetteville, NC 28314
Tel: (910)221-2224
Web Site: www.gcdivinity.org/

Description: Independent religious, 4-year, coed. Calendar: semesters.

■ GREENSBORO COLLEGE

815 W Market St.
Greensboro, NC 27401-1875
Tel: (336)272-7102; Free: 800-346-8226
Fax: (336)271-6634
E-mail: admissions@greensborocollege.edu
Web Site: www.greensboro.edu/

Description: Independent United Methodist, comprehensive, coed. Awards bachelor's and master's degrees. Founded 1838. Setting: 75-acre urban campus with easy access to Charlotte. Total enrollment: 1,264. Faculty: 96 (62 full-time, 34 part-time). Student-undergrad faculty ratio is 13:1. 2,346 applied, 41% were admitted. Full-time: 867 students, 47% women, 53% men. Part-time: 250 students, 72% women, 28% men. Students come from 31 states and territories, 28 other countries, 25% from out-of-state. 0.3% American Indian or Alaska Native, non-Hispanic/Latino; 3% Hispanic/Latino; 22% African American, non-Hispanic/Latino; 1% Asian, non-Hispanic/Latino; 0.3% international. 33% 25 or older, 73% live on campus, 10% transferred in. Retention: 62% of full-time freshmen returned the following year. Academic areas with the most degrees conferred: business/marketing; visual and performing arts; health professions and related sciences. Core. Calendar: semesters. Academic remediation for entering students, ESL program, services for LD students, advanced placement, accelerated degree program, self-designed majors, freshman honors college, honors program, independent study, double major, summer session for credit, part-time degree program, adult/continuing education programs, internships. Off campus study at 7 members of the Greater Greensboro Consortium. Study abroad program. ROTC: Army (c), Air Force (c).

Entrance Requirements: Options: electronic application, early admission, early action, deferred admission, international baccalaureate accepted. Required: high school transcript, SAT or ACT. Recommended: essay, interview. Required for some: 2 recommendations, interview. Entrance:

moderately difficult. Application deadlines: Rolling, 12/15 for early action. Notification: continuous, 1/15 for early action.

Collegiate Environment: Orientation program. Drama-theater group, choral group, marching band, student-run newspaper. Social organizations: 52 open to all; national fraternities, national sororities, local fraternities, local sororities; 2% of eligible men and 2% of eligible women are members. Most popular organizations: Pheta VI, Alpha Z Delta, Student Athletic Advisor Counsel, Pride Productions, United African American Society. Major annual events: Club Carnival, Homecoming, Super Bowl Event. Student services: health clinic, personal-psychological counseling. Campus security: 24-hour patrols, late night transport-escort service, controlled dormitory access. James Addison Jones Library with 108,350 books, 2,970 microform titles, 290 serials, 2,686 audiovisual materials, an OPAC, and a Web page. 180 computers available on campus for general student use. A campuswide network can be accessed from student residence rooms and from off campus.

Community Environment: Greensboro was named for General Nathanael Greene, hero of the Battle of Guilford Courthouse. Textiles are the predominant industry along with the manufacture of cigarettes. The War Memorial Auditorium and Coliseum provides one of the state's finest facilities for conventions, exhibitions, sports events, and shows. Recreation facilities include golf courses, swimming pools, and tennis courts. Part-time employment is available. Points of interest are the Greensboro Historical Museum and on the site of O. Henry's birthplace.

■ GUILFORD COLLEGE

5800 W Friendly Ave.
Greensboro, NC 27410-4173
Tel: (336)316-2000; Free: 800-992-7759
Fax: (336)316-2954
E-mail: admission@guilford.edu
Web Site: www.guilford.edu/

Description: Independent, 4-year, coed, affiliated with Society of Friends. Awards bachelor's degrees. Founded 1837. Setting: 340-acre suburban campus with easy access to Winston Salem, Raleigh. Endowment: $65.9 million. Research spending for the previous fiscal year: $125,000. Educational spending for the previous fiscal year: $6439 per student. Total enrollment: 2,462. Faculty: 190 (124 full-time, 66 part-time). Student-undergrad faculty ratio is 15:1. 2,549 applied, 80% were admitted. 11% from top 10% of their high school class, 38% from top quarter, 76% from top half. Full-time: 2,056 students, 56% women, 44% men. Part-time: 406 students, 65% women, 35% men. Students come from 43 states and territories, 13 other countries, 52% from out-of-state. 0.4% American Indian or Alaska Native, non-Hispanic/Latino; 5% Hispanic/Latino; 25% African American, non-Hispanic/Latino; 3% Asian, non-Hispanic/Latino; 0.04% Native Hawaiian or other Pacific Islander, non-Hispanic/Latino; 1% international. 0% 25 or older, 77% live on campus, 1% transferred in. Retention: 71% of full-time freshmen returned the following year. Academic areas with the most degrees conferred: business/marketing; psychology; social sciences. Core. Calendar: semesters. Academic remediation for entering students, ESL program, services for LD students, advanced placement, accelerated degree program, self-designed majors, honors program, independent study, double major, summer session for credit, part-time degree program, adult/continuing education programs, co-op programs and internships. Off campus study at Greater Greensboro Consortium, Duke University, Bowman Gray School of Medicine at Wake Forest University. Study abroad program.

Entrance Requirements: Options: electronic application, early admission, early action, deferred admission, international baccalaureate accepted. Required: essay, high school transcript, minimum 2 high school GPA. Recommended: minimum 3 high school GPA, 2 recommendations, interview, SAT or ACT. Entrance: moderately difficult. Application deadlines: 2/15, 1/15 for early action. Notification: 4/1, 2/15 for early action. Preference given to Quakers. Transfer credits accepted: Yes. Applicants placed on waiting list: 0. Wait-listed applicants offered admission: 0.

Costs Per Year: Application fee: $25. Comprehensive fee: $41,270 includes full-time tuition ($32,090), mandatory fees ($380), and college room and board ($8800). Room and board charges vary according to board plan and housing facility.

Collegiate Environment: Orientation program. Drama-theater group, choral group, student-run newspaper, radio station. Social organizations: 45 open to all. Most popular organizations: student government, student radio station, student newspaper, Project Community, African-American Cultural Society. Major annual events: Family Weekend, Gender Bender, Serendipity. Student services: health clinic, personal-psychological counseling, women's center.

Campus security: 24-hour emergency response devices and patrols, student patrols, late night transport-escort service, controlled dormitory access. 1,043 college housing spaces available; 927 were occupied in 2012-13. Freshmen guaranteed college housing. On-campus residence required through junior year. Options: coed, men-only, women-only housing available. Hege Library with 256,465 books, 21,538 microform titles, 20,094 serials, 5,119 audiovisual materials, an OPAC, and a Web page. Operations spending for the previous fiscal year: $775,000. 275 computers available on campus for general student use. Computer purchase/lease plans available. A campuswide network can be accessed from student residence rooms and from off campus. Students can access the following: online class registration, network storage. Staffed computer lab on campus (open 24 hours a day) provides training in use of computers, software, and the Internet.
Community Environment: See Greensboro College.

■ **GUILFORD TECHNICAL COMMUNITY COLLEGE**
PO Box 309
Jamestown, NC 27282-0309
Tel: (336)334-4822
E-mail: jlcross@gtcc.edu
Web Site: www.gtcc.edu/
Description: State and locally supported, 2-year, coed. Part of North Carolina Community College System. Awards certificates, diplomas, transfer associate, and terminal associate degrees. Founded 1958. Setting: 158-acre urban campus with easy access to Raleigh, Charlotte, Greensboro. Educational spending for the previous fiscal year: $3393 per student. Total enrollment: 14,793. Faculty: 1,044 (396 full-time, 648 part-time). Student-undergrad faculty ratio is 24:1. 9,181 applied, 100% were admitted. Full-time: 7,903 students, 54% women, 46% men. Part-time: 6,890 students, 59% women, 41% men. Students come from 10 states and territories, 98 other countries, 0.1% from out-of-state. 1% American Indian or Alaska Native, non-Hispanic/Latino; 5% Hispanic/Latino; 46% African American, non-Hispanic/Latino; 3% Asian, non-Hispanic/Latino; 0.1% Native Hawaiian or other Pacific Islander, non-Hispanic/Latino; 1% international. 42% 25 or older, 9% transferred in. Retention: 52% of full-time freshmen returned the following year. Core. Calendar: semesters. Academic remediation for entering students, ESL program, services for LD students, advanced placement, self-designed majors, independent study, distance learning, double major, summer session for credit, part-time degree program, external degree program, adult/continuing education programs, co-op programs and internships. Off campus study at members of the Greater Greensboro Consortium. ROTC: Army (c), Air Force (c).
Entrance Requirements: Open admission except for health-related, aviation maintenance programs, automotive systems, and CCPI. Options: electronic application, early admission, deferred admission, international baccalaureate accepted. Required for some: high school transcript, interview. Entrance: noncompetitive. Application deadline: Rolling. Notification: continuous. Transfer credits accepted: Yes.
Costs Per Year: Application fee: $0. State resident tuition: $1656 full-time, $69 per credit hour part-time. Nonresident tuition: $6264 full-time, $261 per credit hour part-time. Mandatory fees: $167 full-time, $48.60 per term part-time. Full-time tuition and fees vary according to course load and program. Part-time tuition and fees vary according to course load and program.
Collegiate Environment: Orientation program. Drama-theater group. Social organizations: 44 open to all; national sororities, local fraternities; 1% of eligible men and 1% of eligible women are members. Most popular organizations: International Students Association, Steppin' N Style, Surgical Technology, Rotaract, Fellowship of Christian Athletes. Major annual events: Fun Friday at the Fountain, Coffee and Cocoa in the Cafeteria, Founder's Day. Student services: personal-psychological counseling. Campus security: 24-hour emergency response devices and patrols, late night transport-escort service. College housing not available. M. W. Bell Library plus 2 others with 113,818 books, 13,821 serials, 4,723 audiovisual materials, an OPAC, and a Web page. Operations spending for the previous fiscal year: $661,575. 130 computers available on campus for general student use. Computer purchase/lease plans available. A campuswide network can be accessed from off-campus. Students can access the following: online class registration. Staffed computer lab on campus provides training in use of computers, software, and the Internet.
Community Environment: Jamestown neighbors High Point and Greensboro. Primary businesses in Guilford County are textiles, furniture, and numerous other manufacturing concerns. Commercial transportation, one railroad, seven airlines, and recreational facilities are convenient in High Point and Greensboro.

■ **HALIFAX COMMUNITY COLLEGE**
PO Drawer 809
Weldon, NC 27890-0809
Tel: (252)536-4221
Fax: (252)536-4144
E-mail: washingtonj@halifaxcc.edu
Web Site: www.halifaxcc.edu/
Description: State and locally supported, 2-year, coed. Part of North Carolina Community College System. Awards certificates, diplomas, transfer associate, and terminal associate degrees. Founded 1967. Setting: 109-acre rural campus. Endowment: $1.1 million. Total enrollment: 1,142. 2% American Indian or Alaska Native, non-Hispanic/Latino; 2% Hispanic/Latino; 57% African American, non-Hispanic/Latino; 0.2% Asian, non-Hispanic/Latino; 0% Native Hawaiian or other Pacific Islander, non-Hispanic/Latino; 0% international. 53% 25 or older. Retention: 0% of full-time freshmen returned the following year. Core. Calendar: semesters. Academic remediation for entering students, summer session for credit, part-time degree program, adult/continuing education programs, co-op programs.
Entrance Requirements: Open admission. Option: deferred admission. Required: high school transcript. Entrance: noncompetitive. Application deadline: Rolling. Notification: continuous.
Costs Per Year: Application fee: $0. State resident tuition: $1,162 full-time, $69 per credit part-time. Nonresident tuition: $4,234 full-time, $261 per credit part-time.
Collegiate Environment: Campus security: 12-hour patrols by trained security personnel. College housing not available. Halifax Community College Library with 33,267 books, 37 microform titles, 101 serials, 2,195 audiovisual materials, an OPAC, and a Web page. 619 computers available on campus for general student use. A campuswide network can be accessed from off-campus. Students can access the following: online class registration. Staffed computer lab on campus.
Community Environment: Located in the northeastern section of North Carolina, Weldon is in a good agricultural area where the main industries are in textiles and paper goods. Community facilities include churches, a library, historical sites, shopping centers, and medical facilities nearby. There are three convenient lakes, with miles of shoreline, known as the Rockfish Capital of the world.

■ **HARRISON COLLEGE**
2001 Carrington Mill Blvd.
Morrisville, NC 27560
Tel: (800)919-5002
E-mail: Admissions@harrison.edu
Web Site: www.harrison.edu/
Description: Proprietary, 2-year, coed. Part of This campus is part of Harrison College, which has several campuses in Indiana and one in Ohio. Awards transfer associate and terminal associate degrees. Founded 2011. Setting: suburban campus with easy access to Raleigh, NC. Total enrollment: 192. Faculty: 19 (8 full-time, 11 part-time). Student-undergrad faculty ratio is 16:1. 46 applied, 100% were admitted. Full-time: 165 students, 48% women, 52% men. Part-time: 27 students, 56% women, 44% men. Students come from 2 states and territories, 1% from out-of-state. 0% American Indian or Alaska Native, non-Hispanic/Latino; 6% Hispanic/Latino; 49% African American, non-Hispanic/Latino; 1% Asian, non-Hispanic/Latino; 1% Native Hawaiian or other Pacific Islander, non-Hispanic/Latino. 65% 25 or older, 13% transferred in. Retention: 33% of full-time freshmen returned the following year. Advanced placement, distance learning, double major, summer session for credit, part-time degree program, adult/continuing education programs, co-op programs and internships. Off campus study.
Entrance Requirements: Option: electronic application. Required: high school transcript, interview, Wonderlic Scholastic Level Exam (SLE). Entrance: moderately difficult. Application deadlines: Rolling, Rolling for nonresidents. Notification: continuous, continuous for nonresidents. Transfer credits accepted: Yes.
Collegiate Environment: Orientation program. College housing not available.

■ **HAYWOOD COMMUNITY COLLEGE**
185 Freedlander Dr.
Clyde, NC 28721-9453
Tel: (828)627-2821
Fax: (828)627-4513
Web Site: www.haywood.edu/
Description: State and locally supported, 2-year, coed. Part of North

Carolina Community College System. Awards certificates, diplomas, transfer associate, and terminal associate degrees. Founded 1964. Setting: 85-acre rural campus. Total enrollment: 2,127. 39% 25 or older. Calendar: semesters. Academic remediation for entering students, ESL program, services for LD students, advanced placement, independent study, distance learning, double major, part-time degree program, adult/continuing education programs, co-op programs and internships.

Entrance Requirements: Open admission except for nursing, some technical programs. Required: high school transcript. Required for some: interview. Entrance: noncompetitive. Application deadline: Rolling.

Collegiate Environment: Student services: personal-psychological counseling. Campus security: 24-hour patrols. Freedlander Learning Resource Center with 26,788 books and 167 serials.

Community Environment: Haywood is a growing county of 47,000 people with an ever-expanding economy. Fine roads serve the county and new and expanding industry is experiencing a rapid increase. Agriculture is diversifying, and vegetable growing and truck farming share the market with cattle, corn, and tobacco. New and expanding tourist and recreational facilities are being developed. The county's proximity to the Great Smoky Mountains National Park and the world-famous Lake Junaluska Methodist Assembly Grounds make the area a natural tourist attraction. A large ski resort and the nearby lakes and forests have earned the area the distinction of being a winter and summer playground.

■ **HERITAGE BIBLE COLLEGE**
PO Box 1628
Dunn, NC 28335-1628
Tel: (910)892-3178; Free: 800-297-6351
Fax: (910)892-1809
E-mail: tnewton@heritagebiblecollege.edu
Web Site: www.heritagebiblecollege.edu/
Description: Independent Pentecostal Free Will Baptist, 4-year, coed. Awards associate and bachelor's degrees. Founded 1971. Setting: 82-acre small town campus with easy access to Raleigh-Durham. Endowment: $53,446. Educational spending for the previous fiscal year: $6240 per student. Total enrollment: 69. Faculty: 18 (4 full-time, 14 part-time). Student-undergrad faculty ratio is 20:1. Full-time: 34 students, 50% women, 50% men. Part-time: 35 students, 43% women, 57% men. Students come from 7 states and territories, 13% from out-of-state. 77% 25 or older, 13% live on campus, 13% transferred in. Retention: 52% of full-time freshmen returned the following year. Academic area with the most degrees conferred: theology and religious vocations. Core. Calendar: semesters. Academic remediation for entering students, independent study, summer session for credit, external degree program, adult/continuing education programs, internships. Off campus study.

Entrance Requirements: Open admission. Option: international baccalaureate accepted. Required: essay, high school transcript, medical history required for all, immunization record required for some. Required for some: interview. Entrance: minimally difficult. Application deadline: Rolling. Transfer credits accepted: Yes.

Costs Per Year: Application fee: $25. Comprehensive fee: $13,120 includes full-time tuition ($8400), mandatory fees ($720), and college room and board ($4000). College room only: $2700. Room and board charges vary according to board plan and housing facility. Part-time tuition: $280 per credit hour. Part-time mandatory fees: $30 per credit hour.

Collegiate Environment: Orientation program. Choral group. Social organizations: 3 open to all. Major annual event: Arby Carter Lectures. Campus security: controlled dormitory access. Alphin Ellis Learning Center with an OPAC. Operations spending for the previous fiscal year: $36,825. 25 computers available on campus for general student use. A campuswide network can be accessed from student residence rooms and from off campus. Students can access the following: online class registration. Staffed computer lab on campus provides training in use of computers, software, and the Internet.

■ **HIGH POINT UNIVERSITY**
University Station, Montlieu Ave.
High Point, NC 27262-3598
Tel: (336)841-9000; Free: 800-345-6993
Fax: (336)841-5123
E-mail: jmcilrat@highpoint.edu
Web Site: www.highpoint.edu/
Description: Independent United Methodist, comprehensive, coed. Awards bachelor's, master's, and doctoral degrees. Founded 1924. Setting: 320-

acre suburban campus with easy access to Charlotte. Endowment: $36.4 million. Educational spending for the previous fiscal year: $8373 per student. Total enrollment: 4,263. Faculty: 338 (230 full-time, 108 part-time). Student-undergrad faculty ratio is 15:1. 7,663 applied, 64% were admitted. 19% from top 10% of their high school class, 46% from top quarter, 77% from top half. 2 National Merit Scholars, 9 class presidents, 10 valedictorians, 165 student government officers. Full-time: 3,996 students, 59% women, 41% men. Part-time: 74 students, 57% women, 43% men. Students come from 46 states and territories, 29 other countries, 74% from out-of-state. 2% American Indian or Alaska Native, non-Hispanic/Latino; 2% Hispanic/Latino; 6% African American, non-Hispanic/Latino; 1% Asian, non-Hispanic/Latino; 0.02% Native Hawaiian or other Pacific Islander, non-Hispanic/Latino; 1% international. 4% 25 or older, 93% live on campus, 1% transferred in. Retention: 75% of full-time freshmen returned the following year. Academic areas with the most degrees conferred: business/marketing; communication/journalism; visual and performing arts; education. Core. Calendar: semesters. Academic remediation for entering students, ESL program, services for LD students, advanced placement, accelerated degree program, self-designed majors, honors program, independent study, double major, summer session for credit, co-op programs and internships. Off campus study at 7 members of the Greater Greensboro Consortium. Study abroad program. ROTC: Army (c), Air Force (c).

Entrance Requirements: Options: electronic application, early decision, early action, deferred admission, international baccalaureate accepted. Required: high school transcript, minimum 2 high school GPA, 2 recommendations, SAT or ACT. Recommended: essay, minimum 3 high school GPA, interview. Entrance: moderately difficult. Application deadlines: 8/15, 11/1 for early decision, 11/8 for early action. Notification: continuous until 8/15, 11/23 for early decision, 12/9 for early action. SAT Reasoning Test deadline: 8/1. Transfer credits accepted: Yes. Applicants placed on waiting list: 304. Wait-listed applicants offered admission: 81. Early decision applicants: 408. Early decision applicants admitted: 359. Early action applicants: 3,761. Early action applicants admitted: 3,348.

Costs Per Year: Application fee: $50. Comprehensive fee: $39,800. Part-time tuition: $800 per credit hour. Part-time tuition varies according to course load and reciprocity agreements. Tuition: $800 per credit hour part-time. Part-time tuition varies according to course load and reciprocity agreements.

Collegiate Environment: Orientation program. Drama-theater group, choral group, student-run newspaper, radio station. Social organizations: 109 open to all; national fraternities, national sororities, local fraternities, local sororities; 15% of eligible men and 25% of eligible women are members. Most popular organizations: student government, Habitat for Humanity, International Club, Student Activities Board, Honors Club. Major annual events: Homecoming, Family Weekend, Pantherpalooza. Student services: health clinic, personal-psychological counseling. Campus security: 24-hour emergency response devices and patrols, student patrols, late night transport-escort service, controlled dormitory access. 3,148 college housing spaces available; 2,997 were occupied in 2012-13. Freshmen guaranteed college housing. On-campus residence required through sophomore year. Options: coed, men-only, women-only housing available. Smith Library with 288,473 books, 84,000 microform titles, 34,000 serials, 12,500 audiovisual materials, an OPAC, and a Web page. Operations spending for the previous fiscal year: $1.2 million. 1,100 computers available on campus for general student use. Computer purchase/lease plans available. A campuswide network can be accessed from student residence rooms and from off campus. Students can access the following: online class registration. Staffed computer lab on campus provides training in use of computers, software, and the Internet.

Community Environment: The city's name arose from the fact that the community was the highest point, on the original survey, for the old North Carolina Railroad between Goldsboro and Charlotte. Numerous diversified industries, including many furniture manufacturing plants and hosiery mills, are in High Point, the wood furniture manufacturing and hosiery production capital of the world. Parks, golf courses, and a lake provide the facilities for recreation.

■ **ISOTHERMAL COMMUNITY COLLEGE**
PO Box 804
Spindale, NC 28160-0804
Tel: (828)286-3636
Fax: (828)286-8109
E-mail: vsearcy@isothermal.edu
Web Site: www.isothermal.edu/
Description: State-supported, 2-year, coed. Part of North Carolina Com-

munity College System. Awards certificates, diplomas, transfer associate, and terminal associate degrees. Founded 1965. Setting: 120-acre rural campus. Total enrollment: 2,005. Faculty: 114 (60 full-time, 54 part-time). Student-undergrad faculty ratio is 17:1. Full-time: 988 students, 64% women, 36% men. Part-time: 1,017 students, 65% women, 35% men. Students come from 40 states and territories, 3 other countries. 49% 25 or older. Retention: 33% of full-time freshmen returned the following year. Core. Calendar: semesters. Academic remediation for entering students, ESL program, services for LD students, advanced placement, self-designed majors, honors program, summer session for credit, part-time degree program, external degree program, adult/continuing education programs, co-op programs.

Entrance Requirements: Open admission. Options: early admission, deferred admission. Required: high school transcript, placement test. Entrance: noncompetitive. Application deadline: Rolling. Notification: continuous.

Collegiate Environment: Orientation program. Choral group, student-run newspaper, radio station. Student services: personal-psychological counseling. 35,200 books, 289 serials, an OPAC, and a Web page.

Community Environment: Spindale is located 20 miles from Shelby, 28 miles from Hendersonville, and 35 miles from Asheville.

■ **ITT TECHNICAL INSTITUTE (CARY)**
5520 Dillard Dr.
Ste. 100
Cary, NC 27518
Tel: (919)233-2520; Free: 877-203-5533
Web Site: www.itt-tech.edu/
Description: Proprietary, primarily 2-year, coed. Part of ITT Educational Services, Inc. Awards terminal associate and bachelor's degrees.
Entrance Requirements: Entrance: minimally difficult.

■ **ITT TECHNICAL INSTITUTE (CHARLOTTE)**
4135 Southstream Blvd.
Ste. 200
Charlotte, NC 28217
Tel: (704)423-3100; Free: 800-488-0173
Web Site: www.itt-tech.edu/
Description: Proprietary, primarily 2-year, coed. Awards terminal associate and bachelor's degrees.
Entrance Requirements: Entrance: minimally difficult.

■ **ITT TECHNICAL INSTITUTE (CHARLOTTE)**
10926 David Taylor Dr.
Ste. 100
Charlotte, NC 28262
Tel: (704)548-2300; Free: 877-243-7685
Web Site: www.itt-tech.edu/
Description: Proprietary, 4-year, coed. Part of ITT Educational Services, Inc. Awards associate and bachelor's degrees.
Entrance Requirements: Entrance: minimally difficult.

■ **ITT TECHNICAL INSTITUTE (DURHAM)**
3518 Westgate Dr.
Ste. 150
Durham, NC 27707
Tel: (919)401-1400; Free: 877-452-8662
Web Site: www.itt-tech.edu/
Description: Proprietary, 4-year, coed. Awards associate and bachelor's degrees.
Entrance Requirements: Entrance: minimally difficult.

■ **ITT TECHNICAL INSTITUTE (HIGH POINT)**
4050 Piedmont Pky.
Ste. 110
High Point, NC 27265
Tel: (336)819-5900; Free: 877-536-5231
Web Site: www.itt-tech.edu/
Description: Proprietary, primarily 2-year, coed. Part of ITT Educational Services, Inc. Awards terminal associate and bachelor's degrees. Founded 2007.
Entrance Requirements: Entrance: minimally difficult.

■ **JAMES SPRUNT COMMUNITY COLLEGE**
PO Box 398
Kenansville, NC 28349-0398
Tel: (910)296-2400
Fax: (910)296-1222
E-mail: lmatthews@jamessprunt.edu
Web Site: www.jamessprunt.edu/
Description: State-supported, 2-year, coed. Part of North Carolina Community College System. Awards certificates, diplomas, transfer associate, and terminal associate degrees. Founded 1964. Setting: 51-acre rural campus. Endowment: $1.1 million. Educational spending for the previous fiscal year: $2854 per student. Total enrollment: 1,572. Faculty: 128 (60 full-time, 68 part-time). Student-undergrad faculty ratio is 14:1. 585 applied, 50% were admitted. Full-time: 869 students, 75% women, 25% men. Part-time: 703 students, 72% women, 28% men. Students come from 3 states and territories, 1% from out-of-state. 0.4% American Indian or Alaska Native, non-Hispanic/Latino; 9% Hispanic/Latino; 38% African American, non-Hispanic/Latino; 0.2% Asian, non-Hispanic/Latino; 0.1% Native Hawaiian or other Pacific Islander, non-Hispanic/Latino. 49% 25 or older, 13% transferred in. Core. Calendar: semesters. Academic remediation for entering students, ESL program, services for LD students, advanced placement, accelerated degree program, independent study, distance learning, double major, summer session for credit, part-time degree program, co-op programs and internships.
Entrance Requirements: Open admission except for allied health programs. Option: electronic application. Required: high school transcript. Entrance: noncompetitive. Application deadline: Rolling. Notification: continuous. Transfer credits accepted: Yes.
Costs Per Year: Application fee: $0. State resident tuition: $2208 full-time, $69 per semester hour part-time. Nonresident tuition: $8352 full-time, $261 per semester hour part-time. Mandatory fees: $70 full-time, $35 per term part-time. Full-time tuition and fees vary according to course load. Part-time tuition and fees vary according to course load.
Collegiate Environment: Orientation program. Student-run newspaper. Social organizations: 5 open to all; national sororities, local sororities; 1% of women are members. Most popular organizations: Student Nurses Association, Art Club, Alumni Association, National Technical-Vocational Honor Society, Phi Theta Kappa. Major annual events: Christmas Dance/Coronation, Spring Fling, Fall Festival. Student services: personal-psychological counseling. Campus security: day, evening and Saturday trained security personnel. College housing not available. James Sprunt Community College Library with 25,268 books, 92 serials, 200 audiovisual materials, an OPAC, and a Web page. Operations spending for the previous fiscal year: $166,034. 575 computers available on campus for general student use. A campuswide network can be accessed. Students can access the following: online class registration, Online financial aid information. Staffed computer lab on campus provides training in use of computers, software, and the Internet.
Community Environment: Located 40 miles from the principal city of Goldsboro and 4 miles from Interstate 40, Kenansville is a rural community with three churches, a library, and good shopping areas for this size community. The primary businesses of the area are farming, textiles, poultry, and swine production. Good fishing and hunting are available in the area.

■ **JOHNSON C. SMITH UNIVERSITY**
100 Beatties Ford Rd.
Charlotte, NC 28216-5398
Tel: (704)378-1000; Free: 800-782-7303
E-mail: churd@jcsu.edu
Web Site: www.jcsu.edu/
Description: Independent, 4-year, coed. Awards bachelor's degrees. Founded 1867. Setting: 100-acre urban campus with easy access to Atlanta. Endowment: $50.3 million. Research spending for the previous fiscal year: $844,558. Educational spending for the previous fiscal year: $6957 per student. Total enrollment: 1,669. Faculty: 159 (104 full-time, 55 part-time). Student-undergrad faculty ratio is 13:1. 5,064 applied, 38% were admitted. 12% from top 10% of their high school class, 32% from top quarter, 68% from top half. Full-time: 1,606 students, 61% women, 39% men. Part-time: 63 students, 67% women, 33% men. Students come from 34 states and territories, 8 other countries, 48% from out-of-state. 0.1% American Indian or Alaska Native, non-Hispanic/Latino; 5% Hispanic/Latino; 74% African American, non-Hispanic/Latino; 0.4% Asian, non-Hispanic/Latino; 0.1% Native Hawaiian or other Pacific Islander, non-Hispanic/Latino; 3% international. 15% 25 or older, 61% live on campus, 8% transferred in. Retention: 72% of

full-time freshmen returned the following year. Academic areas with the most degrees conferred: business/marketing; social sciences; communication/journalism. Core. Calendar: semesters. Services for LD students, advanced placement, self-designed majors, honors program, independent study, double major, summer session for credit, part-time degree program, adult/continuing education programs, co-op programs and internships. Off campus study at other participating institutions in the Charlotte Area Educational Consortium (CAEC). Study abroad program. ROTC: Army, Air Force (c).

Entrance Requirements: Options: electronic application, early admission, deferred admission, international baccalaureate accepted. Required: high school transcript, SAT or ACT. Recommended: essay, 2 recommendations. Entrance: moderately difficult. Notification: continuous, continuous for nonresidents. Transfer credits accepted: Yes.

Costs Per Year: Application fee: $25. Comprehensive fee: $25,336 includes full-time tuition ($15,466), mandatory fees ($2770), and college room and board ($7100). College room only: $4086. Full-time tuition and fees vary according to course load. Room and board charges vary according to board plan and housing facility. Part-time tuition: $418 per credit hour. Part-time mandatory fees: $292 per term. Part-time tuition and fees vary according to course load.

Collegiate Environment: Orientation program. Drama-theater group, choral group, marching band, student-run newspaper. Social organizations: 50 open to all; national fraternities, national sororities; 5% of eligible men and 4% of eligible women are members. Most popular organizations: International Club, Math Club, Karibbean Vybz, Student Orientation Leaders, Unparalleled Production Evolution. Major annual events: Homecoming, Bullfest Spring Festival, Student Government Association Elections. Student services: health clinic, personal-psychological counseling. Campus security: 24-hour emergency response devices and patrols, late night transport-escort service, controlled dormitory access. 1,316 college housing spaces available; 1,016 were occupied in 2012-13. Freshmen guaranteed college housing. On-campus residence required in freshman year. Options: coed, men-only, women-only housing available. James B. Duke Library with 139,812 books, 4,068 microform titles, 289 serials, 1,471 audiovisual materials, an OPAC, and a Web page. Operations spending for the previous fiscal year: $729,620. 293 computers available on campus for general student use. Computer purchase/lease plans available. A campuswide network can be accessed from student residence rooms and from off campus. Students can access the following: online class registration. Staffed computer lab on campus provides training in use of computers, software, and the Internet.

Community Environment: Charlotte, the largest city of the Carolinas, with a population of more than 610,000, is a commercial and cultural center of the South. The city has tall buildings, huge warehouses, and numerous factories, but the residential sections are extensively gardened and beautifully landscaped. The area is rich in historical landmarks. Charlotte offers all the cultural and recreational facilities of any large city, including sports events, excellent shopping and dining facilities, rock and classical music, concerts, theater, and art. The area is served by Southern Railway and five major airlines. Major highways provide easy access to nearby beaches and mountains.

■ JOHNSON & WALES UNIVERSITY - CHARLOTTE CAMPUS
801 W Trade St.
Charlotte, NC 28202
Tel: (980)598-1000; Free: 866-598-2427
E-mail: clt@admissions.jwu.edu
Web Site: www.jwu.edu/charlotte/
Description: Independent, 4-year, coed. Awards associate and bachelor's degrees. Founded 2004. Total enrollment: 2,587. Faculty: 110 (88 full-time, 22 part-time). Student-undergrad faculty ratio is 27:1. 7,207 applied, 60% were admitted. Full-time: 2,536 students, 58% women, 42% men. Part-time: 51 students, 61% women, 39% men. 66% from out-of-state. 0.3% American Indian or Alaska Native, non-Hispanic/Latino; 4% Hispanic/Latino; 20% African American, non-Hispanic/Latino; 1% Asian, non-Hispanic/Latino; 0.04% Native Hawaiian or other Pacific Islander, non-Hispanic/Latino; 2% international. 10% 25 or older, 48% live on campus, 9% transferred in. Retention: 75% of full-time freshmen returned the following year. Academic areas with the most degrees conferred: family and consumer sciences; business/marketing; parks and recreation. Core. ESL program, services for LD students, advanced placement, accelerated degree program, honors program, independent study, part-time degree program, co-op programs and internships. Study abroad program.
Entrance Requirements: Options: electronic application, early admission, deferred admission. Required: high school transcript. Recommended:

minimum 2 high school GPA. Required for some: interview, SAT or ACT. Entrance: moderately difficult. Application deadline: Rolling. Notification: continuous.
Collegiate Environment: Orientation program. Student-run newspaper. Student services: health clinic, personal-psychological counseling. Campus security: 24-hour emergency response devices and patrols, late night transport-escort service, controlled dormitory access. Johnson & Wales University with an OPAC and a Web page.

■ JOHNSTON COMMUNITY COLLEGE
PO Box 2350
Smithfield, NC 27577-2350
Tel: (919)934-3051
Fax: (919)934-2150
E-mail: pjharrell@johnstoncc.edu
Web Site: www.johnstoncc.edu/
Description: State-supported, 2-year, coed. Part of North Carolina Community College System. Awards certificates, diplomas, transfer associate, and terminal associate degrees. Founded 1969. Setting: 100-acre rural campus. Educational spending for the previous fiscal year: $3284 per student. Total enrollment: 4,216. Faculty: 385 (144 full-time, 241 part-time). Student-undergrad faculty ratio is 14:1. Full-time: 2,075 students, 63% women, 37% men. Part-time: 2,141 students, 69% women, 31% men. 0.5% American Indian or Alaska Native, non-Hispanic/Latino; 7% Hispanic/Latino; 21% African American, non-Hispanic/Latino; 0.2% Asian, non-Hispanic/Latino; 0.2% Native Hawaiian or other Pacific Islander, non-Hispanic/Latino; 1% international. 45% 25 or older. Calendar: semesters. Academic remediation for entering students, services for LD students, advanced placement, honors program, independent study, distance learning, double major, summer session for credit, part-time degree program, adult/continuing education programs, co-op programs.
Entrance Requirements: Open admission except for health sciences programs. Options: electronic application, international baccalaureate accepted. Required: high school transcript, interview, ACCUPLACER. Recommended: SAT or ACT. Entrance: noncompetitive. Application deadline: Rolling. Notification: continuous.
Costs Per Year: Application fee: $0. State resident tuition: $2208 full-time. Nonresident tuition: $8352 full-time. Mandatory fees: $32 full-time. College room and board: $3683.
Collegiate Environment: Choral group. Major annual events: Fall Festival, Spring Fling. Student services: personal-psychological counseling. Campus security: 24-hour patrols. College housing not available. Johnston Community College Library plus 1 other with 36,889 books, 156 serials, 5,624 audiovisual materials, an OPAC, and a Web page. Operations spending for the previous fiscal year: $356,669. 186 computers available on campus for general student use. Students can access the following: online class registration. Staffed computer lab on campus provides training in use of computers.

■ KAPLAN COLLEGE, CHARLOTTE CAMPUS
6070 E Independence Blvd.
Charlotte, NC 28212
Tel: (704)567-3700
Web Site: charlotte.kaplancollege.com/
Description: Proprietary, 2-year, coed. Awards diplomas and terminal associate degrees.

■ KING'S COLLEGE
322 Lamar Ave.
Charlotte, NC 28204-2436
Tel: (704)372-0266; Free: 800-768-2255
Fax: (704)348-2029
Web Site: www.kingscollegecharlotte.edu/
Description: Private, 2-year, coed. Awards diplomas and terminal associate degrees. Founded 1901. Setting: suburban campus. Total enrollment: 529. 1,157 applied, 77% were admitted. Accelerated degree program, internships.

■ LAUREL UNIVERSITY
2314 N Centennial St.
High Point, NC 27265-3197
Tel: (336)889-2262; Free: 855-LaurelU
E-mail: admissions@laureluniversity.edu
Web Site: www.laureluniversity.edu/
Description: Independent interdenominational, comprehensive, coed.

Awards associate, bachelor's, master's, and doctoral degrees. Founded 1932. Setting: 24-acre urban campus. Educational spending for the previous fiscal year: $1500 per student. Total enrollment: 353. Faculty: 37 (3 full-time, 34 part-time). Student-undergrad faculty ratio is 10:1. 161 applied, 39% were admitted. Full-time: 142 students, 51% women, 49% men. Part-time: 136 students, 38% women, 63% men. Students come from 17 states and territories, 12% from out-of-state. 0.3% American Indian or Alaska Native, non-Hispanic/Latino; 1% Hispanic/Latino; 22% African American, non-Hispanic/Latino; 0% Asian, non-Hispanic/Latino; 0% Native Hawaiian or other Pacific Islander, non-Hispanic/Latino; 0% international. 80% 25 or older, 11% transferred in. Retention: 63% of full-time freshmen returned the following year. Academic areas with the most degrees conferred: theology and religious vocations; business/marketing. Core. Calendar: semesters. Academic remediation for entering students, advanced placement, independent study, distance learning, double major, summer session for credit, part-time degree program, adult/continuing education programs, internships. Off campus study at High Point University.

Entrance Requirements: Options: electronic application, early admission, deferred admission. Required: high school transcript, 2 recommendations, interview. Recommended: minimum 2 high school GPA. Required for some: College Board ACCUPLACER Test for English. Entrance: minimally difficult. Application deadline: 8/1. Notification: 8/10.

Collegiate Environment: Orientation program. Most popular organizations: student government, Travel Team, Praise Band. Major annual events: Thanksgiving Banquet, Christmas Banquet, Valentine's Banquet. 48 college housing spaces available; 32 were occupied in 2012-13. No special consideration for freshman housing applicants. Options: men-only, women-only housing available. Temple Library with 37,905 books, 217 serials, an OPAC, and a Web page. Operations spending for the previous fiscal year: $58,989. 7 computers available on campus for general student use. Students can access the following: online class registration. Staffed computer lab on campus.

Community Environment: See High Point University.

■ LEES-MCRAE COLLEGE

PO Box 128
Banner Elk, NC 28604
Tel: (828)898-5241; Free: 800-280-4562
Fax: (828)898-8814
E-mail: admissions@lmc.edu
Web Site: www.lmc.edu/

Description: Independent, 4-year, coed, affiliated with Presbyterian Church (U.S.A.). Awards bachelor's degrees. Founded 1900. Setting: 460-acre rural campus. Total enrollment: 837. Faculty: 88 (43 full-time, 45 part-time). Student-undergrad faculty ratio is 14:1. 1,266 applied, 68% were admitted. 5% from top 10% of their high school class, 21% from top quarter, 54% from top half. Full-time: 830 students, 59% women, 41% men. Part-time: 7 students, 86% women, 14% men. Students come from 39 states and territories, 11 other countries, 32% from out-of-state. 0% American Indian or Alaska Native, non-Hispanic/Latino; 0.5% Hispanic/Latino; 2% African American, non-Hispanic/Latino; 0.1% Asian, non-Hispanic/Latino; 0% Native Hawaiian or other Pacific Islander, non-Hispanic/Latino; 3% international. 22% 25 or older, 63% live on campus, 20% transferred in. Retention: 55% of full-time freshmen returned the following year. Academic areas with the most degrees conferred: education; health professions and related sciences; business/marketing. Core. Calendar: semesters. Academic remediation for entering students, services for LD students, advanced placement, accelerated degree program, honors program, independent study, double major, summer session for credit, part-time degree program, adult/continuing education programs, co-op programs and internships. Off campus study. Study abroad program.

Entrance Requirements: Options: electronic application, early action, international baccalaureate accepted. Required: high school transcript, minimum 2 high school GPA. Required for some: essay, interview, SAT or ACT, Test-optional admission for majority of students. Prospective intercollegiate athletes and Honors Program students are required to submit SAT or ACT scores. Entrance: minimally difficult. Application deadlines: Rolling, Rolling for nonresidents. Notification: continuous, continuous for nonresidents. Transfer credits accepted: Yes.

Costs Per Year: Application fee: $35. Comprehensive fee: $32,950 includes full-time tuition ($23,950), mandatory fees ($500), and college room and board ($8500). Full-time tuition and fees vary according to course load, location, and reciprocity agreements. Room and board charges vary according to housing facility. Part-time tuition: $650 per credit hour. Part-time mandatory

fees: $650 per credit hour. Part-time tuition and fees vary according to course load, location, and reciprocity agreements.

Collegiate Environment: Orientation program. Drama-theater group, choral group. Social organizations: 26 open to all; Service Fraternities and Sororities. Most popular organizations: Student Government Association, Order of the Tower. Major annual event: Mountain Day. Student services: health clinic, personal-psychological counseling. Campus security: 24-hour patrols. 680 college housing spaces available; 527 were occupied in 2012-13. Freshmen guaranteed college housing. Options: coed, men-only, women-only housing available. James H. Carson Library plus 1 other with 215,937 books, 7,194 microform titles, 22,091 serials, 1,485 audiovisual materials, an OPAC, and a Web page.

Community Environment: Banner Elk is in the Blue Ridge Mountains of Western North Carolina, 100 miles from Charlotte and 83 miles northeast of Asheville. Elk River is nearby for trout fishing, and during the winter there is sufficient snow for outdoor winter sports.

■ LENOIR COMMUNITY COLLEGE

PO Box 188
Kinston, NC 28502-0188
Tel: (252)527-6223
E-mail: krhill01@lenoircc.edu
Web Site: www.lenoircc.edu/

Description: State-supported, 2-year, coed. Part of North Carolina Community College System. Awards certificates, diplomas, transfer associate, and terminal associate degrees. Founded 1960. Setting: 86-acre small town campus. Total enrollment: 2,983. Faculty: 345 (95 full-time, 250 part-time). Student-undergrad faculty ratio is 10:1. Full-time: 1,274 students, 59% women, 41% men. Part-time: 1,709 students, 63% women, 37% men. 2% from out-of-state. 0.5% American Indian or Alaska Native, non-Hispanic/Latino; 7% Hispanic/Latino; 35% African American, non-Hispanic/Latino; 1% Asian, non-Hispanic/Latino; 0.1% Native Hawaiian or other Pacific Islander, non-Hispanic/Latino; 0.1% international. 37% 25 or older, 19% transferred in. Core. Calendar: semesters. Academic remediation for entering students, ESL program, advanced placement, distance learning, summer session for credit, part-time degree program, adult/continuing education programs, co-op programs.

Entrance Requirements: Open admission except for allied health programs. Option: early admission. Required: high school transcript. Entrance: noncompetitive. Application deadline: Rolling. Notification: continuous. Transfer credits accepted: Yes.

Collegiate Environment: Orientation program. Choral group, student-run newspaper. Social organizations: 19 open to all. Most popular organizations: Student Government Association, Automotive Club, Electronics Club, Drafting Club, Cosmetology Club. Major annual events: Fall Festival, Spring Joust, Fall Get-Together. Student services: personal-psychological counseling. Campus security: 24-hour emergency response devices and patrols, student patrols. College housing not available. Learning Resources Center plus 1 other with 55,053 books and 381 serials. 116 computers available on campus for general student use. Students can access the following: online class registration. Staffed computer lab on campus.

Community Environment: Kinston is an important bright-leaf tobacco market as well as a grain and livestock producing region. Commercial transportation is convenient. The community facilities include a library with branches, churches representing 25 denominations, a museum, little theatre, arts council, hospitals, good shopping areas, and various civic and service organizations. Good part-time employment opportunities are available for students. Parks, swimming pools, and golf courses provide the recreational facilities for the community.

■ LENOIR-RHYNE UNIVERSITY

625 7th Ave. NE
Hickory, NC 28601
Tel: (828)328-1741; Free: 800-277-5721
Fax: (828)328-7338
E-mail: admission@lr.edu
Web Site: www.lr.edu/

Description: Independent Lutheran, comprehensive, coed. Awards bachelor's and master's degrees. Founded 1891. Setting: small town campus. Total enrollment: 1,860. Faculty: 178 (92 full-time, 86 part-time). Student-undergrad faculty ratio is 14:1. 3,336 applied, 87% were admitted. 18% from top 10% of their high school class, 46% from top quarter, 82% from top half. Full-time: 1,463 students, 61% women, 39% men. Part-time: 132 students, 68% women, 32% men. 18% from out-of-state. 1% American

Indian or Alaska Native, non-Hispanic/Latino; 8% Hispanic/Latino; 28% African American, non-Hispanic/Latino; 1% Asian, non-Hispanic/Latino; 0.4% Native Hawaiian or other Pacific Islander, non-Hispanic/Latino; 4% international. 9% 25 or older, 56% live on campus, 6% transferred in. Retention: 65% of full-time freshmen returned the following year. Academic areas with the most degrees conferred: health professions and related sciences; business/marketing; education. Calendar: semesters. Part-time degree program, adult/continuing education programs. ROTC: Army (c), Air Force (c).

Entrance Requirements: Options: early admission, early action, deferred admission, international baccalaureate accepted. Required: high school transcript, minimum 2.5 high school GPA, SAT or ACT. Recommended: interview. Entrance: moderately difficult. Application deadlines: 8/1, 8/15 for early action. Notification: continuous. SAT Reasoning Test deadline: 8/1.

Costs Per Year: Application fee: $35. Comprehensive fee: $37,514 includes full-time tuition ($27,718) and college room and board ($9796). Part-time tuition: $1100 per credit hour. Part-time tuition varies according to class time.

Collegiate Environment: Campus security: 24-hour emergency response devices and patrols, late night transport-escort service, controlled dormitory access.

Community Environment: Hickory, located in the western Piedmont section, is best known as one of North Carolina's major furniture manufacturing cities. All forms of commercial transportation are available. The community facilities include hospitals, numerous churches, a museum of art, a city library, and various civic and service organizations. Nearby, Lake Hickory offers many recreational opportunities such as boating, fishing, and swimming, golf, and minor league baseball. Hickory is located 50 miles NW of Charlotte and just 40 miles from the Blue Ridge Mountains.

■ **LIVING ARTS COLLEGE**
3000 Wakefield Crossing Dr.
Raleigh, NC 27614
Tel: (919)488-8500; Free: 800-288-7442
E-mail: jwenta@living-arts-college.edu
Web Site: www.higherdigital.com/
Description: Proprietary, primarily 2-year, coed. Awards certificates, diplomas, terminal associate, and bachelor's degrees. Founded 1992. Setting: suburban campus with easy access to Raleigh, NC. Total enrollment: 578. Faculty: 30 (19 full-time, 11 part-time). Student-undergrad faculty ratio is 12:1. 158 applied, 100% were admitted. Full-time: 578 students, 57% women, 43% men. Students come from 5 states and territories, 2 other countries, 3% from out-of-state. 0.3% American Indian or Alaska Native, non-Hispanic/Latino; 5% Hispanic/Latino; 54% African American, non-Hispanic/Latino; 1% Asian, non-Hispanic/Latino; 0% Native Hawaiian or other Pacific Islander, non-Hispanic/Latino; 0% international. 25% 25 or older, 35% live on campus, 0% transferred in. Core. Co-op programs.

Entrance Requirements: Options: early admission, early decision, early action, deferred admission. Required: essay, high school transcript, interview, Portfolio for selected program, Wonderlic aptitude test. Entrance: moderately difficult. Application deadlines: Rolling, Rolling for nonresidents. Notification: continuous, continuous for nonresidents.

Costs Per Year: Application fee: $25. One-time mandatory fee: $275. Tuition: $23,968 full-time. College room only: $7100. Tuition guaranteed not to increase for student's term of enrollment.

Collegiate Environment: Orientation program. Social organizations: 4 open to all. Most popular organizations: MODIV - student council, Student Ambassadors, Firebreathers Animation Studio, NVTHS-National Vocational Technical Honor Society. Major annual events: Career Fair, Student Advising Day/Professional Development, Student Talent Show. Campus security: controlled dormitory access. 78 college housing spaces available; all were occupied in 2012-13. Freshmen given priority for college housing. 320 computers available on campus for general student use. A campuswide network can be accessed. Staffed computer lab on campus provides training in use of computers, software, and the Internet.

■ **LIVINGSTONE COLLEGE**
701 W Monroe St.
Salisbury, NC 28144-5298
Tel: (704)216-6000; Free: 800-835-3435
Fax: (704)216-6217
E-mail: admissions@livingstone.edu
Web Site: www.livingstone.edu/
Description: Independent, 4-year, coed, affiliated with African Methodist Episcopal Zion Church. Awards bachelor's degrees. Founded 1879. Setting:

45-acre small town campus. Endowment: $1.1 million. Educational spending for the previous fiscal year: $5782 per student. Total enrollment: 960. Faculty: 73 (51 full-time, 22 part-time). Student-undergrad faculty ratio is 16:1. 2,093 applied, 98% were admitted. 0.3% from top 10% of their high school class, 3% from top quarter, 15% from top half. Full-time: 947 students, 44% women, 56% men. Part-time: 13 students, 38% women, 62% men. Students come from 34 states and territories, 3 other countries, 43% from out-of-state. 11% 25 or older, 60% live on campus. Academic areas with the most degrees conferred: business/marketing; homeland security, law enforcement, firefighting, and protective services; social sciences. Core. Calendar: semesters. Academic remediation for entering students, advanced placement, honors program, double major, part-time degree program, adult/continuing education programs, co-op programs and internships. ROTC: Army (c).

Entrance Requirements: Options: deferred admission, international baccalaureate accepted. Required: high school transcript, minimum 2.0 high school GPA, SAT or ACT. Entrance: minimally difficult. Application deadline: Rolling. Notification: continuous.

Collegiate Environment: Orientation program. Drama-theater group, choral group, marching band. Social organizations: 35 open to all; national fraternities, national sororities; 25% of eligible men and 30% of eligible women are members. Most popular organizations: Greek Organizations, Modeling Troups, choirs, band, Rotary and Optimist Clubs (Community). Major annual events: Homecoming, Greek Week, Bear Fest (Spring Fling). Student services: health clinic, personal-psychological counseling. Campus security: 24-hour emergency response devices and patrols, late night transport-escort service, controlled dormitory access. Carnegie Library plus 2 others with 75,000 books, 43,400 microform titles, and 135 serials. Operations spending for the previous fiscal year: $176,537. 100 computers available on campus for general student use. A campuswide network can be accessed from student residence rooms. Staffed computer lab on campus provides training in use of computers, software, and the Internet.

Community Environment: See Catawba College.

■ **LOUISBURG COLLEGE**
501 N Main St.
Louisburg, NC 27549-2399
Tel: (919)496-2521; Free: 800-775-0208
Fax: (919)496-1788
E-mail: admissions@louisburg.edu
Web Site: www.louisburg.edu/
Description: Independent United Methodist, 2-year, coed. Awards transfer associate and terminal associate degrees. Founded 1787. Setting: 75-acre small town campus with easy access to Raleigh. Endowment: $9.7 million. Research spending for the previous fiscal year: $20,300. Educational spending for the previous fiscal year: $4329 per student. Total enrollment: 730. Faculty: 83 (45 full-time, 38 part-time). Student-undergrad faculty ratio is 13:1. 1,099 applied, 62% were admitted. 2% from top 10% of their high school class, 5% from top quarter, 19% from top half. Full-time: 717 students, 38% women, 62% men. Part-time: 13 students, 38% women, 62% men. Students come from 22 states and territories, 4 other countries, 34% from out-of-state. 4% 25 or older, 90% live on campus, 7% transferred in. Retention: 76% of full-time freshmen returned the following year. Core. Calendar: semesters. Academic remediation for entering students, services for LD students, advanced placement, accelerated degree program, self-designed majors, freshman honors college, honors program, independent study, distance learning, double major, part-time degree program, adult/continuing education programs. Off campus study.

Entrance Requirements: Option: deferred admission. Required: high school transcript, SAT or ACT. Required for some: interview. Entrance: minimally difficult. Application deadline: Rolling. Notification: continuous.

Collegiate Environment: Orientation program. Drama-theater group, choral group, student-run newspaper, radio station. Social organizations: 12 open to all. Most popular organizations: Student Government Association, Workers Actively Volunteering Energetic Services, Drama Club, Christian Life Council, Ecological Concerns Club. Major annual events: Homecoming, Mud-Volleyball, Spring Dance. Student services: health clinic, personal-psychological counseling. Campus security: 24-hour emergency response devices and patrols, late night transport-escort service, controlled dormitory access. Robbins Library with 60,000 books, 180 serials, 5 audiovisual materials, an OPAC, and a Web page. Operations spending for the previous fiscal year: $148,590. 30 computers available on campus for general student use. A campuswide network can be accessed from student residence rooms and from off campus. Staffed computer lab on campus.

Community Environment: Louisburg, a county seat, is 30 miles from Raleigh, the state capital, where all forms of transportation are available. A hospital, churches, good shopping facilities, and various civic and social organizations are found in the community. There are many part-time job opportunities.

■ **MARS HILL COLLEGE**
PO Box 370
Mars Hill, NC 28754
Tel: (828)689-1307; Free: 866-MHC-4-YOU
Fax: (828)689-1474
E-mail: ehoffmeyer@mhc.edu
Web Site: www.mhc.edu/
Description: Independent Baptist, 4-year, coed. Awards bachelor's and master's degrees. Founded 1856. Setting: 194-acre small town campus. Endowment: $42 million. Educational spending for the previous fiscal year: $6166 per student. Total enrollment: 1,370. Faculty: 184 (85 full-time, 99 part-time). Student-undergrad faculty ratio is 11:1. 2,970 applied, 69% were admitted. 7% from top 10% of their high school class, 25% from top quarter, 57% from top half. Full-time: 1,255 students, 47% women, 53% men. Part-time: 96 students, 66% women, 34% men. Students come from 34 states and territories, 15 other countries, 29% from out-of-state. 2% American Indian or Alaska Native, non-Hispanic/Latino; 2% Hispanic/Latino; 19% African American, non-Hispanic/Latino; 0.4% Asian, non-Hispanic/Latino; 0% Native Hawaiian or other Pacific Islander, non-Hispanic/Latino; 2% international. 17% 25 or older, 68% live on campus, 8% transferred in. Retention: 55% of full-time freshmen returned the following year. Academic areas with the most degrees conferred: business/marketing; education; social sciences. Core. Calendar: semesters. Academic remediation for entering students, ESL program, services for LD students, advanced placement, accelerated degree program, self-designed majors, honors program, independent study, double major, summer session for credit, part-time degree program, adult/continuing education programs, co-op programs and internships. Study abroad program.
Entrance Requirements: Options: electronic application, early admission, deferred admission, international baccalaureate accepted. Required: high school transcript, minimum 2 high school GPA, SAT or ACT. Recommended: essay, minimum 3 high school GPA. Required for some: interview. Entrance: moderately difficult. Application deadline: Rolling. Transfer credits accepted: Yes.
Costs Per Year: Application fee: $25. Comprehensive fee: $34,824 includes full-time tuition ($23,152), mandatory fees ($2484), and college room and board ($9188). College room only: $4948. Part-time tuition: $295 per credit. Part-time tuition varies according to course load.
Collegiate Environment: Orientation program. Drama-theater group, choral group, marching band. Social organizations: 35 open to all; national fraternities, national sororities, local fraternities, local sororities; 19% of eligible men and 28% of eligible women are members. Most popular organizations: Student Government Association, Fellowship of Christian Athletes, Christian Student Movement, Fraternity/Sorority, Athletic Trainers Association. Major annual events: Homecoming, Fall Festival, Spring Fling. Student services: health clinic, personal-psychological counseling. Campus security: 24-hour emergency response devices and patrols, late night transport-escort service, controlled dormitory access. 992 college housing spaces available; 936 were occupied in 2012-13. Freshmen guaranteed college housing. On-campus residence required through sophomore year. Options: men-only, women-only housing available. Renfro Library plus 1 other with 225,784 books, 680,270 microform titles, 513 serials, 72,284 audiovisual materials, an OPAC, and a Web page. Operations spending for the previous fiscal year: $363,455. 188 computers available on campus for general student use. A campuswide network can be accessed from student residence rooms and from off campus. Students can access the following: online class registration. Staffed computer lab on campus provides training in use of computers, software, and the Internet.
Community Environment: Mars Hill is located 17 miles north of Asheville and 10 miles from Marshall. Plane and bus transportation are available. Community facilities include a medical center and convenient shopping.

■ **MARTIN COMMUNITY COLLEGE**
1161 Kehukee Park Rd.
Williamston, NC 27892
Tel: (252)792-1521
Fax: (252)792-4425
Web Site: www.martin.cc.nc.us/
Description: State-supported, 2-year, coed. Part of North Carolina Community College System. Awards certificates, diplomas, transfer associate, and terminal associate degrees. Founded 1968. Setting: 65-acre rural campus. Endowment: $32,015. Educational spending for the previous fiscal year: $1577 per student. Total enrollment: 755. Faculty: 78 (22 full-time, 56 part-time). Student-undergrad faculty ratio is 10:1. Full-time: 475 students, 65% women, 35% men. Part-time: 280 students, 67% women, 33% men. 1% from out-of-state. 0.3% American Indian or Alaska Native, non-Hispanic/Latino; 0.3% Hispanic/Latino; 47% African American, non-Hispanic/Latino; 0.3% Asian, non-Hispanic/Latino; 0% Native Hawaiian or other Pacific Islander, non-Hispanic/Latino. 49% 25 or older, 27% transferred in. Calendar: semesters. Academic remediation for entering students, ESL program, services for LD students, advanced placement, independent study, distance learning, summer session for credit, part-time degree program, internships. Off campus study.
Entrance Requirements: Open admission except for physical therapy assistant and dental assistant programs. Option: electronic application. Required: high school transcript. Required for some: interview. Entrance: noncompetitive. Application deadline: Rolling. Notification: continuous until 8/17. Transfer credits accepted: Yes.
Collegiate Environment: Orientation program. Most popular organizations: Phi Theta Kappa, Student Government Association, Alpha Beta Gamma, Physical Therapy Club, Equine Club. Major annual events: Stampede in the Park, Spring Fling, Fall Festival. Student services: personal-psychological counseling. Campus security: 24-hour emergency response devices, part-time patrols by trained security personnel. Martin Community College Learning Resources Center with 36,443 books, 1,610 microform titles, 215 serials, 10,809 audiovisual materials, and an OPAC. Operations spending for the previous fiscal year: $143,375. 215 computers available on campus for general student use. A campuswide network can be accessed from off-campus. Staffed computer lab on campus.
Community Environment: The college is located in the center of a prosperous agricultural area. Recreational facilities include tennis courts, parks, and several ball fields. The area is ideal for hunting, fishing, and camping. The Senator Bob Martin Eastern Agricultural Center attracts horse shows, rodeos, bull riding, concerts, and many other events.

■ **MAYLAND COMMUNITY COLLEGE**
PO Box 547
Spruce Pine, NC 28777-0547
Tel: (828)765-7351; Free: 800-462-9526
Fax: (828)765-0728
Web Site: www.mayland.edu/
Description: State and locally supported, 2-year, coed. Part of North Carolina Community College System. Awards certificates, diplomas, transfer associate, and terminal associate degrees. Founded 1971. Setting: 38-acre rural campus. Total enrollment: 1,472. 39% 25 or older. Calendar: semesters. Academic remediation for entering students, services for LD students, advanced placement, independent study, distance learning, double major, summer session for credit, part-time degree program, adult/continuing education programs, co-op programs and internships.
Entrance Requirements: Open admission. Options: electronic application, deferred admission. Required: high school transcript. Required for some: CPT required for all for placement, required for admission to nursing program. Entrance: noncompetitive. Application deadline: Rolling. Notification: continuous.
Collegiate Environment: Student services: personal-psychological counseling. Carolyn Munro Wilson Learning Resources Center plus 1 other with 19,041 books, 653 microform titles, 225 serials, 1,707 audiovisual materials, an OPAC, and a Web page.
Community Environment: Mayland Community College is located in the Blue Ridge Mountains of Western North Carolina. The Main Campus is located on Highway 19E, two miles east of Spruce Pine.

■ **MCDOWELL TECHNICAL COMMUNITY COLLEGE**
54 College Dr.
Marion, NC 28752-9724
Tel: (828)652-6021
Fax: (828)652-1014
E-mail: rickw@mcdowelltech.edu
Web Site: www.mcdowelltech.edu/
Description: State-supported, 2-year, coed. Part of North Carolina Community College System. Awards certificates, diplomas, transfer associate, and terminal associate degrees. Founded 1964. Setting: 31-acre rural

campus. Total enrollment: 1,134. Faculty: 58 (40 full-time, 18 part-time). 50% 25 or older. Core. Calendar: semesters. Academic remediation for entering students, ESL program, services for LD students, accelerated degree program, independent study, distance learning, summer session for credit, part-time degree program, adult/continuing education programs, co-op programs.

Entrance Requirements: Open admission except for registered nursing, licensed practical nursing programs. Options: early admission, deferred admission. Required for some: high school transcript. Entrance: noncompetitive. Application deadline: Rolling. Notification: continuous.

Collegiate Environment: Student services: personal-psychological counseling. Campus security: 24-hour emergency response devices. 18,055 books and 156 serials.

Community Environment: Located in the foothills of the Blue Ridge Mountains, Marion enjoys a temperate climate. Trains, buses, and airlines provide the commercial transportation. To serve the people of this community, there are 96 churches and medical facilities. 26 major industries are located here, furnishing part-time job opportunities for students. Outdoor recreational facilities include the Blue Ridge Parkway, Mt Mitchell State Park, Lake James and Lake Tahoma.

■ **MEREDITH COLLEGE**

3800 Hillsborough St.
Raleigh, NC 27607-5298
Tel: (919)760-8600; Free: 800-MEREDITH
Fax: (919)829-2348
E-mail: admissions@meredith.edu
Web Site: www.meredith.edu/

Description: Independent, comprehensive. Awards bachelor's and master's degrees. Founded 1891. Setting: 225-acre urban campus. Endowment: $80.4 million. Educational spending for the previous fiscal year: $9499 per student. Total enrollment: 1,980. Faculty: 207 (121 full-time, 86 part-time). Student-undergrad faculty ratio is 11:1. 1,599 applied, 61% were admitted. 20% from top 10% of their high school class, 48% from top quarter, 82% from top half. 3 valedictorians. Full-time: 1,590 students, 100% women. Part-time: 117 students, 97% women, 3% men. Students come from 30 states and territories, 16 other countries, 11% from out-of-state. 3% Hispanic/Latino; 12% African American, non-Hispanic/Latino; 2% Asian, non-Hispanic/Latino; 3% international. 10% 25 or older, 60% live on campus, 5% transferred in. Retention: 77% of full-time freshmen returned the following year. Academic areas with the most degrees conferred: visual and performing arts; business/marketing; psychology. Core. Calendar: semesters. Academic remediation for entering students, services for LD students, advanced placement, accelerated degree program, self-designed majors, honors program, independent study, double major, summer session for credit, part-time degree program, co-op programs and internships, graduate courses open to undergrads. Off campus study at Cooperating Raleigh Colleges, American University, Marymount College (NY), Drew University. Study abroad program. ROTC: Army (c), Air Force (c).

Entrance Requirements: Options: electronic application, early admission, early decision, deferred admission, international baccalaureate accepted. Required: high school transcript, minimum 2 high school GPA, 2 recommendations, SAT or ACT. Required for some: essay, interview, SAT Subject Tests. Entrance: moderately difficult. Application deadlines: 2/15, 10/15 for early decision. Notification: continuous, 11/1 for early decision. Early decision applicants: 108. Early decision applicants admitted: 54.

Costs Per Year: Application fee: $40. Comprehensive fee: $37,454 includes full-time tuition ($29,106) and college room and board ($8348). Full-time tuition varies according to course load.

Collegiate Environment: Orientation program. Drama-theater group, choral group, student-run newspaper. Social organizations: 90 open to all. Most popular organizations: Student Government Association, Entertainment Association, Recreation Association, Class Organizations, choral groups. Major annual events: Cornhuskin', Day of Celebration, Spring Formal. Student services: health clinic, personal-psychological counseling. Campus security: 24-hour emergency response devices and patrols, late night transport-escort service, controlled dormitory access, self-defense instruction. Carlyle Campbell Library with 139,113 books, 16,116 microform titles, 3,605 serials, 14,731 audiovisual materials, and an OPAC. Operations spending for the previous fiscal year: $1.1 million. 140 computers available on campus for general student use. A campuswide network can be accessed from student residence rooms. Students can access the following: online class registration, laptop computers for full-time students. Staffed computer lab on campus provides training in use of computers, software, and the Internet.

Community Environment: Meredith is located at the western edge of Raleigh, NC, the state capital and home of five other colleges and universities. The area is served by air, bus and rail. The campus is easily accessible from I-40, bordered by US 1 and Wade Avenue, with the front entrance facing Hillsborough Street. Raleigh is a part of the Research Triangle Area, which includes Durham and Chapel Hill, NC. It is a cultural center with the N.C. Museums of Art, History and Natural Science, the North Carolina Symphony and numerous theaters. Meredith itself is a center for many cultural events including the Fletcher School of the Performing Arts and the National Opera Company.

■ **METHODIST UNIVERSITY**

5400 Ramsey St.
Fayetteville, NC 28311-1498
Tel: (910)630-7000; Free: 800-488-7110
Fax: (910)630-7317
E-mail: admissions@methodist.edu
Web Site: www.methodist.edu/

Description: Independent United Methodist, comprehensive, coed. Awards associate, bachelor's, and master's degrees. Founded 1956. Setting: 600-acre suburban campus with easy access to Raleigh-Durham. Endowment: $13.9 million. Educational spending for the previous fiscal year: $18,078 per student. Total enrollment: 2,416. Faculty: 213 (127 full-time, 86 part-time). Student-undergrad faculty ratio is 12:1. 2,904 applied, 63% were admitted. 10% from top 10% of their high school class, 33% from top quarter, 77% from top half. 28 class presidents, 3 valedictorians, 200 student government officers. Full-time: 1,930 students, 45% women, 55% men. Part-time: 287 students, 54% women, 46% men. Students come from 41 states and territories, 53 other countries, 47% from out-of-state. 1% American Indian or Alaska Native, non-Hispanic/Latino; 4% Hispanic/Latino; 22% African American, non-Hispanic/Latino; 1% Asian, non-Hispanic/Latino; 0.4% Native Hawaiian or other Pacific Islander, non-Hispanic/Latino; 5% international. 24% 25 or older, 57% live on campus, 12% transferred in. Retention: 67% of full-time freshmen returned the following year. Academic areas with the most degrees conferred: business/marketing; social sciences; parks and recreation. Core. Calendar: semesters. Academic remediation for entering students, ESL program, services for LD students, advanced placement, accelerated degree program, honors program, independent study, distance learning, double major, summer session for credit, part-time degree program, adult/continuing education programs, co-op programs and internships. Study abroad program. ROTC: Army, Air Force (c).

Entrance Requirements: Options: deferred admission, international baccalaureate accepted. Required: high school transcript, SAT or ACT. Recommended: interview. Required for some: essay, interview. Entrance: moderately difficult. Application deadlines: Rolling, Rolling for nonresidents. Notification: 8/15.

Collegiate Environment: Orientation program. Drama-theater group, choral group, marching band, student-run newspaper. Social organizations: 76 open to all; national fraternities, national sororities, local fraternities, local sororities; 2% of eligible men and 3% of eligible women are members. Most popular organizations: Student Activities Committee, Student Government Association, Student Education Association, Fellowship of Christian Athletes, Residence Hall Association. Major annual events: Homecoming, Spring Fling, Show You Care Day. Student services: health clinic, personal-psychological counseling. Campus security: 24-hour emergency response devices and patrols, student patrols, late night transport-escort service, controlled dormitory access, regular patrol by county sheriff department. Davis Memorial Library plus 1 other with 86,259 books, 62,814 microform titles, 571 serials, an OPAC, and a Web page. Operations spending for the previous fiscal year: $252,675. 200 computers available on campus for general student use. Computer purchase/lease plans available. A campuswide network can be accessed from student residence rooms and from off campus. Students can access the following: online class registration. Staffed computer lab on campus provides training in use of computers, software, and the Internet.

Community Environment: Fayetteville, a community of 105,000, is part of the Carolina Sandhills region in the heart of golf country and two hours from the coast. It is accessible by air, rail, and highway. Its economy is based on agriculture, manufacturing and processing, distribution, and the government. The community has 4 hospitals, a public library with 8 branches, an art guild, theater, art museum, symphony, and brass band. There are 53 public and private golf courses within an hour's drive of the city. Popular sports include golf, tennis, archery, boating, and skating.

■ MID-ATLANTIC CHRISTIAN UNIVERSITY

715 N Poindexter St.
Elizabeth City, NC 27909-4054
Tel: (252)334-2070; Free: 866-996-MACU
Fax: (252)334-2071
E-mail: julie.fields@macuniversity.edu
Web Site: www.macuniversity.edu/

Description: Independent Christian, 4-year, coed. Awards associate and bachelor's degrees. Founded 1948. Setting: 19-acre small town campus with easy access to Norfolk. Endowment: $2.3 million. Educational spending for the previous fiscal year: $24,500 per student. Total enrollment: 165. Faculty: 43 (6 full-time, 37 part-time). Student-undergrad faculty ratio is 10:1. 168 applied, 41% were admitted. 15% from top 10% of their high school class, 19% from top quarter, 54% from top half. Full-time: 126 students, 52% women, 48% men. Part-time: 39 students, 41% women, 59% men. Students come from 17 states and territories, 1 other country, 37% from out-of-state. 0% American Indian or Alaska Native, non-Hispanic/Latino; 4% Hispanic/Latino; 35% African American, non-Hispanic/Latino; 0% Asian, non-Hispanic/Latino; 0% Native Hawaiian or other Pacific Islander, non-Hispanic/Latino; 0% international. 32% 25 or older, 55% live on campus, 15% transferred in. Retention: 57% of full-time freshmen returned the following year. Academic areas with the most degrees conferred: theology and religious vocations; business/marketing; psychology; foreign languages and literature. Core. Calendar: semesters. Academic remediation for entering students, advanced placement, distance learning, double major, summer session for credit, part-time degree program, adult/continuing education programs, internships. ROTC: Army (c).

Entrance Requirements: Options: electronic application, early admission, deferred admission, international baccalaureate accepted. Required: essay, high school transcript, minimum 2 high school GPA, 1 recommendation, reference from church or character reference, SAT or ACT. Required for some: interview. Entrance: minimally difficult. Application deadline: 8/1. Notification: continuous. Transfer credits accepted: Yes.

Costs Per Year: Application fee: $50. Comprehensive fee: $19,940 includes full-time tuition ($12,160) and college room and board ($7780). Full-time tuition varies according to program. Room and board charges vary according to housing facility. Part-time tuition: $380 per credit hour. Part-time tuition varies according to program.

Collegiate Environment: Orientation program. Most popular organizations: Student Advisory Council, Counseling Club. Major annual events: Alumni Rally and Homecoming, Sunday Night Live. Student services: personal-psychological counseling. Campus security: 24-hour emergency response devices, controlled dormitory access. 224 college housing spaces available; 80 were occupied in 2012-13. Freshmen guaranteed college housing. On-campus residence required through senior year. Options: men-only, women-only housing available. Watson-Griffith Library with 35,545 books, 13 microform titles, 208 serials, 2,923 audiovisual materials, an OPAC, and a Web page. Operations spending for the previous fiscal year: $60,462. 24 computers available on campus for general student use. A campuswide network can be accessed from student residence rooms. Students can access the following: online class registration.

■ MITCHELL COMMUNITY COLLEGE

500 W Broad
Statesville, NC 28677-5293
Tel: (704)878-3200
Fax: (704)878-0872
Web Site: www.mitchellcc.edu/

Description: State-supported, 2-year, coed. Part of North Carolina Community College System. Awards certificates, diplomas, transfer associate, and terminal associate degrees. Founded 1852. Setting: 8-acre small town campus with easy access to Charlotte. Total enrollment: 2,687. 39% 25 or older. Core. Calendar: semesters. Academic remediation for entering students, ESL program, services for LD students, advanced placement, distance learning, summer session for credit, part-time degree program, adult/continuing education programs. ROTC: Army (c).

Entrance Requirements: Open admission except for nursing program. Required: high school transcript. Entrance: noncompetitive. Application deadline: Rolling. Notification: continuous.

Collegiate Environment: Choral group. Student services: personal-psychological counseling. Campus security: day and evening security guards. Main library plus 1 other with 37,760 books, 33,426 microform titles, 218 serials, 2,225 audiovisual materials, and an OPAC.

Community Environment: On a plateau, surrounded by the foothills of the Blue Ridge Mountains, Statesville is in the heart of the Piedmont area. Industrial products and textiles, metal, and furniture are produced there. This is also a large milk-producing area. All forms of commercial transportation are available. There are churches of all denominations along with the various civic and service organizations. Excellent part-time job opportunities are available.

■ MONTGOMERY COMMUNITY COLLEGE

1011 Page St.
Troy, NC 27371
Tel: (910)576-6222
E-mail: fryek@montgomery.edu
Web Site: www.montgomery.edu/

Description: State-supported, 2-year, coed. Part of North Carolina Community College System. Awards certificates, diplomas, transfer associate, and terminal associate degrees. Founded 1967. Setting: 159-acre rural campus. Total enrollment: 837. Faculty: 76 (36 full-time, 40 part-time). Full-time: 381 students, 59% women, 41% men. Part-time: 456 students, 69% women, 31% men. Students come from 10 states and territories, 1% from out-of-state. 0.4% American Indian or Alaska Native, non-Hispanic/Latino; 7% Hispanic/Latino; 21% African American, non-Hispanic/Latino; 2% Asian, non-Hispanic/Latino; 0% Native Hawaiian or other Pacific Islander, non-Hispanic/Latino; 0.1% international. 44% 25 or older. Core. Calendar: semesters. Academic remediation for entering students, ESL program, services for LD students, advanced placement, distance learning, summer session for credit, part-time degree program.

Entrance Requirements: Open admission. Options: electronic application, early admission, deferred admission. Required: high school transcript. Entrance: noncompetitive. Application deadline: Rolling. Notification: continuous. Transfer credits accepted: Yes.

Costs Per Year: Application fee: $0. State resident tuition: $2208 full-time, $69 per credit part-time. Nonresident tuition: $8352 full-time, $261 per credit part-time. Mandatory fees: $75 full-time, $75 per year part-time. Part-time tuition and fees vary according to course load.

Collegiate Environment: Orientation program. Social organizations: 12 open to all. Most popular organizations: Student Government Association, Nursing Club, Gunsmithing Society, Medical Assisting Club, Forestry Club. Major annual events: Spring Fling, Polar Volleyball, Holiday Feast. Student services: personal-psychological counseling. Campus security: 24-hour emergency response devices. College housing not available. Montgomery Community College Learning Resource Center with 23,000 books, 100 serials, 1,430 audiovisual materials, an OPAC, and a Web page. 90 computers available on campus for general student use. A campuswide network can be accessed from off-campus. Students can access the following: online class registration. Staffed computer lab on campus provides training in use of computers, software, and the Internet.

Community Environment: Troy is located 50 miles from Greensboro where the main industries are lumber and textiles. Train transportation is available with air travel convenient to Greensboro and Charlotte. The Pee Dee River is 12 miles away providing facilities for water skiing, fishing, and boating.

■ MONTREAT COLLEGE

PO Box 1267
Montreat, NC 28757-1267
Tel: (828)669-8012; Free: 800-622-6968
Fax: (828)669-0120
E-mail: admissions@montreat.edu
Web Site: www.montreat.edu/

Description: Independent, comprehensive, coed, affiliated with Presbyterian Church (U.S.A.). Awards associate, bachelor's, and master's degrees. Founded 1916. Setting: 112-acre small town campus. Total enrollment: 889. Faculty: 90 (26 full-time, 64 part-time). Student-undergrad faculty ratio is 11:1. 854 applied, 51% were admitted. 6% from top 10% of their high school class, 22% from top quarter, 57% from top half. Full-time: 422 students, 47% women, 53% men. Part-time: 344 students, 63% women, 38% men. 25% from out-of-state. 1% American Indian or Alaska Native, non-Hispanic/Latino; 3% Hispanic/Latino; 21% African American, non-Hispanic/Latino; 0.5% Asian, non-Hispanic/Latino; 0% Native Hawaiian or other Pacific Islander, non-Hispanic/Latino; 3% international. 40% 25 or older, 72% live on campus, 6% transferred in. Retention: 50% of full-time freshmen returned the following year. Academic areas with the most degrees conferred: business/marketing; parks and recreation; biological/life sciences. Calendar: semesters. Part-time degree program, adult/continuing education programs.

Entrance Requirements: Options: early admission, deferred admission, international baccalaureate accepted. Required: essay, high school transcript, minimum 2.75 high school GPA, SAT or ACT. Required for some: 1 recommendation, interview. Entrance: moderately difficult. Application deadlines: 8/15, 8/15 for nonresidents. Notification: continuous, continuous for nonresidents. SAT Reasoning Test deadline: 8/9.

Costs Per Year: Application fee: $0. Comprehensive fee: $30,278 includes full-time tuition ($22,684), mandatory fees ($100), and college room and board ($7494). Room and board charges vary according to board plan. Part-time tuition: $600 per credit hour.

Collegiate Environment: Orientation program. Drama-theater group, choral group, student-run newspaper. Student services: health clinic, personal-psychological counseling. Campus security: 24-hour emergency response devices and patrols, controlled dormitory access. Freshmen guaranteed college housing. On-campus residence required through sophomore year. Options: men-only, women-only housing available. L. Nelson Bell Library with an OPAC and a Web page.

Community Environment: Montreat is situated in the beautiful Blue Ridge Mountains, 17 miles from Asheville, and adjacent to the historic town of Black Mountain with picturesque avenues, stores, and restaurants. The climate is recognized as one of the world's finest and the region has long been a major vacation area. Montreat's recreational activities include golf, tennis, skiing, baseball, and basketball, as well as access to the Pisgah National Forest.

■ **MOUNT OLIVE COLLEGE**
634 Henderson St.
Mount Olive, NC 28365
Tel: (919)658-2502; Free: 800-653-0854
Fax: (919)658-8934
E-mail: admissions@moc.edu
Web Site: www.moc.edu/
Description: Independent Free Will Baptist, 4-year, coed. Awards associate and bachelor's degrees. Founded 1951. Setting: 123-acre small town campus with easy access to Raleigh. Total enrollment: 3,855. Faculty: 183 (81 full-time, 102 part-time). Student-undergrad faculty ratio is 26:1. 1,838 applied, 50% were admitted. 10% from top 10% of their high school class, 47% from top quarter, 74% from top half. Full-time: 2,955 students, 69% women, 31% men. Part-time: 900 students, 64% women, 36% men. Students come from 11 other countries, 5% from out-of-state. 67% 25 or older, 11% live on campus. Retention: 60% of full-time freshmen returned the following year. Academic areas with the most degrees conferred: business/marketing; health professions and related sciences; education. Core. Calendar: semester or continuous accelerated programs. Advanced placement, accelerated degree program, freshman honors college, honors program, independent study, double major, summer session for credit, part-time degree program, external degree program, adult/continuing education programs, co-op programs and internships. Off campus study at North Carolina Community College System, East Carolina University, North Carolina State University. ROTC: Air Force (c).
Entrance Requirements: Open admission for those 21 or older or who have 27 hours of transferable credit. Options: electronic application, deferred admission, international baccalaureate accepted. Required: high school transcript. Recommended: 2 recommendations, interview. Required for some: SAT or ACT required for those under 21. Entrance: minimally difficult. Application deadline: 8/18. Notification: continuous. SAT Reasoning Test deadline: 5/15. SAT Subject Test deadline: 5/15. Transfer credits accepted: Yes.
Collegiate Environment: Orientation program. Choral group. Most popular organizations: Student Government Association, Phi Beta Lambda, commuters organization, Christian Student Fellowship, English Society. Major annual events: Pickle Classic Basketball Tournament, Mr. and Miss Mount Olive College, MOOS Day. Student services: health clinic, personal-psychological counseling. Campus security: overnight security patrols; weekend patrols. Moye Library with 77,369 books, 53,922 microform titles, 6,283 audiovisual materials, an OPAC, and a Web page.
Community Environment: Mount Olive is about 15 miles from the county seat, Goldsboro. Buses provide commercial transportation. Numerous civic and service organizations, hospitals in separate towns 15 miles away, churches, and a library contribute to the community. The coast is a one-hour drive for swimming and fresh water fishing; other activities are tennis, softball, and golf.

■ **NASH COMMUNITY COLLEGE**
522 N Old Carriage Rd.
Rocky Mount, NC 27804

Tel: (252)443-4011
Fax: (252)443-0828
E-mail: dgardner@nashcc.edu
Web Site: www.nashcc.edu/
Description: State-supported, 2-year, coed. Part of North Carolina Community College System. Awards certificates, diplomas, transfer associate, and terminal associate degrees. Founded 1967. Setting: 69-acre rural campus. Total enrollment: 2,916. 41% 25 or older. Calendar: semesters. Academic remediation for entering students, ESL program, services for LD students, advanced placement, independent study, distance learning, double major, summer session for credit, part-time degree program, adult/continuing education programs.
Entrance Requirements: Open admission except for nursing, physical therapy assistant, cosmetology, phlebotomy programs. Option: deferred admission. Required: high school transcript. Recommended: interview. Required for some: SAT or ACT, SAT and SAT Subject Tests or ACT, ACT ASSET or ACT COMPASS. Entrance: noncompetitive. Application deadline: Rolling. Notification: continuous.
Collegiate Environment: Orientation program. Student-run newspaper. Campus security: 24-hour emergency response devices, late night transport-escort service. Nash Community College Library plus 1 other with 34,000 books, 110 serials, and an OPAC.
Community Environment: See North Carolina Wesleyan College:

■ **NEW LIFE THEOLOGICAL SEMINARY**
PO Box 790106
Charlotte, NC 28206-7901
Tel: (704)334-6882
Fax: (704)334-6885
Web Site: www.nlts.org/
Description: Independent Christian, comprehensive, coed. Awards associate, bachelor's, and master's degrees. Founded 1996. Setting: 3-acre urban campus. Total enrollment: 98. Faculty: 32 (6 full-time, 26 part-time). Student-undergrad faculty ratio is 6:1. 25 applied, 100% were admitted. Full-time: 48 students, 54% women, 46% men. Part-time: 30 students, 53% women, 47% men. Students come from 8 other countries, 0% from out-of-state. 95% 25 or older, 0% transferred in. Retention: 42% of full-time freshmen returned the following year. Core. Independent study, summer session for credit, part-time degree program, adult/continuing education programs, co-op programs and internships. Off campus study.
Entrance Requirements: Open admission. Required: essay, high school transcript, 2 recommendations, certification of Church membership and involvement. Transfer credits accepted: Yes.
Collegiate Environment: Orientation program. Campus security: 24-hour emergency response devices.

■ **NORTH CAROLINA AGRICULTURAL AND TECHNICAL STATE UNIVERSITY**
1601 E Market St.
Greensboro, NC 27411
Tel: (336)334-7500
Fax: (336)334-7082
E-mail: uadmit@ncat.edu
Web Site: www.ncat.edu/
Description: State-supported, university, coed. Part of University of North Carolina System. Awards bachelor's, master's, and doctoral degrees. Founded 1891. Setting: 200-acre suburban campus with easy access to Charlotte. Total enrollment: 10,881. Faculty: 674 (532 full-time, 142 part-time). 6,692 applied, 66% were admitted. 0% from top 10% of their high school class, 6% from top quarter, 34% from top half. Full-time: 8,278 students, 54% women, 46% men. Part-time: 928 students, 47% women, 53% men. 0.4% American Indian or Alaska Native, non-Hispanic/Latino; 1% Hispanic/Latino; 86% African American, non-Hispanic/Latino; 1% Asian, non-Hispanic/Latino; 0.01% Native Hawaiian or other Pacific Islander, non-Hispanic/Latino; 1% international. 41% live on campus. Retention: 74% of full-time freshmen returned the following year. Academic areas with the most degrees conferred: business/marketing; engineering; communication/journalism. Core. Calendar: semesters. Academic remediation for entering students, advanced placement, accelerated degree program, honors program, distance learning, double major, summer session for credit, part-time degree program, adult/continuing education programs, co-op programs and internships, graduate courses open to undergrads. Off campus study at Bennett College; Elon University; Greensboro College; GTCC; Guilford College; High Point University; UNC-G. Study abroad program. ROTC: Army, Air Force.

Entrance Requirements: Options: early admission, deferred admission, international baccalaureate accepted. Required: high school transcript, minimum 2 high school GPA, SAT or ACT. Entrance: moderately difficult. Application deadlines: Rolling, Rolling for nonresidents. Notification: continuous, continuous for nonresidents. SAT Reasoning Test deadline: 6/1. SAT Subject Test deadline: 6/1. Transfer credits accepted: Yes. Applicants placed on waiting list: 210.

Costs Per Year: Application fee: $45. State resident tuition: $5058 full-time. Nonresident tuition: $15,657 full-time. Full-time tuition varies according to course load and student level. College room and board: $7349. Room and board charges vary according to board plan and housing facility.

Collegiate Environment: Orientation program. Drama-theater group, choral group, marching band, student-run newspaper, radio station. Social organizations: national fraternities, national sororities, local fraternities, local sororities. Most popular organization: student government. Major annual events: Homecoming, Martin Luther King, Jr. Celebration. Student services: health clinic, personal-psychological counseling. Campus security: 24-hour emergency response devices and patrols, late night transport-escort service, controlled dormitory access. F. D. Bluford Library with 702,159 books, 1.1 million microform titles, 3,205 serials, 41,808 audiovisual materials, an OPAC, and a Web page.

Community Environment: See Greensboro College.

■ NORTH CAROLINA CENTRAL UNIVERSITY

1801 Fayetteville St.
Durham, NC 27707-3129
Tel: (919)560-6100; Free: 877-667-7533
E-mail: admissions@nccu.edu
Web Site: www.nccu.edu/

Description: State-supported, comprehensive, coed. Part of University of North Carolina System. Awards bachelor's, master's, and doctoral degrees. Founded 1910. Setting: 115-acre urban campus with easy access to Raleigh. Endowment: $20 million. Research spending for the previous fiscal year: $8.2 million. Total enrollment: 8,604. Faculty: 598 (449 full-time, 149 part-time). Student-undergrad faculty ratio is 15:1. 8,886 applied, 50% were admitted. 5% from top 10% of their high school class, 19% from top quarter, 58% from top half. Full-time: 5,602 students, 66% women, 34% men. Part-time: 1,056 students, 71% women, 29% men. Students come from 40 states and territories, 30 other countries, 10% from out-of-state. 0.3% American Indian or Alaska Native, non-Hispanic/Latino; 2% Hispanic/Latino; 84% African American, non-Hispanic/Latino; 1% Asian, non-Hispanic/Latino; 0.02% Native Hawaiian or other Pacific Islander, non-Hispanic/Latino; 0.5% international. 21% 25 or older, 40% live on campus, 7% transferred in. Retention: 72% of full-time freshmen returned the following year. Academic areas with the most degrees conferred: business/marketing; homeland security, law enforcement, firefighting, and protective services; family and consumer sciences. Core. Calendar: semesters. Academic remediation for entering students, ESL program, services for LD students, advanced placement, accelerated degree program, honors program, independent study, distance learning, double major, summer session for credit, part-time degree program, external degree program, adult/continuing education programs, co-op programs and internships, graduate courses open to undergrads. Off campus study. Study abroad program. ROTC: Army, Air Force.

Entrance Requirements: Options: electronic application, deferred admission, international baccalaureate accepted. Required: high school transcript, minimum 2.3 high school GPA, University of North Carolina System minimum course requirements, SAT or ACT. Entrance: minimally difficult. Application deadline: 8/1. Notification: continuous until 10/15. Preference given to qualified state residents. Transfer credits accepted: Yes.

Costs Per Year: Application fee: $40. State resident tuition: $3244 full-time. Nonresident tuition: $13,817 full-time. College room and board: $9,923. College room only: $6,791. Room and board charges vary according to board plan, housing facility, and location.

Collegiate Environment: Orientation program. Drama-theater group, choral group, marching band, student-run newspaper. Social organizations: national fraternities, national sororities, local fraternities, local sororities. Student services: health clinic, personal-psychological counseling, women's center. Campus security: 24-hour emergency response devices and patrols, student patrols, late night transport-escort service, controlled dormitory access. 2,878 college housing spaces available; 2,535 were occupied in 2012-13. Freshmen given priority for college housing. Option: coed housing available. Shepherd Library plus 2 others with 695,876 books, 179,833 microform titles, 1,952 serials, 4,902 audiovisual materials, an OPAC, and a Web page. 1,262 computers available on campus for general student use. Computer purchase/lease plans available. A campuswide network can be accessed from student residence rooms and from off campus. Students can access the following: online class registration. Staffed computer lab on campus provides training in use of computers, software, and the Internet.

Community Environment: See Duke University.

■ NORTH CAROLINA STATE UNIVERSITY

Raleigh, NC 27695
Tel: (919)515-2011
Fax: (919)515-5039
E-mail: undergrad_admissions@ncsu.edu
Web Site: www.ncsu.edu/

Description: State-supported, university, coed. Part of University of North Carolina System. Awards associate, bachelor's, master's, and doctoral degrees and post-master's certificates. Founded 1887. Setting: 2,110-acre urban campus. Endowment: $635.3 million. Total enrollment: 34,340. Faculty: 1,821 (1,666 full-time, 155 part-time). Student-undergrad faculty ratio is 18:1. 20,435 applied, 50% were admitted. 49% from top 10% of their high school class, 87% from top quarter, 99% from top half. 6 National Merit Scholars, 110 valedictorians. Full-time: 21,821 students, 44% women, 56% men. Part-time: 3,012 students, 42% women, 58% men. Students come from 52 states and territories, 67 other countries, 10% from out-of-state. 0.5% American Indian or Alaska Native, non-Hispanic/Latino; 4% Hispanic/Latino; 8% African American, non-Hispanic/Latino; 5% Asian, non-Hispanic/Latino; 0.05% Native Hawaiian or other Pacific Islander, non-Hispanic/Latino; 2% international. 7% 25 or older, 27% live on campus, 5% transferred in. Retention: 92% of full-time freshmen returned the following year. Academic areas with the most degrees conferred: engineering; business/marketing; biological/life sciences. Core. Calendar: semesters. Academic remediation for entering students, ESL program, services for LD students, advanced placement, accelerated degree program, self-designed majors, honors program, independent study, distance learning, double major, summer session for credit, part-time degree program, adult/continuing education programs, co-op programs and internships, graduate courses open to undergrads. Off campus study at five members of the Cooperating Raleigh Colleges, Duke University, University of North Carolina at Chapel Hill. Study abroad program. ROTC: Army, Naval, Air Force.

Entrance Requirements: Options: electronic application, early action, deferred admission, international baccalaureate accepted. Required: high school transcript, SAT or ACT. Recommended: essay, SAT Subject Tests. Required for some: interview. Entrance: very difficult. Application deadline: 2/1. Notification: continuous. Preference given to state residents. SAT Reasoning Test deadline: 2/1. Transfer credits accepted: Yes.

Costs Per Year: Application fee: $70. State resident tuition: $5748 full-time. Nonresident tuition: $18,913 full-time. Mandatory fees: $2,040 full-time. Full-time tuition and fees vary according to degree level, location, and program. College room and board: $8414. College room only: $5434. Room and board charges vary according to board plan and housing facility.

Collegiate Environment: Orientation program. Drama-theater group, choral group, marching band, student-run newspaper, radio station. Social organizations: 608 open to all; national fraternities, national sororities; 11% of eligible men and 14% of eligible women are members. Most popular organizations: Student Wolfpack Club, Inter-Fraternity Council, Panhellenic Association, Campus Crusade for Christ, Mechanical and Aerospace Engineering Graduate Student Association. Major annual events: Homecoming, Pan-African Week, Krispy Kreme Challenge. Student services: legal services, health clinic, personal-psychological counseling, women's center. Campus security: 24-hour emergency response devices and patrols, student patrols, late night transport-escort service, controlled dormitory access. 7,761 college housing spaces available; 7,683 were occupied in 2012-13. Freshmen given priority for college housing. Options: coed, men-only, women-only housing available. D. H. Hill Library plus 7 others with 4.6 million books, 5.5 million microform titles, 66,571 serials, 35,960 audiovisual materials, an OPAC, and a Web page. 3,024 computers available on campus for general student use. Computer purchase/lease plans available. A campuswide network can be accessed from student residence rooms and from off campus. Students can access the following: online class registration, course materials, online homework submission, online testing/quizzes, financial aid/cashier's office account balances, wiki space, blogging service, Web space, online storage space, on-site OS and virus removal, online/hybrid courses. Staffed computer lab on campus (open 24 hours a day) provides training in use of computers, software, and the Internet.

■ NORTH CAROLINA WESLEYAN COLLEGE

3400 N Wesleyan Blvd.
Rocky Mount, NC 27804-8677
Tel: (252)985-5100; Free: 800-488-6292
Fax: (252)985-5325
E-mail: hjohnson@ncwc.edu
Web Site: www.ncwc.edu/

Description: Independent, 4-year, coed, affiliated with United Methodist Church. Awards bachelor's degrees (also offers adult part-time degree program with significant enrollment not reflected in profile). Founded 1956. Setting: 200-acre suburban campus. Endowment: $9.4 million. Educational spending for the previous fiscal year: $5365 per student. Total enrollment: 1,522. Faculty: 213 (44 full-time, 169 part-time). Student-undergrad faculty ratio is 15:1. 1,634 applied, 47% were admitted. 5% from top 10% of their high school class, 17% from top quarter, 49% from top half. Full-time: 1,154 students, 58% women, 42% men. Part-time: 368 students, 70% women, 30% men. Students come from 24 states and territories, 18 other countries, 12% from out-of-state. 1% American Indian or Alaska Native, non-Hispanic/Latino; 2% Hispanic/Latino; 52% African American, non-Hispanic/Latino; 0.3% Asian, non-Hispanic/Latino; 0.1% Native Hawaiian or other Pacific Islander, non-Hispanic/Latino; 3% international. 54% 25 or older, 41% live on campus, 3% transferred in. Retention: 56% of full-time freshmen returned the following year. Academic areas with the most degrees conferred: business/marketing; homeland security, law enforcement, firefighting, and protective services; psychology. Core. Calendar: semesters. Academic remediation for entering students, services for LD students, advanced placement, accelerated degree program, honors program, independent study, distance learning, double major, summer session for credit, part-time degree program, adult/continuing education programs, co-op programs and internships. ROTC: Army.

Entrance Requirements: Options: electronic application, international baccalaureate accepted. Required: high school transcript, SAT or ACT. Recommended: minimum 2 high school GPA, 2 recommendations, interview. Required for some: essay, interview. Entrance: moderately difficult. Application deadline: Rolling. Notification: continuous. Transfer credits accepted: Yes.

Costs Per Year: Application fee: $45. Comprehensive fee: $35,660 includes full-time tuition ($26,481), mandatory fees ($500), and college room and board ($8679). College room only: $4159. Full-time tuition and fees vary according to location. Room and board charges vary according to housing facility.

Collegiate Environment: Orientation program. Drama-theater group, choral group, marching band, student-run newspaper. Social organizations: 19 open to all; national fraternities, national sororities; 1% of eligible men and 1% of eligible women are members. Most popular organizations: Refuge Campus Ministry, NCWC Cheerleaders, Voices of Triumph, Campus Crusade for Christ, Visions of Beauty. Major annual events: Homecoming Week, Spring Fling, Wesleyan Symposium. Student services: health clinic, personal-psychological counseling. Campus security: 24-hour emergency response devices and patrols, late night transport-escort service, controlled dormitory access. 550 college housing spaces available; 469 were occupied in 2012-13. Freshmen guaranteed college housing. On-campus residence required through sophomore year. Options: coed, men-only, women-only housing available. Elizabeth Braswell Pearsall Library with 265,500 books, 36,062 microform titles, 39,760 serials, 17,840 audiovisual materials, an OPAC, and a Web page. Operations spending for the previous fiscal year: $360,489. 199 computers available on campus for general student use. A campuswide network can be accessed from student residence rooms and from off campus. Staffed computer lab on campus.

Community Environment: Rocky Mount, population 56,600, is located three miles from Interstate 95 in the coastal plain region of the state. It is a progressive industrial and agricultural community, but still maintains its historic heritage. Nash General and Community Hospital are only 10 minutes from campus. Many recreational facilities are easily accessible.

■ PAMLICO COMMUNITY COLLEGE

PO Box 185
Grantsboro, NC 28529-0185
Tel: (252)249-1851
Fax: (252)249-2377
Web Site: www.pamlico.cc.nc.us/

Description: State-supported, 2-year, coed. Part of North Carolina Community College System. Awards certificates, diplomas, transfer associate, and terminal associate degrees. Founded 1963. Setting: 44-acre rural campus. Total enrollment: 300. Faculty: 10 (6 full-time, 4 part-time). 58% 25 or older. Core. Calendar: semesters. Academic remediation for entering students, services for LD students, summer session for credit, part-time degree program, adult/continuing education programs, co-op programs.

Entrance Requirements: Open admission. Options: early admission, deferred admission. Required: high school transcript. Entrance: noncompetitive. Application deadline: Rolling. Notification: continuous.

Collegiate Environment: Student-run newspaper. Student services: personal-psychological counseling. Campus security: evening security guard. Pamlico Community College Library plus 1 other with 19,500 books and 202 serials. 68 computers available on campus for general student use.

■ PFEIFFER UNIVERSITY

PO Box 960
Misenheimer, NC 28109-0960
Tel: (704)463-1360; Free: 800-338-2060
Fax: (704)463-1363
E-mail: admiss@pfeiffer.edu
Web Site: www.pfeiffer.edu/

Description: Independent United Methodist, comprehensive, coed. Awards bachelor's and master's degrees. Founded 1885. Setting: 300-acre rural campus with easy access to Charlotte. Endowment: $15.2 million. Total enrollment: 2,019. Faculty: 150 (76 full-time, 74 part-time). Student-undergrad faculty ratio is 14:1. 912 applied, 71% were admitted. 17% from top 10% of their high school class, 30% from top quarter, 61% from top half. Students come from 36 states and territories, 12 other countries, 18% from out-of-state. 35% 25 or older, 65% live on campus. Retention: 66% of full-time freshmen returned the following year. Academic areas with the most degrees conferred: business/marketing; homeland security, law enforcement, firefighting, and protective services; education. Core. Calendar: semesters. Academic remediation for entering students, ESL program, services for LD students, advanced placement, accelerated degree program, honors program, independent study, double major, summer session for credit, part-time degree program, co-op programs and internships. Study abroad program. ROTC: Army (c).

Entrance Requirements: Options: electronic application, early admission, deferred admission. Required: high school transcript, SAT or ACT. Recommended: minimum 2.0 high school GPA, interview. Required for some: 2 recommendations. Entrance: moderately difficult. Application deadline: Rolling. Notification: continuous.

Collegiate Environment: Orientation program. Drama-theater group, choral group, student-run newspaper. Social organizations: 41 open to all. Most popular organizations: Student Government Association, Religious Life Council, Commuter Student Association, Programming Activities Council, Residence Hall Association. Major annual events: Homecoming, Winterfest, Aprilfest. Student services: health clinic, personal-psychological counseling, women's center. Campus security: 24-hour emergency response devices and patrols, late night transport-escort service, controlled dormitory access. Gustavus A. Pfeiffer Library with 125,972 books, 85,353 microform titles, 288 serials, 3,702 audiovisual materials, an OPAC, and a Web page. 114 computers available on campus for general student use. A campuswide network can be accessed from student residence rooms. Students can access the following: online class registration.

Community Environment: The setting for Misenheimer is a rural area with moderate mild climate. Commercial transportation is available at nearby Salisbury, and airlines at Charlotte. Recreational activities include swimming, boating, hunting and camping.

■ PIEDMONT COMMUNITY COLLEGE

PO Box 1197
Roxboro, NC 27573-1197
Tel: (336)599-1181
Fax: (336)597-3817
Web Site: www.piedmont.cc.nc.us/

Description: State-supported, 2-year, coed. Part of North Carolina Community College System. Awards certificates, diplomas, transfer associate, and terminal associate degrees. Founded 1970. Setting: 178-acre small town campus. Total enrollment: 1,805. Full-time: 819 students, 61% women, 39% men. Part-time: 986 students, 65% women, 35% men. Core. Calendar: semesters. Academic remediation for entering students, ESL program, advanced placement, distance learning, double major, summer session for credit, part-time degree program, adult/continuing education programs, co-op programs. Off campus study at other technical institutes and community colleges in North Carolina.

Entrance Requirements: Open admission except for nursing and medical assisting programs. Options: electronic application, early admission, deferred admission. Required for some: high school transcript. Entrance: noncompetitive. Application deadline: Rolling. Notification: continuous until 9/29.

Collegiate Environment: Drama-theater group, choral group. Student services: personal-psychological counseling. Campus security: routine patrols by the local sheriff's department. College housing not available. Learning Resource Center with 24,166 books and 278 serials.

■ **PIEDMONT INTERNATIONAL UNIVERSITY**
420 S Broad St.
Winston-Salem, NC 27101-5197
Tel: (336)725-8344; Free: 800-937-5097
Fax: (336)725-5522
E-mail: stevensons@piedmontU.edu
Web Site: www.pbc.edu/

Description: Independent Baptist, comprehensive, coed. Awards associate, bachelor's, master's, and doctoral degrees. Founded 1947. Setting: 12-acre urban campus. Total enrollment: 392. 111 applied, 48% were admitted. Full-time: 197 students, 49% women, 51% men. Part-time: 77 students, 36% women, 64% men. Students come from 21 states and territories, 4 other countries, 29% from out-of-state. 0.4% American Indian or Alaska Native, non-Hispanic/Latino; 2% Hispanic/Latino; 5% African American, non-Hispanic/Latino; 1% Asian, non-Hispanic/Latino; 1% Native Hawaiian or other Pacific Islander, non-Hispanic/Latino. 33% 25 or older, 33% live on campus, 50% transferred in. Retention: 57% of full-time freshmen returned the following year. Core. Calendar: semesters. Academic remediation for entering students, advanced placement, double major, summer session for credit, part-time degree program, adult/continuing education programs, internships, graduate courses open to undergrads. Study abroad program.

Entrance Requirements: Open admission. Options: electronic application, early admission, early action, deferred admission. Required: essay, high school transcript, 2 recommendations, medical history, proof of immunization, SAT or ACT. Recommended: minimum 2 high school GPA, interview. Entrance: noncompetitive. Application deadlines: Rolling, 11/1 for early action. Notification: 12/1 for early action. SAT Reasoning Test deadline: 7/1. SAT Subject Test deadline: 7/1.

Costs Per Year: Application fee: $55. Comprehensive fee: $19,605 includes full-time tuition ($12,340), mandatory fees ($855), and college room and board ($6410).

Collegiate Environment: Orientation program. Choral group. Major annual events: Community Service Work Day, Artist Series, CHRISTMAS CONCERT. Campus security: 24-hour emergency response devices, student patrols, late night transport-escort service, controlled dormitory access, security guards on duty from dusk until dawn. George Manuel Memorial Library with 50,000 books and 204 serials.

Community Environment: See Wake Forest University.

■ **PITT COMMUNITY COLLEGE**
Hwy. 11 S, PO Drawer 7007
Greenville, NC 27835-7007
Tel: (252)321-4200
Fax: (252)321-4401
E-mail: pittadm@pcc.pitt.cc.nc.us
Web Site: www.pittcc.edu/

Description: State and locally supported, 2-year, coed. Part of North Carolina Community College System. Awards certificates, diplomas, transfer associate, and terminal associate degrees. Founded 1961. Setting: 172-acre small town campus. Total enrollment: 7,076. Full-time: 3,822 students, 56% women, 44% men. Part-time: 3,254 students, 63% women, 37% men. Core. Calendar: semesters. Academic remediation for entering students, ESL program, services for LD students, advanced placement, independent study, distance learning, double major, summer session for credit, part-time degree program, external degree program, adult/continuing education programs, co-op programs and internships. ROTC: Army.

Entrance Requirements: Open admission except for health science programs. Options: electronic application, deferred admission. Required: high school transcript. Entrance: noncompetitive. Application deadline: Rolling.

Costs Per Year: Application fee: $0. State resident tuition: $2208 full-time, $69 per credit hour part-time. Nonresident tuition: $8352 full-time, $261 per credit hour part-time. Mandatory fees: $86 full-time, $42.75. Part-time tuition and fees vary according to course level.

Collegiate Environment: Orientation program. Student services: personal-psychological counseling. Campus security: 24-hour patrols, student patrols, late night transport-escort service. Pitt Community College Library with 43,302 books, 1,625 microform titles, 242 serials, 4,166 audiovisual materials, an OPAC, and a Web page.

Community Environment: See East Carolina University.

■ **QUEENS UNIVERSITY OF CHARLOTTE**
1900 Selwyn Ave.
Charlotte, NC 28274-0002
Tel: (704)337-2200; Free: 800-849-0202
Fax: (704)337-2403
E-mail: admissions@queens.edu
Web Site: www.queens.edu/

Description: Independent Presbyterian, comprehensive, coed. Awards bachelor's and master's degrees. Founded 1857. Setting: 30-acre suburban campus. Endowment: $84 million. Total enrollment: 2,386. Faculty: 254 (124 full-time, 130 part-time). Student-undergrad faculty ratio is 12:1. 3,472 applied, 53% were admitted. 18% from top 10% of their high school class, 46% from top quarter, 77% from top half. Full-time: 1,450 students, 73% women, 27% men. Part-time: 419 students, 80% women, 20% men. Students come from 30 states and territories, 19 other countries, 40% from out-of-state. 1% American Indian or Alaska Native, non-Hispanic/Latino; 7% Hispanic/Latino; 19% African American, non-Hispanic/Latino; 3% Asian, non-Hispanic/Latino; 0% Native Hawaiian or other Pacific Islander, non-Hispanic/Latino; 1% international. 28% 25 or older, 80% live on campus, 9% transferred in. Retention: 69% of full-time freshmen returned the following year. Academic areas with the most degrees conferred: health professions and related sciences; communication/journalism; business/marketing. Core. Calendar: semesters. Advanced placement, honors program, independent study, double major, summer session for credit, part-time degree program, adult/continuing education programs, internships, graduate courses open to undergrads. Off campus study at members of the Charlotte Area Educational Consortium. Study abroad program. ROTC: Army (c), Air Force (c).

Entrance Requirements: Options: electronic application, deferred admission, international baccalaureate accepted. Required: high school transcript, minimum 2.5 high school GPA, SAT or ACT. Recommended: interview. Required for some: essay, 1 recommendation. Entrance: moderately difficult. Application deadlines: Rolling, Rolling for nonresidents. Notification: continuous, continuous for nonresidents. Transfer credits accepted: Yes.

Costs Per Year: Application fee: $40. Comprehensive fee: $36,988 includes full-time tuition ($27,576) and college room and board ($9412). College room only: $5514. Room and board charges vary according to board plan and housing facility.

Collegiate Environment: Orientation program. Drama-theater group, choral group, student-run newspaper. Social organizations: 40 open to all; national fraternities, national sororities; 13% of eligible men and 18% of eligible women are members. Most popular organizations: Senate, College Union Board, Royal Ambassadors, Students for Black Awareness, International Club. Major annual events: Casino Night, Boar's Head/Yule Log, Homecoming. Student services: health clinic, personal-psychological counseling. Campus security: 24-hour emergency response devices and patrols, late night transport-escort service, controlled dormitory access, Emergency Alert System. 824 college housing spaces available. Freshmen guaranteed college housing. On-campus residence required through junior year. Option: coed housing available. Everett Library with 126,242 books, 1,452 microform titles, 592 serials, an OPAC, and a Web page. 125 computers available on campus for general student use. Computer purchase/lease plans available. A campuswide network can be accessed from student residence rooms and from off campus. Students can access the following: online class registration. Staffed computer lab on campus (open 24 hours a day).

■ **RANDOLPH COMMUNITY COLLEGE**
629 Industrial Park Ave.
Asheboro, NC 27205
Tel: (336)633-0200
Fax: (336)629-4695
E-mail: bhagerman@randolph.edu
Web Site: www.randolph.edu/

Description: State-supported, 2-year, coed. Part of North Carolina Community College System. Awards certificates, diplomas, transfer associate, and terminal associate degrees. Founded 1962. Setting: 40-acre small town campus with easy access to Greensboro, Winston-Salem, High Point. Endowment: $8.7 million. Total enrollment: 2,894. Faculty: 252 (82 full-time,

170 part-time). Student-undergrad faculty ratio is 11:1. 2,792 applied, 100% were admitted. Full-time: 1,066 students, 62% women, 38% men. Part-time: 1,828 students, 67% women, 33% men. Students come from 5 states and territories, 10 other countries, 1% from out-of-state. 1% American Indian or Alaska Native, non-Hispanic/Latino; 9% Hispanic/Latino; 9% African American, non-Hispanic/Latino; 1% Asian, non-Hispanic/Latino; 0.1% Native Hawaiian or other Pacific Islander, non-Hispanic/Latino; 0% international. 36% 25 or older, 17% transferred in. Retention: 56% of full-time freshmen returned the following year. Core. Calendar: semesters. Academic remediation for entering students, ESL program, services for LD students, advanced placement, independent study, distance learning, double major, summer session for credit, part-time degree program, adult/continuing education programs, co-op programs and internships. Off campus study at other members of the North Carolina Community College System.

Entrance Requirements: Open admission. Options: electronic application, deferred admission, international baccalaureate accepted. Entrance: noncompetitive. Application deadline: Rolling. Notification: continuous. Transfer credits accepted: Yes.

Costs Per Year: Application fee: $0. State resident tuition: $2208 full-time, $69 per credit part-time. Nonresident tuition: $8352 full-time, $261 per credit part-time. Mandatory fees: $88 full-time, $2.75 per credit part-time.

Collegiate Environment: Social organizations: 9 open to all. Most popular organizations: Student Government Association, Phi Theta Kappa, Student Nurse Association, Phi Beta Lambda, Campus Crusaders. Major annual events: Fall Fling, Spring Fling, Holiday Party. Student services: personal-psychological counseling. Campus security: 24-hour emergency response devices, security officer during open hours. College housing not available. R. Alton Cox Learning Resources Center with 30,000 books, 5,000 audiovisual materials, an OPAC, and a Web page. 850 computers available on campus for general student use. A campuswide network can be accessed. Students can access the following: online class registration. Staffed computer lab on campus provides training in use of computers, software, and the Internet.

Community Environment: Asheboro is the county seat of Randolph County and is located near the geographical center of the state. The town has grown steadily with the surrounding area, which is mainly agricultural. Community facilities include numerous churches, a library, convenient shopping centers, and the North Carolina State Zoo. Several lakes nearby provide facilities for hunting, fishing, boating, and water skiing.

■ **RICHMOND COMMUNITY COLLEGE**

PO Box 1189
Hamlet, NC 28345-1189
Tel: (910)582-7000
Fax: (910)582-7102
E-mail: daphnes@richmondcc.edu
Web Site: www.richmondcc.edu/

Description: State-supported, 2-year, coed. Part of North Carolina Community College System. Awards diplomas, transfer associate, and terminal associate degrees. Founded 1964. Setting: 163-acre rural campus. Total enrollment: 1,969. Student-undergrad faculty ratio is 20:1. 0% from out-of-state. 49% 25 or older. Calendar: semesters. Academic remediation for entering students, ESL program, advanced placement, self-designed majors, independent study, distance learning, double major, summer session for credit, part-time degree program, adult/continuing education programs, co-op programs and internships.

Entrance Requirements: Open admission except for nursing program. Option: deferred admission. Required: high school transcript. Entrance: noncompetitive. Application deadline: Rolling. Notification: continuous until 8/1.

Collegiate Environment: Student services: personal-psychological counseling. Campus security: 24-hour emergency response devices, security guard during evening hours. Richmond Community College Library with 30,088 books, 236 serials, and an OPAC.

Community Environment: Located 75 miles southeast of Charlotte, Hamlet is a town with a friendly atmosphere. Its primary businesses are manufacturing and textiles. Train and bus transportation is available. Community facilities include churches of various faiths, a library, shopping areas and good medical facilities. Recreational activities include swimming, boating, tennis, and fishing.

■ **ROANOKE-CHOWAN COMMUNITY COLLEGE**

109 Community College Rd.
Ahoskie, NC 27910
Tel: (252)862-1200

Fax: (252)862-1353
Web Site: www.roanokechowan.edu/

Description: State-supported, 2-year, coed. Part of North Carolina Community College System. Awards certificates, diplomas, transfer associate, and terminal associate degrees. Founded 1967. Setting: 39-acre rural campus. Total enrollment: 384. 50% 25 or older. Core. Calendar: semesters. Academic remediation for entering students, distance learning, summer session for credit, part-time degree program, adult/continuing education programs, co-op programs.

Entrance Requirements: Open admission except for nursing program. Option: early admission. Required for some: interview. Entrance: noncompetitive. Application deadline: Rolling. Notification: continuous.

Collegiate Environment: Orientation program. 29,268 books, 207 serials, an OPAC, and a Web page.

Community Environment: See Chowan College.

■ **ROBESON COMMUNITY COLLEGE**

5160 Fayetteville Rd.
Lumberton, NC 28359-1420
Tel: (910)272-3700
Fax: (910)272-3328
E-mail: plocklear@robeson.edu
Web Site: www.robeson.cc.nc.us/

Description: State-supported, 2-year, coed. Part of North Carolina Community College System. Awards transfer associate and terminal associate degrees. Founded 1965. Setting: 78-acre small town campus. Total enrollment: 2,869. Faculty: 114 (44 full-time, 70 part-time). Calendar: semesters. Academic remediation for entering students, services for LD students, distance learning, co-op programs.

Entrance Requirements: Open admission. Options: electronic application, early admission. Required: high school transcript. Entrance: noncompetitive. Application deadline: Rolling. Notification: continuous. Transfer credits accepted: Yes.

Collegiate Environment: Orientation program. Student services: personal-psychological counseling. College housing not available. 39,000 books and 225 serials 100 computers available on campus for general student use. A campuswide network can be accessed from off-campus. Staffed computer lab on campus.

Community Environment: Located in a rural setting in Robeson County, this community is a short distance from Lumberton, the county seat, and has access to all the advantages of that city. Commercial transportation is available. Lumberton is also one of the major tobacco markets; other industries are here along with a number of churches and a library.

■ **ROCKINGHAM COMMUNITY COLLEGE**

PO Box 38
Wentworth, NC 27375-0038
Tel: (336)342-4261
E-mail: admissions@rockinghamcc.edu
Web Site: www.rockinghamcc.edu/

Description: State-supported, 2-year, coed. Part of North Carolina Community College System. Awards certificates, diplomas, transfer associate, and terminal associate degrees. Founded 1964. Setting: 257-acre rural campus. Total enrollment: 2,631. Faculty: 111 (66 full-time, 45 part-time). Student-undergrad faculty ratio is 18:1. Full-time: 1,216 students, 62% women, 38% men. Part-time: 1,415 students, 64% women, 36% men. Students come from 10 states and territories, 8 other countries, 1% from out-of-state. 1% American Indian or Alaska Native, non-Hispanic/Latino; 2% Hispanic/Latino; 25% African American, non-Hispanic/Latino; 0.5% Asian, non-Hispanic/Latino; 0.1% Native Hawaiian or other Pacific Islander, non-Hispanic/Latino; 0.1% international. 41% 25 or older, 18% transferred in. Calendar: semesters. Academic remediation for entering students, advanced placement, self-designed majors, summer session for credit, part-time degree program, adult/continuing education programs, co-op programs.

Entrance Requirements: Open admission except for allied health programs. Options: electronic application, early admission, deferred admission. Entrance: noncompetitive. Application deadline: Rolling. Notification: continuous.

Costs Per Year: Application fee: $0. State resident tuition: $2128 full-time, $66.50 per credit part-time. Nonresident tuition: $8272 full-time, $258.50 per credit part-time. Mandatory fees: $116 full-time. Full-time tuition and fees vary according to course load. Part-time tuition varies according to course load.

Collegiate Environment: Student-run newspaper. Major annual events: Fall

Kickoff, Spring Fling, Blood drive. Student services: personal-psychological counseling. Campus security: 24-hour emergency response devices and patrols. Gerald B. James Library with 2,124 books, 29 microform titles, 433 audiovisual materials, an OPAC, and a Web page. 1,000 computers available on campus for general student use. A campuswide network can be accessed. Students can access the following: online class registration. Staffed computer lab on campus provides training in use of computers, software, and the Internet.

Community Environment: Located near Reidsville and Eden in Rockingham County.

■ ROWAN-CABARRUS COMMUNITY COLLEGE

PO Box 1595
Salisbury, NC 28145-1595
Tel: (704)637-0760
Fax: (704)633-6804
Web Site: www.rccc.edu/

Description: State-supported, 2-year, coed. Part of North Carolina Community College System. Awards diplomas, transfer associate, and terminal associate degrees. Founded 1963. Setting: 100-acre small town campus. Total enrollment: 5,158. 44% 25 or older. Calendar: semesters. Academic remediation for entering students, ESL program, services for LD students, advanced placement, distance learning, summer session for credit, part-time degree program, adult/continuing education programs, co-op programs and internships.

Entrance Requirements: Open admission. Required: high school transcript. Entrance: noncompetitive. Application deadline: Rolling.

Collegiate Environment: Orientation program. Student services: personal-psychological counseling. Campus security: on-campus security during operating hours. Learning Resource Center with 23,005 books and 313 serials.

■ ST. ANDREWS UNIVERSITY

1700 Dogwood Mile
Laurinburg, NC 28352-5598
Tel: (910)277-5000; Free: 800-763-0198
Fax: (910)277-5087
E-mail: admission@sapc.edu
Web Site: www.sapc.edu/

Description: Independent Presbyterian, comprehensive, coed. Administratively affiliated with Webber International University. Awards bachelor's and master's degrees. Founded 1958. Setting: 600-acre small town campus. Total enrollment: 474. Faculty: 53 (27 full-time, 26 part-time). Student-undergrad faculty ratio is 13:1. 826 applied, 69% were admitted. 5% from top 10% of their high school class, 21% from top quarter, 47% from top half. Full-time: 438 students, 54% women, 46% men. Part-time: 22 students, 73% women, 27% men. 51% from out-of-state. 1% American Indian or Alaska Native, non-Hispanic/Latino; 1% Hispanic/Latino; 19% African American, non-Hispanic/Latino; 1% Asian, non-Hispanic/Latino; 7% international. 5% 25 or older, 85% live on campus, 16% transferred in. Retention: 64% of full-time freshmen returned the following year. Academic areas with the most degrees conferred: education; business/marketing; biological/life sciences; interdisciplinary studies. Calendar: semesters. Part-time degree program, adult/continuing education programs.

Entrance Requirements: Options: electronic application, deferred admission, international baccalaureate accepted. Required: high school transcript, SAT or ACT. Recommended: minimum 2 high school GPA. Required for some: essay, interview. Entrance: moderately difficult. Application deadline: Rolling. Notification: continuous. SAT Reasoning Test deadline: 8/1. SAT Subject Test deadline: 8/1.

Costs Per Year: Application fee: $30. Comprehensive fee: $32,050 includes full-time tuition ($22,674) and college room and board ($9376). Full-time tuition varies according to course load and location. Room and board charges vary according to housing facility.

Collegiate Environment: Orientation program. Campus security: 24-hour emergency response devices and patrols, late night transport-escort service. On-campus residence required through senior year. Options: coed, men-only, women-only housing available. DeTamble Library with an OPAC and a Web page.

■ SAINT AUGUSTINE'S COLLEGE

1315 Oakwood Ave.
Raleigh, NC 27610-2298
Tel: (919)516-4000; Free: 800-948-1126

Fax: (919)516-4415
E-mail: jesousa@st-aug.edu
Web Site: www.st-aug.edu/

Description: Independent Episcopal, 4-year, coed. Awards bachelor's degrees. Founded 1867. Setting: 122-acre urban campus. Endowment: $17.7 million. Educational spending for the previous fiscal year: $5860 per student. Total enrollment: 1,506. Faculty: 151 (85 full-time, 66 part-time). Student-undergrad faculty ratio is 14:1. 2,796 applied, 69% were admitted. 0% from top 10% of their high school class, 0% from top quarter, 0% from top half. Full-time: 1,466 students, 49% women, 51% men. Part-time: 40 students, 48% women, 53% men. Students come from 33 states and territories, 10 other countries, 45% from out-of-state. 0% American Indian or Alaska Native, non-Hispanic/Latino; 1% Hispanic/Latino; 97% African American, non-Hispanic/Latino; 0% Asian, non-Hispanic/Latino; 0% Native Hawaiian or other Pacific Islander, non-Hispanic/Latino; 2% international. 12% 25 or older, 79% live on campus, 4% transferred in. Retention: 51% of full-time freshmen returned the following year. Academic areas with the most degrees conferred: business/marketing; social sciences; homeland security, law enforcement, firefighting, and protective services. Calendar: semesters. Services for LD students, advanced placement, accelerated degree program, freshman honors college, honors program, independent study, double major, summer session for credit, part-time degree program, adult/continuing education programs, co-op programs and internships. Off campus study at Consortium - cooperating Raleigh Colleges (Shaw University, Peace College, Meredith College, North Carolina State University). Study abroad program. ROTC: Army, Air Force (c).

Entrance Requirements: Options: electronic application, deferred admission, international baccalaureate accepted. Required: high school transcript, minimum 2 high school GPA, 2 recommendations, medical history, social security card, background check, SAT or ACT. Recommended: minimum 2.5 high school GPA. Required for some: essay, interview. Entrance: moderately difficult. Application deadlines: Rolling, Rolling for nonresidents. Notification: continuous, continuous for nonresidents. SAT Reasoning Test deadline: 8/5. SAT Subject Test deadline: 8/5. Transfer credits accepted: Yes.

Costs Per Year: Application fee: $25. Comprehensive fee: $24,722 includes full-time tuition ($12,364), mandatory fees ($4796), and college room and board ($7562). College room only: $3128. Full-time tuition and fees vary according to course load. Room and board charges vary according to housing facility. Part-time tuition: $515 per credit hour. Part-time mandatory fees: $200 per credit hour. Part-time tuition and fees vary according to course load.

Collegiate Environment: Orientation program. Drama-theater group, choral group, marching band. Social organizations: 44 open to all; national fraternities, national sororities, select social organizations; 17% of eligible men and 15% of eligible women are members. Most popular organizations: Campus Activity Board, Christian Fellowship Organization, Collegiate 100 Black Men of America, Student Government Association/Student Leaders, Falcon Fanatic Pep Squad. Major annual events: Fall and Spring Fling, Homecoming, Community Day. Student services: health clinic, personal-psychological counseling. Campus security: 24-hour emergency response devices and patrols, RAVE - Emergency Notification System. Prezell R. Robinson Library with 100,288 books, 332 microform titles, 330 serials, 710 audiovisual materials, an OPAC, and a Web page. Operations spending for the previous fiscal year: $418,068. 193 computers available on campus for general student use. A campuswide network can be accessed from student residence rooms and from off campus. Students can access the following: online class registration. Staffed computer lab on campus provides training in use of computers, software, and the Internet.

■ SALEM COLLEGE

601 S Church St.
Winston-Salem, NC 27101
Tel: (336)721-2600; Free: 800-327-2536
Fax: (336)724-7102
E-mail: admissions@salem.edu
Web Site: www.salem.edu/

Description: Independent Moravian, comprehensive, coed. Awards bachelor's and master's degrees (only students age 23 or over are eligible to enroll part-time). Founded 1772. Setting: 67-acre urban campus with easy access to Charlotte. Total enrollment: 985. Faculty: 99 (59 full-time, 40 part-time). Student-undergrad faculty ratio is 11:1. 450 applied, 60% were admitted. 36% from top 10% of their high school class, 67% from top quarter, 93% from top half. 4 valedictorians, 24 student government officers. Full-time: 612 students, 98% women, 2% men. Part-time: 152 students, 91% women, 9%

men. Students come from 27 states and territories, 7 other countries, 42% from out-of-state. 39% 25 or older, 86% live on campus, 11% transferred in. Retention: 75% of full-time freshmen returned the following year. Core. Calendar: 4-1-4. Advanced placement, self-designed majors, honors program, independent study, double major, summer session for credit, part-time degree program, adult/continuing education programs, internships. Off campus study at Wake Forest University, American University, Brethren Colleges Abroad (BCA). ROTC: Army (c), Air Force (c).

Entrance Requirements: Options: electronic application, early admission, deferred admission, international baccalaureate accepted. Required: essay, high school transcript, 2 recommendations, SAT or ACT. Recommended: interview. Entrance: moderately difficult. Application deadline: Rolling. Notification: continuous.

Costs Per Year: Application fee: $30. Comprehensive fee: $35,603 includes full-time tuition ($23,478), mandatory fees ($361), and college room and board ($11,764). Part-time tuition: $1328 per course. Part-time mandatory fees: $145 per year.

Collegiate Environment: Orientation program. Drama-theater group, choral group, marching band, student-run newspaper. Social organizations: 41 open to all. Most popular organizations: Student Government Association, Onua, Campus Activities Council, International Club, Ambassadors. Major annual events: Fall Fest, Dance Weekends, Candlelight Christmas Service. Student services: health clinic, personal-psychological counseling. Campus security: 24-hour emergency response devices and patrols, late night transport-escort service, controlled dormitory access. Dale Gramley Library plus 1 other with 152,000 books, 321,695 microform titles, 679 serials, 14,187 audiovisual materials, an OPAC, and a Web page. 54 computers available on campus for general student use. Computer purchase/lease plans available. A campuswide network can be accessed from student residence rooms and from off campus. Staffed computer lab on campus provides training in use of computers.

Community Environment: See Wake Forest University.

■ SAMPSON COMMUNITY COLLEGE
1801 Sunset Ave.
Hwy. 24 W
Clinton, NC 28329-0318
Tel: (910)592-8081
Fax: (910)592-8048
Web Site: www.sampsoncc.edu/

Description: State and locally supported, 2-year, coed. Part of North Carolina Community College System. Awards certificates, diplomas, transfer associate, and terminal associate degrees. Founded 1965. Setting: 55-acre rural campus. Total enrollment: 1,579. Faculty: 95 (45 full-time, 50 part-time). Student-undergrad faculty ratio is 20:1. 712 applied, 100% were admitted. Full-time: 679 students, 73% women, 27% men. Part-time: 900 students, 73% women, 27% men. Students come from 4 states and territories, 1% from out-of-state. 52% 25 or older, 1% transferred in. Core. Calendar: semesters. Academic remediation for entering students, services for LD students, advanced placement, independent study, summer session for credit, part-time degree program, adult/continuing education programs, co-op programs and internships.

Entrance Requirements: Open admission except for nursing program. Option: deferred admission. Required: high school transcript, interview. Recommended: minimum 2.0 high school GPA. Entrance: noncompetitive. Application deadline: Rolling. Notification: continuous.

Collegiate Environment: Orientation program. Social organizations: 7 open to all. Most popular organizations: Student Government Association, Criminal Justice Club, Nursing Student Association, Cosmetology Alliance Club, Phi Beta Lambda. Major annual event: Field Day. Student services: personal-psychological counseling. Campus security: local police patrol. Sampson Community College Library with 25,000 books, 250 serials, an OPAC, and a Web page. 78 computers available on campus for general student use. A campuswide network can be accessed. Staffed computer lab on campus.

Community Environment: The county seat of Sampson County, Clinton is in the coastal plain section of the state. Community facilities have grown as Clinton has grown in population. A complete shopping center is located here, along with churches representing most denominations. A county hospital and numerous civic and service organizations serve the community. 28 industrial firms are based here. Job opportunities are available. Recreational activities include golf, hunting, fishing, and swimming.

■ SANDHILLS COMMUNITY COLLEGE
3395 Airport Rd.
Pinehurst, NC 28374-8299
Tel: (910)692-6185; Free: 800-338-3944
Fax: (910)695-1823
E-mail: robledoi@sandhills.edu
Web Site: www.sandhills.edu/

Description: State-supported, 2-year, coed. Part of North Carolina Community College System. Awards certificates, diplomas, transfer associate, and terminal associate degrees. Founded 1963. Setting: 240-acre small town campus. Endowment: $10.7 million. Educational spending for the previous fiscal year: $3508 per student. Total enrollment: 4,571. Faculty: 409 (145 full-time, 264 part-time). Student-undergrad faculty ratio is 13:1. Core. Calendar: semesters. Academic remediation for entering students, ESL program, services for LD students, advanced placement, independent study, distance learning, double major, summer session for credit, part-time degree program, co-op programs and internships. Off campus study.

Entrance Requirements: Open admission. Options: electronic application, deferred admission. Required: high school transcript. Application deadline: Rolling. Notification: continuous. Transfer credits accepted: Yes.

Collegiate Environment: Orientation program. Drama-theater group, choral group, marching band, student-run newspaper. Social organizations: 21 open to all. Most popular organizations: Rotaract (Service Club - College Affiliate of Rotary International), Student Government Association, Outdoors Club, New Beginning Gospel Choir, Revolutionary Gamers Club. Major annual events: Spring Fling, College Days, Health Career Day. Student services: personal-psychological counseling. Campus security: 24-hour emergency response devices, security on duty until 12 am. Boyd Library with 76,080 books, 107,190 microform titles, 286 serials, 2,317 audiovisual materials, an OPAC, and a Web page. Operations spending for the previous fiscal year: $672,583. 300 computers available on campus for general student use. A campuswide network can be accessed from off-campus. Staffed computer lab on campus.

Community Environment: Pinehurst, established originally as a health resort, has a small town environment. The area of Southern Pines is famous for its dry and mild climate, its golf and tourism as well as for major horse stables. Community facilities include three libraries, a twenty-five acre garden, churches of all denominations, and various civic and service organizations. Recreational activities include golf, tennis, horseback riding, hunting, and fishing.

■ SHAW UNIVERSITY
118 E S St.
Raleigh, NC 27601-2399
Tel: (919)546-8200; Free: 800-214-6683
Fax: (919)546-8271
E-mail: sherlock@shawu.edu
Web Site: www.shawu.edu/

Description: Independent Baptist, comprehensive, coed. Awards associate, bachelor's, and master's degrees. Founded 1865. Setting: 30-acre urban campus. Total enrollment: 2,183. Faculty: 187 (109 full-time, 78 part-time). Student-undergrad faculty ratio is 15:1. 6,207 applied, 54% were admitted. 1% from top 10% of their high school class, 5% from top quarter, 25% from top half. Full-time: 1,879 students, 56% women, 44% men. Part-time: 152 students, 76% women, 24% men. Students come from 30 states and territories, 16 other countries, 32% from out-of-state. 0.05% American Indian or Alaska Native, non-Hispanic/Latino; 0.4% Hispanic/Latino; 86% African American, non-Hispanic/Latino; 0.05% Asian, non-Hispanic/Latino; 2% international. 29% 25 or older, 40% live on campus, 8% transferred in. Academic areas with the most degrees conferred: business/marketing; public administration and social services; homeland security, law enforcement, firefighting, and protective services. Core. Calendar: semesters. Academic remediation for entering students, services for LD students, advanced placement, accelerated degree program, self-designed majors, honors program, independent study, distance learning, double major, summer session for credit, part-time degree program, adult/continuing education programs, internships. Off campus study at Cooperating Raleigh Colleges. Study abroad program. ROTC: Army (c).

Entrance Requirements: Options: electronic application, early admission, deferred admission, international baccalaureate accepted. Required: high school transcript, minimum 2 high school GPA. Recommended: SAT or ACT. Entrance: minimally difficult. Application deadline: 7/30. Notification: continuous. Transfer credits accepted: Yes.

Collegiate Environment: Orientation program. Drama-theater group, choral

group, marching band, student-run newspaper, radio station. Social organizations: national fraternities, national sororities. Most popular organizations: Student Government Association, choir, University band, Shaw Players, academic clubs. Major annual events: University Convocation, Homecoming, Honors Convocation. Student services: health clinic, personal-psychological counseling. Campus security: 24-hour emergency response devices and patrols, late night transport-escort service, 24-hour electronic surveillance cameras. 1,200 college housing spaces available; 818 were occupied in 2012-13. No special consideration for freshman housing applicants. On-campus residence required in freshman year. Options: men-only, women-only housing available. James E. Cheek Learning Resources Center with an OPAC and a Web page.

Community Environment: See Meredith College.

■ SHEPHERDS THEOLOGICAL SEMINARY

6051 Tyron Rd.
Cary, NC 27518
Tel: (919)573-5350
Web Site: shepherds.edu/
Description: Independent religious, comprehensive, coed. Founded 2003. Calendar: semesters.

■ SOUTH COLLEGE–ASHEVILLE

1567 Patton Ave.
Asheville, NC 28806
Tel: (828)252-2486
Web Site: www.southcollegenc.edu/
Description: Proprietary, primarily 2-year, coed. Awards certificates, terminal associate, and bachelor's degrees. Founded 1905. Setting: 8-acre urban campus. Total enrollment: 180. Student-undergrad faculty ratio is 8:1. 0% from out-of-state. 62% 25 or older. Summer session for credit, part-time degree program, adult/continuing education programs.
Entrance Requirements: Open admission. Option: deferred admission. Required: high school transcript, CPAt. Entrance: noncompetitive. Application deadline: Rolling.
Collegiate Environment: Orientation program. Campus security: night security.

■ SOUTH PIEDMONT COMMUNITY COLLEGE

PO Box 126
Polkton, NC 28135-0126
Tel: (704)272-7635; Free: 800-766-0319
E-mail: abaucom@vnet.net
Web Site: www.spcc.edu/
Description: State-supported, 2-year, coed. Part of North Carolina Community College System. Awards certificates, diplomas, transfer associate, and terminal associate degrees. Founded 1962. Setting: 56-acre rural campus with easy access to Charlotte. Endowment: $27,818. Educational spending for the previous fiscal year: $2802 per student. Total enrollment: 2,075. Faculty: 106. Student-undergrad faculty ratio is 17:1. 740 applied, 84% were admitted. 2% from top 10% of their high school class, 5% from top quarter, 10% from top half. Students come from 3 states and territories, 1% from out-of-state. 62% 25 or older. Core. Calendar: semesters. Academic remediation for entering students, ESL program, services for LD students, accelerated degree program, independent study, summer session for credit, part-time degree program, adult/continuing education programs, co-op programs and internships. Off campus study.
Entrance Requirements: Open admission. Options: electronic application, early admission, deferred admission. Required: high school transcript. Entrance: noncompetitive. Application deadline: Rolling. Notification: continuous.
Collegiate Environment: Orientation program. Choral group. Social organizations: 5 open to all. Most popular organizations: Student Association, Phi Beta Lambda, Phi Theta Kappa, Social Services Club, Criminal Justice Club. Major annual events: Spring Fling, Career Day, Christmas Party. Student services: personal-psychological counseling, women's center. Campus security: 24-hour emergency response devices and patrols, evening security. Martin Learning Resource Center with 18,917 books, 170 serials, and an OPAC. Operations spending for the previous fiscal year: $167,634. 150 computers available on campus for general student use. A campuswide network can be accessed from off-campus. Staffed computer lab on campus.
Community Environment: The college is located in the geographic center of the Carolinas and Southeast. Its location is equidistant from the Ap-

palachian and Blue Ridge Mountains and the Grand Strand area of the Atlantic; and is situated halfway between Washington, D.C. and Atlanta, Georgia. The average annual temperature is 61 degrees; the coldest month is January (42.5 degrees), the warmest month is July (78.9 degrees). Annual rainfall is 49 inches.

■ SOUTH UNIVERSITY

3975 Premier Dr.
High Point, NC 27265
Tel: (336)812-7200; Free: 855-268-2187
Fax: (336)812-7390
Web Site: www.southuniversity.edu/high-point.aspx
Description: Proprietary, comprehensive, coed.

■ SOUTHEASTERN BAPTIST THEOLOGICAL SEMINARY

PO Box 1889
Wake Forest, NC 27588-1889
Tel: (919)556-3101; Free: 800-284-6317
Web Site: www.sebts.edu/
Description: Independent Southern Baptist, comprehensive, coed. Awards associate, bachelor's, and master's degrees. Founded 1950. Setting: 300-acre small town campus with easy access to Raleigh. Total enrollment: 2,332. Faculty: 85 (63 full-time, 22 part-time). Student-undergrad faculty ratio is 17:1. 172 applied, 97% were admitted. Full-time: 250 students, 32% women, 68% men. Part-time: 269 students, 49% women, 51% men. Students come from 32 states and territories, 3 other countries, 15% from out-of-state. 94% American Indian or Alaska Native, non-Hispanic/Latino; 2% Hispanic/Latino; 3% African American, non-Hispanic/Latino; 1% international. Core. Calendar: semesters. Academic remediation for entering students, independent study, distance learning, double major, summer session for credit, part-time degree program, adult/continuing education programs, internships, graduate courses open to undergrads. Off campus study.
Entrance Requirements: Open admission. Option: international baccalaureate accepted. Required: essay, high school transcript, SAT or ACT. Required for some: interview. Entrance: minimally difficult. Application deadline: 7/20. Notification: continuous until 8/20. Transfer credits accepted: Yes.
Collegiate Environment: Orientation program. Drama-theater group, choral group. Major annual events: campus-wide spring cook out, Campus-wide fall cook out. Student services: health clinic, personal-psychological counseling, women's center. Campus security: 24-hour emergency response devices and patrols, late night transport-escort service. 7 computers available on campus for general student use. A campuswide network can be accessed from student residence rooms and from off campus. Students can access the following: online class registration. Staffed computer lab on campus.
Community Environment: Wake Forest is located 15 miles north of Raleigh and 22 miles east of Durham on US 1 and NC 98. The seminary is only 25 miles from the Raleigh-Durham Airport. 12 churches, a hospital, a public library, and numerous civic and service organizations are found within the community. A full-time recreational program, supervised by a recreational director, swimming pools, lighted athletic fields, tennis courts, racquetball courts, weight rooms, and two golf courses provide the recreational facilities.

■ SOUTHEASTERN COMMUNITY COLLEGE

PO Box 151
Whiteville, NC 28472-0151
Tel: (910)642-7141
E-mail: start@sccnc.edu
Web Site: www.sccnc.edu/
Description: State-supported, 2-year, coed. Part of North Carolina Community College System. Awards certificates, diplomas, transfer associate, and terminal associate degrees. Founded 1964. Setting: 106-acre rural campus. Educational spending for the previous fiscal year: $1328 per student. Total enrollment: 1,949. Faculty: 91 (75 full-time, 16 part-time). Student-undergrad faculty ratio is 20:1. 890 applied, 100% were admitted. 10% from top 10% of their high school class, 25% from top quarter, 50% from top half. Students come from 2 states and territories, 2 other countries, 1% from out-of-state. 45% 25 or older. Retention: 33% of full-time freshmen returned the following year. Core. Calendar: semesters. Academic remediation for entering students, ESL program, services for LD students, advanced placement, honors program, independent study, distance learning, double major, summer session for credit, part-time degree program, adult/continuing education programs, co-op programs and internships.
Entrance Requirements: Open admission except for nursing, phlebotomy,

medical laboratory technology programs. Options: electronic application, early admission, deferred admission. Required: high school transcript. Entrance: noncompetitive. Application deadline: Rolling.

Collegiate Environment: Orientation program. Drama-theater group, choral group. Social organizations: 6 open to all. Most popular organizations: Student Government Association, Forestry Club, Nursing Club, Environmental Club. Major annual events: High School Senior Day, 8th-Grader Day. Student services: personal-psychological counseling. Campus security: 24-hour emergency response devices. Southeastern Community College Library with 50,297 books, 192 serials, and an OPAC. 80 computers available on campus for general student use. A campuswide network can be accessed. Staffed computer lab on campus.

Community Environment: A rural community with a mean annual temperature of 64 degrees. Bus transportation is convenient, and there is plane service at Wilmington and Fayetteville. Shopping facilities, 14 churches representing a number of denominations, and a hospital are part of the community. A nearby lake, beaches, a golf course, swimming pools, and tennis courts provide recreational opportunities. Part-time employment is limited.

■ SOUTHWESTERN COMMUNITY COLLEGE

447 College Dr.
Sylva, NC 28779
Tel: (828)586-4091; Free: 800-447-7091
Fax: (828)586-4093
E-mail: delos@southwesterncc.edu
Web Site: www.southwesterncc.edu/

Description: State-supported, 2-year, coed. Part of North Carolina Community College System. Awards certificates, diplomas, transfer associate, and terminal associate degrees. Founded 1964. Setting: 77-acre small town campus. Endowment: $2.2 million. Educational spending for the previous fiscal year: $3177 per student. Total enrollment: 2,065. Faculty: 260 (72 full-time, 188 part-time). Student-undergrad faculty ratio is 11:1. Full-time: 841 students, 65% women, 35% men. Part-time: 1,224 students, 63% women, 37% men. Students come from 7 states and territories, 1 other country, 1% from out-of-state. 43% 25 or older, 21% transferred in. Core. Calendar: semesters. Academic remediation for entering students, ESL program, services for LD students, independent study, distance learning, double major, summer session for credit, part-time degree program, adult/continuing education programs, co-op programs. Off campus study at Haywood Community College.

Entrance Requirements: Open admission except for allied health programs. Options: early admission, deferred admission. Required: high school transcript. Recommended: SAT or ACT. Required for some: minimum 2.0 high school GPA, interview. Entrance: noncompetitive. Application deadline: Rolling. Notification: continuous.

Collegiate Environment: Social organizations: 19 open to all. Most popular organizations: Electronics Club, EMT Club, HIT Club, Cyber Crime Club, National Vocational-Technical Honor Society. Major annual events: Spring Fling, Fall Welcome Back, Hullabaloo. Student services: personal-psychological counseling. Campus security: security during hours college is open. Southwestern Community College Library with 37,860 books, 3,579 microform titles, 166 serials, 1,603 audiovisual materials, an OPAC, and a Web page. Operations spending for the previous fiscal year: $130,200. 400 computers available on campus for general student use. A campuswide network can be accessed from off-campus. Staffed computer lab on campus.

■ STANLY COMMUNITY COLLEGE

141 College Dr.
Albemarle, NC 28001-7458
Tel: (704)982-0121
Fax: (704)982-0819
E-mail: dross7926@stanly.edu
Web Site: www.stanly.edu/

Description: State-supported, 2-year, coed. Part of North Carolina Community College System. Awards certificates, diplomas, transfer associate, and terminal associate degrees. Founded 1971. Setting: 150-acre small town campus with easy access to Charlotte. Total enrollment: 3,200. Faculty: 106 (53 full-time, 53 part-time). Student-undergrad faculty ratio is 9:1. 642 applied, 100% were admitted. Students come from 13 states and territories, 3 other countries, 3% from out-of-state. 48% 25 or older. Calendar: semesters. Academic remediation for entering students, ESL program, services for LD students, advanced placement, independent study, distance

learning, double major, summer session for credit, part-time degree program, adult/continuing education programs, co-op programs and internships. Study abroad program.

Entrance Requirements: Open admission except for health sciences programs. Options: electronic application, early admission, deferred admission. Required: high school transcript. Entrance: noncompetitive. Application deadline: Rolling. Notification: continuous. Transfer credits accepted: Yes.

Costs Per Year: State resident tuition: $1656 full-time, $69 per credit hour part-time. Nonresident tuition: $6264 full-time, $261 per credit hour part-time. Mandatory fees: $120 full-time, $59.75 per unit part-time.

Collegiate Environment: Orientation program. Student-run newspaper. Student services: personal-psychological counseling. Campus security: 24-hour emergency response devices and patrols, late night transport-escort service. 23,966 books, 10,586 microform titles, 200 serials, 2,500 audiovisual materials, an OPAC, and a Web page 100 computers available on campus for general student use. A campuswide network can be accessed from off-campus. Students can access the following: online class registration. Staffed computer lab on campus provides training in use of computers, software, and the Internet.

■ STRAYER UNIVERSITY - GREENSBORO CAMPUS

4900 Koger Blvd., Ste. 400
Greensboro, NC 27407
Tel: (336)315-7800
Fax: (336)315-7830
Web Site: www.strayer.edu/campus/greensboro
Description: Proprietary, comprehensive, coed. Awards associate, bachelor's, and master's degrees.

■ STRAYER UNIVERSITY - HUNTERSVILLE CAMPUS

13620 Reese Blvd.
Ste. 130
Huntersville, NC 28078
Tel: (704)379-6800
Fax: (704)379-6830
Web Site: www.strayer.edu/campus/huntersville/
Description: Proprietary, comprehensive, coed. Awards associate, bachelor's, and master's degrees.

■ STRAYER UNIVERSITY - NORTH CHARLOTTE CAMPUS

7870 Commons Park Cir. NW
Concord, NC 28027
Tel: (704)886-6500
Fax: (704)979-3891
Web Site: www.strayer.edu/campus/north-charlotte
Description: Proprietary, comprehensive, coed. Awards associate, bachelor's, and master's degrees.

■ STRAYER UNIVERSITY - NORTH RALEIGH CAMPUS

8701 Wadford Dr.
Raleigh, NC 27616
Tel: (919)878-9900
Fax: (919)878-6625
Web Site: www.strayer.edu/campus/north-raleigh
Description: Proprietary, comprehensive, coed. Awards associate, bachelor's, and master's degrees.

■ STRAYER UNIVERSITY - RTP CAMPUS

4 Copley Pky.
Morrisville, NC 27560
Tel: (919)466-4400
Fax: (919)466-4430
Web Site: www.strayer.edu/campus/rtp
Description: Proprietary, comprehensive, coed. Awards associate, bachelor's, and master's degrees.

■ STRAYER UNIVERSITY - SOUTH CHARLOTTE CAMPUS

9101 Kings Parade Blvd.
Ste. 200
Charlotte, NC 28273
Tel: (704)499-9200
Fax: (704)499-9230
Web Site: www.strayer.edu/campus/south-charlotte

Description: Proprietary, comprehensive, coed. Awards associate, bachelor's, and master's degrees.

■ STRAYER UNIVERSITY - SOUTH RALEIGH CAMPUS
3421 Olympia Dr.
Raleigh, NC 27603
Tel: (919)890-7500
Fax: (919)662-9840
Web Site: www.strayer.edu/campus/south-raleigh
Description: Proprietary, comprehensive, coed. Awards associate, bachelor's, and master's degrees.

■ SURRY COMMUNITY COLLEGE
630 S Main St.
Dobson, NC 27017
Tel: (336)386-8121
Fax: (336)386-8951
E-mail: hazelwoodr@surry.edu
Web Site: www.surry.edu/
Description: State-supported, 2-year, coed. Part of North Carolina Community College System. Awards certificates, diplomas, transfer associate, and terminal associate degrees. Founded 1965. Setting: 100-acre rural campus. Total enrollment: 3,600. Faculty: 450 (150 full-time, 300 part-time). Student-undergrad faculty ratio is 27:1. Students come from 3 states and territories, 4% from out-of-state. 42% 25 or older. Core. Calendar: semesters. Academic remediation for entering students, ESL program, services for LD students, advanced placement, independent study, distance learning, double major, summer session for credit, part-time degree program, adult/continuing education programs, co-op programs and internships. Off campus study at Forsyth Technical Community College, Guilford Technical Community College, Rockingham Community College.
Entrance Requirements: Open admission except for nursing program. Options: electronic application, early admission, deferred admission. Required: high school transcript, CPT. Entrance: noncompetitive.
Collegiate Environment: Orientation program. Drama-theater group, choral group, student-run radio station. Social organizations: 7 open to all. Most popular organizations: Student Government Association, Phi Beta Lambda, Phi Theta Kappa, BSU. Major annual events: Student Appreciation Day, New Student Orientation. Campus security: late night transport-escort service, security guard during day and evening hours. Resource Center with 47,526 books, 10,225 microform titles, 362 serials, an OPAC, and a Web page. 200 computers available on campus for general student use. A campuswide network can be accessed. Staffed computer lab on campus.
Community Environment: A rural community with temperate climate, Dobson is the county seat. Community facilities include a library, United Methodist and Baptist churches, a hospital within 11 miles, some shopping, and several civic and service organizations. There are job opportunities in textile factories and with a poultry processing plant.

■ TRI-COUNTY COMMUNITY COLLEGE
21 Campus Cir.
Murphy, NC 28906-7919
Tel: (828)837-6810
Fax: (828)837-3266
E-mail: jchambers@tricountycc.edu
Web Site: www.tricountycc.edu/
Description: State-supported, 2-year, coed. Part of North Carolina Community College System. Awards certificates, diplomas, transfer associate, and terminal associate degrees. Founded 1964. Setting: 40-acre rural campus. Total enrollment: 1,353. Faculty: 80 (46 full-time, 34 part-time). Student-undergrad faculty ratio is 21:1. 65% 25 or older. Calendar: semesters. Academic remediation for entering students, distance learning, double major, summer session for credit, part-time degree program, adult/continuing education programs, internships. Study abroad program.
Entrance Requirements: Open admission except for nursing, medical assistant programs. Option: electronic application. Required: high school transcript. Recommended: SAT and SAT Subject Tests or ACT. Entrance: noncompetitive. Application deadline: Rolling. Notification: continuous. Preference given to state residents. Transfer credits accepted: Yes.
Collegiate Environment: Orientation program. Student services: personal-psychological counseling. College housing not available. 16,224 books and 306 serials 43 computers available on campus for general student use. A campuswide network can be accessed. Staffed computer lab on campus.
Community Environment: Located in a valley in the central part of

Cherokee County, Murphy has available bus and train transportation; Andrews Airport is 11 miles away. Community facilities include seven church denominations, two hospitals, and a fully equipped clinic. Mountains, streams, lakes, and forests make Murphy a sports lover's paradise. Parks, playgrounds, and other recreational facilities are available, including a complex that offers swimming pools, an 18-hole golf course, and horseback riding.

■ UNIVERSITY OF NORTH CAROLINA AT ASHEVILLE
One University Heights
Asheville, NC 28804-3299
Tel: (828)251-6600; Free: 800-531-9842
Fax: (828)251-6385
E-mail: admissions@unca.edu
Web Site: www.unca.edu/
Description: State-supported, comprehensive, coed. Part of University of North Carolina System. Awards bachelor's and master's degrees. Founded 1927. Setting: 365-acre urban campus. Endowment: $28.6 million. Research spending for the previous fiscal year: $2.1 million. Educational spending for the previous fiscal year: $8539 per student. Total enrollment: 3,751. Faculty: 270 (213 full-time, 57 part-time). Student-undergrad faculty ratio is 14:1. 3,018 applied, 64% were admitted. 22% from top 10% of their high school class, 62% from top quarter, 96% from top half. 4 valedictorians. Full-time: 3,054 students, 57% women, 43% men. Part-time: 639 students, 63% women, 37% men. Students come from 40 states and territories, 23 other countries, 12% from out-of-state. 0.1% American Indian or Alaska Native, non-Hispanic/Latino; 4% Hispanic/Latino; 3% African American, non-Hispanic/Latino; 1% Asian, non-Hispanic/Latino; 0.1% Native Hawaiian or other Pacific Islander, non-Hispanic/Latino; 1% international. 15% 25 or older, 38% live on campus, 9% transferred in. Retention: 78% of full-time freshmen returned the following year. Academic areas with the most degrees conferred: psychology; social sciences; business/marketing. Core. Calendar: semesters. Academic remediation for entering students, services for LD students, advanced placement, self-designed majors, honors program, independent study, distance learning, double major, summer session for credit, part-time degree program, adult/continuing education programs, internships, graduate courses open to undergrads. Off campus study at Asheville Area Educational Consortium. Study abroad program.
Entrance Requirements: Options: electronic application, early action, deferred admission, international baccalaureate accepted. Required: essay, high school transcript, 1 recommendation, minimum course requirement, SAT or ACT. Required for some: interview. Entrance: moderately difficult. Application deadlines: 2/15, 2/15 for nonresidents, 11/15 for early action. Notification: continuous until 12/15, 12/15 for early action. SAT Reasoning Test deadline: 2/15. Transfer credits accepted: Yes.
Costs Per Year: Application fee: $50. State resident tuition: $3476 full-time. Nonresident tuition: $17,292 full-time. Mandatory fees: $2390 full-time. Full-time tuition and fees vary according to course load. College room and board: $7584. College room only: $4348. Room and board charges vary according to housing facility.
Collegiate Environment: Orientation program. Drama-theater group, choral group, student-run newspaper, radio station. Social organizations: 66 open to all; national fraternities, national sororities; 3% of eligible men and 3% of eligible women are members. Most popular organizations: Student Government Association, Underdog Productions, Resident Student Association, Black Student Association, Active Students for a Healthy Environment. Major annual events: Homecoming, Lawn Party, Family Weekend. Student services: health clinic, personal-psychological counseling, women's center. Campus security: 24-hour emergency response devices and patrols, late night transport-escort service, controlled dormitory access. 1,432 college housing spaces available; 1,266 were occupied in 2012-13. Freshmen guaranteed college housing. On-campus residence required in freshman year. Options: coed, men-only, women-only housing available. D. Hiden Ramsey Library with 280,449 books, 182,062 microform titles, 78,979 serials, 8,494 audiovisual materials, an OPAC, and a Web page. Operations spending for the previous fiscal year: $2 million. 477 computers available on campus for general student use. Computer purchase/lease plans available. A campuswide network can be accessed from student residence rooms and from off campus. Students can access the following: online class registration. Staffed computer lab on campus provides training in use of computers, software, and the Internet.

■ THE UNIVERSITY OF NORTH CAROLINA AT CHAPEL HILL
Chapel Hill, NC 27599
Tel: (919)962-2211

E-mail: unchelp@admissions.unc.edu

Web Site: www.unc.edu/

Description: State-supported, university, coed. Part of University of North Carolina System. Awards bachelor's, master's, and doctoral degrees and post-master's certificates. Founded 1789. Setting: 729-acre suburban campus with easy access to Raleigh-Durham. Endowment: $2.2 billion. Research spending for the previous fiscal year: $472.1 million. Educational spending for the previous fiscal year: $25,445 per student. Total enrollment: 29,278. Faculty: 1,936 (1,661 full-time, 275 part-time). Student-undergrad faculty ratio is 14:1. 28,437 applied, 28% were admitted. 79% from top 10% of their high school class, 97% from top quarter, 100% from top half. 99 National Merit Scholars, 210 valedictorians. Full-time: 17,562 students, 59% women, 41% men. Part-time: 941 students, 52% women, 48% men. Students come from 50 states and territories, 94 other countries, 18% from out-of-state. 1% American Indian or Alaska Native, non-Hispanic/Latino; 8% Hispanic/Latino; 9% African American, non-Hispanic/Latino; 8% Asian, non-Hispanic/Latino; 0.03% Native Hawaiian or other Pacific Islander, non-Hispanic/Latino; 3% international. 4% 25 or older, 46% live on campus, 5% transferred in. Retention: 97% of full-time freshmen returned the following year. Academic areas with the most degrees conferred: social sciences; communication/journalism; psychology. Core. Calendar: semesters. ESL program, services for LD students, advanced placement, self-designed majors, honors program, independent study, distance learning, double major, summer session for credit, part-time degree program, internships, graduate courses open to undergrads. Off campus study at North Carolina Central University, Duke University, North Carolina State University, University of North Carolina at Greensboro, University of North Carolina at Charlotte. Study abroad program. ROTC: Army, Naval, Air Force.

Entrance Requirements: Options: electronic application, early action, deferred admission, international baccalaureate accepted. Required: essay, high school transcript, 1 recommendation, counselor's statement, SAT or ACT. Entrance: very difficult. Application deadlines: 1/7, 11/3 for early action. Notification: 3/20, 1/30 for early action. Preference given to state residents. SAT Reasoning Test deadline: 1/31. SAT Subject Test deadline: 1/31. Transfer credits accepted: Yes. Applicants placed on waiting list: 2,986. Waitlisted applicants offered admission: 194. Early action applicants: 13,150. Early action applicants admitted: 5,080.

Costs Per Year: Application fee: $80. State resident tuition: $5823 full-time. Nonresident tuition: $26,575 full-time. Mandatory fees: $1867 full-time. Full-time tuition and fees vary according to program. College room and board: $9734. College room only: $5630. Room and board charges vary according to board plan, housing facility, and location.

Collegiate Environment: Orientation program. Drama-theater group, choral group, marching band, student-run newspaper, radio station. Social organizations: 592 open to all; national fraternities, national sororities; 17% of eligible men and 17% of eligible women are members. Most popular organizations: Campus Y, Carolina Athletic Association, Campus Crusade for Christ (Cornerstone), Residence Hall Association, Black Student Movement. Major annual events: Homecoming, student elections, Fall Fest. Student services: legal services, health clinic, personal-psychological counseling, women's center. Campus security: 24-hour emergency response devices and patrols, late night transport-escort service, controlled dormitory access, crime prevention initiatives (date rape, violence, larceny, etc.), campus-wide emergency alert system, cell phone/GPS security options. 10,223 college housing spaces available; 9,823 were occupied in 2012-13. Freshmen guaranteed college housing. On-campus residence required in freshman year. Options: coed, men-only, women-only housing available. Davis Library plus 14 others with 7.4 million books, 5.3 million microform titles, 104,885 serials, 467,031 audiovisual materials, an OPAC, and a Web page. Operations spending for the previous fiscal year: $42.4 million. 867 computers available on campus for general student use. Computer purchase/lease plans available. A computer is required for all students. A campuswide network can be accessed from student residence rooms and from off campus. Students can access the following: online class registration. Staffed computer lab on campus (open 24 hours a day) provides training in use of computers, software, and the Internet.

■ **THE UNIVERSITY OF NORTH CAROLINA AT CHARLOTTE**

9201 University City Blvd.

Charlotte, NC 28223-0001

Tel: (704)687-2000

Fax: (704)510-6483

E-mail: unccadm@uncc.edu

Web Site: www.uncc.edu/

Description: State-supported, university, coed. Part of University of North Carolina System. Awards bachelor's, master's, and doctoral degrees and post-master's certificates. Founded 1946. Setting: 1,000-acre suburban campus with easy access to Charlotte, NC. Endowment: $140.2 million. Research spending for the previous fiscal year: $20.8 million. Educational spending for the previous fiscal year: $7657 per student. Total enrollment: 26,232. Faculty: 1,412 (1,021 full-time, 391 part-time). Student-undergrad faculty ratio is 19:1. 5,087 applied, 80% were admitted. 19% from top 10% of their high school class, 53% from top quarter, 88% from top half. Full-time: 18,039 students, 49% women, 51% men. Part-time: 3,140 students, 52% women, 48% men. Students come from 46 states and territories, 136 other countries, 7% from out-of-state. 0.5% American Indian or Alaska Native, non-Hispanic/Latino; 7% Hispanic/Latino; 17% African American, non-Hispanic/Latino; 5% Asian, non-Hispanic/Latino; 0.1% Native Hawaiian or other Pacific Islander, non-Hispanic/Latino; 2% international. 20% 25 or older, 25% live on campus, 12% transferred in. Retention: 77% of full-time freshmen returned the following year. Academic areas with the most degrees conferred: business/marketing; social sciences; health professions and related sciences. Core. Calendar: semesters. ESL program, services for LD students, advanced placement, accelerated degree program, freshman honors college, honors program, independent study, distance learning, double major, summer session for credit, part-time degree program, adult/continuing education programs, co-op programs and internships, graduate courses open to undergrads. Off campus study at the Charlotte Area Educational Consortium includes 24 member institutions. Study abroad program. ROTC: Army, Air Force.

Entrance Requirements: Options: electronic application, early admission, early action, international baccalaureate accepted. Required: high school transcript, minimum 2 high school GPA, medical history, no criminal record, SAT or ACT. Required for some: interview. Entrance: moderately difficult. Application deadlines: 7/1, 7/1 for nonresidents, 10/15 for early action. Notification: continuous, continuous for nonresidents, 12/15 for early action. Preference given to state residents. SAT Reasoning Test deadline: 7/1. Transfer credits accepted: Yes.

Costs Per Year: Application fee: $60. State resident tuition: $3453 full-time. Nonresident tuition: $15,982 full-time. Mandatory fees: $2420 full-time. Full-time tuition and fees vary according to course load and program. College room and board: $8130. College room only: $4480. Room and board charges vary according to board plan and housing facility.

Collegiate Environment: Orientation program. Drama-theater group, choral group, student-run newspaper, radio station. Social organizations: 375 open to all; national fraternities, national sororities; 5% of eligible men and 8% of eligible women are members. Most popular organizations: Student Government Association, Student Alumni Ambassadors, Black Student Union, 49er Social and Ballroom Dance, Feminist Student Union. Major annual events: Week of Welcome (WOW), International Festival (IFEST), Student Organization Showcase. Student services: health clinic, personal-psychological counseling. Campus security: 24-hour emergency response devices and patrols, late night transport-escort service, controlled dormitory access. 4,993 college housing spaces available; 4,869 were occupied in 2012-13. No special consideration for freshman housing applicants. Options: coed, men-only, women-only housing available. J. Murrey Atkins Library plus 1 other with 1.1 million books, 2.2 million microform titles, 57,471 serials, 32,948 audiovisual materials, an OPAC, and a Web page. Operations spending for the previous fiscal year: $9.8 million. 1,500 computers available on campus for general student use. A campuswide network can be accessed from student residence rooms and from off campus. Students can access the following: online class registration. Staffed computer lab on campus (open 24 hours a day) provides training in use of computers, software, and the Internet.

■ **THE UNIVERSITY OF NORTH CAROLINA AT GREENSBORO**

1400 Spring Garden St.

Greensboro, NC 27412-5001

Tel: (336)334-5000

Fax: (336)334-4180

E-mail: admissions@uncg.edu

Web Site: www.uncg.edu/

Description: State-supported, university, coed. Part of University of North Carolina System. Awards bachelor's, master's, and doctoral degrees and post-master's certificates. Founded 1891. Setting: 210-acre urban campus. Endowment: $192.5 million. Research spending for the previous fiscal year: $16.9 million. Total enrollment: 18,172. Faculty: 1,006 (783 full-time, 223 part-time). Student-undergrad faculty ratio is 18:1. 10,108 applied, 60% were admitted. 23% from top 10% of their high school class, 48% from top quarter, 80% from top half. Full-time: 12,910 students, 65% women, 35% men. Part-time: 1,764 students, 67% women, 33% men. Students come from 40 states and territories, 46 other countries, 6% from out-of-state. 0.3% American Indian or Alaska Native, non-Hispanic/Latino; 6% Hispanic/Latino; 25% African American, non-Hispanic/Latino; 4% Asian, non-Hispanic/Latino; 0.1% Native Hawaiian or other Pacific Islander, non-Hispanic/Latino; 1% international. 18% 25 or older, 30% live on campus, 11% transferred in. Retention: 76% of full-time freshmen returned the following year. Academic areas with the most degrees conferred: business/marketing; education; health professions and related sciences. Core. Calendar: semesters. Academic remediation for entering students, services for LD students, advanced placement, accelerated degree program, self-designed majors, freshman honors college, honors program, independent study, distance learning, double major, summer session for credit, part-time degree program, adult/continuing education programs, internships, graduate courses open to undergrads. Off campus study at Greater Greensboro Consortium, North Carolina Inter-Institutional Agreement, and UNC Online Inter-institutional Agreement. Study abroad program. ROTC: Army (c), Air Force (c).

Entrance Requirements: Options: electronic application, early admission, international baccalaureate accepted. Required: high school transcript, minimum 2 high school GPA, SAT or ACT. Entrance: moderately difficult. Application deadline: 3/1. Notification: continuous. SAT Reasoning Test deadline: 8/1. Transfer credits accepted: Yes.

Costs Per Year: Application fee: $55. State resident tuition: $3779 full-time, $492 per unit part-time. Nonresident tuition: $17,577 full-time, $2216 per unit part-time. Mandatory fees: $2450 full-time, $91 per hour part-time. Part-time tuition and fees vary according to course load. College room and board: $8948. College room only: $5950. Room and board charges vary according to board plan and housing facility.

Collegiate Environment: Orientation program. Drama-theater group, choral group, marching band, student-run newspaper, radio station. Social organizations: 192 open to all; national fraternities, national sororities. Major annual events: Homecoming, Fall Kick Off, Spring Fling. Student services: health clinic, personal-psychological counseling, women's center. Campus security: 24-hour emergency response devices and patrols, student patrols, late night transport-escort service, controlled dormitory access. 5,014 college housing spaces available; 4,415 were occupied in 2012-13. Freshmen guaranteed college housing. Option: coed housing available. Jackson Library plus 2 others with 1.1 million books, 327,316 microform titles, 52,691 serials, 53,052 audiovisual materials, an OPAC, and a Web page. 360 computers available on campus for general student use. Computer purchase/lease plans available. A campuswide network can be accessed from student residence rooms and from off campus. Students can access the following: online class registration. Staffed computer lab on campus provides training in use of computers, software, and the Internet.

■ THE UNIVERSITY OF NORTH CAROLINA AT PEMBROKE

One University Dr.
Pembroke, NC 28372-1510
Tel: (910)521-6000; Free: 800-949-UNCP
E-mail: jennifer.mcneill@uncp.edu
Web Site: www.uncp.edu/

Description: State-supported, 4-year, coed. Part of University of North Carolina System. Awards bachelor's and master's degrees. Founded 1887. Setting: 200-acre rural campus. Endowment: $15.9 million. Research spending for the previous fiscal year: $576,991. Educational spending for the previous fiscal year: $6332 per student. Total enrollment: 6,269. Faculty: 402 (325 full-time, 77 part-time). Student-undergrad faculty ratio is 15:1. 3,087 applied, 72% were admitted. 11% from top 10% of their high school class, 35% from top quarter, 72% from top half. Full-time: 4,432 students, 58% women, 42% men. Part-time: 1,072 students, 76% women, 24% men. Students come from 19 states and territories, 18 other countries, 3% from out-of-state. 16% American Indian or Alaska Native, non-Hispanic/Latino; 4% Hispanic/Latino; 34% African American, non-Hispanic/Latino; 2% Asian, non-Hispanic/Latino; 0.1% Native Hawaiian or other Pacific Islander, non-Hispanic/Latino; 1% international. 30% 25 or older, 28% live on campus, 9% transferred in. Retention: 64% of full-time freshmen returned the following year. Academic areas with the most degrees conferred: education; business/marketing; social sciences. Core. Calendar: semesters. Academic remediation for entering students, ESL program, services for LD students, advanced placement, accelerated degree program, honors program, distance learning, double major, summer session for credit, part-time degree

program, adult/continuing education programs, co-op programs and internships. Off campus study at Richmond Community College, Fayetteville State University, Sandhills Community College, Southeastern Community College, Fayetteville Technical College. Study abroad program. ROTC: Army, Air Force.

Entrance Requirements: Options: electronic application, deferred admission. Required: high school transcript, SAT or ACT. Recommended: essay, minimum 2 high school GPA. Required for some: 1 recommendation, interview. Entrance: moderately difficult. Application deadline: Rolling. Notification: continuous. SAT Reasoning Test deadline: 7/31. SAT Subject Test deadline: 7/31. Transfer credits accepted: Yes.

Costs Per Year: Application fee: $45. State resident tuition: $3012 full-time. Nonresident tuition: $12,219 full-time. Mandatory fees: $1845 full-time. Full-time tuition and fees vary according to course load and location. College room and board: $7010. College room only: $5500. Room and board charges vary according to board plan, housing facility, and location.

Collegiate Environment: Orientation program. Drama-theater group, choral group, marching band, student-run newspaper, radio station. Social organizations: 90 open to all; national fraternities, national sororities, local fraternities, local sororities; 8% of eligible men and 6% of eligible women are members. Most popular organizations: NAACP, African Student Organization, English Club, International Student Organization, Voices of Serenity and Disabled Student Organization. Major annual events: Pembroke Day, Distinguished Speaker Series, Family Day, Homecoming. Student services: health clinic, personal-psychological counseling. Campus security: 24-hour emergency response devices and patrols, late night transport-escort service, controlled dormitory access. 2,168 college housing spaces available; 1,802 were occupied in 2012-13. Freshmen given priority for college housing. Options: coed, men-only, women-only housing available. Sampson-Livermore Library with 517,987 books, 709,797 microform titles, 65,210 serials, 16,029 audiovisual materials, an OPAC, and a Web page. Operations spending for the previous fiscal year: $3.5 million. 875 computers available on campus for general student use. A campuswide network can be accessed from student residence rooms and from off campus. Students can access the following: online class registration, wireless network, online library, commuter/off campus connection to network, discounted computer software/ hardware. Staffed computer lab on campus provides training in use of computers, software, and the Internet.

■ UNIVERSITY OF NORTH CAROLINA SCHOOL OF THE ARTS

1533 S Main St.
Winston-Salem, NC 27127-2188
Tel: (336)770-3399
Fax: (336)770-3370
E-mail: admissions@uncsa.edu
Web Site: www.uncsa.edu/

Description: State-supported, comprehensive, coed. Part of University of North Carolina System. Awards bachelor's and master's degrees and post-master's certificates. Founded 1963. Setting: 57-acre urban campus. Endowment: $31.6 million. Educational spending for the previous fiscal year: $6150 per student. Total enrollment: 880. Faculty: 170 (129 full-time, 41 part-time). Student-undergrad faculty ratio is 6:1. 16% from top 10% of their high school class, 37% from top quarter, 75% from top half. Full-time: 738 students, 42% women, 58% men. Part-time: 22 students, 32% women, 68% men. Students come from 50 states and territories, 16 other countries, 52% from out-of-state. 1% American Indian or Alaska Native, non-Hispanic/Latino; 8% Hispanic/Latino; 8% African American, non-Hispanic/Latino; 1% Asian, non-Hispanic/Latino; 0.1% Native Hawaiian or other Pacific Islander, non-Hispanic/Latino; 1% international. 6% 25 or older, 58% live on campus, 6% transferred in. Retention: 85% of full-time freshmen returned the following year. Academic area with the most degrees conferred: visual and performing arts. Core. Calendar: trimesters. ESL program, services for LD students, advanced placement, independent study, summer session for credit, internships.

Entrance Requirements: Required: essay, high school transcript, minimum 2.5 high school GPA, 2 recommendations, audition, SAT or ACT. Required for some: interview.

Costs Per Year: State resident tuition: $5870 full-time. Nonresident tuition: $19,015 full-time. Mandatory fees: $2401 full-time. College room and board: $8410. College room only: $4018. Room and board charges vary according to board plan and housing facility.

Collegiate Environment: Orientation program. Drama-theater group, choral group, student-run newspaper. Most popular organizations: Students for Sustainability, Arts & Soul based, Young Americans for Liberty (YAL) awareness. Major annual events: Welcome Back Weekend -targets 1st and 2nd year students, but has participation from student leaders and upperclassmen, FrozeArts - winter event, targets over 300 students, Beaux Arts - end of the year celebration, the Ball alone targets over 500 college students. Student services: health clinic, personal-psychological counseling. Campus security: 24-hour emergency response devices and patrols, late night transport-escort service, controlled dormitory access. 379 college housing spaces available; 348 were occupied in 2012-13. Freshmen guaranteed college housing. On-campus residence required through sophomore year. Option: coed housing available. Semans Library with 122,186 books, 24,957 microform titles, 450 serials, 75,117 audiovisual materials, an OPAC, and a Web page. Operations spending for the previous fiscal year: $1.1 million. 30 computers available on campus for general student use. Computer purchase/lease plans available. A campuswide network can be accessed from student residence rooms and from off campus. Staffed computer lab on campus provides training in use of computers and the Internet.

Community Environment: See Wake Forest University.

■ **THE UNIVERSITY OF NORTH CAROLINA WILMINGTON**

601 S College Rd.

Wilmington, NC 28403-3297

Tel: (910)962-3000

Fax: (910)962-3038

E-mail: admissions@uncw.edu

Web Site: www.uncw.edu/

Description: State-supported, comprehensive, coed. Part of University of North Carolina System. Awards bachelor's, master's, and doctoral degrees and post-master's certificates. Founded 1947. Setting: 656-acre urban campus. Endowment: $62.8 million. Research spending for the previous fiscal year: $17.6 million. Educational spending for the previous fiscal year: $7696 per student. Total enrollment: 13,733. Faculty: 1,027 (639 full-time, 388 part-time). Student-undergrad faculty ratio is 16:1. 11,184 applied, 54% were admitted. 26% from top 10% of their high school class, 65% from top quarter, 95% from top half. Full-time: 11,295 students, 60% women, 40% men. Part-time: 1,053 students, 65% women, 35% men. Students come from 45 states and territories, 54 other countries, 16% from out-of-state. 0.5% American Indian or Alaska Native, non-Hispanic/Latino; 6% Hispanic/Latino; 5% African American, non-Hispanic/Latino; 2% Asian, non-Hispanic/Latino; 0.2% Native Hawaiian or other Pacific Islander, non-Hispanic/Latino; 1% international. 14% 25 or older, 33% live on campus, 13% transferred in. Retention: 86% of full-time freshmen returned the following year. Academic areas with the most degrees conferred: business/marketing; social sciences; education. Core. Calendar: semesters. Academic remediation for entering students, ESL program, services for LD students, advanced placement, accelerated degree program, honors program, independent study, distance learning, double major, summer session for credit, co-op programs and internships. Off campus study. Study abroad program.

Entrance Requirements: Options: electronic application, early admission, early action, deferred admission, international baccalaureate accepted. Required: essay, high school transcript, 1 recommendation, SAT or ACT. Entrance: moderately difficult. Application deadlines: 2/1, 11/1 for early action. Notification: 4/1, 1/20 for early action. SAT Reasoning Test deadline: 2/1. Transfer credits accepted: Yes. Early action applicants: 5,778. Early action applicants admitted: 3,649.

Costs Per Year: Application fee: $60. State resident tuition: $3742 full-time. Nonresident tuition: $15,845 full-time. Mandatory fees: $2,058 full-time. Full-time tuition and fees vary according to course load. College room and board: $8016. College room only: $4620. Room and board charges vary according to board plan and housing facility.

Collegiate Environment: Orientation program. Drama-theater group, choral group, student-run newspaper, radio station. Social organizations: 218 open to all; national fraternities, national sororities; 11% of eligible men and 10% of eligible women are members. Most popular organizations: Student Government Association, Association of Campus Entertainment, Residence Hall Association. Major annual events: Welcome Week, Midnight Madness, Beach Blast. Student services: legal services, health clinic, personal-psychological counseling, women's center. Campus security: 24-hour emergency response devices and patrols, late night transport-escort service, controlled dormitory access. College housing designed to accommodate 4,108 students; 4,259 undergraduates lived in college housing during 2012-13. Freshmen given priority for college housing. Options: coed, women-only housing available. William Madison Randall Library with 1 million books, 746,545 microform titles, 34,029 serials, 86,036 audiovisual materials, an OPAC, and a Web page. Operations spending for the previous fiscal year:

$3 million. 1,650 computers available on campus for general student use. Computer purchase/lease plans available. A campuswide network can be accessed from student residence rooms and from off campus. Students can access the following: online class registration. Staffed computer lab on campus provides training in use of computers, software, and the Internet.

■ **UNIVERSITY OF PHOENIX–CHARLOTTE CAMPUS**

3800 Arco Corporate Dr., Ste. 100

Charlotte, NC 28273-3409

Tel: (704)504-5409; Free: 866-766-0766

Web Site: www.phoenix.edu/

Description: Proprietary, comprehensive, coed. Awards associate, bachelor's, and master's degrees. Founded 2003. Setting: urban campus. Total enrollment: 1,149. Faculty: 141 (18 full-time, 123 part-time). Full-time: 866 students, 67% women, 33% men. 88% 25 or older. Academic areas with the most degrees conferred: business/marketing; computer and information sciences. Core. Calendar: continuous. Services for LD students, advanced placement, accelerated degree program, independent study, distance learning, graduate courses open to undergrads.

Entrance Requirements: Open admission. Options: electronic application, deferred admission. Required: 1 recommendation. Required for some: high school transcript. Entrance: noncompetitive. Application deadline: Rolling.

Collegiate Environment: Campus security: late night transport-escort service. University Library with 16,781 serials and an OPAC. Operations spending for the previous fiscal year: $6.8 million.

■ **UNIVERSITY OF PHOENIX–RALEIGH CAMPUS**

5511 Capital Ctr. Dr.

Ste. 390

Raleigh, NC 27606

Free: 866-766-0766

Web Site: www.phoenix.edu/

Description: Proprietary, comprehensive, coed. Awards bachelor's and master's degrees. Setting: urban campus. Total enrollment: 500. Faculty: 102 (14 full-time, 88 part-time). Full-time: 372 students, 58% women, 42% men. 88% 25 or older. Retention: 29% of full-time freshmen returned the following year. Academic areas with the most degrees conferred: business/marketing; computer and information sciences; homeland security, law enforcement, firefighting, and protective services. Core. Services for LD students, advanced placement, accelerated degree program, independent study, distance learning, graduate courses open to undergrads.

Entrance Requirements: Open admission. Options: electronic application, deferred admission. Required: 1 recommendation. Required for some: high school transcript. Entrance: noncompetitive. Application deadline: Rolling.

Collegiate Environment: Campus security: late night transport-escort service. University Library with 16,781 serials and an OPAC. Operations spending for the previous fiscal year: $6.8 million.

■ **VANCE-GRANVILLE COMMUNITY COLLEGE**

PO Box 917

Henderson, NC 27536-0917

Tel: (252)492-2061

Fax: (252)430-0460

Web Site: www.vgcc.edu/

Description: State-supported, 2-year, coed. Part of North Carolina Community College System. Awards certificates, diplomas, transfer associate, and terminal associate degrees. Founded 1969. Setting: 83-acre rural campus with easy access to Raleigh. Endowment: $3 million. Total enrollment: 4,057. Faculty: 353 (141 full-time, 212 part-time). Student-undergrad faculty ratio is 9:1. 1,765 applied, 100% were admitted. 12% from top 10% of their high school class, 22% from top quarter, 40% from top half. 35 student government officers. Full-time: 1,718 students, 65% women, 35% men. Part-time: 2,339 students, 68% women, 32% men. Students come from 10 states and territories, 15 other countries, 2% from out-of-state. 53% 25 or older, 2% transferred in. Core. Calendar: semesters. Academic remediation for entering students, ESL program, services for LD students, advanced placement, accelerated degree program, distance learning, double major, summer session for credit, part-time degree program, adult/continuing education programs, co-op programs and internships.

Entrance Requirements: Open admission except for nursing, radiology programs, electronics engineering. Options: early admission, deferred admission. Required: high school transcript. Entrance: noncompetitive. Application deadline: Rolling. Notification: continuous. Preference given to district, then state residents.

Collegiate Environment: Orientation program. Drama-theater group. Most popular organizations: Vocational Club, Phi Theta Kappa, Computer Club, Criminal Justice Club, Business Club. Major annual events: Spring Sports Day, College-Wide Olympic Games, Career Day. Student services: personal-psychological counseling. Campus security: 24-hour emergency response devices and patrols. Vance-Granville Community College Learning Resource Center plus 1 other with 38,720 books, 317 serials, an OPAC, and a Web page. 184 computers available on campus for general student use. A campuswide network can be accessed from off-campus. Staffed computer lab on campus.

■ WAKE FOREST UNIVERSITY

PO Box 7373 Reynolda Station
Winston-Salem, NC 27109
Tel: (336)758-5000
Fax: (336)758-6074
E-mail: admissions@wfu.edu
Web Site: www.wfu.edu/

Description: Independent, university, coed. Awards bachelor's, master's, and doctoral degrees. Founded 1834. Setting: 340-acre suburban campus. Total enrollment: 7,432. Faculty: 690 (534 full-time, 156 part-time). Student-undergrad faculty ratio is 11:1. 11,407 applied, 34% were admitted. 79% from top 10% of their high school class, 94% from top quarter, 99% from top half. Full-time: 4,746 students, 52% women, 48% men. Part-time: 69 students, 42% women, 58% men. 77% from out-of-state. 0.3% American Indian or Alaska Native, non-Hispanic/Latino; 5% Hispanic/Latino; 7% African American, non-Hispanic/Latino; 5% Asian, non-Hispanic/Latino; 0.04% Native Hawaiian or other Pacific Islander, non-Hispanic/Latino; 3% international. 0.2% 25 or older, 68% live on campus, 1% transferred in. Retention: 94% of full-time freshmen returned the following year. Academic areas with the most degrees conferred: social sciences; business/marketing; psychology. Calendar: semesters. Services for LD students, advanced placement, honors program, independent study, double major, summer session for credit, part-time degree program, internships. Study abroad program. ROTC: Army.
Entrance Requirements: Options: electronic application, early admission, early decision, international baccalaureate accepted. Required: essay, high school transcript, 1 recommendation. Recommended: interview. Entrance: very difficult. Application deadlines: 1/1, 1/1 for early decision. Notification: 4/1, Rolling for early decision.
Costs Per Year: Application fee: $50. Comprehensive fee: $56,742 includes full-time tuition ($44,200), mandatory fees ($542), and college room and board ($12,000). College room only: $8000. Part-time tuition: $1832 per credit hour.
Collegiate Environment: Drama-theater group, choral group, marching band, student-run newspaper, radio station. Social organizations: national fraternities, national sororities. Student services: health clinic, personal-psychological counseling. Campus security: 24-hour emergency response devices and patrols, late night transport-escort service, controlled dormitory access. Freshmen guaranteed college housing. On-campus residence required through sophomore year. Option: coed housing available.
Community Environment: Wake Forest is located in Piedmont North Carolina, an hour from the Blue Ridge mountains, in the northwestern suburb of Winston-Salem, a city of 150,000 dating from the 1700s. Wake Forest shares a close working relationship with Salem College, Winston-Salem State University, and the North Carolina School of the Arts. Winston-Salem is a city of colleges, business, recreation, and the arts. The numerous points of interest include Reynolda House and Gardens, Old Salem, Wachovia Museum, Southeastern Center of Contemporary Art, Museum of Early Southern Decorative Arts, Nature Science Museum, Tanglewood Estates Park, two annual craft fairs and numerous craft and art galleries.

■ WAKE TECHNICAL COMMUNITY COLLEGE

9101 Fayetteville Rd.
Raleigh, NC 27603-5696
Tel: (919)662-3400
Fax: (919)662-3529
E-mail: srbloomfield@waketech.edu
Web Site: www.waketech.edu/

Description: State and locally supported, 2-year, coed. Part of North Carolina Community College System. Awards certificates, diplomas, transfer associate, and terminal associate degrees. Founded 1958. Setting: 79-acre suburban campus. Total enrollment: 14,747. Student-undergrad faculty ratio is 11:1. 2% from out-of-state. 43% 25 or older. Retention: 71% of full-time

freshmen returned the following year. Calendar: semesters. Academic remediation for entering students, advanced placement, distance learning, summer session for credit, part-time degree program, adult/continuing education programs.
Entrance Requirements: Open admission except for nursing program. Options: electronic application, early admission. Required: high school transcript. Entrance: noncompetitive. Application deadline: Rolling.
Collegiate Environment: Campus security: 24-hour patrols.
Community Environment: See Meredith College.

■ WARREN WILSON COLLEGE

PO Box 9000
Asheville, NC 28815-9000
Tel: (828)298-3325; Free: 800-934-3536
Fax: (828)298-1440
E-mail: admit@warren-wilson.edu
Web Site: www.warren-wilson.edu/

Description: Independent, comprehensive, coed, affiliated with Presbyterian Church (U.S.A.). Awards bachelor's and master's degrees. Founded 1894. Setting: 1,135-acre small town campus. Endowment: $58 million. Educational spending for the previous fiscal year: $9385 per student. Total enrollment: 924. Faculty: 101 (70 full-time, 31 part-time). Student-undergrad faculty ratio is 11:1. 951 applied, 72% were admitted. 21% from top 10% of their high school class, 42% from top quarter, 83% from top half. Full-time: 845 students, 61% women, 39% men. Part-time: 7 students, 71% women, 29% men. Students come from 46 states and territories, 15 other countries, 79% from out-of-state. 0.5% American Indian or Alaska Native, non-Hispanic/Latino; 3% Hispanic/Latino; 4% African American, non-Hispanic/Latino; 2% Asian, non-Hispanic/Latino; 0% Native Hawaiian or other Pacific Islander, non-Hispanic/Latino; 3% international. 3% 25 or older, 89% live on campus, 7% transferred in. Retention: 69% of full-time freshmen returned the following year. Academic areas with the most degrees conferred: natural resources/environmental science; social sciences; interdisciplinary studies. Core. Calendar: semesters. ESL program, services for LD students, advanced placement, self-designed majors, honors program, independent study, double major, summer session for credit, part-time degree program, co-op programs and internships. Off campus study at Duke University, University of North Carolina at Asheville, Mars Hill College. Study abroad program.
Entrance Requirements: Options: electronic application, early admission, early decision, deferred admission. Required: essay, high school transcript, minimum 2.5 high school GPA, 2 recommendations, SAT or ACT. Recommended: interview. Entrance: moderately difficult. Application deadlines: 1/31, 1/31 for nonresidents, 11/15 for early decision. Notification: continuous, continuous for nonresidents, 12/1 for early decision. SAT Reasoning Test deadline: 1/31. SAT Subject Test deadline: 1/31. Transfer credits accepted: Yes. Applicants placed on waiting list: 0. Wait-listed applicants offered admission: 0. Early decision applicants: 56. Early decision applicants admitted: 37.
Costs Per Year: Application fee: $0. Comprehensive fee: $38,336 includes full-time tuition ($29,150), mandatory fees ($390), and college room and board ($8796). College room only: $4398. Full-time tuition and fees vary according to course load. Room and board charges vary according to board plan. Part-time tuition: $1215 per credit hour. Part-time tuition varies according to course load.
Collegiate Environment: Orientation program. Drama-theater group, choral group, student-run newspaper, radio station. Social organizations: 20 open to all. Most popular organizations: Fire Legion (fire-spinning club), BE (Buddhist student organization), Debate Club, Food Not Bombs, Emmaus (Christian student group). Major annual events: Circus, Work Day, Andy Summers Memorial 24-hour Adventure Race. Student services: health clinic, personal-psychological counseling. Campus security: 24-hour emergency response devices and patrols, student patrols, late night transport-escort service, controlled dormitory access. 817 college housing spaces available; 760 were occupied in 2012-13. Freshmen guaranteed college housing. On-campus residence required in freshman year. Options: coed, men-only, women-only housing available. Pew Learning Center and Ellison Library with 106,315 books, 33,852 microform titles, 35,875 serials, 3,764 audiovisual materials, an OPAC, and a Web page. Operations spending for the previous fiscal year: $762,878. 92 computers available on campus for general student use. A campuswide network can be accessed from student residence rooms and from off campus. Students can access the following: online class registration, Home directory and public html for each user, word processing, GIS, Statistical Analysis, Graphica. Staffed computer lab on campus provides training in use of computers, software, and the Internet.

Community Environment: Situated in the Swannanoa Valley among the Blue Ridge Mountains of western North Carolina, the campus is ten miles east of Asheville. Inhabitants enjoy all the conveniences of the smaller local community, and all the advantages of the nearby city.

■ WAYNE COMMUNITY COLLEGE

PO Box 8002
Goldsboro, NC 27533-8002
Tel: (919)735-5151
Fax: (919)736-3204
E-mail: jbmayo@waynecc.edu
Web Site: www.waynecc.edu/

Description: State and locally supported, 2-year, coed. Part of North Carolina Community College System. Awards certificates, diplomas, transfer associate, and terminal associate degrees. Founded 1957. Setting: 175-acre small town campus. Endowment: $92,300. Educational spending for the previous fiscal year: $3548 per student. Total enrollment: 3,822. Faculty: 332 (137 full-time, 195 part-time). Student-undergrad faculty ratio is 20:1. 1,700 applied, 71% were admitted. Full-time: 1,858 students, 59% women, 41% men. Part-time: 1,964 students, 62% women, 38% men. Students come from 47 states and territories, 16% from out-of-state. 1% American Indian or Alaska Native, non-Hispanic/Latino; 7% Hispanic/Latino; 27% African American, non-Hispanic/Latino; 2% Asian, non-Hispanic/Latino; 0.2% Native Hawaiian or other Pacific Islander, non-Hispanic/Latino; 0% international. 33% 25 or older, 18% transferred in. Calendar: semesters. Academic remediation for entering students, ESL program, services for LD students, advanced placement, honors program, distance learning, double major, summer session for credit, part-time degree program, external degree program, adult/continuing education programs, co-op programs.

Entrance Requirements: Open admission except for health occupations programs, BLET. Options: electronic application, international baccalaureate accepted. Required: high school transcript, interview. Recommended: SAT or ACT. Entrance: noncompetitive. Application deadlines: Rolling, Rolling for nonresidents. Notification: continuous, continuous for nonresidents. SAT Reasoning Test deadline: 8/13. Transfer credits accepted: Yes.

Costs Per Year: Application fee: $0. State resident tuition: $2208 full-time. Nonresident tuition: $8352 full-time, $261 per term part-time. Mandatory fees: $92 full-time, $23 per term part-time. Full-time tuition and fees vary according to course load. Part-time tuition and fees vary according to course load.

Collegiate Environment: Orientation program. Choral group. Social organizations: 19 open to all; 10% of eligible men and 10% of eligible women are members. Most popular organizations: Student Government Association, Phi Beta Lambda, Phi Theta Kappa, Criminal Justice, International. Major annual events: SPRING SPECTACULAR, WELCOME BASH, FALL FEST. Student services: personal-psychological counseling. Campus security: 24-hour emergency response devices and patrols. College housing not available. Wayne Community College Library with 35,000 books, 114 serials, 15,000 audiovisual materials, an OPAC, and a Web page. Operations spending for the previous fiscal year: $319,948. 75 computers available on campus for general student use. A campuswide network can be accessed. Students can access the following: online class registration. Staffed computer lab on campus provides training in use of computers, software, and the Internet.

Community Environment: 50% of the state's bright-leaf tobacco is produced within a radius of 60 miles of Goldsboro. The soil and climate also make livestock production and farming important. All forms of commercial transportation are available. Churches of all denominations, a hospital, and medical clinic are a part of the city's facilities. Job opportunities are plentiful. Recreational facilities are good for all outdoor sports.

■ WESTERN CAROLINA UNIVERSITY

Cullowhee, NC 28723
Tel: (828)227-7211; Free: 877-WCU4YOU
E-mail: admiss@email.wcu.edu
Web Site: www.wcu.edu/

Description: State-supported, comprehensive, coed. Part of University of North Carolina System. Awards bachelor's, master's, and doctoral degrees and post-master's certificates. Founded 1889. Setting: 682-acre rural campus. Research spending for the previous fiscal year: $1.5 million. Educational spending for the previous fiscal year: $7015 per student. Total enrollment: 9,608. Faculty: 657 (487 full-time, 170 part-time). Student-undergrad faculty ratio is 15:1. 15,234 applied, 38% were admitted. 13% from top 10% of their high school class, 39% from top quarter, 78% from top

half. Full-time: 6,795 students, 53% women, 47% men. Part-time: 1,184 students, 57% women, 43% men. Students come from 40 states and territories, 15 other countries, 7% from out-of-state. 1% American Indian or Alaska Native, non-Hispanic/Latino; 3% Hispanic/Latino; 7% African American, non-Hispanic/Latino; 1% Asian, non-Hispanic/Latino; 0.1% Native Hawaiian or other Pacific Islander, non-Hispanic/Latino; 1% international. 18% 25 or older, 49% live on campus, 10% transferred in. Retention: 74% of full-time freshmen returned the following year. Academic areas with the most degrees conferred: education; health professions and related sciences; business/marketing. Core. Calendar: semesters. ESL program, services for LD students, advanced placement, self-designed majors, honors program, independent study, distance learning, double major, summer session for credit, part-time degree program, co-op programs and internships, graduate courses open to undergrads. Study abroad program.

Entrance Requirements: Options: electronic application, early admission, early action, international baccalaureate accepted. Required: high school transcript, SAT or ACT. Recommended: SAT. Entrance: moderately difficult. Application deadlines: 3/1, 11/15 for early action. Notification: continuous, 12/15 for early action. SAT Reasoning Test deadline: 7/1. Transfer credits accepted: Yes.

Costs Per Year: Application fee: $55. State resident tuition: $3669 full-time. Nonresident tuition: $13,266 full-time. Mandatory fees: $2810 full-time. Full-time tuition and fees vary according to degree level. College room and board: $7477. College room only: $4429. Room and board charges vary according to board plan and housing facility.

Collegiate Environment: Orientation program. Drama-theater group, choral group, marching band, student-run newspaper, radio station. Social organizations: 150 open to all; national fraternities, national sororities; 9% of eligible men and 7% of eligible women are members. Most popular organizations: WCU Leadership Institute, Physical Therapy Club, UNITY, WCU Gaming Club, WCU Climbing Team. Major annual events: Mountain Heritage Day, Valley Ballyhoo, Homecoming. Student services: health clinic, personal-psychological counseling, women's center. Campus security: 24-hour emergency response devices and patrols, late night transport-escort service, controlled dormitory access. 4,023 college housing spaces available; 3,817 were occupied in 2012-13. Freshmen guaranteed college housing. On-campus residence required in freshman year. Options: coed, men-only, women-only housing available. Hunter Library with 626,918 books, 1.6 million microform titles, 12,465 serials, 17,043 audiovisual materials, an OPAC, and a Web page. Operations spending for the previous fiscal year: $5.2 million. 115 computers available on campus for general student use. Computer purchase/lease plans available. A computer is required for all students. A campuswide network can be accessed from student residence rooms and from off campus. Students can access the following: online class registration. Staffed computer lab on campus provides training in use of computers, software, and the Internet.

Community Environment: Cullowhee is in an area containing several of the most scenic drives in western North Carolina. It is a rural area with bus transportation available. Asheville is nearby and provides an airport for air transportation. Student employment is available in clerical and cafeteria positions. Recreational activities include boating, fishing, water sports, mountain climbing and nature trails. Main shopping facilities are in Asheville.

■ WESTERN PIEDMONT COMMUNITY COLLEGE

1001 Burkemont Ave.
Morganton, NC 28655-4511
Tel: (828)438-6000
Fax: (828)438-6015
E-mail: swilliams@wpcc.edu
Web Site: www.wpcc.edu/

Description: State-supported, 2-year, coed. Part of North Carolina Community College System. Awards certificates, diplomas, transfer associate, and terminal associate degrees. Founded 1964. Setting: 130-acre small town campus. Total enrollment: 3,322. Student-undergrad faculty ratio is 12:1. 0% from out-of-state. 43% 25 or older. Retention: 72% of full-time freshmen returned the following year. Core. Calendar: semesters. Academic remediation for entering students, advanced placement, summer session for credit, part-time degree program, adult/continuing education programs, co-op programs.

Entrance Requirements: Open admission. Required: high school transcript. Entrance: noncompetitive. Application deadline: Rolling. Notification: continuous.

Collegiate Environment: Drama-theater group, student-run newspaper. Student services: personal-psychological counseling, women's center.

Community Environment: Western Piedmont Community College, in Morganton (population 17,000), is situated in the Appalachian foothills of western North Carolina near the Catawba River. Burke County (population 90,000) was established in 1777 and named in honor of the third governor of North Carolina, Thomas Burke. Manufacturing is diversified and includes furniture, textiles, electronics, and assembly plants. The major employer is the State of North Carolina with services at Broughton Hospital, Western Carolina Center, Western Correctional Center, and the North Carolina School for the Deaf. Burke County is located in the fastest growing region of the state but as yet maintains its rural values.

■ **WILKES COMMUNITY COLLEGE**

1328 Collegiate Dr.

Wilkesboro, NC 28697

Tel: (336)838-6100

Fax: (336)838-6277

E-mail: mac.warren@wilkescc.edu

Web Site: www.wilkescc.edu/

Description: State-supported, 2-year, coed. Part of North Carolina Community College System. Awards certificates, diplomas, transfer associate, and terminal associate degrees. Founded 1965. Setting: 140-acre small town campus. Endowment: $2.7 million. Educational spending for the previous fiscal year: $2929 per student. Total enrollment: 2,558. Faculty: 362 (73 full-time, 289 part-time). Student-undergrad faculty ratio is 10:1. 1,215 applied, 100% were admitted. Students come from 13 states and territories, 15 other countries, 1% from out-of-state. 44% 25 or older. Core. Calendar: semesters. Academic remediation for entering students, ESL program, services for LD students, advanced placement, accelerated degree program, independent study, distance learning, double major, summer session for credit, part-time degree program, adult/continuing education programs, co-op programs and internships.

Entrance Requirements: Open admission. Options: electronic application, deferred admission. Required: high school transcript. Entrance: noncompetitive. Application deadline: Rolling. Notification: continuous.

Collegiate Environment: Drama-theater group, choral group, student-run newspaper, radio station. Social organizations: 21 open to all. Most popular organizations: Student Government Association, Phi Theta Kappa, Phi Beta Lambda, Rotaract, Baptist Student Union. Major annual events: Alcohol Awareness Week Activities, Welcome Back Week Activities, Fall Festival. Student services: personal-psychological counseling. Campus security: 24-hour emergency response devices, student patrols, late night transport-escort service. Learning Resources Center with 56,142 books, 1,040 microform titles, 127 serials, 6,867 audiovisual materials, an OPAC, and a Web page. Operations spending for the previous fiscal year: $273,143. 255 computers available on campus for general student use. A campuswide network can be accessed. Students can access the following: campus e-mail system. Staffed computer lab on campus.

Community Environment: Located 50 miles from Winston-Salem, Wilkesboro is the county seat of Wilkes County. The community offers churches of various faiths, shopping areas, and adequate medical facilities. The Kerr Scott Dam and Reservoir provides boating, fishing, water skiing, and swimming. The Blue Ridge Mountains around the Boone area provides winter time sports such as skiing and ice skating.

■ **WILLIAM PEACE UNIVERSITY**

15 E Peace St.

Raleigh, NC 27604-1194

Tel: (919)508-2000; Free: 800-PEACE-47

Fax: (919)508-2328

Web Site: www.peace.edu/

Description: Independent, 4-year, coed, affiliated with Presbyterian Church (U.S.A.). Awards bachelor's degrees. Founded 1857. Setting: 21-acre urban campus with easy access to Raleigh-Cary. Endowment: $40.2 million. Total enrollment: 791. Faculty: 106 (25 full-time, 81 part-time). Student-undergrad faculty ratio is 14:1. 1,238 applied, 61% were admitted. 32% from top 10% of their high school class, 41% from top quarter, 57% from top half. Full-time: 700 students, 83% women, 17% men. Part-time: 91 students, 80% women, 20% men. Students come from 18 states and territories, 1 other country, 6% from out-of-state. 2% American Indian or Alaska Native, non-Hispanic/Latino; 5% Hispanic/Latino; 36% African American, non-Hispanic/Latino; 2% Asian, non-Hispanic/Latino; 0% Native Hawaiian or other Pacific Islander, non-Hispanic/Latino; 0% international. 22% 25 or older, 51% live on campus, 8% transferred in. Retention: 65% of full-time freshmen returned the following year. Academic areas with the most degrees conferred: business/marketing;

psychology; family and consumer sciences. Core. Calendar: semesters. Academic remediation for entering students, services for LD students, advanced placement, accelerated degree program, honors program, independent study, distance learning, double major, summer session for credit, part-time degree program, adult/continuing education programs, internships. Off campus study at Shaw University, North Carolina State University, Meredith College and St. Augustine's University. Study abroad program. ROTC: Army (c), Naval (c), Air Force (c).

Entrance Requirements: Options: electronic application, early admission, early action, deferred admission, international baccalaureate accepted. Required: high school transcript, minimum 2 high school GPA, Dean's Evaluation (transfers), SAT or ACT. Recommended: essay, 2 recommendations, interview, SAT and SAT Subject Tests or ACT, SAT Subject Tests. Entrance: moderately difficult. Application deadlines: Rolling, Rolling for nonresidents, 11/1 for early action. Notification: continuous, continuous for nonresidents, Rolling for early action. SAT Reasoning Test deadline: 7/30. SAT Subject Test deadline: 7/30. Transfer credits accepted: Yes. Early action applicants: 249. Early action applicants admitted: 69.

Costs Per Year: Application fee: $25. Comprehensive fee: $33,041 includes full-time tuition ($23,700), mandatory fees ($200), and college room and board ($9141). College room only: $6186. Full-time tuition and fees vary according to class time, course load, and program. Room and board charges vary according to board plan and housing facility. Part-time tuition: $790 per credit. Part-time tuition varies according to class time, course load, and program.

Collegiate Environment: Orientation program. Drama-theater group, choral group, student-run newspaper. Social organizations: 36 open to all; Gamma Sigma Sigma — National Service Sorority; 4% of women are members. Most popular organizations: Campus Activities Board, Phi Beta Lamda, Gamma Sigma Sigma, Ambassadors for Christ, Class Councils. Major annual events: Late Night Breakfast, Red Rose Ball, athletic events. Student services: health clinic, personal-psychological counseling. Campus security: 24-hour emergency response devices and patrols, late night transport-escort service, controlled dormitory access. 530 college housing spaces available; 385 were occupied in 2012-13. Freshmen given priority for college housing. On-campus residence required through sophomore year. Options: coed, women-only housing available. Lucy Cooper Finch Library with 49,950 books, 2,000 microform titles, 30,600 serials, 1,749 audiovisual materials, an OPAC, and a Web page. 92 computers available on campus for general student use. A campuswide network can be accessed from student residence rooms and from off campus. Students can access the following: online class registration. Staffed computer lab on campus provides training in use of computers, software, and the Internet.

Community Environment: Peace College is located in downtown Raleigh, NC, the state's political, education, and cultural center. The State Capitol, Legislative Building, State Library, and museums lie within a few blocks of campus. Shopping centers, restaurants, coffee shops and clubs are within a 10-block radius. Six other colleges and universities are located in the Raleigh area. The University of North Carolina at Chapel Hill and Duke University are within 25 miles of Peace. Numerous classical and popular concerts, dramatic presentations, and other cultural activities are available on campus, in the community, and in the surrounding Research Triangle Park area.

■ **WILSON COMMUNITY COLLEGE**

902 Herring Ave.

Wilson, NC 27893-3310

Tel: (252)291-1195

Fax: (252)243-7148

E-mail: mwilliams@wilsoncc.edu

Web Site: www.wilsoncc.edu/

Description: State-supported, 2-year, coed. Part of North Carolina Community College System. Awards certificates, diplomas, transfer associate, and terminal associate degrees. Founded 1958. Setting: 35-acre small town campus with easy access to Raleigh. Total enrollment: 1,837. Faculty: 210 (52 full-time, 158 part-time). Student-undergrad faculty ratio is 12:1. Full-time: 897 students, 68% women, 32% men. Part-time: 940 students, 68% women, 32% men. Students come from 3 states and territories, 0% from out-of-state. 1% American Indian or Alaska Native, non-Hispanic/Latino; 5% Hispanic/Latino; 45% African American, non-Hispanic/Latino; 1% Asian, non-Hispanic/Latino; 0.1% Native Hawaiian or other Pacific Islander, non-Hispanic/Latino; 0% international. 49% 25 or older, 27% transferred in. Core. Calendar: semesters. Academic remediation for entering students, ESL program, services for LD students, advanced placement, independent study, distance learning, double major, summer session for credit, part-time degree program, co-op programs and internships.

Entrance Requirements: Open admission except for health occupations programs. Options: electronic application, deferred admission. Required: high school transcript. Entrance: noncompetitive. Application deadline: Rolling. Notification: continuous.

Costs Per Year: Application fee: $0. State resident tuition: $2070 full-time, $69 per credit hour part-time. Nonresident tuition: $7830 full-time, $261 per credit hour part-time. Mandatory fees: $103 full-time, $1.35 per credit hour part-time, $31 per term part-time.

Collegiate Environment: Orientation program. Campus security: 11-hour patrols by trained security personnel; also have a certified sworn Law Enforcement Agency on campus. College housing not available. 38,466 books, 44,853 microform titles, and an OPAC 33 computers available on campus for general student use. A campuswide network can be accessed. Students can access the following: online class registration. Staffed computer lab on campus.

Community Environment: The campus is located in Wilson, NC, a community of 37,000. Raleigh, the capital, is 45 miles west of Wilson.

■ WINGATE UNIVERSITY

PO Box 159
Wingate, NC 28174-0159
Tel: (704)233-8000; Free: 800-755-5550
E-mail: admit@wingate.edu
Web Site: www.wingate.edu/

Description: Independent Baptist, comprehensive, coed. Awards bachelor's, master's, and doctoral degrees and post-master's certificates. Founded 1896. Setting: 330-acre small town campus with easy access to Charlotte. Total enrollment: 2,648. Faculty: 266 (137 full-time, 129 part-time). Student-undergrad faculty ratio is 14:1. 4,862 applied, 81% were admitted. 20% from top 10% of their high school class, 50% from top quarter, 87% from top half. Full-time: 1,714 students, 58% women, 42% men. Part-time: 59 students, 61% women, 39% men. Students come from 33 states and territories, 17 other countries, 17% from out-of-state. 1% American Indian or Alaska Native, non-Hispanic/Latino; 2% Hispanic/Latino; 15% African American, non-Hispanic/Latino; 3% Asian, non-Hispanic/Latino; 0.1% Native Hawaiian or other Pacific Islander, non-Hispanic/Latino; 4% international. 2% 25 or older, 84% live on campus, 3% transferred in. Retention: 71% of full-time freshmen returned the following year. Academic areas with the most degrees conferred: business/marketing; parks and recreation; biological/life sciences. Core. Calendar: semesters. Services for LD students, advanced placement, honors program, independent study, double major, summer session for credit, part-time degree program, internships, graduate courses open to undergrads. Off campus study at members of the Charlotte Area Educational Consortium. Study abroad program. ROTC: Army (c), Air Force (c).

Entrance Requirements: Options: electronic application, early admission, deferred admission, international baccalaureate accepted. Required: high school transcript, minimum 2 high school GPA, SAT or ACT. Recommended: minimum 3 high school GPA, interview. Entrance: moderately difficult. Application deadline: Rolling. Notification: continuous. SAT Reasoning Test deadline: 3/1. Transfer credits accepted: Yes.

Costs Per Year: Application fee: $30. Comprehensive fee: $34,990 includes full-time tuition ($23,620), mandatory fees ($1420), and college room and board ($9950). Room and board charges vary according to board plan. Part-time tuition: $790 per credit hour. Part-time tuition varies according to course load.

Collegiate Environment: Orientation program. Drama-theater group, choral group, marching band, student-run newspaper. Social organizations:

national fraternities, national sororities; 4% of eligible men and 10% of eligible women are members. Most popular organizations: University and Community Assistance Network (UCAN), Theatrix, Fellowship of Christian Athletes, Student Bulldog Club, Student Government Association. Major annual events: International Festival, Homecoming, Spring Fling. Student services: health clinic, personal-psychological counseling. Campus security: 24-hour emergency response devices and patrols, late night transport-escort service, controlled dormitory access. 1,400 undergraduates lived in college housing during 2012-13. Freshmen guaranteed college housing. On-campus residence required through senior year. Options: men-only, women-only housing available. Ethel K. Smith Library with 110,385 books, 6,827 microform titles, 179 serials, 8,508 audiovisual materials, an OPAC, and a Web page. 80 computers available on campus for general student use. A campuswide network can be accessed from student residence rooms and from off campus. Students can access the following: online class registration. Staffed computer lab on campus.

■ WINSTON-SALEM STATE UNIVERSITY

601 Martin Luther King Jr Dr.
Winston-Salem, NC 27110-0003
Tel: (336)750-2000; Free: 800-257-4052
Fax: (336)750-2079
E-mail: Legrandet@wssu.edu
Web Site: www.wssu.edu/

Description: State-supported, comprehensive, coed. Part of University of North Carolina System. Awards bachelor's and master's degrees. Founded 1892. Setting: 94-acre urban campus. Endowment: $19.5 million. Research spending for the previous fiscal year: $1.2 million. Total enrollment: 6,427. Faculty: 336 (334 full-time, 2 part-time). Student-undergrad faculty ratio is 19:1. 4,068 applied, 54% were admitted. 6% from top 10% of their high school class, 24% from top quarter, 65% from top half. Full-time: 5,327 students, 69% women, 31% men. Part-time: 633 students, 79% women, 21% men. Students come from 35 states and territories, 8 other countries, 11% from out-of-state. 31% 25 or older, 36% live on campus, 11% transferred in. Retention: 78% of full-time freshmen returned the following year. Academic areas with the most degrees conferred: health professions and related sciences; business/marketing; social sciences. Core. Calendar: semesters. Academic remediation for entering students, services for LD students, advanced placement, accelerated degree program, freshman honors college, honors program, independent study, distance learning, double major, summer session for credit, part-time degree program, co-op programs and internships. ROTC: Army, Air Force.

Entrance Requirements: Option: deferred admission. Required: high school transcript, SAT or ACT. Recommended: 1 recommendation. Entrance: minimally difficult. Application deadline: 2/15. Notification: 4/1.

Collegiate Environment: Orientation program. Drama-theater group, choral group, marching band, student-run newspaper, radio station. Social organizations: national fraternities, national sororities, local fraternities, local sororities; 5% of eligible men and 5% of eligible women are members. Major annual events: Homecoming, Lyceum Series, International Week. Student services: health clinic, personal-psychological counseling, women's center. Campus security: 24-hour emergency response devices and patrols. O'Kelly Library with an OPAC. Operations spending for the previous fiscal year: $4.1 million. 600 computers available on campus for general student use. A campuswide network can be accessed from student residence rooms and from off campus. Students can access the following: online class registration. Staffed computer lab on campus provides training in use of computers, software, and the Internet.

Community Environment: See Wake Forest University.

■ BISMARCK STATE COLLEGE

PO Box 5587
Bismarck, ND 58506-5587
Tel: (701)224-5400; Free: 800-445-5073
Fax: (701)224-5643
E-mail: karen.erickson@bismarckstate.edu
Web Site: www.bismarckstate.edu/
Description: State-supported, primarily 2-year, coed. Part of North Dakota University System. Awards certificates, diplomas, transfer associate, terminal associate, and bachelor's degrees. Founded 1939. Setting: 100-acre urban campus. Total enrollment: 4,109. Faculty: 370 (124 full-time, 246 part-time). Student-undergrad faculty ratio is 16:1. Full-time: 2,416 students, 44% women, 56% men. Part-time: 1,693 students, 48% women, 52% men. 2% American Indian or Alaska Native, non-Hispanic/Latino; 2% Hispanic/Latino; 3% African American, non-Hispanic/Latino; 0.4% Asian, non-Hispanic/Latino; 0.2% Native Hawaiian or other Pacific Islander, non-Hispanic/Latino; 0.5% international. Academic area with the most degrees conferred: business/marketing. Core. Calendar: semesters. Academic remediation for entering students, advanced placement, distance learning, summer session for credit, part-time degree program, adult/continuing education programs, co-op programs and internships. Study abroad program. ROTC: Army (c), Air Force (c).
Entrance Requirements: Open admission. Options: electronic application, early admission. Required: high school transcript, SAT or ACT. Required for some: interview. Entrance: noncompetitive. Application deadline: Rolling. Notification: continuous.
Collegiate Environment: Drama-theater group, choral group, student-run newspaper, radio station. Campus security: 24-hour emergency response devices and patrols, late night transport-escort service, controlled dormitory access. No special consideration for freshman housing applicants. Options: men-only, women-only housing available. Bismarck State College Library with an OPAC and a Web page.
Community Environment: Bismarck, North Dakota's capital city, is the second largest city with a population of 57,000. Because of its central location, modern shopping centers and Civic Center, the city hosts many state and national conventions. Bismarck is considered the cultural, business and educational center of western and central North Dakota. It is also the medical center for the region with two modern medical centers and clinics. Bismarck has a large city library, a State Historical Library, and numerous libraries related to state and federal offices; a city orchestra, civic chorus, and amateur drama club; and many churches representing various denominations. The city has many parks and recreation areas, a city zoo, three golf courses, and clubs for a variety of recreational activities. The Missouri River and nearby Lake Sakakawea offer boating, fishing and other water sports. Bismarck has transportation service from several major air carriers, commuter airlines, and bus lines. Interstate 94 and U.S. Highway 83 meet in Bismarck. The city has a pleasant summer climate and moderate to severe winters.

■ CANKDESKA CIKANA COMMUNITY COLLEGE

PO Box 269
Fort Totten, ND 58335-0269
Tel: (701)766-4415; Free: 888-783-1463
Fax: (701)766-4077
Web Site: www.littlehoop.edu/
Description: Federally supported, 2-year, coed. Awards certificates, transfer associate, and terminal associate degrees. Founded 1974. Setting: 1-acre small town campus. Total enrollment: 250. Student-undergrad faculty ratio is 9:1. 0% from out-of-state. 42% 25 or older. Core. Calendar: semesters. Academic remediation for entering students, services for LD students, self-designed majors, summer session for credit, part-time degree program, adult/continuing education programs, co-op programs. Off campus study at members of the American Indian Higher Education Consortium.
Entrance Requirements: Open admission. Options: early admission, deferred admission. Entrance: noncompetitive. Application deadline: 8/22. Notification: continuous.
Collegiate Environment: Drama-theater group. Student services: personal-psychological counseling. Campus security: late night transport-escort service. 14,000 books and 66 serials.

■ DAKOTA COLLEGE AT BOTTINEAU

105 Simrall Blvd.
Bottineau, ND 58318-1198
Tel: (701)228-2277; Free: 800-542-6866
Fax: (701)228-5499
E-mail: luann.soland@dakotacollege.edu
Web Site: www.dakotacollege.edu/
Description: State-supported, 2-year, coed. Part of North Dakota University System. Administratively affiliated with Minot State University. Awards certificates, diplomas, transfer associate, and terminal associate degrees. Founded 1906. Setting: 35-acre rural campus. Total enrollment: 773. Faculty: 94 (28 full-time, 66 part-time). Student-undergrad faculty ratio is 10:1. Full-time: 348 students, 53% women, 47% men. Part-time: 425 students, 52% women, 48% men. Students come from 37 states and territories, 4 other countries, 23% from out-of-state. 3% American Indian or Alaska Native, non-Hispanic/Latino; 3% Hispanic/Latino; 6% African American, non-Hispanic/Latino; 1% Asian, non-Hispanic/Latino; 0.1% Native Hawaiian or other Pacific Islander, non-Hispanic/Latino; 3% international. 23% 25 or older. Core. Calendar: semesters. Academic remediation for entering students, services for LD students, advanced placement, distance learning, double major, summer session for credit, part-time degree program, co-op programs. Off campus study at Minot State University (some 2-year programs), Valley City State University (nursing), Bismarck State College (medical assistant); Paramedic (EMT) Technology program via distance delivery to sites in Rugby, ND; Harvey, ND; Hettinger, ND.
Entrance Requirements: Open admission. Options: electronic application, early admission, deferred admission. Required: high school transcript, immunization records, SAT or ACT. Recommended: ACT. Entrance: noncompetitive. Application deadlines: Rolling, Rolling for nonresidents. Transfer credits accepted: Yes.
Collegiate Environment: Orientation program. Drama-theater group, student-run newspaper. Most popular organizations: Student Senate, Wildlife Club/Horticulture Club, Snowboarding Club, Phi Theta Kappa, Delta Epsilon Chi. Major annual events: Smokey's Week, Luau Week, Homecoming Week. Student services: health clinic, personal-psychological counseling. Campus security: controlled dormitory access, security cameras. 263 college housing spaces available; 147 were occupied in 2012-13. Freshmen guaranteed college housing. On-campus residence required through sophomore year. Options: men-only, women-only housing available. Dakota College at Bottineau Library plus 1 other with 41,411 books, 2 microform titles, 5,544 serials, 1,339 audiovisual materials, an OPAC, and a Web page. 58 computers available on campus for general student use. Computer

purchase/lease plans available. A campuswide network can be accessed from student residence rooms and from off campus. Students can access the following: online class registration. Staffed computer lab on campus provides training in use of computers, software, and the Internet.

■ DICKINSON STATE UNIVERSITY

291 Campus Dr.
Dickinson, ND 58601-4896
Tel: (701)483-2507; Free: 800-279-4295
Fax: (701)483-2006
E-mail: dsu.hawk@dickinsonstate.edu
Web Site: www.dickinsonstate.edu/

Description: State-supported, 4-year, coed. Part of North Dakota University System. Awards associate and bachelor's degrees. Founded 1918. Setting: 132-acre small town campus. System endowment: $9.9 million. Educational spending for the previous fiscal year: $5416 per student. Total enrollment: 2,668. Faculty: 233 (94 full-time, 139 part-time). Student-undergrad faculty ratio is 17:1. 693 applied, 97% were admitted. 6% from top 10% of their high school class, 16% from top quarter, 55% from top half. 5 National Merit Scholars, 15 class presidents, 21 valedictorians, 58 student government officers. Full-time: 1,684 students, 59% women, 41% men. Part-time: 984 students, 64% women, 36% men. Students come from 27 states and territories, 27 other countries, 23% from out-of-state. 28% 25 or older, 30% live on campus, 9% transferred in. Retention: 57% of full-time freshmen returned the following year. Academic areas with the most degrees conferred: business/marketing; education; communication/journalism. Core. Calendar: semesters. Academic remediation for entering students, services for LD students, advanced placement, accelerated degree program, self-designed majors, honors program, independent study, distance learning, double major, summer session for credit, part-time degree program, external degree program, adult/continuing education programs, co-op programs and internships. Off campus study. Study abroad program.

Entrance Requirements: Open admission for United States students. Options: electronic application, early admission, deferred admission. Required: high school transcript, medical history, proof of measles-rubella shot, SAT or ACT. Entrance: minimally difficult. Application deadline: Rolling. Notification: continuous. SAT Reasoning Test deadline: 8/15. SAT Subject Test deadline: 8/15. Transfer credits accepted: Yes.

Costs Per Year: Application fee: $35. State resident tuition: $5717 full-time. Nonresident tuition: $11,784 full-time. Full-time tuition varies according to course load and reciprocity agreements. College room and board: $4950. Room and board charges vary according to board plan.

Collegiate Environment: Orientation program. Drama-theater group, choral group, marching band, student-run newspaper. Social organizations: 52 open to all. Most popular organizations: Rodeo Club, Blue Hawk Brigade, chorale, Business Club, Navigators. Major annual events: Homecoming Week, Sure Beats Winter Week, Back to School Week. Student services: health clinic. Campus security: 24-hour emergency response devices and patrols, late night transport-escort service. Stoxen Library with 105,713 books, 8,924 microform titles, 823 serials, an OPAC, and a Web page. Operations spending for the previous fiscal year: $723,988. 216 computers available on campus for general student use. A campuswide network can be accessed from student residence rooms and from off campus. Students can access the following: online class registration. Staffed computer lab on campus provides training in use of computers, software, and the Internet.

Community Environment: Dickinson, population 15,600, is approximately 95 miles from the state capital of Bismarck and is a shipping point for lignite coal, oil, grain, dairy products, meat products, and livestock. Nearby Patterson Lake and Recreational Area and Theodore Roosevelt National Park provide ample opportunities for outdoor sports and activities.

■ FORT BERTHOLD COMMUNITY COLLEGE

220 8th Ave. N
New Town, ND 58763-0490
Tel: (701)627-4738
Fax: (701)627-3609
Web Site: www.fortbertholdcc.edu/

Description: Independent, 2-year, coed. Awards certificates, transfer associate, and terminal associate degrees. Founded 1973. Setting: small town campus. Total enrollment: 323. Student-undergrad faculty ratio is 12:1. 0% from out-of-state. 61% 25 or older. Core. Calendar: semesters. Academic remediation for entering students, summer session for credit, part-time degree program, co-op programs and internships. Off campus study at University of North Dakota, Minot State University.

Entrance Requirements: Open admission except for nursing program. Option: deferred admission. Entrance: noncompetitive. Application deadline: Rolling.

Collegiate Environment: Drama-theater group, student-run newspaper. Student services: legal services, health clinic, personal-psychological counseling.

■ JAMESTOWN COLLEGE

6000 College Ln.
Jamestown, ND 58405
Tel: (701)252-3467; Free: 800-336-2554
Fax: (701)253-4318
E-mail: admissions@jc.edu
Web Site: www.jc.edu/

Description: Independent Presbyterian, comprehensive, coed. Awards bachelor's and master's degrees. Founded 1883. Setting: 110-acre small town campus. Endowment: $27.1 million. Educational spending for the previous fiscal year: $6412 per student. Total enrollment: 945. Faculty: 80 (60 full-time, 20 part-time). Student-undergrad faculty ratio is 13:1. 1,031 applied, 56% were admitted. 15% from top 10% of their high school class, 41% from top quarter, 70% from top half. Full-time: 872 students, 51% women, 49% men. Part-time: 67 students, 52% women, 48% men. Students come from 35 states and territories, 14 other countries, 52% from out-of-state. 1% American Indian or Alaska Native, non-Hispanic/Latino; 5% Hispanic/Latino; 4% African American, non-Hispanic/Latino; 2% Asian, non-Hispanic/Latino; 1% Native Hawaiian or other Pacific Islander, non-Hispanic/Latino; 7% international. 8% 25 or older, 76% live on campus, 8% transferred in. Retention: 68% of full-time freshmen returned the following year. Academic areas with the most degrees conferred: business/marketing; health professions and related sciences; history; parks and recreation; homeland security, law enforcement, firefighting, and protective services; education. Core. Calendar: semesters. Services for LD students, advanced placement, self-designed majors, honors program, independent study, double major, summer session for credit, part-time degree program, adult/continuing education programs, co-op programs and internships. Study abroad program.

Entrance Requirements: Options: electronic application, deferred admission, international baccalaureate accepted. Required: high school transcript, 1 recommendation, SAT or ACT. Recommended: minimum 2.5 high school GPA. Entrance: minimally difficult. Application deadlines: Rolling, Rolling for nonresidents. Transfer credits accepted: Yes.

Costs Per Year: Application fee: $35. Comprehensive fee: $24,668 includes full-time tuition ($17,974), mandatory fees ($450), and college room and board ($6244). College room only: $2754. Full-time tuition and fees vary according to course load, degree level, and program. Room and board charges vary according to housing facility. Part-time tuition: $435 per credit. Part-time tuition varies according to course load, degree level, and program.

Collegiate Environment: Orientation program. Drama-theater group, choral group, student-run newspaper, radio station. Social organizations: 32 open to all. Most popular organizations: Science Club, International Student Organization, Student Media Center, Jimmie Ambassadors, Roots. Major annual events: Homecoming, Family Weekend, Jimmie Jive Week. Student services: personal-psychological counseling. Campus security: late night transport-escort service, controlled dormitory access. 728 college housing spaces available; 660 were occupied in 2012-13. Freshmen guaranteed college housing. On-campus residence required through sophomore year. Option: coed housing available. Raugust Library plus 1 other with 119,052 books, 364 microform titles, 21,781 serials, 9,498 audiovisual materials, an OPAC, and a Web page. Operations spending for the previous fiscal year: $368,950. 300 computers available on campus for general student use. A campuswide network can be accessed from student residence rooms and from off campus. Students can access the following: online class registration. Staffed computer lab on campus provides training in use of computers, software, and the Internet.

Community Environment: In the valley of the James River, Jamestown (population 14,800) was originally the site of Fort Seward, which was established in 1872. Jamestown is located in southeastern North Dakota and is provided transportation by bus lines, air, and major highways. The community has churches, one hospital, a library, two radio stations, and two shopping centers. Parks in the general area provide outdoor recreation facilities. There are several active civic, fraternal, and veteran's organizations in Jamestown.

■ LAKE REGION STATE COLLEGE

1801 College Dr. N
Devils Lake, ND 58301-1598

Tel: (701)662-1600; Free: 800-443-1313
Fax: (701)662-1570
E-mail: samantha.cordrey@lrsc.edu
Web Site: www.lrsc.edu/

Description: State-supported, 2-year, coed. Part of North Dakota University System. Awards certificates, diplomas, transfer associate, and terminal associate degrees. Founded 1941. Setting: 120-acre small town campus. Educational spending for the previous fiscal year: $6099 per student. Total enrollment: 1,974. Faculty: 139 (32 full-time, 107 part-time). Student-undergrad faculty ratio is 14:1. 265 applied, 96% were admitted. Full-time: 524 students, 53% women, 47% men. Part-time: 1,450 students, 58% women, 42% men. Students come from 14 states and territories, 7 other countries, 19% from out-of-state. 5% American Indian or Alaska Native, non-Hispanic/Latino; 3% Hispanic/Latino; 6% African American, non-Hispanic/Latino; 0.1% Asian, non-Hispanic/Latino; 0% Native Hawaiian or other Pacific Islander, non-Hispanic/Latino; 3% international. 19% 25 or older, 10% live on campus, 4% transferred in. Retention: 45% of full-time freshmen returned the following year. Academic area with the most degrees conferred: family and consumer sciences. Core. Calendar: semesters. Academic remediation for entering students, ESL program, honors program, distance learning, double major, summer session for credit, part-time degree program, co-op programs and internships.

Entrance Requirements: Open admission. Option: electronic application. Required: Immunizations records and college transcripts. Required for some: high school transcript, interview, SAT or ACT, COMPASS Test scores must be submitted to be fully admitted (unless exempt). Entrance: noncompetitive. Application deadline: Rolling. Notification: continuous. Transfer credits accepted: Yes.

Costs Per Year: Application fee: $35. State resident tuition: $3065 full-time, $127.71 per credit hour part-time. Nonresident tuition: $3065 full-time, $127.71 per credit hour part-time. Mandatory fees: $843 full-time, $28.03 per credit hour part-time. Full-time tuition and fees vary according to course load, location, and program. Part-time tuition and fees vary according to location and program. College room and board: $5316. Room and board charges vary according to board plan and housing facility.

Collegiate Environment: Orientation program. Drama-theater group, choral group, marching band. Social organizations: 12 open to all. Most popular organizations: Student Senate, Phi Theta Kappa, Delta Epsilon Chi, Phi Theta Lambda, Student Nurse Organization. Major annual events: Orientation week, Sno Daze, Spring Blast. Student services: personal-psychological counseling. Campus security: 24-hour emergency response devices, controlled dormitory access. 200 college housing spaces available; 170 were occupied in 2012-13. No special consideration for freshman housing applicants. Options: coed, men-only, women-only housing available. Paul Hoghaug Library with 47,000 books, 92 serials, 2,000 audiovisual materials, and an OPAC. Operations spending for the previous fiscal year: $127,433. 250 computers available on campus for general student use. Computer purchase/lease plans available. A campuswide network can be accessed from student residence rooms and from off campus. Students can access the following: online class registration.

Community Environment: A center of scenic, historical and recreational attractions, Devils Lake (population 6,816) was named for the largest natural body of water in the state. There are scenic drives, a golf course, a skiway, and camping and recreation facilities at nearby Shelvers Grove, Roosevelt Park, and Lakewood Park. The area is noted for its abundance of ducks and geese. The city has churches of various denominations, hospitals and clinics, a library, six motels, and various civic, fraternal and veteran's organizations. Local recreational facilities include a theatre, baseball, golf, football, bowling alley, swimming pools, hockey, skating, curling, skiing, parks, and playgrounds. Part-time employment is available.

■ MAYVILLE STATE UNIVERSITY

330 3rd St., NE
Mayville, ND 58257-1299
Tel: (701)786-2301; Free: 800-437-4104
Fax: (701)786-4748
E-mail: james.morowski@mayvillestate.edu
Web Site: www.mayvillestate.edu/

Description: State-supported, 4-year, coed. Part of North Dakota University System. Awards associate and bachelor's degrees. Founded 1889. Setting: 60-acre rural campus. Total enrollment: 1,020. Faculty: 81 (41 full-time, 40 part-time). Student-undergrad faculty ratio is 14:1. 311 applied, 60% were admitted. 5% from top 10% of their high school class, 15% from top quarter, 46% from top half. Full-time: 614 students, 48% women, 52% men. Part-

time: 376 students, 70% women, 30% men. Students come from 38 states and territories, 5 other countries, 38% from out-of-state. 2% American Indian or Alaska Native, non-Hispanic/Latino; 4% Hispanic/Latino; 6% African American, non-Hispanic/Latino; 1% Asian, non-Hispanic/Latino; 0.2% Native Hawaiian or other Pacific Islander, non-Hispanic/Latino; 4% international. 24% 25 or older, 48% live on campus, 12% transferred in. Retention: 53% of full-time freshmen returned the following year. Academic areas with the most degrees conferred: education; business/marketing; liberal arts/general studies. Core. Calendar: semesters. Academic remediation for entering students, services for LD students, advanced placement, accelerated degree program, self-designed majors, distance learning, double major, summer session for credit, part-time degree program, adult/continuing education programs, co-op programs and internships. Off campus study at Lake Region State College, Williston State College, North Dakota State College of Science, Northland Community College, Bismarck State College, and Minnesota Technical Colleges; specific agreements for transfer of credits in place for students from Wyoming and Washington Community Colleges. ROTC: Army (c), Air Force (c).

Entrance Requirements: Open admission for freshmen who have completed college preparatory curriculum in high school. Options: electronic application, deferred admission, international baccalaureate accepted. Required: high school transcript, minimum 2 high school GPA, SAT or ACT. Entrance: noncompetitive. Application deadlines: Rolling, Rolling for nonresidents. Notification: continuous until 1/1, continuous for nonresidents. SAT Reasoning Test deadline: 10/1. SAT Subject Test deadline: 10/1. Transfer credits accepted: Yes.

Costs Per Year: Application fee: $35. One-time mandatory fee: $35. State resident tuition: $4484 full-time, $187 per credit hour part-time. Nonresident tuition: $6727 full-time, $280 per credit hour part-time. Mandatory fees: $1709 full-time, $71.22 per credit hour part-time. Full-time tuition and fees vary according to course load and reciprocity agreements. Part-time tuition and fees vary according to course load and reciprocity agreements. College room and board: $4854. College room only: $1874. Room and board charges vary according to board plan and housing facility.

Collegiate Environment: Orientation program. Drama-theater group, choral group, student-run newspaper, radio station. Social organizations: 18 open to all. Most popular organizations: Student Activities Council, Student Education Association, Health and Physical Education Club, Campus Crusade, Student Ambassadors. Major annual events: Homecoming, Spring Fling. Student services: health clinic, personal-psychological counseling. Campus security: controlled dormitory access. 294 college housing spaces available; 267 were occupied in 2012-13. Freshmen guaranteed college housing. On-campus residence required through sophomore year. Options: coed, men-only, women-only housing available. Byrnes-Quanbeck Library plus 1 other with 93,684 books, 14,074 microform titles, 424 serials, 12,262 audiovisual materials, and an OPAC.

Community Environment: Mayville and its twin community, Portland, have a combined population of 2,500 in this rural farming area between Grand Forks and Fargo, North Dakota. The local community offers a city library, many churches, a modern hospital, medical clinic, and dental and optometry offices. A modern business district is also present with air transportation available at airports in Grand Forks and Fargo. A small airport is also located in the community. Housing off campus is abundant, with many choices of apartments, duplexes, and single-family dwellings. Recreational facilities are available for camping, hiking, fishing, golf, skiing, swimming, and horseshoes; a theatre and parks are also available.

■ MINOT STATE UNIVERSITY

500 University Ave., W
Minot, ND 58707-0002
Tel: (701)858-3000; Free: 800-777-0750
Fax: (701)839-6933
E-mail: askmsu@minotstateu.edu
Web Site: www.minotstateu.edu/

Description: State-supported, comprehensive, coed. Part of North Dakota University System. Awards associate, bachelor's, and master's degrees. Founded 1913. Setting: 103-acre small town campus. Total enrollment: 3,560. Faculty: 276 (175 full-time, 101 part-time). Student-undergrad faculty ratio is 13:1. 1,003 applied, 54% were admitted. 12% from top 10% of their high school class, 23% from top quarter, 35% from top half. Full-time: 2,178 students, 61% women, 39% men. Part-time: 1,120 students, 61% women, 39% men. 15% from out-of-state. 3% American Indian or Alaska Native, non-Hispanic/Latino; 4% Hispanic/Latino; 2% African American, non-Hispanic/Latino; 74% Asian, non-Hispanic/Latino; 0.4% Native Hawaiian or other

Pacific Islander, non-Hispanic/Latino; 10% international. 26% 25 or older, 20% live on campus, 9% transferred in. Retention: 65% of full-time freshmen returned the following year. Academic areas with the most degrees conferred: business/marketing; health professions and related sciences; education. Core. Calendar: semesters. Academic remediation for entering students, ESL program, services for LD students, advanced placement, accelerated degree program, self-designed majors, honors program, independent study, distance learning, double major, summer session for credit, part-time degree program, co-op programs and internships, graduate courses open to undergrads. Study abroad program.

Entrance Requirements: Options: electronic application, deferred admission. Required: high school transcript, SAT or ACT. Required for some: minimum 2.5 high school GPA. Entrance: moderately difficult. Application deadlines: Rolling, Rolling for nonresidents. Notification: continuous, continuous for nonresidents. SAT Reasoning Test deadline: 4/1. SAT Subject Test deadline: 4/1. Transfer credits accepted: Yes.

Costs Per Year: Application fee: $35. State resident tuition: $4702 full-time, $246.74 per credit hour part-time. Nonresident tuition: $4702 full-time, $246.74 per credit hour part-time. Mandatory fees: $1219 full-time. Full-time tuition and fees vary according to class time, course load, degree level, location, program, and reciprocity agreements. Part-time tuition varies according to class time, course load, degree level, location, program, and reciprocity agreements. College room and board: $4994. Room and board charges vary according to board plan and housing facility.

Collegiate Environment: Orientation program. Drama-theater group, choral group, marching band, student-run newspaper, radio station. Social organizations: 56 open to all; local fraternities. Most popular organizations: Residence Hall Association, Student Government Association, Beavers on Business, Student Social Work Organization, National Student Speech and Hearing Association. Major annual events: Homecoming Week, Welcome Week, Winter Week. Student services: health clinic, personal-psychological counseling, women's center. Campus security: controlled dormitory access, patrols by trained security personnel. 661 college housing spaces available. Freshmen guaranteed college housing. On-campus residence required in freshman year. Options: coed, men-only, women-only housing available. Gordon B. Olson Library with 419,712 books, 650,538 microform titles, 730 serials, 15,359 audiovisual materials, an OPAC, and a Web page. 450 computers available on campus for general student use. Computer purchase/lease plans available. A campuswide network can be accessed from student residence rooms and from off campus. Students can access the following: online class registration. Staffed computer lab on campus (open 24 hours a day) provides training in use of computers, software, and the Internet.

Community Environment: Minot, population 35,000, began as a tent town of the Great Northern Railroad and now contains the electronic freight classification Gavin Yard. It grew so rapidly that it was called the"Magic City." Today it is a trade center for an area including part of Canada and Montana, as well as northern North Dakota. The town lies within the eastern boundaries of oil-rich Williston Basin and is surrounded by a number of lignite strip mines. The area has good highways, rail, bus, and air lines. Minot has many churches and active civic and fraternal organizations. Part-time job opportunities are available for students.

■ **NORTH DAKOTA STATE COLLEGE OF SCIENCE**
800 N Sixth St.
Wahpeton, ND 58076
Tel: (701)671-2401; Free: 800-342-4325
Fax: (701)671-2332
E-mail: Karen.Reilly@ndscs.edu
Web Site: www.ndscs.nodak.edu/
Description: State-supported, 2-year, coed. Part of North Dakota University System. Awards certificates, diplomas, transfer associate, and terminal associate degrees. Founded 1903. Setting: 125-acre rural campus. Endowment: $12.4 million. Educational spending for the previous fiscal year: $7274 per student. Total enrollment: 3,066. Faculty: 314 (112 full-time, 202 part-time). Student-undergrad faculty ratio is 12:1. 1,322 applied, 74% were admitted. Full-time: 1,807 students, 36% women, 64% men. Part-time: 1,259 students, 58% women, 42% men. Students come from 32 states and territories, 5 other countries, 39% from out-of-state. 2% American Indian or Alaska Native, non-Hispanic/Latino; 2% Hispanic/Latino; 5% African American, non-Hispanic/Latino; 1% Asian, non-Hispanic/Latino; 0.1% Native Hawaiian or other Pacific Islander, non-Hispanic/Latino; 1% international. 18% 25 or older, 51% live on campus, 57% transferred in. Core. Calendar: semesters. Academic remediation for entering students, ESL program,

services for LD students, self-designed majors, independent study, distance learning, double major, summer session for credit, part-time degree program, adult/continuing education programs, co-op programs and internships.

Entrance Requirements: Open admission. Options: electronic application, early admission. Required: high school transcript, ACT. Entrance: noncompetitive. Application deadlines: Rolling, Rolling for nonresidents. Notification: continuous, continuous for nonresidents. SAT Reasoning Test deadline: 12/18. SAT Subject Test deadline: 12/18. Transfer credits accepted: Yes. Applicants placed on waiting list: 0.

Costs Per Year: Application fee: $35. State resident tuition: $4177 full-time, $136.61 per credit hour part-time. Nonresident tuition: $10,175 full-time. Full-time tuition varies according to program and reciprocity agreements. Part-time tuition varies according to program and reciprocity agreements. College room and board: $5164. Room and board charges vary according to board plan and housing facility.

Collegiate Environment: Orientation program. Drama-theater group, choral group, marching band. Most popular organizations: music, Drama Club, Inter-Varsity Christian Fellowship, Cultural Diversity, Habitat for Humanity. Major annual events: Homecoming, Agawasie Day. Student services: legal services, health clinic, personal-psychological counseling. Campus security: 24-hour emergency response devices and patrols, student patrols, late night transport-escort service, controlled dormitory access. 1,200 college housing spaces available; 972 were occupied in 2012-13. Freshmen guaranteed college housing. On-campus residence required in freshman year. Options: coed, men-only, women-only housing available. Mildred Johnson Library with 72,142 books, 10,626 microform titles, 156 serials, 4,488 audiovisual materials, an OPAC, and a Web page. Operations spending for the previous fiscal year: $181,450. 115 computers available on campus for general student use. Computer purchase/lease plans available. A campuswide network can be accessed from student residence rooms and from off campus. Students can access the following: online class registration. Staffed computer lab on campus provides training in use of computers, software, and the Internet.

Community Environment: Wahpeton (population 8,220) is located at the origin of the Red River in southeastern North Dakota. The city is served by a bus line, and U.S. Highway 75, Interstates 29 and 94 and State Highways 13 & 81.

■ **NORTH DAKOTA STATE UNIVERSITY**
1340 N University Ave.
Fargo, ND 58108
Tel: (701)231-8011; Free: 800-488-NDSU
Fax: (701)231-8802
E-mail: ndsu.admission@ndsu.edu
Web Site: www.ndsu.edu/
Description: State-supported, university, coed. Part of North Dakota University System. Awards bachelor's, master's, and doctoral degrees and post-master's certificates. Founded 1890. Setting: 2,100-acre urban campus. Endowment: $372,771. Research spending for the previous fiscal year: $9.3 million. Educational spending for the previous fiscal year: $6050 per student. Total enrollment: 14,443. Faculty: 833 (643 full-time, 190 part-time). Student-undergrad faculty ratio is 18:1. 5,562 applied, 84% were admitted. 16% from top 10% of their high school class, 40% from top quarter, 74% from top half. 8 National Merit Scholars. Full-time: 11,059 students, 44% women, 56% men. Part-time: 1,273 students, 52% women, 48% men. Students come from 47 states and territories, 79 other countries, 55% from out-of-state. 1% American Indian or Alaska Native, non-Hispanic/Latino; 1% Hispanic/Latino; 2% African American, non-Hispanic/Latino; 1% Asian, non-Hispanic/Latino; 0.04% Native Hawaiian or other Pacific Islander, non-Hispanic/Latino; 4% international. 9% 25 or older, 26% live on campus, 6% transferred in. Retention: 80% of full-time freshmen returned the following year. Academic areas with the most degrees conferred: business/marketing; engineering; health professions and related sciences. Core. Calendar: semesters. Services for LD students, advanced placement, self-designed majors, honors program, independent study, distance learning, double major, summer session for credit, part-time degree program, co-op programs and internships, graduate courses open to undergrads. Off campus study at members of the Tri-College University-Concordia College, Moorhead, MN, Minnesota State University Moorhead. Study abroad program. ROTC: Army, Air Force.

Entrance Requirements: Options: electronic application, international baccalaureate accepted. Required: high school transcript, minimum 2.5 high school GPA, SAT or ACT. Entrance: moderately difficult. Application deadline: 8/15. Notification: continuous. SAT Reasoning Test deadline: 8/15. SAT Subject Test deadline: 8/15.

Costs Per Year: Application fee: $35. One-time mandatory fee: $120. State resident tuition: $6135 full-time, $269.94 per credit hour part-time. Nonresident tuition: $16,381 full-time, $720.74 per credit hour part-time. Mandatory fees: $1098 full-time, $45.76 per credit hour part-time. Full-time tuition and fees vary according to program, reciprocity agreements, and student level. Part-time tuition and fees vary according to course load, program, reciprocity agreements, and student level. College room and board: $6910. College room only: $3226. Room and board charges vary according to board plan and housing facility.

Collegiate Environment: Orientation program. Drama-theater group, choral group, marching band, student-run newspaper, radio station. Social organizations: 250 open to all; national fraternities, national sororities; 7% of eligible men and 4% of eligible women are members. Most popular organizations: Saddle and Sirloin, Students Today, Leaders Forever, International Student Association, Chi Alpha Christian Organization, fraternities/sororities. Major annual events: Homecoming, International Students Week, Spring Blast. Student services: health clinic, personal-psychological counseling. Campus security: 24-hour emergency response devices and patrols, student patrols, late night transport-escort service, controlled dormitory access. 4,996 college housing spaces available; 4,005 were occupied in 2012-13. Freshmen guaranteed college housing. On-campus residence required in freshman year. Options: coed, men-only, women-only housing available. North Dakota State University Library plus 3 others with an OPAC and a Web page. Operations spending for the previous fiscal year: $5.1 million. 500 computers available on campus for general student use. Computer purchase/lease plans available. A campuswide network can be accessed from student residence rooms. Students can access the following: online class registration. Staffed computer lab on campus (open 24 hours a day) provides training in use of computers and software.

Community Environment: North Dakota's largest city at 90,599, Fargo is the largest distribution point between Minneapolis and Spokane. Fargo-Moorhead as seen designated as one of the top ten All-American cities for 2000. The metropolitan area has over a hundred manufacturing plants producing agricultural machinery, feed, fertilizers, foodstuffs, and dairy products. In addition, the community contains the largest medical complex between Minneapolis and the West Coast. Recreation facilities in the city's 765-acre park system include three golf courses, a winter sports building, and four swimming pools. There are part-time employment opportunities for students.

■ **RASMUSSEN COLLEGE BISMARCK**
1701 E Century Ave.
Bismarck, ND 58503
Tel: (701)530-9600; Free: 888-549-6755
Fax: (701)530-9604
E-mail: susan.hammerstrom@rasmussen.edu
Web Site: www.rasmussen.edu/

Description: Proprietary, primarily 2-year, coed. Part of Rasmussen College System. Awards certificates, diplomas, transfer associate, terminal associate, and bachelor's degrees. Setting: suburban campus. Total enrollment: 222. Student-undergrad faculty ratio is 22:1. 87% 25 or older. Core. Academic remediation for entering students, accelerated degree program, distance learning, double major, summer session for credit, part-time degree program, adult/continuing education programs, internships.

Entrance Requirements: Options: electronic application, early admission, deferred admission. Required: high school transcript, minimum 2 high school GPA, Internal Exam. Required for some: interview. Entrance: minimally difficult. Application deadline: Rolling. Transfer credits accepted: Yes.

Costs Per Year: Tuition: $12,600 full-time. Mandatory fees: $1800 full-time. Full-time tuition and fees vary according to course level, course load, degree level, location, and program.

Collegiate Environment: Orientation program. College housing not available. Rasmussen College Library - Bismarck with 1,953 books, 20 serials, 235 audiovisual materials, an OPAC, and a Web page. 67 computers available on campus for general student use. A campuswide network can be accessed from off-campus.

■ **RASMUSSEN COLLEGE FARGO**
4012 19th Ave. SW
Fargo, ND 58103
Tel: (701)277-3889; Free: 888-549-6755

Fax: (701)277-5604
E-mail: susan.hammerstrom@rasmussen.edu
Web Site: www.rasmussen.edu/

Description: Proprietary, primarily 2-year, coed. Part of Rasmussen College System. Awards certificates, diplomas, transfer associate, terminal associate, and bachelor's degrees. Founded 1902. Setting: suburban campus. Total enrollment: 400. Student-undergrad faculty ratio is 22:1. 86% 25 or older. Core. Academic remediation for entering students, accelerated degree program, distance learning, double major, summer session for credit, part-time degree program, adult/continuing education programs, internships.

Entrance Requirements: Options: electronic application, early admission, deferred admission. Required: high school transcript, minimum 2 high school GPA, Internal Exam. Required for some: interview. Entrance: minimally difficult. Application deadline: Rolling. Transfer credits accepted: Yes.

Costs Per Year: Tuition: $12,600 full-time. Mandatory fees: $1800 full-time. Full-time tuition and fees vary according to course level, course load, degree level, location, and program.

Collegiate Environment: Orientation program. College housing not available. Rasmussen College Library - Fargo with 1,477 books, 20 serials, 292 audiovisual materials, an OPAC, and a Web page. 87 computers available on campus for general student use. A campuswide network can be accessed from off-campus.

■ **SANFORD COLLEGE OF NURSING**
512 N 7th St.
Bismarck, ND 58501-4494
Tel: (701)323-6271
E-mail: mary.j.smith@sanfordcollege.edu
Web Site: bismarck.sanfordhealth.org/collegeofnursing/index.asp

Description: Independent, upper-level, coed. Administratively affiliated with Sanford Health Bismarck. Awards bachelor's degrees. Founded 1988. Setting: 15-acre small town campus. Total enrollment: 109. Faculty: 13 (10 full-time, 3 part-time). Student-undergrad faculty ratio is 8:1. 127 applied, 58% were admitted. Full-time: 109 students, 89% women, 11% men. Students come from 5 states and territories, 10% from out-of-state. 2% American Indian or Alaska Native, non-Hispanic/Latino; 2% Hispanic/Latino; 5% African American, non-Hispanic/Latino; 1% Asian, non-Hispanic/Latino; 0% Native Hawaiian or other Pacific Islander, non-Hispanic/Latino; 0% international. 35% 25 or older, 59% transferred in. Academic area with the most degrees conferred: health professions and related sciences. Core. Calendar: semesters. Independent study, internships.

Entrance Requirements: Transfer credits accepted: Yes. Applicants placed on waiting list: 6. Wait-listed applicants offered admission: 3. Early action applicants: 2. Early action applicants admitted: 1.

Costs Per Year: Application fee: $40. One-time mandatory fee: $275. Tuition: $10,724 full-time, $446.83 per credit part-time. Mandatory fees: $855 full-time, $71.25 per credit part-time. Part-time tuition and fees vary according to course load.

Collegiate Environment: Orientation program. Social organizations: 2 open to all. Most popular organizations: Student Body Organization, Student Nurses Association. Major annual events: Christmas Party, Annual Picnic, Awards Banquet. Student services: legal services, personal-psychological counseling. Campus security: late night transport-escort service. College housing not available. Sanford Health Sciences Library with 5,049 books, 56 microform titles, 630 serials, 454 audiovisual materials, and an OPAC. 25 computers available on campus for general student use. A campuswide network can be accessed.

■ **SITTING BULL COLLEGE**
1341 92nd St.
Fort Yates, ND 58538-9701
Tel: (701)854-8000
Fax: (701)854-3403
E-mail: melodys@sbcl.edu
Web Site: www.sittingbull.edu/

Description: Independent, 2-year, coed. Awards certificates, transfer associate, and terminal associate degrees. Founded 1973. Setting: rural campus. Endowment: $541,000. Educational spending for the previous fiscal year: $2001 per student. Total enrollment: 214. Faculty: 32 (16 full-time, 16 part-time). Student-undergrad faculty ratio is 6:1. 63 applied, 100% were admitted. 20% from top 10% of their high school class, 30% from top quarter, 50% from top half. 2 class presidents, 2 valedictorians, 10 student government officers. Students come from 2 states and territories, 35% 25 or older. Core. Calendar: semesters. Academic remediation for entering students,

part-time degree program, adult/continuing education programs. Off campus study at members of the American Indian Higher Education Consortium.
Entrance Requirements: Open admission. Option: early admission. Required: high school transcript, medical questionnaire. Entrance: noncompetitive. Application deadline: 9/6. Notification: continuous.
Collegiate Environment: Student-run newspaper. Most popular organizations: student government, Future Teachers, Ikce Oyate Culture Club, Phi Beta Lambda, Ski Club. Major annual events: Homecoming, Thanksgiving Dinner, Student Awards Night. Student services: personal-psychological counseling. Sitting Bull College Library with 10,000 books, 130 serials, and an OPAC. 16 computers available on campus for general student use. Staffed computer lab on campus.

■ **TRINITY BIBLE COLLEGE**
50 S 6th Ave.
Ellendale, ND 58436-7150
Tel: (701)349-3621; Free: 800-523-1603
Fax: (701)349-5443
Web Site: www.trinitybiblecollege.edu/
Description: Independent Assemblies of God, 4-year, coed. Awards associate and bachelor's degrees. Founded 1948. Setting: 28-acre rural campus. Total enrollment: 292. 14% 25 or older. Core. Calendar: semesters. Academic remediation for entering students, advanced placement, accelerated degree program, distance learning, double major, summer session for credit, part-time degree program, internships.
Entrance Requirements: Open admission. Options: deferred admission, international baccalaureate accepted. Required: essay, high school transcript, minimum 2.0 high school GPA, 2 recommendations, health form, evidence of Christian conversion, ACT. Required for some: interview, SAT. Entrance: noncompetitive. Application deadline: Rolling. Notification: continuous.
Collegiate Environment: Orientation program. Drama-theater group, choral group, student-run radio station. Student services: personal-psychological counseling. Campus security: 24-hour emergency response devices, student patrols, late night transport-escort service. Graham Library with 67,868 books, 5,873 microform titles, 227 serials, and 2,258 audiovisual materials.
Community Environment: Ellendale is a rural community (population 1,500) just north of the South Dakota border and 62 miles south of Jamestown on U.S. Highway 281.

■ **TURTLE MOUNTAIN COMMUNITY COLLEGE**
Box 340
Belcourt, ND 58316-0340
Tel: (701)477-7862
Fax: (701)477-7807
E-mail: jlafontaine@tm.edu
Web Site: www.turtle-mountain.cc.nd.us/
Description: Independent, 2-year, coed. Awards certificates, transfer associate, and terminal associate degrees. Founded 1972. Setting: 10-acre rural campus. Total enrollment: 1,058. Student-undergrad faculty ratio is 19:1. 0% from out-of-state. 41% 25 or older. Retention: 57% of full-time freshmen returned the following year. Core. Calendar: semesters. Academic remediation for entering students, part-time degree program, adult/continuing education programs.
Entrance Requirements: Open admission. Options: early admission, deferred admission. Required: high school transcript, ACT. Entrance: noncompetitive. Application deadline: Rolling.
Collegiate Environment: Student services: personal-psychological counseling. Turtle Mountain Community College Library with an OPAC.

■ **UNITED TRIBES TECHNICAL COLLEGE**
3315 University Dr.
Bismarck, ND 58504-7596
Tel: (701)255-3285
E-mail: vgillette@uttc.edu
Web Site: www.uttc.edu/
Description: Federally supported, 2-year, coed. Awards certificates, transfer associate, and terminal associate degrees. Founded 1969. Setting: 105-acre small town campus. Total enrollment: 604. Faculty: 63 (49 full-time, 14 part-time). Student-undergrad faculty ratio is 8:1. 184 applied, 84% were admitted. Full-time: 552 students, 56% women, 44% men. Part-time: 52 students, 63% women, 37% men. Students come from 19 states and territories, 6% from out-of-state. 54% 25 or older, 16% transferred in. Retention: 30% of full-time freshmen returned the following year. Calendar: semesters.

Academic remediation for entering students, honors program, independent study, summer session for credit, part-time degree program, co-op programs.
Entrance Requirements: Open admission. Required: high school transcript. Entrance: noncompetitive. Application deadline: Rolling.
Collegiate Environment: Student-run newspaper. Major annual events: basketball games, Parent Breakfast. Student services: personal-psychological counseling. Campus security: 24-hour emergency response devices and patrols. United Tribes Technical College Library plus 1 other with 6,000 books, 86 serials, an OPAC, and a Web page. 210 computers available on campus for general student use. Staffed computer lab on campus.

■ **UNIVERSITY OF MARY**
7500 University Dr.
Bismarck, ND 58504-9652
Tel: (701)255-7500; Free: 800-288-6279
Fax: (701)255-7687
E-mail: mcheitkamp@umary.edu
Web Site: www.umary.edu/
Description: Independent Roman Catholic, comprehensive, coed. Awards bachelor's, master's, and doctoral degrees. Founded 1959. Setting: 107-acre rural campus. Endowment: $23.4 million. Educational spending for the previous fiscal year: $5531 per student. Total enrollment: 3,135. Faculty: 257 (101 full-time, 156 part-time). Student-undergrad faculty ratio is 17:1. 1,001 applied, 75% were admitted. 16% from top 10% of their high school class, 42% from top quarter, 71% from top half. 31 valedictorians. Full-time: 1,633 students, 62% women, 38% men. Part-time: 497 students, 55% women, 45% men. Students come from 34 states and territories, 13 other countries, 31% from out-of-state. 4% American Indian or Alaska Native, non-Hispanic/Latino; 2% Hispanic/Latino; 3% African American, non-Hispanic/Latino; 1% Asian, non-Hispanic/Latino; 0.5% Native Hawaiian or other Pacific Islander, non-Hispanic/Latino; 1% international. 25% 25 or older, 35% live on campus, 13% transferred in. Retention: 72% of full-time freshmen returned the following year. Academic areas with the most degrees conferred: business/marketing; health professions and related sciences; education. Core. Calendar: 4-4-1. Academic remediation for entering students, services for LD students, advanced placement, accelerated degree program, self-designed majors, honors program, independent study, distance learning, double major, summer session for credit, part-time degree program, external degree program, adult/continuing education programs, co-op programs and internships, graduate courses open to undergrads. Off campus study. Study abroad program.
Entrance Requirements: Options: electronic application, early admission, deferred admission, international baccalaureate accepted. Required: high school transcript, 2.0 College Prep GPA, SAT or ACT. Recommended: minimum 2.5 high school GPA, 2 recommendations. Required for some: essay, interview. Entrance: minimally difficult. Application deadline: Rolling. Transfer credits accepted: Yes.
Costs Per Year: Application fee: $25. Comprehensive fee: $19,890 includes full-time tuition ($13,600) and college room and board ($6290). College room only: $3330. Full-time tuition varies according to course load, degree level, and program. Room and board charges vary according to board plan and housing facility.
Collegiate Environment: Orientation program. Drama-theater group, choral group, student-run newspaper. Social organizations: 28 open to all. Most popular organizations: Collegians for Life, Nursing Students Association, Student Occupational Therapy, UMPHERD, Pre-PT Club. Major annual events: Homecoming activities, Jazz Festival, convocation series. Student services: health clinic, personal-psychological counseling. Campus security: 24-hour emergency response devices and patrols, late night transport-escort service, controlled dormitory access. University of Mary Library with 64,524 books, 210 serials, 4,346 audiovisual materials, and an OPAC. Operations spending for the previous fiscal year: $321,584. 100 computers available on campus for general student use. A campuswide network can be accessed from student residence rooms and from off campus. Students can access the following: online class registration.
Community Environment: Bismarck, North Dakota's capital city, is the second largest city with a population of 57,000. Because of its central location, modern shopping centers and Civic Center, the city hosts many state and national conventions. Bismarck is considered the cultural, business and educational center of western and central North Dakota. It is also the medical center for the region with two modern medical centers and clinics. Bismarck has a large city library, a State Historical Library, and numerous

libraries related to state and federal offices; a city orchestra, civic chorus, and amateur drama club; and many churches representing various denominations. The city has many parks and recreation areas, a city zoo, three golf courses, and clubs for a variety of recreational activities. The Missouri River and nearby Lake Sakakawea offer boating, fishing and other water sports. Bismarck has transportation service from several major air carriers, commuter airlines, and bus lines. Interstate 94 and U.S. Highway 83 meet in Bismarck. The city has a pleasant summer climate and moderate to severe winters.

■ UNIVERSITY OF NORTH DAKOTA

264 Centennial Dr.
Grand Forks, ND 58202
Tel: (701)777-2011; Free: 800-CALL-UND
Fax: (701)777-3650
E-mail: und.enrollmentservices@und.edu
Web Site: www.und.nodak.edu/

Description: State-supported, university, coed. Part of North Dakota University System. Awards bachelor's, master's, and doctoral degrees. Founded 1883. Setting: 550-acre urban campus. Endowment: $13.1 million. Research spending for the previous fiscal year: $47.5 million. Educational spending for the previous fiscal year: $11,710 per student. Total enrollment: 14,697. Faculty: 703 (638 full-time, 65 part-time). 4,857 applied, 43% were admitted. 14% from top 10% of their high school class, 42% from top quarter, 73% from top half. 2 National Merit Scholars. Full-time: 9,334 students, 47% women, 53% men. Part-time: 2,188 students, 38% women, 62% men. Students come from 44 other countries, 57% from out-of-state. 2% American Indian or Alaska Native, non-Hispanic/Latino; 2% Hispanic/Latino; 2% African American, non-Hispanic/Latino; 1% Asian, non-Hispanic/Latino; 0.1% Native Hawaiian or other Pacific Islander, non-Hispanic/Latino; 6% international. 17% 25 or older, 32% live on campus, 8% transferred in. Retention: 77% of full-time freshmen returned the following year. Academic areas with the most degrees conferred: business/marketing; transportation and materials moving; health professions and related sciences. Core. Calendar: semesters. ESL program, services for LD students, advanced placement, accelerated degree program, self-designed majors, honors program, independent study, distance learning, double major, summer session for credit, part-time degree program, adult/continuing education programs, co-op programs and internships, graduate courses open to undergrads. Off campus study. Study abroad program. ROTC: Army, Air Force.

Entrance Requirements: Options: electronic application, deferred admission. Required: high school transcript, SAT or ACT. Recommended: minimum 2.5 high school GPA, ACT. Entrance: minimally difficult.

Costs Per Year: Application fee: $35. State resident tuition: $5938 full-time, $247.40 per credit hour part-time. Nonresident tuition: $15,854 full-time, $660.58 per credit hour part-time. Mandatory fees: $1316 full-time. Full-time tuition and fees vary according to degree level, program, and reciprocity agreements. Part-time tuition varies according to course load, degree level, program, and reciprocity agreements. College room and board: $6332. College room only: $2482. Room and board charges vary according to board plan and housing facility.

Collegiate Environment: Orientation program. Drama-theater group, choral group, marching band, student-run newspaper, radio station. Social organizations: 275 open to all; national fraternities, national sororities; 8% of eligible men and 8% of eligible women are members. Most popular organizations: student government, Greek Life, Association of Residence Halls, University of North Dakota Indian Association, NoDak Nation Student Athletic Boosters. Major annual events: Homecoming, The Big Event (a city wide community event), Athletic events. Student services: legal services, health clinic, personal-psychological counseling, women's center. Campus security: 24-hour emergency response devices and patrols, student patrols, late night transport-escort service, controlled dormitory access, emergency telephones. 3,394 college housing spaces available; 3,304 were occupied in 2012-13. No special consideration for freshman housing applicants. Options: coed, men-only, women-only housing available. Chester Fritz Library plus 2 others with 1.2 million books, 902,192 microform titles, 44,704 serials, 21,669 audiovisual materials, an OPAC, and a Web page. Operations spending for the previous fiscal year: $8.3 million. 1,500 computers available on campus for general student use. Computer purchase/lease plans available. A campuswide network can be accessed from student residence rooms and from off campus. Students can access the following: online class registration. Staffed computer lab on campus provides training in use of computers, software, and the Internet.

■ VALLEY CITY STATE UNIVERSITY

101 College St., SW
Valley City, ND 58072
Tel: (701)845-7990; Free: 800-532-8641
Fax: (701)845-7245
E-mail: kaleen.peterson@vcsu.edu
Web Site: www.vcsu.edu/

Description: State-supported, comprehensive, coed. Part of North Dakota University System. Awards bachelor's and master's degrees. Founded 1890. Setting: 55-acre small town campus. Total enrollment: 1,362. Faculty: 109 (66 full-time, 43 part-time). Student-undergrad faculty ratio is 12:1. 351 applied, 81% were admitted. 6% from top 10% of their high school class, 25% from top quarter, 55% from top half. Full-time: 795 students, 49% women, 51% men. Part-time: 419 students, 67% women, 33% men. Students come from 43 states and territories, 11 other countries, 43% from out-of-state. 1% American Indian or Alaska Native, non-Hispanic/Latino; 4% Hispanic/Latino; 4% African American, non-Hispanic/Latino; 1% Asian, non-Hispanic/Latino; 0.4% Native Hawaiian or other Pacific Islander, non-Hispanic/Latino; 4% international. 33% 25 or older, 24% live on campus, 9% transferred in. Retention: 54% of full-time freshmen returned the following year. Academic areas with the most degrees conferred: education; business/marketing; biological/life sciences. Core. Calendar: semesters. Academic remediation for entering students, services for LD students, self-designed majors, distance learning, double major, summer session for credit, part-time degree program, co-op programs and internships. Off campus study at North Dakota State University. Study abroad program.

Entrance Requirements: Open admission. Options: electronic application, early admission, deferred admission. Required: high school transcript. Required for some: SAT or ACT. Entrance: noncompetitive. Application deadline: Rolling. Notification: continuous. SAT Reasoning Test deadline: 8/15. SAT Subject Test deadline: 8/15. Transfer credits accepted: Yes.

Costs Per Year: Application fee: $35. State resident tuition: $4657 full-time, $155.24 per semester hour part-time. Nonresident tuition: $12,435 full-time, $155.24 per semester hour part-time. Mandatory fees: $1667 full-time. Full-time tuition and fees vary according to course load, location, program, and reciprocity agreements. Part-time tuition varies according to course load, location, program, and reciprocity agreements. College room and board: $5480. College room only: $2040. Room and board charges vary according to board plan and housing facility.

Collegiate Environment: Orientation program. Drama-theater group, choral group. Social organizations: 30 open to all; local fraternities, local sororities; 1% of eligible men and 1% of eligible women are members. Most popular organizations: departmental clubs, Fellowship of Christian Athletes, intramural sports, VCAB, Viking Ambassadors. Major annual events: music and theater productions, homecoming activities, athletic events. Student services: health clinic, personal-psychological counseling. Campus security: controlled dormitory access, security cameras throughout campus. 465 college housing spaces available; 321 were occupied in 2012-13. Freshmen guaranteed college housing. On-campus residence required in freshman year. Options: coed, men-only, women-only housing available. Allen Memorial Library with an OPAC and a Web page. 995 computers available on campus for general student use. Computer purchase/lease plans available. A computer is required for all students. A campuswide network can be accessed from student residence rooms and from off campus. Students can access the following: online class registration. Staffed computer lab on campus provides training in use of computers, software, and the Internet.

Community Environment: Valley City, in the Sheyenne River Valley, is the home of the North Dakota Winter Show, a statewide agricultural fair held in the first week in March. The area is served by buses, railroad, and Interstate Highways 94, 10, and 52.

■ WILLISTON STATE COLLEGE

Box 1326
Williston, ND 58802-1326
Tel: (701)774-4200; Free: 888-863-9455
Fax: (701)774-4211
E-mail: wsc.admission@wsc.nodak.edu
Web Site: www.willistonstate.edu/

Description: State-supported, 2-year, coed. Part of North Dakota University System. Awards certificates, diplomas, transfer associate, and terminal associate degrees. Founded 1957. Setting: 80-acre small town campus. Endowment: $52,200. Educational spending for the previous fiscal year: $4642 per student. Total enrollment: 855. Faculty: 93 (26 full-time, 67 part-time). Student-undergrad faculty ratio is 14:1. 540 applied, 98% were admitted. Students come from 9 states and territories, 3 other countries, 14% from out-of-state. 28% 25 or older, 13% live on campus. Retention: 56% of full-time freshmen returned the following year. Core. Calendar: semesters. Academic remediation for entering students, services for LD students, advanced placement, self-designed majors, honors program, independent study, distance learning, summer session for credit, part-time degree program, co-op programs. Off campus study at Lake Region State College.

Entrance Requirements: Open admission except for practical nursing and physical therapist assistant programs. Option: electronic application. Required: high school transcript. Entrance: noncompetitive. Application deadline: Rolling. Notification: continuous.

Costs Per Year: Application fee: $35. One-time mandatory fee: $35. State resident tuition: $3021 full-time, $100.68 per credit hour part-time. Nonresident tuition: $3021 full-time, $100.68 per credit hour part-time. Mandatory fees: $1161 full-time, $38.68 per credit hour part-time. Full-time tuition and fees vary according to course load, location, and reciprocity agreements. Part-time tuition and fees vary according to course load, location, and reciprocity agreements. College room and board: $7200. College room only: $3770. Room and board charges vary according to board plan and housing facility.

Collegiate Environment: Orientation program. Drama-theater group, choral group, student-run newspaper. Social organizations: 17 open to all; national sororities; 2% of women are members. Most popular organizations: Phi Theta Kappa, PBL, Student Senate, VICA (Vocational Industrial Clubs of America), Student Nurses Association. Major annual events: Winter Carnival, Graduation, Halloween Dance. Student services: personal-psychological counseling. Campus security: controlled dormitory access. Williston State College Library with 16,218 books, 14 microform titles, 214 serials, 475 audiovisual materials, an OPAC, and a Web page. 70 computers available on campus for general student use. Computer purchase/lease plans available. A campuswide network can be accessed from student residence rooms and from off campus. Staffed computer lab on campus.

Community Environment: Midway between two dams, Fort Peck in Montana and Garrison in North Dakota, Williston has been a railroad and distributing center since its earliest days. In the farming and stock-raising region of the oil-rich Williston Basin, the city has more than 1,000 producing wells within its trade territory. This is a rural community with temperate climate. The area is served by bus, rail, and air lines. Good U.S. Highways intersect the city. Community services include 24 churches representing 18 denominations, a public library, museum, community concert association, modern hospital, and clinics. There are also various civic, fraternal, and veteran's organizations here. Local recreation includes theaters, a drive-in, golf clubs, bowling alley, tennis courts, baseball stadium, several softball complexes, and excellent fishing in Garrison Reservoir and the Missouri River.

■ AKRON INSTITUTE OF HERZING UNIVERSITY

1600 S Arlington St.
Ste. 100
Akron, OH 44306
Tel: (330)724-1600; Free: 800-311-0512
Fax: (330)724-9688
Web Site: www.akroninstitute.com/
Description: Proprietary, primarily 2-year, coed. Awards diplomas, terminal associate, and bachelor's degrees. Founded 1970.

■ ALLEGHENY WESLEYAN COLLEGE

2161 Woodsdale Rd.
Salem, OH 44460
Tel: (330)337-6403; Free: 800-292-3153
Fax: (330)337-6255
E-mail: college@awc.edu
Web Site: www.awc.edu/
Description: Independent Wesleyan, 4-year, coed. Awards bachelor's degrees. Total enrollment: 54. 17% 25 or older. Calendar: semesters.
Entrance Requirements: Open admission.

■ ANTIOCH UNIVERSITY MIDWEST

900 Dayton St.
Yellow Springs, OH 45387-1609
Tel: (937)769-1800
Fax: (937)769-1805
E-mail: orobinson@antioch.edu
Web Site: midwest.antioch.edu/
Description: Independent, upper-level, coed. Part of Antioch University. Awards bachelor's and master's degrees and post-master's certificates. Founded 1988. Setting: 100-acre small town campus with easy access to Dayton. Total enrollment: 364. Faculty: 55 (18 full-time, 37 part-time). Student-undergrad faculty ratio is 7:1. Full-time: 55 students, 76% women, 24% men. Part-time: 61 students, 72% women, 28% men. 0% from out-of-state. 4% American Indian or Alaska Native, non-Hispanic/Latino; 1% Hispanic/Latino; 21% African American, non-Hispanic/Latino; 2% Asian, non-Hispanic/Latino; 0% Native Hawaiian or other Pacific Islander, non-Hispanic/Latino; 0% international. 95% 25 or older, 0% live on campus, 27% transferred in. Academic areas with the most degrees conferred: education; business/marketing; liberal arts/general studies. Core. Advanced placement, accelerated degree program, self-designed majors, independent study, distance learning, double major, summer session for credit, part-time degree program, adult/continuing education programs, co-op programs and internships, graduate courses open to undergrads. Off campus study at Southwestern Ohio Consortium of Higher Education (SOCHE) and all Antioch University campuses.
Collegiate Environment: Student services: personal-psychological counseling. Campus security: 24-hour emergency response devices. College housing not available. Olive Kettering Library plus 1 other with 112,436 books, 61,763 serials, 3,700 audiovisual materials, an OPAC, and a Web page. 32 computers available on campus for general student use. A computer is required for all students. A campuswide network can be accessed. Students can access the following: online class registration, online bill pay, and online view of financial aid award letter. Staffed computer lab on campus provides training in use of computers, software, and the Internet.

■ ANTONELLI COLLEGE

124 E Seventh St.
Cincinnati, OH 45202
Tel: (513)241-4338; Free: 877-500-4304
Fax: (513)241-9396
E-mail: admissions.cincinnati@antonellicollege.edu
Web Site: www.antonellicollege.edu/
Description: Proprietary, 2-year, coed. Awards diplomas and terminal associate degrees. Founded 1947. Setting: urban campus. Total enrollment: 377. 55% 25 or older. Core. Honors program, summer session for credit, part-time degree program, internships.
Entrance Requirements: Open admission. Options: early admission, deferred admission. Required: high school transcript, interview. Required for some: art portfolio. Entrance: noncompetitive. Application deadline: Rolling.
Collegiate Environment: Student services: personal-psychological counseling. Campus security: 24-hour emergency response devices, security personnel while classes are in session. Main library plus 1 other with 2,000 books and 30 serials.

■ ART ACADEMY OF CINCINNATI

1212 Jackson St.
Cincinnati, OH 45202
Tel: (513)562-6262; Free: 800-323-5692
Fax: (513)562-8778
E-mail: admissions@artacademy.edu
Web Site: www.artacademy.edu/
Description: Independent, comprehensive, coed. Awards associate, bachelor's, and master's degrees. Founded 1887. Setting: 184-acre urban campus. Endowment: $7 million. Total enrollment: 165. Faculty: 44 (14 full-time, 30 part-time). Student-undergrad faculty ratio is 10:1. 541 applied, 21% were admitted. Full-time: 153 students, 63% women, 37% men. Part-time: 11 students, 55% women, 45% men. Students come from 12 states and territories, 2 other countries, 24% from out-of-state. 8% 25 or older, 18% live on campus, 15% transferred in. Retention: 81% of full-time freshmen returned the following year. Academic area with the most degrees conferred: visual and performing arts. Core. Calendar: semesters. Services for LD students, advanced placement, self-designed majors, honors program, independent study, double major, summer session for credit, part-time degree program, adult/continuing education programs, co-op programs and internships, graduate courses open to undergrads. Off campus study at members of the Greater Cincinnati Consortium of Colleges and Universities, Association of Independent Colleges of Art and Design. Study abroad program.
Entrance Requirements: Options: electronic application, deferred admission. Required: essay, high school transcript, minimum 2.0 high school GPA, 1 recommendation, portfolio, SAT or ACT. Recommended: interview. Entrance: moderately difficult. Application deadline: 6/30. Notification: continuous.
Collegiate Environment: Orientation program. Major annual events: annual field trips to art centers in Chicago and New York, Visiting Artists Lecture Series, Student Exhibitions. Student services: personal-psychological counseling. Campus security: 24-hour emergency response devices and patrols. 40 computers available on campus for general student use. A campuswide network can be accessed. Staffed computer lab on campus provides training in use of computers, software, and the Internet.
Community Environment: The Art Academy is located in Eden Park, a metropolitan park of 184 acres that also contains the Cincinnati Historical

Society. Mirror Lake, the Krohm Conservatory, two dramatic theaters, one outdoor theater and the Ohio River overlook the area.

■ THE ART INSTITUTE OF CINCINNATI

1171 E Kemper Rd.
Cincinnati, OH 45246
Tel: (513)751-1206
Fax: (513)751-1209
Web Site: www.aic-arts.edu/

Description: Independent, 2-year, coed. Awards transfer associate degrees. Founded 1976. Total enrollment: 63. Student-undergrad faculty ratio is 7:1. 116 applied. 17% from out-of-state. 6% 25 or older. Retention: 82% of full-time freshmen returned the following year.

Collegiate Environment: Campus security: 24-hour emergency response devices.

■ THE ART INSTITUTE OF OHIO–CINCINNATI

8845 Governors Hill Dr.
Cincinnati, OH 45249-3317
Tel: (513)833-2400; Free: 866-613-5184
Fax: (877)477-8486
Web Site: www.artinstitutes.edu/cincinnati/

Description: Proprietary, primarily 2-year, coed. Part of Education Management Corporation. Awards diplomas, transfer associate, terminal associate, and bachelor's degrees. Setting: urban campus. Calendar: continuous.

■ ASHLAND UNIVERSITY

401 College Ave.
Ashland, OH 44805-3702
Tel: (419)289-4142; Free: 800-882-1548
Fax: (419)289-5999
E-mail: enrollme@ashland.edu
Web Site: www.exploreashland.com/

Description: Independent, comprehensive, coed, affiliated with Brethren Church. Awards bachelor's, master's, and doctoral degrees and post-master's certificates. Founded 1878. Setting: 135-acre small town campus with easy access to Cleveland. Endowment: $39.4 million. Educational spending for the previous fiscal year: $6661 per student. Total enrollment: 6,491. Faculty: 591 (272 full-time, 319 part-time). Student-undergrad faculty ratio is 13:1. 3,530 applied, 77% were admitted. 22% from top 10% of their high school class, 49% from top quarter, 80% from top half. 18 valedictorians. Full-time: 2,622 students, 59% women, 41% men. Part-time: 524 students, 32% women, 68% men. Students come from 31 states and territories, 19 other countries, 10% from out-of-state. 22% 25 or older, 72% live on campus, 3% transferred in. Retention: 69% of full-time freshmen returned the following year. Academic areas with the most degrees conferred: education; business/marketing; biological/life sciences. Core. Calendar: semesters. Academic remediation for entering students, ESL program, services for LD students, advanced placement, accelerated degree program, self-designed majors, honors program, independent study, distance learning, double major, summer session for credit, part-time degree program, adult/continuing education programs, co-op programs and internships. Off campus study. Study abroad program. ROTC: Army (c), Air Force (c).

Entrance Requirements: Options: electronic application, deferred admission, international baccalaureate accepted. Required: high school transcript, minimum 2.5 high school GPA, Standardized test score for Freshmen applicants, 18 ACT or 870 SAT (Critical Reading and Math), SAT or ACT. Entrance: moderately difficult. Application deadlines: Rolling, Rolling for nonresidents. Notification: continuous. SAT Reasoning Test deadline: 8/15. SAT Subject Test deadline: 8/15. Transfer credits accepted: Yes.

Costs Per Year: Application fee: $0. Comprehensive fee: $38,360 includes full-time tuition ($27,930), mandatory fees ($928), and college room and board ($9502). College room only: $5172. Full-time tuition and fees vary according to location and program. Room and board charges vary according to board plan and housing facility.

Collegiate Environment: Orientation program. Drama-theater group, choral group, marching band, student-run newspaper, radio station. Social organizations: 90 open to all; national fraternities, national sororities; 11% of eligible men and 23% of eligible women are members. Most popular organizations: Campus Activity Board, Fellowship of Christian Athletes, The Well, intramurals, Sororities. Major annual events: Homecoming, Parents' Weekend, Banana Splitin Contest. Student services: health clinic, personal-psychological counseling. Campus security: 24-hour emergency response devices and patrols, student patrols, late night transport-escort service,

controlled dormitory access. 1,884 college housing spaces available; 1,525 were occupied in 2012-13. Freshmen guaranteed college housing. On-campus residence required through junior year. Options: coed, men-only, women-only housing available. Ashland University Library plus 2 others with 205,200 books, 318,000 microform titles, 1,625 serials, 3,550 audiovisual materials, an OPAC, and a Web page. Operations spending for the previous fiscal year: $1.3 million. 760 computers available on campus for general student use. Computer purchase/lease plans available. A campuswide network can be accessed from student residence rooms and from off campus. Students can access the following: online class registration. Staffed computer lab on campus (open 24 hours a day) provides training in use of computers, software, and the Internet.

Community Environment: Five rubber manufacturers in Ashland produce most of the world's toy balloons. Other industries produce spray equipment, hydraulic cylinders, and clothing. Bus transportation is available while Mansfield Airport and Cleveland Airport furnish air transportation. Recreational facilities within the city are good and nearby Mohican State Park provides additional opportunities for fishing and camping.

■ ATS INSTITUTE OF TECHNOLOGY

325 Alpha Park
Highland Heights, OH 44143
Tel: (440)449-1700
Fax: (440)449-1389
E-mail: info@atsinstitute.edu
Web Site: www.atsinstitute.edu/cleveland/

Description: Proprietary, 2-year, coed. Awards diplomas and transfer associate degrees. Setting: suburban campus with easy access to Cleveland. Total enrollment: 353. Academic remediation for entering students, ESL program, advanced placement, accelerated degree program, part-time degree program, external degree program.

Entrance Requirements: Open admission. Required: high school transcript, minimum 2.5 high school GPA, interview, complete background check and physical evaluation, PSB (Psychological Service Bureau) exam is required except for those applying for Bridge program. Required for some: essay, 1 recommendation. Entrance: minimally difficult. Transfer credits accepted: Yes.

Collegiate Environment: Orientation program. Student services: personal-psychological counseling. Campus security: security guard.

■ BALDWIN WALLACE UNIVERSITY

275 Eastland Rd.
Berea, OH 44017-2088
Tel: (440)826-2900; Free: 877-BW-APPLY
Fax: (440)826-3830
E-mail: admission@bw.edu
Web Site: www.bw.edu/

Description: Independent Methodist, comprehensive, coed. Awards bachelor's and master's degrees. Founded 1845. Setting: 120-acre suburban campus with easy access to Cleveland. Endowment: $113.9 million. Research spending for the previous fiscal year: $547,642. Educational spending for the previous fiscal year: $10,135 per student. Total enrollment: 4,173. Faculty: 424 (169 full-time, 255 part-time). Student-undergrad faculty ratio is 15:1. 3,573 applied, 70% were admitted. 28% from top 10% of their high school class, 53% from top quarter, 82% from top half. 21 class presidents, 11 valedictorians, 79 student government officers. Full-time: 3,036 students, 54% women, 46% men. Part-time: 476 students, 65% women, 35% men. Students come from 39 states and territories, 13 other countries, 15% from out-of-state. 0.1% American Indian or Alaska Native, non-Hispanic/Latino; 4% Hispanic/Latino; 8% African American, non-Hispanic/Latino; 1% Asian, non-Hispanic/Latino; 0.03% Native Hawaiian or other Pacific Islander, non-Hispanic/Latino; 1% international. 3% 25 or older, 60% live on campus, 6% transferred in. Retention: 82% of full-time freshmen returned the following year. Academic areas with the most degrees conferred: business/marketing; visual and performing arts; biological/life sciences. Core. Calendar: semesters. Academic remediation for entering students, ESL program, services for LD students, advanced placement, accelerated degree program, self-designed majors, honors program, independent study, distance learning, double major, summer session for credit, part-time degree program, adult/continuing education programs, internships, graduate courses open to undergrads. Off campus study. Study abroad program. ROTC: Army (c), Air Force (c).

Entrance Requirements: Options: electronic application, deferred admission, international baccalaureate accepted. Required: essay, high school

transcript, 1 recommendation. Recommended: minimum 3 high school GPA, interview. Required for some: SAT or ACT. Entrance: moderately difficult. Application deadline: 3/1. Notification: continuous. SAT Reasoning Test deadline: 3/1. Transfer credits accepted: Yes.

Costs Per Year: Application fee: $25. Comprehensive fee: $34,580 includes full-time tuition ($27,060) and college room and board ($7520). College room only: $4340. Full-time tuition varies according to class time, course level, course load, degree level, program, and reciprocity agreements. Room and board charges vary according to housing facility. Part-time tuition: $840 per semester hour. Part-time tuition varies according to class time, course level, course load, degree level, program, and reciprocity agreements.

Collegiate Environment: Orientation program. Drama-theater group, choral group, marching band, student-run newspaper, radio station. Social organizations: 117 open to all; national fraternities, national sororities; 12% of eligible men and 16% of eligible women are members. Most popular organizations: Circle K, Habitat for Humanity, Dance Marathon, Campus Crusade, Black Student Alliance. Major annual events: April Reign, Homecoming, Bach Festival. Student services: health clinic, personal-psychological counseling. Campus security: 24-hour emergency response devices and patrols, student patrols, late night transport-escort service, controlled dormitory access. College housing designed to accommodate 1,782 students; 1,811 undergraduates lived in college housing during 2012-13. Freshmen guaranteed college housing. On-campus residence required through sophomore year. Option: coed housing available. Ritter Library plus 2 others with 225,000 books, 44,000 serials, 2,250 audiovisual materials, an OPAC, and a Web page. Operations spending for the previous fiscal year: $1.8 million. 583 computers available on campus for general student use. A campuswide network can be accessed from student residence rooms. Students can access the following: online class registration. Staffed computer lab on campus (open 24 hours a day) provides training in use of computers, software, and the Internet.

Community Environment: Berea, with its tree-lined streets and picturesque homes, is an ideal college town, yet it is only 20 minutes from the heart of Cleveland, home to many fortune 500 companies and recreational and cultural opportunities.

■ BELMONT COLLEGE

120 Fox Shannon Pl.
Saint Clairsville, OH 43950-9735
Tel: (740)695-9500; Free: 800-423-1188
Fax: (740)695-2247
E-mail: msterling@btc.edu
Web Site: www.belmontcollege.edu/

Description: State-supported, 2-year, coed. Part of Ohio Board of Regents. Awards diplomas and terminal associate degrees. Founded 1971. Setting: 55-acre rural campus. Total enrollment: 1,742. 46% 25 or older. Core. Academic remediation for entering students, independent study, distance learning, summer session for credit, part-time degree program.

Entrance Requirements: Open admission except for nursing, emergency medical technology programs. Option: early admission. Entrance: noncompetitive. Application deadline: Rolling.

Costs Per Year: State resident tuition: $3060 full-time, $102 per credit hour part-time. Nonresident tuition: $6090 full-time, $203 per credit hour part-time. Mandatory fees: $1250 full-time, $41 per credit hour, $10 per term part-time. Full-time tuition and fees vary according to course load and reciprocity agreements. Part-time tuition and fees vary according to course load and reciprocity agreements.

Collegiate Environment: Orientation program. Student services: personal-psychological counseling. 5,612 books and 217 serials.

Community Environment: Belmont Technical College is located in a rural area of Belmont County, Ohio, just 10 miles west of Wheeling, WV. The college is active in the community and exposes students to a variety of activities, including the fine arts.

■ BLUFFTON UNIVERSITY

1 University Dr.
Bluffton, OH 45817
Tel: (419)358-3000; Free: 800-488-3257
Fax: (419)358-3232
E-mail: admissions@bluffton.edu
Web Site: www.bluffton.edu/

Description: Independent Mennonite, 4-year, coed. Awards bachelor's and master's degrees. Founded 1899. Setting: 65-acre small town campus with easy access to Toledo. Endowment: $19.3 million. Educational spending for

the previous fiscal year: $8461 per student. Total enrollment: 1,198. Faculty: 107 (57 full-time, 50 part-time). Student-undergrad faculty ratio is 12:1. 1,807 applied, 58% were admitted. 13% from top 10% of their high school class, 35% from top quarter, 67% from top half. 15 class presidents, 5 valedictorians, 60 student government officers. Full-time: 833 students, 49% women, 51% men. Part-time: 244 students, 63% women, 37% men. Students come from 21 states and territories, 8 other countries, 18% from out-of-state. 0.1% American Indian or Alaska Native, non-Hispanic/Latino; 3% Hispanic/Latino; 7% African American, non-Hispanic/Latino; 0.3% Asian, non-Hispanic/Latino; 0% Native Hawaiian or other Pacific Islander, non-Hispanic/Latino; 1% international. 19% 25 or older, 72% live on campus, 6% transferred in. Retention: 68% of full-time freshmen returned the following year. Academic areas with the most degrees conferred: business/marketing; education; public administration and social services. Core. Calendar: semesters. Academic remediation for entering students, services for LD students, advanced placement, accelerated degree program, self-designed majors, honors program, independent study, distance learning, double major, summer session for credit, part-time degree program, adult/continuing education programs, internships. Off campus study at Christian College Coalition, Council of Independent Colleges. Study abroad program.

Entrance Requirements: Options: electronic application, deferred admission, international baccalaureate accepted. Required: high school transcript, minimum 2.3 high school GPA, 1 recommendation, rank in upper 50% of high school class or 19 on ACT, SAT or ACT. Recommended: interview. Required for some: essay. Entrance: moderately difficult. Application deadline: 8/15. Notification: continuous. Transfer credits accepted: Yes.

Costs Per Year: Application fee: $20. Comprehensive fee: $36,436 includes full-time tuition ($26,976), mandatory fees ($450), and college room and board ($9010). Full-time tuition and fees vary according to course load and reciprocity agreements. Room and board charges vary according to board plan and housing facility. Part-time tuition: $1124 per credit hour. Part-time mandatory fees: $113 per term. Part-time tuition and fees vary according to course load.

Collegiate Environment: Orientation program. Drama-theater group, choral group, student-run newspaper, radio station. Social organizations: 40 open to all. Most popular organizations: Intramurals, Student Senate, Marbeck Center Board, Music Groups/Chorale, Campus Ministries. Major annual events: Homecoming, Midnight Madness, May Day. Student services: health clinic, personal-psychological counseling. Campus security: 24-hour emergency response devices, controlled dormitory access, night security guards. 732 college housing spaces available; 673 were occupied in 2012-13. Freshmen guaranteed college housing. On-campus residence required through senior year. Options: coed, men-only, women-only housing available. Musselman Library with 250,983 books, 137,708 microform titles, 21,350 serials, 5,632 audiovisual materials, an OPAC, and a Web page. Operations spending for the previous fiscal year: $589,542. 170 computers available on campus for general student use. A campuswide network can be accessed from student residence rooms and from off campus. Students can access the following: online class registration. Staffed computer lab on campus provides training in use of computers, software, and the Internet.

■ BOWLING GREEN STATE UNIVERSITY

Bowling Green, OH 43403
Tel: (419)372-2531
E-mail: choosebgsu@bgsu.edu
Web Site: www.bgsu.edu/

Description: State-supported, university, coed. Awards bachelor's, master's, and doctoral degrees and post-master's certificates. Founded 1910. Setting: 1,338-acre small town campus with easy access to Toledo. Endowment: $129.4 million. Research spending for the previous fiscal year: $7 million. Educational spending for the previous fiscal year: $7168 per student. Total enrollment: 17,286. Faculty: 1,067 (814 full-time, 253 part-time). Student-undergrad faculty ratio is 18:1. 16,108 applied, 74% were admitted. 12% from top 10% of their high school class, 36% from top quarter, 70% from top half. 29 valedictorians. Full-time: 13,735 students, 56% women, 44% men. Part-time: 1,080 students, 50% women, 50% men. Students come from 52 states and territories, 45 other countries, 12% from out-of-state. 0.4% American Indian or Alaska Native, non-Hispanic/Latino; 4% Hispanic/Latino; 11% African American, non-Hispanic/Latino; 1% Asian, non-Hispanic/Latino; 0.1% Native Hawaiian or other Pacific Islander, non-Hispanic/Latino; 2% international. 7% 25 or older, 44% live on campus, 4% transferred in. Retention: 70% of full-time freshmen returned the following year. Academic areas with the most degrees conferred: education; business/marketing; visual and performing arts. Core. Calendar: semesters. Academic remediation for entering students, ESL program, services for LD students, advanced placement, accelerated degree program, self-designed majors, honors program, independent study, distance learning, double major, summer session for credit, part-time degree program, adult/continuing education programs, co-op programs and internships, graduate courses open to undergrads. Off campus study at University of Toledo. Study abroad program. ROTC: Army, Air Force.

Entrance Requirements: Options: electronic application, deferred admission, international baccalaureate accepted. Required: high school transcript, SAT or ACT. Required for some: interview. Entrance: moderately difficult. Application deadlines: 7/15, 7/15 for nonresidents. Notification: continuous, continuous for nonresidents. SAT Reasoning Test deadline: 8/1. Transfer credits accepted: Yes.

Costs Per Year: Application fee: $45. State resident tuition: $8913 full-time, $371.40 per credit hour part-time. Nonresident tuition: $16,222 full-time, $676.40 per credit hour part-time. Mandatory fees: $1600 full-time, $66 per credit hour part-time. Full-time tuition and fees vary according to course load and location. Part-time tuition and fees vary according to course load and location. College room and board: $8064. Room and board charges vary according to board plan and housing facility.

Collegiate Environment: Orientation program. Drama-theater group, choral group, marching band, student-run newspaper, radio station. Social organizations: 283 open to all; national fraternities, national sororities; 9% of eligible men and 11% of eligible women are members. Most popular organizations: Dance Marathon, University Activities Organization, BG Undead, H2O, Black Student Union. Major annual events: CampusFest, Homecoming, Move-in Weekend and Week of Welcome. Student services: legal services, health clinic, personal-psychological counseling, women's center. Campus security: 24-hour emergency response devices and patrols, student patrols, late night transport-escort service, controlled dormitory access. 6,871 college housing spaces available; 6,436 were occupied in 2012-13. Freshmen guaranteed college housing. On-campus residence required through sophomore year. Option: coed housing available. William T. Jerome Library with 2 million books, 2.7 million microform titles, 1,532 serials, 212,746 audiovisual materials, an OPAC, and a Web page. Operations spending for the previous fiscal year: $8.2 million. 1,500 computers available on campus for general student use. Computer purchase/lease plans available. A campuswide network can be accessed from student residence rooms and from off campus. Students can access the following: online class registration, wireless networking, ePortfolio, MyFiles, Bursar billing information and payment, online mid-term grade reporting, view and change personal information, order official and unofficial transcripts, check meal plan balance, apply for graduation. Staffed computer lab on campus (open 24 hours a day) provides training in use of computers, software, and the Internet.

Community Environment: Bowling Green, the county seat of Wood County, is located 23 miles south of Toledo. Community facilities in this metropolitan area include libraries, many churches, a hospital, shopping areas, and major civic and service organizations. Lake Erie and the Maumee River provide facilities for recreation.

■ BOWLING GREEN STATE UNIVERSITY-FIRELANDS COLLEGE

One University Dr.
Huron, OH 44839-9791
Tel: (419)433-5560
E-mail: divers@bgsu.edu
Web Site: www.firelands.bgsu.edu/
Description: State-supported, primarily 2-year, coed. Part of Bowling Green State University System. Awards certificates, transfer associate, terminal associate, and bachelor's degrees (also offers some upper-level and graduate courses). Founded 1968. Setting: 216-acre rural campus with easy access to Cleveland, Toledo. Endowment: $3 million. Educational spending for the previous fiscal year: $3381 per student. Total enrollment: 2,397. Faculty: 154 (55 full-time, 99 part-time). Student-undergrad faculty ratio is 19:1. 711 applied, 78% were admitted. 7% from top 10% of their high school class, 19% from top quarter, 54% from top half. Full-time: 1,285 students, 65% women, 35% men. Part-time: 1,112 students, 66% women, 34% men. Students come from 2 states and territories, 0% from out-of-state. 0.5% American Indian or Alaska Native, non-Hispanic/Latino; 4% Hispanic/Latino; 7% African American, non-Hispanic/Latino; 1% Asian, non-Hispanic/Latino; 0.2% Native Hawaiian or other Pacific Islander, non-Hispanic/Latino; 0.04% international. 48% 25 or older, 6% transferred in. Retention: 54% of full-time freshmen returned the following year. Core. Calendar: semesters. Academic remediation for entering students, services for LD students, advanced place-

ment, self-designed majors, honors program, independent study, distance learning, double major, summer session for credit, part-time degree program, adult/continuing education programs, internships. ROTC: Army (c), Air Force (c).

Entrance Requirements: Open admission. Options: electronic application, early admission, deferred admission. Required: high school transcript. Entrance: noncompetitive. Application deadline: 8/6. Notification: continuous. Transfer credits accepted: Yes.

Costs Per Year: Application fee: $45. State resident tuition: $4614 full-time, $192.25 per credit hour part-time. Nonresident tuition: $11,922 full-time, $497.25 per credit hour part-time. Mandatory fees: $236 full-time, $9.15 per credit hour part-time, $117.80 per term part-time. Full-time tuition and fees vary according to location. Part-time tuition and fees vary according to location.

Collegiate Environment: Orientation program. Drama-theater group. Social organizations: 12 open to all. Most popular organizations: Humanity Organized for Peace through Education- H.O.P.E., Science and Environment Club, Speech Activities Organization - Theatre, Visual Communication Technology Organization, intramurals. Major annual events: Beggars Banquet, Welcome Back Cookout, Believe in BG (scholarship fundraiser). Campus security: 24-hour emergency response devices, late night transport-escort service, patrols by trained security personnel. College housing not available. BGSU Firelands College Library with 61,019 books, 3,000 microform titles, 223 serials, 1,958 audiovisual materials, an OPAC, and a Web page. Operations spending for the previous fiscal year: $331,851. 300 computers available on campus for general student use. Computer purchase/lease plans available. A campuswide network can be accessed from off-campus. Students can access the following: online class registration. Staffed computer lab on campus provides training in use of computers, software, and the Internet.

■ BRADFORD SCHOOL

2469 Stelzer Rd.
Columbus, OH 43219
Tel: (614)416-6200; Free: 800-678-7981
Web Site: www.bradfordschoolcolumbus.edu/
Description: Private, 2-year, coed. Awards diplomas and terminal associate degrees. Founded 1911. Setting: suburban campus. Total enrollment: 603. 2,021 applied, 50% were admitted. Calendar: semesters. Accelerated degree program, internships.

■ BROWN MACKIE COLLEGE–AKRON

755 White Pond Dr.
Ste. 101
Akron, OH 44320
Tel: (330)869-3600
Fax: (330)733-5853
Web Site: www.brownmackie.edu/akron/
Description: Proprietary, 2-year, coed. Part of Education Management Corporation. Awards certificates, diplomas, and terminal associate degrees. Founded 1968. Setting: suburban campus.

■ BROWN MACKIE COLLEGE–CINCINNATI

1011 Glendale-Milford Rd.
Cincinnati, OH 45215
Tel: (513)771-2424; Free: 800-888-1445
Web Site: www.brownmackie.edu/cincinnati/
Description: Proprietary, 2-year, coed. Part of Education Management Corporation. Awards certificates, diplomas, and terminal associate degrees. Founded 1927. Setting: suburban campus.

■ BROWN MACKIE COLLEGE–FINDLAY

1700 Fostoria Ave.
Ste. 100
Findlay, OH 45840
Tel: (419)423-2211; Free: 800-842-3687
Fax: (419)423-0725
Web Site: www.brownmackie.edu/findlay/
Description: Proprietary, 2-year, coed. Part of Education Management Corporation. Awards diplomas and terminal associate degrees. Founded 1929. Setting: rural campus. Calendar: continuous.

■ BROWN MACKIE COLLEGE–NORTH CANTON

4300 Munson St. NW
Canton, OH 44718-3674

Tel: (330)494-1214
Web Site: www.brownmackie.edu/northcanton/
Description: Proprietary, 2-year, coed. Part of Education Management Corporation. Awards diplomas and terminal associate degrees. Founded 1929. Setting: suburban campus.

■ **BRYANT & STRATTON COLLEGE**
1700 E 13th St.
Cleveland, OH 44114-3203
Tel: (216)771-1700
Fax: (216)771-1700
Web Site: www.bryantstratton.edu/
Description: Proprietary, 4-year, coed. Part of Bryant and Stratton College, Inc. Awards associate and bachelor's degrees. Founded 1929. Setting: urban campus. Educational spending for the previous fiscal year: $1500 per student. Total enrollment: 524. Faculty: 37 (13 full-time, 24 part-time). Student-undergrad faculty ratio is 10:1. Students come from 2 states and territories, 0% from out-of-state. 59% 25 or older, 10% live on campus. Academic area with the most degrees conferred: business/marketing. Core. Calendar: semesters. Academic remediation for entering students, services for LD students, independent study, distance learning, double major, summer session for credit, part-time degree program, adult/continuing education programs, co-op programs and internships.
Entrance Requirements: Option: deferred admission. Required: high school transcript, interview, entrance evaluation and placement evaluation, TABE. Recommended: SAT or ACT. Entrance: minimally difficult. Application deadline: Rolling.
Collegiate Environment: Orientation program. Student-run newspaper. Most popular organization: student/staff softball. Major annual events: Summer Carnival, Team Spirit Day (hot dog sale). Campus security: controlled dormitory access. 4,466 books, 80 serials, 159 audiovisual materials, and a Web page 66 computers available on campus for general student use. Students can access the following: e-mail. Staffed computer lab on campus.

■ **BRYANT & STRATTON COLLEGE - EASTLAKE CAMPUS**
35350 Curtis Blvd.
Eastlake, OH 44095
Tel: (440)510-1112
Web Site: www.bryantstratton.edu/
Description: Proprietary, primarily 2-year, coed. Part of Bryant and Stratton College, Inc. Awards transfer associate, terminal associate, and bachelor's degrees. Founded 1987. Setting: suburban campus with easy access to Cleveland. Total enrollment: 762. Faculty: 63 (24 full-time, 39 part-time). Student-undergrad faculty ratio is 12:1. 312 applied. Full-time: 490 students, 89% women, 11% men. Part-time: 272 students, 86% women, 14% men. 0% from out-of-state. 63% 25 or older, 1% transferred in. Retention: 28% of full-time freshmen returned the following year. Core. Calendar: semesters. Academic remediation for entering students, advanced placement, independent study, distance learning, summer session for credit, part-time degree program, internships.
Entrance Requirements: Option: deferred admission. Required: high school transcript, interview, entrance evaluation and placement evaluation, CPAt. Recommended: minimum 2 high school GPA, SAT or ACT. Required for some: essay. Entrance: minimally difficult. Application deadline: Rolling.
Collegiate Environment: Orientation program. Student-run newspaper. Social organizations: 6 open to all; 2% of eligible men and 10% of eligible women are members. Most popular organizations: Criminal Justice Club, Rotaract, Medical Assisting Club, International Association of Administrative Professionals (IAAP), Student Senate. Major annual events: Portfolio Development Day, Academic Awards Ceremony. Campus security: 24-hour emergency response devices, late night transport-escort service. Main library plus 1 other with 1,500 books, 19 serials, and an OPAC. Operations spending for the previous fiscal year: $22,554. 300 computers available on campus for general student use. Staffed computer lab on campus provides training in use of computers, software, and the Internet.

■ **BRYANT & STRATTON COLLEGE - PARMA CAMPUS**
12955 Snow Rd.
Parma, OH 44130-1013
Tel: (216)265-3151
Fax: (216)265-0325
E-mail: atinman@bryantstratton.edu
Web Site: www.bryantstratton.edu/
Description: Proprietary, primarily 2-year, coed. Part of Bryant and Stratton

College, Inc. Awards transfer associate, terminal associate, and bachelor's degrees. Founded 1981. Setting: 4-acre suburban campus with easy access to Cleveland. Research spending for the previous fiscal year: $4000. Educational spending for the previous fiscal year: $1335 per student. Total enrollment: 528. Faculty: 57 (16 full-time, 41 part-time). Student-undergrad faculty ratio is 12:1. 2% from top 10% of their high school class, 4% from top quarter, 46% from top half. Full-time: 288 students, 81% women, 19% men. Part-time: 240 students, 82% women, 18% men. 0% from out-of-state. 34% 25 or older. Retention: 60% of full-time freshmen returned the following year. Core. Calendar: semesters. Academic remediation for entering students, independent study, distance learning, double major, summer session for credit, part-time degree program, co-op programs and internships.
Entrance Requirements: Option: deferred admission. Required: high school transcript, interview, entrance evaluation and placement evaluation, CPAt. Recommended: SAT or ACT. Entrance: minimally difficult. Application deadline: Rolling.
Collegiate Environment: Orientation program. Social organizations: 4 open to all. Most popular organizations: SHRM, Student Services Club, Sigma Psi Phi - Lambda Alpha Epsilon, Student Nursing Club, Medical Administrative Assistant Club. Major annual events: Summer Carnival, International Potluck, Halloween Party. Campus security: 24-hour emergency response devices. Main library plus 1 other with 1,500 books, 20 serials, and an OPAC. Operations spending for the previous fiscal year: $52,000. 96 computers available on campus for general student use.

■ **CAPITAL UNIVERSITY**
1 College and Main
Columbus, OH 43209-2394
Tel: (614)236-6011; Free: 866-544-6175
Fax: (614)236-6820
E-mail: asohl@capital.edu
Web Site: www.capital.edu/
Description: Independent, comprehensive, coed, affiliated with Evangelical Lutheran Church in America. Awards bachelor's, master's, and doctoral degrees. Founded 1830. Setting: 48-acre suburban campus with easy access to Columbus. Endowment: $60.6 million. Educational spending for the previous fiscal year: $8761 per student. Total enrollment: 3,584. Faculty: 450 (182 full-time, 268 part-time). Student-undergrad faculty ratio is 11:1. 3,844 applied, 75% were admitted. 21% from top 10% of their high school class, 49% from top quarter, 82% from top half. 14 valedictorians. Full-time: 2,448 students, 56% women, 44% men. Part-time: 272 students, 68% women, 32% men. Students come from 33 states and territories, 12 other countries, 10% from out-of-state. 0.04% American Indian or Alaska Native, non-Hispanic/Latino; 3% Hispanic/Latino; 10% African American, non-Hispanic/Latino; 1% Asian, non-Hispanic/Latino; 0.1% Native Hawaiian or other Pacific Islander, non-Hispanic/Latino; 1% international. 12% 25 or older, 57% live on campus, 3% transferred in. Retention: 75% of full-time freshmen returned the following year. Academic areas with the most degrees conferred: health professions and related sciences; education; business/marketing. Core. Calendar: semesters. ESL program, services for LD students, advanced placement, accelerated degree program, self-designed majors, freshman honors college, honors program, independent study, double major, summer session for credit, part-time degree program, external degree program, adult/continuing education programs, co-op programs and internships. Off campus study at members of the Higher Education Council of Columbus. Study abroad program. ROTC: Army, Air Force (c).
Entrance Requirements: Options: electronic application, deferred admission, international baccalaureate accepted. Required: high school transcript, minimum 2.6 high school GPA, SAT or ACT. Recommended: interview. Required for some: 1 recommendation, audition for Conservatory of Music. Entrance: moderately difficult. Application deadline: 5/1. Notification: 9/30. SAT Reasoning Test deadline: 5/1. Transfer credits accepted: Yes.
Costs Per Year: Application fee: $25. Comprehensive fee: $39,824 includes full-time tuition ($31,364) and college room and board ($8460). Full-time tuition varies according to course load. Room and board charges vary according to board plan and housing facility. Part-time tuition: $1045 per credit hour. Part-time tuition varies according to course load.
Collegiate Environment: Orientation program. Drama-theater group, choral group, student-run newspaper, radio station. Social organizations: 60 open to all; national fraternities, national sororities, local fraternities, local sororities; 17% of eligible men and 19% of eligible women are members. Most popular organizations: Campus Crusade for Christ, student government, University Programming, College Republicans, American Marketing Association. Major annual events: Homecoming, MLK Day of Learning, Up 'til Dawn.

Student services: health clinic, personal-psychological counseling. Campus security: 24-hour emergency response devices and patrols, late night transport-escort service, controlled dormitory access. 1,546 college housing spaces available; 1,489 were occupied in 2012-13. Freshmen guaranteed college housing. On-campus residence required through sophomore year. Option: coed housing available. Blackmore Library with 220,594 books, 148,096 microform titles, 163,236 serials, 85,178 audiovisual materials, an OPAC, and a Web page. Operations spending for the previous fiscal year: $3.4 million. 415 computers available on campus for general student use. A campuswide network can be accessed from student residence rooms and from off campus. Students can access the following: online class registration. Staffed computer lab on campus provides training in use of computers, software, and the Internet.

Community Environment: See Ohio State University - Columbus Campus.

■ CASE WESTERN RESERVE UNIVERSITY

10900 Euclid Ave.
Cleveland, OH 44106
Tel: (216)368-2000
Fax: (216)368-5111
E-mail: admission@case.edu
Web Site: www.case.edu/

Description: Independent, university, coed. Awards bachelor's, master's, and doctoral degrees. Founded 1826. Setting: 155-acre urban campus. Endowment: $1.6 billion. Research spending for the previous fiscal year: $395.3 million. Total enrollment: 10,026. Faculty: 932 (755 full-time, 177 part-time). Student-undergrad faculty ratio is 10:1. 14,778 applied, 54% were admitted. 74% from top 10% of their high school class, 94% from top quarter, 100% from top half. 63 National Merit Scholars, 79 valedictorians. Full-time: 4,260 students, 44% women, 56% men. Part-time: 126 students, 54% women, 46% men. Students come from 49 states and territories, 36 other countries, 59% from out-of-state. 0.2% American Indian or Alaska Native, non-Hispanic/Latino; 5% Hispanic/Latino; 4% African American, non-Hispanic/Latino; 19% Asian, non-Hispanic/Latino; 0.05% Native Hawaiian or other Pacific Islander, non-Hispanic/Latino; 7% international. 2% 25 or older, 77% live on campus, 1% transferred in. Retention: 92% of full-time freshmen returned the following year. Academic areas with the most degrees conferred: engineering; biological/life sciences; social sciences. Core. Calendar: semesters. ESL program, services for LD students, advanced placement, accelerated degree program, self-designed majors, honors program, independent study, double major, summer session for credit, part-time degree program, adult/continuing education programs, co-op programs and internships, graduate courses open to undergrads. Off campus study at Cleveland Institute of Art, Cleveland Institute of Music, 11 other Cleveland area institutions; Fisk University. Study abroad program. ROTC: Army, Air Force (c).

Entrance Requirements: Options: electronic application, early admission, early action, deferred admission, international baccalaureate accepted. Required: essay, high school transcript, 1 recommendation, SAT or ACT. Recommended: interview. Entrance: very difficult. Application deadlines: 1/15, 11/1 for early action. Notification: 3/20, 12/15 for early action. SAT Reasoning Test deadline: 1/15. SAT Subject Test deadline: 1/15. Transfer credits accepted: Yes. Applicants placed on waiting list: 3,480. Wait-listed applicants offered admission: 39. Early action applicants: 3,087. Early action applicants admitted: 2,719.

Costs Per Year: Application fee: $0. One-time mandatory fee: $465. Comprehensive fee: $52,926 includes full-time tuition ($40,120), mandatory fees ($370), and college room and board ($12,436). College room only: $7140. Room and board charges vary according to board plan, housing facility, and student level. Part-time tuition: $1672 per credit hour. Part-time tuition varies according to course load.

Collegiate Environment: Orientation program. Drama-theater group, choral group, marching band, student-run newspaper, radio station. Social organizations: 176 open to all; national fraternities, national sororities, local sororities; 39% of eligible men and 33% of eligible women are members. Most popular organizations: CASE EMS, Habitat for Humanity, international student groups, music/dance groups, Alpha Phi Omega (national service organization). Major annual events: Relay for Life, Thwing Study Over, Spring Fest. Student services: legal services, health clinic, personal-psychological counseling, women's center. Campus security: 24-hour emergency response devices and patrols, student patrols, late night transport-escort service, controlled dormitory access, crime prevention programs. 3,801 college housing spaces available; 3,401 were occupied in 2012-13. Freshmen guaranteed college housing. On-campus residence

required through sophomore year. Option: coed housing available. University Library plus 6 others with 2.9 million books, 111,270 serials, an OPAC, and a Web page. Operations spending for the previous fiscal year: $22.3 million. 298 computers available on campus for general student use. Computer purchase/lease plans available. A campuswide network can be accessed from student residence rooms and from off campus. Students can access the following: online class registration, software library, online reference databases, electronic books and journals, research computing, training. Staffed computer lab on campus provides training in use of computers, software, and the Internet.

Community Environment: The university is located on the eastern edge of Cleveland in University Circle, a 500-acre area of parks, gardens, museums, schools, hospitals, churches and human service institutions. The Cleveland Museum of Art and the Cleveland Orchestra are within walking distance, and downtown Cleveland, offering restaurants, music, theatre, and professional sports, is only ten minutes away by RTA rapid transit. Students also have easy access to many facilities provided by the city of Cleveland and the outlying areas. Among these are Cleveland's well-known "Emerald Necklace" of parks, and Blossom Music Center, the summer home of the Cleveland Orchestra. CWRU also owns a 400-acre farm in Hunting Valley, about 10 miles east of the campus, that is open to students. Recreational facilities include a picnic area, fishing ponds, hiking and ski trails, and buildings for social events.

■ CEDARVILLE UNIVERSITY

251 N Main St.
Cedarville, OH 45314-0601
Tel: (937)766-2211; Free: 800-CEDARVILLE
Fax: (937)766-7575
E-mail: admiss@cedarville.edu
Web Site: www.cedarville.edu/

Description: Independent Baptist, comprehensive, coed. Awards bachelor's, master's, and doctoral degrees. Founded 1887. Setting: 400-acre rural campus with easy access to Columbus, Dayton. System endowment: $19.8 million. Educational spending for the previous fiscal year: $10,200 per student. Total enrollment: 3,380. Faculty: 311 (181 full-time, 130 part-time). Student-undergrad faculty ratio is 14:1. 3,347 applied, 75% were admitted. 33% from top 10% of their high school class, 63% from top quarter, 90% from top half. Full-time: 3,047 students, 53% women, 47% men. Part-time: 173 students, 55% women, 45% men. Students come from 48 states and territories, 16 other countries, 61% from out-of-state. 0.4% American Indian or Alaska Native, non-Hispanic/Latino; 2% Hispanic/Latino; 2% African American, non-Hispanic/Latino; 1% Asian, non-Hispanic/Latino; 0.1% Native Hawaiian or other Pacific Islander, non-Hispanic/Latino; 1% international. 1% 25 or older, 76% live on campus, 3% transferred in. Retention: 85% of full-time freshmen returned the following year. Academic areas with the most degrees conferred: health professions and related sciences; education; business/marketing. Core. Calendar: semesters. Academic remediation for entering students, services for LD students, advanced placement, accelerated degree program, honors program, independent study, distance learning, double major, summer session for credit, part-time degree program, adult/continuing education programs, internships. Off campus study at Au Sable Institute of Environmental Studies, MI, Focus Leadership Institute, CO, International Business Institute, TN. Study abroad program. ROTC: Army (c), Air Force (c).

Entrance Requirements: Options: electronic application, early admission, deferred admission, international baccalaureate accepted. Required: essay, high school transcript, minimum 3 high school GPA, 1 recommendation, Clear testimony of faith in Jesus Christ and evidence of consistent Christian lifestyle, SAT or ACT. Recommended: SAT and SAT Subject Tests or ACT. Required for some: interview. Entrance: moderately difficult. Application deadline: Rolling. Notification: continuous. SAT Reasoning Test deadline: 7/1. Transfer credits accepted: Yes.

Costs Per Year: Application fee: $30. Comprehensive fee: $31,036 includes full-time tuition ($25,496) and college room and board ($5540). College room only: $3140. Room and board charges vary according to board plan. Part-time tuition: $965 per credit. Part-time tuition varies according to course load.

Collegiate Environment: Orientation program. Drama-theater group, choral group, student-run newspaper, radio station. Social organizations: 77 open to all. Most popular organizations: Students in Free Enterprise, Christian Pharmacist Association, Society of Automotive Engineers - SAE, Christian Nursing Association, Cedarville Men's Rugby. Major annual events: Homecoming, Junior/Senior Banquet, ELLIV - Talent/award show. Student services: health clinic, personal-psychological counseling. Campus security: 24-hour emergency response devices and patrols, student patrols, late night transport-escort service, controlled dormitory access. 2,517 college housing spaces available; 2,444 were occupied in 2012-13. Freshmen guaranteed college housing. On-campus residence required through senior year. Options: men-only, women-only housing available. Centennial Library with 239,169 books, 16,862 microform titles, 9,094 serials, 9,254 audiovisual materials, an OPAC, and a Web page. Operations spending for the previous fiscal year: $1.4 million. 2,030 computers available on campus for general student use. A campuswide network can be accessed from student residence rooms and from off campus. Students can access the following: online class registration, over 150 software packages. Staffed computer lab on campus provides training in use of computers, software, and the Internet.

■ CENTRAL OHIO TECHNICAL COLLEGE
1179 University Dr.
Newark, OH 43055-1767
Tel: (740)366-1351; Free: 800-9NEWARK
Fax: (740)366-5047
Web Site: www.cotc.edu/
Description: State-supported, 2-year, coed. Part of Ohio Board of Regents. Awards certificates and terminal associate degrees. Founded 1971. Setting: 155-acre small town campus with easy access to Columbus. Endowment: $1.7 million. Educational spending for the previous fiscal year: $3803 per student. Total enrollment: 4,350. Faculty: 331 (58 full-time, 273 part-time). Student-undergrad faculty ratio is 22:1. 1,578 applied, 100% were admitted. Full-time: 2,213 students, 70% women, 30% men. Part-time: 2,137 students, 75% women, 25% men. Students come from 3 states and territories, 1% from out-of-state. 76% 25 or older, 6% transferred in. Retention: 51% of full-time freshmen returned the following year. Core. Academic remediation for entering students, ESL program, services for LD students, advanced placement, accelerated degree program, distance learning, double major, summer session for credit, part-time degree program, adult/continuing education programs, co-op programs and internships. Off campus study at Ohio State University-Newark Campus, Higher Education Council of Columbus.
Entrance Requirements: Open admission except for health programs. Options: electronic application, early admission, deferred admission. Required: high school transcript. Entrance: noncompetitive. Application deadline: Rolling. Transfer credits accepted: Yes.
Costs Per Year: Application fee: $20. One-time mandatory fee: $40. State resident tuition: $4200 full-time, $175 per semester hour part-time. Nonresident tuition: $6960 full-time, $290 per semester hour part-time.
Collegiate Environment: Orientation program. Drama-theater group, choral group. Social organizations: 15 open to all. Most popular organizations: Student Nurses Organization, Phi Theta Kappa, Forensic Science Club, Campus Chorus, Student Senate. Major annual events: Spring Fling, Annual Blood Battle Blood Drive, Campus Artists and Performers Series. Student services: personal-psychological counseling. Campus security: 24-hour emergency response devices and patrols, student patrols, late night transport-escort service. Newark Campus Library with 45,000 books, 500 serials, an OPAC, and a Web page. Operations spending for the previous fiscal year: $186,828. 110 computers available on campus for general student use. Computer purchase/lease plans available. A campuswide network can be accessed from off-campus. Students can access the following: online class registration. Staffed computer lab on campus provides training in use of computers, software, and the Internet.

■ CENTRAL STATE UNIVERSITY
1400 Brush Row Rd.
Wilberforce, OH 45384
Tel: (937)376-6011; Free: 800-388-2781
Fax: (937)376-6648
E-mail: admissions@centralstate.edu
Web Site: www.centralstate.edu/
Description: State-supported, comprehensive, coed. Part of Ohio Board of Regents. Awards bachelor's and master's degrees. Founded 1887. Setting: 60-acre rural campus with easy access to Dayton. Endowment: $2 million. Research spending for the previous fiscal year: $1.7 million. Educational spending for the previous fiscal year: $5083 per student. Total enrollment: 2,152. Faculty: 243 (112 full-time, 131 part-time). Student-undergrad faculty ratio is 13:1. 7,959 applied, 37% were admitted. 5% from top 10% of their high school class, 12% from top quarter, 29% from top half. Full-time: 1,878 students, 52% women, 48% men. Part-time: 238 students, 61% women, 39% men. Students come from 29 states and territories, 2 other countries,

57% from out-of-state. 0.2% American Indian or Alaska Native, non-Hispanic/Latino; 1% Hispanic/Latino; 96% African American, non-Hispanic/Latino; 0.1% Asian, non-Hispanic/Latino; 0% Native Hawaiian or other Pacific Islander, non-Hispanic/Latino; 0.1% international. 17% 25 or older, 52% live on campus, 6% transferred in. Retention: 43% of full-time freshmen returned the following year. Academic areas with the most degrees conferred: business/marketing; education; communication/journalism; psychology. Core. Calendar: semesters. Services for LD students, honors program, independent study, double major, summer session for credit, part-time degree program, adult/continuing education programs, co-op programs and internships. Off campus study at members of the Southwestern Ohio Council for Higher Education. Study abroad program. ROTC: Army.
Entrance Requirements: Open admission for state residents. Option: electronic application. Required: high school transcript, SAT or ACT. Recommended: interview, ACT. Required for some: essay, minimum 2 high school GPA, 2 recommendations, 2.5 high school GPA for nonresidents. Entrance: minimally difficult. Application deadline: 6/15. Notification: continuous.
Costs Per Year: Application fee: $20. State resident tuition: $3550 full-time. Nonresident tuition: $10,770 full-time. Mandatory fees: $2320 full-time. Full-time tuition and fees vary according to course load. College room and board: $8782. College room only: $4720. Room and board charges vary according to board plan.
Collegiate Environment: Orientation program. Drama-theater group, choral group, marching band, student-run newspaper, radio station. Social organizations: 40 open to all; national fraternities, national sororities, local fraternities, local sororities; 1% of eligible men and 1% of eligible women are members. Most popular organizations: Student Ambassadors, student government, Make it Happen (Inter-Faith), Daughters of Nia Anaya (Social Group), Evolutions (Modeling Troupe). Major annual events: Homecoming, Spring Week, Welcome Week activities. Student services: health clinic, personal-psychological counseling. Campus security: 24-hour emergency response devices and patrols, controlled dormitory access. 1,539 college housing spaces available; 1,049 were occupied in 2012-13. Freshmen guaranteed college housing. On-campus residence required in freshman year. Options: coed, men-only, women-only housing available. Hallie Q. Brown Memorial Library plus 1 other with 256,994 books, 846,839 microform titles, 467 serials, 17,432 audiovisual materials, an OPAC, and a Web page. Operations spending for the previous fiscal year: $1.1 million. 555 computers available on campus for general student use. A campuswide network can be accessed from student residence rooms and from off campus. Students can access the following: online class registration. Staffed computer lab on campus provides training in use of computers, software, and the Internet.
Community Environment: A college community, Wilberforce was named after William Wilberforce, the English philanthropist who fought for the abolition of slave trade. The community is known as a noted African-American cultural center. Part-time employment opportunities are available for students.

■ CHAMBERLAIN COLLEGE OF NURSING (CLEVELAND)
6700 Euclid Ave.
Ste. 201
Cleveland, OH 44103
Tel: (216)361-6005
Web Site: www.chamberlain.edu/
Description: Proprietary, 4-year, coed. Awards bachelor's degrees.
Entrance Requirements: Required: SAT or ACT.
Costs Per Year: Application fee: $95. Tuition: $16,360 full-time, $665 per credit hour part-time. Mandatory fees: $600 full-time.

■ CHAMBERLAIN COLLEGE OF NURSING (COLUMBUS)
1350 Alum Creek Dr.
Columbus, OH 43209
Tel: (614)252-8890; Free: 888-556-8CCN
Web Site: www.chamberlain.edu/
Description: Proprietary, 4-year, coed. Awards associate and bachelor's degrees. Total enrollment: 661. Faculty: 97 (15 full-time, 82 part-time). Student-undergrad faculty ratio is 9:1. Full-time: 258 students, 87% women, 13% men. Part-time: 403 students, 84% women, 16% men. 3% from out-of-state. 0.3% American Indian or Alaska Native, non-Hispanic/Latino; 2% Hispanic/Latino; 14% African American, non-Hispanic/Latino; 3% Asian, non-Hispanic/Latino; 0% Native Hawaiian or other Pacific Islander, non-Hispanic/Latino; 1% international. 56% 25 or older, 0% live on campus, 38% transferred in. Academic area with the most degrees conferred: health professions and related sciences. Calendar: semesters.

Entrance Requirements: Required: SAT or ACT.

Costs Per Year: Tuition: $16,360 full-time, $665 per credit hour part-time. Mandatory fees: $600 full-time. Full-time tuition and fees vary according to course load. Part-time tuition varies according to course load.

■ **CHATFIELD COLLEGE**

20918 State Rte. 251
Saint Martin, OH 45118-9705
Tel: (513)875-3344
Fax: (513)875-3912
E-mail: admissions@chatfield.edu
Web Site: www.chatfield.edu/

Description: Independent, 2-year, coed, affiliated with Roman Catholic Church. Awards transfer associate and terminal associate degrees. Founded 1970. Setting: 200-acre rural campus with easy access to Cincinnati, Dayton. Total enrollment: 244. Student-undergrad faculty ratio is 9:1. 0% from out-of-state. 51% 25 or older. Core. Calendar: semesters. Academic remediation for entering students, advanced placement, summer session for credit, part-time degree program, adult/continuing education programs, internships. Off campus study at 14 members of the Greater Cincinnati Consortium of Colleges and Universities.

Entrance Requirements: Open admission. Options: early admission, deferred admission. Required: high school transcript. Entrance: noncompetitive. Application deadline: Rolling. Notification: continuous.

Collegiate Environment: Orientation program. Drama-theater group, choral group, student-run newspaper. Student services: personal-psychological counseling. Campus security: 12-hour night patrols by security. Chatfield College Library with 19,170 books, 25 serials, and an OPAC.

■ **THE CHRIST COLLEGE OF NURSING AND HEALTH SCIENCES**

2139 Auburn Ave.
Cincinnati, OH 45219
Tel: (513)585-2401
Fax: (513)585-3540
E-mail: bradley.jackson@thechristcollege.edu
Web Site: www.thechristcollege.edu/

Description: Private, 2-year, coed. Awards terminal associate degrees. Setting: urban campus with easy access to Cincinnati. Total enrollment: 346. Faculty: 41 (25 full-time, 16 part-time). Student-undergrad faculty ratio is 7:1. 70 applied, 64% were admitted. Full-time: 202 students, 92% women, 8% men. Part-time: 144 students, 92% women, 8% men. 0% American Indian or Alaska Native, non-Hispanic/Latino; 1% Hispanic/Latino; 10% African American, non-Hispanic/Latino; 1% Asian, non-Hispanic/Latino; 0% Native Hawaiian or other Pacific Islander, non-Hispanic/Latino; 0% international. 38% 25 or older, 22% transferred in. Core. Academic remediation for entering students, services for LD students, advanced placement, summer session for credit.

Entrance Requirements: Required: high school transcript, minimum 2.75 high school GPA, SAT or ACT. Transfer credits accepted: Yes.

Costs Per Year: Application fee: $45. Tuition: $14,060 full-time, $370 per credit hour part-time. Mandatory fees: $800 full-time. Full-time tuition and fees vary according to course load. Part-time tuition varies according to course load.

Collegiate Environment: Orientation program. Student services: personal-psychological counseling. Campus security: 24-hour emergency response devices and patrols, late night transport-escort service. 60 computers available on campus for general student use. A campuswide network can be accessed from off-campus. Students can access the following: online class registration, wireless. Staffed computer lab on campus provides training in use of computers, software, and the Internet.

■ **CINCINNATI CHRISTIAN UNIVERSITY**

2700 Glenway Ave.
Cincinnati, OH 45204-3200
Tel: (513)244-8100; Free: 800-949-4CCU
Fax: (513)244-8140
E-mail: jeffrey.derico@ccuniversity.edu
Web Site: www.ccuniversity.edu/

Description: Independent, upper-level, coed, affiliated with Church of Christ. Awards associate, bachelor's, and master's degrees. Founded 1924. Setting: 40-acre urban campus with easy access to Cincinnati. Total enrollment: 923. Faculty: 82 (34 full-time, 48 part-time). Student-undergrad faculty ratio is 15:1. 215 applied, 94% were admitted. Students come from 12 states and territories, 33% from out-of-state. 0.3% American Indian or Alaska Na-

tive, non-Hispanic/Latino; 1% Hispanic/Latino; 13% African American, non-Hispanic/Latino; 0% Asian, non-Hispanic/Latino; 0% Native Hawaiian or other Pacific Islander, non-Hispanic/Latino; 1% international. 36% 25 or older, 39% live on campus. Retention: 63% of full-time entering class returned the following year. Core. Calendar: semesters. Academic remediation for entering students, services for LD students, advanced placement, accelerated degree program, independent study, distance learning, double major, summer session for credit, part-time degree program, adult/continuing education programs, co-op programs and internships, graduate courses open to undergrads. Off campus study at College of Mount St. Joseph, Cincinnati State Technical & Community College, Greater Cincinnati Consortium of Colleges and Universities.

Entrance Requirements: SAT Reasoning Test deadline: 7/1. Transfer credits accepted: Yes.

Costs Per Year: Application fee: $40. Comprehensive fee: $21,938 includes full-time tuition ($14,766), mandatory fees ($500), and college room and board ($6672). College room only: $2820. Full-time tuition and fees vary according to course load and student level. Room and board charges vary according to board plan, housing facility, and student level. Part-time tuition: $600 per credit. Part-time mandatory fees: $500 per year. Part-time tuition and fees vary according to course load and student level.

Collegiate Environment: Orientation program. Drama-theater group, choral group. Major annual events: Fall College Picnic, Dorm Decorating Contest, Community Service Day. Student services: personal-psychological counseling. Campus security: 24-hour emergency response devices and patrols, student patrols, late night transport-escort service, controlled dormitory access. 408 college housing spaces available; 245 were occupied in 2012-13. On-campus residence required in junior year. Options: men-only, women-only housing available. George Mark Elliot Memorial Library plus 1 other with an OPAC. 45 computers available on campus for general student use. A campuswide network can be accessed from student residence rooms and from off campus. Students can access the following: online class registration. Staffed computer lab on campus provides training in use of computers, software, and the Internet.

■ **CINCINNATI COLLEGE OF MORTUARY SCIENCE**

645 W N Bend Rd.
Cincinnati, OH 45224-1462
Tel: (513)761-2020; Free: 888-377-8433
Fax: (513)761-3333
Web Site: www.ccms.edu/

Description: Independent, 4-year, coed. Awards associate and bachelor's degrees. Founded 1882. Setting: 10-acre urban campus. Educational spending for the previous fiscal year: $13,500 per student. Total enrollment: 165. Faculty: 7 (5 full-time, 2 part-time). Student-undergrad faculty ratio is 33:1. Full-time: 165 students, 52% women, 48% men. Students come from 13 states and territories. 2% Hispanic/Latino; 14% African American, non-Hispanic/Latino. 25% 25 or older, 94% transferred in. Retention: 95% of full-time freshmen returned the following year. Core. Summer session for credit, adult/continuing education programs.

Entrance Requirements: Open admission. Option: deferred admission. Required: high school transcript, minimum 2 high school GPA, SAT or ACT. Application deadline: Rolling. Notification: continuous. Transfer credits accepted: Yes.

Costs Per Year: Application fee: $40. Tuition: $16,875 full-time. Mandatory fees: $400 full-time. Full-time tuition and fees vary according to course load, degree level, and program. Tuition guaranteed not to increase for student's term of enrollment.

Collegiate Environment: Social organizations: local fraternities, local sororities; 57% of eligible men and 43% of eligible women are members. 5,000 books, 30 serials, and a Web page 16 computers available on campus for general student use. Staffed computer lab on campus provides training in use of computers and the Internet.

Community Environment: See University of Cincinnati.

■ **CINCINNATI STATE TECHNICAL AND COMMUNITY COLLEGE**

3520 Central Pky.
Cincinnati, OH 45223-2690
Tel: (513)569-1500; Free: 877-569-0115
Fax: (513)569-1562
E-mail: adm@cincinnatistate.edu
Web Site: www.cincinnatistate.edu/

Description: State-supported, 2-year, coed. Part of Ohio Board of Regents. Awards certificates, transfer associate, and terminal associate degrees.

Founded 1966. Setting: 46-acre urban campus. Total enrollment: 10,995. Faculty: 724 (188 full-time, 536 part-time). Student-undergrad faculty ratio is 18:1. Full-time: 4,206 students, 47% women, 53% men. Part-time: 6,789 students, 56% women, 44% men. Students come from 8 states and territories, 76 other countries, 10% from out-of-state. 1% American Indian or Alaska Native, non-Hispanic/Latino; 1% Hispanic/Latino; 27% African American, non-Hispanic/Latino; 1% Asian, non-Hispanic/Latino; 1% international. 49% 25 or older. Retention: 51% of full-time freshmen returned the following year. Core. Calendar: 5 ten-week terms. Academic remediation for entering students, ESL program, services for LD students, advanced placement, self-designed majors, honors program, independent study, distance learning, double major, summer session for credit, part-time degree program, co-op programs and internships. Off campus study at 12 members of the Greater Cincinnati Consortium of Colleges and Universities.

Entrance Requirements: Open admission. Option: electronic application. Required: high school transcript. Entrance: noncompetitive. Application deadline: Rolling. Notification: continuous.

Collegiate Environment: Orientation program. Drama-theater group. Social organizations: 12 open to all. Most popular organizations: student government, Nursing Student Association, Phi Theta Kappa, American Society of Civil Engineers, Students in Free Enterprise (SIFE). Major annual events: Homecoming, Student Government Picnic, Spirit Week. Student services: personal-psychological counseling. Campus security: 24-hour emergency response devices and patrols, late night transport-escort service. Johnnie Mae Berry Library plus 1 other with 39,802 books, 309 serials, 3,570 audiovisual materials, an OPAC, and a Web page. 150 computers available on campus for general student use. A campuswide network can be accessed from off-campus. Students can access the following: online class registration. Staffed computer lab on campus provides training in use of computers and the Internet.

Community Environment: See University of Cincinnati.

■ **CLARK STATE COMMUNITY COLLEGE**

570 E Leffel Ln.
Springfield, OH 45501-0570
Tel: (937)325-0691
E-mail: admissions@clarkstate.edu
Web Site: www.clarkstate.edu/

Description: State-supported, 2-year, coed. Part of Ohio Board of Regents. Awards certificates, transfer associate, and terminal associate degrees. Founded 1962. Setting: 60-acre suburban campus with easy access to Columbus, Dayton. Endowment: $8.9 million. Educational spending for the previous fiscal year: $2726 per student. Faculty: 552 (74 full-time, 478 part-time). Student-undergrad faculty ratio is 13:1. 3,504 applied, 100% were admitted. Students come from 12 states and territories, 1% from out-of-state. 0.4% American Indian or Alaska Native, non-Hispanic/Latino; 1% Hispanic/Latino; 15% African American, non-Hispanic/Latino; 1% Asian, non-Hispanic/Latino; 0.2% Native Hawaiian or other Pacific Islander, non-Hispanic/Latino; 0.3% international. 48% 25 or older. Retention: 33% of full-time freshmen returned the following year. Core. Academic remediation for entering students, services for LD students, advanced placement, honors program, independent study, distance learning, double major, summer session for credit, part-time degree program, adult/continuing education programs, co-op programs and internships. Off campus study at 22 members of the Southwestern Ohio Council for Higher Education (SOCHE). ROTC: Army (c).

Entrance Requirements: Open admission. Option: electronic application. Recommended: high school transcript. Entrance: noncompetitive. Application deadlines: Rolling, Rolling for nonresidents. Notification: continuous, continuous for nonresidents. Transfer credits accepted: Yes.

Collegiate Environment: Orientation program. Drama-theater group, choral group. Social organizations: 8 open to all. Most popular organizations: Student Senate, Gay Straight Alliance, Student Theatre Guild, Chi Alpha, Creative Writers Club. Major annual events: WoW - Week of Welcome, Welcome Back, Spring Fling. Student services: health clinic, personal-psychological counseling. Campus security: late night transport-escort service. College housing not available. Clark State Community College Library with an OPAC and a Web page. Operations spending for the previous fiscal year: $413,183. 533 computers available on campus for general student use. A campuswide network can be accessed from off-campus. Students can access the following: online class registration. Staffed computer lab on campus provides training in use of computers, software, and the Internet.

Community Environment: See Wittenberg University.

■ **CLEVELAND INSTITUTE OF ART**

11141 E Blvd.
Cleveland, OH 44106-1700
Tel: (216)421-7000; Free: 800-223-4700
Fax: (216)421-7438
E-mail: admissions@cia.edu
Web Site: www.cia.edu/

Description: Independent, 4-year, coed. Awards bachelor's degrees. Founded 1882. Setting: 5-acre urban campus. Endowment: $24.3 million. Educational spending for the previous fiscal year: $15,619 per student. Total enrollment: 556. Faculty: 108 (50 full-time, 58 part-time). Student-undergrad faculty ratio is 9:1. 584 applied, 71% were admitted. 14% from top 10% of their high school class, 34% from top quarter, 72% from top half. Full-time: 550 students, 58% women, 42% men. Part-time: 6 students, 33% women, 67% men. Students come from 31 states and territories, 10 other countries, 30% from out-of-state. 0.2% American Indian or Alaska Native, non-Hispanic/Latino; 4% Hispanic/Latino; 10% African American, non-Hispanic/Latino; 3% Asian, non-Hispanic/Latino; 0% Native Hawaiian or other Pacific Islander, non-Hispanic/Latino; 4% international. 8% 25 or older, 21% live on campus, 5% transferred in. Retention: 79% of full-time freshmen returned the following year. Academic area with the most degrees conferred: visual and performing arts. Core. Calendar: semesters. Academic remediation for entering students, services for LD students, advanced placement, independent study, double major, part-time degree program, internships. Off campus study at Case Western Reserve University, Cross Registration Articulations, Association of Independent Colleges of Art and Design. Study abroad program.

Entrance Requirements: Options: electronic application, early admission, early action. Required: essay, high school transcript, minimum 2 high school GPA, 1 recommendation, portfolio, SAT or ACT. Recommended: interview. Entrance: moderately difficult. Application deadline: 3/1. Notification: continuous. SAT Reasoning Test deadline: 7/1. Transfer credits accepted: Yes. Early action applicants: 54. Early action applicants admitted: 53.

Costs Per Year: Application fee: $30. Comprehensive fee: $48,641 includes full-time tuition ($34,270), mandatory fees ($2239), and college room and board ($12,132). College room only: $6912. Full-time tuition and fees vary according to program, reciprocity agreements, and student level. Room and board charges vary according to board plan. Part-time tuition: $1430 per credit. Part-time mandatory fees: $150 per credit, $115 per term. Part-time tuition and fees vary according to course load, program, reciprocity agreements, and student level.

Collegiate Environment: Orientation program. Drama-theater group, choral group, marching band. Social organizations: 10 open to all; national fraternities, national sororities; 4% of eligible men and 4% of eligible women are members. Most popular organizations: Campus Activities Board, Student Independent Exhibition, International Interior Design Association, Student Leadership Council, Community Service Club. Major annual events: Halloween Party, Student Independent Exhibition, Pink Pig year-end picnic and art auction. Student services: legal services, health clinic, personal-psychological counseling, women's center. Campus security: 24-hour emergency response devices and patrols, late night transport-escort service, controlled dormitory access. 132 college housing spaces available; all were occupied in 2012-13. Freshmen given priority for college housing. On-campus residence required in freshman year. Option: coed housing available. Cleveland Institute of Art Library with 49,785 books, 3,305 microform titles, 139 serials, 930 audiovisual materials, an OPAC, and a Web page. Operations spending for the previous fiscal year: $368,519. 80 computers available on campus for general student use. Computer purchase/lease plans available. A campuswide network can be accessed from student residence rooms. Students can access the following: online class registration, wireless Internet access available throughout campus. Staffed computer lab on campus provides training in use of computers, software, and the Internet.

Community Environment: See Case Western Reserve University.

■ **CLEVELAND INSTITUTE OF ELECTRONICS**

1776 E Seventeenth St.
Cleveland, OH 44114-3636
Tel: (216)781-9400; Free: 800-243-6446
E-mail: instruct@cie-wc.edu
Web Site: www.cie-wc.edu/

Description: Proprietary, 2-year, coed. Awards diplomas and terminal associate degrees (offers only external degree programs conducted through home study). Founded 1934. Total enrollment: 1,675. Faculty: 8 (4 full-time,

4 part-time). Students come from 52 states and territories, 70 other countries, 97% from out-of-state. 85% 25 or older. Core. Calendar: continuous. Accelerated degree program, independent study, distance learning, part-time degree program, external degree program, adult/continuing education programs.

Entrance Requirements: Open admission. Options: electronic application, early admission. Required: high school transcript. Entrance: noncompetitive. Application deadlines: Rolling, Rolling for nonresidents. Notification: continuous, continuous for nonresidents.

Costs Per Year: Tuition: $2075 per term part-time. Tuition guaranteed not to increase for student's term of enrollment.

Collegiate Environment: 5,000 books and 38 serials.

■ CLEVELAND INSTITUTE OF MUSIC
11021 E Blvd.
Cleveland, OH 44106-1776
Tel: (216)791-5000
Fax: (216)791-1530
E-mail: william.fay@case.edu
Web Site: www.cim.edu/

Description: Independent, comprehensive, coed. Awards bachelor's and master's degrees. Founded 1920. Setting: 488-acre urban campus. Total enrollment: 437. Student-undergrad faculty ratio is 7:1. 437 applied, 44% were admitted. 74% from out-of-state. 0% 25 or older. Retention: 90% of full-time freshmen returned the following year. Academic area with the most degrees conferred: visual and performing arts. Calendar: semesters. Academic remediation for entering students, ESL program, advanced placement, accelerated degree program, independent study, distance learning, double major, summer session for credit, internships, graduate courses open to undergrads. Off campus study at Case Western Reserve University. Study abroad program. ROTC: Army (c), Air Force (c).

Entrance Requirements: Options: early admission, deferred admission, international baccalaureate accepted. Required: essay, high school transcript, 2 recommendations, audition. Recommended: interview. Required for some: SAT or ACT. Entrance: very difficult. Application deadline: 12/1. Notification: 4/1.

Collegiate Environment: Orientation program. Choral group. Student services: health clinic, personal-psychological counseling. Campus security: 24-hour emergency response devices and patrols, late night transport-escort service, controlled dormitory access. Cleveland Institute of Music Library with an OPAC and a Web page.

Community Environment: See Case Western Reserve University.

■ CLEVELAND STATE UNIVERSITY
2121 Euclid Ave.
Cleveland, OH 44115
Tel: (216)687-2000; Free: 888-CSU-OHIO
Fax: (216)687-9366
E-mail: admissions@csuohio.edu
Web Site: www.csuohio.edu/

Description: State-supported, university, coed. Part of University System of Ohio. Awards bachelor's, master's, and doctoral degrees and post-master's certificates. Founded 1964. Setting: 82-acre urban campus with easy access to Cleveland, Ohio metro area. Endowment: $47.7 million. Research spending for the previous fiscal year: $16.1 million. Total enrollment: 17,525. Faculty: 1,041 (520 full-time, 521 part-time). Student-undergrad faculty ratio is 19:1. 5,938 applied, 63% were admitted. 12% from top 10% of their high school class, 38% from top quarter, 74% from top half. Full-time: 8,590 students, 54% women, 46% men. Part-time: 3,448 students, 55% women, 45% men. Students come from 41 states and territories, 8 other countries, 3% from out-of-state. 0.3% American Indian or Alaska Native, non-Hispanic/Latino; 4% Hispanic/Latino; 21% African American, non-Hispanic/Latino; 2% Asian, non-Hispanic/Latino; 0.1% Native Hawaiian or other Pacific Islander, non-Hispanic/Latino; 4% international. 35% 25 or older, 8% live on campus, 15% transferred in. Retention: 65% of full-time freshmen returned the following year. Academic areas with the most degrees conferred: business/marketing; health professions and related sciences; social sciences. Core. Calendar: semesters. Academic remediation for entering students, ESL program, services for LD students, advanced placement, accelerated degree program, self-designed majors, freshman honors college, honors program, independent study, distance learning, double major, summer session for credit, part-time degree program, adult/continuing education programs, co-op programs and internships, graduate courses open to undergrads. Off

campus study at University System of Ohio institutions. Study abroad program. ROTC: Army (c), Air Force (c).

Entrance Requirements: Options: electronic application, early action, deferred admission. Required: high school transcript, minimum 2.3 high school GPA, minimum ACT score of 16 or SAT of 770 (combined critical reading and math), SAT or ACT. Entrance: moderately difficult. Application deadlines: 5/15, 5/1 for early action. Notification: continuous. SAT Reasoning Test deadline: 8/10. Transfer credits accepted: Yes.

Costs Per Year: Application fee: $30. State resident tuition: $9264 full-time, $386 per credit hour part-time. Nonresident tuition: $12,386 full-time, $516 per credit hour part-time. Mandatory fees: $50 full-time, $25 per term part-time. Full-time tuition and fees vary according to course load, degree level, and program. Part-time tuition and fees vary according to course load, degree level, and program. College room and board: $11,848. College room only: $7648. Room and board charges vary according to board plan and housing facility.

Collegiate Environment: Orientation program. Drama-theater group, choral group, student-run newspaper, radio station. Social organizations: 244 open to all; national fraternities, national sororities, local fraternities, local sororities; 1% of eligible men and 1% of eligible women are members. Most popular organizations: Friends of India, Chinese Students and Scholars Association, Chi Sigma Iota, Student Nurses Association, Engineers Without Borders. Major annual events: Weeks of Welcome, Springfest, Glow in the Dark Party. Student services: health clinic, personal-psychological counseling, women's center. Campus security: 24-hour emergency response devices and patrols, student patrols, late night transport-escort service, controlled dormitory access, Campus Watch, CSU Alert Notification System, Community Emergency and Response Team (CERT). 1,186 college housing spaces available; 1,007 were occupied in 2012-13. Freshmen guaranteed college housing. Option: coed housing available. Michael Schwartz Library plus 1 other with 539,684 books, 781,569 microform titles, 11,153 serials, 41,766 audiovisual materials, an OPAC, and a Web page. Operations spending for the previous fiscal year: $7.7 million. 736 computers available on campus for general student use. Computer purchase/lease plans available. A campuswide network can be accessed from student residence rooms and from off campus. Students can access the following: online class registration, each general purpose computer lab has a scanner and printer, and students are allowed free black and white printing up to 2,000 pages per semester. Staffed computer lab on campus provides training in use of computers, software, and the Internet.

■ COLLEGE OF MOUNT ST. JOSEPH
5701 Delhi Rd.
Cincinnati, OH 45233-1670
Tel: (513)244-4200; Free: 800-654-9314
Fax: (513)244-4629
E-mail: admissions@mail.msj.edu
Web Site: www.msj.edu/

Description: Independent Roman Catholic, comprehensive, coed. Awards associate, bachelor's, master's, and doctoral degrees. Founded 1920. Setting: 92-acre suburban campus. Endowment: $29.1 million. Educational spending for the previous fiscal year: $8280 per student. Total enrollment: 2,294. Faculty: 233 (118 full-time, 115 part-time). Student-undergrad faculty ratio is 11:1. 1,235 applied, 70% were admitted. 16% from top 10% of their high school class, 39% from top quarter, 73% from top half. Full-time: 1,227 students, 55% women, 45% men. Part-time: 613 students, 81% women, 19% men. Students come from 20 states and territories, 3 other countries, 17% from out-of-state. 0.2% American Indian or Alaska Native, non-Hispanic/Latino; 3% Hispanic/Latino; 9% African American, non-Hispanic/Latino; 0.4% Asian, non-Hispanic/Latino; 0.2% international. 30% 25 or older, 21% live on campus, 5% transferred in. Retention: 77% of full-time freshmen returned the following year. Academic areas with the most degrees conferred: business/marketing; health professions and related sciences; education. Core. Calendar: semesters. Academic remediation for entering students, services for LD students, advanced placement, accelerated degree program, honors program, independent study, distance learning, double major, summer session for credit, part-time degree program, co-op programs and internships, graduate courses open to undergrads. Off campus study at Greater Cincinnati Consortium of Colleges and Universities. Study abroad program. ROTC: Army (c), Air Force (c).

Entrance Requirements: Options: electronic application, deferred admission, international baccalaureate accepted. Required: high school transcript, SAT or ACT. Recommended: minimum 2 high school GPA. Required for some: essay, 2 recommendations, interview. Entrance: moderately difficult.

Application deadline: 8/15. Notification: continuous. SAT Reasoning Test deadline: 8/15. SAT Subject Test deadline: 8/15. Transfer credits accepted: Yes.

Costs Per Year: Application fee: $25. One-time mandatory fee: $200. Comprehensive fee: $33,880 includes full-time tuition ($24,900), mandatory fees ($900), and college room and board ($8080). College room only: $3990. Full-time tuition and fees vary according to course load and reciprocity agreements. Room and board charges vary according to board plan and housing facility. Part-time tuition: $500 per credit hour. Part-time tuition varies according to course load and reciprocity agreements.

Collegiate Environment: Orientation program. Drama-theater group, choral group, student-run newspaper. Social organizations: 35 open to all. Most popular organizations: Student Government Association, Black Student Union, Campus Ministry Leadership Team, Campus Activities Board, Campus Ambassadors. Major annual events: Welcome Back Party, Spring Fest, MSJ Community Trick or Treat. Student services: health clinic, personal-psychological counseling. Campus security: 24-hour emergency response devices and patrols, late night transport-escort service. 519 college housing spaces available; 392 were occupied in 2012-13. Freshmen given priority for college housing. On-campus residence required through sophomore year. Option: coed housing available. Archbishop Alter Library with 95,428 books, 340,000 microform titles, 9,306 serials, 4,149 audiovisual materials, an OPAC, and a Web page. Operations spending for the previous fiscal year: $500,063. 202 computers available on campus for general student use. A campuswide network can be accessed from student residence rooms and from off campus. Students can access the following: online class registration. Staffed computer lab on campus (open 24 hours a day) provides training in use of computers, software, and the Internet.

Community Environment: See University of Cincinnati.

■ THE COLLEGE OF WOOSTER

1189 Beall Ave.
Wooster, OH 44691-2363
Tel: (330)263-2000; Free: 800-877-9905
Fax: (330)263-2621
E-mail: admissions@wooster.edu
Web Site: www.wooster.edu/

Description: Independent, 4-year, coed, affiliated with Presbyterian Church (U.S.A.). Awards bachelor's degrees. Founded 1866. Setting: 240-acre small town campus with easy access to Cleveland. Endowment: $232 million. Research spending for the previous fiscal year: $919,691. Educational spending for the previous fiscal year: $14,355 per student. Total enrollment: 2,080. Faculty: 213 (173 full-time, 40 part-time). Student-undergrad faculty ratio is 12:1. 5,208 applied, 58% were admitted. 41% from top 10% of their high school class, 76% from top quarter, 96% from top half. Full-time: 2,043 students, 55% women, 45% men. Part-time: 37 students, 57% women, 43% men. Students come from 51 states and territories, 50 other countries, 62% from out-of-state. 1% American Indian or Alaska Native, non-Hispanic/Latino; 4% Hispanic/Latino; 9% African American, non-Hispanic/Latino; 3% Asian, non-Hispanic/Latino; 0.05% Native Hawaiian or other Pacific Islander, non-Hispanic/Latino; 6% international. 1% 25 or older, 99% live on campus, 1% transferred in. Retention: 85% of full-time freshmen returned the following year. Academic areas with the most degrees conferred: social sciences; biological/life sciences; history. Core. Calendar: semesters. Services for LD students, advanced placement, self-designed majors, independent study, double major, internships. Off campus study. Study abroad program.

Entrance Requirements: Options: electronic application, early admission, early decision, early action, deferred admission, international baccalaureate accepted. Required: essay, high school transcript, SAT or ACT, SAT or ACT. Recommended: interview. Entrance: moderately difficult. Application deadlines: 2/15, 11/1 for early decision plan 1, 1/15 for early decision plan 2, 11/15 for early action. Notification: 4/1, 11/15 for early decision plan 1, 2/1 for early decision plan 2, 12/31 for early action. SAT Reasoning Test deadline: 3/15. Transfer credits accepted: Yes. Applicants placed on waiting list: 575. Wait-listed applicants offered admission: 19. Early decision applicants: 76. Early decision applicants admitted: 64. Early action applicants: 2,245. Early action applicants admitted: 1,600.

Costs Per Year: Application fee: $40. Comprehensive fee: $49,400 includes full-time tuition ($39,500), mandatory fees ($310), and college room and board ($9590). College room only: $4440. Full-time tuition and fees vary according to course load. Room and board charges vary according to board plan and housing facility. Part-time tuition: $1230 per credit. Part-time tuition varies according to course load.

Collegiate Environment: Orientation program. Drama-theater group, choral

group, marching band, student-run newspaper, radio station. Social organizations: 120 open to all; local fraternities, local sororities, coed fraternity; 15% of eligible men and 20% of eligible women are members. Most popular organizations: Volunteer Network, International Student Association, Inter-Greek Council, Wooster Activities Crew, Women's Athletic and Recreation Association. Major annual events: Winter Gala, Party on the Green, Scot Spirit Day. Student services: health clinic, personal-psychological counseling, women's center. Campus security: 24-hour emergency response devices and patrols, student patrols, late night transport-escort service, controlled dormitory access. Freshmen guaranteed college housing. On-campus residence required through senior year. Options: coed, women-only housing available. The College of Wooster Libraries plus 3 others with 665,839 books, 180,612 microform titles, 73,193 serials, 23,089 audiovisual materials, an OPAC, and a Web page. 450 computers available on campus for general student use. Computer purchase/lease plans available. A computer is required for all students. A campuswide network can be accessed from student residence rooms and from off campus. Students can access the following: online class registration, learning management system, campus blogging site, campus wiki site. Staffed computer lab on campus (open 24 hours a day) provides training in use of computers, software, and the Internet.

Community Environment: City of Wooster population of 25,700, county seat of Wayne County, and leading agricultural region in the United States. In Ohio, Wayne County ranks first in cash receipts from dairy products, cattle and calves, and first in production of hay and oats. The Ohio Agricultural Research and Development Center is second largest in the United States. Companies in the city include Newell Rubbermaid Incorporated, Wooster Brush Company, the Gerstenslager Company, Bell and Howell, Frito-Lay, and others. Other educational institutions include Ohio State University's Agricultural Technical Institute and the Wayne General and Technical College. Wooster has been designated"Tree City, U.S.A." Students have access to Cleveland, Columbus, Pittsburgh, Cincinnati, and Akron.

■ COLUMBUS COLLEGE OF ART & DESIGN

60 Cleveland Ave.
Columbus, OH 43215-1758
Tel: (614)224-9101; Free: 877-997-2223
E-mail: admissions@ccad.edu
Web Site: www.ccad.edu/

Description: Independent, 4-year, coed. Awards bachelor's and master's degrees. Founded 1879. Setting: 17-acre urban campus. Endowment: $8.3 million. Educational spending for the previous fiscal year: $8845 per student. Total enrollment: 1,400. Faculty: 193 (63 full-time, 130 part-time). Student-undergrad faculty ratio is 11:1. 563 applied, 87% were admitted. 5% from top 10% of their high school class, 10% from top quarter, 44% from top half. Full-time: 1,261 students, 60% women, 40% men. Part-time: 114 students, 62% women, 38% men. Students come from 41 states and territories, 16 other countries, 24% from out-of-state. 0.1% American Indian or Alaska Native, non-Hispanic/Latino; 4% Hispanic/Latino; 8% African American, non-Hispanic/Latino; 2% Asian, non-Hispanic/Latino; 0.1% Native Hawaiian or other Pacific Islander, non-Hispanic/Latino; 7% international. 9% 25 or older, 32% live on campus, 0.4% transferred in. Retention: 81% of full-time freshmen returned the following year. Academic area with the most degrees conferred: visual and performing arts. Core. Calendar: semesters. Academic remediation for entering students, ESL program, services for LD students, advanced placement, honors program, independent study, distance learning, double major, summer session for credit, internships. Off campus study at members of the Higher Education Council of Columbus. Study abroad program.

Entrance Requirements: Options: electronic application, deferred admission, international baccalaureate accepted. Required: essay, high school transcript, minimum 2 high school GPA, 1 recommendation, portfolio, SAT or ACT. Recommended: interview. Entrance: moderately difficult. Application deadline: Rolling. Notification: continuous. Transfer credits accepted: Yes.

Costs Per Year: Application fee: $30. Comprehensive fee: $36,014 includes full-time tuition ($27,504), mandatory fees ($1020), and college room and board ($7490). Full-time tuition and fees vary according to course load. Room and board charges vary according to board plan, housing facility, and student level. Part-time tuition: $1146 per credit hour. Part-time tuition and fees vary according to course load.

Collegiate Environment: Orientation program. Social organizations: 40 open to all. Most popular organizations: Student Government Association, Gay Straight Student Alliance, Sanctuary, Environmental Awareness Society, Student Programming Board. Major annual events: Annual Student Art

Exhibition, Big Boo Halloween Party, Family Weekend. Student services: personal-psychological counseling. Campus security: 24-hour emergency response devices and patrols, late night transport-escort service, controlled dormitory access. 440 college housing spaces available; 430 were occupied in 2012-13. Freshmen guaranteed college housing. On-campus residence required in freshman year. Option: coed housing available. Packard Library with 104,908 books, 19,324 microform titles, 300 serials, 3,517 audiovisual materials, an OPAC, and a Web page. Operations spending for the previous fiscal year: $807,330. 485 computers available on campus for general student use. A computer is required for all students. A campuswide network can be accessed. Students can access the following: online class registration, online library. Staffed computer lab on campus provides training in use of computers, software, and the Internet.

Community Environment: See Ohio State University - Columbus Campus.

■ COLUMBUS CULINARY INSTITUTE AT BRADFORD SCHOOL

2435 Stelzer Rd.
Columbus, OH 43219
Free: 877-506-5006
Web Site: www.columbusculinary.com/

Description: Private, 2-year, coed. Awards terminal associate degrees. Founded 2006. Setting: suburban campus. Total enrollment: 204. 811 applied, 49% were admitted. Calendar: semesters.

■ COLUMBUS STATE COMMUNITY COLLEGE

Box 1609
Columbus, OH 43216-1609
Tel: (614)287-2400; Free: 800-621-6407
Fax: (614)287-5117
E-mail: tblaney@cscc.edu
Web Site: www.cscc.edu/

Description: State-supported, 2-year, coed. Part of Ohio Board of Regents. Awards certificates, transfer associate, and terminal associate degrees. Founded 1963. Setting: 75-acre urban campus. Total enrollment: 23,057. 45% 25 or older. Core. Academic remediation for entering students, ESL program, services for LD students, advanced placement, self-designed majors, honors program, distance learning, summer session for credit, part-time degree program, adult/continuing education programs, co-op programs and internships. Off campus study at members of the Higher Education Council of Columbus. ROTC: Army, Air Force (c).

Entrance Requirements: Open admission. Options: early admission, deferred admission. Recommended: high school transcript. Entrance: noncompetitive. Application deadline: Rolling. Notification: continuous.

Collegiate Environment: Choral group. Student services: health clinic, personal-psychological counseling. Campus security: 24-hour emergency response devices and patrols, late night transport-escort service. Educational Resources Center plus 1 other with 38,192 books, 489 serials, 7,903 audiovisual materials, an OPAC, and a Web page.

Community Environment: See Ohio State University - Columbus Campus.

■ CUYAHOGA COMMUNITY COLLEGE

700 Carnegie Ave.
Cleveland, OH 44115-2878
Tel: (216)987-6000; Free: 800-954-8742
Fax: (216)987-5050
Web Site: www.tri-c.edu/

Description: State and locally supported, 2-year, coed. Awards certificates, transfer associate, and terminal associate degrees. Founded 1963. Setting: urban campus. Endowment: $22.5 million. Total enrollment: 30,065. Faculty: 1,673 (359 full-time, 1,314 part-time). Student-undergrad faculty ratio is 18:1. 9,492 applied, 100% were admitted. Full-time: 10,590 students, 55% women, 45% men. Part-time: 19,475 students, 65% women, 35% men. Students come from 32 states and territories, 27 other countries, 1% from out-of-state. 1% American Indian or Alaska Native, non-Hispanic/Latino; 5% Hispanic/Latino; 28% African American, non-Hispanic/Latino; 2% Asian, non-Hispanic/Latino; 0% Native Hawaiian or other Pacific Islander, non-Hispanic/Latino; 1% international. 54% 25 or older, 5% transferred in. Retention: 48% of full-time freshmen returned the following year. Calendar: semesters. ESL program, services for LD students, advanced placement, independent study, distance learning, summer session for credit, part-time degree program, external degree program, adult/continuing education programs, co-op programs.

Entrance Requirements: Open admission. Options: early admission, deferred admission, international baccalaureate accepted. Required for

some: high school transcript. Entrance: noncompetitive. Application deadline: Rolling. Notification: continuous. Transfer credits accepted: Yes.

Costs Per Year: Application fee: $0. Area resident tuition: $2936 full-time, $98 per credit part-time. State resident tuition: $3753 full-time, $125 per credit part-time. Nonresident tuition: $7268 full-time, $242 per credit part-time. College room and board: $5000.

Collegiate Environment: Orientation program. Drama-theater group, choral group, student-run newspaper. Social organizations: 47 open to all. Most popular organizations: Student Senate, Student Nursing Organization, Business Focus, Phi Theta Kappa. Major annual events: Welcome Back, Diversity Day. Student services: health clinic, personal-psychological counseling. Campus security: 24-hour emergency response devices and patrols, late night transport-escort service. College housing not available. Metro Library plus 3 others with 177,767 books, 177,926 microform titles, 1,135 serials, an OPAC, and a Web page. 1,500 computers available on campus for general student use. A campuswide network can be accessed from off-campus. Staffed computer lab on campus.

■ DAVIS COLLEGE

4747 Monroe St.
Toledo, OH 43623-4307
Tel: (419)473-2700; Free: 800-477-7021
E-mail: dstern@daviscollege.edu
Web Site: daviscollege.edu/

Description: Proprietary, 2-year, coed. Awards diplomas and terminal associate degrees. Founded 1858. Setting: 1-acre urban campus with easy access to Detroit. Educational spending for the previous fiscal year: $10,196 per student. Total enrollment: 527. Faculty: 33 (15 full-time, 18 part-time). Student-undergrad faculty ratio is 15:1. 81 applied, 100% were admitted. Full-time: 207 students, 86% women, 14% men. Part-time: 320 students, 86% women, 14% men. Students come from 2 states and territories, 3% from out-of-state. 56% 25 or older, 16% transferred in. Core. Academic remediation for entering students, advanced placement, distance learning, summer session for credit, part-time degree program, adult/continuing education programs, internships.

Entrance Requirements: Options: electronic application, early admission, deferred admission. Required: high school transcript, interview, CPAt. Entrance: minimally difficult. Application deadline: Rolling. Notification: continuous.

Collegiate Environment: Orientation program. Social organizations: 1 open to all. Most popular organization: Student Advisory Board. Major annual events: Spring Parking Lot Event, Christmas Party, Halloween Haunted House. Student services: personal-psychological counseling. Campus security: 24-hour emergency response devices, security cameras for parking lot. Davis College Resource Center with 3,400 books, 107 serials, 191 audiovisual materials, and an OPAC. 116 computers available on campus for general student use. A campuswide network can be accessed from off-campus. Staffed computer lab on campus provides training in use of computers, software, and the Internet.

■ DAYMAR COLLEGE (CHILLICOTHE)

1410 Industrial Dr.
Chillicothe, OH 45601
Tel: (740)774-6300; Free: 877-258-7796
Fax: (740)774-2071
Web Site: www.daymarcollege.edu/

Description: Proprietary, 2-year, coed. Awards certificates and terminal associate degrees. Founded 1976. Total enrollment: 137. 0% from out-of-state. 68% 25 or older. Retention: 55% of full-time freshmen returned the following year.

Entrance Requirements: Open admission.

■ DAYMAR COLLEGE (JACKSON)

980 E Main St.
Jackson, OH 45640
Tel: (740)286-1554; Free: 877-258-7796
Fax: (740)286-4476
Web Site: www.daymarcollege.edu/

Description: Proprietary, 2-year, coed. Awards terminal associate degrees. Founded 1976. Total enrollment: 140. Student-undergrad faculty ratio is 24:1. 0% from out-of-state. 76% 25 or older.

Entrance Requirements: Entrance: noncompetitive.

■ DAYMAR COLLEGE (LANCASTER)

1579 Victor Rd., NW
Lancaster, OH 43130

Tel: (740)687-6126; Free: 877-258-7796
Fax: (740)687-0431
E-mail: hhankinson@daymarcollege.edu
Web Site: www.daymarcollege.edu/
Description: Proprietary, 2-year, coed. Awards terminal associate degrees. Founded 1984. Total enrollment: 67. Student-undergrad faculty ratio is 11:1. 0% from out-of-state. 73% 25 or older.
Entrance Requirements: Entrance: noncompetitive.

■ DAYMAR COLLEGE (NEW BOSTON)

3879 Rhodes Ave.
New Boston, OH 45662
Tel: (740)456-4124; Free: 877-258-7796
Web Site: www.daymarcollege.edu/
Description: Proprietary, 2-year, coed. Awards terminal associate degrees. Total enrollment: 252. Student-undergrad faculty ratio is 35:1. 0% from out-of-state. 67% 25 or older.
Entrance Requirements: Entrance: noncompetitive.

■ DEFIANCE COLLEGE

701 N Clinton St.
Defiance, OH 43512-1610
Tel: (419)784-4010; Free: 800-520-4632
Fax: (419)783-2468
E-mail: bharsha@defiance.edu
Web Site: www.defiance.edu/
Description: Independent, comprehensive, coed, affiliated with United Church of Christ. Awards associate, bachelor's, and master's degrees. Founded 1850. Setting: 150-acre small town campus with easy access to Toledo. Endowment: $14.7 million. Educational spending for the previous fiscal year: $6774 per student. Total enrollment: 1,021. Faculty: 107 (41 full-time, 66 part-time). Student-undergrad faculty ratio is 12:1. 1,854 applied, 67% were admitted. 8% from top 10% of their high school class, 25% from top quarter, 61% from top half. Full-time: 735 students, 45% women, 55% men. Part-time: 197 students, 72% women, 28% men. Students come from 26 states and territories, 4 other countries, 27% from out-of-state. 2% American Indian or Alaska Native, non-Hispanic/Latino; 5% Hispanic/Latino; 11% African American, non-Hispanic/Latino; 1% Asian, non-Hispanic/Latino; 0% Native Hawaiian or other Pacific Islander, non-Hispanic/Latino; 1% international. 20% 25 or older, 44% live on campus, 4% transferred in. Retention: 59% of full-time freshmen returned the following year. Academic areas with the most degrees conferred: business/marketing; education; homeland security, law enforcement, firefighting, and protective services. Core. Calendar: semesters. Academic remediation for entering students, services for LD students, advanced placement, self-designed majors, honors program, independent study, distance learning, double major, summer session for credit, part-time degree program, adult/continuing education programs, co-op programs and internships, graduate courses open to undergrads. Off campus study at Northwest State Community College. Study abroad program.
Entrance Requirements: Options: electronic application, deferred admission, international baccalaureate accepted. Required: high school transcript, minimum 2.25 high school GPA, SAT or ACT. Recommended: interview. Required for some: essay, interview. Entrance: moderately difficult. Application deadline: 8/15. Notification: continuous. Transfer credits accepted: Yes.
Costs Per Year: Application fee: $25. Comprehensive fee: $36,210 includes full-time tuition ($26,740), mandatory fees ($620), and college room and board ($8850). Full-time tuition and fees vary according to program. Room and board charges vary according to board plan and housing facility.
Collegiate Environment: Orientation program. Drama-theater group, choral group, student-run newspaper. Social organizations: 30 open to all; national sororities, local fraternities, service fraternity; 6% of eligible men and 6% of eligible women are members. Most popular organizations: Campus Activities Board, Criminal Justice Society, Student Senate, Black Action Student Association, DC Players. Major annual events: Homecoming, Family Weekend, Dance Marathon. Student services: health clinic, personal-psychological counseling. Campus security: late night transport-escort service, controlled dormitory access. 541 college housing spaces available; 496 were occupied in 2012-13. Freshmen guaranteed college housing. On-campus residence required through junior year. Option: coed housing available. Pilgrim Library with 175,083 books, 7,404 microform titles, 38,108 serials, 27,383 audiovisual materials, an OPAC, and a Web page. Operations spending for the previous fiscal year: $359,644. 200 computers available on campus for general student use. A campuswide network can be accessed from student

residence rooms and from off campus. Staffed computer lab on campus (open 24 hours a day) provides training in use of computers, software, and the Internet.
Community Environment: Defiance College is located in Defiance Ohio, site of Fort Defiance, and birthplace of the Indian Chief Pontiac. Today, Defiance is a community of over 18,000 residents and one of the fastest growing areas in Northwest Ohio. Highly diversified industry and some of the richest farmland in the nation contribute to the areas prosperity. A major shopping mall is 2 blocks north of the campus.

■ DENISON UNIVERSITY

Granville, OH 43023
Tel: (740)587-0810; Free: 800-DENISON
Fax: (740)587-6306
E-mail: admissions@denison.edu
Web Site: www.denison.edu/
Description: Independent, 4-year, coed. Awards bachelor's degrees. Founded 1831. Setting: 800-acre small town campus with easy access to Columbus. Endowment: $585 million. Research spending for the previous fiscal year: $726,353. Educational spending for the previous fiscal year: $16,649 per student. Total enrollment: 2,336. Faculty: 223 (205 full-time, 18 part-time). Student-undergrad faculty ratio is 10:1. 4,757 applied, 50% were admitted. 49% from top 10% of their high school class, 90% from top quarter, 100% from top half. 13 National Merit Scholars, 21 class presidents, 91 valedictorians, 131 student government officers. Full-time: 2,305 students, 58% women, 42% men. Part-time: 31 students, 65% women, 35% men. Students come from 51 states and territories, 36 other countries, 73% from out-of-state. 0.2% American Indian or Alaska Native, non-Hispanic/Latino; 7% Hispanic/Latino; 6% African American, non-Hispanic/Latino; 3% Asian, non-Hispanic/Latino; 0.04% Native Hawaiian or other Pacific Islander, non-Hispanic/Latino; 7% international. 0% 25 or older, 98% live on campus, 1% transferred in. Retention: 89% of full-time freshmen returned the following year. Academic areas with the most degrees conferred: social sciences; biological/life sciences; communication/journalism. Calendar: semesters plus optional May term. Services for LD students, advanced placement, self-designed majors, honors program, independent study, double major, part-time degree program, internships. Off campus study at American University, Great Lakes Colleges Association, Marine Science Consortium. Study abroad program. ROTC: Army (c).
Entrance Requirements: Options: early admission, early decision, deferred admission. Required: essay, high school transcript, 2 recommendations. Recommended: interview. Required for some: SAT or ACT. Entrance: very difficult. Application deadlines: 1/15, 11/15 for early decision plan 1, 1/15 for early decision plan 2. Notification: 4/1, 1/1 for early decision. SAT Reasoning Test deadline: 2/1. Transfer credits accepted: Yes. Early decision applicants: 164. Early decision applicants admitted: 136.
Costs Per Year: Application fee: $40. Comprehensive fee: $52,640 includes full-time tuition ($41,380), mandatory fees ($900), and college room and board ($10,360). College room only: $5700. Room and board charges vary according to board plan and housing facility. Part-time tuition: $1290 per credit. Part-time mandatory fees: $660 per term. Part-time tuition and fees vary according to course load.
Collegiate Environment: Orientation program. Drama-theater group, choral group, student-run newspaper, radio station. Social organizations: 150 open to all; national fraternities, national sororities. Most popular organizations: Community Association, Black Student Union, International Student Association, Student Activities Committee. Major annual events: All-Campus Gala, Academic Awards Convocation, Community Fair and Picnic on registration day. Student services: health clinic, personal-psychological counseling, women's center. Campus security: 24-hour emergency response devices and patrols, student patrols, late night transport-escort service, controlled dormitory access, security lighting, escort service. 2,174 college housing spaces available; 2,092 were occupied in 2012-13. Freshmen guaranteed college housing. On-campus residence required through senior year. Options: coed, men-only, women-only housing available. William Howard Doane Library with 808,820 books, 7,011 microform titles, 900 serials, 28,136 audiovisual materials, an OPAC, and a Web page. Operations spending for the previous fiscal year: $3.1 million.
Community Environment: Of interest are the many beautiful homes in Granville. The town was founded by settlers from the Massachusetts town of the same name in 1805. Granville is a delightful bit of New England tucked in the rolling hills of Central Ohio.

■ **DEVRY UNIVERSITY (COLUMBUS)**
1350 Alum Creek Dr.
Columbus, OH 43209-2705
Tel: (614)253-7291; Free: 866-338-7941
Web Site: www.devry.edu/
Description: Proprietary, comprehensive, coed. Part of DeVry University. Awards associate, bachelor's, and master's degrees. Founded 1952. Setting: urban campus. Total enrollment: 2,476. Faculty: 107 (36 full-time, 71 part-time). Student-undergrad faculty ratio is 23:1. Full-time: 789 students, 40% women, 60% men. Part-time: 1,409 students, 50% women, 50% men. 8% from out-of-state. 1% American Indian or Alaska Native, non-Hispanic/Latino; 2% Hispanic/Latino; 17% African American, non-Hispanic/Latino; 1% Asian, non-Hispanic/Latino; 0.05% Native Hawaiian or other Pacific Islander, non-Hispanic/Latino; 0.4% international. 69% 25 or older, 19% transferred in. Academic areas with the most degrees conferred: business/marketing; computer and information sciences; engineering technologies. Calendar: semesters. Part-time degree program, adult/continuing education programs. ROTC: Army.
Entrance Requirements: Required: high school transcript, interview. Entrance: minimally difficult. Application deadline: Rolling. Notification: continuous.
Costs Per Year: Application fee: $40. Tuition: $16,076 full-time, $609 per credit hour part-time. Mandatory fees: $80 full-time.
Collegiate Environment: Orientation program. College housing not available.

■ **DEVRY UNIVERSITY - COLUMBUS NORTH (COLUMBUS)**
8800 Lyra Dr.
Columbus, OH 43240
Tel: (614)854-7500; Free: 866-338-7941
Web Site: www.devry.edu/
Description: Proprietary, comprehensive, coed. Awards bachelor's and master's degrees.

■ **DEVRY UNIVERSITY (SEVEN HILLS)**
The Genesis Bldg.
6000 Lombardo Ctr., Ste. 200
Seven Hills, OH 44131
Tel: (216)328-8754; Free: 866-338-7941
Fax: (216)328-8764
Web Site: www.devry.edu/
Description: Proprietary, comprehensive, coed. Awards associate, bachelor's, and master's degrees. Calendar: semesters.

■ **EASTERN GATEWAY COMMUNITY COLLEGE**
4000 Sunset Blvd.
Steubenville, OH 43952-3598
Tel: (740)264-5591; Free: 800-68-COLLEGE
Fax: (740)266-2706
E-mail: kltaylor@egcc.edu
Web Site: www.egcc.edu/
Description: State and locally supported, 2-year, coed. Part of Ohio Board of Regents. Awards certificates, transfer associate, and terminal associate degrees. Founded 1966. Setting: 83-acre small town campus with easy access to Pittsburgh. Total enrollment: 2,209. Student-undergrad faculty ratio is 16:1. 1,400 applied, 100% were admitted. Full-time: 1,219 students, 58% women, 42% men. Part-time: 990 students, 63% women, 37% men. 10% from out-of-state. 26% 25 or older. Core. Calendar: semesters. Academic remediation for entering students, services for LD students, accelerated degree program, distance learning, double major, summer session for credit, part-time degree program, adult/continuing education programs, co-op programs. Off campus study at members of the Southeastern Ohio Technical Education Consortium.
Entrance Requirements: Open admission. Options: electronic application, early admission, deferred admission. Required for some: high school transcript, SAT or ACT. Entrance: noncompetitive. Notification: continuous, continuous for nonresidents. Transfer credits accepted: Yes.
Collegiate Environment: Orientation program. Most popular organizations: Student Senate, Phi Theta Kappa. Campus security: 24-hour emergency response devices, day and evening security. Eastern Gateway Community College Library with an OPAC.

■ **EDISON COMMUNITY COLLEGE**
1973 Edison Dr.
Piqua, OH 45356-9253

Tel: (937)778-8600; Free: 800-922-3722
Fax: (937)778-1920
E-mail: vbogart@edisonohio.edu
Web Site: www.edisonohio.edu/
Description: State-supported, 2-year, coed. Part of Ohio Board of Regents' University System of Ohio. Awards certificates, transfer associate, and terminal associate degrees. Founded 1973. Setting: 130-acre small town campus with easy access to Dayton, Columbus, Cincinnati. Endowment: $1.5 million. Educational spending for the previous fiscal year: $3584 per student. Total enrollment: 3,171. Faculty: 221 (49 full-time, 172 part-time). Student-undergrad faculty ratio is 16:1. 633 applied, 100% were admitted. 3% from top 10% of their high school class, 16% from top quarter, 46% from top half. Full-time: 1,036 students, 60% women, 40% men. Part-time: 2,132 students, 67% women, 33% men. Students come from 8 states and territories, 4 other countries, 1% from out-of-state. 0.3% American Indian or Alaska Native, non-Hispanic/Latino; 1% Hispanic/Latino; 3% African American, non-Hispanic/Latino; 1% Asian, non-Hispanic/Latino; 0.04% Native Hawaiian or other Pacific Islander, non-Hispanic/Latino; 0.2% international. 54% 25 or older, 4% transferred in. Retention: 52% of full-time freshmen returned the following year. Core. Calendar: semesters. Academic remediation for entering students, ESL program, services for LD students, advanced placement, accelerated degree program, self-designed majors, honors program, independent study, distance learning, double major, summer session for credit, part-time degree program, adult/continuing education programs, internships. Off campus study at Southwestern Ohio Council for Higher Education.
Entrance Requirements: Open admission except for nursing, medical technology, medical assisting, phlebotomy, physical therapy assisting, social service and early childhood education programs. Option: electronic application. Required: high school transcript, ACT COMPASS. Entrance: noncompetitive. Application deadlines: Rolling, Rolling for nonresidents. Transfer credits accepted: Yes.
Costs Per Year: Application fee: $20. One-time mandatory fee: $20. State resident tuition: $4019 full-time, $133.96 per credit hour part-time. Nonresident tuition: $7429 full-time, $247.62 per credit hour part-time. Mandatory fees: $15 full-time. Full-time tuition and fees vary according to course load, program, and reciprocity agreements. Part-time tuition varies according to course load, program, and reciprocity agreements.
Collegiate Environment: Orientation program. Drama-theater group. Social organizations: 9 open to all. Most popular organizations: Campus Crusade for Christ, Student Ambassadors, Edison Stagelight Players, Writers Club, Edison Photo Society. Student services: health clinic, personal-psychological counseling. Campus security: late night transport-escort service, 18-hour patrols by trained security personnel. College housing not available. Edison Community College Library with 27,433 books, 86,834 microform titles, 75,282 serials, 2,608 audiovisual materials, an OPAC, and a Web page. Operations spending for the previous fiscal year: $414,057. 620 computers available on campus for general student use. Computer purchase/lease plans available. A campuswide network can be accessed from off-campus. Students can access the following: online class registration. Staffed computer lab on campus provides training in use of computers, software, and the Internet.
Community Environment: Located in Piqua, Ohio, Edison State Community College serves Darke, Miami, Shelby, and neighboring counties in west-central Ohio. The region, made up of small-sized and medium-sized towns, has an excellent balance among agricultural, industrial and residential areas.

■ **ETI TECHNICAL COLLEGE OF NILES**
2076 Youngstown-Warren Rd.
Niles, OH 44446-4398
Tel: (330)652-9919
Fax: (330)652-4399
E-mail: dianemarsteller@eticollege.edu
Web Site: eticollege.edu/
Description: Proprietary, 2-year, coed. Awards diplomas and terminal associate degrees. Founded 1989. Setting: 1-acre small town campus with easy access to Cleveland, Pittsburgh. Total enrollment: 212. Faculty: 23 (8 full-time, 15 part-time). Student-undergrad faculty ratio is 7:1. 40 applied, 85% were admitted. 5% from top 10% of their high school class, 10% from top quarter, 50% from top half. Full-time: 143 students, 75% women, 25% men. Part-time: 69 students, 52% women, 48% men. Students come from 2 states and territories, 10% from out-of-state. 45% 25 or older, 8% transferred in. Retention: 0% of full-time freshmen returned the following year. Core.

Calendar: semesters. Academic remediation for entering students, services for LD students, double major, part-time degree program, adult/continuing education programs, internships.

Entrance Requirements: Options: early admission, deferred admission. Required: high school transcript, interview. Recommended: SAT, ACT. Entrance: moderately difficult. Application deadline: Rolling. Notification: continuous. Transfer credits accepted: Yes.

Costs Per Year: Application fee: $50. Tuition: $7854 full-time, $281 per credit part-time. Mandatory fees: $300 full-time, $400 per year part-time. Full-time tuition and fees vary according to course load and program. Part-time tuition and fees vary according to course load and program.

Collegiate Environment: Orientation program. Student-run newspaper. Social organizations: 1 open to all. Most popular organization: student government. Major annual events: Christmas Party, Red Cross Blood Bank, Constitution Day. Campus security: 24-hour emergency response devices. Main Library plus 3 others with 3,000 books, 20 serials, and a Web page. 100 computers available on campus for general student use. Staffed computer lab on campus provides training in use of computers, software, and the Internet.

■ FORTIS COLLEGE (CENTERVILLE)

555 E Alex Bell Rd.
Centerville, OH 45459
Tel: (937)433-3410; Free: 855-4-FORTIS
Fax: (937)435-6516
E-mail: twallace@retstechcenter.com
Web Site: www.fortis.edu/
Description: Proprietary, 2-year, coed. Awards diplomas, transfer associate, and terminal associate degrees. Founded 1953. Setting: 4-acre suburban campus with easy access to Dayton. Endowment: $893. Educational spending for the previous fiscal year: $5000 per student. Total enrollment: 533. Faculty: 122 (41 full-time, 81 part-time). Student-undergrad faculty ratio is 18:1. Full-time: 533 students, 73% women, 27% men. Students come from 2 states and territories, 1% from out-of-state. 47% 25 or older, 1% transferred in. Core. Calendar: semesters. Advanced placement, summer session for credit, internships.

Entrance Requirements: Options: early admission, deferred admission. Required: high school transcript, interview. Entrance: noncompetitive. Application deadline: Rolling.

Collegiate Environment: Orientation program. Campus security: 24-hour emergency response devices. RETS Library with 2,200 books, 27 serials, and 66 audiovisual materials. Operations spending for the previous fiscal year: $11,900. 220 computers available on campus for general student use. A campuswide network can be accessed. Staffed computer lab on campus provides training in use of computers, software, and the Internet.

■ FORTIS COLLEGE (CUYAHOGA FALLS)

2545 Bailey Rd.
Cuyahoga Falls, OH 44221
Tel: (330)923-9959
Fax: (330)923-0886
Web Site: www.fortis.edu/
Description: Proprietary, 2-year, coed. Awards terminal associate degrees. Total enrollment: 741. Student-undergrad faculty ratio is 13:1. 0% from out-of-state. 57% 25 or older.
Entrance Requirements: Entrance: noncompetitive.

■ FORTIS COLLEGE (RAVENNA)

653 Enterprise Pky.
Ravenna, OH 44266
Tel: (330)297-7319; Free: 855-4-FORTIS
Fax: (330)297-7315
Web Site: www.fortis.edu/
Description: Independent, 2-year, coed. Awards certificates and terminal associate degrees. Total enrollment: 482. 168 applied. 57% 25 or older.

■ FRANCISCAN UNIVERSITY OF STEUBENVILLE

1235 University Blvd.
Steubenville, OH 43952-1763
Tel: (740)283-3771; Free: 800-783-6220
Fax: (740)283-6472
E-mail: admissions@franciscan.edu
Web Site: www.franciscan.edu/
Description: Independent Roman Catholic, comprehensive, coed. Awards associate, bachelor's, and master's degrees. Founded 1946. Setting: suburban campus. Total enrollment: 2,823. Faculty: 223 (115 full-time, 108 part-time). Student-undergrad faculty ratio is 15:1. 1,739 applied, 76% were admitted. 29% from top 10% of their high school class, 60% from top quarter, 86% from top half. Full-time: 1,979 students, 62% women, 38% men. Part-time: 152 students, 52% women, 48% men. 79% from out-of-state. 0.2% American Indian or Alaska Native, non-Hispanic/Latino; 8% Hispanic/Latino; 0.4% African American, non-Hispanic/Latino; 1% Asian, non-Hispanic/Latino; 0.1% Native Hawaiian or other Pacific Islander, non-Hispanic/Latino; 1% international. 6% 25 or older, 74% live on campus, 8% transferred in. Retention: 85% of full-time freshmen returned the following year. Academic areas with the most degrees conferred: theology and religious vocations; health professions and related sciences; business/marketing. Calendar: semesters. Part-time degree program, adult/continuing education programs. ROTC: Army, Air Force (c).

Entrance Requirements: Options: deferred admission, international baccalaureate accepted. Required: essay, high school transcript, minimum 2.4 high school GPA, SAT or ACT. Recommended: interview. Required for some: 3 recommendations. Entrance: moderately difficult. Application deadline: Rolling. Notification: continuous. SAT Reasoning Test deadline: 5/1. Applicants placed on waiting list: 74. Wait-listed applicants offered admission: 19.

Costs Per Year: Application fee: $20. Comprehensive fee: $29,580 includes full-time tuition ($21,740), mandatory fees ($440), and college room and board ($7400). College room only: $4280. Room and board charges vary according to board plan. Part-time tuition: $725 per credit hour. Part-time tuition varies according to class time and course load.

Collegiate Environment: Orientation program. Campus security: 24-hour emergency response devices and patrols, student patrols, late night transport-escort service. John Paul II Library with 68 microform titles.

Community Environment: The county seat of Jefferson County, Steubenville is a city in eastern Ohio situated on the Ohio River. An unlimited supply of both deep-mine and strip coal is available in the Steubenville district. Because of the coal and the Ohio River, more steam electricity is generated within a 40-mile radius of the city than in any other area in the world. Steel, iron, and paper are some of the products of industries here.

■ FRANKLIN UNIVERSITY

201 S Grant Ave.
Columbus, OH 43215-5399
Tel: (614)797-4700; Free: 877-341-6300
Fax: (614)224-8027
E-mail: hull@franklin.edu
Web Site: www.franklin.edu/
Description: Independent, comprehensive, coed. Awards associate, bachelor's, and master's degrees. Founded 1902. Setting: 14-acre urban campus. Endowment: $66.8 million. Educational spending for the previous fiscal year: $2944 per student. Total enrollment: 6,885. Faculty: 843 (63 full-time, 780 part-time). Student-undergrad faculty ratio is 12:1. 1,016 applied, 74% were admitted. Full-time: 1,973 students, 59% women, 41% men. Part-time: 3,865 students, 57% women, 43% men. Students come from 48 states and territories, 85 other countries, 21% from out-of-state. 0.3% American Indian or Alaska Native, non-Hispanic/Latino; 3% Hispanic/Latino; 23% African American, non-Hispanic/Latino; 3% Asian, non-Hispanic/Latino; 0.1% Native Hawaiian or other Pacific Islander, non-Hispanic/Latino; 0.4% international. 81% 25 or older, 21% transferred in. Retention: 30% of full-time freshmen returned the following year. Academic areas with the most degrees conferred: business/marketing; computer and information sciences; health professions and related sciences. Core. Calendar: trimesters. Academic remediation for entering students, ESL program, services for LD students, advanced placement, accelerated degree program, self-designed majors, independent study, distance learning, double major, summer session for credit, part-time degree program, adult/continuing education programs, co-op programs and internships, graduate courses open to undergrads. Off campus study at Franklin University has (2 + 2) and (3 + 1) articulation agreements with over 250 community colleges across the United States. Study abroad program. ROTC: Army (c), Air Force (c).

Entrance Requirements: Open admission Certain programs such as Healthcare Information Management and Nursing have specific admissions requirements that other programs do not have. Options: electronic application, deferred admission, international baccalaureate accepted. Required for some: high school transcript. Entrance: noncompetitive. Application deadline: Rolling. Notification: continuous. Transfer credits accepted: Yes.

Costs Per Year: Application fee: $0. One-time mandatory fee: $25. Tuition:

$12,450 full-time, $415 per credit hour part-time. Full-time tuition varies according to degree level and program. Part-time tuition varies according to degree level and program.

Collegiate Environment: Orientation program. Social organizations: Honor Societies, Major/Industry Groups. Campus security: 24-hour emergency response devices, late night transport-escort service, video monitoring capabilities of all public/customer facing locations. College housing not available. The Franklin University Nationwide Library with 102,000 books, an OPAC, and a Web page. Operations spending for the previous fiscal year: $779,779. 500 computers available on campus for general student use. A campuswide network can be accessed from off-campus. Students can access the following: online class registration. Staffed computer lab on campus provides training in use of computers, software, and the Internet.

Community Environment: See Ohio State University - Columbus Campus.

■ GALLIPOLIS CAREER COLLEGE

1176 Jackson Pke.
Ste. 312
Gallipolis, OH 45631
Tel: (740)446-4367; Free: 800-214-0452
Fax: (740)446-4124
E-mail: admissions@gallipoliscareercollege.com
Web Site: www.gallipoliscareercollege.com/

Description: Independent, 2-year, coed. Awards certificates, diplomas, and terminal associate degrees. Founded 1962. Setting: small town campus. Total enrollment: 154. Faculty: 16 (2 full-time, 14 part-time). Student-undergrad faculty ratio is 22:1. Full-time: 145 students, 83% women, 17% men. Part-time: 9 students, 89% women, 11% men. Students come from 2 states and territories, 13% from out-of-state. Core. Academic remediation for entering students, independent study, double major, summer session for credit, part-time degree program, adult/continuing education programs, internships.

Entrance Requirements: Required: high school transcript, interview, Wonderlic aptitude test. Application deadline: Rolling.

Collegiate Environment: Orientation program. Gallipolis Career College Library with 94 audiovisual materials. 28 computers available on campus for general student use. A campuswide network can be accessed. Staffed computer lab on campus.

■ GOD'S BIBLE SCHOOL AND COLLEGE

1810 Young St.
Cincinnati, OH 45202-6838
Tel: (513)721-7944; Free: 800-486-4637
Fax: (513)721-3971
E-mail: sbuckland@gbs.edu
Web Site: www.gbs.edu/

Description: Independent interdenominational, 4-year, coed. Awards associate and bachelor's degrees. Founded 1900. Setting: 14-acre urban campus. Total enrollment: 292. Student-undergrad faculty ratio is 12:1. 93 applied, 90% were admitted. 64% from out-of-state. 27% 25 or older. Retention: 69% of full-time freshmen returned the following year. Core. Calendar: semesters. Academic remediation for entering students, advanced placement, independent study, summer session for credit, part-time degree program, internships.

Entrance Requirements: Required: high school transcript, 3 recommendations, interview, SAT or ACT. Recommended: SAT. Application deadline: 8/18.

Collegiate Environment: Orientation program. Choral group, student-run newspaper. Student services: health clinic. Campus security: 24-hour patrols.

■ GOOD SAMARITAN COLLEGE OF NURSING AND HEALTH SCIENCE

375 Dixmyth Ave.
Cincinnati, OH 45220
Tel: (513)862-2743
Fax: (513)862-3572
Web Site: www.gscollege.edu/

Description: Proprietary, 2-year, coed. Awards terminal associate degrees. Setting: urban campus with easy access to Cincinnati. Total enrollment: 313. Student-undergrad faculty ratio is 7:1. 31 applied, 71% were admitted. 16% from top 10% of their high school class, 34% from top quarter, 50% from top

half. Full-time: 131 students, 87% women, 13% men. Part-time: 182 students, 89% women, 11% men. 7% from out-of-state. 46% 25 or older, 20% transferred in. Core.

Entrance Requirements: Option: electronic application. Required: high school transcript, minimum 2.5 high school GPA, Required average GPA 2.25 in these high school courses: English, Math (Algebra required), Science (Chemistry required), and Social Studies, SAT or ACT. Entrance: minimally difficult. Transfer credits accepted: Yes.

■ HARRISON COLLEGE

3880 Jackpot Rd.
Grove City, OH 43123
Tel: (614)539-8800; Free: 888-544-4422
E-mail: Admissions@harrison.edu
Web Site: www.harrison.edu/

Description: Proprietary, 4-year, coed. Part of This campus is part of Harrison College, which has several campuses in Indiana, one in North Carolina, and a fully online division. Awards associate and bachelor's degrees. Setting: suburban campus with easy access to Columbus, OH. Total enrollment: 201. Faculty: 12 (3 full-time, 9 part-time). Student-undergrad faculty ratio is 10:1. 35 applied, 100% were admitted. Full-time: 142 students, 80% women, 20% men. Part-time: 59 students, 81% women, 19% men. Students come from 3 states and territories, 1% from out-of-state. 0.5% American Indian or Alaska Native, non-Hispanic/Latino; 0.5% Hispanic/Latino; 11% African American, non-Hispanic/Latino; 0.5% Asian, non-Hispanic/Latino; 0% Native Hawaiian or other Pacific Islander, non-Hispanic/Latino; 0% international. 62% 25 or older, 6% transferred in. Retention: 42% of full-time freshmen returned the following year. Advanced placement, distance learning, double major, summer session for credit, part-time degree program, adult/continuing education programs, co-op programs and internships. Off campus study.

Entrance Requirements: Option: electronic application. Required: high school transcript, interview, Wonderlic Scholastic Level Exam (SLE). Entrance: moderately difficult. Application deadlines: Rolling, Rolling for nonresidents. Notification: continuous, continuous for nonresidents. Transfer credits accepted: Yes.

Collegiate Environment: Orientation program. College housing not available.

■ HEIDELBERG UNIVERSITY

310 E Market St.
Tiffin, OH 44883-2462
Tel: (419)448-2000; Free: 800-434-3352
Fax: (419)448-2334
E-mail: jmiller7@heidelberg.edu
Web Site: www.heidelberg.edu/

Description: Independent, comprehensive, coed, affiliated with United Church of Christ. Awards bachelor's and master's degrees. Founded 1850. Setting: 115-acre small town campus with easy access to Cleveland, Columbus, Detroit. Endowment: $32.1 million. Research spending for the previous fiscal year: $875,914. Educational spending for the previous fiscal year: $7111 per student. Total enrollment: 1,317. Faculty: 150 (63 full-time, 87 part-time). Student-undergrad faculty ratio is 13:1. 2,043 applied, 64% were admitted. 12% from top 10% of their high school class, 32% from top quarter, 66% from top half. Full-time: 1,033 students, 48% women, 52% men. Part-time: 80 students, 64% women, 36% men. Students come from 25 states and territories, 12 other countries, 15% from out-of-state. 0.2% American Indian or Alaska Native, non-Hispanic/Latino; 2% Hispanic/Latino; 9% African American, non-Hispanic/Latino; 0.4% Asian, non-Hispanic/Latino; 2% international. 2% 25 or older, 85% live on campus, 4% transferred in. Retention: 65% of full-time freshmen returned the following year. Academic areas with the most degrees conferred: business/marketing; parks and recreation; social sciences. Core. Calendar: semesters. Academic remediation for entering students, ESL program, services for LD students, advanced placement, accelerated degree program, self-designed majors, honors program, independent study, double major, summer session for credit, part-time degree program, adult/continuing education programs, internships, graduate courses open to undergrads. Off campus study at members of the East Central College Consortium. Study abroad program. ROTC: Army (c), Air Force (c).

Entrance Requirements: Options: electronic application, deferred admission, international baccalaureate accepted. Required: high school transcript, minimum 2.5 high school GPA, SAT or ACT. Recommended: essay, interview. Entrance: moderately difficult. Application deadlines: 8/15, 8/15 for nonresidents. Notification: 8/15. SAT Reasoning Test deadline: 8/15. SAT Subject Test deadline: 8/15. Transfer credits accepted: Yes.

Costs Per Year: Application fee: $25. Comprehensive fee: $33,556 includes full-time tuition ($24,000), mandatory fees ($582), and college room and board ($8974). College room only: $4248. Full-time tuition and fees vary according to course load, degree level, and location. Room and board charges vary according to housing facility and location.

Collegiate Environment: Orientation program. Drama-theater group, choral group, student-run newspaper, radio station. Social organizations: 75 open to all; local fraternities, local sororities; 18% of eligible men and 24% of eligible women are members. Most popular organizations: Alpha Phi Omega, BERG Events Council, Student Senate, Campus Fellowship, Black Student Union/World Student Union. Major annual events: Battle of the Bands, Greek Sing, Student Research Conference. Student services: health clinic, personal-psychological counseling. Campus security: 24-hour emergency response devices and patrols, student patrols, late night transport-escort service, controlled dormitory access. Operations spending for the previous fiscal year: $240,134. 125 computers available on campus for general student use. A campuswide network can be accessed from student residence rooms and from off campus. Students can access the following: online class registration. Staffed computer lab on campus provides training in use of computers, software, and the Internet.

Community Environment: The 110-acre campus is located in Tiffin, Ohio, at the intersection of U.S. route 224 and Ohio Route 53, 50 miles southeast of Toledo and 92 miles west of Cleveland. Amtrack stops in Sandusky, Toledo, Lima and Crestline. Churches, civic, service and social service agencies, and private enterprises offer many opportunities for volunteer and class-related experiences. Places of worship are available on campus and in the immediate community for Protestants and Catholics, and within 23 miles for Jewish students.

■ **HERZING UNIVERSITY**

5212 Hill Ave.
Toledo, OH 43615
Tel: (419)776-0300; Free: 800-596-0724
Fax: (419)776-0315
Web Site: www.herzing.edu/toledo

Description: Proprietary, primarily 2-year, coed. Awards diplomas, terminal associate, and bachelor's degrees.

■ **HIRAM COLLEGE**

Box 67
Hiram, OH 44234-0067
Tel: (330)569-3211; Free: 800-362-5280
Fax: (330)569-5944
E-mail: admission@hiram.edu
Web Site: www.hiram.edu/

Description: Independent, comprehensive, coed, affiliated with Christian Church (Disciples of Christ). Awards bachelor's and master's degrees. Founded 1850. Setting: 110-acre rural campus with easy access to Cleveland. Endowment: $60.8 million. Research spending for the previous fiscal year: $105,458. Educational spending for the previous fiscal year: $7848 per student. Total enrollment: 1,324. Faculty: 139 (79 full-time, 60 part-time). Student-undergrad faculty ratio is 13:1. 2,378 applied, 62% were admitted. 17% from top 10% of their high school class, 43% from top quarter, 69% from top half. 11 valedictorians. Full-time: 1,164 students, 56% women, 44% men. Part-time: 149 students, 62% women, 38% men. Students come from 39 states and territories, 25 other countries, 14% from out-of-state. 0.2% American Indian or Alaska Native, non-Hispanic/Latino; 3% Hispanic/Latino; 12% African American, non-Hispanic/Latino; 1% Asian, non-Hispanic/Latino; 0.1% Native Hawaiian or other Pacific Islander, non-Hispanic/Latino; 6% international. 3% 25 or older, 82% live on campus, 6% transferred in. Retention: 75% of full-time freshmen returned the following year. Academic areas with the most degrees conferred: business/marketing; social sciences; biological/life sciences. Core. Calendar: semesters. ESL program, services for LD students, advanced placement, accelerated degree program, self-designed majors, independent study, double major, summer session for credit, part-time degree program, adult/continuing education programs, internships. Off campus study. Study abroad program. ROTC: Army (c).

Entrance Requirements: Options: electronic application, deferred admission, international baccalaureate accepted. Required: high school transcript, SAT or ACT. Recommended: essay, minimum 2.75 high school GPA, 1 recommendation, interview. Entrance: moderately difficult. Application

deadlines: Rolling, Rolling for nonresidents. Notification: continuous, continuous for nonresidents. SAT Reasoning Test deadline: 7/1. Transfer credits accepted: Yes.

Collegiate Environment: Orientation program. Drama-theater group, choral group, marching band, student-run newspaper, radio station. Social organizations: 90 open to all; local fraternities, local sororities; 8% of eligible men and 8% of eligible women are members. Most popular organizations: Student Senate, African American Students United, Outdoors Club, Resident Student Association, Christian Outreach. Major annual events: Homecoming, Springfest, Campus Days. Student services: health clinic, personal-psychological counseling. Campus security: 24-hour emergency response devices and patrols, late night transport-escort service, controlled dormitory access. 1,040 college housing spaces available; 870 were occupied in 2012-13. Freshmen guaranteed college housing. On-campus residence required through junior year. Options: coed, women-only housing available. Hiram College Library with 506,792 books, 131,990 microform titles, 8,890 serials, 22,786 audiovisual materials, an OPAC, and a Web page. Operations spending for the previous fiscal year: $821,359. 100 computers available on campus for general student use. Computer purchase/lease plans available. A computer is required for all students. A campuswide network can be accessed from student residence rooms and from off campus. Students can access the following: online class registration. Staffed computer lab on campus (open 24 hours a day) provides training in use of computers, software, and the Internet.

Community Environment: Located in a dairy and orchard growing area, Hiram is a rural community with numerous buildings in the Western Reserve style. This area has long been famous for the production of maple syrup. Air, bus and train transportation is available. Nearby lakes provide the facilities for boating, swimming, and fishing. Job opportunities are available mainly at the college.

■ **HOCKING COLLEGE**

3301 Hocking Pky.
Nelsonville, OH 45764-9588
Tel: (740)753-3591; Free: 877-462-5464
Fax: (740)753-7065
E-mail: hull_lyn@hocking.edu
Web Site: www.hocking.edu/

Description: State-supported, 2-year, coed. Part of Ohio Board of Regents. Awards certificates, diplomas, transfer associate, and terminal associate degrees. Founded 1968. Setting: 1,600-acre rural campus with easy access to Columbus. Endowment: $2.3 million. Educational spending for the previous fiscal year: $4084 per student. Total enrollment: 5,250. Faculty: 236 (182 full-time, 54 part-time). Students come from 28 states and territories, 3% from out-of-state. 37% 25 or older, 9% live on campus. Core. Academic remediation for entering students, ESL program, services for LD students, advanced placement, accelerated degree program, self-designed majors, distance learning, double major, summer session for credit, part-time degree program, adult/continuing education programs, co-op programs and internships. ROTC: Army (c).

Entrance Requirements: Open admission except for nursing program. Option: electronic application. Required: high school transcript. Entrance: noncompetitive. Application deadline: Rolling. Notification: continuous.

Collegiate Environment: Orientation program. Drama-theater group, choral group. Social organizations: 40 open to all. Most popular organizations: Phi Theta Kappa, Recycling Club, Unity Board, Alpha Beta Gamma, Native American Club. Major annual events: Paul Bunyan Show, Winterfest. Student services: health clinic, personal-psychological counseling, women's center. Campus security: 24-hour emergency response devices and patrols, student patrols, late night transport-escort service. Hocking College Learning Resources Center plus 1 other with 19,663 books, 38,766 microform titles, 223 serials, 8,327 audiovisual materials, an OPAC, and a Web page. Operations spending for the previous fiscal year: $523,820. 280 computers available on campus for general student use. A campuswide network can be accessed from student residence rooms and from off campus. Staffed computer lab on campus.

Community Environment: Nelsonville is a small community on the Hocking River. It is easily accessible from all points north and south in Ohio via US route 33. It is 65 miles from Columbus and is serviced by Greyhound bus lines.

■ **HONDROS COLLEGE**

4140 Executive Pky.
Westerville, OH 43081-3855

Tel: (614)508-7277; Free: 888-HONDROS
Fax: (614)508-7279
Web Site: www.hondros.edu/
Description: Proprietary, 2-year, coed. Awards certificates, transfer associate, and terminal associate degrees. Founded 1981. Total enrollment: 255. 123 applied. 63% 25 or older.
Entrance Requirements: Open admission. Entrance: noncompetitive.
Collegiate Environment: Campus security: 24-hour emergency response devices.

■ INTERNATIONAL COLLEGE OF BROADCASTING
6 S Smithville Rd.
Dayton, OH 45431-1833
Tel: (937)258-8251; Free: 800-517-7284
E-mail: admissions@icbcollege.com
Web Site: www.icbcollege.com/
Description: Private, 2-year, coed. Awards diplomas, transfer associate, and terminal associate degrees. Founded 1968. Setting: 1-acre urban campus with easy access to Dayton. Total enrollment: 77. Faculty: 14 (6 full-time, 8 part-time). 35% 25 or older. Core. Calendar: semesters. Academic remediation for entering students, services for LD students, internships.
Entrance Requirements: Open admission. Option: early admission. Required: high school transcript, interview, Passing Wonderlic Test, Wonderlic aptitude test. Transfer credits accepted: Yes.
Costs Per Year: Application fee: $100. Tuition: $29,120 full-time. Tuition guaranteed not to increase for student's term of enrollment.
Collegiate Environment: Orientation program. Student-run radio station. College housing not available.

■ ITT TECHNICAL INSTITUTE (AKRON)
3428 W Market St.
Akron, OH 44333
Tel: (330)865-8600; Free: 877-818-0154
Web Site: www.itt-tech.edu/
Description: Proprietary, primarily 2-year, coed. Awards terminal associate and bachelor's degrees.
Entrance Requirements: Entrance: minimally difficult.

■ ITT TECHNICAL INSTITUTE (COLUMBUS)
4717 Hilton Corporate Dr.
Columbus, OH 43232
Tel: (614)868-2000; Free: 877-233-8864
Web Site: www.itt-tech.edu/
Description: Proprietary, primarily 2-year, coed. Part of ITT Educational Services, Inc. Awards terminal associate and bachelor's degrees.
Entrance Requirements: Entrance: minimally difficult.

■ ITT TECHNICAL INSTITUTE (DAYTON)
3325 Stop 8 Rd.
Dayton, OH 45414-3425
Tel: (937)264-7700; Free: 800-568-3241
Web Site: www.itt-tech.edu/
Description: Proprietary, primarily 2-year, coed. Part of ITT Educational Services, Inc. Awards terminal associate and bachelor's degrees. Founded 1935. Setting: suburban campus.
Entrance Requirements: Entrance: minimally difficult.

■ ITT TECHNICAL INSTITUTE (HILLIARD)
3781 Park Mill Run Dr.
Hilliard, OH 43026
Tel: (614)771-4888; Free: 888-483-4888
Fax: (614)921-4179
Web Site: www.itt-tech.edu/
Description: Proprietary, primarily 2-year, coed. Part of ITT Educational Services, Inc. Awards terminal associate and bachelor's degrees. Founded 2003.
Entrance Requirements: Entrance: minimally difficult.

■ ITT TECHNICAL INSTITUTE (MAUMEE)
1656 Henthorne Dr.
Ste. B
Maumee, OH 43537
Tel: (419)861-6500; Free: 877-205-4639
Web Site: www.itt-tech.edu/

Description: Proprietary, primarily 2-year, coed. Awards terminal associate and bachelor's degrees.

■ ITT TECHNICAL INSTITUTE (NORWOOD)
4750 Wesley Ave.
Norwood, OH 45212
Tel: (513)531-8300; Free: 800-314-8324
Web Site: www.itt-tech.edu/
Description: Proprietary, primarily 2-year, coed. Part of ITT Educational Services, Inc. Awards transfer associate and bachelor's degrees. Founded 1995.
Entrance Requirements: Entrance: minimally difficult.

■ ITT TECHNICAL INSTITUTE (STRONGSVILLE)
14955 Sprague Rd.
Strongsville, OH 44136
Tel: (440)234-9091; Free: 800-331-1488
Web Site: www.itt-tech.edu/
Description: Proprietary, primarily 2-year, coed. Part of ITT Educational Services, Inc. Awards terminal associate and bachelor's degrees. Founded 1994.
Entrance Requirements: Entrance: minimally difficult.

■ ITT TECHNICAL INSTITUTE (WARRENSVILLE HEIGHTS)
4700 Richmond Rd.
Warrensville Heights, OH 44128
Tel: (216)896-6500; Free: 800-741-3494
Web Site: www.itt-tech.edu/
Description: Proprietary, primarily 2-year, coed. Awards terminal associate and bachelor's degrees. Founded 2005.
Entrance Requirements: Entrance: minimally difficult.

■ ITT TECHNICAL INSTITUTE (YOUNGSTOWN)
1030 N Meridian Rd.
Youngstown, OH 44509-4098
Tel: (330)270-1600; Free: 800-832-5001
Fax: (330)270-8333
Web Site: www.itt-tech.edu/
Description: Proprietary, primarily 2-year, coed. Part of ITT Educational Services, Inc. Awards terminal associate and bachelor's degrees. Founded 1967. Setting: suburban campus.
Entrance Requirements: Entrance: minimally difficult.

■ JAMES A. RHODES STATE COLLEGE
4240 Campus Dr.
Lima, OH 45804-3597
Tel: (419)995-8000
Fax: (419)995-8098
E-mail: cox.t@rhodesstate.edu
Web Site: www.rhodesstate.edu/
Description: State-supported, 2-year, coed. Awards certificates, transfer associate, and terminal associate degrees. Founded 1971. Setting: 565-acre small town campus. Endowment: $1.7 million. Educational spending for the previous fiscal year: $4756 per student. Total enrollment: 3,883. Faculty: 248 (104 full-time, 144 part-time). Student-undergrad faculty ratio is 15:1. 1,691 applied, 100% were admitted. Full-time: 1,548 students, 66% women, 34% men. Part-time: 2,335 students, 70% women, 30% men. Students come from 4 states and territories, 1% from out-of-state. 0.4% American Indian or Alaska Native, non-Hispanic/Latino; 2% Hispanic/Latino; 8% African American, non-Hispanic/Latino; 1% Asian, non-Hispanic/Latino; 0.1% Native Hawaiian or other Pacific Islander, non-Hispanic/Latino; 0% international. 45% 25 or older, 7% transferred in. Retention: 55% of full-time freshmen returned the following year. Core. Academic remediation for entering students, services for LD students, advanced placement, self-designed majors, independent study, distance learning, summer session for credit, part-time degree program, adult/continuing education programs, co-op programs and internships. Off campus study.
Entrance Requirements: Open admission except for allied health programs. Options: electronic application, early admission, deferred admission. Required: high school transcript. Entrance: noncompetitive. Application deadline: Rolling. Notification: continuous until 8/15.
Collegiate Environment: Orientation program. Drama-theater group, choral group, student-run newspaper. Student services: personal-psychological counseling. Campus security: 24-hour emergency response devices and

patrols, student patrols, late night transport-escort service. College housing not available. Rhodes State/Ohio State Library with 80,000 books and an OPAC.

Community Environment: Lima, population 38,608, is an industrial city and the county seat of Allen County. It is 68 miles SSW of Toledo. Its major industries include motor vehicles, steel castings, aircraft parts, machine tools, and building machinery. It is also the center of a diversified agricultural region.

■ **JOHN CARROLL UNIVERSITY**
One John Carroll Blvd.
University Heights, OH 44118-4581
Tel: (216)397-1886; Free: 888-335-6800
Fax: (216)397-3098
E-mail: svitatoe@jcu.edu
Web Site: www.jcu.edu/

Description: Independent Roman Catholic (Jesuit), comprehensive, coed. Awards bachelor's and master's degrees and post-master's certificates. Founded 1886. Setting: 60-acre suburban campus with easy access to Cleveland. Research spending for the previous fiscal year: $5.6 million. Educational spending for the previous fiscal year: $8952 per student. Total enrollment: 3,583. Faculty: 366 (195 full-time, 171 part-time). Student-undergrad faculty ratio is 13:1. 3,490 applied, 81% were admitted. 22% from top 10% of their high school class, 50% from top quarter, 85% from top half. 20 National Merit Scholars, 12 valedictorians, 54 student government officers. Full-time: 2,859 students, 49% women, 51% men. Part-time: 90 students, 37% women, 63% men. Students come from 39 states and territories, 13 other countries, 30% from out-of-state. 0.1% American Indian or Alaska Native, non-Hispanic/Latino; 4% Hispanic/Latino; 4% African American, non-Hispanic/Latino; 2% Asian, non-Hispanic/Latino; 0.03% Native Hawaiian or other Pacific Islander, non-Hispanic/Latino; 2% international. 3% 25 or older, 59% live on campus, 3% transferred in. Retention: 87% of full-time freshmen returned the following year. Academic areas with the most degrees conferred: business/marketing; social sciences; psychology. Core. Calendar: semesters. Services for LD students, advanced placement, self-designed majors, honors program, independent study, double major, summer session for credit, part-time degree program, co-op programs and internships, graduate courses open to undergrads. Off campus study at Northeast Ohio Commission on Higher Education. Study abroad program. ROTC: Army.

Entrance Requirements: Options: electronic application, early admission, early action, deferred admission, international baccalaureate accepted. Required: essay, high school transcript, 1 recommendation, SAT or ACT. Required for some: 2 recommendations, interview. Entrance: moderately difficult. Application deadlines: 2/1, 12/1 for early action. Notification: continuous, 12/20 for early action. SAT Reasoning Test deadline: 3/1. SAT Subject Test deadline: 8/1. Transfer credits accepted: Yes.

Costs Per Year: Application fee: $0. One-time mandatory fee: $325. Comprehensive fee: $44,520 includes full-time tuition ($33,330), mandatory fees ($1150), and college room and board ($10,040). Room and board charges vary according to board plan and housing facility. Part-time tuition: $1016 per credit. Part-time tuition varies according to course load.

Collegiate Environment: Orientation program. Drama-theater group, choral group, student-run newspaper, radio station. Social organizations: 98 open to all; national fraternities, national sororities; 14% of women are members. Most popular organizations: Community Outreach/Volunteer Service Organization, Student Union, Club Sports, Fraternities and Sororities, Carroll News. Major annual events: Homecoming, Streak Week, Christmas Carroll Eve. Student services: health clinic, personal-psychological counseling, women's center. Campus security: 24-hour emergency response devices and patrols, late night transport-escort service, Distinctive Student EMS program fully staffed. 1,819 college housing spaces available; 1,753 were occupied in 2012-13. Freshmen guaranteed college housing. On-campus residence required through sophomore year. Option: coed housing available. Grasselli Library with 778,287 books, 701,253 microform titles, 850 serials, 9,985 audiovisual materials, an OPAC, and a Web page. Operations spending for the previous fiscal year: $3.5 million. 411 computers available on campus for general student use. Computer purchase/lease plans available. A campuswide network can be accessed from student residence rooms and from off campus. Students can access the following: online class registration, campus portal, course management site, online financial aid and billing, online course sites, online housing selection. Staffed computer lab on campus (open 24 hours a day) provides training in use of computers, software, and the Internet.

■ **KAPLAN CAREER INSTITUTE, CLEVELAND CAMPUS**
8720 Brookpark Rd.
Brooklyn, OH 44129
Tel: (216)485-0900; Free: 800-935-1857
Web Site: cleveland.kaplancareerinstitute.com/

Description: Proprietary, 2-year, coed. Awards diplomas and terminal associate degrees.

■ **KAPLAN COLLEGE, DAYTON CAMPUS**
2800 E River Rd.
Dayton, OH 45439
Tel: (937)294-6155; Free: 800-935-1857
Fax: (937)294-2259
Web Site: dayton.kaplancollege.com/

Description: Proprietary, 2-year, coed. Awards diplomas and terminal associate degrees. Founded 1971. Setting: urban campus.

■ **KENT STATE UNIVERSITY**
PO Box 5190
Kent, OH 44242-0001
Tel: (330)672-3000; Free: 800-988-KENT
Fax: (330)672-2499
E-mail: admissions@kent.edu
Web Site: www.kent.edu/

Description: State-supported, university, coed. Part of Kent State University System. Awards associate, bachelor's, master's, and doctoral degrees and post-master's certificates. Founded 1910. Setting: 1,347-acre suburban campus with easy access to Cleveland. System endowment: $85.2 million. Research spending for the previous fiscal year: $21.5 million. Educational spending for the previous fiscal year: $6047 per student. Total enrollment: 28,172. Faculty: 1,688 (908 full-time, 780 part-time). Student-undergrad faculty ratio is 21:1. 15,970 applied, 83% were admitted. 13% from top 10% of their high school class, 37% from top quarter, 74% from top half. Full-time: 19,489 students, 58% women, 42% men. Part-time: 2,947 students, 60% women, 40% men. Students come from 50 states and territories, 64 other countries, 11% from out-of-state. 0.3% American Indian or Alaska Native, non-Hispanic/Latino; 3% Hispanic/Latino; 9% African American, non-Hispanic/Latino; 1% Asian, non-Hispanic/Latino; 0.1% Native Hawaiian or other Pacific Islander, non-Hispanic/Latino; 6% international. 15% 25 or older, 29% live on campus, 6% transferred in. Retention: 77% of full-time freshmen returned the following year. Academic areas with the most degrees conferred: business/marketing; health professions and related sciences; education. Core. Calendar: semesters. Academic remediation for entering students, ESL program, services for LD students, advanced placement, accelerated degree program, self-designed majors, freshman honors college, honors program, independent study, distance learning, double major, summer session for credit, part-time degree program, external degree program, adult/continuing education programs, co-op programs and internships, graduate courses open to undergrads. Off campus study at Cuyahoga Community College, Lorain County Community College, Lakeland Community College. Study abroad program. ROTC: Army, Air Force.

Entrance Requirements: Options: electronic application, early admission, international baccalaureate accepted. Required: high school transcript, minimum 2.5 high school GPA, SAT or ACT. Entrance: moderately difficult. Application deadline: Rolling. Notification: continuous. SAT Reasoning Test deadline: 8/1.

Costs Per Year: Application fee: $40. State resident tuition: $9672 full-time. Nonresident tuition: $17,632 full-time. Full-time tuition varies according to course load. College room and board: $9176. Room and board charges vary according to board plan and housing facility.

Collegiate Environment: Orientation program. Drama-theater group, choral group, marching band, student-run newspaper, radio station. Social organizations: 200 open to all; national fraternities, national sororities, local sororities; 7% of eligible men and 4% of eligible women are members. Most popular organizations: Commuter & Off-Campus Student Organization (COSO), Fashion Student Organization (FSO), Public Relations Students Society of America (PRSSA), Habitat for Humanity, Relay for Life. Major annual events: Back to School Blastoff, Homecoming, FlashFest. Student services: legal services, health clinic, personal-psychological counseling, women's center. Campus security: 24-hour emergency response devices and patrols, student patrols, late night transport-escort service, controlled dormitory access, campus police and fire department, electronic locks on computer labs, studios and laboratory research areas. 6,200 college housing spaces available; all were occupied in 2012-13. Freshmen guaranteed college housing. On-campus residence required through sophomore year. Options: coed, men-only, women-only housing available. Kent State University Libraries and Media Services plus 7 others with 2.3 million books, 1.3 million microform titles, 12,000 serials, 15,578 audiovisual materials, an OPAC, and a Web page. Operations spending for the previous fiscal year: $14.9 million. 2,000 computers available on campus for general student use. Computer purchase/lease plans available. A campuswide network can be accessed from student residence rooms and from off campus. Students can access the following: online class registration. Staffed computer lab on campus (open 24 hours a day) provides training in use of computers, software, and the Internet.

Community Environment: Kent, a city of some 30,000, on the banks of the Cuyahoga River, in Portage County, is situated 11 miles east of Akron, 33 miles south of Cleveland, 40 miles west of Youngstown and 28 miles north of Canton. The community provides students with many places to shop and entertain themselves and places of worship for most major denominations. Recreational activities include fishing, boating, skiing, swimming, and golf. The university is located near two major jetports, Cleveland Hopkins International and Akron-Canton.

■ KENT STATE UNIVERSITY AT ASHTABULA

3300 Lake Rd. W
Ashtabula, OH 44004-2299
Tel: (440)964-3322
Fax: (440)964-4269
E-mail: kanthon2@kent.edu
Web Site: www.ashtabula.kent.edu/

Description: State-supported, primarily 2-year, coed. Part of Kent State University System. Awards certificates, transfer associate, and bachelor's degrees (also offers some upper-level and graduate courses). Founded 1958. Setting: 120-acre small town campus with easy access to Cleveland. Total enrollment: 2,516. Faculty: 126 (53 full-time, 73 part-time). Student-undergrad faculty ratio is 22:1. 565 applied, 99% were admitted. 6% from top 10% of their high school class, 21% from top quarter, 50% from top half. Full-time: 1,268 students, 65% women, 35% men. Part-time: 1,243 students, 65% women, 35% men. Students come from 12 states and territories, 1 other country, 2% from out-of-state. 1% American Indian or Alaska Native, non-Hispanic/Latino; 3% Hispanic/Latino; 5% African American, non-Hispanic/Latino; 1% Asian, non-Hispanic/Latino; 0.04% Native Hawaiian or other Pacific Islander, non-Hispanic/Latino; 0.2% international. 57% 25 or older, 7% transferred in. Retention: 49% of full-time freshmen returned the following year. Core. Calendar: semesters. Academic remediation for entering students, services for LD students, advanced placement, self-designed majors, independent study, distance learning, double major, summer session for credit, part-time degree program, internships. Study abroad program. ROTC: Army (c), Naval (c), Air Force (c).

Entrance Requirements: Open admission except for nursing program. Options: electronic application, early admission, deferred admission. Required: high school transcript. Recommended: SAT or ACT. Required for some: SAT or ACT. Entrance: noncompetitive. Application deadline: Rolling. Notification: continuous. Transfer credits accepted: Yes.

Collegiate Environment: Social organizations: 16 open to all. Most popular organizations: student government, student veterans association, Student Nurses Association, Student Occupational Therapy Association (SOTA), Media Club. Campus security: 24-hour emergency response devices. College housing not available. Kent State at Ashtabula Library with 51,884 books, 273 microform titles, 225 serials, 640 audiovisual materials, an OPAC, and a Web page. 70 computers available on campus for general student use. A campuswide network can be accessed. Students can access the following: online class registration. Staffed computer lab on campus provides training in use of computers, software, and the Internet.

Community Environment: This growing industrial city is on Lake Erie at the mouth of the Ashtabula River. Two municipal parks on Lake Erie have excellent facilities for swimming, boating, and fishing.

■ KENT STATE UNIVERSITY AT EAST LIVERPOOL

400 E 4th St.
East Liverpool, OH 43920-3497
Tel: (330)385-3805
Fax: (330)385-6348
Web Site: www.eliv.kent.edu/

Description: State-supported, primarily 2-year, coed. Part of Kent State University System. Awards certificates, transfer associate, and bachelor's degrees (also offers some upper-level and graduate courses). Founded

1967. Setting: 4-acre small town campus with easy access to Pittsburgh. Total enrollment: 1,505. Faculty: 75 (27 full-time, 48 part-time). Student-undergrad faculty ratio is 24:1. 179 applied, 96% were admitted. 5% from top 10% of their high school class, 18% from top quarter, 51% from top half. Full-time: 818 students, 67% women, 33% men. Part-time: 686 students, 71% women, 29% men. Students come from 8 states and territories, 2 other countries, 5% from out-of-state. 0.3% American Indian or Alaska Native, non-Hispanic/Latino; 2% Hispanic/Latino; 4% African American, non-Hispanic/Latino; 1% Asian, non-Hispanic/Latino; 0% Native Hawaiian or other Pacific Islander, non-Hispanic/Latino; 0.1% international. 50% 25 or older, 5% transferred in. Retention: 52% of full-time freshmen returned the following year. Core. Calendar: semesters. Academic remediation for entering students, services for LD students, advanced placement, accelerated degree program, self-designed majors, freshman honors college, honors program, independent study, distance learning, double major, summer session for credit, part-time degree program, adult/continuing education programs, internships. Study abroad program. ROTC: Army (c), Naval (c), Air Force (c).

Entrance Requirements: Open admission selective admission to some programs. Options: electronic application, early admission, deferred admission. Required: high school transcript. Recommended: SAT or ACT. Required for some: SAT or ACT. Entrance: noncompetitive. Application deadline: Rolling. Notification: continuous. Transfer credits accepted: Yes.

Collegiate Environment: Orientation program. Student-run newspaper. Social organizations: 10 open to all. Most popular organizations: student government, Student Nurses Association, Environmental Club, Occupational Therapist Assistant Club, Physical Therapist Assistant Club. Major annual events: Christmas on Campus, Ohio River Arts Festival, Welcome Back Fest. Campus security: student patrols, late night transport-escort service. College housing not available. Blair Memorial Library with 31,320 books, 135 serials, an OPAC, and a Web page. 72 computers available on campus for general student use. A campuswide network can be accessed. Students can access the following: online class registration. Staffed computer lab on campus provides training in use of computers, software, and the Internet.

Community Environment: East Liverpool is in one of the most scenic sections of the upper Ohio Valley and is a leading pottery center producing semivitreous porcelain ware. Train and bus transportation is available and a local airport is available for private planes. Community facilities include numerous churches, representing 18 denominations, and a library. Thompson park provides facilities for all outdoor sports including winter sports; Beaver Creek provides facilities for camping, fishing, and picnicking.

■ KENT STATE UNIVERSITY AT GEAUGA

14111 Claridon-Troy Rd.
Burton, OH 44021-9500
Tel: (440)834-4187
Fax: (440)834-0919
E-mail: geaugaadmissions@kent.edu
Web Site: www.geauga.kent.edu/

Description: State-supported, 4-year, coed. Part of Kent State University System. Awards associate and bachelor's degrees. Founded 1964. Setting: 87-acre rural campus with easy access to Cleveland. Total enrollment: 2,535. Faculty: 125 (32 full-time, 93 part-time). Student-undergrad faculty ratio is 29:1. 419 applied, 98% were admitted. 1% from top 10% of their high school class, 10% from top quarter, 33% from top half. Full-time: 1,490 students, 62% women, 38% men. Part-time: 1,043 students, 71% women, 29% men. Students come from 12 states and territories, 6 other countries, 1% from out-of-state. 0.4% American Indian or Alaska Native, non-Hispanic/Latino; 2% Hispanic/Latino; 10% African American, non-Hispanic/Latino; 1% Asian, non-Hispanic/Latino; 0.1% Native Hawaiian or other Pacific Islander, non-Hispanic/Latino; 1% international. 46% 25 or older, 7% transferred in. Retention: 53% of full-time freshmen returned the following year. Core. Calendar: semesters. Academic remediation for entering students, services for LD students, advanced placement, accelerated degree program, self-designed majors, independent study, distance learning, double major, summer session for credit, part-time degree program, internships. Study abroad program. ROTC: Army (c), Air Force (c).

Entrance Requirements: Open admission. Options: electronic application, deferred admission, international baccalaureate accepted. Required: high school transcript. Recommended: SAT or ACT. Required for some: SAT or ACT. Entrance: noncompetitive. Application deadlines: Rolling, Rolling for nonresidents. Notification: continuous, continuous for nonresidents. Transfer credits accepted: Yes.

Costs Per Year: Application fee: $30. State resident tuition: $5472 full-time. Nonresident tuition: $13,432 full-time. Full-time tuition varies according to course level and course load.

Collegiate Environment: Orientation program. Most popular organizations: Student Ambassadors, Campus Crusade for Christ, Gaia Society. Major annual events: Beginning of Year Kickoff, Finals Week Activities. Campus security: 24-hour emergency response devices. College housing not available. Kent State University at Geauga Library with 8,300 books, 6,600 serials, an OPAC, and a Web page.

Community Environment: Burton located 30 miles from Cleveland, is primarily a residential area with a few small businesses. Planes and trains are within 18 miles. Community facilities include shopping facilities, churches, and civic and service organizations. Ski resort is nearby for all winter sports.

■ **KENT STATE UNIVERSITY AT SALEM**
2491 State Rte. 45 S
Salem, OH 44460-9412
Tel: (330)332-0361
Fax: (330)332-9256
E-mail: mweekley@kent.edu
Web Site: www.salem.kent.edu/

Description: State-supported, primarily 2-year, coed. Part of Kent State University System. Awards certificates, transfer associate, and bachelor's degrees (also offers some upper-level and graduate courses). Founded 1966. Setting: 98-acre rural campus. Total enrollment: 1,879. Faculty: 123 (46 full-time, 77 part-time). Student-undergrad faculty ratio is 20:1. 446 applied, 98% were admitted. 5% from top 10% of their high school class, 23% from top quarter, 59% from top half. Full-time: 1,266 students, 70% women, 30% men. Part-time: 612 students, 69% women, 31% men. Students come from 11 states and territories, 4 other countries, 1% from out-of-state. 0.4% American Indian or Alaska Native, non-Hispanic/Latino; 1% Hispanic/Latino; 3% African American, non-Hispanic/Latino; 1% Asian, non-Hispanic/Latino; 0% Native Hawaiian or other Pacific Islander, non-Hispanic/Latino; 0.1% international. 46% 25 or older, 7% transferred in. Retention: 59% of full-time freshmen returned the following year. Academic areas with the most degrees conferred: health professions and related sciences; agriculture; natural resources/environmental science. Core. Calendar: semesters. Academic remediation for entering students, services for LD students, advanced placement, accelerated degree program, self-designed majors, freshman honors college, honors program, independent study, distance learning, double major, summer session for credit, part-time degree program, adult/continuing education programs, co-op programs and internships. Study abroad program. ROTC: Army (c), Air Force (c).

Entrance Requirements: Open admission except for radiological technology, human services programs, and honors program. Options: electronic application, early admission, deferred admission, international baccalaureate accepted. Required: high school transcript. Recommended: SAT or ACT. Required for some: essay, SAT or ACT. Entrance: noncompetitive. Application deadlines: Rolling, Rolling for nonresidents. Notification: continuous, continuous for nonresidents. Transfer credits accepted: Yes.

Collegiate Environment: Orientation program. Choral group. Social organizations: 6 open to all. Most popular organizations: Honors Club, Human Services Technology Club, Radiologic Technology Club, Student Government Organization, Students for Professional Nursing. Student services: personal-psychological counseling. Campus security: 24-hour emergency response devices, late night transport-escort service. College housing not available. Kent State Salem Library with 19,000 books, 2,415 microform titles, 163 serials, 158 audiovisual materials, an OPAC, and a Web page.

Community Environment: Known as the"Quaker City" because of its founders, Salem is one of the most productive dairy and fruit growing sections of Ohio. Salem is an area of thriving manufacturing and commercial establishments were full- and part-time employment is available. Centennial Park offers varied recreational facilities.

■ **KENT STATE UNIVERSITY AT STARK**
6000 Frank Ave., NW
Canton, OH 44720-7599
Tel: (330)499-9600
Fax: (330)494-6121
E-mail: starkadmissions@kent.edu
Web Site: www.stark.kent.edu/

Description: State-supported, comprehensive, coed. Part of Kent State University System. Awards associate, bachelor's, and master's degrees. Founded 1967. Setting: 200-acre suburban campus with easy access to Cleveland. Total enrollment: 4,864. Faculty: 255 (110 full-time, 145 part-time). Student-undergrad faculty ratio is 23:1. 1,019 applied, 96% were admitted. 3% from top 10% of their high school class, 17% from top quarter, 44% from top half. Full-time: 3,146 students, 58% women, 42% men. Part-time: 1,670 students, 65% women, 35% men. Students come from 14 states and territories, 5 other countries, 1% from out-of-state. 1% American Indian or Alaska Native, non-Hispanic/Latino; 2% Hispanic/Latino; 8% African American, non-Hispanic/Latino; 1% Asian, non-Hispanic/Latino; 0.1% Native Hawaiian or other Pacific Islander, non-Hispanic/Latino; 0.2% international. 36% 25 or older, 10% transferred in. Retention: 59% of full-time freshmen returned the following year. Academic area with the most degrees conferred: visual and performing arts. Core. Calendar: semesters. Academic remediation for entering students, services for LD students, advanced placement, self-designed majors, honors program, independent study, distance learning, double major, summer session for credit, part-time degree program, adult/continuing education programs, internships. Off campus study at Stark State College of Technology. Study abroad program. ROTC: Army (c), Naval (c), Air Force (c).

Entrance Requirements: Open admission. Options: electronic application, early admission, deferred admission. Required: high school transcript. Recommended: SAT or ACT. Required for some: SAT or ACT. Entrance: noncompetitive. Application deadlines: Rolling, Rolling for nonresidents. Notification: continuous, continuous for nonresidents. Transfer credits accepted: Yes.

Costs Per Year: Application fee: $30. State resident tuition: $5472 full-time. Nonresident tuition: $13,432 full-time. Full-time tuition varies according to course level and course load.

Collegiate Environment: Orientation program. Drama-theater group, choral group. Social organizations: 19 open to all; Campus Ministries, Literary Magazine. Most popular organizations: Club Sunaarashi (Japanese Animation, Magic the Gathering, and Dungeons and Dragons), Rooted in Faith-Bible Club (non-denominational), Kent State Stark Education Association (KSSEA), SCRUBS (nursing organization), Ohio Collegiate Music Education Association (OCMEA). Major annual events: FWOF (Fall Welcome Program), Kentiki (End of Spring Semester Celebration), Student Leadership Academy. Student services: personal-psychological counseling. Campus security: 24-hour emergency response devices, late night transport-escort service. College housing not available. Kent State Stark Library with 81,962 books, 231 serials, 3,590 audiovisual materials, an OPAC, and a Web page. 575 computers available on campus for general student use. Computer purchase/lease plans available. A campuswide network can be accessed from off-campus. Students can access the following: online class registration. Staffed computer lab on campus provides training in use of computers, software, and the Internet.

Community Environment: The Kent State University Stark Campus is a commuter campus located Jackson Township in suburban Canton, Ohio.

■ **KENT STATE UNIVERSITY AT TRUMBULL**
4314 Mahoning Ave., NW
Warren, OH 44483-1998
Tel: (330)847-0571
E-mail: jritter0@kent.edu
Web Site: www.trumbull.kent.edu/

Description: State-supported, primarily 2-year, coed. Part of Kent State University System. Awards certificates, transfer associate, and bachelor's degrees (also offers some upper-level and graduate courses). Founded 1954. Setting: 200-acre suburban campus with easy access to Cleveland. Total enrollment: 3,107. Faculty: 121 (58 full-time, 63 part-time). Student-undergrad faculty ratio is 29:1. 485 applied, 99% were admitted. 6% from top 10% of their high school class, 16% from top quarter, 42% from top half. Full-time: 1,892 students, 62% women, 38% men. Part-time: 1,211 students, 65% women, 35% men. Students come from 16 states and territories, 3 other countries, 1% from out-of-state. 0.2% American Indian or Alaska Native, non-Hispanic/Latino; 3% Hispanic/Latino; 10% African American, non-Hispanic/Latino; 1% Asian, non-Hispanic/Latino; 0% Native Hawaiian or other Pacific Islander, non-Hispanic/Latino; 0.4% international. 51% 25 or older, 7% transferred in. Retention: 47% of full-time freshmen returned the following year. Academic area with the most degrees conferred: liberal arts/general studies. Core. Calendar: semesters. Academic remediation for entering students, services for LD students, advanced placement, self-designed majors, freshman honors college, honors program, independent study, distance learning, double major, summer session for credit, part-time degree program, adult/continuing education programs, internships. Study abroad program. ROTC: Army (c), Air Force (c).

Entrance Requirements: Open admission except for nursing program. Options: electronic application, deferred admission, international baccalaureate accepted. Required: high school transcript. Recommended: SAT or ACT. Required for some: SAT or ACT. Entrance: noncompetitive. Application deadlines: Rolling, Rolling for nonresidents. Notification: continuous, continuous for nonresidents. Transfer credits accepted: Yes.

Collegiate Environment: Orientation program. Drama-theater group. Social organizations: 5 open to all. Most popular organizations: National Student Nurses Association, Spot On Improv Group, ENACTUS, GLOW (Gay, Lesbian, or Whatever), If These Hands Could Talk - ASL. Major annual events: New Student Welcome Day, Halloween Party. Student services: personal-psychological counseling. Campus security: 24-hour emergency response devices, late night transport-escort service, patrols by trained security personnel during open hours. College housing not available. Trumbull Campus Library with 65,951 books, 759 serials, an OPAC, and a Web page. 300 computers available on campus for general student use. A campuswide network can be accessed from off-campus. Students can access the following: online class registration. Staffed computer lab on campus provides training in use of computers, software, and the Internet.

Community Environment: Located in the northeastern part of Ohio, the New England influences brought here by early settlers are still strongly felt. Warren, an industrial city, is in the great Mahoning Valley steel district and also has an active electrical and automotive parts industry. Shopping facilities here are good. Mosquito State Park, located 10 miles north, provides facilities for fishing, boating, swimming and camping. Points of interest are the John Stark Edwards House and the Nelson and Kennedy Ledges State Park.

■ KENT STATE UNIVERSITY AT TUSCARAWAS

330 University Dr., NE
New Philadelphia, OH 44663-9403
Tel: (330)339-3391
Fax: (330)339-3321
E-mail: info@tusc.kent.edu
Web Site: www.tusc.kent.edu/

Description: State-supported, primarily 2-year, coed. Part of Kent State University System. Awards certificates, transfer associate, and bachelor's degrees (also offers some upper-level and graduate courses). Founded 1962. Setting: 172-acre small town campus with easy access to Cleveland. Total enrollment: 2,717. Faculty: 139 (52 full-time, 87 part-time). Student-undergrad faculty ratio is 23:1. 470 applied, 95% were admitted. 6% from top 10% of their high school class, 20% from top quarter, 54% from top half. Full-time: 1,484 students, 57% women, 43% men. Part-time: 1,499 students, 50% women, 50% men. 1% from out-of-state. 0.2% American Indian or Alaska Native, non-Hispanic/Latino; 1% Hispanic/Latino; 2% African American, non-Hispanic/Latino; 1% Asian, non-Hispanic/Latino; 0.2% Native Hawaiian or other Pacific Islander, non-Hispanic/Latino; 0.2% international. 46% 25 or older, 6% transferred in. Retention: 59% of full-time freshmen returned the following year. Academic area with the most degrees conferred: liberal arts/general studies. Core. Calendar: semesters. Academic remediation for entering students, services for LD students, advanced placement, accelerated degree program, self-designed majors, freshman honors college, honors program, independent study, distance learning, double major, summer session for credit, part-time degree program, adult/continuing education programs, internships. Study abroad program.

Entrance Requirements: Open admission except for business administration, education, nursing, veterinary technology, fine and performing arts programs. Options: electronic application, deferred admission. Required: high school transcript. Recommended: SAT or ACT. Required for some: SAT or ACT. Entrance: noncompetitive. Application deadlines: Rolling, Rolling for nonresidents. Notification: continuous, continuous for nonresidents. Transfer credits accepted: Yes.

Collegiate Environment: Orientation program. Drama-theater group, choral group. Social organizations: 18 open to all. Most popular organizations: Society of Manufacturing Engineers, IEEE, Animation Imagineers, Justice Studies Club, Student Activities Council. Major annual events: Spring Awards, Buck Lunches, Commencement. Campus security: 24-hour emergency response devices. College housing not available. Tuscarawas Campus Library with 63,880 books, 2,242 microform titles, 208 serials, 1,179 audiovisual materials, an OPAC, and a Web page. 194 computers available on campus for general student use. A campuswide network can be accessed

from off-campus. Students can access the following: online class registration. Staffed computer lab on campus provides training in use of computers, software, and the Internet.

■ KENYON COLLEGE

Gambier, OH 43022-9623
Tel: (740)427-5000; Free: 800-848-2468
Fax: (740)427-2634
E-mail: admissions@kenyon.edu
Web Site: www.kenyon.edu/

Description: Independent, 4-year, coed. Awards bachelor's degrees. Founded 1824. Setting: 1,200-acre rural campus with easy access to Columbus. Endowment: $187.8 million. Research spending for the previous fiscal year: $627,033. Educational spending for the previous fiscal year: $6783 per student. Total enrollment: 1,667. Faculty: 201 (160 full-time, 41 part-time). Student-undergrad faculty ratio is 10:1. 3,947 applied, 36% were admitted. 52% from top 10% of their high school class, 86% from top quarter, 98% from top half. 11 valedictorians. Full-time: 1,658 students, 53% women, 47% men. Part-time: 9 students, 67% women, 33% men. Students come from 50 states and territories, 41 other countries, 85% from out-of-state. 1% American Indian or Alaska Native, non-Hispanic/Latino; 5% Hispanic/Latino; 3% African American, non-Hispanic/Latino; 7% Asian, non-Hispanic/Latino; 0% Native Hawaiian or other Pacific Islander, non-Hispanic/Latino; 4% international. 0% 25 or older, 98% live on campus, 1% transferred in. Retention: 91% of full-time freshmen returned the following year. Academic areas with the most degrees conferred: social sciences; English; foreign languages and literature. Core. Calendar: semesters. Services for LD students, advanced placement, accelerated degree program, self-designed majors, honors program, independent study, double major. Off campus study. Study abroad program.

Entrance Requirements: Options: electronic application, early admission, early decision, deferred admission, international baccalaureate accepted. Required: essay, high school transcript, counselor recommendation, SAT or ACT. Recommended: 2 recommendations, interview. Entrance: very difficult. Application deadlines: 1/15, 11/15 for early decision plan 1, 1/15 for early decision plan 2. Notification: 4/1, 12/15 for early decision plan 1, 2/1 for early decision plan 2. SAT Reasoning Test deadline: 1/15. SAT Subject Test deadline: 1/15. Transfer credits accepted: Yes. Applicants placed on waiting list: 931. Wait-listed applicants offered admission: 15. Early decision applicants: 390. Early decision applicants admitted: 208.

Costs Per Year: Application fee: $50. Comprehensive fee: $56,810 includes full-time tuition ($43,900), mandatory fees ($1740), and college room and board ($11,170).

Collegiate Environment: Orientation program. Drama-theater group, choral group, student-run newspaper, radio station. Social organizations: 123 open to all; national fraternities, national sororities, local fraternities, local sororities; 14% of eligible men and 16% of eligible women are members. Most popular organizations: student theater organizations, student radio station, musical groups, intramural sports and clubs. Major annual events: Summer Send-off, Philander's Phebruary Phling, Take Back the Night. Student services: health clinic, personal-psychological counseling, women's center. Campus security: 24-hour emergency response devices and patrols, student patrols, late night transport-escort service, controlled dormitory access. 1,704 college housing spaces available; 1,604 were occupied in 2012-13. Freshmen guaranteed college housing. On-campus residence required through senior year. Options: coed, women-only housing available. Olin Library plus 1 other with 655,576 books, 147,806 microform titles, 11,296 serials, 31,769 audiovisual materials, an OPAC, and a Web page. Operations spending for the previous fiscal year: $1.4 million. 450 computers available on campus for general student use. A campuswide network can be accessed from student residence rooms and from off campus. Students can access the following: commercial databases. Staffed computer lab on campus (open 24 hours a day) provides training in use of computers, software, and the Internet.

Community Environment: Gambier, a hamlet in central Ohio, is 47 miles northeast of Columbus, and just east of Mount Vernon. It is a village dating from pre-Civil War days and many buildings of that era still remain.

■ KETTERING COLLEGE

3737 Southern Blvd.
Kettering, OH 45429-1299
Tel: (937)395-8601; Free: 800-433-5262
Fax: (937)395-8333
Web Site: www.kc.edu/

Description: Independent Seventh-day Adventist, comprehensive, coed. Administratively affiliated with Kettering Health Network. Awards associate, bachelor's, and master's degrees. Founded 1967. Setting: 35-acre suburban campus. Total enrollment: 808. Faculty: 70 (55 full-time, 15 part-time). Student-undergrad faculty ratio is 10:1. 204 applied, 50% were admitted. 22% from top 10% of their high school class, 53% from top quarter, 81% from top half. Full-time: 394 students, 81% women, 19% men. Part-time: 347 students, 80% women, 20% men. Students come from 24 states and territories, 3 other countries, 7% from out-of-state. 48% 25 or older, 15% live on campus, 16% transferred in. Retention: 78% of full-time freshmen returned the following year. Academic area with the most degrees conferred: health professions and related sciences. Core. Calendar: semesters. Advanced placement, honors program, independent study, distance learning, summer session for credit, part-time degree program. Off campus study at members of the Southwestern Ohio Council for Higher Education. Study abroad program.

Entrance Requirements: Option: early admission. Required: essay, high school transcript, minimum 2.0 high school GPA, ACT. Recommended: minimum 3.0 high school GPA, interview, SAT. Entrance: moderately difficult. Application deadline: Rolling. Notification: continuous.

Collegiate Environment: Drama-theater group, choral group. Social organizations: 3 open to all. Most popular organizations: Student Association/student life, Campus Ministries. Major annual events: Weeks of Spiritual Emphasis, Nursing Dedication Ceremony, Christmas Party. Student services: health clinic, personal-psychological counseling. Campus security: 24-hour emergency response devices and patrols, late night transport-escort service. Learning Resources Center plus 1 other with 29,390 books, 266 serials, an OPAC, and a Web page. 30 computers available on campus for general student use. A campuswide network can be accessed from student residence rooms and from off campus. Students can access the following: online class registration. Staffed computer lab on campus.

Community Environment: The city is surrounded by rolling, wooded hills and is a suburb of Dayton. The recreational, educational, and cultural advantages of Dayton are enjoyed by the citizens of Kettering also. Kettering is the home of the world's largest supply of electronic components. Community facilities include 37 churches of many denominations and many shopping centers and plazas. Nine golf courses are in the area.

■ **LAKE ERIE COLLEGE**
391 W Washington St.
Painesville, OH 44077-3389
Tel: (440)296-1856; Free: 800-916-0904
Fax: (440)352-3533
E-mail: admissions@lec.edu
Web Site: www.lec.edu/

Description: Independent, comprehensive, coed. Awards bachelor's and master's degrees. Founded 1856. Setting: 48-acre suburban campus with easy access to Cleveland. Endowment: $27.4 million. Educational spending for the previous fiscal year: $8965 per student. Total enrollment: 1,199. Faculty: 114 (41 full-time, 73 part-time). Student-undergrad faculty ratio is 16:1. 1,509 applied, 63% were admitted. 9% from top 10% of their high school class, 38% from top quarter, 70% from top half. 7 valedictorians. Full-time: 944 students, 49% women, 51% men. Part-time: 88 students, 67% women, 33% men. Students come from 27 states and territories, 14 other countries, 24% from out-of-state. 99.9% American Indian or Alaska Native, non-Hispanic/Latino; 2% Hispanic/Latino; 8% African American, non-Hispanic/Latino; 1% Asian, non-Hispanic/Latino; 0% Native Hawaiian or other Pacific Islander, non-Hispanic/Latino; 4% international. 10% 25 or older, 56% live on campus, 5% transferred in. Retention: 64% of full-time freshmen returned the following year. Academic areas with the most degrees conferred: business/marketing; agriculture; education. Core. Calendar: semesters. Services for LD students, advanced placement, accelerated degree program, self-designed majors, honors program, independent study, double major, summer session for credit, part-time degree program, internships, graduate courses open to undergrads. Off campus study at Northeast Ohio Commission on Higher Education. Study abroad program.

Entrance Requirements: Options: electronic application, deferred admission, international baccalaureate accepted. Required: essay, high school transcript, minimum 2.5 high school GPA, SAT or ACT Tests, SAT or ACT. Recommended: interview, AP, CLEP, Institutional Exam. Required for some: high school transcript. Entrance: moderately difficult. Application deadlines: 8/1, 8/1 for nonresidents. Notification: continuous, continuous for nonresidents. SAT Reasoning Test deadline: 8/1. SAT Subject Test deadline: 8/1. Transfer credits accepted: Yes.

Costs Per Year: Application fee: $30. One-time mandatory fee: $350. Comprehensive fee: $35,704 includes full-time tuition ($25,976), mandatory fees ($1392), and college room and board ($8336). College room only: $4054. Full-time tuition and fees vary according to course load, degree level, and program. Room and board charges vary according to board plan. Part-time tuition: $688 per credit hour. Part-time mandatory fees: $51 per credit hour. Part-time tuition and fees vary according to course load, degree level, and program.

Collegiate Environment: Orientation program. Drama-theater group, choral group, marching band. Social organizations: 31 open to all; national fraternities, national sororities; 2% of eligible men and 15% of eligible women are members. Most popular organizations: Student Athlete Advisory Committee, Intercollegiate Horse Show Association, Gamma Phi Beta Sorority, Spanish Club, Student Government Association. Major annual events: Spring Formal, Homecoming, Field Day. Campus security: 24-hour emergency response devices and patrols, late night transport-escort service. 530 college housing spaces available; 522 were occupied in 2012-13. Freshmen given priority for college housing. On-campus residence required through sophomore year. Options: coed, women-only housing available. Lincoln Library with 66,200 books, 11,700 microform titles, 8,300 serials, 1,310 audiovisual materials, an OPAC, and a Web page. Operations spending for the previous fiscal year: $334,162. 78 computers available on campus for general student use. A campuswide network can be accessed from student residence rooms and from off campus. Students can access the following: online class registration. Staffed computer lab on campus provides training in use of computers, software, and the Internet.

Community Environment: Painesville is a city of 30,000 residents located 25 miles east of Cleveland and 3 miles from Lake Erie. The surrounding area boasts numerous fine commercial nurseries, the home of President Garfield, maple sugar industries, and the Holden Arboretum. Lake Erie College sponsors an ongoing series of cultural activities at the B. K. Smith Fine Arts Gallery and the C. K. Rickel Theater on the Lake Erie campus. Other community facilities include a variety of churches, the YMCA, and Morley Library, as well as various civic and service organizations.

■ **LAKELAND COMMUNITY COLLEGE**
7700 Clocktower Dr.
Kirtland, OH 44094-5198
Tel: (440)525-7000; Free: 800-589-8520
Fax: (440)525-4330
Web Site: www.lakeland.cc.oh.us/

Description: State and locally supported, 2-year, coed. Part of Ohio Board of Regents. Awards certificates, transfer associate, and terminal associate degrees. Founded 1967. Setting: 380-acre suburban campus with easy access to Cleveland. Endowment: $354,544. Research spending for the previous fiscal year: $311,937. Educational spending for the previous fiscal year: $4471 per student. Total enrollment: 9,283. Faculty: 673 (120 full-time, 553 part-time). Student-undergrad faculty ratio is 18:1. Full-time: 3,397 students, 54% women, 46% men. Part-time: 5,886 students, 63% women, 37% men. Students come from 6 states and territories, 1% from out-of-state. 0.3% American Indian or Alaska Native, non-Hispanic/Latino; 3% Hispanic/Latino; 16% African American, non-Hispanic/Latino; 1% Asian, non-Hispanic/Latino; 0.1% Native Hawaiian or other Pacific Islander, non-Hispanic/Latino; 0.3% international. 5% transferred in. Retention: 51% of full-time freshmen returned the following year. Core. Calendar: semesters. Academic remediation for entering students, ESL program, services for LD students, advanced placement, independent study, distance learning, summer session for credit, part-time degree program, external degree program, adult/continuing education programs, co-op programs and internships. Off campus study. Study abroad program.

Entrance Requirements: Open admission except for allied health programs. Options: electronic application, early admission, deferred admission. Required: high school transcript, Compass test is required. Entrance: noncompetitive. Application deadline: 9/1. Notification: continuous until 9/1. Transfer credits accepted: Yes.

Costs Per Year: Application fee: $15. Area resident tuition: $3087 full-time, $102.90 per credit hour part-time. State resident tuition: $3936 full-time, $131.20 per credit hour part-time. Nonresident tuition: $8573 full-time, $285.75 per credit hour part-time. Mandatory fees: $29 full-time, $14.25 per term part-time. Full-time tuition and fees vary according to course load. Part-time tuition and fees vary according to course load.

Collegiate Environment: Orientation program. Drama-theater group, choral group, student-run newspaper, radio station. Social organizations: 27 open to all; Phi Theta Kappa; 3% of eligible men and 3% of eligible women are members. Most popular organizations: Campus Activities Board, Lakeland Student Government, Lakeland Signers, Thousand Shoes Skat Dance Team, Gamer's Guild. Major annual events: Halloween Party, Spring Fling Week, Student Leader Awards Banquet & Casino Night. Student services: health clinic, personal-psychological counseling, women's center. Campus security: 24-hour emergency response devices and patrols, student patrols, late night transport-escort service. College housing not available. Lakeland Community College Library with 65,814 books, 248 serials, 4,212 audiovisual materials, an OPAC, and a Web page. Operations spending for the previous fiscal year: $1.1 million. 153 computers available on campus for general student use. A campuswide network can be accessed from off-campus. Students can access the following: online class registration. Staffed computer lab on campus provides training in use of computers, software, and the Internet.

Community Environment: Mentor is located in attractive Lake County, in the northeastern portion of the state along Lake Erie, 20 miles east of Cleveland. The land area amounts to 231 square miles with a total population of 232,800. The county itself consists of two distinctly different areas: a densely populated western end with approximately 68% of the population and a sparsely populated eastern end. The community offers exceptional opportunity for personal and professional growth.

■ **LINCOLN COLLEGE OF TECHNOLOGY (CINCINNATI)**

149 Northland Blvd.
Cincinnati, OH 45246-1122
Tel: (513)874-0432
Web Site: www.lincolnedu.com/

Description: Proprietary, 2-year, coed. Awards certificates and terminal associate degrees. Founded 1972. Setting: suburban campus. Total enrollment: 1,127. 1% from out-of-state. 58% 25 or older. Retention: 38% of full-time freshmen returned the following year. Academic remediation for entering students, summer session for credit.

Entrance Requirements: Open admission. Required for some: CPAt. Entrance: minimally difficult. Application deadline: Rolling. Notification: continuous.

■ **LINCOLN COLLEGE OF TECHNOLOGY (DAYTON)**

111 W First St.
Dayton, OH 45402-3003
Tel: (937)224-0061
Fax: (937)224-0065
Web Site: www.lincolnedu.com/

Description: Proprietary, 2-year, coed. Awards certificates, diplomas, and terminal associate degrees. Founded 1972. Setting: urban campus. Student-undergrad faculty ratio is 28:1. 0% from out-of-state. 37% 25 or older. Retention: 62% of full-time freshmen returned the following year. Summer session for credit.

Entrance Requirements: Open admission. Entrance: minimally difficult. Application deadline: Rolling. Notification: continuous.

■ **LORAIN COUNTY COMMUNITY COLLEGE**

1005 Abbe Rd., N
Elyria, OH 44035
Tel: (440)365-5222; Free: 800-995-5222
Fax: (440)365-6519
E-mail: ssutton@lorainccc.edu
Web Site: www.lorainccc.edu/

Description: State and locally supported, 2-year, coed. Part of Ohio Board of Regents. Awards certificates, transfer associate, and terminal associate degrees. Founded 1963. Setting: 280-acre suburban campus with easy access to Cleveland. Endowment: $21.7 million. Educational spending for the previous fiscal year: $4010 per student. Total enrollment: 12,656. Faculty: 752 (135 full-time, 617 part-time). Student-undergrad faculty ratio is 20:1. 2,283 applied, 100% were admitted. Full-time: 3,918 students, 58% women, 42% men. Part-time: 8,738 students, 66% women, 34% men. Students come from 17 states and territories, 28 other countries, 1% from out-of-state. 1% American Indian or Alaska Native, non-Hispanic/Latino; 8% Hispanic/Latino; 11% African American, non-Hispanic/Latino; 1% Asian, non-Hispanic/Latino; 0% Native Hawaiian or other Pacific Islander, non-Hispanic/Latino; 1% international. 42% 25 or older. Retention: 58% of full-time freshmen returned the following year. Core. Calendar: semesters. Academic remediation for entering students, ESL program, services for LD students, advanced placement, self-designed majors, honors program, independent study, distance learning, double major, summer session for credit, part-time

degree program, external degree program, adult/continuing education programs, co-op programs and internships.

Entrance Requirements: Open admission. Options: early admission, deferred admission. Required for some: high school transcript. Entrance: noncompetitive. Application deadline: Rolling. Notification: continuous.

Collegiate Environment: Orientation program. Drama-theater group, choral group, student-run newspaper, radio station. Social organizations: national fraternities, national sororities. Most popular organizations: Phi Beta Kappa, Black Progressives, Hispanic Club. Major annual events: Fall Picnic, Spring Picnic, Family Fest. Student services: legal services, health clinic, personal-psychological counseling, women's center. Campus security: 24-hour emergency response devices and patrols, late night transport-escort service. College housing not available. Learning Resource Center with 198,984 books, 14,330 microform titles, 3,289 audiovisual materials, and an OPAC. Operations spending for the previous fiscal year: $1.1 million. 400 computers available on campus for general student use. A campuswide network can be accessed from off-campus. Students can access the following: online class registration. Staffed computer lab on campus.

Community Environment: Situated in the far northeast corner of the city of Elyria and 26 miles west of Cleveland, the campus is just four miles from downtown Elyria, a city of over 57,500 and the county seat; eight miles to the north lies Lorain, an industrial community on Lake Erie at the mouth of the Black River; its harbor is one of the best on the Great Lakes. One of Ford Motor Co.'s largest assembly plants is located here with Lake Shore Development. Community facilities include churches representing all denominations, YMCA, YWCA, six hospitals, and all leading civic and service organizations. Boating, fishing, swimming, golf, and tennis are some of the outdoor sports. Job opportunities are excellent. Lakeview Park is noted for its extensive rose garden and colorfully lighted fountain. Cascade Park is a favorite recreation area and is located in the city of Elyria. A rapidly expanding network of major state and interstate highways, including the nearby Ohio Turnpike, makes the college easily reached by automobile.

■ **LOURDES UNIVERSITY**

6832 Convent Blvd.
Sylvania, OH 43560-2898
Tel: (419)885-3211; Free: 800-878-3210
Fax: (419)882-3987
E-mail: AdmissionsLCAdmits@lourdes.edu
Web Site: www.lourdes.edu/

Description: Independent Roman Catholic, comprehensive, coed. Awards associate, bachelor's, and master's degrees. Founded 1958. Setting: 113-acre suburban campus with easy access to Toledo. Endowment: $7.9 million. Educational spending for the previous fiscal year: $3335 per student. Total enrollment: 2,460. Faculty: 280 (99 full-time, 181 part-time). Student-undergrad faculty ratio is 11:1. 1,231 applied, 71% were admitted. 10% from top 10% of their high school class, 31% from top quarter, 62% from top half. Full-time: 1,295 students, 70% women, 30% men. Part-time: 823 students, 80% women, 20% men. Students come from 17 states and territories, 12% from out-of-state. 0.3% American Indian or Alaska Native, non-Hispanic/Latino; 6% Hispanic/Latino; 14% African American, non-Hispanic/Latino; 0.5% Asian, non-Hispanic/Latino; 0.1% Native Hawaiian or other Pacific Islander, non-Hispanic/Latino; 0.3% international. 48% 25 or older, 16% live on campus, 11% transferred in. Retention: 62% of full-time freshmen returned the following year. Academic areas with the most degrees conferred: health professions and related sciences; business/marketing; interdisciplinary studies. Core. Calendar: semesters. Academic remediation for entering students, services for LD students, advanced placement, self-designed majors, independent study, distance learning, double major, summer session for credit, part-time degree program, adult/continuing education programs, internships. Study abroad program. ROTC: Army (c), Air Force (c).

Entrance Requirements: Open admission. Options: electronic application, early admission, deferred admission. Required: high school transcript. Entrance: minimally difficult. Application deadlines: Rolling, Rolling for nonresidents. Notification: continuous, continuous for nonresidents. Transfer credits accepted: Yes.

Costs Per Year: Application fee: $25. Tuition: $17,455 full-time, $582 per credit part-time. Full-time tuition varies according to course load and location. Part-time tuition varies according to course load and location.

Collegiate Environment: Orientation program. Drama-theater group, choral group. Social organizations: 22 open to all. Most popular organizations: Student Government Association, Drama Society, Student Nurses Association, Orbis Ars, Pre-Art Therapy Association. Major annual events: Fall Fest,

Spring Fling, Spike the Spirit. Student services: personal-psychological counseling. Campus security: 24-hour emergency response devices and patrols, late night transport-escort service, controlled dormitory access. 360 college housing spaces available; 269 were occupied in 2012-13. Freshmen given priority for college housing. On-campus residence required through junior year. Option: coed housing available. Duns Scotus Library plus 1 other with 187,314 books, 68,916 serials, 1,747 audiovisual materials, an OPAC, and a Web page. Operations spending for the previous fiscal year: $355,773. 242 computers available on campus for general student use. A campuswide network can be accessed from student residence rooms and from off campus. Students can access the following: online class registration, Sakai/eLearning, LiveText ePortfolio system, RRS news feeds, Facebook, Twitter, online polls, webcasting, panopto, ploycom. Staffed computer lab on campus provides training in use of computers, software, and the Internet.

Community Environment: Sylvania is a suburban area with a temperate climate; plane and bus transportation is available. Job opportunities are good for students. Community facilities include a public library, adequate hospital services, churches, numerous major civic and service organizations, and shopping facilities.

■ **MALONE UNIVERSITY**
2600 Cleveland Ave., NW
Canton, OH 44709
Tel: (330)471-8100; Free: 800-521-1146
Fax: (330)454-6977
E-mail: admissions@malone.edu
Web Site: www.malone.edu/

Description: Independent, comprehensive, coed, affiliated with Evangelical Friends Church-Eastern Region. Awards bachelor's and master's degrees. Founded 1892. Setting: 96-acre suburban campus with easy access to Cleveland. Endowment: $14.7 million. Research spending for the previous fiscal year: $73,429. Educational spending for the previous fiscal year: $7280 per student. Total enrollment: 2,373. Faculty: 223 (106 full-time, 117 part-time). Student-undergrad faculty ratio is 13:1. 1,546 applied, 70% were admitted. 18% from top 10% of their high school class, 46% from top quarter, 76% from top half. 7 valedictorians. Full-time: 1,669 students, 58% women, 42% men. Part-time: 228 students, 64% women, 36% men. Students come from 35 states and territories, 17 other countries, 13% from out-of-state. 0.2% American Indian or Alaska Native, non-Hispanic/Latino; 2% Hispanic/Latino; 8% African American, non-Hispanic/Latino; 1% Asian, non-Hispanic/Latino; 0.2% Native Hawaiian or other Pacific Islander, non-Hispanic/Latino; 1% international. 22% 25 or older, 55% live on campus, 6% transferred in. Retention: 64% of full-time freshmen returned the following year. Academic areas with the most degrees conferred: business/marketing; health professions and related sciences; education. Core. Calendar: semesters. Academic remediation for entering students, services for LD students, advanced placement, accelerated degree program, self-designed majors, honors program, independent study, distance learning, double major, summer session for credit, part-time degree program, adult/continuing education programs, internships, graduate courses open to undergrads. Off campus study at members of the Christian College Consortium, members of the Council for Christian Colleges and Universities. Study abroad program. ROTC: Army (c), Air Force (c).

Entrance Requirements: Options: electronic application, early admission, deferred admission. Required: high school transcript, minimum 2 high school GPA, SAT or ACT. Recommended: interview. Required for some: essay. Entrance: moderately difficult. Application deadlines: Rolling, Rolling for nonresidents. Notification: continuous, continuous for nonresidents. SAT Reasoning Test deadline: 8/1. Transfer credits accepted: Yes.

Costs Per Year: Application fee: $20. Comprehensive fee: $34,334 includes full-time tuition ($24,934), mandatory fees ($744), and college room and board ($8656). College room only: $4412. Room and board charges vary according to board plan. Part-time tuition: $445 per hour. Part-time tuition varies according to course load.

Collegiate Environment: Orientation program. Drama-theater group, choral group, marching band, student-run newspaper, radio station. Social organizations: 45 open to all; 12 honor societies. Most popular organizations: Celebration Worship Services, Student Activities Council, Student Senate, be: Justice, intramural athletics. Major annual events: Homecoming, Christmas celebration, Air Band. Student services: health clinic, personal-psychological counseling. Campus security: 24-hour emergency response devices and patrols, late night transport-escort service, controlled dormitory access. 1,203 college housing spaces available; 1,001 were occupied in

2012-13. Freshmen given priority for college housing. On-campus residence required through junior year. Options: men-only, women-only housing available. Everett L. Cattell Library with 250,747 books, 646,748 microform titles, 50,713 serials, 13,284 audiovisual materials, an OPAC, and a Web page. Operations spending for the previous fiscal year: $808,715. 207 computers available on campus for general student use. Computer purchase/lease plans available. A campuswide network can be accessed from student residence rooms and from off campus. Students can access the following: online class registration, online advising, online financial aid information, and online credit card payments. Staffed computer lab on campus provides training in use of computers, software, and the Internet.

Community Environment: Canton is an industrial, residential, and cultural city of 80,000. The city is the home of the Pro Football Hall of Fame, and birthplace of former president William McKinley. A beautiful Cultural Center for the Arts and an extensive park system enhances the city's beauty and provides many cultural and educational opportunities for the students.

■ **MARIETTA COLLEGE**
215 Fifth St.
Marietta, OH 45750-4000
Tel: (740)376-4000; Free: 800-331-7896
Fax: (740)376-4896
E-mail: admit@marietta.edu
Web Site: www.marietta.edu/

Description: Independent, comprehensive, coed. Awards associate, bachelor's, and master's degrees. Founded 1835. Setting: 90-acre small town campus. Endowment: $61 million. Educational spending for the previous fiscal year: $13,590 per student. Total enrollment: 1,622. Faculty: 173 (110 full-time, 63 part-time). Student-undergrad faculty ratio is 12:1. 4,157 applied, 68% were admitted. 30% from top 10% of their high school class, 56% from top quarter, 84% from top half. Full-time: 1,418 students, 42% women, 58% men. Part-time: 69 students, 61% women, 39% men. Students come from 40 states and territories, 15 other countries, 36% from out-of-state. 0.1% American Indian or Alaska Native, non-Hispanic/Latino; 2% Hispanic/Latino; 6% African American, non-Hispanic/Latino; 1% Asian, non-Hispanic/Latino; 0% Native Hawaiian or other Pacific Islander, non-Hispanic/Latino; 12% international. 0% 25 or older, 76% live on campus, 3% transferred in. Retention: 75% of full-time freshmen returned the following year. Academic areas with the most degrees conferred: business/marketing; communication/journalism; engineering. Core. Calendar: semesters. Academic remediation for entering students, ESL program, services for LD students, advanced placement, accelerated degree program, self-designed majors, honors program, independent study, double major, summer session for credit, part-time degree program, adult/continuing education programs, internships. Off campus study at American University, Stillman College, Central College, Institute of European Studies, Institute of Asian Studies. Study abroad program.

Entrance Requirements: Options: electronic application, early admission, deferred admission, international baccalaureate accepted. Required: essay, high school transcript, minimum 2 high school GPA, 1 recommendation, SAT or ACT. Recommended: minimum 3 high school GPA, interview, SAT Subject Tests. Entrance: moderately difficult. Application deadline: 5/1. Notification: continuous until 5/1. SAT Reasoning Test deadline: 6/1.

Costs Per Year: Application fee: $25. Comprehensive fee: $40,500 includes full-time tuition ($30,090), mandatory fees ($850), and college room and board ($9560). College room only: $5500. Part-time tuition: $990 per credit.

Collegiate Environment: Orientation program. Drama-theater group, choral group, student-run newspaper, radio station. Social organizations: 80 open to all; national fraternities, national sororities, local sororities; 23% of eligible men and 41% of eligible women are members. Most popular organizations: Student Programming Board, student government, Society of Petroleum Engineers, Inter-Varsity Christian Fellowship, Arts and Humanities Council. Major annual events: Homecoming Weekend, Doo Dah Day, Family Weekend. Student services: health clinic, personal-psychological counseling. Campus security: 24-hour emergency response devices and patrols, student patrols, late night transport-escort service, controlled dormitory access. 1,276 college housing spaces available; 1,082 were occupied in 2012-13. Freshmen guaranteed college housing. On-campus residence required through senior year. Options: coed, men-only, women-only housing available. Legacy Library with 449,123 books, 146,583 microform titles, 13,557 serials, 5,031 audiovisual materials, an OPAC, and a Web page. Operations spending for the previous fiscal year: $908,749. 400 computers available on campus for general student use. A campuswide network can be accessed from student residence rooms and from off campus. Staffed computer lab on campus provides training in use of computers, software, and the Internet.

Community Environment: Founded in 1788, Marietta, has the distinction of being the first permanent settlement of America's Northwest Territory. The city is rich in history, with stately homes, brick paved streets, sternwheeler festivals, and an antique row of stores. Students have easy access to the town which is located 1 block from the campus. Large urban cities as Pittsburgh, PA and Columbus, OH are within a two-hour drive. Parkersburg, WV, with a population of 32,000, is 20 minutes away. Transportation is readily available. Part-time employment opportunities are available.

■ **MARION TECHNICAL COLLEGE**
1467 Mount Vernon Ave.
Marion, OH 43302-5694
Tel: (740)389-4636
Fax: (740)389-6136
E-mail: enroll@mtc.edu
Web Site: www.mtc.edu/
Description: State-supported, 2-year, coed. Part of University System of Ohio. Awards certificates, transfer associate, and terminal associate degrees. Founded 1971. Setting: 180-acre small town campus with easy access to Columbus. Total enrollment: 2,765. Faculty: 185 (35 full-time, 150 part-time). Student-undergrad faculty ratio is 18:1. 0.2% American Indian or Alaska Native, non-Hispanic/Latino; 1% Hispanic/Latino; 5% African American, non-Hispanic/Latino; 0.5% Asian, non-Hispanic/Latino; 0.04% international. 49% 25 or older. Retention: 57% of full-time freshmen returned the following year. Academic remediation for entering students, services for LD students, advanced placement, accelerated degree program, self-designed majors, independent study, distance learning, double major, summer session for credit, part-time degree program, adult/continuing education programs, co-op programs and internships. Off campus study at Rhodes State College for Respiratory Care and Occupational Therapist Assistant.
Entrance Requirements: Open admission except for health technologies, allied health, human and social services and criminal justice police academy. Options: electronic application, early admission, deferred admission. Required: high school transcript, COMPASS or ACT. Recommended: interview. Required for some: minimum 2.5 high school GPA, some programs are Limited Enrollment Programs with specific admission criteria, ACT. Entrance: noncompetitive. Application deadlines: Rolling, Rolling for nonresidents. Notification: continuous, continuous for nonresidents. Transfer credits accepted: Yes.
Costs Per Year: Application fee: $20. Area resident tuition: $4282 full-time, $166 part-time. State resident tuition: $4282 full-time, $166 part-time. Nonresident tuition: $6200 full-time, $246 part-time. Mandatory fees: $250 full-time. Full-time tuition and fees vary according to course load, program, and reciprocity agreements. Part-time tuition varies according to course load, program, and reciprocity agreements.
Collegiate Environment: Orientation program. Drama-theater group, choral group. Social organizations: 30 open to all. Most popular organizations: outdoor pursuits, Young Republicans, Economics and Business Club, Psychology Club. Major annual events: Welcome Week, Beat Michigan week. Student services: personal-psychological counseling. College housing not available. Marion Campus Library with 52,000 books, 3,690 microform titles, 251 serials, 1,582 audiovisual materials, an OPAC, and a Web page. 280 computers available on campus for general student use. A campuswide network can be accessed from off-campus. Students can access the following: online class registration. Staffed computer lab on campus provides training in use of computers, software, and the Internet.

■ **MERCY COLLEGE OF OHIO**
2221 Madison Ave.
Toledo, OH 43604
Tel: (419)251-1313; Free: 888-80-MERCY
Fax: (419)251-4116
E-mail: aimee.bishop-stuart@mercycollege.edu
Web Site: www.mercycollege.edu/
Description: Independent, 4-year, coed, affiliated with Roman Catholic Church. Administratively affiliated with Mercy Health Partners. Awards associate and bachelor's degrees. Founded 1993. Setting: urban campus with easy access to Detroit. Endowment: $9.3 million. Educational spending for the previous fiscal year: $3610 per student. Total enrollment: 1,206. Faculty: 166 (64 full-time, 102 part-time). Student-undergrad faculty ratio is 11:1. 68 applied, 74% were admitted. 14% from top 10% of their high school class, 12% from top quarter, 32% from top half. Full-time: 446 students, 89% women, 11% men. Part-time: 759 students, 85% women, 15% men. Students come from 9 states and territories, 26% from out-of-state. 0.4%

American Indian or Alaska Native, non-Hispanic/Latino; 3% Hispanic/Latino; 7% African American, non-Hispanic/Latino; 1% Asian, non-Hispanic/Latino; 0% Native Hawaiian or other Pacific Islander, non-Hispanic/Latino; 0% international. 53% 25 or older, 4% live on campus, 26% transferred in. Retention: 100% of full-time freshmen returned the following year. Academic area with the most degrees conferred: health professions and related sciences. Core. Calendar: semesters. Academic remediation for entering students, services for LD students, advanced placement, independent study, distance learning, double major, summer session for credit, part-time degree program, internships.
Entrance Requirements: Options: electronic application, deferred admission. Required: high school transcript, minimum 2.3 high school GPA. Required for some: SAT or ACT, SAT and SAT Subject Tests or ACT. Entrance: moderately difficult. Application deadline: Rolling. Notification: continuous. Transfer credits accepted: Yes. Applicants placed on waiting list: 34. Wait-listed applicants offered admission: 14.
Collegiate Environment: Orientation program. Social organizations: 4 open to all. Most popular organizations: Student Senate, intramural sports, Student Nurses Association, Phi Theta Kappa. Major annual events: Ahh Day, Welcome Week, Spring Week. Student services: personal-psychological counseling. Campus security: 24-hour patrols, late night transport-escort service, controlled dormitory access. 55 college housing spaces available; all were occupied in 2012-13. No special consideration for freshman housing applicants. Option: coed housing available. Mercy College of Ohio Library with 6,000 books, 128 serials, 681 audiovisual materials, and an OPAC. Operations spending for the previous fiscal year: $296,059. 76 computers available on campus for general student use. A campuswide network can be accessed. Students can access the following: online class registration, billing and payment, degree audit, and transcripts. Staffed computer lab on campus.

■ **MIAMI-JACOBS CAREER COLLEGE (COLUMBUS)**
150 E Gay St.
Columbus, OH 43215
Tel: (614)221-7770
Web Site: www.miamijacobs.edu/
Description: Proprietary, 2-year, coed.

■ **MIAMI-JACOBS CAREER COLLEGE (DAYTON)**
110 N Patterson Blvd.
Dayton, OH 45402
Tel: (937)461-5174
Fax: (937)461-3384
Web Site: www.miamijacobs.edu/
Description: Proprietary, 2-year, coed. Awards certificates, diplomas, and terminal associate degrees. Founded 1860. Setting: small town campus. Total enrollment: 811. 75 applied. 69% 25 or older. Core. Academic remediation for entering students, honors program, distance learning, summer session for credit, part-time degree program, internships. Off campus study at Southwestern Ohio Council for Higher Education.
Entrance Requirements: Options: early admission, deferred admission. Required: essay, high school transcript, interview, Wonderlic aptitude test. Recommended: SAT or ACT. Required for some: ACT. Entrance: minimally difficult. Application deadline: 8/15. Notification: continuous until 8/25.
Collegiate Environment: Student services: personal-psychological counseling. Campus security: late night transport-escort service.
Community Environment: See Wright State University.

■ **MIAMI-JACOBS CAREER COLLEGE (INDEPENDENCE)**
6400 Rockside Rd.
Independence, OH 44131
Tel: (216)834-1400; Free: 866-324-0142
Web Site: www.miamijacobs.edu/
Description: Proprietary, 2-year, coed. Awards certificates and terminal associate degrees. Founded 1970. Total enrollment: 419. Student-undergrad faculty ratio is 12:1. 109 applied, 75% were admitted. 0% from out-of-state. 4% 25 or older.
Entrance Requirements: Entrance: noncompetitive.

■ **MIAMI UNIVERSITY**
Oxford, OH 45056
Tel: (513)529-1809
Fax: (513)529-1550
E-mail: admission@miamioh.edu

Web Site: www.muohio.edu/

Description: State-related, university, coed. Part of Miami University System. Awards associate, bachelor's, master's, and doctoral degrees and post-master's certificates. Founded 1809. Setting: 2,000-acre small town campus with easy access to Cincinnati. System endowment: $387.4 million. Research spending for the previous fiscal year: $16.7 million. Educational spending for the previous fiscal year: $7971 per student. Total enrollment: 17,683. Faculty: 1,114 (841 full-time, 273 part-time). Student-undergrad faculty ratio is 18:1. 20,314 applied, 73% were admitted. 36% from top 10% of their high school class, 68% from top quarter, 96% from top half. 6 National Merit Scholars, 69 valedictorians. Full-time: 14,657 students, 52% women, 48% men. Part-time: 424 students, 49% women, 51% men. Students come from 51 states and territories, 73 other countries, 30% from out-of-state. 0.3% American Indian or Alaska Native, non-Hispanic/Latino; 3% Hispanic/Latino; 4% African American, non-Hispanic/Latino; 2% Asian, non-Hispanic/Latino; 0.1% Native Hawaiian or other Pacific Islander, non-Hispanic/Latino; 6% international. 2% 25 or older, 52% live on campus, 1% transferred in. Retention: 89% of full-time freshmen returned the following year. Academic areas with the most degrees conferred: business/marketing; education; social sciences. Core. Calendar: semesters. ESL program, services for LD students, advanced placement, self-designed majors, honors program, independent study, distance learning, double major, summer session for credit, co-op programs and internships, graduate courses open to undergrads. Off campus study at Greater Cincinnati Consortium of Colleges and Universities. Study abroad program. ROTC: Army (c), Naval, Air Force.

Entrance Requirements: Options: electronic application, early decision, early action, deferred admission, international baccalaureate accepted. Required: essay, high school transcript, 1 recommendation, SAT or ACT. Entrance: moderately difficult. Application deadlines: 2/1, 11/15 for early decision, 12/1 for early action. Notification: 3/15, 12/15 for early decision, 2/1 for early action. SAT Reasoning Test deadline: 2/1. Transfer credits accepted: Yes. Applicants placed on waiting list: 1,715. Wait-listed applicants offered admission: 6. Early decision applicants: 871. Early decision applicants admitted: 692. Early action applicants: 12,469. Early action applicants admitted: 10,673.

Costs Per Year: Application fee: $50. State resident tuition: $13,067 full-time. Nonresident tuition: $28,631 full-time. Mandatory fees: $528 full-time. Full-time tuition and fees vary according to location and program. College room and board: $10,596. College room only: $5250. Room and board charges vary according to board plan and housing facility.

Collegiate Environment: Orientation program. Drama-theater group, choral group, marching band, student-run newspaper, radio station. Social organizations: 344 open to all; national fraternities, national sororities; 24% of eligible men and 25% of eligible women are members. Most popular organizations: College Republicans, CRU (formerly Campus Crusade for Christ), Culinary Association, Pistol Club, Stage Left. Major annual events: Parents' Weekend, Kids' Fest Weekend, Homecoming. Student services: health clinic, personal-psychological counseling, women's center. Campus security: 24-hour emergency response devices and patrols, student patrols, late night transport-escort service, controlled dormitory access. College housing designed to accommodate 7,138 students; 7,271 undergraduates lived in college housing during 2012-13. Freshmen guaranteed college housing. On-campus residence required through sophomore year. Options: coed, men-only, women-only housing available. King Library plus 3 others with 4.2 million books, 276,385 microform titles, 109,477 serials, 2.2 million audiovisual materials, an OPAC, and a Web page. Operations spending for the previous fiscal year: $11.6 million. 1,200 computers available on campus for general student use. Computer purchase/lease plans available. A campuswide network can be accessed from student residence rooms and from off campus. Students can access the following: online class registration. Staffed computer lab on campus (open 24 hours a day) provides training in use of computers, software, and the Internet.

Community Environment: A college town with many beautiful old homes, Oxford, the location of Miami University, is where Professor McGuffey compiled the first of his readers. Recreational facilities provide for tennis, bowling, golf, and swimming. The Hueston Woods State Park also offers swimming, boating, and picnicking areas.

■ **MIAMI UNIVERSITY HAMILTON**
1601 Peck Blvd.
Hamilton, OH 45011-3399
Tel: (513)785-3000
E-mail: nelsona3@muohio.edu
Web Site: www.ham.muohio.edu/

Description: State-supported, comprehensive, coed. Part of Miami University System. Awards associate, bachelor's, and master's degrees (degrees awarded by Miami University main campus). Founded 1968. Setting: 78-acre suburban campus with easy access to Cincinnati. Total enrollment: 4,194. Faculty: 224 (84 full-time, 140 part-time). Student-undergrad faculty ratio is 21:1. Full-time: 3,280 students, 53% women, 47% men. Part-time: 902 students, 62% women, 38% men. 24% 25 or older, 5% transferred in. Core. Calendar: semesters plus summer sessions. Academic remediation for entering students, ESL program, services for LD students, advanced placement, self-designed majors, honors program, distance learning, double major, summer session for credit, part-time degree program, adult/continuing education programs, co-op programs and internships. Study abroad program. ROTC: Naval (c), Air Force (c).

Entrance Requirements: Open admission except for nursing program, transfer students. Option: electronic application. Required: high school transcript. Entrance: noncompetitive. Application deadline: Rolling. Notification: continuous.

Collegiate Environment: Orientation program. Drama-theater group. Social organizations: 16 open to all. Most popular organizations: student government, Campus Activities Committee, Ski Club, Student Nursing Association, OWLS (organization for wiser and world-wide learners). Major annual events: New Student Orientation, Spring Fest, Fall Picnic. Student services: personal-psychological counseling. Campus security: 24-hour emergency response devices and patrols, late night transport-escort service. Rentschler Library with 68,000 books, 400 serials, an OPAC, and a Web page. 300 computers available on campus for general student use. Computer purchase/lease plans available. A campuswide network can be accessed from off-campus. Students can access the following: online class registration. Staffed computer lab on campus provides training in use of computers, software, and the Internet.

Community Environment: The town of Hamilton is easily accessible from most of northern and western Hamilton County via several state and interstate routes. Employment opportunities are good in this area.

■ **MIAMI UNIVERSITY-MIDDLETOWN CAMPUS**
4200 E University Blvd.
Middletown, OH 45042-3497
Tel: (513)727-3200; Free: 866-426-4643
Fax: (513)727-3223
E-mail: cantondm@muohio.edu
Web Site: www.mid.muohio.edu/

Description: State-supported, primarily 2-year, coed. Part of Miami University System. Awards certificates, diplomas, transfer associate, terminal associate, and bachelor's degrees (also offers up to 2 years of most bachelor's degree programs offered at Miami University main campus). Founded 1966. Setting: 141-acre small town campus with easy access to Cincinnati, Dayton. Total enrollment: 2,660. Faculty: 209 (79 full-time, 130 part-time). Student-undergrad faculty ratio is 13:1. 28% 25 or older. Retention: 71% of full-time freshmen returned the following year. Calendar: semesters. Academic remediation for entering students, services for LD students, advanced placement, self-designed majors, independent study, distance learning, double major, summer session for credit, part-time degree program, adult/continuing education programs, co-op programs and internships. Off campus study at members of the Greater Cincinnati Consortium of Colleges and Universities. Study abroad program. ROTC: Air Force (c).

Entrance Requirements: Open admission except for nursing program. Options: electronic application, early admission, deferred admission. Required: high school transcript. Entrance: noncompetitive. Application deadline: Rolling. Notification: continuous.

Collegiate Environment: Orientation program. Social organizations: 28 open to all. Most popular organizations: student radio station, SEAL (Save Every Animal by Learning), Student Advisory Council, Model United Nations, Program Board. Major annual events: Haunted Trails, End of Year Picnic, MUMOXMUH. Student services: personal-psychological counseling, women's center. Campus security: 24-hour patrols, late night transport-escort service. Gardner-Harvey Library with 58,239 microform titles, 540 serials, 4,857 audiovisual materials, an OPAC, and a Web page. 180 computers available on campus for general student use. A campuswide network can be accessed from off-campus. Students can access the following: online class registration. Staffed computer lab on campus.

Community Environment: Middletown, population 51,472, is an industrial city in Butler County, SW Ohio. Its industries include aircraft parts, steel, and paper products.

■ MOUNT CARMEL COLLEGE OF NURSING

127 S Davis Ave.
Columbus, OH 43222
Tel: (614)234-5800; Free: 800-556-6942
E-mail: kcampbell@mccn.edu
Web Site: www.mccn.edu/

Description: Independent, comprehensive, coed. Administratively affiliated with Mount Carmel Health System. Awards bachelor's and master's degrees and post-master's certificates. Founded 1903. Setting: urban campus with easy access to Columbus, Ohio. System endowment: $942,750. Educational spending for the previous fiscal year: $12,924 per student. Total enrollment: 1,056. Faculty: 107 (46 full-time, 61 part-time). Student-undergrad faculty ratio is 13:1. 182 applied, 73% were admitted. 10% from top 10% of their high school class, 55% from top quarter, 95% from top half. Full-time: 635 students, 89% women, 11% men. Part-time: 251 students, 92% women, 8% men. Students come from 16 states and territories, 8% from out-of-state. 0.2% American Indian or Alaska Native, non-Hispanic/Latino; 1% Hispanic/Latino; 6% African American, non-Hispanic/Latino; 1% Asian, non-Hispanic/Latino; 0% Native Hawaiian or other Pacific Islander, non-Hispanic/Latino; 0% international. 33% 25 or older, 10% live on campus, 11% transferred in. Retention: 81% of full-time freshmen returned the following year. Academic area with the most degrees conferred: health professions and related sciences. Core. Calendar: semesters. Advanced placement, accelerated degree program, honors program, distance learning, summer session for credit, adult/continuing education programs. Off campus study at Columbus State Community College, Ohio University Lancaster, The Ohio State University. ROTC: Army (c), Naval (c), Air Force (c).

Entrance Requirements: Option: electronic application. Required: essay, high school transcript, activities/interests resume. Recommended: minimum 3 high school GPA. Required for some: interview, SAT or ACT. Entrance: moderately difficult. Application deadlines: 4/1, 4/1 for nonresidents. Notification: continuous, continuous for nonresidents. Transfer credits accepted: Yes. Applicants placed on waiting list: 10. Wait-listed applicants offered admission: 2.

Costs Per Year: Application fee: $30. One-time mandatory fee: $225. Tuition: $10,633 full-time, $343 per semester hour part-time. Mandatory fees: $732 full-time, $276 per term part-time. Full-time tuition and fees vary according to course level, course load, and student level. Part-time tuition and fees vary according to course level, course load, and student level. College room only: $5000.

Collegiate Environment: Orientation program. Social organizations: 5 open to all. Most popular organizations: Campus Ministry, Student Nurses Association of Mount Carmel (SNAM), Mount Carmel Rho Omicron Chapter of Sigma Theta Tau International Honor Society, Student Government Association (SGA), Student Ambassador Program. Major annual events: Convocation, Graduation. Student services: health clinic, personal-psychological counseling. Campus security: 24-hour emergency response devices and patrols, late night transport-escort service, controlled dormitory access. 144 college housing spaces available; 89 were occupied in 2012-13. Freshmen given priority for college housing. On-campus residence required through sophomore year. Option: coed housing available. The Mount Carmel Health Sciences Library plus 1 other with 95,090 books, 1,554 microform titles, 8,830 serials, 1,051 audiovisual materials, an OPAC, and a Web page. 70 computers available on campus for general student use. A campuswide network can be accessed from off-campus. Students can access the following: online class registration. Staffed computer lab on campus provides training in use of software and the Internet.

■ MOUNT VERNON NAZARENE UNIVERSITY

800 Martinsburg Rd.
Mount Vernon, OH 43050-9500
Tel: (740)392-6868; Free: 866-462-6868
E-mail: admissions@mvnu.edu
Web Site: www.mvnu.edu/

Description: Independent Nazarene, comprehensive, coed. Awards associate, bachelor's, and master's degrees. Founded 1964. Setting: 406-acre small town campus with easy access to Columbus. Endowment: $14.7 million. Educational spending for the previous fiscal year: $6752 per student. Total enrollment: 2,267. Faculty: 235 (100 full-time, 135 part-time). Student-undergrad faculty ratio is 13:1. 1,000 applied, 73% were admitted. 27% from top 10% of their high school class, 51% from top quarter, 80% from top half. 10 valedictorians. Full-time: 1,448 students, 64% women, 36% men. Part-time: 308 students, 69% women, 31% men. Students come from 33 states and territories, 5 other countries, 8% from out-of-state. 0.3% American

Indian or Alaska Native, non-Hispanic/Latino; 2% Hispanic/Latino; 3% African American, non-Hispanic/Latino; 1% Asian, non-Hispanic/Latino; 0.1% Native Hawaiian or other Pacific Islander, non-Hispanic/Latino; 1% international. 29% 25 or older, 80% live on campus, 2% transferred in. Retention: 76% of full-time freshmen returned the following year. Academic areas with the most degrees conferred: business/marketing; public administration and social services; education. Core. Calendar: 4-1-4. Academic remediation for entering students, services for LD students, advanced placement, honors program, independent study, distance learning, double major, summer session for credit, part-time degree program, adult/continuing education programs, internships. Off campus study at Kenyon College, and Coalition for Christian Colleges and Universities. Study abroad program.

Entrance Requirements: Options: electronic application, deferred admission. Required: essay, high school transcript, minimum 2.5 high school GPA, 2 recommendations, SAT or ACT. Entrance: moderately difficult. Application deadline: 7/15. Notification: 9/1. SAT Reasoning Test deadline: 7/15. SAT Subject Test deadline: 7/15. Transfer credits accepted: Yes.

Costs Per Year: Application fee: $25. Comprehensive fee: $30,670 includes full-time tuition ($23,690) and college room and board ($6980). College room only: $3900. Part-time tuition: $658 per credit hour.

Collegiate Environment: Orientation program. Drama-theater group, choral group, student-run newspaper, radio station. Social organizations: 29 open to all. Most popular organizations: Campus Ministry Groups, Student Government Association, Student Education Association, Drama Club, Music Department Ensembles. Major annual events: Welcome Week, Athletic Events and Concerts, Friday Night Live. Student services: health clinic, personal-psychological counseling. Campus security: 24-hour emergency response devices and patrols, late night transport-escort service, controlled dormitory access. 1,146 college housing spaces available; 987 were occupied in 2012-13. Freshmen guaranteed college housing. On-campus residence required through senior year. Options: men-only, women-only housing available. Thorne Library/Learning Resource Center with 107,246 books, 11,439 microform titles, 17,411 serials, 6,212 audiovisual materials, an OPAC, and a Web page. Operations spending for the previous fiscal year: $573,369. 186 computers available on campus for general student use. A campuswide network can be accessed from student residence rooms and from off campus. Staffed computer lab on campus provides training in use of computers, software, and the Internet.

■ MUSKINGUM UNIVERSITY

163 Stormont St.
New Concord, OH 43762
Tel: (740)826-8211; Free: 800-752-6082
Fax: (740)826-8404
E-mail: adminfo@muskingum.edu
Web Site: www.muskingum.edu/

Description: Independent, comprehensive, coed, affiliated with Presbyterian Church (U.S.A.). Awards bachelor's and master's degrees. Founded 1837. Setting: 215-acre small town campus with easy access to Columbus. Total enrollment: 2,099. 1,911 applied. 6% 25 or older. Core. Calendar: semesters. ESL program, services for LD students, advanced placement, accelerated degree program, self-designed majors, independent study, double major, summer session for credit, part-time degree program, external degree program, internships. Off campus study at Case Western Reserve University. Study abroad program.

Entrance Requirements: Options: electronic application, early admission, deferred admission, international baccalaureate accepted. Required: high school transcript, minimum 2.0 high school GPA, 1 recommendation, SAT or ACT. Recommended: essay, minimum 3.0 high school GPA, interview. Entrance: moderately difficult. Application deadline: 6/1. Notification: continuous.

Collegiate Environment: Orientation program. Drama-theater group, choral group, marching band, student-run newspaper, radio station. Social organizations: national fraternities, national sororities, local fraternities, local sororities. Student services: health clinic, personal-psychological counseling, women's center. Campus security: 24-hour emergency response devices and patrols, student patrols, late night transport-escort service. College Library with 233,000 books, 200,000 microform titles, 900 serials, 6,000 audiovisual materials, and a Web page.

Community Environment: New Concord is the boyhood home of John H. Glenn, Jr., the first American astronaut to orbit the earth. Also of interest is the log cabin birthplace of William Rainey Harper, first president of the University of Chicago and an alumnus of Muskingum College. Recreational activities in the area include golf, boating, fishing, hunting, and skating.

■ **NATIONAL COLLEGE (STOW)**

3855 Fishcreek Rd.
Stow, OH 44224
Tel: (330)676-1351
Web Site: www.national-college.edu/
Description: Proprietary, 2-year, coed. Founded 2007.

■ **NATIONAL COLLEGE (YOUNGSTOWN)**

3487 Belmont Ave.
Youngstown, OH 44505
Tel: (330)759-0205
Web Site: www.national-college.edu/
Description: Proprietary, 2-year, coed. Founded 2007.

■ **NORTH CENTRAL STATE COLLEGE**

2441 Kenwood Cir.
Mansfield, OH 44901-0698
Tel: (419)755-4800; Free: 888-755-4899
Fax: (419)755-4750
E-mail: nfletcher@ncstatecollege.edu
Web Site: www.ncstatecollege.edu/
Description: State-supported, 2-year, coed. Part of Ohio Board of Regents. Awards certificates and terminal associate degrees. Founded 1961. Setting: 600-acre suburban campus with easy access to Cleveland, Columbus. Total enrollment: 3,148. 43% 25 or older. Academic remediation for entering students, services for LD students, advanced placement, self-designed majors, independent study, distance learning, summer session for credit, part-time degree program, adult/continuing education programs, internships.
Entrance Requirements: Open admission. Options: early admission, deferred admission. Required for some: high school transcript. Entrance: noncompetitive. Application deadline: Rolling. Notification: continuous.
Collegiate Environment: Orientation program. Choral group, student-run radio station. Student services: personal-psychological counseling. Campus security: 24-hour emergency response devices and patrols, late night transport-escort service. Bromfield Library plus 1 other with 52,700 books, 410 serials, and an OPAC.
Community Environment: See Ohio State University - Mansfield Campus.

■ **NORTHWEST STATE COMMUNITY COLLEGE**

22-600 State Rte. 34
Archbold, OH 43502-9542
Tel: (419)267-5511
Fax: (419)267-3688
E-mail: admissions@northweststate.edu
Web Site: www.northweststate.edu/
Description: State-supported, 2-year, coed. Part of Ohio Board of Regents. Awards certificates, transfer associate, and terminal associate degrees. Founded 1968. Setting: 80-acre rural campus with easy access to Toledo. Educational spending for the previous fiscal year: $4780 per student. Total enrollment: 4,244. Faculty: 309 (42 full-time, 267 part-time). Student-undergrad faculty ratio is 15:1. 1,144 applied, 100% were admitted. 7% from top 10% of their high school class, 16% from top quarter, 40% from top half. Full-time: 881 students, 60% women, 40% men. Part-time: 3,363 students, 38% women, 62% men. Students come from 9 states and territories, 6 other countries, 0.2% from out-of-state. 0.2% American Indian or Alaska Native, non-Hispanic/Latino; 6% Hispanic/Latino; 2% African American, non-Hispanic/Latino; 0.5% Asian, non-Hispanic/Latino; 0% Native Hawaiian or other Pacific Islander, non-Hispanic/Latino; 0% international. 64% 25 or older, 2% transferred in. Retention: 53% of full-time freshmen returned the following year. Core. Calendar: semesters. Academic remediation for entering students, services for LD students, advanced placement, self-designed majors, independent study, distance learning, double major, summer session for credit, part-time degree program, external degree program, adult/continuing education programs, co-op programs and internships. Off campus study.
Entrance Requirements: Open admission. Options: electronic application, early admission, deferred admission. Required: high school transcript. Entrance: noncompetitive. Application deadlines: Rolling, Rolling for nonresidents. Notification: continuous, continuous for nonresidents.
Costs Per Year: Application fee: $20. State resident tuition: $3504 full-time, $146 per credit part-time. Nonresident tuition: $6864 full-time, $286 per credit part-time. Mandatory fees: $60 full-time, $30 per term part-time. Full-time tuition and fees vary according to course load. Part-time tuition and fees vary according to course load.

Collegiate Environment: Orientation program. Student services: personal-psychological counseling. Campus security: 24-hour emergency response devices, security patrols. College housing not available. Northwest State Community College Library with 30,596 books, 124 serials, 3,401 audiovisual materials, an OPAC, and a Web page. Operations spending for the previous fiscal year: $286,662.
Community Environment: The campus is in rural setting with a small town six miles to the north. The major metropolitan area of Toledo is 50 miles northeast, within easy access by major highways.

■ **NOTRE DAME COLLEGE**

4545 College Rd.
South Euclid, OH 44121-4293
Tel: (216)381-1680; Free: 877-NDC-OHIO
Fax: (216)381-3802
E-mail: admissinos@ndc.edu
Web Site: www.notredamecollege.edu/
Description: Independent Roman Catholic, comprehensive, coed. Awards associate, bachelor's, and master's degrees. Founded 1922. Setting: 53-acre suburban campus with easy access to Cleveland. Endowment: $7.7 million. Educational spending for the previous fiscal year: $4807 per student. Total enrollment: 1,393. Faculty: 118 (34 full-time, 84 part-time). Student-undergrad faculty ratio is 13:1. 1,255 applied, 52% were admitted. 6% from top 10% of their high school class, 20% from top quarter, 57% from top half. Full-time: 793 students, 61% women, 39% men. Part-time: 447 students, 75% women, 25% men. Students come from 17 states and territories, 19 other countries, 11% from out-of-state. 22% 25 or older, 44% live on campus, 4% transferred in. Retention: 65% of full-time freshmen returned the following year. Core. Calendar: semesters. Academic remediation for entering students, services for LD students, advanced placement, accelerated degree program, self-designed majors, independent study, distance learning, double major, summer session for credit, part-time degree program, adult/continuing education programs, co-op programs and internships. Off campus study at members of the Northeast Ohio Commission on Higher Education. Study abroad program.
Entrance Requirements: Options: electronic application, deferred admission. Required: essay, high school transcript, minimum 2.0 high school GPA, interview, SAT or ACT. Recommended: minimum 2.5 high school GPA. Entrance: moderately difficult. Application deadline: Rolling. Notification: continuous.
Collegiate Environment: Orientation program. Drama-theater group, choral group, student-run newspaper. Social organizations: 32 open to all. Most popular organizations: Undergraduate Student Senate, Resident Association Board, International Students/Multicultural Club, IHOP (I Help Other People), Bowling Club. Major annual events: Christmas Happening, Finals Week Stress Free Zone, All-Campus Picnic. Student services: personal-psychological counseling. Campus security: 24-hour emergency response devices and patrols, late night transport-escort service, controlled dormitory access. Clara Fritzsche Library with 14,770 microform titles, 9,983 audiovisual materials, and an OPAC. Operations spending for the previous fiscal year: $238,762. 65 computers available on campus for general student use. A campuswide network can be accessed. Staffed computer lab on campus.

■ **OBERLIN COLLEGE**

173 W Lorain St.
Oberlin, OH 44074
Tel: (440)775-8121; Free: 800-622-OBIE
Fax: (440)775-8886
E-mail: college.admissions@oberlin.edu
Web Site: www.oberlin.edu/
Description: Independent, comprehensive, coed. Awards bachelor's and master's degrees. Founded 1833. Setting: 440-acre small town campus with easy access to Cleveland. Endowment: $603.4 million. Total enrollment: 2,974. Faculty: 285. Student-undergrad faculty ratio is 9:1. 7,222 applied, 31% were admitted. 69% from top 10% of their high school class, 90% from top quarter, 99% from top half. 56 National Merit Scholars, 32 valedictorians, 39 student government officers. Full-time: 2,901 students, 55% women, 45% men. Part-time: 47 students, 47% women, 53% men. Students come from 51 states and territories, 44 other countries, 91% from out-of-state. 0.2% American Indian or Alaska Native, non-Hispanic/Latino; 6% Hispanic/Latino; 6% African American, non-Hispanic/Latino; 4% Asian, non-Hispanic/Latino; 0% Native Hawaiian or other Pacific Islander, non-Hispanic/Latino; 6% international. 0% 25 or older, 89% live on campus, 1% transferred in. Reten-

tion: 94% of full-time freshmen returned the following year. Academic areas with the most degrees conferred: English; visual and performing arts; biological/life sciences. Core. Calendar: 4-1-4. ESL program, services for LD students, advanced placement, self-designed majors, honors program, independent study, double major, part-time degree program, internships. Off campus study at Great Lakes Colleges Association. Study abroad program.

Entrance Requirements: Options: electronic application, early admission, early decision, deferred admission, international baccalaureate accepted. Required: essay, high school transcript, 2 recommendations, SAT or ACT. Recommended: SAT Subject Tests. Required for some: interview, audition for applicants to the Conservatory of Music. Entrance: very difficult. Application deadlines: 1/15, 11/15 for early decision plan 1, 1/2 for early decision plan 2. Notification: 4/1, 12/15 for early decision plan 1, 2/1 for early decision plan 2. SAT Reasoning Test deadline: 2/1. Transfer credits accepted: Yes. Applicants placed on waiting list: 1,226. Wait-listed applicants offered admission: 32. Early decision applicants: 385. Early decision applicants admitted: 235.

Collegiate Environment: Orientation program. Drama-theater group, choral group, marching band, student-run newspaper, radio station. Social organizations: 140 open to all. Most popular organizations: Experimental College, Community Outreach, student government, Students Cooperative Association, student radio station. Major annual events: Artist Recital Series, Convocation, The Big Parade. Student services: health clinic, personal-psychological counseling, women's center. Campus security: 24-hour emergency response devices and patrols, student patrols, late night transport-escort service, controlled dormitory access, crime prevention programs. Mudd Center Library plus 3 others with 1.4 million books, 356,864 microform titles, 30,750 serials, 104,227 audiovisual materials, and an OPAC. 340 computers available on campus for general student use. Computer purchase/lease plans available. A campuswide network can be accessed from student residence rooms and from off campus. Students can access the following: online class registration. Staffed computer lab on campus provides training in use of computers, software, and the Internet.

Community Environment: Oberlin College is located 35 miles southwest of Cleveland in a small town.

■ **OHIO BUSINESS COLLEGE (HILLIARD)**
4525 Trueman Blvd.
Hilliard, OH 43026
Tel: (614)891-0124
Web Site: www.ohiobusinesscollege.edu/
Description: Proprietary, 2-year, coed.

■ **OHIO BUSINESS COLLEGE (SANDUSKY)**
5202 Timber Commons Dr.
Sandusky, OH 44870
Tel: (419)627-8345; Free: 888-627-8345
Fax: (419)627-1958
E-mail: sandusky@ohiobusinesscollege.edu
Web Site: www.ohiobusinesscollege.edu/
Description: Proprietary, 2-year, coed. Awards diplomas and transfer associate degrees. Founded 1982. Setting: 1-acre suburban campus. Total enrollment: 451. Student-undergrad faculty ratio is 13:1. 0% from out-of-state. 71% 25 or older.
Entrance Requirements: Required: high school transcript.
Costs Per Year: Application fee: $25. One-time mandatory fee: $40. Tuition: $7740 full-time, $215 per credit hour part-time. Mandatory fees: $360 full-time, $10 per credit hour part-time. Full-time tuition and fees vary according to course load. Part-time tuition and fees vary according to course load. Tuition guaranteed not to increase for student's term of enrollment.

■ **OHIO BUSINESS COLLEGE (SHEFFIELD VILLAGE)**
5095 Waterford Dr.
Sheffield Village, OH 44035
Tel: (440)277-0021; Free: 888-514-3126
Fax: (440)277-7989
Web Site: www.ohiobusinesscollege.edu/
Description: Proprietary, 2-year, coed. Part of Tri State Educational Systems. Awards diplomas and terminal associate degrees. Founded 1903. Total enrollment: 231. 76% 25 or older. Core. Academic remediation for entering students, advanced placement, accelerated degree program, independent study, double major, summer session for credit, part-time degree program, external degree program, adult/continuing education programs, internships.

Entrance Requirements: Open admission. Option: electronic application. Required: high school transcript, interview. Entrance: noncompetitive. Application deadline: Rolling.
Collegiate Environment: Orientation program. Ohio Business College Library with 850 books and 20 serials.

■ **OHIO CHRISTIAN UNIVERSITY**
1476 Lancaster Pke.
Circleville, OH 43113-9487
Tel: (740)474-8896; Free: 877-762-8669
Fax: (740)477-7755
E-mail: enroll@ohiochristian.edu
Web Site: www.ohiochristian.edu/
Description: Independent, 4-year, coed, affiliated with Churches of Christ in Christian Union. Awards associate and bachelor's degrees. Founded 1948. Setting: 40-acre small town campus with easy access to Columbus. Total enrollment: 636. 277 applied. 54% 25 or older. Core. Calendar: semesters. Academic remediation for entering students, services for LD students, advanced placement, self-designed majors, honors program, independent study, double major, summer session for credit, part-time degree program, adult/continuing education programs, internships. Off campus study at Columbus State Community College.
Entrance Requirements: Options: electronic application, early admission. Required: essay, high school transcript, 4 recommendations, medical form. Recommended: SAT. Required for some: interview, ACT. Entrance: minimally difficult. Application deadline: Rolling. Notification: continuous.
Collegiate Environment: Orientation program. Drama-theater group, choral group. Student services: legal services, personal-psychological counseling. Campus security: security checks after midnight. Melvin Maxwell Memorial Library with 37,521 books, 111 serials, 1,995 audiovisual materials, and an OPAC.
Community Environment: Circleville is situated in the central part of the state, 23 miles south of Columbus. A shopping center and a number of civic and service organizations serve the community. The annual Circleville Pumpkin Show features a 350-pound pumpkin pie, five feet in diameter, attracting over 500,000 visitors from throughout the world.

■ **OHIO COLLEGE OF MASSOTHERAPY**
225 Heritage Woods Dr.
Akron, OH 44321
Tel: (330)665-1084; Free: 888-888-4325
Fax: (330)665-5021
E-mail: johna@ocm.edu
Web Site: www.ocm.edu/
Description: Independent, 2-year, coed. Awards terminal associate degrees. Founded 1973. Total enrollment: 282. Calendar: semesters.
Entrance Requirements: Entrance: noncompetitive.

■ **OHIO DOMINICAN UNIVERSITY**
1216 Sunbury Rd.
Columbus, OH 43219-2099
Tel: (614)253-2741; Free: 800-955-6446
Fax: (614)252-0776
E-mail: admissions@ohiodominican.edu
Web Site: www.ohiodominican.edu/
Description: Independent Roman Catholic, comprehensive, coed. Awards associate, bachelor's, and master's degrees. Founded 1911. Setting: 71-acre urban campus. Endowment: $23.2 million. Educational spending for the previous fiscal year: $2836 per student. Total enrollment: 3,052. Faculty: 170 (75 full-time, 95 part-time). Student-undergrad faculty ratio is 14:1. 2,367 applied, 59% were admitted. 9% from top 10% of their high school class, 28% from top quarter, 59% from top half. Full-time: 1,547 students, 57% women, 43% men. Part-time: 733 students, 67% women, 33% men. Students come from 17 states and territories, 11 other countries, 3% from out-of-state. 37% 25 or older, 76% live on campus, 5% transferred in. Retention: 61% of full-time freshmen returned the following year. Academic areas with the most degrees conferred: business/marketing; education; social sciences. Core. Calendar: semesters. Academic remediation for entering students, advanced placement, self-designed majors, honors program, independent study, distance learning, summer session for credit, part-time degree program, internships, graduate courses open to undergrads. Off campus study at members of the Higher Education Council of Columbus. Study abroad program. ROTC: Army (c).
Entrance Requirements: Options: electronic application, deferred admis-

sion, international baccalaureate accepted. Required: high school transcript, minimum 2 high school GPA, interview, SAT or ACT. Required for some: essay. Entrance: moderately difficult. Application deadline: Rolling. Notification: continuous.

Collegiate Environment: Orientation program. Drama-theater group, choral group, student-run newspaper, radio station. Social organizations: 42 open to all. Most popular organizations: Delta Sigma Pi, student government, Panther Activities Council, Black Student Union, Panther Players. Major annual events: Welcome Week, Homecoming Weekend, ODU Day. Student services: health clinic, personal-psychological counseling. Campus security: 24-hour emergency response devices and patrols, late night transport-escort service, controlled dormitory access. 740 college housing spaces available; 614 were occupied in 2012-13. On-campus residence required through junior year. Option: coed housing available. Spangler Library plus 1 other with 128,788 books, 10,853 microform titles, 9,161 serials, 4,173 audiovisual materials, an OPAC, and a Web page. Operations spending for the previous fiscal year: $793,180. 198 computers available on campus for general student use. A campuswide network can be accessed from student residence rooms and from off campus. Students can access the following: online class registration. Staffed computer lab on campus provides training in use of computers, software, and the Internet.

Community Environment: See Ohio State University Columbus Campus.

■ OHIO MID-WESTERN COLLEGE

19 Triangle Park Dr.
Sharonville, OH 45246
Tel: (513)772-9888
Web Site: omw.edu/

Description: Independent Baptist, 4-year, coed. Awards bachelor's degrees. Founded 1972. Total enrollment: 60. 36 applied. 60% 25 or older.

Entrance Requirements: Required: essay, high school transcript.

■ OHIO NORTHERN UNIVERSITY

525 S Main
Ada, OH 45810-1599
Tel: (419)772-2000; Free: 888-408-4ONU
Fax: (419)772-2313
E-mail: admissions-ug@onu.edu
Web Site: www.onu.edu/

Description: Independent, comprehensive, coed, affiliated with United Methodist Church. Awards bachelor's, master's, and doctoral degrees. Founded 1871. Setting: 340-acre small town campus. Total enrollment: 3,557. Faculty: 305 (229 full-time, 76 part-time). Student-undergrad faculty ratio is 12:1. 2,922 applied, 81% were admitted. 35% from top 10% of their high school class, 65% from top quarter, 87% from top half. Full-time: 2,232 students, 46% women, 54% men. Part-time: 397 students, 48% women, 52% men. Students come from 36 states and territories, 29 other countries, 20% from out-of-state. 0.04% American Indian or Alaska Native, non-Hispanic/Latino; 2% Hispanic/Latino; 4% African American, non-Hispanic/Latino; 1% Asian, non-Hispanic/Latino; 0.1% Native Hawaiian or other Pacific Islander, non-Hispanic/Latino; 6% international. 4% 25 or older, 2% transferred in. Retention: 86% of full-time freshmen returned the following year. Academic areas with the most degrees conferred: business/marketing; engineering; health professions and related sciences. Core. Academic remediation for entering students, ESL program, services for LD students, advanced placement, honors program, independent study, distance learning, double major, summer session for credit, part-time degree program, co-op programs and internships. Off campus study. Study abroad program. ROTC: Army (c), Air Force (c).

Entrance Requirements: Options: electronic application, deferred admission, international baccalaureate accepted. Required: high school transcript, SAT or ACT. Recommended: essay, minimum 2.5 high school GPA, 1 recommendation, interview. Entrance: moderately difficult. Application deadlines: 8/15, 8/15 for nonresidents. Notification: continuous, continuous for nonresidents. SAT Reasoning Test deadline: 8/1. Transfer credits accepted: Yes.

Costs Per Year: Application fee: $0. Comprehensive fee: $47,240 includes full-time tuition ($36,480), mandatory fees ($240), and college room and board ($10,520). Full-time tuition and fees vary according to course load, degree level, and program. Room and board charges vary according to board plan, housing facility, and student level. Part-time tuition: $1520 per credit hour. Part-time tuition varies according to course load, degree level, and program.

Collegiate Environment: Orientation program. Drama-theater group, choral

group, marching band, student-run newspaper, radio station. Social organizations: 200 open to all; national fraternities, national sororities; 15% of eligible men and 21% of eligible women are members. Most popular organizations: Habitat for Humanity, Student Planning Committee, Student Senate, Northern Christian Fellowship, marching band. Major annual events: Homecoming, Hypnotist, Mud Volleyball. Student services: legal services, health clinic, personal-psychological counseling. Campus security: 24-hour emergency response devices and patrols, late night transport-escort service, controlled dormitory access. 2,196 college housing spaces available; 1,999 were occupied in 2012-13. Freshmen guaranteed college housing. On-campus residence required through junior year. Options: coed, men-only, women-only housing available. Heterick Memorial Library plus 1 other with an OPAC and a Web page. 533 computers available on campus for general student use. A campuswide network can be accessed from student residence rooms and from off campus. Students can access the following: online class registration. Staffed computer lab on campus (open 24 hours a day) provides training in use of computers, software, and the Internet.

Community Environment: Ada, a community of nearly 5,000 people, is located 15 miles east of Lima, 22 miles south of Findlay, and only 8 miles from I-75. Health services are provided by the university. Some of the usual civic and service organizations are active.

■ THE OHIO STATE UNIVERSITY

Student Academic Services Bldg.
281 W Ln. Ave.
Columbus, OH 43210
Tel: (614)292-6446
Fax: (614)292-4818
E-mail: askabuckeye@osu.edu
Web Site: www.osu.edu/

Description: State-supported, university, coed. Part of Ohio State University System. Awards bachelor's, master's, and doctoral degrees and post-master's certificates. Founded 1870. Setting: 3,469-acre urban campus with easy access to Columbus. Endowment: $2.4 billion. Research spending for the previous fiscal year: $432.1 million. Educational spending for the previous fiscal year: $16,864 per student. Total enrollment: 56,387. Faculty: 4,974 (3,477 full-time, 1,497 part-time). Student-undergrad faculty ratio is 19:1. 25,816 applied, 64% were admitted. 54% from top 10% of their high school class, 89% from top quarter, 99% from top half. 89 National Merit Scholars, 339 valedictorians. Full-time: 38,884 students, 48% women, 52% men. Part-time: 4,174 students, 44% women, 56% men. Students come from 55 states and territories, 72 other countries, 12% from out-of-state. 0.2% American Indian or Alaska Native, non-Hispanic/Latino; 3% Hispanic/Latino; 6% African American, non-Hispanic/Latino; 5% Asian, non-Hispanic/Latino; 0.1% Native Hawaiian or other Pacific Islander, non-Hispanic/Latino; 8% international. 7% 25 or older, 25% live on campus, 6% transferred in. Retention: 92% of full-time freshmen returned the following year. Academic areas with the most degrees conferred: business/marketing; social sciences; engineering. Core. Academic remediation for entering students, ESL program, services for LD students, advanced placement, accelerated degree program, self-designed majors, freshman honors college, honors program, independent study, distance learning, double major, summer session for credit, part-time degree program, adult/continuing education programs, co-op programs and internships, graduate courses open to undergrads. Off campus study at Higher Education Council of Columbus. Study abroad program. ROTC: Army, Naval, Air Force.

Entrance Requirements: Options: electronic application, international baccalaureate accepted. Required: essay, high school transcript, SAT or ACT. Entrance: very difficult. Application deadlines: 2/1, 2/1 for nonresidents. Notification: continuous, continuous for nonresidents. SAT Reasoning Test deadline: 2/1. Transfer credits accepted: Yes. Applicants placed on waiting list: 1,191. Wait-listed applicants offered admission: 0.

Costs Per Year: Application fee: $60. Area resident tuition: $9615 full-time, $401 per credit hour part-time. State resident tuition: $9615 full-time, $401 per credit hour part-time. Nonresident tuition: $25,335 full-time, $1056 per credit hour part-time. Mandatory fees: $422 full-time. Full-time tuition and fees vary according to course load, location, program, and reciprocity agreements. Part-time tuition varies according to course load, location, program, and reciprocity agreements. College room and board: $10,370. College room only: $6020. Room and board charges vary according to board plan, housing facility, and location.

Collegiate Environment: Orientation program. Drama-theater group, choral group, marching band, student-run newspaper, radio station. Social organizations: 1,444 open to all; national fraternities, national sororities, local fraternities, local sororities; 6% of eligible men and 6% of eligible women are members. Most popular organizations: African Student Union, Bisexual, Gay and Lesbian Alliance, Campus Crusade for Christ, University Wide Council of Hispanic Organizations, Asian-American Association. Major annual events: Michigan Week festivities, Welcome Week, Homecoming. Student services: legal services, health clinic, personal-psychological counseling, women's center. Campus security: 24-hour emergency response devices and patrols, student patrols, late night transport-escort service, controlled dormitory access, dorm entrances locked after 9 pm, lighted pathways and sidewalks, self-defense education. 9,936 college housing spaces available. Freshmen guaranteed college housing. On-campus residence required in freshman year. Options: coed, women-only housing available. Thompson Library plus 12 others with 6.2 million books, 6.2 million microform titles, 26,297 serials, 92,109 audiovisual materials, an OPAC, and a Web page. Operations spending for the previous fiscal year: $30.9 million. 295 computers available on campus for general student use. A campuswide network can be accessed from student residence rooms and from off campus. Students can access the following: online class registration, students can apply for admission, register, check grades, pay fees and obtain library resources, including books, online. Staffed computer lab on campus (open 24 hours a day) provides training in use of computers, software, and the Internet.

■ THE OHIO STATE UNIVERSITY AGRICULTURAL TECHNICAL INSTITUTE

1328 Dover Rd.
Wooster, OH 44691
Tel: (330)264-3911; Free: 800-647-8283
E-mail: morris.878@osu.edu
Web Site: www.ati.osu.edu/

Description: State-supported, 2-year, coed. Part of Ohio State University System. Awards certificates, diplomas, transfer associate, and terminal associate degrees. Founded 1971. Setting: small town campus with easy access to Cleveland, Columbus. Endowment: $2.2 million. Total enrollment: 730. Faculty: 70 (33 full-time, 37 part-time). Student-undergrad faculty ratio is 17:1. 636 applied, 91% were admitted. 6% from top 10% of their high school class, 20% from top quarter, 52% from top half. Full-time: 730 students, 43% women, 57% men. Students come from 7 states and territories, 2% from out-of-state. 10% 25 or older, 5% transferred in. Retention: 68% of full-time freshmen returned the following year. Core. Academic remediation for entering students, services for LD students, advanced placement, accelerated degree program, self-designed majors, independent study, distance learning, double major, summer session for credit, part-time degree program, adult/continuing education programs, co-op programs and internships. Study abroad program. ROTC: Army (c), Naval (c), Air Force (c).
Entrance Requirements: Open admission for state residents. Option: electronic application. Required: high school transcript. Required for some: SAT or ACT. Entrance: noncompetitive. Application deadlines: 7/1, 7/1 for nonresidents. Notification: continuous. Transfer credits accepted: Yes.
Costs Per Year: Application fee: $60. Area resident tuition: $7104 full-time, $296 per credit hour part-time. State resident tuition: $7104 full-time, $296 per credit hour part-time. Nonresident tuition: $22,824 full-time, $951 per credit hour part-time. Full-time tuition varies according to course load. Part-time tuition varies according to course load. College room and board: $10,370. College room only: $6020.
Collegiate Environment: Orientation program. Social organizations: 19 open to all. Most popular organizations: Hoof-n-Hide Club, Collegiate FFA, Campus Crusade for Christ, Phi Theta Kappa, Community Council. Major annual events: Welcome Days, Ag Olympics, Fall Barn Dance. Student services: health clinic, personal-psychological counseling. Campus security: 24-hour emergency response devices and patrols, controlled dormitory access. 533 college housing spaces available; 490 were occupied in 2012-13. No special consideration for freshman housing applicants. On-campus residence required in freshman year. Option: coed housing available. Agricultural Technical Institute Library with 9,000 books, 260 serials, 100 audiovisual materials, an OPAC, and a Web page. 85 computers available on campus for general student use. Students can access the following: online class registration. Staffed computer lab on campus.
Community Environment: Wooster, population 25,600, is the county seat of Wayne County and is in a major agricultural area accessible from any area of the state. It is also home to the College of Wooster, and the corporate headquarters of Rubbermaid and other companies including Frito-Lay, Wooster Brush Company, Regal Ware, the Gerstenslager Company, and Bell and Howell. Students also have access to Cleveland, Columbus, Pittsburgh, Cincinnati, and Akron.

■ THE OHIO STATE UNIVERSITY AT LIMA

4240 Campus Dr.
Lima, OH 45804
Tel: (419)995-8600
Fax: (419)995-8483
E-mail: admissions@lima.ohio-state.edu
Web Site: lima.osu.edu/

Description: State-supported, comprehensive, coed. Part of The Ohio State University. Awards associate, bachelor's, and master's degrees. Founded 1960. Setting: 565-acre suburban campus. Research spending for the previous fiscal year: $202,206. Educational spending for the previous fiscal year: $6294 per student. Total enrollment: 64. Faculty: 89 (36 full-time, 53 part-time). Student-undergrad faculty ratio is 18:1. 1,068 applied, 99% were admitted. 8% from top 10% of their high school class, 30% from top quarter, 69% from top half. 4 valedictorians. Full-time: 915 students, 54% women, 46% men. Part-time: 153 students, 59% women, 41% men. Students come from 3 states and territories, 2 other countries, 1% from out-of-state. 0.3% American Indian or Alaska Native, non-Hispanic/Latino; 3% Hispanic/Latino; 5% African American, non-Hispanic/Latino; 1% Asian, non-Hispanic/Latino; 0% Native Hawaiian or other Pacific Islander, non-Hispanic/Latino; 0.2% international. 14% 25 or older, 5% transferred in. Retention: 62% of full-time freshmen returned the following year. Core. Academic remediation for entering students, ESL program, services for LD students, advanced placement, accelerated degree program, self-designed majors, freshman honors college, honors program, independent study, distance learning, double major, summer session for credit, part-time degree program, adult/continuing education programs, co-op programs and internships, graduate courses open to undergrads. Off campus study. Study abroad program. ROTC: Army (c), Naval (c), Air Force (c).
Entrance Requirements: Open admission open admission to in-state students, selective admission for out-of-state students. Option: electronic application. Required: essay, high school transcript, SAT or ACT. Entrance: noncompetitive. Application deadlines: 6/1, 6/1 for nonresidents. Notification: continuous, continuous for nonresidents. SAT Reasoning Test deadline: 6/1. Transfer credits accepted: Yes.
Costs Per Year: Application fee: $60. Area resident tuition: $7140 full-time, $298 per credit hour part-time. State resident tuition: $7140 full-time, $298 per credit hour part-time. Nonresident tuition: $22,860 full-time, $953 per credit hour part-time.
Collegiate Environment: Orientation program. Choral group. Social organizations: 30 open to all. Most popular organizations: Student Senate, Psychology Club, Honors Club, Aggies, Newman Catholic Association. Major annual events: May Week, Welcome Week, Involvement Fair, Walking Taco Day, Blood drives, Comic Book Day. Student services: personal-psychological counseling. Campus security: 24-hour emergency response devices and patrols, student patrols, late night transport-escort service, lighted pathways/sidewalks. College housing not available. Lima Campus Library plus 1 other with 81,572 books, 3,218 microform titles, 276 serials, 1,111 audiovisual materials, an OPAC, and a Web page. 150 computers available on campus for general student use. Computer purchase/lease plans available. A campuswide network can be accessed. Students can access the following: online class registration. Staffed computer lab on campus provides training in use of computers, software, and the Internet.

■ THE OHIO STATE UNIVERSITY AT MARION

1465 Mount Vernon Ave.
Marion, OH 43302-5695
Tel: (740)389-6786
E-mail: moreau.1@osu.edu
Web Site: osumarion.osu.edu/

Description: State-supported, comprehensive, coed. Part of The Ohio State University. Awards associate, bachelor's, and master's degrees. Founded 1958. Setting: 188-acre small town campus with easy access to Columbus. Research spending for the previous fiscal year: $112,166. Educational spending for the previous fiscal year: $5492 per student. Total enrollment: 49. Faculty: 103 (35 full-time, 68 part-time). Student-undergrad faculty ratio is 18:1. 853 applied, 98% were admitted. 11% from top 10% of their high school class, 28% from top quarter, 70% from top half. Full-time: 949 students, 54% women, 46% men. Part-time: 273 students, 55% women, 45% men. Students come from 4 states and territories, 1 other country. 0.4% American Indian or Alaska Native, non-Hispanic/Latino; 2% Hispanic/Latino; 6% African American, non-Hispanic/Latino; 4% Asian, non-Hispanic/Latino; 0.2% Native Hawaiian or other Pacific Islander, non-Hispanic/Latino; 0.1% international. 16% 25 or older, 6% transferred in. Retention: 67% of full-time freshmen returned the following year. Core. Academic remediation for entering students, ESL program, services for LD students, advanced placement, accelerated degree program, self-designed majors, freshman honors college, honors program, independent study, distance learning, double major, summer session for credit, part-time degree program, adult/continuing education programs, co-op programs and internships, graduate courses open to undergrads. Off campus study. Study abroad program. ROTC: Army (c), Naval (c), Air Force (c).

Entrance Requirements: Open admission Open admission for in-state students. Selective admission for out-of-state students. Option: electronic application. Required: essay, high school transcript, SAT or ACT. Entrance: noncompetitive. Application deadlines: 6/1, 6/1 for nonresidents. Notification: continuous, continuous for nonresidents. SAT Reasoning Test deadline: 2/1. Transfer credits accepted: Yes.

Costs Per Year: Application fee: $60. Area resident tuition: $7140 full-time, $298 per credit hour part-time. State resident tuition: $7140 full-time, $298 per credit hour part-time. Nonresident tuition: $22,860 full-time, $953 per credit hour part-time. Full-time tuition varies according to course load and student level. Part-time tuition varies according to course load and student level.

Collegiate Environment: Orientation program. Choral group. Social organizations: 15 open to all. Student services: personal-psychological counseling. Campus security: 24-hour emergency response devices. Marion Campus Library plus 1 other with 6.2 million books, 3,611 microform titles, 75,963 serials, 1,576 audiovisual materials, an OPAC, and a Web page. 128 computers available on campus for general student use. Computer purchase/lease plans available. A campuswide network can be accessed. Students can access the following: online class registration. Staffed computer lab on campus provides training in use of computers, software, and the Internet.

■ THE OHIO STATE UNIVERSITY–MANSFIELD CAMPUS

1680 University Dr.
Mansfield, OH 44906-1599
Tel: (419)755-4011
E-mail: admissions@mansfield.ohio-state.edu
Web Site: www.mansfield.osu.edu/

Description: State-supported, comprehensive, coed. Part of The Ohio State University. Awards associate, bachelor's, and master's degrees. Founded 1958. Setting: 640-acre small town campus with easy access to Columbus, Cleveland. Research spending for the previous fiscal year: $172,590. Educational spending for the previous fiscal year: $5557 per student. Total enrollment: 1,265. Faculty: 92 (40 full-time, 52 part-time). Student-undergrad faculty ratio is 19:1. 1,366 applied, 99% were admitted. 5% from top 10% of their high school class, 26% from top quarter, 62% from top half. 2 valedictorians. Full-time: 1,001 students, 54% women, 46% men. Part-time: 202 students, 52% women, 48% men. Students come from 6 states and territories, 1 other country, 1% from out-of-state. 0.3% American Indian or Alaska Native, non-Hispanic/Latino; 2% Hispanic/Latino; 7% African American, non-Hispanic/Latino; 0.4% Asian, non-Hispanic/Latino; 0% Native Hawaiian or other Pacific Islander, non-Hispanic/Latino; 0.1% international. 17% 25 or older, 17% live on campus, 6% transferred in. Retention: 70% of full-time freshmen returned the following year. Core. Academic remediation for entering students, ESL program, services for LD students, advanced placement, accelerated degree program, self-designed majors, freshman honors college, honors program, independent study, distance learning, double major, summer session for credit, part-time degree program, adult/continuing education programs, co-op programs and internships, graduate courses open to undergrads. Off campus study. Study abroad program. ROTC: Army (c), Naval (c), Air Force (c).

Entrance Requirements: Open admission Open admission for in-state students. Selective admission for out-of-state students. Option: electronic application. Required: essay, high school transcript, SAT or ACT. Entrance: noncompetitive. Application deadlines: 6/1, 6/1 for nonresidents. Notification: continuous, continuous for nonresidents. SAT Reasoning Test deadline: 6/1. Transfer credits accepted: Yes.

Costs Per Year: Application fee: $60. Area resident tuition: $7140 full-time, $298 per credit hour part-time. State resident tuition: $7140 full-time, $298 per credit hour part-time. Nonresident tuition: $22,860 full-time, $953 per credit hour part-time. College room only: $6020.

Collegiate Environment: Orientation program. Drama-theater group, choral group. Social organizations: 28 open to all. Most popular organizations: Campus Activities Board, Campus Crusader for Christ, Club Ed, Multicultural Student Association, Psychology Student Association. Student services:

personal-psychological counseling. Campus security: 24-hour emergency response devices and patrols. 197 college housing spaces available. Option: coed housing available. Bromfield Library plus 1 other with 51,680 books, 1,674 audiovisual materials, an OPAC, and a Web page. 235 computers available on campus for general student use. Computer purchase/lease plans available. A campuswide network can be accessed. Students can access the following: online class registration.

■ THE OHIO STATE UNIVERSITY–NEWARK CAMPUS

1179 University Dr.
Newark, OH 43055-1797
Tel: (740)366-3321
E-mail: barclay.3@osu.edu
Web Site: www.newark.osu.edu/

Description: State-supported, comprehensive, coed. Part of The Ohio State University. Awards associate, bachelor's, and master's degrees. Founded 1957. Setting: 106-acre small town campus with easy access to Columbus. Research spending for the previous fiscal year: $102,956. Educational spending for the previous fiscal year: $4432 per student. Total enrollment: 2,390. Faculty: 151 (50 full-time, 101 part-time). Student-undergrad faculty ratio is 24:1. 2,764 applied, 99% were admitted. 4% from top 10% of their high school class, 22% from top quarter, 59% from top half. 4 valedictorians. Full-time: 1,918 students, 52% women, 48% men. Part-time: 383 students, 58% women, 42% men. Students come from 7 states and territories. 0.3% American Indian or Alaska Native, non-Hispanic/Latino; 2% Hispanic/Latino; 14% African American, non-Hispanic/Latino; 3% Asian, non-Hispanic/Latino; 0.1% Native Hawaiian or other Pacific Islander, non-Hispanic/Latino; 0% international. 11% 25 or older, 8% live on campus, 5% transferred in. Retention: 61% of full-time freshmen returned the following year. Core. Academic remediation for entering students, ESL program, services for LD students, advanced placement, accelerated degree program, self-designed majors, freshman honors college, honors program, independent study, distance learning, double major, summer session for credit, part-time degree program, adult/continuing education programs, co-op programs and internships, graduate courses open to undergrads. Off campus study. Study abroad program. ROTC: Army, Naval (c), Air Force (c).

Entrance Requirements: Open admission Open admission for in-state students. Selective admission for out-of-state students. Option: electronic application. Required: essay, high school transcript, SAT or ACT. Entrance: noncompetitive. Application deadlines: 6/1, 6/1 for nonresidents. Notification: continuous, continuous for nonresidents. SAT Reasoning Test deadline: 6/1. Transfer credits accepted: Yes.

Collegiate Environment: Orientation program. Choral group. Social organizations: 25 open to all. Student services: personal-psychological counseling. Campus security: 24-hour emergency response devices and patrols, late night transport-escort service, self-defense education. 180 college housing spaces available. Option: coed housing available. Newark Campus Library plus 1 other with 4.7 million books, 250 serials, 2,000 audiovisual materials, an OPAC, and a Web page. 132 computers available on campus for general student use. Computer purchase/lease plans available. A campuswide network can be accessed from student residence rooms. Students can access the following: online class registration. Staffed computer lab on campus.

■ OHIO TECHNICAL COLLEGE

1374 E 51st St.
Cleveland, OH 44103
Tel: (216)881-1700; Free: 800-322-7000
Fax: (216)881-9145
E-mail: ohioauto@aol.com
Web Site: www.ohiotechnicalcollege.com/

Description: Proprietary, 2-year, coed. Awards terminal associate degrees. Founded 1969. Total enrollment: 654.

Entrance Requirements: Entrance: noncompetitive.

■ OHIO UNIVERSITY

Athens, OH 45701-2979
Tel: (740)593-1000
Fax: (740)593-4229
E-mail: admissions@ohio.edu
Web Site: www.ohio.edu/

Description: State-supported, university, coed. Part of Ohio Board of Regents, University System of Ohio. Awards associate, bachelor's, master's, and doctoral degrees. Founded 1804. Setting: 1,774-acre small town campus. Endowment: $409 million. Research spending for the previous fiscal year: $33.5 million. Educational spending for the previous fiscal year: $8965 per student. Total enrollment: 27,402. Faculty: 1,229 (852 full-time, 377 part-time). Student-undergrad faculty ratio is 19:1. 17,466 applied, 78% were admitted. 16% from top 10% of their high school class, 42% from top quarter, 81% from top half. 7 National Merit Scholars, 65 valedictorians. Full-time: 16,862 students, 53% women, 47% men. Part-time: 5,823 students, 80% women, 20% men. Students come from 49 states and territories, 61 other countries, 13% from out-of-state. 0.2% American Indian or Alaska Native, non-Hispanic/Latino; 2% Hispanic/Latino; 5% African American, non-Hispanic/Latino; 1% Asian, non-Hispanic/Latino; 0.1% Native Hawaiian or other Pacific Islander, non-Hispanic/Latino; 4% international. 4% 25 or older, 40% live on campus, 3% transferred in. Retention: 79% of full-time freshmen returned the following year. Academic areas with the most degrees conferred: health professions and related sciences; communication/journalism; business/marketing. Core. Academic remediation for entering students, ESL program, services for LD students, advanced placement, accelerated degree program, self-designed majors, freshman honors college, honors program, independent study, distance learning, double major, summer session for credit, part-time degree program, external degree program, adult/continuing education programs, co-op programs and internships, graduate courses open to undergrads. Off campus study. Study abroad program. ROTC: Army, Air Force.

Entrance Requirements: Options: electronic application, early admission, deferred admission, international baccalaureate accepted. Required: high school transcript, SAT or ACT. Recommended: 2 recommendations. Required for some: essay, 2 recommendations, interview, Auditions required for music and dance; interview and portfolio reviews for visual communication, and application supplement for Honors Tutorial College. Entrance: moderately difficult. Application deadlines: 2/1, 2/1 for nonresidents. Notification: continuous, continuous for nonresidents. SAT Reasoning Test deadline: 3/1. SAT Subject Test deadline: 3/1. Transfer credits accepted: Yes. Applicants placed on waiting list: 440. Wait-listed applicants offered admission: 113.

Costs Per Year: Application fee: $45. State resident tuition: $10,282 full-time, $487 per semester hour part-time. Nonresident tuition: $19,246 full-time, $929 per semester hour part-time. Full-time tuition varies according to degree level, location, program, and reciprocity agreements. Part-time tuition varies according to course load, degree level, location, program, and reciprocity agreements. College room and board: $10,010. College room only: $5648. Room and board charges vary according to board plan.

Collegiate Environment: Orientation program. Drama-theater group, choral group, marching band, student-run newspaper, radio station. Social organizations: 420 open to all; national fraternities, national sororities; 7% of eligible men and 8% of eligible women are members. Most popular organizations: Alpha Phi Omega, Golden Key Honor Society, International Student Union, Kappa Delta Pi, Campus Crusade for Christ. Major annual events: Homecoming, International Week, Parents' Weekend. Student services: legal services, health clinic, personal-psychological counseling, women's center. Campus security: 24-hour emergency response devices and patrols, student patrols, late night transport-escort service, controlled dormitory access, electronic dormitory access is being phased in gradually as part of renovations. OU has a fully sworn, 24/7 police department. 8,103 college housing spaces available; 7,268 were occupied in 2012-13. Freshmen guaranteed college housing. On-campus residence required through sophomore year. Options: coed, women-only housing available. Alden Library plus 3 others with 3.3 million books, 2 million microform titles, 62,042 serials, 88,963 audiovisual materials, an OPAC, and a Web page. Operations spending for the previous fiscal year: $13.6 million. 1,000 computers available on campus for general student use. Computer purchase/lease plans available. A campuswide network can be accessed from student residence rooms and from off campus. Students can access the following: online class registration. Staffed computer lab on campus (open 24 hours a day) provides training in use of computers, software, and the Internet.

Community Environment: Athens is a traditional college town with a nonstudent population of approximately 21,000. The city is located about 75 miles southeast of Columbus, the state capital, in the foothills of the Appalachian mountains and on the banks of the Hocking River. Several state parks and thousands of acres of national forests are within easy driving distance and provide ample facilities for swimming, hiking, camping, fishing, and picnicking.

■ **OHIO UNIVERSITY–CHILLICOTHE**

101 University Dr.
Chillicothe, OH 45601

Tel: (740)774-7200; Free: 877-462-6824
Fax: (740)774-7295
E-mail: evelandt@ohio.edu
Web Site: www.chillicothe.ohiou.edu/

Description: State-supported, 4-year, coed. Part of Ohio Board of Regents. Administratively affiliated with Ohio University. Awards associate, bachelor's, and master's degrees. (offers first 2 years of most bachelor's degree programs available at the main campus in Athens; also offers several bachelor's degree programs that can be completed at this campus and several programs exclusive to this campus; also offers some graduate programs). Founded 1946. Setting: 124-acre small town campus with easy access to Columbus. Total enrollment: 2,200. Retention: 0% of full-time freshmen returned the following year. Core. Academic remediation for entering students, services for LD students, advanced placement, distance learning, summer session for credit, part-time degree program, external degree program, adult/continuing education programs, internships. Study abroad program.

Entrance Requirements: Open admission for state residents. Options: electronic application, early admission, deferred admission. Required: high school transcript, COMPASS. Entrance: noncompetitive. Application deadline: 9/1. Notification: continuous. Transfer credits accepted: Yes.

Costs Per Year: Application fee: $20. State resident tuition: $4956 full-time, $222 per credit hour part-time. Nonresident tuition: $6802 full-time, $308 per credit hour part-time. Full-time tuition varies according to course load, location, program, and student level. Part-time tuition varies according to course load, location, program, and student level.

Collegiate Environment: Orientation program. Drama-theater group. Student services: personal-psychological counseling. Campus security: 24-hour emergency response devices, patrols by city police. College housing not available.

■ **OHIO UNIVERSITY–EASTERN**

45425 National Rd.
Saint Clairsville, OH 43950-9724
Tel: (740)695-1720; Free: 800-648-3331
E-mail: howardn@ohio.edu
Web Site: www.eastern.ohiou.edu/

Description: State-supported, comprehensive, coed. Part of Ohio Board of Regents. Awards associate, bachelor's, and master's degrees (also offers some graduate courses). Founded 1957. Setting: 300-acre rural campus. Total enrollment: 751. 26% 25 or older. Core. Academic remediation for entering students, advanced placement, accelerated degree program, self-designed majors, summer session for credit, part-time degree program, external degree program, adult/continuing education programs.

Entrance Requirements: Open admission. Options: early admission, deferred admission. Required: high school transcript. Entrance: noncompetitive. Application deadline: Rolling.

Collegiate Environment: Drama-theater group. 50,000 books, 625 serials, and an OPAC.

■ **OHIO UNIVERSITY–LANCASTER**

1570 Granville Pke.
Lancaster, OH 43130-1097
Tel: (740)654-6711; Free: 888-446-4468
Fax: (740)687-9497
E-mail: fox@ohio.edu
Web Site: www.ohiou.edu/lancaster/

Description: State-supported, comprehensive, coed. Part of Ohio Board of Regents. Awards associate, bachelor's, and master's degrees. Founded 1968. Setting: 360-acre small town campus with easy access to Columbus. Total enrollment: 1,728. 31% 25 or older. Core. Academic remediation for entering students, advanced placement, accelerated degree program, self-designed majors, independent study, distance learning, double major, summer session for credit, part-time degree program, external degree program, adult/continuing education programs, internships. ROTC: Army (c), Air Force (c).

Entrance Requirements: Open admission. Options: electronic application, early admission, deferred admission. Required: high school transcript. Recommended: interview. Entrance: noncompetitive. Application deadline: Rolling. Notification: continuous.

Collegiate Environment: Orientation program. Drama-theater group. Hannah V. McCauley Library with 94,688 books, 369,265 microform titles, 399 serials, 2,759 audiovisual materials, an OPAC, and a Web page.

■ OHIO UNIVERSITY–SOUTHERN CAMPUS

1804 Liberty Ave.

Ironton, OH 45638-2214

Tel: (740)533-4600; Free: 800-626-0513

Fax: (740)533-4632

E-mail: harlow@ohio.edu

Web Site: www.ohiou.edu/

Description: State-supported, comprehensive, coed. Part of Ohio Board of Regents. Awards associate, bachelor's, and master's degrees. Founded 1956. Setting: 9-acre small town campus. Total enrollment: 1,836. 350 applied, 100% were admitted. Students come from 3 states and territories, 50% from out-of-state. 51% 25 or older. Core. Academic remediation for entering students, self-designed majors, summer session for credit, part-time degree program, adult/continuing education programs.

Entrance Requirements: Open admission. Options: electronic application, early admission, deferred admission. Required for some: high school transcript, ACT. Entrance: noncompetitive. Application deadline: Rolling.

Collegiate Environment: Orientation program. Choral group. Student services: legal services. Ohio University-Southern Campus Library with 26,000 books, 19,198 microform titles, 275 serials, 524 audiovisual materials, an OPAC, and a Web page. 185 computers available on campus for general student use. Computer purchase/lease plans available. A campuswide network can be accessed. Students can access the following: online class registration. Staffed computer lab on campus provides training in use of computers, software, and the Internet.

■ OHIO UNIVERSITY–ZANESVILLE

1425 Newark Rd.

Zanesville, OH 43701-2695

Tel: (740)453-0762

Fax: (740)453-6161

E-mail: ouzservices@ohio.edu

Web Site: www.zanesville.ohiou.edu/

Description: State-supported, 4-year, coed. Administratively affiliated with Ohio University. Awards associate and bachelor's degrees (offers first 2 years of most bachelor's degree programs available at the main campus in Athens; also offers several bachelor's degree programs that can be completed at this campus; also offers some graduate courses). Founded 1946. Setting: 179-acre rural campus with easy access to Columbus. Total enrollment: 1,972. Faculty: 130 (31 full-time, 99 part-time). Student-undergrad faculty ratio is 23:1. 546 applied, 91% were admitted. Full-time: 1,090 students, 68% women, 32% men. Part-time: 882 students, 71% women, 29% men. 1% from out-of-state. 0.3% American Indian or Alaska Native, non-Hispanic/Latino; 2% Hispanic/Latino; 3% African American, non-Hispanic/Latino; 0.4% Asian, non-Hispanic/Latino; 0.1% Native Hawaiian or other Pacific Islander, non-Hispanic/Latino; 1% international. 43% 25 or older. Retention: 55% of full-time freshmen returned the following year. Core. Academic remediation for entering students, services for LD students, advanced placement, self-designed majors, independent study, distance learning, double major, summer session for credit, part-time degree program, external degree program, adult/continuing education programs. Off campus study at Muskingum Area Technical College. Study abroad program.

Entrance Requirements: Open admission Admission to the campus is open-enrollment, however admission to a specific degree program may be selective. Option: electronic application. Required: high school transcript. Required for some: SAT or ACT. Entrance: noncompetitive. Application deadline: Rolling. Transfer credits accepted: Yes.

Costs Per Year: Application fee: $20. State resident tuition: $5038 full-time, $219 per semester hour part-time. Nonresident tuition: $6884 full-time, $307 per semester hour part-time. Mandatory fees: $66 full-time.

Collegiate Environment: Orientation program. Drama-theater group, student-run newspaper, radio station. Most popular organizations: Student Senate, Student Nurses Association, Good Intentions Group, Green Bobcats, Habitat for Humanity Club. Major annual events: Spring Fest, Fall Fest. Student services: personal-psychological counseling. Campus security: student patrols, late night transport-escort service, night security. Zanesville Campus Library plus 1 other with 64,227 books, 489 serials, an OPAC, and a Web page. Operations spending for the previous fiscal year: $247,287. 200 computers available on campus for general student use. A campuswide network can be accessed from off-campus. Students can access the following: online class registration. Staffed computer lab on campus.

■ OHIO VALLEY COLLEGE OF TECHNOLOGY

16808 St. Clair Ave.

East Liverpool, OH 43920

Tel: (330)385-1070

Web Site: www.ovct.edu/

Description: Proprietary, 2-year, coed. Awards terminal associate degrees. Founded 1886. Setting: small town campus with easy access to Pittsburgh. Total enrollment: 147. Faculty: 12 (4 full-time, 8 part-time). Student-undergrad faculty ratio is 18:1. Full-time: 132 students, 87% women, 13% men. Part-time: 15 students, 73% women, 27% men. 7% from out-of-state. 50% 25 or older. Core. Calendar: semesters. Summer session for credit, part-time degree program, internships.

Entrance Requirements: Required: high school transcript, interview, COMPASS. Entrance: minimally difficult. Application deadline: Rolling.

Collegiate Environment: Student services: personal-psychological counseling. 72 computers available on campus for general student use. A campuswide network can be accessed. Students can access the following: online campus library. Staffed computer lab on campus provides training in use of computers, software, and the Internet.

■ OHIO WESLEYAN UNIVERSITY

61 S Sandusky St.

Delaware, OH 43015

Tel: (740)368-2000; Free: 800-922-8953

Fax: (740)368-3314

E-mail: amcouch@owu.edu

Web Site: www.owu.edu/

Description: Independent United Methodist, 4-year, coed. Awards bachelor's degrees. Founded 1842. Setting: 200-acre small town campus with easy access to Columbus. Total enrollment: 1,821. Faculty: 219 (142 full-time, 77 part-time). Student-undergrad faculty ratio is 11:1. 3,835 applied, 74% were admitted. 32% from top 10% of their high school class, 63% from top quarter, 89% from top half. Full-time: 1,806 students, 55% women, 45% men. Part-time: 15 students, 47% women, 53% men. 47% from out-of-state. 0.3% American Indian or Alaska Native, non-Hispanic/Latino; 3% Hispanic/Latino; 5% African American, non-Hispanic/Latino; 2% Asian, non-Hispanic/Latino; 0.1% Native Hawaiian or other Pacific Islander, non-Hispanic/Latino; 8% international. 0% 25 or older, 90% live on campus, 2% transferred in. Retention: 83% of full-time freshmen returned the following year. Academic areas with the most degrees conferred: social sciences; biological/life sciences; business/marketing. Calendar: semesters. Services for LD students, self-designed majors, honors program, double major, summer session for credit, internships. Off campus study. Study abroad program.

Entrance Requirements: Options: electronic application, early admission, early decision, early action, deferred admission, international baccalaureate accepted. Required: essay, high school transcript, minimum 2.5 high school GPA, 1 recommendation, SAT or ACT. Recommended: 2 recommendations, interview. Entrance: very difficult. Application deadlines: 3/1, 3/1 for nonresidents, 11/15 for early decision, 12/15 for early action. Notification: 1/15 for early action. SAT Reasoning Test deadline: 3/1. Applicants placed on waiting list: 182. Wait-listed applicants offered admission: 77.

Costs Per Year: Application fee: $35. Comprehensive fee: $49,460 includes full-time tuition ($38,890), mandatory fees ($260), and college room and board ($10,310). College room only: $5500. Room and board charges vary according to board plan.

Collegiate Environment: Orientation program. Drama-theater group, choral group, student-run newspaper, radio station. Social organizations: national fraternities, national sororities. Student services: health clinic. Campus security: 24-hour emergency response devices and patrols, late night transport-escort service, controlled dormitory access. Freshmen guaranteed college housing. On-campus residence required through senior year. Options: coed, women-only housing available. L. A. Beeghly Library with an OPAC and a Web page.

Community Environment: Delaware, a city of 23,000 and county seat of Delaware County, is a 25-minute drive from Columbus, with convenient access by air, highway or bus. The Delaware State Parks provide facilities for fishing, boating, camping, and swimming. An annual event is the Little Brown Jug, which is the largest pacing event in the United States. About half the faculty live within a ten minute walk of student halls and houses, in the architecturally historic northwest section of the city. Ohio Wesleyan is a national school; 50% of the students are from Ohio, while the other 50% represent 40 U.S. states and 54 countries.

■ OTTERBEIN UNIVERSITY

1 S Grove St.
Westerville, OH 43081
Tel: (614)890-3000; Free: 800-488-8144
Fax: (614)823-1200
E-mail: uotterb@otterbein.edu
Web Site: www.otterbein.edu/

Description: Independent United Methodist, comprehensive, coed. Awards bachelor's, master's, and doctoral degrees and post-master's certificates. Founded 1847. Setting: 142-acre suburban campus with easy access to Columbus. Endowment: $70 million. Total enrollment: 2,997. Faculty: 337 (174 full-time, 163 part-time). Student-undergrad faculty ratio is 11:1. 3,190 applied, 79% were admitted. 26% from top 10% of their high school class, 55% from top quarter, 87% from top half. Full-time: 2,282 students, 63% women, 37% men. Part-time: 293 students, 62% women, 38% men. Students come from 40 states and territories, 10 other countries, 10% from out-of-state. 1% American Indian or Alaska Native, non-Hispanic/Latino; 1% Hispanic/Latino; 7% African American, non-Hispanic/Latino; 1% Asian, non-Hispanic/Latino; 0.2% Native Hawaiian or other Pacific Islander, non-Hispanic/Latino; 1% international. 83% 25 or older, 61% live on campus, 4% transferred in. Retention: 75% of full-time freshmen returned the following year. Academic areas with the most degrees conferred: visual and performing arts; business/marketing; health professions and related sciences. Core. Academic remediation for entering students, ESL program, services for LD students, advanced placement, self-designed majors, honors program, double major, summer session for credit, part-time degree program, adult/continuing education programs, internships, graduate courses open to undergrads. Off campus study at American University, University of Pittsburgh (Semester at Sea), members of the Higher Education Council of Columbus. Study abroad program. ROTC: Army (c).

Entrance Requirements: Options: electronic application, deferred admission, international baccalaureate accepted. Required: high school transcript, SAT or ACT. Recommended: minimum 2.5 high school GPA, interview. Required for some: essay, 1 recommendation. Entrance: moderately difficult. Application deadline: 3/1. Notification: continuous. Transfer credits accepted: Yes.

Costs Per Year: Application fee: $25. Comprehensive fee: $39,342 includes full-time tuition ($30,658) and college room and board ($8684). College room only: $4576. Full-time tuition varies according to course load and program. Room and board charges vary according to housing facility. Part-time tuition: $557 per credit hour. Part-time tuition varies according to course load and program.

Collegiate Environment: Orientation program. Drama-theater group, choral group, marching band, student-run newspaper, radio station. Social organizations: 100 open to all; national fraternities, local fraternities, local sororities; 28% of eligible men and 28% of eligible women are members. Most popular organizations: musical groups, Honoraries, academic interest clubs, Governance. Major annual events: Homecoming, Otterbein Christian Fellowship, Martin Luther King, Jr. Convocation. Student services: health clinic, personal-psychological counseling. Campus security: 24-hour emergency response devices and patrols, student patrols, late night transport-escort service, controlled dormitory access, 24-hour locked residence hall entrances. Courtright Memorial Library with 182,629 books, 312,944 microform titles, 1,012 serials, an OPAC, and a Web page. 146 computers available on campus for general student use. A campuswide network can be accessed from student residence rooms and from off campus. Students can access the following: online class registration. Staffed computer lab on campus provides training in use of computers, software, and the Internet.

Community Environment: Westerville was settled in 1813 by Connecticut, New York, and Virginia families, and Quakers from Pennsylvania. The community, seven miles north of Columbus, has excellent city and college libraries, many churches, a modern medical center, and various civic and service organizations. A site of interest is the Hanby House. Hoover Reservoir is located about four miles east, and offers facilities for picnicking, fishing, and boating. Part-time employment is available.

■ OWENS COMMUNITY COLLEGE

PO Box 10000
Toledo, OH 43699-1947
Tel: (419)661-7000; Free: 800-GO-OWENS
E-mail: cory_stine@owens.edu
Web Site: www.owens.edu/

Description: State-supported, 2-year, coed. Awards certificates, transfer as-sociate, and terminal associate degrees. Founded 1966. Setting: 420-acre suburban campus with easy access to Detroit. Endowment: $1.3 million. Educational spending for the previous fiscal year: $4391 per student. Total enrollment: 16,993. Faculty: 1,582 (195 full-time, 1,387 part-time). Student-undergrad faculty ratio is 16:1. 11,378 applied, 100% were admitted. 2% from top 10% of their high school class, 10% from top quarter, 32% from top half. Full-time: 6,061 students, 55% women, 45% men. Part-time: 10,932 students, 48% women, 52% men. Students come from 21 states and territories, 28 other countries, 3% from out-of-state. 0.4% American Indian or Alaska Native, non-Hispanic/Latino; 6% Hispanic/Latino; 14% African American, non-Hispanic/Latino; 1% Asian, non-Hispanic/Latino; 0.1% Native Hawaiian or other Pacific Islander, non-Hispanic/Latino; 1% international. 51% 25 or older, 1% transferred in. Core. Calendar: semesters. Academic remediation for entering students, ESL program, services for LD students, advanced placement, accelerated degree program, honors program, independent study, distance learning, double major, summer session for credit, part-time degree program, adult/continuing education programs, co-op programs and internships. Study abroad program. ROTC: Army (c), Air Force (c).

Entrance Requirements: Open admission health technologies, Peace Officer Academy, early childhood education require high school transcripts and test scores. Options: electronic application, early admission. Recommended: high school transcript. Required for some: minimum 2 high school GPA, interview. Entrance: noncompetitive. Application deadlines: Rolling, Rolling for nonresidents. Notification: continuous, continuous for nonresidents. Transfer credits accepted: Yes.

Costs Per Year: Application fee: $0. State resident tuition: $3,655 full-time, $130.53 per credit hour part-time. Nonresident tuition: $7,744 full-time, $276.56 per credit hour part-time. Mandatory fees: $392 full-time, $15.50 per credit hour part-time, $10 per term part-time. Full-time tuition and fees vary according to course load and reciprocity agreements. Part-time tuition and fees vary according to course load and reciprocity agreements.

Collegiate Environment: Orientation program. Drama-theater group, choral group, student-run newspaper. Social organizations: 63 open to all; Special interest clubs/organizations; 2% of eligible men and 3% of eligible women are members. Most popular organizations: student government, Raising Awareness Club, Environmental Club, First Year Experience, Gamers. Major annual events: Spring Fling, Fall Fest 2 Success, Awareness Events. Campus security: 24-hour emergency response devices and patrols, student patrols, classroom doors that lock from the inside; campus alert system. College housing not available. Owens Community College Library plus 1 other with 36,770 books, 74,868 microform titles, 9,612 serials, 13,470 audiovisual materials, an OPAC, and a Web page. Operations spending for the previous fiscal year: $1.3 million. 3,000 computers available on campus for general student use. Computer purchase/lease plans available. A campuswide network can be accessed from off-campus. Students can access the following: online class registration. Staffed computer lab on campus provides training in use of computers, software, and the Internet.

Community Environment: See University of Toledo.

■ PONTIFICAL COLLEGE JOSEPHINUM

7625 N High St.
Columbus, OH 43235
Tel: (614)885-5585; Free: 888-252-5812
E-mail: acrawford@pcj.edu
Web Site: www.pcj.edu/

Description: Independent Roman Catholic, comprehensive, men only. Awards bachelor's, master's, and doctoral degrees. Founded 1888. Setting: 100-acre suburban campus. Endowment: $41.8 million. Educational spending for the previous fiscal year: $14,542 per student. Total enrollment: 119. Faculty: 22 (13 full-time, 9 part-time). Student-undergrad faculty ratio is 7:1. 8 applied, 75% were admitted. Full-time: 78 students. Students come from 13 states and territories, 3 other countries, 55% from out-of-state. 30% 25 or older, 100% live on campus, 17% transferred in. Retention: 30% of full-time freshmen returned the following year. Academic areas with the most degrees conferred: history; English; area and ethnic studies. Core. Calendar: semesters. Academic remediation for entering students, ESL program, services for LD students, advanced placement, honors program, double major, internships, graduate courses open to undergrads. Off campus study at 2 members of the Theological Cluster.

Entrance Requirements: Required: essay, high school transcript, 3 recommendations, interview, SAT or ACT. Entrance: minimally difficult. Application deadline: 7/31. Preference given to candidates for the priesthood.

Collegiate Environment: Orientation program. Drama-theater group, choral

group. Student services: health clinic, personal-psychological counseling. Campus security: 24-hour emergency response devices, controlled dormitory access. Wehrle Memorial Library with 137,883 books, 1,875 microform titles, 465 serials, and a Web page. Operations spending for the previous fiscal year: $303,425. 10 computers available on campus for general student use. A campuswide network can be accessed from student residence rooms. Staffed computer lab on campus.

Community Environment: See Ohio State University - Columbus Campus.

■ PROFESSIONAL SKILLS INSTITUTE

1505 Holland Rd., Maumee
Toledo, OH 43537
Tel: (419)531-9610
Fax: (419)531-4732
Web Site: www.proskills.com/

Description: Proprietary, 2-year, coed. Awards certificates, diplomas, and terminal associate degrees. Founded 1984. Setting: 2-acre urban campus with easy access to Detroit. Total enrollment: 292. 43 applied. 75% 25 or older. Core. Services for LD students, part-time degree program, internships. Off campus study at Lourdes College.

Entrance Requirements: Required: high school transcript, minimum 2.0 high school GPA, interview, Wonderlic aptitude test. Entrance: moderately difficult. Notification: 9/15.

Collegiate Environment: Student services: health clinic. Campus security: 24-hour emergency response devices, camera, alarm system. Professional Skills Institute Library plus 1 other with 2,200 books, 50 serials, and an OPAC.

■ RABBINICAL COLLEGE OF TELSHE

28400 Euclid Ave.
Wickliffe, OH 44092-2523
Tel: (216)943-5300

Description: Independent Jewish, comprehensive, men only. Awards bachelor's and master's degrees. Total enrollment: 57. Student-undergrad faculty ratio is 7:1. 25% from out-of-state. 14% 25 or older. Retention: 25% of full-time freshmen returned the following year.

Entrance Requirements: Open admission.

■ REMINGTON COLLEGE–CLEVELAND CAMPUS

14445 Broadway Ave.
Cleveland, OH 44125
Tel: (216)475-7520
Fax: (216)475-6055
Web Site: www.remingtoncollege.edu/

Description: Proprietary, 2-year, coed. Awards terminal associate degrees. Setting: 2-acre urban campus. Calendar: continuous. Co-op programs.

■ REMINGTON COLLEGE–CLEVELAND WEST CAMPUS

26350 Brookpark Rd.
North Olmstead, OH 44070
Tel: (440)777-2560
Fax: (440)777-3238
E-mail: james.malley@remingtoncollege.edu
Web Site: www.remingtoncollege.edu/

Description: Proprietary, 2-year, coed. Awards terminal associate degrees. Founded 2003.

■ ROSEDALE BIBLE COLLEGE

2270 Rosedale Rd.
Irwin, OH 43029-9501
Tel: (740)857-1311
Fax: (877)857-1312
E-mail: pweber@rosedale.edu
Web Site: www.rosedale.edu/

Description: Independent Mennonite, 2-year, coed. Awards terminal associate degrees. Founded 1952. Total enrollment: 89. 81 applied, 94% were admitted. Calendar: five six-week terms.

Entrance Requirements: Recommended: SAT or ACT.

■ SCHOOL OF ADVERTISING ART

1725 E David Rd.
Kettering, OH 45440
Tel: (937)294-0592; Free: 877-300-9866
Fax: (937)294-5869

E-mail: Abbie@saa.edu
Web Site: www.saa.edu/

Description: Proprietary, 2-year, coed. Awards diplomas and terminal associate degrees. Founded 1983. Setting: 5-acre suburban campus with easy access to Columbus. Educational spending for the previous fiscal year: $4246 per student. Total enrollment: 116. Faculty: 9 (8 full-time, 1 part-time). Student-undergrad faculty ratio is 14:1. 263 applied, 63% were admitted. Full-time: 116 students, 72% women, 28% men. Students come from 3 states and territories, 2% from out-of-state. 2% Hispanic/Latino; 2% African American, non-Hispanic/Latino; 1% Native Hawaiian or other Pacific Islander, non-Hispanic/Latino; 0% international. 3% 25 or older. Retention: 86% of full-time freshmen returned the following year. Calendar: trimesters.

Entrance Requirements: Option: electronic application. Required: high school transcript, minimum 2 high school GPA, interview. Required for some: essay, 2 recommendations. Entrance: minimally difficult. Transfer credits accepted: Yes.

Collegiate Environment: Orientation program. Major annual events: Halloween Party, Holiday Bowling Party, Fall Picnic. Student services: personal-psychological counseling. saa Library with 590 books, 26 serials, an OPAC, and a Web page. Operations spending for the previous fiscal year: $28,335.

■ SHAWNEE STATE UNIVERSITY

940 Second St.
Portsmouth, OH 45662-4344
Tel: (740)354-3205; Free: 800-959-2SSU
Fax: (740)355-2470
E-mail: btrusz@shawnee.edu
Web Site: www.shawnee.edu/

Description: State-supported, comprehensive, coed. Awards associate, bachelor's, and master's degrees. Founded 1986. Setting: 52-acre small town campus. Endowment: $13.2 million. Educational spending for the previous fiscal year: $5001 per student. Total enrollment: 4,652. Faculty: 328 (152 full-time, 176 part-time). Student-undergrad faculty ratio is 19:1. 4,340 applied, 82% were admitted. 10% from top 10% of their high school class, 28% from top quarter, 60% from top half. Full-time: 3,862 students, 56% women, 44% men. Part-time: 692 students, 67% women, 33% men. Students come from 17 states and territories, 21 other countries, 11% from out-of-state. 1% American Indian or Alaska Native, non-Hispanic/Latino; 1% Hispanic/Latino; 6% African American, non-Hispanic/Latino; 0.4% Asian, non-Hispanic/Latino; 0.05% Native Hawaiian or other Pacific Islander, non-Hispanic/Latino; 1% international. 23% 25 or older, 23% live on campus, 7% transferred in. Retention: 49% of full-time freshmen returned the following year. Academic areas with the most degrees conferred: business/marketing; education; social sciences; visual and performing arts. Core. Calendar: semesters. Academic remediation for entering students, ESL program, services for LD students, advanced placement, accelerated degree program, self-designed majors, honors program, independent study, distance learning, double major, summer session for credit, part-time degree program, adult/continuing education programs, internships. Off campus study. Study abroad program.

Entrance Requirements: Open admission except for allied health programs, nonresident aliens. Options: electronic application, deferred admission. Required: high school transcript. Recommended: ACT, SAT or ACT. Required for some: interview, ACT, SAT or ACT. Entrance: noncompetitive. Application deadlines: Rolling, Rolling for nonresidents. Notification: continuous, continuous for nonresidents. Transfer credits accepted: Yes.

Costs Per Year: Application fee: $0. State resident tuition: $5,918 full-time, $246.60 per credit hour part-time. Nonresident tuition: $10,893 full-time, $453.94 per credit hour part-time. Mandatory fees: $1,070 full-time, $44.58 per credit hour part-time. Full-time tuition and fees vary according to course load and reciprocity agreements. Part-time tuition and fees vary according to course load and reciprocity agreements. College room and board: $9012. College room only: $5478. Room and board charges vary according to board plan and housing facility.

Collegiate Environment: Orientation program. Drama-theater group, choral group, student-run newspaper. Social organizations: 31 open to all; national fraternities, local sororities; 1% of eligible men and 1% of eligible women are members. Most popular organizations: campus ministry, Health Executives and Administrators Learning Society, Student Programming Board, Student Government Association. Major annual events: Homecoming, Springfest, Scare Week. Student services: health clinic, personal-psychological counseling, women's center. Campus security: 24-hour emergency response devices and patrols. College housing designed to accommodate 964 students; 998 undergraduates lived in college housing during 2012-13. Freshmen given priority for college housing. On-campus residence required in freshman year. Option: coed housing available. Shawnee State University Library with 135,302 books, 265,701 microform titles, 58,868 serials, 18,837 audiovisual materials, an OPAC, and a Web page. Operations spending for the previous fiscal year: $1.4 million. 620 computers available on campus for general student use. Computer purchase/lease plans available. A campuswide network can be accessed from student residence rooms and from off campus. Students can access the following: online class registration, financial aid, student billing, courses, student service portal. Staffed computer lab on campus provides training in use of computers, software, and the Internet.

Community Environment: A quaint city of 23,000 residents, Portsmouth is Scioto County's largest retail center and a popular tourist area as well. Its Bonneyfiddle area, with its old-world charm, is a treasure trove for antique buffs, and the winding Ohio River offers opportunities for boating, waterskiing, and fishing. Shawnee State Park provides nature trails, as well as boating, fishing and golf.

■ **SINCLAIR COMMUNITY COLLEGE**
444 W Third St.
Dayton, OH 45402-1460
Tel: (937)512-2500; Free: 800-315-3000
E-mail: ssmith@sinclair.edu
Web Site: www.sinclair.edu/

Description: State and locally supported, 2-year, coed. Part of Ohio Board of Regents. Awards certificates, transfer associate, and terminal associate degrees. Founded 1887. Setting: 50-acre urban campus with easy access to Cincinnati. Total enrollment: 21,561. 0% from out-of-state. 50% 25 or older. Core. Academic remediation for entering students, ESL program, services for LD students, self-designed majors, honors program, independent study, distance learning, summer session for credit, part-time degree program, external degree program, adult/continuing education programs, co-op programs and internships. Off campus study at 17 members of the Southwestern Ohio Council for Higher Education. ROTC: Army (c), Air Force (c).

Entrance Requirements: Open admission except for allied health programs. Options: electronic application, early admission, deferred admission. Required for some: high school transcript, interview. Entrance: noncompetitive. Application deadline: Rolling. Notification: continuous.

Collegiate Environment: Orientation program. Drama-theater group, choral group, student-run newspaper. Social organizations: 55 open to all. Most popular organizations: African-American Men of the Future, Ohio Fellows, Phi Theta Kappa, student government, student newspaper. Major annual events: Welcome Week, Spring Fling, Student Health Fair. Student services: personal-psychological counseling. Campus security: 24-hour emergency response devices and patrols, student patrols, late night transport-escort service. Learning Resources Center with an OPAC and a Web page.

■ **SOUTH UNIVERSITY**
4743 Richmond Rd.
Cleveland, OH 44128
Tel: (216)755-5000; Free: 855-398-9280
Web Site: www.southuniversity.edu/cleveland.aspx
Description: Proprietary, comprehensive, coed. Awards associate, bachelor's, and master's degrees.

■ **SOUTHERN STATE COMMUNITY COLLEGE**
100 Hobart Dr.
Hillsboro, OH 45133-9487
Tel: (937)393-3431
Fax: (937)393-9370
E-mail: wjohnson@sscc.edu
Web Site: www.sscc.edu/

Description: State-supported, 2-year, coed. Awards certificates, transfer associate, and terminal associate degrees. Founded 1975. Setting: 60-acre rural campus. Endowment: $1.9 million. Total enrollment: 2,806. Faculty: 172 (61 full-time, 111 part-time). Student-undergrad faculty ratio is 17:1. 443 applied, 100% were admitted. Full-time: 1,292 students, 66% women, 34% men. Part-time: 1,514 students, 69% women, 31% men. Students come from 2 states and territories, 0% from out-of-state. 0.4% American Indian or Alaska Native, non-Hispanic/Latino; 1% Hispanic/Latino; 2% African American, non-Hispanic/Latino; 0.3% Asian, non-Hispanic/Latino; 0.1% Native Hawaiian or other Pacific Islander, non-Hispanic/Latino; 0% international. Core. Academic remediation for entering students, services for LD students, advanced placement, self-designed majors, independent study, distance

learning, double major, summer session for credit, part-time degree program, co-op programs and internships. Off campus study at 15 members of the Southwestern Ohio Council for Higher Education.

Entrance Requirements: Open admission. Options: electronic application, early admission, deferred admission. Recommended: high school transcript. Entrance: noncompetitive. Application deadline: Rolling. Notification: continuous. Transfer credits accepted: Yes.

Collegiate Environment: Orientation program. Drama-theater group, choral group. Social organizations: 3 open to all. Most popular organizations: Student Government Association, Drama Club. Student services: personal-psychological counseling. College housing not available. Learning Resources Center plus 3 others with 83,421 books, 271 serials, 12,035 audiovisual materials, an OPAC, and a Web page. Operations spending for the previous fiscal year: $637,144. 550 computers available on campus for general student use. A campuswide network can be accessed from off-campus. Students can access the following: online class registration. Staffed computer lab on campus provides training in use of computers, software, and the Internet.

Community Environment: Hillsboro, approximately 40 miles east of Cincinnati, is in a primarily rural setting with small towns and villages.

■ **STARK STATE COLLEGE**
6200 Frank Ave., NW
North Canton, OH 44720-7299
Tel: (330)494-6170; Free: 800-797-8275
Fax: (330)497-6313
E-mail: info@starkstate.edu
Web Site: www.starkstate.edu/

Description: State-related, 2-year, coed. Part of University System of Ohio. Awards certificates, transfer associate, and terminal associate degrees. Founded 1970. Setting: 34-acre suburban campus with easy access to Cleveland. Endowment: $2.8 million. Educational spending for the previous fiscal year: $5452 per student. Total enrollment: 15,536. Faculty: 730 (198 full-time, 532 part-time). Student-undergrad faculty ratio is 23:1. 19% from top quarter of their high school class. Full-time: 5,441 students, 52% women, 48% men. Part-time: 10,095 students, 64% women, 36% men. Students come from 15 states and territories, 6 other countries, 1% from out-of-state. 1% American Indian or Alaska Native, non-Hispanic/Latino; 1% Hispanic/Latino; 19% African American, non-Hispanic/Latino; 1% Asian, non-Hispanic/Latino; 0.1% Native Hawaiian or other Pacific Islander, non-Hispanic/Latino; 0.01% international. 54% 25 or older, 5% transferred in. Retention: 45% of full-time freshmen returned the following year. Core. Calendar: semesters. Academic remediation for entering students, services for LD students, self-designed majors, independent study, distance learning, double major, summer session for credit, part-time degree program, external degree program, adult/continuing education programs, co-op programs. Off campus study at Malone College, University of Akron, Walsh College, Kent State University, Stark Campus.

Entrance Requirements: Required: high school transcript. Recommended: SAT or ACT.

Costs Per Year: State resident tuition: $3495 full-time, $147 per credit hour part-time. Nonresident tuition: $6225 full-time, $238 per credit hour part-time. Mandatory fees: $915 full-time. Full-time tuition and fees vary according to course load and program. Part-time tuition varies according to program.

Collegiate Environment: Orientation program. Student-run newspaper. Social organizations: 21 open to all; national fraternities, national sororities. Most popular organizations: Phi Theta Kappa, Business Student Club, Institute of Management Accountants, Stark State College Association of Medical Assistants, Student Health Information Management Association. Major annual events: Halloween Costume Contest, Make A Difference Day, Spring Festival. Student services: personal-psychological counseling. Campus security: late night transport-escort service, patrols by trained security personnel at anytime the campus is open. College housing not available. Learning Resource Center plus 1 other with 82,728 books, 23,331 serials, an OPAC, and a Web page. Operations spending for the previous fiscal year: $485,582. 1,860 computers available on campus for general student use. A campuswide network can be accessed from off-campus. Students can access the following: online class registration. Staffed computer lab on campus (open 24 hours a day) provides training in use of computers, software, and the Internet.

Community Environment: Set in small city environment - commuter campus only.

■ **STAUTZENBERGER COLLEGE (BRECKSVILLE)**
8001 Katherine Blvd.
Brecksville, OH 44141
Tel: (440)838-1999; Free: 800-437-2997
Web Site: www.sctoday.edu/
Description: Proprietary, 2-year, coed.

■ **STAUTZENBERGER COLLEGE (MAUMEE)**
1796 Indian Wood Cir.
Maumee, OH 43537
Tel: (419)866-0261; Free: 800-552-5099
Fax: (419)867-9821
E-mail: klfitzgerald@stautzenberger.com
Web Site: www.sctoday.edu/maumee/
Description: Proprietary, 2-year, coed. Awards certificates, diplomas, and terminal associate degrees. Setting: urban campus. Total enrollment: 867. Student-undergrad faculty ratio is 26:1. 5% from out-of-state. 62% 25 or older. Retention: 62% of full-time freshmen returned the following year.
Entrance Requirements: Open admission.

■ **STRAYER UNIVERSITY - AKRON CAMPUS**
51 Park W Blvd.
Akron, OH 44320
Tel: (330)734-6700
Fax: (330)835-9060
Web Site: www.strayer.edu/campus/akron
Description: Proprietary, comprehensive, coed. Awards associate, bachelor's, and master's degrees.

■ **STRAYER UNIVERSITY - CINCINNATI CAMPUS**
2135 Dana Ave.
Ste. 300
Cincinnati, OH 45207
Tel: (513)878-3100
Fax: (513)351-2590
Web Site: www.strayer.edu/campus/cincinnati
Description: Proprietary, comprehensive, coed. Awards associate, bachelor's, and master's degrees.

■ **STRAYER UNIVERSITY - COLUMBUS CAMPUS**
8425 Pulsar Pl.
Ste. 400
Columbus, OH 43240
Tel: (614)310-6700
Fax: (614)430-9716
Web Site: www.strayer.edu/campus/columbus/
Description: Proprietary, comprehensive, coed. Awards associate, bachelor's, and master's degrees.

■ **STRAYER UNIVERSITY - FAIRBORN CAMPUS**
2600 Paramount Pl.
Ste. 300
Fairborn, OH 45324
Tel: (937)306-4500
Fax: (937)431-1440
Web Site: www.strayer.edu/campus/fairborn
Description: Proprietary, comprehensive, coed. Awards associate, bachelor's, and master's degrees.

■ **STRAYER UNIVERSITY - FAIRVIEW PARK CAMPUS**
22730 Fairview Ctr. Dr.
Ste. 150
Fairview Park, OH 44126-3616
Tel: (440)471-6400
Fax: (440)716-8050
Web Site: www.strayer.edu/campus/fairview-park
Description: Proprietary, comprehensive, coed. Awards associate, bachelor's, and master's degrees.

■ **STRAYER UNIVERSITY - MASON CAMPUS**
4605 Duke Dr.
Ste. 700
Mason, OH 45040
Tel: (513)234-6450

Fax: (513)204-6920
Web Site: www.strayer.edu/campus/mason/
Description: Proprietary, comprehensive, coed. Awards associate, bachelor's, and master's degrees.

■ **TERRA STATE COMMUNITY COLLEGE**
2830 Napoleon Rd.
Fremont, OH 43420-9670
Tel: (419)334-8400; Free: 866-AT-TERRA
Fax: (419)334-9035
E-mail: ktaylor01@terra.edu
Web Site: www.terra.edu/
Description: State-supported, 2-year, coed. Part of Ohio Board of Regents. Awards certificates, diplomas, transfer associate, and terminal associate degrees. Founded 1968. Setting: 100-acre small town campus with easy access to Toledo. Total enrollment: 3,172. Faculty: 220 (48 full-time, 172 part-time). Student-undergrad faculty ratio is 20:1. 394 applied, 100% were admitted. Full-time: 1,252 students, 59% women, 41% men. Part-time: 1,920 students, 55% women, 45% men. 0.3% American Indian or Alaska Native, non-Hispanic/Latino; 7% Hispanic/Latino; 5% African American, non-Hispanic/Latino; 0.5% Asian, non-Hispanic/Latino; 0% Native Hawaiian or other Pacific Islander, non-Hispanic/Latino; 0.2% international. Core. Calendar: semesters. Academic remediation for entering students, services for LD students, advanced placement, self-designed majors, independent study, distance learning, double major, summer session for credit, part-time degree program, adult/continuing education programs, co-op programs and internships. Off campus study.
Entrance Requirements: Open admission. Options: electronic application, early admission, deferred admission. Required: high school transcript. Entrance: noncompetitive. Application deadline: Rolling. Transfer credits accepted: Yes.
Costs Per Year: Application fee: $0. State resident tuition: $3,056 full-time, $127.32 per semester hour part-time. Nonresident tuition: $4,991 full-time, $207.97 per semester hour part-time. Mandatory fees: $339 full-time, $14.12 per semester hour part-time.
Collegiate Environment: Orientation program. Choral group. Social organizations: 5 open to all. Most popular organizations: Phi Theta Kappa, Student Activities Club, Society of Plastic Engineers, Koinonia, Student Senate. Major annual events: Student Orientation, Commencement, Open House. Student services: legal services, personal-psychological counseling. Campus security: 24-hour emergency response devices. College housing not available. Learning Resource Center with 22,675 books, 59,422 microform titles, 383 serials, an OPAC, and a Web page.

■ **TIFFIN UNIVERSITY**
155 Miami St.
Tiffin, OH 44883-2161
Tel: (419)447-6442; Free: 800-968-6446
Fax: (419)447-9605
E-mail: borichj@tiffin.edu
Web Site: www.tiffin.edu/
Description: Independent, comprehensive, coed. Awards associate, bachelor's, and master's degrees and post-master's certificates. Founded 1888. Setting: 110-acre small town campus with easy access to Toledo. Total enrollment: 6,920. Faculty: 506 (85 full-time, 421 part-time). Student-undergrad faculty ratio is 19:1. 5,228 applied, 39% were admitted. 0% from top 10% of their high school class, 0% from top quarter, 0% from top half. Full-time: 2,766 students, 58% women, 42% men. Part-time: 2,962 students, 68% women, 32% men. Students come from 50 states and territories, 29 other countries, 51% from out-of-state. 1% American Indian or Alaska Native, non-Hispanic/Latino; 1% Hispanic/Latino; 27% African American, non-Hispanic/Latino; 0.3% Asian, non-Hispanic/Latino; 0.1% Native Hawaiian or other Pacific Islander, non-Hispanic/Latino; 1% international. 54% 25 or older, 20% live on campus, 5% transferred in. Retention: 66% of full-time freshmen returned the following year. Academic areas with the most degrees conferred: business/marketing; homeland security, law enforcement, firefighting, and protective services; psychology. Core. Calendar: semesters. Academic remediation for entering students, ESL program, services for LD students, advanced placement, accelerated degree program, freshman honors college, honors program, independent study, distance learning, double major, summer session for credit, external degree program, adult/continuing education programs, internships. Off campus study. Study abroad program. ROTC: Army (c), Air Force (c).
Entrance Requirements: Options: electronic application, international bac-

calaureate accepted. Required: high school transcript. Recommended: minimum 3 high school GPA. Required for some: essay, interview, SAT or ACT. Entrance: moderately difficult. Application deadline: Rolling.

Costs Per Year: Application fee: $20. Comprehensive fee: $30,273 includes full-time tuition ($20,700) and college room and board ($9573). College room only: $4973. Full-time tuition varies according to course load, degree level, location, and program. Room and board charges vary according to board plan and housing facility. Part-time tuition: $690 per credit. Part-time tuition varies according to course load, degree level, location, and program.

Collegiate Environment: Orientation program. Drama-theater group, choral group, marching band, student-run newspaper. Social organizations: 40 open to all; national fraternities, national sororities, local fraternities, local sororities; 1% of eligible men and 1% of eligible women are members. Most popular organizations: Student Government Association, H2O, International Student Association, Global Affairs Organization, Circle K. Major annual events: Late Night Breakfast, Homecoming, faculty vs. student basketball game. Student services: health clinic, personal-psychological counseling, women's center. Campus security: 24-hour emergency response devices, student patrols, late night transport-escort service, controlled dormitory access. 1,050 college housing spaces available; 1,035 were occupied in 2012-13. Freshmen guaranteed college housing. On-campus residence required through sophomore year. Options: coed, men-only, women-only housing available. Pfeiffer Library with 126,557 books, 36,410 microform titles, 17,811 serials, 529 audiovisual materials, an OPAC, and a Web page. 280 computers available on campus for general student use. Computer purchase/lease plans available. A campuswide network can be accessed from student residence rooms and from off campus. Students can access the following: online class registration. Staffed computer lab on campus provides training in use of computers, software, and the Internet.

Community Environment: See Heidelberg College.

■ TRI-STATE BIBLE COLLEGE

506 Margaret St.
South Point, OH 45680-8402
Tel: (740)377-2520
Fax: (740)377-0001
E-mail: recruitment@tsbc.edu
Web Site: www.tsbc.edu/

Description: Independent nondenominational, comprehensive, coed. Awards associate, bachelor's, and master's degrees. Founded 1970. Setting: 4-acre suburban campus. Total enrollment: 65. 86% 25 or older. Calendar: semesters.

Entrance Requirements: Open admission.

■ TRUMBULL BUSINESS COLLEGE

3200 Ridge Rd.
Warren, OH 44484
Tel: (330)369-3200; Free: 888-766-1598
Fax: (330)369-6792
E-mail: admissions@tbc-trumbullbusiness.com
Web Site: www.tbc-trumbullbusiness.com/

Description: Proprietary, 2-year, coed. Awards diplomas and terminal associate degrees. Founded 1972. Setting: 6-acre small town campus. Total enrollment: 417. Student-undergrad faculty ratio is 10:1. 185 applied. 0% from out-of-state. 66% 25 or older. Retention: 47% of full-time freshmen returned the following year. Double major, part-time degree program, adult/continuing education programs. Study abroad program.

Entrance Requirements: Required: high school transcript, interview. Entrance: noncompetitive. Application deadline: Rolling. Notification: continuous until 10/1.

Collegiate Environment: Student-run newspaper.

■ UNION INSTITUTE & UNIVERSITY

440 E McMillan St.
Cincinnati, OH 45206-1925
Tel: (513)861-6400; Free: 800-486-3116
Fax: (513)861-0779
E-mail: jon.mays@myunion.edu
Web Site: www.myunion.edu/

Description: Independent, university, coed. Awards bachelor's, master's, and doctoral degrees and post-master's certificates. Founded 1969. Setting: 5-acre urban campus with easy access to Cincinnati. Endowment: $696,114. Research spending for the previous fiscal year: $205,049. Total enrollment: 1,650. Faculty: 353 (31 full-time, 322 part-time). Student-undergrad faculty

ratio is 9:1. Full-time: 694 students, 57% women, 43% men. Part-time: 468 students, 51% women, 49% men. Students come from 39 states and territories, 1 other country, 12% from out-of-state. 1% American Indian or Alaska Native, non-Hispanic/Latino; 14% Hispanic/Latino; 28% African American, non-Hispanic/Latino; 1% Asian, non-Hispanic/Latino; 0.4% Native Hawaiian or other Pacific Islander, non-Hispanic/Latino; 0% international. 92% 25 or older, 29% transferred in. Retention: 71% of full-time freshmen returned the following year. Academic areas with the most degrees conferred: homeland security, law enforcement, firefighting, and protective services; liberal arts/general studies; family and consumer sciences. Core. Calendar: trimesters some programs offer split (8wk) sessions. Academic remediation for entering students, services for LD students, advanced placement, accelerated degree program, self-designed majors, independent study, distance learning, double major, summer session for credit, part-time degree program, external degree program, adult/continuing education programs, internships, graduate courses open to undergrads. Off campus study.

Entrance Requirements: Options: electronic application, deferred admission. Required: essay, recommendation from program faculty. Recommended: interview. Required for some: high school transcript, 1 recommendation. Entrance: noncompetitive. Application deadlines: Rolling, Rolling for nonresidents. Notification: continuous, continuous for nonresidents. Transfer credits accepted: Yes.

Collegiate Environment: Orientation program. Campus security: 24-hour emergency response devices, late night transport-escort service, security personnel on site during business and class hours. Union Institute & University Library with 60,000 books, 75 serials, 500 audiovisual materials, an OPAC, and a Web page. Operations spending for the previous fiscal year: $5.3 million. 80 computers available on campus for general student use. Computer purchase/lease plans available. A campuswide network can be accessed from off-campus. Students can access the following: online class registration, CampusWeb-online access to basic information and grades. Staffed computer lab on campus provides training in use of computers, software, and the Internet.

■ THE UNIVERSITY OF AKRON

302 Buchtel Common
Akron, OH 44325
Tel: (330)972-7111; Free: 800-655-4884
Fax: (330)972-7676
E-mail: admissions@uakron.edu
Web Site: www.uakron.edu/

Description: State-supported, university, coed. Awards associate, bachelor's, master's, and doctoral degrees and post-master's certificates. Founded 1870. Setting: 223-acre urban campus with easy access to Cleveland. Endowment: $188.4 million. Research spending for the previous fiscal year: $35.2 million. Educational spending for the previous fiscal year: $6703 per student. Total enrollment: 26,580. Faculty: 1,706 (784 full-time, 922 part-time). Student-undergrad faculty ratio is 21:1. 10,854 applied, 97% were admitted. 12% from top 10% of their high school class, 30% from top quarter, 57% from top half. 2 National Merit Scholars, 45 valedictorians. Full-time: 17,045 students, 47% women, 53% men. Part-time: 5,077 students, 51% women, 49% men. Students come from 43 states and territories, 52 other countries, 3% from out-of-state. 0.3% American Indian or Alaska Native, non-Hispanic/Latino; 2% Hispanic/Latino; 16% African American, non-Hispanic/Latino; 2% Asian, non-Hispanic/Latino; 0.2% Native Hawaiian or other Pacific Islander, non-Hispanic/Latino; 1% international. 23% 25 or older, 15% live on campus, 5% transferred in. Retention: 67% of full-time freshmen returned the following year. Academic areas with the most degrees conferred: business/marketing; health professions and related sciences; education. Core. Calendar: semesters. Academic remediation for entering students, ESL program, services for LD students, advanced placement, accelerated degree program, self-designed majors, freshman honors college, honors program, independent study, distance learning, double major, summer session for credit, part-time degree program, external degree program, adult/continuing education programs, co-op programs and internships, graduate courses open to undergrads. Study abroad program. ROTC: Army, Air Force (c).

Entrance Requirements: Open admission Selective admission for eight colleges with open access to two colleges (Summit College Student Success Program and Wayne College). Options: electronic application, early action, deferred admission, international baccalaureate accepted. Required: high school transcript, SAT or ACT. Required for some: essay, 3 recommendations, interview. Entrance: moderately difficult. Application deadlines: 8/11,

11/1 for early action. Notification: 9/15. SAT Reasoning Test deadline: 7/1. SAT Subject Test deadline: 7/1. Transfer credits accepted: Yes.

Costs Per Year: Application fee: $40. State resident tuition: $8284 full-time, $345.15 per credit hour part-time. Nonresident tuition: $16,484 full-time, $686.85 per credit hour part-time. Mandatory fees: $1579 full-time. Full-time tuition and fees vary according to course load, degree level, and location. Part-time tuition varies according to course load, degree level, and location. College room and board: $9878. College room only: $6306. Room and board charges vary according to board plan and housing facility.

Collegiate Environment: Orientation program. Drama-theater group, choral group, marching band, student-run newspaper, radio station. Social organizations: 250 open to all; national fraternities, national sororities, local fraternities; 3% of eligible men and 3% of eligible women are members. Most popular organizations: Associated Student Government, Residence Hall Program Board, American Society of Mechanical Engineers, AK-Rowdies. Major annual events: Homecoming, Student Appreciation Day, Greek Week. Student services: legal services, health clinic, personal-psychological counseling, women's center. Campus security: 24-hour emergency response devices and patrols, student patrols, late night transport-escort service, controlled dormitory access. 3,345 college housing spaces available; 3,137 were occupied in 2012-13. Freshmen given priority for college housing. On-campus residence required in freshman year. Options: coed, men-only, women-only housing available. Bierce Library plus 2 others with 1.3 million books, 1.7 million microform titles, 481,872 serials, 47,258 audiovisual materials, an OPAC, and a Web page. Operations spending for the previous fiscal year: $11.1 million. 3,100 computers available on campus for general student use. Computer purchase/lease plans available. A campuswide network can be accessed from student residence rooms and from off campus. Students can access the following: online class registration, library laptops for student checkout. Staffed computer lab on campus provides training in use of computers, software, and the Internet.

Community Environment: The city is a merchandising center and a vital distribution gateway between the industrial East and the Midwest. The Portage Lakes district south of the city provides facilities for boating, swimming, fishing and ice skating. A number of parks provide additional facilities for skiing and other outdoor activities. A short distance to the north, are the New Gateway Complex, Jacobs Field, home of the Cleveland Indians, Gund Arena, of the Cleveland Cavaliers, and the Rock'n Roll Hall of Fame. To the South is The Pro Football Hall of Fame. Local points of interest are the Akron Art Museum, Blossom Music Center, Canal Park Baseball Stadium, Goodyear Aircraft Hanger, Inventure Place, Perkins Mansion, and the Stan Hywet Hall. Special events are the World Series of Golf, held at the Firestone Country Club, and the All-American Soap Box Derby.

■ **THE UNIVERSITY OF AKRON–WAYNE COLLEGE**
1901 Smucker Rd.
Orrville, OH 44667-9192
Tel: (330)683-2010; Free: 800-221-8308
Fax: (330)684-8989
E-mail: wayneadmissions@uakron.edu
Web Site: www.wayne.uakron.edu/

Description: State-supported, primarily 2-year, coed. Part of The University of Akron. Awards certificates, transfer associate, terminal associate, and bachelor's degrees. Founded 1972. Setting: 157-acre rural campus. Research spending for the previous fiscal year: $1008. Educational spending for the previous fiscal year: $8359 per student. Total enrollment: 2,415. Faculty: 202 (27 full-time, 175 part-time). Student-undergrad faculty ratio is 19:1. 983 applied, 85% were admitted. 5% from top 10% of their high school class, 17% from top quarter, 46% from top half. Full-time: 1,185 students, 56% women, 44% men. Part-time: 1,230 students, 62% women, 38% men. Students come from 2 states and territories, 0% from out-of-state. 0.3% American Indian or Alaska Native, non-Hispanic/Latino; 1% Hispanic/Latino; 3% African American, non-Hispanic/Latino; 1% Asian, non-Hispanic/Latino; 0% Native Hawaiian or other Pacific Islander, non-Hispanic/Latino; 0% international. 30% 25 or older, 3% transferred in. Retention: 49% of full-time freshmen returned the following year. Core. Calendar: semesters. Academic remediation for entering students, services for LD students, advanced placement, honors program, independent study, distance learning, double major, summer session for credit, part-time degree program, adult/continuing education programs, co-op programs and internships. Off campus study at The University of Akron. ROTC: Army (c), Air Force (c).

Entrance Requirements: Open admission. Options: electronic application, early admission, deferred admission. Recommended: SAT or ACT, ACT COMPASS. Required for some: high school transcript, SAT or ACT, ACT

COMPASS. Entrance: noncompetitive. Application deadline: 8/13. Notification: continuous. Transfer credits accepted: Yes.

Costs Per Year: Application fee: $40. State resident tuition: $5,940 full-time, $247.52 per semester hour part-time. Nonresident tuition: $14,281 full-time, $525.55 per semester hour part-time. Mandatory fees: $176 full-time, $7.34 per semester hour part-time. Full-time tuition and fees vary according to course load and location. Part-time tuition and fees vary according to course load and location.

Collegiate Environment: Orientation program. Student services: personal-psychological counseling. Campus security: 24-hour emergency response devices, late night transport-escort service. College housing not available. Wayne College Library with 19,810 books, 109 serials, 1,764 audiovisual materials, an OPAC, and a Web page. Operations spending for the previous fiscal year: $431,995. 280 computers available on campus for general student use. Computer purchase/lease plans available. A campuswide network can be accessed from off-campus. Students can access the following: online class registration. Staffed computer lab on campus provides training in use of computers, software, and the Internet.

Community Environment: Orrville is a thriving community with a diversified business and industry base, best known for being the home of The J. M. Smucker Company. Located 30 miles southwest of Akron and The University of Akron campus, and 50 miles south of Cleveland, the city of Orrville has a population of 8,485. Residents of this area have relatively easy access to metropolitan amenities while enjoying a more relaxed rural-suburban atmosphere. The community park provides many recreational facilities and the Rehm Performing Arts Pavilion is the setting for many musical and cultural events. There are also 26 churches of various denominations, a community library, and a 38 bed hospital in Orville.

■ **UNIVERSITY OF CINCINNATI**
PO Box 210063
Cincinnati, OH 45221
Tel: (513)556-6000
E-mail: admissions@uc.edu
Web Site: www.uc.edu/

Description: State-supported, university, coed. Awards associate, bachelor's, master's, and doctoral degrees and post-master's certificates. Founded 1819. Setting: 137-acre urban campus with easy access to Cincinnati. Endowment: $900.1 million. Research spending for the previous fiscal year: $221.8 million. Educational spending for the previous fiscal year: $11,480 per student. Total enrollment: 33,347. Faculty: 1,195 (1,166 full-time, 29 part-time). Student-undergrad faculty ratio is 18:1. 17,104 applied, 67% were admitted. 20% from top 10% of their high school class, 51% from top quarter, 82% from top half. 40 National Merit Scholars, 58 valedictorians. Full-time: 19,667 students, 48% women, 52% men. Part-time: 3,429 students, 67% women, 33% men. Students come from 51 states and territories, 81 other countries, 13% from out-of-state. 0.2% American Indian or Alaska Native, non-Hispanic/Latino; 3% Hispanic/Latino; 8% African American, non-Hispanic/Latino; 3% Asian, non-Hispanic/Latino; 0.1% Native Hawaiian or other Pacific Islander, non-Hispanic/Latino; 3% international. 16% 25 or older, 19% live on campus, 6% transferred in. Retention: 86% of full-time freshmen returned the following year. Academic areas with the most degrees conferred: business/marketing; health professions and related sciences; engineering. Core. Academic remediation for entering students, ESL program, services for LD students, advanced placement, accelerated degree program, honors program, independent study, distance learning, double major, summer session for credit, part-time degree program, adult/continuing education programs, co-op programs and internships, graduate courses open to undergrads. Off campus study at Greater Cincinnati Consortium of Colleges and Universities. Study abroad program. ROTC: Army, Air Force.

Entrance Requirements: Options: electronic application, deferred admission, international baccalaureate accepted. Required: essay, high school transcript, minimum 2.7 high school GPA, SAT or ACT. Required for some: 2 recommendations, audition. Entrance: moderately difficult. Application deadline: 7/1. Notification: continuous. SAT Reasoning Test deadline: 5/1. Transfer credits accepted: Yes.

Costs Per Year: Application fee: $50. State resident tuition: $9124 full-time, $381 per credit hour part-time. Nonresident tuition: $24,156 full-time, $1017 per credit hour part-time. Mandatory fees: $1660 full-time, $69 per credit hour part-time. Full-time tuition and fees vary according to course load, degree level, location, program, and reciprocity agreements. Part-time tuition and fees vary according to course load, degree level, location, program, and reciprocity agreements. College room and board: $10,170. College room only: $6030. Room and board charges vary according to board plan and housing facility.

Collegiate Environment: Orientation program. Drama-theater group, choral group, marching band, student-run newspaper, radio station. Social organizations: 200 open to all; national fraternities, national sororities, local fraternities, Delta Phi Lambda Asian Interest Sorority; 75% of eligible men and 86% of eligible women are members. Most popular organizations: Navigators, Criminal Justice Society, Serve Beyond Cincinnati, United Black Student Association, Engineering Tribunal. Major annual events: Programs and Activities Council Spring Concert, Sigma Sigma Carnival, Relay for Life. Student services: health clinic, personal-psychological counseling, women's center. Campus security: 24-hour emergency response devices and patrols, late night transport-escort service, controlled dormitory access. 4,075 college housing spaces available; 3,883 were occupied in 2012-13. Freshmen guaranteed college housing. On-campus residence required in freshman year. Options: coed, men-only, women-only housing available. Walter C. Langsam Library plus 13 others with 3.7 million books, 3.4 million microform titles, 103,066 serials, 90,278 audiovisual materials, an OPAC, and a Web page. Operations spending for the previous fiscal year: $21.5 million.

Community Environment: Called by Longfellow,"The Queen City of the West," Cincinnati was founded in 1788 and was named Losantiville. The following year the name was changed to Cincinnati, after the Society of Cincinnati. The city is the third largest in Ohio and is situated on a series of plateaus above the Ohio River surrounded by hills. The altitude varies from 435 to 938 feet. Some of the industries located here are Proctor & Gamble Co., General Electric Co., Ford Motor Co., and the Kroger Co. The Cincinnati Convention-Exposition Center provides facilities for meetings as well as 95,000 square feet of exhibition space. Cultural facilities include the Cincinnati Symphony Orchestra, Art Academy of Cincinnati, and the University of Cincinnati College Conservatory of Music; Cincinnati is famous as a center of music and art. Recreational facilities are numerous. Among the points of interest are the Carew Tower Observatory, Cincinnati Art Museum, Cincinnati Museum of Natural History, King's Island which is a recreational facility, Hebrew Union College Museum, Mount Airy Forest, St. Peter in Chains Cathedral, Stowe House, and Taft Museum.

■ **UNIVERSITY OF CINCINNATI BLUE ASH**
9555 Plainfield Rd.
Cincinnati, OH 45236-1007
Tel: (513)745-5600
Fax: (513)745-5780
Web Site: www.ucblueash.edu/
Description: State-supported, 2-year, coed. Part of University of Cincinnati System. Awards certificates, transfer associate, and terminal associate degrees. Founded 1967. Setting: 120-acre suburban campus. Total enrollment: 4,180. Student-undergrad faculty ratio is 14:1. 3% from out-of-state. 39% 25 or older. Academic remediation for entering students, advanced placement, distance learning, summer session for credit, part-time degree program, adult/continuing education programs. Off campus study at 12 members of the Greater Cincinnati Consortium of Colleges and Universities. ROTC: Army (c), Air Force (c).
Entrance Requirements: Open admission except for allied health programs. Options: electronic application, deferred admission, international baccalaureate accepted. Required: high school transcript. Entrance: noncompetitive. Application deadline: Rolling. Notification: continuous.
Collegiate Environment: Orientation program. Campus security: 24-hour emergency response devices and patrols, student patrols, late night transport-escort service. Raymond Walters College Library with an OPAC and a Web page.
Community Environment: See University of Cincinnati.

■ **UNIVERSITY OF CINCINNATI CLERMONT COLLEGE**
4200 Clermont College Dr.
Batavia, OH 45103-1785
Tel: (513)732-5200
E-mail: jamie.adkins@uc.edu
Web Site: www.ucclermont.edu/
Description: State-supported, 2-year, coed. Part of University of Cincinnati System. Awards certificates, transfer associate, and terminal associate degrees. Founded 1972. Setting: 91-acre rural campus with easy access to Cincinnati. Endowment: $338,141. Educational spending for the previous fiscal year: $2724 per student. Total enrollment: 3,713. Faculty: 336 (77 full-time, 259 part-time). Student-undergrad faculty ratio is 20:1. 1,454 applied, 79% were admitted. Full-time: 2,391 students, 57% women, 43% men. Part-time: 1,322 students, 63% women, 37% men. Students come from 16 states and territories, 21% from out-of-state. 38% 25 or older. Academic

remediation for entering students, services for LD students, advanced placement, self-designed majors, honors program, independent study, distance learning, double major, summer session for credit, part-time degree program, adult/continuing education programs, co-op programs and internships. Off campus study at 11 members of the Greater Cincinnati Consortium of Colleges and Universities. Study abroad program. ROTC: Air Force (c).
Entrance Requirements: Open admission. Options: electronic application, deferred admission. Required: high school transcript. Entrance: noncompetitive. Application deadline: Rolling. Notification: continuous. Transfer credits accepted: Yes.
Collegiate Environment: Orientation program. Drama-theater group, student-run newspaper. Social organizations: 11 open to all. Most popular organizations: Active Minds, Art Collaborative, Education Club, Tribunal. Major annual events: Fall Fest, Winter Fest, Spring Fling. Student services: personal-psychological counseling. Campus security: 24-hour emergency response devices, 24-hour patrols by trained security personnel. UC Clermont College Library with 2,440 microform titles, 80,890 serials, 1,143 audiovisual materials, an OPAC, and a Web page. Operations spending for the previous fiscal year: $276,340. 77 computers available on campus for general student use. A campuswide network can be accessed. Students can access the following: online class registration. Staffed computer lab on campus.
Community Environment: Batavia, the Clermont County seat, is central to the entire county. Clermont County is recognized as the fastest growing county in Ohio. The completion of the Interstate Highway System and belt-freeway have made the Cincinnati metropolitan and Northern Kentucky areas easily accessible.

■ **UNIVERSITY OF DAYTON**
300 College Park
Dayton, OH 45469-1300
Tel: (937)229-1000; Free: 800-837-7433
Fax: (937)229-4545
E-mail: admission@udayton.edu
Web Site: www.udayton.edu/
Description: Independent Roman Catholic, university, coed. Awards bachelor's, master's, and doctoral degrees and post-master's certificates. Founded 1850. Setting: 388-acre suburban campus with easy access to Cincinnati. Endowment: $407.4 million. Research spending for the previous fiscal year: $82.6 million. Educational spending for the previous fiscal year: $12,622 per student. Total enrollment: 11,159. Faculty: 935 (508 full-time, 427 part-time). Student-undergrad faculty ratio is 16:1. 15,101 applied, 55% were admitted. 26% from top 10% of their high school class, 57% from top quarter, 88% from top half. 35 valedictorians. Full-time: 7,462 students, 49% women, 51% men. Part-time: 580 students, 47% women, 53% men. Students come from 50 states and territories, 39 other countries, 43% from out-of-state. 0.3% American Indian or Alaska Native, non-Hispanic/Latino; 2% Hispanic/Latino; 3% African American, non-Hispanic/Latino; 1% Asian, non-Hispanic/Latino; 0.03% Native Hawaiian or other Pacific Islander, non-Hispanic/Latino; 6% international. 3% 25 or older, 75% live on campus, 2% transferred in. Retention: 88% of full-time freshmen returned the following year. Academic areas with the most degrees conferred: business/marketing; engineering; education. Core. Calendar: semesters plus 2 6-week summer terms. Academic remediation for entering students, ESL program, services for LD students, advanced placement, accelerated degree program, self-designed majors, honors program, independent study, distance learning, double major, summer session for credit, part-time degree program, adult/continuing education programs, co-op programs and internships, graduate courses open to undergrads. Off campus study at Southwestern Ohio Council for Higher Education, Chaminade University of Honolulu, St. Mary's University. Study abroad program. ROTC: Army, Air Force (c).
Entrance Requirements: Options: electronic application, early decision, early action, deferred admission, international baccalaureate accepted. Required: essay, high school transcript, 1 recommendation, SAT or ACT. Recommended: interview. Required for some: audition for music, music therapy, music education programs. Entrance: moderately difficult. Application deadline: 12/15 for early action. Notification: 2/1 for early action. SAT Reasoning Test deadline: 3/1. Transfer credits accepted: Yes. Early decision applicants: 11,709. Early decision applicants admitted: 7,439.
Costs Per Year: Comprehensive fee: $43,750 includes full-time tuition ($32,000), mandatory fees ($1400), and college room and board ($10,350). College room only: $6450. Full-time tuition and fees vary according to program. Room and board charges vary according to board plan and hous-

ing facility. Part-time tuition: $1067 per credit hour. Part-time tuition varies according to course load and program.

Collegiate Environment: Orientation program. Drama-theater group, choral group, marching band, student-run newspaper, radio station. Social organizations: 230 open to all; national fraternities, national sororities, local fraternities; 17% of eligible men and 17% of eligible women are members. Most popular organizations: Student Government Association, marching band, Red Scare (basketball student cheering section), Campus Connection, Habitat for Humanity. Major annual events: Christmas on Campus, Parents' Weekend, Up the Organizations Day. Student services: health clinic, personal-psychological counseling, women's center. Campus security: 24-hour emergency response devices and patrols, student patrols, late night transport-escort service, controlled dormitory access, Approximately 1,000 recorded video cameras, automated external defibrillators in high density residential facilities and other key camp. 6,151 college housing spaces available; 6,081 were occupied in 2012-13. Freshmen guaranteed college housing. On-campus residence required through sophomore year. Options: coed, men-only, women-only housing available. Roesch Library plus 3 others with 1.5 million books, 1.5 million microform titles, 73,332 serials, 159,227 audiovisual materials, an OPAC, and a Web page. Operations spending for the previous fiscal year: $11.1 million. 7,675 computers available on campus for general student use. Computer purchase/lease plans available. A campuswide network can be accessed from student residence rooms and from off campus. Students can access the following: online class registration, applications, admission/enrollment status, virtual orientation, online digital resources, online courses, assistive technology, learning management system, multimedia labs, payment, cyber cafes, centrally-licensed, downloadable software and training. Staffed computer lab on campus provides training in use of computers, software, and the Internet.

Community Environment: See Wright State University.

■ THE UNIVERSITY OF FINDLAY

1000 N Main St.
Findlay, OH 45840-3653
Tel: (419)422-8313; Free: 800-548-0932
Fax: (419)424-4822
E-mail: admissions@findlay.edu
Web Site: www.findlay.edu/

Description: Independent, comprehensive, coed, affiliated with Church of God. Awards associate, bachelor's, master's, and doctoral degrees. Founded 1882. Setting: 390-acre urban campus with easy access to Toledo. Endowment: $24.8 million. Educational spending for the previous fiscal year: $10,101 per student. Total enrollment: 4,955. Faculty: 293 (201 full-time, 92 part-time). Student-undergrad faculty ratio is 15:1. 2,655 applied, 68% were admitted. 42% from top 10% of their high school class, 44% from top quarter, 88% from top half. 26 valedictorians. Full-time: 2,496 students, 66% women, 34% men. Part-time: 1,402 students, 60% women, 40% men. Students come from 45 states and territories, 34 other countries, 19% from out-of-state. 0.3% American Indian or Alaska Native, non-Hispanic/Latino; 2% Hispanic/Latino; 3% African American, non-Hispanic/Latino; 1% Asian, non-Hispanic/Latino; 0% Native Hawaiian or other Pacific Islander, non-Hispanic/Latino; 4% international. 18% 25 or older, 40% live on campus, 5% transferred in. Retention: 74% of full-time freshmen returned the following year. Academic areas with the most degrees conferred: health professions and related sciences; business/marketing; agriculture. Core. Calendar: semesters. Academic remediation for entering students, ESL program, services for LD students, advanced placement, accelerated degree program, self-designed majors, honors program, independent study, distance learning, double major, summer session for credit, part-time degree program, adult/continuing education programs, co-op programs and internships, graduate courses open to undergrads. Off campus study. Study abroad program. ROTC: Army (c), Air Force (c).

Entrance Requirements: Options: electronic application, deferred admission, international baccalaureate accepted. Required: essay, high school transcript, minimum 2.3 high school GPA, SAT or ACT. Required for some: interview. Entrance: moderately difficult. Application deadline: Rolling. Notification: continuous. SAT Reasoning Test deadline: 8/1. Transfer credits accepted: Yes.

Costs Per Year: Application fee: $0. Comprehensive fee: $39,056 includes full-time tuition ($28,894), mandatory fees ($904), and college room and board ($9258). College room only: $4620. Part-time tuition: $641 per semester hour. Part-time mandatory fees: $387 per term. Part-time tuition and fees vary according to course load and program.

Collegiate Environment: Orientation program. Drama-theater group, choral

group, marching band, student-run newspaper, radio station. Social organizations: 65 open to all; national fraternities, national sororities; 2% of eligible men and 2% of eligible women are members. Most popular organizations: Campus Program Board, Pre-Vet Club, Horse Club, Circle K, International Club. Major annual events: Homecoming, Family Weekend, Spring Bash. Student services: health clinic, personal-psychological counseling, women's center. Campus security: 24-hour emergency response devices and patrols, late night transport-escort service, controlled dormitory access. 1,400 college housing spaces available; 1,290 were occupied in 2012-13. Freshmen guaranteed college housing. On-campus residence required through sophomore year. Options: coed, men-only, women-only housing available. Shafer Library plus 1 other with 130,416 books, 25,232 microform titles, 51,193 serials, 4,721 audiovisual materials, an OPAC, and a Web page. Operations spending for the previous fiscal year: $941,953. 324 computers available on campus for general student use. Computer purchase/lease plans available. A campuswide network can be accessed from student residence rooms and from off campus. Students can access the following: online class registration. Staffed computer lab on campus provides training in use of computers, software, and the Internet.

Community Environment: Findlay is located in the northwestern part of Ohio, which is both a rich agricultural and manufacturing region. Excellent internship and employment opportunities are available. Recreational activities include swimming, golf, boating, and fishing.

■ UNIVERSITY OF MOUNT UNION

1972 Clark Ave.
Alliance, OH 44601-3993
Tel: (330)821-5320; Free: 800-992-6682
Fax: (330)821-0425
E-mail: admission@mountunion.edu
Web Site: www.mountunion.edu/

Description: Independent United Methodist, comprehensive, coed. Awards bachelor's and master's degrees. Founded 1846. Setting: 122-acre suburban campus with easy access to Cleveland. Endowment: $133.2 million. Educational spending for the previous fiscal year: $8430 per student. Total enrollment: 2,253. Faculty: 236 (128 full-time, 108 part-time). Student-undergrad faculty ratio is 14:1. 2,774 applied, 72% were admitted. 12% from top 10% of their high school class, 32% from top quarter, 70% from top half. Full-time: 2,148 students, 49% women, 51% men. Part-time: 27 students, 48% women, 52% men. Students come from 31 states and territories, 21 other countries, 13% from out-of-state. 0.1% American Indian or Alaska Native, non-Hispanic/Latino; 1% Hispanic/Latino; 6% African American, non-Hispanic/Latino; 0.5% Asian, non-Hispanic/Latino; 0% Native Hawaiian or other Pacific Islander, non-Hispanic/Latino; 3% international. 2% 25 or older, 76% live on campus, 2% transferred in. Retention: 72% of full-time freshmen returned the following year. Academic areas with the most degrees conferred: business/marketing; parks and recreation; education. Core. Calendar: semesters. ESL program, services for LD students, advanced placement, accelerated degree program, self-designed majors, honors program, independent study, distance learning, double major, summer session for credit, part-time degree program, adult/continuing education programs, co-op programs and internships. Off campus study at 6 members of the East Central College Consortium. Study abroad program. ROTC: Army, Air Force (c).

Entrance Requirements: Options: electronic application, early admission, deferred admission. Required: essay, high school transcript, minimum 2 high school GPA, 1 recommendation, SAT or ACT. Recommended: interview. Entrance: moderately difficult. Application deadline: Rolling. Notification: continuous. Transfer credits accepted: Yes.

Costs Per Year: Application fee: $0. Comprehensive fee: $35,130 includes full-time tuition ($26,350), mandatory fees ($300), and college room and board ($8480). Full-time tuition and fees vary according to course load and degree level. Room and board charges vary according to board plan and housing facility. Part-time tuition: $1110 per credit hour. Part-time tuition varies according to course load.

Collegiate Environment: Orientation program. Drama-theater group, choral group, marching band, student-run newspaper, radio station. Social organizations: 74 open to all; national fraternities, national sororities, local sororities; 14% of eligible men and 30% of eligible women are members. Most popular organizations: Alpha Phi Omega, Student Senate, FCA Fellowship of Christian Athletes, Black Student Union, Raider Programming Board. Major annual events: Homecoming, Scholar Day, Schooler Lecture. Student services: health clinic, personal-psychological counseling. Campus security: 24-hour emergency response devices and patrols, late night transport-escort service, controlled dormitory access, 24-hour locked residence hall entrances, outside phones. 1,733 college housing spaces available; 1,626 were occupied in 2012-13. Freshmen guaranteed college housing. On-campus residence required through sophomore year. Options: coed, men-only, women-only housing available. University of Mount Union Library plus 1 other with 293,090 books, 67,365 microform titles, 63,420 serials, 6,911 audiovisual materials, an OPAC, and a Web page. Operations spending for the previous fiscal year: $1.4 million. 265 computers available on campus for general student use. Computer purchase/lease plans available. A campuswide network can be accessed from student residence rooms and from off campus. Students can access the following: online class registration. Staffed computer lab on campus provides training in use of computers, software, and the Internet.

Community Environment: Alliance, population 22,801, is an industrial city located within a circle of large cities, Cleveland, Akron, and Pittsburgh. Heavy steel equipment and forgings are among the products of its industry. Commercial transportation is available. Recreational activities include swimming, golfing, fishing, boating and tennis. The Carnation Festival is an annual event. Part-time employment is available.

■ **UNIVERSITY OF NORTHWESTERN OHIO**
1441 N Cable Rd.
Lima, OH 45805-1498
Tel: (419)227-3141
Fax: (419)229-6926
E-mail: klopp_d@unoh.edu
Web Site: www.unoh.edu/

Description: Independent, 4-year, coed. Awards associate and bachelor's degrees. Founded 1920. Setting: 140-acre small town campus with easy access to Dayton, Toledo. Total enrollment: 3,848. Faculty: 127 (93 full-time, 34 part-time). Student-undergrad faculty ratio is 20:1. 2% from top 10% of their high school class, 9% from top quarter, 34% from top half. 51% from out-of-state. 16% 25 or older, 33% live on campus. Academic areas with the most degrees conferred: business/marketing; health professions and related sciences. Core. Academic remediation for entering students, services for LD students, advanced placement, accelerated degree program, distance learning, double major, summer session for credit, part-time degree program, adult/continuing education programs, co-op programs and internships.

Entrance Requirements: Open admission. Options: electronic application, early admission, deferred admission. Required: high school transcript. Required for some: SAT. Entrance: noncompetitive. Application deadline: Rolling.

Collegiate Environment: Orientation program. Student-run newspaper. Social organizations: 1 open to all. Most popular organization: Students in Free Enterprise (SIFE). Major annual events: Mud Volleyball, Car Show, Intramural Volleyball. Student services: personal-psychological counseling. Campus security: 24-hour emergency response devices and patrols, late night transport-escort service. University of Northwestern Ohio Library with 4,553 books, 95 serials, an OPAC, and a Web page. Operations spending for the previous fiscal year: $36,715. 149 computers available on campus for general student use. A campuswide network can be accessed from off-campus. Staffed computer lab on campus.

■ **UNIVERSITY OF PHOENIX–CINCINNATI CAMPUS**
9050 Centre Pointe Dr., Ste. 250
West Chester, OH 45069-4875
Tel: (513)772-9600; Free: 866-766-0766
Web Site: www.phoenix.edu/

Description: Proprietary, comprehensive, coed. Awards bachelor's and master's degrees. Founded 2003. Setting: urban campus. Total enrollment: 143. Faculty: 47 (6 full-time, 41 part-time). Full-time: 70 students, 60% women, 40% men. 93% 25 or older. Academic areas with the most degrees conferred: business/marketing; computer and information sciences. Core. Calendar: continuous. Services for LD students, advanced placement, accelerated degree program, independent study, distance learning, graduate courses open to undergrads.

Entrance Requirements: Open admission. Options: electronic application, deferred admission. Required: 1 recommendation. Required for some: high school transcript. Entrance: noncompetitive. Application deadline: Rolling.

Collegiate Environment: Campus security: late night transport-escort service. University Library with 16,781 serials, an OPAC, and a Web page. Operations spending for the previous fiscal year: $6.8 million.

■ **UNIVERSITY OF PHOENIX–CLEVELAND CAMPUS**
5005 Rockside Rd., Ste. 130
Independence, OH 44131-2194

Tel: (216)447-8807; Free: 866-766-0766
Web Site: www.phoenix.edu/

Description: Proprietary, comprehensive, coed. Awards associate, bachelor's, and master's degrees. Founded 2000. Setting: urban campus. Total enrollment: 664. Faculty: 123 (10 full-time, 113 part-time). Full-time: 394 students, 73% women, 27% men. 91% 25 or older. Academic areas with the most degrees conferred: business/marketing; health professions and related sciences; computer and information sciences. Core. Calendar: continuous. Services for LD students, advanced placement, accelerated degree program, independent study, distance learning, external degree program, adult/continuing education programs, graduate courses open to undergrads.

Entrance Requirements: Open admission. Options: electronic application, deferred admission. Required: 1 recommendation. Required for some: high school transcript. Entrance: noncompetitive. Application deadline: Rolling.

Collegiate Environment: University Library with 16,781 serials, an OPAC, and a Web page. Operations spending for the previous fiscal year: $6.8 million.

■ **UNIVERSITY OF PHOENIX–COLUMBUS OHIO CAMPUS**
8415 Pulsar Pl.
Columbus, OH 43240-4032
Tel: (614)433-0095; Free: 866-766-0766
Web Site: www.phoenix.edu/

Description: Proprietary, comprehensive, coed. Awards associate, bachelor's, and master's degrees. Founded 2003. Setting: urban campus. Total enrollment: 208. Faculty: 65 (4 full-time, 61 part-time). Full-time: 128 students, 56% women, 44% men. 81% 25 or older. Academic area with the most degrees conferred: business/marketing. Core. Calendar: continuous. Services for LD students, advanced placement, accelerated degree program, independent study, distance learning, graduate courses open to undergrads.

Entrance Requirements: Open admission. Options: electronic application, deferred admission. Required: 1 recommendation. Required for some: high school transcript. Entrance: noncompetitive. Application deadline: Rolling.

Collegiate Environment: Campus security: late night transport-escort service. University Library with 16,781 serials and an OPAC. Operations spending for the previous fiscal year: $6.8 million.

■ **UNIVERSITY OF RIO GRANDE**
218 N College Ave.
Rio Grande, OH 45674
Tel: (740)245-5353; Free: 800-282-7201
Fax: (740)245-9220
E-mail: admissions@rio.edu
Web Site: www.rio.edu/

Description: Independent, comprehensive, coed. Awards associate, bachelor's, and master's degrees. Founded 1876. Setting: 170-acre rural campus. Endowment: $19.2 million. Educational spending for the previous fiscal year: $5229 per student. Total enrollment: 2,278. Faculty: 182 (93 full-time, 89 part-time). Student-undergrad faculty ratio is 16:1. 5,040 applied, 44% were admitted. 3% from top 10% of their high school class, 22% from top quarter, 51% from top half. Full-time: 1,808 students, 61% women, 39% men. Part-time: 391 students, 70% women, 30% men. Students come from 22 states and territories, 10 other countries, 6% from out-of-state. 0.5% American Indian or Alaska Native, non-Hispanic/Latino; 1% Hispanic/Latino; 6% African American, non-Hispanic/Latino; 0.2% Asian, non-Hispanic/Latino; 0.05% Native Hawaiian or other Pacific Islander, non-Hispanic/Latino; 1% international. 41% 25 or older, 20% live on campus, 11% transferred in. Retention: 51% of full-time freshmen returned the following year. Academic areas with the most degrees conferred: business/marketing; education; health professions and related sciences. Core. Calendar: semesters. Academic remediation for entering students, services for LD students, advanced placement, accelerated degree program, self-designed majors, honors program, independent study, distance learning, double major, summer session for credit, part-time degree program, adult/continuing education programs, co-op programs and internships. Study abroad program.

Entrance Requirements: Open admission except for nursing, radiologic technology, education, social work. Option: electronic application. Required: high school transcript, medical history. Recommended: ACT. Entrance: noncompetitive. Application deadline: Rolling. Notification: continuous. Transfer credits accepted: Yes.

Collegiate Environment: Orientation program. Drama-theater group, choral group, student-run newspaper, radio station. Social organizations: 41 open

to all; national fraternities, local fraternities, local sororities; 5% of eligible men and 4% of eligible women are members. Most popular organizations: student government, Honoraries, Bible studies, ENACTA. Major annual events: Community Service Day, Homecoming, Founders Day. Student services: health clinic, personal-psychological counseling. Campus security: 24-hour emergency response devices and patrols, late night transport-escort service, controlled dormitory access. 630 college housing spaces available; 320 were occupied in 2012-13. No special consideration for freshman housing applicants. Options: coed, men-only, women-only housing available. Jeanette Albiez Davis Library plus 2 others with 96,731 books, 850 serials, an OPAC, and a Web page. Operations spending for the previous fiscal year: $353,505. 300 computers available on campus for general student use. A campuswide network can be accessed from student residence rooms and from off campus. Students can access the following: online class registration. Staffed computer lab on campus provides training in use of computers, software, and the Internet.

Community Environment: Less than one mile from campus, the Bob Evans Farm offers canoe and horse rentals, trail rides, hiking, and fishing. A radio-controlled aircraft club meets monthly in good weather. The second weekend of October marks the annual Bob Evans Farm Festival, which brings visitors from surrounding states. Rio Grande students participate heavily in the Farm Festival as part of "Community Service Day" when most college classes are canceled. Annual campus-hosted events include World-Fest, Native American Pow Wow, and Celtic/Welsh festivals. Other recreational facilities within a reasonable driving distance include golf, boating, skiing, rock climbing, white-water rafting, camping, and fishing. A rural community, Rio Grande is located 90 miles southeast of Columbus, 130 miles east of Cincinnati, and 60 miles north of Charleston, WV. Local shopping is found in Jackson and Gallipolis, both within 20 miles. Lare malls are found in Charleston and Huntington, WV, both about 60 miles away. Gallipolis is a picturesque river town, settled on the banks of the Ohio River, one of the annual stops for the historic Delta Queen steamboat. The surrounding area includes active civic and service organizations, church groups, shopping facilities, the Holzer Medical Center, and Holzer Clinic. The Ohio Valley Symphony, the Valley Artist Series, and the French Art Colony provide music, theater, and fine arts cultural events and exhibits. Performances are held either on campus at the Merlyn Ross Fine Arts Center or in Gallipolis at the refurbished Victorian playhouse, the Ariel Theater. Students get special reduced rates to performances. Opportunities for part-time employment are good, primarily in retailing.

■ THE UNIVERSITY OF TOLEDO

2801 W Bancroft
Toledo, OH 43606-3390
Tel: (419)530-4636; Free: 800-5TOLEDO
Fax: (419)530-4940
E-mail: william.pierce@utoledo.edu
Web Site: www.utoledo.edu/

Description: State-supported, university, coed. Awards bachelor's, master's, and doctoral degrees and post-master's certificates. Founded 1872. Setting: 813-acre urban campus with easy access to Detroit. Endowment: $47 million. Research spending for the previous fiscal year: $68.2 million. Educational spending for the previous fiscal year: $9396 per student. Total enrollment: 21,501. Faculty: 1,249 (898 full-time, 351 part-time). Student-undergrad faculty ratio is 19:1. 11,040 applied, 95% were admitted. Full-time: 13,538 students, 49% women, 51% men. Part-time: 3,339 students, 51% women, 49% men. Students come from 55 states and territories, 90 other countries, 15% from out-of-state. 0.2% American Indian or Alaska Native, non-Hispanic/Latino; 4% Hispanic/Latino; 15% African American, non-Hispanic/Latino; 2% Asian, non-Hispanic/Latino; 0.1% Native Hawaiian or other Pacific Islander, non-Hispanic/Latino; 4% international. 16% 25 or older, 15% live on campus, 6% transferred in. Retention: 62% of full-time freshmen returned the following year. Academic areas with the most degrees conferred: health professions and related sciences; business/marketing; engineering. Core. Calendar: semesters. Academic remediation for entering students, ESL program, services for LD students, advanced placement, accelerated degree program, self-designed majors, freshman honors college, honors program, independent study, distance learning, double major, summer session for credit, part-time degree program, adult/continuing education programs, co-op programs and internships, graduate courses open to undergrads. Off campus study at Bowling Green State University, Consortium for Health Education, The Central States Universities, Inc. Study abroad program. ROTC: Army, Air Force (c).

Entrance Requirements: Open admission open admission. Options:

electronic application, deferred admission, international baccalaureate accepted. Required: high school transcript, SAT or ACT. Required for some: minimum 2 high school GPA, CORE high school curriculum. Entrance: noncompetitive. Application deadline: Rolling. Notification: continuous. Transfer credits accepted: Yes.

Costs Per Year: Application fee: $40. State resident tuition: $7,864 full-time, $327.66 per credit hour part-time. Nonresident tuition: $16,984 full-time, $707.66 per credit hour part-time. Mandatory fees: $1,411 full-time, $57.80 per credit hour part-time. Full-time tuition and fees vary according to course load, program, and reciprocity agreements. Part-time tuition and fees vary according to course load, program, and reciprocity agreements. College room and board: $9738. College room only: $6338. Room and board charges vary according to board plan and housing facility.

Collegiate Environment: Orientation program. Drama-theater group, choral group, marching band, student-run newspaper, radio station. Social organizations: 200 open to all; national fraternities, national sororities, local fraternities, local sororities; 6% of eligible men and 3% of eligible women are members. Most popular organizations: student government, University YMCA, Newman Club, International Student Association, Campus Activities and Programming. Major annual events: Homecoming, Songfest, Earthfest. Student services: legal services, health clinic, personal-psychological counseling, women's center. Campus security: 24-hour emergency response devices and patrols, student patrols, late night transport-escort service, controlled dormitory access, bicycle patrols by security staff, crime prevention officer. 3,558 college housing spaces available. On-campus residence required in freshman year. Option: coed housing available. Carlson Library plus 3 others with 1.9 million books, 1.8 million microform titles, 95,498 serials, 11,796 audiovisual materials, an OPAC, and a Web page. Operations spending for the previous fiscal year: $14.8 million. 5,000 computers available on campus for general student use. Computer purchase/lease plans available. A campuswide network can be accessed from student residence rooms and from off campus. Students can access the following: online class registration, online transcripts, student account. Staffed computer lab on campus (open 24 hours a day).

Community Environment: Toledo's importance as a port stems from its location at the mouth of the Maumee River. It is the busiest freshwater port in the world. It ranks second on the Great Lakes, and ninth in the nation in tonnage handled.

■ URBANA UNIVERSITY

579 College Way
Urbana, OH 43078-2091
Tel: (937)484-1400; Free: 800-7-URBANA
Fax: (937)484-1389
E-mail: admiss@urbana.edu
Web Site: www.urbana.edu/

Description: Independent, comprehensive, coed, affiliated with Church of the New Jerusalem. Awards associate, bachelor's, and master's degrees. Founded 1850. Setting: 128-acre small town campus with easy access to Columbus, Dayton. Endowment: $415,000. Educational spending for the previous fiscal year: $14,220 per student. Total enrollment: 1,551. Faculty: 120 (55 full-time, 65 part-time). Student-undergrad faculty ratio is 16:1. 495 applied, 65% were admitted. Full-time: 904 students, 46% women, 54% men. Part-time: 557 students, 64% women, 36% men. 4% from out-of-state. 6% transferred in. Retention: 70% of full-time freshmen returned the following year. Academic areas with the most degrees conferred: education; homeland security, law enforcement, firefighting, and protective services; health professions and related sciences. Core. Calendar: semesters. Academic remediation for entering students, services for LD students, advanced placement, accelerated degree program, self-designed majors, freshman honors college, honors program, independent study, double major, summer session for credit, part-time degree program, adult/continuing education programs, co-op programs and internships. Off campus study at members of the Southwestern Ohio Council for Higher Education.

Entrance Requirements: Options: electronic application, deferred admission. Required: essay, high school transcript, minimum 2.0 high school GPA, SAT or ACT. Recommended: interview. Required for some: 2 recommendations. Entrance: moderately difficult. Application deadline: Rolling. Notification: continuous.

Collegiate Environment: Orientation program. Drama-theater group, choral group, marching band, student-run newspaper, radio station. Social organizations: 20 open to all. Most popular organizations: Student Government Association, Business Club, Education Club, Drama Club, Student Activities Planning Committee. Major annual events: Homecoming, Spring

Fling Week, Founders' Day. Student services: health clinic, personal-psychological counseling. Campus security: 24-hour emergency response devices and patrols, late night transport-escort service. Swedenborg Memorial Library with 61,600 books, 10,000 microform titles, 800 serials, 22,036 audiovisual materials, an OPAC, and a Web page. 75 computers available on campus for general student use. A campuswide network can be accessed from student residence rooms. Staffed computer lab on campus.

Community Environment: Urbana is the county seat of Champaign county and has a population in excess of 12,000 residents. The community has become well known regionally for the restoration of the historic downtown business district. The community provides a modern small-town environment with easy access to major metropolitan areas, being located just 15 minutes from downtown Springfield and 45 minutes from Dayton and Columbus.

■ URSULINE COLLEGE
2550 Lander Rd.
Pepper Pike, OH 44124-4398
Tel: (440)449-4200; Free: 888-URSULINE
Fax: (440)449-2235
E-mail: admission@ursuline.edu
Web Site: www.ursuline.edu/

Description: Independent Roman Catholic, comprehensive, coed. Awards bachelor's, master's, and doctoral degrees and post-master's certificates (applications from men are also accepted). Founded 1871. Setting: 112-acre suburban campus with easy access to Cleveland. Endowment: $33 million. Educational spending for the previous fiscal year: $12,321 per student. Total enrollment: 1,496. Faculty: 202. (70 full-time, 132 part-time). Student-undergrad faculty ratio is 11:1. 470 applied, 58% were admitted. 12% from top 10% of their high school class, 28% from top quarter, 75% from top half. Full-time: 573 students, 92% women, 8% men. Part-time: 306 students, 89% women, 11% men. Students come from 15 states and territories, 6 other countries, 5% from out-of-state. 0.3% American Indian or Alaska Native, non-Hispanic/Latino; 2% Hispanic/Latino; 30% African American, non-Hispanic/Latino; 1% Asian, non-Hispanic/Latino; 0% Native Hawaiian or other Pacific Islander, non-Hispanic/Latino; 2% international. 44% 25 or older, 17% live on campus, 13% transferred in. Retention: 71% of full-time freshmen returned the following year. Academic areas with the most degrees conferred: health professions and related sciences; business/marketing; visual and performing arts. Core. Calendar: semesters. Academic remediation for entering students, services for LD students, advanced placement, accelerated degree program, self-designed majors, independent study, distance learning, double major, summer session for credit, part-time degree program, adult/continuing education programs, co-op programs and internships, graduate courses open to undergrads. Off campus study at Fashion Institute of Technology (FIT) in New York. ROTC: Army (c).

Entrance Requirements: Options: electronic application, deferred admission. Required: essay, high school transcript, 1 recommendation, SAT or ACT. Recommended: minimum 2.5 high school GPA, interview. Entrance: minimally difficult. Application deadlines: 2/1, 2/1 for nonresidents. Notification: continuous, continuous for nonresidents. SAT Reasoning Test deadline: 8/1. SAT Subject Test deadline: 8/1. Transfer credits accepted: Yes.

Costs Per Year: Application fee: $25. Comprehensive fee: $35,660 includes full-time tuition ($26,490), mandatory fees ($270), and college room and board ($8900). College room only: $4546. Full-time tuition and fees vary according to location. Room and board charges vary according to board plan and housing facility. Part-time tuition: $546 per credit. Part-time mandatory fees: $90 per term. Part-time tuition and fees vary according to location.

Collegiate Environment: Orientation program. Drama-theater group, choral group. Social organizations: 29 open to all. Most popular organizations: Student Government Association, Student Nurses of Ursuline College, Fashion Focus, Students United for Black Awareness, Drama Club. Major annual events: Founders' Day, All College Day, Fall Formal. Student services: personal-psychological counseling. Campus security: 24-hour emergency response devices and patrols, late night transport-escort service, controlled dormitory access. 238 college housing spaces available; 150 were occupied in 2012-13. No special consideration for freshman housing applicants. Options: coed, women-only housing available. Ralph M. Besse Library with 208,262 books, 4,675 microform titles, 47,869 serials, 12,727 audiovisual materials, an OPAC, and a Web page. Operations spending for the previous fiscal year: $678,600. 72 computers available on campus for general student use. A campuswide network can be accessed from student residence rooms. Students can access the following: online class registration. Staffed computer lab on campus.

Community Environment: See Case Western Reserve University.

■ VATTEROTT COLLEGE
5025 E Royalton Rd.
Broadview Heights, OH 44147
Tel: (440)526-1660; Free: 888-553-6627
Fax: (440)526-1933
Web Site: www.vatterott.edu/

Description: Proprietary, 2-year, coed. Awards terminal associate degrees. Total enrollment: 236. 46 applied, 93% were admitted. Calendar: semesters.

■ VET TECH INSTITUTE AT BRADFORD SCHOOL
2469 Stelzer Rd.
Columbus, OH 43219
Tel: (614)416-6200; Free: 800-678-7981
Fax: (614)416-5197
Web Site: www.vettechinstitute.edu/

Description: Private, 2-year, coed. Awards terminal associate degrees. Founded 2005. Setting: suburban campus. Total enrollment: 167. 592 applied, 33% were admitted. Accelerated degree program, internships.

■ VIRGINIA MARTI COLLEGE OF ART AND DESIGN
11724 Detroit Ave.
Lakewood, OH 44107-3002
Tel: (216)221-8584
E-mail: qmarti@vmcad.edu
Web Site: www.vmcad.edu/

Description: Proprietary, 2-year, coed. Awards certificates and terminal associate degrees. Founded 1966. Setting: urban campus with easy access to Cleveland. Total enrollment: 271. Student-undergrad faculty ratio is 12:1. 88 applied. 0% from out-of-state. 26% 25 or older. Retention: 62% of full-time freshmen returned the following year. Academic remediation for entering students, summer session for credit, part-time degree program, adult/continuing education programs, internships.

Entrance Requirements: Options: electronic application, early admission, deferred admission. Required: essay, high school transcript, minimum 2 high school GPA, 1 recommendation, interview, CAPS. Required for some: entrance evaluation test. Entrance: moderately difficult. Application deadline: Rolling. Transfer credits accepted: Yes.

Collegiate Environment: Orientation program. Campus security: 24-hour emergency response devices.

■ WALSH UNIVERSITY
2020 E Maple St., NW
North Canton, OH 44720-3396
Tel: (330)499-7090; Free: 800-362-8846
Fax: (330)490-7165
E-mail: admissions@walsh.edu
Web Site: www.walsh.edu/

Description: Independent Roman Catholic, comprehensive, coed. Awards associate, bachelor's, master's, and doctoral degrees. Founded 1958. Setting: 134-acre small town campus with easy access to Cleveland. Endowment: $13.3 million. Research spending for the previous fiscal year: $49,795. Educational spending for the previous fiscal year: $6192 per student. Total enrollment: 2,864. Faculty: 254 (128 full-time, 126 part-time). Student-undergrad faculty ratio is 14:1. 1,621 applied, 78% were admitted. 18% from top 10% of their high school class, 43% from top quarter, 76% from top half. 12 valedictorians. Full-time: 1,922 students, 61% women, 39% men. Part-time: 449 students, 71% women, 29% men. Students come from 20 states and territories, 20 other countries, 3% from out-of-state. 0.3% American Indian or Alaska Native, non-Hispanic/Latino; 2% Hispanic/Latino; 5% African American, non-Hispanic/Latino; 0.5% Asian, non-Hispanic/Latino; 0.04% Native Hawaiian or other Pacific Islander, non-Hispanic/Latino; 2% international. 20% 25 or older, 53% live on campus, 8% transferred in. Retention: 74% of full-time freshmen returned the following year. Academic areas with the most degrees conferred: business/marketing; health professions and related sciences; education. Core. Calendar: semesters. Academic remediation for entering students, ESL program, services for LD students, advanced placement, accelerated degree program, honors program, independent study, distance learning, double major, summer session for credit, part-time degree program, external degree program, adult/continuing education programs, internships, graduate courses open to undergrads. Off campus study at Stark State College, Academic Alliance Cooperative Engineering Program—Youngstown State University. Study abroad program.

Entrance Requirements: Options: electronic application, early admission, deferred admission, international baccalaureate accepted. Required: high school transcript, minimum 2.4 high school GPA, SAT or ACT. Recommended: interview. Required for some: essay, minimum 3 high school GPA, 2 recommendations. Entrance: moderately difficult. Application deadlines: Rolling, Rolling for nonresidents. Notification: continuous, continuous for nonresidents. SAT Reasoning Test deadline: 8/15. Transfer credits accepted: Yes.

Costs Per Year: Application fee: $25. Comprehensive fee: $33,630 includes full-time tuition ($23,550), mandatory fees ($1140), and college room and board ($8940). College room only: $4730. Full-time tuition and fees vary according to location. Room and board charges vary according to board plan and housing facility. Part-time tuition: $785 per credit hour. Part-time mandatory fees: $38 per credit hour. Part-time tuition and fees vary according to course load and location.

Collegiate Environment: Orientation program. Drama-theater group, choral group, marching band, student-run newspaper, radio station. Social organizations: 40 open to all. Most popular organizations: student government, University Programming Board, Business and Communication Club, Behavioral Science Club, Education Club. Major annual events: Homecoming, Walshfest, Finals Week Late Night Breakfast. Student services: health clinic, personal-psychological counseling. Campus security: 24-hour emergency response devices and patrols, late night transport-escort service, controlled dormitory access. 1,045 college housing spaces available; 1,034 were occupied in 2012-13. Freshmen guaranteed college housing. On-campus residence required through senior year. Options: coed, men-only, women-only housing available. Brother Edmond Drouin Library with 277,307 books, 61,193 serials, 13,357 audiovisual materials, an OPAC, and a Web page. Operations spending for the previous fiscal year: $708,369. 371 computers available on campus for general student use. A campuswide network can be accessed from student residence rooms and from off campus. Students can access the following: online class registration. Staffed computer lab on campus provides training in use of computers, software, and the Internet.

Community Environment: Walsh University is conveniently located and easily accessible, near Ohio Interstate 77 in North Canton, a residential suburban area. The Walsh campus, near Canton, which city of about 84,000 with a wide array of cultural, recreational, and athletic activities. Home of the Professional Football Hall of Fame and the President McKinley National Memorial, the city boasts a symphony orchestra, art institute, civic opera, theater guild, and ballet. A number of major employers are headquartered in Stark County, including the Hoover Company, the Timken Company, and Diebold, Inc. 20 miles north of campus is Akron, and within an hour's drive is Cleveland. The Akron-Canton Regional Airport, is north of campus and serves the Canton-Stark County area, as do Amtrak trains and Greyhound buses.

■ WASHINGTON STATE COMMUNITY COLLEGE

710 Colegate Dr.
Marietta, OH 45750-9225
Tel: (740)374-8716
Fax: (740)376-0257
E-mail: rperoni@wscc.edu
Web Site: www.wscc.edu/

Description: State-supported, 2-year, coed. Part of Ohio Board of Regents. Awards certificates, transfer associate, and terminal associate degrees. Founded 1971. Setting: small town campus. Total enrollment: 2,184. Student-undergrad faculty ratio is 18:1. 15% from out-of-state. 44% 25 or older. Core. Academic remediation for entering students, services for LD students, self-designed majors, independent study, double major, summer session for credit, part-time degree program, adult/continuing education programs, internships.

Entrance Requirements: Open admission except for medical laboratory technology, nursing programs. Options: early admission, deferred admission. Recommended: high school transcript. Required for some: high school transcript. Entrance: noncompetitive. Application deadline: Rolling. Notification: continuous.

Collegiate Environment: Choral group. Student services: personal-psychological counseling.

■ WILBERFORCE UNIVERSITY

1055 N Bickett Rd.
Wilberforce, OH 45384
Tel: (937)376-2911; Free: 800-367-8568
Fax: (937)376-4751

E-mail: jjohnson@wilberforce.edu
Web Site: www.wilberforce.edu/

Description: Independent, comprehensive, coed, affiliated with African Methodist Episcopal Church. Awards bachelor's and master's degrees. Founded 1856. Setting: 125-acre rural campus with easy access to Dayton. Total enrollment: 549. 2,321 applied, 43% were admitted. Students come from 14 states and territories, 3 other countries, 60% from out-of-state. 1% American Indian or Alaska Native, non-Hispanic/Latino; 1% Hispanic/Latino; 95% African American, non-Hispanic/Latino; 0% Asian, non-Hispanic/Latino; 0% Native Hawaiian or other Pacific Islander, non-Hispanic/Latino; 0% international. 14% 25 or older. Academic areas with the most degrees conferred: business/marketing; health professions and related sciences; psychology. Core. Calendar: semesters. Academic remediation for entering students, advanced placement, freshman honors college, honors program, independent study, distance learning, double major, external degree program, adult/continuing education programs, co-op programs and internships. Off campus study at 18 members of the Southwestern Ohio Council for Higher Education. Study abroad program. ROTC: Army (c), Air Force (c).

Entrance Requirements: Options: electronic application, early admission, early decision, deferred admission. Required: essay, high school transcript, minimum 2.5 high school GPA, 2 recommendations, SAT or ACT. Entrance: minimally difficult. Application deadline: 7/1. Notification: continuous until 8/1. Transfer credits accepted: Yes.

Costs Per Year: Application fee: $25. Comprehensive fee: $20,946 includes full-time tuition ($14,330) and college room and board ($6616). College room only: $3746. Full-time tuition varies according to course load, location, and program. Part-time tuition: $500 per credit hour. Part-time tuition varies according to course load, location, and program.

Collegiate Environment: Orientation program. Drama-theater group, choral group, student-run newspaper, radio station. Social organizations: national fraternities, national sororities, local fraternities, local sororities. Student services: health clinic, personal-psychological counseling. Campus security: 24-hour emergency response devices and patrols, controlled dormitory access. 850 college housing spaces available. Freshmen guaranteed college housing. On-campus residence required through junior year. Options: coed, men-only, women-only housing available. Rembert E. Stokes Library with 63,000 books, 10,000 microform titles, 650 serials, 500 audiovisual materials, an OPAC, and a Web page.

Community Environment: Located in rural village of Wilberforce with a history of significant activity in the underground railroad of pre-Civil War days. The city of Xenia, Ohio is nearby with a population of 23,600 and is a good shopping center. It provides a resource for field study, cultural and recreational activities plus the close urban centers of Dayton, Springfield, Columbus and Cincinnati.

■ WILMINGTON COLLEGE

1870 Quaker Way
Wilmington, OH 45177
Tel: (937)382-6661; Free: 800-341-9318
Fax: (937)382-7077
E-mail: admissions@wilmington.edu
Web Site: www.wilmington.edu/

Description: Independent Friends, comprehensive, coed. Awards bachelor's and master's degrees. Founded 1870. Setting: small town campus. Total enrollment: 1,458. Faculty: 119 (66 full-time, 53 part-time). Student-undergrad faculty ratio is 14:1. 1,651 applied. 11% from top 10% of their high school class, 36% from top quarter, 70% from top half. Full-time: 1,179 students, 52% women, 48% men. Part-time: 253 students, 60% women, 40% men. 6% from out-of-state. 1% American Indian or Alaska Native, non-Hispanic/Latino; 1% Hispanic/Latino; 11% African American, non-Hispanic/Latino; 0.4% Asian, non-Hispanic/Latino; 0% Native Hawaiian or other Pacific Islander, non-Hispanic/Latino; 1% international. 15% 25 or older, 80% live on campus, 5% transferred in. Retention: 67% of full-time freshmen returned the following year. Academic areas with the most degrees conferred: business/marketing; education; agriculture. Calendar: semesters. Part-time degree program, adult/continuing education programs. ROTC: Army (c).

Entrance Requirements: Option: deferred admission. Required: high school transcript. Recommended: minimum 2.5 high school GPA, 1 recommendation, interview, SAT or ACT. Entrance: moderately difficult. Application deadline: 8/1. Notification: continuous.

Collegiate Environment: Orientation program. Campus security: 24-hour emergency response devices and patrols, late night transport-escort service, controlled dormitory access.

■ WITTENBERG UNIVERSITY

PO Box 720
Springfield, OH 45501-0720
Tel: (937)327-6231; Free: 800-677-7558
Fax: (937)327-6379
E-mail: admission@wittenberg.edu
Web Site: www.wittenberg.edu/

Description: Independent, comprehensive, coed, affiliated with Evangelical Lutheran Church. Awards bachelor's and master's degrees. Founded 1845. Setting: 114-acre suburban campus with easy access to Columbus, Dayton. Endowment: $90.9 million. Research spending for the previous fiscal year: $183,149. Educational spending for the previous fiscal year: $12,322 per student. Total enrollment: 1,894. Faculty: 194 (141 full-time, 53 part-time). Student-undergrad faculty ratio is 11:1. 4,887 applied, 91% were admitted. 23% from top 10% of their high school class, 48% from top quarter, 79% from top half. 33 student government officers. Full-time: 1,784 students, 55% women, 45% men. Part-time: 97 students, 55% women, 45% men. Students come from 43 states and territories, 22 other countries, 27% from out-of-state. 0.2% American Indian or Alaska Native, non-Hispanic/Latino; 3% Hispanic/Latino; 7% African American, non-Hispanic/Latino; 1% Asian, non-Hispanic/Latino; 0% Native Hawaiian or other Pacific Islander, non-Hispanic/Latino; 2% international. 7% 25 or older, 83% live on campus, 2% transferred in. Retention: 78% of full-time freshmen returned the following year. Academic areas with the most degrees conferred: social sciences; business/marketing; biological/life sciences. Core. Calendar: semesters. Academic remediation for entering students, ESL program, advanced placement, self-designed majors, freshman honors college, honors program, independent study, double major, summer session for credit, part-time degree program, adult/continuing education programs, co-op programs and internships. Off campus study at Members of the Southwestern Ohio Council for Higher Education. Study abroad program. ROTC: Army (c), Air Force (c).

Entrance Requirements: Options: electronic application, early admission, early decision, early action, deferred admission, international baccalaureate accepted. Required: essay, high school transcript, interview. Recommended: test scores are optional. Entrance: moderately difficult. Application deadlines: 11/15 for early decision, 12/1 for early action. Notification: continuous, 12/15 for early decision, 1/1 for early action. Preference given to Lutherans, children of alumni, county residents, minorities. Transfer credits accepted: Yes. Early decision applicants: 111. Early decision applicants admitted: 77. Early action applicants: 2,931. Early action applicants admitted: 2,596.

Costs Per Year: Application fee: $40. Comprehensive fee: $47,766 includes full-time tuition ($37,230), mandatory fees ($800), and college room and board ($9736). College room only: $5056. Room and board charges vary according to board plan and housing facility. Part-time tuition: $1241 per credit. Part-time tuition varies according to course load.

Collegiate Environment: Orientation program. Drama-theater group, choral group, student-run newspaper, radio station. Social organizations: 125 open to all; national fraternities, national sororities; 30% of eligible men and 33% of eligible women are members. Most popular organizations: Student Senate, Union Board, choirs, Weaver Chapel Association. Major annual events: New Student Days, Wittfest, Activity Fair. Student services: health clinic, personal-psychological counseling, women's center. Campus security: 24-hour emergency response devices and patrols, student patrols, late night transport-escort service, controlled dormitory access, crime prevention programs. 1,797 college housing spaces available; 1,575 were occupied in 2012-13. Freshmen guaranteed college housing. On-campus residence required through sophomore year. Options: coed, women-only housing available. Thomas Library plus 1 other with 500,552 books, 82,764 microform titles, 23,625 serials, 23,113 audiovisual materials, an OPAC, and a Web page. Operations spending for the previous fiscal year: $2.4 million. 900 computers available on campus for general student use. A campuswide network can be accessed from student residence rooms and from off campus. Students can access the following: online class registration. Staffed computer lab on campus.

Community Environment: Springfield is located 25 miles northeast of Dayton with all forms of commercial transportation available. Community facilities include houses of worship of all denominations, two hospitals, libraries, art and historical museums, Springfield Performing Arts Center, a symphony orchestra, and two theatre groups. Recreational activities include tennis and golf. Job opportunities are available.

■ WRIGHT STATE UNIVERSITY

3640 Colonel Glenn Hwy.
Dayton, OH 45435

Tel: (937)775-3333; Free: 800-247-1770
Fax: (937)775-5795
E-mail: admissions@wright.edu
Web Site: www.wright.edu/

Description: State-supported, university, coed. Part of University System of Ohio. Awards associate, bachelor's, master's, and doctoral degrees and post-master's certificates. Founded 1964. Setting: 557-acre suburban campus with easy access to Columbus. Endowment: $77 million. Research spending for the previous fiscal year: $30.5 million. Educational spending for the previous fiscal year: $7934 per student. Total enrollment: 16,780. Faculty: 647 (642 full-time, 5 part-time). Student-undergrad faculty ratio is 22:1. 8,112 applied, 69% were admitted. 14% from top 10% of their high school class, 33% from top quarter, 65% from top half. Full-time: 10,324 students, 53% women, 47% men. Part-time: 2,819 students, 51% women, 49% men. Students come from 51 states and territories, 40 other countries, 3% from out-of-state. 0.2% American Indian or Alaska Native, non-Hispanic/Latino; 3% Hispanic/Latino; 13% African American, non-Hispanic/Latino; 2% Asian, non-Hispanic/Latino; 0.1% Native Hawaiian or other Pacific Islander, non-Hispanic/Latino; 5% international. 21% 25 or older, 19% live on campus, 8% transferred in. Retention: 56% of full-time freshmen returned the following year. Academic areas with the most degrees conferred: business/marketing; health professions and related sciences; social sciences. Core. Academic remediation for entering students, ESL program, services for LD students, advanced placement, self-designed majors, freshman honors college, honors program, independent study, distance learning, double major, summer session for credit, part-time degree program, adult/continuing education programs, co-op programs and internships, graduate courses open to undergrads. Off campus study at members of the Southwestern Ohio Council for Higher Education. Study abroad program. ROTC: Army, Air Force.

Entrance Requirements: Options: electronic application, early admission, deferred admission, international baccalaureate accepted. Required: high school transcript, SAT or ACT. Recommended: minimum 2 high school GPA. Entrance: minimally difficult. Application deadline: Rolling. Notification: continuous, continuous for nonresidents. SAT Reasoning Test deadline: 8/19. Transfer credits accepted: Yes.

Costs Per Year: Application fee: $30. State resident tuition: $8354 full-time, $378 per credit hour part-time. Nonresident tuition: $16,182 full-time, $738 per credit hour part-time. Full-time tuition varies according to course load. Part-time tuition varies according to course load. College room and board: $8629. College room only: $5689. Room and board charges vary according to housing facility and location.

Collegiate Environment: Orientation program. Drama-theater group, choral group, student-run newspaper, radio station. Social organizations: 200 open to all; national fraternities, national sororities, local fraternities, local sororities; 3% of eligible men and 4% of eligible women are members. Most popular organizations: student government, National Association for the Advancement of Colored People, Interfraternity Council, Panhellenic Council, Golden Key International Honor Society. Major annual events: Spring Fest, Fall Fest, Homecoming. Student services: legal services, health clinic, personal-psychological counseling, women's center. Campus security: 24-hour emergency response devices and patrols, student patrols, late night transport-escort service, controlled dormitory access. 3,000 college housing spaces available; 2,718 were occupied in 2012-13. No special consideration for freshman housing applicants. Option: coed housing available. Paul Laurence Dunbar Library plus 1 other with 910,287 books, 1.4 million microform titles, 36,138 serials, 20,738 audiovisual materials, an OPAC, and a Web page. Operations spending for the previous fiscal year: $9.1 million. 1,700 computers available on campus for general student use. Computer purchase/lease plans available. A campuswide network can be accessed from student residence rooms and from off campus. Students can access the following: online class registration, Student web pages permitted. Staffed computer lab on campus (open 24 hours a day) provides training in use of computers, software, and the Internet.

Community Environment: Located in the Miami Valley at the junction of the Miami, Stillwater, and Mad Rivers in southwestern Ohio, Dayton is the state's fourth largest metropolitan area. Within a twenty-five mile radius, there is a population of over one million. The city lies fifty-four miles north of Cincinnati and seventy-two miles west of Columbus. Dayton International Airport, serviced by most major airlines, offers convenient access to almost any place in the Continental United States and abroad. The river corridor provides twenty-six scenic miles for walking, jogging, or cycling. Dayton also supports the arts, including a philharmonic orchestra, a ballet company, several art galleries and museums, and theater events for adults and children. The Opera Association presents fine productions with top stars on the bill each year.

■ WRIGHT STATE UNIVERSITY, LAKE CAMPUS

7600 State Rte. 703
Celina, OH 45822-2921
Tel: (419)586-0300; Free: 800-237-1477
Fax: (419)586-0358
Web Site: www.wright.edu/lake/

Description: State-supported, 2-year, coed. Part of Ohio Board of Regents. Awards certificates, transfer associate, and terminal associate degrees. Founded 1969. Setting: 173-acre rural campus. Total enrollment: 1,248. Student-undergrad faculty ratio is 28:1. 1% from out-of-state. 25% 25 or older. Retention: 71% of full-time freshmen returned the following year. Core. Academic remediation for entering students, services for LD students, advanced placement, self-designed majors, honors program, summer session for credit, part-time degree program, adult/continuing education programs. Off campus study at members of the Southwestern Ohio Council for Higher Education.

Entrance Requirements: Open admission for state residents. Options: early admission, deferred admission. Required: high school transcript. Recommended: minimum 2.0 high school GPA. Entrance: noncompetitive. Application deadline: Rolling. Notification: continuous.

Collegiate Environment: Drama-theater group, student-run newspaper. Student services: personal-psychological counseling. Campus security: 24-hour emergency response devices.

■ XAVIER UNIVERSITY

3800 Victory Pky.
Cincinnati, OH 45207
Tel: (513)745-3000; Free: 877-XUADMIT
Fax: (513)745-4319
E-mail: xuadmit@xavier.edu
Web Site: www.xu.edu/

Description: Independent Roman Catholic, comprehensive, coed. Awards associate, bachelor's, master's, and doctoral degrees. Founded 1831. Setting: 180-acre urban campus. Endowment: $117 million. Educational spending for the previous fiscal year: $9229 per student. Total enrollment: 6,650. Faculty: 677 (342 full-time, 335 part-time). Student-undergrad faculty ratio is 12:1. 11,232 applied, 68% were admitted. 23% from top 10% of their high school class, 53% from top quarter, 86% from top half. Full-time: 4,066 students, 53% women, 47% men. Part-time: 419 students, 55% women, 45% men. Students come from 49 states and territories, 38 other countries, 44% from out-of-state. 0.4% American Indian or Alaska Native, non-Hispanic/Latino; 4% Hispanic/Latino; 9% African American, non-Hispanic/Latino; 2% Asian, non-Hispanic/Latino; 0.1% Native Hawaiian or other Pacific Islander, non-Hispanic/Latino; 3% international. 9% 25 or older, 50% live on campus, 3% transferred in. Retention: 80% of full-time freshmen returned the following year. Academic areas with the most degrees conferred: business/marketing; liberal arts/general studies; social sciences; health professions and related sciences. Core. Calendar: semesters. Academic remediation for entering students, ESL program, services for LD students, advanced placement, honors program, independent study, double major, summer session for credit, part-time degree program, adult/continuing education programs, co-op programs and internships, graduate courses open to undergrads. Off campus study at 13 members of the Greater Cincinnati Consortium of Colleges and Universities. Study abroad program. ROTC: Army, Air Force (c).

Entrance Requirements: Options: electronic application, deferred admission, international baccalaureate accepted. Required: essay, high school transcript, 1 recommendation, SAT or ACT. Required for some: minimum 3 high school GPA, interview. Entrance: moderately difficult. Application deadline: Rolling. Notification: continuous until 10/15. SAT Reasoning Test deadline: 2/1. Transfer credits accepted: Yes. Applicants placed on waiting list: 119. Wait-listed applicants offered admission: 70.

Costs Per Year: Application fee: $35. Comprehensive fee: $43,740 includes full-time tuition ($32,070), mandatory fees ($930), and college room and board ($10,740). College room only: $5940. Full-time tuition and fees vary according to class time, course load, degree level, location, and program. Room and board charges vary according to board plan and housing facility.

Collegiate Environment: Orientation program. Drama-theater group, choral group, student-run newspaper. Social organizations: 142 open to all. Most popular organizations: Student Government Association, Black Student As-

sociation, X-treme Fans, Alternative Spring Break, Club Sports. Major annual events: Club Day on the Mall, Orientation Leaders (Manresa), Spirit Celebration. Student services: health clinic, personal-psychological counseling, women's center. Campus security: 24-hour emergency response devices and patrols, late night transport-escort service, controlled dormitory access, campus-wide shuttle service. 2,344 college housing spaces available; 2,248 were occupied in 2012-13. Freshmen guaranteed college housing. On-campus residence required through sophomore year. Option: coed housing available. Xavier University Library with 479,256 books, 752,229 microform titles, 58,509 serials, 13,936 audiovisual materials, an OPAC, and a Web page. Operations spending for the previous fiscal year: $2.7 million. 340 computers available on campus for general student use. Computer purchase/lease plans available. A campuswide network can be accessed from student residence rooms and from off campus. Students can access the following: online class registration. Staffed computer lab on campus (open 24 hours a day) provides training in use of computers, software, and the Internet.

Community Environment: See University of Cincinnati.

■ YOUNGSTOWN STATE UNIVERSITY

One University Plz.
Youngstown, OH 44555-0001
Tel: (330)941-3000; Free: 877-468-6978
Fax: (330)941-1998
E-mail: enroll@ysu.edu
Web Site: www.ysu.edu/

Description: State-supported, comprehensive, coed. Awards associate, bachelor's, master's, and doctoral degrees and post-master's certificates. Founded 1908. Setting: 200-acre urban campus with easy access to Cleveland, Pittsburgh. Endowment: $191.1 million. Research spending for the previous fiscal year: $3 million. Educational spending for the previous fiscal year: $5956 per student. Total enrollment: 13,799. Faculty: 1,054 (430 full-time, 624 part-time). Student-undergrad faculty ratio is 18:1. 4,458 applied, 87% were admitted. 11% from top 10% of their high school class, 26% from top quarter, 53% from top half. Full-time: 9,906 students, 51% women, 49% men. Part-time: 2,738 students, 59% women, 41% men. Students come from 38 states and territories, 60 other countries, 11% from out-of-state. 0.3% American Indian or Alaska Native, non-Hispanic/Latino; 3% Hispanic/Latino; 16% African American, non-Hispanic/Latino; 1% Asian, non-Hispanic/Latino; 0.05% Native Hawaiian or other Pacific Islander, non-Hispanic/Latino; 1% international. 27% 25 or older, 10% live on campus, 5% transferred in. Retention: 65% of full-time freshmen returned the following year. Academic areas with the most degrees conferred: education; business/marketing; health professions and related sciences. Core. Calendar: semesters. Academic remediation for entering students, ESL program, services for LD students, advanced placement, accelerated degree program, self-designed majors, honors program, independent study, distance learning, double major, summer session for credit, part-time degree program, adult/continuing education programs, co-op programs and internships, graduate courses open to undergrads. Off campus study at Lorain County Community College, Cuyahoga Community College, North Central State, Lakeland Community College. Study abroad program. ROTC: Army, Air Force (c).

Entrance Requirements: Open admission for all Ohio state residents, and students from Mercer and Lawrence Counties in Pennsylvania. Options: electronic application, early admission, deferred admission, international baccalaureate accepted. Required: high school transcript, SAT or ACT. Required for some: interview. Entrance: noncompetitive. Application deadlines: 8/1, 8/1 for nonresidents. Notification: continuous, continuous for nonresidents. SAT Reasoning Test deadline: 8/1. SAT Subject Test deadline: 8/1. Transfer credits accepted: Yes.

Costs Per Year: Application fee: $40. State resident tuition: $7483 full-time, $312 per credit hour part-time. Nonresident tuition: $13,440 full-time, $560 per credit hour part-time. Mandatory fees: $229 full-time, $10 per credit hour part-time. Full-time tuition and fees vary according to course load. Part-time tuition and fees vary according to course load. College room and board: $8150. Room and board charges vary according to board plan and housing facility.

Collegiate Environment: Orientation program. Drama-theater group, choral group, marching band, student-run newspaper, radio station. Social organizations: 165 open to all; national fraternities, national sororities; 5% of eligible men and 5% of eligible women are members. Most popular organizations: Student Government Association, Omicron Delta Kappa, Golden Key Society, Fraternities/Sororities (IFC, NPHC and Panhellenic Council), History Club. Major annual events: Homecoming, Welcome Week, Penguin Productions Concerts. Student services: health clinic, personal-psychological counseling. Campus security: 24-hour emergency response devices and patrols, student patrols, late night transport-escort service, controlled dormitory access, residence hall patrols. 1,381 college housing spaces available; 1,350 were occupied in 2012-13. No special consideration for freshman housing applicants. Options: coed, women-only housing available. William F. Maag, Jr. Library plus 1 other with 931,931 books, 952,264 microform titles, 44,724 serials, 43,174 audiovisual materials, an OPAC, and a Web page. Operations spending for the previous fiscal year: $3.1 million. 170 computers available on campus for general student use. A campuswide network can be accessed from student residence rooms and from off campus. Students can access the following: online class registration. Staffed computer lab on campus provides training in use of computers, software, and the Internet.

Community Environment: The Youngstown area is a vibrant community, rich in heritage, natural and manmade resources, industry and business, and skilled responsible citizens. It is successfully undergoing a change from basic steelmaking to many diversified industries and businesses. Youngstown is located in bustling Northeast Ohio, five miles from the Pennsylvania line, equidistant between New York and Chicago, and 65 miles from both Pittsburgh and the Ohio River and the ports and beaches of Lake Erie. A network of interstate highways and Youngstown Airport have made it a major transportation center. Residents enjoy the areas lakes, fields, and forests, plus unusual 2,400-acre Mill Creek Park near the heart of the city. There are many churches, numerous fine teaching hospitals, a community playhouse,

symphony orchestra, an outstanding public library system, excellent schools and many other cultural attractions, including the internationally famous Butler Institute of American Arts.

■ ZANE STATE COLLEGE
1555 Newark Rd.
Zanesville, OH 43701-2626
Tel: (740)454-2501; Free: 800-686-8324
E-mail: pyoung@zanestate.edu
Web Site: www.zanestate.edu/

Description: State and locally supported, 2-year, coed. Awards certificates, transfer associate, and terminal associate degrees. Founded 1969. Setting: 170-acre small town campus with easy access to Columbus. Total enrollment: 2,592. Student-undergrad faculty ratio is 19:1. 1% from out-of-state. 49% 25 or older. Retention: 62% of full-time freshmen returned the following year. Core. Academic remediation for entering students, services for LD students, self-designed majors, honors program, summer session for credit, part-time degree program, adult/continuing education programs, co-op programs and internships. Off campus study at Ohio University-Zanesville.

Entrance Requirements: Open admission except for health technology programs. Option: early admission. Required: high school transcript. Recommended: SAT or ACT. Required for some: interview. Entrance: noncompetitive. Application deadline: Rolling. Notification: continuous.

Collegiate Environment: Student-run newspaper. Student services: personal-psychological counseling.

■ **BACONE COLLEGE**
2299 Old Bacone Rd.
Muskogee, OK 74403-1597
Tel: (918)683-4581; Free: 888-682-5514
Fax: (918)682-5514
Web Site: www.bacone.edu/
Description: Independent, 4-year, coed, affiliated with American Baptist Churches in the U.S.A. Awards associate and bachelor's degrees. Founded 1880. Setting: 220-acre small town campus with easy access to Tulsa. Total enrollment: 884. 782 applied. 34% 25 or older. Core. Calendar: semesters. Academic remediation for entering students, services for LD students, advanced placement, accelerated degree program, self-designed majors, summer session for credit, part-time degree program, adult/continuing education programs, co-op programs and internships.
Entrance Requirements: Options: electronic application, early admission, deferred admission, international baccalaureate accepted. Required: high school transcript, minimum 2.0 high school GPA, SAT or ACT. Recommended: ACT. Required for some: essay, interview. Entrance: minimally difficult. Application deadline: Rolling. Notification: continuous.
Collegiate Environment: Orientation program. Drama-theater group, choral group, student-run newspaper. Student services: health clinic, personal-psychological counseling. Campus security: 24-hour emergency response devices, controlled dormitory access, 8-hour patrols by trained security personnel. Bacone College Library with 34,564 books, 18,960 microform titles, 121 serials, 185 audiovisual materials, and an OPAC.
Community Environment: Bacone is a suburban community, one mile from Muskogee, a town of 60,000. All the cultural, recreational, and community services are located in Muskogee.

■ **BROWN MACKIE COLLEGE–OKLAHOMA CITY**
7101 NW Expy.
Ste. 800
Oklahoma City, OK 73132
Tel: (405)621-8000; Free: 888-229-3280
Web Site: www.brownmackie.edu/oklahoma-city/
Description: Proprietary, 2-year, coed. Part of Education Management Corporation. Awards terminal associate degrees.

■ **BROWN MACKIE COLLEGE–TULSA**
4608 S Garnett
Ste. 110
Tulsa, OK 74146
Tel: (918)628-3700; Free: 888-794-8411
Fax: (918)828-9083
Web Site: www.brownmackie.edu/tulsa/
Description: Proprietary, primarily 2-year, coed. Part of Education Management Corporation. Awards diplomas, terminal associate, and bachelor's degrees.

■ **CAMERON UNIVERSITY**
2800 W Gore Blvd.
Lawton, OK 73505-6377
Tel: (580)581-2200; Free: 888-454-7600
Fax: (580)581-5514
E-mail: admissions@cameron.edu

Web Site: www.cameron.edu/
Description: State-supported, comprehensive, coed. Part of Oklahoma State Regents for Higher Education. Awards associate, bachelor's, and master's degrees and post-master's certificates. Founded 1908. Setting: 360-acre small town campus. Endowment: $15.7 million. Research spending for the previous fiscal year: $185,073. Educational spending for the previous fiscal year: $6677 per student. Total enrollment: 6,112. Faculty: 319 (176 full-time, 143 part-time). Student-undergrad faculty ratio is 20:1. 1,336 applied, 99% were admitted. 4% from top 10% of their high school class, 13% from top quarter, 38% from top half. Full-time: 3,734 students, 59% women, 41% men. Part-time: 1,833 students, 64% women, 36% men. Students come from 39 states and territories, 42 other countries, 5% from out-of-state. 6% American Indian or Alaska Native, non-Hispanic/Latino; 10% Hispanic/Latino; 16% African American, non-Hispanic/Latino; 2% Asian, non-Hispanic/Latino; 1% Native Hawaiian or other Pacific Islander, non-Hispanic/Latino; 5% international. 42% 25 or older, 10% live on campus, 8% transferred in. Retention: 57% of full-time freshmen returned the following year. Academic areas with the most degrees conferred: business/marketing; education; psychology. Core. Calendar: semesters. Academic remediation for entering students, services for LD students, advanced placement, accelerated degree program, self-designed majors, honors program, independent study, distance learning, double major, summer session for credit, part-time degree program, adult/continuing education programs, internships, graduate courses open to undergrads. Off campus study at University of Oklahoma, Western Oklahoma State College, Rogers State University. Study abroad program. ROTC: Army.
Entrance Requirements: Open admission Students who are not eligible for a bachelor's or an AS may be admitted into an AAS program. Options: electronic application, deferred admission, international baccalaureate accepted. Required: SAT or ACT. Required for some: high school transcript, Baccalaureate degree: Minimum composite ACT of 20 or SAT of 890 or rank in the top 50% of high school graduation class and have a high school GPA of at least 2.7; AS degree: Meet minimum high school curricular requirements and completed the ACT or SAT; AAS degree: completed ACT or SAT. Entrance: noncompetitive. Application deadlines: Rolling, Rolling for nonresidents. Notification: continuous, continuous for nonresidents. SAT Reasoning Test deadline: 8/15. Transfer credits accepted: Yes.
Costs Per Year: Application fee: $15. State resident tuition: $3225 full-time, $107.50 per credit hour part-time. Nonresident tuition: $10,200 full-time, $340 per credit hour part-time. Mandatory fees: $1545 full-time, $51.50 per credit hour part-time. Full-time tuition and fees vary according to course load, location, and program. Part-time tuition and fees vary according to course load, location, and program. College room and board: $3884. College room only: $1504. Room and board charges vary according to board plan and housing facility.
Collegiate Environment: Orientation program. Drama-theater group, choral group, student-run newspaper. Social organizations: 80 open to all; national fraternities, national sororities, local fraternities, local sororities; 1% of eligible men and 1% of eligible women are members. Most popular organizations: Student Government Association, Programming Activities Council, Nigerian Student Association, International Club, Greek Life. Major annual events: Welcome Week, Homecoming, Foam Dance Party. Student services: health clinic, personal-psychological counseling. Campus security: 24-hour emergency response devices and patrols, late night transport-escort service, controlled dormitory access. 600 college housing spaces available; 565 were occupied in 2012-13. No special consideration for freshman housing ap-

plicants. Options: coed, men-only, women-only housing available. Cameron University Library with 279,907 books, 539,698 microform titles, 29,846 serials, 16,941 audiovisual materials, an OPAC, and a Web page. Operations spending for the previous fiscal year: $1.5 million. 277 computers available on campus for general student use. A campuswide network can be accessed from student residence rooms and from off campus. Students can access the following: online courses, student information system, library, computer labs, mobile app. Staffed computer lab on campus provides training in use of computers, software, and the Internet.

Community Environment: Lawton is a metropolitan area that enjoys a dry, temperate climate. The city is served by two airlines, two railroads for freight, bus service, and a turnpike. Community services include a public library, museum, churches of most denominations, two general and one public health hospital, major civic and fraternal organizations, and good shopping facilities. Part-time employment is available for students. Local recreational facilities include camping, water sports, theaters, and bowling.

■ **CARL ALBERT STATE COLLEGE**
1507 S McKenna
Poteau, OK 74953-5208
Tel: (918)647-1200
Fax: (918)647-1306
Web Site: www.carlalbert.edu/

Description: State-supported, 2-year, coed. Part of Oklahoma State Regents for Higher Education. Awards certificates, transfer associate, and terminal associate degrees. Founded 1934. Setting: 78-acre small town campus. Endowment: $5.7 million. Total enrollment: 2,460. Faculty: 154 (51 full-time, 103 part-time). Student-undergrad faculty ratio is 16:1. 733 applied, 100% were admitted. Full-time: 1,373 students, 64% women, 36% men. Part-time: 1,087 students, 68% women, 32% men. Students come from 16 states and territories, 9 other countries. 35% 25 or older, 12% live on campus. Core. Calendar: semesters. Academic remediation for entering students, part-time degree program, adult/continuing education programs, co-op programs.

Entrance Requirements: Open admission. Required: high school transcript. Entrance: noncompetitive. Application deadline: 8/13. Notification: continuous.

Costs Per Year: Application fee: $0. State resident tuition: $1,234 full-time, $88.80 per credit hour part-time. Nonresident tuition: $2,643 full-time, $188.80 per credit hour part-time. Mandatory fees: $450 per term part-time. College room and board: $1930. College room only: $1650. Room and board charges vary according to board plan.

Collegiate Environment: Orientation program. Drama-theater group, choral group, student-run newspaper, radio station. Social organizations: 25 open to all. Most popular organizations: Student Government Association, Phi Theta Kappa, Baptist Student Union, BACCHUS, Student Physical Therapist Assistant Association. Major annual events: Welcome Week, Homecoming, graduation. Student services: health clinic, personal-psychological counseling. Campus security: security guards. Options: men-only, women-only housing available. Joe E. White Library with 27,200 books, 1,350 serials, and an OPAC. 75 computers available on campus for general student use. A campuswide network can be accessed. Students can access the following: online class registration. Staffed computer lab on campus.

Community Environment: Poteau is located in central eastern Oklahoma in the Cavanal Mountain area. This is the county seat and may be reached by bus lines. Nearby Ouachita National Forest offers excellent recreational facilities.

■ **CLARY SAGE COLLEGE**
3131 S Sheridan
Tulsa, OK 74145
Tel: (918)298-8200
Fax: (918)298-0099
E-mail: rbanuelos@communitycarecollege.edu
Web Site: www.clarysagecollege.com/

Description: Proprietary, 2-year, coed. Part of Dental Directions, Inc. Awards diplomas and terminal associate degrees. Setting: 6-acre urban campus with easy access to Tulsa. Faculty: 23 (all full-time). Student-undergrad faculty ratio is 9:1. Students come from 3 states and territories. Core. Distance learning, part-time degree program, adult/continuing education programs, internships.

Entrance Requirements: Open admission. Option: electronic application. Required: essay, high school transcript, interview. Entrance: noncompetitive.

Application deadlines: Rolling, Rolling for nonresidents. Notification: continuous, continuous for nonresidents. Transfer credits accepted: Yes.

Costs Per Year: Application fee: $100. Tuition: $17,808 full-time. Mandatory fees: $2349 full-time. Full-time tuition and fees vary according to class time, course level, course load, degree level, location, program, and reciprocity agreements.

Collegiate Environment: Orientation program. Social organizations: 1 open to all. Most popular organization: Student Ambassadors. Major annual events: Food Bank Drive, Clothing Drive, Blood Drive. Student services: personal-psychological counseling. Campus security: security guard during hours of operation. College housing not available. 30 computers available on campus for general student use. Computer purchase/lease plans available. A campuswide network can be accessed. Staffed computer lab on campus provides training in use of computers, software, and the Internet.

■ **COMMUNITY CARE COLLEGE**
4242 S Sheridan Rd.
Tulsa, OK 74145
Tel: (918)610-0027
Fax: (918)610-0029
E-mail: tknox@communitycarecollege.edu
Web Site: www.communitycarecollege.edu/

Description: Proprietary, 2-year, coed. Part of Dental Directions, Inc. Awards diplomas and terminal associate degrees. Founded 1995. Setting: 6-acre urban campus. Educational spending for the previous fiscal year: $910 per student. Total enrollment: 942. Faculty: 35 (all full-time). Student-undergrad faculty ratio is 27:1. Full-time: 942 students, 91% women, 9% men. Students come from 14 states and territories, 11% from out-of-state. 10% American Indian or Alaska Native, non-Hispanic/Latino; 4% Hispanic/Latino; 17% African American, non-Hispanic/Latino; 2% Asian, non-Hispanic/Latino; 0% Native Hawaiian or other Pacific Islander, non-Hispanic/Latino; 0% international. 51% 25 or older, 0% transferred in. Core. Calendar: continuous. Services for LD students, independent study, distance learning, adult/continuing education programs, internships.

Entrance Requirements: Open admission. Option: electronic application. Required: essay, high school transcript, interview. Required for some: 1 recommendation. Entrance: noncompetitive. Application deadlines: Rolling, Rolling for nonresidents. Notification: continuous, continuous for nonresidents. Transfer credits accepted: Yes.

Costs Per Year: Application fee: $100. Tuition: $22,084 full-time. Mandatory fees: $2680 full-time. Full-time tuition and fees vary according to class time, course level, course load, degree level, location, program, and reciprocity agreements.

Collegiate Environment: Orientation program. Most popular organization: Student Ambassadors. Major annual events: Food Bank Drive, Clothing Drive, Blood Drive. Student services: personal-psychological counseling. Campus security: campus security personnel are available during school hours. 65 computers available on campus for general student use. A campuswide network can be accessed. Staffed computer lab on campus provides training in use of computers, software, and the Internet.

■ **CONNORS STATE COLLEGE**
Rte. 1 Box 1000
Warner, OK 74469-9700
Tel: (918)463-2931
Web Site: www.connorsstate.edu/

Description: State-supported, 2-year, coed. Part of Oklahoma State Regents for Higher Education. Awards certificates, diplomas, transfer associate, and terminal associate degrees. Founded 1908. Setting: 1,658-acre rural campus. Total enrollment: 2,250. 38% 25 or older. Core. Calendar: semesters. Academic remediation for entering students, advanced placement, accelerated degree program, summer session for credit, part-time degree program, adult/continuing education programs, internships.

Entrance Requirements: Open admission. Options: early admission, deferred admission. Required for some: high school transcript. Entrance: noncompetitive. Application deadline: Rolling.

Collegiate Environment: Drama-theater group, student-run newspaper. Student services: health clinic. Campus security: late night transport-escort service, trained security personnel. Carl Westbrook Library with 63,728 books, 319 serials, and an OPAC.

Community Environment: Warner is a rural community with mild winters and warm to hot summers. The area is provided transportation by bus lines, and U.S. Highways 64 and 266. There are several churches of various denominations, and civic and service clubs within the city. Recreational facilities within the area include theatres, restaurants, and nearby lakes. Within driving distance, there is the Five Civilized Tribes Museum.

■ DEVRY UNIVERSITY

Lakepointe Towers
4013 NW Expy. St., Ste. 100
Oklahoma City, OK 73116
Tel: (405)767-9516; Free: 866-338-7941
Web Site: www.devry.edu/

Description: Proprietary, comprehensive, coed. Awards associate, bachelor's, and master's degrees. Total enrollment: 155. Faculty: 10 (all part-time). Student-undergrad faculty ratio is 27:1. Full-time: 53 students, 38% women, 62% men. Part-time: 58 students, 43% women, 57% men. 2% from out-of-state. 67% 25 or older, 28% transferred in. Academic areas with the most degrees conferred: business/marketing; computer and information sciences. Accelerated degree program, distance learning.

Entrance Requirements: Options: electronic application, deferred admission. Application deadline: Rolling. Notification: continuous. SAT Reasoning Test deadline: 10/31.

■ EAST CENTRAL UNIVERSITY

1100 E 14th St.
Ada, OK 74820-6899
Tel: (580)332-8000
Fax: (580)436-5495
E-mail: KKelley@ecok.edu
Web Site: www.ecok.edu/

Description: State-supported, comprehensive, coed. Part of Oklahoma State Regents for Higher Education. Awards bachelor's and master's degrees. Founded 1909. Setting: 140-acre small town campus with easy access to Oklahoma City. Endowment: $26.4 million. Research spending for the previous fiscal year: $375,414. Educational spending for the previous fiscal year: $2186 per student. Total enrollment: 4,819. Faculty: 277 (167 full-time, 110 part-time). Student-undergrad faculty ratio is 19:1. 999 applied, 95% were admitted. 21% from top 10% of their high school class, 45% from top quarter, 77% from top half. Full-time: 3,039 students, 58% women, 42% men. Part-time: 765 students, 65% women, 35% men. Students come from 37 states and territories, 39 other countries, 8% from out-of-state. 17% American Indian or Alaska Native, non-Hispanic/Latino; 4% Hispanic/Latino; 4% African American, non-Hispanic/Latino; 0.4% Asian, non-Hispanic/Latino; 0.2% Native Hawaiian or other Pacific Islander, non-Hispanic/Latino; 5% international. 27% 25 or older, 28% live on campus, 10% transferred in. Retention: 59% of full-time freshmen returned the following year. Academic areas with the most degrees conferred: health professions and related sciences; education; public administration and social services. Core. Calendar: semesters. Academic remediation for entering students, services for LD students, advanced placement, honors program, independent study, distance learning, double major, summer session for credit, part-time degree program, adult/continuing education programs, internships, graduate courses open to undergrads. Off campus study at Ardmore Higher Education Center. Study abroad program.

Entrance Requirements: Options: electronic application, early admission. Required: high school transcript, SAT or ACT. Recommended: ACT. Required for some: minimum 2.7 high school GPA, rank in upper 50% of high school class. Entrance: minimally difficult. Notification: continuous. Transfer credits accepted: Yes.

Costs Per Year: Application fee: $20. State resident tuition: $3,608 full-time, $120.26 per semester hour part-time. Nonresident tuition: $10,604 full-time, $353.46 per semester hour part-time. Mandatory fees: $1349 full-time, $41.80 per semester hour part-time, $47.50 per term part-time. College room and board: $4824. College room only: $1900. Room and board charges vary according to board plan and housing facility. Tuition guaranteed not to increase for student's term of enrollment.

Collegiate Environment: Orientation program. Drama-theater group, choral group, marching band, student-run newspaper. Social organizations: 88 open to all; national fraternities, national sororities, local fraternities, local sororities; 2% of eligible men and 2% of eligible women are members. Most popular organizations: BACCHUS, Fellowship of Christian Athletes, Human Resources. Major annual events: Homecoming Week, concerts/plays, movie series. Student services: health clinic, personal-psychological counseling. Campus security: 24-hour emergency response devices and patrols, student patrols, late night transport-escort service, agreements with all local, state, federal, and tribal police departments for added crime and violation prevention. 1,126 college housing spaces available; 1,096 were occupied in 2012-

13. No special consideration for freshman housing applicants. On-campus residence required in freshman year. Options: coed, women-only housing available. Linscheid Library with 264,524 books, 355,809 microform titles, 40,969 serials, 11,302 audiovisual materials, an OPAC, and a Web page. Operations spending for the previous fiscal year: $1.2 million. 677 computers available on campus for general student use. A campuswide network can be accessed. Students can access the following: online class registration. Staffed computer lab on campus provides training in use of computers and software.

Community Environment: Ada is the commercial, industrial, service, and medical center for this area. An EPA world-class groundwater research laboratory (Robert S. Kerr Environmental Research Laboratory) and the seat of government of the Chickasaw Indian Nation are located in Ada. Ada's primary commercial employers include a cement plant, a plastics molding operation, and petroleum and cattle industries. The climate is temperate with mild winters. The average temperature is 64 degrees. Ada is approximately 90 miles southeast of Oklahoma City. Community services include a major regional medical center, thirty churches, and many active civic and fraternal organizations. Local recreational facilities include parks, swimming pools, picnic areas, hiking, golf, fishing, hunting, waterskiing, and tennis.

■ EASTERN OKLAHOMA STATE COLLEGE

1301 W Main
Wilburton, OK 74578-4999
Tel: (918)465-2361; Free: 855-534-3672
Fax: (918)465-2431
E-mail: lmiller@eosc.edu
Web Site: www.eosc.edu/

Description: State-supported, 2-year, coed. Part of Oklahoma State Regents for Higher Education. Awards certificates, transfer associate, and terminal associate degrees. Founded 1908. Setting: 4,000-acre rural campus. Total enrollment: 1,772. 26% 25 or older. Core. Calendar: semesters. Academic remediation for entering students, advanced placement, honors program, double major, summer session for credit, part-time degree program, adult/continuing education programs, co-op programs and internships. Off campus study at E. T. Dunlap Higher Education Center, McAlester Higher Education Center.

Entrance Requirements: Open admission for state residents. Options: early admission, deferred admission. Required: high school transcript. Entrance: noncompetitive. Application deadline: Rolling.

Collegiate Environment: Orientation program. Drama-theater group, choral group, student-run newspaper. Student services: personal-psychological counseling. Bill H. Hill Library with 41,639 books, 220 serials, and an OPAC.

Community Environment: Wilburton is a small community located in the San Bois Mountains. The area is served by commercial bus lines, U.S. Route 270 and State Highway 2. A small municipal airport is located here, but commercial airlines are approximately 30 miles distant. Good recreational facilities for outdoor sports include nearby Robber's Cave State Park, and Kiamichi National Forest. The nearest large cities are Muskogee and Fort Smith, Arkansas.

■ FAMILY OF FAITH COLLEGE

30 Kinville
Shawnee, OK 74802
Tel: (405)273-5331
Web Site: www.familyoffaithcollege.edu/

Description: Independent religious, 4-year, coed. Founded 1992. Calendar: semesters.

■ HERITAGE COLLEGE

7100 I-35 Services Rd.
Ste. 7118
Oklahoma City, OK 73149
Tel: (405)631-3399; Free: 888-334-7339
Fax: (405)631-6711
E-mail: info@heritage-education.com
Web Site: www.heritage-education.com/

Description: Proprietary, 2-year, coed. Awards terminal associate degrees. Total enrollment: 767. Student-undergrad faculty ratio is 33:1. 0% from out-of-state. 50% 25 or older. Retention: 85% of full-time freshmen returned the following year.

Entrance Requirements: Open admission. Entrance: noncompetitive.

■ **HILLSDALE FREE WILL BAPTIST COLLEGE**

3701 S I-35 Service Rd.
Moore, OK 73160-1208
Tel: (405)912-9000
Fax: (405)912-9050
E-mail: recruitment@hc.edu
Web Site: www.hc.edu/

Description: Independent Free Will Baptist, comprehensive, coed. Awards associate, bachelor's, and master's degrees. Founded 1959. Setting: 41-acre suburban campus with easy access to Oklahoma City. Total enrollment: 225. Faculty: 47 (13 full-time, 34 part-time). Student-undergrad faculty ratio is 11:1. 167 applied, 45% were admitted. Full-time: 184 students, 34% women, 66% men. Part-time: 18 students, 56% women, 44% men. 9% American Indian or Alaska Native, non-Hispanic/Latino; 7% Hispanic/Latino; 16% African American, non-Hispanic/Latino; 0.5% Asian, non-Hispanic/Latino; 0% Native Hawaiian or other Pacific Islander, non-Hispanic/Latino; 2% international. Retention: 60% of full-time freshmen returned the following year. Academic areas with the most degrees conferred: liberal arts/general studies; education; interdisciplinary studies; psychology; business/marketing. Core. Calendar: semesters. Academic remediation for entering students, ESL program, advanced placement, accelerated degree program, independent study, summer session for credit, part-time degree program, adult/continuing education programs, internships.

Entrance Requirements: Options: electronic application, early admission, deferred admission. Required: high school transcript, 2 recommendations, SAT or ACT. Recommended: minimum 2 high school GPA. Required for some: interview. Entrance: noncompetitive. Transfer credits accepted: Yes.

Costs Per Year: Application fee: $20. Comprehensive fee: $17,350 includes full-time tuition ($9000), mandatory fees ($1880), and college room and board ($6470). College room only: $3020. Full-time tuition and fees according to course load. Room and board charges vary according to board plan and housing facility. Part-time tuition: $375 per credit. Part-time tuition varies according to course load.

Collegiate Environment: Drama-theater group, choral group. Social organizations: local fraternities, local sororities. Student services: personal-psychological counseling. Campus security: 24-hour emergency response devices, controlled dormitory access. 132 college housing spaces available. On-campus residence required through sophomore year. Options: men-only, women-only housing available. Geri Ann Hull Learning Resource Center with 31,137 books, 6,118 microform titles, 79 serials, 541 audiovisual materials, an OPAC, and a Web page. 22 computers available on campus for general student use. A campuswide network can be accessed. Staffed computer lab on campus.

Community Environment: Community transportation is provided by bus and rail. Will Rogers International Airport is 10 minutes away. The city has many churches, a library, and health facilities. Nearby Lake Draper offers water skiing and fishing. There are many businesses in town, and part-time employment is available for students.

■ **ITT TECHNICAL INSTITUTE (OKLAHOMA CITY)**

50 Penn Pl. Office Twr.
1900 NW Expy., Ste. 305R
Oklahoma City, OK 73118
Tel: (405)810-4100; Free: 800-518-1612
Web Site: www.itt-tech.edu/

Description: Proprietary, 4-year, coed. Part of ITT Educational Services, Inc. Awards associate and bachelor's degrees. Founded 2006.

Entrance Requirements: Entrance: minimally difficult.

■ **ITT TECHNICAL INSTITUTE (TULSA)**

4500 S 129th E Ave.
Ste. 152
Tulsa, OK 74134
Tel: (918)615-3900; Free: 800-514-6535
Web Site: www.itt-tech.edu/

Description: Proprietary, primarily 2-year, coed. Awards terminal associate and bachelor's degrees. Founded 2005.

Entrance Requirements: Entrance: minimally difficult.

■ **LANGSTON UNIVERSITY**

PO Box 907
Langston, OK 73050
Tel: (405)466-2231
Fax: (405)466-3381

Web Site: www.langston.edu/

Description: State-supported, comprehensive, coed. Part of Oklahoma State Regents for Higher Education. Awards associate, bachelor's, and master's degrees. Founded 1897. Setting: 40-acre rural campus with easy access to Oklahoma City. Total enrollment: 2,338. Faculty: 205 (140 full-time, 65 part-time). Student-undergrad faculty ratio is 30:1. 3,113 applied, 63% were admitted. Full-time: 1,718 students, 57% women, 43% men. Part-time: 258 students, 72% women, 28% men. Students come from 36 states and territories, 29 other countries, 40% from out-of-state. 1% American Indian or Alaska Native, non-Hispanic/Latino; 0.1% Hispanic/Latino; 87% African American, non-Hispanic/Latino; 1% Native Hawaiian or other Pacific Islander, non-Hispanic/Latino. 20% 25 or older. Academic areas with the most degrees conferred: business/marketing; health professions and related sciences; education. Core. Calendar: semesters. Academic remediation for entering students, ESL program, services for LD students, advanced placement, accelerated degree program, honors program, independent study, distance learning, double major, summer session for credit, part-time degree program, external degree program, adult/continuing education programs, co-op programs and internships, graduate courses open to undergrads. Study abroad program. ROTC: Army (c).

Entrance Requirements: Open admission. Options: electronic application, deferred admission. Required: high school transcript, minimum 2.7 high school GPA, SAT or ACT. Entrance: minimally difficult. Application deadline: Rolling. Transfer credits accepted: Yes.

Costs Per Year: Application fee: $35. State resident tuition: $3030 full-time, $101.85 per credit part-time. Nonresident tuition: $9510 full-time, $317.20 per credit part-time. Mandatory fees: $1255 full-time, $35 per term part-time. Full-time tuition and fees vary according to location and program. Part-time tuition and fees vary according to location and program. College room and board: $8690. College room only: $5930. Room and board charges vary according to board plan, housing facility, and location.

Collegiate Environment: Orientation program. Drama-theater group, choral group, marching band, student-run newspaper, radio station. Social organizations: 22 open to all; national fraternities, national sororities. Most popular organizations: Student Government Association, Student Senate, Sorority and Fraternity (Greek Letter), NAACP, Pre- Alumni Council. Major annual events: Homecoming, Spring Festival, Intramural Sports. Student services: health clinic, personal-psychological counseling, women's center. Campus security: 24-hour emergency response devices and patrols, student patrols, late night transport-escort service, controlled dormitory access. 1,384 undergraduates lived in college housing during 2012-13. Freshmen guaranteed college housing. On-campus residence required through sophomore year. Option: coed housing available. G. Lamar Harrison Library plus 2 others with 97,565 books, 824,457 microform titles, 1,235 serials, 4,974 audiovisual materials, an OPAC, and a Web page. 300 computers available on campus for general student use. A campuswide network can be accessed from student residence rooms and from off campus. Students can access the following: online class registration. Staffed computer lab on campus provides training in use of computers and the Internet.

Community Environment: Langston is a small rural community located 40 miles northeast of Oklahoma City and 90 miles west of Tulsa, OK.

■ **MID-AMERICA CHRISTIAN UNIVERSITY**

3500 SW 119th St.
Oklahoma City, OK 73170-4504
Tel: (405)691-3800; Free: 888-436-3035
Fax: (405)692-5165
E-mail: info@macu.edu
Web Site: www.macu.edu/

Description: Independent, comprehensive, coed, affiliated with Church of God. Awards associate, bachelor's, and master's degrees. Founded 1953. Setting: 145-acre suburban campus. Total enrollment: 869. 53% 25 or older. Core. Calendar: semesters. Academic remediation for entering students, services for LD students, advanced placement, accelerated degree program, distance learning, double major, summer session for credit, part-time degree program, adult/continuing education programs, internships.

Entrance Requirements: Open admission. Option: early admission. Required: high school transcript. Required for some: 2 recommendations, interview. Entrance: noncompetitive. Application deadline: Rolling.

Collegiate Environment: Orientation program. Drama-theater group, choral group, student-run newspaper. Student services: personal-psychological counseling. Campus security: 24-hour patrols, student patrols. Charles Ewing Brown Library with 60,000 books, 12,324 microform titles, 3,906 audiovisual materials, and a Web page.

Community Environment: See Oklahoma City University.

■ MURRAY STATE COLLEGE
One Murray Campus
Tishomingo, OK 73460-3130
Tel: (580)371-2371
Fax: (580)371-9844
E-mail: gmarten@mscok.edu
Web Site: www.mscok.edu/

Description: State-supported, 2-year, coed. Part of Oklahoma State Regents for Higher Education. Awards transfer associate and terminal associate degrees. Founded 1908. Setting: 120-acre rural campus. Total enrollment: 2,674. Faculty: 152 (57 full-time, 95 part-time). Student-undergrad faculty ratio is 20:1. Students come from 19 states and territories, 9 other countries, 4% from out-of-state. 13% American Indian or Alaska Native, non-Hispanic/Latino; 6% Hispanic/Latino; 5% African American, non-Hispanic/Latino; 0.3% Asian, non-Hispanic/Latino; 0.1% Native Hawaiian or other Pacific Islander, non-Hispanic/Latino; 0.1% international. 11% live on campus. Retention: 49% of full-time freshmen returned the following year. Core. Calendar: semesters. Academic remediation for entering students, services for LD students, advanced placement, honors program, distance learning, summer session for credit, part-time degree program, internships.

Entrance Requirements: Open admission. Options: electronic application, early admission. Required: high school transcript, SAT or ACT. Entrance: noncompetitive. Application deadline: Rolling. Notification: continuous.

Costs Per Year: State resident tuition: $2940 full-time, $98 per credit hour part-time. Nonresident tuition: $7650 full-time, $255 per credit hour part-time. Mandatory fees: $695 full-time. Full-time tuition and fees vary according to course level, course load, location, and program. Part-time tuition varies according to course level, course load, location, and program. College room and board: $5800. Room and board charges vary according to board plan and housing facility.

Collegiate Environment: Orientation program. Drama-theater group, choral group. Social organizations: 11 open to all. Student services: personal-psychological counseling. Campus security: 24-hour patrols. Murray State College Library plus 1 other with 19,698 books, 47 serials, 1,316 audiovisual materials, an OPAC, and a Web page. 50 computers available on campus for general student use. Computer purchase/lease plans available. A campuswide network can be accessed. Students can access the following: online class registration. Staffed computer lab on campus provides training in use of computers, software, and the Internet.

Community Environment: Historically noted as the original capital of the Chickasaw Nation, Tishomingo is situated on the banks of Lake Texoma within a wildlife refuge. This is a rural area with a temperate climate. The city is served by five highways. Tishomingo has six churches, a hospital, and major civic, fraternal and veteran's organizations. Local recreational facilities include water sports, hunting, fishing, and hiking.

■ NATIONAL AMERICAN UNIVERSITY
8040 S Sheridan Rd.
Tulsa, OK 74133
Tel: (918)879-8400
Web Site: www.national.edu/
Description: Proprietary, 4-year, coed.

■ NORTHEASTERN OKLAHOMA AGRICULTURAL AND MECHANICAL COLLEGE
200 I St., NE
Miami, OK 74354-6434
Tel: (918)542-8441; Free: 800-464-6636
Fax: (918)542-9759
E-mail: neoadmission@neo.edu
Web Site: www.neo.edu/

Description: State-supported, 2-year, coed. Part of Oklahoma State Regents for Higher Education. Awards certificates, transfer associate, and terminal associate degrees. Founded 1919. Setting: 340-acre small town campus. Total enrollment: 1,899. Faculty: 110 (77 full-time, 33 part-time). Student-undergrad faculty ratio is 17:1. Full-time: 1,396 students, 52% women, 48% men. Part-time: 503 students, 71% women, 29% men. 24% 25 or older. Retention: 58% of full-time freshmen returned the following year. Core. Calendar: semesters. Academic remediation for entering students, services for LD students, advanced placement, distance learning, double major, summer session for credit, part-time degree program, external degree program, adult/continuing education programs, internships.

Entrance Requirements: Open admission. Option: electronic application. Required: high school transcript. Entrance: noncompetitive. Application deadline: Rolling. Notification: continuous.

Collegiate Environment: Drama-theater group, choral group, marching band, student-run newspaper. Social organizations: 50 open to all. Student services: health clinic, personal-psychological counseling. Campus security: 24-hour patrols. Learning Resource Center with 74,000 books, 450 serials, an OPAC, and a Web page. 65 computers available on campus for general student use. Students can access the following: online class registration. Staffed computer lab on campus provides training in use of computers, software, and the Internet.

Community Environment: Miami is headquarters for the Grand Lake recreation area. Items produced by the city's manufacturers include automotive parts, tires and tubes, clothing, food products and boats and accessories. Part-time employment is available. The climate is temperate. There are dormitories and housing units on campus. Good health services are available.

■ NORTHEASTERN STATE UNIVERSITY
600 N Grand
Tahlequah, OK 74464-2399
Tel: (918)456-5511; Free: 800-722-9614
Fax: (918)458-2342
E-mail: cain@nsuok.edu
Web Site: www.nsuok.edu/

Description: State-supported, comprehensive, coed. Part of Regional University System of Oklahoma. Awards bachelor's, master's, and doctoral degrees and post-master's certificates. Founded 1846. Setting: 160-acre small town campus with easy access to Tulsa. Endowment: $12.8 million. Research spending for the previous fiscal year: $905,109. Educational spending for the previous fiscal year: $5119 per student. Total enrollment: 9,361. Faculty: 513 (287 full-time, 226 part-time). Student-undergrad faculty ratio is 20:1. 2,540 applied, 54% were admitted. 19% from top 10% of their high school class, 46% from top quarter, 77% from top half. Full-time: 5,904 students, 59% women, 41% men. Part-time: 2,212 students, 66% women, 34% men. Students come from 29 states and territories, 56 other countries, 6% from out-of-state. 29% American Indian or Alaska Native, non-Hispanic/Latino; 2% Hispanic/Latino; 6% African American, non-Hispanic/Latino; 2% Asian, non-Hispanic/Latino; 0% Native Hawaiian or other Pacific Islander, non-Hispanic/Latino; 2% international. 40% 25 or older, 19% live on campus, 12% transferred in. Retention: 65% of full-time freshmen returned the following year. Academic areas with the most degrees conferred: education; business/marketing; psychology. Core. Calendar: semesters. Academic remediation for entering students, services for LD students, advanced placement, self-designed majors, honors program, independent study, distance learning, double major, summer session for credit, part-time degree program, adult/continuing education programs, co-op programs and internships, graduate courses open to undergrads. ROTC: Army.

Entrance Requirements: Option: deferred admission. Required: high school transcript, minimum 2.7 high school GPA, upper 50% of class or minimum ACT composite of 20, ACT. Required for some: interview. Entrance: moderately difficult. Application deadline: 8/1. Notification: continuous. SAT Reasoning Test deadline: 8/15.

Costs Per Year: Application fee: $25. State resident tuition: $3750 full-time, $125 per credit hour part-time. Nonresident tuition: $10,500 full-time, $350 per credit hour part-time. Mandatory fees: $1107 full-time, $36.90 per credit hour part-time. Full-time tuition and fees vary according to course load and program. Part-time tuition and fees vary according to course load and program. College room and board: $5914. Room and board charges vary according to board plan and housing facility.

Collegiate Environment: Orientation program. Drama-theater group, choral group, marching band, student-run newspaper. Social organizations: 80 open to all; national fraternities, national sororities, local fraternities, local sororities; 2% of eligible men and 1% of eligible women are members. Student services: health clinic, personal-psychological counseling. Campus security: 24-hour emergency response devices and patrols, late night transport-escort service, controlled dormitory access. John Vaughn Library with 429,808 books, 760,516 microform titles, 5,758 serials, 12,266 audiovisual materials, an OPAC, and a Web page. Operations spending for the previous fiscal year: $3.1 million. 1,160 computers available on campus for general student use. Computer purchase/lease plans available. A campuswide network can be accessed from student residence rooms and from off campus. Staffed computer lab on campus (open 24 hours a day) provides training in use of computers, software, and the Internet.

Community Environment: In a region of lakes within the foothills of the Ozark Mountains, Tahlequah is the former capital city of the Cherokee Indian Nation. There are many historic sites and artifacts in the area. The city is accessible by five highways. Community services includes several churches of various denominations, two hospitals, two libraries, and a museum. Apartments provide student housing. There are various civic and fraternal organizations within the city. Limited part-time employment is available for students. Local recreational facilities include boating, fishing, hunting, water skiing, and swimming.

■ NORTHERN OKLAHOMA COLLEGE

1220 E Grand Ave.
Tonkawa, OK 74653-0310
Tel: (580)628-6200
Fax: (580)628-6371
Web Site: www.north-ok.edu/
Description: State-supported, 2-year, coed. Part of Oklahoma State Regents for Higher Education. Awards transfer associate and terminal associate degrees. Founded 1901. Setting: 10-acre rural campus. Total enrollment: 3,050. Faculty: 80 (45 full-time, 35 part-time). Student-undergrad faculty ratio is 35:1. Students come from 4 other countries. 40% 25 or older, 20% live on campus. Calendar: semesters. Academic remediation for entering students, services for LD students, advanced placement, summer session for credit, part-time degree program, adult/continuing education programs.
Entrance Requirements: Open admission except for nursing program. Option: early admission. Required: high school transcript. Entrance: noncompetitive. Application deadline: Rolling.
Collegiate Environment: Drama-theater group, choral group, student-run newspaper, radio station. Social organizations: 15 open to all. Most popular organizations: Phi Theta Kappa, Law Enforcement Club, Fellowship of Christian Athletes, Student Nurses Association, Young Republicans. Major annual events: Homecoming, Drug Awareness Week. Student services: health clinic, personal-psychological counseling. Campus security: 24-hour emergency response devices and patrols. Vineyard Library with 34,458 books and 211 serials. 150 computers available on campus for general student use. Staffed computer lab on campus.
Community Environment: Tonkawa is located 14 miles west of Ponca City and enjoys a mild climate. The city has a public library, churches representing 10 denominations, a nearby hospital, a Chamber of Commerce and other civic, fraternal and veteran's organizations. Housing for students is provided by dormitories and one hotel. There are limited job opportunities for students. Fishing in nearby rivers is considered excellent sport.

■ NORTHWESTERN OKLAHOMA STATE UNIVERSITY

709 Oklahoma Blvd.
Alva, OK 73717-2799
Tel: (580)327-1700
Fax: (580)327-1881
E-mail: wmadair@nwosu.edu
Web Site: www.nwosu.edu/
Description: State-supported, comprehensive, coed. Part of Oklahoma State Regents for Higher Education. Awards bachelor's and master's degrees. Founded 1897. Setting: 70-acre rural campus. Endowment: $21.6 million. Research spending for the previous fiscal year: $88,479. Educational spending for the previous fiscal year: $2608 per student. Total enrollment: 2,295. Faculty: 182 (81 full-time, 101 part-time). Student-undergrad faculty ratio is 14:1. 975 applied, 69% were admitted. 5% from top 10% of their high school class, 24% from top quarter, 59% from top half. Full-time: 1,367 students, 53% women, 47% men. Part-time: 699 students, 54% women, 46% men. Students come from 38 states and territories, 18 other countries, 23% from out-of-state. 6% American Indian or Alaska Native, non-Hispanic/Latino; 6% Hispanic/Latino; 7% African American, non-Hispanic/Latino; 1% Asian, non-Hispanic/Latino; 0.4% Native Hawaiian or other Pacific Islander, non-Hispanic/Latino; 2% international. 20% 25 or older, 35% live on campus, 13% transferred in. Retention: 65% of full-time freshmen returned the following year. Academic areas with the most degrees conferred: business/marketing; education; biological/life sciences. Core. Calendar: semesters. Academic remediation for entering students, services for LD students, advanced placement, honors program, independent study, distance learning, summer session for credit, part-time degree program, adult/continuing education programs, co-op programs and internships, graduate courses open to undergrads. Off campus study at Northern Oklahoma College, Southwestern Oklahoma State University. Study abroad program.

Entrance Requirements: Options: electronic application, early admission. Required: high school transcript, SAT or ACT. Required for some: essay, minimum 2.7 high school GPA, 3 recommendations. Entrance: moderately difficult. Application deadline: Rolling. Notification: continuous. Transfer credits accepted: Yes.
Costs Per Year: Application fee: $15. State resident tuition: $4253 full-time. Nonresident tuition: $10,185 full-time. Mandatory fees: $945 full-time. Full-time tuition and fees vary according to course load, degree level, location, and program. College room and board: $3780. College room only: $1300. Room and board charges vary according to board plan.
Collegiate Environment: Orientation program. Drama-theater group, choral group, marching band, student-run newspaper, radio station. Social organizations: 60 open to all; local fraternities, local sororities. Most popular organizations: Student Government Association, Aggie Club, Phi Beta Lambda, Baptist Student Union. Major annual events: Bahama Breakaway, Homecoming, Family Day. Student services: personal-psychological counseling. Campus security: 24-hour emergency response devices and patrols, late night transport-escort service. 806 college housing spaces available; 700 were occupied in 2012-13. Freshmen guaranteed college housing. On-campus residence required in freshman year. Options: men-only, women-only housing available. J. W. Martin Library plus 1 other with 169,232 books, 95,468 microform titles, 17,100 serials, 1,225 audiovisual materials, an OPAC, and a Web page. Operations spending for the previous fiscal year: $672,522. 260 computers available on campus for general student use. Computer purchase/lease plans available. A campuswide network can be accessed. Students can access the following: online class registration. Staffed computer lab on campus.
Community Environment: Alva is located in northwestern Oklahoma. The average mean temperature is 59.1 degrees. Rainfall averages 16 inches annually. Local public services include a hospital, many churches, five motels, and active civic and fraternal groups. A movie theatre, golf course, municipal swimming pool, park, picnic areas, lighted baseball fields, playgrounds, tennis courts, fishing, and hunting provide recreation and are all easily accessible. Little Sahara State Park and Alabaster Caverns are located approximately 25 miles distant.

■ OKLAHOMA BAPTIST UNIVERSITY

500 W University
Shawnee, OK 74804
Tel: (405)275-2850; Free: 800-654-3285
Fax: (405)878-2046
E-mail: admissions@mail.okbu.edu
Web Site: www.okbu.edu/
Description: Independent Southern Baptist, comprehensive, coed. Awards associate, bachelor's, and master's degrees. Founded 1910. Setting: 125-acre small town campus with easy access to Oklahoma City. Total enrollment: 76. Faculty: 192 (117 full-time, 75 part-time). Student-undergrad faculty ratio is 14:1. 4,909 applied, 62% were admitted. 33% from top 10% of their high school class, 63% from top quarter, 86% from top half. 25 valedictorians. Full-time: 1,731 students, 60% women, 40% men. Part-time: 172 students, 35% women, 65% men. Students come from 39 states and territories, 14 other countries, 36% from out-of-state. 6% American Indian or Alaska Native, non-Hispanic/Latino; 4% Hispanic/Latino; 5% African American, non-Hispanic/Latino; 1% Asian, non-Hispanic/Latino; 0.1% Native Hawaiian or other Pacific Islander, non-Hispanic/Latino; 5% international. 4% 25 or older, 80% live on campus, 6% transferred in. Retention: 75% of full-time freshmen returned the following year. Academic areas with the most degrees conferred: health professions and related sciences; education; visual and performing arts. Core. Calendar: 4-1-4. Academic remediation for entering students, services for LD students, advanced placement, self-designed majors, honors program, independent study, double major, summer session for credit, part-time degree program, co-op programs and internships. Off campus study at St. Gregory's University. Study abroad program. ROTC: Air Force (c).
Entrance Requirements: Options: early admission, deferred admission, international baccalaureate accepted. Required: high school transcript, minimum 2.5 high school GPA, SAT or ACT. Required for some: essay, interview. Entrance: moderately difficult. Application deadline: Rolling. Notification: continuous until 9/1. SAT Reasoning Test deadline: 8/1.
Costs Per Year: One-time mandatory fee: $50. Comprehensive fee: $27,056 includes full-time tuition ($18,954), mandatory fees ($1902), and college room and board ($6200). Full-time tuition and fees vary according to course load. Room and board charges vary according to housing facility. Part-time tuition: $614 per credit hour. Part-time tuition varies according to course load.

Collegiate Environment: Orientation program. Drama-theater group, choral group, student-run newspaper. Social organizations: 50 open to all; local fraternities, local sororities; 10% of eligible men and 15% of eligible women are members. Most popular organizations: Campus Activities Board, University Concert Series, Student Foundation, Blitz Week Activities, Canterbury. Major annual events: Biggie, Freshmen Follies, Spring Affair. Student services: health clinic, personal-psychological counseling. Campus security: 24-hour emergency response devices and patrols, late night transport-escort service, controlled dormitory access. 1,248 college housing spaces available; 1,000 were occupied in 2012-13. Freshmen guaranteed college housing. On-campus residence required through junior year. Options: men-only, women-only housing available. Mabee Learning Center with 230,000 books, 315,000 microform titles, 1,800 serials, 1,600 audiovisual materials, an OPAC, and a Web page. 175 computers available on campus for general student use. Computer purchase/lease plans available. A campuswide network can be accessed from student residence rooms. Students can access the following: online class registration, campus portal, online course work. Staffed computer lab on campus provides training in use of software and the Internet.

Community Environment: On the North Canadian River, Shawnee is in a rich agricultural and oil-producing area. The altitude of the city is 1,080 feet above sea level and the average temperature is 62.3 degrees. It is located near the geographical center of the state approximately 40 miles by interstate highway from Oklahoma City. The area is accessible via bus lines and a municipal airport. There are churches of most denominations and a YMCA in town. Local recreational facilities provide for golf, fishing, tennis, boating, hunting, bowling, and roller skating as well as picnic grounds, three swimming pools, parks, theatres, museums, and one drive-in. Events include horse shows and rodeo. There are various civic, fraternal and veterans' organizations here.

■ OKLAHOMA CHRISTIAN UNIVERSITY

PO Box 11000
Oklahoma City, OK 73136-1100
Tel: (405)425-5000
Fax: (405)425-5208
E-mail: info@oc.edu
Web Site: www.oc.edu/

Description: Independent, comprehensive, coed, affiliated with Church of Christ. Awards bachelor's and master's degrees. Founded 1950. Setting: 200-acre suburban campus. Endowment: $59.7 million. Educational spending for the previous fiscal year: $8860 per student. Total enrollment: 2,271. Faculty: 194 (116 full-time, 78 part-time). Student-undergrad faculty ratio is 13:1. 2,156 applied, 45% were admitted. 27% from top 10% of their high school class, 49% from top quarter, 76% from top half. Full-time: 1,833 students, 49% women, 51% men. Part-time: 77 students, 51% women, 49% men. Students come from 45 states and territories, 38 other countries, 63% from out-of-state. 4% American Indian or Alaska Native, non-Hispanic/Latino; 3% Hispanic/Latino; 3% African American, non-Hispanic/Latino; 1% Asian, non-Hispanic/Latino; 0% Native Hawaiian or other Pacific Islander, non-Hispanic/Latino; 11% international. 4% 25 or older, 80% live on campus, 7% transferred in. Retention: 76% of full-time freshmen returned the following year. Academic areas with the most degrees conferred: business/marketing; engineering; education. Core. Calendar: semesters. Academic remediation for entering students, ESL program, services for LD students, advanced placement, accelerated degree program, honors program, independent study, distance learning, double major, summer session for credit, internships. Off campus study at University of Central Oklahoma. Study abroad program. ROTC: Army (c); Air Force (c).

Entrance Requirements: Options: electronic application, early admission, deferred admission, international baccalaureate accepted. Required: high school transcript, 1 recommendation, SAT or ACT. Entrance: noncompetitive. Application deadline: Rolling. Notification: continuous. SAT Reasoning Test deadline: 8/25. Transfer credits accepted: Yes.

Costs Per Year: Application fee: $25. Comprehensive fee: $24,975 includes full-time tuition ($18,800) and college room and board ($6175). College room only: $3575. Full-time tuition varies according to course load. Room and board charges vary according to board plan and housing facility. Part-time tuition: $783 per credit hour. Part-time tuition varies according to course load.

Collegiate Environment: Orientation program. Drama-theater group, choral group, student-run newspaper, radio station. Social organizations: 19 open to all. Most popular organizations: Outreach, Wishing Well Project, Acting on Aids, Young Republicans, College Democrats. Major annual events:

Homecoming, Spring Sing, First Week Follies. Student services: health clinic, personal-psychological counseling. Campus security: 24-hour emergency response devices and patrols, late night transport-escort service, controlled dormitory access. 1,755 college housing spaces available; 1,533 were occupied in 2012-13. Freshmen guaranteed college housing. On-campus residence required through senior year. Options: men-only, women-only housing available. Tom and Ada Beam Library with 194,874 books, 686,736 microform titles, 36,384 serials, 6,854 audiovisual materials, an OPAC, and a Web page. Operations spending for the previous fiscal year: $549,325. 101 computers available on campus for general student use. A computer is required for all students. A campuswide network can be accessed from student residence rooms and from off campus. Students can access the following: online class registration. Staffed computer lab on campus provides training in use of computers and software.

Community Environment: Oklahoma City has a metropolitan population of 1,083,000. Closer to the University is the smaller suburban community of Edmond, population 74,800. Air transportation is available at Will Rogers World Airport. Many cultural, entertainment, and job opportunities are readily available.

■ OKLAHOMA CITY COMMUNITY COLLEGE

7777 S May Ave.
Oklahoma City, OK 73159-4419
Tel: (405)682-1611
E-mail: jhorinek@occc.edu
Web Site: www.occc.edu/

Description: State-supported, 2-year, coed. Part of Oklahoma State Regents for Higher Education. Awards certificates, transfer associate, and terminal associate degrees. Founded 1969. Setting: 143-acre urban campus. Endowment: $303,207. Educational spending for the previous fiscal year: $3298 per student. Total enrollment: 14,163. Faculty: 766 (150 full-time, 616 part-time). Student-undergrad faculty ratio is 22:1. 5,407 applied, 100% were admitted. Full-time: 4,825 students, 55% women, 45% men. Part-time: 9,338 students, 59% women, 41% men. Students come from 23 states and territories, 41 other countries, 4% from out-of-state. 7% American Indian or Alaska Native, non-Hispanic/Latino; 5% Hispanic/Latino; 10% African American, non-Hispanic/Latino; 5% Asian, non-Hispanic/Latino; 0.4% Native Hawaiian or other Pacific Islander, non-Hispanic/Latino; 0% international. 44% 25 or older. Core. Calendar: semesters. Academic remediation for entering students, ESL program, services for LD students, advanced placement, accelerated degree program, self-designed majors, honors program, independent study, distance learning, double major, summer session for credit, part-time degree program, co-op programs and internships.

Entrance Requirements: Open admission except for applicants whose high school class has not graduated or nursing, occupational therapy, physical therapy, and speech language pathology programs. Option: electronic application. Required: Proof of English Proficiency, All college and university transcripts. Recommended: ACT, SAT or ACT. Required for some: high school transcript, ACT. Entrance: noncompetitive. Application deadlines: Rolling, Rolling for nonresidents. Notification: continuous, continuous for nonresidents. SAT Reasoning Test deadline: 8/19. SAT Subject Test deadline: 8/19. Transfer credits accepted: Yes.

Costs Per Year: Application fee: $25. One-time mandatory fee: $25. State resident tuition: $2,236 full-time, $74.55 per credit part-time. Nonresident tuition: $6,851 full-time, $228.36 per credit part-time. Mandatory fees: $736 full-time, $24.45 per credit part-time.

Collegiate Environment: Orientation program. Drama-theater group, choral group, student-run newspaper. Social organizations: 38 open to all; Phi Theta Kappa (Honorary); 1% of eligible men and 2% of eligible women are members. Most popular organizations: Health Professions Association, Black Student Association, Nursing Student Association, Hispanic Organization Promoting Education (H.O.P.E). Major annual events: Halloween Carnival, Opening Day, Student Awards Ceremony. Student services: personal-psychological counseling. Campus security: 24-hour emergency response devices and patrols, late night transport-escort service. College housing not available. Keith Leftwich Memorial Library with 135,739 books, 20,329 serials, 18,322 audiovisual materials, an OPAC, and a Web page. Operations spending for the previous fiscal year: $1.2 million. 427 computers available on campus for general student use. Computer purchase/lease plans available. A campuswide network can be accessed from off-campus. Students can access the following: online class registration. Staffed computer lab on campus provides training in use of computers, software, and the Internet.

Community Environment: Oklahoma City was born on April 22, 1889, when the population jumped from zero to 10,000 as a result of a unique land run. The city is one of the largest municipalities in the nation, covering a total of 621 square miles. The more than 530,000 residents enjoy temperatures ranging from the mid-80s in July to the mid-30s in January. The community is served by all major forms of transportation. Entertainment, cultural and sports related activities are numerous.

■ **OKLAHOMA CITY UNIVERSITY**
2501 N Blackwelder
Oklahoma City, OK 73106-1402
Tel: (405)208-5000; Free: 800-633-7242
E-mail: michelle.cook@okcu.edu
Web Site: www.okcu.edu/
Description: Independent United Methodist, comprehensive, coed. Awards bachelor's, master's, and doctoral degrees. Founded 1904. Setting: urban campus. Faculty: 342. 58% live on campus. Core. Calendar: semesters. ESL program, services for LD students, advanced placement, accelerated degree program, honors program, independent study, distance learning, double major, summer session for credit, part-time degree program, adult/continuing education programs, internships, graduate courses open to undergrads. Off campus study at American University. Study abroad program. ROTC: Army (c), Naval (c), Air Force (c).
Entrance Requirements: Required: essay, high school transcript, SAT or ACT. Required for some: interview.
Costs Per Year: Comprehensive fee: $37,360 includes full-time tuition ($24,740), mandatory fees ($3450), and college room and board ($9170). College room only: $5090. Room and board charges vary according to board plan and housing facility. Part-time tuition: $840 per credit hour. Tuition guaranteed not to increase for student's term of enrollment.
Collegiate Environment: Orientation program. Drama-theater group, choral group, student-run newspaper. Social organizations: 62 open to all; national fraternities, national sororities, local fraternities, local sororities. Most popular organizations: Tri-Beta, Multicultural Student Association, Student Nursing Associate, Fellowship of Christian Athletes. Major annual events: Oozefest, Free Movie Night, Midnight Breakfast. Student services: health clinic, personal-psychological counseling. Campus security: 24-hour emergency response devices and patrols, late night transport-escort service, controlled dormitory access. 1,305 college housing spaces available. Freshmen given priority for college housing. Options: coed, men-only, women-only housing available. Dulaney Browne Library plus 2 others with 522,263 books, 13,141 microform titles, 51 serials, 15,241 audiovisual materials, and a Web page. 368 computers available on campus for general student use. Computer purchase/lease plans available. A campuswide network can be accessed from student residence rooms and from off campus. Students can access the following: online class registration. Staffed computer lab on campus provides training in use of computers, software, and the Internet.
Community Environment: Oklahoma City, the capital City of Oklahoma, offers a wide variety of cultural, civic, religious, entertainment and sports events in the unique setting of modern facilities and old-fashioned Western hospitality. With more than 1,000,000 people in the metropolitan area, Oklahoma City is a dynamic, growing location with a wide range of opportunities to offer its students. From the State Capitol and the center of Oklahoma's political and governmental activity, to the cultural offerings the Oklahoma City Philharmonic, Lyric Theater, Ballet Oklahoma, Oklahoma Zoo, Omniplex, and more. Oklahoma City stands as a vibrant, growing metropolitan center offerings the Southwest. Out-of-state students are able to make use of the excellent transportation facilities available to the City. Oklahoma City is linked by interstate highways to other major cities in the region, and the City's Will Rogers International Airport, one offerings the busiest in the region, provides jet service coast-to-coast and international flights to Europe, Asia, and South America.

■ **OKLAHOMA PANHANDLE STATE UNIVERSITY**
PO Box 430
Goodwell, OK 73939-0430
Tel: (580)349-2611; Free: 800-664-6778
Fax: (580)349-2302
E-mail: opsu@opsu.edu
Web Site: www.opsu.edu/
Description: State-supported, 4-year, coed. Part of Oklahoma State Regents for Higher Education. Awards associate and bachelor's degrees. Founded 1909. Setting: 40-acre rural campus. Total enrollment: 1,387. Faculty: 91 (65 full-time, 26 part-time). Student-undergrad faculty ratio is

16:1. 316 applied, 100% were admitted. Full-time: 1,116 students, 45% women, 55% men. Part-time: 271 students, 70% women, 30% men. Students come from 25 states and territories, 15 other countries, 50% from out-of-state. 4% American Indian or Alaska Native, non-Hispanic/Latino; 18% Hispanic/Latino; 6% African American, non-Hispanic/Latino; 0.2% Asian, non-Hispanic/Latino; 0% Native Hawaiian or other Pacific Islander, non-Hispanic/Latino; 3% international. 24% 25 or older, 12% transferred in. Retention: 53% of full-time freshmen returned the following year. Academic areas with the most degrees conferred: agriculture; business/marketing; health professions and related sciences; biological/life sciences. Core. Calendar: semesters. Academic remediation for entering students, ESL program, services for LD students, advanced placement, distance learning, double major, summer session for credit.
Entrance Requirements: Options: electronic application, international baccalaureate accepted. Required: high school transcript. Recommended: SAT or ACT. Entrance: noncompetitive. Application deadline: Rolling.
Collegiate Environment: Orientation program. Drama-theater group, choral group, marching band, student-run newspaper, radio station. Social organizations: local fraternities. Major annual events: Fall Homecoming, Annual Rodeo, talent show. Student services: health clinic, personal-psychological counseling. Campus security: safety bars over door latches. McKee Library with an OPAC and a Web page.
Community Environment: Goodwell is located in the center of the Oklahoma Panhandle in Texas County. The climate is cool and arid. The area is served by railroad, and Highway 54. Goodwell has three churches, and various civic, fraternal and veteran's organizations.

■ **OKLAHOMA STATE UNIVERSITY**
Stillwater, OK 74078
Tel: (405)744-5000; Free: 800-852-1255
Fax: (405)744-5285
E-mail: christine.crenshaw@okstate.edu
Web Site: www.okstate.edu/
Description: State-supported, university, coed. Part of Oklahoma State University. Awards bachelor's, master's, and doctoral degrees and post-master's certificates. Founded 1890. Setting: 840-acre small town campus with easy access to Oklahoma City, Tulsa. System endowment: $557.7 million. Research spending for the previous fiscal year: $110.7 million. Educational spending for the previous fiscal year: $8164 per student. Total enrollment: 25,544. Faculty: 1,344 (1,029 full-time, 315 part-time). Student-undergrad faculty ratio is 20:1. 12,056 applied, 78% were admitted. 28% from top 10% of their high school class, 58% from top quarter, 86% from top half. 16 National Merit Scholars. Full-time: 17,549 students, 48% women, 52% men. Part-time: 2,581 students, 46% women, 54% men. Students come from 49 states and territories, 64 other countries, 24% from out-of-state. 6% American Indian or Alaska Native, non-Hispanic/Latino; 4% Hispanic/Latino; 5% African American, non-Hispanic/Latino; 1% Asian, non-Hispanic/Latino; 0.02% Native Hawaiian or other Pacific Islander, non-Hispanic/Latino; 2% international. 13% 25 or older, 45% live on campus, 9% transferred in. Retention: 79% of full-time freshmen returned the following year. Academic areas with the most degrees conferred: business/marketing; agriculture; family and consumer sciences. Core. Calendar: semesters. Academic remediation for entering students, ESL program, services for LD students, advanced placement, accelerated degree program, self-designed majors, freshman honors college, honors program, independent study, distance learning, double major, summer session for credit, part-time degree program, internships. Off campus study. Study abroad program. ROTC: Army, Air Force.
Entrance Requirements: Options: electronic application, deferred admission, international baccalaureate accepted. Required: high school transcript, minimum 3 high school GPA, class rank, SAT or ACT. Required for some: essay, interview. Entrance: moderately difficult. Application deadlines: Rolling, Rolling for nonresidents. Notification: continuous, continuous for nonresidents. Transfer credits accepted: Yes.
Costs Per Year: Application fee: $40. One-time mandatory fee: $95. State resident tuition: $4425 full-time, $147.50 per credit hour part-time. Nonresident tuition: $16,440 full-time, $548 per credit hour part-time. Mandatory fees: $3,016 full-time, $100.55 per credit hour part-time. Full-time tuition and fees vary according to program and student level. Part-time tuition and fees vary according to program and student level. College room and board: $6868. College room only: $3710. Room and board charges vary according to board plan and housing facility.
Collegiate Environment: Orientation program. Drama-theater group, choral group, marching band, student-run newspaper, radio station. Social

organizations: 442 open to all; national fraternities, national sororities. Major annual events: OSU Homecoming, OSU Orange Peel, Remember the Ten Running. Student services: health clinic, personal-psychological counseling, women's center. Campus security: 24-hour emergency response devices and patrols, student patrols, controlled dormitory access. Freshmen guaranteed college housing. On-campus residence required in freshman year. Options: coed, men-only, women-only housing available. Edmon Low Library plus 3 others with an OPAC and a Web page. Operations spending for the previous fiscal year: $17 million.

Community Environment: Stillwater is located in north central Oklahoma. The climate is mild with an average annual temperature of 59.8 degrees and average rainfall of 33.3 inches. The city is accessible by Highways 51 and 177, and nearby U.S. Highways 64 and Interstate 35. There are bus lines to the city. Stillwater has several churches of major denominations, a hospital, two clinics, and a health center. Local recreational facilities include 15 parks, three golf courses, fishing, camping, picnicking, hiking, hunting, boating, water-skiing, theatres, and a drive-in. Rooming houses, apartments and private homes provide housing for students. There is part-time employment available.

■ OKLAHOMA STATE UNIVERSITY INSTITUTE OF TECHNOLOGY

1801 E Fourth St.
Okmulgee, OK 74447-3901
Tel: (918)293-4678; Free: 800-722-4471
E-mail: mary.r.graves@okstate.edu
Web Site: www.osuit.edu/

Description: State-supported, 2-year, coed. Part of Oklahoma State University. Awards transfer associate and terminal associate degrees. Founded 1946. Setting: 160-acre small town campus with easy access to Tulsa. Total enrollment: 2,329. Faculty: 129 (all full-time). Full-time: 1,717 students, 33% women, 67% men. Part-time: 612 students, 58% women, 42% men. Students come from 22 states and territories, 3 other countries. 37% 25 or older, 25% live on campus. Core. Calendar: trimesters. Academic remediation for entering students, services for LD students, advanced placement, summer session for credit, part-time degree program, adult/continuing education programs, internships.

Entrance Requirements: Open admission. Option: deferred admission. Required: high school transcript. Entrance: noncompetitive. Application deadline: Rolling.

Collegiate Environment: Drama-theater group. Social organizations: 32 open to all. Most popular organizations: Student Senate, Junior Ambassadors, Phi Theta Kappa, departmental clubs, Drama Club. Major annual events: Super Weekend, Okmulgee College and Career Day, Auto Show. Student services: health clinic, personal-psychological counseling. Campus security: 24-hour emergency response devices and patrols, late night transport-escort service, controlled dormitory access. Learning Resource Center with 9,965 books, 484 serials, an OPAC, and a Web page. 360 computers available on campus for general student use. Staffed computer lab on campus.

■ OKLAHOMA STATE UNIVERSITY, OKLAHOMA CITY

900 N Portland
Oklahoma City, OK 73107-6120
Tel: (405)947-4421; Free: 800-560-4099
Fax: (405)945-3277
E-mail: wilkylw@osuokc.edu
Web Site: www.osuokc.edu/

Description: State-supported, primarily 2-year, coed. Part of Oklahoma State University. Awards certificates, transfer associate, terminal associate, and bachelor's degrees. Founded 1961. Setting: 110-acre urban campus. Total enrollment: 7,585. Faculty: 389 (85 full-time, 304 part-time). Student-undergrad faculty ratio is 20:1. 562 applied, 100% were admitted. Full-time: 2,510 students, 56% women, 44% men. Part-time: 5,075 students, 64% women, 36% men. Students come from 18 states and territories, 8 other countries, 2% from out-of-state. 4% American Indian or Alaska Native, non-Hispanic/Latino; 8% Hispanic/Latino; 17% African American, non-Hispanic/Latino; 2% Asian, non-Hispanic/Latino; 0% Native Hawaiian or other Pacific Islander, non-Hispanic/Latino; 0.2% international. 51% 25 or older, 11% transferred in. Retention: 40% of full-time freshmen returned the following year. Core. Calendar: semesters. Academic remediation for entering students, services for LD students, advanced placement, honors program, independent study, distance learning, double major, summer session for credit, part-time degree program, co-op programs. Study abroad program.

Entrance Requirements: Open admission except for nursing program. Op-

tions: electronic application, early admission. Required: high school transcript. Entrance: noncompetitive. Application deadline: Rolling. Notification: continuous.

Collegiate Environment: Social organizations: 20 open to all. Most popular organizations: Phi Theta Kappa, Deaf/Hearing Social Club, American Criminal Justice Association, Horticulture Club, Vet-Tech Club. Major annual events: Howdy Week, Halloween Blast, Earth Day Fair. Campus security: 24-hour patrols, late night transport-escort service. College housing not available. Oklahoma State University-Oklahoma City Campus Library with 15,000 books, 300 serials, an OPAC, and a Web page. 800 computers available on campus for general student use. A campuswide network can be accessed from off-campus. Staffed computer lab on campus.

Community Environment: See Oklahoma City University.

■ OKLAHOMA TECHNICAL COLLEGE

4444 S Sheridan
Tulsa, OK 74145
Tel: (918)895-7500
E-mail: rbanuelos@communitycarecollege.edu
Web Site: www.oklahomatechnicalcollege.com/

Description: Proprietary, 2-year, coed. Part of Dental Directions, Inc. Awards diplomas and terminal associate degrees. Setting: 9-acre urban campus with easy access to Tulsa. Faculty: 11 (all full-time). Student-undergrad faculty ratio is 8:1. Students come from 2 states and territories, 2% from out-of-state. Core. Services for LD students, distance learning, adult/continuing education programs, internships.

Entrance Requirements: Open admission. Option: electronic application. Required: essay, high school transcript, interview. Required for some: valid Oklahoma driver's license. Entrance: noncompetitive. Application deadlines: Rolling, Rolling for nonresidents. Notification: continuous, continuous for nonresidents. Transfer credits accepted: Yes.

Costs Per Year: Application fee: $100. Tuition: $25,804 full-time. Mandatory fees: $3280 full-time. Full-time tuition and fees vary according to course load, degree level, location, and program.

Collegiate Environment: Orientation program. Social organizations: 1 open to all. Most popular organization: Student Ambassadors. Major annual events: Food Bank, Clothing Drive, Blood Drive. Student services: personal-psychological counseling. Campus security: Campus security is available during school hours. College housing not available. 12 computers available on campus for general student use. Computer purchase/lease plans available. A campuswide network can be accessed. Staffed computer lab on campus provides training in use of computers, software, and the Internet.

■ OKLAHOMA WESLEYAN UNIVERSITY

2201 Silver Lake Rd.
Bartlesville, OK 74006-6299
Tel: (918)335-6200; Free: 866-222-8226
Fax: (918)335-6229
E-mail: admissions@okwu.edu
Web Site: www.okwu.edu/

Description: Independent, comprehensive, coed, affiliated with Wesleyan Church. Administratively affiliated with The Wesleyan Church. Awards associate, bachelor's, and master's degrees. Founded 1909. Setting: 127-acre small town campus with easy access to Tulsa. Endowment: $3.1 million. Educational spending for the previous fiscal year: $4510 per student. Total enrollment: 1,178. Faculty: 168 (31 full-time, 137 part-time). Student-undergrad faculty ratio is 10:1. 1,880 applied, 66% were admitted. 13% from top 10% of their high school class, 33% from top quarter, 69% from top half. 6 valedictorians. Full-time: 599 students, 51% women, 49% men. Part-time: 484 students, 71% women, 29% men. Students come from 36 states and territories, 20 other countries, 42% from out-of-state. 8% American Indian or Alaska Native, non-Hispanic/Latino; 8% Hispanic/Latino; 7% African American, non-Hispanic/Latino; 1% Asian, non-Hispanic/Latino; 0.1% Native Hawaiian or other Pacific Islander, non-Hispanic/Latino; 4% international. 47% 25 or older, 28% live on campus, 12% transferred in. Retention: 66% of full-time freshmen returned the following year. Academic areas with the most degrees conferred: health professions and related sciences; business/marketing; theology and religious vocations. Core. Calendar: semesters. Academic remediation for entering students, services for LD students, advanced placement, accelerated degree program, self-designed majors, independent study, distance learning, double major, summer session for credit, part-time degree program, external degree program, adult/continuing education programs, co-op programs and internships. Off campus study at Tri-County Technical College, Coalition for Christian Colleges and Universities. Study abroad program.

Entrance Requirements: Open admission. Option: electronic application. Required: high school transcript, ACT score 18 or higher, SAT or ACT. Recommended: minimum 2 high school GPA. Required for some: interview. Entrance: minimally difficult. Application deadlines: Rolling, Rolling for nonresidents. SAT Reasoning Test deadline: 8/15. Transfer credits accepted: Yes.

Costs Per Year: Application fee: $25. Comprehensive fee: $28,380 includes full-time tuition ($19,940), mandatory fees ($1200), and college room and board ($7240). College room only: $3820. Full-time tuition and fees vary according to course load. Room and board charges vary according to board plan and housing facility. Part-time tuition: $795 per credit hour. Part-time mandatory fees: $55 per credit hour, $60 per term.

Collegiate Environment: Orientation program. Drama-theater group, choral group, student-run newspaper. Social organizations: 10 open to all. Most popular organizations: Operation Saturation (Community Service Opportunities), Fellowship of Christian Athletes, Missions Support Groups, intramurals, student government groups. Major annual events: Homecoming activities, Spiritual Emphasis Week, Seasonal banquets. Student services: health clinic, personal-psychological counseling. Campus security: student patrols. Janice and Charles Drake Library with 108,717 books, 21,572 microform titles, 82 serials, 4,942 audiovisual materials, an OPAC, and a Web page. Operations spending for the previous fiscal year: $249,938. 33 computers available on campus for general student use. A campuswide network can be accessed from student residence rooms and from off campus. Students can access the following: online class registration.

■ **ORAL ROBERTS UNIVERSITY**
7777 S Lewis Ave.
Tulsa, OK 74171
Tel: (918)495-6161; Free: 800-678-8876
Fax: (918)495-6222
E-mail: admissions@oru.edu
Web Site: www.oru.edu/

Description: Independent interdenominational, comprehensive, coed. Awards bachelor's, master's, and doctoral degrees. Founded 1963. Setting: 263-acre urban campus. Total enrollment: 3,335. Faculty: 273 (165 full-time, 108 part-time). Student-undergrad faculty ratio is 15:1. 1,557 applied, 52% were admitted. 20% from top 10% of their high school class, 46% from top quarter, 78% from top half. Full-time: 475 students, 52% women, 48% men. Part-time: 5 students, 80% women, 20% men. 41% from out-of-state. 3% American Indian or Alaska Native, non-Hispanic/Latino; 7% Hispanic/Latino; 14% African American, non-Hispanic/Latino; 2% Asian, non-Hispanic/Latino; 0% Native Hawaiian or other Pacific Islander, non-Hispanic/Latino; 5% international. 13% 25 or older, 72% live on campus, 50% transferred in. Academic areas with the most degrees conferred: business/marketing; theology and religious vocations; communication/journalism. Calendar: semesters. Part-time degree program, external degree program, adult/continuing education programs. ROTC: Air Force (c).

Entrance Requirements: Option: deferred admission. Required: essay, high school transcript, minimum 2 high school GPA, 1 recommendation, proof of immunization. Recommended: interview. Required for some: interview. Entrance: moderately difficult. Application deadline: Rolling. Notification: continuous.

Costs Per Year: Application fee: $35. Comprehensive fee: $31,734 includes full-time tuition ($21,696), mandatory fees ($742), and college room and board ($9296). College room only: $4534. Full-time tuition and fees vary according to degree level. Room and board charges vary according to board plan and housing facility. Part-time tuition: $906 per credit hour. Part-time tuition varies according to degree level.

Collegiate Environment: Orientation program. Campus security: 24-hour emergency response devices and patrols, late night transport-escort service. On-campus residence required through senior year. Options: men-only, women-only housing available.

Community Environment: Tulsa is located in northeast Oklahoma. The area has four distinct seasons, and is served by major airlines, bus lines, and U.S. highways. Tulsa is located on the fringe of the southwest's greatest inland vacation and recreation areas. Nearby lakes provide fishing, golf, boating, hunting, and other outdoor sports. Community services include many churches, an Opera Association, Philbrook and Gilcrease Museums, major health facilities, and civic organizations.

■ **PLATT COLLEGE (MOORE)**
201 N Eastern Ave.
Moore, OK 73160

Tel: (405)912-3260
Fax: (405)912-4360
Web Site: www.plattcolleges.edu/

Description: Proprietary, 2-year, coed. Awards terminal associate degrees. Total enrollment: 71. 178 applied, 100% were admitted.

■ **PLATT COLLEGE (OKLAHOMA CITY)**
309 S Ann Arbor Ave.
Oklahoma City, OK 73128
Tel: (405)946-7799
Fax: (405)943-2150
E-mail: klamb@plattcollege.org
Web Site: www.plattcolleges.edu/

Description: Proprietary, 2-year, coed. Awards diplomas and terminal associate degrees. Founded 1979. Setting: urban campus with easy access to Oklahoma City. Total enrollment: 357. Faculty: 27 (16 full-time, 11 part-time). Student-undergrad faculty ratio is 60:1. Full-time: 225 students, 91% women, 9% men. 5% American Indian or Alaska Native, non-Hispanic/Latino; 13% Hispanic/Latino; 30% African American, non-Hispanic/Latino; 2% Asian, non-Hispanic/Latino; 0% Native Hawaiian or other Pacific Islander, non-Hispanic/Latino; 0% international. 57% 25 or older, 0% transferred in. Retention: 0% of full-time freshmen returned the following year. Calendar: continuous. Academic remediation for entering students, part-time degree program, internships.

Entrance Requirements: Open admission. Entrance: noncompetitive. Transfer credits accepted: No.

Collegiate Environment: Orientation program. Major annual events: Constitution Day, Student Appreciation Day, Holiday Party's. Campus security: 24-hour emergency response devices, security officer for evening and Saturday classes. Platt College Learning Resource Center with an OPAC. 30 computers available on campus for general student use. Staffed computer lab on campus provides training in use of computers and the Internet.

■ **PLATT COLLEGE (TULSA)**
3801 S Sheridan Rd.
Tulsa, OK 74145-111
Tel: (918)663-9000
Fax: (918)622-1240
E-mail: susanr@plattcollege.org
Web Site: www.plattcolleges.edu/

Description: Proprietary, 2-year, coed. Awards terminal associate degrees. Founded 1979. Total enrollment: 415. Calendar: continuous.

Entrance Requirements: Entrance: noncompetitive.

■ **REDLANDS COMMUNITY COLLEGE**
1300 S Country Club Rd.
El Reno, OK 73036-5304
Tel: (405)262-2552; Free: 866-415-6367
E-mail: hobsont@redlandscc.edu
Web Site: www.redlandscc.edu/

Description: State-supported, 2-year, coed. Part of Oklahoma State Regents for Higher Education. Awards certificates, transfer associate, and terminal associate degrees. Founded 1938. Setting: 55-acre suburban campus with easy access to Oklahoma City. Total enrollment: 2,560. Faculty: 113 (35 full-time, 78 part-time). Student-undergrad faculty ratio is 24:1. 513 applied, 99% were admitted. Full-time: 915 students, 61% women, 39% men. Part-time: 1,645 students, 67% women, 33% men. 97% from out-of-state. 14% American Indian or Alaska Native, non-Hispanic/Latino; 5% Hispanic/Latino; 6% African American, non-Hispanic/Latino; 1% Asian, non-Hispanic/Latino; 0.1% Native Hawaiian or other Pacific Islander, non-Hispanic/Latino; 0% international. 29% 25 or older, 10% live on campus, 9% transferred in. Retention: 41% of full-time freshmen returned the following year. Core. Calendar: semesters. Academic remediation for entering students, services for LD students, advanced placement, accelerated degree program, honors program, distance learning, double major, summer session for credit, part-time degree program, external degree program, adult/continuing education programs, co-op programs and internships.

Entrance Requirements: Open admission except for nursing, medical laboratory technology programs. Options: electronic application, early admission, deferred admission. Required: high school transcript. Recommended: SAT or ACT. Entrance: noncompetitive. Application deadline: Rolling. Notification: continuous. SAT Reasoning Test deadline: 8/15.

Collegiate Environment: Orientation program. Drama-theater group, choral

group. Social organizations: 11 open to all. Most popular organizations: Nursing Club, Aggie Club, Baptist Student Union, Phi Theta Kappa, Outdoors Club. Major annual events: Back to School Bash, End of Year Party, Career Fair. Campus security: 24-hour patrols. Options: men-only, women-only housing available. Learning Resource Center with an OPAC.

Community Environment: El Reno is located on the south bank of the North Canadian River. The average annual temperature is 60 degrees. The city is served by bus lines, railroad, and an airport. Nearby lakes offer waterskiing, fishing, and boating. El Reno has many community service facilities including a hospital, hotel and many motels, a library, and various civic, service, and fraternal organizations. Part-time job opportunities are good. Local recreational facilities include two movie theatres, drive-ins, parks, tennis, golf, and a municipal swimming pool.

■ ROGERS STATE UNIVERSITY

1701 W Will Rogers Blvd.
Claremore, OK 74017-3252
Tel: (918)343-7777; Free: 800-256-7511
Fax: (918)343-7898
E-mail: info@rsu.edu
Web Site: www.rsu.edu/

Description: State-supported, 4-year, coed. Part of Oklahoma State Regents for Higher Education. Awards associate and bachelor's degrees. Founded 1909. Setting: 40-acre small town campus with easy access to Tulsa. Endowment: $7.6 million. Research spending for the previous fiscal year: $68,619. Educational spending for the previous fiscal year: $4163 per student. Total enrollment: 4,646. Faculty: 281 (106 full-time, 175 part-time). Student-undergrad faculty ratio is 21:1. 1,988 applied, 55% were admitted. 13% from top 10% of their high school class, 32% from top quarter, 60% from top half. Full-time: 2,856 students, 61% women, 39% men. Part-time: 1,790 students, 65% women, 35% men. Students come from 26 states and territories, 29 other countries, 3% from out-of-state. 13% American Indian or Alaska Native, non-Hispanic/Latino; 4% Hispanic/Latino; 3% African American, non-Hispanic/Latino; 1% Asian, non-Hispanic/Latino; 0.1% Native Hawaiian or other Pacific Islander, non-Hispanic/Latino; 1% international. 36% 25 or older, 6% live on campus, 9% transferred in. Retention: 61% of full-time freshmen returned the following year. Academic areas with the most degrees conferred: business/marketing; social sciences; biological/life sciences. Core. Calendar: semesters. Academic remediation for entering students, services for LD students, advanced placement, honors program, independent study, distance learning, double major, summer session for credit, part-time degree program, adult/continuing education programs, co-op programs and internships. Off campus study at Northeast Technology Centers-Afton, Claremore, Kansas, and Pryor, OK; Tri-County Technology Center-Bartlesville, OK; Central Technology Center-Drumright, OK; Tulsa Technology Center-Tulsa, OK. Study abroad program.

Entrance Requirements: Open admission for associate degree programs. Option: electronic application. Required: high school transcript, SAT or ACT. Recommended: ACT. Required for some: minimum 2.75 high school GPA, Baccalaureate degree programs require 20 ACT composite or 2.75 GPA and top 50% rank for admission; Associate degree programs have an open admission policy, ACT COMPASS. Entrance: noncompetitive. Application deadlines: Rolling, Rolling for nonresidents. SAT Reasoning Test deadline: 8/1. Transfer credits accepted: Yes.

Costs Per Year: Application fee: $0. State resident tuition: $3263 full-time, $108.75 per hour part-time. Nonresident tuition: $9788 full-time, $326.25 per hour part-time. Mandatory fees: $1784 full-time, $58.45 per hour part-time, $15 per term part-time. Full-time tuition and fees vary according to course level, course load, location, program, and student level. Part-time tuition and fees vary according to course level, course load, location, program, and student level. College room and board: $6425. Room and board charges vary according to housing facility.

Collegiate Environment: Orientation program. Drama-theater group, choral group, student-run newspaper, radio station. Social organizations: 30 open to all; national fraternities, national sororities; 1% of eligible men and 2% of eligible women are members. Most popular organizations: Community Counseling and Psychology Student Association, Baptist Collegiate Ministry, Native American Student Association, Psychology Students for Social Responsibility, Pre-Professional Health Club. Major annual events: Big Tent Day (during Welcome Week), No Stress Zone Late Night Breakfast (during final exams), Big Thing Day (during Spring Fling). Student services: health clinic, personal-psychological counseling. Campus security: 24-hour emergency response devices and patrols, student patrols, late night transport-escort service, controlled dormitory access, RSU employs only

State certified law enforcement officers and has a comprehensive camera surveillance system. 525 college housing spaces available; 514 were occupied in 2012-13. No special consideration for freshman housing applicants. Option: coed housing available. Stratton Taylor Library with 216,655 books, 17,884 microform titles, 46,559 serials, 2,972 audiovisual materials, an OPAC, and a Web page. Operations spending for the previous fiscal year: $849,120. 237 computers available on campus for general student use. A campuswide network can be accessed from student residence rooms. Students can access the following: online class registration, software to support courses.

■ ROSE STATE COLLEGE

6420 SE 15th St.
Midwest City, OK 73110-2799
Tel: (405)733-7673; Free: 866-621-0987
Fax: (405)733-7399
E-mail: maitson@ms.rose.cc.ok.us
Web Site: www.rose.edu/

Description: State and locally supported, 2-year, coed. Part of Oklahoma State Regents for Higher Education. Awards transfer associate and terminal associate degrees. Founded 1968. Setting: 110-acre suburban campus with easy access to Oklahoma City. Total enrollment: 7,000. Faculty: 412 (143 full-time, 269 part-time). Students come from 18 states and territories, 33 other countries. 60% 25 or older. Core. Calendar: semesters. Academic remediation for entering students, services for LD students, advanced placement, accelerated degree program, honors program, independent study, distance learning, summer session for credit, part-time degree program, adult/continuing education programs, internships. Off campus study. ROTC: Army (c), Air Force (c).

Entrance Requirements: Open admission except for health occupations programs. Options: electronic application, early admission, deferred admission. Required: high school transcript. Entrance: noncompetitive. Application deadline: Rolling. Notification: continuous.

Collegiate Environment: Drama-theater group, choral group, student-run newspaper. Student services: health clinic, personal-psychological counseling, women's center. Campus security: 24-hour patrols. Rose State College Learning Resources Center with 90,000 books, 6,193 microform titles, 443 serials, 9,620 audiovisual materials, an OPAC, and a Web page. Operations spending for the previous fiscal year: $1.3 million. 390 computers available on campus for general student use. A campuswide network can be accessed from off-campus. Staffed computer lab on campus.

Community Environment: See Oklahoma City University.

■ ST. GREGORY'S UNIVERSITY

1900 W MacArthur Dr.
Shawnee, OK 74804-2499
Tel: (405)878-5100; Free: 888-STGREGS
Fax: (405)878-5198
E-mail: admissions@stgregorys.edu
Web Site: www.stgregorys.edu/

Description: Independent Roman Catholic, comprehensive, coed. Awards associate, bachelor's, and master's degrees. Founded 1875. Setting: 640-acre small town campus with easy access to Oklahoma City. Endowment: $9.6 million. Total enrollment: 672. Faculty: 136 (28 full-time, 108 part-time). Student-undergrad faculty ratio is 11:1. 306 applied, 31% were admitted. 18% from top 10% of their high school class, 41% from top quarter, 69% from top half. Full-time: 337 students, 53% women, 47% men. Part-time: 291 students, 59% women, 41% men. Students come from 11 states and territories, 15 other countries, 6% from out-of-state. 8% American Indian or Alaska Native, non-Hispanic/Latino; 10% Hispanic/Latino; 12% African American, non-Hispanic/Latino; 1% Asian, non-Hispanic/Latino; 0% Native Hawaiian or other Pacific Islander, non-Hispanic/Latino; 8% international. 17% 25 or older, 36% live on campus, 11% transferred in. Retention: 41% of full-time freshmen returned the following year. Academic areas with the most degrees conferred: business/marketing; social sciences; theology and religious vocations. Core. Calendar: semesters. Services for LD students, advanced placement, accelerated degree program, honors program, independent study, distance learning, double major, summer session for credit, part-time degree program, external degree program, adult/continuing education programs, co-op programs and internships. Off campus study.

Entrance Requirements: Options: electronic application, deferred admission, international baccalaureate accepted. Required: minimum 2.75 high school GPA, SAT or ACT. Required for some: essay, high school transcript, interview. Entrance: minimally difficult. Application deadline: Rolling. Notification: continuous. Transfer credits accepted: Yes.

Collegiate Environment: Orientation program. Drama-theater group, choral group. Social organizations: 8 open to all; local fraternities, local sororities; 3% of eligible men and 14% of eligible women are members. Most popular organizations: Greek Life, Student Government Association, Pro-Life, Hispanic American Student Association, Campus Ministry. Major annual events: Homecoming, Spring Formal, Spring Fling. Student services: personal-psychological counseling. Campus security: 24-hour emergency response devices and patrols, late night transport-escort service, controlled dormitory access. 400 college housing spaces available; 239 were occupied in 2012-13. Freshmen guaranteed college housing. On-campus residence required through senior year. Options: men-only, women-only housing available. James J. Kelly Library plus 1 other with 88,444 books, 3,496 microform titles, 3,601 serials, 1,484 audiovisual materials, an OPAC, and a Web page. Operations spending for the previous fiscal year: $144,492. 35 computers available on campus for general student use. A campuswide network can be accessed from student residence rooms and from off campus. Students can access the following: online class registration.

■ SEMINOLE STATE COLLEGE
PO Box 351
Seminole, OK 74818-0351
Tel: (405)382-9950
E-mail: lindley_c@ssc.cc.ok.us
Web Site: www.sscok.edu/

Description: State-supported, 2-year, coed. Part of Oklahoma State Regents for Higher Education. Awards diplomas, transfer associate, and terminal associate degrees. Founded 1931. Setting: 40-acre small town campus with easy access to Oklahoma City. Educational spending for the previous fiscal year: $1533 per student. Total enrollment: 2,534. Faculty: 101 (46 full-time, 55 part-time). Student-undergrad faculty ratio is 25:1. Students come from 13 states and territories, 5 other countries, 2% from out-of-state. 47% 25 or older, 8% live on campus. Core. Calendar: semesters. Academic remediation for entering students, services for LD students, advanced placement, accelerated degree program, honors program, independent study, distance learning, summer session for credit, part-time degree program, adult/continuing education programs, co-op programs. Off campus study at Gordon Cooper Technology Center, Wes Watkins Technology Center, Moore-Norman Technology Center.

Entrance Requirements: Open admission. Options: early admission, deferred admission. Required: high school transcript. Recommended: ACT. Entrance: noncompetitive. Application deadline: Rolling. Notification: continuous.

Collegiate Environment: Choral group, student-run newspaper. Social organizations: 21 open to all; local fraternities; 1% of eligible men and 1% of eligible women are members. Most popular organizations: Student Government Association, Native American Student Association, Psi Beta Honor Society, Student Nurses Association, Phi Theta Kappa. Major annual events: Trojan Olympics, SSC Coffee House, Mayfair. Student services: personal-psychological counseling. Campus security: 24-hour patrols, student patrols, late night transport-escort service, controlled dormitory access. Boren Library with 27,507 books, 200 serials, and an OPAC. Operations spending for the previous fiscal year: $205,958. 100 computers available on campus for general student use. A campuswide network can be accessed from off-campus. Staffed computer lab on campus.

Community Environment: Seminole is an urban community enjoying temperate climate. Local transportation services include railroad, bus, and airlines. The city has a public library, 30 churches of various denominations, a hospital, and three clinics. Some part-time employment is available for students. Recreational facilities in Seminole include a theater, a drive-in, bowling, and water sports. The major civic, fraternal and veteran's organizations are active within the immediate community. There are several historic sites located nearby.

■ SOUTHEASTERN OKLAHOMA STATE UNIVERSITY
1405 N 4th Ave.
Durant, OK 74701-0609
Tel: (580)745-2000; Free: 800-435-1327
Fax: (580)745-7490
E-mail: kluke@se.edu
Web Site: www.se.edu/

Description: State-supported, comprehensive, coed. Part of Oklahoma State Regents for Higher Education. Awards bachelor's and master's degrees and post-master's certificates. Founded 1909. Setting: 177-acre small town campus. Endowment: $12 million. Research spending for the previous fiscal year: $564,684. Educational spending for the previous fiscal year: $10,360 per student. Total enrollment: 4,120. Faculty: 262 (142 full-time, 120 part-time). Student-undergrad faculty ratio is 19:1. 1,143 applied, 78% were admitted. 18% from top 10% of their high school class, 41% from top quarter, 73% from top half. 25 valedictorians. Full-time: 2,822 students, 52% women, 48% men. Part-time: 854 students, 63% women, 37% men. Students come from 36 states and territories, 40 other countries, 26% from out-of-state. 30% American Indian or Alaska Native, non-Hispanic/Latino; 3% Hispanic/Latino; 7% African American, non-Hispanic/Latino; 1% Asian, non-Hispanic/Latino; 0.4% Native Hawaiian or other Pacific Islander, non-Hispanic/Latino; 3% international. 34% 25 or older, 19% live on campus, 11% transferred in. Retention: 57% of full-time freshmen returned the following year. Academic areas with the most degrees conferred: education; engineering technologies; liberal arts/general studies. Core. Calendar: semesters. Academic remediation for entering students, services for LD students, advanced placement, accelerated degree program, honors program, independent study, distance learning, double major, summer session for credit, part-time degree program, adult/continuing education programs, internships, graduate courses open to undergrads. Off campus study at Ardmore Higher Education Center, E.T. Dunlap Higher Education Center, Tinker AFB, OKCCC.

Entrance Requirements: Open admission for adults over 21. Required: high school transcript, SAT or ACT. Required for some: interview. Entrance: moderately difficult. Application deadline: Rolling. Notification: continuous.

Costs Per Year: Application fee: $20. State resident tuition: $4427 full-time, $147.55 per credit hour part-time. Nonresident tuition: $12,162 full-time, $257.85 per credit hour part-time. Mandatory fees: $633 full-time, $21.10 per credit hour part-time. Full-time tuition and fees vary according to course level. Part-time tuition and fees vary according to course level and course load. College room and board: $4970. College room only: $2200. Room and board charges vary according to board plan and housing facility.

Collegiate Environment: Orientation program. Drama-theater group, choral group, marching band, student-run newspaper, radio station. Social organizations: 68 open to all; national fraternities, national sororities; 1% of eligible men and 1% of eligible women are members. Most popular organizations: Baptist Collegiate Ministries, Greek Community, Wesley Center, Resident Hall Association. Major annual events: Springfest, Homecoming, Welcome Week/Parent's Day. Student services: health clinic, personal-psychological counseling. Campus security: 24-hour emergency response devices and patrols, late night transport-escort service, controlled dormitory access. 804 college housing spaces available; 624 were occupied in 2012-13. Freshmen guaranteed college housing. On-campus residence required in freshman year. Options: coed, men-only, women-only housing available. Henry B. Bennett Memorial Library with 312,445 books, 589,978 microform titles, 1,152 serials, 10,333 audiovisual materials, an OPAC, and a Web page. Operations spending for the previous fiscal year: $1.2 million. 598 computers available on campus for general student use. A campuswide network can be accessed from student residence rooms. Students can access the following: online class registration, campus Blackboard classes. Staffed computer lab on campus.

Community Environment: Durant is a rural community served by bus line and airport. The community has one hospital, Medical Center of Southeastern Oklahoma, and active civic, fraternal, and veteran's organizations. There are libraries, churches, and motels. Local recreational facilities include hunting, boating, fishing, golf and other sports.

■ SOUTHERN NAZARENE UNIVERSITY
6729 NW 39th Expy.
Bethany, OK 73008
Tel: (405)789-6400; Free: 800-648-9899
Fax: (405)491-6381
E-mail: admiss@snu.edu
Web Site: www.snu.edu/

Description: Independent Nazarene, comprehensive, coed. Awards associate, bachelor's, and master's degrees. Founded 1899. Setting: 40-acre suburban campus with easy access to Oklahoma City. Endowment: $21.6 million. Educational spending for the previous fiscal year: $8446 per student. Total enrollment: 2,184. Faculty: 189 (69 full-time, 120 part-time). Student-undergrad faculty ratio is 18:1. 988 applied, 49% were admitted. 19% from top 10% of their high school class, 44% from top quarter, 75% from top half. 2 National Merit Scholars, 10 valedictorians. Full-time: 1,643 students, 53% women, 47% men. Part-time: 59 students, 56% women, 44% men. Students come from 33 states and territories, 33 other countries, 23% from out-of-state. 6% American Indian or Alaska Native, non-Hispanic/Latino; 6% Hispanic/Latino; 15% African American, non-Hispanic/Latino; 3% Asian, non-Hispanic/Latino; 0.5% Native Hawaiian or other Pacific Islander, non-Hispanic/Latino; 3% international. 33% 25 or older, 71% live on campus, 5% transferred in. Retention: 58% of full-time freshmen returned the following year. Academic areas with the most degrees conferred: business/marketing; family and consumer sciences; health professions and related sciences. Core. Calendar: semesters. Academic remediation for entering students, ESL program, services for LD students, advanced placement, accelerated degree program, self-designed majors, honors program, independent study, distance learning, double major, summer session for credit, part-time degree program, external degree program, adult/continuing education programs, internships, graduate courses open to undergrads. Off campus study at Christian College Coalition Council for Christian Colleges and Universities. Study abroad program. ROTC: Army (c), Air Force (c).

Entrance Requirements: Open admission. Options: electronic application, deferred admission, international baccalaureate accepted. Required: high school transcript, minimum 2 high school GPA, 2 recommendations, interview, SAT or ACT. Recommended: ACT. Entrance: noncompetitive. Application deadline: 8/15. Notification: continuous.

Costs Per Year: Application fee: $35. Comprehensive fee: $28,774 includes full-time tuition ($20,550), mandatory fees ($624), and college room and board ($7600). Room and board charges vary according to board plan and housing facility. Part-time tuition: $639 per credit hour. Part-time tuition varies according to course load.

Collegiate Environment: Orientation program. Drama-theater group, choral group, student-run newspaper. Social organizations: 30 open to all. Most popular organizations: Business Gaming Team, Campus Social Life Committee, intramural sports societies, Choral Society, Inter-Club. Major annual events: Lip Sync Contest, Homecoming, Pow-Wow Weekend. Student services: health clinic, personal-psychological counseling. Campus security: 24-hour emergency response devices, student patrols, late night transport-escort service, controlled dormitory access. 828 college housing spaces available; 799 were occupied in 2012-13. Freshmen guaranteed college housing. On-campus residence required through senior year. Options: men-only, women-only housing available. R. T. Williams Learning Resources Center with 101,117 books, 8 microform titles, 41,048 serials, 8,033 audiovisual materials, an OPAC, and a Web page. Operations spending for the previous fiscal year: $391,464. 120 computers available on campus for general student use. Computer purchase/lease plans available. A computer is required for all students. A campuswide network can be accessed from student residence rooms and from off campus. Staffed computer lab on campus.

Community Environment: Bethany is a metropolitan community in central Oklahoma with a mild climate. Located on U.S. Highway 66, eight miles from Will Rogers Airport, the city also has train service. The community includes active churches, a Chamber of Commerce, nearby health centers and hospitals, and numerous motels. Unusual job opportunities are available for students.

■ SOUTHWESTERN CHRISTIAN UNIVERSITY

PO Box 340
Bethany, OK 73008-0340
Tel: (405)789-7661
E-mail: admissions@swcu.edu
Web Site: www.swcu.edu/

Description: Independent, comprehensive, coed, affiliated with Pentecostal Holiness Church. Awards associate, bachelor's, and master's degrees. Founded 1946. Setting: 7-acre suburban campus with easy access to Oklahoma City. Total enrollment: 450. Student-undergrad faculty ratio is 15:1. 2 valedictorians. Students come from 12 other countries. 30% 25 or older, 50% live on campus. Core. Calendar: semesters. Academic remediation for entering students, advanced placement, distance learning, double major, summer session for credit, part-time degree program, internships, graduate courses open to undergrads. Off campus study at Southern Nazarene University, Rhema Bible Training Center. ROTC: Army (c).

Entrance Requirements: Options: electronic application, early admission, deferred admission. Required: essay, high school transcript, minimum 2.5 high school GPA, 19 ACT or 900 SAT, top 50% rank in class, SAT or ACT. Recommended: interview. Entrance: minimally difficult. Application deadlines: Rolling, Rolling for nonresidents. Notification: continuous, continuous for nonresidents. SAT Reasoning Test deadline: 8/15. SAT Subject Test deadline: 8/15. Transfer credits accepted: Yes.

Costs Per Year: Application fee: $0. Comprehensive fee: $16,560 includes full-time tuition ($11,060), mandatory fees ($500), and college room and board ($5000). Full-time tuition and fees vary according to class time, course load, location, and program. Room and board charges vary according to housing facility. Part-time tuition: $395 per credit hour. Part-time mandatory fees: $250 per term. Part-time tuition and fees vary according to class time, course load, location, and program.

Collegiate Environment: Orientation program. Drama-theater group, choral group. Major annual events: Spring Banquet, Culture Dinner, Chrismon Service. Student services: personal-psychological counseling. Campus security: 24-hour emergency response devices and patrols, student patrols. Springer Learning Center with 38,900 books and 100 serials. 12 computers available on campus for general student use. A campuswide network can be accessed from student residence rooms. Students can access the following: online class registration. Staffed computer lab on campus provides training in use of computers, software, and the Internet.

■ SOUTHWESTERN OKLAHOMA STATE UNIVERSITY

100 Campus Dr.
Weatherford, OK 73096-3098
Tel: (580)772-6611
Fax: (580)774-3795
E-mail: ropers@swosu.edu
Web Site: www.swosu.edu/

Description: State-supported, comprehensive, coed. Awards associate, bachelor's, master's, and doctoral degrees. Founded 1901. Setting: small town campus. Total enrollment: 5,340. Faculty: 234 (215 full-time, 19 part-time). Student-undergrad faculty ratio is 21:1. 1,717 applied, 92% were admitted. 20% from top 10% of their high school class, 44% from top quarter, 76% from top half. Full-time: 3,699 students, 55% women, 45% men. Part-time: 818 students, 69% women, 31% men. 13% from out-of-state. 6% American Indian or Alaska Native, non-Hispanic/Latino; 6% Hispanic/Latino; 6% African American, non-Hispanic/Latino; 2% Asian, non-Hispanic/Latino; 0.4% Native Hawaiian or other Pacific Islander, non-Hispanic/Latino; 2% international. 21% 25 or older, 24% live on campus, 10% transferred in. Retention: 57% of full-time freshmen returned the following year. Academic areas with the most degrees conferred: health professions and related sciences; business/marketing; education. Calendar: semesters. Part-time degree program, adult/continuing education programs.

Entrance Requirements: Option: deferred admission. Required: high school transcript, minimum 2 high school GPA, SAT or ACT. Recommended: ACT. Entrance: minimally difficult. Application deadline: Rolling. Notification: continuous. Preference given to state residents.

Costs Per Year: Application fee: $15. State resident tuition: $4755 full-time. Nonresident tuition: $11,265 full-time. Full-time tuition varies according to program. College room and board: $4240. College room only: $1800. Room and board charges vary according to board plan.

Collegiate Environment: Orientation program. Campus security: late night transport-escort service, controlled dormitory access, 20-hour campus emergency security.

■ SOUTHWESTERN OKLAHOMA STATE UNIVERSITY AT SAYRE

409 E Mississippi St.
Sayre, OK 73662-1236
Tel: (580)928-5533
E-mail: kim.seymour@swosu.edu
Web Site: www.swosu.edu/sayre/

Description: State and locally supported, 2-year, coed. Part of Southwestern Oklahoma State University. Awards diplomas, transfer associate, and terminal associate degrees. Founded 1938. Setting: 6-acre rural campus. Total enrollment: 643. Faculty: 14 (all full-time). Student-undergrad faculty ratio is 18:1. Full-time: 258 students, 75% women, 25% men. Part-time: 385 students, 74% women, 26% men. 5% American Indian or Alaska Native, non-Hispanic/Latino; 6% Hispanic/Latino; 2% African American, non-Hispanic/Latino; 1% Asian, non-Hispanic/Latino; 0.5% Native Hawaiian or other Pacific Islander, non-Hispanic/Latino; 49% 25 or older. Core. Calendar: semesters. Academic remediation for entering students, services for LD students, advanced placement, independent study, distance learning, summer session for credit, part-time degree program, adult/continuing education programs, co-op programs.

Entrance Requirements: Open admission. Required: high school transcript. Required for some: ACT. Entrance: noncompetitive. Application deadline: Rolling.

Collegiate Environment: Oscar McMahan Library with 9,975 books, 45 serials, an OPAC, and a Web page. 100 computers available on campus for general student use. A campuswide network can be accessed. Students can access the following: online class registration. Staffed computer lab on campus.

■ SPARTAN COLLEGE OF AERONAUTICS AND TECHNOLOGY
8820 E Pine St.
Tulsa, OK 74158-2833
Tel: (918)836-6886; Free: 800-331-124
Web Site: www.spartan.edu/
Description: Proprietary, primarily 2-year, men only. Awards certificates, diplomas, terminal associate, and bachelor's degrees. Founded 1928. Setting: 26-acre urban campus. Total enrollment: 1,438. Student-undergrad faculty ratio is 14:1. 844 applied. Full-time: 1,438 students. 76% from out-of-state. 30% 25 or older, 0.2% transferred in. Retention: 66% of full-time freshmen returned the following year. Calendar: calendar terms. Honors program, independent study, co-op programs.
Entrance Requirements: Required: high school transcript. Recommended: interview. Entrance: noncompetitive. Application deadline: Rolling.

■ TULSA COMMUNITY COLLEGE
6111 E Skelly Dr.
Tulsa, OK 74135-6198
Tel: (918)595-7000
Fax: (918)595-7910
E-mail: lbrewer@tulsacc.edu
Web Site: www.tulsacc.edu/
Description: State-supported, 2-year, coed. Part of Oklahoma State Regents for Higher Education. Awards certificates, transfer associate, and terminal associate degrees. Founded 1968. Setting: 160-acre urban campus. Total enrollment: 19,730. Student-undergrad faculty ratio is 20:1. 1% from out-of-state. 43% 25 or older. Retention: 58% of full-time freshmen returned the following year. Core. Calendar: semesters. Academic remediation for entering students, ESL program, services for LD students, advanced placement, accelerated degree program, self-designed majors, freshman honors college, honors program, independent study, distance learning, summer session for credit, part-time degree program, external degree program, adult/continuing education programs, co-op programs and internships. Off campus study.
Entrance Requirements: Open admission except for honors, allied health programs. Option: early admission. Required: high school transcript. Entrance: noncompetitive. Application deadline: Rolling.
Collegiate Environment: Orientation program. Drama-theater group, student-run newspaper. Student services: health clinic, personal-psychological counseling, women's center. Campus security: 24-hour emergency response devices and patrols, student patrols, late night transport-escort service. Learning Resource Center with an OPAC and a Web page.

■ TULSA WELDING SCHOOL
2545 E 11th St.
Tulsa, OK 74104-3909
Tel: (918)587-6789; Free: 888-765-5555
Fax: (918)295-6821
E-mail: dburke@twsweld.com
Web Site: www.weldingschool.com/
Description: Proprietary, 2-year, coed. Administratively affiliated with Tulsa Welding School, Jacksonville Branch. Awards diplomas, transfer associate, and terminal associate degrees. Founded 1949. Setting: 5-acre urban campus. Total enrollment: 604. Faculty: 17 (all full-time). Student-undergrad faculty ratio is 18:1. 37% 25 or older. Core. Calendar: continuous (phased start every 3 weeks).
Entrance Requirements: Entrance: noncompetitive.
Collegiate Environment: Orientation program. Campus security: 24-hour emergency response devices. Technical Resource Center with 403 books and 3 serials. 3 computers available on campus for general student use. A campuswide network can be accessed.

■ UNIVERSITY OF CENTRAL OKLAHOMA
100 N University Dr.
Edmond, OK 73034-5209
Tel: (405)974-2000
Fax: (405)974-4964
E-mail: admituco@uco.edu

Web Site: www.uco.edu/
Description: State-supported, comprehensive, coed. Part of Oklahoma State Regents for Higher Education. Awards associate, bachelor's, and master's degrees. Founded 1890. Setting: 200-acre suburban campus with easy access to Oklahoma City. Endowment: $8.6 million. Research spending for the previous fiscal year: $762,273. Educational spending for the previous fiscal year: $3872 per student. Total enrollment: 17,211. Faculty: 1,024 (461 full-time, 563 part-time). Student-undergrad faculty ratio is 19:1. 4,784 applied, 79% were admitted. 2% from top 10% of their high school class, 7% from top quarter, 25% from top half. 62 valedictorians. Full-time: 11,010 students, 55% women, 45% men. Part-time: 4,369 students, 59% women, 41% men. Students come from 50 states and territories, 91 other countries, 4% from out-of-state. 4% American Indian or Alaska Native, non-Hispanic/Latino; 7% Hispanic/Latino; 9% African American, non-Hispanic/Latino; 3% Asian, non-Hispanic/Latino; 0.2% Native Hawaiian or other Pacific Islander, non-Hispanic/Latino; 7% international. 23% 25 or older, 12% live on campus, 12% transferred in. Retention: 65% of full-time freshmen returned the following year. Academic areas with the most degrees conferred: business/marketing; liberal arts/general studies; education. Core. Calendar: semesters. ESL program, services for LD students, advanced placement, accelerated degree program, honors program, independent study, distance learning, double major, summer session for credit, part-time degree program, internships. ROTC: Army.
Entrance Requirements: Options: electronic application, deferred admission. Required: high school transcript, minimum 2.7 high school GPA, rank in upper 50% of high school class, SAT or ACT. Recommended: SAT, ACT. Required for some: SAT and SAT Subject Tests or ACT. Entrance: minimally difficult. Application deadlines: Rolling, Rolling for nonresidents. Notification: continuous, continuous for nonresidents. SAT Reasoning Test deadline: 8/25. Transfer credits accepted: Yes.
Costs Per Year: Application fee: $40. State resident tuition: $4,460 full-time, $148.65 per credit hour part-time. Nonresident tuition: $12,135 full-time, $404.50 per credit hour part-time. Mandatory fees: $632 full-time, $21.05 per credit hour part-time. Full-time tuition and fees vary according to course load, degree level, and program. Part-time tuition and fees vary according to course load, degree level, and program. College room and board: $6708. Room and board charges vary according to board plan and housing facility. Tuition guaranteed not to increase for student's term of enrollment.
Collegiate Environment: Orientation program. Drama-theater group, choral group, marching band, student-run newspaper, radio station. Social organizations: national fraternities, national sororities; 3% of eligible men and 5% of eligible women are members. Most popular organizations: Student Government Association, Student Programming Board, International Student Council, Panhellenic Council, Interfraternity Council. Major annual events: Stampede Week, Homecoming, Greek Week. Student services: health clinic, personal-psychological counseling. Campus security: 24-hour emergency response devices and patrols, late night transport-escort service. 1,700 college housing spaces available; 1,352 were occupied in 2012-13. No special consideration for freshman housing applicants. Options: coed, men-only, women-only housing available. Max Chambers Library plus 1 other with 526,153 books, 578,619 microform titles, 125,692 serials, 39,845 audiovisual materials, an OPAC, and a Web page. Operations spending for the previous fiscal year: $3.7 million. 88 computers available on campus for general student use. A campuswide network can be accessed from student residence rooms and from off campus. Students can access the following: online class registration. Staffed computer lab on campus.
Community Environment: Edmond is a suburban city 12 miles north of Oklahoma City. All modes of transportation are available to the community. Edmond has churches of most denominations, a movie theatre, numerous parks, a swimming pool, and shopping centers. Part-time employment is plentiful.

■ UNIVERSITY OF OKLAHOMA
660 Parrington Oval
Norman, OK 73019-0390
Tel: (405)325-0311; Free: 800-234-6868
Fax: (405)325-7478
E-mail: ou-pss@ou.edu
Web Site: www.ou.edu/
Description: State-supported, university, coed. Awards bachelor's, master's, and doctoral degrees. Founded 1890. Setting: 3,153-acre suburban campus with easy access to Oklahoma City. Endowment: $784.8 million. Research spending for the previous fiscal year: $94.2 million. Educational spending for the previous fiscal year: $9790 per student. Total enrollment: 27,507.

Faculty: 1,403 (1,152 full-time, 251 part-time). Student-undergrad faculty ratio is 19:1. 11,650 applied, 79% were admitted. 33% from top 10% of their high school class, 66% from top quarter, 93% from top half. 191 National Merit Scholars, 276 valedictorians. Full-time: 18,104 students, 50% women, 50% men. Part-time: 3,005 students, 47% women, 53% men. Students come from 54 states and territories, 111 other countries, 31% from out-of-state. 5% American Indian or Alaska Native, non-Hispanic/Latino; 7% Hispanic/Latino; 5% African American, non-Hispanic/Latino; 5% Asian, non-Hispanic/Latino; 0.2% Native Hawaiian or other Pacific Islander, non-Hispanic/Latino; 5% international. 13% 25 or older, 32% live on campus, 6% transferred in. Retention: 85% of full-time freshmen returned the following year. Academic areas with the most degrees conferred: business/marketing; interdisciplinary studies; communication/journalism; engineering. Core. Calendar: semesters. Academic remediation for entering students, ESL program, services for LD students, advanced placement, accelerated degree program, self-designed majors, freshman honors college, honors program, independent study, distance learning, double major, summer session for credit, part-time degree program, external degree program, adult/continuing education programs, co-op programs and internships, graduate courses open to undergrads. Off campus study. Study abroad program. ROTC: Army, Naval, Air Force.

Entrance Requirements: Options: electronic application, international baccalaureate accepted. Required: essay, high school transcript, 15 specified curricular units, SAT or ACT. Recommended: 1 recommendation. Entrance: moderately difficult. Application deadlines: 4/1, 4/1 for nonresidents. Notification: continuous, continuous for nonresidents. Transfer credits accepted: Yes. Applicants placed on waiting list: 2,878. Wait-listed applicants offered admission: 2,093.

Costs Per Year: Application fee: $40. State resident tuition: $3957 full-time, $131.90 per credit hour part-time. Nonresident tuition: $15,594 full-time, $519.80 per credit hour part-time. Mandatory fees: $3384 full-time, $104.35 per credit hour part-time, $126.50 per term part-time. Full-time tuition and fees vary according to course load, location, program, and reciprocity agreements. Part-time tuition and fees vary according to course load, location, program, and reciprocity agreements. College room and board: $8382. College room only: $4588. Room and board charges vary according to board plan and housing facility. Tuition guaranteed not to increase for student's term of enrollment.

Collegiate Environment: Orientation program. Drama-theater group, choral group, marching band, student-run newspaper, radio station. Social organizations: 467 open to all; national fraternities, national sororities, local fraternities, local sororities; 22% of eligible men and 28% of eligible women are members. Most popular organizations: Campus Activities Council, University of Oklahoma Student Association, OU Cousins, Fraternities/Sororities, The Big Event. Major annual events: The Big Event, Homecoming, Parents and Family Weekend. Student services: legal services, health clinic, personal-psychological counseling, women's center. Campus security: 24-hour emergency response devices and patrols, student patrols, late night transport-escort service, controlled dormitory access, crime prevention programs, police bicycle patrols, self-defense classes. 5,848 college housing spaces available; 4,969 were occupied in 2012-13. Freshmen guaranteed college housing. On-campus residence required in freshman year. Options: coed, men-only, women-only housing available. Bizzell Memorial Library plus 6 others with 5.4 million books, 4.5 million microform titles, 100,157 serials, 7,832 audiovisual materials, an OPAC, and a Web page. Operations spending for the previous fiscal year: $18.7 million. 4,500 computers available on campus for general student use. Computer purchase/lease plans available. A campuswide network can be accessed from student residence rooms and from off campus. Students can access the following: online class registration. Staffed computer lab on campus provides training in use of computers, software, and the Internet.

Community Environment: Norman is a mid-sized city in central Oklahoma with award-winning public schools; cultural offerings, such as theaters and museums; community services including churches, hospitals, a public library; and recreational facilities, including parks, golf courses and nearby Lake Thunderbird. The community is served by major highways, bus lines, and Will Rogers World Airport, located 18 miles north in Oklahoma City. The university operates Max Westheimer Airpark, a general aviation, reliever category airport in Norman.

■ **UNIVERSITY OF OKLAHOMA HEALTH SCIENCES CENTER**
PO Box 26901
Oklahoma City, OK 73190
Tel: (405)271-4000
Fax: (405)271-2480

E-mail: scott-boeh@ouhsc.edu
Web Site: www.ouhsc.edu/
Description: State-supported, upper-level, coed. Part of University of Oklahoma. Awards bachelor's, master's, and doctoral degrees and post-master's certificates. Founded 1890. Setting: 200-acre urban campus with easy access to Oklahoma City. Endowment: $377.5 million. Research spending for the previous fiscal year: $78.7 million. Educational spending for the previous fiscal year: $40 per student. Total enrollment: 3,583. Faculty: 448 (318 full-time, 130 part-time). Student-undergrad faculty ratio is 8:1. Full-time: 827 students, 88% women, 12% men. Part-time: 48 students, 75% women, 25% men. Students come from 47 states and territories, 15 other countries, 13% from out-of-state. 5% American Indian or Alaska Native, non-Hispanic/Latino; 7% Hispanic/Latino; 3% African American, non-Hispanic/Latino; 4% Asian, non-Hispanic/Latino; 0% Native Hawaiian or other Pacific Islander, non-Hispanic/Latino; 0.5% international. 39% 25 or older, 16% live on campus, 46% transferred in. Academic areas with the most degrees conferred: health professions and related sciences; interdisciplinary studies. Calendar: semesters. Advanced placement, honors program, distance learning, summer session for credit, part-time degree program, internships, graduate courses open to undergrads. ROTC: Army (c), Air Force (c).

Costs Per Year: State resident tuition: $3957 full-time, $131.90 per credit hour part-time. Nonresident tuition: $15,594 full-time, $519.80 per semester hour part-time. Mandatory fees: $2095 full-time, $53.95 per credit hour part-time, $238.25 per term part-time. Full-time tuition and fees vary according to course level, course load, degree level, location, program, and student level. Part-time tuition and fees vary according to course level, course load, degree level, location, program, and student level.

Collegiate Environment: Orientation program. Student-run newspaper. Social organizations: 25 open to all; Local chapter of a national fraternity. Most popular organizations: Health Sciences Center Student Association, College of Nursing Student Association, College of Medicine Student Association, Pharmacy Student Counsel, College of Allied Health Student Association. Major annual events: Intramural Sports (programmed through HSC Student Affairs), Campus Activities Board Events, DeStress Fest (programmed by HSC Student Counseling Services). Student services: health clinic, personal-psychological counseling, women's center. Campus security: 24-hour emergency response devices and patrols, late night transport-escort service. 151 college housing spaces available; 19 were occupied in 2012-13. Option: coed housing available. Robert M. Bird Health Sciences Library plus 2 others with 335,340 books, 650 microform titles, 4,941 serials, 6,468 audiovisual materials, an OPAC, and a Web page. Operations spending for the previous fiscal year: $4.9 million. 140 computers available on campus for general student use. Computer purchase/lease plans available. A campuswide network can be accessed from student residence rooms and from off campus. Students can access the following: online class registration, online bursar bill and payment. Staffed computer lab on campus provides training in use of computers, software, and the Internet.

Community Environment: See Oklahoma City University.

■ **UNIVERSITY OF PHOENIX–OKLAHOMA CITY CAMPUS**
6501 N Broadway, Ste. 100
Oklahoma City, OK 73116-8244
Tel: (405)842-8007; Free: 866-766-0766
Web Site: www.phoenix.edu/
Description: Proprietary, comprehensive, coed. Awards bachelor's and master's degrees. Founded 1976. Setting: urban campus. Total enrollment: 801. Faculty: 135 (16 full-time, 119 part-time). Student-undergrad faculty ratio is 13:1. 58 applied, 100% were admitted. 80% 25 or older. Academic areas with the most degrees conferred: business/marketing; computer and information sciences; homeland security, law enforcement, firefighting, and protective services. Core. Calendar: continuous. Services for LD students, advanced placement, accelerated degree program, independent study, distance learning, external degree program, adult/continuing education programs, graduate courses open to undergrads.

Entrance Requirements: Open admission. Options: electronic application, deferred admission. Required: 1 recommendation. Required for some: high school transcript. Entrance: noncompetitive. Application deadline: Rolling.

Collegiate Environment: Campus security: late night transport-escort service. University Library with 16,781 serials, an OPAC, and a Web page. Operations spending for the previous fiscal year: $6.8 million.

■ **UNIVERSITY OF PHOENIX–TULSA CAMPUS**
14002 E 21st St.
Ste. 1000

Tulsa, OK 74134-1412
Tel: (918)622-4877; Free: 866-766-0766
Web Site: www.phoenix.edu/
Description: Proprietary, comprehensive, coed. Awards bachelor's and master's degrees. Founded 1998. Setting: urban campus. Total enrollment: 785. Faculty: 155 (16 full-time, 139 part-time). Full-time: 703 students, 66% women, 34% men. 81% 25 or older. Academic areas with the most degrees conferred: business/marketing; computer and information sciences; homeland security, law enforcement, firefighting, and protective services. Core. Calendar: continuous. Services for LD students, advanced placement, accelerated degree program, independent study, distance learning, external degree program, adult/continuing education programs, graduate courses open to undergrads.
Entrance Requirements: Open admission. Options: electronic application, deferred admission. Required: 1 recommendation. Required for some: high school transcript. Entrance: noncompetitive. Application deadline: Rolling.
Collegiate Environment: Campus security: late night transport-escort service. University Library with 16,781 serials, an OPAC, and a Web page. Operations spending for the previous fiscal year: $6.8 million.

■ **UNIVERSITY OF SCIENCE AND ARTS OF OKLAHOMA**
1727 W Alabama
Chickasha, OK 73018
Tel: (405)224-3140; Free: 800-933-8726
Fax: (405)574-1220
E-mail: usao-admissions@usao.edu
Web Site: www.usao.edu/
Description: State-supported, 4-year, coed. Part of Oklahoma State Regents for Higher Education. Awards bachelor's degrees. Founded 1908. Setting: 75-acre small town campus with easy access to Oklahoma City. Research spending for the previous fiscal year: $156,858. Educational spending for the previous fiscal year: $5086 per student. Total enrollment: 983. Faculty: 89 (55 full-time, 34 part-time). Student-undergrad faculty ratio is 13:1. 597 applied, 39% were admitted. 23% from top 10% of their high school class, 55% from top quarter, 81% from top half. Full-time: 863 students, 65% women, 35% men. Part-time: 120 students, 63% women, 38% men. Students come from 24 states and territories, 19 other countries, 8% from out-of-state. 13% American Indian or Alaska Native, non-Hispanic/Latino; 5% Hispanic/Latino; 4% African American, non-Hispanic/Latino; 1% Asian, non-Hispanic/Latino; 0% Native Hawaiian or other Pacific Islander, non-Hispanic/Latino; 6% international. 22% 25 or older, 44% live on campus, 11% transferred in. Retention: 60% of full-time freshmen returned the following year. Academic areas with the most degrees conferred: education; business/marketing; visual and performing arts. Core. Calendar: trimesters. Academic remediation for entering students, services for LD students, advanced placement, accelerated degree program, self-designed majors, independent study, double major, summer session for credit, part-time degree program, internships. Off campus study.
Entrance Requirements: Options: electronic application, deferred admission. Required: SAT or ACT. Recommended: Option 1: ACT of 24 and (3.0 GPA or top 50% HS Class), Option 2: 3.0 GPA and top 25% HS Class, Option 3: 3.0 GPA in 15-unit HS core and ACT of 22. Required for some: high school transcript, minimum 3 high school GPA, Option 1: ACT of 24 and (3.0 GPA or top 50% HS Class), Option 2: 3.0 GPA and top 25% HS Class, Option 3: 3.0 GPA in 15-unit HS core and ACT of 22. Entrance: moderately difficult. Application deadlines: 9/2, 9/2 for nonresidents. Notification: continuous until 1/2, continuous until 1/2 for nonresidents. SAT Reasoning Test deadline: 9/1. SAT Subject Test deadline: 9/1. Transfer credits accepted: Yes.
Costs Per Year: Application fee: $40. State resident tuition: $4230 full-time, $141 per credit hour part-time. Nonresident tuition: $11,550 full-time, $385 per credit hour part-time. Mandatory fees: $1170 full-time, $39 per credit hour part-time. College room and board: $5160. College room only: $2680. Room and board charges vary according to board plan and housing facility. Tuition guaranteed not to increase for student's term of enrollment.
Collegiate Environment: Orientation program. Drama-theater group, choral group, student-run newspaper. Social organizations: 24 open to all; national fraternities, local sororities; 1% of eligible men and 1% of eligible women are members. Most popular organizations: Student Activities Board, Volunteer Action Council, Psychology Club, Young Democrats, Young Conservatives. Major annual events: Montmartre Festival/Droverstock, Festival of Arts and Ideas, Drover Difference Day. Student services: health clinic, personal-psychological counseling. Campus security: 24-hour emergency response devices and patrols, controlled dormitory access. 504 college housing

spaces available; 431 were occupied in 2012-13. Freshmen guaranteed college housing. On-campus residence required in freshman year. Option: coed housing available. Nash Library with 69,010 books, 72,375 microform titles, 82,980 serials, 2,853 audiovisual materials, an OPAC, and a Web page. Operations spending for the previous fiscal year: $399,660. 175 computers available on campus for general student use. A campuswide network can be accessed from student residence rooms. Staffed computer lab on campus provides training in use of computers, software, and the Internet.
Community Environment: Chickasha is a suburban area southwest of Oklahoma City. Located in the fertile Washita River Valley, the city lies within one of the largest gas fields in the world. The community has rail, bus, and air service. The community includes Catholic and Protestant churches, a hospital, a public library, and major civic, fraternal, and veteran's organizations. Local recreational facilities include theatres and several good lakes within a few miles for boating, fishing and water sports. Some part-time employment is available for students.

■ **UNIVERSITY OF TULSA**
800 S Tucker Dr.
Tulsa, OK 74104-3189
Tel: (918)631-2000; Free: 800-331-3050
Fax: (918)631-2247
E-mail: admission@utulsa.edu
Web Site: www.utulsa.edu/
Description: Independent, university, coed, affiliated with Presbyterian Church (U.S.A.). Awards bachelor's, master's, and doctoral degrees. Founded 1894. Setting: 209-acre urban campus with easy access to Oklahoma City. Endowment: $802.5 million. Research spending for the previous fiscal year: $18.7 million. Educational spending for the previous fiscal year: $15,933 per student. Total enrollment: 4,326. Faculty: 404 (318 full-time, 86 part-time). Student-undergrad faculty ratio is 11:1. 6,984 applied, 41% were admitted. 72% from top 10% of their high school class, 86% from top quarter, 98% from top half. 48 National Merit Scholars, 23 valedictorians. Full-time: 3,007 students, 43% women, 57% men. Part-time: 153 students, 46% women, 54% men. Students come from 42 states and territories, 53 other countries, 47% from out-of-state. 4% American Indian or Alaska Native, non-Hispanic/Latino; 4% Hispanic/Latino; 5% African American, non-Hispanic/Latino; 3% Asian, non-Hispanic/Latino; 0.03% Native Hawaiian or other Pacific Islander, non-Hispanic/Latino; 22% international. 6% 25 or older, 74% live on campus, 4% transferred in. Retention: 86% of full-time freshmen returned the following year. Academic areas with the most degrees conferred: business/marketing; engineering; visual and performing arts. Core. Calendar: semesters. ESL program, services for LD students, advanced placement, accelerated degree program, self-designed majors, honors program, independent study, double major, summer session for credit, part-time degree program, adult/continuing education programs, internships, graduate courses open to undergrads. Study abroad program. ROTC: Air Force (c).
Entrance Requirements: Options: electronic application, early admission, early action, deferred admission, international baccalaureate accepted. Required: essay, high school transcript, 1 recommendation, interview, SAT or ACT. Recommended: minimum 3 high school GPA. Entrance: very difficult. Application deadlines: Rolling, Rolling for nonresidents, 11/1 for early action. Notification: continuous, continuous for nonresidents, 11/22 for early action. SAT Reasoning Test deadline: 8/1. Transfer credits accepted: Yes. Applicants placed on waiting list: 320. Wait-listed applicants offered admission: 320.
Costs Per Year: Application fee: $50. One-time mandatory fee: $485. Comprehensive fee: $44,826 includes full-time tuition ($34,030), mandatory fees ($320), and college room and board ($10,476). College room only: $5800. Full-time tuition and fees vary according to course load. Room and board charges vary according to board plan and housing facility. Part-time tuition: $1221 per credit. Part-time tuition varies according to course load.
Collegiate Environment: Orientation program. Drama-theater group, choral group, marching band, student-run newspaper, radio station. Social organizations: 168 open to all; national fraternities, national sororities; 21% of eligible men and 23% of eligible women are members. Most popular organizations: Student Association, Residence Hall Association, Pre-Professional organizations, intramural sports, Greek life. Major annual events: Homecoming, Springfest, Parents' Weekend. Student services: health clinic, personal-psychological counseling, women's center. Campus security: 24-hour emergency response devices and patrols, late night transport-escort service, controlled dormitory access. 2,502 college housing spaces available; 2,302 were occupied in 2012-13. Freshmen guaranteed

college housing. On-campus residence required through sophomore year. Options: coed, men-only, women-only housing available. McFarlin Library plus 1 other with 1.2 million books, 3.4 million microform titles, 57,304 serials, 23,101 audiovisual materials, an OPAC, and a Web page. Operations spending for the previous fiscal year: $5.3 million. 900 computers available on campus for general student use. Computer purchase/lease plans available. A campuswide network can be accessed from student residence rooms and from off campus. Students can access the following: online class registration. Staffed computer lab on campus (open 24 hours a day) provides training in use of computers, software, and the Internet.

Community Environment: The climate is temperate. The average year-round high temperature is 71 degrees. The population is 382,400. The city features a professional opera company, a national ballet company, a symphony orchestra, museums, art galleries, community theatres, parks, minor league teams in hockey and baseball and recreation and shopping facilities. Public bus transportation is available.

■ **VATTEROTT COLLEGE (TULSA)**
4343 S 118th E Ave., Ste. A
Tulsa, OK 74146
Tel: (918)835-8288; Free: 888-553-6627
Fax: (918)836-9698
E-mail: tulsa@vatterott-college.edu
Web Site: www.vatterott.edu/
Description: Proprietary, 2-year, coed. Part of Vatterott Educational Centers, Inc. Awards diplomas and terminal associate degrees. Setting: 3-acre urban campus. Total enrollment: 146. Faculty: 21 (10 full-time, 11 part-time). Student-undergrad faculty ratio is 12:1. Full-time: 146 students, 38% women, 62% men. 62% 25 or older. Calendar: semesters.
Entrance Requirements: Required: high school transcript.
Collegiate Environment: Orientation program. 10 computers available on campus for general student use. Staffed computer lab on campus provides training in use of computers, software, and the Internet.

■ **VATTEROTT COLLEGE (WARR ACRES)**
5537 NW Expy.
Warr Acres, OK 73132
Tel: (405)234-3600; Free: 888-553-6627
E-mail: mark.hybers@vatterott-college.edu
Web Site: www.vatterott.edu/
Description: Proprietary, 2-year, coed. Awards diplomas, terminal associate, and doctoral degrees. Setting: urban campus. Total enrollment: 367. Faculty: 36 (15 full-time, 21 part-time). Student-undergrad faculty ratio is 11:1. 154 applied, 57% were admitted. 0% from out-of-state. Calendar: semesters.
Entrance Requirements: Required: essay, high school transcript, interview. Entrance: noncompetitive.

Collegiate Environment: Campus security: 24-hour emergency response devices and patrols. 50 computers available on campus for general student use.

■ **WESTERN OKLAHOMA STATE COLLEGE**
2801 N Main St.
Altus, OK 73521-1397
Tel: (580)477-2000
Fax: (580)477-7723
E-mail: larry.paxton@wosc.edu
Web Site: www.wosc.edu/
Description: State-supported, 2-year, coed. Part of Oklahoma State Regents for Higher Education. Awards certificates, transfer associate, and terminal associate degrees. Founded 1926. Setting: 142-acre rural campus. Endowment: $2.5 million. Educational spending for the previous fiscal year: $2376 per student. Total enrollment: 2,061. Faculty: 100 (37 full-time, 63 part-time). Student-undergrad faculty ratio is 20:1. 499 applied, 100% were admitted. 10% from top 10% of their high school class, 20% from top quarter, 50% from top half. 5 valedictorians. Full-time: 859 students, 55% women, 45% men. Part-time: 1,202 students, 60% women, 40% men. Students come from 30 states and territories, 1 other country. 65% 25 or older. Retention: 50% of full-time freshmen returned the following year. Core. Calendar: semesters. Academic remediation for entering students, services for LD students, advanced placement, self-designed majors, honors program, summer session for credit, part-time degree program, adult/continuing education programs. Off campus study at all state institutions in the Oklahoma Higher Education Televised Instructional System.
Entrance Requirements: Open admission. Options: electronic application, early admission. Required: high school transcript. Required for some: ACT. Entrance: noncompetitive. Application deadline: Rolling. Notification: continuous.
Collegiate Environment: Drama-theater group, choral group. Social organizations: national fraternities; 4% of men are members. Most popular organizations: Baptist Student Union, Phi Theta Kappa, Student Senate, Behavioral Science Club, Aggie Club. Major annual events: Homecoming, organizational competitions, basketball games. Student services: personal-psychological counseling. Campus security: 24-hour emergency response devices. Learning Resources Center with 33,000 books, 1,000 serials, an OPAC, and a Web page. Operations spending for the previous fiscal year: $254,402. 50 computers available on campus for general student use. A campuswide network can be accessed from student residence rooms and from off campus. Staffed computer lab on campus.
Community Environment: Altus is an urban community served by bus, railroad, and major interstate highways. The climate is temperate. The community has one hospital, a public library, many churches, and recreational facilities.

■ AMERICAN COLLEGE OF HEALTHCARE SCIENCES

5940 SW Hood Ave.

Portland, OR 97239-3719

Tel: (503)244-0726; Free: 800-487-8839

Fax: (503)244-0727

E-mail: achs@achs.edu

Web Site: www.achs.edu/

Description: Independent, 2-year, coed. Awards certificates, diplomas, terminal associate, and master's degrees. Setting: urban campus. Students come from 50 states and territories, 63 other countries. Retention: 92% of full-time freshmen returned the following year.

Entrance Requirements: Required: essay, high school transcript, standardized test scores, recommendation from Admissions Committee. Required for some: interview. Application deadline: Rolling.

■ THE ART INSTITUTE OF PORTLAND

1122 NW Davis St.

Portland, OR 97209

Tel: (503)228-6528; Free: 888-228-6528

Fax: (503)228-4227

Web Site: www.artinstitutes.edu/portland/

Description: Proprietary, 4-year, coed. Part of Education Management Corporation. Awards associate and bachelor's degrees. Founded 1963. Setting: urban campus.

■ BIRTHINGWAY COLLEGE OF MIDWIFERY

12113 SE Foster Rd.

Portland, OR 97299

Tel: (503)760-3131

E-mail: info@birthingway.edu

Web Site: www.birthingway.edu/

Description: Independent, upper-level, coed. Awards bachelor's degrees. Founded 1993. Total enrollment: 79. Student-undergrad faculty ratio is 10:1. 75% 25 or older. Calendar: 3 semesters.

■ BLUE MOUNTAIN COMMUNITY COLLEGE

2411 NW Carden Ave.

Pendleton, OR 97801-1000

Tel: (541)276-1260

Fax: (541)278-5886

E-mail: tbosworth@bluecc.edu

Web Site: www.bluecc.edu/

Description: State and locally supported, 2-year, coed. Awards certificates, transfer associate, and terminal associate degrees. Founded 1962. Setting: 170-acre rural campus. Total enrollment: 1,782. 51% 25 or older. Core. Academic remediation for entering students, ESL program, services for LD students, advanced placement, distance learning, summer session for credit, part-time degree program, adult/continuing education programs, co-op programs.

Entrance Requirements: Open admission. Option: electronic application. Required: high school transcript. Entrance: noncompetitive. Application deadline: Rolling. Notification: continuous.

Collegiate Environment: Orientation program. Drama-theater group, choral group. Student services: personal-psychological counseling. Blue Mountain Community College Library with 39,026 books, 2,644 microform titles, 271 serials, 1,879 audiovisual materials, an OPAC, and a Web page.

Community Environment: Pendleton, pop. 16,636, is bordered by the Blue Mountains, the Columbia River, and rolling wheat fields with and agriculturally based economy. It is approximately 200 miles from Portland, OR, Spokane, WA, and Boise, ID. Community facilities include a public library, churches of major denominations, a hospital, shopping, and many services and civic organizations. Pendleton is known nationally for its annual event, The Pendleton Roundup. Other activities include a symphony, art shows, and many organized sports for children and adults. For the recreationist, the area offers a wide variety of seasonal sports, including skiing, fishing, hiking, and hunting.

■ CENTRAL OREGON COMMUNITY COLLEGE

2600 NW College Way

Bend, OR 97701-5998

Tel: (541)383-7700

Fax: (541)383-7506

E-mail: welcome@metolius.cocc.edu

Web Site: www.cocc.edu/

Description: District-supported, 2-year, coed. Part of Oregon Community College Association. Awards certificates, transfer associate, and terminal associate degrees. Founded 1949. Setting: 193-acre small town campus. Endowment: $10 million. Total enrollment: 7,132. Faculty: 298 (119 full-time, 179 part-time). Student-undergrad faculty ratio is 25:1. 1,481 applied, 100% were admitted. Full-time: 3,184 students, 52% women, 48% men. Part-time: 3,948 students, 58% women, 42% men. Students come from 10 states and territories, 4% from out-of-state. 2% American Indian or Alaska Native, non-Hispanic/Latino; 7% Hispanic/Latino; 1% African American, non-Hispanic/Latino; 1% Asian, non-Hispanic/Latino; 0.4% Native Hawaiian or other Pacific Islander, non-Hispanic/Latino; 0% international. 48% 25 or older, 1% live on campus. Retention: 53% of full-time freshmen returned the following year. Core. Academic remediation for entering students, ESL program, self-designed majors, independent study, distance learning, double major, summer session for credit, part-time degree program, co-op programs and internships. Study abroad program. ROTC: Army (c).

Entrance Requirements: Open admission except for nursing, emergency medical technology, geographic information systems, medical assistant, dental assistant, fire science programs. Option: electronic application. Entrance: noncompetitive. Application deadline: Rolling. Notification: continuous. Preference given to district residents for nursing program.

Collegiate Environment: Orientation program. Drama-theater group, choral group, student-run newspaper. Social organizations: 25 open to all. Most popular organizations: club sports, student newspaper, Criminal Justice Club, Aviation Club. Major annual events: Graduation Ceremonies, Native American Spring Festival, Jungle Run/Storm the Stairs. Student services: personal-psychological counseling. Campus security: 24-hour emergency response devices and patrols, late night transport-escort service. 100 college housing spaces available; all were occupied in 2012-13. No special consideration for freshman housing applicants. Option: coed housing available. COCC Library plus 1 other with 76,421 books, 114,539 microform titles, 329 serials, 3,570 audiovisual materials, an OPAC, and a Web page. 700 computers available on campus for general student use. A campuswide network can be accessed from student residence rooms and from off campus. Students can access the following: online class registration. Staffed computer lab on campus.

Community Environment: Bend is an extremely scenic town of some 60,000 people located at the foothills of the Oregon's Cascade Mountain range. The college serves a 10,000-square-mile district that includes part of Central Oregon's high desert country east of Bend. The area's primary industries are lumber and tourism. Bus lines connect Bend with other parts of the state. Two airlines serve the nearby town of Redmond, 14 miles distant, with jet air transport. Bend is 157 miles from Portland and 120 miles from Eugene, Oregon. Community facilities include a public library, churches of major denominations, three major shopping malls and many service and civic organizations. Bend is known nationally for its recreational environment. Bordering the 1.6 million-acre Deschutes National Forest, the town affords excellent hunting, fishing, hiking and camping opportunities. The full-facility Mt. Bachelor Ski Area, which is normally open from November through June, is 22 minutes from the college campus. Rain is rare in the area. Bend receives an average snowfall of three feet per year, although the mountainous areas receive considerably more.

■ CHEMEKETA COMMUNITY COLLEGE
4000 Lancaster Dr. NE
Salem, OR 97309
Tel: (503)399-5000
Fax: (503)399-3918
E-mail: admissions@chemeketa.edu
Web Site: www.chemeketa.edu/

Description: State and locally supported, 2-year, coed. Awards certificates, diplomas, transfer associate, and terminal associate degrees. Founded 1955. Setting: 72-acre urban campus with easy access to Portland, OR. Endowment: $3.7 million. Educational spending for the previous fiscal year: $3849 per student. Total enrollment: 12,371. Faculty: 740 (186 full-time, 554 part-time). Student-undergrad faculty ratio is 26:1. Full-time: 6,225 students, 55% women, 45% men. Part-time: 6,146 students, 59% women, 41% men. Students come from 21 states and territories, 20 other countries, 5% from out-of-state. 2% American Indian or Alaska Native, non-Hispanic/Latino; 18% Hispanic/Latino; 1% African American, non-Hispanic/Latino; 2% Asian, non-Hispanic/Latino; 1% Native Hawaiian or other Pacific Islander, non-Hispanic/Latino; 1% international. 52% 25 or older, 1% transferred in. Retention: 61% of full-time freshmen returned the following year. Core. Academic remediation for entering students, ESL program, services for LD students, advanced placement, independent study, distance learning, double major, summer session for credit, part-time degree program, adult/continuing education programs, co-op programs and internships. Study abroad program.

Entrance Requirements: Required for some: high school transcript, interview.

Costs Per Year: State resident tuition: $3690 full-time, $82 per quarter hour part-time. Nonresident tuition: $10,980 full-time, $244 per quarter hour part-time. Mandatory fees: $640 full-time, $14 per quarter hour part-time.

Collegiate Environment: Orientation program. Drama-theater group, choral group, student-run newspaper. Social organizations: 21 open to all. Most popular organizations: Student Center and Multicultural Center (the two largest), Phi Theta Kapa, student government, Juntos (promotes the Latin American culture, leadership development, community service, and higher education), Theater by Storm (all aspects of theater, including acting, technical theater, and management). Major annual events: Into the Streets (Community Service Day) and Earth Day, Indigenous Peoples' Day and Martin Luther King Day, Veterans' Day. Student services: personal-psychological counseling, women's center. Campus security: 24-hour emergency response devices and patrols, late night transport-escort service. College housing not available. Chemeketa Community College Library (CCRLS) with 64,513 books, 1,747 serials, an OPAC, and a Web page. Operations spending for the previous fiscal year: $3 million. 250 computers available on campus for general student use. A campuswide network can be accessed from off-campus. Students can access the following: online class registration. Staffed computer lab on campus provides training in use of computers, software, and the Internet.

Community Environment: See Willamette University.

■ CLACKAMAS COMMUNITY COLLEGE
19600 Molalla Ave.
Oregon City, OR 97045-7998
Tel: (503)657-6958
Fax: (503)650-6654
E-mail: pattyw@clackamas.edu
Web Site: www.clackamas.edu/

Description: District-supported, 2-year, coed. Awards certificates, diplomas, transfer associate, and terminal associate degrees. Founded 1966. Setting: 175-acre suburban campus with easy access to Portland. Endowment: $9.7 million. Educational spending for the previous fiscal year: $3160 per student. Total enrollment: 8,144. Faculty: 577 (148 full-time, 429 part-time). Student-undergrad faculty ratio is 14:1. Full-time: 3,205 students, 52% women, 48% men. Part-time: 4,939 students, 54% women, 46% men. Students come from 21 states and territories, 16 other countries, 1% from out-of-state. 45% 25 or older, 41% transferred in. Retention: 91% of full-time freshmen returned the following year. Core. Academic remediation for entering students, ESL program, services for LD students, advanced placement, accelerated degree program, honors program, independent study, distance learning, double major, summer session for credit, part-time degree program, adult/continuing education programs, co-op programs and internships. Study abroad program.

Entrance Requirements: Open admission except for nursing program, medical assistant, accelerated degree, PSU co-admit. Option: early admission. Entrance: noncompetitive. Application deadline: Rolling.

Collegiate Environment: Orientation program. Drama-theater group, choral group, student-run newspaper. Social organizations: 21 open to all; national fraternities. Most popular organizations: Ski Club, Spanish Club, Phi Theta Kappa, Horticulture Club, Speech Club. Major annual events: Club Fair, Fall Craft Fair, Environmental Week. Student services: personal-psychological counseling, women's center. Campus security: 24-hour emergency response devices and patrols, student patrols, late night transport-escort service. Dye Learning Resource Center plus 1 other with 41,263 books, 99,527 microform titles, 274 serials, 1,141 audiovisual materials, an OPAC, and a Web page. Operations spending for the previous fiscal year: $408,101. 200 computers available on campus for general student use. A campuswide network can be accessed. Students can access the following: online class registration. Staffed computer lab on campus.

Community Environment: Oregon City was the capital of the Old Oregon Territory, founded in 1829. The city is on the bank of the Willamette River where there are 40-foot falls that provide waterpower for the production of paper, batteries, lumber and electric power. A municipal free elevator lifts pedestrians 90 feet up the steep face of a cliff to a residential business district. An observation deck at the top overlooks the downtown area and the falls. The Holly Knoll Museum is 7 miles southeast where antique furniture and harness and horsedrawn vehicles may be seen. The John McLoughlin House National Historic Site was built in 1846.

■ CLATSOP COMMUNITY COLLEGE
1653 Jerome
Astoria, OR 97103-3698
Tel: (503)325-0910; Free: 855-252-8767
Fax: (503)325-5738
E-mail: admissions@clatsopcc.edu
Web Site: www.clatsopcc.edu/

Description: County-supported, 2-year, coed. Awards certificates, transfer associate, and terminal associate degrees. Founded 1958. Setting: 20-acre small town campus. Total enrollment: 1,262. Faculty: 119 (47 full-time, 72 part-time). Student-undergrad faculty ratio is 10:1. 340 applied, 81% were admitted. Full-time: 363 students, 50% women, 50% men. Part-time: 899 students, 43% women, 57% men. 44% 25 or older. Academic remediation for entering students, ESL program, services for LD students, advanced placement, distance learning, summer session for credit, part-time degree program, external degree program, adult/continuing education programs, co-op programs and internships.

Entrance Requirements: Open admission. Recommended: high school transcript. Entrance: noncompetitive. Application deadline: Rolling. Notification: continuous.

Collegiate Environment: Orientation program. Student services: personal-psychological counseling. Campus security: 24-hour emergency response devices, late night transport-escort service. Dora Badollet Library plus 1 other with 48,517 books, 7,000 microform titles, 180 serials, 5,000 audiovisual materials, an OPAC, and a Web page. 76 computers available on campus for general student use. A campuswide network can be accessed. Students can access the following: online class registration. Staffed computer lab on campus provides training in use of software and the Internet.

Community Environment: Located on the Columbia River, about 10 miles from its mouth, Astoria is known principally for its salmon and tuna industries. Astoria's history dates from the winter of 1805 when the Lewis and Clark expedition camped at Fort Clatsop. Many plants here are in the fish canning, curing, and freezing business. At the larger docks, ocean liners load for world ports. Commercial transportation is available. There are a number of churches, a city-owned library, museums, hospitals, and many of the major civic and service organizations in the community. The opportunities are good for part-time employment. Recreational facilities are numerous; lakes, streams, rivers, and the ocean for fishing, swimming, boating, picnicking and digging for clams. During the fishing season, August 1 to September 10, more than 15,000 large fish are taken from the Columbia River near Astoria. Some of the points of interest are the Astoria Column, 125 feet high, which illustrates incidents in the early history of the region, Clatsop County Historical Museum, the Columbia River Maritime Museum, and Fort Astoria. The Astoria Regatta is an annual event.

■ COLUMBIA GORGE COMMUNITY COLLEGE

400 E Scenic Dr.
The Dalles, OR 97058
Tel: (541)296-6182
Fax: (541)298-3104
E-mail: kcarter@cgcc.cc.or.us
Web Site: www.cgcc.cc.or.us/

Description: State-supported, 2-year, coed. Awards certificates, diplomas, transfer associate, and terminal associate degrees. Founded 1977. Setting: 78-acre small town campus. Total enrollment: 1,245. Full-time: 542 students, 59% women, 41% men. Part-time: 703 students, 65% women, 35% men. 5% American Indian or Alaska Native, non-Hispanic/Latino; 7% Hispanic/Latino; 1% African American, non-Hispanic/Latino; 1% Asian, non-Hispanic/Latino; 0.1% Native Hawaiian or other Pacific Islander, non-Hispanic/Latino; 0% international. 48% 25 or older. Retention: 0% of full-time freshmen returned the following year. Academic remediation for entering students, ESL program, services for LD students, honors program, independent study, distance learning, summer session for credit, part-time degree program, co-op programs.

Entrance Requirements: Open admission. Option: electronic application. Transfer credits accepted: Yes.

Costs Per Year: State resident tuition: $2670 full-time, $89 per credit part-time. Nonresident tuition: $2670 full-time, $89 per credit part-time. Mandatory fees: $360 full-time. College room and board: $8610. College room only: $3200. Room and board charges vary according to board plan.

Collegiate Environment: Orientation program. Most popular organizations: Nursing Club, Delta Club, Japanese Culture Club, Environmental Club. Major annual events: Back to School Bash, Spring BBQ, Graduation. Campus security: 24-hour emergency response devices. Columbia Gorge Community College Library with 92,328 books, 48 serials, 2,342 audiovisual materials, an OPAC, and a Web page.

■ CONCORDIA UNIVERSITY

2811 NE Holman
Portland, OR 97211-6099
Tel: (503)288-9371; Free: 800-321-9371
Fax: (503)280-8531
E-mail: admissions@cu-portland.edu
Web Site: www.cu-portland.edu/

Description: Independent, comprehensive, coed, affiliated with Lutheran Church-Missouri Synod. Part of Concordia University System. Awards associate, bachelor's, and master's degrees. Founded 1905. Setting: 13-acre urban campus. Endowment: $7.2 million. Educational spending for the previous fiscal year: $3784 per student. Total enrollment: 3,111. Faculty: 259 (65 full-time, 194 part-time). Student-undergrad faculty ratio is 19:1. 1,961 applied, 54% were admitted. 16% from top 10% of their high school class, 44% from top quarter, 79% from top half. Full-time: 1,147 students, 67% women, 33% men. Part-time: 222 students, 69% women, 31% men. Students come from 36 states and territories, 13 other countries, 42% from out-of-state. 1% American Indian or Alaska Native, non-Hispanic/Latino; 8% Hispanic/Latino; 7% African American, non-Hispanic/Latino; 4% Asian, non-Hispanic/Latino; 2% Native Hawaiian or other Pacific Islander, non-Hispanic/Latino; 1% international. 28% 25 or older, 36% live on campus, 21% transferred in. Retention: 70% of full-time freshmen returned the following year. Academic areas with the most degrees conferred: business/marketing; health professions and related sciences; education. Core. Calendar: semesters. Academic remediation for entering students, ESL program, services for LD students, advanced placement, accelerated degree program, self-designed majors, honors program, independent study, distance learning, double major, summer session for credit, part-time degree program, adult/continuing

education programs, internships. Off campus study at Oregon Independent Colleges Association, Concordia University System. Study abroad program. ROTC: Air Force (c).

Entrance Requirements: Options: electronic application, deferred admission. Required: essay, high school transcript, minimum 2.5 high school GPA, 1 recommendation, SAT or ACT. Recommended: interview. Required for some: interview. Entrance: moderately difficult. Application deadline: Rolling. Notification: continuous. SAT Reasoning Test deadline: 7/1. Transfer credits accepted: Yes.

Collegiate Environment: Orientation program. Drama-theater group, choral group, student-run newspaper. Social organizations: 24 open to all. Most popular organizations: Hawaiian Club, The Navy - athletic boosters, Soccer Club, Ultimate Frisbee Club, Volunteer Corps (Teacher, Service, Athlete). Major annual events: Graduation, MLK Day of Service, Academy Awards (campus). Student services: health clinic, personal-psychological counseling. Campus security: 24-hour emergency response devices and patrols, late night transport-escort service, controlled dormitory access, extensive video camera security of main campus areas. 498 college housing spaces available; 470 were occupied in 2012-13. Freshmen given priority for college housing. On-campus residence required through sophomore year. Option: coed housing available. Concordia University Library plus 2 others with 247,037 books, 185,000 microform titles, 56,440 serials, 30,475 audiovisual materials, an OPAC, and a Web page. Operations spending for the previous fiscal year: $851,000. 100 computers available on campus for general student use. A computer is required for all students. A campuswide network can be accessed from student residence rooms and from off campus. Students can access the following: online class registration, campus wide Wi-Fi. Staffed computer lab on campus provides training in use of computers, software, and the Internet.

■ CORBAN UNIVERSITY

5000 Deer Park Dr., SE
Salem, OR 97317
Tel: (503)581-8600; Free: 800-845-3005
Fax: (503)585-4316
E-mail: admissions@corban.edu
Web Site: www.corban.edu/

Description: Independent Christian, comprehensive, coed. Awards associate, bachelor's, master's, and doctoral degrees. Founded 1935. Setting: 145-acre suburban campus with easy access to Portland. Endowment: $1.6 million. Educational spending for the previous fiscal year: $4518 per student. Total enrollment: 1,160. Faculty: 107 (51 full-time, 56 part-time). Student-undergrad faculty ratio is 13:1. 2,688 applied, 34% were admitted. 26% from top 10% of their high school class, 60% from top quarter, 82% from top half. Full-time: 886 students, 62% women, 38% men. Part-time: 68 students, 59% women, 41% men. Students come from 20 states and territories, 5 other countries, 44% from out-of-state. 3% American Indian or Alaska Native, non-Hispanic/Latino; 6% Hispanic/Latino; 2% African American, non-Hispanic/Latino; 5% Asian, non-Hispanic/Latino; 2% Native Hawaiian or other Pacific Islander, non-Hispanic/Latino; 1% international. 12% 25 or older, 63% live on campus, 5% transferred in. Retention: 68% of full-time freshmen returned the following year. Academic areas with the most degrees conferred: psychology; business/marketing; education. Core. Calendar: semesters. Services for LD students, advanced placement, accelerated degree program, self-designed majors, freshman honors college, honors program, independent study, distance learning, double major, summer session for credit, adult/continuing education programs, co-op programs and internships, graduate courses open to undergrads. Off campus study at Oregon Alliance of Independent Colleges & Universities, Council of Christian Colleges and Universities. Study abroad program. ROTC: Army (c), Air Force (c).

Entrance Requirements: Options: electronic application, international baccalaureate accepted. Required: essay, high school transcript, minimum 2.7 high school GPA, 2 recommendations, SAT or ACT. Entrance: moderately difficult. Application deadline: 8/1. Notification: continuous. SAT Reasoning Test deadline: 8/1. SAT Subject Test deadline: 8/1. Transfer credits accepted: Yes.

Costs Per Year: Application fee: $35. One-time mandatory fee: $100. Comprehensive fee: $34,575 includes full-time tuition ($25,975), mandatory fees ($455), and college room and board ($8145). College room only: $2375. Full-time tuition and fees vary according to course level, degree level, program, and reciprocity agreements. Room and board charges vary according to board plan. Part-time tuition: $1082 per credit hour. Part-time tuition varies according to course level, course load, degree level, program, and reciprocity agreements.

Collegiate Environment: Orientation program. Drama-theater group, choral group, student-run newspaper. Social organizations: 6 open to all. Most popular organizations: Student Fellowship Groups, Poetry Club, Worship Teams, Drama Club, Westrek Hiking Club. Major annual events: Homecoming, Christmas celebration. Student services: health clinic, personal-psychological counseling. Campus security: 24-hour emergency response devices and patrols, student patrols, late night transport-escort service, controlled dormitory access. 557 college housing spaces available; 475 were occupied in 2012-13. Freshmen guaranteed college housing. On-campus residence required through sophomore year. Options: men-only, women-only housing available. Corban University Library with 105,000 books, 4,700 microform titles, 528 serials, 5,000 audiovisual materials, an OPAC, and a Web page. Operations spending for the previous fiscal year: $353,902. 64 computers available on campus for general student use. A campuswide network can be accessed from student residence rooms and from off campus. Staffed computer lab on campus provides training in use of computers, software, and the Internet.

Community Environment: See Willamette University.

■ **DEVRY UNIVERSITY**
9755 SW Barnes Rd.
Ste. 150
Portland, OR 97225-6651
Tel: (503)296-7468; Free: 866-338-7941
Web Site: www.devry.edu/

Description: Proprietary, comprehensive, coed. Part of DeVry University. Awards associate, bachelor's, and master's degrees. Total enrollment: 218. Faculty: 32 (all part-time). Student-undergrad faculty ratio is 11:1. Full-time: 65 students, 34% women, 66% men. Part-time: 66 students, 44% women, 56% men. 18% from out-of-state. 72% 25 or older, 93% transferred in. Academic areas with the most degrees conferred: business/marketing; computer and information sciences. Calendar: semesters. Academic remediation for entering students, services for LD students, advanced placement, accelerated degree program, distance learning, summer session for credit, part-time degree program, adult/continuing education programs.

Entrance Requirements: Options: electronic application, deferred admission, international baccalaureate accepted. Required: high school transcript, interview. Entrance: minimally difficult. Application deadline: Rolling. Notification: continuous. SAT Reasoning Test deadline: 10/31.

Collegiate Environment: Orientation program.

■ **EASTERN OREGON UNIVERSITY**
1 University Blvd.
La Grande, OR 97850-2899
Tel: (541)962-3672; Free: 800-452-8639
Fax: (541)962-3418
E-mail: admissions@eou.edu
Web Site: www.eou.edu/

Description: State-supported, comprehensive, coed. Part of Oregon University System. Awards associate, bachelor's, and master's degrees. Founded 1929. Setting: 121-acre rural campus. Research spending for the previous fiscal year: $344,000. Educational spending for the previous fiscal year: $5210 per student. Total enrollment: 4,298. Faculty: 128 (117 full-time, 11 part-time). Student-undergrad faculty ratio is 24:1. 1,296 applied, 65% were admitted. 15% from top 10% of their high school class, 40% from top quarter, 75% from top half. Full-time: 2,392 students, 60% women, 40% men. Part-time: 1,508 students, 63% women, 37% men. Students come from 49 states and territories, 20 other countries, 29% from out-of-state. 2% American Indian or Alaska Native, non-Hispanic/Latino; 5% Hispanic/Latino; 2% African American, non-Hispanic/Latino; 2% Asian, non-Hispanic/Latino; 1% Native Hawaiian or other Pacific Islander, non-Hispanic/Latino; 1% international. 51% 25 or older, 12% live on campus, 13% transferred in. Retention: 72% of full-time freshmen returned the following year. Academic areas with the most degrees conferred: business/marketing; liberal arts/general studies; education. Core. Services for LD students, advanced placement, self-designed majors, honors program, independent study, distance learning, double major, summer session for credit, part-time degree program, external degree program, adult/continuing education programs, co-op programs and internships. Off campus study at National Student Exchange. Study abroad program. ROTC: Army.

Entrance Requirements: Options: electronic application, early admission, early action, deferred admission, international baccalaureate accepted. Required: high school transcript, minimum 3 high school GPA, SAT or ACT. Required for some: essay, 2 recommendations. Entrance: moderately dif-

ficult. Application deadlines: 8/15, 12/1 for early action. Notification: continuous, 1/15 for early action. SAT Reasoning Test deadline: 9/15. SAT Subject Test deadline: 9/15.

Collegiate Environment: Orientation program. Drama-theater group, choral group, student-run newspaper, radio station. Most popular organizations: Outdoor Club, Island Magic, student radio station, intramurals, student government. Major annual events: Homecoming, Spring Symposium, Fall Honors Convocation. Student services: health clinic, personal-psychological counseling, women's center. Campus security: controlled dormitory access. Pierce Library with an OPAC and a Web page.

■ **EVEREST COLLEGE**
425 SW Washington St.
Portland, OR 97204
Tel: (503)222-3225; Free: 888-741-4270
Fax: (503)228-6926
Web Site: www.everest.edu/

Description: Proprietary, 2-year, coed. Awards terminal associate degrees. Founded 1955. Total enrollment: 737. Student-undergrad faculty ratio is 20:1. 188 applied, 83% were admitted. 0% from out-of-state. 63% 25 or older.

■ **GEORGE FOX UNIVERSITY**
414 N Meridian
Newberg, OR 97132-2697
Tel: (503)538-8383; Free: 800-765-4369
Fax: (503)554-3830
E-mail: admissions@georgefox.edu
Web Site: www.georgefox.edu/

Description: Independent Friends, university, coed. Awards bachelor's, master's, and doctoral degrees and post-master's certificates. Founded 1891. Setting: 108-acre small town campus with easy access to Portland. Endowment: $18 million. Educational spending for the previous fiscal year: $10,813 per student. Total enrollment: 3,484. Faculty: 377 (163 full-time, 214 part-time). Student-undergrad faculty ratio is 13:1. 2,215 applied, 75% were admitted. 31% from top 10% of their high school class, 62% from top quarter, 91% from top half. 1 National Merit Scholar, 22 valedictorians. Full-time: 1,928 students, 59% women, 41% men. Part-time: 256 students, 59% women, 41% men. Students come from 35 states and territories, 31 other countries, 35% from out-of-state. 1% American Indian or Alaska Native, non-Hispanic/Latino; 7% Hispanic/Latino; 2% African American, non-Hispanic/Latino; 4% Asian, non-Hispanic/Latino; 0.5% Native Hawaiian or other Pacific Islander, non-Hispanic/Latino; 6% international. 17% 25 or older, 52% live on campus, 4% transferred in. Retention: 82% of full-time freshmen returned the following year. Academic areas with the most degrees conferred: business/marketing; interdisciplinary studies; health professions and related sciences. Core. Calendar: semesters. Academic remediation for entering students, ESL program, services for LD students, advanced placement, accelerated degree program, self-designed majors, honors program, independent study, distance learning, double major, summer session for credit, part-time degree program, adult/continuing education programs, internships, graduate courses open to undergrads. Off campus study at members of the Christian College Consortium Exchange, Coalition for Christian Colleges and Universities, Oregon Alliance of Independent Colleges and Universities. Study abroad program. ROTC: Air Force (c).

Entrance Requirements: Options: electronic application, early action, deferred admission, international baccalaureate accepted. Required: essay, high school transcript, 2 recommendations, SAT or ACT. Recommended: minimum 2.6 high school GPA, interview. Required for some: interview. Entrance: moderately difficult. Application deadlines: Rolling, 11/15 for early action. Notification: continuous until 10/1, 12/15 for early action. SAT Reasoning Test deadline: 8/1. Transfer credits accepted: Yes. Early action applicants: 1,765. Early action applicants admitted: 1,349.

Costs Per Year: Application fee: $40. Comprehensive fee: $39,590 includes full-time tuition ($29,900), mandatory fees ($330), and college room and board ($9360). College room only: $5460. Room and board charges vary according to board plan. Part-time tuition: $905 per semester hour. Part-time tuition varies according to course load.

Collegiate Environment: Orientation program. Drama-theater group, choral group, student-run newspaper, radio station. Social organizations: 20 open to all. Most popular organizations: student government, Christian Ministries, Orientation Committee, Outdoor Club and Bruin Ambassadors, Blue Zone. Major annual events: Serve Day, Juniors Abroad, Homecoming, Mr. Bruin, Spring Formal. Student services: health clinic, personal-psychological counseling. Campus security: 24-hour emergency response devices and patrols, student patrols, late night transport-escort service, controlled dormitory access, parking lot cameras, and video surveillance of key buildings. 1,242 college housing spaces available; 1,126 were occupied in 2012-13. Freshmen given priority for college housing. On-campus residence required through junior year. Options: men-only, women-only housing available. Murdock Learning Resource Center with 251,000 books, 210,708 microform titles, 57,509 serials, 5,649 audiovisual materials, an OPAC, and a Web page. Operations spending for the previous fiscal year: $745,355. 186 computers available on campus for general student use. A campuswide network can be accessed from student residence rooms and from off campus. Students can access the following: online class registration, online acceptance of financial aid. Staffed computer lab on campus provides training in use of computers, software, and the Internet.

Community Environment: Located 24 miles southwest of Portland, Newberg has a number of churches, a community hospital, and various civic and service organizations. Commercial transportation is easily accessible. Part-time employment is available.

■ **GUTENBERG COLLEGE**
1883 University St.
Eugene, OR 97403
Tel: (541)683-5141
Fax: (541)683-6997
E-mail: tstollar@gutenberg.edu
Web Site: www.gutenberg.edu/
Description: Independent Christian, 4-year, coed. Awards bachelor's degrees. Setting: urban campus. Educational spending for the previous fiscal year: $5741 per student. Total enrollment: 38. Faculty: 10 (8 full-time, 2 part-time). Student-undergrad faculty ratio is 6:1. 14 applied, 64% were admitted. Full-time: 38 students, 39% women, 61% men. Students come from 15 states and territories, 3 other countries, 53% from out-of-state. 10% 25 or older, 75% live on campus, 0% transferred in. Retention: 70% of full-time freshmen returned the following year. Academic area with the most degrees conferred: liberal arts/general studies. Core.
Entrance Requirements: Required: essay, high school transcript, 2 recommendations, interview, SAT. Entrance: moderately difficult. Application deadline: 3/1. Notification: 9/10.
Collegiate Environment: Orientation program. Choral group. Major annual events: Junior Tea, President's Dinner, Student Art Show. Operations spending for the previous fiscal year: $1840. 2 computers available on campus for general student use. Staffed computer lab on campus.

■ **HEALD COLLEGE–PORTLAND**
6035 NE 78th Ct.
Portland, OR 97218
Tel: (503)229-0492; Free: 800-88-HEALD
Fax: (503)229-0498
E-mail: portlandinfo@heald.edu
Web Site: www.heald.edu/
Description: Independent, 2-year, coed. Awards certificates, diplomas, transfer associate, and terminal associate degrees. Founded 1863. Total enrollment: 733. Student-undergrad faculty ratio is 21:1. 9% from out-of-state. 58% 25 or older. Academic remediation for entering students, advanced placement, summer session for credit, part-time degree program, internships.
Entrance Requirements: Open admission. Options: early admission, deferred admission. Required: high school transcript, interview. Entrance: minimally difficult. Application deadline: Rolling. Notification: continuous.
Collegiate Environment: Learning Resource Center with an OPAC.

■ **ITT TECHNICAL INSTITUTE (PORTLAND)**
9500 NE Cascades Pky.
Portland, OR 97220
Tel: (503)255-6500; Free: 800-234-5488
Fax: (503)255-6135
Web Site: www.itt-tech.edu/
Description: Proprietary, primarily 2-year, coed. Part of ITT Educational Services, Inc. Awards terminal associate and bachelor's degrees. Founded 1971. Setting: urban campus.
Entrance Requirements: Entrance: minimally difficult.

■ **ITT TECHNICAL INSTITUTE (SALEM)**
4825 Commercial St. SE
Ste. 100

Salem, OR 97302-2177
Tel: (503)576-2300; Free: 877-273-7397
Web Site: www.itt-tech.edu/
Description: Proprietary, 4-year, coed. Awards associate and bachelor's degrees.
Entrance Requirements: Entrance: minimally difficult.

■ **KLAMATH COMMUNITY COLLEGE**
7390 S 6th St.
Klamath Falls, OR 97603
Tel: (541)882-3521
E-mail: garlock@klamathcc.edu
Web Site: www.klamathcc.edu/
Description: State-supported, 2-year, coed. Awards certificates, transfer associate, and terminal associate degrees. Founded 1996. Setting: 58-acre small town campus. Endowment: $129,870. Educational spending for the previous fiscal year: $3310 per student. Total enrollment: 1,148. Faculty: 129 (28 full-time, 101 part-time). Student-undergrad faculty ratio is 14:1. Full-time: 385 students, 60% women, 40% men. Part-time: 763 students, 59% women, 41% men. Students come from 2 states and territories, 0.1% from out-of-state. 6% American Indian or Alaska Native, non-Hispanic/Latino; 13% Hispanic/Latino; 1% African American, non-Hispanic/Latino; 1% Asian, non-Hispanic/Latino; 0.2% Native Hawaiian or other Pacific Islander, non-Hispanic/Latino; 0% international. 52% 25 or older, 14% transferred in. Retention: 58% of full-time freshmen returned the following year. Core. Academic remediation for entering students, ESL program, services for LD students, advanced placement, self-designed majors, independent study, distance learning, double major, summer session for credit, co-op programs and internships.
Entrance Requirements: Open admission. Option: electronic application. Required: high school transcript. Entrance: noncompetitive. Application deadlines: Rolling, Rolling for nonresidents. Notification: continuous, continuous for nonresidents. Transfer credits accepted: Yes.
Costs Per Year: State resident tuition: $2988 full-time, $83 per credit part-time. Nonresident tuition: $5796 full-time, $161 per credit part-time. Mandatory fees: $12 full-time, $12 per credit part-time. Tuition guaranteed not to increase for student's term of enrollment.
Collegiate Environment: Orientation program. Social organizations: 12 open to all; Multiple student clubs; 10% of eligible men and 15% of eligible women are members. Most popular organizations: Phi Beta Lambda, Hispanic Club, Future Farmers of America, Veterans Club, Business Club. Major annual events: Welcome Back Barbecue, Luau, Halloween Bash. Student services: personal-psychological counseling. Campus security: 24-hour emergency response devices. Learning Resource Center with an OPAC. Operations spending for the previous fiscal year: $317,891.

■ **LANE COMMUNITY COLLEGE**
4000 E 30th Ave.
Eugene, OR 97405-0640
Tel: (541)747-4501
Fax: (541)744-3995
Web Site: www.lanecc.edu/
Description: State and locally supported, 2-year, coed. Awards certificates, transfer associate, and terminal associate degrees. Founded 1964. Setting: 240-acre suburban campus. Total enrollment: 8,618. 46% 25 or older. Core. Academic remediation for entering students, ESL program, services for LD students, advanced placement, summer session for credit, part-time degree program, adult/continuing education programs, internships.
Entrance Requirements: Open admission. Option: early admission. Entrance: noncompetitive. Application deadline: Rolling. Notification: continuous. Preference given to district residents.
Collegiate Environment: Orientation program. Drama-theater group, choral group, student-run newspaper, radio station. Student services: legal services, health clinic, personal-psychological counseling, women's center. Campus security: 24-hour emergency response devices and patrols, student patrols, late night transport-escort service. Lane Community College Library plus 1 other with 67,051 books, 513 serials, an OPAC, and a Web page.
Community Environment: See University of Oregon.

■ **LE CORDON BLEU COLLEGE OF CULINARY ARTS IN PORTLAND**
921 SW Morrison St.
Ste. 400
Portland, OR 97205
Tel: (503)223-2245; Free: 888-891-6222

Fax: (503)223-0126
Web Site: www.wci.edu/
Description: Proprietary, 2-year, coed. Awards terminal associate degrees. Founded 1983. Total enrollment: 1,025. Calendar: continuous.
Entrance Requirements: Entrance: noncompetitive.

■ LEWIS & CLARK COLLEGE
0615 SW Palatine Hill Rd.
Portland, OR 97219-7899
Tel: (503)768-7000; Free: 800-444-4111
Fax: (503)768-7055
E-mail: admissions@lclark.edu
Web Site: www.lclark.edu/
Description: Independent, comprehensive, coed. Awards bachelor's, master's, and doctoral degrees and post-master's certificates. Founded 1867. Setting: 137-acre suburban campus with easy access to Portland. Endowment: $182.3 million. Research spending for the previous fiscal year: $3.6 million. Educational spending for the previous fiscal year: $13,833 per student. Total enrollment: 3,703. Faculty: 417 (239 full-time, 178 part-time). Student-undergrad faculty ratio is 12:1. 6,488 applied, 64% were admitted. 37% from top 10% of their high school class, 76% from top quarter, 98% from top half. Full-time: 2,120 students, 60% women, 40% men. Part-time: 30 students, 53% women, 47% men. Students come from 51 states and territories, 46 other countries, 80% from out-of-state. 1% American Indian or Alaska Native, non-Hispanic/Latino; 7% Hispanic/Latino; 2% African American, non-Hispanic/Latino; 3% Asian, non-Hispanic/Latino; 0.1% Native Hawaiian or other Pacific Islander, non-Hispanic/Latino; 9% international. 3% 25 or older, 70% live on campus, 2% transferred in. Retention: 89% of full-time freshmen returned the following year. Academic areas with the most degrees conferred: social sciences; psychology; biological/life sciences; visual and performing arts. Core. Calendar: semesters. ESL program, services for LD students, advanced placement, accelerated degree program, self-designed majors, honors program, independent study, double major, summer session for credit, internships. Off campus study. Study abroad program.
Entrance Requirements: Options: electronic application, early action, deferred admission, international baccalaureate accepted. Required: essay, high school transcript, minimum 2 high school GPA, 'portfolio path' applicants submit samples of writing, SAT or ACT, or academic portfolio. Students may apply via Portfolio Path where test scores are optional. Recommended: minimum 3 high school GPA, interview. Required for some: 4 recommendations, SAT or ACT. Entrance: very difficult. Application deadlines: 1/15, 1/15 for nonresidents, 11/1 for early action. Notification: 4/1, 4/1 for nonresidents, 1/1 for early action. SAT Reasoning Test deadline: 3/1. Transfer credits accepted: Yes. Applicants placed on waiting list: 423. Waitlisted applicants offered admission: 27.
Costs Per Year: Application fee: $50. Comprehensive fee: $52,564 includes full-time tuition ($41,568), mandatory fees ($360), and college room and board ($10,636). College room only: $5722. Room and board charges vary according to board plan and housing facility. Part-time tuition: $1999 per credit hour.
Collegiate Environment: Orientation program. Drama-theater group, choral group, student-run newspaper, radio station. Student services: health clinic, personal-psychological counseling, women's center. Campus security: 24-hour emergency response devices and patrols, student patrols, late night transport-escort service, controlled dormitory access. 1,400 college housing spaces available; 1,394 were occupied in 2012-13. Freshmen guaranteed college housing. On-campus residence required through sophomore year. Options: coed, women-only housing available. Aubrey Watzek Library plus 2 others with 586,144 books, 420,400 microform titles, 23,851 audiovisual materials, an OPAC, and a Web page. Operations spending for the previous fiscal year: $5.9 million. 428 computers available on campus for general student use. Computer purchase/lease plans available. A campuswide network can be accessed from student residence rooms and from off campus. Students can access the following: online class registration. Staffed computer lab on campus provides training in use of computers, software, and the Internet.
Community Environment: See Portland State University.

■ LINFIELD COLLEGE
900 SE Baker St.
McMinnville, OR 97128-6894
Tel: (503)883-2200; Free: 800-640-2287
Fax: (503)883-2472

E-mail: admission@linfield.edu
Web Site: www.linfield.edu/
Description: Independent American Baptist Churches in the USA, 4-year, coed. Part of Linfield College includes the Linfield College McMinnville Campus; the School of Nursing in Portland, Oregon; and the Linfield College Adult Degree Program. Awards bachelor's degrees. Founded 1849. Setting: 193-acre small town campus with easy access to Portland. System endowment: $78.1 million. Total enrollment: 1,663. Faculty: 196 (119 full-time, 77 part-time). Student-undergrad faculty ratio is 11:1. 2,338 applied, 83% were admitted. 27% from top 10% of their high school class, 38% from top quarter, 92% from top half. 7 class presidents, 24 valedictorians, 21 student government officers. Full-time: 1,633 students, 61% women, 39% men. Part-time: 30 students, 57% women, 43% men. Students come from 21 states and territories, 20 other countries, 46% from out-of-state. 1% American Indian or Alaska Native, non-Hispanic/Latino; 8% Hispanic/Latino; 2% African American, non-Hispanic/Latino; 6% Asian, non-Hispanic/Latino; 0.5% Native Hawaiian or other Pacific Islander, non-Hispanic/Latino; 6% international. 2% 25 or older, 75% live on campus, 3% transferred in. Retention: 88% of full-time freshmen returned the following year. Academic areas with the most degrees conferred: business/marketing; social sciences; parks and recreation. Core. Calendar: 4-1-4. ESL program, services for LD students, advanced placement, accelerated degree program, self-designed majors, independent study, distance learning, double major, summer session for credit, part-time degree program, external degree program, adult/continuing education programs, internships. Off campus study at American Baptist Colleges and Universities. Study abroad program. ROTC: Air Force (c).
Entrance Requirements: Options: electronic application, early action, deferred admission, international baccalaureate accepted. Required: essay, high school transcript, 1 recommendation, SAT or ACT. Recommended: interview. Entrance: moderately difficult. Application deadlines: 2/15, 11/15 for early action. Notification: 4/1, 1/15 for early action. SAT Reasoning Test deadline: 2/15. Transfer credits accepted: Yes. Early action applicants: 702. Early action applicants admitted: 686.
Costs Per Year: Comprehensive fee: $43,828 includes full-time tuition ($34,000), mandatory fees ($328), and college room and board ($9500). College room only: $5180. Full-time tuition and fees vary according to location. Room and board charges vary according to board plan, housing facility, and location. Part-time tuition: $1059 per semester hour. Part-time tuition varies according to course load and location.
Collegiate Environment: Orientation program. Drama-theater group, choral group, student-run newspaper, radio station. Social organizations: 40 open to all; national fraternities, national sororities, local fraternities, local sororities; 21% of eligible men and 24% of eligible women are members. Most popular organizations: Fellowship of Christian Athletes, Linfield Ultimate Players Association, Hawaiian Club, International Club, Outdoor Club. Major annual events: Luau, Wildstock, Monthly Comedy Series. Student services: health clinic, personal-psychological counseling. Campus security: 24-hour emergency response devices and patrols, late night transport-escort service, controlled dormitory access. 1,367 college housing spaces available; 1,301 were occupied in 2012-13. Freshmen guaranteed college housing. On-campus residence required through junior year. Options: coed, men-only, women-only housing available. Jereld R. Nicholson Library with 184,441 books, 17,491 microform titles, 985 serials, 38,152 audiovisual materials, an OPAC, and a Web page. 250 computers available on campus for general student use. Computer purchase/lease plans available. A campuswide network can be accessed from student residence rooms and from off campus. Students can access the following: online class registration. Staffed computer lab on campus provides training in use of computers, software, and the Internet.
Community Environment: Nestled in the heart of the Willamette Valley, McMinnville is a classic college town where students are quickly welcomed into the community. Downtown McMinnville boasts a charming historic shopping district, which includes art galleries, antique shops, coffeehouses, and nationally renowned restaurants like Nick's Italian Cafe, as well as a variety of job opportunities. Linfield students have many chances to get acquainted with their McMinnville neighbors while going to the Cinema 8 Multiplex or the Moonlight Theater and Pizzeria, attending community theatre productions or becoming members of one of the town's 28 churches.

■ LINN-BENTON COMMUNITY COLLEGE
6500 SW Pacific Blvd.
Albany, OR 97321
Tel: (541)917-4999
Fax: (541)917-4838

E-mail: admissions@linnbenton.edu

Web Site: www.linnbenton.edu/

Description: State and locally supported, 2-year, coed. Awards certificates, transfer associate, and terminal associate degrees. Founded 1966. Setting: 104-acre small town campus. Total enrollment: 6,922. Faculty: 510 (156 full-time, 354 part-time). Student-undergrad faculty ratio is 20:1. 2,772 applied. Full-time: 3,556 students, 48% women, 52% men. Part-time: 3,366 students, 53% women, 47% men. 1% American Indian or Alaska Native, non-Hispanic/Latino; 6% Hispanic/Latino; 2% African American, non-Hispanic/Latino; 1% Asian, non-Hispanic/Latino; 0% Native Hawaiian or other Pacific Islander, non-Hispanic/Latino; 0.3% international. Core. Academic remediation for entering students, ESL program, services for LD students, advanced placement, self-designed majors, independent study, distance learning, summer session for credit, part-time degree program, adult/continuing education programs, co-op programs and internships. Study abroad program. ROTC: Army (c), Air Force (c).

Entrance Requirements: Open admission. Options: electronic application, deferred admission. Required for some: high school transcript. Entrance: noncompetitive. Application deadline: Rolling. Preference given to district residents.

Collegiate Environment: Orientation program. Drama-theater group, choral group, student-run newspaper. Social organizations: 18 open to all. Most popular organizations: EBOP Club, Multicultural Club, Campus Family Co-op, Horticulture Club, Collegiate Secretary Club. Major annual events: Martin Luther King Celebration, Spring Daze, Children's Winter Festival. Student services: personal-psychological counseling. Campus security: 24-hour emergency response devices and patrols, student patrols, late night transport-escort service. Linn-Benton Community College Library with 42,561 books, 1,172 microform titles, 91 serials, 8,758 audiovisual materials, an OPAC, and a Web page. 500 computers available on campus for general student use. A campuswide network can be accessed from off-campus. Students can access the following: online class registration. Staffed computer lab on campus.

Community Environment: Noted for its rare metals industries, Albany is also in the fertile Willamette Valley, a rich timber area; the valley is one of the leading producers of rye grass seed and mint. The rare metals industries produce tantalum, tungsten, zirconium, hafnium, columbium, and molybdenum. Other manufactured products are plywood lumber, furniture, and mill machinery. The average rainfall is 39.7 inches. Community facilities include a number of churches, a YMCA, Boys Club, a hospital, and many clinics, excellent shopping areas, and a number of civic and service organizations. Part-time jobs are available. Recreational activities are swimming, tennis, and other sports. The World's Champion Timber Carnival in July draws loggers from all over to compete in log rolling, tree topping, axe throwing, and other events.

■ **MARYLHURST UNIVERSITY**

17600 Pacific Hwy.

Marylhurst, OR 97036-0261

Tel: (503)636-8141; Free: 800-634-9982

Fax: (503)636-9526

E-mail: admissions@marylhurst.edu

Web Site: www.marylhurst.edu/

Description: Independent Roman Catholic, comprehensive, coed. Awards bachelor's and master's degrees and post-master's certificates. Founded 1893. Setting: 63-acre suburban campus with easy access to Portland. Endowment: $15.2 million. Educational spending for the previous fiscal year: $4243 per student. Total enrollment: 1,722. Faculty: 263 (55 full-time, 208 part-time). Student-undergrad faculty ratio is 7:1. 33 applied, 70% were admitted. Full-time: 228 students, 73% women, 27% men. Part-time: 611 students, 70% women, 30% men. Students come from 33 states and territories, 15 other countries, 23% from out-of-state. 1% American Indian or Alaska Native, non-Hispanic/Latino; 5% Hispanic/Latino; 4% African American, non-Hispanic/Latino; 3% Asian, non-Hispanic/Latino; 1% Native Hawaiian or other Pacific Islander, non-Hispanic/Latino; 7% international. 80% 25 or older, 16% transferred in. Retention: 66% of full-time freshmen returned the following year. Academic areas with the most degrees conferred: business/marketing; interdisciplinary studies; visual and performing arts; liberal arts/general studies. Core. ESL program, services for LD students, advanced placement, accelerated degree program, self-designed majors, independent study, distance learning, double major, summer session for credit, part-time degree program, adult/continuing education programs, internships. Off campus study at member of the Oregon Alliance of Independent Colleges & Universities (OAICU). Study abroad program.

Entrance Requirements: Options: electronic application, deferred admission. Required: essay, high school transcript, minimum 2.5 high school GPA. Required for some: 2 recommendations, interview. Entrance: noncompetitive. Application deadline: Rolling. Notification: continuous. Transfer credits accepted: Yes.

Collegiate Environment: Choral group, student-run newspaper. Most popular organizations: Marylhurst's Writer's Club, Marylhurst Gerontology Association, Solutions: Marylhurst Mediation Resource, Marylhurst S.A.F.E. Community: Sexual Acceptance for Everyone, LABY: Labyrinth Alliance Balances You. Student services: personal-psychological counseling. Campus security: security is available during campus hours. Shoen Library with 109,963 books, 191 microform titles, 23,286 serials, 4,425 audiovisual materials, an OPAC, and a Web page. Operations spending for the previous fiscal year: $850,528. 50 computers available on campus for general student use. A campuswide network can be accessed from off-campus. Students can access the following: online class registration. Staffed computer lab on campus provides training in use of computers, software, and the Internet.

■ **MOUNT ANGEL SEMINARY**

Saint Benedict, OR 97373

Tel: (503)845-3951

E-mail: admissions@mtangel.edu

Web Site: www.mountangelabbey.org/seminary/

Description: Independent Roman Catholic, comprehensive. Awards bachelor's, master's, and doctoral degrees (only candidates for the priesthood are admitted). Founded 1887. Setting: 75-acre rural campus with easy access to Portland. Total enrollment: 181. 73 applied, 100% were admitted. 51% 25 or older. Core. Calendar: semesters. Academic remediation for entering students, ESL program, advanced placement, part-time degree program, adult/continuing education programs, graduate courses open to undergrads. Off campus study at Oregon Independent Colleges Association.

Entrance Requirements: Required: essay, high school transcript, minimum 2.0 high school GPA, 2 recommendations. Recommended: interview, SAT. Entrance: moderately difficult. Application deadline: 7/15. Notification: continuous. Preference given to Catholic seminarians.

Collegiate Environment: Orientation program. Choral group. Student services: health clinic, personal-psychological counseling. Campus security: 24-hour emergency response devices, patrols by police officers. Mount Angel Abbey Library with 240,000 books and 775 serials.

■ **MT. HOOD COMMUNITY COLLEGE**

26000 SE Stark St.

Gresham, OR 97030-3300

Tel: (503)491-6422

Fax: (503)491-7388

Web Site: www.mhcc.edu/

Description: State and locally supported, 2-year, coed. Awards certificates, diplomas, transfer associate, and terminal associate degrees. Founded 1966. Setting: 212-acre suburban campus with easy access to Portland. Research spending for the previous fiscal year: $75,611. Total enrollment: 8,771. Faculty: 638 (173 full-time, 465 part-time). Student-undergrad faculty ratio is 25:1. Full-time: 3,178 students, 53% women, 47% men. Part-time: 5,593 students, 57% women, 43% men. Students come from 16 states and territories, 6 other countries. 56% 25 or older. Core. Academic remediation for entering students, ESL program, services for LD students, advanced placement, summer session for credit, part-time degree program, adult/continuing education programs, co-op programs and internships. Study abroad program.

Entrance Requirements: Open admission except for allied health, some professional-technical programs. Options: early admission, deferred admission. Required for some: high school transcript, minimum 2.0 high school GPA. Entrance: noncompetitive. Application deadline: Rolling. Notification: continuous. Preference given to state residents.

Collegiate Environment: Drama-theater group, choral group, student-run newspaper, radio station. Student services: health clinic, personal-psychological counseling, women's center. Campus security: 24-hour emergency response devices and patrols, student patrols, late night transport-escort service. Library Resource Center with 64,000 books and 412 serials. 100 computers available on campus for general student use. Staffed computer lab on campus.

■ **MULTNOMAH UNIVERSITY**

8435 NE Glisan St.

Portland, OR 97220-5898

Tel: (503)255-0332; Free: 877-251-6560
Fax: (503)254-1268
E-mail: admiss@multnomah.edu
Web Site: www.multnomah.edu/
Description: Independent interdenominational, comprehensive, coed. Awards bachelor's and master's degrees. Founded 1936. Setting: 22-acre urban campus. Endowment: $6.8 million. Educational spending for the previous fiscal year: $5482 per student. Total enrollment: 850. Faculty: 89 (33 full-time, 56 part-time). Student-undergrad faculty ratio is 15:1. 118 applied, 64% were admitted. 0% from top 10% of their high school class, 22% from top quarter, 100% from top half. Full-time: 414 students, 42% women, 58% men. Part-time: 89 students, 33% women, 67% men. Students come from 25 states and territories, 4 other countries, 50% from out-of-state. 0.4% American Indian or Alaska Native, non-Hispanic/Latino; 6% Hispanic/Latino; 3% African American, non-Hispanic/Latino; 2% Asian, non-Hispanic/Latino; 1% Native Hawaiian or other Pacific Islander, non-Hispanic/Latino; 1% international. 35% 25 or older, 42% live on campus, 15% transferred in. Retention: 60% of full-time freshmen returned the following year. Academic areas with the most degrees conferred: theology and religious vocations; education; social sciences; communication/journalism. Core. Calendar: semesters. Academic remediation for entering students, services for LD students, advanced placement, double major, summer session for credit, part-time degree program, adult/continuing education programs, internships.
Entrance Requirements: Options: electronic application, deferred admission, international baccalaureate accepted. Required: essay, high school transcript, minimum 2.5 high school GPA, 2 recommendations, SAT or ACT. Entrance: moderately difficult. Notification: continuous. SAT Reasoning Test deadline: 8/1. Transfer credits accepted: Yes.
Costs Per Year: Application fee: $40. Comprehensive fee: $28,440 includes full-time tuition ($20,990), mandatory fees ($250), and college room and board ($7200). Full-time tuition and fees vary according to course load, location, and program. Room and board charges vary according to housing facility. Part-time tuition: $655 per semester hour. Part-time tuition and fees vary according to course load, location, and program.
Collegiate Environment: Orientation program. Drama-theater group, choral group. Most popular organizations: Day of Outreach, Prayer for the Persecuted, Multnomah Soccer Club, The Beautiful Response, Student World Outreach Team. Major annual events: Fall Retreat, Fall Banquet, Junior-Senior Banquet. Student services: health clinic, personal-psychological counseling. Campus security: 24-hour emergency response devices and patrols, late night transport-escort service, controlled dormitory access. 308 college housing spaces available; 166 were occupied in 2012-13. Freshmen guaranteed college housing. On-campus residence required through junior year. Options: men-only, women-only housing available. John Mitchell Library with 103,434 books, 3,565 microform titles, 294 serials, 7,469 audiovisual materials, and an OPAC. Operations spending for the previous fiscal year: $163,687. 36 computers available on campus for general student use. A campuswide network can be accessed from student residence rooms and from off campus. Students can access the following: online class registration. Staffed computer lab on campus provides training in use of computers and software.
Community Environment: See Portland State University.

■ **NEW HOPE CHRISTIAN COLLEGE**
2155 Bailey Hill Rd.
Eugene, OR 97405
Tel: (541)485-1780; Free: 800-322-2638
Fax: (541)343-5801
E-mail: sarahslater@newhope.edu
Web Site: www.newhope.edu/
Description: Independent, 4-year, coed, affiliated with Open Bible Standard Churches. Awards bachelor's degrees. Founded 1925. Setting: 40-acre suburban campus. Total enrollment: 143. Faculty: 25 (9 full-time, 16 part-time). Student-undergrad faculty ratio is 11:1. 165 applied, 22% were admitted. Full-time: 134 students, 39% women, 61% men. Part-time: 9 students, 44% women, 56% men. 0% American Indian or Alaska Native, non-Hispanic/Latino; 3% Hispanic/Latino; 3% African American, non-Hispanic/Latino; 1% Asian, non-Hispanic/Latino; 1% Native Hawaiian or other Pacific Islander, non-Hispanic/Latino; 1% international. 24% 25 or older, 20% transferred in. Retention: 60% of full-time freshmen returned the following year. Calendar: semesters. Part-time degree program.
Entrance Requirements: Options: electronic application, deferred admission. Required: essay, high school transcript, minimum 2 high school GPA, 2 recommendations. Entrance: minimally difficult. Application deadline: 8/1. Notification: continuous.

Collegiate Environment: Orientation program. Campus security: 24-hour emergency response devices, student patrols, controlled dormitory access.
Community Environment: See University of Oregon.

■ **NORTHWEST CHRISTIAN UNIVERSITY**
828 E 11th Ave.
Eugene, OR 97401-3745
Tel: (541)343-1641; Free: 877-463-6622
Fax: (541)684-7317
E-mail: admissions@nwcu.edu
Web Site: www.nwcu.edu/
Description: Independent Christian, comprehensive, coed. Awards associate, bachelor's, and master's degrees. Founded 1895. Setting: 8-acre urban campus with easy access to Portland. Endowment: $10 million. Educational spending for the previous fiscal year: $3595 per student. Total enrollment: 635. Faculty: 75 (25 full-time, 50 part-time). Student-undergrad faculty ratio is 13:1. 273 applied, 66% were admitted. Full-time: 356 students, 61% women, 39% men. Part-time: 100 students, 65% women, 35% men. Students come from 15 states and territories, 19% from out-of-state. 1% American Indian or Alaska Native, non-Hispanic/Latino; 6% Hispanic/Latino; 1% African American, non-Hispanic/Latino; 2% Asian, non-Hispanic/Latino; 1% Native Hawaiian or other Pacific Islander, non-Hispanic/Latino; 0% international. 37% 25 or older, 31% live on campus, 11% transferred in. Retention: 71% of full-time freshmen returned the following year. Academic areas with the most degrees conferred: business/marketing; education; psychology. Core. Academic remediation for entering students, services for LD students, advanced placement, accelerated degree program, self-designed majors, independent study, distance learning, double major, summer session for credit, part-time degree program, adult/continuing education programs, internships, graduate courses open to undergrads. Off campus study at University of Oregon, Lane Community College. Study abroad program.
Entrance Requirements: Options: electronic application, deferred admission, international baccalaureate accepted. Required: essay, minimum 2.5 high school GPA, SAT or ACT. Recommended: interview. Required for some: high school transcript. Entrance: moderately difficult. Application deadlines: Rolling, Rolling for nonresidents. Notification: continuous, continuous for nonresidents. Transfer credits accepted: Yes.
Costs Per Year: Application fee: $0. Comprehensive fee: $32,480 includes full-time tuition ($24,780), mandatory fees ($100), and college room and board ($7600). Full-time tuition and fees vary according to course load. Room and board charges vary according to board plan and housing facility. Part-time tuition: $825 per credit. Part-time mandatory fees: $100 per year. Part-time tuition and fees vary according to course load.
Collegiate Environment: Orientation program. Drama-theater group, choral group, student-run newspaper. Most popular organizations: Community Life Groups, Circle K, Believers Building Bonds through Boardgames, Parable. Major annual event: Beacon Nights. Student services: personal-psychological counseling. Campus security: 24-hour emergency response devices and patrols, late night transport-escort service, controlled dormitory access, late-night patrols by trained security personnel. 139 undergraduates lived in college housing during 2012-13. Freshmen guaranteed college housing. On-campus residence required in freshman year. Options: men-only, women-only housing available. Edward P. Kellenberger Library with 74,000 books, 874 microform titles, 25,125 serials, an OPAC, and a Web page. Operations spending for the previous fiscal year: $310,108. 60 computers available on campus for general student use. A campuswide network can be accessed from student residence rooms and from off campus. Students can access the following: online class registration. Staffed computer lab on campus provides training in use of computers, software, and the Internet.
Community Environment: See University of Oregon.

■ **OREGON COAST COMMUNITY COLLEGE**
400 SE College Way
Newport, OR 97366
Tel: (541)265-2283
E-mail: webinfo@occc.cc.or.us
Web Site: www.oregoncoastcc.org
Description: Public, 2-year, coed. Administratively affiliated with Clatsop Community College. Awards certificates, transfer associate, and terminal associate degrees. Founded 1987. Setting: 24-acre small town campus. Educational spending for the previous fiscal year: $4987 per student. Total enrollment: 536. Faculty: 42 (10 full-time, 32 part-time). Student-undergrad faculty ratio is 15:1. 93 applied, 100% were admitted. Full-time: 188

students, 62% women, 38% men. Part-time: 348 students, 59% women, 41% men. Students come from 2 states and territories, 1% from out-of-state. 2% American Indian or Alaska Native, non-Hispanic/Latino; 2% Hispanic/Latino; 1% African American, non-Hispanic/Latino; 2% Asian, non-Hispanic/Latino; 0.4% Native Hawaiian or other Pacific Islander, non-Hispanic/Latino; 0% international. 54% 25 or older, 12% transferred in. Retention: 53% of full-time freshmen returned the following year. Core. Academic remediation for entering students, ESL program, services for LD students, honors program, distance learning, summer session for credit, part-time degree program, co-op programs and internships.

Entrance Requirements: Open admission. Option: international baccalaureate accepted. Required for some: essay, 2 recommendations, interview, nursing entrance exam. Entrance: noncompetitive. Transfer credits accepted: Yes.

Costs Per Year: Application fee: $0. State resident tuition: $3564 full-time, $99 per credit part-time. Nonresident tuition: $7704 full-time, $214 per credit part-time. Mandatory fees: $252 full-time, $7 per credit part-time. Full-time tuition and fees vary according to course load and program. Part-time tuition and fees vary according to course load and program.

Collegiate Environment: Orientation program. Most popular organizations: Psych club, Triangle club, Writing club, ASG. Major annual events: Fall Welcome, Oregon transfer day. Campus security: 24-hour emergency response devices. College housing not available. Oregon Coast Community College Library with 63,302 books, 50 serials, 2,079 audiovisual materials, an OPAC, and a Web page. Operations spending for the previous fiscal year: $149,097. 40 computers available on campus for general student use. A campuswide network can be accessed. Staffed computer lab on campus provides training in use of computers, software, and the Internet.

■ OREGON COLLEGE OF ART & CRAFT

8245 SW Barnes Rd.
Portland, OR 97225
Tel: (503)297-5544; Free: 800-390-0632
Fax: (503)297-3155
E-mail: aboerner@ocac.edu
Web Site: www.ocac.edu/

Description: Independent, comprehensive, coed. Awards bachelor's degrees. Founded 1907. Setting: 10-acre urban campus with easy access to Portland. Endowment: $3.7 million. Total enrollment: 164. Faculty: 37 (8 full-time, 29 part-time). Student-undergrad faculty ratio is 9:1. 71 applied, 27% were admitted. 8% from top 10% of their high school class, 38% from top quarter, 77% from top half. Full-time: 133 students, 75% women, 25% men. Part-time: 31 students, 77% women, 23% men. Students come from 21 states and territories, 3 other countries, 35% from out-of-state. 2% American Indian or Alaska Native, non-Hispanic/Latino; 7% Hispanic/Latino; 0% African American, non-Hispanic/Latino; 1% Asian, non-Hispanic/Latino; 1% Native Hawaiian or other Pacific Islander, non-Hispanic/Latino; 2% international. 43% 25 or older, 10% live on campus, 16% transferred in. Retention: 86% of full-time freshmen returned the following year. Academic area with the most degrees conferred: visual and performing arts. Core. Calendar: semesters. Services for LD students, advanced placement, independent study, part-time degree program, adult/continuing education programs, internships. Off campus study at AICAD Mobility Program, OAICU Cross-Registration. Study abroad program.

Entrance Requirements: Options: electronic application, deferred admission, international baccalaureate accepted. Required: essay, high school transcript, minimum 2 high school GPA, 2 recommendations, portfolio that includes 12 to 20 pieces of studio artwork. Recommended: SAT, ACT. Required for some: interview. Entrance: moderately difficult. Application deadlines: Rolling, Rolling for nonresidents. Notification: continuous, continuous for nonresidents. SAT Reasoning Test deadline: 8/15. SAT Subject Test deadline: 8/15. Transfer credits accepted: Yes.

Collegiate Environment: Orientation program. Social organizations: 2 open to all; Student Commonwealth, Ceramics Club; 1% of eligible men and 1% of eligible women are members. Most popular organization: Student Commonwealth. Major annual events: Annual Student and Alumni Holiday Sale, Annual Student Awards Ceremony, Thesis Presentations. Student services: personal-psychological counseling. Campus security: 24-hour emergency response devices, late night transport-escort service. 17 college housing spaces available; all were occupied in 2012-13. Freshmen given priority for college housing. Option: coed housing available. Oregon College of Art and Craft Library plus 1 other with 9,000 books, 90 serials, and an OPAC. Operations spending for the previous fiscal year: $122,098. 15 computers available on campus for general student use. A campuswide network can be accessed

from student residence rooms and from off campus. Staffed computer lab on campus provides training in use of computers, software, and the Internet.

■ OREGON HEALTH & SCIENCE UNIVERSITY

3181 SW Sam Jackson Park Rd.
Portland, OR 97239-3098
Tel: (503)494-8311
Fax: (503)494-5738
E-mail: andersje@ohsu.edu
Web Site: www.ohsu.edu/

Description: State-related, upper-level, coed. Awards bachelor's, master's, and doctoral degrees and post-master's certificates. Founded 1974. Setting: 120-acre urban campus. Total enrollment: 2,849. Faculty: 111 (73 full-time, 38 part-time). Student-undergrad faculty ratio is 7:1. Full-time: 141 students, 87% women, 13% men. Part-time: 684 students, 82% women, 18% men. 1% American Indian or Alaska Native, non-Hispanic/Latino; 6% Hispanic/Latino; 2% African American, non-Hispanic/Latino; 5% Asian, non-Hispanic/Latino; 0.1% Native Hawaiian or other Pacific Islander, non-Hispanic/Latino; 0.5% international. Academic area with the most degrees conferred: health professions and related sciences. Core. Advanced placement, accelerated degree program, distance learning, summer session for credit, part-time degree program, graduate courses open to undergrads. Off campus study at Oregon Consortium of Nursing Education.

Entrance Requirements: Transfer credits accepted: Yes. Applicants placed on waiting list: 129. Wait-listed applicants offered admission: 46.

Collegiate Environment: Orientation program. Choral group, student-run newspaper. Social organizations: 60 open to all; national fraternities. Student services: health clinic, personal-psychological counseling. Campus security: 24-hour emergency response devices and patrols, late night transport-escort service. College housing not available. OHSU Main Library with 315,470 books, 2,121 serials, 1,554 audiovisual materials, an OPAC, and a Web page. Operations spending for the previous fiscal year: $5.8 million.

■ OREGON INSTITUTE OF TECHNOLOGY

3201 Campus Dr.
Klamath Falls, OR 97601-8801
Tel: (541)885-1000; Free: 800-422-2017
Fax: (541)885-1115
E-mail: carl.thomas@oit.edu
Web Site: www.oit.edu/

Description: State-supported, comprehensive, coed. Part of Oregon University System. Awards associate, bachelor's, and master's degrees. Founded 1947. Setting: 173-acre small town campus. Total enrollment: 3,911. Faculty: 257 (144 full-time, 113 part-time). Student-undergrad faculty ratio is 20:1. 713 applied, 93% were admitted. 18% from top 10% of their high school class, 52% from top quarter, 87% from top half. Full-time: 2,148 students, 46% women, 54% men. Part-time: 1,733 students, 50% women, 50% men. 25% from out-of-state. 1% American Indian or Alaska Native, non-Hispanic/Latino; 6% Hispanic/Latino; 1% African American, non-Hispanic/Latino; 4% Asian, non-Hispanic/Latino; 1% Native Hawaiian or other Pacific Islander, non-Hispanic/Latino; 2% international. 13% live on campus, 13% transferred in. Retention: 73% of full-time freshmen returned the following year. Academic areas with the most degrees conferred: health professions and related sciences; engineering technologies; engineering. Core. Academic remediation for entering students, services for LD students, advanced placement, distance learning, double major, summer session for credit, part-time degree program, external degree program, co-op programs and internships, graduate courses open to undergrads. Off campus study at Portland State University. Study abroad program. ROTC: Army (c).

Entrance Requirements: Options: electronic application, deferred admission. Required: high school transcript, minimum 3 high school GPA, SAT or ACT. Entrance: moderately difficult. Application deadline: 10/1. Notification: continuous.

Collegiate Environment: Orientation program. Choral group, student-run newspaper, radio station. Social organizations: national fraternities. Most popular organizations: Phi Delta Theta, Christian Fellowship, International Club, Society of Women Engineers, Association of Student Mechanical Engineers. Major annual events: Super Club Sign-Up, Homecoming, talent show. Student services: health clinic, personal-psychological counseling. Campus security: 24-hour emergency response devices and patrols, late night transport-escort service.

Community Environment: Klamath Falls is located nearly equidistant from Portland, OR, San Francisco, CA, and Reno, NV. Bus, train and air transportation is available. A local phenomenon is a stratum of hot water underlying certain sections of the city, which is used to heat homes and offices. Numerous lakes are in Klamath County, including Crater Lake National Park. Outdoor recreation of all sorts is readily available and enjoyed year-round.

■ OREGON STATE UNIVERSITY

Corvallis, OR 97331
Tel: (541)737-1000; Free: 800-291-4192
Fax: (541)737-6157
E-mail: osuadmit@oregonstate.edu
Web Site: www.oregonstate.edu/

Description: State-supported, university, coed. Part of Oregon University System. Awards bachelor's, master's, and doctoral degrees and post-master's certificates. Founded 1868. Setting: 422-acre small town campus. Endowment: $403.6 million. Research spending for the previous fiscal year: $196.6 million. Educational spending for the previous fiscal year: $9553 per student. Total enrollment: 26,393. Faculty: 1,345 (945 full-time, 400 part-time). Student-undergrad faculty ratio is 21:1. 12,330 applied, 79% were admitted. 26% from top 10% of their high school class, 55% from top quarter, 90% from top half. Full-time: 17,795 students, 46% women, 54% men. Part-time: 4,017 students, 51% women, 49% men. Students come from 50 states and territories, 62 other countries, 21% from out-of-state. 1% American Indian or Alaska Native, non-Hispanic/Latino; 7% Hispanic/Latino; 1% African American, non-Hispanic/Latino; 7% Asian, non-Hispanic/Latino; 1% Native Hawaiian or other Pacific Islander, non-Hispanic/Latino; 5% international. 17% 25 or older, 20% live on campus, 8% transferred in. Retention: 81% of full-time freshmen returned the following year. Academic areas with the most degrees conferred: engineering; business/marketing; family and consumer sciences. Core. Academic remediation for entering students, ESL program, services for LD students, advanced placement, accelerated degree program, self-designed majors, freshman honors college, honors program, independent study, distance learning, double major, summer session for credit, part-time degree program, external degree program, co-op programs and internships, graduate courses open to undergrads. Off campus study at members of the National Student Exchange, members of the Western Interstate Commission for Higher Education. Study abroad program. ROTC: Army, Naval, Air Force.

Entrance Requirements: Options: electronic application, early action, deferred admission. Required: essay, high school transcript, minimum 3 high school GPA, SAT or ACT. Required for some: SAT Subject Tests. Entrance: moderately difficult. Application deadlines: 9/1, 11/1 for early action. Notification: continuous. SAT Reasoning Test deadline: 9/1. Transfer credits accepted: Yes.

Costs Per Year: Application fee: $50. One-time mandatory fee: $300. State resident tuition: $6660 full-time, $185 per credit hour part-time. Nonresident tuition: $20,844 full-time, $579 per credit hour part-time. Mandatory fees: $1478 full-time, $450.57 per term part-time. Full-time tuition and fees vary according to course load and program. Part-time tuition and fees vary according to course load and program. College room and board: $10,563. College room only: $7130. Room and board charges vary according to board plan and housing facility.

Collegiate Environment: Orientation program. Drama-theater group, choral group, marching band, student-run newspaper, radio station. Social organizations: 300 open to all; national fraternities, national sororities; 9% of eligible men and 9% of eligible women are members. Most popular organizations: Associated Students of OSU, International Students of OSU, Graduate Students Organization, Campus Crusade, MECHA. Major annual events: Civil War Football Game, Homecoming, Parents' Weekend. Student services: legal services, health clinic, personal-psychological counseling, women's center. Campus security: 24-hour emergency response devices and patrols, student patrols, late night transport-escort service, controlled dormitory access, crime prevention office. 4,307 college housing spaces available; 3,982 were occupied in 2012-13. Freshmen given priority for college housing. Option: coed housing available. Valley Library with 2 million books, 2.2 million microform titles, 39,000 serials, 27,256 audiovisual materials, an OPAC, and a Web page. Operations spending for the previous fiscal year: $12.6 million. 2,179 computers available on campus for general student use. Computer purchase/lease plans available. A campuswide network can be accessed from student residence rooms and from off campus. Students can access the following: online class registration. Staffed computer lab on campus (open 24 hours a day) provides training in use of computers, software, and the Internet.

Community Environment: Corvallis is situated in the Willamette Valley which is noted for crops and dairy goods. Air, rail and bus transportation is

available. The community includes churches of major denominations, a hospital, library, shopping areas, and civic, fraternal, and veteran's organizations. The Willamette River is nearby for fishing and boating, and the Pacific Coast is a 50-mile drive. Part-time employment opportunities are fair.

■ OREGON STATE UNIVERSITY–CASCADES

2600 NW College Way
Bend, OR 97701
Tel: (541)322-3100
E-mail: cascadeadmit@osucascades.edu
Web Site: www.osucascades.edu/

Description: State-supported, comprehensive, coed. Part of Oregon University System. Awards bachelor's and master's degrees. Founded 2001. Setting: 193-acre small town campus. Total enrollment: 611. Student-undergrad faculty ratio is 15:1. Students come from 15 states and territories, 1 other country, 5% from out-of-state. 44% 25 or older. Services for LD students, advanced placement, double major, summer session for credit, internships. Study abroad program.

Entrance Requirements: Option: international baccalaureate accepted. Application deadlines: Rolling, Rolling for nonresidents. Notification: continuous, continuous for nonresidents.

Collegiate Environment: Orientation program. Student-run newspaper. Student services: personal-psychological counseling, women's center.

■ PACIFIC NORTHWEST COLLEGE OF ART

1241 NW Johnson St.
Portland, OR 97209
Tel: (503)226-4391
Fax: (503)226-3587
E-mail: admissions@pnca.edu
Web Site: www.pnca.edu/

Description: Independent, comprehensive, coed. Awards bachelor's and master's degrees. Founded 1909. Setting: 2-acre urban campus with easy access to Portland. Endowment: $14.8 million. Educational spending for the previous fiscal year: $10,071 per student. Total enrollment: 551. Faculty: 101 (26 full-time, 75 part-time). Student-undergrad faculty ratio is 9:1. Full-time: 392 students, 66% women, 34% men. Part-time: 54 students, 74% women, 26% men. Students come from 27 states and territories, 4 other countries, 73% from out-of-state. 2% American Indian or Alaska Native, non-Hispanic/Latino; 5% Hispanic/Latino; 2% African American, non-Hispanic/Latino; 5% Asian, non-Hispanic/Latino; 0.2% Native Hawaiian or other Pacific Islander, non-Hispanic/Latino; 0.4% international. 21% 25 or older, 21% live on campus, 17% transferred in. Retention: 56% of full-time freshmen returned the following year. Academic area with the most degrees conferred: visual and performing arts. Core. Calendar: semesters. Services for LD students, advanced placement, self-designed majors, independent study, summer session for credit, part-time degree program, co-op programs and internships. Off campus study at Reed College, Oregon Independent Colleges Association, Association of Independent Colleges of Art and Design. Study abroad program.

Entrance Requirements: Options: electronic application, deferred admission. Required: essay, high school transcript, portfolio of artwork. Recommended: minimum 2 high school GPA, interview. Entrance: minimally difficult. Application deadlines: Rolling, Rolling for nonresidents. Notification: continuous, continuous for nonresidents. Transfer credits accepted: Yes. Applicants placed on waiting list: 0. Wait-listed applicants offered admission: 0.

Costs Per Year: Application fee: $0. Tuition: $29,442 full-time, $1227 per credit part-time. Mandatory fees: $1150 full-time, $43 per credit part-time. Part-time tuition and fees vary according to course load. College room only: $10,890.

Collegiate Environment: Orientation program. Major annual events: Time-Based Arts Festival, Focus Week; Thesis Orals and Workshops, Commencement. Student services: personal-psychological counseling. Campus security: 24-hour emergency response devices, late night transport-escort service, controlled dormitory access, entrance security guards during open hours. 130 college housing spaces available; 94 were occupied in 2012-13. Freshmen guaranteed college housing. On-campus residence required in freshman year. Option: coed housing available. Charles Vorhies Fine Arts Library with 28,076 books, 145 serials, 3,422 audiovisual materials, an OPAC, and a Web page. Operations spending for the previous fiscal year: $300,199. 300 computers available on campus for general student use. Computer purchase/lease plans available. A campuswide network can be accessed from student residence rooms and from off campus. Students can

access the following: online class registration. Staffed computer lab on campus provides training in use of computers, software, and the Internet.
Community Environment: See Portland State University.

■ **PACIFIC UNIVERSITY**
2043 College Way
Forest Grove, OR 97116-1797
Tel: (503)357-6151; Free: 877-722-8648
Fax: (503)352-3191
E-mail: admissions@pacificu.edu
Web Site: www.pacificu.edu/
Description: Independent, comprehensive, coed. Awards bachelor's, master's, and doctoral degrees and post-master's certificates. Founded 1849. Setting: 60-acre small town campus with easy access to Portland. Total enrollment: 3,416. 2,618 applied, 85% were admitted. Full-time: 1,658 students, 57% women, 43% men. Part-time: 58 students, 72% women, 28% men. 49% from out-of-state. 1% American Indian or Alaska Native, non-Hispanic/Latino; 9% Hispanic/Latino; 1% African American, non-Hispanic/Latino; 13% Asian, non-Hispanic/Latino; 2% Native Hawaiian or other Pacific Islander, non-Hispanic/Latino; 2% international. 9% 25 or older, 5% transferred in. Retention: 82% of full-time freshmen returned the following year. Academic areas with the most degrees conferred: parks and recreation; visual and performing arts; social sciences. Calendar: semesters. ROTC: Army (c), Air Force (c).
Entrance Requirements: Options: electronic application, deferred admission, international baccalaureate accepted. Required: essay, high school transcript, minimum 3 high school GPA, 1 recommendation, SAT or ACT. Recommended: interview. Entrance: moderately difficult. Application deadline: 8/15. Notification: continuous. SAT Reasoning Test deadline: 8/15. SAT Subject Test deadline: 8/15.
Costs Per Year: Application fee: $40. Comprehensive fee: $45,252 includes full-time tuition ($35,260) and college room and board ($9992). Room and board charges vary according to board plan and housing facility.
Collegiate Environment: Orientation program. Campus security: 24-hour emergency response devices and patrols, late night transport-escort service, controlled dormitory access. Freshmen guaranteed college housing. On-campus residence required through sophomore year. Option: coed housing available. Pacific University Library with an OPAC and a Web page.
Community Environment: Located 30 miles west of Portland, Forest Grove (population 19,600) is the home of Pacific University, the first school to be chartered in the Oregon Territory. Part-time employment is available. Community facilities include 15 churches, 2 libraries, a hospital, and various civic and service organizations. Bus transportation is available. The Pacific Coast beaches are an hour's drive and skiing on Mt. Hood is 90 minutes away.

■ **PIONEER PACIFIC COLLEGE (CLACKAMAS)**
8800 SE Sunnyside Rd.
Clackamas, OR 97015
Free: 866-772-4636
E-mail: inquiries@pioneerpacific.edu
Web Site: www.pioneerpacific.edu/
Description: Proprietary, 4-year, coed. Awards associate and bachelor's degrees. Setting: urban campus.
Entrance Requirements: Required: high school transcript. Required for some: essay, interview.

■ **PIONEER PACIFIC COLLEGE (WILSONVILLE)**
27501 SW Pky. Ave.
Wilsonville, OR 97070
Tel: (503)682-3903; Free: 866-PPC-INFO
Fax: (503)682-1514
E-mail: inquiries@pioneerpacific.edu
Web Site: www.pioneerpacific.edu/
Description: Proprietary, 4-year, coed. Awards associate and bachelor's degrees. Founded 1981. Setting: suburban campus with easy access to Portland. Faculty: 119 (49 full-time, 70 part-time). Student-undergrad faculty ratio is 15:1. Core. Calendar: continuous. Accelerated degree program, honors program, internships.
Entrance Requirements: Open admission. Option: international baccalaureate accepted. Required: high school transcript, interview, CPAt. Required for some: essay. Entrance: noncompetitive. Application deadline: Rolling.
Collegiate Environment: Orientation program. Social organizations: 1 open to all. Most popular organization: Phi Beta Lambda. Major annual event: an-

nual picnic. Pioneer Pacific College Library with 2,500 books. Operations spending for the previous fiscal year: $17,280. 300 computers available on campus for general student use. Computer purchase/lease plans available. A campuswide network can be accessed. Students can access the following: eglobal library.

■ **PIONEER PACIFIC COLLEGE–EUGENE/SPRINGFIELD BRANCH**
3800 Sports Way
Springfield, OR 97477
Free: 866-772-4636
E-mail: inquiries@pioneerpacific.edu
Web Site: www.pioneerpacific.edu/
Description: Proprietary, 4-year, coed. Awards associate and bachelor's degrees. Setting: urban campus.
Entrance Requirements: Required: high school transcript. Required for some: essay, interview.

■ **PORTLAND COMMUNITY COLLEGE**
PO Box 19000
Portland, OR 97280-0990
Tel: (503)244-6111
Fax: (503)452-4988
Web Site: www.pcc.edu/
Description: State and locally supported, 2-year, coed. Awards certificates, diplomas, transfer associate, and terminal associate degrees. Founded 1961. Setting: 400-acre urban campus. Total enrollment: 24,353. 52% 25 or older. Academic remediation for entering students, ESL program, services for LD students, advanced placement, independent study, distance learning, double major, summer session for credit, part-time degree program, external degree program, adult/continuing education programs, co-op programs and internships. Off campus study at Governors State University, Marylhurst University, members of the Oregon University System. Study abroad program.
Entrance Requirements: Open admission. Options: electronic application, international baccalaureate accepted. Entrance: noncompetitive. Application deadline: Rolling.
Collegiate Environment: Orientation program. Drama-theater group, choral group, student-run newspaper. Student services: personal-psychological counseling, women's center. Campus security: 24-hour emergency response devices and patrols, late night transport-escort service. Main library plus 4 others with 91,472 books, 40 microform titles, 820 serials, 247 audiovisual materials, an OPAC, and a Web page. 1,572 computers available on campus for general student use. Computer purchase/lease plans available. A campuswide network can be accessed from off-campus. Students can access the following: online class registration. Staffed computer lab on campus.
Community Environment: See Portland State University.

■ **PORTLAND STATE UNIVERSITY**
PO Box 751
Portland, OR 97207-0751
Tel: (503)725-3000; Free: 800-547-8887
Fax: (503)725-5525
E-mail: mtrifi@pdx.edu
Web Site: www.pdx.edu/
Description: State-supported, university, coed. Part of Oregon University System. Awards bachelor's, master's, and doctoral degrees. Founded 1946. Setting: 49-acre urban campus with easy access to Portland. Total enrollment: 28,731. Faculty: 1,734 (941 full-time, 793 part-time). Student-undergrad faculty ratio is 15:1. Full-time: 14,517 students, 52% women, 48% men. Part-time: 8,653 students, 53% women, 47% men. 12% from out-of-state. 1% American Indian or Alaska Native, non-Hispanic/Latino; 8% Hispanic/Latino; 3% African American, non-Hispanic/Latino; 8% Asian, non-Hispanic/Latino; 1% Native Hawaiian or other Pacific Islander, non-Hispanic/Latino; 6% international. Retention: 74% of full-time freshmen returned the following year. Academic areas with the most degrees conferred: social sciences; business/marketing; liberal arts/general studies. Core. Academic remediation for entering students, ESL program, services for LD students, advanced placement, accelerated degree program, freshman honors college, honors program, independent study, distance learning, double major, summer session for credit, part-time degree program, adult/continuing education programs, co-op programs and internships, graduate courses open to undergrads. Off campus study at other members of the Oregon University System. Study abroad program. ROTC: Army, Air Force (c).

Entrance Requirements: Options: electronic application, early admission, deferred admission. Required: high school transcript, minimum 3 high school GPA, SAT or ACT. Entrance: moderately difficult. Application deadlines: Rolling, Rolling for nonresidents. Notification: continuous, continuous for nonresidents. Transfer credits accepted: Yes.

Costs Per Year: Application fee: $50. One-time mandatory fee: $300. State resident tuition: $6390 full-time, $142 per credit hour part-time. Nonresident tuition: $21,600 full-time, $480 per credit hour part-time. Mandatory fees: $1263 full-time, $17 per credit hour part-time, $98 per term part-time. Full-time tuition and fees vary according to program and reciprocity agreements. Part-time tuition and fees vary according to program. College room and board: $11,019. College room only: $7650. Room and board charges vary according to board plan and housing facility.

Collegiate Environment: Orientation program. Drama-theater group, choral group, student-run newspaper, radio station. Social organizations: 174 open to all; national fraternities, national sororities, local fraternities, local sororities. Student services: legal services, health clinic, personal-psychological counseling, women's center. Campus security: 24-hour emergency response devices and patrols, late night transport-escort service, controlled dormitory access. Freshmen guaranteed college housing. Option: coed housing available. Branford P. Millar Library plus 1 other with an OPAC and a Web page.

Community Environment: Portland lies along both sides of the Willamette River at its juncture with the Columbia River, where there is a splendid port deep enough for the largest ships to dock. Portland has a beautiful background of snowcapped mountain peaks to the north and east, and because of the Japanese Current, enjoys a mild and equable climate. The Columbia River Highway is a beautiful drive, particularly through the Columbia River Gorge with cliffs 2,000 feet high. The Columbia and Willamette Rivers nearby offer year-round water sports, the ocean beach is also nearby, and skiing is available at nearby Mount Hood. Part-time employment and commercial transportation are available. Some of the points of interest are the Hoyt Arboretum, Oregon Art Institute, Oregon Historical Center, Oregon Museum of Science and Industry, Crystal Spring Rhododendron Garden, Washington Park Zoo, Japanese Gardens, World Forestry Center, and the Washington Park Rose Test Gardens.

■ REED COLLEGE
3203 SE Woodstock Blvd.
Portland, OR 97202-8199
Tel: (503)771-1112; Free: 800-547-4750
Fax: (503)777-7553
E-mail: admission@reed.edu
Web Site: www.reed.edu/

Description: Independent, 4-year, coed. Awards bachelor's and master's degrees. Founded 1908. Setting: 116-acre urban campus. Endowment: $450.1 million. Research spending for the previous fiscal year: $1.2 million. Educational spending for the previous fiscal year: $18,451 per student. Total enrollment: 1,455. Faculty: 139 (130 full-time, 9 part-time). Student-undergrad faculty ratio is 10:1. 3,131 applied, 36% were admitted. 63% from top 10% of their high school class, 85% from top quarter, 98% from top half. 12 valedictorians. Full-time: 1,395 students, 54% women, 46% men. Part-time: 37 students, 73% women, 27% men. Students come from 50 states and territories, 44 other countries, 87% from out-of-state. 1% American Indian or Alaska Native, non-Hispanic/Latino; 9% Hispanic/Latino; 3% African American, non-Hispanic/Latino; 8% Asian, non-Hispanic/Latino; 0.1% Native Hawaiian or other Pacific Islander, non-Hispanic/Latino; 6% international. 2% 25 or older, 67% live on campus, 2% transferred in. Retention: 92% of full-time freshmen returned the following year. Academic areas with the most degrees conferred: social sciences; biological/life sciences; English. Core. Calendar: semesters. Academic remediation for entering students, services for LD students, advanced placement, independent study, double major, part-time degree program, co-op programs and internships. Off campus study at Howard University, Sarah Lawrence College, Sea Education Association. Study abroad program.

Entrance Requirements: Options: electronic application, early admission, early decision, deferred admission, international baccalaureate accepted. Required: essay, high school transcript, 2 recommendations, SAT or ACT. Recommended: interview, SAT Subject Tests, International citizens who have an SAT critical reading score below 600 are strongly recommended to submit TOEFL or IELTS scores. Entrance: most difficult. Application deadlines: 1/15, 11/15 for early decision plan 1, 12/20 for early decision plan 2. Notification: 4/1, 12/15 for early decision plan 1, 2/1 for early decision plan 2. SAT Reasoning Test deadline: 3/1. SAT Subject Test deadline: 3/1.

Transfer credits accepted: Yes. Applicants placed on waiting list: 748. Waitlisted applicants offered admission: 56. Early decision applicants: 186. Early decision applicants admitted: 115.

Costs Per Year: Application fee: $50. Comprehensive fee: $55,920 includes full-time tuition ($44,200), mandatory fees ($260), and college room and board ($11,460). College room only: $5960. Room and board charges vary according to board plan and housing facility. Part-time tuition: $1903 per semester hour. Part-time tuition varies according to course load.

Collegiate Environment: Orientation program. Drama-theater group, choral group, student-run newspaper, radio station. Social organizations: 105 open to all. Most popular organizations: GreenBoard, Canyon Day, Reed Outing Club, Bike Co-op, Comic Book Reading Room. Major annual events: Renaissance Faire, Paideia, Reed Arts Weekend. Student services: health clinic, personal-psychological counseling, women's center. Campus security: 24-hour emergency response devices and patrols, student patrols, late night transport-escort service, controlled dormitory access, 24-hour emergency dispatch. 950 college housing spaces available; 897 were occupied in 2012-13. Freshmen guaranteed college housing. On-campus residence required in freshman year. Options: coed, women-only housing available. Eric V. Hauser Memorial Library with 629,871 books, 180,996 microform titles, 17,169 serials, 31,456 audiovisual materials, an OPAC, and a Web page. Operations spending for the previous fiscal year: $4.3 million. 434 computers available on campus for general student use. Computer purchase/lease plans available. A campuswide network can be accessed from student residence rooms and from off campus. Students can access the following: online class registration. Staffed computer lab on campus (open 24 hours a day) provides training in use of computers, software, and the Internet.

Community Environment: See Portland State University.

■ ROGUE COMMUNITY COLLEGE
3345 Redwood Hwy.
Grants Pass, OR 97527-9298
Tel: (541)956-7500
E-mail: csullivan@roguecc.edu
Web Site: www.roguecc.edu/

Description: State and locally supported, 2-year, coed. Awards certificates, transfer associate, and terminal associate degrees. Founded 1970. Setting: 84-acre rural campus. Endowment: $6.4 million. Research spending for the previous fiscal year: $86,310. Educational spending for the previous fiscal year: $3638 per student. Total enrollment: 5,556. Faculty: 408 (77 full-time, 331 part-time). Student-undergrad faculty ratio is 18:1. Full-time: 2,312 students, 55% women, 45% men. Part-time: 3,244 students, 60% women, 40% men. Students come from 22 states and territories, 3 other countries, 2% from out-of-state. 2% American Indian or Alaska Native, non-Hispanic/Latino; 12% Hispanic/Latino; 1% African American, non-Hispanic/Latino; 2% Asian, non-Hispanic/Latino; 1% Native Hawaiian or other Pacific Islander, non-Hispanic/Latino; 0.1% international. 52% 25 or older, 69% transferred in. Core. Academic remediation for entering students, ESL program, services for LD students, advanced placement, independent study, distance learning, double major, summer session for credit, part-time degree program, adult/continuing education programs, co-op programs and internships. Study abroad program.

Entrance Requirements: Open admission except for nursing, human services, emergency medical technology, apprenticeship, dental assisting, massage therapy programs. Options: electronic application, early admission. Entrance: noncompetitive. Application deadlines: Rolling, Rolling for nonresidents. Preference given to local residents. Transfer credits accepted: Yes.

Costs Per Year: Application fee: $0. State resident tuition: $3132 full-time, $87 per credit hour part-time. Nonresident tuition: $3852 full-time, $107 per credit hour part-time. Mandatory fees: $549 full-time, $4 per credit hour part-time, $135 per term part-time. Full-time tuition and fees vary according to course load. Part-time tuition and fees vary according to course load.

Collegiate Environment: Orientation program. Drama-theater group, choral group, student-run newspaper. Student services: personal-psychological counseling. Campus security: 24-hour emergency response devices and patrols, late night transport-escort service. Rogue Community College Library with 33,000 books, 275 serials, and an OPAC. Operations spending for the previous fiscal year: $895,569. 700 computers available on campus for general student use. A campuswide network can be accessed from off-campus. Students can access the following: online class registration. Staffed computer lab on campus provides training in use of computers, software, and the Internet.

Community Environment: See Southern Oregon State College.

■ SOUTHERN OREGON UNIVERSITY

1250 Siskiyou Blvd.
Ashland, OR 97520
Tel: (541)552-7672
Fax: (541)552-6329
E-mail: admissions@sou.edu
Web Site: www.sou.edu/

Description: State-supported, comprehensive, coed. Part of Oregon University System. Awards bachelor's and master's degrees and post-master's certificates. Founded 1926. Setting: 175-acre small town campus. Endowment: $20.1 million. Research spending for the previous fiscal year: $1.1 million. Educational spending for the previous fiscal year: $6318 per student. Total enrollment: 6,307. Faculty: 334 (199 full-time, 135 part-time). Student-undergrad faculty ratio is 20:1. 2,063 applied, 92% were admitted. Full-time: 3,874 students, 55% women, 45% men. Part-time: 1,786 students, 62% women, 38% men. Students come from 45 states and territories, 18 other countries, 31% from out-of-state. 2% American Indian or Alaska Native, non-Hispanic/Latino; 9% Hispanic/Latino; 2% African American, non-Hispanic/Latino; 2% Asian, non-Hispanic/Latino; 1% Native Hawaiian or other Pacific Islander, non-Hispanic/Latino; 2% international. 28% 25 or older, 24% live on campus, 11% transferred in. Retention: 68% of full-time freshmen returned the following year. Academic areas with the most degrees conferred: business/marketing; psychology; visual and performing arts. Core. Academic remediation for entering students, ESL program, services for LD students, advanced placement, accelerated degree program, self-designed majors, freshman honors college, honors program, independent study, distance learning, double major, summer session for credit, part-time degree program, adult/continuing education programs, co-op programs and internships. Off campus study at National Student Exchange, other members of the Oregon University System. Study abroad program. ROTC: Army.

Entrance Requirements: Options: electronic application, early admission, deferred admission, international baccalaureate accepted. Required: high school transcript, minimum 2.75 high school GPA, SAT or ACT. Required for some: essay, SAT Subject Tests. Entrance: moderately difficult. Application deadline: Rolling. Notification: continuous. SAT Reasoning Test deadline: 9/1. SAT Subject Test deadline: 9/1. Transfer credits accepted: Yes.

Costs Per Year: Application fee: $50. State resident tuition: $6183 full-time. Nonresident tuition: $18,900 full-time. Mandatory fees: $1338 full-time. Full-time tuition and fees vary according to course load, program, and reciprocity agreements. College room and board: $9918. College room only: $5400. Room and board charges vary according to board plan and housing facility.

Collegiate Environment: Orientation program. Drama-theater group, choral group, student-run newspaper, radio station. Social organizations: 65 open to all. Most popular organizations: Native American Student Union, International Student Association, Impact (religious club), Ho'opa'a Hawaii Club, Omicron Delta Kappa. Major annual events: Southern Oregon Arts and Research Symposium, International Week, One World (performing arts series). Student services: legal services, health clinic, personal-psychological counseling, women's center. Campus security: 24-hour emergency response devices and patrols, student patrols, late night transport-escort service, controlled dormitory access. 1,100 college housing spaces available; 1,000 were occupied in 2012-13. Freshmen guaranteed college housing. On-campus residence required in freshman year. Option: coed housing available. Lenn and Dixie Hannon Library with 400,861 books, 800,548 microform titles, 3,571 serials, 10,492 audiovisual materials, an OPAC, and a Web page. Operations spending for the previous fiscal year: $2.4 million. 750 computers available on campus for general student use. Computer purchase/lease plans available. A campuswide network can be accessed from student residence rooms and from off campus. Students can access the following: online class registration, Online account information including bill payment, online employee records for student workers. Staffed computer lab on campus provides training in use of computers, software, and the Internet.

Community Environment: Ashland, a town of 20,000 people, is nestled at the base of the Sikiyou Mountains in the Rogue Valley of Oregon. Culturally the community has gained national recognition through the Oregon Shakespearean festival and associated legitimate theatres, annually drawing over 300,000 patrons. The town is surrounded by natural forests, mountain lakes and rivers, spectacular for outdoor sports and ecological studies. For the skier, it's only 30 minutes to the 7,000 foot Mt. Ashland Ski Resort.

■ SOUTHWESTERN OREGON COMMUNITY COLLEGE

1988 Newmark Ave.
Coos Bay, OR 97420-2912
Tel: (541)888-2525; Free: 800-962-2838
E-mail: lwells@socc.edu
Web Site: www.socc.edu/

Description: State and locally supported, 2-year, coed. Awards certificates, diplomas, transfer associate, and terminal associate degrees. Founded 1961. Setting: 125-acre small town campus. Endowment: $769,894. Educational spending for the previous fiscal year: $2340 per student. Total enrollment: 2,206. 5% from out-of-state. 38% 25 or older. Core. Academic remediation for entering students, ESL program, services for LD students, advanced placement, distance learning, summer session for credit, part-time degree program, adult/continuing education programs, co-op programs and internships.

Entrance Requirements: Open admission except for culinary institute, nursing, emergency medical technology programs, surgical technician, pharmacy technician programs. Option: early admission. Required for some: high school transcript. Entrance: noncompetitive. Application deadline: Rolling. Notification: continuous.

Costs Per Year: Application fee: $30. One-time mandatory fee: $30. State resident tuition: $3444 full-time, $82 per credit hour part-time. Nonresident tuition: $3444 full-time, $82 per credit hour part-time. Mandatory fees: $1320 full-time, $24 per credit hour part-time, $26. Full-time tuition and fees vary according to program. College room and board: $7876. Room and board charges vary according to board plan.

Collegiate Environment: Orientation program. Drama-theater group, choral group, student-run newspaper. Major annual events: Orientation, Fall Funk Fest, Swocc Stock. Campus security: controlled dormitory access. Southwestern Oregon Community College Library with 40,505 books, 1,836 microform titles, 218 serials, 3,673 audiovisual materials, an OPAC, and a Web page. Operations spending for the previous fiscal year: $343,207. 65 computers available on campus for general student use. A campuswide network can be accessed. Students can access the following: online class registration. Staffed computer lab on campus.

Community Environment: Coos Bay is an important seaport and trading center as well as one of the world's largest lumber export points. Community facilities include a library, hospital, churches representing many major denominations, and civic and service organizations. Coos Bay and adjacent North Bend are the shopping centers for southwestern Oregon. The Golden and Silver Falls State Park is 24 miles away, offering facilities for picnicking, camping, and fishing, as do Millicoma-Myrtle Grove State Park and Shore Acres State Park. Opportunities for part-time employment are good.

■ TILLAMOOK BAY COMMUNITY COLLEGE

4301 Third St.
Tillamook, OR 97141
Tel: (503)842-8222
Fax: (503)842-2214
E-mail: gates@tillamookbay.cc
Web Site: www.tbcc.cc.or.us/

Description: District-supported, 2-year, coed. Administratively affiliated with Portland Community College. Awards certificates, diplomas, transfer associate, and terminal associate degrees. Founded 1984. Total enrollment: 310. Faculty: 36 (6 full-time, 30 part-time). Student-undergrad faculty ratio is 8:1. 0% from out-of-state. 45% 25 or older.

Entrance Requirements: Recommended: high school transcript.

Collegiate Environment: Campus security: evening security guard.

■ TREASURE VALLEY COMMUNITY COLLEGE

650 College Blvd.
Ontario, OR 97914-3423
Tel: (541)889-6493
Fax: (541)881-2721
E-mail: clbell@tvcc.cc
Web Site: www.tvcc.cc.or.us/

Description: State and locally supported, 2-year, coed. Awards certificates, transfer associate, and terminal associate degrees. Founded 1962. Setting: 95-acre small town campus. Endowment: $2 million. Total enrollment: 2,010. Faculty: 140 (48 full-time, 92 part-time). Student-undergrad faculty ratio is 11:1. 652 applied, 100% were admitted. Full-time: 997 students, 56% women, 44% men. Part-time: 1,013 students, 69% women, 31% men. Students come from 12 states and territories, 2 other countries, 68% from out-of-state. 38% 25 or older, 6% live on campus, 18% transferred in. Core. Academic remediation for entering students, ESL program, services for LD students, advanced placement, accelerated degree program, honors program, independent study, distance learning, summer session for credit, part-time degree program, external degree program, adult/continuing education programs, co-op programs and internships. ROTC: Army (c).

Entrance Requirements: Open admission. Options: early admission, deferred admission. Entrance: noncompetitive. Application deadline: Rolling. Notification: continuous.

Collegiate Environment: Orientation program. Drama-theater group, choral group, marching band. Student services: health clinic, personal-psychological counseling. Campus security: student patrols, controlled dormitory access. Treasure Valley Community College Library with 28,000 books, 150 serials, and an OPAC. 70 computers available on campus for general student use. A campuswide network can be accessed. Students can access the following: online class registration. Staffed computer lab on campus provides training in use of computers, software, and the Internet.

Community Environment: Ontario, one mile from the Oregon-Idaho state line, lies in an agricultural area that produces potatoes, onions, sugar beets, corn, and hay. All forms of commercial transportation are available. Community facilities include the Malheur County Library, a hospital, and several civic and service organizations. Mule, deer, and antelope hunting on the vast rangeland, and fishing on Owyhee Lake and the Malheur and Snake Rivers attract the sportsman. Semiprecious stones may be found in Malheur County. Skiing may be enjoyed at nearby ski resorts. Job opportunities are available.

■ **UMPQUA COMMUNITY COLLEGE**
PO Box 967
Roseburg, OR 97470-0226
Tel: (541)440-4600
Fax: (541)440-4612
E-mail: Richard.Robles@umpqua.edu
Web Site: www.umpqua.edu/

Description: State and locally supported, 2-year, coed. Awards certificates, transfer associate, and terminal associate degrees. Founded 1964. Setting: 100-acre rural campus. Endowment: $3.7 million. Educational spending for the previous fiscal year: $2667 per student. Total enrollment: 2,607. Faculty: 167 (63 full-time, 104 part-time). Student-undergrad faculty ratio is 20:1. 221 applied, 100% were admitted. Full-time: 1,313 students, 56% women, 44% men. Part-time: 1,294 students, 60% women, 40% men. Students come from 5 states and territories, 2 other countries. 2% American Indian or Alaska Native, non-Hispanic/Latino; 5% Hispanic/Latino; 1% African American, non-Hispanic/Latino; 1% Asian, non-Hispanic/Latino; 0.3% Native Hawaiian or other Pacific Islander, non-Hispanic/Latino; 0.1% international. 52% 25 or older, 17% transferred in. Retention: 50% of full-time freshmen returned the following year. Core. Academic remediation for entering students, ESL program, services for LD students, advanced placement, accelerated degree program, honors program, independent study, distance learning, summer session for credit, part-time degree program, adult/continuing education programs, co-op programs and internships. Study abroad program.

Entrance Requirements: Open admission except for registered nursing and emergency medical technology programs. Options: electronic application, early admission, deferred admission. Recommended: high school transcript. Entrance: noncompetitive. Application deadline: Rolling.

Costs Per Year: Application fee: $25. State resident tuition: $4253 full-time. Nonresident tuition: $9383 full-time. Mandatory fees: $304 full-time.

Collegiate Environment: Orientation program. Drama-theater group, choral group, student-run newspaper. Social organizations: 10 open to all. Most popular organizations: Phi Theta Kappa, Computer Club, Phi Beta Lambda, Nursing Club, Umpqua Accounting Associates. Major annual events: Student Government Sponsored Quarterly BBQ, Transfer College Day, New Student Orientation. Student services: personal-psychological counseling. Campus security: 24-hour emergency response devices and patrols. College housing not available. Umpqua Community College Library with 41,000 books, 350 serials, an OPAC, and a Web page. Operations spending for the previous fiscal year: $364,912. 429 computers available on campus for general student use. A campuswide network can be accessed from off-campus. Students can access the following: online class registration. Staffed computer lab on campus provides training in use of computers, software, and the Internet.

Community Environment: Roseburg is the county seat of Douglas County, one of the largest lumber centers in the country. Roseburg is also a noted sheep producing area. The town is the headquarters for the Umpqua National Forest, where good salmon and trout fishing may be enjoyed and in season, hunting of deer, elk, bear, and cougar is permitted.

■ **UNIVERSITY OF OREGON**
Eugene, OR 97403
Tel: (541)346-3111; Free: 800-232-3825
Fax: (541)346-5815
E-mail: uoadmit@uoregon.edu
Web Site: www.uoregon.edu/

Description: State-supported, university, coed. Part of Oregon University System. Awards bachelor's, master's, and doctoral degrees. Founded 1872. Setting: 295-acre urban campus. Endowment: $493.5 million. Research spending for the previous fiscal year: $121.7 million. Educational spending for the previous fiscal year: $10,839 per student. Total enrollment: 24,518. Faculty: 1,505 (1,039 full-time, 466 part-time). Student-undergrad faculty ratio is 19:1. 21,263 applied, 74% were admitted. 28% from top 10% of their high school class, 63% from top quarter, 94% from top half. 7 National Merit Scholars. Full-time: 18,847 students, 52% women, 48% men. Part-time: 1,962 students, 49% women, 51% men. Students come from 53 states and territories, 75 other countries, 35% from out-of-state. 1% American Indian or Alaska Native, non-Hispanic/Latino; 7% Hispanic/Latino; 2% African American, non-Hispanic/Latino; 5% Asian, non-Hispanic/Latino; 1% Native Hawaiian or other Pacific Islander, non-Hispanic/Latino; 11% international. 9% 25 or older, 20% live on campus, 7% transferred in. Retention: 85% of full-time freshmen returned the following year. Academic areas with the most degrees conferred: social sciences; business/marketing; communication/journalism. Core. ESL program, services for LD students, advanced placement, self-designed majors, honors program, independent study, distance learning, double major, summer session for credit, part-time degree program, co-op programs and internships, graduate courses open to undergrads. Off campus study at National Student Exchange. Study abroad program. ROTC: Army, Air Force (c).

Entrance Requirements: Options: electronic application, early action, international baccalaureate accepted. Required: essay, high school transcript, 15 college preparatory units, SAT or ACT. Recommended: minimum 3 high school GPA. Required for some: 2 recommendations, SAT and SAT Subject Tests or ACT. Entrance: moderately difficult. Application deadlines: 1/15, 11/1 for early action. Notification: 10/1, 12/15 for early action. SAT Reasoning Test deadline: 2/15. SAT Subject Test deadline: 2/15. Transfer credits accepted: Yes. Applicants placed on waiting list: 1,714. Wait-listed applicants offered admission: 479.

Costs Per Year: Application fee: $50. One-time mandatory fee: $347. State resident tuition: $8010 full-time, $178 per credit hour part-time. Nonresident tuition: $27,360 full-time, $608 per credit hour part-time. Mandatory fees: $1300 full-time. Full-time tuition and fees vary according to course load. Part-time tuition varies according to course load. College room and board: $10,580. Room and board charges vary according to board plan and housing facility.

Collegiate Environment: Orientation program. Drama-theater group, choral group, marching band, student-run newspaper, radio station. Social organizations: 250 open to all; national fraternities, national sororities, local fraternities, local sororities. Most popular organizations: political and environmental action, cultural organizations, major-specific organizations, community service organizations, club sports. Major annual events: University Day, Homecoming, ASUO Fall and Spring Street Faires. Student services: legal services, health clinic, personal-psychological counseling, women's center. Campus security: 24-hour emergency response devices and patrols, late night transport-escort service, controlled dormitory access. 4,200 college housing spaces available; 4,015 were occupied in 2012-13. Freshmen given priority for college housing. Option: coed housing available. Knight Library plus 5 others with 3.1 million books, 3 million microform titles, 90,000 serials, 112,492 audiovisual materials, an OPAC, and a Web page. Operations spending for the previous fiscal year: $21.6 million. 1,118 computers available on campus for general student use. A campuswide network can be accessed from student residence rooms and from off campus. Students can access the following: online class registration. Staffed computer lab on campus provides training in use of computers, software, and the Internet.

Community Environment: Eugene, the center of a vast recreational area, is an important high-technology and software center. Bicycles are a major form of student transportation. Airline, bus and train transportation are available. Eugene's facilities include more than 80 churches, a large public library, a YMCA, YWCA, three hospitals, and a number of motels. Eugene is 60 miles east of the Pacific Ocean and 60 miles west of the Cascade Mountains. The Willamette National Forest nearby provides fine hunting and fishing opportunities and skiing is enjoyed at the Hoodoo Ski Bowl and Willamette Pass Ski area.

■ UNIVERSITY OF PHOENIX–OREGON CAMPUS

13221 SW 68th Pky., Ste. 500

Tigard, OR 97223

Tel: (503)670-0590; Free: 866-766-0766

Fax: (503)670-0614

Web Site: www.phoenix.edu/

Description: Proprietary, comprehensive, coed. Awards bachelor's and master's degrees. Founded 1976. Setting: urban campus. Total enrollment: 1,265. Faculty: 253 (31 full-time, 222 part-time). Full-time: 1,042 students, 57% women, 43% men. 87% 25 or older. Academic areas with the most degrees conferred: business/marketing; computer and information sciences; public administration and social services. Core. Calendar: continuous. Services for LD students, advanced placement, accelerated degree program, independent study, distance learning, external degree program, adult/continuing education programs, graduate courses open to undergrads.

Entrance Requirements: Open admission. Options: electronic application, deferred admission. Required: 1 recommendation. Required for some: high school transcript. Entrance: noncompetitive. Application deadline: Rolling.

Collegiate Environment: Campus security: late night transport-escort service. University Library with 16,781 serials, an OPAC, and a Web page. Operations spending for the previous fiscal year: $6.8 million.

■ UNIVERSITY OF PORTLAND

5000 N Willamette Blvd.

Portland, OR 97203-5798

Tel: (503)943-7911; Free: 888-627-5601

Fax: (503)943-7399

E-mail: admissions@up.edu

Web Site: www.up.edu/

Description: Independent Roman Catholic, comprehensive, coed. Awards bachelor's, master's, and doctoral degrees and post-master's certificates. Founded 1901. Setting: 125-acre urban campus. Endowment: $80 million. Research spending for the previous fiscal year: $798,000. Educational spending for the previous fiscal year: $10,178 per student. Total enrollment: 3,981. Faculty: 335 (213 full-time, 122 part-time). Student-undergrad faculty ratio is 13:1. 8,696 applied, 67% were admitted. 45% from top 10% of their high school class, 75% from top quarter, 95% from top half. Full-time: 3,320 students, 59% women, 41% men. Part-time: 82 students, 61% women, 39% men. 65% from out-of-state. 0.3% American Indian or Alaska Native, non-Hispanic/Latino; 9% Hispanic/Latino; 1% African American, non-Hispanic/Latino; 10% Asian, non-Hispanic/Latino; 1% Native Hawaiian or other Pacific Islander, non-Hispanic/Latino; 3% international. 3% 25 or older, 55% live on campus, 2% transferred in. Retention: 89% of full-time freshmen returned the following year. Academic areas with the most degrees conferred: health professions and related sciences; business/marketing; engineering. Core. Calendar: semesters. Services for LD students, advanced placement, honors program, independent study, double major, summer session for credit, part-time degree program, adult/continuing education programs, internships, graduate courses open to undergrads. Off campus study. Study abroad program. ROTC: Army, Air Force.

Entrance Requirements: Options: electronic application, deferred admission, international baccalaureate accepted. Required: essay, high school transcript, 1 recommendation, SAT or ACT. Recommended: SAT, ACT. Entrance: moderately difficult. Application deadline: 6/1. Notification: continuous. SAT Reasoning Test deadline: 2/1. Transfer credits accepted: Yes.

Costs Per Year: Application fee: $50. Tuition: $35,120 full-time, $1100 per credit hour part-time. Mandatory fees: $140 full-time. Full-time tuition and fees vary according to program. Part-time tuition varies according to course load and program. College room only: $7290. Room charges vary according to housing facility.

Collegiate Environment: Orientation program. Drama-theater group, choral group, student-run newspaper, radio station. Social organizations: 40 open to all. Most popular organizations: English Society, International Club, Hawaiian Club, rugby club, Social Science Club. Major annual events: Homecoming Dance, Dance of the Decades, Hawaiian Luau. Student services: health clinic, personal-psychological counseling. Campus security: 24-hour emergency response devices and patrols, student patrols, late night transport-escort service, controlled dormitory access. 1,600 college housing spaces available. Freshmen guaranteed college housing. On-campus residence required in freshman year. Options: coed, men-only, women-only housing available. Wilson M. Clark Library plus 1 other with 219,693 books, 41,624 microform titles, 6,830 serials, 15,002 audiovisual materials, an OPAC, and a Web page. Operations spending for the previous fiscal year: $3.8 million. 575 computers available on campus for general student use. A campuswide network can be accessed from student residence rooms and from off campus. Students can access the following: online class registration. Staffed computer lab on campus (open 24 hours a day) provides training in use of computers, software, and the Internet.

Community Environment: See Portland State University.

■ WARNER PACIFIC COLLEGE

2219 SE 68th Ave.

Portland, OR 97215-4099

Tel: (503)517-1000; Free: 800-804-1510

Fax: (503)788-7425

E-mail: admiss@warnerpacific.edu

Web Site: www.warnerpacific.edu/

Description: Independent, 4-year, coed, affiliated with Church of God. Awards associate, bachelor's, and master's degrees. Founded 1937. Setting: 15-acre urban campus with easy access to Portland. Endowment: $7.7 million. Educational spending for the previous fiscal year: $6630 per student. Total enrollment: 1,333. Faculty: 116 (24 full-time, 92 part-time). Student-undergrad faculty ratio is 22:1. 514 applied, 61% were admitted. Full-time: 1,166 students, 63% women, 37% men. Part-time: 15 students, 40% women, 60% men. Students come from 26 states and territories, 18 other countries, 42% from out-of-state. 13% 25 or older, 19% live on campus, 10% transferred in. Retention: 60% of full-time freshmen returned the following year. Academic areas with the most degrees conferred: social sciences; business/marketing; theology and religious vocations. Core. Calendar: semesters. Academic remediation for entering students, services for LD students, advanced placement, accelerated degree program, self-designed majors, honors program, independent study, double major, summer session for credit, part-time degree program, adult/continuing education programs, co-op programs and internships. Off campus study at Mt. Hood Community College, Concordia College (OR), Oregon Independent Colleges Association, Council for Christian Colleges and Universities (CCCU), Food for the Hungry Go Ed program. Study abroad program. ROTC: Air Force (c).

Entrance Requirements: Options: electronic application, international baccalaureate accepted. Required: essay, high school transcript, minimum 2.5 high school GPA, SAT or ACT. Recommended: minimum 3 high school GPA, interview, SAT Subject Tests. Required for some: 1 recommendation, interview. Entrance: moderately difficult. Application deadline: Rolling. Notification: continuous.

Collegiate Environment: Orientation program. Drama-theater group, choral group, student-run newspaper. Most popular organizations: Associated Students of Warner Pacific College, yearbook, College Activities Board, Fellowship of Christian Athletes. Major annual events: Homecoming, spring and winter banquets, Midnight Barbecue and Breakfast. Student services: health clinic, personal-psychological counseling. Campus security: 24-hour emergency response devices and patrols, student patrols, late night transport-escort service, controlled dormitory access. 292 college housing spaces available; 265 were occupied in 2012-13. Freshmen given priority for college housing. On-campus residence required through junior year. Options: men-only, women-only housing available. Otto F. Linn Library with 87,653 books, an OPAC, and a Web page. Operations spending for the previous fiscal year: $419,726. 90 computers available on campus for general student use. A campuswide network can be accessed from student residence rooms and from off campus. Students can access the following: online class registration.

Community Environment: See Portland State University.

■ WESTERN OREGON UNIVERSITY

345 N Monmouth Ave.

Monmouth, OR 97361-1394

Tel: (503)838-8000; Free: 877-877-1593

Fax: (503)838-8067

E-mail: wolfgram@wou.edu

Web Site: www.wou.edu/

Description: State-supported, comprehensive, coed. Part of Oregon University System. Awards bachelor's and master's degrees. Founded 1856. Setting: 157-acre rural campus with easy access to Portland. Research spending for the previous fiscal year: $8 million. Educational spending for the previous fiscal year: $5937 per student. Total enrollment: 6,187. Faculty: 406 (191 full-time, 215 part-time). Student-undergrad faculty ratio is 20:1. 2,841 applied, 88% were admitted. 10% from top 10% of their high school class, 32% from top quarter, 68% from top half. Full-time: 4,797 students, 60% women, 40% men. Part-time: 700 students, 55% women, 45% men. Students come from 33 states and territories, 22 other countries, 12% from out-of-state. 2% American Indian or Alaska Native, non-Hispanic/Latino; 6% Hispanic/Latino; 4% African American, non-Hispanic/Latino; 3% Asian, non-Hispanic/Latino; 3% Native Hawaiian or other Pacific Islander, non-Hispanic/Latino; 5% international. 17% 25 or older, 11% transferred in. Retention: 70% of full-time freshmen returned the following year. Academic areas with the most degrees conferred: education; business/marketing; psychology. Core. Academic remediation for entering students, ESL program, services for LD students, advanced placement, self-designed majors, freshman honors college, honors program, independent study, distance learning, double major, summer session for credit, part-time degree program, internships, graduate courses open to undergrads. Off campus study at other members of the Oregon University System. Study abroad program. ROTC: Army, Naval (c).

Entrance Requirements: Options: electronic application, deferred admission, international baccalaureate accepted. Required: high school transcript, minimum 2.75 high school GPA, general college preparatory program completion. Entrance: moderately difficult. Application deadline: Rolling. Notification: continuous. Transfer credits accepted: Yes.

Costs Per Year: Application fee: $50. State resident tuition: $8529 full-time. Nonresident tuition: $21,114 full-time. Tuition guaranteed not to increase for student's term of enrollment.

Collegiate Environment: Orientation program. Drama-theater group, choral group, student-run newspaper. Social organizations: 50 open to all. Most popular organizations: Model United Nations, Multicultural Student Union, Oregon Student Association, Alternative Spring Break (community service), M.E.Ch.A. Major annual events: Homecoming, Holiday Tree Lighting, Alcohol Awareness Week. Student services: health clinic, personal-psychological counseling, women's center. Campus security: 24-hour emergency response devices and patrols, student patrols, late night transport-escort service, controlled dormitory access. 1,350 college housing spaces available; 1,280 were occupied in 2012-13. Freshmen given priority for college housing. On-campus residence required in freshman year. Option: coed housing available. Wayne and Lynn Hamersly Library with 227,707 books, 2,158 serials, 8,010 audiovisual materials, an OPAC, and a Web page. Operations spending for the previous fiscal year: $2 million. 411 computers available on campus for general student use. A campuswide network can be accessed from student residence rooms and from off campus. Students can access the following: online class registration. Staffed computer lab on campus.

Community Environment: Located in Monmouth, a town of 7,500, Western is 15 miles from Salem, the state capital, and is midway between the state's two largest cities, Portland and Eugene. Western is a short drive from the famed Oregon Coast to the west and the majestic Cascade Mountains to the east. Monmouth is located in the Willamette Valley. The University is the town's main employer and serves as the cultural and athletic center for the area.

■ **WILLAMETTE UNIVERSITY**
900 State St.
Salem, OR 97301-3931
Tel: (503)370-6300; Free: 877-542-2787
Fax: (503)375-5363
E-mail: libarts@willamette.edu
Web Site: www.willamette.edu/

Description: Independent United Methodist, comprehensive, coed. Awards bachelor's, master's, and doctoral degrees. Founded 1842. Setting: 72-acre urban campus with easy access to Portland. Endowment: $205.2 million. Research spending for the previous fiscal year: $3.2 million. Educational spending for the previous fiscal year: $12,775 per student. Total enrollment: 2,933. Faculty: 320 (243 full-time, 77 part-time). Student-undergrad faculty ratio is 10:1. 6,462 applied, 83% were admitted. 38% from top 10% of their high school class, 66% from top quarter, 92% from top half. Full-time: 1,968 students, 55% women, 45% men. Part-time: 135 students, 53% women, 47% men. Students come from 43 states and territories, 20 other countries, 73% from out-of-state. 1% American Indian or Alaska Native, non-Hispanic/Latino; 9% Hispanic/Latino; 2% African American, non-Hispanic/Latino; 7% Asian, non-Hispanic/Latino; 1% Native Hawaiian or other Pacific Islander, non-Hispanic/Latino; 1% international. 1% 25 or older, 68% live on campus, 2% transferred in. Retention: 86% of full-time freshmen returned the following year. Academic areas with the most degrees conferred: social sciences; English; visual and performing arts. Core. Calendar: semesters. Services for LD students, advanced placement, accelerated degree program, self-designed majors, independent study, double major, part-time degree program, internships, graduate courses open to undergrads. Off campus study at American University, Urban Life Center (Chicago, IL). Study abroad program. ROTC: Army (c), Air Force (c).

Entrance Requirements: Options: electronic application, early action, deferred admission, international baccalaureate accepted. Required: essay, high school transcript, minimum 2 high school GPA, 1 recommendation, SAT or ACT. Recommended: interview. Required for some: interview. Entrance: very difficult. Application deadlines: 2/1, 11/1 for early action. Notification: continuous until 4/1, 12/15 for early action. SAT Reasoning Test deadline: 2/1. Transfer credits accepted: Yes. Applicants placed on waiting list: 48. Wait-listed applicants offered admission: 0. Early action applicants: 3,563. Early action applicants admitted: 3,029.

Costs Per Year: Application fee: $50. Comprehensive fee: $50,694 includes full-time tuition ($40,560), mandatory fees ($314), and college room and board ($9820). Full-time tuition and fees vary according to course load. Room and board charges vary according to board plan and housing facility. Part-time tuition: $5070 per course. Part-time tuition varies according to course load.

Collegiate Environment: Orientation program. Drama-theater group, choral group, student-run newspaper, radio station. Social organizations: national fraternities, national sororities. Student services: health clinic, personal-psychological counseling, women's center. Campus security: 24-hour emergency response devices and patrols, student patrols, late night transport-escort service, controlled dormitory access. Freshmen guaranteed college housing. On-campus residence required through sophomore year. Option: coed housing available. Mark O. Hatfield Library plus 1 other with an OPAC and a Web page. Operations spending for the previous fiscal year: $3.2 million.

Community Environment: Salem, the capital city, has a population of 148,750. All forms of commercial transportation are available. Recreational activities include tennis, fishing, swimming, boating, riding, and hiking. Ski area facilities and the Pacific Ocean are nearby. Part-time employment is available. Points of interest are Bush Park, a large city park planted with rare trees and shrubs, Salem Art Center, Mission Mill Museum and the Oregon State Capitol.

■ ALBRIGHT COLLEGE

13th and Bern Sts.
Reading, PA 19612-5234
Tel: (610)921-2381; Free: 800-252-1856
Fax: (610)921-7530
E-mail: admission@albright.edu
Web Site: www.albright.edu/

Description: Independent, comprehensive, coed, affiliated with United Methodist Church. Awards bachelor's and master's degrees. Founded 1856. Setting: 118-acre suburban campus with easy access to Philadelphia. Endowment: $51.3 million. Educational spending for the previous fiscal year: $9537 per student. Total enrollment: 1,690. Faculty: 173 (113 full-time, 60 part-time). Student-undergrad faculty ratio is 12:1. 6,132 applied, 49% were admitted. 22% from top 10% of their high school class, 48% from top quarter, 76% from top half. Full-time: 1,589 students, 56% women, 44% men. Part-time: 36 students, 69% women, 31% men. Students come from 23 states and territories, 17 other countries, 36% from out-of-state. 1% American Indian or Alaska Native, non-Hispanic/Latino; 10% Hispanic/Latino; 20% African American, non-Hispanic/Latino; 4% Asian, non-Hispanic/Latino; 0% Native Hawaiian or other Pacific Islander, non-Hispanic/Latino; 5% international. 1% 25 or older, 65% live on campus, 3% transferred in. Retention: 75% of full-time freshmen returned the following year. Academic areas with the most degrees conferred: business/marketing; social sciences; psychology. Core. Calendar: 4-1-4. ESL program, services for LD students, advanced placement, accelerated degree program, self-designed majors, honors program, independent study, double major, summer session for credit, part-time degree program, adult/continuing education programs, internships, graduate courses open to undergrads. Off campus study at The Washington Center, National Theatre Centre. Study abroad program. ROTC: Army (c).

Entrance Requirements: Options: electronic application, early admission, deferred admission, international baccalaureate accepted. Required: essay, high school transcript, 1 recommendation, secondary school report (guidance department), students applying tests optional, must complete an on-campus admission interview. Recommended: interview, SAT, ACT, SAT or ACT. Entrance: moderately difficult. Application deadline: Rolling. Notification: continuous. SAT Reasoning Test deadline: 4/1. Transfer credits accepted: Yes.

Costs Per Year: Application fee: $25. Comprehensive fee: $46,660 includes full-time tuition ($35,860), mandatory fees ($800), and college room and board ($10,000). College room only: $5550. Full-time tuition and fees vary according to degree level. Room and board charges vary according to board plan and housing facility. Part-time tuition: $4483 per course. Part-time tuition varies according to degree level.

Collegiate Environment: Orientation program. Drama-theater group, choral group, student-run newspaper, radio station. Social organizations: 69 open to all; national fraternities, national sororities; 14% of eligible men and 20% of eligible women are members. Most popular organizations: Greek Organizations (combined), Alpha Phi Omega (service organization), Albright College Activities Council, Student Government Association, Newspaper. Major annual events: Homecoming, Spring Fever Weekend/Foozeball, Greek Week. Student services: health clinic, personal-psychological counseling, women's center. Campus security: 24-hour emergency response devices and patrols, student patrols, late night transport-escort service, controlled dormitory access, E2 Campus Text messaging, Rape Aggression Defense Training, Marked Patrol Cars, Partnership with Reading PD, PA

State Police. 1,168 college housing spaces available; 1,056 were occupied in 2012-13. Freshmen guaranteed college housing. On-campus residence required through sophomore year. Options: coed, men-only, women-only housing available. F. W. Gingrich Library plus 1 other with 254,367 books, 99,513 microform titles, 5,693 serials, 10,489 audiovisual materials, an OPAC, and a Web page. Operations spending for the previous fiscal year: $1.1 million. 372 computers available on campus for general student use. A campuswide network can be accessed from student residence rooms and from off campus. Students can access the following: online class registration, online financial statements, housing choices, course management systems. Staffed computer lab on campus provides training in use of computers, software, and the Internet.

Community Environment: The Reading and Berks County area has a temperate climate. The community is served by U.S. air and several bus companies. Reading is world famous for its outlet shopping. The city has many churches representing major denominations, a symphony orchestra, two major hospitals, four museums, several theaters, and beautiful park and recreational facilities. It is within easy driving distance from major metropolitan areas such as Philadelphia, New York City, Washington, D.C., and Baltimore, MD.

■ ALLEGHENY COLLEGE

520 N Main St.
Meadville, PA 16335
Tel: (814)332-3100; Free: 800-521-5293
Fax: (814)337-0431
E-mail: admissions@allegheny.edu
Web Site: www.allegheny.edu/

Description: Independent, 4-year, coed. Awards bachelor's degrees. Founded 1815. Setting: 565-acre suburban campus. Endowment: $146.5 million. Research spending for the previous fiscal year: $880,681. Educational spending for the previous fiscal year: $12,070 per student. Total enrollment: 2,140. Faculty: 200 (165 full-time, 35 part-time). Student-undergrad faculty ratio is 12:1. 4,795 applied, 63% were admitted. 40% from top 10% of their high school class, 70% from top quarter, 93% from top half. 16 National Merit Scholars, 19 valedictorians, 11 student government officers. Full-time: 2,104 students, 54% women, 46% men. Part-time: 36 students, 64% women, 36% men. Students come from 42 states and territories, 34 other countries, 44% from out-of-state. 0.1% American Indian or Alaska Native, non-Hispanic/Latino; 5% Hispanic/Latino; 5% African American, non-Hispanic/Latino; 3% Asian, non-Hispanic/Latino; 0% Native Hawaiian or other Pacific Islander, non-Hispanic/Latino; 1% international. 0% 25 or older, 90% live on campus, 1% transferred in. Retention: 89% of full-time freshmen returned the following year. Academic areas with the most degrees conferred: biological/life sciences; social sciences; psychology. Core. Calendar: semesters. ESL program, services for LD students, advanced placement, self-designed majors, independent study, double major, internships. Off campus study at Washington Semester, American University, Washington DC; Duke University Marine Biological Laboratory, Beaufort NC and Bermuda; Ecosystems Center in Woods Hole Massachusetts; New York Arts Program; Oak Ridge Science Semester, Tennessee; The Philadelphia Center; Newberry Seminar Research in Humanities, Chicago IL. Study abroad program.

Entrance Requirements: Options: electronic application, early admission, early decision, deferred admission, international baccalaureate accepted. Required: essay, high school transcript, 2 recommendations, college preparatory program, standardized test scores, SAT or ACT. Recommended: interview. Entrance: very difficult. Application deadlines: 2/15, 11/15 for early decision. Notification: 4/1, 12/15 for early decision. SAT Reasoning Test deadline: 2/15. SAT Subject Test deadline: 2/15. Transfer credits accepted: Yes. Applicants placed on waiting list: 216. Wait-listed applicants offered admission: 26. Early decision applicants: 127. Early decision applicants admitted: 60.

Costs Per Year: Application fee: $35. Comprehensive fee: $49,020 includes full-time tuition ($38,710), mandatory fees ($390), and college room and board ($9920). College room only: $5220. Room and board charges vary according to board plan and housing facility. Part-time tuition: $1613 per credit hour. Part-time mandatory fees: $195 per term. Part-time tuition and fees vary according to course load.

Collegiate Environment: Orientation program. Drama-theater group, choral group, student-run newspaper, radio station. Social organizations: 103 open to all; national fraternities, national sororities, social service; 28% of eligible men and 34% of eligible women are members. Most popular organizations: student government, Gators Activity Programming, Alpha Phi Omega (service fraternity), Outing Club, Greek life. Major annual events: Make A Difference Day, Orchesis Dance Performance, Springfest. Student services: health clinic, personal-psychological counseling. Campus security: 24-hour emergency response devices and patrols, late night transport-escort service, controlled dormitory access, local police patrol, emergency alert system, self defense education, compliance program. College housing designed to accommodate 1,844 students; 1,871 undergraduates lived in college housing during 2012-13. Freshmen guaranteed college housing. On-campus residence required through senior year. Options: coed, men-only, women-only housing available. Lawrence Lee Pelletier Library with 318,041 books, 506,608 microform titles, 20,867 serials, 146,139 audiovisual materials, an OPAC, and a Web page. Operations spending for the previous fiscal year: $2.1 million. 207 computers available on campus for general student use. Computer purchase/lease plans available. A campuswide network can be accessed from student residence rooms and from off campus. Students can access the following: online class registration, placement testing, course catalog, class lists, book buy, repair service, transcript review and ordering, billing, payroll time cards, internet kiosks, dataports for laptops, campus organizations, financial aid.

Community Environment: Population 14,000, Meadville, the seat of Crawford County, is in a rich agricultural and active vacation area. The community lies on the western Appalachian slope. The area is served by plane, bus and interstate highways. There are many churches, a public library, active arts organizations, and a large medical center within the community. Most civic, fraternal, and veteran's organizations are represented here. Local recreational facilities include five movie screens, a professional theater, parks, lakes, and picnic groves. Activities include fishing, boating, hunting, swimming, golf, tennis, a major summer jazz festival, hot-air balloon festival, and folk-art festival. Part-time employment is available.

■ **ALVERNIA UNIVERSITY**

400 Saint Bernardine St.
Reading, PA 19607-1799
Tel: (610)796-8200
Fax: (610)796-8336
E-mail: admissions@alvernia.edu
Web Site: www.alvernia.edu/

Description: Independent Roman Catholic, comprehensive, coed. Awards associate, bachelor's, master's, and doctoral degrees. Founded 1958. Setting: 121-acre suburban campus with easy access to Philadelphia. Endowment: $19.7 million. Educational spending for the previous fiscal year: $5890 per student. Total enrollment: 2,891. Faculty: 292 (102 full-time, 190 part-time). Student-undergrad faculty ratio is 12:1. 1,864 applied, 80% were admitted. 8% from top 10% of their high school class, 29% from top quarter, 67% from top half. Full-time: 1,689 students, 66% women, 34% men. Part-time: 658 students, 83% women, 17% men. Students come from 18 states and territories, 4 other countries, 24% from out-of-state. 0.1% American Indian or Alaska Native, non-Hispanic/Latino; 8% Hispanic/Latino; 12% African American, non-Hispanic/Latino; 1% Asian, non-Hispanic/Latino; 0.1% Native Hawaiian or other Pacific Islander, non-Hispanic/Latino; 0.2% international. 9% 25 or older, 57% live on campus, 4% transferred in. Retention: 75% of full-time freshmen returned the following year. Academic areas with the most degrees conferred: health professions and related sciences; business/marketing; education. Core. Calendar: semesters. Academic remediation for entering students, ESL program, services for LD students, advanced placement, accelerated degree program, self-designed majors,

honors program, independent study, distance learning, double major, summer session for credit, part-time degree program, adult/continuing education programs, internships, graduate courses open to undergrads. Off campus study at Washington Center for Internships and Academic Seminars. Study abroad program. ROTC: Army (c).

Entrance Requirements: Options: electronic application, deferred admission, international baccalaureate accepted. Required: essay, high school transcript, SAT or ACT. Recommended: minimum 2 high school GPA, 1 recommendation. Required for some: 2 recommendations, interview. Entrance: moderately difficult. Application deadline: Rolling. Notification: continuous. SAT Reasoning Test deadline: 8/1. Transfer credits accepted: Yes.

Costs Per Year: Application fee: $25. Comprehensive fee: $39,250 includes full-time tuition ($28,500), mandatory fees ($560), and college room and board ($10,190). College room only: $5070. Full-time tuition and fees vary according to class time and reciprocity agreements. Room and board charges vary according to board plan and housing facility. Part-time tuition: $780 per credit hour. Part-time tuition varies according to class time and course load.

Collegiate Environment: Orientation program. Drama-theater group, choral group, student-run newspaper. Social organizations: 38 open to all. Most popular organizations: Student Government Association, Student Nurses Association of Alvernia (ASNA), Criminal Justice Association (CJA), Sport Management Association (SMA), Science Association. Major annual events: Spring Fling Weekend, Homecoming and Family Weekend, Winter Formal. Student services: health clinic, personal-psychological counseling. Campus security: 24-hour patrols, late night transport-escort service, controlled dormitory access. 930 college housing spaces available; 887 were occupied in 2012-13. Freshmen guaranteed college housing. On-campus residence required in freshman year. Option: coed housing available. Dr. Frank A. Franco Library Learning Center with 89,361 books, 41,005 serials, 2,140 audiovisual materials, an OPAC, and a Web page. 426 computers available on campus for general student use. A campuswide network can be accessed from student residence rooms. Students can access the following: online class registration. Staffed computer lab on campus provides training in use of computers, software, and the Internet.

Community Environment: Alvernia College is located in a tree-lined neighborhood three miles south of the city of Reading. The 85-acre campus adjoins Angelica Lake. Public transportation provides service to within walking distance of the campus. Alvernia is noted for its accessibility to metropolitan and historical areas of interest. Near enough to New York, Philadelphia, and Baltimore to share their cultural and educational opportunities, the college is only a short distance from the Amish country in nearby Lancaster and York counties.

■ **ANTONELLI INSTITUTE**

300 Montgomery Ave.
Erdenheim, PA 19038
Tel: (215)836-2222; Free: 800-722-7871
Fax: (215)836-2794
Web Site: www.antonelli.edu/

Description: Proprietary, 2-year, coed. Awards terminal associate degrees. Founded 1938. Setting: 15-acre suburban campus with easy access to Philadelphia. Total enrollment: 183. 270 applied, 85% were admitted. Calendar: semesters. Adult/continuing education programs.

Entrance Requirements: Open admission.

■ **ARCADIA UNIVERSITY**

450 S Easton Rd.
Glenside, PA 19038-3295
Tel: (215)572-2900; Free: 877-ARCADIA
Fax: (215)572-4049
E-mail: admiss@arcadia.edu
Web Site: www.arcadia.edu/

Description: Independent, comprehensive, coed, affiliated with Presbyterian Church (U.S.A.). Awards bachelor's, master's, and doctoral degrees. Founded 1853. Setting: 71-acre suburban campus with easy access to Philadelphia. Endowment: $52.9 million. Educational spending for the previous fiscal year: $22,343 per student. Total enrollment: 4,027. Faculty: 487 (145 full-time, 342 part-time). Student-undergrad faculty ratio is 12:1. 9,044 applied, 57% were admitted. 27% from top 10% of their high school class, 58% from top quarter, 89% from top half. Full-time: 2,155 students, 69% women, 31% men. Part-time: 205 students, 62% women, 38% men. Students come from 39 states and territories, 13 other countries, 37% from out-of-state. 0.3% American Indian or Alaska Native, non-Hispanic/Latino; 5% Hispanic/Latino; 8% African American, non-Hispanic/Latino; 4% Asian, non-Hispanic/Latino; 0.04% Native Hawaiian or other Pacific Islander, non-Hispanic/Latino; 1% international. 7% 25 or older, 52% live on campus, 6% transferred in. Retention: 79% of full-time freshmen returned the following year. Academic areas with the most degrees conferred: business/marketing; biological/life sciences; psychology. Core. Calendar: semesters. ESL program, services for LD students, advanced placement, accelerated degree program, self-designed majors, honors program, independent study, distance learning, double major, summer session for credit, part-time degree program, co-op programs and internships, graduate courses open to undergrads. Off campus study. Study abroad program.

Entrance Requirements: Options: electronic application, deferred admission, international baccalaureate accepted. Required: essay, high school transcript, 2 recommendations, SAT or ACT. Recommended: minimum 3 high school GPA, interview. Required for some: portfolio, audition. Entrance: moderately difficult. Application deadline: 3/1. Notification: continuous until 9/1.

Costs Per Year: Application fee: $30. Comprehensive fee: $47,770 includes full-time tuition ($34,960), mandatory fees ($660), and college room and board ($12,150). Full-time tuition and fees vary according to course load, degree level, and program. Room and board charges vary according to board plan.

Collegiate Environment: Orientation program. Drama-theater group, choral group, student-run newspaper, radio station. Most popular organizations: Student Program Board, Residence Hall Council, student government, Arcadia Christian Fellowship, Student Alumni Association. Major annual events: Mr. Beaver Contest, Woodstock, Spring Fling. Student services: health clinic, personal-psychological counseling. Campus security: 24-hour emergency response devices and patrols, student patrols, late night transport-escort service, controlled dormitory access. 1,294 college housing spaces available; 1,235 were occupied in 2012-13. Freshmen guaranteed college housing. Options: coed, women-only housing available. Bette E. Landman Library with 157,438 books, 260,495 microform titles, 982 serials, and 2,745 audiovisual materials. 120 computers available on campus for general student use. A campuswide network can be accessed from student residence rooms and from off campus. Students can access the following: online class registration. Staffed computer lab on campus.

Community Environment: Population 7,914. Glenside is a suburb of Philadelphia served by railroad, buses, and major highways. There are many churches in the immediate area as well as various civic and fraternal organizations. Local recreational facilities include golf courses, ice rinks, parks, and a swimming pool.

■ THE ART INSTITUTE OF PHILADELPHIA
1622 Chestnut St.
Philadelphia, PA 19103
Tel: (215)567-7080; Free: 800-275-2474
Web Site: www.artinstitutes.edu/philadelphia/
Description: Proprietary, 4-year, coed. Part of Education Management Corporation. Awards associate and bachelor's degrees. Founded 1966. Setting: urban campus.

■ THE ART INSTITUTE OF PITTSBURGH
420 Blvd. of the Allies
Pittsburgh, PA 15219
Tel: (412)263-6600; Free: 800-275-2470
Fax: (412)263-6667
Web Site: www.artinstitutes.edu/pittsburgh/
Description: Proprietary, 4-year, coed. Part of Education Management Corporation. Awards associate and bachelor's degrees. Founded 1921. Setting: urban campus.

■ THE ART INSTITUTE OF YORK–PENNSYLVANIA
1409 Williams Rd.
York, PA 17402-9012
Tel: (717)755-2300; Free: 800-864-7725
Fax: (717)840-1951
Web Site: www.artinstitutes.edu/york/
Description: Proprietary, primarily 2-year, coed. Part of Education Management Corporation. Awards terminal associate and bachelor's degrees. Founded 1952. Setting: suburban campus.

■ BAPTIST BIBLE COLLEGE OF PENNSYLVANIA
538 Venard Rd.
Clarks Summit, PA 18411-1297

Tel: (570)586-2400; Free: 800-451-7664
Fax: (570)585-9400
E-mail: admissions@bbc.edu
Web Site: www.bbc.edu/
Description: Independent Baptist, comprehensive, coed. Awards associate, bachelor's, master's, and doctoral degrees. Founded 1932. Setting: 124-acre suburban campus. Endowment: $2.1 million. Educational spending for the previous fiscal year: $5466 per student. Total enrollment: 1,001. Faculty: 47 (41 full-time, 6 part-time). Student-undergrad faculty ratio is 11:1. 834 applied, 81% were admitted. 35% from top 10% of their high school class, 50% from top quarter, 75% from top half. Full-time: 568 students, 52% women, 48% men. Part-time: 154 students, 43% women, 57% men. Students come from 34 states and territories, 86 other countries, 51% from out-of-state. 0.4% American Indian or Alaska Native, non-Hispanic/Latino; 2% Hispanic/Latino; 3% African American, non-Hispanic/Latino; 1% Asian, non-Hispanic/Latino; 0.1% Native Hawaiian or other Pacific Islander, non-Hispanic/Latino; 0.1% international. 9% 25 or older, 91% live on campus, 7% transferred in. Retention: 47% of full-time freshmen returned the following year. Academic areas with the most degrees conferred: theology and religious vocations; education; psychology. Core. Calendar: semesters. Academic remediation for entering students, ESL program, advanced placement, self-designed majors, independent study, distance learning, double major, summer session for credit, part-time degree program, external degree program, adult/continuing education programs, internships, graduate courses open to undergrads. ROTC: Army (c), Naval (c), Air Force (c).

Entrance Requirements: Options: electronic application, early admission, deferred admission, international baccalaureate accepted. Required: essay, high school transcript, 3 recommendations, Christian testimony, SAT or ACT. Required for some: interview. Entrance: minimally difficult. Application deadline: 8/15. Notification: continuous. Transfer credits accepted: Yes.

Costs Per Year: Application fee: $40. Comprehensive fee: $26,890 includes full-time tuition ($18,420), mandatory fees ($1290), and college room and board ($7180). College room only: $2560. Room and board charges vary according to board plan. Part-time tuition: $614 per credit. Part-time mandatory fees: $43 per credit.

Collegiate Environment: Orientation program. Drama-theater group, choral group. Major annual events: Homecoming Day, Spring and Fall Plays, Spring Banquet. Student services: health clinic, personal-psychological counseling. Campus security: 24-hour patrols, student patrols, controlled dormitory access. 720 college housing spaces available; 471 were occupied in 2012-13. Freshmen guaranteed college housing. On-campus residence required through senior year. Options: men-only, women-only housing available. Murphy Memorial Library with 92,250 books, 4,550 microform titles, 26,222 serials, 3,666 audiovisual materials, an OPAC, and a Web page. Operations spending for the previous fiscal year: $232,867. 25 computers available on campus for general student use. A campuswide network can be accessed from student residence rooms. Students can access the following: online class registration. Staffed computer lab on campus.

Community Environment: Population of 5,000. Served by bus; major airport serves Scranton; train serves Harrisburg (100 miles). Public transportation serves campus. The community has a public library, nearby hospitals, recreational facilities, and many local parks. Part-time employment opportunities are excellent.

■ BERKS TECHNICAL INSTITUTE
2205 Ridgewood Rd.
Wyomissing, PA 19610-1168
Tel: (610)372-1722; Free: 866-591-8384
Fax: (610)376-4684
E-mail: abrussolo@berks.edu
Web Site: www.berks.edu/
Description: Proprietary, 2-year, coed. Part of Delta Career Education Corporation. Awards diplomas, transfer associate, and terminal associate degrees. Founded 1977. Setting: 8-acre small town campus. Total enrollment: 609. Faculty: 54 (37 full-time, 17 part-time). Full-time: 490 students, 50% women, 50% men. Part-time: 119 students, 59% women, 41% men. 12% 25 or older. Core. Calendar: semesters. Part-time degree program, co-op programs.

Entrance Requirements: Option: early admission. Required: high school transcript, interview. Required for some: CPAt and COMPASS. Entrance: noncompetitive.

Collegiate Environment: Orientation program. Campus security: 24-hour emergency response devices. Learning Resource Center with 3,000 books, 35 serials, 290 audiovisual materials, and an OPAC. 8 computers available on campus for general student use. A campuswide network can be accessed. Students can access the following: online class registration. Staffed computer lab on campus.

■ BIDWELL TRAINING CENTER

1815 Metropolitan St.
Pittsburgh, PA 15233
Tel: (412)323-4000; Free: 800-516-1800
Fax: (412)321-2120
E-mail: admissions@mcg-btc.org
Web Site: www.bidwell-training.org/

Description: Independent, 2-year, coed. Awards certificates and terminal associate degrees. Founded 1968. Total enrollment: 194. Student-undergrad faculty ratio is 12:1. 27 applied, 100% were admitted. 0% from out-of-state. 72% 25 or older.

■ BLOOMSBURG UNIVERSITY OF PENNSYLVANIA

400 E Second St.
Bloomsburg, PA 17815-1301
Tel: (570)389-4000
E-mail: buadmiss@bloomu.edu
Web Site: www.bloomu.edu/

Description: State-supported, comprehensive, coed. Part of Pennsylvania State System of Higher Education. Awards bachelor's, master's, and doctoral degrees. Founded 1839. Setting: 282-acre rural campus. Endowment: $21.3 million. Research spending for the previous fiscal year: $482,086. Educational spending for the previous fiscal year: $6242 per student. Total enrollment: 9,950. Faculty: 519 (414 full-time, 105 part-time). Student-undergrad faculty ratio is 21:1. 10,379 applied, 68% were admitted. 9% from top 10% of their high school class, 28% from top quarter, 68% from top half. Full-time: 8,642 students, 57% women, 43% men. Part-time: 559 students, 57% women, 43% men. Students come from 31 states and territories, 19 other countries, 11% from out-of-state. 0.1% American Indian or Alaska Native, non-Hispanic/Latino; 4% Hispanic/Latino; 7% African American, non-Hispanic/Latino; 1% Asian, non-Hispanic/Latino; 0.1% Native Hawaiian or other Pacific Islander, non-Hispanic/Latino; 2% international. 4% 25 or older, 42% live on campus, 5% transferred in. Retention: 78% of full-time freshmen returned the following year. Academic areas with the most degrees conferred: business/marketing; education; health professions and related sciences. Core. Calendar: semesters. Academic remediation for entering students, ESL program, services for LD students, advanced placement, honors program, independent study, distance learning, double major, summer session for credit, part-time degree program, co-op programs and internships, graduate courses open to undergrads. Off campus study at B.S. Ed. Early Childhood Education, Luzerne County Community College (degree completion), B.S. Ed. Early Childhood Education, Lehigh Carbon Community College (degree completion), B.S. Ed. Early Childhood Education, Harrisburg Area Community College at the Dixon Center (degree completion), Engineering Science 3+2 program with Wilkes University and Pennsylvania State University. Study abroad program. ROTC: Army, Air Force (c).

Entrance Requirements: Options: electronic application, early admission, early action, deferred admission. Required: high school transcript, SAT or ACT. Entrance: moderately difficult. Application deadlines: Rolling, Rolling for nonresidents, 10/31 for early action. Notification: continuous until 10/1, continuous until 10/1 for nonresidents. Preference given to state residents. SAT Reasoning Test deadline: 12/30. Transfer credits accepted: Yes. Applicants placed on waiting list: 0. Wait-listed applicants offered admission: 0.

Costs Per Year: Application fee: $35. State resident tuition: $6428 full-time, $268 per credit part-time. Nonresident tuition: $16,070 full-time, $670 per credit part-time. Mandatory fees: $1915 full-time, $70.25 per credit part-time, $55 per term part-time. Full-time tuition and fees vary according to course load and location. Part-time tuition and fees vary according to course load and location. College room and board: $7498. College room only: $4598. Room and board charges vary according to board plan and housing facility.

Collegiate Environment: Orientation program. Drama-theater group, choral group, marching band, student-run newspaper, radio station. Social organizations: 203 open to all; national fraternities, national sororities, local fraternities, local sororities; 7% of eligible men and 9% of eligible women are members. Most popular organizations: Living and Learning Communities, Band and Music Groups, Greek Organizations, Residence Hall Councils. Major annual events: Homecoming, Renaissance Jamboree, Parents/Family Weekend. Student services: health clinic, personal-psychological counseling, women's center. Campus security: 24-hour emergency response devices and patrols, late night transport-escort service, controlled dormitory

access, monitored surveillance cameras. 3,627 college housing spaces available; 3,441 were occupied in 2012-13. Freshmen guaranteed college housing. On-campus residence required in freshman year. Option: coed housing available. Andruss Library with 552,492 books, 2.1 million microform titles, 13,890 audiovisual materials, an OPAC, and a Web page. 1,567 computers available on campus for general student use. Computer purchase/lease plans available. A campuswide network can be accessed from student residence rooms and from off campus. Students can access the following: online class registration. Staffed computer lab on campus.

Community Environment: Population 12,915. Bloomsburg is located 40 miles southeast of Williamsport. Average winter temperature is 31 degrees; with a summer mean temperature of 70 degrees. The area is served by railroad, bus, and airlines. The community has multiple lodging accommodations, several churches of various denominations, a public library, and a hospital. There are numerous civic, fraternal and veteran's organizations in the area. Part-time employment is available.

■ BRADFORD SCHOOL

125 W Station Sq. Dr.
Pittsburgh, PA 15219
Tel: (412)391-6710; Free: 800-391-6810
Fax: (412)471-6714
Web Site: www.bradfordpittsburgh.edu/

Description: Private, 2-year, coed. Awards diplomas and terminal associate degrees. Founded 1968. Setting: urban campus. Total enrollment: 441. 915 applied, 87% were admitted. Accelerated degree program, internships.

■ BRYN ATHYN COLLEGE OF THE NEW CHURCH

2965 College Dr.
Bryn Athyn, PA 19009-0717
Tel: (267)502-2543; Free: 800-767-9552
Fax: (267)502-2658
E-mail: admissions@brynathyn.edu
Web Site: www.brynathyn.edu/

Description: Independent, comprehensive, coed, affiliated with Church of the New Jerusalem. Part of The Academy of the New Church. Awards associate, bachelor's, master's, and doctoral degrees. Founded 1876. Setting: 130-acre suburban campus with easy access to Philadelphia. System endowment: $59.3 million. Research spending for the previous fiscal year: $388,904. Educational spending for the previous fiscal year: $15,826 per student. Total enrollment: 257. Faculty: 63 (27 full-time, 36 part-time). Student-undergrad faculty ratio is 6:1. 456 applied, 45% were admitted. Full-time: 235 students, 55% women, 45% men. Part-time: 7 students, 57% women, 43% men. Students come from 20 states and territories, 10 other countries, 40% from out-of-state. 0.4% American Indian or Alaska Native, non-Hispanic/Latino; 5% Hispanic/Latino; 15% African American, non-Hispanic/Latino; 3% Asian, non-Hispanic/Latino; 0.4% Native Hawaiian or other Pacific Islander, non-Hispanic/Latino; 11% international. 2% 25 or older, 2% transferred in. Retention: 80% of full-time freshmen returned the following year. Academic areas with the most degrees conferred: interdisciplinary studies; biological/life sciences; education; psychology. Core. Calendar: trimesters. Academic remediation for entering students, ESL program, services for LD students, advanced placement, accelerated degree program, self-designed majors, independent study, part-time degree program, co-op programs and internships. Study abroad program. ROTC: Army (c), Air Force (c).

Entrance Requirements: Options: electronic application, deferred admission. Required: essay, high school transcript, minimum 2 high school GPA, 1 recommendation, interest in the writings of Emanuel Swedenborg, SAT or ACT. Required for some: interview. Entrance: minimally difficult. Notification: continuous. Transfer credits accepted: Yes. Applicants placed on waiting list: 5.

Costs Per Year: Application fee: $0. Comprehensive fee: $27,982 includes full-time tuition ($16,498), mandatory fees ($1224), and college room and board ($10,260). Part-time tuition: $635 per credit hour. Part-time mandatory fees: $45 per credit hour.

Collegiate Environment: Orientation program. Drama-theater group, choral group, student-run newspaper. Social organizations: 11 open to all; 42% of eligible men and 57% of eligible women are members. Most popular organizations: C.A.R.E. (Community Service), Social council, International Student Organization, Peer Advisory Council, student government. Major annual events: Charter Day, Service Day, Graduation. Student services: health clinic, personal-psychological counseling. Campus security: 24-hour emergency response devices, controlled dormitory access, 18-hour patrols by trained personnel. 216 college housing spaces available; 172 were occupied in 2012-13. Freshmen guaranteed college housing. Options: men-only, women-only housing available. Swedenborg Library plus 1 other with 144,475 books, 3,593 microform titles, 148 serials, 2,017 audiovisual materials, an OPAC, and a Web page. Operations spending for the previous fiscal year: $553,410. 18 computers available on campus for general student use. A campuswide network can be accessed from student residence rooms and from off campus. Students can access the following: online class registration. Staffed computer lab on campus provides training in use of computers and software.

■ BRYN MAWR COLLEGE

101 N Merion Ave.
Bryn Mawr, PA 19010-2899
Tel: (610)526-5000; Free: 800-BMC-1885
Fax: (610)526-7471
E-mail: admissions@brynmawr.edu
Web Site: www.brynmawr.edu/

Description: Independent, university. Awards bachelor's, master's, and doctoral degrees. Founded 1885. Setting: 135-acre suburban campus with easy access to Philadelphia. Endowment: $671.1 million. Research spending for the previous fiscal year: $2.1 million. Educational spending for the previous fiscal year: $24,385 per student. Total enrollment: 1,774. Faculty: 201 (163 full-time, 38 part-time). Student-undergrad faculty ratio is 8:1. 2,626 applied, 41% were admitted. 68% from top 10% of their high school class, 93% from top quarter, 100% from top half. 6 valedictorians. Full-time: 1,309 students, 100% women. Part-time: 13 students, 100% women. Students come from 48 states and territories, 59 other countries, 83% from out-of-state. 0.1% American Indian or Alaska Native, non-Hispanic/Latino; 9% Hispanic/Latino; 6% African American, non-Hispanic/Latino; 13% Asian, non-Hispanic/Latino; 0.2% Native Hawaiian or other Pacific Islander, non-Hispanic/Latino; 19% international. 1% 25 or older, 93% live on campus, 1% transferred in. Retention: 90% of full-time freshmen returned the following year. Academic areas with the most degrees conferred: social sciences; foreign languages and literature; English. Core. Calendar: semesters. Academic remediation for entering students, services for LD students, advanced placement, accelerated degree program, self-designed majors, independent study, double major, summer session for credit, internships, graduate courses open to undergrads. Off campus study at Haverford College, Swarthmore College, University of Pennsylvania, Spelman College, Villanova University, Temple University. Study abroad program. ROTC: Air Force (c).
Entrance Requirements: Options: electronic application, early admission, early decision, deferred admission, international baccalaureate accepted. Required: essay, high school transcript, 3 recommendations, SAT and SAT Subject Tests or ACT. Recommended: interview. Entrance: most difficult. Application deadlines: 1/15, 11/15 for early decision plan 1, 1/1 for early decision plan 2. Notification: 4/1, 12/15 for early decision plan 1, 2/1 for early decision plan 2. SAT Subject Test deadline: 1/15. Applicants placed on waiting list: 846. Wait-listed applicants offered admission: 5. Early decision applicants: 194. Early decision applicants admitted: 109.
Costs Per Year: Application fee: $50. Comprehensive fee: $55,586 includes full-time tuition ($41,260), mandatory fees ($986), and college room and board ($13,340). College room only: $7620. Part-time tuition: $5160 per course.
Collegiate Environment: Orientation program. Drama-theater group, choral group, student-run newspaper. Social organizations: 100 open to all. Most popular organizations: musical and theater groups, community service, Student Government Association, International Students Association, cultural groups. Major annual events: Fall Frolic, Lantern Night, May Day. Student services: health clinic, personal-psychological counseling, women's center. Campus security: 24-hour emergency response devices and patrols, late night transport-escort service, controlled dormitory access, shuttle bus service, awareness programs, bicycle registration, security Web site. 1,221 college housing spaces available; 1,204 were occupied in 2012-13. Freshmen guaranteed college housing. On-campus residence required in freshman year. Options: coed, women-only housing available. Canaday with 949,276 books, 72,074 serials, 10,433 audiovisual materials, an OPAC, and a Web page. Operations spending for the previous fiscal year: $5.5 million. 200 computers available on campus for general student use. A campuswide network can be accessed from student residence rooms and from off campus. Students can access the following: online class registration. Staffed computer lab on campus.
Community Environment: Population 4,382, Bryn Mawr is a suburban area

11 miles from Philadelphia. The immediate area has two clinics and a hospital, a public library, and churches of major denominations. Nearby Philadelphia offers all the facilities of a large city. Part-time employment opportunities are limited.

■ BUCKNELL UNIVERSITY

One Dent Dr.
Lewisburg, PA 17837
Tel: (570)577-2000
Fax: (570)577-3760
E-mail: admissions@bucknell.edu
Web Site: www.bucknell.edu/

Description: Independent, comprehensive, coed. Awards bachelor's and master's degrees. Founded 1846. Setting: 446-acre small town campus. Endowment: $599.2 million. Research spending for the previous fiscal year: $2.6 million. Educational spending for the previous fiscal year: $18,398 per student. Total enrollment: 3,618. Faculty: 386 (361 full-time, 25 part-time). Student-undergrad faculty ratio is 10:1. 8,291 applied, 27% were admitted. 66% from top 10% of their high school class, 89% from top quarter, 99% from top half. 10 National Merit Scholars, 15 valedictorians. Full-time: 3,515 students, 52% women, 48% men. Part-time: 21 students, 76% women, 24% men. Students come from 45 states and territories, 66 other countries, 76% from out-of-state. 0.03% American Indian or Alaska Native, non-Hispanic/Latino; 5% Hispanic/Latino; 3% African American, non-Hispanic/Latino; 3% Asian, non-Hispanic/Latino; 0% Native Hawaiian or other Pacific Islander, non-Hispanic/Latino; 5% international. 1% 25 or older, 86% live on campus, 1% transferred in. Retention: 95% of full-time freshmen returned the following year. Academic areas with the most degrees conferred: social sciences; engineering; business/marketing. Calendar: semesters. Services for LD students, advanced placement, self-designed majors, honors program, independent study, double major, summer session for credit, part-time degree program, internships, graduate courses open to undergrads. Off campus study at American University, Semester at Sea. Study abroad program. ROTC: Army.
Entrance Requirements: Options: electronic application, early decision, deferred admission, international baccalaureate accepted. Required: essay, high school transcript, 1 recommendation, SAT or ACT. Entrance: most difficult. Application deadlines: 1/15, 11/15 for early decision plan 1, 1/15 for early decision plan 2. Notification: 4/1, 12/15 for early decision plan 1, 2/15 for early decision plan 2. Preference given to children of alumni. SAT Reasoning Test deadline: 1/15. Transfer credits accepted: Yes. Applicants placed on waiting list: 2,348. Wait-listed applicants offered admission: 3. Early decision applicants: 717. Early decision applicants admitted: 437.
Costs Per Year: Application fee: $60. Comprehensive fee: $58,160 includes full-time tuition ($46,646), mandatory fees ($256), and college room and board ($11,258). College room only: $6622. Room and board charges vary according to board plan and housing facility. Part-time tuition: $5121 per course.
Collegiate Environment: Orientation program. Drama-theater group, choral group, student-run newspaper, radio station. Social organizations: 135 open to all; national fraternities, national sororities; 52% of eligible men and 59% of eligible women are members. Most popular organizations: Alpha Phi Omega, Outing Club, Activities and Campus Events, Catholic Campus Ministries, CALVIN and HOBBES. Major annual events: Homecoming, Chrysalis Ball, Family Weekend. Student services: health clinic, personal-psychological counseling, women's center. Campus security: 24-hour emergency response devices and patrols, student patrols, late night transport-escort service, controlled dormitory access, well-lit pathways, self-defense education, safety/security orientation. 3,017 college housing spaces available; 2,979 were occupied in 2012-13. Freshmen guaranteed college housing. On-campus residence required through senior year. Options: coed, men-only housing available. Ellen Clarke Bertrand Library plus 2 others with 992,242 books, 20,301 microform titles, 45,589 serials, 16,470 audiovisual materials, an OPAC, and a Web page. Operations spending for the previous fiscal year: $6.2 million. 970 computers available on campus for general student use. A campuswide network can be accessed from student residence rooms and from off campus. Students can access the following: online class registration. Staffed computer lab on campus provides training in use of computers, software, and the Internet.
Community Environment: Lewisburg, population 5,500, is the county seat and the commercial center of a prosperous farming area. Some industries in the city produce textiles, furniture, business forms, and electronic materials. Some part-time employment is available.

■ **BUCKS COUNTY COMMUNITY COLLEGE**
275 Swamp Rd.
Newtown, PA 18940-1525
Tel: (215)968-8000
Fax: (215)968-8110
E-mail: barlowm@bucks.edu
Web Site: www.bucks.edu/
Description: County-supported, 2-year, coed. Awards certificates, transfer associate, and terminal associate degrees. Founded 1964. Setting: 200-acre suburban campus with easy access to Philadelphia. Endowment: $4.6 million. Total enrollment: 10,252. Faculty: 577 (172 full-time, 405 part-time). Student-undergrad faculty ratio is 21:1. 4,963 applied, 98% were admitted. Full-time: 3,378 students, 51% women, 49% men. Part-time: 6,874 students, 58% women, 42% men. Students come from 12 states and territories, 1% from out-of-state. 1% American Indian or Alaska Native, non-Hispanic/Latino; 5% Hispanic/Latino; 5% African American, non-Hispanic/Latino; 3% Asian, non-Hispanic/Latino; 0.1% Native Hawaiian or other Pacific Islander, non-Hispanic/Latino; 1% international. 31% 25 or older, 76% transferred in. Core. Calendar: semesters. Academic remediation for entering students, ESL program, services for LD students, advanced placement, self-designed majors, independent study, distance learning, summer session for credit, part-time degree program, external degree program, adult/continuing education programs, co-op programs and internships.
Entrance Requirements: Open admission except for nursing, chef's apprentice, woodworking. Options: electronic application, early admission. Required: high school transcript. Required for some: essay, interview. Entrance: noncompetitive. Transfer credits accepted: Yes.
Costs Per Year: Application fee: $0. Area resident tuition: $3510 full-time, $117 per credit hour part-time. State resident tuition: $7020 full-time, $234 per credit hour part-time. Nonresident tuition: $10,530 full-time, $351 per credit hour part-time. Mandatory fees: $1124 full-time, $63 per credit hour part-time. Full-time tuition and fees vary according to program. Part-time tuition and fees vary according to program.
Collegiate Environment: Orientation program. Drama-theater group, choral group, student-run newspaper. Social organizations: 46 open to all. Most popular organizations: Phi Theta Kappa, Inter-Varsity Christian Fellowship, Drama Club, Habitat for Humanity, Future Teachers Organization. Major annual events: Spring Fling, Welcome Week, Halloween Party. Student services: personal-psychological counseling, women's center. Campus security: 24-hour emergency response devices and patrols, late night transport-escort service. College housing not available. Bucks County Community College Library with 131,156 books, 36 microform titles, 268 serials, 1,828 audiovisual materials, an OPAC, and a Web page. 750 computers available on campus for general student use. A campuswide network can be accessed from off-campus. Students can access the following: online class registration, e-mail, online course work, WebCT, Canvas. Staffed computer lab on campus provides training in use of computers, software, and the Internet.
Community Environment: Population 2,256. Newtown is a suburb of Philadelphia located approximately 20 miles from the heart of the downtown area.

■ **BUTLER COUNTY COMMUNITY COLLEGE**
107 College Dr.
Butler, PA 16003-1203
Tel: (724)287-8711; Free: 888-826-2829
Fax: (724)285-6047
E-mail: pattie.bajoszik@bc3.edu
Web Site: www.bc3.edu/
Description: County-supported, 2-year, coed. Awards certificates, diplomas, transfer associate, and terminal associate degrees. Founded 1965. Setting: 300-acre rural campus with easy access to Pittsburgh. Total enrollment: 3,656. Faculty: 335 (64 full-time, 271 part-time). Student-undergrad faculty ratio is 20:1. Full-time: 1,967 students, 55% women, 45% men. Part-time: 1,689 students, 67% women, 33% men. 35% 25 or older. Core. Calendar: semesters. Academic remediation for entering students, ESL program, services for LD students, advanced placement, summer session for credit, part-time degree program, adult/continuing education programs, co-op programs and internships.
Entrance Requirements: Open admission except for nursing, metrology, physical therapy, medical assistant technologies programs. Required: high school transcript. Required for some: interview. Entrance: noncompetitive. Application deadline: 8/15. Notification: continuous until 8/15.
Collegiate Environment: Orientation program. Student services: personal-

psychological counseling. Campus security: 24-hour emergency response devices, late night transport-escort service. John A. Beck, Jr. Library with 70,000 books and 305 serials. 350 computers available on campus for general student use. Students can access the following: online class registration. Staffed computer lab on campus provides training in use of computers, software, and the Internet.
Community Environment: In a region rich in coal, oil, natural gas and limestone, Butler's industries produce steel, cement, oil, glass, and metal products. The climate is temperate, and the average annual temperature is 50.6 degrees. The community has access to rail and air, and services include hospitals, churches, a library, YMCA, and YWCA. Local recreation includes boating, swimming, skiing, golf, parks, and movie theaters. Part-time employment is available.

■ **CABRINI COLLEGE**
610 King of Prussia Rd.
Radnor, PA 19087-3698
Tel: (610)902-8100; Free: 800-848-1003
Fax: (610)902-8309
E-mail: admit@cabrini.edu
Web Site: www.cabrini.edu/
Description: Independent Roman Catholic, comprehensive, coed. Awards bachelor's and master's degrees. Founded 1957. Setting: 112-acre suburban campus with easy access to Philadelphia. Endowment: $12.7 million. Educational spending for the previous fiscal year: $7401 per student. Total enrollment: 2,801. Faculty: 293 (75 full-time, 218 part-time). Student-undergrad faculty ratio is 13:1. 2,608 applied, 73% were admitted. 4% from top 10% of their high school class, 25% from top quarter, 49% from top half. Full-time: 1,298 students, 64% women, 36% men. Part-time: 107 students, 51% women, 49% men. Students come from 21 states and territories, 16 other countries, 39% from out-of-state. 0.1% American Indian or Alaska Native, non-Hispanic/Latino; 5% Hispanic/Latino; 10% African American, non-Hispanic/Latino; 2% Asian, non-Hispanic/Latino; 1% Native Hawaiian or other Pacific Islander, non-Hispanic/Latino; 0.3% international. 6% 25 or older, 59% live on campus, 4% transferred in. Retention: 74% of full-time freshmen returned the following year. Academic areas with the most degrees conferred: business/marketing; education; communication/journalism. Core. Calendar: semesters. Academic remediation for entering students, services for LD students, advanced placement, self-designed majors, honors program, independent study, double major, summer session for credit, part-time degree program, adult/continuing education programs, co-op programs and internships, graduate courses open to undergrads. Off campus study at Eastern University, Rosemont College, Valley Forge Military College, SouthEastern Pennsylvania Consortium for Higher Education. Study abroad program. ROTC: Army (c), Air Force (c).
Entrance Requirements: Options: electronic application, deferred admission, international baccalaureate accepted. Required: high school transcript, minimum 2 high school GPA, SAT or ACT. Recommended: essay, minimum 3 high school GPA, 3 recommendations, interview. Entrance: moderately difficult. Application deadlines: Rolling, Rolling for nonresidents. SAT Reasoning Test deadline: 5/1. Transfer credits accepted: Yes.
Costs Per Year: Application fee: $35. Tuition: $28,090 full-time. Mandatory fees: $910 full-time.
Collegiate Environment: Orientation program. Drama-theater group, choral group, student-run newspaper, radio station. Social organizations: 50 open to all. Most popular organizations: Student Government Association, Campus Activities and Programming Board, Colleges Against Cancer/Relay for Life, Psychology Club, Habitat for Humanity. Major annual events: Cabrini Day, Family Weekend, SGA Formal. Student services: health clinic, personal-psychological counseling. Campus security: 24-hour emergency response devices and patrols, student patrols, late night transport-escort service, controlled dormitory access, resident assistants and directors on nightly duty. 837 college housing spaces available; 812 were occupied in 2012-13. Freshmen given priority for college housing. Options: coed, women-only housing available. Holy Spirit Library with 140,160 books, 53,883 serials, 2,583 audiovisual materials, an OPAC, and a Web page. Operations spending for the previous fiscal year: $867,184. 575 computers available on campus for general student use. A campuswide network can be accessed from student residence rooms and from off campus. Students can access the following: online class registration, account balances and other services. Staffed computer lab on campus (open 24 hours a day) provides training in use of the Internet.
Community Environment: See Villanova University.

■ **CAIRN UNIVERSITY**
200 Manor Ave.
Langhorne, PA 19047-2990
Tel: (215)752-5800; Free: 800-RUN-2-PBU
Fax: (215)752-5812
E-mail: admissions@pbu.edu
Web Site: cairn.edu/
Description: Independent nondenominational, comprehensive, coed. Awards bachelor's and master's degrees. Founded 1913. Setting: 105-acre suburban campus with easy access to Philadelphia. Endowment: $9.6 million. Educational spending for the previous fiscal year: $5509 per student. Total enrollment: 1,200. Faculty: 115 (46 full-time, 69 part-time). Student-undergrad faculty ratio is 15:1. 466 applied, 72% were admitted. 12% from top 10% of their high school class, 18% from top quarter, 40% from top half. Full-time: 877 students, 52% women, 48% men. Part-time: 75 students, 51% women, 49% men. 45% from out-of-state. 1% American Indian or Alaska Native, non-Hispanic/Latino; 4% Hispanic/Latino; 16% African American, non-Hispanic/Latino; 4% Asian, non-Hispanic/Latino; 0% Native Hawaiian or other Pacific Islander, non-Hispanic/Latino; 2% international. 19% 25 or older, 55% live on campus, 10% transferred in. Retention: 75% of full-time freshmen returned the following year. Academic areas with the most degrees conferred: education; public administration and social services; business/marketing. Core. Calendar: semesters. Academic remediation for entering students, services for LD students, advanced placement, accelerated degree program, honors program, double major, summer session for credit, part-time degree program, adult/continuing education programs, internships, graduate courses open to undergrads. Off campus study. Study abroad program. ROTC: Air Force (c).
Entrance Requirements: Options: electronic application, early admission, deferred admission, international baccalaureate accepted. Required: essay, high school transcript, minimum 2 high school GPA, SAT or ACT. Recommended: interview. Required for some: interview. Entrance: moderately difficult. Application deadlines: Rolling, Rolling for nonresidents. Notification: continuous, continuous for nonresidents. Transfer credits accepted: Yes.
Costs Per Year: Application fee: $25. Tuition: $22,250 full-time, $660 per credit part-time. Mandatory fees: $205 full-time. Full-time tuition and fees vary according to course load and location. Part-time tuition varies according to course load and location. College room only: $4625. Room charges vary according to location.
Collegiate Environment: Orientation program. Drama-theater group, choral group, student-run newspaper. Social organizations: 25 open to all. Most popular organizations: Student Senate, Chi Beta Sigma (Social Work Club), Students in Free Enterprise, Student Missionary Fellowship, Culture & Arts Association. Major annual events: Homecoming events, Hoedown, Missions Conference. Student services: health clinic, personal-psychological counseling. Campus security: 24-hour emergency response devices and patrols, student patrols, late night transport-escort service, controlled dormitory access. 662 college housing spaces available; 516 were occupied in 2012-13. Freshmen guaranteed college housing. On-campus residence required through senior year. Options: men-only, women-only housing available. Masland Learning Resource Center with 136,348 books, 63,817 microform titles, 21,052 serials, 10,177 audiovisual materials, an OPAC, and a Web page. Operations spending for the previous fiscal year: $896,364. 79 computers available on campus for general student use. Computer purchase/lease plans available. A campuswide network can be accessed from student residence rooms and from off campus. Students can access the following: online class registration. Staffed computer lab on campus provides training in use of computers, software, and the Internet.

■ **CALIFORNIA UNIVERSITY OF PENNSYLVANIA**
250 University Ave.
California, PA 15419-1394
Tel: (724)938-4000; Free: 888-412-0479
Fax: (724)938-4138
Web Site: www.calu.edu/
Description: State-supported, comprehensive, coed. Part of Pennsylvania State System of Higher Education. Awards associate, bachelor's, and master's degrees and post-master's certificates. Founded 1852. Setting: 188-acre small town campus with easy access to Pittsburgh. Endowment: $189.6 million. Total enrollment: 8,608. Faculty: 404 (248 full-time, 156 part-time). Student-undergrad faculty ratio is 19:1. 5,313 applied, 47% were admitted. 8% from top 10% of their high school class, 29% from top quarter, 64% from top half. Full-time: 5,827 students, 51% women, 49% men. Part-time: 856 students, 59% women, 41% men. 10% from out-of-state. 0.1%

American Indian or Alaska Native, non-Hispanic/Latino; 1% Hispanic/Latino; 8% African American, non-Hispanic/Latino; 0.4% Asian, non-Hispanic/Latino; 0.1% Native Hawaiian or other Pacific Islander, non-Hispanic/Latino; 0.5% international. 20% 25 or older, 28% live on campus, 10% transferred in. Retention: 78% of full-time freshmen returned the following year. Academic areas with the most degrees conferred: business/marketing; health professions and related sciences; parks and recreation. Calendar: semesters. Part-time degree program, external degree program, adult/continuing education programs. ROTC: Army.
Entrance Requirements: Options: early admission, deferred admission. Required: high school transcript, SAT or ACT. Entrance: moderately difficult. Application deadline: Rolling. Notification: continuous.
Costs Per Year: Application fee: $25. State resident tuition: $6428 full-time, $268 per credit hour part-time. Nonresident tuition: $10,286 full-time, $429 per credit hour part-time. Mandatory fees: $2588 full-time. Full-time tuition and fees vary according to location and student level. Part-time tuition varies according to location and student level. College room and board: $10,172. College room only: $6592. Room and board charges vary according to board plan and housing facility.
Collegiate Environment: Orientation program. Drama-theater group, choral group, marching band, student-run newspaper, radio station. Social organizations: national fraternities, national sororities. Student services: legal services, health clinic, personal-psychological counseling, women's center. Campus security: 24-hour emergency response devices and patrols, student patrols, late night transport-escort service, residence hall entrances staffed 24/7, fire suppression and smoke detection systems, security staff are trained police officers. Freshmen guaranteed college housing. On-campus residence required through sophomore year. Options: coed, men-only, women-only housing available.
Community Environment: Population 5,072. California is located 35 miles south of Pittsburgh on the Monogahela River. This is a coal mining region of the Appalachian Foothills. Some part-time employment is available.

■ **CAMBRIA-ROWE BUSINESS COLLEGE (INDIANA)**
422 S 13th St.
Indiana, PA 15701
Tel: (724)463-0222; Free: 800-NEW-CAREER
Fax: (724)463-7246
E-mail: sbell-leger@crbc.net
Web Site: www.crbc.net/
Description: Proprietary, 2-year, coed. Awards diplomas, transfer associate, and terminal associate degrees. Founded 1959. Setting: 1-acre small town campus. Total enrollment: 101. Faculty: 8 (all full-time). Student-undergrad faculty ratio is 13:1. 65 applied, 78% were admitted. 12% from top 10% of their high school class, 33% from top quarter, 68% from top half. Full-time: 98 students, 88% women, 12% men. Part-time: 3 students, 100% women.
Costs Per Year: Tuition: $11,950 full-time. Mandatory fees: $1030 full-time.

■ **CAMBRIA-ROWE BUSINESS COLLEGE (JOHNSTOWN)**
221 Central Ave.
Johnstown, PA 15902-2494
Tel: (814)536-5168; Free: 800-NEWCAREER
Fax: (814)536-5160
E-mail: admissions@crbc.net
Web Site: www.crbc.net/
Description: Proprietary, 2-year, coed. Awards diplomas, transfer associate, and terminal associate degrees. Founded 1891. Setting: small town campus with easy access to Pittsburgh. Total enrollment: 180. Student-undergrad faculty ratio is 15:1. 80 applied, 90% were admitted. 0% from out-of-state. 51% 25 or older. Core. Advanced placement, accelerated degree program, summer session for credit, part-time degree program, adult/continuing education programs.
Entrance Requirements: Options: electronic application, early admission. Required: high school transcript, entrance exam. Recommended: interview. Entrance: minimally difficult. Application deadline: Rolling. Notification: continuous.
Collegiate Environment: Orientation program.

■ **CAREER TRAINING ACADEMY (MONROEVILLE)**
4314 Old William Penn Hwy.
Ste. 103
Monroeville, PA 15146
Tel: (412)372-3900; Free: 866-673-7773
Fax: (412)373-4262

E-mail: admissions@careerta.edu
Web Site: www.careerta.edu/
Description: Proprietary, 2-year, coed. Awards certificates and terminal associate degrees. Founded 1986. Total enrollment: 35.
Entrance Requirements: Required: essay, high school transcript, interview. Entrance: noncompetitive.
Collegiate Environment: Orientation program.

■ **CAREER TRAINING ACADEMY (NEW KENSINGTON)**
950 Fifth Ave.
New Kensington, PA 15068-6301
Tel: (724)337-1000; Free: 866-673-7773
Fax: (724)335-7140
E-mail: admissions@careeta.edu
Web Site: www.careerta.edu/
Description: Proprietary, 2-year, coed. Awards diplomas and terminal associate degrees (profile includes branch campuses in Monroeville and Pittsburgh, PA). Founded 1986. Faculty: 22 (14 full-time, 8 part-time). Student-undergrad faculty ratio is 20:1.
Entrance Requirements: Required: essay, high school transcript, minimum 1.5 high school GPA, interview. Application deadline: Rolling. Notification: continuous.
Collegiate Environment: Student services: personal-psychological counseling.

■ **CAREER TRAINING ACADEMY (PITTSBURGH)**
1500 Northway Mall
Ste. 200
Pittsburgh, PA 15237
Tel: (412)367-4000; Free: 866-673-7773
E-mail: admission3@careerta.edu
Web Site: www.careerta.edu/
Description: Proprietary, 2-year, coed. Awards diplomas and terminal associate degrees. Setting: suburban campus with easy access to Pittsburgh. Total enrollment: 70. Faculty: 9 (7 full-time, 2 part-time). Student-undergrad faculty ratio is 9:1. Full-time: 70 students, 93% women, 7% men. 0% from out-of-state. 4% Hispanic/Latino; 33% African American, non-Hispanic/Latino; 1% Native Hawaiian or other Pacific Islander, non-Hispanic/Latino. 49% 25 or older, 0% transferred in. Calendar: continuous. Academic remediation for entering students, services for LD students, advanced placement, co-op programs and internships.
Entrance Requirements: Required: essay, high school transcript, minimum 1.5 high school GPA, interview. Entrance: noncompetitive. Application deadlines: Rolling, Rolling for nonresidents. Transfer credits accepted: Yes.
Costs Per Year: Application fee: $30. Tuition: $12,218 full-time. Full-time tuition varies according to program. Tuition guaranteed not to increase for student's term of enrollment.
Collegiate Environment: Orientation program. Campus security: 24-hour emergency response devices, late night transport-escort service. College housing not available. 22 computers available on campus for general student use.

■ **CARLOW UNIVERSITY**
3333 Fifth Ave.
Pittsburgh, PA 15213-3165
Tel: (412)578-6000; Free: 800-333-CARLOW
Fax: (412)578-6668
E-mail: admissions@carlow.edu
Web Site: www.carlow.edu/
Description: Independent Roman Catholic, comprehensive, coed. Awards bachelor's, master's, and doctoral degrees and post-master's certificates. Founded 1929. Setting: 14-acre urban campus with easy access to Pittsburgh. Endowment: $16.6 million. Educational spending for the previous fiscal year: $6342 per student. Total enrollment: 2,967. Faculty: 280 (98 full-time, 182 part-time). Student-undergrad faculty ratio is 11:1. 1,169 applied, 61% were admitted. 16% from top 10% of their high school class, 39% from top quarter, 78% from top half. Full-time: 1,040 students, 93% women, 7% men. Part-time: 915 students, 72% women, 28% men. Students come from 17 states and territories, 11 other countries, 4% from out-of-state. 1% American Indian or Alaska Native, non-Hispanic/Latino; 2% Hispanic/Latino; 19% African American, non-Hispanic/Latino; 1% Asian, non-Hispanic/Latino; 0% Native Hawaiian or other Pacific Islander, non-Hispanic/Latino; 0.4% international. 31% 25 or older, 27% live on campus, 10% transferred in. Retention: 70% of full-time freshmen returned the following year. Academic

areas with the most degrees conferred: health professions and related sciences; education; business/marketing. Core. Calendar: semesters. Academic remediation for entering students, services for LD students, advanced placement, accelerated degree program, honors program, independent study, distance learning, double major, summer session for credit, part-time degree program, adult/continuing education programs, co-op programs and internships, graduate courses open to undergrads. Off campus study at 9 members of the Pittsburgh Council on Higher Education. Study abroad program. ROTC: Army (c), Naval (c), Air Force (c).
Entrance Requirements: Options: electronic application, deferred admission, international baccalaureate accepted. Required: high school transcript, SAT or ACT. Recommended: essay, minimum 2.5 high school GPA, interview. Entrance: moderately difficult. Application deadline: Rolling. Notification: continuous. SAT Reasoning Test deadline: 7/1. SAT Subject Test deadline: 7/1. Transfer credits accepted: Yes.
Costs Per Year: Application fee: $20. Comprehensive fee: $34,068 includes full-time tuition ($24,230), mandatory fees ($208), and college room and board ($9630). College room only: $4924. Full-time tuition and fees vary according to course load, program, and reciprocity agreements. Room and board charges vary according to board plan. Part-time tuition: $770 per credit hour. Part-time tuition varies according to course load, program, and reciprocity agreements.
Collegiate Environment: Orientation program. Drama-theater group, choral group. Social organizations: 20 open to all; Service sororities. Most popular organizations: Student Government Association, Campus Activities, SPiRiT (Student Ambassadors), SNAP (Student Nursing Association), PSEA (School Education Association). Major annual events: Spring Fair, Fashion for Kids' Sake, Campus Activities Fair. Student services: health clinic, personal-psychological counseling. Campus security: 24-hour emergency response devices and patrols, late night transport-escort service, controlled dormitory access. 416 college housing spaces available; 359 were occupied in 2012-13. No special consideration for freshman housing applicants. Options: men-only, women-only housing available. Grace Library with 132,930 books, 11,775 microform titles, 5,625 audiovisual materials, an OPAC, and a Web page. Operations spending for the previous fiscal year: $654,140. 162 computers available on campus for general student use. A campuswide network can be accessed from student residence rooms and from off campus. Students can access the following: online class registration.
Community Environment: The campus occupies 14 acres in the Oakland section of Pittsburgh, which is the educational heart of the city. Carlow is within walking distance of several other colleges and universities, and students enjoy all the educational and social opportunities this collection of institutions offers. The school is just 10 minutes from downtown Pittsburgh. The metropolitan center of Western Pennsylvania and one of the country's largest corporate headquarters, Pittsburgh is rich in educational, medical, entertainment, cultural, and business activities. Pittsburgh is also noted for its professional sports teams, ballet and theater companies, outdoor art festivals and river regattas, and multiple venues that attract a wide range of entertainment.

■ **CARNEGIE MELLON UNIVERSITY**
5000 Forbes Ave.
Pittsburgh, PA 15213-3891
Tel: (412)268-2000
Fax: (412)268-7838
E-mail: undergraduate-admissions@andrew.cmu.edu
Web Site: www.cmu.edu/
Description: Independent, university, coed. Awards bachelor's, master's, and doctoral degrees and post-master's certificates. Founded 1900. Setting: 145-acre urban campus. Endowment: $987.1 million. Research spending for the previous fiscal year: $392.6 million. Educational spending for the previous fiscal year: $63,000 per student. Total enrollment: 12,569. 17,313 applied, 28% were admitted. 76% from top 10% of their high school class, 93% from top quarter, 99% from top half. Full-time: 6,083 students, 43% women, 57% men. Part-time: 196 students, 37% women, 63% men. Students come from 49 states and territories, 78 other countries, 82% from out-of-state. 0.1% American Indian or Alaska Native, non-Hispanic/Latino; 7% Hispanic/Latino; 5% African American, non-Hispanic/Latino; 22% Asian, non-Hispanic/Latino; 0% Native Hawaiian or other Pacific Islander, non-Hispanic/Latino; 18% international. 0% 25 or older, 64% live on campus, 1% transferred in. Retention: 95% of full-time freshmen returned the following year. Academic areas with the most degrees conferred: engineering; computer and information sciences; visual and performing arts. Core. Calendar: semesters. Services for LD students, advanced placement, self-designed majors,

independent study, distance learning, double major, summer session for credit, part-time degree program, co-op programs and internships, graduate courses open to undergrads. Off campus study at members of the Pittsburgh Council on Higher Education. Study abroad program. ROTC: Army, Naval, Air Force.

Entrance Requirements: Options: electronic application, early admission, early decision, deferred admission, international baccalaureate accepted. Required: essay, high school transcript, 2 recommendations, SAT or ACT, SAT Subject Tests. Recommended: interview. Required for some: audition/portfolio for certain majors/BFA. Entrance: most difficult. Application deadlines: 1/1, 11/1 for early decision plan 1, 12/1 for early decision plan 2. Notification: 4/15, 12/15 for early decision plan 1, 1/15 for early decision plan 2. SAT Reasoning Test deadline: 1/1. SAT Subject Test deadline: 1/1. Applicants placed on waiting list: 3,664. Wait-listed applicants offered admission: 97. Early decision applicants: 965. Early decision applicants admitted: 342.

Costs Per Year: Application fee: $70. Comprehensive fee: $59,632 includes full-time tuition ($46,670), mandatory fees ($972), and college room and board ($11,990). College room only: $7070. Full-time tuition and fees vary according to student level. Room and board charges vary according to board plan and housing facility.

Collegiate Environment: Orientation program. Drama-theater group, choral group, marching band, student-run newspaper, radio station. Social organizations: 279 open to all; national fraternities, national sororities, NPC, IFC, NPHC, and Multicultural Organizations. Most popular organizations: Student Senate, Alpha Phi Omega, Tartan Club, Spirit Club, Greek Community. Major annual events: Carnival, Homecoming, Drama performances. Student services: legal services, health clinic, personal-psychological counseling, women's center. Campus security: 24-hour emergency response devices and patrols, late night transport-escort service, controlled dormitory access. 4,104 college housing spaces available; 3,989 were occupied in 2012-13. Freshmen guaranteed college housing. On-campus residence required in freshman year. Options: coed, men-only, women-only housing available. Hunt Library plus 5 others with 1.1 million books, 1.2 million microform titles, 136,638 serials, 33,112 audiovisual materials, an OPAC, and a Web page. 421 computers available on campus for general student use. A campuswide network can be accessed from student residence rooms and from off campus. Students can access the following: online class registration. Staffed computer lab on campus provides training in use of computers, software, and the Internet.

Community Environment: See University of Pittsburgh.

■ **CEDAR CREST COLLEGE**
100 College Dr.
Allentown, PA 18104-6196
Tel: (610)437-4471; Free: 800-360-1222
Fax: (610)606-4647
E-mail: astewart@cedarcrest.edu
Web Site: www.cedarcrest.edu/

Description: Independent, comprehensive, coed, affiliated with United Church of Christ. Awards bachelor's and master's degrees. Founded 1867. Setting: 84-acre suburban campus with easy access to Philadelphia. Endowment: $18.9 million. Educational spending for the previous fiscal year: $10,440 per student. Total enrollment: 1,567. Faculty: 156 (74 full-time, 82 part-time). Student-undergrad faculty ratio is 10:1. 1,155 applied, 61% were admitted. 16% from top 10% of their high school class, 52% from top quarter, 85% from top half. Full-time: 700 students, 97% women, 3% men. Part-time: 659 students, 92% women, 8% men. 14% from out-of-state. 45% 25 or older, 30% live on campus, 5% transferred in. Retention: 70% of full-time freshmen returned the following year. Academic areas with the most degrees conferred: health professions and related sciences; psychology; biological/life sciences. Core. Calendar: semesters. Academic remediation for entering students, services for LD students, advanced placement, self-designed majors, honors program, independent study, double major, summer session for credit, part-time degree program, internships, graduate courses open to undergrads. Off campus study at 6 members of the Lehigh Valley Association of Independent Colleges, American University. ROTC: Army (c).

Entrance Requirements: Options: electronic application, early admission, deferred admission, international baccalaureate accepted. Required: essay, high school transcript, SAT or ACT. Recommended: minimum 2 high school GPA, interview. Required for some: 2 recommendations. Entrance: moderately difficult. Application deadline: Rolling. Notification: continuous.

Costs Per Year: Application fee: $0. Comprehensive fee: $41,186 includes full-time tuition ($31,196) and college room and board ($9990). College room

only: $5160. Full-time tuition varies according to class time, course load, and program. Room and board charges vary according to board plan and housing facility.

Collegiate Environment: Orientation program. Drama-theater group, choral group, student-run newspaper, radio station. Social organizations: 51 open to all. Most popular organizations: Alpha Phi Omega, Forensic Science Student Organization, Crestiad Student Newspaper, Student Activities Board, Student Government Association. Major annual events: Dink Donut Night, Fall Fest, Midnight Breakfast. Student services: health clinic, personal-psychological counseling. Campus security: 24-hour emergency response devices and patrols, late night transport-escort service, controlled dormitory access, crime prevention programs. 550 college housing spaces available; 418 were occupied in 2012-13. Freshmen guaranteed college housing. Option: women-only housing available. Frank M. Cressman Library with 149,853 books, 14,979 microform titles, 28,278 serials, 19,726 audiovisual materials, an OPAC, and a Web page. Operations spending for the previous fiscal year: $633,955. 285 computers available on campus for general student use. Computer purchase/lease plans available. A campuswide network can be accessed from student residence rooms and from off campus. Students can access the following: online class registration. Staffed computer lab on campus provides training in use of computers, software, and the Internet.

Community Environment: Population 107,000, Allentown is located on the Lehigh River within 55 miles of Philadelphia and 90 miles from New York City. It is Pennsylvania's third largest industrial market. Diversified manufacturing includes machinery and tools, trucks, electric appliances, electronic equipment, apparel, cement, and gas-generating equipment. The area has good transportation facilities including four railroad lines, air service, and bus lines. The community has many churches representing various denominations. Four hospitals, a dental hospital, a library system, a museum, and an Equity theatre company are located here. Local recreational facilities encompass volleyball, baseball, tennis, basketball, swimming, hiking, band concerts, opera, community theatre, five radio stations, and many movie theatres. Part-time employment is available for students.

■ **CENTRAL PENN COLLEGE**
College Hill & Valley Roads
Summerdale, PA 17093-0309
Tel: (717)732-0702; Free: 800-759-2727
Fax: (717)732-5254
E-mail: rebeccacummins@centralpenn.edu
Web Site: www.centralpenn.edu/

Description: Proprietary, 4-year, coed. Awards associate and bachelor's degrees. Founded 1881. Setting: 35-acre small town campus with easy access to Harrisburg. Total enrollment: 1,342. Faculty: 133 (27 full-time, 106 part-time). Student-undergrad faculty ratio is 14:1. 1,182 applied, 35% were admitted. Full-time: 636 students, 61% women, 39% men. Part-time: 706 students, 70% women, 30% men. Students come from 19 states and territories, 1 other country, 5% from out-of-state. 0.1% American Indian or Alaska Native, non-Hispanic/Latino; 3% Hispanic/Latino; 19% African American, non-Hispanic/Latino; 1% Asian, non-Hispanic/Latino; 0% Native Hawaiian or other Pacific Islander, non-Hispanic/Latino; 0% international. 59% 25 or older, 18% live on campus, 0% transferred in. Retention: 55% of full-time freshmen returned the following year. Academic areas with the most degrees conferred: business/marketing; homeland security, law enforcement, firefighting, and protective services; computer and information sciences. Core. Academic remediation for entering students, advanced placement, honors program, independent study, distance learning, double major, summer session for credit, part-time degree program, adult/continuing education programs, internships. Study abroad program.

Entrance Requirements: Option: electronic application. Required: essay, high school transcript, minimum 2 high school GPA, interview. Recommended: SAT or ACT. Required for some: some majors have special requirements. Entrance: minimally difficult. Application deadlines: Rolling, Rolling for nonresidents. Notification: continuous, continuous for nonresidents. Transfer credits accepted: Yes.

Costs Per Year: Application fee: $0. Comprehensive fee: $23,127 includes full-time tuition ($15,372), mandatory fees ($795), and college room and board ($6960). College room only: $5220. Full-time tuition and fees vary according to course load and program. Room and board charges vary according to board plan and housing facility. Part-time tuition: $427 per credit hour. Part-time mandatory fees: $265 per term. Part-time tuition and fees vary according to course load and program.

Collegiate Environment: Orientation program. Choral group, student-run

newspaper. Social organizations: 14 open to all; honor and community service organizations. Most popular organizations: International Travel Club, Student Government Association, Toastmasters, Student Ambassadors. Major annual events: Family Fall Harvest, Common Hour, Business Casual Day. Student services: personal-psychological counseling. Campus security: 24-hour emergency response devices and patrols, late night transport-escort service. 450 college housing spaces available; 236 were occupied in 2012-13. Freshmen given priority for college housing. Options: men-only, women-only housing available. Charles T Jones Leadership Library plus 1 other with 104,174 books, 71 serials, 879 audiovisual materials, an OPAC, and a Web page. 100 computers available on campus for general student use. A campuswide network can be accessed from student residence rooms and from off campus. Students can access the following: online class registration. Staffed computer lab on campus provides training in use of computers, software, and the Internet.

Community Environment: Located in the small town of Summerdale, Pennsylvania, Central Penn is just across the river from Harrisburg. As the state capital, Harrisburg is home to a variety of recreational, cultural, historic, and sporting attractions.

■ **CHATHAM UNIVERSITY**
Woodland Rd.
Pittsburgh, PA 15232-2826
Tel: (412)365-1100; Free: 800-837-1290
Fax: (412)365-1609
E-mail: MSCOTT2@chatham.edu
Web Site: www.chatham.edu/

Description: Independent, university. Awards bachelor's, master's, and doctoral degrees and post-master's certificates. Founded 1869. Setting: 427-acre urban campus. Endowment: $58.9 million. Educational spending for the previous fiscal year: $8131 per student. Total enrollment: 2,178. Faculty: 323 (101 full-time, 222 part-time). Student-undergrad faculty ratio is 10:1. 727 applied, 60% were admitted. 24% from top 10% of their high school class, 53% from top quarter, 83% from top half. Full-time: 629 students, 99% women, 0.3% men. Part-time: 293 students, 83% women, 17% men. Students come from 31 states and territories, 29 other countries, 19% from out-of-state. 0% American Indian or Alaska Native, non-Hispanic/Latino; 2% Hispanic/Latino; 10% African American, non-Hispanic/Latino; 2% Asian, non-Hispanic/Latino; 0% Native Hawaiian or other Pacific Islander, non-Hispanic/Latino; 9% international. 20% 25 or older, 53% live on campus, 21% transferred in. Retention: 76% of full-time freshmen returned the following year. Academic areas with the most degrees conferred: health professions and related sciences; visual and performing arts; psychology. Core. Calendar: 4-4-1. ESL program, services for LD students, advanced placement, accelerated degree program, self-designed majors, honors program, independent study, distance learning, double major, summer session for credit, part-time degree program, adult/continuing education programs, co-op programs and internships, graduate courses open to undergrads. Off campus study at members of the Pittsburgh Council on Higher Education. Study abroad program. ROTC: Army (c), Naval (c), Air Force (c).

Entrance Requirements: Options: electronic application, early admission, deferred admission, international baccalaureate accepted. Required: essay, high school transcript, minimum 2 high school GPA, 1 recommendation. Recommended: interview, Consider SAT or ACT if submitted. Entrance: moderately difficult. Application deadline: 8/1. Notification: continuous. SAT Reasoning Test deadline: 8/1. Transfer credits accepted: Yes.

Costs Per Year: Application fee: $35. Comprehensive fee: $42,440 includes full-time tuition ($31,294), mandatory fees ($1160), and college room and board ($9986). College room only: $5061. Room and board charges vary according to board plan and housing facility. Part-time tuition: $759 per credit. Part-time tuition varies according to course load.

Collegiate Environment: Orientation program. Drama-theater group, choral group, student-run newspaper. Social organizations: 37 open to all. Most popular organizations: Chatham Student Government, Residence Hall Council, Chatham University Dance Team, Creative Writing Club & MFA Writing Council, Graduate Student Assembly. Major annual events: Spring Formal, Eggnog & Holiday Ball, Battle of the Classes. Student services: health clinic, personal-psychological counseling. Campus security: 24-hour emergency response devices and patrols, late night transport-escort service, controlled dormitory access, self-defense education, well-lighted pathways and sidewalks. 363 college housing spaces available; 350 were occupied in 2012-13. Freshmen guaranteed college housing. On-campus residence required through sophomore year. Option: women-only housing available. Jennie King Mellon Library with 91,318 books, 22,356 microform titles,

31,656 serials, 1,253 audiovisual materials, an OPAC, and a Web page. Operations spending for the previous fiscal year: $1.5 million. 250 computers available on campus for general student use. A computer is required for all students. A campuswide network can be accessed from student residence rooms and from off campus. Students can access the following: online class registration. Staffed computer lab on campus provides training in use of computers, software, and the Internet.

Community Environment: See University of Pittsburgh.

■ **CHESTNUT HILL COLLEGE**
9601 Germantown Ave.
Philadelphia, PA 19118-2693
Tel: (215)248-7000; Free: 800-248-0052
Fax: (215)248-7056
E-mail: williamss@chc.edu
Web Site: www.chc.edu/

Description: Independent Roman Catholic, comprehensive, coed. Awards associate, bachelor's, master's, and doctoral degrees and post-master's certificates (profile includes figures from both traditional and accelerated (part-time) programs). Founded 1924. Setting: 75-acre suburban campus with easy access to Philadelphia. Total enrollment: 2,301. Faculty: 354 (87 full-time, 267 part-time). Student-undergrad faculty ratio is 9:1. 2,173 applied, 66% were admitted. 13% from top 10% of their high school class, 30% from top quarter, 65% from top half. Full-time: 1,249 students, 68% women, 32% men. Part-time: 332 students, 78% women, 22% men. Students come from 24 states and territories, 41 other countries, 23% from out-of-state. 0.1% American Indian or Alaska Native, non-Hispanic/Latino; 7% Hispanic/Latino; 36% African American, non-Hispanic/Latino; 1% Asian, non-Hispanic/Latino; 1% Native Hawaiian or other Pacific Islander, non-Hispanic/Latino; 2% international. 40% 25 or older, 32% live on campus, 5% transferred in. Retention: 74% of full-time freshmen returned the following year. Academic areas with the most degrees conferred: education; business/marketing; public administration and social services. Core. Calendar: semesters. Academic remediation for entering students, ESL program, services for LD students, advanced placement, self-designed majors, honors program, independent study, double major, summer session for credit, part-time degree program, adult/continuing education programs, internships, graduate courses open to undergrads. Off campus study at Sisters of St. Joseph Consortium (7 institutions across the United States: St. Catherine University MN, Aquinas College MA, Avila College MO, Chestnut Hill College PA, Elms College MA, Elms College MA, Fontbonne College MO, Mater Dei College NY, Regis College MA, College of Saint Rose NY) AND Southeastern Penna Consortium (8 institutions in metropolitan area: Arcadia University, Cabrini College, Chestnut Hill College, Gwynedd-Mercy College, Holy Family University, Immaculata University, Neumann University, Rosemont College). Study abroad program.

Entrance Requirements: Open admission An open admissions policy applies only to the students in the School of Continuing and Professional Studies, an undergraduate school for working adults with course delivery in six eight-week sessions each year. Options: electronic application, deferred admission, international baccalaureate accepted. Required: high school transcript, SAT or ACT. Recommended: essay, minimum 2 high school GPA. Required for some: interview. Entrance: moderately difficult. Application deadlines: Rolling, Rolling for nonresidents. Notification: continuous, continuous for nonresidents. SAT Reasoning Test deadline: 7/31. Transfer credits accepted: Yes.

Costs Per Year: Application fee: $35. Comprehensive fee: $41,045 includes full-time tuition ($31,000), mandatory fees ($170), and college room and board ($9875). Room and board charges vary according to housing facility. Part-time tuition: $665 per credit hour.

Collegiate Environment: Orientation program. Drama-theater group, choral group, student-run newspaper, radio station. Social organizations: 30 open to all. Most popular organizations: student government, Mask and Foil Drama Club, African American Awareness Society, Campus Ministry Community Service Group, Business Club. Major annual events: Fall Fest/Homecoming, Christmas decorating/celebrations, Spring Fling. Student services: health clinic, personal-psychological counseling. Campus security: 24-hour emergency response devices and patrols, late night transport-escort service, controlled dormitory access. 525 college housing spaces available; 466 were occupied in 2012-13. Freshmen guaranteed college housing. Option: coed housing available. Logue Library with 134,862 books, 219,532 microform titles, 22,156 serials, 1,776 audiovisual materials, an OPAC, and a Web page. Operations spending for the previous fiscal year: $525,042. 70 computers available on campus for general student use. A campuswide network can be accessed from student residence rooms. Students can access the following: online class registration. Staffed computer lab on campus provides training in use of computers, software, and the Internet.

Community Environment: Chestnut Hill College is located in a 45-acre suburban setting of Philadelphia. Historic homes, a regional art museum, a well-respected arboretum, stables, and quaint specialty shops are within two miles of the campus, which is 30 minutes from Center-city Philadelphia. Villanova University, Saint Joseph's University, the University of Pennsylvania, Drexel University, and LaSalle University are nearby.

■ **CHEYNEY UNIVERSITY OF PENNSYLVANIA**
1837 University Cir.
Cheyney, PA 19319
Tel: (610)399-2000; Free: 800-CHEYNEY
Fax: (610)399-2099
E-mail: ehilton@cheyney.edu
Web Site: www.cheyney.edu/
Description: State-supported, comprehensive, coed. Part of Pennsylvania State System of Higher Education. Awards associate, bachelor's, and master's degrees. Founded 1837. Setting: 275-acre suburban campus with easy access to Philadelphia. Total enrollment: 1,284. Faculty: 107 (70 full-time, 37 part-time). Student-undergrad faculty ratio is 14:1. 1,582 applied, 87% were admitted. 3% from top 10% of their high school class, 13% from top quarter, 38% from top half. Full-time: 1,160 students, 51% women, 49% men. Part-time: 64 students, 61% women, 39% men. Students come from 15 states and territories, 21% from out-of-state. 0% American Indian or Alaska Native, non-Hispanic/Latino; 3% Hispanic/Latino; 93% African American, non-Hispanic/Latino; 0% Asian, non-Hispanic/Latino; 0% Native Hawaiian or other Pacific Islander, non-Hispanic/Latino; 0% international. 13% 25 or older, 74% live on campus, 8% transferred in. Retention: 65% of full-time freshmen returned the following year. Academic areas with the most degrees conferred: business/marketing; social sciences; psychology. Core. Calendar: semesters. Academic remediation for entering students, services for LD students, honors program, independent study, distance learning, double major, summer session for credit, part-time degree program, adult/continuing education programs, co-op programs and internships, graduate courses open to undergrads. Off campus study at West Chester University of Pennsylvania. Study abroad program. ROTC: Army (c).
Entrance Requirements: Options: electronic application, deferred admission. Required: essay, high school transcript, SAT, ACT, SAT and SAT Subject Tests or ACT. Recommended: interview. Required for some: 3 recommendations. Entrance: minimally difficult. Application deadline: 3/31. Notification: continuous. Preference given to state residents. SAT Reasoning Test deadline: 6/15. SAT Subject Test deadline: 6/15.
Costs Per Year: Application fee: $20. One-time mandatory fee: $150. State resident tuition: $6600 full-time, $275 per credit hour part-time. Nonresident tuition: $10,872 full-time, $453 per credit hour part-time. Mandatory fees: $2436 full-time, $15 per credit hour part-time, $454. Full-time tuition and fees vary according to course load. Part-time tuition and fees vary according to course load. College room and board: $11,552. College room only: $7552. Room and board charges vary according to board plan and housing facility.
Collegiate Environment: Orientation program. Drama-theater group, choral group, marching band, student-run newspaper, radio station. Social organizations: national fraternities, national sororities, local fraternities, local sororities. Most popular organizations: NAACP, Student Government Association, Alpha Kappa Alpha, Kappa Alpha Psi, Alpha Phi Alpha. Major annual events: Founders' Day, Homecoming, Commencement. Student services: health clinic, personal-psychological counseling. Campus security: 24-hour emergency response devices and patrols. Freshmen given priority for college housing. Options: coed, men-only, women-only housing available. Leslie Pickney Hill with an OPAC.
Community Environment: Cheyney's campus looks out on open fields and wooded hills in one of Pennsylvania's most scenic areas, yet the campus is less than an hour from Philadelphia. The summer temperatures range from 70 to 90 degrees, with winter ranges from 20 to 50 degrees. The area is served by bus and railroad. All major religious denominations are represented in town. There are very few shopping facilities in the immediate area. Part-time employment is available in neighboring community.

■ **CLARION UNIVERSITY OF PENNSYLVANIA**
890 Wood St.
Clarion, PA 16214
Tel: (814)393-2000; Free: 800-672-7171
Fax: (814)393-2030

E-mail: wbailey@clarion.edu
Web Site: www.clarion.edu/
Description: State-supported, comprehensive, coed. Part of Pennsylvania State System of Higher Education. Awards associate, bachelor's, and master's degrees and post-master's certificates. Founded 1867. Setting: 100-acre rural campus. Total enrollment: 6,520. Faculty: 387 (273 full-time, 114 part-time). Student-undergrad faculty ratio is 17:1. 3,408 applied, 77% were admitted. 9% from top 10% of their high school class, 25% from top quarter, 50% from top half. Full-time: 4,609 students, 60% women, 40% men. Part-time: 909 students, 75% women, 25% men. 5% from out-of-state. 0.1% American Indian or Alaska Native, non-Hispanic/Latino; 1% Hispanic/Latino; 6% African American, non-Hispanic/Latino; 0.4% Asian, non-Hispanic/Latino; 0.1% Native Hawaiian or other Pacific Islander, non-Hispanic/Latino; 1% international. 16% 25 or older, 25% live on campus, 6% transferred in. Retention: 70% of full-time freshmen returned the following year. Academic areas with the most degrees conferred: business/marketing; education; health professions and related sciences. Core. Calendar: semesters. Academic remediation for entering students, ESL program, services for LD students, advanced placement, accelerated degree program, honors program, independent study, distance learning, double major, summer session for credit, part-time degree program, adult/continuing education programs, co-op programs and internships, graduate courses open to undergrads. Off campus study at California University of PA; Edinboro University of Pennsylvania. Study abroad program. ROTC: Army (c).
Entrance Requirements: Option: deferred admission. Required: high school transcript, SAT or ACT. Recommended: essay, 2 recommendations, interview. Required for some: essay, interview, NLN Test for ASN Program, International TOEFL or TSE or IELTS students. Entrance: minimally difficult. Application deadlines: Rolling, Rolling for nonresidents. Notification: continuous, continuous for nonresidents. SAT Reasoning Test deadline: 8/11. Transfer credits accepted: Yes.
Costs Per Year: Application fee: $30. State resident tuition: $9141 full-time. Nonresident tuition: $12,861 full-time. Full-time tuition varies according to course level and course load. College room and board: $7186. Room and board charges vary according to board plan, housing facility, and location.
Collegiate Environment: Orientation program. Drama-theater group, choral group, marching band, student-run newspaper, radio station. Social organizations: 142 open to all; national fraternities, national sororities, local fraternities, local sororities; 6% of eligible men and 8% of eligible women are members. Most popular organizations: Circle K, Psychology Club, Council for Exceptional Children, Animae Club, Allies. Major annual events: Activities Day, Homecoming / Autumn Leaf Parade, Campusfest Concert. Student services: health clinic, personal-psychological counseling, women's center. Campus security: 24-hour emergency response devices and patrols, student patrols, controlled dormitory access. 2,113 college housing spaces available. Freshmen guaranteed college housing. On-campus residence required in freshman year. Options: coed, men-only, women-only housing available. Carlson Library with 474,723 books, 1.5 million microform titles, 33,515 serials, 8,293 audiovisual materials, an OPAC, and a Web page. 386 computers available on campus for general student use. A campuswide network can be accessed from student residence rooms and from off campus. Students can access the following: online class registration, Online Learning Management System, web-based personal disk space, other online student services (financial aid, billing etc.). Staffed computer lab on campus provides training in use of computers, software, and the Internet.
Community Environment: Clarion is in a rural area located near Cook Forest State Park and Allegheny National Forest. The area offers excellent hunting and fishing. The city has a public library, historical museum, nine churches, a hospital, and good shopping facilities. Two airports with commercial commuter and charter service are located within easy driving distance.

■ **COMMONWEALTH TECHNICAL INSTITUTE**
727 Goucher St.
Johnstown, PA 15905-3092
Tel: (814)255-8200; Free: 800-762-4211
E-mail: rhalza@state.pa.us
Web Site: www.portal.state.pa.us/portal/server.pt/community/commonwealth_technical_institute/10361
Description: State-supported, 2-year, coed. Awards certificates, diplomas, and terminal associate degrees. Setting: 12-acre suburban campus. Total enrollment: 275. Faculty: 33 (all full-time). Student-undergrad faculty ratio is 10:1. 113 applied, 89% were admitted. Full-time: 275 students, 35% women,

65% men. 1% from out-of-state. Retention: 64% of full-time freshmen returned the following year. Calendar: trimesters. Academic remediation for entering students.

Entrance Requirements: Open admission. Recommended: high school transcript. Required for some: high school transcript. Entrance: noncompetitive. Application deadline: Rolling. Notification: continuous. Preference given to disabled students.

Collegiate Environment: Drama-theater group, choral group. Student services: health clinic, personal-psychological counseling. Campus security: 24-hour patrols. Commonwealth Technical Institute at the Hiram G.Andrews Center Library with 4,294 books, 62 serials, and 470 audiovisual materials.

■ COMMUNITY COLLEGE OF ALLEGHENY COUNTY

800 Allegheny Ave.
Pittsburgh, PA 15233-1894
Tel: (412)323-2323
Web Site: www.ccac.edu/

Description: County-supported, 2-year, coed. Awards certificates, diplomas, transfer associate, and terminal associate degrees. Founded 1966. Setting: 242-acre urban campus. Total enrollment: 18,913. Faculty: 1,188 (260 full-time, 928 part-time). Student-undergrad faculty ratio is 20:1. Full-time: 7,101 students, 55% women, 45% men. Part-time: 11,812 students, 62% women, 38% men. 2% from out-of-state. 0.4% American Indian or Alaska Native, non-Hispanic/Latino; 1% Hispanic/Latino; 18% African American, non-Hispanic/Latino; 2% Asian, non-Hispanic/Latino; 0.1% Native Hawaiian or other Pacific Islander, non-Hispanic/Latino; 0.1% international. 46% 25 or older, 0% transferred in. Calendar: semesters. Part-time degree program.

Entrance Requirements: Recommended: high school transcript. Entrance: noncompetitive. Application deadline: Rolling. Notification: continuous.

Collegiate Environment: Campus security: 24-hour emergency response devices and patrols, late night transport-escort service. College housing not available.

■ COMMUNITY COLLEGE OF BEAVER COUNTY

One Campus Dr.
Monaca, PA 15061-2588
Tel: (724)775-8561; Free: 800-335-0222
Fax: (724)728-7599
E-mail: admissions@ccbc.edu
Web Site: www.ccbc.edu/

Description: State-supported, 2-year, coed. Awards certificates, diplomas, transfer associate, and terminal associate degrees. Founded 1966. Setting: 75-acre small town campus with easy access to Pittsburgh. Total enrollment: 2,779. Student-undergrad faculty ratio is 16:1. 2% from out-of-state. 33% 25 or older. Core. Calendar: semesters. Academic remediation for entering students, services for LD students, advanced placement, independent study, distance learning, double major, summer session for credit, part-time degree program, adult/continuing education programs, co-op programs and internships. Off campus study at Geneva College, Pennsylvania State University Beaver Campus of the Commonwealth College, La Roche College, Robert Morris College.

Entrance Requirements: Open admission except for nursing, medical laboratory technology programs. Option: early admission. Required: interview. Recommended: high school transcript. Entrance: noncompetitive. Application deadline: Rolling. Notification: continuous.

Collegiate Environment: Social organizations: local fraternities, local sororities. Campus security: 24-hour emergency response devices and patrols, late night transport-escort service. College housing not available.

Community Environment: Beaver County covers 436 square miles of rolling hills and valleys in southwestern Pennsylvania. Professional sporting events, world-renowned museums, and numerous cultural events are within commuting distance in nearby Pittsburgh.

■ COMMUNITY COLLEGE OF PHILADELPHIA

1700 Spring Garden St.
Philadelphia, PA 19130-3991
Tel: (215)751-8010
E-mail: admissions@ccp.edu
Web Site: www.ccp.edu/

Description: State and locally supported, 2-year, coed. Awards certificates, diplomas, transfer associate, and terminal associate degrees. Founded 1964. Setting: 14-acre urban campus. Total enrollment: 39,500. Faculty: 1,109 (427 full-time, 682 part-time). Students come from 50 other countries. 53% 25 or older. Core. Calendar: semesters. Academic remediation for

entering students, ESL program, services for LD students, advanced placement, accelerated degree program, self-designed majors, honors program, independent study, distance learning, summer session for credit, part-time degree program, external degree program, adult/continuing education programs, co-op programs and internships. Off campus study at Bucks, Delaware and Montgomery Community Colleges. Study abroad program. ROTC: Army (c).

Entrance Requirements: Open admission except for allied health, mental health/social service, engineering science programs. Options: electronic application, early admission, deferred admission. Required for some: high school transcript, allied health and nursing programs have specific entry requirements. Entrance: noncompetitive. Application deadline: Rolling. Notification: continuous. Preference given to city residents.

Costs Per Year: Application fee: $20. Area resident tuition: $4980 full-time, $148 per credit hour part-time. State resident tuition: $8828 full-time, $296 per credit hour part-time. Nonresident tuition: $12,676 full-time, $444 per credit hour part-time. Full-time tuition varies according to program. Part-time tuition varies according to program.

Collegiate Environment: Orientation program. Drama-theater group, choral group, student-run newspaper. Social organizations: 30 open to all; Phi Theta Kappa. Most popular organizations: Philadelphia L.E.A.D.S, Phi Theta Kappa, Student Government Association, Vanguard Student Newspaper, Fundraising Club. Major annual events: Spring Fling, International Festival, Senior Cruise. Student services: personal-psychological counseling, women's center. Campus security: 24-hour emergency response devices and patrols, phone/alert systems in classrooms/buildings. College housing not available. Main Campus Library plus 2 others with 110,000 books, 420 serials, an OPAC, and a Web page. 350 computers available on campus for general student use. Computer purchase/lease plans available. Students can access the following: online class registration. Staffed computer lab on campus.

Community Environment: See Temple University.

■ CONSOLIDATED SCHOOL OF BUSINESS (LANCASTER)

2124 Ambassador Cir.
Lancaster, PA 17603
Tel: (717)394-6211; Free: 800-541-8298
Fax: (717)394-6213
E-mail: lpaul@csb.edu
Web Site: www.csb.edu/

Description: Proprietary, 2-year, coed. Awards diplomas and terminal associate degrees. Founded 1986. Setting: 4-acre suburban campus with easy access to Philadelphia. Total enrollment: 182. Faculty: 25 (24 full-time, 1 part-time). Student-undergrad faculty ratio is 15:1. Full-time: 179 students, 86% women, 14% men. Part-time: 3 students, 67% women, 33% men. Students come from 2 states and territories, 1% from out-of-state. 59% 25 or older. Core. Calendar: continuous. Services for LD students, accelerated degree program, self-designed majors, honors program, independent study, part-time degree program, internships.

Entrance Requirements: Open admission. Option: electronic application. Required: high school transcript, interview. Entrance: minimally difficult. Application deadline: Rolling. Transfer credits accepted: Yes.

Collegiate Environment: Orientation program. Social organizations: 1 open to all. Most popular organization: Community Service Club. Major annual events: Holiday Party, Student Appreciation Day. 120 computers available on campus for general student use. Staffed computer lab on campus provides training in use of computers, software, and the Internet.

■ CONSOLIDATED SCHOOL OF BUSINESS (YORK)

1605 Clugston Rd.
York, PA 17404
Tel: (717)764-9550; Free: 800-520-0691
Fax: (717)764-9469
E-mail: sswanger@csb.edu
Web Site: www.csb.edu/

Description: Proprietary, 2-year, coed. Awards diplomas and terminal associate degrees. Founded 1981. Setting: 6-acre suburban campus with easy access to Baltimore. Total enrollment: 176. Faculty: 21 (18 full-time, 3 part-time). Student-undergrad faculty ratio is 15:1. 41% 25 or older. Core. Calendar: continuous. Services for LD students, accelerated degree program, honors program, independent study, double major, part-time degree program, internships.

Entrance Requirements: Open admission. Option: electronic application. Required: high school transcript, interview. Entrance: minimally difficult. Application deadline: Rolling.

Collegiate Environment: Student-run newspaper. 120 computers available on campus for general student use. A campuswide network can be accessed. Staffed computer lab on campus.

■ **CURTIS INSTITUTE OF MUSIC**

1726 Locust St.
Philadelphia, PA 19103-6107
Tel: (215)893-5252
Fax: (215)893-7900
E-mail: chris.hodges@curtis.edu
Web Site: www.curtis.edu/

Description: Independent, comprehensive, coed. Awards bachelor's and master's degrees. Founded 1924. Setting: urban campus. Total enrollment: 164. 1% 25 or older. Core. Calendar: semesters. ESL program, advanced placement, accelerated degree program. Off campus study.

Entrance Requirements: Option: early admission. Required: essay, high school transcript, 2 recommendations, audition. Entrance: most difficult. Application deadline: 12/11. Notification: continuous.

Collegiate Environment: Orientation program. Student services: health clinic, personal-psychological counseling. Campus security: 24-hour patrols. The Rock Resource Center with 70,000 books.

Community Environment: See Temple University.

■ **DEAN INSTITUTE OF TECHNOLOGY**

1501 W Liberty Ave.
Pittsburgh, PA 15226-1103
Tel: (412)531-4433
Fax: (412)531-4435
Web Site: www.deantech.edu/

Description: Proprietary, 2-year, coed. Awards diplomas and terminal associate degrees. Founded 1947. Setting: 2-acre urban campus. Total enrollment: 132. 91% 25 or older. Core. Part-time degree program.

Entrance Requirements: Open admission. Options: early admission, deferred admission. Entrance: noncompetitive. Application deadline: Rolling.

Collegiate Environment: Campus security: 24-hour emergency response devices. 2,500 books and 25 serials.

■ **DELAWARE COUNTY COMMUNITY COLLEGE**

901 S Media Line Rd.
Media, PA 19063-1094
Tel: (610)359-5000
E-mail: admiss@dccc.edu
Web Site: www.dccc.edu/

Description: State and locally supported, 2-year, coed. Awards certificates, transfer associate, and terminal associate degrees. Founded 1967. Setting: 123-acre suburban campus with easy access to Philadelphia. Endowment: $3.8 million. Total enrollment: 13,248. Faculty: 802 (143 full-time, 659 part-time). Student-undergrad faculty ratio is 24:1. 4,818 applied, 100% were admitted. Students come from 9 states and territories, 53 other countries, 1% from out-of-state. 0.2% American Indian or Alaska Native, non-Hispanic/Latino; 2% Hispanic/Latino; 25% African American, non-Hispanic/Latino; 4% Asian, non-Hispanic/Latino; 0.1% Native Hawaiian or other Pacific Islander, non-Hispanic/Latino. 56% 25 or older. Retention: 61% of full-time freshmen returned the following year. Calendar: semesters. Academic remediation for entering students, ESL program, services for LD students, advanced placement, self-designed majors, independent study, distance learning, double major, summer session for credit, part-time degree program, adult/continuing education programs, co-op programs and internships.

Entrance Requirements: Open admission except for international students, nursing, respiratory therapy, surgical technology, plumbing apprentice, municipal police training programs, paramedic, perioperative nursing. Option: early admission. Required: high school transcript. Entrance: noncompetitive. Application deadlines: Rolling, Rolling for nonresidents. Notification: continuous, continuous for nonresidents. Preference given to residents of sponsoring school districts for nursing, respiratory therapy, surgical technology programs. Transfer credits accepted: Yes.

Collegiate Environment: Orientation program. Drama-theater group, student-run newspaper, radio station. Social organizations: 15 open to all. Most popular organizations: Business Society, Phi Theta Kappa, Student Government Association, Campus Bible Fellowship, Engineering Club. Student services: health clinic, personal-psychological counseling. Campus security: 24-hour emergency response devices and patrols, late night

transport-escort service. Delaware County Community College Library with 55,779 books, 7,922 microform titles, 249 serials, 2,863 audiovisual materials, an OPAC, and a Web page.

Community Environment: Media, population 5,451, is in central Delaware County. The city is located 20 miles from Philadelphia with all its cultural, educational, and recreational opportunities.

■ **DELAWARE VALLEY COLLEGE**

700 E Butler Ave.
Doylestown, PA 18901-2697
Tel: (215)345-1500; Free: 800-2DELVAL
Fax: (215)345-5277
E-mail: admitme@devalcol.edu
Web Site: www.delval.edu/

Description: Independent, comprehensive, coed. Awards associate, bachelor's, and master's degrees. Founded 1896. Setting: 600-acre suburban campus with easy access to Philadelphia. Endowment: $33.1 million. Research spending for the previous fiscal year: $225,713. Educational spending for the previous fiscal year: $7034 per student. Total enrollment: 2,253. Faculty: 195 (83 full-time, 112 part-time). Student-undergrad faculty ratio is 15:1. 1,652 applied, 74% were admitted. 15% from top 10% of their high school class, 42% from top quarter, 75% from top half. Full-time: 1,712 students, 61% women, 39% men. Part-time: 271 students, 54% women, 46% men. 37% from out-of-state. 1% American Indian or Alaska Native, non-Hispanic/Latino; 3% Hispanic/Latino; 4% African American, non-Hispanic/Latino; 1% Asian, non-Hispanic/Latino; 0.1% Native Hawaiian or other Pacific Islander, non-Hispanic/Latino; 0% international. 13% 25 or older, 61% live on campus, 7% transferred in. Retention: 75% of full-time freshmen returned the following year. Academic areas with the most degrees conferred: agriculture; business/marketing; biological/life sciences. Core. Calendar: semesters. Academic remediation for entering students, services for LD students, advanced placement, accelerated degree program, honors program, independent study, distance learning, double major, summer session for credit, part-time degree program, adult/continuing education programs, internships. Study abroad program.

Entrance Requirements: Options: electronic application, deferred admission. Required: high school transcript, 1 recommendation, SAT or ACT. Recommended: minimum 2.75 high school GPA, interview. Required for some: minimum 3 high school GPA. Entrance: moderately difficult. Application deadline: 5/1. Notification: continuous. SAT Reasoning Test deadline: 6/1. SAT Subject Test deadline: 6/1.

Costs Per Year: Application fee: $50. Comprehensive fee: $43,008 includes full-time tuition ($29,696), mandatory fees ($2050), and college room and board ($11,262). College room only: $5106. Part-time tuition: $818 per credit.

Collegiate Environment: Orientation program. Drama-theater group, choral group, student-run newspaper, radio station. Social organizations: local fraternities, local sororities. Student services: health clinic, personal-psychological counseling. Campus security: 24-hour patrols, late night transport-escort service, controlled dormitory access. Joseph Krauskopf Memorial Library with an OPAC and a Web page.

Community Environment: Doylestown, population 19,000, and founded in 1745, is in Bucks County, one of the finest farming sections of the state. The city is located 30 miles north of Philadelphia, and can be reached by rail, bus, and good highways. There are several churches, a hospital, public library, historical society, and more than 50 civic, fraternal, and veteran's organizations in the community. Local recreational facilities include theaters, a swimming pool, bowling lanes, and a radio station. Part-time employment is available.

■ **DESALES UNIVERSITY**

2755 Station Ave.
Center Valley, PA 18034-9568
Tel: (610)282-1100
Fax: (610)282-2254
E-mail: derrick.wetzell@desales.edu
Web Site: www.desales.edu/

Description: Independent Roman Catholic, comprehensive, coed. Awards bachelor's, master's, and doctoral degrees and post-master's certificates. Founded 1964. Setting: 480-acre suburban campus. Endowment: $48.1 million. Educational spending for the previous fiscal year: $8698 per student. Total enrollment: 3,255. Faculty: 308 (105 full-time, 203 part-time). Student-undergrad faculty ratio is 14:1. 2,353 applied, 72% were admitted. 33% from top 10% of their high school class, 45% from top quarter, 78% from top half.

Full-time: 1,782 students, 58% women, 42% men. Part-time: 686 students, 69% women, 31% men. Students come from 31 states and territories, 5 other countries, 64% from out-of-state. 1% American Indian or Alaska Native, non-Hispanic/Latino; 8% Hispanic/Latino; 4% African American, non-Hispanic/Latino; 2% Asian, non-Hispanic/Latino; 0.1% Native Hawaiian or other Pacific Islander, non-Hispanic/Latino; 0% international. 25% 25 or older, 67% live on campus, 4% transferred in. Retention: 83% of full-time freshmen returned the following year. Academic areas with the most degrees conferred: business/marketing; health professions and related sciences; visual and performing arts. Core. Calendar: semesters. Academic remediation for entering students, services for LD students, advanced placement, accelerated degree program, self-designed majors, honors program, independent study, distance learning, double major, summer session for credit, part-time degree program, external degree program, co-op programs and internships, graduate courses open to undergrads. Off campus study. Study abroad program. ROTC: Army (c).

Entrance Requirements: Option: electronic application. Required: essay, high school transcript, SAT or ACT. Recommended: interview. Entrance: moderately difficult. Application deadline: 8/1. Transfer credits accepted: Yes.

Costs Per Year: Comprehensive fee: $41,120 includes full-time tuition ($29,000), mandatory fees ($1150), and college room and board ($10,970). Full-time tuition and fees vary according to course load, degree level, and program. Room and board charges vary according to board plan and housing facility. Part-time tuition: $1210 per credit hour. Part-time tuition varies according to course load, degree level, and program.

Collegiate Environment: Orientation program. Drama-theater group, choral group, marching band, student-run newspaper, radio station. Social organizations: 47 open to all. Most popular organizations: DSU Equestrian Team, PA Student Society, Colleges Against Cancer, Colleges Against Cancer, CEO (Creative Exploration Organization), SHARE. Major annual events: Spring Fling and Fall Fest, Battle of the Bands, Winter Carnival. Student services: personal-psychological counseling. Campus security: 24-hour emergency response devices and patrols, late night transport-escort service, controlled dormitory access. 1,156 college housing spaces available; 1,045 were occupied in 2012-13. Freshmen guaranteed college housing. On-campus residence required in freshman year. Options: men-only, women-only housing available. Trexler Library with 163,208 books, 467,889 microform titles, 251 serials, 7,901 audiovisual materials, an OPAC, and a Web page. Operations spending for the previous fiscal year: $1 million. 200 computers available on campus for general student use. A campuswide network can be accessed from student residence rooms and from off campus. Students can access the following: online class registration. Staffed computer lab on campus.

Community Environment: Center Valley is a suburban area that enjoys a temperate climate. Lehigh Valley is accessible by air, bus, and car (Route 309), and the nearby towns are Allentown (population 107,000) and Bethlehem (population 73,000).

■ **DEVRY UNIVERSITY (FORT WASHINGTON)**
1140 Virginia Dr.
Fort Washington, PA 19034
Tel: (215)591-5700; Free: 866-338-7941
Web Site: www.devry.edu/
Description: Proprietary, comprehensive, coed. Part of DeVry University. Awards associate, bachelor's, and master's degrees. Founded 2002. Total enrollment: 809. Faculty: 150 (19 full-time, 131 part-time). Student-undergrad faculty ratio is 7:1. Full-time: 257 students, 30% women, 70% men. Part-time: 403 students, 39% women, 61% men. 17% from out-of-state. 1% American Indian or Alaska Native, non-Hispanic/Latino; 9% Hispanic/Latino; 26% African American, non-Hispanic/Latino; 4% Asian, non-Hispanic/Latino; 0% Native Hawaiian or other Pacific Islander, non-Hispanic/Latino; 1% international. 57% 25 or older, 14% transferred in. Academic areas with the most degrees conferred: business/marketing; computer and information sciences; engineering technologies. Calendar: semesters. Part-time degree program, adult/continuing education programs.
Entrance Requirements: Required: high school transcript, interview. Entrance: minimally difficult. Application deadline: Rolling. Notification: continuous.
Costs Per Year: Application fee: $40. Tuition: $16,076 full-time, $609 per credit hour part-time. Mandatory fees: $80 full-time.
Collegiate Environment: Orientation program. College housing not available.

■ **DEVRY UNIVERSITY (KING OF PRUSSIA)**
150 Allendale Rd., Buillding 3, Ste. 3201
King of Prussia, PA 19406-2926
Tel: (610)205-3130; Free: 866-338-7941
Web Site: www.devry.edu/
Description: Proprietary, comprehensive, coed. Awards bachelor's and master's degrees. Calendar: semesters.

■ **DEVRY UNIVERSITY (PHILADELPHIA)**
Philadelphia Downtown Ctr.
1800 JFK Blvd., Ste. 104
Philadelphia, PA 19103-7421
Free: 866-338-7941
Web Site: www.devry.edu/
Description: Proprietary, comprehensive, coed. Awards associate, bachelor's, and master's degrees.

■ **DEVRY UNIVERSITY (PITTSBURGH)**
FreeMarkets Ctr.
210 Sixth Ave., Ste. 200
Pittsburgh, PA 15222-2606
Tel: (412)642-9072; Free: 866-338-7941
Web Site: www.devry.edu/
Description: Proprietary, comprehensive, coed. Awards bachelor's and master's degrees. Calendar: semesters.

■ **DICKINSON COLLEGE**
PO Box 1773
Carlisle, PA 17013-2896
Tel: (717)243-5121; Free: 800-644-1773
Fax: (717)245-1442
E-mail: admit@dickinson.edu
Web Site: www.dickinson.edu/
Description: Independent, 4-year, coed. Awards bachelor's degrees. Founded 1773. Setting: 180-acre suburban campus with easy access to Harrisburg. Endowment: $325.7 million. Research spending for the previous fiscal year: $3.1 million. Educational spending for the previous fiscal year: $18,621 per student. Total enrollment: 2,386. Faculty: 253 (210 full-time, 43 part-time). Student-undergrad faculty ratio is 10:1. 5,818 applied, 40% were admitted. 48% from top 10% of their high school class, 78% from top quarter, 96% from top half. Full-time: 2,341 students, 56% women, 44% men. Part-time: 45 students, 27% women, 73% men. Students come from 43 states and territories, 48 other countries, 77% from out-of-state. 0.04% American Indian or Alaska Native, non-Hispanic/Latino; 6% Hispanic/Latino; 3% African American, non-Hispanic/Latino; 2% Asian, non-Hispanic/Latino; 0.04% Native Hawaiian or other Pacific Islander, non-Hispanic/Latino; 7% international. 1% 25 or older, 95% live on campus, 1% transferred in. Retention: 91% of full-time freshmen returned the following year. Academic areas with the most degrees conferred: social sciences; biological/life sciences; area and ethnic studies; business/marketing. Core. Calendar: semesters. ESL program, services for LD students, advanced placement, accelerated degree program, self-designed majors, independent study, double major, summer session for credit, part-time degree program, adult/continuing education programs, internships. Off campus study at The Washington Center, University of Pennsylvania, Woods Hole Oceanographic Institution, Consortium Exchange: Dickinson College, Franklin and Marshall College, Gettysburg College. Study abroad program. ROTC: Army.
Entrance Requirements: Options: electronic application, early decision, early action, deferred admission, international baccalaureate accepted. Required: essay, high school transcript, 2 recommendations. Recommended: minimum 3 high school GPA, interview, SAT or ACT. Entrance: very difficult. Application deadlines: 2/1, 2/1 for nonresidents, 11/15 for early decision plan 1, 1/15 for early decision plan 2, 12/1 for early action. Notification: 3/20, 3/20 for nonresidents, 12/15 for early decision plan 1, 2/15 for early decision plan 2, 2/1 for early action. SAT Reasoning Test deadline: 2/1. SAT Subject Test deadline: 2/1. Transfer credits accepted: Yes. Applicants placed on waiting list: 1,157. Wait-listed applicants offered admission: 17. Early decision applicants: 412. Early decision applicants admitted: 307. Early action applicants: 2,636. Early action applicants admitted: 1,296.
Costs Per Year: Application fee: $65. One-time mandatory fee: $25. Comprehensive fee: $55,729 includes full-time tuition ($44,101), mandatory fees ($450), and college room and board ($11,178). College room only:

$5765. Room and board charges vary according to board plan and housing facility. Part-time tuition: $5515 per course. Part-time mandatory fees: $56 per course.

Collegiate Environment: Orientation program. Drama-theater group, choral group, student-run newspaper, radio station. Social organizations: 122 open to all; national fraternities, national sororities, local sororities; 11% of eligible men and 29% of eligible women are members. Most popular organizations: Student Senate, CommServ, Multi-Organization Board, Hillel, Spectrum. Major annual events: Activities Night, Relay for Life, All College Formal. Student services: health clinic, personal-psychological counseling, women's center. Campus security: 24-hour emergency response devices and patrols, student patrols, late night transport-escort service, controlled dormitory access. College housing designed to accommodate 2,018 students; 2,041 undergraduates lived in college housing during 2012-13. Freshmen guaranteed college housing. On-campus residence required through senior year. Option: coed housing available. Waidner-Spahr Library with 547,711 books, 168,703 microform titles, 5,192 serials, 86,231 audiovisual materials, an OPAC, and a Web page. Operations spending for the previous fiscal year: $3.1 million. 1,081 computers available on campus for general student use. Computer purchase/lease plans available. A campuswide network can be accessed from student residence rooms and from off campus. Students can access the following: online class registration. Staffed computer lab on campus (open 24 hours a day) provides training in use of computers, software, and the Internet.

Community Environment: Carlisle, population 18,000, is in the Cumberland Valley located at the western edge of Harrisburg, the state capital. It is 3 miles from I-76 and I-81, and within 2-3 hours of Baltimore, Washington and Philadelphia. Founded in 1751, it was the focus of the Scotch-Irish colonists who settled in Pennsylvania in the pre-revolutionary period. Several historic figures made their homes in Carlisle during the revolutionary period. Numerous buildings of Colonial and Federal architecture, many of native limestone, have been restored in the historic district of Carlisle. The eastern most ranges of the Appalachian Mountains are within a few miles of the downtown area, and the Appalachian Trail passes within five miles. Four state parks provide opportunities for hiking, fishing, hunting, and water and winter sports. The Carlisle Hospital, a variety of theatres, restaurants, and churches, three amusement parks, and public golf courses are within easy reach.

■ **DOUGLAS EDUCATION CENTER**
130 Seventh St.
Monessen, PA 15062
Tel: (724)684-3684; Free: 800-413-6013
Fax: (724)684-7463
Web Site: www.dec.edu/

Description: Proprietary, 2-year, coed. Awards diplomas and terminal associate degrees. Founded 1904. Setting: small town campus with easy access to Pittsburgh. Educational spending for the previous fiscal year: $4633 per student. Total enrollment: 334. Faculty: 37 (13 full-time, 24 part-time). Student-undergrad faculty ratio is 16:1. Full-time: 334 students, 66% women, 34% men. Students come from 49 states and territories, 4 other countries, 32% from out-of-state. 1% American Indian or Alaska Native, non-Hispanic/Latino; 4% Hispanic/Latino; 4% African American, non-Hispanic/Latino; 1% Asian, non-Hispanic/Latino; 1% Native Hawaiian or other Pacific Islander, non-Hispanic/Latino; 1% international. 61% 25 or older, 0% transferred in. Retention: 87% of full-time freshmen returned the following year. Core. Advanced placement.

Entrance Requirements: Open admission. Required: high school transcript, interview, Wonderlic aptitude test. Entrance: minimally difficult. Application deadlines: Rolling, Rolling for nonresidents. Notification: continuous, continuous for nonresidents. Transfer credits accepted: Yes.

Collegiate Environment: Orientation program. Campus security: 24-hour emergency response devices. Douglas Education Center Library / Learning Resource Center plus 2 others with 126 serials, 820 audiovisual materials, and an OPAC. Operations spending for the previous fiscal year: $135,000. 97 computers available on campus for general student use. Computer purchase/lease plans available. A computer is required for all students. A campuswide network can be accessed. Students can access the following: online Student Accounts/Financial Aid. Staffed computer lab on campus provides training in use of computers, software, and the Internet.

■ **DREXEL UNIVERSITY**
3141 Chestnut St.
Philadelphia, PA 19104-2875

Tel: (215)895-2000; Free: 800-2-DREXEL
Fax: (215)895-5939
E-mail: enroll@drexel.edu
Web Site: www.drexel.edu/

Description: Independent, university, coed. Awards associate, bachelor's, master's, and doctoral degrees and post-master's certificates. Founded 1891. Setting: 96-acre urban campus with easy access to Philadelphia. Endowment: $555.4 million. Research spending for the previous fiscal year: $119.2 million. Total enrollment: 25,500. Faculty: 2,014 (1,061 full-time, 953 part-time). Student-undergrad faculty ratio is 14:1. 40,586 applied, 75% were admitted. 34% from top 10% of their high school class, 65% from top quarter, 92% from top half. Full-time: 13,072 students, 43% women, 57% men. Part-time: 2,804 students, 59% women, 41% men. Students come from 51 states and territories, 121 other countries, 51% from out-of-state. 0.2% American Indian or Alaska Native, non-Hispanic/Latino; 6% Hispanic/Latino; 6% African American, non-Hispanic/Latino; 12% Asian, non-Hispanic/Latino; 1% Native Hawaiian or other Pacific Islander, non-Hispanic/Latino; 11% international. 18% 25 or older, 28% live on campus, 9% transferred in. Retention: 85% of full-time freshmen returned the following year. Academic areas with the most degrees conferred: health professions and related sciences; business/marketing; engineering. Core. Academic remediation for entering students, ESL program, services for LD students, advanced placement, accelerated degree program, self-designed majors, freshman honors college, honors program, independent study, distance learning, double major, summer session for credit, part-time degree program, adult/continuing education programs, co-op programs and internships, graduate courses open to undergrads. Study abroad program. ROTC: Army, Naval (c), Air Force (c).

Entrance Requirements: Options: electronic application, early admission, early decision, deferred admission. Required: essay, high school transcript, minimum 2 high school GPA, SAT or ACT. Recommended: 2 recommendations, interview. Entrance: moderately difficult. Application deadlines: 1/15, 11/15 for early decision. Notification: continuous, 12/15 for early decision. SAT Reasoning Test deadline: 1/15. Transfer credits accepted: Yes.

Costs Per Year: Application fee: $75. Comprehensive fee: $51,920 includes full-time tuition ($35,135), mandatory fees ($2370), and college room and board ($14,415). College room only: $8730. Full-time tuition and fees vary according to course load, location, program, and student level. Room and board charges vary according to board plan and housing facility. Part-time tuition: $970 per credit. Part-time tuition varies according to course load and program.

Collegiate Environment: Orientation program. Drama-theater group, choral group, student-run newspaper, radio station. Social organizations: 363 open to all; national fraternities, national sororities, local fraternities, local sororities; 9% of eligible men and 8% of eligible women are members. Most popular organizations: student government, Black Student Union, Society of Hispanic Professional Engineers, Society of Minority Engineers and Scientists, Campus Activities Board. Major annual events: Spring Jam, Welcome Back, Homecoming. Student services: health clinic, personal-psychological counseling. Campus security: 24-hour emergency response devices and patrols, late night transport-escort service, controlled dormitory access. 3,900 college housing spaces available. Freshmen guaranteed college housing. On-campus residence required in freshman year. Option: coed housing available. W. W. Hagerty Library plus 3 others with 625,531 books, 18,133 microform titles, 32,850 serials, 6,853 audiovisual materials, an OPAC, and a Web page. 8,000 computers available on campus for general student use. A computer is required for all students. A campuswide network can be accessed from student residence rooms and from off campus. Students can access the following: online class registration. Staffed computer lab on campus.

Community Environment: Philadelphia, a metropolitan city with historical significance, provides considerable cultural, social, and recreational resources, as well as excellent shopping and dining. Transportation includes public transit, major highways, Amtrak, and Philadelphia International Airport.

■ **DUBOIS BUSINESS COLLEGE**
1 Beaver Dr.
DuBois, PA 15801-2401
Tel: (814)371-6920; Free: 800-692-6213
E-mail: dotylj@dbcollege.com
Web Site: www.dbcollege.com/

Description: Proprietary, 2-year, coed. Awards diplomas and terminal associate degrees. Founded 1885. Setting: 4-acre rural campus. Total enrollment: 233. 33% 25 or older. Core. Academic remediation for entering students, accelerated degree program, double major, summer session for credit, part-time degree program.

Entrance Requirements: Options: electronic application, deferred admission. Required: high school transcript, interview. Entrance: moderately difficult. Application deadline: Rolling. Notification: continuous.

Collegiate Environment: Orientation program. Student-run newspaper. Social organizations: national fraternities, national sororities. Student services: personal-psychological counseling. Campus security: late night transport-escort service, controlled dormitory access. DuBois Business College Main Campus Library with 2,100 books, 10 serials, and a Web page.

Community Environment: See Penn State University, DuBois Campus.

■ **DUQUESNE UNIVERSITY**

600 Forbes Ave.
Pittsburgh, PA 15282-0001
Tel: (412)396-6000; Free: 800-456-0590
Fax: (412)396-5779
E-mail: admissions@duq.edu
Web Site: www.duq.edu/

Description: Independent Roman Catholic, university, coed. Awards bachelor's, master's, and doctoral degrees and post-master's certificates. Founded 1878. Setting: 50-acre urban campus with easy access to Pittsburgh. Endowment: $177.2 million. Research spending for the previous fiscal year: $15.1 million. Educational spending for the previous fiscal year: $10,698 per student. Total enrollment: 9,956. Faculty: 987 (486 full-time, 501 part-time). Student-undergrad faculty ratio is 14:1. 6,659 applied, 75% were admitted. 29% from top 10% of their high school class, 60% from top quarter, 90% from top half. 31 valedictorians. Full-time: 5,650 students, 58% women, 42% men. Part-time: 182 students, 45% women, 55% men. Students come from 43 states and territories, 49 other countries, 25% from out-of-state. 0.2% American Indian or Alaska Native, non-Hispanic/Latino; 3% Hispanic/Latino; 4% African American, non-Hispanic/Latino; 2% Asian, non-Hispanic/Latino; 0.03% Native Hawaiian or other Pacific Islander, non-Hispanic/Latino; 4% international. 6% 25 or older, 59% live on campus, 3% transferred in. Retention: 89% of full-time freshmen returned the following year. Academic areas with the most degrees conferred: business/marketing; health professions and related sciences; biological/life sciences; communication/journalism. Core. Calendar: semesters. Academic remediation for entering students, ESL program, services for LD students, advanced placement, accelerated degree program, self-designed majors, freshman honors college, honors program, independent study, distance learning, double major, summer session for credit, part-time degree program, external degree program, adult/continuing education programs, internships, graduate courses open to undergrads. Off campus study at Carlow University, Carnegie Mellon University, Chatham University, Community College of Allegheny County, LaRoche College, Pittsburgh Theological Seminary, Point Park University, Robert Morris University, University of Pittsburgh. Study abroad program. ROTC: Army, Naval (c), Air Force (c).

Entrance Requirements: Options: electronic application, early admission, early decision, early action, deferred admission, international baccalaureate accepted. Required: essay, high school transcript, 1 recommendation, SAT or ACT. Recommended: minimum 3 high school GPA, interview. Required for some: audition for School of Music applicants; Physical Therapy freshman-40 hours of volunteer, paid, or shadowing experience before start of freshman year. Entrance: moderately difficult. Application deadlines: 7/1, 11/1 for early decision, 12/1 for early action. Notification: continuous until 10/1, 12/15 for early decision, 1/15 for early action. SAT Reasoning Test deadline: 7/1. Transfer credits accepted: Yes. Early decision applicants: 136. Early decision applicants admitted: 81. Early action applicants: 1,608. Early action applicants admitted: 861.

Costs Per Year: Application fee: $50. Comprehensive fee: $40,232 includes full-time tuition ($27,668), mandatory fees ($2366), and college room and board ($10,198). College room only: $5562. Full-time tuition and fees vary according to program. Room and board charges vary according to board plan and housing facility. Part-time tuition: $902 per credit. Part-time mandatory fees: $92 per credit. Part-time tuition and fees vary according to program.

Collegiate Environment: Orientation program. Drama-theater group, choral group, marching band, student-run newspaper, radio station. Social organizations: 200 open to all; national fraternities, national sororities, local fraternities; 17% of eligible men and 19% of eligible women are members. Most popular organizations: Duquesne University Volunteers (DUV), Red and Blue Crew, Student Government Association, Duquesne Program

Council, Residence Hall Association. Major annual events: Orientation, Night of Lights, ISO Night (International Dinner). Student services: health clinic, personal-psychological counseling. Campus security: 24-hour emergency response devices and patrols, late night transport-escort service, controlled dormitory access, cameras monitor exterior 24 hours/day; card access for buildings; 8 Code Blue Emergency service stations; outside warning siren system. 3,796 college housing spaces available; 3,774 were occupied in 2012-13. Freshmen guaranteed college housing. On-campus residence required through sophomore year. Options: coed, men-only, women-only housing available. Gumberg Library with 739,768 books, 252,149 microform titles, 101,861 serials, 89,421 audiovisual materials, an OPAC, and a Web page. Operations spending for the previous fiscal year: $7.1 million. 1,000 computers available on campus for general student use. Computer purchase/lease plans available. A campuswide network can be accessed from student residence rooms and from off campus. Students can access the following: online class registration. Staffed computer lab on campus (open 24 hours a day) provides training in use of computers, software, and the Internet.

Community Environment: Located adjacent to downtown Pittsburgh, Duquesne University's modern hilltop campus is readily accessible to the business, entertainment, and shopping centers of the city, while still offering students the privacy and peace of its own self-enclosed 43-acre site. Long noted as one of the world's great corporate centers, Pittsburgh combines the features of urban living with many of the charms and personal characteristics of a much smaller town. The world-renowned Pittsburgh Symphony Orchestra, Pittsburgh Opera, and Pittsburgh Ballet Theatre all perform regularly in the elegant Heinz Hall for the Performing Arts and the Benedum Center. The theatergoer can choose from productions of the Pittsburgh Public Theatre, local college drama departments and programs, and a wide variety of summer and after dinner club theatres. Duquesne students can visit such points of interest as The Pittsburgh Zoo, Carnegie Museum of Art and History, Scaife Gallery, the Conservatory Aviary, Carnegie Science Center and Buhl Planetarium, Pittsburgh History and Landmarks Museum, Duquesne Incline and Phipps Conservatory. Market Square, a redeveloped area in the heart of downtown Pittsburgh, and the Oakland-Shadyside area in the eastern end of the city are two of the major entertainment and nightlife centers. The success of the various professional and major college sports teams has won for Pittsburgh the title of"City of Champions.".

■ **EAST STROUDSBURG UNIVERSITY OF PENNSYLVANIA**

200 Prospect St.
East Stroudsburg, PA 18301-2999
Tel: (570)422-3211; Free: 877-230-5547
Fax: (570)422-3933
E-mail: undergrads@po-box.esu.edu
Web Site: www.esu.edu/

Description: State-supported, comprehensive, coed. Part of Pennsylvania State System of Higher Education. Awards associate, bachelor's, and master's degrees. Founded 1893. Setting: 256-acre small town campus. Endowment: $10.3 million. Research spending for the previous fiscal year: $634,192. Educational spending for the previous fiscal year: $6108 per student. Total enrollment: 7,353. Faculty: 319 (262 full-time, 57 part-time). Student-undergrad faculty ratio is 24:1. 6,520 applied, 81% were admitted. 8% from top 10% of their high school class, 24% from top quarter, 58% from top half. Full-time: 6,056 students, 55% women, 45% men. Part-time: 600 students, 57% women, 43% men. Students come from 26 states and territories, 23 other countries, 25% from out-of-state. 0.3% American Indian or Alaska Native, non-Hispanic/Latino; 4% Hispanic/Latino; 7% African American, non-Hispanic/Latino; 2% Asian, non-Hispanic/Latino; 4% Native Hawaiian or other Pacific Islander, non-Hispanic/Latino; 1% international. 8% 25 or older, 43% live on campus, 10% transferred in. Retention: 78% of full-time freshmen returned the following year. Academic areas with the most degrees conferred: education; business/marketing; health professions and related sciences. Core. Calendar: semesters. Academic remediation for entering students, services for LD students, advanced placement, accelerated degree program, self-designed majors, honors program, independent study, distance learning, double major, summer session for credit, part-time degree program, adult/continuing education programs, internships, graduate courses open to undergrads. Off campus study at National Student Exchange, Wallops Island Consortium. Study abroad program. ROTC: Army, Air Force (c).

Entrance Requirements: Options: electronic application, international baccalaureate accepted. Required: SAT or ACT. Required for some: high school transcript. Entrance: moderately difficult. Application deadline: 4/1. Notification: 5/1. Preference given to state residents. SAT Reasoning Test deadline: 4/1. Transfer credits accepted: Yes. Applicants placed on waiting list: 0.

Costs Per Year: Application fee: $45. State resident tuition: $6428 full-time. Nonresident tuition: $16,070 full-time. Mandatory fees: $1,887 full-time. Full-time tuition and fees vary according to course load. College room and board: $9176. College room only: $6718. Room and board charges vary according to board plan and housing facility.

Collegiate Environment: Orientation program. Drama-theater group, choral group, marching band, student-run newspaper, radio station. Social organizations: 100 open to all; national fraternities, national sororities; 5% of eligible men and 4% of eligible women are members. Most popular organizations: Student Senate, Stage II, Council for Exceptional Children, United Campus Ministry/ESU Christian Fellowship, University Band/Vocal Performing Choirs. Major annual events: Welcome Week, Homecoming, Greek Week. Student services: health clinic, personal-psychological counseling, women's center. Campus security: 24-hour emergency response devices and patrols, late night transport-escort service, controlled dormitory access. Kemp Library with 569,096 books, 1.4 million microform titles, 3,900 serials, 39,227 audiovisual materials, an OPAC, and a Web page. Operations spending for the previous fiscal year: $2 million. 500 computers available on campus for general student use. A campuswide network can be accessed from student residence rooms and from off campus. Students can access the following: online class registration, Online classes. Students can connect through the wireless network. Staffed computer lab on campus provides training in use of computers, software, and the Internet.

Community Environment: Population 10,621. East Stroudsburg is an urban area with temperate climate. The community is served by bus lines and Routes 611, 80 and 191. The community has a public library, YMCA, a hospital, good shopping facilities, and churches of major denominations. Part-time employment opportunities are excellent. The area offers good recreational facilities with nearby resorts.

■ EASTERN UNIVERSITY
1300 Eagle Rd.
Saint Davids, PA 19087-3696
Tel: (610)341-5800; Free: 800-452-0996
Fax: (610)341-1723
E-mail: ugadm@eastern.edu
Web Site: www.eastern.edu/

Description: Independent Christian, comprehensive, coed. Awards associate, bachelor's, master's, and doctoral degrees. Founded 1952. Setting: 114-acre suburban campus with easy access to Philadelphia. Total enrollment: 4,263. Faculty: 568 (174 full-time, 394 part-time). Student-undergrad faculty ratio is 11:1. 1,463 applied, 70% were admitted. 18% from top 10% of their high school class, 32% from top quarter, 77% from top half. Full-time: 2,179 students, 68% women, 32% men. Part-time: 522 students, 75% women, 25% men. 44% from out-of-state. 0.3% American Indian or Alaska Native, non-Hispanic/Latino; 11% Hispanic/Latino; 23% African American, non-Hispanic/Latino; 2% Asian, non-Hispanic/Latino; 0.1% Native Hawaiian or other Pacific Islander, non-Hispanic/Latino; 2% international. 4% 25 or older, 72% live on campus, 3% transferred in. Retention: 80% of full-time freshmen returned the following year. Academic areas with the most degrees conferred: business/marketing; education; health professions and related sciences. Core. Calendar: semesters. Academic remediation for entering students, ESL program, advanced placement, accelerated degree program, self-designed majors, honors program, independent study, distance learning, summer session for credit, part-time degree program, adult/continuing education programs, internships, graduate courses open to undergrads. Off campus study at all American Baptist-related colleges, Cabrini College, Rosemont College. Study abroad program. ROTC: Army (c), Air Force (c).

Entrance Requirements: Options: electronic application, early admission, deferred admission, international baccalaureate accepted. Required: essay, high school transcript, minimum 2 high school GPA, 1 recommendation, SAT or ACT. Recommended: 2 recommendations, interview. Entrance: moderately difficult. Application deadlines: Rolling, Rolling for nonresidents. Notification: continuous, continuous for nonresidents. Transfer credits accepted: Yes.

Costs Per Year: Application fee: $25. One-time mandatory fee: $50. Comprehensive fee: $37,654 includes full-time tuition ($27,900), mandatory fees ($140), and college room and board ($9614). College room only: $5150. Full-time tuition and fees vary according to course load, degree level, and program. Room and board charges vary according to housing facility and location. Part-time tuition: $580 per credit. Part-time tuition varies according to course load, degree level, and program.

Collegiate Environment: Orientation program. Drama-theater group, choral group, student-run newspaper, radio station. Social organizations: 40 open to all. Most popular organizations: Habitat for Humanity, Evangelical for the Promotion of Education, Black Student League, Students in Free Enterprise, Fellowship of Christian Athletes. Major annual events: Homecoming Weekend, Spring Banquet, Concerts. Student services: health clinic, personal-psychological counseling, women's center. Campus security: 24-hour emergency response devices and patrols, late night transport-escort service, controlled dormitory access, emergency call boxes. 1,242 college housing spaces available; 1,116 were occupied in 2012-13. Freshmen guaranteed college housing. On-campus residence required through senior year. Option: coed housing available. Warner Library plus 1 other with 473,190 books, 869,487 microform titles, 79,525 serials, 17,421 audiovisual materials, an OPAC, and a Web page. 125 computers available on campus for general student use. A campuswide network can be accessed from student residence rooms and from off campus. Students can access the following: online class registration. Staffed computer lab on campus.

■ EDINBORO UNIVERSITY OF PENNSYLVANIA
Edinboro, PA 16444
Tel: (814)732-2000; Free: 888-846-2676
Fax: (814)732-2420
E-mail: eup_admissions@edinboro.edu
Web Site: www.edinboro.edu/

Description: State-supported, comprehensive, coed. Part of Pennsylvania State System of Higher Education. Awards associate, bachelor's, and master's degrees and post-master's certificates. Founded 1857. Setting: 585-acre small town campus. Endowment: $8.3 million. Research spending for the previous fiscal year: $53,875. Total enrollment: 7,462. Faculty: 410 (338 full-time, 72 part-time). Student-undergrad faculty ratio is 18:1. 3,992 applied, 75% were admitted. 4% from top 10% of their high school class, 15% from top quarter, 47% from top half. Full-time: 5,565 students, 58% women, 42% men. Part-time: 525 students, 59% women, 41% men. Students come from 32 states and territories, 33 other countries, 14% from out-of-state. 0.2% American Indian or Alaska Native, non-Hispanic/Latino; 3% Hispanic/Latino; 7% African American, non-Hispanic/Latino; 1% Asian, non-Hispanic/Latino; 0.1% Native Hawaiian or other Pacific Islander, non-Hispanic/Latino; 1% international. 13% 25 or older, 37% live on campus, 4% transferred in. Retention: 68% of full-time freshmen returned the following year. Academic areas with the most degrees conferred: visual and performing arts; education; health professions and related sciences. Core. Calendar: semesters. Academic remediation for entering students, services for LD students, advanced placement, self-designed majors, freshman honors college, honors program, independent study, distance learning, double major, summer session for credit, part-time degree program, adult/continuing education programs, internships, graduate courses open to undergrads. Off campus study at members of the Northwestern Pennsylvania Planning Council for Higher Education, Gannon University, Mercyhurst College, Hamot Medical Center, Pennsylvania State University at Erie, The Behrend College, Clarion University of Pennsylvania, Slippery Rock University of Pennsylvania, University of Pittsburgh, Case-Western University. Study abroad program. ROTC: Army.

Entrance Requirements: Options: electronic application, deferred admission, international baccalaureate accepted. Required: high school transcript, SAT or ACT. Recommended: minimum 2.5 high school GPA. Required for some: essay, 1 recommendation, interview, music auditions. Entrance: moderately difficult. Notification: continuous. SAT Reasoning Test deadline: 8/15. Transfer credits accepted: Yes.

Costs Per Year: Application fee: $30. State resident tuition: $6428 full-time, $268 per credit part-time. Nonresident tuition: $9642 full-time, $402 per credit part-time. Mandatory fees: $2,150 full-time, $90 per credit part-time. Part-time tuition and fees vary according to course load. College room and board: $7362. College room only: $5200. Room and board charges vary according to board plan.

Collegiate Environment: Orientation program. Drama-theater group, choral group, marching band, student-run newspaper, radio station. Social organizations: 200 open to all; national fraternities, national sororities; 2% of eligible men and 2% of eligible women are members. Most popular organizations: Student Government Association, University Programming Board, Greek Life, Recreational Sports, Student Concert Series. Major annual events: Homecoming, Concerts, Welcome Week/Club Rush. Student services: legal services, health clinic, personal-psychological counseling, women's center. Campus security: 24-hour emergency response devices and patrols, controlled dormitory access, self-defense education. 2,940 college housing spaces available; 2,277 were occupied in 2012-13. Freshmen guaranteed college housing. On-campus residence required through sophomore year. Option: coed housing available. Baron-Forness Library plus 1 other with 485,338 books, 691,742 microform titles, 1,024 serials, 10,412 audiovisual materials, an OPAC, and a Web page. Operations spending for the previous fiscal year: $870,912. 4,420 computers available on campus for general student use. Computer purchase/lease plans available. A campuswide network can be accessed from student residence rooms. Students can access the following: online class registration, software. Staffed computer lab on campus provides training in use of computers, software, and the Internet.

Community Environment: Population 6,737, Edinboro lies approximately 18 miles south of Erie, Pennsylvania. The community has several churches that represent various denominations. Bus and highway transportation is available. Local recreational facilities include hunting, boating, swimming, fishing, golf, and skiing. Edinboro Lake, which is one mile from the campus, has three beaches.

■ ELIZABETHTOWN COLLEGE

One Alpha Dr.
Elizabethtown, PA 17022-2298
Tel: (717)361-1000
E-mail: admissions@etown.edu
Web Site: www.etown.edu/

Description: Independent, 4-year, coed, affiliated with Church of the Brethren. Awards bachelor's and master's degrees. Founded 1899. Setting: 201-acre small town campus with easy access to Baltimore, Philadelphia. Endowment: $54.8 million. Educational spending for the previous fiscal year: $11,541 per student. Total enrollment: 1,911. Faculty: 212 (131 full-time, 81 part-time). Student-undergrad faculty ratio is 12:1. 3,732 applied, 70% were admitted. 33% from top 10% of their high school class, 61% from top quarter, 89% from top half. 9 valedictorians, 70 student government officers. Full-time: 1,858 students, 65% women, 35% men. Part-time: 27 students, 59% women, 41% men. Students come from 27 states and territories, 26 other countries, 31% from out-of-state. 0.3% American Indian or Alaska Native, non-Hispanic/Latino; 2% Hispanic/Latino; 3% African American, non-Hispanic/Latino; 2% Asian, non-Hispanic/Latino; 0.2% Native Hawaiian or other Pacific Islander, non-Hispanic/Latino; 4% international. 1% 25 or older, 88% live on campus, 1% transferred in. Retention: 86% of full-time freshmen returned the following year. Academic areas with the most degrees conferred: business/marketing; biological/life sciences; social sciences. Core. Calendar: semesters. ESL program, services for LD students, advanced placement, honors program, independent study, distance learning, double major, summer session for credit, internships. Off campus study at American University. Study abroad program.

Entrance Requirements: Options: electronic application, deferred admission, international baccalaureate accepted. Required: essay, high school transcript, minimum 2 high school GPA, 2 recommendations, SAT or ACT. Recommended: minimum 3 high school GPA, interview. Required for some: interview. Entrance: moderately difficult. Application deadline: 3/1. Notification: continuous. SAT Reasoning Test deadline: 3/1. Transfer credits accepted: Yes. Applicants placed on waiting list: 101. Wait-listed applicants offered admission: 10.

Costs Per Year: Application fee: $30. Comprehensive fee: $47,600 includes full-time tuition ($38,200) and college room and board ($9400). College room only: $4650. Full-time tuition varies according to course load. Room and board charges vary according to board plan and housing facility. Part-time tuition: $925 per credit hour. Part-time tuition and fees vary according to course load.

Collegiate Environment: Orientation program. Drama-theater group, choral group, student-run newspaper, radio station. Social organizations: 80 open to all. Most popular organizations: Students in Free Enterprise (SIFE), Emotion Dance Club, Student Senate, Acappella groups, religious groups. Major annual events: Into the Streets Service Weekend, TGIS Weekend, Homecoming. Student services: personal-psychological counseling. Campus security: 24-hour emergency response devices and patrols, student patrols, late night transport-escort service, controlled dormitory access, self-defense workshops, crime prevention program. College housing designed to accommodate 1,616 students; 1,630 undergraduates lived in college housing during 2012-13. Freshmen guaranteed college housing. On-campus residence required through senior year. Options: coed, women-only housing available. High Library plus 1 other with 260,258 books, 23,672 microform titles, 28,901 serials, 9,242 audiovisual materials, an OPAC, and a Web page. Operations spending for the previous fiscal year: $1.2 million. 200 computers

available on campus for general student use. Computer purchase/lease plans available. A campuswide network can be accessed from student residence rooms and from off campus. Students can access the following: online class registration, file space, personal web page, financial aid, student billing, residence hall selection, personal and group blogs. Staffed computer lab on campus provides training in use of computers, software, and the Internet.

Community Environment: Population 18,900. Located in Lancaster County, Elizabethtown enjoys the advantages of the neighboring communities' facilities. This suburb has a library, several churches, and major fraternal and civic organizations within the immediate locale. Some part-time employment is available.

■ ELIZABETHTOWN COLLEGE SCHOOL OF CONTINUING AND PROFESSIONAL STUDIES

One Alpha Dr.
Elizabethtown, PA 17022
Tel: (717)361-3750
Web Site: www.etowndegrees.com/
Description: Independent religious, comprehensive, coed.

■ ERIE BUSINESS CENTER, MAIN

246 W Ninth St.
Erie, PA 16501-1392
Tel: (814)456-7504; Free: 800-352-3743
Fax: (814)456-4882
E-mail: admissions@eriebc.edu
Web Site: www.eriebc.edu/
Description: Proprietary, 2-year, coed. Awards certificates, diplomas, and terminal associate degrees. Founded 1884. Setting: 1-acre urban campus with easy access to Cleveland, Buffalo. Total enrollment: 332. Student-undergrad faculty ratio is 15:1. 1% from out-of-state. 62% 25 or older. Core. Calendar: trimesters. Advanced placement, independent study, summer session for credit, part-time degree program, adult/continuing education programs.

Entrance Requirements: Option: deferred admission. Required: high school transcript, interview, Wonderlic aptitude test. Entrance: minimally difficult. Application deadline: Rolling. Notification: continuous.

Collegiate Environment: Orientation program. Drama-theater group. Campus security: 24-hour emergency response devices, security guard. EBC Blackmer Library with an OPAC.

■ ERIE BUSINESS CENTER, SOUTH

170 Cascade Galleria
New Castle, PA 16101-3950
Tel: (724)658-9066; Free: 800-722-6227
Fax: (724)658-3083
E-mail: admissions@eriebcs.com
Web Site: www.eriebc.edu/newcastle/
Description: Proprietary, 2-year, coed. Administratively affiliated with Erie Business Center - Main Campus. Awards diplomas, transfer associate, and terminal associate degrees. Founded 1894. Setting: 1-acre small town campus with easy access to Pittsburgh. Total enrollment: 100. Faculty: 4 (2 full-time, 2 part-time). 45 applied, 87% were admitted. 60% 25 or older. Retention: 80% of full-time freshmen returned the following year. Core. Academic remediation for entering students, part-time degree program, adult/continuing education programs, internships.

Entrance Requirements: Options: electronic application, deferred admission. Required: essay, high school transcript, Wonderlic aptitude test. Recommended: interview, SAT or ACT, SAT and SAT Subject Tests or ACT. Entrance: moderately difficult. Application deadline: Rolling.

Collegiate Environment: Orientation program. Social organizations: 6 open to all. Most popular organizations: student government, Business Club, Medical Club, Travel Club, Ambassadors Club. Major annual events: Winter Formal, Christmas Party, Kennywood Park Fun Day. Student services: personal-psychological counseling. Campus security: 24-hour patrols. 1,725 books, 20 serials, and 8 audiovisual materials 60 computers available on campus for general student use. A campuswide network can be accessed. Staffed computer lab on campus provides training in use of computers, software, and the Internet.

■ ERIE INSTITUTE OF TECHNOLOGY

940 Millcreek Mall
Erie, PA 16565

Tel: (814)868-9900; Free: 866-868-3743
Fax: (814)868-9977
E-mail: info@erieit.edu
Web Site: www.erieit.edu/
Description: Independent, 2-year, coed. Awards certificates and terminal associate degrees. Founded 1991. Total enrollment: 279. Student-undergrad faculty ratio is 11:1. 7% from out-of-state. 58% 25 or older. Calendar: semesters.
Entrance Requirements: Open admission. Required: high school transcript, interview/tour, Wonderlic Basic Skills. Entrance: noncompetitive.

■ EVEREST INSTITUTE
100 Forbes Ave.
Ste. 1200
Pittsburgh, PA 15222
Tel: (412)261-4520; Free: 888-741-4270
Fax: (412)261-4546
Web Site: www.everest.edu/
Description: Proprietary, 2-year, coed. Awards diplomas and transfer associate degrees. Founded 1840. Setting: urban campus. Total enrollment: 827. 69 applied. 1% from out-of-state. 42% 25 or older. Retention: 44% of full-time freshmen returned the following year. Summer session for credit, part-time degree program, adult/continuing education programs.
Entrance Requirements: Option: deferred admission. Required: CPAt. Entrance: moderately difficult. Application deadline: Rolling.
Collegiate Environment: Orientation program. Campus security: 24-hour emergency response devices.

■ FORTIS INSTITUTE (ERIE)
5757 W 26th St.
Erie, PA 16506
Tel: (814)838-7673
Fax: (814)838-8642
E-mail: geuliano@tsbi.org
Web Site: www.fortis.edu/
Description: Private, 2-year, coed. Awards terminal associate degrees. Total enrollment: 1,603. Student-undergrad faculty ratio is 17:1. 40% from out-of-state. 58% 25 or older. Retention: 63% of full-time freshmen returned the following year.
Entrance Requirements: Required: interview.

■ FORTIS INSTITUTE (FORTY FORT)
166 Slocum St.
Forty Fort, PA 18704
Tel: (570)288-8400
Fax: (717)287-7936
Web Site: www.fortis.edu/
Description: Proprietary, 2-year, coed. Awards diplomas, transfer associate, and terminal associate degrees. Founded 1984. Total enrollment: 402. 41 applied. 46% 25 or older.

■ FRANKLIN & MARSHALL COLLEGE
PO Box 3003
Lancaster, PA 17604-3003
Tel: (717)291-3911; Free: 877-678-9111
Fax: (717)291-4389
E-mail: julie.kerich@fandm.edu
Web Site: www.fandm.edu/
Description: Independent, 4-year, coed. Awards bachelor's degrees. Founded 1787. Setting: 209-acre suburban campus with easy access to Philadelphia. Total enrollment: 2,365. Faculty: 288 (229 full-time, 59 part-time). Student-undergrad faculty ratio is 9:1. 5,174 applied, 39% were admitted. Full-time: 2,307 students, 52% women, 48% men. Part-time: 58 students, 50% women, 50% men. Students come from 42 states and territories, 41 other countries, 70% from out-of-state. 0.1% American Indian or Alaska Native, non-Hispanic/Latino; 6% Hispanic/Latino; 4% African American, non-Hispanic/Latino; 4% Asian, non-Hispanic/Latino; 0.04% Native Hawaiian or other Pacific Islander, non-Hispanic/Latino; 10% international. 1% 25 or older, 99% live on campus, 1% transferred in. Retention: 92% of full-time freshmen returned the following year. Academic areas with the most degrees conferred: social sciences; interdisciplinary studies; biological/life sciences. Core. Calendar: semesters. Services for LD students, advanced placement, accelerated degree program, self-designed

majors, independent study, double major, summer session for credit, internships. Off campus study at Central Pennsylvania Consortium. Study abroad program. ROTC: Army (c).
Entrance Requirements: Options: electronic application, early admission, early decision, deferred admission, international baccalaureate accepted. Required: essay, high school transcript, 2 recommendations, Common Application Supplement. Required for some: interview. Entrance: very difficult. Application deadlines: 1/15, 1/15 for nonresidents, 11/15 for early decision plan 1, 1/15 for early decision plan 2. Notification: 4/1, 4/1 for nonresidents, 12/15 for early decision plan 1, 2/15 for early decision plan 2. SAT Reasoning Test deadline: 2/1. SAT Subject Test deadline: 2/1. Transfer credits accepted: Yes. Applicants placed on waiting list: 1,330. Wait-listed applicants offered admission: 31.
Costs Per Year: Application fee: $60. One-time mandatory fee: $200. Comprehensive fee: $56,110 includes full-time tuition ($44,260), mandatory fees ($100), and college room and board ($11,750). College room only: $7330. Room and board charges vary according to board plan and housing facility. Part-time tuition: $5533 per course.
Collegiate Environment: Orientation program. Drama-theater group, choral group, student-run newspaper, radio station. Social organizations: 115 open to all; national fraternities, national sororities; 28% of eligible men and 34% of eligible women are members. Most popular organizations: Intervarsity, Hillel, Mi Gente Latina, Cia Bella, F&M Players. Major annual events: The Halloween Party, Spring Arts, Flapjack Fest. Student services: health clinic, personal-psychological counseling, women's center. Campus security: 24-hour emergency response devices and patrols, late night transport-escort service, controlled dormitory access, residence hall security, campus security connected to city police and fire company. 2,306 college housing spaces available. Freshmen guaranteed college housing. On-campus residence required through senior year. Option: coed housing available. Shadek-Fackenthal Library plus 1 other with 544,913 books, 346,078 microform titles, 2,357 serials, 13,410 audiovisual materials, an OPAC, and a Web page. 125 computers available on campus for general student use. A campuswide network can be accessed from student residence rooms and from off campus. Students can access the following: online class registration, online degree audit, unofficial transcripts, course material. Staffed computer lab on campus provides training in use of computers, software, and the Internet.
Community Environment: Metropolitan area of 300,000; vital, historic city.

■ GANNON UNIVERSITY
109 University Sq.
Erie, PA 16541-0001
Tel: (814)871-7000; Free: 800-GANNONU
Fax: (814)871-5803
E-mail: admissions@gannon.edu
Web Site: www.gannon.edu/
Description: Independent Roman Catholic, university, coed. Awards bachelor's, master's, and doctoral degrees and post-master's certificates. Founded 1925. Setting: 37-acre urban campus with easy access to Cleveland, Buffalo, Pittsburgh. Endowment: $41.3 million. Research spending for the previous fiscal year: $1.4 million. Educational spending for the previous fiscal year: $8286 per student. Total enrollment: 4,008. Faculty: 363 (202 full-time, 161 part-time). Student-undergrad faculty ratio is 13:1. 3,859 applied, 83% were admitted. 21% from top 10% of their high school class, 49% from top quarter, 80% from top half. 10 valedictorians. Full-time: 2,525 students, 59% women, 41% men. Part-time: 483 students, 51% women, 49% men. Students come from 35 states and territories, 24 other countries, 24% from out-of-state. 0.4% American Indian or Alaska Native, non-Hispanic/Latino; 2% Hispanic/Latino; 6% African American, non-Hispanic/Latino; 1% Asian, non-Hispanic/Latino; 0.2% Native Hawaiian or other Pacific Islander, non-Hispanic/Latino; 5% international. 9% 25 or older, 45% live on campus, 4% transferred in. Retention: 80% of full-time freshmen returned the following year. Academic areas with the most degrees conferred: health professions and related sciences; business/marketing; parks and recreation. Core. Calendar: semesters plus 2 summer sessions. Academic remediation for entering students, ESL program, services for LD students, advanced placement, accelerated degree program, honors program, independent study, distance learning, double major, summer session for credit, part-time degree program, adult/continuing education programs, co-op programs and internships, graduate courses open to undergrads. Off campus study. Study abroad program. ROTC: Army.
Entrance Requirements: Options: electronic application, early admission, deferred admission, international baccalaureate accepted. Required: high

school transcript, minimum 2 high school GPA, SAT or ACT. Recommended: essay, counselor's recommendation. Required for some: minimum 3 high school GPA, 3 recommendations, interview. Entrance: moderately difficult. Application deadline: Rolling. SAT Reasoning Test deadline: 7/1. Transfer credits accepted: Yes. Applicants placed on waiting list: 66. Wait-listed applicants offered admission: 16.

Costs Per Year: Application fee: $25. Comprehensive fee: $38,486 includes full-time tuition ($27,000), mandatory fees ($546), and college room and board ($10,940). College room only: $5740. Full-time tuition and fees vary according to class time, course load, and program. Room and board charges vary according to board plan and housing facility. Part-time tuition: $650 per credit hour. Part-time mandatory fees: $18 per credit hour. Part-time tuition and fees vary according to class time, course load, and program.

Collegiate Environment: Orientation program. Drama-theater group, choral group, student-run newspaper, radio station. Social organizations: 58 open to all; national fraternities, national sororities; 11% of eligible men and 13% of eligible women are members. Most popular organizations: Student Occupational Therapy Association, GU Habitat for Humanity, Phi Eta Sigma, Activities Programming Board, GU Society of Physician Assistants. Major annual events: Homecoming, GIVE Day (Gannon's Invitation to Volunteer Everywhere), Springtopia. Student services: health clinic, personal-psychological counseling. Campus security: 24-hour emergency response devices and patrols, student patrols, late night transport-escort service, controlled dormitory access, security cameras. 1,338 college housing spaces available; 1,222 were occupied in 2012-13. Freshmen guaranteed college housing. On-campus residence required through sophomore year. Option: coed housing available. Nash Library with 266,136 books, 193,200 microform titles, 58,039 serials, 4,079 audiovisual materials, an OPAC, and a Web page. Operations spending for the previous fiscal year: $1.5 million. 380 computers available on campus for general student use. A campuswide network can be accessed from student residence rooms and from off campus. Students can access the following: online class registration. Staffed computer lab on campus provides training in use of computers and the Internet.

Community Environment: Pennsylvania's third largest city and its only port on the Great Lakes, Erie is a city of widely diversified industry and commerce. A public library was built on the waterfront and an observation tower to celebrate the city's bicentennial. The area is served by rail, air, and bus lines. The community has many churches representing the major denominations, numerous civic and fraternal organizations, and community health clinics and hospitals. Local facilities include theatres, restaurants, shops, golf courses, city parks, Presque Isle State Park, fishing, ice fishing, boating, beach volleyball, and skating. Part-time employment opportunities are excellent.

■ **GENEVA COLLEGE**
3200 College Ave.
Beaver Falls, PA 15010-3599
Tel: (724)846-5100; Free: 800-847-8255
Fax: (724)847-6687
E-mail: admissions@geneva.edu
Web Site: www.geneva.edu/

Description: Independent, comprehensive, coed, affiliated with Reformed Presbyterian Church of North America. Awards associate, bachelor's, and master's degrees (also offers non-traditional programs in Philadelphia and western Pennsylvania with significant enrollment not reflected in profile). Founded 1848. Setting: 55-acre small town campus with easy access to Pittsburgh. Endowment: $31.9 million. Educational spending for the previous fiscal year: $8822 per student. Total enrollment: 1,646. Faculty: 202 (86 full-time, 116 part-time). Student-undergrad faculty ratio is 13:1. 1,588 applied, 72% were admitted. 17% from top 10% of their high school class, 45% from top quarter, 81% from top half. Full-time: 1,312 students, 48% women, 52% men. Part-time: 30 students, 50% women, 50% men. Students come from 39 states and territories, 5 other countries, 29% from out-of-state. 0.2% American Indian or Alaska Native, non-Hispanic/Latino; 1% Hispanic/Latino; 3% African American, non-Hispanic/Latino; 1% Asian, non-Hispanic/Latino; 0% Native Hawaiian or other Pacific Islander, non-Hispanic/Latino; 1% international. 4% 25 or older, 71% live on campus, 3% transferred in. Retention: 79% of full-time freshmen returned the following year. Academic areas with the most degrees conferred: business/marketing; education; theology and religious vocations. Core. Calendar: semesters. Academic remediation for entering students, ESL program, services for LD students, advanced placement, accelerated degree program, self-designed majors, honors program, independent study, double major, summer session for credit, part-

time degree program, adult/continuing education programs, co-op programs and internships, graduate courses open to undergrads. Off campus study at Council for Christian Colleges and Universities, Community College of Beaver County, Roberts Wesleyan University, Arcadia University, Art Institute of Pittsburgh. Study abroad program. ROTC: Army (c).

Entrance Requirements: Options: electronic application, early admission, early action, deferred admission, international baccalaureate accepted. Required: essay, high school transcript, minimum 2 high school GPA, SAT or ACT. Recommended: minimum 3 high school GPA, 2 recommendations, interview. Required for some: interview. Entrance: moderately difficult. Application deadline: Rolling. Notification: continuous. Transfer credits accepted: Yes.

Costs Per Year: Application fee: $40. Comprehensive fee: $34,470 includes full-time tuition ($25,220) and college room and board ($9250). Full-time tuition varies according to course load. Room and board charges vary according to board plan. Part-time tuition: $850 per credit. Part-time tuition varies according to course load.

Collegiate Environment: Orientation program. Drama-theater group, choral group, marching band, student-run newspaper, radio station. Social organizations: 50 open to all. Most popular organizations: marching band, Genevans Choir, ministry groups, intermurals, discipleship groups. Major annual events: Homecoming, My Generation Night, Midnight Madness. Student services: health clinic, personal-psychological counseling. Campus security: 24-hour emergency response devices and patrols, late night transport-escort service, controlled dormitory access. 969 college housing spaces available; 946 were occupied in 2012-13. Freshmen guaranteed college housing. On-campus residence required through senior year. Options: men-only, women-only housing available. McCartney Library plus 3 others with 171,865 books, 232,933 microform titles, 689 serials, 19,645 audiovisual materials, an OPAC, and a Web page. Operations spending for the previous fiscal year: $645,245. 150 computers available on campus for general student use. A campuswide network can be accessed from student residence rooms and from off campus. Students can access the following: online class registration. Staffed computer lab on campus provides training in use of computers, software, and the Internet.

Community Environment: Rich in natural resources and historical heritage, Beaver County supports commercial and industrial growth as well as a thriving agribusiness enterprise. 18,000 acres of park lands, excellent health care facilities, and numerous churches of various denominations help to meet needs of residents. Public transportation is accessible and proximity to Pittsburgh makes cultural and professional sports events available year-round. Part-time employment is available.

■ **GETTYSBURG COLLEGE**
300 N Washington St.
Gettysburg, PA 17325-1483
Tel: (717)337-6000; Free: 800-431-0803
Fax: (717)337-6008
E-mail: admiss@gettysburg.edu
Web Site: www.gettysburg.edu/

Description: Independent, 4-year, coed, affiliated with Evangelical Lutheran Church in America. Awards bachelor's degrees. Founded 1832. Setting: 200-acre suburban campus with easy access to Baltimore and Washington, DC. Endowment: $231.5 million. Total enrollment: 2,597. Faculty: 312 (220 full-time, 92 part-time). Student-undergrad faculty ratio is 10:1. 5,620 applied, 40% were admitted. 72% from top 10% of their high school class, 92% from top quarter, 99% from top half. Full-time: 2,573 students, 53% women, 47% men. Part-time: 24 students, 58% women, 42% men. Students come from 37 states and territories, 31 other countries, 73% from out-of-state. 0.04% American Indian or Alaska Native, non-Hispanic/Latino; 4% Hispanic/Latino; 3% African American, non-Hispanic/Latino; 2% Asian, non-Hispanic/Latino; 0% Native Hawaiian or other Pacific Islander, non-Hispanic/Latino; 2% international. 1% 25 or older, 92% live on campus, 1% transferred in. Retention: 91% of full-time freshmen returned the following year. Academic areas with the most degrees conferred: social sciences; biological/life sciences; business/marketing. Core. Calendar: semesters. Advanced placement, self-designed majors, independent study, double major, adult/continuing education programs, internships. Off campus study at 2 members of the Central Pennsylvania Consortium. Study abroad program. ROTC: Army (c).

Entrance Requirements: Options: electronic application, early admission, early decision, deferred admission, international baccalaureate accepted. Required: essay, high school transcript, 2 recommendations, SAT or ACT. Recommended: minimum 3 high school GPA, interview, extracurricular activities, SAT Subject Tests. Entrance: most difficult. Application deadlines:

2/1, 11/15 for early decision plan 1, 1/15 for early decision plan 2. Notification: 4/1, 12/15 for early decision plan 1, 2/15 for early decision plan 2. Early decision applicants: 470. Early decision applicants admitted: 343.

Costs Per Year: Application fee: $60. Comprehensive fee: $54,770 includes full-time tuition ($44,210) and college room and board ($10,560). Room and board charges vary according to board plan and housing facility.

Collegiate Environment: Orientation program. Drama-theater group, choral group, marching band, student-run newspaper, radio station. Social organizations: 120 open to all; national fraternities, national sororities; 38% of eligible men and 33% of eligible women are members. Most popular organizations: community service, music, athletics, student government. Major annual events: family weekend programs, Thanksgiving Dinner, Snowball. Student services: health clinic, personal-psychological counseling, women's center. Campus security: 24-hour emergency response devices and patrols, late night transport-escort service, controlled dormitory access. 2,260 college housing spaces available; all were occupied in 2012-13. Freshmen guaranteed college housing. On-campus residence required through senior year. Options: coed, men-only, women-only housing available. Musselman Library with 406,218 books, 71,368 microform titles, 52,619 serials, 27,935 audiovisual materials, an OPAC, and a Web page. 291 computers available on campus for general student use. Computer purchase/lease plans available. A campuswide network can be accessed from student residence rooms and from off campus. Students can access the following: online class registration. Staffed computer lab on campus (open 24 hours a day) provides training in use of computers and software.

Community Environment: Historic area of 20,000 with easy access to Harrisburg, PA, Washington, DC, and Baltimore, MD. The college borders the town and the 3800-acre National Park. A wide variety of recreational opportunities are available.

■ GROVE CITY COLLEGE

100 Campus Dr.
Grove City, PA 16127-2104
Tel: (724)458-2000
Fax: (724)458-3395
E-mail: admissions@gcc.edu
Web Site: www.gcc.edu/

Description: Independent Presbyterian, 4-year, coed. Awards bachelor's degrees. Founded 1876. Setting: 180-acre small town campus with easy access to Pittsburgh. Endowment: $92.3 million. Research spending for the previous fiscal year: $189,724. Educational spending for the previous fiscal year: $7920 per student. Total enrollment: 2,506. Faculty: 228 (133 full-time, 95 part-time). Student-undergrad faculty ratio is 15:1. 1,481 applied, 84% were admitted. 43% from top 10% of their high school class, 81% from top quarter, 95% from top half. 11 National Merit Scholars, 18 class presidents, 42 valedictorians, 135 student government officers. Full-time: 2,469 students, 50% women, 50% men. Part-time: 37 students, 43% women, 57% men. Students come from 45 states and territories, 8 other countries, 54% from out-of-state. 0.3% American Indian or Alaska Native, non-Hispanic/Latino; 1% Hispanic/Latino; 1% African American, non-Hispanic/Latino; 2% Asian, non-Hispanic/Latino; 0% Native Hawaiian or other Pacific Islander, non-Hispanic/Latino; 1% international. 0% 25 or older, 94% live on campus, 1% transferred in. Retention: 91% of full-time freshmen returned the following year. Academic areas with the most degrees conferred: business/marketing; biological/life sciences; education. Core. Calendar: semesters. Services for LD students, advanced placement, independent study, distance learning, double major, summer session for credit, internships. Off campus study. Study abroad program. ROTC: Army (c).

Entrance Requirements: Options: electronic application, early admission, early decision, deferred admission, international baccalaureate accepted. Required: essay, high school transcript, 2 recommendations, SAT or ACT. Recommended: interview. Entrance: moderately difficult. Application deadlines: 2/1, 11/15 for early decision. Notification: 3/15, 12/15 for early decision. Preference given to legacies. SAT Reasoning Test deadline: 3/1. Transfer credits accepted: Yes. Applicants placed on waiting list: 165. Wait-listed applicants offered admission: 27. Early decision applicants: 391. Early decision applicants admitted: 358.

Costs Per Year: Application fee: $50. Comprehensive fee: $22,988 includes full-time tuition ($14,880) and college room and board ($8108). Full-time tuition varies according to course load. Room and board charges vary according to housing facility. Part-time tuition: $465 per credit.

Collegiate Environment: Orientation program. Drama-theater group, choral group, marching band, student-run newspaper, radio station. Social organizations: 145 open to all; local fraternities, local sororities; 16% of

eligible men and 17% of eligible women are members. Most popular organizations: Salt Company, Warriors for Christ, Orientation Board, Orchesis, Touring Choir. Major annual events: Homecoming, Parents' Weekend, President's Gala. Student services: health clinic, personal-psychological counseling. Campus security: 24-hour emergency response devices and patrols, student patrols, late night transport-escort service, controlled dormitory access, security cameras located around campus and in parking lots. 2,338 college housing spaces available; 2,329 were occupied in 2012-13. Freshmen guaranteed college housing. On-campus residence required through senior year. Options: men-only, women-only housing available. Henry Buhl Library with 162,000 books, 4,000 microform titles, 112 serials, 3,500 audiovisual materials, an OPAC, and a Web page. Operations spending for the previous fiscal year: $1.3 million. 50 computers available on campus for general student use. Computer purchase/lease plans available. A computer is required for all students. A campuswide network can be accessed from student residence rooms and from off campus. Students can access the following: online class registration. Staffed computer lab on campus provides training in use of computers, software, and the Internet.

Community Environment: Grove City, population 7,800, is an urban community that produces compressors, gas and diesel engines, soldering equipment and linemen's supplies. The city has a hospital, several churches, a library, theatre, YMCA, and various civic and fraternal organizations. You can experience big-city shopping at the Grove City Factory Shops located just outside of town. Local recreation includes hunting, fishing, golf, football, baseball, swimming, tennis, basketball, bowling, boating, and ice and roller skating.

■ GWYNEDD-MERCY COLLEGE

Sumneytown Pke.
Gwynedd Valley, PA 19437-0901
Tel: (215)646-7300; Free: 800-DIAL-GMC
Fax: (215)641-5556
E-mail: admissions@gmc.edu
Web Site: www.gmc.edu/

Description: Independent Roman Catholic, comprehensive, coed. Awards associate, bachelor's, and master's degrees and post-master's certificates. Founded 1948. Setting: 170-acre suburban campus with easy access to Philadelphia. Endowment: $7.4 million. Educational spending for the previous fiscal year: $8009 per student. Total enrollment: 2,710. Faculty: 272 (80 full-time, 192 part-time). Student-undergrad faculty ratio is 16:1. 1,187 applied, 87% were admitted. 4% from top 10% of their high school class, 21% from top quarter, 52% from top half. Full-time: 2,122 students, 75% women, 25% men. Part-time: 225 students, 76% women, 24% men. Students come from 13 states and territories, 47 other countries, 10% from out-of-state. 0.3% American Indian or Alaska Native, non-Hispanic/Latino; 3% Hispanic/Latino; 26% African American, non-Hispanic/Latino; 3% Asian, non-Hispanic/Latino; 0.1% international. 43% 25 or older, 31% live on campus, 13% transferred in. Retention: 81% of full-time freshmen returned the following year. Academic areas with the most degrees conferred: business/marketing; health professions and related sciences; education. Core. Calendar: semesters. Academic remediation for entering students, ESL program, advanced placement, accelerated degree program, freshman honors college, honors program, independent study, double major, summer session for credit, part-time degree program, adult/continuing education programs, co-op programs and internships, graduate courses open to undergrads.

Entrance Requirements: Options: electronic application, deferred admission. Required: high school transcript, SAT or ACT. Required for some: essay, interview. Entrance: moderately difficult. Application deadlines: Rolling, Rolling for nonresidents. Notification: continuous, continuous for nonresidents. Applicants placed on waiting list: 25. Wait-listed applicants offered admission: 0.

Costs Per Year: Application fee: $25. Comprehensive fee: $38,190 includes full-time tuition ($27,740), mandatory fees ($600), and college room and board ($9850). Full-time tuition and fees vary according to program. Room and board charges vary according to board plan and housing facility. Part-time tuition: $600 per credit hour. Part-time tuition varies according to program.

Collegiate Environment: Orientation program. Choral group, student-run newspaper. Social organizations: 30 open to all. Most popular organizations: Voices of Gwynedd, Athletic Association, student government, Program Board, Peer Mentors. Major annual events: Fall Fest, Carol Night, International Night. Student services: health clinic, personal-psychological counseling. Campus security: 24-hour emergency response devices and patrols, late night transport-escort service. Lourdes Library plus 1 other with

105,070 books, 15,315 microform titles, 667 serials, 11,448 audiovisual materials, an OPAC, and a Web page. Operations spending for the previous fiscal year: $620,000. 218 computers available on campus for general student use. Computer purchase/lease plans available. A campuswide network can be accessed from student residence rooms and from off campus. Students can access the following: online class registration. Staffed computer lab on campus provides training in use of computers, software, and the Internet.

Community Environment: Gwynedd Valley is a suburban location with the community located 20 miles from Center City, Philadelphia, which has cultural, recreational, and community service opportunities. The immediate locale has churches, recreational facilities, shopping malls, movies and restaurants.

■ **HARCUM COLLEGE**
750 Montgomery Ave.
Bryn Mawr, PA 19010-3476
Tel: (610)525-4100
Fax: (610)526-6147
E-mail: enroll@harcum.edu
Web Site: www.harcum.edu/
Description: Independent, 2-year, coed. Awards certificates, transfer associate, and terminal associate degrees. Founded 1915. Setting: 12-acre suburban campus with easy access to Philadelphia. Educational spending for the previous fiscal year: $5673 per student. Total enrollment: 1,154. Faculty: 190 (36 full-time, 154 part-time). Student-undergrad faculty ratio is 12:1. 485 applied, 65% were admitted. 20% live on campus. Retention: 64% of full-time freshmen returned the following year. Core. Calendar: semesters. Academic remediation for entering students, ESL program, services for LD students, advanced placement, accelerated degree program, honors program, independent study, distance learning, summer session for credit, part-time degree program, adult/continuing education programs, internships. Off campus study.
Entrance Requirements: Options: electronic application, deferred admission, international baccalaureate accepted. Required: high school transcript, minimum 2 high school GPA. Recommended: essay, SAT or ACT. Required for some: 1 recommendation, interview. Entrance: minimally difficult. Application deadline: Rolling. Notification: continuous.
Collegiate Environment: Orientation program. Social organizations: 10 open to all. Most popular organizations: OATS (Organization for Animal Tech Students), Student Association of Dental Hygienist of America, Student Nurses Association, Dental Assisting Club, HAECY (Organization for Early Childhood Development). Major annual events: College Transfer Fair, Semester Kick-off, Health and Wellness Fair. Student services: health clinic, personal-psychological counseling. Campus security: 24-hour emergency response devices and patrols, late night transport-escort service, controlled dormitory access. Harcum College Library with 39,994 books, 298 serials, 1,905 audiovisual materials, an OPAC, and a Web page. Operations spending for the previous fiscal year: $239,085. 86 computers available on campus for general student use. A campuswide network can be accessed from student residence rooms and from off campus. Students can access the following: online class registration. Staffed computer lab on campus provides training in use of computers, software, and the Internet.
Community Environment: Located in Bryn Mawr, Harcum College is neighbor to Villanova University, St. Joseph's University, Bryn Mawr College, Cabrini College, Eastern College, among others. Historical and residential, the local community offers many shops, banks, and activities for students. The city of Philadelphia is just 25 minutes away by car or train.

■ **HARRISBURG AREA COMMUNITY COLLEGE**
1 HACC Dr.
Harrisburg, PA 17110-2999
Tel: (717)780-2300; Free: 800-ABC-HACC
Fax: (717)231-7674
E-mail: admit@hacc.edu
Web Site: www.hacc.edu/
Description: State and locally supported, 2-year, coed. Awards certificates, diplomas, transfer associate, and terminal associate degrees. Founded 1964. Setting: 212-acre urban campus. Endowment: $32.1 million. Research spending for the previous fiscal year: $6700. Educational spending for the previous fiscal year: $6337 per student. Total enrollment: 21,945. Faculty: 980 (327 full-time, 653 part-time). Student-undergrad faculty ratio is 22:1. Full-time: 6,882 students, 55% women, 45% men. Part-time: 15,063 students, 66% women, 34% men. Students come from 10 states and ter-

ritories, 58 other countries, 1% from out-of-state. 0.4% American Indian or Alaska Native, non-Hispanic/Latino; 9% Hispanic/Latino; 12% African American, non-Hispanic/Latino; 2% Asian, non-Hispanic/Latino; 0.2% Native Hawaiian or other Pacific Islander, non-Hispanic/Latino; 2% international. 43% 25 or older, 0% live on campus, 0% transferred in. Core. Calendar: semesters. Academic remediation for entering students, ESL program, services for LD students, advanced placement, self-designed majors, honors program, independent study, distance learning, double major, summer session for credit, part-time degree program, adult/continuing education programs, internships. Study abroad program. ROTC: Army.
Entrance Requirements: Open admission except for allied health, chef's apprenticeship programs. Options: electronic application, early admission, deferred admission. Required for some: high school transcript, 1 recommendation, interview. Entrance: noncompetitive. Application deadline: Rolling. Transfer credits accepted: Yes.
Costs Per Year: Application fee: $35. Area resident tuition: $4185 full-time, $139.50 per credit hour part-time. State resident tuition: $5850 full-time, $195 per credit hour part-time. Nonresident tuition: $8775 full-time, $292.50 per credit hour part-time. Mandatory fees: $1170 full-time.
Collegiate Environment: Orientation program. Drama-theater group, student-run newspaper. Social organizations: 28 open to all. Most popular organizations: Student Government Association, Phi Theta Kappa, African American Student Association, Mosiaco Club, Fourth Estate. Campus security: 24-hour emergency response devices and patrols, late night transport-escort service. College housing not available. McCormick Library plus 6 others with 155,069 books, 1,711 microform titles, 855 serials, 8,449 audiovisual materials, an OPAC, and a Web page. Operations spending for the previous fiscal year: $3.5 million. 696 computers available on campus for general student use. Computer purchase/lease plans available. A campuswide network can be accessed. Students can access the following: online class registration. Staffed computer lab on campus.
Community Environment: Population 47,472. On the Susquehanna River, Harrisburg lies between mountains which rise abruptly to the north and west and rolling hills which slope to the south and east. Extensive coal and iron mines in the vicinity furnish raw materials for the city's large steel plants. Part-time employment opportunities are good. Harrisburg is a metropolitan area served by airlines, railroad, and bus lines. The community has state and public libraries, a State Museum, several hospitals, and major civic, fraternal and veteran's organizations. Shopping facilities are excellent. Local recreational opportunities include theatres, summer theatres, parks, golf, professional hockey, and water sports.

■ **HARRISBURG UNIVERSITY OF SCIENCE AND TECHNOLOGY**
326 Market St.
Harrisburg, PA 17101
Tel: (717)901-5100; Free: 866-HBG-UNIV
Fax: (717)901-5150
E-mail: tdawson@harrisburgu.edu
Web Site: www.HarrisburgU.edu/
Description: Independent, comprehensive, coed. Awards bachelor's and master's degrees. Founded 2005. Setting: urban campus. Research spending for the previous fiscal year: $557,211. Educational spending for the previous fiscal year: $8864 per student. Total enrollment: 322. Faculty: 40 (12 full-time, 28 part-time). Student-undergrad faculty ratio is 11:1. Full-time: 202 students, 47% women, 53% men. Part-time: 21 students, 43% women, 57% men. Students come from 5 states and territories, 1 other country, 5% from out-of-state. 0.4% American Indian or Alaska Native, non-Hispanic/Latino; 9% Hispanic/Latino; 25% African American, non-Hispanic/Latino; 7% Asian, non-Hispanic/Latino; 0% Native Hawaiian or other Pacific Islander, non-Hispanic/Latino; 0% international. 20% 25 or older, 30% live on campus, 5% transferred in. Retention: 60% of full-time freshmen returned the following year. Academic areas with the most degrees conferred: physical sciences; computer and information sciences. Core. Calendar: semesters. Academic remediation for entering students, services for LD students, advanced placement, self-designed majors, independent study, double major, summer session for credit, part-time degree program, adult/continuing education programs, internships, graduate courses open to undergrads.
Entrance Requirements: Option: electronic application. Required: high school transcript. Recommended: essay, interview, SAT or ACT. Entrance: minimally difficult. Application deadline: Rolling. Notification: continuous. Transfer credits accepted: Yes.
Costs Per Year: Application fee: $0. Tuition: $23,900 full-time, $1000 per credit hour part-time. Full-time tuition varies according to degree level. Part-time tuition varies according to course load and degree level. College room only: $6340. Room charges vary according to housing facility.

Collegiate Environment: Orientation program. Student services: personal-psychological counseling. Campus security: 24-hour emergency response devices and patrols, trained security personnel during all university operating hours. Information Commons with 40,000 books, 45 serials, an OPAC, and a Web page. Operations spending for the previous fiscal year: $119,386. 10 computers available on campus for general student use. Computer purchase/lease plans available. A computer is required for all students. A campuswide network can be accessed from student residence rooms and from off campus. Staffed computer lab on campus.

■ HAVERFORD COLLEGE

370 Lancaster Ave.
Haverford, PA 19041-1392
Tel: (610)896-1000
Fax: (610)896-1338
E-mail: admitme@haverford.edu
Web Site: www.haverford.edu/

Description: Independent, 4-year, coed. Awards bachelor's degrees. Founded 1833. Setting: 200-acre suburban campus with easy access to Philadelphia. Endowment: $387.6 million. Research spending for the previous fiscal year: $1.3 million. Educational spending for the previous fiscal year: $65,341 per student. Total enrollment: 1,205. Faculty: 138 (118 full-time, 20 part-time). Student-undergrad faculty ratio is 8:1. 3,626 applied, 23% were admitted. 92% from top 10% of their high school class, 100% from top quarter, 100% from top half. 18 valedictorians. Full-time: 1,205 students, 53% women, 47% men. Students come from 44 states and territories, 42 other countries, 86% from out-of-state. 0.2% American Indian or Alaska Native, non-Hispanic/Latino; 9% Hispanic/Latino; 6% African American, non-Hispanic/Latino; 7% Asian, non-Hispanic/Latino; 0% Native Hawaiian or other Pacific Islander, non-Hispanic/Latino; 4% international. 0% 25 or older, 99% live on campus, 0.4% transferred in. Retention: 96% of full-time freshmen returned the following year. Academic areas with the most degrees conferred: social sciences; English; biological/life sciences. Core. Calendar: semesters. Services for LD students, advanced placement, self-designed majors, independent study, double major, internships. Off campus study at University of Pennsylvania, Swarthmore College, Bryn Mawr College. Study abroad program.

Entrance Requirements: Options: electronic application, early admission, early decision, deferred admission, international baccalaureate accepted. Required: essay, 2 recommendations, SAT and SAT Subject Tests or ACT. Recommended: interview. Required for some: high school transcript. Entrance: most difficult. Application deadlines: 1/15, 11/15 for early decision. Notification: 4/15, 12/15 for early decision. Preference given to children of alumni. Transfer credits accepted: Yes. Applicants placed on waiting list: 869. Wait-listed applicants offered admission: 3. Early decision applicants: 281. Early decision applicants admitted: 134.

Costs Per Year: Application fee: $60. One-time mandatory fee: $210. Comprehensive fee: $56,992 includes full-time tuition ($43,310), mandatory fees ($392), and college room and board ($13,290). College room only: $7570.

Collegiate Environment: Orientation program. Drama-theater group, choral group, student-run newspaper, radio station. Social organizations: 229 open to all. Most popular organizations: Volunteer Programs, student government, choral groups, Multicultural Groups, Orientation Team/Residential Life Leaders. Major annual events: Haverfest/May Day, Snowball, Athletic Events Against Swarthmore. Student services: health clinic, personal-psychological counseling, women's center. Campus security: 24-hour emergency response devices and patrols, late night transport-escort service, controlled dormitory access. 1,233 college housing spaces available; 1,205 were occupied in 2012-13. Freshmen guaranteed college housing. On-campus residence required in freshman year. Option: coed housing available. Magill Library plus 4 others with 592,894 books, 8,039 microform titles, 16,280 audiovisual materials, an OPAC, and a Web page. Operations spending for the previous fiscal year: $3.9 million. 300 computers available on campus for general student use. A campuswide network can be accessed from student residence rooms and from off campus. Students can access the following: online class registration. Staffed computer lab on campus (open 24 hours a day) provides training in use of computers, software, and the Internet.

Community Environment: The school has cooperative arrangements with several colleges and universities (see Bryn Mawr College, Swarthmore College, University of Pennsylvania) and is located near many colleges and universities in metropolitan Philadelphia area.

■ HOLY FAMILY UNIVERSITY

9801 Frankford Ave.
Philadelphia, PA 19114
Tel: (215)637-7700
Fax: (215)281-1022
E-mail: admissions@holyfamily.edu
Web Site: www.holyfamily.edu/

Description: Independent Roman Catholic, comprehensive, coed. Awards associate, bachelor's, master's, and doctoral degrees and post-master's certificates. Founded 1954. Setting: 47-acre suburban campus with easy access to Philadelphia. Endowment: $11.5 million. Educational spending for the previous fiscal year: $8598 per student. Total enrollment: 3,094. Faculty: 375 (95 full-time, 280 part-time). Student-undergrad faculty ratio is 12:1. 1,400 applied, 67% were admitted. 8% from top 10% of their high school class, 32% from top quarter, 68% from top half. Full-time: 1,544 students, 75% women, 25% men. Part-time: 595 students, 73% women, 27% men. Students come from 16 states and territories, 9 other countries, 18% from out-of-state. 0.2% American Indian or Alaska Native, non-Hispanic/Latino; 6% Hispanic/Latino; 8% African American, non-Hispanic/Latino; 4% Asian, non-Hispanic/Latino; 0.05% Native Hawaiian or other Pacific Islander, non-Hispanic/Latino; 0.5% international. 20% 25 or older, 17% live on campus, 8% transferred in. Retention: 76% of full-time freshmen returned the following year. Academic areas with the most degrees conferred: health professions and related sciences; education; business/marketing. Core. Calendar: semesters. Academic remediation for entering students, ESL program, services for LD students, advanced placement, accelerated degree program, freshman honors college, honors program, independent study, double major, summer session for credit, part-time degree program, adult/continuing education programs, co-op programs and internships, graduate courses open to undergrads. Study abroad program.

Entrance Requirements: Options: electronic application, deferred admission, international baccalaureate accepted. Required: essay, high school transcript, minimum 2 high school GPA, 2 recommendations, SAT or ACT. Recommended: interview. Entrance: minimally difficult. Application deadlines: Rolling, Rolling for nonresidents. Notification: continuous, continuous for nonresidents. Transfer credits accepted: Yes.

Costs Per Year: Application fee: $25. Comprehensive fee: $37,940 includes full-time tuition ($24,940), mandatory fees ($650), and college room and board ($12,350). College room only: $6650. Full-time tuition and fees vary according to course load and program. Room and board charges vary according to board plan and housing facility. Part-time tuition: $535 per credit hour. Part-time mandatory fees: $60 per term. Part-time tuition and fees vary according to course load and program.

Collegiate Environment: Orientation program. Drama-theater group, choral group, student-run newspaper. Social organizations: 30 open to all; 15% of men are members. Most popular organizations: Students at Your Service (S. A.Y.S.), student government, Campus Ministry Team, Habitat for Humanity, Tri-lite. Major annual events: Christmas Rose, Charter Day, Stress Reduction Week. Student services: health clinic, personal-psychological counseling. Campus security: 24-hour emergency response devices and patrols, late night transport-escort service, controlled dormitory access, video surveillance. 353 college housing spaces available; 261 were occupied in 2012-13. Freshmen given priority for college housing. Option: coed housing available. Holy Family University Library plus 1 other with 145,442 books, 3,980 microform titles, 21,932 serials, 5,407 audiovisual materials, an OPAC, and a Web page. Operations spending for the previous fiscal year: $1.2 million. 350 computers available on campus for general student use. A campuswide network can be accessed from student residence rooms and from off campus. Students can access the following: online class registration. Staffed computer lab on campus provides training in use of computers, software, and the Internet.

Community Environment: The main campus of Holy Family College is located on 46 acres in the residential Torresdale section of northeast Philadelphia near the boundary with Bucks County, Pennsylvania. The main campus is easily reached by public transportation. The Newtown campus is located on 85 acres in the heart of suburban Bucks County, Pennsylvania. It is situated very close to the Newtown exit of Interstate-95.

■ HUSSIAN SCHOOL OF ART

The Bourse - Ste. 300
111 S Independence Mall E
Philadelphia, PA 19106
Tel: (215)981-0900
Fax: (215)864-9115

E-mail: info@hussianart.edu

Web Site: www.hussianart.edu/

Description: Proprietary, 2-year, coed. Awards transfer associate and terminal associate degrees. Founded 1946. Setting: 1-acre urban campus. Total enrollment: 136. Faculty: 26 (3 full-time, 23 part-time). 116 applied, 97% were admitted. Full-time: 136 students, 26% women, 74% men. Students come from 4 states and territories, 20% from out-of-state. 2% 25 or older, 0% transferred in. Retention: 65% of full-time freshmen returned the following year. Core. Calendar: semesters. Independent study, internships.

Entrance Requirements: Options: electronic application, deferred admission. Required: high school transcript, interview, art portfolio. Entrance: minimally difficult. Application deadline: Rolling. Notification: continuous.

Collegiate Environment: Major annual events: Senior Showcase/May, Open House/November. Campus security; security guard during open hours. 58 computers available on campus for general student use. A computer is required for all students. A campuswide network can be accessed. Staffed computer lab on campus provides training in use of computers, software, and the Internet.

■ **IMMACULATA UNIVERSITY**

1145 King Rd.

Immaculata, PA 19345

Tel: (610)647-4400; Free: 877-428-6329

Fax: (610)251-1668

E-mail: admiss@immaculata.edu

Web Site: www.immaculata.edu/

Description: Independent Roman Catholic, comprehensive, coed. Awards associate, bachelor's, master's, and doctoral degrees. Founded 1920. Setting: 400-acre suburban campus with easy access to Philadelphia. Total enrollment: 4,117. Faculty: 426 (102 full-time, 324 part-time). Student-undergrad faculty ratio is 10:1. 1,650 applied, 80% were admitted. Full-time: 1,175 students, 72% women, 28% men. Part-time: 1,708 students, 83% women, 17% men. 21% from out-of-state. 0.2% American Indian or Alaska Native, non-Hispanic/Latino; 4% Hispanic/Latino; 16% African American, non-Hispanic/Latino; 3% Asian, non-Hispanic/Latino; 0.1% Native Hawaiian or other Pacific Islander, non-Hispanic/Latino; 1% international. 59% 25 or older, 19% live on campus, 2% transferred in. Retention: 80% of full-time freshmen returned the following year. Academic areas with the most degrees conferred: health professions and related sciences; business/marketing; education. Calendar: semesters. ROTC: Army (c).

Entrance Requirements: Option: electronic application. Required: high school transcript, minimum 2 high school GPA, SAT or ACT. Recommended: minimum 3 high school GPA, interview. Required for some: essay. Entrance: moderately difficult. Application deadline: Rolling. Notification: continuous. SAT Reasoning Test deadline: 3/1.

Costs Per Year: Application fee: $35. Comprehensive fee: $40,740 includes full-time tuition ($29,000) and college room and board ($11,740). College room only: $6280. Full-time tuition varies according to student level. Room and board charges vary according to board plan and housing facility. Part-time tuition: $470 per credit hour. Tuition guaranteed not to increase for student's term of enrollment.

Collegiate Environment: Orientation program. Campus security: 24-hour emergency response devices and patrols, late night transport-escort service, controlled dormitory access. Freshmen guaranteed college housing. Options: coed, men-only, women-only housing available.

Community Environment: Immaculata is a suburban area with a temperate climate. An airport, railroad, and bus lines serve the area. The school is located in Chester County, twenty miles west of Philadelphia, at the junction of routes 30 and 352. The community has a public library, churches of major denominations, two hospitals, and several large shopping centers. There are active civic and fraternal organizations within the area.

■ **INDIANA UNIVERSITY OF PENNSYLVANIA**

Indiana, PA 15705-1087

Tel: (724)357-2100; Free: 800-442-6830

Fax: (724)357-2685

E-mail: admissions-inquiry@iup.edu

Web Site: www.iup.edu/

Description: State-supported, university, coed. Part of Pennsylvania State System of Higher Education. Awards associate, bachelor's, master's, and doctoral degrees and post-master's certificates. Founded 1875. Setting: 374-acre small town campus with easy access to Pittsburgh. Endowment: $47.9 million. Research spending for the previous fiscal year: $1.2 million. Educational spending for the previous fiscal year: $8224 per student. Total

enrollment: 15,379. Faculty: 708 (620 full-time, 88 part-time). Student-undergrad faculty ratio is 18:1. 12,333 applied, 61% were admitted. 8% from top 10% of their high school class, 27% from top quarter, 60% from top half. Full-time: 12,195 students, 55% women, 45% men. Part-time: 863 students, 51% women, 49% men. Students come from 38 states and territories, 43 other countries, 7% from out-of-state. 0.1% American Indian or Alaska Native, non-Hispanic/Latino; 3% Hispanic/Latino; 11% African American, non-Hispanic/Latino; 1% Asian, non-Hispanic/Latino; 0.01% Native Hawaiian or other Pacific Islander, non-Hispanic/Latino; 2% international. 6% 25 or older, 83% live on campus, 5% transferred in. Retention: 75% of full-time freshmen returned the following year. Academic areas with the most degrees conferred: business/marketing; social sciences; health professions and related sciences. Core. Calendar: semesters. Academic remediation for entering students, ESL program, services for LD students, advanced placement, accelerated degree program, freshman honors college, honors program, independent study, distance learning, double major, summer session for credit, part-time degree program, external degree program, adult/continuing education programs, co-op programs and internships, graduate courses open to undergrads. Off campus study at 14 members of the Marine Science Consortium, The Art Institute of Pittsburgh, National Student Exchange. Study abroad program. ROTC: Army.

Entrance Requirements: Options: electronic application, early admission, deferred admission, international baccalaureate accepted. Required: high school transcript, SAT or ACT. Recommended: essay, 2 recommendations. Entrance: moderately difficult. Application deadline: Rolling. Notification: 9/1. Transfer credits accepted: Yes.

Costs Per Year: Application fee: $50. State resident tuition: $6428 full-time, $268 per credit hour part-time. Nonresident tuition: $16,070 full-time, $670 per credit hour part-time. Mandatory fees: $2244 full-time, $52 per credit hour part-time, $203 per term part-time. Full-time tuition and fees vary according to course load and reciprocity agreements. Part-time tuition and fees vary according to course load and reciprocity agreements. College room and board: $10,466. College room only: $7740. Room and board charges vary according to board plan, housing facility, and location.

Collegiate Environment: Orientation program. Drama-theater group, choral group, marching band, student-run newspaper, radio station. Social organizations: 307 open to all; national fraternities, national sororities; 6% of eligible men and 6% of eligible women are members. Most popular organizations: Student Government Association, Panhellenic Association, Interfraternity Council, Amplify, NAACP. Major annual events: Homecoming, Family Weekend, IUP Day. Student services: legal services, health clinic, personal-psychological counseling. Campus security: 24-hour emergency response devices and patrols, late night transport-escort service, controlled dormitory access. 4,460 college housing spaces available; 4,402 were occupied in 2012-13. Freshmen guaranteed college housing. On-campus residence required in freshman year. Options: coed, women-only housing available. Stapleton Library with 888,056 books, 2.4 million microform titles, 32,718 serials, 50,101 audiovisual materials, an OPAC, and a Web page. Operations spending for the previous fiscal year: $3.8 million. 2,363 computers available on campus for general student use. Computer purchase/lease plans available. A computer is required for all students. A campuswide network can be accessed from student residence rooms and from off campus. Students can access the following: online class registration. Staffed computer lab on campus (open 24 hours a day) provides training in use of computers, software, and the Internet.

Community Environment: Population 15,000. Indiana is known as the"Christmas Tree Capital of the World" and is the birthplace of actor Jimmy Stewart. The town is located 50 miles northeast of Pittsburgh in the foothills of the beautiful Allegheny Mountains. Indiana has churches of all denominations, a library, a recreation center, a hospital, and various civic, fraternal and veteran's organizations. Local recreational facilities include golf courses, theatres, swimming pool, ice skating rink, tennis, baseball fields, a grandstand and an outdoor stage. Some part-time employment is available.

■ **ITT TECHNICAL INSTITUTE (DUNMORE)**

1000 Meade St.

Dunmore, PA 18512

Tel: (570)330-0600; Free: 800-774-9791

Web Site: www.itt-tech.edu/

Description: Proprietary, 2-year, coed. Part of ITT Educational Services, Inc. Awards diplomas and terminal associate degrees.

■ **ITT TECHNICAL INSTITUTE (HARRISBURG)**

449 Eisenhower Blvd., Ste. 100

Harrisburg, PA 17111

Tel: (717)565-1700; Free: 800-847-4756
Web Site: www.itt-tech.edu/
Description: Proprietary, 2-year, coed. Part of ITT Educational Services, Inc. Awards diplomas and terminal associate degrees.
Entrance Requirements: Entrance: minimally difficult.

■ **ITT TECHNICAL INSTITUTE (LEVITTOWN)**
311 Veterans Hwy.
Levittown, PA 19056
Tel: (215)244-8871; Free: 866-488-8324
Web Site: www.itt-tech.edu/
Description: Proprietary, 2-year, coed. Part of ITT Educational Services, Inc. Awards diplomas and terminal associate degrees. Founded 2000.
Entrance Requirements: Entrance: minimally difficult.

■ **ITT TECHNICAL INSTITUTE (PITTSBURGH)**
10 Pky. Ctr.
Pittsburgh, PA 15220-3801
Tel: (412)937-9150; Free: 800-353-8324
Web Site: www.itt-tech.edu/
Description: Proprietary, 2-year, coed. Part of ITT Educational Services, Inc. Awards diplomas and terminal associate degrees.
Entrance Requirements: Entrance: minimally difficult.

■ **ITT TECHNICAL INSTITUTE (PLYMOUTH MEETING)**
220 W Germantown Pke.
Ste. 100
Plymouth Meeting, PA 19462
Tel: (610)491-8004; Free: 866-902-8324
Web Site: www.itt-tech.edu/
Description: Proprietary, 2-year, coed. Part of ITT Educational Services, Inc. Awards diplomas and terminal associate degrees. Founded 2002.
Entrance Requirements: Entrance: minimally difficult.

■ **ITT TECHNICAL INSTITUTE (TARENTUM)**
100 Pittsburgh Mills Cir.
Ste. 100
Tarentum, PA 15084
Tel: (724)274-1400; Free: 800-488-0121
Web Site: www.itt-tech.edu/
Description: Proprietary, 2-year, coed. Part of ITT Educational Services, Inc. Awards diplomas and terminal associate degrees.
Entrance Requirements: Entrance: minimally difficult.

■ **JNA INSTITUTE OF CULINARY ARTS**
1212 S Broad St.
Philadelphia, PA 19146
Tel: (215)468-8800
Fax: (215)468-8838
Web Site: www.culinaryarts.com/
Description: Proprietary, 2-year, coed. Awards terminal associate degrees. Founded 1988. Setting: urban campus with easy access to Philadelphia. Educational spending for the previous fiscal year: $4322 per student. Total enrollment: 65. Full-time: 65 students, 45% women, 55% men. 26% Hispanic/Latino; 57% African American, non-Hispanic/Latino; 3% Asian, non-Hispanic/Latino. Calendar: continuous.
Entrance Requirements: Entrance: noncompetitive.

■ **JOHNSON COLLEGE**
3427 N Main Ave.
Scranton, PA 18508-1495
Tel: (570)342-6404; Free: 800-2WE-WORK
Fax: (570)348-2181
E-mail: admit@johnson.edu
Web Site: www.johnson.edu/
Description: Independent, 2-year, coed. Awards terminal associate degrees. Founded 1912. Setting: 65-acre urban campus. Total enrollment: 376. Faculty: 23 (21 full-time, 2 part-time). Student-undergrad faculty ratio is 17:1. Full-time: 363 students, 27% women, 73% men. Part-time: 13 students, 54% women, 46% men. 20% 25 or older. Retention: 69% of full-time freshmen returned the following year. Core. Calendar: semesters. Academic remediation for entering students, services for LD students, summer session for credit, part-time degree program, adult/continuing education programs, internships.

Entrance Requirements: Options: electronic application, deferred admission. Required: essay, high school transcript. Recommended: SAT. Required for some: interview, SAT. Entrance: minimally difficult. Application deadline: 5/1.
Collegiate Environment: Orientation program. Most popular organizations: student government, Social Force Club, trade/technical/clinical clubs. Major annual events: Activity Day, Career Day, Parents' Day. Student services: personal-psychological counseling. Campus security: 24-hour emergency response devices. Johnson Technical Institute Library with 4,473 books, 118 serials, an OPAC, and a Web page. 75 computers available on campus for general student use. Staffed computer lab on campus.

■ **JUNIATA COLLEGE**
1700 Moore St.
Huntingdon, PA 16652-2119
Tel: (814)641-3000; Free: 877-JUNIATA
Fax: (814)641-3100
E-mail: admissions@juniata.edu
Web Site: www.juniata.edu/
Description: Independent, comprehensive, coed, affiliated with Church of the Brethren. Awards bachelor's and master's degrees. Founded 1876. Setting: 110-acre small town campus. Endowment: $77.4 million. Research spending for the previous fiscal year: $387,675. Educational spending for the previous fiscal year: $10,215 per student. Total enrollment: 1,565. Faculty: 143 (104 full-time, 39 part-time). Student-undergrad faculty ratio is 13:1. 2,418 applied, 66% were admitted. 42% from top 10% of their high school class, 74% from top quarter, 99% from top half. 6 National Merit Scholars, 7 valedictorians. Full-time: 1,500 students, 55% women, 45% men. Part-time: 58 students, 52% women, 48% men. Students come from 30 states and territories, 43 other countries, 30% from out-of-state. 0.3% American Indian or Alaska Native, non-Hispanic/Latino; 4% Hispanic/Latino; 3% African American, non-Hispanic/Latino; 2% Asian, non-Hispanic/Latino; 0% Native Hawaiian or other Pacific Islander, non-Hispanic/Latino; 9% international. 2% 25 or older, 81% live on campus, 2% transferred in. Retention: 90% of full-time freshmen returned the following year. Academic areas with the most degrees conferred: biological/life sciences; business/marketing; education. Core. Calendar: semesters. ESL program, services for LD students, advanced placement, accelerated degree program, self-designed majors, independent study, double major, summer session for credit, part-time degree program, internships. Off campus study at Philadelphia Urban Semester, Washington Center, University of Oregon, Great Lakes Colleges Associates, Philadelphia Center, Washington Internship Institute. Study abroad program.
Entrance Requirements: Options: electronic application, early admission, early decision, early action, deferred admission, international baccalaureate accepted. Required: essay, high school transcript, minimum 3 high school GPA, 1 recommendation. Recommended: interview, SAT or ACT. Entrance: moderately difficult. Application deadlines: 3/15, 11/15 for early decision, 1/1 for early action. Notification: continuous, 12/23 for early decision, 1/30 for early action. SAT Reasoning Test deadline: 3/15. Transfer credits accepted: Yes. Applicants placed on waiting list: 61. Early decision applicants: 210. Early decision applicants admitted: 116. Early action applicants: 1,146. Early action applicants admitted: 193.
Costs Per Year: Application fee: $30. Comprehensive fee: $47,370 includes full-time tuition ($36,410), mandatory fees ($760), and college room and board ($10,200). College room only: $5380. Full-time tuition and fees vary according to course load and program. Room and board charges vary according to board plan. Part-time tuition: $1500 per credit hour.
Collegiate Environment: Orientation program. Drama-theater group, choral group, student-run newspaper, radio station. Social organizations: 85 open to all. Most popular organizations: Student Government Association, Juniata Activities Board (JAB), Colleges Against Cancer, Habitat for Humanity, Model UN. Major annual events: Mountain Day, Madrigal Dinner and Dance, SpringFest. Student services: health clinic, personal-psychological counseling, women's center. Campus security: 24-hour emergency response devices and patrols, student patrols, late night transport-escort service, controlled dormitory access, fire safety training, adopt-an-officer program, security web site, weather/terror alerts, travel forecast, crime statistics. 1,222 college housing spaces available; 1,205 were occupied in 2012-13. Freshmen guaranteed college housing. On-campus residence required through senior year. Options: coed, women-only housing available. Beeghly Library with 430,000 books, 400 microform titles, 11,000 serials, 2,800 audiovisual materials, and an OPAC. Operations spending for the previous fiscal year: $1 million. 340 computers available on campus for general student use. A

computer is required for all students. A campuswide network can be accessed from student residence rooms and from off campus. Students can access the following: online class registration. Staffed computer lab on campus provides training in use of computers, software, and the Internet.
Community Environment: Huntingdon, population 6,800, on the Juniata River, is in one of the most scenic sections of the state. It was founded on the site of an Indian Village called Standing Stone. The city is the county seat and lies approximately 30 miles east of Altoona. The area is served by railroad. Penn State (32 miles away) offers cultural and social activities. Nearby state parks, forests, and the Raystown Lake recreation area provide excellent camping, fishing, canoeing, hunting, swimming, and boating opportunities. In winter ski slopes are less than 40 miles away.

■ **KAPLAN CAREER INSTITUTE, BROOMALL CAMPUS**
1991 Sproul Rd.
Ste. 42
Broomall, PA 19008
Tel: (610)353-7630; Free: 800-935-1857
Web Site: broomall.kaplancareerinstitute.com/
Description: Proprietary, 2-year, coed. Awards diplomas and terminal associate degrees. Founded 1958. Setting: small town campus.

■ **KAPLAN CAREER INSTITUTE, FRANKLIN MILLS CAMPUS**
177 Franklin Mills Blvd.
Philadelphia, PA 19154
Tel: (215)612-6600; Free: 800-935-1857
Web Site: franklin-mills.kaplancareerinstitute.com/
Description: Proprietary, 2-year, coed. Awards diplomas and terminal associate degrees. Founded 1981. Setting: suburban campus.

■ **KAPLAN CAREER INSTITUTE, HARRISBURG CAMPUS**
5650 Derry St.
Harrisburg, PA 17111-3518
Tel: (717)558-1300; Free: 800-935-1857
Fax: (717)564-3779
Web Site: harrisburg.kaplancareerinstitute.com/
Description: Proprietary, 2-year, coed. Awards diplomas and terminal associate degrees. Founded 1918. Setting: suburban campus.

■ **KAPLAN CAREER INSTITUTE, PHILADELPHIA CAMPUS**
3010 Market St.
Philadelphia, PA 19104
Tel: (215)594-4000; Free: 800-935-1857
Web Site: philadelphia.kaplancareerinstitute.com/
Description: Proprietary, 2-year, coed. Awards diplomas and terminal associate degrees.

■ **KAPLAN CAREER INSTITUTE, PITTSBURGH CAMPUS**
933 Penn Ave.
Pittsburgh, PA 15222
Tel: (412)261-2647; Free: 800-935-1857
Web Site: pittsburgh.kaplancareerinstitute.com/
Description: Proprietary, 2-year, coed. Awards diplomas and terminal associate degrees. Founded 1963. Setting: urban campus. Calendar: continuous.

■ **KEYSTONE COLLEGE**
One College Green
La Plume, PA 18440
Tel: (570)945-5141; Free: 877-4-COLLEGE
E-mail: admissions@keystone.edu
Web Site: www.keystone.edu/
Description: Independent, 4-year, coed. Awards associate and bachelor's degrees. Founded 1868. Setting: 270-acre small town campus. Endowment: $6.7 million. Educational spending for the previous fiscal year: $5640 per student. Total enrollment: 1,683. Faculty: 244 (68 full-time, 176 part-time). Student-undergrad faculty ratio is 12:1. 1,192 applied, 70% were admitted. Full-time: 1,388 students, 58% women, 42% men. Part-time: 282 students, 68% women, 32% men. Students come from 11 other countries, 13% from out-of-state. 0.2% American Indian or Alaska Native, non-Hispanic/Latino; 3% Hispanic/Latino; 4% African American, non-Hispanic/Latino; 1% Asian, non-Hispanic/Latino; 0.1% Native Hawaiian or other Pacific Islander, non-Hispanic/Latino; 1% international. 24% 25 or older, 29% live on campus, 8% transferred in. Retention: 61% of full-time freshmen returned the following

year. Academic areas with the most degrees conferred: education; business/marketing; homeland security, law enforcement, firefighting, and protective services. Core. Calendar: semesters. Academic remediation for entering students, ESL program, services for LD students, advanced placement, honors program, independent study, distance learning, double major, summer session for credit, part-time degree program, adult/continuing education programs, co-op programs and internships. Study abroad program. ROTC: Army (c), Air Force (c).
Entrance Requirements: Options: electronic application, early admission, deferred admission, international baccalaureate accepted. Required: essay, high school transcript, 1 recommendation, SAT or ACT. Recommended: interview. Required for some: interview, art portfolio for visual arts and art education. Entrance: minimally difficult. Application deadline: 6/1. Notification: continuous. SAT Reasoning Test deadline: 6/1. SAT Subject Test deadline: 8/1. Transfer credits accepted: Yes.
Costs Per Year: Application fee: $30. One-time mandatory fee: $500. Comprehensive fee: $31,000 includes full-time tuition ($20,300), mandatory fees ($900), and college room and board ($9800). College room only: $4950. Room and board charges vary according to board plan and housing facility. Part-time tuition: $400 per credit. Part-time mandatory fees: $225 per term. Part-time tuition and fees vary according to course load.
Collegiate Environment: Orientation program. Drama-theater group, choral group, student-run newspaper, radio station. Social organizations: 24 open to all. Most popular organizations: Art Society, Inter-Hall Council, O.P.E.N. (Opposing Prejudice Ending Negativity), S.M.A.R.T. (Sports Management and Recreation Team), Eco Club. Major annual events: Keystone College Leadership Conference, Welcome Back Carnival, Spring Fling Block Party. Student services: health clinic, personal-psychological counseling. Campus security: 24-hour emergency response devices and patrols, student patrols, late night transport-escort service, controlled dormitory access. 446 college housing spaces available; 425 were occupied in 2012-13. Freshmen guaranteed college housing. On-campus residence required in freshman year. Options: coed, women-only housing available. Miller Library with 108,836 books, 3,352 microform titles, 27,458 serials, 2,602 audiovisual materials, an OPAC, and a Web page. Operations spending for the previous fiscal year: $496,940. 100 computers available on campus for general student use. A campuswide network can be accessed from student residence rooms and from off campus. Students can access the following: online class registration. Staffed computer lab on campus provides training in use of computers, software, and the Internet.
Community Environment: Population of Scranton is 73,120. The city is provided transportation by bus and air. Air facilities are located near Scranton. This is a semirural community with many churches and synagogues close at hand. There are service clubs active locally. Five modern hospitals are easily accessible. Local recreation includes movies, museum, art galleries, professional sports, lakes, streams, ski slopes, hunting, and fishing areas.

■ **KEYSTONE TECHNICAL INSTITUTE**
2301 Academy Dr.
Harrisburg, PA 17112
Tel: (717)545-4747; Free: 800-400-3322
Fax: (717)901-9090
E-mail: info@acadcampus.com
Web Site: www.kti.edu/
Description: Proprietary, 2-year, coed. Awards diplomas, transfer associate, and terminal associate degrees. Founded 1980. Setting: 8-acre suburban campus. Total enrollment: 207. 47% 25 or older. Calendar: continuous. Advanced placement, internships.
Entrance Requirements: Open admission. Required: high school transcript, interview. Entrance: noncompetitive. Application deadline: Rolling.
Collegiate Environment: Orientation program. Student-run newspaper. Resource Center with 1,620 books, 30 serials, 30 audiovisual materials, and an OPAC.

■ **KING'S COLLEGE**
133 N River St.
Wilkes-Barre, PA 18711-0801
Tel: (570)208-5900; Free: 888-KINGSPA
Fax: (570)208-5971
E-mail: admissions@kings.edu
Web Site: www.kings.edu/
Description: Independent Roman Catholic, comprehensive, coed. Awards associate, bachelor's, and master's degrees. Founded 1946. Setting: 48-

acre urban campus. Endowment: $49.5 million. Research spending for the previous fiscal year: $46,211. Educational spending for the previous fiscal year: $9569 per student. Total enrollment: 2,494. Faculty: 237 (136 full-time, 101 part-time). Student-undergrad faculty ratio is 13:1. 2,967 applied, 70% were admitted. 14% from top 10% of their high school class, 34% from top quarter, 70% from top half. Full-time: 1,981 students, 49% women, 51% men. Part-time: 237 students, 57% women, 43% men. Students come from 19 states and territories, 2 other countries, 28% from out-of-state. 0.2% American Indian or Alaska Native, non-Hispanic/Latino; 6% Hispanic/Latino; 3% African American, non-Hispanic/Latino; 2% Asian, non-Hispanic/Latino; 0.1% Native Hawaiian or other Pacific Islander, non-Hispanic/Latino; 0.1% international. 3% 25 or older, 52% live on campus, 4% transferred in. Retention: 78% of full-time freshmen returned the following year. Academic areas with the most degrees conferred: business/marketing; health professions and related sciences; biological/life sciences; education. Core. Calendar: semesters. Services for LD students, advanced placement, accelerated degree program, self-designed majors, honors program, independent study, distance learning, double major, summer session for credit, part-time degree program, adult/continuing education programs, internships. Off campus study at Misericordia University, Wilkes University. Study abroad program. ROTC: Army, Air Force (c).

Entrance Requirements: Options: electronic application, deferred admission, international baccalaureate accepted. Required: essay, high school transcript. Recommended: interview, SAT or ACT. Entrance: moderately difficult. Application deadlines: Rolling, Rolling for nonresidents. Notification: continuous, continuous for nonresidents. Transfer credits accepted: Yes.

Costs Per Year: Application fee: $30. Comprehensive fee: $40,194 includes full-time tuition ($29,174) and college room and board ($11,020). College room only: $5380. Room and board charges vary according to board plan. Part-time tuition: $530 per credit hour.

Collegiate Environment: Orientation program. Drama-theater group, choral group, student-run newspaper, radio station. Social organizations: 50 open to all. Most popular organizations: Association of Campus Events, Student Government Association, Accounting Association, International/Multicultural Club, Biology Club. Major annual events: Homecoming, Friends and Family Weekend, All College Ball. Student services: health clinic, personal-psychological counseling, women's center. Campus security: 24-hour emergency response devices and patrols, late night transport-escort service, controlled dormitory access. 1,077 college housing spaces available; 1,026 were occupied in 2012-13. Freshmen guaranteed college housing. On-campus residence required through sophomore year. Options: coed, men-only, women-only housing available. D. Leonard Corgan Library with 184,383 books, 579,888 microform titles, 15,165 serials, 2,885 audiovisual materials, an OPAC, and a Web page. Operations spending for the previous fiscal year: $1.3 million. 470 computers available on campus for general student use. Computer purchase/lease plans available. A campuswide network can be accessed from student residence rooms and from off campus. Students can access the following: online class registration. Staffed computer lab on campus provides training in use of computers, software, and the Internet.

■ KUTZTOWN UNIVERSITY OF PENNSYLVANIA

15200 Kutztown Rd.
Kutztown, PA 19530-0730
Tel: (610)683-4000; Free: 877-628-1915
Fax: (610)683-1375
E-mail: admissions@kutztown.edu
Web Site: www.kutztown.edu/

Description: State-supported, comprehensive, coed. Part of Pennsylvania State System of Higher Education. Awards bachelor's and master's degrees. Founded 1866. Setting: 289-acre rural campus with easy access to Philadelphia. Endowment: $15.3 million. Research spending for the previous fiscal year: $488,467. Educational spending for the previous fiscal year: $6367 per student. Total enrollment: 9,804. Faculty: 464 (423 full-time, 41 part-time). Student-undergrad faculty ratio is 20:1. 9,730 applied, 68% were admitted. 5% from top 10% of their high school class, 22% from top quarter, 60% from top half. Full-time: 8,641 students, 57% women, 43% men. Part-time: 494 students, 55% women, 45% men. Students come from 22 states and territories, 24 other countries, 11% from out-of-state. 0.2% American Indian or Alaska Native, non-Hispanic/Latino; 6% Hispanic/Latino; 7% African American, non-Hispanic/Latino; 1% Asian, non-Hispanic/Latino; 0.1% Native Hawaiian or other Pacific Islander, non-Hispanic/Latino; 1% international. 6% 25 or older, 46% live on campus, 8% transferred in. Retention: 71% of full-time freshmen returned the following year. Academic areas

with the most degrees conferred: business/marketing; education; visual and performing arts. Core. Calendar: semesters. Academic remediation for entering students, services for LD students, advanced placement, accelerated degree program, self-designed majors, honors program, independent study, distance learning, double major, summer session for credit, part-time degree program, adult/continuing education programs, internships. Off campus study at members of the Marine Science Consortium, Pennsylvania Consortium for International Education. Study abroad program. ROTC: Army (c).

Entrance Requirements: Options: electronic application, early admission, deferred admission, international baccalaureate accepted. Required: high school transcript, minimum 2 high school GPA, SAT or ACT. Required for some: audition for music; portfolio and/or art test for arts, SAT Subject Tests. Entrance: moderately difficult. Application deadline: Rolling. Notification: continuous. SAT Reasoning Test deadline: 4/1. Transfer credits accepted: Yes.

Costs Per Year: Application fee: $35. One-time mandatory fee: $238. State resident tuition: $6428 full-time, $268 per credit hour part-time. Nonresident tuition: $16,070 full-time, $670 per credit hour part-time. Mandatory fees: $2168 full-time, $90.43 per credit hour part-time. Part-time tuition and fees vary according to course load. College room and board: $8890. College room only: $5552. Room and board charges vary according to board plan and housing facility.

Collegiate Environment: Orientation program. Drama-theater group, choral group, marching band, student-run newspaper, radio station. Social organizations: 218 open to all; national fraternities, national sororities; 5% of eligible men and 4% of eligible women are members. Most popular organizations: Student Government Board, Student Pennsylvania State Education Association, National Art Education Association, Residence Hall Association, Association of Campus Events. Major annual events: Homecoming, Family Day, Bear Fest. Student services: health clinic, personal-psychological counseling, women's center. Campus security: 24-hour emergency response devices and patrols, student patrols, late night transport-escort service, secondary door electronic alarm system in residence halls, 24-hour student desk personnel at main entrance of residence halls. 4,600 college housing spaces available; 4,111 were occupied in 2012-13. Freshmen guaranteed college housing. Options: coed, women-only housing available. Rohrbach Library with 401,094 books, 1.3 million microform titles, 74,591 serials, 6,341 audiovisual materials, an OPAC, and a Web page. Operations spending for the previous fiscal year: $3.6 million. 1,075 computers available on campus for general student use. Computer purchase/lease plans available. A campuswide network can be accessed from student residence rooms. Students can access the following: online class registration.

Community Environment: Kutztown is a rural, small town located on U.S. Route 222, midway between Reading and Allentown, one and a half hours from Philadelphia, and three hours from New York City. Airports are located in Allentown and Reading, with bus transportation provided daily to Philadelphia and New York as well as to local destinations. The community has churches, civic organizations, and hospitals are located in nearby Reading and Allentown. Area recreation includes golf, bowling, tennis, hunting, fishing, swimming, basketball, football, theatre, nature study at Hawk Mountain Sanctuary, and the annual Kutztown Folk Festival.

■ LA ROCHE COLLEGE

9000 Babcock Blvd.
Pittsburgh, PA 15237-5898
Tel: (412)367-9300; Free: 800-838-4LRC
Fax: (412)536-1075
E-mail: admissions@laroche.edu
Web Site: www.laroche.edu/

Description: Independent, comprehensive, coed, affiliated with Roman Catholic Church. Awards associate, bachelor's, and master's degrees. Founded 1963. Setting: 43-acre suburban campus. Endowment: $4.4 million. Educational spending for the previous fiscal year: $6025 per student. Total enrollment: 1,465. Faculty: 194 (59 full-time, 135 part-time). Student-undergrad faculty ratio is 12:1. 1,587 applied, 52% were admitted. 8% from top 10% of their high school class, 11% from top quarter, 56% from top half. 1 valedictorian. Full-time: 1,103 students, 56% women, 44% men. Part-time: 242 students, 65% women, 35% men. Students come from 13 states and territories, 29 other countries, 8% from out-of-state. 0% American Indian or Alaska Native, non-Hispanic/Latino; 2% Hispanic/Latino; 6% African American, non-Hispanic/Latino; 1% Asian, non-Hispanic/Latino; 0% Native Hawaiian or other Pacific Islander, non-Hispanic/Latino; 11% international. 21% 25 or older, 47% live on campus, 15% transferred in. Retention: 66% of full-time freshmen returned the following year. Academic areas with the most degrees conferred: business/marketing; health professions and related sciences; psychology. Core. Calendar: semesters plus summer term. Academic remediation for entering students, ESL program, services for LD students, advanced placement, accelerated degree program, self-designed majors, honors program, independent study, distance learning, double major, summer session for credit, part-time degree program, adult/continuing education programs, internships, graduate courses open to undergrads. Study abroad program. ROTC: Army (c), Air Force (c).

Entrance Requirements: Options: electronic application, early admission, deferred admission, international baccalaureate accepted. Required: high school transcript, minimum 2 high school GPA, 2 recommendations, SAT or ACT. Recommended: essay, minimum 3 high school GPA, interview. Entrance: minimally difficult. Application deadline: Rolling. Notification: 9/15. Transfer credits accepted: Yes.

Costs Per Year: Application fee: $50. Comprehensive fee: $33,790 includes full-time tuition ($23,328), mandatory fees ($730), and college room and board ($9732). College room only: $6160. Full-time tuition and fees vary according to student level. Room and board charges vary according to board plan and housing facility. Part-time tuition: $595 per credit hour.

Collegiate Environment: Orientation program. Drama-theater group, choral group, student-run newspaper, radio station. Social organizations: 52 open to all. Most popular organizations: American Society of Interior Design, student government, Visions (environmental club), Helping Hands. Major annual events: Gateway Clipper Cruise, Festival of Lights, Globe Fashion Show. Student services: health clinic, personal-psychological counseling. Campus security: 24-hour emergency response devices and patrols, student patrols, late night transport-escort service, controlled dormitory access. 591 college housing spaces available; 515 were occupied in 2012-13. Freshmen guaranteed college housing. Option: coed housing available. John J. Wright Library with 110,000 books, 30,000 microform titles, 548 serials, 1,002 audiovisual materials, an OPAC, and a Web page. Operations spending for the previous fiscal year: $391,979. 164 computers available on campus for general student use. Computer purchase/lease plans available. A campuswide network can be accessed. Students can access the following: online class registration. Staffed computer lab on campus.

Community Environment: The college is located just ten miles north of the center of Pittsburgh. The campus has an ideal combination of rural and urban life: within a five-mile radius of its own natural beauty are the recreational facilities and wooded expanse of North Park and the shops, restaurants and theaters of the McKnight Road malls.

■ LA SALLE UNIVERSITY

1900 W Olney Ave.
Philadelphia, PA 19141-1199
Tel: (215)951-1000; Free: 800-328-1910
Fax: (215)951-1656
E-mail: admiss@lasalle.edu
Web Site: www.lasalle.edu/

Description: Independent Roman Catholic, comprehensive, coed. Awards associate, bachelor's, master's, and doctoral degrees and post-master's certificates. Founded 1863. Setting: 130-acre urban campus with easy access to Philadelphia. Endowment: $71.7 million. Research spending for the previous fiscal year: $873,568. Educational spending for the previous fiscal year: $9021 per student. Total enrollment: 6,580. Faculty: 457 (245 full-time, 212 part-time). Student-undergrad faculty ratio is 12:1. 6,101 applied, 73% were admitted. 17% from top 10% of their high school class, 40% from top quarter, 74% from top half. Full-time: 3,557 students, 61% women, 39% men. Part-time: 959 students, 78% women, 22% men. Students come from 40 states and territories, 27 other countries, 38% from out-of-state. 0.4% American Indian or Alaska Native, non-Hispanic/Latino; 10% Hispanic/Latino; 18% African American, non-Hispanic/Latino; 5% Asian, non-Hispanic/Latino; 0.1% Native Hawaiian or other Pacific Islander, non-Hispanic/Latino; 1% international. 2% 25 or older, 54% live on campus, 3% transferred in. Retention: 80% of full-time freshmen returned the following year. Academic areas with the most degrees conferred: health professions and related sciences; business/marketing; communication/journalism. Core. Calendar: semesters. Academic remediation for entering students, ESL program, services for LD students, advanced placement, accelerated degree program, self-designed majors, freshman honors college, honors program, independent study, distance learning, double major, summer session for credit, part-time degree program, adult/continuing education programs, co-op programs and internships, graduate courses open to undergrads. Off campus study at Chestnut Hill College. Study abroad program. ROTC: Army (c), Air Force (c).

Entrance Requirements: Options: electronic application, early admission, early decision, early action, deferred admission, international baccalaureate accepted. Required: essay, high school transcript, 1 recommendation, SAT or ACT, SAT or ACT. Recommended: interview. Entrance: moderately difficult. Application deadline: 11/15 for early action. Notification: continuous, 12/15 for early action. Transfer credits accepted: Yes. Early action applicants: 2,041. Early action applicants admitted: 1,726.

Costs Per Year: Application fee: $35. One-time mandatory fee: $150. Comprehensive fee: $48,860 includes full-time tuition ($36,250), mandatory fees ($400), and college room and board ($12,210). College room only: $6430. Full-time tuition and fees vary according to course load and program. Room and board charges vary according to board plan and housing facility. Part-time tuition: $500 per credit hour. Part-time mandatory fees: $125 per term. Part-time tuition and fees vary according to course load and program.

Collegiate Environment: Orientation program. Drama-theater group, choral group, student-run newspaper, radio station. Social organizations: 90 open to all; national fraternities, national sororities, local fraternities, local sororities; 6% of eligible men and 13% of eligible women are members. Most popular organizations: Student Government Association, Community service organization, La Salle Entertainment Organization, The Explorer (yearbook), The Masque (theater group). Major annual events: Branch Out Day, Homecoming, Spring Fling. Student services: health clinic, personal-psychological counseling, women's center. Campus security: 24-hour emergency response devices and patrols, student patrols, late night transport-escort service, controlled dormitory access. 2,095 college housing spaces available; 1,971 were occupied in 2012-13. Freshmen guaranteed college housing. Options: coed, men-only, women-only housing available. Connelly Library with 420,000 books, 9,754 microform titles, 60,705 serials, 13,000 audiovisual materials, an OPAC, and a Web page. Operations spending for the previous fiscal year: $2.4 million. 1,100 computers available on campus for general student use. Computer purchase/lease plans available. A campuswide network can be accessed from student residence rooms and from off campus. Students can access the following: online class registration, Blackboard Course Management System. Staffed computer lab on campus provides training in use of computers, software, and the Internet.

Community Environment: See Temple University.

■ LACKAWANNA COLLEGE

501 Vine St.
Scranton, PA 18509
Tel: (570)961-7810; Free: 877-346-3552
Fax: (570)961-7858
E-mail: muchals@lackawanna.edu
Web Site: www.lackawanna.edu/

Description: Independent, 2-year, coed. Awards certificates, diplomas, transfer associate, and terminal associate degrees. Founded 1894. Setting: 4-acre urban campus. Endowment: $1.9 million. Educational spending for the previous fiscal year: $5380 per student. Total enrollment: 1,387. Faculty: 215 (32 full-time, 183 part-time). Student-undergrad faculty ratio is 13:1. 809 applied, 64% were admitted. Full-time: 999 students, 48% women, 52% men. Part-time: 388 students, 61% women, 39% men. Students come from 13 states and territories, 10% from out-of-state. 28% 25 or older, 17% live on campus, 10% transferred in. Retention: 34% of full-time freshmen returned the following year. Core. Calendar: semesters. Academic remediation for entering students, ESL program, services for LD students, double major, summer session for credit, part-time degree program, adult/continuing education programs, co-op programs and internships. ROTC: Army (c), Air Force (c).

Entrance Requirements: Open admission. Options: electronic application, early admission, deferred admission. Required: high school transcript, interview. Recommended: SAT, ACT, SAT or ACT. Entrance: noncompetitive. Application deadlines: Rolling, Rolling for nonresidents. Transfer credits accepted: Yes.

Costs Per Year: Application fee: $30. Comprehensive fee: $19,980 includes full-time tuition ($12,000), mandatory fees ($280), and college room and board ($7700). Part-time tuition: $410 per credit hour.

Collegiate Environment: Orientation program. Drama-theater group, choral group, student-run newspaper. Social organizations: 10 open to all; Phi Theta Kappa; Phi Beta Lambda. Most popular organizations: student government, Student/Alumni Association, United Cultures Leadership Association, Green Falcons: Sustainability Action Group, Sonography Club. Major annual events: Homecoming Activities, Spring Fling, College/Career Fair. Campus security: 24-hour emergency response devices and patrols, late night transport-escort service, controlled dormitory access, patrols by college liaison staff. Seeley Memorial Library with 17,068 books, 52 serials, 1,120 audiovisual materials, an OPAC, and a Web page. Operations spending for the previous fiscal year: $187,244. 202 computers available on campus for general student use. A campuswide network can be accessed from student residence rooms and from off campus. Students can access the following: online class registration. Staffed computer lab on campus provides training in use of computers and the Internet.

■ **LAFAYETTE COLLEGE**
Easton, PA 18042-1798
Tel: (610)330-5000
Fax: (610)330-5127
E-mail: hydem@lafayette.edu
Web Site: www.lafayette.edu/

Description: Independent, 4-year, coed, affiliated with Presbyterian Church (U.S.A.). Awards bachelor's degrees. Founded 1826. Setting: 340-acre suburban campus with easy access to New York City, Philadelphia. Endowment: $700 million. Research spending for the previous fiscal year: $643,489. Educational spending for the previous fiscal year: $20,167 per student. Total enrollment: 2,488. Faculty: 258 (217 full-time, 41 part-time). Student-undergrad faculty ratio is 11:1. 62% from top 10% of their high school class, 88% from top quarter, 97% from top half. 4 National Merit Scholars, 12 valedictorians. Full-time: 2,438 students, 47% women, 53% men. Part-time: 50 students, 44% women, 56% men. Students come from 47 states and territories, 37 other countries, 78% from out-of-state. 0.2% American Indian or Alaska Native, non-Hispanic/Latino; 6% Hispanic/Latino; 5% African American, non-Hispanic/Latino; 3% Asian, non-Hispanic/Latino; 0.1% Native Hawaiian or other Pacific Islander, non-Hispanic/Latino; 5% international. 1% 25 or older, 92% live on campus, 0.5% transferred in. Retention: 95% of full-time freshmen returned the following year. Academic areas with the most degrees conferred: social sciences; engineering; biological/life sciences. Core. Calendar: semesters plus interim January program. Academic remediation for entering students, services for LD students, advanced placement, accelerated degree program, self-designed majors, honors program, independent study, double major, summer session for credit, part-time degree program, internships. Off campus study at 5 members of the Lehigh Valley Association of Independent Colleges (Lehigh University, Muhlenberg College, Moravian College, DeSales University, Cedar Crest College), American University. Study abroad program. ROTC: Army (c).

Entrance Requirements: Required: essay, high school transcript, 1 recommendation, SAT or ACT. Recommended: interview, SAT Subject Tests.

Costs Per Year: One-time mandatory fee: $700. Comprehensive fee: $57,050 includes full-time tuition ($43,580), mandatory fees ($390), and college room and board ($13,080). College room only: $8090. Full-time tuition and fees vary according to course load. Room and board charges vary according to board plan, housing facility, and student level. Part-time tuition: $5450 per course. Part-time tuition varies according to course load.

Collegiate Environment: Orientation program. Drama-theater group, choral group, student-run newspaper, radio station. Social organizations: 250 open to all; national fraternities, national sororities, social dorms; 25% of eligible men and 30% of eligible women are members. Major annual events: Homecoming, Earth Day, Lafayette-Lehigh Weekend. Student services: health clinic, personal-psychological counseling, women's center. Campus security: 24-hour emergency response devices and patrols, student patrols, late night transport-escort service, controlled dormitory access. 2,308 college housing spaces available; 2,200 were occupied in 2012-13. Freshmen guaranteed college housing. On-campus residence required through senior year. Options: coed, men-only, women-only housing available. Skillman Library plus 2 others with an OPAC and a Web page. Operations spending for the previous fiscal year: $2.1 million. 690 computers available on campus for general student use. A campuswide network can be accessed from student residence rooms and from off campus. Students can access the following: online class registration. Staffed computer lab on campus provides training in use of computers, software, and the Internet.

Community Environment: Population 26,000, Easton is located at the confluence of the Lehigh and Delaware Rivers in the Lehigh Valley. The area is served by bus lines and a county airport. The valley has a YMCA, YWCA, nine hospitals, four public libraries, many churches and synagogues, a community concert association, and numerous civic and fraternal organizations. Recreational activities include baseball, softball, tennis, bowling, golf, boating, swimming, hunting, and fishing.

■ **LANCASTER BIBLE COLLEGE**
901 Eden Rd.
Lancaster, PA 17601
Tel: (717)569-7071; Free: 800-544-7335
Fax: (717)560-8213
E-mail: admissions@lbc.edu
Web Site: www.lbc.edu/

Description: Independent nondenominational, comprehensive, coed. Awards associate, bachelor's, and master's degrees. Founded 1933. Setting: 100-acre suburban campus with easy access to Philadelphia. Endowment: $5.6 million. Educational spending for the previous fiscal year: $5017 per student. Total enrollment: 958. Faculty: 86 (44 full-time, 42 part-time). Student-undergrad faculty ratio is 15:1. 192 applied, 57% were admitted. 16% from top 10% of their high school class, 37% from top quarter, 84% from top half. Full-time: 560 students, 51% women, 49% men. Part-time: 226 students, 52% women, 48% men. Students come from 23 states and territories, 4 other countries, 27% from out-of-state. 17% 25 or older, 54% live on campus, 9% transferred in. Retention: 68% of full-time freshmen returned the following year. Academic areas with the most degrees conferred: theology and religious vocations; education. Core. Calendar: semesters. Academic remediation for entering students, services for LD students, advanced placement, independent study, double major, summer session for credit, part-time degree program, adult/continuing education programs, internships, graduate courses open to undergrads. Study abroad program.

Entrance Requirements: Options: early admission, deferred admission. Required: essay, high school transcript, minimum 2.0 high school GPA, 3 recommendations, SAT or ACT. Required for some: interview. Entrance: minimally difficult. Application deadline: Rolling. Notification: continuous.

Collegiate Environment: Orientation program. Drama-theater group, choral group, student-run newspaper. Social organizations: 19 open to all. Most popular organizations: Student Government Association, Student Missionary Fellowship, International Student Fellowship, Resident Affairs Council, Student Intramural Association. Major annual events: Homecoming, Missions Conference, Spiritual Life Week. Student services: health clinic, personal-psychological counseling. Campus security: student patrols, late night transport-escort service, controlled dormitory access. Lancaster Bible College Library with 132,599 books, 30,248 microform titles, 6,852 serials, and an OPAC. Operations spending for the previous fiscal year: $361,437. 50 computers available on campus for general student use. A campuswide network can be accessed from student residence rooms. Staffed computer lab on campus.

■ **LANCASTER GENERAL COLLEGE OF NURSING & HEALTH SCIENCES**
410 N Lime St.
Lancaster, PA 17602
Tel: (717)544-4912; Free: 800-622-5443
Fax: (717)290-5970
E-mail: lgc_admissions@lancastergeneral.org
Web Site: www.lancastergeneralcollege.edu/content/

Description: Independent, primarily 2-year, coed. Awards certificates, terminal associate, and bachelor's degrees. Founded 1903. Setting: urban campus with easy access to Harrisburg. Endowment: $1 million. Research spending for the previous fiscal year: $72,666. Educational spending for the previous fiscal year: $13,875 per student. Total enrollment: 1,375. Faculty: 168 (63 full-time, 105 part-time). Student-undergrad faculty ratio is 8:1. 517 applied, 28% were admitted. Full-time: 503 students, 86% women, 14% men. Part-time: 872 students, 84% women, 16% men. 2% from out-of-state. 0.2% American Indian or Alaska Native, non-Hispanic/Latino; 4% Hispanic/Latino; 5% African American, non-Hispanic/Latino; 3% Asian, non-Hispanic/Latino; 0.3% Native Hawaiian or other Pacific Islander, non-Hispanic/Latino; 0% international. 52% 25 or older, 25% transferred in. Academic area with the most degrees conferred: health professions and related sciences. Core. Services for LD students, advanced placement, accelerated degree program, distance learning, summer session for credit, part-time degree program, adult/continuing education programs.

Entrance Requirements: Option: electronic application. Required: minimum 3 high school GPA, 2 recommendations, Official GED transcript may be substituted in lieu of high school transcript. SAT or ACT scores required if graduated from high school within last 2 years. Official transcripts of all institutions attended, SAT or ACT. Required for some: essay, high school transcript. Entrance: moderately difficult. Application deadline: 2/1. Notification: continuous. SAT Reasoning Test deadline: 2/1. SAT Subject Test deadline: 2/1. Transfer credits accepted: Yes.

Costs Per Year: Application fee: $60. Tuition: $18,800 full-time, $425 per credit part-time. Mandatory fees: $1350 full-time, $250 per term part-time. Full-time tuition and fees vary according to program. Part-time tuition and fees vary according to program.
Collegiate Environment: Orientation program. Social organizations: Soccer Club, Distance Running Club. Most popular organizations: Student Government Association, Soccer Club, Distance Running. Student services: health clinic, personal-psychological counseling. Campus security: 24-hour emergency response devices and patrols, late night transport-escort service. College housing not available. Health Sciences Library with 60,590 books, 17,719 serials, 112 audiovisual materials, an OPAC, and a Web page. Operations spending for the previous fiscal year: $221,188. 98 computers available on campus for general student use. A campuswide network can be accessed from off-campus. Students can access the following: online class registration. Staffed computer lab on campus provides training in use of computers and software.

■ **LANSDALE SCHOOL OF BUSINESS**
201 Church Rd.
North Wales, PA 19454-4148
Tel: (215)699-5700; Free: 800-219-0486
Fax: (215)699-8770
E-mail: mjohnson@lsb.edu
Web Site: www.lsb.edu/
Description: Proprietary, 2-year, coed. Awards certificates, diplomas, transfer associate, and terminal associate degrees. Founded 1918. Setting: suburban campus with easy access to Philadelphia. Total enrollment: 372. 73% 25 or older. Core. Calendar: semesters. Accelerated degree program, honors program, independent study, double major, summer session for credit, part-time degree program, adult/continuing education programs, internships. Off campus study.
Entrance Requirements: Required: high school transcript, interview. Entrance: minimally difficult. Application deadline: Rolling.
Collegiate Environment: Orientation program. Student-run newspaper. Lansdale School of Business Library with 2,000 books, 125 serials, an OPAC, and a Web page.

■ **LAUREL BUSINESS INSTITUTE**
11-15 Penn St.
Uniontown, PA 15401
Tel: (724)439-4900
Fax: (724)439-3607
E-mail: ldolan@laurel.edu
Web Site: www.laurel.edu/lbi/
Description: Proprietary, 2-year, coed. Awards certificates, diplomas, transfer associate, and terminal associate degrees. Founded 1985. Setting: 10-acre small town campus with easy access to Pittsburgh. Educational spending for the previous fiscal year: $3576 per student. Total enrollment: 305. Faculty: 25 (16 full-time, 9 part-time). Student-undergrad faculty ratio is 16:1. 415 applied, 59% were admitted. Full-time: 305 students, 77% women, 23% men. 50% 25 or older. Retention: 80% of full-time freshmen returned the following year. Core. Calendar: trimesters. Advanced placement, honors program, independent study, double major, part-time degree program, adult/continuing education programs, co-op programs and internships.
Entrance Requirements: Open admission. Options: electronic application, deferred admission. Required: essay, high school transcript, interview, Wonderlic aptitude test. Entrance: minimally difficult. Application deadline: Rolling. Notification: continuous.
Costs Per Year: Application fee: $55. One-time mandatory fee: $150. Comprehensive fee: $12,326 includes full-time tuition ($8190), mandatory fees ($900), and college room and board ($3236). Full-time tuition and fees vary according to course load and program. Part-time tuition: $285 per credit hour. Part-time tuition and fees vary according to course load and program.
Collegiate Environment: Orientation program. Student Learning Center with 1,537 books and 41 serials. 75 computers available on campus for general student use. A campuswide network can be accessed from off-campus. Staffed computer lab on campus.

■ **LAUREL TECHNICAL INSTITUTE (MEADVILLE)**
847 N Main St.
Ste. 204
Meadville, PA 16335
Tel: (814)724-0700
Fax: (814)724-2777

E-mail: lti.admission@laurel.edu
Web Site: www.laurel.edu/lti/
Description: Proprietary, 2-year, coed. Awards certificates, diplomas, and terminal associate degrees. Founded 1987.
Entrance Requirements: Required: high school transcript, interview, Wonderlic Scholastic Level Exam (SLE).
Costs Per Year: Application fee: $50. One-time mandatory fee: $150. Comprehensive fee: $12,326 includes full-time tuition ($8190), mandatory fees ($900), and college room and board ($3236). Full-time tuition and fees vary according to course load and program. Part-time tuition: $285 per credit hour. Part-time tuition and fees vary according to course load and program.

■ **LAUREL TECHNICAL INSTITUTE (SHARON)**
335 Boyd Dr.
Sharon, PA 16146
Tel: (724)983-0700
Fax: (724)983-8355
E-mail: info@biop.edu
Web Site: www.laurel.edu/lti/
Description: Proprietary, 2-year, coed. Awards certificates, diplomas, and terminal associate degrees. Founded 1926. Setting: 2-acre small town campus. Educational spending for the previous fiscal year: $4300 per student. Total enrollment: 106. Faculty: 9 (5 full-time, 4 part-time). Student-undergrad faculty ratio is 16:1. 49 applied, 80% were admitted. 14% from top 10% of their high school class, 27% from top quarter, 59% from top half. Full-time: 98 students, 93% women, 7% men. Part-time: 8 students, 100% women. 71% 25 or older, 2% transferred in.
Entrance Requirements: Required: high school transcript, interview, ACT.
Costs Per Year: One-time mandatory fee: $150. Comprehensive fee: $12,326 includes full-time tuition ($8190), mandatory fees ($900), and college room and board ($3236). Full-time tuition and fees vary according to course load and program. Part-time tuition: $285 per credit hour. Part-time mandatory fees: $450 per term. Part-time tuition and fees vary according to course load and program.

■ **LE CORDON BLEU INSTITUTE OF CULINARY ARTS IN PITTSBURGH**
717 Liberty Ave.
Pittsburgh, PA 15222-3500
Tel: (412)566-2433; Free: 888-314-8222
Fax: (412)566-2434
Web Site: www.chefs.edu/Pittsburgh
Description: Proprietary, 2-year, coed. Awards terminal associate degrees. Founded 1986. Setting: urban campus. Total enrollment: 996. 1,489 applied. 26% 25 or older. Core. Calendar: semesters. Academic remediation for entering students, services for LD students, double major, internships.
Entrance Requirements: Option: electronic application. Required: high school transcript, interview. Recommended: essay. Required for some: entrance examination.
Collegiate Environment: Orientation program. L. Edwin Brown Library and Resource Center with 5,000 books, 100 serials, 350 audiovisual materials, an OPAC, and a Web page.

■ **LEBANON VALLEY COLLEGE**
101 N College Ave.
Annville, PA 17003-1400
Tel: (717)867-6100; Free: 866-LVC-4ADM
Fax: (717)867-6124
E-mail: admission@lvc.edu
Web Site: www.lvc.edu/
Description: Independent United Methodist, comprehensive, coed. Awards associate, bachelor's, master's, and doctoral degrees. Founded 1866. Setting: 340-acre small town campus. Endowment: $51 million. Educational spending for the previous fiscal year: $8507 per student. Total enrollment: 1,984. Faculty: 219 (103 full-time, 116 part-time). Student-undergrad faculty ratio is 12:1. 3,012 applied, 66% were admitted. 38% from top 10% of their high school class, 69% from top quarter, 93% from top half. 1 National Merit Scholar, 2 class presidents, 6 valedictorians, 17 student government officers. Full-time: 1,618 students, 55% women, 45% men. Part-time: 126 students, 57% women, 43% men. Students come from 22 states and territories, 3 other countries, 21% from out-of-state. 0.2% American Indian or Alaska Native, non-Hispanic/Latino; 4% Hispanic/Latino; 2% African American, non-Hispanic/Latino; 1% Asian, non-Hispanic/Latino; 0.1% Native Hawaiian or other Pacific Islander, non-Hispanic/Latino; 0.2% international. 4% 25 or

older, 76% live on campus, 3% transferred in. Retention: 86% of full-time freshmen returned the following year. Academic areas with the most degrees conferred: business/marketing; education; visual and performing arts. Core. Calendar: semesters. Academic remediation for entering students, services for LD students, advanced placement, self-designed majors, independent study, double major, summer session for credit, part-time degree program, adult/continuing education programs, internships. Off campus study at The Philadelphia Center, The Washington Center of Internships and Academic Seminars. Study abroad program.

Entrance Requirements: Options: electronic application, international baccalaureate accepted. Required: high school transcript. Recommended: 2 recommendations, interview. Required for some: essay, audition for music majors. Entrance: moderately difficult. Application deadline: Rolling. Notification: continuous. Transfer credits accepted: Yes.

Costs Per Year: Application fee: $30. Comprehensive fee: $43,650 includes full-time tuition ($33,670), mandatory fees ($800), and college room and board ($9180). College room only: $4480. Room and board charges vary according to board plan and housing facility. Part-time tuition: $575 per credit. Part-time tuition varies according to class time and degree level.

Collegiate Environment: Orientation program. Drama-theater group, choral group, marching band, student-run newspaper, radio station. Social organizations: 85 open to all; national fraternities, national sororities, local fraternities; 10% of eligible men and 9% of eligible women are members. Most popular organizations: LVC PSEA, Corner Stone, College Against Cancer, Wig and Buckle Theater Group, Habitat for Humanity. Major annual events: Valley Fest Weekend, Wig and Buckle Theater Productions, Christmas at the Valley. Student services: health clinic, personal-psychological counseling, women's center. Campus security: 24-hour emergency response devices and patrols, late night transport-escort service, controlled dormitory access, residence hall entrances locked 24 hours a day. College housing designed to accommodate 1,276 students; 1,282 undergraduates lived in college housing during 2012-13. Freshmen guaranteed college housing. On-campus residence required through senior year. Option: coed housing available. Bishop Library with 309,609 books, 9,214 microform titles, 3,000 serials, 19,432 audiovisual materials, an OPAC, and a Web page. Operations spending for the previous fiscal year: $1.4 million. 192 computers available on campus for general student use. Computer purchase/lease plans available. A campuswide network can be accessed from student residence rooms and from off campus. Students can access the following: online class registration. Staffed computer lab on campus provides training in use of computers, software, and the Internet.

Community Environment: Population 4,500. Annville is located seven miles east of Hershey. The area has a temperate climate. The city has many churches that represent various denominations, a public library, three hospitals that are easily accessible, and major civic, fraternal, and veteran's organizations. Community recreational facilities include theaters and radio and TV stations. Community concerts are also available.

■ LEHIGH CARBON COMMUNITY COLLEGE

4525 Education Park Dr.
Schnecksville, PA 18078-2598
Tel: (610)799-2121
Fax: (610)799-1527
E-mail: admissions@lccc.edu
Web Site: www.lccc.edu/

Description: State and locally supported, 2-year, coed. Awards certificates, diplomas, transfer associate, and terminal associate degrees. Founded 1967. Setting: 254-acre suburban campus with easy access to Philadelphia. Endowment: $2.4 million. Educational spending for the previous fiscal year: $2967 per student. Total enrollment: 7,323. Faculty: 399 (89 full-time, 310 part-time). Student-undergrad faculty ratio is 22:1. 4,566 applied, 100% were admitted. Full-time: 2,725 students, 53% women, 47% men. Part-time: 6,155 students, 48% women, 52% men. Students come from 11 states and territories, 15 other countries, 0.3% from out-of-state. 0.1% American Indian or Alaska Native, non-Hispanic/Latino; 18% Hispanic/Latino; 5% African American, non-Hispanic/Latino; 2% Asian, non-Hispanic/Latino; 0% Native Hawaiian or other Pacific Islander, non-Hispanic/Latino; 0.2% international. 39% 25 or older, 46% transferred in. Core. Calendar: semesters. Academic remediation for entering students, ESL program, services for LD students, advanced placement, honors program, independent study, distance learning, summer session for credit, part-time degree program, external degree program, co-op programs and internships. ROTC: Army (c).

Entrance Requirements: Open admission except for allied health, aviation, veterinary technician programs. Option: electronic application. Required for

some: essay, high school transcript, interview, TEAS (for those applying to Nursing Program). Entrance: noncompetitive. Application deadlines: Rolling, Rolling for nonresidents. Notification: continuous, continuous for nonresidents. Transfer credits accepted: Yes.

Costs Per Year: Area resident tuition: $2880 full-time, $96 per credit part-time. State resident tuition: $6030 full-time, $201 per credit part-time. Nonresident tuition: $9180 full-time, $306 per credit part-time. Mandatory fees: $510 full-time, $17 per credit part-time.

Collegiate Environment: Orientation program. Drama-theater group, choral group. Social organizations: 21 open to all. Most popular organizations: Phi Theta Kappa, Criminal Justice/Justice Society, Psychology Club, Student Government Association, Teacher Education Student Association (TESA). Major annual events: Freshman Orientation, Spring Awards Program, Athletic Events. Student services: personal-psychological counseling. Campus security: 24-hour emergency response devices. College housing not available. Rothrock Library with 90,968 books, 336 serials, 7,563 audiovisual materials, an OPAC, and a Web page. Operations spending for the previous fiscal year: $1.2 million. 1,100 computers available on campus for general student use. Computer purchase/lease plans available. A campuswide network can be accessed. Students can access the following: online class registration. Staffed computer lab on campus.

Community Environment: See Muhlenberg College.

■ LEHIGH UNIVERSITY

27 Memorial Dr. W
Bethlehem, PA 18015-3094
Tel: (610)758-3000
Fax: (610)758-4361
E-mail: admissions@lehigh.edu
Web Site: www.lehigh.edu/

Description: Independent, university, coed. Awards bachelor's, master's, and doctoral degrees and post-master's certificates. Founded 1865. Setting: 1,600-acre suburban campus with easy access to Philadelphia. Endowment: $1 billion. Research spending for the previous fiscal year: $34.5 million. Educational spending for the previous fiscal year: $26,847 per student. Total enrollment: 7,080. Faculty: 691 (493 full-time, 198 part-time). Student-undergrad faculty ratio is 10:1. 11,529 applied, 33% were admitted. 64% from top 10% of their high school class, 92% from top quarter, 100% from top half. Full-time: 4,824 students, 43% women, 57% men. Part-time: 59 students, 37% women, 63% men. Students come from 52 states and territories, 50 other countries, 74% from out-of-state. 0.04% American Indian or Alaska Native, non-Hispanic/Latino; 8% Hispanic/Latino; 4% African American, non-Hispanic/Latino; 6% Asian, non-Hispanic/Latino; 0.02% Native Hawaiian or other Pacific Islander, non-Hispanic/Latino; 6% international. 0% 25 or older, 69% live on campus, 1% transferred in. Retention: 94% of full-time freshmen returned the following year. Academic areas with the most degrees conferred: business/marketing; engineering; social sciences. Calendar: semesters. ESL program, services for LD students, advanced placement, accelerated degree program, honors program, independent study, distance learning, double major, summer session for credit, external degree program, co-op programs and internships, graduate courses open to undergrads. Off campus study at members of the Lehigh Valley Association of Independent Colleges, American University. Study abroad program. ROTC: Army.

Entrance Requirements: Options: electronic application, early admission, early decision, deferred admission. Required: essay, high school transcript, 2 recommendations, SAT or ACT. Entrance: most difficult. Application deadlines: 1/1, 11/15 for early decision plan 1, 1/15 for early decision plan 2. Notification: 4/1, 12/15 for early decision plan 1, 2/15 for early decision plan 2. SAT Reasoning Test deadline: 1/31. SAT Subject Test deadline: 1/31. Transfer credits accepted: Yes. Applicants placed on waiting list: 3,595. Wait-listed applicants offered admission: 0. Early decision applicants: 950. Early decision applicants admitted: 602.

Costs Per Year: Application fee: $70. Comprehensive fee: $53,450 includes full-time tuition ($41,920), mandatory fees ($300), and college room and board ($11,230). College room only: $6450. Room and board charges vary according to board plan and housing facility. Part-time tuition: $1750 per credit hour.

Collegiate Environment: Orientation program. Drama-theater group, choral group, marching band, student-run newspaper, radio station. Social organizations: 225 open to all; national fraternities, national sororities. Most popular organizations: WLVR Radio Station, Association of Student Alumni, University Productions, Accounting Club, Phi Sigma Pi. Major annual events: Sundaze, Lehigh/Lafayette Spirit Week, International Week. Student services: health clinic, personal-psychological counseling, women's center. Campus security: 24-hour emergency response devices and patrols, student patrols, late night transport-escort service, controlled dormitory access. 2,461 college housing spaces available; 2,437 were occupied in 2012-13. Freshmen guaranteed college housing. On-campus residence required through sophomore year. Option: coed housing available. E. W. Fairchild-Martindale Library plus 1 other with 1.2 million books, 1.7 million microform titles, 55,210 serials, 7,232 audiovisual materials, an OPAC, and a Web page. 605 computers available on campus for general student use. Computer purchase/lease plans available. A campuswide network can be accessed from student residence rooms and from off campus. Students can access the following: online class registration. Staffed computer lab on campus provides training in use of computers, software, and the Internet.

Community Environment: Population: 72,900. Bethlehem is famous for the Moravian Community, the Bach Choir, the corporate headquarters of Bethlehem Steel and Lehigh University. The historic area of Bethlehem has many 18th century buildings still in use; others are being restored by active community groups. The town contains 6 colonial and Victorian museums. The Bach Festival is held annually in May in Packer Chapel on the Lehigh campus.

■ **LINCOLN TECHNICAL INSTITUTE (ALLENTOWN)**

5151 Tilghman St.
Allentown, PA 18104-3298
Tel: (610)398-5300
Web Site: www.lincolnedu.com/
Description: Proprietary, 2-year, coed. Part of Lincoln Technical Institute, Inc. Awards diplomas and terminal associate degrees. Founded 1949. Setting: 10-acre suburban campus with easy access to Philadelphia. Total enrollment: 539. Core. Calendar: semesters. Summer session for credit.
Entrance Requirements: Open admission. Option: early admission. Required: high school transcript, interview. Entrance: noncompetitive. Application deadline: Rolling.
Collegiate Environment: Orientation program.

■ **LINCOLN TECHNICAL INSTITUTE (PHILADELPHIA)**

9191 Torresdale Ave.
Philadelphia, PA 19136-1595
Tel: (215)335-0800
Fax: (215)335-1443
E-mail: jkuntz@lincolntech.com
Web Site: www.lincolnedu.com/
Description: Proprietary, 2-year, coed. Part of Lincoln Technical Institute, Inc. Awards terminal associate degrees. Founded 1946. Setting: 3-acre suburban campus. Total enrollment: 499. 31% 25 or older. Core. Calendar: modular. Part-time degree program, adult/continuing education programs, co-op programs.
Entrance Requirements: Open admission. Option: deferred admission. Required: high school transcript, minimum 2.0 high school GPA, interview. Entrance: noncompetitive. Application deadline: Rolling.
Collegiate Environment: Student-run newspaper. Campus security: 16-hour patrols by trained security personnel.

■ **LINCOLN UNIVERSITY**

PO Box 179
Lincoln University, PA 19352
Tel: (484)365-8000; Free: 800-790-0191
E-mail: admiss@lincoln.edu
Web Site: www.lincoln.edu/
Description: State-related, comprehensive, coed. Awards bachelor's and master's degrees. Founded 1854. Setting: 422-acre rural campus with easy access to Philadelphia. Endowment: $36.6 million. Research spending for the previous fiscal year: $1.8 million. Educational spending for the previous fiscal year: $10,900 per student. Total enrollment: 2,101. Faculty: 146 (95 full-time, 51 part-time). Student-undergrad faculty ratio is 17:1. 6,642 applied, 25% were admitted. Full-time: 1,569 students, 60% women, 40% men. Part-time: 109 students, 72% women, 28% men. Students come from 31 states and territories, 21 other countries, 57% from out-of-state. 0.2% American Indian or Alaska Native, non-Hispanic/Latino; 0.4% Hispanic/Latino; 79% African American, non-Hispanic/Latino; 0.2% Asian, non-Hispanic/Latino; 0% Native Hawaiian or other Pacific Islander, non-Hispanic/Latino; 3% international. 6% 25 or older. 98% live on campus, 3% transferred in. Retention: 67% of full-time freshmen returned the following year. Academic areas with the most degrees conferred: business/marketing;

social sciences; communication/journalism. Core. Calendar: semesters. Services for LD students, advanced placement, honors program, independent study, double major, summer session for credit, part-time degree program, internships, graduate courses open to undergrads. Off campus study. Study abroad program. ROTC: Army (c), Air Force (c).
Entrance Requirements: Options: electronic application, deferred admission. Required: essay, high school transcript, minimum 2 high school GPA, 2 recommendations, SAT or ACT. Recommended: interview. Entrance: moderately difficult. Application deadline: Rolling.
Costs Per Year: Application fee: $20. State resident tuition: $7018 full-time, $295 per credit hour part-time. Nonresident tuition: $11,602 full-time, $487 per credit hour part-time. Full-time tuition varies according to student level. Part-time tuition varies according to course load. College room and board: $8554. College room only: $4564. Room and board charges vary according to board plan and housing facility.
Collegiate Environment: Orientation program. Drama-theater group, choral group, marching band, student-run newspaper, radio station. Social organizations: national fraternities, national sororities. Most popular organizations: The Gospel Ensemble, Ziana Fashion Club, We R One, Council of Independent Organizations. Major annual events: Homecoming, Spring Fling, Pump Handle. Student services: health clinic, personal-psychological counseling, women's center. Campus security: 24-hour emergency response devices and patrols, late night transport-escort service, controlled dormitory access. 1,768 college housing spaces available; 1,632 were occupied in 2012-13. Freshmen given priority for college housing. Options: coed, men-only, women-only housing available. Langston Hughes Memorial Libarary with 159,884 books, 300,800 microform titles, 561 serials, 1,413 audiovisual materials, and an OPAC. 1,000 computers available on campus for general student use. A campuswide network can be accessed from student residence rooms. Students can access the following: online class registration. Staffed computer lab on campus provides training in use of computers, software, and the Internet.

■ **LOCK HAVEN UNIVERSITY OF PENNSYLVANIA**

401 N Fairview St.
Lock Haven, PA 17745-2390
Tel: (570)893-2011; Free: 800-233-8978
Fax: (570)893-2201
E-mail: admissions@lhup.edu
Web Site: www.lhup.edu/
Description: State-supported, comprehensive, coed. Part of Pennsylvania State System of Higher Education. Awards associate, bachelor's, and master's degrees. Founded 1870. Setting: 165-acre rural campus. Endowment: $9.3 million. Research spending for the previous fiscal year: $64,304. Educational spending for the previous fiscal year: $6348 per student. Total enrollment: 5,328. Faculty: 245 (230 full-time, 15 part-time). Student-undergrad faculty ratio is 21:1. 4,498 applied, 56% were admitted. 9% from top 10% of their high school class, 20% from top quarter, 36% from top half. Full-time: 4,638 students, 56% women, 44% men. Part-time: 331 students, 67% women, 33% men. Students come from 26 states and territories, 22 other countries, 7% from out-of-state. 0.3% American Indian or Alaska Native, non-Hispanic/Latino; 2% Hispanic/Latino; 8% African American, non-Hispanic/Latino; 1% Asian, non-Hispanic/Latino; 0.02% Native Hawaiian or other Pacific Islander, non-Hispanic/Latino; 1% international. 9% 25 or older, 37% live on campus, 6% transferred in. Retention: 69% of full-time freshmen returned the following year. Academic areas with the most degrees conferred: parks and recreation; business/marketing; homeland security, law enforcement, firefighting, and protective services; education; health professions and related sciences. Core. Calendar: semesters. Academic remediation for entering students, ESL program, services for LD students, advanced placement, self-designed majors, freshman honors college, honors program, independent study, distance learning, double major, summer session for credit, part-time degree program, adult/continuing education programs, co-op programs and internships, graduate courses open to undergrads. Off campus study at Pennsylvania Consortium for International Education. Study abroad program. ROTC: Army.
Entrance Requirements: Options: electronic application, deferred admission. Required: high school transcript, SAT or ACT. Recommended: interview. Required for some: essay. Entrance: moderately difficult. Application deadline: Rolling. Notification: continuous.
Costs Per Year: Application fee: $25. One-time mandatory fee: $25. State resident tuition: $6428 full-time. Nonresident tuition: $14,070 full-time. Mandatory fees: $2136 full-time. Full-time tuition and fees vary according to

course load and location. College room and board: $8016. College room only: $4712. Room and board charges vary according to board plan and housing facility.

Collegiate Environment: Orientation program. Drama-theater group, choral group, marching band, student-run newspaper, radio station. Social organizations: 150 open to all; national fraternities, national sororities; 3% of eligible men and 4% of eligible women are members. Most popular organizations: student government, Residence Hall Association. Major annual events: Homecoming, Family Day, Campus Craze. Student services: health clinic, personal-psychological counseling, women's center. Campus security: 24-hour emergency response devices and patrols, late night transport-escort service, controlled dormitory access. 1,764 college housing spaces available; all were occupied in 2012-13. Freshmen given priority for college housing. On-campus residence required in freshman year. Option: coed housing available. Stevenson Library with an OPAC and a Web page. Operations spending for the previous fiscal year: $2.1 million. 290 computers available on campus for general student use. A campuswide network can be accessed from student residence rooms and from off campus. Students can access the following: online class registration. Staffed computer lab on campus (open 24 hours a day).

Community Environment: Population 8,700, Loch Haven was laid out at the site of old Fort Reed, which was erected to protect the frontier settlers from the Indians. The fort was evacuated in the great runaway of 1778. Today, lumbering is a major industry and paper products are produced here. The city lies in a central mountainous region with a moderate climate. Local recreation includes hunting, fishing, boating, hang gliding, and skiing. Private homes provide supplemental student housing.

■ **LUZERNE COUNTY COMMUNITY COLLEGE**
1333 S Prospect St.
Nanticoke, PA 18634-9804
Tel: (570)740-0300; Free: 800-377-5222
E-mail: admissions@luzerne.edu
Web Site: www.luzerne.edu/

Description: County-supported, 2-year, coed. Awards certificates, diplomas, transfer associate, and terminal associate degrees. Founded 1966. Setting: 122-acre suburban campus with easy access to Philadelphia. Total enrollment: 6,579. Faculty: 489 (115 full-time, 374 part-time). Student-undergrad faculty ratio is 20:1. 2,558 applied, 100% were admitted. Full-time: 3,335 students, 55% women, 45% men. Part-time: 3,244 students, 64% women, 36% men. 0% from out-of-state. 0.2% American Indian or Alaska Native, non-Hispanic/Latino; 7% Hispanic/Latino; 4% African American, non-Hispanic/Latino; 2% Asian, non-Hispanic/Latino; 0.2% Native Hawaiian or other Pacific Islander, non-Hispanic/Latino; 0.03% international. 36% 25 or older, 0% transferred in. Retention: 55% of full-time freshmen returned the following year. Core. Calendar: semesters. Academic remediation for entering students, services for LD students, advanced placement, accelerated degree program, distance learning, summer session for credit, part-time degree program, external degree program, internships. ROTC: Air Force (c).

Entrance Requirements: Open admission except for health sciences programs. Options: early admission, deferred admission. Recommended: high school transcript. Entrance: noncompetitive. Application deadline: Rolling.

Collegiate Environment: Orientation program. Student-run newspaper, radio station. Social organizations: 25 open to all. Most popular organizations: student government, Circle K, Nursing Forum, Science Club, SADAH. Major annual events: Alumni Career Fair, College Night, Craft Festival. Campus security: 24-hour patrols. College housing not available. Learning Resources Center plus 1 other with 60,000 books, 35,500 microform titles, 744 serials, 3,000 audiovisual materials, an OPAC, and a Web page. 150 computers available on campus for general student use. A campuswide network can be accessed. Staffed computer lab on campus.

■ **LYCOMING COLLEGE**
700 College Pl.
Williamsport, PA 17701-5192
Tel: (570)321-4000; Free: 800-345-3920
Fax: (570)321-4337
E-mail: admissions@lycoming.edu
Web Site: www.lycoming.edu/

Description: Independent United Methodist, 4-year, coed. Awards bachelor's degrees. Founded 1812. Setting: 35-acre small town campus. Endowment: $155.2 million. Educational spending for the previous fiscal year: $7713 per student. Total enrollment: 1,365. Faculty: 119 (81 full-time,

38 part-time). Student-undergrad faculty ratio is 14:1. 1,723 applied, 72% were admitted. 20% from top 10% of their high school class, 46% from top quarter, 78% from top half. 12 class presidents, 7 valedictorians, 19 student government officers. Full-time: 1,342 students, 56% women, 44% men. Part-time: 23 students, 43% women, 57% men. Students come from 29 states and territories, 10 other countries, 34% from out-of-state. 0.2% American Indian or Alaska Native, non-Hispanic/Latino; 3% Hispanic/Latino; 5% African American, non-Hispanic/Latino; 1% Asian, non-Hispanic/Latino; 0% Native Hawaiian or other Pacific Islander, non-Hispanic/Latino; 3% international. 3% 25 or older, 92% live on campus, 2% transferred in. Retention: 81% of full-time freshmen returned the following year. Academic areas with the most degrees conferred: visual and performing arts; business/marketing; social sciences. Core. Calendar: semesters. Services for LD students, advanced placement, accelerated degree program, self-designed majors, honors program, independent study, double major, summer session for credit, part-time degree program, internships. Off campus study at members of the Student Enrichment Semester. Study abroad program. ROTC: Army (c).

Entrance Requirements: Options: electronic application, deferred admission, international baccalaureate accepted. Required: essay, high school transcript, 2 recommendations. Recommended: minimum 2.3 high school GPA, interview, SAT or ACT. Entrance: moderately difficult. Application deadline: 3/1. Notification: continuous. SAT Reasoning Test deadline: 3/1. SAT Subject Test deadline: 3/1. Transfer credits accepted: Yes.

Costs Per Year: Application fee: $35. One-time mandatory fee: $225. Comprehensive fee: $42,176 includes full-time tuition ($32,096), mandatory fees ($660), and college room and board ($9420). Room and board charges vary according to board plan and housing facility. Part-time tuition: $1003 per contact hour. Part-time tuition varies according to course load.

Collegiate Environment: Orientation program. Drama-theater group, choral group, student-run newspaper, radio station. Social organizations: 81 open to all; national fraternities, national sororities, local sororities; 18% of eligible men and 20% of eligible women are members. Most popular organizations: Campus Activities Board, Lycoming Dance Club, Habitat for Humanity, Circle K, United Campus Ministry. Major annual events: Major Concert, Homecoming Weekend, Family Weekend. Student services: health clinic, personal-psychological counseling. Campus security: 24-hour emergency response devices and patrols, student patrols, late night transport-escort service, controlled dormitory access. 1,217 college housing spaces available; 1,096 were occupied in 2012-13. Freshmen guaranteed college housing. On-campus residence required through senior year. Options: coed, women-only housing available. Snowden Library plus 1 other with 293,188 books, 195,401 microform titles, 19,311 serials, 881 audiovisual materials, an OPAC, and a Web page. Operations spending for the previous fiscal year: $1.1 million. 165 computers available on campus for general student use. Computer purchase/lease plans available. A campuswide network can be accessed from student residence rooms and from off campus. Students can access the following: online class registration, Online financial aid, free printing up to a limit. Staffed computer lab on campus provides training in use of computers, software, and the Internet.

Community Environment: Population 30,000. This town, in a scenic mountainous region on the west branch of the Susquehanna River, was known as a great lumber center until the 1890s. As the forests were depleted, it became a manufacturing city and now has a diversified production including steel wire rope, computer components, batteries, flashbulbs, radio tubes, power piping, chemicals, lumber and its byproducts, aircraft engines, textiles, furniture, leather, and mobile homes. The area is provided transportation by bus and air lines. The community has many churches representing various faiths. There are two hospitals, numerous health agencies, a library, a community cultural center, a museum, and various civic, fraternal and veteran's organizations in the immediate area. Part-time employment is available. Local recreation includes boating, golf, hiking, picnic areas, fishing, hunting, skiing, and cycling.

■ **MANOR COLLEGE**
700 Fox Chase Rd.
Jenkintown, PA 19046
Tel: (215)885-2360
E-mail: ftadmiss@manor.edu
Web Site: www.manor.edu/

Description: Independent Byzantine Catholic, 2-year, coed. Awards certificates, diplomas, transfer associate, and terminal associate degrees. Founded 1947. Setting: 35-acre small town campus with easy access to Philadelphia. Total enrollment: 926. Student-undergrad faculty ratio is 10:1.

712 applied, 49% were admitted. Students come from 4 states and territories, 2% from out-of-state. 0% American Indian or Alaska Native, non-Hispanic/Latino; 6% Hispanic/Latino; 28% African American, non-Hispanic/Latino; 3% Asian, non-Hispanic/Latino; 0.1% Native Hawaiian or other Pacific Islander, non-Hispanic/Latino; 0.1% international. 50% 25 or older. Core. Calendar: semesters. Academic remediation for entering students, ESL program, advanced placement, honors program, independent study, distance learning, double major, summer session for credit, part-time degree program, adult/continuing education programs, internships.

Entrance Requirements: Options: electronic application, deferred admission. Required: high school transcript, interview, SAT or ACT. Entrance: minimally difficult. Application deadline: Rolling. Notification: continuous.

Collegiate Environment: Orientation program. Choral group. Student services: personal-psychological counseling. Campus security: 24-hour emergency response devices and patrols. Option: coed housing available. Basileiad Library with 41,688 books, 97 serials, an OPAC, and a Web page.

■ MANSFIELD UNIVERSITY OF PENNSYLVANIA

Academy St.
Mansfield, PA 16933
Tel: (570)662-4000; Free: 800-577-6826
Fax: (570)662-4121
E-mail: admissions@mnsfld.edu
Web Site: www.mansfield.edu/

Description: State-supported, comprehensive, coed. Part of Pennsylvania State System of Higher Education. Awards associate, bachelor's, and master's degrees. Founded 1857. Setting: 174-acre small town campus. Total enrollment: 3,131. Faculty: 188 (137 full-time, 51 part-time). Student-undergrad faculty ratio is 17:1. 1,995 applied, 94% were admitted. 7% from top 10% of their high school class, 29% from top quarter, 64% from top half. Full-time: 2,557 students, 57% women, 43% men. Part-time: 267 students, 72% women, 28% men. 20% from out-of-state. 1% American Indian or Alaska Native, non-Hispanic/Latino; 3% Hispanic/Latino; 8% African American, non-Hispanic/Latino; 1% Asian, non-Hispanic/Latino; 0.1% Native Hawaiian or other Pacific Islander, non-Hispanic/Latino; 1% international. 13% 25 or older, 52% live on campus, 9% transferred in. Retention: 72% of full-time freshmen returned the following year. Academic areas with the most degrees conferred: visual and performing arts; health professions and related sciences; homeland security, law enforcement, firefighting, and protective services. Calendar: semesters. Part-time degree program, adult/continuing education programs. ROTC: Army (c).

Entrance Requirements: Options: electronic application, early admission, deferred admission, international baccalaureate accepted. Required: high school transcript, SAT or ACT. Recommended: essay, minimum 2.5 high school GPA. Required for some: interview. Entrance: moderately difficult. Application deadline: Rolling. Notification: continuous.

Costs Per Year: Application fee: $25. State resident tuition: $6428 full-time, $268 per credit hour part-time. Nonresident tuition: $16,070 full-time, $670 per credit hour part-time. Mandatory fees: $2498 full-time. Part-time tuition varies according to course load. College room and board: $8592. College room only: $5780. Room and board charges vary according to board plan and housing facility.

Collegiate Environment: Orientation program. Campus security: 24-hour emergency response devices and patrols, student patrols, late night transport-escort service, controlled dormitory access. Freshmen guaranteed college housing. On-campus residence required through sophomore year. Option: coed housing available.

Community Environment: Population 3,354, Mansfield is a rural town located on the north-central border of Pennsylvania at the intersection of U.S. Highways 6 and 15. It is mild in summer and often near freezing in winter. The community is served by bus lines. Ski slopes, camping areas, lakes, and hiking trails are all within an hours drive. Other recreational activities include river-rafting, cross-country skiing, fishing, and hunting.

■ MARYWOOD UNIVERSITY

2300 Adams Ave.
Scranton, PA 18509-1598
Tel: (570)348-6211; Free: 866-279-9663
Fax: (570)961-4763
E-mail: yourfuture@marywood.edu
Web Site: www.marywood.edu/

Description: Independent Roman Catholic, comprehensive, coed. Awards bachelor's, master's, and doctoral degrees and post-master's certificates. Founded 1915. Setting: 122-acre suburban campus. Endowment: $39.6 mil-

lion. Research spending for the previous fiscal year: $471,228. Educational spending for the previous fiscal year: $8474 per student. Total enrollment: 3,479. Faculty: 398 (150 full-time, 248 part-time). Student-undergrad faculty ratio is 13:1. 2,284 applied, 69% were admitted. 18% from top 10% of their high school class, 48% from top quarter, 88% from top half. Full-time: 2,106 students, 70% women, 30% men. Part-time: 161 students, 65% women, 35% men. Students come from 32 states and territories, 21 other countries, 27% from out-of-state. 0.1% American Indian or Alaska Native, non-Hispanic/Latino; 3% Hispanic/Latino; 1% African American, non-Hispanic/Latino; 2% Asian, non-Hispanic/Latino; 0.05% Native Hawaiian or other Pacific Islander, non-Hispanic/Latino; 1% international. 8% 25 or older, 49% live on campus, 6% transferred in. Retention: 81% of full-time freshmen returned the following year. Academic areas with the most degrees conferred: health professions and related sciences; education; visual and performing arts. Core. Calendar: semesters. ESL program, services for LD students, advanced placement, self-designed majors, honors program, independent study, double major, summer session for credit, part-time degree program, adult/continuing education programs, internships, graduate courses open to undergrads. Off campus study at University of Scranton; consortium - cross registration: OCICU - on-line consortium of Independent Colleges and Universities. Study abroad program. ROTC: Army (c), Air Force (c).

Entrance Requirements: Options: electronic application, early admission, deferred admission. Required: essay, high school transcript, 1 recommendation, SAT or ACT. Recommended: interview. Required for some: interview, art majors require portfolio, music majors require audition. Entrance: moderately difficult. Application deadline: Rolling. Notification: continuous. SAT Reasoning Test deadline: 9/1. Transfer credits accepted: Yes.

Costs Per Year: Application fee: $35. Comprehensive fee: $44,006 includes full-time tuition ($29,340), mandatory fees ($1100), and college room and board ($13,566). College room only: $7634. Full-time tuition and fees vary according to course load. Room and board charges vary according to board plan and housing facility.

Collegiate Environment: Orientation program. Drama-theater group, choral group, student-run newspaper, radio station. Social organizations: 60 open to all; local sororities. Most popular organizations: Anime and Japanese Club, Diversity United, Marywood Aviators, Marywood Players, International Club. Major annual events: Family Weekend, Homecoming, Spring Fling. Student services: health clinic, personal-psychological counseling. Campus security: 24-hour emergency response devices and patrols, late night transport-escort service, controlled dormitory access, apartments with deadbolts, self-defense education, lighted pathways, seminars on safety. 1,088 college housing spaces available; 1,038 were occupied in 2012-13. Freshmen guaranteed college housing. On-campus residence required through sophomore year. Options: coed, men-only, women-only housing available. Learning Resources Center plus 1 other with 206,578 books, 378,259 microform titles, 34,057 serials, 28,007 audiovisual materials, an OPAC, and a Web page. Operations spending for the previous fiscal year: $343,269. 460 computers available on campus for general student use. A campuswide network can be accessed from student residence rooms and from off campus. Students can access the following: online class registration, degree audit, student account management. Staffed computer lab on campus (open 24 hours a day) provides training in use of computers, software, and the Internet.

Community Environment: The city of Scranton is a regional center for business, health care, social services, and recreation in northeastern Pennsylvania. It is 120 miles west of New York City and 115 miles north of Philadelphia. Sports, special events, music, theater, and parks are available. The nearby Pocono Mountains region offers six major ski areas, resorts, campgrounds, snowmobiling, canoeing, whitewater rafting, and various other activities. The Scranton area is home to seven other colleges and universities in addition to Marywood.

■ MCCANN SCHOOL OF BUSINESS & TECHNOLOGY

2650 Woodglen Rd.
Pottsville, PA 17901
Tel: (570)622-7622
Fax: (570)622-7770
Web Site: www.mccannschool.com/

Description: Proprietary, 2-year, coed. Awards certificates, diplomas, transfer associate, and terminal associate degrees. Founded 1897. Setting: small town campus. Total enrollment: 1,657. 53% 25 or older. Core. Services for LD students, advanced placement, double major, summer session for credit, part-time degree program, co-op programs and internships.

Entrance Requirements: Open admission. Option: electronic application. Required: high school transcript, minimum 2 high school GPA, interview, GED or High School Attestation form, Wonderlic aptitude test. Entrance: minimally difficult. Application deadline: Rolling.

Collegiate Environment: Orientation program. Most popular organizations: Medical Club, Criminal Justice Club, Student Ambassador Club, Marketing Club, IT Club. Major annual events: Family First/Safety First, Student Appreciation Day, Relay for Life fundraising Event. Campus security: controlled dormitory access. College housing not available. McCann Main Library plus 2 others with 1,850 books and 26 serials. 103 computers available on campus for general student use. A campuswide network can be accessed from off-campus. Staffed computer lab on campus provides training in use of computers, software, and the Internet.

■ **MERCYHURST NORTH EAST**

16 W Division St.
North East, PA 16428
Tel: (717)725-6100; Free: 866-846-6042
E-mail: neadmiss@mercyhurst.edu
Web Site: northeast.mercyhurst.edu/

Description: Independent Roman Catholic, primarily 2-year, coed. Awards certificates, terminal associate, and bachelor's degrees. Founded 1991. Calendar: 4-3-3.

Costs Per Year: Comprehensive fee: $24,657 includes full-time tuition ($14,400), mandatory fees ($1500), and college room and board ($8757). College room only: $4494. Full-time tuition and fees vary according to course load, location, and program. Room and board charges vary according to board plan and housing facility. Part-time tuition: $3000 per term. Part-time mandatory fees: $400 per term. Part-time tuition and fees vary according to course load, location, and program.

■ **MERCYHURST UNIVERSITY**

501 E 38th St.
Erie, PA 16546
Tel: (814)824-2000; Free: 800-825-1926
Fax: (814)824-2071
E-mail: ccoons@mercyhurst.edu
Web Site: www.mercyhurst.edu/

Description: Independent Roman Catholic, comprehensive, coed. Awards associate, bachelor's, and master's degrees. Founded 1926. Setting: 88-acre suburban campus with easy access to Buffalo. Endowment: $26.9 million. Total enrollment: 3,122. Faculty: 249 (158 full-time, 91 part-time). Student-undergrad faculty ratio is 14:1. 2,961 applied, 77% were admitted. 22% from top 10% of their high school class, 29% from top quarter, 87% from top half. 6 class presidents, 19 valedictorians, 28 student government officers. Full-time: 2,607 students, 56% women, 44% men. Part-time: 183 students, 69% women, 31% men. Students come from 41 states and territories, 31 other countries, 48% from out-of-state. 0.4% American Indian or Alaska Native, non-Hispanic/Latino; 2% Hispanic/Latino; 4% African American, non-Hispanic/Latino; 1% Asian, non-Hispanic/Latino; 0% Native Hawaiian or other Pacific Islander, non-Hispanic/Latino; 7% international. 9% 25 or older, 68% live on campus, 3% transferred in. Retention: 81% of full-time freshmen returned the following year. Academic areas with the most degrees conferred: business/marketing; interdisciplinary studies; homeland security, law enforcement, firefighting, and protective services. Core. Calendar: 4-3-3. Academic remediation for entering students, services for LD students, advanced placement, accelerated degree program, self-designed majors, honors program, independent study, distance learning, double major, summer session for credit, part-time degree program, adult/continuing education programs, co-op programs and internships, graduate courses open to undergrads. Off campus study. Study abroad program. ROTC: Army (c), Air Force (c).

Entrance Requirements: Options: electronic application, deferred admission, international baccalaureate accepted. Required: essay, high school transcript, SAT or ACT. Recommended: interview, SAT Subject Tests. Required for some: 1 recommendation. Entrance: moderately difficult. Application deadlines: Rolling, Rolling for nonresidents. Notification: continuous until 11/1, continuous until 11/1 for nonresidents. SAT Reasoning Test deadline: 8/1. SAT Subject Test deadline: 8/1. Transfer credits accepted: Yes.

Costs Per Year: Application fee: $30. Comprehensive fee: $39,141 includes full-time tuition ($27,150), mandatory fees ($1887), and college room and board ($10,104). College room only: $5118. Full-time tuition and fees vary according to class time, course load, degree level, location, and program.

Room and board charges vary according to board plan, housing facility, and location. Part-time tuition: $905 per semester hour. Part-time tuition varies according to class time, course load, degree level, location, and program.

Collegiate Environment: Orientation program. Drama-theater group, choral group, student-run newspaper, radio station. Social organizations: 82 open to all. Most popular organizations: student government, chorus, Admission Ambassadors, Amnesty International, The Merciad. Major annual events: Christmas on Campus, Homecoming, Parents' Weekend. Student services: health clinic, personal-psychological counseling. Campus security: 24-hour emergency response devices and patrols, campus-wide camera system. 2,130 college housing spaces available; 1,998 were occupied in 2012-13. Freshmen guaranteed college housing. On-campus residence required through sophomore year. Options: coed, men-only, women-only housing available. Hammermill Library with 140,000 books, 53,137 microform titles, 275 serials, 5,500 audiovisual materials, an OPAC, and a Web page. 350 computers available on campus for general student use. A campuswide network can be accessed from student residence rooms and from off campus. Students can access the following: online class registration. Staffed computer lab on campus provides training in use of computers, software, and the Internet.

Community Environment: See Gannon University.

■ **MESSIAH COLLEGE**

One College Ave.
Mechanicsburg, PA 17055
Tel: (717)766-2511; Free: 800-233-4220
Fax: (717)796-5374
E-mail: admiss@messiah.edu
Web Site: www.messiah.edu/

Description: Independent interdenominational, comprehensive, coed. Awards bachelor's and master's degrees and post-master's certificates. Founded 1909. Setting: 485-acre small town campus. Endowment: $120.3 million. Educational spending for the previous fiscal year: $11,398 per student. Total enrollment: 3,017. Faculty: 312 (175 full-time, 137 part-time). Student-undergrad faculty ratio is 13:1. 3,149 applied, 64% were admitted. 34% from top 10% of their high school class, 66% from top quarter, 89% from top half. 8 National Merit Scholars, 19 valedictorians. Full-time: 2,710 students, 61% women, 39% men. Part-time: 88 students, 60% women, 40% men. Students come from 37 states and territories, 27 other countries, 40% from out-of-state. 0.1% American Indian or Alaska Native, non-Hispanic/Latino; 3% Hispanic/Latino; 2% African American, non-Hispanic/Latino; 2% Asian, non-Hispanic/Latino; 0.1% Native Hawaiian or other Pacific Islander, non-Hispanic/Latino; 2% international. 2% 25 or older, 87% live on campus, 3% transferred in. Retention: 87% of full-time freshmen returned the following year. Academic areas with the most degrees conferred: education; business/marketing; health professions and related sciences. Core. Calendar: semesters. ESL program, services for LD students, advanced placement, accelerated degree program, self-designed majors, freshman honors college, honors program, independent study, distance learning, double major, summer session for credit, part-time degree program, adult/continuing education programs, co-op programs and internships. Off campus study at Christian College Consortium, Council for Christian Colleges and Universities. Study abroad program.

Entrance Requirements: Options: electronic application, deferred admission, international baccalaureate accepted. Required: essay, high school transcript, 1 recommendation. Recommended: interview, SAT or ACT. Required for some: SAT or ACT. Entrance: moderately difficult. Application deadline: Rolling. Notification: continuous. Transfer credits accepted: Yes. Applicants placed on waiting list: 2. Wait-listed applicants offered admission: 1.

Costs Per Year: Application fee: $30. Comprehensive fee: $39,540 includes full-time tuition ($29,650), mandatory fees ($820), and college room and board ($9070). College room only: $4800. Room and board charges vary according to board plan, housing facility, and location. Part-time tuition: $1235 per credit hour.

Collegiate Environment: Orientation program. Drama-theater group, choral group, student-run newspaper, radio station. Social organizations: 66 open to all. Most popular organizations: Outreach teams, student government, choral groups and ensembles, Small Group Program, Outdoors Club. Major annual events: Family Weekend, Homecoming, Christmas Tradition Banquet. Student services: health clinic, personal-psychological counseling. Campus security: 24-hour emergency response devices and patrols, student patrols, late night transport-escort service, controlled dormitory access, bicycle patrols, security lighting, self-defense classes, prevention/awareness programs. College housing designed to accommodate 2,383 students; 2,435 undergraduates lived in college housing during 2012-13. Freshmen guaranteed college housing. On-campus residence required through senior year. Options: coed, men-only, women-only housing available. Murray Library with 282,906 books, 620 microform titles, 86,618 serials, 20,546 audiovisual materials, an OPAC, and a Web page. Operations spending for the previous fiscal year: $1.9 million. 571 computers available on campus for general student use. Computer purchase/lease plans available. A campuswide network can be accessed from student residence rooms and from off campus. Students can access the following: online class registration, access to software. Staffed computer lab on campus (open 24 hours a day) provides training in use of computers, software, and the Internet.

Community Environment: Population of Harrisburg 47,472. Grantham is a semirural community in south-central Pennsylvania located 12 miles southwest of the state capital, Harrisburg - providing easy access to urban centers such Harrisburg, Philadelphia, Baltimore, and Washington, D.C.

■ **METROPOLITAN CAREER CENTER COMPUTER TECHNOLOGY INSTITUTE**

100 S Broad St.
Ste. 830
Philadelphia, PA 19110
Tel: (215)568-9215
Fax: (215)568-3511
Web Site: www.careersinit.org/

Description: Independent, 2-year, coed. Awards terminal associate degrees. Founded 1974. Total enrollment: 110. Student-undergrad faculty ratio is 16:1. 66 applied, 53% were admitted. 0% from out-of-state. 85% 25 or older. Calendar: semesters.

■ **MILLERSVILLE UNIVERSITY OF PENNSYLVANIA**

PO Box 1002
Millersville, PA 17551-0302
Tel: (717)872-3011; Free: 800-MU-ADMIT
E-mail: admissions@millersville.edu
Web Site: www.millersville.edu/

Description: State-supported, comprehensive, coed. Part of Pennsylvania State System of Higher Education. Awards associate, bachelor's, and master's degrees and post-master's certificates. Founded 1855. Setting: 250-acre small town campus. Endowment: $2 million. Research spending for the previous fiscal year: $304,773. Educational spending for the previous fiscal year: $5805 per student. Total enrollment: 8,368. Faculty: 442 (281 full-time, 161 part-time). Student-undergrad faculty ratio is 22:1. 6,665 applied, 63% were admitted. 10% from top 10% of their high school class, 37% from top quarter, 76% from top half. Full-time: 6,675 students, 55% women, 45% men. Part-time: 749 students, 54% women, 46% men. Students come from 23 states and territories, 57 other countries, 4% from out-of-state. 0.2% American Indian or Alaska Native, non-Hispanic/Latino; 7% Hispanic/Latino; 8% African American, non-Hispanic/Latino; 2% Asian, non-Hispanic/Latino; 0.1% Native Hawaiian or other Pacific Islander, non-Hispanic/Latino; 1% international. 10% 25 or older, 30% live on campus, 8% transferred in. Retention: 79% of full-time freshmen returned the following year. Academic areas with the most degrees conferred: education; business/marketing; social sciences. Core. Calendar: 4-1-4. Academic remediation for entering students, services for LD students, advanced placement, accelerated degree program, honors program, independent study, distance learning, double major, summer session for credit, part-time degree program, adult/continuing education programs, co-op programs and internships, graduate courses open to undergrads. Off campus study at Franklin and Marshall College, Lancaster Theological Seminary, Wallops Island Consortium. Study abroad program. ROTC: Army.

Entrance Requirements: Options: electronic application, early admission, deferred admission, international baccalaureate accepted. Required: high school transcript, minimum 2 high school GPA, SAT or ACT. Recommended: essay, 1 recommendation. Required for some: essay, 1 recommendation, interview. Entrance: moderately difficult. Application deadlines: Rolling, Rolling for nonresidents. Notification: continuous, continuous for nonresidents. Transfer credits accepted: Yes. Applicants placed on waiting list: 402. Wait-listed applicants offered admission: 399.

Costs Per Year: Application fee: $50. State resident tuition: $6428 full-time, $268 per credit part-time. Nonresident tuition: $16,070 full-time, $670 per credit part-time. Mandatory fees: $2,172 full-time, $75.75 per credit part-time, $15. Part-time tuition and fees vary according to course load. College

room and board: $9234. College room only: $5378. Room and board charges vary according to board plan and housing facility.

Collegiate Environment: Orientation program. Drama-theater group, choral group, marching band, student-run newspaper, radio station. Social organizations: 166 open to all; national fraternities, national sororities, local sororities; 3% of eligible men and 5% of eligible women are members. Most popular organizations: MUTV 99, University Christian Fellowship, Marching Band, University Activities Board (UAB), Student Senate. Major annual events: Organization Outbreak, Homecoming, Superfest. Student services: health clinic, personal-psychological counseling, women's center. Campus security: 24-hour emergency response devices and patrols, student patrols, late night transport-escort service, controlled dormitory access, crime awareness programs, self-defense education, shuttle buses, lighted pathways / sidewalks. 2,284 college housing spaces available; 2,216 were occupied in 2012-13. Freshmen guaranteed college housing. On-campus residence required through sophomore year. Option: coed housing available. Helen A. Ganser Library with 363,250 books, 81,771 microform titles, 77,665 serials, 4,528 audiovisual materials, an OPAC, and a Web page. Operations spending for the previous fiscal year: $3 million. 430 computers available on campus for general student use. A campuswide network can be accessed from student residence rooms and from off campus. Students can access the following: online class registration. Staffed computer lab on campus provides training in use of computers, software, and the Internet.

Community Environment: Population 7,583, Millersville is a suburban community adjacent to Lancaster. The climate is temperate. There is air and train service, bus lines, and major highways are easily accessible. The community has churches, theatres, hospitals, and shopping facilities located in Lancaster. Major civic, fraternal and veteran's organizations are represented here.

■ **MISERICORDIA UNIVERSITY**

301 Lake St.
Dallas, PA 18612-1098
Tel: (570)674-6400; Free: 866-262-6363
Fax: (570)675-2441
E-mail: admiss@misericordia.edu
Web Site: www.misericordia.edu/

Description: Independent Roman Catholic, comprehensive, coed. Awards bachelor's, master's, and doctoral degrees and post-master's certificates. Founded 1924. Setting: 120-acre small town campus. Endowment: $25.4 million. Educational spending for the previous fiscal year: $7312 per student. Total enrollment: 3,012. Faculty: 323 (111 full-time, 212 part-time). Student-undergrad faculty ratio is 12:1. 2,526 applied, 58% were admitted. 23% from top 10% of their high school class, 52% from top quarter, 83% from top half. Full-time: 1,767 students, 65% women, 35% men. Part-time: 660 students, 77% women, 23% men. Students come from 21 states and territories, 1 other country, 21% from out-of-state. 0.1% American Indian or Alaska Native, non-Hispanic/Latino; 3% Hispanic/Latino; 1% African American, non-Hispanic/Latino; 1% Asian, non-Hispanic/Latino; 0.04% international. 27% 25 or older, 45% live on campus, 5% transferred in. Retention: 86% of full-time freshmen returned the following year. Academic areas with the most degrees conferred: health professions and related sciences; business/marketing; education; psychology; liberal arts/general studies. Core. Calendar: semesters. Services for LD students, advanced placement, accelerated degree program, self-designed majors, honors program, independent study, distance learning, double major, summer session for credit, part-time degree program, external degree program, adult/continuing education programs, co-op programs and internships, graduate courses open to undergrads. Off campus study at King's College (PA), Wilkes University. Study abroad program. ROTC: Army (c), Air Force (c).

Entrance Requirements: Options: electronic application, early admission, deferred admission, international baccalaureate accepted. Required: high school transcript, SAT or ACT. Recommended: interview. Required for some: essay, minimum 2.5 high school GPA, 2 recommendations. Entrance: moderately difficult. Application deadlines: Rolling, Rolling for nonresidents. Notification: continuous, continuous for nonresidents. Transfer credits accepted: Yes. Applicants placed on waiting list: 70. Wait-listed applicants offered admission: 5.

Costs Per Year: Application fee: $25. Comprehensive fee: $38,420 includes full-time tuition ($25,890), mandatory fees ($1340), and college room and board ($11,190). College room only: $6530. Room and board charges vary according to board plan and housing facility. Part-time tuition: $495 per credit. Part-time tuition varies according to class time, degree level, and location.

Collegiate Environment: Orientation program. Drama-theater group, choral group, student-run newspaper, radio station. Social organizations: 40 open to all. Most popular organizations: MSOTA, Peer Associates, Physical Therapy club, Varsity 'M' Club, Education Club. Major annual events: Homecoming, Snowball Week, Spring Fest Weekend/ Great Hunt. Student services: health clinic, personal-psychological counseling, women's center. Campus security: 24-hour emergency response devices and patrols, late night transport-escort service, controlled dormitory access. 1,014 college housing spaces available; all were occupied in 2012-13. Freshmen given priority for college housing. Option: coed housing available. Mary Kintz Bevevino Library with 550,890 books, 4,871 microform titles, 24,992 serials, 11,800 audiovisual materials, an OPAC, and a Web page. Operations spending for the previous fiscal year: $1.1 million. 150 computers available on campus for general student use. Computer purchase/lease plans available. A campuswide network can be accessed from student residence rooms and from off campus. Students can access the following: online class registration, student leadership transcript. Staffed computer lab on campus provides training in use of computers, software, and the Internet.

Community Environment: The community of Dallas surrounding College Misericordia has a suburban atmosphere. It is located just nine miles from the city of Wilkes-Barre. The area provides shopping centers, a mall, cinemas, sporting events and a variety of cultural activities. Also nearby are Pennsylvania's largest natural lake, two state parks, the ski resorts of the Poconos, and five other colleges. New York and Philadelphia are within a two-hour drive. Public transportation is available to and from the campus.

■ MONTGOMERY COUNTY COMMUNITY COLLEGE

340 DeKalb Pke.
Blue Bell, PA 19422-0796
Tel: (215)641-6300
Fax: (215)653-0585
E-mail: admrec@admin.mc3.edu
Web Site: www.mc3.edu/

Description: County-supported, 2-year, coed. Awards certificates, transfer associate, and terminal associate degrees. Founded 1964. Setting: 186-acre suburban campus with easy access to Philadelphia. Total enrollment: 13,645. Faculty: 778 (191 full-time, 587 part-time). Student-undergrad faculty ratio is 20:1. 11,557 applied, 100% were admitted. Full-time: 5,013 students, 50% women, 50% men. Part-time: 8,632 students, 59% women, 41% men. Students come from 9 states and territories, 104 other countries, 0.2% from out-of-state. 0.3% American Indian or Alaska Native, non-Hispanic/Latino; 6% Hispanic/Latino; 14% African American, non-Hispanic/Latino; 6% Asian, non-Hispanic/Latino; 0.2% Native Hawaiian or other Pacific Islander, non-Hispanic/Latino; 2% international. 36% 25 or older, 4% transferred in. Retention: 61% of full-time freshmen returned the following year. Core. Calendar: semesters. Academic remediation for entering students, ESL program, services for LD students, advanced placement, accelerated degree program, self-designed majors, honors program, independent study, distance learning, summer session for credit, part-time degree program, adult/continuing education programs, co-op programs and internships. Study abroad program.

Entrance Requirements: Open admission except for dental hygiene, nursing, medical laboratory technology, automotive technology programs. Options: electronic application, early admission, deferred admission. Required: high school transcript. Required for some: interview. Entrance: noncompetitive. Notification: continuous. Preference given to county residents given preferred admission to certain programs.

Costs Per Year: Application fee: $25. Area resident tuition: $3360 full-time, $112 per credit hour part-time. State resident tuition: $7020 full-time, $224 per credit hour part-time. Nonresident tuition: $10,680 full-time, $336 per credit hour part-time. Mandatory fees: $690 full-time, $23 per credit hour part-time.

Collegiate Environment: Orientation program. Drama-theater group, choral group, student-run newspaper, radio station. Social organizations: 50 open to all. Most popular organizations: student government, Thrive (Christian Fellowship), radio station, Drama Club, African - American Student League. Major annual events: Student Club and Involvement Fair, Drama Club Productions, Film Festivals. Student services: health clinic, personal-psychological counseling. Campus security: 24-hour emergency response devices and patrols, late night transport-escort service, bicycle patrol. College housing not available. The Brendlinger Library/Branch Library Pottstown Campus with 87,136 books, 378 serials, 12,948 audiovisual materials, an OPAC, and a Web page. 1,087 computers available on campus for general student use. Computer purchase/lease plans available.

A campuswide network can be accessed from off-campus. Students can access the following: online class registration. Staffed computer lab on campus provides training in use of computers, software, and the Internet.

Community Environment: Rural community (under 2,500). Suburban campus environment. 5 miles from (north) Norristown. Some bus transportation. Approximately 45 minute commute to Philadelphia. Surrounding industries include pharmaceutical and chemical-product companies; some farming.

■ MOORE COLLEGE OF ART & DESIGN

20th and the Pky.
Philadelphia, PA 19103
Tel: (215)568-4515; Free: 800-523-2025
Fax: (215)568-3547
E-mail: enroll@moore.edu
Web Site: www.moore.edu/

Description: Independent, 4-year, women only. Awards bachelor's and master's degrees. Founded 1848. Setting: 3-acre urban campus with easy access to Philadelphia. Endowment: $13.7 million. Total enrollment: 529. Faculty: 136 (24 full-time, 112 part-time). Student-undergrad faculty ratio is 8:1. 607 applied, 54% were admitted. Full-time: 451 students. Part-time: 31 students. Students come from 29 states and territories, 12 other countries, 42% from out-of-state. 1% American Indian or Alaska Native, non-Hispanic/Latino; 5% Hispanic/Latino; 16% African American, non-Hispanic/Latino; 4% Asian, non-Hispanic/Latino; 1% Native Hawaiian or other Pacific Islander, non-Hispanic/Latino; 3% international. 14% 25 or older, 9% transferred in. Retention: 73% of full-time freshmen returned the following year. Academic areas with the most degrees conferred: visual and performing arts; education. Core. Calendar: semesters. Academic remediation for entering students, services for LD students, advanced placement, independent study, double major, summer session for credit, part-time degree program, external degree program, co-op programs and internships. Study abroad program.

Entrance Requirements: Options: electronic application, deferred admission. Required: high school transcript, minimum 2.5 high school GPA, 1 recommendation, portfolio review. Recommended: essay, interview. Required for some: minimum 3 high school GPA, SAT or ACT. Entrance: moderately difficult. Application deadline: 8/15. Notification: continuous. Transfer credits accepted: Yes.

Costs Per Year: Application fee: $40. One-time mandatory fee: $241. Tuition: $31,654 full-time, $1321 per credit part-time. Mandatory fees: $1084 full-time, $543 per year part-time. Full-time tuition and fees vary according to course load. Part-time tuition and fees vary according to course load. College room only: $12,298.

Collegiate Environment: Orientation program. Most popular organizations: Student Government Association, Student Orientation Staff, yearbook, Residence Life Staff, Business Scholars in the Arts. Major annual events: Visionary Woman Awards, Fashion Show, Student and Senior Shows. Student services: health clinic, personal-psychological counseling. Campus security: 24-hour patrols, late night transport-escort service, controlled dormitory access. 164 college housing spaces available. Freshmen guaranteed college housing. Option: women-only housing available. Connelly Library plus 1 other with 49,000 books, 1,070 audiovisual materials, an OPAC, and a Web page. Operations spending for the previous fiscal year: $64,524.

Community Environment: See Temple University.

■ MORAVIAN COLLEGE

1200 Main St.
Bethlehem, PA 18018-6650
Tel: (610)861-1300; Free: 800-441-3191
Fax: (610)861-3956
E-mail: admissions@moravian.edu
Web Site: www.moravian.edu/

Description: Independent, comprehensive, coed, affiliated with Moravian Church. Awards bachelor's and master's degrees. Founded 1742. Setting: 60-acre suburban campus with easy access to Philadelphia. Endowment: $91.6 million. Research spending for the previous fiscal year: $157,051. Educational spending for the previous fiscal year: $13,118 per student. Total enrollment: 1,909. Faculty: 167 (100 full-time, 67 part-time). Student-undergrad faculty ratio is 12:1. 2,034 applied, 79% were admitted. 17% from top 10% of their high school class, 47% from top quarter, 78% from top half. 1 National Merit Scholar, 1 class president, 1 valedictorian, 16 student government officers. Full-time: 1,459 students, 59% women, 41% men. Part-time: 123 students, 79% women, 21% men. Students come from 20 states and territories, 7 other countries, 32% from out-of-state. 0.1% American Indian or Alaska Native, non-Hispanic/Latino; 7% Hispanic/Latino; 3% African American, non-Hispanic/Latino; 2% Asian, non-Hispanic/Latino; 0.2% Native Hawaiian or other Pacific Islander, non-Hispanic/Latino; 0.3% international. 3% 25 or older, 73% live on campus, 5% transferred in. Retention: 76% of full-time freshmen returned the following year. Academic areas with the most degrees conferred: business/marketing; social sciences; health professions and related sciences. Core. Calendar: semesters. Services for LD students, advanced placement, self-designed majors, honors program, independent study, double major, summer session for credit, part-time degree program, adult/continuing education programs, co-op programs and internships, graduate courses open to undergrads. Off campus study at Five other members of the Lehigh Valley Association of Independent Colleges, Washington Semester. Study abroad program. ROTC: Army (c).

Entrance Requirements: Options: electronic application, deferred admission, international baccalaureate accepted. Required: essay, high school transcript, 2 recommendations. Recommended: interview, SAT, ACT, SAT or ACT. Entrance: moderately difficult. Application deadline: 3/1. Notification: 3/15. SAT Reasoning Test deadline: 3/1.

Costs Per Year: Application fee: $40. Comprehensive fee: $44,630 includes full-time tuition ($33,919), mandatory fees ($565), and college room and board ($10,146). College room only: $5676. Room and board charges vary according to board plan and housing facility. Part-time tuition: $942.25 per credit hour. Part-time tuition varies according to class time.

Collegiate Environment: Orientation program. Drama-theater group, choral group, marching band, student-run newspaper, radio station. Social organizations: 100 open to all; national fraternities, national sororities, local fraternities; 14% of eligible men and 24% of eligible women are members. Most popular organizations: United Student Government, Moravian College Choir, Habitat for Humanity, Student Nurses Association, Moravian College Theatre Company. Major annual events: Homecoming, Christmas Vespers, Annual Concert. Student services: health clinic, personal-psychological counseling. Campus security: 24-hour emergency response devices and patrols, late night transport-escort service, controlled dormitory access. 1,196 college housing spaces available; 1,015 were occupied in 2012-13. Freshmen guaranteed college housing. On-campus residence required through senior year. Options: coed, men-only, women-only housing available. Reeves Library with 337,468 books, 2,200 microform titles, 49,280 serials, 3,817 audiovisual materials, an OPAC, and a Web page. Operations spending for the previous fiscal year: $2.3 million. 180 computers available on campus for general student use. Computer purchase/lease plans available. A campuswide network can be accessed from student residence rooms and from off campus. Staffed computer lab on campus provides training in use of computers, software, and the Internet.

Community Environment: Town of about 75,000 residential neighborhood.

■ MOUNT ALOYSIUS COLLEGE
7373 Admiral Peary Hwy.
Cresson, PA 16630-1999
Tel: (814)886-4131; Free: 888-823-2220
Fax: (814)886-2978
E-mail: admissions@mtaloy.edu
Web Site: www.mtaloy.edu/

Description: Independent Roman Catholic, comprehensive, coed. Awards associate, bachelor's, and master's degrees. Founded 1939. Setting: 193-acre small town campus. Total enrollment: 1,768. Faculty: 184 (67 full-time, 117 part-time). Student-undergrad faculty ratio is 13:1. 1,546 applied, 69% were admitted. Full-time: 1,241 students, 71% women, 29% men. Part-time: 465 students, 75% women, 25% men. 3% from out-of-state. 0.2% American Indian or Alaska Native, non-Hispanic/Latino; 1% Hispanic/Latino; 1% African American, non-Hispanic/Latino; 0.2% Asian, non-Hispanic/Latino; 0% Native Hawaiian or other Pacific Islander, non-Hispanic/Latino; 1% international. 30% 25 or older, 33% live on campus, 9% transferred in. Retention: 66% of full-time freshmen returned the following year. Academic areas with the most degrees conferred: business/marketing; health professions and related sciences; liberal arts/general studies. Core. Calendar: semesters. Academic remediation for entering students, advanced placement, accelerated degree program, self-designed majors, honors program, independent study, distance learning, double major, summer session for credit, part-time degree program, external degree program, internships. Study abroad program.

Entrance Requirements: Options: electronic application, early admission, deferred admission, international baccalaureate accepted. Required: high

school transcript, SAT or ACT. Recommended: interview, SAT, ACT. Required for some: essay, interview. Entrance: minimally difficult. Application deadline: Rolling. Notification: continuous. SAT Reasoning Test deadline: 8/1. Transfer credits accepted: Yes. Applicants placed on waiting list: 0. Wait-listed applicants offered admission: 0.

Collegiate Environment: Orientation program. Drama-theater group, choral group, student-run newspaper. Social organizations: 44 open to all. Most popular organizations: student government, Campus Activity Board, Student Athletic Advisory Committee, Spirit Team, Dance Team. Major annual events: Club Fair, Mountie Madness, MAC's Got Talent. Student services: health clinic, personal-psychological counseling. Campus security: 24-hour emergency response devices and patrols, student patrols, late night transport-escort service, controlled dormitory access. 505 college housing spaces available; 499 were occupied in 2012-13. Freshmen guaranteed college housing. On-campus residence required through sophomore year. Option: coed housing available. Mount Aloysius College Library with 90,750 books, 5,351 microform titles, 164 serials, 3,448 audiovisual materials, an OPAC, and a Web page. 120 computers available on campus for general student use. Computer purchase/lease plans available. A campuswide network can be accessed from student residence rooms and from off campus. Students can access the following: online class registration. Staffed computer lab on campus provides training in use of computers, software, and the Internet.

Community Environment: Population 4,200. Cresson is a rural community with a moderately humid climate and relatively high temperatures in summer. The area is served by bus, highway, and an airport at Martinsburg 45 minutes away. The city has two Catholic, a Methodist, Presbyterian, Christian, and Missionary Alliance Churches. There are several civic, fraternal, and veteran's organizations within the area. Theatres, concerts, sport events, and other recreational facilities are located in nearby Altoona and Johnstown. There are part-time employment opportunities for students on campus.

■ MUHLENBERG COLLEGE
2400 Chew St.
Allentown, PA 18104-5586
Tel: (484)664-3100
Fax: (484)664-3234
E-mail: adm@muhlenberg.edu
Web Site: www.muhlenberg.edu/

Description: Independent, 4-year, coed, affiliated with Lutheran Church. Awards associate and bachelor's degrees. Founded 1848. Setting: 75-acre suburban campus with easy access to Philadelphia. Endowment: $149.4 million. Research spending for the previous fiscal year: $444,871. Educational spending for the previous fiscal year: $15,011 per student. Total enrollment: 2,422. Faculty: 262 (166 full-time, 96 part-time). Student-undergrad faculty ratio is 12:1. 5,023 applied, 46% were admitted. 45% from top 10% of their high school class, 77% from top quarter, 96% from top half. Full-time: 2,301 students, 59% women, 41% men. Part-time: 121 students, 54% women, 46% men. Students come from 39 states and territories, 9 other countries, 79% from out-of-state. 0.2% American Indian or Alaska Native, non-Hispanic/Latino; 3% Hispanic/Latino; 3% African American, non-Hispanic/Latino; 2% Asian, non-Hispanic/Latino; 0.1% Native Hawaiian or other Pacific Islander, non-Hispanic/Latino; 0.4% international. 3% 25 or older, 91% live on campus, 0.4% transferred in. Retention: 94% of full-time freshmen returned the following year. Academic areas with the most degrees conferred: business/marketing; visual and performing arts; biological/life sciences. Core. Calendar: semesters. Services for LD students, advanced placement, accelerated degree program, self-designed majors, honors program, independent study, double major, summer session for credit, part-time degree program, adult/continuing education programs, internships. Off campus study at 6 members of the Lehigh Valley Association of Independent Colleges. Study abroad program. ROTC: Army (c).

Entrance Requirements: Options: electronic application, early admission, early decision, deferred admission, international baccalaureate accepted. Required: essay, high school transcript, 2 recommendations. Recommended: interview. Required for some: interview, graded paper, SAT or ACT. Entrance: very difficult. Application deadlines: 2/15, 2/1 for early decision. Notification: 3/15, Rolling for early decision. SAT Reasoning Test deadline: 2/15. Applicants placed on waiting list: 1,691. Wait-listed applicants offered admission: 22. Early decision applicants: 392. Early decision applicants admitted: 312.

Costs Per Year: Application fee: $50. Comprehensive fee: $52,650 includes full-time tuition ($41,225), mandatory fees ($285), and college room and

board ($11,140). College room only: $7175. Room and board charges vary according to board plan, housing facility, and location.

Collegiate Environment: Orientation program. Drama-theater group, choral group, student-run newspaper, radio station. Social organizations: 123 open to all; national fraternities, national sororities; 14% of eligible men and 17% of eligible women are members. Most popular organizations: Theater Association, Environmental Action Team, Jefferson School Partnership, Select Choir, Habitat for Humanity. Major annual events: Homecoming, Jefferson School Field Day, Family Weekend. Student services: health clinic, personal-psychological counseling. Campus security: 24-hour emergency response devices and patrols, late night transport-escort service, controlled dormitory access. 1,996 college housing spaces available; 1,892 were occupied in 2012-13. Freshmen guaranteed college housing. On-campus residence required through senior year. Options: coed, women-only housing available. Trexler Library, Muhlenberg College with 419,790 books, 359,462 microform titles, 38,453 serials, 12,836 audiovisual materials, an OPAC, and a Web page. Operations spending for the previous fiscal year: $3 million. 471 computers available on campus for general student use. Computer purchase/lease plans available. A campuswide network can be accessed from student residence rooms and from off campus. Students can access the following: online class registration. Staffed computer lab on campus (open 24 hours a day) provides training in use of computers, software, and the Internet.

Community Environment: Population 107,000. Allentown is located on the Lehigh River. It is Pennsylvania's third largest industrial market. Diversified manufacturing includes machinery and tools, trucks, electrical appliances, electronic equipment, apparel, cement, and gas-generating equipment. Other industries manufacture metal products, batteries, foodstuffs, textiles, and shoes. The area has good transportation facilities including four railroad lines, air service, and bus lines. The community has many churches representing various denominations. Four hospitals, a dental hospital, a library system, a museum and an Equity theater company are located here. Local recreational facilities encompass volleyball, baseball, tennis, basketball, pools, hiking, band concerts, opera, community theatre, five radio stations, and many motion picture and drive-in theatres. Part-time employment is available for students.

■ NEUMANN UNIVERSITY

One Neumann Dr.
Aston, PA 19014-1298
Tel: (610)459-0905; Free: 800-963-8626
E-mail: neumann@neumann.edu
Web Site: www.neumann.edu/

Description: Independent Roman Catholic, comprehensive, coed. Awards associate, bachelor's, master's, and doctoral degrees and post-master's certificates. Founded 1965. Setting: 50-acre suburban campus with easy access to Philadelphia. Endowment: $22.3 million. Total enrollment: 3,100. Faculty: 308 (95 full-time, 213 part-time). Student-undergrad faculty ratio is 14:1. 3,567 applied, 71% were admitted. Full-time: 2,166 students, 63% women, 37% men. Part-time: 508 students, 73% women, 27% men. Students come from 24 states and territories, 33% from out-of-state. 0.3% American Indian or Alaska Native, non-Hispanic/Latino; 3% Hispanic/Latino; 19% African American, non-Hispanic/Latino; 1% Asian, non-Hispanic/Latino; 0.1% Native Hawaiian or other Pacific Islander, non-Hispanic/Latino; 2% international. 17% 25 or older, 40% live on campus, 5% transferred in. Retention: 74% of full-time freshmen returned the following year. Academic areas with the most degrees conferred: liberal arts/general studies; health professions and related sciences; education. Core. Calendar: semesters. Academic remediation for entering students, services for LD students, advanced placement, accelerated degree program, self-designed majors, freshman honors college, honors program, independent study, distance learning, double major, summer session for credit, part-time degree program, adult/continuing education programs, co-op programs and internships, graduate courses open to undergrads. Off campus study. Study abroad program. ROTC: Army (c).

Entrance Requirements: Options: electronic application, deferred admission. Required: high school transcript, minimum 2 high school GPA, SAT or ACT. Recommended: interview. Entrance: minimally difficult. Application deadline: 4/1. Notification: continuous. SAT Reasoning Test deadline: 8/1. Transfer credits accepted: Yes.

Costs Per Year: Application fee: $40. Comprehensive fee: $35,302 includes full-time tuition ($23,262), mandatory fees ($970), and college room and board ($11,070). College room only: $6510. Room and board charges vary according to board plan. Part-time tuition: $531 per credit hour. Part-time mandatory fees: $50 per semester hour.

Collegiate Environment: Orientation program. Drama-theater group, choral group, student-run newspaper, radio station. Social organizations: 34 open to all. Most popular organizations: student government, Student Activities Board, Black Student Union, Boogie Knights, Neumann Media. Major annual events: Homecoming, Halloween Carnival, Winter Formal. Student services: health clinic, personal-psychological counseling. Campus security: 24-hour emergency response devices and patrols, late night transport-escort service, controlled dormitory access. 917 college housing spaces available; all were occupied in 2012-13. Freshmen given priority for college housing. Option: coed housing available. Neumann University Library plus 1 other with 64,000 books, 94,000 serials, 3,000 audiovisual materials, an OPAC, and a Web page. 400 computers available on campus for general student use. Computer purchase/lease plans available. A campuswide network can be accessed from student residence rooms and from off campus. Staffed computer lab on campus provides training in use of computers, software, and the Internet.

Community Environment: Population of Philadelphia 1,463,281. Aston is a suburban township serving a commuter population from the Tri-state area of Philadelphia, Wilmington and South Jersey. The city enjoys temperate climate. Local historical sites include Valley Forge National Park, Brandywine Battlefield, and many others. Nearby Philadelphia offers all the cultural, recreational, and community service facilities normally found in a metropolis. The immediate area is served by railroad and bus lines with an airport located 10 miles away. There are three hospitals and numerous shopping centers in the area. Part-time employment opportunities are good.

■ NEW CASTLE SCHOOL OF TRADES

New Castle Youngstown Rd., Rte. 422 RD1
Pulaski, PA 16143-9721
Tel: (724)964-8811; Free: 800-837-8299
Web Site: www.ncstrades.com/

Description: Independent, 2-year, coed. Part of Educational Enterprises Incorporated. Awards diplomas and transfer associate degrees. Founded 1945. Setting: 20-acre rural campus with easy access to Cleveland. Total enrollment: 441. 251 applied, 100% were admitted. 54% 25 or older.

Entrance Requirements: Required: high school transcript, interview, Wonderlic aptitude test. Required for some: essay.

Collegiate Environment: Student services: personal-psychological counseling. Campus security: 24-hour emergency response devices.

■ NEWPORT BUSINESS INSTITUTE (LOWER BURRELL)

945 Greensburg Rd.
Lower Burrell, PA 15068-3929
Tel: (724)339-7542; Free: 800-752-7695
Fax: (724)339-2950
E-mail: admissions@newportbusiness.com
Web Site: www.nbi.edu/

Description: Proprietary, 2-year, coed. Awards certificates, diplomas, and terminal associate degrees. Founded 1895. Setting: 4-acre small town campus with easy access to Pittsburgh. Total enrollment: 64. Student-undergrad faculty ratio is 10:1. 0% from out-of-state. 59% 25 or older. Advanced placement, self-designed majors, double major, internships.

Entrance Requirements: Open admission. Option: early admission. Required: high school transcript. Recommended: interview. Entrance: noncompetitive. Application deadline: Rolling. Notification: continuous.

Collegiate Environment: Student-run newspaper. Student services: personal-psychological counseling. Campus security: security system.

■ NEWPORT BUSINESS INSTITUTE (WILLIAMSPORT)

941 W Third St.
Williamsport, PA 17701-5855
Tel: (570)326-2869
Fax: (570)326-2136
E-mail: admissions2_NBI@Comcast.net
Web Site: www.nbi.edu/

Description: Proprietary, 2-year, coed. Awards terminal associate degrees. Founded 1955. Setting: small town campus. Total enrollment: 108. Faculty: 26 (6 full-time, 20 part-time). Student-undergrad faculty ratio is 9:1. 23 applied, 100% were admitted. Full-time: 108 students, 92% women, 8% men. 0% American Indian or Alaska Native, non-Hispanic/Latino; 1% Hispanic/Latino; 18% African American, non-Hispanic/Latino; 0% Asian, non-Hispanic/Latino; 0% Native Hawaiian or other Pacific Islander, non-Hispanic/Latino; 0% international. 69% 25 or older, 16% transferred in. Distance learning, summer session for credit, part-time degree program, internships.

Entrance Requirements: Options: electronic application, deferred admission. Required: high school transcript, interview. Entrance: moderately difficult. Application deadline: Rolling. Transfer credits accepted: Yes.

Collegiate Environment: Orientation program. Most popular organization: Student Council. 4 computers available on campus for general student use. Computer purchase/lease plans available. A computer is required for all students.

■ NORTHAMPTON COMMUNITY COLLEGE

3835 Green Pond Rd.
Bethlehem, PA 18020-7599
Tel: (610)861-5300
E-mail: jrmccarthy@northampton.edu
Web Site: www.northampton.edu/

Description: State and locally supported, 2-year, coed. Awards certificates, diplomas, transfer associate, and terminal associate degrees. Founded 1967. Setting: 165-acre suburban campus with easy access to Philadelphia. Endowment: $30.3 million. Educational spending for the previous fiscal year: $3304 per student. Total enrollment: 11,018. Faculty: 697 (120 full-time, 577 part-time). Student-undergrad faculty ratio is 22:1. 4,699 applied, 100% were admitted. 1% from top 10% of their high school class, 8% from top quarter, 35% from top half. Full-time: 4,668 students, 53% women, 47% men. Part-time: 6,350 students, 64% women, 36% men. Students come from 24 states and territories, 52 other countries, 2% from out-of-state. 0.3% American Indian or Alaska Native, non-Hispanic/Latino; 18% Hispanic/Latino; 11% African American, non-Hispanic/Latino; 2% Asian, non-Hispanic/Latino; 0.2% Native Hawaiian or other Pacific Islander, non-Hispanic/Latino; 1% international. 35% 25 or older, 2% live on campus, 8% transferred in. Core. Calendar: semesters. Academic remediation for entering students, ESL program, services for LD students, advanced placement, self-designed majors, honors program, independent study, distance learning, summer session for credit, part-time degree program, adult/continuing education programs, internships. Off campus study. Study abroad program.

Entrance Requirements: Open admission except for allied health, veterinary technician and culinary arts programs. Options: electronic application, deferred admission. Recommended: high school transcript. Required for some: high school transcript, minimum 2.5 high school GPA, interview, interview for rad and veterinary. Entrance: noncompetitive. Application deadlines: Rolling, Rolling for nonresidents. Notification: continuous, continuous for nonresidents. Transfer credits accepted: Yes.

Costs Per Year: Application fee: $25. Area resident tuition: $2550 full-time, $85 per credit hour part-time. State resident tuition: $5100 full-time, $170 per credit hour part-time. Nonresident tuition: $7650 full-time, $255 per credit hour part-time. Mandatory fees: $1020 full-time, $34 per credit hour part-time. Full-time tuition and fees vary according to course load. Part-time tuition and fees vary according to course load. College room and board: $7676. College room only: $4386. Room and board charges vary according to board plan and housing facility.

Collegiate Environment: Orientation program. Drama-theater group, choral group, student-run newspaper, radio station. Social organizations: 60 open to all. Most popular organizations: Phi Theta Kappa, Student Senate, College and Hospital Association of Radiologic Technologies Students (CHARTS), American Dental Hygiene Association (ADHA), International Student Organization. Major annual events: Fall Quad Fest, Souper Bowl Party/Club Fair, Student Celebration. Student services: health clinic, personal-psychological counseling. Campus security: 24-hour emergency response devices and patrols, controlled dormitory access. 268 college housing spaces available; 262 were occupied in 2012-13. No special consideration for freshman housing applicants. Option: coed housing available. Paul & Harriett Mack Library with 111,697 books, 197 serials, 11,981 audiovisual materials, an OPAC, and a Web page. Operations spending for the previous fiscal year: $1.3 million. 1,236 computers available on campus for general student use. Computer purchase/lease plans available. A campuswide network can be accessed from student residence rooms and from off campus. Students can access the following: online class registration. Staffed computer lab on campus provides training in use of computers, software, and the Internet.

■ OAKBRIDGE ACADEMY OF ARTS

1250 Greensburg Rd.
Lower Burrell, PA 15068
Tel: (724)335-5336; Free: 800-734-5601
Fax: (724)335-3367
E-mail: mbelferman@oaa.edu

Web Site: oaa.edu/

Description: Proprietary, 2-year, coed. Awards transfer associate and terminal associate degrees. Founded 1972. Setting: 2-acre small town campus with easy access to Pittsburgh. Total enrollment: 60. Student-undergrad faculty ratio is 14:1. 0% from out-of-state. 15% 25 or older. Core. Academic remediation for entering students, advanced placement, internships.

Entrance Requirements: Option: electronic application. Required: high school transcript, portfolio. Application deadline: 8/31.

Collegiate Environment: Orientation program. Campus security: 24-hour emergency response devices. Robert J. Mullen Memorial Library with a Web page.

■ ORLEANS TECHNICAL INSTITUTE

2770 Red Lion Rd.
Philadelphia, PA 19114
Tel: (215)728-4700
Fax: (215)745-1689
E-mail: stinsd@jevs.org
Web Site: www.orleanstech.edu/

Description: Independent, 2-year, coed. Awards diplomas, transfer associate, and terminal associate degrees. Setting: 9-acre urban campus with easy access to Philadelphia. Educational spending for the previous fiscal year: $3750 per student. Total enrollment: 533. Faculty: 48 (27 full-time, 21 part-time). Student-undergrad faculty ratio is 13:1. Full-time: 400 students, 33% women, 67% men. Part-time: 133 students, 21% women, 79% men. Students come from 3 states and territories, 5% from out-of-state. 0.2% American Indian or Alaska Native, non-Hispanic/Latino; 11% Hispanic/Latino; 49% African American, non-Hispanic/Latino; 2% Asian, non-Hispanic/Latino; 1% Native Hawaiian or other Pacific Islander, non-Hispanic/Latino; 0% international. 61% 25 or older, 1% transferred in. Core. Calendar: trimesters. Academic remediation for entering students, summer session for credit, part-time degree program, co-op programs and internships.

Entrance Requirements: Option: electronic application. Required: high school transcript, interview, Wonderlic. Entrance: minimally difficult. Application deadline: Rolling. Transfer credits accepted: Yes.

Collegiate Environment: Orientation program. Campus security: 24-hour emergency response devices. Orleans Technical Institute Library and Learning Resource Center plus 1 other with 804 books, 27 serials, 7 audiovisual materials, an OPAC, and a Web page. Operations spending for the previous fiscal year: $37,000. 166 computers available on campus for general student use. A campuswide network can be accessed. Staffed computer lab on campus provides training in use of computers, software, and the Internet.

■ PACE INSTITUTE

606 Ct. St.
Reading, PA 19601
Tel: (610)375-1212
Fax: (610)375-1924
Web Site: www.paceinstitute.com/

Description: Private, 2-year, coed. Awards diplomas, transfer associate, and terminal associate degrees. Founded 1977. Total enrollment: 274. Faculty: 14 (6 full-time, 8 part-time). Student-undergrad faculty ratio is 18:1. 95% 25 or older.

■ PEIRCE COLLEGE

1420 Pine St.
Philadelphia, PA 19102-4699
Tel: (215)545-6400; Free: 888-467-3472
Fax: (215)546-5996
E-mail: info@peirce.edu
Web Site: www.peirce.edu/

Description: Independent, 4-year, coed. Awards associate and bachelor's degrees. Founded 1865. Setting: 1-acre urban campus. Endowment: $17.3 million. Educational spending for the previous fiscal year: $6685 per student. Total enrollment: 2,261. Faculty: 149 (37 full-time, 112 part-time). Student-undergrad faculty ratio is 17:1. Full-time: 817 students, 74% women, 26% men. Part-time: 1,444 students, 72% women, 28% men. Students come from 27 states and territories, 22 other countries, 11% from out-of-state. 0.4% American Indian or Alaska Native, non-Hispanic/Latino; 7% Hispanic/Latino; 68% African American, non-Hispanic/Latino; 1% Asian, non-Hispanic/Latino; 0.04% Native Hawaiian or other Pacific Islander, non-Hispanic/Latino; 0.3% international. 79% 25 or older. Retention: 0% of full-time freshmen returned the following year. Academic areas with the most degrees conferred: business/marketing; law/legal studies; computer and information sciences. Core. Calendar: semesters. Services for LD students, advanced placement, accelerated degree program, distance learning, summer session for credit, part-time degree program, adult/continuing education programs, co-op programs and internships.

Entrance Requirements: Open admission selective admissions into the Professional Studies degree completion program. Option: electronic application. Required: high school transcript. Entrance: noncompetitive. Application deadlines: Rolling, Rolling for nonresidents. Notification: continuous, continuous for nonresidents. Transfer credits accepted: Yes.

Costs Per Year: Application fee: $50. Tuition: $15,450 full-time, $515 per credit hour part-time. Mandatory fees: $1050 full-time, $105 per course part-time.

Collegiate Environment: Orientation program. Social organizations: Program Student Associations. Major annual events: Commencement, Academic Awards Ceremony, Student Appreciation Day. Campus security: 24-hour emergency response devices and patrols, late night transport-escort service, 24-hour security cameras. College housing not available. Peirce College Library with 124,667 books, 70 serials, 109 audiovisual materials, an OPAC, and a Web page. Operations spending for the previous fiscal year: $298,200. 46 computers available on campus for general student use. Computer purchase/lease plans available. A computer is required for all students. A campuswide network can be accessed from off-campus. Students can access the following: online class registration. Staffed computer lab on campus provides training in use of computers, software, and the Internet.

■ **PENN COMMERCIAL BUSINESS AND TECHNICAL SCHOOL**
242 Oak Spring Rd.
Washington, PA 15301
Tel: (724)222-5330; Free: 888-309-7484
Fax: (724)222-4722
E-mail: mjoyce@penn-commercial.com
Web Site: www.penncommercial.net/

Description: Proprietary, 2-year, coed. Awards certificates, diplomas, transfer associate, and terminal associate degrees. Founded 1929. Setting: 1-acre small town campus with easy access to Pittsburgh. Total enrollment: 435. 165 applied. 67% 25 or older. Academic remediation for entering students, summer session for credit, part-time degree program.

Entrance Requirements: Open admission. Options: early admission, deferred admission. Required: high school transcript. Entrance: noncompetitive. Application deadline: Rolling. Notification: continuous.

Collegiate Environment: Student-run newspaper. Main library plus 1 other with 400 books and 60 serials.

■ **PENN STATE ABINGTON**
1600 Woodland Rd.
Abington, PA 19001
Tel: (215)881-7300
E-mail: abingtonadmissions@psu.edu
Web Site: www.abington.psu.edu/

Description: State-related, 4-year, coed. Part of Pennsylvania State University. Awards associate and bachelor's degrees (enrollment figures include students enrolled at The Graduate School at Penn State who are taking courses at this location). Founded 1950. Setting: small town campus. Total enrollment: 3,516. Faculty: 226 (108 full-time, 118 part-time). Student-undergrad faculty ratio is 20:1. 3,221 applied, 78% were admitted. 11% from top 10% of their high school class, 32% from top quarter, 69% from top half. Full-time: 2,728 students, 49% women, 51% men. Part-time: 778 students, 61% women, 39% men. 7% from out-of-state. 0.2% American Indian or Alaska Native, non-Hispanic/Latino; 8% Hispanic/Latino; 15% African American, non-Hispanic/Latino; 16% Asian, non-Hispanic/Latino; 0.1% Native Hawaiian or other Pacific Islander, non-Hispanic/Latino; 2% international. 16% 25 or older, 0% live on campus, 5% transferred in. Retention: 74% of full-time freshmen returned the following year. Academic areas with the most degrees conferred: business/marketing; psychology; homeland security, law enforcement, firefighting, and protective services. Calendar: semesters. Part-time degree program, external degree program, adult/continuing education programs. ROTC: Army, Air Force (c).

Entrance Requirements: Options: electronic application, early admission, deferred admission, international baccalaureate accepted. Required: high school transcript, SAT or ACT. Recommended: essay. Required for some: interview. Entrance: very difficult. Application deadline: Rolling. Notification: continuous.

Costs Per Year: Application fee: $50. State resident tuition: $12,474 full-time, $504 per credit hour part-time. Nonresident tuition: $19,030 full-time, $793 per credit hour part-time. Mandatory fees: $882 full-time. Full-time tuition and fees vary according to course level, degree level, location, program, and student level. Part-time tuition varies according to course level, course load, degree level, location, program, and student level.

Collegiate Environment: Orientation program. Campus security: 24-hour emergency response devices and patrols. College housing not available.

■ **PENN STATE ALTOONA**
3000 Ivyside Park
Altoona, PA 16601-3760
Tel: (814)949-5000; Free: 800-848-9843
Fax: (814)949-5011
E-mail: aaadmit@psu.edu
Web Site: www.aa.psu.edu/

Description: State-related, 4-year, coed. Part of Pennsylvania State University. Awards associate and bachelor's degrees (enrollment figures include students enrolled at The Graduate School at Penn State who are taking courses at this location). Founded 1939. Setting: suburban campus. Total enrollment: 3,863. Faculty: 292 (174 full-time, 118 part-time). Student-undergrad faculty ratio is 18:1. 5,700 applied, 85% were admitted. 5% from top 10% of their high school class, 25% from top quarter, 74% from top half. Full-time: 3,660 students, 46% women, 54% men. Part-time: 203 students, 62% women, 38% men. 19% from out-of-state. 0.1% American Indian or Alaska Native, non-Hispanic/Latino; 4% Hispanic/Latino; 8% African American, non-Hispanic/Latino; 2% Asian, non-Hispanic/Latino; 0.03% Native Hawaiian or other Pacific Islander, non-Hispanic/Latino; 2% international. 8% 25 or older, 24% live on campus, 2% transferred in. Retention: 84% of full-time freshmen returned the following year. Academic areas with the most degrees conferred: business/marketing; engineering; homeland security, law enforcement, firefighting, and protective services. Calendar: semesters. ROTC: Army, Air Force.

Entrance Requirements: Options: electronic application, early admission, deferred admission, international baccalaureate accepted. Required: high school transcript, SAT or ACT. Recommended: essay. Required for some: interview. Entrance: very difficult. Application deadline: Rolling. Notification: continuous.

Costs Per Year: Application fee: $50. State resident tuition: $13,018 full-time, $542 per credit hour part-time. Nonresident tuition: $19,912 full-time, $830 per credit hour part-time. Mandatory fees: $882 full-time. Full-time tuition and fees vary according to course level, degree level, location, program, and student level. Part-time tuition varies according to course level, course load, degree level, location, program, and student level. College room and board: $9690. College room only: $4910. Room and board charges vary according to board plan, housing facility, and location.

Collegiate Environment: Orientation program. Campus security: 24-hour emergency response devices and patrols, late night transport-escort service. Option: coed housing available.

■ **PENN STATE BEAVER**
100 University Dr.
Monaca, PA 15061
Tel: (724)773-3800
Fax: (724)773-3557
E-mail: br-admissions@psu.edu
Web Site: www.br.psu.edu/

Description: State-related, primarily 2-year, coed. Part of Pennsylvania State University. Awards certificates, transfer associate, terminal associate, and bachelor's degrees. Founded 1964. Setting: small town campus. Total enrollment: 759. Faculty: 64 (34 full-time, 30 part-time). Student-undergrad faculty ratio is 15:1. 670 applied, 87% were admitted. 8% from top 10% of their high school class, 30% from top quarter, 67% from top half. Full-time: 634 students, 42% women, 58% men. Part-time: 125 students, 60% women, 40% men. 8% from out-of-state. 0.2% American Indian or Alaska Native, non-Hispanic/Latino; 4% Hispanic/Latino; 11% African American, non-Hispanic/Latino; 2% Asian, non-Hispanic/Latino; 0.3% Native Hawaiian or other Pacific Islander, non-Hispanic/Latino; 1% international. 12% 25 or older, 22% live on campus, 4% transferred in. Retention: 71% of full-time freshmen returned the following year. Academic areas with the most degrees conferred: business/marketing; psychology; computer and information sciences. Calendar: semesters. Adult/continuing education programs.

Entrance Requirements: Options: electronic application, early admission, deferred admission. Required: high school transcript, SAT or ACT. Recommended: essay. Required for some: interview. Entrance: moderately difficult. Application deadline: Rolling. Notification: continuous.

Costs Per Year: Application fee: $50. State resident tuition: $12,474 full-time, $504 per credit hour part-time. Nonresident tuition: $19,030 full-time, $793 per credit hour part-time. Mandatory fees: $876 full-time. Full-time tuition and fees vary according to course level, degree level, location, program, and student level. Part-time tuition varies according to course level, course load, degree level, location, program, and student level. College room and board: $9690. College room only: $4910. Room and board charges vary according to board plan, housing facility, and location.

Collegiate Environment: Orientation program. Freshmen guaranteed college housing. Option: coed housing available.

■ **PENN STATE BERKS**
Tulpehocken Rd.
Reading, PA 19610-6009
Tel: (610)396-6000
E-mail: admissionsbk@psu.edu
Web Site: www.bk.psu.edu/

Description: State-related, 4-year, coed. Part of Pennsylvania State University. Awards associate and bachelor's degrees (enrollment figures include students enrolled at The Graduate School at Penn State who are taking courses at this location). Founded 1924. Setting: suburban campus. Total enrollment: 2,747. Faculty: 217 (121 full-time, 96 part-time). Student-undergrad faculty ratio is 17:1. 2,570 applied, 83% were admitted. 7% from top 10% of their high school class, 27% from top quarter, 65% from top half. Full-time: 2,432 students, 45% women, 55% men. Part-time: 311 students, 42% women, 58% men. 8% from out-of-state. 0.1% American Indian or Alaska Native, non-Hispanic/Latino; 9% Hispanic/Latino; 9% African American, non-Hispanic/Latino; 4% Asian, non-Hispanic/Latino; 0.04% Native Hawaiian or other Pacific Islander, non-Hispanic/Latino; 1% international. 11% 25 or older, 29% live on campus, 4% transferred in. Retention: 80% of full-time freshmen returned the following year. Academic areas with the most degrees conferred: business/marketing; psychology; education. Calendar: semesters. Part-time degree program, adult/continuing education programs. ROTC: Army (c).

Entrance Requirements: Options: electronic application, early admission, deferred admission, international baccalaureate accepted. Required: high school transcript, SAT or ACT. Recommended: essay. Required for some: interview. Entrance: very difficult. Application deadline: Rolling. Notification: continuous.

Costs Per Year: Application fee: $50. State resident tuition: $13,018 full-time, $542 per credit hour part-time. Nonresident tuition: $19,912 full-time, $830 per credit hour part-time. Mandatory fees: $882 full-time. Full-time tuition and fees vary according to course level, degree level, location, program, and student level. Part-time tuition varies according to course level, course load, degree level, location, program, and student level. College room and board: $10,560. College room only: $5780. Room and board charges vary according to board plan, housing facility, and location.

Collegiate Environment: Orientation program. Campus security: 24-hour emergency response devices and patrols, late night transport-escort service, controlled dormitory access. Option: coed housing available.

■ **PENN STATE BRANDYWINE**
25 Yearsley Mill Rd.
Media, PA 19063-5596
Tel: (610)892-1200
E-mail: bwadmissions@psu.edu
Web Site: www.brandywine.psu.edu/

Description: State-related, primarily 2-year, coed. Part of Pennsylvania State University. Awards certificates, transfer associate, terminal associate, and bachelor's degrees. Founded 1966. Setting: small town campus. Total enrollment: 1,581. Faculty: 131 (60 full-time, 71 part-time). Student-undergrad faculty ratio is 17:1. 1,279 applied, 79% were admitted. 6% from top 10% of their high school class, 24% from top quarter, 59% from top half. Full-time: 1,338 students, 44% women, 56% men. Part-time: 243 students, 43% women, 57% men. 6% from out-of-state. 0.2% American Indian or Alaska Native, non-Hispanic/Latino; 5% Hispanic/Latino; 13% African American, non-Hispanic/Latino; 9% Asian, non-Hispanic/Latino; 0.1% Native Hawaiian or other Pacific Islander, non-Hispanic/Latino; 1% international. 12% 25 or older, 0% live on campus, 4% transferred in. Retention: 71% of full-time freshmen returned the following year. Academic areas with the most degrees conferred: business/marketing; family and consumer sciences;

communication/journalism. Calendar: semesters. Adult/continuing education programs. ROTC: Army (c), Air Force (c).

Entrance Requirements: Options: electronic application, early admission, deferred admission. Required: high school transcript, SAT or ACT. Recommended: essay. Required for some: interview. Entrance: moderately difficult. Application deadline: Rolling. Notification: continuous.

Costs Per Year: Application fee: $50. State resident tuition: $12,474 full-time, $504 per credit hour part-time. Nonresident tuition: $19,030 full-time, $793 per credit hour part-time. Mandatory fees: $882 full-time. Full-time tuition and fees vary according to course level, degree level, location, program, and student level. Part-time tuition varies according to course level, course load, degree level, location, program, and student level.

Collegiate Environment: Orientation program. Campus security: late night transport-escort service, part-time trained security personnel. College housing not available.

■ **PENN STATE DUBOIS**
College Pl.
DuBois, PA 15801-3199
Tel: (814)375-4700; Free: 800-346-7627
E-mail: duboisinfo@psi.edu
Web Site: www.ds.psu.edu/

Description: State-related, primarily 2-year, coed. Part of Pennsylvania State University. Awards certificates, transfer associate, terminal associate, and bachelor's degrees. Founded 1935. Setting: small town campus. Total enrollment: 705. Faculty: 79 (46 full-time, 33 part-time). Student-undergrad faculty ratio is 11:1. 439 applied, 88% were admitted. 11% from top 10% of their high school class, 31% from top quarter, 66% from top half. Full-time: 554 students, 49% women, 51% men. Part-time: 150 students, 62% women, 38% men. 2% from out-of-state. 0.3% American Indian or Alaska Native, non-Hispanic/Latino; 1% Hispanic/Latino; 2% African American, non-Hispanic/Latino; 1% Asian, non-Hispanic/Latino; 0% Native Hawaiian or other Pacific Islander, non-Hispanic/Latino; 1% international. 27% 25 or older, 0% live on campus, 2% transferred in. Retention: 71% of full-time freshmen returned the following year. Academic areas with the most degrees conferred: family and consumer sciences; business/marketing; liberal arts/general studies. Calendar: semesters. Adult/continuing education programs.

Entrance Requirements: Options: electronic application, early admission, deferred admission. Required: high school transcript, SAT or ACT. Recommended: essay. Required for some: interview. Entrance: moderately difficult. Application deadline: Rolling. Notification: continuous.

Costs Per Year: Application fee: $50. State resident tuition: $12,474 full-time, $504 per credit hour part-time. Nonresident tuition: $19,030 full-time, $793 per credit hour part-time. Mandatory fees: $770 full-time. Full-time tuition and fees vary according to course level, degree level, location, program, and student level. Part-time tuition varies according to course level, course load, degree level, location, program, and student level.

Collegiate Environment: Orientation program. College housing not available.

■ **PENN STATE ERIE, THE BEHREND COLLEGE**
4701 College Dr.
Erie, PA 16563-0001
Tel: (814)898-6000; Free: 866-374-3378
E-mail: behrend.admissions@psu.edu
Web Site: www.pserie.psu.edu/

Description: State-related, comprehensive, coed. Part of Pennsylvania State University. Awards associate, bachelor's, and master's degrees. Founded 1948. Setting: 725-acre suburban campus. Total enrollment: 4,149. Faculty: 299 (241 full-time, 58 part-time). Student-undergrad faculty ratio is 15:1. 3,437 applied, 84% were admitted. 13% from top 10% of their high school class, 40% from top quarter, 83% from top half. Full-time: 3,723 students, 35% women, 65% men. Part-time: 342 students, 42% women, 58% men. 10% from out-of-state. 0.1% American Indian or Alaska Native, non-Hispanic/Latino; 3% Hispanic/Latino; 4% African American, non-Hispanic/Latino; 2% Asian, non-Hispanic/Latino; 0.1% Native Hawaiian or other Pacific Islander, non-Hispanic/Latino; 3% international. 9% 25 or older, 41% live on campus, 3% transferred in. Retention: 82% of full-time freshmen returned the following year. Academic areas with the most degrees conferred: business/marketing; engineering; engineering technologies. Calendar: semesters. Part-time degree program, adult/continuing education programs. ROTC: Army.

Entrance Requirements: Options: electronic application, early admission, deferred admission, international baccalaureate accepted. Required: high school transcript, SAT or ACT. Recommended: essay. Required for some: interview. Entrance: very difficult. Application deadline: Rolling. Notification: continuous.

Costs Per Year: Application fee: $50. State resident tuition: $13,018 full-time, $542 per credit hour part-time. Nonresident tuition: $19,912 full-time, $830 per credit hour part-time. Mandatory fees: $882 full-time. Full-time tuition and fees vary according to course level, degree level, location, program, and student level. Part-time tuition varies according to course level, course load, degree level, location, program, and student level. College room and board: $9690. College room only: $4910. Room and board charges vary according to board plan, housing facility, and location.

Collegiate Environment: Orientation program. Campus security: 24-hour emergency response devices and patrols, student patrols, late night transport-escort service, controlled dormitory access. Options: coed, men-only, women-only housing available.

■ **PENN STATE FAYETTE, THE EBERLY CAMPUS**
1 University Dr.
Uniontown, PA 15401-0519
Tel: (724)430-4100; Free: 877-568-4130
Fax: (724)430-4184
E-mail: feadm@psu.edu
Web Site: www.fe.psu.edu/
Description: State-related, primarily 2-year, coed. Part of Pennsylvania State University. Awards certificates, transfer associate, terminal associate, and bachelor's degrees. Founded 1934. Setting: small town campus. Total enrollment: 867. Faculty: 96 (53 full-time, 43 part-time). Student-undergrad faculty ratio is 11:1. 610 applied, 89% were admitted. 12% from top 10% of their high school class, 33% from top quarter, 70% from top half. Full-time: 680 students, 49% women, 51% men. Part-time: 187 students, 74% women, 26% men. 5% from out-of-state. 0.2% American Indian or Alaska Native, non-Hispanic/Latino; 1% Hispanic/Latino; 3% African American, non-Hispanic/Latino; 1% Asian, non-Hispanic/Latino; 0.1% Native Hawaiian or other Pacific Islander, non-Hispanic/Latino; 2% international. 29% 25 or older, 0% live on campus, 4% transferred in. Retention: 69% of full-time freshmen returned the following year. Academic areas with the most degrees conferred: health professions and related sciences; business/marketing; family and consumer sciences. Calendar: semesters. Adult/continuing education programs. ROTC: Army.
Entrance Requirements: Options: electronic application, early admission, deferred admission. Required: high school transcript, SAT or ACT. Recommended: essay. Required for some: interview. Entrance: moderately difficult. Application deadline: Rolling. Notification: continuous.
Costs Per Year: Application fee: $50. State resident tuition: $12,474 full-time, $504 per credit hour part-time. Nonresident tuition: $19,030 full-time, $793 per credit hour part-time. Mandatory fees: $826 full-time. Full-time tuition and fees vary according to course level, degree level, location, program, and student level. Part-time tuition varies according to course level, course load, degree level, location, program, and student level.
Collegiate Environment: Orientation program. Campus security: student patrols, 8-hour patrols by trained security personnel. College housing not available.

■ **PENN STATE GREATER ALLEGHENY**
4000 University Dr.
McKeesport, PA 15132-7698
Tel: (412)675-9000
E-mail: psuga@psu.edu
Web Site: www.ga.psu.edu/
Description: State-related, primarily 2-year, coed. Part of Pennsylvania State University. Awards certificates, transfer associate, terminal associate, bachelor's, and master's degrees. Founded 1947. Setting: small town campus. Total enrollment: 635. Faculty: 62 (38 full-time, 24 part-time). Student-undergrad faculty ratio is 13:1. 699 applied, 80% were admitted. 11% from top 10% of their high school class, 34% from top quarter, 69% from top half. Full-time: 582 students, 43% women, 57% men. Part-time: 53 students, 42% women, 58% men. 9% from out-of-state. 0% American Indian or Alaska Native, non-Hispanic/Latino; 4% Hispanic/Latino; 24% African American, non-Hispanic/Latino; 2% Asian, non-Hispanic/Latino; 0.2% Native Hawaiian or other Pacific Islander, non-Hispanic/Latino; 5% international. 11% 25 or older, 27% live on campus, 4% transferred in. Retention: 75% of full-time freshmen returned the following year. Academic areas with the most degrees conferred: psychology; business/marketing; communication/journalism. Calendar: semesters. Adult/continuing education programs.

Entrance Requirements: Options: electronic application, early admission, deferred admission. Required: high school transcript, SAT or ACT. Recommended: essay. Required for some: interview. Entrance: moderately difficult. Application deadline: Rolling. Notification: continuous.
Costs Per Year: Application fee: $50. State resident tuition: $12,474 full-time, $504 per credit hour part-time. Nonresident tuition: $19,030 full-time, $793 per credit hour part-time. Mandatory fees: $882 full-time. Full-time tuition and fees vary according to course level, degree level, location, program, and student level. Part-time tuition varies according to course level, course load, degree level, location, program, and student level. College room and board: $9690. College room only: $4910. Room and board charges vary according to board plan, housing facility, and location.
Collegiate Environment: Orientation program. Campus security: 24-hour patrols, controlled dormitory access. Freshmen guaranteed college housing. Option: coed housing available.

■ **PENN STATE HARRISBURG**
777 W Harrisburg Pke.
Middletown, PA 17057-4898
Tel: (717)948-6000; Free: 800-222-2056
E-mail: hbgadmit@psu.edu
Web Site: www.hbg.psu.edu/
Description: State-related, comprehensive, coed. Part of Pennsylvania State University. Awards associate, bachelor's, master's, and doctoral degrees. Founded 1966. Setting: small town campus. Total enrollment: 4,376. Faculty: 341 (217 full-time, 124 part-time). Student-undergrad faculty ratio is 14:1. 2,792 applied, 80% were admitted. 10% from top 10% of their high school class, 36% from top quarter, 80% from top half. Full-time: 2,905 students, 41% women, 59% men. Part-time: 521 students, 60% women, 40% men. 13% from out-of-state. 0.3% American Indian or Alaska Native, non-Hispanic/Latino; 5% Hispanic/Latino; 10% African American, non-Hispanic/Latino; 7% Asian, non-Hispanic/Latino; 0.1% Native Hawaiian or other Pacific Islander, non-Hispanic/Latino; 5% international. 21% 25 or older, 12% live on campus, 10% transferred in. Retention: 81% of full-time freshmen returned the following year. Academic areas with the most degrees conferred: business/marketing; engineering; education. Calendar: semesters. Part-time degree program, adult/continuing education programs. ROTC: Army (c).
Entrance Requirements: Options: electronic application, early admission, deferred admission, international baccalaureate accepted. Required: high school transcript, SAT or ACT. Recommended: essay. Required for some: interview. Entrance: very difficult. Application deadline: Rolling. Notification: continuous.
Costs Per Year: Application fee: $50. State resident tuition: $13,018 full-time, $542 per credit hour part-time. Nonresident tuition: $19,912 full-time, $830 per credit hour part-time. Mandatory fees: $882 full-time. Full-time tuition and fees vary according to course level, degree level, location, program, and student level. Part-time tuition varies according to course level, course load, degree level, location, program, and student level. College room and board: $11,000. College room only: $6220. Room and board charges vary according to board plan, housing facility, and location.
Collegiate Environment: Orientation program. Campus security: 24-hour emergency response devices and patrols, student patrols, late night transport-escort service, controlled dormitory access.

■ **PENN STATE HAZLETON**
Hazleton, PA 18201-1291
Tel: (570)450-3000; Free: 800-279-8495
E-mail: admissions-hn@psu.edu
Web Site: www.hn.psu.edu/
Description: State-related, primarily 2-year, coed. Part of Pennsylvania State University. Awards certificates, transfer associate, terminal associate, and bachelor's degrees. Founded 1934. Setting: small town campus. Total enrollment: 1,060. Faculty: 80 (54 full-time, 26 part-time). Student-undergrad faculty ratio is 16:1. 1,179 applied, 86% were admitted. 7% from top 10% of their high school class, 28% from top quarter, 61% from top half. Full-time: 1,000 students, 45% women, 55% men. Part-time: 60 students, 52% women, 48% men. 28% from out-of-state. 0.3% American Indian or Alaska Native, non-Hispanic/Latino; 15% Hispanic/Latino; 16% African American, non-Hispanic/Latino; 4% Asian, non-Hispanic/Latino; 0.1% Native Hawaiian or other Pacific Islander, non-Hispanic/Latino; 1% international. 9% 25 or older, 45% live on campus, 4% transferred in. Retention: 78% of full-time freshmen returned the following year. Academic areas with the most degrees

conferred; business/marketing; liberal arts/general studies; computer and information sciences. Calendar: semesters. Adult/continuing education programs. ROTC: Army, Air Force (c).

Entrance Requirements: Options: electronic application, early admission, deferred admission. Required: high school transcript, SAT or ACT. Recommended: essay. Required for some: interview. Entrance: moderately difficult. Application deadline: Rolling. Notification: continuous.

Costs Per Year: Application fee: $50. State resident tuition: $12,474 full-time, $504 per credit hour part-time. Nonresident tuition: $19,030 full-time, $793 per credit hour part-time. Mandatory fees: $826 full-time. Full-time tuition and fees vary according to course level, degree level, location, program, and student level. Part-time tuition varies according to course level, course load, degree level, location, program, and student level. College room and board: $9690. College room only: $4910. Room and board charges vary according to board plan, housing facility, and location.

Collegiate Environment: Orientation program. Campus security: 24-hour patrols, late night transport-escort service, controlled dormitory access. Freshmen guaranteed college housing. Option: coed housing available.

■ PENN STATE LEHIGH VALLEY
2809 Saucon Valley Rd.
Fogelsville, PA 18051-9999
Tel: (610)285-5000
E-mail: admissions-lv@psu.edu
Web Site: www.lv.psu.edu/

Description: State-related, primarily 2-year, coed. Part of Pennsylvania State University. Awards certificates, transfer associate, terminal associate, and bachelor's degrees (enrollment figures include students enrolled at The Graduate School at Penn State who are taking courses at this location). Founded 1912. Setting: rural campus. Total enrollment: 945. Faculty: 90 (35 full-time, 55 part-time). Student-undergrad faculty ratio is 15:1. 909 applied, 85% were admitted. 12% from top 10% of their high school class, 35% from top quarter, 68% from top half. Full-time: 728 students, 43% women, 57% men. Part-time: 179 students, 46% women, 54% men. 4% from out-of-state. 0% American Indian or Alaska Native, non-Hispanic/Latino; 15% Hispanic/Latino; 5% African American, non-Hispanic/Latino; 10% Asian, non-Hispanic/Latino; 0.1% Native Hawaiian or other Pacific Islander, non-Hispanic/Latino; 1% international. 14% 25 or older, 0% live on campus, 5% transferred in. Retention: 81% of full-time freshmen returned the following year. Academic areas with the most degrees conferred: education; business/marketing; psychology. Calendar: semesters. Adult/continuing education programs. ROTC: Army (c).

Entrance Requirements: Options: electronic application, early admission, deferred admission. Required: high school transcript, SAT or ACT. Entrance: moderately difficult. Application deadline: Rolling. Notification: continuous.

Costs Per Year: Application fee: $50. State resident tuition: $12,474 full-time, $504 per credit hour part-time. Nonresident tuition: $19,030 full-time, $793 per credit hour part-time. Mandatory fees: $876 full-time. Full-time tuition and fees vary according to course level, degree level, location, program, and student level. Part-time tuition varies according to course level, course load, degree level, location, program, and student level.

Collegiate Environment: Orientation program. College housing not available.

■ PENN STATE MONT ALTO
1 Campus Dr.
Mont Alto, PA 17237-9703
Tel: (717)749-6000; Free: 800-392-6173
E-mail: psuma@psu.edu
Web Site: www.ma.psu.edu/

Description: State-related, primarily 2-year, coed. Part of Pennsylvania State University. Awards certificates, transfer associate, terminal associate, and bachelor's degrees. Founded 1929. Setting: small town campus. Total enrollment: 1,107. Faculty: 108 (57 full-time, 51 part-time). Student-undergrad faculty ratio is 13:1. 827 applied, 83% were admitted. 12% from top 10% of their high school class, 33% from top quarter, 69% from top half. Full-time: 831 students, 52% women, 48% men. Part-time: 275 students, 67% women, 33% men. 17% from out-of-state. 0% American Indian or Alaska Native, non-Hispanic/Latino; 4% Hispanic/Latino; 11% African American, non-Hispanic/Latino; 2% Asian, non-Hispanic/Latino; 0% Native Hawaiian or other Pacific Islander, non-Hispanic/Latino; 1% international. 22% 25 or older, 29% live on campus, 4% transferred in. Retention: 74% of full-time freshmen returned the following year. Academic areas with the most degrees conferred: health professions and related sciences; family and

consumer sciences; business/marketing. Calendar: semesters. Adult/continuing education programs. ROTC: Army (c).

Entrance Requirements: Options: electronic application, early admission, deferred admission. Required: high school transcript, SAT or ACT. Recommended: essay. Required for some: interview. Entrance: moderately difficult. Application deadline: Rolling. Notification: continuous.

Costs Per Year: Application fee: $50. State resident tuition: $12,474 full-time, $504 per credit hour part-time. Nonresident tuition: $19,030 full-time, $793 per credit hour part-time. Mandatory fees: $882 full-time. Full-time tuition and fees vary according to course level, degree level, location, program, and student level. Part-time tuition varies according to course level, course load, degree level, location, program, and student level. College room and board: $9690. College room only: $4910. Room and board charges vary according to board plan, housing facility, and location.

Collegiate Environment: Orientation program. Campus security: 24-hour patrols, controlled dormitory access. Freshmen guaranteed college housing. Option: coed housing available.

■ PENN STATE NEW KENSINGTON
3550 Seventh St. Rd.
New Kensington, PA 15068
Tel: (724)334-5466; Free: 888-968-7297
Fax: (724)334-6111
E-mail: nkadmissions@psu.edu
Web Site: www.nk.psu.edu/

Description: State-related, primarily 2-year, coed. Part of Pennsylvania State University. Awards certificates, transfer associate, terminal associate, bachelor's, and master's degrees. Founded 1958. Setting: small town campus. Total enrollment: 715. Faculty: 78 (37 full-time, 41 part-time). Student-undergrad faculty ratio is 12:1. 477 applied, 74% were admitted. 11% from top 10% of their high school class, 31% from top quarter, 74% from top half. Full-time: 558 students, 37% women, 63% men. Part-time: 157 students, 52% women, 48% men. 2% from out-of-state. 0.2% American Indian or Alaska Native, non-Hispanic/Latino; 2% Hispanic/Latino; 3% African American, non-Hispanic/Latino; 1% Asian, non-Hispanic/Latino; 0% Native Hawaiian or other Pacific Islander, non-Hispanic/Latino; 1% international. 22% 25 or older, 0% live on campus, 7% transferred in. Retention: 71% of full-time freshmen returned the following year. Academic areas with the most degrees conferred: business/marketing; computer and information sciences; communication/journalism. Calendar: semesters. External degree program, adult/continuing education programs. ROTC: Air Force (c).

Entrance Requirements: Options: electronic application, early admission, deferred admission. Required: high school transcript, SAT or ACT. Recommended: essay. Required for some: interview. Entrance: moderately difficult. Application deadline: Rolling. Notification: continuous.

Costs Per Year: Application fee: $50. State resident tuition: $504 per credit part-time. Nonresident tuition: $793 per credit part-time. Part-time tuition varies according to course level, course load, degree level, location, program, and student level.

Collegiate Environment: Orientation program. Campus security: part-time trained security personnel.

■ PENN STATE SCHUYLKILL
200 University Dr.
Schuylkill Haven, PA 17972-2208
Tel: (570)385-6000
E-mail: sl-admissions@psu.edu
Web Site: www.sl.psu.edu/

Description: State-related, primarily 2-year, coed. Part of Pennsylvania State University. Awards certificates, transfer associate, terminal associate, and bachelor's degrees (bachelor's degree programs completed at the Harrisburg campus). Founded 1934. Setting: small town campus. Total enrollment: 867. Faculty: 68 (44 full-time, 24 part-time). Student-undergrad faculty ratio is 15:1. 693 applied, 81% were admitted. 11% from top 10% of their high school class, 28% from top quarter, 63% from top half. Full-time: 696 students, 55% women, 45% men. Part-time: 171 students, 71% women, 29% men. 18% from out-of-state. 0.2% American Indian or Alaska Native, non-Hispanic/Latino; 6% Hispanic/Latino; 29% African American, non-Hispanic/Latino; 1% Asian, non-Hispanic/Latino; 0.2% Native Hawaiian or other Pacific Islander, non-Hispanic/Latino; 1% international. 16% 25 or older, 32% live on campus, 5% transferred in. Retention: 69% of full-time freshmen returned the following year. Academic areas with the most degrees conferred: homeland security, law enforcement, firefighting, and protective services; psychology; business/marketing. Calendar: semesters. External degree program, adult/continuing education programs.

Entrance Requirements: Options: electronic application, early admission, deferred admission. Required: high school transcript, SAT or ACT. Entrance: moderately difficult. Application deadline: Rolling. Notification: continuous.

Costs Per Year: Application fee: $50. State resident tuition: $12,474 full-time, $504 per credit part-time. Nonresident tuition: $19,030 full-time, $793 per credit part-time. Mandatory fees: $770 full-time. Full-time tuition and fees vary according to course level, degree level, location, program, and student level. Part-time tuition varies according to course level, course load, degree level, location, program, and student level.

Collegiate Environment: Orientation program. Campus security: 24-hour patrols, controlled dormitory access.

■ **PENN STATE SHENANGO**
147 Shenango Ave.
Sharon, PA 16146-1537
Tel: (724)983-2803
Fax: (724)983-2820
E-mail: psushenango@psu.edu
Web Site: www.shenango.psu.edu/

Description: State-related, 4-year, coed. Part of Pennsylvania State University. Awards associate and bachelor's degrees. Founded 1965. Setting: small town campus. Total enrollment: 578. Faculty: 68 (30 full-time, 38 part-time). Student-undergrad faculty ratio is 10:1. 229 applied, 69% were admitted. 8% from top 10% of their high school class, 25% from top quarter, 65% from top half. Full-time: 336 students, 64% women, 36% men. Part-time: 242 students, 68% women, 32% men. 19% from out-of-state. 0% American Indian or Alaska Native, non-Hispanic/Latino; 2% Hispanic/Latino; 9% African American, non-Hispanic/Latino; 0.2% Asian, non-Hispanic/Latino; 0.4% Native Hawaiian or other Pacific Islander, non-Hispanic/Latino; 0% international. 54% 25 or older, 9% transferred in. Retention: 56% of full-time freshmen returned the following year. Academic areas with the most degrees conferred: health professions and related sciences; family and consumer sciences; business/marketing. Calendar: semesters. Adult/continuing education programs.

Entrance Requirements: Options: electronic application, early admission, deferred admission. Required: high school transcript, SAT or ACT. Recommended: essay. Required for some: interview. Entrance: moderately difficult. Application deadline: Rolling. Notification: continuous.

Costs Per Year: Application fee: $50. State resident tuition: $12,474 full-time, $504 per credit part-time. Nonresident tuition: $19,030 full-time, $793 per credit part-time. Mandatory fees: $770 full-time. Full-time tuition and fees vary according to course level, degree level, location, program, and student level. Part-time tuition varies according to course level, course load, degree level, location, program, and student level.

Collegiate Environment: Orientation program. College housing not available.

■ **PENN STATE UNIVERSITY PARK**
201 Old Main
University Park, PA 16802-1503
Tel: (814)865-4700
E-mail: admissions@psu.edu
Web Site: www.psu.edu/

Description: State-related, university, coed. Part of Pennsylvania State University. Awards associate, bachelor's, master's, and doctoral degrees. Founded 1855. Setting: 8,556-acre small town campus with easy access to Harrisburg. System endowment: $1.9 billion. Total enrollment: 45,783. Faculty: 2,910 (2,518 full-time, 392 part-time). Student-undergrad faculty ratio is 17:1. 47,552 applied, 54% were admitted. 41% from top 10% of their high school class, 84% from top quarter, 98% from top half. Full-time: 37,917 students, 46% women, 54% men. Part-time: 1,275 students, 41% women, 59% men. Students come from 53 states and territories, 98 other countries, 30% from out-of-state. 0.1% American Indian or Alaska Native, non-Hispanic/Latino; 5% Hispanic/Latino; 4% African American, non-Hispanic/Latino; 5% Asian, non-Hispanic/Latino; 0.1% Native Hawaiian or other Pacific Islander, non-Hispanic/Latino; 8% international. 2% 25 or older, 36% live on campus, 1% transferred in. Retention: 92% of full-time freshmen returned the following year. Academic areas with the most degrees conferred: business/marketing; engineering; communication/journalism. Core. Calendar: semesters. Academic remediation for entering students, ESL program, services for LD students, advanced placement, accelerated degree program, self-designed majors, freshman honors college, honors

program, independent study, distance learning, double major, summer session for credit, part-time degree program, external degree program, adult/continuing education programs, co-op programs and internships, graduate courses open to undergrads. Off campus study. Study abroad program. ROTC: Army, Naval, Air Force.

Entrance Requirements: Options: electronic application, early admission, deferred admission, international baccalaureate accepted. Required: high school transcript, SAT or ACT. Recommended: essay. Required for some: interview. Entrance: very difficult. Application deadline: Rolling. Notification: continuous. Transfer credits accepted: Yes.

Costs Per Year: Application fee: $50. State resident tuition: $15,562 full-time, $648 per credit part-time. Nonresident tuition: $27,864 full-time, $1161 per credit part-time. Mandatory fees: $882 full-time. Full-time tuition and fees vary according to course level, degree level, location, program, and student level. Part-time tuition varies according to course level, course load, degree level, location, program, and student level. College room and board: $9690. College room only: $4910. Room and board charges vary according to board plan, housing facility, and location.

Collegiate Environment: Orientation program. Drama-theater group, choral group, marching band, student-run newspaper, radio station. Social organizations: 914 open to all; national fraternities, national sororities; 14% of eligible men and 13% of eligible women are members. Major annual events: Homecoming, Four Diamonds Dance Marathon, Parents' Weekend. Student services: health clinic, personal-psychological counseling, women's center. Campus security: 24-hour emergency response devices and patrols, student patrols, late night transport-escort service, controlled dormitory access. 13,808 college housing spaces available; 13,009 were occupied in 2012-13. Freshmen guaranteed college housing. On-campus residence required in freshman year. Options: coed, men-only, women-only housing available. Pattee/Paterno Library plus 26 others with 5.4 million books, 3.8 million microform titles, 131,358 serials, 129,550 audiovisual materials, an OPAC, and a Web page. 6,150 computers available on campus for general student use. Computer purchase/lease plans available. A campuswide network can be accessed from student residence rooms and from off campus. Students can access the following: online class registration. Staffed computer lab on campus (open 24 hours a day) provides training in use of computers, software, and the Internet.

■ **PENN STATE WILKES-BARRE**
PO PSU
Lehman, PA 18627-0217
Tel: (570)675-2171
E-mail: wbadmissions@psu.edu
Web Site: www.wb.psu.edu/

Description: State-related, primarily 2-year, coed. Part of Pennsylvania State University. Awards certificates, transfer associate, terminal associate, and bachelor's degrees (enrollment figures include students enrolled at The Graduate School at Penn State who are taking courses at this location). Founded 1916. Setting: rural campus. Total enrollment: 647. Faculty: 58 (33 full-time, 25 part-time). Student-undergrad faculty ratio is 14:1. 472 applied, 82% were admitted. 14% from top 10% of their high school class, 33% from top quarter, 68% from top half. Full-time: 539 students, 30% women, 70% men. Part-time: 78 students, 40% women, 60% men. 6% from out-of-state. 0.2% American Indian or Alaska Native, non-Hispanic/Latino; 5% Hispanic/Latino; 5% African American, non-Hispanic/Latino; 1% Asian, non-Hispanic/Latino; 0.2% Native Hawaiian or other Pacific Islander, non-Hispanic/Latino; 1% international. 9% 25 or older, 0% live on campus, 4% transferred in. Retention: 84% of full-time freshmen returned the following year. Academic areas with the most degrees conferred: engineering; business/marketing; computer and information sciences. Calendar: semesters. Adult/continuing education programs. ROTC: Army (c), Air Force (c).

Entrance Requirements: Options: electronic application, early admission, deferred admission. Required: high school transcript, SAT or ACT. Recommended: essay. Required for some: interview. Entrance: moderately difficult. Application deadline: Rolling. Notification: continuous.

Costs Per Year: Application fee: $50. State resident tuition: $12,474 full-time, $504 per credit hour part-time. Nonresident tuition: $19,030 full-time, $793 per credit hour part-time. Mandatory fees: $764 full-time. Full-time tuition and fees vary according to course level, degree level, location, program, and student level. Part-time tuition varies according to course level, course load, degree level, location, program, and student level.

Collegiate Environment: Orientation program. College housing not available.

■ PENN STATE WORTHINGTON SCRANTON

120 Ridge View Dr.

Dunmore, PA 18512-1699

Tel: (570)963-2500

Fax: (570)963-2535

E-mail: wsadmissions@psu.edu

Web Site: www.sn.psu.edu/

Description: State-related, primarily 2-year, coed. Part of Pennsylvania State University. Awards certificates, transfer associate, terminal associate, and bachelor's degrees. Founded 1923. Setting: small town campus. Total enrollment: 1,234. Faculty: 99 (51 full-time, 48 part-time). Student-undergrad faculty ratio is 16:1. 722 applied, 82% were admitted. 4% from top 10% of their high school class, 22% from top quarter, 53% from top half. Full-time: 990 students, 51% women, 49% men. Part-time: 244 students, 63% women, 37% men. 3% from out-of-state, 0.3% American Indian or Alaska Native, non-Hispanic/Latino; 5% Hispanic/Latino; 2% African American, non-Hispanic/Latino; 5% Asian, non-Hispanic/Latino; 0.1% Native Hawaiian or other Pacific Islander, non-Hispanic/Latino; 0.4% international. 22% 25 or older, 0% live on campus, 4% transferred in. Retention: 69% of full-time freshmen returned the following year. Academic areas with the most degrees conferred: business/marketing; health professions and related sciences; family and consumer sciences. Calendar: semesters. Adult/continuing education programs. ROTC: Army (c), Air Force (c).

Entrance Requirements: Options: electronic application, early admission, deferred admission. Required: high school transcript, SAT or ACT. Recommended: essay. Required for some: interview. Entrance: moderately difficult. Application deadline: Rolling. Notification: continuous.

Costs Per Year: Application fee: $50. State resident tuition: $12,474 full-time, $504 per credit hour part-time. Nonresident tuition: $19,030 full-time, $793 per credit hour part-time. Mandatory fees: $756 full-time. Full-time tuition and fees vary according to course level, degree level, location, program, and student level. Part-time tuition varies according to course level, course load, degree level, location, program, and student level.

Collegiate Environment: Orientation program. College housing not available.

■ PENN STATE YORK

1031 Edgecomb Ave.

York, PA 17403

Tel: (717)771-4000; Free: 800-778-6227

Fax: (717)771-4062

E-mail: ykadmission@psu.edu

Web Site: www.yk.psu.edu/

Description: State-related, primarily 2-year, coed. Part of Pennsylvania State University. Awards certificates, transfer associate, terminal associate, bachelor's, and master's degrees (also offers up to 2 years of most bachelor's degree programs offered at University Park campus). Founded 1926. Setting: suburban campus. Total enrollment: 1,208. Faculty: 103 (52 full-time, 51 part-time). Student-undergrad faculty ratio is 14:1. 1,329 applied, 84% were admitted. 8% from top 10% of their high school class, 26% from top quarter, 64% from top half. Full-time: 829 students, 42% women, 58% men. Part-time: 326 students, 46% women, 54% men. 10% from out-of-state. 0.1% American Indian or Alaska Native, non-Hispanic/Latino; 7% Hispanic/Latino; 9% African American, non-Hispanic/Latino; 5% Asian, non-Hispanic/Latino; 0% Native Hawaiian or other Pacific Islander, non-Hispanic/Latino; 5% international. 25% 25 or older, 0% live on campus, 4% transferred in. Retention: 76% of full-time freshmen returned the following year. Academic areas with the most degrees conferred: business/marketing; computer and information sciences; family and consumer sciences. Calendar: semesters. Adult/continuing education programs.

Entrance Requirements: Options: electronic application, early admission, deferred admission. Required: high school transcript, SAT or ACT. Recommended: essay. Required for some: interview. Entrance: moderately difficult. Application deadline: Rolling. Notification: continuous.

Costs Per Year: Application fee: $50. State resident tuition: $12,474 full-time, $504 per credit hour part-time. Nonresident tuition: $19,030 full-time, $793 per credit hour part-time. Mandatory fees: $764 full-time. Full-time tuition and fees vary according to course level, degree level, location, program, and student level. Part-time tuition varies according to course level, course load, degree level, location, program, and student level.

Collegiate Environment: Orientation program. College housing not available.

■ PENNCO TECH

3815 Otter St.

Bristol, PA 19007-3696

Tel: (215)824-3200; Free: 800-575-9399

E-mail: admissions@penncotech.com

Web Site: www.penncotech.com/

Description: Proprietary, 2-year, coed. Part of Pennco Institutes, Inc. Awards certificates, diplomas, and terminal associate degrees. Founded 1961. Setting: 7-acre suburban campus with easy access to Philadelphia. Educational spending for the previous fiscal year: $8200 per student. Total enrollment: 400. Faculty: 40 (30 full-time, 10 part-time). Student-undergrad faculty ratio is 18:1. 229 applied. Full-time: 245 students, 22% women, 78% men. Part-time: 155 students, 16% women, 84% men. Students come from 6 states and territories, 3% from out-of-state. 40% 25 or older, 3% live on campus, 1% transferred in. Retention: 78% of full-time freshmen returned the following year. Calendar: modular. Academic remediation for entering students, advanced placement, double major, adult/continuing education programs.

Entrance Requirements: Required: high school transcript, minimum 2 high school GPA, interview, Interview and school visit, exam at campus. Required for some: essay. Entrance: minimally difficult. Application deadline: Rolling. Transfer credits accepted: Yes.

Costs Per Year: Application fee: $100. Tuition: $21,500 full-time. Full-time tuition varies according to class time, course load, and program. College room only: $4000.

Collegiate Environment: Orientation program. Major annual events: Toys for Tots, Food Drives, Coat Drives. Campus security: 24-hour emergency response devices, controlled dormitory access. Resource Center with 6,000 books, 30 serials, and a Web page. Operations spending for the previous fiscal year: $5000. 14 computers available on campus for general student use. Staffed computer lab on campus provides training in use of computers, software, and the Internet.

■ PENNSYLVANIA ACADEMY OF THE FINE ARTS

128 N Broad St.

Philadelphia, PA 19102

Tel: (215)972-7600

E-mail: admissions@pafa.edu

Web Site: www.pafa.edu/

Description: Independent, comprehensive, coed. Founded 1805. Setting: urban campus. Calendar: semesters.

Entrance Requirements: Application deadline: 3/1.

■ PENNSYLVANIA COLLEGE OF ART & DESIGN

204 N Prince St.

Lancaster, PA 17608-0059

Tel: (717)396-7833

Fax: (717)396-1339

E-mail: admissions@pcad.edu

Web Site: www.pcad.edu/

Description: Independent, 4-year, coed. Awards bachelor's degrees. Founded 1982. Setting: urban campus with easy access to Philadelphia, Baltimore. Total enrollment: 248. Faculty: 54 (14 full-time, 40 part-time). Student-undergrad faculty ratio is 9:1. 375 applied, 40% were admitted. 90% from top half of their high school class. Full-time: 225 students, 68% women, 32% men. Part-time: 23 students, 57% women, 43% men. Students come from 12 states and territories, 26% from out-of-state. 0% American Indian or Alaska Native, non-Hispanic/Latino; 6% Hispanic/Latino; 5% African American, non-Hispanic/Latino; 2% Asian, non-Hispanic/Latino; 0% Native Hawaiian or other Pacific Islander, non-Hispanic/Latino; 0% international. 6% 25 or older, 8% transferred in. Retention: 59% of full-time freshmen returned the following year. Academic area with the most degrees conferred: visual and performing arts. Core. Calendar: semesters. Advanced placement, internships.

Entrance Requirements: Options: electronic application, deferred admission. Required: essay, high school transcript, minimum 2.5 high school GPA, interview, portfolio. Recommended: SAT, ACT. Required for some: 2 recommendations. Entrance: moderately difficult. Application deadline: Rolling. Notification: continuous.

Costs Per Year: Application fee: $40. Tuition: $18,700 full-time, $779 per credit part-time. Mandatory fees: $980 full-time. Part-time tuition varies according to course load.

Collegiate Environment: Orientation program. Social organizations: 2 open to all. Most popular organizations: Student Council, Anime Club, Student

AIGA, Society of Illustrators - Student Group. Major annual events: Halloween Party, Thanksgiving Feast, Spring Picnic. Campus security: late night transport-escort service, trained evening/weekend security personnel. College housing not available. Pennsylvania College of Art & Design Library with 29,895 books, 81 serials, 1,263 audiovisual materials, an OPAC, and a Web page. 86 computers available on campus for general student use. A computer is required for all students. A campuswide network can be accessed. Staffed computer lab on campus provides training in use of computers and the Internet.

■ PENNSYLVANIA COLLEGE OF TECHNOLOGY

One College Ave.
Williamsport, PA 17701-5778
Tel: (570)326-3761; Free: 800-367-9222
Fax: (570)321-5551
E-mail: admissions@pct.edu
Web Site: www.pct.edu/

Description: State-related, 4-year, coed. Administratively affiliated with The Pennsylvania State University. Awards associate and bachelor's degrees. Founded 1965. Setting: 997-acre small town campus. Total enrollment: 5,671. Faculty: 477 (294 full-time, 183 part-time). Student-undergrad faculty ratio is 17:1. 3,598 applied, 88% were admitted. Full-time: 4,764 students, 33% women, 67% men. Part-time: 893 students, 62% women, 38% men. Students come from 36 states and territories, 11 other countries, 11% from out-of-state. 0.2% American Indian or Alaska Native, non-Hispanic/Latino; 3% Hispanic/Latino; 4% African American, non-Hispanic/Latino; 1% Asian, non-Hispanic/Latino; 0.1% Native Hawaiian or other Pacific Islander, non-Hispanic/Latino; 1% international. 21% 25 or older, 30% live on campus, 9% transferred in. Retention: 66% of full-time freshmen returned the following year. Academic areas with the most degrees conferred: engineering technologies; business/marketing; health professions and related sciences. Core. Calendar: semesters. Academic remediation for entering students, ESL program, services for LD students, advanced placement, self-designed majors, independent study, distance learning, summer session for credit, part-time degree program, co-op programs and internships. Off campus study at Lycoming College, The Pennsylvania State University, and Bucknell University for some of the U.S. Army ROTC Programs. Study abroad program. ROTC: Army.

Entrance Requirements: Open admission. Options: electronic application, early admission, deferred admission. Required for some: high school transcript, college transcripts if transfer applicant, SAT. Entrance: noncompetitive. Application deadline: 7/1. Transfer credits accepted: Yes.

Costs Per Year: Application fee: $50. State resident tuition: $12,000 full-time, $400 per credit hour part-time. Nonresident tuition: $15,630 full-time, $521 per credit hour part-time. Mandatory fees: $2370 full-time, $79 per credit hour part-time. Full-time tuition and fees vary according to course load and program. Part-time tuition and fees vary according to course load and program. College room and board: $10,500. College room only: $5994. Room and board charges vary according to board plan and housing facility.

Collegiate Environment: Orientation program. Student-run radio station. Social organizations: 56 open to all; national fraternities, local fraternities. Most popular organizations: Student Government Association, Residence Hall Association, Wildcats Event Board, Association of Computing Machinery, Campus Ministry International. Major annual events: Career Expo/Career Fairs, WEB FESTS & EVENTS, WinterFest, Mardi Gras Bash, Parent & Family Weekend. Student services: health clinic, personal-psychological counseling. Campus security: 24-hour emergency response devices and patrols, late night transport-escort service, controlled dormitory access. 1,725 college housing spaces available; all were occupied in 2012-13. No special consideration for freshman housing applicants. Option: coed housing available. Penn College Madigan Library plus 1 other with 140,885 books, 16,344 microform titles, 62,601 serials, 621 audiovisual materials, an OPAC, and a Web page. 1,785 computers available on campus for general student use. A campuswide network can be accessed from student residence rooms and from off campus. Students can access the following: online class registration. Staffed computer lab on campus provides training in use of computers, software, and the Internet.

Community Environment: The main campus is in Williamsport, a city known internationally as the home of Little League Baseball. Williamsport (population 30,100) is the seat of Lycoming County (population 117,600); it offers the advantages of a city situated in a rural environment. The surrounding area is an outdoor-lovers' paradise, with hunting, fishing, hiking, camping, backpacking, and more, just minutes from downtown.

■ PENNSYLVANIA HIGHLANDS COMMUNITY COLLEGE

101 Community College Way
Johnstown, PA 15904
Tel: (814)262-6400
E-mail: jmaul@pennhighlands.edu
Web Site: www.pennhighlands.edu/

Description: State and locally supported, 2-year, coed. Awards certificates, diplomas, transfer associate, and terminal associate degrees. Founded 1994. Setting: small town campus. Total enrollment: 2,543. Student-undergrad faculty ratio is 13:1. Students come from 4 states and territories, 2% from out-of-state. 45% 25 or older. Retention: 34% of full-time freshmen returned the following year. Core. Calendar: semesters. Academic remediation for entering students, services for LD students, advanced placement, honors program, independent study, distance learning, part-time degree program, adult/continuing education programs, co-op programs and internships.

Entrance Requirements: Open admission. Entrance: noncompetitive.

Collegiate Environment: Orientation program. Pennsylvania Highlands Community College Main Library plus 1 other with an OPAC and a Web page. Operations spending for the previous fiscal year: $144,750.

■ PENNSYLVANIA INSTITUTE OF TECHNOLOGY

800 Manchester Ave.
Media, PA 19063
Tel: (610)892-1500; Free: 800-422-0025
Fax: (610)892-1510
E-mail: info@pit.edu
Web Site: www.pit.edu/

Description: Independent, 2-year, coed. Awards certificates, transfer associate, and terminal associate degrees. Founded 1953. Setting: 12-acre small town campus with easy access to Philadelphia. Total enrollment: 763. Faculty: 91 (22 full-time, 69 part-time). Student-undergrad faculty ratio is 13:1. Full-time: 505 students, 75% women, 25% men. Part-time: 258 students, 76% women, 24% men. 1% American Indian or Alaska Native, non-Hispanic/Latino; 6% Hispanic/Latino; 60% African American, non-Hispanic/Latino; 2% Asian, non-Hispanic/Latino; 0% Native Hawaiian or other Pacific Islander, non-Hispanic/Latino; 0.1% international. 43% 25 or older. Retention: 50% of full-time freshmen returned the following year. Core. Calendar: semesters. Academic remediation for entering students, advanced placement, summer session for credit, part-time degree program, adult/continuing education programs, co-op programs.

Entrance Requirements: Options: electronic application, deferred admission. Required: high school transcript, interview. Recommended: essay. Required for some: 2 recommendations. Entrance: noncompetitive. Application deadline: 9/19. Notification: continuous until 9/19.

Costs Per Year: Application fee: $25. Tuition: $11,250 full-time, $375 per credit part-time. Mandatory fees: $1500 full-time, $50 per credit part-time. Full-time tuition and fees vary according to program. Part-time tuition and fees vary according to course load and program.

Collegiate Environment: Orientation program. Student services: personal-psychological counseling. Campus security: 24-hour emergency response devices. College housing not available. Pennsylvania Institute of Technology Library/Learning Resource Center with 16,500 books, 217 serials, an OPAC, and a Web page. 400 computers available on campus for general student use. Staffed computer lab on campus.

■ PENNSYLVANIA SCHOOL OF BUSINESS

406 W Hamilton St.
Allentown, PA 18101
Tel: (610)841-3333
E-mail: wbarber@pennschoolofbusiness.edu
Web Site: www.psb.edu/

Description: Private, 2-year, coed. Awards certificates, transfer associate, and terminal associate degrees. Founded 1978. Total enrollment: 401. 50% 25 or older.

Entrance Requirements: Open admission.

■ PHILADELPHIA UNIVERSITY

School House Ln. and Henry Ave.
Philadelphia, PA 19144
Tel: (215)951-2700
Fax: (215)951-2907
E-mail: admissions@philau.edu
Web Site: www.philau.edu/

Description: Independent, comprehensive, coed. Awards associate, bachelor's, master's, and doctoral degrees and post-master's certificates. Founded 1884. Setting: 100-acre suburban campus. Total enrollment: 3,540. Faculty: 488 (114 full-time, 374 part-time). Student-undergrad faculty ratio is 13:1. 3,602 applied, 72% were admitted. 17% from top 10% of their high school class, 43% from top quarter, 78% from top half. Full-time: 2,679 students, 65% women, 35% men. Part-time: 209 students, 71% women, 29% men. 0.1% American Indian or Alaska Native, non-Hispanic/Latino; 6% Hispanic/Latino; 12% African American, non-Hispanic/Latino; 4% Asian, non-Hispanic/Latino; 0.1% Native Hawaiian or other Pacific Islander, non-Hispanic/Latino; 3% international. 8% transferred in. Retention: 71% of full-time freshmen returned the following year. Academic areas with the most degrees conferred: business/marketing; visual and performing arts; architecture. Calendar: semesters. Part-time degree program, adult/continuing education programs.

Entrance Requirements: Options: electronic application, deferred admission. Required: high school transcript, SAT or ACT. Recommended: essay, 2 recommendations, interview. Entrance: moderately difficult. Application deadline: Rolling. Notification: continuous. SAT Reasoning Test deadline: 7/1.

Costs Per Year: Application fee: $40. Comprehensive fee: $42,052 includes full-time tuition ($31,874) and college room and board ($10,178). College room only: $5032. Full-time tuition varies according to degree level and program. Room and board charges vary according to board plan and housing facility.

Collegiate Environment: Orientation program. Campus security: 24-hour emergency response devices and patrols, late night transport-escort service, controlled dormitory access. Freshmen guaranteed college housing. Options: coed, women-only housing available.

Community Environment: This suburban campus is 15 minutes from the heart of Philadelphia.

■ PITTSBURGH INSTITUTE OF AERONAUTICS

PO Box 10897
Pittsburgh, PA 15236-0897
Tel: (412)462-9011; Free: 800-444-1440
Fax: (412)466-0513
E-mail: admissions@pia.edu
Web Site: www.pia.edu/

Description: Independent, 2-year, coed. Awards transfer associate and terminal associate degrees. Founded 1929. Setting: suburban campus. Total enrollment: 571. Faculty: 37 (31 full-time, 6 part-time). Student-undergrad faculty ratio is 17:1. 85 applied, 100% were admitted. Full-time: 571 students, 4% women, 96% men. Students come from 12 states and territories, 4 other countries, 35% from out-of-state. 30% 25 or older. Core. Academic remediation for entering students, advanced placement.

Entrance Requirements: Open admission. Option: deferred admission. Recommended: high school transcript, interview. Entrance: noncompetitive. Application deadline: Rolling. Notification: continuous.

Collegiate Environment: Student services: personal-psychological counseling. Technical Library with 15,000 books and 35 serials. 30 computers available on campus for general student use. Staffed computer lab on campus.

■ PITTSBURGH INSTITUTE OF MORTUARY SCIENCE, INCORPORATED

5808 Baum Blvd.
Pittsburgh, PA 15206-3706
Tel: (412)362-8500
Fax: (412)362-1684
E-mail: pims5808@aol.com
Web Site: www.pims.edu/

Description: Independent, 2-year, coed. Awards diplomas, transfer associate, and terminal associate degrees. Founded 1939. Setting: urban campus. Total enrollment: 193. Faculty: 24 (2 full-time, 22 part-time). Student-undergrad faculty ratio is 13:1. Full-time: 85 students, 51% women, 49% men. Part-time: 108 students, 37% women, 63% men. Students come from 12 states and territories, 1 other country, 37% from out-of-state. 53% 25 or older, 0% transferred in. Core. Calendar: trimesters. Academic remediation for entering students, services for LD students, distance learning, part-time degree program, adult/continuing education programs.

Entrance Requirements: Open admission. Options: electronic application, international baccalaureate accepted. Required: essay, high school

transcript, minimum 2 high school GPA, 2 recommendations, interview, immunizations. Entrance: noncompetitive. Application deadline: Rolling. Notification: continuous.

Collegiate Environment: Orientation program. Campus security: 24-hour emergency response devices. William J. Musmanno Memorial Library with 2,547 books, 48 serials, 284 audiovisual materials, an OPAC, and a Web page. 10 computers available on campus for general student use. A campuswide network can be accessed from off-campus. Staffed computer lab on campus provides training in use of computers, software, and the Internet.

■ PITTSBURGH TECHNICAL INSTITUTE

1111 McKee Rd.
Oakdale, PA 15071
Tel: (412)809-5100; Free: 800-784-9675
Fax: (412)809-5388
E-mail: goodlin.nancy@pti.edu
Web Site: www.pti.edu/

Description: Proprietary, 2-year, coed. Awards certificates and terminal associate degrees. Founded 1946. Setting: 180-acre suburban campus with easy access to Pittsburgh. Total enrollment: 1,791. Faculty: 116 (65 full-time, 51 part-time). Student-undergrad faculty ratio is 28:1. 2,126 applied, 84% were admitted. Full-time: 1,792 students, 43% women, 57% men. Students come from 15 states and territories, 18% from out-of-state. 0.2% American Indian or Alaska Native, non-Hispanic/Latino; 1% Hispanic/Latino; 9% African American, non-Hispanic/Latino; 1% Asian, non-Hispanic/Latino; 0% Native Hawaiian or other Pacific Islander, non-Hispanic/Latino. 20% 25 or older, 40% live on campus, 13% transferred in. Retention: 63% of full-time freshmen returned the following year. Core. Academic remediation for entering students, services for LD students, advanced placement, distance learning, double major, co-op programs and internships.

Entrance Requirements: Open admission background check for surg tech, safety & security, practical nursing, patient care tech, smart building tech, massage; entrance exam for practical nursing; rank in top 1/2 of secondary school class for computer prog. & top 4/5 for graphic design & multimedia. Options: electronic application, deferred admission, international baccalaureate accepted. Required: high school transcript. Recommended: interview. Required for some: essay, certain programs require a criminal background check; some programs require applicants to be in top 50-80% of class; Practical Nursing requires entrance exam. Application deadlines: Rolling, Rolling for nonresidents. Notification: continuous, continuous for nonresidents. Transfer credits accepted: Yes.

Costs Per Year: Application fee: $0. Comprehensive fee: $23,777 includes full-time tuition ($15,524) and college room and board ($8253). Full-time tuition varies according to course load and program. Room and board charges vary according to housing facility. Tuition guaranteed not to increase for student's term of enrollment.

Collegiate Environment: Orientation program. Drama-theater group, choral group. Social organizations: 10 open to all. Most popular organizations: American Society of Travel Agents (ASTA), MEDICS Club, Alpha Beta Gamma (ABG), Drama Club, Direct Connect. Major annual events: PTI Carnival, PTI Ocktoberfest, Casino Night. Student services: personal-psychological counseling. Campus security: 24-hour emergency response devices and patrols, controlled dormitory access. 831 college housing spaces available; all were occupied in 2012-13. Freshmen guaranteed college housing. Option: coed housing available. Library Resource Center with 10,776 books, 128 serials, 2,036 audiovisual materials, and an OPAC. 1,000 computers available on campus for general student use. A campuswide network can be accessed from student residence rooms and from off campus. Staffed computer lab on campus provides training in use of computers, software, and the Internet.

■ POINT PARK UNIVERSITY

201 Wood St.
Pittsburgh, PA 15222-1984
Tel: (412)391-4100; Free: 800-321-0129
Fax: (412)391-1980
E-mail: enroll@pointpark.edu
Web Site: www.pointpark.edu/

Description: Independent, comprehensive, coed. Awards associate, bachelor's, and master's degrees. Founded 1960. Setting: urban campus. Endowment: $26.7 million. Research spending for the previous fiscal year: $254,472. Educational spending for the previous fiscal year: $7670 per student. Total enrollment: 3,827. Faculty: 442 (133 full-time, 309 part-time).

Student-undergrad faculty ratio is 13:1. 3,673 applied, 76% were admitted. 10% from top 10% of their high school class, 30% from top quarter, 66% from top half. 72 student government officers. Full-time: 2,537 students, 59% women, 41% men. Part-time: 688 students, 56% women, 44% men. Students come from 26 states and territories, 23 other countries, 21% from out-of-state. 0.1% American Indian or Alaska Native, non-Hispanic/Latino; 3% Hispanic/Latino; 17% African American, non-Hispanic/Latino; 1% Asian, non-Hispanic/Latino; 0% Native Hawaiian or other Pacific Islander, non-Hispanic/Latino; 2% international. 26% 25 or older, 25% live on campus, 14% transferred in. Retention: 74% of full-time freshmen returned the following year. Academic areas with the most degrees conferred: visual and performing arts; business/marketing; communication/journalism. Core. Calendar: semesters. Academic remediation for entering students, ESL program, services for LD students, advanced placement, accelerated degree program, self-designed majors, honors program, independent study, distance learning, double major, summer session for credit, part-time degree program, adult/continuing education programs, co-op programs and internships, graduate courses open to undergrads. Off campus study at Fellow members of the Pittsburgh Council on Higher Education: Carlow University, Carnegie Mellon University, Chatham University, Community College of Allegheny County, Duquesne University, La Roche College, Pittsburgh Theological Seminary, Robert Morris University, and the University of Pittsburgh. Study abroad program. ROTC: Army (c), Air Force (c).
Entrance Requirements: Options: electronic application, deferred admission, international baccalaureate accepted. Required: high school transcript, SAT or ACT. Recommended: essay, minimum 2.5 high school GPA. Required for some: 2 recommendations, interview, audition. Entrance: moderately difficult. Application deadline: Rolling. Notification: continuous. Transfer credits accepted: Yes.
Costs Per Year: Application fee: $40. Comprehensive fee: $33,190 includes full-time tuition ($24,020), mandatory fees ($1170), and college room and board ($8000). College room only: $4720. Full-time tuition and fees vary according to program. Room and board charges vary according to board plan and housing facility.
Collegiate Environment: Orientation program. Drama-theater group, student-run newspaper, radio station. Social organizations: 40 open to all. Most popular organizations: student radio station, The Body Christian Fellowship, Dance Club, Campus Activities Board, Action Sports Club. Major annual events: Pioneer Community (Service) Day, Spring Fling, Freshman Riverboat Cruise. Student services: personal-psychological counseling. Campus security: 24-hour emergency response devices and patrols, late night transport-escort service, controlled dormitory access, 24-hour security desk, video security. 1,022 college housing spaces available; 978 were occupied in 2012-13. Freshmen guaranteed college housing. Options: coed, women-only housing available. Point Park University Library with 153,990 books, 16,275 microform titles, 171 serials, 7,266 audiovisual materials, an OPAC, and a Web page. Operations spending for the previous fiscal year: $749,348. 309 computers available on campus for general student use. Computer purchase/lease plans available. A campuswide network can be accessed from student residence rooms. Students can access the following: online class registration. Staffed computer lab on campus.
Community Environment: The college is centrally located in the city of Pittsburgh, population 316,700. See also University of Pittsburgh, Pittsburgh Campus.

■ **PRISM CAREER INSTITUTE**
6800 Market St.
Upper Darby, PA 19082
Tel: (610)789-6700; Free: 800-571-2213
E-mail: dgentile@pjaschool.com
Web Site: www.prismcareerinstitute.edu/
Description: Proprietary, 2-year, coed. Part of Prism Education Group. Awards diplomas and terminal associate degrees. Founded 1981. Setting: suburban campus. Total enrollment: 244. Faculty: 28 (5 full-time, 23 part-time). Student-undergrad faculty ratio is 19:1. Full-time: 244 students, 85% women, 15% men. Students come from 2 states and territories, 1% from out-of-state. 61% 25 or older, 0% transferred in. Core. Academic remediation for entering students, advanced placement, independent study, double major, internships.
Entrance Requirements: Required: essay, interview, writing sample, high school diploma or equivalent, Wonderlic aptitude test. Entrance: moderately difficult.
Collegiate Environment: Orientation program. Campus security: 24-hour

emergency response devices. Ford Library plus 1 other with 2,350 books, 7 serials, and 40 audiovisual materials. Operations spending for the previous fiscal year: $24,185.

■ **READING AREA COMMUNITY COLLEGE**
PO Box 1706
Reading, PA 19603-1706
Tel: (610)372-4721
Fax: (610)375-8255
E-mail: mmitchell@racc.edu
Web Site: www.racc.edu/
Description: County-supported, 2-year, coed. Awards certificates, diplomas, transfer associate, and terminal associate degrees. Founded 1971. Setting: 14-acre urban campus with easy access to Philadelphia. Endowment: $745,770. Total enrollment: 4,682. Faculty: 228 (68 full-time, 160 part-time). Student-undergrad faculty ratio is 24:1. 2,318 applied, 100% were admitted. Full-time: 2,009 students, 62% women, 38% men. Part-time: 2,673 students, 71% women, 29% men. Students come from 10 other countries. 47% 25 or older. Retention: 37% of full-time freshmen returned the following year. Core. Academic remediation for entering students, ESL program, services for LD students, self-designed majors, summer session for credit, part-time degree program, external degree program, adult/continuing education programs, co-op programs.
Entrance Requirements: Open admission. Options: electronic application, early admission, deferred admission. Required for some: essay, high school transcript, interview, background/criminal check, physical exam, proof of insurance, TOEFL. Entrance: noncompetitive. Application deadlines: Rolling, Rolling for nonresidents.
Costs Per Year: Application fee: $0. Area resident tuition: $2970 full-time, $99 per credit part-time. State resident tuition: $5940 full-time, $198 per credit part-time. Nonresident tuition: $8910 full-time, $297 per credit part-time. Mandatory fees: $1380 full-time, $46 per credit part-time.
Collegiate Environment: Student-run newspaper. Student services: personal-psychological counseling, women's center. Campus security: 24-hour patrols. Yocum Library with 25,541 books, 284 serials, an OPAC, and a Web page. 90 computers available on campus for general student use. A campuswide network can be accessed. Students can access the following: online class registration. Staffed computer lab on campus provides training in use of computers, software, and the Internet.
Community Environment: Reading is located about 60 miles north of Philadelphia and approximately 2 1/2 hours by bus or car to New York City.

■ **THE RESTAURANT SCHOOL AT WALNUT HILL COLLEGE**
4207 Walnut St.
Philadelphia, PA 19104-3518
Tel: (215)222-4200
Fax: (215)222-4219
E-mail: tmorelli@walnuthillcollege.edu
Web Site: www.walnuthillcollege.edu/
Description: Proprietary, primarily 2-year, coed. Awards terminal associate and bachelor's degrees. Founded 1974. Setting: 2-acre urban campus. Research spending for the previous fiscal year: $137,880. Educational spending for the previous fiscal year: $5570 per student. Total enrollment: 402. Faculty: 19 (18 full-time, 1 part-time). Student-undergrad faculty ratio is 22:1. 174 applied, 97% were admitted. 2 valedictorians. Full-time: 402 students, 56% women, 44% men. Students come from 4 other countries, 29% from out-of-state. 4% Hispanic/Latino; 14% African American, non-Hispanic/Latino; 2% Asian, non-Hispanic/Latino. 12% 25 or older, 0% live on campus, 10% transferred in. Academic area with the most degrees conferred: personal and culinary services. Part-time degree program, internships.
Entrance Requirements: Open admission. Options: electronic application, early admission, early decision, deferred admission. Required: essay, high school transcript, 2 recommendations, interview. Recommended: minimum 2 high school GPA, SAT or ACT. Required for some: entrance exam. Application deadline: Rolling. Transfer credits accepted: Yes. Early decision applicants: 56. Early decision applicants admitted: 55.
Costs Per Year: Application fee: $50. One-time mandatory fee: $200. Tuition: $19,050 full-time. Mandatory fees: $3675 full-time. College room only: $4600. Room charges vary according to housing facility.
Collegiate Environment: Orientation program. Social organizations: student clubs. Most popular organizations: Wine Club, Book Club, Coffee & Tea Club, Craft Club, Flair Bartending. Major annual events: Freshman Showcase, First Class, Club Fairs. Campus security: 24-hour emergency

response devices and patrols, student patrols, controlled dormitory access. Alumni Resource Center with a Web page. Operations spending for the previous fiscal year: $20,500. 60 computers available on campus for general student use. A campuswide network can be accessed from student residence rooms and from off campus. Students can access the following: All students receive an IPad. Staffed computer lab on campus provides training in use of computers and the Internet.

■ ROBERT MORRIS UNIVERSITY

6001 University Blvd.
Moon Township, PA 15108-1189
Tel: (412)262-8200; Free: 800-762-0097
Fax: (412)262-8619
E-mail: admissionsoffice@rmu.edu
Web Site: www.rmu.edu/

Description: Independent, university, coed. Awards bachelor's, master's, and doctoral degrees. Founded 1921. Setting: 230-acre suburban campus with easy access to Pittsburgh. Endowment: $26.4 million. Educational spending for the previous fiscal year: $8051 per student. Total enrollment: 5,181. Faculty: 469 (196 full-time, 273 part-time). Student-undergrad faculty ratio is 15:1. 5,220 applied, 82% were admitted. 17% from top 10% of their high school class, 44% from top quarter, 80% from top half. 9 valedictorians. Full-time: 3,643 students, 44% women, 56% men. Part-time: 501 students, 61% women, 39% men. Students come from 38 states and territories, 39 other countries, 16% from out-of-state. 0.2% American Indian or Alaska Native, non-Hispanic/Latino; 2% Hispanic/Latino; 7% African American, non-Hispanic/Latino; 1% Asian, non-Hispanic/Latino; 0.1% Native Hawaiian or other Pacific Islander, non-Hispanic/Latino; 4% international. 17% 25 or older, 43% live on campus, 10% transferred in. Retention: 76% of full-time freshmen returned the following year. Academic areas with the most degrees conferred: business/marketing; health professions and related sciences; communication/journalism. Core. Calendar: semesters. Academic remediation for entering students, services for LD students, accelerated degree program, honors program, independent study, distance learning, double major, summer session for credit, part-time degree program, adult/continuing education programs, co-op programs and internships, graduate courses open to undergrads. Off campus study at Pittsburgh Council on Higher Education. Study abroad program. ROTC: Army, Air Force (c).

Entrance Requirements: Options: electronic application, deferred admission, international baccalaureate accepted. Required: high school transcript, minimum 2.5 high school GPA, SAT or ACT. Recommended: essay, minimum 3 high school GPA, interview. Required for some: interview. Entrance: minimally difficult. Application deadline: 7/1. Notification: continuous until 9/1. SAT Reasoning Test deadline: 7/1. SAT Subject Test deadline: 7/1. Transfer credits accepted: Yes. Applicants placed on waiting list: 95. Wait-listed applicants offered admission: 37.

Costs Per Year: Application fee: $30. Comprehensive fee: $35,424 includes full-time tuition ($23,410), mandatory fees ($654), and college room and board ($11,360). College room only: $5370. Full-time tuition and fees vary according to degree level and program. Room and board charges vary according to board plan and housing facility. Part-time tuition: $760 per credit hour. Part-time mandatory fees: $30 per credit hour. Part-time tuition and fees vary according to course load, degree level, and program.

Collegiate Environment: Orientation program. Drama-theater group, choral group, marching band, student-run newspaper, radio station. Social organizations: 137 open to all; national fraternities, national sororities; 10% of eligible men and 8% of eligible women are members. Most popular organizations: Student Government Association, Residence Hall Association, R-MOVE, National Society of Collegiate Scholars, Black Student Union. Major annual events: Snowball, Homecoming, Spring Fest. Student services: health clinic, personal-psychological counseling. Campus security: 24-hour emergency response devices and patrols, late night transport-escort service, controlled dormitory access. 1,533 college housing spaces available; all were occupied in 2012-13. Freshmen given priority for college housing. On-campus residence required in freshman year. Options: coed, men-only, women-only housing available. Robert Morris University Library with 115,350 books, 210,274 microform titles, 19,143 serials, 3,042 audiovisual materials, an OPAC, and a Web page. Operations spending for the previous fiscal year: $1.7 million. 300 computers available on campus for general student use. Computer purchase/lease plans available. A campuswide network can be accessed from student residence rooms and from off campus. Students can access the following: online class registration, online payment. Staffed computer lab on campus (open 24 hours a day) provides training in use of computers, software, and the Internet.

■ ROSEDALE TECHNICAL INSTITUTE

215 Beecham Dr.
Ste. 2
Pittsburgh, PA 15205-9791
Tel: (412)521-6200; Free: 800-521-6262
Fax: (412)521-9277
E-mail: admissions@rosedaletech.org
Web Site: www.rosedaletech.org/

Description: Independent, 2-year, coed. Awards diplomas and terminal associate degrees. Founded 1949. Setting: 6-acre suburban campus. Total enrollment: 200. Faculty: 18 (14 full-time, 4 part-time). Student-undergrad faculty ratio is 13:1. 156 applied, 65% were admitted. Calendar: semesters.

■ ROSEMONT COLLEGE

1400 Montgomery Ave.
Rosemont, PA 19010-1699
Tel: (610)527-0200; Free: 888-2-ROSEMONT
Fax: (610)527-1041
E-mail: admissions@rosemont.edu
Web Site: www.rosemont.edu/

Description: Independent Roman Catholic, comprehensive, coed. Awards bachelor's and master's degrees. Founded 1921. Setting: 56-acre suburban campus with easy access to Philadelphia. Endowment: $13.6 million. Educational spending for the previous fiscal year: $6339 per student. Total enrollment: 908. Faculty: 139 (28 full-time, 111 part-time). Student-undergrad faculty ratio is 10:1. 941 applied, 50% were admitted. 0% from top 10% of their high school class, 0% from top quarter, 0% from top half. 4 class presidents, 2 valedictorians, 15 student government officers. Full-time: 426 students, 66% women, 34% men. Part-time: 98 students, 76% women, 24% men. Students come from 11 states and territories, 14 other countries, 20% from out-of-state. 0% American Indian or Alaska Native, non-Hispanic/Latino; 7% Hispanic/Latino; 35% African American, non-Hispanic/Latino; 4% Asian, non-Hispanic/Latino; 0% Native Hawaiian or other Pacific Islander, non-Hispanic/Latino; 2% international. 10% 25 or older, 70% live on campus, 5% transferred in. Retention: 80% of full-time freshmen returned the following year. Academic areas with the most degrees conferred: business/marketing; communication/journalism; psychology. Core. Calendar: semesters. Academic remediation for entering students, ESL program, services for LD students, advanced placement, accelerated degree program, self-designed majors, honors program, independent study, double major, summer session for credit, part-time degree program, adult/continuing education programs, internships, graduate courses open to undergrads. Off campus study at Villanova University, Eastern University and the SEPCHE Consortium whose members include: Arcadia University, Cabrini College, Chestnut Hill College, Gwynedd-Mercy College, Holy Family University, Immaculata University and Neuman University. Study abroad program. ROTC: Army (c).

Entrance Requirements: Options: electronic application, early admission, deferred admission, international baccalaureate accepted. Required: essay, high school transcript, 2 recommendations, SAT or ACT. Recommended: minimum 3 high school GPA, interview. Entrance: moderately difficult. Application deadline: Rolling. Notification: 8/1. SAT Reasoning Test deadline: 8/1. Transfer credits accepted: Yes.

Costs Per Year: Application fee: $0. Comprehensive fee: $43,330 includes full-time tuition ($30,000), mandatory fees ($950), and college room and board ($12,380). Full-time tuition and fees vary according to course load and program. Room and board charges vary according to board plan and housing facility. Part-time tuition: $1140 per credit hour. Part-time tuition varies according to course load and program.

Collegiate Environment: Orientation program. Drama-theater group, choral group, student-run newspaper. Social organizations: 27 open to all. Most popular organizations: student government, Triad, Jest and Gesture, Best Buddies, Political Science Club. Major annual events: Oktoberfest/Family Weekend, Founders' Day/Spring Fling, Annual Concert of the Petaltones. Student services: legal services, health clinic, personal-psychological counseling, women's center. Campus security: 24-hour emergency response devices and patrols, late night transport-escort service, controlled dormitory access. 300 college housing spaces available; all were occupied in 2012-13. Freshmen guaranteed college housing. On-campus residence required through junior year. Options: coed, women-only housing available. Kistler Library plus 1 other with 165,425 books, 22,908 microform titles, 16,370 serials, 3,425 audiovisual materials, an OPAC, and a Web page. Operations spending for the previous fiscal year: $393,365. 100 computers available on campus for general student use. A campuswide network can be accessed from student residence rooms and from off campus. Students can access the following: online class registration. Staffed computer lab on campus provides training in use of software and the Internet.

Community Environment: See Villanova University.

■ **SAINT CHARLES BORROMEO SEMINARY, OVERBROOK**
100 E Wynnewood Rd.
Wynnewood, PA 19096
Tel: (610)667-3394
Web Site: www.scs.edu/

Description: Independent Roman Catholic, comprehensive, coed. Awards bachelor's and master's degrees (also offers coed part-time programs). Founded 1832. Setting: 77-acre suburban campus with easy access to Philadelphia. Total enrollment: 218. Faculty: 33 (16 full-time, 17 part-time). Student-undergrad faculty ratio is 6:1. 8 applied, 100% were admitted. 72% from top 10% of their high school class, 33% from top quarter, 67% from top half. Full-time: 74 students, 100% men. Part-time: 24 students, 71% women, 29% men. Students come from 6 states and territories, 13% from out-of-state. 0% American Indian or Alaska Native, non-Hispanic/Latino; 9% Hispanic/Latino; 0% African American, non-Hispanic/Latino; 2% Asian, non-Hispanic/Latino; 0% Native Hawaiian or other Pacific Islander, non-Hispanic/Latino; 0% international. 2% 25 or older, 100% live on campus, 5% transferred in. Retention: 78% of full-time freshmen returned the following year. Core. Calendar: semesters. Academic remediation for entering students, ESL program, advanced placement, accelerated degree program, independent study, summer session for credit, adult/continuing education programs, graduate courses open to undergrads.

Entrance Requirements: Options: deferred admission, international baccalaureate accepted. Required: essay, high school transcript, minimum 2 high school GPA, 3 recommendations, interview, sponsorship by diocese or religious community. Recommended: SAT or ACT. Entrance: moderately difficult. Application deadline: 7/15. Notification: continuous.

Costs Per Year: Application fee: $0. Comprehensive fee: $31,210 includes full-time tuition ($17,950), mandatory fees ($1200), and college room and board ($12,060). Part-time tuition: $880 per course.

Collegiate Environment: Orientation program. Drama-theater group, choral group, student-run newspaper. Most popular organizations: Seminarians for Life, Student Council. Student services: health clinic, personal-psychological counseling. Campus security: 24-hour emergency response devices and patrols. 150 college housing spaces available; 74 were occupied in 2012-13. Freshmen guaranteed college housing. On-campus residence required through senior year. Option: men-only housing available. Ryan Memorial Library with 148,379 books, 1,905 microform titles, 292 serials, 17,853 audiovisual materials, an OPAC, and a Web page. 60 computers available on campus for general student use. A campuswide network can be accessed.

■ **SAINT FRANCIS UNIVERSITY**
PO Box 600, 117 Evergreen Dr.
Loretto, PA 15940-0600
Tel: (814)472-3000; Free: 866-DIAL-SFU
Fax: (814)472-3044
E-mail: rbeener@francis.edu
Web Site: www.francis.edu/

Description: Independent Roman Catholic, comprehensive, coed. Awards associate, bachelor's, master's, and doctoral degrees. Founded 1847. Setting: 600-acre rural campus. Endowment: $34.7 million. Research spending for the previous fiscal year: $1.6 million. Educational spending for the previous fiscal year: $8684 per student. Total enrollment: 2,451. Faculty: 203 (113 full-time, 90 part-time). Student-undergrad faculty ratio is 14:1. 1,687 applied, 74% were admitted. 24% from top 10% of their high school class, 52% from top quarter, 83% from top half. 10 valedictorians. Full-time: 1,598 students, 61% women, 39% men. Part-time: 174 students, 62% women, 38% men. Students come from 40 states and territories, 25% from out-of-state. 0.1% American Indian or Alaska Native, non-Hispanic/Latino; 2% Hispanic/Latino; 7% African American, non-Hispanic/Latino; 1% Asian, non-Hispanic/Latino; 4% international. 2% 25 or older, 88% live on campus, 2% transferred in. Retention: 78% of full-time freshmen returned the following year. Academic areas with the most degrees conferred: health professions and related sciences; business/marketing; biological/life sciences. Core. Calendar: semesters. Academic remediation for entering students, advanced placement, accelerated degree program, self-designed majors, freshman honors college, honors program, independent study, distance learning, double major, summer session for credit, part-time degree program, external degree program, adult/continuing education programs, internships, graduate

courses open to undergrads. Off campus study at Washington Semester, CCSA. Study abroad program. ROTC: Army.

Entrance Requirements: Options: electronic application, deferred admission, international baccalaureate accepted. Required: essay, high school transcript, 1 recommendation, SAT or ACT. Recommended: interview. Required for some: interview. Entrance: moderately difficult. Application deadlines: Rolling, Rolling for nonresidents. SAT Reasoning Test deadline: 8/15. SAT Subject Test deadline: 8/15.

Costs Per Year: Application fee: $30. One-time mandatory fee: $100. Comprehensive fee: $40,338 includes full-time tuition ($28,942), mandatory fees ($1050), and college room and board ($10,346). College room only: $5198. Full-time tuition and fees vary according to course load, degree level, program, and student level. Room and board charges vary according to board plan and housing facility. Part-time tuition: $909 per credit hour. Part-time mandatory fees: $432 per credit hour. Part-time tuition and fees vary according to class time, degree level, and program.

Collegiate Environment: Orientation program. Drama-theater group, choral group, marching band, student-run newspaper, radio station. Social organizations: 80 open to all; national fraternities, national sororities, local sororities, national Greek-lettered service organizations; 21% of eligible men and 25% of eligible women are members. Most popular organizations: Student Activities Organization, Club Baseball, Student Government Association, Best Buddies, Ultimate Frisbee Club. Major annual events: Parents' Weekend, Homecoming, Spring Fest. Student services: health clinic, personal-psychological counseling. Campus security: 24-hour emergency response devices and patrols, late night transport-escort service, controlled dormitory access. 1,500 college housing spaces available; 1,475 were occupied in 2012-13. Freshmen guaranteed college housing. On-campus residence required through junior year. Options: men-only, women-only housing available. Pasquerilla Library with 99,500 books, 39,800 serials, 3,642 audiovisual materials, an OPAC, and a Web page. Operations spending for the previous fiscal year: $1.1 million. 75 computers available on campus for general student use. Computer purchase/lease plans available. A computer is required for all students. A campuswide network can be accessed from student residence rooms and from off campus. Students can access the following: online class registration, wireless access throughout all of campus. Staffed computer lab on campus provides training in use of computers, software, and the Internet.

■ **SAINT JOSEPH'S UNIVERSITY**
5600 City Ave.
Philadelphia, PA 19131-1395
Tel: (610)660-1000; Free: 800-BE-A-HAWK
E-mail: admit@sju.edu
Web Site: www.sju.edu/

Description: Independent Roman Catholic (Jesuit), comprehensive, coed. Awards associate, bachelor's, master's, and doctoral degrees and post-master's certificates. Founded 1851. Setting: 105-acre suburban campus. Endowment: $168.8 million. Research spending for the previous fiscal year: $4.1 million. Educational spending for the previous fiscal year: $11,401 per student. Total enrollment: 8,805. Faculty: 786 (310 full-time, 476 part-time). Student-undergrad faculty ratio is 13:1. 7,386 applied, 78% were admitted. 25% from top 10% of their high school class, 53% from top quarter, 84% from top half. Full-time: 4,433 students, 51% women, 49% men. Part-time: 909 students, 59% women, 41% men. Students come from 37 states and territories, 29 other countries, 53% from out-of-state. 0.1% American Indian or Alaska Native, non-Hispanic/Latino; 5% Hispanic/Latino; 7% African American, non-Hispanic/Latino; 2% Asian, non-Hispanic/Latino; 0.1% Native Hawaiian or other Pacific Islander, non-Hispanic/Latino; 1% international. 10% 25 or older, 59% live on campus, 1% transferred in. Retention: 89% of full-time freshmen returned the following year. Academic areas with the most degrees conferred: business/marketing; social sciences; education. Core. Calendar: semesters. ESL program, services for LD students, advanced placement, accelerated degree program, self-designed majors, honors program, independent study, distance learning, double major, summer session for credit, part-time degree program, adult/continuing education programs, co-op programs and internships, graduate courses open to undergrads. Off campus study at members of the Jesuit Student Exchange. Study abroad program. ROTC: Army (c), Naval (c), Air Force.

Entrance Requirements: Options: electronic application, early action, deferred admission, international baccalaureate accepted. Required: essay, high school transcript, SAT or ACT. Entrance: moderately difficult. Application deadlines: 2/1, 11/15 for early action. Notification: 3/15, 12/25 for early action. SAT Reasoning Test deadline: 2/1. Transfer credits accepted: Yes. Applicants placed on waiting list: 573. Wait-listed applicants offered admission: 76. Early action applicants: 4,047. Early action applicants admitted: 3,577.

Costs Per Year: Application fee: $60. Comprehensive fee: $50,630 includes full-time tuition ($37,670), mandatory fees ($160), and college room and board ($12,800). College room only: $8105. Full-time tuition and fees vary according to course load. Room and board charges vary according to board plan and housing facility. Part-time tuition: $500 per credit.

Collegiate Environment: Orientation program. Drama-theater group, choral group, student-run newspaper, radio station. Social organizations: 105 open to all; national fraternities, national sororities; 9% of eligible men and 19% of eligible women are members. Most popular organizations: Student Union Board, Hand-in-Hand, 54th Airborne / Booster Club, Appalachian Experience, Weekly Service. Major annual events: Community Day / Global Community Day, spring concert, Hawk-A-Palooza. Student services: health clinic, personal-psychological counseling. Campus security: 24-hour emergency response devices and patrols, late night transport-escort service, controlled dormitory access, 24-hour shuttle/escort service, bicycle patrols. 2,732 undergraduates lived in college housing during 2012-13. Freshmen guaranteed college housing. On-campus residence required through sophomore year. Options: coed, men-only, women-only housing available. Post Learning Commons and Drexel Library plus 1 other with 353,000 books, 861,000 microform titles, 57,900 serials, 4,500 audiovisual materials, an OPAC, and a Web page. Operations spending for the previous fiscal year: $1.7 million. 825 computers available on campus for general student use. Computer purchase/lease plans available. A campuswide network can be accessed from student residence rooms and from off campus. Students can access the following: online class registration. Staffed computer lab on campus provides training in use of computers, software, and the Internet.

■ SAINT VINCENT COLLEGE
300 Fraser Purchase Rd.
Latrobe, PA 15650-2690
Tel: (724)532-6600; Free: 800-782-5549
Fax: (724)537-4554
E-mail: admission@stvincent.edu
Web Site: www.stvincent.edu/

Description: Independent Roman Catholic, comprehensive, coed. Awards bachelor's and master's degrees. Founded 1846. Setting: 200-acre suburban campus with easy access to Pittsburgh. Total enrollment: 1,766. 1,696 applied, 66% were admitted. 23% from top 10% of their high school class, 52% from top quarter, 80% from top half. Full-time: 1,481 students, 48% women, 52% men. Part-time: 85 students, 47% women, 53% men. 16% from out-of-state. 0.2% American Indian or Alaska Native, non-Hispanic/Latino; 3% Hispanic/Latino; 5% African American, non-Hispanic/Latino; 1% Asian, non-Hispanic/Latino; 0.1% Native Hawaiian or other Pacific Islander, non-Hispanic/Latino; 1% international. 4% 25 or older, 67% live on campus, 2% transferred in. Retention: 81% of full-time freshmen returned the following year. Academic areas with the most degrees conferred: business/marketing; education; biological/life sciences. Calendar: semesters. Part-time degree program, external degree program. ROTC: Army (c), Air Force (c).

Entrance Requirements: Options: electronic application, early admission, deferred admission, international baccalaureate accepted. Required: essay, high school transcript, minimum 2.5 high school GPA, SAT or ACT. Recommended: minimum 3.2 high school GPA, 3 recommendations, interview. Required for some: interview. Entrance: moderately difficult. Application deadline: 4/1. Notification: continuous until 10/1.

Costs Per Year: Application fee: $25. Comprehensive fee: $38,738 includes full-time tuition ($28,542), mandatory fees ($602), and college room and board ($9594). College room only: $5098. Room and board charges vary according to board plan and housing facility.

Collegiate Environment: Orientation program. Campus security: 24-hour emergency response devices and patrols, late night transport-escort service, controlled dormitory access, limited access to residence halls on weekends. Freshmen given priority for college housing. On-campus residence required in freshman year. Option: coed housing available.

Community Environment: Population 8,654. Located in the Laurel Highlands region of the Allegheny Mountains, Latrobe is 35 miles east of Pittsburgh. The area is accessible by air, railroad and major highways. There is a county airport adjacent to campus. The community has a public library, churches and a synagogue and multiple shopping malls.

■ SANFORD-BROWN INSTITUTE–PITTSBURGH
421 Seventh Ave.
Pittsburgh, PA 15219-1907

Tel: (412)281-2600; Free: 888-270-6333
Fax: (412)281-0319
Web Site: www.sanfordbrown.edu/

Description: Proprietary, 2-year, coed. Awards terminal associate degrees. Founded 1980. Setting: urban campus. Total enrollment: 472. 44% 25 or older. Core. Calendar: continuous. Academic remediation for entering students, ESL program, services for LD students, advanced placement, accelerated degree program, adult/continuing education programs, co-op programs and internships.

Entrance Requirements: Options: electronic application, early admission, deferred admission. Required: high school transcript, interview. Recommended: SAT or ACT, SAT Subject Tests. Entrance: minimally difficult.

Collegiate Environment: Orientation program. Campus security: 24-hour emergency response devices, 14-hour security patrols Monday through Friday. Campus Library with 1,687 books and 1,403 serials.

■ SETON HILL UNIVERSITY
Seton Hill Dr.
Greensburg, PA 15601
Tel: (724)834-2200; Free: 800-826-6234
Fax: (724)830-4611
E-mail: admit@setonhill.edu
Web Site: www.setonhill.edu/

Description: Independent Roman Catholic, comprehensive, coed. Awards bachelor's and master's degrees and post-master's certificates. Founded 1883. Setting: 200-acre small town campus with easy access to Pittsburgh. Endowment: $30 million. Educational spending for the previous fiscal year: $8585 per student. Total enrollment: 2,091. Faculty: 196 (98 full-time, 98 part-time). Student-undergrad faculty ratio is 14:1. 2,150 applied, 66% were admitted. 20% from top 10% of their high school class, 45% from top quarter, 77% from top half. Full-time: 1,475 students, 64% women, 36% men. Part-time: 198 students, 67% women, 33% men. Students come from 32 states and territories, 13 other countries, 23% from out-of-state. 0.2% American Indian or Alaska Native, non-Hispanic/Latino; 3% Hispanic/Latino; 10% African American, non-Hispanic/Latino; 0.3% Asian, non-Hispanic/Latino; 0% Native Hawaiian or other Pacific Islander, non-Hispanic/Latino; 2% international. 8% 25 or older, 46% live on campus, 5% transferred in. Retention: 78% of full-time freshmen returned the following year. Academic areas with the most degrees conferred: business/marketing; visual and performing arts; psychology. Core. Calendar: semesters. Academic remediation for entering students, ESL program, services for LD students, advanced placement, self-designed majors, honors program, independent study, distance learning, double major, summer session for credit, part-time degree program, adult/continuing education programs, internships, graduate courses open to undergrads. Off campus study. Study abroad program. ROTC: Army.

Entrance Requirements: Options: electronic application, deferred admission, international baccalaureate accepted. Required: essay, high school transcript, 1 recommendation, portfolio for art, audition for music and theatre. Recommended: interview, SAT or ACT. Entrance: moderately difficult. Application deadlines: Rolling, Rolling for nonresidents. Notification: continuous, continuous for nonresidents. SAT Reasoning Test deadline: 8/1. Transfer credits accepted: Yes.

Costs Per Year: Application fee: $35. Comprehensive fee: $39,394 includes full-time tuition ($28,350), mandatory fees ($1100), and college room and board ($9944). Full-time tuition and fees vary according to course load and program. Room and board charges vary according to board plan and housing facility. Part-time tuition: $760 per credit hour. Part-time mandatory fees: $25 per credit hour, $50 per term. Part-time tuition and fees vary according to course load and program.

Collegiate Environment: Orientation program. Drama-theater group, choral group, marching band, student-run newspaper. Social organizations: 43 open to all; academic honor societies; 25% of eligible men and 25% of eligible women are members. Most popular organizations: Student Body Activities Council, Future Greek leaders, Peer Ministry Council, Biology Club, intramurals. Major annual events: homecoming weekend, Christmas on the Hill, Midnight Breakfast. Student services: health clinic, personal-psychological counseling. Campus security: 24-hour emergency response devices and patrols, late night transport-escort service, controlled dormitory access, emergency phones throughout camps, campus alert system, safety committee. 774 college housing spaces available; 749 were occupied in 2012-13. Freshmen guaranteed college housing. On-campus residence required in freshman year. Options: coed, men-only, women-only housing available. Reeves Memorial Library with 116,912 books, 5,190 microform titles, 295 serials, 5,509 audiovisual materials, an OPAC, and a Web page. Operations spending for the previous fiscal year: $513,097. 50 computers available on campus for general student use. Computer purchase/lease plans available. A campuswide network can be accessed from student residence rooms and from off campus. Students can access the following: online class registration. Staffed computer lab on campus provides training in use of computers, software, and the Internet.

■ SHIPPENSBURG UNIVERSITY OF PENNSYLVANIA

1871 Old Main Dr.
Shippensburg, PA 17257-2299
Tel: (717)477-7447; Free: 800-822-8028
Fax: (717)477-1273
E-mail: admiss@ship.edu
Web Site: www.ship.edu/

Description: State-supported, comprehensive, coed. Part of Pennsylvania State System of Higher Education. Awards bachelor's and master's degrees and post-master's certificates. Founded 1871. Setting: 200-acre rural campus. Endowment: $27.4 million. Research spending for the previous fiscal year: $774,001. Educational spending for the previous fiscal year: $7380 per student. Total enrollment: 7,724. Faculty: 397 (329 full-time, 68 part-time). Student-undergrad faculty ratio is 20:1. 6,402 applied, 81% were admitted. 8% from top 10% of their high school class, 26% from top quarter, 59% from top half. 71 student government officers. Full-time: 6,363 students, 50% women, 50% men. Part-time: 349 students, 57% women, 43% men. Students come from 21 states and territories, 15 other countries, 6% from out-of-state. 0.2% American Indian or Alaska Native, non-Hispanic/Latino; 3% Hispanic/Latino; 8% African American, non-Hispanic/Latino; 1% Asian, non-Hispanic/Latino; 0.1% Native Hawaiian or other Pacific Islander, non-Hispanic/Latino; 0.3% international. 6% 25 or older, 33% live on campus, 5% transferred in. Retention: 68% of full-time freshmen returned the following year. Academic areas with the most degrees conferred: business/marketing; education; homeland security, law enforcement, firefighting, and protective services. Core. Calendar: semesters. Academic remediation for entering students, services for LD students, advanced placement, accelerated degree program, honors program, independent study, distance learning, double major, summer session for credit, part-time degree program, co-op programs and internships, graduate courses open to undergrads. Off campus study at Cooperative Agreement with Wilson College, Marine Science Consortium, Cooperative Program with Art Institutes International, Visiting Student Program with Fashion Institute of Technology, and Visiting Student Program with PASSHE Schools. Study abroad program. ROTC: Army.

Entrance Requirements: Options: electronic application, early admission, early action, deferred admission, international baccalaureate accepted. Required: high school transcript, SAT or ACT. Recommended: essay, class rank, letters of recommendation optional. Required for some: interview. Entrance: moderately difficult. Application deadline: Rolling. Notification: continuous. Transfer credits accepted: Yes.

Costs Per Year: Application fee: $30. State resident tuition: $6428 full-time, $268 per credit hour part-time. Nonresident tuition: $14,464 full-time, $603 per credit hour part-time. Mandatory fees: $2726 full-time, $113 per credit hour part-time. College room and board: $7910. College room only: $4180. Room and board charges vary according to board plan and housing facility.

Collegiate Environment: Orientation program. Drama-theater group, choral group, marching band, student-run newspaper, radio station. Social organizations: 120 open to all; national fraternities, national sororities; 6% of eligible men and 7% of eligible women are members. Major annual events: Homecoming, Parents' Days, Spring Fest. Student services: health clinic, personal-psychological counseling, women's center. Campus security: 24-hour emergency response devices and patrols, late night transport-escort service, controlled dormitory access, surveillance cameras in certain parking lots and buildings, foot, vehicular and bicycle patrols by security officers. 2,641 college housing spaces available; 2,191 were occupied in 2012-13. Freshmen guaranteed college housing. On-campus residence required in freshman year. Option: coed housing available. Ezra Lehman Memorial Library plus 1 other with 369,525 books, 1.3 million microform titles, 19,975 serials, 72,734 audiovisual materials, an OPAC, and a Web page. Operations spending for the previous fiscal year: $2.8 million. 1,100 computers available on campus for general student use. A campuswide network can be accessed from student residence rooms and from off campus. Students can access the following: online class registration, personal Web pages. Staffed computer lab on campus.

Community Environment: Located in south-central Pennsylvania, Shippensburg, population 5,600, is a semirural community. The area has 32 churches of various denominations, a library, and many civic and fraternal organizations. Recreational activities include fishing, hunting, swimming, football, baseball, and bowling. Limited part-time employment opportunities are available.

■ SLIPPERY ROCK UNIVERSITY OF PENNSYLVANIA

1 Morrow Way
Slippery Rock, PA 16057-1383
Tel: (724)738-9000; Free: 800-SRU-9111
Fax: (724)738-2098
E-mail: asktherock@sru.edu
Web Site: www.sru.edu/

Description: State-supported, comprehensive, coed. Part of Pennsylvania State System of Higher Education. Awards bachelor's, master's, and doctoral degrees. Founded 1889. Setting: 650-acre small town campus with easy access to Pittsburgh. Endowment: $18.5 million. Research spending for the previous fiscal year: $239,584. Educational spending for the previous fiscal year: $5387 per student. Total enrollment: 8,559. Faculty: 407 (355 full-time, 52 part-time). Student-undergrad faculty ratio is 20:1. 6,276 applied, 63% were admitted. 12% from top 10% of their high school class, 37% from top quarter, 80% from top half. Full-time: 7,308 students, 56% women, 44% men. Part-time: 552 students, 67% women, 33% men. Students come from 36 states and territories, 37 other countries, 11% from out-of-state. 0.1% American Indian or Alaska Native, non-Hispanic/Latino; 2% Hispanic/Latino; 5% African American, non-Hispanic/Latino; 0.5% Asian, non-Hispanic/Latino; 0.03% Native Hawaiian or other Pacific Islander, non-Hispanic/Latino; 1% international. 8% 25 or older, 36% live on campus, 8% transferred in. Retention: 81% of full-time freshmen returned the following year. Academic areas with the most degrees conferred: health professions and related sciences; education; business/marketing. Core. Calendar: semesters. Academic remediation for entering students, services for LD students, advanced placement, self-designed majors, honors program, independent study, distance learning, double major, summer session for credit, part-time degree program, adult/continuing education programs, internships, graduate courses open to undergrads. Off campus study at members of the Marine Science Consortium. Study abroad program. ROTC: Army.

Entrance Requirements: Options: electronic application, deferred admission, international baccalaureate accepted. Required: high school transcript, minimum 2 high school GPA, SAT or ACT. Entrance: moderately difficult. Application deadline: Rolling. Notification: continuous until 6/15. SAT Reasoning Test deadline: 5/1. Transfer credits accepted: Yes.

Costs Per Year: Application fee: $30. State resident tuition: $6428 full-time, $268 per credit hour part-time. Nonresident tuition: $9642 full-time, $536 per credit hour part-time. Mandatory fees: $2,319 full-time, $96.77 per credit hour part-time. Full-time tuition and fees vary according to course load and degree level. Part-time tuition and fees vary according to course load and degree level. College room and board: $9364. College room only: $6206. Room and board charges vary according to board plan and housing facility.

Collegiate Environment: Orientation program. Drama-theater group, choral group, marching band, student-run newspaper, radio station. Social organizations: 170 open to all; national fraternities, national sororities; 6% of eligible men and 7% of eligible women are members. Most popular organizations: Exercise Science Society, Down Hill Ski and Snowboard Club, Pre Physical Therapy Club, Interfraternity Council, Panhellenic Council. Major annual events: Homecoming, Family Day, concerts. Student services: legal services, health clinic, personal-psychological counseling, women's center. Campus security: 24-hour emergency response devices and patrols, late night transport-escort service, controlled dormitory access. 2,800 college housing spaces available; 2,785 were occupied in 2012-13. Freshmen guaranteed college housing. On-campus residence required in freshman year. Option: coed housing available. Bailey Library with 717,847 books, 1.5 million microform titles, 56,899 serials, 28,474 audiovisual materials, an OPAC, and a Web page. Operations spending for the previous fiscal year: $2.8 million. 1,305 computers available on campus for general student use. Computer purchase/lease plans available. A campuswide network can be accessed from student residence rooms and from off campus. Students can access the following: online class registration. Staffed computer lab on campus provides training in use of computers, software, and the Internet.

Community Environment: Population 3,000, Slippery Rock is located approximately an hour's drive from Pittsburgh. The climate is pleasant both in winter and in summer. There are several Protestant and Catholic churches in the community. The area has good highways and bus service. Local recreation includes hunting, fishing, boating, swimming, golf, and theatres, all easily accessible. Rooms are available in private homes. Many special interest and veteran's clubs are active in the community.

■ SOUTH HILLS SCHOOL OF BUSINESS & TECHNOLOGY (ALTOONA)
508 58th St.
Altoona, PA 16602
Tel: (814)944-6134
Fax: (814)944-4684
E-mail: hemerick@southhills.edu
Web Site: www.southhills.edu/
Description: Proprietary, 2-year, coed. Awards certificates, diplomas, transfer associate, and terminal associate degrees. Founded 2001. Total enrollment: 189. Faculty: 11 (10 full-time, 1 part-time). Student-undergrad faculty ratio is 13:1. 102 applied, 60% were admitted. 10% from top 10% of their high school class, 15% from top quarter, 75% from top half. 6 National Merit Scholars, 1 class president, 2 valedictorians, 3 student government officers. Full-time: 189 students, 67% women, 33% men. 0% from out-of-state. 24% 25 or older, 0% transferred in. Retention: 77% of full-time freshmen returned the following year. Calendar: trimesters. Independent study, double major, summer session for credit, part-time degree program, internships.
Entrance Requirements: Option: electronic application. Required: essay, high school transcript, interview, COMPASS. Entrance: moderately difficult. Application deadline: 9/1.
Collegiate Environment: Orientation program. Social organizations: 6 open to all. Most popular organizations: Student Forum, Phi Beta Lambda, Student Ambassadors, HOSA, Tech Team. Major annual events: Spring Fling, Summer and Fall Picnics, Alumni Reunions. 93 computers available on campus for general student use. A campuswide network can be accessed. Staffed computer lab on campus provides training in use of computers, software, and the Internet.

■ SOUTH HILLS SCHOOL OF BUSINESS & TECHNOLOGY (STATE COLLEGE)
480 Waupelani Dr.
State College, PA 16801-4516
Tel: (814)234-7755; Free: 888-282-7427
Fax: (814)234-0926
E-mail: admissions@southhills.edu
Web Site: www.southhills.edu/
Description: Proprietary, 2-year, coed. Awards certificates, diplomas, transfer associate, and terminal associate degrees (also includes Altoona campus). Founded 1970. Setting: 6-acre small town campus. Total enrollment: 707. 690 applied, 79% were admitted. 0% from out-of-state. 33% 25 or older. Advanced placement, independent study, distance learning, double major, part-time degree program, internships.
Entrance Requirements: Option: electronic application. Required: high school transcript, minimum 1.5 high school GPA, interview, CPAt. Recommended: minimum 3.0 high school GPA. Required for some: essay, 2 recommendations. Entrance: minimally difficult. Application deadline: 9/2.
Collegiate Environment: Orientation program. Student-run newspaper. Social organizations: 6 open to all. Most popular organizations: Phi Beta Lambda, South Hills Executives, Student Forum, newspaper. Major annual events: school picnics, school trips. Campus security: 24-hour emergency response devices.

■ STRAYER UNIVERSITY - ALLENTOWN CAMPUS
3800 Sierra Cir.
Ste. 300
Center Valley, PA 18034
Tel: (484)809-7770
Fax: (610)791-0210
Web Site: www.strayer.edu/campus/allentown/
Description: Proprietary, comprehensive, coed. Awards associate, bachelor's, and master's degrees.

■ STRAYER UNIVERSITY - CENTER CITY CAMPUS
1601 Cherry St., Ste. 100
Philadelphia, PA 19102
Tel: (267)256-0200
Fax: (267)256-0230
Web Site: www.strayer.edu/campus/center-city
Description: Proprietary, comprehensive, coed. Awards associate, bachelor's, and master's degrees.

■ STRAYER UNIVERSITY - DELAWARE COUNTY CAMPUS
760 W Sproul Rd., Ste. 200
Springfield, PA 19064-1215
Tel: (610)604-7700
Fax: (610)543-6599
Web Site: www.strayer.edu/campus/delaware-county
Description: Proprietary, comprehensive, coed. Awards associate, bachelor's, and master's degrees.

■ STRAYER UNIVERSITY - KING OF PRUSSIA CAMPUS
234 Mall Blvd.
Ste. G-50
King of Prussia, PA 19406
Tel: (610)992-1700
Fax: (610)992-9777
Web Site: www.strayer.edu/campus/king-prussia
Description: Proprietary, comprehensive, coed. Awards associate, bachelor's, and master's degrees.

■ STRAYER UNIVERSITY - LOWER BUCKS COUNTY CAMPUS
3800 Horizon Blvd., Ste. 100
Trevose, PA 19053
Tel: (215)953-5999
Fax: (215)953-9464
Web Site: www.strayer.edu/campus/lower-bucks-county/
Description: Proprietary, comprehensive, coed. Awards associate, bachelor's, and master's degrees.

■ STRAYER UNIVERSITY - PENN CENTER WEST CAMPUS
One Penn Ctr. W, Ste. 320
Pittsburgh, PA 15276
Tel: (412)747-7800
Fax: (412)747-7830
Web Site: www.strayer.edu/campus/penn-center-west/
Description: Proprietary, comprehensive, coed. Awards associate, bachelor's, and master's degrees.

■ STRAYER UNIVERSITY - WARRENDALE CAMPUS
802 Warrendale Village Dr.
Warrendale, PA 15086
Tel: (724)799-2900
Fax: (724)933-7877
Web Site: www.strayer.edu/campus/warrendale
Description: Proprietary, comprehensive, coed. Awards associate, bachelor's, and master's degrees.

■ SUSQUEHANNA UNIVERSITY
514 University Ave.
Selinsgrove, PA 17870
Tel: (570)374-0101; Free: 800-326-9672
Fax: (570)372-2722
E-mail: suadmiss@susqu.edu
Web Site: www.susqu.edu/
Description: Independent, 4-year, coed, affiliated with Evangelical Lutheran Church in America. Awards bachelor's degrees (also offers evening associate degree program limited to local adult students). Founded 1858. Setting: 306-acre small town campus with easy access to Harrisburg. Endowment: $121.2 million. Research spending for the previous fiscal year: $254,876. Educational spending for the previous fiscal year: $11,613 per student. Total enrollment: 2,215. Faculty: 254 (141 full-time, 113 part-time). Student-undergrad faculty ratio is 12:1. 3,458 applied, 76% were admitted. 22% from top 10% of their high school class, 55% from top quarter, 84% from top half. 1 National Merit Scholar, 10 class presidents, 6 valedictorians, 61 student government officers. Full-time: 2,142 students, 55% women, 45% men. Part-time: 55 students, 51% women, 49% men. Students come from 35 states and territories, 17 other countries, 49% from out-of-state. 0.1% American Indian or Alaska Native, non-Hispanic/Latino; 5% Hispanic/Latino; 5% African American, non-Hispanic/Latino; 1% Asian, non-Hispanic/Latino; 0.2% Native Hawaiian or other Pacific Islander, non-Hispanic/Latino; 1% international. 1% 25 or older, 77% live on campus, 2% transferred in. Retention: 84% of full-time freshmen returned the following year. Academic areas with the most degrees conferred: business/marketing; communication/journalism; social sciences. Core. Calendar: semesters. Services for LD students, advanced placement, accelerated degree program, self-designed

majors, honors program, independent study, distance learning, double major, summer session for credit, part-time degree program, internships. Off campus study at Lutheran College-Washington Consortium semester in Arlington, Virginia. Study abroad program. ROTC: Army (c).

Entrance Requirements: Options: electronic application, early admission, early decision, deferred admission, international baccalaureate accepted. Required: essay, high school transcript, minimum 2.5 high school GPA, 1 recommendation. Recommended: minimum 3 high school GPA, interview, SAT or ACT. Required for some: writing portfolio, auditions for music programs. Entrance: moderately difficult. Application deadlines: 3/1, 12/1 for early decision. Notification: continuous until 12/15, 12/15 for early decision. SAT Reasoning Test deadline: 3/1. SAT Subject Test deadline: 3/1. Transfer credits accepted: Yes. Applicants placed on waiting list: 196. Wait-listed applicants offered admission: 13. Early decision applicants: 164. Early decision applicants admitted: 127.

Costs Per Year: Application fee: $35. Comprehensive fee: $47,280 includes full-time tuition ($36,800), mandatory fees ($480), and college room and board ($10,000). College room only: $5250. Room and board charges vary according to board plan and housing facility. Part-time tuition: $1170 per semester hour.

Collegiate Environment: Orientation program. Drama-theater group, choral group, student-run newspaper, radio station. Social organizations: 145 open to all; national fraternities, national sororities; 16% of eligible men and 14% of eligible women are members. Most popular organizations: Student Government Association, community service organizations, music performance groups, theater performance groups, intramurals and outdoor recreation. Major annual events: Fall Musical, Spring Weekend, Homecoming. Student services: health clinic, personal-psychological counseling. Campus security: 24-hour emergency response devices and patrols, late night transport-escort service, controlled dormitory access. 1,852 college housing spaces available; 1,782 were occupied in 2012-13. Freshmen guaranteed college housing. On-campus residence required through junior year. Option: coed housing available. Blough-Weis Library plus 1 other with 370,668 books, 32,499 microform titles, 66,321 serials, 10,437 audiovisual materials, an OPAC, and a Web page. Operations spending for the previous fiscal year: $1.6 million. 300 computers available on campus for general student use. Computer purchase/lease plans available. A campuswide network can be accessed from student residence rooms and from off campus. Students can access the following: online class registration, class listings and assignments, online voting booth. Staffed computer lab on campus (open 24 hours a day) provides training in use of computers, software, and the Internet.

Community Environment: Population 5,400. The beautiful Susquehanna River winds through this quiet town. Route 80 is one half hour north and the Pennsylvania Turnpike is one hour south of campus. Selinsgrove is 50 miles north of Harrisburg. Limited part-time employment is available.

■ **SWARTHMORE COLLEGE**

500 College Ave.
Swarthmore, PA 19081-1397
Tel: (610)328-8000; Free: 800-667-3110
Fax: (610)328-8673
E-mail: admissions@swarthmore.edu
Web Site: www.swarthmore.edu/

Description: Independent, 4-year, coed. Awards bachelor's degrees. Founded 1864. Setting: 425-acre suburban campus with easy access to Philadelphia. Endowment: $1.5 billion. Research spending for the previous fiscal year: $3.4 million. Educational spending for the previous fiscal year: $29,966 per student. Total enrollment: 1,552. Faculty: 205 (171 full-time, 34 part-time). Student-undergrad faculty ratio is 8:1. 6,589 applied, 14% were admitted. 92% from top 10% of their high school class, 99% from top quarter, 100% from top half. 22 National Merit Scholars, 30 valedictorians. Full-time: 1,537 students, 51% women, 49% men. Part-time: 15 students, 67% women, 33% men. Students come from 53 states and territories, 44 other countries, 88% from out-of-state. 0.3% American Indian or Alaska Native, non-Hispanic/Latino; 13% Hispanic/Latino; 6% African American, non-Hispanic/Latino; 14% Asian, non-Hispanic/Latino; 8% international. 0.1% 25 or older, 93% live on campus, 1% transferred in. Retention: 97% of full-time freshmen returned the following year. Academic areas with the most degrees conferred: social sciences; biological/life sciences; visual and performing arts. Core. Calendar: semesters. Services for LD students, advanced placement, accelerated degree program, self-designed majors, honors program, independent study, double major, co-op programs and internships. Off campus study at Cross-registration is available at Bryn Mawr and Haverford

colleges, and the University of Pennsylvania Cooperative exchange programs are available with Tufts University and Harvey Mudd, Pomona, Mills, and Middlebury colleges. Study abroad is encouraged and is available to students of all academic majors. Study abroad program. ROTC: Army (c), Naval (c), Air Force (c).

Entrance Requirements: Options: electronic application, early decision, deferred admission, international baccalaureate accepted. Required: essay, high school transcript, 3 recommendations, SAT and SAT Subject Tests or ACT. Required for some: Statement of good standing from prior institution(s) for transfer applicants. Entrance: most difficult. Application deadlines: 1/1, 1/1 for nonresidents, 11/15 for early decision plan 1, 1/1 for early decision plan 2. Notification: 4/1, 4/1 for nonresidents, 12/15 for early decision plan 1, 2/15 for early decision plan 2. SAT Reasoning Test deadline: 1/1. SAT Subject Test deadline: 1/1. Transfer credits accepted: Yes. Wait-listed applicants offered admission: 8. Early decision applicants: 575. Early decision applicants admitted: 180.

Costs Per Year: Application fee: $60. Comprehensive fee: $55,750 includes full-time tuition ($42,744), mandatory fees ($336), and college room and board ($12,670). College room only: $6500. Room and board charges vary according to board plan.

Collegiate Environment: Orientation program. Drama-theater group, choral group, student-run newspaper, radio station. Social organizations: 150 open to all; national fraternities, local fraternities; 14% of men are members. Most popular organizations: community service and activist groups, club sports and intramurals, social/cultural clubs, music/acappella groups, political and debate clubs. Major annual events: Yule Ball, Midnight Breakfast, Spring Fling. Student services: health clinic, personal-psychological counseling, women's center. Campus security: 24-hour emergency response devices and patrols, late night transport-escort service. 1,429 college housing spaces available; 1,372 were occupied in 2012-13. Freshmen guaranteed college housing. On-campus residence required in freshman year. Options: coed, men-only, women-only housing available. McCabe Library plus 6 others with 1.4 million books, 197,376 microform titles, 17,233 serials, 30,146 audiovisual materials, an OPAC, and a Web page. Operations spending for the previous fiscal year: $5.6 million. 332 computers available on campus for general student use. Computer purchase/lease plans available. A campuswide network can be accessed from student residence rooms and from off campus. Students can access the following: online class registration, Course materials and academic software are available online for many courses. Staffed computer lab on campus provides training in use of computers, software, and the Internet.

Community Environment: Swarthmore, population 6,146, is in a suburban area 11 miles from Philadelphia. The climate is temperate. There is bus and rail service to Philadelphia, New York and Washington. Philadelphia International Airport is 15 minutes from campus by car, with a college shuttle before and after breaks and public rail service year-round. The immediate community has a library and churches of various denominations. There are hospitals nearby. For civic services, recreation and cultural facilities, see Philadelphia.

■ **TALMUDICAL YESHIVA OF PHILADELPHIA**

6063 Drexel Rd.
Philadelphia, PA 19131-1296
Tel: (215)473-1212
Fax: (215)477-5065

Description: Independent Jewish, 4-year, men only. Awards bachelor's degrees (also offers some graduate courses). Founded 1953. Setting: 3-acre urban campus. Total enrollment: 112. 51 applied. Core. Calendar: trimesters. Academic remediation for entering students, honors program, internships. Study abroad program.

Entrance Requirements: Options: early admission, deferred admission. Required: high school transcript, 1 recommendation, interview, oral examination. Entrance: moderately difficult. Application deadline: 7/15. Notification: 8/5.

Collegiate Environment: Student services: health clinic, personal-psychological counseling. Campus security: controlled dormitory access, night security patrol. 4,800 books and 300 serials.

■ **TEMPLE UNIVERSITY**

1801 N Broad St.
Philadelphia, PA 19122-6096
Tel: (215)204-7000; Free: 888-340-2222
Fax: (215)204-5694
E-mail: tuadm@temple.edu

Web Site: www.temple.edu/

Description: State-related, university, coed. Awards associate, bachelor's, master's, and doctoral degrees and post-master's certificates. Founded 1884. Setting: 330-acre urban campus with easy access to Philadelphia. Endowment: $277.5 million. Research spending for the previous fiscal year: $109.8 million. Educational spending for the previous fiscal year: $12,237 per student. Total enrollment: 36,744. Faculty: 2,888 (1,452 full-time, 1,436 part-time). Student-undergrad faculty ratio is 15:1. 18,731 applied, 67% were admitted. 18% from top 10% of their high school class, 51% from top quarter, 89% from top half. Full-time: 24,382 students, 51% women, 49% men. Part-time: 3,185 students, 50% women, 50% men. Students come from 52 states and territories, 66 other countries, 18% from out-of-state. 0.2% American Indian or Alaska Native, non-Hispanic/Latino; 5% Hispanic/Latino; 13% African American, non-Hispanic/Latino; 10% Asian, non-Hispanic/Latino; 0.1% Native Hawaiian or other Pacific Islander, non-Hispanic/Latino; 3% international. 13% 25 or older, 14% live on campus, 10% transferred in. Retention: 87% of full-time freshmen returned the following year. Academic areas with the most degrees conferred: business/marketing; visual and performing arts; communication/journalism. Core. Calendar: semesters. Academic remediation for entering students, ESL program, services for LD students, advanced placement, accelerated degree program, self-designed majors, honors program, independent study, distance learning, double major, summer session for credit, part-time degree program, external degree program, adult/continuing education programs, co-op programs and internships, graduate courses open to undergrads. Off campus study at Messiah College. Study abroad program. ROTC: Army, Naval (c), Air Force (c).

Entrance Requirements: Options: electronic application, deferred admission, international baccalaureate accepted. Required: essay, high school transcript, SAT or ACT. Recommended: minimum 3 high school GPA. Entrance: moderately difficult. Application deadline: 3/1. Notification: continuous. SAT Reasoning Test deadline: 3/1. Transfer credits accepted: Yes. Applicants placed on waiting list: 1,168. Wait-listed applicants offered admission: 512.

Costs Per Year: Application fee: $55. State resident tuition: $13,006 full-time, $502 per credit hour part-time. Nonresident tuition: $22,832 full-time, $813 per credit hour part-time. Mandatory fees: $590 full-time. Full-time tuition and fees vary according to course load, program, reciprocity agreements, and student level. Part-time tuition varies according to course load, program, reciprocity agreements, and student level. College room and board: $10,276. College room only: $6956. Room and board charges vary according to board plan and housing facility.

Collegiate Environment: Orientation program. Drama-theater group, choral group, marching band, student-run newspaper, radio station. Social organizations: 329 open to all; national fraternities, national sororities; 4% of eligible men and 4% of eligible women are members. Most popular organizations: Temple Film Collective, Habitat for Humanity, Feminist Majority Leadership Alliance, Alpha Epsilon Delta (Pre-professional students with interests in pursuing careers in healthcare), The Spanish Club. Major annual events: Spring Fling, Homecoming, Cherry and White Day. Student services: legal services, health clinic, personal-psychological counseling. Campus security: 24-hour emergency response devices and patrols, late night transport-escort service, controlled dormitory access. 5,382 college housing spaces available; 4,697 were occupied in 2012-13. Freshmen guaranteed college housing. Option: coed housing available. Paley Library plus 14 others with 3.4 million microform titles, 67,942 serials, 41,441 audiovisual materials, an OPAC, and a Web page. Operations spending for the previous fiscal year: $21.9 million. 3,670 computers available on campus for general student use. Computer purchase/lease plans available. A campuswide network can be accessed from student residence rooms and from off campus. Students can access the following: online class registration, student accounts, Web hosting. Staffed computer lab on campus (open 24 hours a day) provides training in use of computers, software, and the Internet.

Community Environment: "Birthplace of the Nation", Philadelphia has retained much of the charm of its colonial origins even while developing into one of the great industrial cities of the world. Population of the greater metropolitan area is over 2,000,000. Distinctive colonial characteristics such as the Liberty Bell and Independence Hall blend with evidence of vast manufacturing. Narrow cobblestone streets may be found within blocks of the business district. The city has museums, churches of all denominations, many libraries (including the first Free Library in the United States), Fairmon Park (the largest city park in the U.S.), a zoo, planetarium, major league and collegiate sports teams, numerous cultural and entertainment facilities, and all the fraternal, civic, and community service organizations of any large metropolis. Local recreation includes golf, tennis, horseback riding, hunting, boating, fishing, and swimming.

■ **THADDEUS STEVENS COLLEGE OF TECHNOLOGY**
750 E King St.
Lancaster, PA 17602-3198
Tel: (717)299-7730; Free: 800-842-3832
Fax: (717)391-6929
Web Site: www.stevenscollege.edu/

Description: State-supported, 2-year, coed. Awards transfer associate and terminal associate degrees. Founded 1905. Setting: 33-acre urban campus with easy access to Philadelphia. Total enrollment: 789. Student-undergrad faculty ratio is 13:1. 1,565 applied. 0% from out-of-state. 5% 25 or older. Retention: 71% of full-time freshmen returned the following year. Calendar: semesters. Academic remediation for entering students, advanced placement.

Entrance Requirements: Options: electronic application, deferred admission. Required: essay, high school transcript, minimum 2.0 high school GPA, ASSET Test. Required for some: interview. Entrance: moderately difficult. Application deadline: 6/30. Notification: continuous until 7/15. Preference given to needy students, indigent orphans.

Collegiate Environment: Orientation program. Campus security: 24-hour emergency response devices. K.W. Schuler Learning Resources Center with an OPAC and a Web page.

■ **THIEL COLLEGE**
75 College Ave.
Greenville, PA 16125-2181
Tel: (724)589-2000; Free: 800-248-4435
Fax: (724)589-2013
E-mail: admissions@thiel.edu
Web Site: www.thiel.edu/

Description: Independent, 4-year, coed, affiliated with Evangelical Lutheran Church in America. Awards associate and bachelor's degrees. Founded 1866. Setting: 135-acre rural campus with easy access to Cleveland, Pittsburgh. Endowment: $20.9 million. Educational spending for the previous fiscal year: $7011 per student. Total enrollment: 1,109. Faculty: 105 (58 full-time, 47 part-time). Student-undergrad faculty ratio is 14:1. 2,541 applied, 65% were admitted. 9% from top 10% of their high school class, 28% from top quarter, 60% from top half. Full-time: 1,065 students, 46% women, 54% men. Part-time: 44 students, 68% women, 32% men. Students come from 20 states and territories, 6 other countries, 34% from out-of-state. 1% American Indian or Alaska Native, non-Hispanic/Latino; 2% Hispanic/Latino; 8% African American, non-Hispanic/Latino; 0.1% Asian, non-Hispanic/Latino; 0% Native Hawaiian or other Pacific Islander, non-Hispanic/Latino; 1% international. 6% 25 or older, 89% live on campus, 4% transferred in. Retention: 58% of full-time freshmen returned the following year. Academic areas with the most degrees conferred: business/marketing; biological/life sciences; psychology. Core. Calendar: semesters. Academic remediation for entering students, services for LD students, advanced placement, honors program, independent study, distance learning, double major, summer session for credit, part-time degree program, adult/continuing education programs, co-op programs and internships. Off campus study at American University, Art Institute of Pittsburgh, Bryant and Stratton Business Institute (Buffalo, NY), Community College of Allegheny County, Drew University, Harrisburg Area Community College, Union College (KY). Study abroad program.

Entrance Requirements: Options: electronic application, deferred admission, international baccalaureate accepted. Required: essay, high school transcript, minimum 2 high school GPA, 1 recommendation, SAT or ACT. Required for some: interview. Entrance: moderately difficult. Application deadlines: Rolling, Rolling for nonresidents. Notification: continuous, continuous for nonresidents. SAT Reasoning Test deadline: 7/1. SAT Subject Test deadline: 8/1. Transfer credits accepted: Yes.

Costs Per Year: Application fee: $35. One-time mandatory fee: $300. Comprehensive fee: $36,108 includes full-time tuition ($24,208), mandatory fees ($1780), and college room and board ($10,120). College room only: $5060. Room and board charges vary according to board plan and housing facility. Part-time tuition: $808 per credit. Part-time mandatory fees: $890 per term. Part-time tuition and fees vary according to course load.

Collegiate Environment: Orientation program. Drama-theater group, choral group, marching band, student-run newspaper, radio station. Social organizations: 30 open to all; national fraternities, national sororities, local fraternities; 25% of eligible men and 28% of eligible women are members. Most popular organizations: Thiel Players Theatre Group, student government, Thiel Choir, Ski Club, Thiel Christian Fellowship. Major annual events: Homecoming, Student Activities Concerts, Farewell Festival. Student services: health clinic, personal-psychological counseling. Campus security: 24-hour emergency response devices and patrols, late night transport-escort service, controlled dormitory access. Langenheim Memorial Library with 200,540 books, 150,125 microform titles, 412 serials, 450 audiovisual materials, an OPAC, and a Web page. Operations spending for the previous fiscal year: $398,564. 130 computers available on campus for general student use. Computer purchase/lease plans available. A computer is required for all students. A campuswide network can be accessed from student residence rooms. Students can access the following: online class registration. Staffed computer lab on campus provides training in use of computers, software, and the Internet.

Community Environment: Local industry is devoted principally to the manufacture of steel, cars, tanks, structural steel and other steel and aluminum products. Greenville is a small town of 10,000 situated halfway between Erie and Pittsburgh. Cleveland and Youngstown are also with 1 to 1 1/2 hours driving. The community is served by railroad, bus lines, and airlines located at nearby Youngstown airport. Greenville has numerous churches, public library, hospital, and excellent shopping and restaurants. Part-time employment is available. Local recreational facilities include a symphony orchestra, theatre and a number of civic parks. Nearby lakes provide boating, swimming, fishing, water skiing, and golf courses. There are various civic, fraternal, and veteran's organizations active in the community.

■ THOMAS JEFFERSON UNIVERSITY
Eleventh and Walnut Sts.
Philadelphia, PA 19107
Tel: (215)955-6000; Free: 877-533-3247
Fax: (215)503-7241
E-mail: chpadmissions@mail.tju.edu
Web Site: www.jefferson.edu/
Description: Independent, university, coed. Awards associate, bachelor's, master's, and doctoral degrees. Founded 1824. Setting: 13-acre urban campus. Total enrollment: 3,326. Student-undergrad faculty ratio is 15:1. 61% 25 or older. Core. Calendar: semesters. Academic remediation for entering students, services for LD students, advanced placement, accelerated degree program, honors program, independent study, distance learning, double major, part-time degree program, adult/continuing education programs, co-op programs, graduate courses open to undergrads. Off campus study. Study abroad program. ROTC: Air Force (c).
Entrance Requirements: Option: deferred admission. Required: essay, minimum 3.0 high school GPA, 2 recommendations, interview. Recommended: SAT or ACT. Required for some: high school transcript, NET. Entrance: moderately difficult. Application deadline: Rolling. Notification: continuous.
Collegiate Environment: Orientation program. Choral group. Student services: health clinic, personal-psychological counseling. Campus security: 24-hour emergency response devices and patrols, late night transport-escort service, controlled dormitory access. Scott Memorial Library plus 1 other with a Web page.

■ TRIANGLE TECH INC–BETHLEHEM
Lehigh Valley Industrial Park IV
31 S Commerce Way
Bethlehem, PA 18017
Tel: (610)691-1300
Web Site: www.triangle-tech.edu/
Description: Proprietary, 2-year, coed. Awards terminal associate degrees. Setting: urban campus. Total enrollment: 140. Faculty: 10 (8 full-time, 2 part-time). Student-undergrad faculty ratio is 15:1. 109 applied, 99% were admitted. Full-time: 140 students, 4% women, 96% men. Students come from 2 states and territories, 11% from out-of-state. 34% 25 or older, 4% transferred in. Core.
Entrance Requirements: Open admission. Required: high school transcript, interview, high school diploma or GED, tour of school, TABE test for student advising. Entrance: noncompetitive. Transfer credits accepted: Yes.
Collegiate Environment: Orientation program. 27 computers available on campus for general student use.

■ TRIANGLE TECH, INC.–DUBOIS SCHOOL
PO Box 551
DuBois, PA 15801-0551

Tel: (814)371-2090; Free: 800-874-8324
Fax: (814)371-9227
E-mail: tkucic@triangle-tech.com
Web Site: www.triangle-tech.edu/
Description: Proprietary, 2-year, coed. Part of Triangle Tech Group, Inc. Awards diplomas and terminal associate degrees. Founded 1944. Setting: 5-acre small town campus. Total enrollment: 329. Faculty: 21 (all full-time). Student-undergrad faculty ratio is 15:1. 246 applied, 100% were admitted. Full-time: 329 students, 3% women, 97% men. Students come from 2 states and territories, 1 other country, 0% from out-of-state. 48% 25 or older. Core. Calendar: semesters. Academic remediation for entering students, advanced placement. Off campus study at all other campuses of Triangle Tech.
Entrance Requirements: Option: deferred admission. Required: high school transcript, minimum 2 high school GPA, interview. Entrance: minimally difficult. Application deadline: Rolling. Transfer credits accepted: Yes.
Collegiate Environment: Orientation program. Social organizations: 1 open to all. Most popular organization: Student Council. Major annual events: Christmas Luncheon, Student Appreciation Luncheon. Library Resource Center with 1,200 books, 15 serials, and 60 audiovisual materials. 54 computers available on campus for general student use. A campuswide network can be accessed. Staffed computer lab on campus provides training in use of computers, software, and the Internet.

■ TRIANGLE TECH, INC.–ERIE SCHOOL
2000 Liberty St.
Erie, PA 16502-2594
Tel: (814)453-6016; Free: 800-TRI-TECH
Fax: (814)454-2818
Web Site: www.triangle-tech.edu/
Description: Proprietary, 2-year, coed. Part of Triangle Tech Group, Inc. Awards transfer associate and terminal associate degrees. Founded 1976. Setting: 1-acre urban campus. Total enrollment: 176. Faculty: 16 (14 full-time, 2 part-time). Student-undergrad faculty ratio is 12:1. 76 applied, 100% were admitted. Full-time: 176 students, 5% women, 95% men. Students come from 3 states and territories, 10% from out-of-state. 65% 25 or older, 0% transferred in. Core. Calendar: semesters. Academic remediation for entering students, services for LD students, advanced placement.
Entrance Requirements: Option: deferred admission. Required: high school transcript, interview. Entrance: minimally difficult. Application deadline: Rolling.
Collegiate Environment: Orientation program. Social organizations: 1 open to all. Campus security: 24-hour emergency response devices. 1,000 books and 15 serials 50 computers available on campus for general student use. Staffed computer lab on campus provides training in use of computers, software, and the Internet.

■ TRIANGLE TECH, INC.–PITTSBURGH SCHOOL
1940 Perrysville Ave.
Pittsburgh, PA 15214-3897
Tel: (412)359-1000; Free: 800-874-8324
Fax: (412)359-1012
E-mail: info@triangle-tech.edu
Web Site: www.triangle-tech.edu/
Description: Proprietary, 2-year, coed. Part of Triangle Tech Group, Inc. Awards diplomas, transfer associate, and terminal associate degrees. Founded 1944. Setting: 5-acre urban campus. Total enrollment: 265. Student-undergrad faculty ratio is 12:1. 4% from out-of-state. 44% 25 or older. Retention: 78% of full-time freshmen returned the following year. Core. Calendar: semesters. Academic remediation for entering students.
Entrance Requirements: Required: high school transcript, minimum 2.0 high school GPA, interview. Entrance: moderately difficult. Application deadline: Rolling.
Collegiate Environment: Campus security: 16-hour patrols by trained security personnel.

■ TRIANGLE TECH, INC.–SUNBURY SCHOOL
191 Performance Rd.
Sunbury, PA 17801
Tel: (570)988-0700
Web Site: www.triangle-tech.edu/
Description: Proprietary, 2-year, coed. Awards terminal associate degrees. Setting: 4-acre rural campus. Total enrollment: 170. Faculty: 15 (14 full-time, 1 part-time). Student-undergrad faculty ratio is 12:1. 76 applied, 100% were

admitted. Full-time: 170 students, 2% women, 98% men. Students come from 2 states and territories, 0.01% from out-of-state. 39% 25 or older. Retention: 75% of full-time freshmen returned the following year. Core. Calendar: semesters. Advanced placement, co-op programs.

Entrance Requirements: Required: high school transcript.

Collegiate Environment: Orientation program. Main library plus 1 other with 300 books, 50 serials, and 25 audiovisual materials. 26 computers available on campus for general student use.

■ TRIANGLE TECH–GREENSBURG SCHOOL
222 E Pittsburgh St.
Ste. A
Greensburg, PA 15601-3304
Tel: (724)832-1050; Free: 800-874-8324
Web Site: www.triangle-tech.edu/

Description: Proprietary, 2-year, coed. Part of Triangle Tech Group, Inc. Awards diplomas and terminal associate degrees. Founded 1944. Setting: 1-acre small town campus with easy access to Pittsburgh. Total enrollment: 260. Faculty: 21 (all full-time). Student-undergrad faculty ratio is 12:1. 247 applied, 100% were admitted. Full-time: 260 students, 2% women, 98% men. 0% from out-of-state. 45% 25 or older. Core. Calendar: semesters. Academic remediation for entering students, advanced placement, summer session for credit, adult/continuing education programs.

Entrance Requirements: Option: deferred admission. Required: high school transcript, interview. Entrance: moderately difficult. Application deadline: Rolling. Transfer credits accepted: Yes.

Collegiate Environment: Orientation program. Student services: personal-psychological counseling. Triangle Tech Library plus 1 other with 550 books and 15 serials. 55 computers available on campus for general student use. A campuswide network can be accessed. Staffed computer lab on campus provides training in use of computers, software, and the Internet.

■ THE UNIVERSITY OF THE ARTS
320 S Broad St.
Philadelphia, PA 19102-4944
Tel: (215)717-6000; Free: 800-616-ARTS
Fax: (215)717-6045
E-mail: admissions@uarts.edu
Web Site: www.uarts.edu/

Description: Independent, comprehensive, coed. Awards bachelor's and master's degrees. Founded 1870. Setting: 21-acre urban campus. Total enrollment: 2,126. Faculty: 505 (121 full-time, 384 part-time). Student-undergrad faculty ratio is 8:1. 1,634 applied, 69% were admitted. Full-time: 1,867 students, 57% women, 43% men. Part-time: 42 students, 57% women, 43% men. Students come from 41 states and territories, 16 other countries, 63% from out-of-state. 0.4% American Indian or Alaska Native, non-Hispanic/Latino; 7% Hispanic/Latino; 13% African American, non-Hispanic/Latino; 3% Asian, non-Hispanic/Latino; 1% Native Hawaiian or other Pacific Islander, non-Hispanic/Latino; 6% international. 5% 25 or older, 33% live on campus, 6% transferred in. Retention: 81% of full-time freshmen returned the following year. Academic areas with the most degrees conferred: visual and performing arts; education; communication/journalism. Core. Calendar: semesters. Academic remediation for entering students, ESL program, services for LD students, advanced placement, accelerated degree program, honors program, independent study, double major, summer session for credit, part-time degree program, internships, graduate courses open to undergrads. Off campus study at University of the Sciences in Philadelphia. Study abroad program.

Entrance Requirements: Options: electronic application, deferred admission. Required: essay, high school transcript, 1 recommendation, Interview recommended for all; audition or portfolio required for performing arts programs; portfolio required for design, visual arts, film programs, essay required for all programs. Recommended: minimum 2 high school GPA, interview. Required for some: interview, SAT or ACT. Entrance: moderately difficult. Application deadlines: Rolling, Rolling for nonresidents. Notification: continuous, continuous for nonresidents. Transfer credits accepted: Yes.

Costs Per Year: Application fee: $60. Comprehensive fee: $47,540 includes full-time tuition ($34,840) and college room and board ($12,700). College room only: $8200. Room and board charges vary according to board plan and housing facility.

Collegiate Environment: Orientation program. Drama-theater group, choral group. Social organizations: 17 open to all. Most popular organizations: Student Council, Gallery One, African Diaspora Collective, UArts Literary Society, The Fifth Circle (fencing). Major annual events: Late Night

Breakfasts, Midterm Block Party, Cafe Series. Student services: health clinic, personal-psychological counseling. Campus security: 24-hour emergency response devices and patrols, late night transport-escort service, crime prevention workshops and seminars. 593 college housing spaces available; all were occupied in 2012-13. Freshmen given priority for college housing. Option: coed housing available. Albert M. Greenfield Library plus 1 other with 108,274 books, 461 microform titles, 16,655 serials, 27,091 audiovisual materials, an OPAC, and a Web page. 368 computers available on campus for general student use. A computer is required for all students. A campuswide network can be accessed from student residence rooms. Students can access the following: online class registration. Staffed computer lab on campus provides training in use of computers and software.

Community Environment: The campus is located in the heart of Philadelphia's cultural community. The area has theaters, museums, galleries, music and dance facilities, restaurants of many ethnic varieties, and major department stores and shops. Philadelphia offers a broad mix of experiences of historical importance. The city is also known as a supporter of the arts. Urban and sophisticated, it is at the same time a series of small, close-knit neighborhoods. Fairmount Park, the largest municipal park in the world, provides facilities for boating, fishing, hiking, biking, picnicking, and relaxing.

■ UNIVERSITY OF PENNSYLVANIA
3451 Walnut St.
Philadelphia, PA 19104
Tel: (215)898-5000
Web Site: www.upenn.edu/

Description: Independent, university, coed. Awards associate, bachelor's, master's, and doctoral degrees and post-master's certificates (also offers evening program with significant enrollment not reflected in profile). Founded 1740. Setting: 302-acre urban campus. Endowment: $6.8 billion. Research spending for the previous fiscal year: $720.2 million. Educational spending for the previous fiscal year: $45,599 per student. Total enrollment: 21,339. Faculty: 2,250 (1,437 full-time, 813 part-time). Student-undergrad faculty ratio is 6:1. 31,218 applied, 13% were admitted. 94% from top 10% of their high school class, 99% from top quarter, 100% from top half. Full-time: 9,374 students, 50% women, 50% men. Part-time: 308 students, 50% women, 50% men. Students come from 54 states and territories, 101 other countries, 84% from out-of-state. 0.2% American Indian or Alaska Native, non-Hispanic/Latino; 9% Hispanic/Latino; 7% African American, non-Hispanic/Latino; 19% Asian, non-Hispanic/Latino; 0.1% Native Hawaiian or other Pacific Islander, non-Hispanic/Latino; 12% international. 1% 25 or older, 56% live on campus, 1% transferred in. Retention: 98% of full-time freshmen returned the following year. Academic areas with the most degrees conferred: business/marketing; social sciences; health professions and related sciences; engineering. Core. Calendar: semesters plus 2 5-week summer sessions. Academic remediation for entering students, ESL program, services for LD students, advanced placement, accelerated degree program, self-designed majors, honors program, independent study, distance learning, double major, summer session for credit, part-time degree program, adult/continuing education programs, co-op programs and internships, graduate courses open to undergrads. Off campus study at Bryn Mawr College, Haverford College, Swarthmore College. Study abroad program. ROTC: Army (c), Naval, Air Force (c).

Entrance Requirements: Options: electronic application, early admission, early decision, deferred admission, international baccalaureate accepted. Required: essay, high school transcript, 2 recommendations, SAT and SAT Subject Tests or ACT. Entrance: most difficult. Application deadlines: 1/1, 11/1 for early decision. Notification: 4/1, 12/15 for early decision. SAT Reasoning Test deadline: 1/1. SAT Subject Test deadline: 1/1. Applicants placed on waiting list: 2,017. Wait-listed applicants offered admission: 87. Early decision applicants: 4,527. Early decision applicants admitted: 1,143.

Costs Per Year: Application fee: $75. Comprehensive fee: $56,106 includes full-time tuition ($39,088), mandatory fees ($4650), and college room and board ($12,368). College room only: $7952. Room and board charges vary according to board plan and housing facility. Part-time tuition: $4989 per course. Part-time mandatory fees: $543 per course. Part-time tuition and fees vary according to course load.

Collegiate Environment: Orientation program. Drama-theater group, choral group, marching band, student-run newspaper, radio station. Social organizations: 350 open to all; national fraternities, national sororities; 30% of eligible men and 27% of eligible women are members. Most popular organizations: Kite and Key Society, Social Planning and Events Committee, Hillel at Penn, Sports Club Council, Interfraternity Council. Major annual events: Homecoming, Spring Fling, Hey Day. Student services: legal services, health clinic, personal-psychological counseling, women's center. Campus security: 24-hour emergency response devices and patrols, late night transport-escort service, controlled dormitory access. 5,662 college housing spaces available; 5,646 were occupied in 2012-13. Freshmen guaranteed college housing. Option: coed housing available. Van Pelt Library plus 15 others with 6.1 million books, 4.2 million microform titles, 109,467 serials, 125,811 audiovisual materials, an OPAC, and a Web page. Operations spending for the previous fiscal year: $58.8 million.

Community Environment: Philadelphia is a large city with the feel of small villages; many with distinct characters. It is a center of history, culture and business, opera, symphony and ballet, museums, major sports teams and theater. The city is ideally located near both seashore and ski resorts.

■ **UNIVERSITY OF PHOENIX–HARRISBURG CAMPUS**

4050 Crums Mill Rd.
Harrisburg, PA 17112
Tel: (717)540-3300; Free: 866-766-0766
Web Site: www.phoenix.edu/

Description: Proprietary, comprehensive, coed. Awards associate, bachelor's, master's, and doctoral degrees.

■ **UNIVERSITY OF PHOENIX–PHILADELPHIA CAMPUS**

170 S Warner Rd.
Ste. 200
Wayne, PA 19087-2121
Tel: (610)989-0880; Free: 866-766-0766
Fax: (610)989-0881
Web Site: www.phoenix.edu/

Description: Proprietary, comprehensive, coed. Awards bachelor's and master's degrees. Founded 1999. Setting: urban campus. Total enrollment: 883. Faculty: 177 (24 full-time, 153 part-time). Full-time: 778 students, 72% women, 28% men. 80% 25 or older. Academic areas with the most degrees conferred: business/marketing; computer and information sciences; homeland security, law enforcement, firefighting, and protective services. Core. Calendar: continuous. Services for LD students, advanced placement, accelerated degree program, independent study, distance learning, external degree program, adult/continuing education programs, graduate courses open to undergrads.

Entrance Requirements: Open admission. Options: electronic application, deferred admission. Required: 1 recommendation. Required for some: high school transcript. Entrance: noncompetitive. Application deadline: Rolling.

Collegiate Environment: Campus security: late night transport-escort service. University Library with 16,781 serials, an OPAC, and a Web page. Operations spending for the previous fiscal year: $6.8 million.

■ **UNIVERSITY OF PHOENIX–PITTSBURGH CAMPUS**

Penn Ctr. W Six
Ste. 100
Pittsburgh, PA 15276
Tel: (412)747-9000; Free: 866-766-0766
Fax: (412)747-0676
Web Site: www.phoenix.edu/

Description: Proprietary, comprehensive, coed. Awards bachelor's and master's degrees. Founded 2001. Setting: urban campus. Total enrollment: 101. Faculty: 79 (8 full-time, 71 part-time). 5 applied, 100% were admitted. Full-time: 82 students, 49% women, 51% men. 95% 25 or older. Academic areas with the most degrees conferred: business/marketing; computer and information sciences; homeland security, law enforcement, firefighting, and protective services. Core. Calendar: continuous. Services for LD students, advanced placement, accelerated degree program, independent study, distance learning, external degree program, adult/continuing education programs, graduate courses open to undergrads.

Entrance Requirements: Open admission. Options: electronic application, deferred admission. Required: 1 recommendation. Required for some: high school transcript. Entrance: noncompetitive. Application deadline: Rolling.

Collegiate Environment: Campus security: late night transport-escort service. University Library with 16,781 serials, an OPAC, and a Web page. Operations spending for the previous fiscal year: $6.9 million.

■ **UNIVERSITY OF PITTSBURGH**

4200 Fifth Ave.
Pittsburgh, PA 15260
Tel: (412)624-4141

Fax: (412)648-8815
E-mail: oafa@pitt.edu
Web Site: www.pitt.edu/

Description: State-related, university, coed. Part of Commonwealth System of Higher Education. Awards bachelor's, master's, and doctoral degrees and post-master's certificates. Founded 1787. Setting: 132-acre urban campus with easy access to Pittsburgh. Endowment: $2.6 billion. Research spending for the previous fiscal year: $677.7 million. Total enrollment: 28,769. Faculty: 2,206 (1,594 full-time, 612 part-time). Student-undergrad faculty ratio is 14:1. 24,871 applied, 56% were admitted. 52% from top 10% of their high school class, 86% from top quarter, 99% from top half. Full-time: 17,256 students, 50% women, 50% men. Part-time: 1,173 students, 52% women, 48% men. Students come from 52 states and territories, 45 other countries, 25% from out-of-state. 0.1% American Indian or Alaska Native, non-Hispanic/Latino; 2% Hispanic/Latino; 6% African American, non-Hispanic/Latino; 6% Asian, non-Hispanic/Latino; 0.1% Native Hawaiian or other Pacific Islander, non-Hispanic/Latino; 3% international. 8% 25 or older, 44% live on campus, 5% transferred in. Retention: 93% of full-time freshmen returned the following year. Academic areas with the most degrees conferred: social sciences; business/marketing; health professions and related sciences. Core. Calendar: semesters plus summer term. Academic remediation for entering students, ESL program, services for LD students, advanced placement, accelerated degree program, self-designed majors, freshman honors college, honors program, independent study, distance learning, double major, summer session for credit, part-time degree program, external degree program, adult/continuing education programs, co-op programs and internships, graduate courses open to undergrads. Off campus study at 10 other institutions in the surrounding area. Study abroad program. ROTC: Army, Naval (c), Air Force.

Entrance Requirements: Options: electronic application, international baccalaureate accepted. Required: high school transcript, SAT or ACT. Recommended: essay, interview, SAT and SAT Subject Tests or ACT, SAT Subject Tests. Entrance: moderately difficult. Application deadline: Rolling. Notification: continuous. Transfer credits accepted: Yes. Applicants placed on waiting list: 1,191. Wait-listed applicants offered admission: 31.

Costs Per Year: Application fee: $45. State resident tuition: $15,730 full-time, $655 per credit part-time. Nonresident tuition: $25,420 full-time, $1059 per credit part-time. Mandatory fees: $860 full-time, $214. Full-time tuition and fees vary according to location and program. Part-time tuition and fees vary according to location and program. College room and board: $9870. College room only: $5950. Room and board charges vary according to board plan, housing facility, and location.

Collegiate Environment: Orientation program. Drama-theater group, choral group, marching band, student-run newspaper, radio station. Social organizations: 485 open to all; national fraternities, national sororities; 11% of eligible men and 9% of eligible women are members. Most popular organizations: Resident Student Association, Black Action Society, Engineering Student Council, Interfraternity Council, Panhellenic Association. Major annual events: Homecoming Laser and Fireworks Show, Fall Fest, Bigelow Bash. Student services: health clinic, personal-psychological counseling. Campus security: 24-hour emergency response devices and patrols, late night transport-escort service, controlled dormitory access, on-call van transportation. 7,291 college housing spaces available; all were occupied in 2012-13. Freshmen guaranteed college housing. Options: coed, women-only housing available. Hillman Library plus 14 others with 6.7 million books, 5.5 million microform titles, 279,272 serials, 1.2 million audiovisual materials, an OPAC, and a Web page. Operations spending for the previous fiscal year: $45.4 million. 2,000 computers available on campus for general student use. Computer purchase/lease plans available. A campuswide network can be accessed from student residence rooms and from off campus. Students can access the following: online class registration, online class listings, online tuition payment. Staffed computer lab on campus (open 24 hours a day) provides training in use of computers, software, and the Internet.

Community Environment: Pittsburgh is a city of hills, rivers, and bridges, and a mixture of traditional and contemporary lifestyles. Accessible by air, bus, and rail its attractions include concerts, folk festivals, the Pittsburgh Symphony, Phipps Conservatory, professional sports, museums, libraries, parks, and art galleries.

■ **UNIVERSITY OF PITTSBURGH AT BRADFORD**

300 Campus Dr.
Bradford, PA 16701-2812
Tel: (814)362-7500; Free: 800-872-1787

Fax: (814)362-7578

E-mail: monti@pitt.edu

Web Site: www.upb.pitt.edu/

Description: State-related, 4-year, coed. Administratively affiliated with University of Pittsburgh System. Awards associate and bachelor's degrees. Founded 1963. Setting: 317-acre small town campus with easy access to Buffalo. Endowment: $18.5 million. Research spending for the previous fiscal year: $888,295. Educational spending for the previous fiscal year: $5232 per student. Total enrollment: 1,518. Faculty: 155 (71 full-time, 84 part-time). Student-undergrad faculty ratio is 17:1. 940 applied, 45% were admitted. 8% from top 10% of their high school class, 27% from top quarter, 64% from top half. Full-time: 1,378 students, 54% women, 46% men. Part-time: 140 students, 64% women, 36% men. Students come from 25 states and territories, 12 other countries, 16% from out-of-state. 0.5% American Indian or Alaska Native, non-Hispanic/Latino; 3% Hispanic/Latino; 9% African American, non-Hispanic/Latino; 3% Asian, non-Hispanic/Latino; 3% international. 14% 25 or older, 62% live on campus, 7% transferred in. Retention: 72% of full-time freshmen returned the following year. Academic areas with the most degrees conferred: business/marketing; social sciences; education. Core. Calendar: semesters. Academic remediation for entering students, services for LD students, advanced placement, accelerated degree program, independent study, distance learning, double major, summer session for credit, part-time degree program, adult/continuing education programs, internships. Off campus study at University of Pittsburgh - Oakland, University of Pittsburgh - Greensburg, University of Pittsburgh - Johnstown, University of Pittsburgh - Titusville. Study abroad program. ROTC: Army (c).

Entrance Requirements: Options: electronic application, deferred admission, international baccalaureate accepted. Required: high school transcript, minimum 2 high school GPA, SAT or ACT. Recommended: essay, 2 recommendations, interview. Required for some: minimum 3 high school GPA. Entrance: minimally difficult. Application deadlines: Rolling, Rolling for nonresidents. Notification: continuous, continuous for nonresidents. SAT Reasoning Test deadline: 7/1. Transfer credits accepted: Yes. Applicants placed on waiting list: 0. Wait-listed applicants offered admission: 0.

Costs Per Year: Application fee: $45. One-time mandatory fee: $90. State resident tuition: $11,970 full-time, $498 per credit hour part-time. Nonresident tuition: $22,366 full-time, $931 per credit hour part-time. Mandatory fees: $840 full-time, $135 per term part-time. Full-time tuition and fees vary according to course load and program. Part-time tuition and fees vary according to course load and program. College room and board: $7960. College room only: $4920. Room and board charges vary according to board plan and housing facility.

Collegiate Environment: Orientation program. Drama-theater group, choral group, student-run newspaper, radio station. Social organizations: 53 open to all; national fraternities, national sororities, local fraternities, local sororities; 5% of eligible men and 3% of eligible women are members. Most popular organizations: Student Government Association, Student Activities Board, The Source (student newspaper), Alpha Phi Omega, WDRQ (student radio station). Major annual events: Alumni Weekend, Winter Weekend, Spring Fling. Student services: health clinic, personal-psychological counseling. Campus security: 24-hour emergency response devices and patrols, late night transport-escort service, controlled dormitory access. 938 college housing spaces available; 926 were occupied in 2012-13. Freshmen guaranteed college housing. On-campus residence required in freshman year. Option: coed housing available. T. Edward and Tullah Hanley Library with 99,223 books, 1,055 microform titles, 231 serials, 3,895 audiovisual materials, an OPAC, and a Web page. Operations spending for the previous fiscal year: $16,672. 120 computers available on campus for general student use. A campuswide network can be accessed from student residence rooms and from off campus. Students can access the following: online class registration, online bills. Staffed computer lab on campus provides training in use of computers, software, and the Internet.

■ **UNIVERSITY OF PITTSBURGH AT GREENSBURG**

150 Finoli Dr.

Greensburg, PA 15601-5860

Tel: (724)837-7040

Fax: (724)836-9901

E-mail: upgadmit@pitt.edu

Web Site: www.greensburg.pitt.edu/

Description: State-related, 4-year, coed. Part of University of Pittsburgh system. Awards bachelor's degrees. Founded 1963. Setting: 219-acre small town campus with easy access to Pittsburgh. Total enrollment: 1,733.

Faculty: 133 (73 full-time, 60 part-time). Student-undergrad faculty ratio is 18:1. 1,262 applied, 93% were admitted. 11% from top 10% of their high school class, 30% from top quarter, 80% from top half. Full-time: 1,606 students, 50% women, 50% men. Part-time: 127 students, 46% women, 54% men. Students come from 20 states and territories, 6 other countries, 2% from out-of-state. 0.1% American Indian or Alaska Native, non-Hispanic/Latino; 3% Hispanic/Latino; 5% African American, non-Hispanic/Latino; 3% Asian, non-Hispanic/Latino; 0% Native Hawaiian or other Pacific Islander, non-Hispanic/Latino; 2% international. 10% 25 or older, 40% live on campus, 8% transferred in. Retention: 74% of full-time freshmen returned the following year. Academic areas with the most degrees conferred: business/marketing; psychology; biological/life sciences. Core. Calendar: semesters. Academic remediation for entering students, services for LD students, advanced placement, accelerated degree program, self-designed majors, independent study, distance learning, double major, summer session for credit, part-time degree program, adult/continuing education programs, internships. Off campus study at Seton Hill College, other units of the University of Pittsburgh, Westmoreland County Community College. Study abroad program. ROTC: Army (c), Air Force (c).

Entrance Requirements: Options: electronic application, early admission, deferred admission. Required: high school transcript, minimum 2.5 high school GPA, SAT or ACT. Recommended: essay, interview. Entrance: moderately difficult. Application deadlines: 8/1, 8/1 for nonresidents. Notification: continuous. SAT Reasoning Test deadline: 7/1. Transfer credits accepted: Yes.

Costs Per Year: Application fee: $45. State resident tuition: $11,970 full-time, $498 per credit hour part-time. Nonresident tuition: $22,366 full-time, $931 per credit hour part-time. Mandatory fees: $920 full-time, $174 per term part-time. College room and board: $8730. Room and board charges vary according to board plan and housing facility.

Collegiate Environment: Orientation program. Drama-theater group, choral group, student-run newspaper, radio station. Social organizations: 40 open to all. Most popular organizations: Habitat for Humanity, Student Government Association, Student Activities Board, Outdoor Adventure and Community Service, Freshmen Honor Society - Phi Eta Sigma. Major annual events: Into the Streets - community volunteer event, Big Bang - fall term kick-off, Up All Night - end of term event. Student services: health clinic, personal-psychological counseling. Campus security: 24-hour emergency response devices and patrols, late night transport-escort service, controlled dormitory access. 615 college housing spaces available; 558 were occupied in 2012-13. No special consideration for freshman housing applicants. Option: coed housing available. Millstein Library with 75,000 books, 418 serials, an OPAC, and a Web page. 174 computers available on campus for general student use. A campuswide network can be accessed from student residence rooms and from off campus. Students can access the following: online class registration. Staffed computer lab on campus provides training in use of computers, software, and the Internet.

■ **UNIVERSITY OF PITTSBURGH AT JOHNSTOWN**

450 Schoolhouse Rd.

Johnstown, PA 15904-2990

Tel: (814)269-7000; Free: 800-765-4875

Fax: (814)269-7044

E-mail: upjadmit@pitt.edu

Web Site: www.upj.pitt.edu/

Description: State-related, 4-year, coed. Part of University of Pittsburgh System. Awards associate and bachelor's degrees. Founded 1927. Setting: 655-acre suburban campus with easy access to Pittsburgh. Total enrollment: 2,957. 1,613 applied, 88% were admitted. 11% from top 10% of their high school class, 34% from top quarter, 71% from top half. 8 valedictorians. Full-time: 2,849 students, 46% women, 54% men. Part-time: 108 students, 51% women, 49% men. Students come from 14 states and territories, 12 other countries, 2% from out-of-state. 0.1% American Indian or Alaska Native, non-Hispanic/Latino; 2% Hispanic/Latino; 3% African American, non-Hispanic/Latino; 1% Asian, non-Hispanic/Latino; 0.1% Native Hawaiian or other Pacific Islander, non-Hispanic/Latino; 1% international. 6% 25 or older, 59% live on campus, 3% transferred in. Retention: 74% of full-time freshmen returned the following year. Academic areas with the most degrees conferred: business/marketing; education; engineering technologies. Core. Calendar: semesters. Services for LD students, advanced placement, accelerated degree program, self-designed majors, independent study, distance learning, double major, summer session for credit, part-time degree program, adult/continuing education programs, co-op programs and internships. Off campus study at members of the Pittsburgh Council on Higher Education. Study abroad program.

Entrance Requirements: Options: electronic application, early admission, deferred admission, international baccalaureate accepted. Required: high school transcript, minimum 2 high school GPA, SAT or ACT. Recommended: essay, 3 recommendations. Required for some: interview. Entrance: moderately difficult. Application deadlines: Rolling, Rolling for nonresidents. Notification: continuous, continuous for nonresidents. SAT Reasoning Test deadline: 5/1.

Costs Per Year: Application fee: $45. State resident tuition: $11,970 full-time, $498 per credit hour part-time. Nonresident tuition: $22,366 full-time, $931 per credit hour part-time. Mandatory fees: $922 full-time. Full-time tuition and fees vary according to program. Part-time tuition varies according to program. College room and board: $8230. College room only: $5180. Room and board charges vary according to board plan and housing facility.

Collegiate Environment: Orientation program. Drama-theater group, choral group, student-run newspaper, radio station. Social organizations: 95 open to all; national fraternities, national sororities; 8% of eligible men and 11% of eligible women are members. Most popular organizations: Dance Ensemble, Student Senate, Programming Board, academic clubs. Major annual events: Homecoming, Greek Week. Student services: health clinic, personal-psychological counseling. Campus security: 24-hour emergency response devices and patrols, late night transport-escort service, controlled dormitory access. Owen Library with 145,547 books, 20,728 microform titles, 450 serials, an OPAC, and a Web page. 222 computers available on campus for general student use. Computer purchase/lease plans available. A campuswide network can be accessed from student residence rooms and from off campus. Students can access the following: online class registration. Staffed computer lab on campus provides training in use of computers, software, and the Internet.

■ UNIVERSITY OF PITTSBURGH AT TITUSVILLE
504 E Main St.
Titusville, PA 16354
Tel: (814)827-4400; Free: 888-878-0462
Fax: (814)827-4448
E-mail: wyant@pitt.edu
Web Site: www.upt.pitt.edu/

Description: State-related, 2-year, coed. Part of University of Pittsburgh System. Awards transfer associate and terminal associate degrees. Founded 1963. Setting: 10-acre small town campus. Endowment: $850,000. Total enrollment: 388. Faculty: 59 (25 full-time, 34 part-time). Student-undergrad faculty ratio is 15:1. 9% from top 10% of their high school class, 26% from top quarter, 68% from top half. 1 valedictorian. Full-time: 313 students, 63% women, 37% men. Part-time: 75 students, 76% women, 24% men. Students come from 15 states and territories, 8% from out-of-state. 0% American Indian or Alaska Native, non-Hispanic/Latino; 4% Hispanic/Latino; 14% African American, non-Hispanic/Latino; 2% Asian, non-Hispanic/Latino; 0% Native Hawaiian or other Pacific Islander, non-Hispanic/Latino. 14% 25 or older, 42% live on campus, 4% transferred in. Core. Calendar: semesters. Academic remediation for entering students, advanced placement, distance learning, summer session for credit, part-time degree program, internships. Study abroad program.

Entrance Requirements: Required: high school transcript, minimum 2 high school GPA, SAT or ACT. Recommended: interview. Required for some: essay, 3 recommendations.

Costs Per Year: State resident tuition: $10,544 full-time, $439 per credit hour part-time. Nonresident tuition: $19,918 full-time, $829 per credit hour part-time. Mandatory fees: $780 full-time. Full-time tuition and fees vary according to program. Part-time tuition varies according to program. College room and board: $9364. College room only: $4982. Room and board charges vary according to board plan.

Collegiate Environment: Orientation program. Drama-theater group, choral group. Social organizations: 20 open to all. Most popular organizations: Phi Theta Kappa, BSU, SAB, Dining Club, Diversity Club. Major annual events: Talent Show, semi-formal dance, Stress Relief Week. Student services: health clinic. Campus security: 24-hour emergency response devices and patrols, late night transport-escort service, controlled dormitory access. 300 college housing spaces available; 163 were occupied in 2012-13. Freshmen guaranteed college housing. On-campus residence required through sophomore year. Option: coed housing available. Haskell Memorial Library with 49,256 books, 1,358 microform titles, 126 serials, and an OPAC. 74 computers available on campus for general student use. A campuswide network can be accessed from student residence rooms and from off campus. Students can access the following: online class registration. Staffed computer lab on campus provides training in use of computers, software, and the Internet.

■ UNIVERSITY OF THE SCIENCES
600 S 43rd St.
Philadelphia, PA 19104-4495
Tel: (215)596-8800; Free: 888-996-8747
Fax: (215)895-1100
E-mail: admit@usciences.edu
Web Site: www.usciences.edu

Description: Independent, university, coed. Awards bachelor's, master's, and doctoral degrees. Founded 1821. Setting: 35-acre urban campus. Endowment: $154.2 million. Research spending for the previous fiscal year: $4.5 million. Educational spending for the previous fiscal year: $13,340 per student. Total enrollment: 2,770. Faculty: 323 (187 full-time, 136 part-time). Student-undergrad faculty ratio is 10:1. 4,307 applied, 56% were admitted. 46% from top 10% of their high school class, 79% from top quarter, 97% from top half. 18 valedictorians. Full-time: 2,406 students, 61% women, 39% men. Part-time: 30 students, 60% women, 40% men. Students come from 34 states and territories, 13 other countries, 56% from out-of-state. 0.2% American Indian or Alaska Native, non-Hispanic/Latino; 3% Hispanic/Latino; 5% African American, non-Hispanic/Latino; 36% Asian, non-Hispanic/Latino; 0.4% Native Hawaiian or other Pacific Islander, non-Hispanic/Latino; 2% international. 5% 25 or older, 32% live on campus, 4% transferred in. Retention: 84% of full-time freshmen returned the following year. Academic areas with the most degrees conferred: health professions and related sciences; biological/life sciences; psychology; physical sciences. Core. Calendar: semesters. Academic remediation for entering students, services for LD students, advanced placement, honors program, distance learning, double major, summer session for credit, part-time degree program, adult/continuing education programs, co-op programs and internships, graduate courses open to undergrads. Off campus study at University of the Arts. Study abroad program. ROTC: Army (c), Air Force (c).

Entrance Requirements: Options: electronic application, deferred admission, international baccalaureate accepted. Required: high school transcript, SAT or ACT. Recommended: minimum 3 high school GPA, SAT. Entrance: moderately difficult. Application deadline: Rolling. Notification: continuous.

Collegiate Environment: Orientation program. Drama-theater group, choral group, student-run newspaper. Social organizations: 65 open to all; national fraternities, national sororities, local fraternities, local sororities. Most popular organizations: student government, Bharat, Academy of Students of Pharmacy, Student Physical Therapy Association, Asian Student Association. Major annual events: Greek Week, Student Appreciation Day, Parent's Weekend. Student services: health clinic, personal-psychological counseling. Campus security: 24-hour emergency response devices and patrols, late night transport-escort service, controlled dormitory access. 767 college housing spaces available; 711 were occupied in 2012-13. Freshmen guaranteed college housing. On-campus residence required through sophomore year. Option: coed housing available. Joseph W. England Library plus 1 other with 87,125 books, 27,642 microform titles, 9,817 serials, an OPAC, and a Web page. Operations spending for the previous fiscal year: $1.9 million. 350 computers available on campus for general student use. Computer purchase/lease plans available. A campuswide network can be accessed from student residence rooms and from off campus. Students can access the following: online class registration. Staffed computer lab on campus provides training in use of computers, software, and the Internet.

■ THE UNIVERSITY OF SCRANTON
800 Linden St.
Scranton, PA 18510
Tel: (570)941-7400; Free: 888-SCRANTON
Fax: (570)941-5928
E-mail: admissions@scranton.edu
Web Site: www.scranton.edu/

Description: Independent Roman Catholic (Jesuit), comprehensive, coed. Awards bachelor's, master's, and doctoral degrees and post-master's certificates. Founded 1888. Setting: 50-acre urban campus. Endowment: $125.2 million. Educational spending for the previous fiscal year: $31,431 per student. Total enrollment: 5,898. Faculty: 522 (272 full-time, 250 part-time). Student-undergrad faculty ratio is 11:1. 9,672 applied, 69% were admitted. 29% from top 10% of their high school class, 64% from top quarter, 92% from top half. 11 valedictorians. Full-time: 3,847 students, 55% women, 45% men. Part-time: 194 students, 55% women, 45% men. Students come from 24 states and territories, 12 other countries, 58% from out-of-state. 0.2% American Indian or Alaska Native, non-Hispanic/Latino; 7% Hispanic/Latino; 2% African American, non-Hispanic/Latino; 3% Asian, non-Hispanic/Latino; 0.03% Native Hawaiian or other Pacific Islander, non-Hispanic/

Latino; 0.4% international. 3% 25 or older, 64% live on campus, 2% transferred in. Retention: 87% of full-time freshmen returned the following year. Academic areas with the most degrees conferred: business/marketing; health professions and related sciences; biological/life sciences. Core. Calendar: 4-1-4. Academic remediation for entering students, services for LD students, advanced placement, accelerated degree program, self-designed majors, honors program, independent study, distance learning, double major, summer session for credit, part-time degree program, adult/continuing education programs, internships, graduate courses open to undergrads. Off campus study at Marywood University. Study abroad program. ROTC: Army, Air Force (c).

Entrance Requirements: Options: electronic application, early admission, early action, deferred admission, international baccalaureate accepted. Required: essay, high school transcript, 1 recommendation, SAT or ACT. Required for some: interview. Entrance: moderately difficult. Application deadlines: 3/1, 11/15 for early action. Notification: continuous until 1/15, 12/15 for early action. SAT Reasoning Test deadline: 3/1. Transfer credits accepted: Yes. Applicants placed on waiting list: 1,087. Wait-listed applicants offered admission: 57. Early action applicants: 4,990. Early action applicants admitted: 4,075.

Costs Per Year: Application fee: $0. Comprehensive fee: $50,260 includes full-time tuition ($37,106), mandatory fees ($350), and college room and board ($12,804). College room only: $7500. Room and board charges vary according to board plan and housing facility. Part-time tuition: $955 per credit.

Collegiate Environment: Orientation program. Drama-theater group, choral group, student-run newspaper, radio station. Social organizations: 80 open to all. Most popular organizations: Service-oriented student clubs, United Colors, Retreat Programs, Biology/Pre-Medicine clubs, Pre-Law Society. Major annual events: Spring Fling, Senior Formal, President's Ball. Student services: health clinic, personal-psychological counseling, women's center. Campus security: 24-hour emergency response devices and patrols, student patrols, late night transport-escort service, controlled dormitory access, sprinkler systems in all University-owned housing. 2,640 college housing spaces available; 2,578 were occupied in 2012-13. Freshmen guaranteed college housing. On-campus residence required through sophomore year. Options: coed, men-only, women-only housing available. Harry and Jeanette Weinberg Memorial Library with 486,650 books, 26,241 microform titles, 45,972 serials, an OPAC, and a Web page. Operations spending for the previous fiscal year: $4.1 million. 973 computers available on campus for general student use. Computer purchase/lease plans available. A campuswide network can be accessed from student residence rooms and from off campus. Students can access the following: online class registration. Staffed computer lab on campus (open 24 hours a day) provides training in use of computers, software, and the Internet.

Community Environment: Settled in the late eighteenth century, Scranton is the commercial and industrial center of northeast Pennsylvania. Scranton's manufactured items include textiles, clothing, electronic equipment, furniture, plastic, canvas, and metal products. Lying in the Appalachian Mountains on the Lackawana River, Scranton is 10 minutes from the Montage Ski and Recreation Area. Also of interest are the Everhart Museum of Natural History, Science, and Art, Steamtown, and McDade State Park and Coal Mine Tour.

■ **URSINUS COLLEGE**
Box 1000, Main St.
Collegeville, PA 19426-1000
Tel: (610)409-3000
Fax: (610)489-0627
E-mail: admissions@ursinus.edu
Web Site: www.ursinus.edu/

Description: Independent, 4-year, coed. Awards bachelor's degrees. Founded 1869. Setting: 168-acre suburban campus with easy access to Philadelphia. Endowment: $91.7 million. Research spending for the previous fiscal year: $379,324. Educational spending for the previous fiscal year: $12,681 per student. Total enrollment: 1,742. Faculty: 194 (125 full-time, 69 part-time). Student-undergrad faculty ratio is 12:1. 6,125 applied, 57% were admitted. 45% from top 10% of their high school class, 77% from top quarter, 95% from top half. 2 National Merit Scholars, 7 class presidents, 6 valedictorians, 94 student government officers. Full-time: 1,718 students, 54% women, 46% men. Part-time: 24 students, 38% women, 63% men. Students come from 32 states and territories, 14 other countries, 47% from out-of-state. 0% 25 or older, 95% live on campus, 1% transferred in. Retention: 89% of full-time freshmen returned the following year. Academic areas

with the most degrees conferred: social sciences; biological/life sciences; parks and recreation. Core. Calendar: semesters. ESL program, advanced placement, self-designed majors, honors program, independent study, double major, part-time degree program, internships. Off campus study at Howard University, American University, Butler University. Study abroad program.

Entrance Requirements: Options: electronic application, early admission, early decision, early action, deferred admission, international baccalaureate accepted. Required: essay, high school transcript, graded paper. Recommended: 2 recommendations, interview. Required for some: SAT or ACT, offers a SAT Report Option for students who are in the top ten percent of their class (if their school provides class rank) or a 3.5 GPA (if school does not offer class rank). Entrance: very difficult. Application deadlines: 2/15, 1/15 for early decision, 12/15 for early action. Notification: 4/1, 2/1 for early decision, 1/15 for early action. SAT Reasoning Test deadline: 2/15. SAT Subject Test deadline: 2/15. Transfer credits accepted: Yes. Applicants placed on waiting list: 515. Wait-listed applicants offered admission: 72. Early decision applicants: 211. Early decision applicants admitted: 102. Early action applicants: 4,901. Early action applicants admitted: 2,921.

Collegiate Environment: Orientation program. Drama-theater group, choral group, student-run newspaper, radio station. Social organizations: 105 open to all; national fraternities, national sororities, local fraternities, local sororities; 10% of eligible men and 13% of eligible women are members. Most popular organizations: Environmental Action Committee, Habitat for Humanity, Campus Activities Board, Relay for Life, Multicultural Student Union. Major annual events: Homecoming, Air Band Competition, Spring Fling. Student services: health clinic, personal-psychological counseling. Campus security: 24-hour emergency response devices and patrols, late night transport-escort service, student EMT Corps for first aid/emergency first response. Myrin Library plus 2 others with 420,000 books, 202,000 microform titles, 25,900 serials, 32,000 audiovisual materials, an OPAC, and a Web page. Operations spending for the previous fiscal year: $956,971. 1,655 computers available on campus for general student use. Computer purchase/lease plans available. A computer is required for all students. A campuswide network can be accessed from student residence rooms and from off campus. Students can access the following: online class registration. Staffed computer lab on campus provides training in use of computers, software, and the Internet.

Community Environment: Collegeville is 25 miles northwest of Philadelphia. Within a one-hour drive are museums, libraries, historical sights, educational institutions, recreational facilities, and theaters. Part-time employment is available.

■ **VALLEY FORGE CHRISTIAN COLLEGE**
1401 Charlestown Rd.
Phoenixville, PA 19460
Tel: (610)935-0450; Free: 800-432-8322
E-mail: admissions@vfcc.edu
Web Site: www.vfcc.edu/

Description: Independent Assemblies of God, comprehensive, coed. Awards associate, bachelor's, and master's degrees. Founded 1938. Setting: 106-acre small town campus with easy access to Philadelphia. Endowment: $1.2 million. Total enrollment: 1,204. Faculty: 77 (31 full-time, 46 part-time). Student-undergrad faculty ratio is 19:1. 533 applied, 73% were admitted. 12% from top 10% of their high school class, 29% from top quarter, 59% from top half. Full-time: 834 students, 52% women, 48% men. Part-time: 316 students, 51% women, 49% men. Students come from 39 states and territories, 5 other countries, 47% from out-of-state. 13% 25 or older, 84% live on campus, 7% transferred in. Retention: 69% of full-time freshmen returned the following year. Academic areas with the most degrees conferred: theology and religious vocations; education; psychology. Core. Calendar: semesters. Academic remediation for entering students, ESL program, advanced placement, honors program, independent study, distance learning, double major, summer session for credit, part-time degree program, external degree program, adult/continuing education programs, internships, graduate courses open to undergrads. Study abroad program.

Entrance Requirements: Open admission. Options: electronic application, early admission, deferred admission. Required: essay, high school transcript, 1 recommendation, SAT or ACT. Required for some: interview. Entrance: minimally difficult. Application deadline: 8/1. Notification: continuous. SAT Reasoning Test deadline: 8/1. Transfer credits accepted: Yes.

Collegiate Environment: Orientation program. Drama-theater group, choral group, student-run newspaper. Social organizations: 15 open to all. Most popular organizations: Prison Ministries Organization-Men's and Women's,

Homeless Outreach Ministry, Audience of One Drama Team. Major annual events: Homecoming, Missions Convention, Spiritual Emphasis Week. Student services; health clinic, personal-psychological counseling. Campus security: 24-hour emergency response devices and patrols, student patrols, late night transport-escort service, controlled dormitory access, 16-hour patrols by trained security personnel. Storms Research Center with 74,386 books, 175 serials, 2,982 audiovisual materials, and an OPAC. Operations spending for the previous fiscal year: $453,311. 86 computers available on campus for general student use. Computer purchase/lease plans available. A campuswide network can be accessed from student residence rooms and from off campus. Students can access the following: online class registration. Staffed computer lab on campus provides training in use of computers, software, and the Internet.

Community Environment: Phoenixville is a quiet residential town on the boundary of Valley Forge State Park and is approximately 40 miles from Philadelphia. The climate is temperate. The immediate area provides an abundance of shopping areas and malls, as well as religious, medical and professional services. Recreational opportunities include picnicking, fishing, swimming, boating, camping, and tennis. There are considerable job opportunities available.

■ **VALLEY FORGE MILITARY COLLEGE**
1001 Eagle Rd.
Wayne, PA 19087-3695
Tel: (610)989-1200; Free: 800-234-8362
Fax: (610)688-1545
E-mail: admissions@vfmac.edu
Web Site: www.vfmac.edu/
Description: Independent, 2-year, coed. Awards transfer associate degrees. Founded 1928. Setting: 120-acre suburban campus with easy access to Philadelphia. Endowment: $7.2 million. Educational spending for the previous fiscal year: $6368 per student. Faculty: 26 (16 full-time, 10 part-time). Student-undergrad faculty ratio is 10:1. Students come from 6 other countries, 85% from out-of-state. 100% live on campus. Core. Calendar: 4-1-4. Academic remediation for entering students, ESL program, advanced placement. ROTC: Army, Air Force (c).
Entrance Requirements: Options: early admission, deferred admission. Required: high school transcript, guidance counselor/teacher evaluation form, SAT or ACT. Recommended: minimum 2.0 high school GPA, interview. Entrance: moderately difficult. Application deadline: 8/2. Notification: continuous.
Collegiate Environment: Orientation program. Drama-theater group, choral group, marching band, student-run newspaper. Social organizations: 12 open to all; national fraternities; 20% of men are members. Most popular organizations: Rotaract, Young Republicans, Phi Theta Kappa, Business Club, Criminal Justice Club. Major annual events: class trip, Winter Ball, Field Day. Student services: health clinic, personal-psychological counseling. Campus security: 24-hour patrols, student patrols. Baker Library with 75,830 books, 70,220 microform titles, 189 serials, 326 audiovisual materials, and an OPAC. 44 computers available on campus for general student use. A campuswide network can be accessed from student residence rooms and from off campus. Staffed computer lab on campus.

■ **VET TECH INSTITUTE**
125 7th St.
Pittsburgh, PA 15222-3400
Tel: (412)391-7021; Free: 800-570-0693
Fax: (412)232-4348
Web Site: www.vettechinstitute.edu/
Description: Private, 2-year, coed. Awards terminal associate degrees. Founded 1958. Setting: urban campus. Total enrollment: 340. 541 applied, 62% were admitted. Accelerated degree program, summer session for credit, internships.

■ **VILLANOVA UNIVERSITY**
800 Lancaster Ave.
Villanova, PA 19085-1699
Tel: (610)519-4500
Fax: (610)519-6450
E-mail: gotovu@villanova.edu
Web Site: www.villanova.edu/
Description: Independent Roman Catholic, comprehensive, coed. Awards bachelor's, master's, and doctoral degrees and post-master's certificates. Founded 1842. Setting: 254-acre suburban campus with easy access to Philadelphia. Endowment: $370.3 million. Research spending for the previous fiscal year: $7.8 million. Educational spending for the previous fiscal year: $15,212 per student. Total enrollment: 10,661. Faculty: 951 (590 full-time, 361 part-time). Student-undergrad faculty ratio is 11:1. 15,394 applied, 44% were admitted. 64% from top 10% of their high school class, 89% from top quarter, 97% from top half. 16 National Merit Scholars, 28 valedictorians. Full-time: 6,603 students, 51% women, 49% men. Part-time: 508 students, 46% women, 54% men. Students come from 51 states and territories, 50 other countries, 76% from out-of-state. 0.04% American Indian or Alaska Native, non-Hispanic/Latino; 7% Hispanic/Latino; 5% African American, non-Hispanic/Latino; 6% Asian, non-Hispanic/Latino; 0.1% Native Hawaiian or other Pacific Islander, non-Hispanic/Latino; 3% international. 5% 25 or older, 70% live on campus, 2% transferred in. Retention: 94% of full-time freshmen returned the following year. Academic areas with the most degrees conferred: business/marketing; health professions and related sciences; engineering. Core. Calendar: semesters. ESL program, services for LD students, advanced placement, accelerated degree program, honors program, independent study, distance learning, double major, summer session for credit, part-time degree program, adult/continuing education programs, co-op programs and internships, graduate courses open to undergrads. Off campus study at Rosemont College is an off-campus consortium institution. Study abroad program. ROTC: Army, Naval, Air Force (c).
Entrance Requirements: Options: electronic application, early admission, early action, deferred admission, international baccalaureate accepted. Required: essay, high school transcript, 1 recommendation, Test Scores (SAT or ACT), SAT or ACT. Entrance: very difficult. Application deadlines: 1/7, 1/7 for nonresidents, 11/1 for early action. Notification: 4/1, 4/1 for nonresidents, 12/20 for early action. SAT Reasoning Test deadline: 1/7. Transfer credits accepted: Yes. Applicants placed on waiting list: 4,950. Waitlisted applicants offered admission: 152. Early action applicants: 6,986. Early action applicants admitted: 2,875.
Costs Per Year: Application fee: $80. Comprehensive fee: $54,110 includes full-time tuition ($42,150), mandatory fees ($590), and college room and board ($11,370). College room only: $6020. Room and board charges vary according to board plan and housing facility. Part-time tuition: $1760 per credit. Part-time mandatory fees: $30 per year. Part-time tuition and fees vary according to class time and program.
Collegiate Environment: Orientation program. Drama-theater group, choral group, marching band, student-run newspaper, radio station. Social organizations: 265 open to all; national fraternities, national sororities; 19% of eligible men and 33% of eligible women are members. Most popular organizations: Blue Key Society, New Student Orientation Counselor Program, Special Olympics, Campus Activities Team, Student Government Association. Major annual events: St. Thomas of Villanova Day of Service, PA Special Olympics Fall Festival, Villanova Hoops Mania. Student services: health clinic, personal-psychological counseling. Campus security: 24-hour emergency response devices and patrols, late night transport-escort service, controlled dormitory access, Nova Alert - email, text messaging re: emergency situations. 4,400 college housing spaces available; all were occupied in 2012-13. Freshmen guaranteed college housing. Options: coed, men-only, women-only housing available. Falvey Memorial Library plus 1 other with 755,000 books, 700,000 microform titles, 12,000 serials, 9,250 audiovisual materials, an OPAC, and a Web page. Operations spending for the previous fiscal year: $11.9 million. 6,609 computers available on campus for general student use. Computer purchase/lease plans available. A computer is required for all students. A campuswide network can be accessed from student residence rooms and from off campus. Students can access the following: online class registration, learning management system with anti-plagiarism software, testing software, online faculty hours, videoconferencing; electronic portfolios; data vaulting/backup service; emergency notification system; Citrix-based library of advanced software. Staffed computer lab on campus (open 24 hours a day) provides training in use of computers, software, and the Internet.
Community Environment: The"Main Line" is a suburban residential area located 12 miles due west of downtown Philadelphia, which includes the towns of Radnor, Rosemont, Villanova, St. Davids, Wayne, Haverford, and Merion Station. The mean temperature for the area is 54.3 degrees. The area is served by Amtrak and local commuter rail lines, regional bus lines, and the Schuylkill Expressway. The total locale has more than 200 civic, social, and church groups. There are art centers, theater groups, a symphony orchestra, several museums, many libraries, two hospitals, and good shopping facilities. Local recreation facilities include golf courses, swimming pools, skating rinks, parks, and playgrounds.

■ WASHINGTON & JEFFERSON COLLEGE

60 S Lincoln St.
Washington, PA 15301
Tel: (724)222-4400; Free: 888-WANDJAY
Fax: (724)223-5271
E-mail: admission@washjeff.edu
Web Site: www.washjeff.edu/
Description: Independent, 4-year, coed. Awards bachelor's degrees. Founded 1781. Setting: 60-acre suburban campus with easy access to Pittsburgh. Endowment: $103.8 million. Research spending for the previous fiscal year: $2.3 million. Educational spending for the previous fiscal year: $14,845 per student. Total enrollment: 1,429. Faculty: 151 (113 full-time, 38 part-time). Student-undergrad faculty ratio is 11:1. 6,504 applied, 41% were admitted. 32% from top 10% of their high school class, 57% from top quarter, 91% from top half. 1 class president, 13 valedictorians, 58 student government officers. Full-time: 1,419 students, 51% women, 49% men. Part-time: 10 students, 70% women, 30% men. Students come from 35 states and territories, 18 other countries, 27% from out-of-state. 1% American Indian or Alaska Native, non-Hispanic/Latino; 3% Hispanic/Latino; 3% African American, non-Hispanic/Latino; 2% Asian, non-Hispanic/Latino; 0.1% Native Hawaiian or other Pacific Islander, non-Hispanic/Latino; 3% international. 1% 25 or older, 91% live on campus, 2% transferred in. Academic areas with the most degrees conferred: business/marketing; social sciences; biological/life sciences. Core. Calendar: 4-1-4. Academic remediation for entering students, services for LD students, advanced placement, accelerated degree program, self-designed majors, honors program, independent study, double major, summer session for credit, part-time degree program, internships. Off campus study at Community College of Allegheny County (CCAC). Study abroad program. ROTC: Army, Air Force (c).
Entrance Requirements: Options: electronic application, early admission, early decision, early action, deferred admission, international baccalaureate accepted. Required: essay, high school transcript, 1 recommendation. Recommended: interview. Required for some: interview. Entrance: very difficult. Application deadlines: 3/1, 12/1 for early decision, 1/15 for early action. Notification: 3/15, 12/15 for early decision, 2/15 for early action. SAT Reasoning Test deadline: 3/1. SAT Subject Test deadline: 3/1. Transfer credits accepted: Yes. Applicants placed on waiting list: 46. Wait-listed applicants offered admission: 6. Early decision applicants: 13. Early decision applicants admitted: 5. Early action applicants: 2,806. Early action applicants admitted: 1,425.
Costs Per Year: Application fee: $25. Comprehensive fee: $48,270 includes full-time tuition ($37,850), mandatory fees ($460), and college room and board ($9960). College room only: $5970. Full-time tuition and fees vary according to reciprocity agreements. Room and board charges vary according to board plan and housing facility. Part-time tuition: $950 per credit hour. Part-time tuition varies according to course load.
Collegiate Environment: Orientation program. Drama-theater group, choral group, student-run newspaper, radio station. Social organizations: 72 open to all; national fraternities, national sororities; 37% of eligible men and 43% of eligible women are members. Most popular organizations: Student Government Association, Student Activities Board, Black Student Union, The Newman Club, W&J American Mock Trial Association. Major annual events: talent show, spring concert, Greek Week. Student services: health clinic, personal-psychological counseling, women's center. Campus security: 24-hour emergency response devices and patrols, late night transport-escort service, controlled dormitory access, security cameras monitored 24/7 throughout campus, card access to buildings. 1,418 college housing spaces available; 1,307 were occupied in 2012-13. Freshmen guaranteed college housing. On-campus residence required through senior year. Options: coed, men-only, women-only housing available. U. Grant Miller Library plus 4 others with 165,500 books, 15,557 microform titles, 41,280 serials, 10,002 audiovisual materials, an OPAC, and a Web page. Operations spending for the previous fiscal year: $1 million. 450 computers available on campus for general student use. Computer purchase/lease plans available. A campuswide network can be accessed from student residence rooms and from off campus. Students can access the following: online class registration. Staffed computer lab on campus (open 24 hours a day) provides training in use of computers, software, and the Internet.

■ WAYNESBURG UNIVERSITY

51 W College St.
Waynesburg, PA 15370-1222
Tel: (724)627-8191; Free: 800-225-7393
Fax: (724)627-8124

E-mail: admissions@waynesburg.edu
Web Site: www.waynesburg.edu/
Description: Independent, comprehensive, coed, affiliated with Presbyterian Church (U.S.A.). Awards bachelor's, master's, and doctoral degrees. Founded 1849. Setting: 30-acre small town campus with easy access to Pittsburgh. Total enrollment: 2,270. Faculty: 278 (76 full-time, 202 part-time). Student-undergrad faculty ratio is 14:1. 1,827 applied, 76% were admitted. 18% from top 10% of their high school class, 44% from top quarter, 80% from top half. Full-time: 1,464 students, 59% women, 41% men. Part-time: 166 students, 81% women, 19% men. Students come from 33 states and territories, 4 other countries, 18% from out-of-state. 0.5% American Indian or Alaska Native, non-Hispanic/Latino; 1% Hispanic/Latino; 4% African American, non-Hispanic/Latino; 0.5% Asian, non-Hispanic/Latino; 0% Native Hawaiian or other Pacific Islander, non-Hispanic/Latino; 0.2% international. 14% 25 or older, 64% live on campus, 3% transferred in. Retention: 83% of full-time freshmen returned the following year. Academic areas with the most degrees conferred: health professions and related sciences; business/marketing; communication/journalism. Core. Calendar: semesters. Services for LD students, advanced placement, accelerated degree program, honors program, independent study, distance learning, double major, summer session for credit, part-time degree program, adult/continuing education programs, internships. Study abroad program. ROTC: Army (c).
Entrance Requirements: Options: electronic application, early admission. Required: high school transcript, minimum 2.75 high school GPA, SAT or ACT. Recommended: minimum 3 high school GPA, interview. Required for some: essay, 2 recommendations. Entrance: moderately difficult. Application deadline: Rolling. Notification: continuous. SAT Reasoning Test deadline: 8/30. SAT Subject Test deadline: 8/30.
Costs Per Year: Application fee: $20. Comprehensive fee: $28,060 includes full-time tuition ($19,450), mandatory fees ($360), and college room and board ($8250). College room only: $4170. Full-time tuition and fees vary according to class time. Room and board charges vary according to board plan. Part-time tuition: $820 per credit hour. Part-time mandatory fees: $16 per credit hour. Part-time tuition and fees vary according to class time, course load, and location.
Collegiate Environment: Orientation program. Drama-theater group, choral group, marching band, student-run newspaper, radio station. Social organizations: 53 open to all. Most popular organizations: Student Senate, Student Activities Board, Student Nurses Association, Christian Fellowship. Major annual events: Homecoming, Spring Week, Charter Day. Student services: health clinic, personal-psychological counseling. Campus security: 24-hour emergency response devices and patrols, late night transport-escort service, controlled dormitory access. 1,041 college housing spaces available; 1,039 were occupied in 2012-13. Freshmen guaranteed college housing. On-campus residence required through junior year. Options: men-only, women-only housing available. Waynesburg College Library with 100,000 books, 5,097 microform titles, 1,206 serials, 3,327 audiovisual materials, an OPAC, and a Web page. 150 computers available on campus for general student use. A campuswide network can be accessed from student residence rooms and from off campus. Students can access the following: online class registration. Staffed computer lab on campus.
Community Environment: Population 4,142, Waynesburg is located 50 miles from Pittsburgh in southwestern Pennsylvania. The climate is moderate. Community service facilities include a library, several churches, a hospital, hotels, motels, and rooming houses. There is bus service available. Local recreation includes theatres, hunting, boating, fishing, golf, and movies. Many civic, fraternal and veteran's organizations are active in the community.

■ WEST CHESTER UNIVERSITY OF PENNSYLVANIA

University Ave. and High St.
West Chester, PA 19383
Tel: (610)436-1000
E-mail: ugadmiss@wcupa.edu
Web Site: www.wcupa.edu/
Description: State-supported, comprehensive, coed. Part of Pennsylvania State System of Higher Education. Awards bachelor's and master's degrees and post-master's certificates. Founded 1871. Setting: 409-acre suburban campus with easy access to Philadelphia. Endowment: $16.6 million. Research spending for the previous fiscal year: $1.8 million. Educational spending for the previous fiscal year: $6248 per student. Total enrollment: 15,411. Faculty: 890 (605 full-time, 285 part-time). Student-undergrad faculty ratio is 18:1. 14,356 applied, 50% were admitted. 12% from top 10% of their high school class, 42% from top quarter, 85% from top half. 14 valedictori-

ans. Full-time: 12,133 students, 60% women, 40% men. Part-time: 1,164 students, 54% women, 46% men. Students come from 28 states and territories, 66 other countries, 12% from out-of-state. 0.1% American Indian or Alaska Native, non-Hispanic/Latino; 5% Hispanic/Latino; 9% African American, non-Hispanic/Latino; 2% Asian, non-Hispanic/Latino; 0.1% Native Hawaiian or other Pacific Islander, non-Hispanic/Latino; 0.4% international. 9% 25 or older, 40% live on campus, 10% transferred in. Retention: 85% of full-time freshmen returned the following year. Academic areas with the most degrees conferred: education; health professions and related sciences; business/marketing. Core. Calendar: semesters. Academic remediation for entering students, services for LD students, advanced placement, accelerated degree program, self-designed majors, freshman honors college, honors program, independent study, distance learning, double major, summer session for credit, part-time degree program, adult/continuing education programs, internships, graduate courses open to undergrads. Off campus study at member of the National Student Exchange. Study abroad program. ROTC: Army, Air Force (c).

Entrance Requirements: Options: electronic application, deferred admission, international baccalaureate accepted. Required: essay, high school transcript, SAT or ACT, SAT or ACT. Recommended: minimum 3 high school GPA. Required for some: interview. Entrance: moderately difficult. Application deadline: Rolling. Notification: continuous. SAT Reasoning Test deadline: 2/1. Transfer credits accepted: Yes. Applicants placed on waiting list: 2,285. Wait-listed applicants offered admission: 0.

Costs Per Year: Application fee: $45. State resident tuition: $6428 full-time, $268 per credit hour part-time. Nonresident tuition: $16,070 full-time, $670 per credit hour part-time. Mandatory fees: $2,192 full-time, $80.33 per credit hour part-time, $11.08. Full-time tuition and fees vary according to course load. Part-time tuition and fees vary according to course load. College room and board: $6786. College room only: $4848. Room and board charges vary according to board plan and housing facility.

Collegiate Environment: Orientation program. Drama-theater group, choral group, marching band, student-run newspaper, radio station. Social organizations: 238 open to all; national fraternities, national sororities; 7% of eligible men and 10% of eligible women are members. Most popular organizations: Student Government Association, Residence Hall Association, Inter-Greek Council, Sports Club Council, Campus Crusade for Christ. Major annual events: Spring Weekend, Homecoming, Martin Luther King Day of Service. Student services: legal services, health clinic, personal-psychological counseling, women's center. Campus security: 24-hour emergency response devices and patrols, late night transport-escort service, controlled dormitory access, officers are on site 24/7, 365. Camera systems in campus residence halls, recreational and classroom facilities and outdoor areas. 4,860 college housing spaces available; 4,835 were occupied in 2012-13. Freshmen given priority for college housing. Option: coed housing available. Francis Harvey Green Library plus 1 other with 1.4 million books, 926,451 microform titles, 7,090 serials, 199,454 audiovisual materials, an OPAC, and a Web page. Operations spending for the previous fiscal year: $5.7 million. 1,900 computers available on campus for general student use. Computer purchase/lease plans available. A campuswide network can be accessed from student residence rooms and from off campus. Students can access the following: online class registration. Staffed computer lab on campus provides training in use of computers, software, and the Internet.

Community Environment: Population 18,000. Essentially a residential and college community, West Chester is the county seat of a region rich in colonial history. Local industries include pharmaceuticals, firefighting foam, electrical appliances, air compressors, tags and labels, and refrigerated cabinets. The average January temperature is 31.5 degrees, and the average July temperature is 75 degrees. The community is provided transportation by railroad, bus lines, and an airport nearby. There are several churches, a YMCA, hospital, and public library serving the community. Local recreation includes swimming, bowling, volleyball, tennis, hunting, fishing, and golf. Civic and fraternal organizations are active within the area.

■ **WESTMINSTER COLLEGE**
319 S Market St.
New Wilmington, PA 16172-0001
Tel: (724)946-8761; Free: 800-942-8033
Fax: (724)946-7171
E-mail: tokarbp@westminster.edu
Web Site: www.westminster.edu/
Description: Independent, comprehensive, coed, affiliated with Presbyterian Church (U.S.A.). Awards bachelor's and master's degrees. Founded 1852. Setting: 350-acre small town campus with easy access to Pittsburgh. Total

enrollment: 1,608. Faculty: 163 (104 full-time, 59 part-time). Student-undergrad faculty ratio is 12:1. 3,824 applied, 61% were admitted. 22% from top 10% of their high school class, 62% from top quarter, 93% from top half. Full-time: 1,511 students, 59% women, 41% men. Part-time: 55 students, 76% women, 24% men. 18% 25 or older, 73% live on campus, 2% transferred in. Retention: 88% of full-time freshmen returned the following year. Academic areas with the most degrees conferred: education; business/marketing; communication/journalism. Core. Calendar: semesters. Advanced placement, self-designed majors, honors program, independent study, double major, summer session for credit, part-time degree program, adult/continuing education programs, internships, graduate courses open to undergrads. Off campus study at members of the East Central College Consortium. Study abroad program. ROTC: Army (c).

Entrance Requirements: Option: deferred admission. Required: essay, high school transcript, minimum 2 high school GPA, 2 recommendations, SAT or ACT. Recommended: minimum 3 high school GPA, interview. Entrance: moderately difficult. Application deadline: 5/1. Notification: continuous.

Costs Per Year: Application fee: $35. Comprehensive fee: $40,980 includes full-time tuition ($30,320), mandatory fees ($1090), and college room and board ($9570). Room and board charges vary according to board plan and housing facility. Part-time tuition: $970 per credit hour.

Collegiate Environment: Orientation program. Drama-theater group, choral group, marching band, student-run newspaper, radio station. Social organizations: 85 open to all; national fraternities, national sororities. Most popular organizations: student government, Habitat for Humanity, established service teams. Major annual events: Homecoming, Christmas Vespers, Greek Week. Student services: health clinic, personal-psychological counseling. Campus security: 24-hour patrols, late night transport-escort service. McGill Memorial Library plus 1 other with an OPAC and a Web page.

■ **WESTMORELAND COUNTY COMMUNITY COLLEGE**
145 Pavilion Ln.
Youngwood, PA 15697
Tel: (724)925-4000; Free: 800-262-2103
Fax: (724)925-1150
E-mail: admission@wccc.edu
Web Site: www.wccc.edu/
Description: County-supported, 2-year, coed. Awards certificates, diplomas, transfer associate, and terminal associate degrees. Founded 1970. Setting: 85-acre rural campus with easy access to Pittsburgh. Endowment: $488,371. Educational spending for the previous fiscal year: $2655 per student. Total enrollment: 6,571. Faculty: 521 (81 full-time, 440 part-time). Student-undergrad faculty ratio is 18:1. 2,778 applied, 100% were admitted. Full-time: 2,974 students, 60% women, 40% men. Part-time: 3,597 students, 69% women, 31% men. Students come from 5 states and territories, 0.1% from out-of-state. 0.2% American Indian or Alaska Native, non-Hispanic/Latino; 1% Hispanic/Latino; 4% African American, non-Hispanic/Latino; 1% Asian, non-Hispanic/Latino; 0.1% Native Hawaiian or other Pacific Islander, non-Hispanic/Latino; 0% international. 40% 25 or older, 2% transferred in. Retention: 56% of full-time freshmen returned the following year. Core. Calendar: semesters. Academic remediation for entering students, ESL program, services for LD students, advanced placement, honors program, independent study, distance learning, double major, summer session for credit, part-time degree program, adult/continuing education programs, co-op programs and internships. Off campus study at Seton Hill College, University of Pittsburgh.

Entrance Requirements: Open admission except for nursing, dental services, and radiologic technology programs. Options: electronic application, early admission. Entrance: noncompetitive. Application deadline: Rolling. Notification: continuous.

Costs Per Year: Application fee: $15. Area resident tuition: $2700 full-time, $90 per credit part-time. State resident tuition: $5400 full-time, $180 per credit part-time. Nonresident tuition: $8100 full-time, $270 per credit part-time. Mandatory fees: $630 full-time, $21 per credit part-time. Full-time tuition and fees vary according to course load. Part-time tuition and fees vary according to course load.

Collegiate Environment: Orientation program. Drama-theater group, choral group. Social organizations: 26 open to all; Phi Theta Kappa and Sigma Alpha Pi. Most popular organizations: Phi Theta Kappa, Sigma Alpha Pi Leadership Society, Criminal Justice Fraternity, Gay Straight Alliance, SADAA/SADHA. Major annual events: Family Fest, Red Cross Blood Drive, Casino Night. Student services: personal-psychological counseling. Campus security: 24-hour emergency response devices and patrols, late night transport-escort service. College housing not available. Westmoreland County Community College Learning Resources Center with 64,000 books, 62,000 microform titles, 250 serials, 3,500 audiovisual materials, an OPAC, and a Web page. Operations spending for the previous fiscal year: $341,060. 1,021 computers available on campus for general student use. A campuswide network can be accessed from off-campus. Students can access the following: online class registration. Staffed computer lab on campus provides training in use of computers, software, and the Internet.

■ **WIDENER UNIVERSITY**
One University Pl.
Chester, PA 19013-5792
Tel: (610)499-4000; Free: 888-WIDENER
Fax: (610)499-4676
E-mail: admissions.office@widener.edu
Web Site: www.widener.edu/
Description: Independent, comprehensive, coed. Awards associate, bachelor's, master's, and doctoral degrees. Founded 1821. Setting: 110-acre suburban campus with easy access to Philadelphia. Endowment: $72.8 million. Research spending for the previous fiscal year: $163,000. Educational spending for the previous fiscal year: $15,170 per student. Total enrollment: 6,238. Faculty: 656 (317 full-time, 339 part-time). Student-undergrad faculty ratio is 12:1. 4,863 applied, 66% were admitted. 12% from top 10% of their high school class, 35% from top quarter, 72% from top half. Full-time: 2,741 students, 54% women, 46% men. Part-time: 557 students, 70% women, 30% men. 40% from out-of-state. 0.5% American Indian or Alaska Native, non-Hispanic/Latino; 3% Hispanic/Latino; 16% African American, non-Hispanic/Latino; 3% Asian, non-Hispanic/Latino; 0.2% Native Hawaiian or other Pacific Islander, non-Hispanic/Latino; 2% international. 14% 25 or older, 50% live on campus, 5% transferred in. Retention: 71% of full-time freshmen returned the following year. Academic areas with the most degrees conferred: business/marketing; health professions and related sciences; engineering. Core. Calendar: semesters. Academic remediation for entering students, ESL program, services for LD students, advanced placement, accelerated degree program, self-designed majors, honors program, independent study, distance learning, double major, summer session for credit, part-time degree program, adult/continuing education programs, co-op programs and internships, graduate courses open to undergrads. Off campus study. Study abroad program. ROTC: Army, Naval (c), Air Force (c).
Entrance Requirements: Options: electronic application, deferred admission, international baccalaureate accepted. Required: essay, high school transcript, SAT or ACT. Recommended: interview. Required for some: minimum 2.85 high school GPA. Entrance: moderately difficult. Application deadline: Rolling. Notification: continuous. Applicants placed on waiting list: 100. Wait-listed applicants offered admission: 5.
Costs Per Year: Application fee: $35. Comprehensive fee: $48,630 includes full-time tuition ($35,764), mandatory fees ($618), and college room and board ($12,248). College room only: $6300. Full-time tuition and fees vary according to class time, course load, and program. Room and board charges vary according to board plan and housing facility. Part-time tuition: $1190 per credit hour.
Collegiate Environment: Orientation program. Drama-theater group, choral group, student-run newspaper, radio station. Social organizations: 80 open to all; national fraternities, national sororities; 10% of eligible men and 9% of eligible women are members. Most popular organizations: WDNR Radio, Black Student Union, volunteer services, rugby club, Theatre Widener. Major annual events: Spring Carnival, Greek Week, Homecoming. Student services: health clinic, personal-psychological counseling. Campus security: 24-hour emergency response devices and patrols, late night transport-escort service, controlled dormitory access, blue light emergency phones located throughout campus. 1,772 college housing spaces available; 1,565 were occupied in 2012-13. Freshmen guaranteed college housing. On-campus residence required through sophomore year. Options: coed, men-only, women-only housing available. Wolfgram Memorial Library with 208,847 books, 174,211 microform titles, 2,695 serials, 6,719 audiovisual materials, an OPAC, and a Web page. 710 computers available on campus for general student use. A campuswide network can be accessed from student residence rooms and from off campus. Students can access the following: online class registration. Staffed computer lab on campus provides training in use of computers, software, and the Internet.

■ **WILKES UNIVERSITY**
84 W S St.
Wilkes-Barre, PA 18766-0002
Tel: (570)408-5000; Free: 800-945-5378
Fax: (570)408-7820
E-mail: admissions@wilkes.edu
Web Site: www.wilkes.edu/
Description: Independent, comprehensive, coed. Awards bachelor's, master's, and doctoral degrees. Founded 1933. Setting: 25-acre urban campus. Endowment: $35.7 million. Research spending for the previous fiscal year: $1.5 million. Educational spending for the previous fiscal year: $7911 per student. Total enrollment: 5,030. Faculty: 407 (160 full-time, 247 part-time). Student-undergrad faculty ratio is 14:1. 2,998 applied, 76% were admitted. 25% from top 10% of their high school class, 53% from top quarter, 87% from top half. Full-time: 2,095 students, 49% women, 51% men. Part-time: 207 students, 47% women, 53% men. Students come from 18 states and territories, 10 other countries, 17% from out-of-state. 0.1% American Indian or Alaska Native, non-Hispanic/Latino; 4% Hispanic/Latino; 4% African American, non-Hispanic/Latino; 3% Asian, non-Hispanic/Latino; 0.04% Native Hawaiian or other Pacific Islander, non-Hispanic/Latino; 5% international. 8% 25 or older, 37% live on campus, 7% transferred in. Retention: 80% of full-time freshmen returned the following year. Academic areas with the most degrees conferred: business/marketing; liberal arts/general studies; health professions and related sciences. Core. Calendar: semesters. Academic remediation for entering students, ESL program, services for LD students, advanced placement, accelerated degree program, self-designed majors, honors program, independent study, distance learning, double major, summer session for credit, part-time degree program, external degree program, adult/continuing education programs, co-op programs and internships, graduate courses open to undergrads. Off campus study. Study abroad program. ROTC: Army (c), Air Force.
Entrance Requirements: Options: electronic application, early admission, deferred admission, international baccalaureate accepted. Required: high school transcript, SAT or ACT. Recommended: interview. Required for some: 2 recommendations. Entrance: moderately difficult. Application deadline: Rolling. Notification: 8/30. Transfer credits accepted: Yes.
Costs Per Year: Application fee: $40. Comprehensive fee: $41,360 includes full-time tuition ($27,908), mandatory fees ($1418), and college room and board ($12,034). College room only: $7228. Room and board charges vary according to board plan and housing facility. Part-time tuition: $775 per credit hour. Part-time mandatory fees: $64 per credit hour.
Collegiate Environment: Orientation program. Drama-theater group, choral group, student-run newspaper, radio station. Social organizations: 65 open to all. Student services: health clinic, personal-psychological counseling. Campus security: 24-hour emergency response devices and patrols, late night transport-escort service, controlled dormitory access. 850 college housing spaces available; 783 were occupied in 2012-13. Freshmen guaranteed college housing. On-campus residence required through sophomore year. Options: coed, men-only, women-only housing available. Eugene S. Farley Library with an OPAC. 868 computers available on campus for general student use. Computer purchase/lease plans available. A campuswide network can be accessed from student residence rooms and from off campus. Students can access the following: online class registration. Staffed computer lab on campus provides training in use of computers, software, and the Internet.

■ **THE WILLIAMSON FREE SCHOOL OF MECHANICAL TRADES**
106 S New Middletown Rd.
Media, PA 19063
Tel: (610)566-1776
Fax: (610)566-6502
E-mail: jmerillat@williamson.edu
Web Site: www.williamson.edu/
Description: Independent, 2-year, men only. Awards diplomas and terminal associate degrees. Founded 1888. Setting: 222-acre small town campus with easy access to Philadelphia. Total enrollment: 270. Faculty: (29 full-time). Student-undergrad faculty ratio is 12:1. 412 applied, 24% were admitted. 10% from top 10% of their high school class, 25% from top quarter, 65% from top half. Full-time: 270 students. Students come from 7 states and territories, 15% from out-of-state. 0% 25 or older, 100% live on campus, 0% transferred in. Core. Calendar: semesters. Academic remediation for entering students, independent study. Off campus study at Delaware County Community College.
Entrance Requirements: Required: essay, high school transcript, minimum 2 high school GPA, interview, average performance or better on the Armed Services Vocational Aptitude Battery (ASVAB), Armed Services Vocational Aptitude Battery. Required for some: 3 recommendations. Entrance:

moderately difficult. Application deadline: 2/28. Preference given to financially deserving young men. Applicants placed on waiting list: 30. Wait-listed applicants offered admission: 7.

Collegiate Environment: Orientation program. Choral group, student-run newspaper. Most popular organizations: Campus Crusade for Christ, Skills USA. Major annual events: Homecoming, Alumni Day, Founder's Day. Student services: health clinic, personal-psychological counseling. Campus security: evening patrols, gate security. Shrigley Library plus 3 others with 1,600 books and 70 serials. 165 computers available on campus for general student use. Staffed computer lab on campus.

■ **WILSON COLLEGE**
1015 Philadelphia Ave.
Chambersburg, PA 17201-1285
Tel: (717)264-4141; Free: 800-421-8402
Fax: (717)264-1578
E-mail: admissions@wilson.edu
Web Site: www.wilson.edu/
Description: Independent, comprehensive, coed, affiliated with Presbyterian Church (U.S.A.). Awards associate, bachelor's, and master's degrees. Founded 1869. Setting: 300-acre small town campus. Endowment: $60.5 million. Educational spending for the previous fiscal year: $7663 per student. Total enrollment: 746. Faculty: 85 (45 full-time, 40 part-time). Student-undergrad faculty ratio is 10:1. 407 applied, 56% were admitted. 21% from top 10% of their high school class, 52% from top quarter, 82% from top half. 0% American Indian or Alaska Native, non-Hispanic/Latino; 3% Hispanic/Latino; 5% African American, non-Hispanic/Latino; 0% Asian, non-Hispanic/Latino; 0% Native Hawaiian or other Pacific Islander, non-Hispanic/Latino; 4% international. 74% live on campus. Retention: 76% of full-time freshmen returned the following year. Academic areas with the most degrees conferred: health professions and related sciences; social sciences; business/marketing. Core. Calendar: 4-1-4. Academic remediation for entering students, services for LD students, advanced placement, self-designed majors, honors program, independent study, distance learning, double major, summer session for credit, part-time degree program, adult/continuing education programs, internships. Off campus study at Shippensburg University of Pennsylvania, Gettysburg College. Study abroad program. ROTC: Army (c).
Entrance Requirements: Options: electronic application, early admission, deferred admission, international baccalaureate accepted. Required: essay, high school transcript, 1 recommendation, college preparatory program that includes 4 units of English, 4 units of History/Civics, 3 units of Mathematics (preferably Algebra I, II or Geometry), 2 units of same Foreign Language, and 2 units of Natural Sciences with lab. Recommended: minimum 2.75 high school GPA, interview. Required for some: SAT or ACT, SAT/ACT optional for students with high school GPA of 3.0 and specified college prep curriculum from regionally accredited schools; TOEFL/IELTS/STEP for international students. Entrance: moderately difficult. Application deadlines: Rolling, Rolling for nonresidents. Notification: continuous, continuous for nonresidents. Transfer credits accepted: Yes.
Collegiate Environment: Orientation program. Drama-theater group, choral group, student-run newspaper. Social organizations: 47 open to all. Most popular organizations: Muhibbah Club, Orchesis Club, student newspaper, student government, Campus Activity Board. Major annual events: White Dinner, Thanksgiving Dinner, Spring Fling/May Court. Student services: health clinic, personal-psychological counseling, women's center. Campus security: 24-hour emergency response devices and patrols, late night transport-escort service, controlled dormitory access. Stewart Library with 144,044 books, 11,144 microform titles, 150 serials, 1,376 audiovisual materials, an OPAC, and a Web page. Operations spending for the previous fiscal year: $288,760. 96 computers available on campus for general student use. A campuswide network can be accessed from student residence rooms. Students can access the following: online class registration, online databases. Staffed computer lab on campus.
Community Environment: Population 17,900, Chambersburg was occupied three times during the Civil War and burned in 1864 when it refused to pay an indemnity of $100,000. Today, this diversified manufacturing community is also considered the state's largest producer of apples and peaches. The city has 2 libraries, a hospital, and many churches and historic sites. Part-time employment is available for students both on and off campus.

■ **WYOTECH BLAIRSVILLE**
500 Innovation Dr.
Blairsville, PA 15717

Tel: (724)459-9500; Free: 888-577-7559
Fax: (724)459-6499
E-mail: tsmyers@wyotech.edu
Web Site: www.wyotech.edu/
Description: Proprietary, 2-year, coed. Awards diplomas and terminal associate degrees. Founded 2002. Total enrollment: 1,200. Calendar: 9-month program.
Entrance Requirements: Required: high school transcript. Entrance: moderately difficult.

■ **YESHIVA BETH MOSHE**
930 Hickory St.
Scranton, PA 18505-2124
Tel: (717)346-1747
Description: Independent Jewish, comprehensive, men only. Awards bachelor's, master's, and doctoral degrees. Founded 1965. Total enrollment: 54. Calendar: semesters.
Entrance Requirements: Open admission. Required: high school transcript, interview, oral examination.

■ **YORK COLLEGE OF PENNSYLVANIA**
York, PA 17405-7199
Tel: (717)846-7788; Free: 800-455-8018
E-mail: admissions@ycp.edu
Web Site: www.ycp.edu/
Description: Independent, comprehensive, coed. Awards bachelor's, master's, and doctoral degrees and post-master's certificates. Founded 1787. Setting: 190-acre suburban campus with easy access to Baltimore. Endowment: $61.7 million. Educational spending for the previous fiscal year: $8076 per student. Total enrollment: 5,439. Faculty: 550 (189 full-time, 361 part-time). Student-undergrad faculty ratio is 16:1. 9,283 applied, 74% were admitted. 8% from top 10% of their high school class, 35% from top quarter, 76% from top half. Full-time: 4,595 students, 54% women, 46% men. Part-time: 587 students, 67% women, 33% men. Students come from 31 states and territories, 5 other countries, 40% from out-of-state. 0.1% American Indian or Alaska Native, non-Hispanic/Latino; 5% Hispanic/Latino; 5% African American, non-Hispanic/Latino; 1% Asian, non-Hispanic/Latino; 0.1% Native Hawaiian or other Pacific Islander, non-Hispanic/Latino; 0.2% international. 12% 25 or older, 55% live on campus, 5% transferred in. Retention: 73% of full-time freshmen returned the following year. Academic areas with the most degrees conferred: business/marketing; health professions and related sciences; education. Core. Calendar: semesters. Services for LD students, advanced placement, self-designed majors, independent study, double major, summer session for credit, part-time degree program, co-op programs and internships, graduate courses open to undergrads. Study abroad program. ROTC: Army (c).
Entrance Requirements: Options: electronic application, deferred admission, international baccalaureate accepted. Required: high school transcript, minimum 2 high school GPA, SAT or ACT. Recommended: essay, 1 recommendation. Required for some: interview. Entrance: moderately difficult. Application deadlines: 8/15, 8/15 for nonresidents. Notification: continuous, continuous for nonresidents. SAT Reasoning Test deadline: 8/15. SAT Subject Test deadline: 8/15. Transfer credits accepted: Yes.
Costs Per Year: Application fee: $0. Comprehensive fee: $26,590 includes full-time tuition ($15,350), mandatory fees ($1660), and college room and board ($9580). College room only: $5380. Full-time tuition and fees vary according to program. Room and board charges vary according to board plan and housing facility. Part-time tuition: $475 per credit. Part-time mandatory fees: $360 per term.
Collegiate Environment: Orientation program. Drama-theater group, choral group, student-run newspaper, radio station. Social organizations: 80 open to all; national fraternities, national sororities; 9% of eligible men and 8% of eligible women are members. Most popular organizations: Pre-Med Society, Ski and Outdoor Club, Habitat for Humanity, Students in Free Enterprise (SIFE), WVYC Radio Station. Major annual events: Spartapalooza, Spring Weekend, Fall Fest. Student services: health clinic, personal-psychological counseling. Campus security: 24-hour emergency response devices and patrols, student patrols, late night transport-escort service, controlled dormitory access. 2,575 college housing spaces available; 2,523 were occupied in 2012-13. Freshmen guaranteed college housing. On-campus residence required through senior year. Option: coed housing available. Schmidt Library with 429,072 books, 250,000 microform titles, 40,557 serials, an OPAC, and a Web page. Operations spending for the previous fiscal year: $2 million. 1,054 computers available on campus for general student use. A

campuswide network can be accessed from student residence rooms and from off campus. Students can access the following: online class registration. Staffed computer lab on campus provides training in use of computers, software, and the Internet.

Community Environment: York College is located in the heart of one of the most naturally beautiful and historically rich sections of Pennsylvania. Traveling by car, York is just four hours from New York and Pittsburgh, less than two hours from Philadelphia and Washington, DC, and an hour from Baltimore. The area has much to offer, including great local food, interesting places to visit and shop, and parks, lakes, and miles of trails that afford opportunities for picnicking, hiking, and skiing. On the practical side, there is a shopping center, a bank, and York Hospital within walking distance of the campus. Culture is an important part of York's heritage as well. The York Symphony Orchestra, the York Little Theater, and the Strand-Capitol Performing Arts Center bring well-known performing artists to the area. Throughout the year, numerous galleries exhibit a wide variety of artwork.

■ YORKTOWNE BUSINESS INSTITUTE

W Seventh Ave.
York, PA 17404
Tel: (717)846-5000; Free: 800-840-1004
Fax: (717)848-4584
Web Site: www.ybi.edu/

Description: Proprietary, 2-year, coed. Awards diplomas, transfer associate, and terminal associate degrees. Founded 1976. Setting: 1-acre small town campus with easy access to Baltimore. Total enrollment: 254. Student-undergrad faculty ratio is 16:1. 75 applied. 0% from out-of-state. 60% 25 or older. Retention: 50% of full-time freshmen returned the following year. Calendar: semesters.

Entrance Requirements: Required: high school transcript, interview. Required for some: admissions test. Entrance: minimally difficult. Application deadline: Rolling.

Collegiate Environment: Orientation program.

■ YTI CAREER INSTITUTE–ALTOONA

2900 Fairway Dr.
Altoona, PA 16602
Tel: (814)944-5643

Web Site: www.yti.edu/
Description: Proprietary, 2-year, coed.

■ YTI CAREER INSTITUTE–CAPITAL REGION

401 E Winding Hill Rd.
Mechanicsburg, PA 17055
Tel: (717)761-1481
Fax: (717)761-0558
Web Site: www.yti.edu/
Description: Proprietary, 2-year, coed. Founded 1982.

■ YTI CAREER INSTITUTE–YORK

1405 Williams Rd.
York, PA 17402-9017
Tel: (717)757-1100; Free: 800-557-6335
Fax: (717)757-4964
Web Site: www.yti.edu/

Description: Private, 2-year, coed. Part of York Technical Institute, LLC. Awards diplomas and terminal associate degrees. Founded 1967. Setting: suburban campus with easy access to Harrisburg. Educational spending for the previous fiscal year: $4293 per student. Total enrollment: 680. Faculty: 69 (48 full-time, 21 part-time). Student-undergrad faculty ratio is 15:1. Full-time: 680 students, 44% women, 56% men. Students come from 9 states and territories, 2% from out-of-state. 0.1% American Indian or Alaska Native, non-Hispanic/Latino; 9% Hispanic/Latino; 9% African American, non-Hispanic/Latino; 1% Asian, non-Hispanic/Latino; 0.3% Native Hawaiian or other Pacific Islander, non-Hispanic/Latino. 45% 25 or older. Core. Calendar: continuous. Academic remediation for entering students, advanced placement, co-op programs and internships.

Entrance Requirements: Open admission. Required: high school transcript, minimum 2 high school GPA, interview, ACT COMPASS. Recommended: admissions test. Entrance: noncompetitive.

Costs Per Year: Application fee: $50. One-time mandatory fee: $50. Tuition: $15,000 full-time. Full-time tuition varies according to location and program.

Collegiate Environment: Orientation program. Student services: personal-psychological counseling. 250 computers available on campus for general student use. A campuswide network can be accessed. Staffed computer lab on campus.

Rhode Island

■ **BROWN UNIVERSITY**
One Prospect St.
Providence, RI 02912
Tel: (401)863-1000
Fax: (401)863-9300
E-mail: admission_undergraduate@brown.edu
Web Site: www.brown.edu/
Description: Independent, university, coed. Awards bachelor's, master's, and doctoral degrees. Founded 1764. Setting: 140-acre urban campus with easy access to Boston. Endowment: $2.5 billion. Total enrollment: 8,885. Faculty: 977 (794 full-time, 183 part-time). Student-undergrad faculty ratio is 9:1. 28,742 applied, 10% were admitted. 94% from top 10% of their high school class, 99% from top quarter, 100% from top half. Full-time: 6,117 students, 52% women, 48% men. Part-time: 318 students, 68% women, 32% men. Students come from 52 states and territories, 95% from out-of-state. 0.3% American Indian or Alaska Native, non-Hispanic/Latino; 10% Hispanic/Latino; 6% African American, non-Hispanic/Latino; 12% Asian, non-Hispanic/Latino; 0.1% Native Hawaiian or other Pacific Islander, non-Hispanic/Latino; 12% international. 1% 25 or older. Retention: 97% of full-time freshmen returned the following year. Academic areas with the most degrees conferred: social sciences; biological/life sciences; mathematics and statistics; interdisciplinary studies; visual and performing arts; English. Calendar: semesters. Services for LD students, advanced placement, self-designed majors, honors program, independent study, double major, summer session for credit, adult/continuing education programs, internships, graduate courses open to undergrads. Off campus study. Study abroad program. ROTC: Army (c).
Entrance Requirements: Options: electronic application, early decision, deferred admission, international baccalaureate accepted. Required: essay, high school transcript, 2 recommendations, Common application; Brown University supplement, SAT and SAT Subject Tests or ACT. Recommended: interview. Entrance: most difficult. Application deadlines: 1/1, 11/1 for early decision. Notification: 4/1, 12/15 for early decision. SAT Reasoning Test deadline: 1/1. SAT Subject Test deadline: 1/1. Transfer credits accepted: Yes. Early decision applicants: 2,923. Early decision applicants admitted: 555.
Costs Per Year: Application fee: $75. Comprehensive fee: $55,016 includes full-time tuition ($42,808), mandatory fees ($950), and college room and board ($11,258). College room only: $6974. Room and board charges vary according to board plan.
Collegiate Environment: Orientation program. Drama-theater group, choral group, marching band, student-run newspaper, radio station. Social organizations: national fraternities, national sororities, local fraternities, local sororities. Student services: health clinic, personal-psychological counseling, women's center. Campus security: 24-hour emergency response devices and patrols, late night transport-escort service, controlled dormitory access. Freshmen guaranteed college housing. On-campus residence required through junior year. Options: coed, women-only housing available. John D. Rockefeller Library plus 7 others with an OPAC and a Web page.
Community Environment: In its early days, Providence was a shipping and shipbuilding town, running the Triangular Trade route with slaves, rum, and molasses between Africa, the West Indies and the colonies. Providence, the second largest city in New England, is the industrial and commercial center in addition to being the capital of Rhode Island. The city is one of the largest manufacturing centers in the world and excels in several branches of the metal and rubber industries. Textile manufacturing is of first importance.

Historical sites and points of interest include Cathedral of St. John, Cathedral of St. Peter and St. Paul, John Brown House, the Arcade (oldest shopping center in the U.S.), Museum of the Rhode Island School of Design, Waterplace Park, the Athenaeum (oldest library in the U.S.), the Rhode Island Historical Society, Round Top Church, and the State House.

■ **BRYANT UNIVERSITY**
1150 Douglas Pke.
Smithfield, RI 02917
Tel: (401)232-6000; Free: 800-622-7001
Fax: (401)232-6741
E-mail: admission@bryant.edu
Web Site: www.bryant.edu/
Description: Independent, comprehensive, coed. Administratively affiliated with Bryant University. Awards bachelor's and master's degrees. Founded 1863. Setting: 428-acre suburban campus with easy access to Boston, Providence. Endowment: $141.8 million. Research spending for the previous fiscal year: $5.4 million. Educational spending for the previous fiscal year: $8430 per student. Total enrollment: 3,418. Faculty: 308 (168 full-time, 140 part-time). Student-undergrad faculty ratio is 15:1. 5,997 applied, 62% were admitted. 18% from top 10% of their high school class, 53% from top quarter, 88% from top half. 1 class president, 1 valedictorian, 91 student government officers. Full-time: 3,078 students, 42% women, 58% men. Part-time: 102 students, 41% women, 59% men. Students come from 31 states and territories, 65 other countries, 87% from out-of-state. 0.5% American Indian or Alaska Native, non-Hispanic/Latino; 5% Hispanic/Latino; 4% African American, non-Hispanic/Latino; 3% Asian, non-Hispanic/Latino; 0.1% Native Hawaiian or other Pacific Islander, non-Hispanic/Latino; 8% international. 2% 25 or older, 81% live on campus, 3% transferred in. Retention: 88% of full-time freshmen returned the following year. Academic areas with the most degrees conferred: business/marketing; communication/journalism; mathematics and statistics. Core. Calendar: semesters. ESL program, services for LD students, advanced placement, honors program, independent study, double major, summer session for credit, part-time degree program, adult/continuing education programs, internships. Study abroad program. ROTC: Army.
Entrance Requirements: Options: electronic application, early decision, early action, deferred admission, international baccalaureate accepted. Required: essay, high school transcript, 1 recommendation, senior year first-quarter grades; SAT Reasoning Test or ACT results. Recommended: minimum 3.3 high school GPA, 2 recommendations, interview. Entrance: moderately difficult. Application deadlines: 2/15, 2/15 for nonresidents, 11/15 for early decision plan 1, 1/15 for early decision plan 2, 12/1 for early action. Notification: 3/21, 3/21 for nonresidents, 12/15 for early decision plan 1, 2/15 for early decision plan 2, 1/15 for early action. SAT Subject Test deadline: 2/1. Transfer credits accepted: Yes. Applicants placed on waiting list: 865. Wait-listed applicants offered admission: 95. Early decision applicants: 160. Early decision applicants admitted: 116.
Costs Per Year: Application fee: $50. Comprehensive fee: $50,898 includes full-time tuition ($36,872), mandatory fees ($362), and college room and board ($13,664). College room only: $8020. Room and board charges vary according to board plan and housing facility. Part-time tuition: $806.89 per credit hour. Part-time tuition varies according to course load.
Collegiate Environment: Orientation program. Drama-theater group, choral group, student-run newspaper, radio station. Social organizations: 114 open to all; national fraternities, national sororities; 6% of eligible men and 7% of

The College Blue Book, 41st Edition

959

eligible women are members. Most popular organizations: Bryant Outdoor Activities Club, Student Programming Board, Rhythm and Pride Dance Team, WJMF Radio, Bryant Players (drama club). Major annual events: Reunion@Homecoming, REDay (Research & Engagement Day), Festival of Lights. Student services: health clinic, personal-psychological counseling, women's center. Campus security: 24-hour emergency response devices and patrols, late night transport-escort service, controlled dormitory access, 24 full-time staff; 20 patrol officers on foot, bike, golf cart, and car; Entry Control Station staffed 24/7 at only campus entry point. 2,882 college housing spaces available; 2,545 were occupied in 2012-13. Freshmen guaranteed college housing. Options: coed, women-only housing available. Douglas and Judith Krupp Library plus 1 other with 282,176 books, 14,541 microform titles, 68,915 serials, 2,137 audiovisual materials, an OPAC, and a Web page. Operations spending for the previous fiscal year: $1.5 million. 559 computers available on campus for general student use. Computer purchase/lease plans available. A computer is required for all students. A campuswide network can be accessed from student residence rooms and from off campus. Students can access the following: online class registration, e-mail, online library, wireless network, student Web hosts. Staffed computer lab on campus provides training in use of computers, software, and the Internet.

Community Environment: The college is located in the midst of the social, cultural, and recreational center that is southern New England. Its 392-acre campus offers the best of two worlds: the security of its suburban location with easy access to the excitement of the city. The setting, the campus, and the ultramodern facilities have been designed to maximize the interaction between faculty, students and administrators. This integrative atmosphere contributes to an individualistic approach to education and fosters an intimate relationship among all segments of the college community.

■ COMMUNITY COLLEGE OF RHODE ISLAND

400 E Ave.
Warwick, RI 02886-1807
Tel: (401)825-1000
Fax: (401)825-2418
E-mail: webadmission@ccri.edu
Web Site: www.ccri.edu/

Description: State-supported, 2-year, coed. Awards certificates, diplomas, transfer associate, and terminal associate degrees. Founded 1964. Setting: 205-acre urban campus with easy access to Boston. Total enrollment: 17,884. Faculty: 859 (332 full-time, 527 part-time). Student-undergrad faculty ratio is 20:1. 6,655 applied, 98% were admitted. Full-time: 5,857 students, 52% women, 48% men. Part-time: 12,027 students, 64% women, 36% men. Students come from 17 states and territories, 4% from out-of-state. 1% American Indian or Alaska Native, non-Hispanic/Latino; 17% Hispanic/Latino; 9% African American, non-Hispanic/Latino; 3% Asian, non-Hispanic/Latino; 0.04% Native Hawaiian or other Pacific Islander, non-Hispanic/Latino; 0.1% international. 39% 25 or older. Core. Calendar: semesters. Academic remediation for entering students, ESL program, services for LD students, advanced placement, honors program, independent study, distance learning, double major, summer session for credit, part-time degree program, external degree program, adult/continuing education programs, co-op programs and internships. Off campus study at Rhode Island College, University of Rhode Island. Study abroad program. ROTC: Army (c).

Entrance Requirements: Open admission except for nursing, dental, radiography, physical therapist assistant, computer programming, engineering, cardio-respiratory care, medical laboratory technician, occupational therapy assistant. Option: deferred admission. Entrance: noncompetitive. Application deadline: Rolling. Notification: continuous. Preference given to state residents, New England Regional Student Program applicants.

Costs Per Year: Application fee: $20. State resident tuition: $3624 full-time, $165 per credit hour part-time. Nonresident tuition: $10,256 full-time, $490 per semester hour part-time. Mandatory fees: $326 full-time, $12 per credit hour part-time, $30 per term part-time. Full-time tuition and fees vary according to program. Part-time tuition and fees vary according to course load and program.

Collegiate Environment: Orientation program. Drama-theater group, choral group, student-run newspaper. Social organizations: 75 open to all. Most popular organizations: Distributive Education Clubs of America, Theater group - Players, Skills USA, Phi Theta Kappa, student government. Major annual events: Student Welcome—All Clubs Day, Thanksgiving Leadership Conference, Theatre Productions. Student services: health clinic, personal-psychological counseling. Campus security: 24-hour emergency response devices and patrols. College housing not available. Community College of

Rhode Island Learning Resources Center plus 3 others with an OPAC and a Web page. 1,200 computers available on campus for general student use. A campuswide network can be accessed from off-campus. Students can access the following: online class registration. Staffed computer lab on campus provides training in use of computers, software, and the Internet.

■ JOHNSON & WALES UNIVERSITY

8 Abbott Park Pl.
Providence, RI 02903-3703
Tel: (401)598-1000; Free: 800-342-5598
Fax: (401)598-1835
E-mail: pvd@admissions.jwu.edu
Web Site: www.jwu.edu/providence/

Description: Independent, comprehensive, coed. Awards associate, bachelor's, master's, and doctoral degrees and post-master's certificates (branch locations in Charlotte, NC; Denver, CO; North Miami, FL). Founded 1914. Setting: 47-acre urban campus with easy access to Boston. Total enrollment: 10,974. Faculty: 519 (294 full-time, 225 part-time). Student-undergrad faculty ratio is 27:1. 13,850 applied, 70% were admitted. Full-time: 8,843 students, 55% women, 45% men. Part-time: 860 students, 56% women, 44% men. 81% from out-of-state. 0.3% American Indian or Alaska Native, non-Hispanic/Latino; 7% Hispanic/Latino; 7% African American, non-Hispanic/Latino; 2% Asian, non-Hispanic/Latino; 0.01% Native Hawaiian or other Pacific Islander, non-Hispanic/Latino; 9% international. 11% 25 or older, 42% live on campus, 7% transferred in. Retention: 75% of full-time freshmen returned the following year. Academic areas with the most degrees conferred: business/marketing; personal and culinary services; family and consumer sciences. Core. Academic remediation for entering students, ESL program, services for LD students, advanced placement, accelerated degree program, freshman honors college, honors program, independent study, summer session for credit, part-time degree program, adult/continuing education programs, co-op programs and internships, graduate courses open to undergrads. Study abroad program. ROTC: Army.

Entrance Requirements: Options: electronic application, early admission, deferred admission, international baccalaureate accepted. Required: high school transcript. Recommended: minimum 2 high school GPA. Required for some: essay, minimum 2.75 high school GPA, interview, SAT or ACT. Entrance: moderately difficult. Application deadline: Rolling. Notification: continuous.

Collegiate Environment: Orientation program. Student-run newspaper. Social organizations: national fraternities, national sororities, local fraternities, local sororities. Student services: health clinic, personal-psychological counseling, women's center. Campus security: 24-hour emergency response devices and patrols, student patrols, late night transport-escort service. Johnson & Wales University Library with an OPAC and a Web page.

■ MATER ECCLESIAE COLLEGE

60 Austin Ave.
Greenville, RI 02828
Tel: (401)949-2820
E-mail: info@mecollege.org
Web Site: www.mecollege.edu/

Description: Independent Roman Catholic, 4-year, women only. Awards bachelor's degrees.

Entrance Requirements: Required: high school transcript, 2 recommendations, SAT or ACT. Recommended: minimum 2.5 high school GPA.

■ NEW ENGLAND INSTITUTE OF TECHNOLOGY

One New England Tech Blvd.
East Greenwich, RI 02818
Tel: (401)467-7744; Free: 800-736-7744
E-mail: jjessup@neit.edu
Web Site: www.neit.edu/

Description: Independent, 4-year, coed. Awards associate, bachelor's, and master's degrees. Founded 1940. Setting: 225-acre suburban campus with easy access to Boston. Total enrollment: 2,764. Faculty: 294 (119 full-time, 175 part-time). Full-time: 2,320 students, 28% women, 72% men. Part-time: 393 students, 28% women, 72% men. Students come from 8 states and territories, 13 other countries. 1% American Indian or Alaska Native, non-Hispanic/Latino; 7% Hispanic/Latino; 5% African American, non-Hispanic/Latino; 2% Asian, non-Hispanic/Latino; 0.1% Native Hawaiian or other Pacific Islander, non-Hispanic/Latino; 3% international. Core. Academic remediation for entering students, services for LD students, advanced placement, accelerated degree program, self-designed majors, distance learning, double major, summer session for credit, part-time degree program, adult/continuing education programs, co-op programs and internships.

Entrance Requirements: Open admission. Options: electronic application, early admission, deferred admission. Required: high school transcript, interview, basic skills testing, Ronald P. Carver reading test used for placement. Portfolios required for advanced standing. Entrance: noncompetitive. Application deadline: Rolling. Transfer credits accepted: Yes.

Costs Per Year: Application fee: $25. Tuition: $20,870 full-time, $390 per credit hour part-time. Mandatory fees: $1125 full-time. Full-time tuition and fees vary according to degree level and program. Part-time tuition varies according to degree level and program. Tuition guaranteed not to increase for student's term of enrollment.

Collegiate Environment: Social organizations: 21 open to all. Most popular organizations: Skills USA, Game Developers Network, Vet Tech, Student Occupational Therapy Association, Phi Theta Kappa (International Honor Society). Student services: personal-psychological counseling. Campus security: security personnel during open hours. College housing not available. Library with 56,257 books, 26,235 serials, 1,366 audiovisual materials, an OPAC, and a Web page. 1,000 computers available on campus for general student use. A campuswide network can be accessed from off-campus. Students can access the following: online class registration. Staffed computer lab on campus provides training in use of computers, software, and the Internet.

■ **PROVIDENCE COLLEGE**
1 Cunningham Sq.
Providence, RI 02918
Tel: (401)865-1000; Free: 800-721-6444
Fax: (401)865-2826
E-mail: pcadmiss@providence.edu
Web Site: www.providence.edu/

Description: Independent Roman Catholic, comprehensive, coed. Awards associate, bachelor's, and master's degrees. Founded 1917. Setting: 105-acre suburban campus with easy access to Boston. Endowment: $166 million. Research spending for the previous fiscal year: $819,158. Educational spending for the previous fiscal year: $11,817 per student. Total enrollment: 4,336. Faculty: 395 (310 full-time, 85 part-time). Student-undergrad faculty ratio is 12:1. 37% from top 10% of their high school class, 69% from top quarter, 95% from top half. 10 National Merit Scholars, 29 class presidents, 12 valedictorians, 195 student government officers. Full-time: 3,802 students, 57% women, 43% men. Part-time: 8 students, 38% women, 63% men. Students come from 38 states and territories, 26 other countries, 88% from out-of-state. 0.2% American Indian or Alaska Native, non-Hispanic/Latino; 5% Hispanic/Latino; 4% African American, non-Hispanic/Latino; 1% Asian, non-Hispanic/Latino; 0.2% Native Hawaiian or other Pacific Islander, non-Hispanic/Latino; 2% international. 0% 25 or older, 78% live on campus, 1% transferred in. Retention: 90% of full-time freshmen returned the following year. Academic areas with the most degrees conferred: business/marketing; social sciences; biological/life sciences. Core. Calendar: semesters. Services for LD students, advanced placement, self-designed majors, honors program, independent study, distance learning, double major, summer session for credit, part-time degree program, adult/continuing education programs, co-op programs and internships, graduate courses open to undergrads. Study abroad program. ROTC: Army.

Entrance Requirements: Required: essay, high school transcript, 2 recommendations. Recommended: Test scores are considered if submitted.

Costs Per Year: Comprehensive fee: $54,646 includes full-time tuition ($41,350), mandatory fees ($856), and college room and board ($12,440). College room only: $7170. Full-time tuition and fees vary according to degree level and student level. Room and board charges vary according to board plan and housing facility. Part-time tuition: $1477 per credit. Part-time tuition varies according to degree level.

Collegiate Environment: Orientation program. Drama-theater group, choral group, student-run newspaper, radio station. Social organizations: 90 open to all. Most popular organizations: Board of Multicultural Student Activities, Board of Programmers, Student Congress, Campus Ministry, Future Friar Executives. Major annual events: Annual Concert or Comedy Show, Late Night Madness, BOP Clam Jam. Student services: health clinic, personal-psychological counseling. Campus security: 24-hour emergency response devices and patrols, student patrols, late night transport-escort service, controlled dormitory access. 3,088 college housing spaces available; 2,972 were occupied in 2012-13. Freshmen guaranteed college housing. On-campus residence required through sophomore year. Options: coed, men-only, women-only housing available. Phillips Memorial Library with 1.1 mil-

lion books, 62,487 microform titles, 46,805 serials, 225 audiovisual materials, an OPAC, and a Web page. Operations spending for the previous fiscal year: $3.4 million. 390 computers available on campus for general student use. Computer purchase/lease plans available. A campuswide network can be accessed from student residence rooms and from off campus. Students can access the following: online class registration. Staffed computer lab on campus provides training in use of computers, software, and the Internet.

Community Environment: See Brown University.

■ **RHODE ISLAND COLLEGE**
600 Mount Pleasant Ave.
Providence, RI 02908-1991
Tel: (401)456-8000; Free: 800-669-5760
Fax: (401)456-8379
E-mail: admissions@ric.edu
Web Site: www.ric.edu/

Description: State-supported, comprehensive, coed. Awards bachelor's, master's, and doctoral degrees and post-master's certificates. Founded 1854. Setting: 180-acre suburban campus with easy access to Boston. Endowment: $15.7 million. Research spending for the previous fiscal year: $12 million. Educational spending for the previous fiscal year: $12,919 per student. Total enrollment: 8,869. Faculty: 743 (327 full-time, 416 part-time). Student-undergrad faculty ratio is 14:1. 4,492 applied, 69% were admitted. 10% from top 10% of their high school class, 33% from top quarter, 75% from top half. Full-time: 5,533 students, 66% women, 34% men. Part-time: 2,020 students, 68% women, 32% men. Students come from 29 states and territories, 14% from out-of-state. 0.2% American Indian or Alaska Native, non-Hispanic/Latino; 11% Hispanic/Latino; 7% African American, non-Hispanic/Latino; 2% Asian, non-Hispanic/Latino; 0.1% Native Hawaiian or other Pacific Islander, non-Hispanic/Latino; 0.1% international. 23% 25 or older, 14% live on campus, 10% transferred in. Retention: 75% of full-time freshmen returned the following year. Academic areas with the most degrees conferred: business/marketing; education; psychology. Core. Calendar: semesters. Academic remediation for entering students, services for LD students, advanced placement, self-designed majors, honors program, independent study, double major, summer session for credit, part-time degree program, adult/continuing education programs, internships, graduate courses open to undergrads. Off campus study at Community College of Rhode Island, Providence College, University of Rhode Island. Study abroad program. ROTC: Army (c).

Entrance Requirements: Options: electronic application, early admission. Required: essay, high school transcript, 1 recommendation, one letter from guidance counselor, SAT or ACT. Recommended: minimum 3 high school GPA. Required for some: interview. Entrance: moderately difficult. Application deadlines: 3/15, 3/15 for nonresidents. Notification: continuous, continuous for nonresidents. SAT Reasoning Test deadline: 3/15. SAT Subject Test deadline: 3/15. Transfer credits accepted: Yes.

Costs Per Year: Application fee: $50. State resident tuition: $6530 full-time, $272 per credit part-time. Nonresident tuition: $17,228 full-time, $670 per credit part-time. Mandatory fees: $1068 full-time, $32 per credit part-time, $72 per term part-time. Part-time tuition and fees vary according to course load. College room and board: $9534. College room only: $5424. Room and board charges vary according to housing facility.

Collegiate Environment: Orientation program. Drama-theater group, choral group, student-run newspaper, radio station. Social organizations: 80 open to all; national fraternities, national sororities, local sororities; 3% of eligible men and 4% of eligible women are members. Most popular organizations: student government, newspaper (The Anchor), campus radio station (WXIN), Programming Board, Resident Student Association. Major annual events: Anchor Madness, Spring RIC End, Campus Activities Day. Student services: health clinic, personal-psychological counseling, women's center. Campus security: 24-hour emergency response devices and patrols, late night transport-escort service, controlled dormitory access. 1,194 college housing spaces available; 1,109 were occupied in 2012-13. Freshmen given priority for college housing. Options: coed, women-only housing available. Adams Library with 802,729 books, 1.3 million microform titles, 1.3 million serials, 6,704 audiovisual materials, an OPAC, and a Web page. Operations spending for the previous fiscal year: $2.8 million. 220 computers available on campus for general student use. Computer purchase/lease plans available. A campuswide network can be accessed from student residence rooms and from off campus. Students can access the following: online class registration. Staffed computer lab on campus provides training in use of computers, software, and the Internet.

■ RHODE ISLAND SCHOOL OF DESIGN

2 College St.
Providence, RI 02903-2784
Tel: (401)454-6100; Free: 800-364-7473
Fax: (401)454-6309
E-mail: admissions@risd.edu
Web Site: www.risd.edu/

Description: Independent, comprehensive, coed. Awards bachelor's and master's degrees. Founded 1877. Setting: 13-acre urban campus with easy access to Boston. Endowment: $283.5 million. Educational spending for the previous fiscal year: $18,465 per student. Total enrollment: 2,386. Faculty: 530 (147 full-time, 383 part-time). Student-undergrad faculty ratio is 9:1. 3,113 applied, 25% were admitted. Full-time: 1,971 students, 67% women, 33% men. Students come from 35 states and territories, 56 other countries, 93% from out-of-state. 0.2% American Indian or Alaska Native, non-Hispanic/Latino; 7% Hispanic/Latino; 2% African American, non-Hispanic/Latino; 18% Asian, non-Hispanic/Latino; 0.1% Native Hawaiian or other Pacific Islander, non-Hispanic/Latino; 21% international. 2% 25 or older, 70% live on campus, 4% transferred in. Retention: 93% of full-time freshmen returned the following year. Academic areas with the most degrees conferred: visual and performing arts; architecture; family and consumer sciences. Core. Calendar: 4-1-4. Academic remediation for entering students, ESL program, services for LD students, advanced placement, honors program, independent study, double major, co-op programs and internships. Off campus study at Brown University, Association of Independent Colleges of Art and Design. Study abroad program.

Entrance Requirements: Options: electronic application, early admission, early decision, deferred admission. Required: essay, high school transcript, portfolio, drawing assignments, SAT or ACT. Recommended: 3 recommendations. Entrance: very difficult. Application deadlines: 2/1, 11/1 for early decision. Notification: 3/15, 12/1 for early decision. SAT Reasoning Test deadline: 2/1. Transfer credits accepted: Yes.

Costs Per Year: Application fee: $60. Comprehensive fee: $53,312 includes full-time tuition ($41,022), mandatory fees ($310), and college room and board ($11,980). College room only: $6280. Room and board charges vary according to board plan and housing facility.

Collegiate Environment: Orientation program. Drama-theater group, choral group, student-run newspaper. Social organizations: 70 open to all; Student Alliance, clubs. Most popular organizations: athletic clubs, Industrial Design Club, Korean Students Association, Lesbian/Gay/Bisexual Alliance. Major annual events: Artists' Ball, Student and Alumni Art Sale, RISD Apparel Show. Student services: legal services, health clinic, personal-psychological counseling. Campus security: 24-hour emergency response devices and patrols, late night transport-escort service, controlled dormitory access. 1,485 college housing spaces available; all were occupied in 2012-13. Freshmen guaranteed college housing. On-campus residence required through sophomore year. Option: coed housing available. Fleet Library with 143,693 books, 1,544 serials, 5,132 audiovisual materials, an OPAC, and a Web page. Operations spending for the previous fiscal year: $1.8 million. 400 computers available on campus for general student use. Computer purchase/lease plans available. A campuswide network can be accessed from student residence rooms and from off campus. Students can access the following: online class registration. Staffed computer lab on campus provides training in use of computers, software, and the Internet.

Community Environment: See Brown University.

■ ROGER WILLIAMS UNIVERSITY

1 Old Ferry Rd.
Bristol, RI 02809
Tel: (401)253-1040; Free: 800-458-7144
Fax: (401)254-3557
E-mail: admit@rwu.edu
Web Site: www.rwu.edu/

Description: Independent, comprehensive, coed. Awards associate; bachelor's, master's, and doctoral degrees. Founded 1956. Setting: 140-acre small town campus with easy access to Boston. Endowment: $59.2 million. Research spending for the previous fiscal year: $2.2 million. Educational spending for the previous fiscal year: $12,373 per student. Total enrollment: 5,274. Faculty: 511 (224 full-time, 287 part-time). Student-undergrad faculty ratio is 15:1. 8,969 applied, 77% were admitted. 15% from top 10% of their high school class, 47% from top quarter, 83% from top half. Full-time: 3,774 students, 49% women, 51% men. Part-time: 617 students, 44% women, 56% men. Students come from 42 states and territories, 51 other countries, 82% from out-of-state. 0.3% American Indian or Alaska Na-

tive, non-Hispanic/Latino; 5% Hispanic/Latino; 2% African American, non-Hispanic/Latino; 1% Asian, non-Hispanic/Latino; 0% Native Hawaiian or other Pacific Islander, non-Hispanic/Latino; 4% international. 37% 25 or older, 63% live on campus, 2% transferred in. Retention: 78% of full-time freshmen returned the following year. Academic areas with the most degrees conferred: business/marketing; homeland security, law enforcement, firefighting, and protective services; architecture; psychology; law/legal studies. Core. Calendar: semesters. ESL program, services for LD students, advanced placement, accelerated degree program, self-designed majors, freshman honors college, honors program, independent study, distance learning, double major, summer session for credit, part-time degree program, external degree program, adult/continuing education programs, co-op programs and internships, graduate courses open to undergrads. Study abroad program. ROTC: Army (c).

Entrance Requirements: Options: electronic application, early action, deferred admission, international baccalaureate accepted. Required: essay, high school transcript, 1 recommendation. Required for some: Programs that require portfolio reviews, auditions, specific preparatory courses for admission include visual arts studies, graphic design communications, architecture, creative writing, dance and theater, SAT or ACT. Entrance: moderately difficult. Application deadlines: 2/1, 2/1 for nonresidents, 11/1 for early action. Notification: continuous until 2/15, continuous until 2/15 for nonresidents, 12/5 for early action. SAT Reasoning Test deadline: 2/1. Transfer credits accepted: Yes. Applicants placed on waiting list: 337. Wait-listed applicants offered admission: 7. Early action applicants: 3,835. Early action applicants admitted: 501.

Costs Per Year: Application fee: $50. Comprehensive fee: $45,788 includes full-time tuition ($29,976), mandatory fees ($1692), and college room and board ($14,120). College room only: $7610. Full-time tuition and fees vary according to class time, course load, and program. Room and board charges vary according to board plan and housing facility. Part-time tuition: $939 per course. Part-time tuition varies according to class time. Tuition guaranteed not to increase for student's term of enrollment.

Collegiate Environment: Orientation program. Drama-theater group, choral group, student-run newspaper, radio station. Social organizations: 70 open to all. Most popular organizations: Campus Entertainment Network, Dance Club, Inter Residence Hall Association, WQRI 88.3 radio station, Inter Class Council. Major annual events: Spring Week/Winter Weekend, Midnight Madness, Student Involvement Fair. Student services: health clinic, personal-psychological counseling, women's center. Campus security: 24-hour emergency response devices and patrols, student patrols, late night transport-escort service, controlled dormitory access. 2,860 college housing spaces available; 1,802 were occupied in 2012-13. Freshmen guaranteed college housing. On-campus residence required through sophomore year. Option: coed housing available. Roger Williams University Library plus 1 other with 536,679 books, 140,792 microform titles, 62,451 serials, 115,642 audiovisual materials, an OPAC, and a Web page. Operations spending for the previous fiscal year: $3.1 million. 270 computers available on campus for general student use. A campuswide network can be accessed from student residence rooms and from off campus. Students can access the following: online class registration. Staffed computer lab on campus.

■ SALVE REGINA UNIVERSITY

100 Ochre Point Ave.
Newport, RI 02840-4192
Tel: (401)847-6650; Free: 888-GO SALVE
Fax: (401)848-2823
E-mail: sruadmis@salve.edu
Web Site: www.salve.edu/

Description: Independent Roman Catholic, comprehensive, coed. Awards associate, bachelor's, master's, and doctoral degrees and post-master's certificates. Founded 1934. Setting: 75-acre suburban campus with easy access to Boston, Providence. Endowment: $44.3 million. Research spending for the previous fiscal year: $371,000. Educational spending for the previous fiscal year: $7914 per student. Total enrollment: 2,615. Faculty: 236 (115 full-time, 121 part-time). Student-undergrad faculty ratio is 15:1. 4,824 applied, 70% were admitted. 18% from top 10% of their high school class, 49% from top quarter, 85% from top half. Full-time: 1,974 students, 69% women, 31% men. Part-time: 79 students, 75% women, 25% men. Students come from 38 states and territories, 19 other countries, 78% from out-of-state. 0.3% American Indian or Alaska Native, non-Hispanic/Latino; 6% Hispanic/Latino; 2% African American, non-Hispanic/Latino; 1% Asian, non-Hispanic/Latino; 0.05% Native Hawaiian or other Pacific Islander, non-Hispanic/Latino; 2% international. 3% 25 or older, 60% live on campus, 2% transferred in. Retention: 82% of full-time freshmen returned the following year. Academic areas with the most degrees conferred: business/marketing; education; health professions and related sciences. Core. Calendar: semesters. ESL program, services for LD students, advanced placement, accelerated degree program, honors program, independent study, double major, summer session for credit, part-time degree program, adult/continuing education programs, internships, graduate courses open to undergrads. Off campus study. Study abroad program. ROTC: Army (c).

Entrance Requirements: Options: electronic application, early action, deferred admission, international baccalaureate accepted. Required: essay, high school transcript, 2 recommendations. Recommended: minimum 2.7 high school GPA. Required for some: SAT or ACT. Entrance: moderately difficult. Application deadlines: 2/1, 11/1 for early action. Notification: 12/25, 12/25 for early action. Transfer credits accepted: Yes. Applicants placed on waiting list: 271. Wait-listed applicants offered admission: 9. Early action applicants: 1,803. Early action applicants admitted: 1,318.

Costs Per Year: Application fee: $50. Comprehensive fee: $45,850 includes full-time tuition ($33,450), mandatory fees ($500), and college room and board ($11,900). Full-time tuition and fees vary according to course load and location. Room and board charges vary according to board plan and housing facility. Part-time tuition: $1115 per credit. Part-time mandatory fees: $40 per term. Part-time tuition and fees vary according to course load and location.

Collegiate Environment: Orientation program. Drama-theater group, choral group, student-run newspaper, radio station. Social organizations: 47 open to all. Most popular organizations: Orpheus Musical Society, Student Government Association, Student Outdoor Adventures, Student Nurse Organization, Stagefright Theatre Company. Major annual events: Family Weekend, Spring Weekend. Student services: health clinic, personal-psychological counseling. Campus security: 24-hour emergency response devices and patrols, late night transport-escort service, controlled dormitory access. 1,263 college housing spaces available; 1,196 were occupied in 2012-13. Freshmen guaranteed college housing. On-campus residence required through sophomore year. Options: coed, men-only, women-only housing available. McKillop Library with an OPAC and a Web page. Operations spending for the previous fiscal year: $1.4 million. 163 computers available on campus for general student use. Computer purchase/lease plans available. A campuswide network can be accessed from student residence rooms and from off campus. Students can access the following: online class registration. Staffed computer lab on campus provides training in use of computers, software, and the Internet.

Community Environment: Newport, RI, an island community and home of Salve Regina, was founded in 1639 and thrived as a Colonial seaport. Today, yachting and sailing regattas still fill its harbor and the Museum of Yachting displays America's Cup memorabilia. The Newport Historical Society and Newport Preservation Society support the City-by-the-Sea's bountiful historic and architectural legacy, including colonial structures, Victorian cottages, and Gilded Age mansions. The Cliff Walk and Ocean Drive provide stirring ocean vistas. The Redwood Library is the oldest library building in the United States in continuous use. The Newport Art museum exhibitions focus on the art of Newport and New England. The Newport Casino, which contains the Tennis Hall of Fame, hosts international tennis matches on its grass courts. World-acclaimed musicians perform at the Newport Music Festival. Opportunities abound for students to participate in the rich historical and cultural aspects of the community through university-sponsored work-study, volunteer, and intern programs.

■ **UNIVERSITY OF RHODE ISLAND**
Kingston, RI 02881
Tel: (401)874-1000
Fax: (401)874-5523
E-mail: lynch@uri.edu
Web Site: www.uri.edu/

Description: State-supported, university, coed. Administratively affiliated with Rhode Island Hospital, Community College of Rhode Island. Awards bachelor's, master's, and doctoral degrees. Founded 1892. Setting: 1,200-acre small town campus. Total enrollment: 16,451. Faculty: 1,169 (645 full-time, 524 part-time). Student-undergrad faculty ratio is 16:1. 20,637 applied, 77% were admitted. 17% from top 10% of their high school class, 48% from top quarter, 83% from top half. Full-time: 11,945 students, 54% women, 46% men. Part-time: 1,453 students, 57% women, 43% men. Students come from 43 states and territories, 40 other countries, 39% from out-of-state. 0.3% American Indian or Alaska Native, non-Hispanic/Latino; 8% Hispanic/Latino; 5% African American, non-Hispanic/Latino; 3% Asian, non-Hispanic/Latino; 0.1% Native Hawaiian or other Pacific Islander, non-Hispanic/Latino; 1% international. 11% 25 or older, 44% live on campus, 5% transferred in. Retention: 81% of full-time freshmen returned the following year. Academic areas with the most degrees conferred: business/marketing; health professions and related sciences; communication/journalism. Core. Calendar: semesters. Academic remediation for entering students, ESL program, services for LD students, advanced placement, accelerated degree program, honors program, independent study, distance learning, double major, summer session for credit, part-time degree program, adult/continuing education programs, co-op programs and internships, graduate courses open to undergrads. Off campus study at National Student Exchange, New England Land Grant University Exchange Program. Study abroad program. ROTC: Army.

Entrance Requirements: Options: electronic application, early admission, early action, deferred admission, international baccalaureate accepted. Required: essay, high school transcript, 1 recommendation, minimum of 18 units of college preparatory work, SAT or ACT. Entrance: moderately difficult. Application deadlines: 2/1, 2/1 for nonresidents, 12/1 for early action. Notification: 3/31, 3/31 for nonresidents, 1/31 for early action. Preference given to state residents. SAT Reasoning Test deadline: 2/1. Transfer credits accepted: Yes. Applicants placed on waiting list: 1,559. Wait-listed applicants offered admission: 108.

Costs Per Year: Application fee: $65. State resident tuition: $10,878 full-time. Nonresident tuition: $26,444 full-time. Mandatory fees: $1572 full-time. Full-time tuition and fees vary according to course load, location, and reciprocity agreements.

Collegiate Environment: Orientation program. Drama-theater group, choral group, marching band, student-run newspaper, radio station. Social organizations: 100 open to all; national fraternities, national sororities. Most popular organizations: Student Entertainment Committee, student radio station, Intramural sport clubs, Student Alumni Association, student newspaper. Major annual events: Family Weekend, Homecoming, Springfest. Student services: health clinic, personal-psychological counseling, women's center. Campus security: 24-hour emergency response devices and patrols, student patrols, late night transport-escort service, controlled dormitory access. 6,917 college housing spaces available; 6,140 were occupied in 2012-13. Freshmen guaranteed college housing. Option: coed housing available. Robert L. Carothers Library & Learning Commons plus 3 others with 1.7 million microform titles, 27,048 serials, 12,976 audiovisual materials, an OPAC, and a Web page. 2,500 computers available on campus for general student use. Computer purchase/lease plans available. A campuswide network can be accessed from student residence rooms and from off campus. Students can access the following: online class registration. Staffed computer lab on campus.

Community Environment: The quiet village of Kingston was founded about 1700. Some of the many interesting houses here date from pre-Revolutionary days. Community facilities include churches of all faiths, a museum, art center, hospitals, and numerous major civic, fraternal and veteran's organizations. Recreational activities include boating, fishing, golf, skiing, and summer theatre. International and deep-sea yacht races are special events. Many part-time jobs are available.

■ AIKEN TECHNICAL COLLEGE

PO Drawer 696
Aiken, SC 29802-0696
Tel: (803)593-9231
E-mail: sommersl@atc.edu
Web Site: www.atc.edu/

Description: State and locally supported, 2-year, coed. Part of South Carolina State Board for Technical and Comprehensive Education. Awards certificates, diplomas, transfer associate, and terminal associate degrees. Founded 1972. Setting: 88-acre rural campus. Endowment: $4.1 million. Total enrollment: 3,045. Faculty: 184 (59 full-time, 125 part-time). Student-undergrad faculty ratio is 31:1. 2,001 applied, 41% were admitted. Full-time: 1,315 students, 59% women, 41% men. Part-time: 1,730 students, 68% women, 32% men. 10% from out-of-state. 1% American Indian or Alaska Native, non-Hispanic/Latino; 2% Hispanic/Latino; 33% African American, non-Hispanic/Latino; 1% Asian, non-Hispanic/Latino; 0.3% Native Hawaiian or other Pacific Islander, non-Hispanic/Latino; 0.03% international. 40% 25 or older, 11% transferred in. Retention: 23% of full-time freshmen returned the following year. Core. Calendar: semesters. Academic remediation for entering students, services for LD students, advanced placement, summer session for credit, part-time degree program, co-op programs and internships. Off campus study at University of South Carolina-Aiken.

Entrance Requirements: Open admission except for nursing program. Options: electronic application, deferred admission. Recommended: high school transcript. Entrance: noncompetitive. Application deadlines: Rolling, Rolling for nonresidents. Notification: continuous, continuous for nonresidents. Transfer credits accepted: Yes.

Costs Per Year: Application fee: $0. Area resident tuition: $3576 full-time, $149 per credit hour part-time. State resident tuition: $3936 full-time, $164 per credit hour part-time. Nonresident tuition: $9600 full-time, $400 per credit hour part-time. Mandatory fees: $290 full-time, $5 per credit hour part-time, $85 per term part-time. Full-time tuition and fees vary according to course load and reciprocity agreements. Part-time tuition and fees vary according to course load and reciprocity agreements.

Collegiate Environment: Orientation program. Student services: personal-psychological counseling. Campus security: 24-hour emergency response devices and patrols, late night transport-escort service. Aiken Technical College Library with 62,235 books, 165 serials, an OPAC, and a Web page.

■ ALLEN UNIVERSITY

1530 Harden St.
Columbia, SC 29204
Tel: (803)254-4165; Free: 877-625-5368
Fax: (803)376-5731
E-mail: tparker@allenuniversity.edu
Web Site: www.allenuniversity.edu/

Description: Independent African Methodist Episcopal, 4-year, coed. Awards bachelor's degrees. Founded 1870. Setting: suburban campus. Total enrollment: 827. Faculty: 41 (29 full-time, 12 part-time). 1,937 applied, 72% were admitted. Full-time: 804 students, 56% women, 44% men. Part-time: 23 students, 57% women, 43% men. 25% from out-of-state. 30% 25 or older, 7% transferred in. Retention: 62% of full-time freshmen returned the following year. Academic areas with the most degrees conferred: business/marketing; social sciences; biological/life sciences. Core. Calendar: semesters. Academic remediation for entering students, honors program,

independent study, summer session for credit, part-time degree program, adult/continuing education programs, co-op programs and internships. Study abroad program. ROTC: Army (c).

Entrance Requirements: Open admission. Option: electronic application. Required: essay, high school transcript, 2 recommendations. Recommended: SAT or ACT. Entrance: minimally difficult. Application deadline: 7/31. Transfer credits accepted: Yes.

Costs Per Year: Application fee: $20. Comprehensive fee: $17,500 includes full-time tuition ($11,540), mandatory fees ($400), and college room and board ($5560). College room only: $1850. Full-time tuition and fees vary according to course load. Room and board charges vary according to housing facility. Part-time tuition: $450 per credit hour. Part-time mandatory fees: $531 per term. Part-time tuition and fees vary according to course load.

Collegiate Environment: Orientation program. Choral group, student-run newspaper. Social organizations: 6 open to all; national fraternities, local fraternities, local sororities, NAACP. Most popular organizations: International Students Club, Social Science Club, Gospel Choir, NAACP, Phi Beta Lambda and BASIC. Major annual events: Homecoming, Religious Emphasis Week, Black History Month observance. Student services: health clinic, personal-psychological counseling. Campus security: 24-hour emergency response devices and patrols, controlled dormitory access. J. S. Flipper Library with 50,000 books and 175 serials.

Community Environment: See University of South Carolina.

■ ANDERSON UNIVERSITY

316 Blvd.
Anderson, SC 29621-4035
Tel: (864)231-2000; Free: 800-542-3594
Fax: (864)231-2004
E-mail: admissions@andersonuniversity.edu
Web Site: www.andersonuniversity.edu/

Description: Independent Baptist, comprehensive, coed. Awards bachelor's, master's, and doctoral degrees. Founded 1911. Setting: 271-acre suburban campus with easy access to Greenville. Endowment: $32.2 million. Educational spending for the previous fiscal year: $4425 per student. Total enrollment: 2,922. Faculty: 302 (115 full-time, 187 part-time). Student-undergrad faculty ratio is 15:1. 2,060 applied, 72% were admitted. 39% from top 10% of their high school class, 61% from top quarter, 86% from top half. 8 valedictorians, 42 student government officers. Full-time: 2,152 students, 64% women, 36% men. Part-time: 478 students, 68% women, 32% men. Students come from 35 states and territories, 22 other countries, 18% from out-of-state. 1% American Indian or Alaska Native, non-Hispanic/Latino; 3% Hispanic/Latino; 11% African American, non-Hispanic/Latino; 1% Asian, non-Hispanic/Latino; 1% Native Hawaiian or other Pacific Islander, non-Hispanic/Latino; 1% international. 22% 25 or older, 54% live on campus, 4% transferred in. Retention: 77% of full-time freshmen returned the following year. Academic areas with the most degrees conferred: business/marketing; education; visual and performing arts. Core. Calendar: semesters. Academic remediation for entering students, services for LD students, advanced placement, accelerated degree program, honors program, independent study, distance learning, double major, summer session for credit, part-time degree program, adult/continuing education programs, co-op programs and internships. Study abroad program. ROTC: Army (c), Air Force (c).

Entrance Requirements: Options: electronic application, deferred admission. Required: high school transcript, SAT or ACT. Recommended:

minimum 2.9 high school GPA. Required for some: essay, 2 recommendations, interview. Entrance: minimally difficult. Application deadline: 7/1. Notification: continuous.

Costs Per Year: Application fee: $25. Comprehensive fee: $31,138 includes full-time tuition ($20,820), mandatory fees ($1970), and college room and board ($8348). College room only: $4316. Full-time tuition and fees vary according to course load and program. Room and board charges vary according to board plan and housing facility. Part-time tuition: $515 per credit hour. Part-time tuition varies according to program.

Collegiate Environment: Orientation program. Drama-theater group, choral group, student-run newspaper. Social organizations: 29 open to all. Most popular organizations: Baptist Campus Ministries, Fellowship of Christian Athletes, Student Government Association, Gamma Beta Phi, Student Alumni Council. Major annual events: CORE-Campus Organizations Recruitment Event, Christmas First Night, Founders' Day Convocation. Student services: health clinic, personal-psychological counseling. Campus security: 24-hour emergency response devices and patrols, late night transport-escort service, controlled dormitory access. 1,280 college housing spaces available; 1,260 were occupied in 2012-13. No special consideration for freshman housing applicants. On-campus residence required through sophomore year. Options: men-only, women-only housing available. Thrift Library with 82,615 books, 6,849 microform titles, 160 serials, 7,131 audiovisual materials, an OPAC, and a Web page. 192 computers available on campus for general student use. A campuswide network can be accessed from student residence rooms and from off campus. Students can access the following: online class registration. Staffed computer lab on campus (open 24 hours a day) provides training in use of computers, software, and the Internet.

Community Environment: Located in the Piedmont Plateau section, Anderson enjoys moderate climate and is a busy manufacturing town with 32 textile plants and many other factories. The area is accessed by major highways, air, bus, and limited rail service. The community has a countywide library system, churches of many denominations, hotel and motels, hospitals, shopping malls, and various civic and fraternal organizations. Local recreation includes theatres, bowling, tennis, excellent golf facilities, two large lakes, swimming, boating, fishing, hunting, and other outdoor sports. Part-time employment is available.

■ THE ART INSTITUTE OF CHARLESTON
24 N Market St.
Charleston, SC 29401
Tel: (843)727-3500; Free: 866-211-0107
Fax: (843)727-3440
Web Site: www.artinstitutes.edu/charleston/
Description: Proprietary, 4-year, coed. Part of Education Management Corporation. Awards associate and bachelor's degrees. Founded 2007. Setting: urban campus.

■ BENEDICT COLLEGE
1600 Harden St.
Columbia, SC 29204
Tel: (803)256-4220; Free: 800-868-6598
Fax: (803)253-5167
E-mail: thompsop@benedict.edu
Web Site: www.benedict.edu/
Description: Independent Baptist, 4-year, coed. Awards bachelor's degrees. Founded 1870. Setting: 20-acre urban campus. Total enrollment: 2,641. 10% 25 or older. Calendar: semesters. Advanced placement, honors program, summer session for credit, part-time degree program, adult/continuing education programs, internships. ROTC: Army, Air Force (c).
Entrance Requirements: Open admission. Options: early admission, deferred admission. Required: high school transcript. Entrance: minimally difficult. Application deadline: Rolling. Notification: continuous until 7/31.
Costs Per Year: Application fee: $25. Comprehensive fee: $26,390 includes full-time tuition ($16,354), mandatory fees ($1932), and college room and board ($8104). Part-time tuition: $515 per credit hour. Part-time mandatory fees: $60 per credit hour. Part-time tuition and fees vary according to course load.
Collegiate Environment: Orientation program. Campus security: 24-hour emergency response devices and patrols. Benjamin Payton Learning Resource Center with 114,770 books, 35,754 microform titles, 320 serials, 5,954 audiovisual materials, and a Web page.
Community Environment: See University of South Carolina.

■ BOB JONES UNIVERSITY
1700 Wade Hampton Blvd.
Greenville, SC 29614

Tel: (864)242-5100; Free: 800-BJANDME
E-mail: admission@bju.edu
Web Site: www.bju.edu/
Description: Independent Christian, university, coed. Awards associate, bachelor's, master's, and doctoral degrees and post-master's certificates. Founded 1927. Setting: 225-acre urban campus. Total enrollment: 3,469. Faculty: 260 (198 full-time, 62 part-time). Student-undergrad faculty ratio is 15:1. 1,437 applied, 73% were admitted. 8% from top 10% of their high school class, 17% from top quarter, 36% from top half. Full-time: 2,802 students, 57% women, 43% men. Part-time: 174 students, 54% women, 46% men. Students come from 52 states and territories, 90 other countries, 75% from out-of-state. 0.2% American Indian or Alaska Native, non-Hispanic/Latino; 2% Hispanic/Latino; 1% African American, non-Hispanic/Latino; 2% Asian, non-Hispanic/Latino; 0.3% Native Hawaiian or other Pacific Islander, non-Hispanic/Latino; 5% international. 3% 25 or older, 74% live on campus, 3% transferred in. Retention: 83% of full-time freshmen returned the following year. Academic areas with the most degrees conferred: education; visual and performing arts; business/marketing. Core. Calendar: semesters. ESL program, services for LD students, advanced placement, accelerated degree program, distance learning, summer session for credit, part-time degree program, adult/continuing education programs, internships. Off campus study.
Entrance Requirements: Options: electronic application, international baccalaureate accepted. Required: essay, high school transcript, 3 recommendations, ACT. Entrance: minimally difficult. Application deadline: 8/1. Transfer credits accepted: Yes.
Costs Per Year: Application fee: $0. Comprehensive fee: $19,220 includes full-time tuition ($12,820), mandatory fees ($610), and college room and board ($5790). Full-time tuition and fees vary according to program. Part-time tuition: $624 per credit hour. Part-time tuition varies according to program.
Collegiate Environment: Orientation program. Drama-theater group, choral group, student-run newspaper, radio station. Social organizations: 30 open to all; Intra-societies. Most popular organizations: Community Relations Council, Extension Ministries, Societies, Mission Prayer Band, University Business Association. Major annual events: Bible conference, Artist series, Missions Emphasis Week. Student services: health clinic, personal-psychological counseling. Campus security: 24-hour patrols, student patrols, late night transport-escort service, controlled dormitory access, 24/7 emergency dispatcher. 3,344 college housing spaces available; 2,212 were occupied in 2012-13. Freshmen guaranteed college housing. On-campus residence required through senior year. Options: men-only, women-only housing available. J.S. Mack plus 2 others with 315,486 books, 493,302 microform titles, 27,310 serials, 17,294 audiovisual materials, an OPAC, and a Web page. 450 computers available on campus for general student use. Computer purchase/lease plans available. A campuswide network can be accessed from student residence rooms and from off campus. Students can access the following: online class registration. Staffed computer lab on campus provides training in use of computers, software, and the Internet.

■ BROWN MACKIE COLLEGE–GREENVILLE
Two Liberty Sq.
75 Beattie Pl., Ste. 100
Greenville, SC 29601
Tel: (864)239-5300; Free: 877-479-8465
Fax: (864)232-4094
Web Site: www.brownmackie.edu/greenville/
Description: Proprietary, primarily 2-year, coed. Part of Education Management Corporation. Awards certificates, terminal associate, and bachelor's degrees.

■ CENTRAL CAROLINA TECHNICAL COLLEGE
506 N Guignard Dr.
Sumter, SC 29150-2499
Tel: (803)778-1961; Free: 800-221-8711
Fax: (803)773-4859
E-mail: wrightb@cctech.edu
Web Site: www.cctech.edu/
Description: State-supported, 2-year, coed. Part of South Carolina State Board for Technical and Comprehensive Education. Awards certificates, diplomas, transfer associate, and terminal associate degrees. Founded 1963. Setting: 70-acre small town campus with easy access to Columbia, SC. Endowment: $1.4 million. Total enrollment: 4,522. Faculty: 258 (99 full-time, 159 part-time). Student-undergrad faculty ratio is 17:1. Full-time: 1,607

students, 63% women, 37% men. Part-time: 2,915 students, 74% women, 26% men. 1% from out-of-state. 0.1% American Indian or Alaska Native, non-Hispanic/Latino; 2% Hispanic/Latino; 48% African American, non-Hispanic/Latino; 1% Asian, non-Hispanic/Latino; 0.02% Native Hawaiian or other Pacific Islander, non-Hispanic/Latino; 0% international. 49% 25 or older, 7% transferred in. Core. Calendar: semesters. Academic remediation for entering students, services for LD students, advanced placement, accelerated degree program, independent study, distance learning, summer session for credit, part-time degree program, external degree program, adult/continuing education programs, co-op programs and internships.

Entrance Requirements: Open admission except for selected health science programs. Option: electronic application. Required: COMPASS/ASSET. Required for some: high school transcript, SAT, ACT, SAT or ACT. Entrance: noncompetitive. Application deadline: Rolling. Transfer credits accepted: Yes.

Costs Per Year: Application fee: $0. Area resident tuition: $3584 full-time, $150 per credit hour part-time. State resident tuition: $4178 full-time, $175 per credit hour part-time. Nonresident tuition: $6232 full-time, $260 per credit hour part-time. Full-time tuition varies according to program. Part-time tuition varies according to program.

Collegiate Environment: Orientation program. Social organizations: 7 open to all. Most popular organizations: Creative Arts Society, Phi Theta Kappa, Computer Club, National Student Nurses Association (local chapter), Natural Resources Management Club. Major annual events: Spring Fling, Student Appreciation Day, Centralfest. Student services: personal-psychological counseling. Campus security: 24-hour emergency response devices, student patrols, security patrols parking lots and halls during working hours and off-duty police officers are deployed on main campus during peak hours. Central Carolina Technical College Library with 27,878 books, 135 serials, 2,778 audiovisual materials, an OPAC, and a Web page. Operations spending for the previous fiscal year: $241,681. 850 computers available on campus for general student use. A campuswide network can be accessed from off-campus. Students can access the following: online class registration, student account and grade information. Staffed computer lab on campus.

Community Environment: See Morris College.

■ **CHARLESTON SOUTHERN UNIVERSITY**
PO Box 118087
Charleston, SC 29423-8087
Tel: (843)863-7000; Free: 800-947-7474
E-mail: enroll@csuniv.edu
Web Site: www.charlestonsouthern.edu/
Description: Independent Baptist, comprehensive, coed. Awards bachelor's and master's degrees. Founded 1964. Setting: 500-acre suburban campus. Endowment: $13.5 million. Educational spending for the previous fiscal year: $6137 per student. Total enrollment: 3,130. Faculty: 298 (172 full-time, 126 part-time). Student-undergrad faculty ratio is 13:1. 2,734 applied, 82% were admitted. 10% from top 10% of their high school class, 37% from top quarter, 63% from top half. Full-time: 2,482 students, 63% women, 37% men. Part-time: 297 students, 66% women, 34% men. Students come from 40 states and territories, 22 other countries, 15% from out-of-state. 1% American Indian or Alaska Native, non-Hispanic/Latino; 3% Hispanic/Latino; 29% African American, non-Hispanic/Latino; 1% Asian, non-Hispanic/Latino; 0.04% Native Hawaiian or other Pacific Islander, non-Hispanic/Latino; 1% international. 14% 25 or older, 49% live on campus, 8% transferred in. Retention: 57% of full-time freshmen returned the following year. Core. Calendar: 4-4-1. Academic remediation for entering students, services for LD students, advanced placement, accelerated degree program, honors program, double major, summer session for credit, part-time degree program, internships. Off campus study at Charleston Higher Education Consortium, University of North Carolina System, Clemson University. ROTC: Air Force.

Entrance Requirements: Option: international baccalaureate accepted. Required: high school transcript, minimum 2 high school GPA, SAT or ACT. Required for some: essay, 1 recommendation, interview. Entrance: moderately difficult. Application deadline: Rolling. Notification: continuous.

Costs Per Year: Application fee: $40. Comprehensive fee: $30,740 includes full-time tuition ($22,050), mandatory fees ($40), and college room and board ($8650). Part-time tuition: $470 per credit. Part-time mandatory fees: $40 per term.

Collegiate Environment: Orientation program. Drama-theater group, choral group, marching band, student-run newspaper. Social organizations: 20 open to all; national fraternities, national sororities, local fraternities, local sororities. Most popular organizations: student government, Baptist Student

Union, Fellowship of Christian Athletes. Major annual events: Convocation, Homecoming. Student services: personal-psychological counseling. Campus security: 24-hour emergency response devices and patrols, late night transport-escort service. College housing designed to accommodate 1,134 students; 1,150 undergraduates lived in college housing during 2012-13. Freshmen given priority for college housing. On-campus residence required through sophomore year. Options: men-only, women-only housing available. L. Mendel Rivers Library with 192,600 books, 215,900 microform titles, 1,111 serials, an OPAC, and a Web page. 250 computers available on campus for general student use. A campuswide network can be accessed from student residence rooms and from off campus. Students can access the following: online class registration, online course work. Staffed computer lab on campus.

Community Environment: See The Citadel.

■ **THE CITADEL, THE MILITARY COLLEGE OF SOUTH CAROLINA**
171 Moultrie St.
Charleston, SC 29409
Tel: (843)953-5000; Free: 800-868-1842
Fax: (843)953-7084
E-mail: john.powell@citadel.edu
Web Site: www.citadel.edu/
Description: State-supported, comprehensive, coed. Awards bachelor's and master's degrees and post-master's certificates. Founded 1842. Setting: 300-acre suburban campus. Endowment: $58.2 million. Research spending for the previous fiscal year: $427,049. Educational spending for the previous fiscal year: $5970 per student. Total enrollment: 3,499. Faculty: 266 (182 full-time, 84 part-time). Student-undergrad faculty ratio is 13:1. 2,557 applied, 80% were admitted. 12% from top 10% of their high school class, 33% from top quarter, 71% from top half. Full-time: 2,438 students, 7% women, 93% men. Part-time: 191 students, 40% women, 60% men. Students come from 44 states and territories, 8 other countries, 44% from out-of-state. 1% American Indian or Alaska Native, non-Hispanic/Latino; 6% Hispanic/Latino; 8% African American, non-Hispanic/Latino; 2% Asian, non-Hispanic/Latino; 0.2% Native Hawaiian or other Pacific Islander, non-Hispanic/Latino; 1% international. 8% 25 or older, 100% live on campus, 4% transferred in. Retention: 84% of full-time freshmen returned the following year. Academic areas with the most degrees conferred: business/marketing; engineering; homeland security, law enforcement, firefighting, and protective services. Core. Calendar: semesters. ESL program, services for LD students, advanced placement, honors program, independent study, distance learning, double major, summer session for credit, part-time degree program, co-op programs and internships. Off campus study at 4 members of the Charleston Higher Education Consortium. Study abroad program. ROTC: Army, Naval, Air Force.

Entrance Requirements: Options: electronic application, international baccalaureate accepted. Required: high school transcript, SAT or ACT. Recommended: interview. Entrance: moderately difficult. Application deadline: Rolling. Notification: continuous. Preference given to state residents.

Costs Per Year: Application fee: $40. State resident tuition: $10,523 full-time, $410 per credit part-time. Nonresident tuition: $28,776 full-time, $743 per credit part-time. Mandatory fees: $1249 full-time. College room and board: $6115.

Collegiate Environment: Orientation program. Choral group, marching band, student-run newspaper. Social organizations: 100 open to all. Most popular organizations: The Republican Society, Semper Fi Society, HESS Majors, Rod & Gun Club, Cordell Airborne Rangers. Major annual events: Parents' Day, Homecoming, Corps Day. Student services: health clinic, personal-psychological counseling. Campus security: 24-hour patrols. 2,330 college housing spaces available; 2,272 were occupied in 2012-13. Freshmen guaranteed college housing. On-campus residence required through senior year. Option: coed housing available. Daniel Library with 193,992 books, 1.2 million microform titles, 74,476 serials, 5,538 audiovisual materials, an OPAC, and a Web page. Operations spending for the previous fiscal year: $1.7 million. 350 computers available on campus for general student use. A campuswide network can be accessed from student residence rooms and from off campus. Students can access the following: online class registration. Staffed computer lab on campus provides training in use of computers, software, and the Internet.

■ **CLAFLIN UNIVERSITY**
400 Magnolia St.
Orangeburg, SC 29115
Tel: (803)535-5097; Free: 800-922-1276

Fax: (803)531-2860
E-mail: mike.zeigler.@claflin.edu
Web Site: www.claflin.edu/
Description: Independent United Methodist, comprehensive, coed. Awards bachelor's and master's degrees. Founded 1869. Setting: 46-acre small town campus with easy access to Columbia. Endowment: $19 million. Research spending for the previous fiscal year: $6 million. Educational spending for the previous fiscal year: $22,152 per student. Total enrollment: 1,946. Faculty: 153 (121 full-time, 32 part-time). Student-undergrad faculty ratio is 14:1. 4,394 applied, 53% were admitted. 13% from top 10% of their high school class, 31% from top quarter, 66% from top half. Full-time: 1,830 students, 65% women, 35% men. Part-time: 53 students, 70% women, 30% men. Students come from 27 states and territories, 15 other countries, 19% from out-of-state. 0.3% American Indian or Alaska Native, non-Hispanic/Latino; 2% Hispanic/Latino; 92% African American, non-Hispanic/Latino; 0.2% Asian, non-Hispanic/Latino; 0% Native Hawaiian or other Pacific Islander, non-Hispanic/Latino; 3% international. 15% 25 or older, 71% live on campus, 6% transferred in. Retention: 74% of full-time freshmen returned the following year. Academic areas with the most degrees conferred: business/marketing; social sciences; homeland security, law enforcement, firefighting, and protective services. Core. Calendar: semesters. Academic remediation for entering students, advanced placement, freshman honors college, honors program, independent study, summer session for credit, part-time degree program, adult/continuing education programs, co-op programs and internships. Off campus study at South Carolina State University, Medical University of South Carolina, Orangeburg-Calhoun Technical College, Clemson University. ROTC: Army (c).
Entrance Requirements: Options: electronic application, deferred admission, international baccalaureate accepted. Required: essay, high school transcript, minimum 2 high school GPA, SAT or ACT. Recommended: SAT Subject Tests. Entrance: minimally difficult. Application deadline: Rolling. Notification: continuous.
Costs Per Year: Application fee: $30. Comprehensive fee: $22,464 includes full-time tuition ($13,974), mandatory fees ($450), and college room and board ($8040). College room only: $3420. Full-time tuition and fees vary according to class time. Room and board charges vary according to housing facility. Part-time tuition: $582 per credit hour. Part-time tuition varies according to class time.
Collegiate Environment: Orientation program. Drama-theater group, choral group, student-run newspaper. Social organizations: 64 open to all; national fraternities, national sororities; 3% of eligible men and 6% of eligible women are members. Major annual events: Homecoming, Spring Convocation, Honors and Awards Convocation. Student services: health clinic, personal-psychological counseling. Campus security: 24-hour emergency response devices and patrols, student patrols, controlled dormitory access. 1,179 college housing spaces available; 1,104 were occupied in 2012-13. Freshmen given priority for college housing. Options: men-only, women-only housing available. H. V. Manning Library plus 1 other with 166,505 books, 67,123 microform titles, 409 serials, 1,287 audiovisual materials, an OPAC, and a Web page. Operations spending for the previous fiscal year: $549,531. 530 computers available on campus for general student use. A campuswide network can be accessed from student residence rooms and from off campus. Students can access the following: online class registration. Staffed computer lab on campus.

■ **CLEMSON UNIVERSITY**
Clemson, SC 29634
Tel: (864)656-3311
Fax: (864)656-2464
E-mail: cuadmissions@clemson.edu
Web Site: www.clemson.edu/
Description: State-supported, university, coed. Awards bachelor's, master's, and doctoral degrees and post-master's certificates. Founded 1889. Setting: 1,400-acre small town campus. Endowment: $453.5 million. Research spending for the previous fiscal year: $123.6 million. Educational spending for the previous fiscal year: $9544 per student. Total enrollment: 20,768. Faculty: 1,157 (1,051 full-time, 106 part-time). Student-undergrad faculty ratio is 18:1. 18,500 applied, 58% were admitted. 54% from top 10% of their high school class, 84% from top quarter, 97% from top half. 31 National Merit Scholars. Full-time: 15,643 students, 47% women, 53% men. Part-time: 919 students, 37% women, 63% men. Students come from 53 states and territories, 84 other countries, 29% from out-of-state. 0.2% American Indian or Alaska Native, non-Hispanic/Latino; 3% Hispanic/Latino; 6% African American, non-Hispanic/Latino; 2% Asian, non-Hispanic/Latino; 0.1% Native

Hawaiian or other Pacific Islander, non-Hispanic/Latino; 1% international. 4% 25 or older, 37% live on campus, 7% transferred in. Retention: 91% of full-time freshmen returned the following year. Academic areas with the most degrees conferred: business/marketing; engineering; biological/life sciences. Core. Calendar: semesters. Academic remediation for entering students, ESL program, services for LD students, advanced placement, freshman honors college, honors program, independent study, distance learning, double major, summer session for credit, part-time degree program, co-op programs and internships, graduate courses open to undergrads. Off campus study. Study abroad program. ROTC: Army, Air Force.
Entrance Requirements: Options: electronic application, international baccalaureate accepted. Required: high school transcript, SAT or ACT. Recommended: essay. Entrance: moderately difficult. Application deadline: 5/1. Notification: continuous. Preference given to state residents. SAT Reasoning Test deadline: 4/30. SAT Subject Test deadline: 4/30. Applicants placed on waiting list: 1,820. Wait-listed applicants offered admission: 4.
Costs Per Year: Application fee: $70. State resident tuition: $13,076 full-time. Nonresident tuition: $29,720 full-time. Full-time tuition varies according to course load, location, and program. College room and board: $7552. Room and board charges vary according to board plan, housing facility, and location.
Collegiate Environment: Orientation program. Drama-theater group, choral group, marching band, student-run newspaper, radio station. Social organizations: 350 open to all; national fraternities, national sororities; 20% of eligible men and 33% of eligible women are members. Most popular organizations: student government, Fellowship of Christian Athletes, Tiger Band. Major annual events: Homecoming/Tigerama, Welcome Back Festival, Campus Sweep. Student services: legal services, health clinic, personal-psychological counseling. Campus security: 24-hour emergency response devices and patrols, late night transport-escort service, controlled dormitory access. 6,145 college housing spaces available; 5,845 were occupied in 2012-13. Freshmen guaranteed college housing. On-campus residence required in freshman year. Options: coed, men-only, women-only housing available. Robert Muldrow Cooper Library plus 1 other with 1.2 million books, 1.2 million microform titles, 5,587 serials, an OPAC, and a Web page. Operations spending for the previous fiscal year: $14 million. 1,250 computers available on campus for general student use. Computer purchase/lease plans available. A computer is required for all students. A campuswide network can be accessed from student residence rooms and from off campus. Students can access the following: online class registration. Staffed computer lab on campus provides training in use of computers, software, and the Internet.
Community Environment: Clemson is located in the foothills of the Blue Ridge Mountains approximately 135 miles from Charlotte and Atlanta. The average temperature is 61 degrees. The area is served by U.S. Highways 76 and 123, and air service is available nearby. Clemson has several churches of different denominations, a library, YMCA, concert series, and Little Theatre. Hotels, apartments, and rooming houses provide additional student housing. Local recreational facilities include fishing, hunting, golf, tennis, swimming, sailing, and skiing. Job opportunities are available.

■ **CLINTON JUNIOR COLLEGE**
PO Box 968, 1029 Crawford Rd.
Rock Hill, SC 29730
Tel: (803)327-7402; Free: 877-837-9645
Fax: (803)327-3261
E-mail: rcopeland@clintonjrcollege.org
Web Site: www.clintonjuniorcollege.edu/
Description: Independent, 2-year, coed, affiliated with African Methodist Episcopal Zion Church. Awards terminal associate degrees. Founded 1894. Total enrollment: 148. Student-undergrad faculty ratio is 15:1. 45% from out-of-state. 17% 25 or older. Calendar: semesters.
Entrance Requirements: Entrance: noncompetitive.

■ **COASTAL CAROLINA UNIVERSITY**
PO Box 261954
Conway, SC 29528-6054
Tel: (843)347-3161; Free: 800-277-7000
Fax: (843)349-2127
E-mail: admissions@coastal.edu
Web Site: www.coastal.edu/
Description: State-supported, comprehensive, coed. Awards bachelor's and master's degrees and post-master's certificates. Founded 1954. Setting: 630-acre suburban campus. Endowment: $30.1 million. Research spending

for the previous fiscal year: $2.3 million. Educational spending for the previous fiscal year: $5785 per student. Total enrollment: 9,335. Faculty: 645 (378 full-time, 267 part-time). Student-undergrad faculty ratio is 17:1. 10,993 applied, 74% were admitted. 8% from top 10% of their high school class, 28% from top quarter, 66% from top half. Full-time: 7,916 students, 53% women, 47% men. Part-time: 830 students, 56% women, 44% men. Students come from 45 states and territories, 51 other countries, 47% from out-of-state. 0.3% American Indian or Alaska Native, non-Hispanic/Latino; 3% Hispanic/Latino; 20% African American, non-Hispanic/Latino; 1% Asian, non-Hispanic/Latino; 0.1% Native Hawaiian or other Pacific Islander, non-Hispanic/Latino; 2% international. 9% 25 or older, 38% live on campus, 9% transferred in. Retention: 60% of full-time freshmen returned the following year. Academic areas with the most degrees conferred: business/marketing; biological/life sciences; parks and recreation. Core. Calendar: semesters. Services for LD students, advanced placement, accelerated degree program, self-designed majors, honors program, independent study, distance learning, double major, summer session for credit, part-time degree program, adult/continuing education programs, co-op programs and internships, graduate courses open to undergrads. Study abroad program. ROTC: Army.

Entrance Requirements: Options: electronic application, deferred admission, international baccalaureate accepted. Required: high school transcript, minimum 2 high school GPA, SAT or ACT. Recommended: essay, 1 recommendation, interview. Entrance: moderately difficult. Application deadline: 6/1. Notification: continuous until 10/1. Preference given to state residents. SAT Reasoning Test deadline: 5/1. Transfer credits accepted: Yes.

Costs Per Year: Application fee: $45. State resident tuition: $9680 full-time, $407 per credit hour part-time. Nonresident tuition: $21,970 full-time, $920 per credit hour part-time. Mandatory fees: $80 full-time. Full-time tuition and fees vary according to course load and degree level. Part-time tuition varies according to course load and degree level. College room and board: $7700. College room only: $5000. Room and board charges vary according to board plan and housing facility.

Collegiate Environment: Orientation program. Drama-theater group, choral group, marching band, student-run newspaper, radio station. Social organizations: 159 open to all; national fraternities, national sororities; 8% of eligible men and 9% of eligible women are members. Most popular organizations: Student Government Association, Campus Activities Board, STAR (Students Taking Active Responsibility), SCREAM (Student Spirit Organization), Leadership Challenge. Major annual events: Homecoming, Cino Day, Relay for Life. Student services: health clinic, personal-psychological counseling, women's center. Campus security: 24-hour emergency response devices and patrols, late night transport-escort service. College housing designed to accommodate 3,290 students; 3,514 undergraduates lived in college housing during 2012-13. Freshmen guaranteed college housing. On-campus residence required through sophomore year. Option: coed housing available. Kimbel Library with 236,625 books, 4,650 microform titles, 82,600 serials, 7,117 audiovisual materials, an OPAC, and a Web page. Operations spending for the previous fiscal year: $2.9 million. 987 computers available on campus for general student use. Computer purchase/lease plans available. A campuswide network can be accessed from student residence rooms and from off campus. Students can access the following: online class registration. Staffed computer lab on campus provides training in use of computers, software, and the Internet.

Community Environment: Coastal Carolina University is located nine miles from the bustling resort area of Myrtle Beach, SC. Recreational and entertainment options provide many opportunities for internships for the Professional Golf Management and Resort Tourism programs, as well as part-time employment opportunities. Brookgreen Gardens, one of the world's finest outdoor sculpture gardens, provides a tranquil setting for relaxation, while Broadway on the Beach provides entertainment, shopping, and dining attractions.

■ **COKER COLLEGE**
300 E College Ave.
Hartsville, SC 29550
Tel: (843)383-8000; Free: 800-950-1908
Fax: (843)383-8056
E-mail: admissions@coker.edu
Web Site: www.coker.edu/
Description: Independent, comprehensive, coed. Awards bachelor's and master's degrees (also offers evening program with significant enrollment not reflected in profile). Founded 1908. Setting: 37-acre small town campus with easy access to Charlotte. Endowment: $23.2 million. Research spending for the previous fiscal year: $142,091. Educational spending for the

previous fiscal year: $6995 per student. Total enrollment: 1,163. Faculty: 103 (63 full-time, 40 part-time). Student-undergrad faculty ratio is 14:1. 902 applied, 58% were admitted. 15% from top 10% of their high school class, 31% from top quarter, 63% from top half. Full-time: 1,005 students, 65% women, 35% men. Part-time: 150 students, 78% women, 22% men. Students come from 31 states and territories, 9 other countries, 15% from out-of-state. 1% American Indian or Alaska Native, non-Hispanic/Latino; 3% Hispanic/Latino; 40% African American, non-Hispanic/Latino; 0.3% Asian, non-Hispanic/Latino; 0.3% Native Hawaiian or other Pacific Islander, non-Hispanic/Latino; 2% international. 37% 25 or older, 46% live on campus, 9% transferred in. Retention: 69% of full-time freshmen returned the following year. Academic areas with the most degrees conferred: business/marketing; social sciences; education. Core. Calendar: semesters. Services for LD students, advanced placement, self-designed majors, honors program, independent study, distance learning, double major, summer session for credit, part-time degree program, adult/continuing education programs, internships. Off campus study. Study abroad program.

Entrance Requirements: Options: electronic application, deferred admission, international baccalaureate accepted. Required: high school transcript, SAT or ACT. Entrance: moderately difficult. Application deadlines: 8/1, 8/1 for nonresidents. Notification: continuous, continuous for nonresidents. SAT Reasoning Test deadline: 7/31. SAT Subject Test deadline: 7/31. Transfer credits accepted: Yes.

Costs Per Year: Application fee: $25. Comprehensive fee: $32,186 includes full-time tuition ($24,576) and college room and board ($7610). College room only: $3620. Full-time tuition varies according to course load, location, and program. Room and board charges vary according to board plan and housing facility.

Collegiate Environment: Orientation program. Drama-theater group, choral group. Most popular organization: Student Government Association. Major annual events: Bandfest, Crew Race, COW Days (Coker Olympics of Winter). Student services: health clinic, personal-psychological counseling. Campus security: 24-hour patrols, late night transport-escort service, controlled dormitory access. 502 college housing spaces available; all were occupied in 2012-13. Freshmen guaranteed college housing. On-campus residence required through junior year. Option: coed housing available. The Charles W. and Joan S. Coker Library-Information Technology Center plus 1 other with 73,507 books, 15,760 microform titles, 145 serials, 3,080 audiovisual materials, an OPAC, and a Web page. Operations spending for the previous fiscal year: $439,956. 44 computers available on campus for general student use. A campuswide network can be accessed from student residence rooms. Students can access the following: online class registration. Staffed computer lab on campus provides training in use of computers and the Internet.

Community Environment: Coker College is located in Hartsville, a community of approximately 20,000 people. It is located in the northeastern part of the state, 20 miles off I-95, and approximately a two-hour drive from South Carolina's beautiful beaches and mountains. The climate is temperate and mild year-round. There is a township library and many churches of various denominations. Florence airport is 24 miles away. Part-time employment is available for students. Local recreational facilities include two theaters, Lake Robinson, Prestwood Lake, golf, tennis, two city parks, and racing. There are various civic and fraternal organizations that are active within the community. Health service facilities are available.

■ **COLLEGE OF CHARLESTON**
66 George St.
Charleston, SC 29424-0001
Tel: (843)953-5507
E-mail: admissions@cofc.edu
Web Site: www.cofc.edu/
Description: State-supported, comprehensive, coed. Awards bachelor's and master's degrees and post-master's certificates (also offers graduate degree programs through University of Charleston, South Carolina). Founded 1770. Setting: 52-acre urban campus. Endowment: $55.9 million. Research spending for the previous fiscal year: $8 million. Educational spending for the previous fiscal year: $6386 per student. Total enrollment: 11,723. Faculty: 957 (541 full-time, 416 part-time). Student-undergrad faculty ratio is 16:1. 11,962 applied, 68% were admitted. 31% from top 10% of their high school class, 67% from top quarter, 94% from top half. Full-time: 9,760 students, 63% women, 37% men. Part-time: 746 students, 52% women, 48% men. Students come from 51 states and territories, 63 other countries, 38% from out-of-state. 0.1% American Indian or Alaska Native, non-Hispanic/Latino; 4% Hispanic/Latino; 6% African American, non-Hispanic/Latino; 2% Asian,

non-Hispanic/Latino; 0.2% Native Hawaiian or other Pacific Islander, non-Hispanic/Latino; 1% international. 8% 25 or older, 31% live on campus, 7% transferred in. Retention: 82% of full-time freshmen returned the following year. Academic areas with the most degrees conferred: business/marketing; social sciences; visual and performing arts. Core. Calendar: semesters. ESL program, services for LD students, advanced placement, accelerated degree program, honors program, independent study, distance learning, double major, summer session for credit, part-time degree program, adult/continuing education programs, co-op programs and internships, graduate courses open to undergrads. Off campus study at National Student Exchange, Medical University of South Carolina, Trident Technical College, The Citadel, Charleston Southern University. Study abroad program. ROTC: Air Force (c).

Entrance Requirements: Options: electronic application, early action, deferred admission, international baccalaureate accepted. Required: essay, high school transcript, SAT or ACT, SAT or ACT. Entrance: moderately difficult. Application deadlines: 4/1, 11/1 for early action. Notification: 5/15, 12/15 for early action. SAT Reasoning Test deadline: 4/1. Transfer credits accepted: Yes. Applicants placed on waiting list: 578. Wait-listed applicants offered admission: 71. Early action applicants: 6,782. Early action applicants admitted: 5,012.

Costs Per Year: Application fee: $50. State resident tuition: $9918 full-time, $413 per semester hour part-time. Nonresident tuition: $25,304 full-time, $1054 per semester hour part-time. Full-time tuition varies according to degree level. Part-time tuition varies according to course load and degree level. College room and board: $10,461. College room only: $7111. Room and board charges vary according to board plan and housing facility.

Collegiate Environment: Orientation program. Drama-theater group, choral group, student-run newspaper, radio station. Social organizations: 200 open to all; national fraternities, national sororities, local fraternities, local sororities; 14% of eligible men and 21% of eligible women are members. Most popular organizations: Student Government Association, Cougar Activities Board, Intramural basketball, Black Student Union, Cisternyard Student Media. Major annual events: Homecoming Spirit Cup Competition, Pep Supper, GeorgeStock and Welcome Week. Student services: legal services, health clinic, personal-psychological counseling, women's center. Campus security: 24-hour emergency response devices and patrols, student patrols, late night transport-escort service, controlled dormitory access. 3,375 college housing spaces available; 3,115 were occupied in 2012-13. Freshmen guaranteed college housing. Options: coed, men-only, women-only housing available. Marlene and Nathan Addlestone Library plus 1 other with 832,011 books, 880,146 microform titles, 72,792 serials, 10,284 audiovisual materials, an OPAC, and a Web page. Operations spending for the previous fiscal year: $6 million. 750 computers available on campus for general student use. Computer purchase/lease plans available. A campuswide network can be accessed from student residence rooms and from off campus. Students can access the following: online class registration. Staffed computer lab on campus provides training in use of computers, software, and the Internet.

Community Environment: See The Citadel.

■ **COLUMBIA COLLEGE**
1301 Columbia College Dr.
Columbia, SC 29203-5998
Tel: (803)786-3012; Free: 800-277-1301
Fax: (803)786-3674
E-mail: admissions@colacoll.edu
Web Site: www.columbiasc.edu/

Description: Independent United Methodist, comprehensive. Awards bachelor's, master's, and doctoral degrees. Founded 1854. Setting: 33-acre suburban campus. Endowment: $19 million. Educational spending for the previous fiscal year: $5858 per student. Total enrollment: 1,263. Faculty: 134 (72 full-time, 62 part-time). Student-undergrad faculty ratio is 12:1. 771 applied, 65% were admitted. 19% from top 10% of their high school class, 55% from top quarter, 81% from top half. Full-time: 828 students, 99% women, 1% men. Part-time: 260 students, 91% women, 9% men. Students come from 24 states and territories, 6 other countries, 10% from out-of-state. 0.4% American Indian or Alaska Native, non-Hispanic/Latino; 3% Hispanic/Latino; 41% African American, non-Hispanic/Latino; 1% Asian, non-Hispanic/Latino; 0% Native Hawaiian or other Pacific Islander, non-Hispanic/Latino; 1% international. 28% 25 or older, 44% live on campus, 13% transferred in. Retention: 60% of full-time freshmen returned the following year. Academic areas with the most degrees conferred: education; business/marketing; public administration and social services. Core. Calendar: semesters. Academic remediation for entering students, advanced placement, self-designed majors, honors program, independent study, distance learning,

double major, summer session for credit, part-time degree program, adult/continuing education programs, internships. Off campus study. Study abroad program. ROTC: Army (c), Naval (c), Air Force (c).

Entrance Requirements: Option: electronic application. Required: high school transcript, minimum 2 high school GPA, 1 recommendation, SAT or ACT. Recommended: essay. Required for some: interview. Entrance: moderately difficult. Application deadline: 8/1. SAT Reasoning Test deadline: 7/1.

Costs Per Year: Application fee: $25. Comprehensive fee: $34,228 includes full-time tuition ($26,800), mandatory fees ($450), and college room and board ($6978). College room only: $3496. Full-time tuition and fees vary according to class time. Room and board charges vary according to board plan and housing facility. Part-time tuition: $710 per semester hour. Part-time tuition varies according to course load.

Collegiate Environment: Orientation program. Drama-theater group, choral group, student-run newspaper. Social organizations: 53 open to all. Most popular organizations: Student Government Association, African-American Student Association, Columbia College Activities Board, Heavenly Creations Gospel Choir, Student Christian Association. Major annual events: Ludy Bowl, Follies, Mom's Day/Dad's Night. Student services: health clinic, personal-psychological counseling, women's center. Campus security: 24-hour emergency response devices and patrols, late night transport-escort service, controlled dormitory access. 590 college housing spaces available; 495 were occupied in 2012-13. Freshmen guaranteed college housing. On-campus residence required through sophomore year. Option: women-only housing available. J. Drake Edens Library plus 1 other with 126,124 books, 7,756 microform titles, 152 serials, 3,728 audiovisual materials, an OPAC, and a Web page. Operations spending for the previous fiscal year: $614,354. 165 computers available on campus for general student use. Computer purchase/lease plans available. A campuswide network can be accessed from student residence rooms. Students can access the following: online class registration. Staffed computer lab on campus (open 24 hours a day) provides training in use of computers, software, and the Internet.

■ **COLUMBIA INTERNATIONAL UNIVERSITY**
PO Box 3122
Columbia, SC 29230-3122
Tel: (803)754-4100; Free: 800-777-2227
Fax: (803)786-4209
E-mail: yesciu@ciu.edu
Web Site: www.ciu.edu/

Description: Independent nondenominational, university, coed. Awards associate, bachelor's, master's, and doctoral degrees. Founded 1923. Setting: 450-acre suburban campus. Endowment: $12.7 million. Educational spending for the previous fiscal year: $5308 per student. Total enrollment: 953. Faculty: 84 (46 full-time, 38 part-time). Student-undergrad faculty ratio is 14:1. 320 applied, 64% were admitted. 17% from top 10% of their high school class, 45% from top quarter, 73% from top half. Full-time: 489 students, 49% women, 51% men. Part-time: 45 students, 64% women, 36% men. Students come from 35 states and territories, 9 other countries, 47% from out-of-state. 0.2% American Indian or Alaska Native, non-Hispanic/Latino; 4% Hispanic/Latino; 7% African American, non-Hispanic/Latino; 2% Asian, non-Hispanic/Latino; 0.4% Native Hawaiian or other Pacific Islander, non-Hispanic/Latino; 2% international. 17% 25 or older, 77% live on campus, 7% transferred in. Retention: 80% of full-time freshmen returned the following year. Academic areas with the most degrees conferred: theology and religious vocations; liberal arts/general studies; psychology. Core. Calendar: semesters. Academic remediation for entering students, services for LD students, advanced placement, independent study, distance learning, double major, summer session for credit, co-op programs and internships, graduate courses open to undergrads. Off campus study. Study abroad program.

Entrance Requirements: Options: electronic application, deferred admission, international baccalaureate accepted. Required: essay, minimum 2 high school GPA, 3 recommendations, SAT or ACT. Required for some: high school transcript, interview, SAT or ACT scores. Entrance: minimally difficult. Application deadlines: 7/1, 7/1 for nonresidents. Notification: continuous, continuous for nonresidents. SAT Reasoning Test deadline: 7/1. SAT Subject Test deadline: 7/1. Transfer credits accepted: Yes.

Costs Per Year: Application fee: $45. One-time mandatory fee: $825. Comprehensive fee: $25,836 includes full-time tuition ($18,200), mandatory fees ($540), and college room and board ($7096). College room only: $3548. Full-time tuition and fees vary according to course load, program, and reciprocity agreements. Room and board charges vary according to board plan and housing facility. Part-time tuition: $750 per credit hour. Part-time mandatory fees: $10 per credit, $120 per term. Part-time tuition and fees vary according to course load, program, and reciprocity agreements.

Collegiate Environment: Orientation program. Drama-theater group, choral group, student-run newspaper. Social organizations: 9 open to all; 25% of eligible men and 30% of eligible women are members. Most popular organizations: Student Union, Mu Kappa, Student Missions Connection, GradLife, African American Fellowship Ministries. Major annual events: World Christian Week, Homecoming, Winter Formal Banquet. Student services: health clinic, personal-psychological counseling. Campus security: 24-hour emergency response devices and patrols, late night transport-escort service. 375 college housing spaces available; 367 were occupied in 2012-13. Freshmen guaranteed college housing. On-campus residence required through senior year. Options: men-only, women-only housing available. G. Allen Fleece Library with 124,737 books, 6,785 microform titles, 162 serials, 1,963 audiovisual materials, an OPAC, and a Web page. Operations spending for the previous fiscal year: $468,462. 106 computers available on campus for general student use. A campuswide network can be accessed from student residence rooms and from off campus. Students can access the following: online class registration. Staffed computer lab on campus provides training in use of computers, software, and the Internet.

Community Environment: See University of South Carolina.

■ **CONVERSE COLLEGE**
580 E Main St.
Spartanburg, SC 29302-0006
Tel: (864)596-9000; Free: 800-766-1125
Fax: (864)596-9158
E-mail: admissions@converse.edu
Web Site: www.converse.edu/

Description: Independent, comprehensive. Awards bachelor's and master's degrees and post-master's certificates. Founded 1889. Setting: 70-acre urban campus. Endowment: $76.9 million. Educational spending for the previous fiscal year: $8426 per student. Total enrollment: 1,221. Faculty: 83 (76 full-time, 7 part-time). Student-undergrad faculty ratio is 11:1. 1,383 applied, 51% were admitted. 18% from top 10% of their high school class, 43% from top quarter, 80% from top half. Full-time: 608 students, 100% women. Part-time: 82 students, 100% women. Students come from 26 states and territories, 11 other countries, 24% from out-of-state. 0.1% American Indian or Alaska Native, non-Hispanic/Latino; 3% Hispanic/Latino; 8% African American, non-Hispanic/Latino; 1% Asian, non-Hispanic/Latino; 0.1% Native Hawaiian or other Pacific Islander, non-Hispanic/Latino; 1% international. 15% 25 or older, 80% live on campus, 2% transferred in. Retention: 76% of full-time freshmen returned the following year. Academic areas with the most degrees conferred: visual and performing arts; education; biological/life sciences; psychology. Core. Calendar: 4-2-4. ESL program, services for LD students, advanced placement, self-designed majors, honors program, independent study, distance learning, double major, summer session for credit, part-time degree program, adult/continuing education programs, co-op programs and internships, graduate courses open to undergrads. Off campus study at Wofford College. Study abroad program. ROTC: Army (c).

Entrance Requirements: Options: electronic application, international baccalaureate accepted. Required: high school transcript, 1 recommendation, SAT or ACT. Recommended: essay, minimum 3 high school GPA. Required for some: interview. Entrance: moderately difficult. Application deadlines: Rolling, Rolling for nonresidents. Notification: continuous, continuous for nonresidents. SAT Reasoning Test deadline: 8/1. Transfer credits accepted: Yes.

Costs Per Year: Application fee: $0. Comprehensive fee: $37,130 includes full-time tuition ($28,276) and college room and board ($8854). Full-time tuition varies according to course load and program. Room and board charges vary according to board plan, housing facility, and student level. Part-time tuition: $850 per credit hour. Part-time tuition varies according to program.

Collegiate Environment: Orientation program. Drama-theater group, choral group, student-run newspaper. Social organizations: 55 open to all. Most popular organizations: student government, student volunteer services, Student Christian Organization, Student Activities Committee, Athletic Association. Major annual events: 1889 Day, Founders' Day, Spring Concert. Student services: health clinic, personal-psychological counseling, women's center. Campus security: 24-hour emergency response devices and patrols, late night transport-escort service, controlled dormitory access. 550 college housing spaces available; all were occupied in 2012-13. Freshmen guaranteed college housing. On-campus residence required through senior year. Option: women-only housing available. Mickel Library with 160,850

books, 88,961 microform titles, 49,024 serials, 22,434 audiovisual materials, an OPAC, and a Web page. Operations spending for the previous fiscal year: $624,628. 140 computers available on campus for general student use. A campuswide network can be accessed from student residence rooms and from off campus. Students can access the following: online class registration. Staffed computer lab on campus provides training in use of computers, software, and the Internet.

Community Environment: One of the leading textile manufacturing cities in the South, Spartanburg is also one of the largest peach shipping centers in the world. The city was named after the Spartan Regiment, which represented this community in the Revolutionary War. The community is located in the Piedmont section of South Carolina and has an average temperature of 60 degrees. Airlines, railroads, and bus lines serve the area. There are many churches representing various denominations, 3 hospitals, libraries, a YMCA Family Center, and various civic and fraternal groups serving the city. Motels, hotels, and rooming houses are available for guests. Local recreation includes football, basketball, baseball, golf, stock car racing, swimming, tennis, picnicking, water skiing, theater, and series of concerts. Part-time employment is available.

■ **DENMARK TECHNICAL COLLEGE**
1126 Solomon Blatt Blvd.
Denmark, SC 29042-0327
Tel: (803)793-5100
Fax: (803)793-5942
E-mail: troyk@denmarktech.edu
Web Site: www.denmarktech.edu/

Description: State-supported, 2-year, coed. Part of South Carolina State Board for Technical and Comprehensive Education. Awards certificates, diplomas, transfer associate, and terminal associate degrees. Founded 1948. Setting: 53-acre rural campus. Total enrollment: 2,003. Faculty: 49 (34 full-time, 15 part-time). Student-undergrad faculty ratio is 21:1. Full-time: 1,821 students, 53% women, 47% men. Part-time: 182 students, 59% women, 41% men. 3% from out-of-state. 0.05% American Indian or Alaska Native, non-Hispanic/Latino; 0.2% Hispanic/Latino; 96% African American, non-Hispanic/Latino. 41% 25 or older, 2% transferred in. Retention: 54% of full-time freshmen returned the following year. Calendar: semesters. Academic remediation for entering students, advanced placement, independent study, distance learning, summer session for credit, part-time degree program, adult/continuing education programs, co-op programs and internships. Off campus study at Voorhees College, South Carolina State University.

Entrance Requirements: Open admission. Options: electronic application, early admission, deferred admission. Required: high school transcript, ACT, ASSET, COMPASS, and TEAS (Nursing). Recommended: SLED Check, TEAS Testing, Drug Test, PPD Test (all requirement for LPN), SAT or ACT. Required for some: essay. Entrance: noncompetitive. Application deadlines: Rolling, Rolling for nonresidents. Notification: continuous, continuous for nonresidents. Transfer credits accepted: Yes.

Costs Per Year: Application fee: $10. State resident tuition: $2662 full-time. Nonresident tuition: $5014 full-time. College room and board: $3566. College room only: $1762.

Collegiate Environment: Orientation program. Choral group. Social organizations: 25 open to all. Most popular organizations: Student Government Association, DTC Choir, athletics, Phi Theta Kappa Internal Honor Society, Esquire Club (men and women). Major annual events: Homecoming, Commencement, Coronation. Student services: health clinic, personal-psychological counseling. Campus security: 24-hour patrols, late night transport-escort service, 24-hour emergency contact line/alarm devices. 396 college housing spaces available; 378 were occupied in 2012-13. Freshmen given priority for college housing. Options: men-only, women-only housing available. Denmark Technical College Learning Resources Center with 18,735 books, 2,650 microform titles, 195 serials, 802 audiovisual materials, and an OPAC. 325 computers available on campus for general student use. A campuswide network can be accessed from student residence rooms. Staffed computer lab on campus provides training in use of computers, software, and the Internet.

■ **ECPI COLLEGE OF TECHNOLOGY (COLUMBIA)**
250 Berryhill Rd., No.300
Columbia, SC 29210
Tel: (803)772-3333; Free: 866-708-6168
Web Site: www.ecpi.edu/

Description: Proprietary, primarily 2-year, coed. Awards diplomas, terminal associate, and bachelor's degrees.

■ ECPI COLLEGE OF TECHNOLOGY (GREENVILLE)
1001 Keys Dr., No.100
Greenville, SC 29615
Tel: (864)288-2828; Free: 866-708-6171
Web Site: www.ecpi.edu/
Description: Proprietary, primarily 2-year, coed. Awards diplomas, terminal associate, and bachelor's degrees.

■ ECPI COLLEGE OF TECHNOLOGY (NORTH CHARLESTON)
7410 Northside Dr.
Ste. 100
North Charleston, SC 29420
Tel: (843)414-0350; Free: 866-708-6166
Web Site: www.ecpi.edu/
Description: Proprietary, primarily 2-year, coed. Awards diplomas, terminal associate, and bachelor's degrees.

■ ERSKINE COLLEGE
2 Washington St.
Due West, SC 29639
Tel: (864)379-2131; Free: 800-241-8721
Fax: (864)379-8759
E-mail: young@erskine.edu
Web Site: www.erskine.edu/
Description: Independent, comprehensive, coed, affiliated with Associate Reformed Presbyterian Church. Administratively affiliated with Erskine Theological Seminary. Awards bachelor's, master's, and doctoral degrees. Founded 1839. Setting: 90-acre rural campus. Endowment: $43.6 million. Total enrollment: 811. Faculty: 70 (41 full-time, 29 part-time). Student-undergrad faculty ratio is 11:1. 500 applied, 75% were admitted. 39% from top 10% of their high school class, 65% from top quarter, 87% from top half. Full-time: 541 students, 54% women, 46% men. Part-time: 12 students, 25% women, 75% men. Students come from 19 states and territories, 8 other countries, 24% from out-of-state. 0% American Indian or Alaska Native, non-Hispanic/Latino; 1% Hispanic/Latino; 8% African American, non-Hispanic/Latino; 1% Asian, non-Hispanic/Latino; 0% Native Hawaiian or other Pacific Islander, non-Hispanic/Latino; 4% international. 1% 25 or older, 89% live on campus, 3% transferred in. Retention: 77% of full-time freshmen returned the following year. Academic areas with the most degrees conferred: biological/life sciences; business/marketing; education. Core. Calendar: 4-1-4. Advanced placement, independent study, double major, summer session for credit, part-time degree program, internships, graduate courses open to undergrads. Off campus study at other colleges having a 4-1-4 calendar. Study abroad program.
Entrance Requirements: Options: electronic application, early admission, early action, deferred admission, international baccalaureate accepted. Required: essay, high school transcript, 1 recommendation, SAT or ACT. Recommended: interview. Entrance: moderately difficult. Application deadlines: Rolling, 11/1 for early action. Notification: continuous, 11/15 for early action. Preference given to members of Associate Reformed Presbyterian Church. SAT Reasoning Test deadline: 8/15.
Collegiate Environment: Orientation program. Drama-theater group, choral group, student-run newspaper, radio station. Social organizations: 51 open to all. Most popular organizations: literary societies, religious organizations, Student Government Organization, publications, honor societies. Major annual events: Fall Fest, Spring Fling, Homecoming. Student services: health clinic, personal-psychological counseling. Campus security: 24-hour patrols, late night transport-escort service, controlled dormitory access. McCain Library with 217,947 books, 63,064 microform titles, 1,125 serials, 2,979 audiovisual materials, an OPAC, and a Web page. Operations spending for the previous fiscal year: $499,606.
Community Environment: Due West is a town of approximately 1,300 residents. It enjoys a temperate climate. There is easy access to Interstate Routes 26 and 85, and the cities of Anderson, Greenwood, and Greenville are nearby. The major metropolitan areas of Atlanta and Charlotte are within a 2.5-hour drive. The college arranges transportation to meet students arriving at these points by train, bus or plane. Local recreational facilities include tennis courts, a swimming pool, movies and a physical education/athletic center.

■ FLORENCE-DARLINGTON TECHNICAL COLLEGE
2715 W Lucas St.
Florence, SC 29501-0548
Tel: (843)661-8324; Free: 800-228-5745

Fax: (843)661-8306
E-mail: shelley.fortin@fdtc.edu
Web Site: www.fdtc.edu/
Description: State-supported, 2-year, coed. Part of South Carolina State Board for Technical and Comprehensive Education. Awards certificates, diplomas, transfer associate, and terminal associate degrees. Founded 1963. Setting: 100-acre small town campus with easy access to Columbia. Total enrollment: 5,242. Student-undergrad faculty ratio is 26:1. 2% from out-of-state. 39% 25 or older. Core. Calendar: semesters. Academic remediation for entering students, ESL program, advanced placement, summer session for credit, part-time degree program, adult/continuing education programs, internships. Study abroad program. ROTC: Army (c).
Entrance Requirements: Open admission. Option: deferred admission. Entrance: noncompetitive. Application deadline: 8/1.
Collegiate Environment: Choral group, student-run newspaper. Student services: personal-psychological counseling. Campus security: 24-hour emergency response devices and patrols, late night transport-escort service.
Community Environment: Agriculture and industry support the economy of Florence. There are several diversified manufacturing companies within the area. Florence can be called an urban and a suburban community. It is located approximately 50 miles from the Atlantic Ocean resort areas. The city enjoys a temperate climate. Community services include public library, hospitals, museums, many churches of various denominations, and major civic, fraternal, and veteran's organizations. Local entertainment and recreation encompasses the Little Theatre group, movie theatres, a YMCA, a Civic Center, swimming, hunting, golf, tennis, and ice hockey.

■ FORREST COLLEGE
601 E River St.
Anderson, SC 29624
Tel: (864)225-7653
Fax: (864)261-7471
E-mail: janieturmon@forrestcollege.com
Web Site: www.forrestcollege.edu/
Description: Proprietary, 2-year, coed. Awards certificates, diplomas, transfer associate, and terminal associate degrees. Founded 1946. Setting: 3-acre rural campus. Total enrollment: 120. Faculty: 20 (2 full-time, 18 part-time). Student-undergrad faculty ratio is 6:1. Full-time: 86 students, 90% women, 10% men. Part-time: 34 students, 88% women, 12% men. Students come from 2 states and territories, 1% from out-of-state. 62% 25 or older, 0% transferred in. Core. Advanced placement, independent study, double major, summer session for credit, part-time degree program, co-op programs and internships.
Entrance Requirements: Required: essay, high school transcript, minimum 2 high school GPA, interview, Gates-McGinnity. Recommended: minimum 2.5 high school GPA.
Costs Per Year: Tuition: $8820 full-time, $245 per credit part-time. Mandatory fees: $375 full-time.
Collegiate Environment: Orientation program. Campus security: 24-hour emergency response devices, late night transport-escort service. College housing not available. Forrest Junior College Library with 40,000 books, 225 serials, 2,200 audiovisual materials, and an OPAC. Operations spending for the previous fiscal year: $12,000. 50 computers available on campus for general student use. Computer purchase/lease plans available. A campuswide network can be accessed from off-campus. Staffed computer lab on campus.

■ FRANCIS MARION UNIVERSITY
PO Box 100547
Florence, SC 29502-0547
Tel: (843)661-1362; Free: 800-368-7551
Fax: (843)661-4635
E-mail: admission@fmarion.edu
Web Site: www.fmarion.edu/
Description: State-supported, comprehensive, coed. Awards bachelor's and master's degrees and post-master's certificates. Founded 1970. Setting: 400-acre rural campus. Endowment: $25 million. Research spending for the previous fiscal year: $183,785. Educational spending for the previous fiscal year: $6069 per student. Total enrollment: 4,093. Faculty: 270 (206 full-time, 64 part-time). Student-undergrad faculty ratio is 16:1. 3,908 applied, 59% were admitted. 14% from top 10% of their high school class, 46% from top quarter, 80% from top half. 16 valedictorians. Full-time: 3,395 students, 67% women, 33% men. Part-time: 385 students, 68% women, 32% men. Students come from 31 states and territories, 16 other countries, 4% from

out-of-state. 1% American Indian or Alaska Native, non-Hispanic/Latino; 1% Hispanic/Latino; 47% African American, non-Hispanic/Latino; 1% Asian, non-Hispanic/Latino; 0.1% Native Hawaiian or other Pacific Islander, non-Hispanic/Latino; 1% international. 9% 25 or older, 40% live on campus, 8% transferred in. Retention: 65% of full-time freshmen returned the following year. Academic areas with the most degrees conferred: business/marketing; health professions and related sciences; biological/life sciences. Core. Calendar: semesters. Services for LD students, advanced placement, accelerated degree program, honors program, independent study, distance learning, double major, summer session for credit, part-time degree program, adult/continuing education programs, internships, graduate courses open to undergrads. Off campus study at University of South Carolina, Florence-Darlington Technical College, Clemson University. Study abroad program. ROTC: Army.

Entrance Requirements: Options: electronic application, early admission, deferred admission, international baccalaureate accepted. Required: high school transcript, minimum 2 high school GPA, SAT or ACT. Entrance: moderately difficult. Application deadlines: 8/15, 8/15 for nonresidents. Notification: 9/1, 9/1 for nonresidents. SAT Reasoning Test deadline: 8/17. Transfer credits accepted: Yes.

Costs Per Year: Application fee: $32. State resident tuition: $8708 full-time, $435.40 per credit hour part-time. Nonresident tuition: $17,416 full-time, $870.80 per credit hour part-time. Mandatory fees: $358 full-time. Full-time tuition and fees vary according to program. Part-time tuition varies according to course load and program. College room and board: $6820. College room only: $3842. Room and board charges vary according to board plan and housing facility.

Collegiate Environment: Orientation program. Drama-theater group, choral group, student-run newspaper. Social organizations: 60 open to all; national fraternities, national sororities; 1% of eligible men and 2% of eligible women are members. Most popular organizations: Baptist Collegiate Ministries, University Programming Board, National Pan-Hellenic Association, Student Alumni Association, Student Government Association. Major annual events: Homecoming, Arts International, University Programming Board Activities. Student services: health clinic, personal-psychological counseling. Campus security: 24-hour emergency response devices and patrols, late night transport-escort service, controlled dormitory access. 1,539 college housing spaces available; 1,517 were occupied in 2012-13. Freshmen given priority for college housing. Options: men-only, women-only housing available. James A. Rogers Library plus 1 other with 415,592 books, 500,000 microform titles, 860 serials, 9,242 audiovisual materials, an OPAC, and a Web page. Operations spending for the previous fiscal year: $1.9 million. 634 computers available on campus for general student use. A campuswide network can be accessed from student residence rooms and from off campus. Students can access the following: online class registration, Blackboard. Staffed computer lab on campus provides training in use of computers, software, and the Internet.

Community Environment: See Florence-Darlington Technical College.

■ FURMAN UNIVERSITY

3300 Poinsett Hwy.
Greenville, SC 29613
Tel: (864)294-2000
Fax: (864)294-3127
E-mail: admissions@furman.edu
Web Site: www.furman.edu/

Description: Independent, comprehensive, coed. Awards bachelor's and master's degrees. Founded 1826. Setting: 800-acre suburban campus. Endowment: $550.3 million. Research spending for the previous fiscal year: $2.1 million. Educational spending for the previous fiscal year: $21,109 per student. Total enrollment: 2,915. Faculty: 268 (240 full-time, 28 part-time). Student-undergrad faculty ratio is 11:1. 6,035 applied, 77% were admitted. 40% from top 10% of their high school class, 72% from top quarter, 92% from top half. 12 National Merit Scholars, 12 valedictorians, 174 student government officers. Full-time: 2,623 students, 57% women, 43% men. Part-time: 130 students, 54% women, 46% men. Students come from 46 states and territories, 53 other countries, 71% from out-of-state. 0.1% American Indian or Alaska Native, non-Hispanic/Latino; 3% Hispanic/Latino; 5% African American, non-Hispanic/Latino; 2% Asian, non-Hispanic/Latino; 0.04% Native Hawaiian or other Pacific Islander, non-Hispanic/Latino; 3% international. 0% 25 or older, 96% live on campus, 1% transferred in. Retention: 90% of full-time freshmen returned the following year. Academic areas with the most degrees conferred: social sciences; business/marketing; visual and performing arts. Core. Calendar: 3-2-3. Services for LD students,

advanced placement, accelerated degree program, self-designed majors, independent study, double major, summer session for credit, part-time degree program, adult/continuing education programs, internships, graduate courses open to undergrads. Study abroad program. ROTC: Army.

Entrance Requirements: Options: electronic application, early decision, early action, international baccalaureate accepted. Required: essay, high school transcript. Recommended: interview, SAT or ACT. Entrance: moderately difficult. Application deadlines: 1/15, 11/1 for early decision, 11/15 for early action. Notification: 4/2, 12/1 for early decision, 2/1 for early action. Preference given to children of alumni. SAT Reasoning Test deadline: 1/15. Transfer credits accepted: Yes. Applicants placed on waiting list: 76. Wait-listed applicants offered admission: 3. Early decision applicants: 131. Early decision applicants admitted: 112. Early action applicants: 2,970. Early action applicants admitted: 2,542.

Costs Per Year: Application fee: $50. Comprehensive fee: $52,041 includes full-time tuition ($41,152), mandatory fees ($380), and college room and board ($10,509). College room only: $5704. Room and board charges vary according to board plan and housing facility. Part-time tuition: $1286 per credit. Part-time tuition varies according to course load.

Collegiate Environment: Orientation program. Drama-theater group, choral group, marching band, student-run newspaper, radio station. Social organizations: 183 open to all; national fraternities, national sororities; 38% of eligible men and 51% of eligible women are members. Most popular organizations: Collegiate Educational Service Corps, Fellowship of Christian Athletes, Baptist Student Union, Student Activities Board, Furman Singers. Major annual events: Homecoming Spirit Competition, May Day-Play Day, Beach Weekend. Student services: health clinic, personal-psychological counseling, women's center. Campus security: 24-hour emergency response devices and patrols, student patrols, late night transport-escort service, controlled dormitory access. 2,550 college housing spaces available; all were occupied in 2012-13. Freshmen guaranteed college housing. On-campus residence required through senior year. Options: coed, men-only, women-only housing available. James Buchanan Duke Library plus 2 others with 595,000 books, 811,000 microform titles, 130,000 serials, an OPAC, and a Web page. Operations spending for the previous fiscal year: $4.2 million. 425 computers available on campus for general student use. Computer purchase/lease plans available. A campuswide network can be accessed from student residence rooms and from off campus. Students can access the following: online class registration. Staffed computer lab on campus provides training in use of computers, software, and the Internet.

Community Environment: An industrial city, Greenville is in an important manufacturing region with very diverse industry. It is a metropolitan community that enjoys a temperate climate. Part-time employment is available. The city is served by air, rail and bus lines. Community facilities include a performing arts center, 16,000 seat arena, public library, art museum, YMCA, YWCA, 5 general and 1 children's hospital, and over 400 churches that represent major denominations. Local recreation includes several community theatre groups, lakes and rivers for water sports, mountains for hiking and camping, and most major sports, including golf and minor league baseball and hockey teams.

■ GOLF ACADEMY OF AMERICA

3268 Waccamaw Blvd.
Myrtle Beach, SC 29579
Tel: (843)236-0481
Web Site: www.golfacademy.edu/
Description: Proprietary, 2-year, coed. Calendar: semesters.

■ GREENVILLE TECHNICAL COLLEGE

PO Box 5616
Greenville, SC 29606-5616
Tel: (864)250-8111; Free: 800-723-0673
Fax: (864)250-8534
E-mail: carolyn.watkins@gvltec.edu
Web Site: www.gvltec.edu/

Description: State-supported, 2-year, coed. Part of South Carolina State Board for Technical and Comprehensive Education. Awards certificates, diplomas, transfer associate, and terminal associate degrees. Founded 1962. Setting: 407-acre urban campus. Total enrollment: 15,089. Student-undergrad faculty ratio is 20:1. 2% from out-of-state. 45% 25 or older. Core. Calendar: semesters. Academic remediation for entering students, advanced placement, summer session for credit, part-time degree program, adult/continuing education programs, co-op programs.

Entrance Requirements: Open admission except for allied health, nursing programs. Options: early admission, deferred admission. Required: high school transcript. Recommended: SAT, ACT ASSET, or ACT COMPASS. Entrance: noncompetitive. Application deadline: Rolling. Notification: continuous until 8/20.

Costs Per Year: Application fee: $35. Area resident tuition: $3866 full-time. State resident tuition: $4190 full-time. Nonresident tuition: $7910 full-time. Mandatory fees: $60 full-time. Full-time tuition and fees vary according to course load.

Collegiate Environment: Campus security: 24-hour emergency response devices and patrols, student patrols, late night transport-escort service.

Community Environment: See Furman University.

■ HORRY-GEORGETOWN TECHNICAL COLLEGE

2050 Hwy. 501
Conway, SC 29528-6066
Tel: (843)347-3186
Fax: (843)347-4207
E-mail: george.swindoll@hgtc.edu
Web Site: www.hgtc.edu/

Description: State and locally supported, 2-year, coed. Part of South Carolina State Board for Technical and Comprehensive Education. Awards certificates, diplomas, transfer associate, and terminal associate degrees. Founded 1966. Setting: small town campus. Total enrollment: 7,698. Faculty: 417 (134 full-time, 283 part-time). Student-undergrad faculty ratio is 16:1. Full-time: 2,936 students, 58% women, 42% men. Part-time: 4,762 students, 70% women, 30% men. 0.5% American Indian or Alaska Native, non-Hispanic/Latino; 3% Hispanic/Latino; 23% African American, non-Hispanic/Latino; 1% Asian, non-Hispanic/Latino; 0.2% Native Hawaiian or other Pacific Islander, non-Hispanic/Latino; 0.2% international. 44% 25 or older. Retention: 54% of full-time freshmen returned the following year. Core. Calendar: semesters. Academic remediation for entering students, services for LD students, advanced placement, summer session for credit, part-time degree program, adult/continuing education programs, co-op programs and internships.

Entrance Requirements: Open admission. Option: early admission. Required for some: high school transcript. Application deadline: Rolling. Notification: continuous.

Collegiate Environment: Orientation program. Student services: personal-psychological counseling. College housing not available. Conway Campus Learning Resource Center plus 2 others with a Web page. 300 computers available on campus for general student use. A campuswide network can be accessed from off-campus. Staffed computer lab on campus.

Community Environment: The college is located at the center of the largest tourist recreational environment along the Eastern Seaboard. Over 75 miles of white sand beaches as well as golf courses, restaurants, and hotels abound in the area. Air and bus service is available and Highway 17, the "Kings Highway", is the major coastal route in the area. Major arts and entertainment centers, libraries, churches, as well as numerous fraternal and civic organizations serve the community. There are extensive part-time employment opportunities for students, especially from March through September, the height of the tourist season.

■ ITT TECHNICAL INSTITUTE (COLUMBIA)

1628 Browning Rd.
Ste. 180
Columbia, SC 29210
Tel: (803)216-6000; Free: 800-242-5158
Web Site: www.itt-tech.edu/

Description: Proprietary, primarily 2-year, coed. Part of ITT Educational Services, Inc. Awards terminal associate and bachelor's degrees.

■ ITT TECHNICAL INSTITUTE (GREENVILLE)

Independence Corporate Park
6 Independence Pointe
Greenville, SC 29615
Tel: (864)288-0777; Free: 800-932-4488
Fax: (864)297-0053
Web Site: www.itt-tech.edu/

Description: Proprietary, primarily 2-year, coed. Part of ITT Educational Services, Inc. Awards terminal associate and bachelor's degrees. Founded 1992.

Entrance Requirements: Entrance: minimally difficult.

■ ITT TECHNICAL INSTITUTE (MYRTLE BEACH)

9654 N Kings Hwy.
Ste. 101
Myrtle Beach, SC 29572
Tel: (843)497-7820; Free: 877-316-7054
Web Site: www.itt-tech.edu/

Description: Proprietary, primarily 2-year, coed. Part of ITT Educational Services, Inc. Awards terminal associate and bachelor's degrees.

■ ITT TECHNICAL INSTITUTE (NORTH CHARLESTON)

2431 W Aviation Ave.
North Charleston, SC 29406
Tel: (843)745-5700; Free: 877-291-0900
Web Site: www.itt-tech.edu/

Description: Proprietary, primarily 2-year, coed. Part of ITT Educational Services, Inc. Awards terminal associate and bachelor's degrees.

■ LANDER UNIVERSITY

320 Stanley Ave.
Greenwood, SC 29649-2099
Tel: (864)388-8000; Free: 888-452-6337
Fax: (864)388-8125
E-mail: admissions@lander.edu
Web Site: www.lander.edu/

Description: State-supported, comprehensive, coed. Part of South Carolina Commission on Higher Education. Awards bachelor's and master's degrees. Founded 1872. Setting: 120-acre small town campus. Educational spending for the previous fiscal year: $4069 per student. Total enrollment: 3,049. Faculty: 249 (164 full-time, 85 part-time). Student-undergrad faculty ratio is 16:1. 3,342 applied, 42% were admitted. 13% from top 10% of their high school class, 45% from top quarter, 80% from top half. Full-time: 2,706 students, 69% women, 31% men. Part-time: 263 students, 71% women, 29% men. Students come from 23 states and territories, 28 other countries, 5% from out-of-state. 0.3% American Indian or Alaska Native, non-Hispanic/Latino; 1% Hispanic/Latino; 34% African American, non-Hispanic/Latino; 0.4% Asian, non-Hispanic/Latino; 0.2% Native Hawaiian or other Pacific Islander, non-Hispanic/Latino; 3% international. 9% 25 or older, 45% live on campus, 7% transferred in. Retention: 61% of full-time freshmen returned the following year. Academic areas with the most degrees conferred: business/marketing; health professions and related sciences; education. Core. Calendar: semesters plus 3 summer sessions. Academic remediation for entering students, services for LD students, advanced placement, honors program, independent study, distance learning, double major, summer session for credit, part-time degree program, adult/continuing education programs, co-op programs and internships, graduate courses open to undergrads. Off campus study. Study abroad program. ROTC: Army.

Entrance Requirements: Options: electronic application, international baccalaureate accepted. Required: high school transcript, minimum 2 high school GPA, SAT or ACT scores, SAT or ACT. Recommended: interview. Entrance: moderately difficult. Application deadlines: Rolling, Rolling for nonresidents. Notification: continuous, continuous for nonresidents.

Collegiate Environment: Orientation program. Drama-theater group, choral group, student-run newspaper, radio station. Social organizations: 65 open to all; national fraternities, national sororities, local fraternities, local sororities; 11% of eligible men and 12% of eligible women are members. Most popular organizations: Students Promoting Intelligent Choices and Experiences (S.P.I.C.E.), Lander Association of Biological Science, Minorities on the Move (MOM), Presidential Ambassadors, Lander Dance Company. Major annual events: Miss Lander Pageant, Homecoming, Graduation. Student services: health clinic, personal-psychological counseling. Campus security: 24-hour emergency response devices and patrols, late night transport-escort service, controlled dormitory access. 1,578 college housing spaces available. Freshmen given priority for college housing. Options: coed, women-only housing available. Jackson Library with 186,690 books, 156,387 microform titles, 657 serials, an OPAC, and a Web page. 300 computers available on campus for general student use. Computer purchase/lease plans available. A computer is required for all students. A campuswide network can be accessed from student residence rooms and from off campus. Students can access the following: online class registration. Staffed computer lab on campus provides training in use of computers, software, and the Internet.

Community Environment: Greenwood, an industrial city noted for its production of textiles, is located in west-central South Carolina. The climate is temperate and mild. Five rail lines, commercial air service, buses, and major highways serve the community. Public service facilities include one hospital and various health centers, an area mental health center, churches of all denominations, a library, and a YMCA. There are several motels, shopping, and various civic and fraternal organizations within the immediate area. Recreation includes several swimming pools, two recreation centers, 3 golf courses, baseball, football, tennis, basketball, and nearby Greenwood State Park, which provides water sports and picnic areas. Part-time employment is available.

■ **LIMESTONE COLLEGE**
1115 College Dr.
Gaffney, SC 29340-3799
Tel: (864)489-7151; Free: 800-795-7151
Fax: (864)487-8706
E-mail: lhobbs@limestone.edu
Web Site: www.limestone.edu/
Description: Independent, 4-year, coed. Awards associate, bachelor's, and master's degrees. Founded 1845. Setting: 123-acre suburban campus with easy access to Charlotte. Endowment: $12.5 million. Educational spending for the previous fiscal year: $4596 per student. Total enrollment: 937. Faculty: 91 (68 full-time, 23 part-time). Student-undergrad faculty ratio is 12:1. 1,389 applied, 55% were admitted. 6% from top 10% of their high school class, 21% from top quarter, 53% from top half. Full-time: 879 students, 42% women, 58% men. Part-time: 23 students, 30% women, 70% men. Students come from 36 states and territories, 21 other countries, 51% from out-of-state. 1% American Indian or Alaska Native, non-Hispanic/Latino; 4% Hispanic/Latino; 22% African American, non-Hispanic/Latino; 0.4% Asian, non-Hispanic/Latino; 0% Native Hawaiian or other Pacific Islander, non-Hispanic/Latino; 9% international. 3% 25 or older, 50% live on campus, 7% transferred in. Retention: 53% of full-time freshmen returned the following year. Academic areas with the most degrees conferred: business/marketing; education; parks and recreation. Core. Calendar: semesters. Academic remediation for entering students, services for LD students, advanced placement, accelerated degree program, self-designed majors, honors program, independent study, distance learning, double major, summer session for credit, part-time degree program, adult/continuing education programs, internships. ROTC: Army (c).
Entrance Requirements: Option: electronic application. Required: high school transcript, minimum 2 high school GPA, SAT or ACT. Recommended: 2 recommendations, interview. Required for some: Students whose native language is not English are required to submit a score of 500 or above on the TOEFL test or have proof they have successfully completed an ESL program and/or have a satisfactory score on the SAT or ACT. Entrance: minimally difficult. Application deadlines: Rolling, Rolling for nonresidents. Notification: continuous, continuous for nonresidents. SAT Reasoning Test deadline: 9/1. Transfer credits accepted: Yes.
Costs Per Year: Application fee: $25. Comprehensive fee: $29,880 includes full-time tuition ($22,080) and college room and board ($7800). College room only: $3900. Full-time tuition varies according to class time and course load. Room and board charges vary according to housing facility. Part-time tuition: $920 per semester hour. Part-time tuition varies according to class time.
Collegiate Environment: Orientation program. Drama-theater group, choral group. Social organizations: 15 open to all; national fraternities; 3% of men are members. Most popular organizations: Fellowship of Christian Athletes, Student Government Association, Student Alumni Leadership Council, Students in Free Enterprise (SIFE), Limestone Activities Board. Major annual events: Christmas On Campus, Homecoming, Saints Festival. Student services: health clinic, personal-psychological counseling. Campus security: 24-hour patrols, late night transport-escort service, controlled dormitory access. 540 college housing spaces available; 441 were occupied in 2012-13. Freshmen given priority for college housing. On-campus residence required through junior year. Options: men-only, women-only housing available. A. J. Eastwood Library plus 1 other with 182,759 books, 2,907 microform titles, 36,338 serials, 18,380 audiovisual materials, an OPAC, and a Web page. Operations spending for the previous fiscal year: $493,836. 134 computers available on campus for general student use. A campuswide network can be accessed from student residence rooms and from off campus. Students can access the following: online class registration.
Community Environment: Once predominately a cotton-textile manufacturing city, Gaffney has many diversified industries today including the manufacture of frozen foods, roller bearings, clothes, gloves, rugs, clay and concrete products. The surrounding agricultural area is a major producer of peaches, and also grain and livestock. The city is located 2 miles from Interstate I-85. Approximately 45 miles north is the Charlotte International

Airport, and 40 miles south is the Greenville-Spartanburg International Airport. The community has several churches representing many denominations, and many civic and service organizations.

■ **MEDICAL UNIVERSITY OF SOUTH CAROLINA**
179 Ashley Ave.
Charleston, SC 29425
Tel: (843)792-2300
Fax: (843)792-3764
E-mail: hudsonly@musc.edu
Web Site: www.musc.edu/
Description: State-supported, upper-level, coed. Awards bachelor's, master's, and doctoral degrees and post-master's certificates. Founded 1824. Setting: 82-acre urban campus. System endowment: $230.3 million. Research spending for the previous fiscal year: $169.2 million. Educational spending for the previous fiscal year: $69,072 per student. Total enrollment: 2,679. Faculty: 223 (153 full-time, 70 part-time). Student-undergrad faculty ratio is 2:1. Full-time: 197 students, 79% women, 21% men. Part-time: 3 students, 100% women. Students come from 23 states and territories, 10% from out-of-state. 1% American Indian or Alaska Native, non-Hispanic/Latino; 6% Hispanic/Latino; 11% African American, non-Hispanic/Latino; 3% Asian, non-Hispanic/Latino; 0% Native Hawaiian or other Pacific Islander, non-Hispanic/Latino; 0% international. 61% 25 or older, 0% transferred in. Academic area with the most degrees conferred: health professions and related sciences. Calendar: semesters. Services for LD students, accelerated degree program, distance learning, internships. Off campus study at Charleston Higher Education Consortium, University of South Carolina, University Center of Greenville, Francis Marion University. ROTC: Air Force (c).
Entrance Requirements: Transfer credits accepted: No.
Costs Per Year: Application fee: $95. One-time mandatory fee: $485. State resident tuition: $14,298 full-time, $647 per semester hour part-time. Nonresident tuition: $24,300 full-time, $1124 per semester hour part-time. Mandatory fees: $1140 full-time, $1296. Full-time tuition and fees vary according to program. Part-time tuition and fees vary according to course load and program.
Collegiate Environment: Orientation program. Choral group. Social organizations: 77 open to all. Most popular organizations: MUSC Student Government Association, Multicultural Group Advisory Board, Public Health Interest Group, International Association, Crisis Ministries. Major annual events: Alhambra, Back to School Party, Halloween Horror Cruise. Student services: legal services, health clinic, personal-psychological counseling. Campus security: 24-hour emergency response devices and patrols, late night transport-escort service. Medical University of South Carolina Library plus 1 other with 151,763 books, 15 microform titles, 20,173 serials, 1,819 audiovisual materials, an OPAC, and a Web page. Operations spending for the previous fiscal year: $6.1 million. 200 computers available on campus for general student use. A campuswide network can be accessed from off-campus. Students can access the following: online class registration. Staffed computer lab on campus (open 24 hours a day) provides training in use of computers, software, and the Internet.
Community Environment: See The Citadel.

■ **MIDLANDS TECHNICAL COLLEGE**
PO Box 2408
Columbia, SC 29202-2408
Tel: (803)738-1400; Free: 800-922-8038
Fax: (803)738-7784
E-mail: admissions@midlandstech.edu
Web Site: www.midlandstech.edu/
Description: State and locally supported, 2-year, coed. Part of South Carolina State Board for Technical and Comprehensive Education. Awards certificates, diplomas, transfer associate, and terminal associate degrees. Founded 1974. Setting: 113-acre suburban campus. Endowment: $5.1 million. Educational spending for the previous fiscal year: $3729 per student. Total enrollment: 12,078. Faculty: 733 (216 full-time, 517 part-time). Student-undergrad faculty ratio is 20:1. 5,753 applied, 65% were admitted. Full-time: 5,697 students, 54% women, 46% men. Part-time: 6,381 students, 67% women, 33% men. Students come from 30 states and territories, 3% from out-of-state. 1% American Indian or Alaska Native, non-Hispanic/Latino; 2% Hispanic/Latino; 35% African American, non-Hispanic/Latino; 2% Asian, non-Hispanic/Latino; 0.04% Native Hawaiian or other Pacific Islander, non-Hispanic/Latino; 0.05% international. 41% 25 or older, 10% transferred in. Calendar: semesters. Academic remediation for entering students, ESL

program, services for LD students, advanced placement, self-designed majors, distance learning, double major, summer session for credit, part-time degree program, adult/continuing education programs, co-op programs and internships.

Entrance Requirements: Open admission except for health science/ nursing program. Options: electronic application, early admission, deferred admission. Recommended: high school transcript, SAT or ACT. Required for some: interview, ACT ASSET. Entrance: minimally difficult. Application deadline: Rolling. Notification: continuous.

Collegiate Environment: Orientation program. Drama-theater group, student-run newspaper. Campus security: 24-hour emergency response devices and patrols, late night transport-escort service. Midlands Technical College Library with 98,507 books, 330 microform titles, 423 serials, 2,114 audiovisual materials, an OPAC, and a Web page. Operations spending for the previous fiscal year: $1.2 million. 229 computers available on campus for general student use. A campuswide network can be accessed from off-campus. Students can access the following: online class registration. Staffed computer lab on campus provides training in use of computers, software, and the Internet.

Community Environment: See University of South Carolina.

■ **MILLER-MOTTE TECHNICAL COLLEGE**
8085 Rivers Ave.
Ste. E
Charleston, SC 29406
Tel: (843)574-0101; Free: 800-923-4162
Fax: (843)266-3434
E-mail: juliasc@miller-mott.net
Web Site: www.miller-motte.edu/

Description: Proprietary, 2-year, coed. Part of Delta Career Education Corporation. Awards certificates, diplomas, and terminal associate degrees. Founded 2000. Setting: urban campus. Total enrollment: 764. 352 applied. 57% 25 or older. Distance learning, part-time degree program.

Entrance Requirements: Open admission. Required: high school transcript, interview, Wonderlic.

Collegiate Environment: 150 computers available on campus for general student use.

■ **MORRIS COLLEGE**
100 W College St.
Sumter, SC 29150-3599
Tel: (803)934-3200; Free: 866-853-1345
Fax: (803)773-3687
E-mail: dcalhoun@morris.edu
Web Site: www.morris.edu/

Description: Independent, 4-year, coed, affiliated with Baptist Educational and Missionary Convention of South Carolina. Awards bachelor's degrees. Founded 1908. Setting: 34-acre small town campus. Endowment: $12.8 million. Educational spending for the previous fiscal year: $6968 per student. Total enrollment: 874. Faculty: 67 (49 full-time, 18 part-time). Student-undergrad faculty ratio is 16:1. 2,946 applied, 85% were admitted. 0.4% from top 10% of their high school class, 10% from top quarter, 31% from top half. Full-time: 863 students, 58% women, 42% men. Part-time: 11 students, 73% women, 27% men. Students come from 19 states and territories, 21% from out-of-state. 0.1% Hispanic/Latino; 93% African American, non-Hispanic/ Latino. 11% 25 or older, 78% live on campus, 6% transferred in. Retention: 40% of full-time freshmen returned the following year. Academic areas with the most degrees conferred: homeland security, law enforcement, firefighting, and protective services; business/marketing; biological/life sciences. Core. Calendar: semesters. Academic remediation for entering students, advanced placement, accelerated degree program, honors program, double major, summer session for credit, adult/continuing education programs, co-op programs and internships. Study abroad program. ROTC: Army.

Entrance Requirements: Open admission. Options: electronic application, deferred admission. Required: high school transcript, minimum 2 high school GPA, medical examination. Required for some: interview. Entrance: noncompetitive. Application deadlines: Rolling, Rolling for nonresidents. Notification: continuous, continuous for nonresidents. Transfer credits accepted: Yes.

Costs Per Year: Application fee: $20. Comprehensive fee: $15,606 includes full-time tuition ($10,520), mandatory fees ($320), and college room and board ($4766). College room only: $2030. Part-time tuition: $438 per credit hour. Part-time mandatory fees: $320 per term.

Collegiate Environment: Orientation program. Drama-theater group, choral group, student-run newspaper, radio station. Social organizations: 60 open to all; national fraternities, national sororities; 4% of eligible men and 3% of eligible women are members. Most popular organizations: Student Government Association, New Emphasis on Nontraditional Students (NEONS), Block M Club, Pre Alumni Council, Baptist Student Union. Major annual events: Coronation of Miss Morris College, Fall Harvest Rally, Homecoming Week. Student services: health clinic, personal-psychological counseling. Campus security: 24-hour patrols, controlled dormitory access, cameras in select locations. 688 college housing spaces available; 682 were occupied in 2012-13. Freshmen given priority for college housing. Options: men-only, women-only housing available. Richardson-Johnson Learning Resources Center with 123,331 books, 228,277 microform titles, 370 serials, 3,024 audiovisual materials, and an OPAC. Operations spending for the previous fiscal year: $1.4 million. 252 computers available on campus for general student use. A campuswide network can be accessed from student residence rooms and from off campus. Students can access the following: online class registration. Staffed computer lab on campus provides training in use of computers, software, and the Internet.

Community Environment: Sumter was named for General Thomas Sumter, "The Gamecock of the Revolution." The community is served by two bus lines and is 50 miles from an airport and 35 miles from rail service. The mean summer temperature is 90 degrees, and the mean winter temperature is 40 degrees. The city has many churches of various faiths, as well as a public library. Sumter offers both large natural parks and many lakes, and is famed for its Swan Lake Iris Gardens. Sports and recreation go hand-in-hand with the compatible climate and natural resources found in the community, and includes four theatres, a skating rink, bowling, and night-lit tennis courts.

■ **NEWBERRY COLLEGE**
2100 College St.
Newberry, SC 29108-2197
Tel: (803)276-5010; Free: 800-845-4955
E-mail: admissions@newberry.edu
Web Site: www.newberry.edu/

Description: Independent Evangelical Lutheran, 4-year, coed. Awards bachelor's degrees. Founded 1856. Setting: 90-acre small town campus with easy access to Columbia, Greenville. Endowment: $20.3 million. Educational spending for the previous fiscal year: $5886 per student. Total enrollment: 1,042. Faculty: 121 (65 full-time, 56 part-time). Student-undergrad faculty ratio is 12:1. 858 applied, 61% were admitted. 12% from top 10% of their high school class, 28% from top quarter, 66% from top half. Full-time: 1,012 students, 43% women, 57% men. Part-time: 30 students, 60% women, 40% men. Students come from 28 states and territories, 19 other countries, 18% from out-of-state. 0.3% American Indian or Alaska Native, non-Hispanic/ Latino; 3% Hispanic/Latino; 25% African American, non-Hispanic/Latino; 1% Asian, non-Hispanic/Latino; 0% Native Hawaiian or other Pacific Islander, non-Hispanic/Latino; 3% international. 8% 25 or older, 72% live on campus, 6% transferred in. Retention: 68% of full-time freshmen returned the following year. Academic areas with the most degrees conferred: business/ marketing; education; parks and recreation; biological/life sciences; health professions and related sciences. Core. Calendar: semesters. Academic remediation for entering students, services for LD students, advanced placement, accelerated degree program, self-designed majors, honors program, independent study, double major, summer session for credit, part-time degree program, adult/continuing education programs, internships. Study abroad program. ROTC: Army (c).

Entrance Requirements: Options: electronic application, deferred admission, international baccalaureate accepted. Required: essay, high school transcript, minimum 2 high school GPA, SAT or ACT. Recommended: 1 recommendation, interview. Entrance: moderately difficult. Application deadline: Rolling. Notification: continuous. SAT Reasoning Test deadline: 7/31. SAT Subject Test deadline: 7/31. Transfer credits accepted: Yes.

Costs Per Year: Application fee: $30. Comprehensive fee: $32,800 includes full-time tuition ($22,050), mandatory fees ($1750), and college room and board ($9000). College room only: $4500. Full-time tuition and fees vary according to class time, course load, and student level. Room and board charges vary according to board plan and housing facility. Part-time tuition: $525 per hour. Part-time tuition varies according to class time, course load, and student level. Tuition guaranteed not to increase for student's term of enrollment.

Collegiate Environment: Orientation program. Drama-theater group, choral group, marching band, student-run newspaper, radio station. Social

organizations: 30 open to all; national fraternities, national sororities; 15% of eligible men and 10% of eligible women are members. Most popular organizations: Future Educators Association, Multi Cultural Student Association, American Chemistry Society, Blue Key Honor Club, Baptist Collegiate Ministry. Major annual events: Homecoming, Fun Day, FAL Event- Drunk Sex or Date Rape (Speaking Engagement). Student services: health clinic, personal-psychological counseling. Campus security: 24-hour emergency response devices and patrols, late night transport-escort service, controlled dormitory access. 833 college housing spaces available; 754 were occupied in 2012-13. Freshmen given priority for college housing. On-campus residence required through senior year. Options: coed, men-only, women-only housing available. Wessels Library with 64,368 books, 7,003 microform titles, 87 serials, 1,333 audiovisual materials, an OPAC, and a Web page. Operations spending for the previous fiscal year: $79,706. 22 computers available on campus for general student use. A campuswide network can be accessed from student residence rooms and from off campus. Students can access the following: online class registration. Staffed computer lab on campus.

Community Environment: Newberry is located in the Piedmont region of South Carolina between Lakes Murray and Greenwood. The city enjoys mild weather. Community services include churches of many denominations, a hospital, a county library, and various civic and fraternal organizations. Local recreation and facilities include a swimming pool, barbecue facilities, parks, theaters, fishing, boating, swimming, and camping on nearby lakes. Part-time employment is available for college students.

■ NORTH GREENVILLE UNIVERSITY
PO Box 1892
Tigerville, SC 29688-1892
Tel: (864)977-7000; Free: 800-468-6642
Fax: (864)977-7177
E-mail: ksewell@ngu.edu
Web Site: www.ngu.edu/

Description: Independent Southern Baptist, comprehensive, coed. Awards bachelor's, master's, and doctoral degrees. Founded 1892. Setting: 330-acre rural campus with easy access to Greenville. Educational spending for the previous fiscal year: $5110 per student. Total enrollment: 2,428. Faculty: 183 (127 full-time, 56 part-time). Student-undergrad faculty ratio is 14:1. 1,392 applied, 60% were admitted. 22% from top 10% of their high school class, 48% from top quarter, 81% from top half. 2 National Merit Scholars, 35 class presidents, 28 valedictorians, 100 student government officers. Full-time: 1,980 students, 50% women, 50% men. Part-time: 235 students, 61% women, 39% men. Students come from 35 states and territories, 11 other countries, 29% from out-of-state. 0.2% American Indian or Alaska Native, non-Hispanic/Latino; 2% Hispanic/Latino; 7% African American, non-Hispanic/Latino; 0.5% Asian, non-Hispanic/Latino; 0% Native Hawaiian or other Pacific Islander, non-Hispanic/Latino; 0.4% international. 14% 25 or older, 68% live on campus, 7% transferred in. Retention: 69% of full-time freshmen returned the following year. Academic areas with the most degrees conferred: business/marketing; theology and religious vocations; liberal arts/general studies. Core. Calendar: semesters. Academic remediation for entering students, ESL program, services for LD students, advanced placement, accelerated degree program, self-designed majors, freshman honors college, honors program, independent study, distance learning, double major, summer session for credit, part-time degree program, co-op programs and internships, graduate courses open to undergrads. Study abroad program. ROTC: Army (c).

Entrance Requirements: Options: electronic application, early admission, deferred admission, international baccalaureate accepted. Required: high school transcript, SAT or ACT. Recommended: minimum 2 high school GPA, CPT. Required for some: interview, CPT. Entrance: minimally difficult. Application deadline: 8/22. Notification: continuous. Preference given to Baptists. SAT Reasoning Test deadline: 8/26. SAT Subject Test deadline: 8/26. Transfer credits accepted: Yes.

Costs Per Year: Application fee: $25. Comprehensive fee: $22,100 includes full-time tuition ($13,936) and college room and board ($8164). Full-time tuition varies according to course load. Room and board charges vary according to housing facility. Part-time tuition: $240 per unit.

Collegiate Environment: Orientation program. Drama-theater group, choral group, marching band, student-run newspaper, radio station. Social organizations: 21 open to all. Most popular organizations: Baptist Student Union, Fellowship of Christians in Service, Fellowship of Christian Athletes, Black Student Fellowship, Education Club. Major annual events: Homecoming, Founders' Day, Miss NGU Pageant. Student services: health clinic,

personal-psychological counseling. Campus security: 24-hour emergency response devices and patrols, late night transport-escort service, controlled dormitory access. 1,560 college housing spaces available; 1,510 were occupied in 2012-13. Freshmen guaranteed college housing. On-campus residence required through sophomore year. Options: men-only, women-only housing available. Hester Memorial Library with 50,000 books, 2,930 microform titles, 536 serials, 5,644 audiovisual materials, an OPAC, and a Web page. Operations spending for the previous fiscal year: $650,036. 95 computers available on campus for general student use. A campuswide network can be accessed from student residence rooms and from off campus. Students can access the following: online class registration. Staffed computer lab on campus provides training in use of computers.

Community Environment: Tigerville is a rural area adjacent to Greenville in the foothills of the Blue Ridge Mountains. The climate is temperate. There are several civic and fraternal organizations and a Baptist Church in the community. Part-time employment is available. Local recreation includes hunting, fishing, rafting, fine arts and the advantages of nearby Greenville.

■ NORTHEASTERN TECHNICAL COLLEGE
PO Drawer 1007
Cheraw, SC 29520-1007
Tel: (843)921-6900; Free: 800-921-7399
Fax: (843)537-6148
E-mail: mpace@netc.edu
Web Site: www.netc.edu/

Description: State and locally supported, 2-year, coed. Part of South Carolina State Board for Technical and Comprehensive Education. Awards certificates, diplomas, transfer associate, and terminal associate degrees. Founded 1967. Setting: 59-acre rural campus. Endowment: $31,355. Educational spending for the previous fiscal year: $2999 per student. Total enrollment: 976. Student-undergrad faculty ratio is 25:1. 468 applied, 100% were admitted. Full-time: 446 students, 67% women, 33% men. Part-time: 530 students, 76% women, 24% men. Students come from 3 states and territories, 1% from out-of-state. 43% 25 or older, 3% transferred in. Core. Calendar: semesters. Academic remediation for entering students, advanced placement, independent study, distance learning, part-time degree program, adult/continuing education programs. Study abroad program.

Entrance Requirements: Open admission except for nursing program. Options: electronic application, early admission. Required: high school transcript, interview, COMPASS. Required for some: SAT. Entrance: noncompetitive. Application deadline: 8/4. Notification: continuous.

Collegiate Environment: Orientation program. Social organizations: 2 open to all. Most popular organizations: Student Government Association, Alpha Beta Delta. Major annual events: Field Day, Christmas refreshments. Student services: personal-psychological counseling. Campus security: 24-hour emergency response devices. Northeastern Technical College Library with 24,129 books, 1,113 audiovisual materials, an OPAC, and a Web page. Operations spending for the previous fiscal year: $158,573. 125 computers available on campus for general student use. A campuswide network can be accessed from off-campus. Staffed computer lab on campus.

Community Environment: Cheraw is a small community enjoying mild climate year-round. The city has a public library, a shopping center, churches of many denominations, and good medical facilities. There are several service and civic organizations active in the area.

■ ORANGEBURG-CALHOUN TECHNICAL COLLEGE
3250 St. Matthews Rd., NE
Orangeburg, SC 29118-8299
Tel: (803)536-0311; Free: 800-813-6519
Fax: (803)535-1388
Web Site: www.octech.edu/

Description: State and locally supported, 2-year, coed. Part of State Board for Technical and Comprehensive Education, South Carolina. Awards certificates, diplomas, transfer associate, and terminal associate degrees. Founded 1968. Setting: 100-acre small town campus with easy access to Columbia. Total enrollment: 3,219. Faculty: 163 (75 full-time, 88 part-time). Student-undergrad faculty ratio is 20:1. Full-time: 1,538 students, 66% women, 34% men. Part-time: 1,681 students, 68% women, 32% men. Students come from 11 states and territories, 1 other country. 38% 25 or older. Calendar: semesters. Academic remediation for entering students, services for LD students, advanced placement, self-designed majors, independent study, distance learning, summer session for credit, part-time degree program, adult/continuing education programs, co-op programs and internships.

Entrance Requirements: Open admission. Required: high school transcript. Required for some: interview. Entrance: noncompetitive. Application deadline: Rolling. Notification: continuous.

Collegiate Environment: Orientation program. Student services: personal-psychological counseling. Campus security: 24-hour emergency response devices and patrols. Gressette Learning Center plus 1 other with 43,500 books, 143 serials, 2,253 audiovisual materials, and an OPAC. 361 computers available on campus for general student use. A campuswide network can be accessed from off-campus. Students can access the following: online class registration.

Community Environment: See South Carolina State University.

■ PIEDMONT TECHNICAL COLLEGE

620 N Emerald Rd.
Greenwood, SC 29648-1467
Tel: (864)941-8324; Free: 800-868-5528
Fax: (864)941-8555
Web Site: www.ptc.edu/

Description: State-supported, 2-year, coed. Part of South Carolina State Board for Technical and Comprehensive Education. Awards certificates, diplomas, transfer associate, and terminal associate degrees. Founded 1966. Setting: 60-acre small town campus. Endowment: $1.1 million. Research spending for the previous fiscal year: $124,427. Educational spending for the previous fiscal year: $2515 per student. Total enrollment: 4,911. Faculty: 233 (103 full-time, 130 part-time). Student-undergrad faculty ratio is 18:1. 890 applied, 100% were admitted. Students come from 2 states and territories, 5 other countries, 1% from out-of-state. 38% 25 or older. Calendar: semesters. Academic remediation for entering students, services for LD students, advanced placement, independent study, distance learning, summer session for credit, part-time degree program, adult/continuing education programs, co-op programs and internships.

Entrance Requirements: Open admission except for nursing, health sciences programs. Options: electronic application, early admission, deferred admission. Required: high school transcript. Recommended: interview. Entrance: noncompetitive. Application deadline: Rolling. Notification: continuous until 8/20.

Collegiate Environment: Orientation program. Choral group. Social organizations: 18 open to all. Most popular organizations: National Honor Society, Career Peers (student volunteers), Student Nurses Association, Psychology Club, Ebony Club. Major annual events: Spring Activities Day, club fairs, Fall Convocation/Back to School Bash. Student services: personal-psychological counseling, women's center. Campus security: 24-hour emergency response devices and patrols, late night transport-escort service. Piedmont Technical College Library with 27,497 books, 4,497 microform titles, 345 serials, 1,501 audiovisual materials, an OPAC, and a Web page. Operations spending for the previous fiscal year: $221,086. 320 computers available on campus for general student use. A campuswide network can be accessed from off-campus. Staffed computer lab on campus.

Community Environment: In additions to Greenwood county campus, Piedmont has 6 county center campuses serving students of the service area which includes Abbeville, Laurens, Edgefield, McCormick, Saluda, and Newberry.

■ PRESBYTERIAN COLLEGE

503 S Broad St.
Clinton, SC 29325
Tel: (864)833-2820; Free: 800-930-7583
Fax: (864)833-8481
E-mail: bjfortman@presby.edu
Web Site: www.presby.edu/

Description: Independent, 4-year, coed, affiliated with Presbyterian Church (U.S.A.). Awards bachelor's and doctoral degrees. Founded 1880. Setting: 240-acre small town campus with easy access to Greenville, Spartanburg. Endowment: $75 million. Educational spending for the previous fiscal year: $10,300 per student. Total enrollment: 1,403. Faculty: 126 (98 full-time, 28 part-time). Student-undergrad faculty ratio is 14:1. 1,438 applied, 58% were admitted. 31% from top 10% of their high school class, 67% from top quarter, 88% from top half. Full-time: 1,149 students, 56% women, 44% men. Part-time: 23 students, 65% women, 35% men. Students come from 35 states and territories, 27 other countries, 34% from out-of-state. 1% American Indian or Alaska Native, non-Hispanic/Latino; 2% Hispanic/Latino; 10% African American, non-Hispanic/Latino; 1% Asian, non-Hispanic/Latino; 0% Native Hawaiian or other Pacific Islander, non-Hispanic/Latino; 2% international. 0% 25 or older, 97% live on campus, 1% transferred in. Reten-

tion: 86% of full-time freshmen returned the following year. Academic areas with the most degrees conferred: business/marketing; biological/life sciences; social sciences. Core. Calendar: semesters. Services for LD students, advanced placement, honors program, independent study, double major, summer session for credit, internships. Off campus study at Gulf Coast Marine Laboratory, American University. Study abroad program. ROTC: Army.

Entrance Requirements: Options: electronic application, early admission, early decision, early action, deferred admission, international baccalaureate accepted. Required: essay, high school transcript, 1 recommendation, SAT or ACT. Recommended: interview. Entrance: very difficult. Application deadlines: 6/30, 6/30 for nonresidents, 11/1 for early decision, 11/15 for early action. Notification: 3/15, 3/15 for nonresidents, 12/1 for early decision, 12/15 for early action. SAT Reasoning Test deadline: 6/30. Transfer credits accepted: Yes. Applicants placed on waiting list: 20. Early decision applicants: 54. Early decision applicants admitted: 35. Early action applicants: 738. Early action applicants admitted: 457.

Costs Per Year: Comprehensive fee: $41,430 includes full-time tuition ($30,080), mandatory fees ($2600), and college room and board ($8750). College room only: $4260. Full-time tuition and fees vary according to reciprocity agreements. Room and board charges vary according to board plan and housing facility.

Collegiate Environment: Orientation program. Drama-theater group, choral group, student-run newspaper, radio station. Social organizations: 85 open to all; national fraternities, national sororities; 41% of eligible men and 47% of eligible women are members. Most popular organizations: Student Volunteer Services, intramural sports, Student Union Board, Fellowship of Christian Athletes, Student Government Association. Major annual events: Homecoming, Special Olympics, Spring Fling. Student services: health clinic, personal-psychological counseling. Campus security: 24-hour emergency response devices and patrols, late night transport-escort service, controlled dormitory access. 1,151 college housing spaces available; 1,126 were occupied in 2012-13. Freshmen guaranteed college housing. On-campus residence required through senior year. Options: coed, men-only, women-only housing available. James H. Thomason Library with 140,467 books, 1,072 microform titles, 8,094 serials, 12,117 audiovisual materials, an OPAC, and a Web page. Operations spending for the previous fiscal year: $1.1 million. 100 computers available on campus for general student use. A campuswide network can be accessed from student residence rooms and from off campus. Students can access the following: online class registration. Staffed computer lab on campus provides training in use of computers, software, and the Internet.

Community Environment: Located in the Piedmont section of South Carolina, Clinton is approximately 64 miles northwest of Columbia. The annual mean January temperature is 43.6 degrees; July 79.9 degrees. The community has air and bus service and is adjacent to U.S. Highway 76, I-385; I-26. There are many churches of various denominations, a hospital, hotels and motels in town. Part-time employment is available. Local recreational facilities include tennis, golf, theatre and swimming; nearby Lake Greenwood provides boating, fishing and hunting. Various civic, fraternal and veteran's organizations are active in the community.

■ SOUTH CAROLINA STATE UNIVERSITY

300 College St. NE
Orangeburg, SC 29117-0001
Tel: (803)536-7000; Free: 800-260-5956
Fax: (803)536-8990
E-mail: admissions@scsu.edu
Web Site: www.scsu.edu/

Description: State-supported, comprehensive, coed. Part of South Carolina Commission on Higher Education. Awards bachelor's, master's, and doctoral degrees and post-master's certificates. Founded 1896. Setting: 160-acre small town campus. Endowment: $766,537. Research spending for the previous fiscal year: $16.8 million. Educational spending for the previous fiscal year: $7457 per student. Total enrollment: 4,326. Faculty: 279 (216 full-time, 63 part-time). Student-undergrad faculty ratio is 17:1. 3,267 applied, 96% were admitted. 6% from top 10% of their high school class, 43% from top quarter, 50% from top half. Full-time: 3,480 students, 54% women, 46% men. Part-time: 264 students, 60% women, 40% men. Students come from 34 states and territories, 19 other countries, 16% from out-of-state. 0.1% American Indian or Alaska Native, non-Hispanic/Latino; 1% Hispanic/Latino; 96% African American, non-Hispanic/Latino; 0.4% Asian, non-Hispanic/Latino; 0% Native Hawaiian or other Pacific Islander, non-Hispanic/Latino; 0.03% international. 10% 25 or older, 60% live on campus, 6% transferred in. Retention: 65% of full-time freshmen returned the following year. Academic areas with the most degrees conferred: business/marketing; family and consumer sciences; biological/life sciences; education; engineering technologies. Core. Calendar: semesters. Advanced placement, honors program, independent study, distance learning, summer session for credit, part-time degree program, adult/continuing education programs, co-op programs and internships. Off campus study at National Student Exchange. Study abroad program. ROTC: Army, Air Force (c).

Entrance Requirements: Options: electronic application, deferred admission. Required: high school transcript, minimum 2 high school GPA, SAT or ACT. Recommended: SAT Subject Tests. Entrance: minimally difficult. Application deadline: 7/31. Notification: continuous.

Costs Per Year: Application fee: $25. State resident tuition: $8688 full-time. Nonresident tuition: $17,600 full-time. Mandatory fees: $570 full-time. College room and board: $9286. College room only: $6300. Room and board charges vary according to housing facility.

Collegiate Environment: Orientation program. Drama-theater group, choral group, marching band, student-run newspaper. Social organizations: 75 open to all; national fraternities, national sororities, local fraternities, local sororities; 20% of eligible men and 20% of eligible women are members. Most popular organizations: student government, Campus Activity Board, NAACP, United Voices of Christ, student media. Major annual events: Spring Convocation, Smith-Hammond Middleton Memorial Program, Bulldog Fest. Student services: health clinic, personal-psychological counseling. Campus security: 24-hour emergency response devices and patrols, late night transport-escort service, controlled dormitory access. Miller F. Whittaker Library with 313,329 books, 1 million microform titles, 3,031 serials, an OPAC, and a Web page. Operations spending for the previous fiscal year: $1.3 million. 600 computers available on campus for general student use. A campuswide network can be accessed. Students can access the following: online class registration. Staffed computer lab on campus.

Community Environment: Orangeburg is in an agricultural and dairying area. Its industries include textiles, wood products, meat packing, chemicals, and baking goods. This is a suburban community with a temperate climate. Airline service is available at nearby Columbia. Railroad and bus lines serve the immediate community. There is a public library, churches of major denominations, a hospital, and major civic and fraternal organizations. Some part-time employment is available. Local recreation includes four theatres, swimming, fishing and many sports.

■ **SOUTH UNIVERSITY**
9 Science Ct.
Columbia, SC 29203
Tel: (803)799-9082; Free: 866-629-3031
Fax: (803)799-9038
Web Site: www.southuniversity.edu/columbia/
Description: Proprietary, comprehensive, coed. Part of Education Management Corporation. Awards associate, bachelor's, and master's degrees. Founded 1935.

■ **SOUTHERN METHODIST COLLEGE**
541 Broughton St.
Orangeburg, SC 29115
Tel: (803)534-7826
E-mail: jcourson@smcollege.edu
Web Site: www.smcollege.edu/
Description: Independent Southern Methodist, 4-year, coed. Awards associate and bachelor's degrees. Founded 1956. Setting: 50-acre small town campus. Total enrollment: 236. 81% 25 or older. Core. Academic remediation for entering students, services for LD students, advanced placement, accelerated degree program, honors program, independent study, double major, summer session for credit, part-time degree program, adult/continuing education programs, co-op programs and internships. Off campus study at Wesley Institute.

Entrance Requirements: Options: early admission, early action, deferred admission. Required: essay, high school transcript, 3 recommendations, interview, health certificate, SAT or ACT. Entrance: minimally difficult. Application deadlines: 7/15, 7/15 for early action. Notification: continuous until 7/22.

Collegiate Environment: Orientation program. No special consideration for freshman housing applicants. Options: men-only, women-only housing available. Lynn Corbett Library with 21,743 books, 10,000 microform titles, 60 serials, and 171 audiovisual materials.

Community Environment: See South Carolina State University.

■ **SOUTHERN WESLEYAN UNIVERSITY**
907 Wesleyan Dr.
Central, SC 29630-1020
Tel: (864)644-5000; Free: 800-CU-AT-SWU
Fax: (864)644-5900
E-mail: broe@swu.edu
Web Site: www.swu.edu/
Description: Independent, comprehensive, coed, affiliated with Wesleyan Church. Awards associate, bachelor's, and master's degrees. Founded 1906. Setting: 350-acre small town campus. Endowment: $3.5 million. Educational spending for the previous fiscal year: $4075 per student. Total enrollment: 1,883. Faculty: 193 (57 full-time, 136 part-time). Student-undergrad faculty ratio is 18:1. 575 applied, 94% were admitted. 13% from top 10% of their high school class, 43% from top quarter, 75% from top half. Full-time: 1,440 students, 60% women, 40% men. Part-time: 16 students, 56% women, 44% men. Students come from 25 states and territories, 9 other countries, 16% from out-of-state. 1% American Indian or Alaska Native, non-Hispanic/Latino; 2% Hispanic/Latino; 27% African American, non-Hispanic/Latino; 0.4% Asian, non-Hispanic/Latino; 0% Native Hawaiian or other Pacific Islander, non-Hispanic/Latino; 1% international. 57% 25 or older, 55% live on campus, 6% transferred in. Retention: 70% of full-time freshmen returned the following year. Academic areas with the most degrees conferred: business/marketing; education; psychology. Core. Calendar: semesters. Academic remediation for entering students, ESL program, services for LD students, advanced placement, accelerated degree program, self-designed majors, honors program, independent study, distance learning, double major, summer session for credit, part-time degree program, adult/continuing education programs, internships. Off campus study at Clemson University, Clemson, SC; Tri-County Technical College, Pendleton, SC; Council for Christian Colleges and Universities, Los Angels, CA, Martha's Vineyard, MA, Washington, DC. Study abroad program. ROTC: Army (c), Air Force (c).

Entrance Requirements: Options: electronic application, deferred admission. Required: high school transcript, minimum 2.3 high school GPA, SAT or ACT. Required for some: interview. Entrance: minimally difficult. Application deadline: 8/1. Notification: continuous. SAT Reasoning Test deadline: 8/1. SAT Subject Test deadline: 8/1. Transfer credits accepted: Yes.

Collegiate Environment: Orientation program. Drama-theater group, choral group. Social organizations: 12 open to all. Most popular organizations: Student Government Association, Student Missions Focus, Ministry Teams, Music Club, Ignite student athlete fellowship group. Major annual events: Homecoming, Spiritual Emphasis Week, Christmas Banquet. Student services: health clinic, personal-psychological counseling. Campus security: 24-hour emergency response devices, late night security patrols until 2:00 am, restricted access to campus after midnight. Rickman Library with 116,475 books, 2,160 microform titles, 278 serials, 5,730 audiovisual materials, an OPAC, and a Web page. Operations spending for the previous fiscal year: $503,465. 95 computers available on campus for general student use. A campuswide network can be accessed from student residence rooms and from off campus. Students can access the following: online class registration. Staffed computer lab on campus provides training in use of computers, software, and the Internet.

Community Environment: Central is located in the Piedmont section of South Carolina, between Atlanta, Georgia, and Charlotte, North Carolina. The community is five miles North of Clemson and is located near the metropolitan area of Greenville.

■ **SPARTANBURG COMMUNITY COLLEGE**
Business I-85 & New Cut Rd.
Spartanburg, SC 29305-4386
Tel: (864)592-4600; Free: 866-591-3700
E-mail: admissions@stcsc.edu
Web Site: www.sccsc.edu/
Description: State-supported, 2-year, coed. Part of South Carolina State Board for Technical and Comprehensive Education. Awards certificates, diplomas, transfer associate, and terminal associate degrees. Founded 1961. Setting: 104-acre suburban campus with easy access to Charlotte. Educational spending for the previous fiscal year: $3530 per student. Total enrollment: 6,036. Faculty: 380. Student-undergrad faculty ratio is 16:1. Full-time: 2,868 students, 57% women, 43% men. Part-time: 3,168 students, 64% women, 36% men. Students come from 10 states and territories, 3 other countries, 2% from out-of-state. 1% American Indian or Alaska Native, non-Hispanic/Latino; 5% Hispanic/Latino; 23% African American, non-Hispanic/Latino; 3% Asian, non-Hispanic/Latino; 0.1% Native Hawaiian or

other Pacific Islander, non-Hispanic/Latino; 0.03% international. 36% 25 or older, 9% transferred in. Retention: 58% of full-time freshmen returned the following year. Core. Calendar: semesters condensed semesters plus summer sessions. Academic remediation for entering students, ESL program, services for LD students, advanced placement, distance learning, summer session for credit, part-time degree program, adult/continuing education programs, co-op programs.

Entrance Requirements: Open admission. Options: electronic application, early admission, international baccalaureate accepted. Required: high school transcript, high school diploma, GED or equivalent. Recommended: interview. Required for some: SAT or ACT. Entrance: noncompetitive. Application deadline: Rolling. Notification: continuous. Transfer credits accepted: Yes.

Collegiate Environment: Orientation program. Drama-theater group, student-run newspaper, Social organizations: 5 open to all. Student services: personal-psychological counseling, women's center. Campus security: 24-hour emergency response devices and patrols. College housing not available. Spartanburg Community College Library with 40,078 books, 295 serials, an OPAC, and a Web page. Operations spending for the previous fiscal year: $753,545. 1,500 computers available on campus for general student use. A campuswide network can be accessed from off-campus. Students can access the following: online class registration. Staffed computer lab on campus provides training in use of computers, software, and the Internet.

Community Environment: See Converse College.

■ **SPARTANBURG METHODIST COLLEGE**
1000 Powell Mill Rd.
Spartanburg, SC 29301
Tel: (864)587-4000; Free: 800-772-7286
Fax: (864)587-4355
E-mail: admiss@smcsc.edu
Web Site: www.smcsc.edu/
Description: Independent Methodist, 2-year, coed. Awards transfer associate and terminal associate degrees. Founded 1911. Setting: 110-acre suburban campus with easy access to Charlotte. Endowment: $16.6 million. Educational spending for the previous fiscal year: $2791 per student. Total enrollment: 811. Faculty: 48 (28 full-time, 20 part-time). Student-undergrad faculty ratio is 23:1. 1,265 applied, 64% were admitted. 2% from top 10% of their high school class, 18% from top quarter, 56% from top half. Full-time: 785 students, 48% women, 52% men. Part-time: 26 students, 58% women, 42% men. Students come from 9 states and territories, 3 other countries, 4% from out-of-state. 0.2% American Indian or Alaska Native, non-Hispanic/Latino; 6% Hispanic/Latino; 29% African American, non-Hispanic/Latino; 1% Asian, non-Hispanic/Latino; 0% Native Hawaiian or other Pacific Islander, non-Hispanic/Latino; 0.4% international. 1% 25 or older, 66% live on campus, 4% transferred in. Retention: 0% of full-time freshmen returned the following year. Core. Calendar: semesters. Academic remediation for entering students, ESL program, services for LD students, advanced placement, honors program, independent study, summer session for credit, part-time degree program.

Entrance Requirements: Options: electronic application, deferred admission. Required: essay, high school transcript, minimum 2 high school GPA, high school rank considered along with other criteria, SAT or ACT. Recommended: interview. Required for some: interview. Entrance: minimally difficult. Application deadline: Rolling. Notification: continuous. Transfer credits accepted: Yes.

Costs Per Year: Application fee: $20. One-time mandatory fee: $175. Comprehensive fee: $24,021 includes full-time tuition ($14,882), mandatory fees ($903), and college room and board ($8236). Full-time tuition and fees vary according to course load. Part-time tuition: $402 per semester hour. Part-time tuition varies according to course load.

Collegiate Environment: Orientation program. Drama-theater group, choral group, student-run newspaper. Social organizations: 14 open to all. Most popular organizations: College Christian Movement, Alpha Phi Omega, Campus Union, Fellowship of Christian Athletes, Kappa Sigma Alpha. Major annual events: College Wide Day of Service, Homecoming. Student services: health clinic, personal-psychological counseling. Campus security: 24-hour emergency response devices and patrols, student patrols, late night transport-escort service, controlled dormitory access. 596 college housing spaces available; 518 were occupied in 2012-13. Freshmen guaranteed college housing. Options: coed, men-only, women-only housing available. Marie Blair Burgess Learning Resource Center plus 1 other with 75,000 books, 2,900 microform titles, 5,000 serials, 3,150 audiovisual materials, an OPAC, and a Web page. Operations spending for the previous fiscal year:

$242,114. 60 computers available on campus for general student use. A campuswide network can be accessed from student residence rooms and from off campus. Staffed computer lab on campus provides training in use of computers, software, and the Internet.
Community Environment: See Converse College.

■ **STRAYER UNIVERSITY - CHARLESTON CAMPUS**
5010 Wetland Crossing
North Charleston, SC 29418
Tel: (843)746-5100
Fax: (843)746-5130
Web Site: www.strayer.edu/campus/charleston/
Description: Proprietary, comprehensive, coed. Awards associate, bachelor's, and master's degrees.

■ **STRAYER UNIVERSITY - COLUMBIA CAMPUS**
200 Ctr. Point Cir., Ste. 300
Columbia, SC 29210
Tel: (803)750-2500
Fax: (803)750-2530
Web Site: www.strayer.edu/campus/columbia
Description: Proprietary, comprehensive, coed. Awards associate, bachelor's, and master's degrees.

■ **STRAYER UNIVERSITY - GREENVILLE CAMPUS**
555 N Pleasantburg Dr.
Ste. 300
Greenville, SC 29607
Tel: (864)250-7000
Fax: (864)232-3611
Web Site: www.strayer.edu/campus/greenville
Description: Proprietary, comprehensive, coed. Awards associate, bachelor's, and master's degrees.

■ **TECHNICAL COLLEGE OF THE LOWCOUNTRY**
921 Ribaut Rd.
Beaufort, SC 29901-1288
Tel: (843)525-8324
E-mail: rcole@tcl.edu
Web Site: www.tcl.edu/
Description: State-supported, 2-year, coed. Part of South Carolina Technical and Comprehensive Education System. Awards certificates, diplomas, transfer associate, and terminal associate degrees. Founded 1972. Setting: 12-acre small town campus. Total enrollment: 2,511. Student-undergrad faculty ratio is 15:1. Students come from 4 states and territories. Calendar: semesters. Academic remediation for entering students, advanced placement, distance learning, summer session for credit, part-time degree program, adult/continuing education programs.
Entrance Requirements: Options: early admission, deferred admission. Required: ACT ASSET. Recommended: SAT and SAT Subject Tests or ACT. Entrance: noncompetitive. Application deadline: Rolling.
Collegiate Environment: Orientation program. Campus security: security during class hours. College housing not available.

■ **TRI-COUNTY TECHNICAL COLLEGE**
PO Box 587, 7900 Hwy. 76
Pendleton, SC 29670-0587
Tel: (864)646-8361
E-mail: infocent@tctc.edu
Web Site: www.tctc.edu/
Description: State-supported, 2-year, coed. Part of South Carolina State Board for Technical and Comprehensive Education. Awards certificates, diplomas, transfer associate, and terminal associate degrees. Founded 1962. Setting: 100-acre rural campus. Total enrollment: 5,730. Student-undergrad faculty ratio is 21:1. 5% from out-of-state. 30% 25 or older. Retention: 45% of full-time freshmen returned the following year. Calendar: semesters. Academic remediation for entering students, advanced placement, distance learning, summer session for credit, part-time degree program, adult/continuing education programs. Study abroad program. ROTC: Army (c), Air Force (c).
Entrance Requirements: Open admission except for allied health programs. Option: early admission. Entrance: noncompetitive. Application deadline: Rolling. Notification: continuous.

Collegiate Environment: Campus security: 24-hour emergency response devices and patrols.

■ **TRIDENT TECHNICAL COLLEGE**
PO Box 118067
Charleston, SC 29423-8067
Tel: (843)574-6111
Fax: (843)574-6109
E-mail: Clara.Martin@tridenttech.edu
Web Site: www.tridenttech.edu/

Description: State and locally supported, 2-year, coed. Part of South Carolina State Board for Technical and Comprehensive Education. Awards certificates, diplomas, transfer associate, and terminal associate degrees. Founded 1964. Setting: urban campus. Total enrollment: 17,224. Faculty: 869 (326 full-time, 543 part-time). Student-undergrad faculty ratio is 21:1. Full-time: 7,557 students, 58% women, 42% men. Part-time: 9,667 students, 65% women, 35% men. Students come from 71 other countries, 3% from out-of-state. 1% American Indian or Alaska Native, non-Hispanic/Latino; 4% Hispanic/Latino; 32% African American, non-Hispanic/Latino; 2% Asian, non-Hispanic/Latino; 0.3% Native Hawaiian or other Pacific Islander, non-Hispanic/Latino. 44% 25 or older, 6% transferred in. Core. Calendar: semesters. Part-time degree program. Off campus study at Summerville Site at Trolley Road, Dorchester County QuickJobs Training Center, St. Paul's Parish Site, Wando Partner, Mt. Pleasant.

Entrance Requirements: Open admission except for nursing and allied health programs. Options: electronic application, early admission. Required for some: high school transcript. Entrance: noncompetitive. Application deadline: 8/6. Notification: continuous.

Costs Per Year: Application fee: $30. Area resident tuition: $3834 full-time, $153.45 per credit hour part-time. State resident tuition: $4236 full-time, $170.25 per credit hour part-time. Nonresident tuition: $7122 full-time, $290.45 per credit hour part-time. Mandatory fees: $100 full-time. Full-time tuition and fees vary according to course load.

Collegiate Environment: Orientation program. Drama-theater group, student-run newspaper, radio station. Social organizations: 52 open to all. Most popular organizations: Phi Theta Kappa, Lex Artis Paralegal Society, Hospitality and Culinary Student Association, Partnership for Change in Communities and Families, Society of Student Leaders. Student services: personal-psychological counseling. Campus security: 24-hour emergency response devices and patrols, late night transport-escort service. College housing not available. Learning Resource Center plus 3 others with 113,550 books, 265 serials, 5,659 audiovisual materials, an OPAC, and a Web page. 1,700 computers available on campus for general student use. A campus-wide network can be accessed from off-campus. Students can access the following: online class registration. Staffed computer lab on campus provides training in use of computers, software, and the Internet.

Community Environment: North Charleston is a suburb located just eight miles from downtown Charleston. The community enjoys all the cultural, recreational and civic advantages of the nearby larger community, yet retains an air of the small town. There are good shopping areas, churches, parks and theatres.

■ **UNIVERSITY OF PHOENIX–COLUMBIA CAMPUS**
1001 Pinnacle Point Dr., Ste. 200
Columbia, SC 29223
Tel: (803)699-5096; Free: 866-766-0766
Web Site: www.phoenix.edu/

Description: Proprietary, comprehensive, coed. Awards bachelor's, master's, and doctoral degrees.

■ **UNIVERSITY OF SOUTH CAROLINA**
Columbia, SC 29208
Tel: (803)777-7000; Free: 800-868-5872
E-mail: admissions-ugrad@sc.edu
Web Site: www.sc.edu/

Description: State-supported, university, coed. Part of University of South Carolina System. Awards bachelor's, master's, and doctoral degrees and post-master's certificates. Founded 1801. Setting: 444-acre urban campus. Endowment: $513.9 million. Research spending for the previous fiscal year: $145.8 million. Educational spending for the previous fiscal year: $9339 per student. Total enrollment: 31,288. Faculty: 2,051 (1,397 full-time, 654 part-time). Student-undergrad faculty ratio is 17:1. 23,429 applied, 61% were admitted. 30% from top 10% of their high school class, 67% from top quarter, 94% from top half. 47 National Merit Scholars, 66 valedictorians. Full-time:

21,646 students, 54% women, 46% men. Part-time: 1,717 students, 48% women, 52% men. Students come from 53 states and territories, 115 other countries, 31% from out-of-state. 0.3% American Indian or Alaska Native, non-Hispanic/Latino; 4% Hispanic/Latino; 11% African American, non-Hispanic/Latino; 3% Asian, non-Hispanic/Latino; 0.1% Native Hawaiian or other Pacific Islander, non-Hispanic/Latino; 1% international. 7% 25 or older, 36% live on campus, 8% transferred in. Retention: 87% of full-time freshmen returned the following year. Academic areas with the most degrees conferred: business/marketing; biological/life sciences; social sciences. Core. Calendar: semesters. ESL program, services for LD students, advanced placement, accelerated degree program, self-designed majors, freshman honors college, honors program, independent study, distance learning, double major, summer session for credit, part-time degree program, adult/continuing education programs, co-op programs and internships, graduate courses open to undergrads. Study abroad program. ROTC: Army, Naval, Air Force.

Entrance Requirements: Options: electronic application, early action, international baccalaureate accepted. Required: high school transcript, minimum 2 high school GPA, SAT or ACT. Entrance: moderately difficult. Application deadlines: 12/1, 10/15 for early action. Notification: 12/20 for early action. SAT Reasoning Test deadline: 2/1. Transfer credits accepted: Yes. Early action applicants: 9,983. Early action applicants admitted: 5,598.

Costs Per Year: Application fee: $50. State resident tuition: $10,088 full-time, $421 per credit hour part-time. Nonresident tuition: $27,244 full-time, $1136 per credit hour part-time. Mandatory fees: $400 full-time. Full-time tuition and fees vary according to program and reciprocity agreements. Part-time tuition varies according to course load. College room and board: $8459. College room only: $5624. Room and board charges vary according to board plan, housing facility, and location.

Collegiate Environment: Orientation program. Drama-theater group, choral group, marching band, student-run newspaper, radio station. Social organizations: 387 open to all; national fraternities, national sororities; 13% of eligible men and 28% of eligible women are members. Most popular organizations: Social Work Student Association, Friendship Association of Chinese Students and Scholars, Alpha Lambda Delta, Residence Hall Association, Student Bar Association. Major annual events: Homecoming Week, Carolina-Clemson Blood Drive, Welcome Week. Student services: health clinic, personal-psychological counseling, women's center. Campus security: 24-hour emergency response devices and patrols, student patrols, late night transport-escort service, controlled dormitory access. 7,329 college housing spaces available. Freshmen guaranteed college housing. On-campus residence required in freshman year. Options: coed, men-only, women-only housing available. Thomas Cooper Library plus 7 others with 4.5 million books, 5.5 million microform titles, 66,105 audiovisual materials, an OPAC, and a Web page. Operations spending for the previous fiscal year: $21.3 million. 2,800 computers available on campus for general student use. Computer purchase/lease plans available. A campuswide network can be accessed from student residence rooms and from off campus. Students can access the following: online class registration. Staffed computer lab on campus (open 24 hours a day) provides training in use of computers, software, and the Internet.

Community Environment: Columbia is located in the Midlands, halfway between the coast and the mountains - an easy two-and-a-half hour drive to some of the nicest beaches on the East Coast and some of the Carolinas' best hiking trails. A few blocks east of the university lies bustling Five Points, a longtime favorite of students for it boutiques, bookstores, restaurants, and bars. West of the university lies the Congaree Vista, a more upscale shopping and eating district. As the state's capital city, Columbia is home to the state government, as well as several other colleges and universities. Culture and entertainment abound. The city has several theatre groups, an art museum, and an art center that brings in major musical, dance, and theatre entertainment. For relaxation on Columbia's balmy spring-like days, downtown's Finlay Park is close by, and nearby Lake Murray offers swimming, camping, and fishing.

■ **UNIVERSITY OF SOUTH CAROLINA AIKEN**
471 University Pky.
Aiken, SC 29801-6309
Tel: (803)648-6851; Free: 888-WOW-USCA
Fax: (803)641-3727
E-mail: admit@usca.edu
Web Site: www.usca.edu/

Description: State-supported, comprehensive, coed. Part of University of South Carolina System. Awards bachelor's and master's degrees. Founded

1961. Setting: 453-acre suburban campus with easy access to Columbia. Endowment: $18.3 million. Research spending for the previous fiscal year: $806,097. Educational spending for the previous fiscal year: $5388 per student. Total enrollment: 3,210. Faculty: 237 (142 full-time, 95 part-time). Student-undergrad faculty ratio is 16:1. 2,619 applied, 51% were admitted. 13% from top 10% of their high school class, 41% from top quarter, 77% from top half. Full-time: 2,427 students, 65% women, 35% men. Part-time: 696 students, 65% women, 35% men. Students come from 30 states and territories, 24 other countries, 10% from out-of-state. 0.4% American Indian or Alaska Native, non-Hispanic/Latino; 4% Hispanic/Latino; 28% African American, non-Hispanic/Latino; 1% Asian, non-Hispanic/Latino; 0.1% Native Hawaiian or other Pacific Islander, non-Hispanic/Latino; 2% international. 15% 25 or older, 27% live on campus, 9% transferred in. Retention: 68% of full-time freshmen returned the following year. Academic areas with the most degrees conferred: business/marketing; health professions and related sciences; education. Core. Calendar: semesters. ESL program, services for LD students, advanced placement, self-designed majors, honors program, independent study, distance learning, double major, summer session for credit, part-time degree program, adult/continuing education programs, co-op programs and internships. Off campus study at other units of the University of South Carolina System. Study abroad program.

Entrance Requirements: Options: electronic application, early admission, deferred admission, international baccalaureate accepted. Required: high school transcript, SAT or ACT. Entrance: moderately difficult. Application deadlines: 8/1, 8/1 for nonresidents. Notification: continuous, continuous for nonresidents. SAT Reasoning Test deadline: 8/1. Transfer credits accepted: Yes.

Costs Per Year: Application fee: $45. State resident tuition: $8734 full-time, $380 per credit hour part-time. Nonresident tuition: $17,490 full-time, $760 per credit hour part-time. Mandatory fees: $290 full-time, $9 per credit hour part-time, $25 per term part-time. Full-time tuition and fees vary according to reciprocity agreements. Part-time tuition and fees vary according to course load and reciprocity agreements. College room and board: $6780. Room and board charges vary according to board plan and housing facility.

Collegiate Environment: Orientation program. Drama-theater group, choral group, student-run newspaper. Social organizations: 87 open to all; national fraternities, national sororities; 9% of eligible men and 7% of eligible women are members. Most popular organizations: student government, Pacesetters, Student Alumni Ambassadors, African-American Student Alliance, Pacer Union Board. Major annual events: Homecoming Week, leadership training events, Black History Month. Student services: health clinic, personal-psychological counseling. Campus security: 24-hour emergency response devices and patrols, late night transport-escort service, controlled dormitory access. 968 college housing spaces available; 841 were occupied in 2012-13. Freshmen given priority for college housing. Option: coed housing available. Gregg-Graniteville Library with 283,111 books, 79,433 microform titles, 4,425 serials, 4,167 audiovisual materials, an OPAC, and a Web page. Operations spending for the previous fiscal year: $1.2 million. 550 computers available on campus for general student use. A campuswide network can be accessed from student residence rooms and from off campus. Students can access the following: online class registration. Staffed computer lab on campus (open 24 hours a day) provides training in use of computers, software, and the Internet.

Community Environment: Aiken, population c. 27,490, is the seat of Aiken County and is about 17 miles from Augusta, Georgia.

■ **UNIVERSITY OF SOUTH CAROLINA BEAUFORT**
One University Blvd.
Bluffton, SC 29909
Tel: (843)208-8000
E-mail: mrwilli5@uscb.edu
Web Site: www.uscb.edu/

Description: State-supported, 4-year, coed. Part of University of South Carolina System. Awards bachelor's degrees. Founded 1959. Setting: 200-acre suburban campus. Total enrollment: 1,874. Faculty: 141 (59 full-time, 82 part-time). Student-undergrad faculty ratio is 18:1. 1,434 applied, 75% were admitted. Students come from 38 states and territories, 14 other countries, 22% from out-of-state. 0.4% American Indian or Alaska Native, non-Hispanic/Latino; 6% Hispanic/Latino; 19% African American, non-Hispanic/Latino; 1% Asian, non-Hispanic/Latino; 0.2% Native Hawaiian or other Pacific Islander, non-Hispanic/Latino; 0.5% international. 26% 25 or older, 20% live on campus. Retention: 54% of full-time freshmen returned the following year. Academic areas with the most degrees conferred: business/marketing; health professions and related sciences; social sci-

ences; education; psychology. Core. Calendar: semesters. Services for LD students, advanced placement, independent study, distance learning, double major, summer session for credit, part-time degree program, adult/continuing education programs, internships. Study abroad program.

Entrance Requirements: Options: electronic application, deferred admission, international baccalaureate accepted. Required: high school transcript, Specific college prep classes required from high school, SAT or ACT. Recommended: minimum 2 high school GPA. Entrance: minimally difficult. Application deadline: Rolling. Notification: continuous. Transfer credits accepted: Yes.

Costs Per Year: Application fee: $40. One-time mandatory fee: $150. State resident tuition: $8172 full-time, $344 per credit hour part-time. Nonresident tuition: $17,570 full-time, $734 per credit hour part-time. Mandatory fees: $386 full-time, $14 per credit hour part-time, $25 per term part-time. Full-time tuition and fees vary according to course load, program, reciprocity agreements, and student level. Part-time tuition and fees vary according to course load, program, reciprocity agreements, and student level. College room and board: $6910. College room only: $4850. Room and board charges vary according to board plan, housing facility, and student level.

Collegiate Environment: Orientation program. Drama-theater group, student-run newspaper. Social organizations: 8 open to all; local fraternities, local sororities. Most popular organizations: Student Government Association, Gamma Beta Phi, Black Student Organization, Business Club, Environmental Awareness Club. Major annual events: student cookouts, Christmas Party, Spring Fling. Student services: personal-psychological counseling. Campus security: 24-hour emergency response devices, evening security service. University of South Carolina at Beaufort Library plus 1 other with 84,865 books, 146 serials, an OPAC, and a Web page.

■ **UNIVERSITY OF SOUTH CAROLINA LANCASTER**
PO Box 889
Lancaster, SC 29721-0889
Tel: (803)313-7000
Fax: (803)313-7106
E-mail: vinsons@mailbox.sc.edu
Web Site: usclancaster.sc.edu/

Description: State-supported, 2-year, coed. Part of University of South Carolina System. Awards transfer associate and terminal associate degrees. Founded 1959. Setting: 17-acre small town campus with easy access to Charlotte. Educational spending for the previous fiscal year: $4680 per student. Total enrollment: 1,593. Faculty: 105 (63 full-time, 42 part-time). Student-undergrad faculty ratio is 14:1. 557 applied, 99% were admitted. 8% from top 10% of their high school class, 13% from top quarter, 50% from top half. 1 valedictorian. Students come from 10 states and territories, 2 other countries, 1% from out-of-state. 13% 25 or older. Calendar: semesters. Academic remediation for entering students, services for LD students, advanced placement, honors program, independent study, distance learning, part-time degree program, internships.

Entrance Requirements: Open admission. Options: electronic application, early admission. Required: high school transcript, SAT or ACT. Entrance: noncompetitive. Application deadlines: Rolling, Rolling for nonresidents. Notification: continuous, continuous for nonresidents. Transfer credits accepted: Yes.

Collegiate Environment: Orientation program. Drama-theater group, student-run newspaper. Student services: personal-psychological counseling. Medford Library with 82,000 books, 150 serials, an OPAC, and a Web page. 40 computers available on campus for general student use. A campuswide network can be accessed. Students can access the following: online class registration. Staffed computer lab on campus.

■ **UNIVERSITY OF SOUTH CAROLINA SALKEHATCHIE**
PO Box 617
Allendale, SC 29810-0617
Tel: (803)584-3446; Free: 800-922-5500
E-mail: cdbrown@mailbox.sc.edu
Web Site: uscsalkehatchie.sc.edu/

Description: State-supported, 2-year, coed. Part of University of South Carolina System. Awards transfer associate and terminal associate degrees. Founded 1965. Setting: 95-acre rural campus. Total enrollment: 1,173. Student-undergrad faculty ratio is 16:1. 554 applied. 4% from out-of-state. 25% 25 or older. Retention: 45% of full-time freshmen returned the following year. Core. Calendar: semesters. Academic remediation for entering students, advanced placement, distance learning, summer session for credit, part-time degree program, adult/continuing education programs.

Entrance Requirements: Option: electronic application. Required: high school transcript, minimum 2 high school GPA, SAT or ACT. Entrance: noncompetitive. Application deadline: Rolling. Transfer credits accepted: Yes.

Collegiate Environment: Orientation program. Social organizations: Student Government and Campus Ambassadors. Campus security: 24-hour emergency response devices. College housing not available. Salkehatchie Learning Resource Center with an OPAC and a Web page.

■ **UNIVERSITY OF SOUTH CAROLINA SUMTER**
200 Miller Rd.
Sumter, SC 29150-2498
Tel: (803)775-8727
E-mail: kbritton@usc.sumter.edu
Web Site: www.uscsumter.edu/

Description: State-supported, 2-year, coed. Part of University of South Carolina System. Awards transfer associate degrees. Founded 1966. Setting: 50-acre urban campus. Endowment: $1.8 million. Research spending for the previous fiscal year: $25,459. Educational spending for the previous fiscal year: $4064 per student. Total enrollment: 1,206. Faculty: 66 (41 full-time, 25 part-time). Student-undergrad faculty ratio is 19:1. 698 applied, 58% were admitted. 12% from top 10% of their high school class, 34% from top quarter, 67% from top half. 1 class president, 3 student government officers, 5% from out-of-state. 19% 25 or older. Retention: 57% of full-time freshmen returned the following year. Core. Calendar: semesters. Services for LD students, advanced placement, honors program, independent study, distance learning, summer session for credit, part-time degree program, adult/continuing education programs. ROTC: Army (c), Air Force (c).

Entrance Requirements: Options: electronic application, international baccalaureate accepted. Required: high school transcript, minimum 2.0 high school GPA, SAT or ACT. Entrance: moderately difficult. Application deadline: 8/8.

Costs Per Year: Application fee: $40. State resident tuition: $5892 full-time, $246 per credit hour part-time. Nonresident tuition: $14,766 full-time, $616 per credit hour part-time. Mandatory fees: $246 full-time, $15 per credit hour part-time, $25 per term part-time. Full-time tuition and fees vary according to student level. Part-time tuition and fees vary according to student level.

Collegiate Environment: Orientation program. Drama-theater group, choral group. Social organizations: 16 open to all. Most popular organizations: Association of African-American Students, Baptist Student Union, Student Education Association, Gamecock Ambassadors, Environmental Club. Major annual events: Convocation, Alcohol Awareness Week Festival, Martin Luther King, Jr. Day festivities. Student services: personal-psychological counseling. Campus security: 24-hour patrols, late night transport-escort service. University of South Carolina at Sumter Library with 81,114 books, 12,938 microform titles, 1,114 serials, an OPAC, and a Web page. Operations spending for the previous fiscal year: $302,089. 355 computers available on campus for general student use. A campuswide network can be accessed from off-campus. Students can access the following: online class registration, online course evaluation, online student surveys. Staffed computer lab on campus.

■ **UNIVERSITY OF SOUTH CAROLINA UNION**
PO Drawer 729
Union, SC 29379-0729
Tel: (864)427-3681
E-mail: tyoung@gwm.sc.edu
Web Site: uscunion.sc.edu/

Description: State-supported, 2-year, coed. Part of University of South Carolina System. Awards transfer associate degrees. Founded 1965. Setting: small town campus with easy access to Charlotte. Total enrollment: 500. Faculty: 38 (10 full-time, 28 part-time). Student-undergrad faculty ratio is 14:1. 5% from top 10% of their high school class, 15% from top quarter, 50% from top half. Full-time: 250 students, 60% women, 40% men. Part-time: 250 students, 60% women, 40% men. 33% 25 or older. Calendar: semesters. Part-time degree program.

Entrance Requirements: Required: high school transcript, SAT or ACT. Entrance: minimally difficult. Application deadline: Rolling. Transfer credits accepted: Yes.

Costs Per Year: Application fee: $40. State resident tuition: $2900 full-time. Nonresident tuition: $7200 full-time. Mandatory fees: $249 full-time, $249 per credit hour part-time. Full-time tuition and fees vary according to course load, degree level, and student level. Part-time fees vary according to student level.

Collegiate Environment: Orientation program. Drama-theater group, choral group, student-run newspaper. Social organizations: 12 open to all; CLUB BASEBALL. College housing not available. 60 computers available on campus for general student use. A campuswide network can be accessed from off-campus. Students can access the following: online class registration. Staffed computer lab on campus provides training in use of computers.

■ **UNIVERSITY OF SOUTH CAROLINA UPSTATE**
800 University Way
Spartanburg, SC 29303-4999
Tel: (864)503-5000; Free: 800-277-8727
Fax: (864)503-5201
E-mail: dstewart@uscupstate.edu
Web Site: www.uscupstate.edu/

Description: State-supported, comprehensive, coed. Part of University of South Carolina System. Awards bachelor's and master's degrees. Founded 1967. Setting: 300-acre urban campus with easy access to Charlotte. Endowment: $3.6 million. Research spending for the previous fiscal year: $187,230. Educational spending for the previous fiscal year: $4743 per student. Total enrollment: 5,561. Faculty: 406 (211 full-time, 195 part-time). Student-undergrad faculty ratio is 17:1. 3,012 applied, 65% were admitted. 12% from top 10% of their high school class, 37% from top quarter, 78% from top half. 2 valedictorians. Full-time: 4,225 students, 67% women, 33% men. Part-time: 1,202 students, 58% women, 42% men. Students come from 29 states and territories, 26 other countries, 4% from out-of-state. 0.3% American Indian or Alaska Native, non-Hispanic/Latino; 4% Hispanic/Latino; 27% African American, non-Hispanic/Latino; 2% Asian, non-Hispanic/Latino; 0.1% Native Hawaiian or other Pacific Islander, non-Hispanic/Latino; 2% international. 22% 25 or older, 18% live on campus. Retention: 67% of full-time freshmen returned the following year. Academic areas with the most degrees conferred: health professions and related sciences; education; business/marketing. Core. Calendar: semesters. Academic remediation for entering students, ESL program, services for LD students, advanced placement, accelerated degree program, self-designed majors, honors program, independent study, distance learning, double major, summer session for credit, part-time degree program, adult/continuing education programs, co-op programs and internships. Off campus study at Wofford College, Greenville Higher Education Consortium. Study abroad program. ROTC: Army (c).

Entrance Requirements: Options: electronic application, deferred admission, international baccalaureate accepted. Required: high school transcript, minimum 2 high school GPA, college preparatory courses, SAT or ACT. Entrance: moderately difficult. Notification: continuous. Transfer credits accepted: Yes.

Costs Per Year: Application fee: $40. State resident tuition: $9442 full-time, $403 per semester hour part-time. Nonresident tuition: $19,164 full-time, $815 per semester hour part-time. Mandatory fees: $450 full-time, $165 per term part-time. Full-time tuition and fees vary according to course load and program. Part-time tuition and fees vary according to course load and program. College room and board: $7250. College room only: $4450. Room and board charges vary according to board plan and housing facility.

Collegiate Environment: Orientation program. Drama-theater group, choral group, student-run newspaper. Social organizations: 75 open to all; national fraternities, national sororities; 1% of eligible men and 2% of eligible women are members. Most popular organizations: African-American Association, Campus Activity Board, Student Nurses Association, Student Government Association, Impact. Major annual events: Premier Fall Kick-Off, Technology Fair, Angel Tree Program. Student services: health clinic, personal-psychological counseling, women's center. Campus security: 24-hour emergency response devices and patrols, late night transport-escort service, campus security cameras. 1,004 college housing spaces available; 931 were occupied in 2012-13. Freshmen given priority for college housing. Option: coed housing available. University of South Carolina Upstate Library with 402,358 books, 48,584 microform titles, 63,583 serials, 7,413 audiovisual materials, an OPAC, and a Web page. Operations spending for the previous fiscal year: $2 million. 430 computers available on campus for general student use. A campuswide network can be accessed from student residence rooms. Students can access the following: online class registration. Staffed computer lab on campus.

Community Environment: Spartanburg, South Carolina, is one of the fastest-growing communities in the region, located on the thriving Interstate 85 corridor about three hours from Atlanta and an hour and a half from Charlotte, North Carolina. The Blue Ridge Mountains are less than an hour away; South Carolina's Grand Strand and historic Low Country are a four-hour drive in the other direction. The area has a growing international presence, and arts and cultural activities that would be the envy of many larger cities.

■ VIRGINIA COLLEGE IN SPARTANBURG

8150 Warren H. Abernathy Hwy.
Spartanburg, SC 29301
Tel: (864)504-3200
Web Site: www.vc.edu/
Description: Proprietary, 2-year, coed. Founded 2011.

■ VOORHEES COLLEGE

213 Wiggins Dr.
Denmark, SC 29042
Tel: (803)780-1234; Free: 866-685-9904
Fax: (803)793-5773
E-mail: williej@voorhees.edu
Web Site: www.voorhees.edu/
Description: Independent Episcopal, 4-year, coed. Awards bachelor's degrees. Founded 1897. Setting: 350-acre rural campus. Endowment: $5 million. Educational spending for the previous fiscal year: $10,522 per student. Total enrollment: 701. Faculty: 56 (38 full-time, 18 part-time). Student-undergrad faculty ratio is 16:1. 2,569 applied, 70% were admitted. Full-time: 671 students, 56% women, 44% men. Part-time: 30 students, 50% women, 50% men. Students come from 15 states and territories, 5 other countries, 28% from out-of-state. 19% 25 or older, 74% live on campus, 5% transferred in. Retention: 64% of full-time freshmen returned the following year. Core. Calendar: semesters. Academic remediation for entering students, advanced placement, honors program, double major, summer session for credit, part-time degree program, adult/continuing education programs, co-op programs and internships. ROTC: Army (c).
Entrance Requirements: Options: electronic application, deferred admission. Required: high school transcript, minimum 2 high school GPA, secondary school GPA. Recommended: SAT or ACT. Required for some: interview. Entrance: moderately difficult. Application deadline: Rolling.
Costs Per Year: Application fee: $25. Comprehensive fee: $18,126 includes full-time tuition ($10,180), mandatory fees ($600), and college room and board ($7346). College room only: $3676. Room and board charges vary according to housing facility. Part-time tuition: $335 per credit hour.
Collegiate Environment: Orientation program. Drama-theater group, choral group, student-run newspaper, radio station. Social organizations: 30 open to all; national fraternities, national sororities; 15% of eligible men and 10% of eligible women are members. Major annual events: Founders' Day, Homecoming, Fall Convocation. Student services: health clinic, personal-psychological counseling. Campus security: 24-hour emergency response devices and patrols, student patrols, late night transport-escort service. Wright-Potts Library with 107,260 books, 24,266 microform titles, 408 serials, 1,172 audiovisual materials, an OPAC, and a Web page. Operations spending for the previous fiscal year: $213,167. 300 computers available on campus for general student use. A campuswide network can be accessed from student residence rooms and from off campus. Students can access the following: online class registration. Staffed computer lab on campus provides training in use of computers, software, and the Internet.
Community Environment: Denmark is a rural community located in south central South Carolina. The climate is temperate. There is a public library, local hospitals and several churches representing various denominations. The Lions Club, Masonic Lodge, and Woodmen of the World are active within the community. Recreation includes golf, swimming, boating, fishing and a local theatre.

■ WILLIAMSBURG TECHNICAL COLLEGE

601 Martin Luther King, Jr Ave.
Kingstree, SC 29556-4197
Tel: (843)355-4110; Free: 800-768-2021
Fax: (843)355-4296
E-mail: wrighta@wiltech.edu
Web Site: www.wiltech.edu/
Description: State-supported, 2-year, coed. Part of South Carolina State Board for Technical and Comprehensive Education. Awards certificates, diplomas, transfer associate, and terminal associate degrees. Founded 1969. Setting: 41-acre rural campus. Total enrollment: 640. Student-undergrad faculty ratio is 11:1. 0% from out-of-state. 44% 25 or older. Retention: 62% of full-time freshmen returned the following year. Calendar:

semesters. Academic remediation for entering students, distance learning, summer session for credit, part-time degree program, adult/continuing education programs.
Entrance Requirements: Open admission. Options: early admission, deferred admission. Required: high school transcript. Entrance: noncompetitive. Application deadline: Rolling. Notification: continuous.
Collegiate Environment: Campus security: late night transport-escort service.

■ WINTHROP UNIVERSITY

701 Oakland Ave.
Rock Hill, SC 29733
Tel: (803)323-2211; Free: 800-763-0230
Fax: (803)323-2137
E-mail: admissions@winthrop.edu
Web Site: www.winthrop.edu/
Description: State-supported, comprehensive, coed. Part of South Carolina Commission on Higher Education. Awards bachelor's and master's degrees and post-master's certificates. Founded 1886. Setting: 448-acre suburban campus with easy access to Charlotte. Endowment: $32.5 million. Research spending for the previous fiscal year: $6.3 million. Educational spending for the previous fiscal year: $6804 per student. Total enrollment: 6,170. Faculty: 525 (286 full-time, 239 part-time). Student-undergrad faculty ratio is 15:1. 4,316 applied, 71% were admitted. 19% from top 10% of their high school class, 83% from top half. Full-time: 4,462 students, 68% women, 32% men. Part-time: 567 students, 65% women, 35% men. Students come from 34 states and territories, 37 other countries, 8% from out-of-state. 0.5% American Indian or Alaska Native, non-Hispanic/Latino; 2% Hispanic/Latino; 30% African American, non-Hispanic/Latino; 1% Asian, non-Hispanic/Latino; 0.5% Native Hawaiian or other Pacific Islander, non-Hispanic/Latino; 3% international. 9% 25 or older, 47% live on campus, 8% transferred in. Retention: 73% of full-time freshmen returned the following year. Academic areas with the most degrees conferred: business/marketing; education; visual and performing arts. Core. Calendar: semesters. Services for LD students, advanced placement, honors program, independent study, distance learning, double major, summer session for credit, part-time degree program, adult/continuing education programs, co-op programs and internships, graduate courses open to undergrads. Off campus study at National Student Exchange, 19 members of the Charlotte Area Educational Consortium. Study abroad program. ROTC: Army (c), Air Force (c).
Entrance Requirements: Options: electronic application, deferred admission, international baccalaureate accepted. Required: high school transcript, minimum 3 high school GPA, SAT or ACT. Required for some: essay. Entrance: moderately difficult. Application deadlines: 5/1, 5/1 for nonresidents. Notification: continuous. SAT Reasoning Test deadline: 5/1. Transfer credits accepted: Yes.
Costs Per Year: Application fee: $40. State resident tuition: $13,026 full-time, $543 per credit hour part-time. Nonresident tuition: $24,476 full-time, $1020 per credit hour part-time. Full-time tuition varies according to degree level and reciprocity agreements. Part-time tuition varies according to degree level. College room and board: $7464. College room only: $4674. Room and board charges vary according to board plan and housing facility.
Collegiate Environment: Orientation program. Drama-theater group, choral group, student-run newspaper, radio station. Social organizations: 158 open to all; national fraternities, national sororities; 1% of eligible men and 1% of eligible women are members. Most popular organizations: Association of Ebonites, WU Crew, Greek Life, DiGiorgio Student Union, Campus Ministries. Major annual events: Homecoming, Greek Week, Convocation. Student services: health clinic, personal-psychological counseling. Campus security: 24-hour emergency response devices and patrols, late night transport-escort service, controlled dormitory access. 2,578 college housing spaces available; 2,378 were occupied in 2012-13. Freshmen guaranteed college housing. On-campus residence required in freshman year. Options: coed, men-only, women-only housing available. Dacus Library plus 1 other with 499,697 books, 1.3 million microform titles, 1,492 serials, 24,100 audiovisual materials, an OPAC, and a Web page. Operations spending for the previous fiscal year: $2.9 million. 620 computers available on campus for general student use. Computer purchase/lease plans available. A campuswide network can be accessed from student residence rooms and from off campus. Students can access the following: online class registration, vast majority of university services are available online. Staffed computer lab on campus (open 24 hours a day) provides training in use of computers, software, and the Internet.
Community Environment: Rock Hill is a small progressive city of nearly

50,000 residents located 30 miles below Charlotte, North Carolina. The city is uniquely situated to offer the advantages of both small town living and big city amenities. Diversified industry fuels a growing local economy which produces textiles, wood, paper, concrete, plastic and chemical products. Rock Hill's facilities include the Museum of York County (featuring the world's largest collection of hooved African animals); Winthrop Galleries, host to local, national and international artists; Winthrop Coliseum, Glencairn Gardens, a six acre garden spot; and Cherry Park, a 68 acre recreation park featuring five major league baseball and softball diamonds, which attracts major tournaments from throughout the United States. Opportunities for recreation in the mild piedmont climate are plentiful. The city maintains a system of 28 parks that offer athletic fields and courts, play areas, fitness, walking and jogging trails, and amphitheaters. Lakes 20 minutes away are a convenient destination for water sports and sailing.

■ **WOFFORD COLLEGE**
429 N Church St.
Spartanburg, SC 29303-3663
Tel: (864)597-4000
Fax: (864)597-4149
E-mail: admission@wofford.edu
Web Site: www.wofford.edu/
Description: Independent, 4-year, coed, affiliated with United Methodist Church. Awards bachelor's degrees. Founded 1854. Setting: 170-acre urban campus with easy access to Charlotte. Endowment: $154.2 million. Educational spending for the previous fiscal year: $10,945 per student. Total enrollment: 1,588. Faculty: 153 (128 full-time, 25 part-time). Student-undergrad faculty ratio is 11:1. 3,197 applied, 63% were admitted. 54% from top 10% of their high school class, 79% from top quarter, 97% from top half. 3 National Merit Scholars, 11 class presidents, 16 valedictorians, 32 student government officers. Full-time: 1,543 students, 49% women, 51% men. Part-time: 45 students, 42% women, 58% men. Students come from 27 states and territories, 3 other countries, 52% from out-of-state. 0.2% American Indian or Alaska Native, non-Hispanic/Latino; 3% Hispanic/Latino; 8% African American, non-Hispanic/Latino; 3% Asian, non-Hispanic/Latino; 0.1% Native Hawaiian or other Pacific Islander, non-Hispanic/Latino; 2% international. 0% 25 or older, 93% live on campus, 2% transferred in. Retention: 90% of full-time freshmen returned the following year. Academic areas with the most degrees conferred: business/marketing; biological/life sciences; foreign languages and literature. Core. Calendar: 4-1-4. Advanced placement, accelerated degree program, self-designed majors, independent study, double major, summer session for credit, part-time degree program, internships. Off campus study at Converse College, University of South Carolina-Upstate. Study abroad program. ROTC: Army.
Entrance Requirements: Options: electronic application, early admission, early decision, deferred admission, international baccalaureate accepted. Required: essay, high school transcript, SAT or ACT. Recommended: 2 recommendations, interview. Entrance: very difficult. Application deadlines: 2/1, 11/1 for early decision. Notification: 3/15, 12/5 for early decision. SAT Reasoning Test deadline: 2/1. Transfer credits accepted: Yes. Applicants placed on waiting list: 78. Wait-listed applicants offered admission: 4. Early decision applicants: 715. Early decision applicants admitted: 515.
Costs Per Year: Application fee: $35. Comprehensive fee: $45,795 includes full-time tuition ($35,515) and college room and board ($10,280).
Collegiate Environment: Orientation program. Drama-theater group, choral group, student-run newspaper. Social organizations: 98 open to all; national fraternities, national sororities; 43% of eligible men and 55% of eligible women are members. Most popular organizations: Ultimate Frisbee Club, W.A.C. (Wofford Activities Council), Psychology Kingdom, Beta Beta Beta (Biology), Twin Towers (Service). Major annual events: Homecoming, Family

Weekend, Phi Beta Kappa Day. Student services: health clinic, personal-psychological counseling. Campus security: 24-hour emergency response devices and patrols, late night transport-escort service, controlled dormitory access. 1,475 college housing spaces available; 1,425 were occupied in 2012-13. Freshmen given priority for college housing. On-campus residence required through senior year. Option: coed housing available. Sandor Teszler Library with 188,153 books, 42,432 microform titles, 47,796 serials, 5,514 audiovisual materials, an OPAC, and a Web page. 200 computers available on campus for general student use. A campuswide network can be accessed from student residence rooms and from off campus. Students can access the following: online class registration. Staffed computer lab on campus provides training in use of computers, software, and the Internet.
Community Environment: Spartanburg County (population 271,000) is a thriving, rapidly growing Sunbelt business center that is particularly well known for its international community. Wofford students live in a downtown setting near restaurants, churches of all denominations, shopping districts, a busy arts center, and four other college campuses. Memorial Auditorium, Wofford's next-door neighbor, features concerts, touring Broadway plays, and other special attractions. Several major airlines serve the convenient Greenville-Spartanburg Airport, which is only twenty miles from the campus. Interstate highways 26 and 85 intersect at Spartanburg. Charlotte, Atlanta, historic Charleston, and South Carolina's world-famous coastal resorts are all within a pleasant afternoon drive.

■ **YORK TECHNICAL COLLEGE**
452 S Anderson Rd.
Rock Hill, SC 29730-3395
Tel: (803)327-8000
Fax: (803)327-8059
E-mail: kaldridge@yorktech.com
Web Site: www.yorktech.com/
Description: State-supported, 2-year, coed. Part of South Carolina State Board for Technical and Comprehensive Education. Awards certificates, diplomas, transfer associate, and terminal associate degrees. Founded 1961. Setting: 110-acre small town campus with easy access to Charlotte. Total enrollment: 4,731. Faculty: 267 (128 full-time, 139 part-time). Student-undergrad faculty ratio is 16:1. Full-time: 2,279 students, 60% women, 40% men. Part-time: 2,452 students, 65% women, 35% men. 2% from out-of-state. 39% 25 or older. Core. Calendar: semesters. Academic remediation for entering students, ESL program, services for LD students, advanced placement, honors program, distance learning, summer session for credit, part-time degree program, adult/continuing education programs, co-op programs and internships. Off campus study at Charlotte Area Educational Consortium.
Entrance Requirements: Open admission except for health and human services program. Option: electronic application. Required for some: high school transcript, SAT, ACT, or ACT ASSET, ACT COMPASS. Entrance: noncompetitive. Application deadline: Rolling. Notification: continuous.
Collegiate Environment: Orientation program. Social organizations: 16 open to all. Most popular organizations: Jacobin Society, Phi Theta Kappa, Student Government Association, Phi Beta Lambda, Student Activities Board. Major annual events: Welcome Back Blast, Health Fair. Campus security: 24-hour patrols, late night transport-escort service. Anne Springs Close Library with 26,947 books, 50,574 microform titles, 475 serials, an OPAC, and a Web page. 250 computers available on campus for general student use. A campuswide network can be accessed from off-campus. Students can access the following: online class registration, grades, course search, account detail, placement test scores. Staffed computer lab on campus provides training in use of computers.
Community Environment: See Winthrop University.

■ AUGUSTANA COLLEGE
2001 S Summit Ave.
Sioux Falls, SD 57197
Tel: (605)274-0770; Free: 800-727-2844
Fax: (605)274-5518
E-mail: admission@augie.edu
Web Site: www.augie.edu/
Description: Independent, comprehensive, coed, affiliated with Evangelical Lutheran Church in America. Awards bachelor's and master's degrees. Founded 1860. Setting: 100-acre urban campus. Endowment: $55.7 million. Research spending for the previous fiscal year: $1.5 million. Educational spending for the previous fiscal year: $10,241 per student. Total enrollment: 1,839. Faculty: 206 (134 full-time, 72 part-time). Student-undergrad faculty ratio is 11:1. 1,415 applied, 76% were admitted. 35% from top 10% of their high school class, 67% from top quarter, 91% from top half. 29 valedictorians. Full-time: 1,694 students, 60% women, 40% men. Part-time: 77 students, 49% women, 51% men. Students come from 31 states and territories, 43 other countries, 54% from out-of-state. 0.2% American Indian or Alaska Native, non-Hispanic/Latino; 1% Hispanic/Latino; 1% African American, non-Hispanic/Latino; 1% Asian, non-Hispanic/Latino; 0% Native Hawaiian or other Pacific Islander, non-Hispanic/Latino; 7% international. 3% 25 or older, 78% live on campus, 4% transferred in. Retention: 83% of full-time freshmen returned the following year. Academic areas with the most degrees conferred: education; health professions and related sciences; biological/life sciences. Core. Calendar: 4-1-4. Academic remediation for entering students, services for LD students, advanced placement, self-designed majors, honors program, independent study, distance learning, double major, summer session for credit, part-time degree program, co-op programs and internships. Off campus study at Higher Education Consortium for Urban Affairs (HECUA), Lutheran College, Washington D.C., American University, Washington D.C., Midwest Lutheran Colleges January/Interim term exchange. Study abroad program. ROTC: Army (c), Air Force (c).
Entrance Requirements: Options: electronic application, deferred admission, international baccalaureate accepted. Required: essay, high school transcript, minimum 2.7 high school GPA, 1 recommendation, SAT or ACT, minimum ACT score of 20. Recommended: interview. Entrance: moderately difficult. Application deadlines: Rolling, Rolling for nonresidents. Notification: continuous until 10/1, continuous until 10/1 for nonresidents. SAT Reasoning Test deadline: 8/1. Transfer credits accepted: Yes.
Costs Per Year: Application fee: $0. Comprehensive fee: $34,406 includes full-time tuition ($27,380), mandatory fees ($400), and college room and board ($6626). College room only: $3214. Full-time tuition and fees vary according to course load and degree level. Room and board charges vary according to board plan and housing facility. Part-time tuition: $420 per credit hour. Part-time tuition varies according to course load and degree level.
Collegiate Environment: Orientation program. Drama-theater group, choral group, student-run newspaper. Social organizations: 87 open to all; Academic Honor Greek Society. Most popular organizations: Augieholics (student athletics support organization), intramurals, Union Board of Governors (student union), Augie Green, Campus Ministries. Major annual events: Community Service Day, An Augustan Christmas (Vespers), Viking Days (Homecoming). Student services: health clinic, personal-psychological counseling. Campus security: 24-hour emergency response devices and patrols, late night transport-escort service, controlled dormitory access, Special 'day lighting' night lights throughout the campus grounds. 1,486 college housing spaces available; 1,223 were occupied in 2012-13. Freshmen

guaranteed college housing. On-campus residence required through junior year. Option: coed housing available. Mikkelsen Library with 276,842 books, 8,269 microform titles, 20,385 serials, 6,604 audiovisual materials, an OPAC, and a Web page. Operations spending for the previous fiscal year: $1.1 million. 286 computers available on campus for general student use. Computer purchase/lease plans available. A campuswide network can be accessed from student residence rooms and from off campus. Students can access the following: online class registration. Staffed computer lab on campus (open 24 hours a day) provides training in use of computers, software, and the Internet.
Community Environment: See University of Sioux Falls.

■ BLACK HILLS STATE UNIVERSITY
1200 University St.
Spearfish, SD 57799
Tel: (605)642-6011; Free: 800-255-2478
E-mail: admissions@bhsu.edu
Web Site: www.bhsu.edu/
Description: State-supported, comprehensive, coed. Part of South Dakota State University System. Awards associate, bachelor's, and master's degrees and post-master's certificates. Founded 1883. Setting: 123-acre small town campus. Total enrollment: 4,412. 1,476 applied, 94% were admitted. 10% from top 10% of their high school class, 28% from top quarter, 63% from top half. Full-time: 2,623 students, 59% women, 41% men. Part-time: 1,386 students, 68% women, 32% men. 22% from out-of-state. 27% 25 or older, 2% transferred in. Retention: 61% of full-time freshmen returned the following year. Core. Calendar: semesters. Academic remediation for entering students, services for LD students, advanced placement, accelerated degree program, honors program, independent study, distance learning, double major, summer session for credit, part-time degree program, co-op programs and internships, graduate courses open to undergrads. Off campus study at South Dakota State University. ROTC: Army.
Entrance Requirements: Option: electronic application. Required: high school transcript, minimum 2.0 high school GPA in core curriculum, SAT or ACT. Entrance: minimally difficult. Application deadline: 7/18.
Costs Per Year: Application fee: $20. State resident tuition: $7320 full-time. Nonresident tuition: $9184 full-time. College room and board: $5641. College room only: $2834.
Collegiate Environment: Orientation program. Drama-theater group, choral group, student-run newspaper, radio station. Social organizations: national fraternities, national sororities. Most popular organizations: Student Activities Committee, student government. Major annual events: Swarm Days, Big 100 Week. Student services: health clinic, personal-psychological counseling. Campus security: 24-hour patrols, late night transport-escort service, controlled dormitory access. 220 computers available on campus for general student use. A campuswide network can be accessed from student residence rooms and from off campus. Students can access the following: online class registration. Staffed computer lab on campus provides training in use of computers, software, and the Internet.
Community Environment: Spearfish, population 9,355, is in a beautiful agricultural valley at the mouth of Spearfish Canyon. There are libraries, museums, churches, hospitals, and a number of civic and service organizations in the community and surrounding area. Recreational activities include hunting, fishing, hiking, skiing, golf, and boating. The Black Hills Passion Play is presented during the summer months in a specially constructed amphitheater. Part-time employment is available.

■ COLORADO TECHNICAL UNIVERSITY SIOUX FALLS

3901 W 59th St.
Sioux Falls, SD 57108
Tel: (605)361-0200
Fax: (605)361-5954
Web Site: www.coloradotech.edu/Sioux-Falls

Description: Proprietary, comprehensive, coed. Administratively affiliated with Colorado Technical University. Awards associate, bachelor's, and master's degrees. Founded 1965. Setting: 3-acre urban campus. Total enrollment: 912. Faculty: 82. Full-time: 490 students, 63% women, 37% men. Part-time: 326 students, 65% women, 35% men. 2% from out-of-state. 17% 25 or older, 17% transferred in. Academic areas with the most degrees conferred: business/marketing; homeland security, law enforcement, firefighting, and protective services; computer and information sciences. Core. Advanced placement, accelerated degree program, distance learning, double major, summer session for credit, part-time degree program, adult/continuing education programs, co-op programs and internships, graduate courses open to undergrads. ROTC: Army (c).

Entrance Requirements: Options: electronic application, deferred admission, international baccalaureate accepted. Required: interview. Entrance: minimally difficult. Application deadlines: Rolling, Rolling for nonresidents. Notification: continuous, continuous for nonresidents.

Collegiate Environment: Orientation program. 25 computers available on campus for general student use. A campuswide network can be accessed. Staffed computer lab on campus.

■ DAKOTA STATE UNIVERSITY

820 N Washington
Madison, SD 57042-1799
Tel: (605)256-5111; Free: 888-DSU-9988
Fax: (605)256-5316
E-mail: yourfuture@dsu.edu
Web Site: www.dsu.edu/

Description: State-supported, comprehensive, coed. Part of South Dakota Board of Regents. Awards associate, bachelor's, master's, and doctoral degrees. Founded 1881. Setting: 56-acre rural campus with easy access to Sioux Falls. Endowment: $7.7 million. Research spending for the previous fiscal year: $1.3 million. Educational spending for the previous fiscal year: $3419 per student. Total enrollment: 3,110. Faculty: 119 (92 full-time, 27 part-time). Student-undergrad faculty ratio is 18:1. 742 applied, 89% were admitted. 5% from top 10% of their high school class, 20% from top quarter, 52% from top half. Full-time: 1,190 students, 38% women, 62% men. Part-time: 1,682 students, 60% women, 40% men. Students come from 41 states and territories, 13 other countries, 26% from out-of-state. 1% American Indian or Alaska Native, non-Hispanic/Latino; 3% Hispanic/Latino; 2% African American, non-Hispanic/Latino; 1% Asian, non-Hispanic/Latino; 0.2% Native Hawaiian or other Pacific Islander, non-Hispanic/Latino; 3% international. 25% 25 or older, 33% live on campus, 10% transferred in. Retention: 60% of full-time freshmen returned the following year. Academic areas with the most degrees conferred: computer and information sciences; business/marketing; education. Core. Calendar: semesters. Academic remediation for entering students, ESL program, services for LD students, advanced placement, honors program, independent study, distance learning, double major, summer session for credit, part-time degree program, adult/continuing education programs, co-op programs and internships, graduate courses open to undergrads. Off campus study at South Dakota State University, University of South Dakota, Northern State University, Black Hills State University, South Dakota School of Mines and Technology, Southeast Technical Institute, Lake Area Technical Institute, Mitchell Tech, Western Dakota Tech, and Northwest Iowa Community College. Study abroad program. ROTC: Air Force (c).

Entrance Requirements: Options: electronic application, deferred admission, international baccalaureate accepted. Required: high school transcript, minimum 2.6 high school GPA, rank in top 60% of high school class, 18 or higher ACT or 870 SAT (Combined Math and Critical Reading), SAT or ACT. Entrance: minimally difficult. Application deadlines: Rolling, Rolling for nonresidents. Notification: continuous, continuous for nonresidents. SAT Reasoning Test deadline: 9/1. Transfer credits accepted: Yes.

Costs Per Year: Application fee: $20. State resident tuition: $3726 full-time, $124 per credit hour part-time. Nonresident tuition: $5591 full-time, $186 per credit hour part-time. Mandatory fees: $4224 full-time. Full-time tuition and fees vary according to location and reciprocity agreements. Part-time tuition varies according to location and reciprocity agreements. College room and board: $5235. College room only: $2770. Room and board charges vary according to board plan and housing facility.

Collegiate Environment: Orientation program. Drama-theater group, choral group, student-run newspaper, radio station. Social organizations: 36 open to all. Most popular organizations: Gaming Club, Students in Free Enterprise (SIFE), Phi Beta Lambda Business Club, Student Senate, Student Activities Board. Major annual events: Homecoming, Convocation, Frost Bites Week. Student services: health clinic, personal-psychological counseling. Campus security: late night transport-escort service, controlled dormitory access, night watchman. 659 college housing spaces available; 532 were occupied in 2012-13. Freshmen guaranteed college housing. On-campus residence required through sophomore year. Options: coed, men-only housing available. Karl E. Mundt Library & Learning Commons plus 1 other with 167,349 books, 3,381 microform titles, 26,233 serials, 885 audiovisual materials, an OPAC, and a Web page. Operations spending for the previous fiscal year: $653,406. 165 computers available on campus for general student use. Computer purchase/lease plans available. A computer is required for all students. A campuswide network can be accessed from student residence rooms and from off campus. Students can access the following: online class registration, wireless computing initiative requires full-time students to have a tablet computer. Staffed computer lab on campus (open 24 hours a day).

Community Environment: Dakota State University is located in the heart of the Midwest, in Madison, South Dakota, just minutes from Interstates 29 and 90, which are major highways. Two nearby lakes provide the best in outdoor recreation. In the summer, this includes water sports, fishing and camping, followed in the fall and winter by hunting, snowmobiling, cross-country skiing and more. One of South Dakota's finest state parks provides excellent facilities for all of these activities. Cultural events are provided by a local arts association, a summer theater group and through college-sponsored events. Madison is also located just an hour away from the state's largest city, Sioux Falls.

■ DAKOTA WESLEYAN UNIVERSITY

1200 W University Ave.
Mitchell, SD 57301-4398
Tel: (605)995-2600; Free: 800-333-8506
Fax: (605)995-2699
E-mail: admissions@dwu.edu
Web Site: www.dwu.edu/

Description: Independent United Methodist, comprehensive, coed. Awards associate, bachelor's, and master's degrees. Founded 1885. Setting: 50-acre small town campus. Endowment: $20.9 million. Research spending for the previous fiscal year: $138,654. Educational spending for the previous fiscal year: $5526 per student. Total enrollment: 836. Faculty: 70 (50 full-time, 20 part-time). Student-undergrad faculty ratio is 11:1. 659 applied, 73% were admitted. 9% from top 10% of their high school class, 36% from top quarter, 75% from top half. Full-time: 688 students, 53% women, 47% men. Part-time: 70 students, 64% women, 36% men. Students come from 29 states and territories, 2 other countries, 26% from out-of-state. 1% American Indian or Alaska Native, non-Hispanic/Latino; 2% Hispanic/Latino; 3% African American, non-Hispanic/Latino; 1% Asian, non-Hispanic/Latino; 0% Native Hawaiian or other Pacific Islander, non-Hispanic/Latino; 1% international. 14% 25 or older, 45% live on campus, 12% transferred in. Retention: 67% of full-time freshmen returned the following year. Academic areas with the most degrees conferred: health professions and related sciences; business/marketing; education. Core. Calendar: semesters. Academic remediation for entering students, services for LD students, advanced placement, self-designed majors, honors program, independent study, distance learning, double major, summer session for credit, part-time degree program, co-op programs and internships. Off campus study. Study abroad program. ROTC: Army.

Entrance Requirements: Option: electronic application. Required: high school transcript, SAT or ACT. Recommended: minimum 2 high school GPA. Entrance: moderately difficult. Application deadline: 8/27. Notification: continuous.

Costs Per Year: Application fee: $25. Comprehensive fee: $28,550 includes full-time tuition ($21,750) and college room and board ($6800). College room only: $2900. Room and board charges vary according to board plan and housing facility.

Collegiate Environment: Orientation program. Drama-theater group, choral group, student-run newspaper. Social organizations: 27 open to all. Most popular organizations: Future Teachers Organization, Student Nurses Association, Multi-Culture Club, Human Services Club, Student Ministry Council. Major annual events: Blue and White Days (Homecoming), Spring Week, Family Life Conference. Student services: health clinic, personal-psychological counseling. Campus security: 24-hour emergency response devices, student patrols, late night transport-escort service, controlled dormitory access, campus patrol from 2am to 6am by special request only. 429 college housing spaces available; 402 were occupied in 2012-13. Freshmen guaranteed college housing. On-campus residence required through sophomore year. Options: coed, men-only, women-only housing available. George and Eleanor McGovern Library plus 1 other with 132,114 books, 64,397 microform titles, 1,058 serials, 11,021 audiovisual materials, an OPAC, and a Web page. Operations spending for the previous fiscal year: $305,460. 100 computers available on campus for general student use. A campuswide network can be accessed from student residence rooms and from off campus. Students can access the following: online class registration, portal, course management system. Staffed computer lab on campus provides training in use of computers, software, and the Internet.

Community Environment: Located in the James River Valley, Mitchell (population 15,000) is one of the most fertile and diversified agricultural areas in the United States. Products are corn, sorghum, small grain, cattle and hogs. Mitchell is the trading center for the surrounding counties. Community facilities include shopping areas, churches, a library, YMCA, 2 hospitals and a number of the customary civic and service organizations. Recreational activities include boating, fishing, swimming and pheasant hunting.

■ GLOBE UNIVERSITY–SIOUX FALLS

5101 S Broadband Ln.
Sioux Falls, SD 57108-2208
Tel: (605)977-0705; Free: 866-437-0705
Fax: (605)977-0784
Web Site: www.globeuniversity.edu/

Description: Proprietary, 4-year, coed. Part of Globe Education Network (GEN) which is composed of Globe University, Minnesota School of Business, Broadview University, The Institute of Production and Recording and Minnesota School of Cosmetology. Awards associate and bachelor's degrees. Setting: 3-acre small town campus. Total enrollment: 368. Faculty: 36 (12 full-time, 24 part-time). Student-undergrad faculty ratio is 14:1. Full-time: 156 students, 78% women, 22% men. Part-time: 212 students, 86% women, 14% men. Students come from 6 states and territories, 3% from out-of-state. 1% American Indian or Alaska Native, non-Hispanic/Latino; 2% Hispanic/Latino; 2% African American, non-Hispanic/Latino; 1% Asian, non-Hispanic/Latino; 1% Native Hawaiian or other Pacific Islander, non-Hispanic/Latino; 0% international. 37% 25 or older, 18% transferred in. Retention: 56% of full-time freshmen returned the following year. Academic areas with the most degrees conferred: health professions and related sciences; law/legal studies. Core. Academic remediation for entering students, services for LD students, advanced placement, accelerated degree program, summer session for credit, part-time degree program, adult/continuing education programs, internships.

Entrance Requirements: Option: electronic application. Required: high school transcript, interview, ACCUPLACER is required of all applicants unless documentation of a minimum ACT composite score of 21 or documentation of a minimum composite score of 1485 on the SAT is presented. Required for some: essay, 2 recommendations, GED certificate in lieu of high school transcript. Application deadlines: Rolling, Rolling for nonresidents. Notification: continuous, continuous for nonresidents. Transfer credits accepted: Yes.

Costs Per Year: Application fee: $50. Tuition: $15,300 full-time, $460 per credit part-time. Mandatory fees: $1548 full-time, $43 per credit part-time. Full-time tuition and fees vary according to course level, course load, degree level, location, and program. Part-time tuition and fees vary according to course level, course load, degree level, location, and program.

Collegiate Environment: Orientation program. Social organizations: Program specific student led organizations. Major annual events: Service Learning Projects, Applied Learning Projects, Student Appreciation Events. Campus security: 24-hour emergency response devices, late night transport-escort service. Sioux Falls Campus Library with 1,960 books, 53,138 serials, 71 audiovisual materials, an OPAC, and a Web page. 47 computers available on campus for general student use. A campuswide network can be accessed. Students can access the following: online class registration. Staffed computer lab on campus provides training in use of computers, software, and the Internet.

■ KILIAN COMMUNITY COLLEGE

300 E 6th St.
Sioux Falls, SD 57104-6014
Tel: (605)221-3100; Free: 800-888-1147

Fax: (605)336-2606
E-mail: info@killian.edu
Web Site: www.kilian.edu/

Description: Independent, 2-year, coed. Awards certificates, transfer associate, and terminal associate degrees. Founded 1977. Setting: 2-acre urban campus. Total enrollment: 294. Faculty: 34 (5 full-time, 29 part-time). Student-undergrad faculty ratio is 8:1. 159 applied, 62% were admitted. Full-time: 37 students, 65% women, 35% men. Part-time: 257 students, 67% women, 33% men. Students come from 3 states and territories, 2% from out-of-state. 9% American Indian or Alaska Native, non-Hispanic/Latino; 3% Hispanic/Latino; 12% African American, non-Hispanic/Latino; 1% Asian, non-Hispanic/Latino; 0% Native Hawaiian or other Pacific Islander, non-Hispanic/Latino; 0% international. 57% 25 or older, 10% transferred in. Retention: 0% of full-time freshmen returned the following year. Core. Calendar: trimesters. Academic remediation for entering students, ESL program, services for LD students, advanced placement, independent study, distance learning, double major, summer session for credit, part-time degree program. Off campus study at Presentation College, Aberdeen, SD.

Entrance Requirements: Open admission. Options: electronic application, deferred admission. Required: high school transcript. Entrance: noncompetitive. Application deadlines: Rolling, Rolling for nonresidents. Transfer credits accepted: Yes.

Costs Per Year: Application fee: $25. Tuition: $9900 full-time, $275 per credit hour part-time. Mandatory fees: $330 full-time, $110 per term part-time.

Collegiate Environment: Orientation program. Social organizations: 2 open to all. Most popular organizations: Phi Theta Kappa, Students in Free Enterprise (SIFE), Student Leadership. Student services: personal-psychological counseling. Campus security: late night transport-escort service. College housing not available. Sioux Falls Public Library with 78,000 books, 395 serials, an OPAC, and a Web page. 48 computers available on campus for general student use. A campuswide network can be accessed. Staffed computer lab on campus provides training in use of computers, software, and the Internet.

■ LAKE AREA TECHNICAL INSTITUTE

1201 Arrow Ave.
Watertown, SD 57201
Tel: (605)882-5284; Free: 800-657-4344
E-mail: latiinfo@lati.tec.sd.us
Web Site: www.lakeareatech.edu/

Description: State-supported, 2-year, coed. Awards diplomas and terminal associate degrees. Founded 1964. Setting: 40-acre small town campus. Total enrollment: 1,600. Faculty: 97 (95 full-time, 2 part-time). Student-undergrad faculty ratio is 16:1. 1,689 applied, 60% were admitted. 2% American Indian or Alaska Native, non-Hispanic/Latino; 1% Hispanic/Latino; 1% African American, non-Hispanic/Latino; 0% Asian, non-Hispanic/Latino; 0% Native Hawaiian or other Pacific Islander, non-Hispanic/Latino; 0% international. Retention: 81% of full-time freshmen returned the following year. Core. Calendar: semesters. Academic remediation for entering students, services for LD students, internships.

Entrance Requirements: Option: electronic application. Required: high school transcript, ACT. Required for some: essay, 3 recommendations, interview. Entrance: minimally difficult. Transfer credits accepted: Yes.

Collegiate Environment: Orientation program. College housing not available. Leonard H. Timmerman Library plus 1 other with 5,000 books and 128 serials.

■ MITCHELL TECHNICAL INSTITUTE

821 N Capital
Mitchell, SD 57301
Tel: (605)995-3024; Free: 800-684-1969
Fax: (605)996-3299
E-mail: clayton.deuter@mitchelltech.edu
Web Site: www.mitchelltech.edu/

Description: State-supported, 2-year, coed. Part of South Dakota Board of Education. Awards certificates, diplomas, and terminal associate degrees. Founded 1968. Setting: 90-acre rural campus. Endowment: $1.4 million. Educational spending for the previous fiscal year: $3931 per student. Total enrollment: 1,089. Faculty: 83 (71 full-time, 12 part-time). Student-undergrad faculty ratio is 13:1. 996 applied, 59% were admitted. 1% from top 10% of their high school class, 6% from top quarter, 32% from top half. Full-time: 873 students, 32% women, 68% men. Part-time: 216 students, 46% women, 54% men. Students come from 14 states and territories, 6% from out-of-state. 4% American Indian or Alaska Native, non-Hispanic/Latino; 1% Hispanic/Latino; 0.1% African American, non-Hispanic/Latino; 0.1% Asian, non-Hispanic/Latino; 0% Native Hawaiian or other Pacific Islander, non-Hispanic/Latino; 0% international. 25% 25 or older, 9% live on campus, 10% transferred in. Core. Calendar: semesters. Academic remediation for entering students, services for LD students, advanced placement, distance learning, summer session for credit, part-time degree program, co-op programs and internships.

Entrance Requirements: Open admission except for some programs. Option: electronic application. Required: high school transcript. Recommended: minimum 2 high school GPA. Required for some: essay, interview, SAT or ACT, COMPASS. Entrance: minimally difficult. Application deadlines: Rolling, Rolling for nonresidents. Notification: continuous, continuous for nonresidents. Transfer credits accepted: Yes. Applicants placed on waiting list: 25.

Costs Per Year: One-time mandatory fee: $999. State resident tuition: $3564 full-time, $99 per credit hour part-time. Nonresident tuition: $3564 full-time, $99 per credit hour part-time. Mandatory fees: $2890 full-time, $73 per credit hour part-time. Full-time tuition and fees vary according to course load and program. Part-time tuition and fees vary according to course load and program.

Collegiate Environment: Orientation program. Social organizations: 5 open to all. Most popular organizations: Student Representative Board, Skills USA, Post-Secondary Agricultural Students, Rodeo Club, Student Veterans Organization. Major annual events: Orientation Week, Christmas Party for Children, Winter Week. Student services: personal-psychological counseling. 96 college housing spaces available. No special consideration for freshman housing applicants. Instructional Services Center with 3,000 books, 100 serials, 300 audiovisual materials, and an OPAC. Operations spending for the previous fiscal year: $14,700. 120 computers available on campus for general student use. Computer purchase/lease plans available. A campuswide network can be accessed. Staffed computer lab on campus provides training in use of computers, software, and the Internet.

■ **MOUNT MARTY COLLEGE**
1105 W 8th St.
Yankton, SD 57078-3724
Tel: (605)668-1011; Free: 800-658-4552
Fax: (605)668-1607
E-mail: paula.tacke@mtmc.edu
Web Site: www.mtmc.edu/

Description: Independent Roman Catholic, comprehensive, coed. Awards associate, bachelor's, and master's degrees. Founded 1936. Setting: 80-acre small town campus. Endowment: $15 million. Educational spending for the previous fiscal year: $5423 per student. Total enrollment: 1,178. Faculty: 61 (49 full-time, 12 part-time). Student-undergrad faculty ratio is 10:1. 434 applied, 71% were admitted. 12% from top 10% of their high school class, 32% from top quarter, 66% from top half. Full-time: 553 students, 67% women, 33% men. Part-time: 483 students, 50% women, 50% men. Students come from 15 states and territories, 2 other countries, 45% from out-of-state. 4% American Indian or Alaska Native, non-Hispanic/Latino; 8% Hispanic/Latino; 3% African American, non-Hispanic/Latino; 1% Asian, non-Hispanic/Latino; 0.4% Native Hawaiian or other Pacific Islander, non-Hispanic/Latino; 0% international. 27% 25 or older, 70% live on campus, 6% transferred in. Retention: 68% of full-time freshmen returned the following year. Academic areas with the most degrees conferred: health professions and related sciences; education; business/marketing. Core. Calendar: semesters. Academic remediation for entering students, services for LD students, advanced placement, accelerated degree program, self-designed majors, honors program, independent study, distance learning, double major, summer session for credit, part-time degree program, adult/continuing education programs, co-op programs and internships. Off campus study at members of the Colleges of Mid-America. ROTC: Army (c).

Entrance Requirements: Options: electronic application, early admission, deferred admission. Required: high school transcript, minimum 2 high school GPA, SAT or ACT. Recommended: interview. Entrance: minimally difficult. Application deadline: Rolling. Notification: continuous. SAT Reasoning Test deadline: 8/30. SAT Subject Test deadline: 8/30. Transfer credits accepted: Yes.

Costs Per Year: Application fee: $35. Comprehensive fee: $28,520 includes full-time tuition ($20,300), mandatory fees ($1830), and college room and board ($6390). Full-time tuition and fees vary according to location. Room and board charges vary according to board plan. Part-time tuition: $325 per credit hour. Part-time tuition varies according to course load and location.

Collegiate Environment: Orientation program. Drama-theater group, choral group, student-run newspaper. Social organizations: 40 open to all. Most popular organizations: Campus Ministry, Student Government Association, Nursing Club, Education Club, Theater Club. Major annual events: Homecoming, October Service Blitz, Blue and Gold Days. Student services: health clinic, personal-psychological counseling. Campus security: 24-hour emergency response devices and patrols, late night transport-escort service. 390 college housing spaces available; 337 were occupied in 2012-13. Freshmen guaranteed college housing. On-campus residence required through senior year. Options: men-only, women-only housing available. Mount Marty College Library with 79,660 books, 12,733 microform titles, 307 serials, 8,358 audiovisual materials, and a Web page. Operations spending for the previous fiscal year: $207,532. 12 computers available on campus for general student use. Computer purchase/lease plans available. A computer is required for all students. A campuswide network can be accessed from student residence rooms and from off campus. Students can access the following: online class registration. Staffed computer lab on campus provides training in use of computers, software, and the Internet.

Community Environment: Yankton is situated on the Missouri River, 60 miles northwest of Sioux City, Iowa, and 80 miles southwest of Sioux Falls, S.D. The city is located four miles downstream from Gavins Point Dam, and Lewis and Clark Lake, which provides some of the best fishing, swimming, boating, and picnicking areas in the Midwest. The All-American city served as the first capital of Dakota Territory and is known as the Mother City of the Dakotas. Its 14,000 friendly people take a deep interest in the activities of the college.

■ **NATIONAL AMERICAN UNIVERSITY (ELLSWORTH AFB)**
1000 Ellsworth St.
Ste. 2400B
Ellsworth AFB, SD 57706
Tel: (605)718-6550
Web Site: www.national.edu/

Description: Proprietary, 2-year, coed. Awards terminal associate degrees. Total enrollment: 209.

Entrance Requirements: Entrance: noncompetitive.

■ **NATIONAL AMERICAN UNIVERSITY (RAPID CITY)**
321 Kansas City St.
Rapid City, SD 57701
Tel: (605)394-4800; Free: 800-209-4090
Fax: (605)394-4871
E-mail: abeck@national.edu
Web Site: www.national.edu/

Description: Proprietary, comprehensive, coed. Part of National College. Awards associate, bachelor's, and master's degrees. Founded 1941. Setting: 8-acre urban campus. Endowment: $30,000. Research spending for the previous fiscal year: $35,000. Educational spending for the previous fiscal year: $3320 per student. Total enrollment: 518. Faculty: 47 (13 full-time, 34 part-time). Student-undergrad faculty ratio is 26:1. Full-time: 350 students, 65% women, 35% men. Part-time: 131 students, 63% women, 37% men. Students come from 22 states and territories, 6 other countries, 15% from out-of-state. 55% 25 or older, 21% live on campus, 10% transferred in. Retention: 52% of full-time freshmen returned the following year. Academic areas with the most degrees conferred: business/marketing; health professions and related sciences; computer and information sciences. Core. Academic remediation for entering students, ESL program, services for LD students, advanced placement, accelerated degree program, independent study, distance learning, summer session for credit, part-time degree program, external degree program, adult/continuing education programs, co-op programs and internships. ROTC: Army (c).

Entrance Requirements: Open admission. Options: electronic application, early admission, deferred admission. Recommended: interview, ACT. Required for some: high school transcript. Entrance: noncompetitive. Application deadline: Rolling. Notification: continuous.

Collegiate Environment: Orientation program. Social organizations: local fraternities, local sororities; 6% of eligible men and 7% of eligible women are members. Most popular organizations: Student Senate, Phi Beta Lambda, Dormitory Council, Student Association of Legal Assistants, President's Advisory Council. Major annual events: blood drives, Community Clean-Up. Student services: personal-psychological counseling. Campus security: 24-hour emergency response devices, controlled dormitory access, part-time security personnel. Jefferson Library with 31,018 books, 268 serials, and a Web page. 50 computers available on campus for general student use. A campuswide network can be accessed. Staffed computer lab on campus.

Community Environment: National College is located in a community of about 57,000 residents. Rapid City is a retail hub for several Midwestern states. Rapid City shops, entertainment facilities, and a wide array of dining establishments offer a"big city" feel. A strong Rapid City economy provides many part-time employment opportunities while students are in school. Only 20 minutes away lies one of the most popular tourist areas in the world—Mount Rushmore—which is nestled in the majestic Black Hills. From Rushmore Mall and the Dahl Fine Arts Center to wilderness mountain biking and downhill skiing, Rapid City offers the social and cultural diversity that students desire.

■ NATIONAL AMERICAN UNIVERSITY–SIOUX FALLS BRANCH

2801 S Kiwanis Ave.
Ste. 100
Sioux Falls, SD 57105-4293
Tel: (605)334-5430; Free: 800-388-5430
E-mail: lhoutsma@national.edu
Web Site: www.national.edu/

Description: Proprietary, comprehensive, coed. Part of National College. Awards associate, bachelor's, and master's degrees. Founded 1941. Setting: urban campus. Total enrollment: 375. Faculty: 35 (all part-time). 9 applied, 100% were admitted. Students come from 6 states and territories. 76% 25 or older. Core. Academic remediation for entering students, ESL program, advanced placement, accelerated degree program, distance learning, double major, summer session for credit, part-time degree program, adult/continuing education programs, co-op programs and internships.

Entrance Requirements: Open admission. Options: electronic application, deferred admission. Required: high school transcript, interview. Entrance: noncompetitive. Application deadline: Rolling. Notification: continuous.

Collegiate Environment: Orientation program. Campus security: 24-hour emergency response devices. Main library plus 1 other with 1,580 books, 57 serials, and a Web page. 60 computers available on campus for general student use. A campuswide network can be accessed. Staffed computer lab on campus.

■ NORTHERN STATE UNIVERSITY

1200 S Jay St.
Aberdeen, SD 57401-7198
Tel: (605)626-3011; Free: 800-678-5330
Fax: (605)626-3022
E-mail: admission2@northern.edu
Web Site: www.northern.edu/

Description: State-supported, comprehensive, coed. Part of South Dakota Board of Regents. Awards associate, bachelor's, and master's degrees. Founded 1901. Setting: 72-acre small town campus. Endowment: $18.4 million. Total enrollment: 3,449. Faculty: 101 (89 full-time, 12 part-time). Student-undergrad faculty ratio is 19:1. 1,142 applied, 90% were admitted. 9% from top 10% of their high school class, 21% from top quarter, 56% from top half. Full-time: 1,557 students, 54% women, 46% men. Part-time: 1,410 students, 64% women, 36% men. Students come from 37 states and territories, 14 other countries, 19% from out-of-state. 1% American Indian or Alaska Native, non-Hispanic/Latino; 2% Hispanic/Latino; 1% African American, non-Hispanic/Latino; 0.4% Asian, non-Hispanic/Latino; 0.4% Native Hawaiian or other Pacific Islander, non-Hispanic/Latino; 8% international. 24% 25 or older, 26% live on campus, 4% transferred in. Retention: 69% of full-time freshmen returned the following year. Academic areas with the most degrees conferred: business/marketing; physical sciences; education; social sciences. Core. Calendar: semesters. Academic remediation for entering students, ESL program, services for LD students, advanced placement, accelerated degree program, self-designed majors, freshman honors college, honors program, independent study, distance learning, double major, summer session for credit, part-time degree program, adult/continuing education programs, co-op programs and internships, graduate courses open to undergrads. Off campus study at National Student Exchange. Study abroad program.

Entrance Requirements: Options: electronic application, early admission, deferred admission. Required: high school transcript, minimum 2.6 high school GPA, SAT or ACT. Entrance: minimally difficult. Notification: continuous. SAT Reasoning Test deadline: 9/1.

Costs Per Year: Application fee: $20. State resident tuition: $3726 full-time. Nonresident tuition: $5590 full-time. Mandatory fees: $3543 full-time. Full-time tuition and fees vary according to course level, course load, and reciprocity agreements. College room and board: $6147. College room only: $2703. Room and board charges vary according to board plan.

Collegiate Environment: Orientation program. Drama-theater group, choral group, marching band, student-run newspaper. Social organizations: 100 open to all. Most popular organizations: Student Ambassadors, Choices, honor society, Native American Student Association, International Student Association. Major annual events: Homecoming-Gypsy Days, I Hate Winter, Commencement. Student services: legal services, health clinic, personal-psychological counseling, women's center. Campus security: 24-hour emergency response devices, controlled dormitory access, evening patrols. 840 college housing spaces available; 835 were occupied in 2012-13. On-campus residence required through sophomore year. Option: coed housing available. Beulah Williams Library with 215,000 books, 403,198 microform titles, 71,639 serials, 3,191 audiovisual materials, an OPAC, and a Web page. 135 computers available on campus for general student use. A campuswide network can be accessed from student residence rooms and from off campus. Students can access the following: online class registration. Staffed computer lab on campus.

■ OGLALA LAKOTA COLLEGE

490 Piya Wiconi Rd.
Kyle, SD 57752-0490
Tel: (605)455-6000
Fax: (605)455-2787
E-mail: lmeseteth@olc.edu
Web Site: www.olc.edu/

Description: State and locally supported, comprehensive, coed. Awards associate, bachelor's, and master's degrees. Founded 1970. Setting: rural campus. Total enrollment: 1,000. Students come from 2 states and territories. 70% 25 or older. Core. Calendar: semesters. Academic remediation for entering students, accelerated degree program, summer session for credit, part-time degree program, adult/continuing education programs, co-op programs and internships. Off campus study at American Indian Higher Education Consortium.

Entrance Requirements: Open admission. Option: early admission. Preference given to Native Americans.

Collegiate Environment: Social organizations: 10 open to all. Oglala Lakota College Learning Resource Center with 15,000 books and 150 serials. 65 computers available on campus for general student use.

■ PRESENTATION COLLEGE

1500 N Main St.
Aberdeen, SD 57401-1299
Tel: (605)225-1634; Free: 800-437-6060
Fax: (605)229-8518
E-mail: admit@presentation.edu
Web Site: www.presentation.edu/

Description: Independent Roman Catholic, 4-year, coed. Awards associate and bachelor's degrees. Founded 1951. Setting: 100-acre small town campus. Endowment: $7.6 million. Educational spending for the previous fiscal year: $5610 per student. Total enrollment: 748. Faculty: 73 (46 full-time, 27 part-time). Student-undergrad faculty ratio is 10:1. 340 applied, 74% were admitted. Full-time: 465 students, 66% women, 34% men. Part-time: 283 students, 80% women, 20% men. Students come from 23 states and territories, 3 other countries, 57% from out-of-state. 6% American Indian or Alaska Native, non-Hispanic/Latino; 4% Hispanic/Latino; 8% African American, non-Hispanic/Latino; 1% Asian, non-Hispanic/Latino; 1% Native Hawaiian or other Pacific Islander, non-Hispanic/Latino; 0.5% international. 40% 25 or older, 21% live on campus, 19% transferred in. Retention: 49% of full-time freshmen returned the following year. Academic areas with the most degrees conferred: health professions and related sciences; business/marketing; public administration and social services. Core. Calendar: semesters. Academic remediation for entering students, advanced placement, accelerated degree program, distance learning, double major, summer session for credit, part-time degree program, external degree program, adult/continuing education programs, co-op programs and internships. Off campus study at Kilian Community College, Sioux Falls, SD.

Entrance Requirements: Option: electronic application. Required: high school transcript, SAT or ACT. Recommended: minimum 2 high school GPA. Required for some: 2 recommendations, GED, if applicable; college transcripts. Entrance: noncompetitive. Application deadline: Rolling. Notification: continuous. SAT Reasoning Test deadline: 8/12. SAT Subject Test deadline: 8/12. Transfer credits accepted: Yes.

Costs Per Year: Application fee: $25. One-time mandatory fee: $195. Comprehensive fee: $23,314 includes full-time tuition ($16,664), mandatory fees ($150), and college room and board ($6500). College room only:

$5300. Full-time tuition and fees vary according to course load, location, and program. Room and board charges vary according to board plan. Part-time tuition: $617 per credit hour. Part-time tuition varies according to course load, location, and program.

Collegiate Environment: Orientation program. Choral group. Social organizations: 17 open to all. Most popular organizations: Wellness/athletics, National Student Nursing Association, Social Work Organization, Rad Tech Organization, Student Ambassadors. Major annual events: Homecoming, Spring Fling. Student services: health clinic, personal-psychological counseling. Campus security: 24-hour emergency response devices, late night transport-escort service, controlled dormitory access. College housing designed to accommodate 137 students; 159 undergraduates lived in college housing during 2012-13. Freshmen guaranteed college housing. On-campus residence required through sophomore year. Options: men-only, women-only housing available. Presentation College Library plus 1 other with 87,546 books, 27 microform titles, 86,106 serials, 2,226 audiovisual materials, an OPAC, and a Web page. Operations spending for the previous fiscal year: $210,763. 35 computers available on campus for general student use. Computer purchase/lease plans available. A computer is required for all students. A campuswide network can be accessed from student residence rooms. Students can access the following: online class registration, wireless network has 100% coverage for students. Staffed computer lab on campus provides training in use of computers, software, and the Internet.

Community Environment: Aberdeen is a regional retail and market center with a population of 25,000. It is served by two major U.S. highways, and daily airline service.

■ **SINTE GLESKA UNIVERSITY**
101 Antelope Lake Cir.
Mission, SD 57555
Tel: (605)856-8100
Fax: (605)747-2098
Web Site: www.sintegleska.edu/
Description: Independent, comprehensive, coed. Awards associate, bachelor's, and master's degrees. Founded 1970. Setting: 52-acre rural campus. Total enrollment: 971. 70% 25 or older. Core. Calendar: semesters. Academic remediation for entering students, honors program, distance learning, double major, summer session for credit, part-time degree program, adult/continuing education programs, internships. Off campus study at American Indian Higher Education Consortium.
Entrance Requirements: Open admission. Required: high school transcript. Entrance: noncompetitive. Application deadline: 8/20. Notification: continuous until 8/30.
Collegiate Environment: Student services: personal-psychological counseling, women's center. Campus security: late night transport-escort service. Sinte Gleska University Library with 25,000 books, 80 serials, and an OPAC.

■ **SISSETON-WAHPETON COLLEGE**
Old Agency Box 689
Sisseton, SD 57262
Tel: (605)698-3966
E-mail: dredday@swc.tc
Web Site: www.swc.tc/
Description: Federally supported, 2-year, coed. Awards certificates, transfer associate, and terminal associate degrees. Founded 1979. Setting: 2-acre rural campus. Total enrollment: 237. Faculty: 30 (10 full-time, 20 part-time). Student-undergrad faculty ratio is 10:1. 67 applied, 94% were admitted. Full-time: 181 students, 72% women, 28% men. Part-time: 56 students, 86% women, 14% men. 2% from out-of-state. 42% 25 or older, 0.4% transferred in. Core. Calendar: semesters. Academic remediation for entering students, double major, summer session for credit, part-time degree program, adult/continuing education programs, co-op programs and internships. Off campus study at members of the American Indian Higher Education Consortium.
Entrance Requirements: Open admission. Required: high school transcript, COMPASS test. Recommended: minimum 2 high school GPA, interview. Required for some: Certificate of Indian Blood for enrolled tribal members. Entrance: noncompetitive. Application deadlines: Rolling, 7/8 for nonresidents.
Collegiate Environment: Orientation program. Social organizations: 5 open to all. Most popular organizations: AIHEC, AISES, Student Senate, Student Nurses Association, AIBL. Major annual event: AIHEC. Student services: personal-psychological counseling. Campus security: 24-hour emergency response devices. Sisseton-Wahpeton Community College Library with

15,481 books, 8 microform titles, 162 serials, 885 audiovisual materials, an OPAC, and a Web page. 30 computers available on campus for general student use. Computer purchase/lease plans available. A campuswide network can be accessed from off-campus. Staffed computer lab on campus (open 24 hours a day) provides training in use of computers, software, and the Internet.

■ **SOUTH DAKOTA SCHOOL OF MINES AND TECHNOLOGY**
501 E Saint Joseph St.
Rapid City, SD 57701-3995
Tel: (605)394-2511; Free: 800-544-8162
Fax: (605)394-2914
E-mail: admissions@sdsmt.edu
Web Site: www.sdsmt.edu/
Description: State-supported, university, coed. Part of South Dakota State Board of Regents University System. Awards associate, bachelor's, master's, and doctoral degrees. Founded 1885. Setting: 120-acre suburban campus. Endowment: $42.5 million. Research spending for the previous fiscal year: $22.7 million. Educational spending for the previous fiscal year: $3964 per student. Total enrollment: 2,311. Faculty: 153 (130 full-time, 23 part-time). Student-undergrad faculty ratio is 15:1. 1,030 applied, 88% were admitted. 21% from top 10% of their high school class, 54% from top quarter, 83% from top half. Full-time: 1,636 students, 21% women, 79% men. Part-time: 372 students, 48% women, 52% men. Students come from 38 states and territories, 22 other countries, 41% from out-of-state. 2% American Indian or Alaska Native, non-Hispanic/Latino; 2% Hispanic/Latino; 1% African American, non-Hispanic/Latino; 1% Asian, non-Hispanic/Latino; 0.2% Native Hawaiian or other Pacific Islander, non-Hispanic/Latino; 3% international. 18% 25 or older, 32% live on campus, 4% transferred in. Retention: 78% of full-time freshmen returned the following year. Academic areas with the most degrees conferred: engineering; physical sciences; interdisciplinary studies. Core. Calendar: semesters. Academic remediation for entering students, ESL program, services for LD students, advanced placement, independent study, distance learning, summer session for credit, part-time degree program, adult/continuing education programs, co-op programs and internships, graduate courses open to undergrads. Off campus study. Study abroad program. ROTC: Army.
Entrance Requirements: Options: electronic application, international baccalaureate accepted. Required: high school transcript, SAT or ACT. Recommended: minimum 2.75 high school GPA, SAT or ACT. Required for some: SAT or ACT. Entrance: moderately difficult. Application deadlines: Rolling, Rolling for nonresidents. Notification: continuous, continuous for nonresidents. SAT Reasoning Test deadline: 8/15. SAT Subject Test deadline: 8/15. Transfer credits accepted: Yes.
Collegiate Environment: Orientation program. Drama-theater group, choral group, student-run newspaper, radio station. Social organizations: 79 open to all; national fraternities, national sororities; 15% of eligible men and 16% of eligible women are members. Most popular organizations: ASCE (American Society of Civil Engineers), ASME (American Society of Mechanical Engineers), Drill and Crucible Club, Tau Beta Pi, Formula SAE (Mini Indy race car team). Major annual events: Homecoming/M Week, Engineers' Week, Fall Career Fair. Student services: health clinic, personal-psychological counseling. Campus security: 24-hour emergency response devices and patrols, student patrols, late night transport-escort service, controlled dormitory access. Devereaux Library with 236,080 books, 19,195 microform titles, 22,933 serials, 8,516 audiovisual materials, an OPAC, and a Web page. Operations spending for the previous fiscal year: $344,568. 105 computers available on campus for general student use. Computer purchase/lease plans available. A computer is required for all students. A campuswide network can be accessed from student residence rooms and from off campus. Students can access the following: online class registration, laptop rental, our whole campus has wireless connections. Staffed computer lab on campus (open 24 hours a day) provides training in use of computers, software, and the Internet.
Community Environment: Rapid City, founded in 1876, two years after gold was discovered in the Black Hills, is now a trading center and tourist headquarters of the Black Hills area. All commercial transportation is available. Community facilities include many churches, museums, hospitals, a library, radio stations, three TV stations, and a number of the major civic and service organizations.

■ **SOUTH DAKOTA STATE UNIVERSITY**
Box 2201
Brookings, SD 57007

Tel: (605)688-4151; Free: 800-952-3541
Fax: (605)688-6384
E-mail: sdsu.admissions@sdstate.edu
Web Site: www.sdstate.edu/

Description: State-supported, university, coed. Part of South Dakota Board of Regents. Awards associate, bachelor's, master's, and doctoral degrees and post-master's certificates. Founded 1881. Setting: 272-acre small town campus. Total enrollment: 12,583. Faculty: 693 (533 full-time, 160 part-time). Student-undergrad faculty ratio is 17:1. 4,725 applied, 92% were admitted. 11% from top 10% of their high school class, 36% from top quarter, 69% from top half. 3 National Merit Scholars, 75 valedictorians. Full-time: 8,562 students, 49% women, 51% men. Part-time: 2,556 students, 64% women, 36% men. Students come from 50 states and territories, 63 other countries, 30% from out-of-state. 1% American Indian or Alaska Native, non-Hispanic/Latino; 2% Hispanic/Latino; 1% African American, non-Hispanic/Latino; 1% Asian, non-Hispanic/Latino; 0.1% Native Hawaiian or other Pacific Islander, non-Hispanic/Latino; 2% international. 13% 25 or older, 42% live on campus, 7% transferred in. Retention: 75% of full-time freshmen returned the following year. Academic areas with the most degrees conferred: health professions and related sciences; agriculture; social sciences. Core. Calendar: semesters. Academic remediation for entering students, services for LD students, advanced placement, accelerated degree program, freshman honors college, honors program, independent study, distance learning, double major, summer session for credit, part-time degree program, adult/continuing education programs, co-op programs and internships, graduate courses open to undergrads. Off campus study at National Student Exchange. Study abroad program. ROTC: Army, Air Force.

Entrance Requirements: Options: electronic application, international baccalaureate accepted. Required: high school transcript, minimum 2.6 high school GPA, SAT or ACT. Entrance: minimally difficult. Application deadline: Rolling. Notification: continuous. SAT Reasoning Test deadline: 9/1. Transfer credits accepted: Yes.

Costs Per Year: Application fee: $20. State resident tuition: $3897 full-time, $129.90 per credit hour part-time. Nonresident tuition: $5843 full-time, $194.75 per credit hour part-time. Mandatory fees: $3507 full-time. Full-time tuition and fees vary according to course level, course load, degree level, location, program, and reciprocity agreements. Part-time tuition varies according to course level, course load, degree level, location, program, and reciprocity agreements. College room and board: $5586. College room only: $2839. Room and board charges vary according to board plan and housing facility.

Collegiate Environment: Orientation program. Drama-theater group, choral group, marching band, student-run newspaper, radio station. Social organizations: 200 open to all; national fraternities, national sororities; 3% of eligible men and 2% of eligible women are members. Major annual events: Hobo Day, Spring Fling, Festival of Cultures. Student services: legal services, health clinic, personal-psychological counseling, women's center. Campus security: 24-hour emergency response devices and patrols, student patrols, late night transport-escort service, controlled dormitory access. 3,995 college housing spaces available. Freshmen guaranteed college housing. On-campus residence required through sophomore year. Option: coed housing available. H. M. Briggs Library with 790,900 books, 96,395 microform titles, 32,900 serials, 4,503 audiovisual materials, an OPAC, and a Web page. Operations spending for the previous fiscal year: $3.6 million. 437 computers available on campus for general student use. Computer purchase/lease plans available. A campuswide network can be accessed from student residence rooms and from off campus. Students can access the following: online class registration. Staffed computer lab on campus (open 24 hours a day) provides training in use of computers, software, and the Internet.

Community Environment: Brookings is located in the eastern part of the state, an agriculturally rich area with diversified farming influenced by research done at South Dakota State University. Located 55 miles from Sioux Falls, the community facilities include a library, 23 churches, an hospital, and many civic and service clubs. Recreational activities include deer and pheasant hunting, golf, and water sports at the center lake region.

■ **SOUTHEAST TECHNICAL INSTITUTE**
2320 N Career Ave.
Sioux Falls, SD 57107-1301
Tel: (605)367-7624; Free: 800-247-0789
E-mail: scott.dorman@southeasttech.edu
Web Site: www.southeasttech.edu/

Description: State-supported, 2-year, coed. Awards certificates, diplomas,

and terminal associate degrees. Founded 1968. Setting: 138-acre urban campus. Endowment: $768,716. Educational spending for the previous fiscal year: $4593 per student. Total enrollment: 2,632. Faculty: 201 (88 full-time, 113 part-time). Student-undergrad faculty ratio is 18:1. 3,119 applied, 42% were admitted. Full-time: 1,900 students, 46% women, 54% men. Part-time: 731 students, 67% women, 33% men. Students come from 11 states and territories, 8% from out-of-state. 2% American Indian or Alaska Native, non-Hispanic/Latino; 2% Hispanic/Latino; 2% African American, non-Hispanic/Latino; 1% Asian, non-Hispanic/Latino; 0.4% Native Hawaiian or other Pacific Islander, non-Hispanic/Latino; 0% international. 27% 25 or older, 8% live on campus, 14% transferred in. Retention: 56% of full-time freshmen returned the following year. Calendar: semesters. Academic remediation for entering students, services for LD students, advanced placement, independent study, distance learning, double major, summer session for credit, part-time degree program, internships.

Entrance Requirements: Option: electronic application. Required: high school transcript, minimum 2.2 high school GPA. Recommended: ACT. Required for some: interview, background check and drug testing for certain programs. Entrance: minimally difficult. Application deadlines: Rolling, Rolling for nonresidents. Notification: continuous, continuous for nonresidents. Transfer credits accepted: Yes.

Costs Per Year: Application fee: $0. State resident tuition: $3120 full-time, $104 per credit hour part-time. Nonresident tuition: $3120 full-time, $104 per credit hour part-time. Mandatory fees: $2670 full-time, $89 per credit hour part-time. Full-time tuition and fees vary according to program. Part-time tuition and fees vary according to program. College room only: $4650.

Collegiate Environment: Orientation program. Social organizations: 6 open to all. Most popular organizations: VICA (Vocational Industrial Clubs of America), American Landscape Contractors Association. Major annual events: Student Picnic, Movie/Pizza Night. Student services: personal-psychological counseling. Campus security: 24-hour patrols, late night transport-escort service, controlled dormitory access. 200 college housing spaces available; all were occupied in 2012-13. No special consideration for freshman housing applicants. Option: coed housing available. Southeast Library with 10,643 books, 1 microform title, 158 serials, an OPAC, and a Web page. Operations spending for the previous fiscal year: $94,322. 70 computers available on campus for general student use. Computer purchase/lease plans available. A computer is required for all students. A campuswide network can be accessed from student residence rooms and from off campus. Students can access the following: online class registration, online official transcript request, online enrollment verification. Staffed computer lab on campus provides training in use of computers, software, and the Internet.

■ **UNIVERSITY OF SIOUX FALLS**
1101 W 22nd St.
Sioux Falls, SD 57105-1699
Tel: (605)331-5000; Free: 800-888-1047
Fax: (605)331-6615
E-mail: admissions@usiouxfalls.edu
Web Site: www.usiouxfalls.edu/

Description: Independent American Baptist Churches in the USA, comprehensive, coed. Awards associate, bachelor's, and master's degrees and post-master's certificates. Founded 1883. Setting: 24-acre suburban campus. Endowment: $17.2 million. Educational spending for the previous fiscal year: $5286 per student. Total enrollment: 1,564. Faculty: 140 (60 full-time, 80 part-time). Student-undergrad faculty ratio is 15:1. 645 applied, 97% were admitted. 18% from top 10% of their high school class, 40% from top quarter, 73% from top half. Full-time: 1,011 students, 52% women, 48% men. Part-time: 232 students, 56% women, 44% men. Students come from 30 states and territories, 5 other countries, 32% from out-of-state. 15% 25 or older, 47% live on campus, 7% transferred in. Retention: 68% of full-time freshmen returned the following year. Academic areas with the most degrees conferred: business/marketing; health professions and related sciences; biological/life sciences; education. Core. Calendar: 4-1-4. Academic remediation for entering students, services for LD students, advanced placement, accelerated degree program, self-designed majors, honors program, independent study, distance learning, double major, summer session for credit, part-time degree program, adult/continuing education programs, internships, graduate courses open to undergrads. Off campus study at Colleges of Mid-America, Augustana College (SD), North American Baptist Seminary, Christian College Coalition. Study abroad program. ROTC: Air Force.

Entrance Requirements: Options: electronic application, international bac-

calaureate accepted. Required: high school transcript, SAT or ACT. Recommended: essay, minimum 2.8 high school GPA. Required for some: 2 recommendations, interview. Entrance: moderately difficult. Application deadline: Rolling. Notification: continuous. Transfer credits accepted: Yes.

Collegiate Environment: Orientation program. Drama-theater group, choral group, student-run newspaper, radio station. Social organizations: 25 open to all. Most popular organizations: Fellowship of Christian Athletes, Campus Ministry Outreach, Student Senate, Association of Cougar Education Students (ACES), 1980's Music Video Remake Club. Major annual events: Homecoming, Madrigals, Campus Olympics. Student services: personal-psychological counseling. Campus security: 24-hour emergency response devices and patrols, student patrols, late night transport-escort service, controlled dormitory access. Norman B. Mears Library with 85,713 books, 3,665 microform titles, 378 serials, an OPAC, and a Web page. Operations spending for the previous fiscal year: $277,060. 150 computers available on campus for general student use. A campuswide network can be accessed from student residence rooms and from off campus. Students can access the following: online class registration. Staffed computer lab on campus provides training in use of computers, software, and the Internet.

Community Environment: Sioux Falls, population 139,500, is a commercial and industrial center. Credit card corporations, banking, retailing and meat packing are the leading industries of the community. Air and bus transportation are available. Community facilities include churches of many denominations, hospitals, an art center, and excellent shopping. Recreation includes all winter sports, water sports, hunting, and fishing. Part-time employment opportunities are excellent.

■ THE UNIVERSITY OF SOUTH DAKOTA

414 E Clark St.
Vermillion, SD 57069-2390
Tel: (605)677-5011; Free: 877-269-6837
Fax: (605)677-6753
E-mail: admiss@usd.edu
Web Site: www.usd.edu/

Description: State-supported, university, coed. Part of South Dakota Board of Regents. Awards associate, bachelor's, master's, and doctoral degrees and post-master's certificates. Founded 1862. Setting: 275-acre small town campus. Endowment: $157.5 million. Research spending for the previous fiscal year: $15.7 million. Educational spending for the previous fiscal year: $8520 per student. Total enrollment: 10,284. Faculty: 579 (436 full-time, 143 part-time). Student-undergrad faculty ratio is 17:1. 3,443 applied, 89% were admitted. 14% from top 10% of their high school class, 33% from top quarter, 71% from top half. Full-time: 4,629 students, 59% women, 41% men. Part-time: 3,061 students, 69% women, 31% men. Students come from 50 states and territories, 86 other countries, 38% from out-of-state. 2% American Indian or Alaska Native, non-Hispanic/Latino; 3% Hispanic/Latino; 2% African American, non-Hispanic/Latino; 1% Asian, non-Hispanic/Latino; 0.2% Native Hawaiian or other Pacific Islander, non-Hispanic/Latino; 1% international. 22% 25 or older, 26% live on campus, 9% transferred in. Retention: 75% of full-time freshmen returned the following year. Academic areas with the most degrees conferred: business/marketing; health professions and related sciences; education. Core. Calendar: semesters. Academic remediation for entering students, ESL program, services for LD students, advanced placement, accelerated degree program, self-designed majors, honors program, independent study, distance learning, double major, summer session for credit, part-time degree program, external degree program, adult/continuing education programs, co-op programs and internships. Off campus study at National Student Exchange. Study abroad program. ROTC: Army.

Entrance Requirements: Options: electronic application, early admission, deferred admission. Required: high school transcript, SAT or ACT. Recommended: minimum 2 high school GPA. Entrance: moderately difficult. Application deadline: Rolling. Notification: continuous. SAT Reasoning Test deadline: 8/9. SAT Subject Test deadline: 8/9. Transfer credits accepted: Yes.

Costs Per Year: Application fee: $20. State resident tuition: $3897 full-time, $129.30 per credit hour part-time. Nonresident tuition: $5,842 full-time, $194.75 per credit hour part-time. Mandatory fees: $3807 full-time, $126.90 per credit hour part-time. Full-time tuition and fees vary according to course load. Part-time tuition and fees vary according to course load. College room and board: $6648. College room only: $3433. Room and board charges vary according to board plan and housing facility.

Collegiate Environment: Orientation program. Drama-theater group, choral group, marching band, student-run newspaper, radio station. Social organizations: 132 open to all; national fraternities, national sororities; 18% of eligible men and 14% of eligible women are members. Most popular organizations: Program Council, Residence Hall Association, Student Ambassadors, Delta Sigma Pi. Major annual events: Dakota Days, Strollers, Rockfest. Student services: legal services, health clinic, personal-psychological counseling. Campus security: 24-hour emergency response devices and patrols, student patrols, late night transport-escort service, controlled dormitory access. 2,283 college housing spaces available; 1,852 were occupied in 2012-13. Freshmen guaranteed college housing. On-campus residence required through sophomore year. Options: coed, men-only, women-only housing available. I. D. Weeks Library plus 2 others with 716,915 books, 740,794 microform titles, 1,950 serials, 48,921 audiovisual materials, and an OPAC. 917 computers available on campus for general student use. A campuswide network can be accessed from student residence rooms and from off campus. Students can access the following: online class registration. Staffed computer lab on campus (open 24 hours a day) provides training in use of computers, software, and the Internet.

Community Environment: Vermillion is situated on a bluff overlooking the Missouri and Vermillion Rivers and was named for the red clay on the riverbanks. There is a public library, museums, churches of a number of denominations, a hospital, and major civic and service organizations. Shopping facilities are excellent. Part-time employment opportunities are good. There are a number of recreational activities, and hunting and fishing opportunities are excellent.

■ WESTERN DAKOTA TECHNICAL INSTITUTE

800 Mickelson Dr.
Rapid City, SD 57703
Tel: (605)394-4034; Free: 800-544-8765
E-mail: jill.elder@wdt.edu
Web Site: www.wdt.edu/

Description: State-supported, 2-year, coed. Awards certificates, diplomas, and terminal associate degrees. Founded 1968. Setting: 5-acre small town campus. Educational spending for the previous fiscal year: $4203 per student. Total enrollment: 1,019. Faculty: 123 (45 full-time, 78 part-time). Student-undergrad faculty ratio is 18:1. 1,110 applied, 73% were admitted. 4% from top 10% of their high school class, 13% from top quarter, 38% from top half. Full-time: 785 students, 46% women, 54% men. Part-time: 234 students, 55% women, 45% men. Students come from 11 states and territories, 3% from out-of-state. 13% American Indian or Alaska Native, non-Hispanic/Latino; 4% Hispanic/Latino; 1% African American, non-Hispanic/Latino; 1% Asian, non-Hispanic/Latino; 0.2% Native Hawaiian or other Pacific Islander, non-Hispanic/Latino; 0% international. 45% 25 or older, 8% transferred in. Retention: 67% of full-time freshmen returned the following year. Core. Calendar: semesters. Academic remediation for entering students, services for LD students, advanced placement, independent study, distance learning, summer session for credit, part-time degree program, internships.

Entrance Requirements: Open admission. Option: electronic application. Required: high school transcript, Placement test. Recommended: minimum 2 high school GPA, SAT or ACT. Required for some: essay, 3 recommendations, interview. Entrance: noncompetitive. Application deadline: 8/1. Notification: continuous until 8/15. Transfer credits accepted: Yes.

Costs Per Year: Application fee: $20. One-time mandatory fee: $250. State resident tuition: $3564 full-time, $99 per credit hour part-time. Nonresident tuition: $3564 full-time, $99 per credit hour part-time. Mandatory fees: $2887 full-time, $80 per credit hour part-time. Full-time tuition and fees vary according to course load and program. Part-time tuition and fees vary according to course load.

Collegiate Environment: Orientation program. Campus security: 24-hour video surveillance. College housing not available. Western Dakota Technical Institute Library with 8,211 books, 87 serials, 133 audiovisual materials, an OPAC, and a Web page. Operations spending for the previous fiscal year: $142,334. 32 computers available on campus for general student use. A computer is required for all students. A campuswide network can be accessed. Students can access the following: online class registration. Staffed computer lab on campus provides training in use of computers, software, and the Internet.

Tennessee

■ **AMERICAN BAPTIST COLLEGE OF AMERICAN BAPTIST THEOLOGICAL SEMINARY**
1800 Baptist World Ctr. Dr.
Nashville, TN 37207
Tel: (615)256-1463
E-mail: admissions@abcnash.edu
Web Site: www.abcnash.edu/
Description: Independent Baptist, 4-year, coed. Awards bachelor's degrees. Founded 1924. Setting: 52-acre urban campus. Endowment: $875,540. Educational spending for the previous fiscal year: $8892 per student. Total enrollment: 122. Faculty: 12 (5 full-time, 7 part-time). Student-undergrad faculty ratio is 10:1. 16 applied, 69% were admitted. Full-time: 90 students, 27% women, 73% men. Part-time: 19 students, 21% women, 79% men. Students come from 11 states and territories, 9% from out-of-state. 69% 25 or older, 63% live on campus, 9% transferred in. Retention: 61% of full-time freshmen returned the following year. Academic area with the most degrees conferred: theology and religious vocations. Core. Calendar: semesters. Academic remediation for entering students, double major, summer session for credit, part-time degree program, adult/continuing education programs. Off campus study at American Baptist College (Augusta, GA).
Entrance Requirements: Open admission. Options: electronic application, deferred admission. Required: essay, high school transcript, minimum 2 high school GPA, 2 recommendations. Required for some: interview. Entrance: noncompetitive. Application deadlines: 8/5, 8/5 for nonresidents. Notification: 8/12, 8/12 for nonresidents. Transfer credits accepted: Yes.
Costs Per Year: Application fee: $30. Tuition: $8688 full-time. Mandatory fees: $317 full-time. College room only: $2000.
Collegiate Environment: Orientation program. Choral group. Social organizations: 6 open to all; national fraternities, local fraternities. Most popular organizations: Student Government Association, Vespers Service, Baptist Student Union, Choir, Greek Letter Fraternity and Hoi Adelphoi Fraternity. Major annual events: Garnett-Nabrit Lectures, ABC Days and Discovery Week, Presidential Scholarship Banquet. 50 college housing spaces available; 22 were occupied in 2012-13. No special consideration for freshman housing applicants. Options: coed, men-only, women-only housing available. T. L. Holcolm Library with 33,676 books, 180 serials, and an OPAC. Operations spending for the previous fiscal year: $54,092. 10 computers available on campus for general student use. A campuswide network can be accessed from student residence rooms and from off campus. Students can access the following: online class registration, IT support person on campus during regular campus hours. Staffed computer lab on campus provides training in use of computers, software, and the Internet.

■ **ANTHEM CAREER COLLEGE**
5865 Shelby Oaks Cir.
Ste. 100
Memphis, TN 38134
Tel: (901)432-3800; Free: 866-381-5623
Fax: (901)387-1181
Web Site: www.anthem.edu/memphis-tennessee/
Description: Proprietary, 2-year, coed. Awards terminal associate degrees. Founded 2003. Total enrollment: 1,101. Calendar: semesters.
Entrance Requirements: Entrance: noncompetitive.

■ **ANTHEM CAREER COLLEGE–NASHVILLE**
560 Royal Pky.
Nashville, TN 37214
Tel: (615)232-3700; Free: 866-381-5791
Fax: (615)902-9766
Web Site: anthem.edu/nashville-tennessee/
Description: Proprietary, 2-year, coed. Awards terminal associate degrees. Founded 1999. Total enrollment: 1,319. Calendar: semesters.
Entrance Requirements: Entrance: noncompetitive.

■ **AQUINAS COLLEGE**
4210 Harding Rd.
Nashville, TN 37205-2005
Tel: (615)297-7545; Free: 800-649-9956
Fax: (615)297-7970
E-mail: hansomc@aquinascollege.edu
Web Site: www.aquinascollege.edu/
Description: Independent Roman Catholic, 4-year, coed. Administratively affiliated with The Dominican Sisters of the Saint Cecilia Congregation. Awards associate and bachelor's degrees. Founded 1961. Setting: 92-acre urban campus. Total enrollment: 747. Faculty: 91 (34 full-time, 57 part-time). Student-undergrad faculty ratio is 8:1. 82 applied, 65% were admitted. Full-time: 255 students, 80% women, 20% men. Part-time: 466 students, 88% women, 12% men. 0.1% American Indian or Alaska Native, non-Hispanic/Latino; 2% Hispanic/Latino; 13% African American, non-Hispanic/Latino; 2% Asian, non-Hispanic/Latino; 1% Native Hawaiian or other Pacific Islander, non-Hispanic/Latino; 0% international. 77% 25 or older, 18% transferred in. Retention: 80% of full-time freshmen returned the following year. Academic areas with the most degrees conferred: business/marketing; health professions and related sciences; liberal arts/general studies; education. Core. Calendar: semesters. Academic remediation for entering students, advanced placement, accelerated degree program, independent study, summer session for credit, part-time degree program, co-op programs and internships.
Entrance Requirements: Open admission. Options: electronic application, deferred admission. Required: high school transcript, minimum 2.2 high school GPA. Required for some: essay, SAT or ACT. Entrance: minimally difficult. Application deadline: Rolling. Notification: continuous. SAT Reasoning Test deadline: 8/15. SAT Subject Test deadline: 8/15.
Collegiate Environment: Orientation program. Student-run newspaper. Campus security: 24-hour emergency response devices, patrols by security after class hours.
Community Environment: See Vanderbilt University.

■ **ARGOSY UNIVERSITY, NASHVILLE**
100 Centerview Dr., Ste. 225
Nashville, TN 37214
Tel: (615)525-2800; Free: 866-833-6598
Fax: (615)369-0601
Web Site: www.argosy.edu/nashville/
Description: Proprietary, university, coed. Awards bachelor's, master's, and doctoral degrees. Founded 2001. Calendar: semesters.

■ **THE ART INSTITUTE OF TENNESSEE–NASHVILLE**
100 Centerview Dr., Ste. 250
Nashville, TN 37214
Tel: (615)874-1067; Free: 866-747-5770
Web Site: www.artinstitutes.edu/nashville/

Description: Proprietary, 4-year, coed. Part of Education Management Corporation. Awards associate and bachelor's degrees. Founded 2006. Setting: urban campus.

■ AUSTIN PEAY STATE UNIVERSITY

601 College St.
Clarksville, TN 37044
Tel: (931)221-7011; Free: 800-844-2778
Fax: (931)221-5994
E-mail: admissions@apsu.edu
Web Site: www.apsu.edu/

Description: State-supported, comprehensive, coed. Part of Tennessee Board of Regents. Awards associate, bachelor's, and master's degrees and post-master's certificates. Founded 1927. Setting: 169-acre suburban campus with easy access to Nashville. Endowment: $6.8 million. Research spending for the previous fiscal year: $2.2 million. Educational spending for the previous fiscal year: $2811 per student. Total enrollment: 10,597. Faculty: 615 (350 full-time, 265 part-time). Student-undergrad faculty ratio is 19:1. 3,453 applied, 86% were admitted. 13% from top 10% of their high school class, 34% from top quarter, 70% from top half. Full-time: 6,994 students, 60% women, 40% men. Part-time: 2,741 students, 58% women, 42% men. Students come from 40 states and territories, 23 other countries, 11% from out-of-state. 1% American Indian or Alaska Native, non-Hispanic/Latino; 5% Hispanic/Latino; 19% African American, non-Hispanic/Latino; 2% Asian, non-Hispanic/Latino; 0.3% Native Hawaiian or other Pacific Islander, non-Hispanic/Latino; 0.3% international. 37% 25 or older, 14% live on campus, 9% transferred in. Retention: 67% of full-time freshmen returned the following year. Academic areas with the most degrees conferred: business/marketing; health professions and related sciences; education. Core. Calendar: semesters. Academic remediation for entering students, ESL program, services for LD students, advanced placement, accelerated degree program, honors program, independent study, distance learning, double major, summer session for credit, part-time degree program, adult/continuing education programs, co-op programs and internships, graduate courses open to undergrads. Study abroad program. ROTC: Army, Air Force (c).

Entrance Requirements: Options: electronic application, early admission, deferred admission. Required: high school transcript. Required for some: minimum 2.75 high school GPA, SAT or ACT. Entrance: moderately difficult. Application deadline: 8/1. Notification: continuous. SAT Reasoning Test deadline: 8/1. SAT Subject Test deadline: 8/1. Transfer credits accepted: Yes.

Costs Per Year: Application fee: $15. One-time mandatory fee: $75. State resident tuition: $5424 full-time, $226 per credit hour part-time. Nonresident tuition: $19,512 full-time, $813 per credit hour part-time. Mandatory fees: $1224 full-time. Full-time tuition and fees vary according to location and program. Part-time tuition varies according to location and program. College room and board: $7380. College room only: $4600. Room and board charges vary according to board plan and housing facility.

Collegiate Environment: Orientation program. Drama-theater group, choral group, marching band, student-run newspaper, radio station. Social organizations: 117 open to all; national fraternities, national sororities; 9% of eligible men and 9% of eligible women are members. Student services: health clinic, personal-psychological counseling. Campus security: 24-hour emergency response devices and patrols, student patrols, late night transport-escort service, controlled dormitory access. 1,454 college housing spaces available; 1,363 were occupied in 2012-13. Freshmen guaranteed college housing. On-campus residence required in freshman year. Options: coed, men-only, women-only housing available. Felix G. Woodward Library with 368,661 books, 672,137 microform titles, 34,899 serials, 6,933 audiovisual materials, an OPAC, and a Web page. Operations spending for the previous fiscal year: $2.5 million. 825 computers available on campus for general student use. Computer purchase/lease plans available. A campuswide network can be accessed from student residence rooms and from off campus. Students can access the following: online class registration. Staffed computer lab on campus provides training in use of computers.

Community Environment: Clarksville, an urban area, was founded in 1784 and was named for General George Rogers Clark. Bus transportation is available. Community facilities include a number of churches, a hospital, a public library, and major civic and service organizations. Water sports are enjoyed on the Cumberland River and nearby lakes. Some part-time employment is available.

■ BAPTIST COLLEGE OF HEALTH SCIENCES

1003 Monroe Ave.
Memphis, TN 38104
Tel: (901)227-4330; Free: 866-575-2247
E-mail: Lissa.Morgan@bchs.edu
Web Site: www.bchs.edu/

Description: Independent Southern Baptist, 4-year, coed. Administratively affiliated with Baptist Memorial Health Care. Awards bachelor's degrees. Founded 1994. Setting: urban campus. Total enrollment: 1,043. Faculty: 107 (59 full-time, 48 part-time). Student-undergrad faculty ratio is 9:1. 490 applied, 27% were admitted. Full-time: 489 students, 89% women, 11% men. Part-time: 554 students, 91% women, 9% men. 34% from out-of-state. 0.1% American Indian or Alaska Native, non-Hispanic/Latino; 0.5% Hispanic/Latino; 37% African American, non-Hispanic/Latino; 2% Asian, non-Hispanic/Latino. 10% live on campus, 24% transferred in. Retention: 83% of full-time freshmen returned the following year. Academic area with the most degrees conferred: health professions and related sciences. Core. Calendar: trimesters. Services for LD students, advanced placement, accelerated degree program, distance learning, summer session for credit, part-time degree program.

Entrance Requirements: Option: electronic application. Required: high school transcript, minimum 2.75 high school GPA, immunizations, health physical, ACT. Required for some: interview. Entrance: moderately difficult. Application deadline: 5/1. SAT Reasoning Test deadline: 5/1. SAT Subject Test deadline: 5/1. Transfer credits accepted: Yes. Applicants placed on waiting list: 151. Wait-listed applicants offered admission: 0.

Costs Per Year: Application fee: $25. Tuition: $10,980 full-time, $366 per credit hour part-time. Mandatory fees: $890 full-time. College room only: $2200. Room charges vary according to housing facility.

Collegiate Environment: Orientation program. Most popular organizations: Student Government Association, Student Nursing Association, Allied Health Organization. Major annual events: Spiritual Renewal Week, Convocation, Graduation. Student services: health clinic, personal-psychological counseling. Campus security: 24-hour emergency response devices, late night transport-escort service, controlled dormitory access, trained security personnel. 92 college housing spaces available. No special consideration for freshman housing applicants. Option: coed housing available. Health Sciences Library with an OPAC and a Web page.

■ BELHAVEN UNIVERSITY

5100 Poplar Ave., Ste. 200
Memphis, TN 38137
Tel: (901)888-3343
Fax: (901)888-0771
E-mail: memphisadmission@belhaven.edu
Web Site: memphis.belhaven.edu/

Description: Independent Presbyterian, comprehensive, coed. Awards associate, bachelor's, and master's degrees. Founded 1997. Calendar: semesters.

Entrance Requirements: Required: high school transcript. Required for some: essay, resume.

■ BELMONT UNIVERSITY

1900 Belmont Blvd.
Nashville, TN 37212-3757
Tel: (615)460-6000
E-mail: david.mee@belmont.edu
Web Site: www.belmont.edu/

Description: Independent Christian, university, coed. Awards bachelor's, master's, and doctoral degrees and post-master's certificates. Founded 1951. Setting: 77-acre urban campus. Endowment: $73.8 million. Educational spending for the previous fiscal year: $9080 per student. Total enrollment: 6,665. Faculty: 735 (306 full-time, 429 part-time). Student-undergrad faculty ratio is 13:1. 4,046 applied, 84% were admitted. 35% from top 10% of their high school class, 62% from top quarter, 91% from top half. Full-time: 4,906 students, 59% women, 41% men. Part-time: 383 students, 62% women, 38% men. Students come from 50 states and territories, 21 other countries, 63% from out-of-state. 0.2% American Indian or Alaska Native, non-Hispanic/Latino; 4% Hispanic/Latino; 4% African American, non-Hispanic/Latino; 1% Asian, non-Hispanic/Latino; 0.02% Native Hawaiian or other Pacific Islander, non-Hispanic/Latino; 1% international. 8% 25 or older, 50% live on campus, 10% transferred in. Retention: 82% of full-time freshmen returned the following year. Academic areas with the most degrees conferred: business/marketing; health professions and related sciences;

visual and performing arts. Core. Calendar: semesters. ESL program, advanced placement, accelerated degree program, self-designed majors, honors program, independent study, distance learning, double major, summer session for credit, part-time degree program, adult/continuing education programs, co-op programs and internships, graduate courses open to undergrads. Off campus study at Cool Springs Center. Study abroad program. ROTC: Army (c), Naval (c), Air Force (c).

Entrance Requirements: Options: electronic application, early admission, deferred admission, international baccalaureate accepted. Required: essay, high school transcript, minimum 3 high school GPA, 2 recommendations, resume of activities, SAT or ACT. Required for some: interview. Entrance: moderately difficult. Application deadline: 8/1. Notification: continuous. SAT Reasoning Test deadline: 8/1.

Costs Per Year: Application fee: $50. Comprehensive fee: $38,550 includes full-time tuition ($24,900), mandatory fees ($1230), and college room and board ($12,420). College room only: $8200. Full-time tuition and fees vary according to class time, course load, and location. Room and board charges vary according to board plan, housing facility, and location. Part-time tuition: $950 per credit hour. Part-time mandatory fees: $840 per year. Part-time tuition and fees vary according to course load.

Collegiate Environment: Orientation program. Drama-theater group, choral group, marching band, student-run newspaper, radio station. Social organizations: 80 open to all; national fraternities, national sororities; 6% of eligible men and 8% of eligible women are members. Most popular organizations: Service Corp, Alpha Sigma Tau, Phi Mu, Phi Kappa Tau, MOB. Major annual events: Fall Festival, Homecoming, Towering Traditions. Student services: health clinic, personal-psychological counseling, women's center. Campus security: 24-hour emergency response devices and patrols, late night transport-escort service, controlled dormitory access, bicycle patrol. 2,710 college housing spaces available; 2,626 were occupied in 2012-13. Freshmen guaranteed college housing. On-campus residence required through sophomore year. Options: men-only, women-only housing available. Lila D. Bunch Library plus 1 other with 232,140 books, 29,999 microform titles, 788 serials, 34,506 audiovisual materials, an OPAC, and a Web page. Operations spending for the previous fiscal year: $1.2 million. 500 computers available on campus for general student use. Computer purchase/lease plans available. A campuswide network can be accessed from student residence rooms and from off campus. Students can access the following: online class registration, individual student information via BANNER Web. Staffed computer lab on campus provides training in use of computers, software, and the Internet.

Community Environment: See Vanderbilt University.

■ **BETHEL UNIVERSITY**
325 Cherry Ave.
McKenzie, TN 38201
Tel: (731)352-4000
Fax: (731)352-4069
E-mail: hodgest@bethelu.edu
Web Site: www.bethelu.edu/

Description: Independent Cumberland Presbyterian, comprehensive, coed. Awards bachelor's and master's degrees. Founded 1842. Setting: 100-acre small town campus. Endowment: $8.1 million. Educational spending for the previous fiscal year: $5423 per student. Total enrollment: 4,295. Faculty: 291 (97 full-time, 194 part-time). Student-undergrad faculty ratio is 19:1. 1,057 applied, 54% were admitted. 2 National Merit Scholars, 2 valedictorians, 8 student government officers. Full-time: 1,876 students, 54% women, 46% men. Part-time: 848 students, 67% women, 33% men. Students come from 25 states and territories, 19 other countries, 9% from out-of-state. 55% 25 or older, 29% live on campus, 2% transferred in. Retention: 64% of full-time freshmen returned the following year. Academic areas with the most degrees conferred: business/marketing; education; health professions and related sciences. Core. Calendar: semesters. Academic remediation for entering students, services for LD students, advanced placement, accelerated degree program, self-designed majors, honors program, independent study, distance learning, double major, summer session for credit, part-time degree program, adult/continuing education programs, co-op programs and internships, graduate courses open to undergrads. Off campus study at Tennessee Technological University, University of Memphis.

Entrance Requirements: Open admission for non-traditional undergraduate program. Options: electronic application, early admission, deferred admission. Required: high school transcript, minimum 2 high school GPA. Recommended: SAT or ACT. Required for some: essay, interview. Entrance: minimally difficult. Application deadline: Rolling. Notification: continuous.

Costs Per Year: Application fee: $30. Comprehensive fee: $22,884 includes full-time tuition ($13,870), mandatory fees ($650), and college room and board ($8364). Full-time tuition and fees vary according to program. Part-time tuition: $433 per credit hour. Part-time tuition varies according to course load and program.

Collegiate Environment: Orientation program. Drama-theater group, choral group, marching band. Social organizations: 17 open to all; local fraternities, local sororities; 20% of eligible men and 15% of eligible women are members. Most popular organizations: Campus Crusade for Christ, STEA (Education), Student Government Association, Students in Free Enterprise (SIFE), Arete. Major annual events: Convocation, school-wide dances, Homecoming. Student services: personal-psychological counseling. Campus security: night patrols by trained security personnel. Burroughs Learning Center plus 1 other with 45,000 books, 111,700 serials, 538 audiovisual materials, an OPAC, and a Web page. Operations spending for the previous fiscal year: $6.3 million. 12 computers available on campus for general student use. Computer purchase/lease plans available. A computer is required for all students. A campuswide network can be accessed from student residence rooms. Students can access the following: online class registration. Staffed computer lab on campus provides training in use of computers, software, and the Internet.

■ **BRYAN COLLEGE**
721 Bryan Dr.
Dayton, TN 37321
Tel: (423)775-2041; Free: 800-277-9522
Fax: (423)775-7330
E-mail: admissions@bryan.edu
Web Site: www.bryan.edu/

Description: Independent interdenominational, comprehensive, coed. Awards associate, bachelor's, and master's degrees. Founded 1930. Setting: 100-acre small town campus. Total enrollment: 1,304. Faculty: 66 (43 full-time, 23 part-time). Student-undergrad faculty ratio is 23:1. 897 applied, 53% were admitted. Full-time: 1,029 students, 54% women, 46% men. Part-time: 193 students, 48% women, 52% men. 50% from out-of-state. 0.2% American Indian or Alaska Native, non-Hispanic/Latino; 2% Hispanic/Latino; 5% African American, non-Hispanic/Latino; 1% Asian, non-Hispanic/Latino; 1% international. 1% 25 or older, 82% live on campus, 3% transferred in. Academic areas with the most degrees conferred: business/marketing; communication/journalism; education. Core. Calendar: semesters. Academic remediation for entering students, advanced placement, honors program, independent study, distance learning, double major, summer session for credit, part-time degree program, adult/continuing education programs, internships. Study abroad program.

Entrance Requirements: Options: electronic application, early action, deferred admission, international baccalaureate accepted. Required: essay, high school transcript, minimum 2 high school GPA, 3 recommendations, SAT or ACT. Required for some: interview. Entrance: moderately difficult. Application deadlines: Rolling, 5/1 for early action. Notification: continuous, Rolling for early action. SAT Reasoning Test deadline: 8/10. SAT Subject Test deadline: 8/10.

Collegiate Environment: Orientation program. Drama-theater group, choral group, student-run newspaper. Student services: health clinic, personal-psychological counseling. Campus security: student patrols, late night transport-escort service, controlled dormitory access, police patrols. Ironside Memorial Library with an OPAC and a Web page.

Community Environment: Dayton is located 38 miles from Chattanooga, enjoying a very desirable climate the year round. Air and bus transportation are convenient. Community facilities include some 20 churches representing Protestant and Roman Catholic faiths, a public library, a hospital, and motels. TVA lakes provide fishing and water sports. Part-time employment is available for students. The East Tennessee Strawberry Festival is held in May.

■ **CARSON-NEWMAN UNIVERSITY**
1646 Russell Ave.
Jefferson City, TN 37760
Tel: (865)471-2000; Free: 800-678-9061
Fax: (865)471-3502
E-mail: cnadmiss@cn.edu
Web Site: www.cn.edu/

Description: Independent Southern Baptist, comprehensive, coed. Awards associate, bachelor's, and master's degrees. Founded 1851. Setting: 90-acre small town campus with easy access to Knoxville. Endowment: $45.8

million. Educational spending for the previous fiscal year: $7294 per student. Total enrollment: 1,967. Faculty: 206 (111 full-time, 95 part-time). Student-undergrad faculty ratio is 12:1. 2,917 applied, 66% were admitted. 27% from top 10% of their high school class, 47% from top quarter, 73% from top half. Full-time: 1,573 students, 53% women, 47% men. Part-time: 73 students, 55% women, 45% men. Students come from 30 states and territories, 23 other countries, 22% from out-of-state. 0.3% American Indian or Alaska Native, non-Hispanic/Latino; 2% Hispanic/Latino; 10% African American, non-Hispanic/Latino; 0.4% Asian, non-Hispanic/Latino; 0.1% Native Hawaiian or other Pacific Islander, non-Hispanic/Latino; 3% international. 6% 25 or older, 51% live on campus, 6% transferred in. Retention: 60% of full-time freshmen returned the following year. Academic areas with the most degrees conferred: education; business/marketing; health professions and related sciences. Core. Calendar: semesters. Academic remediation for entering students, ESL program, services for LD students, advanced placement, accelerated degree program, self-designed majors, honors program, summer session for credit, part-time degree program, adult/continuing education programs, internships, graduate courses open to undergrads. Off campus study. Study abroad program. ROTC: Army, Air Force (c).

Entrance Requirements: Options: electronic application, deferred admission, international baccalaureate accepted. Required: high school transcript, minimum 2.25 high school GPA, medical history, SAT or ACT. Recommended: interview. Required for some: essay, interview. Entrance: moderately difficult. Application deadline: 8/1. Notification: continuous.

Costs Per Year: Application fee: $25. Comprehensive fee: $29,058 includes full-time tuition ($21,660), mandatory fees ($992), and college room and board ($6406). Full-time tuition and fees vary according to class time and course load. Room and board charges vary according to board plan, gender, and housing facility. Part-time tuition: $900 per credit hour.

Collegiate Environment: Orientation program. Drama-theater group, choral group, marching band, student-run newspaper. Social organizations: 63 open to all; national fraternities, national sororities, local fraternities, local sororities; 5% of eligible men and 5% of eligible women are members. Most popular organizations: Baptist Student Union, Fellowship of Christian Athletes, Student Government Association, Student Ambassadors Association, Columbians. Major annual events: Welcome Week, Beach Fest, homecoming. Student services: health clinic, personal-psychological counseling. Campus security: 24-hour emergency response devices and patrols, late night transport-escort service, controlled dormitory access. 1,427 college housing spaces available. Freshmen guaranteed college housing. On-campus residence required through junior year. Options: men-only, women-only housing available. Stephens-Burnett Library plus 1 other with 283,517 books, 276,403 microform titles, 3,966 serials, an OPAC, and a Web page. Operations spending for the previous fiscal year: $771,598. 200 computers available on campus for general student use. A campuswide network can be accessed from student residence rooms and from off campus. Staffed computer lab on campus.

Community Environment: Jefferson City is located 27 miles from Knoxville, a city of approximately 400,000. Plane and bus transportation are available. Recreational activities include fishing, water skiing, swimming, and boating at Cherokee and Douglas Lakes, a short drive away. Skiing is available in the Great Smoky Mountains National Park. Part-time employment opportunities are available.

■ **CHATTANOOGA COLLEGE–MEDICAL, DENTAL AND TECHNICAL CAREERS**
3805 Brainerd Rd.
Chattanooga, TN 37411-3798
Tel: (423)624-0077; Free: 877-313-2373
Web Site: www.chattanoogacollege.edu/
Description: Proprietary, 2-year, coed. Awards transfer associate degrees. Total enrollment: 147. 58% 25 or older.
Entrance Requirements: Open admission.
Costs Per Year: Application fee: $75. One-time mandatory fee: $25. Tuition: $9515 full-time. Mandatory fees: $2600 full-time. Full-time tuition and fees vary according to degree level and program. Tuition guaranteed not to increase for student's term of enrollment.

■ **CHATTANOOGA STATE COMMUNITY COLLEGE**
4501 Amnicola Hwy.
Chattanooga, TN 37406-1097
Tel: (423)697-4400; Free: 866-547-3733
Fax: (423)697-4709
E-mail: brad.mccormick@chattanoogastate.edu

Web Site: www.chattanoogastate.edu/
Description: State-supported, 2-year, coed. Part of Tennessee Board of Regents. Awards certificates, diplomas, transfer associate, and terminal associate degrees. Founded 1965. Setting: 100-acre urban campus. Endowment: $6.8 million. Educational spending for the previous fiscal year: $2224 per student. Total enrollment: 10,438. Faculty: 699 (224 full-time, 475 part-time). Student-undergrad faculty ratio is 19:1. 1,758 applied, 100% were admitted. Full-time: 1,061 students, 56% women, 44% men. Part-time: 525 students, 59% women, 41% men. Students come from 23 states and territories, 9 other countries, 11% from out-of-state. 0.2% American Indian or Alaska Native, non-Hispanic/Latino; 2% Hispanic/Latino; 18% African American, non-Hispanic/Latino; 1% Asian, non-Hispanic/Latino. 41% 25 or older, 99.9% transferred in. Core. Calendar: semesters. Academic remediation for entering students, services for LD students, advanced placement, accelerated degree program, honors program, independent study, distance learning, double major, summer session for credit, part-time degree program, external degree program, adult/continuing education programs, co-op programs and internships.

Entrance Requirements: Open admission. Options: electronic application, early admission, deferred admission. Recommended: high school transcript. Required for some: high school transcript, interview. Entrance: noncompetitive. Application deadlines: Rolling, Rolling for nonresidents. Notification: continuous, continuous for nonresidents. Transfer credits accepted: Yes.

Costs Per Year: Application fee: $15. State resident tuition: $3555 full-time, $135 per credit hour part-time. Nonresident tuition: $13,683 full-time, $422 per credit hour part-time. Mandatory fees: $315 full-time. Full-time tuition and fees vary according to course load. Part-time tuition varies according to course load.

Collegiate Environment: Orientation program. Drama-theater group, choral group, student-run newspaper. Social organizations: 35 open to all. Most popular organizations: Black Student Association, Adult Connections, Human Services Specialists, Student Government Association, Student Nurses Association. Major annual events: Fun in the Sun, Oktoberfest, Wellness Festival. Student services: personal-psychological counseling, women's center. Campus security: 24-hour emergency response devices and patrols, late night transport-escort service. Augusta R. Kolwyck Library with 161,086 books, 256 serials, 3,680 audiovisual materials, an OPAC, and a Web page. Operations spending for the previous fiscal year: $203,619. 500 computers available on campus for general student use. A campuswide network can be accessed from off-campus. Students can access the following: online class registration. Staffed computer lab on campus provides training in use of computers, software, and the Internet.

Community Environment: Located in southeastern Tennessee on the Tennessee River, Chattanooga is an important industrial center with over 500 manufacturing plants. All forms of commercial transportation are convenient. Part-time employment is available. Recreational facilities are plentiful, Chickamauga Lake, formed by the TVA dam, provides a wonderful place for water sports, and fishing; also there are other lakes, rivers and streams, and Harrison Bay State Park and Hamilton County State Park for other activities. Chattanooga has a number of city parks, and five golf courses for activities within the city. Some points of interest are Lookout Mountain, Lookout Mountain Incline Railway, Rock City Gardens, the Ruby Falls-Lookout Mountain Caves, and the Chattanooga Choo-Choo.

■ **CHRISTIAN BROTHERS UNIVERSITY**
650 E Pky. S
Memphis, TN 38104-5581
Tel: (901)321-3000; Free: 877-321-4CBU
Fax: (901)321-3202
E-mail: admissions@cbu.edu
Web Site: www.cbu.edu/
Description: Independent Roman Catholic, comprehensive, coed. Awards bachelor's and master's degrees. Founded 1871. Setting: 75-acre urban campus with easy access to Memphis. Endowment: $26.9 million. Total enrollment: 1,598. Faculty: 153 (104 full-time, 49 part-time). Student-undergrad faculty ratio is 11:1. 1,943 applied, 48% were admitted. 38% from top 10% of their high school class, 66% from top quarter, 89% from top half. 1 valedictorian. Full-time: 1,079 students, 56% women, 44% men. Part-time: 158 students, 70% women, 30% men. Students come from 27 states and territories, 25 other countries, 20% from out-of-state. 0.3% American Indian or Alaska Native, non-Hispanic/Latino; 5% Hispanic/Latino; 36% African American, non-Hispanic/Latino; 5% Asian, non-Hispanic/Latino; 0.1% Native Hawaiian or other Pacific Islander, non-Hispanic/Latino; 4% international. 17% 25 or older, 40% live on campus, 6% transferred in. Retention: 72% of

full-time freshmen returned the following year. Academic areas with the most degrees conferred: business/marketing; engineering; psychology. Core. Calendar: semesters. Services for LD students, advanced placement, accelerated degree program, honors program, independent study, distance learning, double major, summer session for credit, part-time degree program, adult/continuing education programs, internships, graduate courses open to undergrads. Off campus study at Greater Memphis Consortium. Study abroad program. ROTC: Army (c), Naval (c), Air Force (c).

Entrance Requirements: Options: electronic application, deferred admission. Required: essay, high school transcript, minimum 2 high school GPA, SAT or ACT. Recommended: interview. Required for some: 2 recommendations. Entrance: moderately difficult. Application deadline: 8/1. Notification: 12/1. SAT Reasoning Test deadline: 5/1.

Costs Per Year: Application fee: $25. Comprehensive fee: $33,424 includes full-time tuition ($26,694), mandatory fees ($590), and college room and board ($6140). Full-time tuition and fees vary according to class time and program. Room and board charges vary according to board plan and housing facility. Part-time tuition: $936 per credit hour. Part-time mandatory fees: $115 per term. Part-time tuition and fees vary according to class time, course load, and program.

Collegiate Environment: Orientation program. Drama-theater group, choral group. Social organizations: 37 open to all; national fraternities, national sororities, local sororities; 25% of eligible men and 19% of eligible women are members. Most popular organizations: Black Student Association, BACCHUS Alcohol Awareness Group, Intercultural Club, The Chosen Generation, Lasallian Collegians. Major annual events: Homecoming Week, Sofapalooza. Student services: health clinic, personal-psychological counseling. Campus security: 24-hour emergency response devices and patrols, student patrols, late night transport-escort service, controlled dormitory access. 550 college housing spaces available; 443 were occupied in 2012-13. Freshmen given priority for college housing. On-campus residence required through sophomore year. Options: coed, men-only, women-only housing available. Plough Memorial Library and Media Center with 101,898 books, 61,523 microform titles, 371 serials, 2,004 audiovisual materials, an OPAC, and a Web page. Operations spending for the previous fiscal year: $530,977. 310 computers available on campus for general student use. A campuswide network can be accessed from student residence rooms and from off campus. Students can access the following: online class registration, online class listings, course assignments. Staffed computer lab on campus provides training in use of computers, software, and the Internet.

Community Environment: See University of Memphis.

■ **CLEVELAND STATE COMMUNITY COLLEGE**
PO Box 3570
Cleveland, TN 37320-3570
Tel: (423)472-7141; Free: 800-604-2722
Fax: (423)478-6255
E-mail: SBayne@clevelandstatecc.edu
Web Site: www.clevelandstatecc.edu/

Description: State-supported, 2-year, coed. Part of Tennessee Board of Regents. Awards certificates, transfer associate, and terminal associate degrees. Founded 1967. Setting: 83-acre suburban campus. Endowment: $6.4 million. Educational spending for the previous fiscal year: $2710 per student. Total enrollment: 3,640. Faculty: 194 (71 full-time, 123 part-time). Student-undergrad faculty ratio is 22:1. 1,619 applied, 48% were admitted. Full-time: 1,920 students, 57% women, 43% men. Part-time: 1,720 students, 69% women, 31% men. Students come from 7 states and territories, 3 other countries, 1% from out-of-state. 0.3% American Indian or Alaska Native, non-Hispanic/Latino; 0.3% Hispanic/Latino; 6% African American, non-Hispanic/Latino; 1% Asian, non-Hispanic/Latino; 0.2% international. 36% 25 or older, 5% transferred in. Core. Calendar: semesters. Academic remediation for entering students, services for LD students, advanced placement, honors program, independent study, distance learning, double major, summer session for credit, part-time degree program, external degree program, adult/continuing education programs, co-op programs and internships. Off campus study at Chattanooga State Technical Community College.

Entrance Requirements: Open admission except for nursing, medical assistant programs. Options: electronic application, early admission, deferred admission. Required: high school transcript. Entrance: noncompetitive. Application deadline: Rolling. Notification: continuous.

Costs Per Year: Application fee: $10. State resident tuition: $3402 full-time, $135 per credit hour part-time. Nonresident tuition: $14,034 full-time, $557

per credit hour part-time. Mandatory fees: $269 full-time, $14.25 per credit hour part-time, $22 per term part-time. Full-time tuition and fees vary according to course load.

Collegiate Environment: Orientation program. Choral group, student-run newspaper. Social organizations: 20 open to all; 21% of eligible men and 79% of eligible women are members. Most popular organizations: Human Services/Social Work, Computer Aided Design, Phi Theta Kappa, Student Nursing Association, Early Childhood Education. Major annual events: Career Fair, Octoberfest, Q.E.P. (Quality Enhancement Plan) Picnic. Student services: personal-psychological counseling. Campus security: 24-hour emergency response devices and patrols. College housing not available. Cleveland State Community College Library with 153,456 books, 26,803 microform titles, 1,137 serials, 8,142 audiovisual materials, an OPAC, and a Web page. Operations spending for the previous fiscal year: $405,761. 720 computers available on campus for general student use. A campuswide network can be accessed from off-campus. Students can access the following: online class registration. Staffed computer lab on campus provides training in use of computers, software, and the Internet.

Community Environment: Cleveland was first settled in 1837 and served as headquarters for both General Grant and General Sherman during the Civil War. The city is in the heart of the great Tennessee Valley and is the gateway to the awe inspiring Cherokee National Forest. The climate is mild-temperate, long warm summers, and short mild winters. All forms of commercial transportation are available. The community facilities include a public library, many churches representing all denominations, YMCA, a hospital, community theatre, concert series, and a number of the usual civic and service organizations. Nearby, TVA lakes offer facilities for swimming, fishing, boating, and skiing; the city facilities provide for other activities such as tennis and golf. Part-time employment is available.

■ **COLUMBIA STATE COMMUNITY COLLEGE**
PO Box 1315
Columbia, TN 38402-1315
Tel: (931)540-2722
Fax: (931)540-2535
E-mail: scruggs@coscc.cc.tn.us
Web Site: www.columbiastate.edu/

Description: State-supported, 2-year, coed. Awards certificates, transfer associate, and terminal associate degrees. Founded 1966. Setting: 179-acre small town campus with easy access to Nashville. Total enrollment: 4,633. 1,093 applied, 100% were admitted. 33% 25 or older. Core. Calendar: semesters. Academic remediation for entering students, services for LD students, advanced placement, honors program, double major, summer session for credit, part-time degree program, adult/continuing education programs.

Entrance Requirements: Option: early admission. Required: high school transcript. Entrance: noncompetitive. Application deadline: Rolling.

Costs Per Year: Application fee: $10. State resident tuition: $3402 full-time, $135 per credit hour part-time. Nonresident tuition: $14,034 full-time, $557 per credit hour part-time. Mandatory fees: $271 full-time, $16.32 per credit hour part-time, $83 per term part-time. Full-time tuition and fees vary according to course load. Part-time tuition and fees vary according to course load.

Collegiate Environment: Orientation program. Drama-theater group. Student services: health clinic, personal-psychological counseling. Campus security: 24-hour patrols. John W. Finney Memorial Learning Resources Center with 61,200 books, 460 serials, and an OPAC.

Community Environment: A metropolitan community with temperate climate, Columbia is the boyhood home of James K. Polk. In Bluegrass country, it is noted for its diversified industry and agriculture. Particularly notable are the phosphate industry, and the Saturn automobile plant. Numerous civic and service organizations and excellent shopping facilities are part of the community. Outstanding recreational facilities include city parks, tennis courts, swimming pools, golf courses, and many TVA lakes for swimming, boating, fishing, and skiing. The National Tennessee Walking Horse Spring Jubilee is held each May in Maury County Park, three miles west. The Maury County Fair is an annual event. There are good opportunities for part-time employment.

■ **CONCORDE CAREER COLLEGE**
5100 Poplar Ave.
Ste. 132
Memphis, TN 38137
Tel: (901)761-9494
Fax: (901)761-3293

E-mail: dvickers@concorde.edu

Web Site: www.concorde.edu/

Description: Proprietary, 2-year, coed. Awards terminal associate degrees. Founded 1969. Total enrollment: 1,113. Student-undergrad faculty ratio is 24:1. 383 applied, 100% were admitted. 2% from out-of-state. 57% 25 or older.

Entrance Requirements: Required: high school transcript.

■ CUMBERLAND UNIVERSITY

1 Cumberland Sq.

Lebanon, TN 37087

Tel: (615)444-2562; Free: 800-467-0562

Fax: (615)444-2569

E-mail: admissions@cumberland.edu

Web Site: www.cumberland.edu/

Description: Independent, comprehensive, coed. Awards associate, bachelor's, and master's degrees. Founded 1842. Setting: 44-acre small town campus with easy access to Nashville. Endowment: $8.4 million. Educational spending for the previous fiscal year: $5203 per student. Total enrollment: 1,375. Faculty: 122 (48 full-time, 74 part-time). Student-undergrad faculty ratio is 15:1. 592 applied, 56% were admitted. 15% from top 10% of their high school class, 49% from top quarter, 77% from top half. 2 class presidents, 2 valedictorians, 1 student government officer. Full-time: 965 students, 54% women, 46% men. Part-time: 155 students, 66% women, 34% men. Students come from 26 states and territories, 19 other countries, 10% from out-of-state. 0.4% American Indian or Alaska Native, non-Hispanic/Latino; 3% Hispanic/Latino; 11% African American, non-Hispanic/Latino; 1% Asian, non-Hispanic/Latino; 0% Native Hawaiian or other Pacific Islander, non-Hispanic/Latino; 3% international. 22% 25 or older, 30% live on campus, 17% transferred in. Retention: 68% of full-time freshmen returned the following year. Academic areas with the most degrees conferred: health professions and related sciences; business/marketing; education. Core. Calendar: semesters. Academic remediation for entering students, services for LD students, advanced placement, accelerated degree program, freshman honors college, honors program, double major, summer session for credit, part-time degree program, adult/continuing education programs, co-op programs and internships, graduate courses open to undergrads. ROTC: Army.

Entrance Requirements: Options: electronic application, deferred admission, international baccalaureate accepted. Required: high school transcript, SAT or ACT. Recommended: essay, minimum 2.5 high school GPA, SAT. Required for some: 3 recommendations. Entrance: moderately difficult. Application deadline: Rolling. Notification: continuous.

Costs Per Year: Application fee: $25. One-time mandatory fee: $100. Comprehensive fee: $28,000 includes full-time tuition ($19,200), mandatory fees ($1000), and college room and board ($7800). Full-time tuition and fees vary according to degree level. Room and board charges vary according to housing facility. Part-time tuition: $800 per credit hour. Part-time tuition varies according to course load and degree level.

Collegiate Environment: Orientation program. Drama-theater group, choral group, marching band, student-run newspaper, radio station. Social organizations: 15 open to all; national fraternities, national sororities; 6% of eligible men and 3% of eligible women are members. Most popular organizations: African-American Student Association, Baptist Collegiate Ministry, Law and Government Club, Student Government Association, Student Nurses' Association. Major annual events: Homecoming, Spring Fling Week, Coming Home. Student services: personal-psychological counseling. Campus security: 24-hour emergency response devices and patrols, late night transport-escort service. Doris and Harry Vise Library with 112,112 books, 245 microform titles, 232 serials, 1,871 audiovisual materials, an OPAC, and a Web page. 150 computers available on campus for general student use. A campuswide network can be accessed from student residence rooms and from off campus. Staffed computer lab on campus provides training in use of computers and software.

Community Environment: Named for the Biblical Lebanon because of the tall cedars found in the area. There are TVA Lakes on three sides of the town, and the Cedars of Lebanon State Park is on the fourth side. Bus transportation is available. Nashville Airport is 25 miles away. Community facilities include three libraries, many churches of major denominations, hospitals and clinic, four major shopping areas and a number of the civic and service organizations. Recreational facilities are excellent for fishing, boating, hunting, swimming, and water skiing.

■ DAYMAR INSTITUTE (CLARKSVILLE)

1860 Wilma Rudolph Blvd.

Clarksville, TN 37040

Tel: (931)552-7600

Fax: (931)552-3624

E-mail: aprather@daymarinstitute.edu

Web Site: www.daymarinstitute.edu/

Description: Proprietary, 4-year, coed. Awards associate and bachelor's degrees. Founded 1987. Setting: small town campus. Total enrollment: 532. Faculty: 39 (20 full-time, 19 part-time). Student-undergrad faculty ratio is 7:1. Full-time: 381 students, 78% women, 22% men. Part-time: 151 students, 80% women, 20% men. Students come from 12 states and territories, 2 other countries, 16% from out-of-state. 62% 25 or older, 0% transferred in. Core. Services for LD students, honors program, independent study, distance learning, double major, part-time degree program, co-op programs and internships.

Entrance Requirements: Open admission. Required: high school transcript, interview. Entrance: noncompetitive. Application deadline: Rolling. Notification: continuous. Transfer credits accepted: Yes.

Collegiate Environment: Orientation program. Social organizations: honor society. Major annual events: Spring Softball League, Annual Pic-Nic, Fall Festival.

■ DAYMAR INSTITUTE (MURFREESBORO)

415 Golden Bear Ct.

Murfreesboro, TN 37128

Web Site: www.daymarinstitute.edu/

Description: Proprietary, 4-year, coed.

■ DAYMAR INSTITUTE (NASHVILLE)

340 Plus Park Blvd.

Nashville, TN 37217

Tel: (615)361-7555

Web Site: www.daymarinstitute.edu/

Description: Proprietary, 2-year, coed. Awards transfer associate and terminal associate degrees. Founded 1884. Setting: 5-acre suburban campus. Total enrollment: 286. 52% 25 or older. Core. Calendar: semesters. Academic remediation for entering students, summer session for credit, part-time degree program, internships.

Entrance Requirements: Open admission. Option: deferred admission. Required: high school transcript. Entrance: noncompetitive. Application deadline: Rolling. Notification: continuous.

Collegiate Environment: Student-run newspaper. Student services: personal-psychological counseling. Campus security: 24-hour emergency response devices. 3,250 books, 20 serials, and a Web page.

■ DEVRY UNIVERSITY (MEMPHIS)

6401 Poplar Ave., Ste. 600

Memphis, TN 38119

Tel: (901)537-2560; Free: 866-338-7941

Fax: (901)682-1326

Web Site: www.devry.edu/

Description: Proprietary, comprehensive, coed. Awards associate, bachelor's, and master's degrees. Founded 2007. Total enrollment: 172. Full-time: 44 students, 80% women, 20% men. Part-time: 43 students, 51% women, 49% men. 21% from out-of-state. 75% 25 or older, 22% transferred in. Academic area with the most degrees conferred: business/marketing. Accelerated degree program, distance learning.

Entrance Requirements: Option: deferred admission. Application deadline: Rolling. Notification: continuous. SAT Reasoning Test deadline: 10/31.

■ DEVRY UNIVERSITY (NASHVILLE)

3343 Perimeter Hill Dr., Ste. 200

Nashville, TN 37211-4147

Tel: (615)445-3456; Free: 866-338-7941

Web Site: www.devry.edu/

Description: Proprietary, comprehensive, coed. Awards associate, bachelor's, and master's degrees.

■ DYERSBURG STATE COMMUNITY COLLEGE

1510 Lake Rd.

Dyersburg, TN 38024

Tel: (731)286-3200

Fax: (731)286-3325

E-mail: jcaviness@dscc.edu

Web Site: www.dscc.edu/

Description: State-supported, 2-year, coed. Part of Tennessee Board of Regents. Awards certificates, transfer associate, and terminal associate degrees. Founded 1969. Setting: 100-acre small town campus with easy access to Memphis. Endowment: $5.4 million. Total enrollment: 3,590. Faculty: 204 (67 full-time, 137 part-time). Student-undergrad faculty ratio is 18:1. 3% from top 10% of their high school class, 13% from top quarter, 40% from top half. Full-time: 1,601 students, 64% women, 36% men. Part-time: 1,989 students, 68% women, 32% men. Students come from 2 states and territories, 2 other countries. 0.01% from out-of-state. 1% American Indian or Alaska Native, non-Hispanic/Latino; 2% Hispanic/Latino; 20% African American, non-Hispanic/Latino; 0.4% Asian, non-Hispanic/Latino; 0.1% Native Hawaiian or other Pacific Islander, non-Hispanic/Latino. 45% 25 or older, 6% transferred in. Retention: 54% of full-time freshmen returned the following year. Core. Calendar: semesters. Academic remediation for entering students, services for LD students, advanced placement, honors program, independent study, distance learning, double major, summer session for credit, part-time degree program, adult/continuing education programs.

Entrance Requirements: Required: high school transcript, SAT or ACT, An official copy of ACT scores is required for all first-time degree-seeking students under the age of 21. ACT scores may be used only if the ACT scores are no older than three years. Official SAT scores may be accepted in lieu of ACT scores. The COMPASS is required by student who are over 21.

Costs Per Year: State resident tuition: $3531 full-time, $135 per credit hour part-time. Nonresident tuition: $13,659 full-time, $590 per credit hour part-time. Mandatory fees: $291 full-time, $145.50 per term part-time. Full-time tuition and fees vary according to course load. Part-time tuition and fees vary according to course load.

Collegiate Environment: Orientation program. Drama-theater group, choral group. Social organizations: 9 open to all. Most popular organizations: Psychology Club, Phi Theta Kappa, student government, Media Club, Criminal Justice Association. Major annual events: Spring Fling, Homecoming, FOCUS-Open House. Student services: personal-psychological counseling. Campus security: 24-hour patrols. College housing not available. Learning Resource Center with 66,892 books, 35 serials, 479 audiovisual materials, an OPAC, and a Web page. Operations spending for the previous fiscal year: $497,699. 916 computers available on campus for general student use. A campuswide network can be accessed from off-campus. Students can access the following: online class registration. Staffed computer lab on campus provides training in use of computers, software, and the Internet.

■ EAST TENNESSEE STATE UNIVERSITY

807 University Pky.

Johnson City, TN 37614

Tel: (423)439-1000; Free: 800-462-3878

Fax: (423)439-5770

E-mail: go2etsu@etsu.edu

Web Site: www.etsu.edu/

Description: State-supported, university, coed. Part of State University and Community College System of Tennessee; Tennessee Board of Regents. Awards bachelor's, master's, and doctoral degrees and post-master's certificates. Founded 1911. Setting: 366-acre small town campus. Endowment: $100.1 million. Research spending for the previous fiscal year: $5.6 million. Educational spending for the previous fiscal year: $3387 per student. Total enrollment: 15,133. Faculty: 845 (562 full-time, 283 part-time). Student-undergrad faculty ratio is 19:1. 5,124 applied, 89% were admitted. 19% from top 10% of their high school class, 45% from top quarter, 77% from top half. Full-time: 10,234 students, 56% women, 44% men. Part-time: 2,033 students, 61% women, 39% men. Students come from 44 states and territories, 45 other countries, 12% from out-of-state. 0.4% American Indian or Alaska Native, non-Hispanic/Latino; 2% Hispanic/Latino; 6% African American, non-Hispanic/Latino; 1% Asian, non-Hispanic/Latino; 0.1% Native Hawaiian or other Pacific Islander, non-Hispanic/Latino; 2% international. 23% 25 or older, 20% live on campus, 10% transferred in. Retention: 66% of full-time freshmen returned the following year. Academic areas with the most degrees conferred: health professions and related sciences; business/marketing; liberal arts/general studies. Core. Calendar: semesters. ESL program, services for LD students, advanced placement, self-designed majors, freshman honors college, honors program, independent study, distance learning, double major, summer session for credit, part-time degree program, external degree program, adult/continuing education programs,

co-op programs and internships, graduate courses open to undergrads. Off campus study at Milligan College, Emmanuel School of Religion. Study abroad program. ROTC: Army.

Entrance Requirements: Options: electronic application, early admission, international baccalaureate accepted. Required: high school transcript, minimum 2.3 high school GPA, 2.3 high school GPA or 19 ACT, SAT or ACT. Entrance: moderately difficult. Application deadlines: Rolling, Rolling for nonresidents. Notification: continuous, continuous for nonresidents. SAT Reasoning Test deadline: 8/15. Transfer credits accepted: Yes.

Collegiate Environment: Orientation program. Drama-theater group, choral group, student-run newspaper, radio station. Social organizations: national fraternities, national sororities; 5% of eligible men and 5% of eligible women are members. Most popular organizations: honor societies, Volunteer ETSU, religious groups, residence hall councils. Major annual events: Homecoming, Greek Week, Winter Cruise. Student services: health clinic, personal-psychological counseling, women's center. Campus security: 24-hour emergency response devices and patrols, student patrols, late night transport-escort service, controlled dormitory access. 3,067 college housing spaces available. No special consideration for freshman housing applicants. Options: coed, men-only, women-only housing available. Sherrod Library plus 2 others with 1.1 million books, 1.7 million microform titles, 3,714 serials, an OPAC, and a Web page. Operations spending for the previous fiscal year: $3.3 million. 1,400 computers available on campus for general student use. Computer purchase/lease plans available. A campuswide network can be accessed from student residence rooms. Students can access the following: online class registration. Staffed computer lab on campus (open 24 hours a day) provides training in use of computers, software, and the Internet.

Community Environment: Johnson City, Kingsport and Bristol compose the Tri-Cities area, which is Tennessee's fifth largest metropolitan area, having one million people living within a 50-mile radius. Johnson City, a progressive city with a population of approximately 58,700, is located close to the state lines of Virginia, Kentucky, West Virginia, North Carolina and South Carolina. Recreational opportunities abound and include boating and water skiing on major TVA lakes, a variety of snow skiing resorts featuring downhill and cross-country, mountain hiking trails including easy access to the Appalachian Trail, and white water rafting. Interstate highways I-40, I-81 and I-26 provide access by automobile, with Tri-Cities Regional Airport providing access by commercial airlines. All major religious denominations are represented.

■ L'ECOLE CULINAIRE

1245 N Germantown Pky.

Cordova, TN 38016

Tel: (901)754-7115

Web Site: www.lecole.edu/memphis/

Description: Proprietary, 2-year, coed.

■ FISK UNIVERSITY

1000 17th Ave., N

Nashville, TN 37208-3051

Tel: (615)329-8500; Free: 888-702-0022

Fax: (615)329-8576

E-mail: admit@fisk.edu

Web Site: www.fisk.edu/

Description: Independent, comprehensive, coed, affiliated with United Church of Christ. Awards bachelor's and master's degrees. Founded 1866. Setting: 40-acre urban campus. Endowment: $12.1 million. Research spending for the previous fiscal year: $3.1 million. Educational spending for the previous fiscal year: $8070 per student. Total enrollment: 635. Faculty: 80 (59 full-time, 21 part-time). Student-undergrad faculty ratio is 9:1. 1,031 applied, 65% were admitted. 18% from top 10% of their high school class, 39% from top quarter, 71% from top half. 20 class presidents, 25 student government officers. Full-time: 560 students, 66% women, 34% men. Part-time: 34 students, 59% women, 41% men. Students come from 34 states and territories, 8 other countries, 76% from out-of-state. 5% 25 or older, 68% live on campus, 4% transferred in. Retention: 75% of full-time freshmen returned the following year. Academic areas with the most degrees conferred: psychology; social sciences; English. Core. Calendar: semesters. Advanced placement, self-designed majors, honors program, independent study, double major, co-op programs and internships, graduate courses open to undergrads. Off campus study at 4 members of the Nashville University Center, 17 other institutions. Study abroad program. ROTC: Army (c), Naval (c).

Entrance Requirements: Option: electronic application. Required: essay, high school transcript, minimum 2.5 high school GPA, 2 recommendations, SAT or ACT. Entrance: moderately difficult. Application deadlines: 3/1, 3/1 for nonresidents. Notification: continuous, continuous for nonresidents.

Collegiate Environment: Orientation program. Drama-theater group, choral group, student-run newspaper, radio station. Social organizations: 55 open to all; national fraternities, national sororities; 25% of eligible men and 20% of eligible women are members. Most popular organizations: Student Government Association, State Clubs, Students in Free Enterprise (SIFE), Students for Change, Caribbean Student Association. Major annual events: Homecoming, Arts Festival, Jubilee Day Convocation. Student services: personal-psychological counseling. Campus security: 24-hour patrols, late night transport-escort service. John Hope and Aurelia E. Franklin Library with 127,070 books, 111,224 microform titles, 221 serials, 3,880 audiovisual materials, an OPAC, and a Web page. Operations spending for the previous fiscal year: $505,794. 40 computers available on campus for general student use. Computer purchase/lease plans available. A campuswide network can be accessed from student residence rooms and from off campus. Staffed computer lab on campus provides training in use of computers, software, and the Internet.

Community Environment: See Vanderbilt University.

■ FORTIS INSTITUTE

1025 Hwy. 111
Cookeville, TN 38501
Tel: (931)526-3660; Free: 855-4-FORTIS
Fax: (931)372-2603
Web Site: www.fortis.edu/

Description: Proprietary, 2-year, coed. Awards certificates, diplomas, and terminal associate degrees. Founded 1970. Setting: 4-acre small town campus. Total enrollment: 283. 237 applied. 60% 25 or older. Core. Internships.

Entrance Requirements: Required: high school transcript, interview, Wonderlic aptitude test. Recommended: minimum 2.0 high school GPA, 2 recommendations. Entrance: noncompetitive. Application deadline: Rolling. Notification: continuous.

Collegiate Environment: Orientation program.

■ FOUNTAINHEAD COLLEGE OF TECHNOLOGY

10208 Technology Dr.
Knoxville, TN 37932
Tel: (865)688-9422; Free: 888-218-7335
Fax: (865)688-2419
E-mail: joel.southern@fountainheadcollege.edu
Web Site: www.fountainheadcollege.edu/

Description: Proprietary, primarily 2-year, coed. Awards transfer associate, terminal associate, and bachelor's degrees. Founded 1947. Setting: 2-acre suburban campus. Total enrollment: 230. Faculty: 23 (11 full-time, 12 part-time). Student-undergrad faculty ratio is 9:1. 0% from out-of-state. 82% of full-time freshmen returned the following year. Core. Calendar: semesters. Accelerated degree program, distance learning, double major, summer session for credit.

Entrance Requirements: Open admission. Required: high school transcript, interview. Required for some: SAT or ACT. Entrance: noncompetitive. Application deadline: Rolling. Notification: continuous. Transfer credits accepted: Yes.

Costs Per Year: Tuition: $485 per credit hour part-time. Tuition guaranteed not to increase for student's term of enrollment.

Collegiate Environment: Campus security: 24-hour emergency response devices. College housing not available. Library and Resource Center with an OPAC and a Web page. Operations spending for the previous fiscal year: $6000.

■ FREED-HARDEMAN UNIVERSITY

158 E Main St.
Henderson, TN 38340-2399
Tel: (731)989-6000; Free: 800-FHU-FHU-1
Fax: (731)989-6047
E-mail: jaskew@fhu.edu
Web Site: www.fhu.edu/

Description: Independent, comprehensive, coed, affiliated with Church of Christ. Awards associate, bachelor's, master's, and doctoral degrees and post-master's certificates. Founded 1869. Setting: 120-acre small town campus. Endowment: $35.4 million. Educational spending for the previous

fiscal year: $7870 per student. Total enrollment: 1,904. Faculty: 149 (90 full-time, 59 part-time). Student-undergrad faculty ratio is 12:1. 1,010 applied, 44% were admitted. 33% from top 10% of their high school class, 54% from top quarter, 82% from top half. Full-time: 1,289 students, 56% women, 44% men. Part-time: 160 students, 53% women, 48% men. Students come from 33 states and territories, 20 other countries, 42% from out-of-state. 0.4% American Indian or Alaska Native, non-Hispanic/Latino; 1% Hispanic/Latino; 5% African American, non-Hispanic/Latino; 0.3% Asian, non-Hispanic/Latino; 2% international. 4% 25 or older, 82% live on campus, 5% transferred in. Retention: 71% of full-time freshmen returned the following year. Academic areas with the most degrees conferred: education; interdisciplinary studies; business/marketing. Core. Calendar: semesters. Academic remediation for entering students, services for LD students, advanced placement, accelerated degree program, self-designed majors, freshman honors college, honors program, independent study, distance learning, double major, summer session for credit, part-time degree program, co-op programs and internships, graduate courses open to undergrads. Off campus study at Union University. Study abroad program.

Entrance Requirements: Options: electronic application, deferred admission, international baccalaureate accepted. Required: high school transcript, minimum 2.25 high school GPA, ACT and/or SAT scores, SAT or ACT. Recommended: essay. Required for some: interview. Entrance: moderately difficult. Application deadline: Rolling. Notification: continuous. Transfer credits accepted: Yes.

Costs Per Year: Application fee: $0. Comprehensive fee: $27,764 includes full-time tuition ($20,468) and college room and board ($7296). College room only: $3980. Room and board charges vary according to board plan and housing facility. Part-time tuition: $642 per credit hour.

Collegiate Environment: Orientation program. Drama-theater group, choral group, student-run newspaper, radio station. Social organizations: 18 open to all; There are 6 co-ed social clubs on campus. Most popular organizations: Student Government Association, University Program Council, Campus Delegate Team, Student Alumni Association, College Republicans. Major annual events: Makin' Music, Homecoming, Lectureship. Student services: health clinic, personal-psychological counseling. Campus security: 24-hour patrols, controlled dormitory access. 1,271 college housing spaces available; 1,094 were occupied in 2012-13. Freshmen guaranteed college housing. On-campus residence required through senior year. Options: men-only, women-only housing available. Loden-Daniel Library with 298,750 books, 23,524 serials, 49,582 audiovisual materials, an OPAC, and a Web page. Operations spending for the previous fiscal year: $160,854. 63 computers available on campus for general student use. Computer purchase/lease plans available. A computer is required for all students. A campuswide network can be accessed from student residence rooms and from off campus. Students can access the following: online class registration. Staffed computer lab on campus provides training in use of computers, software, and the Internet.

Community Environment: Henderson is a rural town of 5,500 with an airport within 25 miles. A metropolitan area, Jackson, (population 62,000) is located within 15 miles and Memphis is only 80 miles away. The community facilities include churches, good shopping facilities, and some major civic and service organizations. The Tennessee River, Kentucky Lake, Chickasaw State Park, and Pickwick Dam provide a number of facilities for all kinds of water sports and other recreation. Some part-time employment is available.

■ HUNTINGTON COLLEGE OF HEALTH SCIENCES

1204 -D Kenesaw, Sequoyah Hills Ctr.
Knoxville, TN 37919-7736
Tel: (865)524-8079; Free: 800-290-4226
Fax: (865)524-8339
E-mail: studentservices@hchs.edu
Web Site: www.hchs.edu/

Description: Proprietary, comprehensive, coed. Awards associate, bachelor's, and master's degrees (offers only external degree programs conducted through home study). Founded 1984. Setting: suburban campus. Research spending for the previous fiscal year: $18,000. Total enrollment: 460. Faculty: 20 (3 full-time, 17 part-time). Student-undergrad faculty ratio is 29:1. 33 applied, 100% were admitted. Full-time: 400 students, 64% women, 36% men. Students come from 49 states and territories, 15 other countries, 98% from out-of-state. 90% 25 or older, 46% transferred in. Retention: 10% of full-time freshmen returned the following year. Academic area with the most degrees conferred: health professions and related sciences. Core. Calendar: continuous. Academic remediation for entering students, self-designed majors, independent study, distance learning, summer session for credit, part-time degree program, external degree program, adult/continuing education programs, graduate courses open to undergrads.

Entrance Requirements: Open admission. Options: electronic application, deferred admission, international baccalaureate accepted. Recommended: minimum 2 high school GPA. Required for some: high school transcript, interview. Entrance: noncompetitive. Application deadline: Rolling. Notification: continuous. Transfer credits accepted: Yes.

Costs Per Year: Application fee: $75. Tuition: $199 per semester hour part-time. Part-time tuition varies according to course load and program.

■ ITT TECHNICAL INSTITUTE (CHATTANOOGA)
5600 Brainerd Rd., Ste. G-1
Chattanooga, TN 37411
Tel: (423)510-6800; Free: 877-474-8312
Web Site: www.itt-tech.edu/
Description: Proprietary, primarily 2-year, coed. Part of ITT Educational Services, Inc. Awards terminal associate and bachelor's degrees.
Entrance Requirements: Entrance: minimally difficult.

■ ITT TECHNICAL INSTITUTE (CORDOVA)
7260 Goodlett Farms Pky.
Cordova, TN 38016
Tel: (901)381-0200; Free: 866-444-5141
Web Site: www.itt-tech.edu/
Description: Proprietary, primarily 2-year, coed. Part of ITT Educational Services, Inc. Awards terminal associate and bachelor's degrees. Founded 1994. Setting: suburban campus.
Entrance Requirements: Entrance: minimally difficult.

■ ITT TECHNICAL INSTITUTE (JOHNSON CITY)
4721 Lake Park Dr.
Ste. 100
Johnson City, TN 37615
Tel: (423)952-4400; Free: 877-301-9691
Web Site: www.itt-tech.edu/
Description: Proprietary, primarily 2-year, coed. Awards terminal associate and bachelor's degrees.
Entrance Requirements: Entrance: minimally difficult.

■ ITT TECHNICAL INSTITUTE (KNOXVILLE)
9123 Executive Park Dr.
Knoxville, TN 37923
Tel: (865)671-2800; Free: 800-671-2801
Fax: (865)691-0337
Web Site: www.itt-tech.edu/
Description: Proprietary, primarily 2-year, coed. Part of ITT Educational Services, Inc. Awards terminal associate and bachelor's degrees. Founded 1988. Setting: suburban campus.
Entrance Requirements: Entrance: minimally difficult.

■ ITT TECHNICAL INSTITUTE (NASHVILLE)
2845 Elm Hill Pke.
Nashville, TN 37214
Tel: (615)889-8700; Free: 800-331-8386
Fax: (615)872-7209
Web Site: www.itt-tech.edu/
Description: Proprietary, primarily 2-year, coed. Part of ITT Educational Services, Inc. Awards terminal associate and bachelor's degrees. Founded 1984. Setting: urban campus.
Entrance Requirements: Entrance: minimally difficult.

■ JACKSON STATE COMMUNITY COLLEGE
2046 N Pky.
Jackson, TN 38301-3797
Tel: (731)424-3520; Free: 800-355-5722
Fax: (731)425-2647
E-mail: awinchester@jscc.edu
Web Site: www.jscc.edu/
Description: State-supported, 2-year, coed. Part of Tennessee Board of Regents. Awards certificates, diplomas, transfer associate, and terminal associate degrees. Founded 1967. Setting: 97-acre suburban campus with easy access to Memphis. Endowment: $800,579. Educational spending for the previous fiscal year: $4115 per student. Total enrollment: 5,109. Faculty: 306 (98 full-time, 208 part-time). Student-undergrad faculty ratio is 21:1.

Students come from 7 states and territories, 3 other countries. 37% 25 or older. Retention: 49% of full-time freshmen returned the following year. Core. Calendar: semesters. Academic remediation for entering students, services for LD students, advanced placement, honors program, independent study, distance learning, summer session for credit, part-time degree program, external degree program, adult/continuing education programs, co-op programs and internships. Off campus study. ROTC: Army.

Entrance Requirements: Open admission except for allied health programs. Option: electronic application. Required: SAT or ACT, COMPASS. Recommended: ACT. Required for some: high school transcript. Entrance: noncompetitive. Application deadlines: 8/23, 8/23 for nonresidents. Notification: continuous, continuous for nonresidents. Preference given to state residents. Transfer credits accepted: Yes.

Collegiate Environment: Orientation program. Drama-theater group, choral group. Social organizations: 7 open to all. Most popular organizations: Spanish Club, Philosophy Club, Nation Against Genocide, FFA/Agriculture Club, Biology Club. Major annual events: Welcome Back Bash, Health and Career Fair, Alcohol Awareness. Student services: personal-psychological counseling. Campus security: 24-hour patrols, late night transport-escort service, field camera surveillance. Jackson State Community College Library with 56,024 books, 26,381 microform titles, 105 serials, 2,128 audiovisual materials, an OPAC, and a Web page. Operations spending for the previous fiscal year: $582,993. 1,000 computers available on campus for general student use. A campuswide network can be accessed from off-campus. Students can access the following: online class registration. Staffed computer lab on campus provides training in use of computers, software, and the Internet.

Community Environment: Jackson, at one time a small cotton port, is now a trading and shipping center. All forms of commercial transportation are available. Because of direct access to major thoroughfares, Jackson is one of the fastest growing cities in Tennessee and is the trade center for a large populated area. Its facilities include hospitals, clinics, many churches, an art association, and symphony orchestra. The city is known as the home and burial place of John Luther "Casey" Jones, who became a part of American folklore and a legend of early railroading. The Casey Jones Railroad Museum may be seen here.

■ JOHN A. GUPTON COLLEGE
1616 Church St.
Nashville, TN 37203-2920
Tel: (615)327-3927
Fax: (615)321-4518
E-mail: purcell@guptoncollege.edu
Web Site: www.guptoncollege.edu/
Description: Independent, 2-year, coed. Awards diplomas, transfer associate, and terminal associate degrees. Founded 1946. Setting: 1-acre urban campus with easy access to Nashville. Endowment: $60,000. Educational spending for the previous fiscal year: $2837 per student. Total enrollment: 138. Faculty: 13 (2 full-time, 11 part-time). Student-undergrad faculty ratio is 8:1. 74 applied, 49% were admitted. Full-time: 67 students, 55% women, 45% men. Part-time: 71 students, 51% women, 49% men. Students come from 3 states and territories, 1% from out-of-state. 1% American Indian or Alaska Native, non-Hispanic/Latino; 22% African American, non-Hispanic/Latino. 32% 25 or older, 11% live on campus, 14% transferred in. Calendar: semesters. Part-time degree program.

Entrance Requirements: Option: deferred admission. Required: essay, high school transcript, 2 recommendations, ACT. Entrance: minimally difficult. Application deadline: Rolling. Transfer credits accepted: Yes.

Costs Per Year: Application fee: $50. Tuition: $9440 full-time, $295 per semester hour part-time. Mandatory fees: $70 full-time. Full-time tuition and fees vary according to course load. Part-time tuition varies according to course load. College room only: $3600.

Collegiate Environment: Orientation program. Campus security: controlled dormitory access, day patrols. 14 college housing spaces available; all were occupied in 2012-13. No special consideration for freshman housing applicants. Option: coed housing available. Memorial Library with 4,000 books, 54 serials, and a Web page. 8 computers available on campus for general student use. Staffed computer lab on campus provides training in use of computers and the Internet.

■ JOHNSON UNIVERSITY
7900 Johnson Dr.
Knoxville, TN 37998-1001
Tel: (865)573-4517; Free: 800-827-2122
Fax: (865)251-2337

E-mail: twingfield@jbc.edu

Web Site: www.johnsonu.edu/

Description: Independent, comprehensive, coed, affiliated with Christian Churches and Churches of Christ. Awards associate, bachelor's, master's, and doctoral degrees. Founded 1893. Setting: 175-acre rural campus. Endowment: $99.9 million. Educational spending for the previous fiscal year: $5916 per student. Total enrollment: 816. Faculty: 62 (34 full-time, 28 part-time). Student-undergrad faculty ratio is 14:1. 466 applied, 66% were admitted. Full-time: 649 students, 47% women, 53% men. Part-time: 31 students, 52% women, 48% men. Students come from 34 states and territories, 13 other countries, 72% from out-of-state. 1% American Indian or Alaska Native, non-Hispanic/Latino; 3% Hispanic/Latino; 2% African American, non-Hispanic/Latino; 0.3% Asian, non-Hispanic/Latino; 0.1% Native Hawaiian or other Pacific Islander, non-Hispanic/Latino; 2% international. 3% 25 or older, 85% live on campus, 17% transferred in. Retention: 69% of full-time freshmen returned the following year. Academic areas with the most degrees conferred: education; family and consumer sciences; area and ethnic studies. Core. Calendar: semesters. Academic remediation for entering students, ESL program, services for LD students, advanced placement, accelerated degree program, honors program, independent study, distance learning, double major, summer session for credit, part-time degree program, adult/continuing education programs, co-op programs and internships, graduate courses open to undergrads. Study abroad program.

Entrance Requirements: Options: electronic application, deferred admission, international baccalaureate accepted. Required: essay, high school transcript, 3 recommendations, SAT or ACT. Required for some: interview, ACT. Entrance: moderately difficult. Application deadline: 7/1. Notification: continuous. Transfer credits accepted: Yes.

Collegiate Environment: Orientation program. Choral group, student-run radio station. Social organizations: 3 open to all. Most popular organizations: Quest, Timothy Club, International Harvesters. Major annual events: Homecoming, Founders' Day, Miller and Scott Christmas Banquet. Student services: health clinic, personal-psychological counseling. Campus security: 24-hour emergency response devices, student patrols, controlled dormitory access. Glass Memorial Library plus 1 other with 111,776 books, 20,223 microform titles, 310 serials, 14,710 audiovisual materials, an OPAC, and a Web page. Operations spending for the previous fiscal year: $327,185.

Community Environment: The college is located in the rural community of Kimberlin Heights within a 20-minute drive of Knoxville where shopping, jobs, recreation, hospitals, churches, and civic cultural, and service organizations are abundant.

■ **KAPLAN CAREER INSTITUTE, NASHVILLE CAMPUS**

750 Envious Ln.

Nashville, TN 37217

Tel: (615)279-8300; Free: 800-935-1857

Fax: (615)297-6678

Web Site: nashville.kaplancareerinstitute.com/

Description: Proprietary, 2-year, coed. Awards certificates, diplomas, and terminal associate degrees. Founded 1981.

■ **KING COLLEGE**

1350 King College Rd.

Bristol, TN 37620-2699

Tel: (423)968-1187; Free: 800-362-0014

Fax: (423)968-4456

E-mail: admissions@king.edu

Web Site: www.king.edu/

Description: Independent, comprehensive, coed, affiliated with Presbyterian Church (U.S.A.). Awards bachelor's and master's degrees and post-master's certificates. Founded 1867. Setting: 135-acre suburban campus. Endowment: $29.1 million. Research spending for the previous fiscal year: $38,943. Educational spending for the previous fiscal year: $4315 per student. Total enrollment: 2,342. Faculty: 212 (86 full-time, 126 part-time). Student-undergrad faculty ratio is 16:1. 1,090 applied, 72% were admitted. 17% from top 10% of their high school class, 42% from top quarter, 74% from top half. Full-time: 1,843 students, 65% women, 35% men. Part-time: 120 students, 57% women, 43% men. Students come from 31 states and territories, 29 other countries, 37% from out-of-state. 0.3% American Indian or Alaska Native, non-Hispanic/Latino; 2% Hispanic/Latino; 5% African American, non-Hispanic/Latino; 0.5% Asian, non-Hispanic/Latino; 0.1% Native Hawaiian or other Pacific Islander, non-Hispanic/Latino; 3% international. 47% 25 or older, 42% live on campus, 5% transferred in. Retention: 75% of full-time freshmen returned the following year. Academic areas with the most degrees

conferred: health professions and related sciences; business/marketing; computer and information sciences. Core. Calendar: semesters. Services for LD students, advanced placement, self-designed majors, honors program, independent study, distance learning, double major, summer session for credit, part-time degree program, adult/continuing education programs, co-op programs and internships. Off campus study at Virginia Intermont College. Study abroad program. ROTC: Army (c).

Entrance Requirements: Options: electronic application, early admission, deferred admission, international baccalaureate accepted. Required: high school transcript, minimum 2.4 high school GPA, SAT or ACT. Required for some: essay. Entrance: moderately difficult. Application deadlines: Rolling, Rolling for nonresidents. Notification: continuous, continuous for nonresidents. SAT Reasoning Test deadline: 7/31. Transfer credits accepted: Yes.

Costs Per Year: Application fee: $20. Comprehensive fee: $33,140 includes full-time tuition ($23,608), mandatory fees ($1352), and college room and board ($8180). College room only: $4108. Full-time tuition and fees vary according to course load and program. Room and board charges vary according to board plan. Part-time tuition: $600 per credit hour. Part-time tuition varies according to course load and program.

Collegiate Environment: Orientation program. Drama-theater group, choral group, student-run newspaper. Social organizations: 35 open to all. Most popular organizations: Student Government Association, Campus Life Committee, World Christian Fellowship, Fellowship of Christian Athletes, Drama Club. Major annual events: Fall Ball and Fall Play, Dogwood/Alumni Weekend, Parents' Weekend. Student services: personal-psychological counseling. Campus security: 24-hour patrols, late night transport-escort service, controlled dormitory access. 493 college housing spaces available; 327 were occupied in 2012-13. Freshmen guaranteed college housing. On-campus residence required through junior year. Options: men-only, women-only housing available. E. W. King Library with 104,697 books, 62,173 microform titles, 349 serials, 7,009 audiovisual materials, an OPAC, and a Web page. Operations spending for the previous fiscal year: $583,805. 90 computers available on campus for general student use. A campuswide network can be accessed from student residence rooms and from off campus. Students can access the following: online class registration, student portal.

Community Environment: Located in the beautiful Southern Highlands, Bristol is a twin city on the Tennessee-Virginia state line. Four distinct seasons offer year-round recreation. With three access points to the Appalachian trail within an hour's drive from campus, students can quickly escape to a wilderness playground. Nearby Cherokee and Jefferson National Forests provide more than 250,000 acres of unspoiled woodlands for hiking and camping. More than 40 square miles of inland lakes and freshwater streams await water enthusiasts, including South Holston Lake, site of the world's third largest earthen dam. Several major ski resorts are located within an hour's drive. NASCAR fans enjoy the world's fastest half-mile track at the Bristol Motor Speedway, and Bristol's Viking Hall Civic Center serves as a stop for top-name concerts, sporting events and community-sponsored shows and bazaars.

■ **LANE COLLEGE**

545 Ln. Ave.

Jackson, TN 38301-4598

Tel: (731)426-7500; Free: 800-960-7533

Fax: (731)426-7559

E-mail: jmorris@lanecollege.edu

Web Site: www.lanecollege.edu/

Description: Independent, 4-year, coed, affiliated with Christian Methodist Episcopal Church. Awards bachelor's degrees. Founded 1882. Setting: 25-acre suburban campus with easy access to Memphis. Endowment: $4.1 million. Educational spending for the previous fiscal year: $4431 per student. Total enrollment: 1,512. Faculty: 91 (90 full-time, 1 part-time). Student-undergrad faculty ratio is 17:1. 5,324 applied, 33% were admitted. 3% from top 10% of their high school class, 12% from top quarter, 39% from top half. Full-time: 1,484 students, 51% women, 49% men. Part-time: 28 students, 57% women, 43% men. Students come from 29 states and territories, 37% from out-of-state. 0% American Indian or Alaska Native, non-Hispanic/Latino; 0% Hispanic/Latino; 100% African American, non-Hispanic/Latino; 0% international. 9% 25 or older, 61% live on campus, 6% transferred in. Retention: 50% of full-time freshmen returned the following year. Academic areas with the most degrees conferred: business/marketing; biological/life sciences; homeland security, law enforcement, firefighting, and protective services. Core. Calendar: semesters. Academic remediation for entering students, advanced placement, accelerated degree program, honors program, independent study, summer session for credit, part-time degree program, adult/continuing education programs, co-op programs and internships. Off campus study. Study abroad program.

Entrance Requirements: Options: electronic application, deferred admission. Required: high school transcript, 2 recommendations, SAT or ACT. Entrance: minimally difficult. Application deadlines: Rolling, Rolling for nonresidents. Notification: continuous. SAT Reasoning Test deadline: 7/15.

Costs Per Year: Application fee: $0. Comprehensive fee: $14,600 includes full-time tuition ($7860), mandatory fees ($700), and college room and board ($6040). Full-time tuition and fees vary according to course load. Part-time tuition: $330 per credit hour. Part-time mandatory fees: $700 per year. Part-time tuition and fees vary according to course load.

Collegiate Environment: Orientation program. Drama-theater group, choral group, marching band. Social organizations: 36 open to all; national fraternities, national sororities, discipline specific academic clubs; 1% of eligible men and 5% of eligible women are members. Most popular organizations: Student Government Association, Pre-Law Club, Student Christian Association, Drama Club, Sociology Club. Major annual events: Homecoming, Founder's Day, Convocation/Weekly Chapel. Student services: health clinic, personal-psychological counseling. Campus security: 24-hour emergency response devices and patrols, late night transport-escort service, surveillance cameras, lighted parking areas. 1,234 college housing spaces available; 808 were occupied in 2012-13. Freshmen given priority for college housing. On-campus residence required in freshman year. Options: men-only, women-only housing available. Chambers-McClure Academic Center with 152,039 books, 191 microform titles, 9,751 serials, 1,013 audiovisual materials, an OPAC, and a Web page. Operations spending for the previous fiscal year: $405,954. 258 computers available on campus for general student use. A campuswide network can be accessed from student residence rooms and from off campus. Students can access the following: online admissions and advising. Staffed computer lab on campus provides training in use of computers and the Internet.

Community Environment: See Jackson State Community College.

■ **LEE UNIVERSITY**
PO Box 3450
Cleveland, TN 37320-3450
Tel: (423)614-8000; Free: 800-533-9930
Fax: (423)614-8533
E-mail: admissions@leeuniversity.edu
Web Site: www.leeuniversity.edu/

Description: Independent, comprehensive, coed, affiliated with Church of God. Awards bachelor's and master's degrees and post-master's certificates. Founded 1918. Setting: 104-acre small town campus with easy access to Chattanooga. Endowment: $12 million. Research spending for the previous fiscal year: $309,658. Educational spending for the previous fiscal year: $5586 per student. Total enrollment: 4,954. Faculty: 388 (157 full-time, 231 part-time). Student-undergrad faculty ratio is 18:1. 26% from top 10% of their high school class, 52% from top quarter, 79% from top half. Full-time: 3,834 students, 58% women, 42% men. Part-time: 731 students, 51% women, 49% men. Students come from 50 states and territories, 57 other countries, 56% from out-of-state. 0.4% American Indian or Alaska Native, non-Hispanic/Latino; 4% Hispanic/Latino; 6% African American, non-Hispanic/Latino; 1% Asian, non-Hispanic/Latino; 0.2% Native Hawaiian or other Pacific Islander, non-Hispanic/Latino; 5% international. 17% 25 or older, 48% live on campus, 5% transferred in. Retention: 73% of full-time freshmen returned the following year. Academic areas with the most degrees conferred: education; business/marketing; theology and religious vocations. Core. Calendar: semesters. Academic remediation for entering students, ESL program, services for LD students, advanced placement, honors program, independent study, distance learning, double major, summer session for credit, part-time degree program, external degree program, adult/continuing education programs, co-op programs and internships. Off campus study. Study abroad program.

Entrance Requirements: Required: high school transcript, minimum 2 high school GPA, MMR immunization record, SAT or ACT. Required for some: 3 recommendations.

Costs Per Year: Comprehensive fee: $20,512 includes full-time tuition ($13,200), mandatory fees ($550), and college room and board ($6762). College room only: $3502. Full-time tuition and fees vary according to course load, location, and program. Room and board charges vary according to board plan and housing facility. Part-time tuition: $550 per credit hour. Part-time mandatory fees: $550 per credit hour. Part-time tuition and fees vary according to course load, location, and program.

Collegiate Environment: Orientation program. Drama-theater group, choral group, student-run newspaper. Social organizations: 76 open to all; local fraternities, local sororities; 7% of eligible men and 8% of eligible women are members. Most popular organizations: Student Leadership Council, Pioneers for Christ, International Student Fellowship, Big Pal Little Pal, Back Yard Ministry. Major annual events: Homecoming, Dorm Wars, Lee Day. Student services: health clinic, personal-psychological counseling. Campus security: 24-hour emergency response devices and patrols, late night transport-escort service, controlled dormitory access. 2,082 college housing spaces available; 2,013 were occupied in 2012-13. Freshmen guaranteed college housing. On-campus residence required through sophomore year. Options: men-only, women-only housing available. William G. Squires Library plus 2 others with 240,059 books, 51,332 microform titles, 311 serials, 2,070 audiovisual materials, an OPAC, and a Web page. Operations spending for the previous fiscal year: $1.2 million. 410 computers available on campus for general student use. A campuswide network can be accessed from student residence rooms and from off campus. Students can access the following: online class registration.

Community Environment: See Cleveland State Community College.

■ **LEMOYNE-OWEN COLLEGE**
807 Walker Ave.
Memphis, TN 38126-6595
Tel: (901)774-9090; Free: 800-737-7778
Fax: (901)942-6272
E-mail: samuel_king@loc.edu
Web Site: www.loc.edu/

Description: Independent, 4-year, coed, affiliated with United Church of Christ. Awards bachelor's degrees. Founded 1862. Setting: 15-acre urban campus. Endowment: $15.1 million. Educational spending for the previous fiscal year: $7184 per student. Total enrollment: 592. Faculty: 88 (55 full-time, 33 part-time). Student-undergrad faculty ratio is 10:1. 673 applied, 51% were admitted. Full-time: 501 students, 65% women, 35% men. Part-time: 91 students, 64% women, 36% men. Students come from 12 states and territories, 4 other countries, 12% from out-of-state. 40% 25 or older, 25% live on campus, 30% transferred in. Retention: 43% of full-time freshmen returned the following year. Academic areas with the most degrees conferred: business/marketing; education; homeland security, law enforcement, firefighting, and protective services. Core. Calendar: semesters. Academic remediation for entering students, services for LD students, advanced placement, accelerated degree program, honors program, independent study, double major, summer session for credit, part-time degree program, co-op programs and internships. Off campus study at Greater Memphis Consortium. Study abroad program. ROTC: Army (c), Air Force (c).

Entrance Requirements: Open admission. Options: electronic application, international baccalaureate accepted. Required: essay, high school transcript, minimum 2.0 high school GPA, 2 recommendations, interview, SAT or ACT. Entrance: minimally difficult. Application deadline: 4/1.

Collegiate Environment: Orientation program. Drama-theater group, choral group, student-run newspaper. Social organizations: 35 open to all; national fraternities, national sororities; 35% of eligible men and 65% of eligible women are members. Most popular organizations: Greek Fraternities and Sororities, Black Business Students Association, National Black Student Accountant Club, Gospel Choir, Pre-Alumni organization. Major annual events: Homecoming, Honors Week, Black History Month. Student services: health clinic, personal-psychological counseling. Campus security: 24-hour patrols, late night transport-escort service, controlled dormitory access. 223 computers available on campus for general student use. A campuswide network can be accessed from off-campus. Students can access the following: online class registration. Staffed computer lab on campus.

Community Environment: See University of Memphis.

■ **LINCOLN COLLEGE OF TECHNOLOGY**
1524 Gallatin Ave.
Nashville, TN 37206-3298
Tel: (615)226-3990; Free: 800-228-6232
Fax: (615)262-8488
E-mail: wpruitt@nadcedu.com
Web Site: www.lincolnedu.com/campus/nashville-tn

Description: Proprietary, 2-year, coed. Awards diplomas and terminal associate degrees. Founded 1919. Setting: 13-acre urban campus. Total enrollment: 1,306. Faculty: 77 (73 full-time, 4 part-time). Student-undergrad faculty ratio is 30:1. 2,924 applied, 89% were admitted. Full-time: 1,306 students, 0.4% women, 99% men. Students come from 50 states and territories, 83% from out-of-state. 5% 25 or older, 21% live on campus. Calendar: continuous. Advanced placement, honors program, co-op programs.

Entrance Requirements: Option: deferred admission. Required: high school transcript. Recommended: SAT or ACT. Required for some: interview. Entrance: minimally difficult. Application deadline: Rolling.

Costs Per Year: Application fee: $100. Comprehensive fee: $35,600 includes full-time tuition ($25,700), mandatory fees ($100), and college room and board ($9800). College room only: $5880. Full-time tuition and fees vary according to degree level and program. Room and board charges vary according to housing facility. Tuition guaranteed not to increase for student's term of enrollment.

Collegiate Environment: Orientation program. Campus security: 24-hour emergency response devices and patrols. NADC Library with 1,309 books and 69 serials. 40 computers available on campus for general student use. A campuswide network can be accessed. Staffed computer lab on campus (open 24 hours a day) provides training in use of computers.

■ **LINCOLN MEMORIAL UNIVERSITY**
6965 Cumberland Gap Pky.
Harrogate, TN 37752-1901
Tel: (423)869-3611; Free: 800-325-0900
Fax: (423)869-6250
E-mail: admissions@lmunet.edu
Web Site: www.lmunet.edu/

Description: Independent, comprehensive, coed. Awards associate, bachelor's, master's, and doctoral degrees and post-master's certificates. Founded 1897. Setting: 1,000-acre small town campus. Endowment: $14 million. Educational spending for the previous fiscal year: $6794 per student. Total enrollment: 4,338. Faculty: 275 (191 full-time, 84 part-time). Student-undergrad faculty ratio is 13:1. 990 applied, 65% were admitted. Full-time: 1,416 students, 69% women, 31% men. Part-time: 435 students, 79% women, 21% men. Students come from 46 states and territories, 25 other countries, 36% from out-of-state. 0.2% American Indian or Alaska Native, non-Hispanic/Latino; 2% Hispanic/Latino; 4% African American, non-Hispanic/Latino; 1% Asian, non-Hispanic/Latino; 0% Native Hawaiian or other Pacific Islander, non-Hispanic/Latino; 3% international. 29% 25 or older, 36% live on campus, 16% transferred in. Retention: 67% of full-time freshmen returned the following year. Academic areas with the most degrees conferred: health professions and related sciences; business/marketing; education. Core. Calendar: semesters. Academic remediation for entering students, ESL program, advanced placement, accelerated degree program, honors program, independent study, distance learning, double major, summer session for credit, part-time degree program, adult/continuing education programs, internships, graduate courses open to undergrads.

Entrance Requirements: Options: electronic application, international baccalaureate accepted. Required: high school transcript, minimum 2.3 high school GPA, immunization records, financial aid application, SAT or ACT. Entrance: moderately difficult. Application deadline: Rolling. Notification: continuous. Transfer credits accepted: Yes.

Costs Per Year: Application fee: $50. Comprehensive fee: $26,200 includes full-time tuition ($18,960), mandatory fees ($500), and college room and board ($6740). Room and board charges vary according to board plan and housing facility. Part-time tuition: $790 per credit hour. Part-time tuition varies according to course load.

Collegiate Environment: Orientation program. Drama-theater group, choral group, student-run radio station. Social organizations: 40 open to all; local fraternities, local sororities; 2% of eligible men and 6% of eligible women are members. Most popular organizations: Students in Free Enterprise (SIFE), Baptist Campus Ministries, Pre-Med Club, Fishing Club, Earth Club. Major annual events: Founder's Day, Convocation, SGA Fall and Spring Campus Clean UP. Student services: health clinic, personal-psychological counseling. Campus security: 24-hour emergency response devices and patrols. 890 college housing spaces available. No special consideration for freshman housing applicants. Options: coed, men-only, women-only housing available. Carnegie-Vincent Library with 323,046 books, 100,745 microform titles, 334 serials, 4,064 audiovisual materials, an OPAC, and a Web page. Operations spending for the previous fiscal year: $116,616.

■ **LIPSCOMB UNIVERSITY**
One University Park Dr.
Nashville, TN 37204-3951
Tel: (615)966-1000; Free: 877-582-4766

Fax: (615)966-1804
E-mail: admissions@lipscomb.edu
Web Site: www.lipscomb.edu/

Description: Independent, comprehensive, coed, affiliated with Church of Christ. Awards associate, bachelor's, master's, and doctoral degrees. Founded 1891. Setting: 75-acre suburban campus. Endowment: $56.7 million. Educational spending for the previous fiscal year: $9980 per student. Total enrollment: 4,254. Faculty: 490 (189 full-time, 301 part-time). Student-undergrad faculty ratio is 12:1. 3,022 applied, 52% were admitted. 25% from top 10% of their high school class, 50% from top quarter, 78% from top half. 16 National Merit Scholars, 13 valedictorians. Full-time: 2,491 students, 58% women, 42% men. Part-time: 249 students, 62% women, 38% men. Students come from 48 states and territories, 35 other countries, 30% from out-of-state. 0.04% American Indian or Alaska Native, non-Hispanic/Latino; 6% Hispanic/Latino; 7% African American, non-Hispanic/Latino; 2% Asian, non-Hispanic/Latino; 0.1% Native Hawaiian or other Pacific Islander, non-Hispanic/Latino; 2% international. 14% 25 or older, 52% live on campus, 5% transferred in. Retention: 76% of full-time freshmen returned the following year. Academic areas with the most degrees conferred: business/marketing; biological/life sciences; health professions and related sciences. Core. Calendar: semesters. Academic remediation for entering students, services for LD students, advanced placement, accelerated degree program, freshman honors college, honors program, independent study, distance learning, double major, summer session for credit, adult/continuing education programs, internships, graduate courses open to undergrads. Study abroad program. ROTC: Army (c), Air Force (c).

Entrance Requirements: Options: electronic application, early admission, deferred admission, international baccalaureate accepted. Required: high school transcript, minimum 2.25 high school GPA, 1 recommendation, interview, SAT or ACT. Recommended: essay. Entrance: moderately difficult. Application deadline: Rolling. Notification: continuous. SAT Reasoning Test deadline: 8/15. SAT Subject Test deadline: 8/15. Transfer credits accepted: Yes.

Costs Per Year: Application fee: $50. Comprehensive fee: $33,978 includes full-time tuition ($22,978), mandatory fees ($1776), and college room and board ($9224). College room only: $5184. Full-time tuition and fees vary according to course load. Room and board charges vary according to board plan and housing facility. Part-time tuition: $960 per hour. Part-time mandatory fees: $75 per credit hour. Part-time tuition and fees vary according to course load.

Collegiate Environment: Orientation program. Drama-theater group, choral group, student-run newspaper, radio station. Social organizations: 67 open to all; local fraternities, local sororities; 14% of eligible men and 16% of eligible women are members. Most popular organizations: Sigma Pi Beta, business fraternities, Multicultural Association, Alpha Phi Chi men's service club, Pi Kappa Sigma women's service club. Major annual events: Homecoming, Singarama (annual spring student talent show), Annual Service Day for students, faculty, and staff. Student services: health clinic, personal-psychological counseling. Campus security: 24-hour emergency response devices and patrols, late night transport-escort service, controlled dormitory access. 1,450 college housing spaces available; 1,431 were occupied in 2012-13. Freshmen given priority for college housing. On-campus residence required through junior year. Options: men-only, women-only housing available. Beaman Library plus 1 other with 274,396 books, 93,410 microform titles, 712 serials, an OPAC, and a Web page. Operations spending for the previous fiscal year: $1.8 million. 175 computers available on campus for general student use. A campuswide network can be accessed from student residence rooms and from off campus. Students can access the following: online class registration. Staffed computer lab on campus provides training in use of computers, software, and the Internet.

Community Environment: Lipscomb University is a vital part of Nashville, the capital of Tennessee, and a regional and national center for education, business, and culture. Nashville is centrally located and easy to reach. Half the population of the United States is within 600 miles of its borders. There are 3 major interstates in addition to Nashville International Airport. Nashville abounds in history and culture. From antebellum mansions like the Hermitage, home of President Andrew Jackson, to Cheekwood Botanical Gardens, the Parthenon, and the Tennessee State Museum, Nashville offers abundant resources to strengthen and complement student education.

■ **MARTIN METHODIST COLLEGE**
433 W Madison St.
Pulaski, TN 38478-2716
Tel: (931)363-9868; Free: 800-467-1273

Fax: (931)363-9818

E-mail: admit@martinmethodist.edu

Web Site: www.martinmethodist.edu/

Description: Independent United Methodist, 4-year, coed. Awards associate and bachelor's degrees. Founded 1870. Setting: 6-acre small town campus with easy access to Nashville. Total enrollment: 924. 22% 25 or older. Core. Calendar: semesters. Academic remediation for entering students, ESL program, services for LD students, advanced placement, honors program, independent study, double major, summer session for credit, part-time degree program, adult/continuing education programs, internships.

Entrance Requirements: Options: electronic application, early admission, deferred admission. Required: high school transcript, minimum 2.0 high school GPA, SAT or ACT. Recommended: essay, interview. Entrance: minimally difficult. Application deadline: 8/26. Notification: continuous.

Collegiate Environment: Orientation program. Drama-theater group, choral group. Campus security: controlled dormitory access. Warden Memorial Library with 84,000 books, 19,000 microform titles, 664 serials, 996 audiovisual materials, an OPAC, and a Web page.

Community Environment: Located in south-central Tennessee where the climate is mild, Pulaski, between Nashville, Tennessee, and Huntsville, Alabama, is a small, friendly town with much civic pride.

■ MARYVILLE COLLEGE

502 E Lamar Alexander Pky.

Maryville, TN 37804-5907

Tel: (865)981-8000; Free: 800-597-2687

Fax: (865)983-0581

E-mail: admissions@maryvillecollege.edu

Web Site: www.maryvillecollege.edu/

Description: Independent Presbyterian, 4-year, coed. Awards bachelor's degrees. Founded 1819. Setting: 350-acre suburban campus. Educational spending for the previous fiscal year: $9065 per student. Total enrollment: 1,093. Faculty: 106 (67 full-time, 39 part-time). Student-undergrad faculty ratio is 12:1. 2,114 applied, 66% were admitted. 26% from top 10% of their high school class, 51% from top quarter, 84% from top half. Full-time: 1,050 students, 56% women, 44% men. Part-time: 43 students, 53% women, 47% men. Students come from 31 states and territories, 24 other countries, 19% from out-of-state. 1% American Indian or Alaska Native, non-Hispanic/Latino; 3% Hispanic/Latino; 5% African American, non-Hispanic/Latino; 1% Asian, non-Hispanic/Latino; 0.1% Native Hawaiian or other Pacific Islander, non-Hispanic/Latino; 4% international. 5% 25 or older, 66% live on campus, 5% transferred in. Retention: 72% of full-time freshmen returned the following year. Academic areas with the most degrees conferred: business/marketing; psychology; education. Core. Calendar: 4-1-4. Academic remediation for entering students, ESL program, services for LD students, advanced placement, self-designed majors, honors program, independent study, double major, summer session for credit, part-time degree program, internships. Off campus study at Argonne National Laboratory, Oak Ridge National Laboratories, Woods Hole Oceanographic Institute, and Patuxent River Laboratory. Study abroad program.

Entrance Requirements: Options: electronic application, early admission, deferred admission, international baccalaureate accepted. Required: high school transcript, minimum 2.5 high school GPA, 1 recommendation, SAT or ACT. Recommended: minimum 3 high school GPA. Required for some: essay, interview. Entrance: moderately difficult. Application deadline: 3/1. Notification: continuous until 4/1. SAT Reasoning Test deadline: 7/15. Transfer credits accepted: Yes.

Costs Per Year: Application fee: $0. Comprehensive fee: $41,022 includes full-time tuition ($30,410), mandatory fees ($722), and college room and board ($9890). College room only: $4908. Full-time tuition and fees vary according to course load. Room and board charges vary according to board plan and housing facility. Part-time tuition: $800 per credit hour. Part-time tuition varies according to course load.

Collegiate Environment: Orientation program. Drama-theater group, choral group, student-run newspaper. Social organizations: 65 open to all. Most popular organizations: Voices of Praise, student government, Student Programming Board, Global Citizenship, Peer Mentors. Major annual events: Homecoming, Blister in the Sun, Spring Fling. Student services: health clinic, personal-psychological counseling. Campus security: 24-hour emergency response devices and patrols, late night transport-escort service, controlled dormitory access, campus-wide emergency alert system via cell phones, home phones, and email. 861 college housing spaces available; 796 were occupied in 2012-13. Freshmen guaranteed college housing. On-campus residence required through senior year. Options: coed, men-only, women-

only housing available. Lamar Memorial Library plus 1 other with 331,157 books, 8,977 microform titles, 28,146 serials, 5,929 audiovisual materials, an OPAC, and a Web page. 290 computers available on campus for general student use. A campuswide network can be accessed from student residence rooms and from off campus. Students can access the following: online class registration. Staffed computer lab on campus provides training in use of computers, software, and the Internet.

Community Environment: Maryville was founded in 1819 and named for Mary Blount, wife of Governor William Blount. The town is located near the entrance of the Great Smoky Mountains National Park. Bus and air transportation is available. Fishing, boating, water skiing, golfing, and hiking are favorite sports in the county. Maryville is a suburban community located 15 miles from Knoxville in a metropolitan area of half a million.

■ MEMPHIS COLLEGE OF ART

Overton Park, 1930 Poplar Ave.

Memphis, TN 38104-2764

Tel: (901)272-5100; Free: 800-727-1088

Fax: (901)272-5104

E-mail: amoore@mca.edu

Web Site: www.mca.edu/

Description: Independent, comprehensive, coed. Awards bachelor's and master's degrees. Founded 1936. Setting: 200-acre urban campus. Total enrollment: 433. Faculty: 61 (26 full-time, 35 part-time). Student-undergrad faculty ratio is 10:1. 544 applied, 45% were admitted. Full-time: 343 students, 65% women, 35% men. Part-time: 34 students, 59% women, 41% men. Students come from 26 states and territories, 7 other countries, 55% from out-of-state. 0% American Indian or Alaska Native, non-Hispanic/Latino; 6% Hispanic/Latino; 18% African American, non-Hispanic/Latino; 2% Asian, non-Hispanic/Latino; 0% Native Hawaiian or other Pacific Islander, non-Hispanic/Latino; 2% international. 10% 25 or older, 44% live on campus, 6% transferred in. Retention: 76% of full-time freshmen returned the following year. Academic area with the most degrees conferred: visual and performing arts. Core. Calendar: semesters. Academic remediation for entering students, services for LD students, advanced placement, independent study, summer session for credit, part-time degree program, adult/continuing education programs, internships, graduate courses open to undergrads. Off campus study at Greater Memphis Consortium, Association of Independent Colleges of Art and Design. Study abroad program.

Entrance Requirements: Options: electronic application, deferred admission, international baccalaureate accepted. Required: high school transcript, minimum 2 high school GPA, portfolio, SAT or ACT. Recommended: essay, interview. Entrance: moderately difficult. Application deadline: Rolling. Notification: continuous. Transfer credits accepted: Yes.

Costs Per Year: Application fee: $25. Comprehensive fee: $34,250 includes full-time tuition ($25,600), mandatory fees ($650), and college room and board ($8000). College room only: $6000. Full-time tuition and fees vary according to degree level and program. Room and board charges vary according to housing facility. Part-time tuition: $1117 per credit. Part-time mandatory fees: $650 per year. Part-time tuition and fees vary according to course load, degree level, and program.

Collegiate Environment: Orientation program. Student-run newspaper. Social organizations: 7 open to all. Most popular organizations: Student Alliance, Photo Club, Design Club-AIGA, Clay Club. Major annual events: Holiday Bazaar, Student Day Community Dinner, End of the Year Party. Student services: personal-psychological counseling. Campus security: 24-hour emergency response devices and patrols, late night transport-escort service, controlled dormitory access. 100 computers available on campus for general student use. Computer purchase/lease plans available. Staffed computer lab on campus provides training in use of software and the Internet.

Community Environment: Memphis is a friendly city. It's large enough to support a cultural life of high quality, but small enough not to overwhelm. The cost of living is low. The school is located in midtown, near the Mississippi River.

■ MID-AMERICA BAPTIST THEOLOGICAL SEMINARY

2095 Appling Rd.

Cordova, TN 38016

Tel: (901)751-8453; Free: 800-968-4508

Fax: (901)751-8454

E-mail: info@mabts.edu

Web Site: www.mabts.edu/

Description: Independent Southern Baptist, comprehensive, men only.

Awards associate, master's, and doctoral degrees. Founded 1972. Setting: suburban campus with easy access to Memphis. Endowment: $3.6 million. Total enrollment: 327. Faculty: 27 (all full-time). Student-undergrad faculty ratio is 15:1. Full-time: 29 students. Part-time: 22 students. Students come from 26 states and territories. Core. Calendar: semesters. Summer session for credit, part-time degree program, graduate courses open to undergrads.
Entrance Requirements: Open admission. Required: 2 recommendations. Required for some: high school transcript. Entrance: noncompetitive. Application deadline: 8/4.
Collegiate Environment: Campus security: 24-hour emergency response devices. Ora Byram Allison Memorial Library with 119,000 books, 931 serials, an OPAC, and a Web page. Operations spending for the previous fiscal year: $217,748. 10 computers available on campus for general student use. Staffed computer lab on campus.

■ **MIDDLE TENNESSEE STATE UNIVERSITY**
1301 E Main St.
Murfreesboro, TN 37132
Tel: (615)898-2300; Free: 800-331-MTSU
E-mail: admissions@mtsu.edu
Web Site: www.mtsu.edu/
Description: State-supported, university, coed. Part of Tennessee Board of Regents. Awards bachelor's, master's, and doctoral degrees and post-master's certificates. Founded 1911. Setting: 500-acre urban campus with easy access to Nashville. Endowment: $64.7 million. Research spending for the previous fiscal year: $10.4 million. Educational spending for the previous fiscal year: $5075 per student. Total enrollment: 25,394. 9,405 applied, 67% were admitted. 17% from top 10% of their high school class, 42% from top quarter, 78% from top half. Full-time: 18,403 students, 52% women, 48% men. Part-time: 3,968 students, 54% women, 46% men. 4% from out-of-state. 0.3% American Indian or Alaska Native, non-Hispanic/Latino; 4% Hispanic/Latino; 19% African American, non-Hispanic/Latino; 3% Asian, non-Hispanic/Latino; 0.1% Native Hawaiian or other Pacific Islander, non-Hispanic/Latino. 24% 25 or older, 17% live on campus, 9% transferred in. Academic areas with the most degrees conferred: business/marketing; visual and performing arts; education. Calendar: semesters. Part-time degree program, adult/continuing education programs. ROTC: Army, Air Force (c).
Entrance Requirements: Option: international baccalaureate accepted. Required: high school transcript, minimum 3 high school GPA, SAT or ACT. Required for some: essay. Entrance: moderately difficult. Application deadline: Rolling. Notification: continuous.
Costs Per Year: Application fee: $25. State resident tuition: $5616 full-time, $234 per credit hour part-time. Nonresident tuition: $20,232 full-time, $843 per credit hour part-time. Mandatory fees: $1594 full-time. Full-time tuition and fees vary according to course load. Part-time tuition varies according to course load. College room and board: $7532. Room and board charges vary according to board plan and housing facility.
Collegiate Environment: Orientation program. Drama-theater group, choral group, marching band, student-run newspaper, radio station. Social organizations: national fraternities, national sororities, local sororities. Student services: legal services, health clinic, personal-psychological counseling, women's center. Campus security: 24-hour emergency response devices and patrols, student patrols, late night transport-escort service, controlled dormitory access. No special consideration for freshman housing applicants. Options: coed, men-only, women-only housing available. Operations spending for the previous fiscal year: $9 million.
Community Environment: Murfreesboro is a small city of about 60,000 that is 32 miles southeast of the state capital, Nashville. Capital of the state from 1819 to 1825, Murfreesboro is a city proud of its history, but one that is changing with the times. Community and area facilities include historical landmarks such as Stones River Battlefield and Old Fort Park. Facilities range from an amphitheater to tennis courts, growing industries, charming old homes, new apartment complexes, churches, numerous recreational areas including many for water sports, the Veteran's Hospital. Because of its geographic location in the center of the state, MTSU is easily accessible from any direction.

■ **MILLER-MOTTE TECHNICAL COLLEGE**
1820 Business Park Dr.
Clarksville, TN 37040
Tel: (931)553-0071
Fax: (931)552-2916
E-mail: lisateague@hotmail.com

Web Site: www.miller-motte.edu/
Description: Proprietary, 2-year, coed. Awards terminal associate degrees. Founded 1916. Total enrollment: 516.
Entrance Requirements: Entrance: noncompetitive.

■ **MILLIGAN COLLEGE**
PO Box 500
Milligan College, TN 37682
Tel: (423)461-8700; Free: 800-262-8337
Fax: (423)461-8960
E-mail: admissions@milligan.edu
Web Site: www.milligan.edu/
Description: Independent Christian, comprehensive, coed. Awards bachelor's and master's degrees. Founded 1866. Setting: 181-acre suburban campus. Endowment: $17.3 million. Educational spending for the previous fiscal year: $6004 per student. Total enrollment: 1,208. Faculty: 134 (68 full-time, 66 part-time). Student-undergrad faculty ratio is 13:1. 603 applied, 70% were admitted. 37% from top 10% of their high school class, 65% from top quarter, 89% from top half. Full-time: 901 students, 60% women, 40% men. Part-time: 83 students, 58% women, 42% men. Students come from 34 states and territories, 16 other countries, 35% from out-of-state. 0.4% American Indian or Alaska Native, non-Hispanic/Latino; 3% Hispanic/Latino; 5% African American, non-Hispanic/Latino; 1% Asian, non-Hispanic/Latino; 0% Native Hawaiian or other Pacific Islander, non-Hispanic/Latino; 2% international. 11% 25 or older, 74% live on campus, 9% transferred in. Retention: 80% of full-time freshmen returned the following year. Academic areas with the most degrees conferred: health professions and related sciences; business/marketing; education. Core. Calendar: semesters. Academic remediation for entering students, advanced placement, independent study, distance learning, double major, summer session for credit, part-time degree program, adult/continuing education programs, co-op programs and internships, graduate courses open to undergrads. Off campus study at East Tennessee State University. Study abroad program. ROTC: Army (c).
Entrance Requirements: Options: electronic application, deferred admission, international baccalaureate accepted. Required: essay, high school transcript, minimum 2 high school GPA, 2 recommendations, SAT or ACT. Recommended: minimum 3 high school GPA. Required for some: interview. Entrance: moderately difficult. Application deadline: 8/1. Notification: continuous. Transfer credits accepted: Yes.
Costs Per Year: Application fee: $30. Comprehensive fee: $32,610 includes full-time tuition ($25,735), mandatory fees ($1025), and college room and board ($5850). College room only: $2850. Full-time tuition and fees vary according to course load. Room and board charges vary according to housing facility.
Collegiate Environment: Orientation program. Drama-theater group, choral group, student-run newspaper, radio station. Social organizations: 31 open to all. Most popular organizations: Social Affairs Committee, Buffalo Ramblers, Concert Council, Volunteer Milligan, Students for Life. Major annual events: Wonderful Wednesday, Spirit Week, SUB7 Coffeehouse. Student services: health clinic, personal-psychological counseling. Campus security: 24-hour emergency response devices and patrols, late night transport-escort service. P. H. Welshimer Memorial Library with 145,605 books, 11,097 serials, 3,205 audiovisual materials, an OPAC, and a Web page. Operations spending for the previous fiscal year: $312,436. 97 computers available on campus for general student use. A campuswide network can be accessed from student residence rooms and from off campus. Students can access the following: online class registration. Staffed computer lab on campus provides training in use of computers, software, and the Internet.

■ **MOTLOW STATE COMMUNITY COLLEGE**
PO Box 8500
Lynchburg, TN 37352-8500
Tel: (931)393-1500; Free: 800-654-4877
Fax: (931)393-1681
E-mail: smason@mscc.edu
Web Site: www.mscc.edu/
Description: State-supported, 2-year, coed. Part of Tennessee Board of Regents. Awards certificates, transfer associate, and terminal associate degrees. Founded 1969. Setting: 187-acre rural campus with easy access to Nashville. Endowment: $4.6 million. Educational spending for the previous fiscal year: $1898 per student. Total enrollment: 4,580. Faculty: 236 (87 full-time, 149 part-time). 5,010 applied, 30% were admitted. Full-time: 1,791

students, 59% women, 41% men. Part-time: 2,789 students, 64% women, 36% men. Students come from 12 states and territories, 25 other countries, 1% from out-of-state. 0.3% American Indian or Alaska Native, non-Hispanic/Latino; 3% Hispanic/Latino; 10% African American, non-Hispanic/Latino; 2% Asian, non-Hispanic/Latino; 0.1% Native Hawaiian or other Pacific Islander, non-Hispanic/Latino; 0.2% international. 28% 25 or older, 7% transferred in. Core. Calendar: semesters. Academic remediation for entering students, services for LD students, advanced placement, accelerated degree program, honors program, independent study, distance learning, double major, summer session for credit, part-time degree program, adult/continuing education programs, co-op programs. Study abroad program.

Entrance Requirements: Open admission except for nursing program. Options: electronic application, early admission, deferred admission. Required: high school transcript. Entrance: noncompetitive. Application deadline: 8/13. Notification: continuous.

Costs Per Year: Application fee: $10. State resident tuition: $3516 full-time. Nonresident tuition: $13,368 full-time.

Collegiate Environment: Orientation program. Drama-theater group, choral group. Social organizations: 9 open to all. Most popular organizations: PTK Club, Communication Club, Student Government Association, Art Club, Baptist Student Union. Major annual events: Buck Barbecue, a play for children, basketball homecoming. Student services: personal-psychological counseling. Campus security: 24-hour patrols, late night transport-escort service. College housing not available. Clayton-Glass Library with 194,392 books, 4,725 microform titles, 9,411 serials, 5,430 audiovisual materials, an OPAC, and a Web page. Operations spending for the previous fiscal year: $548,968. 477 computers available on campus for general student use. A campuswide network can be accessed from off-campus. Students can access the following: online class registration. Staffed computer lab on campus provides training in use of computers.

Community Environment: Tullahoma is located in the southwest corner of Coffee County, not far from Shelbyville. See University of Tennessee - Space Institute.

■ **NASHVILLE STATE COMMUNITY COLLEGE**
120 White Bridge Rd.
Nashville, TN 37209-4515
Tel: (615)353-3333; Free: 800-272-7363
Fax: (615)353-3243
E-mail: beth.mahan@nscc.edu
Web Site: www.nscc.edu/
Description: State-supported, 2-year, coed. Part of Tennessee Board of Regents. Awards certificates, transfer associate, and terminal associate degrees. Founded 1970. Setting: 85-acre urban campus. Educational spending for the previous fiscal year: $3020 per student. Total enrollment: 7,077. Faculty: 403 (136 full-time, 267 part-time). Student-undergrad faculty ratio is 18:1. Full-time: 2,556 students, 53% women, 47% men. Part-time: 4,521 students, 61% women, 39% men. Students come from 36 states and territories, 55 other countries, 2% from out-of-state. 55% 25 or older, 3% transferred in. Core. Calendar: semesters. Academic remediation for entering students, ESL program, services for LD students, advanced placement, distance learning, summer session for credit, part-time degree program, adult/continuing education programs, co-op programs. Off campus study.
Entrance Requirements: Open admission except for occupational therapy, automotive services technology, surgical technology programs. Options: electronic application, deferred admission. Required: high school transcript, SAT or ACT. Entrance: noncompetitive. Application deadlines: Rolling, Rolling for nonresidents. Notification: continuous, continuous for nonresidents. Preference given to state residents.
Costs Per Year: Application fee: $5. State resident tuition: $3465 full-time, $145 per credit hour part-time. Nonresident tuition: $13,593 full-time, $567 per credit hour part-time. Mandatory fees: $225 full-time. Part-time tuition varies according to course load.
Collegiate Environment: Orientation program. Student-run newspaper. Social organizations: 7 open to all. Most popular organizations: Data Processing Management Association, Occupational Therapy Club, Phi Theta Kappa, Student Government Association, Black Student Association. Major annual events: Fall Festival, Spring Fling, Diversity Day. Campus security: 24-hour emergency response devices and patrols, late night transport-escort service. Jane G. Kisber Memorial Library with 38,502 books, 275 serials, an OPAC, and a Web page. Operations spending for the previous fiscal year: $405,872. 518 computers available on campus for general student use. A campuswide network can be accessed from off-campus. Students can access the following: online class registration. Staffed computer lab on campus.

Community Environment: See Vanderbilt University.

■ **NATIONAL COLLEGE OF BUSINESS AND TECHNOLOGY (BRISTOL)**
1328 Hwy. 11 W
Bristol, TN 37620
Tel: (423)878-4440; Free: 888-9-JOBREADY
Web Site: www.national-college.edu/
Description: Proprietary, primarily 2-year, coed. Part of National College of Business and Technology. Awards diplomas, terminal associate, and bachelor's degrees. Founded 1992. Setting: small town campus. Core. Services for LD students, advanced placement, honors program, double major, summer session for credit, part-time degree program, internships.
Entrance Requirements: Open admission. Option: electronic application. Required: high school transcript. Recommended: interview. Entrance: noncompetitive. Application deadline: Rolling.
Collegiate Environment: Orientation program.

■ **NATIONAL COLLEGE OF BUSINESS AND TECHNOLOGY (KNOXVILLE)**
8415 Kingston Pke.
Knoxville, TN 37919
Tel: (865)539-2011; Free: 888-9-JOBREADY
Fax: (865)539-2049
Web Site: www.national-college.edu/
Description: Proprietary, 2-year, coed. Part of National College of Business and Technology. Awards diplomas and terminal associate degrees. Founded 2003. Setting: 2-acre suburban campus.

■ **NATIONAL COLLEGE OF BUSINESS AND TECHNOLOGY (NASHVILLE)**
1638 Bell Rd.
Nashville, TN 37211
Tel: (615)333-3344; Free: 888-9-JOBREADY
Web Site: www.national-college.edu/
Description: Proprietary, 2-year, coed. Part of National College of Business and Technology. Awards diplomas and terminal associate degrees. Founded 1915. Setting: 1-acre urban campus. Core. Services for LD students, honors program, double major, summer session for credit, part-time degree program.
Entrance Requirements: Open admission. Option: electronic application. Recommended: interview. Entrance: noncompetitive. Application deadline: Rolling. Notification: continuous.
Collegiate Environment: Orientation program.

■ **NORTH CENTRAL INSTITUTE**
168 Jack Miller Blvd.
Clarksville, TN 37042
Tel: (931)431-9700; Free: 800-603-4116
Fax: (931)431-9771
E-mail: admissions@nci.edu
Web Site: www.nci.edu/
Description: Proprietary, 2-year, coed. Awards terminal associate degrees. Founded 1988. Setting: 14-acre suburban campus. Total enrollment: 88. Student-undergrad faculty ratio is 10:1. 29% from out-of-state. 73% 25 or older. Core. Calendar: continuous. Advanced placement, independent study, summer session for credit, part-time degree program, external degree program.
Entrance Requirements: Open admission. Options: electronic application, early admission. Required: proof of high school. Recommended: high school transcript. Entrance: noncompetitive. Application deadline: Rolling. Notification: continuous.
Collegiate Environment: Social organizations: national fraternities. Campus security: 24-hour emergency response devices.

■ **NORTHEAST STATE COMMUNITY COLLEGE**
PO Box 246
Blountville, TN 37617-0246
Tel: (423)323-3191; Free: 800-836-7822
Fax: (423)323-0215
E-mail: jpharr@northeaststate.edu
Web Site: www.northeaststate.edu/
Description: State-supported, 2-year, coed. Part of Tennessee Board of Regents. Awards certificates, transfer associate, and terminal associate

degrees. Founded 1966. Setting: 100-acre small town campus. Endowment: $4 million. Educational spending for the previous fiscal year: $3908 per student. Total enrollment: 5,470. Faculty: 268 (107 full-time, 161 part-time). Student-undergrad faculty ratio is 11:1. 3,286 applied, 100% were admitted. 10% from top 10% of their high school class, 20% from top quarter, 40% from top half. Full-time: 2,927 students, 53% women, 47% men. Part-time: 2,543 students, 55% women, 45% men. Students come from 3 states and territories, 2 other countries, 3% from out-of-state. 47% 25 or older, 5% transferred in. Retention: 58% of full-time freshmen returned the following year. Core. Calendar: semesters. Academic remediation for entering students, services for LD students, advanced placement, honors program, distance learning, double major, summer session for credit, part-time degree program, co-op programs.

Entrance Requirements: Open admission. Option: electronic application. Required: high school transcript, minimum 2 high school GPA. Entrance: noncompetitive. Application deadline: Rolling. Notification: continuous. Preference given to state residents.

Collegiate Environment: Orientation program. Drama-theater group, student-run radio station. Social organizations: 23 open to all. Most popular organizations: Phi Theta Kappa, Student Government Association, Student Tennessee Education Association, Students in Free Enterprise (SIFE), Student Ambassadors. Major annual events: Spring Fling, Club Fair, Fall Finale. Student services: health clinic, personal-psychological counseling. Campus security: 24-hour emergency response devices and patrols, late night transport-escort service. Wayne G. Basler Library plus 1 other with 50,553 books, 56,349 microform titles, 388 serials, 8,861 audiovisual materials, an OPAC, and a Web page. Operations spending for the previous fiscal year: $880,553. 910 computers available on campus for general student use. A campuswide network can be accessed from off-campus. Students can access the following: online class registration, online transcripts. Staffed computer lab on campus.

Community Environment: Blountville is located in the center of the Tri-Cities triangle of Bristol-Kingsport-Johnson City, approximately 15 miles from each city. Chemical, defense, manufacturing, and banking industries are numerous. The medical industry is a growing part of the economy. The Northeast Tennessee area is bordered by Virginia and North Carolina and is less than a day's drive to both East Coast recreation areas and large metropolitan areas such as Atlanta, GA, and Washington, DC. A system of TVA lakes offer warm weather recreation and snow skiing is a short drive away in the winter. Part-time employment is available.

■ NOSSI COLLEGE OF ART

590 Cheron Rd.
Goodlettsville, TN 37072
Tel: (615)851-1088; Free: 888-986-ARTS
Fax: (615)851-1087
E-mail: admissions@nossi.edu
Web Site: www.nossi.edu/

Description: Independent, primarily 2-year, coed. Awards transfer associate, terminal associate, and bachelor's degrees. Setting: 10-acre urban campus with easy access to Nashville. Total enrollment: 478. Faculty: 37 (6 full-time, 31 part-time). Student-undergrad faculty ratio is 10:1. 210 applied, 63% were admitted. Students come from 12 states and territories, 1 other country, 12% from out-of-state. 0% American Indian or Alaska Native, non-Hispanic/Latino; 4% Hispanic/Latino; 20% African American, non-Hispanic/Latino; 1% Asian, non-Hispanic/Latino; 0% Native Hawaiian or other Pacific Islander, non-Hispanic/Latino; 0.2% international. 9% 25 or older. Retention: 72% of full-time freshmen returned the following year. Core. Calendar: semesters. Services for LD students, independent study, summer session for credit, internships.

Entrance Requirements: Options: electronic application, early admission. Required: essay, high school transcript, interview, portfolio of work for Associate or Bachelor of Graphic Art and Design program and the Bachelor of Illustration program. Transfer credits accepted: Yes.

Collegiate Environment: Orientation program. Social organizations: national fraternities, The Creative's Group. Campus security: campus has a gated entrance, all doors are kept locked. College housing not available. Learning Resource Center with an OPAC. 125 computers available on campus for general student use. A computer is required for all students.

■ O'MORE COLLEGE OF DESIGN

423 S Margin St.
Franklin, TN 37064-2816
Tel: (615)794-4254; Free: 888-662-1970

Fax: (615)790-1662
E-mail: tbagsby@omorecollege.edu
Web Site: www.omorecollege.edu/

Description: Independent, 4-year, coed. Awards bachelor's degrees. Founded 1970. Setting: 6-acre small town campus with easy access to Nashville. Total enrollment: 205. Faculty: 46 (16 full-time, 30 part-time). Student-undergrad faculty ratio is 7:1. 69 applied, 55% were admitted. Full-time: 177 students, 86% women, 14% men. Part-time: 28 students, 93% women, 7% men. Students come from 18 states and territories, 3 other countries, 16% from out-of-state. 2% American Indian or Alaska Native, non-Hispanic/Latino; 2% Hispanic/Latino; 3% African American, non-Hispanic/Latino; 4% Asian, non-Hispanic/Latino; 2% international. 23% 25 or older, 14% transferred in. Academic area with the most degrees conferred: visual and performing arts. Core. Calendar: semesters. Advanced placement, independent study, double major, summer session for credit, part-time degree program, co-op programs and internships. Off campus study at Middle Tennessee State University. Study abroad program.

Entrance Requirements: Options: electronic application, deferred admission, international baccalaureate accepted. Required: minimum 2.7 high school GPA, SAT or ACT. Required for some: essay, high school transcript, interview, Departmental Requirement for Admissions (Sewing Sample for Fashion Design). Entrance: moderately difficult. Application deadlines: 7/31, 7/31 for nonresidents. Notification: continuous, continuous for nonresidents. SAT Reasoning Test deadline: 7/31. SAT Subject Test deadline: 7/31. Transfer credits accepted: Yes.

Costs Per Year: Application fee: $50. Tuition: $25,000 full-time, $1041 per credit hour part-time. Part-time tuition varies according to course load.

Collegiate Environment: Orientation program. Most popular organizations: American Society for Interior Design, Student Government Association, O'More Fashion Merchandising Association, Visual Communications Forum, International Interior Design Association. Major annual events: Spring Social, Homecoming/Croquet Tournament, Halloween Masquerade. Campus security: 24-hour emergency response devices and patrols, security cards at The Factory campus (off-campus). College housing not available. McAfee Library with 4,725 books, 65 serials, 124 audiovisual materials, and an OPAC. 20 computers available on campus for general student use. A computer is required for all students. A campuswide network can be accessed. Students can access the following: library card catalog. Staffed computer lab on campus provides training in use of software.

■ PELLISSIPPI STATE COMMUNITY COLLEGE

PO Box 22990
Knoxville, TN 37933-0990
Tel: (865)694-6400
Web Site: www.pstcc.edu/

Description: State-supported, 2-year, coed. Part of Tennessee Board of Regents. Awards transfer associate and terminal associate degrees. Founded 1974. Setting: 144-acre suburban campus. Total enrollment: 10,297. Student-undergrad faculty ratio is 24:1. 3,834 applied, 100% were admitted. 1% from out-of-state. 33% 25 or older. Retention: 60% of full-time freshmen returned the following year. Core. Calendar: semesters. Academic remediation for entering students, ESL program, services for LD students, advanced placement, self-designed majors, freshman honors college, honors program, distance learning, double major, summer session for credit, part-time degree program, adult/continuing education programs, co-op programs and internships.

Entrance Requirements: Open admission. Options: electronic application, early admission, deferred admission. Required: high school transcript. Required for some: SAT or ACT. Entrance: noncompetitive. Application deadline: Rolling. Notification: continuous.

Collegiate Environment: Orientation program. Drama-theater group, choral group, student-run newspaper. Student services: personal-psychological counseling. Campus security: 24-hour patrols. Educational Resources Center plus 1 other with 72,644 books, 330 serials, an OPAC, and a Web page.

Community Environment: Located in Tennessee's third largest metropolitan area, Pellissippi State comprehensively serves the greater Knox and Blount County area and extends its engineering technology offerings to Anderson, Loudon, Roane, Cumberland, Campbell, Fentress, Scott, and Morgan Counties. The main campus is located west of Knoxville in Knox County. The city of Knoxville lies on the Tennessee River, about 40 miles from the Great Smoky Mountains National Park. Knoxville's population approaches 180,000, with approximately 655,000 in the metropolitan area. The city supports a wide variety of cultural and sports activities. The city is a business center in the East Tennessee Valley with markets in tobacco, livestock, marble, and zinc. It is home to the state's flagship higher education institution: the University of Tennessee. The headquarters of the Tennessee Valley Authority are also located in the city.

■ REMINGTON COLLEGE–MEMPHIS CAMPUS

2710 Nonconnah Blvd.
Memphis, TN 38132
Tel: (901)291-4200
Fax: (901)396-8310
E-mail: randal.hayes@remingtoncollege.edu
Web Site: www.remingtoncollege.edu/
Description: Proprietary, primarily 2-year, coed. Awards transfer associate and bachelor's degrees.

■ REMINGTON COLLEGE–NASHVILLE CAMPUS

441 Donelson Pke.
Ste. 150
Nashville, TN 37214
Tel: (615)889-5520
Fax: (615)889-5528
E-mail: frank.vivelo@remingtoncollege.edu
Web Site: www.remingtoncollege.edu/
Description: Proprietary, 2-year, coed. Awards terminal associate degrees. Founded 2003.

■ RHODES COLLEGE

2000 N Pky.
Memphis, TN 38112-1690
Tel: (901)843-3000; Free: 800-844-5969
Fax: (901)843-3719
E-mail: adminfo@rhodes.edu
Web Site: www.rhodes.edu/
Description: Independent, comprehensive, coed. Awards bachelor's and master's degrees (master's degree in accounting only). Founded 1848. Setting: 100-acre urban campus with easy access to Memphis. Endowment: $271.5 million. Research spending for the previous fiscal year: $1.3 million. Educational spending for the previous fiscal year: $15,528 per student. Total enrollment: 1,927. Faculty: 207 (171 full-time, 36 part-time). Student-undergrad faculty ratio is 10:1. 4,138 applied, 55% were admitted. 49% from top 10% of their high school class, 78% from top quarter, 96% from top half. Full-time: 1,899 students, 59% women, 41% men. Part-time: 17 students, 71% women, 29% men. Students come from 47 states and territories, 19 other countries, 73% from out-of-state. 1% American Indian or Alaska Native, non-Hispanic/Latino; 3% Hispanic/Latino; 6% African American, non-Hispanic/Latino; 6% Asian, non-Hispanic/Latino; 0% Native Hawaiian or other Pacific Islander, non-Hispanic/Latino; 4% international. 0% 25 or older, 71% live on campus, 1% transferred in. Retention: 90% of full-time freshmen returned the following year. Academic areas with the most degrees conferred: social sciences; biological/life sciences; business/marketing. Core. Calendar: semesters. Services for LD students, advanced placement, self-designed majors, honors program, independent study, double major, summer session for credit, part-time degree program, co-op programs and internships, graduate courses open to undergrads. Off campus study at Memphis College of Art, University of Memphis, Christian Brothers University. Study abroad program. ROTC: Army (c), Air Force (c).
Entrance Requirements: Options: electronic application, early admission, early decision, early action, deferred admission, international baccalaureate accepted. Required: essay, high school transcript, 2 recommendations, SAT or ACT. Recommended: interview. Entrance: very difficult. Application deadlines: 1/15, 1/15 for nonresidents, 11/1 for early decision plan 1, 1/1 for early decision plan 2, 11/15 for early action. Notification: 4/1, 4/1 for nonresidents, 12/1 for early decision plan 1, 2/1 for early decision plan 2, 1/15 for early action. SAT Reasoning Test deadline: 1/15. Transfer credits accepted: Yes. Applicants placed on waiting list: 435. Wait-listed applicants offered admission: 0. Early decision applicants: 99. Early decision applicants admitted: 30.
Costs Per Year: Application fee: $45. Comprehensive fee: $47,596 includes full-time tuition ($37,782), mandatory fees ($310), and college room and board ($9504). Room and board charges vary according to board plan and housing facility. Part-time tuition: $1590 per credit hour.
Collegiate Environment: Orientation program. Drama-theater group, choral group, student-run newspaper, radio station. Social organizations: 103 open to all; national fraternities, national sororities; 37% of eligible men and 54%

of eligible women are members. Most popular organizations: Health Professions Society, Rhodes Outdoors Club, Kinney, RhodeKill (ultimate frisbee), Reformed University Fellowship. Major annual events: Relay for Life, Rites of Spring (Rhodes Activity Board sponsored concert), Crawfish Boil. Student services: health clinic, personal-psychological counseling, women's center. Campus security: 24-hour emergency response devices and patrols, student patrols, late night transport-escort service, 24-hour monitored security cameras in parking areas, fenced campus with monitored access at night. 1,370 college housing spaces available; 1,360 were occupied in 2012-13. Freshmen guaranteed college housing. On-campus residence required through sophomore year. Options: coed, men-only, women-only housing available. Paul Barret, Jr. Library with 302,807 books, 106,853 microform titles, 8,094 serials, 13,346 audiovisual materials, an OPAC, and a Web page. Operations spending for the previous fiscal year: $1.8 million. 220 computers available on campus for general student use. A campuswide network can be accessed from student residence rooms and from off campus. Students can access the following: online class registration. Staffed computer lab on campus provides training in use of computers, software, and the Internet.
Community Environment: See University of Memphis.

■ ROANE STATE COMMUNITY COLLEGE

276 Patton Ln.
Harriman, TN 37748-5011
Tel: (865)354-3000; Free: 866-462-7722
Fax: (865)882-4562
E-mail: admissions@roanestate.edu
Web Site: www.roanestate.edu/
Description: State-supported, 2-year, coed. Part of Tennessee Board of Regents. Awards certificates, transfer associate, and terminal associate degrees. Founded 1971. Setting: 104-acre small town campus with easy access to Knoxville. Endowment: $18,348. Total enrollment: 5,353. Faculty: 359 (136 full-time, 223 part-time). Student-undergrad faculty ratio is 18:1. 2,389 applied, 99% were admitted. Full-time: 2,987 students, 64% women, 36% men. Part-time: 2,366 students, 71% women, 29% men. Students come from 12 states and territories, 15 other countries, 1% from out-of-state. 39% 25 or older, 7% transferred in. Retention: 55% of full-time freshmen returned the following year. Core. Calendar: semesters. Academic remediation for entering students, services for LD students, advanced placement, accelerated degree program, freshman honors college, honors program, independent study, distance learning, double major, summer session for credit, part-time degree program, adult/continuing education programs, co-op programs and internships. Off campus study. ROTC: Army (c), Air Force (c).
Entrance Requirements: Open admission except for allied health, nursing, computer technology programs. Options: electronic application, early admission, deferred admission. Required: high school transcript. Entrance: noncompetitive. Application deadline: Rolling. Notification: continuous. Preference given to state residents.
Collegiate Environment: Orientation program. Drama-theater group, choral group, student-run newspaper. Social organizations: 21 open to all. Most popular organizations: Baptist Student Union, American Chemical Society, Physical Therapy Student Association, Student Artists At Roane State (S.T.A.R.S.), Phi Theta Kappa. Major annual events: Thanksgiving Feast, Spring Fling, Children's Egg Hunt. Student services: health clinic, personal-psychological counseling. Campus security: 24-hour patrols. Roane State Community College Library plus 3 others with 103,404 books, an OPAC, and a Web page. Operations spending for the previous fiscal year: $523,386. 750 computers available on campus for general student use. A campuswide network can be accessed. Students can access the following: online class registration. Staffed computer lab on campus.
Community Environment: Harriman is located near the cities of Kingston and Rockwood and is easily accessible via U.S. highways.

■ SEWANEE: THE UNIVERSITY OF THE SOUTH

735 University Ave.
Sewanee, TN 37383-1000
Tel: (931)598-1000; Free: 800-522-2234
Fax: (931)598-1145
E-mail: admiss@sewanee.edu
Web Site: www.sewanee.edu/
Description: Independent Episcopal, comprehensive, coed. Awards bachelor's, master's, and doctoral degrees and post-master's certificates. Founded 1857. Setting: 13,000-acre small town campus. Endowment: $319

million. Research spending for the previous fiscal year: $558,249. Educational spending for the previous fiscal year: $14,880 per student. Total enrollment: 1,557. Faculty: 181 (136 full-time, 45 part-time). Student-undergrad faculty ratio is 10:1. 3,369 applied, 59% were admitted. 35% from top 10% of their high school class, 66% from top quarter, 93% from top half. Full-time: 1,455 students, 52% women, 48% men. Part-time: 23 students, 65% women, 35% men. Students come from 43 states and territories, 23 other countries, 74% from out-of-state. 0% American Indian or Alaska Native, non-Hispanic/Latino; 3% Hispanic/Latino; 4% African American, non-Hispanic/Latino; 2% Asian, non-Hispanic/Latino; 0.1% Native Hawaiian or other Pacific Islander, non-Hispanic/Latino; 3% international. 0% 25 or older, 96% live on campus, 1% transferred in. Retention: 86% of full-time freshmen returned the following year. Academic areas with the most degrees conferred: social sciences; English; visual and performing arts. Core. Calendar: semesters. Services for LD students; advanced placement, self-designed majors, independent study, double major, summer session for credit, internships, graduate courses open to undergrads. Study abroad program.

Entrance Requirements: Options: electronic application, early admission, early decision, deferred admission. Required: essay, high school transcript, 2 recommendations. Recommended: interview, SAT or ACT. Required for some: TEOFL for International Students. Entrance: very difficult. Application deadlines: 2/1, 11/15 for early decision plan 1, 1/2 for early decision plan 2. Notification: 3/17, 12/17 for early decision plan 1, 2/8 for early decision plan 2. SAT Reasoning Test deadline: 2/1. SAT Subject Test deadline: 2/1. Transfer credits accepted: Yes. Applicants placed on waiting list: 507. Wait-listed applicants offered admission: 18. Early decision applicants: 119. Early decision applicants admitted: 89.

Costs Per Year: Application fee: $45. Comprehensive fee: $45,970 includes full-time tuition ($35,484), mandatory fees ($272), and college room and board ($10,214). College room only: $5302. Full-time tuition and fees vary according to student level. Room and board charges vary according to student level. Part-time tuition: $1250 per credit hour. Tuition guaranteed not to increase for student's term of enrollment.

Collegiate Environment: Orientation program. Drama-theater group, choral group, student-run newspaper, radio station. Social organizations: 100 open to all; national fraternities, national sororities, local fraternities, local sororities; 67% of eligible men and 71% of eligible women are members. Most popular organizations: Sewanee Outing Program, Community Service Council, Student Activities Programming Board, student radio station, BACCHUS (alcohol and drug education). Major annual events: Homecoming, Parents' Weekend, Fall and Spring Party weekends. Student services: legal services, health clinic, personal-psychological counseling, women's center. Campus security: 24-hour emergency response devices and patrols, late night transport-escort service, controlled dormitory access, security lighting. 1,500 college housing spaces available; 1,418 were occupied in 2012-13. Freshmen guaranteed college housing. On-campus residence required through senior year. Options: coed, men-only, women-only housing available. Jessie Ball duPont Library with 1.2 million books, 331,251 microform titles, 12,546 serials, 25,569 audiovisual materials, an OPAC, and a Web page. Operations spending for the previous fiscal year: $2.9 million. 370 computers available on campus for general student use. Computer purchase/lease plans available. A campuswide network can be accessed from student residence rooms and from off campus. Students can access the following: online class registration. Staffed computer lab on campus (open 24 hours a day) provides training in use of computers, software, and the Internet.

Community Environment: Sewanee is located on the Cuberland Plateau. It has an average temperature of 57 degrees and an average rainfall of 58 inches. Summer nights are cool and there is some snow in the winter. Churches, a hospital and clinic, and several civic and service organizations are a part of the community. Job opportunities are limited. Seventeen lakes in the surrounding area provide facilities for a number of sports, swimming, boating, fishing, and skating. Other activities are hunting, camping, mountain climbing, golf and tennis. There are many tourist attractions in this area.

■ SOUTH COLLEGE
720 N Fifth Ave.
Knoxville, TN 37917
Tel: (865)524-3043
Fax: (865)673-8019
E-mail: whosea@southcollegetn.edu
Web Site: www.southcollegetn.edu/
Description: Proprietary, comprehensive, coed. Awards associate,

bachelor's, and master's degrees. Founded 1882. Setting: 2-acre urban campus. Total enrollment: 825. Student-undergrad faculty ratio is 16:1. 47 applied, 100% were admitted. 0% from out-of-state. 60% 25 or older. Retention: 35% of full-time freshmen returned the following year. Core. Advanced placement, double major, summer session for credit, part-time degree program, adult/continuing education programs, internships.

Entrance Requirements: Options: early admission, deferred admission. Required: high school transcript, interview. Entrance: moderately difficult. Application deadline: 10/1.

Collegiate Environment: Orientation program. Campus security: evening and morning security patrols. Knoxville Business College Library with a Web page.

■ SOUTHERN ADVENTIST UNIVERSITY
PO Box 370
Collegedale, TN 37315-0370
Tel: (423)236-2000; Free: 800-768-8437
Fax: (423)236-1000
E-mail: admissions@southern.edu
Web Site: www.southern.edu/
Description: Independent Seventh-day Adventist, comprehensive, coed. Awards associate, bachelor's, and master's degrees and post-master's certificates. Founded 1892. Setting: 1,000-acre small town campus with easy access to Chattanooga. Endowment: $21.1 million. Research spending for the previous fiscal year: $38,289. Educational spending for the previous fiscal year: $9639 per student. Total enrollment: 3,053. Faculty: 269 (146 full-time, 123 part-time). Student-undergrad faculty ratio is 15:1. 1,452 applied, 80% were admitted. 1 National Merit Scholar. Full-time: 2,323 students, 54% women, 46% men. Part-time: 409 students, 59% women, 41% men. Students come from 49 states and territories, 69% from out-of-state. 0.4% American Indian or Alaska Native, non-Hispanic/Latino; 18% Hispanic/Latino; 12% African American, non-Hispanic/Latino; 5% Asian, non-Hispanic/Latino; 1% Native Hawaiian or other Pacific Islander, non-Hispanic/Latino; 4% international. 11% 25 or older, 61% live on campus, 7% transferred in. Retention: 72% of full-time freshmen returned the following year. Academic areas with the most degrees conferred: health professions and related sciences; business/marketing; visual and performing arts. Core. Calendar: semesters. ESL program, services for LD students, advanced placement, honors program, independent study, double major, summer session for credit, internships, graduate courses open to undergrads. Off campus study. Study abroad program.

Entrance Requirements: Options: deferred admission, international baccalaureate accepted. Required: high school transcript, minimum 2.25 high school GPA, SAT or ACT. Required for some: essay. Entrance: moderately difficult. Application deadline: Rolling. Notification: continuous. SAT Reasoning Test deadline: 8/30. SAT Subject Test deadline: 8/30. Transfer credits accepted: Yes.

Costs Per Year: Application fee: $25. Comprehensive fee: $24,708 includes full-time tuition ($18,324), mandatory fees ($800), and college room and board ($5584). College room only: $3484. Room and board charges vary according to housing facility. Part-time tuition: $774 per semester hour. Part-time tuition varies according to course load.

Collegiate Environment: Orientation program. Drama-theater group, choral group, student-run newspaper, radio station. Social organizations: 10 open to all. Most popular organizations: Student Association, Black Christian Union, Campus Ministries. Major annual events: SA Welcome-Back Party, SA Mid-Winter Party, Strawberry Festival. Student services: health clinic, personal-psychological counseling. Campus security: 24-hour patrols, late night transport-escort service, controlled dormitory access. McKee Library with 170,176 books, 390,279 microform titles, 56,047 serials, 4,457 audiovisual materials, an OPAC, and a Web page. Operations spending for the previous fiscal year: $1.3 million. 200 computers available on campus for general student use. A campuswide network can be accessed from student residence rooms and from off campus. Students can access the following: online class registration. Staffed computer lab on campus.

Community Environment: Collegedale is located 18 miles east of Chattanooga where the recreation areas of the TVA lake system are within 10 miles. There are residence halls for the students; part-time employment opportunities are available.

■ SOUTHWEST TENNESSEE COMMUNITY COLLEGE
PO Box 780
Memphis, TN 38101-0780
Tel: (901)333-5000; Free: 877-717-STCC

Fax: (901)333-4273
E-mail: cmeziere@southwest.tn.edu
Web Site: www.southwest.tn.edu/
Description: State-supported, 2-year, coed. Part of Tennessee Board of Regents. Awards certificates, transfer associate, and terminal associate degrees. Founded 2000. Setting: 100-acre urban campus. Total enrollment: 13,016. 3,064 applied, 100% were admitted. 2% from out-of-state. 45% 25 or older. Core. Calendar: semesters. Academic remediation for entering students, ESL program, services for LD students, advanced placement, accelerated degree program, self-designed majors, distance learning, double major, summer session for credit, part-time degree program, adult/continuing education programs, co-op programs and internships. ROTC: Army (c), Air Force (c).
Entrance Requirements: Open admission. Options: early admission, deferred admission. Required: high school transcript. Entrance: noncompetitive. Application deadline: 9/1. Notification: continuous until 9/1.
Collegiate Environment: Orientation program. Drama-theater group, choral group, student-run newspaper. Social organizations: 18 open to all. Most popular organizations: Human Key Society, NAACP, Black Student Association, Honor Society, Collegiate Secretaries. Major annual events: College Transfer Day, International Night, Career Day. Student services: personal-psychological counseling. Campus security: 24-hour emergency response devices and patrols, late night transport-escort service. Infonet Library plus 4 others with 87,280 books, 10,066 microform titles, 522 serials, 10,588 audiovisual materials, an OPAC, and a Web page.
Community Environment: See University of Memphis.

■ **STRAYER UNIVERSITY - KNOXVILLE CAMPUS**
10118 Parkside Dr.
Ste. 200
Knoxville, TN 37922
Tel: (865)288-6000
Fax: (865)288-6030
Web Site: www.strayer.edu/campus/knoxville/
Description: Proprietary, comprehensive, coed. Awards associate, bachelor's, and master's degrees.

■ **STRAYER UNIVERSITY - NASHVILLE CAMPUS**
1809 Dabbs Ave.
Nashville, TN 37210
Tel: (615)871-2260
Fax: (615)391-5330
Web Site: www.strayer.edu/campus/nashville
Description: Proprietary, comprehensive, coed. Awards associate, bachelor's, and master's degrees.

■ **STRAYER UNIVERSITY - SHELBY CAMPUS**
7275 Appling Farms Pky.
Memphis, TN 38133
Tel: (901)383-6750
Fax: (901)373-8700
Web Site: www.strayer.edu/campus/shelby
Description: Proprietary, comprehensive, coed. Awards associate, bachelor's, and master's degrees.

■ **STRAYER UNIVERSITY - THOUSAND OAKS CAMPUS**
2620 Thousand Oaks Blvd.
Ste. 1100
Memphis, TN 38118
Tel: (901)369-0835
Fax: (901)565-9400
Web Site: www.strayer.edu/campus/thousand-oaks
Description: Proprietary, comprehensive, coed. Awards associate, bachelor's, and master's degrees.

■ **TENNESSEE STATE UNIVERSITY**
3500 John A Merritt Blvd.
Nashville, TN 37209-1561
Tel: (615)963-5000
Fax: (615)963-5108
E-mail: vsmith@tnstate.edu
Web Site: www.tnstate.edu/
Description: State-supported, comprehensive, coed. Part of Tennessee Board of Regents. Awards associate, bachelor's, and master's degrees and

post-master's certificates. Founded 1912. Setting: 450-acre urban campus. Research spending for the previous fiscal year: $2.4 million. Total enrollment: 8,775. Faculty: 603 (434 full-time, 169 part-time). Student-undergrad faculty ratio is 15:1. 5,307 applied, 58% were admitted. Full-time: 5,277 students, 61% women, 39% men. Part-time: 1,503 students, 68% women, 32% men. Students come from 46 states and territories, 11 other countries, 21% from out-of-state. 0.1% American Indian or Alaska Native, non-Hispanic/Latino; 1% Hispanic/Latino; 77% African American, non-Hispanic/Latino; 1% Asian, non-Hispanic/Latino; 3% international. 29% 25 or older, 39% live on campus, 10% transferred in. Retention: 55% of full-time freshmen returned the following year. Academic areas with the most degrees conferred: liberal arts/general studies; health professions and related sciences; business/marketing. Core. Calendar: semesters. Academic remediation for entering students, services for LD students, accelerated degree program, freshman honors college, honors program, independent study, summer session for credit, part-time degree program, external degree program, adult/continuing education programs, co-op programs and internships. Off campus study at Volunteer State Community College, Meharry Medical College. ROTC: Army (c), Naval (c), Air Force.
Entrance Requirements: Option: electronic application. Required: high school transcript, SAT or ACT. Required for some: 3 recommendations. Entrance: minimally difficult. Application deadline: 8/1. Notification: continuous until 8/15. Preference given to state residents.
Collegiate Environment: Orientation program. Drama-theater group, choral group, marching band, student-run newspaper, radio station. Social organizations: 103 open to all; national fraternities, national sororities, local fraternities, local sororities; 12% of eligible men and 12% of eligible women are members. Most popular organizations: Honda Civic Bowl, Jazz Ensemble, Honors Program. Major annual events: Homecoming, Greek shows, student elections. Student services: health clinic, personal-psychological counseling, women's center. Campus security: 24-hour patrols, controlled dormitory access. 3,200 college housing spaces available; all were occupied in 2012-13. Freshmen given priority for college housing. Options: coed, men-only, women-only housing available. Martha M. Brown/Lois H. Daniel Library plus 1 other with 630,890 books, 899,731 microform titles, an OPAC, and a Web page. Operations spending for the previous fiscal year: $3.9 million. 1,025 computers available on campus for general student use. A campuswide network can be accessed from student residence rooms and from off campus. Students can access the following: online class registration. Staffed computer lab on campus provides training in use of computers, software, and the Internet.
Community Environment: See Vanderbilt University.

■ **TENNESSEE TECHNOLOGICAL UNIVERSITY**
N Dixie Ave.
Cookeville, TN 38505
Tel: (931)372-3101; Free: 800-255-8881
Fax: (931)372-6250
E-mail: admissions@tntech.edu
Web Site: www.tntech.edu/
Description: State-supported, university, coed. Part of Tennessee Board of Regents. Awards bachelor's, master's, and doctoral degrees and post-master's certificates. Founded 1915. Setting: 235-acre small town campus. Endowment: $50 million. Research spending for the previous fiscal year: $12 million. Educational spending for the previous fiscal year: $6161 per student. Total enrollment: 11,538. Faculty: 640 (389 full-time, 251 part-time). Student-undergrad faculty ratio is 21:1. 4,553 applied, 94% were admitted. 24% from top 10% of their high school class, 50% from top quarter, 82% from top half. 3 National Merit Scholars. Full-time: 8,506 students, 47% women, 53% men. Part-time: 930 students, 50% women, 50% men. Students come from 43 states and territories, 60 other countries, 4% from out-of-state. 0.4% American Indian or Alaska Native, non-Hispanic/Latino; 2% Hispanic/Latino; 4% African American, non-Hispanic/Latino; 1% Asian, non-Hispanic/Latino; 0.1% Native Hawaiian or other Pacific Islander, non-Hispanic/Latino; 3% international. 15% 25 or older, 30% live on campus, 8% transferred in. Retention: 76% of full-time freshmen returned the following year. Academic areas with the most degrees conferred: interdisciplinary studies; business/marketing; engineering. Core. Calendar: semesters. Academic remediation for entering students, ESL program, services for LD students, advanced placement, accelerated degree program, honors program, independent study, distance learning, double major, summer session for credit, part-time degree program, adult/continuing education programs, co-op programs and internships. Off campus study at Roane State Community College-Oak Ridge, TN and Pellissippi State Community College-Knoxville, TN. Study abroad program. ROTC: Army, Air Force (c).

Entrance Requirements: Options: electronic application, early admission, deferred admission, international baccalaureate accepted. Required: high school transcript, minimum 2.5 high school GPA, SAT or ACT. Recommended: interview, ACT. Entrance: moderately difficult. Application deadline: 8/1. Notification: continuous. Preference given to state residents. Transfer credits accepted: Yes.

Costs Per Year: Application fee: $25. State resident tuition: $6724 full-time, $310 per credit hour part-time. Nonresident tuition: $20,884 full-time, $900 per credit hour part-time. Full-time tuition varies according to course load and program. Part-time tuition varies according to course load and program. College room and board: $7642. College room only: $3980. Room and board charges vary according to board plan and housing facility.

Collegiate Environment: Orientation program. Drama-theater group, choral group, marching band, student-run newspaper, radio station. Social organizations: 216 open to all; national fraternities, national sororities; 10% of eligible men and 10% of eligible women are members. Most popular organizations: Baptist Collegiate Center, Fellowship of Christian Athletes, University Christian Student Center, Residence Hall Association. Major annual events: Homecoming, Greek Week, Career Day. Student services: health clinic, personal-psychological counseling, women's center. Campus security: 24-hour emergency response devices and patrols, late night transport-escort service, student safety organization, lighted pathways. Angelo and Jennette Volpe Library and Media Center with 704,377 books, 1.5 million microform titles, 1,636 serials, 19,784 audiovisual materials, an OPAC, and a Web page. Operations spending for the previous fiscal year: $2.5 million. 227 computers available on campus for general student use. A campuswide network can be accessed from student residence rooms. Students can access the following: online class registration, 590 additional computers are available for student use in individual departmental labs. Staffed computer lab on campus provides training in use of computers, software, and the Internet.

Community Environment: Cookeville, located in middle Tennessee, is predominantly an agricultural area. Bus transportation is available. Churches of most denominations, libraries, a hospital, and various civic and service organizations serve the community. Recreational activities include swimming, softball, baseball, tennis, and golf. Center Hill Dam and Reservoir are nearby for many other sports, such as boating, water sports, fishing, and camping.

■ **TENNESSEE TEMPLE UNIVERSITY**
1815 Union Ave.
Chattanooga, TN 37404-3587
Tel: (423)493-4100; Free: 800-553-4050
Fax: (423)493-4497
E-mail: eric.lovett@tntemple.edu
Web Site: www.tntemple.edu/

Description: Independent Baptist, comprehensive, coed. Awards associate, bachelor's, master's, and doctoral degrees. Founded 1946. Setting: 55-acre urban campus. Total enrollment: 623. 1,892 applied. 27% 25 or older. Core. Calendar: semesters. Academic remediation for entering students, advanced placement, independent study, distance learning, double major, summer session for credit, part-time degree program, internships, graduate courses open to undergrads.

Entrance Requirements: Options: electronic application, deferred admission, international baccalaureate accepted. Required: high school transcript, minimum 2.0 high school GPA, 3 recommendations, interview, health and immunization report, SAT or ACT. Required for some: essay. Entrance: minimally difficult. Application deadline: 8/20. Notification: continuous.

Collegiate Environment: Orientation program. Drama-theater group, choral group, student-run newspaper, radio station. Social organizations: societies for men and women. Student services: health clinic, personal-psychological counseling. Campus security: 24-hour emergency response devices and patrols, late night transport-escort service. Cierpke Memorial Library with 150,711 books and 76 serials.

Community Environment: The university is located near downtown Chattanooga, which sits in the valley of Lookout Mountain. The campus is only minutes from all of the downtown attractions and two malls.

■ **TENNESSEE WESLEYAN COLLEGE**
204 E College St.
Athens, TN 37303
Tel: (423)745-7504; Free: 800-PICK-TWC
Fax: (423)744-9968
E-mail: admissions@twcnet.edu

Web Site: www.twcnet.edu/

Description: Independent United Methodist, comprehensive, coed. Awards bachelor's and master's degrees (profile includes information for both the main and branch campuses). Founded 1857. Setting: 40-acre small town campus with easy access to Knoxville, Chattanooga. Total enrollment: 1,116. Faculty: 106 (55 full-time, 51 part-time). Student-undergrad faculty ratio is 15:1. 851 applied, 76% were admitted. 8% from top 10% of their high school class, 35% from top quarter, 81% from top half. Full-time: 1,026 students, 64% women, 36% men. Part-time: 80 students, 58% women, 43% men. Students come from 28 states and territories, 21 other countries, 9% from out-of-state. 0.2% American Indian or Alaska Native, non-Hispanic/Latino; 1% Hispanic/Latino; 6% African American, non-Hispanic/Latino; 1% Asian, non-Hispanic/Latino; 0.2% Native Hawaiian or other Pacific Islander, non-Hispanic/Latino; 4% international. 21% 25 or older, 30% live on campus, 18% transferred in. Retention: 62% of full-time freshmen returned the following year. Academic areas with the most degrees conferred: business/marketing; health professions and related sciences; education. Core. Calendar: semesters. Academic remediation for entering students, services for LD students, advanced placement, accelerated degree program, self-designed majors, honors program, independent study, double major, summer session for credit, part-time degree program, adult/continuing education programs, internships. Off campus study. Study abroad program.

Entrance Requirements: Options: electronic application, deferred admission, international baccalaureate accepted. Required: essay, high school transcript, minimum 2.25 high school GPA, 1 recommendation, SAT or ACT. Required for some: interview. Entrance: minimally difficult. SAT Subject Test deadline: 7/1.

Collegiate Environment: Orientation program. Drama-theater group, choral group, student-run newspaper. Social organizations: 45 open to all; national sororities, local fraternities, local sororities; 10% of eligible men and 12% of eligible women are members. Campus security: 24-hour patrols, late night transport-escort service, controlled dormitory access, night patrols by trained security personnel. 350 college housing spaces available; 300 were occupied in 2012-13. Freshmen guaranteed college housing. On-campus residence required through senior year. Options: men-only, women-only housing available. Merner-Pfeiffer Library plus 1 other with an OPAC and a Web page. 150 computers available on campus for general student use. A campuswide network can be accessed from student residence rooms. Students can access the following: online class registration. Staffed computer lab on campus (open 24 hours a day) provides training in use of computers, software, and the Internet.

Community Environment: Athens is the county seat of McMinn County, located between Chattanooga and Knoxville. The town is an industrial community providing jobs for approximately 13,000 people and serving as a shopping center for 50,000 rural residents. Recreational activities in the beautiful mountainous area include big game hunting, fresh water fishing, rafting, kayaking, hiking, and many other sports.

■ **TREVECCA NAZARENE UNIVERSITY**
333 Murfreesboro Rd.
Nashville, TN 37210-2877
Tel: (615)248-1200; Free: 888-210-4TNU
Fax: (615)248-7728
E-mail: admissions_und@trevecca.edu
Web Site: www.trevecca.edu/

Description: Independent Nazarene, comprehensive, coed. Awards associate, bachelor's, master's, and doctoral degrees. Founded 1901. Setting: 65-acre urban campus. Endowment: $20.1 million. Educational spending for the previous fiscal year: $6187 per student. Total enrollment: 2,472. Faculty: 223 (89 full-time, 134 part-time). Student-undergrad faculty ratio is 15:1. 930 applied, 99% were admitted. Full-time: 1,071 students, 54% women, 46% men. Part-time: 396 students, 56% women, 44% men. Students come from 38 states and territories, 13 other countries, 34% from out-of-state. 1% American Indian or Alaska Native, non-Hispanic/Latino; 2% Hispanic/Latino; 8% African American, non-Hispanic/Latino; 1% Asian, non-Hispanic/Latino; 0.1% Native Hawaiian or other Pacific Islander, non-Hispanic/Latino; 2% international. 30% 25 or older, 48% live on campus, 5% transferred in. Retention: 74% of full-time freshmen returned the following year. Academic areas with the most degrees conferred: business/marketing; education; visual and performing arts; homeland security, law enforcement, firefighting, and protective services. Core. Calendar: semesters. Academic remediation for entering students, services for LD students, advanced placement, distance learning, double major, summer session for credit, adult/continuing education programs, internships. Study abroad program. ROTC: Army (c).

Entrance Requirements: Options: electronic application, early admission, deferred admission. Required: high school transcript, minimum 2.5 high school GPA, ACT composite score of 18 or above, or SAT Critical Reading + Math score of 860 or above; enrollment fee; medical history and immunization records, SAT or ACT. Entrance: moderately difficult. Application deadline: 8/1. Notification: continuous. SAT Reasoning Test deadline: 8/29. Transfer credits accepted: Yes.

Costs Per Year: Application fee: $25. Comprehensive fee: $28,778 includes full-time tuition ($20,790), mandatory fees ($500), and college room and board ($7488). College room only: $3744. Full-time tuition and fees vary according to course load and program. Room and board charges vary according to board plan. Part-time tuition: $803 per credit hour. Part-time tuition varies according to course load and program.

Collegiate Environment: Orientation program. Drama-theater group, choral group, marching band, student-run newspaper. Major annual events: Homecoming Week, Friday Night Live, Trojan Idol. Student services: health clinic, personal-psychological counseling. Campus security: 24-hour patrols, late night transport-escort service, weather alert warning system (phone, email, siren). 730 college housing spaces available; 680 were occupied in 2012-13. On-campus residence required through senior year. Options: men-only, women-only housing available. Waggoner Library with 151,985 books, 735 serials, an OPAC, and a Web page. Operations spending for the previous fiscal year: $1.1 million. 200 computers available on campus for general student use. A campuswide network can be accessed from student residence rooms and from off campus. Students can access the following: online class registration, Non-traditional and graduate student registered through Academic Records. Staffed computer lab on campus.

Community Environment: See Vanderbilt University.

■ **TUSCULUM COLLEGE**
60 Shiloh Rd.
Greeneville, TN 37743-9997
Tel: (423)636-7300; Free: 800-729-0256
Fax: (423)638-7166
E-mail: admissions@tusculum.edu
Web Site: www.tusculum.edu/

Description: Independent Presbyterian, comprehensive, coed. Awards bachelor's and master's degrees. Founded 1794. Setting: 140-acre small town campus. Endowment: $16.8 million. Total enrollment: 2,199. Faculty: 224 (77 full-time, 147 part-time). Student-undergrad faculty ratio is 16:1. 2,825 applied, 72% were admitted. 10% from top 10% of their high school class, 26% from top quarter, 61% from top half. Full-time: 1,913 students, 56% women, 44% men. Part-time: 67 students, 79% women, 21% men. Students come from 31 states and territories, 15 other countries, 19% from out-of-state. 1% American Indian or Alaska Native, non-Hispanic/Latino; 2% Hispanic/Latino; 13% African American, non-Hispanic/Latino; 0.3% Asian, non-Hispanic/Latino; 0.1% Native Hawaiian or other Pacific Islander, non-Hispanic/Latino; 2% international. 45% 25 or older, 65% live on campus, 3% transferred in. Retention: 57% of full-time freshmen returned the following year. Academic areas with the most degrees conferred: business/marketing; education; parks and recreation. Core. Calendar: semesters. Academic remediation for entering students, services for LD students, advanced placement, self-designed majors, honors program, independent study, double major, summer session for credit, part-time degree program, adult/continuing education programs, internships. Study abroad program.

Entrance Requirements: Options: electronic application, early admission, deferred admission. Required: essay, high school transcript, minimum 2 high school GPA, SAT or ACT. Recommended: interview. Required for some: 3 recommendations. Entrance: moderately difficult. Application deadline: Rolling. Transfer credits accepted: Yes.

Costs Per Year: Application fee: $0. Comprehensive fee: $30,750 includes full-time tuition ($22,250) and college room and board ($8500). College room only: $5110.

Collegiate Environment: Orientation program. Drama-theater group, choral group, marching band, student-run newspaper, radio station. Social organizations: 21 open to all. Most popular organizations: Pioneer Newspaper, Bonwondi, Campus Activities Board, Fellowship of Christian Athletes, Tusculana (yearbook). Major annual events: Opening Convocation, Honors Convocation, Lantern Festival. Student services: health clinic, personal-psychological counseling, women's center. Campus security: 24-hour emergency response devices and patrols, student patrols, late night transport-escort service, controlled dormitory access, trained security personnel on duty. 598 college housing spaces available; 565 were occupied in 2012-13. Freshmen guaranteed college housing. On-campus residence

required through junior year. Options: coed, men-only, women-only housing available. Thomas J. Garland Library plus 2 others with 49,905 books, 17,771 microform titles, 1,000 serials, an OPAC, and a Web page. 200 computers available on campus for general student use. A campuswide network can be accessed from student residence rooms and from off campus. Students can access the following: online class registration. Staffed computer lab on campus (open 24 hours a day) provides training in use of computers.

Community Environment: Greeneville, in Greene County, the birthplace of Davy Crockett, is accessible by bus and rail. The city has a full-time recreational director who supervises a year-round program in addition to the hunting, boating, fishing, golf, whitewater rafting, and cycling available in the area. Nearby is the Andrew Johnson Wildlife Management Area.

■ **UNION UNIVERSITY**
1050 Union University Dr.
Jackson, TN 38305-3697
Tel: (731)668-1818; Free: 800-33-UNION
Fax: (731)661-5187
E-mail: rgraves@uu.edu
Web Site: www.uu.edu/

Description: Independent Southern Baptist, comprehensive, coed. Awards associate, bachelor's, master's, and doctoral degrees and post-master's certificates. Founded 1823. Setting: 360-acre small town campus with easy access to Memphis. Endowment: $30.2 million. Research spending for the previous fiscal year: $250,000. Educational spending for the previous fiscal year: $24,030 per student. Total enrollment: 3,996. Faculty: 248 (242 full-time, 6 part-time). Student-undergrad faculty ratio is 11:1. 2,051 applied, 75% were admitted. 41% from top 10% of their high school class, 67% from top quarter, 87% from top half. 10 National Merit Scholars, 20 valedictorians. Full-time: 2,212 students, 62% women, 38% men. Part-time: 617 students, 50% women, 50% men. Students come from 44 states and territories, 36 other countries, 32% from out-of-state. 0.2% American Indian or Alaska Native, non-Hispanic/Latino; 2% Hispanic/Latino; 14% African American, non-Hispanic/Latino; 1% Asian, non-Hispanic/Latino; 0.1% Native Hawaiian or other Pacific Islander, non-Hispanic/Latino; 2% international. 3% 25 or older, 63% live on campus, 4% transferred in. Retention: 92% of full-time freshmen returned the following year. Academic areas with the most degrees conferred: health professions and related sciences; interdisciplinary studies; education. Core. Calendar: 4-1-4. Academic remediation for entering students, ESL program, services for LD students, advanced placement, accelerated degree program, honors program, independent study, distance learning, double major, summer session for credit, part-time degree program, adult/continuing education programs, co-op programs and internships, graduate courses open to undergrads. Off campus study at Freed-Hardeman University, Council for Christian Colleges and Universities. Study abroad program. ROTC: Army (c).

Entrance Requirements: Options: electronic application, early admission, early action, deferred admission, international baccalaureate accepted. Required: high school transcript, minimum 2.5 high school GPA, SAT or ACT. Recommended: essay, interview, SAT Subject Tests. Required for some: 3 recommendations. Entrance: moderately difficult. Application deadlines: Rolling, 12/1 for early action. Notification: 8/1, 12/15 for early action.

Costs Per Year: Application fee: $35. Comprehensive fee: $34,080 includes full-time tuition ($24,940), mandatory fees ($710), and college room and board ($8430). Full-time tuition and fees vary according to class time, course load, degree level, location, and program. Room and board charges vary according to board plan and housing facility. Part-time tuition: $845 per credit hour. Part-time tuition and fees vary according to class time, course load, degree level, location, and program.

Collegiate Environment: Orientation program. Drama-theater group, choral group, student-run newspaper. Social organizations: 52 open to all; national fraternities, national sororities; 25% of eligible men and 21% of eligible women are members. Most popular organizations: Campus Ministries, Student Government Association, Student Activities Council, Students in Free Enterprise (SIFE). Major annual events: Campus Day, All-Sing Contest, Homecoming. Student services: health clinic, personal-psychological counseling. Campus security: 24-hour emergency response devices and patrols, student patrols, late night transport-escort service. 1,180 college housing spaces available; 1,100 were occupied in 2012-13. Freshmen given priority for college housing. On-campus residence required through junior year. Options: men-only, women-only housing available. Emma Waters Summar Library plus 1 other with 218,154 books, 79,079 microform titles, 20,585 serials, 18,442 audiovisual materials, an OPAC, and a Web page.

Operations spending for the previous fiscal year: $1.3 million. 236 computers available on campus for general student use. A campuswide network can be accessed from student residence rooms and from off campus. Students can access the following: online class registration. Staffed computer lab on campus provides training in use of computers, software, and the Internet.
Community Environment: Jackson is a city of 55,000 that is 75 miles from Memphis and 125 miles from Nashville. There are 3 other colleges located in the same town.

■ **UNIVERSITY OF MEMPHIS**
Memphis, TN 38152
Tel: (901)678-2000; Free: 800-669-2678
Fax: (901)678-3053
E-mail: bmeredith@memphis.edu
Web Site: www.memphis.edu/
Description: State-supported, university, coed. Part of Tennessee Board of Regents. Awards bachelor's, master's, and doctoral degrees and post-master's certificates. Founded 1912. Setting: 1,160-acre urban campus. Total enrollment: 22,139. Faculty: 1,517 (862 full-time, 655 part-time). Student-undergrad faculty ratio is 14:1. 6,798 applied, 62% were admitted. 1% from top 10% of their high school class, 42% from top quarter, 79% from top half. Full-time: 12,728 students, 59% women, 41% men. Part-time: 4,919 students, 64% women, 36% men. 10% from out-of-state. 0.3% American Indian or Alaska Native, non-Hispanic/Latino; 3% Hispanic/Latino; 39% African American, non-Hispanic/Latino; 3% Asian, non-Hispanic/Latino; 0.1% Native Hawaiian or other Pacific Islander, non-Hispanic/Latino; 1% international. 29% 25 or older, 14% live on campus, 9% transferred in. Retention: 76% of full-time freshmen returned the following year. Academic areas with the most degrees conferred: business/marketing; education; interdisciplinary studies. Core. Calendar: semesters. Academic remediation for entering students, ESL program, services for LD students, advanced placement, accelerated degree program, self-designed majors, honors program, independent study, distance learning, double major, summer session for credit, part-time degree program, external degree program, adult/continuing education programs, co-op programs and internships, graduate courses open to undergrads. Off campus study. Study abroad program. ROTC: Army, Naval, Air Force.
Entrance Requirements: Options: electronic application, early admission, international baccalaureate accepted. Required: high school transcript, SAT or ACT. Required for some: minimum 2 high school GPA, 2 recommendations, interview. Entrance: moderately difficult. Application deadline: 7/1. Notification: continuous. SAT Reasoning Test deadline: 7/1.
Costs Per Year: Application fee: $25. State resident tuition: $6978 full-time, $277 per credit hour part-time. Nonresident tuition: $22,428 full-time, $890 per credit hour part-time. Mandatory fees: $1256 full-time, $82.50 per credit hour part-time. Full-time tuition and fees vary according to course load, degree level, program, and reciprocity agreements. Part-time tuition and fees vary according to course load, degree level, and program. College room and board: $6860. Room and board charges vary according to board plan and housing facility.
Collegiate Environment: Orientation program. Drama-theater group, choral group, marching band, student-run newspaper, radio station. Social organizations: 186 open to all; national fraternities, national sororities, local sororities; 7% of eligible men and 5% of eligible women are members. Most popular organizations: Blue Crew, Up 'til Dawn, Black Student Association. Major annual events: Homecoming, Springfest, Black History Month. Student services: health clinic, personal-psychological counseling, women's center. Campus security: 24-hour emergency response devices and patrols, student patrols, late night transport-escort service, controlled dormitory access. 2,413 college housing spaces available; 2,342 were occupied in 2012-13. Options: coed, men-only, women-only housing available. McWherter Library plus 4 others with 1.5 million books, 3.6 million microform titles, 6,771 serials, 34,093 audiovisual materials, an OPAC, and a Web page. 1,600 computers available on campus for general student use. A campuswide network can be accessed from student residence rooms and from off campus. Students can access the following: online class registration. Staffed computer lab on campus (open 24 hours a day).
Community Environment: Memphis, with a metropolitan area population of over one million, is one of the South's largest and most attractive cities. As a primary medical, educational, communication, distribution, and transportation center, Memphis offers a rich and full range of research opportunities and cultural experiences. The city, known worldwide for its musical heritage, has many fine restaurants, museums, and theaters, as well as one of the nation's largest urban park systems. All forms of commercial transportation

are available. Opportunities are numerous for part-time employment. Annual events include the St. Jude Liberty Bowl Football Classic, the Memphis in May International Festival, the Great River Carnival, and the Mid-South Fair. Some of the points of interest are the Brooks Memorial Art Gallery, Chuclissa Indian Villiage and Museum, Elvis Presley's Graceland, Mud Island, Libertyland, and the Great American Pyramid.

■ **UNIVERSITY OF PHOENIX–CHATTANOOGA CAMPUS**
1208 Pointe Centre Dr.
Chattanooga, TN 37421-3707
Tel: (423)499-2500; Free: 866-766-0766
Web Site: www.phoenix.edu/
Description: Proprietary, comprehensive, coed. Awards associate, bachelor's, master's, and doctoral degrees.

■ **UNIVERSITY OF PHOENIX–MEMPHIS CAMPUS**
65 Germantown Ct.
Cordova, TN 38018
Tel: (901)751-1086; Free: 866-766-0766
Web Site: www.phoenix.edu/
Description: Proprietary, comprehensive, coed. Awards bachelor's, master's, and doctoral degrees.

■ **UNIVERSITY OF PHOENIX–NASHVILLE CAMPUS**
616 Marriott Dr., Ste. 150
Nashville, TN 37214-5048
Tel: (615)872-0188; Free: 866-766-0766
Web Site: www.phoenix.edu/
Description: Proprietary, comprehensive, coed. Awards bachelor's and master's degrees. Founded 2003. Setting: urban campus. Total enrollment: 917. Faculty: 129 (16 full-time, 113 part-time). Full-time: 751 students, 64% women, 36% men. 84% 25 or older. Academic areas with the most degrees conferred: business/marketing; computer and information sciences; health professions and related sciences. Core. Calendar: continuous. Services for LD students, advanced placement, accelerated degree program, independent study, distance learning, graduate courses open to undergrads.
Entrance Requirements: Open admission. Options: electronic application, deferred admission. Required: 1 recommendation. Required for some: high school transcript. Entrance: noncompetitive. Application deadline: Rolling.
Collegiate Environment: Campus security: late night transport-escort service. University Library with 16,781 serials and an OPAC. Operations spending for the previous fiscal year: $6.8 million.

■ **THE UNIVERSITY OF TENNESSEE**
Knoxville, TN 37996
Tel: (865)974-1000
E-mail: admissions@utk.edu
Web Site: www.utk.edu/
Description: State-supported, university, coed. Part of University of Tennessee System. Awards bachelor's, master's, and doctoral degrees. Founded 1794. Setting: 560-acre urban campus. Endowment: $532.5 million. Research spending for the previous fiscal year: $264.4 million. Total enrollment: 29,833. Faculty: 2,008 (1,680 full-time, 328 part-time). Student-undergrad faculty ratio is 17:1. 14,398 applied, 67% were admitted. 50% from top 10% of their high school class, 90% from top quarter, 100% from top half. Full-time: 19,588 students, 49% women, 51% men. Part-time: 1,328 students, 50% women, 50% men. Students come from 48 states and territories, 103 other countries, 8% from out-of-state. 0.3% American Indian or Alaska Native, non-Hispanic/Latino; 3% Hispanic/Latino; 7% African American, non-Hispanic/Latino; 3% Asian, non-Hispanic/Latino; 0.1% Native Hawaiian or other Pacific Islander, non-Hispanic/Latino; 1% international. 9% 25 or older, 37% live on campus, 6% transferred in. Retention: 85% of full-time freshmen returned the following year. Academic areas with the most degrees conferred: business/marketing; social sciences; psychology. Core. Calendar: semesters. ESL program, services for LD students, advanced placement, accelerated degree program, self-designed majors, freshman honors college, honors program, independent study, distance learning, double major, summer session for credit, part-time degree program, external degree program, co-op programs and internships, graduate courses open to undergrads. Off campus study at National Student Exchange. Study abroad program. ROTC: Army, Air Force.
Entrance Requirements: Options: electronic application, international baccalaureate accepted. Required: essay, high school transcript, minimum 2 high school GPA, specific high school units, SAT or ACT. Recommended: 1

recommendation. Entrance: moderately difficult. Application deadline: 12/1. Notification: 3/31. SAT Reasoning Test deadline: 12/1. Transfer credits accepted: Yes.

Costs Per Year: Application fee: $40. State resident tuition: $7802 full-time, $326 per hour part-time. Nonresident tuition: $25,992 full-time, $1085 per hour part-time. Mandatory fees: $1290 full-time, $62 per hour part-time. Full-time tuition and fees vary according to course level, program, and reciprocity agreements. Part-time tuition and fees vary according to course level, program, and reciprocity agreements. College room and board: $8752. Room and board charges vary according to board plan and housing facility.

Collegiate Environment: Orientation program. Drama-theater group, choral group, marching band, student-run newspaper, radio station. Social organizations: national fraternities, national sororities; 13% of eligible men and 21% of eligible women are members. Most popular organizations: Fraternities/Sororities, Religious organizations, Central Program Council, Black Cultural Programming Committee, Student Government Association. Major annual events: Welcome Week, Homecoming, Volapalooza. Student services: health clinic, personal-psychological counseling, women's center. Campus security: 24-hour emergency response devices and patrols, late night transport-escort service, controlled dormitory access, security cameras on all building entrances; card entry into the living sections of residence hall buildings. 7,534 college housing spaces available; 7,195 were occupied in 2012-13. Freshmen guaranteed college housing. On-campus residence required in freshman year. Options: coed, men-only, women-only housing available. John C. Hodges Library plus 5 others with 3.1 million books, 4.7 million microform titles, 58,765 serials, 80,122 audiovisual materials, an OPAC, and a Web page. Operations spending for the previous fiscal year: $24.3 million. 1,000 computers available on campus for general student use. Computer purchase/lease plans available. A campuswide network can be accessed from student residence rooms and from off campus. Students can access the following: online class registration, Blackboard Course Management System. Staffed computer lab on campus (open 24 hours a day) provides training in use of computers, software, and the Internet.

■ THE UNIVERSITY OF TENNESSEE AT CHATTANOOGA

615 McCallie Ave.
Chattanooga, TN 37403-2598
Tel: (423)425-4111; Free: 800-UTC.MOCS
Fax: (423)425-4157
E-mail: lee-pierce@utc.edu
Web Site: www.utc.edu/

Description: State-supported, comprehensive, coed. Part of University of Tennessee System. Awards bachelor's, master's, and doctoral degrees and post-master's certificates. Founded 1886. Setting: 120-acre urban campus with easy access to Atlanta. Total enrollment: 11,660. Faculty: 751 (438 full-time, 313 part-time). Student-undergrad faculty ratio is 18:1. 7,677 applied, 76% were admitted. 43% from top quarter of their high school class, 85% from top half. Full-time: 8,904 students, 55% women, 45% men. Part-time: 1,255 students, 56% women, 44% men. 6% from out-of-state. 0.3% American Indian or Alaska Native, non-Hispanic/Latino; 3% Hispanic/Latino; 12% African American, non-Hispanic/Latino; 2% Asian, non-Hispanic/Latino; 0% Native Hawaiian or other Pacific Islander, non-Hispanic/Latino; 1% international. 14% 25 or older, 31% live on campus, 9% transferred in. Retention: 67% of full-time freshmen returned the following year. Academic areas with the most degrees conferred: business/marketing; education; psychology. Core. Calendar: semesters. Academic remediation for entering students, ESL program, services for LD students, advanced placement, honors program, independent study, distance learning, double major, summer session for credit, part-time degree program, adult/continuing education programs, co-op programs and internships, graduate courses open to undergrads. Off campus study. Study abroad program. ROTC: Army.

Entrance Requirements: Options: electronic application, deferred admission, international baccalaureate accepted. Required: high school transcript, SAT or ACT. Recommended: essay. Entrance: moderately difficult. Application deadlines: 8/1, 8/1 for nonresidents. Notification: continuous, continuous for nonresidents. SAT Reasoning Test deadline: 5/1. Transfer credits accepted: Yes.

Costs Per Year: Application fee: $30. State resident tuition: $5722 full-time, $238 per credit hour part-time. Nonresident tuition: $20,068 full-time, $836 per credit hour part-time. Mandatory fees: $1490 full-time, $190 per credit hour part-time. College room and board: $8300. Room and board charges vary according to board plan and housing facility.

Collegiate Environment: Orientation program. Drama-theater group, choral group, marching band, student-run newspaper, radio station. Social

organizations: national fraternities, national sororities. Most popular organizations: Student Government Association, Black Student Association, Association for Campus Entertainment, International Student Association, Baptist Student Union. Major annual event: Homecoming Week. Student services: health clinic, personal-psychological counseling. Campus security: 24-hour emergency response devices and patrols, late night transport-escort service, controlled dormitory access. Freshmen given priority for college housing. On-campus residence required in freshman year. Option: coed housing available. Lupton Library plus 1 other with an OPAC and a Web page. Operations spending for the previous fiscal year: $1.4 million. 965 computers available on campus for general student use. A campuswide network can be accessed from student residence rooms and from off campus. Students can access the following: online class registration, pay fees. Staffed computer lab on campus provides training in use of computers, software, and the Internet.

■ THE UNIVERSITY OF TENNESSEE AT MARTIN

University St.
Martin, TN 38238-1000
Tel: (731)881-7000; Free: 800-829-8861
Fax: (731)881-7029
E-mail: jrayburn@utm.edu
Web Site: www.utm.edu/

Description: State-supported, comprehensive, coed. Part of University of Tennessee System. Awards bachelor's and master's degrees. Founded 1900. Setting: 250-acre small town campus. Endowment: $25.7 million. Research spending for the previous fiscal year: $551,090. Educational spending for the previous fiscal year: $5931 per student. Total enrollment: 7,751. Faculty: 563 (290 full-time, 273 part-time). Student-undergrad faculty ratio is 18:1. 3,730 applied, 76% were admitted. 19% from top 10% of their high school class, 50% from top quarter, 85% from top half. 2 National Merit Scholars, 24 valedictorians, 97 student government officers. Full-time: 6,082 students, 57% women, 43% men. Part-time: 1,244 students, 66% women, 34% men. Students come from 58 states and territories, 18 other countries, 4% from out-of-state. 0.3% American Indian or Alaska Native, non-Hispanic/Latino; 2% Hispanic/Latino; 16% African American, non-Hispanic/Latino; 1% Asian, non-Hispanic/Latino; 0% Native Hawaiian or other Pacific Islander, non-Hispanic/Latino; 2% international. 21% 25 or older, 32% live on campus, 7% transferred in. Retention: 76% of full-time freshmen returned the following year. Academic areas with the most degrees conferred: business/marketing; education; interdisciplinary studies. Core. Calendar: semesters. ESL program, services for LD students, advanced placement, accelerated degree program, self-designed majors, honors program, independent study, distance learning, double major, summer session for credit, part-time degree program, adult/continuing education programs, co-op programs and internships, graduate courses open to undergrads. Off campus study at Gulf Coast Research Laboratory. Study abroad program. ROTC: Army.

Entrance Requirements: Options: electronic application, early admission, deferred admission, international baccalaureate accepted. Required: high school transcript, minimum 2.5 high school GPA, SAT or ACT. Entrance: moderately difficult. Application deadline: Rolling. Notification: 8/1. SAT Reasoning Test deadline: 8/1. SAT Subject Test deadline: 8/1. Transfer credits accepted: Yes.

Costs Per Year: Application fee: $30. State resident tuition: $5978 full-time, $249 per credit hour part-time. Nonresident tuition: $19,134 full-time, $798 per credit hour part-time. Mandatory fees: $1071 full-time, $46 per credit hour part-time. Part-time tuition and fees vary according to course load. College room and board: $5593. College room only: $2720. Room and board charges vary according to board plan and housing facility.

Collegiate Environment: Orientation program. Drama-theater group, choral group, marching band, student-run newspaper, radio station. Social organizations: 179 open to all; national fraternities, national sororities, local sororities; 15% of eligible men and 15% of eligible women are members. Most popular organizations: Student Government Association, Student Activities Council, Sigma Theta Tau, Gamma Beta Phi, Student Tennessee Education Association. Major annual events: Quad City, UTM Rodeo-n-Roundup Days, SAC-Lip Sync during Homecoming. Student services: health clinic, personal-psychological counseling, women's center. Campus security: 24-hour emergency response devices and patrols, student patrols, controlled dormitory access. 2,382 college housing spaces available; 2,112 were occupied in 2012-13. Freshmen given priority for college housing. On-campus residence required in freshman year. Options: men-only, women-only housing available. Paul Meek Library with 379,072 books, 709,972 microform titles, 1,010 serials, 17,122 audiovisual materials, an OPAC, and a Web page. Operations spending for the previous fiscal year: $1.1 million. 843 computers available on campus for general student use. A campuswide network can be accessed from student residence rooms and from off campus. Students can access the following: online class registration, online fee payments, degree progress, financial aid data, housing applications, transcripts. Staffed computer lab on campus (open 24 hours a day) provides training in use of computers, software, and the Internet.

■ VANDERBILT UNIVERSITY
Nashville, TN 37240-1001
Tel: (615)322-7311; Free: 800-288-0432
Fax: (615)343-7765
E-mail: admissions@vanderbilt.edu
Web Site: www.vanderbilt.edu/

Description: Independent, university, coed. Awards bachelor's, master's, and doctoral degrees. Founded 1873. Setting: 330-acre urban campus. Endowment: $3.4 billion. Research spending for the previous fiscal year: $543.1 million. Total enrollment: 12,710. Faculty: 1,148 (919 full-time, 229 part-time). Student-undergrad faculty ratio is 8:1. 28,348 applied, 14% were admitted. 90% from top 10% of their high school class, 98% from top quarter, 100% from top half. 236 National Merit Scholars, 165 valedictorians, 233 student government officers. Full-time: 6,731 students, 50% women, 50% men. Part-time: 65 students, 37% women, 63% men. Students come from 52 states and territories, 44 other countries, 87% from out-of-state. 0.3% American Indian or Alaska Native, non-Hispanic/Latino; 8% Hispanic/Latino; 8% African American, non-Hispanic/Latino; 8% Asian, non-Hispanic/Latino; 0.04% Native Hawaiian or other Pacific Islander, non-Hispanic/Latino; 5% international. 0% 25 or older, 86% live on campus, 3% transferred in. Retention: 96% of full-time freshmen returned the following year. Academic areas with the most degrees conferred: social sciences; engineering; interdisciplinary studies. Core. Calendar: semesters. ESL program, services for LD students, advanced placement, accelerated degree program, self-designed majors, honors program, independent study, double major, summer session for credit, co-op programs and internships, graduate courses open to undergrads. Off campus study. Study abroad program. ROTC: Army, Naval, Air Force (c).

Entrance Requirements: Options: electronic application, early admission, early decision, deferred admission, international baccalaureate accepted. Required: essay, high school transcript, 3 recommendations, 3 letters of recommendation (two from teachers in core subject areas and one from counselor), SAT or ACT. Entrance: most difficult. Application deadlines: 1/3, 11/1 for early decision plan 1, 1/3 for early decision plan 2. Notification: 4/1, 12/15 for early decision plan 1, 2/15 for early decision plan 2. SAT Reasoning Test deadline: 1/3. SAT Subject Test deadline: 1/3. Transfer credits accepted: Yes. Applicants placed on waiting list: 5,653. Wait-listed applicants offered admission: 253. Early decision applicants: 2,823. Early decision applicants admitted: 691.

Costs Per Year: Application fee: $50. Comprehensive fee: $55,936 includes full-time tuition ($41,088), mandatory fees ($1030), and college room and board ($13,818). College room only: $9028. Room and board charges vary according to board plan.

Collegiate Environment: Orientation program. Drama-theater group, choral group, marching band, student-run newspaper, radio station. Social organizations: 510 open to all; national fraternities, national sororities. Major annual events: Rites of Spring, Great Performances, Accolade Homecoming Ball. Student services: health clinic, personal-psychological counseling, women's center. Campus security: 24-hour emergency response devices and patrols, student patrols, late night transport-escort service, controlled dormitory access. 5,695 college housing spaces available. Freshmen guaranteed college housing. On-campus residence required in freshman year. Options: coed, men-only, women-only housing available. Jean and Alexander Heard Library plus 7 others with 2.6 million books, 241,054 microform titles, 78,041 serials, 69,255 audiovisual materials, an OPAC, and a Web page.

Community Environment: Nashville, Tennessee's capital city, is one of the South's foremost centers for insurance, publishing, healthcare, and music. Ranking high among American cities in"quality of life" surveys, it offers four-star restaurants, sprawling shopping complexes, and entertainment to suit all tastes. The Tennessee Repertory Theatre, Community Concerts, Broadway touring companies, classical ensembles and the Nashville Symphony Orchestra, and the Circle Players perform regularly. The Tennessee Performing Arts Center continually hosts major orchestral and theatrical groups from throughout the nation. Among the attractions that bring visitors to Nashville each year are the Cheekwood Botanical Gardens and Fine Arts

Center, the Cumberland Museum and Science Center, the Nashville Arena, and the Tennessee State Museum. Nashville is also home of an NFL team, the Tennessee Titans, and a NHS team, the Nashville Predators.

■ VATTEROTT COLLEGE
2655 Dividend Dr.
Memphis, TN 38132
Tel: (901)761-5730; Free: 888-553-6627
Fax: (901)763-2897
Web Site: www.vatterott.edu/

Description: Proprietary, 2-year, coed. Awards terminal associate degrees. Founded 2004. Total enrollment: 233. 156 applied, 45% were admitted. Calendar: semesters.

■ VICTORY UNIVERSITY
255 N Highland St.
Memphis, TN 38111
Tel: (901)320-9700; Free: 800-960-9777
Fax: (901)320-9709
E-mail: admissions@victory.edu
Web Site: www.victory.edu/

Description: Independent, comprehensive, coed. Awards associate, bachelor's, and master's degrees. Founded 1941. Setting: 7-acre urban campus with easy access to Memphis. Educational spending for the previous fiscal year: $2736 per student. Total enrollment: 740. Faculty: 63 (35 full-time, 28 part-time). Student-undergrad faculty ratio is 12:1. 145 applied, 29% were admitted. 0% from top 10% of their high school class, 17% from top quarter, 33% from top half. Full-time: 449 students, 74% women, 26% men. Part-time: 245 students, 75% women, 25% men. Students come from 13 states and territories, 4 other countries, 8% from out-of-state. 0% American Indian or Alaska Native, non-Hispanic/Latino; 1% Hispanic/Latino; 80% African American, non-Hispanic/Latino; 0.3% Asian, non-Hispanic/Latino; 0.4% Native Hawaiian or other Pacific Islander, non-Hispanic/Latino; 1% international. 78% 25 or older, 13% transferred in. Retention: 70% of full-time freshmen returned the following year. Academic areas with the most degrees conferred: business/marketing; education; psychology. Core. Calendar: semesters. Academic remediation for entering students, services for LD students, advanced placement, accelerated degree program, self-designed majors, honors program, independent study, distance learning, double major, summer session for credit, part-time degree program, adult/continuing education programs. Off campus study. Study abroad program.

Entrance Requirements: Options: electronic application, deferred admission, international baccalaureate accepted. Required: minimum 2 high school GPA. Recommended: interview. Required for some: essay, high school transcript, 3 recommendations, transfer students must have a 2.0 college GPA, SAT or ACT. Entrance: minimally difficult. Application deadline: Rolling. Notification: continuous. Transfer credits accepted: Yes.

Collegiate Environment: Orientation program. Drama-theater group, choral group, student-run newspaper. Social organizations: SHRM, SIFE, STEA, SGA. Major annual events: Operation Christmas Child, Thanksgiving Celebration. Campus security: 24-hour patrols. J.W. and Dorothy Bell Library with 108,524 books, 111,884 microform titles, 1,015 serials, 2,194 audiovisual materials, an OPAC, and a Web page. Operations spending for the previous fiscal year: $190,328. 31 computers available on campus for general student use. A campuswide network can be accessed. Students can access the following: online class registration. Staffed computer lab on campus provides training in use of computers, software, and the Internet.

Community Environment: See University of Memphis.

■ VISIBLE MUSIC COLLEGE
200 Madison Ave.
Memphis, TN 38103
Tel: (901)381-3939
Web Site: visible.edu/

Description: Independent, 4-year, coed.

■ VOLUNTEER STATE COMMUNITY COLLEGE
1480 Nashville Pke.
Gallatin, TN 37066-3188
Tel: (615)452-8600; Free: 888-335-8722
Fax: (615)230-3577
E-mail: admissions@volstate.edu
Web Site: www.volstate.edu/

Description: State-supported, 2-year, coed. Part of Tennessee Board of

Regents. Awards certificates, transfer associate, and terminal associate degrees. Founded 1970. Setting: 100-acre suburban campus with easy access to Nashville. Endowment: $122,153. Educational spending for the previous fiscal year: $2286 per student. Total enrollment: 8,177. Faculty: 368 (153 full-time, 215 part-time). Student-undergrad faculty ratio is 23:1. 2,132 applied, 100% were admitted. Full-time: 3,619 students, 58% women, 42% men. Part-time: 4,558 students, 66% women, 34% men. Students come from 13 states and territories, 10 other countries, 1% from out-of-state. 0.5% American Indian or Alaska Native, non-Hispanic/Latino; 3% Hispanic/Latino; 9% African American, non-Hispanic/Latino; 2% Asian, non-Hispanic/Latino; 0.02% Native Hawaiian or other Pacific Islander, non-Hispanic/Latino; 0.4% international. 33% 25 or older, 7% transferred in. Core. Calendar: semesters. Academic remediation for entering students, ESL program, services for LD students, advanced placement, accelerated degree program, honors program, independent study, distance learning, double major, summer session for credit, part-time degree program, adult/continuing education programs, internships. Study abroad program.

Entrance Requirements: Open admission. Options: electronic application, early admission, deferred admission. Required: high school transcript. Required for some: minimum 2 high school GPA, interview, SAT or ACT. Entrance: noncompetitive. Application deadline: 8/25. Notification: continuous. SAT Reasoning Test deadline: 8/25. SAT Subject Test deadline: 8/25. Transfer credits accepted: Yes.

Costs Per Year: Application fee: $20. State resident tuition: $3673 full-time, $135 per credit hour part-time. Nonresident tuition: $14,305 full-time, $557 per credit hour part-time. Mandatory fees: $271 full-time, $22 per term part-time. Full-time tuition and fees vary according to course load. Part-time tuition and fees vary according to course load.

Collegiate Environment: Orientation program. Drama-theater group, choral group, student-run newspaper, radio station. Social organizations: 18 open to all. Most popular organizations: Gamma Beta Phi, Returning Woman's Organization, Phi Theta Kappa, Student Government Association, The Settler. Major annual events: Homecoming, Pioneer Field Day, Fall Fling. Student services: personal-psychological counseling. Campus security: 24-hour emergency response devices and patrols, late night transport-escort service. College housing not available. Thigpen Learning Resource Center with 178,186 books, 3,055 microform titles, 156 serials, 2,018 audiovisual materials, an OPAC, and a Web page. Operations spending for the previous fiscal year: $122,020. 800 computers available on campus for general student use. A campuswide network can be accessed from off-campus. Students can access the following: online class registration. Staffed computer lab on campus.

Community Environment: See Vanderbilt University.

■ **WALTERS STATE COMMUNITY COLLEGE**
500 S Davy Crockett Pky.
Morristown, TN 37813-6899
Tel: (423)585-2600; Free: 800-225-4770
E-mail: mike.campbell@ws.edu
Web Site: www.ws.edu/

Description: State-supported, 2-year, coed. Part of Tennessee Board of Regents. Awards certificates, transfer associate, and terminal associate degrees. Founded 1970. Setting: 100-acre small town campus. Endowment: $7.6 million. Total enrollment: 6,853. Faculty: 388 (141 full-time, 247 part-time). Student-undergrad faculty ratio is 22:1. 2,515 applied, 100% were admitted. 10% from top 10% of their high school class, 25% from top quarter, 65% from top half. Full-time: 3,591 students, 59% women, 41% men. Part-time: 3,262 students, 66% women, 34% men. Students come from 11 states and territories, 9 other countries, 1% from out-of-state. 5% transferred in. Retention: 58% of full-time freshmen returned the following year. Core. Calendar: semesters. Academic remediation for entering students, advanced placement, accelerated degree program, freshman honors college, honors program, distance learning, summer session for credit, part-time degree program, adult/continuing education programs. ROTC: Army (c).

Entrance Requirements: Open admission. Option: early admission. Required: high school transcript, SAT or ACT. Entrance: noncompetitive. Application deadline: Rolling. Notification: continuous. Transfer credits accepted: Yes.

Collegiate Environment: Choral group, student-run newspaper. Student services: health clinic. Campus security: 24-hour emergency response devices and patrols, late night transport-escort service. Walters State Library with 154,995 books, 28,218 serials, 6,393 audiovisual materials, an OPAC, and a Web page. Operations spending for the previous fiscal year: $725,009. 686 computers available on campus for general student use. A

campuswide network can be accessed from off-campus. Students can access the following: online class registration. Staffed computer lab on campus.

Community Environment: Known as the City Between the Lakes, Morristown is centrally located in the college's 10-county service area. It has become a market center for the region with the establishment of a shopping mall as well as a growing industrial center. Farming remains an important part of the local economy with primary crops of light burley tobacco, corn, hay, and wheat. The lakes provide for fishing, swimming, hunting, and picnicking. Scenic drives lead to the nearby Great Smoky Mountains, Clinch Mountain, and the larger urban areas to both the north and south.

■ **WATKINS COLLEGE OF ART, DESIGN, & FILM**
2298 Rosa L. Parks Blvd.
Nashville, TN 37228
Tel: (615)383-4848
Fax: (615)383-4849
E-mail: admissions@watkins.edu
Web Site: www.watkins.edu/

Description: Independent, 4-year, coed. Awards bachelor's degrees. Founded 1885. Setting: 13-acre urban campus. Endowment: $1.8 million. Educational spending for the previous fiscal year: $3657 per student. Total enrollment: 378. Faculty: 57 (20 full-time, 37 part-time). Student-undergrad faculty ratio is 10:1. 89 applied, 94% were admitted. Students come from 27 states and territories, 6 other countries, 25% from out-of-state. 1% American Indian or Alaska Native, non-Hispanic/Latino; 5% Hispanic/Latino; 8% African American, non-Hispanic/Latino; 1% Asian, non-Hispanic/Latino; 1% Native Hawaiian or other Pacific Islander, non-Hispanic/Latino; 2% international. 28% 25 or older, 24% live on campus. Retention: 60% of full-time freshmen returned the following year. Academic area with the most degrees conferred: visual and performing arts. Core. Calendar: semesters. Services for LD students, advanced placement, independent study, summer session for credit, part-time degree program, co-op programs and internships.

Entrance Requirements: Options: electronic application, early admission, deferred admission, international baccalaureate accepted. Required: essay, high school transcript, minimum 2.6 high school GPA, 1 recommendation, SAT or ACT. Recommended: interview. Required for some: high school transcript, artistic exercises, optional portfolio. Entrance: moderately difficult. Application deadline: 7/15. Notification: 8/1. SAT Reasoning Test deadline: 7/15. SAT Subject Test deadline: 7/15. Transfer credits accepted: Yes.

Costs Per Year: Application fee: $50. Tuition: $20,250 full-time, $675 per credit part-time. Mandatory fees: $1650 full-time, $55 per credit part-time. College room only: $6380.

Collegiate Environment: Orientation program. Social organizations: 7 open to all. Most popular organizations: Company Q (art society), Film club, sports club, student government. Major annual events: Welcome BBQ, YART Sale, Talent Show. Student services: health clinic, personal-psychological counseling. Campus security: 24-hour emergency response devices and patrols, late night transport-escort service, controlled dormitory access, monitored 24 hour camera security. 96 college housing spaces available; all were occupied in 2012-13. Freshmen given priority for college housing. On-campus residence required in freshman year. Options: men-only, women-only housing available. The Watkins Library plus 1 other with 18,944 books, 56 serials, 3,572 audiovisual materials, an OPAC, and a Web page. Operations spending for the previous fiscal year: $152,373. 200 computers available on campus for general student use. A campuswide network can be accessed from student residence rooms and from off campus. Students can access the following: online class registration. Staffed computer lab on campus provides training in use of computers, software, and the Internet.

■ **WELCH COLLEGE**
3606 W End Ave.
Nashville, TN 37205-2498
Tel: (615)844-5000; Free: 800-763-9222
Fax: (615)269-6028
E-mail: dmouser@welch.edu
Web Site: www.fwbbc.edu/

Description: Independent Free Will Baptist, 4-year, coed. Awards associate and bachelor's degrees. Founded 1942. Setting: 10-acre urban campus with easy access to Nashville. Endowment: $1.3 million. Educational spending for the previous fiscal year: $5979 per student. Total enrollment: 315. Faculty: 37 (14 full-time, 23 part-time). Student-undergrad faculty ratio is 9:1. 148 applied, 51% were admitted. 22% from top 10% of their high school class,

42% from top quarter, 60% from top half. Full-time: 203 students, 54% women, 46% men. Part-time: 112 students, 46% women, 54% men. Students come from 23 states and territories, 2 other countries, 48% from out-of-state. 0% American Indian or Alaska Native, non-Hispanic/Latino; 2% Hispanic/Latino; 10% African American, non-Hispanic/Latino; 0% Asian, non-Hispanic/Latino; 0% Native Hawaiian or other Pacific Islander, non-Hispanic/Latino; 1% international. 20% 25 or older, 73% live on campus, 7% transferred in. Retention: 69% of full-time freshmen returned the following year. Academic areas with the most degrees conferred: theology and religious vocations; education; psychology. Core. Calendar: semesters. Academic remediation for entering students, advanced placement, self-designed majors, distance learning, double major, summer session for credit, part-time degree program, internships. ROTC: Army (c), Air Force (c). **Entrance Requirements:** Open admission. Options: electronic application, early admission, deferred admission, international baccalaureate accepted. Required: essay, high school transcript, 3 recommendations, medical history, SAT or ACT. Entrance: noncompetitive. Application deadlines: Rolling, Rolling for nonresidents. Notification: continuous, continuous for nonresidents. Preference given to Free Will Baptists. SAT Reasoning Test deadline: 9/15. Transfer credits accepted: Yes.

Costs Per Year: Application fee: $35. Comprehensive fee: $22,448 includes full-time tuition ($14,820), mandatory fees ($986), and college room and board ($6642). Room and board charges vary according to board plan. Part-time tuition: $494 per credit.

Collegiate Environment: Orientation program. Drama-theater group, choral group. Social organizations: 17 open to all. Most popular organizations: GMF-Global Missions Fellowship, Four Women's Societies, Four Men's Societies. Major annual events: Project Pumpkin, Semi-Annual Red Cross Blood Drive, Christmas on Richland (choral presentation). Student services: personal-psychological counseling. Campus security: 24-hour emergency response devices, student patrols, late night transport-escort service, controlled dormitory access. 335 college housing spaces available; 150 were occupied in 2012-13. Freshmen guaranteed college housing. On-campus residence required through senior year. Options: men-only, women-only housing available. Welch Library with 69,829 books, 75,056 microform titles, 6,494 serials, 5,108 audiovisual materials, and an OPAC. Operations spend-

ing for the previous fiscal year: $197,000. 41 computers available on campus for general student use. A campuswide network can be accessed from student residence rooms. Staffed computer lab on campus.
Community Environment: See Vanderbilt University.

■ **WILLIAMSON CHRISTIAN COLLEGE**
200 Seaboard Ln.
Franklin, TN 37067
Tel: (615)771-7821
Fax: (615)771-7810
E-mail: mary@williamsoncc.edu
Web Site: www.williamsoncc.edu/

Description: Independent interdenominational, 4-year, coed. Awards associate and bachelor's degrees. Founded 1997. Setting: 1-acre suburban campus with easy access to Nashville. Educational spending for the previous fiscal year: $1453 per student. Total enrollment: 64. Faculty: 17 (5 full-time, 12 part-time). Student-undergrad faculty ratio is 5:1. Full-time: 55 students, 55% women, 45% men. Part-time: 9 students, 78% women, 22% men. Students come from 2 states and territories, 0% from out-of-state. 76% 25 or older, 14% transferred in. Retention: 100% of full-time freshmen returned the following year. Academic areas with the most degrees conferred: theology and religious vocations; business/marketing. Core. Calendar: semesters. Accelerated degree program, independent study, distance learning, double major, part-time degree program, external degree program, adult/continuing education programs, internships.
Entrance Requirements: Options: early admission, deferred admission, international baccalaureate accepted. Required: high school transcript. Required for some: interview, SAT or ACT. Entrance: noncompetitive. Application deadline: 9/1. Notification: continuous until 10/1.
Collegiate Environment: Orientation program. Major annual event: semi-professional baseball game. Student services: health clinic, personal-psychological counseling. John W. Neth, Jr. Library with 14,384 books, 16,607 serials, 189 audiovisual materials, and an OPAC. Operations spending for the previous fiscal year: $5848. 3 computers available on campus for general student use.

■ ABILENE CHRISTIAN UNIVERSITY

ACU Box 29100
Abilene, TX 79699-9100
Tel: (325)674-2000
E-mail: info@admissions.acu.edu
Web Site: www.acu.edu/

Description: Independent, comprehensive, coed, affiliated with Church of Christ. Awards associate, bachelor's, master's, and doctoral degrees and post-master's certificates. Founded 1906. Setting: 208-acre urban campus. Endowment: $307.1 million. Research spending for the previous fiscal year: $783,293. Educational spending for the previous fiscal year: $8305 per student. Total enrollment: 4,367. Faculty: 346 (243 full-time, 103 part-time). Student-undergrad faculty ratio is 14:1. 8,440 applied, 45% were admitted. 23% from top 10% of their high school class, 58% from top quarter, 88% from top half. 6 National Merit Scholars, 17 valedictorians. Full-time: 3,408 students, 56% women, 44% men. Part-time: 218 students, 50% women, 50% men. Students come from 52 states and territories, 43 other countries, 19% from out-of-state. 0.3% American Indian or Alaska Native, non-Hispanic/Latino; 10% Hispanic/Latino; 7% African American, non-Hispanic/Latino; 1% Asian, non-Hispanic/Latino; 0.1% Native Hawaiian or other Pacific Islander, non-Hispanic/Latino; 5% international. 0% 25 or older, 44% live on campus, 2% transferred in. Retention: 75% of full-time freshmen returned the following year. Academic areas with the most degrees conferred: business/marketing; education; communication/journalism. Core. Calendar: semesters. ESL program, services for LD students, advanced placement, self-designed majors, honors program, independent study, distance learning, double major, summer session for credit, part-time degree program, adult/continuing education programs, internships, graduate courses open to undergrads. Off campus study at McMurry University, Hardin-Simmons University, Texas Tech University, The University of Texas at Arlington. Study abroad program.

Entrance Requirements: Options: electronic application, early admission, early action, international baccalaureate accepted. Required: high school transcript, SAT or ACT. Required for some: essay. Entrance: moderately difficult. Application deadline: 2/15. Notification: 3/15. SAT Reasoning Test deadline: 2/15. SAT Subject Test deadline: 2/15. Transfer credits accepted: Yes. Early action applicants: 4,185. Early action applicants admitted: 1,508.

Costs Per Year: Application fee: $50. Comprehensive fee: $37,150 includes full-time tuition ($28,350) and college room and board ($8800). College room only: $3980. Full-time tuition varies according to course load. Room and board charges vary according to board plan and housing facility. Part-time tuition: $950 per credit. Part-time tuition varies according to course load.

Collegiate Environment: Orientation program. Drama-theater group, choral group, marching band, student-run newspaper, radio station. Social organizations: 95 open to all; local fraternities, local sororities; 24% of eligible men and 25% of eligible women are members. Most popular organizations: Student Association, Graduate Students Association, Spring Break Campaigns, International Students Association, LYNAY. Major annual events: homecoming, Sing Song, Welcome Week. Student services: health clinic, personal-psychological counseling. Campus security: 24-hour emergency response devices and patrols, student patrols, late night transport-escort service, controlled dormitory access. 1,856 college housing spaces available; 1,598 were occupied in 2012-13. Freshmen guaranteed college housing. On-campus residence required through sophomore year. Options: men-only, women-only housing available. Brown Library with 558,009 books, 1.2 million microform titles, 42,083 serials, 66,358 audiovisual materials, an OPAC, and a Web page. Operations spending for the previous fiscal year: $2.1 million. 860 computers available on campus for general student use. Computer purchase/lease plans available. A campuswide network can be accessed from student residence rooms and from off campus. Students can access the following: online class registration. Staffed computer lab on campus provides training in use of computers, software, and the Internet.

Community Environment: Abilene, Texas, has the reputation of being a friendly and caring community. USA Today's annual "Make a Difference Day" issue has recognized Abilene's community efforts in each of the past three years. Abilene is located 150 miles west of the Dallas/Ft. Worth metroplex and has a population of about 115,000. Its climate is warm and sunny, with an occasional light snow some winters. Residents of Abilene are served by shopping malls, major restaurant chains, specialty shops, two hospitals, and a regional airport. Abilene is the home of Dyess Air Force Base. The city is second only to Houston in cultural events per capita in Texas, and has one of the lowest crime rates in the state. Part-time employment is available.

■ ALVIN COMMUNITY COLLEGE

3110 Mustang Rd.
Alvin, TX 77511-4898
Tel: (281)756-3500
Fax: (281)756-3854
E-mail: info@alvincollege.edu
Web Site: www.alvincollege.edu/

Description: State and locally supported, 2-year, coed. Awards certificates, diplomas, transfer associate, and terminal associate degrees. Founded 1949. Setting: 114-acre suburban campus with easy access to Houston. Total enrollment: 5,794. Faculty: 262 (98 full-time, 164 part-time). Student-undergrad faculty ratio is 17:1. Full-time: 1,560 students, 52% women, 48% men. Part-time: 4,234 students, 55% women, 45% men. 2% American Indian or Alaska Native, non-Hispanic/Latino; 4% Hispanic/Latino; 10% African American, non-Hispanic/Latino; 5% Asian, non-Hispanic/Latino; 0.3% Native Hawaiian or other Pacific Islander, non-Hispanic/Latino; 0% international. 35% 25 or older. Core. Calendar: semesters. Academic remediation for entering students, ESL program, services for LD students, advanced placement, accelerated degree program, self-designed majors, honors program, independent study, distance learning, double major, summer session for credit, part-time degree program, adult/continuing education programs, internships. Study abroad program.

Entrance Requirements: Open admission. Option: electronic application. Required for some: high school transcript. Entrance: noncompetitive. Application deadline: Rolling.

Costs Per Year: Application fee: $0. Area resident tuition: $1008 full-time, $42 per credit hour part-time. State resident tuition: $2016 full-time, $84 per credit hour part-time. Nonresident tuition: $3120 full-time, $130 per credit hour part-time. Mandatory fees: $414 full-time, $202. Full-time tuition and fees vary according to program. Part-time tuition and fees vary according to program.

Collegiate Environment: Orientation program. Student services: personal-psychological counseling. Campus security: 24-hour patrols, late night transport-escort service. Alvin Community College Library with an OPAC and a Web page.

Community Environment: Population 22,000, Alvin is a suburban community located 30 minutes from Houston, Galveston, and NASA. The city is served by a private airport, railroad, bus line, and State Routes 6 and 35.

There are churches of major denominations, a public library, and hospital. Public recreation includes a theatre, bowling, fishing, and boating. Major civic, fraternal, and veteran's organizations are active in Alvin.

■ AMARILLO COLLEGE
PO Box 447
Amarillo, TX 79178-0001
Tel: (806)371-5000; Free: 800-227-8784
Fax: (806)371-5370
E-mail: askac@actx.edu
Web Site: www.actx.edu/

Description: State and locally supported, 2-year, coed. Awards certificates, transfer associate, and terminal associate degrees. Founded 1929. Setting: 1,542-acre urban campus. Endowment: $29 million. Faculty: 443 (222 full-time, 221 part-time). 1% American Indian or Alaska Native, non-Hispanic/Latino; 32% Hispanic/Latino; 5% African American, non-Hispanic/Latino; 3% Asian, non-Hispanic/Latino; 0% Native Hawaiian or other Pacific Islander, non-Hispanic/Latino; 0% international. 36% 25 or older. Retention: 52% of full-time freshmen returned the following year. Core. Calendar: semesters. Academic remediation for entering students, ESL program, services for LD students, advanced placement, freshman honors college, honors program, distance learning, summer session for credit, part-time degree program, adult/continuing education programs, co-op programs.

Entrance Requirements: Open admission. Options: early admission, deferred admission. Required: high school transcript. Entrance: noncompetitive. Notification: continuous.

Costs Per Year: Application fee: $0. Area resident tuition: $1842 full-time, $76.75 per semester hour part-time. State resident tuition: $2778 full-time, $115.75 per semester hour part-time. Nonresident tuition: $4242 full-time, $176.75 per semester hour part-time. Full-time tuition varies according to course load. Part-time tuition varies according to course load.

Collegiate Environment: Orientation program. Drama-theater group, choral group, student-run newspaper, radio station. Social organizations: 2 open to all. Most popular organizations: Student Government Association, College Republicans. Major annual events: Fall Fest, Badgerama, Spring Fling. Campus security: 24-hour emergency response devices, late night transport-escort service, Campus police patrol Monday through Saturday, 0700 to 2300. College housing not available. Lynn Library Learning Center plus 2 others with 62,076 books, 24,020 serials, an OPAC, and a Web page. Operations spending for the previous fiscal year: $576,899. 1,000 computers available on campus for general student use. A campuswide network can be accessed. Students can access the following: online class registration. Staffed computer lab on campus provides training in use of computers, software, and the Internet.

Community Environment: Population 183,021. Situated on the high plains of the Texas Panhandle, Amarillo is the capital of the oil and as industry. Pipelines from adjacent fields extend as far as the east coast. The average temperature ranges from 37.4 degrees in winter to 76 degrees in summer. The community is provided transportation by bus, and airlines, as well as five interstate highways and one state highway. Amarillo has many churches representing various faiths, public libraries, museums, several hospitals, a YMCA, and various civic, fraternal, and veteran's organizations. Part-time employment is available. Off-campus housing is plentiful.

■ AMBERTON UNIVERSITY
1700 Eastgate Dr.
Garland, TX 75041-5595
Tel: (972)279-6511
Fax: (972)279-9773
E-mail: advisor@amberton.edu
Web Site: www.amberton.edu/

Description: Independent nondenominational, upper-level, coed. Awards bachelor's and master's degrees. Founded 1971. Setting: 5-acre suburban campus with easy access to Dallas-Fort Worth. Endowment: $10 million. Educational spending for the previous fiscal year: $7400 per student. Total enrollment: 1,461. Faculty: 40 (15 full-time, 25 part-time). Student-undergrad faculty ratio is 25:1. Full-time: 165 students, 55% women, 45% men. Part-time: 157 students, 66% women, 34% men. 0% from out-of-state. 0% American Indian or Alaska Native, non-Hispanic/Latino; 8% Hispanic/Latino; 32% African American, non-Hispanic/Latino; 7% Asian, non-Hispanic/Latino; 0% Native Hawaiian or other Pacific Islander, non-Hispanic/Latino; 0% international. 98% 25 or older. Academic areas with the most degrees conferred: business/marketing; interdisciplinary studies. Core. Calendar: 4 10-week terms. Self-designed majors, distance learning, summer session for

credit, part-time degree program, external degree program, adult/continuing education programs, internships, graduate courses open to undergrads.

Entrance Requirements: Transfer credits accepted: Yes.

Costs Per Year: Application fee: $0. Tuition: $5640 full-time.

Collegiate Environment: Campus security: 24-hour emergency response devices and patrols. Library Resource Center plus 1 other with 21,000 books, 120 serials, an OPAC, and a Web page. Operations spending for the previous fiscal year: $100,000. 30 computers available on campus for general student use. Staffed computer lab on campus provides training in use of computers, software, and the Internet.

■ AMERICAN INTERCONTINENTAL UNIVERSITY HOUSTON
9999 Richmond Ave.
Houston, TX 77042
Tel: (832)242-5788; Free: 888-607-9888
Fax: (832)242-5775
Web Site: www.aiuniv.edu/

Description: Proprietary, comprehensive, coed. Administratively affiliated with American InterContinental University. Awards associate, bachelor's, and master's degrees. Founded 2003. Total enrollment: 474. Faculty: 32. Full-time: 330 students, 53% women, 47% men. Part-time: 85 students, 56% women, 44% men. 53% 25 or older, 12% transferred in. Academic areas with the most degrees conferred: business/marketing; visual and performing arts; computer and information sciences. Core. Calendar: five 10-week terms. Academic remediation for entering students, accelerated degree program, distance learning, part-time degree program, adult/continuing education programs, co-op programs.

Entrance Requirements: Options: electronic application, deferred admission, international baccalaureate accepted. Required: essay, high school transcript, interview. Application deadline: Rolling. Notification: continuous.

Collegiate Environment: Orientation program. 149 computers available on campus for general student use. Computer purchase/lease plans available. A computer is required for all students. A campuswide network can be accessed. Students can access the following: online class registration, online campus bookstore. Staffed computer lab on campus.

■ ANGELINA COLLEGE
PO Box 1768
Lufkin, TX 75902-1768
Tel: (936)639-1301
Fax: (936)639-4299
E-mail: jthomas@angelina.edu
Web Site: www.angelina.cc.tx.us/

Description: State and locally supported, 2-year, coed. Awards certificates, diplomas, transfer associate, and terminal associate degrees. Founded 1968. Setting: 140-acre small town campus. Total enrollment: 5,422. Student-undergrad faculty ratio is 8:1. 1% from out-of-state. 29% 25 or older. Core. Calendar: semesters. Academic remediation for entering students, services for LD students, advanced placement, self-designed majors, honors program, distance learning, double major, summer session for credit, part-time degree program, adult/continuing education programs, co-op programs and internships. Off campus study. ROTC: Army (c).

Entrance Requirements: Open admission. Options: electronic application, early admission, deferred admission. Required: high school transcript. Entrance: noncompetitive. Application deadline: Rolling. Notification: continuous.

Collegiate Environment: Orientation program. Drama-theater group, choral group, student-run newspaper. Social organizations: local fraternities, local sororities. Student services: personal-psychological counseling. Campus security: 24-hour patrols. Angelina College Library with 37,000 books, 270 serials, and an OPAC.

Community Environment: Population 33,500. Lufkin derives most of its income from the lumber and paper-making industries, two iron foundries and one chromium corporation. This urban community is headquarters for four national forests. The climate is temperate and mild. Lufkin is served by three railroad lines, airlines, and U.S. Routes 59 and 69. The community has a public library, 20 churches, three hospitals, and many civic, fraternal, and veteran's organizations. Part-time employment opportunities are unlimited. Local recreation includes theatres, hunting, fishing, boating, nearby Rayburn Lake, baseball, and swimming pools.

■ ANGELO STATE UNIVERSITY
2601 W Ave. N
San Angelo, TX 76909

Tel: (325)942-2555; Free: 800-946-8627
Fax: (325)942-2038
E-mail: admissions@angelo.edu
Web Site: www.angelo.edu/
Description: State-supported, comprehensive, coed. Part of Texas Tech University System. Awards bachelor's, master's, and doctoral degrees. Founded 1928. Setting: 268-acre urban campus. Endowment: $119.1 million. Research spending for the previous fiscal year: $936,325. Educational spending for the previous fiscal year: $7832 per student. Total enrollment: 6,886. Faculty: 356 (274 full-time, 82 part-time). Student-undergrad faculty ratio is 20:1. 2,588 applied, 90% were admitted. 10% from top 10% of their high school class, 33% from top quarter, 68% from top half. 27 valedictorians. Full-time: 5,076 students, 54% women, 46% men. Part-time: 930 students, 59% women, 41% men. Students come from 37 states and territories, 25 other countries, 3% from out-of-state. 1% American Indian or Alaska Native, non-Hispanic/Latino; 28% Hispanic/Latino; 1% African American, non-Hispanic/Latino; 1% Asian, non-Hispanic/Latino; 0.2% Native Hawaiian or other Pacific Islander, non-Hispanic/Latino; 2% international. 16% 25 or older, 32% live on campus, 7% transferred in. Retention: 59% of full-time freshmen returned the following year. Academic areas with the most degrees conferred: interdisciplinary studies; business/marketing; psychology. Core. Calendar: semesters. Academic remediation for entering students, ESL program, advanced placement, honors program, independent study, distance learning, double major, summer session for credit, part-time degree program, internships, graduate courses open to undergrads. Study abroad program. ROTC: Air Force.
Entrance Requirements: Options: electronic application, early admission, deferred admission, international baccalaureate accepted. Required: high school transcript, high school class rank, SAT or ACT. Entrance: moderately difficult. Application deadlines: Rolling, Rolling for nonresidents. Notification: continuous, continuous for nonresidents. SAT Reasoning Test deadline: 8/27. Transfer credits accepted: Yes.
Costs Per Year: Application fee: $35. State resident tuition: $4994 full-time, $166.58 per credit hour part-time. Nonresident tuition: $15,524 full-time, $517.58 per credit hour part-time. Mandatory fees: $2499 full-time, $28 per credit hour part-time, $631.25 per term part-time. College room and board: $8026. College room only: $5298. Room and board charges vary according to board plan and housing facility.
Collegiate Environment: Orientation program. Drama-theater group, choral group, marching band, student-run newspaper, radio station. Social organizations: 114 open to all; national fraternities, national sororities; 3% of eligible men and 4% of eligible women are members. Most popular organizations: Association of Mexican-American Students, Block and Bridle Club, Air force ROTC, University Center Program Council, Baptist Student Union. Major annual events: Homecoming, Parents' Day, Rambunctious Weekend. Student services: health clinic, personal-psychological counseling. Campus security: 24-hour emergency response devices and patrols, student patrols, late night transport-escort service, controlled dormitory access. 2,060 college housing spaces available; 1,979 were occupied in 2012-13. On-campus residence required through sophomore year. Option: coed housing available. Porter Henderson Library plus 1 other with 584,809 books, 961,404 microform titles, 45,713 serials, 22,160 audiovisual materials, an OPAC, and a Web page. Operations spending for the previous fiscal year: $2.9 million. 640 computers available on campus for general student use. Computer purchase/lease plans available. A campuswide network can be accessed from student residence rooms and from off campus. Students can access the following: online class registration, online courses, tuition payments, purchase books, purchase parking permits, university calendar, library card catalog and library resources. Discounted hardware and software programs for personally owned computers. Staffed computer lab on campus (open 24 hours a day) provides training in use of computers, software, and the Internet.
Community Environment: Population approx 88,000. San Angelo is an attractive city located in the heart of West Texas ranch country. San Angelo and the surrounding area provide a readily accessible social and physical environment for cultural and recreational activities so essential to the university community. Three nearby lakes make water sports a popular attraction among students and those living in San Angelo.

■ **ARGOSY UNIVERSITY, DALLAS**
5001 Lyndon B. Johnson Fwy.
Heritage Sq.
Farmers Branch, TX 75244
Tel: (214)890-9900; Free: 866-954-9900

Fax: (214)656-3900
Web Site: www.argosy.edu/dallas/
Description: Proprietary, university, coed. Part of Education Management Corporation. Awards bachelor's, master's, and doctoral degrees. Founded 2002. Setting: urban campus. Calendar: semesters.

■ **ARLINGTON BAPTIST COLLEGE**
3001 W Division
Arlington, TX 76012-3425
Tel: (817)461-8741
Fax: (817)274-1138
E-mail: jtaylor@arlingtonbaptistcollege.edu
Web Site: www.arlingtonbaptistcollege.edu/
Description: Independent Baptist, comprehensive, coed. Awards bachelor's and master's degrees. Founded 1939. Setting: 32-acre urban campus with easy access to Dallas-Fort Worth. Endowment: $17,000. Educational spending for the previous fiscal year: $4400 per student. Total enrollment: 241. Faculty: 17 (12 full-time, 5 part-time). Student-undergrad faculty ratio is 16:1. 86 applied, 100% were admitted. 2% from top 10% of their high school class, 21% from top quarter, 47% from top half. Full-time: 198 students, 45% women, 55% men. Part-time: 22 students, 41% women, 59% men. Students come from 15 states and territories, 6 other countries, 17% from out-of-state. 2% American Indian or Alaska Native, non-Hispanic/Latino; 8% Hispanic/Latino; 18% African American, non-Hispanic/Latino; 0% Asian, non-Hispanic/Latino; 0% Native Hawaiian or other Pacific Islander, non-Hispanic/Latino; 1% international. 35% 25 or older, 46% live on campus, 18% transferred in. Retention: 51% of full-time freshmen returned the following year. Academic areas with the most degrees conferred: theology and religious vocations; education. Core. Calendar: semesters. Academic remediation for entering students, advanced placement, independent study, distance learning, double major, summer session for credit, part-time degree program, internships.
Entrance Requirements: Options: electronic application, early admission, deferred admission, international baccalaureate accepted. Required: essay, high school transcript, 1 recommendation, pastoral recommendation, medical examination. Required for some: interview. Entrance: noncompetitive. Application deadline: Rolling. Notification: continuous. Preference given to professing Christians. Transfer credits accepted: Yes.
Costs Per Year: Application fee: $15. Comprehensive fee: $12,640 includes full-time tuition ($7100), mandatory fees ($740), and college room and board ($4800). Full-time tuition and fees vary according to course load. Part-time tuition: $220 per credit hour. Part-time mandatory fees: $740 per term. Part-time tuition and fees vary according to course load.
Collegiate Environment: Orientation program. Drama-theater group, choral group. Most popular organizations: Student Missionary Association, 4-12 Group. Major annual events: First Saturday Night Back, Homecoming Weekend, Fellowship Week. Student services: personal-psychological counseling. Campus security: controlled dormitory access, night security guards. Earl K. Oldham with 49,393 books, 10 microform titles, 20 serials, 548 audiovisual materials, and an OPAC. Operations spending for the previous fiscal year: $90,666. 25 computers available on campus for general student use. A campuswide network can be accessed from student residence rooms. Students can access the following: online class registration. Staffed computer lab on campus provides training in use of computers, software, and the Internet.
Community Environment: See University of Texas at Arlington.

■ **THE ART INSTITUTE OF AUSTIN**
101 W Louis Henna Blvd.
Ste. 100
Austin, TX 78728
Tel: (512)691-1707; Free: 866-583-7952
Web Site: www.artinstitutes.edu/austin
Description: Proprietary, 4-year, coed. Part of Education Management Corporation. Awards associate and bachelor's degrees.

■ **THE ART INSTITUTE OF DALLAS**
8080 Park Ln.
Ste. 100
Dallas, TX 75231-5993
Tel: (214)692-8080; Free: 800-275-4243
Fax: (214)750-9460
Web Site: www.artinstitutes.edu/dallas/
Description: Proprietary, comprehensive, coed. Part of Education Manage-

ment Corporation. Awards associate, bachelor's, and master's degrees. Founded 1978. Setting: 2-acre urban campus.

■ THE ART INSTITUTE OF FORT WORTH
7000 Calmont Ave.
Ste. 150
Fort Worth, TX 76116
Tel: (817)210-0808; Free: 888-422-9686
Fax: (817)210-0901
Web Site: www.artinstitutes.edu/fort-worth/
Description: Proprietary, 4-year, coed. Awards associate and bachelor's degrees.

■ THE ART INSTITUTE OF HOUSTON
1900 Yorktown St.
Houston, TX 77056
Tel: (713)623-2040; Free: 800-275-4244
Fax: (713)966-2797
Web Site: www.artinstitutes.edu/houston/
Description: Proprietary, 4-year, coed. Part of Education Management Corporation. Awards associate and bachelor's degrees. Founded 1978. Setting: urban campus.

■ THE ART INSTITUTE OF HOUSTON - NORTH
10740 N Gessner Dr.
Ste. 190
Houston, TX 77064
Free: 866-830-4450
Web Site: www.artinstitutes.edu/houston-north
Description: Proprietary, 4-year, coed. Awards associate and bachelor's degrees.

■ THE ART INSTITUTE OF SAN ANTONIO
1000 IH-10 W, Ste. 200
San Antonio, TX 78230
Tel: (210)338-7320; Free: 888-222-0040
Fax: (210)338-7321
Web Site: www.artinstitutes.edu/san-antonio/
Description: Proprietary, 4-year, coed. Awards associate and bachelor's degrees.

■ ATI TECHNICAL TRAINING CENTER
6627 Maple Ave.
Dallas, TX 75235
Tel: (214)263-4284; Free: 888-209-8264
Fax: (214)358-7500
Web Site: www.aticareertraining.edu/
Description: Proprietary, 2-year, coed. Awards certificates degrees. Total enrollment: 568.
Entrance Requirements: Open admission. Entrance: noncompetitive.

■ AUSTIN COLLEGE
900 N Grand Ave.
Sherman, TX 75090-4400
Tel: (903)813-2000; Free: 800-526-4276
Fax: (903)813-3198
E-mail: admission@austincollege.edu
Web Site: www.austincollege.edu/
Description: Independent Presbyterian, comprehensive, coed. Awards bachelor's and master's degrees. Founded 1849. Setting: 60-acre small town campus with easy access to Dallas-Fort Worth. Endowment: $119.5 million. Research spending for the previous fiscal year: $180,874. Total enrollment: 1,260. Faculty: 123 (94 full-time, 29 part-time). Student-undergrad faculty ratio is 12:1. 3,003 applied, 59% were admitted. 36% from top 10% of their high school class, 70% from top quarter, 96% from top half. Full-time: 1,235 students, 52% women, 48% men. Part-time: 7 students, 43% women, 57% men. Students come from 35 states and territories, 9 other countries, 9% from out-of-state. 0.5% American Indian or Alaska Native, non-Hispanic/Latino; 12% Hispanic/Latino; 4% African American, non-Hispanic/Latino; 13% Asian, non-Hispanic/Latino; 0.1% Native Hawaiian or other Pacific Islander, non-Hispanic/Latino; 2% international. 1% 25 or older, 75% live on campus, 3% transferred in. Retention: 77% of full-time freshmen returned the following year. Academic areas with the most degrees conferred: social sciences; psychology; business/marketing. Core. Calendar:

4-1-4. Advanced placement, self-designed majors, honors program, independent study, double major, summer session for credit, part-time degree program, adult/continuing education programs, internships, graduate courses open to undergrads. Off campus study. Study abroad program.
Entrance Requirements: Options: electronic application, early admission, deferred admission, international baccalaureate accepted. Required: essay, high school transcript, 2 recommendations, SAT or ACT. Recommended: minimum 3 high school GPA, interview. Required for some: interview. Entrance: very difficult. Application deadline: 5/1. Applicants placed on waiting list: 13. Wait-listed applicants offered admission: 1.
Costs Per Year: Application fee: $0. One-time mandatory fee: $25. Comprehensive fee: $44,545 includes full-time tuition ($33,645), mandatory fees ($185), and college room and board ($10,715). Full-time tuition and fees vary according to student level. Room and board charges vary according to board plan. Part-time tuition: $1220 per contact hour.
Collegiate Environment: Orientation program. Drama-theater group, choral group, student-run newspaper. Social organizations: 50 open to all; local fraternities, local sororities; 27% of eligible men and 27% of eligible women are members. Most popular organizations: Fellowship of Christian Athletes, Campus Activity Board, Indian Cultural Association, Student Development Board, International Relations Club. Major annual events: Homecoming, Earth Day, Spring Fest. Student services: health clinic, personal-psychological counseling. Campus security: 24-hour emergency response devices and patrols, late night transport-escort service, controlled dormitory access. 951 college housing spaces available; 881 were occupied in 2012-13. Freshmen guaranteed college housing. On-campus residence required through junior year. Options: coed, men-only, women-only housing available. Abell Library with 227,390 books, 175,059 microform titles, 29,547 serials, 6,404 audiovisual materials, an OPAC, and a Web page. 160 computers available on campus for general student use. A campuswide network can be accessed from student residence rooms and from off campus. Students can access the following: online class registration. Staffed computer lab on campus.
Community Environment: Sherman, population 37,000, is a retail trade and industrial center located in north central Texas 60 miles north of Dallas. The climate is mild and temperate. The average annual temperature is 64 degrees. Two bus lines, and U.S. Highways 82 and 75 serve the area. The community has a library, two hospitals, a shopping mall, two theatres, and various civic and fraternal organizations. Local recreation includes golf, bowling, skating, hunting, and on Lake Texoma with a 1,250 mile shoreline, fishing, swimming, water skiing, and boating. Part-time employment is available.

■ AUSTIN COMMUNITY COLLEGE
5930 Middle Fiskville Rd.
Austin, TX 78752-4390
Tel: (512)223-7000
Fax: (512)223-7665
E-mail: admission@austincc.edu
Web Site: www.austincc.edu/
Description: State and locally supported, 2-year, coed. Awards certificates, transfer associate, and terminal associate degrees. Founded 1972. Setting: urban campus with easy access to Austin. Endowment: $4.5 million. Total enrollment: 43,315. Faculty: 2,060 (626 full-time, 1,434 part-time). Student-undergrad faculty ratio is 19:1. 1% American Indian or Alaska Native, non-Hispanic/Latino; 28% Hispanic/Latino; 8% African American, non-Hispanic/Latino; 5% Asian, non-Hispanic/Latino; 0.2% Native Hawaiian or other Pacific Islander, non-Hispanic/Latino; 3% international. 41% 25 or older. Core. Calendar: semesters. Academic remediation for entering students, ESL program, services for LD students, advanced placement, accelerated degree program, honors program, independent study, distance learning, summer session for credit, part-time degree program, adult/continuing education programs, co-op programs and internships. ROTC: Army (c), Air Force (c).
Entrance Requirements: Open admission. Options: electronic application, international baccalaureate accepted. Required: high school transcript. Entrance: noncompetitive. Application deadline: Rolling. Transfer credits accepted: Yes.
Costs Per Year: Application fee: $0. Area resident tuition: $1860 full-time, $62 per credit hour part-time. State resident tuition: $6720 full-time, $224 per credit hour part-time. Nonresident tuition: $9240 full-time, $308 per credit hour part-time. Mandatory fees: $480 full-time, $16 per credit hour part-time. Full-time tuition and fees vary according to course load. Part-time tuition and fees vary according to course load.

Collegiate Environment: Orientation program. Student-run newspaper. Social organizations: 51 open to all; Clubs and Organizations. Most popular organizations: Intramurals, Student Government Association (SGA), Phi Theta Kappa (PTK), Center for Student Political Studies (CSPS), Circle K International (CKI). Major annual events: Welcome Week, Riverbat Bash, Nite in the Life. Student services: personal-psychological counseling. Campus security: 24-hour emergency response devices and patrols, late night transport-escort service. College housing not available. Main library plus 8 others with 190,539 books, 52,057 serials, 16,875 audiovisual materials, an OPAC, and a Web page. 637 computers available on campus for general student use. Computer purchase/lease plans available. A campuswide network can be accessed. Students can access the following: online class registration. Staffed computer lab on campus provides training in use of computers, software, and the Internet.

Community Environment: See University of Texas at Austin.

■ **AUSTIN GRADUATE SCHOOL OF THEOLOGY**

7640 Guadalupe St.
Austin, TX 78752
Tel: (512)476-2772; Free: 866-AUS-GRAD
Fax: (512)476-3919
E-mail: registrar@austingrad.edu
Web Site: www.austingrad.edu/

Description: Independent, upper-level, coed, affiliated with Church of Christ. Awards bachelor's and master's degrees. Founded 1917. Setting: 2-acre urban campus with easy access to Austin. Endowment: $3.6 million. Total enrollment: 60. Faculty: 10 (4 full-time, 6 part-time). 7 applied, 100% were admitted. 1% from out-of-state. 83% 25 or older. Retention: 81% of full-time entering class returned the following year. Core. Calendar: semesters. Summer session for credit, part-time degree program, adult/continuing education programs.

Collegiate Environment: Orientation program. Social organizations: 1 open to all. Most popular organization: Student Association. Major annual events: Christmas Party, spring picnic, Chili Cook-Off. Campus security: 24-hour emergency response devices. David Worley Library with 29,728 books, 120 serials, an OPAC, and a Web page. Operations spending for the previous fiscal year: $107,714. 8 computers available on campus for general student use. A campuswide network can be accessed from off-campus. Staffed computer lab on campus.

■ **BAPTIST MISSIONARY ASSOCIATION THEOLOGICAL SEMINARY**

1530 E Pine St.
Jacksonville, TX 75766-5407
Tel: (903)586-2501; Free: 800-259-5673
E-mail: attebery@bmats.edu
Web Site: www.bmats.edu/

Description: Independent Baptist, comprehensive, coed. Awards associate, bachelor's, and master's degrees. Founded 1955. Setting: 17-acre small town campus. Endowment: $1.2 million. Total enrollment: 117. Faculty: 11 (5 full-time, 6 part-time). 9 applied. Full-time: 23 students, 13% women, 87% men. Part-time: 33 students, 18% women, 82% men. 82% 25 or older, 29% live on campus. Academic area with the most degrees conferred: theology and religious vocations. Core. Calendar: semesters. Independent study, distance learning, summer session for credit, part-time degree program, adult/continuing education programs, internships, graduate courses open to undergrads.

Entrance Requirements: Open admission. Required: 3 recommendations, interview, Church approval statement. Entrance: noncompetitive. Application deadline: 7/25. Notification: continuous. Transfer credits accepted: Yes.

Costs Per Year: Application fee: $35. Tuition: $140 per hour part-time. Mandatory fees: $75 per term part-time. Part-time tuition and fees vary according to course load and location.

Collegiate Environment: Major annual events: Bible lectures, Thanksgiving meal, Back-to-school picnic. Student services: personal-psychological counseling. 30 college housing spaces available. No special consideration for freshman housing applicants. Options: men-only, women-only housing available. Kellar Library with 75,000 books, 947 microform titles, 453 serials, 5,886 audiovisual materials, and an OPAC. 3 computers available on campus for general student use. A campuswide network can be accessed.

■ **BAPTIST UNIVERSITY OF THE AMERICAS**

8019 S Pan Am Expy.
San Antonio, TX 78224-2701
Tel: (210)924-4338; Free: 800-721-1396

Fax: (210)924-2701
E-mail: david.natividad@bua.edu
Web Site: www.bua.edu/

Description: Independent Baptist, 4-year, coed. Awards associate and bachelor's degrees (associate degree in Cross-Cultural Studies). Founded 1947. Setting: 90-acre urban campus with easy access to San Antonio. System endowment: $1.9 million. Educational spending for the previous fiscal year: $286,182 per student. Total enrollment: 175. Faculty: 7 (all full-time). Student-undergrad faculty ratio is 12:1. 66 applied, 53% were admitted. Full-time: 25 students, 52% women, 48% men. Part-time: 2 students, 50% women, 50% men. Students come from 12 states and territories, 16 other countries, 5% from out-of-state. 1% American Indian or Alaska Native, non-Hispanic/Latino; 6% Hispanic/Latino; 6% African American, non-Hispanic/Latino; 87% international. 55% 25 or older, 96% transferred in. Retention: 31% of full-time freshmen returned the following year. Academic areas with the most degrees conferred: theology and religious vocations; foreign languages and literature; business/marketing. Core. Calendar: semesters. Academic remediation for entering students, ESL program, services for LD students, advanced placement, independent study, double major, part-time degree program, internships.

Entrance Requirements: Open admission. Option: electronic application. Required: essay, high school transcript, 3 recommendations, Meningitis Vaccine for students under 30 years; Application Fee and 1 year prepaid tuition for international students. Recommended: SAT and SAT Subject Tests or ACT, ACCUPLACER, THEA (Texas Higher Education Assessment). Required for some: interview, ACCUPLACER, THEA (Texas Higher Education Assessment). Entrance: noncompetitive. Application deadlines: 2/15, 2/15 for nonresidents. Notification: continuous. Transfer credits accepted: Yes.

Costs Per Year: Application fee: $25. Comprehensive fee: $8660 includes full-time tuition ($4800), mandatory fees ($480), and college room and board ($3380). College room only: $2500. Part-time tuition: $200 per credit. Part-time mandatory fees: $20 per hour.

Collegiate Environment: Orientation program. Choral group. Social organizations: 3 open to all. Most popular organizations: Communities In Schools, Missions Society, Navigators, Student Council/Embajadores, BSM. Major annual events: Rudy Sanchez Conference/Rollins Lectures, Student Orientation/Inauguration of Student Council, President's Picnic. Student services: personal-psychological counseling. Campus security: 24-hour emergency response devices, student patrols, late night transport-escort service, Gate code is required to enter the residence area. 182 college housing spaces available. Options: coed, men-only, women-only housing available. Learning Resource Center with 23,290 books, 11,430 serials, 7,643 audiovisual materials, an OPAC, and a Web page. Operations spending for the previous fiscal year: $11 million. 22 computers available on campus for general student use. A campuswide network can be accessed from student residence rooms. Staffed computer lab on campus provides training in use of computers, software, and the Internet.

■ **BAYLOR UNIVERSITY**

Waco, TX 76798
Tel: (254)710-1011; Free: 800-BAYLORU
E-mail: admissions@baylor.edu
Web Site: www.baylor.edu/

Description: Independent Baptist, university, coed. Awards bachelor's, master's, and doctoral degrees and post-master's certificates. Founded 1845. Setting: 1,000-acre urban campus with easy access to Dallas-Fort Worth. Endowment: $964.2 million. Total enrollment: 15,364. Faculty: 1,238 (888 full-time, 350 part-time). Student-undergrad faculty ratio is 15:1. 27,828 applied, 61% were admitted. 39% from top 10% of their high school class, 73% from top quarter, 97% from top half. 80 National Merit Scholars. Full-time: 12,615 students, 59% women, 41% men. Part-time: 303 students, 62% women, 38% men. Students come from 51 states and territories, 73 other countries, 22% from out-of-state. 0.3% American Indian or Alaska Native, non-Hispanic/Latino; 14% Hispanic/Latino; 7% African American, non-Hispanic/Latino; 6% Asian, non-Hispanic/Latino; 0.03% Native Hawaiian or other Pacific Islander, non-Hispanic/Latino; 3% international. 2% 25 or older, 39% live on campus, 3% transferred in. Retention: 87% of full-time freshmen returned the following year. Academic areas with the most degrees conferred: business/marketing; health professions and related sciences; biological/life sciences. Core. Calendar: semesters. Services for LD students, advanced placement, accelerated degree program, self-designed majors, honors program, double major, summer session for credit, part-time degree program, internships, graduate courses open to undergrads. Study abroad program. ROTC: Army, Air Force.

Entrance Requirements: Options: electronic application, early admission, early action, international baccalaureate accepted. Required: high school transcript, SAT or ACT. Recommended: interview. Required for some: essay, minimum 2.5 high school GPA, 2 recommendations. Entrance: moderately difficult. Application deadlines: 2/1, 11/1 for early action. Notification: 3/15, 1/15 for early action. SAT Reasoning Test deadline: 2/1. Applicants placed on waiting list: 3,415. Wait-listed applicants offered admission: 32.

Costs Per Year: Application fee: $50. Comprehensive fee: $46,885 includes full-time tuition ($32,574), mandatory fees ($3563), and college room and board ($10,748). College room only: $5312. Room and board charges vary according to board plan and housing facility. Part-time tuition: $1357 per semester hour. Part-time mandatory fees: $142 per semester hour.

Collegiate Environment: Orientation program. Drama-theater group, choral group, marching band, student-run newspaper, radio station. Social organizations: 285 open to all; national fraternities, national sororities, local fraternities, local sororities; 13% of eligible men and 21% of eligible women are members. Most popular organizations: The Bear Pit, Alpha Lambda Delta, Delta Epsilon Iota, National Society of Collegiate Scholars, American Medical Student Association. Major annual events: Diadeloso (Student Day of Fun), Homecoming, All-University Sing. Student services: legal services, health clinic, personal-psychological counseling. Campus security: 24-hour emergency response devices and patrols, late night transport-escort service, controlled dormitory access, bicycle patrols. 5,209 college housing spaces available; 5,109 were occupied in 2012-13. Freshmen guaranteed college housing. On-campus residence required in freshman year. Options: men-only, women-only housing available. Moody Memorial Library plus 8 others with 3 million books, 2.2 million microform titles, 82,294 serials, 99,615 audiovisual materials, an OPAC, and a Web page.

Community Environment: The campus adjoins the historic Brazos River in Waco, a Central Texas city of 110,000 people. The climate is temperate with a mean annual temperature of 67.4 degrees, and an average rainfall of 35 inches. Waco is reached by interstate, airlines, railroad, and bus lines. There are almost 200 churches of various faiths, public hospitals and a veteran's hospital, excellent libraries, and convenient shopping facilities in the area. Nineteen civic clubs and many fraternal organizations are active in Waco. Local recreation includes boating, swimming, fishing, picnicking, bowling, biking, golfing, hiking, tennis, parks, a zoo, and Lake Waco. Part-time employment is available for students.

■ BLINN COLLEGE
902 College Ave.
Brenham, TX 77833-4049
Tel: (979)830-4000
E-mail: recruit@blinn.edu
Web Site: www.blinn.edu/

Description: State and locally supported, 2-year, coed. Awards certificates, diplomas, transfer associate, and terminal associate degrees. Founded 1883. Setting: 100-acre small town campus with easy access to Houston. Endowment: $29.8 million. Total enrollment: 14,016. Faculty: 575 (215 full-time, 360 part-time). Student-undergrad faculty ratio is 24:1. 3,825 applied, 100% were admitted. Full-time: 7,505 students, 48% women, 52% men. Part-time: 6,511 students, 56% women, 44% men. Students come from 36 states and territories, 42 other countries, 1% from out-of-state. 14% 25 or older, 9% live on campus, 32% transferred in. Core. Calendar: semesters. Academic remediation for entering students, ESL program, services for LD students, advanced placement, freshman honors college, distance learning, double major, summer session for credit, part-time degree program, adult/continuing education programs.

Entrance Requirements: Open admission. Options: electronic application, early admission, deferred admission. Required: high school transcript. Entrance: noncompetitive. Application deadline: Rolling.

Collegiate Environment: Orientation program. Drama-theater group, choral group, marching band, student-run newspaper. Social organizations: 42 open to all. Most popular organizations: Student Government Association, Phi Theta Kappa, Baptist student ministries, Blinn Ethnic Student Organization, Circle K. Major annual events: Homecoming, Blinnfest, Transfer Day. Student services: personal-psychological counseling. Campus security: 24-hour emergency response devices and patrols, controlled dormitory access. W. L. Moody, Jr. Library plus 1 other with 130,000 books, 700 serials, an OPAC, and a Web page. Operations spending for the previous fiscal year: $745,933. 1,200 computers available on campus for general student use. A campuswide network can be accessed from student residence rooms and from off campus. Students can access the following: online class registration. Staffed computer lab on campus.

Community Environment: Population 10,900. Brenham is a suburban community enjoying temperate climate. The city has libraries, and churches of various denominations. Railroad, bus lines, and major highways serve the area. Part-time employment is available for students. There are motels and apartment houses available for student housing. Brenham has hospitals, and civic and fraternal organizations are active within the area. Local recreation includes theaters, hunting, fishing, golf, and sports.

■ BRAZOSPORT COLLEGE
500 College Dr.
Lake Jackson, TX 77566-3199
Tel: (979)230-3000
Fax: (979)230-3443
E-mail: wade.wilson@brazosport.edu
Web Site: www.brazosport.edu/

Description: State and locally supported, primarily 2-year, coed. Awards certificates, transfer associate, terminal associate, and bachelor's degrees. Founded 1968. Setting: 160-acre small town campus with easy access to Houston. Total enrollment: 3,893. Student-undergrad faculty ratio is 17:1. 0% from out-of-state. 32% 25 or older. Retention: 52% of full-time freshmen returned the following year. Calendar: semesters. Academic remediation for entering students, advanced placement, honors program, distance learning, summer session for credit, part-time degree program, adult/continuing education programs, co-op programs and internships.

Entrance Requirements: Open admission. Options: early admission, deferred admission. Required for some: high school transcript. Entrance: noncompetitive. Application deadline: 8/15.

Costs Per Year: Application fee: $0. Area resident tuition: $1770 full-time, $59 per credit part-time. State resident tuition: $2790 full-time, $93 per credit part-time. Nonresident tuition: $4200 full-time, $140 per credit part-time. Mandatory fees: $525 full-time, $17.50 per credit part-time. Full-time tuition and fees vary according to course level, course load, degree level, and student level. Part-time tuition and fees vary according to course level, course load, degree level, and student level.

Collegiate Environment: Orientation program. Drama-theater group, choral group, student-run newspaper. Campus security: 24-hour patrols. Brazosport College Library with 66,025 books, 345 serials, an OPAC, and a Web page.

Community Environment: Population 27,000, Lake Jackson is located 50 miles south of Houston. Major cities in the district are Lake Jackson and Freeport (population 12,600), located on a stretch of beach on the Gulf Coast. The area is serviced by rail, four major highways, commuter planes, and good local bus service. Recreation in the area includes fishing, surfing, swimming, and other water sports in the Gulf of Mexico.

■ BROOKHAVEN COLLEGE
3939 Valley View Ln.
Farmers Branch, TX 75244-4997
Tel: (972)860-4700
Fax: (972)860-4897
E-mail: bhcAdmissions@dcccd.edu
Web Site: www.brookhavencollege.edu/

Description: County-supported, 2-year, coed. Part of Dallas County Community College District System. Awards certificates, transfer associate, and terminal associate degrees. Founded 1978. Setting: 200-acre suburban campus with easy access to Dallas-Fort Worth. Educational spending for the previous fiscal year: $4289 per student. Total enrollment: 13,705. Faculty: 545 (129 full-time, 416 part-time). Student-undergrad faculty ratio is 23:1. Full-time: 2,889 students, 50% women, 50% men. Part-time: 10,816 students, 61% women, 39% men. Students come from 28 states and territories, 10 other countries, 0.4% from out-of-state. 1% American Indian or Alaska Native, non-Hispanic/Latino; 30% Hispanic/Latino; 18% African American, non-Hispanic/Latino; 11% Asian, non-Hispanic/Latino; 0.2% Native Hawaiian or other Pacific Islander, non-Hispanic/Latino; 1% international. 50% 25 or older, 7% transferred in. Core. Calendar: semesters. Academic remediation for entering students, ESL program, services for LD students, advanced placement, self-designed majors, honors program, independent study, distance learning, summer session for credit, part-time degree program, adult/continuing education programs, co-op programs and internships. Off campus study. Study abroad program.

Entrance Requirements: Open admission Admission to nursing program requires the HESI A2 exam to be taken at Brookhaven. Admission is selective for some programs. Options: electronic application, early admission, deferred admission, international baccalaureate accepted. Required: high school transcript, STAAR test scores or an approved test for Reading, Writing and Math course placement. Test scores used for placement, not admission, purposes. Certain programs require specific tests. Required for some: Admission to the nursing program is based on a point system consisting of three parts: (1) HESI score, (2)GPA of prerequisite courses, and (3) completion of support courses. Entrance: noncompetitive. Application deadline: Rolling. Transfer credits accepted: Yes.

Costs Per Year: Application fee: $0. Area resident tuition: $1560 full-time, $52 per credit part-time. State resident tuition: $2910 full-time, $97 per credit part-time. Nonresident tuition: $4590 full-time, $153 per credit part-time.

Collegiate Environment: Orientation program. Drama-theater group, choral group, student-run newspaper. Student services: health clinic, personal-psychological counseling. Campus security: 24-hour emergency response devices and patrols, late night transport-escort service. College housing not available. Brookhaven College Learning Resources Center plus 1 other with an OPAC and a Web page.

■ BROWN MACKIE COLLEGE–DALLAS/FT. WORTH

2200 N Hwy. 121
Ste. 270
Bedford, TX 76021
Tel: (817)799-0500
Web Site: www.brownmackie.edu/dallas/
Description: Proprietary, 4-year, coed.

■ BROWN MACKIE COLLEGE–SAN ANTONIO

4715 Fredericksburg Rd.
Ste. 100
San Antonio, TX 78229
Tel: (210)460-1714; Free: 877-460-1714
Web Site: www.brownmackie.edu/san-antonio
Description: Proprietary, 4-year, coed. Part of Education Management Corporation. Awards associate and bachelor's degrees.

■ CAREER POINT COLLEGE

4522 Fredericksburg Rd.
San Antonio, TX 78201
Tel: (210)732-3000
Web Site: www.careerpointcollege.edu/
Description: Proprietary, 4-year, coed.

■ CEDAR VALLEY COLLEGE

3030 N Dallas Ave.
Lancaster, TX 75134-3799
Tel: (972)860-8201
Web Site: www.cedarvalleycollege.edu/
Description: State-supported, 2-year, coed. Part of Dallas County Community College District System. Awards certificates, transfer associate, and terminal associate degrees. Founded 1977. Setting: 353-acre suburban campus with easy access to Dallas-Fort Worth. Total enrollment: 5,886. Student-undergrad faculty ratio is 23:1. 1% from out-of-state. 42% 25 or older. Core. Calendar: semesters. Academic remediation for entering students, ESL program, services for LD students, advanced placement, distance learning, summer session for credit, part-time degree program, co-op programs. ROTC: Army (c).

Entrance Requirements: Open admission. Options: electronic application, early admission. Entrance: noncompetitive. Application deadline: Rolling. Notification: continuous.

Collegiate Environment: Orientation program. Drama-theater group, choral group. Student services: health clinic, personal-psychological counseling. Campus security: 24-hour emergency response devices and patrols, late night transport-escort service. Cedar Valley College Library with an OPAC and a Web page.

■ CENTER FOR ADVANCED LEGAL STUDIES

3910 Kirby Dr.
Ste. 200
Houston, TX 77098-4151
Tel: (713)529-2778; Free: 800-446-6931
Fax: (713)523-2715
E-mail: james.scheffer@paralegal.edu
Web Site: www.paralegal.edu/
Description: Proprietary, 2-year, coed. Awards terminal associate degrees.

Founded 1987. Total enrollment: 198. Faculty: 25 (2 full-time, 23 part-time). Student-undergrad faculty ratio is 17:1. Full-time: 176 students, 88% women, 12% men. 60% 25 or older.

Entrance Requirements: Required: essay. Required for some: high school transcript, transcript testing. Application deadline: Rolling.

Collegiate Environment: Orientation program. 30 computers available on campus for general student use. A campuswide network can be accessed from off-campus.

■ CENTRAL TEXAS COLLEGE

PO Box 1800
Killeen, TX 76540-1800
Tel: (254)526-7161; Free: 800-792-3348
E-mail: admrec@ctcd.edu
Web Site: www.ctcd.edu/
Description: State and locally supported, 2-year, coed. Awards certificates, transfer associate, and terminal associate degrees. Founded 1967. Setting: 500-acre suburban campus with easy access to Austin. Endowment: $3.5 million. Educational spending for the previous fiscal year: $1060 per student. Total enrollment: 24,498. Faculty: 2,413 (252 full-time, 2,161 part-time). Student-undergrad faculty ratio is 11:1. 4,163 students, 60% women, 40% men. Part-time: 20,335 students, 42% women, 58% men. Students come from 50 states and territories, 38 other countries, 19% from out-of-state. 61% 25 or older, 1% live on campus, 7% transferred in. Retention: 58% of full-time freshmen returned the following year. Core. Calendar: semesters. Academic remediation for entering students, ESL program, services for LD students, advanced placement, accelerated degree program, self-designed majors, distance learning, summer session for credit, part-time degree program, external degree program, adult/continuing education programs, internships. ROTC: Army.

Entrance Requirements: Open admission. Options: electronic application, early admission, deferred admission. Required: high school transcript, minimum 2 high school GPA. Entrance: noncompetitive. Application deadline: Rolling. Transfer credits accepted: Yes.

Collegiate Environment: Drama-theater group, student-run newspaper. Social organizations: 18 open to all; national fraternities. Most popular organizations: International Student Association, We Can Do It Club, Students in Free Enterprise (SIFE), Student Nurses Association, NAACP. Major annual events: Graduation, Annual Job Fair, Wellness Fair. Campus security: 24-hour emergency response devices and patrols. Oveta Culp Hobby Memorial Library with 80,381 books, 173,023 microform titles, 467 serials, an OPAC, and a Web page. Operations spending for the previous fiscal year: $901,433. 130 computers available on campus for general student use. A campuswide network can be accessed from student residence rooms and from off campus. Students can access the following: online class registration. Staffed computer lab on campus provides training in use of computers and the Internet.

Community Environment: Population 100,200. Killeen is considered an outstanding recreation area with beautiful lakes and streams located nearby. The climate is temperate. All types of transportation are accessible. The community has shopping centers, medical facilities, and churches of many different faiths. Part-time employment is available.

■ CHAMBERLAIN COLLEGE OF NURSING

10025 Equity Dr.
Houston, TX 77041
Tel: (713)277-9800
Web Site: www.chamberlain.edu/
Description: Proprietary, 4-year, coed. Awards bachelor's degrees. Total enrollment: 231. Faculty: 6 (3 full-time, 3 part-time). Student-undergrad faculty ratio is 22:1. Full-time: 103 students, 92% women, 8% men. Part-time: 128 students, 88% women, 12% men. 4% from out-of-state. 0% American Indian or Alaska Native, non-Hispanic/Latino; 11% Hispanic/Latino; 35% African American, non-Hispanic/Latino; 9% Asian, non-Hispanic/Latino; 1% Native Hawaiian or other Pacific Islander, non-Hispanic/Latino; 0.4% international. 71% 25 or older, 0% live on campus, 42% transferred in.

Entrance Requirements: Required: SAT or ACT. Entrance: moderately difficult. Application deadline: Rolling. Notification: continuous.

Costs Per Year: Application fee: $95. Tuition: $16,360 full-time, $665 per credit hour part-time. Mandatory fees: $600 full-time. Full-time tuition and fees vary according to course load. Part-time tuition varies according to course load.

Collegiate Environment: College housing not available.

■ CISCO COLLEGE
101 College Heights
Cisco, TX 76437-9321
Tel: (254)442-5000
Fax: (254)442-5100
E-mail: oodom@cjc.edu
Web Site: www.cisco.edu/

Description: State and locally supported, 2-year, coed. Awards certificates, transfer associate, and terminal associate degrees. Founded 1940. Setting: 40-acre rural campus. Total enrollment: 4,022. Faculty: 120. Student-undergrad faculty ratio is 18:1. 1,227 applied, 100% were admitted. Full-time: 1,601 students, 59% women, 41% men. Part-time: 2,421 students, 73% women, 27% men. Students come from 40 states and territories. 12% live on campus. Retention: 56% of full-time freshmen returned the following year. Core. Calendar: semesters. Academic remediation for entering students, advanced placement, summer session for credit, part-time degree program. ROTC: Army (c).

Entrance Requirements: Open admission. Option: early admission. Required: high school transcript. Recommended: SAT, ACT. Entrance: noncompetitive. Application deadline: Rolling.

Collegiate Environment: Orientation program. Drama-theater group, marching band. Most popular organizations: Christian Athletes Association, Agricultural Club. Major annual events: Homecoming, Ranch Day. Campus security: late night transport-escort service. Maner Library with 34,000 books, 173 serials, an OPAC, and a Web page. 300 computers available on campus for general student use. A campuswide network can be accessed from student residence rooms and from off campus. Students can access the following: online class registration. Staffed computer lab on campus (open 24 hours a day) provides training in use of computers and the Internet.

Community Environment: Population 3,833. Cisco is a rural community that enjoys a temperate climate. The community is served by railroad, bus lines, and highways 80, 380, 183, 206 and Interstate-20. Local service facilities include a hospital, Rotary Club, Lions Club, and Veterans of Foreign Wars and Veterans of World War I. Merchants in the community provide jobs for many students. Recreation includes nearby Lake Cisco for boating, fishing, and water sports.

■ CLARENDON COLLEGE
PO Box 968
Clarendon, TX 79226-0968
Tel: (806)874-3571; Free: 800-687-9737
E-mail: martha.smith@clarendoncollege.edu
Web Site: www.clarendoncollege.edu/

Description: State and locally supported, 2-year, coed. Awards certificates, transfer associate, and terminal associate degrees. Founded 1898. Setting: 109-acre rural campus. Endowment: $2.1 million. Educational spending for the previous fiscal year: $2130 per student. Total enrollment: 1,583. Faculty: 94 (36 full-time, 58 part-time). Student-undergrad faculty ratio is 19:1. 498 applied, 100% were admitted. Students come from 14 states and territories, 2 other countries, 4% from out-of-state. 1% American Indian or Alaska Native, non-Hispanic/Latino; 19% Hispanic/Latino; 6% African American, non-Hispanic/Latino; 1% Asian, non-Hispanic/Latino; 0% Native Hawaiian or other Pacific Islander, non-Hispanic/Latino; 0.3% international. 29% 25 or older, 21% live on campus. Core. Calendar: semesters. Academic remediation for entering students, ESL program, services for LD students, advanced placement, independent study, distance learning, double major, summer session for credit, part-time degree program, adult/continuing education programs.

Entrance Requirements: Open admission. Options: electronic application, early admission, international baccalaureate accepted. Required: high school transcript. Required for some: interview. Entrance: noncompetitive. Application deadlines: Rolling, Rolling for nonresidents. Notification: continuous, continuous for nonresidents. Transfer credits accepted: Yes.

Collegiate Environment: Orientation program. Drama-theater group, choral group. Campus security: 8-hour patrols by trained security personnel, Emergency notification system through text messaging. Vera Dial Dickey Library plus 1 other with 21,027 books, 1,018 microform titles, 10,588 serials, 448 audiovisual materials, an OPAC, and a Web page. Operations spending for the previous fiscal year: $127,571. 57 computers available on campus for general student use. A campuswide network can be accessed from student residence rooms and from off campus. Students can access the following: online class registration. Staffed computer lab on campus.

Community Environment: Population 2,021. A rural community, Clarendon is the center of a ranching and farming area 54 miles southwest of Amarillo.

The climate is temperate with an average temperature of 61 degrees, and rainfall average of 23 inches. The area is served by railroad, bus lines, and Highways 70 and U.S. 287. The community has many churches, a hospital and clinic, museum, and adequate shopping facilities. Local recreation includes a city park, theatres, a Youth Center, golf course, hunting and fishing, all sports, and Greenbelt Lake with a 35-mile shoreline. Part-time employment is available.

■ COASTAL BEND COLLEGE
3800 Charco Rd.
Beeville, TX 78102-2197
Tel: (361)358-2838; Free: 866-262-2838
Fax: (361)354-2254
E-mail: register@coastalbend.edu
Web Site: www.coastalbend.edu/

Description: County-supported, 2-year, coed. Awards certificates, transfer associate, and terminal associate degrees. Founded 1965. Setting: 100-acre rural campus. Endowment: $514,263. Educational spending for the previous fiscal year: $1632 per student. Total enrollment: 3,142. Faculty: 151 (85 full-time, 66 part-time). Student-undergrad faculty ratio is 14:1. 1,048 applied, 100% were admitted. Full-time: 1,186 students, 65% women, 35% men. Part-time: 1,956 students, 61% women, 39% men. Students come from 2 states and territories, 1 other country, 1% from out-of-state. 26% 25 or older, 5% live on campus, 70% transferred in. Core. Calendar: semesters. Academic remediation for entering students, services for LD students, advanced placement, distance learning, summer session for credit, part-time degree program, adult/continuing education programs, co-op programs and internships.

Entrance Requirements: Open admission. Options: electronic application, deferred admission. Required: high school transcript. Entrance: noncompetitive. Application deadlines: Rolling, Rolling for nonresidents. Notification: continuous, continuous for nonresidents.

Collegiate Environment: Orientation program. Social organizations: 15 open to all. Most popular organizations: student government, Computer Science Club, Creative Writing Club, Drama Club, Art Club. Major annual events: Transfer Day, Job Fair, CBC Day. Student services: personal-psychological counseling. Campus security: 24-hour emergency response devices, night security. Grady C. Hogue Learning Resource Center with 43,004 books, 3,636 microform titles, 1,341 serials, 2,179 audiovisual materials, an OPAC, and a Web page. Operations spending for the previous fiscal year: $549,751. 970 computers available on campus for general student use. A campuswide network can be accessed from off-campus. Students can access the following: online class registration. Staffed computer lab on campus.

■ COLLEGE OF BIBLICAL STUDIES–HOUSTON
7000 Regency Sq. Blvd.
Houston, TX 77036
Tel: (713)785-5995
Fax: (713)785-5998
E-mail: admissions@cbshouston.edu
Web Site: www.cbshouston.edu/

Description: Independent nondenominational, 4-year, coed. Awards associate and bachelor's degrees. Founded 1979. Setting: 12-acre urban campus with easy access to Houston. Endowment: $1.4 million. Total enrollment: 643. 0% from out-of-state. Core. Calendar: trimesters. ESL program, services for LD students, accelerated degree program, honors program, independent study, summer session for credit, part-time degree program, adult/continuing education programs.

Entrance Requirements: Open admission. Option: electronic application. Required: essay, high school transcript. Entrance: noncompetitive. Transfer credits accepted: Yes.

Collegiate Environment: Orientation program. Most popular organization: Student Ministries. Major annual event: Student Appreciation Week. Campus security: 24-hour emergency response devices, late night transport-escort service, hourly patrols by trained security guards and police. College housing not available. College of Biblical Studies Library with 40,000 books, 359 microform titles, 609 serials, and 515 audiovisual materials. 25 computers available on campus for general student use. Students can access the following: online class registration. Staffed computer lab on campus provides training in use of computers, software, and the Internet.

■ THE COLLEGE OF HEALTH CARE PROFESSIONS
240 NW Mall Blvd.
Houston, TX 77092

Tel: (713)862-2633; Free: 800-487-6728
Fax: (713)746-5466
Web Site: www.chcp.edu/
Description: Proprietary, 2-year, coed. Awards certificates and terminal associate degrees. Founded 1988. Total enrollment: 392. Student-undergrad faculty ratio is 49:1. 126 applied, 100% were admitted. 0% from out-of-state. 48% 25 or older. Calendar: semesters.
Entrance Requirements: Required: high school transcript.

■ **COLLEGE OF THE MAINLAND**
1200 Amburn Rd.
Texas City, TX 77591-2499
Tel: (409)938-1211; Free: 888-258-8859
Fax: (409)938-1306
E-mail: sem@com.edu
Web Site: www.com.edu/
Description: State and locally supported, 2-year, coed. Awards certificates, diplomas, transfer associate, and terminal associate degrees. Founded 1967. Setting: 120-acre suburban campus with easy access to Houston. Endowment: $1.3 million. Educational spending for the previous fiscal year: $2461 per student. Total enrollment: 3,561. Faculty: 205 (100 full-time, 105 part-time). Student-undergrad faculty ratio is 14:1. Full-time: 1,093 students, 55% women, 45% men. Part-time: 2,468 students, 62% women, 38% men. 0.02% from out-of-state. 38% 25 or older, 16% transferred in. Retention: 58% of full-time freshmen returned the following year. Core. Calendar: semesters. Academic remediation for entering students, ESL program, services for LD students, honors program, distance learning, summer session for credit, part-time degree program, adult/continuing education programs, co-op programs.
Entrance Requirements: Open admission. Options: electronic application, early admission, deferred admission. Recommended: SAT or ACT. Required for some: high school transcript. Entrance: noncompetitive. Application deadline: Rolling. Notification: continuous.
Collegiate Environment: Orientation program. Drama-theater group, choral group. Social organizations: 25 open to all. Most popular organizations: Student Activities Board, Student Government Association, Biology Club, Collegiate High Schools Club NuPsi, Phi Theta Kappa. Major annual events: Club kickoffs, cultural events, entertainment programs. Student services: personal-psychological counseling, women's center. Campus security: 24-hour emergency response devices and patrols, student patrols. COM Library plus 1 other with 84,128 books, 19,000 serials, 492 audiovisual materials, an OPAC, and a Web page. Operations spending for the previous fiscal year: $105,668.
Community Environment: Population 44,200 Texas City is a suburban community located approximately 40 miles from the center of Houston.

■ **THE COLLEGE OF SAINTS JOHN FISHER & THOMAS MORE**
3020 Lubbock St.
Fort Worth, TX 76109-2323
Tel: (817)923-8459
Fax: (817)924-3206
E-mail: peter.capani@fishermore.edu
Web Site: www.fishermore.edu/
Description: Independent, 4-year, coed, affiliated with Roman Catholic Church. Awards associate and bachelor's degrees. Founded 1981. Setting: 1-acre urban campus with easy access to Dallas-Fort Worth. Educational spending for the previous fiscal year: $16,345 per student. Total enrollment: 21. Faculty: 9 (8 full-time, 1 part-time). Student-undergrad faculty ratio is 8:1. 13 applied, 100% were admitted. 75% from top 10% of their high school class, 80% from top quarter, 100% from top half. Full-time: 21 students, 48% women, 52% men. Students come from 9 states and territories, 67% from out-of-state. 0% American Indian or Alaska Native, non-Hispanic/Latino; 10% Hispanic/Latino; 5% African American, non-Hispanic/Latino; 0% Asian, non-Hispanic/Latino; 5% Native Hawaiian or other Pacific Islander, non-Hispanic/Latino; 0% international. 10% 25 or older, 91% live on campus, 10% transferred in. Retention: 91% of full-time freshmen returned the following year. Academic area with the most degrees conferred: liberal arts/general studies. Core. Calendar: semesters. Distance learning. ROTC: Army (c).
Entrance Requirements: Options: electronic application, international baccalaureate accepted. Required: essay, high school transcript, minimum 2.5 high school GPA, 2 recommendations, interview, Transcripts of all postsecondary work attempted, ACT / SAT / GRE scores, SAT or ACT. Entrance: very difficult. Application deadlines: 6/22, 6/21 for nonresidents. Notification: 7/31, 7/31 for nonresidents. SAT Reasoning Test deadline: 6/22. Transfer credits accepted: No.

Costs Per Year: Application fee: $25. Comprehensive fee: $10,000 includes full-time tuition ($8000) and college room and board ($2000).
Collegiate Environment: Orientation program. Choral group, student-run radio station. Major annual events: First day of term - Holy Mass, procession and Fellowship meal (BBQ in Fall), Matriculation and Holy Mass, Graduation and Holy Mass. Student services: health clinic, personal-psychological counseling. Campus security: 24-hour emergency response devices and patrols, late night transport-escort service. 19 undergraduates lived in college housing during 2012-13. On-campus residence required through senior year. Options: men-only, women-only housing available. The College of Saint Thomas More Library with 15,000 books and an OPAC. Operations spending for the previous fiscal year: $10,000.

■ **COLLIN COUNTY COMMUNITY COLLEGE DISTRICT**
3452 Spur 399
McKinney, TX 75069
Tel: (972)599-3100
Fax: (972)758-5468
E-mail: tfields@collin.edu
Web Site: www.collin.edu/
Description: State and locally supported, 2-year, coed. Awards certificates, transfer associate, and terminal associate degrees. Founded 1985. Setting: 333-acre suburban campus with easy access to Dallas-Fort Worth. Endowment: $4.3 million. Educational spending for the previous fiscal year: $3003 per student. Total enrollment: 27,424. Faculty: 1,163 (419 full-time, 744 part-time). Student-undergrad faculty ratio is 24:1. 5,091 applied, 100% were admitted. Full-time: 9,755 students, 53% women, 47% men. Part-time: 17,669 students, 58% women, 42% men. Students come from 48 states and territories, 109 other countries, 2% from out-of-state. 0.4% American Indian or Alaska Native, non-Hispanic/Latino; 18% Hispanic/Latino; 11% African American, non-Hispanic/Latino; 8% Asian, non-Hispanic/Latino; 0.3% Native Hawaiian or other Pacific Islander, non-Hispanic/Latino; 3% international. 35% 25 or older, 9% transferred in. Retention: 62% of full-time freshmen returned the following year. Core. Calendar: semesters. Academic remediation for entering students, ESL program, services for LD students, advanced placement, honors program, distance learning, summer session for credit, part-time degree program, adult/continuing education programs, co-op programs and internships. ROTC: Air Force (c).
Entrance Requirements: Open admission except for selective admissions to some programs. Options: electronic application, international baccalaureate accepted. Required: high school transcript. Entrance: noncompetitive. Application deadlines: Rolling, Rolling for nonresidents. Notification: continuous, continuous for nonresidents. Transfer credits accepted: Yes.
Costs Per Year: Application fee: $0. Area resident tuition: $810 full-time, $34 per credit hour part-time. State resident tuition: $1830 full-time, $68 per credit hour part-time. Nonresident tuition: $3480 full-time, $123 per credit hour part-time. Mandatory fees: $214 full-time.
Collegiate Environment: Orientation program. Drama-theater group, choral group. Social organizations: 48 open to all. Most popular organizations: student government, Phi Theta Kappa, Baptist Student Ministry, National Society of Leadership Success, Political Science Club. Major annual events: Welcome Week events, Get the Scoop on Student Groups, Safe Break activities. Student services: personal-psychological counseling. Campus security: 24-hour emergency response devices and patrols, late night transport-escort service. College housing not available. Spring Creek Library, Preston Ridge Library, Central Park Library plus 3 others with 178,212 books, 581 microform titles, 888 serials, 32,095 audiovisual materials, an OPAC, and a Web page. Operations spending for the previous fiscal year: $2.6 million. 478 computers available on campus for general student use. A campuswide network can be accessed. Students can access the following: online class registration. Staffed computer lab on campus provides training in use of computers.

■ **COMMONWEALTH INSTITUTE OF FUNERAL SERVICE**
415 Barren Springs Dr.
Houston, TX 77090
Tel: (281)873-0262; Free: 800-628-1580
Fax: (281)873-5232
E-mail: p.moreno@commonwealth.edu
Web Site: www.commonwealth.edu/
Description: Independent, 2-year, coed. Awards certificates and terminal associate degrees. Founded 1988. Setting: urban campus with easy access to Houston. Total enrollment: 122. 55 applied, 100% were admitted. 52% 25 or older. Core. External degree program, adult/continuing education programs.

Entrance Requirements: Required: high school transcript. Recommended: SAT or ACT. Required for some: Wonderlic aptitude test or THEA. Entrance: moderately difficult. Application deadline: Rolling. Notification: continuous.
Collegiate Environment: Social organizations: local fraternities. Campus security: 24-hour emergency response devices, daytime trained security personnel. Commonwealth Institute Library and York Learning Resource Center with 1,500 books and 12 serials. 15 computers available on campus for general student use. Staffed computer lab on campus provides training in use of computers, software, and the Internet.

■ **COMPUTER CAREER CENTER**
6101 Montana Ave.
El Paso, TX 79925
Tel: (915)779-8031; Free: 866-442-4197
Web Site: www.vistacollege.edu/
Description: Proprietary, 2-year, coed. Awards certificates, diplomas, transfer associate, and terminal associate degrees. Founded 1985. Setting: urban campus. Total enrollment: 351. 55% 25 or older. Calendar: 8 six-week terms.
Entrance Requirements: Open admission. Entrance: noncompetitive.

■ **CONCORDIA UNIVERSITY TEXAS**
11400 Concordia University Dr.
Austin, TX 78726
Tel: (512)486-2000; Free: 800-865-4282
Fax: (512)459-8517
E-mail: admissions@concordia.edu
Web Site: www.concordia.edu/
Description: Independent, comprehensive, coed, affiliated with Lutheran Church-Missouri Synod. Part of Concordia University System. Awards associate, bachelor's, and master's degrees. Founded 1926. Setting: 385-acre urban campus with easy access to Austin. Endowment: $12.1 million. Educational spending for the previous fiscal year: $4814 per student. Total enrollment: 2,584. Faculty: 278 (67 full-time, 211 part-time). Student-undergrad faculty ratio is 10:1. 930 applied, 95% were admitted. 14% from top 10% of their high school class, 45% from top quarter, 75% from top half. Full-time: 1,223 students, 61% women, 39% men. Part-time: 368 students, 70% women, 30% men. Students come from 26 states and territories, 2 other countries, 13% from out-of-state. 1% American Indian or Alaska Native, non-Hispanic/Latino; 20% Hispanic/Latino; 14% African American, non-Hispanic/Latino; 2% Asian, non-Hispanic/Latino; 0% Native Hawaiian or other Pacific Islander, non-Hispanic/Latino; 1% international. 1% 25 or older, 7% live on campus, 14% transferred in. Retention: 57% of full-time freshmen returned the following year. Academic areas with the most degrees conferred: business/marketing; health professions and related sciences; education. Core. Calendar: semesters. Academic remediation for entering students, services for LD students, advanced placement, accelerated degree program, honors program, independent study, double major, summer session for credit, part-time degree program, adult/continuing education programs, internships. Study abroad program. ROTC: Army (c), Air Force (c).
Entrance Requirements: Options: electronic application, early admission, deferred admission, international baccalaureate accepted. Required: high school transcript, minimum 2.5 high school GPA, SAT or ACT. Required for some: essay, interview. Entrance: moderately difficult. Application deadline: Rolling. Notification: continuous. SAT Reasoning Test deadline: 8/1. Transfer credits accepted: Yes.
Costs Per Year: Application fee: $25. Comprehensive fee: $32,060 includes full-time tuition ($23,600) and college room and board ($8460). Full-time tuition varies according to course load, degree level, and program. Room and board charges vary according to board plan.
Collegiate Environment: Orientation program. Drama-theater group, choral group, student-run newspaper, radio station. Social organizations: 19 open to all; non-Greek social and service organizations; 8% of eligible men and 12% of eligible women are members. Most popular organizations: student government, Business Club (The Executives), Education Club, Student Nursing Association, Student Athlete Advisory Committee. Major annual events: Tornado Tuesday, Coffee House, Spring Banquet. Student services: personal-psychological counseling. Campus security: student patrols, late night transport-escort service, controlled dormitory access. 270 college housing spaces available; 254 were occupied in 2012-13. Freshmen guaranteed college housing. On-campus residence required in freshman year. Option: coed housing available. Concordia University Library plus 1 other with 80,000 books, 10,500 microform titles, 21,000 serials, 300

audiovisual materials, an OPAC, and a Web page. Operations spending for the previous fiscal year: $282,489. 25 computers available on campus for general student use. A campuswide network can be accessed from student residence rooms and from off campus. Students can access the following: online class registration. Staffed computer lab on campus provides training in use of software and the Internet.

■ **COURT REPORTING INSTITUTE OF DALLAS**
1341 W Mockingbird Ln.
Ste. 200E
Dallas, TX 75247
Tel: (214)350-9722; Free: 888-841-3557
Fax: (214)631-0143
Web Site: www.crid.com/
Description: Proprietary, 2-year, coed. Awards transfer associate and terminal associate degrees. Founded 1978. Setting: urban campus. Total enrollment: 1,018. 69% 25 or older.
Entrance Requirements: Open admission. Option: early decision. Required: high school transcript, interview. Entrance: noncompetitive.
Collegiate Environment: Student-run newspaper. Campus security: 24-hour patrols, late night transport-escort service.

■ **COURT REPORTING INSTITUTE OF HOUSTON**
13101 NW Fwy., Ste. 100
Houston, TX 77040
Tel: (713)996-8300; Free: 888-841-3557
Web Site: www.crid.com/
Description: Proprietary, 2-year, coed. Awards diplomas and terminal associate degrees. Founded 2002.

■ **THE CRISWELL COLLEGE**
4010 Gaston Ave.
Dallas, TX 75246-1537
Tel: (214)821-5433; Free: 800-899-0012
Fax: (214)818-1310
Web Site: www.criswell.edu/
Description: Independent, comprehensive, coed, affiliated with Southern Baptist Convention. Awards associate, bachelor's, and master's degrees. Founded 1970. Setting: 1-acre urban campus. Calendar: semesters. Summer session for credit, part-time degree program.
Entrance Requirements: Entrance: minimally difficult.
Collegiate Environment: Orientation program. Campus security: 24-hour emergency response devices and patrols, late night transport-escort service.

■ **CULINARY INSTITUTE LENOTRE**
7070 Allensby
Houston, TX 77022-4322
Tel: (713)692-0077; Free: 888-LENOTRE
Fax: (713)692-7399
Web Site: www.culinaryinstitute.edu/
Description: Proprietary, 2-year, coed. Awards terminal associate degrees. Setting: urban campus. Total enrollment: 403. Student-undergrad faculty ratio is 12:1. Students come from 6 states and territories, 3 other countries, 6% from out-of-state. 0% American Indian or Alaska Native, non-Hispanic/Latino; 40% Hispanic/Latino; 22% African American, non-Hispanic/Latino; 2% Asian, non-Hispanic/Latino; 0.2% Native Hawaiian or other Pacific Islander, non-Hispanic/Latino; 0% international. 55% 25 or older. Core. Academic remediation for entering students, co-op programs and internships. Study abroad program.
Entrance Requirements: Required: essay, high school transcript, minimum 2 high school GPA, interview. Entrance: noncompetitive. Transfer credits accepted: Yes.
Collegiate Environment: Orientation program. College housing not available. 12 computers available on campus for general student use. A campuswide network can be accessed from off-campus. Staffed computer lab on campus provides training in use of computers, software, and the Internet.

■ **DALLAS BAPTIST UNIVERSITY**
3000 Mountain Creek Pky.
Dallas, TX 75211-9299
Tel: (214)333-7100; Free: 800-460-1328
Fax: (214)333-5447
E-mail: admiss@dbu.edu

Web Site: www.dbu.edu/

Description: Independent, comprehensive, coed, affiliated with Baptist General Convention of Texas. Awards associate, bachelor's, master's, and doctoral degrees and post-master's certificates. Founded 1965. Setting: 293-acre suburban campus with easy access to Dallas-Fort Worth. Endowment: $31.6 million. Educational spending for the previous fiscal year: $6763 per student. Total enrollment: 5,622. Faculty: 568 (129 full-time, 439 part-time). Student-undergrad faculty ratio is 15:1. 2,692 applied, 41% were admitted. 21% from top 10% of their high school class, 48% from top quarter, 81% from top half. 6 valedictorians. Full-time: 2,437 students, 56% women, 44% men. Part-time: 1,076 students, 61% women, 39% men. Students come from 46 states and territories, 43 other countries, 6% from out-of-state. 1% American Indian or Alaska Native, non-Hispanic/Latino; 11% Hispanic/Latino; 17% African American, non-Hispanic/Latino; 2% Asian, non-Hispanic/Latino; 0.1% Native Hawaiian or other Pacific Islander, non-Hispanic/Latino; 6% international. 38% 25 or older, 49% live on campus, 8% transferred in. Retention: 71% of full-time freshmen returned the following year. Academic areas with the most degrees conferred: business/marketing; interdisciplinary studies; theology and religious vocations; psychology. Core. Calendar: 4-1-4. Academic remediation for entering students, ESL program, services for LD students, advanced placement, accelerated degree program, honors program, independent study, distance learning, double major, summer session for credit, part-time degree program, adult/continuing education programs, internships, graduate courses open to undergrads. Off campus study at Council for Christian Colleges and Universities. Study abroad program. ROTC: Army (c), Air Force (c).

Entrance Requirements: Options: electronic application, early admission, deferred admission, international baccalaureate accepted. Required: essay, high school transcript, minimum 2.5 high school GPA, rank in upper 50% of high school class, SAT or ACT. Recommended: interview. Entrance: moderately difficult. Application deadlines: Rolling, Rolling for nonresidents. Notification: continuous, continuous for nonresidents. Transfer credits accepted: Yes.

Costs Per Year: Application fee: $25. Comprehensive fee: $27,608 includes full-time tuition ($20,910), mandatory fees ($200), and college room and board ($6498). College room only: $2590. Room and board charges vary according to board plan and housing facility. Part-time tuition: $697 per credit hour. Part-time mandatory fees: $100 per term.

Collegiate Environment: Orientation program. Drama-theater group, choral group. Social organizations: 51 open to all; local fraternities, local sororities; 10% of eligible men and 14% of eligible women are members. Most popular organizations: Ministry Fellowship, Baptist Student Ministry, Student Government Association, Student Education Association, International Student Organization. Major annual events: Homecoming, Freshman Orientation/Student Welcome and Transition Week (SWAT), Midnight Madness. Student services: health clinic, personal-psychological counseling. Campus security: 24-hour emergency response devices and patrols, late night transport-escort service, controlled dormitory access. 1,802 college housing spaces available; 1,719 were occupied in 2012-13. Freshmen given priority for college housing. On-campus residence required through senior year. Options: men-only, women-only housing available. Vance Memorial Library with 291,615 books, 520,463 microform titles, 23,978 serials, 8,255 audiovisual materials, an OPAC, and a Web page. Operations spending for the previous fiscal year: $1.4 million. 214 computers available on campus for general student use. A campuswide network can be accessed from student residence rooms and from off campus. Students can access the following: online class registration. Staffed computer lab on campus provides training in use of computers, software, and the Internet.

Community Environment: See University of Texas at Dallas.

■ **DALLAS CHRISTIAN COLLEGE**
2700 Christian Pky.
Dallas, TX 75234-7299
Tel: (972)241-3371; Free: 800-688-1029
Fax: (972)241-8021
E-mail: bvance@dallas.edu
Web Site: www.dallas.edu/

Description: Independent, 4-year, coed, affiliated with Christian Churches and Churches of Christ. Awards associate and bachelor's degrees. Founded 1950. Setting: 22-acre urban campus with easy access to Dallas-Fort Worth. Endowment: $169,907. Educational spending for the previous fiscal year: $4645 per student. Total enrollment: 322. Faculty: 56 (8 full-time, 48 part-time). Student-undergrad faculty ratio is 16:1. 107 applied, 64% were admitted. 12% from top 10% of their high school class, 31% from top quarter, 64%

from top half. Full-time: 227 students, 42% women, 58% men. Part-time: 95 students, 43% women, 57% men. Students come from 31 states and territories, 4 other countries, 20% from out-of-state. 2% American Indian or Alaska Native, non-Hispanic/Latino; 18% Hispanic/Latino; 20% African American, non-Hispanic/Latino; 1% Asian, non-Hispanic/Latino; 0% Native Hawaiian or other Pacific Islander, non-Hispanic/Latino; 1% international. 40% 25 or older, 41% live on campus, 18% transferred in. Retention: 67% of full-time freshmen returned the following year. Academic areas with the most degrees conferred: theology and religious vocations; business/marketing; psychology. Core. Calendar: semesters. Academic remediation for entering students, advanced placement, accelerated degree program, independent study, distance learning, double major, summer session for credit, part-time degree program, internships.

Entrance Requirements: Options: electronic application, deferred admission, international baccalaureate accepted. Required: essay, high school transcript, minimum 2 high school GPA, 2 recommendations, SAT or ACT. Required for some: interview. Entrance: minimally difficult. Application deadline: Rolling. Preference given to Christians. Transfer credits accepted: Yes.

Collegiate Environment: Orientation program. Drama-theater group, choral group, student-run newspaper. Major annual events: Day of Service, National Missionary Convention, Skip Day. Student services: personal-psychological counseling. Campus security: controlled dormitory access. Crawford Library with an OPAC and a Web page. Operations spending for the previous fiscal year: $108,378. 16 computers available on campus for general student use. A campuswide network can be accessed from student residence rooms. Students can access the following: online class registration. Staffed computer lab on campus.

Community Environment: A manufacturing, financial and distributing center, Dallas is a center for scientifically oriented industry in the electronics and aerospace fields and ranks high in cotton, oil and consumer goods production. The city also houses a principal banking and insurance complex. Dallas is a transportation hub for rail, bus and airlines.

■ **DALLAS INSTITUTE OF FUNERAL SERVICE**
3909 S Buckner Blvd.
Dallas, TX 75227
Tel: (214)388-5466; Free: 800-235-5444
Fax: (214)388-0316
E-mail: difs@dallasinstitute.edu
Web Site: www.dallasinstitute.edu/

Description: Independent, 2-year, coed. Awards certificates, transfer associate, and terminal associate degrees. Founded 1945. Setting: 4-acre urban campus with easy access to Dallas-Fort Worth. Total enrollment: 141. Student-undergrad faculty ratio is 17:1. Full-time: 141 students, 47% women, 53% men. Students come from 7 states and territories, 11% from out-of-state. 52% 25 or older, 0% transferred in. Services for LD students, distance learning.

Entrance Requirements: Open admission. Required: high school transcript. Entrance: noncompetitive.

Collegiate Environment: Campus security: 24-hour emergency response devices.

■ **DEL MAR COLLEGE**
101 Baldwin Blvd.
Corpus Christi, TX 78404-3897
Tel: (361)698-1200; Free: 800-652-3357
Fax: (361)698-1559
E-mail: fjordan@delmar.edu
Web Site: www.delmar.edu/

Description: State and locally supported, 2-year, coed. Awards certificates, transfer associate, and terminal associate degrees. Founded 1935. Setting: 159-acre urban campus. Educational spending for the previous fiscal year: $3578 per student. Total enrollment: 12,007. Faculty: 560 (267 full-time, 293 part-time). Student-undergrad faculty ratio is 18:1. Students come from 43 states and territories, 57 other countries, 1% from out-of-state. 38% 25 or older. Core. Calendar: semesters. Academic remediation for entering students, ESL program, services for LD students, advanced placement, accelerated degree program, freshman honors college, honors program, distance learning, double major, summer session for credit, part-time degree program, adult/continuing education programs, co-op programs and internships. Off campus study. ROTC: Army.

Entrance Requirements: Open admission except for allied health programs. Options: electronic application, early admission, deferred admission, international baccalaureate accepted. Required: high school transcript. Entrance: noncompetitive. Application deadline: Rolling. Transfer credits accepted: Yes.

Collegiate Environment: Orientation program. Drama-theater group, choral group, student-run newspaper, radio station. Social organizations: 25 open to all. Most popular organizations: Phi Theta Kappa, Alpha Beta Gamma, Student Government Association. Student services: personal-psychological counseling. Campus security: 24-hour emergency response devices and patrols. White Library plus 1 other with 127,717 books, 739 serials, an OPAC, and a Web page. Operations spending for the previous fiscal year: $2.6 million. 800 computers available on campus for general student use. A campuswide network can be accessed from off-campus. Students can access the following: online class registration. Staffed computer lab on campus provides training in use of computers, software, and the Internet.

Community Environment: See Texas A&M University Corpus Christi.

■ DEVRY UNIVERSITY (HOUSTON)

11125 Equity Dr.
Houston, TX 77041
Tel: (713)973-3100; Free: 866-338-7941
Web Site: www.devry.edu/

Description: Proprietary, comprehensive, coed. Awards associate, bachelor's, and master's degrees. Total enrollment: 1,332. Faculty: 165 (25 full-time, 140 part-time). Student-undergrad faculty ratio is 11:1. Full-time: 431 students, 48% women, 52% men. Part-time: 639 students, 53% women, 47% men. 8% from out-of-state. 1% American Indian or Alaska Native, non-Hispanic/Latino; 29% Hispanic/Latino; 33% African American, non-Hispanic/Latino; 4% Asian, non-Hispanic/Latino; 0.3% Native Hawaiian or other Pacific Islander, non-Hispanic/Latino; 1% international. 71% 25 or older, 16% transferred in. Academic areas with the most degrees conferred: business/marketing; computer and information sciences; engineering technologies. Calendar: semesters.

Entrance Requirements: Entrance: minimally difficult. Application deadline: Rolling. Notification: continuous.

Costs Per Year: Application fee: $40. Tuition: $16,076 full-time, $609 per credit hour part-time. Mandatory fees: $80 full-time.

■ DEVRY UNIVERSITY (IRVING)

4800 Regent Blvd.
Irving, TX 75063-2439
Tel: (972)929-6777; Free: 866-338-7941
Web Site: www.devry.edu/

Description: Proprietary, comprehensive, coed. Part of DeVry University. Awards associate, bachelor's, and master's degrees. Founded 1969. Setting: suburban campus. Total enrollment: 1,220. Faculty: 102 (38 full-time, 64 part-time). Student-undergrad faculty ratio is 11:1. Full-time: 337 students, 28% women, 72% men. Part-time: 589 students, 39% women, 61% men. 13% from out-of-state. 1% American Indian or Alaska Native, non-Hispanic/Latino; 22% Hispanic/Latino; 27% African American, non-Hispanic/Latino; 3% Asian, non-Hispanic/Latino; 0.1% Native Hawaiian or other Pacific Islander, non-Hispanic/Latino; 1% international. 68% 25 or older, 14% transferred in. Academic areas with the most degrees conferred: business/marketing; computer and information sciences; engineering technologies. Calendar: semesters. Part-time degree program, adult/continuing education programs.

Entrance Requirements: Required: high school transcript, interview. Entrance: minimally difficult. Application deadline: Rolling. Notification: continuous.

Costs Per Year: Application fee: $40. Tuition: $16,076 full-time, $609 per credit hour part-time. Mandatory fees: $80 full-time.

Collegiate Environment: Orientation program. College housing not available.

■ DEVRY UNIVERSITY (RICHARDSON)

Richardson Ctr.
2201 N Central Expy.
Richardson, TX 75080
Tel: (972)792-7450; Free: 866-338-7941
Fax: (972)437-6892
Web Site: www.devry.edu/

Description: Proprietary, comprehensive, coed. Awards bachelor's and master's degrees. Calendar: semesters.

■ EAST TEXAS BAPTIST UNIVERSITY

One Tiger Dr.
Marshall, TX 75670-1498

Tel: (903)935-7963; Free: 800-804-ETBU
Fax: (903)938-1705
E-mail: admissions@etbu.edu
Web Site: www.etbu.edu/

Description: Independent Baptist, comprehensive, coed. Awards bachelor's and master's degrees. Founded 1912. Setting: 200-acre small town campus. Endowment: $59.4 million. Research spending for the previous fiscal year: $3200. Educational spending for the previous fiscal year: $6417 per student. Total enrollment: 1,290. Faculty: 118 (70 full-time, 48 part-time). Student-undergrad faculty ratio is 13:1. 1,462 applied, 58% were admitted. 12% from top 10% of their high school class, 42% from top quarter, 79% from top half. 1 valedictorian. Full-time: 1,085 students, 53% women, 47% men. Part-time: 156 students, 58% women, 42% men. Students come from 20 states and territories, 5 other countries, 9% from out-of-state. 1% American Indian or Alaska Native, non-Hispanic/Latino; 11% Hispanic/Latino; 19% African American, non-Hispanic/Latino; 1% Asian, non-Hispanic/Latino; 0.1% Native Hawaiian or other Pacific Islander, non-Hispanic/Latino; 1% international. 5% 25 or older, 84% live on campus, 8% transferred in. Retention: 52% of full-time freshmen returned the following year. Academic areas with the most degrees conferred: education; health professions and related sciences; interdisciplinary studies. Core. Calendar: semesters 4-4-1. Services for LD students, advanced placement, accelerated degree program, self-designed majors, honors program, independent study, distance learning, double major, summer session for credit, part-time degree program, adult/continuing education programs, internships, graduate courses open to undergrads. Off campus study. Study abroad program.

Entrance Requirements: Options: electronic application, international baccalaureate accepted. Required: high school transcript, SAT or ACT. Required for some: interview. Entrance: moderately difficult. Application deadlines: 8/17, 8/17 for nonresidents. Notification: continuous, continuous for nonresidents. SAT Reasoning Test deadline: 8/17. Transfer credits accepted: Yes.

Costs Per Year: Application fee: $25. Comprehensive fee: $27,675 includes full-time tuition ($20,670), mandatory fees ($860), and college room and board ($6145). College room only: $2540. Room and board charges vary according to board plan and housing facility. Part-time tuition: $689 per credit hour. Part-time mandatory fees: $35 per credit hour.

Collegiate Environment: Orientation program. Drama-theater group, choral group, marching band, student-run newspaper, radio station. Social organizations: 37 open to all; local fraternities, local sororities; 3% of eligible men and 1% of eligible women are members. Most popular organizations: Baptist Student Ministry, Fellowship of Christian Athletes, Texas Nursing Students Association, Student Government Association, Spirit Program. Major annual events: Christmas on the Hill, F5, Annual concert. Student services: personal-psychological counseling. Campus security: 24-hour emergency response devices and patrols, controlled dormitory access. 979 college housing spaces available; 947 were occupied in 2012-13. Freshmen guaranteed college housing. On-campus residence required through senior year. Options: men-only, women-only housing available. Mamye Jarrett Library with 2.4 million books, 10,000 microform titles, 25,000 serials, 108,982 audiovisual materials, an OPAC, and a Web page. Operations spending for the previous fiscal year: $601,350. 200 computers available on campus for general student use. A campuswide network can be accessed from student residence rooms and from off campus. Students can access the following: online class registration. Staffed computer lab on campus provides training in use of computers, software, and the Internet.

Community Environment: See Wiley College.

■ EASTFIELD COLLEGE

3737 Motley Dr.
Mesquite, TX 75150-2099
Tel: (972)860-7100
Fax: (972)860-8373
E-mail: efc@dcccd.edu
Web Site: www.efc.dcccd.edu/

Description: State and locally supported, 2-year, coed. Part of Dallas County Community College District System. Awards certificates, transfer associate, and terminal associate degrees. Founded 1970. Setting: 244-acre suburban campus with easy access to Dallas-Fort Worth. Educational spending for the previous fiscal year: $4091 per student. Total enrollment: 12,403. Faculty: 564 (121 full-time, 443 part-time). Student-undergrad faculty ratio is 24:1. 3,200 applied, 100% were admitted. Full-time: 3,026 students, 53% women, 47% men. Part-time: 9,377 students, 60% women, 40% men. Students come from 7 states and territories, 26 other countries, 1% from out-of-state. 37% 25 or older, 2% transferred in. Core. Calendar: semesters. Academic remediation for entering students, ESL program, services for LD students, advanced placement, honors program, distance learning, summer session for credit, part-time degree program, adult/continuing education programs, co-op programs.

Entrance Requirements: Open admission. Options: early admission, deferred admission. Recommended: high school transcript. Entrance: noncompetitive. Application deadline: Rolling. Notification: continuous.

Collegiate Environment: Drama-theater group, choral group, student-run newspaper. Most popular organizations: LULAC, Rodeo Club, Phi Theta Kappa, Rising Star, Communications Club. Major annual events: Student Leadership Academy, back to school parties, performing artists and speakers series. Student services: health clinic, personal-psychological counseling, women's center. Campus security: 24-hour emergency response devices and patrols. Eastfield College Learning Resource Center with 66,988 books, 48,976 microform titles, 415 serials, 2,620 audiovisual materials, an OPAC, and a Web page. Operations spending for the previous fiscal year: $580,478. 50 computers available on campus for general student use. A campuswide network can be accessed from off-campus. Students can access the following: online class registration. Staffed computer lab on campus.

Community Environment: See University of Texas at Dallas.

■ **EL CENTRO COLLEGE**
801 Main St.
Dallas, TX 75202-3604
Tel: (214)860-2037
Fax: (214)860-2335
E-mail: rgarza@dcccd.edu
Web Site: www.elcentrocollege.edu/

Description: County-supported, 2-year, coed. Part of Dallas County Community College District System. Awards certificates, transfer associate, and terminal associate degrees. Founded 1966. Setting: 2-acre urban campus. Total enrollment: 10,101. Faculty: 493 (135 full-time, 358 part-time). Student-undergrad faculty ratio is 19:1. 2,962 applied, 100% were admitted. Full-time: 2,314 students, 67% women, 33% men. Part-time: 7,787 students, 65% women, 35% men. Students come from 49 other countries, 1% from out-of-state. 0.3% American Indian or Alaska Native, non-Hispanic/Latino; 38% Hispanic/Latino; 19% African American, non-Hispanic/Latino; 3% Asian, non-Hispanic/Latino; 0.05% Native Hawaiian or other Pacific Islander, non-Hispanic/Latino; 0.3% international. 46% 25 or older, 74% transferred in. Retention: 39% of full-time freshmen returned the following year. Core. Calendar: semesters. Academic remediation for entering students, ESL program, services for LD students, advanced placement, freshman honors college, honors program, distance learning, double major, summer session for credit, part-time degree program, adult/continuing education programs, co-op programs and internships. ROTC: Army (c).

Entrance Requirements: Open admission except for allied health, culinary arts programs. Options: electronic application, early admission. Required for some: high school transcript, 1 recommendation. Entrance: noncompetitive. Application deadline: Rolling.

Costs Per Year: Application fee: $0. Area resident tuition: $1248 full-time, $52 per credit hour part-time. State resident tuition: $2328 full-time, $97 per credit hour part-time. Nonresident tuition: $3672 full-time, $153 per credit hour part-time. Full-time tuition varies according to program. Part-time tuition varies according to program.

Collegiate Environment: Orientation program. Choral group. Social organizations: 38 open to all. Most popular organizations: Phi Theta Kappa, student government, Paralegal Student Association, El Centro Computer Society, Conflict Resolution Society. Major annual events: Student Recognition, African American Read In, Spring and Fall Semester Welcome Festivals. Student services: health clinic, personal-psychological counseling. Campus security: 24-hour emergency response devices and patrols, late night transport-escort service, e-mail and text message alerts. College housing not available. El Centro College Library with 77,902 books, 7,420 microform titles, 224 serials, 585 audiovisual materials, an OPAC, and a Web page. 1,317 computers available on campus for general student use. A campuswide network can be accessed from off-campus. Students can access the following: online class registration. Staffed computer lab on campus.

Community Environment: See University of Texas at Dallas.

■ **EL PASO COMMUNITY COLLEGE**
PO Box 20500
El Paso, TX 79998-0500

Tel: (915)831-2000
Fax: (915)831-6145
E-mail: daryleh@epcc.edu
Web Site: www.epcc.edu/

Description: County-supported, 2-year, coed. Awards certificates, transfer associate, and terminal associate degrees. Founded 1969. Setting: urban campus. Total enrollment: 30,723. Faculty: 1,452 (415 full-time, 1,037 part-time). Full-time: 11,886 students, 60% women, 40% men. Part-time: 18,837 students, 56% women, 44% men. 0.4% American Indian or Alaska Native, non-Hispanic/Latino; 85% Hispanic/Latino; 2% African American, non-Hispanic/Latino; 1% Asian, non-Hispanic/Latino; 0.1% Native Hawaiian or other Pacific Islander, non-Hispanic/Latino; 2% international. 30% 25 or older. Core. Calendar: semesters. Academic remediation for entering students, ESL program, services for LD students, advanced placement, honors program, distance learning, summer session for credit, part-time degree program, external degree program, adult/continuing education programs, co-op programs and internships. Off campus study at University of Texas at El Paso. ROTC: Army (c).

Entrance Requirements: Open admission. Options: early admission, deferred admission. Entrance: noncompetitive. Application deadline: 8/3.

Costs Per Year: Application fee: $10. State resident tuition: $1848 full-time, $67 per hour part-time. Nonresident tuition: $2496 full-time, $94 per hour part-time. Mandatory fees: $240 full-time, $10 per hour part-time.

Collegiate Environment: Drama-theater group, choral group, student-run newspaper, radio station. Student services: personal-psychological counseling. Campus security: 24-hour patrols, late night transport-escort service. El Paso Community College Learning Resource Center plus 4 others with 220,150 books, 2,356 microform titles, 807 serials, 14,734 audiovisual materials, an OPAC, and a Web page.

Community Environment: See University of Texas - El Paso.

■ **EVEREST COLLEGE (ARLINGTON)**
300 Six Flags Dr.
Ste. 200
Arlington, TX 76011
Tel: (817)652-7790
Fax: (817)649-6033
Web Site: www.everest.edu/

Description: Proprietary, 2-year, coed. Awards terminal associate degrees. Founded 2003. Total enrollment: 783. Student-undergrad faculty ratio is 18:1. 199 applied, 75% were admitted. 0% out-of-state. 51% 25 or older. Calendar: 6 or 12 week terms.

Entrance Requirements: Required: high school transcript.

■ **EVEREST COLLEGE (DALLAS)**
6080 N Central Expy.
Dallas, TX 75206
Tel: (214)234-4850; Free: 888-741-4270
Fax: (214)696-6208
Web Site: www.everest.edu/

Description: Proprietary, 2-year, coed. Awards terminal associate degrees. Founded 2003. Total enrollment: 1,261. Student-undergrad faculty ratio is 30:1. 357 applied, 63% were admitted. 0% from out-of-state. 43% 25 or older. Calendar: 6 or 12 week terms.

■ **EVEREST COLLEGE (FORT WORTH)**
5237 N Riverside Dr.
Ste. 100
Fort Worth, TX 76137
Tel: (817)838-3000; Free: 888-741-4270
Fax: (817)838-2040
Web Site: www.everest.edu/

Description: Proprietary, 2-year, coed. Awards certificates and terminal associate degrees. Founded 2004. Total enrollment: 939. Student-undergrad faculty ratio is 27:1. 162 applied, 90% were admitted. 0% from out-of-state. 54% 25 or older.

■ **FRANK PHILLIPS COLLEGE**
Box 5118
Borger, TX 79008-5118
Tel: (806)274-5311
Fax: (806)274-6835
E-mail: mstevens@fpctx.edu
Web Site: www.fpctx.edu/

Description: State and locally supported, 2-year, coed. Awards certificates, transfer associate, and terminal associate degrees. Founded 1948. Setting: 60-acre small town campus. Endowment: $919,464. Total enrollment: 1,247. Faculty: 75 (35 full-time, 40 part-time). Student-undergrad faculty ratio is 18:1. Full-time: 686 students, 53% women, 47% men. Part-time: 561 students, 57% women, 43% men. Students come from 15 states and territories, 6 other countries, 10% from out-of-state. 20% 25 or older, 20% live on campus, 6% transferred in. Retention: 52% of full-time freshmen returned the following year. Core. Calendar: semesters. Academic remediation for entering students, services for LD students, advanced placement, accelerated degree program, honors program, distance learning, summer session for credit, part-time degree program, adult/continuing education programs, co-op programs and internships.

Entrance Requirements: Open admission. Options: electronic application, early admission, deferred admission. Required: high school transcript. Entrance: noncompetitive. Application deadline: 8/25. Notification: continuous until 8/25. Transfer credits accepted: Yes.

Collegiate Environment: Orientation program. Choral group. Student services: personal-psychological counseling. Campus security: 24-hour emergency response devices and patrols, controlled dormitory access. James W. Dillard Library with 45,631 books, 14,360 serials, 1,143 audiovisual materials, and an OPAC. Operations spending for the previous fiscal year: $153,853.

Community Environment: Population 13,305, one of the youngest towns in Texas, Borger was born as an oil boomtown in 1926. Today it is the center of the Panhandle gas reservoir, which produces more natural gas and allied products than any other field in the world. The community enjoys temperate climate. Air, rail, and bus service is available. Community services include a public library, churches of major denominations, a hospital, major civic, fraternal, and veteran's organizations, and shopping facilities. Local recreation includes theaters, golf, and other sports. Lake Meredith also offers recreational opportunities. The Oil Show, Rodeo, and Art Show are held annually. Part-time employment is available.

■ **GALVESTON COLLEGE**
4015 Ave. Q
Galveston, TX 77550-7496
Tel: (409)763-6551
Fax: (409)762-9367
E-mail: calcala@gc.edu
Web Site: www.gc.edu/

Description: State and locally supported, 2-year, coed. Awards certificates, transfer associate, and terminal associate degrees. Founded 1967. Setting: 11-acre urban campus with easy access to Houston. Endowment: $3.4 million. Research spending for the previous fiscal year: $13.1 million. Educational spending for the previous fiscal year: $13,143 per student. Total enrollment: 2,230. Faculty: 101 (55 full-time, 46 part-time). Student-undergrad faculty ratio is 11:1. Full-time: 851 students, 61% women, 39% men. Part-time: 1,379 students, 67% women, 33% men. Students come from 26 states and territories, 2% from out-of-state. 36% 25 or older, 33% transferred in. Retention: 51% of full-time freshmen returned the following year. Core. Calendar: semesters. Services for LD students, advanced placement, distance learning, summer session for credit, part-time degree program, adult/continuing education programs, co-op programs and internships. Off campus study at Brazosport College, College of the Mainland.

Entrance Requirements: Open admission except for allied health programs. Required for some: high school transcript. Entrance: noncompetitive. Application deadline: Rolling. Notification: continuous.

Collegiate Environment: Orientation program. Choral group. Social organizations: 17 open to all. Most popular organizations: student government, Phi Theta Kappa, Student Nurses Association, ATTC, Hispanic Student Organization. Major annual events: College Night, back to school activity, Business Symposium. Student services: personal-psychological counseling. Campus security: 24-hour emergency response devices and patrols, late night transport-escort service. David Glenn Hunt Memorial Library with 45,193 books, 54 microform titles, 4,000 serials, 1,500 audiovisual materials, an OPAC, and a Web page. Operations spending for the previous fiscal year: $553,667. 173 computers available on campus for general student use. A campuswide network can be accessed. Students can access the following: online class registration. Staffed computer lab on campus (open 24 hours a day) provides training in use of computers, software, and the Internet.

Community Environment: Galveston is a port and recreational city. Major business activities include the tourist, maritime, and banking industries.

Known as the "playground of the Southwest," Galveston has an average maximum temperature of 74.9 degrees, and an average minimum of 65.2 degrees. The climate is semitropical. The community is reached by rail, bus, and air. There are churches of various faiths, a library, YMCA, YWCA, medical facilities, a civic orchestra, Little Theatre, civic music association, an art league, and various fraternal, civic, and veteran's organizations in the community. Local recreation includes 32 miles of hard sand beaches, bathing, motoring, water sports, boating, deep-sea fishing, golf, and horseback riding. Part-time employment is abundant.

■ **GRAYSON COUNTY COLLEGE**
6101 Grayson Dr.
Denison, TX 75020-8299
Tel: (903)465-6030
Fax: (903)463-5284
E-mail: hallt@grayson.edu
Web Site: www.grayson.edu/

Description: State and locally supported, 2-year, coed. Awards certificates, diplomas, transfer associate, and terminal associate degrees. Founded 1964. Setting: 500-acre rural campus. Total enrollment: 4,856. Student-undergrad faculty ratio is 33:1. 5% from out-of-state. 43% 25 or older. Core. Calendar: semesters. Academic remediation for entering students, ESL program, advanced placement, honors program, summer session for credit, part-time degree program, adult/continuing education programs.

Entrance Requirements: Open admission. Options: early admission, deferred admission. Entrance: noncompetitive. Application deadline: 8/31. Notification: continuous.

Collegiate Environment: Drama-theater group.

Community Environment: Population 23,648. Principal industries in this manufacturing city include railroad cars, furniture, fishing lures, wigs, pickup campers, mattresses, venetian blinds, food processing and pipes. This is a metropolitan community served by railway transite and bus lines. The community has a library, over 40 churches representing most denominations, four hospitals, and various civic, fraternal and veteran's organizations. Some part-time job opportunities are available. Local recreation includes nearby lakes featuring all water sports, and three downtown theater complexes.

■ **HALLMARK COLLEGE OF TECHNOLOGY**
10401 IH 10 W
San Antonio, TX 78230
Tel: (210)690-9000
Fax: (210)697-8225
E-mail: slross@hallmarkcollege.edu
Web Site: www.hallmarkcollege.edu/

Description: Independent, primarily 2-year, coed. Administratively affiliated with Hallmark College of Aeronautics, Branch Campus, Hallmark College of Technology-Main Campus. Awards certificates, terminal associate, bachelor's, and master's degrees. Founded 1969. Setting: 3-acre suburban campus. Total enrollment: 356. Faculty: 43 (20 full-time, 23 part-time). Student-undergrad faculty ratio is 8:1. Full-time: 356 students, 55% women, 45% men. 0% from out-of-state. 0% American Indian or Alaska Native, non-Hispanic/Latino; 55% Hispanic/Latino; 15% African American, non-Hispanic/Latino; 1% Asian, non-Hispanic/Latino; 0.3% Native Hawaiian or other Pacific Islander, non-Hispanic/Latino; 0% international. 49% 25 or older, 0% transferred in. Calendar: continuous. Advanced placement, accelerated degree program, distance learning, internships.

Entrance Requirements: Option: international baccalaureate accepted. Required: high school transcript, interview, tour, application requirements differ depending on program of enrollment, Wonderlic aptitude test, SAT/ACT is used for entrance to some degree programs. Required for some: essay, SAT or ACT. Entrance: moderately difficult. Application deadline: Rolling. Notification: continuous. Transfer credits accepted: Yes.

Collegiate Environment: Orientation program. Social organizations: 1 open to all; Alpha Beta Kappa Honor Society. Most popular organization: Alpha Beta Kappa Honor Society. Major annual events: Student Appreciation Day, Student Mentoring Program, Student Enhancement Program. Campus security: 24-hour emergency response devices. College housing not available. 227 computers available on campus for general student use. A campuswide network can be accessed from off-campus. Staffed computer lab on campus provides training in use of computers, software, and the Internet.

■ **HALLMARK INSTITUTE OF AERONAUTICS**
8901 Wetmore Rd.
San Antonio, TX 78216

Tel: (210)826-1000

Fax: (210)826-3707

E-mail: sross@hallmarkcollege.edu

Web Site: www.hallmarkcollege.edu/programs/school-of-aeronautics/

Description: Private, 2-year, coed. Administratively affiliated with Hallmark College of Technology. Awards diplomas and terminal associate degrees. Setting: 2-acre urban campus with easy access to San Antonio. Total enrollment: 227. Faculty: 17 (all full-time). Student-undergrad faculty ratio is 17:1. Full-time: 227 students, 7% women, 93% men. 0% from out-of-state. 0% American Indian or Alaska Native, non-Hispanic/Latino; 49% Hispanic/Latino; 10% African American, non-Hispanic/Latino; 1% Asian, non-Hispanic/Latino; 0.4% Native Hawaiian or other Pacific Islander, non-Hispanic/Latino; 0% international. 54% 25 or older, 0% live on campus, 2% transferred in. Core. Calendar: continuous. Academic remediation for entering students.

Entrance Requirements: Option: international baccalaureate accepted. Required: high school transcript, interview, assessment, tour, background check. Entrance: moderately difficult. Application deadline: Rolling. Notification: continuous. Transfer credits accepted: Yes.

Collegiate Environment: Orientation program. Social organizations: 1 open to all; Alpha Beta Kappa National Honor Society; 10% of eligible men and 30% of eligible women are members. Major annual event: Student Appreciation Day. Campus security: 24-hour emergency response devices and patrols. College housing not available. 30 computers available on campus for general student use. A campuswide network can be accessed. Staffed computer lab on campus provides training in use of computers, software, and the Internet.

■ **HARDIN-SIMMONS UNIVERSITY**

2200 Hickory St.

Abilene, TX 79698-0001

Tel: (325)670-1000; Free: 877-464-7889

Fax: (325)677-8351

E-mail: breynolds@hsutx.edu

Web Site: www.hsutx.edu/

Description: Independent Baptist, comprehensive, coed. Awards bachelor's, master's, and doctoral degrees and post-master's certificates. Founded 1891. Setting: 220-acre urban campus. Endowment: $120.4 million. Educational spending for the previous fiscal year: $9381 per student. Total enrollment: 2,301. Faculty: 206 (137 full-time, 69 part-time). Student-undergrad faculty ratio is 13:1. 1,823 applied, 54% were admitted. 24% from top 10% of their high school class, 54% from top quarter, 83% from top half. 8 valedictorians. Full-time: 1,622 students, 52% women, 48% men. Part-time: 231 students, 45% women, 55% men. Students come from 27 states and territories, 17 other countries, 4% from out-of-state. 1% American Indian or Alaska Native, non-Hispanic/Latino; 14% Hispanic/Latino; 7% African American, non-Hispanic/Latino; 1% Asian, non-Hispanic/Latino; 0.1% Native Hawaiian or other Pacific Islander, non-Hispanic/Latino; 2% international. 8% 25 or older, 44% live on campus, 9% transferred in. Retention: 66% of full-time freshmen returned the following year. Academic areas with the most degrees conferred: education; business/marketing; parks and recreation. Core. Calendar: semesters. Academic remediation for entering students, services for LD students, advanced placement, accelerated degree program, honors program, independent study, distance learning, double major, summer session for credit, part-time degree program, adult/continuing education programs, internships, graduate courses open to undergrads. Off campus study at Abilene Christian University, McMurry University. Study abroad program.

Entrance Requirements: Options: electronic application, deferred admission, international baccalaureate accepted. Required: high school transcript, minimum 2 high school GPA, SAT or ACT. Required for some: 3 recommendations. Entrance: moderately difficult. Application deadline: Rolling. Notification: continuous. SAT Reasoning Test deadline: 8/15. Transfer credits accepted: Yes.

Costs Per Year: Application fee: $50. Comprehensive fee: $30,252 includes full-time tuition ($22,350), mandatory fees ($1110), and college room and board ($6792). College room only: $3400. Full-time tuition and fees vary according to program. Room and board charges vary according to board plan and housing facility. Part-time tuition: $745 per credit hour. Part-time mandatory fees: $200 per term. Part-time tuition and fees vary according to course load and program. Tuition guaranteed not to increase for student's term of enrollment.

Collegiate Environment: Orientation program. Drama-theater group, choral group, marching band, student-run newspaper. Social organizations: 57 open to all; local fraternities, local sororities; 3% of eligible men and 5% of

eligible women are members. Most popular organizations: Baptist Student Ministry, Alpha Phi Omega, Student Congress, Fellowship of Christian Athletes, Unity Group. Major annual events: Homecoming, All-School Sing, Western Heritage Day. Student services: health clinic, personal-psychological counseling. Campus security: 24-hour emergency response devices and patrols, late night transport-escort service, controlled dormitory access. 1,095 college housing spaces available; 813 were occupied in 2012-13. Freshmen guaranteed college housing. On-campus residence required through sophomore year. Options: men-only, women-only housing available. Richardson Library plus 1 other with 380,336 books, 19,628 microform titles, 38,670 serials, 17,844 audiovisual materials, an OPAC, and a Web page. Operations spending for the previous fiscal year: $1.9 million. 258 computers available on campus for general student use. A campuswide network can be accessed from student residence rooms and from off campus. Students can access the following: online class registration. Staffed computer lab on campus provides training in use of computers, software, and the Internet.

Community Environment: See Abilene Christian University.

■ **HILL COLLEGE**

112 Lamar Dr.

Hillsboro, TX 76645

Tel: (254)582-2555

E-mail: diharvey@hill-college.cc.tx.us

Web Site: www.hillcollege.edu/

Description: District-supported, 2-year, coed. Awards certificates, transfer associate, and terminal associate degrees. Founded 1923. Setting: 80-acre small town campus with easy access to Dallas-Fort Worth. Total enrollment: 3,556. 26% 25 or older. Core. Calendar: semesters. Academic remediation for entering students, ESL program, services for LD students, advanced placement, honors program, distance learning, double major, summer session for credit, part-time degree program, adult/continuing education programs, co-op programs and internships.

Entrance Requirements: Open admission. Options: early admission, deferred admission. Required: high school transcript. Entrance: noncompetitive. Application deadline: Rolling.

Collegiate Environment: Orientation program. Drama-theater group, choral group. Campus security: late night transport-escort service, controlled dormitory access, security officers. Hill College Library plus 1 other with 40,000 books, 3,161 microform titles, 300 serials, 500 audiovisual materials, an OPAC, and a Web page.

■ **HOUSTON BAPTIST UNIVERSITY**

7502 Fondren Rd.

Houston, TX 77074-3298

Tel: (281)649-3000; Free: 800-696-3210

Fax: (281)649-3209

E-mail: eborges@hbu.edu

Web Site: www.hbu.edu/

Description: Independent Baptist, comprehensive, coed. Awards bachelor's and master's degrees. Founded 1960. Setting: 150-acre urban campus with easy access to Houston. Endowment: $83.7 million. Educational spending for the previous fiscal year: $6676 per student. Total enrollment: 2,589. Faculty: 225 (115 full-time, 110 part-time). Student-undergrad faculty ratio is 15:1. 11,738 applied, 35% were admitted. 27% from top 10% of their high school class, 60% from top quarter, 85% from top half. Full-time: 1,875 students, 65% women, 35% men. Part-time: 177 students, 66% women, 34% men. Students come from 24 states and territories, 27 other countries, 3% from out-of-state. 0.1% American Indian or Alaska Native, non-Hispanic/Latino; 28% Hispanic/Latino; 19% African American, non-Hispanic/Latino; 12% Asian, non-Hispanic/Latino; 0.3% Native Hawaiian or other Pacific Islander, non-Hispanic/Latino; 4% international. 15% 25 or older, 34% live on campus, 9% transferred in. Retention: 68% of full-time freshmen returned the following year. Academic areas with the most degrees conferred: business/marketing; biological/life sciences; education. Core. Calendar: semesters. Academic remediation for entering students, services for LD students, accelerated degree program, freshman honors college, honors program, independent study, distance learning, double major, summer session for credit, part-time degree program, adult/continuing education programs, internships, graduate courses open to undergrads. Off campus study. Study abroad program. ROTC: Army (c), Naval (c), Air Force (c).

Entrance Requirements: Options: electronic application, early admission, international baccalaureate accepted. Required: high school transcript, SAT or ACT. Required for some: essay, interview. Entrance: moderately difficult.

Application deadline: Rolling. Notification: continuous. SAT Reasoning Test deadline: 8/20. Transfer credits accepted: Yes.

Costs Per Year: Application fee: $0. Comprehensive fee: $34,430 includes full-time tuition ($26,280), mandatory fees ($1650), and college room and board ($6500). College room only: $3550. Room and board charges vary according to board plan and housing facility. Part-time tuition: $1100 per credit hour. Part-time mandatory fees: $825 per term. Part-time tuition and fees vary according to course load.

Collegiate Environment: Orientation program. Drama-theater group, choral group, student-run newspaper. Social organizations: 47 open to all; national fraternities, national sororities, local fraternities, local sororities; 10% of eligible men and 9% of eligible women are members. Most popular organizations: Alpha Epsilon Delta, Alpha Phi Omega, Association of Student Educators, Alpha Kappa Psi, Phi Mu. Major annual events: Homecoming, Midnight Madness, Opening Convocation. Student services: health clinic, personal-psychological counseling. Campus security: 24-hour emergency response devices and patrols, late night transport-escort service, controlled dormitory access. 1,037 college housing spaces available; 758 were occupied in 2012-13. Freshmen guaranteed college housing. On-campus residence required through sophomore year. Options: coed, men-only, women-only housing available. Moody Library with 322,277 books, 128,564 microform titles, 74,186 serials, 8,385 audiovisual materials, an OPAC, and a Web page. Operations spending for the previous fiscal year: $1.1 million. 100 computers available on campus for general student use. A campuswide network can be accessed from student residence rooms. Students can access the following: online class registration. Staffed computer lab on campus provides training in use of computers and software.

Community Environment: See University of Houston.

■ HOUSTON COMMUNITY COLLEGE SYSTEM

3100 Main St.
Houston, TX 77002
Tel: (713)718-2000; Free: 877-422-6111
Fax: (713)718-2111
Web Site: www.hccs.edu/

Description: State and locally supported, 2-year, coed. Awards certificates, transfer associate, and terminal associate degrees. Founded 1971. Setting: urban campus. Total enrollment: 58,476. Full-time: 18,476 students, 56% women, 44% men. Part-time: 40,000 students, 60% women, 40% men. 2% from out-of-state. 0.2% American Indian or Alaska Native, non-Hispanic/Latino; 31% Hispanic/Latino; 31% African American, non-Hispanic/Latino; 9% Asian, non-Hispanic/Latino; 0.3% Native Hawaiian or other Pacific Islander, non-Hispanic/Latino; 10% international. 43% 25 or older, 7% transferred in. Core. Calendar: semesters. Part-time degree program, adult/continuing education programs. ROTC: Army (c), Air Force (c).

Entrance Requirements: Open admission except for allied health programs. Required for some: high school transcript, interview. Entrance: noncompetitive. Application deadline: Rolling.

Collegiate Environment: Drama-theater group, student-run newspaper. Student services: personal-psychological counseling. Campus security: 24-hour emergency response devices and patrols, late night transport-escort service. College housing not available.

■ HOWARD COLLEGE

1001 Birdwell Ln.
Big Spring, TX 79720
Tel: (915)264-5000; Free: 866-HC-HAWKS
Fax: (915)264-5082
E-mail: trichardson@howardcollege.edu
Web Site: www.howardcollege.edu/

Description: State and locally supported, 2-year, coed. Part of Howard County Junior College District System. Awards certificates, transfer associate, and terminal associate degrees. Founded 1945. Setting: 120-acre small town campus. Endowment: $1.2 million. Educational spending for the previous fiscal year: $1636 per student. Total enrollment: 4,103. Faculty: 243 (144 full-time, 99 part-time). Student-undergrad faculty ratio is 14:1. Full-time: 1,636 students, 60% women, 40% men. Part-time: 2,467 students, 62% women, 38% men. 29% 25 or older, 8% live on campus. Retention: 54% of full-time freshmen returned the following year. Core. Calendar: semesters. Academic remediation for entering students, ESL program, services for LD students, advanced placement, independent study, distance learning, summer session for credit, part-time degree program, adult/continuing education programs, co-op programs and internships.

Entrance Requirements: Open admission. Options: electronic application,

early admission. Required: high school transcript. Entrance: noncompetitive. Application deadline: Rolling. Notification: continuous until 8/31. Transfer credits accepted: Yes.

Costs Per Year: Application fee: $0. Area resident tuition: $2010 full-time, $57 per credit hour part-time. State resident tuition: $3030 full-time, $89 per credit hour part-time. Nonresident tuition: $4540 full-time, $138 per credit hour part-time. Mandatory fees: $212 full-time. Full-time tuition and fees vary according to course load and location. Part-time tuition varies according to course load and location. College room and board: $4180. College room only: $1400.

Collegiate Environment: Orientation program. Drama-theater group, choral group. Social organizations: 10 open to all. Most popular organizations: Phi Theta Kappa, Student Government Association, Mexican-American Student Association, Baptist Student Ministries. Major annual events: Talent Shows, Awards Convocation, Athletic Events/Games. Student services: personal-psychological counseling. Campus security: 24-hour emergency response devices and patrols. Howard College Library with 30,921 books, 47,555 microform titles, 16,006 serials, 1,710 audiovisual materials, an OPAC, and a Web page. Operations spending for the previous fiscal year: $351,428. 300 computers available on campus for general student use. A campuswide network can be accessed from student residence rooms and from off campus. Students can access the following: online class registration. Staffed computer lab on campus provides training in use of computers, software, and the Internet.

Community Environment: Big Spring, population 24,250, is an urban community noted for its varied industries, which include oil refining and production, petrochemical manufacturing, one carbon black plants, two bottling plants, and an ammonia plant. The climate is temperate and dry. The community is served by air, rail, and bus lines. There is a public library, YMCA, many churches of various faiths, three general and one Veteran's hospital, a crippled children's rehabilitation center, three theatres, good shopping facilities, and various civic, fraternal, and veteran's organizations in the area. Local recreation includes skating, bowling, and water sports on nearby lakes. Part-time employment opportunities are limited.

■ HOWARD PAYNE UNIVERSITY

1000 Fisk St.
Brownwood, TX 76801-2715
Tel: (325)646-2502; Free: 800-880-4478
Fax: (325)649-8905
E-mail: enroll@hputx.edu
Web Site: www.hputx.edu/

Description: Independent, comprehensive, coed, affiliated with Baptist General Convention of Texas. Awards associate, bachelor's, and master's degrees. Founded 1889. Setting: 80-acre small town campus. Endowment: $45.5 million. Educational spending for the previous fiscal year: $7922 per student. Total enrollment: 1,130. Faculty: 120 (82 full-time, 38 part-time). Student-undergrad faculty ratio is 11:1. 1,554 applied, 50% were admitted. 13% from top 10% of their high school class, 35% from top quarter, 65% from top half. 3 valedictorians. Full-time: 930 students, 48% women, 52% men. Part-time: 161 students, 61% women, 39% men. Students come from 10 states and territories, 2% from out-of-state. 1% American Indian or Alaska Native, non-Hispanic/Latino; 17% Hispanic/Latino; 8% African American, non-Hispanic/Latino; 0.4% Asian, non-Hispanic/Latino; 0.2% Native Hawaiian or other Pacific Islander, non-Hispanic/Latino; 0.4% international. 9% 25 or older, 62% live on campus, 5% transferred in. Retention: 61% of full-time freshmen returned the following year. Academic areas with the most degrees conferred: education; business/marketing; theology and religious vocations. Core. Calendar: semesters. Academic remediation for entering students, services for LD students, advanced placement, honors program, independent study, distance learning, double major, summer session for credit, part-time degree program, internships, graduate courses open to undergrads. Off campus study. Study abroad program.

Entrance Requirements: Options: electronic application, early admission, international baccalaureate accepted. Required: high school transcript, minimum 3 high school GPA, SAT or ACT. Recommended: essay. Required for some: 3 recommendations, interview, ACCUPLACER. Entrance: moderately difficult. Application deadlines: Rolling, Rolling for nonresidents. Notification: continuous, continuous for nonresidents. SAT Reasoning Test deadline: 8/1. Transfer credits accepted: Yes.

Costs Per Year: Application fee: $0. Comprehensive fee: $30,000 includes full-time tuition ($21,800), mandatory fees ($1400), and college room and board ($6800). Full-time tuition and fees vary according to course load, location, and program. Room and board charges vary according to board plan and housing facility. Part-time tuition: $700 per credit hour. Part-time tuition varies according to location and program.

Collegiate Environment: Orientation program. Drama-theater group, choral group, marching band, student-run newspaper. Social organizations: 13 open to all; national fraternities, national sororities, local fraternities, local sororities; 9% of eligible men and 5% of eligible women are members. Most popular organizations: Baptist Student Ministry, Fellowship of Christian Athletes, Student Government Association, Student Foundation, Student Activities Council. Major annual events: Family Weekend, Homecoming, Stinger Daze. Student services: health clinic, personal-psychological counseling. Campus security: 24-hour emergency response devices and patrols, late night transport-escort service, controlled dormitory access. 756 college housing spaces available; 575 were occupied in 2012-13. Freshmen guaranteed college housing. On-campus residence required through sophomore year. Options: men-only, women-only housing available. Walker Memorial Library with 115,049 books, 56,536 microform titles, 34,952 serials, 1,099 audiovisual materials, an OPAC, and a Web page. Operations spending for the previous fiscal year: $262,444. 260 computers available on campus for general student use. A campuswide network can be accessed from student residence rooms and from off campus. Staffed computer lab on campus provides training in use of computers, software, and the Internet.

Community Environment: Population 20,000. Brownwood is located 26 miles from the geographic center of the state, which designates the community "deep in the heart of Texas." The annual average temperature is 66.7 degrees, with an average annual rainfall of 27.4 inches. Railroad, airlines, and bus lines serve the area. The community has many churches of various faiths, a public library, two hospitals, and various civic, fraternal and veteran's organizations. Recreation includes Lake Brownwood with fishing, hunting, boating, water skiing, bathing, and picnicking; many city parks, golf course, municipal swimming pool, tennis courts, and five ball parks.

■ **HUSTON-TILLOTSON UNIVERSITY**
900 Chicon St.
Austin, TX 78702-2795
Tel: (512)505-3000
Fax: (512)505-3190
E-mail: slstinson@htu.edu
Web Site: www.htu.edu/
Description: Independent interdenominational, 4-year, coed. Awards bachelor's degrees. Founded 1875. Setting: 23-acre urban campus. Endowment: $8.3 million. Research spending for the previous fiscal year: $23,201. Total enrollment: 904. Faculty: 81 (49 full-time, 32 part-time). Student-undergrad faculty ratio is 14:1. 739 applied, 76% were admitted. 6% from top 10% of their high school class, 24% from top quarter, 56% from top half. Full-time: 766 students, 49% women, 51% men. Part-time: 123 students, 58% women, 42% men. Students come from 24 states and territories, 13 other countries, 6% from out-of-state. 19% Hispanic/Latino; 69% African American, non-Hispanic/Latino; 4% international. 11% 25 or older, 39% live on campus, 30% transferred in. Retention: 50% of full-time freshmen returned the following year. Academic areas with the most degrees conferred: business/marketing; parks and recreation; education; homeland security, law enforcement, firefighting, and protective services. Core. Calendar: semesters. Academic remediation for entering students, services for LD students, advanced placement, honors program, independent study, distance learning, double major, summer session for credit, co-op programs and internships. Study abroad program. ROTC: Army (c).
Entrance Requirements: Options: electronic application, deferred admission, international baccalaureate accepted. Required: high school transcript, minimum 2.3 high school GPA, university admission application, SAT or ACT. Required for some: essay, interview. Entrance: moderately difficult. Application deadline: 7/1. SAT Reasoning Test deadline: 7/1. SAT Subject Test deadline: 7/1.
Costs Per Year: Application fee: $25. Comprehensive fee: $20,000 includes full-time tuition ($11,020), mandatory fees ($2034), and college room and board ($6946). College room only: $2966. Full-time tuition and fees vary according to course load. Room and board charges vary according to housing facility. Part-time tuition: $368 per credit hour. Part-time tuition varies according to course load.
Collegiate Environment: Orientation program. Drama-theater group, choral group. Social organizations: 32 open to all; national fraternities, national sororities, local fraternities, local sororities; 3% of eligible men and 8% of eligible women are members. Most popular organizations: Campus Ministries, Zeta Phi Beta Sorority, Inc., Alpha Phi Alpha Fraternity, Inc., The Gentlemen's Club, Pre-Alumni Council. Major annual events: Coronation,

Charter Day, Graduation Day. Student services: health clinic, personal-psychological counseling. Campus security: 24-hour emergency response devices and patrols, late night transport-escort service, controlled dormitory access. Downs-Jones Library with 96,798 books, 69,945 microform titles, 43,342 serials, 10,147 audiovisual materials, an OPAC, and a Web page. Operations spending for the previous fiscal year: $318,846. 350 computers available on campus for general student use. A campuswide network can be accessed from student residence rooms and from off campus. Students can access the following: online class registration. Staffed computer lab on campus.
Community Environment: See University of Texas at Austin.

■ **ITT TECHNICAL INSTITUTE (ARLINGTON)**
551 Ryan Plz. Dr.
Arlington, TX 76011
Tel: (817)794-5100; Free: 888-288-4950
Fax: (817)275-8446
Web Site: www.itt-tech.edu/
Description: Proprietary, primarily 2-year, coed. Part of ITT Educational Services, Inc. Awards terminal associate and bachelor's degrees. Founded 1982. Setting: suburban campus.
Entrance Requirements: Entrance: minimally difficult.

■ **ITT TECHNICAL INSTITUTE (AUSTIN)**
6330 E Hwy. 290, Ste. 150
Austin, TX 78723-1061
Tel: (512)467-6800; Free: 800-431-0677
Web Site: www.itt-tech.edu/
Description: Proprietary, primarily 2-year, coed. Part of ITT Educational Services, Inc. Awards terminal associate and bachelor's degrees. Founded 1985. Setting: urban campus.
Entrance Requirements: Entrance: minimally difficult.

■ **ITT TECHNICAL INSTITUTE (DESOTO)**
921 W Belt Line Rd.
Ste. 181
DeSoto, TX 75115
Tel: (972)274-8600; Free: 877-854-5728
Web Site: www.itt-tech.edu/
Description: Proprietary, primarily 2-year, coed. Awards terminal associate and bachelor's degrees.
Entrance Requirements: Entrance: minimally difficult.

■ **ITT TECHNICAL INSTITUTE (HOUSTON)**
2950 S Gessner
Houston, TX 77063-3751
Tel: (713)952-2294; Free: 800-235-4787
Web Site: www.itt-tech.edu/
Description: Proprietary, primarily 2-year, coed. Part of ITT Educational Services, Inc. Awards terminal associate and bachelor's degrees. Founded 1983. Setting: urban campus.
Entrance Requirements: Entrance: minimally difficult.

■ **ITT TECHNICAL INSTITUTE (HOUSTON)**
15651 N Fwy.
Houston, TX 77090
Tel: (281)873-0512
Fax: (281)873-0518
Web Site: www.itt-tech.edu/
Description: Proprietary, primarily 2-year, coed. Part of ITT Educational Services, Inc. Awards terminal associate and bachelor's degrees. Founded 1985. Setting: suburban campus.
Entrance Requirements: Entrance: minimally difficult.

■ **ITT TECHNICAL INSTITUTE (RICHARDSON)**
2101 Waterview Pky.
Richardson, TX 75080
Tel: (972)690-9100; Free: 888-488-5761
Web Site: www.itt-tech.edu/
Description: Proprietary, primarily 2-year, coed. Part of ITT Educational Services, Inc. Awards terminal associate and bachelor's degrees. Founded 1989. Setting: suburban campus.
Entrance Requirements: Entrance: minimally difficult.

■ ITT TECHNICAL INSTITUTE (SAN ANTONIO)

5700 NW Pky.
San Antonio, TX 78249-3303
Tel: (210)694-4612; Free: 800-880-0570
Fax: (210)694-4651
Web Site: www.itt-tech.edu/
Description: Proprietary, primarily 2-year, coed. Part of ITT Educational Services, Inc. Awards terminal associate and bachelor's degrees. Founded 1988. Setting: urban campus.
Entrance Requirements: Entrance: minimally difficult.

■ ITT TECHNICAL INSTITUTE (WACO)

3700 S Jack Kultgen Expy.
Ste. 100
Waco, TX 76706
Tel: (254)881-2200; Free: 877-201-7143
Web Site: www.itt-tech.edu/
Description: Proprietary, primarily 2-year, coed. Part of ITT Educational Services, Inc. Awards terminal associate and bachelor's degrees.

■ ITT TECHNICAL INSTITUTE (WEBSTER)

1001 Magnolia Ave.
Webster, TX 77598
Tel: (281)316-4700; Free: 888-488-9347
Web Site: www.itt-tech.edu/
Description: Proprietary, primarily 2-year, coed. Part of ITT Educational Services, Inc. Awards terminal associate and bachelor's degrees. Founded 1995.
Entrance Requirements: Entrance: minimally difficult.

■ JACKSONVILLE COLLEGE

105 B J Albritton Dr.
Jacksonville, TX 75766-4759
Tel: (903)586-2518; Free: 800-256-8522
E-mail: admissions@jacksonville-college.org
Web Site: www.jacksonville-college.edu/
Description: Independent Baptist, 2-year, coed. Awards diplomas, transfer associate, and terminal associate degrees. Founded 1899. Setting: 20-acre small town campus. Total enrollment: 327. Student-undergrad faculty ratio is 15:1. 7% from out-of-state. 17% 25 or older. Core. Calendar: semesters. Academic remediation for entering students, advanced placement, summer session for credit, part-time degree program, adult/continuing education programs.
Entrance Requirements: Open admission. Options: electronic application, early admission. Required for some: SAT, ACT, THEA. Entrance: noncompetitive. Application deadline: 8/15. Notification: continuous until 7/1.
Collegiate Environment: Drama-theater group, choral group. Student services: health clinic, personal-psychological counseling. Campus security: 24-hour emergency response devices, evening security personnel.
Community Environment: Population 14,000, Jacksonville is a small community enjoying temperate climate. The average annual rainfall is approximately 45 inches. The community is reached by way of railroad, major airlines, bus lines and highways. Community service facilities include many churches, two hospitals, a public library, and a local radio station. There are parks and facilities for golf, hunting, fishing, rodeos, and swimming. Various civic and fraternal organizations are active in the area. Part-time employment is available.

■ JARVIS CHRISTIAN COLLEGE

PR 7631 @ U S Hwy. 80 E
Hawkins, TX 75765-1470
Tel: (903)769-5700
Fax: (903)769-4842
E-mail: mlambert@jarvis.edu
Web Site: www.jarvis.edu/
Description: Independent, 4-year, coed, affiliated with Christian Church (Disciples of Christ). Awards bachelor's degrees. Founded 1912. Setting: 465-acre rural campus. Endowment: $11.6 million. Educational spending for the previous fiscal year: $11,499 per student. Total enrollment: 603. Faculty: 46 (32 full-time, 14 part-time). Student-undergrad faculty ratio is 16:1. 774 applied, 100% were admitted. 0% from top 10% of their high school class, 13% from top quarter, 35% from top half. Full-time: 560 students, 43% women, 57% men. Part-time: 43 students, 47% women, 53% men. Students come from 20 states and territories, 11% from out-of-state. 0.3% American Indian or Alaska Native, non-Hispanic/Latino; 7% Hispanic/Latino; 85% African American, non-Hispanic/Latino; 0% Asian, non-Hispanic/Latino; 0.2% Native Hawaiian or other Pacific Islander, non-Hispanic/Latino; 0% international. 6% 25 or older, 88% live on campus, 17% transferred in. Retention: 55% of full-time freshmen returned the following year. Academic areas with the most degrees conferred: interdisciplinary studies; education; business/marketing; biological/life sciences. Core. Calendar: semesters. Academic remediation for entering students, ESL program, advanced placement, self-designed majors, honors program, double major, summer session for credit, co-op programs and internships. Off campus study at University of Texas at Arlington, University of Texas at Tyler, University of North Texas.
Entrance Requirements: Open admission. Option: electronic application. Required: high school transcript. Recommended: minimum 2 high school GPA. Entrance: minimally difficult. Application deadlines: 8/1, 8/1 for nonresidents. Notification: 8/15, 8/15 for nonresidents. Transfer credits accepted: Yes.
Costs Per Year: Application fee: $50. Comprehensive fee: $19,552 includes full-time tuition ($10,090), mandatory fees ($1279), and college room and board ($8183). College room only: $5174. Room and board charges vary according to housing facility. Part-time tuition: $420.40 per semester hour. Part-time mandatory fees: $1279 per year.
Collegiate Environment: Orientation program. Drama-theater group, choral group. Social organizations: 16 open to all; national fraternities, national sororities; 88% of eligible men and 12% of eligible women are members. Most popular organizations: Student Government Association, Pre-Alumni Club, Student Ministers' Association, Women 2 Women, Panhellenic Council. Major annual events: Homecoming/Founders' Week, Miss Jarvis Coronation, Annual Christmas Concert. Student services: health clinic. Campus security: 24-hour emergency response devices and patrols. 700 college housing spaces available; 520 were occupied in 2012-13. No special consideration for freshman housing applicants. Options: men-only, women-only housing available. Olin Library with 84,192 books, 135 microform titles, 121 serials, 431 audiovisual materials, and an OPAC. Operations spending for the previous fiscal year: $21,060. 100 computers available on campus for general student use. A campuswide network can be accessed from student residence rooms. Students can access the following: online class registration. Staffed computer lab on campus provides training in use of computers, software, and the Internet.
Community Environment: Hawkins is located in southwestern Wood County, population 41,776. The area enjoys moderate, temperate climate. Serviced by U.S. Highway 80 and bus lines, there are churches of many denominations, a hospital and clinic, and various civic, fraternal, and veteran's organizations. Local recreation includes camping and hunting, with rivers, creeks, springs and lakes furnishing opportunities for fishing and boating.

■ KAPLAN COLLEGE, ARLINGTON CAMPUS

2241 S Watson Rd.
Arlington, TX 76010
Free: 800-935-1857
Web Site: arlington.kaplancollege.com/
Description: Proprietary, 2-year, coed. Awards diplomas and terminal associate degrees.

■ KAPLAN COLLEGE, BEAUMONT CAMPUS

6115 Eastex Fwy.
Beaumont, TX 77706
Tel: (409)347-5900; Free: 800-935-1857
Web Site: beaumont.kaplancollege.com/
Description: Proprietary, 2-year, coed. Awards diplomas and terminal associate degrees. Calendar: continuous.

■ KAPLAN COLLEGE, BROWNSVILLE CAMPUS

1900 N Expy.
Ste. O
Brownsville, TX 78521
Tel: (956)547-8200
Web Site: brownsville.kaplancollege.com/
Description: Proprietary, 2-year, coed. Awards diplomas and terminal associate degrees.

■ KAPLAN COLLEGE, CORPUS CHRISTI CAMPUS

1620 S Padre Island Dr.
Ste. 600

Corpus Christi, TX 78416

Tel: (361)852-2900

Web Site: corpus-christi.kaplancollege.com/

Description: Proprietary, 2-year, coed. Awards diplomas and terminal associate degrees.

■ KAPLAN COLLEGE, DALLAS CAMPUS

12005 Ford Rd.

Ste. 100

Dallas, TX 75234

Tel: (972)385-1446; Free: 800-935-1857

Fax: (972)385-0641

Web Site: dallas.kaplancollege.com/

Description: Proprietary, 2-year, coed. Awards diplomas and terminal associate degrees. Founded 1987.

■ KAPLAN COLLEGE, EL PASO CAMPUS

8360 Burnham Rd.

Ste. 100

El Paso, TX 79907

Web Site: el-paso.kaplancollege.com/

Description: Proprietary, 2-year, coed. Awards diplomas and terminal associate degrees.

■ KAPLAN COLLEGE, FORT WORTH CAMPUS

2001 Beach St.

Ste. 201

Fort Worth, TX 76103

Tel: (817)413-2000

Web Site: fort-worth.kaplancollege.com/

Description: Proprietary, 2-year, coed. Awards diplomas and terminal associate degrees.

■ KAPLAN COLLEGE, LAREDO CAMPUS

6410 McPherson Rd.

Laredo, TX 78041

Tel: (956)717-5909; Free: 800-935-1857

Web Site: laredo.kaplancollege.com/

Description: Proprietary, 2-year, coed. Awards diplomas and terminal associate degrees.

■ KAPLAN COLLEGE, LUBBOCK CAMPUS

1421 Ninth St.

Lubbock, TX 79401

Tel: (806)765-7051; Free: 800-935-1857

Web Site: lubbock.kaplancollege.com/

Description: Proprietary, 2-year, coed. Awards diplomas and terminal associate degrees.

■ KAPLAN COLLEGE, MCALLEN CAMPUS

1500 S Jackson Rd.

McAllen, TX 78503

Tel: (956)630-1499; Free: 800-935-1857

Web Site: mcallen.kaplancollege.com/

Description: Proprietary, 2-year, coed.

■ KAPLAN COLLEGE, SAN ANTONIO CAMPUS

6441 NW Loop 410

San Antonio, TX 78238

Tel: (210)308-8584; Free: 800-935-1857

Web Site: wsan-antonio.kaplancollege.com/

Description: Proprietary, 2-year, coed. Awards certificates, diplomas, and terminal associate degrees.

■ KAPLAN COLLEGE, SAN ANTONIO–SAN PEDRO AREA CAMPUS

7142 San Pedro Ave.

Ste. 100

San Antonio, TX 78216

Tel: (210)733-0777; Free: 800-935-1857

Web Site: nsan-antonio.kaplancollege.com/

Description: Proprietary, 2-year, coed. Awards diplomas and terminal associate degrees.

■ KD STUDIO

2600 Stemmons Fwy., No.117

Dallas, TX 75207

Tel: (214)638-0484; Free: 877-278-2283

Fax: (214)630-5140

E-mail: tataylor@kdstudio.com

Web Site: www.kdstudio.com/

Description: Proprietary, 2-year, coed. Awards terminal associate degrees. Founded 1979. Setting: urban campus. Educational spending for the previous fiscal year: $2405 per student. Total enrollment: 177. Faculty: 28 (all full-time). Student-undergrad faculty ratio is 6:1. 21 applied, 100% were admitted. 9% from out-of-state. 18% Hispanic/Latino; 46% African American, non-Hispanic/Latino; 2% Asian, non-Hispanic/Latino. 27% 25 or older. Retention: 69% of full-time freshmen returned the following year. Core. Calendar: semesters. Co-op programs.

Entrance Requirements: Open admission. Option: deferred admission. Required: essay, high school transcript, interview, audition. Entrance: noncompetitive. Application deadline: Rolling. Transfer credits accepted: Yes.

Collegiate Environment: Drama-theater group. Social organizations: 1 open to all. Most popular organization: Student Council. Major annual events: In-house plays/productions, Halloween Costume contest, Monthly movie nights. Campus security: 24-hour emergency response devices and patrols. KD Studio Library with 800 books and 15 serials. Operations spending for the previous fiscal year: $20,693. 5 computers available on campus for general student use. Staffed computer lab on campus provides training in use of computers, software, and the Internet.

■ KILGORE COLLEGE

1100 Broadway Blvd.

Kilgore, TX 75662-3299

Tel: (903)984-8531

Fax: (903)983-8607

E-mail: register@kilgore.cc.tx.us

Web Site: www.kilgore.edu/

Description: State and locally supported, 2-year, coed. Awards certificates, transfer associate, and terminal associate degrees. Founded 1935. Setting: 35-acre small town campus with easy access to Dallas-Fort Worth. Educational spending for the previous fiscal year: $7916 per student. Total enrollment: 6,231. Faculty: 398 (155 full-time, 243 part-time). Student-undergrad faculty ratio is 17:1. Full-time: 2,858 students, 59% women, 41% men. Part-time: 3,373 students, 66% women, 34% men. Students come from 25 states and territories, 28 other countries, 1% from out-of-state. 0.5% American Indian or Alaska Native, non-Hispanic/Latino; 13% Hispanic/Latino; 21% African American, non-Hispanic/Latino; 1% Asian, non-Hispanic/Latino; 0.1% Native Hawaiian or other Pacific Islander, non-Hispanic/Latino; 1% international. 33% 25 or older, 7% live on campus, 7% transferred in. Retention: 52% of full-time freshmen returned the following year. Core. Calendar: semesters. Academic remediation for entering students, ESL program, services for LD students, advanced placement, self-designed majors, distance learning, summer session for credit, part-time degree program, adult/continuing education programs, co-op programs and internships.

Entrance Requirements: Open admission except for associate degree allied health programs. Options: electronic application, early admission. Required: high school transcript. Required for some: interview. Entrance: noncompetitive. Application deadlines: Rolling, Rolling for nonresidents. Transfer credits accepted: Yes.

Costs Per Year: Application fee: $0. Area resident tuition: $696 full-time, $29 per semester hour part-time. State resident tuition: $2304 full-time, $96 per semester hour part-time. Nonresident tuition: $3456 full-time, $144 per semester hour part-time. Mandatory fees: $672 full-time. College room and board: $4270. Room and board charges vary according to board plan and housing facility.

Collegiate Environment: Orientation program. Drama-theater group, choral group, marching band, student-run newspaper. Student services: personal-psychological counseling. Campus security: 24-hour emergency response devices and patrols. 500 college housing spaces available; all were occupied in 2012-13. No special consideration for freshman housing applicants. Options: coed, men-only, women-only housing available. Randolph C. Watson Library plus 1 other with 65,000 books, 394 microform titles, 6,679 serials, 13,351 audiovisual materials, an OPAC, and a Web page. 500 computers available on campus for general student use. A campuswide network can be accessed from student residence rooms and from off campus. Students can access the following: online class registration. Staffed computer lab on campus provides training in use of the Internet.

Community Environment: Kilgore, population 11,800, is a suburban area enjoying temperate climate and four distinct seasons. The area is reached by bus, rail, air, and Interstate Highway 20, U.S. 259, and State 31. The community has over 40 churches representing various faiths, a library, medical facilities, and many civic, fraternal, and veteran's organizations. There are apartments available for student housing. Local recreation facilities include a swimming pool, tennis courts, picnic areas, bowling alleys, theatres, go-cart track, golf course, as well as water skiing, fishing, camping, and hunting. Part-time employment is available.

■ LAMAR INSTITUTE OF TECHNOLOGY

855 E Lavaca
Beaumont, TX 77705
Tel: (409)880-8321; Free: 800-950-6989
Web Site: www.lit.edu/
Description: State-supported, 2-year, coed. Awards certificates and terminal associate degrees. Founded 1995. Total enrollment: 2,711. Faculty: 157. Calendar: semesters.
Entrance Requirements: Entrance: noncompetitive.

■ LAMAR STATE COLLEGE–ORANGE

410 Front St.
Orange, TX 77630
Tel: (409)883-7750
Fax: (409)882-3374
Web Site: www.lsco.edu/
Description: State-supported, 2-year, coed. Part of Texas State University System. Awards certificates, transfer associate, and terminal associate degrees. Founded 1969. Setting: 21-acre small town campus. Total enrollment: 2,005. Faculty: 96 (50 full-time, 46 part-time). Student-undergrad faculty ratio is 19:1. Full-time: 929 students, 71% women, 29% men. Part-time: 1,076 students, 75% women, 25% men. 38% 25 or older. Retention: 45% of full-time freshmen returned the following year. Calendar: semesters. Academic remediation for entering students, distance learning, double major, summer session for credit, part-time degree program, internships.
Entrance Requirements: Open admission except for some programs. Required: high school transcript. Entrance: noncompetitive. Application deadline: Rolling. Notification: continuous.
Collegiate Environment: Orientation program. Campus security: 24-hour emergency response devices, late night transport-escort service. Lamar State College-Orange Library plus 1 other with 71,092 books, 1,306 serials, 288 audiovisual materials, and an OPAC. 70 computers available on campus for general student use. A campuswide network can be accessed from off-campus. Staffed computer lab on campus provides training in use of computers and the Internet.

■ LAMAR STATE COLLEGE–PORT ARTHUR

PO Box 310
Port Arthur, TX 77641-0310
Tel: (409)983-4921; Free: 800-477-5872
Fax: (409)984-6032
E-mail: nichoca@lamarpa.edu
Web Site: www.lamarpa.edu/
Description: State-supported, 2-year, coed. Part of Texas State University System. Awards certificates, transfer associate, and terminal associate degrees. Founded 1909. Setting: 34-acre suburban campus with easy access to Houston. Total enrollment: 2,208. Student-undergrad faculty ratio is 18:1. 0% from out-of-state. 17% 25 or older. Core. Calendar: semesters. Academic remediation for entering students, ESL program, services for LD students, advanced placement, accelerated degree program, honors program, independent study, distance learning, double major, summer session for credit, part-time degree program, adult/continuing education programs, co-op programs and internships. Off campus study at Lamar University-Beaumont, Lamar University-Orange. ROTC: Army (c).
Entrance Requirements: Open admission. Options: early admission, deferred admission. Required: high school transcript. Required for some: interview. Entrance: noncompetitive. Application deadline: Rolling. Notification: continuous.
Collegiate Environment: Orientation program. Drama-theater group, choral group. Social organizations: local fraternities, local sororities. Student services: personal-psychological counseling. Campus security: 24-hour emergency response devices, student patrols, late night transport-escort service. Gates Memorial Library with an OPAC and a Web page.

■ LAMAR UNIVERSITY

4400 Martin Luther King Pky.
Beaumont, TX 77710
Tel: (409)880-7011
Fax: (409)880-8463
E-mail: admissions@lamar.edu
Web Site: www.lamar.edu/
Description: State-supported, university, coed. Part of Texas State University System. Awards associate, bachelor's, master's, and doctoral degrees. Founded 1923. Setting: 200-acre suburban campus with easy access to Houston. Total enrollment: 14,288. Faculty: 645 (403 full-time, 242 part-time). Student-undergrad faculty ratio is 20:1. 4,929 applied, 88% were admitted. 14% from top 10% of their high school class, 36% from top quarter, 72% from top half. Full-time: 7,003 students, 57% women, 43% men. Part-time: 2,797 students, 63% women, 37% men. Students come from 39 states and territories, 38 other countries, 2% from out-of-state. 1% American Indian or Alaska Native, non-Hispanic/Latino; 10% Hispanic/Latino; 32% African American, non-Hispanic/Latino; 4% Asian, non-Hispanic/Latino; 0.01% Native Hawaiian or other Pacific Islander, non-Hispanic/Latino; 2% international. 28% 25 or older, 7% transferred in. Retention: 56% of full-time freshmen returned the following year. Academic areas with the most degrees conferred: business/marketing; interdisciplinary studies; health professions and related sciences. Core. Calendar: semesters. Academic remediation for entering students, ESL program, services for LD students, advanced placement, accelerated degree program, self-designed majors, honors program, summer session for credit, part-time degree program, co-op programs and internships, graduate courses open to undergrads. Off campus study.
Entrance Requirements: Options: electronic application, early admission. Required: high school transcript, SAT or ACT. Required for some: essay, SAT Subject Tests. Entrance: minimally difficult. Application deadline: 8/1. Notification: continuous. Transfer credits accepted: Yes.
Costs Per Year: Application fee: $0. State resident tuition: $6240 full-time, $208 per credit hour part-time. Nonresident tuition: $18,270 full-time, $609 per credit hour part-time. Mandatory fees: $2771 full-time. Full-time tuition and fees vary according to course load. Part-time tuition varies according to course load. College room and board: $7966. College room only: $5098. Room and board charges vary according to board plan.
Collegiate Environment: Orientation program. Drama-theater group, choral group, student-run newspaper. Social organizations: 181 open to all; national fraternities, national sororities; 5% of eligible men and 3% of eligible women are members. Major annual events: Midnight Madness, Homecoming, Springfest. Student services: health clinic, personal-psychological counseling. Campus security: 24-hour emergency response devices and patrols, student patrols, late night transport-escort service. 2,515 college housing spaces available. Option: coed housing available. Mary and John Gray Library with 526,180 books, 320,666 microform titles, 26,618 serials, 7,218 audiovisual materials, an OPAC, and a Web page. 120 computers available on campus for general student use. A campuswide network can be accessed from student residence rooms and from off campus. Staffed computer lab on campus.
Community Environment: Beaumont and the surrounding area form one of the largest concentrations of petroleum refineries in the nation. Top manufactures of the area include deep sea and dry-land oil-drilling equipment and oil-processing apparatus. The city is located on the Neches River approximately 20 miles north of the Gulf of Mexico. The climate is mild the year round. Airlines, railroad, and bus lines serve the community. The community has many churches representing various faiths, three libraries, YMCA, and YWCA, several hospitals, and various civic and fraternal organizations. Part-time employment is available.

■ LAREDO COMMUNITY COLLEGE

W End Washington St.
Laredo, TX 78040-4395
Tel: (956)722-0521
Fax: (956)721-5493
Web Site: www.laredo.edu/
Description: State and locally supported, 2-year, coed. Awards certificates, transfer associate, and terminal associate degrees. Founded 1946. Setting: 186-acre urban campus. Endowment: $2 million. Total enrollment: 8,152. Faculty: 343 (203 full-time, 140 part-time). Student-undergrad faculty ratio is 18:1. 987 applied, 100% were admitted. Full-time: 3,044 students, 57%

women, 43% men. Part-time: 5,108 students, 59% women, 41% men. Students come from 4 states and territories, 5 other countries, 8% from out-of-state. 34% 25 or older. Retention: 86% of full-time freshmen returned the following year. Core. Calendar: semesters. Academic remediation for entering students, ESL program, services for LD students, advanced placement, freshman honors college, honors program, independent study, distance learning, double major, summer session for credit, part-time degree program, adult/continuing education programs, internships.

Entrance Requirements: Open admission. Options: early admission, deferred admission. Required: high school transcript. Recommended: SAT, ACT. Entrance: noncompetitive. Application deadline: Rolling.

Collegiate Environment: Drama-theater group, choral group, student-run newspaper. Student services: personal-psychological counseling, women's center. Campus security: 24-hour emergency response devices and patrols, student patrols. Yeary Library with 88,006 books, 555 serials, and an OPAC.

Community Environment: Population approximately 208,000. A chief port of entry into Mexico, Laredo is separated from Nuevo Laredo, Mexico, by the Rio Grande. This is a metropolitan community located in the center of a rich cattle, oil, gas and agricultural district. It is a major import-export center. The city is reached by airlines, railroad, and bus service. The climate is temperate and dry. Laredo has a public library, churches of major denominations, two hospitals, and various civic and fraternal organizations. Shopping facilities are good. Part-time employment is available for students. Local recreation includes theaters, water sports, and most major sports.

■ **LE CORDON BLEU COLLEGE OF CULINARY ARTS IN AUSTIN**
3110 Esperanza Crossing
Ste. 100
Austin, TX 78758
Tel: (512)323-2511; Free: 888-559-7222
Fax: (512)323-2126
E-mail: ppaulette@txca.com
Web Site: www.chefs.edu/Austin
Description: Independent, 2-year, coed. Awards certificates, diplomas, transfer associate, and terminal associate degrees. Setting: urban campus. Total enrollment: 948. Student-undergrad faculty ratio is 27:1. 10% from out-of-state. 38% 25 or older. Retention: 67% of full-time freshmen returned the following year. Calendar: continuous.
Entrance Requirements: Open admission. Required: essay, high school transcript. Application deadline: Rolling.
Collegiate Environment: Campus security: 24-hour emergency response devices.

■ **LEE COLLEGE**
PO Box 818
Baytown, TX 77522-0818
Tel: (281)427-5611
Fax: (281)425-6831
E-mail: bgriffit@lee.edu
Web Site: www.lee.edu/
Description: District-supported, 2-year, coed. Awards certificates, transfer associate, and terminal associate degrees. Founded 1934. Setting: 35-acre suburban campus with easy access to Houston. Endowment: $5.2 million. Total enrollment: 5,347. Faculty: 399 (185 full-time, 214 part-time). Student-undergrad faculty ratio is 14:1. Full-time: 1,795 students, 62% women, 38% men. Part-time: 3,552 students, 48% women, 52% men. Students come from 17 states and territories, 44 other countries, 5% from out-of-state. 50% 25 or older, 1% transferred in. Core. Calendar: semesters. Academic remediation for entering students, ESL program, advanced placement, honors program, independent study, distance learning, summer session for credit, part-time degree program, adult/continuing education programs, co-op programs and internships. ROTC: Army (c).
Entrance Requirements: Open admission except for nursing program. Options: early admission, deferred admission. Required for some: high school transcript. Entrance: noncompetitive. Application deadline: Rolling. Notification: continuous.
Collegiate Environment: Orientation program. Drama-theater group, choral group, student-run newspaper. Social organizations: 27 open to all. Most popular organizations: Student Congress, Health Information Student Association, Lee College Awareness, Digital Information Society, ASHRAE (Air Conditioning Society of Heat and Refrigeration Engineers). Major annual events: Fall Fiesta, Spring Fling, Annual Blood Drive. Student services: personal-psychological counseling. Campus security: 24-hour patrols, late night transport-escort service, emergency telephones. Erma Wood Carlson

Learning Resource Center with 100,000 books, 660 serials, an OPAC, and a Web page. 800 computers available on campus for general student use. A campuswide network can be accessed. Staffed computer lab on campus.
Community Environment: Population 68,000. Baytown is located midway between Houston and the open sea on the Houston Ship Channel. The city is a consolidation of three towns: Baytown, Goose Creek, and Pelly. There are many churches in the immediate area, and four hospitals are easily accessible.

■ **LETOURNEAU UNIVERSITY**
PO Box 7001
Longview, TX 75607-7001
Tel: (903)233-3000; Free: 800-759-8811
Fax: (903)233-3411
E-mail: admissions@letu.edu
Web Site: www.letu.edu/
Description: Independent nondenominational, comprehensive, coed. Awards associate, bachelor's, and master's degrees. Founded 1946. Setting: 162-acre suburban campus. Total enrollment: 2,843. Faculty: 232 (96 full-time, 136 part-time). Student-undergrad faculty ratio is 15:1. 1,684 applied, 43% were admitted. 50% from top 10% of their high school class, 70% from top quarter, 93% from top half. Full-time: 1,343 students, 30% women, 70% men. Part-time: 1,107 students, 72% women, 28% men. 44% from out-of-state. 1% American Indian or Alaska Native, non-Hispanic/Latino; 9% Hispanic/Latino; 12% African American, non-Hispanic/Latino; 1% Asian, non-Hispanic/Latino; 0.1% Native Hawaiian or other Pacific Islander, non-Hispanic/Latino; 4% international. 45% 25 or older, 72% live on campus, 4% transferred in. Retention: 78% of full-time freshmen returned the following year. Academic areas with the most degrees conferred: business/marketing; education; engineering. Calendar: semesters. Part-time degree program, adult/continuing education programs.
Entrance Requirements: Options: electronic application, deferred admission. Required: SAT or ACT. Entrance: moderately difficult. Application deadline: Rolling. Notification: continuous. SAT Reasoning Test deadline: 6/1.
Costs Per Year: Application fee: $35. Comprehensive fee: $33,480 includes full-time tuition ($24,050), mandatory fees ($490), and college room and board ($8940). Room and board charges vary according to board plan. Part-time tuition: $959 per credit hour. Part-time tuition varies according to course load.
Collegiate Environment: Orientation program. Campus security: 24-hour emergency response devices and patrols, late night transport-escort service, controlled dormitory access, University police department. Freshmen guaranteed college housing. On-campus residence required through junior year. Options: coed, men-only, women-only housing available.
Community Environment: Population 75,600. Oil is the major source of economy for this community. Longview has a city library, community center, two hospitals, and a number of medical clinics. Major civic and fraternal clubs are active in the area. Longview is reached by airlines, railroad, and bus lines. Residence halls and apartments furnish student housing. Local recreation includes theatres, symphony, parks, swimming, hunting, fishing, golf, and water skiing. Part-time employment is available.

■ **LONE STAR COLLEGE–CYFAIR**
9191 Barker Cypress Rd.
Cypress, TX 77433-1383
Tel: (281)290-3200
E-mail: cfc.info@lonestar.edu
Web Site: www.lonestar.edu/cyfair
Description: State and locally supported, 2-year, coed. Part of Lone Star College System. Awards certificates, diplomas, transfer associate, and terminal associate degrees. Founded 2002. Setting: suburban campus with easy access to Houston. Total enrollment: 18,906. Faculty: 1,041 (196 full-time, 845 part-time). Student-undergrad faculty ratio is 27:1. 3,041 applied, 100% were admitted. Full-time: 6,314 students, 55% women, 45% men. Part-time: 12,592 students, 60% women, 40% men. Students come from 65 other countries, 0% from out-of-state. 0.3% American Indian or Alaska Native, non-Hispanic/Latino; 37% Hispanic/Latino; 15% African American, non-Hispanic/Latino; 9% Asian, non-Hispanic/Latino; 0% international. 33% 25 or older. Core. Calendar: semesters. Academic remediation for entering students, ESL program, services for LD students, advanced placement, accelerated degree program, honors program, independent study, distance learning, double major, summer session for credit, part-time degree program, adult/continuing education programs, co-op programs and internships. Study abroad program.

Entrance Requirements: Open admission. Options: electronic application, early admission. Entrance: noncompetitive. Transfer credits accepted: Yes.

Costs Per Year: Application fee: $0. Area resident tuition: $960 full-time, $480 per year part-time. State resident tuition: $2640 full-time, $1320 per year part-time. Nonresident tuition: $3000 full-time, $1500 per year part-time. Mandatory fees: $448 full-time, $192 per year part-time, $64 per year part-time. Full-time tuition and fees vary according to program. Part-time tuition and fees vary according to program.

Collegiate Environment: Orientation program. Drama-theater group, choral group. Major annual events: Fall Festival, Spring Fling, Commencement. Student services: personal-psychological counseling. Campus security: 24-hour emergency response devices and patrols, late night transport-escort service. College housing not available. LSC-CyFair Library with an OPAC and a Web page.

■ **LONE STAR COLLEGE–KINGWOOD**

20000 Kingwood Dr.
Kingwood, TX 77339-3801
Tel: (281)312-1600
Fax: (281)312-1477
E-mail: kingwoodadvising@lonestar.edu
Web Site: www.lonestar.edu/kingwood.htm

Description: State and locally supported, 2-year, coed. Part of Lone Star College System. Awards certificates, transfer associate, and terminal associate degrees. Founded 1984. Setting: 264-acre suburban campus with easy access to Houston. Total enrollment: 11,947. Faculty: 625 (130 full-time, 495 part-time). Student-undergrad faculty ratio is 23:1. 1,481 applied, 100% were admitted. Full-time: 4,147 students, 62% women, 38% men. Part-time: 7,800 students, 66% women, 34% men. Students come from 35 other countries, 0% from out-of-state. 0.4% American Indian or Alaska Native, non-Hispanic/Latino; 24% Hispanic/Latino; 17% African American, non-Hispanic/Latino; 3% Asian, non-Hispanic/Latino; 0% international. 41% 25 or older. Core. Calendar: semesters. Academic remediation for entering students, ESL program, services for LD students, advanced placement, accelerated degree program, honors program, independent study, distance learning, double major, summer session for credit, part-time degree program, adult/continuing education programs, co-op programs and internships. Study abroad program.

Entrance Requirements: Open admission. Options: electronic application, early admission. Entrance: noncompetitive. Application deadline: Rolling.

Costs Per Year: Application fee: $0. Area resident tuition: $960 full-time, $480 per year part-time. State resident tuition: $2640 full-time, $1320 per year part-time. Nonresident tuition: $3000 full-time, $1500 per year part-time. Mandatory fees: $448 full-time, $192 per year part-time, $64 per year part-time.

Collegiate Environment: Orientation program. Drama-theater group, choral group. Major annual events: Fall Festival, Spring Fling, Commencement. Student services: personal-psychological counseling. Campus security: 24-hour emergency response devices and patrols, late night transport-escort service. College housing not available. LSC-Kingwood Library with an OPAC and a Web page.

■ **LONE STAR COLLEGE–MONTGOMERY**

3200 College Park Dr.
Conroe, TX 77384
Tel: (936)273-7000
Fax: (936)273-7234
E-mail: mc.advising@lonestar.edu
Web Site: www.lonestar.edu/montgomery

Description: State and locally supported, 2-year, coed. Part of Lone Star College System. Awards certificates, transfer associate, and terminal associate degrees. Founded 1995. Setting: suburban campus with easy access to Houston. Total enrollment: 13,250. Faculty: 700 (156 full-time, 544 part-time). Student-undergrad faculty ratio is 24:1. 1,965 applied, 100% were admitted. Full-time: 4,655 students, 59% women, 41% men. Part-time: 8,595 students, 65% women, 35% men. Students come from 56 other countries, 0% from out-of-state. 0.5% American Indian or Alaska Native, non-Hispanic/Latino; 24% Hispanic/Latino; 12% African American, non-Hispanic/Latino; 4% Asian, non-Hispanic/Latino; 0% international. 39% 25 or older. Core. Calendar: semesters. Academic remediation for entering students, ESL program, services for LD students, advanced placement, honors program, independent study, distance learning, double major, summer session for credit, part-time degree program, adult/continuing education programs, co-op programs and internships. Study abroad program.

Entrance Requirements: Open admission. Options: electronic application, early admission. Entrance: noncompetitive. Application deadline: Rolling. Transfer credits accepted: Yes.

Costs Per Year: Area resident tuition: $960 full-time, $480 per year part-time. State resident tuition: $2640 full-time, $1320 per year part-time. Nonresident tuition: $3000 full-time, $1500 per year part-time. Mandatory fees: $448 full-time, $192 per year part-time, $64 per year part-time.

Collegiate Environment: Orientation program. Drama-theater group, choral group, student-run newspaper. Most popular organizations: Campus Crusade for Christ, Criminal Justice Club, Phi Theta Kappa, Latino-American Student Association, African-American Cultural Awareness. Major annual events: Career Day, College/University Transfer Day. Student services: personal-psychological counseling. Campus security: 24-hour emergency response devices and patrols, late night transport-escort service. College housing not available. LSC-Montgomery Library with an OPAC and a Web page.

■ **LONE STAR COLLEGE–NORTH HARRIS**

2700 W W Thorne Dr.
Houston, TX 77073-3499
Tel: (281)618-5400
E-mail: nhcounselor@lonestar.edu
Web Site: www.lonestar.edu/northharris

Description: State and locally supported, 2-year, coed. Part of Lone Star College System. Awards certificates, transfer associate, and terminal associate degrees. Founded 1972. Setting: suburban campus with easy access to Houston. Total enrollment: 18,756. Faculty: 998 (214 full-time, 784 part-time). Student-undergrad faculty ratio is 23:1. 2,696 applied, 100% were admitted. Full-time: 5,800 students, 61% women, 40% men. Part-time: 12,956 students, 64% women, 36% men. Students come from 46 other countries, 0% from out-of-state. 0.2% American Indian or Alaska Native, non-Hispanic/Latino; 35% Hispanic/Latino; 32% African American, non-Hispanic/Latino; 5% Asian, non-Hispanic/Latino. 43% 25 or older. Core. Calendar: semesters. Academic remediation for entering students, ESL program, services for LD students, advanced placement, honors program, independent study, distance learning, double major, summer session for credit, part-time degree program, adult/continuing education programs, co-op programs and internships. Study abroad program.

Entrance Requirements: Open admission except for nursing, respiratory therapy programs. Options: electronic application, early admission. Entrance: noncompetitive. Application deadline: Rolling. Transfer credits accepted: Yes.

Costs Per Year: Application fee: $0. Area resident tuition: $960 full-time, $480 per year part-time. State resident tuition: $2640 full-time, $1320 per year part-time. Nonresident tuition: $3000 full-time, $1320 per year part-time. Mandatory fees: $448 full-time, $192 per year part-time, $64 per year part-time.

Collegiate Environment: Orientation program. Drama-theater group, choral group, student-run newspaper. Social organizations: 33 open to all; local fraternities. Most popular organizations: Student Government Association, Phi Theta Kappa, Ambassadors, honors student organizations, Soccer Club. Major annual events: Fall Festival, Cajun Fest, Spring Fling/Health Fair. Student services: personal-psychological counseling, women's center. Campus security: 24-hour emergency response devices and patrols, late night transport-escort service. LSC-North Harris Library with an OPAC and a Web page.

■ **LONE STAR COLLEGE–TOMBALL**

30555 Tomball Pky.
Tomball, TX 77375-4036
Tel: (281)351-3300
Fax: (281)351-3384
E-mail: tcinfo@lonestar.edu
Web Site: www.lonestar.edu/tomball

Description: State and locally supported, 2-year, coed. Part of Lone Star College System. Awards certificates, transfer associate, and terminal associate degrees. Founded 1988. Setting: suburban campus with easy access to Houston. Total enrollment: 9,454. Faculty: 540 (115 full-time, 425 part-time). Student-undergrad faculty ratio is 18:1. 1,115 applied, 100% were admitted. Full-time: 3,024 students, 61% women, 39% men. Part-time: 6,430 students, 64% women, 36% men. Students come from 30 other countries, 0% from out-of-state. 0.4% American Indian or Alaska Native, non-Hispanic/Latino; 21% Hispanic/Latino; 13% African American, non-Hispanic/Latino; 5% Asian, non-Hispanic/Latino; 0% international. 37% 25 or older. Core. Calendar:

semesters. Academic remediation for entering students, ESL program, services for LD students, advanced placement, honors program, independent study, distance learning, double major, summer session for credit, part-time degree program, adult/continuing education programs, co-op programs and internships. Study abroad program.

Entrance Requirements: Open admission. Options: electronic application, early admission. Entrance: noncompetitive. Application deadline: Rolling. Transfer credits accepted: Yes.

Costs Per Year: Application fee: $0. Area resident tuition: $960 full-time. State resident tuition: $1320 full-time. Nonresident tuition: $1500 full-time. Mandatory fees: $448 full-time, $192 per year part-time, $64 per year part-time. Full-time tuition and fees vary according to program. Part-time fees vary according to program.

Collegiate Environment: Orientation program. Drama-theater group, choral group, student-run newspaper. Most popular organizations: Phi Theta Kappa, Occupational Therapy OTA, Veterinary Technicians Student Organization, STARS, Student Nurses Association. Major annual events: Spring Fling, Winter Wonderland, Fall Festival. Student services: personal-psychological counseling. Campus security: 24-hour emergency response devices and patrols, late night transport-escort service, trained security personnel during open hours. College housing not available. LSC-Tomball Community Library with an OPAC and a Web page.

■ LUBBOCK CHRISTIAN UNIVERSITY

5601 19th St.
Lubbock, TX 79407-2099
Tel: (806)796-8800; Free: 800-933-7601
Fax: (806)796-8917
E-mail: admissions@lcu.edu
Web Site: www.lcu.edu/

Description: Independent, comprehensive, coed, affiliated with Church of Christ. Awards bachelor's and master's degrees. Founded 1957. Setting: 120-acre suburban campus. Endowment: $12.7 million. Educational spending for the previous fiscal year: $5942 per student. Total enrollment: 2,135. Faculty: 187 (95 full-time, 92 part-time). Student-undergrad faculty ratio is 13:1. 979 applied, 93% were admitted. 12% from top 10% of their high school class, 40% from top quarter, 72% from top half. Full-time: 1,334 students, 59% women, 41% men. Part-time: 306 students, 64% women, 36% men. Students come from 28 states and territories, 20 other countries, 11% from out-of-state. 1% American Indian or Alaska Native, non-Hispanic/Latino; 22% Hispanic/Latino; 7% African American, non-Hispanic/Latino; 0.3% Asian, non-Hispanic/Latino; 0.4% Native Hawaiian or other Pacific Islander, non-Hispanic/Latino; 2% international. 22% 25 or older, 65% live on campus, 13% transferred in. Retention: 65% of full-time freshmen returned the following year. Academic areas with the most degrees conferred: health professions and related sciences; business/marketing; education. Core. Calendar: semesters. Academic remediation for entering students, ESL program, services for LD students, advanced placement, honors program, distance learning, double major, summer session for credit, part-time degree program, adult/continuing education programs, internships, graduate courses open to undergrads. Study abroad program. ROTC: Army (c), Air Force (c).

Entrance Requirements: Option: electronic application. Required: high school transcript, SAT or ACT. Entrance: moderately difficult. Application deadline: 8/1. Notification: continuous. SAT Reasoning Test deadline: 8/15. Transfer credits accepted: Yes.

Costs Per Year: Application fee: $25. Comprehensive fee: $24,434 includes full-time tuition ($16,350), mandatory fees ($1410), and college room and board ($6674). Full-time tuition and fees vary according to degree level and program. Room and board charges vary according to board plan and housing facility. Part-time tuition: $525 per semester hour. Part-time mandatory fees: $540 per term. Part-time tuition and fees vary according to course load, degree level, and program.

Collegiate Environment: Orientation program. Drama-theater group, choral group, student-run newspaper. Social organizations: 23 open to all; local fraternities, local sororities; 15% of eligible men and 13% of eligible women are members. Major annual events: Masterfollies, Homecoming, Spiritual Development Week. Student services: health clinic, personal-psychological counseling. Campus security: 24-hour patrols. 802 college housing spaces available; 572 were occupied in 2012-13. Freshmen guaranteed college housing. On-campus residence required through sophomore year. Options: men-only, women-only housing available. University Library with 128,890 books, 2,250 microform titles, 416 serials, 254 audiovisual materials, an OPAC, and a Web page. Operations spending for the previous fiscal year:

$704,789. 169 computers available on campus for general student use. A campuswide network can be accessed from student residence rooms and from off campus. Students can access the following: online class registration. Staffed computer lab on campus provides training in use of computers, software, and the Internet.

Community Environment: Population 209,737. The industrial, agricultural and educational center of the South Plains of Texas, Lubbock is the third largest inland cotton market in the Nation. There are also many oil wells in the community. This metropolitan center is called"The Hub of the Plains." The climate is mild and arid. Community service facilities include over 200 churches, county libraries, hospitals, a planetarium, museum, and municipal auditorium. There are four TV stations, seven radio stations, four golf courses, movie theaters, drive-ins, hunting, water skiing, horseback riding, and many other forms of recreation available in the area. Part-time employment is available. The city is served by railroad, airlines, and a bus line.

■ MCLENNAN COMMUNITY COLLEGE

1400 College Dr.
Waco, TX 76708-1499
Tel: (254)299-8622
E-mail: vjefferson@mclennan.edu
Web Site: www.mclennan.edu/

Description: County-supported, 2-year, coed. Awards certificates, transfer associate, and terminal associate degrees. Founded 1965. Setting: 200-acre urban campus. Total enrollment: 7,794. Faculty: 389. 2,362 applied, 100% were admitted. Full-time: 3,467 students, 63% women, 37% men. Part-time: 4,327 students, 70% women, 30% men. 2% from out-of-state. 45% 25 or older. Core. Calendar: semesters. Academic remediation for entering students, services for LD students, advanced placement, honors program, distance learning, summer session for credit, part-time degree program, adult/continuing education programs, co-op programs and internships. Off campus study at Baylor University. Study abroad program. ROTC: Air Force (c).

Entrance Requirements: Open admission except for health careers programs. Option: early admission. Required: high school transcript, THEA. Entrance: noncompetitive. Application deadline: Rolling. Notification: continuous until 9/2.

Collegiate Environment: Orientation program. Drama-theater group, choral group, student-run newspaper. Major annual event: Highland Games. Student services: personal-psychological counseling. Campus security: 24-hour emergency response devices and patrols. McLennan Community College Library with 93,000 books, 130,000 microform titles, 400 serials, an OPAC, and a Web page. 425 computers available on campus for general student use. A campuswide network can be accessed from off-campus. Staffed computer lab on campus.

Community Environment: See Baylor University.

■ MCMURRY UNIVERSITY

S 14th and Sayles
Abilene, TX 79697
Tel: (325)793-3800; Free: 800-460-2392
Fax: (325)691-6599
E-mail: admissions@mcm.edu
Web Site: www.mcm.edu/

Description: Independent United Methodist, comprehensive, coed. Awards bachelor's and master's degrees. Founded 1923. Setting: 43-acre suburban campus. Endowment: $61.4 million. Educational spending for the previous fiscal year: $8169 per student. Total enrollment: 1,368. Faculty: 126 (80 full-time, 46 part-time). Student-undergrad faculty ratio is 13:1. 1,568 applied, 55% were admitted. 11% from top 10% of their high school class, 34% from top quarter, 69% from top half. Full-time: 1,151 students, 49% women, 51% men. Part-time: 214 students, 43% women, 57% men. Students come from 27 states and territories, 11 other countries, 6% from out-of-state. 1% American Indian or Alaska Native, non-Hispanic/Latino; 18% Hispanic/Latino; 15% African American, non-Hispanic/Latino; 1% Asian, non-Hispanic/Latino; 0.2% Native Hawaiian or other Pacific Islander, non-Hispanic/Latino; 2% international. 17% 25 or older, 47% live on campus, 13% transferred in. Retention: 60% of full-time freshmen returned the following year. Academic areas with the most degrees conferred: business/marketing; education; social sciences. Core. Calendar: semesters plus May term. Academic remediation for entering students, services for LD students, advanced placement, accelerated degree program, self-designed majors, honors program, independent study, double major, summer session for credit, part-time degree program, adult/continuing education programs, internships. Study abroad program.

Entrance Requirements: Options: electronic application, deferred admission, international baccalaureate accepted. Required: essay, high school transcript, minimum 2 high school GPA, Official ACT or SAT score report, SAT or ACT. Required for some: 3 recommendations, interview. Entrance: moderately difficult. Application deadlines: 8/15, 8/5 for nonresidents. Notification: continuous, continuous for nonresidents. SAT Reasoning Test deadline: 8/15. Transfer credits accepted: Yes.

Costs Per Year: Application fee: $25. One-time mandatory fee: $175. Comprehensive fee: $30,765 includes full-time tuition ($23,305) and college room and board ($7460). College room only: $3636. Full-time tuition varies according to course load. Room and board charges vary according to board plan and housing facility. Part-time tuition: $728 per credit hour. Part-time tuition varies according to course load.

Collegiate Environment: Orientation program. Drama-theater group, choral group, marching band, student-run newspaper. Social organizations: 20 open to all; local fraternities, local sororities; 16% of eligible men and 19% of eligible women are members. Most popular organizations: Alpha Phi Omega, Religious Life Council, McMurry Student Government, Campus Activity Board, Servant Leadership. Major annual events: Homecoming, Spring Thing, Spring McMadness. Student services: health clinic, personal-psychological counseling. Campus security: 24-hour emergency response devices and patrols, late night transport-escort service, controlled dormitory access. 659 college housing spaces available; 604 were occupied in 2012-13. Freshmen guaranteed college housing. On-campus residence required through junior year. Options: coed, men-only, women-only housing available. Jay-Rollins Library with 249,273 books, 4,473 microform titles, 551 serials, 799 audiovisual materials, an OPAC, and a Web page. Operations spending for the previous fiscal year: $341,092. 130 computers available on campus for general student use. Computer purchase/lease plans available. A computer is required for all students. A campuswide network can be accessed from student residence rooms and from off campus. Students can access the following: online class registration, Moodle. Staffed computer lab on campus provides training in use of computers and software.

■ **MESSENGER COLLEGE**
PO Box 1207
Euless, TX 76039
Free: 800-385-8940
E-mail: info@messengercollege.edu
Web Site: www.messengercollege.edu/

Description: Independent Pentecostal, 4-year, coed. Awards associate and bachelor's degrees. Founded 1987. Setting: 16-acre suburban campus with easy access to Springfield. Endowment: $319,026. Educational spending for the previous fiscal year: $1026 per student. Total enrollment: 70. Faculty: 14 (6 full-time, 8 part-time). 13 applied, 77% were admitted. 5 valedictorians, 5 student government officers. Full-time: 58 students, 55% women, 45% men. Part-time: 12 students, 25% women, 75% men. 23% 25 or older, 23% transferred in. Retention: 77% of full-time freshmen returned the following year. Core. Calendar: semesters. Academic remediation for entering students, honors program, independent study, distance learning, double major, part-time degree program, external degree program, co-op programs and internships.

Entrance Requirements: Option: electronic application. Required: essay, high school transcript, minimum 2.0 high school GPA, 3 recommendations, health form, SAT or ACT. Required for some: interview. Entrance: moderately difficult. Application deadline: 8/14. Notification: 8/25.

Collegiate Environment: Orientation program. Choral group. Student services: personal-psychological counseling. Campus security: 24-hour emergency response devices, student patrols. McDole-McDonald Library with 36,278 books, 114 serials, and an OPAC. Operations spending for the previous fiscal year: $38,864. 5 computers available on campus for general student use. A campuswide network can be accessed from student residence rooms. Staffed computer lab on campus provides training in use of computers and software.

■ **MIDLAND COLLEGE**
3600 N Garfield
Midland, TX 79705-6399
Tel: (432)685-4500
Fax: (432)685-4714
E-mail: jmartinez@midland.edu
Web Site: www.midland.edu/

Description: State and locally supported, 4-year, coed. Awards associate and bachelor's degrees. Founded 1969. Setting: 163-acre suburban campus. Endowment: $34.7 million. Educational spending for the previous fiscal year: $6525 per student. Total enrollment: 5,530. Faculty: 271 (135 full-time, 136 part-time). Student-undergrad faculty ratio is 16:1. Full-time: 1,627 students, 61% women, 39% men. Part-time: 3,903 students, 60% women, 40% men. Students come from 28 states and territories, 39 other countries, 2% from out-of-state. 0.3% American Indian or Alaska Native, non-Hispanic/Latino; 44% Hispanic/Latino; 7% African American, non-Hispanic/Latino; 1% Asian, non-Hispanic/Latino; 0.1% Native Hawaiian or other Pacific Islander, non-Hispanic/Latino; 0.1% international. 4% transferred in. Retention: 0% of full-time freshmen returned the following year. Academic area with the most degrees conferred: business/marketing. Core. Calendar: semesters. Academic remediation for entering students, services for LD students, advanced placement, honors program, distance learning, summer session for credit, adult/continuing education programs.

Entrance Requirements: Open admission except for nursing, respiratory therapy, radiological technology programs. Required: high school transcript. Entrance: noncompetitive. Application deadlines: Rolling, Rolling for nonresidents. Notification: continuous, continuous for nonresidents. Transfer credits accepted: Yes.

Costs Per Year: Application fee: $0. Area resident tuition: $2160 full-time. State resident tuition: $3450 full-time. Nonresident tuition: $4620 full-time. Full-time tuition varies according to course level, course load, degree level, program, and reciprocity agreements. College room and board: $4650. College room only: $2200.

Collegiate Environment: Orientation program. Drama-theater group, choral group, student-run newspaper. Social organizations: 20 open to all; Student Organized clubs with Faculty Sponsor; 20% of eligible men and 80% of eligible women are members. Most popular organizations: OIKOS, Midland College Latin American Student Society, Student Government Association, Student Nurses Association, Baptist Student Ministries. Major annual events: Homecoming Night, Chappapalooza, Club Fair. Student services: personal-psychological counseling. Campus security: 24-hour patrols, controlled dormitory access. 300 college housing spaces available; 225 were occupied in 2012-13. No special consideration for freshman housing applicants. Options: coed, men-only, women-only housing available. Murray Fasken Learning Resource Center with 65,760 books, 91,046 microform titles, 300 serials, 359 audiovisual materials, an OPAC, and a Web page. Operations spending for the previous fiscal year: $481,425. 950 computers available on campus for general student use. A campuswide network can be accessed from student residence rooms and from off campus. Students can access the following: online class registration. Staffed computer lab on campus provides training in use of computers, software, and the Internet.

■ **MIDWESTERN STATE UNIVERSITY**
3410 Taft Blvd.
Wichita Falls, TX 76308
Tel: (940)397-4000; Free: 800-842-1922
Fax: (940)397-4302
E-mail: admissions@mwsu.edu
Web Site: www.mwsu.edu/

Description: State-supported, comprehensive, coed. Awards associate, bachelor's, and master's degrees. Founded 1922. Setting: 255-acre urban campus. Total enrollment: 5,916. Faculty: 342 (224 full-time, 118 part-time). Student-undergrad faculty ratio is 17:1. 2,090 applied, 75% were admitted. 12% from top 10% of their high school class, 28% from top quarter, 74% from top half. 20 valedictorians. Full-time: 3,823 students, 57% women, 43% men. Part-time: 1,415 students, 59% women, 41% men. Students come from 26 states and territories, 51 other countries, 8% from out-of-state. 1% American Indian or Alaska Native, non-Hispanic/Latino; 13% Hispanic/Latino; 13% African American, non-Hispanic/Latino; 3% Asian, non-Hispanic/Latino; 0.3% Native Hawaiian or other Pacific Islander, non-Hispanic/Latino; 7% international. 29% 25 or older, 23% live on campus, 11% transferred in. Retention: 71% of full-time freshmen returned the following year. Academic areas with the most degrees conferred: health professions and related sciences; business/marketing; interdisciplinary studies. Core. Calendar: semesters. Academic remediation for entering students, ESL program, services for LD students, advanced placement, honors program, independent study, distance learning, double major, summer session for credit, part-time degree program, adult/continuing education programs, internships, graduate courses open to undergrads. Study abroad program. ROTC: Air Force (c).

Entrance Requirements: Options: electronic application, early action. Required: essay, high school transcript, SAT or ACT. Entrance: moderately difficult. Application deadline: 8/7. Notification: continuous. SAT Reasoning Test deadline: 8/7. SAT Subject Test deadline: 8/7. Transfer credits accepted: Yes.

Costs Per Year: Application fee: $25. Area resident tuition: $4845 full-time. State resident tuition: $4548 full-time, $161.50 per credit part-time. Nonresident tuition: $6795 full-time, $226.50 per credit part-time. Mandatory fees: $2393 full-time, $68.50 per credit part-time, $199 per term part-time. Full-time tuition and fees vary according to course load, location, and program. Part-time tuition and fees vary according to course load, location, and program. College room and board: $6350. College room only: $3350. Room and board charges vary according to board plan and housing facility.

Collegiate Environment: Orientation program. Drama-theater group, choral group, marching band, student-run newspaper. Social organizations: 75 open to all; national fraternities, national sororities; 4% of eligible men and 6% of eligible women are members. Most popular organizations: Caribbean Students Organization, Baptist Student Ministry, Catholic Campus Ministry, African Students Organization, University Programming Board. Major annual events: Homecoming, Welcome Week, Family Day. Student services: legal services, health clinic, personal-psychological counseling. Campus security: 24-hour emergency response devices and patrols, controlled dormitory access. 1,364 college housing spaces available; 1,297 were occupied in 2012-13. Freshmen given priority for college housing. On-campus residence required through sophomore year. Options: coed, men-only, women-only housing available. Moffett Library with 462,657 books, 219,063 microform titles, 884 serials, 10,476 audiovisual materials, an OPAC, and a Web page. 405 computers available on campus for general student use. A campuswide network can be accessed from student residence rooms and from off campus. Students can access the following: online class registration. Staffed computer lab on campus (open 24 hours a day) provides training in use of computers, software, and the Internet.

Community Environment: Population 100,000. A distributing point for both southern Oklahoma and northwestern Texas, Wichita Falls is one of the important trade centers of the Southwest. The community has a library, museum, two hospitals, 3 YMCA's and YWCA. Various civic, fraternal and veteran's organizations serve the city. Part-time employment is available. Local recreational facilities include theatres, nightclubs, bowling, skating, boating, fishing, municipal golf course, and two country club golf courses.

■ MOUNTAIN VIEW COLLEGE

4849 W Illinois Ave.
Dallas, TX 75211-6599
Tel: (214)860-8600
Fax: (214)860-8570
E-mail: ghall@dcccd.edu
Web Site: www.mountainviewcollege.edu/

Description: State and locally supported, 2-year, coed. Part of Dallas County Community College District System. Awards certificates, transfer associate, and terminal associate degrees. Founded 1970. Setting: 200-acre urban campus. Total enrollment: 8,463. Faculty: 377 (77 full-time, 300 part-time). Student-undergrad faculty ratio is 27:1. 0% from out-of-state. 0.4% American Indian or Alaska Native, non-Hispanic/Latino; 50% Hispanic/Latino; 27% African American, non-Hispanic/Latino; 5% Asian, non-Hispanic/Latino; 0.3% international. 37% 25 or older. Retention: 45% of full-time freshmen returned the following year. Core. Calendar: semesters. Academic remediation for entering students, ESL program, services for LD students, advanced placement, freshman honors college, honors program, independent study, distance learning, double major, summer session for credit, part-time degree program, external degree program, adult/continuing education programs, co-op programs and internships.

Entrance Requirements: Open admission. Options: electronic application, early admission, deferred admission. Required: high school transcript. Entrance: noncompetitive. Application deadline: Rolling. Notification: continuous.

Collegiate Environment: Orientation program. Drama-theater group, choral group. Student services: health clinic, personal-psychological counseling. Campus security: 24-hour patrols, late night transport-escort service.

Community Environment: See University of Texas at Dallas.

■ NAVARRO COLLEGE

3200 W 7th Ave.
Corsicana, TX 75110-4899
Tel: (903)874-6501; Free: 800-628-2776
E-mail: david.edwards@navarrocollege.edu
Web Site: www.navarrocollege.edu/

Description: State and locally supported, 2-year, coed. Awards certificates, diplomas, transfer associate, and terminal associate degrees. Founded 1946. Setting: 275-acre small town campus with easy access to Dallas-Fort Worth. Total enrollment: 4,411. Faculty: 380 (99 full-time, 281 part-time). 4,411 applied, 100% were admitted. 10% from top 10% of their high school class, 40% from top half. Full-time: 2,516 students, 51% women, 49% men. Part-time: 1,895 students, 66% women, 34% men. Students come from 22 states and territories, 30 other countries. 35% 25 or older, 25% live on campus. Retention: 100% of full-time freshmen returned the following year. Core. Calendar: semesters. Academic remediation for entering students, services for LD students, advanced placement, self-designed majors, honors program, summer session for credit, part-time degree program, adult/continuing education programs, co-op programs.

Entrance Requirements: Open admission. Option: early admission. Required: high school transcript. Entrance: noncompetitive.

Collegiate Environment: Drama-theater group, choral group, marching band. Social organizations: 35 open to all; local sororities. Most popular organizations: Student Government Association, Phi Theta Kappa, Ebony Club, Que Pasa. Major annual events: Homecoming, Bulldog Bash, Mr. NC contest. Student services: personal-psychological counseling. Campus security: 24-hour patrols. Richard M. Sanchez Library with 40,000 books and 250 serials. 80 computers available on campus for general student use. Staffed computer lab on campus.

Community Environment: Navarro College is located in historic Corsicana, Texas. The economy is diversified and part-time jobs are available for students. The local climate is moderate to mild. The area is served by bus and major highways. There are several churches, a library, YMCA, and outstanding medical facilities. Residents can enjoy restaurants, shopping, and local fine arts events as well as excellent recreational facilities for boating, water skiing, fishing, golf, and hunting. Annual events include rodeo finals, bicycle races, and food festivals.

■ NORTH AMERICAN COLLEGE

3203 N Sam Houston Pky. W
Houston, TX 77038
Tel: (832)230-5555
Web Site: www.northamerican.edu/

Description: Independent, 4-year, coed. Calendar: semesters.

■ NORTH CENTRAL TEXAS COLLEGE

1525 W California St.
Gainesville, TX 76240-4699
Tel: (940)668-7731
Fax: (940)668-6049
E-mail: mcarroll@nctc.edu
Web Site: www.nctc.edu/

Description: State and locally supported, 2-year, coed. Awards certificates, diplomas, transfer associate, and terminal associate degrees. Founded 1924. Setting: 132-acre suburban campus with easy access to Dallas-Fort Worth. Endowment: $4.3 million. Research spending for the previous fiscal year: $87,984. Educational spending for the previous fiscal year: $2051 per student. Total enrollment: 9,156. Faculty: 395 (123 full-time, 272 part-time). Student-undergrad faculty ratio is 25:1. 1,964 applied, 100% were admitted. Students come from 14 states and territories, 21 other countries, 5% from out-of-state. 33% 25 or older, 1% live on campus. Retention: 68% of full-time freshmen returned the following year. Core. Calendar: semesters. Academic remediation for entering students, services for LD students, advanced placement, distance learning, summer session for credit, part-time degree program, adult/continuing education programs, co-op programs and internships. ROTC: Army (c).

Entrance Requirements: Open admission except for allied health, legal assistant, equine technology, occupational therapy assistant programs. Options: electronic application, early admission, international baccalaureate accepted. Required: high school transcript. Entrance: noncompetitive. Application deadlines: Rolling, Rolling for nonresidents. Transfer credits accepted: Yes.

Collegiate Environment: Orientation program. Drama-theater group, choral group. Social organizations: 15 open to all. Most popular organizations: Student Nursing Association, Residence Hall Association, Cosmetology Student Association, Student Government Association - Gainesville, Gainesville Program Council. Major annual events: Welcome Back Party, NCTC's Got Talent. Student services: personal-psychological counseling. Campus security: late night transport-escort service, controlled dormitory access, cameras added to campus. North Central Texas College Library plus 1 other with 44,861 books, 273 serials, and an OPAC. Operations spending for the previous fiscal year: $426,946. 60 computers available on campus for general student use. A campuswide network can be accessed from off-campus. Staffed computer lab on campus.

Community Environment: Population 16,500. Gainesville is a rural community that enjoys a temperate climate. The area is reached by bus lines. There is a public library, churches of major denominations, a local hospital, and over 80 civic, fraternal and veteran's organizations in the city. Part-time employment is limited. Local recreation includes boating, tennis, fishing, and golf.

■ **NORTH LAKE COLLEGE**

5001 N MacArthur Blvd.

Irving, TX 75038-3899

Tel: (972)273-3000

Web Site: www.northlakecollege.edu/

Description: County-supported, 2-year, coed. Part of Dallas County Community College District System. Awards certificates, transfer associate, and terminal associate degrees. Founded 1977. Setting: 250-acre suburban campus with easy access to Dallas-Fort Worth. Research spending for the previous fiscal year: $1465. Total enrollment: 10,174. Faculty: 504 (95 full-time, 409 part-time). Student-undergrad faculty ratio is 21:1. Full-time: 3,171 students, 47% women, 53% men. Part-time: 7,003 students, 57% women, 43% men. Students come from 18 states and territories, 23 other countries, 9% from out-of-state. 38% 25 or older, 8% transferred in. Retention: 55% of full-time freshmen returned the following year. Core. Calendar: semesters. Academic remediation for entering students, ESL program, services for LD students, advanced placement, accelerated degree program, independent study, distance learning, double major, summer session for credit, part-time degree program, external degree program, adult/continuing education programs, co-op programs and internships. Off campus study. Study abroad program.

Entrance Requirements: Open admission. Options: electronic application, early admission. Recommended: high school transcript. Entrance: noncompetitive. Application deadline: Rolling. Notification: continuous. Transfer credits accepted: Yes.

Costs Per Year: Application fee: $0. Area resident tuition: $1350 full-time, $45 per credit hour part-time. State resident tuition: $2550 full-time, $83 per credit hour part-time. Nonresident tuition: $3960 full-time, $132 per credit hour part-time.

Collegiate Environment: Orientation program. Drama-theater group, choral group, student-run newspaper. Major annual events: International Day, Career Day. Student services: health clinic, personal-psychological counseling. Campus security: 24-hour emergency response devices, student patrols, late night transport-escort service. North Lake College Library plus 3 others with 35,000 books, 500 microform titles, 400 serials, 1,200 audiovisual materials, an OPAC, and a Web page. Operations spending for the previous fiscal year: $501,000. 250 computers available on campus for general student use. A campuswide network can be accessed. Students can access the following: online class registration. Staffed computer lab on campus provides training in use of computers, software, and the Internet.

■ **NORTHEAST TEXAS COMMUNITY COLLEGE**

PO Box 1307

Mount Pleasant, TX 75456-1307

Tel: (903)572-1911; Free: 800-870-0142

Fax: (903)572-6712

Web Site: www.ntcc.edu/

Description: State and locally supported, 2-year, coed. Awards certificates, transfer associate, and terminal associate degrees. Founded 1985. Setting: 175-acre rural campus. Total enrollment: 1,010. 17% 25 or older. Core. Calendar: semesters. Academic remediation for entering students, ESL program, services for LD students, advanced placement, independent study, distance learning, summer session for credit, part-time degree program, adult/continuing education programs, co-op programs.

Entrance Requirements: Open admission. Option: early admission. Required: high school transcript. Entrance: noncompetitive. Application deadline: Rolling.

Collegiate Environment: Orientation program. Drama-theater group, choral group, student-run newspaper. Student services: personal-psychological counseling, women's center. Campus security: 24-hour patrols. Learning Resource Center with 24,501 books and 325 serials.

■ **NORTHWEST VISTA COLLEGE**

3535 N Ellison Dr.

San Antonio, TX 78251

Tel: (210)348-2000

E-mail: elang@accd.edu

Web Site: www.alamo.edu/nvc/

Description: State and locally supported, 2-year, coed. Part of Alamo Community College District System. Awards transfer associate and terminal associate degrees. Founded 1995. Setting: 137-acre urban campus. Total enrollment: 8,519. Faculty: 497 (83 full-time, 414 part-time). Student-undergrad faculty ratio is 12:1. 74% 25 or older. Calendar: semesters. Academic remediation for entering students, ESL program, services for LD students, advanced placement, independent study, distance learning, double major, summer session for credit, part-time degree program, co-op programs and internships. Off campus study. Study abroad program.

Entrance Requirements: Required: high school transcript. Entrance: noncompetitive.

Collegiate Environment: Drama-theater group, student-run newspaper. Student services: health clinic, personal-psychological counseling. Campus security: 24-hour emergency response devices, student patrols, late night transport-escort service. Manzanillo Hall with a Web page.

■ **NORTHWOOD UNIVERSITY, TEXAS CAMPUS**

1114 W FM 1382

Cedar Hill, TX 75104-1204

Tel: (972)291-1541; Free: 800-927-9663

Fax: (972)291-3824

E-mail: txadmit@northwood.edu

Web Site: www.northwood.edu/

Description: Independent, comprehensive, coed. Administratively affiliated with Northwood University (MI). Awards bachelor's and master's degrees. Founded 1966. Setting: 360-acre small town campus with easy access to Dallas-Fort Worth. Total enrollment: 587. Faculty: 44 (20 full-time, 24 part-time). Student-undergrad faculty ratio is 19:1. 452 applied, 59% were admitted. 8% from top 10% of their high school class, 27% from top quarter, 65% from top half. Full-time: 521 students, 42% women, 58% men. Part-time: 13 students, 38% women, 62% men. Students come from 14 states and territories, 19 other countries, 6% from out-of-state. 1% American Indian or Alaska Native, non-Hispanic/Latino; 49% Hispanic/Latino; 23% African American, non-Hispanic/Latino; 3% Asian, non-Hispanic/Latino; 39% international. 7% 25 or older, 36% live on campus, 14% transferred in. Retention: 58% of full-time freshmen returned the following year. Academic areas with the most degrees conferred: business/marketing; parks and recreation. Core. Academic remediation for entering students, advanced placement, accelerated degree program, honors program, distance learning, double major, summer session for credit, part-time degree program, external degree program, adult/continuing education programs, internships. Off campus study. Study abroad program.

Entrance Requirements: Options: electronic application, early admission, deferred admission, international baccalaureate accepted. Required: essay, high school transcript, minimum 2 high school GPA, SAT or ACT. Recommended: 1 recommendation, interview. Entrance: moderately difficult. Application deadlines: 8/1, 8/1 for nonresidents. Notification: continuous, continuous for nonresidents. SAT Reasoning Test deadline: 8/1. Transfer credits accepted: Yes.

Costs Per Year: Application fee: $25. Comprehensive fee: $30,103 includes full-time tuition ($20,040), mandatory fees ($956), and college room and board ($9107). College room only: $4907. Room and board charges vary according to board plan. Part-time tuition: $776 per semester hour.

Collegiate Environment: Orientation program. Drama-theater group, choral group, student-run newspaper. Social organizations: local fraternities, local sororities; 3% of eligible men and 3% of eligible women are members. Most popular organizations: Association of Entertainment and Sports Management, In-Line Hockey Club, Alpha Nu Omega, Alpha Omega, Delta Epsilon Chi. Major annual events: Haunted Forest, International Fest, Sanity Inn. Student services: health clinic, personal-psychological counseling. Campus security: 24-hour emergency response devices and patrols, student patrols, late night transport-escort service, controlled dormitory access. 260 college housing spaces available; 124 were occupied in 2012-13. Freshmen guaranteed college housing. On-campus residence required in freshman year. Options: men-only, women-only housing available. 73 computers available on campus for general student use. A campuswide network can be accessed from student residence rooms and from off campus. Students can access the following: online class registration. Staffed computer lab on campus.

■ **ODESSA COLLEGE**
201 W University Ave.
Odessa, TX 79764-7127
Tel: (432)335-6400
Fax: (432)335-6860
E-mail: thilliard@odessa.edu
Web Site: www.odessa.edu/
Description: State and locally supported, 2-year, coed. Awards certificates, transfer associate, and terminal associate degrees. Founded 1946. Setting: 87-acre urban campus. Endowment: $813,199. Educational spending for the previous fiscal year: $4129 per student. Total enrollment: 5,132. Faculty: 236 (118 full-time, 118 part-time). Student-undergrad faculty ratio is 19:1. 344 applied, 100% were admitted. Students come from 20 states and territories, 2% from out-of-state. 41% 25 or older, 4% live on campus. Retention: 44% of full-time freshmen returned the following year. Core. Calendar: semesters. Academic remediation for entering students, services for LD students, advanced placement, independent study, distance learning, summer session for credit, part-time degree program, adult/continuing education programs, co-op programs and internships.
Entrance Requirements: Open admission except for allied health programs. Options: electronic application, early admission, deferred admission. Entrance: noncompetitive. Application deadline: Rolling. Notification: continuous.
Collegiate Environment: Choral group. Social organizations: 13 open to all. Most popular organizations: Baptist Student Union, Student Government Association, Rodeo Club, Physical Therapy Assistant Club, American Chemical Society. Major annual events: Back-to-School Picnic, Homecoming, Spring Fest. Student services: personal-psychological counseling. Campus security: 24-hour emergency response devices and patrols, late night transport-escort service, controlled dormitory access. Murry H. Fly Learning Resources Center with 123,000 books, 8,300 microform titles, 350 serials, 6,800 audiovisual materials, an OPAC, and a Web page. Operations spending for the previous fiscal year: $418,772. 300 computers available on campus for general student use. A campuswide network can be accessed from student residence rooms and from off campus. Staffed computer lab on campus.
Community Environment: Population of Odessa 93,500; of Midland 99,200. Odessa is one of the largest domestic oilfield supply centers in Texas. The community enjoys a mild climate. The city is reached by airlines, two bus lines, and railroad. Churches representing all denominations, two hospitals, a library, and many civic and fraternal organizations serve the area. Part-time employment is available. Local recreation includes theatres, bowling alleys, hunting, ice skating, and sports.

■ **OUR LADY OF THE LAKE UNIVERSITY OF SAN ANTONIO**
411 SW 24th St.
San Antonio, TX 78207-4689
Tel: (210)434-6711; Free: 800-436-6558
Fax: (210)436-0824
E-mail: admission@lake.ollusa.edu
Web Site: www.ollusa.edu/
Description: Independent Roman Catholic, comprehensive, coed. Awards bachelor's, master's, and doctoral degrees and post-master's certificates. Founded 1895. Setting: 75-acre urban campus. Total enrollment: 2,751. Faculty: 249 (101 full-time, 148 part-time). Student-undergrad faculty ratio is 15:1. 2,129 applied, 48% were admitted. 22% from top 10% of their high school class, 49% from top quarter, 18% from top half. Full-time: 1,278 students, 73% women, 27% men. Part-time: 310 students, 77% women, 23% men. 2% from out-of-state. 1% American Indian or Alaska Native, non-Hispanic/Latino; 63% Hispanic/Latino; 8% African American, non-Hispanic/Latino; 1% Asian, non-Hispanic/Latino; 0.4% Native Hawaiian or other Pacific Islander, non-Hispanic/Latino; 1% international. 37% 25 or older, 12% transferred in. Retention: 60% of full-time freshmen returned the following year. Academic areas with the most degrees conferred: business/marketing; psychology; education. Core. Calendar: semesters plus 2 summer sessions. Academic remediation for entering students, services for LD students, advanced placement, accelerated degree program, honors program, independent study, distance learning, double major, summer session for credit, part-time degree program, adult/continuing education programs, co-op programs and internships, graduate courses open to undergrads. Off campus study at United Colleges of San Antonio. Study abroad program. ROTC: Army (c), Air Force (c).
Entrance Requirements: Options: electronic application, deferred admission, international baccalaureate accepted. Required: high school transcript,

SAT or ACT. Required for some: interview. Entrance: moderately difficult. Application deadline: Rolling. Notification: continuous. SAT Reasoning Test deadline: 1/15. SAT Subject Test deadline: 8/15. Transfer credits accepted: Yes.
Collegiate Environment: Orientation program. Drama-theater group, choral group, student-run newspaper. Social organizations: 60 open to all; local sororities; 15% of eligible men and 35% of eligible women are members. Most popular organizations: Student Government Association, Leadership Institute for Freshman Excellence, Health Occupations Student of America, Epsilon Sigma Alpha Service Sorority, University Programming Council. Major annual events: Spirit Day, Candlelight. Student services: health clinic, personal-psychological counseling, women's center. Campus security: 24-hour emergency response devices and patrols, late night transport-escort service, controlled dormitory access. The Sueltenfuss Library with 93,551 books, 1,000 microform titles, 600 serials, 7,140 audiovisual materials, an OPAC, and a Web page. 230 computers available on campus for general student use. A campuswide network can be accessed from student residence rooms and from off campus. Students can access the following: online class registration. Staffed computer lab on campus (open 24 hours a day).
Community Environment: See San Antonio College.

■ **PALO ALTO COLLEGE**
1400 W Villaret
San Antonio, TX 78224-2499
Tel: (210)921-5000
E-mail: pacar@accd.edu
Web Site: www.alamo.edu/pac/
Description: State and locally supported, 2-year, coed. Part of Alamo Community College District System. Awards certificates, transfer associate, and terminal associate degrees. Founded 1987. Setting: urban campus. Total enrollment: 8,021. Faculty: 475 (197 full-time, 278 part-time). Student-undergrad faculty ratio is 19:1. 1,163 applied, 100% were admitted. Students come from 50 states and territories, 1% from out-of-state. 31% 25 or older. Core. Calendar: semesters. Academic remediation for entering students, ESL program, summer session for credit, part-time degree program, adult/continuing education programs, co-op programs.
Entrance Requirements: Open admission. Option: early admission. Required: high school transcript. Entrance: noncompetitive. Application deadline: Rolling.
Collegiate Environment: Drama-theater group, student-run newspaper. Social organizations: 20 open to all. Most popular organizations: Catholic Campus Ministries, International Club, Veterinary Technician Association, Movimiento Estudiantil Chicano De Aztlan, Phi Theta Kappa. Major annual events: PACFest, PAChanga. Student services: health clinic, personal-psychological counseling. Campus security: 24-hour emergency response devices and patrols. Operations spending for the previous fiscal year: $1 million. 300 computers available on campus for general student use. A campuswide network can be accessed from off-campus. Staffed computer lab on campus.

■ **PANOLA COLLEGE**
1109 W Panola St.
Carthage, TX 75633-2397
Tel: (903)693-2000
E-mail: bsimpson@panola.edu
Web Site: www.panola.edu/
Description: State and locally supported, 2-year, coed. Awards certificates, transfer associate, and terminal associate degrees. Founded 1947. Setting: 35-acre small town campus. Endowment: $2.4 million. Research spending for the previous fiscal year: $3980. Total enrollment: 2,562. Faculty: 140 (64 full-time, 76 part-time). Student-undergrad faculty ratio is 19:1. Full-time: 1,134 students, 66% women, 34% men. Part-time: 1,428 students, 73% women, 27% men. Students come from 23 states and territories, 11 other countries, 8% from out-of-state. 1% American Indian or Alaska Native, non-Hispanic/Latino; 7% Hispanic/Latino; 22% African American, non-Hispanic/Latino; 1% Asian, non-Hispanic/Latino; 0% Native Hawaiian or other Pacific Islander, non-Hispanic/Latino; 1% international. 34% 25 or older, 8% live on campus, 12% transferred in. Retention: 39% of full-time freshmen returned the following year. Core. Calendar: semesters. Academic remediation for entering students, ESL program, services for LD students, advanced placement, distance learning, summer session for credit, part-time degree program, co-op programs.
Entrance Requirements: Open admission except for nursing, occupational

therapy assisting, vocational nursing programs. Options: electronic application, early admission. Recommended: high school transcript. Required for some: high school transcript. Entrance: noncompetitive. Application deadlines: Rolling, Rolling for nonresidents. Notification: continuous, continuous for nonresidents.

Costs Per Year: Area resident tuition: $750 full-time, $67 per semester hour part-time. State resident tuition: $1950 full-time, $107 per semester hour part-time. Nonresident tuition: $2790 full-time, $135 per semester hour part-time. Mandatory fees: $1260 full-time. College room and board: $4800.

Collegiate Environment: Orientation program. Drama-theater group, choral group, student-run newspaper. Social organizations: 25 open to all; honor fraternity and academic area fraternities; 4% of eligible men and 7% of eligible women are members. Most popular organizations: Student Government Organization, Student Occupational Therapy Assistant Club, Baptist Student Ministries, Texas Nursing Student Association, Phi Theta Kappa. Major annual events: Fall and Spring Health Fairs, Fall Frolic, Spring Fling. Campus security: controlled dormitory access. 213 college housing spaces available; all were occupied in 2012-13. No special consideration for freshman housing applicants. Option: coed housing available. M. P. Baker Library with 103,639 books, 293 microform titles, 31,932 serials, 4,870 audiovisual materials, an OPAC, and a Web page. Operations spending for the previous fiscal year: $420,026. 562 computers available on campus for general student use. A campuswide network can be accessed from student residence rooms and from off campus. Students can access the following: online class registration. Staffed computer lab on campus provides training in use of computers, software, and the Internet.

Community Environment: Population 6,611, Carthage is in a rural area with a temperate climate. The community is served by rail, bus, and U.S. Routes 59 and 79. Facilities include a public library, hospital, churches of eight denominations, theatres, a 35-mile lake shoreline for all water sports, a swimming pool, bowling alley, golf courses. Several rodeos and livestock shows are held annually. Part-time employment is somewhat limited.

■ **PARIS JUNIOR COLLEGE**
2400 Clarksville St.
Paris, TX 75460-6298
Tel: (903)785-7661; Free: 800-232-5804
E-mail: sreece@parisjc.edu
Web Site: www.parisjc.edu/

Description: State and locally supported, 2-year, coed. Awards certificates, diplomas, transfer associate, and terminal associate degrees. Founded 1924. Setting: 54-acre rural campus. Endowment: $14.8 million. Educational spending for the previous fiscal year: $3054 per student. Total enrollment: 5,513. Faculty: 250 (96 full-time, 154 part-time). Student-undergrad faculty ratio is 23:1. 1,072 applied, 100% were admitted. Full-time: 2,567 students, 57% women, 43% men. Part-time: 2,946 students, 63% women, 37% men. Students come from 22 states and territories, 7 other countries, 3% from out-of-state. 2% American Indian or Alaska Native, non-Hispanic/Latino; 10% Hispanic/Latino; 12% African American, non-Hispanic/Latino; 1% Asian, non-Hispanic/Latino; 0.1% Native Hawaiian or other Pacific Islander, non-Hispanic/Latino; 0.2% international. 31% 25 or older, 4% live on campus, 35% transferred in. Retention: 52% of full-time freshmen returned the following year. Core. Calendar: semesters. Academic remediation for entering students, ESL program, services for LD students, advanced placement, distance learning, summer session for credit, part-time degree program, adult/continuing education programs, co-op programs.

Entrance Requirements: Open admission except for allied health programs. Options: electronic application, early admission, international baccalaureate accepted. Required: high school transcript. Entrance: noncompetitive. Application deadlines: Rolling, Rolling for nonresidents. Transfer credits accepted: Yes.

Costs Per Year: Application fee: $0. Area resident tuition: $1740 full-time, $50 per credit hour part-time. State resident tuition: $2670 full-time, $81 per credit hour part-time. Nonresident tuition: $4080 full-time, $128 per credit hour part-time. Mandatory fees: $240 full-time. Full-time tuition and fees vary according to course load, location, and program. Part-time tuition varies according to course load, location, and program.

Collegiate Environment: Orientation program. Drama-theater group, choral group, student-run newspaper. Social organizations: Student Government, PTK, drama, student interest. Most popular organizations: Student Government Organization, Blends Club for all ethic groups. Major annual events: Homecoming, year-end cookout, weekly activities. Student services: personal-psychological counseling. Campus security: 24-hour emergency response devices and patrols, late night transport-escort service, controlled

dormitory access. 336 college housing spaces available; 237 were occupied in 2012-13. No special consideration for freshman housing applicants. Options: men-only, women-only housing available. Mike Rheudasil Learning Center with 38,150 books, 404 serials, and an OPAC. 82 computers available on campus for general student use. Students can access the following: online class registration. Staffed computer lab on campus provides training in use of computers, software, and the Internet.

Community Environment: Population 26,500, Paris, a farming and industrial center, has a modern attractiveness which is the result of planned reconstruction following a fire that swept the town in 1916. Today the local industries produce furniture, light bulb parts, clothing, and food items. Located in the heart of Red River Valley, the area has a mean annual temperature of 63.9 degrees. There are four rail lines, two bus lines, five main highways, and an airport approximately seven miles away to serve the community. A public library, theatres, two hospitals, and civic and fraternal organizations are active in the city. Local recreation includes the parks, bowling, golf, and nearby Pat Mayse Lake providing boating, swimming, and fishing.

■ **PAUL QUINN COLLEGE**
3837 Simpson-Stuart Rd.
Dallas, TX 75241-4331
Tel: (214)376-1000; Free: 877-346-1063
Fax: (214)302-3559
Web Site: www.pqc.edu/

Description: Independent African Methodist Episcopal, 4-year, coed. Awards bachelor's degrees. Founded 1872. Setting: 132-acre suburban campus. Endowment: $5.3 million. Educational spending for the previous fiscal year: $12,400 per student. Total enrollment: 193. Faculty: 17 (10 full-time, 7 part-time). Student-undergrad faculty ratio is 11:1. 305 applied, 96% were admitted. 0% from top 10% of their high school class, 16% from top quarter, 28% from top half. 7 student government officers. Full-time: 145 students, 51% women, 49% men. Part-time: 48 students, 56% women, 44% men. Students come from 21 states and territories, 1 other country, 19% from out-of-state. 1% American Indian or Alaska Native, non-Hispanic/Latino; 11% Hispanic/Latino; 83% African American, non-Hispanic/Latino; 0% Asian, non-Hispanic/Latino; 0% Native Hawaiian or other Pacific Islander, non-Hispanic/Latino; 1% international. 35% 25 or older, 39% live on campus, 19% transferred in. Retention: 43% of full-time freshmen returned the following year. Academic areas with the most degrees conferred: homeland security, law enforcement, firefighting, and protective services; education; computer and information sciences. Core. Calendar: semesters. Academic remediation for entering students, services for LD students, honors program, independent study, summer session for credit, part-time degree program, external degree program, adult/continuing education programs, co-op programs and internships. Off campus study.

Entrance Requirements: Option: electronic application. Required: essay, high school transcript, minimum 2.5 high school GPA, interview, medical history, SAT or ACT scores, SAT or ACT. Entrance: moderately difficult. Application deadlines: 6/1, 6/1 for nonresidents. Notification: continuous, continuous for nonresidents. SAT Reasoning Test deadline: 6/1. SAT Subject Test deadline: 6/1. Transfer credits accepted: Yes.

Costs Per Year: Application fee: $25. Comprehensive fee: $18,800 includes full-time tuition ($9300), mandatory fees ($2150), and college room and board ($7350). College room only: $3600. Full-time tuition and fees vary according to course load. Room and board charges vary according to board plan. Part-time tuition: $387.50 per semester hour. Part-time tuition varies according to course load.

Collegiate Environment: Orientation program. Drama-theater group, choral group, marching band. Social organizations: 5 open to all; national fraternities, national sororities, local fraternities, local sororities; 43% of eligible men and 48% of eligible women are members. Most popular organizations: Student Ambassadors, NAACP, Student Government Association, intramurals, Honda Campus All Star Challenge (academic quiz bowl). Major annual events: Homecoming, Spring Fest, intramural sports. Student services: health clinic, personal-psychological counseling. Campus security: 24-hour patrols. 228 college housing spaces available; 118 were occupied in 2012-13. Freshmen given priority for college housing. On-campus residence required through sophomore year. Option: coed housing available. Zale Library plus 1 other with 87,000 books and 167 serials. Operations spending for the previous fiscal year: $450,000. 50 computers available on campus for general student use. A campuswide network can be accessed from student residence rooms. Students can access the following: online class registration. Staffed computer lab on campus provides training in use of computers, software, and the Internet.

Community Environment: See University of Texas at Dallas.

■ PIMA MEDICAL INSTITUTE

10201 Katy Fwy.

Houston, TX 77024

Tel: (712)778-0778

E-mail: cluebke@pmi.edu

Web Site: www.pmi.edu/

Description: Proprietary, 2-year, coed. Setting: urban campus. Core. Distance learning, co-op programs and internships.

Entrance Requirements: Required: high school transcript, interview, Wonderlic Scholastic Level Exam (SLE).

Collegiate Environment: Orientation program.

■ PRAIRIE VIEW A&M UNIVERSITY

PO Box 519

Prairie View, TX 77446-0519

Tel: (936)857-3311

Fax: (936)857-2699

E-mail: megooch@pvamu.edu

Web Site: www.pvamu.edu/

Description: State-supported, university, coed. Part of Texas A&M University System. Awards bachelor's, master's, and doctoral degrees. Founded 1878. Setting: 1,502-acre small town campus with easy access to Houston. Total enrollment: 8,336. Faculty: 461 (379 full-time, 82 part-time). Student-undergrad faculty ratio is 17:1. 9,602 applied, 41% were admitted. 5% from top 10% of their high school class, 19% from top quarter, 55% from top half. Full-time: 6,281 students, 59% women, 41% men. Part-time: 476 students, 60% women, 40% men. 6% from out-of-state. 0.1% American Indian or Alaska Native, non-Hispanic/Latino; 6% Hispanic/Latino; 84% African American, non-Hispanic/Latino; 2% Asian, non-Hispanic/Latino; 0.1% Native Hawaiian or other Pacific Islander, non-Hispanic/Latino; 1% international. 0.1% 25 or older, 25% live on campus, 6% transferred in. Academic areas with the most degrees conferred: health professions and related sciences; business/marketing; homeland security, law enforcement, firefighting, and protective services. Core. Calendar: semesters. Academic remediation for entering students, services for LD students, advanced placement, accelerated degree program, honors program, independent study, distance learning, double major, summer session for credit, part-time degree program, co-op programs and internships, graduate courses open to undergrads. Off campus study. Study abroad program. ROTC: Army, Naval.

Entrance Requirements: Options: electronic application, deferred admission. Required: high school transcript, minimum 2.5 high school GPA, SAT or ACT. Entrance: moderately difficult. Application deadline: 6/1. Notification: continuous. SAT Reasoning Test deadline: 8/1. Transfer credits accepted: Yes.

Costs Per Year: Application fee: $25. State resident tuition: $5,393 full-time, $179.77 per credit hour part-time. Nonresident tuition: $15,923 full-time, $530.77 per credit hour part-time. Mandatory fees: $2345 full-time, $78.17 per credit hour part-time. Full-time tuition and fees vary according to course load, program, and reciprocity agreements. Part-time tuition and fees vary according to course load, program, and reciprocity agreements. College room and board: $7,467. Room and board charges vary according to board plan, housing facility, and student level.

Collegiate Environment: Orientation program. Drama-theater group, choral group, marching band, student-run newspaper, radio station. Social organizations: 29 open to all; national fraternities, national sororities, local fraternities, local sororities. Most popular organizations: National Society of Black Engineers, National Association of Black Accountants, National Organization of Black Chemists and Chemical Engineers, Toastmasters International, Baptist Student Movement. Major annual events: Homecoming, The Yard Show, Mister & Miss Prairie View. Student services: health clinic, personal-psychological counseling. Campus security: 24-hour emergency response devices and patrols, late night transport-escort service, controlled dormitory access. 3,519 college housing spaces available; all were occupied in 2012-13. Freshmen given priority for college housing. Options: men-only, women-only housing available. John B. Coleman Library plus 1 other with 1.2 million books, 712,183 microform titles, 42,660 serials, 3,255 audiovisual materials, an OPAC, and a Web page. 4,400 computers available on campus for general student use. A campuswide network can be accessed from student residence rooms and from off campus. Students can access the following: online class registration. Staffed computer lab on campus provides training in use of the Internet.

■ RANGER COLLEGE

1100 College Cir.

Ranger, TX 76470

Tel: (254)647-3234

Web Site: www.rangercollege.edu/

Description: State-related, 2-year, coed. Awards transfer associate and terminal associate degrees. Founded 1926. Setting: 100-acre rural campus with easy access to Dallas-Fort Worth. Total enrollment: 843. Faculty: 51 (28 full-time, 23 part-time). 15% from top 10% of their high school class, 75% from top half. Students come from 7 states and territories, 4 other countries. 45% live on campus. Core. Calendar: semesters. Academic remediation for entering students, advanced placement, self-designed majors, freshman honors college, honors program, summer session for credit, part-time degree program, adult/continuing education programs.

Entrance Requirements: Open admission. Option: early admission. Entrance: noncompetitive. Application deadline: Rolling. Notification: continuous.

Collegiate Environment: Choral group, marching band. Student services: health clinic, personal-psychological counseling. Campus security: controlled dormitory access. Golemon Library with 24,211 books and 133 serials. 42 computers available on campus for general student use. Staffed computer lab on campus.

Community Environment: Population 2,535. Ranger's name was derived from a camp of Texas Rangers, organized near here to protect settlers from marauding Indians. In 1917, oil was discovered and the community expanded. Today, there are several churches representing the major denominations. The community is reached by railroad and interstate highway. Local recreation includes fishing, swimming, boating, water skiing, a municipally owned swimming pool, hunting for deer, duck, dove, squirrel, and rabbit. Part-time employment is limited.

■ REMINGTON COLLEGE–DALLAS CAMPUS

1800 Eastgate Dr.

Garland, TX 75041

Tel: (972)686-7878

Fax: (972)686-5116

E-mail: shonda.wisenhunt@remingtoncollege.edu

Web Site: www.remingtoncollege.edu/

Description: Proprietary, 2-year, coed. Awards terminal associate degrees. Founded 1987.

■ REMINGTON COLLEGE–FORT WORTH CAMPUS

300 E Loop 820

Fort Worth, TX 76112

Tel: (817)451-0017; Free: 800-560-6192

Fax: (817)496-1257

E-mail: marcia.kline@remingtoncollege.edu

Web Site: www.remingtoncollege.edu/

Description: Proprietary, 2-year, coed. Awards terminal associate degrees.

■ REMINGTON COLLEGE–HOUSTON CAMPUS

3110 Hayes Rd.

Ste. 380

Houston, TX 77082

Tel: (281)899-1240

Fax: (281)597-8466

E-mail: kevin.wilkinson@remingtoncollege.edu

Web Site: www.remingtoncollege.edu/

Description: Proprietary, 2-year, coed. Awards terminal associate degrees.

■ REMINGTON COLLEGE–HOUSTON SOUTHEAST

20985 Interstate 45 S

Webster, TX 77598

E-mail: lori.minor@remingtoncollege.edu

Web Site: www.remingtoncollege.edu/

Description: Proprietary, 2-year, coed. Awards terminal associate degrees.

■ REMINGTON COLLEGE–NORTH HOUSTON CAMPUS

11310 Greens Crossing Blvd.

Ste. 300

Houston, TX 77067

E-mail: edmund.flores@remingtoncollege.edu

Web Site: www.remingtoncollege.edu/

Description: Proprietary, 2-year, coed. Awards transfer associate and terminal associate degrees.

■ **RICE UNIVERSITY**
6100 Main St.
Houston, TX 77251-1892
Tel: (713)348-0000; Free: 800-527-OWLS
Fax: (713)348-5323
E-mail: admi@rice.edu
Web Site: www.rice.edu/
Description: Independent, university, coed. Awards bachelor's, master's, and doctoral degrees. Founded 1912. Setting: 300-acre urban campus with easy access to Houston. Endowment: $4.4 billion. Research spending for the previous fiscal year: $87.7 million. Educational spending for the previous fiscal year: $40,970 per student. Total enrollment: 6,484. Faculty: 771 (676 full-time, 95 part-time). Student-undergrad faculty ratio is 6:1. 15,133 applied, 17% were admitted. 90% from top 10% of their high school class, 97% from top quarter, 100% from top half. 63 class presidents, 185 student government officers. Full-time: 7,821 students, 75% women, 25% men. Part-time: 45 students, 29% women, 71% men. Students come from 53 states and territories, 51 other countries, 48% from out-of-state. 0.2% American Indian or Alaska Native, non-Hispanic/Latino; 14% Hispanic/Latino; 7% African American, non-Hispanic/Latino; 21% Asian, non-Hispanic/Latino; 0.1% Native Hawaiian or other Pacific Islander, non-Hispanic/Latino; 11% international. 0% 25 or older, 72% live on campus, 1% transferred in. Retention: 96% of full-time freshmen returned the following year. Academic areas with the most degrees conferred: engineering; social sciences; biological/life sciences. Core. Calendar: semesters. ESL program, services for LD students, advanced placement, accelerated degree program, self-designed majors, honors program, independent study, double major, summer session for credit, internships, graduate courses open to undergrads. Off campus study. Study abroad program. ROTC: Army (c), Naval, Air Force (c).
Entrance Requirements: Options: electronic application, early decision, deferred admission, international baccalaureate accepted. Required: essay, high school transcript, 2 recommendations, SAT and 2 SAT Subject Tests OR ACT with Writing. Recommended: interview. Required for some: portfolio for architecture; audition for music. Entrance: most difficult. Application deadlines: 1/1, 11/1 for early decision. Notification: 4/1, 12/15 for early decision. SAT Reasoning Test deadline: 1/1. SAT Subject Test deadline: 1/1. Transfer credits accepted: Yes. Applicants placed on waiting list: 2,304. Wait-listed applicants offered admission: 52. Early decision applicants: 1,230. Early decision applicants admitted: 306.
Costs Per Year: Application fee: $75. One-time mandatory fee: $520. Comprehensive fee: $51,942 includes full-time tuition ($38,260), mandatory fees ($682), and college room and board ($13,000). College room only: $8800.
Collegiate Environment: Orientation program. Drama-theater group, choral group, marching band, student-run newspaper, radio station. Social organizations: 240 open to all. Most popular organizations: Drama Club, volunteer program, intramural sports, college government, Marching Owl Band. Major annual events: Annual Bike Relay Race and Parade, Campus-wide formals, Homecoming. Student services: health clinic, personal-psychological counseling, women's center. Campus security: 24-hour emergency response devices and patrols, late night transport-escort service, controlled dormitory access. 2,827 college housing spaces available; 2,738 were occupied in 2012-13. Freshmen given priority for college housing. Option: coed housing available. Fondren Library with 2.8 million books, 3.4 million microform titles, 128,472 serials, 77,458 audiovisual materials, an OPAC, and a Web page. Operations spending for the previous fiscal year: $31.4 million. 543 computers available on campus for general student use. A campuswide network can be accessed from student residence rooms and from off campus. Students can access the following: online class registration. Staffed computer lab on campus.

■ **RICHLAND COLLEGE**
12800 Abrams Rd.
Dallas, TX 75243-2199
Tel: (972)238-6106
Fax: (972)238-6957
Web Site: www.rlc.dcccd.edu/
Description: State and locally supported, 2-year, coed. Part of Dallas County Community College District System. Awards transfer associate and terminal associate degrees. Founded 1972. Setting: 250-acre suburban campus. Total enrollment: 14,128. Faculty: 665 (165 full-time, 500 part-time).

Students come from 24 states and territories, 21 other countries. 47% 25 or older. Core. Calendar: semesters. Academic remediation for entering students, ESL program, services for LD students, advanced placement, freshman honors college, honors program, summer session for credit, part-time degree program, adult/continuing education programs, co-op programs. Study abroad program.
Entrance Requirements: Open admission. Option: early admission. Required for some: high school transcript. Entrance: noncompetitive. Application deadline: Rolling. Notification: continuous.
Collegiate Environment: Drama-theater group, choral group, student-run newspaper. Student services: health clinic, personal-psychological counseling, women's center. Campus security: 24-hour emergency response devices and patrols, late night transport-escort service, emergency call boxes. Richland College Library with 63,000 books and 350 serials. 400 computers available on campus for general student use.

■ **RIO GRANDE BIBLE INSTITUTE**
4300 S US Hwy. 281
Edinburg, TX 78539
Tel: (956)380-8100
Fax: (956)380-8256
E-mail: admisiones@riogrande.edu
Web Site: www.riogrande.edu/
Description: Independent Christian, 4-year, coed. Awards bachelor's degrees.
Entrance Requirements: Required: doctrinal statement.

■ **ST. EDWARD'S UNIVERSITY**
3001 S Congress Ave.
Austin, TX 78704
Tel: (512)448-8400; Free: 800-555-0164
Fax: (512)448-8492
E-mail: seu.admit@stedwards.edu
Web Site: www.gotostedwards.com/
Description: Independent Roman Catholic, comprehensive, coed. Awards bachelor's and master's degrees. Founded 1885. Setting: 160-acre urban campus. Endowment: $54.2 million. Educational spending for the previous fiscal year: $9333 per student. Total enrollment: 5,095. Faculty: 532 (214 full-time, 318 part-time). Student-undergrad faculty ratio is 13:1. 4,209 applied, 63% were admitted. 20% from top 10% of their high school class, 55% from top quarter, 88% from top half. 5 valedictorians. Full-time: 3,449 students, 61% women, 39% men. Part-time: 789 students, 61% women, 39% men. Students come from 45 states and territories, 43 other countries, 11% from out-of-state. 1% American Indian or Alaska Native, non-Hispanic/Latino; 35% Hispanic/Latino; 4% African American, non-Hispanic/Latino; 2% Asian, non-Hispanic/Latino; 0.2% Native Hawaiian or other Pacific Islander, non-Hispanic/Latino; 7% international. 5% 25 or older, 38% live on campus, 5% transferred in. Retention: 79% of full-time freshmen returned the following year. Academic areas with the most degrees conferred: business/marketing; communication/journalism; psychology. Core. Calendar: semesters. Academic remediation for entering students, services for LD students, advanced placement, honors program, double major, summer session for credit, part-time degree program, adult/continuing education programs, internships. Study abroad program. ROTC: Army (c), Air Force (c).
Entrance Requirements: Options: electronic application, deferred admission, international baccalaureate accepted. Required: essay, high school transcript, 1 recommendation, SAT or ACT. Recommended: interview. Entrance: moderately difficult. Application deadlines: 5/1, 5/1 for nonresidents. Notification: continuous, continuous for nonresidents. SAT Reasoning Test deadline: 5/1. Transfer credits accepted: Yes. Applicants placed on waiting list: 315. Wait-listed applicants offered admission: 81.
Costs Per Year: Application fee: $50. Comprehensive fee: $44,674 includes full-time tuition ($33,320), mandatory fees ($400), and college room and board ($10,954). College room only: $6024. Full-time tuition and fees vary according to course load and degree level. Room and board charges vary according to board plan and housing facility. Part-time tuition: $1112 per credit hour. Part-time mandatory fees: $50 per term. Part-time tuition and fees vary according to course load and degree level.
Collegiate Environment: Orientation program. Drama-theater group, choral group, student-run newspaper, radio station. Social organizations: 120 open to all. Most popular organizations: Academy of Science, Promoting Respect, Inclusion, Diversity and Empowerment (PRIDE), Psychological Society, Outdoor Adventure Club, Students for Sustainability. Major annual events:

Hillfest, Involvement Fair, Student Homecoming Events. Student services: health clinic, personal-psychological counseling. Campus security: 24-hour emergency response devices and patrols, late night transport-escort service, controlled dormitory access, self-defense education, informal discussions, pamphlets, posters, alcohol awareness meetings, lighted pathways and sidewalks. 1,381 college housing spaces available; 1,360 were occupied in 2012-13. Freshmen guaranteed college housing. On-campus residence required in freshman year. Options: coed, women-only housing available. St. Edward's University Library with 293,706 books, 2,122 serials, 17,687 audiovisual materials, an OPAC, and a Web page. Operations spending for the previous fiscal year: $1.7 million. 790 computers available on campus for general student use. A campuswide network can be accessed from student residence rooms. Students can access the following: online class registration, online library, ability to change address and biographical data, look at transcripts, pull up statements of account, grades, online progress reports and degree audit, campus job postings, student timesheets, financial aid information. Staffed computer lab on campus (open 24 hours a day) provides training in use of computers, software, and the Internet.

■ ST. MARY'S UNIVERSITY
1 Camino Santa Maria
San Antonio, TX 78228-8507
Tel: (210)436-3011; Free: 800-FOR-STMU
Fax: (210)431-6742
E-mail: uadm@stmarytx.edu
Web Site: www.stmarytx.edu/

Description: Independent Roman Catholic, comprehensive, coed. Awards bachelor's, master's, and doctoral degrees. Founded 1852. Setting: 135-acre urban campus with easy access to San Antonio. Endowment: $134.4 million. Research spending for the previous fiscal year: $729,252. Educational spending for the previous fiscal year: $9459 per student. Total enrollment: 3,988. Faculty: 393 (205 full-time, 188 part-time). Student-undergrad faculty ratio is 13:1. 5,581 applied, 55% were admitted. 31% from top 10% of their high school class, 60% from top quarter, 87% from top half. 3 valedictorians. Full-time: 2,323 students, 58% women, 42% men. Part-time: 136 students, 54% women, 46% men. Students come from 32 states and territories, 12 other countries, 8% from out-of-state. 0.3% American Indian or Alaska Native, non-Hispanic/Latino; 73% Hispanic/Latino; 3% African American, non-Hispanic/Latino; 3% Asian, non-Hispanic/Latino; 0.2% Native Hawaiian or other Pacific Islander, non-Hispanic/Latino; 3% international. 10% 25 or older, 59% live on campus, 5% transferred in. Retention: 76% of full-time freshmen returned the following year. Academic areas with the most degrees conferred: business/marketing; social sciences; biological/life sciences. Core. Calendar: semesters. Academic remediation for entering students, ESL program, services for LD students, advanced placement, honors program, independent study, distance learning, double major, summer session for credit, part-time degree program, adult/continuing education programs, co-op programs and internships, graduate courses open to undergrads. Off campus study at University of the Incarnate Word, Our Lady of the Lake University of San Antonio, Oblate School of Theology, University of Dayton, Chaminade University, University of Notre Dame. Study abroad program. ROTC: Army, Air Force (c).
Entrance Requirements: Options: electronic application, deferred admission, international baccalaureate accepted. Required: high school transcript, SAT or ACT. Recommended: essay, minimum 2 high school GPA, interview. Entrance: moderately difficult. Application deadline: Rolling. Notification: continuous. SAT Reasoning Test deadline: 6/1. Transfer credits accepted: Yes.
Costs Per Year: Application fee: $30. Comprehensive fee: $33,390 includes full-time tuition ($24,520) and college room and board ($8870). College room only: $5210. Full-time tuition varies according to course load. Room and board charges vary according to board plan and housing facility.
Collegiate Environment: Orientation program. Drama-theater group, choral group, student-run newspaper. Social organizations: 102 open to all; national fraternities, national sororities, local fraternities; 20% of eligible men and 16% of eligible women are members. Most popular organizations: Beta Beta Beta Biology Society, St. Mary's University Society of Honor Scholars, American Chemical Society of Students, Mexican Student Organization, Alpha Phi Omega. Major annual events: Fiesta Oyster Bake, President Peace Commission Symposia, Continuing the Heritage Service Day. Student services: health clinic, personal-psychological counseling. Campus security: 24-hour emergency response devices and patrols, late night transport-escort service, controlled dormitory access. 1,402 college housing spaces available; 1,355 were occupied in 2012-13. Freshmen given priority for college

housing. On-campus residence required in freshman year. Option: coed housing available. Louis J. Blume Library plus 1 other with 339,662 books, 344,297 microform titles, 36,954 serials, 8,400 audiovisual materials, an OPAC, and a Web page. Operations spending for the previous fiscal year: $3.6 million. 200 computers available on campus for general student use. Computer purchase/lease plans available. A computer is required for all students. A campuswide network can be accessed from student residence rooms and from off campus. Students can access the following: online class registration. Staffed computer lab on campus provides training in use of computers, software, and the Internet.

■ ST. PHILIP'S COLLEGE
1801 Martin Luther King Dr.
San Antonio, TX 78203-2098
Tel: (210)486-2000
Fax: (210)531-4831
E-mail: pvelasco@alamo.edu
Web Site: www.alamo.edu/spc/

Description: District-supported, 2-year, coed. Part of Alamo Community College District. Awards certificates, diplomas, transfer associate, and terminal associate degrees. Founded 1898. Setting: 68-acre urban campus with easy access to San Antonio. Educational spending for the previous fiscal year: $3861 per student. Total enrollment: 10,710. Faculty: 398 (173 full-time, 225 part-time). Student-undergrad faculty ratio is 15:1. Full-time: 2,232 students, 55% women, 45% men. Part-time: 8,478 students, 57% women, 43% men. Students come from 45 states and territories, 11 other countries, 1% from out-of-state. 0.4% American Indian or Alaska Native, non-Hispanic/Latino; 50% Hispanic/Latino; 13% African American, non-Hispanic/Latino; 2% Asian, non-Hispanic/Latino; 0% Native Hawaiian or other Pacific Islander, non-Hispanic/Latino; 0.3% international. 44% 25 or older, 10% transferred in. Core. Calendar: semesters. Academic remediation for entering students, ESL program, services for LD students, advanced placement, honors program, independent study, distance learning, double major, summer session for credit, part-time degree program, adult/continuing education programs, co-op programs and internships. Off campus study. Study abroad program. ROTC: Army (c).
Entrance Requirements: Open admission special requirements for nursing and certain allied health programs. Options: electronic application, early admission. Required: high school transcript. Entrance: noncompetitive. Application deadline: Rolling. Notification: continuous. Transfer credits accepted: Yes.
Costs Per Year: Application fee: $0. Area resident tuition: $2008 full-time, $80 per credit hour part-time. State resident tuition: $5470 full-time, $195 per credit hour part-time. Nonresident tuition: $10,660 full-time, $368 per credit hour part-time. Mandatory fees: $30 full-time, $1 per credit hour part-time. Full-time tuition and fees vary according to program. Part-time tuition and fees vary according to program.
Collegiate Environment: Orientation program. Drama-theater group, choral group. Social organizations: 6 open to all. Most popular organizations: student government, Future United Latino Leaders of Change, Anime. Major annual events: Culture Fest, Hispanic Heritage Month, Black History Month. Student services: health clinic, women's center. Campus security: 24-hour emergency response devices and patrols, late night transport-escort service. College housing not available. Library plus 1 other with 112,745 books, 14,156 microform titles, 107 serials, 11,520 audiovisual materials, an OPAC, and a Web page. 2,623 computers available on campus for general student use. A campuswide network can be accessed from off-campus. Students can access the following: online class registration. Staffed computer lab on campus provides training in use of computers, software, and the Internet.

■ SAM HOUSTON STATE UNIVERSITY
Huntsville, TX 77341
Tel: (936)294-1111; Free: 866-232-7528
E-mail: admissions@shsu.edu
Web Site: www.shsu.edu/

Description: State-supported, university, coed. Part of Texas State University System. Awards bachelor's, master's, and doctoral degrees. Founded 1879. Setting: 1,256-acre small town campus with easy access to Houston. Endowment: $49.7 million. Research spending for the previous fiscal year: $4.9 million. Educational spending for the previous fiscal year: $2114 per student. Total enrollment: 18,461. Faculty: 797 (620 full-time, 177 part-time). Student-undergrad faculty ratio is 25:1. 9,315 applied, 65% were admitted. 13% from top 10% of their high school class, 42% from top quarter, 85% from top half. Full-time: 12,968 students, 57% women, 43% men. Part-time: 2,643 students, 60% women, 40% men. Students come from 47 states and territories, 58 other countries, 1% from out-of-state. 0.4% American Indian or Alaska Native, non-Hispanic/Latino; 17% Hispanic/Latino; 17% African American, non-Hispanic/Latino; 1% Asian, non-Hispanic/Latino; 0.1% Native Hawaiian or other Pacific Islander, non-Hispanic/Latino; 1% international. 16% 25 or older, 25% live on campus, 15% transferred in. Retention: 71% of full-time freshmen returned the following year. Academic areas with the most degrees conferred: business/marketing; homeland security, law enforcement, firefighting, and protective services; interdisciplinary studies. Core. Calendar: semesters. Academic remediation for entering students, ESL program, services for LD students, accelerated degree program, honors program, independent study, distance learning, double major, summer session for credit, part-time degree program, external degree program, internships, graduate courses open to undergrads. Off campus study at The University Center, American Institute for Foreign Study. Study abroad program. ROTC: Army.

Entrance Requirements: Options: electronic application, early admission, international baccalaureate accepted. Required: high school transcript, SAT or ACT. Entrance: moderately difficult. Application deadlines: 8/1, 8/1 for nonresidents. Notification: continuous, continuous for nonresidents. SAT Reasoning Test deadline: 8/1. SAT Subject Test deadline: 8/1. Transfer credits accepted: Yes.

Costs Per Year: Application fee: $45. State resident tuition: $5610 full-time. Nonresident tuition: $16,140 full-time. Mandatory fees: $2510 full-time. Full-time tuition and fees vary according to course level, course load, location, and program. College room and board: $8092. Room and board charges vary according to board plan and housing facility.

Collegiate Environment: Orientation program. Drama-theater group, choral group, marching band, student-run newspaper, radio station. Social organizations: national fraternities, national sororities, local fraternities, local sororities; 40% of eligible men and 30% of eligible women are members. Most popular organizations: Chi Alpha Christian Fellowship, Non-Traditional Student Organization, Sigma Alpha Pi Leadership Society, Baptist Student Ministry, Bearkats for Life. Major annual events: Bearkat Alley (Football Tailgate Parties), Tree of Light ceremony, Sam Jam carnival. Student services: legal services, health clinic, personal-psychological counseling. Campus security: 24-hour emergency response devices and patrols, student patrols, late night transport-escort service, controlled dormitory access. 3,297 college housing spaces available; 3,267 were occupied in 2012-13. Freshmen guaranteed college housing. On-campus residence required in freshman year. Options: coed, men-only, women-only housing available. Newton Gresham Library plus 1 other with 1.3 million books, 1.2 million microform titles, 27,987 audiovisual materials, an OPAC, and a Web page. Operations spending for the previous fiscal year: $6.2 million. 1,600 computers available on campus for general student use. A campuswide network can be accessed from student residence rooms and from off campus. Students can access the following: online class registration. Staffed computer lab on campus (open 24 hours a day) provides training in use of computers, software, and the Internet.

Community Environment: Huntsville, population 36,699, is located in the pine belt 70 miles north of Houston. This was the home of General Sam Houston, and local museums commemorate his honor. The average temperatures are 51.1 degrees in winter and 82.6 degrees in summer. The community has a hospital, various fraternal, civic, and veteran's organizations, and is served by bus and U.S. Highway I-45. A nearby state park offers fishing, boating, swimming, picnicking, and camping. Part-time employment is available.

■ **SAN ANTONIO COLLEGE**
1300 San Pedro Ave.
San Antonio, TX 78212-4299
Tel: (210)733-2000
Fax: (210)733-2200
Web Site: www.alamo.edu/sac/
Description: State and locally supported, 2-year, coed. Part of Alamo Community College District System. Awards certificates, transfer associate, and terminal associate degrees. Founded 1925. Setting: 45-acre urban campus. Total enrollment: 21,800. Faculty: 1,000 (407 full-time, 593 part-time). Student-undergrad faculty ratio is 22:1. Full-time: 8,375 students, 57% women, 43% men. Part-time: 13,425 students, 62% women, 38% men. Students come from 54 states and territories, 112 other countries, 3% from out-of-state. 36% 25 or older, 8% transferred in. Core. Calendar: semesters. Academic remediation for entering students, ESL program, services for LD students, advanced placement, honors program, independent study,

distance learning, summer session for credit, part-time degree program, adult/continuing education programs, co-op programs and internships. ROTC: Army, Air Force (c).

Entrance Requirements: Open admission. Option: early admission. Required: ACT ASSET, THEA, ACCUPLACER. Recommended: high school transcript. Required for some: high school transcript. Entrance: noncompetitive. Application deadline: Rolling.

Costs Per Year: Application fee: $0. Area resident tuition: $2008 full-time, $480 per term part-time. State resident tuition: $5470 full-time, $1172 per term part-time. Nonresident tuition: $10,660 full-time, $2210 per term part-time. Mandatory fees: $30 full-time, $1 per credit hour part-time.

Collegiate Environment: Orientation program. Drama-theater group, choral group, student-run newspaper, radio station. Student services: health clinic, personal-psychological counseling, women's center. Campus security: 24-hour emergency response devices and patrols, late night transport-escort service. San Antonio College Library and Media Services with 233,714 books, 9,765 microform titles, 1,498 serials, an OPAC, and a Web page. 1,700 computers available on campus for general student use. A campuswide network can be accessed from off-campus. Students can access the following: online class registration. Staffed computer lab on campus.

Community Environment: Population 1,256,509. Called the cradle of Texas liberty because of its history, San Antonio is the birthplace of the rough riders and the home of the Alamo. San Antonio is a mixture of its early Spanish background and a modern metropolis. Skyscrapers exist alongside 18th-century adobe restorations. There are many historic sites to be seen in the area. The transportation to and within the city is excellent. There are local and transcontinental bus lines. More than 500 churches representing most denominations, many civic and fraternal organizations, hospitals and museums serve the community. San Antonio has a symphony orchestra and an art museum. The annual Fiesta San Jacinto, Everett Colborn World's Championship Rodeo, and Grand Opera Festival are held here. Local recreation includes 56 parks, sunken garden theater, golf courses, polo fields, baseball diamonds, tennis courts, bridle paths, picnic grounds, swimming pools, hunting, fishing, and boating. Part-time employment is available.

■ **SAN JACINTO COLLEGE DISTRICT**
4624 Fairmont Pky.
Pasadena, TX 77504-3323
Tel: (281)998-6150
E-mail: Wanda.Munson@sjcd.edu
Web Site: www.sanjac.edu/
Description: State and locally supported, 2-year, coed. Awards certificates, transfer associate, and terminal associate degrees. Founded 1961. Setting: 445-acre suburban campus with easy access to Houston. Endowment: $3.2 million. Educational spending for the previous fiscal year: $3112 per student. Total enrollment: 28,721. Faculty: 1,248 (517 full-time, 731 part-time). Student-undergrad faculty ratio is 20:1. 11,631 applied, 100% were admitted. Full-time: 8,625 students, 55% women, 45% men. Part-time: 20,096 students, 58% women, 42% men. Students come from 44 states and territories, 76 other countries, 1% from out-of-state. 0.3% American Indian or Alaska Native, non-Hispanic/Latino; 44% Hispanic/Latino; 9% African American, non-Hispanic/Latino; 5% Asian, non-Hispanic/Latino; 0.1% Native Hawaiian or other Pacific Islander, non-Hispanic/Latino; 1% international. 30% 25 or older, 26% transferred in. Calendar: semesters. Academic remediation for entering students, ESL program, services for LD students, advanced placement, accelerated degree program, self-designed majors, honors program, distance learning, double major, summer session for credit, part-time degree program, adult/continuing education programs, co-op programs. Study abroad program. ROTC: Army (c), Air Force (c).

Entrance Requirements: Open admission special requirements for health science program (Psychological Service Bureau test); interview required for nursing programs and EMT programs. Options: electronic application, early admission. Required: high school transcript. Required for some: interview. Entrance: noncompetitive. Transfer credits accepted: Yes.

Costs Per Year: Area resident tuition: $1312 full-time, $43 per credit hour part-time. State resident tuition: $2296 full-time, $84 per credit hour part-time. Nonresident tuition: $3496 full-time, $134 per credit hour part-time. Mandatory fees: $280 full-time. Full-time tuition and fees vary according to course load. Part-time tuition varies according to course load.

Collegiate Environment: Orientation program. Drama-theater group, choral group, student-run newspaper. Social organizations: 84 open to all; local fraternities, local sororities. Most popular organizations: Phi Theta Kappa, Nurses Association, Student Government Association, ABG Radiography, Texas Student Education Association. Major annual events: Fall Welcome

Mixer, Raven Pep Rally, Discovery Lecture Series. Campus security: 24-hour emergency response devices and patrols, late night transport-escort service. College housing not available. Lee Davis Library (C), Edwin E. Lehr (N), and Parker Williams (S) with 283,963 books, 97 microform titles, 1,303 serials, 2,809 audiovisual materials, an OPAC, and a Web page. Operations spending for the previous fiscal year: $1.8 million. 471 computers available on campus for general student use. A campuswide network can be accessed from off-campus. Students can access the following: online class registration. Staffed computer lab on campus provides training in use of computers, software, and the Internet.

■ **SCHREINER UNIVERSITY**

2100 Memorial Blvd.

Kerrville, TX 78028-5697

Tel: (830)896-5411; Free: 800-343-4919

Fax: (830)792-7226

E-mail: admissions@schreiner.edu

Web Site: www.schreiner.edu/

Description: Independent Presbyterian, comprehensive, coed. Awards associate, bachelor's, and master's degrees. Founded 1923. Setting: 175-acre small town campus with easy access to San Antonio, Austin. Endowment: $51.2 million. Educational spending for the previous fiscal year: $6005 per student. Total enrollment: 1,126. Faculty: 119 (56 full-time, 63 part-time). Student-undergrad faculty ratio is 14:1. 1,153 applied, 63% were admitted. 13% from top 10% of their high school class, 40% from top quarter, 74% from top half. Full-time: 1,015 students, 56% women, 44% men. Part-time: 53 students, 70% women, 30% men. 3% from out-of-state. 0.4% American Indian or Alaska Native, non-Hispanic/Latino; 28% Hispanic/Latino; 4% African American, non-Hispanic/Latino; 1% Asian, non-Hispanic/Latino; 0.1% Native Hawaiian or other Pacific Islander, non-Hispanic/Latino; 0.5% international. 13% 25 or older, 66% live on campus, 7% transferred in. Retention: 71% of full-time freshmen returned the following year. Academic areas with the most degrees conferred: business/marketing; psychology; education; visual and performing arts; parks and recreation. Core. Calendar: semesters. Academic remediation for entering students, services for LD students, advanced placement, accelerated degree program, self-designed majors, honors program, independent study, double major, summer session for credit, part-time degree program, co-op programs and internships, graduate courses open to undergrads. Study abroad program.

Entrance Requirements: Options: electronic application, deferred admission, international baccalaureate accepted. Required: essay, high school transcript, SAT or ACT. Recommended: interview. Entrance: moderately difficult. Application deadline: 5/1. Notification: continuous.

Costs Per Year: Application fee: $25. One-time mandatory fee: $25. Comprehensive fee: $31,602 includes full-time tuition ($20,940), mandatory fees ($600), and college room and board ($10,062). Room and board charges vary according to board plan and housing facility. Part-time tuition: $894 per credit hour. Part-time mandatory fees: $300 per term.

Collegiate Environment: Orientation program. Drama-theater group, choral group, student-run newspaper. Social organizations: 19 open to all; national fraternities, national sororities; 9% of eligible men and 16% of eligible women are members. Most popular organizations: Student Senate, Greek Life, Campus Ministry, honor societies, Hall Councils. Major annual events: BINGO Night, Fall Ball, Comedy Nights. Student services: health clinic, personal-psychological counseling. Campus security: 24-hour emergency response devices and patrols, late night transport-escort service. 753 college housing spaces available. Freshmen guaranteed college housing. On-campus residence required through junior year. Option: coed housing available. W. M. Logan Library with 110,300 books, 593 microform titles, 225 serials, 720 audiovisual materials, an OPAC, and a Web page. Operations spending for the previous fiscal year: $527,262. 120 computers available on campus for general student use. Computer purchase/lease plans available. A campuswide network can be accessed from student residence rooms and from off campus. Students can access the following: online class registration. Staffed computer lab on campus provides training in use of computers, software, and the Internet.

Community Environment: Population 22,000. In the rugged hill region by the Guadalupe River, Kerrville is a popular summer and winter resort area. The hill country is famous for fishing and hunting. The city is located 65 miles northwest of San Antonio and enjoys moderate climate. The community has churches of major denominations, a hospital, and various civic, fraternal, and veteran's organizations. Local recreation includes theatres, boating, fishing, water skiing, and deer and turkey hunting. Job opportunities are available.

■ **SOUTH PLAINS COLLEGE**

1401 S College Ave.

Levelland, TX 79336-6595

Tel: (806)894-9611

Fax: (806)897-3167

E-mail: arangel@southplainscollege.edu

Web Site: www.southplainscollege.edu/

Description: State and locally supported, 2-year, coed. Awards certificates, transfer associate, and terminal associate degrees. Founded 1958. Setting: 177-acre small town campus. Endowment: $3 million. Educational spending for the previous fiscal year: $1432 per student. Total enrollment: 9,444. Faculty: 454 (271 full-time, 183 part-time). Student-undergrad faculty ratio is 20:1. 3,189 applied, 100% were admitted. 10% from top 10% of their high school class, 32% from top quarter, 60% from top half. 8 valedictorians. Full-time: 4,382 students, 51% women, 49% men. Part-time: 5,062 students, 57% women, 43% men. Students come from 21 states and territories, 8 other countries, 4% from out-of-state. 39% 25 or older, 10% live on campus, 10% transferred in. Retention: 45% of full-time freshmen returned the following year. Core. Calendar: semesters. Academic remediation for entering students, services for LD students, advanced placement, accelerated degree program, distance learning, double major, summer session for credit, part-time degree program, adult/continuing education programs, internships. Off campus study. Study abroad program. ROTC: Army (c), Air Force (c).

Entrance Requirements: Open admission. Options: electronic application, early admission. Required: high school transcript. Recommended: ACT, SAT Subject Tests. Entrance: noncompetitive. Application deadlines: Rolling, Rolling for nonresidents. Notification: continuous, continuous for nonresidents. Transfer credits accepted: Yes.

Costs Per Year: Application fee: $0. Area resident tuition: $864 full-time, $36 per hour part-time. State resident tuition: $1329 full-time, $48 per hour part-time. Nonresident tuition: $1776 full-time, $64 per hour part-time. Mandatory fees: $1250 full-time. College room and board: $3100.

Collegiate Environment: Orientation program. Drama-theater group, choral group, student-run newspaper, radio station. Most popular organizations: student government, Phi Beta Kappa, Bleacher Bums, Law Enforcement Association. Major annual events: Homecoming, Spring Fling, Miss Cap Rock Pageant. Student services: health clinic. Campus security: 24-hour emergency response devices and patrols, controlled dormitory access. 715 college housing spaces available; all were occupied in 2012-13. Freshmen given priority for college housing. On-campus residence required through sophomore year. Options: men-only, women-only housing available. South Plains College Library plus 1 other with 70,000 books, 310 serials, and an OPAC. 130 computers available on campus for general student use. Computer purchase/lease plans available. A campuswide network can be accessed from student residence rooms and from off campus. Students can access the following: online class registration. Staffed computer lab on campus provides training in use of computers, software, and the Internet.

Community Environment: Levelland, population 12,777, a rural community enjoying a temperate climate. The area is served by bus, an airport, and Routes 114 and 385. The city has a public library, hospital, churches of major denominations, theatres, and active civic, fraternal, and veteran's organizations. Local recreation includes outdoor sports and rodeo. Part-time employment is available.

■ **SOUTH TEXAS COLLEGE**

3201 W Pecan

McAllen, TX 78501

Tel: (956)618-8323; Free: 800-742-7822

Fax: (956)928-4445

E-mail: mshebbar@southtexascollege.edu

Web Site: www.southtexascollege.edu/

Description: District-supported, primarily 2-year, coed. Awards certificates, transfer associate, terminal associate, and bachelor's degrees. Founded 1993. Setting: 20-acre suburban campus. Endowment: $222,114. Total enrollment: 19,827. Faculty: 629 (434 full-time, 195 part-time). Student-undergrad faculty ratio is 25:1. 25% from top quarter of their high school class, 34% from top half. Full-time: 7,027 students, 57% women, 43% men. Part-time: 12,800 students, 59% women, 41% men. 0% from out-of-state. 27% 25 or older. Retention: 57% of full-time freshmen returned the following year. Calendar: semesters. Academic remediation for entering students, services for LD students, accelerated degree program, summer session for credit, part-time degree program, adult/continuing education programs, co-op programs. Off campus study at University of Texas-Pan American. ROTC: Army (c).

Entrance Requirements: Open admission. Options: early admission, deferred admission. Required: high school transcript. Required for some: THEA. Entrance: noncompetitive. Application deadline: Rolling.

Collegiate Environment: Orientation program. Most popular organizations: Beta Epsilon Mu Honor Society, Automotive Technology Club, Child Care and Development Association Club, Heating, Air Conditioning, and Ventilation Club, Writing in Literary Discussion Club. Major annual events: Career Day, Cinco de Mayo, Thanksgiving Food Drive. Student services: personal-psychological counseling. Campus security: 24-hour emergency response devices and patrols, late night transport-escort service. Learning Resources Center with 15,811 books, 192 serials, an OPAC, and a Web page. Operations spending for the previous fiscal year: $144,832. 2,550 computers available on campus for general student use. A campuswide network can be accessed from off-campus. Students can access the following: online class registration. Staffed computer lab on campus provides training in use of computers, software, and the Internet.

■ **SOUTH UNIVERSITY**
810 Hesters Crossing Rd., Ste. 220
Austin, TX 78681
Fax: (512)516-8680
Web Site: www.southuniversity.edu/austin.aspx
Description: Proprietary, comprehensive, coed. Awards associate, bachelor's, and master's degrees.

■ **SOUTHERN METHODIST UNIVERSITY**
6425 Boaz
Dallas, TX 75275
Tel: (214)768-2000; Free: 800-323-0672
E-mail: ugadmission@smu.edu
Web Site: www.smu.edu/
Description: Independent, university, coed, affiliated with United Methodist Church. Awards bachelor's, master's, and doctoral degrees. Founded 1911. Setting: 235-acre suburban campus. Endowment: $1.2 billion. Research spending for the previous fiscal year: $22.1 million. Educational spending for the previous fiscal year: $16,525 per student. Total enrollment: 10,893. Faculty: 1,155 (723 full-time, 432 part-time). Student-undergrad faculty ratio is 11:1. 11,217 applied, 54% were admitted. 47% from top 10% of their high school class, 76% from top quarter, 96% from top half. Full-time: 5,999 students, 51% women, 49% men. Part-time: 250 students, 53% women, 47% men. Students come from 50 states and territories, 66 other countries, 48% from out-of-state. 0.4% American Indian or Alaska Native, non-Hispanic/Latino; 12% Hispanic/Latino; 6% African American, non-Hispanic/Latino; 7% Asian, non-Hispanic/Latino; 0.2% Native Hawaiian or other Pacific Islander, non-Hispanic/Latino; 7% international. 5% 25 or older, 32% live on campus, 5% transferred in. Retention: 91% of full-time freshmen returned the following year. Academic areas with the most degrees conferred: business/marketing; social sciences; engineering. Core. Calendar: semesters. Academic remediation for entering students, ESL program, services for LD students, advanced placement, accelerated degree program, self-designed majors, honors program, independent study, distance learning, double major, summer session for credit, part-time degree program, adult/continuing education programs, co-op programs and internships, graduate courses open to undergrads. Study abroad program. ROTC: Army, Air Force (c).

Entrance Requirements: Options: electronic application, early action, deferred admission, international baccalaureate accepted. Required: high school transcript, minimum 2 high school GPA, 1 recommendation, statement of good standing from prior institution(s), SAT or ACT. Recommended: essay, minimum 2.7 high school GPA. Required for some: SAT Subject Tests. Entrance: moderately difficult. Application deadlines: 3/15, 11/1 for early action. Notification: continuous, 12/31 for early action. SAT Reasoning Test deadline: 3/15. Transfer credits accepted: Yes. Applicants placed on waiting list: 1,057. Wait-listed applicants offered admission: 125.

Costs Per Year: Application fee: $60. Comprehensive fee: $57,755 includes full-time tuition ($38,870), mandatory fees ($4930), and college room and board ($13,955). Room and board charges vary according to board plan and housing facility. Part-time tuition: $1624 per credit hour. Part-time tuition varies according to course load.

Collegiate Environment: Orientation program. Drama-theater group, choral group, marching band, student-run newspaper, radio station. Social organizations: 180 open to all; national fraternities, national sororities; 32% of eligible men and 43% of eligible women are members. Most popular organizations: Program Council, Student Senate, Student Foundation,

Residence Hall Association, SPARC (Students Promoting Awareness, Responsibility, and Citizenship). Major annual events: Homecoming, Sing Song, Mane Event (All-School Block Party). Student services: health clinic, personal-psychological counseling, women's center. Campus security: 24-hour emergency response devices and patrols, late night transport-escort service, controlled dormitory access. 2,525 college housing spaces available; 1,959 were occupied in 2012-13. Freshmen guaranteed college housing. On-campus residence required in freshman year. Option: coed housing available. Central University Library plus 7 others with 3.1 million books, 843,365 microform titles, 18,482 serials, 58,610 audiovisual materials, an OPAC, and a Web page. Operations spending for the previous fiscal year: $17 million. 758 computers available on campus for general student use. A campuswide network can be accessed from student residence rooms and from off campus. Students can access the following: online class registration, online billing/payment processing. Staffed computer lab on campus provides training in use of computers, software, and the Internet.

Community Environment: See University of Texas at Dallas.

■ **SOUTHWEST INSTITUTE OF TECHNOLOGY**
5424 Hwy. 290 W, Ste. 200
Austin, TX 78735-8800
Tel: (512)892-2640
Fax: (512)892-1045
Web Site: www.swse.net/
Description: Proprietary, 2-year, coed. Awards diplomas, transfer associate, and terminal associate degrees. Setting: 1-acre urban campus. Total enrollment: 29. Student-undergrad faculty ratio is 7:1. 0% from out-of-state. 55% 25 or older. Retention: 67% of full-time freshmen returned the following year. Calendar: continuous.
Entrance Requirements: Open admission.

■ **SOUTHWEST TEXAS JUNIOR COLLEGE**
2401 Garner Field Rd.
Uvalde, TX 78801-6297
Tel: (830)278-4401
Web Site: www.swtjc.edu/
Description: State and locally supported, 2-year, coed. Awards certificates, transfer associate, and terminal associate degrees. Founded 1946. Setting: 97-acre small town campus with easy access to San Antonio. Total enrollment: 4,350. Faculty: 166 (66 full-time, 100 part-time). Students come from 2 states and territories, 4 other countries. 34% 25 or older, 9% live on campus. Core. Calendar: semesters. Academic remediation for entering students, ESL program, advanced placement, honors program, summer session for credit, part-time degree program, external degree program, adult/continuing education programs.

Entrance Requirements: Open admission. Options: electronic application, early admission, deferred admission. Required: high school transcript. Entrance: noncompetitive. Application deadline: Rolling. Notification: continuous. Preference given to local residents.

Collegiate Environment: Orientation program. Drama-theater group, student-run newspaper. Social organizations: 25 open to all. Most popular organizations: Catholic Students Club, Business Administration Club. Major annual event: Spring Palms Festival. Student services: health clinic, personal-psychological counseling. Campus security: 24-hour patrols, controlled dormitory access. Will C. Miller Memorial Library with 30,890 books and 285 serials. 300 computers available on campus for general student use. Staffed computer lab on campus.

Community Environment: Population 16,400. Uvalde is located at the base of the Texas Hill Country 75 miles west of San Antonio and is known for its agriculture production; hunting for deer, wild turkey, quail and doves; and fishing. The climate is moderate. City services include a memorial hospital, public library, community theatre in the historic Grand Opera House, U.S. Vice-President John Nance Garner Memorial Museum, and churches of various denominations. Uvalde is reached by buslines, major highways and a private airport. Dormitories, apartments and rental houses provide student housing. Local recreation includes six screen theater complex, 18-hole golf course, parks, two rivers, private clubs, various community celebrations.

■ **SOUTHWESTERN ADVENTIST UNIVERSITY**
100 Hillcrest Dr.
Keene, TX 76059
Tel: (817)645-3921; Free: 800-433-2240
Fax: (817)556-4744
E-mail: rahneeka@swau.edu

Web Site: www.swau.edu/

Description: Independent Seventh-day Adventist, comprehensive, coed. Awards associate, bachelor's, and master's degrees. Founded 1894. Setting: 150-acre small town campus with easy access to Dallas-Fort Worth. Endowment: $7.2 million. Educational spending for the previous fiscal year: $7849 per student. Total enrollment: 807. Faculty: 78 (52 full-time, 26 part-time). Student-undergrad faculty ratio is 11:1. 1,218 applied, 56% were admitted. 20% from top 10% of their high school class, 35% from top quarter, 60% from top half. 6 valedictorians, 15 student government officers. Full-time: 625 students, 60% women, 40% men. Part-time: 156 students, 59% women, 41% men. Students come from 31 states and territories, 42 other countries, 28% from out-of-state. 0% American Indian or Alaska Native, non-Hispanic/Latino; 31% Hispanic/Latino; 14% African American, non-Hispanic/Latino; 3% Asian, non-Hispanic/Latino; 1% Native Hawaiian or other Pacific Islander, non-Hispanic/Latino; 19% international. 18% 25 or older, 40% live on campus, 11% transferred in. Retention: 61% of full-time freshmen returned the following year. Academic areas with the most degrees conferred: health professions and related sciences; education; business/marketing. Core. Calendar: semesters. Academic remediation for entering students, ESL program, services for LD students, advanced placement, accelerated degree program, self-designed majors, honors program, independent study, double major, summer session for credit, part-time degree program, external degree program, adult/continuing education programs, internships, graduate courses open to undergrads. Off campus study at Tarleton State University, Loma Linda University, Andrews University. Study abroad program.

Entrance Requirements: Options: electronic application, deferred admission. Required: high school transcript, minimum 2 high school GPA, SAT or ACT. Required for some: essay, 1 recommendation, interview. Entrance: minimally difficult. Application deadline: 8/31. Notification: 9/1. Transfer credits accepted: Yes.

Costs Per Year: Application fee: $25. Comprehensive fee: $24,432 includes full-time tuition ($17,400) and college room and board ($7032). College room only: $3420. Full-time tuition varies according to course load and program. Room and board charges vary according to board plan. Part-time tuition: $725 per credit. Part-time tuition varies according to course load and program.

Collegiate Environment: Orientation program. Drama-theater group, choral group, student-run newspaper, radio station. Social organizations: 10 open to all. Most popular organizations: Student Association, Students in Free Enterprise (SIFE), Education/Psychology Club, Theology Club, Nursing Club. Major annual events: Mimosa Memories, Student Appreciation Week. Student services: health clinic, personal-psychological counseling. Campus security: 24-hour emergency response devices, student patrols. 425 college housing spaces available; 300 were occupied in 2012-13. Freshmen guaranteed college housing. On-campus residence required through sophomore year. Options: men-only, women-only housing available. Chan Shun Centennial Library with 135,453 books, 4,500 serials, an OPAC, and a Web page. Operations spending for the previous fiscal year: $443,145. 100 computers available on campus for general student use. A campuswide network can be accessed from student residence rooms and from off campus. Students can access the following: online class registration. Staffed computer lab on campus provides training in use of computers, software, and the Internet.

Community Environment: Population 5,952. Keene is a small community in a rural area. The climate is temperate. The city is reached by bus lines and U.S. Route 67. There is a local Seventh Day Adventist Church. A shopping center is located seven miles distant. Part-time employment is available.

■ **SOUTHWESTERN ASSEMBLIES OF GOD UNIVERSITY**

1200 Sycamore St.
Waxahachie, TX 75165-5735
Tel: (972)937-4010; Free: 888-937-7248
E-mail: bbrooks@sagu.edu
Web Site: www.sagu.edu/

Description: Independent, comprehensive, coed, affiliated with Assemblies of God. Awards associate, bachelor's, and master's degrees. Founded 1927. Setting: 70-acre small town campus with easy access to Dallas-Fort Worth. Endowment: $4 million. Educational spending for the previous fiscal year: $4704 per student. Total enrollment: 2,064. Faculty: 142 (69 full-time, 73 part-time). Student-undergrad faculty ratio is 16:1. Full-time: 1,458 students, 48% women, 52% men. Part-time: 284 students, 53% women, 47% men. Students come from 49 states and territories, 11 other countries, 40% from

out-of-state. 85% live on campus, 15% transferred in. Retention: 67% of full-time freshmen returned the following year. Academic areas with the most degrees conferred: theology and religious vocations; education; liberal arts/general studies. Core. Calendar: semesters. Academic remediation for entering students, services for LD students, advanced placement, independent study, distance learning, double major, summer session for credit, part-time degree program, external degree program, adult/continuing education programs, internships, graduate courses open to undergrads. ROTC: Air Force (c).

Entrance Requirements: Options: early admission, deferred admission. Required: essay, high school transcript, minimum 2 high school GPA, 1 recommendation, medical history, evidence of approved Christian character, SAT or ACT. Entrance: noncompetitive. Application deadline: Rolling. SAT Reasoning Test deadline: 8/15. Transfer credits accepted: Yes.

Costs Per Year: Application fee: $35. Comprehensive fee: $23,414 includes full-time tuition ($15,750), mandatory fees ($880), and college room and board ($6784). College room only: $3590. Room and board charges vary according to housing facility. Part-time tuition: $525 per credit.

Collegiate Environment: Orientation program. Drama-theater group, choral group, student-run newspaper. Social organizations: 16 open to all. Most popular organizations: Student Congress, Southwestern Missions Association, Street Hope, Gold Jackets, Women in Ministry. Major annual events: All School Fellowship/Battle of the Dorms, Homecoming, Class Night. Student services: health clinic, personal-psychological counseling. Campus security: 24-hour patrols, late night transport-escort service, controlled dormitory access, 2 dorms electronic access; 4 dorms key access to rooms, camera surveillance, 24 hour dispatch monitored fire alarm systems (offsite). P. C. Nelson Memorial Library plus 1 other with 108,207 books, 99,782 microform titles, 350 serials, 5,126 audiovisual materials, an OPAC, and a Web page. Operations spending for the previous fiscal year: $102,529. 96 computers available on campus for general student use. A campuswide network can be accessed from student residence rooms and from off campus. Students can access the following: online class registration. Staffed computer lab on campus provides training in use of computers and the Internet.

Community Environment: Population 25,500, Waxahachie is the capital of Ellis County. It is located 28 miles south of Dallas and 40 miles southeast of Fort Worth. The area can be reached by rail, bus, and major highways. Community facilities include a medical center, a hospital and health clinic, many churches of various denominations, and several civic and fraternal organizations. Local recreation includes baseball, bowling, golf, hunting, boating, and fishing. Apartments and part-time employment are available.

■ **SOUTHWESTERN CHRISTIAN COLLEGE**

Box 10
200 Bowser St.
Terrell, TX 75160
Tel: (972)524-3341
Web Site: www.swcc.edu/

Description: Independent, 4-year, coed, affiliated with Church of Christ. Awards associate and bachelor's degrees. Founded 1949. Setting: 25-acre small town campus with easy access to Dallas-Fort Worth. 80% live on campus. Core. Calendar: semesters. Academic remediation for entering students, part-time degree program.

Entrance Requirements: Open admission. Options: early admission, deferred admission. Required: high school transcript, 2 recommendations, immunization record. Entrance: noncompetitive. Application deadline: 8/1.

Collegiate Environment: Orientation program. Choral group, student-run newspaper. Social organizations: national fraternities, national sororities, local fraternities, local sororities. Campus security: 24-hour patrols. Hogan Stewart Learning Center with 25,687 books and 158 serials.

Community Environment: Terrell is a suburban community enjoying dry, temperate climate. The city is reached by bus, railroad, and major highways. Community services include many churches representing most major denominations, hospitals, a public library, YMCA, and YWCA. There are theatres, parks, and nearby lakes for water sports. Part-time employment opportunities are limited. Various civic, fraternal and veteran's organizations are active in Terrell. Small city and all necessary items are within walking distance.

■ **SOUTHWESTERN UNIVERSITY**

1001 E University Ave.
Georgetown, TX 78626
Tel: (512)863-6511; Free: 800-252-3166
Fax: (512)863-6511

E-mail: admission@southwestern.edu
Web Site: www.southwestern.edu/
Description: Independent Methodist, 4-year, coed. Awards bachelor's degrees. Founded 1840. Setting: 700-acre suburban campus with easy access to Austin. Endowment: $250.6 million. Research spending for the previous fiscal year: $236,379. Educational spending for the previous fiscal year: $15,172 per student. Total enrollment: 1,394. Faculty: 165 (117 full-time, 48 part-time). Student-undergrad faculty ratio is 10:1. 2,795 applied, 61% were admitted. 41% from top 10% of their high school class, 75% from top quarter, 97% from top half. 2 National Merit Scholars, 10 valedictorians. Full-time: 1,376 students, 61% women, 39% men. Part-time: 18 students, 44% women, 56% men. Students come from 33 states and territories, 6 other countries, 10% from out-of-state. 1% American Indian or Alaska Native, non-Hispanic/Latino; 18% Hispanic/Latino; 3% African American, non-Hispanic/Latino; 4% Asian, non-Hispanic/Latino; 0.2% Native Hawaiian or other Pacific Islander, non-Hispanic/Latino; 1% international. 1% 25 or older, 78% live on campus, 3% transferred in. Retention: 86% of full-time freshmen returned the following year. Academic areas with the most degrees conferred: social sciences; business/marketing; biological/life sciences. Core. Calendar: semesters. Services for LD students, advanced placement, self-designed majors, honors program, independent study, double major, summer session for credit, internships. Off campus study at GLCA Arts Program in New York; Southwestern University students also participate in the Washington D.C. semesters but grades are assigned by SU faculty rather than another institution. Study abroad program.
Entrance Requirements: Options: electronic application, early admission, early action, deferred admission, international baccalaureate accepted. Required: essay, high school transcript, 1 recommendation, Counselor recommendation; teacher and parent recommendation optional, SAT or ACT. Recommended: interview. Required for some: interview. Entrance: very difficult. Application deadlines: Rolling, Rolling for nonresidents, 11/15 for early action. Notification: 4/1, 4/1 for nonresidents, 2/15 for early action. SAT Reasoning Test deadline: 3/1. Transfer credits accepted: Yes. Applicants placed on waiting list: 75. Wait-listed applicants offered admission: 6.
Costs Per Year: Application fee: $0. Comprehensive fee: $46,250 includes full-time tuition ($35,240) and college room and board ($11,010). College room only: $5650. Room and board charges vary according to board plan and housing facility. Part-time tuition: $1470 per credit hour. Part-time tuition varies according to course load.
Collegiate Environment: Orientation program. Drama-theater group, choral group, student-run newspaper, radio station. Social organizations: 99 open to all; national fraternities, national sororities, Sigma Phi Lamba, Kappa Upsilon Chi, Kappa Delta Chi; 29% of eligible men and 20% of eligible women are members. Most popular organizations: Student Peace Alliance (SPA), Students for Environmental Activism & Knowledge (SEAK), Alpha Phi Omega, Men's IFC, Women's Panhellenic. Major annual events: Late Night Breakfast, Annual large act concert, MallBall. Student services: health clinic, personal-psychological counseling. Campus security: 24-hour emergency response devices and patrols, student patrols, late night transport-escort service, controlled dormitory access. 1,134 college housing spaces available; 1,013 were occupied in 2012-13. Freshmen guaranteed college housing. On-campus residence required through sophomore year. Options: coed, men-only, women-only housing available. A. Frank Smith Jr. Library Center with 392,200 books, 65,157 microform titles, 86,856 serials, 21,338 audiovisual materials, an OPAC, and a Web page. Operations spending for the previous fiscal year: $2.1 million. 410 computers available on campus for general student use. A campuswide network can be accessed from student residence rooms and from off campus. Students can access the following: online class registration, transcripts. Staffed computer lab on campus (open 24 hours a day) provides training in use of computers, software, and the Internet.
Community Environment: Population 39,000, Georgetown enjoys the advantage of being a small town yet is only 26 miles from the state capital, Austin. The climate is moderate, both in winter and summer. The community is served by rail, bus lines, Austin-Bergstrom International Airport, and Interstate Highway 35 and has a modern hospital and clinic. Located in the heart of the highland lakes region, recreational opportunities include fishing, boating, and water sports. Part-time employment is available.

■ **STEPHEN F. AUSTIN STATE UNIVERSITY**
1936 N St.
Nacogdoches, TX 75962
Tel: (936)468-2011; Free: 800-731-2902
Fax: (936)468-3849

E-mail: admissions@sfasu.edu
Web Site: www.sfasu.edu/
Description: State-supported, comprehensive, coed. Awards bachelor's, master's, and doctoral degrees. Founded 1923. Setting: 412-acre small town campus. Endowment: $50.2 million. Research spending for the previous fiscal year: $5.5 million. Total enrollment: 12,999. Faculty: 673 (500 full-time, 173 part-time). Student-undergrad faculty ratio is 20:1. 11,463 applied, 56% were admitted. 14% from top 10% of their high school class, 43% from top quarter, 78% from top half. 30 valedictorians. Full-time: 9,632 students, 63% women, 37% men. Part-time: 1,666 students, 62% women, 38% men. Students come from 42 states and territories, 30 other countries, 2% from out-of-state. 1% American Indian or Alaska Native, non-Hispanic/Latino; 13% Hispanic/Latino; 24% African American, non-Hispanic/Latino; 1% Asian, non-Hispanic/Latino; 0.03% Native Hawaiian or other Pacific Islander, non-Hispanic/Latino; 1% international. 11% 25 or older, 42% live on campus, 9% transferred in. Retention: 63% of full-time freshmen returned the following year. Academic areas with the most degrees conferred: business/marketing; interdisciplinary studies; health professions and related sciences. Core. Calendar: semesters. Academic remediation for entering students, services for LD students, advanced placement, accelerated degree program, self-designed majors, freshman honors college, honors program, independent study, distance learning, double major, summer session for credit, part-time degree program, adult/continuing education programs, co-op programs and internships, graduate courses open to undergrads. Off campus study. Study abroad program. ROTC: Army.
Entrance Requirements: Options: electronic application, international baccalaureate accepted. Required: high school transcript, SAT or ACT. Entrance: moderately difficult. Application deadlines: Rolling, Rolling for nonresidents. Notification: continuous, continuous for nonresidents. Transfer credits accepted: Yes.
Costs Per Year: Application fee: $35. State resident tuition: $5756 full-time, $191.86 per credit hour part-time. Nonresident tuition: $16,286 full-time, $542.86 per credit hour part-time. Mandatory fees: $2172 full-time, $154 per credit hour part-time. Full-time tuition and fees vary according to course load, degree level, and location. Part-time tuition and fees vary according to course load, degree level, and location. College room and board: $8476. Room and board charges vary according to board plan and housing facility.
Collegiate Environment: Orientation program. Drama-theater group, choral group, marching band, student-run newspaper, radio station. Social organizations: 218 open to all; national fraternities, national sororities; 13% of eligible men and 9% of eligible women are members. Most popular organizations: Residence Hall Association, Baptist Student Ministries, Greek Life, Student Activities Association, Student Government Association. Major annual events: Homecoming, Spring Fest, Jacks Back Welcome Week. Student services: legal services, health clinic, personal-psychological counseling. Campus security: 24-hour emergency response devices and patrols, student patrols, late night transport-escort service, controlled dormitory access. 4,898 college housing spaces available; 4,714 were occupied in 2012-13. Freshmen guaranteed college housing. On-campus residence required through sophomore year. Options: coed, men-only, women-only housing available. Ralph W. Steen Library with 745,165 books, 861,034 microform titles, 1,138 serials, 25,373 audiovisual materials, an OPAC, and a Web page. Operations spending for the previous fiscal year: $4 million. 1,000 computers available on campus for general student use. A campuswide network can be accessed from student residence rooms and from off campus. Students can access the following: online class registration. Staffed computer lab on campus provides training in use of computers, software, and the Internet.
Community Environment: Population 30,800. Nacogdoches is one of the oldest settlements in Texas. This is a rural community enjoying temperate climate. There are more than 30 churches representing 15 different denominations, a library, museums, two hospitals, garden clubs, and major civic and fraternal organizations within the community. Nacogdoches is reached by railroad, bus lines, and Highways 59, 259, 7 and 21. Part-time employment is available. Local recreation includes movie theatres, several lakes for boating, swimming, and other water sports, and national forests for hiking, picnicking and hunting.

■ **STRAYER UNIVERSITY - CEDAR HILL CAMPUS**
610 Uptown Blvd.
Ste. 3500
Cedar Hill, TX 75104
Tel: (469)454-3400
Fax: (972)293-1800

Web Site: www.strayer.edu/campus/cedar-hill
Description: Proprietary, comprehensive, coed. Awards associate, bachelor's, and master's degrees.

■ **STRAYER UNIVERSITY - IRVING CAMPUS**
7701 Las Colinas Ridge
Ste. 450
Irving, TX 75063
Tel: (214)429-3900
Fax: (214)910-8499
Web Site: www.strayer.edu/campus/irving
Description: Proprietary, comprehensive, coed. Awards associate, bachelor's, and master's degrees.

■ **STRAYER UNIVERSITY - KATY CAMPUS**
14511 Old Katy Rd.
Ste. 200
Houston, TX 77079
Tel: (281)619-9200
Fax: (281)752-4111
Web Site: www.strayer.edu/campus/katy
Description: Proprietary, comprehensive, coed. Awards associate, bachelor's, and master's degrees.

■ **STRAYER UNIVERSITY - NORTH AUSTIN CAMPUS**
8501 N Mo-pac Expy.
Ste. 100
Austin, TX 78759
Tel: (512)568-3300
Fax: (512)340-9130
Web Site: www.strayer.edu/campus/north-austin
Description: Proprietary, comprehensive, coed. Awards associate, bachelor's, and master's degrees.

■ **STRAYER UNIVERSITY - NORTHWEST HOUSTON CAMPUS**
10940 W Sam Houston Pky. N
Ste. 200
Houston, TX 77064
Tel: (281)949-1800
Fax: (281)469-0090
Web Site: www.strayer.edu/campus/northwest-houston
Description: Proprietary, comprehensive, coed. Awards associate, bachelor's, and master's degrees.

■ **STRAYER UNIVERSITY - PLANO CAMPUS**
2701 N Dallas Pky.
Ste. 300
Plano, TX 75093
Tel: (972)535-3700
Fax: (972)608-2099
Web Site: www.strayer.edu/campus/plano
Description: Proprietary, comprehensive, coed. Awards associate, bachelor's, and master's degrees.

■ **SUL ROSS STATE UNIVERSITY**
PO Box C - 114
Alpine, TX 79832
Tel: (432)837-8011; Free: 888-722-7778
Fax: (432)837-8334
E-mail: admissions@sulross.edu
Web Site: www.sulross.edu/
Description: State-supported, comprehensive, coed. Part of Texas State University System. Awards associate, bachelor's, and master's degrees. Founded 1920. Setting: 640-acre rural campus. Total enrollment: 1,782. Faculty: 175 (120 full-time, 55 part-time). Student-undergrad faculty ratio is 14:1. 1,106 applied, 97% were admitted. 6% from top 10% of their high school class, 14% from top quarter, 35% from top half. Full-time: 1,003 students, 45% women, 55% men. Part-time: 233 students, 52% women, 48% men. 2% from out-of-state. 1% American Indian or Alaska Native, non-Hispanic/Latino; 51% Hispanic/Latino; 9% African American, non-Hispanic/Latino; 0.5% Asian, non-Hispanic/Latino; 0.2% Native Hawaiian or other Pacific Islander, non-Hispanic/Latino; 0% international. 33% 25 or older, 31% live on campus. Retention: 45% of full-time freshmen returned the following year. Academic areas with the most degrees conferred: interdisciplinary

studies; homeland security, law enforcement, firefighting, and protective services; business/marketing. Calendar: semesters. Part-time degree program.
Entrance Requirements: Options: early decision, deferred admission. Required: high school transcript, SAT or ACT. Recommended: interview. Entrance: noncompetitive. Application deadline: Rolling. Notification: continuous. Early decision applicants: 58. Early decision applicants admitted: 58.
Collegiate Environment: Campus security: 24-hour patrols, late night transport-escort service. Freshmen guaranteed college housing. On-campus residence required through sophomore year. Option: coed housing available.
Community Environment: Population 6,065, Alpine, located between El Paso on the west and Del Rio on the east, is known for its Highland Hereford breed of cattle. The city is also the gateway to travel to Big Bend National Park, Fort Davis National Historic Sites, Davis Mountains State Park, and McDonald Observatory. The climate in the area is mild. Railroad, commuter airline, and three bus lines serve the community. Local recreation includes baseball, hunting, golf, fishing, a theatre, and Summer Theatre during July and August. There is a hospital, library, and churches of various denominations within the city. Part-time employment is available.

■ **TARLETON STATE UNIVERSITY**
Box T-0001
Tarleton Station
Stephenville, TX 76402
Tel: (254)968-9000; Free: 800-687-8236
Fax: (254)968-9920
E-mail: uadm@tarleton.edu
Web Site: www.tarleton.edu/
Description: State-supported, comprehensive, coed. Part of Texas A&M University System. Awards associate, bachelor's, master's, and doctoral degrees. Founded 1899. Setting: 175-acre small town campus with easy access to Fort Worth. Endowment: $36.2 million. Research spending for the previous fiscal year: $8.8 million. Total enrollment: 10,279. Faculty: 601 (311 full-time, 290 part-time). Student-undergrad faculty ratio is 19:1. 4,643 applied, 76% were admitted. 9% from top 10% of their high school class, 23% from top quarter, 76% from top half. Full-time: 7,057 students, 59% women, 41% men. Part-time: 1,860 students, 61% women, 39% men. Students come from 40 states and territories, 22 other countries, 2% from out-of-state. 1% American Indian or Alaska Native, non-Hispanic/Latino; 13% Hispanic/Latino; 6% African American, non-Hispanic/Latino; 1% Asian, non-Hispanic/Latino; 0.1% Native Hawaiian or other Pacific Islander, non-Hispanic/Latino; 1% international. 23% 25 or older, 30% live on campus, 14% transferred in. Retention: 67% of full-time freshmen returned the following year. Academic areas with the most degrees conferred: interdisciplinary studies; business/marketing; agriculture. Core. Calendar: semesters. Academic remediation for entering students, services for LD students, advanced placement, accelerated degree program, honors program, independent study, distance learning, double major, summer session for credit, part-time degree program, adult/continuing education programs, co-op programs and internships, graduate courses open to undergrads. Off campus study. Study abroad program. ROTC: Army.
Entrance Requirements: Options: electronic application, early action, international baccalaureate accepted. Required: high school transcript, SAT or ACT. Entrance: moderately difficult. Application deadlines: 7/22, 3/1 for early action. SAT Reasoning Test deadline: 7/22. Transfer credits accepted: Yes.
Costs Per Year: Application fee: $30. State resident tuition: $4,619 full-time, $153.97 per credit hour part-time. Nonresident tuition: $15,149 full-time, $504.97 per credit hour part-time. Mandatory fees: $2,320 full-time. Full-time tuition and fees vary according to course load and degree level. Part-time tuition varies according to course load and degree level. College room and board: $7336. College room only: $3972. Room and board charges vary according to board plan and housing facility.
Collegiate Environment: Orientation program. Drama-theater group, choral group, marching band, student-run newspaper, radio station. Social organizations: 117 open to all; national fraternities, national sororities. Most popular organizations: Student Government Association, Student Programming Association, Kappa Delta Rho, Delta Zeta, Chi Alpha. Major annual events: Homecoming, Halloween Carnival, Vegas Night. Student services: legal services, health clinic, personal-psychological counseling. Campus security: 24-hour emergency response devices and patrols, student patrols, late night transport-escort service, controlled dormitory access. 2,711 college housing spaces available; 2,693 were occupied in 2012-13. Freshmen

guaranteed college housing. On-campus residence required through sophomore year. Options: coed, men-only, women-only housing available. Dick Smith Library plus 1 other with 400,000 books, 25,800 serials, an OPAC, and a Web page. Operations spending for the previous fiscal year: $2.1 million. 1,000 computers available on campus for general student use. A campuswide network can be accessed from student residence rooms and from off campus. Students can access the following: online class registration. Staffed computer lab on campus.

Community Environment: Stephenville, Texas, with a population of 15,900 is located in west central Texas, approximately 60 miles from the Ft. Worth/Dallas metroplex. With a typically mild climate average rainfall of 32 inches yearly, the region is commonly known as the Cross Timbers area, a term that refers to the many varieties of oak trees, including a heavy concentration of the live oak tree. Community services include churches of all denominations, a full-service hospital, including a new emergency wing and 24 hour care flight service, libraries and dozens of restaurants and shopping options. Railroad, bus, and a local airport are available. In addition, the Dallas/Ft. Worth International Airport is within a one and one-half hour drive.

■ **TARRANT COUNTY COLLEGE DISTRICT**
1500 Houston St.
Fort Worth, TX 76102-6599
Tel: (817)515-5100
Fax: (817)515-5295
E-mail: vikas.rajpurohit@tccd.edu
Web Site: www.tccd.edu/
Description: County-supported, 2-year, coed. Awards certificates, transfer associate, and terminal associate degrees. Founded 1967. Setting: 667-acre urban campus with easy access to Dallas-Fort Worth. Endowment: $5.8 million. Total enrollment: 50,062. Faculty: 1,861 (648 full-time, 1,213 part-time). Student-undergrad faculty ratio is 28:1. 9,924 applied, 100% were admitted. Full-time: 17,530 students, 56% women, 44% men. Part-time: 32,302 students, 61% women, 39% men. Students come from 39 states and territories. 1% American Indian or Alaska Native, non-Hispanic/Latino; 24% Hispanic/Latino; 19% African American, non-Hispanic/Latino; 6% Asian, non-Hispanic/Latino; 0.2% Native Hawaiian or other Pacific Islander, non-Hispanic/Latino; 1% international. 37% 25 or older. Core. Calendar: semesters. Academic remediation for entering students, ESL program, services for LD students, advanced placement, honors program, distance learning, summer session for credit, part-time degree program, adult/continuing education programs. ROTC: Army (c), Air Force (c).
Entrance Requirements: Open admission except for nursing, allied health programs. Options: electronic application, early admission. Entrance: noncompetitive. Application deadline: Rolling.
Costs Per Year: Application fee: $0. Area resident tuition: $1320 full-time, $55 per credit hour part-time. State resident tuition: $2064 full-time, $86 per credit hour part-time. Nonresident tuition: $4920 full-time, $205 per credit hour part-time. Full-time tuition varies according to course load and program. Part-time tuition varies according to course load and program.
Collegiate Environment: Orientation program. Drama-theater group, choral group, student-run newspaper. Social organizations: 48 open to all. Student services: health clinic, personal-psychological counseling. Campus security: 24-hour emergency response devices and patrols, late night transport-escort service. College housing not available. 197,352 books, 14,681 microform titles, 1,649 serials, 18,833 audiovisual materials, an OPAC, and a Web page 2,000 computers available on campus for general student use. Students can access the following: online class registration. Staffed computer lab on campus.

■ **TEMPLE COLLEGE**
2600 S First St.
Temple, TX 76504-7435
Tel: (254)298-8282
E-mail: carey.rose@templejc.edu
Web Site: www.templejc.edu/
Description: District-supported, 2-year, coed. Awards certificates, transfer associate, and terminal associate degrees. Founded 1926. Setting: 106-acre suburban campus with easy access to Austin. Endowment: $638,964. Educational spending for the previous fiscal year: $3327 per student. Total enrollment: 5,547. Faculty: 284 (126 full-time, 158 part-time). Student-undergrad faculty ratio is 18:1. 625 applied, 100% were admitted. Full-time: 2,160 students, 65% women, 35% men. Part-time: 3,373 students, 68% women, 32% men. Students come from 30 states and territories, 9 other countries, 2% from out-of-state. 1% American Indian or Alaska Native, non-

Hispanic/Latino; 20% Hispanic/Latino; 19% African American, non-Hispanic/Latino; 2% Asian, non-Hispanic/Latino; 0.2% Native Hawaiian or other Pacific Islander, non-Hispanic/Latino; 0.1% international. 38% 25 or older, 7% transferred in. Core. Calendar: semesters. Academic remediation for entering students, ESL program, services for LD students, advanced placement, distance learning, summer session for credit, part-time degree program, adult/continuing education programs, co-op programs and internships. Off campus study at East Williamson County Higher Education Center, Taylor, TX; Cameron Education Center, Cameron, TX; McClennan Community College (Radiologic Technology), Texas BioScience Institute, Temple TX. Study abroad program.
Entrance Requirements: Open admission except for health programs with clinical requirements. Options: electronic application, early admission, international baccalaureate accepted. Recommended: high school transcript. Required for some: high school transcript. Entrance: noncompetitive. Application deadline: Rolling. Transfer credits accepted: Yes.
Costs Per Year: Application fee: $0. Area resident tuition: $2640 full-time, $88 per semester hour part-time. State resident tuition: $4620 full-time, $154 per semester hour part-time. Nonresident tuition: $7020 full-time, $330 per semester hour part-time. Mandatory fees: $150 full-time, $24 per course part-time, $48 per term part-time. Full-time tuition and fees vary according to course load and program. Part-time tuition and fees vary according to course load and program. College room and board: $7696.
Collegiate Environment: Orientation program. Drama-theater group, choral group. Social organizations: 18 open to all; academic, service, and honor societies. Most popular organizations: Baptist Student Ministries, student government, Phi Theta Kappa, Delta Epsilon Chi, Nursing Student Organization. Major annual events: Fall Festival, Spring Fling. Campus security: 24-hour emergency response devices and patrols. No special consideration for freshman housing applicants. Option: coed housing available. Hubert Dawson Library with 58,907 books, 45,814 microform titles, 271 serials, 2,900 audiovisual materials, an OPAC, and a Web page. Operations spending for the previous fiscal year: $467,913. 102 computers available on campus for general student use. A campuswide network can be accessed from student residence rooms. Students can access the following: online class registration. Staffed computer lab on campus provides training in use of computers, software, and the Internet.
Community Environment: Population 55,447. Temple today is a medical center visited annually by thousands of patients. Located in central Texas, the city enjoys a temperate climate. The community has air, rail, and bus service available. Community service facilities include four excellent hospitals, many churches representing all major denominations, a library, and several hotels and motels. There are various civic, fraternal, and veteran's organizations active in the area. Local recreation includes hunting, fishing, boating, water skiing, and most water sports at nearby Lake Belton. Part-time employment is available.

■ **TEXARKANA COLLEGE**
2500 N Robison Rd.
Texarkana, TX 75599-0001
Tel: (903)838-4541
Fax: (903)832-5030
E-mail: linda.bennett@texarkanacollege.edu
Web Site: www.texarkanacollege.edu/
Description: State and locally supported, 2-year, coed. Awards certificates, transfer associate, and terminal associate degrees. Founded 1927. Setting: 90-acre urban campus. Total enrollment: 4,111. Faculty: 227 (96 full-time, 131 part-time). Student-undergrad faculty ratio is 20:1. Students come from 7 states and territories, 27% from out-of-state. 1% American Indian or Alaska Native, non-Hispanic/Latino; 5% Hispanic/Latino; 23% African American, non-Hispanic/Latino; 1% Asian, non-Hispanic/Latino; 0.05% Native Hawaiian or other Pacific Islander, non-Hispanic/Latino; 0% international. 2% live on campus. Core. Calendar: semesters. Academic remediation for entering students, services for LD students, advanced placement, summer session for credit, part-time degree program, adult/continuing education programs, co-op programs.
Entrance Requirements: Open admission. Option: early admission. Required: high school transcript. Recommended: Interview recommended for nursing program. Must have meningitis vaccine before student can start. Entrance: noncompetitive. Application deadline: Rolling.
Costs Per Year: Application fee: $0. Area resident tuition: $1170 full-time, $39 per semester hour part-time. State resident tuition: $2430 full-time, $81 per semester hour part-time. Nonresident tuition: $3600 full-time, $120 per semester hour part-time. Mandatory fees: $660 full-time. Full-time tuition and

fees vary according to course load. Part-time tuition varies according to course load. College room only: $2000.

Collegiate Environment: Orientation program. Drama-theater group, choral group, student-run newspaper, radio station. Social organizations: 16 open to all. Most popular organizations: Black Student Association, Earth Club, Baptist Student Union, 21st Century Democrats, Young Republicans. Major annual events: Octoberfest, Spring Fest. Student services: personal-psychological counseling. Campus security: 24-hour patrols. 125 college housing spaces available; 120 were occupied in 2012-13. No special consideration for freshman housing applicants. Palmer Memorial Library with 46,700 books and 646 serials. 110 computers available on campus for general student use. A campuswide network can be accessed. Staffed computer lab on campus.

Community Environment: Texarkana is located on the Arkansas-Texas border which runs approximately through the center of town. A trading center, there are many railroad lines coming into the area. The community has two hospitals, motels and hotels, and various civic, fraternal and veteran's organizations. Local recreation includes golf, hunting, fishing, boating, and water skiing. Part-time employment is available.

■ TEXAS A&M HEALTH SCIENCE CENTER
301 Tarrow St.
7th Fl.
College Station, TX 77840
Tel: (979)458-7200
Fax: (979)458-7202
Web Site: www.tamhsc.edu/

Description: State-supported, upper-level, coed. Part of Texas A&M University System Health Science Center. Awards bachelor's, master's, and doctoral degrees and post-master's certificates. Founded 1999. Setting: urban campus. Total enrollment: 544. Faculty: 255 (137 full-time, 118 part-time). Full-time: 60 students, 97% women, 3% men. 3% from out-of-state. 19% 25 or older, 50% transferred in. Academic area with the most degrees conferred: health professions and related sciences. Core. Calendar: semesters. Services for LD students.

Collegiate Environment: Orientation program. Student services: health clinic, personal-psychological counseling. Campus security: 24-hour emergency response devices and patrols, late night transport-escort service, electronically operated building access.

■ TEXAS A&M INTERNATIONAL UNIVERSITY
5201 University Blvd.
Laredo, TX 78041-1900
Tel: (956)326-2001; Free: 888-489-2648
Fax: (956)326-2348
E-mail: adms@tamiu.edu
Web Site: www.tamiu.edu/

Description: State-supported, comprehensive, coed. Part of Texas A&M University System. Awards bachelor's, master's, and doctoral degrees. Founded 1969. Setting: 300-acre urban campus. Endowment: $34.3 million. Research spending for the previous fiscal year: $2.8 million. Educational spending for the previous fiscal year: $4736 per student. Total enrollment: 7,213. Faculty: 306 (169 full-time, 137 part-time). Student-undergrad faculty ratio is 21:1. 4,569 applied, 48% were admitted. 23% from top 10% of their high school class, 53% from top quarter, 86% from top half. Full-time: 3,918 students, 57% women, 43% men. Part-time: 2,466 students, 60% women, 40% men. Students come from 22 states and territories, 22 other countries, 1% from out-of-state. 0.05% American Indian or Alaska Native, non-Hispanic/Latino; 94% Hispanic/Latino; 1% African American, non-Hispanic/Latino; 1% Asian, non-Hispanic/Latino; 0% Native Hawaiian or other Pacific Islander, non-Hispanic/Latino; 2% international. 17% 25 or older, 11% live on campus, 7% transferred in. Retention: 72% of full-time freshmen returned the following year. Academic areas with the most degrees conferred: business/marketing; interdisciplinary studies; health professions and related sciences. Core. Calendar: semesters. Academic remediation for entering students, ESL program, services for LD students; advanced placement, honors program, independent study, distance learning, double major, summer session for credit, part-time degree program, internships, graduate courses open to undergrads. Study abroad program. ROTC: Army.

Entrance Requirements: Options: electronic application, early admission, deferred admission, international baccalaureate accepted. Required: high school transcript, SAT or ACT. Entrance: moderately difficult. Application deadline: 7/1. Notification: 7/15. SAT Reasoning Test deadline: 7/1. SAT Subject Test deadline: 7/1. Transfer credits accepted: Yes.

Costs Per Year: Application fee: $0. State resident tuition: $6838 full-time. Nonresident tuition: $17,368 full-time. Full-time tuition varies according to course load. College room and board: $6275. Room and board charges vary according to board plan and housing facility.

Collegiate Environment: Orientation program. Drama-theater group, choral group, marching band, student-run newspaper. Social organizations: 55 open to all; national fraternities, national sororities, local fraternities; 3% of eligible men and 3% of eligible women are members. Most popular organizations: National Student Speech Language Hearing Association (NSSLHA), Association of International Students (AIS), Tri-Beta Biological Honor Society, Student Nurses' Association, STAR Club. Major annual events: Spirit Week, Welcome Week, Hispanic Heritage Month - Loteria. Student services: health clinic, personal-psychological counseling, women's center. Campus security: 24-hour emergency response devices and patrols, late night transport-escort service, controlled dormitory access, provide training to faculty, staff, a new students on active shooter. Interoperable communications with local, county, state, federal. 686 college housing spaces available; 670 were occupied in 2012-13. No special consideration for freshman housing applicants. Option: coed housing available. Sue and Radcliff Killam Library with 476,656 books, 854,479 microform titles, 54,115 serials, 6,427 audiovisual materials, an OPAC, and a Web page. Operations spending for the previous fiscal year: $3 million. 970 computers available on campus for general student use. A campuswide network can be accessed. Students can access the following: online class registration. Staffed computer lab on campus provides training in use of computers, software, and the Internet.

■ TEXAS A&M UNIVERSITY
College Station, TX 77843
Tel: (979)845-3211
E-mail: admissions@tamu.edu
Web Site: www.tamu.edu/

Description: State-supported, university, coed. Part of Texas A&M University System. Awards bachelor's, master's, and doctoral degrees. Founded 1876. Setting: 5,200-acre suburban campus with easy access to Houston. System endowment: $7.6 billion. Research spending for the previous fiscal year: $693.4 million. Educational spending for the previous fiscal year: $13,713 per student. Total enrollment: 50,227. Faculty: 2,451 (2,034 full-time, 417 part-time). Student-undergrad faculty ratio is 22:1. 27,798 applied, 67% were admitted. 60% from top 10% of their high school class, 91% from top quarter, 99% from top half. 159 National Merit Scholars, 260 valedictorians. Full-time: 36,219 students, 48% women, 52% men. Part-time: 3,884 students, 47% women, 53% men. Students come from 53 states and territories, 87 other countries, 3% from out-of-state. 0.3% American Indian or Alaska Native, non-Hispanic/Latino; 18% Hispanic/Latino; 3% African American, non-Hispanic/Latino; 5% Asian, non-Hispanic/Latino; 0.1% Native Hawaiian or other Pacific Islander, non-Hispanic/Latino; 2% international. 2% 25 or older, 25% live on campus, 5% transferred in. Retention: 92% of full-time freshmen returned the following year. Academic areas with the most degrees conferred: business/marketing; engineering; agriculture. Core. Calendar: semesters. Academic remediation for entering students, ESL program, services for LD students, advanced placement, accelerated degree program, honors program, independent study, distance learning, double major, summer session for credit, part-time degree program, co-op programs and internships, graduate courses open to undergrads. Off campus study at Texas A&M University at Galveston. Study abroad program. ROTC: Army, Naval, Air Force.

Entrance Requirements: Options: electronic application, international baccalaureate accepted. Required: essay, high school transcript, SAT or ACT. Entrance: moderately difficult. Application deadline: 1/15. Notification: continuous. Preference given to students graduating in the top 10% of Texas high schools. SAT Reasoning Test deadline: 2/1. Applicants placed on waiting list: 0. Wait-listed applicants offered admission: 0.

Costs Per Year: Application fee: $60. State resident tuition: $5297 full-time, $176.55 per credit hour part-time. Nonresident tuition: $21,827 full-time, $727.55 per credit hour part-time. Mandatory fees: $3209 full-time. Full-time tuition and fees vary according to program. Part-time tuition varies according to program. College room and board: $8400. Room and board charges vary according to board plan, housing facility, and location.

Collegiate Environment: Orientation program. Drama-theater group, choral group, marching band, student-run newspaper, radio station. Social organizations: 700 open to all; national fraternities, national sororities, local fraternities, local sororities; 6% of eligible men and 13% of eligible women are members. Most popular organizations: Memorial Student Center, Corps of Cadets, Fish Camp, student government. Major annual events: Big Event,

Parents' Weekend, Aggie Muster. Student services: legal services, health clinic, personal-psychological counseling, women's center. Campus security: 24-hour emergency response devices and patrols, late night transport-escort service, controlled dormitory access, student escorts. 9,512 college housing spaces available; 9,168 were occupied in 2012-13. No special consideration for freshman housing applicants. Options: coed, men-only, women-only housing available. Sterling C. Evans Library plus 7 others with 4.5 million books, 5.6 million microform titles, 160,576 serials, 87,912 audiovisual materials, an OPAC, and a Web page. Operations spending for the previous fiscal year: $35.4 million. 1,961 computers available on campus for general student use. A campuswide network can be accessed from student residence rooms and from off campus. Students can access the following: online class registration. Staffed computer lab on campus (open 24 hours a day) provides training in use of computers, software, and the Internet.

■ TEXAS A&M UNIVERSITY AT GALVESTON
PO Box 1675
Galveston, TX 77553-1675
Tel: (409)740-4400
Fax: (409)740-4709
E-mail: seaaggie@tamug.edu
Web Site: www.tamug.edu/
Description: State-supported, comprehensive, coed. Part of Texas A&M University System. Awards bachelor's and master's degrees. Founded 1962. Setting: 122-acre suburban campus with easy access to Houston. Endowment: $2.2 million. Research spending for the previous fiscal year: $4.1 million. Educational spending for the previous fiscal year: $7362 per student. Total enrollment: 1,774. Faculty: 170 (117 full-time, 53 part-time). Student-undergrad faculty ratio is 12:1. 1,257 applied, 77% were admitted. 12% from top 10% of their high school class, 48% from top quarter, 76% from top half. 1 National Merit Scholar, 1 valedictorian. Full-time: 1,591 students, 39% women, 61% men. Part-time: 128 students, 49% women, 51% men. Students come from 45 states and territories, 6 other countries, 18% from out-of-state. 5% 25 or older, 37% live on campus, 7% transferred in. Retention: 79% of full-time freshmen returned the following year. Academic areas with the most degrees conferred: biological/life sciences; business/marketing; engineering. Core. Calendar: semesters. Academic remediation for entering students, ESL program, advanced placement, accelerated degree program, independent study, double major, summer session for credit, part-time degree program, co-op programs and internships, graduate courses open to undergrads. Study abroad program. ROTC: Naval.
Entrance Requirements: Options: electronic application, early admission, deferred admission. Required: essay, high school transcript, SAT or ACT. Recommended: 2 recommendations, community involvement, SAT Subject Tests. Required for some: interview. Entrance: moderately difficult. Application deadline: Rolling. Notification: continuous.
Collegiate Environment: Orientation program. Drama-theater group, choral group, student-run newspaper. Social organizations: 37 open to all. Most popular organizations: Sail Club, Caving Club, Dive Club, rowing club, Rifle Drill Team. Major annual events: Aggie Muster, Spring Fest, Maritime Ball. Student services: health clinic, personal-psychological counseling. Campus security: 24-hour emergency response devices and patrols. Jack K. Williams Library with 56,589 books, 54,187 microform titles, 640 serials, an OPAC, and a Web page. Operations spending for the previous fiscal year: $929,967. 122 computers available on campus for general student use. A campuswide network can be accessed from student residence rooms and from off campus. Students can access the following: online class registration, degree plan progress, billing statement. Staffed computer lab on campus provides training in use of computers, software, and the Internet.

■ TEXAS A&M UNIVERSITY–COMMERCE
PO Box 3011
Commerce, TX 75429-3011
Tel: (903)886-5081; Free: 888-868-2682
Fax: (903)886-5888
E-mail: admissions@tamu-commerce.edu
Web Site: www.tamuc.edu/
Description: State-supported, university, coed. Part of Texas A&M University System. Awards bachelor's, master's, and doctoral degrees. Founded 1889. Setting: 1,883-acre small town campus with easy access to Dallas-Fort Worth. Endowment: $14.7 million. Research spending for the previous fiscal year: $2 million. Educational spending for the previous fiscal year: $5695 per student. Total enrollment: 11,187. Faculty: 610 (335 full-time, 275 part-time). Student-undergrad faculty ratio is 17:1. 3,516 applied,

65% were admitted. 15% from top 10% of their high school class, 42% from top quarter, 75% from top half. Full-time: 3,303 students, 55% women, 45% men. Part-time: 3,465 students, 63% women, 37% men. Students come from 31 states and territories, 18 other countries, 1% from out-of-state. 1% American Indian or Alaska Native, non-Hispanic/Latino; 14% Hispanic/Latino; 19% African American, non-Hispanic/Latino; 2% Asian, non-Hispanic/Latino; 0.1% Native Hawaiian or other Pacific Islander, non-Hispanic/Latino; 4% international. 36% 25 or older, 17% live on campus, 18% transferred in. Academic areas with the most degrees conferred: interdisciplinary studies; business/marketing; parks and recreation. Core. Calendar: semesters. Academic remediation for entering students, services for LD students, advanced placement, honors program, independent study, distance learning, double major, summer session for credit, part-time degree program, adult/continuing education programs, co-op programs and internships. Off campus study at Federation of North Texas Area Universities. Study abroad program.
Entrance Requirements: Options: electronic application, early admission. Required: high school transcript, SAT or ACT. Entrance: moderately difficult. Application deadline: 8/15. Notification: continuous. Transfer credits accepted: Yes.
Costs Per Year: State resident tuition: $6583 full-time, $159.68 per semester hour part-time. Nonresident tuition: $17,113 full-time. Mandatory fees: $1793 full-time. Full-time tuition and fees vary according to course load. Part-time tuition varies according to course load. College room and board: $3,627. College room only: $2,062. Room and board charges vary according to board plan and housing facility.
Collegiate Environment: Orientation program. Drama-theater group, choral group, marching band, student-run newspaper, radio station. Social organizations: 100 open to all; national fraternities, national sororities. Major annual events: Homecoming, Family Day, Sam Rayburn Leadership Institute. Student services: legal services, health clinic, personal-psychological counseling. Campus security: 24-hour emergency response devices and patrols, controlled dormitory access. 2,328 college housing spaces available; 1,132 were occupied in 2012-13. Freshmen guaranteed college housing. On-campus residence required in freshman year. Options: coed, men-only, women-only housing available. Gee Library with an OPAC and a Web page. Operations spending for the previous fiscal year: $3 million. 313 computers available on campus for general student use. Computer purchase/lease plans available. A campuswide network can be accessed from student residence rooms and from off campus. Students can access the following: online class registration. Staffed computer lab on campus.

■ TEXAS A&M UNIVERSITY–CORPUS CHRISTI
6300 Ocean Dr.
Corpus Christi, TX 78412-5503
Tel: (361)825-5700; Free: 800-482-6822
Fax: (361)825-5810
E-mail: monica.martinez@tamucc.edu
Web Site: www.tamucc.edu/
Description: State-supported, university, coed. Part of Texas A&M University System. Awards bachelor's, master's, and doctoral degrees. Founded 1947. Setting: 240-acre suburban campus. Endowment: $4.5 million. Research spending for the previous fiscal year: $14.7 million. Educational spending for the previous fiscal year: $6551 per student. Total enrollment: 10,162. Faculty: 547 (317 full-time, 230 part-time). Student-undergrad faculty ratio is 21:1. 5,732 applied, 85% were admitted. 13% from top 10% of their high school class, 39% from top quarter, 77% from top half. Full-time: 6,512 students, 59% women, 41% men. Part-time: 1,763 students, 63% women, 37% men. Students come from 45 states and territories, 42 other countries, 3% from out-of-state. 1% American Indian or Alaska Native, non-Hispanic/Latino; 43% Hispanic/Latino; 5% African American, non-Hispanic/Latino; 5% Asian, non-Hispanic/Latino; 0% Native Hawaiian or other Pacific Islander, non-Hispanic/Latino; 4% international. 23% 25 or older, 16% live on campus, 10% transferred in. Retention: 60% of full-time freshmen returned the following year. Academic areas with the most degrees conferred: business/marketing; interdisciplinary studies; health professions and related sciences. Core. Calendar: semesters. Academic remediation for entering students, ESL program, services for LD students, advanced placement, honors program, independent study, distance learning, double major, summer session for credit, part-time degree program, co-op programs and internships. Off campus study at Texas A&M University at Galveston. Study abroad program. ROTC: Army.
Entrance Requirements: Option: electronic application. Required: high school transcript, minimum 2 high school GPA, SAT or ACT. Entrance: moderately difficult. Application deadlines: 7/1, 7/1 for nonresidents. Notifica-

tion: continuous, continuous for nonresidents. SAT Reasoning Test deadline: 7/1. SAT Subject Test deadline: 7/1. Transfer credits accepted: Yes.

Collegiate Environment: Orientation program. Drama-theater group, choral group, marching band, student-run newspaper. Social organizations: 75 open to all; national fraternities, national sororities, local fraternities, local sororities; 5% of eligible men and 5% of eligible women are members. Most popular organizations: Student Accounting Society, Student Art Association, Islander Cultural Alliance, Graduate Student Association, Student Nurses Association. Major annual events: Island Day, Waves of Welcome, Wellness Expo. Student services: health clinic, personal-psychological counseling, women's center. Campus security: 24-hour emergency response devices and patrols, late night transport-escort service, controlled dormitory access. Mary and Jeff Bell Library with 731,586 books, 536,059 microform titles, 1,901 serials, 6,012 audiovisual materials, an OPAC, and a Web page. Operations spending for the previous fiscal year: $2 million. 500 computers available on campus for general student use. A campuswide network can be accessed from student residence rooms and from off campus. Students can access the following: online class registration. Staffed computer lab on campus provides training in use of computers, software, and the Internet.

■ **TEXAS A&M UNIVERSITY–KINGSVILLE**
700 University Blvd.
Kingsville, TX 78363
Tel: (361)593-2111; Free: 800-687-6000
E-mail: laura.knippers@tamuk.edu
Web Site: www.tamuk.edu/

Description: State-supported, university, coed. Part of Texas A&M University System. Awards bachelor's, master's, and doctoral degrees. Founded 1925. Setting: 255-acre small town campus. Endowment: $15 million. Research spending for the previous fiscal year: $16.3 million. Educational spending for the previous fiscal year: $3511 per student. Total enrollment: 7,234. Faculty: 399 (267 full-time, 132 part-time). Student-undergrad faculty ratio is 20:1. 4,920 applied, 93% were admitted. 11% from top 10% of their high school class, 35% from top quarter, 73% from top half. Full-time: 4,864 students, 48% women, 52% men. Part-time: 1,103 students, 55% women, 45% men. Students come from 32 states and territories, 28 other countries, 2% from out-of-state. 0.3% American Indian or Alaska Native, non-Hispanic/Latino; 67% Hispanic/Latino; 6% African American, non-Hispanic/Latino; 1% Asian, non-Hispanic/Latino; 0.1% Native Hawaiian or other Pacific Islander, non-Hispanic/Latino; 1% international. 16% 25 or older, 9% transferred in. Retention: 62% of full-time freshmen returned the following year. Academic areas with the most degrees conferred: engineering; business/marketing; agriculture. Core. Calendar: semesters. Academic remediation for entering students, ESL program, services for LD students, advanced placement, honors program, distance learning, double major, summer session for credit, part-time degree program, co-op programs and internships, graduate courses open to undergrads. Off campus study. Study abroad program. ROTC: Army.

Entrance Requirements: Open admission for the college of arts and sciences. Options: electronic application, early admission, deferred admission. Required: high school transcript, SAT or ACT. Recommended: minimum 2 high school GPA. Required for some: interview. Entrance: moderately difficult. Application deadline: Rolling. Notification: continuous. Transfer credits accepted: Yes.

Costs Per Year: Application fee: $15. State resident tuition: $6940 full-time. Nonresident tuition: $17,560 full-time. Full-time tuition varies according to course load and degree level. College room and board: $7484. College room only: $3674. Room and board charges vary according to board plan and housing facility.

Collegiate Environment: Orientation program. Drama-theater group, choral group, marching band, student-run newspaper, radio station. Social organizations: 28 open to all; national fraternities, national sororities, local fraternities, local sororities. Most popular organizations: Catholic Student Organization, Baptist Student Ministry, Gamerz Elite, Javelina Students for Sustainability, Aggie Club. Major annual events: Homecoming, Fall Carnival, Spring Fling. Student services: health clinic, personal-psychological counseling, women's center. Campus security: 24-hour emergency response devices and patrols, late night transport-escort service, controlled dormitory access. 2,329 college housing spaces available; 2,167 were occupied in 2012-13. Freshmen guaranteed college housing. On-campus residence required in freshman year. Options: coed, men-only, women-only housing available. James C. Jernigan Library with 797,368 books, 654,959 microform titles, 34,176 serials, 10,113 audiovisual materials, an OPAC, and a Web page. Operations spending for the previous fiscal year: $2.5 million. 170

computers available on campus for general student use. A campuswide network can be accessed from student residence rooms and from off campus. Students can access the following: online class registration, Blackboard. Staffed computer lab on campus provides training in use of computers and software.

■ **TEXAS A&M UNIVERSITY–SAN ANTONIO**
One University Way
San Antonio, TX 78224
Tel: (210)784-1000
E-mail: jennifer.zamarripa@tamusa.tamus.edu
Web Site: www.tamusa.tamus.edu/

Description: State-supported, comprehensive, coed. Awards bachelor's and master's degrees.

Entrance Requirements: Required: high school transcript. Application deadline: 8/15.

■ **TEXAS A&M UNIVERSITY–TEXARKANA**
PO Box 5518
Texarkana, TX 75505-5518
Tel: (903)223-3000
Fax: (903)832-8890
E-mail: admissions@tamut.edu
Web Site: www.tamut.edu/

Description: State-supported, upper-level, coed. Part of Texas A&M University System. Awards bachelor's and master's degrees. Founded 1971. Setting: 1-acre small town campus. Total enrollment: 1,653. Student-undergrad faculty ratio is 11:1. 62% 25 or older. Core. Calendar: semesters. Services for LD students, advanced placement, self-designed majors, independent study, distance learning, summer session for credit, part-time degree program, internships, graduate courses open to undergrads.

Collegiate Environment: Orientation program. Student-run newspaper. Campus security: 24-hour patrols, late night transport-escort service. John F. Moss Library plus 1 other with an OPAC and a Web page.

■ **TEXAS CHRISTIAN UNIVERSITY**
2800 S University Dr.
Fort Worth, TX 76129-0002
Tel: (817)257-7000; Free: 800-828-3764
E-mail: frogmail@tcu.edu
Web Site: www.tcu.edu/

Description: Independent, university, coed, affiliated with Christian Church (Disciples of Christ). Awards bachelor's, master's, and doctoral degrees and post-master's certificates. Founded 1873. Setting: 277-acre suburban campus with easy access to Dallas-Fort Worth. Endowment: $1.1 billion. Research spending for the previous fiscal year: $10.2 million. Educational spending for the previous fiscal year: $14,178 per student. Total enrollment: 9,727. Faculty: 886 (572 full-time, 314 part-time). Student-undergrad faculty ratio is 13:1. 19,335 applied, 41% were admitted. 43% from top 10% of their high school class, 75% from top quarter, 96% from top half. Full-time: 8,145 students, 60% women, 40% men. Part-time: 311 students, 51% women, 49% men. Students come from 51 states and territories, 66 other countries, 33% from out-of-state. 1% American Indian or Alaska Native, non-Hispanic/Latino; 10% Hispanic/Latino; 5% African American, non-Hispanic/Latino; 2% Asian, non-Hispanic/Latino; 0.2% Native Hawaiian or other Pacific Islander, non-Hispanic/Latino; 4% international. 4% 25 or older, 47% live on campus, 5% transferred in. Retention: 90% of full-time freshmen returned the following year. Academic areas with the most degrees conferred: business/marketing; communication/journalism; health professions and related sciences. Core. Calendar: semesters. ESL program, services for LD students, advanced placement, accelerated degree program, freshman honors college, honors program, independent study, distance learning, double major, summer session for credit, part-time degree program, internships, graduate courses open to undergrads. Study abroad program. ROTC: Army, Air Force.

Entrance Requirements: Options: electronic application, early action, deferred admission, international baccalaureate accepted. Required: essay, high school transcript, 1 recommendation, SAT or ACT. Recommended: 2 recommendations, interview. Entrance: very difficult. Application deadlines: 2/15, 11/1 for early action. Notification: 4/1, 1/1 for early action. SAT Reasoning Test deadline: 2/15. SAT Subject Test deadline: 2/15. Transfer credits accepted: Yes. Applicants placed on waiting list: 2,666. Wait-listed applicants offered admission: 269. Early action applicants: 10,368. Early action applicants admitted: 4,969.

Costs Per Year: Application fee: $40. Tuition: $36,500 full-time. Mandatory fees: $90 full-time.

Collegiate Environment: Orientation program. Drama-theater group, choral group, marching band, student-run newspaper, radio station. Social organizations: 210 open to all; national fraternities, national sororities, local fraternities, local sororities, local coed music fraternities; 42% of eligible men and 51% of eligible women are members. Major annual events: Opening Concert, Homecoming, Christmas Tree lighting. Student services: health clinic, personal-psychological counseling, women's center. Campus security: 24-hour emergency response devices and patrols, late night transport-escort service, controlled dormitory access, emergency call boxes, video surveillance in parking lots, self-defense education, lighted sidewalks, emergency notification system. College housing designed to accommodate 3,650 students; 3,900 undergraduates lived in college housing during 2012-13. Freshmen guaranteed college housing. On-campus residence required through sophomore year. Options: coed, men-only, women-only housing available. Mary Couts Burnett Library with 1.4 million books, 511,455 microform titles, 75,302 serials, 67,946 audiovisual materials, an OPAC, and a Web page. Operations spending for the previous fiscal year: $7.3 million. 1,400 computers available on campus for general student use. A campus-wide network can be accessed from student residence rooms and from off campus. Students can access the following: online class registration. Staffed computer lab on campus (open 24 hours a day) provides training in use of computers, software, and the Internet.

Community Environment: The University is easily accessible to a variety of recreational, educational, and professional opportunities in the Fort Worth/Dallas metroplex. Major museums, parks, theatres, churches, and restaurants are within a few miles from the campus.

■ **TEXAS COLLEGE**
2404 N Grand Ave.
Tyler, TX 75712-4500
Tel: (903)593-8311; Free: 800-306-6299
E-mail: jroberts@texascollege.edu
Web Site: www.texascollege.edu/

Description: Independent, 4-year, coed, affiliated with Christian Methodist Episcopal Church. Awards associate and bachelor's degrees. Founded 1894. Setting: 25-acre urban campus. Endowment: $1.3 million. Educational spending for the previous fiscal year: $2225 per student. Total enrollment: 883. Faculty: 35. Student-undergrad faculty ratio is 25:1. Full-time: 841 students, 41% women, 59% men. Part-time: 19 students, 68% women, 32% men. Students come from 26 states and territories, 1 other country, 14% from out-of-state. 9% Hispanic/Latino; 87% African American, non-Hispanic/Latino; 0.1% Asian, non-Hispanic/Latino; 0.1% international. 16% 25 or older, 31% live on campus, 21% transferred in. Retention: 46% of full-time freshmen returned the following year. Core. Calendar: semesters. Academic remediation for entering students, services for LD students, advanced placement, accelerated degree program, honors program, independent study, distance learning, double major, summer session for credit, part-time degree program, adult/continuing education programs.

Entrance Requirements: Open admission. Options: electronic application, early admission. Required: high school transcript, minimum 2 high school GPA, SAT or ACT. Entrance: noncompetitive. Application deadlines: Rolling, Rolling for nonresidents. Notification: continuous, continuous for nonresidents. Transfer credits accepted: Yes.

Costs Per Year: Application fee: $20. Comprehensive fee: $16,686 includes full-time tuition ($7996), mandatory fees ($1690), and college room and board ($7000). College room only: $3600.

Collegiate Environment: Orientation program. Choral group, marching band. Social organizations: national fraternities, national sororities, local fraternities, local sororities. Most popular organizations: Omega Psi Phi, Delta Sigma Theta, Pre-Alumni Council. Major annual events: Springfest, Homecoming, Religious Emphasis Week. Student services: health clinic, personal-psychological counseling. Campus security: 24-hour emergency response devices and patrols, late night transport-escort service. D. R. Glass Library with 80,500 books, 24,513 microform titles, 71 serials, 1,266 audiovisual materials, an OPAC, and a Web page. Operations spending for the previous fiscal year: $58,715. 252 computers available on campus for general student use. Computer purchase/lease plans available. A campuswide network can be accessed from student residence rooms. Staffed computer lab on campus provides training in use of computers, software, and the Internet.

■ **TEXAS LUTHERAN UNIVERSITY**
1000 W Ct. St.
Seguin, TX 78155-5999
Tel: (830)372-8000; Free: 800-771-8521
Fax: (830)372-8096
E-mail: toliver@tlu.edu
Web Site: www.tlu.edu/

Description: Independent, comprehensive, coed, affiliated with Evangelical Lutheran Church. Awards bachelor's and master's degrees. Founded 1891. Setting: 196-acre suburban campus with easy access to San Antonio, Austin. Endowment: $79 million. Research spending for the previous fiscal year: $43,534. Educational spending for the previous fiscal year: $6661 per student. Total enrollment: 1,318. Faculty: 129 (74 full-time, 55 part-time). Student-undergrad faculty ratio is 14:1. 1,852 applied, 53% were admitted. 19% from top 10% of their high school class, 49% from top quarter, 87% from top half. 1 valedictorian. Full-time: 1,246 students, 53% women, 47% men. Part-time: 65 students, 54% women, 46% men. Students come from 19 states and territories, 6 other countries, 3% from out-of-state. 0.5% American Indian or Alaska Native, non-Hispanic/Latino; 28% Hispanic/Latino; 9% African American, non-Hispanic/Latino; 1% Asian, non-Hispanic/Latino; 0.1% Native Hawaiian or other Pacific Islander, non-Hispanic/Latino; 0.5% international. 6% 25 or older, 56% live on campus, 5% transferred in. Retention: 67% of full-time freshmen returned the following year. Academic areas with the most degrees conferred: business/marketing; parks and recreation; psychology. Core. Calendar: semesters. Services for LD students, advanced placement, honors program, independent study, double major, summer session for credit, part-time degree program, internships. Study abroad program. ROTC: Army (c), Air Force (c).

Entrance Requirements: Options: electronic application, deferred admission, international baccalaureate accepted. Required: essay, high school transcript, 2 recommendations, SAT or ACT. Recommended: interview. Required for some: minimum 2 high school GPA. Entrance: moderately difficult. Application deadline: Rolling. Notification: 8/1.

Costs Per Year: Application fee: $40. Comprehensive fee: $32,330 includes full-time tuition ($24,860), mandatory fees ($130), and college room and board ($7340). College room only: $3800. Room and board charges vary according to board plan and housing facility. Part-time tuition: $825 per semester hour.

Collegiate Environment: Orientation program. Drama-theater group, choral group, student-run newspaper. Social organizations: 52 open to all; local fraternities, local sororities; 30% of eligible men and 54% of eligible women are members. Most popular organizations: Campus Ministry, Mexican American Student Association, Student Government Association, Black Student Union. Major annual events: KROST Symposium, Christmas Vespers, Spring Fling. Student services: health clinic, personal-psychological counseling, women's center. Campus security: 24-hour emergency response devices and patrols, late night transport-escort service, controlled dormitory access. 935 college housing spaces available; 702 were occupied in 2012-13. Freshmen guaranteed college housing. On-campus residence required through senior year. Options: coed, men-only, women-only housing available. Blumberg Memorial Library with 216,518 books, 119,086 microform titles, 16,259 serials, 2,997 audiovisual materials, an OPAC, and a Web page. Operations spending for the previous fiscal year: $723,093. 243 computers available on campus for general student use. A campuswide network can be accessed from student residence rooms and from off campus. Students can access the following: online class registration, free printing. Staffed computer lab on campus provides training in use of computers.

Community Environment: Population 24,230, Seguin is a suburban community enjoying temperate climate. The city is reached by Interstate 10. There is a library, a museum, churches representing 10 different denominations, and a hospital serving the community. Various job opportunities are available here. Various civic, fraternal and veteran's organizations are active in Seguin. Nearby Lake McQueeney offers water skiing.

■ **TEXAS SCHOOL OF BUSINESS, FRIENDSWOOD CAMPUS**
3208 Farm to Market Rd. 528
Friendswood, TX 77546
Web Site: www.friendswood.tsb.edu/

Description: Proprietary, 2-year, coed. Awards diplomas and terminal associate degrees.

■ **TEXAS SCHOOL OF BUSINESS, HOUSTON NORTH CAMPUS**
711 E Airtex Dr.
Houston, TX 77073

Tel: (281)443-8900

Web Site: www.north.tsb.edu/

Description: Proprietary, 2-year, coed. Awards diplomas and terminal associate degrees.

■ **TEXAS SOUTHERN UNIVERSITY**

3100 Cleburne Ave.

Houston, TX 77004-4584

Tel: (713)313-7011

Fax: (713)527-7842

E-mail: eservices@em.tsu.edu

Web Site: www.tsu.edu/

Description: State-supported, university, coed. Part of Texas Higher Education Coordinating Board. Awards bachelor's, master's, and doctoral degrees. Founded 1947. Setting: 147-acre urban campus. Endowment: $35.4 million. Research spending for the previous fiscal year: $7.5 million. Educational spending for the previous fiscal year: $10,401 per student. Total enrollment: 9,646. Faculty: 602 (370 full-time, 232 part-time). Student-undergrad faculty ratio is 19:1. 9,393 applied, 53% were admitted. 5% from top 10% of their high school class, 22% from top quarter, 58% from top half. Full-time: 5,905 students, 57% women, 43% men. Part-time: 1,116 students, 59% women, 41% men. Students come from 42 states and territories, 23 other countries, 11% from out-of-state. 0.3% American Indian or Alaska Native, non-Hispanic/Latino; 5% Hispanic/Latino; 86% African American, non-Hispanic/Latino; 2% Asian, non-Hispanic/Latino; 4% international. 25% 25 or older, 24% live on campus, 11% transferred in. Retention: 61% of full-time freshmen returned the following year. Academic areas with the most degrees conferred: business/marketing; health professions and related sciences; biological/life sciences; communication/journalism. Core. Calendar: semesters. Academic remediation for entering students, ESL program, services for LD students, accelerated degree program, honors program, independent study, distance learning, summer session for credit, part-time degree program, external degree program, adult/continuing education programs, co-op programs and internships, graduate courses open to undergrads. Off campus study at Houston Community College Pinemont Center, North Harris College Career Center. Study abroad program. ROTC: Army, Naval (c), Air Force (c).

Entrance Requirements: Open admission. Options: electronic application, early admission, early decision. Required: high school transcript, minimum 2 high school GPA. Required for some: SAT or ACT. Entrance: noncompetitive. Application deadline: 8/15. Notification: 8/28. SAT Reasoning Test deadline: 8/15. SAT Subject Test deadline: 8/15.

Costs Per Year: Application fee: $42. State resident tuition: $7646 full-time. Nonresident tuition: $16,946 full-time. Full-time tuition varies according to course level, course load, degree level, and program. College room and board: $10,566. Room and board charges vary according to board plan, housing facility, and location.

Collegiate Environment: Orientation program. Drama-theater group, choral group, marching band, student-run newspaper, radio station. Social organizations: 58 open to all; national fraternities, national sororities, local fraternities, local sororities. Most popular organizations: Debate Team, University Program Council, Student Government Association, Band. Major annual events: Homecoming Festival, Labor Day Classic Game, Spring Festival. Student services: legal services, health clinic, personal-psychological counseling. Campus security: 24-hour emergency response devices and patrols, student patrols, late night transport-escort service. 1,600 college housing spaces available. Freshmen guaranteed college housing. Options: coed, men-only, women-only housing available. Robert J. Terry Library plus 2 others with 261,506 books, 504,149 microform titles, 1,774 serials, an OPAC, and a Web page.

Community Environment: See University of Houston.

■ **TEXAS SOUTHMOST COLLEGE**

80 Fort Brown

Brownsville, TX 78520-4991

Tel: (956)882-8200; Free: 877-882-8721

Web Site: www.utb.edu/

Description: District-supported, 2-year, coed. Part of University of Texas System. Awards certificates, transfer associate, and terminal associate degrees. Founded 1926. Setting: 65-acre urban campus. Calendar: semesters. Summer session for credit, part-time degree program.

Entrance Requirements: Open admission. Entrance: noncompetitive. Application deadline: 8/1.

Collegiate Environment: Campus security: 24-hour emergency response devices and patrols.

■ **TEXAS STATE TECHNICAL COLLEGE HARLINGEN**

1902 N Loop 499

Harlingen, TX 78550-3697

Tel: (956)364-4000; Free: 800-852-8784

Fax: (956)364-5140

E-mail: paula.arredondo@harlingen.tstc.edu

Web Site: www.harlingen.tstc.edu/

Description: State-supported, 2-year, coed. Part of Texas State Technical College System. Awards certificates, transfer associate, and terminal associate degrees. Founded 1967. Setting: 125-acre small town campus. Total enrollment: 5,509. Faculty: 215 (157 full-time, 58 part-time). Student-undergrad faculty ratio is 19:1. Full-time: 2,361 students, 45% women, 55% men. Part-time: 3,148 students, 58% women, 42% men. Students come from 18 states and territories, 2 other countries, 0.4% from out-of-state. 0.1% American Indian or Alaska Native, non-Hispanic/Latino; 88% Hispanic/Latino; 1% African American, non-Hispanic/Latino; 1% Asian, non-Hispanic/Latino; 0.1% Native Hawaiian or other Pacific Islander, non-Hispanic/Latino; 0.1% international. 33% 25 or older, 5% live on campus, 6% transferred in. Core. Calendar: semesters. Academic remediation for entering students, ESL program, services for LD students, distance learning, double major, summer session for credit, part-time degree program, adult/continuing education programs, co-op programs and internships.

Entrance Requirements: Open admission except for dental hygiene, dental assistant, health information technology programs. Options: electronic application, early admission, deferred admission. Required: high school transcript. Entrance: noncompetitive. Application deadline: Rolling. Notification: continuous.

Costs Per Year: Application fee: $0. State resident tuition: $3240 full-time, $90 per credit hour part-time. Nonresident tuition: $9144 full-time, $254 per credit hour part-time. Mandatory fees: $1656 full-time. Full-time tuition and fees vary according to course load and program. Part-time tuition varies according to course load and program. College room and board: $2775. College room only: $2175. Room and board charges vary according to board plan and housing facility.

Collegiate Environment: Orientation program. Student-run newspaper. Most popular organizations: Student Government Association, VICA (Vocational Industrial Clubs of America), Business Professionals of America. Major annual events: Oktoberfest, Miss TSTC Pageant, Techsan Day. Student services: health clinic, personal-psychological counseling, women's center. Campus security: 24-hour emergency response devices and patrols, late night transport-escort service, night watchman for housing area. 377 college housing spaces available; 270 were occupied in 2012-13. No special consideration for freshman housing applicants. Options: men-only, women-only housing available. Dr. J. Gilbert Leal Learning Resource Center with 23,506 books, 80 serials, 649 audiovisual materials, an OPAC, and a Web page. 2,000 computers available on campus for general student use. Computer purchase/lease plans available. A campuswide network can be accessed. Students can access the following: online class registration. Staffed computer lab on campus.

■ **TEXAS STATE TECHNICAL COLLEGE WACO**

3801 Campus Dr.

Waco, TX 76705-1695

Tel: (254)799-3611; Free: 800-792-8784

E-mail: marcus.balch@tstc.edu

Web Site: waco.tstc.edu/

Description: State-supported, 2-year, coed. Part of Texas State Technical College System. Awards certificates, transfer associate, and terminal associate degrees. Founded 1965. Setting: 200-acre suburban campus. Total enrollment: 4,277. Faculty: 283 (253 full-time, 30 part-time). Student-undergrad faculty ratio is 17:1. 1,016 applied, 100% were admitted. Full-time: 6,367 students, 22% women, 78% men. Part-time: 1,962 students, 24% women, 76% men. 1% from out-of-state. 1% American Indian or Alaska Native, non-Hispanic/Latino; 18% Hispanic/Latino; 17% African American, non-Hispanic/Latino; 1% Asian, non-Hispanic/Latino; 0.2% Native Hawaiian or other Pacific Islander, non-Hispanic/Latino; 0% international. 36% 25 or older, 17% transferred in. Retention: 52% of full-time freshmen returned the following year. Calendar: trimesters. Academic remediation for entering students, services for LD students, distance learning, summer session for credit, part-time degree program, adult/continuing education programs, co-op programs and internships.

Entrance Requirements: Open admission. Options: electronic application, early admission. Required: high school transcript, ACCUPLACER. Required for some: interview. Entrance: noncompetitive. Application deadline: Rolling. Notification: continuous. Transfer credits accepted: Yes.

Costs Per Year: Application fee: $0. State resident tuition: $2238 full-time, $93 per credit hour part-time. Nonresident tuition: $6096 full-time, $254 per credit hour part-time. Mandatory fees: $1104 full-time, $1104 per year part-time. College room only: $2440. Room charges vary according to housing facility and location.

Collegiate Environment: Orientation program. Social organizations: 25 open to all. Most popular organizations: Student Ambassador Association, SkillsUSA, Student Leadership Council, Phi Theta Kappa, Hispanic Student Association. Major annual events: DIA Techsana, Christmas Parade, Halloween Festival. Student services: health clinic, personal-psychological counseling, women's center. Campus security: 24-hour emergency response devices and patrols, late night transport-escort service, controlled dormitory access. 1,781 college housing spaces available. On-campus residence required in freshman year. Options: coed, men-only, women-only housing available. Texas State Technical College-Waco Campus Library with 52,296 books, 1.1 million microform titles, 235,477 serials, 5,335 audiovisual materials, an OPAC, and a Web page. 1,300 computers available on campus for general student use. Computer purchase/lease plans available. A campuswide network can be accessed from student residence rooms and from off campus. Students can access the following: online class registration, various software packages. Staffed computer lab on campus (open 24 hours a day) provides training in use of computers, software, and the Internet.

■ TEXAS STATE TECHNICAL COLLEGE WEST TEXAS

300 College Dr.
Sweetwater, TX 79556-4108
Tel: (915)235-7300; Free: 800-592-8784
Fax: (915)235-7359
E-mail: maria.aquirre@sweetwater.tstc.edu
Web Site: www.westtexas.tstc.edu/

Description: State-supported, 2-year, coed. Part of Texas State Technical College System. Awards certificates and terminal associate degrees. Founded 1970. Setting: 115-acre small town campus. Endowment: $100,429. Educational spending for the previous fiscal year: $12,438 per student. Total enrollment: 1,689. Faculty: 116 (89 full-time, 27 part-time). Student-undergrad faculty ratio is 7:1. 248 applied, 100% were admitted. Full-time: 299 students, 33% women, 67% men. Part-time: 1,390 students, 44% women, 56% men. Students come from 18 states and territories, 3% from out-of-state. 35% 25 or older, 14% live on campus, 10% transferred in. Core. Calendar: semesters. Academic remediation for entering students, services for LD students, advanced placement, distance learning, summer session for credit, part-time degree program, adult/continuing education programs, co-op programs and internships.

Entrance Requirements: Open admission. Options: electronic application, early admission, deferred admission. Required: high school transcript, ACCUPLACER primarily; also accept THEA, TASP, SAT and ACTTHEA. Entrance: noncompetitive. Application deadline: Rolling. Notification: continuous.

Collegiate Environment: Orientation program. Social organizations: 25 open to all. Most popular organizations: Student Government Association, Association of Information Technology Professionals (AITP), Mexican-American Student Club, Autobody Club (AUB), Vocational Nurses Association. Major annual events: Techsan Day, Valentine's Dinner and Dance, Halloween Party. Student services: health clinic, personal-psychological counseling. Campus security: 24-hour patrols. Texas State Technical College West Texas Library with 59,711 books, 212,050 serials, 681 audiovisual materials, an OPAC, and a Web page. 500 computers available on campus for general student use. Computer purchase/lease plans available. A computer is required for all students. A campuswide network can be accessed from student residence rooms and from off campus. Students can access the following: online class registration. Staffed computer lab on campus provides training in use of computers, software, and the Internet.

■ TEXAS STATE TECHNICAL COLLEGE–MARSHALL

2650 E End Blvd. S
Marshall, TX 75671
Tel: (903)935-1010; Free: 888-382-8782
E-mail: Pat.Robbins@marshall.tstc.edu
Web Site: www.marshall.tstc.edu/

Description: State-supported, 2-year, coed. Part of Texas State Technical College System. Awards certificates and terminal associate degrees. Founded 1991. Total enrollment: 705. Faculty: 41 (30 full-time, 11 part-time). Student-undergrad faculty ratio is 12:1. Full-time: 322 students, 25% women, 75% men. Part-time: 383 students, 39% women, 61% men. 26% 25 or older. Retention: 49% of full-time freshmen returned the following year. Calendar: semesters.

Entrance Requirements: Required: high school transcript. Entrance: noncompetitive.

Collegiate Environment: Orientation program. 500 computers available on campus for general student use. Computer purchase/lease plans available. A campuswide network can be accessed from student residence rooms. Students can access the following: online class registration. Staffed computer lab on campus provides training in use of computers, software, and the Internet.

■ TEXAS STATE UNIVERSITY–SAN MARCOS

601 University Dr.
San Marcos, TX 78666
Tel: (512)245-2111
Fax: (512)245-8044
E-mail: admissions@txstate.edu
Web Site: www.txstate.edu/

Description: State-supported, university, coed. Part of Texas State University System. Awards bachelor's, master's, and doctoral degrees. Founded 1899. Setting: 423-acre suburban campus with easy access to San Antonio, Austin. Endowment: $111.4 million. Research spending for the previous fiscal year: $31.9 million. Educational spending for the previous fiscal year: $1980 per student. Total enrollment: 34,225. Faculty: 1,590 (1,196 full-time, 394 part-time). Student-undergrad faculty ratio is 20:1. 10,418 applied, 66% were admitted. 11% from top 10% of their high school class, 47% from top quarter, 90% from top half. 2 National Merit Scholars, 22 valedictorians. Full-time: 24,223 students, 56% women, 44% men. Part-time: 5,235 students, 52% women, 48% men. Students come from 49 states and territories, 42 other countries, 1% from out-of-state. 0.4% American Indian or Alaska Native, non-Hispanic/Latino; 29% Hispanic/Latino; 6% African American, non-Hispanic/Latino; 2% Asian, non-Hispanic/Latino; 0.1% Native Hawaiian or other Pacific Islander, non-Hispanic/Latino; 1% international. 16% 25 or older, 20% live on campus, 13% transferred in. Retention: 77% of full-time freshmen returned the following year. Academic areas with the most degrees conferred: business/marketing; interdisciplinary studies; visual and performing arts. Core. Calendar: semesters. Academic remediation for entering students, ESL program, services for LD students, advanced placement, accelerated degree program, freshman honors college, honors program, independent study, distance learning, double major, summer session for credit, part-time degree program, adult/continuing education programs, internships, graduate courses open to undergrads. Off campus study at The University of Texas at San Antonio, Round Rock Multi Institutional Teaching Center. Study abroad program. ROTC: Army, Air Force.

Entrance Requirements: Options: electronic application, early admission, deferred admission. Required: essay, high school transcript, SAT or ACT. Recommended: SAT, ACT. Entrance: moderately difficult. Application deadlines: 5/1, 5/1 for nonresidents. Notification: continuous. SAT Reasoning Test deadline: 5/1. Transfer credits accepted: Yes.

Costs Per Year: Application fee: $60. State resident tuition: $6510 full-time, $217 per credit hour part-time. Nonresident tuition: $17,040 full-time, $568 per credit hour part-time. Mandatory fees: $2262 full-time, $52 per credit hour part-time, $396 per term part-time. Full-time tuition and fees vary according to course load and degree level. Part-time tuition and fees vary according to course load and degree level. College room and board: $7070. College room only: $4670. Room and board charges vary according to board plan and housing facility.

Collegiate Environment: Orientation program. Drama-theater group, choral group, marching band, student-run newspaper, radio station. Social organizations: 364 open to all; national fraternities, national sororities, local fraternities, local sororities, Religious, multi-cultural, honors, professional; 5% of eligible men and 5% of eligible women are members. Most popular organizations: Non-traditional Students Association, Student Association for Campus Activities, Association Student Government, Annual Martin Luther King Jr. Commemoration. Major annual events: Homecoming, Springfest, Cricket Fest. Student services: legal services, health clinic, personal-psychological counseling. Campus security: 24-hour emergency response devices and patrols, late night transport-escort service, controlled dormitory access. 6,561 college housing spaces available; 5,898 were occupied in

2012-13. Freshmen guaranteed college housing. On-campus residence required through sophomore year. Options: coed, men-only, women-only housing available. Alkek Library plus 1 other with 1.6 million books, 1.9 million microform titles, 14,762 serials, 276,124 audiovisual materials, an OPAC, and a Web page. Operations spending for the previous fiscal year: $14.4 million. 1,792 computers available on campus for general student use. Computer purchase/lease plans available. A campuswide network can be accessed from student residence rooms and from off campus. Students can access the following: online class registration. Staffed computer lab on campus (open 24 hours a day) provides training in use of computers, software, and the Internet.

Community Environment: The university is located in San Marcos, a historic community of 37,000 on I-35 located between San Antonio, 45 miles to the south, and Austin, 30 miles to the north. Both cities are within commuting distance of San Marcos and have major airports. San Marcos has a municipal airport. The central Texas climate offers sunshine most of the year with moderate to cool winters and warm to hot summers. The area enjoys a healthy economy bolstered by clean, light industry, active tourism, and well-preserved historic districts. It is the home to churches of many denominations and various civic organizations. Local recreation includes golfing, fishing, hunting, swimming,"tubing," canoeing and other outdoor activities. Annual celebrations include Chilympiad, Sights and Sounds of Christmas, Summerfest, Cinco de Mayo, and weekly summer concerts in the park.

■ **TEXAS TECH UNIVERSITY**
Lubbock, TX 79409
Tel: (806)742-2011
Fax: (806)742-3055
Web Site: www.ttu.edu/

Description: State-supported, university, coed. Part of Texas Tech University System. Awards bachelor's, master's, and doctoral degrees. Founded 1923. Setting: 1,839-acre urban campus. Endowment: $491.6 million. Research spending for the previous fiscal year: $142.8 million. Educational spending for the previous fiscal year: $5026 per student. Total enrollment: 32,327. Faculty: 1,348 (1,153 full-time, 195 part-time). Student-undergrad faculty ratio is 24:1. 17,569 applied, 66% were admitted. 21% from top 10% of their high school class, 56% from top quarter, 87% from top half. 8 National Merit Scholars, 105 valedictorians. Full-time: 23,453 students, 45% women, 55% men. Part-time: 2,610 students, 45% women, 55% men. Students come from 56 states and territories, 78 other countries, 5% from out-of-state. 1% American Indian or Alaska Native, non-Hispanic/Latino; 18% Hispanic/Latino; 5% African American, non-Hispanic/Latino; 3% Asian, non-Hispanic/Latino; 0.1% Native Hawaiian or other Pacific Islander, non-Hispanic/Latino; 3% international. 10% 25 or older, 24% live on campus, 10% transferred in. Retention: 82% of full-time freshmen returned the following year. Academic areas with the most degrees conferred: business/marketing; engineering; family and consumer sciences. Core. Calendar: semesters. Academic remediation for entering students, ESL program, services for LD students, advanced placement, accelerated degree program, self-designed majors, freshman honors college, honors program, independent study, distance learning, double major, summer session for credit, part-time degree program, external degree program, co-op programs and internships, graduate courses open to undergrads. Off campus study at South Plains College. Study abroad program. ROTC: Army, Air Force.

Entrance Requirements: Options: electronic application, early admission, international baccalaureate accepted. Required: high school transcript, SAT or ACT. Recommended: essay. Entrance: moderately difficult. Application deadline: 3/1. Notification: continuous. SAT Reasoning Test deadline: 8/1. SAT Subject Test deadline: 8/1. Transfer credits accepted: Yes. Applicants placed on waiting list: 344. Wait-listed applicants offered admission: 241.

Costs Per Year: Application fee: $60. State resident tuition: $6077 full-time, $203 per credit hour part-time. Nonresident tuition: $16,607 full-time, $554 per credit hour part-time. Mandatory fees: $2865 full-time, $35 per credit hour part-time, $908. Full-time tuition and fees vary according to course load, location, and reciprocity agreements. Part-time tuition and fees vary according to course load, location, and reciprocity agreements. College room and board: $8275. College room only: $4380. Room and board charges vary according to board plan and housing facility.

Collegiate Environment: Orientation program. Drama-theater group, choral group, marching band, student-run newspaper. Social organizations: 440 open to all; national fraternities, national sororities, local fraternities, local sororities; 12% of eligible men and 18% of eligible women are members. Most popular organizations: Red Raider Club, Alpha Lambda Delta, Phi Eta Sigma, Paradigm, Campus Crusade for Christ. Major annual events:

Homecoming, Carol of Lights, Arbor Day. Student services: legal services, health clinic, personal-psychological counseling. Campus security: 24-hour emergency response devices and patrols, late night transport-escort service, controlled dormitory access. Texas Tech Library plus 3 others with 2.7 million books, 2.1 million microform titles, 58,040 serials, 57,532 audiovisual materials, an OPAC, and a Web page. Operations spending for the previous fiscal year: $22.3 million. 3,000 computers available on campus for general student use. Computer purchase/lease plans available. A campuswide network can be accessed from student residence rooms and from off campus. Students can access the following: online class registration, online degree plans, accounts, transcripts, schedules. Staffed computer lab on campus provides training in use of computers, software, and the Internet.

Community Environment: Lubbock, with a population of nearly 210,000, is located on top of the caprock on the South Plains of Texas. Its climate is excellent, with over 3,550 hours of sunshine every year. Summers are dry and not extremely hot, while winters are dry and moderate (average rainfall is only 18 inches). An average annual temperature of 60 degrees coupled with the average noon humidity of 46 percent combine to make Lubbock comfortable year-round. The city lies 320 miles west of Dallas, and an equal distance 320 miles south east of Albuquerque, New Mexico. Several airlines and an interstate bus line serve the city, as well as four U.S. highways, including an interstate highway.

■ **TEXAS WESLEYAN UNIVERSITY**
1201 Wesleyan St.
Fort Worth, TX 76105-1536
Tel: (817)531-4444; Free: 800-580-8980
Fax: (817)531-7515
E-mail: admissions@txwes.edu
Web Site: www.txwes.edu/

Description: Independent United Methodist, comprehensive, coed. Awards bachelor's, master's, and doctoral degrees. Founded 1890. Setting: 74-acre urban campus with easy access to Dallas-Fort Worth. Endowment: $47.9 million. Research spending for the previous fiscal year: $35,842. Total enrollment: 3,204. Faculty: 274 (173 full-time, 101 part-time). Student-undergrad faculty ratio is 15:1. 2,107 applied, 55% were admitted. 16% from top 10% of their high school class, 40% from top quarter, 80% from top half. Full-time: 1,233 students, 56% women, 44% men. Part-time: 561 students, 61% women, 39% men. Students come from 22 states and territories, 29 other countries, 4% from out-of-state. 1% American Indian or Alaska Native, non-Hispanic/Latino; 21% Hispanic/Latino; 17% African American, non-Hispanic/Latino; 2% Asian, non-Hispanic/Latino; 0.1% Native Hawaiian or other Pacific Islander, non-Hispanic/Latino; 8% international. 20% 25 or older, 25% live on campus, 15% transferred in. Retention: 65% of full-time freshmen returned the following year. Academic areas with the most degrees conferred: business/marketing; education; interdisciplinary studies. Core. Calendar: semesters. Academic remediation for entering students, services for LD students, advanced placement, accelerated degree program, honors program, independent study, distance learning, double major, summer session for credit, part-time degree program, external degree program, internships, graduate courses open to undergrads. Off campus study. Study abroad program. ROTC: Army, Air Force (c).

Entrance Requirements: Options: electronic application, deferred admission, international baccalaureate accepted. Required: minimum 2 high school GPA, SAT or ACT. Required for some: essay, high school transcript. Entrance: moderately difficult. Application deadline: Rolling. Notification: continuous. SAT Reasoning Test deadline: 8/15. SAT Subject Test deadline: 8/15.

Costs Per Year: Comprehensive fee: $28,310 includes full-time tuition ($18,722), mandatory fees ($2118), and college room and board ($7470). College room only: $4380. Full-time tuition and fees vary according to course load. Room and board charges vary according to housing facility. Part-time tuition: $635 per credit hour. Part-time mandatory fees: $80 per credit hour. Part-time tuition and fees vary according to course load.

Collegiate Environment: Orientation program. Drama-theater group, choral group, student-run newspaper. Social organizations: 27 open to all; national fraternities, national sororities, local fraternities, local sororities; 3% of eligible men and 3% of eligible women are members. Most popular organizations: Gamma Phi Beta, Alpha Xi Delta, Kappa Alpha Order, Lambda Kappa Kappa, Burleson BLUE. Major annual events: We Are Wesleyan Concert, RAM JAM, University College Day. Student services: health clinic, personal-psychological counseling. Campus security: 24-hour emergency response devices and patrols, student patrols, late night transport-escort service, controlled dormitory access. 439 college housing spaces available; 381 were occupied in 2012-13. Option: coed housing available. Eunice and James L. West Library plus 1 other with 270,924 books, 20,069 microform titles, 232 serials, 6,113 audiovisual materials, an OPAC, and a Web page. Operations spending for the previous fiscal year: $475,544. 478 computers available on campus for general student use. A campuswide network can be accessed from student residence rooms and from off campus. Students can access the following: online class registration. Staffed computer lab on campus (open 24 hours a day) provides training in use of software and the Internet.

Community Environment: The campus is located in the Dallas/Fort Worth metropolitan area. Local public transportation is available in close proximity to the regional international airport, trains and buses. There are world-famous museums, cultural events, and professional football, basketball, baseball, and soccer teams in the area. The economy is widely diverse.

■ TEXAS WOMAN'S UNIVERSITY

304 Administration Dr.
Denton, TX 76201
Tel: (940)898-2000; Free: 866-809-6130
Fax: (940)898-3198
E-mail: admissions@twu.edu
Web Site: www.twu.edu/

Description: State-supported, university, coed. Awards bachelor's, master's, and doctoral degrees and post-master's certificates. Founded 1901. Setting: 270-acre suburban campus with easy access to Dallas-Fort Worth. Endowment: $10.7 million. Research spending for the previous fiscal year: $3.4 million. Educational spending for the previous fiscal year: $4631 per student. Total enrollment: 15,168. Faculty: 886 (418 full-time, 468 part-time). Student-undergrad faculty ratio is 21:1. 4,268 applied, 86% were admitted. 16% from top 10% of their high school class, 46% from top quarter, 80% from top half. Full-time: 6,575 students, 91% women, 9% men. Part-time: 2,868 students, 88% women, 12% men. 1% from out-of-state. 1% American Indian or Alaska Native, non-Hispanic/Latino; 22% Hispanic/Latino; 21% African American, non-Hispanic/Latino; 8% Asian, non-Hispanic/Latino; 0.1% Native Hawaiian or other Pacific Islander, non-Hispanic/Latino; 1% international. 39% 25 or older, 20% live on campus, 16% transferred in. Retention: 68% of full-time freshmen returned the following year. Academic areas with the most degrees conferred: health professions and related sciences; business/marketing; interdisciplinary studies. Core. Calendar: semesters. Academic remediation for entering students, services for LD students, advanced placement, accelerated degree program, honors program, independent study, distance learning, double major, summer session for credit, part-time degree program, adult/continuing education programs, co-op programs and internships, graduate courses open to undergrads. Off campus study at Federation of North Texas Area Universities. Study abroad program. ROTC: Army (c), Air Force (c).

Entrance Requirements: Open admission. Options: electronic application, early admission, deferred admission, international baccalaureate accepted. Required: high school transcript, minimum 2 high school GPA. Required for some: SAT or ACT. Entrance: minimally difficult. Application deadline: 7/15. Notification: 8/15. Preference given to students graduating in the top 10% of class. SAT Reasoning Test deadline: 7/15. SAT Subject Test deadline: 7/15. Transfer credits accepted: Yes.

Costs Per Year: Application fee: $50. State resident tuition: $5156 full-time, $171.84 per credit hour part-time. Nonresident tuition: $15,685 full-time, $522.84 per credit hour part-time. Mandatory fees: $1547 full-time. Full-time tuition and fees vary according to course load, program, and reciprocity agreements. Part-time tuition varies according to course load, program, and reciprocity agreements. College room and board: $6930. College room only: $3582. Room and board charges vary according to board plan and housing facility.

Collegiate Environment: Orientation program. Drama-theater group, choral group, student-run newspaper. Social organizations: 109 open to all; national fraternities, national sororities, local fraternities, local sororities; 0.1% of eligible men and 6% of eligible women are members. Most popular organizations: Helping Hands, Athenian Honor Society, Campus Activities Board, Nursing Student Organization, Graduate Library and Information Studies Association. Major annual events: Spring Fling, Family Day, Athletic events. Student services: health clinic, personal-psychological counseling. Campus security: 24-hour emergency response devices and patrols, late night transport-escort service, controlled dormitory access. 1,803 college housing spaces available. Freshmen guaranteed college housing. On-campus residence required through sophomore year. Options: coed, women-only housing available. Blagg-Huey Library plus 1 other with 580,832 books, 19,387 microform titles, 55,756 serials, 15,411 audiovisual materials, an

OPAC, and a Web page. Operations spending for the previous fiscal year: $2.8 million. 1,380 computers available on campus for general student use. A campuswide network can be accessed from student residence rooms and from off campus. Students can access the following: online class registration. Staffed computer lab on campus provides training in use of computers, software, and the Internet.

■ TRINITY UNIVERSITY

One Trinity Pl.
San Antonio, TX 78212-7200
Tel: (210)999-7011; Free: 800-TRINITY
Fax: (210)999-8164
E-mail: admissions@trinity.edu
Web Site: www.trinity.edu/

Description: Independent, comprehensive, coed, affiliated with Presbyterian Church. Awards bachelor's and master's degrees. Founded 1869. Setting: 113-acre urban campus. Endowment: $915.9 million. Research spending for the previous fiscal year: $1 million. Educational spending for the previous fiscal year: $13,269 per student. Total enrollment: 2,525. Faculty: 309 (240 full-time, 69 part-time). Student-undergrad faculty ratio is 9:1. 4,402 applied, 64% were admitted. 47% from top 10% of their high school class, 81% from top quarter, 98% from top half. 11 National Merit Scholars. Full-time: 2,317 students, 54% women, 46% men. Part-time: 36 students, 50% women, 50% men. Students come from 46 states and territories, 70 other countries, 29% from out-of-state. 0.5% American Indian or Alaska Native, non-Hispanic/Latino; 15% Hispanic/Latino; 4% African American, non-Hispanic/Latino; 8% Asian, non-Hispanic/Latino; 0.04% Native Hawaiian or other Pacific Islander, non-Hispanic/Latino; 7% international. 1% 25 or older, 74% live on campus, 1% transferred in. Retention: 89% of full-time freshmen returned the following year. Academic areas with the most degrees conferred: business/marketing; social sciences; communication/journalism. Core. Calendar: semesters. Services for LD students, advanced placement, accelerated degree program, honors program, independent study, double major, summer session for credit, part-time degree program, internships. Study abroad program. ROTC: Air Force (c).

Entrance Requirements: Options: electronic application, early decision, early action, deferred admission, international baccalaureate accepted. Required: essay, high school transcript, 2 recommendations, SAT or ACT. Recommended: interview. Entrance: very difficult. Application deadlines: 2/1, 11/1 for early decision, 11/1 for early action. Notification: 4/1, 12/1 for early decision, 12/15 for early action. SAT Reasoning Test deadline: 2/1. Applicants placed on waiting list: 269. Wait-listed applicants offered admission: 50. Early decision applicants: 41. Early decision applicants admitted: 37. Early action applicants: 2,638. Early action applicants admitted: 1,966.

Costs Per Year: Application fee: $50. Comprehensive fee: $44,184 includes full-time tuition ($32,578), mandatory fees ($1110), and college room and board ($10,496). College room only: $6520. Full-time tuition and fees vary according to course load. Room and board charges vary according to board plan. Part-time tuition: $1357 per credit hour. Part-time tuition varies according to course load.

Collegiate Environment: Orientation program. Drama-theater group, choral group, student-run newspaper, radio station. Social organizations: local fraternities, local sororities; 15% of eligible men and 21% of eligible women are members. Most popular organizations: Voluntary Action Center, Alpha Phi Omega, Association of Student Representatives, Activities Council, Multicultural Network. Major annual events: Homecoming, Trinity Night at the San Antonio Spurs game, Tower Party. Student services: health clinic, personal-psychological counseling. Campus security: 24-hour emergency response devices and patrols, late night transport-escort service, controlled dormitory access. 1,823 college housing spaces available; 1,799 were occupied in 2012-13. Freshmen guaranteed college housing. On-campus residence required through junior year. Option: coed housing available. Elizabeth Huth Coates Library plus 1 other with 307,774 microform titles, 2,500 serials, 36,208 audiovisual materials, an OPAC, and a Web page. Operations spending for the previous fiscal year: $3.7 million. 450 computers available on campus for general student use. Computer purchase/lease plans available. A campuswide network can be accessed from student residence rooms and from off campus. Students can access the following: online class registration. Staffed computer lab on campus (open 24 hours a day) provides training in use of computers, software, and the Internet.

Community Environment: San Antonio, population of more than one million, is the 8th largest city in the United States and is rich in history. It has a healthy economy and supports many cultural, and recreational activities. An international airport provides wide access.

■ **TRINITY VALLEY COMMUNITY COLLEGE**
100 Cardinal Dr.
Athens, TX 75751-2765
Tel: (903)677-TVCC
Web Site: www.tvcc.edu/
Description: State and locally supported, 2-year, coed. Awards certificates, diplomas, transfer associate, and terminal associate degrees. Founded 1946. Setting: 65-acre rural campus with easy access to Dallas-Fort Worth. Endowment: $2.9 million. Educational spending for the previous fiscal year: $3135 per student. Total enrollment: 7,579. Faculty: 255 (138 full-time, 117 part-time). Student-undergrad faculty ratio is 26:1. Full-time: 3,035 students, 62% women, 38% men. Part-time: 4,544 students, 61% women, 39% men. Students come from 27 states and territories, 11 other countries, 1% from out-of-state. 39% 25 or older, 12% live on campus. Core. Calendar: semesters. Academic remediation for entering students, ESL program, services for LD students, advanced placement, honors program, independent study, distance learning, double major, summer session for credit, part-time degree program, adult/continuing education programs, co-op programs and internships.
Entrance Requirements: Open admission. Options: electronic application, early admission. Required: high school transcript. Entrance: noncompetitive. Application deadline: Rolling. Notification: continuous. Transfer credits accepted: Yes.
Collegiate Environment: Orientation program. Drama-theater group, choral group, marching band, student-run newspaper. Social organizations: 5 open to all. Most popular organizations: Student Senate, Phi Theta Kappa, Delta Epsilon Chi. Major annual events: Homecoming, Cardinal Beauty Pageant, Cardette Spring Show. Student services: personal-psychological counseling. Campus security: 24-hour emergency response devices and patrols, controlled dormitory access. Ginger Murchison Learning Resource Center plus 3 others with 54,940 books, 7,051 microform titles, 257 serials, 1,954 audiovisual materials, an OPAC, and a Web page. Operations spending for the previous fiscal year: $679,055. 66 computers available on campus for general student use. A campuswide network can be accessed from student residence rooms. Students can access the following: online class registration. Staffed computer lab on campus provides training in use of computers, software, and the Internet.
Community Environment: Population 12,559, Athens is a rural community located approximately 70 miles from Dallas. The climate is unusually mild and dry. The average high temperature is 95 degrees, and the low temperature range is 18 to 30 degrees, with an annual rainfall of 25 inches. Airport facilities, bus lines, and six major highways provide transportation for the city. There is a hospital, libraries, churches of various denominations, and various civic and fraternal organizations. Recreation includes theaters, drive-ins, hunting, fishing, golf, boating, tennis, parks, and swimming pools. Part-time employment is available.

■ **TYLER JUNIOR COLLEGE**
PO Box 9020
Tyler, TX 75711-9020
Tel: (903)510-2200; Free: 800-687-5680
E-mail: jcha@tjc.edu
Web Site: www.tjc.edu/
Description: State and locally supported, 2-year, coed. Awards certificates, transfer associate, and terminal associate degrees. Founded 1926. Setting: 85-acre suburban campus. Educational spending for the previous fiscal year: $3139 per student. Total enrollment: 11,374. Faculty: 559 (283 full-time, 276 part-time). Student-undergrad faculty ratio is 21:1. 2,811 applied, 100% were admitted. Full-time: 6,344 students, 55% women, 45% men. Part-time: 5,030 students, 61% women, 39% men. Students come from 34 states and territories, 27 other countries, 3% from out-of-state. 1% American Indian or Alaska Native, non-Hispanic/Latino; 13% Hispanic/Latino; 23% African American, non-Hispanic/Latino; 1% Asian, non-Hispanic/Latino; 0.1% Native Hawaiian or other Pacific Islander, non-Hispanic/Latino; 1% international. 28% 25 or older, 9% live on campus, 6% transferred in. Retention: 49% of full-time freshmen returned the following year. Core. Calendar: semesters. Academic remediation for entering students, ESL program, services for LD students, advanced placement, accelerated degree program, freshman honors college, honors program, distance learning, summer session for credit, part-time degree program, adult/continuing education programs.
Entrance Requirements: Open admission. Options: electronic application, early admission, international baccalaureate accepted. Required: high school transcript. Entrance: noncompetitive. Application deadline: Rolling. Notification: continuous. Preference given to district residents. Transfer credits accepted: Yes.

Costs Per Year: Application fee: $0. Area resident tuition: $900 full-time, $30 per credit hour part-time. State resident tuition: $2280 full-time, $76 per credit hour part-time. Nonresident tuition: $2880 full-time, $96 per credit hour part-time. Mandatory fees: $1362 full-time, $39 per credit part-time, $100 per term part-time. College room and board: $6400.
Collegiate Environment: Orientation program. Drama-theater group, choral group, marching band, student-run newspaper. Social organizations: 48 open to all; national fraternities, national sororities, local fraternities, local sororities; 5% of eligible men and 5% of eligible women are members. Most popular organizations: student government, religious affiliation clubs, Phi Theta Kappa. Major annual events: Homecoming, Annual Career Day, Fall Preview. Student services: health clinic, personal-psychological counseling. Campus security: 24-hour emergency response devices and patrols, controlled dormitory access. 1,060 college housing spaces available; all were occupied in 2012-13. No special consideration for freshman housing applicants. Options: men-only, women-only housing available. Vaughn Library and Learning Resource Center with 104,000 books, 10,000 serials, and an OPAC. Operations spending for the previous fiscal year: $414,729. 79 computers available on campus for general student use. A campuswide network can be accessed from student residence rooms and from off campus. Students can access the following: online class registration. Staffed computer lab on campus.
Community Environment: Tyler, population 91,936, was incorporated in 1846 and named for President John Tyler who was responsible for bringing Texas into the Union. Industry is varied with production of fieldgrown rose bushes for shipment throughout the United States, an economic mainstay. Located in the Pine region of East Texas, the community is reached by rail, bus, and air, as well as eight major highways. Community facilities include a symphony orchestra, a library system, hospitals, and medical facilities with Tyler being the medical center for East Texas. Local recreation includes golf courses, parks, and nearby Tyler State Park and Lake Tyler. Part-time employment is available.

■ **UNIVERSAL TECHNICAL INSTITUTE**
721 Lockhaven Dr.
Houston, TX 77073-5598
Tel: (281)443-6262; Free: 800-510-5072
Web Site: www.uti.edu/
Description: Proprietary, 2-year, coed. Awards diplomas and terminal associate degrees. Founded 1983. Total enrollment: 1,897. Student-undergrad faculty ratio is 22:1. 27% from out-of-state. 15% 25 or older. Retention: 71% of full-time freshmen returned the following year.
Entrance Requirements: Open admission.

■ **UNIVERSITY OF DALLAS**
1845 E Northgate Dr.
Irving, TX 75062-4736
Tel: (972)721-5000; Free: 800-628-6999
Fax: (972)721-5017
E-mail: ugadmis@udallas.edu
Web Site: www.udallas.edu/
Description: Independent Roman Catholic, university, coed. Awards bachelor's, master's, and doctoral degrees and post-master's certificates. Founded 1955. Setting: 215-acre suburban campus with easy access to Dallas-Fort Worth. Endowment: $45.6 million. Research spending for the previous fiscal year: $111,336. Total enrollment: 2,725. Faculty: 235 (127 full-time, 108 part-time). Student-undergrad faculty ratio is 12:1. 1,082 applied, 88% were admitted. 43% from top 10% of their high school class, 66% from top quarter, 87% from top half. 14 National Merit Scholars, 8 valedictorians. Full-time: 1,332 students, 51% women, 49% men. Part-time: 24 students, 42% women, 58% men. Students come from 49 states and territories, 12 other countries, 55% from out-of-state. 0.4% American Indian or Alaska Native, non-Hispanic/Latino; 16% Hispanic/Latino; 1% African American, non-Hispanic/Latino; 4% Asian, non-Hispanic/Latino; 0.1% Native Hawaiian or other Pacific Islander, non-Hispanic/Latino; 3% international. 2% 25 or older, 63% live on campus, 3% transferred in. Retention: 80% of full-time freshmen returned the following year. Academic areas with the most degrees conferred: English; social sciences; business/marketing. Core. Calendar: semesters. Services for LD students, advanced placement, self-designed majors, independent study, double major, summer session for credit, part-time degree program, internships, graduate courses open to undergrads. Off campus study. Study abroad program. ROTC: Army (c), Air Force (c).
Entrance Requirements: Options: electronic application, early action, deferred admission, international baccalaureate accepted. Required: essay,

high school transcript, 2 recommendations, SAT or ACT. Required for some: interview. Entrance: moderately difficult. Application deadlines: 3/1, 3/1 for nonresidents, 12/1 for early action. Notification: continuous, 1/15 for early action. SAT Reasoning Test deadline: 4/1. Transfer credits accepted: Yes.

Costs Per Year: Application fee: $40. Comprehensive fee: $40,960 includes full-time tuition ($29,140), mandatory fees ($1930), and college room and board ($9890). College room only: $5690. Room and board charges vary according to board plan and housing facility. Part-time tuition: $1210 per credit. Part-time mandatory fees: $1930 per year.

Collegiate Environment: Orientation program. Drama-theater group, choral group, student-run newspaper. Social organizations: 42 open to all. Most popular organizations: SPUD (Programming Board), Residence Hall Association, student government, Best Buddies, Alpha Phi Omega. Major annual events: Charity Week, Groundhog, Mallapalooza. Student services: health clinic, personal-psychological counseling. Campus security: 24-hour emergency response devices and patrols, late night transport-escort service, controlled dormitory access. 740 college housing spaces available; all were occupied in 2012-13. Freshmen guaranteed college housing. On-campus residence required through junior year. Options: men-only, women-only housing available. William A. Blakley Library with 245,228 books, 4,536 microform titles, 1,310 serials, 1,317 audiovisual materials, an OPAC, and a Web page. Operations spending for the previous fiscal year: $1.5 million. 125 computers available on campus for general student use. Computer purchase/lease plans available. A campuswide network can be accessed from student residence rooms and from off campus. Students can access the following: online class registration. Staffed computer lab on campus (open 24 hours a day).

Community Environment: Population 193,600. Irving is a suburb of Dallas. The community enjoys a temperate climate. Transportation facilities in the community include a railroad, bus lines, excellent highways, and air lines at nearby Dallas and Fort Worth airports. The city has a public library, YMCA, many churches of various faiths, and hospital facilities. Some part-time employment is available. Local recreation includes four theaters, water sports on nearby lakes, and athletic facilities of neighboring communities. There are major civic, fraternal and veteran's organizations active in the area. The Dallas-Ft. Worth area has a population of nearly 3,000,000.

■ UNIVERSITY OF HOUSTON

4800 Calhoun Rd.
Houston, TX 77204
Tel: (713)743-1000
Fax: (713)743-9633
E-mail: jdfuller@central.uh.edu
Web Site: www.uh.edu/

Description: State-supported, university, coed. Part of University of Houston System. Awards bachelor's, master's, and doctoral degrees. Founded 1927. Setting: 594-acre urban campus. Endowment: $359 million. Research spending for the previous fiscal year: $92.8 million. Educational spending for the previous fiscal year: $6197 per student. Total enrollment: 40,747. Faculty: 1,966 (1,383 full-time, 583 part-time). Student-undergrad faculty ratio is 22:1. 17,020 applied, 56% were admitted. 32% from top 10% of their high school class, 68% from top quarter, 92% from top half. Full-time: 23,578 students, 50% women, 50% men. Part-time: 9,061 students, 48% women, 52% men. Students come from 52 states and territories, 119 other countries, 2% from out-of-state. 0.2% American Indian or Alaska Native, non-Hispanic/Latino; 28% Hispanic/Latino; 12% African American, non-Hispanic/Latino; 21% Asian, non-Hispanic/Latino; 0.3% Native Hawaiian or other Pacific Islander, non-Hispanic/Latino; 4% international. 20% 25 or older, 16% live on campus, 13% transferred in. Retention: 83% of full-time freshmen returned the following year. Academic areas with the most degrees conferred: business/marketing; social sciences; psychology. Core. Calendar: semesters. Academic remediation for entering students, ESL program, services for LD students, advanced placement, self-designed majors, freshman honors college, honors program, independent study, distance learning, double major, summer session for credit, part-time degree program, adult/continuing education programs, co-op programs and internships, graduate courses open to undergrads. Off campus study at University of Texas Health Science Center, Baylor College of Medicine, Rice University, Texas Southern University. Study abroad program. ROTC: Army, Naval (c), Air Force.

Entrance Requirements: Option: electronic application. Required: high school transcript, SAT or ACT scores, SAT or ACT. Entrance: moderately difficult. Application deadline: 4/1. Notification: continuous. SAT Reasoning Test deadline: 4/1. Transfer credits accepted: Yes.

Costs Per Year: Application fee: $50. State resident tuition: $8970 full-time.

Nonresident tuition: $19,500 full-time. Mandatory fees: $918 full-time. Full-time tuition and fees vary according to course level, course load, degree level, program, and student level.

Collegiate Environment: Orientation program. Drama-theater group, choral group, marching band, student-run newspaper. Social organizations: 479 open to all; national fraternities, national sororities; 4% of eligible men and 3% of eligible women are members. Most popular organizations: Student Government Association, Residence Hall Association, Metropolitan Volunteer Program, Student Governing Board- Honors College, Student Alumni Connection. Major annual events: Homecoming, Welcome Back to Campus Event, Frontier Fiesta. Student services: legal services, health clinic, personal-psychological counseling, women's center. Campus security: 24-hour emergency response devices and patrols, student patrols, late night transport-escort service, controlled dormitory access, vehicle assistance. 5,350 college housing spaces available; 4,920 were occupied in 2012-13. No special consideration for freshman housing applicants. Option: coed housing available. M.D. Anderson Library plus 4 others with 2.3 million books, 6 million microform titles, 77,827 serials, 31,106 audiovisual materials, an OPAC, and a Web page. Operations spending for the previous fiscal year: $17.6 million. 997 computers available on campus for general student use. Computer purchase/lease plans available. A campuswide network can be accessed from student residence rooms and from off campus. Students can access the following: online class registration. Staffed computer lab on campus (open 24 hours a day) provides training in use of computers, software, and the Internet.

Community Environment: Population 2,016,582. Although Houston lies 50 miles inland, it is a major seaport due to the conversion of Buffalo Bayou into the Houston Ship Channel. The city was named in honor of Sam Houston, hero of the Battle of San Jacinto. The community has excellent air, bus, and railroad facilities. Many points of interest in the city include L. B. Johnson Manned Spacecraft Center, Texas Medical Center, Jones Hall, Wortham Theatre, Emron Baseball Field, Burke Barker Planetarium, Museum of Fine Arts, Contemporary Arts Museum, Zoological Gardens, and the San Jacinto Battleground and Monument, the Astrodome and Battleship U.S.S. Texas. There are over one thousand churches representing all the major denominations, excellent medical facilities, ample shopping centers, and good student housing in the area. Full- and part-time employment is available.

■ UNIVERSITY OF HOUSTON–CLEAR LAKE

2700 Bay Area Blvd.
Houston, TX 77058-1098
Tel: (281)283-7600
Fax: (281)283-2530
E-mail: admissions@uhcl.edu
Web Site: www.uhcl.edu/

Description: State-supported, upper-level, coed. Part of University of Houston System. Awards bachelor's, master's, and doctoral degrees and post-master's certificates. Founded 1971. Setting: 524-acre suburban campus with easy access to Houston. Total enrollment: 8,155. Faculty: 484 (247 full-time, 237 part-time). Student-undergrad faculty ratio is 17:1. 2,177 applied, 73% were admitted. Full-time: 2,143 students, 67% women, 33% men. Part-time: 2,647 students, 68% women, 32% men. Students come from 9 states and territories, 27 other countries, 0% from out-of-state. 0.3% American Indian or Alaska Native, non-Hispanic/Latino; 32% Hispanic/Latino; 9% African American, non-Hispanic/Latino; 6% Asian, non-Hispanic/Latino; 0.2% Native Hawaiian or other Pacific Islander, non-Hispanic/Latino; 2% international. 49% 25 or older, 22% transferred in. Academic areas with the most degrees conferred: business/marketing; interdisciplinary studies; psychology. Core. Calendar: semesters. Academic remediation for entering students, ESL program, services for LD students, advanced placement, independent study, distance learning, double major, summer session for credit, part-time degree program, co-op programs and internships, graduate courses open to undergrads. Off campus study. Study abroad program.

Entrance Requirements: Transfer credits accepted: Yes.

Costs Per Year: Application fee: $45. State resident tuition: $5326 full-time, $178 per credit hour part-time. Nonresident tuition: $17,110 full-time, $572 per credit hour part-time. Mandatory fees: $1254 full-time, $486 per term part-time. Full-time tuition and fees vary according to course load and program. Part-time tuition and fees vary according to course load and program. College room only: $8354. Room charges vary according to housing facility.

Collegiate Environment: Orientation program. Student-run newspaper. Social organizations: 61 open to all. Most popular organizations: Beta Alpha Psi, National Society of Leadership and Success, Applied Behavior Student

Analysis Student Organization, Student Government Association, Accounting Association. Major annual events: Student Organization Expo, Global Expo, Student Leadership Conference. Student services: health clinic, personal-psychological counseling, women's center. Campus security: 24-hour emergency response devices and patrols, student patrols, late night transport-escort service. Option: coed housing available. Alfred R. Neuman Library with an OPAC and a Web page. 800 computers available on campus for general student use. A campuswide network can be accessed from off-campus. Students can access the following: online class registration. Staffed computer lab on campus provides training in use of computers, software, and the Internet.

Community Environment: A planned community 20 miles south of Houston, and 35 miles from Galveston, Texas. Mixture of education and space related employers. Many cultural activities available, both in the Clear Lake area, and within easy access of Houston. Abundance of outdoor recreational opportunities.

■ **UNIVERSITY OF HOUSTON–DOWNTOWN**

One Main St.
Houston, TX 77002
Tel: (713)221-8000
Fax: (713)221-8157
E-mail: uhdadmit@uhd.edu
Web Site: www.uhd.edu/

Description: State-supported, comprehensive, coed. Part of University of Houston System. Awards bachelor's and master's degrees. Founded 1974. Setting: 24-acre urban campus. Endowment: $35.5 million. Research spending for the previous fiscal year: $2.2 million. Educational spending for the previous fiscal year: $4428 per student. Total enrollment: 13,916. Faculty: 673 (337 full-time, 336 part-time). Student-undergrad faculty ratio is 20:1. 4,194 applied, 91% were admitted. 7% from top 10% of their high school class, 27% from top quarter, 63% from top half. Full-time: 6,768 students, 58% women, 42% men. Part-time: 6,941 students, 62% women, 38% men. Students come from 28 states and territories, 65 other countries, 0% from out-of-state. 0.4% American Indian or Alaska Native, non-Hispanic/Latino; 38% Hispanic/Latino; 27% African American, non-Hispanic/Latino; 8% Asian, non-Hispanic/Latino; 0.2% Native Hawaiian or other Pacific Islander, non-Hispanic/Latino; 5% international. 49% 25 or older, 16% transferred in. Retention: 67% of full-time freshmen returned the following year. Academic areas with the most degrees conferred: business/marketing; liberal arts/general studies; interdisciplinary studies. Core. Calendar: semesters. Academic remediation for entering students, ESL program, services for LD students, advanced placement, independent study, distance learning, double major, summer session for credit, part-time degree program, internships, graduate courses open to undergrads. Off campus study. Study abroad program. ROTC: Army (c), Air Force (c).

Entrance Requirements: Open admission. Options: electronic application, international baccalaureate accepted. Required: high school transcript. Recommended: SAT or ACT. Required for some: SAT or ACT. Entrance: noncompetitive. Application deadline: 6/1. Notification: continuous. SAT Reasoning Test deadline: 7/15. Transfer credits accepted: Yes.

Costs Per Year: Application fee: $35. State resident tuition: $4875 full-time, $162.50 per credit hour part-time. Nonresident tuition: $15,405 full-time, $513.50 per credit hour part-time. Mandatory fees: $1122 full-time, $162.50 per credit hour part-time. Full-time tuition and fees vary according to course load and program. Part-time tuition and fees vary according to course load and program.

Collegiate Environment: Orientation program. Drama-theater group, student-run newspaper. Social organizations: national fraternities, national sororities; 1% of eligible men and 1% of eligible women are members. Most popular organizations: Bilingual Education Student Organization, Student Government Association, Alpha Phi Sigma, American Marketing Association, Professional Accounting Society. Major annual events: Activities Day, Fall Family Festival, Culture on the Bayou. Student services: legal services, health clinic, personal-psychological counseling. Campus security: 24-hour emergency response devices and patrols, late night transport-escort service. College housing not available. W. I. Dykes Library with 197,361 books, 5,688 microform titles, 9,731 serials, 3,536 audiovisual materials, an OPAC, and a Web page. Operations spending for the previous fiscal year: $4.1 million. 583 computers available on campus for general student use. A campuswide network can be accessed from off-campus. Students can access the following: online class registration. Staffed computer lab on campus.

■ **UNIVERSITY OF HOUSTON–VICTORIA**

3007 N Ben Wilson St.
Victoria, TX 77901-4450
Tel: (361)570-4848; Free: 877-970-4848
Fax: (361)572-9377
E-mail: worthamt@uhv.edu
Web Site: www.uhv.edu/

Description: State-supported, upper-level, coed. Part of University of Houston System. Awards bachelor's and master's degrees and post-master's certificates. Founded 1973. Setting: 20-acre small town campus. Endowment: $14.5 million. Research spending for the previous fiscal year: $142,161. Educational spending for the previous fiscal year: $7712 per student. Total enrollment: 4,335. Faculty: 212 (128 full-time, 84 part-time). Student-undergrad faculty ratio is 18:1. 2,455 applied, 51% were admitted. Full-time: 1,254 students, 65% women, 35% men. Part-time: 1,410 students, 69% women, 31% men. 0% from out-of-state. 0.1% American Indian or Alaska Native, non-Hispanic/Latino; 29% Hispanic/Latino; 16% African American, non-Hispanic/Latino; 6% Asian, non-Hispanic/Latino; 0.3% Native Hawaiian or other Pacific Islander, non-Hispanic/Latino; 1% international. 58% 25 or older, 12% live on campus, 16% transferred in. Retention: 55% of full-time entering class returned the following year. Academic areas with the most degrees conferred: business/marketing; education; health professions and related sciences. Core. Calendar: semesters. Accelerated degree program, honors program, independent study, distance learning, double major, part-time degree program, adult/continuing education programs, internships, graduate courses open to undergrads. Study abroad program. ROTC: Air Force (c).

Entrance Requirements: SAT Reasoning Test deadline: 8/21. Transfer credits accepted: Yes.

Costs Per Year: Application fee: $0. State resident tuition: $4809 full-time, $160 per credit hour part-time. Nonresident tuition: $15,338 full-time, $511 per credit hour part-time. Mandatory fees: $1308 full-time, $61 per credit hour part-time. Full-time tuition and fees vary according to course level and course load. Part-time tuition and fees vary according to course level and course load. College room and board: $7042. Room and board charges vary according to board plan and housing facility.

Collegiate Environment: Orientation program. Student services: personal-psychological counseling. Campus security: 24-hour emergency response devices and patrols, controlled dormitory access. Option: coed housing available. VC/UHV Library plus 1 other with an OPAC and a Web page. Operations spending for the previous fiscal year: $497,565.

Community Environment: The campus is located in Victoria, a city of 58,000 inhabitants at the center of the South Texas Crossroads in the heart of the Golden Gulf Coast. This expanding city on the banks of the Guadalupe River is more than 150 years old, and is one of the first three towns chartered by The Republic of Texas. The city is near the Gulf of Mexico and is a popular coastal route between Houston and Mexico. The home of many petrochemical companies, such as DuPont, Alcoa, and Union Carbide, it is surrounded by vast expanses of ranchland.

■ **UNIVERSITY OF THE INCARNATE WORD**

4301 Broadway
San Antonio, TX 78209-6397
Tel: (210)829-6000; Free: 800-749-WORD
Fax: (210)829-3921
E-mail: hrodrig1@uiwtx.edu
Web Site: www.uiw.edu/

Description: Independent Roman Catholic, comprehensive, coed. Awards associate, bachelor's, master's, and doctoral degrees. Founded 1881. Setting: 200-acre urban campus with easy access to San Antonio. Endowment: $100 million. Research spending for the previous fiscal year: $593,342. Educational spending for the previous fiscal year: $6172 per student. Total enrollment: 8,442. Faculty: 533 (280 full-time, 253 part-time). Student-undergrad faculty ratio is 14:1. 3,784 applied, 94% were admitted. 18% from top 10% of their high school class, 41% from top quarter, 76% from top half. 3 valedictorians. Full-time: 4,388 students, 64% women, 36% men. Part-time: 2,016 students, 60% women, 40% men. Students come from 50 states and territories, 38 other countries, 5% from out-of-state. 0.4% American Indian or Alaska Native, non-Hispanic/Latino; 59% Hispanic/Latino; 7% African American, non-Hispanic/Latino; 2% Asian, non-Hispanic/Latino; 0.2% Native Hawaiian or other Pacific Islander, non-Hispanic/Latino; 4% international. 37% 25 or older, 18% live on campus, 13% transferred in. Retention: 75% of full-time freshmen returned the following year. Academic areas with the most degrees conferred: business/marketing; health professions and related sciences; biological/life sciences. Core. Calendar: semesters. Academic remediation for entering students, ESL program, services for LD students, advanced placement, accelerated degree program, freshman honors college, honors program, independent study, distance learning, double major, summer session for credit, part-time degree program, adult/continuing education programs, co-op programs and internships, graduate courses open to undergrads. Off campus study at United College of San Antonio Consortium for exchange of course offerings and of faculty members with Our Lady of the Lake University of San Antonio, St. Mary's University of San Antonio, and Oblate School of Theology. Study abroad program. ROTC: Army (c), Air Force (c).

Entrance Requirements: Options: electronic application, deferred admission. Required: high school transcript, SAT or ACT. Recommended: minimum 2 high school GPA, letter(s) of recommendation recommended for all, required for some. Required for some: essay, interview. Entrance: moderately difficult. Application deadlines: Rolling, Rolling for nonresidents. Notification: continuous, continuous for nonresidents. Transfer credits accepted: Yes.

Costs Per Year: Application fee: $20. Comprehensive fee: $33,784 includes full-time tuition ($22,800), mandatory fees ($890), and college room and board ($10,094), College room only: $5980. Full-time tuition and fees vary according to course load, degree level, location, program, and reciprocity agreements. Room and board charges vary according to board plan and housing facility. Part-time tuition: $755 per credit hour. Part-time tuition varies according to course load, degree level, location, program, and reciprocity agreements.

Collegiate Environment: Orientation program. Drama-theater group, choral group, marching band, student-run newspaper, radio station. Social organizations: 77 open to all; national fraternities, national sororities, local sororities; 40% of eligible men and 60% of eligible women are members. Most popular organizations: Society of Leadership and Success, Pre-Pharmacy Association, Alpha Sigma Alpha, Lambda Chi Alpha, Student Government Association House. Major annual events: Light the Way, UIW homecoming (football), President's Spaghetti Dinner. Student services: health clinic, personal-psychological counseling. Campus security: 24-hour emergency response devices and patrols, late night transport-escort service, controlled dormitory access. 1,241 college housing spaces available; 1,146 were occupied in 2012-13. Freshmen guaranteed college housing. Options: coed, men-only, women-only housing available. J.E. and M.E. Mabee Library plus 1 other with 273,468 books, 301,272 microform titles, 70,017 serials, 11,350 audiovisual materials, an OPAC, and a Web page. Operations spending for the previous fiscal year: $857,188. 185 computers available on campus for general student use. Computer purchase/lease plans available. A computer is required for all students. A campuswide network can be accessed from student residence rooms and from off campus. Students can access the following: online class registration, Ports available in general use area and other locations. Also dedicated computers for graduate/doctoral students. Staffed computer lab on campus provides training in use of computers, software, and the Internet.

Community Environment: See San Antonio College.

■ **UNIVERSITY OF MARY HARDIN-BAYLOR**

900 College St.

Belton, TX 76513

Tel: (254)295-8642; Free: 800-727-8642

Fax: (254)295-4535

E-mail: admission@umhb.edu

Web Site: www.umhb.edu/

Description: Independent Southern Baptist, comprehensive, coed. Awards bachelor's, master's, and doctoral degrees. Founded 1845. Setting: 220-acre small town campus with easy access to Austin. Endowment: $59.6 million. Research spending for the previous fiscal year: $141,266. Total enrollment: 3,287. Faculty: 286 (146 full-time, 140 part-time). Student-undergrad faculty ratio is 16:1. 8,847 applied, 36% were admitted. Full-time: 2,652 students, 61% women, 39% men. Part-time: 274 students, 62% women, 38% men. Students come from 24 states and territories, 20 other countries, 2% from out-of-state. 1% American Indian or Alaska Native, non-Hispanic/Latino; 15% Hispanic/Latino; 14% African American, non-Hispanic/Latino; 1% Asian, non-Hispanic/Latino; 0.4% Native Hawaiian or other Pacific Islander, non-Hispanic/Latino; 2% international. 17% 25 or older, 50% live on campus, 10% transferred in. Retention: 68% of full-time freshmen returned the following year. Academic areas with the most degrees conferred: health professions and related sciences; education; business/marketing. Core. Calendar: semesters. Academic remediation for entering students, ESL

program, services for LD students, advanced placement, accelerated degree program, honors program, independent study, distance learning, double major, summer session for credit, part-time degree program, internships, graduate courses open to undergrads. Study abroad program. ROTC: Army, Air Force (c).

Entrance Requirements: Options: electronic application, early admission, deferred admission. Required: high school transcript, SAT or ACT. Required for some: essay, interview. Entrance: moderately difficult. Application deadlines: Rolling, Rolling for nonresidents. Notification: continuous, continuous for nonresidents. Transfer credits accepted: Yes.

Costs Per Year: Application fee: $35. Comprehensive fee: $30,770 includes full-time tuition ($21,900), mandatory fees ($2250), and college room and board ($6620). Full-time tuition and fees vary according to course load and degree level. Room and board charges vary according to board plan and housing facility. Part-time tuition: $765 per credit hour. Part-time mandatory fees: $75 per credit hour, $50 per term. Part-time tuition and fees vary according to course load and degree level.

Collegiate Environment: Orientation program. Drama-theater group, choral group, marching band, student-run newspaper. Social organizations: 51 open to all. Most popular organizations: Baptist Student Ministry, Student Government Association, Residence Hall Association, Campus Activities Board, Focus. Major annual events: Homecoming, Easter Pageant, Play Day. Student services: health clinic, personal-psychological counseling. Campus security: 24-hour emergency response devices and patrols, late night transport-escort service, controlled dormitory access, campus police force, lighted pathways and sidewalks. 1,558 college housing spaces available; 1,487 were occupied in 2012-13. Freshmen given priority for college housing. On-campus residence required through sophomore year. Options: men-only, women-only housing available. Townsend Memorial Library plus 1 other with 145,212 books, 10,277 microform titles, 693 serials, 8,460 audiovisual materials, an OPAC, and a Web page. Operations spending for the previous fiscal year: $813,806. 275 computers available on campus for general student use. Computer purchase/lease plans available. A campuswide network can be accessed from student residence rooms and from off campus. Students can access the following: online class registration. Staffed computer lab on campus.

Community Environment: Belton, population 15,530, located in central Texas, has a mild climate. The community is served by railroad lines, bus lines, U.S. Highway I-35 and Texas State 317. There is an airport 15 miles away. Local community services include a library, museum, several churches, a hospital, and various civic, fraternal and veteran's organizations. The city is a one-hour drive from Waco and Austin for out-of-town entertainment. Belton has nearby Lake Belton for fishing, water skiing, swimming, and speed boat races. Part-time employment is available.

■ **UNIVERSITY OF NORTH TEXAS**

1155 Union Cir. No.311425

Denton, TX 76203

Tel: (940)565-2000; Free: 800-868-8211

Fax: (940)565-2408

E-mail: jasiel.perez@unt.edu

Web Site: www.unt.edu/

Description: State-supported, university, coed. Part of University of North Texas System. Awards bachelor's, master's, and doctoral degrees. Founded 1890. Setting: 875-acre suburban campus with easy access to Dallas-Fort Worth. Endowment: $113 million. Total enrollment: 35,836. Faculty: 1,489 (985 full-time, 504 part-time). Student-undergrad faculty ratio is 23:1. 14,853 applied, 64% were admitted. 17% from top 10% of their high school class, 47% from top quarter, 89% from top half. Full-time: 23,346 students, 53% women, 47% men. Part-time: 5,610 students, 49% women, 51% men. 4% from out-of-state. 1% American Indian or Alaska Native, non-Hispanic/Latino; 19% Hispanic/Latino; 13% African American, non-Hispanic/Latino; 5% Asian, non-Hispanic/Latino; 0.1% Native Hawaiian or other Pacific Islander, non-Hispanic/Latino; 3% international. 18% 25 or older, 19% live on campus, 13% transferred in. Retention: 79% of full-time freshmen returned the following year. Academic areas with the most degrees conferred: business/marketing; interdisciplinary studies; social sciences. Core. Calendar: semesters. Academic remediation for entering students, ESL program, services for LD students, advanced placement, accelerated degree program, freshman honors college, honors program, independent study, distance learning, double major, summer session for credit, part-time degree program, co-op programs and internships, graduate courses open to undergrads. Off campus study. Study abroad program. ROTC: Army, Air Force.

Entrance Requirements: Options: electronic application, early admission, deferred admission, international baccalaureate accepted. Required: high school transcript, SAT or ACT. Required for some: essay. Entrance: moderately difficult. Application deadline: 8/1. Notification: continuous. SAT Reasoning Test deadline: 8/10. Transfer credits accepted: Yes.

Costs Per Year: Application fee: $60. State resident tuition: $6488 full-time. Nonresident tuition: $17,018 full-time. Mandatory fees: $2590 full-time. College room and board: $7150. Room and board charges vary according to board plan and housing facility.

Collegiate Environment: Orientation program. Drama-theater group, choral group, marching band, student-run newspaper, radio station. Social organizations: national fraternities, national sororities; 5% of eligible men and 4% of eligible women are members. Most popular organizations: Student Government Association, Residence Hall Association, Panhellenic Association, Interfraternity Council, College Life. Major annual events: Homecoming, University Day, Homecoming bonfire. Student services: legal services, health clinic, personal-psychological counseling, women's center. Campus security: 24-hour emergency response devices and patrols, late night transport-escort service, controlled dormitory access. Freshmen given priority for college housing. On-campus residence required in freshman year. Options: coed, women-only housing available. Willis Library plus 4 others with an OPAC and a Web page.

Community Environment: Denton is a community of approximately 73,050. Texas' largest and most modern airport, Dallas - Fort Worth International, is only a short drive from Denton.

■ UNIVERSITY OF PHOENIX–AUSTIN CAMPUS

10801 N Mopac
Austin, TX 78759
Tel: (512)344-1400; Free: 866-766-0766
Web Site: www.phoenix.edu/

Description: Proprietary, comprehensive, coed. Awards associate, bachelor's, master's, and doctoral degrees.

■ UNIVERSITY OF PHOENIX–DALLAS CAMPUS

Churchill Twr.
12400 Coit Rd., Ste. 200
Dallas, TX 75251-2009
Tel: (972)385-1055; Free: 866-766-0766
Fax: (972)385-1700
Web Site: www.phoenix.edu/

Description: Proprietary, comprehensive, coed. Awards bachelor's and master's degrees. Founded 2001. Setting: urban campus. Total enrollment: 1,371. Faculty: 181 (15 full-time, 166 part-time). Full-time: 1,075 students, 64% women, 36% men. 90% 25 or older. Academic areas with the most degrees conferred: business/marketing; public administration and social services. Core. Calendar: continuous. Services for LD students, advanced placement, accelerated degree program, independent study, distance learning, external degree program, adult/continuing education programs, graduate courses open to undergrads.

Entrance Requirements: Open admission. Options: electronic application, deferred admission. Required: 1 recommendation. Required for some: high school transcript. Entrance: noncompetitive. Application deadline: Rolling.

Collegiate Environment: Campus security: late night transport-escort service. 16,781 serials, an OPAC, and a Web pageOperations spending for the previous fiscal year: $6.8 million.

■ UNIVERSITY OF PHOENIX–HOUSTON CAMPUS

11451 Katy Fwy.
Ste. 100
Houston, TX 77079-2004
Tel: (281)596-0363; Free: 866-766-0766
Fax: (281)596-0336
Web Site: www.phoenix.edu/

Description: Proprietary, comprehensive, coed. Awards bachelor's and master's degrees. Founded 2001. Setting: urban campus. Total enrollment: 2,748. Faculty: 325 (16 full-time, 309 part-time). Full-time: 2,286 students, 68% women, 32% men. 89% 25 or older. Academic areas with the most degrees conferred: business/marketing; health professions and related sciences. Core. Calendar: continuous. Services for LD students, advanced placement, accelerated degree program, independent study, distance learning, external degree program, adult/continuing education programs, graduate courses open to undergrads.

Entrance Requirements: Open admission. Options: electronic application,

deferred admission. Required: 1 recommendation. Required for some: high school transcript. Entrance: noncompetitive. Application deadline: Rolling.

Collegiate Environment: Campus security: late night transport-escort service. University Library with 16,781 serials, an OPAC, and a Web page. Operations spending for the previous fiscal year: $6.8 million.

■ UNIVERSITY OF PHOENIX–SAN ANTONIO CAMPUS

8200 IH-10 W, Ste. 900
San Antonio, TX 78230
Tel: (210)524-2100; Free: 866-766-0766
Web Site: www.phoenix.edu/

Description: Proprietary, comprehensive, coed. Awards bachelor's, master's, and doctoral degrees.

■ UNIVERSITY OF ST. THOMAS

3800 Montrose Blvd.
Houston, TX 77006-4696
Tel: (713)522-7911; Free: 800-856-8565
Fax: (713)525-3558
E-mail: admissions@stthom.edu
Web Site: www.stthom.edu/

Description: Independent Roman Catholic, comprehensive, coed. Awards bachelor's, master's, and doctoral degrees. Founded 1947. Setting: 20-acre urban campus. System endowment: $64.7 million. Educational spending for the previous fiscal year: $10,186 per student. Total enrollment: 3,711. Faculty: 335 (153 full-time, 182 part-time). Student-undergrad faculty ratio is 11:1. 863 applied, 80% were admitted. 53% from top 10% of their high school class, 60% from top quarter, 71% from top half. 3 valedictorians. Full-time: 1,255 students, 65% women, 35% men. Part-time: 371 students, 55% women, 45% men. Students come from 31 states and territories, 38 other countries, 4% from out-of-state. 0.3% American Indian or Alaska Native, non-Hispanic/Latino; 37% Hispanic/Latino; 5% African American, non-Hispanic/Latino; 12% Asian, non-Hispanic/Latino; 0.1% Native Hawaiian or other Pacific Islander, non-Hispanic/Latino; 8% international. 25% 25 or older, 17% live on campus, 9% transferred in. Retention: 79% of full-time freshmen returned the following year. Academic areas with the most degrees conferred: business/marketing; social sciences; liberal arts/general studies. Core. Calendar: semesters. Services for LD students, advanced placement, accelerated degree program, self-designed majors, honors program, independent study, distance learning, double major, summer session for credit, part-time degree program, adult/continuing education programs, internships, graduate courses open to undergrads. Off campus study at University of Houston, Glassell School of Art, Notre Dame, Texas A&M, Texas Women University. Study abroad program. ROTC: Army (c), Air Force (c).

Entrance Requirements: Options: electronic application, early action, deferred admission, international baccalaureate accepted. Required: essay, high school transcript, minimum 2.8 high school GPA, 1070 SAT (Critical Reading and Math) or 23 ACT, SAT or ACT. Entrance: moderately difficult. Application deadlines: 5/1, 5/1 for nonresidents, 11/1 for early action. Notification: continuous until 11/15, continuous until 11/15 for nonresidents, 12/15 for early action. Transfer credits accepted: Yes.

Costs Per Year: Application fee: $25. Comprehensive fee: $34,790 includes full-time tuition ($26,550), mandatory fees ($340), and college room and board ($7900). College room only: $4800. Full-time tuition and fees vary according to course load. Room and board charges vary according to board plan and housing facility. Part-time tuition: $885 per credit hour. Part-time tuition varies according to course load.

Collegiate Environment: Orientation program. Drama-theater group, choral group, student-run newspaper. Social organizations: 80 open to all. Most popular organizations: Health Occupations Students of America (HOSA), Nursing Student Association, Student Activities Board (SAB), American Chemical Society, Soccer. Major annual events: Neewollah-Annual Halloween party, Late Night Breakfast, Deck the Mall. Student services: personal-psychological counseling. Campus security: 24-hour emergency response devices and patrols, late night transport-escort service, controlled dormitory access. 346 college housing spaces available; 274 were occupied in 2012-13. Freshmen given priority for college housing. Option: coed housing available. Doherty Library plus 4 others with 317,207 books, 611,292 microform titles, 58,251 serials, 13,190 audiovisual materials, an OPAC, and a Web page. Operations spending for the previous fiscal year: $1.9 million. 316 computers available on campus for general student use. Computer purchase/lease plans available. A campuswide network can be accessed from student residence rooms. Students can access the following: online class registration. Staffed computer lab on campus.

■ THE UNIVERSITY OF TEXAS AT ARLINGTON

701 S Nedderman Dr.
Arlington, TX 76019
Tel: (817)272-2011
Fax: (817)272-5656
E-mail: admissions@uta.edu
Web Site: www.uta.edu/

Description: State-supported, university, coed. Part of University of Texas System. Awards bachelor's, master's, and doctoral degrees and post-master's certificates. Founded 1895. Setting: 420-acre urban campus with easy access to Dallas-Fort Worth. Endowment: $83.3 million. Research spending for the previous fiscal year: $56.9 million. Educational spending for the previous fiscal year: $2651 per student. Total enrollment: 33,239. Faculty: 1,399 (845 full-time, 554 part-time). Student-undergrad faculty ratio is 23:1. 10,280 applied, 59% were admitted. 27% from top 10% of their high school class, 73% from top quarter, 98% from top half. Full-time: 16,164 students, 52% women, 48% men. Part-time: 9,597 students, 63% women, 37% men. Students come from 49 states and territories, 65 other countries, 23% from out-of-state. 0.4% American Indian or Alaska Native, non-Hispanic/Latino; 24% Hispanic/Latino; 15% African American, non-Hispanic/Latino; 11% Asian, non-Hispanic/Latino; 0.2% Native Hawaiian or other Pacific Islander, non-Hispanic/Latino; 4% international. 36% 25 or older, 11% live on campus, 34% transferred in. Retention: 76% of full-time freshmen returned the following year. Academic areas with the most degrees conferred: health professions and related sciences; business/marketing; interdisciplinary studies. Core. Calendar: semesters. Academic remediation for entering students, ESL program, services for LD students, advanced placement, self-designed majors, freshman honors college, honors program, independent study, distance learning, double major, summer session for credit, part-time degree program, adult/continuing education programs, co-op programs and internships, graduate courses open to undergrads. Off campus study. Study abroad program. ROTC: Army, Air Force (c).

Entrance Requirements: Options: electronic application, deferred admission. Required: high school transcript, class rank, SAT or ACT. Entrance: moderately difficult. Application deadline: 6/1. Notification: continuous. SAT Reasoning Test deadline: 6/1. Transfer credits accepted: Yes.

Costs Per Year: Application fee: $50. State resident tuition: $8878 full-time. Nonresident tuition: $19,408 full-time. Full-time tuition varies according to course level, course load, and program. College room and board: $7708. College room only: $4028. Room and board charges vary according to board plan and housing facility.

Collegiate Environment: Orientation program. Drama-theater group, choral group, marching band, student-run newspaper, radio station. Social organizations: 300 open to all; national fraternities, national sororities, local fraternities, local sororities; 4% of eligible men and 2% of eligible women are members. Most popular organizations: Baptist Student Ministry, Association of Mexican American Students, Latin American Student Association, Asian Student Association, African Student Association. Major annual events: Campus Elections, Bed Races, Activity Fair Days. Student services: legal services, health clinic, personal-psychological counseling. Campus security: 24-hour emergency response devices and patrols, late night transport-escort service, controlled dormitory access, remote emergency telephones, bicycle patrols, crime prevention program, student shuttle service. 5,102 college housing spaces available; 4,078 were occupied in 2012-13. No special consideration for freshman housing applicants. Options: coed, men-only, women-only housing available. Central Library plus 2 others with 1.6 million books, 1.5 million microform titles, 37,479 serials, 8,881 audiovisual materials, an OPAC, and a Web page. Operations spending for the previous fiscal year: $11.9 million. 500 computers available on campus for general student use. A campuswide network can be accessed from student residence rooms and from off campus. Students can access the following: online class registration. Staffed computer lab on campus provides training in use of computers and the Internet.

■ THE UNIVERSITY OF TEXAS AT AUSTIN

Austin, TX 78712-1111
Tel: (512)471-3434
Fax: (512)475-7475
E-mail: kedra.ishop@austin.utexas.edu
Web Site: www.utexas.edu/

Description: State-supported, university, coed. Part of University of Texas

System. Awards bachelor's, master's, and doctoral degrees. Founded 1883. Setting: 431-acre urban campus with easy access to San Antonio. Endowment: $2.9 billion. Research spending for the previous fiscal year: $490.2 million. Educational spending for the previous fiscal year: $12,854 per student. Total enrollment: 52,186. Faculty: 3,034 (2,735 full-time, 299 part-time). Student-undergrad faculty ratio is 18:1. 35,431 applied, 47% were admitted. 72% from top 10% of their high school class, 91% from top quarter, 98% from top half. Full-time: 37,083 students, 52% women, 48% men. Part-time: 2,872 students, 46% women, 54% men. Students come from 53 states and territories, 99 other countries, 5% from out-of-state. 0.3% American Indian or Alaska Native, non-Hispanic/Latino; 21% Hispanic/Latino; 4% African American, non-Hispanic/Latino; 18% Asian, non-Hispanic/Latino; 0.1% Native Hawaiian or other Pacific Islander, non-Hispanic/Latino; 5% international. 5% 25 or older, 19% live on campus, 7% transferred in. Retention: 93% of full-time freshmen returned the following year. Academic areas with the most degrees conferred: social sciences; business/marketing; engineering; communication/journalism. Core. Calendar: semesters. Academic remediation for entering students, ESL program, services for LD students, advanced placement, accelerated degree program, self-designed majors, honors program, independent study, distance learning, double major, summer session for credit, part-time degree program, co-op programs and internships, graduate courses open to undergrads. Off campus study at MD/PHD program with UTMB; MBA/MA program with Tecnologico de Monterrey-Campus Santa Fe; MSSW/M.Div program with Austin Presbyterian Theological Seminary; MSSW/MPH program with UT Health Science Center, Houston; MGPS/MPH program with UT Health Science Center, School of Public Health (Austin Regional Campus); MPAff/MPH with UT Health Science Center, School of Public Health (Austin Regional Campus); Ph.D. in Translational Science with UT Health Science Center at San Antonio and UT San Antonio. Study abroad program. ROTC: Army, Naval, Air Force.

Entrance Requirements: Options: electronic application, international baccalaureate accepted. Required: essay, high school transcript, SAT or ACT. Entrance: very difficult. Application deadline: 12/1. Notification: continuous. Preference given to Texas high school graduates in the top ranks of their class. SAT Reasoning Test deadline: 12/31. Transfer credits accepted: Yes. Applicants placed on waiting list: 321. Wait-listed applicants offered admission: 34.

Costs Per Year: Application fee: $75. State resident tuition: $9792 full-time. Nonresident tuition: $33,060 full-time. Full-time tuition varies according to course load and program. College room and board: $10,946. Room and board charges vary according to housing facility.

Collegiate Environment: Orientation program. Drama-theater group, choral group, marching band, student-run newspaper, radio station. Social organizations: 1,100 open to all; national fraternities, national sororities; 3% of eligible men and 5% of eligible women are members. Most popular organizations: Alpha Phi Omega, Student Events Center, Texas Exes-Student Chapter, Longhorn Band Student Organization, Student Volunteer Board. Major annual events: Gone to Texas (Freshman welcome), 40 Acres Fest, Commencement. Student services: legal services, health clinic, personal-psychological counseling, women's center. Campus security: 24-hour emergency response devices and patrols, late night transport-escort service, controlled dormitory access. 8,244 college housing spaces available; 7,598 were occupied in 2012-13. Freshmen given priority for college housing. Options: coed, men-only, women-only housing available. Perry-Castaneda Library plus 17 others with 10.9 million books, 6.7 million microform titles, 103,589 serials, 13.3 million audiovisual materials, an OPAC, and a Web page. Operations spending for the previous fiscal year: $31.1 million. 3,150 computers available on campus for general student use. A campuswide network can be accessed from student residence rooms and from off campus. Students can access the following: online class registration. Staffed computer lab on campus provides training in use of computers, software, and the Internet.

■ THE UNIVERSITY OF TEXAS AT BROWNSVILLE

80 Fort Brown
Brownsville, TX 78520-4991
Tel: (956)544-8200; Free: 877-UTBTSC1
Fax: (956)544-8832
E-mail: admissions@utb.edu
Web Site: www.utb.edu/

Description: State-supported, comprehensive, coed. Part of University of Texas System. Awards associate, bachelor's, master's, and doctoral degrees. Founded 1973. Setting: 380-acre urban campus. Endowment: $8.7 million. Research spending for the previous fiscal year: $8.3 million.

Educational spending for the previous fiscal year: $2846 per student. Total enrollment: 13,713. Faculty: 642 (380 full-time, 262 part-time). Student-undergrad faculty ratio is 21:1. 2,341 applied, 100% were admitted. 8% from top 10% of their high school class, 25% from top quarter, 54% from top half. 5% from out-of-state. 32% 25 or older, 2% live on campus. Retention: 57% of full-time freshmen returned the following year. Academic areas with the most degrees conferred: interdisciplinary studies; business/marketing; psychology. Core. Calendar: semesters. Academic remediation for entering students, ESL program, services for LD students, advanced placement, independent study, distance learning, double major, summer session for credit, part-time degree program, co-op programs and internships, graduate courses open to undergrads. Off campus study. Study abroad program. ROTC: Army.

Entrance Requirements: Open admission. Options: electronic application, early admission, international baccalaureate accepted. Required: high school transcript, minimum 2 high school GPA. Entrance: noncompetitive. Application deadline: 7/1. Transfer credits accepted: Yes.

Costs Per Year: Application fee: $0. State resident tuition: $3743 full-time, $155.95 per credit hour part-time. Nonresident tuition: $12,167 full-time, $506.95 per credit hour part-time. Mandatory fees: $1373 full-time, $469.12 per term part-time. Full-time tuition and fees vary according to class time, course level, course load, location, and program. Part-time tuition and fees vary according to class time, course level, course load, location, and program. College room and board: $6602. Room and board charges vary according to board plan.

Collegiate Environment: Orientation program. Choral group, student-run newspaper. Social organizations: 62 open to all; local fraternities, local sororities; 4% of eligible men and 4% of eligible women are members. Most popular organizations: Alpha Chi, Anime Viewing Club, Counseling and Guidance Student Association, Gorgas Science, Alpha Chi Psi. Major annual events: Halloween Extravaganza, Fiesta de Paseo, Bougainvillea Ball. Student services: legal services, health clinic, personal-psychological counseling. Campus security: 24-hour emergency response devices and patrols, late night transport-escort service. 458 college housing spaces available. No special consideration for freshman housing applicants. Option: coed housing available. University Boulevard Library plus 1 other with an OPAC and a Web page. 332 computers available on campus for general student use. Computer purchase/lease plans available. A campuswide network can be accessed from student residence rooms. Students can access the following: online class registration. Staffed computer lab on campus provides training in use of computers, software, and the Internet.

■ **THE UNIVERSITY OF TEXAS AT DALLAS**
800 W Campbell Rd.
Richardson, TX 75080
Tel: (972)883-2111; Free: 800-889-2443
Fax: (972)883-6803
E-mail: interest@utdallas.edu
Web Site: www.utdallas.edu/

Description: State-supported, university, coed. Part of University of Texas System. Awards bachelor's, master's, and doctoral degrees. Founded 1969. Setting: 500-acre suburban campus with easy access to Dallas-Fort Worth. Endowment: $273.6 million. Research spending for the previous fiscal year: $90.6 million. Educational spending for the previous fiscal year: $14,821 per student. Total enrollment: 19,727. Faculty: 940 (664 full-time, 276 part-time). Student-undergrad faculty ratio is 21:1. 7,079 applied, 52% were admitted. 42% from top 10% of their high school class, 73% from top quarter, 92% from top half. 63 National Merit Scholars, 27 valedictorians. Full-time: 9,505 students, 43% women, 57% men. Part-time: 2,524 students, 46% women, 54% men. Students come from 47 states and territories, 73 other countries, 4% from out-of-state. 0.3% American Indian or Alaska Native, non-Hispanic/Latino; 16% Hispanic/Latino; 6% African American, non-Hispanic/Latino; 25% Asian, non-Hispanic/Latino; 0.1% Native Hawaiian or other Pacific Islander, non-Hispanic/Latino; 5% international. 24% 25 or older, 25% live on campus, 14% transferred in. Retention: 85% of full-time freshmen returned the following year. Academic areas with the most degrees conferred: business/marketing; biological/life sciences; psychology. Core. Calendar: semesters. Academic remediation for entering students, services for LD students, advanced placement, accelerated degree program, self-designed majors, freshman honors college, honors program, independent study, distance learning, double major, summer session for credit, part-time degree program, adult/continuing education programs, co-op programs and internships, graduate courses open to undergrads. Study abroad program. ROTC: Army (c), Air Force (c).

Entrance Requirements: Options: electronic application, deferred admission, international baccalaureate accepted. Required: essay, high school transcript, SAT or ACT. Recommended: 3 recommendations. Required for some: interview, THEA. Entrance: very difficult. Application deadline: 7/1. Notification: continuous. SAT Reasoning Test deadline: 8/1. SAT Subject Test deadline: 8/1. Transfer credits accepted: Yes.

Costs Per Year: Application fee: $50. State resident tuition: $11,592 full-time, $386.40 per credit hour part-time. Nonresident tuition: $29,266 full-time, $975.53 per credit hour part-time. Full-time tuition varies according to course load and degree level. Part-time tuition varies according to course load and degree level. College room and board: $9050. Room and board charges vary according to board plan and housing facility. Tuition guaranteed not to increase for student's term of enrollment.

Collegiate Environment: Orientation program. Drama-theater group, choral group, student-run newspaper, radio station. Social organizations: 275 open to all; national fraternities, national sororities, local fraternities, local sororities; 3% of eligible men and 2% of eligible women are members. Most popular organizations: Student Government Association, Golden Key National Honor Society, Muslim Students Association, Indian Student Association, Friendship Association of Chinese Students and Scholars. Major annual events: Jazz Concert, Homecoming dance, Holiday Sing. Student services: legal services, health clinic, personal-psychological counseling, women's center. Campus security: 24-hour emergency response devices and patrols, student patrols, late night transport-escort service, controlled dormitory access. 3,633 college housing spaces available; 2,964 were occupied in 2012-13. Freshmen given priority for college housing. Option: coed housing available. Eugene McDermott Library plus 1 other with 2.6 million books, 2.9 million microform titles, 836,388 serials, 14,411 audiovisual materials, an OPAC, and a Web page. Operations spending for the previous fiscal year: $8.3 million. 168 computers available on campus for general student use. Computer purchase/lease plans available. A campuswide network can be accessed from student residence rooms and from off campus. Students can access the following: online class registration. Staffed computer lab on campus provides training in use of computers, software, and the Internet.

■ **THE UNIVERSITY OF TEXAS AT EL PASO**
500 W University Ave.
El Paso, TX 79968-0001
Tel: (915)747-5000; Free: 877-74MINER
Fax: (915)747-5122
E-mail: futureminer@utep.edu
Web Site: www.utep.edu/

Description: State-supported, university, coed. Part of University of Texas System. Awards bachelor's, master's, and doctoral degrees and post-master's certificates. Founded 1913. Setting: 360-acre urban campus. Total enrollment: 22,749. Faculty: 1,215 (701 full-time, 514 part-time). Student-undergrad faculty ratio is 21:1. 6,240 applied, 99% were admitted. 17% from top 10% of their high school class, 40% from top quarter, 69% from top half. Full-time: 12,681 students, 53% women, 47% men. Part-time: 6,536 students, 56% women, 44% men. Students come from 53 states and territories, 41 other countries, 3% from out-of-state. 0.2% American Indian or Alaska Native, non-Hispanic/Latino; 81% Hispanic/Latino; 3% African American, non-Hispanic/Latino; 1% Asian, non-Hispanic/Latino; 0.1% Native Hawaiian or other Pacific Islander, non-Hispanic/Latino; 5% international. 27% 25 or older, 10% transferred in. Retention: 72% of full-time freshmen returned the following year. Academic areas with the most degrees conferred: education; business/marketing; health professions and related sciences. Core. Calendar: semesters. Academic remediation for entering students, ESL program, services for LD students, advanced placement, accelerated degree program, honors program, independent study, distance learning, double major, summer session for credit, part-time degree program, adult/continuing education programs, co-op programs and internships, graduate courses open to undergrads. Off campus study at National Student Exchange. Study abroad program. ROTC: Army, Air Force.

Entrance Requirements: Option: deferred admission. Required: high school transcript. Required for some: SAT or ACT. Entrance: minimally difficult. Application deadline: 7/31. Transfer credits accepted: Yes.

Collegiate Environment: Orientation program. Drama-theater group, choral group, marching band, student-run newspaper, radio station. Social organizations: national fraternities, national sororities. Student services: legal services, health clinic, personal-psychological counseling, women's center. Campus security: 24-hour emergency response devices and patrols, late night transport-escort service. 428 college housing spaces available. Option:

coed housing available. University Library with 1.3 million books, 2 million microform titles, 3,065 serials, and 194,088 audiovisual materials.

■ THE UNIVERSITY OF TEXAS HEALTH SCIENCE CENTER AT HOUSTON

PO Box 20036
Houston, TX 77225-0036
Tel: (713)500-3333
Fax: (713)500-3026
E-mail: registrar@uth.tmc.edu
Web Site: www.uthouston.edu/

Description: State-supported, upper-level, coed. Part of University of Texas System. Awards bachelor's, master's, and doctoral degrees and post-master's certificates. Founded 1972. Setting: urban campus with easy access to Houston. Total enrollment: 4,489. Full-time: 563 students, 83% women, 17% men. Students come from 7 states and territories, 7 other countries, 1% from out-of-state. 0.4% American Indian or Alaska Native, non-Hispanic/Latino; 9% Hispanic/Latino; 7% African American, non-Hispanic/Latino; 13% Asian, non-Hispanic/Latino; 0% Native Hawaiian or other Pacific Islander, non-Hispanic/Latino; 4% international. 0% 25 or older, 0% transferred in. Academic area with the most degrees conferred: health professions and related sciences. Core. Calendar: semesters. Accelerated degree program, independent study, distance learning, summer session for credit, part-time degree program, internships, graduate courses open to undergrads. ROTC: Army (c).

Entrance Requirements: Transfer credits accepted: Yes.

Collegiate Environment: Orientation program. Student-run newspaper. Most popular organizations: Student Inter-council (SIC), School of Nursing Student Government Organization (School of Nursing), Student Council (Dental Branch), Student Senate (Medical School), SPH Student Association (School of Public Health). Major annual event: UT Medics Community Projects. Student services: health clinic, personal-psychological counseling. Campus security: 24-hour emergency response devices and patrols, late night transport-escort service, controlled access to all buildings. College housing not available.

■ THE UNIVERSITY OF TEXAS HEALTH SCIENCE CENTER AT SAN ANTONIO

7703 Floyd Curl Dr.
San Antonio, TX 78229-3900
Tel: (210)567-7000
Fax: (210)567-2685
Web Site: www.uthscsa.edu/

Description: State-supported, upper-level, coed. Part of University of Texas System. Awards bachelor's, master's, and doctoral degrees. Founded 1976. Setting: 100-acre suburban campus. Total enrollment: 3,093. Student-undergrad faculty ratio is 3:1. 32 applied. 0% from out-of-state. 54% 25 or older. Core. Calendar: semesters. Distance learning, summer session for credit, part-time degree program, adult/continuing education programs. ROTC: Army (c), Air Force (c).

Collegiate Environment: Campus security: 24-hour emergency response devices and patrols, late night transport-escort service.

■ THE UNIVERSITY OF TEXAS MEDICAL BRANCH

301 University Blvd.
Galveston, TX 77555
Tel: (409)772-1011
Fax: (409)772-5056
E-mail: enrollment.services@utmb.edu
Web Site: www.utmb.edu/

Description: State-supported, comprehensive, coed. Part of University of Texas System. Awards bachelor's, master's, and doctoral degrees and post-master's certificates. Founded 1891. Setting: 85-acre small town campus with easy access to Houston. Endowment: $368.5 million. Research spending for the previous fiscal year: $145.2 million. Total enrollment: 2,430. Full-time: 315 students, 81% women, 19% men. Part-time: 177 students, 79% women, 21% men. Students come from 5 states and territories, 12 other countries, 1% from out-of-state. 65% 25 or older. Academic area with the most degrees conferred: health professions and related sciences. Core. Calendar: semesters (early semester). Services for LD students, advanced placement, accelerated degree program, independent study, distance learning, summer session for credit, part-time degree program, internships.

Entrance Requirements: Options: electronic application, international bac-

calaureate accepted. Entrance: very difficult. Preference given to state residents. Transfer credits accepted: Yes.

Collegiate Environment: Orientation program. Student-run newspaper. Social organizations: 40 open to all; national fraternities, local fraternities. Most popular organizations: Texas Medical Association, American Medical Student Association, American Medical Women's Association, Texas Association Latin American Medical Students, National Medical Student Association. Major annual events: Quest and Orientation, All Sports Day, Primary Care Day. Student services: legal services, health clinic, personal-psychological counseling. Campus security: 24-hour emergency response devices and patrols, late night transport-escort service. Moody Medical Library with an OPAC and a Web page.

■ THE UNIVERSITY OF TEXAS OF THE PERMIAN BASIN

4901 E University Blvd.
Odessa, TX 79762-0001
Tel: (432)552-2020; Free: 866-552-UTPB
Fax: (432)552-2109
E-mail: admissions@utpb.edu
Web Site: www.utpb.edu/

Description: State-supported, comprehensive, coed. Part of University of Texas System. Awards bachelor's and master's degrees. Founded 1969. Setting: 600-acre urban campus. Endowment: $32.8 million. Research spending for the previous fiscal year: $1.5 million. Educational spending for the previous fiscal year: $24,955 per student. Total enrollment: 4,021. Faculty: 186 (108 full-time, 78 part-time). Student-undergrad faculty ratio is 21:1. 1,007 applied, 86% were admitted. 25% from top 10% of their high school class, 55% from top quarter, 90% from top half. Full-time: 2,507 students, 56% women, 44% men. Part-time: 1,345 students, 58% women, 42% men. Students come from 33 states and territories, 20 other countries, 3% from out-of-state. 1% American Indian or Alaska Native, non-Hispanic/Latino; 47% Hispanic/Latino; 5% African American, non-Hispanic/Latino; 3% Asian, non-Hispanic/Latino; 0.3% Native Hawaiian or other Pacific Islander, non-Hispanic/Latino; 1% international. 27% 25 or older, 15% live on campus, 13% transferred in. Retention: 66% of full-time freshmen returned the following year. Academic areas with the most degrees conferred: business/marketing; social sciences; family and consumer sciences. Core. Calendar: semesters. Academic remediation for entering students, ESL program, services for LD students, advanced placement, honors program, independent study, distance learning, double major, summer session for credit, part-time degree program, internships, graduate courses open to undergrads. Study abroad program.

Entrance Requirements: Options: electronic application, early admission, deferred admission. Required: high school transcript, SAT or ACT. Entrance: moderately difficult. Application deadline: 7/14. Notification: continuous. SAT Reasoning Test deadline: 7/15. Transfer credits accepted: Yes.

Costs Per Year: Application fee: $0. State resident tuition: $5,037 full-time, $167.86 per credit hour part-time. Nonresident tuition: $15,566 full-time, $518.86 per credit hour part-time. Mandatory fees: $1,422 full-time, $52.44 per credit hour part-time, $576.80 per term part-time. Full-time tuition and fees vary according to course load and location. Part-time tuition and fees vary according to course load and location. College room and board: $7616. College room only: $4532. Room and board charges vary according to board plan and housing facility.

Collegiate Environment: Orientation program. Drama-theater group, choral group, student-run newspaper. Social organizations: 43 open to all; national fraternities; 14% of eligible men and 23% of eligible women are members. Most popular organizations: National Society of Leadership and Success (NSLS), Baptist Student Ministries (BSM), Students In Philanthropy (SIP), Catholic Student Association (CSA), Black Leadership Council (BLC). Major annual events: Welcome Week Activities, Homecoming Activities, The Big Party. Student services: health clinic, personal-psychological counseling. Campus security: 24-hour patrols, late night transport-escort service. 620 college housing spaces available; 511 were occupied in 2012-13. No special consideration for freshman housing applicants. Option: coed housing available. J. Conrad Dunagan Library with 287,808 books, 1.2 million microform titles, 42,005 serials, 1,506 audiovisual materials, an OPAC, and a Web page. Operations spending for the previous fiscal year: $950,923. 170 computers available on campus for general student use. A campuswide network can be accessed from student residence rooms and from off campus. Students can access the following: online class registration. Staffed computer lab on campus provides training in use of computers, software, and the Internet.

Community Environment: Metropolitan area of Odessa-Midland, population 237,000. International Airport and Interstate Highway 20 access to campus.

■ THE UNIVERSITY OF TEXAS AT SAN ANTONIO

One UTSA Cir.
San Antonio, TX 78249-0617
Tel: (210)458-4011; Free: 800-669-0919
E-mail: prospects@utsa.edu
Web Site: www.utsa.edu/

Description: State-supported, university, coed. Part of University of Texas System. Awards bachelor's, master's, and doctoral degrees. Founded 1969. Setting: 600-acre suburban campus. Research spending for the previous fiscal year: $51.1 million. Total enrollment: 30,474. Student-undergrad faculty ratio is 23:1. 15,239 applied, 73% were admitted. 13% from top 10% of their high school class, 51% from top quarter, 89% from top half. Full-time: 21,186 students, 47% women, 53% men. Part-time: 4,793 students, 47% women, 53% men. 3% from out-of-state. 0.2% American Indian or Alaska Native, non-Hispanic/Latino; 47% Hispanic/Latino; 10% African American, non-Hispanic/Latino; 5% Asian, non-Hispanic/Latino; 0.2% Native Hawaiian or other Pacific Islander, non-Hispanic/Latino; 4% international. 24% 25 or older, 12% live on campus, 9% transferred in. Retention: 63% of full-time freshmen returned the following year. Academic areas with the most degrees conferred: business/marketing; interdisciplinary studies; biological/life sciences. Core. Calendar: semesters. Academic remediation for entering students, ESL program, services for LD students, advanced placement, honors program, independent study, distance learning, double major, summer session for credit, part-time degree program, adult/continuing education programs, co-op programs and internships, graduate courses open to undergrads. Off campus study at National Student Exchange. Study abroad program. ROTC: Army, Air Force.

Entrance Requirements: Options: electronic application, international baccalaureate accepted. Required: high school transcript, SAT or ACT. Recommended: essay, 1 recommendation. Application deadlines: 6/1, 6/1 for nonresidents. Notification: continuous, continuous for nonresidents. SAT Reasoning Test deadline: 6/1. Transfer credits accepted: Yes.

Costs Per Year: Application fee: $40. State resident tuition: $5928 full-time, $197.60 per hour part-time. Nonresident tuition: $16,458 full-time, $548.60 per hour part-time. Mandatory fees: $2491 full-time. Full-time tuition and fees vary according to course load and degree level. Part-time tuition varies according to course load and degree level. College room and board: $9693. College room only: $6651. Room and board charges vary according to board plan and housing facility.

Collegiate Environment: Orientation program. Choral group, marching band, student-run newspaper, radio station. Social organizations: 297 open to all; national fraternities, national sororities; 2% of eligible men and 2% of eligible women are members. Most popular organizations: Student Government Association, Hispanic Student Association, Black Student Union, GLBTQ, Marching Band. Major annual events: Best Fest, Fiesta UTSA, Party on the Paseo. Student services: health clinic, personal-psychological counseling, women's center. Campus security: 24-hour emergency response devices and patrols, late night transport-escort service, controlled dormitory access, close to 1,000 security cameras, Reverse 911 emergency telephone notification system, and Giant Voice speaker arrays. 3,647 college housing spaces available; 3,501 were occupied in 2012-13. No special consideration for freshman housing applicants. Option: coed housing available. John Peace Library plus 3 others with 1.7 million books, 2.9 million microform titles, 76,419 serials, 56,842 audiovisual materials, an OPAC, and a Web page. 542 computers available on campus for general student use. A campuswide network can be accessed from student residence rooms and from off campus. Students can access the following: online class registration. Staffed computer lab on campus (open 24 hours a day) provides training in use of computers and the Internet.

■ THE UNIVERSITY OF TEXAS AT TYLER

3900 University Blvd.
Tyler, TX 75799-0001
Tel: (903)566-7000; Free: 800-UTTYLER
Fax: (903)566-7068
E-mail: admissions@uttyler.edu
Web Site: www.uttyler.edu/

Description: State-supported, comprehensive, coed. Part of University of Texas System. Awards bachelor's, master's, and doctoral degrees. Founded 1971. Setting: 200-acre urban campus. Total enrollment: 6,858. Faculty: 449

(292 full-time, 157 part-time). Student-undergrad faculty ratio is 16:1. 2,012 applied, 80% were admitted. 11% from top 10% of their high school class, 43% from top quarter, 78% from top half. Full-time: 4,072 students, 57% women, 43% men. Part-time: 1,167 students, 61% women, 39% men. 2% from out-of-state. 0.4% American Indian or Alaska Native, non-Hispanic/Latino; 12% Hispanic/Latino; 10% African American, non-Hispanic/Latino; 2% Asian, non-Hispanic/Latino; 0.2% Native Hawaiian or other Pacific Islander, non-Hispanic/Latino; 1% international. 27% 25 or older, 14% live on campus, 19% transferred in. Retention: 64% of full-time freshmen returned the following year. Academic areas with the most degrees conferred: health professions and related sciences; business/marketing; interdisciplinary studies. Calendar: semesters. Part-time degree program, adult/continuing education programs.

Entrance Requirements: Options: electronic application, deferred admission, international baccalaureate accepted. Required: high school transcript, SAT or ACT. Entrance: moderately difficult. Application deadline: 8/20. Notification: continuous. SAT Reasoning Test deadline: 8/20. SAT Subject Test deadline: 8/20.

Costs Per Year: Application fee: $40. State resident tuition: $5370 full-time, $50 per semester hour part-time. Nonresident tuition: $15,900 full-time, $401 per semester hour part-time. Mandatory fees: $1852 full-time. Full-time tuition and fees vary according to course load. Part-time tuition varies according to course load. College room and board: $8979. College room only: $5679. Room and board charges vary according to board plan and housing facility.

Collegiate Environment: Orientation program. Campus security: 24-hour emergency response devices and patrols, late night transport-escort service, controlled dormitory access. Freshmen given priority for college housing. On-campus residence required in freshman year. Option: coed housing available.

■ THE UNIVERSITY OF TEXAS–PAN AMERICAN

1201 W University Dr.
Edinburg, TX 78539
Tel: (956)381-2011
E-mail: admissions@utpa.edu
Web Site: www.utpa.edu/

Description: State-supported, comprehensive, coed. Part of University of Texas System. Awards bachelor's, master's, and doctoral degrees. Founded 1927. Setting: 331-acre small town campus with easy access to McAllen-Edinburg-Mission. Endowment: $61.2 million. Research spending for the previous fiscal year: $9 million. Total enrollment: 19,302. Faculty: 775 (640 full-time, 135 part-time). Student-undergrad faculty ratio is 22:1. 9,313 applied, 62% were admitted. 21% from top 10% of their high school class, 53% from top quarter, 83% from top half. Full-time: 12,491 students, 55% women, 45% men. Part-time: 4,475 students, 56% women, 44% men. Students come from 35 states and territories, 52 other countries, 1% from out-of-state. 0.1% American Indian or Alaska Native, non-Hispanic/Latino; 91% Hispanic/Latino; 1% African American, non-Hispanic/Latino; 1% Asian, non-Hispanic/Latino; 0.1% Native Hawaiian or other Pacific Islander, non-Hispanic/Latino; 2% international. 20% 25 or older, 4% live on campus, 7% transferred in. Retention: 75% of full-time freshmen returned the following year. Academic areas with the most degrees conferred: business/marketing; health professions and related sciences; interdisciplinary studies. Core. Calendar: semesters. Academic remediation for entering students, ESL program, services for LD students, advanced placement, accelerated degree program, honors program, independent study, distance learning, double major, summer session for credit, part-time degree program, adult/continuing education programs, co-op programs and internships, graduate courses open to undergrads. Study abroad program. ROTC: Army.

Entrance Requirements: Option: electronic application. Required: high school transcript, minimum 2 high school GPA, SAT or ACT. Required for some: interview. Entrance: noncompetitive. Application deadline: 8/11. Notification: continuous. SAT Reasoning Test deadline: 8/11. SAT Subject Test deadline: 8/11.

Costs Per Year: Application fee: $0. State resident tuition: $4,168 full-time, $173.65 per credit hour part-time. Nonresident tuition: $12,592 full-time, $533.60 per credit hour part-time. Mandatory fees: $997 full-time, $41.53 per credit hour part-time. Full-time tuition and fees vary according to course load and degree level. Part-time tuition and fees vary according to course load and degree level. College room and board: $5656. College room only: $3400. Room and board charges vary according to board plan and housing facility.

Collegiate Environment: Orientation program. Drama-theater group, choral

group, student-run newspaper. Social organizations: national fraternities, national sororities, local sororities. Major annual events: Hispanic Engineering, Science, and Technology Week, Homecoming. Student services: health clinic, personal-psychological counseling. Campus security: 24-hour emergency response devices and patrols, late night transport-escort service. No special consideration for freshman housing applicants. Options: coed, men-only, women-only housing available. University Library with an OPAC and a Web page.

Community Environment: Population 62,735. Edinburg is located in the subtropical lower Rio Grande Valley of Texas and enjoys a mild year-round climate. The average summer maximum temperature is about 90 degrees, with winter average of 70 degrees. The community is served by bus lines and U.S. Highway 281. Edinburg has a hospital and major civic, fraternal and veteran's organizations. Part-time employment is available. Local recreation includes hunting, fishing, golf, and swimming in the Gulf of Mexico approximately 70 miles away.

■ **VERNON COLLEGE**
4400 College Dr.
Vernon, TX 76384-4092
Tel: (940)552-6291
Fax: (940)553-1753
Web Site: www.vernoncollege.edu/
Description: State and locally supported, 2-year, coed. Awards certificates, transfer associate, and terminal associate degrees. Founded 1970. Setting: 100-acre small town campus. Total enrollment: 3,163. Student-undergrad faculty ratio is 17:1. 4% from out-of-state. 35% 25 or older. Core. Calendar: semesters. Academic remediation for entering students, services for LD students, advanced placement, distance learning, double major, summer session for credit, part-time degree program, adult/continuing education programs, co-op programs and internships.
Entrance Requirements: Open admission. Options: electronic application, early admission. Entrance: noncompetitive. Application deadline: Rolling.
Collegiate Environment: Drama-theater group, choral group. Social organizations: 3 open to all. Most popular organizations: Student Government Association, Baptist Student Union. Major annual event: Sports Day. Student services: health clinic, personal-psychological counseling. Campus security: 24-hour patrols. Wright Library with 29,000 books, 200 serials, an OPAC, and a Web page. 100 computers available on campus for general student use. A campuswide network can be accessed. Students can access the following: online class registration. Staffed computer lab on campus.

■ **VET TECH INSTITUTE OF HOUSTON**
4669 SW Fwy.
Ste. 100
Houston, TX 77027
Tel: (713)629-1500; Free: 800-275-2736
Fax: (713)629-0059
Web Site: www.vettechinstitute.edu/
Description: Private, 2-year, coed. Awards terminal associate degrees. Founded 1958. Setting: suburban campus. Total enrollment: 239. 570 applied, 66% were admitted. Accelerated degree program, internships.
Collegiate Environment: College housing not available.

■ **VICTORIA COLLEGE**
2200 E Red River
Victoria, TX 77901-4494
Tel: (361)573-3291; Free: 877-843-4369
Fax: (361)572-3850
E-mail: registrar@victoriacollege.edu
Web Site: www.victoriacollege.edu/
Description: County-supported, 2-year, coed. Awards certificates, transfer associate, and terminal associate degrees. Founded 1925. Setting: 80-acre urban campus. Endowment: $2.3 million. Educational spending for the previous fiscal year: $1410 per student. Total enrollment: 4,484. Faculty: 306 (106 full-time, 200 part-time). Student-undergrad faculty ratio is 18:1. 3,972 applied, 18% were admitted. Full-time: 1,482 students, 60% women, 40% men. Part-time: 3,002 students, 69% women, 31% men. Students come from 15 states and territories, 9 other countries, 1% from out-of-state. 1% American Indian or Alaska Native, non-Hispanic/Latino; 39% Hispanic/Latino; 5% African American, non-Hispanic/Latino; 1% Asian, non-Hispanic/Latino; 0.04% Native Hawaiian or other Pacific Islander, non-Hispanic/Latino; 0.2% international. 34% 25 or older, 57% transferred in. Core. Calendar: semesters. Academic remediation for entering students, services for LD

students, advanced placement, distance learning, summer session for credit, part-time degree program, adult/continuing education programs.
Entrance Requirements: Open admission. Option: electronic application. Required: high school transcript. Entrance: noncompetitive. Application deadline: Rolling. Transfer credits accepted: Yes.
Collegiate Environment: Orientation program. Drama-theater group, choral group. Most popular organization: Student Senate. Major annual event: VC Pirates Day. Student services: personal-psychological counseling. Campus security: 24-hour emergency response devices. College housing not available. Victoria College Library with 150,000 books and 1,500 serials. Operations spending for the previous fiscal year: $466,045. 225 computers available on campus for general student use. A campuswide network can be accessed from off-campus. Students can access the following: online class registration. Staffed computer lab on campus provides training in use of computers, software, and the Internet.
Community Environment: Population 61,790. After the battle of San Jacinto, the first military capital of the new republic was established here in Victoria. Today, the area is known for its cattle raising. The city is located 25 miles from the Gulf of Mexico. Local industries include chemicals, sand and gravel mining, and oil and gas production. Part-time employment is limited. The climate is mild. Victoria is reached by bus and airline connections. The community has several churches. Local recreation includes salt water fishing, boating, swimming and water skiing in the Gulf of Mexico, a municipal park and golf courses.

■ **VIRGINIA COLLEGE IN AUSTIN**
6301 E Hwy. 290
Austin, TX 78723
Tel: (512)371-3500
Fax: (512)371-3502
Web Site: www.vc.edu/
Description: Proprietary, 2-year, coed. Awards terminal associate degrees. Founded 2002. Total enrollment: 865. Student-undergrad faculty ratio is 16:1. 0% from out-of-state. 65% 25 or older. Retention: 85% of full-time freshmen returned the following year.

■ **WADE COLLEGE**
INFOMart, 1950 Stemmons Fwy.
Ste. 4080, LB 562
Dallas, TX 75207
Tel: (214)637-3530; Free: 800-624-4850
Fax: (214)637-0827
E-mail: jandalman@wadecollege.edu
Web Site: www.wadecollege.edu/
Description: Proprietary, primarily 2-year, coed. Awards transfer associate, terminal associate, and bachelor's degrees. Founded 1965. Setting: 175-acre urban campus. Total enrollment: 238. Faculty: 18 (9 full-time, 9 part-time). Student-undergrad faculty ratio is 15:1. 5% from out-of-state. 31% 25 or older. Retention: 49% of full-time freshmen returned the following year. Core. Calendar: trimesters. Academic remediation for entering students, advanced placement, double major, summer session for credit, part-time degree program.
Entrance Requirements: Open admission. Option: electronic application. Required: high school transcript, interview. Entrance: minimally difficult. Application deadline: Rolling. Transfer credits accepted: Yes.
Collegiate Environment: Orientation program. Social organizations: 1 open to all. Most popular organization: Merchandising Design Student Association. Campus security: 24-hour emergency response devices and patrols, late night transport-escort service, controlled dormitory access. College Library with 4,782 books, 109 serials, 147 audiovisual materials, an OPAC, and a Web page.

■ **WAYLAND BAPTIST UNIVERSITY**
1900 W Seventh St.
Plainview, TX 79072-6998
Tel: (806)291-1000; Free: 800-588-1928
Fax: (806)291-1960
E-mail: admityou@wbu.edu
Web Site: www.wbu.edu/
Description: Independent Baptist, comprehensive, coed. Awards associate, bachelor's, and master's degrees (branch locations in Anchorage, AK; Amarillo, TX; Luke Air Force Base, AZ; Glorieta, NM; Aiea, HI; Lubbock, TX; San Antonio, TX; Wichita Falls, TX). Founded 1908. Setting: 80-acre small town campus. Endowment: $68.5 million. Educational spending for the previ-

ous fiscal year: $8849 per student. Total enrollment: 1,824. Faculty: 153 (101 full-time, 52 part-time). Student-undergrad faculty ratio is 10:1. 556 applied, 97% were admitted. 9% from top 10% of their high school class, 28% from top quarter, 57% from top half. 2 valedictorians. Full-time: 1,011 students, 43% women, 57% men. Part-time: 374 students, 51% women, 49% men. Students come from 43 states and territories, 20 other countries, 17% from out-of-state. 1% American Indian or Alaska Native, non-Hispanic/Latino; 29% Hispanic/Latino; 14% African American, non-Hispanic/Latino; 1% Asian, non-Hispanic/Latino; 0.2% Native Hawaiian or other Pacific Islander, non-Hispanic/Latino; 3% international. 18% 25 or older, 53% live on campus, 7% transferred in. Retention: 48% of full-time freshmen returned the following year. Academic areas with the most degrees conferred: business/marketing; education; liberal arts/general studies. Core. Calendar: semesters. Academic remediation for entering students, services for LD students, advanced placement, accelerated degree program, honors program, distance learning, double major, summer session for credit, part-time degree program, external degree program, adult/continuing education programs, graduate courses open to undergrads. Study abroad program. ROTC: Army (c), Air Force (c).

Entrance Requirements: Option: electronic application. Required: high school transcript, SAT or ACT. Required for some: interview. Entrance: minimally difficult. Application deadline: 8/1. Notification: continuous. Transfer credits accepted: Yes.

Costs Per Year: Application fee: $35. Comprehensive fee: $18,787 includes full-time tuition ($13,650), mandatory fees ($980), and college room and board ($4,157). College room only: $1368. Full-time tuition and fees vary according to course load and location. Room and board charges vary according to board plan and housing facility. Part-time tuition: $455 per credit hour. Part-time mandatory fees: $110 per term. Part-time tuition and fees vary according to course load and location.

Collegiate Environment: Orientation program. Drama-theater group, choral group, marching band, student-run newspaper, radio station. Social organizations: 35 open to all; national fraternities, national sororities; 2% of eligible men and 2% of eligible women are members. Most popular organization: student government. Major annual events: Homecoming, Big Weekend, Pioneer Pride Week. Student services: health clinic, personal-psychological counseling. Campus security: 24-hour emergency response devices and patrols, security lighting, campus police department. 870 college housing spaces available; 738 were occupied in 2012-13. Freshmen guaranteed college housing. On-campus residence required through junior year. Options: men-only, women-only housing available. J.E. and L.E. Mabee Learning Resource Center with 131,163 books, 283,041 microform titles, 2,661 serials, 11,893 audiovisual materials, an OPAC, and a Web page. Operations spending for the previous fiscal year: $702,429. 231 computers available on campus for general student use. Computer purchase/lease plans available. A campuswide network can be accessed from student residence rooms and from off campus. Students can access the following: online class registration. Staffed computer lab on campus provides training in use of computers, software, and the Internet.

Community Environment: Population 21,900. Plainview is an agricultural and industrial community located on the High Plains of Northwest Texas. The area is served by railroad, bus, and U.S. Highway 70 and Interstate 27; State Highways 194 and FM400. The city has many churches, a municipal airport, a memorial library, YMCA, and one hospital as well as several clinics to serve the community. Local recreation includes five swimming pools, summer baseball programs, golf courses, theatres, miniature golf, bowling facilities, and boating facilities. There are a great many civic and fraternal groups active in the area. Part-time employment is available.

■ WEATHERFORD COLLEGE

225 College Park Ave.
Weatherford, TX 76086-5699
Tel: (817)594-5471; Free: 800-287-5471
Fax: (817)598-6205
E-mail: willingham@wc.edu
Web Site: www.wc.edu/

Description: State and locally supported, 2-year, coed. Awards certificates, diplomas, transfer associate, and terminal associate degrees. Founded 1869. Setting: 94-acre small town campus with easy access to Dallas-Fort Worth. Total enrollment: 4,528. Faculty: 220 (95 full-time, 125 part-time). Student-undergrad faculty ratio is 22:1. 23% 25 or older, 7% live on campus. Core. Calendar: semesters. Academic remediation for entering students, services for LD students, self-designed majors, freshman honors college,

honors program, distance learning, summer session for credit, part-time degree program, adult/continuing education programs, co-op programs and internships. ROTC: Air Force (c).

Entrance Requirements: Open admission. Option: early admission. Required for some: high school transcript. Entrance: noncompetitive. Application deadline: Rolling. Notification: continuous.

Collegiate Environment: Orientation program. Drama-theater group, choral group. Social organizations: 21 open to all. Most popular organizations: Black Awareness Student Organization, Criminal Justice Club, Phi Theta Kappa. Major annual events: Homecoming, Halloween Dance, Family Weekend. Student services: personal-psychological counseling. Campus security: 24-hour emergency response devices and patrols, late night transport-escort service. Weatherford College Library with 59,499 books, 362 serials, an OPAC, and a Web page. 85 computers available on campus for general student use. A campuswide network can be accessed from off-campus. Students can access the following: online class registration, online catalog. Staffed computer lab on campus provides training in use of computers and the Internet.

Community Environment: Weatherford, population 23,300, is the county seat of Parker County. In a diversified crop and livestock market, watermelons are their best known product. Cutting horse ranches are a major market. It can be reached by rail, bus, and air lines, and Interstate 20. The climate is mild with a mean average temperature of 64 degrees and an average rainfall of 31.6 inches. There is a city library, a local hospital, several churches representing the major denominations, and various civic and fraternal organizations. The Parker Plaza Shopping Center and College Park Shopping Center serve the surrounding area. Local recreation includes Weatherford Lake with boating, fishing, and swimming, a local picnic grounds, golf, and three public parks. Part-time employment opportunities are very limited.

■ WEST TEXAS A&M UNIVERSITY

2501 4th Ave.
Canyon, TX 79016-0001
Tel: (806)651-2000; Free: 800-99-WTAMU
Fax: (806)651-2126
E-mail: kmoore@mail.wtamu.edu
Web Site: www.wtamu.edu/

Description: State-supported, comprehensive, coed. Part of Texas A&M University System. Awards bachelor's, master's, and doctoral degrees. Founded 1909. Setting: 128-acre small town campus. Endowment: $48.4 million. Research spending for the previous fiscal year: $5.1 million. Educational spending for the previous fiscal year: $5296 per student. Total enrollment: 7,909. Faculty: 384 (266 full-time, 118 part-time). Student-undergrad faculty ratio is 20:1. 4,109 applied, 69% were admitted. 15% from top 10% of their high school class, 43% from top quarter, 78% from top half. 19 valedictorians. Full-time: 5,226 students, 55% women, 45% men. Part-time: 1,362 students, 55% women, 45% men. Students come from 47 states and territories, 35 other countries, 9% from out-of-state. 1% American Indian or Alaska Native, non-Hispanic/Latino; 23% Hispanic/Latino; 5% African American, non-Hispanic/Latino; 1% Asian, non-Hispanic/Latino; 0.1% Native Hawaiian or other Pacific Islander, non-Hispanic/Latino; 2% international. 22% 25 or older, 26% live on campus, 13% transferred in. Retention: 62% of full-time freshmen returned the following year. Academic areas with the most degrees conferred: interdisciplinary studies; business/marketing; liberal arts/general studies. Core. Calendar: semesters. Academic remediation for entering students, ESL program, services for LD students, advanced placement, honors program, independent study, distance learning, double major, summer session for credit, part-time degree program, adult/continuing education programs, co-op programs and internships. Study abroad program.

Entrance Requirements: Options: electronic application, deferred admission. Required: high school transcript, class rank and Texas high school curriculum or equivalent, SAT or ACT. Entrance: moderately difficult. Application deadline: Rolling. Notification: continuous.

Costs Per Year: Application fee: $25. State resident tuition: $4730 full-time, $165 per credit hour part-time. Nonresident tuition: $5630 full-time, $195 per credit hour part-time. Mandatory fees: $2060 full-time, $66 per credit hour part-time, $182. Full-time tuition and fees vary according to course load. Part-time tuition and fees vary according to course load. College room and board: $5000. Room and board charges vary according to board plan and housing facility.

Collegiate Environment: Orientation program. Drama-theater group, choral group, marching band, student-run newspaper, radio station. Social

organizations: 130 open to all; national fraternities, national sororities; 6% of eligible men and 6% of eligible women are members. Most popular organizations: Residence Hall Association, National Society for Leadership and Success, student government, Students in Free Enterprise (SIFE), Baptist Student Ministries. Major annual events: Buffalo Branding, Workathon, Homecoming. Student services: health clinic, personal-psychological counseling. Campus security: 24-hour emergency response devices and patrols, late night transport-escort service, controlled dormitory access. 2,034 college housing spaces available; 1,693 were occupied in 2012-13. Freshmen guaranteed college housing. On-campus residence required through sophomore year. Options: coed, men-only, women-only housing available. Cornette Library with 1.2 million books, 1.3 million microform titles, 19,264 serials, 4,976 audiovisual materials, an OPAC, and a Web page. Operations spending for the previous fiscal year: $2.2 million. 1,200 computers available on campus for general student use. Computer purchase/lease plans available. A campuswide network can be accessed from student residence rooms and from off campus. Students can access the following: online class registration. Staffed computer lab on campus (open 24 hours a day) provides training in use of computers, software, and the Internet.

■ **WESTERN TECHNICAL COLLEGE (EL PASO)**
9624 Plz. Cir.
El Paso, TX 79927
Tel: (915)532-3737
E-mail: bterrell@wtc-ep.edu
Web Site: www.westerntech.edu/
Description: Private, 2-year, coed. Awards certificates, transfer associate, and terminal associate degrees. Total enrollment: 825. Faculty: 130 (98 full-time, 32 part-time). Student-undergrad faculty ratio is 18:1. Calendar: continuous.
Entrance Requirements: Open admission. Options: early admission, deferred admission.
Collegiate Environment: 25 computers available on campus for general student use. Computer purchase/lease plans available. A campuswide network can be accessed from off-campus. Staffed computer lab on campus.

■ **WESTERN TECHNICAL COLLEGE (EL PASO)**
9451 Diana
El Paso, TX 79930-2610
Tel: (915)566-9621; Free: 800-201-9232
E-mail: lpena@westerntech.edu
Web Site: www.westerntech.edu/
Description: Private, 2-year, coed. Awards certificates and terminal associate degrees. Total enrollment: 545. Student-undergrad faculty ratio is 12:1. 177 applied. 8% from out-of-state. 49% 25 or older. Retention: 69% of full-time freshmen returned the following year.
Entrance Requirements: Entrance: noncompetitive.

■ **WESTERN TEXAS COLLEGE**
6200 College Ave.
Snyder, TX 79549
Tel: (325)573-8511; Free: 888-GO-TO-WTC
E-mail: jclifton@wtc.cc.tx.us
Web Site: www.wtc.edu/
Description: State and locally supported, 2-year, coed. Awards certificates, transfer associate, and terminal associate degrees. Founded 1969. Setting: 165-acre small town campus. Total enrollment: 2,473. Student-undergrad faculty ratio is 21:1. 5% from out-of-state. 26% 25 or older. Retention: 50% of full-time freshmen returned the following year. Core. Calendar: semesters. Academic remediation for entering students, services for LD students, advanced placement, self-designed majors, summer session for credit, part-time degree program, adult/continuing education programs, internships.
Entrance Requirements: Open admission. Options: early admission, deferred admission. Required: high school transcript. Entrance: noncompetitive. Application deadline: Rolling. Notification: continuous.
Collegiate Environment: Drama-theater group, choral group, student-run newspaper. Student services: personal-psychological counseling. Campus security: 24-hour emergency response devices and patrols. Western Texas College Resource Center with a Web page.
Community Environment: Snyder is a small rural city, population 10,580. Agriculture and oil are important industries.

■ **WHARTON COUNTY JUNIOR COLLEGE**
911 Boling Hwy.
Wharton, TX 77488-3298

Tel: (979)532-4560
E-mail: albertb@wcjc.edu
Web Site: www.wcjc.edu/
Description: State and locally supported, 2-year, coed. Awards certificates, transfer associate, and terminal associate degrees. Founded 1946. Setting: 90-acre rural campus with easy access to Houston. Total enrollment: 6,115. Faculty: 257 (136 full-time, 121 part-time). Student-undergrad faculty ratio is 22:1. 5% from top 10% of their high school class, 50% from top half. Students come from 8 states and territories, 5 other countries. 30% 25 or older, 5% live on campus. Core. Calendar: semesters. Academic remediation for entering students, advanced placement, self-designed majors, summer session for credit, part-time degree program, adult/continuing education programs.
Entrance Requirements: Open admission. Required: high school transcript, minimum 2.0 high school GPA. Entrance: noncompetitive. Application deadline: 8/14.
Collegiate Environment: Drama-theater group. Student services: personal-psychological counseling. Campus security: 24-hour patrols. J. M. Hodges Library with 51,478 books and 536 serials. 350 computers available on campus for general student use. Staffed computer lab on campus.
Community Environment: Population 9,374, Wharton is situated on the banks of the Colorado River, 45 miles from the Gulf of Mexico. The community is served by bus lines, a municipal airport, and U.S. Highway 59. Community facilities include a county library, hospital and clinic, several churches of various faiths, and many civic and fraternal organizations. It also has a museum, theatre, concert series, health club, municipal swimming pool, hunting, and fishing. An annual Wharton County Youth Rodeo is held here. Part-time employment is available.

■ **WILEY COLLEGE**
711 Wiley Ave.
Marshall, TX 75670-5199
Tel: (903)927-3300; Free: 800-658-6889
Fax: (903)938-8100
E-mail: ajones@wileyc.edu
Web Site: www.wileyc.edu/
Description: Independent, 4-year, coed, affiliated with United Methodist Church. Awards associate and bachelor's degrees. Founded 1873. Setting: 58-acre small town campus. Endowment: $3.9 million. Educational spending for the previous fiscal year: $15,881 per student. Total enrollment: 925. Faculty: 80 (51 full-time, 29 part-time). Student-undergrad faculty ratio is 15:1. 976 applied, 40% were admitted. 1% from top quarter of their high school class, 2% from top half. Full-time: 803 students, 59% women, 41% men. Part-time: 122 students, 61% women, 39% men. Students come from 25 states and territories, 7 other countries, 45% from out-of-state. 39% 25 or older, 51% live on campus, 11% transferred in. Retention: 100% of full-time freshmen returned the following year. Academic areas with the most degrees conferred: business/marketing; social sciences; education. Core. Calendar: semesters. Academic remediation for entering students, self-designed majors, summer session for credit, part-time degree program, adult/continuing education programs. Off campus study at Howard University. Study abroad program.
Entrance Requirements: Open admission. Options: electronic application, early admission, deferred admission, international baccalaureate accepted. Required: high school transcript, 1 recommendation. Recommended: SAT or ACT. Entrance: minimally difficult. Application deadline: 8/1. Notification: continuous until 8/10.
Costs Per Year: Application fee: $10. One-time mandatory fee: $80. Comprehensive fee: $17,734 includes full-time tuition ($9240), mandatory fees ($2142), and college room and board ($6352). College room only: $3082. Full-time tuition and fees vary according to program. Room and board charges vary according to board plan. Part-time tuition: $309 per credit hour. Part-time mandatory fees: $1040 per term. Part-time tuition and fees vary according to program.
Collegiate Environment: Orientation program. Drama-theater group, student-run newspaper. Social organizations: national fraternities, national sororities. Student services: health clinic, personal-psychological counseling. Campus security: 24-hour patrols, controlled dormitory access. T. Winston Cole, Sr. Library with 24,000 books, 40,000 microform titles, and 23,000 serials. Operations spending for the previous fiscal year: $52,832. 198 computers available on campus for general student use. Computer purchase/lease plans available. A campuswide network can be accessed from student residence rooms and from off campus. Students can access the following: online class registration.
Community Environment: Population 24,000. Marshall is located at the

junction of Highways U.S. 59 and 80 and Interstate 20, approximately 40 miles west of Shreveport, and 150 miles east of Dallas. The climate is temperate and mild. Natural gas fields surround the city. Railroad and bus lines serve the community, and Harrison County Memorial Airport located three miles east offers airline facilities. There are many churches of various faiths, hospitals, radio stations, and public library serving the area. Skilled and unskilled employment opportunities are available. Local recreation includes camping, fishing, and hunting.

■ **ARGOSY UNIVERSITY, SALT LAKE CITY**
121 W Election Rd., Ste. 300
Draper, UT 84020
Free: 888-639-4756
Web Site: www.argosy.edu/locations/salt-lake-city/
Description: Proprietary, university, coed. Awards associate, bachelor's, master's, and doctoral degrees. Founded 2008.

■ **THE ART INSTITUTE OF SALT LAKE CITY**
121 W Election Rd.
Ste. 100
Draper, UT 84020-9492
Free: 800-978-0096
Web Site: www.artinstitutes.edu/SaltLakeCity/
Description: Proprietary, 4-year, coed. Part of Education Management Corporation. Awards associate and bachelor's degrees.

■ **BRIGHAM YOUNG UNIVERSITY**
Provo, UT 84602-1001
Tel: (801)422-1211
Fax: (801)422-5278
E-mail: admissions@byu.edu
Web Site: www.byu.edu/
Description: Independent, university, coed, affiliated with The Church of Jesus Christ of Latter-day Saints. Part of Church Education System (CES) of The Church of Jesus Christ of Latter-day Saints. Awards bachelor's, master's, and doctoral degrees. Founded 1875. Setting: 557-acre suburban campus with easy access to Salt Lake City. Total enrollment: 34,409. Faculty: 1,739 (1,226 full-time, 513 part-time). Student-undergrad faculty ratio is 23:1. 12,557 applied, 55% were admitted. 53% from top 10% of their high school class, 84% from top quarter, 98% from top half. Full-time: 28,338 students, 49% women, 51% men. Part-time: 2,722 students, 48% women, 52% men. 63% from out-of-state. 0.4% American Indian or Alaska Native, non-Hispanic/Latino; 5% Hispanic/Latino; 0.4% African American, non-Hispanic/Latino; 2% Asian, non-Hispanic/Latino; 1% Native Hawaiian or other Pacific Islander, non-Hispanic/Latino; 4% international. 10% 25 or older, 19% live on campus, 3% transferred in. Retention: 89% of full-time freshmen returned the following year. Academic areas with the most degrees conferred: business/marketing; biological/life sciences; education. Calendar: semesters. Part-time degree program, external degree program, adult/continuing education programs. Off campus study at BYU Salt Lake Center. ROTC: Army, Air Force.
Entrance Requirements: Options: electronic application, early admission, deferred admission. Required: essay, high school transcript, 1 recommendation, interview, SAT or ACT. Entrance: moderately difficult. Application deadline: 2/1. Notification: continuous. SAT Reasoning Test deadline: 2/1.
Costs Per Year: Application fee: $35. Comprehensive fee: $11,910 includes full-time tuition ($4710) and college room and board ($7200). Room and board charges vary according to board plan, housing facility, and location. Part-time tuition: $242 per credit hour. Part-time tuition varies according to course load.
Collegiate Environment: Orientation program. Campus security: 24-hour emergency response devices and patrols, late night transport-escort service, controlled dormitory access. No special consideration for freshman housing

applicants. Options: men-only, women-only housing available. Harold B. Lee Library plus 2 others with an OPAC and a Web page.
Community Environment: Located 45 miles from Salt Lake City. Local industries also produce steel, computer software, pig iron, and foundry products. The community may be reached by air, railroad, bus lines, and Highways 6, 91, 89, 50, and Interstate 15. The community has hospitals, shopping centers, and national monuments nearby. Part-time employment is available. Local recreation includes hunting, fishing, picnicking, hiking, swimming, boating, water-skiing, horseback riding, golf, tennis, ice skating, bobsledding, and snow skiing.

■ **BROADVIEW UNIVERSITY–LAYTON**
869 W Hill Field Rd.
Layton, UT 84041
Tel: (801)660-6000; Free: 866-253-7744
Fax: (801)660-6001
E-mail: rbaxter@broadviewuniversity.edu
Web Site: www.broadviewuniversity.edu/
Description: Proprietary, 4-year, coed. Part of Globe Education Network (GEN) which is composed of Globe University, Minnesota School of Business, Broadview University, The Institute of Production and Recording and Minnesota School of Cosmetology. Awards associate and bachelor's degrees. Setting: 3 suburban campus. Total enrollment: 434. Faculty: 30 (7 full-time, 23 part-time). Student-undergrad faculty ratio is 20:1. Full-time: 74 students, 68% women, 32% men. Part-time: 360 students, 79% women, 21% men. 0% from out-of-state. 1% American Indian or Alaska Native, non-Hispanic/Latino; 7% Hispanic/Latino; 3% African American, non-Hispanic/Latino; 1% Asian, non-Hispanic/Latino; 1% Native Hawaiian or other Pacific Islander, non-Hispanic/Latino; 0% international. 42% 25 or older, 71% transferred in. Retention: 75% of full-time freshmen returned the following year. Academic areas with the most degrees conferred: business/marketing; parks and recreation; law/legal studies. Core. Academic remediation for entering students, services for LD students, advanced placement, accelerated degree program, summer session for credit, part-time degree program, adult/continuing education programs, internships.
Entrance Requirements: Option: electronic application. Required: high school transcript, interview, High school transcript or GED, ACCUPLACER is required of all applicants unless documentation of a minimum ACT composite score of 21 or documentation of a minimum composite score of 1485 on the SAT is presented. Required for some: essay, 2 recommendations. Application deadlines: Rolling, Rolling for nonresidents. Notification: continuous, continuous for nonresidents. Transfer credits accepted: Yes.
Costs Per Year: Application fee: $50. Tuition: $14,400 full-time, $435 per credit part-time. Mandatory fees: $1548 full-time, $43 per credit part-time. Full-time tuition and fees vary according to course load, degree level, location, and program. Part-time tuition and fees vary according to course load, degree level, location, and program.
Collegiate Environment: Orientation program. Social organizations: Program specific student led organizations. Major annual events: Service Learning Projects, Applied Learning Projects, Student Appreciation Events. Campus security: 24-hour emergency response devices, late night transport-escort service. Layton Campus Library with 2,095 books, 53,137 serials, 201 audiovisual materials, an OPAC, and a Web page. 66 computers available on campus for general student use. A campuswide network can be ac-

cessed. Students can access the following: online class registration. Staffed computer lab on campus provides training in use of computers, software, and the Internet.

■ BROADVIEW UNIVERSITY–OREM

898 N 1200 W
Orem, UT 84057
Tel: (801)822-5800; Free: 877-822-5838
Fax: (801)822-5801
Web Site: www.broadviewuniversity.edu/
Description: Proprietary, 4-year, coed. Part of Globe Education Network (GEN) which is composed of Globe University, Minnesota School of Business, Broadview University, The Institute of Production and Recording and Minnesota School of Cosmetology. Awards associate and bachelor's degrees. Setting: 3-acre small town campus. Total enrollment: 285. Faculty: 25 (11 full-time, 14 part-time). Student-undergrad faculty ratio is 17:1. Full-time: 81 students, 69% women, 31% men. Part-time: 204 students, 74% women, 26% men. Students come from 2 states and territories, 0.4% from out-of-state. 1% American Indian or Alaska Native, non-Hispanic/Latino; 8% Hispanic/Latino; 1% African American, non-Hispanic/Latino; 1% Asian, non-Hispanic/Latino; 0.4% Native Hawaiian or other Pacific Islander, non-Hispanic/Latino; 0% international. 42% 25 or older, 19% transferred in. Retention: 25% of full-time freshmen returned the following year. Academic area with the most degrees conferred: business/marketing. Core. Academic remediation for entering students, services for LD students, advanced placement, accelerated degree program, summer session for credit, part-time degree program, adult/continuing education programs, internships.
Entrance Requirements: Option: electronic application. Required: high school transcript, interview, High school transcript or GED, ACCUPLACER is required of all applicants unless documentation of a minimum ACT composite score of 21 or documentation of a minimum composite score of 1485 on the SAT is presented. Required for some: essay, 2 recommendations. Application deadlines: Rolling, Rolling for nonresidents. Notification: continuous, continuous for nonresidents. Transfer credits accepted: Yes.
Costs Per Year: Application fee: $50. Tuition: $14,400 full-time, $435 per credit part-time. Mandatory fees: $1548 full-time, $43 per credit part-time. Full-time tuition and fees vary according to course level, course load, degree level, location, and program. Part-time tuition and fees vary according to course level, course load, degree level, location, and program.
Collegiate Environment: Orientation program. Social organizations: Program specific student led organizations. Major annual events: Service Learning Projects, Applied Learning Projects, Student Appreciation Events. Campus security: 24-hour emergency response devices, late night transport-escort service. Orem Campus Library with 2,197 books, 53,137 serials, 83 audiovisual materials, an OPAC, and a Web page. 47 computers available on campus for general student use. A campuswide network can be accessed. Students can access the following: online class registration. Staffed computer lab on campus provides training in use of computers, software, and the Internet.

■ BROADVIEW UNIVERSITY–SALT LAKE CITY

240 E Morris Ave.
Salt Lake City, UT 84115
Tel: (801)300-4300; Free: 877-801-8889
Fax: (801)300-4301
Web Site: www.broadviewuniversity.edu/
Description: Proprietary, 4-year, coed. Part of Globe Education Network (GEN) which is composed of Globe University, Minnesota School of Business, Broadview University, The Institute of Production and Recording and Minnesota School of Cosmetology. Awards associate and bachelor's degrees. Setting: 3-acre urban campus. Total enrollment: 34. Faculty: 8 (5 full-time, 3 part-time). Student-undergrad faculty ratio is 9:1. Full-time: 12 students, 17% women, 83% men. Part-time: 22 students, 45% women, 55% men. 0% from out-of-state. 0% American Indian or Alaska Native, non-Hispanic/Latino; 21% Hispanic/Latino; 3% African American, non-Hispanic/Latino; 12% Asian, non-Hispanic/Latino; 0% Native Hawaiian or other Pacific Islander, non-Hispanic/Latino; 0% international. 19% 25 or older, 29% transferred in. Retention: 0% of full-time freshmen returned the following year. Core. Academic remediation for entering students, services for LD students, advanced placement, accelerated degree program, summer session for credit, part-time degree program, adult/continuing education programs, internships.
Entrance Requirements: Option: electronic application. Required: high school transcript, interview, ACCUPLACER is required of all applicants un-

less documentation of a minimum ACT composite score of 21 or documentation of a minimum composite score of 1485 on the SAT is presented. Required for some: essay, 2 recommendations, GED certificate in lieu of high school transcript. Application deadlines: Rolling, Rolling for nonresidents. Notification: continuous, continuous for nonresidents. Transfer credits accepted: Yes.
Costs Per Year: Application fee: $50. Tuition: $14,400 full-time, $460 per credit part-time. Mandatory fees: $1548 full-time, $43 per credit part-time. Full-time tuition and fees vary according to course level, course load, degree level, location, and program. Part-time tuition and fees vary according to course level, course load, degree level, location, and program.
Collegiate Environment: Orientation program. Social organizations: Program specific student led organizations. Major annual events: Service Learning Projects, Applied Learning Projects, Student Appreciation Events. Campus security: 24-hour emergency response devices, late night transport-escort service. Broadview Entertainment Arts University Campus Library with 1,957 books, 53,116 serials, an OPAC, and a Web page. 43 computers available on campus for general student use. A campuswide network can be accessed. Students can access the following: online class registration. Staffed computer lab on campus provides training in use of computers, software, and the Internet.

■ BROADVIEW UNIVERSITY–WEST JORDAN

1902 W 7800 S
West Jordan, UT 84088
Tel: (801)304-4224; Free: 866-304-4224
Fax: (801)304-4229
E-mail: kcooper@utahcollege.edu
Web Site: www.broadviewuniversity.edu/
Description: Proprietary, comprehensive, coed. Part of Globe Education Network (GEN) which is composed of Globe University, Minnesota School of Business, Broadview University, The Institute of Production and Recording and Minnesota School of Cosmetology. Awards associate, bachelor's, and master's degrees. Setting: 4-acre urban campus. Total enrollment: 702. Faculty: 72 (26 full-time, 46 part-time). Student-undergrad faculty ratio is 15:1. Full-time: 134 students, 73% women, 27% men. Part-time: 567 students, 79% women, 21% men. Students come from 4 states and territories, 0.4% from out-of-state. 2% American Indian or Alaska Native, non-Hispanic/Latino; 7% Hispanic/Latino; 2% African American, non-Hispanic/Latino; 1% Asian, non-Hispanic/Latino; 1% Native Hawaiian or other Pacific Islander, non-Hispanic/Latino; 0% international. 41% 25 or older, 14% transferred in. Retention: 20% of full-time freshmen returned the following year. Academic areas with the most degrees conferred: law/legal studies; parks and recreation; business/marketing. Core. Academic remediation for entering students, services for LD students, advanced placement, accelerated degree program, summer session for credit, part-time degree program, adult/continuing education programs, internships.
Entrance Requirements: Option: electronic application. Required: high school transcript, interview, High school transcript or GED, ACCUPLACER is required of all applicants unless documentation of a minimum ACT composite score of 21 or documentation of a minimum composite score of 1485 on the SAT is presented. Required for some: essay, 2 recommendations. Application deadlines: Rolling, Rolling for nonresidents. Notification: continuous, continuous for nonresidents. Transfer credits accepted: Yes.
Costs Per Year: Application fee: $50. Tuition: $14,400 full-time, $460 per credit part-time. Mandatory fees: $1548 full-time, $43 per credit part-time. Full-time tuition and fees vary according to course level, course load, degree level, location, and program. Part-time tuition and fees vary according to course level, course load, degree level, location, and program.
Collegiate Environment: Orientation program. Social organizations: Program specific student led organizations. Major annual events: Service Learning Projects, Applied Learning Projects, Student Appreciation Events. Campus security: 24-hour emergency response devices, late night transport-escort service. West Jordan Campus Library with 7,016 books, 63,753 serials, 3,112 audiovisual materials, an OPAC, and a Web page. 78 computers available on campus for general student use. A campuswide network can be accessed. Students can access the following: online class registration. Staffed computer lab on campus provides training in use of computers, software, and the Internet.

■ DEVRY UNIVERSITY

9350 S 150 E, Ste. 420
Sandy, UT 84070
Tel: (801)565-5110; Free: 866-338-7941

Fax: (801)561-1710

Web Site: www.devry.edu/

Description: Proprietary, comprehensive, coed. Awards associate, bachelor's, and master's degrees. Total enrollment: 147. Faculty: 19 (all part-time). Student-undergrad faculty ratio is 13:1. Full-time: 45 students, 33% women, 67% men. Part-time: 53 students, 34% women, 66% men. 5% from out-of-state. 80% 25 or older, 33% transferred in. Academic area with the most degrees conferred: business/marketing. Accelerated degree program, distance learning.

Entrance Requirements: Options: electronic application, deferred admission. Application deadline: Rolling. Notification: continuous. SAT Reasoning Test deadline: 10/31.

■ **DIXIE STATE COLLEGE OF UTAH**

225 S 700 E

Saint George, UT 84770-3876

Tel: (435)652-7500

Fax: (435)656-4005

E-mail: ldavenport@dixie.edu

Web Site: www.dixie.edu/

Description: State-supported, 4-year, coed. Part of Utah System of Higher Education. Awards associate and bachelor's degrees. Founded 1911. Setting: 117-acre small town campus. Endowment: $13.5 million. Research spending for the previous fiscal year: $48,230. Educational spending for the previous fiscal year: $2489 per student. Total enrollment: 9,044. 4,894 applied, 63% were admitted. 8% from top 10% of their high school class, 27% from top quarter, 59% from top half. Full-time: 5,473 students, 52% women, 48% men. Part-time: 3,571 students, 53% women, 47% men. Students come from 51 states and territories, 19 other countries, 14% from out-of-state. 1% American Indian or Alaska Native, non-Hispanic/Latino; 7% Hispanic/Latino; 2% African American, non-Hispanic/Latino; 1% Asian, non-Hispanic/Latino; 2% Native Hawaiian or other Pacific Islander, non-Hispanic/Latino; 1% international. 37% 25 or older, 3% live on campus, 6% transferred in. Retention: 57% of full-time freshmen returned the following year. Academic areas with the most degrees conferred: business/marketing; education; interdisciplinary studies. Core. Calendar: semesters. Academic remediation for entering students, ESL program, services for LD students, advanced placement, accelerated degree program, self-designed majors, honors program, independent study, distance learning, double major, summer session for credit, part-time degree program, adult/continuing education programs, co-op programs and internships. Off campus study. Study abroad program. ROTC: Army.

Entrance Requirements: Open admission. Options: electronic application, early admission, deferred admission. Required: high school transcript. Recommended: SAT or ACT. Entrance: noncompetitive. Application deadlines: 8/15, 8/15 for nonresidents. Notification: continuous, continuous for nonresidents. Transfer credits accepted: Yes.

Costs Per Year: Application fee: $35. State resident tuition: $4089 full-time, $144.54 per credit hour part-time. Nonresident tuition: $11,721 full-time, $462.53 per credit hour part-time. Mandatory fees: $620 full-time, $310 per term part-time. Full-time tuition and fees vary according to course load. Part-time tuition and fees vary according to course load. College room and board: $4348. College room only: $1550. Room and board charges vary according to board plan and housing facility.

Collegiate Environment: Orientation program. Drama-theater group, choral group, marching band, student-run newspaper, radio station. Most popular organizations: Dixie Spirit, Outdoor Club, Association of Women Students, intramurals. Major annual events: Homecoming, D-Week, Week of Welcome. Student services: health clinic, personal-psychological counseling. Campus security: 24-hour emergency response devices and patrols. Val A. Browning Library with 166,120 books, 11,078 microform titles, 190 serials, 10,757 audiovisual materials, an OPAC, and a Web page. Operations spending for the previous fiscal year: $1.3 million. 400 computers available on campus for general student use. Computer purchase/lease plans available. A campuswide network can be accessed from student residence rooms. Students can access the following: online class registration. Staffed computer lab on campus provides training in use of computers, software, and the Internet.

■ **EVEREST COLLEGE**

3280 W 3500 S

West Valley City, UT 84119

Tel: (801)840-4800; Free: 888-741-4270

Fax: (801)969-0828

Web Site: www.everest.edu/

Description: Proprietary, 2-year, coed. Part of Corinthian Colleges, Inc. Awards diplomas, transfer associate, and terminal associate degrees. Founded 1982. Setting: suburban campus. Total enrollment: 179. Student-undergrad faculty ratio is 20:1. 134 applied. 0% from out-of-state. 46% 25 or older. Retention: 93% of full-time freshmen returned the following year. Core. Academic remediation for entering students, advanced placement, distance learning, summer session for credit, part-time degree program.

Entrance Requirements: Option: deferred admission. Required: high school transcript, interview, CPAt. Recommended: SAT or ACT. Entrance: noncompetitive. Application deadline: Rolling.

Collegiate Environment: Orientation program.

■ **INDEPENDENCE UNIVERSITY**

5295 S Commerce Dr.

Salt Lake City, UT 84107

Tel: (800)221-7374; Free: 800-972-5149

Fax: (801)263-0345

Web Site: www.independence.edu/

Description: Proprietary, comprehensive, coed. Awards associate, bachelor's, and master's degrees (offers primarily external degree programs). Founded 1978. Setting: 2-acre urban campus with easy access to San Diego. Calendar: continuous. Distance learning, part-time degree program, external degree program.

Entrance Requirements: Open admission. Option: deferred admission. Required: high school transcript. Recommended: employment in a health science field. Required for some: employment in a health science field. Entrance: noncompetitive. Application deadline: Rolling.

■ **ITT TECHNICAL INSTITUTE**

920 W Levoy Dr.

Murray, UT 84123-2500

Tel: (801)263-3313; Free: 800-365-2136

Web Site: www.itt-tech.edu/

Description: Proprietary, primarily 2-year, coed. Part of ITT Educational Services, Inc. Awards terminal associate and bachelor's degrees. Founded 1984. Setting: suburban campus.

Entrance Requirements: Entrance: minimally difficult.

■ **LDS BUSINESS COLLEGE**

95 N 300 W

Salt Lake City, UT 84101

Tel: (801)524-8100; Free: 800-999-5767

Fax: (801)524-1900

E-mail: DFellows@ldsbc.edu

Web Site: www.ldsbc.edu/

Description: Independent, 2-year, coed, affiliated with The Church of Jesus Christ of Latter-day Saints. Part of Latter-day Saints Church Educational System. Awards certificates, transfer associate, and terminal associate degrees. Founded 1886. Setting: 2-acre urban campus with easy access to Salt Lake City. Total enrollment: 2,191. Faculty: 142 (14 full-time, 128 part-time). Student-undergrad faculty ratio is 25:1. 878 applied, 93% were admitted. Full-time: 1,589 students, 47% women, 53% men. Part-time: 602 students, 47% women, 53% men. Students come from 37 states and territories, 60 other countries, 45% from out-of-state. 0.5% American Indian or Alaska Native, non-Hispanic/Latino; 11% Hispanic/Latino; 0.2% African American, non-Hispanic/Latino; 1% Asian, non-Hispanic/Latino; 2% Native Hawaiian or other Pacific Islander, non-Hispanic/Latino; 13% international. 21% 25 or older, 34% transferred in. Retention: 48% of full-time freshmen returned the following year. Core. Calendar: semesters. Academic remediation for entering students, services for LD students, advanced placement, summer session for credit, part-time degree program, adult/continuing education programs, internships. ROTC: Army (c), Air Force (c).

Entrance Requirements: Open admission. Options: electronic application, deferred admission. Required: essay, high school transcript, interview. Recommended: SAT or ACT. Entrance: noncompetitive. Application deadlines: Rolling, Rolling for nonresidents. Notification: continuous, continuous for nonresidents. Transfer credits accepted: Yes.

Costs Per Year: Application fee: $35. Tuition: $3060 full-time, $128 per credit hour part-time. Full-time tuition varies according to course load. Part-time tuition varies according to course load.

Collegiate Environment: Orientation program. Drama-theater group, choral group. Major annual events: BCs Got Talent, Winter Formal, New Student Orientation. Campus security: 24-hour emergency response devices and patrols. College housing not available. LDS Business College Library with 115,920 books, 121 serials, 1,128 audiovisual materials, an OPAC, and a Web page. 350 computers available on campus for general student use. A campuswide network can be accessed from off-campus. Students can access the following: online class registration. Staffed computer lab on campus provides training in use of computers, software, and the Internet.

■ **MIDWIVES COLLEGE OF UTAH**
1174 E 2700 S, Ste. 2
Salt Lake City, UT 84106
Tel: (801)764-9068; Free: 866-680-2756
Fax: (801)434-8704
E-mail: office@midwifery.edu
Web Site: www.midwifery.edu/
Description: Independent, comprehensive, women only. Awards associate, bachelor's, and master's degrees. Founded 1980. Setting: suburban campus with easy access to Salt Lake City. Educational spending for the previous fiscal year: $1500 per student. Total enrollment: 130. Faculty: 8. Part-time: 130 students. Retention: 93% of full-time freshmen returned the following year. Academic area with the most degrees conferred: health professions and related sciences. Core. Calendar: semesters. Graduate courses open to undergrads.
Entrance Requirements: Option: electronic application. Required: essay, high school transcript, interview. Entrance: noncompetitive. Application deadline: 7/29. Notification: 8/8.
Collegiate Environment: Orientation program.

■ **NEUMONT UNIVERSITY**
10701 S River Front Pky., Ste. 300
South Jordan, UT 84095
Tel: (801)438-1100; Free: 888-NEUMONT
Fax: (801)438-1111
E-mail: karick.heaton@neumont.edu
Web Site: www.neumont.edu/
Description: Proprietary, comprehensive, coed. Awards bachelor's and master's degrees. Founded 2002. Setting: suburban campus with easy access to Salt Lake City. Total enrollment: 366. Faculty: 26 (13 full-time, 13 part-time). Student-undergrad faculty ratio is 21:1. 596 applied, 81% were admitted. Full-time: 366 students, 10% women, 90% men. 80% live on campus. Retention: 69% of full-time freshmen returned the following year. Academic area with the most degrees conferred: computer and information sciences. Core. Services for LD students, accelerated degree program.
Entrance Requirements: Option: electronic application. Required: essay, high school transcript, SAT or ACT. Recommended: 2 recommendations, interview. Entrance: moderately difficult. Application deadline: Rolling. SAT Reasoning Test deadline: 10/1. SAT Subject Test deadline: 10/1. Transfer credits accepted: Yes.
Costs Per Year: Application fee: $35. Tuition: $21,600 full-time, $495 per unit part-time. Mandatory fees: $1500 full-time. College room only: $4230.
Collegiate Environment: Orientation program. Choral group. Social organizations: 15 open to all. Most popular organizations: Neumont Tactical Federation, Epically Good Gamer's Group, Beyond The Screen Order, Rhythm Rockers Gaming Association, Unified Student Government. Major annual events: Week-One Done, Quarterly Coding Competition, Project Showcase. Student services: health clinic, personal-psychological counseling. 400 college housing spaces available; 300 were occupied in 2012-13. Freshmen guaranteed college housing. Options: men-only, women-only housing available.

■ **PROVO COLLEGE**
1450 W 820 N
Provo, UT 84601
Tel: (801)818-8900; Free: 877-777-5886
Fax: (801)375-9728
E-mail: gordonp@provocollege.org
Web Site: www.provocollege.edu/
Description: Proprietary, 2-year, coed. Awards terminal associate degrees. Founded 1984. Total enrollment: 656.
Entrance Requirements: Entrance: noncompetitive.

■ **SALT LAKE COMMUNITY COLLEGE**
PO Box 30808
Salt Lake City, UT 84130-0808
Tel: (801)957-4111

Fax: (801)957-4958
E-mail: kathy.thompson@slcc.edu
Web Site: www.slcc.edu/
Description: State-supported, 2-year, coed. Part of Utah System of Higher Education. Awards certificates, diplomas, transfer associate, and terminal associate degrees. Founded 1948. Setting: 114-acre urban campus with easy access to Salt Lake City. Endowment: $826,231. Total enrollment: 28,967. Faculty: 1,479 (341 full-time, 1,138 part-time). Student-undergrad faculty ratio is 21:1. 2,769 applied, 100% were admitted. Full-time: 9,091 students, 49% women, 51% men. Part-time: 19,876 students, 53% women, 47% men. 1% American Indian or Alaska Native, non-Hispanic/Latino; 12% Hispanic/Latino; 2% African American, non-Hispanic/Latino; 3% Asian, non-Hispanic/Latino; 1% Native Hawaiian or other Pacific Islander, non-Hispanic/Latino; 1% international. 47% 25 or older, 4% transferred in. Core. Calendar: semesters. Academic remediation for entering students, ESL program, services for LD students, advanced placement, self-designed majors, distance learning, double major, summer session for credit, part-time degree program, co-op programs and internships. Study abroad program. ROTC: Army (c), Air Force (c).
Entrance Requirements: Open admission except for health science programs. Options: electronic application, early admission. Entrance: noncompetitive. Application deadline: Rolling. Transfer credits accepted: Yes.
Collegiate Environment: Orientation program. Drama-theater group, choral group, marching band, student-run newspaper, radio station. Social organizations: local fraternities, local sororities. Student services: health clinic, personal-psychological counseling. Campus security: 24-hour emergency response devices and patrols, late night transport-escort service. College housing not available. Markosian Library plus 2 others with 152,537 books, 3,900 microform titles, 21,736 serials, 20,645 audiovisual materials, an OPAC, and a Web page. Operations spending for the previous fiscal year: $2.2 million.
Community Environment: The capital of the state, Salt Lake City, is located at the foot of the beautiful Wasatch Mountains. The Great Salt Lake is northwest of the city was founded by Brigham Young and his followers, and many of the original buildings may still be seen. The city is a metropolis today enjoying excellent transportation facilities. There are five libraries, a law library, many churches of various denominations, hospitals, and clinics to serve the community. Some part-time employment is available. Local recreation facilities includes 23 parks, golf courses, fishing, hunting, bowling, skiing, several theatres, and outdoor sports. There are excellent shopping facilities located here. The Utah State Fair is held annually as well as the Music Festival.

■ **SNOW COLLEGE**
150 E College Ave.
Ephraim, UT 84627-1203
Tel: (435)283-7000
Fax: (435)283-6879
E-mail: snowcollege@snow.edu
Web Site: www.snow.edu/
Description: State-supported, 2-year, coed. Part of Utah System of Higher Education. Awards certificates, diplomas, transfer associate, and terminal associate degrees. Founded 1888. Setting: 50-acre rural campus. Endowment: $6.2 million. Research spending for the previous fiscal year: $21,046. Educational spending for the previous fiscal year: $4682 per student. Total enrollment: 4,465. Faculty: 319 (115 full-time, 204 part-time). Student-undergrad faculty ratio is 19:1. 2,764 applied, 100% were admitted. Full-time: 2,943 students, 55% women, 45% men. Part-time: 1,522 students, 46% women, 54% men. Students come from 34 states and territories, 12 other countries, 6% from out-of-state. 1% American Indian or Alaska Native, non-Hispanic/Latino; 3% Hispanic/Latino; 1% African American, non-Hispanic/Latino; 0.5% Asian, non-Hispanic/Latino; 2% Native Hawaiian or other Pacific Islander, non-Hispanic/Latino; 2% international. 12% 25 or older, 2% transferred in. Retention: 47% of full-time freshmen returned the following year. Core. Calendar: semesters. Academic remediation for entering students, ESL program, services for LD students, advanced placement, honors program, independent study, summer session for credit, part-time degree program, external degree program, adult/continuing education programs, co-op programs.
Entrance Requirements: Open admission. Options: electronic application, early admission. Required: high school transcript. Recommended: SAT or ACT. Entrance: noncompetitive. Application deadline: 6/15. Notification: continuous.

Collegiate Environment: Orientation program. Drama-theater group, choral group, student-run newspaper, radio station. Most popular organizations: Phi Beta Lambda, Latter-Day Saints Singers, International Student Society, BAAD Club (Alcohol and Drug Prevention), Dead Cats Society (Life Science Club). Major annual events: Orientation, Homecoming, Miss Snow/Mr. Snow. Student services: health clinic, personal-psychological counseling. Campus security: 24-hour emergency response devices and patrols, student patrols, late night transport-escort service. Eccles Library with 51,352 books, 22,044 microform titles, 201 serials, 6,676 audiovisual materials, an OPAC, and a Web page. Operations spending for the previous fiscal year: $633,709. 400 computers available on campus for general student use. A campuswide network can be accessed from student residence rooms and from off campus. Students can access the following: online class registration. Staffed computer lab on campus provides training in use of software.

Community Environment: Ephraim is a small, rural, college town located in central Utah. The area has a moderate climate with four definite seasons. The community is reached by bus lines and Highway 89. The city has four churches in the immediate vicinity and others in the surrounding area, a hospital 13 miles distant, and a clinic in the town. Public restaurants, motels, and limited entertainment facilities are available. Student housing and part-time employments opportunities are available in the community. Local recreation includes boating, fishing, hunting, cross-country skiing, golf, and winter sports. The county fairs and local festivities highlight the heritages of local communities.

■ **SOUTHERN UTAH UNIVERSITY**
351 W University Blvd.
Cedar City, UT 84720-2498
Tel: (435)586-7700
Fax: (435)586-5475
E-mail: admissioninfo@suu.edu
Web Site: www.suu.edu/
Description: State-supported, comprehensive, coed. Part of Utah System of Higher Education. Awards associate, bachelor's, and master's degrees. Founded 1897. Setting: 130-acre small town campus. Endowment: $7.8 million. Research spending for the previous fiscal year: $153,129. Educational spending for the previous fiscal year: $4316 per student. Total enrollment: 8,297. Faculty: 420 (254 full-time, 166 part-time). Student-undergrad faculty ratio is 21:1. 6,375 applied, 57% were admitted. 17% from top 10% of their high school class, 41% from top quarter, 77% from top half. Full-time: 5,552 students, 54% women, 46% men. Part-time: 2,081 students, 58% women, 42% men. Students come from 48 states and territories, 30 other countries, 16% from out-of-state. 2% American Indian or Alaska Native, non-Hispanic/Latino; 5% Hispanic/Latino; 1% African American, non-Hispanic/Latino; 1% Asian, non-Hispanic/Latino; 1% Native Hawaiian or other Pacific Islander, non-Hispanic/Latino; 4% international. 20% 25 or older, 11% live on campus, 5% transferred in. Retention: 66% of full-time freshmen returned the following year. Academic areas with the most degrees conferred: education; business/marketing; health professions and related sciences. Core. Calendar: semesters. Academic remediation for entering students, ESL program, services for LD students, advanced placement, honors program, independent study, distance learning, double major, summer session for credit, part-time degree program, adult/continuing education programs, co-op programs and internships, graduate courses open to undergrads. Study abroad program. ROTC: Army.
Entrance Requirements: Options: electronic application, deferred admission, international baccalaureate accepted. Required: high school transcript, SAT or ACT. Entrance: moderately difficult. Application deadlines: 5/1, 5/1 for nonresidents. Notification: continuous, continuous for nonresidents. SAT Reasoning Test deadline: 5/1. Transfer credits accepted: Yes.
Costs Per Year: Application fee: $50. State resident tuition: $4960 full-time, $233 per credit hour part-time. Nonresident tuition: $16,368 full-time, $773 per credit hour part-time. Mandatory fees: $616 full-time, $308 per term part-time. Full-time tuition and fees vary according to program. Part-time tuition and fees vary according to course load and program. College room only: $2878. Room charges vary according to housing facility.
Collegiate Environment: Orientation program. Drama-theater group, choral group, student-run newspaper, radio station. Social organizations: national fraternities, national sororities, local sororities. Student services: health clinic, personal-psychological counseling, women's center. Campus security: 24-hour emergency response devices, student patrols, late night transport-escort service, controlled dormitory access. Option: coed housing available. Gerald R Sherratt Library with 235,062 books, 38,720 microform titles, 711 serials, 11,879 audiovisual materials, an OPAC, and a Web page. Opera-

tions spending for the previous fiscal year: $2.2 million. 1,040 computers available on campus for general student use. A campuswide network can be accessed from student residence rooms and from off campus. Students can access the following: online class registration. Staffed computer lab on campus provides training in use of computers, software, and the Internet.
Community Environment: Cedar City is located within a few hours of the Grand Canyon, Lake Powell, Cedar Breaks National Monument, Bryce Canyon, Zion National Park and other scenic wonders. It is 2 1/2 hours from Las Vegas. Cedar City is accessible by airlines, railroad, bus lines, and major highways. The community has churches representing most denominations, a hospital, public library, and a museum. Student housing is available in the community. Various civic, fraternal, and veteran's organizations are active in the area. Local recreation includes indoor and outdoor theatres, hunting, fishing, skiing, golf, and boating. There is a shopping center in the area.

■ **STEVENS-HENAGER COLLEGE–OGDEN/WEST HAVEN**
1890 S 1350 W
Ogden, UT 84401
Tel: (801)394-7791; Free: 800-622-2640
Fax: (801)393-1745
Web Site: www.stevenshenager.edu/
Description: Proprietary, comprehensive, coed. Awards associate, bachelor's, and master's degrees. Founded 1891. Setting: 1-acre urban campus with easy access to Salt Lake City. Total enrollment: 371. Student-undergrad faculty ratio is 18:1. 5% from out-of-state. 54% 25 or older. Retention: 78% of full-time freshmen returned the following year. Part-time degree program, adult/continuing education programs.
Entrance Requirements: Open admission. Options: early admission, deferred admission. Required: high school transcript, Wonderlic aptitude test. Recommended: SAT or ACT. Entrance: noncompetitive. Application deadline: Rolling. Notification: continuous.

■ **STRAYER UNIVERSITY - SANDY CAMPUS**
9815 S Monroe St.
Ste. 200
Sandy, UT 84070
Tel: (801)432-5000
Fax: (801)561-5700
Web Site: www.strayer.edu/campus/sandy
Description: Proprietary, comprehensive, coed. Awards associate, bachelor's, and master's degrees.

■ **UNIVERSITY OF PHOENIX–UTAH CAMPUS**
5373 S Green St.
Salt Lake City, UT 84123-4617
Tel: (801)263-1444; Free: 866-766-0766
Fax: (801)269-9766
Web Site: www.phoenix.edu/
Description: Proprietary, comprehensive, coed. Awards bachelor's and master's degrees. Founded 1984. Setting: urban campus. Total enrollment: 3,169. Faculty: 406 (57 full-time, 349 part-time). 75 applied, 100% were admitted. Full-time: 1,936 students, 45% women, 55% men. 90% 25 or older. Academic areas with the most degrees conferred: business/marketing; computer and information sciences; health professions and related sciences. Core. Calendar: continuous. Services for LD students, advanced placement, accelerated degree program, independent study, distance learning, external degree program, adult/continuing education programs, graduate courses open to undergrads.
Entrance Requirements: Open admission. Options: electronic application, deferred admission. Required for some: high school transcript. Entrance: noncompetitive. Application deadline: Rolling.
Collegiate Environment: Campus security: late night transport-escort service. University Library with 16,871 serials, an OPAC, and a Web page. Operations spending for the previous fiscal year: $6.8 million.

■ **UNIVERSITY OF UTAH**
201 S University St.
Salt Lake City, UT 84112-1107
Tel: (801)581-7200; Free: 800-685-8856
Fax: (801)585-3034
E-mail: mremsburg@sa.utah.edu
Web Site: www.utah.edu/
Description: State-supported, university, coed. Part of Utah System of

Higher Education. Awards bachelor's, master's, and doctoral degrees and post-master's certificates. Founded 1850. Setting: 1,535-acre urban campus with easy access to Salt Lake City. Endowment: $544 million. Research spending for the previous fiscal year: $313.8 million. Educational spending for the previous fiscal year: $15,126 per student. Total enrollment: 32,388. Faculty: 2,116 (1,506 full-time, 610 part-time). Student-undergrad faculty ratio is 13:1. 11,118 applied, 83% were admitted. 24% from top 10% of their high school class, 48% from top quarter, 82% from top half. Full-time: 17,518 students, 45% women, 55% men. Part-time: 7,322 students, 44% women, 56% men. Students come from 53 states and territories, 118 other countries, 18% from out-of-state. 1% American Indian or Alaska Native, non-Hispanic/Latino; 8% Hispanic/Latino; 1% African American, non-Hispanic/Latino; 5% Asian, non-Hispanic/Latino; 1% Native Hawaiian or other Pacific Islander, non-Hispanic/Latino; 6% international. 31% 25 or older, 14% live on campus, 8% transferred in. Retention: 88% of full-time freshmen returned the following year. Academic areas with the most degrees conferred: social sciences; business/marketing; communication/journalism. Core. Calendar: semesters. ESL program, services for LD students, advanced placement, accelerated degree program, self-designed majors, freshman honors college, honors program, independent study, distance learning, double major, summer session for credit, part-time degree program, co-op programs and internships, graduate courses open to undergrads. Off campus study at members of the National Student Exchange. Study abroad program. ROTC: Army, Naval, Air Force.

Entrance Requirements: Options: electronic application, early admission, deferred admission, international baccalaureate accepted. Required: high school transcript, minimum 2.6 high school GPA, ACT, SAT or ACT. Recommended: minimum 3 high school GPA. Required for some: essay. Entrance: moderately difficult. Application deadlines: 4/1, 4/1 for nonresidents. Notification: continuous, continuous for nonresidents. SAT Reasoning Test deadline: 6/1. SAT Subject Test deadline: 6/1. Transfer credits accepted: Yes.

Costs Per Year: Application fee: $45. State resident tuition: $6200 full-time, $174 per credit hour part-time. Nonresident tuition: $21,704 full-time, $599 per credit hour part-time. Mandatory fees: $938 full-time. Full-time tuition and fees vary according to course level, course load, degree level, program, and student level. Part-time tuition varies according to course level, course load, degree level, program, and student level. College room and board: $7155. College room only: $3719. Room and board charges vary according to board plan, housing facility, and location.

Collegiate Environment: Orientation program. Drama-theater group, choral group, marching band, student-run newspaper, radio station. Social organizations: 487 open to all; national fraternities, national sororities, local fraternities, local sororities; 3% of eligible men and 4% of eligible women are members. Most popular organizations: Latter-Day Saints Student Association, Lowell Bennion Community Service Center, Newman Center, Center for Ethnic Student Affairs. Major annual events: Welcome Week, Redfest, Homecoming. Student services: legal services, health clinic, personal-psychological counseling, women's center. Campus security: 24-hour emergency response devices and patrols, student patrols, late night transport-escort service, controlled dormitory access. 3,800 college housing spaces available; 3,000 were occupied in 2012-13. No special consideration for freshman housing applicants. Options: coed, men-only, women-only housing available. J. Willard Marriott Library plus 3 others with 4.2 million books, 3 million microform titles, 86,266 serials, 96,897 audiovisual materials, an OPAC, and a Web page. Operations spending for the previous fiscal year: $23 million. 3,000 computers available on campus for general student use. A campuswide network can be accessed from student residence rooms and from off campus. Students can access the following: online class registration, online classes. Staffed computer lab on campus provides training in use of computers, software, and the Internet.

Community Environment: The capital of the state, Salt Lake City, is located at the foot of the beautiful Wasatch Mountains. The Great Salt Lake is northwest of the city, and the desert is only a few miles away to the west. The city was founded by Brigham Young and his followers, and many of the original buildings may still be seen. The city is a metropolis today enjoying excellent transportation facilities. There are five libraries, a law library, many churches of various denominations, hospitals, and clinics to serve the community. Salt Lake City is the headquarters of the Church of Jesus Christ of Latter Day Saints, and is noted for Temple Square and the Mormon Temple and Tabernacle. Part-time employment is available. Local recreation facilities includes parks, golf courses, fishing, hunting, bowling, skiing, theatres, and outdoor sports. There are excellent shopping facilities located here. The Utah State Fair is held annually.

■ UTAH STATE UNIVERSITY

Old Main Hill
Logan, UT 84322
Tel: (435)797-1000; Free: 800-488-8108
Fax: (435)797-3900
E-mail: admit@usu.edu
Web Site: www.usu.edu/

Description: State-supported, university, coed. Part of Utah System of Higher Education. Awards associate, bachelor's, master's, and doctoral degrees. Founded 1888. Setting: 456-acre urban campus. Endowment: $209.2 million. Research spending for the previous fiscal year: $120.8 million. Educational spending for the previous fiscal year: $6027 per student. Total enrollment: 28,786. Faculty: 1,074 (870 full-time, 204 part-time). Student-undergrad faculty ratio is 23:1. 9,052 applied, 97% were admitted. 19% from top 10% of their high school class, 43% from top quarter, 74% from top half. Full-time: 15,469 students, 52% women, 48% men. Part-time: 9,976 students, 60% women, 40% men. Students come from 53 states and territories, 46 other countries, 23% from out-of-state. 2% American Indian or Alaska Native, non-Hispanic/Latino; 5% Hispanic/Latino; 1% African American, non-Hispanic/Latino; 1% Asian, non-Hispanic/Latino; 0.3% Native Hawaiian or other Pacific Islander, non-Hispanic/Latino; 2% international. 27% 25 or older, 7% transferred in. Retention: 72% of full-time freshmen returned the following year. Academic areas with the most degrees conferred: business/marketing; education; social sciences. Core. Calendar: semesters. Academic remediation for entering students, ESL program, services for LD students, advanced placement, accelerated degree program, self-designed majors, freshman honors college, honors program, independent study, distance learning, double major, summer session for credit, part-time degree program, adult/continuing education programs, co-op programs and internships, graduate courses open to undergrads. Off campus study at Weber State University. Study abroad program. ROTC: Army, Air Force.

Entrance Requirements: Options: electronic application, deferred admission, international baccalaureate accepted. Required: high school transcript, SAT or ACT. Recommended: minimum 2.75 high school GPA. Entrance: moderately difficult. Application deadline: Rolling. Notification: continuous. SAT Reasoning Test deadline: 8/26. SAT Subject Test deadline: 8/26. Transfer credits accepted: Yes.

Costs Per Year: Application fee: $40. State resident tuition: $5,273 full-time. Nonresident tuition: $16,976 full-time. Mandatory fees: $910 full-time. Full-time tuition and fees vary according to course load, location, program, and reciprocity agreements. College room and board: $5620. College room only: $1920. Room and board charges vary according to board plan and housing facility.

Collegiate Environment: Orientation program. Drama-theater group, choral group, marching band, student-run newspaper, radio station. Social organizations: 270 open to all; national fraternities, national sororities; 2% of eligible men and 2% of eligible women are members. Most popular organizations: Latter-Day Saints Student Association, multicultural clubs, volunteer groups, college councils. Major annual events: Homecoming, Halloween Howl, A-Day. Student services: legal services, health clinic, personal-psychological counseling, women's center. Campus security: 24-hour emergency response devices and patrols, student patrols, late night transport-escort service, video monitors in pedestrian tunnels. No special consideration for freshman housing applicants. Options: coed, men-only, women-only housing available. Merrill-Cazier Library plus 4 others with 1.6 million books, 2.7 million microform titles, 10,749 serials, 17,711 audiovisual materials, an OPAC, and a Web page. Operations spending for the previous fiscal year: $10.1 million. 1,000 computers available on campus for general student use. Computer purchase/lease plans available. A campuswide network can be accessed from student residence rooms and from off campus. Students can access the following: online class registration. Staffed computer lab on campus provides training in use of computers, software, and the Internet.

Community Environment: Located in the fertile Cache Valley, Logan is the headquarters for the adjacent Cache National Forest. The Cache Valley was originally an ancient lakebed 500 feet deep, and shorelines of the lake are still visible along the foothills. Today, the community has excellent transportation with airlines, railroad, and bus connections. Major highways enter the city from four directions. Dairying is an important economic feature of the community, and the city has one of the largest Swiss cheese factories in the world. Some part-time employment is available. Local recreation includes hunting, fishing, skiing, and all the water sports.

■ UTAH VALLEY UNIVERSITY

800 W University Pky.
Orem, UT 84058-5999
Tel: (801)222-8000
Fax: (801)225-4677
E-mail: info@uvsc.edu
Web Site: www.uvu.edu/

Description: State-supported, comprehensive, coed, affiliated with Advent Christian Church. Part of Utah System of Higher Education. Awards associate, bachelor's, and master's degrees. Founded 1941. Setting: 422-acre suburban campus with easy access to Salt Lake City. Total enrollment: 31,562. Faculty: 1,717 (582 full-time, 1,135 part-time). Student-undergrad faculty ratio is 23:1. 6,722 applied, 100% were admitted. 4% from top 10% of their high school class, 17% from top quarter, 45% from top half. Full-time: 16,742 students, 44% women, 56% men. Part-time: 14,663 students, 44% women, 56% men. Students come from 55 states and territories, 46 other countries, 10% from out-of-state. 1% American Indian or Alaska Native, non-Hispanic/Latino; 9% Hispanic/Latino; 1% African American, non-Hispanic/Latino; 1% Asian, non-Hispanic/Latino; 1% Native Hawaiian or other Pacific Islander, non-Hispanic/Latino; 2% international. 43% 25 or older, 5% transferred in. Retention: 61% of full-time freshmen returned the following year. Academic areas with the most degrees conferred: business/marketing; psychology; education. Core. Calendar: semesters. Academic remediation for entering students, ESL program, services for LD students, advanced placement, self-designed majors, honors program, independent study, distance learning, double major, summer session for credit, part-time degree program, co-op programs and internships, graduate courses open to undergrads. Off campus study at Wasatch Campus, North Valley Campus, Spanish Fork Campus, National Guard Building. Study abroad program. ROTC: Army, Air Force (c).

Entrance Requirements: Open admission. Options: electronic application, deferred admission, international baccalaureate accepted. Required: ACT or SAT, or Accuplacer, SAT or ACT. Required for some: high school transcript. Entrance: noncompetitive. Application deadlines: 8/15, 8/15 for nonresidents. Notification: continuous. SAT Reasoning Test deadline: 8/15. SAT Subject Test deadline: 8/15. Transfer credits accepted: Yes.

Costs Per Year: Application fee: $35. State resident tuition: $4122 full-time, $137.40 per credit part-time. Nonresident tuition: $12,854 full-time, $428.47 per credit part-time. Mandatory fees: $664 full-time, $28.86 per credit part-time, $332 per term part-time.

Collegiate Environment: Orientation program. Drama-theater group, choral group, student-run newspaper. Social organizations: 118 open to all. Most popular organizations: LDSSA Orem Institute, Center for the Advancement of Leadership. Major annual events: Homecoming, Club All-Nighter, Club Rush. Student services: legal services, health clinic, personal-psychological counseling, women's center. Campus security: 24-hour patrols. College housing not available. Utah Valley University Library plus 1 other with 228,000 books, 53 microform titles, 568 serials, 20,788 audiovisual materials, an OPAC, and a Web page. 1,000 computers available on campus for general student use. A campuswide network can be accessed from off-campus. Students can access the following: online class registration. Staffed computer lab on campus.

Community Environment: See Brigham Young University.

■ WEBER STATE UNIVERSITY

1001 University Cir.
Ogden, UT 84408-1001
Tel: (801)626-6000; Free: 800-848-7770
Fax: (801)626-6747
E-mail: admissions@weber.edu
Web Site: www.weber.edu/

Description: State-supported, comprehensive, coed. Part of Utah System of Higher Education. Awards associate, bachelor's, and master's degrees. Founded 1889. Setting: 526-acre urban campus with easy access to Salt Lake City. Endowment: $74.9 million. Research spending for the previous fiscal year: $974,648. Educational spending for the previous fiscal year: $3723 per student. Total enrollment: 26,532. Faculty: 976 (439 full-time, 537 part-time). Student-undergrad faculty ratio is 24:1. 5,561 applied, 100% were admitted. Full-time: 11,784 students, 51% women, 49% men. Part-time: 14,084 students, 55% women, 45% men. Students come from 52 states and territories, 45 other countries, 8% from out-of-state. 0.4% American Indian or Alaska Native, non-Hispanic/Latino; 9% Hispanic/Latino; 1% African American, non-Hispanic/Latino; 1% Asian, non-Hispanic/Latino; 0.3% Native Hawaiian or other Pacific Islander, non-Hispanic/Latino; 2% international.

42% 25 or older, 3% live on campus, 3% transferred in. Retention: 74% of full-time freshmen returned the following year. Academic areas with the most degrees conferred: health professions and related sciences; business/marketing; history. Core. Calendar: semesters. Academic remediation for entering students, ESL program, services for LD students, advanced placement, accelerated degree program, self-designed majors, freshman honors college, honors program, independent study, distance learning, double major, summer session for credit, part-time degree program, external degree program, adult/continuing education programs, co-op programs and internships, graduate courses open to undergrads. Off campus study at Utah State University, Southern Utah University, Dixie College, Utah Valley University, Salt Lake Community College. Study abroad program. ROTC: Army, Naval, Air Force.

Entrance Requirements: Open admission. Options: electronic application, early admission, deferred admission, international baccalaureate accepted. Required: high school transcript. Recommended: SAT or ACT. Required for some: ACCUPLACER. Entrance: noncompetitive. Application deadline: 8/21. Notification: continuous. SAT Reasoning Test deadline: 7/1. SAT Subject Test deadline: 7/1.

Costs Per Year: Application fee: $30. State resident tuition: $3961 full-time, $165 per credit hour part-time. Nonresident tuition: $12,058 full-time, $502 per credit hour part-time. Mandatory fees: $800 full-time, $33 per credit hour part-time. Full-time tuition and fees vary according to course load and degree level. Part-time tuition and fees vary according to course load and degree level. College room and board: $5200. Room and board charges vary according to board plan and housing facility.

Collegiate Environment: Orientation program. Drama-theater group, choral group, marching band, student-run newspaper, radio station. Social organizations: 229 open to all; national fraternities, national sororities, local fraternities, local sororities; 12% of eligible men and 15% of eligible women are members. Most popular organizations: LDSSA (Latter-day Saint Student Association), SAA (Student Alumni Association), GSA (Gay-Straight Alliance), Chinese Club, Golden Key Honor Society. Major annual events: Homecoming, Graduation, Student Elections. Student services: legal services, health clinic, personal-psychological counseling, women's center. Campus security: 24-hour emergency response devices and patrols, student patrols, late night transport-escort service, controlled dormitory access. 864 college housing spaces available; 798 were occupied in 2012-13. No special consideration for freshman housing applicants. Options: men-only, women-only housing available. Stewart Library with 708,606 books, 623,973 microform titles, 793 serials, 22,957 audiovisual materials, an OPAC, and a Web page. Operations spending for the previous fiscal year: $2.9 million. 358 computers available on campus for general student use. A campuswide network can be accessed from student residence rooms and from off campus. Students can access the following: online class registration. Staffed computer lab on campus provides training in use of computers.

Community Environment: Located at the confluence of the Weber and Ogden Rivers, this community is an important railroad distribution center for products directed to west coast markets. Mormon pioneers settled the community. The climate is temperate with four distinct seasons. Ogden is reached by railroad, airlines, and highways. The community has many churches representing over 30 denominations. There are two hospitals, four health centers, a library and branch, 2 major shopping malls, and various civic and fraternal organizations serving the area. There are also five TV stations and a radio station. Part-time employment is available. Local recreation includes fishing, hunting, swimming, skiing, boating, picnicking, camping, golfing, and horseback riding.

■ WESTERN GOVERNORS UNIVERSITY

4001 S 700 E, Ste. 700
Salt Lake City, UT 84107
Tel: (801)274-3280; Free: 866-225-5948
Fax: (801)274-3305
E-mail: admissions@wgu.edu
Web Site: www.wgu.edu/

Description: Independent, comprehensive, coed. Awards bachelor's and master's degrees. Founded 1998. Total enrollment: 9,022. 12,273 applied. 92% 25 or older. Core. Calendar: continuous. Services for LD students, accelerated degree program, independent study, distance learning, double major, part-time degree program, external degree program, adult/continuing education programs.

Entrance Requirements: Option: electronic application. Required for some: high school transcript. Entrance: minimally difficult.

Collegiate Environment: Orientation program. WGU Central Library (online) with a Web page.

■ WESTMINSTER COLLEGE

1840 S 1300, E
Salt Lake City, UT 84105-3697
Tel: (801)484-7651; Free: 800-748-4753
Fax: (801)484-3252
E-mail: admission@westminstercollege.edu
Web Site: www.westminstercollege.edu/

Description: Independent, comprehensive, coed. Awards bachelor's and master's degrees. Founded 1875. Setting: 27-acre suburban campus. Endowment: $56.7 million. Research spending for the previous fiscal year: $42,176. Educational spending for the previous fiscal year: $9036 per student. Total enrollment: 3,301. Faculty: 410 (155 full-time, 255 part-time). Student-undergrad faculty ratio is 10:1. 3,764 applied, 70% were admitted. 22% from top 10% of their high school class, 56% from top quarter, 87% from top half. 3 National Merit Scholars, 13 valedictorians. Full-time: 2,260 students, 55% women, 45% men. Part-time: 266 students, 42% women, 58% men. 38% from out-of-state. 1% American Indian or Alaska Native, non-Hispanic/Latino; 9% Hispanic/Latino; 1% African American, non-Hispanic/Latino; 3% Asian, non-Hispanic/Latino; 0.5% Native Hawaiian or other Pacific Islander, non-Hispanic/Latino; 5% international. 16% 25 or older, 27% live on campus, 7% transferred in. Retention: 78% of full-time freshmen returned the following year. Academic areas with the most degrees conferred: business/marketing; health professions and related sciences; social sciences. Core. Calendar: 4-4-1. Academic remediation for entering students, ESL program, services for LD students, advanced placement, accelerated degree program, self-designed majors, freshman honors college, honors program, independent study, distance learning, double major, summer session for credit, part-time degree program, external degree program, co-op programs and internships. Off campus study. Study abroad program. ROTC: Army (c), Naval (c), Air Force (c).

Entrance Requirements: Options: electronic application, deferred admission, international baccalaureate accepted. Required: essay, high school transcript, minimum 2.5 high school GPA, 1 recommendation, SAT or ACT. Recommended: interview. Entrance: moderately difficult. Application deadlines: Rolling, Rolling for nonresidents. Notification: continuous, continuous for nonresidents. SAT Reasoning Test deadline: 8/1. Transfer credits accepted: Yes.

Costs Per Year: Application fee: $50. Comprehensive fee: $36,100 includes full-time tuition ($27,720), mandatory fees ($490), and college room and board ($7890). Full-time tuition and fees vary according to course load and program. Room and board charges vary according to board plan. Part-time tuition: $1155 per credit hour. Part-time tuition varies according to course load and program.

Collegiate Environment: Orientation program. Drama-theater group, choral group, student-run newspaper. Social organizations: 65 open to all. Most popular organizations: Associated Students of Westminster College (Student Government), Associated Residents of Westminster College (Residential Government), Westminster Ski and Snowboard Club (WSSC), V-Day, Westminster Entrepreneurship Club. Major annual events: Halloween Dance, Welcome Back, Late Night Breakfast. Student services: health clinic, personal-psychological counseling. Campus security: 24-hour emergency response devices and patrols, student patrols, late night transport-escort service, controlled dormitory access. 809 college housing spaces available. Freshmen given priority for college housing. On-campus residence required in freshman year. Option: coed housing available. Giovale Library plus 1 other with 218,288 books, 256,323 microform titles, 22,033 serials, 5,999 audiovisual materials, an OPAC, and a Web page. Operations spending for the previous fiscal year: $1.1 million. 244 computers available on campus for general student use. A computer is required for all students. A campuswide network can be accessed from student residence rooms and from off campus. Students can access the following: online class registration. Staffed computer lab on campus provides training in use of computers, software, and the Internet.

■ BENNINGTON COLLEGE

One College Dr.
Bennington, VT 05201
Tel: (802)442-5401; Free: 800-833-6845
Fax: (802)447-4269
E-mail: admissions@bennington.edu
Web Site: www.bennington.edu/

Description: Independent, comprehensive, coed. Awards bachelor's and master's degrees. Founded 1932. Setting: 440-acre small town campus with easy access to Albany, NY. Endowment: $15.4 million. Educational spending for the previous fiscal year: $19,909 per student. Total enrollment: 826. Faculty: 89 (64 full-time, 25 part-time). Student-undergrad faculty ratio is 9:1. 1,236 applied, 63% were admitted. 35% from top 10% of their high school class, 67% from top quarter, 93% from top half. Full-time: 684 students, 64% women, 36% men. Part-time: 4 students, 75% women, 25% men. Students come from 46 states and territories, 36 other countries, 96% from out-of-state. 0% American Indian or Alaska Native, non-Hispanic/Latino; 5% Hispanic/Latino; 2% African American, non-Hispanic/Latino; 2% Asian, non-Hispanic/Latino; 0% Native Hawaiian or other Pacific Islander, non-Hispanic/Latino; 7% international. 1% 25 or older, 95% live on campus, 2% transferred in. Retention: 83% of full-time freshmen returned the following year. Academic areas with the most degrees conferred: visual and performing arts; social sciences; English. Calendar: semesters plus winter work term in January and February. Services for LD students, accelerated degree program, self-designed majors, independent study, double major, part-time degree program, internships, graduate courses open to undergrads. Off campus study at The Association of Vermont Independent Colleges (AVIC) Semester Exchange Program provides Bennington students the opportunity to study away for a term at any of the following partner institutions: Burlington College, Champlain College, College of St. Joseph, Goddard College, Green Mountain College, Landmark College, Marlboro College, Middlebury College, New England Culinary Institute, Norwich University, Saint Michaels College, Southern Vermont College, Sterling College. Study abroad program.

Entrance Requirements: Options: electronic application, early admission, early decision, early action, deferred admission, international baccalaureate accepted. Required: essay, high school transcript, 2 recommendations, graded analytic paper. Recommended: interview. Entrance: very difficult. Application deadlines: 1/3, 11/15 for early decision plan 1, 1/3 for early decision plan 2, 12/1 for early action. Notification: 4/1, 12/20 for early decision plan 1, 2/1 for early decision plan 2, 2/1 for early action. SAT Reasoning Test deadline: 1/3. SAT Subject Test deadline: 1/3. Transfer credits accepted: Yes. Applicants placed on waiting list: 175. Wait-listed applicants offered admission: 27. Early decision applicants: 50. Early decision applicants admitted: 21. Early action applicants: 358. Early action applicants admitted: 240.

Costs Per Year: Application fee: $60. Comprehensive fee: $56,990 includes full-time tuition ($43,070), mandatory fees ($1150), and college room and board ($12,770). College room only: $6850. Part-time tuition: $1440 per credit hour.

Collegiate Environment: Orientation program. Drama-theater group, choral group, student-run newspaper. Social organizations: 37 open to all; 25% of eligible men and 30% of eligible women are members. Most popular organizations: Program Activity Council, Bennington Free Press, Student Endowment for the Arts, SILO: Student Journal of Arts and Letters, Bennington Zombie Defense: Humans vs. Zombies Game. Major annual events: Sunfest, Midnight Breakfast, Convocation. Student services: health clinic, personal-psychological counseling. Campus security: 24-hour emergency response devices and patrols, late night transport-escort service, prevention/awareness program. 661 college housing spaces available; 620 were occupied in 2012-13. Freshmen guaranteed college housing. On-campus residence required through senior year. Option: coed housing available. Crossett Library plus 1 other with 125,000 books, 14,500 serials, 6,000 audiovisual materials, an OPAC, and a Web page. Operations spending for the previous fiscal year: $759,251. 100 computers available on campus for general student use. A campuswide network can be accessed from student residence rooms and from off campus. Staffed computer lab on campus provides training in use of computers, software, and the Internet.

Community Environment: Situated on 550 acres in the foothills of Vermont's Green Mountains, Bennington College is a short drive from some of the region's top ski resorts. The College is four miles from the village of Bennington and one mile from North Bennington. Twenty miles to the south is Williamstown, MA, and the Berkshires, home to the nationally renowned museums The Clark Institute and MASSMoCA, while featuring such esteemed performing arts venues as the Williamstown Theatre Festival, Jacob's Pillow, and Tanglewood. Twenty miles north is Manchester, VT, and its fine restaurants and shopping, as well as a state-of-the-art ice skating rink. Approximately 40 miles to the west is Albany, NY, which provides numerous amenities as well as rail transportation to Boston, New York City, and elsewhere. Local historical sites include the Bennington Museum, Bennington Battle Monument, and Old First Church, where poet Robert Frost is buried.

■ BURLINGTON COLLEGE

95 N Ave.
Burlington, VT 05401-2998
Tel: (802)862-9616; Free: 800-862-9616
Fax: (802)658-0071
E-mail: admissions@burlington.edu
Web Site: www.burlington.edu/

Description: Independent, comprehensive, coed. Awards associate, bachelor's, and master's degrees. Founded 1972. Setting: 32-acre urban campus with easy access to Montreal. Endowment: $100,784. Educational spending for the previous fiscal year: $13,055 per student. Total enrollment: 187. Faculty: 76 (5 full-time, 71 part-time). Student-undergrad faculty ratio is 6:1. 180 applied, 86% were admitted. 5% from top 10% of their high school class, 19% from top quarter, 38% from top half. Full-time: 144 students, 50% women, 50% men. Part-time: 41 students, 39% women, 61% men. Students come from 23 states and territories, 5 other countries, 46% from out-of-state. 1% American Indian or Alaska Native, non-Hispanic/Latino; 2% Hispanic/Latino; 1% African American, non-Hispanic/Latino; 1% Asian, non-Hispanic/Latino; 0% Native Hawaiian or other Pacific Islander, non-Hispanic/Latino; 2% international. 24% 25 or older, 17% live on campus, 16% transferred in. Retention: 40% of full-time freshmen returned the following year. Academic areas with the most degrees conferred: visual and performing arts; psychology; English. Core. Calendar: semesters. Services for LD students, advanced placement, self-designed majors, independent study, distance learning, double major, summer session for credit, part-time degree program, external degree program, internships. Off campus study at Community College of Vermont, Vermont Law School, Central Maine Community College, Champlain College and St. Michael's College, VT. Study abroad program.

Entrance Requirements: Options: electronic application, deferred admission, international baccalaureate accepted. Required: essay, high school transcript, minimum 2 high school GPA, 2 recommendations. Recommended: interview. Required for some: art portfolio. Entrance: moderately difficult. Application deadlines: 8/15, 8/15 for nonresidents. Notification: continuous, continuous for nonresidents. Transfer credits accepted: Yes.

Costs Per Year: Application fee: $50. Tuition: $22,410 full-time. Full-time tuition varies according to course load and program. College room only: $6870. Room charges vary according to housing facility.

Collegiate Environment: Orientation program. Social organizations: student government and student occupy groups. Most popular organization: Student Association. Major annual events: Graduation, student film festivals, Convocation. Student services: legal services. Campus security: student patrols. Burlington College Library with 20,390 books, 31,594 serials, 2,640 audiovisual materials, an OPAC, and a Web page. Operations spending for the previous fiscal year: $61,578. 19 computers available on campus for general student use. A campuswide network can be accessed from off-campus. Staffed computer lab on campus provides training in use of computers, software, and the Internet.

Community Environment: With five other colleges in the area, Burlington offers a wealth of cultural, economic and recreational opportunities, but still offers a friendly, small-city ambiance. Human-scale neighborhoods, and the college's governance structure itself, give students the chance to get involved, and make a difference.

■ CASTLETON STATE COLLEGE
Castleton, VT 05735
Tel: (802)468-5611; Free: 800-639-8521
Fax: (802)468-1476
E-mail: info@castleton.edu
Web Site: www.castleton.edu/

Description: State-supported, comprehensive, coed. Part of Vermont State Colleges System. Awards associate, bachelor's, and master's degrees and post-master's certificates. Founded 1787. Setting: 165-acre rural campus. Endowment: $4.9 million. Research spending for the previous fiscal year: $22,771. Educational spending for the previous fiscal year: $6026 per student. Total enrollment: 2,156. Faculty: 234 (92 full-time, 142 part-time). Student-undergrad faculty ratio is 14:1. 2,737 applied, 76% were admitted. 5% from top 10% of their high school class, 21% from top quarter, 61% from top half. Full-time: 1,906 students, 50% women, 50% men. Part-time: 153 students, 68% women, 32% men. Students come from 26 states and territories, 9 other countries, 30% from out-of-state. 1% American Indian or Alaska Native, non-Hispanic/Latino; 2% Hispanic/Latino; 1% African American, non-Hispanic/Latino; 1% Asian, non-Hispanic/Latino; 0% Native Hawaiian or other Pacific Islander, non-Hispanic/Latino; 1% international. 6% 25 or older, 54% live on campus, 9% transferred in. Retention: 70% of full-time freshmen returned the following year. Academic areas with the most degrees conferred: business/marketing; parks and recreation; health professions and related sciences. Core. Calendar: semesters. Academic remediation for entering students, services for LD students, advanced placement, self-designed majors, honors program, independent study, double major, summer session for credit, part-time degree program, co-op programs and internships. Off campus study at Vermont State Colleges (Johnson, Lyndon, Vermont Technical College, Community College of Vermont). Study abroad program. ROTC: Army.

Entrance Requirements: Options: electronic application, deferred admission. Required: essay, high school transcript, minimum 2.5 high school GPA, 2 recommendations, SAT or ACT. Recommended: interview. Entrance: moderately difficult. Application deadlines: Rolling, Rolling for nonresidents. Notification: continuous, continuous for nonresidents. SAT Reasoning Test deadline: 5/1. Transfer credits accepted: Yes.

Costs Per Year: Application fee: $40. One-time mandatory fee: $200. State resident tuition: $9312 full-time, $388 per credit part-time. Nonresident tuition: $23,040 full-time, $960 per credit part-time. Mandatory fees: $974 full-time, $40 per credit part-time. Full-time tuition and fees vary according to program. Part-time tuition and fees vary according to course load and program. College room and board: $9138. College room only: $5442. Room and board charges vary according to board plan.

Collegiate Environment: Orientation program. Drama-theater group, choral group, marching band, student-run newspaper, radio station. Social organizations: 40 open to all. Most popular organizations: community service, clubs in the academic majors, Women's issues organization, Spanish and International, Skiing/Snowboarding. Major annual events: Soundings, Spring Weekend, Fall Festival. Student services: health clinic,

personal-psychological counseling. Campus security: 24-hour emergency response devices and patrols, student patrols, late night transport-escort service, controlled dormitory access. 1,100 college housing spaces available; 1,050 were occupied in 2012-13. Freshmen guaranteed college housing. On-campus residence required in freshman year. Option: coed housing available. Calvin Coolidge Library with 206,845 books, 613,114 microform titles, 49,645 serials, 15,520 audiovisual materials, an OPAC, and a Web page. Operations spending for the previous fiscal year: $1.1 million. 250 computers available on campus for general student use. Computer purchase/lease plans available. A campuswide network can be accessed from student residence rooms and from off campus. Staffed computer lab on campus provides training in use of computers, software, and the Internet.

Community Environment: Adjacent to outstanding ski and summer resorts, the area is rural and surrounded by Vermont's beautiful lakes and mountains.

■ CHAMPLAIN COLLEGE
PO Box 670
Burlington, VT 05402-0670
Tel: (802)860-2700; Free: 800-570-5858
Fax: (802)862-2772
E-mail: admission@champlain.edu
Web Site: www.champlain.edu/

Description: Independent, comprehensive, coed. Awards associate, bachelor's, and master's degrees. Founded 1878. Setting: 21-acre suburban campus with easy access to Montreal. Endowment: $10.2 million. Educational spending for the previous fiscal year: $7620 per student. Total enrollment: 3,233. Faculty: 350 (103 full-time, 247 part-time). Student-undergrad faculty ratio is 13:1. 4,444 applied, 74% were admitted. 16% from top 10% of their high school class, 34% from top quarter, 68% from top half. Full-time: 2,236 students, 37% women, 63% men. Part-time: 557 students, 50% women, 50% men. Students come from 53 states and territories, 21 other countries, 67% from out-of-state. 0.4% American Indian or Alaska Native, non-Hispanic/Latino; 3% Hispanic/Latino; 2% African American, non-Hispanic/Latino; 1% Asian, non-Hispanic/Latino; 0.2% Native Hawaiian or other Pacific Islander, non-Hispanic/Latino; 0.4% international. 23% 25 or older, 49% live on campus, 3% transferred in. Retention: 79% of full-time freshmen returned the following year. Academic areas with the most degrees conferred: business/marketing; computer and information sciences; visual and performing arts. Core. Calendar: semesters. Services for LD students, advanced placement, independent study, distance learning, double major, summer session for credit, part-time degree program, adult/continuing education programs, co-op programs and internships. Off campus study. Study abroad program. ROTC: Army (c).

Entrance Requirements: Options: electronic application, early decision, international baccalaureate accepted. Required: essay, high school transcript, SAT or ACT. Recommended: 1 recommendation, interview. Required for some: SAT Subject Tests. Entrance: moderately difficult. Application deadlines: 1/31, 11/15 for early decision plan 1, 1/15 for early decision plan 2. Notification: 3/25, 12/15 for early decision plan 1, 2/15 for early decision plan 2. SAT Reasoning Test deadline: 2/1. SAT Subject Test deadline: 2/1. Transfer credits accepted: Yes. Applicants placed on waiting list: 88. Wait-listed applicants offered admission: 15. Early decision applicants: 304. Early decision applicants admitted: 248.

Costs Per Year: Comprehensive fee: $44,850 includes full-time tuition ($31,250), mandatory fees ($100), and college room and board ($13,500). Part-time tuition: $1240 per credit hour.

Collegiate Environment: Orientation program. Drama-theater group, choral group, student-run newspaper. Most popular organizations: Diversity Champlain, International Club, community service organization, Champlain Players (theater group), Outing Club/Skiing Snowboarding Club. Major annual events: Parents' Weekend, Halloween Masquerade Dance, Spring Meltdown. Student services: health clinic, personal-psychological counseling. Campus security: 24-hour emergency response devices and patrols, late night transport-escort service, controlled dormitory access. 1,393 college housing spaces available; 1,292 were occupied in 2012-13. Freshmen guaranteed college housing. Option: coed housing available. Miller Information Commons with 170,000 books, 700 microform titles, 50,000 serials, an OPAC, and a Web page. Operations spending for the previous fiscal year: $1.2 million. 563 computers available on campus for general student use. A campuswide network can be accessed from student residence rooms and from off campus. Students can access the following: online class registration. Staffed computer lab on campus provides training in use of software.

Community Environment: Burlington offers the best of both worlds: the excitement of life in the city and the tranquility and recreational splendor of the northern Vermont countryside. Three blocks from the Champlain campus, the Church Street Marketplace provides an exciting collection of more than 100 shops, services, and restaurants. Within one hour's drive are five major ski resorts: Stowe, Sugarbush, Bolton Valley, Mad River Glen, and Smugglers' Notch.

■ **COLLEGE OF ST. JOSEPH**

71 Clement Rd.
Rutland, VT 05701-3899
Tel: (802)773-5900; Free: 877-270-9998
E-mail: admissions@csj.edu
Web Site: www.csj.edu/

Description: Independent Roman Catholic, comprehensive, coed. Awards associate, bachelor's, and master's degrees. Founded 1950. Setting: 117-acre small town campus. Endowment: $4.5 million. Educational spending for the previous fiscal year: $4345 per student. Total enrollment: 377. Faculty: 58 (12 full-time, 46 part-time). Student-undergrad faculty ratio is 10:1. 146 applied, 69% were admitted. 1% from top 10% of their high school class, 20% from top quarter, 50% from top half. 5 student government officers. Full-time: 164 students, 58% women, 42% men. Part-time: 73 students, 67% women, 33% men. Students come from 19 states and territories, 26% from out-of-state. 1% American Indian or Alaska Native, non-Hispanic/Latino; 1% Hispanic/Latino; 10% African American, non-Hispanic/Latino. 38% 25 or older, 33% live on campus, 13% transferred in. Retention: 53% of full-time freshmen returned the following year. Academic areas with the most degrees conferred: psychology; business/marketing; English. Core. Calendar: semesters. Academic remediation for entering students, services for LD students, advanced placement, accelerated degree program, independent study, double major, summer session for credit, part-time degree program, adult/continuing education programs, internships, graduate courses open to undergrads.

Entrance Requirements: Options: electronic application, early admission, deferred admission, international baccalaureate accepted. Required: essay, high school transcript, minimum 2 high school GPA, 2 recommendations, SAT or ACT. Recommended: interview. Entrance: minimally difficult. Application deadlines: Rolling, Rolling for nonresidents. Notification: continuous, continuous for nonresidents. Transfer credits accepted: Yes.

Costs Per Year: Application fee: $25. Comprehensive fee: $30,000 includes full-time tuition ($20,125), mandatory fees ($475), and college room and board ($9400). Full-time tuition and fees vary according to course load, degree level, and program. Room and board charges vary according to housing facility. Part-time tuition: $260 per credit. Part-time tuition and fees vary according to course load, degree level, and program.

Collegiate Environment: Orientation program. Choral group. Social organizations: 14 open to all. Most popular organizations: Humans vs. Zombies Club, Business Club, Human Services Club, Student Government Association, Cooking Club. Major annual events: Bonfire/DJ, Beach Barbecue, Oktoberfest. Student services: personal-psychological counseling. Campus security: 24-hour emergency response devices, trained security personnel from 8 pm to 6 am. Giorgetti Library with 115,615 books, 19,739 microform titles, 64 serials, 1,419 audiovisual materials, and an OPAC. Operations spending for the previous fiscal year: $124,238. 33 computers available on campus for general student use. A campuswide network can be accessed. Students can access the following: online statements/ability to pay tuition online. Staffed computer lab on campus provides training in use of computers, software, and the Internet.

Community Environment: Rutland, though a small city of 30,000, is the third largest city in Vermont. All forms of commercial transportation are available. The community includes churches, a hospital, library, museum, community concert series, and a number of civic and service organizations. Recreational areas provide facilities for boating, swimming, fishing, camping, horseback riding, hunting, mountain climbing, and cross-country and alpine skiing at nearby Pico and Killington Ski areas. Rutland is the headquarters for the Green Mountain National Forest.

■ **COMMUNITY COLLEGE OF VERMONT**

660 Elm St.
Montpelier, VT 05602
Tel: (802)828-2800
Fax: (802)828-2805
E-mail: adam.warrington@ccv.edu
Web Site: www.ccv.edu/

Description: State-supported, 2-year, coed. Part of Vermont State Colleges

System. Awards certificates, transfer associate, and terminal associate degrees. Founded 1970. Setting: rural campus. Total enrollment: 6,908. Faculty: 735 (all part-time). Student-undergrad faculty ratio is 13:1. 1,805 applied, 63% were admitted. Students come from 18 states and territories, 3% from out-of-state. 1% American Indian or Alaska Native, non-Hispanic/Latino; 2% Hispanic/Latino; 3% African American, non-Hispanic/Latino; 2% Asian, non-Hispanic/Latino; 0% Native Hawaiian or other Pacific Islander, non-Hispanic/Latino; 0.03% international. 50% 25 or older. Core. Calendar: semesters. Academic remediation for entering students, ESL program, services for LD students, advanced placement, accelerated degree program, self-designed majors, independent study, distance learning, double major, summer session for credit, part-time degree program, external degree program, adult/continuing education programs, co-op programs and internships. Study abroad program.

Entrance Requirements: Open admission. Option: electronic application. Recommended: SAT or ACT. Required for some: ACCUPLACER assessments are required for degree seeking applicants and some continuing education applicants. SAT/ACT scores as well as college transcripts may be used to waive the Accuplacers. Entrance: noncompetitive. Application deadlines: Rolling, Rolling for nonresidents. Notification: continuous, continuous for nonresidents. Transfer credits accepted: Yes.

Costs Per Year: Application fee: $0. State resident tuition: $6690 full-time, $223 per credit hour part-time. Nonresident tuition: $13,380 full-time, $446 per credit hour part-time. Mandatory fees: $150 full-time, $50 per term part-time.

Collegiate Environment: Orientation program. College housing not available. Hartness Library plus 1 other with 59,000 books, 36,500 serials, 6,200 audiovisual materials, an OPAC, and a Web page. 880 computers available on campus for general student use. A campuswide network can be accessed from off-campus. Students can access the following: online class registration. Staffed computer lab on campus provides training in use of computers, software, and the Internet.

■ **GODDARD COLLEGE**

123 Pitkin Rd.
Plainfield, VT 05667-9432
Tel: (802)454-8311; Free: 800-906-8312.
Fax: (802)454-1029
E-mail: admissions@goddard.edu
Web Site: www.goddard.edu/

Description: Independent, comprehensive, coed. Awards bachelor's and master's degrees. Founded 1938. Setting: 200-acre rural campus. Endowment: $932,377. Research spending for the previous fiscal year: $120,000. Total enrollment: 703. Faculty: 104 (14 full-time, 90 part-time). 10 applied, 70% were admitted. Full-time: 244 students, 70% women, 30% men. Students come from 38 states and territories, 3 other countries, 85% from out-of-state. 59% 25 or older, 24% transferred in. Retention: 63% of full-time freshmen returned the following year. Core. Calendar: semesters. Services for LD students, advanced placement, self-designed majors, independent study, distance learning, double major, external degree program, adult/continuing education programs, internships. Off campus study.

Entrance Requirements: Options: electronic application, deferred admission, international baccalaureate accepted. Required: essay, high school transcript, 2 recommendations, interview. Recommended: four years of English, Mathematics, Social Studies, Natural Sciences; three years of lab science and two years of a foreign language. Entrance: moderately difficult. Application deadlines: Rolling, Rolling for nonresidents. Notification: continuous, continuous for nonresidents. Transfer credits accepted: Yes.

Costs Per Year: Application fee: $20. Comprehensive fee: $15,610 includes full-time tuition ($14,036), mandatory fees ($182), and college room and board ($1392). College room only: $672. Full-time tuition and fees vary according to location, program, and reciprocity agreements. Room and board charges vary according to location.

Collegiate Environment: Orientation program. Student-run radio station. Major annual events: graduating senior project presentations, student cabarets. Student services: personal-psychological counseling. Campus security: 24-hour patrols, patrols by trained security personnel 9 pm to 6 am. 125 college housing spaces available. Options: coed, women-only housing available. Eliot Pratt Center with 70,000 books, 19 serials, 325 audiovisual materials, an OPAC, and a Web page. Operations spending for the previous fiscal year: $206,452. 55 computers available on campus for general student use. A computer is required for all students. A campuswide network can be accessed from student residence rooms and from off campus. Students can access the following: library services. Staffed computer lab on campus provides training in use of computers, software, and the Internet.

Community Environment: Located in the Upper Valley of Winooski River, this rural setting has the typical beauty of northern New England surrounded by the lower ranges of the Green Mountains. Winters are cold with heavy snow for good skiing. Opportunities are few for part-time employment.

■ **GREEN MOUNTAIN COLLEGE**
One Brennan Cir.
Poultney, VT 05764-1199
Tel: (802)287-8000; Free: 800-776-6675
Fax: (802)287-8099
E-mail: admiss@greenmtn.edu
Web Site: www.greenmtn.edu/
Description: Independent, comprehensive, coed. Awards bachelor's and master's degrees. Founded 1834. Setting: 155-acre small town campus. Endowment: $2.9 million. Research spending for the previous fiscal year: $230,302. Educational spending for the previous fiscal year: $7150 per student. Total enrollment: 858. Faculty: 82 (49 full-time, 33 part-time). Student-undergrad faculty ratio is 14:1. 1,496 applied, 72% were admitted. 8% from top 10% of their high school class, 20% from top quarter, 50% from top half. Full-time: 736 students, 55% women, 45% men. Part-time: 25 students, 52% women, 48% men. Students come from 33 states and territories, 12 other countries, 87% from out-of-state. 4% 25 or older, 80% live on campus, 6% transferred in. Retention: 70% of full-time freshmen returned the following year. Academic areas with the most degrees conferred: business/marketing; natural resources/environmental science; psychology. Core. Calendar: semesters. ESL program, services for LD students, advanced placement, accelerated degree program, self-designed majors, honors program, independent study, distance learning, double major, summer session for credit, part-time degree program, adult/continuing education programs, co-op programs and internships, graduate courses open to undergrads. Off campus study at Castleton State College, The Eco League. Study abroad program.
Entrance Requirements: Options: electronic application, deferred admission, international baccalaureate accepted. Required: essay, high school transcript, 1 recommendation. Recommended: minimum 2.5 high school GPA, interview, SAT or ACT. Required for some: interview. Entrance: moderately difficult. Application deadline: Rolling. Notification: continuous until 8/1. Transfer credits accepted: Yes.
Collegiate Environment: Orientation program. Drama-theater group, choral group, student-run newspaper, radio station. Social organizations: 32 open to all. Most popular organizations: Student Government Association, Green Mountain College Ultimate Frisbee, Diversity, College Programming Board, International Awareness Club. Major annual events: Welsh Harvest Festival, Earth Week, Midnight Breakfast. Student services: personal-psychological counseling. Campus security: 24-hour emergency response devices and patrols, late night transport-escort service. Griswold Library with 112,000 books, 65,548 microform titles, 312 serials, 2,960 audiovisual materials, an OPAC, and a Web page. Operations spending for the previous fiscal year: $344,822. 92 computers available on campus for general student use. A campuswide network can be accessed from student residence rooms and from off campus. Students can access the following: online class registration, personal network folders, electronic course folders. Staffed computer lab on campus provides training in use of computers, software, and the Internet.
Community Environment: Poultney is in a small town community with a typical New England climate. Train and bus stations and airport are within 20 minutes. Lake Saint Catherine provides facilities for water sports, and other facilities in nearby areas offer winter sports. Pico and Killington Ski resorts, as well as 4 other major ski resorts.

■ **JOHNSON STATE COLLEGE**
337 College Hill
Johnson, VT 05656
Tel: (802)635-2356; Free: 800-635-2356
Fax: (802)635-1230
E-mail: jscadmissions@jsc.edu
Web Site: www.jsc.edu/
Description: State-supported, comprehensive, coed. Part of Vermont State Colleges System. Awards associate, bachelor's, and master's degrees and post-master's certificates. Founded 1828. Setting: 350-acre rural campus with easy access to Montreal. Endowment: $2.3 million. Educational spending for the previous fiscal year: $6102 per student. Total enrollment: 1,882. Faculty: 137 (50 full-time, 87 part-time). Student-undergrad faculty ratio is 16:1. 1,291 applied, 86% were admitted. 6% from top 10% of their high

school class, 12% from top quarter, 31% from top half. Full-time: 1,048 students, 58% women, 42% men. Part-time: 599 students, 76% women, 24% men. Students come from 18 states and territories, 20 other countries, 19% from out-of-state. 1% American Indian or Alaska Native, non-Hispanic/Latino; 1% Hispanic/Latino; 3% African American, non-Hispanic/Latino; 1% Asian, non-Hispanic/Latino; 0% Native Hawaiian or other Pacific Islander, non-Hispanic/Latino; 0.1% international. 35% 25 or older, 60% live on campus, 10% transferred in. Retention: 64% of full-time freshmen returned the following year. Academic areas with the most degrees conferred: liberal arts/general studies; business/marketing; psychology. Core. Calendar: semesters. ESL program, services for LD students, advanced placement, accelerated degree program, honors program, independent study, distance learning, double major, summer session for credit, part-time degree program, external degree program, co-op programs and internships, graduate courses open to undergrads. Off campus study at Vermont State Colleges System, National Student Exchange. Study abroad program. ROTC: Army (c).
Entrance Requirements: Options: electronic application, early admission, early action, deferred admission, international baccalaureate accepted. Required: essay, high school transcript, minimum 2 high school GPA, 1 recommendation, SAT or ACT. Recommended: minimum 2.5 high school GPA, interview. Entrance: moderately difficult. Application deadlines: Rolling, Rolling for nonresidents. Notification: continuous, continuous for nonresidents.
Costs Per Year: Application fee: $40. State resident tuition: $9312 full-time, $372 per credit part-time. Nonresident tuition: $20,976 full-time, $832 per credit part-time. Mandatory fees: $1231 full-time. Full-time tuition and fees vary according to course load. Part-time tuition varies according to course load. College room and board: $9138. College room only: $5442. Room and board charges vary according to board plan.
Collegiate Environment: Orientation program. Drama-theater group, choral group, student-run newspaper, radio station. Social organizations: 35 open to all. Most popular organizations: SERVE (Break Away), A Global partnership: Students for Children's Right, Ski/Snowboarding Club, Dance Club, Christian Fellowship Club. Major annual events: Winterfest, Casino Night (to benefit the Lamoille County United Way), Dance Ensemble Performances. Student services: health clinic, personal-psychological counseling, women's center. Campus security: 24-hour emergency response devices and patrols, student patrols, late night transport-escort service, controlled dormitory access. 600 college housing spaces available; 540 were occupied in 2012-13. Freshmen given priority for college housing. On-campus residence required through sophomore year. Option: coed housing available. Willey Library plus 1 other with 156,427 books, 180,373 microform titles, 471 serials, 8,237 audiovisual materials, and an OPAC. Operations spending for the previous fiscal year: $735,339. 160 computers available on campus for general student use. A campuswide network can be accessed from student residence rooms and from off campus. Students can access the following: online class registration. Staffed computer lab on campus provides training in use of computers, software, and the Internet.
Community Environment: The 350-acre hilltop campus of Johnson State is home for more than 1,500 students. Its location, in the heart of the Green Mountains, places it just minutes away from some of the East's finest skiing and snowboarding at Stowe and Smuggler's Notch. Students have access to our on-campus snowboard park. Its modern facilities include one of the finest performing arts centers in northern New England.

■ **LANDMARK COLLEGE**
River Rd. S
Putney, VT 05346
Tel: (802)387-4767
Fax: (802)387-4779
E-mail: admissions@landmark.edu
Web Site: www.landmark.edu/
Description: Independent, primarily 2-year, coed. Awards transfer associate, terminal associate, and bachelor's degrees. Founded 1983. Setting: 125-acre small town campus. Endowment: $14.9 million. Educational spending for the previous fiscal year: $51,751 per student. Total enrollment: 465. Faculty: 78 (all full-time). Student-undergrad faculty ratio is 6:1. 254 applied, 79% were admitted. Full-time: 465 students, 34% women, 66% men. Students come from 36 states and territories, 11 other countries, 94% from out-of-state. 0.2% American Indian or Alaska Native, non-Hispanic/Latino; 3% Hispanic/Latino; 6% African American, non-Hispanic/Latino; 2% Asian, non-Hispanic/Latino; 0% Native Hawaiian or other Pacific Islander, non-Hispanic/Latino; 3% international. 4% 25 or older, 95% live on campus, 18%

transferred in. Retention: 60% of full-time freshmen returned the following year. Core. Calendar: semesters. Academic remediation for entering students, services for LD students, advanced placement, distance learning, summer session for credit, internships. Study abroad program.

Entrance Requirements: Options: electronic application, deferred admission, international baccalaureate accepted. Required: essay, high school transcript, 2 recommendations, interview, diagnosis of LD and/or ADHD and cognitive testing, Wechsler Adult Intelligence Scale III and Nelson Denny Reading Test. Entrance: moderately difficult. Application deadline: Rolling. Notification: continuous. Transfer credits accepted: Yes.

Costs Per Year: Application fee: $75. Comprehensive fee: $59,930 includes full-time tuition ($49,500), mandatory fees ($130), and college room and board ($10,300). College room only: $5300. Room and board charges vary according to board plan and housing facility.

Collegiate Environment: Orientation program. Drama-theater group, choral group, student-run newspaper, radio station. Social organizations: 16 open to all. Most popular organizations: Student Government Association, Campus Activities Board, Phi Theta Kappa Honor Society, Equestrian Club, PBL Business Club. Major annual events: Charity Casino Night, Spring Fest, Spring Semiformal Dance. Student services: health clinic, personal-psychological counseling, women's center. Campus security: 24-hour emergency response devices and patrols, late night transport-escort service, controlled dormitory access. 507 college housing spaces available; 465 were occupied in 2012-13. Freshmen guaranteed college housing. On-campus residence required in freshman year. Option: coed housing available. Landmark College Library with 32,786 books, 20 microform titles, 165 serials, 1,535 audiovisual materials, an OPAC, and a Web page. Operations spending for the previous fiscal year: $318,477. 50 computers available on campus for general student use. Computer purchase/lease plans available. A computer is required for all students. A campuswide network can be accessed from student residence rooms and from off campus. Students can access the following: Online access to assignment grades, attendance, and other course data, pay bills, view/print unofficial transcripts. Staffed computer lab on campus provides training in use of computers, software, and the Internet.

■ LYNDON STATE COLLEGE

PO Box 919
Lyndonville, VT 05851-0919
Tel: (802)626-6200; Free: 800-225-1998
Fax: (802)626-6335
E-mail: admissions@lyndonstate.edu
Web Site: www.lyndonstate.edu/

Description: State-supported, comprehensive, coed. Part of Vermont State Colleges System. Awards associate, bachelor's, and master's degrees. Founded 1911. Setting: 175-acre rural campus. Endowment: $2.8 million. Total enrollment: 1,436. Faculty: 160 (58 full-time, 102 part-time). Student-undergrad faculty ratio is 15:1. 1,021 applied, 93% were admitted. 12% from top 10% of their high school class, 22% from top quarter, 69% from top half. Full-time: 1,213 students, 45% women, 55% men. Part-time: 110 students, 57% women, 43% men. Students come from 19 states and territories, 11 other countries, 39% from out-of-state. 1% American Indian or Alaska Native, non-Hispanic/Latino; 2% Hispanic/Latino; 2% African American, non-Hispanic/Latino; 1% Asian, non-Hispanic/Latino; 0% Native Hawaiian or other Pacific Islander, non-Hispanic/Latino; 0.4% international. 8% 25 or older, 51% live on campus, 6% transferred in. Retention: 59% of full-time freshmen returned the following year. Academic areas with the most degrees conferred: parks and recreation; business/marketing; visual and performing arts. Core. Calendar: semesters. Academic remediation for entering students, services for LD students, advanced placement, accelerated degree program, self-designed majors, honors program, independent study, double major, summer session for credit, part-time degree program, adult/continuing education programs, co-op programs and internships. Study abroad program. ROTC: Air Force (c).

Entrance Requirements: Options: electronic application, early admission, deferred admission. Required: high school transcript, minimum 2 high school GPA, 1 recommendation, SAT or ACT. Recommended: minimum 3 high school GPA, interview. Required for some: essay, minimum 3 high school GPA. Entrance: moderately difficult. Application deadline: Rolling. Notification: continuous.

Costs Per Year: Application fee: $36. State resident tuition: $8928 full-time. Nonresident tuition: $19,200 full-time. Mandatory fees: $936 full-time. Full-time tuition and fees vary according to course load. College room and board: $8786. Room and board charges vary according to board plan and housing facility.

Collegiate Environment: Orientation program. Drama-theater group, choral group, student-run newspaper, radio station. Social organizations: 40 open to all. Most popular organizations: American Meteorological Society, ASSIST (A Society of Students in Service Together), Student Senate, Campus Activities Board, Outing Club. Major annual events: Winter Weekend, Spring Weekend, Winter Ball. Student services: health clinic, personal-psychological counseling. Campus security: 24-hour emergency response devices, student patrols, late night transport-escort service, controlled dormitory access. Samuel Read Hall Library with 109,629 books, 32,327 microform titles, 16,468 serials, an OPAC, and a Web page. 125 computers available on campus for general student use. A campuswide network can be accessed from student residence rooms and from off campus. Staffed computer lab on campus (open 24 hours a day).

Community Environment: Lyndon is a rural community in the northeastern part of Vermont with community facilities that include churches of major denominations, civic and service organizations, a library, two hospitals, and good shopping areas. A ski resort at Burke Mountain and Jay Peak provide facilities for skiing and other winter sports.

■ MARLBORO COLLEGE

PO Box A, S Rd.
Marlboro, VT 05344
Tel: (802)257-4333; Free: 800-343-0049
E-mail: admissions@marlboro.edu
Web Site: www.marlboro.edu/

Description: Independent, comprehensive, coed. Awards bachelor's and master's degrees. Founded 1946. Setting: 350-acre rural campus. Endowment: $36.8 million. Educational spending for the previous fiscal year: $18,240 per student. Total enrollment: 267. Faculty: 49 (40 full-time, 9 part-time). Student-undergrad faculty ratio is 6:1. 279 applied, 75% were admitted. Full-time: 260 students, 51% women, 49% men. Part-time: 7 students, 43% women, 57% men. Students come from 34 states and territories, 3 other countries, 85% from out-of-state. 1% American Indian or Alaska Native, non-Hispanic/Latino; 2% Hispanic/Latino; 1% African American, non-Hispanic/Latino; 3% Asian, non-Hispanic/Latino; 0% Native Hawaiian or other Pacific Islander, non-Hispanic/Latino; 0% international. 3% 25 or older, 80% live on campus, 6% transferred in. Retention: 77% of full-time freshmen returned the following year. Academic areas with the most degrees conferred: visual and performing arts; social sciences; English. Calendar: semesters. Services for LD students, advanced placement, accelerated degree program, self-designed majors, independent study, double major, part-time degree program, internships, graduate courses open to undergrads. Off campus study at Brattleboro School of Music, School for International Training. Study abroad program.

Entrance Requirements: Options: electronic application, early admission, early decision, early action, deferred admission, international baccalaureate accepted. Required: essay, high school transcript, 2 recommendations, analytical essay. Recommended: interview. Required for some: interview. Entrance: moderately difficult. Application deadlines: 3/1, 11/15 for early decision, 1/15 for early action. Notification: continuous until 3/15, 12/1 for early decision, 2/1 for early action. SAT Reasoning Test deadline: 3/1. Transfer credits accepted: Yes. Early decision applicants: 5. Early decision applicants admitted: 3. Early action applicants: 123. Early action applicants admitted: 91.

Costs Per Year: Application fee: $50. Comprehensive fee: $47,570 includes full-time tuition ($36,300), mandatory fees ($1340), and college room and board ($9930). College room only: $5470. Full-time tuition and fees vary according to program. Part-time tuition: $1210 per credit. Part-time mandatory fees: $210 per year. Part-time tuition and fees vary according to course load and program.

Collegiate Environment: Orientation program. Drama-theater group, choral group, student-run newspaper, radio station. Social organizations: 22 open to all. Most popular organizations: outdoor program, theater, farm program, Gay/Lesbian/Bisexual Alliance, madrigal and a cappella groups. Major annual events: Work Day, Broomball Tournament, Queer Homecoming. Student services: health clinic, personal-psychological counseling, women's center. Campus security: 24-hour emergency response devices and patrols. Rice-Aron Library with 75,000 books, 5,000 microform titles, 40,000 serials, 4,177 audiovisual materials, an OPAC, and a Web page. Operations spending for the previous fiscal year: $270,370. 47 computers available on campus for general student use. Computer purchase/lease plans available. A campuswide network can be accessed from student residence rooms and from off campus. Students can access the following: online class registration. Staffed computer lab on campus (open 24 hours a day) provides training in use of computers, software, and the Internet.

Community Environment: Marlboro is located on the scenic Molly Stark Trail near Hogback Mountain which offers a panoramic view of the area. Recreational activities include canoeing, kayaking, cross country skiing, hiking, rock climbing, and biking. The Marlboro Summer Music Festival is an annual event.

■ **MIDDLEBURY COLLEGE**
Middlebury, VT 05753-6002
Tel: (802)443-5000
Fax: (802)443-2056
E-mail: admissions@middlebury.edu
Web Site: www.middlebury.edu/
Description: Independent, comprehensive, coed. Awards bachelor's, master's, and doctoral degrees. Founded 1800. Setting: 350-acre small town campus. Total enrollment: 2,516. Faculty: 337 (255 full-time, 82 part-time). Student-undergrad faculty ratio is 9:1. 8,847 applied, 17% were admitted. 21% from top 10% of their high school class, 82% from top quarter, 96% from top half. Full-time: 2,493 students, 51% women, 49% men. Part-time: 23 students, 43% women, 57% men. Students come from 55 states and territories, 68 other countries, 94% from out-of-state. 0.2% American Indian or Alaska Native, non-Hispanic/Latino; 7% Hispanic/Latino; 2% African American, non-Hispanic/Latino; 6% Asian, non-Hispanic/Latino; 0% Native Hawaiian or other Pacific Islander, non-Hispanic/Latino; 9% international. 0% 25 or older, 97% live on campus, 0.4% transferred in. Retention: 97% of full-time freshmen returned the following year. Academic areas with the most degrees conferred: social sciences; biological/life sciences; area and ethnic studies. Core. Calendar: 4-1-4. Services for LD students, advanced placement, accelerated degree program, self-designed majors, honors program, independent study, double major, summer session for credit, internships. Off campus study at Swarthmore College, Berea College, Bucknell University, Eckerd College, St. Olaf College, American University, Williams College (Mystic Seaport Program), Institute for Architecture and Urban Studies. Study abroad program. ROTC: Army (c).
Entrance Requirements: Options: electronic application, early admission, early decision, deferred admission, international baccalaureate accepted. Required: essay, high school transcript, 3 recommendations. Recommended: interview. Entrance: most difficult. Application deadlines: 1/1, 11/10 for early decision plan 1, 1/1 for early decision plan 2. Notification: 3/31, 12/15 for early decision plan 1, 2/15 for early decision plan 2. SAT Reasoning Test deadline: 1/1. SAT Subject Test deadline: 1/1. Applicants placed on waiting list: 1,679. Wait-listed applicants offered admission: 78. Early decision applicants: 959. Early decision applicants admitted: 316.
Costs Per Year: Application fee: $65. Comprehensive fee: $55,570 includes full-time tuition ($43,731) and college room and board ($11,839).
Collegiate Environment: Orientation program. Drama-theater group, choral group, student-run newspaper, radio station. Social organizations: 185 open to all. Major annual events: Senior Week, Winter Carnival, Student Concert Series. Student services: health clinic, personal-psychological counseling, women's center. Campus security: 24-hour patrols, student patrols, late night transport-escort service, controlled dormitory access. 2,420 college housing spaces available; all were occupied in 2012-13. Freshmen guaranteed college housing. On-campus residence required through junior year. Option: coed housing available. Davis Family Library plus 1 other with 1.9 million books, 770 microform titles, 87,815 serials, 36,408 audiovisual materials, an OPAC, and a Web page. 250 computers available on campus for general student use. Computer purchase/lease plans available. A campuswide network can be accessed from student residence rooms and from off campus. Students can access the following: online class registration, helpline, personal Web pages, file servers. Staffed computer lab on campus provides training in use of computers, software, and the Internet.
Community Environment: Middlebury, population 8,000, is located between Burlington and Rutland. Churches, libraries, and various civic and service organizations serve the community. The college's Bread Loaf Mountain is nearby and has facilities for skiing and other winter sports. The College owns and operates an 18-hole golf course, an alpine ski area, and 2 cross-country ski areas. Other sports facilities in the area provide for tennis and horseback riding. Lake Champlain and Green Mountain National Forest are nearby and provide numerous additional facilities.

■ **NEW ENGLAND CULINARY INSTITUTE**
56 College St.
Montpelier, VT 05602-9720
Tel: (802)223-6324; Free: 877-223-6324
Fax: (802)223-0634

E-mail: janknutsen@neci.edu
Web Site: www.neci.edu/
Description: Proprietary, primarily 2-year, coed. Awards certificates, terminal associate, and bachelor's degrees. Founded 1980. Setting: small town campus. Endowment: $291,550. Total enrollment: 569. Faculty: 85 (70 full-time, 15 part-time). Student-undergrad faculty ratio is 8:1. 376 applied, 92% were admitted. 32% 25 or older, 80% live on campus. Core. Services for LD students, advanced placement, accelerated degree program, honors program, independent study, distance learning, co-op programs and internships.
Entrance Requirements: Options: electronic application, early admission, deferred admission. Required: essay, high school transcript, 1 recommendation. Required for some: interview. Entrance: moderately difficult. Application deadline: Rolling.
Collegiate Environment: Orientation program. Student-run newspaper. Social organizations: 10 open to all; 75% of eligible men and 25% of eligible women are members. Most popular organizations: American Culinary Federation, Toastmasters, Ice Carving Club. Major annual events: skiing trips, annual chef vs. student softball games and BBQ, talent show. Student services: personal-psychological counseling. Campus security: 24-hour emergency response devices, student patrols, patrols in the evening. New England Culinary Institute Library with 2,400 books, 30 serials, and an OPAC. Operations spending for the previous fiscal year: $12,000. 14 computers available on campus for general student use. Computer purchase/lease plans available. A campuswide network can be accessed from student residence rooms. Staffed computer lab on campus.

■ **NORWICH UNIVERSITY**
158 Harmon Dr.
Northfield, VT 05663
Tel: (802)485-2000; Free: 800-468-6679
Fax: (802)485-2580
E-mail: nuadm@norwich.edu
Web Site: www.norwich.edu/
Description: Independent, comprehensive, coed. Awards bachelor's and master's degrees. Founded 1819. Setting: 1,125-acre small town campus with easy access to Burlington. Endowment: $160.1 million. Research spending for the previous fiscal year: $978,000. Educational spending for the previous fiscal year: $7225 per student. Total enrollment: 3,452. Faculty: 327 (161 full-time, 166 part-time). Student-undergrad faculty ratio is 12:1. 3,135 applied, 65% were admitted. 16% from top 10% of their high school class, 44% from top quarter, 77% from top half. Full-time: 2,192 students, 25% women, 75% men. Part-time: 35 students, 6% women, 94% men. Students come from 30 states and territories, 8 other countries, 85% from out-of-state. 1% American Indian or Alaska Native, non-Hispanic/Latino; 3% Hispanic/Latino; 2% African American, non-Hispanic/Latino; 2% Asian, non-Hispanic/Latino; 0.2% Native Hawaiian or other Pacific Islander, non-Hispanic/Latino; 1% international. 3% 25 or older, 82% live on campus, 4% transferred in. Retention: 85% of full-time freshmen returned the following year. Academic areas with the most degrees conferred: homeland security, law enforcement, firefighting, and protective services; business/marketing; engineering. Calendar: semesters. Academic remediation for entering students, ESL program, services for LD students, advanced placement, honors program, independent study, distance learning, double major, summer session for credit, part-time degree program, external degree program, adult/continuing education programs, co-op programs and internships, graduate courses open to undergrads. Study abroad program. ROTC: Army, Naval, Air Force.
Entrance Requirements: Option: electronic application. Required: essay, high school transcript, SAT or ACT. Recommended: minimum 2 high school GPA, 2 recommendations, interview. Required for some: portfolio. Entrance: moderately difficult. Application deadline: Rolling. Notification: continuous.
Costs Per Year: Application fee: $35. Comprehensive fee: $42,758 includes full-time tuition ($30,048), mandatory fees ($1734), and college room and board ($10,976).
Collegiate Environment: Orientation program. Drama-theater group, choral group, marching band, student-run newspaper, radio station. Social organizations: 45 open to all. Most popular organizations: DREAM, NUEMS, IEEE, CJSA, Politeia/Model UN. Major annual events: Regimental Ball Weekend, Junior Weekend, Homecoming/Alumni Weekend. Student services: health clinic, personal-psychological counseling. Campus security: 24-hour emergency response devices and patrols, late night transport-escort service. 1,598 college housing spaces available; all were occupied in 2012-13. Freshmen guaranteed college housing. On-campus residence required through senior year. Option: coed housing available. Kreitzberg Library with

280,000 books, 99,100 microform titles, 904 serials, 1,501 audiovisual materials, an OPAC, and a Web page. Operations spending for the previous fiscal year: $1.6 million. 200 computers available on campus for general student use. A campuswide network can be accessed from student residence rooms and from off campus. Staffed computer lab on campus (open 24 hours a day) provides training in use of computers, software, and the Internet.

Community Environment: A rural community in the central section of Vermont, Northfield is 11 miles south of Montpelier, the state capital. Rail, bus and air transportation is available. Recreational activities include skiing, hiking, bicycling, fishing, and hunting.

■ **SAINT MICHAEL'S COLLEGE**
One Winooski Park
Colchester, VT 05439
Tel: (802)654-2000; Free: 800-762-8000
Fax: (802)654-2242
E-mail: admission@smcvt.edu
Web Site: www.smcvt.edu/

Description: Independent Roman Catholic, comprehensive, coed. Awards bachelor's and master's degrees and post-master's certificates. Founded 1904. Setting: 440-acre suburban campus with easy access to Montreal. Endowment: $69.7 million. Research spending for the previous fiscal year: $621,928. Educational spending for the previous fiscal year: $11,607 per student. Total enrollment: 2,410. Faculty: 217 (155 full-time, 62 part-time). Student-undergrad faculty ratio is 12:1. 4,578 applied, 78% were admitted. 27% from top 10% of their high school class, 59% from top quarter, 83% from top half. 20 class presidents, 11 valedictorians, 85 student government officers. Full-time: 1,948 students, 54% women, 46% men. Part-time: 23 students, 48% women, 52% men. Students come from 35 states and territories, 16 other countries, 79% from out-of-state. 0.2% American Indian or Alaska Native, non-Hispanic/Latino; 4% Hispanic/Latino; 2% African American, non-Hispanic/Latino; 2% Asian, non-Hispanic/Latino; 0% Native Hawaiian or other Pacific Islander, non-Hispanic/Latino; 2% international. 1% 25 or older, 96% live on campus, 2% transferred in. Retention: 90% of full-time freshmen returned the following year. Academic areas with the most degrees conferred: business/marketing; social sciences; psychology. Core. Calendar: semesters. ESL program, services for LD students, advanced placement, self-designed majors, honors program, independent study, distance learning, double major, summer session for credit, part-time degree program, internships, graduate courses open to undergrads. Off campus study at American University, Georgetown University, Boston University (journalism), Boston University, the International Partnership for Service Learning and Leadership (Lakota Nation: American Indian Studies Program), Semester exchange program with Vermont Private Colleges. Study abroad program. ROTC: Army (c), Air Force (c).

Entrance Requirements: Options: electronic application, early action, deferred admission, international baccalaureate accepted. Required: essay, high school transcript. Recommended: minimum 3 high school GPA, 3 recommendations, interview, SAT or ACT, Saint Michael's is a test-optional institution. Therefore, you do not have to submit standardized test scores (SAT Reasoning Test or ACT with Writing) to be considered for admission. Entrance: moderately difficult. Application deadlines: 2/1, 11/1 for early action. Notification: 4/1, 1/1 for early action. SAT Reasoning Test deadline: 2/1. Transfer credits accepted: Yes. Applicants placed on waiting list: 280. Wait-listed applicants offered admission: 21. Early action applicants: 2,863. Early action applicants admitted: 2,179.

Costs Per Year: Application fee: $50. Comprehensive fee: $48,740 includes full-time tuition ($38,690), mandatory fees ($325), and college room and board ($9725). Full-time tuition and fees vary according to course load. Room and board charges vary according to board plan and housing facility. Part-time tuition: $1290 per credit hour. Part-time tuition varies according to course load.

Collegiate Environment: Orientation program. Drama-theater group, choral group, student-run newspaper, radio station. Social organizations: 50 open to all. Most popular organizations: Student Association (governing board), Mobilization of Volunteer Efforts (MOVE), WWPV-FM (student run radio station), Wilderness Program, student newspaper/online publication (The Defender). Major annual events: Homecoming (Fall), Martin Luther King, Jr. Convocation (Winter), Family Weekend (spring). Student services: health clinic, personal-psychological counseling, women's center. Campus security: 24-hour emergency response devices and patrols, student patrols, late night transport-escort service, controlled dormitory access, bicycle patrols; Fire and Rescue Squad serving the surrounding community with professionally

trained student volunteers. 1,900 college housing spaces available; 1,855 were occupied in 2012-13. Freshmen guaranteed college housing. On-campus residence required through senior year. Options: coed, men-only, women-only housing available. Durick Library with 417,800 books, 137,000 microform titles, 82,500 serials, 13,100 audiovisual materials, an OPAC, and a Web page. Operations spending for the previous fiscal year: $2.1 million. 490 computers available on campus for general student use. Computer purchase/lease plans available. A campuswide network can be accessed from student residence rooms and from off campus. Students can access the following: online class registration. Staffed computer lab on campus provides training in use of computers, software, and the Internet.

■ **SOUTHERN VERMONT COLLEGE**
982 Mansion Dr.
Bennington, VT 05201
Tel: (802)442-5427
Fax: (802)447-4695
E-mail: admissions@svc.edu
Web Site: www.svc.edu/

Description: Independent, 4-year, coed. Awards associate and bachelor's degrees. Founded 1926. Setting: 371-acre small town campus with easy access to Albany, NY. Endowment: $1.2 million. Educational spending for the previous fiscal year: $4680 per student. Total enrollment: 530. Faculty: 54 (26 full-time, 28 part-time). Student-undergrad faculty ratio is 14:1. 463 applied, 75% were admitted. Full-time: 470 students, 64% women, 36% men. Part-time: 60 students, 73% women, 27% men. Students come from 13 states and territories, 4 other countries, 66% from out-of-state. 0.4% American Indian or Alaska Native, non-Hispanic/Latino; 5% Hispanic/Latino; 8% African American, non-Hispanic/Latino; 2% Asian, non-Hispanic/Latino; 0% Native Hawaiian or other Pacific Islander, non-Hispanic/Latino; 3% international. 16% 25 or older, 55% live on campus, 12% transferred in. Retention: 53% of full-time freshmen returned the following year. Academic areas with the most degrees conferred: health professions and related sciences; psychology; homeland security, law enforcement, firefighting, and protective services. Core. Calendar: semesters. Academic remediation for entering students, services for LD students, advanced placement, accelerated degree program, self-designed majors, independent study, distance learning, double major, summer session for credit, part-time degree program, external degree program, adult/continuing education programs, co-op programs and internships. Off campus study at Consortium of Vermont Colleges, Hudson Mohawk Association of Colleges and Universities. Study abroad program.

Entrance Requirements: Options: electronic application, early admission, deferred admission, international baccalaureate accepted. Required: essay, high school transcript, 2 recommendations, SAT or ACT. Recommended: minimum 2 high school GPA, interview. Required for some: interview, Deans report and college transcripts for transfer students. Entrance: minimally difficult. Application deadlines: Rolling, Rolling for nonresidents. Notification: continuous, continuous for nonresidents. Transfer credits accepted: Yes.

Costs Per Year: Application fee: $30. Comprehensive fee: $31,218 includes full-time tuition ($21,000), mandatory fees ($275), and college room and board ($9943). College room only: $4924. Full-time tuition and fees vary according to program. Room and board charges vary according to board plan and housing facility. Part-time tuition: $800 per credit. Part-time tuition varies according to course load and program.

Collegiate Environment: Orientation program. Drama-theater group. Social organizations: 15 open to all. Most popular organizations: Student Government Association, Mountaineer Event Board, Japanese Culture and Anime Club, Big Brothers Big Sisters, Moosecorps. Major annual events: Homecoming Weekend, Moosapalooza, Fall Fest. Student services: health clinic, personal-psychological counseling. Campus security: 24-hour patrols, late night transport-escort service, controlled dormitory access. Southern Vermont College Library with 20,270 books, 33,000 serials, 774 audiovisual materials, an OPAC, and a Web page. Operations spending for the previous fiscal year: $170,782. 50 computers available on campus for general student use. A campuswide network can be accessed from student residence rooms and from off campus. Students can access the following: online class registration. Staffed computer lab on campus provides training in use of computers, software, and the Internet.

Community Environment: See Bennington College.

■ **STERLING COLLEGE**
PO Box 72
Craftsbury Common, VT 05827-0072

Tel: (802)586-7711; Free: 800-648-3591
E-mail: lbirdsall@sterlingcollege.edu
Web Site: www.sterlingcollege.edu/
Description: Independent, 4-year, coed. Awards bachelor's degrees. Founded 1958. Setting: 430-acre rural campus. Endowment: $876,051. Educational spending for the previous fiscal year: $14,884 per student. Total enrollment: 95. Faculty: 17 (10 full-time, 7 part-time). Student-undergrad faculty ratio is 6:1. 53 applied, 91% were admitted. Full-time: 82 students, 52% women, 48% men. Part-time: 13 students, 46% women, 54% men. 79% from out-of-state. 2% Hispanic/Latino; 1% African American, non-Hispanic/Latino; 1% Asian, non-Hispanic/Latino. 16% 25 or older, 72% live on campus, 17% transferred in. Retention: 55% of full-time freshmen returned the following year. Academic areas with the most degrees conferred: liberal arts/general studies; biological/life sciences; agriculture. Core. Calendar: semesters. Services for LD students, advanced placement, self-designed majors, independent study, double major, summer session for credit, internships. Off campus study at Association of Vermont Independent Colleges (AVIC) Semester Exchange Program. Study abroad program.
Entrance Requirements: Options: electronic application, early admission, early action, deferred admission, international baccalaureate accepted. Required: essay, high school transcript, 2 recommendations. Recommended: minimum 2 high school GPA, interview. Entrance: moderately difficult. Application deadlines: Rolling, 12/15 for early action. Notification: continuous, 1/15 for early action. Transfer credits accepted: Yes. Applicants placed on waiting list: 0. Wait-listed applicants offered admission: 0.
Costs Per Year: Application fee: $35. Comprehensive fee: $37,092 includes full-time tuition ($28,410), mandatory fees ($350), and college room and board ($8332). Full-time tuition and fees vary according to course load. Room and board charges vary according to board plan. Part-time tuition: $900 per credit. Part-time tuition varies according to course load.
Collegiate Environment: Orientation program. Drama-theater group, choral group. Most popular organizations: Outing Club, Timbersports Team, Student Union, Art Club, Musical Groups. Major annual events: Contra Dances, Harvest Barbeque, Open Mic nights. Student services: health clinic, personal-psychological counseling. Campus security: 24-hour pager. 95 college housing spaces available; 79 were occupied in 2012-13. Freshmen guaranteed college housing. Option: coed housing available. Brown Library plus 1 other with 14,888 books, 42,476 serials, 778 audiovisual materials, an OPAC, and a Web page. Operations spending for the previous fiscal year: $107,893. 18 computers available on campus for general student use. A campuswide network can be accessed from student residence rooms. Staffed computer lab on campus (open 24 hours a day) provides training in use of computers, software, and the Internet.

■ UNIVERSITY OF VERMONT

Burlington, VT 05405
Tel: (802)656-3131
E-mail: admissions@uvm.edu
Web Site: www.uvm.edu/
Description: State-supported, university, coed. Awards bachelor's, master's, and doctoral degrees and post-master's certificates. Founded 1791. Setting: 459-acre suburban campus. Endowment: $299 million. Total enrollment: 13,097. Faculty: 755 (606 full-time, 149 part-time). Student-undergrad faculty ratio is 17:1. 21,808 applied, 77% were admitted. 34% from top 10% of their high school class, 71% from top quarter, 96% from top half. 5 National Merit Scholars, 35 valedictorians. Full-time: 9,956 students, 56% women, 44% men. Part-time: 1,255 students, 61% women, 39% men. Students come from 49 states and territories, 30 other countries, 67% from out-of-state. 0.3% American Indian or Alaska Native, non-Hispanic/Latino; 4% Hispanic/Latino; 1% African American, non-Hispanic/Latino; 2% Asian, non-Hispanic/Latino; 0.1% Native Hawaiian or other Pacific Islander, non-Hispanic/Latino; 2% international. 3% 25 or older, 51% live on campus, 4% transferred in. Retention: 85% of full-time freshmen returned the following year. Academic areas with the most degrees conferred: social sciences; natural resources/environmental science; business/marketing. Calendar: semesters. Services for LD students, advanced placement, self-designed majors, freshman honors college, honors program, independent study, distance learning, double major, summer session for credit, part-time degree program, adult/continuing education programs, co-op programs and internships, graduate courses open to undergrads. Off campus study. Study abroad program. ROTC: Army.
Entrance Requirements: Options: electronic application, early action, deferred admission, international baccalaureate accepted. Required: essay, high school transcript, 1 recommendation, SAT or ACT. Entrance:

moderately difficult. Application deadlines: 1/15, 11/1 for early action. Notification: 3/31, 12/15 for early action. Preference given to Vermont residents. Transfer credits accepted: Yes. Applicants placed on waiting list: 2,471. Wait-listed applicants offered admission: 92.
Costs Per Year: Application fee: $55. State resident tuition: $13,344 full-time. Nonresident tuition: $33,672 full-time. Mandatory fees: $1910 full-time. College room and board: $10,094. Room and board charges vary according to board plan and housing facility.
Collegiate Environment: Orientation program. Drama-theater group, choral group, student-run newspaper, radio station. Social organizations: 150 open to all; national fraternities, national sororities, local fraternities; 6% of eligible men and 5% of eligible women are members. Most popular organizations: Volunteers in Action, Outing Club, Ski and Snowboard Club. Major annual events: Springfest, Homecoming. Student services: legal services, health clinic, personal-psychological counseling, women's center. Campus security: 24-hour emergency response devices and patrols, late night transport-escort service, controlled dormitory access. 5,508 college housing spaces available; 5,304 were occupied in 2012-13. Freshmen guaranteed college housing. On-campus residence required through sophomore year. Option: coed housing available. Bailey-Howe Library plus 2 others with 2.6 million books, 2 million microform titles, 30,000 serials, 55,310 audiovisual materials, an OPAC, and a Web page. 850 computers available on campus for general student use. Computer purchase/lease plans available. A campuswide network can be accessed from student residence rooms and from off campus. Students can access the following: online class registration, Web pages, online course support.
Community Environment: Burlington is Vermont's largest city and, while the University is a significant resource, the city has many cultural, recreational, and social offerings. Burlington is a tourist and business center with a rich history and significant business development.

■ VERMONT TECHNICAL COLLEGE

PO Box 500
Randolph Center, VT 05061-0500
Tel: (802)728-1000; Free: 800-442-VTC1
Fax: (802)728-1390
E-mail: admissions@vtc.edu
Web Site: www.vtc.edu/
Description: State-supported, 4-year, coed. Part of Vermont State Colleges System. Awards associate and bachelor's degrees. Founded 1866. Setting: 544-acre rural campus. Total enrollment: 1,645. Faculty: 194 (76 full-time, 118 part-time). Student-undergrad faculty ratio is 11:1. 825 applied, 63% were admitted. 4% from top 10% of their high school class, 25% from top quarter, 61% from top half. Full-time: 1,141 students, 37% women, 63% men. Part-time: 504 students, 59% women, 41% men. 12% from out-of-state. 2% American Indian or Alaska Native, non-Hispanic/Latino; 2% Hispanic/Latino; 2% African American, non-Hispanic/Latino; 2% Asian, non-Hispanic/Latino; 0.1% Native Hawaiian or other Pacific Islander, non-Hispanic/Latino; 0% international. 32% 25 or older, 12% transferred in. Retention: 69% of full-time freshmen returned the following year. Academic areas with the most degrees conferred: engineering technologies; business/marketing; computer and information sciences. Core. Calendar: semesters. Academic remediation for entering students, ESL program, services for LD students, advanced placement, accelerated degree program, honors program, independent study, distance learning, double major, summer session for credit, part-time degree program, co-op programs and internships. ROTC: Army (c).
Entrance Requirements: Option: electronic application. Required: high school transcript. Recommended: minimum 3 high school GPA, 2 recommendations, interview. Required for some: essay, 2 recommendations, interview, SAT or ACT. Entrance: moderately difficult. Application deadline: Rolling. Notification: continuous.
Costs Per Year: Application fee: $40. State resident tuition: $11,088 full-time, $480 per credit hour part-time. Nonresident tuition: $21,192 full-time, $918 per credit hour part-time. Mandatory fees: $1456 full-time. Full-time tuition and fees vary according to course load and program. Part-time tuition varies according to program. College room and board: $8786. College room only: $5232. Room and board charges vary according to board plan.
Collegiate Environment: Orientation program. Choral group, student-run radio station. Social organizations: 25 open to all. Most popular organizations: Student Council (student government), Adventurer's Guild (board and video gaming), WVTC (student radio station), Outing Club, Veterinary Technology Club. Major annual events: October Fiesta, Late-Night Breakfast (spring and fall). Student services: health clinic. Campus security: 24-hour emergency response devices and patrols, late night transport-escort service,

controlled dormitory access: 600 college housing spaces available. On-campus residence required through sophomore year. Option: coed housing available. Hartness Library with 59,000 books, 856 microform titles, 36,500 serials, 6,200 audiovisual materials, an OPAC, and a Web page. 480 computers available on campus for general student use. A campuswide network can be accessed from student residence rooms and from off campus. Students can access the following: online class registration, online

(network) file storage, wireless network. Staffed computer lab on campus (open 24 hours a day) provides training in use of computers, software, and the Internet.

Community Environment: Randolph Center is a rural area, four miles from Randolph. A library, hospital, churches, shopping facilities, and several civic and service organizations serve the town. Outdoor sports include golf, fishing, hunting, skiing, ice skating, and tennis.

■ **ADVANCED TECHNOLOGY INSTITUTE**
5700 Southern Blvd.
Virginia Beach, VA 23462
Tel: (757)490-1241; Free: 888-468-1093
Web Site: www.auto.edu/
Description: Proprietary, 2-year, coed. Awards certificates and terminal associate degrees. Total enrollment: 827. Student-undergrad faculty ratio is 24:1. 431 applied, 75% were admitted. 26% from out-of-state. 45% 25 or older.

■ **ARGOSY UNIVERSITY, WASHINGTON DC**
1550 Wilson Blvd., Ste. 600
Arlington, VA 22209
Tel: (703)526-5800; Free: 866-703-2777
Fax: (703)526-5850
Web Site: www.argosy.edu/washingtondc/
Description: Proprietary, university, coed. Part of Argosy Education Group. Awards bachelor's, master's, and doctoral degrees. Founded 1994. Setting: urban campus. Calendar: semesters.

■ **THE ART INSTITUTE OF VIRGINIA BEACH**
Two Columbus Ctr.
4500 Main St., Ste. 100
Virginia Beach, VA 23462
Tel: (757)493-6700; Free: 877-437-4428
Fax: (757)493-6800
Web Site: www.artinstitutes.edu/virginia-beach/
Description: Proprietary, 4-year, coed. Awards associate and bachelor's degrees.

■ **THE ART INSTITUTE OF WASHINGTON**
1820 N Fort Meyer Dr.
Arlington, VA 22209
Tel: (703)358-9550; Free: 877-303-3771
Fax: (703)358-9759
Web Site: www.artinstitutes.edu/arlington/
Description: Proprietary, 4-year, coed. Part of Education Management Corporation. Awards associate and bachelor's degrees. Founded 2000. Setting: urban campus.

■ **THE ART INSTITUTE OF WASHINGTON–DULLES**
The Corporate Office Park at Dulles Town Ctr.
21000 Atlantic Blvd., Ste. 100
Sterling, VA 20166
Tel: (571)449-4400; Free: 888-627-5008
Fax: (571)449-4500
Web Site: www.artinstitutes.edu/washington-dulles/
Description: Proprietary, 4-year, coed. Awards associate and bachelor's degrees.

■ **AVERETT UNIVERSITY**
420 W Main St.
Danville, VA 24541-3692
Tel: (434)791-5600; Free: 800-AVERETT
Fax: (434)791-5637

E-mail: joel.nester@averett.edu
Web Site: www.averett.edu/
Description: Independent, comprehensive, coed, affiliated with Baptist General Association of Virginia. Awards associate, bachelor's, and master's degrees. Founded 1859. Setting: 252-acre small town campus with easy access to Greensboro, Raleigh, Durham, and Cary. Endowment: $24.7 million. Total enrollment: 914. Faculty: 118 (61 full-time, 57 part-time). Student-undergrad faculty ratio is 10:1. 2,477 applied, 58% were admitted. 8% from top 10% of their high school class, 39% from top quarter, 73% from top half. Full-time: 870 students, 47% women, 53% men. Part-time: 22 students, 64% women, 36% men. Students come from 23 states and territories, 15 other countries, 30% from out-of-state. 1% American Indian or Alaska Native, non-Hispanic/Latino; 3% Hispanic/Latino; 27% African American, non-Hispanic/Latino; 1% Asian, non-Hispanic/Latino; 0% Native Hawaiian or other Pacific Islander, non-Hispanic/Latino; 9% international. 9% 25 or older, 57% live on campus, 9% transferred in. Retention: 62% of full-time freshmen returned the following year. Academic areas with the most degrees conferred: business/marketing; homeland security, law enforcement, firefighting, and protective services; health professions and related sciences. Core. Calendar: semesters. Academic remediation for entering students, services for LD students, advanced placement, accelerated degree program, self-designed majors, honors program, independent study, distance learning, double major, summer session for credit, part-time degree program, external degree program, adult/continuing education programs, co-op programs and internships, graduate courses open to undergrads. Off campus study. Study abroad program.
Entrance Requirements: Options: electronic application, international baccalaureate accepted. Required: high school transcript, minimum 2.5 high school GPA, High school diploma, SAT or ACT, TOEFL for International students. Recommended: essay, 1 recommendation. Entrance: moderately difficult. Application deadlines: 8/1, 8/1 for nonresidents. Notification: continuous, continuous for nonresidents. SAT Reasoning Test deadline: 8/15. Transfer credits accepted: Yes.
Costs Per Year: Application fee: $0. Comprehensive fee: $34,320 includes full-time tuition ($25,950) and college room and board ($8370). College room only: $5650. Full-time tuition varies according to course load, degree level, location, and program. Room and board charges vary according to board plan and housing facility. Part-time tuition: $1080 per credit hour. Part-time tuition varies according to course load, degree level, location, and program.
Collegiate Environment: Orientation program. Drama-theater group, choral group, student-run newspaper. Social organizations: 30 open to all; national fraternities; 2% of men are members. Most popular organizations: Student Government Association, Campus Activities Board, Christian Student Union, Averett Gospel Choir, Pi Kappa Phi. Major annual events: Homecoming, Spring Formal, Late Night Breakfast. Student services: personal-psychological counseling. Campus security: 24-hour emergency response devices and patrols, late night transport-escort service, controlled dormitory access. 537 college housing spaces available; 503 were occupied in 2012-13. Freshmen given priority for college housing. On-campus residence required through junior year. Options: coed, men-only, women-only housing available. Blount Library with 117,920 books, 101,773 microform titles, 39,575 serials, 905 audiovisual materials, an OPAC, and a Web page. Operations spending for the previous fiscal year: $250,986. 150 computers available on campus for general student use. A campuswide network can be accessed from student residence rooms. Students can access the following: online class registration.

■ AVIATION INSTITUTE OF MAINTENANCE–CHESAPEAKE

2211 S Military Hwy.
Chesapeake, VA 23320
Tel: (757)363-2121; Free: 888-349-5387
Web Site: www.aviationmaintenance.edu/
Description: Proprietary, 2-year, coed. Awards certificates and terminal associate degrees. Total enrollment: 201. Student-undergrad faculty ratio is 11:1. 14% from out-of-state. 70% 25 or older. Retention: 54% of full-time freshmen returned the following year.
Entrance Requirements: Required: high school diploma or GED.

■ AVIATION INSTITUTE OF MAINTENANCE–MANASSAS

9821 Godwin Dr.
Manassas, VA 20110
Tel: (703)257-5515; Free: 888-349-5387
Fax: (703)257-5523
Web Site: www.aviationmaintenance.edu/
Description: Proprietary, 2-year, coed. Awards certificates and terminal associate degrees. Total enrollment: 140. Student-undergrad faculty ratio is 12:1. 24% from out-of-state. 60% 25 or older. Retention: 38% of full-time freshmen returned the following year.
Entrance Requirements: Required: high school diploma or GED.

■ BETHEL COLLEGE

1705 Todds Ln.
Hampton, VA 23666
Tel: (757)826-1426
Web Site: bethel-college.com/
Description: Independent religious, 4-year, coed. Founded 1996. Calendar: semesters.

■ BLUE RIDGE COMMUNITY COLLEGE

PO Box 80
Weyers Cave, VA 24486-0080
Tel: (540)234-9261; Free: 888-750-2722
E-mail: bakerb@brcc.edu
Web Site: www.brcc.edu/
Description: State-supported, 2-year, coed. Part of Virginia Community College System. Awards certificates, diplomas, transfer associate, and terminal associate degrees. Founded 1967. Setting: 65-acre rural campus. Total enrollment: 4,466. Student-undergrad faculty ratio is 22:1. 1% from out-of-state. 32% 25 or older. Retention: 57% of full-time freshmen returned the following year. Calendar: semesters. Academic remediation for entering students, ESL program, services for LD students, advanced placement, honors program, distance learning, double major, summer session for credit, part-time degree program, adult/continuing education programs, co-op programs and internships. Off campus study. Study abroad program.
Entrance Requirements: Open admission except for veterinary technology, nursing programs. Options: electronic application, early admission. Required: College Preparedness Test. Required for some: high school transcript, interview. Entrance: noncompetitive. Application deadline: Rolling. Notification: continuous.
Collegiate Environment: Orientation program. Student services: personal-psychological counseling, women's center. Campus security: 24-hour emergency response devices and patrols, late night transport-escort service. Houff Library with an OPAC and a Web page.
Community Environment: Weyers Cave is a rural community located near Staunton and Harrisonburg.

■ BLUEFIELD COLLEGE

3000 College Dr.
Bluefield, VA 24605-1799
Tel: (276)326-3682; Free: 800-872-0175
Fax: (276)326-4288
E-mail: mhipes@bluefield.edu
Web Site: www.bluefield.edu/
Description: Independent Southern Baptist, 4-year, coed. Awards bachelor's degrees. Founded 1922. Setting: 82-acre small town campus. Endowment: $5.4 million. Total enrollment: 828. Faculty: 107 (37 full-time, 70 part-time). Student-undergrad faculty ratio is 13:1. 6% from top 10% of their high school class, 27% from top quarter, 65% from top half. Full-time: 766 students, 52% women, 48% men. Part-time: 62 students, 60% women, 40% men. Students come from 26 states and territories, 4 other countries, 23% from out-of-state. 0.5% American Indian or Alaska Native, non-Hispanic/

Latino; 2% Hispanic/Latino; 24% African American, non-Hispanic/Latino; 2% Asian, non-Hispanic/Latino; 0% Native Hawaiian or other Pacific Islander, non-Hispanic/Latino; 0.5% international. 44% 25 or older, 65% live on campus, 7% transferred in. Retention: 61% of full-time freshmen returned the following year. Academic areas with the most degrees conferred: business/marketing; psychology; homeland security, law enforcement, firefighting, and protective services. Core. Calendar: semesters. Academic remediation for entering students, services for LD students, advanced placement, accelerated degree program, honors program, distance learning, double major, summer session for credit, adult/continuing education programs, co-op programs and internships. Study abroad program.
Entrance Requirements: Required: high school transcript, minimum 2 high school GPA, SAT/ACT scores, SAT or ACT. Required for some: essay.
Costs Per Year: Comprehensive fee: $28,700 includes full-time tuition ($21,060) and college room and board ($7640). College room only: $2990. Full-time tuition varies according to course load and program. Room and board charges vary according to housing facility. Part-time tuition: $880 per credit. Part-time tuition varies according to course load and program.
Collegiate Environment: Orientation program. Drama-theater group, choral group, student-run newspaper. Social organizations: 13 open to all; local fraternities, local sororities; 15% of eligible men and 20% of eligible women are members. Most popular organizations: Baptist Collegiate Ministries, Fellowship of Christian Athletes, Student Union Board, Student Government Association, Arts Club. Major annual events: Homecoming Dance, Spring Formal, Mud Pig Day. Student services: personal-psychological counseling. Campus security: controlled dormitory access, night security patrols. 329 college housing spaces available; 317 were occupied in 2012-13. Freshmen given priority for college housing. On-campus residence required through junior year. Options: men-only, women-only housing available. Easley Library with 47,000 books, 16,310 serials, 3,477 audiovisual materials, an OPAC, and a Web page. Operations spending for the previous fiscal year: $61,345. 110 computers available on campus for general student use. A campuswide network can be accessed from student residence rooms. Students can access the following: online class registration, career assessment tests, library database.
Community Environment: A suburban area in the Virginia Highlands, Bluefield is a center of diversified industry. Products of its industries are fabric dyes, mattresses, hardwood flooring, textiles, and mining equipment. All commercial transportation is available. Public libraries, churches, hospitals, and a number of civic and service organizations are a part of the community. Nearby mountains provide opportunities for numerous recreational activities. Some part-time employment is available.

■ BON SECOURS MEMORIAL COLLEGE OF NURSING

8550 Magellan Pky.
Ste. 1100
Richmond, VA 23227-1149
Tel: (804)627-5300; Free: 866-238-7414
Web Site: www.bsmcon.edu/
Description: Independent, 4-year, coed.

■ BRIDGEWATER COLLEGE

402 E College St.
Bridgewater, VA 22812-1599
Tel: (540)828-8000; Free: 800-759-8328
Fax: (540)828-5481
E-mail: admissions@bridgewater.edu
Web Site: www.bridgewater.edu/
Description: Independent, 4-year, coed, affiliated with Church of the Brethren. Awards bachelor's degrees. Founded 1880. Setting: 300-acre small town campus. Endowment: $65.4 million. Educational spending for the previous fiscal year: $6070 per student. Total enrollment: 1,760. Faculty: 138 (106 full-time, 32 part-time). Student-undergrad faculty ratio is 15:1. 6,079 applied, 54% were admitted. 17% from top 10% of their high school class, 49% from top quarter, 82% from top half. 4 National Merit Scholars, 4 valedictorians, 23 student government officers. Full-time: 1,748 students, 56% women, 44% men. Part-time: 12 students, 42% women, 58% men. Students come from 28 states and territories, 10 other countries, 22% from out-of-state. 0.3% American Indian or Alaska Native, non-Hispanic/Latino; 3% Hispanic/Latino; 8% African American, non-Hispanic/Latino; 1% Asian, non-Hispanic/Latino; 0.1% Native Hawaiian or other Pacific Islander, non-Hispanic/Latino; 1% international. 1% 25 or older, 84% live on campus, 4% transferred in. Retention: 77% of full-time freshmen returned the following year. Academic areas with the most degrees conferred: parks and

recreation; business/marketing; biological/life sciences. Core. Calendar: 4-1-4. Services for LD students, advanced placement, honors program, independent study, double major, summer session for credit, part-time degree program, adult/continuing education programs, internships. Off campus study. Study abroad program.

Entrance Requirements: Options: electronic application, deferred admission, international baccalaureate accepted. Required: high school transcript, minimum 2.5 high school GPA, 1 recommendation, SAT or ACT. Recommended: minimum 2.8 high school GPA, interview. Required for some: interview. Entrance: moderately difficult. Application deadlines: Rolling, Rolling for nonresidents. Notification: continuous, continuous for nonresidents. SAT Reasoning Test deadline: 4/15. Transfer credits accepted: Yes. Applicants placed on waiting list: 54. Wait-listed applicants offered admission: 3.

Costs Per Year: Application fee: $30. Comprehensive fee: $39,880 includes full-time tuition ($28,500), mandatory fees ($590), and college room and board ($10,790). College room only: $5490. Room and board charges vary according to housing facility. Part-time tuition: $980 per credit hour. Part-time mandatory fees: $40 per term.

Collegiate Environment: Orientation program. Drama-theater group, choral group, student-run newspaper, radio station. Social organizations: 42 open to all. Most popular organizations: Equestrian Club, Student Ambassadors, Campus Crusade for Christ (CRU), Eagle Productions (program board), Habitat for Humanity. Major annual events: Homecoming, Welcome Week, SpringFest Concert. Student services: health clinic, personal-psychological counseling. Campus security: 24-hour emergency response devices and patrols, controlled dormitory access, emergency alert system. 1,485 college housing spaces available; 1,471 were occupied in 2012-13. Freshmen guaranteed college housing. On-campus residence required through senior year. Options: coed, men-only, women-only housing available. Alexander Mack Memorial Library with 139,194 books, 2,152 microform titles, 42,475 serials, 5,609 audiovisual materials, an OPAC, and a Web page. Operations spending for the previous fiscal year: $893,128. 203 computers available on campus for general student use. Computer purchase/lease plans available. A campuswide network can be accessed from student residence rooms and from off campus. Students can access the following: online class registration, Moodle (course management system), campus bulletin board system.

Community Environment: Bridgewater is located in the Shenandoah Valley, seven miles south of Harrisonburg. The community facilities include churches, banks, restaurants, parks, museums, and shops. The city, its suburbs and the surrounding area offer entertainment, fine dining experiences, a shopping mall, libraries, a hospital, historic towns, civil war battlefields, the George Washington National Forest, the Massanutten Four Seasons Resort, the Shenandoah Regional Airport, various civic organizations, and events at James Madison University Convocation Center. The College is conveniently located 10 minutes from Harrisonburg, 50 minutes from Charlottesville, an hour and 40 minutes from Roanoke and approximately 2 hours from Richmond or Washington, D.C.

■ **BRYANT & STRATTON COLLEGE - RICHMOND CAMPUS**
8141 Hull St. Rd.
Richmond, VA 23235-6411
Tel: (804)745-2444
Fax: (804)499-7799
E-mail: tlawson@bryanstratton.edu
Web Site: www.bryantstratton.edu/
Description: Proprietary, primarily 2-year, coed. Part of Bryant and Stratton Business Institute, Inc. Awards terminal associate and bachelor's degrees. Founded 1952. Setting: suburban campus. Total enrollment: 572. Faculty: 49 (14 full-time, 35 part-time). Student-undergrad faculty ratio is 10:1. Full-time: 280 students, 80% women, 20% men. Part-time: 292 students, 85% women, 15% men. 0% from out-of-state. 84% 25 or older, 7% transferred in. Academic area with the most degrees conferred: business/marketing. Core. Calendar: semesters. Academic remediation for entering students, advanced placement, independent study, distance learning, double major, summer session for credit, part-time degree program, adult/continuing education programs, internships.
Entrance Requirements: Option: deferred admission. Required: high school transcript, interview, entrance evaluation and placement evaluation, TABE, CPAt. Recommended: SAT or ACT. Entrance: minimally difficult. Application deadline: Rolling.
Collegiate Environment: Orientation program. Social organizations: 7 open to all. Most popular organizations: Phi Beta Lambda, Alpha Beta Gamma, Student Council, Medical Assisting Club, Paralegal Club. Major annual

events: Portfolio Development Day, Meet and Greet the Faculty and Staff, Spring Fling. Campus security: late night transport-escort service. Bryant and Stratton Library with 3,176 books and 84 serials. 50 computers available on campus for general student use. A campuswide network can be accessed. Staffed computer lab on campus.

■ **BRYANT & STRATTON COLLEGE - VIRGINIA BEACH**
301 Centre Pointe Dr.
Virginia Beach, VA 23462-4417
Tel: (757)499-7900
Fax: (757)499-7799
E-mail: dmsoutherland@bryantstratton.edu
Web Site: www.bryantstratton.edu/
Description: Proprietary, primarily 2-year, coed. Part of Bryant and Stratton Business Institute, Inc. Awards terminal associate and bachelor's degrees. Founded 1952. Setting: suburban campus. Total enrollment: 595. Faculty: 60 (20 full-time, 40 part-time). Student-undergrad faculty ratio is 12:1. 259 applied, 88% were admitted. Full-time: 267 students, 71% women, 29% men. Part-time: 328 students, 82% women, 18% men. Students come from 2 states and territories, 1% from out-of-state. 64% 25 or older, 10% transferred in. Academic area with the most degrees conferred: business/marketing. Core. Calendar: semesters. Academic remediation for entering students, services for LD students, advanced placement, independent study, double major, summer session for credit, part-time degree program, adult/continuing education programs, internships.
Entrance Requirements: Open admission. Option: electronic application. Required: essay, high school transcript, interview, CPAt. Entrance: minimally difficult. Application deadline: Rolling.
Collegiate Environment: Orientation program. Student-run newspaper. Campus security: 24-hour emergency response devices, late night transport-escort service. Campus Library with 8,700 books, 8,271 microform titles, 124 serials, 447 audiovisual materials, an OPAC, and a Web page. 100 computers available on campus for general student use. A campuswide network can be accessed. Staffed computer lab on campus provides training in use of computers, software, and the Internet.

■ **CENTRAL VIRGINIA COMMUNITY COLLEGE**
3506 Wards Rd.
Lynchburg, VA 24502-2498
Tel: (434)832-7600; Free: 800-562-3060
Fax: (434)832-7626
Web Site: www.cvcc.vccs.edu/
Description: State-supported, 2-year, coed. Part of Virginia Community College System. Awards certificates, diplomas, transfer associate, and terminal associate degrees. Founded 1966. Setting: 104-acre suburban campus. Total enrollment: 5,420. Student-undergrad faculty ratio is 19:1. 0% from out-of-state. 33% 25 or older. Core. Calendar: semesters. Academic remediation for entering students, services for LD students, advanced placement, independent study, distance learning, summer session for credit, part-time degree program, co-op programs and internships.
Entrance Requirements: Open admission. Options: early admission, deferred admission. Entrance: noncompetitive. Application deadline: Rolling. Notification: continuous.
Collegiate Environment: Orientation program. Drama-theater group, student-run newspaper. Student services: personal-psychological counseling. Campus security: 24-hour emergency response devices. Bedford Learning Resources Center with an OPAC and a Web page.
Community Environment: See Lynchburg College.

■ **CENTURA COLLEGE (CHESAPEAKE)**
932 Ventures Way
Chesapeake, VA 23320
Tel: (757)549-2121; Free: 877-575-5627
Fax: (757)548-1196
Web Site: www.centuracollege.edu/
Description: Proprietary, 2-year, coed. Awards terminal associate degrees. Founded 1982. Total enrollment: 212. Student-undergrad faculty ratio is 24:1. 2% from out-of-state. 60% 25 or older.

■ **CENTURA COLLEGE (NEWPORT NEWS)**
616 Denbigh Blvd.
Newport News, VA 23608
Tel: (757)874-2121; Free: 877-575-5627
Fax: (757)874-3857

E-mail: admdircpen@centura.edu
Web Site: www.centuracollege.edu/
Description: Proprietary, 2-year, coed. Awards diplomas and terminal associate degrees. Founded 1969. Total enrollment: 250. Student-undergrad faculty ratio is 8:1. 0% from out-of-state. 20% 25 or older.

■ **CENTURA COLLEGE (NORFOLK)**
7020 N Military Hwy.
Norfolk, VA 23518
Tel: (757)853-2121; Free: 877-575-5627
Fax: (757)852-9017
Web Site: www.centuracollege.edu/
Description: Proprietary, 2-year, coed. Awards diplomas and terminal associate degrees. Total enrollment: 380. Student-undergrad faculty ratio is 17:1. 0% from out-of-state. 53% 25 or older.

■ **CENTURA COLLEGE (NORTH CHESTERFIELD)**
7914 Midlothian Tpke.
North Chesterfield, VA 23235-5230
Tel: (804)330-0111; Free: 877-575-5627
Fax: (804)330-3809
Web Site: www.centuracollege.edu/
Description: Proprietary, 2-year, coed. Awards certificates and terminal associate degrees. Total enrollment: 290. Student-undergrad faculty ratio is 10:1. 0% from out-of-state. 58% 25 or older.
Entrance Requirements: Entrance: noncompetitive.

■ **CENTURA COLLEGE (RICHMOND)**
7001 W Broad St.
Richmond, VA 23294
Tel: (804)672-2300; Free: 877-575-5627
Fax: (804)672-3338
Web Site: www.centuracollege.edu/
Description: Proprietary, 2-year, coed. Awards diplomas and terminal associate degrees. Total enrollment: 200. Student-undergrad faculty ratio is 21:1. 0% from out-of-state. 49% 25 or older.

■ **CENTURA COLLEGE (VIRGINIA BEACH)**
2697 Dean Dr.
Ste. 100
Virginia Beach, VA 23452
Tel: (757)340-2121; Free: 877-575-5627
Fax: (757)340-9704
Web Site: www.centuracollege.edu/
Description: Proprietary, primarily 2-year, coed. Awards terminal associate and bachelor's degrees. Founded 1969. Total enrollment: 1,639. Student-undergrad faculty ratio is 35:1. 86% from out-of-state. 72% 25 or older.
Entrance Requirements: Entrance: noncompetitive.

■ **CHAMBERLAIN COLLEGE OF NURSING**
2450 Crystal Dr.
Arlington, VA 22202
Tel: (703)416-7300; Free: 888-556-8CCN
Web Site: www.chamberlain.edu/
Description: Proprietary, 4-year, coed. Awards bachelor's degrees. Total enrollment: 348. Faculty: 21 (10 full-time, 11 part-time). Student-undergrad faculty ratio is 19:1. Full-time: 221 students, 88% women, 12% men. Part-time: 127 students, 85% women, 15% men. 43% from out-of-state. 0.3% American Indian or Alaska Native, non-Hispanic/Latino; 14% Hispanic/Latino; 35% African American, non-Hispanic/Latino; 7% Asian, non-Hispanic/Latino; 1% Native Hawaiian or other Pacific Islander, non-Hispanic/Latino; 3% international. 72% 25 or older, 0% live on campus, 34% transferred in. Academic area with the most degrees conferred: health professions and related sciences. Calendar: semesters.
Entrance Requirements: Required: SAT or ACT.
Costs Per Year: Tuition: $16,360 full-time, $665 per credit hour part-time. Mandatory fees: $600 full-time. Full-time tuition and fees vary according to course load. Part-time tuition varies according to course load.

■ **CHRISTENDOM COLLEGE**
134 Christendom Dr.
Front Royal, VA 22630-5103
Tel: (540)636-2900; Free: 800-877-5456
Fax: (540)636-1655

E-mail: tmcfadden@christendom.edu
Web Site: www.christendom.edu/
Description: Independent Roman Catholic, comprehensive, coed. Awards associate, bachelor's, and master's degrees. Founded 1977. Setting: 100-acre rural campus with easy access to Washington, DC. Endowment: $3.1 million. Educational spending for the previous fiscal year: $5077 per student. Total enrollment: 453. Faculty: 44 (21 full-time, 23 part-time). Student-undergrad faculty ratio is 13:1. 254 applied, 83% were admitted. 50% from top 10% of their high school class, 75% from top quarter, 100% from top half. Full-time: 381 students, 58% women, 42% men. Part-time: 7 students, 57% women, 43% men. Students come from 45 states and territories, 5 other countries, 75% from out-of-state. 3% 25 or older, 95% live on campus, 2% transferred in. Retention: 83% of full-time freshmen returned the following year. Academic areas with the most degrees conferred: history; social sciences; theology and religious vocations. Core. Calendar: semesters. Academic remediation for entering students, services for LD students, advanced placement, accelerated degree program, independent study, double major, summer session for credit, co-op programs and internships, graduate courses open to undergrads. Study abroad program.
Entrance Requirements: Options: electronic application, early admission, early action. Required: essay, high school transcript, 2 recommendations, SAT or ACT. Recommended: minimum 3 high school GPA, interview. Entrance: moderately difficult. Application deadlines: 3/1, 12/1 for early action. Notification: 4/1, 12/15 for early action. SAT Reasoning Test deadline: 8/1. Transfer credits accepted: Yes. Applicants placed on waiting list: 0. Wait-listed applicants offered admission: 0. Early action applicants: 143. Early action applicants admitted: 130.
Costs Per Year: Application fee: $25. Comprehensive fee: $31,000 includes full-time tuition ($22,050), mandatory fees ($670), and college room and board ($8280).
Collegiate Environment: Orientation program. Drama-theater group, choral group, student-run newspaper. Social organizations: 15 open to all. Most popular organizations: drama, choir, Shield of Roses, Legion of Mary, debate team. Major annual events: Christmas Dinner Dance, St. Patrick's Day, Spring Formal. Student services: health clinic, personal-psychological counseling. Campus security: 24-hour emergency response devices, late night transport-escort service, night patrols by trained security personnel. 339 college housing spaces available; all were occupied in 2012-13. Freshmen guaranteed college housing. On-campus residence required through senior year. Options: men-only, women-only housing available. St. John the Evangelist Library with 90,000 books, 1,000 microform titles, 250 serials, an OPAC, and a Web page. Operations spending for the previous fiscal year: $271,069. 60 computers available on campus for general student use. Staffed computer lab on campus provides training in use of computers and the Internet.
Community Environment: Located in northwestern Virginia, the College community offers a wide variety of attractions. Visitors can choose from a wide variety of facilities and activities: fine restaurants, historic Bed & Breakfasts, Civil War battlefields, countless hiking trails, numerous golf courses, and tours of Skyline Drive and Skyline Caverns.

■ **CHRISTOPHER NEWPORT UNIVERSITY**
One Ave. of the Arts
Newport News, VA 23606-2998
Tel: (757)594-7000; Free: 800-333-4268
Fax: (757)594-7333
E-mail: admit@cnu.edu
Web Site: www.cnu.edu/
Description: State-supported, comprehensive, coed. Awards bachelor's and master's degrees. Founded 1960. Setting: 260-acre suburban campus with easy access to Virginia Beach. Endowment: $16.3 million. Research spending for the previous fiscal year: $1.4 million. Educational spending for the previous fiscal year: $5421 per student. Total enrollment: 5,186. Faculty: 392 (258 full-time, 134 part-time). Student-undergrad faculty ratio is 17:1. 6,831 applied, 65% were admitted. 18% from top 10% of their high school class, 51% from top quarter, 92% from top half. Full-time: 4,926 students, 57% women, 43% men. Part-time: 120 students, 48% women, 52% men. Students come from 28 states and territories, 35 other countries, 6% from out-of-state. 0.2% American Indian or Alaska Native, non-Hispanic/Latino; 5% Hispanic/Latino; 8% African American, non-Hispanic/Latino; 2% Asian, non-Hispanic/Latino; 0.2% Native Hawaiian or other Pacific Islander, non-Hispanic/Latino; 0.2% international. 2% 25 or older, 68% live on campus, 4% transferred in. Retention: 85% of full-time freshmen returned the following year. Academic areas with the most degrees conferred: social sciences;

communication/journalism; biological/life sciences. Core. Calendar: semesters. Services for LD students, advanced placement, self-designed majors, honors program, independent study, double major, summer session for credit, internships, graduate courses open to undergrads. Off campus study at Virginia Tidewater Consortium (VTC) arrangements, members include College of William and Mary, Eastern Shore Community College, Eastern Virginia Medical School, Hampton University, Joint Forces Staff College, Norfolk State University, Old Dominion University, Paul D. Camp Community College, Regent University, Thomas Nelson Community College, Tidewater Community College, and Virginia Wesleyan College. Study abroad program. ROTC: Army.

Entrance Requirements: Options: electronic application, early admission, early decision, early action, deferred admission, international baccalaureate accepted. Required: essay, high school transcript, minimum 3 high school GPA. Required for some: 2 recommendations, interview, SAT or ACT. Entrance: very difficult. Application deadlines: 2/1, 11/15 for early decision, 12/1 for early action. Notification: 3/15, 12/15 for early decision, 1/15 for early action. SAT Reasoning Test deadline: 5/1. SAT Subject Test deadline: 8/1. Transfer credits accepted: Yes. Applicants placed on waiting list: 813. Wait-listed applicants offered admission: 7. Early decision applicants: 430. Early decision applicants admitted: 338. Early action applicants: 2,843. Early action applicants admitted: 2,148.

Costs Per Year: Application fee: $50. State resident tuition: $6210 full-time, $258 per credit hour part-time. Nonresident tuition: $15,364 full-time, $641 per credit hour part-time. Mandatory fees: $4362 full-time, $181 per credit hour part-time. Full-time tuition and fees vary according to course load. Part-time tuition and fees vary according to course load. College room and board: $9728. College room only: $6358. Room and board charges vary according to board plan and housing facility.

Collegiate Environment: Orientation program. Drama-theater group, choral group, marching band, student-run newspaper, radio station. Social organizations: 225 open to all; national fraternities, national sororities; 6% of eligible men and 9% of eligible women are members. Most popular organizations: Intervarsity, Alpha Delta Pi, Alpha Sigma Alpha, Gamma Phi Beta, Phi Mu. Major annual events: Homecoming, Fall Fest, Day of Service. Student services: health clinic, personal-psychological counseling. Campus security: 24-hour emergency response devices and patrols, late night transport-escort service, controlled dormitory access, campus-based University Police; Emergency Notification System; Crime Prevention Programs. College housing designed to accommodate 3,259 students; 3,407 undergraduates lived in college housing during 2012-13. Freshmen guaranteed college housing. On-campus residence required through junior year. Option: coed housing available. Paul and Rosemary Trible Library with 241,050 books, 199,289 microform titles, 53,190 serials, 7,143 audiovisual materials, an OPAC, and a Web page. Operations spending for the previous fiscal year: $3.2 million. 450 computers available on campus for general student use. A campuswide network can be accessed from student residence rooms and from off campus. Students can access the following: online class registration, online degree audit. Staffed computer lab on campus (open 24 hours a day) provides training in use of computers, software, and the Internet.

Community Environment: The 125-acre campus located in Newport News, VA, is easily accessible to residents of that city. The campus is centrally located between recreational centers at Colonial Williamsburg and the Norfolk/Virginia Beach resorts.

■ THE COLLEGE OF WILLIAM AND MARY

PO Box 8795
Williamsburg, VA 23187-8795
Tel: (757)221-4000
Fax: (757)221-1242
E-mail: admission@wm.edu
Web Site: www.wm.edu/

Description: State-supported, university, coed. Awards bachelor's, master's, and doctoral degrees and post-master's certificates. Founded 1693. Setting: 1,200-acre small town campus with easy access to Richmond. Endowment: $644.2 million. Research spending for the previous fiscal year: $48.2 million. Educational spending for the previous fiscal year: $11,681 per student. Total enrollment: 8,258. Student-undergrad faculty ratio is 12:1. 13,660 applied, 32% were admitted. 79% from top 10% of their high school class, 97% from top quarter, 100% from top half. Full-time: 6,097 students, 55% women, 45% men. Part-time: 74 students, 57% women, 43% men. Students come from 55 states and territories, 54 other countries, 32% from out-of-state. 0.3% American Indian or Alaska Native, non-Hispanic/Latino; 9% Hispanic/Latino; 7% African American, non-Hispanic/Latino; 6% Asian, non-Hispanic/Latino;

0.1% Native Hawaiian or other Pacific Islander, non-Hispanic/Latino; 4% international. 2% 25 or older, 72% live on campus, 3% transferred in. Retention: 96% of full-time freshmen returned the following year. Academic areas with the most degrees conferred: social sciences; business/marketing; biological/life sciences. Core. Calendar: semesters. Services for LD students, advanced placement, accelerated degree program, self-designed majors, honors program, independent study, double major, summer session for credit, part-time degree program, internships, graduate courses open to undergrads. Off campus study. Study abroad program. ROTC: Army.

Entrance Requirements: Options: electronic application, early admission, early decision, deferred admission, international baccalaureate accepted. Required: essay, high school transcript, 1 recommendation, SAT or ACT. Recommended: 2 recommendations, SAT Subject Tests. Entrance: most difficult. Application deadlines: 1/1, 11/1 for early decision. Notification: 4/1, 12/1 for early decision. Preference given to Virginia residents. SAT Reasoning Test deadline: 1/24. SAT Subject Test deadline: 1/24. Transfer credits accepted: Yes. Applicants placed on waiting list: 3,518. Wait-listed applicants offered admission: 147. Early decision applicants: 1,167. Early decision applicants admitted: 564.

Costs Per Year: Application fee: $70. State resident tuition: $13,570 full-time. Nonresident tuition: $37,344 full-time. College room and board: $9072. College room only: $5790. Room and board charges vary according to board plan and housing facility.

Collegiate Environment: Orientation program. Drama-theater group, choral group, student-run newspaper, radio station. Social organizations: 375 open to all; national fraternities, national sororities; 25% of eligible men and 29% of eligible women are members. Most popular organizations: Alma Mater Productions, Student Assembly, College Partnership for Kids, Residence Hall Association, Alpha Phi Omega. Major annual events: Yule Log Ceremony, King and Queen Ball, Opening Convocation Exercises. Student services: legal services, health clinic, personal-psychological counseling. Campus security: 24-hour emergency response devices and patrols, late night transport-escort service, controlled dormitory access, The WMPD is a State certified law enforcement agency with 33 employees, providing law enforcement services for the College. 4,379 college housing spaces available; 4,260 were occupied in 2012-13. Freshmen guaranteed college housing. On-campus residence required in freshman year. Option: coed housing available. Earl Gregg Swem plus 7 others with 2.7 million books, 7,454 serials, 44,405 audiovisual materials, an OPAC, and a Web page. Operations spending for the previous fiscal year: $10.7 million. 300 computers available on campus for general student use. Computer purchase/lease plans available. A computer is required for all students. A campuswide network can be accessed from student residence rooms. Students can access the following: online class registration.

Community Environment: Williamsburg, the historic capital of Colonial Virginia, has been restored as nearly as possible to its 18th-century appearance. The Colonial Williamsburg project has been made possible by the generous provisions of the late John D. Rockefeller, Jr. The restored town offers excellent facilities, and the colonial shops on Merchant's Square provide historical interest. Williamsburg is a popular tourist center and has recreational activities such as fishing, boating, golf, and hunting. Major historic points of interest include William and Mary's Sir Christopher Wren Building (1695), the Bruton Parish Church, the Capitol, Governor's Palace, Peyton Randolph House, Raleigh Tavern, and the Wythe House.

■ CULINARY INSTITUTE OF VIRGINIA

2428 Almeda Ave., Ste. 316
Norfolk, VA 23513
Tel: (757)853-3508; Free: 866-619-CHEF
Fax: (757)857-4869
E-mail: hsadmissions@chefva.com
Web Site: www.chefva.com/

Description: Proprietary, 4-year, coed. Administratively affiliated with ECPI College of Technology. Awards associate and bachelor's degrees. Setting: urban campus. Faculty: 19 (16 full-time, 3 part-time). Core. Academic remediation for entering students, advanced placement, internships.

Entrance Requirements: Option: electronic application. Required: interview. Entrance: minimally difficult. Application deadline: Rolling. Notification: continuous. Transfer credits accepted: Yes.

Collegiate Environment: Orientation program. Campus security: trained evening security personnel. 96 computers available on campus for general student use. Staffed computer lab on campus provides training in use of software and the Internet.

◼ DABNEY S. LANCASTER COMMUNITY COLLEGE
1000 Dabney Dr.
Clifton Forge, VA 24422
Tel: (540)863-2800; Free: 877-73-DSLCC
Fax: (540)863-2915
E-mail: lwferguson@dslcc.edu
Web Site: www.dslcc.edu/
Description: State-supported, 2-year, coed. Part of Virginia Community College System. Awards certificates, diplomas, transfer associate, and terminal associate degrees. Founded 1964. Setting: 117-acre rural campus. Endowment: $3.3 million. Educational spending for the previous fiscal year: $14,138 per student. Total enrollment: 1,538. Faculty: 97 (23 full-time, 74 part-time). Student-undergrad faculty ratio is 16:1. Full-time: 479 students, 54% women, 46% men. Part-time: 1,059 students, 53% women, 47% men. Students come from 8 states and territories, 3% from out-of-state. 1% American Indian or Alaska Native, non-Hispanic/Latino; 1% Hispanic/Latino; 6% African American, non-Hispanic/Latino; 0.4% Asian, non-Hispanic/Latino; 0% Native Hawaiian or other Pacific Islander, non-Hispanic/Latino; 0% international. 28% 25 or older, 26% transferred in. Calendar: semesters. Academic remediation for entering students, services for LD students, advanced placement, honors program, independent study, distance learning, summer session for credit, part-time degree program, adult/continuing education programs, co-op programs and internships. Study abroad program.
Entrance Requirements: Recommended: high school transcript, interview.
Costs Per Year: State resident tuition: $2808 full-time, $117 per credit part-time. Nonresident tuition: $7046 full-time, $293.60 per credit part-time. Mandatory fees: $240 full-time, $120 per year part-time.
Collegiate Environment: Orientation program. Social organizations: Phi Theta Kappa. Major annual events: Spring Picnic, Fall Picnic. Student services: personal-psychological counseling. Campus security: 24-hour emergency response devices. College housing not available. DSLCC Library plus 1 other with 34,397 books, 853 serials, 1,260 audiovisual materials, and an OPAC. Operations spending for the previous fiscal year: $215,886. 300 computers available on campus for general student use. A campuswide network can be accessed. Students can access the following: online class registration. Staffed computer lab on campus provides training in use of the Internet.
Community Environment: A rural community, Clifton Forge is served by limited modes of transportation. Libraries, churches of major denominations, a hospital, and various civic and service organizations are part of the community. Some part-time job opportunities are available. A state park, lakes and streams provide facilities for fishing and outdoor sports; other activities include baseball, basketball, football, tennis, canoeing, backpacking and skiing.

◼ DANVILLE COMMUNITY COLLEGE
1008 S Main St.
Danville, VA 24541-4088
Tel: (434)797-2222; Free: 800-560-4291
Fax: (434)797-8541
E-mail: cpulliam@dcc.vccs.edu
Web Site: www.dcc.vccs.edu/
Description: State-supported, 2-year, coed. Part of Virginia Community College System. Awards certificates, diplomas, transfer associate, and terminal associate degrees. Founded 1967. Setting: 76-acre urban campus. Total enrollment: 4,387. Student-undergrad faculty ratio is 18:1. 1% from out-of-state. 36% 25 or older. Core. Calendar: semesters. Academic remediation for entering students, advanced placement, honors program, distance learning, summer session for credit, part-time degree program, adult/continuing education programs, co-op programs.
Entrance Requirements: Open admission. Options: early admission, deferred admission. Required: high school transcript. Entrance: noncompetitive. Application deadline: Rolling. Notification: continuous. Preference given to district residents.
Collegiate Environment: Campus security: 24-hour patrols. Learning Resource Center with an OPAC and a Web page.
Community Environment: See Averett College.

◼ DEVRY UNIVERSITY (ARLINGTON)
2450 Crystal Dr.
Arlington, VA 22202
Tel: (703)414-4000; Free: 866-338-7941
Fax: (703)414-4040

Web Site: www.devry.edu/
Description: Proprietary, comprehensive, coed. Part of DeVry University. Awards associate, bachelor's, and master's degrees. Founded 2001. Total enrollment: 808. Faculty: 181 (15 full-time, 166 part-time). Student-undergrad faculty ratio is 7:1. Full-time: 258 students, 34% women, 66% men. Part-time: 284 students, 27% women, 73% men. 59% from out-of-state. 0.4% American Indian or Alaska Native, non-Hispanic/Latino; 11% Hispanic/Latino; 48% African American, non-Hispanic/Latino; 4% Asian, non-Hispanic/Latino; 1% Native Hawaiian or other Pacific Islander, non-Hispanic/Latino; 5% international. 61% 25 or older, 13% transferred in. Academic areas with the most degrees conferred: business/marketing; engineering; computer and information sciences. Calendar: semesters. Part-time degree program, adult/continuing education programs.
Entrance Requirements: Required: high school transcript, interview. Entrance: minimally difficult. Application deadline: Rolling. Notification: continuous.
Costs Per Year: Application fee: $40. Tuition: $16,076 full-time, $609 per credit hour part-time. Mandatory fees: $80 full-time.
Collegiate Environment: College housing not available.

◼ DEVRY UNIVERSITY (CHESAPEAKE)
1317 Executive Blvd., Ste. 100
Chesapeake, VA 23320-3671
Tel: (757)382-5680; Free: 866-338-7941
Web Site: www.devry.edu/
Description: Proprietary, comprehensive, coed. Awards associate, bachelor's, and master's degrees.

◼ DEVRY UNIVERSITY (MANASSAS)
10432 Balls Ford Rd., Ste. 130
Manassas, VA 20109-3173
Tel: (703)396-6611; Free: 866-338-7941
Web Site: www.devry.edu/
Description: Proprietary, comprehensive, coed. Awards bachelor's and master's degrees. Calendar: semesters.

◼ EASTERN MENNONITE UNIVERSITY
1200 Park Rd.
Harrisonburg, VA 22802-2462
Tel: (540)432-4000; Free: 800-368-2665
Fax: (540)432-4444
E-mail: admiss@emu.edu
Web Site: www.emu.edu/
Description: Independent Mennonite, comprehensive, coed. Awards associate, bachelor's, and master's degrees. Founded 1917. Setting: 93-acre small town campus. Endowment: $19.5 million. Research spending for the previous fiscal year: $179,657. Educational spending for the previous fiscal year: $12,861 per student. Total enrollment: 1,519. Faculty: 205 (104 full-time, 101 part-time). Student-undergrad faculty ratio is 10:1. 919 applied, 70% were admitted. 17% from top 10% of their high school class, 44% from top quarter, 80% from top half. Full-time: 1,061 students, 65% women, 35% men. Part-time: 63 students, 48% women, 52% men. Students come from 37 states and territories, 18 other countries, 44% from out-of-state. 0.2% American Indian or Alaska Native, non-Hispanic/Latino; 7% Hispanic/Latino; 7% African American, non-Hispanic/Latino; 2% Asian, non-Hispanic/Latino; 0% Native Hawaiian or other Pacific Islander, non-Hispanic/Latino; 3% international. 6% 25 or older, 60% live on campus, 6% transferred in. Retention: 81% of full-time freshmen returned the following year. Academic areas with the most degrees conferred: liberal arts/general studies; health professions and related sciences; visual and performing arts. Core. Calendar: semesters. ESL program, services for LD students, advanced placement, honors program, independent study, distance learning, double major, summer session for credit, part-time degree program, adult/continuing education programs, internships, graduate courses open to undergrads. Off campus study at Council for Christian Colleges and Universities, Brethren College Abroad. Study abroad program.
Entrance Requirements: Options: electronic application, deferred admission, international baccalaureate accepted. Required: high school transcript, minimum 2.2 high school GPA, Community Lifestyle Commitment, SAT or ACT. Recommended: interview. Required for some: 2 recommendations. Entrance: moderately difficult. Application deadline: Rolling. Notification: continuous. Transfer credits accepted: Yes.
Costs Per Year: Application fee: $25. Comprehensive fee: $38,770 includes

full-time tuition ($28,940), mandatory fees ($140), and college room and board ($9690). Room and board charges vary according to board plan and housing facility.

Collegiate Environment: Orientation program. Drama-theater group, choral group, student-run newspaper. Social organizations: 35 open to all. Most popular organizations: Young People's Christian Association, Student Government Association, Student Education Association, Creation Care Council, Black Student Union. Major annual events: Fall Festival, Multicultural Week, Spring Fling. Student services: health clinic, personal-psychological counseling. Campus security: 24-hour emergency response devices, controlled dormitory access, night watchman. 657 college housing spaces available; 542 were occupied in 2012-13. Freshmen guaranteed college housing. On-campus residence required through junior year. Option: coed housing available. Sadie Hartzler Library with 168,896 books, 74,906 microform titles, 781 serials, 4,738 audiovisual materials, an OPAC, and a Web page. Operations spending for the previous fiscal year: $659,290. 154 computers available on campus for general student use. A campuswide network can be accessed from student residence rooms and from off campus. Students can access the following: online class registration.

Community Environment: The college is located in the heart of Virginia's beautiful Shenandoah Valley, near a national park.

■ **EASTERN SHORE COMMUNITY COLLEGE**
29300 Lankford Hwy.
Melfa, VA 23410-3000
Tel: (757)789-1789; Free: 877-871-8455
Fax: (757)789-1739
E-mail: bsmith@es.vccs.edu
Web Site: www.es.vccs.edu/

Description: State-supported, 2-year, coed. Part of Virginia Community College System. Awards certificates, transfer associate, and terminal associate degrees. Founded 1971. Setting: 117-acre rural campus with easy access to Hampton Roads/Virginia Beach, Norfolk. Total enrollment: 1,332. Faculty: 57 (18 full-time, 39 part-time). Student-undergrad faculty ratio is 13:1. Students come from 3 states and territories, 2% from out-of-state. Core. Calendar: semesters. Academic remediation for entering students, services for LD students, distance learning, summer session for credit, part-time degree program, adult/continuing education programs, internships. Off campus study at members of the Virginia Tidewater Consortium for Continuing Higher Education.

Entrance Requirements: Open admission except for practical nursing program. Option: electronic application. Required: high school transcript, high school diploma, The Virginia Community College System (VCCS) has a placement test designed for and utilized by all schools in its system. Entrance: noncompetitive. Application deadline: Rolling. Notification: continuous. Preference given to Residents of Accomack or Northampton counties. Transfer credits accepted: Yes.

Collegiate Environment: Orientation program. Social organizations: 6 open to all. Most popular organizations: All Christians Together in Service (ACTS), Phi Theta Kappa, Phi Beta Lambda, The Electronics Club, SNAP Photography Club. Major annual events: Heritage Celebration, Science Fair, Phi Theta Kappa Lecture Series. Campus security: security guards, day and night during classes when the college is in session. College housing not available. Learning Resources Center plus 1 other with 25,000 books, 102 serials, an OPAC, and a Web page. 75 computers available on campus for general student use. A campuswide network can be accessed from off-campus. Students can access the following: online class registration. Staffed computer lab on campus provides training in use of computers, software, and the Internet.

Community Environment: Located midway down the Delmarva Peninsula, which separates Chesapeake Bay from the Atlantic Ocean, Melfa has a population of 450. The area is known for vegetables, poultry, oysters, fish, sailing, and swimming.

■ **ECPI COLLEGE OF TECHNOLOGY (GLEN ALLEN)**
4305 Cox Rd.
Glen Allen, VA 23060
Tel: (804)934-0100; Free: 800-986-1200
Fax: (804)934-0054
E-mail: jpope@ecpi.edu
Web Site: www.ecpi.edu/

Description: Proprietary, 4-year, coed. Awards associate and bachelor's degrees. Setting: urban campus with easy access to Richmond. Total enrollment: 473. Student-undergrad faculty ratio is 15:1. 148 applied, 82% were

admitted. Full-time: 473 students, 38% women, 62% men. Students come from 2 states and territories, 1% from out-of-state. 48% 25 or older. Calendar: semesters.

Entrance Requirements: Required: high school transcript, interview. Recommended: SAT, SAT and SAT Subject Tests or ACT, SAT Subject Tests. Entrance: moderately difficult. Application deadline: Rolling. Notification: continuous.

Collegiate Environment: Most popular organizations: CSI, OPMA, SETA, NVTHS, ITE. Campus security: building and parking lot security.

■ **ECPI COLLEGE OF TECHNOLOGY (MANASSAS)**
10021 Balls Ford Rd.
Manassas, VA 20109
Tel: (703)330-5300; Free: 866-708-6172
Fax: (703)369-0530
Web Site: www.ecpi.edu/

Description: Proprietary, 4-year, coed. Awards associate and bachelor's degrees.

■ **ECPI COLLEGE OF TECHNOLOGY (NEWPORT NEWS)**
1001 Omni Blvd., No.100
Newport News, VA 23606
Tel: (757)838-9191; Free: 866-499-0335
Fax: (757)827-5351
Web Site: www.ecpi.edu/

Description: Proprietary, 4-year, coed. Awards associate and bachelor's degrees. Founded 1966. Setting: suburban campus. Total enrollment: 556. Faculty: 130 (66 full-time, 64 part-time). Student-undergrad faculty ratio is 16:1. Full-time: 556 students, 39% women, 61% men. Students come from 34 states and territories, 2% from out-of-state. 64% 25 or older, 77% transferred in. Core. Calendar: trimesters. Advanced placement, freshman honors college, honors program, summer session for credit, part-time degree program, adult/continuing education programs, internships.

Entrance Requirements: Option: deferred admission. Required: high school transcript, minimum 2.0 high school GPA, interview. Recommended: SAT, SAT or ACT, SAT Subject Tests. Entrance: moderately difficult. Notification: continuous.

Collegiate Environment: Orientation program. Social organizations: 6 open to all. Most popular organizations: SETA, IEEE, NVTHS, Accounting Society, CSI. Major annual events: Commencement, picnic. Student services: personal-psychological counseling. Campus security: building and parking lot security. ECPI-Virginia Beach Library with 13,014 books, 168 serials, an OPAC, and a Web page. 100 computers available on campus for general student use. A campuswide network can be accessed from off-campus. Staffed computer lab on campus.

■ **ECPI COLLEGE OF TECHNOLOGY (RICHMOND)**
800 Moorefield Park Dr.
Richmond, VA 23236
Tel: (804)330-5533; Free: 800-986-1200
E-mail: agerard@ecpi.edu
Web Site: www.ecpi.edu/

Description: Proprietary, primarily 2-year, coed. Awards certificates, diplomas, terminal associate, and bachelor's degrees. Founded 1966. Setting: urban campus. Total enrollment: 865. Faculty: 38 (20 full-time, 18 part-time). Student-undergrad faculty ratio is 18:1. 136 applied, 80% were admitted. Full-time: 865 students, 33% women, 67% men. Students come from 2 states and territories, 1% from out-of-state. 46% 25 or older. Retention: 75% of full-time freshmen returned the following year. Core. Calendar: semesters. Advanced placement, freshman honors college, honors program, summer session for credit, part-time degree program, adult/continuing education programs, internships.

Entrance Requirements: Option: deferred admission. Required: high school transcript, interview. Recommended: SAT, SAT Subject Tests. Entrance: moderately difficult. Application deadline: Rolling. Notification: continuous.

Collegiate Environment: Orientation program. Most popular organization: National Technical Honor Society. Major annual events: Student Appreciation Day bar-b-q (twice yearly), Graduation Ceremony—June. Campus security: building and parking lot security. ECPI-Richmond Library with 3,165 books, 81 serials, an OPAC, and a Web page. 491 computers available on campus for general student use. A campuswide network can be accessed from off-campus. Staffed computer lab on campus.

■ ECPI COLLEGE OF TECHNOLOGY (VIRGINIA BEACH)

5555 Greenwich Rd.
Virginia Beach, VA 23462
Tel: (757)671-7171; Free: 866-499-0336
E-mail: rballance@ecpi.edu
Web Site: www.ecpi.edu/

Description: Proprietary, 4-year, coed. Awards associate and bachelor's degrees. Founded 1966. Setting: 8-acre suburban campus. Total enrollment: 13,717. Faculty: 1,371 (563 full-time, 808 part-time). Student-undergrad faculty ratio is 17:1. 1,328 applied, 80% were admitted. Full-time: 13,717 students, 58% women, 42% men. Students come from 6 states and territories, 10% from out-of-state. 1% American Indian or Alaska Native, non-Hispanic/Latino; 5% Hispanic/Latino; 41% African American, non-Hispanic/Latino; 3% Asian, non-Hispanic/Latino; 0.02% Native Hawaiian or other Pacific Islander, non-Hispanic/Latino; 0.01% international. 44% 25 or older. Retention: 73% of full-time freshmen returned the following year. Academic areas with the most degrees conferred: computer and information sciences; homeland security, law enforcement, firefighting, and protective services; engineering technologies. Core. Calendar: continuous. Academic remediation for entering students, advanced placement, accelerated degree program, freshman honors college, honors program, independent study, distance learning, double major, summer session for credit, part-time degree program, adult/continuing education programs, internships. Off campus study. Study abroad program.

Entrance Requirements: Options: electronic application, deferred admission. Required: high school transcript, interview, ACT. Recommended: SAT, SAT or ACT, SAT Subject Tests. Entrance: moderately difficult. Notification: continuous.

Collegiate Environment: Orientation program. Social organizations: national fraternities, national sororities, local fraternities, local sororities; 24% of eligible men and 22% of eligible women are members. Most popular organizations: Student Electronic Technicians Association (SETA), Institute of Electrical & Electronic Engineers (IEEE), Phi Theta Kappa Honor Society, Information Technology Exchange (ITE), Medical Student Association. Major annual events: picnic, Fall Fest. Student services: personal-psychological counseling. Campus security: building and parking lot security. ECPI-Virginia Beach Library plus 10 others with 111,114 books, 293 serials, 1,154 audiovisual materials, an OPAC, and a Web page. 6,500 computers available on campus for general student use. A campuswide network can be accessed from off-campus. Students can access the following: online class registration. Staffed computer lab on campus provides training in use of computers, software, and the Internet.

■ EMORY & HENRY COLLEGE

PO Box 947
Emory, VA 24327-0947
Tel: (276)944-4121; Free: 800-848-5493
Fax: (276)944-6934
E-mail: ehadmiss@ehc.edu
Web Site: www.ehc.edu/

Description: Independent United Methodist, 4-year, coed. Awards bachelor's and master's degrees. Founded 1836. Setting: 330-acre rural campus. Total enrollment: 945. Faculty: 120 (72 full-time, 48 part-time). Student-undergrad faculty ratio is 10:1. 1,217 applied, 72% were admitted. 20% from top 10% of their high school class, 45% from top quarter, 80% from top half. Full-time: 874 students, 47% women, 53% men. Part-time: 23 students, 48% women, 52% men. 36% from out-of-state. 0.4% American Indian or Alaska Native, non-Hispanic/Latino; 2% Hispanic/Latino; 10% African American, non-Hispanic/Latino; 0.4% Asian, non-Hispanic/Latino; 0% Native Hawaiian or other Pacific Islander, non-Hispanic/Latino; 1% international. 3% 25 or older, 77% live on campus, 3% transferred in. Retention: 72% of full-time freshmen returned the following year. Academic areas with the most degrees conferred: social sciences; education; psychology. Core. Calendar: semesters. Academic remediation for entering students, services for LD students, advanced placement, self-designed majors, honors program, independent study, double major, summer session for credit, external degree program, co-op programs and internships. Study abroad program.

Entrance Requirements: Options: electronic application, early action, international baccalaureate accepted. Required: high school transcript, SAT or ACT. Recommended: essay, interview. Application deadlines: Rolling, Rolling for nonresidents, 12/1 for early action. Notification: continuous, continuous for nonresidents, 1/1 for early action. Transfer credits accepted: Yes.

Costs Per Year: Application fee: $0. Comprehensive fee: $37,548 includes full-time tuition ($28,122) and college room and board ($9426). College room only: $4782. Full-time tuition varies according to course load, degree level, and location. Room and board charges vary according to board plan, housing facility, and location. Part-time tuition: $1125 per credit hour. Part-time tuition varies according to course load, degree level, and location.

Collegiate Environment: Orientation program. Drama-theater group, choral group, student-run newspaper, radio station. Social organizations: local fraternities, local sororities; 15% of eligible men and 30% of eligible women are members. Major annual events: Martin Luther King Jr. Day Celebration, Service Plunge, Lyceums. Student services: health clinic, personal-psychological counseling. Campus security: 24-hour emergency response devices and patrols, late night transport-escort service, controlled dormitory access. Freshmen guaranteed college housing. On-campus residence required through junior year. Options: coed, men-only, women-only housing available. Kelly Library with an OPAC and a Web page.

Community Environment: Emory, in the Virginia Highlands, is approximately 20 miles north of Bristol, VA, just off exit 26 of I-81. The area is known for its scenic beauty, recreational opportunities, and abundance of talented craftspeople. In Abingdon, an historic town dating from the middle 1700's, the annual Virginia Highlands Festival brings together artists and craftspeople from throughout the eastern U.S. Just twenty minutes from the college campus is Mt. Rogers National Recreational Area, featuring numerous campgrounds, mountain streams, and miles of the Appalachian Trail.

■ EVEREST COLLEGE

801 N Quincy St.
Ste. 500
Arlington, VA 22203
Tel: (703)248-8887
Fax: (703)351-2202
Web Site: www.everest.edu/

Description: Proprietary, 2-year, coed. Awards certificates and terminal associate degrees. Founded 2001. Setting: urban campus. Total enrollment: 919. 226 applied. 77% from out-of-state. 41% 25 or older. Retention: 81% of full-time freshmen returned the following year.

■ FERRUM COLLEGE

PO Box 1000
Ferrum, VA 24088
Tel: (540)365-2121; Free: 800-868-9797
Fax: (540)365-4266
E-mail: admissions@ferrum.edu
Web Site: www.ferrum.edu/

Description: Independent United Methodist, 4-year, coed. Awards bachelor's degrees. Founded 1913. Setting: 720-acre rural campus. Endowment: $39.5 million. Educational spending for the previous fiscal year: $5821 per student. Total enrollment: 1,510. Faculty: 125 (79 full-time, 46 part-time). Student-undergrad faculty ratio is 16:1. 2,589 applied, 92% were admitted. 8% from top 10% of their high school class, 19% from top quarter, 48% from top half. Full-time: 1,487 students, 45% women, 55% men. Part-time: 23 students, 70% women, 30% men. Students come from 12 states and territories, 7 other countries, 18% from out-of-state. 0.5% American Indian or Alaska Native, non-Hispanic/Latino; 4% Hispanic/Latino; 33% African American, non-Hispanic/Latino; 0.1% Asian, non-Hispanic/Latino; 0.2% Native Hawaiian or other Pacific Islander, non-Hispanic/Latino; 1% international. 2% 25 or older, 90% live on campus, 5% transferred in. Retention: 53% of full-time freshmen returned the following year. Academic areas with the most degrees conferred: business/marketing; public administration and social services; liberal arts/general studies. Core. Calendar: semesters. Academic remediation for entering students, services for LD students, advanced placement, self-designed majors, honors program, double major, summer session for credit, adult/continuing education programs, internships. Study abroad program.

Entrance Requirements: Options: electronic application, early admission, deferred admission, international baccalaureate accepted. Required: high school transcript, SAT or ACT. Recommended: essay, minimum 2 high school GPA, 2 recommendations, interview. Required for some: interview. Entrance: minimally difficult. Application deadline: Rolling. Notification: continuous. SAT Reasoning Test deadline: 8/1. Applicants placed on waiting list: 0. Wait-listed applicants offered admission: 0.

Costs Per Year: Application fee: $25. Comprehensive fee: $36,555 includes full-time tuition ($27,310), mandatory fees ($115), and college room and board ($9130). Part-time tuition: $545 per credit hour.

Collegiate Environment: Orientation program. Drama-theater group, choral group, student-run newspaper, radio station. Social organizations: national sororities, local fraternities, local sororities. Most popular organizations: Student Government Association, Agriculture Club, BACCHUS, Panther Productions, African American Student Association, Students in Free Enterprise (SIFE). Major annual events: Homecoming, Folklife Festival, Spring Fling. Student services: health clinic, personal-psychological counseling. Campus security: 24-hour emergency response devices and patrols, student patrols, late night transport-escort service, controlled dormitory access. 1,412 college housing spaces available; 1,360 were occupied in 2012-13. Freshmen guaranteed college housing. On-campus residence required through senior year. Options: coed, women-only housing available. Stanley Library plus 1 other with 15,427 books, 17,752 microform titles, 39,336 serials, 2,699 audiovisual materials, an OPAC, and a Web page. Operations spending for the previous fiscal year: $620,250. 89 computers available on campus for general student use. A campuswide network can be accessed from student residence rooms and from off campus. Students can access the following: online class registration. Staffed computer lab on campus provides training in use of computers, software, and the Internet.

Community Environment: Located in the Blue Ridge Mountains of Virginia, Ferrum has an ideal environment for study and cultural enrichment. The College's proximity to the mountains and lakes enables students to enjoy outdoor activities such as hiking, camping, fishing, boating, swimming and skiing. Ferrum is 35 miles south of Roanoke, Virginia, which has excellent shopping, living, cultural and recreational facilities. Bus service and air transportation are available in Roanoke.

■ **FORTIS COLLEGE (NORFOLK)**
6300 Ctr. Dr.
Ste. 100
Norfolk, VA 23502
Tel: (757)499-5447
Web Site: www.fortis.edu/
Description: Proprietary, 2-year, coed.

■ **FORTIS COLLEGE (RICHMOND)**
2000 Westmoreland St.
Ste. A
Richmond, VA 23230
Tel: (804)323-1020
Web Site: www.fortis.edu/
Description: Proprietary, 2-year, coed.

■ **GEORGE MASON UNIVERSITY**
4400 University Dr.
Fairfax, VA 22030
Tel: (703)993-1000
E-mail: sdvorak@gmu.edu
Web Site: www.gmu.edu/
Description: State-supported, university, coed. Awards bachelor's, master's, and doctoral degrees and post-master's certificates. Founded 1957. Setting: 817-acre suburban campus with easy access to Washington, DC. Endowment: $51.7 million. Research spending for the previous fiscal year: $96.8 million. Total enrollment: 32,961. Faculty: 2,379 (1,210 full-time, 1,169 part-time). Student-undergrad faculty ratio is 16:1. 14,703 applied, 66% were admitted. 21% from top 10% of their high school class, 36% from top quarter, 37% from top half. Full-time: 16,265 students, 52% women, 48% men. Part-time: 4,388 students, 50% women, 50% men. Students come from 50 states and territories, 125 other countries, 11% from out-of-state. 0.2% American Indian or Alaska Native, non-Hispanic/Latino; 11% Hispanic/Latino; 9% African American, non-Hispanic/Latino; 17% Asian, non-Hispanic/Latino; 0.5% Native Hawaiian or other Pacific Islander, non-Hispanic/Latino; 4% international. 23% 25 or older, 28% live on campus, 10% transferred in. Retention: 86% of full-time freshmen returned the following year. Academic areas with the most degrees conferred: business/marketing; social sciences; English. Core. Calendar: semesters. ESL program, services for LD students, advanced placement, accelerated degree program, self-designed majors, freshman honors college, honors program, independent study, distance learning, double major, summer session for credit, part-time degree program, adult/continuing education programs, co-op programs and internships, graduate courses open to undergrads. Off campus study at Members of the Consortium of Universities of the Washington Metropolitan Area. Study abroad program. ROTC: Army, Air Force (c).
Entrance Requirements: Options: electronic application, early admission,

early action, deferred admission, international baccalaureate accepted. Required: essay, high school transcript, minimum 2 high school GPA. Recommended: minimum 3.5 high school GPA, SAT and SAT Subject Tests or ACT. Required for some: 3 recommendations, Audition required for School of Dance and School of Music applicants; portfolio required for Art and Visual Technology BFA and Computer Game Design BFA applicants. Interview and audition or portfolio required for School of Theater applicants, SAT or ACT. Entrance: moderately difficult. Application deadlines: 1/15, 1/15 for nonresidents, 11/9 for early action. Notification: 4/1, 4/1 for nonresidents, 12/15 for early action. SAT Reasoning Test deadline: 1/15. SAT Subject Test deadline: 1/15. Transfer credits accepted: Yes. Applicants placed on waiting list: 1,737. Wait-listed applicants offered admission: 158. Early action applicants: 4,624. Early action applicants admitted: 3,215.

Costs Per Year: Application fee: $60. One-time mandatory fee: $180. State resident tuition: $7010 full-time, $292.08 per credit hour part-time. Nonresident tuition: $25,154 full-time, $1,048.08 per credit hour part-time. Mandatory fees: $2610 full-time, $108.75 per credit hour part-time. Full-time tuition and fees vary according to course load. Part-time tuition and fees vary according to course load. College room and board: $9250. College room only: $5510. Room and board charges vary according to board plan and housing facility.

Collegiate Environment: Orientation program. Drama-theater group, choral group, student-run newspaper, radio station. Social organizations: 396 open to all; national fraternities, national sororities, Multicultural, Religious, and Special Interest. Most popular organizations: Catholic Campus Ministry, Muslim Student Association, National Society of Collegiate Scholars, Campus Crusade for Christ, Institute of Electrical and Electronics Engineers. Major annual events: Mason Day, Welcome Week, Homecoming. Student services: health clinic, personal-psychological counseling, women's center. Campus security: 24-hour emergency response devices and patrols, student patrols, late night transport-escort service, controlled dormitory access. 6,083 college housing spaces available; 5,748 were occupied in 2012-13. Freshmen guaranteed college housing. Option: coed housing available. Fenwick Library plus 4 others with 2.5 million books, 3.3 million microform titles, 11,200 serials, 50,500 audiovisual materials, an OPAC, and a Web page. Operations spending for the previous fiscal year: $23.3 million. 629 computers available on campus for general student use. Computer purchase/lease plans available. A campuswide network can be accessed from student residence rooms and from off campus. Students can access the following: online class registration. Staffed computer lab on campus provides training in use of computers, software, and the Internet.

Community Environment: Fairfax is a rapidly growing residential area on the western fringes of Washington, DC. Shopping facilities, commercial transportation, recreation activities, part-time employment and moderate-to-expensive rental apartments are available nearby.

■ **GERMANNA COMMUNITY COLLEGE**
2130 Germanna Hwy.
Locust Grove, VA 22508-2102
Tel: (540)727-3000
Fax: (540)727-3207
Web Site: www.germanna.edu/
Description: State-supported, 2-year, coed. Part of Virginia Community College System. Awards certificates, transfer associate, and terminal associate degrees. Founded 1970. Setting: 100-acre suburban campus with easy access to Washington, DC. Total enrollment: 7,035. Faculty: 372 (69 full-time, 303 part-time). Student-undergrad faculty ratio is 19:1. 1,338 applied, 100% were admitted. Full-time: 2,296 students, 57% women, 43% men. Part-time: 4,739 students, 65% women, 35% men. 28% 25 or older. Calendar: semesters. Academic remediation for entering students, ESL program, services for LD students, advanced placement, independent study, distance learning, double major, summer session for credit, part-time degree program. Off campus study at University of Mary Washington, other members of the Virginia Community College System. Study abroad program.
Entrance Requirements: Open admission except for nursing program. Options: electronic application, early admission. Required for some: high school transcript. Entrance: noncompetitive. Application deadline: Rolling. Notification: continuous.
Collegiate Environment: Orientation program. Drama-theater group. Most popular organizations: Student Nurses Association, Student Government Association, Phi Theta Kappa. Student services: personal-psychological counseling. Campus security: 24-hour patrols. Locust Grove Campus Library plus 2 others with 124,808 books, 1,083 microform titles, 208 serials, 2,382 audiovisual materials, an OPAC, and a Web page. 55 computers available

on campus for general student use. Students can access the following: online class registration. Staffed computer lab on campus provides training in use of computers, software, and the Internet.

■ HAMPDEN-SYDNEY COLLEGE

PO Box 667
Hampden-Sydney, VA 23943
Tel: (434)223-6000; Free: 800-755-0733
Fax: (434)223-6346
E-mail: hsapp@hsc.edu
Web Site: www.hsc.edu/

Description: Independent, 4-year, men only, affiliated with Presbyterian Church (U.S.A.). Awards bachelor's degrees. Founded 1776. Setting: 1,340-acre rural campus with easy access to Richmond. Endowment: $129 million. Research spending for the previous fiscal year: $52,769. Educational spending for the previous fiscal year: $11,079 per student. Total enrollment: 1,080. Faculty: 106 (94 full-time, 12 part-time). Student-undergrad faculty ratio is 11:1. 2,630 applied, 56% were admitted. 13% from top 10% of their high school class, 28% from top quarter, 87% from top half. 1 class president, 4 valedictorians, 32 student government officers. Full-time: 1,080 students. Students come from 33 states and territories, 19 other countries, 29% from out-of-state. 1% American Indian or Alaska Native, non-Hispanic/Latino; 2% Hispanic/Latino; 9% African American, non-Hispanic/Latino; 1% Asian, non-Hispanic/Latino; 0% Native Hawaiian or other Pacific Islander, non-Hispanic/Latino; 1% international. 0% 25 or older, 95% live on campus, 2% transferred in. Retention: 78% of full-time freshmen returned the following year. Academic areas with the most degrees conferred: social sciences; history; business/marketing. Core. Calendar: semesters. Academic remediation for entering students, advanced placement, honors program, independent study, double major, summer session for credit, internships. Off campus study at Seven-College Exchange Program, Longwood College Cooperative Program. Study abroad program. ROTC: Army (c).

Entrance Requirements: Options: electronic application, early admission, early decision, early action, international baccalaureate accepted. Required: essay, high school transcript, minimum 2 high school GPA, 2 recommendations, SAT or ACT. Recommended: minimum 3 high school GPA, interview, SAT Subject Tests. Entrance: moderately difficult. Application deadlines: 3/1, 11/15 for early decision, 1/15 for early action. Notification: 4/15, 12/15 for early decision, 2/15 for early action. SAT Reasoning Test deadline: 3/1. SAT Subject Test deadline: 3/1. Transfer credits accepted: Yes. Early decision applicants: 108. Early decision applicants admitted: 38. Early action applicants: 2,050. Early action applicants admitted: 1,207.

Costs Per Year: Application fee: $30. Comprehensive fee: $46,736 includes full-time tuition ($34,498), mandatory fees ($1072), and college room and board ($11,166). Room and board charges vary according to board plan and housing facility.

Collegiate Environment: Orientation program. Drama-theater group, choral group, student-run newspaper, radio station. Social organizations: 73 open to all; national fraternities; 34% of eligible undergrads are members. Most popular organizations: Republican Society, Pre-Health Society, Outdoors Club, Tiger Athletic Club, Pre-Law Society. Major annual events: Homecoming, Greek Weekend, Macon Week/Midwinters. Student services: health clinic, personal-psychological counseling. Campus security: 24-hour emergency response devices and patrols. 1,122 college housing spaces available; 1,000 were occupied in 2012-13. Freshmen guaranteed college housing. On-campus residence required through senior year. Option: men-only housing available. Walter M. Bortz III Library with 267,595 books, 43,798 serials, 6,538 audiovisual materials, an OPAC, and a Web page. Operations spending for the previous fiscal year: $205,618. 200 computers available on campus for general student use. Computer purchase/lease plans available. A campuswide network can be accessed from student residence rooms and from off campus. Students can access the following: online class registration. Staffed computer lab on campus provides training in use of computers, software, and the Internet.

■ HAMPTON UNIVERSITY

Hampton, VA 23668
Tel: (757)727-5000; Free: 800-624-3328
Fax: (757)727-5084
E-mail: derrickboone@hamptonu.edu
Web Site: www.hamptonu.edu/

Description: Independent, comprehensive, coed. Awards associate, bachelor's, master's, and doctoral degrees and post-master's certificates. Founded 1868. Setting: 314-acre urban campus with easy access to Norfolk.

Endowment: $240 million. Research spending for the previous fiscal year: $13.3 million. Educational spending for the previous fiscal year: $29,631 per student. Total enrollment: 4,754. Faculty: 330 (323 full-time, 7 part-time). Student-undergrad faculty ratio is 10:1. 14,503 applied, 36% were admitted. 20% from top 10% of their high school class, 45% from top quarter, 90% from top half. 224 National Merit Scholars, 31 class presidents, 49 valedictorians, 98 student government officers. Full-time: 3,464 students, 64% women, 36% men. Part-time: 387 students, 61% women, 39% men. Students come from 45 states and territories, 33 other countries, 51% from out-of-state. 0.1% American Indian or Alaska Native, non-Hispanic/Latino; 1% Hispanic/Latino; 94% African American, non-Hispanic/Latino; 1% Asian, non-Hispanic/Latino; 0% Native Hawaiian or other Pacific Islander, non-Hispanic/Latino; 1% international. 11% 25 or older, 53% live on campus, 5% transferred in. Retention: 76% of full-time freshmen returned the following year. Academic areas with the most degrees conferred: business/marketing; psychology; health professions and related sciences. Core. Calendar: semesters. Academic remediation for entering students, services for LD students, advanced placement, accelerated degree program, honors program, independent study, distance learning, double major, summer session for credit, part-time degree program, adult/continuing education programs, co-op programs and internships, graduate courses open to undergrads. Off campus study at 11 members of the Virginia Tidewater Consortium for Continuing Higher Education. Study abroad program. ROTC: Army, Naval.

Entrance Requirements: Options: electronic application, early admission, early action, deferred admission, international baccalaureate accepted. Required: essay, high school transcript, minimum 2.5 high school GPA, 3 recommendations, SAT or ACT. Entrance: moderately difficult. Application deadlines: 3/1, 11/1 for early action. Notification: 12/31 for early action. SAT Reasoning Test deadline: 6/15. Transfer credits accepted: Yes. Early action applicants: 2,873. Early action applicants admitted: 404.

Costs Per Year: Application fee: $35. Comprehensive fee: $29,954 includes full-time tuition ($18,618), mandatory fees ($2106), and college room and board ($9230). College room only: $4800. Full-time tuition and fees vary according to course load, degree level, location, and program. Room and board charges vary according to board plan, housing facility, and location. Part-time tuition: $472 per credit. Part-time tuition varies according to course load and location.

Collegiate Environment: Orientation program. Drama-theater group, choral group, marching band, student-run newspaper, radio station. Social organizations: 80 open to all; national fraternities, national sororities; 5% of eligible men and 4% of eligible women are members. Most popular organizations: student government, student leaders, Student Union Board, student recruitment team, resident assistants. Major annual events: Homecoming, Founders Day, Convocation. Student services: health clinic, personal-psychological counseling, women's center. Campus security: 24-hour emergency response devices and patrols, controlled dormitory access, emergency call boxes. 3,066 college housing spaces available; 1,997 were occupied in 2012-13. Freshmen given priority for college housing. Options: coed, men-only, women-only housing available. William R. and Norma B. Harvey Library plus 4 others with 526,154 books, 1.1 million microform titles, 32,187 serials, 5,835 audiovisual materials, an OPAC, and a Web page. 1,300 computers available on campus for general student use. Computer purchase/lease plans available. A campuswide network can be accessed from student residence rooms and from off campus. Students can access the following: online class registration, Banner Systems. Staffed computer lab on campus provides training in use of computers, software, and the Internet.

Community Environment: Hampton is the oldest English settlement still in existence in the nation; the city was settled in 1610. Hampton is the center of the fishing industry of Virginia. All modes of transportation are available. The Syms-Eaton Academy, first free school of America, and Hampton University, of which Booker T. Washington was an alumnus, are only two of the area's important sites. St. John's Church, which survived a partial burning during the Civil War, is another historic point of interest. Its most precious relic is communion silver made in 1618. The window dedicated to Pocahontas was donated by Indian students at Hampton Institute.

■ HOLLINS UNIVERSITY

PO Box 9603
Roanoke, VA 24020-1603
Tel: (540)362-6000; Free: 800-456-9595
Fax: (540)362-6218
E-mail: huadm@hollins.edu

Web Site: www.hollins.edu/

Description: Independent, comprehensive. Awards bachelor's and master's degrees and post-master's certificates. Founded 1842. Setting: 475-acre suburban campus. Endowment: $154.5 million. Research spending for the previous fiscal year: $23,000. Educational spending for the previous fiscal year: $15,399 per student. Total enrollment: 794. Faculty: 105 (71 full-time, 34 part-time). Student-undergrad faculty ratio is 9:1. 814 applied, 66% were admitted. 18% from top 10% of their high school class, 61% from top quarter, 89% from top half. Full-time: 594 students, 100% women. Part-time: 19 students, 100% women. Students come from 42 states and territories, 13 other countries, 43% from out-of-state. 0.3% American Indian or Alaska Native, non-Hispanic/Latino; 5% Hispanic/Latino; 11% African American, non-Hispanic/Latino; 2% Asian, non-Hispanic/Latino; 0.3% Native Hawaiian or other Pacific Islander, non-Hispanic/Latino; 5% international. 10% 25 or older, 77% live on campus, 2% transferred in. Retention: 70% of full-time freshmen returned the following year. Academic areas with the most degrees conferred: English; visual and performing arts; social sciences. Core. Calendar: 4-1-4. Services for LD students, advanced placement, accelerated degree program, self-designed majors, independent study, double major, part-time degree program, adult/continuing education programs, internships, graduate courses open to undergrads. Off campus study at member of the Seven-College Exchange Program. Study abroad program.

Entrance Requirements: Options: electronic application, early admission, early decision, early action, deferred admission, international baccalaureate accepted. Required: essay, high school transcript, 2 recommendations, SAT or ACT. Recommended: interview. Entrance: moderately difficult. Application deadlines: Rolling, 11/1 for early decision, 12/1 for early action. Notification: continuous, 11/15 for early decision, 12/15 for early action. SAT Reasoning Test deadline: 8/1. Transfer credits accepted: Yes. Applicants placed on waiting list: 7. Early decision applicants: 12. Early decision applicants admitted: 11. Early action applicants: 170. Early action applicants admitted: 156.

Costs Per Year: Application fee: $40. Comprehensive fee: $43,295 includes full-time tuition ($31,490), mandatory fees ($585), and college room and board ($11,220). College room only: $6700. Part-time tuition: $986 per credit hour. Part-time mandatory fees: $148.75 per term.

Collegiate Environment: Orientation program. Drama-theater group, choral group, student-run newspaper, radio station. Social organizations: 30 open to all. Most popular organizations: Student Government Association, SHARE (volunteer group), Hollins Activity Board, Student Athletic Association, Black Student Alliance. Major annual events: Literary Festival, Founders' Day, Tinker Day. Student services: health clinic, personal-psychological counseling, women's center. Campus security: 24-hour emergency response devices and patrols, late night transport-escort service, controlled dormitory access, emergency call boxes. 679 college housing spaces available; 464 were occupied in 2012-13. Freshmen guaranteed college housing. On-campus residence required through senior year. Option: women-only housing available. Wyndham Robertson Library plus 1 other with 626,085 books, 12,985 microform titles, 38,349 serials, 13,796 audiovisual materials, an OPAC, and a Web page. Operations spending for the previous fiscal year: $927,643. 100 computers available on campus for general student use. Computer purchase/lease plans available. A campuswide network can be accessed from student residence rooms and from off campus. Students can access the following: online class registration, applications software. Staffed computer lab on campus (open 24 hours a day) provides training in use of computers, software, and the Internet.

Community Environment: In this suburban area, the city of Roanoke is the business, cultural, and commercial center of Southwest Virginia. Air and bus transportation are available in Roanoke. Other community facilities of Roanoke are accessible to the students. There is also a symphony, opera company, ballet company, theatre company, art and science museums, and a farmers' market.

■ **ITT TECHNICAL INSTITUTE (CHANTILLY)**

14420 Abermarle Point Pl.

Ste. 100

Chantilly, VA 20151

Tel: (703)263-2541; Free: 888-895-8324

Web Site: www.itt-tech.edu/

Description: Proprietary, primarily 2-year, coed. Part of ITT Educational Services, Inc. Awards terminal associate and bachelor's degrees. Founded 2002.

Entrance Requirements: Entrance: minimally difficult.

■ **ITT TECHNICAL INSTITUTE (NORFOLK)**

863 Glenrock Rd., Ste. 100

Norfolk, VA 23502-3701

Tel: (757)466-1260; Free: 888-253-8324

Web Site: www.itt-tech.edu/

Description: Proprietary, primarily 2-year, coed. Part of ITT Educational Services, Inc. Awards terminal associate and bachelor's degrees. Founded 1988. Setting: suburban campus.

Entrance Requirements: Entrance: minimally difficult.

■ **ITT TECHNICAL INSTITUTE (RICHMOND)**

300 Gateway Centre Pky.

Richmond, VA 23235

Tel: (804)330-4992; Free: 888-330-4888

Web Site: www.itt-tech.edu/

Description: Proprietary, primarily 2-year, coed. Part of ITT Educational Services, Inc. Awards terminal associate and bachelor's degrees. Founded 1999.

Entrance Requirements: Entrance: minimally difficult.

■ **ITT TECHNICAL INSTITUTE (SALEM)**

2159 Apperson Dr.

Salem, VA 24153

Tel: (540)989-2500; Free: 877-208-6132

Web Site: www.itt-tech.edu/

Description: Proprietary, primarily 2-year, coed. Awards terminal associate and bachelor's degrees.

Entrance Requirements: Entrance: minimally difficult.

■ **ITT TECHNICAL INSTITUTE (SPRINGFIELD)**

7300 Boston Blvd.

Springfield, VA 22153

Tel: (703)440-9535; Free: 866-817-8324

Fax: (703)440-9561

Web Site: www.itt-tech.edu/

Description: Proprietary, primarily 2-year, coed. Part of ITT Educational Services, Inc. Awards terminal associate and bachelor's degrees. Founded 2002.

Entrance Requirements: Entrance: minimally difficult.

■ **J. SARGEANT REYNOLDS COMMUNITY COLLEGE**

PO Box 85622

Richmond, VA 23285-5622

Tel: (804)371-3000

Fax: (804)371-3650

E-mail: kpettis-walden@reynolds.edu

Web Site: www.reynolds.edu/

Description: State-supported, 2-year, coed. Part of Virginia Community College System. Awards certificates, transfer associate, and terminal associate degrees. Founded 1972. Setting: 207-acre suburban campus. Total enrollment: 13,370. Full-time: 1,054 students, 52% women, 48% men. Part-time: 1,126 students, 54% women, 46% men. 1% American Indian or Alaska Native, non-Hispanic/Latino; 3% Hispanic/Latino; 37% African American, non-Hispanic/Latino; 4% Asian, non-Hispanic/Latino. Calendar: semesters. Academic remediation for entering students, ESL program, services for LD students, advanced placement, independent study, distance learning, summer session for credit, part-time degree program, adult/continuing education programs, internships. Off campus study at Rappahannock Community College, Southside Virginia Community College.

Entrance Requirements: Open admission. Option: electronic application. Required: high school transcript. Required for some: interview. Entrance: noncompetitive. Application deadline: Rolling. Notification: continuous.

Collegiate Environment: Orientation program. Drama-theater group. Student services: personal-psychological counseling. Campus security: 24-hour emergency response devices and patrols, late night transport-escort service, security during open hours. J. Sargeant Reynolds Community College Library plus 3 others with 101,858 books, 45,875 serials, 2,483 audiovisual materials, an OPAC, and a Web page.

Community Environment: See University of Richmond.

■ **JAMES MADISON UNIVERSITY**

800 S Main St.

Harrisonburg, VA 22807

Tel: (540)568-6211

Fax: (540)568-3332
E-mail: admissions@jmu.edu
Web Site: www.jmu.edu/

Description: State-supported, comprehensive, coed. Awards bachelor's, master's, and doctoral degrees and post-master's certificates (also offers specialist in education degree). Founded 1908. Setting: 721-acre small town campus. Endowment: $59.6 million. Research spending for the previous fiscal year: $9.9 million. Educational spending for the previous fiscal year: $6626 per student. Total enrollment: 19,722. Faculty: 1,400 (924 full-time, 476 part-time). Student-undergrad faculty ratio is 16:1. 22,864 applied, 60% were admitted. 26% from top 10% of their high school class, 70% from top quarter, 98% from top half. Full-time: 17,086 students, 60% women, 40% men. Part-time: 814 students, 50% women, 50% men. Students come from 48 states and territories, 60 other countries, 27% from out-of-state. 0.2% American Indian or Alaska Native, non-Hispanic/Latino; 4% Hispanic/Latino; 4% African American, non-Hispanic/Latino; 5% Asian, non-Hispanic/Latino; 0.4% Native Hawaiian or other Pacific Islander, non-Hispanic/Latino; 1% international. 2% 25 or older, 36% live on campus, 4% transferred in. Retention: 91% of full-time freshmen returned the following year. Academic areas with the most degrees conferred: business/marketing; health professions and related sciences; communication/journalism. Core. Calendar: semesters. ESL program, services for LD students, advanced placement, accelerated degree program, self-designed majors, freshman honors college, honors program, independent study, distance learning, double major, summer session for credit, part-time degree program, adult/continuing education programs, internships, graduate courses open to undergrads. Off campus study at Distance Learning for Virginia Educators (DLVE): A degree for teachers who work with hearing impaired students. Partners are: JMU, Hampton University, and Longwood University. Visual Impairment (VI): A program for teachers who work with visually impaired students. JMU and GMU partner on this program. Study abroad program. ROTC: Army, Air Force (c).

Entrance Requirements: Options: electronic application, early action, deferred admission, international baccalaureate accepted. Required: high school transcript, SAT or ACT. Recommended: minimum 3 high school GPA. Entrance: very difficult. Application deadlines: 1/15, 11/1 for early action. Notification: 4/1, 1/1 for early action. Preference given to state residents. SAT Reasoning Test deadline: 1/15. Transfer credits accepted: Yes. Applicants placed on waiting list: 3,406. Wait-listed applicants offered admission: 165.

Costs Per Year: Application fee: $50. Area resident tuition: $169 per credit hour part-time. State resident tuition: $5104 full-time. Nonresident tuition: $19,582 full-time, $633 per credit hour part-time. Mandatory fees: $4072 full-time. College room and board: $8873. College room only: $4451. Room and board charges vary according to board plan.

Collegiate Environment: Orientation program. Drama-theater group, choral group, marching band, student-run newspaper, radio station. Social organizations: national fraternities, national sororities. Student services: health clinic, personal-psychological counseling, women's center. Campus security: 24-hour emergency response devices and patrols, student patrols, late night transport-escort service, controlled dormitory access, lighted pathways. College housing designed to accommodate 6,213 students; 6,301 undergraduates lived in college housing during 2012-13. Freshmen guaranteed college housing. On-campus residence required in freshman year. Option: coed housing available. Carrier Library plus 2 others with 761,026 books, 369,319 microform titles, 15,464 serials, 83,175 audiovisual materials, an OPAC, and a Web page. Operations spending for the previous fiscal year: $10.3 million. 600 computers available on campus for general student use. Computer purchase/lease plans available. A campuswide network can be accessed from student residence rooms and from off campus. Students can access the following: online class registration. Staffed computer lab on campus (open 24 hours a day) provides training in use of computers, software, and the Internet.

Community Environment: Located in the geographic center of Shenandoah Valley, Harrisonburg is an attractive city of 30,000 people. The Shenandoah National Park and the George Washington National Forest are here. All forms of commercial transportation are available. Community facilities include a number of churches, a library, hospital, and various civic and service organizations. Recreational facilities are available for camping, fishing, and picnicking. A snow skiing resort is also nearby.

■ **JEFFERSON COLLEGE OF HEALTH SCIENCES**
PO Box 13186
Roanoke, VA 24031-3186

Tel: (540)985-8483; Free: 888-985-8483
Fax: (540)985-9773
E-mail: jomckeon@jchs.edu
Web Site: www.jchs.edu/

Description: Independent, comprehensive, coed. Awards associate, bachelor's, and master's degrees. Founded 1982. Setting: 1-acre urban campus. Endowment: $1.6 million. Educational spending for the previous fiscal year: $9844 per student. Total enrollment: 1,032. Faculty: 128 (69 full-time, 59 part-time). Student-undergrad faculty ratio is 10:1. 572 applied, 39% were admitted. Full-time: 636 students, 82% women, 18% men. Part-time: 197 students, 86% women, 14% men. Students come from 22 states and territories, 10 other countries, 4% from out-of-state. 0.2% American Indian or Alaska Native, non-Hispanic/Latino; 1% Hispanic/Latino; 11% African American, non-Hispanic/Latino; 1% Asian, non-Hispanic/Latino; 0.1% Native Hawaiian or other Pacific Islander, non-Hispanic/Latino; 0.1% international. 45% 25 or older, 5% live on campus, 27% transferred in. Retention: 71% of full-time freshmen returned the following year. Academic areas with the most degrees conferred: health professions and related sciences; biological/life sciences. Core. Calendar: semesters. ESL program, services for LD students, advanced placement, accelerated degree program, independent study, distance learning, double major, summer session for credit, part-time degree program, adult/continuing education programs, co-op programs and internships. Off campus study.

Entrance Requirements: Options: electronic application, deferred admission, international baccalaureate accepted. Required: high school transcript, minimum 2 high school GPA, SAT or ACT. Recommended: SAT. Required for some: interview. Entrance: moderately difficult. Application deadline: Rolling. Notification: continuous. Transfer credits accepted: Yes. Applicants placed on waiting list: 20. Wait-listed applicants offered admission: 0.

Collegiate Environment: Orientation program. Choral group, student-run newspaper. Social organizations: 5 open to all. Most popular organizations: Jefferson Activities Group (JAG), Student Ambassadors, Hands of Healing, American Medical Students Association (AMSA), Student Nurses Association. Major annual events: Organization and Wellness Day, Spirit Day, Halloween Party. Student services: personal-psychological counseling. Campus security: 24-hour emergency response devices and patrols, late night transport-escort service, controlled dormitory access. JCHS Library with 6,042 books, 16 microform titles, 233 serials, 424 audiovisual materials, an OPAC, and a Web page. 72 computers available on campus for general student use. A campuswide network can be accessed from student residence rooms. Students can access the following: online class registration. Staffed computer lab on campus provides training in use of computers, software, and the Internet.

■ **JOHN TYLER COMMUNITY COLLEGE**
13101 Jefferson Davis Hwy.
Chester, VA 23831-5316
Tel: (804)796-4000; Free: 800-552-3490
Fax: (804)796-4163
Web Site: www.jtcc.edu/

Description: State-supported, 2-year, coed. Part of Virginia Community College System. Awards certificates, transfer associate, and terminal associate degrees. Founded 1967. Setting: 160-acre suburban campus with easy access to Richmond. Total enrollment: 10,145. Faculty: 542 (119 full-time, 423 part-time). Student-undergrad faculty ratio is 20:1. Full-time: 2,820 students, 57% women, 43% men. Part-time: 7,325 students, 58% women, 42% men. 1% American Indian or Alaska Native, non-Hispanic/Latino; 6% Hispanic/Latino; 25% African American, non-Hispanic/Latino; 3% Asian, non-Hispanic/Latino; 0% Native Hawaiian or other Pacific Islander, non-Hispanic/Latino; 0.2% international. Retention: 51% of full-time freshmen returned the following year. Core. Calendar: semesters. Academic remediation for entering students, services for LD students, advanced placement, honors program, distance learning, summer session for credit, part-time degree program, external degree program, adult/continuing education programs. Off campus study. Study abroad program. ROTC: Army (c).

Entrance Requirements: Open admission. Options: early admission, deferred admission. Recommended: high school transcript. Entrance: noncompetitive. Application deadline: Rolling. Notification: continuous. Preference given to district residents.

Costs Per Year: Application fee: $0. State resident tuition: $2988 full-time, $124.50 per credit hour part-time. Nonresident tuition: $7598 full-time, $316.10 per credit hour part-time. Mandatory fees: $50 full-time, $25 per term part-time. Full-time tuition and fees vary according to course load. Part-time tuition and fees vary according to course load.

Collegiate Environment: Drama-theater group, choral group. Social organizations: 23 open to all. Most popular organizations: Phi Theta Kappa -TauRho, Phi Theta Kappa - BOO, Art Club, Elements of Life Club, Funeral Services Club. Major annual event: Fool for Art. Campus security: 24-hour emergency response devices and patrols. College housing not available. John Tyler Community College Learning Resource and Technology Center with 52,000 books, 10,150 serials, 1,335 audiovisual materials, an OPAC, and a Web page. 2,115 computers available on campus for general student use. A campuswide network can be accessed from off-campus. Students can access the following: online class registration. Staffed computer lab on campus provides training in use of computers, software, and the Internet.

Community Environment: Located 10 miles from Richmond, the state capital, and Petersburg.

■ **LIBERTY UNIVERSITY**
1971 University Blvd.
Lynchburg, VA 24502
Tel: (434)582-2000; Free: 800-543-5317
Fax: (434)582-2304
E-mail: admissions@liberty.edu
Web Site: www.liberty.edu/
Description: Independent nondenominational, comprehensive, coed. Awards associate, bachelor's, master's, and doctoral degrees and post-master's certificates (also offers external degree program with significant enrollment not reflected in profile). Founded 1971. Setting: 6,500-acre suburban campus. Total enrollment: 12,645. Faculty: 629 (532 full-time, 97 part-time). Student-undergrad faculty ratio is 23:1. 25,976 applied, 23% were admitted. 22% from top 10% of their high school class, 50% from top quarter, 78% from top half. Full-time: 11,231 students, 52% women, 48% men. Part-time: 350 students, 48% women, 52% men. Students come from 78 other countries, 58% from out-of-state. 0.4% American Indian or Alaska Native, non-Hispanic/Latino; 3% Hispanic/Latino; 7% African American, non-Hispanic/Latino; 1% Asian, non-Hispanic/Latino; 0.2% Native Hawaiian or other Pacific Islander, non-Hispanic/Latino; 6% international. 3% 25 or older, 61% live on campus, 6% transferred in. Retention: 81% of full-time freshmen returned the following year. Academic areas with the most degrees conferred: business/marketing; health professions and related sciences; psychology. Core. Calendar: semesters. Academic remediation for entering students, ESL program, services for LD students, advanced placement, accelerated degree program, self-designed majors, honors program, independent study, distance learning, double major, summer session for credit, part-time degree program, external degree program, co-op programs and internships, graduate courses open to undergrads. Off campus study. Study abroad program. ROTC: Army, Air Force (c).
Entrance Requirements: Options: electronic application, international baccalaureate accepted. Required: essay, high school transcript, minimum 2 high school GPA, SAT or ACT. Recommended: minimum 2 high school GPA. Entrance: minimally difficult. Application deadlines: Rolling, Rolling for nonresidents. Notification: continuous, continuous for nonresidents. Transfer credits accepted: Yes.
Costs Per Year: Application fee: $40. Comprehensive fee: $28,868 includes full-time tuition ($19,486), mandatory fees ($1406), and college room and board ($7976). Full-time tuition and fees vary according to course load. Room and board charges vary according to housing facility. Part-time tuition: $650 per credit hour. Part-time mandatory fees: $1550 per year. Part-time tuition and fees vary according to course load.
Collegiate Environment: Orientation program. Drama-theater group, choral group, marching band, student-run newspaper, radio station. Most popular organization: Campus Serve. Major annual events: Coffeehouse, Homecoming, Block Party. Student services: health clinic, personal-psychological counseling. Campus security: 24-hour patrols, late night transport-escort service, 24-hour emergency dispatch. 7,287 college housing spaces available; 6,497 were occupied in 2012-13. Freshmen guaranteed college housing. On-campus residence required through senior year. Options: men-only, women-only housing available. A. Pierre Guillermin Integrated Learning Resource Center plus 1 other with 402,115 books, 544,149 microform titles, 75,441 serials, 141,171 audiovisual materials, an OPAC, and a Web page. 800 computers available on campus for general student use. A campuswide network can be accessed from student residence rooms and from off campus. Students can access the following: online class registration. Staffed computer lab on campus provides training in use of computers, software, and the Internet.
Community Environment: Lynchburg, with a population of 67,000, is in the heart of Virginia on the south bank of the historic James River, with the

scenic Blue Ridge Mountains nearby. The city is over 200 years old and is noted for its culture, beauty and educational advantages. It is at the crossroads of U.S. highways 29 and 460 and has adequate transportation facilities by bus, railway and air.

■ **LONGWOOD UNIVERSITY**
201 High St.
Farmville, VA 23909
Tel: (434)395-2000; Free: 800-281-4677
Fax: (434)395-2332
E-mail: admissions@longwood.edu
Web Site: www.longwood.edu/
Description: State-supported, comprehensive, coed. Part of The State Council of Higher Education for Virginia. Awards bachelor's and master's degrees and post-master's certificates. Founded 1839. Setting: 60-acre small town campus with easy access to Richmond. Endowment: $49.9 million. Research spending for the previous fiscal year: $153,909. Educational spending for the previous fiscal year: $7407 per student. Total enrollment: 4,834. Faculty: 288 (225 full-time, 63 part-time). Student-undergrad faculty ratio is 18:1. 4,166 applied, 78% were admitted. 12% from top 10% of their high school class, 39% from top quarter, 79% from top half. Full-time: 3,963 students, 67% women, 33% men. Part-time: 392 students, 61% women, 39% men. Students come from 25 states and territories, 15 other countries, 4% from out-of-state. 0.2% American Indian or Alaska Native, non-Hispanic/Latino; 4% Hispanic/Latino; 7% African American, non-Hispanic/Latino; 1% Asian, non-Hispanic/Latino; 0.2% Native Hawaiian or other Pacific Islander, non-Hispanic/Latino; 1% international. 2% 25 or older, 71% live on campus, 5% transferred in. Retention: 79% of full-time freshmen returned the following year. Academic areas with the most degrees conferred: liberal arts/general studies; business/marketing; social sciences. Core. Calendar: semesters. ESL program, services for LD students, advanced placement, accelerated degree program, honors program, independent study, distance learning, double major, summer session for credit, part-time degree program, internships, graduate courses open to undergrads. Off campus study at Hampden-Sydney College. Study abroad program. ROTC: Army.
Entrance Requirements: Options: electronic application, early admission, early action, deferred admission, international baccalaureate accepted. Required: essay, high school transcript, SAT or ACT. Entrance: moderately difficult. Application deadlines: 3/1, 3/1 for nonresidents, 12/1 for early action. Notification: 6/1, 6/1 for nonresidents, 1/15 for early action. Transfer credits accepted: Yes. Early action applicants: 1,980. Early action applicants admitted: 1,080.
Costs Per Year: Application fee: $50. State resident tuition: $6120 full-time, $204 per credit hour part-time. Nonresident tuition: $17,760 full-time, $592 per credit hour part-time. Mandatory fees: $4770 full-time, $159 per credit hour part-time. Full-time tuition and fees vary according to course load. Part-time tuition and fees vary according to course load. College room and board: $8448. College room only: $5524. Room and board charges vary according to board plan, housing facility, and location.
Collegiate Environment: Orientation program. Drama-theater group, choral group, student-run newspaper, radio station. Social organizations: 125 open to all; national fraternities, national sororities; 21% of eligible men and 18% of eligible women are members. Most popular organizations: Student Government Association, Alpha Phi Omega, Inter-Varsity Christian Fellowship, Longwood Ambassadors, Wellness Advocates. Major annual events: Oktoberfest, Spring Weekend, Rock The Block. Student services: health clinic, personal-psychological counseling. Campus security: 24-hour emergency response devices and patrols, late night transport-escort service, controlled dormitory access. 2,972 college housing spaces available; 2,863 were occupied in 2012-13. Freshmen guaranteed college housing. On-campus residence required through sophomore year. Options: coed, women-only housing available. The Janet D. Greenwood Library with 478,036 books, 667,657 microform titles, 64,000 serials, 20,242 audiovisual materials, an OPAC, and a Web page. Operations spending for the previous fiscal year: $3.2 million. 315 computers available on campus for general student use. Computer purchase/lease plans available. A computer is required for all students. A campuswide network can be accessed from student residence rooms and from off campus. Students can access the following: online class registration. Staffed computer lab on campus provides training in use of computers, software, and the Internet.
Community Environment: Farmville is a small residential town. Bus transportation is available. Most major religious denominations are represented, and a community hospital is 5 blocks from campus. Nearby state parks provide swimming, boating, camping and hiking facilities.

■ LORD FAIRFAX COMMUNITY COLLEGE

173 Skirmisher Ln.
Middletown, VA 22645
Tel: (540)868-7000; Free: 800-906-LFCC
Fax: (540)868-7100
E-mail: kbucher@lfcc.edu
Web Site: www.lfcc.edu/

Description: State-supported, 2-year, coed. Part of Virginia Community College System. Awards certificates, transfer associate, and terminal associate degrees. Founded 1969. Setting: 100-acre rural campus with easy access to Washington, DC. Total enrollment: 6,644. Student-undergrad faculty ratio is 22:1. 1% from out-of-state. 28% 25 or older. Retention: 60% of full-time freshmen returned the following year. Core. Calendar: semesters. Academic remediation for entering students, services for LD students, advanced placement, honors program, distance learning, summer session for credit, part-time degree program, adult/continuing education programs, co-op programs.

Entrance Requirements: Open admission. Option: early admission. Recommended: high school transcript. Entrance: noncompetitive. Application deadline: Rolling. Notification: continuous.

Collegiate Environment: Drama-theater group. Student services: personal-psychological counseling, women's center. Campus security: late night transport-escort service. Learning Resources Center with an OPAC.

Community Environment: The area is rural and does not offer public transportation. There is medium industry and seasonal employment in the apple industry.

■ LYNCHBURG COLLEGE

1501 Lakeside Dr.
Lynchburg, VA 24501-3199
Tel: (434)544-8100; Free: 800-426-8101
Fax: (434)544-8653
E-mail: admissions@lynchburg.edu
Web Site: www.lynchburg.edu/

Description: Independent, comprehensive, coed, affiliated with Christian Church (Disciples of Christ). Awards bachelor's, master's, and doctoral degrees and post-master's certificates. Founded 1903. Setting: 214-acre suburban campus. Endowment: $74.6 million. Total enrollment: 2,756. Faculty: 297 (186 full-time, 111 part-time). Student-undergrad faculty ratio is 11:1. 4,474 applied, 67% were admitted. 10% from top 10% of their high school class, 37% from top quarter, 75% from top half. Full-time: 2,088 students, 59% women, 41% men. Part-time: 123 students, 67% women, 33% men. Students come from 33 states and territories, 13 other countries, 33% from out-of-state. 0.4% American Indian or Alaska Native, non-Hispanic/Latino; 3% Hispanic/Latino; 10% African American, non-Hispanic/Latino; 1% Asian, non-Hispanic/Latino; 0.05% Native Hawaiian or other Pacific Islander, non-Hispanic/Latino; 1% international. 6% 25 or older, 77% live on campus, 4% transferred in. Retention: 73% of full-time freshmen returned the following year. Academic areas with the most degrees conferred: social sciences; health professions and related sciences; business/marketing. Core. Calendar: semesters. Services for LD students, advanced placement, accelerated degree program, honors program, independent study, distance learning, double major, summer session for credit, part-time degree program, adult/continuing education programs, internships, graduate courses open to undergrads. Off campus study at Lynchburg College, Randolph College, and Sweet Briar College are members of the Tri-College Consortium in which students of the three colleges may take classes at the other two colleges at no charge (if their home college does not offer the class(es) of interest). Study abroad program.

Entrance Requirements: Options: electronic application, early admission, early decision, deferred admission. Required: high school transcript, SAT or ACT. Recommended: essay, 2 recommendations, interview. Entrance: moderately difficult. Application deadlines: Rolling, 11/15 for early decision. Notification: continuous, 12/15 for early decision. Transfer credits accepted: Yes. Early decision applicants: 226. Early decision applicants admitted: 92.

Costs Per Year: Application fee: $30. Comprehensive fee: $40,685 includes full-time tuition ($31,060), mandatory fees ($945), and college room and board ($8680). College room only: $4360. Room and board charges vary according to board plan and housing facility. Part-time tuition: $430 per credit hour. Part-time mandatory fees: $5.10 per credit hour. Part-time tuition and fees vary according to course load.

Collegiate Environment: Orientation program. Drama-theater group, choral group, student-run newspaper. Social organizations: 80 open to all; national fraternities, national sororities; 4% of eligible men and 8% of eligible women are members. Most popular organizations: Student Government Association,

Student Activities Board, Enrollment Student Ambassadors, Emergency Services, Greek Life. Major annual events: Homecoming, Turkey Bowl, Sibs-n-Kids Weekend. Student services: health clinic, personal-psychological counseling. Campus security: 24-hour emergency response devices and patrols, late night transport-escort service, controlled dormitory access. Freshmen guaranteed college housing. On-campus residence required through junior year. Option: coed housing available. Knight-Capron Library with 322,751 books, 454,996 microform titles, 261 serials, 8,418 audiovisual materials, an OPAC, and a Web page. 300 computers available on campus for general student use. A campuswide network can be accessed from student residence rooms. Students can access the following: online class registration. Staffed computer lab on campus provides training in use of computers and the Internet.

Community Environment: Founded in 1786, Lynchburg is rich in history. It is a modern community with diversified industry in a traditional, handsome setting. Although it has a metropolitan area population of 214,000, Lynchburg maintains intimate contact with the countryside since it is very near the Blue Ridge Mountains and is in the center of perhaps the most historic of states. Washington, D.C., is less than 4 hours away, Williamsburg approximately 3, and Richmond about 2 1/2. The area provides excellent climate, convenient shopping, and many cultural opportunities. There is an active Lynchburg Fine Arts Center, and professional musical and theatrical groups visit. Some of the 7 colleges in the area also present fine arts programs.

■ MARY BALDWIN COLLEGE

201 E Frederick St.
Staunton, VA 24401-3610
Tel: (540)887-7000; Free: 800-468-2262
Fax: (540)886-6634
E-mail: rpalmer@mbc.edu
Web Site: www.mbc.edu/

Description: Independent, comprehensive, coed. Awards bachelor's and master's degrees. Founded 1842. Setting: 54-acre small town campus. Endowment: $31.9 million. Educational spending for the previous fiscal year: $8187 per student. Total enrollment: 1,804. Faculty: 128 (76 full-time, 52 part-time). Student-undergrad faculty ratio is 12:1. 4,909 applied, 54% were admitted. 19% from top 10% of their high school class, 53% from top quarter, 84% from top half. Full-time: 1,035 students, 96% women, 4% men. Part-time: 491 students, 88% women, 12% men. Students come from 35 states and territories, 8 other countries, 40% from out-of-state. 1% American Indian or Alaska Native, non-Hispanic/Latino; 6% Hispanic/Latino; 27% African American, non-Hispanic/Latino; 2% Asian, non-Hispanic/Latino; 0.1% Native Hawaiian or other Pacific Islander, non-Hispanic/Latino; 3% international. 2% 25 or older, 48% live on campus, 2% transferred in. Retention: 69% of full-time freshmen returned the following year. Academic areas with the most degrees conferred: social sciences; interdisciplinary studies; psychology. Core. Calendar: 4-1-4. Academic remediation for entering students, ESL program, services for LD students, advanced placement, accelerated degree program, self-designed majors, freshman honors college, honors program, independent study, double major, part-time degree program, external degree program, adult/continuing education programs, internships, graduate courses open to undergrads. Off campus study at members of the Seven-College Exchange Program. Study abroad program. ROTC: Army, Naval (c), Air Force (c).

Entrance Requirements: Options: electronic application, early admission, early decision, deferred admission, international baccalaureate accepted. Required: high school transcript, minimum 2 high school GPA, 1 recommendation, SAT or ACT. Recommended: interview. Entrance: moderately difficult. Application deadlines: Rolling, 11/15 for early decision. Notification: continuous, 12/1 for early decision. SAT Reasoning Test deadline: 7/8. SAT Subject Test deadline: 7/8. Early decision applicants: 25. Early decision applicants admitted: 14.

Costs Per Year: Application fee: $35. One-time mandatory fee: $100. Comprehensive fee: $37,120 includes full-time tuition ($28,360), mandatory fees ($360), and college room and board ($8400). College room only: $5360. Full-time tuition and fees vary according to degree level. Room and board charges vary according to housing facility. Part-time tuition: $427 per semester hour. Part-time mandatory fees: $427 per semester hour. Part-time tuition and fees vary according to degree level.

Collegiate Environment: Orientation program. Drama-theater group, choral group, marching band, student-run newspaper, radio station. Social organizations: 57 open to all. Most popular organizations: International Club council, Minority Clubs United, Student Senate, Baldwin Program Board,

Resident Hall Association. Major annual events: Apple Day, Junior Dads Weekend, Christmas Cheer. Student services: health clinic, personal-psychological counseling. Campus security: 24-hour emergency response devices and patrols, late night transport-escort service, controlled dormitory access. 760 college housing spaces available; 576 were occupied in 2012-13. Freshmen guaranteed college housing. On-campus residence required through senior year. Option: women-only housing available. Grafton Library with 147,624 books, 65,502 microform titles, 36,606 serials, 7,907 audiovisual materials, an OPAC, and a Web page. Operations spending for the previous fiscal year: $349,500. 244 computers available on campus for general student use. A campuswide network can be accessed from student residence rooms and from off campus. Students can access the following: online class registration, 100% wireless. Staffed computer lab on campus (open 24 hours a day) provides training in use of computers, software, and the Internet.

Community Environment: Staunton, one of the oldest cities west of the Blue Ridge Mountains, originated the city manager form of government. Annual snowfall here is 16 inches. All modes of commercial transportation are available. Community facilities include a public library, YMCA, hospital, many churches, shopping areas, and civic and service organizations. Recreational activities include golf, tennis, skiing, horseback riding, bowling, swimming, fishing, and hunting. Some of the points of interest are the birthplace of Woodrow Wilson, the Old Trinity Church, and American Frontier Museum. Opportunities for part-time work are available.

■ **MARYMOUNT UNIVERSITY**
2807 N Glebe Rd.
Arlington, VA 22207-4299
Tel: (703)522-5600; Free: 800-548-7638
Fax: (703)522-0349
E-mail: admissions@marymount.edu
Web Site: www.marymount.edu/
Description: Independent, comprehensive, coed, affiliated with Roman Catholic Church. Awards bachelor's, master's, and doctoral degrees and post-master's certificates. Founded 1950. Setting: 21-acre suburban campus with easy access to Washington, DC. Endowment: $23 million. Educational spending for the previous fiscal year: $8783 per student. Total enrollment: 3,702. Faculty: 370 (157 full-time, 213 part-time). Student-undergrad faculty ratio is 13:1. 1,945 applied, 80% were admitted. 14% from top 10% of their high school class, 31% from top quarter, 74% from top half. Full-time: 2,175 students, 70% women, 30% men. Part-time: 295 students, 72% women, 28% men. Students come from 39 states and territories, 57 other countries, 37% from out-of-state. 0.3% American Indian or Alaska Native, non-Hispanic/Latino; 15% Hispanic/Latino; 16% African American, non-Hispanic/Latino; 8% Asian, non-Hispanic/Latino; 0.5% Native Hawaiian or other Pacific Islander, non-Hispanic/Latino; 10% international. 23% 25 or older, 34% live on campus, 15% transferred in. Retention: 74% of full-time freshmen returned the following year. Academic areas with the most degrees conferred: health professions and related sciences; business/marketing; visual and performing arts. Core. Calendar: semesters plus 2 summer terms. Academic remediation for entering students, ESL program, services for LD students, advanced placement, accelerated degree program, self-designed majors, honors program, independent study, distance learning, double major, summer session for credit, part-time degree program, internships, graduate courses open to undergrads. Off campus study at Consortium of Universities of the Washington Metropolitan Area. Study abroad program. ROTC: Army (c).

Entrance Requirements: Options: electronic application, deferred admission, international baccalaureate accepted. Required: essay, high school transcript, minimum 2.5 high school GPA, 1 recommendation, SAT or ACT. Recommended: interview. Required for some: interview. Entrance: moderately difficult. Application deadline: Rolling. Notification: continuous. Transfer credits accepted: Yes.

Costs Per Year: Application fee: $40. One-time mandatory fee: $360. Comprehensive fee: $37,980 includes full-time tuition ($26,100), mandatory fees ($330), and college room and board ($11,550). Room and board charges vary according to housing facility. Part-time tuition: $850 per credit hour.

Collegiate Environment: Orientation program. Drama-theater group, choral group, student-run newspaper. Social organizations: 42 open to all. Most popular organizations: Fashion Club, Student Nurses Association, International Club, Activities Programming Board, Blue Harmony (show choir). Major annual events: Portfolio in Motion Fashion Show, Snowball Winter Dance, International Week. Student services: health clinic, personal-

psychological counseling. Campus security: 24-hour emergency response devices and patrols, late night transport-escort service, controlled dormitory access. 858 college housing spaces available; 844 were occupied in 2012-13. Freshmen given priority for college housing. On-campus residence required through sophomore year. Options: coed, men-only, women-only housing available. Emerson C. Reinsch Library plus 1 other with 241,177 books, 198,465 microform titles, 57,490 serials, 14,019 audiovisual materials, an OPAC, and a Web page. Operations spending for the previous fiscal year: $2.7 million. 350 computers available on campus for general student use. A campuswide network can be accessed from student residence rooms and from off campus. Students can access the following: online class registration, online drive space. Staffed computer lab on campus provides training in use of software and the Internet.

Community Environment: Located in Arlington, Virginia, just minutes from Washington, DC, Marymount provides students with an easy access to the resources of the nation's capital, including the Library of Congress, the National Archives, the Smithsonian Institution, the John F. Kennedy Center for the Performing Arts, and the Capitol. The University location offers both professional and scholarly opportunities for faculty; the opportunity to bring leaders from government, commerce, and the professions to the University campus; resources for instruction and research; internships placements for students; and employment opportunities for graduates.

■ **MILLER-MOTTE TECHNICAL COLLEGE**
4444 Electric Rd.
Roanoke, VA 24018
Tel: (540)597-1010
Web Site: www.miller-motte.edu/
Description: Proprietary, 2-year, coed.

■ **MOUNTAIN EMPIRE COMMUNITY COLLEGE**
3441 Mountain Empire Rd.
Big Stone Gap, VA 24219
Tel: (276)523-2400
E-mail: khall@me.vccs.edu
Web Site: www.mecc.edu/
Description: State-supported, 2-year, coed. Part of Virginia Community College System. Awards certificates, transfer associate, and terminal associate degrees. Founded 1972. Setting: rural campus. Total enrollment: 3,404. Faculty: 202 (40 full-time, 162 part-time). Students come from 10 states and territories, 3% from out-of-state. 0.2% American Indian or Alaska Native, non-Hispanic/Latino; 0.3% Hispanic/Latino; 2% African American, non-Hispanic/Latino; 0.3% Asian, non-Hispanic/Latino; 0% Native Hawaiian or other Pacific Islander, non-Hispanic/Latino; 0% international. 32% 25 or older. Retention: 48% of full-time freshmen returned the following year. Calendar: semesters. Academic remediation for entering students, advanced placement, self-designed majors, independent study, distance learning, double major, summer session for credit, part-time degree program, external degree program, adult/continuing education programs, co-op programs and internships.

Entrance Requirements: Open admission except for nursing (RN) and respiratory therapy programs. Options: electronic application, early admission, deferred admission. Required: high school transcript. Required for some: minimum 2 high school GPA. Entrance: noncompetitive. Application deadline: Rolling. Notification: continuous. Transfer credits accepted: Yes.

Collegiate Environment: Orientation program. Drama-theater group. Social organizations: 13 open to all. Most popular organizations: Phi Theta Kappa, Healing Hands, Rho Nu (SNAV), Students in Free Enterprise (SIFE), Merits. Major annual events: Spring Fling, Home Crafts Day, Pro-Art. Student services: personal-psychological counseling. Campus security: 24-hour emergency response devices and patrols. Wampler Library with 44,136 books, 8,352 microform titles, 148 serials, an OPAC, and a Web page. 400 computers available on campus for general student use. A campuswide network can be accessed from off-campus. Students can access the following: online class registration. Staffed computer lab on campus provides training in use of computers and software.

Community Environment: Big Stone Gap is a rural community in the southwest corner of Virginia, situated in the Cumberland Mountains. It has a population of 5,854. Many state parks and recreational areas are within an easy drive of the campus. Kingsport, Tennessee is approximately 30 miles south of the campus.

■ **NATIONAL COLLEGE (CHARLOTTESVILLE)**
3926 Seminole Trl.
Charlottesville, VA 22911

Tel: (434)295-0136; Free: 888-9-JOBREADY
Fax: (434)986-1344
Web Site: www.national-college.edu/
Description: Proprietary, 2-year, coed. Part of National College of Business and Technology. Awards certificates, diplomas, and terminal associate degrees. Founded 1975. Setting: small town campus with easy access to Richmond. Core. Services for LD students, advanced placement, honors program, double major, summer session for credit, part-time degree program, internships.
Entrance Requirements: Open admission. Option: electronic application. Recommended: interview. Required for some: high school transcript. Entrance: noncompetitive. Application deadline: Rolling.
Collegiate Environment: Orientation program.

■ **NATIONAL COLLEGE (DANVILLE)**
336 Old Riverside Dr.
Danville, VA 24541
Tel: (434)793-6822; Free: 888-9-JOBREADY
Fax: (434)793-3634
Web Site: www.national-college.edu/
Description: Proprietary, primarily 2-year, coed. Part of National College of Business and Technology. Awards diplomas, terminal associate, and bachelor's degrees. Founded 1975. Setting: small town campus. Summer session for credit, part-time degree program.
Entrance Requirements: Open admission. Option: electronic application. Recommended: interview. Required for some: high school transcript. Entrance: noncompetitive. Application deadline: Rolling.
Collegiate Environment: Orientation program.

■ **NATIONAL COLLEGE (HARRISONBURG)**
1515 Country Club Rd.
Harrisonburg, VA 22802
Tel: (540)432-0943; Free: 888-9-JOBREADY
Fax: (540)986-1344
Web Site: www.national-college.edu/
Description: Proprietary, primarily 2-year, coed. Part of National College of Business and Technology. Awards diplomas, terminal associate, and bachelor's degrees. Founded 1988. Setting: small town campus. Core. Services for LD students, advanced placement, honors program, double major, summer session for credit, part-time degree program, internships.
Entrance Requirements: Open admission. Option: electronic application. Recommended: interview. Required for some: high school transcript. Entrance: noncompetitive. Application deadline: Rolling. Notification: continuous.
Collegiate Environment: Orientation program.

■ **NATIONAL COLLEGE (LYNCHBURG)**
104 Candlewood Ct.
Lynchburg, VA 24502-2653
Tel: (434)239-3500; Free: 888-9-JOBREADY
Fax: (434)986-1344
Web Site: www.national-college.edu/
Description: Proprietary, primarily 2-year, coed. Part of National College of Business and Technology. Awards diplomas, terminal associate, and bachelor's degrees. Founded 1979. Setting: 2-acre small town campus. Core. Services for LD students, advanced placement, honors program, double major, summer session for credit, part-time degree program, internships.
Entrance Requirements: Open admission. Option: electronic application. Recommended: interview. Required for some: high school transcript. Entrance: noncompetitive. Application deadline: Rolling.
Collegiate Environment: Orientation program.

■ **NATIONAL COLLEGE (MARTINSVILLE)**
905 Memorial Blvd. N
Martinsville, VA 24112
Tel: (276)632-5621; Free: 888-9-JOBREADY
Fax: (276)986-1344
Web Site: www.national-college.edu/
Description: Proprietary, 2-year, coed. Part of National College of Business and Technology. Awards diplomas and terminal associate degrees. Founded 1975. Setting: small town campus. Core. Services for LD students, advanced placement, honors program, double major, summer session for credit, part-time degree program, internships.

Entrance Requirements: Open admission. Option: electronic application. Recommended: interview. Required for some: high school transcript. Entrance: noncompetitive. Application deadline: Rolling.
Collegiate Environment: Orientation program.

■ **NATIONAL COLLEGE (SALEM)**
1813 E Main St.
Salem, VA 24153
Tel: (540)986-1800; Free: 888-9-JOBREADY
Fax: (540)986-1344
Web Site: www.national-college.edu/
Description: Proprietary, primarily 2-year, coed. Part of National College of Business and Technology. Awards certificates, diplomas, transfer associate, terminal associate, bachelor's, and master's degrees. Founded 1886. Setting: 3-acre urban campus. Academic remediation for entering students, advanced placement, summer session for credit, part-time degree program.
Entrance Requirements: Open admission. Required: high school transcript. Recommended: interview. Entrance: noncompetitive. Application deadline: Rolling. Notification: continuous.
Collegiate Environment: Orientation program.

■ **NEW RIVER COMMUNITY COLLEGE**
PO Box 1127
Dublin, VA 24084-1127
Tel: (540)674-3600; Free: 866-462-6722
Fax: (540)674-3644
E-mail: nrtaylm@nr.edu
Web Site: www.nr.edu/
Description: State-supported, 2-year, coed. Part of Virginia Community College System. Awards certificates, diplomas, transfer associate, and terminal associate degrees. Founded 1969. Setting: 100-acre rural campus. Endowment: $1.9 million. Total enrollment: 4,345. Faculty: 206 (51 full-time, 155 part-time). Student-undergrad faculty ratio is 22:1. Full-time: 2,008 students, 49% women, 51% men. Part-time: 2,337 students, 56% women, 44% men. Students come from 22 states and territories, 21 other countries, 3% from out-of-state. 40% 25 or older, 5% transferred in. Calendar: semesters. Academic remediation for entering students, services for LD students, advanced placement, distance learning, double major, summer session for credit, part-time degree program, external degree program, adult/continuing education programs, co-op programs and internships.
Entrance Requirements: Open admission. Options: early admission, deferred admission. Required for some: high school transcript. Entrance: noncompetitive. Application deadline: Rolling. Notification: continuous. Preference given to local residents.
Collegiate Environment: Most popular organizations: Student Government Association, Phi Beta Lambda, Instrument Society of America, Human Service Organization, Sign Language Club. Major annual events: Fall Bash, Freaky Friday, Spring Fling. Student services: personal-psychological counseling. Campus security: 24-hour patrols. New River Community College Library with 33,993 books, 258 serials, and an OPAC. Operations spending for the previous fiscal year: $551,572. 120 computers available on campus for general student use. A campuswide network can be accessed. Staffed computer lab on campus.

■ **NORFOLK STATE UNIVERSITY**
700 Park Ave.
Norfolk, VA 23504
Tel: (757)823-8600; Free: 800-274-1821
Fax: (757)823-9435
E-mail: admissions@nsu.edu
Web Site: www.nsu.edu/
Description: State-supported, comprehensive, coed. Part of State Council of Higher Education for Virginia. Awards associate, bachelor's, master's, and doctoral degrees. Founded 1935. Setting: 134-acre urban campus. Total enrollment: 8,343. Faculty: 417 (278 full-time, 139 part-time). Student-undergrad faculty ratio is 19:1. 4,226 applied, 67% were admitted. 13% from top 10% of their high school class, 26% from top quarter, 43% from top half. Full-time: 6,263 students, 62% women, 38% men. Part-time: 1,192 students, 73% women, 27% men. 16% from out-of-state. 0.2% American Indian or Alaska Native, non-Hispanic/Latino; 2% Hispanic/Latino; 84% African American, non-Hispanic/Latino; 1% Asian, non-Hispanic/Latino; 0.1% Native Hawaiian or other Pacific Islander, non-Hispanic/Latino; 0.5% international. 26% 25 or older, 38% live on campus, 8% transferred in. Retention: 73% of full-time freshmen returned the following year. Academic areas with the most

degrees conferred: natural resources/environmental science; business/marketing; health professions and related sciences. Calendar: semesters. ROTC: Army, Naval.

Entrance Requirements: Options: electronic application, deferred admission. Required: high school transcript, minimum 2.3 high school GPA, SAT or ACT. Entrance: moderately difficult.

Costs Per Year: State resident tuition: $6860 full-time, $252 per credit hour part-time. Nonresident tuition: $20,343 full-time, $702 per credit hour part-time. Full-time tuition varies according to course load. Part-time tuition varies according to course load. College room and board: $8130. Room and board charges vary according to board plan and housing facility.

Collegiate Environment: Orientation program. Campus security: 24-hour emergency response devices and patrols, late night transport-escort service. Options: men-only, women-only housing available.

Community Environment: See Old Dominion University.

■ NORTHERN VIRGINIA COMMUNITY COLLEGE

4001 Wakefield Chapel Rd.
Annandale, VA 22003-3796
Tel: (703)323-3000
Web Site: www.nvcc.edu/

Description: State-supported, 2-year, coed. Part of Virginia Community College System. Awards certificates, transfer associate, and terminal associate degrees. Founded 1965. Setting: 435-acre suburban campus with easy access to Washington, DC. Total enrollment: 41,266. 42% 25 or older. Core. Calendar: semesters. Academic remediation for entering students, ESL program, services for LD students, advanced placement, honors program, distance learning, double major, summer session for credit, part-time degree program, external degree program, adult/continuing education programs, co-op programs. Study abroad program.

Entrance Requirements: Open admission except for veterinary technology, dental hygiene, other health-related programs. Options: early admission, deferred admission. Required for some: high school transcript. Entrance: noncompetitive. Application deadline: Rolling. Notification: continuous.

Collegiate Environment: Student-run newspaper. Campus security: 24-hour emergency response devices, campus police. 228,009 books, 132,449 microform titles, 1,949 serials, 12,227 audiovisual materials, an OPAC, and a Web page.

Community Environment: Northern Virginia Community College is a five campus college located in the suburban communities of Northern Virginia, just outside Washington, D.C. The Northern Virginia region is rapidly growing, provides excellent job opportunities and has high quality public schools and community services. Part-time job opportunities are excellent for students and graduates of the occupational and technical programs and career placements attractive. Students seeking transfer to a university to earn a Bachelor's degree can enroll in appropriate programs that parallel most university programs.

■ OLD DOMINION UNIVERSITY

5115 Hampton Blvd.
Norfolk, VA 23529
Tel: (757)683-3000; Free: 800-348-7926
Fax: (757)683-5357
E-mail: admissions@odu.edu
Web Site: www.odu.edu/

Description: State-supported, university, coed. Awards bachelor's, master's, and doctoral degrees and post-master's certificates. Founded 1930. Setting: 251-acre urban campus with easy access to Virginia Beach. Endowment: $168.1 million. Research spending for the previous fiscal year: $47.3 million. Educational spending for the previous fiscal year: $6633 per student. Total enrollment: 24,670. Faculty: 1,294 (757 full-time, 537 part-time). Student-undergrad faculty ratio is 21:1. 10,656 applied, 72% were admitted. 9% from top 10% of their high school class, 33% from top quarter, 78% from top half. 9 valedictorians. Full-time: 14,949 students, 53% women, 47% men. Part-time: 4,663 students, 56% women, 44% men. Students come from 47 states and territories, 69 other countries, 7% from out-of-state. 0.4% American Indian or Alaska Native, non-Hispanic/Latino; 6% Hispanic/Latino; 25% African American, non-Hispanic/Latino; 4% Asian, non-Hispanic/Latino; 1% Native Hawaiian or other Pacific Islander, non-Hispanic/Latino; 1% international. 27% 25 or older, 24% live on campus, 12% transferred in. Retention: 80% of full-time freshmen returned the following year. Academic areas with the most degrees conferred: business/marketing; health professions and related sciences; social sciences. Core. Calendar: semesters. ESL program, services for LD students, advanced placement, accelerated

degree program, self-designed majors, freshman honors college, honors program, independent study, distance learning, double major, summer session for credit, part-time degree program, adult/continuing education programs, co-op programs and internships, graduate courses open to undergrads. Off campus study at Virginia Tidewater Consortium. Study abroad program. ROTC: Army, Naval.

Entrance Requirements: Options: electronic application, early admission, early action, deferred admission, international baccalaureate accepted. Required: high school transcript, minimum 2.7 high school GPA, test scores, SAT or ACT. Recommended: essay, 1 recommendation. Entrance: moderately difficult. Application deadlines: 2/1, 2/1 for nonresidents, 12/1 for early action. Notification: continuous, continuous for nonresidents, 1/15 for early action. SAT Reasoning Test deadline: 6/1. SAT Subject Test deadline: 6/1. Transfer credits accepted: Yes. Early action applicants: 4,963. Early action applicants admitted: 3,769.

Costs Per Year: Application fee: $50. State resident tuition: $8190 full-time, $273 per credit hour part-time. Nonresident tuition: $23,097 full-time, $769 per credit hour part-time. Mandatory fees: $260 full-time, $59 per term part-time. College room and board: $9066. College room only: $5210. Room and board charges vary according to board plan and housing facility.

Collegiate Environment: Orientation program. Drama-theater group, choral group, marching band, student-run newspaper, radio station. Social organizations: 321 open to all; national fraternities, national sororities; 4% of eligible men and 3% of eligible women are members. Most popular organizations: Student Activities Council, F.O.R.E.I.G.N.E.R.S, Veteran Student Association, Anime Club, Ebony Impact Gospel Choir. Major annual events: Homecoming, Main Street Organization Fair, Relay for Life. Student services: health clinic, personal-psychological counseling, women's center. Campus security: 24-hour emergency response devices and patrols, student patrols, late night transport-escort service, controlled dormitory access. 4,607 college housing spaces available; all were occupied in 2012-13. Freshmen given priority for college housing. Options: coed, women-only housing available. Patricia W. and Douglas Perry Library plus 3 others with 2.5 million books, 1.9 million microform titles, 10,754 serials, 53,473 audiovisual materials, an OPAC, and a Web page. Operations spending for the previous fiscal year: $483,230. 1,130 computers available on campus for general student use. A campuswide network can be accessed from student residence rooms and from off campus. Students can access the following: online class registration, online courses. Staffed computer lab on campus (open 24 hours a day) provides training in use of computers, software, and the Internet.

Community Environment: See Virginia Wesleyan College.

■ PATRICK HENRY COLLEGE

Ten Patrick Henry Cir.
Purcellville, VA 20132
Tel: (540)338-1776
Fax: (540)338-8707
E-mail: admissions@phc.edu
Web Site: www.phc.edu/

Description: Independent nondenominational, 4-year, coed. Awards bachelor's degrees. Founded 1999. Setting: 106-acre small town campus with easy access to Washington, DC. Total enrollment: 345. Faculty: 47 (22 full-time, 25 part-time). Student-undergrad faculty ratio is 10:1. 239 applied, 79% were admitted. Full-time: 296 students, 48% women, 52% men. Part-time: 49 students, 43% women, 57% men. Students come from 43 states and territories, 86% from out-of-state. 0.3% American Indian or Alaska Native, non-Hispanic/Latino; 2% Hispanic/Latino; 1% African American, non-Hispanic/Latino; 3% Asian, non-Hispanic/Latino; 1% Native Hawaiian or other Pacific Islander, non-Hispanic/Latino. 1% 25 or older, 90% live on campus, 3% transferred in. Retention: 88% of full-time freshmen returned the following year. Academic areas with the most degrees conferred: social sciences; communication/journalism; history. Core. Calendar: semesters. Advanced placement, independent study, summer session for credit, internships. Off campus study.

Entrance Requirements: Options: electronic application, early action, deferred admission. Required: essay, high school transcript, 2 recommendations, interview, Official transcripts from all colleges attended; Reading List, SAT or ACT. Entrance: very difficult. Application deadlines: 6/15, 11/1 for early action. Notification: continuous. SAT Reasoning Test deadline: 6/15. Transfer credits accepted: No.

Costs Per Year: Application fee: $40. Comprehensive fee: $36,036 includes full-time tuition ($25,570), mandatory fees ($250), and college room and board ($10,216). Full-time tuition and fees vary according to course load.

Room and board charges vary according to board plan. Part-time tuition: $1065 per credit hour. Part-time tuition varies according to course level and course load.

Collegiate Environment: Orientation program. Drama-theater group, choral group, student-run newspaper. Social organizations: 16 open to all. Most popular organizations: Drama Club, Eden Troupe, student government, chorale, College Republicans, Debate/Moot Court. Major annual events: Homecoming, Harmonic Comedy, Eden Troupe productions. Campus security: 24-hour emergency response devices, student patrols, late night transport-escort service, controlled dormitory access, after hours patrols by trained security personnel. 288 college housing spaces available; 275 were occupied in 2012-13. Freshmen given priority for college housing. On-campus residence required through sophomore year. Options: men-only, women-only housing available. Patrick Henry College Library with 26,539 books, 7 microform titles, 33,069 serials, 509 audiovisual materials, an OPAC, and a Web page. Operations spending for the previous fiscal year: $636,879. 6 computers available on campus for general student use. Computer purchase/lease plans available. A computer is required for all students. A campuswide network can be accessed from student residence rooms. Students can access the following: online class registration.

■ PATRICK HENRY COMMUNITY COLLEGE

PO Box 5311
Martinsville, VA 24115-5311
Tel: (276)638-8777
Fax: (276)656-0247
Web Site: www.ph.vccs.edu/

Description: State-supported, 2-year, coed. Part of Virginia Community College System. Awards transfer associate and terminal associate degrees. Founded 1962. Setting: 137-acre rural campus. Total enrollment: 3,501. Faculty: 149 (49 full-time, 100 part-time). Students come from 4 states and territories. 60% 25 or older. Retention: 49% of full-time freshmen returned the following year. Calendar: semesters. Academic remediation for entering students, services for LD students, advanced placement, independent study, distance learning, summer session for credit, part-time degree program, adult/continuing education programs, co-op programs and internships.

Entrance Requirements: Open admission except for nursing program. Options: electronic application, early admission, deferred admission. Required: high school transcript. Entrance: noncompetitive. Application deadline: Rolling. Notification: continuous. Preference given to district residents.

Collegiate Environment: Orientation program. Drama-theater group. Most popular organizations: Student Government Association, Student Support Services, Phi Theta Kappa, Gospel Choir, Black Student Association. Major annual events: Fall Festival, Spring Play Day, Awards Banquet. Campus security: 24-hour emergency response devices and patrols, late night transport-escort service. Lester Library with 26,160 books, 259 serials, an OPAC, and a Web page. Operations spending for the previous fiscal year: $84,738. 505 computers available on campus for general student use. Computer purchase/lease plans available. A campuswide network can be accessed from off-campus. Staffed computer lab on campus provides training in use of computers, software, and the Internet.

Community Environment: Martinsville is an important textile and furniture market as well as an industrial city with a wide range of products. It provides all forms of commercial transportation. Job opportunities are excellent and shopping is good. Philpott Reservoir, about 19 miles northwest of Martinsville, is a popular spot for fishing, boating, water skiing, and swimming. Other facilities within the city provide for swimming, baseball, and football.

■ PAUL D. CAMP COMMUNITY COLLEGE

PO Box 737, 100 N College Dr.
Franklin, VA 23851-0737
Tel: (757)569-6700
E-mail: tjones@pdc.edu
Web Site: www.pdc.edu/

Description: State-supported, 2-year, coed. Part of Virginia Community College System. Awards certificates, transfer associate, and terminal associate degrees. Founded 1971. Setting: 99-acre small town campus. Endowment: $500,000. Total enrollment: 1,579. Faculty: 161 (18 full-time, 143 part-time). Student-undergrad faculty ratio is 16:1. 597 applied, 100% were admitted. 5% from top 10% of their high school class, 20% from top quarter, 45% from top half. Students come from 2 states and territories, 2 other countries, 1% from out-of-state. 38% African American, non-Hispanic/Latino. 40% 25 or older. Retention: 66% of full-time freshmen returned the following year. Core.

Calendar: semesters. Academic remediation for entering students, advanced placement, honors program, independent study, distance learning, summer session for credit, part-time degree program, adult/continuing education programs, co-op programs and internships. Off campus study at members of the Virginia Consortium for Continuing Higher Education.

Entrance Requirements: Open admission. Options: electronic application, deferred admission. Required: high school transcript. Entrance: noncompetitive. Application deadline: Rolling. Notification: continuous. Preference given to state residents. Transfer credits accepted: Yes.

Costs Per Year: Application fee: $0. State resident tuition: $3,964 full-time, $122.03 per credit part-time. Nonresident tuition: $9,802 full-time, $298 per credit part-time. Mandatory fees: $9.65 per credit part-time.

Collegiate Environment: Student-run newspaper. Most popular organizations: African-American History Club, Phi Beta Lambda, Phi Theta Kappa, Student Government Association, student newspaper. Campus security: late night transport-escort service. College housing not available. Paul D. Camp Community College Library with 22,000 books, 200 serials, and an OPAC. Operations spending for the previous fiscal year: $258,883. 298 computers available on campus for general student use. A campuswide network can be accessed. Students can access the following: online class registration. Staffed computer lab on campus provides training in use of computers, software, and the Internet.

Community Environment: Franklin is in a rural setting with a population of 8,594.

■ PIEDMONT VIRGINIA COMMUNITY COLLEGE

501 College Dr.
Charlottesville, VA 22902-7589
Tel: (434)977-3900
Fax: (434)971-8232
E-mail: mwalsh@pvcc.edu
Web Site: www.pvcc.edu/

Description: State-supported, 2-year, coed. Part of Virginia Community College System. Awards certificates, transfer associate, and terminal associate degrees. Founded 1972. Setting: 114-acre suburban campus with easy access to Richmond. Total enrollment: 5,693. Faculty: (74 full-time). Full-time: 1,179 students, 54% women, 46% men. Part-time: 4,514 students, 61% women, 39% men. Students come from 15 states and territories. 0.3% American Indian or Alaska Native, non-Hispanic/Latino; 4% Hispanic/Latino; 14% African American, non-Hispanic/Latino; 4% Asian, non-Hispanic/Latino; 0.1% Native Hawaiian or other Pacific Islander, non-Hispanic/Latino; 0.4% international. 46% 25 or older, 6% transferred in. Core. Calendar: semesters. Academic remediation for entering students, ESL program, services for LD students, advanced placement, honors program, independent study, distance learning, summer session for credit, part-time degree program, adult/continuing education programs, co-op programs and internships. ROTC: Army (c).

Entrance Requirements: Open admission Certain health and life sciences programs do not have open admission. Options: electronic application, early admission, deferred admission. Required for some: high school transcript, Admission to programs in Nursing, Practical Nursing, Radiography, Sonography, Surgical Technology, Emergency Medical Services, Health Information Management, and Patient Admissions Coordination is competitive and/or requires completion of specific prerequisites. Entrance: noncompetitive. Application deadline: Rolling. Notification: continuous. Transfer credits accepted: Yes.

Costs Per Year: Application fee: $0. State resident tuition: $3510 full-time, $117 per credit hour part-time. Nonresident tuition: $9,592 full-time, $293.60 per credit hour part-time. Mandatory fees: $320 full-time, $10.65 per credit hour part-time. Full-time tuition and fees vary according to course load. Part-time tuition and fees vary according to course load.

Collegiate Environment: Orientation program. Drama-theater group, choral group, student-run newspaper. Social organizations: 45 open to all. Major annual events: plays and concerts, fall/spring picnics. Campus security: 24-hour emergency response devices and patrols, late night transport-escort service. College housing not available. Jessup Library with 37,261 books, 12 microform titles, 139 serials, 1,058 audiovisual materials, an OPAC, and a Web page. 171 computers available on campus for general student use. A campuswide network can be accessed from off-campus. Students can access the following: online class registration. Staffed computer lab on campus provides training in use of computers, software, and the Internet.

Community Environment: Charlottesville is situated in the foothills of the Blue Ridge Mountains. The area has many old homes and estates. Albemarle County is renown for its horses, dogs and fruit orchards. Outdoor activities available include: golf, tennis, hunting, fishing and hiking. Points of interest are the Lewis and Clark Memorial, Monticello, and the University of Virginia. Commercial transportation and part-time employment are available.

■ RADFORD UNIVERSITY

801 E Main St.
Radford, VA 24142
Tel: (540)831-5000
Fax: (540)831-5138
E-mail: admissions@radford.edu
Web Site: www.radford.edu/

Description: State-supported, comprehensive, coed. Awards bachelor's, master's, and doctoral degrees and post-master's certificates. Founded 1910. Setting: 191-acre small town campus. Endowment: $42.9 million. Research spending for the previous fiscal year: $539,784. Educational spending for the previous fiscal year: $7339 per student. Total enrollment: 9,573. Faculty: 663 (411 full-time, 252 part-time). Student-undergrad faculty ratio is 19:1. 8,192 applied, 76% were admitted. 6% from top 10% of their high school class, 22% from top quarter, 61% from top half. 10 National Merit Scholars, 4 valedictorians. Full-time: 8,288 students, 56% women, 44% men. Part-time: 322 students, 52% women, 48% men. Students come from 42 states and territories, 59 other countries, 5% from out-of-state. 0.4% American Indian or Alaska Native, non-Hispanic/Latino; 4% Hispanic/Latino; 8% African American, non-Hispanic/Latino; 2% Asian, non-Hispanic/Latino; 0.3% Native Hawaiian or other Pacific Islander, non-Hispanic/Latino; 1% international. 6% 25 or older, 36% live on campus, 9% transferred in. Retention: 74% of full-time freshmen returned the following year. Academic areas with the most degrees conferred: business/marketing; interdisciplinary studies; health professions and related sciences. Core. Calendar: semesters. Services for LD students, advanced placement, accelerated degree program, self-designed majors, honors program, independent study, distance learning, double major, summer session for credit, part-time degree program, internships, graduate courses open to undergrads. Off campus study at Southwest Virginia Higher Education Center, Roanoke Higher Education Center. Study abroad program. ROTC: Army.

Entrance Requirements: Options: electronic application, early admission, early action, deferred admission, international baccalaureate accepted. Required: high school transcript, SAT or ACT. Recommended: essay. Entrance: moderately difficult. Application deadlines: 2/1, 12/1 for early action. Notification: 4/1, 1/15 for early action. SAT Reasoning Test deadline: 4/1. Transfer credits accepted: Yes. Applicants placed on waiting list: 962. Wait-listed applicants offered admission: 104.

Costs Per Year: Application fee: $50. State resident tuition: $5702 full-time, $238 per credit hour part-time. Nonresident tuition: $16,826 full-time, $701 per credit hour part-time. Mandatory fees: $2888 full-time, $121 per credit hour part-time. Part-time tuition and fees vary according to course load. College room and board: $7881. College room only: $4307. Room and board charges vary according to board plan and housing facility.

Collegiate Environment: Orientation program. Drama-theater group, choral group, student-run newspaper, radio station. Social organizations: 240 open to all; national fraternities, national sororities. Most popular organizations: Think in Pink, National Society for Collegiate Scholars, Sigma Sigma Sigma (Greek sorority), The American Sign Language Club, Gay-Straight Alliance. Major annual events: Club Fair, Family Weekend, Highlander Homecoming. Student services: health clinic, personal-psychological counseling. Campus security: 24-hour emergency response devices and patrols, late night transport-escort service, controlled dormitory access. 3,185 college housing spaces available; 3,150 were occupied in 2012-13. Freshmen guaranteed college housing. On-campus residence required through sophomore year. Option: coed housing available. McConnell Library with 644,750 books, 1.4 million microform titles, 9,772 serials, 27,118 audiovisual materials, an OPAC, and a Web page. Operations spending for the previous fiscal year: $4.1 million. 772 computers available on campus for general student use. Computer purchase/lease plans available. A campuswide network can be accessed from student residence rooms and from off campus. Students can access the following: online class registration, online financial aid status and student accounts payable. Staffed computer lab on campus (open 24 hours a day) provides training in use of computers, software, and the Internet.

Community Environment: Located on the banks of the scenic New River in the foothills of the beautiful Blue Ridge Mountains, the city of Radford, Virginia (population 14,500), is 45 miles southwest of Roanoke. First settled in 1756, the city features a number of churches, a public library, hospital, and many civic and service organizations. The city is clean and the weather is

moderate. Outdoor sports enthusiasts can enjoy nearby Claytor Lake, the New River, the Appalachian Trail and many other streams, lakes and trails in close proximity.

■ RANDOLPH COLLEGE

2500 Rivermont Ave.
Lynchburg, VA 24503
Tel: (434)947-8000; Free: 800-745-7692
Fax: (434)947-8996
E-mail: admissions@randolphcollege.edu
Web Site: www.randolphcollege.edu/

Description: Independent Methodist, comprehensive, coed. Awards bachelor's and master's degrees. Founded 1891. Setting: 100-acre suburban campus. Total enrollment: 645. Faculty: 74 (69 full-time, 5 part-time). Student-undergrad faculty ratio is 9:1. 892 applied, 83% were admitted. 22% from top 10% of their high school class, 55% from top quarter, 85% from top half. Full-time: 609 students, 63% women, 37% men. Part-time: 14 students, 64% women, 36% men. 59% from out-of-state. 0.3% American Indian or Alaska Native, non-Hispanic/Latino; 6% Hispanic/Latino; 9% African American, non-Hispanic/Latino; 2% Asian, non-Hispanic/Latino; 0% Native Hawaiian or other Pacific Islander, non-Hispanic/Latino; 14% international. 91% live on campus, 5% transferred in. Retention: 80% of full-time freshmen returned the following year. Academic areas with the most degrees conferred: social sciences; visual and performing arts; biological/life sciences. Calendar: semesters. Part-time degree program, adult/continuing education programs.

Entrance Requirements: Options: electronic application, early admission, early action, deferred admission, international baccalaureate accepted. Required: essay, high school transcript, 2 recommendations, SAT or ACT. Recommended: interview. Entrance: moderately difficult. Application deadlines: 3/1, 12/1 for early action. Notification: continuous, 1/1 for early action. SAT Reasoning Test deadline: 3/1. Transfer credits accepted: Yes.

Costs Per Year: Application fee: $35. Comprehensive fee: $42,330 includes full-time tuition ($31,030), mandatory fees ($510), and college room and board ($10,790).

Collegiate Environment: Orientation program. Campus security: 24-hour emergency response devices and patrols, late night transport-escort service. Freshmen guaranteed college housing. On-campus residence required through senior year. Options: coed, women-only housing available.

■ RANDOLPH-MACON COLLEGE

PO Box 5005
Ashland, VA 23005-5505
Tel: (804)752-7200; Free: 800-888-1762
Fax: (804)752-4707
E-mail: admissions@rmc.edu
Web Site: www.rmc.edu/

Description: Independent United Methodist, 4-year, coed. Awards bachelor's degrees. Founded 1830. Setting: 120-acre suburban campus with easy access to Richmond. Endowment: $120.8 million. Educational spending for the previous fiscal year: $9602 per student. Total enrollment: 1,312. Faculty: 148 (93 full-time, 55 part-time). Student-undergrad faculty ratio is 12:1. 4,155 applied, 54% were admitted. 20% from top 10% of their high school class, 49% from top quarter, 88% from top half. 3 class presidents, 1 valedictorian, 36 student government officers. Full-time: 1,286 students, 53% women, 47% men. Part-time: 26 students, 31% women, 69% men. Students come from 31 states and territories, 20 other countries, 26% from out-of-state. 1% American Indian or Alaska Native, non-Hispanic/Latino; 4% Hispanic/Latino; 12% African American, non-Hispanic/Latino; 2% Asian, non-Hispanic/Latino; 0% Native Hawaiian or other Pacific Islander, non-Hispanic/Latino; 3% international. 2% 25 or older, 78% live on campus, 3% transferred in. Retention: 80% of full-time freshmen returned the following year. Academic areas with the most degrees conferred: business/marketing; social sciences; psychology. Core. Calendar: 4-1-4. Academic remediation for entering students, services for LD students, advanced placement, accelerated degree program, honors program, independent study, double major, summer session for credit, part-time degree program, internships. Off campus study at members of the Seven-College Exchange Program. Study abroad program. ROTC: Army (c).

Entrance Requirements: Options: electronic application, early admission, early action, deferred admission, international baccalaureate accepted. Required: essay, high school transcript, minimum 2 high school GPA, 1 recommendation, SAT or ACT. Recommended: interview, SAT Subject Tests. Eritrance: moderately difficult. Application deadlines: 3/1, 11/15 for early action. Notification: 4/1, 1/1 for early action. SAT Subject Test deadline: 6/1. Applicants placed on waiting list: 297. Wait-listed applicants offered admission: 9. Early action applicants: 3,524. Early action applicants admitted: 1,920.

Costs Per Year: Application fee: $30. One-time mandatory fee: $100. Comprehensive fee: $43,925 includes full-time tuition ($32,625), mandatory fees ($900), and college room and board ($10,400). College room only: $5755. Full-time tuition and fees vary according to reciprocity agreements. Room and board charges vary according to board plan and housing facility. Part-time tuition: $3625 per course. Part-time mandatory fees: $135 per year.

Collegiate Environment: Orientation program. Drama-theater group, choral group, student-run newspaper, radio station. Social organizations: 85 open to all; national fraternities, national sororities; 34% of eligible men and 35% of eligible women are members. Most popular organizations: Residence Hall Association, Campus Activities Board, Student Government Association, Drama Guild, Student Honors Association. Major annual events: Dance Marathon, football game against Hampden-Sydney College, Springfest. Student services: health clinic, personal-psychological counseling, women's center. Campus security: 24-hour emergency response devices and patrols, late night transport-escort service, controlled dormitory access. 1,005 college housing spaces available; 986 were occupied in 2012-13. Freshmen guaranteed college housing. On-campus residence required through junior year. Options: coed, men-only, women-only housing available. McGraw-Page Library plus 1 other with 298,194 books, 337,227 microform titles, 44,078 serials, 12,439 audiovisual materials, an OPAC, and a Web page. 356 computers available on campus for general student use. Computer purchase/lease plans available. A campuswide network can be accessed from student residence rooms and from off campus. Students can access the following: online class registration. Staffed computer lab on campus.

Community Environment: Ashland is a suburban area 15 miles from Richmond, and 90 miles south of Washington DC. Community facilities include a public library, six churches, 2 medical centers, and a number of civic and service organizations.

■ RAPPAHANNOCK COMMUNITY COLLEGE

12745 College Dr.
Glenns, VA 23149-2616
Tel: (804)758-6700; Free: 800-836-9381
Fax: (804)758-3852
Web Site: www.rappahannock.edu/

Description: State and locally supported, 2-year, coed. Part of Virginia Community College System. Awards certificates, diplomas, transfer associate, and terminal associate degrees. Founded 1970. Setting: rural campus. Total enrollment: 3,711. 42% 25 or older. Calendar: semesters. Academic remediation for entering students, services for LD students, honors program, distance learning, summer session for credit, part-time degree program, adult/continuing education programs, internships. Off campus study.

Entrance Requirements: Open admission. Options: electronic application, early admission. Entrance: noncompetitive. Application deadline: Rolling. Notification: continuous.

Costs Per Year: Application fee: $0. State resident tuition: $2808 full-time, $117 per credit hour part-time. Nonresident tuition: $7046 full-time, $293.60 per credit hour part-time. Mandatory fees: $281 full-time, $11.69 per credit hour part-time. Full-time tuition and fees vary according to course load. Part-time tuition and fees vary according to course load.

Collegiate Environment: Orientation program. Student services: personal-psychological counseling.

Community Environment: Glenns is centrally located in the Rappahannock River Tidewaters serving a 13-county region.

■ REGENT UNIVERSITY

1000 Regent University Dr.
Virginia Beach, VA 23464-9800
Tel: (757)226-4127; Free: 800-373-5504
E-mail: kbaker@regent.edu
Web Site: www.regent.edu/

Description: Independent Christian, comprehensive, coed. Awards associate, bachelor's, master's, and doctoral degrees and post-master's certificates. Founded 1977. Setting: 70-acre suburban campus. Endowment: $181 million. Research spending for the previous fiscal year: $67,161. Educational spending for the previous fiscal year: $7437 per student. Total enrollment: 5,863. Faculty: 569 (171 full-time, 398 part-time). Student-undergrad faculty ratio is 16:1. 1,497 applied, 83% were admitted. Full-time:

1,442 students, 62% women, 38% men. Part-time: 990 students, 64% women, 36% men. Students come from 50 states and territories, 14 other countries, 52% from out-of-state. 0.4% American Indian or Alaska Native, non-Hispanic/Latino; 5% Hispanic/Latino; 19% African American, non-Hispanic/Latino; 2% Asian, non-Hispanic/Latino; 2% international. 57% 25 or older, 18% live on campus, 18% transferred in. Retention: 78% of full-time freshmen returned the following year. Academic areas with the most degrees conferred: business/marketing; psychology; communication/journalism. Core. Calendar: trimesters. Academic remediation for entering students, services for LD students, advanced placement, distance learning, double major, summer session for credit, part-time degree program, external degree program, adult/continuing education programs, internships, graduate courses open to undergrads. Off campus study at The Virginia Tidewater Consortium for Higher Education (VTC) is a consortium of higher education institutions including Christopher Newport University, Hampton University, Norfolk State University, Old Dominion University, Paul D. Camp Community College, Regent University, Thomas Nelson Community College, Tidewater Community College, and Virginia Wesleyan College. Study abroad program. ROTC: Army (c), Naval (c).

Entrance Requirements: Options: electronic application, deferred admission. Required: essay. Required for some: high school transcript, minimum 3 high school GPA, SAT or ACT. Entrance: minimally difficult. Application deadlines: 8/1, 8/1 for nonresidents. Notification: continuous, continuous for nonresidents. SAT Reasoning Test deadline: 5/1. Transfer credits accepted: Yes.

Costs Per Year: Application fee: $50. Comprehensive fee: $24,390 includes full-time tuition ($15,300), mandatory fees ($660), and college room and board ($8430). College room only: $5460. Full-time tuition and fees vary according to course level, course load, program, and student level. Room and board charges vary according to housing facility. Part-time tuition: $510 per credit hour. Part-time mandatory fees: $510 per credit hour, $330 per term. Part-time tuition and fees vary according to course level, course load, program, and student level.

Collegiate Environment: Orientation program. Drama-theater group, choral group, student-run newspaper. Social organizations: 40 open to all; national fraternities, national sororities. Most popular organizations: Regent Undergraduate Council, Students in Free Enterprise (SIFE), Psychology Club, Student Alumni Ambassadors, Regent Undergraduate Debate Association. Major annual events: Back to School BBQ, Harvest Festival, Christmas Ball. Student services: personal-psychological counseling. Campus security: 24-hour emergency response devices and patrols, student patrols, late night transport-escort service, controlled dormitory access. 470 college housing spaces available; 445 were occupied in 2012-13. Freshmen given priority for college housing. On-campus residence required in freshman year. Options: men-only, women-only housing available. Regent University Library plus 1 other with 546,641 books, 593,318 microform titles, 568 serials, 33,221 audiovisual materials, an OPAC, and a Web page. Operations spending for the previous fiscal year: $2.2 million. 69 computers available on campus for general student use. A campuswide network can be accessed from student residence rooms and from off campus. Students can access the following: online class registration. Staffed computer lab on campus provides training in use of computers, software, and the Internet.

■ RICHARD BLAND COLLEGE OF THE COLLEGE OF WILLIAM AND MARY

11301 Johnson Rd.
Petersburg, VA 23805-7100
Tel: (804)862-6100
Fax: (804)862-6189
Web Site: www.rbc.edu/

Description: State-supported, 2-year, coed. Administratively affiliated with College of William and Mary. Awards transfer associate degrees. Founded 1961. Setting: 712-acre rural campus with easy access to Richmond. Total enrollment: 1,634. Faculty: 71 (33 full-time, 38 part-time). Student-undergrad faculty ratio is 25:1. 897 applied, 89% were admitted. 6% from top 10% of their high school class, 20% from top quarter, 48% from top half. Full-time: 1,038 students, 62% women, 38% men. Part-time: 596 students, 67% women, 33% men. Students come from 5 states and territories, 2 other countries, 1% from out-of-state. 11% 25 or older, 6% transferred in. Retention: 59% of full-time freshmen returned the following year. Core. Calendar: semesters. Academic remediation for entering students, services for LD students, advanced placement, accelerated degree program, summer session for credit, part-time degree program. ROTC: Army (c).

Entrance Requirements: Option: electronic application. Required: essay, high school transcript, minimum 2 high school GPA, in-state residency form. Recommended: SAT or ACT. Required for some: interview. Entrance: minimally difficult. Application deadline: 8/15. Notification: continuous.

Collegiate Environment: Orientation program. Drama-theater group, choral group, student-run newspaper. Social organizations: 20 open to all. Most popular organizations: RBC Newspaper, Student Ambassadors, student government, Spanish Club, Biology Club. Major annual events: Fall Orientation, International Forum. Campus security: 24-hour emergency response devices and patrols, controlled dormitory access, full-time dedicated Campus Police Force. Richard Bland College Library with 126,242 books, 3,842 microform titles, 9,000 serials, 4,253 audiovisual materials, an OPAC, and a Web page. 130 computers available on campus for general student use. A campuswide network can be accessed from student residence rooms and from off campus. Students can access the following: online class registration. Staffed computer lab on campus provides training in use of computers, software, and the Internet.

■ **ROANOKE COLLEGE**
221 College Ln.
Salem, VA 24153-3794
Tel: (540)375-2500; Free: 800-388-2276
Fax: (540)375-2267
E-mail: admissions@roanoke.edu
Web Site: www.roanoke.edu/
Description: Independent, 4-year, coed, affiliated with Evangelical Lutheran Church in America. Awards bachelor's degrees. Founded 1842. Setting: 80-acre suburban campus. Endowment: $116.4 million. Research spending for the previous fiscal year: $386,652. Educational spending for the previous fiscal year: $12,258 per student. Total enrollment: 2,060. Faculty: 212 (165 full-time, 47 part-time). Student-undergrad faculty ratio is 11:1. 4,264 applied, 69% were admitted. 25% from top 10% of their high school class, 51% from top quarter, 87% from top half. 1 National Merit Scholar, 13 class presidents, 10 valedictorians, 69 student government officers. Full-time: 1,987 students, 59% women, 41% men. Part-time: 73 students, 42% women, 58% men. Students come from 39 states and territories, 24 other countries, 46% from out-of-state. 0.3% American Indian or Alaska Native, non-Hispanic/Latino; 4% Hispanic/Latino; 4% African American, non-Hispanic/Latino; 1% Asian, non-Hispanic/Latino; 0.05% Native Hawaiian or other Pacific Islander, non-Hispanic/Latino; 2% international. 3% 25 or older, 74% live on campus, 4% transferred in. Retention: 81% of full-time freshmen returned the following year. Academic areas with the most degrees conferred: business/marketing; social sciences; psychology. Core. Calendar: semesters. ESL program, services for LD students, advanced placement, accelerated degree program, honors program, independent study, double major, summer session for credit, part-time degree program, adult/continuing education programs, internships. Off campus study at Hollins University cross registration, Lutheran College Washington, DC Semester. Study abroad program.
Entrance Requirements: Options: electronic application, early admission, early decision, deferred admission, international baccalaureate accepted. Required: high school transcript, SAT or ACT. Recommended: essay, 3 recommendations, interview. Entrance: moderately difficult. Application deadlines: 3/15, 11/1 for early decision. Notification: continuous until 4/1, 12/1 for early decision. SAT Reasoning Test deadline: 3/15. Transfer credits accepted: Yes. Applicants placed on waiting list: 212. Wait-listed applicants offered admission: 93. Early decision applicants: 133. Early decision applicants admitted: 69.
Costs Per Year: Application fee: $30. One-time mandatory fee: $125. Comprehensive fee: $47,996 includes full-time tuition ($35,108), mandatory fees ($1364), and college room and board ($11,524). College room only: $5310. Full-time tuition and fees vary according to reciprocity agreements. Room and board charges vary according to board plan and housing facility. Part-time tuition: $1680 per course. Part-time mandatory fees: $38 per term. Part-time tuition and fees vary according to course load and reciprocity agreements.
Collegiate Environment: Orientation program. Drama-theater group, choral group, student-run newspaper, radio station. Social organizations: 100 open to all; national fraternities, national sororities, Co-educational service fraternity; 22% of eligible men and 26% of eligible women are members. Most popular organizations: Outdoor Adventures, Habitat for Humanity, Honors Association, Campus Activities Board, Inter-Varsity Christian Fellowship. Major annual events: President's Ball, Alumni Weekend, Winterfest. Student services: health clinic, personal-psychological counseling. Campus security: 24-hour emergency response devices and patrols, late night

transport-escort service, controlled dormitory access, Campus emergency phones, Maroon Alert system. 1,576 college housing spaces available; 1,476 were occupied in 2012-13. Freshmen guaranteed college housing. On-campus residence required through senior year. Options: coed, women-only housing available. Fintel Library with 278,233 books, 156,310 microform titles, 45,544 serials, 9,942 audiovisual materials, an OPAC, and a Web page. Operations spending for the previous fiscal year: $1.1 million. 207 computers available on campus for general student use. Computer purchase/lease plans available. A campuswide network can be accessed from student residence rooms and from off campus. Students can access the following: online class registration, discounts on computer hardware and software purchases, free Microsoft Office software, free security software. Staffed computer lab on campus provides training in use of computers, software, and the Internet.

Community Environment: Salem is located in the heart of the Roanoke Valley between the Blue Ridge Mountains to the east, and the Allegheny Mountains to the west. Many national manufacturing companies contribute to the diversified industry of Salem. Plane and bus transportation are available. Part-time employment opportunities are excellent. The Dixie Caverns subterranean wonderland is seven miles away. State parks, the Blue Ridge Parkway & the Appalachian Trail provide outdoor activities, and facilities within the city provide for tennis, skating, and golf.

■ **SENTARA COLLEGE OF HEALTH SCIENCES**
1441 Crossways Blvd.
Crossways I, Ste. 105
Chesapeake, VA 23320
Tel: (757)388-2900
Web Site: www.sentara.edu/
Description: Proprietary, 4-year, coed.

■ **SHENANDOAH UNIVERSITY**
1460 University Dr.
Winchester, VA 22601-5195
Tel: (540)665-4500; Free: 800-432-2266
Fax: (540)665-4627
E-mail: admit@su.edu
Web Site: www.su.edu/
Description: Independent United Methodist, comprehensive, coed. Awards bachelor's, master's, and doctoral degrees and post-master's certificates. Founded 1875. Setting: 125-acre small town campus with easy access to Baltimore and Washington, DC. Endowment: $52.7 million. Research spending for the previous fiscal year: $65,136. Educational spending for the previous fiscal year: $12,417 per student. Total enrollment: 4,176. Faculty: 404 (230 full-time, 174 part-time). Student-undergrad faculty ratio is 10:1. 1,833 applied, 85% were admitted. Full-time: 1,837 students, 56% women, 44% men. Part-time: 565 students, 84% women, 16% men. Students come from 35 states and territories, 28 other countries, 36% from out-of-state. 2% American Indian or Alaska Native, non-Hispanic/Latino; 3% Hispanic/Latino; 12% African American, non-Hispanic/Latino; 4% Asian, non-Hispanic/Latino; 1% Native Hawaiian or other Pacific Islander, non-Hispanic/Latino; 3% international. 14% 25 or older, 55% live on campus, 5% transferred in. Retention: 80% of full-time freshmen returned the following year. Academic areas with the most degrees conferred: health professions and related sciences; visual and performing arts; education. Core. Calendar: semesters. ESL program, services for LD students, advanced placement, accelerated degree program, self-designed majors, independent study, distance learning, double major, summer session for credit, part-time degree program, adult/continuing education programs, co-op programs and internships, graduate courses open to undergrads. Off campus study. Study abroad program.
Entrance Requirements: Options: electronic application, deferred admission, international baccalaureate accepted. Required: high school transcript, 1 recommendation, SAT or ACT. Required for some: essay, minimum 3 high school GPA, interview. Applicants are strongly recommended to indicate community and extra-curricular involvement. Conservatory applicants are also required to successfully complete an audition. Entrance: moderately difficult. Application deadline: Rolling. Notification: continuous. Transfer credits accepted: Yes.
Costs Per Year: Application fee: $30. Comprehensive fee: $37,090 includes full-time tuition ($27,550), mandatory fees ($300), and college room and board ($9240). Full-time tuition and fees vary according to course load, location, program, and student level. Room and board charges vary according to board plan and housing facility. Part-time tuition: $800 per credit hour. Part-time tuition varies according to course load, location, program, and student level.

Collegiate Environment: Orientation program. Drama-theater group, choral group, student-run newspaper, radio station. Social organizations: 49 open to all; 2% of eligible men and 1% of eligible women are members. Most popular organizations: Student Government Association, The Graduate Student Association, Campus Activities Network, American Pharmacists Association Academy of Student Pharmacists, Kappa Psi Pharmaceutical Fraternity, Inc. Major annual events: Homecoming, Spring Fling Weekend, Sun Block Party. Student services: health clinic, personal-psychological counseling, women's center. Campus security: 24-hour emergency response devices and patrols, late night transport-escort service, controlled dormitory access, side door alarms. 890 college housing spaces available; 822 were occupied in 2012-13. Freshmen guaranteed college housing. Option: coed housing available. Alson H. Smith Jr. Library plus 1 other with 211,976 books, 57,500 microform titles, 76,250 serials, 20,325 audiovisual materials, an OPAC, and a Web page. Operations spending for the previous fiscal year: $1.6 million. 35 computers available on campus for general student use. Computer purchase/lease plans available. A campuswide network can be accessed from student residence rooms and from off campus. Students can access the following: online class registration, online student account information. Staffed computer lab on campus provides training in use of computers, software, and the Internet.

Community Environment: Winchester/Frederick County, a community of approximately 70,000 persons, is located 72 miles from Washington, D.C. near the northern end of the historic Shenandoah Valley. Winchester was founded in 1732 and played an important part in the French and Indian War and the Civil War. Bus transportation is available. Community facilities include a public library, museums, churches of major denominations, a medical center, excellent shopping areas, and a number of various civic and service organizations. Winchester is the host to the Shenandoah Apple Blossom Festival. George Washington began his career in Winchester in 1748 as surveyor to Lord Fairfax. Some of the historical points of interest are Abram's Delight (the Hollingsworth Home), Sheridan's Headquarters, "Stonewall" Jackson's Headquarters, Glen Burnie (home of James Wood), and Washington's Office.

■ **SKYLINE COLLEGE**

5234 Airport Rd. NW
Roanoke, VA 24012
Tel: (540)563-8080; Free: 866-708-6178
Fax: (540)362-5400
E-mail: wmerchant@ecpi.edu
Web Site: www.skyline.edu/

Description: Proprietary, 4-year, coed. Awards associate and bachelor's degrees. Founded 1966. Setting: 3-acre suburban campus. Total enrollment: 321. Faculty: 46 (21 full-time, 25 part-time). Student-undergrad faculty ratio is 11:1. 52 applied, 81% were admitted. Full-time: 321 students, 59% women, 41% men. Students come from 4 states and territories, 2% from out-of-state. 0% American Indian or Alaska Native, non-Hispanic/Latino; 2% Hispanic/Latino; 28% African American, non-Hispanic/Latino; 0% Asian, non-Hispanic/Latino; 0% Native Hawaiian or other Pacific Islander, non-Hispanic/Latino; 0% international. 42% 25 or older. Retention: 54% of full-time freshmen returned the following year. Academic areas with the most degrees conferred: computer and information sciences; engineering technologies; health professions and related sciences. Core. Calendar: semesters. Academic remediation for entering students, advanced placement, accelerated degree program, honors program, independent study, distance learning, double major, summer session for credit, part-time degree program, adult/continuing education programs, internships. Off campus study. Study abroad program.

Entrance Requirements: Options: electronic application, deferred admission. Required: high school transcript, interview, ACT. Recommended: SAT, SAT Subject Tests. Entrance: moderately difficult. Application deadline: Rolling. Notification: continuous.

Collegiate Environment: Orientation program. Social organizations: 3 open to all. Most popular organizations: National Vocational Technical Honor Society, Electronics Technician's Association, American Red Cross blood mobile drives. Major annual events: picnic and potlucks, Christmas lunch, Student Appreciation Days. Campus security: building and parking lot security. Skyline-Roanoke Library plus 2 others with 70,534 books, 46 serials, 164 audiovisual materials, an OPAC, and a Web page. 120 computers available on campus for general student use. A campuswide network can be accessed from off-campus. Students can access the following: online class registration. Staffed computer lab on campus provides training in use of computers, software, and the Internet.

■ **SOUTH UNIVERSITY (GLEN ALLEN)**

2151 Old Brick Rd.
Glen Allen, VA 23060
Tel: (804)727-6800; Free: 888-422-5076
Fax: (804)727-6790
Web Site: www.southuniversity.edu/richmond
Description: Proprietary, comprehensive, coed. Awards associate, bachelor's, and master's degrees.

■ **SOUTH UNIVERSITY (VIRGINIA BEACH)**

301 Bendix Rd., Ste. 100
Virginia Beach, VA 23452
Tel: (757)493-6900; Free: 877-206-1845
Fax: (757)493-6990
Web Site: www.southuniversity.edu/virginia-beach
Description: Proprietary, comprehensive, coed. Awards associate, bachelor's, and master's degrees.

■ **SOUTHERN VIRGINIA UNIVERSITY**

One College Hill Dr.
Buena Vista, VA 24416
Tel: (540)261-8400; Free: 800-229-8420
Fax: (540)261-8559
E-mail: admissions@southernvirginia.edu
Web Site: www.svu.edu/
Description: Independent Latter-day Saints, 4-year, coed. Awards bachelor's degrees. Founded 1867. Setting: 155-acre small town campus. Endowment: $1 million. Educational spending for the previous fiscal year: $5102 per student. Total enrollment: 749. Faculty: 69 (34 full-time, 35 part-time). Student-undergrad faculty ratio is 16:1. 1,346 applied, 52% were admitted. 17% from top 10% of their high school class, 36% from top quarter, 72% from top half. Full-time: 714 students, 54% women, 46% men. Part-time: 35 students, 49% women, 51% men. Students come from 47 states and territories, 17 other countries, 74% from out-of-state. 4% 25 or older, 65% live on campus, 13% transferred in. Retention: 48% of full-time freshmen returned the following year. Academic areas with the most degrees conferred: parks and recreation; visual and performing arts; business/marketing. Core. Calendar: semesters. Summer session for credit, co-op programs. Study abroad program. ROTC: Army (c).

Entrance Requirements: Required: high school transcript, ecclesiastical endorsement, SAT or ACT. Recommended: minimum 2.0 high school GPA. Required for some: essay, interview. Entrance: moderately difficult. Application deadline: 7/31.

Collegiate Environment: Orientation program. Drama-theater group, choral group. Most popular organizations: Student Association, LDS Institute of Religion. Student services: health clinic, personal-psychological counseling. Campus security: 24-hour emergency response devices and patrols. Von Canon Library with 107,630 books, 37,000 serials, 4,350 audiovisual materials, and an OPAC.

■ **SOUTHSIDE VIRGINIA COMMUNITY COLLEGE**

109 Campus Dr.
Alberta, VA 23821-9719
Tel: (434)949-1000
Fax: (434)949-7863
E-mail: rhina.jones@sv.vccs.edu
Web Site: www.southside.edu/
Description: State-supported, 2-year, coed. Part of Virginia Community College System. Awards certificates, diplomas, transfer associate, and terminal associate degrees. Founded 1970. Setting: 207-acre rural campus. Endowment: $1.3 million. Educational spending for the previous fiscal year: $4120 per student. Total enrollment: 6,353. Faculty: 290 (73 full-time, 217 part-time). Student-undergrad faculty ratio is 17:1. 438 applied, 100% were admitted. Full-time: 1,924 students, 65% women, 35% men. Part-time: 4,429 students, 61% women, 39% men. Students come from 5 states and territories, 0.1% from out-of-state. 49% 25 or older. Core. Calendar: semesters. Academic remediation for entering students, services for LD students, advanced placement, honors program, distance learning, summer session for credit, part-time degree program. Off campus study at Hampden-Sydney College, Saint Paul's College, Longwood College. Study abroad program. ROTC: Army (c).

Entrance Requirements: Open admission except for nursing program. Options: electronic application, deferred admission. Required: high school transcript, interview. Entrance: noncompetitive. Application deadline: Rolling. Notification: continuous. Preference given to district residents.

Costs Per Year: Application fee: $0. State resident tuition: $3510 full-time, $117 per credit hour part-time. Nonresident tuition: $8808 full-time, $293.60 per credit hour part-time. Mandatory fees: $300 full-time, $10 per credit hour part-time. Full-time tuition and fees vary according to course load. Part-time tuition and fees vary according to course load.

Collegiate Environment: Orientation program. Choral group. Most popular organizations: Student Forum, Phi Theta Kappa, Phi Beta Lambda, Alpha Delta Omega. Major annual events: women's festivals, cultural events, Kwanza celebration. Julian M. Howell Library plus 1 other with 28,752 books, 122 serials, 2,678 audiovisual materials, an OPAC, and a Web page. Operations spending for the previous fiscal year: $300,000. 200 computers available on campus for general student use. A campuswide network can be accessed. Students can access the following: online class registration, e-mail. Staffed computer lab on campus.

Community Environment: See Hampden-Sydney College.

■ **SOUTHWEST VIRGINIA COMMUNITY COLLEGE**
PO Box SVCC
Richlands, VA 24641
Tel: (276)964-2555; Free: 800-822-7822
Fax: (276)964-9307
E-mail: dionne.cook@sw.edu
Web Site: www.sw.edu/

Description: State-supported, 2-year, coed. Part of Virginia Community College System. Awards certificates, diplomas, transfer associate, and terminal associate degrees. Founded 1968. Setting: 100-acre rural campus. Endowment: $8.7 million. Educational spending for the previous fiscal year: $5222 per student. Total enrollment: 2,766. Faculty: 226 (49 full-time, 177 part-time). Student-undergrad faculty ratio is 16:1. 15% from top 10% of their high school class. Full-time: 1,159 students, 58% women, 42% men. Part-time: 1,607 students, 62% women, 38% men. Students come from 4 states and territories, 2% from out-of-state. 0.4% American Indian or Alaska Native, non-Hispanic/Latino; 1% Hispanic/Latino; 3% African American, non-Hispanic/Latino; 1% Asian, non-Hispanic/Latino; 0.1% Native Hawaiian or other Pacific Islander, non-Hispanic/Latino; 0.1% international. 33% 25 or older, 19% transferred in. Retention: 57% of full-time freshmen returned the following year. Core. Calendar: semesters. Academic remediation for entering students, advanced placement, accelerated degree program, honors program, distance learning, double major, summer session for credit, part-time degree program, adult/continuing education programs, internships. Off campus study.

Entrance Requirements: Open admission except for allied health, engineering programs. Options: electronic application, early admission, deferred admission. Required: high school transcript, interview, VCCS Math and English Assessments. Entrance: noncompetitive. Application deadline: Rolling. Preference given to service region residents. Transfer credits accepted: Yes.

Collegiate Environment: Choral group. Social organizations: 23 open to all. Most popular organizations: Phi Theta Kappa, Phi Beta Lambda, Intervoice, Helping Minds Club, Project ACHEIVE. Major annual events: Back to School Bash, End of the Year Bash, Annual Halloween Costume Contest. Student services: personal-psychological counseling. Campus security: 24-hour emergency response devices and patrols, student patrols, heavily saturated camera system. College housing not available. Southwest Virginia Community College Library with 111,000 books, 950 serials, 1,000 audiovisual materials, an OPAC, and a Web page. Operations spending for the previous fiscal year: $87,000. 475 computers available on campus for general student use. A campuswide network can be accessed from off-campus. Students can access the following: online class registration. Staffed computer lab on campus provides training in use of computers and the Internet.

Community Environment: Richlands is a rural community in the Appalachian Mountain region. Bus and plane transportation are available. The main industries of the area are agriculture, mining, and manufacturing.

■ **STRATFORD UNIVERSITY (FALLS CHURCH)**
7777 Leesburg Pke.
Ste. 100 S
Falls Church, VA 22043
Tel: (703)821-8570; Free: 800-444-0804
Fax: (703)556-9892
E-mail: jray@stratford.edu
Web Site: www.stratford.edu/

Description: Proprietary, comprehensive, coed. Administratively affiliated with Stratford University. Awards associate, bachelor's, and master's degrees. Founded 1976. Setting: suburban campus with easy access to Washington, DC. Educational spending for the previous fiscal year: $7384 per student. Total enrollment: 955. Faculty: 110 (19 full-time, 91 part-time). Student-undergrad faculty ratio is 88:1. 218 applied, 29% were admitted. Full-time: 141 students, 59% women, 41% men. Part-time: 463 students, 54% women, 46% men. 52% from out-of-state. 48% 25 or older. Retention: 52% of full-time freshmen returned the following year. Academic areas with the most degrees conferred: personal and culinary services; computer and information sciences; business/marketing. Core. Academic remediation for entering students, ESL program, advanced placement, accelerated degree program, distance learning, summer session for credit, part-time degree program, co-op programs and internships.

Entrance Requirements: Open admission. Options: electronic application, deferred admission, international baccalaureate accepted. Required: essay, proof of high school graduation or equivalent is required for all students; personal statement, transcript, and letters of recommendation are only required for the Nursing program. Entrance: noncompetitive. Application deadlines: Rolling, Rolling for nonresidents. Notification: continuous, continuous for nonresidents. Transfer credits accepted: Yes.

Costs Per Year: Application fee: $50. Tuition: $370 per quarter hour part-time. Mandatory fees: $100.

Collegiate Environment: Orientation program. Major annual event: International Events. Campus security: 24-hour emergency response devices. College housing not available. Stratford University Library with 7,649 books, 75 serials, 283 audiovisual materials, and an OPAC. Operations spending for the previous fiscal year: $217,113. 104 computers available on campus for general student use. A campuswide network can be accessed from off-campus. Students can access the following: online class registration. Staffed computer lab on campus provides training in use of computers, software, and the Internet.

■ **STRATFORD UNIVERSITY (GLEN ALLEN)**
11104 W Broad St.
Glen Allen, VA 23060
Tel: (804)290-4231; Free: 877-373-5173
Web Site: www.stratford.edu/

Description: Proprietary, comprehensive, coed. Awards bachelor's and master's degrees. Setting: suburban campus. Total enrollment: 486. Faculty: 23 (2 full-time, 21 part-time). Student-undergrad faculty ratio is 21:1. Full-time: 363 students, 65% women, 35% men. 0.4% American Indian or Alaska Native, non-Hispanic/Latino; 3% Hispanic/Latino; 45% African American, non-Hispanic/Latino; 21% Asian, non-Hispanic/Latino; 0.2% Native Hawaiian or other Pacific Islander, non-Hispanic/Latino. Retention: 63% of full-time freshmen returned the following year. Core. Academic remediation for entering students, independent study, part-time degree program, external degree program, adult/continuing education programs, co-op programs and internships.

Collegiate Environment: Orientation program.

■ **STRATFORD UNIVERSITY (NEWPORT NEWS)**
836 J. Clyde Morris Blvd.
Newport News, VA 23601
Tel: (757)873-4235; Free: 855-873-4235
Web Site: www.stratford.edu/

Description: Proprietary, comprehensive, coed. Awards associate, bachelor's, and master's degrees. Setting: urban campus. Total enrollment: 158. Faculty: 19 (3 full-time, 16 part-time). Student-undergrad faculty ratio is 4:1. 0% from top 10% of their high school class, 0% from top quarter, 0% from top half. Full-time: 24 students, 54% women, 46% men. Part-time: 128 students, 66% women, 34% men. 4% Hispanic/Latino; 86% African American, non-Hispanic/Latino; 0% international. 71% 25 or older, 4% transferred in. Retention: 83% of full-time freshmen returned the following year. Core. Academic remediation for entering students, services for LD students, accelerated degree program, distance learning, summer session for credit, part-time degree program, external degree program, co-op programs.

Entrance Requirements: Required: essay, high school transcript, interview.

Costs Per Year: Tuition: $14,895 full-time, $370 per credit part-time. Mandatory fees: $100 full-time. Full-time tuition and fees vary according to course load and program. Part-time tuition varies according to course load and program.

Collegiate Environment: Orientation program. Major annual events: Dress for Success Fashion Show, Optimal Resume Workshops, APA Workshops. Campus security: 24-hour emergency response devices, security officer during evening hours / classes. College housing not available. Learning Resource Center plus 1 other with 1,078 books, 20 serials, an OPAC, and a Web page. 19 computers available on campus for general student use. A campuswide network can be accessed from off-campus. Staffed computer lab on campus provides training in use of computers, software, and the Internet.

■ STRATFORD UNIVERSITY (WOODBRIDGE)

14349 Gideon Dr.
Woodbridge, VA 22192
Free: 888-546-1250
E-mail: admissions@stratford.edu
Web Site: www.stratford.edu/

Description: Proprietary, comprehensive, coed. Awards associate, bachelor's, and master's degrees. Setting: suburban campus. Faculty: 51 (15 full-time, 36 part-time). Full-time: 96 students, 67% women, 33% men. Part-time: 598 students, 74% women, 26% men. Academic remediation for entering students, advanced placement, accelerated degree program, independent study, distance learning, double major, summer session for credit, part-time degree program, adult/continuing education programs, co-op programs and internships. Off campus study.

Entrance Requirements: Open admission. Option: electronic application. Transfer credits accepted: Yes.

Collegiate Environment: Stratford University Woodbridge Campus Library with 4,228 books, 28 serials, 5 audiovisual materials, an OPAC, and a Web page. 100 computers available on campus for general student use. A campuswide network can be accessed from off-campus. Students can access the following: online class registration.

■ STRAYER UNIVERSITY - ALEXANDRIA CAMPUS

2730 Eisenhower Ave.
Alexandria, VA 22314
Tel: (703)317-2626
Fax: (703)329-9602
Web Site: www.strayer.edu/campus/alexandria

Description: Proprietary, comprehensive, coed. Awards associate, bachelor's, and master's degrees.

■ STRAYER UNIVERSITY - ARLINGTON CAMPUS

2121 15th St. N
Arlington, VA 22201
Tel: (703)892-5100
Fax: (703)769-2677
Web Site: www.strayer.edu/campus/arlington

Description: Proprietary, comprehensive, coed. Awards associate, bachelor's, and master's degrees.

■ STRAYER UNIVERSITY - CHESAPEAKE CAMPUS

676 Independence Pky.
Ste. 300
Chesapeake, VA 23320
Tel: (757)382-9900
Fax: (757)547-6078
Web Site: www.strayer.edu/campus/chesapeake/

Description: Proprietary, comprehensive, coed. Awards associate, bachelor's, and master's degrees.

■ STRAYER UNIVERSITY - CHESTERFIELD CAMPUS

2820 Waterford Lake Dr.
Ste. 100
Midlothian, VA 23112
Tel: (804)763-6300
Fax: (804)763-6304
Web Site: www.strayer.edu/campus/chesterfield/

Description: Proprietary, comprehensive, coed. Awards associate, bachelor's, and master's degrees.

■ STRAYER UNIVERSITY - FREDERICKSBURG CAMPUS

150 Riverside Pky.
Ste. 100
Fredericksburg, VA 22406
Tel: (540)374-4300

Web Site: www.strayer.edu/campus/fredericksburg
Description: Proprietary, comprehensive, coed. Awards associate, bachelor's, and master's degrees.

■ STRAYER UNIVERSITY - HENRICO CAMPUS

11501 Nuckols Rd.
Glen Allen, VA 23059
Tel: (804)527-1000
Fax: (804)527-6963
Web Site: www.strayer.edu/campus/henrico
Description: Proprietary, comprehensive, coed. Awards associate, bachelor's, and master's degrees. Founded 1892.

■ STRAYER UNIVERSITY - LOUDOUN CAMPUS

45150 Russell Branch Pky.
Ste. 200
Ashburn, VA 20147
Tel: (703)729-8800
Fax: (703)729-8820
Web Site: www.strayer.edu/campus/loudoun
Description: Proprietary, comprehensive, coed. Awards associate, bachelor's, and master's degrees.

■ STRAYER UNIVERSITY - MANASSAS CAMPUS

9990 Battleview Pky.
Manassas, VA 20109
Tel: (703)330-8400
Fax: (703)330-8135
Web Site: www.strayer.edu/campus/manassas
Description: Proprietary, comprehensive, coed. Awards associate, bachelor's, and master's degrees.

■ STRAYER UNIVERSITY - NEWPORT NEWS CAMPUS

99 Old Oyster Point Rd.
Unit 1
Newport News, VA 23602
Tel: (757)873-3100
Fax: (757)873-3131
Web Site: www.strayer.edu/campus/newport-news
Description: Proprietary, comprehensive, coed. Awards associate, bachelor's, and master's degrees.

■ STRAYER UNIVERSITY - VIRGINIA BEACH CAMPUS

249 Central Park Ave., Ste. 350
Virginia Beach, VA 23462
Tel: (757)493-6000
Fax: (757)493-6030
Web Site: www.strayer.edu/campus/virginia-beach
Description: Proprietary, comprehensive, coed. Awards associate, bachelor's, and master's degrees.

■ STRAYER UNIVERSITY - WOODBRIDGE CAMPUS

13385 Minnieville Rd.
Woodbridge, VA 22192
Tel: (703)878-2800
Fax: (703)878-2993
Web Site: www.strayer.edu/campus/woodbridge
Description: Proprietary, comprehensive, coed. Awards associate, bachelor's, and master's degrees.

■ SWEET BRIAR COLLEGE

Sweet Briar, VA 24595
Tel: (434)381-6100; Free: 800-381-6142
Fax: (434)381-6173
E-mail: admissions@sbc.edu
Web Site: www.sbc.edu/

Description: Independent, 4-year, women only. Awards bachelor's and master's degrees. Founded 1901. Setting: 3,250-acre rural campus. Endowment: $84.7 million. Research spending for the previous fiscal year: $571,376. Educational spending for the previous fiscal year: $20,997 per student. Total enrollment: 739. Faculty: 97 (78 full-time, 19 part-time). Student-undergrad faculty ratio is 8:1. 763 applied, 79% were admitted. 24% from top 10% of their high school class, 53% from top quarter, 87% from top half. Full-time: 695 students. Part-time: 28 students. Students come from 43 states and territories, 6 other countries, 50% from out-of-state. 2% American Indian or Alaska Native, non-Hispanic/Latino; 6% Hispanic/Latino; 9% African American, non-Hispanic/Latino; 3% Asian, non-Hispanic/Latino; 0.4% Native Hawaiian or other Pacific Islander, non-Hispanic/Latino; 1% international. 1% 25 or older, 93% live on campus, 2% transferred in. Retention: 74% of full-time freshmen returned the following year. Academic areas with the most degrees conferred: social sciences; business/marketing; biological/life sciences. Core. Calendar: semesters. Services for LD students, advanced placement, accelerated degree program, self-designed majors, honors program, independent study, double major, summer session for credit, part-time degree program, adult/continuing education programs, co-op programs and internships. Off campus study at Seven-College Exchange Program, Tri-College Exchange Program, American University. Study abroad program.

Entrance Requirements: Options: electronic application, deferred admission, international baccalaureate accepted. Required: essay, high school transcript, 2 recommendations, SAT or ACT. Recommended: interview. Required for some: portfolio with courses taken, list of texts covered, essay about homeschooling, campus visit, interview for homeschooled applicants. Entrance: moderately difficult. Application deadline: 2/1. Notification: continuous. SAT Reasoning Test deadline: 2/1. Transfer credits accepted: Yes.

Costs Per Year: Application fee: $40. Comprehensive fee: $43,765 includes full-time tuition ($31,850), mandatory fees ($475), and college room and board ($11,440). Room and board charges vary according to board plan. Part-time tuition: $885 per credit hour.

Collegiate Environment: Orientation program. Drama-theater group, choral group, student-run newspaper, radio station. Social organizations: 50 open to all. Most popular organizations: Student Government Association, Campus Events Organization, Interclub Council, PnP, Environmental Club. Major annual events: Spring Fling, Homecoming, Winter Mixer. Student services: health clinic, personal-psychological counseling. Campus security: 24-hour emergency response devices and patrols, late night transport-escort service, controlled dormitory access, front gate security. 625 college housing spaces available; 524 were occupied in 2012-13. Freshmen guaranteed college housing. On-campus residence required through senior year. Option: women-only housing available. Mary Helen Cochran Library plus 2 others with 384,462 books, 400,008 microform titles, 56,403 serials, 10,107 audiovisual materials, an OPAC, and a Web page. 128 computers available on campus for general student use. Computer purchase/lease plans available. A campuswide network can be accessed from student residence rooms and from off campus. Students can access the following: online class registration. Staffed computer lab on campus (open 24 hours a day) provides training in use of computers, software, and the Internet.

Community Environment: Sweet Briar is located on U.S. 29, 165 miles southwest of Washington, D.C., 50 miles south of Charlottesville, VA., and 100 miles west of Richmond. The nearest shopping area is in the town of Amherst, two miles north of Sweet Briar. Lynchburg, home of three other colleges, is 12 miles south of Sweet Briar. The Blue Ridge Mountains, visible a few miles to the west, offer numerous recreational possibilities, including the ski slopes at Wintergreen.

■ THOMAS NELSON COMMUNITY COLLEGE
PO Box 9407
Hampton, VA 23670-0407
Tel: (757)825-2700
E-mail: admissions@tncc.edu
Web Site: www.tncc.edu/

Description: State-supported, 2-year, coed. Part of Virginia Community College System. Awards certificates, diplomas, transfer associate, and terminal associate degrees. Founded 1968. Setting: 85-acre suburban campus with easy access to Virginia Beach. Total enrollment: 10,942. Student-undergrad faculty ratio is 22:1. Calendar: semesters. Academic remediation for entering students, ESL program, services for LD students, advanced placement, accelerated degree program, honors program, distance learning, summer session for credit, part-time degree program, adult/continuing education programs, co-op programs and internships. Off campus study.

Entrance Requirements: Open admission. Options: electronic application, early admission, deferred admission. Recommended: high school transcript. Required for some: interview. Entrance: noncompetitive. Application deadline: Rolling. Notification: continuous. Transfer credits accepted: Yes.

Costs Per Year: Application fee: $0. State resident tuition: $3735 full-time, $124.50 per credit hour part-time. Nonresident tuition: $9498 full-time, $316.60 per credit hour part-time. Mandatory fees: $43 full-time, $21.65 per term part-time.

Collegiate Environment: Orientation program. Drama-theater group, choral group. Most popular organizations: Phi Theta Kappa, Student Nurses Association, International Club, Student Government Association. Major annual events: Fall Festival, Spring Fest, Literature Circles. Student services: personal-psychological counseling. Campus security: 24-hour emergency response devices and patrols, late night transport-escort service. Thomas Nelson Community College Library with an OPAC and a Web page. 111 computers available on campus for general student use. A campuswide network can be accessed. Students can access the following: online class registration. Staffed computer lab on campus provides training in use of computers, software, and the Internet.

Community Environment: See Hampton University.

■ TIDEWATER COMMUNITY COLLEGE
121 College Pl.
Norfolk, VA 23510
Tel: (757)822-1122
Fax: (757)822-1060
E-mail: CentralRecords@tcc.edu
Web Site: www.tcc.edu/

Description: State-supported, 2-year, coed. Part of Virginia Community College System. Awards certificates, diplomas, transfer associate, and terminal associate degrees. Founded 1968. Setting: 520-acre suburban campus. Endowment: $7.1 million. Total enrollment: 30,447. Faculty: 1,219 (325 full-time, 894 part-time). Student-undergrad faculty ratio is 29:1. Students come from 53 states and territories, 10% from out-of-state. 45% 25 or older. Core. Calendar: semesters. Academic remediation for entering students, ESL program, services for LD students, advanced placement, accelerated degree program, honors program, independent study, distance learning, summer session for credit, part-time degree program, adult/continuing education programs, co-op programs and internships. Off campus study at members of the Virginia Tidewater Consortium for Continuing Higher Education.

Entrance Requirements: Open admission. Options: early admission, deferred admission. Entrance: noncompetitive. Application deadline: Rolling. Notification: continuous.

Collegiate Environment: Orientation program. Drama-theater group, student-run newspaper. Student services: personal-psychological counseling, women's center. Campus security: 24-hour patrols. Main library plus 5 others with 147,126 books, 913 serials, an OPAC, and a Web page. Operations spending for the previous fiscal year: $535,000.

Community Environment: A metropolitan area, Tidewater is located on the Chesapeake Bay, and has been a strategic military location in this country's conflicts because of its shipbuilding and ship repair. All forms of commercial transportation are available. Recreational activities are numerous, all water sports are enjoyed on nearby beaches. There is excellent hunting and fishing in the area also. Part-time employment opportunities are limited.

■ UNIVERSITY OF MANAGEMENT AND TECHNOLOGY
1901 N Fort Myers Dr.
Arlington, VA 22209
Tel: (703)516-0035; Free: 800-924-4883
Fax: (703)516-0985
E-mail: admissions@umtweb.edu
Web Site: www.umtweb.edu/

Description: Proprietary, comprehensive, coed. Awards associate, bachelor's, and master's degrees and post-master's certificates. Founded 1998. Setting: urban campus with easy access to Washington, DC. Calendar: continuous. Graduate courses open to undergrads.

■ UNIVERSITY OF MARY WASHINGTON
1301 College Ave.
Fredericksburg, VA 22401-5358
Tel: (540)654-1000; Free: 800-468-5614
Fax: (540)654-1073
E-mail: admit@umw.edu
Web Site: www.umw.edu/

Description: State-supported, comprehensive, coed. Awards bachelor's and master's degrees. Founded 1908. Setting: 176-acre small town campus with easy access to Richmond, Washington, DC. Endowment: $38.1 million. Research spending for the previous fiscal year: $338,020. Educational spending for the previous fiscal year: $5914 per student. Total enrollment: 5,093. Faculty: 386 (244 full-time, 142 part-time). Student-undergrad faculty ratio is 14:1. 4,847 applied, 77% were admitted. 23% from top 10% of their high school class, 58% from top quarter, 94% from top half. 3 National Merit

Scholars, 109 student government officers. Full-time: 3,881 students, 65% women, 35% men. Part-time: 634 students, 62% women, 38% men. Students come from 38 states and territories, 23 other countries, 15% from out-of-state. 0.2% American Indian or Alaska Native, non-Hispanic/Latino; 6% Hispanic/Latino; 6% African American, non-Hispanic/Latino; 5% Asian, non-Hispanic/Latino; 0% Native Hawaiian or other Pacific Islander, non-Hispanic/Latino; 1% international. 10% 25 or older, 60% live on campus, 7% transferred in. Retention: 83% of full-time freshmen returned the following year. Academic areas with the most degrees conferred: social sciences; English; interdisciplinary studies. Core. Calendar: semesters. Services for LD students, advanced placement, accelerated degree program, self-designed majors, honors program, independent study, distance learning, double major, summer session for credit, part-time degree program, adult/continuing education programs, co-op programs and internships, graduate courses open to undergrads. Study abroad program. ROTC: Army (c).

Entrance Requirements: Options: electronic application, early admission, early action, deferred admission, international baccalaureate accepted. Required: essay, high school transcript, SAT or ACT. Recommended: SAT Subject Tests. Entrance: very difficult. Application deadlines: 2/1, 11/15 for early action. Notification: 4/1, 1/31 for early action. Preference given to state residents. SAT Reasoning Test deadline: 2/1. SAT Subject Test deadline: 2/1. Transfer credits accepted: Yes. Applicants placed on waiting list: 352. Wait-listed applicants offered admission: 73. Early action applicants: 1,648. Early action applicants admitted: 1,459.

Costs Per Year: Application fee: $50. One-time mandatory fee: $60. State resident tuition: $4686 full-time, $200 per credit hour part-time. Nonresident tuition: $17,000 full-time, $712 per credit hour part-time. Mandatory fees: $4560 full-time, $129 per credit hour part-time, $30 per term part-time. Part-time tuition and fees vary according to course load and location. College room and board: $10,238. College room only: $5384. Room and board charges vary according to board plan and housing facility.

Collegiate Environment: Orientation program. Drama-theater group, choral group, student-run newspaper, radio station. Social organizations: 134 open to all. Most popular organizations: Students Helping Honduras, Black Student Association, Giant Productions (campus entertainment group), PRISM, Cheap Seats Cinema. Major annual events: Fall Homecoming, Junior Ring Week, Multicultural Fair. Student services: health clinic, personal-psychological counseling. Campus security: 24-hour emergency response devices and patrols, student patrols, late night transport-escort service, controlled dormitory access, self-defense and safety classes. 2,820 college housing spaces available; 2,541 were occupied in 2012-13. Freshmen guaranteed college housing. On-campus residence required through sophomore year. Options: coed, men-only, women-only housing available. Simpson Library plus 2 others with 424,417 books, 610,498 microform titles, 62,985 serials, 2,206 audiovisual materials, an OPAC, and a Web page. Operations spending for the previous fiscal year: $2.4 million. 306 computers available on campus for general student use. Computer purchase/lease plans available. A campuswide network can be accessed from student residence rooms and from off campus. Students can access the following: online class registration, Library resources, foreign languages resources, course management system. Staffed computer lab on campus provides training in use of computers, software, and the Internet.

Community Environment: Fredericksburg is located an hour south of Washington, DC and an hour north of Richmond, in one of the fastest growing regions in the state. One of the most historic cities in the country, Fredericksburg was the childhood home of George Washington and was the site of several major battles of the Civil War. Today the surrounding metropolitan population reaches upwards of 150,000 people yet still maintains the charm of a small town. The 40-block Historic District is located within easy walking distance of the campus and includes fine shopping, restaurants, movie theaters as well as historic attractions. Located on I-95, Fredericksburg offers access to both Washington and Richmond by Amtrak, various bus lines, and transportation service to National Airport in Washington and Richmond International. Fredericksburg is on the regularly scheduled commuter rail to Washington.

■ UNIVERSITY OF PHOENIX–NORTHERN VIRGINIA CAMPUS

11730 Plz. American Dr., Ste. 2000
Reston, VA 20190
Tel: (703)435-4402; Free: 866-766-0766
Web Site: www.phoenix.edu/
Description: Proprietary, comprehensive, coed. Awards bachelor's and master's degrees. Setting: urban campus. Total enrollment: 419. Faculty: 102 (12 full-time, 90 part-time). Full-time: 309 students, 46% women, 54%

men. 87% 25 or older. Academic areas with the most degrees conferred: business/marketing; computer and information sciences; public administration and social services. Core. Services for LD students, advanced placement, accelerated degree program, independent study, distance learning, graduate courses open to undergrads.

Entrance Requirements: Open admission. Options: electronic application, deferred admission. Required: 1 recommendation. Required for some: high school transcript. Entrance: noncompetitive. Application deadline: Rolling.

Collegiate Environment: Campus security: late night transport-escort service. University Library with 16,781 serials and an OPAC. Operations spending for the previous fiscal year: $6.8 million.

■ UNIVERSITY OF PHOENIX–RICHMOND CAMPUS

6600 W Broad St.
Richmond, VA 23230
Tel: (804)288-3390; Free: 866-766-0766
Web Site: www.phoenix.edu/
Description: Proprietary, comprehensive, coed. Awards bachelor's and master's degrees. Setting: urban campus. Total enrollment: 129. Faculty: 81 (8 full-time, 73 part-time). Full-time: 89 students, 67% women, 33% men. 89% 25 or older. Academic areas with the most degrees conferred: history; computer and information sciences. Core. Services for LD students, advanced placement, accelerated degree program, independent study, distance learning, graduate courses open to undergrads.

Entrance Requirements: Open admission. Options: electronic application, deferred admission. Required: 1 recommendation. Required for some: high school transcript. Entrance: noncompetitive. Application deadline: Rolling.

Collegiate Environment: Campus security: late night transport-escort service. University Library with 16,781 serials and an OPAC. Operations spending for the previous fiscal year: $6.8 million.

■ UNIVERSITY OF RICHMOND

28 Westhampton Way
University of Richmond, VA 23173
Tel: (804)289-8000; Free: 800-700-1662
Fax: (804)287-6003
E-mail: admissions@richmond.edu
Web Site: www.richmond.edu/
Description: Independent, comprehensive, coed. Awards bachelor's, master's, and doctoral degrees. Founded 1830. Setting: 350-acre suburban campus. Endowment: $1.9 billion. Research spending for the previous fiscal year: $7 million. Educational spending for the previous fiscal year: $18,193 per student. Total enrollment: 3,626. Faculty: 427 (320 full-time, 107 part-time). Student-undergrad faculty ratio is 9:1. 10,232 applied, 30% were admitted. 59% from top 10% of their high school class, 89% from top quarter, 99% from top half. 7 National Merit Scholars, 50 class presidents, 12 valedictorians. Full-time: 3,031 students, 55% women, 45% men. Part-time: 43 students, 37% women, 63% men. Students come from 48 states and territories, 71 other countries, 79% from out-of-state. 0.2% American Indian or Alaska Native, non-Hispanic/Latino; 6% Hispanic/Latino; 8% African American, non-Hispanic/Latino; 6% Asian, non-Hispanic/Latino; 0.03% Native Hawaiian or other Pacific Islander, non-Hispanic/Latino; 8% international. 1% 25 or older, 89% live on campus, 2% transferred in. Retention: 93% of full-time freshmen returned the following year. Academic areas with the most degrees conferred: business/marketing; social sciences; biological/life sciences. Core. Calendar: semesters. ESL program, services for LD students, advanced placement, self-designed majors, honors program, independent study, double major, summer session for credit, part-time degree program, internships. Off campus study at American University Washington Semester Program, Duke University Marine Sciences Laboratory, Marine Biological Laboratory Semester in Environmental Science - Woods Hole. Study abroad program. ROTC: Army.

Entrance Requirements: Options: electronic application, early decision, deferred admission, international baccalaureate accepted. Required: essay, high school transcript, 1 recommendation, SAT or ACT. Entrance: very difficult. Application deadlines: 1/15, 11/15 for early decision plan 1, 1/15 for early decision plan 2. Notification: 4/1, 12/15 for early decision plan 1, 2/15 for early decision plan 2. SAT Reasoning Test deadline: 1/15. SAT Subject Test deadline: 1/15. Transfer credits accepted: Yes. Applicants placed on waiting list: 3,939. Wait-listed applicants offered admission: 13. Early decision applicants: 818. Early decision applicants admitted: 333.

Costs Per Year: Application fee: $50. Comprehensive fee: $55,590 includes full-time tuition ($45,320) and college room and board ($10,270). College room only: $4650. Full-time tuition varies according to course load. Room and board charges vary according to board plan and housing facility. Part-time tuition: $2266 per credit hour. Part-time tuition varies according to course load.

Collegiate Environment: Orientation program. Drama-theater group, choral group, student-run newspaper, radio station. Social organizations: 118 open to all; national fraternities, national sororities; 13% of eligible men and 27% of eligible women are members. Most popular organizations: Club Sports, Richmond Rowdies - Facilitates school spirit at athletic events, Alpha Phi Omega Service Fraternity, InterVarsity Christian Fellowship, Student Government Associations. Major annual events: Homecoming, Pig Roast, Ring Dance. Student services: health clinic, personal-psychological counseling, women's center. Campus security: 24-hour emergency response devices and patrols, late night transport-escort service, controlled dormitory access, campus police. 2,790 college housing spaces available; 2,649 were occupied in 2012-13. Freshmen guaranteed college housing. Options: coed, men-only, women-only housing available. Boatwright Memorial Library plus 2 others with 839,555 books, 141,297 microform titles, 92,748 serials, 30,034 audiovisual materials, an OPAC, and a Web page. Operations spending for the previous fiscal year: $12.4 million. 1,018 computers available on campus for general student use. Computer purchase/lease plans available. A campuswide network can be accessed from student residence rooms and from off campus. Students can access the following: online class registration. Staffed computer lab on campus provides training in use of computers, software, and the Internet.

■ UNIVERSITY OF VIRGINIA

Charlottesville, VA 22903
Tel: (434)924-0311
Fax: (434)924-3587
E-mail: undergrad-admission@virginia.edu
Web Site: www.virginia.edu/

Description: State-supported, university, coed. Awards bachelor's, master's, and doctoral degrees and post-master's certificates. Founded 1819. Setting: 1,167-acre suburban campus with easy access to Richmond. Endowment: $4.7 billion. Research spending for the previous fiscal year: $344.9 million. Educational spending for the previous fiscal year: $15,556 per student. Total enrollment: 23,907. Faculty: 1,307 (1,243 full-time, 64 part-time). Student-undergrad faculty ratio is 16:1. 27,193 applied, 30% were admitted. 93% from top 10% of their high school class, 98% from top quarter, 99% from top half. Full-time: 14,931 students, 54% women, 46% men. Part-time: 891 students, 55% women, 45% men. Students come from 48 states and territories, 120 other countries, 26% from out-of-state. 0.1% American Indian or Alaska Native, non-Hispanic/Latino; 5% Hispanic/Latino; 6% African American, non-Hispanic/Latino; 11% Asian, non-Hispanic/Latino; 0.1% Native Hawaiian or other Pacific Islander, non-Hispanic/Latino; 6% international. 4% 25 or older, 41% live on campus, 4% transferred in. Retention: 97% of full-time freshmen returned the following year. Academic areas with the most degrees conferred: social sciences; engineering; business/marketing. Core. Calendar: semesters. ESL program, services for LD students, advanced placement, accelerated degree program, self-designed majors, honors program, independent study, double major, summer session for credit, part-time degree program, adult/continuing education programs, co-op programs and internships, graduate courses open to undergrads. Study abroad program. ROTC: Army, Naval, Air Force.

Entrance Requirements: Options: electronic application, early action, deferred admission, international baccalaureate accepted. Required: essay, high school transcript, 1 recommendation, SAT or ACT. Recommended: SAT Subject Tests, SAT or ACT plus optional ACT writing test (ACT alone does not satisfy requirement). At least two SAT subject tests (student's choice) are recommended. Entrance: very difficult. Application deadlines: 1/1, 11/1 for early action. Notification: 4/1, 1/31 for early action. Preference given to state residents, children of alumni. SAT Reasoning Test deadline: 1/1. SAT Subject Test deadline: 1/1. Transfer credits accepted: Yes. Applicants placed on waiting list: 4,393. Wait-listed applicants offered admission: 284. Early action applicants: 10,817. Early action applicants admitted: 3,171.

Costs Per Year: Application fee: $60. State resident tuition: $10,016 full-time. Nonresident tuition: $36,720 full-time. Mandatory fees: $2442 full-time. Full-time tuition and fees vary according to program. College room and board: $9717. College room only: $5337. Room and board charges vary according to board plan and housing facility.

Collegiate Environment: Orientation program. Drama-theater group, choral group, marching band, student-run newspaper, radio station. Social organizations: national fraternities, national sororities, local fraternities, local sororities; 21% of eligible men and 22% of eligible women are members.

Most popular organizations: Madison House, student government, university guides, University Union, The Cavalier Daily. Major annual events: Family Weekend, Homecoming, Finals Weekend. Student services: legal services, health clinic, personal-psychological counseling, women's center. Campus security: 24-hour emergency response devices and patrols, late night transport-escort service, controlled dormitory access. 6,213 college housing spaces available; 5,584 were occupied in 2012-13. Freshmen guaranteed college housing. On-campus residence required in freshman year. Option: coed housing available. Alderman Library plus 14 others with 5.7 million books, 5 million microform titles, 124,721 serials, 155,852 audiovisual materials, an OPAC, and a Web page. Operations spending for the previous fiscal year: $32.7 million. 372 computers available on campus for general student use. Computer purchase/lease plans available. A campuswide network can be accessed from student residence rooms and from off campus. Students can access the following: online class registration, online course management tool. Staffed computer lab on campus (open 24 hours a day) provides training in use of computers, software, and the Internet.

Community Environment: Charlottesville, situated in the foothills of the Blue Ridge Mountains, was the home of Thomas Jefferson and James Monroe. Numerous old homes and estates in Charlottesville and the surrounding areas, reveal Jefferson's architectural influence. All forms of commercial transportation are available. Albemarle County is known for its horses, dogs, fox hunting, and for its peach and apple orchards. The many outdoor activities include golf, tennis, hunting, fishing, and hiking. Some part-time employment is available for students. Points of interest include the Lewis and Clark Memorial, Monticello, the home of Thomas Jefferson, Old Courthouse, and the University of Virginia-founded by Thomas Jefferson.

■ THE UNIVERSITY OF VIRGINIA'S COLLEGE AT WISE

1 College Ave.
Wise, VA 24293
Tel: (276)328-0100; Free: 888-282-9324
Fax: (276)328-0251
E-mail: admissions@uvawise.edu
Web Site: www.uvawise.edu/

Description: State-supported, 4-year, coed. Part of University of Virginia. Awards bachelor's degrees. Founded 1954. Setting: 396-acre small town campus. Endowment: $50.8 million. Research spending for the previous fiscal year: $54,669. Educational spending for the previous fiscal year: $5007 per student. Total enrollment: 2,420. Faculty: 196 (90 full-time, 106 part-time). Student-undergrad faculty ratio is 17:1. 971 applied, 83% were admitted. 17% from top 10% of their high school class, 19% from top quarter, 76% from top half. 6 valedictorians. Full-time: 1,522 students, 50% women, 50% men. Part-time: 898 students, 82% women, 18% men. Students come from 17 states and territories, 10 other countries, 5% from out-of-state. 0.2% American Indian or Alaska Native, non-Hispanic/Latino; 2% Hispanic/Latino; 9% African American, non-Hispanic/Latino; 1% Asian, non-Hispanic/Latino; 0% Native Hawaiian or other Pacific Islander, non-Hispanic/Latino; 0.1% international. 37% 25 or older, 38% live on campus, 6% transferred in. Retention: 70% of full-time freshmen returned the following year. Academic areas with the most degrees conferred: education; business/marketing; social sciences; biological/life sciences. Core. Calendar: semesters. Academic remediation for entering students, services for LD students, advanced placement, accelerated degree program, self-designed majors, honors program, independent study, distance learning, double major, summer session for credit, part-time degree program, adult/continuing education programs, co-op programs and internships. ROTC: Army.

Entrance Requirements: Options: early admission, early action, international baccalaureate accepted. Required: high school transcript, minimum 2.3 high school GPA, SAT or ACT. Recommended: 2 recommendations. Entrance: moderately difficult. Application deadlines: 8/1, 2/1 for early action. Notification: 8/20, 2/15 for early action. SAT Reasoning Test deadline: 5/1. Early action applicants: 421. Early action applicants admitted: 188.

Costs Per Year: Application fee: $25. State resident tuition: $8509 full-time, $200 per credit hour part-time. Nonresident tuition: $23,565 full-time, $808 per credit hour part-time. Mandatory fees: $71 per credit hour part-time. Part-time tuition and fees vary according to course load. College room and board: $9440. College room only: $5642. Room and board charges vary according to board plan and housing facility.

Collegiate Environment: Orientation program. Drama-theater group, choral group, marching band, student-run newspaper, radio station. Social organizations: 60 open to all; national fraternities, national sororities, local fraternities, local sororities; 9% of eligible men and 8% of eligible women are members. Most popular organizations: student government, Student Activities Board, Multicultural Association, Residence Hall Association, intramurals. Major annual events: Holly Ball, Homecoming, Jam for Man. Student services: health clinic, personal-psychological counseling. Campus security: 24-hour emergency response devices and patrols, student patrols, late night transport-escort service, self-defense, informal discussions, pamphlets/posters/films, and crime prevention office. 749 college housing spaces available; 648 were occupied in 2012-13. No special consideration for freshman housing applicants. On-campus residence required in freshman year. Options: coed, men-only, women-only housing available. Wyllie Library with 159,245 books, 66,117 microform titles, 3,634 serials, 2,279 audiovisual materials, an OPAC, and a Web page. Operations spending for the previous fiscal year: $777,269. 300 computers available on campus for general student use. Computer purchase/lease plans available. A campuswide network can be accessed from student residence rooms and from off campus. Students can access the following: online class registration. Staffed computer lab on campus provides training in use of computers, software, and the Internet.

■ VALLEY FORGE CHRISTIAN COLLEGE WOODBRIDGE CAMPUS
13909 Smoketown Rd.
Woodbridge, VA 22192
Tel: (703)580-4810; Free: 800-432-8322
Fax: (703)580-4806
Web Site: www.vfcc.edu/woodbridge/
Description: Independent Assemblies of God, 4-year, coed. Administratively affiliated with Valley Forge Christian College. Awards associate and bachelor's degrees. Setting: suburban campus with easy access to Washington, DC. Total enrollment: 131. Faculty: 36 (4 full-time, 32 part-time). Student-undergrad faculty ratio is 6:1. 53 applied, 81% were admitted. Full-time: 59 students, 56% women, 44% men. Part-time: 72 students, 67% women, 33% men. 0% American Indian or Alaska Native, non-Hispanic/Latino; 11% Hispanic/Latino; 32% African American, non-Hispanic/Latino; 0% Asian, non-Hispanic/Latino; 2% Native Hawaiian or other Pacific Islander, non-Hispanic/Latino; 3% international. Academic areas with the most degrees conferred: education; psychology; theology and religious vocations. Core. Academic remediation for entering students, services for LD students, advanced placement, independent study, distance learning, double major, summer session for credit, part-time degree program, adult/continuing education programs, co-op programs and internships. Off campus study.
Entrance Requirements: Required: essay, high school transcript, minimum 1.5 high school GPA, interview, Pastor's Recommendation. Entrance: minimally difficult. Application deadlines: Rolling, Rolling for nonresidents. Notification: continuous, continuous for nonresidents. Transfer credits accepted: Yes.
Costs Per Year: Application fee: $75. Tuition: $8398 full-time. Mandatory fees: $500 full-time.
Collegiate Environment: Orientation program. Campus security: 24-hour emergency response devices. 40 computers available on campus for general student use. Students can access the following: online class registration. Staffed computer lab on campus provides training in use of computers, software, and the Internet.

■ VIRGINIA COLLEGE IN RICHMOND
7200 Midlothian Tpke.
Richmond, VA 23225
Tel: (804)977-5100
Web Site: www.vc.edu/
Description: Proprietary, 2-year, coed. Founded 2011.

■ VIRGINIA COMMONWEALTH UNIVERSITY
901 W Franklin St.
Richmond, VA 23284-9005
Tel: (804)828-0100; Free: 800-841-3638
Fax: (804)828-1899
E-mail: schallor@vcu.edu
Web Site: www.vcu.edu/
Description: State-supported, university, coed. Awards bachelor's, master's, and doctoral degrees and post-master's certificates. Founded 1838. Setting: 144-acre urban campus. Endowment: $438.1 million. Research spending for the previous fiscal year: $136.3 million. Educational spending for the previous fiscal year: $10,477 per student. Total enrollment: 31,752. Faculty: 3,253 (2,048 full-time, 1,205 part-time). Student-undergrad faculty ratio is 18:1. 15,750 applied, 60% were admitted. 20% from top 10% of their high school class, 53% from top quarter, 88% from top half. Full-time: 20,010 students,

56% women, 44% men. Part-time: 3,941 students, 56% women, 44% men. Students come from 48 states and territories, 109 other countries, 7% from out-of-state. 0.3% American Indian or Alaska Native, non-Hispanic/Latino; 7% Hispanic/Latino; 18% African American, non-Hispanic/Latino; 12% Asian, non-Hispanic/Latino; 0.3% Native Hawaiian or other Pacific Islander, non-Hispanic/Latino; 3% international. 13% 25 or older, 22% live on campus, 8% transferred in. Retention: 85% of full-time freshmen returned the following year. Academic areas with the most degrees conferred: business/marketing; visual and performing arts; health professions and related sciences. Core. Calendar: semesters. Academic remediation for entering students, ESL program, services for LD students, advanced placement, accelerated degree program, self-designed majors, freshman honors college, honors program, independent study, distance learning, double major, summer session for credit, part-time degree program, adult/continuing education programs, co-op programs and internships, graduate courses open to undergrads. Off campus study. Study abroad program. ROTC: Army (c).
Entrance Requirements: Options: electronic application, early admission. Required: high school transcript, SAT or ACT scores, SAT or ACT. Application deadline: 1/15. Notification: 12/1. SAT Reasoning Test deadline: 2/1. Applicants placed on waiting list: 494. Wait-listed applicants offered admission: 0.
Costs Per Year: Application fee: $40. State resident tuition: $7860 full-time, $327.50 per credit hour part-time. Nonresident tuition: $21,275 full-time, $886.46 per credit hour part-time. Mandatory fees: $2,025 full-time, $77.67 per credit hour part-time. College room and board: $8748. Room and board charges vary according to board plan and housing facility.
Collegiate Environment: Orientation program. Drama-theater group, choral group, student-run newspaper, radio station. Social organizations: 496 open to all; national fraternities, national sororities, local fraternities, local sororities; 7% of eligible men and 6% of eligible women are members. Major annual events: Welcome Week and Homecoming, 2011 Intercultural Festival, Fall Fest. Student services: health clinic, personal-psychological counseling, women's center. Campus security: 24-hour emergency response devices and patrols, student patrols, late night transport-escort service, controlled dormitory access, security personnel in residence halls, RAD classes and special event coverage. 5,321 college housing spaces available; 5,156 were occupied in 2012-13. Option: coed housing available. Cabell Library and Thompkins McCaw Library with 2.5 million books, 3.3 million microform titles, 61,000 serials, 39,184 audiovisual materials, an OPAC, and a Web page. Operations spending for the previous fiscal year: $17.9 million. 1,500 computers available on campus for general student use. Computer purchase/lease plans available. A computer is required for all students. A campuswide network can be accessed from student residence rooms and from off campus. Students can access the following: online class registration. Staffed computer lab on campus provides training in use of computers, software, and the Internet.
Community Environment: See University of Richmond.

■ VIRGINIA HIGHLANDS COMMUNITY COLLEGE
100 VHCC Dr. Abingdon
Abingdon, VA 24212
Tel: (276)739-2400; Free: 877-207-6115
Fax: (276)739-2590
E-mail: kcheers@vhcc.edu
Web Site: www.vhcc.edu/
Description: State-supported, 2-year, coed. Part of Virginia Community College System. Awards certificates, diplomas, transfer associate, and terminal associate degrees. Founded 1967. Setting: 100-acre small town campus. Total enrollment: 2,580. Faculty: 97 (58 full-time, 39 part-time). 15% from top 10% of their high school class, 35% from top quarter, 65% from top half. Full-time: 1,001 students, 52% women, 48% men. Part-time: 1,579 students, 55% women, 45% men. Students come from 7 states and territories, 9% from out-of-state. 52% 25 or older, 7% transferred in. Retention: 47% of full-time freshmen returned the following year. Calendar: semesters. Academic remediation for entering students, services for LD students, advanced placement, summer session for credit, part-time degree program, adult/continuing education programs, co-op programs.
Entrance Requirements: Open admission except for nursing, radiology, physical therapy programs. Options: early admission, deferred admission. Required: high school transcript. Entrance: noncompetitive. Application deadline: Rolling. Notification: continuous. Preference given to district, then state residents.
Costs Per Year: State resident tuition: $3810 full-time, $127 per credit part-time. Nonresident tuition: $9570 full-time, $319 per credit part-time. Full-time

tuition varies according to course load and reciprocity agreements. Part-time tuition varies according to course load and reciprocity agreements.

Collegiate Environment: Orientation program. Drama-theater group, choral group. Student services: personal-psychological counseling. 29,683 books and 174 serials 240 computers available on campus for general student use. A campuswide network can be accessed from off-campus. Staffed computer lab on campus.

Community Environment: Abingdon is known as a handicraft center as well as being the largest burley tobacco market and the largest livestock auction in Virginia. Commercial transportation is available. The Blue Ridge and Holston Mountains are nearby providing facilities for many outdoor activities.

■ **VIRGINIA INTERMONT COLLEGE**

1013 Moore St.

Bristol, VA 24201

Tel: (276)669-6101; Free: 800-451-1842

Fax: (276)669-5763

E-mail: genevaperkins@vic.edu

Web Site: www.vic.edu/

Description: Independent religious, 4-year, coed. Awards bachelor's degrees. Founded 1884. Setting: 13-acre small town campus. Endowment: $4.1 million. Educational spending for the previous fiscal year: $7412 per student. Total enrollment: 496. Faculty: 96 (41 full-time, 55 part-time). Student-undergrad faculty ratio is 8:1. 286 applied, 99% were admitted. 9% from top 10% of their high school class, 39% from top quarter, 70% from top half. 4 valedictorians. Full-time: 447 students, 68% women, 32% men. Part-time: 49 students, 76% women, 24% men. Students come from 34 states and territories, 8 other countries, 44% from out-of-state. 1% American Indian or Alaska Native, non-Hispanic/Latino; 2% Hispanic/Latino; 8% African American, non-Hispanic/Latino; 0.4% Asian, non-Hispanic/Latino; 0% Native Hawaiian or other Pacific Islander, non-Hispanic/Latino; 2% international. 23% 25 or older, 50% live on campus, 10% transferred in. Retention: 61% of full-time freshmen returned the following year. Academic areas with the most degrees conferred: interdisciplinary studies; visual and performing arts; agriculture. Core. Calendar: semesters. Academic remediation for entering students, services for LD students, advanced placement, accelerated degree program, honors program, independent study, double major, summer session for credit, part-time degree program, adult/continuing education programs, internships. Off campus study at King College - Bristol, TN. Study abroad program.

Entrance Requirements: Options: electronic application, early admission, early decision, deferred admission, international baccalaureate accepted. Required: essay, high school transcript, minimum 2.5 high school GPA, SAT or ACT. Required for some: interview, 2 letters of recommendation for students applying to Honors Program. Entrance: minimally difficult. Application deadlines: Rolling, Rolling for nonresidents, 1/1 for early decision. Notification: continuous, continuous for nonresidents, 2/15 for early decision. SAT Reasoning Test deadline: 8/15. Transfer credits accepted: Yes.

Costs Per Year: Application fee: $0. Comprehensive fee: $32,411 includes full-time tuition ($24,542), mandatory fees ($100), and college room and board ($7769). College room only: $3760. Full-time tuition and fees vary according to course level, course load, program, and reciprocity agreements. Room and board charges vary according to board plan and housing facility. Part-time tuition: $491 per credit hour. Part-time tuition varies according to course level, course load, program, and reciprocity agreements.

Collegiate Environment: Orientation program. Drama-theater group, student-run newspaper. Social organizations: 17 open to all. Most popular organizations: Intermont Green, FCA Fellowship of Christian Athletes, Student Government Association, Sport Management Club, International Issues Club. Major annual events: Family Weekend, Spring Fling/Spirit Week, May Court. Student services: health clinic, personal-psychological counseling. Campus security: 24-hour emergency response devices and patrols, late night transport-escort service. 363 college housing spaces available; 252 were occupied in 2012-13. Freshmen guaranteed college housing. On-campus residence required through junior year. Option: coed housing available. J. F. Hicks Library with 166,729 books, 60 serials, 1,650 audiovisual materials, an OPAC, and a Web page. Operations spending for the previous fiscal year: $130,588. 100 computers available on campus for general student use. A campuswide network can be accessed from student residence rooms and from off campus. Students can access the following: online class registration. Staffed computer lab on campus.

Community Environment: The name"Intermont" meaning"among the mountains," is descriptive of the College's setting. Virginia Intermont is

located in Bristol, VA, off Exit 5 of Interstate 81, almost halfway between Roanoke, VA and Knoxville, TN. The campus is situated only eight blocks from the city's downtown district and two miles from the Bristol Mall.

■ **VIRGINIA INTERNATIONAL UNIVERSITY**

11200 Waples Mill Rd.

Fairfax, VA 22030

Tel: (703)591-7042; Free: 800-514-6848

Fax: (703)591-7048

E-mail: admissions@viu.edu

Web Site: www.viu.edu/

Description: Proprietary, comprehensive, coed. Awards bachelor's and master's degrees.

■ **VIRGINIA MILITARY INSTITUTE**

Lexington, VA 24450

Tel: (540)464-7207; Free: 800-767-4207

Fax: (540)464-7746

E-mail: admissions@vmi.edu

Web Site: www.vmi.edu/

Description: State-supported, 4-year, coed. Awards bachelor's degrees. Founded 1839. Setting: 134-acre small town campus. Total enrollment: 1,569. Faculty: 180 (119 full-time, 61 part-time). Student-undergrad faculty ratio is 11:1. 1,598 applied, 56% were admitted. 13% from top 10% of their high school class, 40% from top quarter, 86% from top half. Full-time: 1,569 students, 9% women, 91% men. 40% from out-of-state. 0.3% American Indian or Alaska Native, non-Hispanic/Latino; 4% Hispanic/Latino; 5% African American, non-Hispanic/Latino; 5% Asian, non-Hispanic/Latino; 0% Native Hawaiian or other Pacific Islander, non-Hispanic/Latino; 2% international. 100% live on campus, 2% transferred in. Retention: 83% of full-time freshmen returned the following year. Academic areas with the most degrees conferred: social sciences; engineering; history. Core. Calendar: semesters. Services for LD students, advanced placement, honors program, independent study, double major, summer session for credit, internships. Study abroad program. ROTC: Army, Naval, Air Force.

Entrance Requirements: Options: electronic application, early admission, early decision, international baccalaureate accepted. Required: high school transcript, SAT or ACT. Recommended: essay, 2 recommendations, interview. Entrance: moderately difficult. Application deadlines: 2/1, 11/15 for early decision. Notification: continuous, 12/15 for early decision. SAT Reasoning Test deadline: 5/1. Transfer credits accepted: Yes. Applicants placed on waiting list: 253. Wait-listed applicants offered admission: 4. Early decision applicants: 282. Early decision applicants admitted: 192.

Costs Per Year: Application fee: $40. State resident tuition: $6880 full-time. Nonresident tuition: $26,856 full-time. Mandatory fees: $6955 full-time. College room and board: $7733.

Collegiate Environment: Orientation program. Drama-theater group, choral group, marching band, student-run newspaper. Most popular organizations: Newman Club, Officers Christian Fellowship, strength and fitness organizations, Promaji, Pre-Law Society. Major annual events: New Market Day, Parents' Weekend, Founders' Day. Student services: health clinic, personal-psychological counseling. Campus security: 24-hour emergency response devices and patrols, student patrols. Preston Library with an OPAC and a Web page.

Community Environment: VMI offers a small town flavor, with a hallowed history and breathtaking scenery.

■ **VIRGINIA POLYTECHNIC INSTITUTE AND STATE UNIVERSITY**

Blacksburg, VA 24061

Tel: (540)231-6000

Fax: (540)231-3242

E-mail: vtadmiss@vt.edu

Web Site: www.vt.edu/

Description: State-supported, university, coed. Awards associate, bachelor's, master's, and doctoral degrees and post-master's certificates. Founded 1872. Setting: 2,600-acre small town campus. Endowment: $594.8 million. Total enrollment: 31,087. Faculty: 1,579 (1,306 full-time, 273 part-time). Student-undergrad faculty ratio is 16:1. 20,191 applied, 70% were admitted. 44% from top 10% of their high school class, 84% from top quarter, 99% from top half. Full-time: 23,366 students, 42% women, 58% men. Part-time: 493 students, 38% women, 62% men. Students come from 113 other countries. 0.2% American Indian or Alaska Native, non-Hispanic/Latino; 5% Hispanic/Latino; 3% African American, non-Hispanic/Latino; 8% Asian, non-Hispanic/Latino; 0.1% Native Hawaiian or other Pacific Islander, non-

Hispanic/Latino; 3% international. 36% live on campus, 4% transferred in. Retention: 91% of full-time freshmen returned the following year. Academic areas with the most degrees conferred: engineering; business/marketing; biological/life sciences. Core. Calendar: semesters. ESL program, services for LD students, advanced placement, accelerated degree program, honors program, independent study, distance learning, double major, summer session for credit, part-time degree program, adult/continuing education programs, co-op programs and internships, graduate courses open to undergrads. Study abroad program. ROTC: Army, Naval, Air Force.

Entrance Requirements: Options: electronic application, early admission, early decision, deferred admission, international baccalaureate accepted. Required: high school transcript, SAT or ACT. Recommended: minimum 3 high school GPA. Required for some: SAT and SAT Subject Tests or ACT. Entrance: moderately difficult. Application deadlines: 1/15, 11/1 for early decision. Notification: 4/1, 12/15 for early decision. Applicants placed on waiting list: 2,217. Wait-listed applicants offered admission: 110. Early decision applicants: 2,121. Early decision applicants admitted: 1,108.

Costs Per Year: Application fee: $60. State resident tuition: $9187 full-time. Nonresident tuition: $23,575 full-time. College room and board: $7406. College room only: $4190. Room and board charges vary according to board plan.

Collegiate Environment: Orientation program. Drama-theater group, choral group, marching band, student-run newspaper, radio station. Social organizations: 700 open to all; national fraternities, national sororities, local fraternities. Most popular organizations: Virginia Tech Union, Student Government Association, international student organizations. Major annual events: The Big Event, International Street Fair, Homecoming Week. Student services: legal services, health clinic, personal-psychological counseling, women's center. Campus security: 24-hour emergency response devices and patrols, student patrols, late night transport-escort service, controlled dormitory access. 9,100 college housing spaces available; all were occupied in 2012-13. Freshmen guaranteed college housing. On-campus residence required in freshman year. Options: coed, men-only, women-only housing available. Newman Library plus 2 others with 2.4 million books, 6.3 million microform titles, 27,150 serials, 18,185 audiovisual materials, an OPAC, and a Web page. 8,000 computers available on campus for general student use. A computer is required for all students. A campuswide network can be accessed from student residence rooms and from off campus. Students can access the following: online class registration. Staffed computer lab on campus (open 24 hours a day) provides training in use of computers, software, and the Internet.

Community Environment: Blacksburg is a town with a population of 39,000 located on a plateau between the Blue Ridge and Allegheny Mountains, 38 miles southwest of Roanoke. Bus service is convenient and free to the university community. Civic and service organizations are active and welcome student participation. Outdoor recreation opportunities include hiking, horseback riding, fishing, swimming, boating, water skiing, and camping. Nearby are the Jefferson National Forest, the Appalachian Trail, the New River, and other parks and lakes.

■ VIRGINIA STATE UNIVERSITY

1 Hayden Dr.
Petersburg, VA 23806-0001
Tel: (804)524-5000; Free: 800-871-7611
Fax: (804)524-5055
E-mail: ilogan@vsu.edu
Web Site: www.vsu.edu/

Description: State-supported, comprehensive, coed. Part of State Council of Higher Education for Virginia. Awards associate, bachelor's, master's, and doctoral degrees. Founded 1882. Setting: 236-acre suburban campus with easy access to Richmond. Endowment: $24 million. Research spending for the previous fiscal year: $5.8 million. Educational spending for the previous fiscal year: $7313 per student. Total enrollment: 6,208. Faculty: 426 (284 full-time, 142 part-time). 5,754 applied, 94% were admitted. 5% from top 10% of their high school class, 20% from top quarter, 54% from top half. Full-time: 5,082 students, 60% women, 40% men. Part-time: 488 students, 61% women, 39% men. Students come from 39 states and territories, 30% from out-of-state. 0.2% American Indian or Alaska Native, non-Hispanic/Latino; 1% Hispanic/Latino; 85% African American, non-Hispanic/Latino; 0.2% Asian, non-Hispanic/Latino; 0% Native Hawaiian or other Pacific Islander, non-Hispanic/Latino; 0% international. 8% 25 or older, 7% transferred in. Retention: 65% of full-time freshmen returned the following year. Academic areas with the most degrees conferred: business/marketing; homeland security, law enforcement, firefighting, and protective services;

communication/journalism; education. Core. Calendar: semesters. Services for LD students, advanced placement, self-designed majors, honors program, independent study, double major, summer session for credit, part-time degree program, adult/continuing education programs, co-op programs and internships. Off campus study. Study abroad program. ROTC: Army.

Entrance Requirements: Options: electronic application, international baccalaureate accepted. Required: essay, high school transcript, minimum 2.2 high school GPA, 2 recommendations, SAT or ACT. Entrance: minimally difficult. Application deadline: 5/1. Notification: continuous. SAT Reasoning Test deadline: 7/1. Transfer credits accepted: Yes.

Costs Per Year: Application fee: $25. State resident tuition: $4550 full-time, $311 per credit hour part-time. Nonresident tuition: $12,988 full-time, $663 per credit hour part-time. Mandatory fees: $2870 full-time, $10 per credit hour part-time. Full-time tuition and fees vary according to course load and program. Part-time tuition and fees vary according to course load and program. College room and board: $9680. College room only: $5816. Room and board charges vary according to board plan and housing facility.

Collegiate Environment: Orientation program. Drama-theater group, choral group, marching band, student-run newspaper. Social organizations: 54 open to all; national fraternities, national sororities, local fraternities, local sororities. Most popular organizations: AbstraKt Entertainment, Golden Key Honor Society, The Betterment of Brothers and Sisters, Diversified Virtue Entertainment, Sankofa. Major annual events: Homecoming, Spring Fling, Welcome to the Land of Troy. Student services: health clinic, personal-psychological counseling. Campus security: 24-hour emergency response devices and patrols, late night transport-escort service, controlled dormitory access. 3,088 college housing spaces available; 2,867 were occupied in 2012-13. Freshmen given priority for college housing. On-campus residence required in freshman year. Options: coed, men-only, women-only housing available. Johnston Memorial Library with 357,262 books, 761,221 microform titles, 7,823 serials, 28,427 audiovisual materials, an OPAC, and a Web page. Operations spending for the previous fiscal year: $2.9 million. 2,500 computers available on campus for general student use. A campuswide network can be accessed from student residence rooms and from off campus. Students can access the following: online class registration. Staffed computer lab on campus (open 24 hours a day).

Community Environment: The immediate environs of the university offer an exciting atmosphere involving a variety of interesting sites and events for leisure-time activities. The Petersburg National Battlefield and Old Blandford Church are historical landmarks that are recognized in the National Historical Register. Other popular attractions include museums, art exhibits, parks, the Petersburg Symphony, and theatrical groups. The close proximity of Virginia's capital, Richmond, 25 minutes north, enhances the"VSU experience." Colonial Williamsburg and nearby Busch Gardens; Norfolk, home of one of America's busiest seaports; Virginia Beach, the top tourist attraction in the state; and the Blue Ridge Mountains are within easy driving distance.

■ VIRGINIA UNION UNIVERSITY

1500 N Lombardy St.
Richmond, VA 23220-1170
Tel: (804)257-5600; Free: 800-368-3227
E-mail: slspellman@vuu.edu
Web Site: www.vuu.edu/

Description: Independent Baptist, comprehensive, coed. Awards bachelor's, master's, and doctoral degrees. Founded 1865. Setting: 84-acre urban campus. System endowment: $25.3 million. Educational spending for the previous fiscal year: $6136 per student. Total enrollment: 1,710. Faculty: 114 (77 full-time, 37 part-time). Student-undergrad faculty ratio is 15:1. 6,910 applied, 95% were admitted. 3% from top 10% of their high school class, 21% from top quarter, 49% from top half. Full-time: 1,296 students, 53% women, 47% men. Part-time: 37 students, 51% women, 49% men. Students come from 29 states and territories, 50% from out-of-state. 0.1% American Indian or Alaska Native, non-Hispanic/Latino; 1% Hispanic/Latino; 97% African American, non-Hispanic/Latino; 0.1% Asian, non-Hispanic/Latino; 0% Native Hawaiian or other Pacific Islander, non-Hispanic/Latino; 0.1% international. 6% 25 or older, 4% transferred in. Retention: 55% of full-time freshmen returned the following year. Academic areas with the most degrees conferred: law/legal studies; business/marketing; social sciences. Core. Calendar: semesters. Academic remediation for entering students, ESL program, advanced placement, honors program, summer session for credit, adult/continuing education programs, co-op programs and internships. Off campus study at University of Richmond, Virginia Commonwealth University, Virginia State University. ROTC: Army (c).

Entrance Requirements: Options: electronic application, deferred admis-

sion. Required: high school transcript, minimum 2.25 high school GPA, SAT or ACT. Recommended: essay, minimum 2.5 high school GPA, 3 recommendations. Required for some: interview. Entrance: moderately difficult. Application deadline: Rolling. Notification: continuous. SAT Reasoning Test deadline: 6/30. SAT Subject Test deadline: 6/30. Transfer credits accepted: Yes. Applicants placed on waiting list: 4. Wait-listed applicants offered admission: 0.

Costs Per Year: Application fee: $25. Comprehensive fee: $22,302 includes full-time tuition ($13,314), mandatory fees ($1316), and college room and board ($7672). College room only: $3600. Full-time tuition and fees vary according to course level and course load. Room and board charges vary according to housing facility. Part-time tuition: $422 per credit hour. Part-time mandatory fees: $40 per credit hour. Part-time tuition and fees vary according to course level and course load.

Collegiate Environment: Orientation program. Drama-theater group, choral group, marching band, student-run newspaper. Social organizations: 51 open to all; national fraternities, national sororities; 10% of eligible men and 10% of eligible women are members. Most popular organizations: Student Government Association, NAACP, NPHC-VUU Chapter (National Pan-Hellenic Council), Mr. and Miss Royal Court. Major annual events: Homecoming, The Annual John Malcus Ellison Convocation, Founder's Day. Student services: health clinic, personal-psychological counseling. Campus security: 24-hour emergency response devices and patrols, controlled dormitory access. 778 college housing spaces available; 729 were occupied in 2012-13. Freshmen given priority for college housing. Options: coed, men-only, women-only housing available. L. Douglas Wilder Learning Resource Center and Library plus 1 other with 181,484 books, 150,761 microform titles, 307 serials, 4,531 audiovisual materials, and an OPAC. Operations spending for the previous fiscal year: $762,166. 200 computers available on campus for general student use. A campuswide network can be accessed from student residence rooms. Students can access the following: online class registration, academic research databases. Staffed computer lab on campus provides training in use of the Internet.

Community Environment: See University of Richmond.

■ **VIRGINIA UNIVERSITY OF LYNCHBURG**
2058 Garfield Ave.
Lynchburg, VA 24501-6417
Tel: (804)528-5276
Fax: (804)528-4257
E-mail: cglass@vul.edu
Web Site: www.vul.edu/

Description: Independent Baptist, comprehensive, coed. Awards associate, bachelor's, master's, and doctoral degrees. Founded 1886. Setting: urban campus. Educational spending for the previous fiscal year: $5550 per student. Total enrollment: 327. Faculty: 66 (22 full-time, 44 part-time). Student-undergrad faculty ratio is 9:1. Full-time: 138 students, 57% women, 43% men. Part-time: 95 students, 47% women, 53% men. Students come from 3 states and territories, 1% from out-of-state. 61% 25 or older, 14% live on campus, 19% transferred in. Retention: 100% of full-time freshmen returned the following year. Academic areas with the most degrees conferred: business/marketing; social sciences. Core. Calendar: semesters. Academic remediation for entering students, services for LD students, advanced placement, independent study, distance learning, summer session for credit, part-time degree program, external degree program, adult/continuing education programs, graduate courses open to undergrads.

Entrance Requirements: Open admission. Option: international baccalaureate accepted. Required: high school transcript. Entrance: noncompetitive. Application deadlines: Rolling, Rolling for nonresidents. Notification: continuous, continuous for nonresidents. Transfer credits accepted: Yes.

Collegiate Environment: Orientation program. Choral group. Social organizations: 3 open to all. Most popular organizations: choir, community service, intramural basketball. Major annual events: Founder's Day, Sacrificial Day, Multicultural Day. Student services: health clinic, personal-psychological counseling. Campus security: 24-hour emergency response devices, monitored camera security system with electronic backup saved. Mary Jane Cachelin Library with an OPAC. 10 computers available on campus for general student use. A campuswide network can be accessed from student residence rooms and from off campus. Staffed computer lab on campus provides training in use of computers, software, and the Internet.

■ **VIRGINIA WESLEYAN COLLEGE**
1584 Wesleyan Dr.
Norfolk, VA 23502-5599

Tel: (757)455-3200; Free: 800-737-8684
Fax: (757)461-5238
E-mail: admissions@vwc.edu
Web Site: www.vwc.edu/

Description: Independent United Methodist, 4-year, coed. Awards bachelor's degrees. Founded 1961. Setting: 300-acre urban campus with easy access to Norfolk, Virginia Beach. Endowment: $48.6 million. Educational spending for the previous fiscal year: $8788 per student. Total enrollment: 1,431. Faculty: 119 (91 full-time, 28 part-time). Student-undergrad faculty ratio is 12:1. 3,890 applied, 86% were admitted. 13% from top 10% of their high school class, 42% from top quarter, 80% from top half. Full-time: 1,288 students, 63% women, 37% men. Part-time: 143 students, 70% women, 30% men. Students come from 32 states and territories, 5 other countries, 25% from out-of-state. 0.5% American Indian or Alaska Native, non-Hispanic/Latino; 7% Hispanic/Latino; 23% African American, non-Hispanic/Latino; 1% Asian, non-Hispanic/Latino; 0.3% Native Hawaiian or other Pacific Islander, non-Hispanic/Latino; 1% international. 15% 25 or older, 61% live on campus, 7% transferred in. Retention: 67% of full-time freshmen returned the following year. Academic areas with the most degrees conferred: business/marketing; social sciences; homeland security, law enforcement, firefighting, and protective services; education. Core. Calendar: 4-1-4. Academic remediation for entering students, services for LD students, advanced placement, self-designed majors, freshman honors college, honors program, independent study, double major, summer session for credit, part-time degree program, adult/continuing education programs, internships. Off campus study at Old Dominion University, Norfolk State University, Virginia Tidewater Consortium for Higher Education. Study abroad program. ROTC: Army (c).

Entrance Requirements: Options: electronic application, international baccalaureate accepted. Required: essay, high school transcript, minimum 2.5 high school GPA. Required for some: interview, SAT or ACT. Entrance: moderately difficult. Application deadline: Rolling. Notification: continuous. SAT Reasoning Test deadline: 7/1. Transfer credits accepted: Yes.

Costs Per Year: Application fee: $40. One-time mandatory fee: $300. Comprehensive fee: $40,690 includes full-time tuition ($31,532), mandatory fees ($650), and college room and board ($8508). Full-time tuition and fees vary according to course load. Room and board charges vary according to board plan and housing facility. Part-time tuition: $1314 per credit hour. Part-time tuition varies according to course load.

Collegiate Environment: Orientation program. Drama-theater group, choral group, student-run newspaper, radio station. Social organizations: 60 open to all; national fraternities, national sororities; 10% of eligible men and 15% of eligible women are members. Most popular organizations: Wesleyan Activities Council, Community service, Student Government Association, student newspaper, Black Student Union. Major annual events: Homecoming, Lake Taylor Music Festival, Seafood Party in the Dell. Student services: health clinic, personal-psychological counseling, women's center. Campus security: 24-hour emergency response devices and patrols, late night transport-escort service, controlled dormitory access, well-lit pathways. 845 college housing spaces available; 842 were occupied in 2012-13. Freshmen guaranteed college housing. On-campus residence required through senior year. Options: coed, women-only housing available. H. C. Hofheimer II Library with 191,446 books, 15,953 microform titles, 37,500 serials, 4,393 audiovisual materials, an OPAC, and a Web page. 130 computers available on campus for general student use. Computer purchase/lease plans available. A campuswide network can be accessed from student residence rooms. Students can access the following: online class registration. Staffed computer lab on campus (open 24 hours a day) provides training in use of computers, software, and the Internet.

Community Environment: Tidewater, Virginia, is the cultural center of the Commonwealth. Norfolk features the Chrysler Museum, MacArthur Memorial, Scope Arena, Chrysler Hall for professional theatre, an opera house, and is headquarters of the Virginia Orchestra Group, Feldman String Quartet, and the Tidewater Ballet Association. Virginia Beach, in addition to its world-famous beaches, is proud of Seashore State Park, the Little Theater, Edgar Cayce's Association for Research and Enlightenment, the Virginia Beach Pops and other groups. Within one hour's driving time are Colonial Williamsburg, Yorktown and Jamestown, several nationally known museums including the Mariners Museum, and Busch Gardens.

■ **VIRGINIA WESTERN COMMUNITY COLLEGE**
PO Box 14007
Roanoke, VA 24038
Tel: (540)857-7311

Fax: (540)857-7204

Web Site: www.virginiawestern.edu/

Description: State-supported, 2-year, coed. Part of Virginia Community College System. Awards certificates, transfer associate, and terminal associate degrees. Founded 1966. Setting: 70-acre suburban campus. Endowment: $3 million. Educational spending for the previous fiscal year: $3832 per student. Total enrollment: 8,440. Student-undergrad faculty ratio is 23:1. Full-time: 2,568 students, 51% women, 49% men. Part-time: 5,872 students, 56% women, 44% men. Students come from 9 states and territories, 54 other countries, 2% from out-of-state. 0.4% American Indian or Alaska Native, non-Hispanic/Latino; 3% Hispanic/Latino; 14% African American, non-Hispanic/Latino; 2% Asian, non-Hispanic/Latino; 0.2% Native Hawaiian or other Pacific Islander, non-Hispanic/Latino; 0.5% international. 38% 25 or older, 4% transferred in. Retention: 55% of full-time freshmen returned the following year. Core. Calendar: semesters. Academic remediation for entering students, ESL program, services for LD students, advanced placement, honors program, independent study, distance learning, double major, summer session for credit, part-time degree program, co-op programs and internships.

Entrance Requirements: Open admission except for health technology programs. Options: electronic application, early admission, deferred admission. Recommended: high school transcript. Required for some: high school transcript. Entrance: noncompetitive. Application deadline: Rolling. Notification: continuous. Preference given to local residents.

Costs Per Year: Application fee: $0. State resident tuition: $3,242 full-time, $135.09 per credit hour part-time. Nonresident tuition: $7,853 full-time, $327.19 per credit hour part-time. Full-time tuition varies according to program. Part-time tuition varies according to program.

Collegiate Environment: Drama-theater group, student-run newspaper. Student services: personal-psychological counseling. Campus security: 24-hour emergency response devices and patrols, late night transport-escort service. College housing not available. Brown Library with an OPAC and a Web page.

Community Environment: Roanoke is a manufacturing, regional service and trading center, and a metropolitan area with all modes of transportation available. Community facilities include libraries, YMCA, YWCA, many churches, hospitals, and a number of the civic and service organizations. Part-time employment opportunities are available to certain students. Roanoke is headquarters for the Norfolk and Western Railway System and the Blue Ridge Parkway. Smith Mountain Lake is a favorite water recreation area. Carvin's Cove Lake nine and one-half miles north offers fishing, boating, and picnicking. Some of the points of interest are the Crystal Spring, Mill Mountain, and Transportation Museum.

■ **WASHINGTON AND LEE UNIVERSITY**

Lexington, VA 24450-0303

Tel: (540)458-8400

Fax: (540)463-8062

E-mail: admissions@wlu.edu

Web Site: www.wlu.edu/

Description: Independent, comprehensive, coed. Awards bachelor's, master's, and doctoral degrees. Founded 1749. Setting: 430-acre small town campus. Endowment: $1.3 billion. Research spending for the previous fiscal year: $2.7 million. Educational spending for the previous fiscal year: $28,546 per student. Total enrollment: 2,302. Faculty: 311 (242 full-time, 69 part-time). Student-undergrad faculty ratio is 8:1. 5,972 applied, 19% were admitted. 80% from top 10% of their high school class, 98% from top quarter, 100% from top half. 14 National Merit Scholars, 36 valedictorians, 40 student government officers. Full-time: 1,835 students, 49% women, 51% men. Part-time: 3 students, 67% women, 33% men. Students come from 53 states and territories, 31 other countries, 86% from out-of-state. 0.2% American Indian or Alaska Native, non-Hispanic/Latino; 3% Hispanic/Latino; 3% African American, non-Hispanic/Latino; 3% Asian, non-Hispanic/Latino; 0% Native Hawaiian or other Pacific Islander, non-Hispanic/Latino; 4% international. 0% 25 or older, 59% live on campus, 0.2% transferred in. Retention: 95% of full-time freshmen returned the following year. Academic areas with the most degrees conferred: social sciences; business/marketing; biological/life sciences. Core. Calendar: 4-4-2. Services for LD students, advanced placement, self-designed majors, honors program, independent study, double major, internships, graduate courses open to undergrads. Off campus study at Hampden-Sydney, Mary Baldwin, Randolph-Macon, Randolph, Sweet Briar College and Hollins University in the Seven-College Exchange (program designed primarily for juniors in Virginia); also Bates College in Lewiston, ME; Morehouse College and Spelman College in Atlanta, GA; and the Virginia Military Institute in Lexington, VA. Study abroad program. ROTC: Army (c).

Entrance Requirements: Options: electronic application, early decision, deferred admission, international baccalaureate accepted. Required: high school transcript, 3 recommendations, SAT or ACT. Recommended: essay, interview, SAT Subject Tests, 2 unrelated SAT subject tests are recommended, but not required. Entrance: most difficult. Application deadlines: 1/1, 11/1 for early decision plan 1, 1/1 for early decision plan 2. Notification: 4/1, 12/21 for early decision plan 1, 2/1 for early decision plan 2. SAT Reasoning Test deadline: 2/15. Transfer credits accepted: Yes. Applicants placed on waiting list: 2,002. Wait-listed applicants offered admission: 89. Early decision applicants: 610. Early decision applicants admitted: 261.

Costs Per Year: Application fee: $50. Comprehensive fee: $52,812 includes full-time tuition ($42,425), mandatory fees ($937), and college room and board ($9450). College room only: $3840. Room and board charges vary according to board plan and housing facility. Part-time tuition: $1515 per credit hour.

Collegiate Environment: Orientation program. Drama-theater group, choral group, student-run newspaper, radio station. Social organizations: 129 open to all; national fraternities, national sororities; 81% of eligible men and 82% of eligible women are members. Most popular organizations: Mock Convention, General Activities Board, Nabors Service League, Outing Club, Sports Clubs. Major annual events: Fancy Dress Ball, Homecoming, Alumni Weekend. Student services: health clinic, personal-psychological counseling, women's center. Campus security: 24-hour emergency response devices and patrols, late night transport-escort service, controlled dormitory access, Emergency Alert System. 1,267 college housing spaces available; 1,074 were occupied in 2012-13. Freshmen guaranteed college housing. On-campus residence required through sophomore year. Options: coed, men-only, women-only housing available. James G. Leyburn Library plus 2 others with 973,445 books, 1.4 million microform titles, 11,794 serials, 18,522 audiovisual materials, an OPAC, and a Web page. Operations spending for the previous fiscal year: $4.9 million. 176 computers available on campus for general student use. A campuswide network can be accessed from student residence rooms and from off campus. Students can access the following: online class registration. Staffed computer lab on campus provides training in use of computers, software, and the Internet.

Community Environment: Lexington is located in the Shenandoah Valley of Virginia between the Blue Ridge and Allegheny Mountains. Two of the greatest Confederate heroes, Robert E. Lee and Thomas J. "Stonewall" Jackson, lived and are buried in Lexington, the "Shrine of the South." Bus transportation is available. Some of the points of interest are the Natural Bridge, Lee Chapel, Home of "Stonewall" Jackson, Virginia Military Institute, and Washington and Lee University. Cyrus McCormick, inventor of the reaper, lived nearby. Lexington is also the home of the Virginia Horse Center.

■ **WESTWOOD COLLEGE–ANNANDALE CAMPUS**

7619 Little River Tpke., 5th Fl.

Annandale, VA 22003

Tel: (706)642-3633; Free: 877-305-0049

Web Site: www.westwood.edu/

Description: Proprietary, 4-year, coed. Part of Westwood Colleges, Inc. Awards associate and bachelor's degrees. Total enrollment: 473. Faculty: 74.

■ **WESTWOOD COLLEGE–ARLINGTON BALLSTON CAMPUS**

4420 N Fairfax Dr.

Arlington, VA 22203

Tel: (703)243-1662; Free: 877-268-5278

Web Site: www.westwood.edu/

Description: Proprietary, 4-year, coed. Part of Westwood Colleges, Inc. Awards associate and bachelor's degrees. Total enrollment: 473. Faculty: 57.

■ **WORLD COLLEGE**

5193 Shore Dr., Ste. 105

Virginia Beach, VA 23455-2500

Tel: (757)464-4600; Free: 800-243-6446

E-mail: instruct@cie-wc.edu

Web Site: www.worldcollege.edu/

Description: Proprietary, 4-year, coed. Awards bachelor's degrees (offers only external degree programs). Founded 1992. Setting: suburban campus. Total enrollment: 489. Faculty: 5 (3 full-time, 2 part-time). Students come

from 50 states and territories, 25 other countries. 94% 25 or older. Academic areas with the most degrees conferred: computer and information sciences; engineering technologies. Core. Calendar: semesters. Accelerated degree program, independent study, distance learning, part-time degree program, external degree program, adult/continuing education programs.
Entrance Requirements: Open admission. Options: electronic application, early admission. Required: high school transcript. Entrance: noncompetitive. Application deadline: Rolling. Notification: continuous.

■ **WYTHEVILLE COMMUNITY COLLEGE**
1000 E Main St.
Wytheville, VA 24382-3308
Tel: (276)223-4700; Free: 800-468-1195
Fax: (276)223-4778
E-mail: kalexander@wcc.vccs.edu
Web Site: www.wcc.vccs.edu/
Description: State-supported, 2-year, coed. Part of Virginia Community College System. Awards certificates, diplomas, transfer associate, and terminal associate degrees. Founded 1967. Setting: 141-acre rural campus. Total enrollment: 3,792. Faculty: 216 (43 full-time, 173 part-time). Student-undergrad faculty ratio is 23:1. 0% from out-of-state. 0.3% American Indian or Alaska Native, non-Hispanic/Latino; 1% Hispanic/Latino; 7% African American, non-Hispanic/Latino; 1% Asian, non-Hispanic/Latino; 0.1% Native Hawaiian or other Pacific Islander, non-Hispanic/Latino. 33% 25 or older.

Retention: 59% of full-time freshmen returned the following year. Core. Calendar: semesters. Academic remediation for entering students, services for LD students, advanced placement, independent study, distance learning, summer session for credit, part-time degree program, external degree program, adult/continuing education programs.
Entrance Requirements: Open admission. Option: early admission. Required: high school transcript. Required for some: interview. Entrance: noncompetitive. Application deadline: Rolling. Notification: continuous. Preference given to service region residents for allied health programs.
Costs Per Year: State resident tuition: $3810 full-time, $117 per credit part-time. Nonresident tuition: $9573 full-time, $294 per credit part-time. Mandatory fees: $320 full-time, $10 per credit part-time.
Collegiate Environment: Drama-theater group, student-run newspaper. Campus security: 24-hour emergency response devices and patrols. College housing not available.
Community Environment: Wytheville is located in a rich agricultural and cattle-raising area with most forms of commercial transportation available. A growing number of industries are located in the area, providing good part-time employment opportunities. Community facilities include a public library, churches, Jewish Synagogues in the neighboring towns of Bluefield and Bristol, a hospital, shopping areas, and a number of the civic and service organizations. Claytor Lake and the Jefferson National Forest provide opportunities for hunting, fishing, camping, and picnicking; other facilities within the city offer swimming and golf.

■ ANTIOCH UNIVERSITY SEATTLE

2326 Sixth Ave.
Seattle, WA 98121-1814
Tel: (206)441-5352; Free: 888-268-4477
E-mail: admissions@antiochseattle.edu
Web Site: www.antiochsea.edu/
Description: Independent, university, coed. Part of Antioch University. Awards bachelor's, master's, and doctoral degrees. Founded 1975. Setting: urban campus. Total enrollment: 1,080. Student-undergrad faculty ratio is 8:1. 64 applied. 95% from out-of-state. 91% 25 or older. Summer session for credit.
Entrance Requirements: Options: electronic application, deferred admission. Entrance: noncompetitive.

■ ARGOSY UNIVERSITY, SEATTLE

2601-A Elliott Ave.
Seattle, WA 98121
Tel: (206)283-4500; Free: 866-283-2777
Fax: (206)393-3592
Web Site: www.argosy.edu/seattle/
Description: Proprietary, university, coed. Part of Education Management Corporation. Awards bachelor's, master's, and doctoral degrees. Founded 1995. Setting: urban campus. Calendar: semesters.

■ THE ART INSTITUTE OF SEATTLE

2323 Elliott Ave.
Seattle, WA 98121-1642
Tel: (206)448-6600; Free: 800-275-2471
Fax: (206)269-0275
Web Site: www.artinstitutes.edu/seattle/
Description: Proprietary, primarily 2-year, coed. Part of Education Management Corporation. Awards diplomas, terminal associate, and bachelor's degrees. Founded 1982. Setting: urban campus.

■ BASTYR UNIVERSITY

14500 Juanita Dr., NE
Kenmore, WA 98028-4966
Tel: (425)823-1300
Fax: (425)823-6222
E-mail: admissions@bastyr.edu
Web Site: www.bastyr.edu/
Description: Independent, upper-level, coed. Awards bachelor's, master's, and doctoral degrees and post-master's certificates. Founded 1978. Setting: 51-acre suburban campus with easy access to Seattle. Total enrollment: 1,028. Faculty: 160 (66 full-time, 94 part-time). Full-time: 187 students, 81% women, 19% men. Part-time: 34 students, 88% women, 12% men. Students come from 24 states and territories, 7 other countries, 25% from out-of-state. 1% American Indian or Alaska Native, non-Hispanic/Latino; 5% Hispanic/Latino; 3% African American, non-Hispanic/Latino; 9% Asian, non-Hispanic/Latino; 0.5% Native Hawaiian or other Pacific Islander, non-Hispanic/Latino; 7% international. 58% 25 or older, 10% live on campus, 44% transferred in. Academic areas with the most degrees conferred: health professions and related sciences; personal and culinary services; family and consumer sci-

ences. Independent study, double major, summer session for credit, part-time degree program, co-op programs and internships, graduate courses open to undergrads.
Costs Per Year: Application fee: $60. Tuition: $21,090 full-time, $590 per credit hour part-time. Mandatory fees: $900 full-time. Full-time tuition and fees vary according to course load and program. Part-time tuition varies according to course load and program. College room only: $7050. Room charges vary according to housing facility.
Collegiate Environment: Orientation program. Social organizations: 47 open to all. Most popular organizations: Naturopaths Without Borders, Nature Club, Multicultural Student Association of Natural Medicine, Environmental Action Team, Venture Grant. Major annual events: Community Day, Talent/No Talent Show, Graduation Party and Dance. Student services: health clinic, personal-psychological counseling. Campus security: student patrols, late night transport-escort service, controlled dormitory access. Option: coed housing available. Bastyr University Library with 19,859 books, 177 serials, 5,876 audiovisual materials, an OPAC, and a Web page. 71 computers available on campus for general student use. A campuswide network can be accessed from student residence rooms and from off campus. Staffed computer lab on campus.

■ BATES TECHNICAL COLLEGE

1101 S Yakima Ave.
Tacoma, WA 98405-4895
Tel: (253)596-1500
E-mail: registration@bates.ctc.edu
Web Site: www.bates.ctc.edu/
Description: State-supported, 2-year, coed. Part of Washington State Board for Community and Technical Colleges. Awards certificates, diplomas, and terminal associate degrees. Setting: urban campus with easy access to Seattle. Total enrollment: 5,463. 68% 25 or older.
Entrance Requirements: Open admission. Application deadline: Rolling. Notification: continuous.
Collegiate Environment: Student-run newspaper, radio station. Campus security: 24-hour emergency response devices, on-campus weekday security to 10 pm.

■ BELLEVUE COLLEGE

3000 Landerholm Cir., SE
Bellevue, WA 98007-6484
Tel: (425)564-1000
Fax: (425)564-2261
Web Site: www.bcc.ctc.edu/
Description: State-supported, primarily 2-year, coed. Part of Washington State Board for Community and Technical Colleges. Awards certificates, transfer associate, terminal associate, and bachelor's degrees. Founded 1966. Setting: 96-acre suburban campus with easy access to Seattle. Total enrollment: 12,305. 37% 25 or older. Core. Academic remediation for entering students, ESL program, services for LD students, advanced placement, honors program, independent study, distance learning, summer session for credit, part-time degree program, co-op programs and internships.
Entrance Requirements: Open admission. Option: electronic application. Entrance: noncompetitive. Application deadline: Rolling.
Collegiate Environment: Orientation program. Drama-theater group, student-run newspaper, radio station. Student services: health clinic,

personal-psychological counseling, women's center. Bellevue Community College Library with 42,000 books, 485 serials, an OPAC, and a Web page.
Community Environment: Bellevue is a suburban community of Seattle and enjoys temperate climate with an average rainfall of 33.5 inches. The city has churches of most denominations, a hospital, good shopping facilities, and major civic and fraternal organizations serving the area.

■ **BELLINGHAM TECHNICAL COLLEGE**
3028 Lindbergh Ave.
Bellingham, WA 98225
Tel: (360)752-7000
Fax: (360)676-2798
E-mail: erunestr@btc.ctc.edu
Web Site: www.btc.ctc.edu/
Description: State-supported, 2-year, coed. Part of Washington State Board for Community and Technical Colleges (SBCTC). Awards certificates, transfer associate, and terminal associate degrees. Founded 1957. Setting: 21-acre suburban campus with easy access to Vancouver. Total enrollment: 2,864. Faculty: 189 (126 full-time, 63 part-time). Student-undergrad faculty ratio is 24:1. 0% from out-of-state. 61% 25 or older. Core. Academic remediation for entering students, ESL program, services for LD students, distance learning, summer session for credit, part-time degree program, internships.
Entrance Requirements: Open admission. Options: early admission, deferred admission. Required: ACCUPLACER entrance exam or waiver. Required for some: high school transcript, some programs have prerequisites. Entrance: noncompetitive. Application deadlines: Rolling, Rolling for nonresidents. Transfer credits accepted: Yes.
Collegiate Environment: Orientation program. Major annual event: Diversity celebrations. Student services: personal-psychological counseling. Information Technology Resource Center with an OPAC and a Web page.

■ **BIG BEND COMMUNITY COLLEGE**
7662 Chanute St., NE
Moses Lake, WA 98837-3299
Tel: (509)762-5351; Free: 877-745-1212
Fax: (509)762-6243
E-mail: admissions@bigbend.edu
Web Site: www.bigbend.edu/
Description: State-supported, 2-year, coed. Administratively affiliated with Washington State Board for Community & Technical Colleges. Awards certificates, transfer associate, and terminal associate degrees. Founded 1962. Setting: 159-acre small town campus. Total enrollment: 1,946. Student-undergrad faculty ratio is 20:1. Full-time: 1,390 students, 54% women, 46% men. Part-time: 556 students, 64% women, 36% men. 1% American Indian or Alaska Native, non-Hispanic/Latino; 34% Hispanic/Latino; 1% African American, non-Hispanic/Latino; 1% Asian, non-Hispanic/Latino; 0.1% Native Hawaiian or other Pacific Islander, non-Hispanic/Latino; 0.4% international. 35% 25 or older, 5% live on campus. Core. Academic remediation for entering students, ESL program, services for LD students, advanced placement, distance learning, summer session for credit, part-time degree program, co-op programs.
Entrance Requirements: Open admission except for aviation and nursing programs. Options: electronic application, early admission, deferred admission. Required for some: high school transcript. Entrance: noncompetitive. Application deadline: Rolling. Notification: continuous. Transfer credits accepted: Yes.
Costs Per Year: Application fee: $30. One-time mandatory fee: $30. State resident tuition: $3687 full-time, $112 per credit hour part-time. Nonresident tuition: $4550 full-time, $125 per credit hour part-time. Mandatory fees: $150 full-time, $5 per credit hour part-time. Full-time tuition and fees vary according to course load and program. Part-time tuition and fees vary according to course load and program. College room and board: $6900. College room only: $2700.
Collegiate Environment: Orientation program. Choral group. Student services: personal-psychological counseling. Campus security: 24-hour emergency response devices, student patrols, late night transport-escort service, controlled dormitory access, daytime security on campus during the week, student security in dorms four evenings a week, Enhanced Campus Notification System. No special consideration for freshman housing applicants. Option: coed housing available. Big Bend Community College Library with 42,647 books, 6,455 microform titles, 115 serials, 4,124 audiovisual materials, an OPAC, and a Web page. 120 computers available on campus for general student use. A campuswide network can be accessed

from student residence rooms and from off campus. Students can access the following: online class registration, Online catalog, Online New Student Orientation. Staffed computer lab on campus.
Community Environment: Moses Lake is an important agricultural processing and shipping center for the Columbia Basin. This is a rural area with dry climate. The community has a library, many churches, a museum, a hospital and clinics, and modern shopping facilities. Local recreation includes lakes for fishing, swimming, boating, water skiing, and hydroplane boat races, as well as picnic areas and hunting areas for geese and pheasant. The community has major civic, fraternal and veteran's organizations. Grant County Fair, and a rodeo and parade are held here annually. Part-time employment is available.

■ **CARRINGTON COLLEGE–SPOKANE**
10102 E Knox Ave.
Ste. 200
Spokane, WA 99206
Tel: (509)532-8888
Web Site: carrington.edu/
Description: Proprietary, 2-year, coed. Part of Carrington Colleges Group, Inc. Awards certificates and terminal associate degrees. Founded 1976. Total enrollment: 448. Faculty: 28 (11 full-time, 17 part-time). Student-undergrad faculty ratio is 27:1. Full-time: 448 students, 82% women, 18% men. 4% American Indian or Alaska Native, non-Hispanic/Latino; 5% Hispanic/Latino; 2% African American, non-Hispanic/Latino; 2% Asian, non-Hispanic/Latino; 0.4% Native Hawaiian or other Pacific Islander, non-Hispanic/Latino; 0% international. 50% 25 or older.
Entrance Requirements: Required: essay, high school transcript, interview, Entrance test administered by Carrington College.
Collegiate Environment: College housing not available.

■ **CASCADIA COMMUNITY COLLEGE**
18345 Campus Way, NE
Bothell, WA 98011
Tel: (425)352-8000
Fax: (425)398-5730
E-mail: admissions@cascadia.edu
Web Site: www.cascadia.edu/
Description: State-supported, 2-year, coed. Awards certificates, transfer associate, and terminal associate degrees. Founded 1999. Setting: 128-acre suburban campus. Total enrollment: 2,834. Faculty: 127 (41 full-time, 86 part-time). Student-undergrad faculty ratio is 18:1. Full-time: 1,544 students, 50% women, 50% men. Part-time: 1,290 students, 51% women, 49% men. Students come from 2 states and territories, 0% from out-of-state. 0.3% American Indian or Alaska Native, non-Hispanic/Latino; 8% Hispanic/Latino; 1% African American, non-Hispanic/Latino; 8% Asian, non-Hispanic/Latino; 1% Native Hawaiian or other Pacific Islander, non-Hispanic/Latino; 4% international. 20% 25 or older, 21% transferred in. Core. Academic remediation for entering students, ESL program, services for LD students, advanced placement, accelerated degree program, independent study, distance learning, double major, summer session for credit, part-time degree program, adult/continuing education programs, co-op programs and internships. Off campus study. Study abroad program.
Entrance Requirements: Open admission. Option: electronic application. Entrance: noncompetitive. Application deadlines: Rolling, Rolling for nonresidents. Notification: continuous, continuous for nonresidents.
Costs Per Year: Application fee: $0. State resident tuition: $3606 full-time, $106.84 per credit part-time. Nonresident tuition: $3606 full-time, $278.84 per credit part-time. Full-time tuition varies according to course load and program. Part-time tuition varies according to course load and program.
Collegiate Environment: Orientation program. Drama-theater group, student-run newspaper. Campus security: 24-hour emergency response devices, late night transport-escort service. College housing not available. UWB/CCC Campus Library with 73,749 books, 11,231 microform titles, 850 serials, 6,100 audiovisual materials, an OPAC, and a Web page.

■ **CENTRAL WASHINGTON UNIVERSITY**
400 E University Way
Ellensburg, WA 98926
Tel: (509)963-1111; Free: 866-298-4968
Fax: (509)963-3022
E-mail: cwuadmis@cwu.edu
Web Site: www.cwu.edu/
Description: State-supported, comprehensive, coed. Awards bachelor's and

master's degrees. Founded 1891. Setting: 380-acre small town campus. Total enrollment: 11,320. Faculty: 589 (427 full-time, 162 part-time). Student-undergrad faculty ratio is 21:1. 4,553 applied, 78% were admitted. Full-time: 9,435 students, 51% women, 49% men. Part-time: 1,335 students, 51% women, 49% men. 7% from out-of-state. 0.4% American Indian or Alaska Native, non-Hispanic/Latino; 9% Hispanic/Latino; 3% African American, non-Hispanic/Latino; 4% Asian, non-Hispanic/Latino; 0.4% Native Hawaiian or other Pacific Islander, non-Hispanic/Latino; 2% international. 23% 25 or older, 26% live on campus, 15% transferred in. Retention: 78% of full-time freshmen returned the following year. Academic areas with the most degrees conferred: business/marketing; education; social sciences. Part-time degree program. ROTC: Army, Air Force.

Entrance Requirements: Options: electronic application, international baccalaureate accepted. Required: high school transcript, minimum 2 high school GPA, SAT or ACT. Required for some: essay, interview. Entrance: moderately difficult. Application deadline: 4/1. Notification: continuous.

Costs Per Year: Application fee: $50. State resident tuition: $7962 full-time, $241.60 per credit hour part-time. Nonresident tuition: $18,607 full-time, $596 per credit hour part-time. Mandatory fees: $984 full-time. Part-time tuition varies according to course load. College room and board: $9240, Room and board charges vary according to board plan and housing facility.

Collegiate Environment: Orientation program. Campus security: 24-hour emergency response devices and patrols, late night transport-escort service, controlled dormitory access.

Community Environment: Ellensburg is a small university town in central Washington. The climate is mild and dry. The community has several churches, three libraries, a hospital and infirmary. Ellensburg may be reached by railroad, bus lines, and Interstate 90 and 82. Local recreation includes camping, hiking, river rafting, rodeo, snow sports, fishing, hunting, boating, skiing and golf. There are many job opportunities available at the university. Various civic and fraternal organizations are active in the community.

■ CENTRALIA COLLEGE
600 Centralia College Blvd.
Centralia, WA 98531-4099
Tel: (360)736-9391
E-mail: admissions@centralia.edu
Web Site: www.centralia.edu/

Description: State-supported, 2-year, coed. Part of Washington State Board for Community and Technical Colleges. Awards certificates, transfer associate, and terminal associate degrees. Founded 1925. Setting: 31-acre small town campus. Total enrollment: 3,574. Student-undergrad faculty ratio is 20:1. 0% from out-of-state. 54% 25 or older. Core. Academic remediation for entering students, ESL program, services for LD students, advanced placement, freshman honors college, honors program, independent study, distance learning, summer session for credit, part-time degree program, external degree program, adult/continuing education programs, co-op programs. Study abroad program.

Entrance Requirements: Open admission except for nursing program. Options: electronic application, international baccalaureate accepted. Required: high school transcript. Entrance: noncompetitive. Application deadline: Rolling. Notification: continuous until 9/15.

Collegiate Environment: Orientation program. Drama-theater group, choral group, marching band, student-run newspaper, radio station. Student services: personal-psychological counseling. Campus security: 24-hour patrols, student patrols, late night transport-escort service. Kirk Library with an OPAC and a Web page.

■ CITY UNIVERSITY OF SEATTLE
11900 NE First St.
Bellevue, WA 98005
Tel: (425)637-1010; Free: 888-42-CITYU
Fax: (425)277-2437
E-mail: info@cityu.edu
Web Site: www.cityu.edu/

Description: Independent, comprehensive, coed. Awards associate, bachelor's, master's, and doctoral degrees and post-master's certificates. Founded 1973. Setting: 1-acre urban campus with easy access to Seattle. Educational spending for the previous fiscal year: $5199 per student. Total enrollment: 2,065. Faculty: 332 (47 full-time, 285 part-time). Student-undergrad faculty ratio is 15:1. 86 applied, 100% were admitted. Full-time: 532 students, 55% women, 45% men. Part-time: 503 students, 55% women, 45% men. Students come from 45 states and territories, 24 other countries,

0% from out-of-state. 9% American Indian or Alaska Native, non-Hispanic/Latino; 6% Hispanic/Latino; 6% African American, non-Hispanic/Latino; 4% Asian, non-Hispanic/Latino; 1% Native Hawaiian or other Pacific Islander, non-Hispanic/Latino; 10% international. 74% 25 or older, 13% transferred in. Academic areas with the most degrees conferred: business/marketing; education; computer and information sciences. Core. ESL program, services for LD students, advanced placement, accelerated degree program, self-designed majors, independent study, distance learning, double major, summer session for credit, part-time degree program, adult/continuing education programs, internships. Study abroad program.

Entrance Requirements: Open admission. Options: electronic application, deferred admission, international baccalaureate accepted. Recommended: high school transcript. Entrance: noncompetitive. Application deadlines: Rolling, Rolling for nonresidents. Notification: continuous, continuous for nonresidents. Transfer credits accepted: Yes.

Costs Per Year: Application fee: $50. Tuition: $15,600 full-time, $368 per credit hour part-time. Full-time tuition varies according to course level, course load, degree level, location, program, and reciprocity agreements. Part-time tuition varies according to course level, course load, degree level, location, program, and reciprocity agreements.

Collegiate Environment: Orientation program. Student services: personal-psychological counseling. Campus security: 24-hour emergency response devices. College housing not available. City University Library with 46,663 books, 551,736 microform titles, 75,430 serials, 13,000 audiovisual materials, an OPAC, and a Web page. Operations spending for the previous fiscal year: $1.2 million. 148 computers available on campus for general student use. A campuswide network can be accessed from off-campus. Students can access the following: online class registration. Staffed computer lab on campus.

■ CLARK COLLEGE
1933 Fort Vancouver Way
Vancouver, WA 98663-3598
Tel: (360)992-2000
E-mail: admissions@clark.edu
Web Site: www.clark.edu/

Description: State-supported, 2-year, coed. Part of Washington State Board for Community and Technical Colleges. Awards certificates, diplomas, transfer associate, and terminal associate degrees. Founded 1933. Setting: 101-acre urban campus with easy access to Portland. Total enrollment: 12,314. Faculty: 689 (202 full-time, 487 part-time). Student-undergrad faculty ratio is 17:1. 1,844 applied, 100% were admitted. 4% from out-of-state. 1% American Indian or Alaska Native, non-Hispanic/Latino; 8% Hispanic/Latino; 2% African American, non-Hispanic/Latino; 4% Asian, non-Hispanic/Latino; 0.5% Native Hawaiian or other Pacific Islander, non-Hispanic/Latino; 1% international. 41% 25 or older. Part-time degree program, adult/continuing education programs. ROTC: Army (c), Air Force (c).

Entrance Requirements: Options: electronic application, early admission, deferred admission, international baccalaureate accepted. Entrance: noncompetitive. Application deadline: 9/7. Notification: continuous. Transfer credits accepted: Yes.

Costs Per Year: Application fee: $20. Area resident tuition: $4154 full-time, $110.46 per credit hour part-time. State resident tuition: $4544 full-time, $123.46 per credit hour part-time. Nonresident tuition: $9389 full-time, $282.46 per credit hour part-time. Full-time tuition varies according to course load and reciprocity agreements. Part-time tuition varies according to course load and reciprocity agreements.

Collegiate Environment: Orientation program. Campus security: 24-hour patrols, late night transport-escort service, security staff during hours of operation. College housing not available.

Community Environment: The oldest city in the state, Vancouver is located at the head of the deep-water navigation of the Columbia River. This is an industrial city with job opportunities for students. The city is served by rail, bus and major highways. Local recreation includes fishing, hunting, boating, skiing, and nearby beaches.

■ CLOVER PARK TECHNICAL COLLEGE
4500 Steilacoom Blvd., SW
Lakewood, WA 98499
Tel: (253)589-5678
Web Site: www.cptc.edu/

Description: State-supported, 2-year, coed. Part of Washington State Community and Technical College System. Awards certificates and terminal associate degrees. Founded 1942. Total enrollment: 9,829. 85% 25 or older.

Core. Academic remediation for entering students, ESL program, services for LD students, accelerated degree program, distance learning, part-time degree program, co-op programs and internships.

Entrance Requirements: Open admission. Options: electronic application, international baccalaureate accepted. Required for some: high school transcript, interview. Entrance: noncompetitive. Application deadline: 9/27. Notification: continuous until 9/27.

Collegiate Environment: Orientation program. Student-run newspaper. Most popular organizations: Accounting Numbers Club, Auto Tech Club, Computer Users Club, Social Services Club. Major annual events: Veteran's Day Celebration, Martin Luther King, Jr. Celebration, car show. Student services: personal-psychological counseling. Campus security: 24-hour patrols, late night transport-escort service. CPTC Library with 11,219 books, 97 serials, 2,322 audiovisual materials, an OPAC, and a Web page.

■ **COLUMBIA BASIN COLLEGE**
2600 N 20th Ave.
Pasco, WA 99301-3397
Tel: (509)547-0511
Fax: (509)546-0401
E-mail: admissions@columbiabasin.edu
Web Site: www.columbiabasin.edu/
Description: State-supported, 2-year, coed. Part of Washington State Board for Community and Technical Colleges. Awards transfer associate and terminal associate degrees. Founded 1955. Setting: 156-acre small town campus. Total enrollment: 6,978. Student-undergrad faculty ratio is 22:1. 2% from out-of-state. 41% 25 or older. Retention: 58% of full-time freshmen returned the following year. Core. Academic remediation for entering students, ESL program, services for LD students, advanced placement, accelerated degree program, distance learning, summer session for credit, part-time degree program, adult/continuing education programs, co-op programs and internships.

Entrance Requirements: Open admission except for nursing program. Options: electronic application, international baccalaureate accepted. Required: high school transcript. Entrance: noncompetitive. Application deadline: Rolling. Notification: continuous.

Collegiate Environment: Orientation program. Drama-theater group, choral group, student-run newspaper. Student services: personal-psychological counseling, women's center. Campus security: 24-hour patrols. Columbia Basin College Library with an OPAC and a Web page.

■ **CORNISH COLLEGE OF THE ARTS**
1000 Lenora St.
Seattle, WA 98102-4696
Tel: (206)726-5151; Free: 800-726-ARTS
Fax: (206)720-1011
E-mail: admissions@cornish.edu
Web Site: www.cornish.edu/
Description: Independent, 4-year, coed. Awards bachelor's degrees. Founded 1914. Setting: 4-acre urban campus. Endowment: $6.6 million. Educational spending for the previous fiscal year: $10,971 per student. Total enrollment: 834. Faculty: 165 (55 full-time, 110 part-time). Student-undergrad faculty ratio is 6:1. 1,406 applied, 58% were admitted. Full-time: 834 students, 67% women, 33% men. Students come from 37 states and territories, 11 other countries, 43% from out-of-state. 1% American Indian or Alaska Native, non-Hispanic/Latino; 7% Hispanic/Latino; 3% African American, non-Hispanic/Latino; 6% Asian, non-Hispanic/Latino; 0.5% Native Hawaiian or other Pacific Islander, non-Hispanic/Latino; 2% international. 12% 25 or older, 11% transferred in. Retention: 64% of full-time freshmen returned the following year. Academic area with the most degrees conferred: visual and performing arts. Core. Calendar: semesters. Services for LD students, advanced placement, independent study, summer session for credit, co-op programs and internships. Study abroad program.

Entrance Requirements: Options: electronic application, deferred admission, international baccalaureate accepted. Required: essay, high school transcript, minimum 2.5 high school GPA, portfolio or audition. Recommended: 2 recommendations, interview, SAT or ACT. Required for some: 2 recommendations. Entrance: moderately difficult. Application deadline: 8/15. Notification: continuous. Transfer credits accepted: Yes.

Collegiate Environment: Orientation program. Drama-theater group, choral group. Most popular organizations: Student Leadership Council, Black Student Alliance, Sigma Alpha Phi, AIGA, Cheese Tasting. Major annual events: Spring Festival/ Drag Show, Cabaret, BFA Art Show. Student services: personal-psychological counseling. Campus security: 24-hour

emergency response devices and patrols, late night transport-escort service, controlled dormitory access. Cornish Library with 26,629 books, 154 serials, 50,511 audiovisual materials, an OPAC, and a Web page. Operations spending for the previous fiscal year: $73,468. 28 computers available on campus for general student use. A campuswide network can be accessed from student residence rooms and from off campus. Students can access the following: online class registration. Staffed computer lab on campus provides training in use of computers, software, and the Internet.

Community Environment: Urban.

■ **DEVRY UNIVERSITY (BELLEVUE)**
600 108th Ave. NE, Ste. 230
Bellevue, WA 98004-5110
Tel: (425)455-2242; Free: 866-338-7941
Fax: (425)455-2322
Web Site: www.devry.edu/
Description: Proprietary, comprehensive, coed. Awards bachelor's and master's degrees. Calendar: semesters.

■ **DEVRY UNIVERSITY (FEDERAL WAY)**
3600 S 344th Way
Federal Way, WA 98001
Tel: (253)943-2800; Free: 866-338-7941
Web Site: www.devry.edu/
Description: Proprietary, comprehensive, coed. Part of DeVry University. Awards associate, bachelor's, and master's degrees. Founded 2001. Setting: suburban campus. Total enrollment: 643. Faculty: 89 (14 full-time, 75 part-time). Student-undergrad faculty ratio is 10:1. Full-time: 250 students, 28% women, 72% men. Part-time: 252 students, 33% women, 67% men. 12% from out-of-state. 1% American Indian or Alaska Native, non-Hispanic/Latino; 9% Hispanic/Latino; 13% African American, non-Hispanic/Latino; 6% Asian, non-Hispanic/Latino; 2% Native Hawaiian or other Pacific Islander, non-Hispanic/Latino; 0.4% international. 73% 25 or older, 18% transferred in. Academic areas with the most degrees conferred: business/marketing; computer and information sciences; engineering; engineering technologies. Calendar: semesters. Part-time degree program, adult/continuing education programs.

Entrance Requirements: Option: electronic application. Required: high school transcript, interview. Entrance: minimally difficult. Application deadline: Rolling. Notification: continuous.

Costs Per Year: Application fee: $40. Tuition: $16,076 full-time, $609 per credit hour part-time. Mandatory fees: $80 full-time.

Collegiate Environment: Orientation program. College housing not available.

■ **DIGIPEN INSTITUTE OF TECHNOLOGY**
9931 Willows Rd. NE
Redmond, WA 98052
Tel: (425)558-0299
Fax: (425)558-0299
E-mail: admissions@digipen.edu
Web Site: www.digipen.edu/
Description: Proprietary, comprehensive, coed. Awards bachelor's and master's degrees. Founded 1988. Setting: 3-acre suburban campus with easy access to Seattle. Total enrollment: 1,041. Faculty: 95 (47 full-time, 48 part-time). Student-undergrad faculty ratio is 15:1. 468 applied, 44% were admitted. Students come from 22 other countries, 47% from out-of-state. 0.2% American Indian or Alaska Native, non-Hispanic/Latino; 5% Hispanic/Latino; 1% African American, non-Hispanic/Latino; 6% Asian, non-Hispanic/Latino; 0.2% Native Hawaiian or other Pacific Islander, non-Hispanic/Latino; 17% international. 23% 25 or older. Retention: 72% of full-time freshmen returned the following year. Academic areas with the most degrees conferred: computer and information sciences; communication technologies; engineering. Calendar: semesters. Academic remediation for entering students, ESL program, services for LD students, advanced placement, accelerated degree program, independent study, double major, summer session for credit, internships, graduate courses open to undergrads. Study abroad program.

Entrance Requirements: Options: electronic application, deferred admission, international baccalaureate accepted. Required: essay, high school transcript, minimum 2.5 high school GPA. Recommended: 2 recommendations. Required for some: art portfolio for BFA in Digital Art and Animation applicants; specific essay requirements for Game Design applicants; audition portfolio for BA in Music and Sound Design applicants, SAT or ACT.

Entrance: minimally difficult. Application deadlines: Rolling, Rolling for nonresidents. Notification: continuous, continuous for nonresidents. Transfer credits accepted: Yes.

Costs Per Year: Application fee: $35. One-time mandatory fee: $150. Comprehensive fee: $37,001 includes full-time tuition ($26,400), mandatory fees ($160), and college room and board ($10,441). Full-time tuition and fees vary according to course load and program. Room and board charges vary according to board plan and housing facility. Part-time tuition: $15,460 per year. Part-time tuition varies according to course load and program.

Collegiate Environment: Orientation program. Social organizations: student run clubs/associations. Most popular organizations: Game Testing Club, Guilty Gear Club, Student Association, Audio Freaks, Game Design Club. Major annual events: Halloween Pageant, LAN Party, Humans vs. Zombies. Student services: personal-psychological counseling. Campus security: late night transport-escort service, controlled dormitory access, onsite security during campus hours. 122 college housing spaces available. Freshmen given priority for college housing. Option: coed housing available. DigiPen Library with 29 serials, an OPAC, and a Web page. 1,200 computers available on campus for general student use. A campuswide network can be accessed. Students can access the following: online class registration. Staffed computer lab on campus provides training in use of computers, software, and the Internet.

■ **EASTERN WASHINGTON UNIVERSITY**
526 5th St.
Cheney, WA 99004-2431
Tel: (509)359-6200
Fax: (509)359-4330
E-mail: admissions@ewu.edu
Web Site: www.ewu.edu/

Description: State-supported, comprehensive, coed. Awards bachelor's, master's, and doctoral degrees and post-master's certificates. Founded 1882. Setting: 335-acre suburban campus with easy access to Spokane. Endowment: $21 million. Research spending for the previous fiscal year: $1.3 million. Educational spending for the previous fiscal year: $6302 per student. Total enrollment: 12,587. Faculty: 649 (413 full-time, 236 part-time). Student-undergrad faculty ratio is 23:1. Full-time: 9,557 students, 55% women, 45% men. Part-time: 1,803 students, 57% women, 43% men. Students come from 46 states and territories, 20 other countries, 6% from out-of-state. 1% American Indian or Alaska Native, non-Hispanic/Latino; 11% Hispanic/Latino; 4% African American, non-Hispanic/Latino; 3% Asian, non-Hispanic/Latino; 0.4% Native Hawaiian or other Pacific Islander, non-Hispanic/Latino; 3% international. 22% 25 or older, 20% live on campus, 12% transferred in. Retention: 76% of full-time freshmen returned the following year. Academic areas with the most degrees conferred: business/marketing; health professions and related sciences; education. Core. Academic remediation for entering students, ESL program, services for LD students, advanced placement, accelerated degree program, self-designed majors, honors program, independent study, distance learning, double major, summer session for credit, part-time degree program, co-op programs and internships, graduate courses open to undergrads. Off campus study at Intercollegiate Center for Nursing. Study abroad program. ROTC: Army.

Entrance Requirements: Required: high school transcript, minimum 2 high school GPA, SAT or ACT. Recommended: minimum 3 high school GPA. Required for some: essay.

Costs Per Year: State resident tuition: $7425 full-time, $247.50 per credit part-time. Nonresident tuition: $18,168 full-time, $605.60 per credit part-time. Mandatory fees: $551 full-time, $551 per year part-time. Full-time tuition and fees vary according to program and reciprocity agreements. Part-time tuition and fees vary according to program and reciprocity agreements. College room and board: $8412. College room only: $4500. Room and board charges vary according to board plan and housing facility.

Collegiate Environment: Orientation program. Drama-theater group, choral group, marching band, student-run newspaper, radio station. Social organizations: 73 open to all; national fraternities, national sororities, local fraternities, local sororities, Clubs/Organizations and EPIC outdoor adventures; 5% of eligible men and 5% of eligible women are members. Most popular organizations: Circle K International, Saudi Club, Gamers Club, Hui O Hawaii, Sportsman's Club. Major annual events: Homecoming Week, Cinco do Mayo, Neighbor Festival. Student services: health clinic, personal-psychological counseling, women's center. Campus security: 24-hour emergency response devices and patrols, student patrols, late night transport-escort service, controlled dormitory access, emergency call boxes. College housing designed to accommodate 2,066 students; 2,405

undergraduates lived in college housing during 2012-13. Freshmen given priority for college housing. Option: coed housing available. John F. Kennedy Library with 846,241 books, 820,642 microform titles, 75,183 serials, 56,880 audiovisual materials, an OPAC, and a Web page. Operations spending for the previous fiscal year: $4.2 million. 1,012 computers available on campus for general student use. Computer purchase/lease plans available. A campuswide network can be accessed from student residence rooms and from off campus. Students can access the following: online class registration, 15 gb network disk storage per student; discounted Microsoft and Adobe software; laptops, still and video cameras, projectors for checkout; print credit; black white laser, color laser, and color photo options, large format print service. Staffed computer lab on campus provides training in use of computers, software, and the Internet.

Community Environment: Cheney is located 16 miles southwest of Spokane. The community is reached by major highways, rail, bus, and air lines with Spokane Airport approximately 11 miles away. The city has many churches and various civic, fraternal, and veteran's organizations. Local recreation includes hunting, fishing, skiing, and swimming on nearby lakes. Part-time employment is available.

■ **EDMONDS COMMUNITY COLLEGE**
20000 68th Ave. W
Lynnwood, WA 98036
Tel: (425)640-1500
Fax: (425)640-1159
E-mail: nanci.froemming@edcc.edu
Web Site: www.edcc.edu/

Description: State and locally supported, 2-year, coed. Part of Washington State Board for Community and Technical Colleges. Awards certificates, transfer associate, and terminal associate degrees. Founded 1967. Setting: 115-acre suburban campus with easy access to Seattle. Endowment: $2.7 million. Educational spending for the previous fiscal year: $3600 per student. Total enrollment: 8,435. Faculty: 480 (145 full-time, 335 part-time). Student-undergrad faculty ratio is 21:1. 1,770 applied, 100% were admitted. Full-time: 3,656 students, 53% women, 47% men. Part-time: 4,779 students, 61% women, 39% men. Students come from 55 other countries, 2% from out-of-state. 11% 25 or older, 0.5% transferred in. Core. Academic remediation for entering students, ESL program, services for LD students, advanced placement, self-designed majors, honors program, distance learning, summer session for credit, part-time degree program, adult/continuing education programs, co-op programs and internships. Off campus study at other community colleges in Washington. Study abroad program.

Entrance Requirements: Open admission. Options: electronic application, early admission, deferred admission. Entrance: noncompetitive. Application deadline: Rolling. Notification: continuous.

Collegiate Environment: Orientation program. Drama-theater group, choral group, student-run newspaper. Social organizations: 40 open to all. Most popular organizations: Phi Theta Kappa, AITP, AAWCC, International Club, Pottery/Art Club. Major annual events: Commencement, campus barbecues, music performances. Student services: personal-psychological counseling, women's center. Campus security: 24-hour emergency response devices and patrols, student patrols, late night transport-escort service. Edmonds Community College Library with 47,947 books, 51 microform titles, 312 serials, 7,735 audiovisual materials, an OPAC, and a Web page. Operations spending for the previous fiscal year: $915,656. 735 computers available on campus for general student use. A campuswide network can be accessed from off-campus. Students can access the following: online class registration. Staffed computer lab on campus.

Community Environment: Lynnwood overlooks the Puget Sound and the Olympic Mountains, and is connected with the Olympic Peninsula by ferry. This is a large, rapidly growing suburban community. The city has a large public marina, good shopping facilities, and good recreation areas. There is a public library, churches, and theatres. Good skiing and winter sports may be found within an hour's drive.

■ **EVEREST COLLEGE**
120 NE 136th Ave.
Ste. 130
Vancouver, WA 98684
Tel: (360)254-3282; Free: 888-741-4270
E-mail: rschiffhauer@cci.edu
Web Site: www.everest.edu/

Description: Proprietary, 2-year, coed. Awards diplomas and terminal associate degrees. Founded 1979. Total enrollment: 340. Faculty: 25 (8 full-time, 17 part-time). Student-undergrad faculty ratio is 14:1. Retention: 83% of full-time freshmen returned the following year.

Entrance Requirements: Required: interview, placement exam. Recommended: interview. Entrance: moderately difficult. Application deadline: Rolling.

Collegiate Environment: Most popular organization: Student Ambassador. 130 computers available on campus for general student use.

■ EVERETT COMMUNITY COLLEGE

2000 Twr. St.
Everett, WA 98201-1327
Tel: (425)388-9100
Fax: (425)388-9173
E-mail: admissions@everettcc.edu
Web Site: www.everettcc.edu/

Description: State-supported, 2-year, coed. Part of Washington State Board for Community and Technical Colleges. Awards certificates, diplomas, transfer associate, and terminal associate degrees. Founded 1941. Setting: 22-acre suburban campus with easy access to Seattle. Total enrollment: 7,562. Faculty: 369 (135 full-time, 234 part-time). Student-undergrad faculty ratio is 24:1. Full-time: 3,707 students, 57% women, 43% men. Part-time: 3,855 students, 57% women, 43% men. Students come from 24 other countries, 3% from out-of-state. 32% 25 or older, 3% transferred in. Retention: 46% of full-time freshmen returned the following year. Core. Academic remediation for entering students, ESL program, services for LD students, advanced placement, independent study, distance learning, summer session for credit, part-time degree program, adult/continuing education programs, co-op programs and internships. Study abroad program.

Entrance Requirements: Open admission except for some programs such as cosmetology, aviation, criminal justice, fire science, nursing, and medical assisting. Options: electronic application, early admission, deferred admission. Required: ACT ASSET, ACT COMPASS. Recommended: high school transcript. Entrance: noncompetitive. Application deadline: Rolling. Notification: continuous.

Collegiate Environment: Orientation program. Drama-theater group, choral group, student-run newspaper. Social organizations: 30 open to all. Most popular organizations: United Native American Council, Nippon Friendship Club, Student Nurses Association, International Students Club, Math, Engineering and Science Student Organization. Major annual events: Student Activities Kick-off, Campus Awareness Days, Artist and Lecture Series. Student services: personal-psychological counseling, women's center. Campus security: 24-hour emergency response devices and patrols, late night transport-escort service. John Terrey Library/Media Center with an OPAC and a Web page. 900 computers available on campus for general student use. A campuswide network can be accessed from off-campus. Students can access the following: online class registration. Staffed computer lab on campus.

Community Environment: Located on a natural landlocked harbor at the mouth of the Snohomish River, Everett looks across the Sound at the snowy crags of the Olympic Range. The chief industries of the area are lumbering and the manufacture of airplanes. Railroad lines, bus lines, and Interstate 5 serve the community. More than 60 churches of major denominations, two hospitals, and a library are within the immediate community. Local recreation includes a civic auditorium and stadium, ballfields, tennis courts, roller rinks, bowling alleys, golf courses, outdoor theaters, hunting, fishing, and boating. Skiing areas are a few hours away. Part-time employment is available for students.

■ THE EVERGREEN STATE COLLEGE

2700 Evergreen Pky., NW
Olympia, WA 98505
Tel: (360)867-6000
Fax: (360)867-6577
E-mail: admissions@evergreen.edu
Web Site: www.evergreen.edu/

Description: State-supported, comprehensive, coed. Part of Washington State Public Baccalaureate Institution. Awards bachelor's and master's degrees. Founded 1967. Setting: 1,000-acre rural campus with easy access to Seattle. Endowment: $7.4 million. Research spending for the previous fiscal year: $74,862. Educational spending for the previous fiscal year: $8281 per student. Total enrollment: 4,509. Faculty: 240 (176 full-time, 64 part-time). Student-undergrad faculty ratio is 21:1. 1,650 applied, 98% were admitted. 13% from top 10% of their high school class, 30% from top quarter, 58% from top half. Full-time: 3,872 students, 53% women, 47% men. Part-

time: 321 students, 55% women, 45% men. Students come from 49 states and territories, 26 other countries, 25% from out-of-state. 2% American Indian or Alaska Native, non-Hispanic/Latino; 7% Hispanic/Latino; 5% African American, non-Hispanic/Latino; 3% Asian, non-Hispanic/Latino; 0.5% Native Hawaiian or other Pacific Islander, non-Hispanic/Latino; 1% international. 34% 25 or older, 20% live on campus, 18% transferred in. Retention: 72% of full-time freshmen returned the following year. Academic areas with the most degrees conferred: liberal arts/general studies; interdisciplinary studies. Services for LD students, advanced placement, accelerated degree program, self-designed majors, independent study, double major, summer session for credit, part-time degree program, internships, graduate courses open to undergrads. Off campus study at Jackson School of International Studies at University of Washington; Consortium for Innovative Environments in Learning (CIEL) (Alverno College, Daemen College, Fairhaven College at Western Washington University, Hampshire College, Johnston Center for Integrative Studies at University of Redlands, Marlboro College, The New College at the University of Alabama, New College of Florida, Pitzer College, Prescott College, Richard Stockton College of New Jersey). Study abroad program.

Entrance Requirements: Options: electronic application, deferred admission, international baccalaureate accepted. Required: high school transcript, minimum 2 high school GPA, SAT or ACT. Recommended: essay. Required for some: essay. Entrance: moderately difficult. Application deadline: 2/1. Notification: continuous until 11/1. Preference given to Eligible veterans or National Guard members. SAT Reasoning Test deadline: 2/1. Transfer credits accepted: Yes.

Costs Per Year: Application fee: $50. State resident tuition: $7812 full-time, $260.40 per credit hour part-time. Nonresident tuition: $18,978 full-time, $632.60 per credit hour part-time. Mandatory fees: $583 full-time, $7.85 per credit hour part-time, $3 per term part-time. Full-time tuition and fees vary according to course load, location, and program. Part-time tuition and fees vary according to course load, location, and program. College room and board: $9240. College room only: $6150. Room and board charges vary according to board plan, housing facility, location, and student level.

Collegiate Environment: Orientation program. Drama-theater group, choral group, student-run newspaper, radio station. Social organizations: 58 open to all. Most popular organizations: Bike Shop, Women's Resource Center, Asian Pacific Islander Coalition, Freedom First Dance Collective, Community Gardens. Major annual events: Harvest Festival, Student Activities Fair, Arts and Crafts Fair. Student services: health clinic, personal-psychological counseling, women's center. Campus security: 24-hour emergency response devices and patrols, student patrols, late night transport-escort service, controlled dormitory access. 990 college housing spaces available; 836 were occupied in 2012-13. Freshmen guaranteed college housing. Option: coed housing available. Daniel J. Evans Library with 291,772 books, 60,345 microform titles, 30,107 serials, 10,793 audiovisual materials, an OPAC, and a Web page. 470 computers available on campus for general student use. A campuswide network can be accessed from student residence rooms and from off campus. Students can access the following: online class registration, Online payment, student accounts history, financial aid records, academic history, housing application, evaluations. Staffed computer lab on campus provides training in use of computers, software, and the Internet.

Community Environment: Olympia is a seaport community of 37,000, located at the southernmost tip of Puget Sound. The Pacific Ocean is about an hour's drive west of the campus. The rain forests of the Olympic Peninsula lie to the northwest, and the Cascade mountain range is a few hours east of the campus. Seattle, 60 miles from campus, offers all the cultural and recreational activities typically found in a large city.

■ GONZAGA UNIVERSITY

502 E Boone Ave.
Spokane, WA 99258
Tel: (509)328-4220; Free: 800-322-2584
Fax: (509)324-5780
E-mail: admissions@gonzaga.edu
Web Site: www.gonzaga.edu/

Description: Independent Roman Catholic, comprehensive, coed. Awards bachelor's, master's, and doctoral degrees and post-master's certificates. Founded 1887. Setting: 130-acre urban campus. Endowment: $148.3 million. Research spending for the previous fiscal year: $2.3 million. Educational spending for the previous fiscal year: $9897 per student. Total enrollment: 7,781. Faculty: 784 (408 full-time, 376 part-time). Student-undergrad faculty ratio is 11:1. 6,991 applied, 67% were admitted. 38% from top 10% of their high school class, 73% from top quarter, 93% from top half.

2 National Merit Scholars, 133 class presidents, 471 student government officers. Full-time: 4,805 students, 54% women, 46% men. Part-time: 101 students, 47% women, 53% men. Students come from 46 states and territories, 19 other countries, 51% from out-of-state. 1% American Indian or Alaska Native, non-Hispanic/Latino; 8% Hispanic/Latino; 1% African American, non-Hispanic/Latino; 4% Asian, non-Hispanic/Latino; 0.5% Native Hawaiian or other Pacific Islander, non-Hispanic/Latino; 2% international. 3% 25 or older, 58% live on campus, 3% transferred in. Retention: 94% of full-time freshmen returned the following year. Academic areas with the most degrees conferred: business/marketing; social sciences; engineering. Core. Calendar: semesters. ESL program, services for LD students, advanced placement, accelerated degree program, honors program, independent study, double major, summer session for credit, part-time degree program, adult/continuing education programs, internships. Off campus study at American University. Study abroad program. ROTC: Army.

Entrance Requirements: Options: electronic application, early action, deferred admission, international baccalaureate accepted. Required: essay, high school transcript, minimum 3 high school GPA, 1 recommendation, SAT or ACT. Recommended: interview. Entrance: moderately difficult. Application deadlines: 2/1, 11/15 for early action. Notification: 3/15, 1/15 for early action. SAT Reasoning Test deadline: 2/15. Transfer credits accepted: Yes. Applicants placed on waiting list: 553. Wait-listed applicants offered admission: 173. Early action applicants: 3,583. Early action applicants admitted: 2,417.

Costs Per Year: Application fee: $50. Comprehensive fee: $42,382 includes full-time tuition ($33,160), mandatory fees ($492), and college room and board ($8730). College room only: $4580. Full-time tuition and fees vary according to course load, location, program, reciprocity agreements, and student level. Room and board charges vary according to board plan and housing facility. Part-time tuition: $885 per credit hour. Part-time tuition varies according to course load, location, program, reciprocity agreements, and student level.

Collegiate Environment: Orientation program. Drama-theater group, choral group, student-run newspaper, radio station. Social organizations: 95 open to all. Most popular organizations: Student Body Association, Search, Circle K, Encore, Knights and Setons. Major annual events: new student orientation events, Spring Formal, Aprilfest. Student services: health clinic, personal-psychological counseling. Campus security: 24-hour emergency response devices and patrols, late night transport-escort service, controlled dormitory access. 3,086 college housing spaces available; 2,801 were occupied in 2012-13. Freshmen guaranteed college housing. On-campus residence required through sophomore year. Options: coed, men-only, women-only housing available. Ralph E. and Helen Higgins Foley Center plus 2 others with 286,482 books, 58,763 serials, 10,562 audiovisual materials, an OPAC, and a Web page. Operations spending for the previous fiscal year: $5.9 million. 400 computers available on campus for general student use. Computer purchase/lease plans available. A campuswide network can be accessed from student residence rooms and from off campus. Students can access the following: online class registration. Staffed computer lab on campus provides training in use of computers, software, and the Internet.

Community Environment: See Spokane Falls Community College.

■ **GRAYS HARBOR COLLEGE**
1620 Edward P Smith Dr.
Aberdeen, WA 98520-7599
Tel: (360)532-9020; Free: 800-562-4830
Fax: (360)538-4293
Web Site: www.ghc.edu/

Description: State-supported, 2-year, coed. Part of Washington State Board for Community and Technical Colleges. Awards certificates, diplomas, transfer associate, and terminal associate degrees. Founded 1930. Setting: 125-acre small town campus. Endowment: $8.3 million. Research spending for the previous fiscal year: $915,120. Educational spending for the previous fiscal year: $5369 per student. Total enrollment: 2,526. Faculty: 132 (61 full-time, 71 part-time). Student-undergrad faculty ratio is 19:1. Full-time: 1,589 students, 50% women, 50% men. Part-time: 937 students, 52% women, 48% men. Students come from 11 states and territories, 1 other country, 1% from out-of-state. 4% American Indian or Alaska Native, non-Hispanic/Latino; 4% Hispanic/Latino; 3% African American, non-Hispanic/Latino; 2% Asian, non-Hispanic/Latino; 0.1% Native Hawaiian or other Pacific Islander, non-Hispanic/Latino; 0.1% international. 52% 25 or older, 17% transferred in. Retention: 57% of full-time freshmen returned the following year. Core. Academic remediation for entering students, ESL program, services for LD students, advanced placement, accelerated degree program, honors program, independent study, distance learning, double major, summer ses-

sion for credit, part-time degree program, external degree program, adult/continuing education programs, co-op programs and internships. Study abroad program.

Entrance Requirements: Open admission. Options: electronic application, early admission. Recommended: high school transcript. Entrance: noncompetitive. Application deadline: Rolling. Notification: continuous.

Costs Per Year: Application fee: $0. State resident tuition: $3965 full-time, $106.27 per credit hour part-time. Nonresident tuition: $9200 full-time, $278.27 per credit hour part-time. Mandatory fees: $416 full-time, $9.24 per credit hour part-time. Full-time tuition and fees vary according to course load and program. Part-time tuition and fees vary according to program.

Collegiate Environment: Orientation program. Drama-theater group, choral group, student-run newspaper. Social organizations: 14 open to all. Most popular organizations: Phi Theta Kappa, TYEE, Student Nurses Association, Human Services Student Association, Student Council. Major annual events: sporting events, Bishop Center, drama events. Student services: personal-psychological counseling, women's center. Campus security: 24-hour emergency response devices, late night transport-escort service. Spellman Library with 40,000 books, 240 serials, an OPAC, and a Web page. Operations spending for the previous fiscal year: $411,181. 400 computers available on campus for general student use. A campuswide network can be accessed. Students can access the following: online class registration. Staffed computer lab on campus.

Community Environment: Aberdeen is located in a heavily wooded area and is known chiefly for its lumbering and fishing. The area has good harbors where the fishing fleet anchors. The city has mild winters and cool summers, with up to 75 inches of rainfall per year. Aberdeen may be reached by bus and state highways. There is a public library, YMCA, two hospitals, churches of major denominations, theatres, public parks, and civic, fraternal, and veteran's organizations serving the community. Local recreation includes hunting, fishing, golf, swimming, tennis, and skiing three hours drive away. Part-time employment is available.

■ **GREEN RIVER COMMUNITY COLLEGE**
12401 SE 320th St.
Auburn, WA 98092-3699
Tel: (253)833-9111
Fax: (253)288-3454
Web Site: www.greenriver.edu/

Description: State-supported, 2-year, coed. Part of Washington State Board for Community and Technical Colleges. Awards certificates, diplomas, transfer associate, and terminal associate degrees. Founded 1965. Setting: 168-acre small town campus with easy access to Seattle. Total enrollment: 8,205. Faculty: 436 (134 full-time, 302 part-time). Student-undergrad faculty ratio is 23:1. Students come from 41 other countries. 29% 25 or older. Retention: 61% of full-time freshmen returned the following year. Core. Academic remediation for entering students, ESL program, services for LD students, advanced placement, distance learning, summer session for credit, part-time degree program, adult/continuing education programs, co-op programs and internships. Off campus study. Study abroad program.

Entrance Requirements: Open admission except for nursing, physical therapy, and occupational therapy programs. Options: electronic application, early admission, deferred admission. Required for some: high school transcript. Entrance: noncompetitive. Application deadline: Rolling. Notification: continuous. Transfer credits accepted: Yes.

Costs Per Year: Application fee: $0. State resident tuition: $3999 full-time, $106.84 per credit part-time. Nonresident tuition: $4400 full-time, $119.84 per credit part-time. Mandatory fees: $442 full-time, $68 per credit part-time. Full-time tuition and fees vary according to course load. Part-time tuition and fees vary according to course load.

Collegiate Environment: Orientation program. Drama-theater group, choral group, student-run newspaper, radio station. Student services: health clinic, personal-psychological counseling, women's center. Campus security: 24-hour emergency response devices and patrols, student patrols, late night transport-escort service. Holman Library with 32,500 books, 2,100 serials, 4,471 audiovisual materials, an OPAC, and a Web page.

Community Environment: Auburn is a suburban community in the Seattle area. It is located approximately 30 miles from the heart of downtown Seattle. The climate is mild. Auburn may be reached by railroad, the Seattle airport, and major highways. One library, several churches, a museum, YMCA, general hospital, and clinics serve the community. Local recreation includes a city park, a golf club, community theater, a nearby beach and rivers, hunting for deer, bear, birds and elk, lake fishing, water sports, skiing and mountain climbing. Some part-time employment is available. Various civic and fraternal organizations are active in the community. There are good shopping facilities.

■ HERITAGE UNIVERSITY

3240 Fort Rd.
Toppenish, WA 98948-9599
Tel: (509)865-8500; Free: 888-272-6190
Fax: (509)865-4469
E-mail: admissions@heritage.edu
Web Site: www.heritage.edu/

Description: Independent, comprehensive, coed. Awards associate, bachelor's, and master's degrees. Founded 1982. Setting: 10-acre rural campus. Total enrollment: 1,115. Student-undergrad faculty ratio is 10:1. 0% from out-of-state. 59% 25 or older. Retention: 68% of full-time freshmen returned the following year. Core. Calendar: semesters. Academic remediation for entering students, ESL program, services for LD students, advanced placement, self-designed majors, honors program, independent study, double major, summer session for credit, part-time degree program, adult/continuing education programs, co-op programs and internships, graduate courses open to undergrads.
Entrance Requirements: Open admission. Options: early admission, early decision, deferred admission. Required: high school transcript. Required for some: interview, SAT or ACT. Entrance: noncompetitive. Application deadline: Rolling. Notification: continuous.
Costs Per Year: Application fee: $0. Tuition: $15,480 full-time.
Collegiate Environment: Orientation program. Student-run newspaper. Student services: personal-psychological counseling. Campus security: 24-hour emergency response devices. Library and Resource Center with 62,463 books, 30,100 serials, an OPAC, and a Web page.
Community Environment: Toppenish is located twenty miles south of Yakima, in the fertile lower Yakima Valley which produces fruit and hops and supports agricultural related industries. The climate is mild and dry. Toppenish has churches representing most denominations, a hospital, symphony, civic theatre, community concert series, and arts events. Local recreation includes swimming, skiing, boating, fishing, hunting, and golf. Local events include the Toppenish Rodeo and Pow-Wow, the Cinco de Mayo celebrations, and Yakima Indian Nation Cultural Center events.

■ HIGHLINE COMMUNITY COLLEGE

2400 S 240th St.
Des Moines, WA 98198-9800
Tel: (206)878-3710
Fax: (206)870-3782
Web Site: www.highline.edu/

Description: State-supported, 2-year, coed. Part of Washington State Board for Community and Technical Colleges. Awards certificates, diplomas, transfer associate, and terminal associate degrees. Founded 1961. Setting: 81-acre suburban campus with easy access to Seattle. Endowment: $1.4 million. Educational spending for the previous fiscal year: $3719 per student. Total enrollment: 6,743. Faculty: 360 (144 full-time, 216 part-time). Student-undergrad faculty ratio is 19:1. 4,445 applied, 100% were admitted. Full-time: 3,932 students, 56% women, 44% men. Part-time: 2,811 students, 61% women, 39% men. Students come from 6 states and territories, 50 other countries, 1% from out-of-state. 1% American Indian or Alaska Native, non-Hispanic/Latino; 7% Hispanic/Latino; 11% African American, non-Hispanic/Latino; 15% Asian, non-Hispanic/Latino; 1% Native Hawaiian or other Pacific Islander, non-Hispanic/Latino; 7% international. 51% 25 or older, 71% transferred in. Retention: 57% of full-time freshmen returned the following year. Core. Academic remediation for entering students, ESL program, services for LD students, advanced placement, self-designed majors, freshman honors college, honors program, independent study, distance learning, summer session for credit, part-time degree program, co-op programs and internships. Off campus study. Study abroad program. ROTC: Army (c), Air Force (c).
Entrance Requirements: Open admission. Option: electronic application. Entrance: noncompetitive. Application deadline: Rolling. Transfer credits accepted: Yes.
Costs Per Year: Application fee: $26. Area resident tuition: $107 per credit part-time. State resident tuition: $4000 full-time, $120 per credit part-time. Nonresident tuition: $4400 full-time, $279 per credit part-time. Mandatory fees: $75 full-time, $107 per credit part-time, $75 per term part-time. Full-time tuition and fees vary according to course load and program. Part-time tuition and fees vary according to course load and program.

Collegiate Environment: Orientation program. Drama-theater group, choral group, student-run newspaper. Social organizations: 47 open to all. Most popular organizations: Black Student Union, Pacific Islander Club, Friends of Bosnia, United Latino Association, Muslim Student Association. Major annual event: Thunderweek (Fall opening week). Student services: personal-psychological counseling, women's center. Campus security: 24-hour emergency response devices and patrols, late night transport-escort service. Highline Community College Library with 57,678 books, 585 serials, an OPAC, and a Web page. Operations spending for the previous fiscal year: $1.7 million. 300 computers available on campus for general student use. A campuswide network can be accessed. Students can access the following: online class registration, online degree planning. Staffed computer lab on campus provides training in use of computers, software, and the Internet.
Community Environment: Overlooking the Puget Sound, Des Moines is a suburb of Seattle, approximately 15 miles from the heart of downtown. (See Seattle University.) The community has all the advantages of a small town, and yet is easily accessible to all the cultural, recreational, and civic opportunities of the neighboring community.

■ ITT TECHNICAL INSTITUTE (EVERETT)

1615 75th St. SW
Everett, WA 98203
Tel: (425)583-0200; Free: 800-272-3791
Web Site: www.itt-tech.edu/

Description: Proprietary, primarily 2-year, coed. Part of ITT Educational Services, Inc. Awards terminal associate and bachelor's degrees.
Entrance Requirements: Entrance: minimally difficult.

■ ITT TECHNICAL INSTITUTE (SEATTLE)

12720 Gateway Dr., Ste. 100
Seattle, WA 98168-3333
Tel: (206)244-3300; Free: 800-422-2029
Web Site: www.itt-tech.edu/

Description: Proprietary, primarily 2-year, coed. Part of ITT Educational Services, Inc. Awards terminal associate and bachelor's degrees. Founded 1932. Setting: urban campus.
Entrance Requirements: Entrance: minimally difficult.

■ ITT TECHNICAL INSTITUTE (SPOKANE VALLEY)

13518 E Indiana Ave.
Spokane Valley, WA 99216
Tel: (509)926-2900; Free: 800-777-8324
Web Site: www.itt-tech.edu/

Description: Proprietary, primarily 2-year, coed. Part of ITT Educational Services, Inc. Awards terminal associate and bachelor's degrees. Founded 1985. Setting: suburban campus.
Entrance Requirements: Entrance: minimally difficult.

■ LAKE WASHINGTON INSTITUTE OF TECHNOLOGY

11605 132nd Ave. NE
Kirkland, WA 98034-8506
Tel: (425)739-8100
E-mail: info@lwtc.edu
Web Site: www.lwtech.edu/

Description: State-supported, 2-year, coed. Part of Washington State Board for Community and Technical Colleges. Awards certificates, transfer associate, and terminal associate degrees. Founded 1949. Setting: 57-acre suburban campus with easy access to Seattle. Total enrollment: 3,996. Academic remediation for entering students, ESL program, services for LD students, advanced placement, summer session for credit, co-op programs and internships.
Entrance Requirements: Open admission except for allied health programs. Option: early admission. Required for some: high school transcript. Entrance: noncompetitive. Application deadline: Rolling. Notification: continuous.
Collegiate Environment: Student services: personal-psychological counseling, women's center. Campus security: 24-hour emergency response devices, late night transport-escort service, parking lot security, security cameras. Lake Washington Technical College Library/Media Center with 18,300 books, 770 serials, an OPAC, and a Web page.

■ LOWER COLUMBIA COLLEGE

PO Box 3010
Longview, WA 98632-0310

Tel: (360)442-2000; Free: 866-900-2311
Fax: (360)442-2109
E-mail: registration@lowercolumbia.edu
Web Site: www.lowercolumbia.edu/

Description: State-supported, 2-year, coed. Part of Washington State Board for Community and Technical Colleges. Awards certificates, diplomas, transfer associate, and terminal associate degrees. Founded 1934. Setting: 39-acre rural campus with easy access to Portland. Endowment: $12 million. Educational spending for the previous fiscal year: $8342 per student. Total enrollment: 4,252. Faculty: 222 (69 full-time, 153 part-time). Student-undergrad faculty ratio is 24:1. Full-time: 2,579 students, 59% women, 41% men. Part-time: 1,673 students, 69% women, 31% men. Students come from 7 states and territories, 2 other countries, 2% from out-of-state. 2% American Indian or Alaska Native, non-Hispanic/Latino; 6% Hispanic/Latino; 2% African American, non-Hispanic/Latino; 2% Asian, non-Hispanic/Latino; 0.1% Native Hawaiian or other Pacific Islander, non-Hispanic/Latino; 0.02% international. 55% 25 or older, 11% transferred in. Retention: 53% of full-time freshmen returned the following year. Core. Academic remediation for entering students, ESL program, services for LD students, advanced placement, self-designed majors, independent study, distance learning, summer session for credit, part-time degree program, external degree program, adult/continuing education programs, co-op programs and internships.

Entrance Requirements: Open admission. Option: electronic application. Recommended: high school transcript. Entrance: noncompetitive. Application deadline: Rolling. Notification: continuous. Transfer credits accepted: Yes.

Costs Per Year: Application fee: $14.35. One-time mandatory fee: $30. State resident tuition: $4,275 full-time, $114.69 per credit part-time. Nonresident tuition: $4,813 full-time, $129.13 per credit part-time. Mandatory fees: $274 full-time, $7.85 per credit part-time. Full-time tuition and fees vary according to course load and reciprocity agreements. Part-time tuition and fees vary according to course load and reciprocity agreements.

Collegiate Environment: Orientation program. Drama-theater group, choral group. Social organizations: 24 open to all; student clubs and organizations. Most popular organizations: Phi Theta Kappa, Biological Society, Electric Vehicle Club, American Sign Language Club, Global Medical Brigade. Major annual events: Welcome Back Week, Winterfest, Red Devil Days. Student services: personal-psychological counseling. Campus security: 24-hour emergency response devices and patrols. College housing not available. Alan Thompson Library plus 1 other with 38,841 books, 130 serials, 4,573 audiovisual materials, an OPAC, and a Web page. Operations spending for the previous fiscal year: $378,438.

Community Environment: Longview is a planned city located on the banks of the Columbia and Cowlitz Rivers. The city is 50 miles north of Portland, Oregon, and has a mild climate. There are several churches, a public library, YMCA and two hospitals accessible. Longview may be reached by five railroad lines, and an airport. Local recreation includes theatres, boating, fishing, golf, hunting, skiing, and other sports. Part-time employment is available for students. Hotels, motels, and apartments are available for student housing. The community has several large shopping centers.

■ NORTH SEATTLE COMMUNITY COLLEGE
9600 College Way N
Seattle, WA 98103-3599
Tel: (206)527-3600
Fax: (206)527-3635
E-mail: arrc@seattlecolleges.edu
Web Site: www.northseattle.edu/

Description: State-supported, 2-year, coed. Part of Seattle Community College District. Awards certificates, diplomas, transfer associate, and terminal associate degrees. Founded 1970. Setting: 65-acre urban campus. Endowment: $4.4 million. Educational spending for the previous fiscal year: $4522 per student. Total enrollment: 6,303. Faculty: 304 (88 full-time, 216 part-time). Student-undergrad faculty ratio is 20:1. 5,726 applied, 100% were admitted. Full-time: 1,953 students, 52% women, 48% men. Part-time: 4,350 students, 63% women, 37% men. Students come from 50 states and territories, 39 other countries, 5% from out-of-state. 1% American Indian or Alaska Native, non-Hispanic/Latino; 7% Hispanic/Latino; 7% African American, non-Hispanic/Latino; 12% Asian, non-Hispanic/Latino; 1% Native Hawaiian or other Pacific Islander, non-Hispanic/Latino. 65% 25 or older, 23% transferred in. Core. Academic remediation for entering students, ESL program, services for LD students, advanced placement, independent study, distance learning, summer session for credit, part-time degree program, external degree program, adult/continuing education programs, co-op programs and internships. Study abroad program. ROTC: Army (c).

Entrance Requirements: Open admission. Options: electronic application, early admission, deferred admission. Required: high school transcript. Required for some: essay, English/Math Placement Test. Entrance: noncompetitive. Application deadline: Rolling. Notification: continuous until 9/24.

Collegiate Environment: Orientation program. Drama-theater group, choral group. Social organizations: 25 open to all. Most popular organizations: Muslim Students Association, Indonesian Community Club, Literary Guild, Phi Theta Kappa, Vietnamese Student Association. Major annual events: Cinco de Mayo, Welcome Back BBQ and Success Fair, Spring Fest. Student services: personal-psychological counseling, women's center. Campus security: 24-hour emergency response devices, late night transport-escort service, patrols by security. North Seattle Community College Library with 52,496 books, 152,522 microform titles, 594 serials, an OPAC, and a Web page. 1,600 computers available on campus for general student use. A campuswide network can be accessed from off-campus. Students can access the following: online class registration. Staffed computer lab on campus.

Community Environment: See Seattle University.

■ NORTHWEST COLLEGE OF ART & DESIGN
16301 Creative Dr., NE
Poulsbo, WA 98370
Tel: (360)779-9993; Free: 800-769-ARTS
Fax: (360)779-9933
E-mail: mstoddard@nca.edu
Web Site: www.ncad.edu/

Description: Proprietary, 4-year, coed. Awards bachelor's degrees. Founded 1982. Setting: 26-acre small town campus with easy access to Seattle. Core. Calendar: semesters. Double major, summer session for credit, internships.

Entrance Requirements: Option: deferred admission. Required: essay, high school transcript, minimum 2.5 high school GPA, 3 recommendations, interview, portfolio. Entrance: moderately difficult. Application deadline: 6/1. Notification: continuous.

Collegiate Environment: Orientation program. Major annual events: Student Art Shows, Open House. 28 computers available on campus for general student use. Students can access the following: graphics programs, word processing. Staffed computer lab on campus.

■ NORTHWEST INDIAN COLLEGE
2522 Kwina Rd.
Bellingham, WA 98226
Tel: (360)676-2772; Free: 866-676-2772
Fax: (360)738-0136
E-mail: admissions@nwic.edu
Web Site: www.nwic.edu/

Description: Federally supported, primarily 2-year, coed. Awards certificates, transfer associate, terminal associate, and bachelor's degrees (also offers bachelor's degree in elementary education in conjunction with Washington State University). Founded 1978. Setting: 5-acre rural campus. Total enrollment: 609. Student-undergrad faculty ratio is 13:1. 17% from out-of-state. 54% 25 or older. Core. Academic remediation for entering students, self-designed majors, summer session for credit, part-time degree program, external degree program, adult/continuing education programs, co-op programs and internships. Study abroad program.

Entrance Requirements: Open admission. Required: high school transcript. Entrance: noncompetitive. Notification: continuous. Preference given to Native Americans.

Collegiate Environment: Drama-theater group, choral group, student-run newspaper. Student services: personal-psychological counseling.

■ NORTHWEST SCHOOL OF WOODEN BOATBUILDING
42 N Water St.
Port Hadlock, WA 98339
Tel: (360)385-4948
Fax: (360)385-5089
E-mail: info@nwboatschool.org
Web Site: www.nwboatschool.org/

Description: Independent, 2-year, coed. Awards diplomas and terminal associate degrees. Founded 1980. Calendar: semesters.

■ NORTHWEST UNIVERSITY
5520 108th Ave., NE
Kirkland, WA 98033

Tel: (425)822-8266; Free: 800-669-3781
Fax: (425)425-0148
E-mail: admissions@northwestu.edu
Web Site: www.northwestu.edu/

Description: Independent, comprehensive, coed, affiliated with Assemblies of God. Awards associate, bachelor's, master's, and doctoral degrees. Founded 1934. Setting: 56-acre suburban campus with easy access to Seattle. Endowment: $9.3 million. Educational spending for the previous fiscal year: $5945 per student. Total enrollment: 1,612. Faculty: 206 (58 full-time, 148 part-time). Student-undergrad faculty ratio is 13:1. 749 applied, 64% were admitted. Full-time: 1,163 students, 61% women, 39% men. Part-time: 192 students, 45% women, 55% men. Students come from 29 states and territories, 16 other countries, 6% from out-of-state. 1% American Indian or Alaska Native, non-Hispanic/Latino; 8% Hispanic/Latino; 4% African American, non-Hispanic/Latino; 5% Asian, non-Hispanic/Latino; 1% Native Hawaiian or other Pacific Islander, non-Hispanic/Latino; 2% international. 63% 25 or older, 55% live on campus, 15% transferred in. Retention: 86% of full-time freshmen returned the following year. Academic areas with the most degrees conferred: theology and religious vocations; business/marketing; health professions and related sciences. Core. Calendar: semesters. Academic remediation for entering students, ESL program, advanced placement, accelerated degree program, independent study, double major, summer session for credit, part-time degree program, adult/continuing education programs, co-op programs and internships. Study abroad program. ROTC: Army (c), Air Force (c).

Entrance Requirements: Options: electronic application, early action, deferred admission, international baccalaureate accepted. Required: essay, high school transcript, minimum 2.3 high school GPA, 2 recommendations, SAT or ACT. Required for some: interview. Entrance: moderately difficult. Application deadlines: 8/1, 1/15 for early action. Notification: continuous, 2/15 for early action. SAT Reasoning Test deadline: 8/1. Transfer credits accepted: Yes. Early action applicants: 450. Early action applicants admitted: 359.

Collegiate Environment: Orientation program. Drama-theater group, choral group, student-run newspaper, radio station. Social organizations: 19 open to all. Most popular organizations: Student Ministries, Pursuit (worship service), Northwest University Business Club, Environmental Stewardship Club. Major annual events: Christmas Party, Floor Olympics, The Evening Formal Event. Student services: health clinic, personal-psychological counseling. Campus security: 24-hour emergency response devices and patrols, late night transport-escort service, controlled dormitory access. 650 college housing spaces available; 627 were occupied in 2012-13. Freshmen guaranteed college housing. On-campus residence required through sophomore year. Options: men-only, women-only housing available. Hurst Library with 100,356 books, 56,202 microform titles, 13,443 serials, 1,053 audiovisual materials, an OPAC, and a Web page. Operations spending for the previous fiscal year: $603,826. 134 computers available on campus for general student use. A campuswide network can be accessed from student residence rooms and from off campus. Students can access the following: online class registration, online classes. Staffed computer lab on campus provides training in use of computers, software, and the Internet.

■ **OLYMPIC COLLEGE**
1600 Chester Ave.
Bremerton, WA 98337-1699
Tel: (360)792-6050; Free: 800-259-6718
Fax: (360)792-2135
E-mail: jfyllingness@olympic.edu
Web Site: www.olympic.edu/

Description: State-supported, primarily 2-year, coed. Part of Washington State Board for Community and Technical Colleges. Awards certificates, diplomas, transfer associate, terminal associate, and bachelor's degrees. Founded 1946. Setting: 33-acre suburban campus with easy access to Seattle. Total enrollment: 8,260. Faculty: 472 (122 full-time, 350 part-time). 3,126 applied, 100% were admitted. 2% American Indian or Alaska Native, non-Hispanic/Latino; 6% Hispanic/Latino; 5% African American, non-Hispanic/Latino; 8% Asian, non-Hispanic/Latino; 1% international. 49% 25 or older. Core. Academic remediation for entering students, ESL program, services for LD students, advanced placement, honors program, independent study, distance learning, summer session for credit, part-time degree program, adult/continuing education programs, co-op programs and internships. Off campus study at Brandman University, Evergreen State College, University of Washington-Tacoma, Western Governors University and other community colleges in Washington.

Entrance Requirements: Open admission except for nursing, medical office assistant program, physical therapy. Option: electronic application. Required for some: high school transcript. Entrance: noncompetitive. Application deadlines: Rolling, Rolling for nonresidents. Transfer credits accepted: Yes.

Costs Per Year: Application fee: $0. State resident tuition: $3,523 full-time, $106.84 per credit hour part-time. Nonresident tuition: $3,943 full-time, $119.84 per credit hour part-time. Mandatory fees: $195 full-time. Full-time tuition and fees vary according to course load and degree level. Part-time tuition varies according to course load and degree level.

Collegiate Environment: Orientation program. Drama-theater group, choral group, student-run newspaper. Most popular organizations: Phi Theta Kappa, International Student Club, MESA/STEM club, Armed Services, ASL. Major annual events: Commencement, Student Appreciation Day, End of the School Year BBQ. Student services: personal-psychological counseling. Campus security: 24-hour emergency response devices and patrols, student patrols, late night transport-escort service. College housing not available. Haselwood Library with an OPAC and a Web page. 1,300 computers available on campus for general student use. A campuswide network can be accessed. Students can access the following: online class registration. Staffed computer lab on campus provides training in use of computers, software, and the Internet.

Community Environment: Bremerton is a metropolitan community enjoying mild summer and winter temperatures. The major local industry is shipbuilding. The community has a library, hospital, churches of most denominations, and active civic, fraternal, and veteran's organizations. Rooming and boarding houses and small apartments are available for student housing. Local recreation includes sports, cultural events, boating, skiing, and snow boarding, all within a 3 hr. drive. Job opportunities are available for students.

■ **PACIFIC LUTHERAN UNIVERSITY**
Tacoma, WA 98447
Tel: (253)531-6900; Free: 800-274-6758
Fax: (253)536-5136
E-mail: admission@plu.edu
Web Site: www.plu.edu/

Description: Independent, comprehensive, coed, affiliated with Evangelical Lutheran Church in America. Awards bachelor's and master's degrees. Founded 1890. Setting: 156-acre suburban campus with easy access to Seattle. Endowment: $73.2 million. Research spending for the previous fiscal year: $433,087. Educational spending for the previous fiscal year: $12,228 per student. Total enrollment: 3,473. Faculty: 254 (204 full-time, 50 part-time). Student-undergrad faculty ratio is 15:1. 3,550 applied, 74% were admitted. 37% from top 10% of their high school class, 67% from top quarter, 86% from top half. Full-time: 3,028 students, 62% women, 38% men. Part-time: 138 students, 57% women, 43% men. Students come from 44 states and territories, 24 other countries, 23% from out-of-state. 1% American Indian or Alaska Native, non-Hispanic/Latino; 7% Hispanic/Latino; 3% African American, non-Hispanic/Latino; 6% Asian, non-Hispanic/Latino; 0.5% Native Hawaiian or other Pacific Islander, non-Hispanic/Latino; 4% international. 9% 25 or older, 49% live on campus, 7% transferred in. Retention: 83% of full-time freshmen returned the following year. Academic areas with the most degrees conferred: social sciences; health professions and related sciences; business/marketing. Core. Calendar: 4-1-4. Services for LD students, advanced placement, self-designed majors, honors program, independent study, double major, summer session for credit, part-time degree program, co-op programs and internships, graduate courses open to undergrads. Study abroad program. ROTC: Army.

Entrance Requirements: Options: electronic application, early admission, deferred admission, international baccalaureate accepted. Required: essay, high school transcript, 1 recommendation, SAT or ACT. Recommended: minimum 2.5 high school GPA. Required for some: interview. Entrance: moderately difficult. Application deadline: Rolling. Notification: continuous. Transfer credits accepted: Yes.

Costs Per Year: Application fee: $40. Comprehensive fee: $44,840 includes full-time tuition ($34,440), mandatory fees ($300), and college room and board ($10,100). College room only: $4870. Full-time tuition and fees vary according to course load. Room and board charges vary according to board plan and housing facility. Part-time mandatory fees: $1030 per semester hour. Part-time fees vary according to course load.

Collegiate Environment: Orientation program. Drama-theater group, choral group, student-run newspaper, radio station. Social organizations: 64 open to all. Most popular organizations: Ignite, Circle K, Adult Students Club, Residence Hall Government, Inter-Varsity Fellowship. Major annual events: Homecoming, Convocation, All-Campus Picnics. Student services: health clinic, personal-psychological counseling, women's center. Campus security: 24-hour emergency response devices and patrols, student patrols, late night transport-escort service, controlled dormitory access. 1,725 college housing spaces available; 1,665 were occupied in 2012-13. Freshmen guaranteed college housing. On-campus residence required through sophomore year. Options: coed, women-only housing available. Mortvedt Library with 337;167 books, 240,061 microform titles, 5,808 serials, 14,299 audiovisual materials, an OPAC, and a Web page. Operations spending for the previous fiscal year: $2.8 million. 435 computers available on campus for general student use. A campuswide network can be accessed from student residence rooms and from off campus. Students can access the following: online class registration. Staffed computer lab on campus provides training in use of computers, software, and the Internet.

Community Environment: The third largest city in Washington, Tacoma is a shipping, industrial, and distribution center located in the Puget Sound region. The city has diversified industries including electrochemicals, food and beverage processing, clothing manufacturing, iron and steel works, and shipyards. The city has several parks, a public library system, museums, hospitals, and many civic and fraternal organizations serving the community. Transportation is provided by railroads, airlines, twelve bus lines, and major highways. Its residents enjoy easy access to ocean beaches, the many waterways of Puget Sound, and Mt. Rainier, Olympic, and North Cascades National Parks. Nearby lakes and streams offer excellent fishing and numerous water sports.

■ **PENINSULA COLLEGE**

1502 E Lauridsen Blvd.
Port Angeles, WA 98362-2779
Tel: (360)452-9277; Free: 877-452-9277
Fax: (360)457-8100
E-mail: admissions@pencol.edu
Web Site: www.pc.ctc.edu/

Description: State-supported, primarily 2-year, coed. Part of Washington State Community and Technical Colleges. Awards certificates, transfer associate, terminal associate, and bachelor's degrees. Founded 1961. Setting: 75-acre small town campus. Total enrollment: 3,321. Faculty: 156 (57 full-time, 99 part-time). Student-undergrad faculty ratio is 21:1. Academic remediation for entering students, ESL program, services for LD students, advanced placement, honors program, distance learning, summer session for credit, part-time degree program, adult/continuing education programs, internships.

Entrance Requirements: Open admission except for management, nursing, industrial electronics, business computer systems programs, massage therapy programs. Required for some: high school transcript. Entrance: noncompetitive. Application deadline: Rolling. Notification: continuous.

Collegiate Environment: Orientation program. Student-run newspaper. Student services: women's center. Campus security: 8-hour patrols by trained security personnel. John D Glann Library with 33,736 books and 383 serials.

Community Environment: Called the gateway to Olympic National Park, Port Angeles is a popular resort and tourist area located between the Olympic Mountains and Strait of Juan de Fuca. The area enjoys temperate climate with temperature ranges from 30 to 80 degrees. Average rainfall is 22.8 inches. The city may be reached by airlines and highways. There are libraries, churches representing many denominations, a YMCA, and a modern hospital. Local recreation includes theatres, parks, concerts, plays, swimming, golf, skiing, bowling, hiking, crabbing, fishing, sailing and other sports. The community has many civic organizations, a symphony orchestra, choral and theater groups.

■ **PIERCE COLLEGE AT PUYALLUP**

1601 39th Ave. SE
Puyallup, WA 98374
Tel: (253)840-8400
Fax: (253)840-8423
Web Site: www.pierce.ctc.edu/

Description: State-supported, 2-year, coed. Part of Washington State Board for Community and Technical Colleges. Awards certificates, diplomas, transfer associate, and terminal associate degrees. Founded 1967. Setting: 140-acre suburban campus with easy access to Seattle. Total enrollment: 13,294. Faculty: 600. Students come from 12 other countries. 56% 25 or older. Core. Academic remediation for entering students, ESL program, services for LD students, advanced placement, independent study, distance learning, summer session for credit, part-time degree program, adult/

continuing education programs, co-op programs and internships. Off campus study. Study abroad program. ROTC: Army (c).

Entrance Requirements: Open admission except for international students, veterinary technology, dental hygiene and nursing programs. Options: electronic application, early admission. Entrance: noncompetitive. Application deadlines: Rolling, Rolling for nonresidents. Notification: continuous, continuous for nonresidents. Transfer credits accepted: Yes.

Costs Per Year: Application fee: $0. State resident tuition: $2836 full-time, $107 per credit hour part-time. Nonresident tuition: $3104 full-time, $120 per credit hour part-time. Mandatory fees: $228 full-time, $9.25 per credit hour part-time. Full-time tuition and fees vary according to course load and location. Part-time tuition and fees vary according to course load and location.

Collegiate Environment: Orientation program. Drama-theater group, choral group, student-run newspaper. Social organizations: 20 open to all. Most popular organizations: Student Life, Phi Theta Kappa, Dental Hygiene Association, Veterinary Technology Association. Student services: women's center. Campus security: 24-hour emergency response devices and patrols, late night transport-escort service. College housing not available. 55,000 books and 425 serials 350 computers available on campus for general student use. Staffed computer lab on campus.

■ **PIMA MEDICAL INSTITUTE (RENTON)**

555 S Renton Village Pl.
Renton, WA 98057
Tel: (425)228-9600
E-mail: rpanerio@pmi.edu
Web Site: www.pmi.edu/

Description: Proprietary, 2-year, coed. Setting: urban campus. Core. Distance learning, co-op programs and internships.

Entrance Requirements: Required: high school transcript, interview, Wonderlic Scholastic Level Exam (SLE).

Collegiate Environment: Orientation program.

■ **PIMA MEDICAL INSTITUTE (SEATTLE)**

9709 Third Ave. NE
Ste. 400
Seattle, WA 98115
Tel: (206)322-6100; Free: 888-477-PIMA
Fax: (206)324-1985
Web Site: www.pmi.edu/

Description: Proprietary, primarily 2-year, coed. Part of Vocational Training Institutes, Inc. Awards certificates, terminal associate, and bachelor's degrees. Founded 1989. Setting: urban campus. Total enrollment: 357. 57% 25 or older. Calendar: modular. Distance learning.

Entrance Requirements: Required: interview, Wonderlic aptitude test. Required for some: high school transcript. Entrance: minimally difficult.

■ **RENTON TECHNICAL COLLEGE**

3000 NE Fourth St.
Renton, WA 98056
Tel: (425)235-2352
Fax: (425)235-7832
Web Site: www.rtc.edu/

Description: State-supported, 2-year, coed. Part of Washington State Board for Community and Technical Colleges. Awards certificates, diplomas, and terminal associate degrees. Founded 1942. Setting: 30-acre suburban campus with easy access to Seattle. Research spending for the previous fiscal year: $59,756. Educational spending for the previous fiscal year: $3093 per student. Total enrollment: 9,301. Faculty: 282 (84 full-time, 198 part-time). Student-undergrad faculty ratio is 15:1. Students come from 9 states and territories, 13 other countries. 71% 25 or older. Academic remediation for entering students, ESL program, services for LD students, advanced placement, self-designed majors, distance learning, summer session for credit, part-time degree program, adult/continuing education programs, co-op programs and internships.

Entrance Requirements: Open admission. Option: early admission. Recommended: interview. Required for some: high school transcript. Entrance: noncompetitive. Application deadline: Rolling. Notification: continuous.

Costs Per Year: Application fee: $25. State resident tuition: $5735 full-time, $106.26 per credit hour part-time. Nonresident tuition: $6308 full-time, $119.26 per credit hour part-time. Full-time tuition varies according to course load.

Collegiate Environment: Orientation program. Major annual events: Graduation, Orientation. Campus security: patrols by security, security system. Renton Technical College Library with 12,876 books, 684 microform titles, 2,316 serials, 321 audiovisual materials, and an OPAC. Operations spending for the previous fiscal year: $169,650. 96 computers available on campus for general student use. A campuswide network can be accessed. Staffed computer lab on campus.

■ **SAINT MARTIN'S UNIVERSITY**
5000 Abbey Way SE
Lacey, WA 98503
Tel: (360)491-4700; Free: 800-368-8803
Fax: (360)459-4124
E-mail: admissions@stmartin.edu
Web Site: www.stmartin.edu/

Description: Independent Roman Catholic, comprehensive, coed. Awards bachelor's and master's degrees and post-master's certificates. Founded 1895. Setting: 380-acre suburban campus with easy access to Seattle. Endowment: $16.4 million. Research spending for the previous fiscal year: $22,699. Educational spending for the previous fiscal year: $6936 per student. Total enrollment: 1,823. Faculty: 218 (73 full-time, 145 part-time). Student-undergrad faculty ratio is 12:1. 808 applied, 82% were admitted. 26% from top 10% of their high school class, 51% from top quarter, 82% from top half. Full-time: 1,143 students, 52% women, 48% men. Part-time: 336 students, 44% women, 56% men. Students come from 29 states and territories, 7 other countries, 25% from out-of-state. 1% American Indian or Alaska Native, non-Hispanic/Latino; 11% Hispanic/Latino; 8% African American, non-Hispanic/Latino; 5% Asian, non-Hispanic/Latino; 2% Native Hawaiian or other Pacific Islander, non-Hispanic/Latino; 6% international. 32% 25 or older, 33% live on campus, 12% transferred in. Retention: 74% of full-time freshmen returned the following year. Academic areas with the most degrees conferred: business/marketing; psychology; engineering. Core. Calendar: semesters. Academic remediation for entering students, ESL program, services for LD students, advanced placement, accelerated degree program, independent study, distance learning, double major, summer session for credit, part-time degree program, adult/continuing education programs, co-op programs and internships, graduate courses open to undergrads. Off campus study at American University. Study abroad program. ROTC: Army (c), Air Force (c).
Entrance Requirements: Options: electronic application, international baccalaureate accepted. Required: essay, high school transcript, minimum 2.5 high school GPA, 1 recommendation, SAT or ACT. Required for some: interview. Entrance: moderately difficult. Notification: 8/15. SAT Reasoning Test deadline: 7/1. SAT Subject Test deadline: 7/1. Transfer credits accepted: Yes.
Costs Per Year: Comprehensive fee: $39,494 includes full-time tuition ($29,500), mandatory fees ($334), and college room and board ($9660). College room only: $4820. Full-time tuition and fees vary according to degree level, location, and program. Room and board charges vary according to board plan. Part-time tuition: $990 per credit. Part-time tuition varies according to course load, degree level, location, and program.
Collegiate Environment: Orientation program. Drama-theater group, choral group, student-run newspaper. Social organizations: 24 open to all. Most popular organizations: International Club, Minorities in Action, Hui O Hawaii, American Society of Civil Engineers, Chemistry. Major annual events: Luau, Homecoming, Career Fair. Student services: health clinic, personal-psychological counseling. Campus security: 24-hour emergency response devices and patrols, student patrols, late night transport-escort service, controlled dormitory access. 630 college housing spaces available; 498 were occupied in 2012-13. Freshmen guaranteed college housing. On-campus residence required through sophomore year. Option: coed housing available. O'Grady Library with 110,072 books, 162,535 microform titles, 2,920 serials, 2,352 audiovisual materials, an OPAC, and a Web page. Operations spending for the previous fiscal year: $1 million. 80 computers available on campus for general student use. A campuswide network can be accessed from student residence rooms. Students can access the following: online class registration. Staffed computer lab on campus provides training in use of computers, software, and the Internet.

■ **SEATTLE CENTRAL COMMUNITY COLLEGE**
1701 Broadway
Seattle, WA 98122-2400
Tel: (206)587-3800
Web Site: www.seattlecentral.edu/
Description: State-supported, 2-year, coed. Part of Seattle Community Col-

lege District System. Awards certificates, transfer associate, and terminal associate degrees. Founded 1966. Setting: 15-acre urban campus. Total enrollment: 7,774. 1% from out-of-state. 49% 25 or older. Core. Academic remediation for entering students, ESL program, services for LD students, summer session for credit, part-time degree program, external degree program, adult/continuing education programs, co-op programs and internships. ROTC: Army (c), Naval (c), Air Force (c).
Entrance Requirements: Open admission except for nursing program. Entrance: noncompetitive. Application deadline: Rolling.
Collegiate Environment: Orientation program. Drama-theater group, choral group, student-run newspaper. Social organizations: 30 open to all. Most popular organizations: Triangle Club, African Brothers of Unity, MECHA, Asian/Pacific Islander Student Union, Sea-King Club for the Deaf. Major annual events: Student Studies Institute, Student Leadership. Student services: personal-psychological counseling, women's center. Campus security: 24-hour emergency response devices.
Community Environment: See Seattle University.

■ **SEATTLE PACIFIC UNIVERSITY**
3307 Third Ave. W
Seattle, WA 98119-1997
Tel: (206)281-2000; Free: 800-366-3344
E-mail: admissions@spu.edu
Web Site: www.spu.edu/
Description: Independent Free Methodist, comprehensive, coed. Awards bachelor's, master's, and doctoral degrees and post-master's certificates. Founded 1891. Setting: 35-acre urban campus. Total enrollment: 4,095. Faculty: 348 (202 full-time, 146 part-time). Student-undergrad faculty ratio is 15:1. 4,559 applied, 17% were admitted. 26% from top 10% of their high school class, 57% from top quarter, 87% from top half. 5 National Merit Scholars. Full-time: 3,107 students, 66% women, 34% men. Part-time: 142 students, 70% women, 30% men. Students come from 43 states and territories, 36 other countries, 37% from out-of-state. 0.4% American Indian or Alaska Native, non-Hispanic/Latino; 8% Hispanic/Latino; 4% African American, non-Hispanic/Latino; 10% Asian, non-Hispanic/Latino; 0.03% Native Hawaiian or other Pacific Islander, non-Hispanic/Latino; 1% international. 7% 25 or older, 54% live on campus, 7% transferred in. Retention: 84% of full-time freshmen returned the following year. Academic areas with the most degrees conferred: business/marketing; social sciences; health professions and related sciences. Core. Academic remediation for entering students, services for LD students, advanced placement, self-designed majors, honors program, independent study, distance learning, double major, summer session for credit, part-time degree program, external degree program, adult/continuing education programs, internships, graduate courses open to undergrads. Off campus study at 13 members of the Coalition for Christian Colleges and Universities. Study abroad program. ROTC: Army (c), Naval (c), Air Force (c).
Entrance Requirements: Options: electronic application, early admission, early action, international baccalaureate accepted. Required: essay, high school transcript, minimum 2.5 high school GPA, 2 recommendations, SAT or ACT. Recommended: interview. Required for some: SAT and SAT Subject Tests or ACT, SAT Subject Tests. Entrance: moderately difficult. Application deadlines: 2/1, 11/15 for early action. Notification: 3/1, 1/5 for early action. SAT Reasoning Test deadline: 2/1. SAT Subject Test deadline: 2/1. Transfer credits accepted: Yes. Applicants placed on waiting list: 896. Wait-listed applicants offered admission: 207.
Costs Per Year: Application fee: $50. Comprehensive fee: $41,559 includes full-time tuition ($31,701), mandatory fees ($366), and college room and board ($9492). College room only: $5190. Room and board charges vary according to board plan and housing facility. Part-time tuition: $881 per credit hour. Part-time mandatory fees: $122 per term. Part-time tuition and fees vary according to course load.
Collegiate Environment: Orientation program. Drama-theater group, choral group, student-run newspaper, radio station. Social organizations: 50 open to all. Most popular organizations: Centurions, Falconettes, forensics organization, Amnesty International, University Players. Major annual events: Homecoming, spring picnic, ivy cutting event. Student services: health clinic, personal-psychological counseling. Campus security: 24-hour emergency response devices and patrols, student patrols, late night transport-escort service, closed-circuit TV monitors. 1,732 college housing spaces available; 1,695 were occupied in 2012-13. Freshmen guaranteed college housing. On-campus residence required through sophomore year. Option: coed housing available. Seattle Pacific University Library with 217,369 books, 497,248 microform titles, 2,729 serials, 7,417 audiovisual

materials, an OPAC, and a Web page. 150 computers available on campus for general student use. A campuswide network can be accessed from student residence rooms and from off campus. Students can access the following: online class registration. Staffed computer lab on campus provides training in use of computers and software.

Community Environment: See Seattle University.

■ SEATTLE UNIVERSITY

902 12th Ave.
Seattle, WA 98122-1090
Tel: (206)296-6000; Free: 800-426-7123
Fax: (206)296-5656
E-mail: admissions@seattleu.edu
Web Site: www.seattleu.edu/

Description: Independent Roman Catholic, comprehensive, coed. Awards bachelor's, master's, and doctoral degrees and post-master's certificates. Founded 1891. Setting: 50-acre urban campus with easy access to Seattle. Total enrollment: 7,484. Faculty: 739 (504 full-time, 235 part-time). Student-undergrad faculty ratio is 12:1. 6,862 applied, 71% were admitted. 26% from top 10% of their high school class, 58% from top quarter, 89% from top half. Full-time: 4,364 students, 59% women, 41% men. Part-time: 225 students, 59% women, 41% men. Students come from 48 states and territories, 48 other countries, 44% from out-of-state. 1% American Indian or Alaska Native, non-Hispanic/Latino; 9% Hispanic/Latino; 4% African American, non-Hispanic/Latino; 16% Asian, non-Hispanic/Latino; 1% Native Hawaiian or other Pacific Islander, non-Hispanic/Latino; 10% international. 8% 25 or older, 41% live on campus, 10% transferred in. Retention: 87% of full-time freshmen returned the following year. Academic areas with the most degrees conferred: business/marketing; health professions and related sciences; social sciences. Core. ESL program, services for LD students, advanced placement, accelerated degree program, self-designed majors, freshman honors college, honors program, independent study, double major, summer session for credit, part-time degree program, adult/continuing education programs, internships, graduate courses open to undergrads. Off campus study at Photographic Center Northwest. Study abroad program. ROTC: Army, Naval (c), Air Force (c).

Entrance Requirements: Options: electronic application, early action, deferred admission, international baccalaureate accepted. Required: essay, high school transcript, minimum 2.5 high school GPA, 2 recommendations, SAT or ACT. Entrance: moderately difficult. Application deadlines: Rolling, 11/15 for early action. Notification: continuous until 3/1, 12/23 for early action. SAT Reasoning Test deadline: 7/1. SAT Subject Test deadline: 7/1. Transfer credits accepted: Yes. Applicants placed on waiting list: 924. Waitlisted applicants offered admission: 14.

Costs Per Year: Application fee: $50. Comprehensive fee: $45,096 includes full-time tuition ($34,200), mandatory fees ($600), and college room and board ($10,296). Full-time tuition and fees vary according to course load. Room and board charges vary according to board plan and housing facility. Part-time tuition: $760 per credit hour. Part-time tuition varies according to course load.

Collegiate Environment: Orientation program. Drama-theater group, choral group, student-run newspaper, radio station. Social organizations: 78 open to all. Most popular organizations: student government, Center for Service, Hawaiian Club, International Student Club, Dance Marathon. Major annual events: International Student Dinner, Luau, Quadstock. Student services: health clinic, personal-psychological counseling, women's center. Campus security: 24-hour emergency response devices and patrols, late night transport-escort service, controlled dormitory access, bicycle patrols. 2,085 college housing spaces available; 1,940 were occupied in 2012-13. Freshmen guaranteed college housing. On-campus residence required through sophomore year. Option: coed housing available. Lemieux Library plus 1 other with 293,806 books, 578,876 microform titles, 1,569 serials, 6,099 audiovisual materials, an OPAC, and a Web page. 467 computers available on campus for general student use. Computer purchase/lease plans available. A campuswide network can be accessed from student residence rooms and from off campus. Students can access the following: online class registration. Staffed computer lab on campus (open 24 hours a day) provides training in use of the Internet.

Community Environment: Built upon the hills between Lake Washington and Puget Sound, Seattle is the metropolis of the Pacific Northwest. A fine protected harbor makes the city one of the world's great seaports. The community has a prosperous fishing industry, and is important for shipping of fir, red cedar and salmon. Other industries in the area include software and computer-related industries, aerospace and related fields, foundries,

electronics, marine science firms and the processing of food and forest products. The summer average temperature is 63 degrees, and the winter average is 42 degrees. Mountains surround the city and 193 miles of waterfront accommodate oceangoing vessels. The community has 45 parks, art galleries, museums, year-round theater, and opera. There are churches representing all major denominations, and civic, fraternal and veteran's organizations active in the area. Part-time employment is available. Professional sport teams include the Seahawks (football), Mariners (baseball), and Sonics (basketball).

■ SHORELINE COMMUNITY COLLEGE

16101 Greenwood Ave. N
Shoreline, WA 98133-5696
Tel: (206)546-4101
Fax: (206)546-4599
Web Site: www.shore.ctc.edu/

Description: State-supported, 2-year, coed. Part of Washington State Board for Community and Technical Colleges. Awards certificates, diplomas, and transfer associate degrees. Founded 1964. Setting: 80-acre suburban campus. Total enrollment: 8,591. Faculty: 415 (155 full-time, 260 part-time). Student-undergrad faculty ratio is 21:1. 45% 25 or older. Academic remediation for entering students, ESL program, services for LD students, advanced placement, summer session for credit, part-time degree program, adult/continuing education programs, co-op programs and internships. Study abroad program.

Entrance Requirements: Open admission. Required: high school transcript. Recommended: ACT ASSET or ACT COMPASS. Entrance: noncompetitive. Application deadline: Rolling.

Collegiate Environment: Orientation program. Student services: personal-psychological counseling, women's center. Campus security: 24-hour emergency response devices and patrols. Ray W. Howard Library/Media Center with 79,554 books, 1,735 serials, an OPAC, and a Web page. 385 computers available on campus for general student use. Students can access the following: online class registration. Staffed computer lab on campus provides training in use of computers and software.

Community Environment: See Seattle University.

■ SKAGIT VALLEY COLLEGE

2405 College Way
Mount Vernon, WA 98273-5899
Tel: (360)416-7600
Fax: (360)416-7890
E-mail: karenmarie.bade@skagit.edu
Web Site: www.skagit.edu/

Description: State-supported, 2-year, coed. Part of Washington State Board for Community and Technical Colleges. Awards certificates, diplomas, transfer associate, and terminal associate degrees. Founded 1926. Setting: 85-acre small town campus with easy access to Seattle. Endowment: $3.2 million. Total enrollment: 6,858. Faculty: 301. Student-undergrad faculty ratio is 22:1. 3,321 applied, 60% were admitted. Students come from 4 states and territories, 23 other countries, 3% from out-of-state. 68% 25 or older, 1% live on campus. Core. Academic remediation for entering students, ESL program, services for LD students, advanced placement, accelerated degree program, self-designed majors, independent study, distance learning, summer session for credit, part-time degree program, external degree program, adult/continuing education programs, co-op programs and internships. Study abroad program.

Entrance Requirements: Open admission except for some programs. Options: electronic application, deferred admission. Required for some: high school transcript, interview. Entrance: noncompetitive. Application deadline: Rolling.

Collegiate Environment: Orientation program. Drama-theater group, choral group, student-run newspaper, radio station. Social organizations: 42 open to all. Most popular organizations: Phi Theta Kappa, Calling All Colors, Business Management Training, Human Services, Paralegal Club. Major annual events: Cardinal Day, Honors Banquet, Commencement. Student services: personal-psychological counseling, women's center. Campus security: 24-hour patrols, late night transport-escort service, telephone/pager system. Norwood Cole Library with 78,631 books, 46,186 microform titles, 359 serials, 2,599 audiovisual materials, an OPAC, and a Web page. 200 computers available on campus for general student use. A campuswide network can be accessed from off-campus. Staffed computer lab on campus.

Community Environment: Agriculture, mixed industries and tourism are the principal industries in this city located on the Skagit River. The climate here is moderate with neither cold nor hot extremes. Mount Vernon is accessible by railroad, bus lines and major highways and is 90 minutes from the Seattle Pacific Airport by automobile. The community has several churches, two hospitals and YMCA serving the residents. Local recreation includes hunting, fishing, skiing, golfing, boating, swimming, salt water or fresh water sports and nearby mountains and forests recreation areas. Various fraternal and civic organizations are found within the community.

■ **SOUTH PUGET SOUND COMMUNITY COLLEGE**
2011 Mottman Rd., SW
Olympia, WA 98512-6292
Tel: (360)754-7711
Fax: (360)664-9407
E-mail: hdearborn@spcc.edu
Web Site: www.spscc.ctc.edu/
Description: State-supported, 2-year, coed. Part of Washington State Board for Community and Technical Colleges. Awards certificates, diplomas, transfer associate, and terminal associate degrees. Founded 1970. Setting: 102-acre suburban campus with easy access to Seattle. Educational spending for the previous fiscal year: $4709 per student. Total enrollment: 4,955. Faculty: 263 (88 full-time, 175 part-time). Student-undergrad faculty ratio is 18:1. 525 applied, 100% were admitted. Full-time: 2,693 students, 53% women, 47% men. Part-time: 2,262 students, 64% women, 36% men. Students come from 16 states and territories, 27 other countries, 0.4% from out-of-state. 1% American Indian or Alaska Native, non-Hispanic/Latino; 8% Hispanic/Latino; 2% African American, non-Hispanic/Latino; 5% Asian, non-Hispanic/Latino; 1% Native Hawaiian or other Pacific Islander, non-Hispanic/Latino; 1% international. 42% 25 or older, 33% transferred in. Retention: 59% of full-time freshmen returned the following year. Core. Academic remediation for entering students, ESL program, services for LD students, advanced placement, distance learning, summer session for credit, part-time degree program, adult/continuing education programs, co-op programs and internships. Study abroad program. ROTC: Army (c).
Entrance Requirements: Open admission except for nursing, fire protection, dental assisting programs. Options: electronic application, early admission, deferred admission. Entrance: noncompetitive. Application deadlines: Rolling, Rolling for nonresidents. Notification: continuous, continuous for nonresidents. Transfer credits accepted: Yes.
Collegiate Environment: Orientation program. Drama-theater group, student-run newspaper. Social organizations: 20 open to all. Most popular organizations: Building Revolution by Increasing Community Knowledge (BRICK), Christian Club, Welding Club, Automotive Club, Psychology/Sociology Club. Major annual events: Career Fair, International Celebration, Cinco de Mayo Celebration. Student services: personal-psychological counseling. Campus security: 24-hour emergency response devices and patrols, late night transport-escort service. College housing not available. Library/Media Center plus 1 other with 115,056 books, 63,122 serials, 5,515 audiovisual materials, an OPAC, and a Web page. 250 computers available on campus for general student use. A campuswide network can be accessed from off-campus. Students can access the following: online class registration. Staffed computer lab on campus provides training in use of computers, software, and the Internet.

■ **SOUTH SEATTLE COMMUNITY COLLEGE**
6000 16th Ave., SW
Seattle, WA 98106-1499
Tel: (206)764-5300
E-mail: kimmanderb@sccd.ctc.edu
Web Site: southseattle.edu/
Description: State-supported, 2-year, coed. Part of Seattle Community College District System. Awards certificates, diplomas, transfer associate, and terminal associate degrees. Founded 1970. Setting: 65-acre urban campus. Total enrollment: 6,769. Faculty: 285 (75 full-time, 210 part-time). Students come from 24 other countries. 54% 25 or older. Academic remediation for entering students, ESL program, services for LD students, advanced placement, summer session for credit, part-time degree program, adult/continuing education programs. Off campus study at 9 community colleges in the Seattle metropolitan area.
Entrance Requirements: Open admission except for international students. Option: early admission. Entrance: noncompetitive. Application deadline: Rolling.
Collegiate Environment: Drama-theater group, choral group, student-run newspaper. Most popular organizations: Phi Theta Kappa, Vietnamese Club, Afro-American Club, Delta Epsilon Chi, International Student Clubs. Major

annual events: Rainbow Festival, Holiday Dinner. Student services: personal-psychological counseling, women's center. Campus security: 24-hour emergency response devices and patrols. South Seattle Community College Instructional Resource Center with 34,000 books, 350 serials, an OPAC, and a Web page. 300 computers available on campus for general student use. A campuswide network can be accessed. Staffed computer lab on campus.

■ **SPOKANE COMMUNITY COLLEGE**
1810 N Greene St.
Spokane, WA 99217-5399
Tel: (509)533-7000; Free: 800-248-5644
Fax: (509)533-8839
E-mail: mlee@ccs.spokane.edu
Web Site: www.scc.spokane.edu/
Description: State-supported, 2-year, coed. Part of Washington State Board for Community and Technical Colleges. Awards certificates, diplomas, transfer associate, and terminal associate degrees. Founded 1963. Setting: 108-acre urban campus. Endowment: $33,508. Total enrollment: 6,982. Faculty: 509 (296 full-time, 213 part-time). Student-undergrad faculty ratio is 14:1. Full-time: 4,393 students, 57% women, 43% men. Part-time: 2,589 students, 49% women, 51% men. 3% from out-of-state. 32% 25 or older, 28% transferred in. Core. Academic remediation for entering students, ESL program, services for LD students, advanced placement, self-designed majors, independent study, distance learning, summer session for credit, part-time degree program, adult/continuing education programs, co-op programs and internships. ROTC: Army (c).
Entrance Requirements: Open admission. Options: early admission, deferred admission. Recommended: high school transcript. Entrance: noncompetitive. Application deadline: Rolling. Notification: continuous.
Collegiate Environment: Orientation program. Drama-theater group, student-run newspaper. Social organizations: 25 open to all. Most popular organizations: VICA (Vocational Industrial Clubs of America), Delta Epsilon Chi, Intercultural Student Organization, Rho Beta Psi, Student Awareness League. Major annual events: Spring Fling, Celebration of Cultures, Job Fair. Campus security: 24-hour emergency response devices and patrols, student patrols, late night transport-escort service. Learning Resources Center plus 1 other with 38,967 books, 466 serials, and an OPAC. Operations spending for the previous fiscal year: $786,010. 700 computers available on campus for general student use. A campuswide network can be accessed. Students can access the following: online class registration. Staffed computer lab on campus.
Community Environment: See Spokane Falls Community College.

■ **SPOKANE FALLS COMMUNITY COLLEGE**
3410 W Fort George Wright Dr.
Spokane, WA 99224-5288
Tel: (509)533-3500; Free: 888-509-7944
Fax: (509)533-3433
Web Site: www.spokanefalls.edu/
Description: State-supported, 2-year, coed. Part of State Board for Washington Community and Technical Colleges. Awards certificates, diplomas, transfer associate, and terminal associate degrees. Founded 1967. Setting: 125-acre urban campus. Total enrollment: 5,658. Faculty: 545 (164 full-time, 381 part-time). Student-undergrad faculty ratio is 27:1. Full-time: 3,974 students, 55% women, 45% men. Part-time: 1,684 students, 62% women, 38% men. 19% 25 or older. Core. Academic remediation for entering students, ESL program, services for LD students, advanced placement, self-designed majors, summer session for credit, part-time degree program, adult/continuing education programs, co-op programs and internships. ROTC: Army (c).
Entrance Requirements: Open admission. Options: early admission, deferred admission. Recommended: high school transcript. Entrance: noncompetitive. Application deadline: Rolling. Notification: continuous.
Collegiate Environment: Drama-theater group, choral group, student-run newspaper, radio station. Social organizations: 30 open to all. Most popular organizations: DECA, Associated Men Students, Associated Women Students, chorale, Forensics Club. Major annual events: Spring Fling, Winter Fest, Club Orientation Week. Student services: personal-psychological counseling, women's center. Campus security: late night transport-escort service, 24-hour emergency dispatch. Learning Resources Center plus 1 other with 58,000 books, 705 serials, and an OPAC. 400 computers available on campus for general student use. A campuswide network can be accessed. Students can access the following: online class registration. Staffed computer lab on campus.

Community Environment: The second largest city in the state, Spokane has diversified natural resources including timber lands, tremendous waterpower, and mineral wealth. There are many industries in the area, and part-time work is available. The city is considered the economic and cultural capital of the region between the Rockies and the Cascades. The mean temperature is 47 degrees. Two airports, and several private fields, railroads, and bus lines serve the area. Over 200 churches of all denominations, a public library system, several hospitals, and many civic and fraternal organizations are active here. There are military establishments representing all the services within the area. The community has many fine cultural and recreational facilities as well as excellent shopping facilities.

■ **TACOMA COMMUNITY COLLEGE**
6501 S 19th St.
Tacoma, WA 98466
Tel: (253)566-5000
Fax: (253)566-5376
Web Site: www.tacomacc.edu/
Description: State-supported, 2-year, coed. Part of Washington State Board for Community and Technical Colleges. Awards certificates, diplomas, transfer associate, and terminal associate degrees. Founded 1965. Setting: 150-acre urban campus with easy access to Seattle. Total enrollment: 6,318. Student-undergrad faculty ratio is 21:1. 2% from out-of-state. 44% 25 or older. Retention: 56% of full-time freshmen returned the following year. Academic remediation for entering students, advanced placement, distance learning, summer session for credit, part-time degree program, adult/continuing education programs. Off campus study at members of the Concurrent Enrollment Program. Study abroad program. ROTC: Army (c).
Entrance Requirements: Open admission except for some vocational programs. Option: early admission. Entrance: noncompetitive. Application deadline: Rolling.
Collegiate Environment: Orientation program. Campus security: Sonitrol electronic system.
Community Environment: The third largest city in Washington, Tacoma is a shipping, industrial and distributing center located in the Puget Sound region. The city has diversified industries including electrochemicals, food and beverage processing, clothing manufacturing, iron, steel, and shipyards. The area is provided transportation by rail, air, bus, and major highways. The city has many parks, a public library system, museums, hospitals, and many civic and fraternal organizations to serve the community. Tacoma is near Mt. Rainier National park and its residents enjoy easy access to ocean beaches, the many waterways of Puget Sound, and Olympic and North Cascades National Parks. Nearby lakes and streams offer excellent fishing.

■ **TRINITY LUTHERAN COLLEGE**
2802 Wetmore Ave.
Issaquah, WA 98029-9299
Tel: (425)249-4800; Free: 800-843-5659
Fax: (425)392-0404
E-mail: tracy.sisk@tlc.edu
Web Site: www.tlc.edu/
Description: Independent Lutheran, 4-year, coed. Awards associate and bachelor's degrees. Founded 1944. Setting: 1-acre urban campus with easy access to Seattle. Total enrollment: 163. Faculty: 23 (10 full-time, 13 part-time). Student-undergrad faculty ratio is 7:1. 231 applied, 72% were admitted. Students come from 21 states and territories, 6 other countries, 22% from out-of-state. 1% American Indian or Alaska Native, non-Hispanic/Latino; 18% Hispanic/Latino; 7% African American, non-Hispanic/Latino; 5% Asian, non-Hispanic/Latino; 2% Native Hawaiian or other Pacific Islander, non-Hispanic/Latino; 0% international. 24% 25 or older. Academic areas with the most degrees conferred: psychology; theology and religious vocations; education. Core. Academic remediation for entering students, ESL program, services for LD students, advanced placement, independent study, double major, part-time degree program, internships. Off campus study at Concordia University (OR). Study abroad program.
Entrance Requirements: Options: electronic application, early admission, deferred admission. Required: essay, high school transcript, minimum 2 high school GPA, 1 recommendation, SAT or ACT. Required for some: interview. Entrance: minimally difficult. Application deadline: 9/14. Transfer credits accepted: Yes.
Costs Per Year: Application fee: $30. Comprehensive fee: $30,616 includes full-time tuition ($23,283), mandatory fees ($500), and college room and board ($6833). College room only: $5833. Room and board charges vary according to board plan and housing facility. Part-time tuition: $910 per credit

hour. Part-time mandatory fees: $910 per credit hour, $150 per year. Part-time tuition and fees vary according to course load and program.
Collegiate Environment: Orientation program. Drama-theater group, choral group. Social organizations: 8 open to all. Most popular organizations: Environmental Commission, student government, Worship Commission, Global Concerns, Activities Commission. Major annual events: Day of Jubilee, Spring Retreat, Insanity Night. Student services: health clinic, personal-psychological counseling. Campus security: 24-hour emergency response devices, student patrols, controlled dormitory access. Trinity Lutheran College with 31,000 books, 217 serials, an OPAC, and a Web page. Operations spending for the previous fiscal year: $147,806. 15 computers available on campus for general student use. A campuswide network can be accessed from student residence rooms and from off campus. Students can access the following: online class registration. Staffed computer lab on campus (open 24 hours a day) provides training in use of software and the Internet.

■ **UNIVERSITY OF PHOENIX–EASTERN WASHINGTON CAMPUS**
8775 E Mission Ave.
Spokane, WA 99212-2531
Tel: (509)327-2443; Free: 866-766-0766
Web Site: www.phoenix.edu/
Description: Proprietary, comprehensive, coed. Awards bachelor's and master's degrees. Founded 2003. Setting: urban campus. Total enrollment: 44. Faculty: 43 (5 full-time, 38 part-time). Student-undergrad faculty ratio is 9:1. Full-time: 37 students, 54% women, 46% men. 92% 25 or older. Academic areas with the most degrees conferred: business/marketing; computer and information sciences; homeland security, law enforcement, firefighting, and protective services. Core. Calendar: continuous. Services for LD students, advanced placement, accelerated degree program, independent study, distance learning, graduate courses open to undergrads.
Entrance Requirements: Open admission. Options: electronic application, deferred admission. Required: 1 recommendation. Required for some: high school transcript. Entrance: noncompetitive. Application deadline: Rolling.
Collegiate Environment: Campus security: late night transport-escort service. University Library with 16,781 serials and an OPAC. Operations spending for the previous fiscal year: $6.8 million.

■ **UNIVERSITY OF PHOENIX–WASHINGTON CAMPUS**
7100 Fort Dent Way, Ste. 100
Tukwila, WA 98188
Tel: (206)268-5800; Free: 866-766-0766
Fax: (206)241-8848
Web Site: www.phoenix.edu/
Description: Proprietary, comprehensive, coed. Awards bachelor's and master's degrees. Founded 1997. Setting: urban campus. Total enrollment: 749. Faculty: 159 (14 full-time, 145 part-time). Full-time: 572 students, 56% women, 44% men. 90% 25 or older. Academic areas with the most degrees conferred: business/marketing; computer and information sciences; interdisciplinary studies. Core. Calendar: continuous. Services for LD students, advanced placement, accelerated degree program, independent study, distance learning, external degree program, adult/continuing education programs, graduate courses open to undergrads.
Entrance Requirements: Open admission. Options: electronic application, deferred admission, international baccalaureate accepted. Required: 1 recommendation. Required for some: high school transcript. Entrance: noncompetitive. Application deadline: Rolling.
Collegiate Environment: Campus security: late night transport-escort service. University Library with 16,781 serials, an OPAC, and a Web page. Operations spending for the previous fiscal year: $6.8 million.

■ **UNIVERSITY OF PUGET SOUND**
1500 N Warner St.
Tacoma, WA 98416
Tel: (253)879-3100; Free: 800-396-7191
Fax: (253)879-3500
E-mail: admission@pugetsound.edu
Web Site: www.pugetsound.edu/
Description: Independent, comprehensive, coed. Awards bachelor's, master's, and doctoral degrees. Founded 1888. Setting: 97-acre urban campus with easy access to Seattle. Endowment: $250.5 million. Research spending for the previous fiscal year: $941,000. Educational spending for the previous fiscal year: $17,000 per student. Total enrollment: 2,857. Faculty: 281 (228 full-time, 53 part-time). Student-undergrad faculty ratio is 12:1.

4,470 applied, 82% were admitted. 36% from top 10% of their high school class, 67% from top quarter, 93% from top half. 30 National Merit Scholars. Full-time: 2,555 students, 57% women, 43% men. Part-time: 23 students, 35% women, 65% men. Students come from 45 states and territories, 15 other countries, 76% from out-of-state. 1% American Indian or Alaska Native, non-Hispanic/Latino; 7% Hispanic/Latino; 2% African American, non-Hispanic/Latino; 7% Asian, non-Hispanic/Latino; 0.1% Native Hawaiian or other Pacific Islander, non-Hispanic/Latino; 1% international. 2% 25 or older, 57% live on campus, 2% transferred in. Retention: 86% of full-time freshmen returned the following year. Academic areas with the most degrees conferred: social sciences; business/marketing; biological/life sciences. Core. Calendar: semesters. Services for LD students, advanced placement, self-designed majors, honors program, independent study, double major, summer session for credit, part-time degree program, co-op programs and internships. Study abroad program. ROTC: Army (c).

Entrance Requirements: Options: electronic application, early admission, early decision, deferred admission, international baccalaureate accepted. Required: essay, high school transcript, 2 recommendations, SAT or ACT. Recommended: minimum 3 high school GPA, interview. Entrance: moderately difficult. Application deadlines: 1/15, 11/1 for early decision plan 1, 1/2 for early decision plan 2. Notification: 4/1, 12/15 for early decision plan 1, 2/15 for early decision plan 2. SAT Reasoning Test deadline: 1/15. Transfer credits accepted: Yes. Applicants placed on waiting list: 367. Wait-listed applicants offered admission: 80. Early decision applicants: 129. Early decision applicants admitted: 114.

Costs Per Year: Application fee: $50. Comprehensive fee: $52,648 includes full-time tuition ($41,640), mandatory fees ($228), and college room and board ($10,780). College room only: $5940. Full-time tuition and fees vary according to course load. Room and board charges vary according to board plan and housing facility. Part-time tuition: $5250 per unit. Part-time tuition varies according to course load.

Collegiate Environment: Orientation program. Drama-theater group, choral group, student-run newspaper, radio station. Social organizations: 98 open to all; national fraternities, national sororities; 22% of eligible men and 26% of eligible women are members. Most popular organizations: Puget Sound Outdoors, Repertory Dance Group, Hui-O-Hawaii, Student Theatre Productions, Relay for Life. Major annual events: Log Jam opening weekend of fall semester, Hui-O-Hawaii Luau/Spring Family Weekend, Midnight Breakfast. Student services: health clinic, personal-psychological counseling. Campus security: 24-hour emergency response devices and patrols, student patrols, late night transport-escort service, controlled dormitory access, 24-hour locked residence hall entrances, surveillance cameras, and emergency telephone towers. 1,611 college housing spaces available; 1,461 were occupied in 2012-13. Freshmen guaranteed college housing. On-campus residence required through sophomore year. Option: coed housing available. Collins Memorial Library with 538,304 books, 125,177 microform titles, 44,875 serials, 19,583 audiovisual materials, an OPAC, and a Web page. Operations spending for the previous fiscal year: $5.5 million. 320 computers available on campus for general student use. A campuswide network can be accessed from student residence rooms and from off campus. Students can access the following: online class registration, financial aid, admission, student employment. Staffed computer lab on campus (open 24 hours a day) provides training in use of computers, software, and the Internet.

Community Environment: Founded in 1888, the campus is located in residential North Tacoma. Thirty miles south of Seattle and easily accessible from Interstate 5, Tacoma is a dynamic city of 187,200 people. The university occupies 38 buildings on a 97 acre park-like campus; architecture is Tudor Gothic with its distinctive red-brick pattern arches and porticoes. Located close to the shores of Puget Sound and a short distance from ski slopes and the Pacific Ocean, the University is also the center for much of Tacoma's cultural life. Tacoma also features Point Defiance Zoo and Aquarium, many parks, a public library system, museums and hospitals.

■ **UNIVERSITY OF WASHINGTON**

Seattle, WA 98195
Tel: (206)543-2100
Web Site: www.washington.edu/

Description: State-supported, university, coed. Awards bachelor's, master's, and doctoral degrees and post-master's certificates. Founded 1861. Setting: 703-acre urban campus. Total enrollment: 42,428. Faculty: 3,602 (2,818 full-time, 784 part-time). Student-undergrad faculty ratio is 13:1. 24,540 applied, 58% were admitted. 92% from top 10% of their high school class, 98% from top quarter, 100% from top half. Full-time: 25,863 students, 52% women, 48% men. Part-time: 3,154 students, 50% women, 50% men. 14% from out-of-state. 1% American Indian or Alaska Native, non-Hispanic/Latino; 6%

Hispanic/Latino; 3% African American, non-Hispanic/Latino; 26% Asian, non-Hispanic/Latino; 1% Native Hawaiian or other Pacific Islander, non-Hispanic/Latino; 7% international. 9% 25 or older, 11% live on campus, 6% transferred in. Retention: 93% of full-time freshmen returned the following year. Academic areas with the most degrees conferred: social sciences; business/marketing; biological/life sciences. Part-time degree program, adult/continuing education programs. ROTC: Army, Naval, Air Force.

Entrance Requirements: Options: electronic application, early admission, international baccalaureate accepted. Required: essay, minimum 2 high school GPA, SAT or ACT. Required for some: high school transcript. Entrance: moderately difficult. Application deadline: 12/1. SAT Reasoning Test deadline: 12/31. Transfer credits accepted: Yes. Applicants placed on waiting list: 2,519. Wait-listed applicants offered admission: 284.

Costs Per Year: Application fee: $60. State resident tuition: $11,305 full-time. Nonresident tuition: $28,860 full-time. Full-time tuition varies according to course load.

Collegiate Environment: Orientation program. Campus security: 24-hour emergency response devices and patrols, late night transport-escort service, controlled dormitory access.

■ **UNIVERSITY OF WASHINGTON, BOTHELL**

18115 Campus Way, NE
Bothell, WA 98011-8246
Tel: (425)352-5000
E-mail: freshmen@uwb.edu
Web Site: www.uwb.edu/

Description: State-supported, comprehensive, coed. Part of University of Washington. Awards bachelor's and master's degrees. Founded 1990. Setting: 128-acre suburban campus with easy access to Seattle. Endowment: $2.8 million. Research spending for the previous fiscal year: $5 million. Educational spending for the previous fiscal year: $7344 per student. Total enrollment: 4,159. Faculty: 219 (146 full-time, 73 part-time). Student-undergrad faculty ratio is 21:1. 2,419 applied, 72% were admitted. Full-time: 3,030 students, 49% women, 51% men. Part-time: 607 students, 53% women, 47% men. Students come from 19 states and territories, 27 other countries, 2% from out-of-state. 1% American Indian or Alaska Native, non-Hispanic/Latino; 6% Hispanic/Latino; 4% African American, non-Hispanic/Latino; 22% Asian, non-Hispanic/Latino; 1% Native Hawaiian or other Pacific Islander, non-Hispanic/Latino; 5% international. 28% 25 or older, 7% live on campus, 17% transferred in. Retention: 78% of full-time freshmen returned the following year. Academic areas with the most degrees conferred: business/marketing; health professions and related sciences; interdisciplinary studies. Core. Services for LD students, advanced placement, self-designed majors, honors program, independent study, double major, summer session for credit, part-time degree program, adult/continuing education programs, co-op programs and internships, graduate courses open to undergrads. Off campus study at University of Washington Seattle and University of Washington Tacoma. Study abroad program. ROTC: Army (c), Naval (c), Air Force (c).

Entrance Requirements: Options: electronic application, early admission, deferred admission, international baccalaureate accepted. Required: essay, high school transcript, minimum 2 high school GPA, SAT or ACT. Entrance: moderately difficult. Application deadline: 1/15. Notification: continuous. Transfer credits accepted: Yes.

Collegiate Environment: Orientation program. Student-run newspaper. Social organizations: 108 open to all. Most popular organizations: Campus Events Board, Collegiate DECA, Associated Students of University of Washington Bothell (ASUWB), Recreation Programs, Diversity Programs. Major annual events: Welcome Week, Intercultural Night, SpringFest. Student services: personal-psychological counseling. Campus security: 24-hour emergency response devices and patrols, late night transport-escort service. 268 college housing spaces available; 251 were occupied in 2012-13. Freshmen given priority for college housing. Option: coed housing available. Campus Library with 99,520 books, 12,342 microform titles, 429 serials, 8,348 audiovisual materials, an OPAC, and a Web page. Operations spending for the previous fiscal year: $2.6 million. 400 computers available on campus for general student use. A campuswide network can be accessed from student residence rooms. Students can access the following: online class registration, online course management system. Staffed computer lab on campus provides training in use of computers, software, and the Internet.

■ **UNIVERSITY OF WASHINGTON, TACOMA**

1900 Commerce St.
Tacoma, WA 98402-3100

Tel: (253)692-4000; Free: 800-736-7750
E-mail: megan61@u.washington.edu
Web Site: www.tacoma.washington.edu/
Description: State-supported, comprehensive, coed. Part of University of Washington. Awards bachelor's, master's, and doctoral degrees and post-master's certificates. Founded 1990. Setting: 46-acre urban campus with easy access to Seattle. Total enrollment: 3,906. Faculty: 232 (148 full-time, 84 part-time). Student-undergrad faculty ratio is 19:1. 1,166 applied, 82% were admitted. Full-time: 2,825 students, 53% women, 47% men. Part-time: 536 students, 57% women, 43% men. 2% from out-of-state. 1% American Indian or Alaska Native, non-Hispanic/Latino; 8% Hispanic/Latino; 7% African American, non-Hispanic/Latino; 15% Asian, non-Hispanic/Latino; 1% Native Hawaiian or other Pacific Islander, non-Hispanic/Latino; 3% international. 39% 25 or older, 0% live on campus, 24% transferred in. Retention: 73% of full-time freshmen returned the following year. Academic areas with the most degrees conferred: business/marketing; social sciences; psychology. Core. Academic remediation for entering students, ESL program, services for LD students, advanced placement, accelerated degree program, self-designed majors, honors program, independent study, distance learning, double major, summer session for credit, part-time degree program, co-op programs and internships, graduate courses open to undergrads. Study abroad program. ROTC: Army (c), Naval (c), Air Force (c).
Entrance Requirements: Options: electronic application, early decision, deferred admission, international baccalaureate accepted. Required: essay, minimum 2 high school GPA, SAT or ACT. Required for some: high school transcript. Entrance: minimally difficult. Application deadline: 6/1. Notification: continuous. SAT Reasoning Test deadline: 6/1. SAT Subject Test deadline: 6/1. Transfer credits accepted: Yes.
Costs Per Year: Application fee: $60. Area resident tuition: $11,305 full-time, $376 part-time. Nonresident tuition: $28,860 full-time, $962 part-time. Mandatory fees: $597 full-time.
Collegiate Environment: Orientation program. Choral group, student-run newspaper. Social organizations: 29 open to all. Most popular organizations: Accounting Student Association, International Student Association, Partners in Action to Transform Healthcare (PATH), Asian Pacific Islander Student Union (APISU)I, TacPack. Major annual events: Block Party, O.S.C.A.R.S., RSO Canned Food Drive. Student services: health clinic, personal-psychological counseling. Campus security: 24-hour emergency response devices and patrols, late night transport-escort service, key card access to buildings after hours. No special consideration for freshman housing applicants. Option: coed housing available. University of Washington Tacoma Library with 7.5 million books, 7.8 million microform titles, 63,575 serials, 136,325 audiovisual materials, an OPAC, and a Web page.

■ **WALLA WALLA COMMUNITY COLLEGE**
500 Tausick Way
Walla Walla, WA 99362-9267
Tel: (509)522-2500; Free: 877-992-9922
Fax: (509)527-3361
Web Site: www.wwcc.edu/
Description: State-supported, 2-year, coed. Part of Washington State Board for Community and Technical Colleges. Awards certificates, diplomas, transfer associate, and terminal associate degrees. Founded 1967. Setting: 125-acre small town campus. Total enrollment: 4,910. Student-undergrad faculty ratio is 17:1. 22% from out-of-state. 56% 25 or older. Retention: 60% of full-time freshmen returned the following year. Academic remediation for entering students, advanced placement, distance learning, summer session for credit, part-time degree program, external degree program, adult/continuing education programs. Off campus study at other members of the Washington State Board for Community and Technical Colleges.
Entrance Requirements: Open admission. Option: electronic application. Recommended: high school transcript. Required for some: interview. Entrance: noncompetitive. Application deadline: Rolling.
Collegiate Environment: Orientation program. Campus security: student patrols, late night transport-escort service. Walla Walla Community College Library with an OPAC.
Community Environment: Walla Walla is rich agricultural area in southern Washington near the Oregon State line. The chief crop is wheat. The area has excellent highways, a commuter airline and buslines serving the community. The climate is mild. Local recreation includes hunting, boating, fishing, camping and skiing in the nearby mountains. There are churches representing most denominations, health facilities and shopping centers in the area. All major lodges and service clubs are active here. Frontier days and a rodeo are held annually in September.

■ **WALLA WALLA UNIVERSITY**
204 S College Ave.
College Place, WA 99324-1198
Tel: (509)527-2615; Free: 800-541-8900
Fax: (509)527-2397
Web Site: www.wallawalla.edu/
Description: Independent Seventh-day Adventist, comprehensive, coed. Awards associate, bachelor's, and master's degrees. Founded 1892. Setting: 77-acre small town campus. Total enrollment: 1,940. Faculty: 202 (115 full-time, 87 part-time). Student-undergrad faculty ratio is 13:1. 626 applied, 89% were admitted. Full-time: 1,583 students, 49% women, 51% men. Part-time: 127 students, 56% women, 44% men. 62% from out-of-state. 1% American Indian or Alaska Native, non-Hispanic/Latino; 11% Hispanic/Latino; 2% African American, non-Hispanic/Latino; 4% Asian, non-Hispanic/Latino; 0.4% Native Hawaiian or other Pacific Islander, non-Hispanic/Latino; 6% international. 10% 25 or older, 64% live on campus, 7% transferred in. Retention: 83% of full-time freshmen returned the following year. Academic areas with the most degrees conferred: health professions and related sciences; business/marketing; engineering. Core. Academic remediation for entering students, services for LD students, advanced placement, freshman honors college, honors program, independent study, distance learning, double major, summer session for credit, part-time degree program, co-op programs and internships, graduate courses open to undergrads. Off campus study. Study abroad program.
Entrance Requirements: Options: electronic application, early decision, deferred admission. Required: high school transcript, minimum 2.5 high school GPA, SAT or ACT. Recommended: ACT. Entrance: moderately difficult. Application deadline: Rolling. Notification: continuous. SAT Reasoning Test deadline: 9/27. SAT Subject Test deadline: 9/1.
Costs Per Year: Application fee: $40. Comprehensive fee: $31,347 includes full-time tuition ($24,822), mandatory fees ($555), and college room and board ($5970). College room only: $3360. Room and board charges vary according to board plan and housing facility.
Collegiate Environment: Orientation program. Drama-theater group, choral group, student-run newspaper, radio station. Most popular organizations: Associated Students of Walla Walla University, Campus Ministries, Village Club, OPS Club (Men's residence hall club), AGA Club (women's residence hall club). Major annual events: CommUnity, weekly school assembly, Service Day, community projects, Welcome Back Bash, school year kick-off. Student services: health clinic, personal-psychological counseling. Campus security: 24-hour emergency response devices and patrols, student patrols, late night transport-escort service, controlled dormitory access. Freshmen guaranteed college housing. On-campus residence required through junior year. Options: men-only, women-only housing available. Peterson Memorial Library plus 3 others with an OPAC and a Web page.
Community Environment: College Place is a residential community adjacent to Walla Walla. The climate is temperate. Three miles away, all major forms of transportation are available. The immediate community has four churches and two hospitals. Part-time employment opportunities are fair.

■ **WASHINGTON STATE UNIVERSITY**
Pullman, WA 99164
Tel: (509)335-3564; Free: 888-468-6978
E-mail: admissions@wsu.edu
Web Site: www.wsu.edu/
Description: State-supported, university, coed. Awards bachelor's, master's, and doctoral degrees and post-master's certificates. Founded 1890. Setting: 620-acre small town campus with easy access to Spokane. Endowment: $638.4 million. Research spending for the previous fiscal year: $144.9 million. Educational spending for the previous fiscal year: $8586 per student. Total enrollment: 27,679. Faculty: 1,701 (1,224 full-time, 477 part-time). Student-undergrad faculty ratio is 15:1. 14,825 applied, 76% were admitted. 26% from top 10% of their high school class, 46% from top quarter, 78% from top half. 8 National Merit Scholars. Full-time: 20,082 students, 49% women, 51% men. Part-time: 3,053 students, 59% women, 41% men. 7% from out-of-state. 1% American Indian or Alaska Native, non-Hispanic/Latino; 9% Hispanic/Latino; 3% African American, non-Hispanic/Latino; 5% Asian, non-Hispanic/Latino; 0.4% Native Hawaiian or other Pacific Islander, non-Hispanic/Latino; 4% international. 18% 25 or older, 26% live on campus, 10% transferred in. Retention: 82% of full-time freshmen returned the following year. Academic areas with the most degrees conferred: business/marketing; social sciences; communication/journalism. Core. Calendar: semesters. ESL program, services for LD students, advanced placement,

accelerated degree program, self-designed majors, honors program, independent study, distance learning, double major, summer session for credit, part-time degree program, external degree program, adult/continuing education programs, co-op programs and internships, graduate courses open to undergrads. Off campus study at University of Idaho, National Student Exchange; Nursing Consortia: Eastern Washington University and Whitworth University. Study abroad program. ROTC: Army, Naval (c), Air Force.

Entrance Requirements: Options: electronic application, international baccalaureate accepted. Required: high school transcript, minimum 2 high school GPA, SAT or ACT. Recommended: essay. Entrance: moderately difficult. Application deadlines: 1/31, 1/7 for nonresidents. Notification: continuous until 11/1, continuous until 11/1 for nonresidents. Transfer credits accepted: Yes.

Costs Per Year: Application fee: $50. State resident tuition: $10,874 full-time, $569 per credit hour part-time. Nonresident tuition: $23,956 full-time, $1141 per credit hour part-time. Mandatory fees: $1426 full-time. Full-time tuition and fees vary according to location and reciprocity agreements. Part-time tuition varies according to course load, location, and reciprocity agreements. College room and board: $10,524. College room only: $6626. Room and board charges vary according to board plan, housing facility, and location.

Collegiate Environment: Orientation program. Drama-theater group, choral group, marching band, student-run newspaper, radio station. Social organizations: 380 open to all; national fraternities, national sororities; 21% of eligible men and 22% of eligible women are members. Most popular organizations: Panhellenic Association - Sororities, Interfraternity Council - Fraternities, Student Entertainment Board, International Students Council, ChiLaStAI (Chicana/o Latina/o Student Alliance. Major annual events: Up All Night, Springfest, Cougfest. Student services: legal services, health clinic, personal-psychological counseling, women's center. Campus security: 24-hour emergency response devices and patrols, student patrols, late night transport-escort service, controlled dormitory access. 6,538 college housing spaces available; 5,800 were occupied in 2012-13. Freshmen guaranteed college housing. On-campus residence required in freshman year. Options: coed, men-only, women-only housing available. Holland and Terrell Libraries plus 7 others with 2.4 million books, 4 million microform titles, 51,210 serials, 52,119 audiovisual materials, an OPAC, and a Web page. Operations spending for the previous fiscal year: $14.6 million. 2,500 computers available on campus for general student use. A campuswide network can be accessed from student residence rooms and from off campus. Students can access the following: online class registration. Staffed computer lab on campus provides training in use of computers, software, and the Internet.

Community Environment: Pullman is located 7 miles west of the Idaho border. The summer temperature averages in the 80s and the winter temperature averages around 30 degrees. The area is accessible by airlines and bus lines. There are 30 churches, a public library, and various civic, fraternal, and veteran's organizations serving the community. Local recreation includes four parks, baseball diamonds, swimming pools, theaters, bowling alleys, a golf course, tennis courts and nearby lakes and rivers offering swimming, boating and skating.

■ **WASHINGTON STATE UNIVERSITY SPOKANE**
412 E Spokane Falls Blvd.
Spokane, WA 99210-1495
Tel: (509)358-7500
Fax: (509)358-7505
Web Site: www.spokane.wsu.edu/
Description: State-supported, upper-level, coed. Founded 1989. Calendar: semesters.

■ **WASHINGTON STATE UNIVERSITY TRI-CITIES**
2710 University Dr.
Richland, WA 99352-1671
Tel: (509)372-7000
Fax: (509)372-7100
Web Site: www.tricity.wsu.edu/
Description: State-supported, comprehensive, coed. Founded 1989. Calendar: semesters.

■ **WASHINGTON STATE UNIVERSITY VANCOUVER**
14204 NE Salmon Creek Ave.
Vancouver, WA 98686
Tel: (360)546-9788

Fax: (360)546-9041
Web Site: www.vancouver.wsu.edu/
Description: State-supported, comprehensive, coed. Awards bachelor's and master's degrees. Founded 1989. Calendar: semesters.

■ **WENATCHEE VALLEY COLLEGE**
1300 Fifth St.
Wenatchee, WA 98801-1799
Tel: (509)682-6800
Fax: (509)664-2511
E-mail: cescobedo@wvc.edu
Web Site: www.wvc.edu/
Description: State and locally supported, 2-year, coed. Part of Washington State Board for Community and Technical Colleges. Awards certificates, diplomas, transfer associate, and terminal associate degrees. Founded 1939. Setting: 56-acre rural campus. Total enrollment: 3,637. Core. Academic remediation for entering students, ESL program, services for LD students, advanced placement, independent study, distance learning, summer session for credit, part-time degree program, external degree program, adult/continuing education programs, co-op programs.

Entrance Requirements: Open admission except for allied health programs. Options: electronic application, early admission, deferred admission. Required for some: high school transcript. Entrance: noncompetitive. Application deadline: Rolling.

Collegiate Environment: Drama-theater group, choral group, student-run newspaper. Campus security: 24-hour patrols, evening and late night security patrols. John Brown Library plus 1 other with 32,000 books, 220 serials, an OPAC, and a Web page.

Community Environment: Situated at the confluence of the Wenatchee and Columbia Rivers, Wenatchee is known as the apple capital of the world. In the eastern foothills of the Cascade Mountains, the city has a temperate climate with four definite seasons. The average maximum temperature is 75 degrees, with an average minimum of 28 degrees, with an average rainfall of 9.58 inches. The community is accessible by bus, air, and major highways. There are almost 40 churches representing various denominations, a YMCA, YWCA, library, museum, theatres, medical facilities, motels, hotels, good shopping, and many civic and fraternal organizations. Local recreation includes hunting, boating, fishing, golf, and skiing. A state apple blossom festival is held annually. Part-time employment is available.

■ **WESTERN WASHINGTON UNIVERSITY**
516 High St.
Bellingham, WA 98225-5996
Tel: (360)650-3000
E-mail: admit@wwu.edu
Web Site: www.wwu.edu/
Description: State-supported, comprehensive, coed. Awards bachelor's and master's degrees and post-master's certificates. Founded 1893. Setting: 223-acre small town campus with easy access to Seattle, Vancouver. Total enrollment: 14,833. Faculty: 783 (516 full-time, 267 part-time). Student-undergrad faculty ratio is 21:1. 9,785 applied, 80% were admitted. 23% from top 10% of their high school class, 55% from top quarter, 89% from top half. Full-time: 12,860 students, 56% women, 44% men. Part-time: 1,042 students, 48% women, 52% men. Students come from 48 states and territories, 36 other countries, 9% from out-of-state. 1% American Indian or Alaska Native, non-Hispanic/Latino; 6% Hispanic/Latino; 2% African American, non-Hispanic/Latino; 6% Asian, non-Hispanic/Latino; 0.2% Native Hawaiian or other Pacific Islander, non-Hispanic/Latino; 1% international. 8% 25 or older, 32% live on campus, 7% transferred in. Retention: 85% of full-time freshmen returned the following year. Academic areas with the most degrees conferred: business/marketing; social sciences; psychology; communication/journalism; visual and performing arts; education; English. Core. ESL program, services for LD students, advanced placement, accelerated degree program, self-designed majors, honors program, independent study, distance learning, double major, summer session for credit, co-op programs and internships, graduate courses open to undergrads. Off campus study at National Student Exchange. Study abroad program.

Entrance Requirements: Options: electronic application, deferred admission, international baccalaureate accepted. Required: high school transcript, SAT or ACT. Recommended: essay. Entrance: moderately difficult. Application deadline: 3/1. Notification: 4/15. SAT Reasoning Test deadline: 1/31. Applicants placed on waiting list: 905. Wait-listed applicants offered admission: 454.

Costs Per Year: Application fee: $55. State resident tuition: $8022 full-time,

$267 per credit hour part-time. Nonresident tuition: $18,369 full-time, $612 per credit hour part-time. Mandatory fees: $783 full-time, $26 per credit hour part-time. Full-time tuition and fees vary according to course load, location, and reciprocity agreements. Part-time tuition and fees vary according to course load, location, and reciprocity agreements. College room and board: $9372. Room and board charges vary according to board plan, housing facility, and location.

Collegiate Environment: Orientation program. Drama-theater group, choral group, student-run newspaper, radio station. Social organizations: 200 open to all. Most popular organizations: intramurals, Residence Hall Association, Associated Students, Outdoor Center, Ethnic Student Center. Major annual events: Fall New Student Convocation, Information Faire, Earth Day. Student services: legal services, health clinic, personal-psychological counseling, women's center. Campus security: 24-hour emergency response devices and patrols, student patrols, late night transport-escort service, controlled dormitory access. 4,166 college housing spaces available; 4,081 were occupied in 2012-13. Freshmen guaranteed college housing. Option: coed housing available. Wilson Library plus 1 other with 1.4 million books, 2 million microform titles, 11,500 serials, 48,672 audiovisual materials, an OPAC, and a Web page. 2,408 computers available on campus for general student use. A campuswide network can be accessed from student residence rooms and from off campus. Students can access the following: online class registration. Staffed computer lab on campus.

Community Environment: Bellingham overlooks Puget Sound and the San Juan Islands. The city enjoys a temperate climate with a summer temperature seldom exceeding 73 degrees, and winter temperatures range from 28 to 55 degrees. There are frequently winters without snow, and the average rainfall is 34 inches. County industries include shipbuilding, food processing, oil refining, and manufacturing of aluminum, cement, plywood, and paper products. There is also a commercial fishing fleet. The community has hospitals, theatres, and major civic and fraternal organizations. Local recreation includes hiking, fishing, sailing, golf, baseball, softball, and bowling. Mt. Baker for skiing and climbing is 50 miles away. Part-time employment is available.

■ **WHATCOM COMMUNITY COLLEGE**
237 W Kellogg Rd.
Bellingham, WA 98226-8003
Tel: (360)676-2170
Fax: (360)676-2171
E-mail: admit@whatcom.ctc.edu
Web Site: www.whatcom.ctc.edu/
Description: State-supported, 2-year, coed. Part of Washington State Board for Community and Technical Colleges. Awards certificates, diplomas, transfer associate, and terminal associate degrees. Founded 1970. Setting: 52-acre small town campus with easy access to Vancouver. Endowment: $2 million. Total enrollment: 4,127. Faculty: 225 (75 full-time, 150 part-time). Students come from 35 other countries, 5% from out-of-state. 30% 25 or older. Core. Academic remediation for entering students, ESL program, services for LD students, advanced placement, accelerated degree program, self-designed majors, honors program, independent study, distance learning, summer session for credit, part-time degree program, external degree program, adult/continuing education programs, co-op programs and internships. Study abroad program.
Entrance Requirements: Open admission. Option: electronic application. Entrance: noncompetitive. Application deadline: Rolling. Notification: continuous.
Collegiate Environment: Orientation program. Drama-theater group, choral group, student-run newspaper. Social organizations: 15 open to all. Most popular organizations: Japanime, Ethnic Student Association, Queer/Straight Alliance, Phi Theta Kappa, International Friendship Club. Major annual events: Commencement, Spring BBQ, Fall Welcome. Student services: personal-psychological counseling. Campus security: 24-hour emergency response devices. Whatcom Community College Library with 14,680 books, 41,682 microform titles, 193 serials, 3,653 audiovisual materials, an OPAC, and a Web page. 100 computers available on campus for general student use. Students can access the following: online class registration. Staffed computer lab on campus.

■ **WHITMAN COLLEGE**
345 Boyer Ave.
Walla Walla, WA 99362-2083
Tel: (509)527-5111; Free: 877-462-9448
Fax: (509)527-4967

E-mail: admission@whitman.edu
Web Site: www.whitman.edu/
Description: Independent, 4-year, coed. Awards bachelor's degrees. Founded 1859. Setting: 117-acre small town campus. Endowment: $401 million. Research spending for the previous fiscal year: $229,000. Educational spending for the previous fiscal year: $12,957 per student. Total enrollment: 1,539. Faculty: 205 (146 full-time, 59 part-time). Student-undergrad faculty ratio is 9:1. 2,854 applied, 49% were admitted. 62% from top 10% of their high school class, 89% from top quarter, 100% from top half. 42 National Merit Scholars, 18 class presidents, 39 valedictorians. Full-time: 1,508 students, 57% women, 43% men. Part-time: 31 students, 55% women, 45% men. Students come from 48 states and territories, 23 other countries, 66% from out-of-state. 1% American Indian or Alaska Native, non-Hispanic/Latino; 6% Hispanic/Latino; 1% African American, non-Hispanic/Latino; 8% Asian, non-Hispanic/Latino; 0.2% Native Hawaiian or other Pacific Islander, non-Hispanic/Latino; 3% international. 1% 25 or older, 67% live on campus, 1% transferred in. Retention: 94% of full-time freshmen returned the following year. Academic areas with the most degrees conferred: social sciences; biological/life sciences; physical sciences. Core. Calendar: semesters. Services for LD students, advanced placement, accelerated degree program, self-designed majors, honors program, independent study, double major, co-op programs. Off campus study at American University, Associated Colleges of the Midwest, Great Lakes Colleges Association, Columbia University. Study abroad program.
Entrance Requirements: Options: electronic application, early decision, deferred admission, international baccalaureate accepted. Required: essay, high school transcript, 1 recommendation, SAT or ACT. Recommended: interview. Entrance: very difficult. Application deadlines: 1/15, 11/15 for early decision. Notification: 4/1, 12/18 for early decision. SAT Reasoning Test deadline: 1/15. SAT Subject Test deadline: 1/15. Transfer credits accepted: Yes. Applicants placed on waiting list: 671. Wait-listed applicants offered admission: 10. Early decision applicants: 148. Early decision applicants admitted: 117.
Costs Per Year: Application fee: $50. Comprehensive fee: $52,666 includes full-time tuition ($41,790), mandatory fees ($316), and college room and board ($10,560). College room only: $4880. Room and board charges vary according to board plan and housing facility. Part-time tuition: $1741 per credit.
Collegiate Environment: Orientation program. Drama-theater group, choral group, student-run newspaper, radio station. Social organizations: 60 open to all; national fraternities, national sororities; 51% of eligible men and 37% of eligible women are members. Most popular organizations: Associated Students, Outdoor Program, Center for Community Service. Major annual events: Choral Contest, Interest House Block Party, One-Act Play Contest. Student services: health clinic, personal-psychological counseling, women's center. Campus security: 24-hour emergency response devices and patrols, student patrols, late night transport-escort service, controlled dormitory access. 882 college housing spaces available; 860 were occupied in 2012-13. Freshmen guaranteed college housing. On-campus residence required through sophomore year. Options: coed, women-only housing available. Penrose Library plus 1 other with 560,749 books, 30,122 serials, 8,180 audiovisual materials, an OPAC, and a Web page. Operations spending for the previous fiscal year: $2.3 million. 397 computers available on campus for general student use. A campuswide network can be accessed from student residence rooms and from off campus. Students can access the following: online class registration, course registration information. Staffed computer lab on campus (open 24 hours a day).

■ **WHITWORTH UNIVERSITY**
300 W Hawthorne Rd.
Spokane, WA 99251-0001
Tel: (509)777-1000; Free: 800-533-4668
Fax: (509)777-3773
E-mail: admission@whitworth.edu
Web Site: www.whitworth.edu/
Description: Independent Presbyterian, comprehensive, coed. Awards bachelor's and master's degrees and post-master's certificates. Founded 1890. Setting: 200-acre suburban campus. Endowment: $98.9 million. Research spending for the previous fiscal year: $1.2 million. Educational spending for the previous fiscal year: $9094 per student. Total enrollment: 2,568. Faculty: 331 (170 full-time, 161 part-time). Student-undergrad faculty ratio is 11:1. 6,932 applied, 52% were admitted. Full-time: 2,300 students, 59% women, 41% men. Part-time: 48 students, 48% women, 52% men. Students come from 34 states and territories, 27 other countries, 43% from

out-of-state. 1% American Indian or Alaska Native, non-Hispanic/Latino; 7% Hispanic/Latino; 1% African American, non-Hispanic/Latino; 3% Asian, non-Hispanic/Latino; 0.2% Native Hawaiian or other Pacific Islander, non-Hispanic/Latino; 2% international. 1% 25 or older, 4% transferred in. Retention: 85% of full-time freshmen returned the following year. Academic areas with the most degrees conferred: business/marketing; social sciences; physical sciences. Core. Calendar: 4-1-4. ESL program, services for LD students, advanced placement, self-designed majors, honors program, independent study, double major, summer session for credit, part-time degree program, adult/continuing education programs, co-op programs and internships, graduate courses open to undergrads. Off campus study at 3 members of the Intercollegiate Center for Nursing, 2 members of the Intercollegiate Language Study Consortium. Study abroad program. ROTC: Army (c).

Entrance Requirements: Options: electronic application, early admission, early action, deferred admission, international baccalaureate accepted. Required: essay, high school transcript. Required for some: interview, SAT, ACT, SAT or ACT, SAT and SAT Subject Tests or ACT, SAT Subject Tests. Entrance: moderately difficult. Application deadlines: 3/1, 12/1 for early action. Notification: 12/20 for early action. SAT Reasoning Test deadline: 5/1. SAT Subject Test deadline: 5/1. Applicants placed on waiting list: 790. Waitlisted applicants offered admission: 73.

Costs Per Year: Application fee: $0. Comprehensive fee: $43,710 includes full-time tuition ($33,676), mandatory fees ($670), and college room and board ($9364). College room only: $5076. Room and board charges vary according to board plan and housing facility. Part-time tuition: $1403 per credit.

Collegiate Environment: Orientation program. Drama-theater group, choral group, student-run newspaper, radio station. Social organizations: 80 open to all. Most popular organizations: International Club, Young Life, En Christo, Hawaiian Club, intramural sports. Major annual events: Homecoming, Community Building Day, Spring Fest. Student services: health clinic, personal-psychological counseling. Campus security: 24-hour emergency response devices and patrols, late night transport-escort service, controlled dormitory access. 1,396 college housing spaces available; all were occupied in 2012-13. Freshmen guaranteed college housing. On-campus residence required through sophomore year. Options: coed, men-only, women-only housing available. Harriet Cheney Cowles Library with 286,049 books, 70,460 microform titles, 2,953 serials, 9,036 audiovisual materials, an OPAC, and a Web page. 280 computers available on campus for general student use. A campuswide network can be accessed from student residence rooms and from off campus. Students can access the following: online class registration. Staffed computer lab on campus.

Community Environment: See Spokane Community College.

■ **YAKIMA VALLEY COMMUNITY COLLEGE**
PO Box 22520
Yakima, WA 98907-2520

Tel: (509)574-4600
Fax: (509)574-6860
E-mail: admis@yvcc.edu
Web Site: www.yvcc.edu/

Description: State-supported, 2-year, coed. Part of Washington State Board for Community and Technical Colleges. Awards certificates, transfer associate, and terminal associate degrees. Founded 1928. Setting: 20-acre small town campus. Total enrollment: 4,479. Faculty: 319 (106 full-time, 213 part-time). Student-undergrad faculty ratio is 20:1. 496 applied, 100% were admitted. Full-time: 2,786 students, 62% women, 38% men. Part-time: 1,693 students, 69% women, 31% men. 36% 25 or older, 1% live on campus. Core. Academic remediation for entering students, ESL program, services for LD students, advanced placement, distance learning, summer session for credit, part-time degree program, adult/continuing education programs, co-op programs and internships.

Entrance Requirements: Open admission except for nursing, dental hygiene, radiological technology, allied health programs. Required: placement testing, ACT COMPASS. Recommended: high school transcript. Required for some: high school transcript, interview. Entrance: noncompetitive. Application deadline: 8/12. Notification: continuous until 9/12.

Costs Per Year: Application fee: $20. State resident tuition: $4,000 full-time, $106.84 per credit hour part-time. Nonresident tuition: $4,400 full-time, $119.84 per credit hour part-time. Mandatory fees: $338 full-time, $9 per credit hour part-time. Full-time tuition and fees vary according to course load. Part-time tuition and fees vary according to course load. College room only: $3240. Room charges vary according to housing facility.

Collegiate Environment: Orientation program. Drama-theater group, choral group. Student services: personal-psychological counseling. Campus security: 24-hour emergency response devices, student patrols, late night transport-escort service, controlled dormitory access. Raymond Library with 44,715 books, 21,056 serials, 3,709 audiovisual materials, and an OPAC. 375 computers available on campus for general student use. A campuswide network can be accessed. Students can access the following: online class registration, degree audit and financial aid information. Staffed computer lab on campus provides training in use of software and the Internet.

Community Environment: Located in the fertile Yakima Valley known as the "Fruit Bowl of the Nation," the area produces cherries, peaches, pears, apples, and other small fruit. The climate is mild and dry with an average of 302 days of sun per year. The community is served by railroad, air, and main arterial highways. Local recreation includes swimming, skiing, boating, fishing, hunting and golf. Part-time employment is available for students. There are churches representing most of the religious denominations, as well as many civic and fraternal organizations serving the community. Many "western" type celebrations are held in the area. Yakima was named an "All-American City" in 1994.

■ ALDERSON-BROADDUS COLLEGE

101 College Hill Dr.
Philippi, WV 26416
Tel: (304)457-1700; Free: 800-263-1549
Fax: (304)457-6239
E-mail: admissions@ab.edu
Web Site: www.ab.edu/

Description: Independent, comprehensive, coed, affiliated with American Baptist Churches in the U.S.A. Awards associate, bachelor's, and master's degrees. Founded 1871. Setting: 170-acre rural campus. Endowment: $18.2 million. Research spending for the previous fiscal year: $212,893. Educational spending for the previous fiscal year: $6739 per student. Total enrollment: 870. Faculty: 97 (65 full-time, 32 part-time). Student-undergrad faculty ratio is 12:1. 3,726 applied, 41% were admitted. 12% from top 10% of their high school class, 31% from top quarter, 66% from top half. Full-time: 777 students, 47% women, 53% men. Part-time: 49 students, 71% women, 29% men. Students come from 28 states and territories, 8 other countries, 47% from out-of-state. 0.2% American Indian or Alaska Native, non-Hispanic/Latino; 2% Hispanic/Latino; 16% African American, non-Hispanic/Latino; 2% Asian, non-Hispanic/Latino; 0% Native Hawaiian or other Pacific Islander, non-Hispanic/Latino; 2% international. 8% 25 or older, 76% live on campus, 6% transferred in. Retention: 66% of full-time freshmen returned the following year. Academic areas with the most degrees conferred: health professions and related sciences; biological/life sciences; business/marketing. Core. Calendar: semesters. Services for LD students, advanced placement, honors program, independent study, double major, summer session for credit, part-time degree program, internships. Study abroad program.

Entrance Requirements: Options: electronic application, deferred admission. Required: high school transcript, minimum 2 high school GPA, SAT and SAT Subject Tests or ACT. Required for some: 3 recommendations, interview. Entrance: moderately difficult. Application deadline: Rolling. Notification: 8/31. SAT Reasoning Test deadline: 8/1. SAT Subject Test deadline: 8/1. Transfer credits accepted: Yes.

Costs Per Year: Application fee: $0. Comprehensive fee: $29,976 includes full-time tuition ($22,530), mandatory fees ($210), and college room and board ($7236). Room and board charges vary according to housing facility. Part-time tuition: $751 per credit.

Collegiate Environment: Orientation program. Drama-theater group, choral group, marching band, student-run newspaper, radio station. Social organizations: 49 open to all; local fraternities, local sororities; 5% of eligible men and 4% of eligible women are members. Most popular organizations: AAPA/Hu C. Myers Society, Alpha Beta Nu, Student Athletic Advisory Committee, Sigma Alpha Iota, Kappa Xi Omega. Major annual events: Homecoming, Battler Pride Days, Boo Crew. Student services: health clinic, personal-psychological counseling. Campus security: 24-hour patrols, controlled dormitory access, emergency notification system, lighted pathways and sidewalks. 640 college housing spaces available; 624 were occupied in 2012-13. Freshmen guaranteed college housing. On-campus residence required through senior year. Options: coed, women-only housing available. Pickett Library with 50,000 books, 11,000 serials, 1,500 audiovisual materials, an OPAC, and a Web page. Operations spending for the previous fiscal year: $239,238. 100 computers available on campus for general student use. A campuswide network can be accessed from student residence rooms and from off campus. Students can access the following: course materials, student record information. Staffed computer lab on campus provides training in use of computers, software, and the Internet.

Community Environment: Philippi is a rural community enjoying a moderate climate ranging from balmy summers to snowy winters. There are churches of major denominations, a hospital, clinic, and more than 50 civic, fraternal, and veteran's organizations active in the community. Local recreation includes swimming, bowling, theater, and major outdoor sports. Skiing and whitewater rafting are within minutes of the campus. Some part-time employment is available.

■ AMERICAN PUBLIC UNIVERSITY SYSTEM

111 W Congress St.
Charles Town, WV 25414
Free: 877-755-2787
E-mail: info@apus.edu
Web Site: www.apus.edu/

Description: Proprietary, comprehensive, coed. Administratively affiliated with American Military University/American Public University. Awards associate, bachelor's, and master's degrees (profile includes American Public University, American Military University and American Community College). Founded 1991. Setting: rural campus with easy access to Washington, DC. Total enrollment: 58,115. Full-time: 3,287 students, 54% women, 46% men. Part-time: 42,485 students, 37% women, 63% men. Students come from 58 states and territories, 77 other countries. 1% American Indian or Alaska Native, non-Hispanic/Latino; 11% Hispanic/Latino; 22% African American, non-Hispanic/Latino; 2% Asian, non-Hispanic/Latino; 1% Native Hawaiian or other Pacific Islander, non-Hispanic/Latino; 1% international. 80% 25 or older, 12% transferred in. Academic areas with the most degrees conferred: homeland security, law enforcement, firefighting, and protective services; business/marketing; interdisciplinary studies. Core. Calendar: courses start on the first Monday of each month. Services for LD students, advanced placement, independent study, distance learning, summer session for credit, part-time degree program, external degree program, internships.

Entrance Requirements: Open admission. Options: electronic application, deferred admission, international baccalaureate accepted. Required: high school transcript, orientation (no-fee). Entrance: noncompetitive. Application deadlines: Rolling, Rolling for nonresidents. Transfer credits accepted: Yes.

Costs Per Year: Application fee: $0. Tuition: $6000 full-time, $250 per credit hour part-time. Mandatory fees: $400 full-time, $50 per course part-time.

Collegiate Environment: Orientation program. College housing not available. APUS Online Library with 150,000 books, 35,000 serials, an OPAC, and a Web page.

■ APPALACHIAN BIBLE COLLEGE

161 College Dr.
Bradley, WV 25818
Tel: (304)877-6428; Free: 800-678-9ABC
E-mail: admissions2@abc.edu
Web Site: www.abc.edu/

Description: Independent nondenominational, comprehensive, coed. Awards associate, bachelor's, and master's degrees. Founded 1950. Setting: 110-acre small town campus. Endowment: $316,677. Total enrollment: 302. Faculty: 18 (11 full-time, 7 part-time). Student-undergrad faculty ratio is 17:1. 133 applied, 56% were admitted. Full-time: 209 students, 52% women, 48% men. Part-time: 77 students, 38% women, 62% men. Students come from 25 states and territories, 6 other countries, 75% from out-of-state. 1% American Indian or Alaska Native, non-Hispanic/Latino; 2% Hispanic/Latino; 1% African American, non-Hispanic/Latino; 0.4% Asian, non-Hispanic/Latino; 1% international. 0% 25 or older, 95% live on campus, 9% transferred in. Retention: 74% of full-time freshmen returned the following year. Academic area with the most degrees conferred: theology and religious vocations. Core. Calendar: semesters. Academic remediation for entering students, advanced placement, self-designed majors, honors program, independent study, distance learning, double major, summer session for credit, part-time degree program, adult/continuing education programs, internships, graduate courses open to undergrads.

Entrance Requirements: Open admission. Options: electronic application, early admission, international baccalaureate accepted. Required: essay, high school transcript, 3 recommendations, interview, SAT or ACT. Recommended: minimum 2.5 high school GPA. Required for some: interview. Entrance: noncompetitive. Application deadline: Rolling. SAT Reasoning Test deadline: 8/15. SAT Subject Test deadline: 8/15.

Costs Per Year: Application fee: $20. Comprehensive fee: $18,310 includes full-time tuition ($10,800), mandatory fees ($940), and college room and board ($6570). Full-time tuition and fees vary according to course load and program. Room and board charges vary according to housing facility. Part-time tuition: $340 per credit hour. Part-time mandatory fees: $34 per credit hour, $365 per term. Part-time tuition and fees vary according to program.

Collegiate Environment: Orientation program. Drama-theater group, choral group. Major annual events: Spring Music Festival, Christmas Concert, Bible Conference. Student services: health clinic, personal-psychological counseling. Campus security: 24-hour emergency response devices, patrols by trained security personnel. 236 college housing spaces available; 195 were occupied in 2012-13. Freshmen guaranteed college housing. On-campus residence required through senior year. Options: men-only, women-only housing available. John Van Pufflen Library with 44,944 books, 985 microform titles, 347 serials, and an OPAC. 30 computers available on campus for general student use. A campuswide network can be accessed from student residence rooms and from off campus.

Community Environment: Bradley is a rural community enjoying temperate climate. There is a railroad line 15 miles distant, an airline 14 miles away, buses, and Highways I-77, I-64, 19, 21, and 16 to serve the community. The city has 5 churches and a Lions Club. Within walking distance is Crossroads Mall. The community provides numerous part-time employment opportunities, and enjoys all the cultural, recreational, and medical facilities of nearby Beckley.

■ BETHANY COLLEGE

Main St.
Bethany, WV 26032
Tel: (304)829-7000; Free: 800-922-7611
Fax: (304)829-7142
E-mail: admission@bethanywv.edu
Web Site: www.bethanywv.edu/

Description: Independent, comprehensive, coed, affiliated with Christian Church (Disciples of Christ). Awards bachelor's and master's degrees. Founded 1840. Setting: 1,300-acre rural campus with easy access to Pittsburgh. Total enrollment: 842. Faculty: 78 (47 full-time, 31 part-time). Student-undergrad faculty ratio is 14:1. 1,523 applied, 43% were admitted. 8% from top 10% of their high school class, 9% from top quarter, 18% from top half. Full-time: 809 students, 40% women, 60% men. Part-time: 3 students, 33% women, 67% men. Students come from 29 states and territories, 4 other countries, 79% from out-of-state. 0% American Indian or Alaska Native, non-Hispanic/Latino; 2% Hispanic/Latino; 20% African American, non-Hispanic/Latino; 0.4% Asian, non-Hispanic/Latino; 0% Native Hawaiian or other Pacific Islander, non-Hispanic/Latino; 1% international. 2% 25 or older, 94% live on campus, 4% transferred in. Retention: 63% of full-time freshmen returned the following year. Academic areas with the most degrees conferred: education; psychology; communication/journalism. Core. Calendar: 4-1-4. Academic remediation for entering students, ESL program, services for LD students, advanced placement, accelerated degree program, self-designed majors, independent study, distance learning, double major, summer session for credit, part-time degree program, internships. Off campus study at Art Institute of Pittsburgh. Study abroad program.

Entrance Requirements: Options: electronic application, deferred admission, international baccalaureate accepted. Required: essay, high school transcript, minimum 2 high school GPA, 1 recommendation, documentation of student involvement, SAT or ACT. Recommended: interview. Required for

some: interview. Entrance: moderately difficult. Application deadlines: Rolling, Rolling for nonresidents. Notification: 8/15, 8/15 for nonresidents. Transfer credits accepted: Yes.

Costs Per Year: Application fee: $0. Comprehensive fee: $34,326 includes full-time tuition ($23,880), mandatory fees ($900), and college room and board ($9546). College room only: $5000. Room and board charges vary according to board plan and housing facility. Part-time tuition: $675 per credit hour. Part-time mandatory fees: $112.50 per term.

Collegiate Environment: Orientation program. Drama-theater group, choral group, marching band, student-run newspaper, radio station. Social organizations: national fraternities, national sororities, local sororities; 20% of eligible men and 35% of eligible women are members. Most popular organizations: Student Board of Governors, Outdoor Club, Model United Nations, Public Relations Society, International Student Association. Major annual events: Homecoming, Mardi Gras, Spring Weekend. Student services: health clinic, personal-psychological counseling. Campus security: 24-hour emergency response devices and patrols, late night transport-escort service, controlled dormitory access. 870 college housing spaces available; 760 were occupied in 2012-13. Freshmen guaranteed college housing. On-campus residence required through senior year. Options: coed, men-only, women-only housing available. T. W. Phillips Memorial Library plus 1 other with 300,000 books, 546 microform titles, 17,000 serials, 1,937 audiovisual materials, an OPAC, and a Web page. 145 computers available on campus for general student use. A campuswide network can be accessed from student residence rooms and from off campus. Students can access the following: online class registration. Staffed computer lab on campus (open 24 hours a day) provides training in use of software and the Internet.

■ BLUE RIDGE COMMUNITY AND TECHNICAL COLLEGE

13650 Apple Harvest Dr.
Martinsburg, WV 254013
Tel: (304)260-4380
Fax: (304)260-4376
E-mail: bneal@blueridgectc.edu
Web Site: www.blueridgectc.edu/

Description: State-supported, 2-year, coed. Awards certificates, transfer associate, and terminal associate degrees. Founded 1974. Setting: small town campus. Total enrollment: 4,317. Faculty: 169 (59 full-time, 110 part-time). Student-undergrad faculty ratio is 23:1. Full-time: 1,161 students, 64% women, 36% men. Part-time: 3,156 students, 69% women, 31% men. 5% from out-of-state. 0.4% American Indian or Alaska Native, non-Hispanic/Latino; 3% Hispanic/Latino; 15% African American, non-Hispanic/Latino; 1% Asian, non-Hispanic/Latino; 0.2% Native Hawaiian or other Pacific Islander, non-Hispanic/Latino; 0% international. 57% 25 or older, 4% transferred in. Retention: 54% of full-time freshmen returned the following year. Core. Academic remediation for entering students, ESL program, services for LD students, advanced placement, accelerated degree program, independent study, double major, part-time degree program, adult/continuing education programs, internships.

Entrance Requirements: Open admission. Option: deferred admission. Required: high school transcript. Recommended: SAT and SAT Subject Tests or ACT. Required for some: interview. Entrance: noncompetitive. Transfer credits accepted: Yes.

Costs Per Year: Application fee: $25. State resident tuition: $3120 full-time, $130 per credit hour part-time. Nonresident tuition: $5616 full-time, $234 per credit hour part-time. Full-time tuition varies according to course load. Part-time tuition varies according to course load.

Collegiate Environment: Orientation program. Drama-theater group. Social organizations: national fraternities. Student services: personal-psychological counseling. Campus security: late night transport-escort service. College housing not available. Operations spending for the previous fiscal year: $20,000. 63 computers available on campus for general student use. A campuswide network can be accessed. Students can access the following: online class registration. Staffed computer lab on campus provides training in use of computers, software, and the Internet.

■ BLUEFIELD STATE COLLEGE

219 Rock St.
Bluefield, WV 24701-2198
Tel: (304)327-4000; Free: 800-654-7798
Fax: (304)327-7747
E-mail: bscadmit@bluefieldstate.edu
Web Site: www.bluefieldstate.edu/

Description: State-supported, 4-year, coed. Part of West Virginia Higher

Education Policy Commission. Awards associate and bachelor's degrees. Founded 1895. Setting: 45-acre small town campus. Total enrollment: 1,935. Faculty: 140 (74 full-time, 66 part-time). Student-undergrad faculty ratio is 17:1. 1,026 applied, 47% were admitted. 2% from top 10% of their high school class, 25% from top quarter, 64% from top half. Full-time: 1,583 students, 62% women, 38% men. Part-time: 352 students, 74% women, 26% men. 3% from out-of-state. 0.1% American Indian or Alaska Native, non-Hispanic/Latino; 1% Hispanic/Latino; 10% African American, non-Hispanic/Latino; 0.2% Asian, non-Hispanic/Latino; 0% Native Hawaiian or other Pacific Islander, non-Hispanic/Latino; 3% international. 42% 25 or older, 0% live on campus, 12% transferred in. Retention: 53% of full-time freshmen returned the following year. Academic areas with the most degrees conferred: liberal arts/general studies; engineering technologies; business/marketing. Calendar: semesters. Part-time degree program, adult/continuing education programs.

Entrance Requirements: Options: early admission, deferred admission. Required: high school transcript, minimum 2 high school GPA, SAT or ACT. Entrance: noncompetitive. Application deadline: Rolling. Notification: continuous.

Costs Per Year: Application fee: $0. Area resident tuition: $217 per credit hour part-time. State resident tuition: $314 per credit hour part-time. Nonresident tuition: $414 per credit hour part-time.

Collegiate Environment: Orientation program. Drama-theater group, choral group, student-run newspaper, radio station. Social organizations: national fraternities, national sororities, local fraternities, local sororities. Student services: health clinic, personal-psychological counseling. Campus security: 24-hour emergency response devices and patrols, student patrols. College housing not available.

Community Environment: At the foot of the East River Mountain, high in the Appalachian chain, Bluefield is situated at the southern tip of West Virginia, bordering on the Virginia state line. The city is the commercial and industrial center for the surrounding area. The climate is temperate with a mean annual temperature of 53.7 degrees and an average rainfall of 38.52 inches. Due to a high altitude and low humidity, the city known as"Nature's Air Conditioned City." Bluefield is accessible by airlines, bus lines, and major highways. There are many churches representing most denominations, community health facilities, and major civic, fraternal, and veteran's organizations to serve the community. Local recreation includes nearby Bluestone Reservoir and lakes for fishing, swimming, and boating; municipal swimming pools, golf, a football stadium, tennis courts, softball, and Little Theatre group.

■ **BRIDGEMONT COMMUNITY & TECHNICAL COLLEGE**
405 Fayette Pke.
Montgomery, WV 25136
Tel: (304)442-3149
Web Site: www.bridgemont.edu/
Description: County-supported, 2-year, coed. Awards certificates and terminal associate degrees. Total enrollment: 760. 30% 25 or older.
Entrance Requirements: Open admission.

■ **CONCORD UNIVERSITY**
Vermillion St.
Athens, WV 24712-1000
Tel: (304)384-3115; Free: 888-384-5249
Fax: (304)384-9044
E-mail: admissions@concord.edu
Web Site: www.concord.edu/
Description: State-supported, comprehensive, coed. Part of State College System of West Virginia. Awards associate, bachelor's, and master's degrees. Founded 1872. Setting: 100-acre rural campus. Endowment: $22.2 million. Research spending for the previous fiscal year: $73,305. Educational spending for the previous fiscal year: $6053 per student. Total enrollment: 2,888. Faculty: 216 (126 full-time, 90 part-time). Student-undergrad faculty ratio is 16:1. 2,495 applied, 49% were admitted. 17% from top 10% of their high school class, 46% from top quarter, 80% from top half. Full-time: 2,377 students, 57% women, 43% men. Part-time: 275 students, 66% women, 34% men. Students come from 29 states and territories, 22 other countries, 20% from out-of-state. 0.2% American Indian or Alaska Native, non-Hispanic/Latino; 1% Hispanic/Latino; 6% African American, non-Hispanic/Latino; 1% Asian, non-Hispanic/Latino; 0% Native Hawaiian or other Pacific Islander, non-Hispanic/Latino; 3% international. 27% 25 or older, 32% live on campus, 10% transferred in. Retention: 62% of full-time freshmen returned the following year. Academic areas with the most degrees conferred: educa-

tion; business/marketing; liberal arts/general studies. Core. Calendar: semesters. Academic remediation for entering students, ESL program, services for LD students, advanced placement, accelerated degree program, self-designed majors, honors program, independent study, distance learning, double major, summer session for credit, part-time degree program, external degree program, adult/continuing education programs, co-op programs and internships, graduate courses open to undergrads. Off campus study. Study abroad program.

Entrance Requirements: Options: electronic application, early admission, early decision, international baccalaureate accepted. Required: high school transcript, minimum 2 high school GPA, SAT or ACT. Recommended: interview. Required for some: essay, interview. Entrance: minimally difficult. Application deadlines: Rolling, 1/15 for nonresidents. Notification: continuous. Transfer credits accepted: Yes. Early decision applicants: 334. Early decision applicants admitted: 175.

Costs Per Year: Application fee: $0. State resident tuition: $5716 full-time, $238 per credit part-time. Nonresident tuition: $12,698 full-time, $529 per credit part-time. Full-time tuition varies according to course load. Part-time tuition varies according to course load. College room and board: $7386. College room only: $3762. Room and board charges vary according to housing facility.

Collegiate Environment: Orientation program. Drama-theater group, choral group, marching band, student-run newspaper, radio station. Social organizations: 62 open to all; national fraternities, national sororities, local fraternities, local sororities; 20% of eligible men and 25% of eligible women are members. Most popular organizations: Service Groups, student government, student-run publications, intramurals, Student Activities Committee. Major annual events: Homecoming, CU Community Fair, Spring Fling. Student services: health clinic, personal-psychological counseling. Campus security: 24-hour emergency response devices and patrols, student patrols, late night transport-escort service, controlled dormitory access. 1,125 college housing spaces available; 1,091 were occupied in 2012-13. Freshmen guaranteed college housing. On-campus residence required through senior year. Options: coed, men-only, women-only housing available. J. Frank Marsh Library with 168,164 books, 240,089 microform titles, 140 serials, an OPAC, and a Web page. Operations spending for the previous fiscal year: $539,164. 350 computers available on campus for general student use. A campuswide network can be accessed from student residence rooms and from off campus. Students can access the following: online class registration. Staffed computer lab on campus.

Community Environment: Located in the mountains in a quiet rural area, this is an excellent atmosphere for students. The climate is moderate with cool summers. Local recreation includes good hunting and fishing. Pipestem State Park and Winterplace Ski Resort are located nearby.

■ **DAVIS & ELKINS COLLEGE**
100 Campus Dr.
Elkins, WV 26241-3996
Tel: (304)637-1900; Free: 800-624-3157
Fax: (304)637-1800
E-mail: admiss@davisandelkins.edu
Web Site: www.dewv.edu/
Description: Independent Presbyterian, 4-year, coed. Awards associate and bachelor's degrees. Founded 1904. Setting: 170-acre small town campus. Endowment: $22.7 million. Educational spending for the previous fiscal year: $7510 per student. Total enrollment: 640. Faculty: 64 (44 full-time, 20 part-time). Student-undergrad faculty ratio is 10:1. 351 applied, 75% were admitted. 11% from top 10% of their high school class, 28% from top quarter, 50% from top half. Full-time: 568 students, 63% women, 37% men. Part-time: 72 students, 78% women, 22% men. Students come from 19 states and territories, 21 other countries, 34% from out-of-state. 24% 25 or older, 49% live on campus, 10% transferred in. Retention: 66% of full-time freshmen returned the following year. Academic areas with the most degrees conferred: business/marketing; education; parks and recreation. Core. Calendar: 4-1-4. ESL program, services for LD students, advanced placement, accelerated degree program, self-designed majors, honors program, independent study, double major, summer session for credit, part-time degree program, external degree program, adult/continuing education programs, co-op programs and internships. Study abroad program.

Entrance Requirements: Options: electronic application, early admission, deferred admission, international baccalaureate accepted. Required: high school transcript, minimum 2.0 high school GPA, SAT or ACT. Recommended: essay, interview. Required for some: essay, 2 recommendations, interview. Entrance: moderately difficult. Application deadline: Rolling. Notification: continuous.

Costs Per Year: Application fee: $35. Comprehensive fee: $31,850 includes full-time tuition ($23,500) and college room and board ($8350). Full-time tuition varies according to course load. Room and board charges vary according to board plan.

Collegiate Environment: Orientation program. Drama-theater group, choral group, student-run newspaper, radio station. Social organizations: 42 open to all; national fraternities, national sororities; 4% of eligible men and 8% of eligible women are members. Most popular organizations: Beta Alpha Beta, campus radio station, Student Nurses Association, Student Education Association, International Student Organization. Major annual events: Parents' Weekend, Alumni Homecoming Weekend, Deja vu Weekend. Student services: health clinic, personal-psychological counseling. Campus security: 24-hour emergency response devices, late night transport-escort service, controlled dormitory access, late night security personnel. Booth Library with 226,705 books, 222,871 microform titles, 1,422 serials, 6,190 audiovisual materials, an OPAC, and a Web page. Operations spending for the previous fiscal year: $266,454. 80 computers available on campus for general student use. Computer purchase/lease plans available. A campuswide network can be accessed from student residence rooms and from off campus. Staffed computer lab on campus provides training in use of computers, software, and the Internet.

Community Environment: Elkins is located in the foothills of the Alleghenies and is the headquarters for the nearby Monongahela National Forest. The community is accessible by auto and airline. The climate is temperate. Elkins has several churches of various denominations, a hospital, YMCA, and major civic and fraternal organizations. The nearby national forest offers excellent trout streams, hunting, camping, 4 modern ski resorts, and bathing beaches. An annual autumn State Forest Festival is held here. Part-time employment is limited.

■ **EASTERN WEST VIRGINIA COMMUNITY AND TECHNICAL COLLEGE**
HC 65 Box 402
Moorefield, WV 26836
Tel: (304)434-8000; Free: 877-982-2322
E-mail: askeast@eastern.wvnet.edu
Web Site: www.eastern.wvnet.edu/
Description: State-supported, 2-year, coed. Awards certificates, transfer associate, and terminal associate degrees. Founded 1999. Setting: rural campus. Total enrollment: 639. Student-undergrad faculty ratio is 20:1. 0% from out-of-state. 44% 25 or older. Calendar: semesters. Academic remediation for entering students, services for LD students, advanced placement, self-designed majors, independent study, distance learning, double major, part-time degree program, external degree program, internships.

■ **EVEREST INSTITUTE**
5514 Big Tyler Rd.
Cross Lanes, WV 25313-1390
Tel: (304)776-6290; Free: 888-741-4270
Web Site: www.everest.edu/
Description: Proprietary, 2-year, coed. Part of Corinthian Colleges, Inc. Awards certificates, diplomas, and transfer associate degrees. Founded 1938. Setting: small town campus. Total enrollment: 487. 191 applied. 0% from out-of-state. 44% 25 or older. Retention: 75% of full-time freshmen returned the following year. Core. Academic remediation for entering students, internships.
Entrance Requirements: Option: deferred admission. Required: high school transcript, interview. Entrance: moderately difficult. Application deadline: Rolling. Notification: continuous.
Collegiate Environment: Orientation program.

■ **FAIRMONT STATE UNIVERSITY**
1201 Locust Ave.
Fairmont, WV 26554
Tel: (304)367-4000; Free: 800-641-5678
Fax: (304)367-4789
E-mail: admit@fairmontstate.edu
Web Site: www.fairmontstate.edu/
Description: State-supported, comprehensive, coed. Part of State College System of West Virginia. Awards associate, bachelor's, and master's degrees. Founded 1865. Setting: 120-acre small town campus. Endowment: $16.8 million. Research spending for the previous fiscal year: $114,674. Educational spending for the previous fiscal year: $5886 per student. Total enrollment: 4,451. Faculty: 326 (171 full-time, 155 part-time). Student-

undergrad faculty ratio is 17:1. 2,326 applied, 66% were admitted. 8% from top 10% of their high school class, 25% from top quarter, 51% from top half. Full-time: 3,573 students, 55% women, 45% men. Part-time: 539 students, 69% women, 31% men. Students come from 27 states and territories, 25 other countries, 7% from out-of-state. 0.2% American Indian or Alaska Native, non-Hispanic/Latino; 2% Hispanic/Latino; 5% African American, non-Hispanic/Latino; 0.4% Asian, non-Hispanic/Latino; 0.1% Native Hawaiian or other Pacific Islander, non-Hispanic/Latino; 2% international. 27% 25 or older, 18% live on campus, 9% transferred in. Retention: 64% of full-time freshmen returned the following year. Academic areas with the most degrees conferred: business/marketing; liberal arts/general studies; engineering technologies. Core. Calendar: semesters. Academic remediation for entering students, ESL program, services for LD students, advanced placement, accelerated degree program, honors program, independent study, distance learning, double major, summer session for credit, part-time degree program, adult/continuing education programs, co-op programs and internships, graduate courses open to undergrads. Off campus study at Pierpont Community & Technical College. Study abroad program. ROTC: Army, Air Force (c).

Entrance Requirements: Option: electronic application. Required: high school transcript, SAT or ACT. Recommended: minimum 2 high school GPA. Entrance: minimally difficult. Application deadline: Rolling. Notification: continuous. Transfer credits accepted: Yes.

Costs Per Year: Application fee: $0. State resident tuition: $5804 full-time, $243 per credit hour part-time. Nonresident tuition: $12,240 full-time, $510 per credit hour part-time. Full-time tuition varies according to location. Part-time tuition varies according to course load and location. College room and board: $7686. College room only: $4186. Room and board charges vary according to board plan and housing facility.

Collegiate Environment: Orientation program. Drama-theater group, choral group, marching band, student-run newspaper. Social organizations: 80 open to all; national fraternities, national sororities, local fraternities; 2% of eligible men and 2% of eligible women are members. Most popular organizations: Alpha Phi Omega, Circle K, Society for Non-traditional Students, Criminal Justice Club, Honors Association. Major annual events: Homecoming, Student Leadership Conference, Alcohol Awareness Week. Student services: legal services, health clinic, personal-psychological counseling. Campus security: 24-hour emergency response devices and patrols, student patrols, controlled dormitory access. 1,180 college housing spaces available; all were occupied in 2012-13. Freshmen guaranteed college housing. On-campus residence required through sophomore year. Options: coed, men-only, women-only housing available. Musick Library with 280,000 books, 27,500 microform titles, 895 serials, an OPAC, and a Web page. Operations spending for the previous fiscal year: $1.5 million. 1,350 computers available on campus for general student use. Computer purchase/lease plans available. A campuswide network can be accessed from student residence rooms and from off campus. Students can access the following: online class registration. Staffed computer lab on campus (open 24 hours a day) provides training in use of computers, software, and the Internet.

Community Environment: The College's 80-acre campus, with its twelve major buildings, is attractively located in Fairmont, West Virginia. Approximately ninety miles south of Pittsburgh on Interstate 79, Fairmont, with a population of about 19,000, is the county seat of Marion County.

■ **GLENVILLE STATE COLLEGE**
200 High St.
Glenville, WV 26351-1200
Tel: (304)462-7361; Free: 800-924-2010
Fax: (304)462-8619
E-mail: ashley.weir@glenville.edu
Web Site: www.glenville.edu/
Description: State-supported, 4-year, coed. Part of West Virginia Higher Education Policy Commission. Awards associate and bachelor's degrees. Founded 1872. Setting: 331-acre rural campus. Endowment: $13.4 million. Research spending for the previous fiscal year: $637,816. Educational spending for the previous fiscal year: $9692 per student. Total enrollment: 1,857. Faculty: 112 (68 full-time, 44 part-time). Student-undergrad faculty ratio is 19:1. 1,246 applied, 82% were admitted. 12% from top 10% of their high school class, 20% from top quarter, 57% from top half. Full-time: 1,188 students, 45% women, 55% men. Part-time: 669 students, 37% women, 63% men. Students come from 23 states and territories, 4 other countries, 14% from out-of-state. 0% American Indian or Alaska Native, non-Hispanic/Latino; 2% Hispanic/Latino; 16% African American, non-Hispanic/Latino. 34% 25 or older, 33% live on campus, 4% transferred in. Retention: 70% of

full-time freshmen returned the following year. Academic areas with the most degrees conferred: education; social sciences; business/marketing. Core. Calendar: semesters. Academic remediation for entering students, services for LD students, advanced placement, accelerated degree program, self-designed majors, honors program, distance learning, double major, summer session for credit, part-time degree program, external degree program, adult/continuing education programs, co-op programs and internships. Off campus study. Study abroad program. ROTC: Army.

Entrance Requirements: Open admission. Options: electronic application, deferred admission. Required: high school transcript, minimum 3 high school GPA, college preparatory program, SAT or ACT. Required for some: interview. Entrance: noncompetitive. Application deadlines: Rolling, Rolling for nonresidents. Notification: continuous, continuous for nonresidents. Preference given to Hidden Promise Consortium. SAT Reasoning Test deadline: 12/14. SAT Subject Test deadline: 12/14. Transfer credits accepted: Yes.

Costs Per Year: Application fee: $20. State resident tuition: $5860 full-time, $244 per credit hour part-time. Nonresident tuition: $13,824 full-time, $576 per credit hour part-time. Mandatory fees: $244 per credit hour part-time. Full-time tuition varies according to course load. College room and board: $8400. College room only: $4830. Room and board charges vary according to board plan and housing facility.

Collegiate Environment: Orientation program. Drama-theater group, choral group, marching band, student-run newspaper. Social organizations: 41 open to all; national fraternities, local fraternities, local sororities; 4% of eligible men and 4% of eligible women are members. Most popular organizations: Music Educators National Conference, Student Government Association, Student Support Services, Student Advisory Committee, Glenville Student Action. Major annual events: Homecoming, GSC Week, Convocation. Student services: health clinic, personal-psychological counseling. Campus security: 24-hour emergency response devices and patrols, student patrols, late night transport-escort service, controlled dormitory access. Robert F. Kidd Library with 116,220 books, 604,256 microform titles, 22,835 serials, 2,968 audiovisual materials, an OPAC, and a Web page. Operations spending for the previous fiscal year: $423,707. 183 computers available on campus for general student use. A campuswide network can be accessed from student residence rooms and from off campus. Students can access the following: online class registration, WebVista, Wimba Classroom. Staffed computer lab on campus provides training in use of computers, software, and the Internet.

Community Environment: Glenville is located in the approximate geographical center of the state. Interstate 79 passes within 15 miles of the campus. Glenville has 5 churches, a modern clinic, motel, and several civic and fraternal organizations. Within the area there are facilities for hunting, fishing, golf, baseball, softball. A state park is located 6 miles away. Job opportunities are available. An annual West Virginia Folk Festival is held each year in June.

■ **HUNTINGTON JUNIOR COLLEGE**
900 Fifth Ave.
Huntington, WV 25701-2004
Tel: (304)697-7550; Free: 800-344-4522
Fax: (304)697-7554
Web Site: www.huntingtonjuniorcollege.com/
Description: Proprietary, 2-year, coed. Awards terminal associate degrees. Founded 1936. Setting: urban campus. Total enrollment: 745. 68% 25 or older. Core. Academic remediation for entering students, services for LD students, summer session for credit, part-time degree program.
Entrance Requirements: Open admission. Required: high school transcript. Entrance: minimally difficult. Application deadline: Rolling.
Collegiate Environment: Orientation program. 1,900 books and 35 serials.

■ **ITT TECHNICAL INSTITUTE**
5183 US Rte. 60
Bldg. 1, Ste. 40
Huntington, WV 25705
Tel: (304)733-8700; Free: 800-224-4695
Web Site: www.itt-tech.edu/
Description: Proprietary, 2-year, coed. Part of ITT Educational Services, Inc. Awards terminal associate degrees.
Entrance Requirements: Entrance: minimally difficult.

■ **KANAWHA VALLEY COMMUNITY AND TECHNICAL COLLEGE**
2001 Union Carbide Dr.
South Charleston, WV 25303

Tel: (304)205-6600
E-mail: castosb@wvstateu.edu
Web Site: www.kvctc.edu/
Description: County-supported, 2-year, coed. Part of West Council for Community and Technical College Education. Awards certificates, transfer associate, and terminal associate degrees. Setting: 5,219-acre suburban campus. Educational spending for the previous fiscal year: $2562 per student. Total enrollment: 1,717. Faculty: 87 (35 full-time, 52 part-time). 2,704 applied, 63% were admitted. Full-time: 1,064 students, 61% women, 39% men. Part-time: 653 students, 73% women, 27% men. 7% from out-of-state. 51% 25 or older, 6% transferred in. Retention: 61% of full-time freshmen returned the following year. Academic remediation for entering students, ESL program, services for LD students, advanced placement, self-designed majors, independent study, distance learning, double major, summer session for credit, external degree program, adult/continuing education programs, co-op programs and internships. Study abroad program.
Entrance Requirements: Required: high school transcript, ACT. Recommended: essay.
Collegiate Environment: Campus security: 24-hour emergency response devices and patrols, late night transport-escort service, controlled dormitory access. Drain Jordan Library plus 1 other with 221,184 books, 495 serials, an OPAC, and a Web page.

■ **MARSHALL UNIVERSITY**
One John Marshall Dr.
Huntington, WV 25755
Tel: (304)696-3170; Free: 800-642-3499
Fax: (304)696-3135
E-mail: admissions@marshall.edu
Web Site: www.marshall.edu/
Description: State-supported, university, coed. Part of University System of West Virginia. Awards associate, bachelor's, master's, and doctoral degrees and post-master's certificates. Founded 1837. Setting: 100-acre urban campus. Research spending for the previous fiscal year: $12.8 million. Educational spending for the previous fiscal year: $7673 per student. Total enrollment: 13,708. Faculty: 768 (519 full-time, 249 part-time). Student-undergrad faculty ratio is 19:1. 2,889 applied, 80% were admitted. Full-time: 8,561 students, 55% women, 45% men. Part-time: 1,324 students, 59% women, 41% men. Students come from 45 states and territories, 35 other countries, 24% from out-of-state. 0.3% American Indian or Alaska Native, non-Hispanic/Latino; 2% Hispanic/Latino; 6% African American, non-Hispanic/Latino; 1% Asian, non-Hispanic/Latino; 0.1% Native Hawaiian or other Pacific Islander, non-Hispanic/Latino; 1% international. 20% 25 or older, 24% live on campus, 7% transferred in. Retention: 71% of full-time freshmen returned the following year. Academic areas with the most degrees conferred: liberal arts/general studies; business/marketing; education. Core. Calendar: semesters. Academic remediation for entering students, ESL program, services for LD students, advanced placement, accelerated degree program, honors program, independent study, distance learning, double major, summer session for credit, part-time degree program, adult/continuing education programs, co-op programs and internships, graduate courses open to undergrads. Off campus study at National Student Exchange. Study abroad program. ROTC: Army.
Entrance Requirements: Options: electronic application, deferred admission, international baccalaureate accepted. Required: SAT or ACT. Required for some: high school transcript. Entrance: moderately difficult. Application deadline: Rolling. Notification: continuous.
Costs Per Year: Application fee: $30. State resident tuition: $4860 full-time, $202.75 per credit hour part-time. Nonresident tuition: $12,860 full-time, $536 per credit hour part-time. Mandatory fees: $1070 full-time. Full-time tuition and fees vary according to degree level, location, program, and reciprocity agreements. Part-time tuition varies according to course load, degree level, location, program, and reciprocity agreements. College room and board: $8988. College room only: $5570. Room and board charges vary according to board plan and housing facility.
Collegiate Environment: Orientation program. Drama-theater group, choral group, marching band, student-run newspaper, radio station. Social organizations: 75 open to all; national fraternities, national sororities; 8% of eligible men and 4% of eligible women are members. Most popular organizations: Campus Crusade for Christ, Gamma Beta Phi, The International Students' Organization, Newman Association, Phi Alpha Theta. Major annual events: Homecoming, Spring Fest, Independence Daze. Student services: legal services, health clinic, personal-psychological counseling, women's center. Campus security: 24-hour emergency response devices and patrols,

student patrols, late night transport-escort service, controlled dormitory access. 2,503 college housing spaces available; 2,368 were occupied in 2012-13. Freshmen guaranteed college housing. On-campus residence required through sophomore year. Options: coed, women-only housing available. John Deaver Drinko Library plus 1 other with 1.9 million books, 1 million microform titles, 33,622 serials, 43,396 audiovisual materials, an OPAC, and a Web page. Operations spending for the previous fiscal year: $4 million. 1,461 computers available on campus for general student use. Computer purchase/lease plans available. A campuswide network can be accessed from student residence rooms and from off campus. Students can access the following: online class registration, Virtual Computer Lab - MU Remote and Web Conferencing. Staffed computer lab on campus (open 24 hours a day) provides training in use of computers, software, and the Internet.

Community Environment: Huntington is a busy river terminal and serves as the shipping point for millions of tons of coal mined annually from the great bituminous fields to the south of the city. It is also the center of a large natural gas and oil-producing area. The annual mean temperature is 56.6 degrees with an annual rainfall of 41.8 inches. The community is accessed by bus, rail, and air. There are medical facilities, a public library, YMCA, YWCA, and over 140 churches of various denominations serving the area. Recreation includes municipal swimming pools, roller skating rinks, golf, tennis, bowling, boating, the Memorial Field House, theatres, and the Huntington Civic Center which attracts top entertainment. Part-time employment is available.

■ **MOUNTAIN STATE COLLEGE**
1508 Spring St.
Parkersburg, WV 26101-3993
Tel: (304)485-5487; Free: 800-841-0201
Fax: (304)485-3524
E-mail: jsutton@msc.edu
Web Site: www.msc.edu/

Description: Proprietary, 2-year, coed. Awards diplomas and terminal associate degrees. Founded 1888. Setting: small town campus. Total enrollment: 166. Faculty: 11 (7 full-time, 4 part-time). Student-undergrad faculty ratio is 17:1. Full-time: 166 students, 83% women, 17% men. Students come from 2 states and territories, 0% from out-of-state. 55% 25 or older, 4% transferred in. Retention: 70% of full-time freshmen returned the following year. Core. Honors program, independent study, distance learning, double major, part-time degree program, internships.

Entrance Requirements: Required: interview, CPAt. Entrance: minimally difficult.

Collegiate Environment: Orientation program. Student services: personal-psychological counseling. Mountain State College Library with an OPAC. 30 computers available on campus for general student use. Staffed computer lab on campus.

■ **MOUNTWEST COMMUNITY & TECHNICAL COLLEGE**
One John Marshall Dr.
Huntington, WV 25755
Free: 866-676-5533
E-mail: admissions@marshall.edu
Web Site: www.mctc.edu/

Description: County-supported, 2-year, coed. Part of Community and Technical College System of West Virginia. Awards certificates and terminal associate degrees. Setting: 70-acre urban campus. Endowment: $27,466. Educational spending for the previous fiscal year: $3554 per student. Total enrollment: 2,534. Faculty: 156 (49 full-time, 107 part-time). Student-undergrad faculty ratio is 21:1. 601 applied, 100% were admitted. Full-time: 1,400 students, 50% women, 50% men. Part-time: 1,134 students, 39% women, 61% men. Students come from 26 states and territories, 5 other countries, 16% from out-of-state. 47% 25 or older, 9% transferred in. Retention: 43% of full-time freshmen returned the following year. Core. Calendar: semesters. Academic remediation for entering students, ESL program, services for LD students, accelerated degree program, independent study, distance learning, double major, summer session for credit, part-time degree program, co-op programs and internships. Off campus study. ROTC: Army.

Entrance Requirements: Open admission. Options: electronic application, deferred admission, international baccalaureate accepted. Required: high school transcript, minimum 2 high school GPA. Entrance: noncompetitive. Application deadline: Rolling. Notification: continuous.

Collegiate Environment: Orientation program. Drama-theater group, choral group, marching band, student-run newspaper, radio station. Social organizations: national fraternities, national sororities. Student services: legal

services, health clinic, personal-psychological counseling, women's center. Campus security: 24-hour emergency response devices and patrols, controlled dormitory access. John Deaver Drinko Library plus 2 others with 1.6 million books, 1.2 million microform titles, 22,591 serials, 209,391 audiovisual materials, an OPAC, and a Web page. 1,461 computers available on campus for general student use. A campuswide network can be accessed from student residence rooms and from off campus. Students can access the following: online class registration. Staffed computer lab on campus.

■ **NEW RIVER COMMUNITY AND TECHNICAL COLLEGE**
167 Dye Dr.
Beckley, WV 25801
Tel: (304)255-5821
E-mail: awithers@newriver.edu
Web Site: www.newriver.edu/

Description: County-supported, 2-year, coed. Awards certificates, transfer associate, and terminal associate degrees. Founded 2003. Total enrollment: 2,232. 41% 25 or older.

■ **OHIO VALLEY UNIVERSITY**
One Campus View Dr.
Vienna, WV 26105-8000
Tel: (304)865-6000; Free: 877-446-8668
Fax: (304)865-6001
E-mail: admissions@ovu.edu
Web Site: www.ovu.edu/

Description: Independent, comprehensive, coed, affiliated with Church of Christ. Awards associate, bachelor's, and master's degrees. Founded 1960. Setting: 299-acre small town campus. Endowment: $1.3 million. Educational spending for the previous fiscal year: $3307 per student. Total enrollment: 478. Faculty: 83 (22 full-time, 61 part-time). Student-undergrad faculty ratio is 10:1. 751 applied, 42% were admitted. 23% from top 10% of their high school class, 18% from top quarter, 24% from top half. Full-time: 386 students, 43% women, 57% men. Part-time: 50 students, 70% women, 30% men. Students come from 31 states and territories, 11 other countries, 59% from out-of-state. 0.2% American Indian or Alaska Native, non-Hispanic/Latino; 3% Hispanic/Latino; 7% African American, non-Hispanic/Latino; 0.2% Asian, non-Hispanic/Latino; 0% Native Hawaiian or other Pacific Islander, non-Hispanic/Latino; 8% international. 23% 25 or older, 53% live on campus, 10% transferred in. Retention: 46% of full-time freshmen returned the following year. Academic areas with the most degrees conferred: business/marketing; education; psychology. Core. Calendar: semesters. Academic remediation for entering students, ESL program, services for LD students, advanced placement, self-designed majors, honors program, independent study, distance learning, double major, summer session for credit, part-time degree program, adult/continuing education programs, co-op programs and internships, graduate courses open to undergrads. Off campus study at The Washington Center. Study abroad program.

Entrance Requirements: Options: electronic application, early admission, early action, deferred admission. Required: high school transcript, SAT or ACT, SAT and SAT Subject Tests or ACT. Required for some: essay, interview. Entrance: minimally difficult. Application deadline: 8/30. Notification: continuous. SAT Reasoning Test deadline: 8/1. SAT Subject Test deadline: 8/1. Transfer credits accepted: Yes.

Costs Per Year: Application fee: $0. Comprehensive fee: $25,650 includes full-time tuition ($17,000), mandatory fees ($1750), and college room and board ($6900). College room only: $3500. Full-time tuition and fees vary according to course load. Room and board charges vary according to board plan and housing facility. Part-time tuition: $475 per credit. Part-time mandatory fees: $75 per credit. Part-time tuition and fees vary according to course load.

Collegiate Environment: Orientation program. Drama-theater group, choral group, student-run newspaper. Social organizations: 11 open to all; local fraternities, local sororities, Social Clubs; 54% of eligible men and 54% of eligible women are members. Most popular organizations: Social Clubs, intramural sports, Theatre Production, Acappella Choir, Ambassadors. Major annual events: OVU Homecoming, OVU Expressions, Winter/Spring Banquets. Campus security: 24-hour emergency response devices and patrols, controlled dormitory access. 46 undergraduates lived in college housing during 2012-13. Freshmen guaranteed college housing. On-campus residence required through sophomore year. Options: men-only, women-only housing available. Operations spending for the previous fiscal year: $109,668. 45 computers available on campus for general student use. A campuswide network can be accessed from student residence rooms. Students can access the following: online class registration. Staffed computer lab on campus provides training in use of computers, software, and the Internet.

■ PIERPONT COMMUNITY & TECHNICAL COLLEGE

1201 Locust Ave.
Fairmont, WV 26554
Tel: (304)367-4892; Free: 800-641-5678
Fax: (304)367-4692
Web Site: www.pierpont.edu/

Description: State-supported, 2-year, coed. Administratively affiliated with Fairmont State College. Awards certificates, transfer associate, and terminal associate degrees. Founded 1974. Setting: 90-acre small town campus. Endowment: $9.9 million. Research spending for the previous fiscal year: $602,614. Educational spending for the previous fiscal year: $3500 per student. Total enrollment: 2,852. Faculty: 495 (232 full-time, 263 part-time). Student-undergrad faculty ratio is 18:1. 1,339 applied, 92% were admitted. 4% from top quarter of their high school class, 10% from top half. Full-time: 1,672 students, 61% women, 39% men. Part-time: 1,180 students, 58% women, 42% men. Students come from 14 states and territories, 6 other countries, 3% from out-of-state. 31% 25 or older, 12% live on campus, 5% transferred in. Retention: 60% of full-time freshmen returned the following year. Core. Calendar: semesters. Summer session for credit, part-time degree program, external degree program, adult/continuing education programs.

Entrance Requirements: Open admission except for health career programs. Options: electronic application, deferred admission, international baccalaureate accepted. Required: SAT or ACT. Recommended: high school transcript. Entrance: minimally difficult. Application deadline: Rolling. Notification: continuous.

Collegiate Environment: Orientation program. Drama-theater group, choral group, marching band, student-run newspaper. Social organizations: 90 open to all; national fraternities, national sororities; 4% of eligible men and 3% of eligible women are members. Student services: health clinic, personal-psychological counseling. 1,150 computers available on campus for general student use. Computer purchase/lease plans available. A campuswide network can be accessed from student residence rooms and from off campus. Students can access the following: online class registration. Staffed computer lab on campus (open 24 hours a day) provides training in use of computers, software, and the Internet.

■ POTOMAC STATE COLLEGE OF WEST VIRGINIA UNIVERSITY

101 Fort Ave.
Keyser, WV 26726-2698
Tel: (304)788-6800; Free: 800-262-7332
Fax: (304)788-6939
E-mail: go2psc@mail.wvu.edu
Web Site: www.potomacstatecollege.edu/

Description: State-supported, primarily 2-year, coed. Part of West Virginia Higher Education Policy Commission. Awards transfer associate, terminal associate, and bachelor's degrees. Founded 1901. Setting: 18-acre small town campus. Total enrollment: 1,781. Faculty: 95 (42 full-time, 53 part-time). Student-undergrad faculty ratio is 25:1. 7% from top 10% of their high school class, 22% from top quarter, 49% from top half. Full-time: 1,436 students, 50% women, 50% men. Part-time: 345 students, 64% women, 36% men. Students come from 19 states and territories, 2 other countries, 31% from out-of-state. 1% American Indian or Alaska Native, non-Hispanic/Latino; 2% Hispanic/Latino; 17% African American, non-Hispanic/Latino; 0.3% Asian, non-Hispanic/Latino; 0.1% Native Hawaiian or other Pacific Islander, non-Hispanic/Latino; 0.2% international. 14% 25 or older, 28% live on campus, 3% transferred in. Retention: 46% of full-time freshmen returned the following year. Academic areas with the most degrees conferred: homeland security, law enforcement, firefighting, and protective services; business/marketing. Core. Calendar: semesters. Academic remediation for entering students, services for LD students, advanced placement, honors program, independent study, distance learning, double major, summer session for credit, part-time degree program, adult/continuing education programs, internships. Study abroad program.

Entrance Requirements: Open admission for West Virginia residents. Options: electronic application, international baccalaureate accepted. Required: high school transcript. Recommended: SAT or ACT. Entrance: noncompetitive. Application deadline: Rolling. Transfer credits accepted: Yes.

Collegiate Environment: Orientation program. Drama-theater group, choral group, student-run newspaper. Social organizations: 17 open to all. Most popular organizations: Community Chorus, Circle K, Agriculture and Forestry Club, Catamounts Against Cancer, intramural program. Major annual events: Homecoming, Spring Fest, Commencement. Student services: health clinic, personal-psychological counseling. Campus security: 24-hour patrols, late night transport-escort service, controlled dormitory access. 650 college housing spaces available; 635 were occupied in 2012-13. Freshmen given priority for college housing. On-campus residence required through sophomore year. Option: coed housing available. Mary F. Shipper Library with 51,028 books, 98,621 microform titles, 286 serials, 1,253 audiovisual materials, and an OPAC. Operations spending for the previous fiscal year: $142,600. 35 computers available on campus for general student use. Computer purchase/lease plans available. A campuswide network can be accessed from student residence rooms. Students can access the following: online class registration. Staffed computer lab on campus.

Community Environment: During the Civil War, the country around Keyser was a frequent battleground. The community was a supply point for, alternately, the Union Army and the Confederate forces. It changed hands 14 times in 4 years of war. The climate is temperate. There are churches of many denominations, libraries, a hospital and various civic, fraternal, and veteran's organizations serving the area. The city has good shopping facilities and is accessible by railroad, buses, and U.S. Highways 48,50 and 220. Residence Halls provide student housing. Part-time employment is available. Local recreation includes hunting, boating, fishing, golf, swimming, skiing, and tennis.

■ SALEM INTERNATIONAL UNIVERSITY

223 W Main St.
Salem, WV 26426-0500
Tel: (304)782-5011; Free: 888-235-5024
E-mail: admissions@salemiu.edu
Web Site: www.salemu.edu/

Description: Independent, comprehensive, coed. Awards associate, bachelor's, and master's degrees and post-master's certificates. Founded 1888. Setting: 300-acre rural campus. Total enrollment: 850. Faculty: 60 (26 full-time, 34 part-time). Student-undergrad faculty ratio is 18:1. Full-time: 631 students, 62% women, 38% men. Students come from 13 states and territories, 13 other countries, 59% from out-of-state. 1% American Indian or Alaska Native, non-Hispanic/Latino; 5% Hispanic/Latino; 23% African American, non-Hispanic/Latino; 0.5% Asian, non-Hispanic/Latino; 0.2% Native Hawaiian or other Pacific Islander, non-Hispanic/Latino; 5% international. 40% 25 or older, 32% live on campus. Retention: 43% of full-time freshmen returned the following year. Academic areas with the most degrees conferred: business/marketing; homeland security, law enforcement, firefighting, and protective services; education. Core. Calendar: modular. Academic remediation for entering students, ESL program, services for LD students, advanced placement, accelerated degree program, independent study, distance learning, double major, summer session for credit, part-time degree program, internships, graduate courses open to undergrads. Off campus study at West Virginia Association of Independent Colleges and Universities. Study abroad program.

Entrance Requirements: Required: high school transcript, minimum 2 high school GPA. Recommended: essay, interview. Required for some: interview, SAT or ACT.

Costs Per Year: Comprehensive fee: $21,100 includes full-time tuition ($13,050), mandatory fees ($1650), and college room and board ($6400). College room only: $2400. Full-time tuition and fees vary according to degree level and program. Part-time tuition: $435 per credit. Part-time mandatory fees: $55 per credit. Part-time tuition and fees vary according to degree level and program.

Collegiate Environment: Orientation program. Social organizations: 25 open to all; national fraternities, national sororities, local fraternities, local sororities; 1% of eligible men and 1% of eligible women are members. Most popular organizations: student government, Alpha Phi Omega, Gamma Beta Phi. Major annual events: Homecoming, Spring Fling, Convocation. Student services: personal-psychological counseling. Campus security: 24-hour emergency response devices and patrols. 599 college housing spaces available; 199 were occupied in 2012-13. Freshmen guaranteed college housing. On-campus residence required in freshman year. Options: coed, men-only, women-only housing available. Benedum Library with 61,654 books, 485,126 microform titles, 43 serials, 1,203 audiovisual materials, an OPAC, and a Web page. 104 computers available on campus for general student use. A campuswide network can be accessed from student residence rooms and from off campus. Students can access the following: online class registration. Staffed computer lab on campus provides training in use of computers, software, and the Internet.

Community Environment: Tucked into a quiet valley, Salem-Teikyo University is surrounded by the scenic mountains for which West Virginia is known. Nearby parks provide excellent hiking, biking, white water rafting, skiing and fishing locations. Although the atmosphere is rural, students are within minutes of shopping malls, cinemas, fine restaurants, and the Benedum Airport. There is easy access to metropolitan areas such as Pittsburgh, Washington, D.C., and New York.

■ **SHEPHERD UNIVERSITY**
PO Box 5000
Shepherdstown, WV 25443
Tel: (304)876-5000; Free: 800-344-5231
Fax: (304)876-5165
E-mail: admissions@shepherd.edu
Web Site: www.shepherd.edu/

Description: State-supported, comprehensive, coed. Part of West Virginia Higher Education Policy Commission. Awards bachelor's and master's degrees. Founded 1871. Setting: 320-acre small town campus with easy access to Washington, DC. Endowment: $25.4 million. Research spending for the previous fiscal year: $243,500. Educational spending for the previous fiscal year: $4462 per student. Total enrollment: 4,326. Faculty: 367 (142 full-time, 225 part-time). Student-undergrad faculty ratio is 18:1. 2,023 applied, 81% were admitted. Full-time: 3,484 students, 58% women, 42% men. Part-time: 686 students, 56% women, 44% men. Students come from 48 states and territories, 16 other countries, 37% from out-of-state. 1% American Indian or Alaska Native, non-Hispanic/Latino; 3% Hispanic/Latino; 7% African American, non-Hispanic/Latino; 2% Asian, non-Hispanic/Latino; 0.1% Native Hawaiian or other Pacific Islander, non-Hispanic/Latino; 0.4% international. 19% 25 or older, 34% live on campus, 11% transferred in. Retention: 63% of full-time freshmen returned the following year. Academic areas with the most degrees conferred: liberal arts/general studies; business/marketing; education. Core. Calendar: semesters. Academic remediation for entering students, services for LD students, advanced placement, honors program, independent study, distance learning, double major, summer session for credit, part-time degree program, adult/continuing education programs, co-op programs and internships, graduate courses open to undergrads. Study abroad program. ROTC: Air Force (c).

Entrance Requirements: Options: electronic application, early admission, early action, deferred admission, international baccalaureate accepted. Required: high school transcript, minimum 2 high school GPA, SAT or ACT. Recommended: essay, minimum 3 high school GPA, 3 recommendations. Entrance: moderately difficult. Application deadlines: Rolling, Rolling for nonresidents, 11/15 for early action. Notification: continuous until 8/15, continuous until 8/15 for nonresidents, 12/15 for early action. SAT Reasoning Test deadline: 8/15. Transfer credits accepted: Yes. Early action applicants: 797. Early action applicants admitted: 672.

Costs Per Year: Application fee: $45. State resident tuition: $5834 full-time, $237 per credit hour part-time. Nonresident tuition: $15,136 full-time, $625 per credit hour part-time. Full-time tuition varies according to program and reciprocity agreements. Part-time tuition varies according to program. College room and board: $8424. Room and board charges vary according to board plan and housing facility.

Collegiate Environment: Orientation program. Drama-theater group, choral group, marching band, student-run newspaper, radio station. Social organizations: 92 open to all; national fraternities, national sororities; 3% of eligible men and 4% of eligible women are members. Most popular organizations: Relay for Life, Sigma Sigma Sigma, Ram Marching Band, Student Government Association, Delta Zeta. Major annual events: Homecoming, Midnight Breakfast, Late Night in the Zone. Student services: health clinic, personal-psychological counseling. Campus security: 24-hour emergency response devices and patrols, late night transport-escort service, controlled dormitory access, student security in academic buildings, RAVE emergency alert system. 1,302 college housing spaces available; 1,237 were occupied in 2012-13. Freshmen given priority for college housing. On-campus residence required through senior year. Option: coed housing available. Ruth Scarborough Library with 285,494 books, 89,682 microform titles, 45,260 serials, 10,226 audiovisual materials, an OPAC, and a Web page. Operations spending for the previous fiscal year: $1.4 million. 451 computers available on campus for general student use. A campuswide network can be accessed from student residence rooms. Students can access the following: online class registration, personal Web pages. Staffed computer lab on campus provides training in use of computers, software, and the Internet.

Community Environment: Shepherdstown is a small town of about 5,000 located near Martinsburg, Charles Town and Harpers Ferry, West Virginia, and Hagerstown, Maryland. The town was established by English and German farmers who had crossed the river from Maryland before 1730. There are many historic sites in the area. The climate is temperate and the community is reached by State Route 45. There are 10 churches, 4 libraries, and 4 hospitals nearby. Some part-time employment is available in the surrounding area.

■ **SOUTHERN WEST VIRGINIA COMMUNITY AND TECHNICAL COLLEGE**
Dempsey Branch Rd.
Mount Gay, WV 25637-2900
Tel: (304)792-7160
Fax: (304)792-7096
E-mail: admissions@southern.wvnet.edu
Web Site: southernwv.edu/

Description: State-supported, 2-year, coed. Part of State College System of West Virginia. Awards certificates, transfer associate, and terminal associate degrees. Founded 1971. Setting: 23-acre rural campus. Total enrollment: 1,900. Faculty: 171 (66 full-time, 105 part-time). Student-undergrad faculty ratio is 20:1. 603 applied, 100% were admitted. 5% from top 10% of their high school class, 12% from top quarter, 32% from top half. Full-time: 1,192 students, 71% women, 29% men. Part-time: 708 students, 77% women, 23% men. Students come from 3 states and territories, 9% from out-of-state. 24% 25 or older, 5% transferred in. Core. Calendar: semesters. Academic remediation for entering students, services for LD students, advanced placement, summer session for credit, part-time degree program, external degree program, adult/continuing education programs, co-op programs.

Entrance Requirements: Open admission except for nursing, medical laboratory technology, radiological technology programs. Options: early admission, deferred admission. Required: high school transcript. Entrance: noncompetitive. Application deadline: Rolling. Notification: continuous.

Collegiate Environment: Drama-theater group. Student services: personal-psychological counseling. Harless Library plus 1 other with 66,400 books, 1,200 microform titles, 12,400 serials, 6,000 audiovisual materials, an OPAC, and a Web page. 92 computers available on campus for general student use. A campuswide network can be accessed from off-campus. Staffed computer lab on campus.

■ **STRAYER UNIVERSITY - TEAYS VALLEY CAMPUS**
100 Corporate Ctr. Dr.
Scott Depot, WV 25560
Tel: (304)760-1700
Fax: (304)757-1430
Web Site: www.strayer.edu/campus/teays-valley
Description: Proprietary, comprehensive, coed. Awards associate, bachelor's, and master's degrees.

■ **UNIVERSITY OF CHARLESTON**
2300 MacCorkle Ave., SE
Charleston, WV 25304-1099
Tel: (304)357-4800; Free: 800-995-GOUC
Fax: (304)357-4781
E-mail: admissions@ucwv.edu
Web Site: www.ucwv.edu/

Description: Independent, comprehensive, coed. Awards associate, bachelor's, master's, and doctoral degrees. Founded 1888. Setting: 40-acre urban campus. Total enrollment: 1,427. Faculty: 126 (83 full-time, 43 part-time). Student-undergrad faculty ratio is 15:1. 1,641 applied, 56% were admitted. 37% from top 10% of their high school class, 70% from top quarter, 91% from top half. Full-time: 993 students, 59% women, 41% men. Part-time: 33 students, 70% women, 30% men. Students come from 35 states and territories, 32 other countries, 37% from out-of-state. 0.4% American Indian or Alaska Native, non-Hispanic/Latino; 3% Hispanic/Latino; 12% African American, non-Hispanic/Latino; 1% Asian, non-Hispanic/Latino; 0% Native Hawaiian or other Pacific Islander, non-Hispanic/Latino; 10% international. 12% 25 or older, 61% live on campus, 14% transferred in. Retention: 70% of full-time freshmen returned the following year. Academic areas with the most degrees conferred: business/marketing; biological/life sciences; health professions and related sciences. Core. Calendar: semesters. Academic remediation for entering students, ESL program, services for LD students, advanced placement, accelerated degree program, self-designed majors, independent study, distance learning, double major, summer session for credit, part-time degree program, adult/continuing education programs, co-op programs and internships, graduate courses open to undergrads. Study abroad program. ROTC: Army.

Entrance Requirements: Options: electronic application, early admission, deferred admission, international baccalaureate accepted. Required: high school transcript, minimum 2.25 high school GPA, SAT or ACT. Recommended: essay. Required for some: interview. Entrance: moderately difficult. Application deadlines: Rolling, Rolling for nonresidents. Notification: continuous, continuous for nonresidents. Transfer credits accepted: Yes.

Costs Per Year: Application fee: $25. Comprehensive fee: $34,700 includes full-time tuition ($25,500), mandatory fees ($200), and college room and board ($9000). College room only: $4900. Full-time tuition and fees vary according to location and student level. Room and board charges vary according to board plan, housing facility, and location. Part-time tuition: $900 per credit hour. Part-time tuition varies according to course load, location, and program.

Collegiate Environment: Orientation program. Choral group, student-run newspaper. Social organizations: 29 open to all; national fraternities, national sororities, local sororities. Most popular organizations: Student Activities Board, American Society of Interior Designers, Student Government Association, Capito Association of Nursing Students, International Student Organization. Major annual events: Governor's Cup Regatta, Homecoming, Family Weekend. Student services: health clinic, personal-psychological counseling. Campus security: 24-hour emergency response devices and patrols, student patrols, late night transport-escort service, controlled dormitory access, radio connection to city police and ambulance. 826 college housing spaces available. Freshmen guaranteed college housing. On-campus residence required through sophomore year. Option: coed housing available. Schoenbaum Library plus 1 other with 94,267 books, 229,551 microform titles, 150 serials, 5,000 audiovisual materials, an OPAC, and a Web page. 200 computers available on campus for general student use. A campuswide network can be accessed from student residence rooms and from off campus. Students can access the following: online class registration. Staffed computer lab on campus provides training in use of software.

Community Environment: Charleston, with a metropolitan population of 307,700, is the state capital, as well as the cultural, social, political, and economic center of West Virginia. Located in the Kanawha Valley, near the foothills of the Appalachian Mountains, it offers scenic tranquility as well as the convenience and excitement of a modern city. Downtown Charleston, just a 5-minute drive from campus, offers social and cultural opportunities that can be found only in a large city.

■ **VALLEY COLLEGE OF TECHNOLOGY**
287 Aikens Ctr.
Martinsburg, WV 25404
Tel: (304)263-0979
Fax: (304)263-2413
E-mail: gkennedy@vct.edu
Web Site: www.vct.edu/
Description: Proprietary, 2-year, coed. Awards certificates and terminal associate degrees. Founded 1983. Setting: suburban campus. Total enrollment: 47. Faculty: 6 (4 full-time, 2 part-time). Student-undergrad faculty ratio is 14:1. Full-time: 47 students, 94% women, 6% men. Calendar: continuous.
Entrance Requirements: Required: high school transcript, interview.

■ **WEST LIBERTY UNIVERSITY**
208 University Dr.
West Liberty, WV 26074
Tel: (304)336-5000; Free: 866-WESTLIB
Fax: (304)336-8285
E-mail: wladmsn1@westliberty.edu
Web Site: www.westliberty.edu/
Description: State-supported, comprehensive, coed. Part of West Virginia Higher Education Policy Commission. Awards associate, bachelor's, and master's degrees. Founded 1837. Setting: rural campus. Total enrollment: 2,804. Faculty: 240 (144 full-time, 96 part-time). Student-undergrad faculty ratio is 14:1. 1,860 applied, 28% were admitted. 11% from top 10% of their high school class, 38% from top quarter, 75% from top half. Full-time: 2,331 students, 57% women, 43% men. Part-time: 387 students, 67% women, 33% men. Students come from 26 states and territories, 38 other countries, 28% from out-of-state. 0.1% American Indian or Alaska Native, non-Hispanic/Latino; 1% Hispanic/Latino; 4% African American, non-Hispanic/Latino; 1% Asian, non-Hispanic/Latino; 0.04% Native Hawaiian or other Pacific Islander, non-Hispanic/Latino; 2% international. 11% 25 or older, 47%

live on campus, 9% transferred in. Retention: 71% of full-time freshmen returned the following year. Academic areas with the most degrees conferred: business/marketing; health professions and related sciences; education. Calendar: semesters. Academic remediation for entering students, services for LD students, advanced placement, accelerated degree program, self-designed majors, honors program, independent study, distance learning, double major, summer session for credit, part-time degree program, external degree program, adult/continuing education programs, co-op programs and internships. Off campus study. Study abroad program.

Entrance Requirements: Option: electronic application. Required: high school transcript, minimum 2 high school GPA, SAT or ACT. Recommended: interview. Entrance: minimally difficult. Application deadline: Rolling. Notification: continuous. SAT Reasoning Test deadline: 8/1. SAT Subject Test deadline: 8/1. Transfer credits accepted: Yes.

Costs Per Year: Application fee: $0. State resident tuition: $5530 full-time, $230.42 per credit hour part-time. Nonresident tuition: $13,140 full-time, $547.50 per credit hour part-time. Mandatory fees: $275 full-time. Full-time tuition and fees vary according to course load, degree level, and program. Part-time tuition varies according to course load, degree level, and program. College room and board: $8200. College room only: $4720. Room and board charges vary according to board plan and housing facility.

Collegiate Environment: Orientation program. Campus security: 24-hour emergency response devices and patrols, controlled dormitory access. No special consideration for freshman housing applicants. Options: coed, men-only, women-only housing available. Paul N. Elbin Library plus 1 other with an OPAC.

Community Environment: West Liberty is located 10 miles from the city limits of Wheeling. There are 2 Protestant churches and a visiting priest for Catholic students. Famous Oglebay Park, 6 miles from the campus, is used for recreation. Job opportunities are good in the area. There are dormitories, campus health services, and an infirmary for students. Fraternities and sororities are prominent here.

■ **WEST VIRGINIA BUSINESS COLLEGE (NUTTER FORT)**
116 Pennsylvania Ave.
Nutter Fort, WV 26301
Tel: (304)624-7695
Fax: (304)622-2149
E-mail: info@wvbc.edu
Web Site: www.wvbc.edu/
Description: Independent, 2-year, coed. Awards certificates and terminal associate degrees. Founded 1980. Total enrollment: 1,224. Student-undergrad faculty ratio is 36:1. 735 applied, 95% were admitted. 0% from out-of-commonwealth. 44% 25 or older.

■ **WEST VIRGINIA BUSINESS COLLEGE (WHEELING)**
1052 Main St.
Wheeling, WV 26003
Tel: (304)232-0361
Fax: (304)232-0363
E-mail: wvbcwheeling@stratuswave.net
Web Site: www.wvbc.edu/
Description: Proprietary, 2-year, coed. Awards diplomas and terminal associate degrees. Founded 1881. Setting: 5-acre urban campus. Total enrollment: 78. Faculty: 10 (all part-time). Student-undergrad faculty ratio is 6:1. 12 applied, 100% were admitted. 0% from out-of-state. 50% 25 or older.
Collegiate Environment: Orientation program.

■ **WEST VIRGINIA JUNIOR COLLEGE–BRIDGEPORT**
176 Thompson Dr.
Bridgeport, WV 26330
Tel: (304)363-8824; Free: 800-470-5627
E-mail: apratt@wvjcinfo.net
Web Site: www.wvjcinfo.net/
Description: Proprietary, 2-year, coed. Part of West Virginia Junior College-Charleston, WV; West Virginia Junior College-Morgantown, WV; Pennsylvania Institute of Health & Technology-Uniontown, PA; Ohio Institute of Health & Technology, E. Liverpool, OH. Administratively affiliated with West Virginia Junior College-Charleston, WV (Main Campus). Awards transfer associate and terminal associate degrees. Founded 1922. Setting: 3-acre small town campus with easy access to Pittsburgh. Total enrollment: 507. Faculty: 19 (10 full-time, 9 part-time). Student-undergrad faculty ratio is 15:1. Full-time: 507 students, 83% women, 17% men. Students come from 4 states and territories, 0% from out-of-state. 0.4% African American, non-Hispanic/Latino.

30% 25 or older, 20% transferred in. Retention: 74% of full-time freshmen returned the following year. Core. Services for LD students, independent study, distance learning, summer session for credit, co-op programs and internships.

Entrance Requirements: Open admission. Option: electronic application. Required: essay, minimum 2.5 high school GPA, interview, Applicants are required to meet with an Admissions Representative. Recommended: high school transcript, SAT or ACT. Required for some: 1 recommendation. Entrance: minimally difficult. Application deadline: Rolling. Notification: continuous. Transfer credits accepted: Yes.

Collegiate Environment: Orientation program. Social organizations: 5 open to all; Each discipline has a Club; 50% of eligible men and 50% of eligible women are members. Most popular organizations: Medical Club, Business Club, Computer Club, Dental Assisting Club, Pharmacy Tech Club. Major annual events: Annual Alumni Picnic, Thanksgiving Covered Dish Dinner, Graduation. Campus security: 24-hour emergency response devices. College housing not available. WVJC Resource Center plus 1 other with an OPAC. Operations spending for the previous fiscal year: $10,000. 150 computers available on campus for general student use. A campuswide network can be accessed from student residence rooms and from off campus. Students can access the following: online class registration. Staffed computer lab on campus provides training in use of computers, software, and the Internet.

■ **WEST VIRGINIA JUNIOR COLLEGE–CHARLESTON**
1000 Virginia St. E
Charleston, WV 25301-2817
Tel: (304)345-2820; Free: 800-924-5208
Web Site: www.wvjc.edu/

Description: Proprietary, 2-year, coed. Awards terminal associate degrees. Founded 1892. Setting: urban campus. Total enrollment: 201. Student-undergrad faculty ratio is 17:1. 52% 25 or older. Retention: 61% of full-time freshmen returned the following year. Summer session for credit, part-time degree program, adult/continuing education programs.

Entrance Requirements: Open admission. Entrance: noncompetitive. Application deadline: Rolling.

■ **WEST VIRGINIA JUNIOR COLLEGE–MORGANTOWN**
148 Willey St.
Morgantown, WV 26505-5521
Tel: (304)296-8282
Web Site: www.wvjcmorgantown.edu/

Description: Proprietary, 2-year, coed. Awards terminal associate degrees (also offers non-degree programs with significant enrollment not reflected in profile). Founded 1922. Setting: small town campus with easy access to Pittsburgh. Total enrollment: 150. Student-undergrad faculty ratio is 32:1. 3% from out-of-state. 39% 25 or older. Retention: 64% of full-time freshmen returned the following year. Adult/continuing education programs.

Entrance Requirements: Open admission. Required: high school transcript, interview. Entrance: noncompetitive. Application deadline: Rolling. Notification: continuous.

■ **WEST VIRGINIA NORTHERN COMMUNITY COLLEGE**
1704 Market St.
Wheeling, WV 26003-3699
Tel: (304)233-5900
Fax: (304)233-5900
E-mail: jfike@northern.wvnet.edu
Web Site: www.wvncc.edu/

Description: State-supported, 2-year, coed. Awards certificates, transfer associate, and terminal associate degrees. Founded 1972. Setting: small town campus with easy access to Pittsburgh. Endowment: $659,426. Educational spending for the previous fiscal year: $1552 per student. Total enrollment: 2,505. Faculty: 190 (58 full-time, 132 part-time). 350 applied, 100% were admitted. 5% from top 10% of their high school class, 10% from top quarter, 19% from top half. Full-time: 1,156 students, 67% women, 33% men. Part-time: 1,349 students, 69% women, 31% men. Students come from 14 states and territories, 24% from out-of-state. 0.3% American Indian or Alaska Native, non-Hispanic/Latino; 0.4% Hispanic/Latino; 5% African American, non-Hispanic/Latino; 0.4% Asian, non-Hispanic/Latino; 0% Native Hawaiian or other Pacific Islander, non-Hispanic/Latino; 0% international. 50% 25 or older, 12% transferred in. Core. Calendar: semesters. Academic remediation for entering students, services for LD students, advanced placement, accelerated degree program, self-designed majors, honors program, distance

learning, double major, summer session for credit, part-time degree program, adult/continuing education programs, co-op programs and internships.

Entrance Requirements: Open admission except for health science programs. Options: electronic application, early admission, deferred admission. Recommended: Compass. Required for some: high school transcript, Compass. Entrance: noncompetitive. Application deadline: Rolling. Transfer credits accepted: Yes.

Costs Per Year: Application fee: $0. State resident tuition: $2256 full-time. Nonresident tuition: $7416 full-time. Mandatory fees: $390 full-time. Full-time tuition and fees vary according to course load, location, program, reciprocity agreements, and student level.

Collegiate Environment: Orientation program. Student-run newspaper. Social organizations: Phi Theta Kappa; 23% of eligible men and 77% of eligible women are members. Most popular organization: Community Outreach Opportunity Program (COOP). Campus security: police officer on staff during the day at Main Campus, security personnel during evening and during night classes. College housing not available. Wheeling B&O Campus Library plus 2 others with 36,650 books, 8 microform titles, 188 serials, 3,495 audiovisual materials, an OPAC, and a Web page. Operations spending for the previous fiscal year: $121,220. 300 computers available on campus for general student use. A campuswide network can be accessed. Students can access the following: online class registration, Student Portal.

Community Environment: Wheeling, one of the country's most liveable small cities, is a one-hour drive from Pittsburgh, PA, and a two-hour drive from Columbus, OH. It is in a central area of approximately 150,000 people. Many cultural and recreational facilities are available, including 1,500-acre Oglebay Park and 250-acre Wheeling Park. Excellent local recreation areas provide opportunities for camping, hiking, skiing, swimming, golf, and other such activities.

■ **WEST VIRGINIA STATE UNIVERSITY**
PO Box 1000
Institute, WV 25112-1000
Tel: (304)766-3000; Free: 800-987-2112
Fax: (304)766-4158
Web Site: www.wvstateu.edu/

Description: State-supported, comprehensive, coed. Part of State College System of West Virginia. Awards bachelor's and master's degrees. Founded 1891. Setting: 98-acre suburban campus. Total enrollment: 2,644. Faculty: 179 (119 full-time, 60 part-time). Student-undergrad faculty ratio is 15:1. 798 applied, 84% were admitted. Students come from 22 states and territories, 4 other countries, 8% from out-of-state. 37% 25 or older, 7% live on campus. Retention: 54% of full-time freshmen returned the following year. Academic areas with the most degrees conferred: liberal arts/general studies; education; business/marketing. Core. Calendar: semesters. Academic remediation for entering students, services for LD students, advanced placement, accelerated degree program, summer session for credit, part-time degree program, external degree program, adult/continuing education programs, co-op programs and internships. ROTC: Army.

Entrance Requirements: Options: electronic application, early admission. Required: high school transcript. Recommended: SAT. Required for some: SAT or ACT. Entrance: minimally difficult. Application deadline: 8/11. Notification: continuous.

Costs Per Year: Application fee: $0. State resident tuition: $5442 full-time, $222 per credit hour part-time. Nonresident tuition: $12,720 full-time, $525 per credit hour part-time. Full-time tuition varies according to course load and program. Part-time tuition varies according to course load and program. College room and board: $6698. College room only: $3382. Room and board charges vary according to board plan and housing facility.

Collegiate Environment: Orientation program. Choral group, marching band, student-run newspaper. Social organizations: 22 open to all; national fraternities, national sororities; 1% of eligible men and 1% of eligible women are members. Major annual event: Homecoming. Student services: health clinic, personal-psychological counseling. Campus security: 24-hour emergency response devices and patrols, late night transport-escort service. On-campus residence required in freshman year. Options: men-only, women-only housing available. Drain-Jordan Library with 190,067 books, 64,877 microform titles, 355 serials, 4,694 audiovisual materials, and an OPAC.

Community Environment: Institute is a suburb of Charleston and is reached by railroad, bus lines, feeder airlines, and a local transit system. There are churches of major denominations and community services in the easily accessible neighboring community. Part-time employment is available.

■ WEST VIRGINIA UNIVERSITY

University Ave.
Morgantown, WV 26506
Tel: (304)293-0111; Free: 800-344-9881
Fax: (304)293-3080
E-mail: marilyn.potts@mail.wvu.edu
Web Site: www.wvu.edu/

Description: State-supported, university, coed. Part of West Virginia Higher Education Policy Commission. Awards bachelor's, master's, and doctoral degrees. Founded 1867. Setting: 1,400-acre small town campus with easy access to Pittsburgh. Endowment: $403.6 million. Research spending for the previous fiscal year: $143.6 million. Educational spending for the previous fiscal year: $9872 per student. Total enrollment: 29,707. Faculty: 1,360 (1,004 full-time, 356 part-time). Student-undergrad faculty ratio is 23:1. 16,521 applied, 85% were admitted. 17% from top 10% of their high school class, 41% from top quarter, 75% from top half. Full-time: 21,118 students, 45% women, 55% men. Part-time: 1,709 students, 57% women, 43% men. Students come from 52 states and territories, 71 other countries, 47% from out-of-state. 0.2% American Indian or Alaska Native, non-Hispanic/Latino; 3% Hispanic/Latino; 4% African American, non-Hispanic/Latino; 2% Asian, non-Hispanic/Latino; 0.1% Native Hawaiian or other Pacific Islander, non-Hispanic/Latino; 3% international. 8% 25 or older, 24% live on campus, 5% transferred in. Retention: 77% of full-time freshmen returned the following year. Academic areas with the most degrees conferred: business/marketing; interdisciplinary studies; engineering. Core. Calendar: semesters. Academic remediation for entering students, ESL program, services for LD students, advanced placement, accelerated degree program, self-designed majors, honors program, independent study, distance learning, double major, summer session for credit, part-time degree program, external degree program, adult/continuing education programs, internships, graduate courses open to undergrads. Off campus study at Academic Common Market, Garrett County Community College. Study abroad program. ROTC: Army, Air Force.

Entrance Requirements: Option: international baccalaureate accepted. Required: high school transcript, minimum 2 high school GPA, SAT or ACT. Required for some: essay, minimum 2.25 high school GPA. Entrance: moderately difficult. Application deadline: 8/1. Preference given to state residents. SAT Reasoning Test deadline: 8/1. Transfer credits accepted: Yes.

Costs Per Year: Application fee: $45. State resident tuition: $6090 full-time, $254 per credit hour part-time. Nonresident tuition: $18,868 full-time, $786 per credit hour part-time. Full-time tuition varies according to location, program, and reciprocity agreements. Part-time tuition varies according to course load, location, program, and reciprocity agreements. College room and board: $8782. Room and board charges vary according to board plan, housing facility, and location.

Collegiate Environment: Orientation program. Drama-theater group, choral group, marching band, student-run newspaper, radio station. Social organizations: 390 open to all; national fraternities, national sororities; 8% of eligible men and 7% of eligible women are members. Most popular organizations: Residential Hall Association, Alpha Phi Omega, WVU Greek System, Mountaineer Maniacs, Campus Crusade for Christ. Major annual events: Mountaineer Week, Fall Fest, Parents' Weekend and Homecoming. Student services: legal services, health clinic, personal-psychological counseling, women's center. Campus security: 24-hour emergency response devices and patrols, student patrols, late night transport-escort service, controlled dormitory access, patrol officers just for housing. 5,781 college housing spaces available; all were occupied in 2012-13. Freshmen guaranteed college housing. On-campus residence required in freshman year. Options: coed, men-only, women-only housing available. Downtown Library Complex plus 5 others with 1.9 million books, 2.4 million microform titles, 59,860 serials, 31,594 audiovisual materials, an OPAC, and a Web page. Operations spending for the previous fiscal year: $14.1 million. 2,500 computers available on campus for general student use. Computer purchase/lease plans available. A campuswide network can be accessed from student residence rooms and from off campus. Students can access the following: online class registration. Staffed computer lab on campus provides training in use of computers, software, and the Internet.

Community Environment: West Virginia University's main campus is located in Morgantown, a small city of 30,000 in the Appalachian Mountains on West Virginia's northern border. Although the state is rural and the community quiet, Greater Morgantown is within easy traveling distance, on modern interstate highways, of the metropolitan areas of Pittsburgh, about 70 miles north, and Baltimore and Washington, D.C., about 200 miles to the east. The community has churches of various denominations, two hospitals, a city library, and various civic and fraternal organizations. Local recreation is available through the city's park system which includes several municipal pools and an ice skating rink. The area has golf courses, 1,800-acre Cheat Lake, whitewater rafting, and nearby Cooper's Rock State Forest. A half dozen snow skiing areas are within easy driving distance, as are some of the best remaining wilderness areas in the eastern United States.

■ WEST VIRGINIA UNIVERSITY INSTITUTE OF TECHNOLOGY

405 Fayette Pke.
Montgomery, WV 25136
Tel: (304)442-3071; Free: 888-554-8324
Fax: (304)442-3097
E-mail: Tech-Admissions@mail.wvu.edu
Web Site: www.wvutech.edu/

Description: State-supported, comprehensive, coed. Administratively affiliated with West Virginia University. Awards bachelor's degrees. Founded 1895. Setting: 200-acre small town campus. Endowment: $1.9 million. Research spending for the previous fiscal year: $770,000. Educational spending for the previous fiscal year: $7800 per student. Total enrollment: 1,107. Faculty: 99 (78 full-time, 21 part-time). Student-undergrad faculty ratio is 11:1. 1,033 applied, 51% were admitted. 19% from top 10% of their high school class, 50% from top quarter, 78% from top half. Full-time: 840 students, 38% women, 63% men. Part-time: 267 students, 45% women, 55% men. Students come from 29 states and territories, 20 other countries, 17% from out-of-state. 1% American Indian or Alaska Native, non-Hispanic/Latino; 2% Hispanic/Latino; 6% African American, non-Hispanic/Latino; 2% Asian, non-Hispanic/Latino; 0.1% Native Hawaiian or other Pacific Islander, non-Hispanic/Latino; 3% international. 37% 25 or older, 28% live on campus, 10% transferred in. Retention: 45% of full-time freshmen returned the following year. Academic areas with the most degrees conferred: engineering; liberal arts/general studies; engineering technologies. Core. Calendar: semesters. Academic remediation for entering students, services for LD students, advanced placement, self-designed majors, independent study, distance learning, double major, summer session for credit, part-time degree program, co-op programs and internships. Study abroad program. ROTC: Army.

Entrance Requirements: Options: electronic application, early admission. Required: high school transcript, minimum 2 high school GPA, Must have minimum ACT composite score of 18 or 870 SAT math + verbal; Requirement waived for students having 3.0 HS GPA or higher, SAT or ACT. Required for some: TOEFL or IELTS. Entrance: minimally difficult. Application deadlines: Rolling, Rolling for nonresidents. Notification: continuous until 8/15, continuous for nonresidents. SAT Reasoning Test deadline: 8/16. SAT Subject Test deadline: 8/16. Transfer credits accepted: Yes.

Costs Per Year: Application fee: $0. State resident tuition: $5558 full-time. Nonresident tuition: $13,980 full-time. Full-time tuition varies according to program. College room and board: $8414. College room only: $4968. Room and board charges vary according to board plan and housing facility.

Collegiate Environment: Orientation program. Drama-theater group, student-run newspaper. Social organizations: 40 open to all; national fraternities, national sororities, local sororities. Most popular organizations: Christian Student Union, Student Activities Board, Alpha Phi Omega, Student Government Association, American Society of Mechanical Engineers. Major annual events: Homecoming, Light Up Old Main, Pre-Exam Jam. Student services: health clinic, personal-psychological counseling. Campus security: 24-hour emergency response devices and patrols. 400 college housing spaces available; 310 were occupied in 2012-13. Freshmen guaranteed college housing. On-campus residence required through sophomore year. Option: coed housing available. Vining Library plus 1 other with 166,292 books, 431,948 microform titles, 605 serials, an OPAC, and a Web page. Operations spending for the previous fiscal year: $650,000. 200 computers available on campus for general student use. A campuswide network can be accessed from student residence rooms and from off campus. Students can access the following: online class registration, electronic course materials through eCampus. Staffed computer lab on campus provides training in use of software.

Community Environment: The community has nearby plants that include the world's largest producer of ferro alloys for steel and a steam-produced electric power plant. Montgomery may be reached by bus lines and Amtrak.

■ WEST VIRGINIA UNIVERSITY AT PARKERSBURG

300 Campus Dr.
Parkersburg, WV 26104
Tel: (304)424-8000; Free: 800-WVA-WVUP
E-mail: christine.post@mail.wvu.edu

Web Site: www.wvup.edu/

Description: State-supported, primarily 2-year, coed. Administratively affiliated with West Virginia University. Awards certificates, transfer associate, terminal associate, and bachelor's degrees. Founded 1961. Setting: 120-acre small town campus. Total enrollment: 4,223. Student-undergrad faculty ratio is 24:1. 1% from out-of-state. 44% 25 or older. Retention: 57% of full-time freshmen returned the following year. Core. Calendar: semesters. Academic remediation for entering students, ESL program, services for LD students, advanced placement, independent study, distance learning, summer session for credit, part-time degree program, co-op programs and internships. Study abroad program.

Entrance Requirements: Open admission except for nursing, bachelor of science degree programs, surgical technology, paramedic science. Options: electronic application, early admission, deferred admission. Required for some: high school transcript. Entrance: noncompetitive. Application deadlines: Rolling, Rolling for nonresidents. Notification: continuous, continuous for nonresidents.

Collegiate Environment: Orientation program. Drama-theater group, student-run newspaper. Student services: health clinic, personal-psychological counseling. WVUP Library with an OPAC and a Web page.

■ **WEST VIRGINIA WESLEYAN COLLEGE**
59 College Ave.
Buckhannon, WV 26201
Tel: (304)473-8000; Free: 800-722-9933
Fax: (304)472-2571
E-mail: admission@wvwc.edu
Web Site: www.wvwc.edu/

Description: Independent, comprehensive, coed, affiliated with United Methodist Church. Awards bachelor's and master's degrees. Founded 1890. Setting: 180-acre small town campus. Endowment: $34 million. Educational spending for the previous fiscal year: $6123 per student. Total enrollment: 1,394. Faculty: 156 (89 full-time, 67 part-time). Student-undergrad faculty ratio is 12:1. 2,008 applied, 78% were admitted. 26% from top 10% of their high school class, 51% from top quarter, 80% from top half. 6 valedictorians. Full-time: 1,289 students, 54% women, 46% men. Part-time: 26 students, 42% women, 58% men. Students come from 34 states and territories, 17 other countries, 41% from out-of-state. 0.2% American Indian or Alaska Native, non-Hispanic/Latino; 2% Hispanic/Latino; 11% African American, non-Hispanic/Latino; 0.2% Asian, non-Hispanic/Latino; 0.3% Native Hawaiian or other Pacific Islander, non-Hispanic/Latino; 4% international. 3% 25 or older, 76% live on campus, 5% transferred in. Retention: 64% of full-time freshmen returned the following year. Academic areas with the most degrees conferred: business/marketing; education; health professions and related sciences. Core. Calendar: semesters. Academic remediation for entering students, ESL program, services for LD students, advanced placement, self-designed majors, honors program, independent study, double major, summer session for credit, part-time degree program, internships, graduate courses open to undergrads. Off campus study. Study abroad program.

Entrance Requirements: Options: electronic application, deferred admission. Required: high school transcript, SAT or ACT. Recommended: essay, interview. Required for some: SAT Subject Tests. Entrance: moderately difficult. Notification: continuous. SAT Reasoning Test deadline: 7/1. SAT Subject Test deadline: 7/1.

Costs Per Year: Application fee: $35. Comprehensive fee: $34,534 includes full-time tuition ($25,650), mandatory fees ($1144), and college room and board ($7740). Full-time tuition and fees vary according to course load. Room and board charges vary according to board plan and housing facility.

Collegiate Environment: Orientation program. Drama-theater group, choral group, student-run newspaper, radio station. Social organizations: 84 open to all; national fraternities, national sororities; 25% of eligible men and 25% of eligible women are members. Most popular organizations: Campus Activities Board, Green Club, Students in Free Enterprise (SIFE), Wesleyan Ambassadors. Major annual events: Founders' Day/Homecoming, Festival of Lessons and Carols, Spring Weekend. Student services: health clinic, personal-psychological counseling. Campus security: 24-hour emergency response devices and patrols, student patrols, late night transport-escort service, controlled dormitory access. 1,348 college housing spaces available; 1,038 were occupied in 2012-13. Freshmen guaranteed college housing. On-campus residence required through senior year. Options: coed, men-only, women-only housing available. Annie Merner Pfeifer Library with 130,000 books, 14,500 serials, 6,000 audiovisual materials, an OPAC, and a Web page.

Community Environment: Buckhannon is a rural community supported by

agriculture, coal, natural gas, and local industries. The climate is temperate with an average annual temperature of 53 degrees. Bus and airlines are accessible 25 miles distant at Clarksburg. The community has a public library, restaurants, hotels, churches of most denominations, 1 hospital, and a YWCA. Part-time employment is available. Buckhannon is the home of the West Virginia Strawberry Festival. Local recreation includes hunting, fishing, boating, skiing, white-water rafting, and most outdoor sports. Civic, fraternal, and veterans' organizations are active in the area.

■ **WHEELING JESUIT UNIVERSITY**
316 Washington Ave.
Wheeling, WV 26003-6295
Tel: (304)243-2000; Free: 800-624-6992
Fax: (304)243-2397
E-mail: bloy@wju.edu
Web Site: www.wju.edu/

Description: Independent Roman Catholic (Jesuit), comprehensive, coed. Awards bachelor's, master's, and doctoral degrees and post-master's certificates. Founded 1954. Setting: 65-acre suburban campus with easy access to Pittsburgh. Endowment: $19.2 million. Research spending for the previous fiscal year: $7 million. Educational spending for the previous fiscal year: $8325 per student. Total enrollment: 1,563. Faculty: 156 (90 full-time, 66 part-time). Student-undergrad faculty ratio is 11:1. 1,401 applied, 63% were admitted. 18% from top 10% of their high school class, 48% from top quarter, 83% from top half. Full-time: 929 students, 54% women, 46% men. Part-time: 244 students, 74% women, 26% men. Students come from 28 states and territories, 16 other countries, 68% from out-of-state. 0% American Indian or Alaska Native, non-Hispanic/Latino; 2% Hispanic/Latino; 4% African American, non-Hispanic/Latino; 2% Asian, non-Hispanic/Latino; 0.4% Native Hawaiian or other Pacific Islander, non-Hispanic/Latino; 3% international. 17% 25 or older, 84% live on campus, 4% transferred in. Retention: 72% of full-time freshmen returned the following year. Academic areas with the most degrees conferred: health professions and related sciences; business/marketing; liberal arts/general studies. Core. Calendar: semesters. Academic remediation for entering students, ESL program, services for LD students, advanced placement, accelerated degree program, self-designed majors, honors program, independent study, distance learning, double major, summer session for credit, part-time degree program, external degree program, adult/continuing education programs, internships, graduate courses open to undergrads. Off campus study at Bethany College, Belmont Technical College, members of the Jesuit Student Exchange. Study abroad program.

Entrance Requirements: Options: electronic application, deferred admission, international baccalaureate accepted. Required: high school transcript, SAT or ACT. Recommended: essay, minimum 3 high school GPA, 2 recommendations, interview. Required for some: interview. Entrance: moderately difficult. Application deadline: Rolling. Notification: continuous. SAT Reasoning Test deadline: 8/1. Transfer credits accepted: Yes.

Costs Per Year: Application fee: $25. Comprehensive fee: $30,640 includes full-time tuition ($24,650), mandatory fees ($990), and college room and board ($5000). Room and board charges vary according to board plan and housing facility. Part-time tuition: $675 per credit hour.

Collegiate Environment: Orientation program. Drama-theater group, choral group, student-run newspaper, radio station. Social organizations: 26 open to all. Most popular organizations: Campus Activity Board (CAB), Theater Guild, Student Senate, International Student Club, Campus Ministry. Major annual events: Culture Fest, Last Blast Carnival, Homecoming/Family Weekend. Student services: health clinic, personal-psychological counseling. Campus security: 24-hour emergency response devices and patrols, student patrols, late night transport-escort service, controlled dormitory access. 979 college housing spaces available; 749 were occupied in 2012-13. Freshmen guaranteed college housing. On-campus residence required through senior year. Options: coed, men-only, women-only housing available. Bishop Hodges Library with 282,379 books, 135,030 microform titles, 232 serials, 45,450 audiovisual materials, an OPAC, and a Web page. Operations spending for the previous fiscal year: $385,387. 215 computers available on campus for general student use. A campuswide network can be accessed from student residence rooms and from off campus. Students can access the following: online class registration.

Community Environment: Wheeling, one of the country's most liveable small cities, is a one-hour drive from Pittsburgh, PA and a two-hour drive from Columbus, OH. In a central area of approximately 150,000 people, many cultural and recreational facilities are available for golf, camping, hiking, skiing, and swimming, including 1,500-acre Oglebay Park and 250-acre Wheeling Park.

■ ALVERNO COLLEGE

3400 S 43rd St.
Milwaukee, WI 53234-3922
Tel: (414)382-6000; Free: 800-933-3401
Fax: (414)382-6354
E-mail: admissions@alverno.edu
Web Site: www.alverno.edu/

Description: Independent Roman Catholic, comprehensive. Awards associate, bachelor's, and master's degrees and post-master's certificates (also offers weekend program with significant enrollment not reflected in profile). Founded 1887. Setting: 46-acre urban campus. Endowment: $19.8 million. Research spending for the previous fiscal year: $721,236. Educational spending for the previous fiscal year: $6547 per student. Total enrollment: 2,522. Faculty: 269 (119 full-time, 150 part-time). Student-undergrad faculty ratio is 10:1. 643 applied, 65% were admitted. 16% from top 10% of their high school class, 30% from top quarter, 60% from top half. Full-time: 1,412 students, 100% women. Part-time: 520 students, 99% women, 1% men. Students come from 11 states and territories, 12 other countries, 4% from out-of-state. 1% American Indian or Alaska Native, non-Hispanic/Latino; 17% Hispanic/Latino; 18% African American, non-Hispanic/Latino; 5% Asian, non-Hispanic/Latino; 0.2% Native Hawaiian or other Pacific Islander, non-Hispanic/Latino; 1% international. 36% 25 or older, 11% live on campus, 10% transferred in. Retention: 72% of full-time freshmen returned the following year. Academic areas with the most degrees conferred: health professions and related sciences; business/marketing; education. Core. Calendar: semesters. Academic remediation for entering students, services for LD students, advanced placement, self-designed majors, independent study, double major, summer session for credit, part-time degree program, adult/continuing education programs, internships. Study abroad program. ROTC: Army (c), Air Force (c).

Entrance Requirements: Options: electronic application, deferred admission, international baccalaureate accepted. Required: essay, high school transcript, 2.0 on any college work, ACT or SAT, SAT or ACT. Recommended: minimum 2 high school GPA, interview. Entrance: moderately difficult. Application deadline: Rolling. Notification: continuous. Transfer credits accepted: Yes.

Costs Per Year: Application fee: $20. Comprehensive fee: $29,176 includes full-time tuition ($21,576), mandatory fees ($550), and college room and board ($7050). Full-time tuition and fees vary according to program. Room and board charges vary according to board plan and housing facility. Part-time tuition: $899 per credit hour. Part-time tuition varies according to program.

Collegiate Environment: Orientation program. Drama-theater group, choral group, student-run newspaper, radio station. Social organizations: 37 open to all; local sororities; 1% of women are members. Most popular organizations: Student Nurses Association, Team Green, Alverno Student Wisconsin Education Association, Circle K, Gay-Straight Alliance. Major annual events: Convocation, Student Involvement Fair, Community Day. Student services: health clinic, personal-psychological counseling. Campus security: 24-hour emergency response devices and patrols, late night transport-escort service, controlled dormitory access, well-lit parking lots and pathways, emergency first-aid and CPR, crisis intervention team and plan in place. 269 college housing spaces available; 212 were occupied in 2012-13. Freshmen guaranteed college housing. Option: women-only housing available. Alverno College Library with 177,846 books, 246,730 microform titles, 46,569 serials, 4,828 audiovisual materials, an OPAC, and a Web page. Operations spending for the previous fiscal year: $958,369. 624 computers available on campus for general student use. A campuswide network can be accessed from student residence rooms and from off campus. Students can access the following: online class registration. Staffed computer lab on campus provides training in use of computers, software, and the Internet.

Community Environment: See Milwaukee Area Technical College.

■ THE ART INSTITUTE OF WISCONSIN

320 E Buffalo St.
Ste. 600
Milwaukee, WI 53202
Tel: (414)978-5000; Free: 877-285-4234
Fax: (414)978-5182
Web Site: www.artinstitutes.edu/milwaukee

Description: Proprietary, 4-year, coed. Part of Education Management Corporation. Awards associate and bachelor's degrees.

■ BELLIN COLLEGE

3201 Eaton Rd.
Green Bay, WI 54305
Tel: (920)433-3560; Free: 800-236-8707
Fax: (920)433-7416
E-mail: admissio@bcon.edu
Web Site: www.bellincollege.edu/

Description: Independent, comprehensive, coed. Administratively affiliated with Bellin Health System. Awards bachelor's and master's degrees. Founded 1909. Setting: urban campus. Total enrollment: 304. 92 applied. 22% 25 or older. Core. Calendar: semesters. Advanced placement, accelerated degree program, independent study, distance learning, summer session for credit, part-time degree program. Off campus study at University of Wisconsin-Green Bay. ROTC: Army (c).

Entrance Requirements: Option: electronic application. Required: high school transcript, minimum 3.25 high school GPA, 3 recommendations, interview, ACT. Recommended: minimum 3.25 high school GPA. Entrance: moderately difficult. Application deadline: Rolling. Notification: continuous.

Collegiate Environment: Orientation program. Student services: health clinic, personal-psychological counseling. Campus security: 24-hour patrols, late night transport-escort service, electronically operated building access after hours. Meredith B. and John M. Rose Library with 7,000 books, 225 serials, and 600 audiovisual materials.

■ BELOIT COLLEGE

700 College St.
Beloit, WI 53511-5596
Tel: (608)363-2000; Free: 800-9-BELOIT
Fax: (608)363-2075
E-mail: admiss@beloit.edu
Web Site: www.beloit.edu/

Description: Independent, 4-year, coed. Awards bachelor's degrees. Founded 1846. Setting: 65-acre small town campus with easy access to Chicago, Milwaukee. Endowment: $113.7 million. Research spending for the previous fiscal year: $68,777. Educational spending for the previous fiscal year: $15,136 per student. Total enrollment: 1,359. Faculty: 137 (115 full-time, 22 part-time). Student-undergrad faculty ratio is 11:1. 2,205 applied, 67% were admitted. 34% from top 10% of their high school class, 74% from top quarter, 97% from top half. Full-time: 1,290 students, 59% women, 41% men. Part-time: 69 students, 65% women, 35% men. Students come from 51 states and territories, 36 other countries, 80% from out-of-state. 0.4% American Indian or Alaska Native, non-Hispanic/Latino; 8% Hispanic/Latino; 4% African American, non-Hispanic/Latino; 2% Asian, non-Hispanic/Latino; 0.1% Native Hawaiian or other Pacific Islander, non-Hispanic/Latino; 10% international. 2% 25 or older, 94% live on campus, 0% transferred in. Retention: 91% of full-time freshmen returned the following year. Academic areas with the most degrees conferred: social sciences; foreign languages and literature; English. Core. Calendar: semesters. ESL program, services for LD students, advanced placement, self-designed majors, independent study, double major, summer session for credit, adult/continuing education programs, internships. Off campus study at University of Wisconsin-Madison, American University, Rush University, Duke University, Associated Colleges of the Midwest. Study abroad program.

Entrance Requirements: Options: electronic application, early admission, early decision, early action, deferred admission, international baccalaureate accepted. Required: essay, 1 recommendation, SAT or ACT. Recommended: interview. Entrance: very difficult. Application deadlines: 1/15, 1/15 for nonresidents, 12/1 for early decision, 10/1 for early action. Notification: 5/1, 12/15 for early action. Transfer credits accepted: Yes. Applicants placed on waiting list: 74. Wait-listed applicants offered admission: 2.

Costs Per Year: Application fee: $0. Comprehensive fee: $57,506 includes full-time tuition ($49,970), mandatory fees ($280), and college room and board ($7256). College room only: $4256. Room and board charges vary according to board plan.

Collegiate Environment: Orientation program. Drama-theater group, choral group, student-run newspaper, radio station. Social organizations: 103 open to all; national fraternities, national sororities, local fraternities, local sororities; 8% of eligible men and 6% of eligible women are members. Most popular organizations: Science Fiction and Fantasy Association, Black Students Union, Alliance, International Club, Ballroom Dancing Club. Major annual events: Folk 'n' Blues Festival, International Symposium, Advising Day. Student services: health clinic, personal-psychological counseling, women's center. Campus security: 24-hour emergency response devices and patrols, late night transport-escort service, controlled dormitory access. 1,144 college housing spaces available. Freshmen guaranteed college housing. On-campus residence required through junior year. Options: coed, women-only housing available. Morse Library and Black Information Center with 505,586 books, 7,314 microform titles, 1,052 serials, 9,301 audiovisual materials, an OPAC, and a Web page. Operations spending for the previous fiscal year: $1.3 million. 100 computers available on campus for general student use. A campuswide network can be accessed from student residence rooms and from off campus. Staffed computer lab on campus provides training in use of computers, software, and the Internet.

Community Environment: Beloit College is located in Beloit, Wisconsin (population 36,000), 90 miles northwest of Chicago, 50 miles south of Madison, and 70 miles southwest of Milwaukee. Students take advantage of the varied resources offered by these three major metropolitan areas, as well as those offered by the city of Beloit itself. Beloit's hospital, clinics, manufacturers, and various civic and service organizations provide numerous internship, job shadowing, enrichment, and community outreach opportunities. Year-round sports and recreation areas are available in southern Wisconsin and northern Illinois. There is direct bus service from O'Hare International Airport, and the same bus continues on to the University of Wisconsin in Madison.

■ **BLACKHAWK TECHNICAL COLLEGE**
PO Box 5009
Janesville, WI 53547-5009
Tel: (608)758-6900
Fax: (608)757-9407
E-mail: erobinson@blackhawk.edu
Web Site: www.blackhawk.edu/

Description: District-supported, 2-year, coed. Part of Wisconsin Technical College System. Awards transfer associate and terminal associate degrees. Founded 1968. Setting: 84-acre small town campus. Educational spending for the previous fiscal year: $7239 per student. Total enrollment: 2,967. Faculty: 357 (96 full-time, 261 part-time). Student-undergrad faculty ratio is 11:1. Full-time: 1,306 students, 53% women, 47% men. Part-time: 1,661 students, 69% women, 31% men. Students come from 2 states and territories, 1% from out-of-state. 0.5% American Indian or Alaska Native, non-Hispanic/Latino; 10% Hispanic/Latino; 10% African American, non-Hispanic/Latino; 1% Asian, non-Hispanic/Latino; 0.2% Native Hawaiian or other

Pacific Islander, non-Hispanic/Latino; 0% international. 53% 25 or older. Retention: 83% of full-time freshmen returned the following year. Core. Calendar: semesters. Academic remediation for entering students, ESL program, services for LD students, advanced placement, accelerated degree program, self-designed majors, independent study, distance learning, summer session for credit, part-time degree program, adult/continuing education programs, co-op programs and internships.

Entrance Requirements: Open admission. Option: electronic application. Required: high school transcript. Entrance: noncompetitive. Application deadline: Rolling. Notification: continuous. Preference given to district residents.

Costs Per Year: Application fee: $30. State resident tuition: $3507 full-time, $116.90 per credit part-time. Nonresident tuition: $5261 full-time, $175.35 per credit part-time. Mandatory fees: $455 full-time, $5.85 per credit part-time. Full-time tuition and fees vary according to course load. Part-time tuition and fees vary according to course load.

Collegiate Environment: Orientation program. Student-run newspaper. Social organizations: 17 open to all. Most popular organizations: student government, Association of Information Technology Professionals, Criminal Justice, Epicurean Club, Phi Theta Kappa Honor Society. Major annual events: Fall Carnival, Winter Social, Back Yard Bash. Campus security: student patrols. College housing not available. Blackhawk Technical College Library with 101,024 books, 12,000 microform titles, 300 serials, 5,889 audiovisual materials, an OPAC, and a Web page. Operations spending for the previous fiscal year: $314,055. 125 computers available on campus for general student use. A campuswide network can be accessed. Students can access the following: online class registration. Staffed computer lab on campus.

■ **BRYANT & STRATTON COLLEGE - MILWAUKEE CAMPUS**
310 W Wisconsin Ave.
Ste. 500 E
Milwaukee, WI 53202-2618
Tel: (414)276-5200
Web Site: www.bryantstratton.edu/

Description: Proprietary, primarily 2-year, coed. Part of Bryant and Stratton College, Inc. Awards terminal associate and bachelor's degrees. Founded 1863. Setting: urban campus. Educational spending for the previous fiscal year: $1427 per student. Total enrollment: 828. Faculty: 102 (19 full-time, 83 part-time). Student-undergrad faculty ratio is 13:1. 433 applied, 89% were admitted. Full-time: 460 students, 84% women, 16% men. Part-time: 368 students, 84% women, 16% men. 0% from out-of-state. 33% transferred in. Retention: 70% of full-time freshmen returned the following year. Core. Calendar: semesters. Academic remediation for entering students, advanced placement, independent study, distance learning, double major, summer session for credit, part-time degree program, adult/continuing education programs, co-op programs and internships.

Entrance Requirements: Option: electronic application. Required: high school transcript, interview, entrance and placement evaluations, CPAt; ACCUPLACER. Recommended: SAT or ACT. Entrance: minimally difficult. Application deadline: Rolling. Notification: continuous.

Collegiate Environment: Orientation program. Student-run newspaper. Most popular organizations: Phi Beta Lambda, Association of Information Technology Professionals, Allied Health Association, Institute of Management Accountants, Student Advisory Board. Major annual events: Portfolio Development Day, Career Fair, All-School Picnic. Campus security: 24-hour emergency response devices and patrols. Bryant and Stratton College Library plus 1 other with 120 serials and 100 audiovisual materials. Operations spending for the previous fiscal year: $20,915. 130 computers available on campus for general student use. A campuswide network can be accessed from off-campus. Staffed computer lab on campus provides training in use of computers, software, and the Internet.

■ **BRYANT & STRATTON COLLEGE - WAUWATOSA CAMPUS**
10950 W Potter Rd.
Wauwatosa, WI 53226
Tel: (414)302-7000
Web Site: www.bryantstratton.edu/

Description: Proprietary, 4-year, coed. Awards associate and bachelor's degrees. Setting: suburban campus with easy access to Milwaukee. Total enrollment: 1,264. Student-undergrad faculty ratio is 10:1. Students come from 2 states and territories. 48% 25 or older. Retention: 88% of full-time freshmen returned the following year. Calendar: semesters. Academic remediation for entering students, services for LD students, advanced placement, independent study, distance learning, double major, part-time degree program, adult/continuing education programs, co-op programs and internships.

Entrance Requirements: Option: electronic application. Required: high school transcript, interview, entrance and placement evaluation, TABE, CPAt. Recommended: SAT or ACT. Application deadline: Rolling. Notification: continuous.

Collegiate Environment: Orientation program. 125 computers available on campus for general student use. A campuswide network can be accessed. Students can access the following: online class registration. Staffed computer lab on campus provides training in use of computers.

■ CARDINAL STRITCH UNIVERSITY

6801 N Yates Rd.
Milwaukee, WI 53217-3985
Tel: (414)410-4000; Free: 800-347-8822
Fax: (414)410-4239
E-mail: admityou@stritch.edu
Web Site: www.stritch.edu/

Description: Independent Roman Catholic, comprehensive, coed. Awards associate, bachelor's, master's, and doctoral degrees and post-master's certificates. Founded 1937. Setting: 40-acre suburban campus with easy access to Milwaukee. Endowment: $21.1 million. Educational spending for the previous fiscal year: $3288 per student. Total enrollment: 4,641. Faculty: 431 (105 full-time, 326 part-time). 955 applied, 48% were admitted. Full-time: 2,350 students, 65% women, 35% men. Part-time: 432 students, 66% women, 34% men. Students come from 21 states and territories, 2 other countries, 13% from out-of-state. 0.4% American Indian or Alaska Native, non-Hispanic/Latino; 6% Hispanic/Latino; 24% African American, non-Hispanic/Latino; 2% Asian, non-Hispanic/Latino; 0.1% Native Hawaiian or other Pacific Islander, non-Hispanic/Latino; 2% international. 69% 25 or older, 5% live on campus, 5% transferred in. Academic areas with the most degrees conferred: business/marketing; education; health professions and related sciences. Core. Calendar: semesters. Academic remediation for entering students, ESL program, services for LD students, advanced placement, accelerated degree program, self-designed majors, honors program, independent study, distance learning, double major, summer session for credit, part-time degree program, external degree program, adult/continuing education programs, co-op programs and internships, graduate courses open to undergrads. Off campus study at Concordia University Wisconsin, Saint Francis Seminary, Sacred Heart School of Theology.

Entrance Requirements: Options: electronic application, deferred admission, international baccalaureate accepted. Required: essay, high school transcript, minimum 2 high school GPA, SAT or ACT. Recommended: interview. Entrance: moderately difficult. Application deadline: 8/1. Notification: continuous. Transfer credits accepted: Yes.

Costs Per Year: Application fee: $0. Comprehensive fee: $31,360 includes full-time tuition ($23,680), mandatory fees ($650), and college room and board ($7030). College room only: $1900. Full-time tuition and fees vary according to degree level and program. Room and board charges vary according to board plan. Part-time tuition: $740 per credit hour. Part-time mandatory fees: $460 per year. Part-time tuition and fees vary according to course load, degree level, and program.

Collegiate Environment: Orientation program. Drama-theater group, choral group, student-run newspaper, radio station. Social organizations: 35 open to all. Most popular organizations: Residence Hall Association, Student Government Association, Student Activities Board. Major annual events: Christmas Dinner/Dance, Homecoming, Spring Semi-formal Dance. Student services: health clinic, personal-psychological counseling. Campus security: 24-hour emergency response devices and patrols, late night transport-escort service. 387 college housing spaces available; 300 were occupied in 2012-13. Option: coed housing available. Cardinal Stritch University Library plus 1 other with 124,897 books, 180,550 microform titles, 667 serials, an OPAC, and a Web page. Operations spending for the previous fiscal year: $947,541. 549 computers available on campus for general student use. Computer purchase/lease plans available. A campuswide network can be accessed from student residence rooms and from off campus. Students can access the following: online class registration. Staffed computer lab on campus provides training in use of computers, software, and the Internet.

Community Environment: See Milwaukee Area Technical College.

■ CARROLL UNIVERSITY

100 NE Ave.
Waukesha, WI 53186-5593
Tel: (262)547-1211; Free: 800-CARROLL
Fax: (262)524-7139
E-mail: info@carrollu.edu
Web Site: www.carrollu.edu/

Description: Independent Presbyterian, comprehensive, coed. Awards bachelor's, master's, and doctoral degrees. Founded 1846. Setting: 52-acre suburban campus with easy access to Milwaukee. Endowment: $32.7 million. Educational spending for the previous fiscal year: $17,074 per student. Total enrollment: 3,385. Faculty: 330 (127 full-time, 203 part-time). Student-undergrad faculty ratio is 15:1. 2,512 applied, 79% were admitted. 25% from top 10% of their high school class, 53% from top quarter, 86% from top half. Full-time: 2,675 students, 67% women, 33% men. Part-time: 464 students, 62% women, 38% men. Students come from 25 states and territories, 25 other countries, 23% from out-of-state. 15% 25 or older, 52% live on campus, 6% transferred in. Retention: 75% of full-time freshmen returned the following year. Academic areas with the most degrees conferred: health professions and related sciences; business/marketing; education. Core. Calendar: semesters. Academic remediation for entering students, ESL program, services for LD students, advanced placement, self-designed majors, honors program, independent study, distance learning, double major, summer session for credit, part-time degree program, adult/continuing education programs, internships, graduate courses open to undergrads. Study abroad program. ROTC: Army (c), Air Force (c).

Entrance Requirements: Options: electronic application, deferred admission, international baccalaureate accepted. Required: high school transcript, minimum 2 high school GPA, 1 recommendation, SAT or ACT. Recommended: interview, ACT. Required for some: essay. Entrance: moderately difficult. Application deadline: Rolling. Notification: 8/20. SAT Reasoning Test deadline: 7/1. SAT Subject Test deadline: 7/1. Transfer credits accepted: Yes.

Collegiate Environment: Orientation program. Drama-theater group, choral group, student-run newspaper, radio station. Social organizations: 53 open to all; national sororities, local fraternities; 10% of eligible men and 11% of eligible women are members. Most popular organizations: College Activities Board, Student Senate, Black Student Union, Intervarsity Christian Fellowship, Latin American Student Organization. Major annual events: Homecoming, Parents' Weekend, Spring Fling. Student services: health clinic, personal-psychological counseling. Campus security: 24-hour emergency response devices and patrols, student patrols, late night transport-escort service, controlled dormitory access. Todd Wehr Memorial Library with 150,000 books, 27,227 microform titles, 65,200 serials, 2,539 audiovisual materials, an OPAC, and a Web page. Operations spending for the previous fiscal year: $1.5 million. 400 computers available on campus for general student use. Computer purchase/lease plans available. A campuswide network can be accessed from student residence rooms and from off campus. Students can access the following: online class registration. Staffed computer lab on campus provides training in use of computers, software, and the Internet.

■ CARTHAGE COLLEGE

2001 Alford Park Dr.
Kenosha, WI 53140
Tel: (262)551-8500; Free: 800-351-4058
Fax: (262)551-5762
E-mail: admissions@carthage.edu
Web Site: www.carthage.edu/

Description: Independent, comprehensive, coed, affiliated with Evangelical Lutheran Church in America. Awards bachelor's and master's degrees. Founded 1847. Setting: 72-acre suburban campus with easy access to Chicago, Milwaukee. Endowment: $48.6 million. Total enrollment: 2,778. Faculty: (137 full-time). Student-undergrad faculty ratio is 15:1. 4,687 applied, 77% were admitted. 18% from top 10% of their high school class, 73% from top half. Full-time: 2,233 students, 56% women, 44% men. Part-time: 427 students, 73% women, 27% men. Students come from 31 states and territories, 16 other countries, 72% from out-of-state. 12% 25 or older, 68% live on campus, 3% transferred in. Retention: 75% of full-time freshmen returned the following year. Academic areas with the most degrees conferred: business/marketing; education; social sciences. Core. Calendar: 4-1-4. Services for LD students, advanced placement, accelerated degree program, self-designed majors, honors program, independent study, double major, summer session for credit, part-time degree program, adult/continuing education programs, co-op programs and internships. Off campus study at University of Wisconsin-Parkside, Marquette University. Study abroad program. ROTC: Army (c), Air Force (c).

Entrance Requirements: Options: electronic application, early admission, early action, deferred admission, international baccalaureate accepted. Required: high school transcript, SAT or ACT. Recommended: essay, interview. Required for some: essay, 2 recommendations, interview. Entrance: moderately difficult. Application deadlines: Rolling, 7/26 for early action. Notification: continuous, 9/15 for early action.

Costs Per Year: Application fee: $25. Comprehensive fee: $42,000 includes full-time tuition ($33,000) and college room and board ($9000). Room and board charges vary according to board plan and housing facility.

Collegiate Environment: Orientation program. Drama-theater group, choral group, student-run newspaper, radio station. Social organizations: 90 open to all; national fraternities, national sororities, local fraternities, local sororities; 22% of eligible men and 25% of eligible women are members. Most popular organizations: Residence Life Council, Alpha Lambda Delta, Circle K, Inter-Varsity Christian Fellowship, Pals-n-Partners. Major annual events: Homecoming, May Madness, Casino Night. Student services: health clinic, personal-psychological counseling. Campus security: 24-hour emergency response devices and patrols, student patrols, late night transport-escort service, controlled dormitory access. Hedberg Library with 128,551 books, 7,149 microform titles, 425 serials, 4,361 audiovisual materials, an OPAC, and a Web page. 250 computers available on campus for general student use. Computer purchase/lease plans available. A campuswide network can be accessed from student residence rooms and from off campus. Students can access the following: online class registration. Staffed computer lab on campus provides training in use of computers, software, and the Internet.

Community Environment: See Gateway Technical College.

■ CHIPPEWA VALLEY TECHNICAL COLLEGE

620 W Clairemont Ave.
Eau Claire, WI 54701-6162
Tel: (715)833-6307; Free: 800-547-2882
Fax: (715)833-6470
E-mail: infocenter@cvtc.edu
Web Site: www.cvtc.edu/

Description: District-supported, 2-year, coed. Part of Wisconsin Technical College System. Awards certificates, diplomas, transfer associate, and terminal associate degrees. Founded 1912. Setting: 255-acre urban campus. Educational spending for the previous fiscal year: $7720 per student. Total enrollment: 6,086. Faculty: 491 (225 full-time, 266 part-time). Student-undergrad faculty ratio is 14:1. Full-time: 2,640 students, 45% women, 55% men. Part-time: 3,446 students, 62% women, 38% men. 2% from out-of-state. 1% American Indian or Alaska Native, non-Hispanic/Latino; 2% Hispanic/Latino; 1% African American, non-Hispanic/Latino; 4% Asian, non-Hispanic/Latino; 0.1% Native Hawaiian or other Pacific Islander, non-Hispanic/Latino; 0% international. 44% 25 or older. Calendar: semesters. Academic remediation for entering students, ESL program, services for LD students, advanced placement, accelerated degree program, self-designed majors, honors program, independent study, distance learning, double major, summer session for credit, part-time degree program, adult/continuing education programs, co-op programs and internships.

Entrance Requirements: Open admission Many programs have admission requirements which must be met prior to being accepted. Options: electronic application, early admission, deferred admission. Required: Compass, ACCUPLACER. Recommended: ACT. Required for some: high school transcript. Entrance: noncompetitive. Application deadline: Rolling. Notification: continuous. Transfer credits accepted: Yes.

Costs Per Year: Application fee: $30. State resident tuition: $3524 full-time, $116.90 per credit part-time. Nonresident tuition: $5260 full-time, $175.35 per credit part-time. Mandatory fees: $291 full-time, $291 per term part-time. Full-time tuition and fees vary according to course load and reciprocity agreements. Part-time tuition and fees vary according to course load and reciprocity agreements. College room and board: $6452.

Collegiate Environment: Orientation program. Social organizations: 30 open to all; Phi Theta Kappa, Academic Honor Society. Most popular organization: Collegiate DECA. Major annual events: Campus picnic, Transfer Fair. Student services: health clinic, personal-psychological counseling. Campus security: 24-hour emergency response devices, late night transport-escort service, security cameras. College housing not available. The Learning Center with an OPAC and a Web page. Operations spending for the previous fiscal year: $335,166. 1,700 computers available on campus for general student use. A campuswide network can be accessed from off-campus. Students can access the following: online class registration. Staffed computer lab on campus provides training in use of computers, software, and the Internet.

Community Environment: See University of Wisconsin Eau Claire.

■ COLLEGE OF MENOMINEE NATION

PO Box 1179
Keshena, WI 54135
Tel: (715)799-5600; Free: 800-567-2344
Fax: (715)799-1308
E-mail: tjames@menominee.edu
Web Site: www.menominee.edu/

Description: Independent, 2-year, coed. Awards certificates, transfer associate, and terminal associate degrees. Founded 1993. Total enrollment: 634. Student-undergrad faculty ratio is 16:1. 0% from out-of-state. 58% 25 or older. Calendar: semesters.

Entrance Requirements: Open admission. Required: high school transcript, ACCUPLACER. Entrance: noncompetitive. Application deadline: 8/14.

■ COLUMBIA COLLEGE OF NURSING

4425 N Port Washington Rd.
Milwaukee, WI 53212
Tel: (414)961-3530
E-mail: ewade@ccon.edu
Web Site: www.ccon.edu/

Description: Independent, 4-year, coed. Awards bachelor's degrees (nursing degree is awarded in conjunction with Mount Mary College). Founded 1901. Setting: 1-acre urban campus with easy access to Milwaukee. Endowment: $700,000. Research spending for the previous fiscal year: $69,321. Educational spending for the previous fiscal year: $6858 per student. Total enrollment: 169. Faculty: 21 (18 full-time, 3 part-time). Student-undergrad faculty ratio is 9:1. 13% from top 10% of their high school class, 65% from top quarter, 91% from top half. Full-time: 154 students, 95% women, 5% men. Part-time: 15 students, 100% women. Students come from 3 states and territories, 4% from out-of-state. 1% American Indian or Alaska Native, non-Hispanic/Latino; 4% Hispanic/Latino; 8% African American, non-Hispanic/Latino; 2% Asian, non-Hispanic/Latino; 0% international. 44% 25 or older, 14% transferred in. Retention: 88% of full-time freshmen returned the following year. Academic area with the most degrees conferred: health professions and related sciences. Core. Calendar: semesters. Academic remediation for entering students, advanced placement, honors program, independent study, double major, summer session for credit, part-time degree program, co-op programs. Off campus study at Mount Mary College, Milwaukee, WI. Study abroad program.

Entrance Requirements: Option: electronic application. Required: high school transcript, minimum 2.8 high school GPA, minimum 2.8 GPA in college level natural and social sciences, SAT or ACT. Recommended: essay, 1 recommendation. Required for some: essay, interview. Entrance: moderately difficult. Transfer credits accepted: Yes.

Collegiate Environment: Orientation program. Social organizations: 2 open to all; Student Nurse Organization; 1% of eligible men and 13% of eligible women are members. Most popular organizations: Student Senate, Student Nurses Association. Major annual events: Holiday Party, Spring Banquet, Student Luncheon. Student services: health clinic, personal-psychological counseling. Campus security: 24-hour emergency response devices and patrols, student patrols, late night transport-escort service, security card entrances to academic areas. Columbia St. Mary's Library with 12,000 books and 5,000 serials. Operations spending for the previous fiscal year: $72,129. 46 computers available on campus for general student use. A campuswide network can be accessed from student residence rooms and from off campus. Students can access the following: online class registration. Staffed computer lab on campus provides training in use of computers, software, and the Internet.

■ CONCORDIA UNIVERSITY WISCONSIN

12800 N Lake Shore Dr.
Mequon, WI 53097-2402
Tel: (262)243-5700; Free: 888-628-9472
Fax: (262)243-4351
E-mail: admission@cuw.edu
Web Site: www.cuw.edu/

Description: Independent, comprehensive, coed, affiliated with Lutheran Church-Missouri Synod. Part of Concordia University System. Awards associate, bachelor's, master's, and doctoral degrees and post-master's certificates. Founded 1881. Setting: 192-acre suburban campus with easy access to Milwaukee. Total enrollment: 7,751. Faculty: 382 (162 full-time, 220 part-time). Student-undergrad faculty ratio is 14:1. 2,517 applied, 70%

were admitted. 16% from top 10% of their high school class, 40% from top quarter, 75% from top half. Full-time: 2,876 students, 62% women, 38% men. Part-time: 1,543 students, 71% women, 29% men. 20% from out-of-state. 1% American Indian or Alaska Native, non-Hispanic/Latino; 2% Hispanic/Latino; 18% African American, non-Hispanic/Latino; 2% Asian, non-Hispanic/Latino; 0.1% Native Hawaiian or other Pacific Islander, non-Hispanic/Latino; 1% international. 46% 25 or older, 41% live on campus, 4% transferred in. Retention: 74% of full-time freshmen returned the following year. Academic areas with the most degrees conferred: business/marketing; health professions and related sciences; education. Core. Calendar: 4-1-4. Academic remediation for entering students, ESL program, services for LD students, advanced placement, accelerated degree program, self-designed majors, independent study, distance learning, double major, summer session for credit, part-time degree program, adult/continuing education programs, internships. Off campus study at Milwaukee Area Technical College, Milwaukee Institute of Art and Design, Cardinal Stritch University, Mount Mary College. Study abroad program.

Entrance Requirements: Option: international baccalaureate accepted. Required: high school transcript, minimum 2 high school GPA, ACT. Recommended: interview. Required for some: essay, minimum 3 high school GPA, 3 recommendations. Entrance: moderately difficult. Application deadline: 8/15. Notification: continuous. SAT Reasoning Test deadline: 8/15.

Costs Per Year: Application fee: $35. Comprehensive fee: $33,020 includes full-time tuition ($23,970) and college room and board ($9050). Full-time tuition varies according to program. Room and board charges vary according to board plan.

Collegiate Environment: Orientation program. Drama-theater group, choral group, student-run newspaper, radio station. Student services: health clinic, personal-psychological counseling. Campus security: 24-hour patrols, student patrols, late night transport-escort service, controlled dormitory access. 1,245 college housing spaces available. Freshmen given priority for college housing. Options: men-only, women-only housing available. Rinker Memorial Library with an OPAC. 225 computers available on campus for general student use. A campuswide network can be accessed from student residence rooms and from off campus. Staffed computer lab on campus.

Community Environment: See Milwaukee Area Technical College.

■ DEVRY UNIVERSITY (MILWAUKEE)
411 E Wisconsin Ave.
Ste. 300
Milwaukee, WI 53202
Tel: (414)278-7677; Free: 866-338-7941
Fax: (414)278-0137
Web Site: www.devry.edu/

Description: Proprietary, comprehensive, coed. Part of DeVry University. Awards associate, bachelor's, and master's degrees. Total enrollment: 213. Faculty: 29 (1 full-time, 28 part-time). Student-undergrad faculty ratio is 9:1. Full-time: 35 students, 51% women, 49% men. Part-time: 93 students, 51% women, 49% men. 2% from out-of-state. 72% 25 or older, 17% transferred in. Calendar: semesters. Academic remediation for entering students, services for LD students, advanced placement, accelerated degree program, distance learning, summer session for credit, part-time degree program, adult/continuing education programs.

Entrance Requirements: Options: electronic application, deferred admission, international baccalaureate accepted. Required: high school transcript, interview. Entrance: minimally difficult. Application deadline: Rolling. Notification: continuous. SAT Reasoning Test deadline: 10/31.

■ DEVRY UNIVERSITY (WAUKESHA)
N14 W23833 Stone Ridge Dr., Ste. 450
Waukesha, WI 53188-1157
Tel: (262)347-2911; Free: 866-338-7941
Web Site: www.devry.edu/

Description: Proprietary, comprehensive, coed. Awards bachelor's and master's degrees. Calendar: semesters.

■ EDGEWOOD COLLEGE
1000 Edgewood College Dr.
Madison, WI 53711-1997
Tel: (608)663-4861; Free: 800-444-4861
Fax: (608)663-3291
E-mail: admissions@edgewood.edu
Web Site: www.edgewood.edu/

Description: Independent Roman Catholic, comprehensive, coed. Awards

bachelor's, master's, and doctoral degrees. Founded 1927. Setting: 55-acre urban campus. Endowment: $17.5 million. Educational spending for the previous fiscal year: $8705 per student. Total enrollment: 3,064. Faculty: 319 (153 full-time, 166 part-time). Student-undergrad faculty ratio is 11:1. 1,382 applied, 73% were admitted. 13% from top 10% of their high school class, 44% from top quarter, 80% from top half. 4 valedictorians. Full-time: 1,671 students, 69% women, 31% men. Part-time: 357 students, 74% women, 26% men. Students come from 17 states and territories, 38 other countries, 6% from out-of-state. 0.3% American Indian or Alaska Native, non-Hispanic/Latino; 5% Hispanic/Latino; 3% African American, non-Hispanic/Latino; 2% Asian, non-Hispanic/Latino; 0.1% Native Hawaiian or other Pacific Islander, non-Hispanic/Latino; 3% international. 23% 25 or older, 27% live on campus, 10% transferred in. Retention: 79% of full-time freshmen returned the following year. Academic areas with the most degrees conferred: business/marketing; health professions and related sciences; education. Core. Calendar: semesters. Academic remediation for entering students, services for LD students, advanced placement, accelerated degree program, self-designed majors, honors program, independent study, distance learning, double major, summer session for credit, part-time degree program, adult/continuing education programs, co-op programs and internships, graduate courses open to undergrads. Off campus study at University of Wisconsin-Madison, Online Consortium of Independent Colleges & Universities (OCICU). Study abroad program. ROTC: Army (c), Naval (c), Air Force (c).

Entrance Requirements: Options: electronic application, deferred admission, international baccalaureate accepted. Required: high school transcript, minimum 2.5 high school GPA. Students must meet two of the following three requirements. Students must present a cumulative high school GPA of 2.5 on a 4.0 scale, a rank in the top 50% of their high school graduating class and/or a composite score of 18 on the ACT or an equivalent SAT score, SAT or ACT. Required for some: essay, 2 recommendations, interview. Entrance: moderately difficult. Application deadline: 8/14. Notification: continuous. SAT Reasoning Test deadline: 8/1. Transfer credits accepted: Yes.

Costs Per Year: Application fee: $25. Comprehensive fee: $32,216 includes full-time tuition ($23,740) and college room and board ($8476). Full-time tuition varies according to degree level. Room and board charges vary according to housing facility. Part-time tuition: $747 per credit. Part-time tuition varies according to course load and degree level.

Collegiate Environment: Orientation program. Drama-theater group, choral group, student-run newspaper. Social organizations: 48 open to all; 3% of eligible men and 7% of eligible women are members. Most popular organizations: Circle K, Student Education Association, Student Government Association, Rotaract, Ambassadors. Major annual events: Homecoming, Winterfrost, Leadership Conference. Student services: health clinic, personal-psychological counseling. Campus security: 24-hour emergency response devices and patrols, student patrols, late night transport-escort service, controlled dormitory access, lighted pathways/sidewalks. 555 college housing spaces available; 554 were occupied in 2012-13. Freshmen guaranteed college housing. On-campus residence required through sophomore year. Options: coed, women-only housing available. Oscar Rennebohm Library with 92,054 books, 9,524 microform titles, 26,700 serials, 5,845 audiovisual materials, an OPAC, and a Web page. Operations spending for the previous fiscal year: $783,550. 100 computers available on campus for general student use. Computer purchase/lease plans available. A campuswide network can be accessed from student residence rooms and from off campus. Students can access the following: online class registration, Online library. Staffed computer lab on campus.

Community Environment: See University of Wisconsin - Madison.

■ FOX VALLEY TECHNICAL COLLEGE
1825 N Bluemound
Appleton, WI 54912-2277
Tel: (920)735-5600; Free: 800-735-3882
Fax: (920)735-2582
Web Site: www.fvtc.edu/

Description: State and locally supported, 2-year, coed. Part of Wisconsin Technical College System. Awards certificates, diplomas, and terminal associate degrees. Founded 1967. Setting: 100-acre suburban campus. Endowment: $2.1 million. Educational spending for the previous fiscal year: $10,171 per student. Total enrollment: 10,948. Faculty: 917 (327 full-time, 590 part-time). Student-undergrad faculty ratio is 11:1. 1,396 applied, 76% were admitted. Full-time: 2,902 students, 41% women, 59% men. Part-time: 8,046 students, 52% women, 48% men. Students come from 15 states and territories, 14 other countries, 1% from out-of-state. 1% American Indian or

Alaska Native, non-Hispanic/Latino; 3% Hispanic/Latino; 2% African American, non-Hispanic/Latino; 4% Asian, non-Hispanic/Latino; 0.2% Native Hawaiian or other Pacific Islander, non-Hispanic/Latino; 0.1% international. 48% 25 or older. Core. Calendar: semesters. Academic remediation for entering students, ESL program, services for LD students, advanced placement, accelerated degree program, self-designed majors, independent study, distance learning, double major, summer session for credit, part-time degree program, co-op programs and internships. Off campus study. Study abroad program.

Entrance Requirements: Open admission. Options: electronic application, early admission, deferred admission. Required: high school transcript. Entrance: noncompetitive. Application deadline: Rolling.

Costs Per Year: Application fee: $30. State resident tuition: $3507 full-time, $116.90 per credit part-time. Nonresident tuition: $5261 full-time, $175.35 per credit part-time. Mandatory fees: $471 full-time, $15.70 per credit part-time.

Collegiate Environment: Orientation program. Student-run newspaper. Social organizations: 48 open to all. Most popular organizations: Student Government Association, Phi Theta Kappa, Culinary Arts, Student Nurses, Post Secondary Agribusiness. Major annual events: Drive in Movie, Lecture Series, Family Carnival. Student services: health clinic, personal-psychological counseling. Campus security: 24-hour emergency response devices, late night transport-escort service, 16-hour patrols by trained security personnel. College housing not available. William M. Sirek Educational Resource Center with 99,130 books, 182 serials, 6,884 audiovisual materials, an OPAC, and a Web page. Operations spending for the previous fiscal year: $484,187. 275 computers available on campus for general student use. A campuswide network can be accessed from off-campus. Students can access the following: online class registration, personal Web pages. Staffed computer lab on campus provides training in use of computers, software, and the Internet.

■ GATEWAY TECHNICAL COLLEGE

3520 30th Ave.
Kenosha, WI 53144-1690
Tel: (262)564-2200
Fax: (262)564-2201
E-mail: admissions@gtc.edu
Web Site: www.gtc.edu/

Description: State and locally supported, 2-year, coed. Part of Wisconsin Technical College System. Awards certificates, diplomas, and terminal associate degrees. Founded 1911. Setting: 10-acre urban campus with easy access to Chicago, Milwaukee. Total enrollment: 8,720. Student-undergrad faculty ratio is 16:1. Full-time: 1,717 students, 48% women, 52% men. Part-time: 7,003 students, 64% women, 36% men. Students come from 7 states and territories, 2 other countries, 1% from out-of-state. 1% American Indian or Alaska Native, non-Hispanic/Latino; 12% Hispanic/Latino; 15% African American, non-Hispanic/Latino; 1% Asian, non-Hispanic/Latino; 0.1% Native Hawaiian or other Pacific Islander, non-Hispanic/Latino; 0% international. 55% 25 or older, 1% transferred in. Retention: 64% of full-time freshmen returned the following year. Core. Calendar: semesters. Academic remediation for entering students, ESL program, services for LD students, advanced placement, self-designed majors, independent study, distance learning, double major, summer session for credit, part-time degree program, co-op programs and internships.

Entrance Requirements: Open admission except for health occupations programs. Options: electronic application, early admission, deferred admission. Required: high school transcript. Entrance: noncompetitive. Application deadline: Rolling. Notification: continuous. Transfer credits accepted: Yes.

Collegiate Environment: Student-run newspaper, radio station. Most popular organization: International Club. Student services: personal-psychological counseling. Campus security: 24-hour emergency response devices and patrols, late night transport-escort service. College housing not available. Library/Learning Resources Center plus 3 others with 46,103 books, 18 microform titles, 173 serials, 4,438 audiovisual materials, an OPAC, and a Web page.

Community Environment: Located on the shore of Lake Michigan, Kenosha (population 95,240) has an excellent harbor with 83% of its shoreline providing recreation. It is surrounded by a prosperous agricultural area and is one of the chief industrial centers of the state. Both Chicago and Milwaukee are an hour away. Points of interest are the Hall of Fame, Art Museum, County Historical Society, and Petrifying Springs Park.

■ GLOBE UNIVERSITY–APPLETON

5045 W Grande Market Dr.
Grand Chute, WI 54913
Tel: (920)384-1100
E-mail: jordanklein@globeuniversity.edu
Web Site: www.globeuniversity.edu

Description: Proprietary, 4-year, coed. Part of Globe Education Network (GEN) which is composed of Globe University, Minnesota School of Business, Broadview University, The Institute of Production and Recording and Minnesota School of Cosmetology. Awards associate and bachelor's degrees. Setting: 4-acre small town campus. Total enrollment: 47. Faculty: 27 (7 full-time, 20 part-time). Student-undergrad faculty ratio is 9:1. Full-time: 18 students, 72% women, 28% men. Part-time: 29 students, 90% women, 10% men. Students come from 2 states and territories, 0% from out-of-state. 2% American Indian or Alaska Native, non-Hispanic/Latino; 4% Hispanic/Latino; 2% African American, non-Hispanic/Latino; 0% Asian, non-Hispanic/Latino; 0% Native Hawaiian or other Pacific Islander, non-Hispanic/Latino; 0% international. 14% 25 or older, 30% transferred in. Retention: 0% of full-time freshmen returned the following year. Core. Academic remediation for entering students, services for LD students, advanced placement, accelerated degree program, summer session for credit, part-time degree program, adult/continuing education programs, internships.

Entrance Requirements: Option: electronic application. Required: high school transcript, interview, High school transcript or GED, ACCUPLACER is required of all applicants unless documentation of a minimum ACT composite score of 21 or documentation of a minimum composite score of 1485 on the SAT is presented. Required for some: essay, 2 recommendations. Application deadlines: Rolling, Rolling for nonresidents. Notification: continuous, continuous for nonresidents. Transfer credits accepted: Yes.

Costs Per Year: Application fee: $50. Tuition: $15,300 full-time, $460 per credit part-time. Mandatory fees: $1548 full-time, $43 per credit part-time. Full-time tuition and fees vary according to course load, degree level, location, and program. Part-time tuition and fees vary according to course load, degree level, location, and program.

Collegiate Environment: Orientation program. Social organizations: Program specific student led organizations. Major annual events: Service Learning Projects, Applied Learning Projects, Student Appreciation Events. Campus security: 24-hour emergency response devices, late night transport-escort service. Appleton Campus Library with 1,944 books, 53,138 serials, 4 audiovisual materials, an OPAC, and a Web page. 52 computers available on campus for general student use. A campuswide network can be accessed. Students can access the following: online class registration. Staffed computer lab on campus provides training in use of computers, software, and the Internet.

■ GLOBE UNIVERSITY–EAU CLAIRE

4955 Bullis Farm Rd.
Eau Claire, WI 54701-5168
Tel: (715)855-6600; Free: 377-303-6060
E-mail: jkampa@globeuniversity.edu
Web Site: www.globeuniversity.edu/

Description: Proprietary, 4-year, coed. Part of Globe Education Network (GEN) which is composed of Globe University, Minnesota School of Business, Broadview University, The Institute of Production and Recording and Minnesota School of Cosmetology. Awards associate and bachelor's degrees. Setting: 5-acre small town campus with easy access to Minneapolis-St. Paul. Total enrollment: 719. Faculty: 54 (9 full-time, 45 part-time). Student-undergrad faculty ratio is 19:1. Full-time: 274 students, 73% women, 27% men. Part-time: 445 students, 83% women, 17% men. 0% from out-of-state. 1% American Indian or Alaska Native, non-Hispanic/Latino; 1% Hispanic/Latino; 0.1% African American, non-Hispanic/Latino; 2% Asian, non-Hispanic/Latino; 0% Native Hawaiian or other Pacific Islander, non-Hispanic/Latino; 0% international. 42% 25 or older, 15% transferred in. Retention: 79% of full-time freshmen returned the following year. Academic areas with the most degrees conferred: business/marketing; health professions and related sciences; law/legal studies. Core. Academic remediation for entering students, services for LD students, advanced placement, accelerated degree program, summer session for credit, part-time degree program, adult/continuing education programs, internships.

Entrance Requirements: Option: electronic application. Required: high school transcript, interview, ACCUPLACER is required of all applicants unless documentation of a minimum ACT composite score of 21 or documentation of a minimum composite score of 1485 on the SAT is presented. Required for some: essay, 2 recommendations, GED certificate in lieu of high school transcript. Application deadlines: Rolling, Rolling for nonresidents. Notification: continuous, continuous for nonresidents. Transfer credits accepted: Yes.

Costs Per Year: Application fee: $50. Tuition: $15,300 full-time, $460 per credit part-time. Mandatory fees: $1548 full-time, $43 per credit part-time. Full-time tuition and fees vary according to course load, degree level, location, and program. Part-time tuition and fees vary according to course load, degree level, location, and program.

Collegiate Environment: Orientation program. Social organizations: Program specific student led organizations. Major annual events: Service Learning Projects, Applied Learning Projects, Student Appreciation Events. Campus security: 24-hour emergency response devices, late night transport-escort service. Eau Claire Campus Library with 2,151 books, 53,138 serials, 20 audiovisual materials, an OPAC, and a Web page. 64 computers available on campus for general student use. A campuswide network can be accessed. Students can access the following: online class registration. Staffed computer lab on campus provides training in use of computers, software, and the Internet.

■ GLOBE UNIVERSITY–GREEN BAY

2620 Development Dr.
Bellevue, WI 54311
Tel: (920)264-1600
E-mail: bfrancour@globeuniversity.edu
Web Site: www.globeuniversity.edu/

Description: Proprietary, 4-year, coed. Part of Globe Education Network (GEN) which is composed of Globe University, Minnesota School of Business, Broadview University, The Institute of Production and Recording and Minnesota School of Cosmetology. Awards associate and bachelor's degrees. Setting: 5-acre urban campus. Total enrollment: 215. Faculty: 40 (9 full-time, 31 part-time). Student-undergrad faculty ratio is 8:1. Full-time: 117 students, 86% women, 14% men. Part-time: 98 students, 88% women, 12% men. Students come from 4 states and territories, 4% from out-of-state. 3% American Indian or Alaska Native, non-Hispanic/Latino; 2% Hispanic/Latino; 2% African American, non-Hispanic/Latino; 1% Asian, non-Hispanic/Latino; 0% Native Hawaiian or other Pacific Islander, non-Hispanic/Latino; 0% international. 23% 25 or older, 53% transferred in. Core. Academic remediation for entering students, services for LD students, advanced placement, accelerated degree program, summer session for credit, adult/continuing education programs, internships.

Entrance Requirements: Option: electronic application. Required: high school transcript, interview. Required for some: essay, 2 recommendations, GED certificate in lieu of high school transcript. Application deadlines: Rolling, Rolling for nonresidents. Notification: continuous, continuous for nonresidents. Transfer credits accepted: Yes.

Costs Per Year: Application fee: $50. Tuition: $15,300 full-time, $460 per credit part-time. Mandatory fees: $1548 full-time. Full-time tuition and fees vary according to course load, degree level, location, and program. Part-time tuition varies according to course load, degree level, location, and program.

Collegiate Environment: Orientation program. Social organizations: Program specific student led organizations. Major annual events: Service Learning Projects, Applied Learning Projects, Student Appreciation Events. Campus security: 24-hour emergency response devices, late night transport-escort service. Green Bay Campus Library with 1,594 books, 53,144 serials, 15 audiovisual materials, an OPAC, and a Web page. 46 computers available on campus for general student use. A campuswide network can be accessed. Students can access the following: online class registration. Staffed computer lab on campus provides training in use of computers, software, and the Internet.

■ GLOBE UNIVERSITY–LA CROSSE

2651 Midwest Dr.
Onalaska, WI 54650
Tel: (608)779-2600
E-mail: csimonson@globeuniversity.edu
Web Site: www.globeuniversity.edu/

Description: Proprietary, 4-year, coed. Part of Globe Education Network (GEN) which is composed of Globe University, Minnesota School of Business, Broadview University, The Institute of Production and Recording and Minnesota School of Cosmetology. Awards associate and bachelor's degrees. Setting: 4 small town campus. Total enrollment: 534. Faculty: 37 (10 full-time, 27 part-time). Student-undergrad faculty ratio is 9:1. Full-time: 412 students, 74% women, 26% men. Part-time: 122 students, 83% women, 17% men. Students come from 4 states and territories, 3% from out-of-state.

1% American Indian or Alaska Native, non-Hispanic/Latino; 1% Hispanic/Latino; 2% African American, non-Hispanic/Latino; 2% Asian, non-Hispanic/Latino; 0% Native Hawaiian or other Pacific Islander, non-Hispanic/Latino; 0% international. 48% 25 or older, 24% transferred in. Retention: 40% of full-time freshmen returned the following year. Core. Academic remediation for entering students, services for LD students, advanced placement, accelerated degree program, summer session for credit, part-time degree program, adult/continuing education programs, internships.

Entrance Requirements: Option: electronic application. Required: high school transcript, interview, ACCUPLACER is required of all applicants unless documentation of a minimum ACT composite score of 21 or documentation of a minimum composite score of 1485 on the SAT is presented. Required for some: essay, 2 recommendations, GED certificate in lieu of high school transcript. Application deadlines: Rolling, Rolling for nonresidents. Notification: continuous, continuous for nonresidents. Transfer credits accepted: Yes.

Costs Per Year: Application fee: $50. Tuition: $15,300 full-time, $460 per credit part-time. Mandatory fees: $1548 full-time, $43 per credit part-time. Full-time tuition and fees vary according to course load, degree level, location, and program. Part-time tuition and fees vary according to course load, degree level, location, and program.

Collegiate Environment: Orientation program. Social organizations: Program specific student led organizations. Major annual events: Service Learning Projects, Applied Learning Projects, Student Appreciation Events. Campus security: 24-hour emergency response devices, late night transport-escort service. La Crosse Campus Liibrary with 1,946 books, 53,138 serials, 50 audiovisual materials, an OPAC, and a Web page. 67 computers available on campus for general student use. A campuswide network can be accessed. Students can access the following: online class registration. Staffed computer lab on campus provides training in use of computers, software, and the Internet.

■ GLOBE UNIVERSITY–MADISON EAST

4901 Eastpark Blvd.
Madison, WI 53718
Tel: (608)216-9400
E-mail: brittanykuntson@globeuniversity.edu
Web Site: www.globeuniversity.edu/

Description: Proprietary, 4-year, coed. Part of Globe Education Network (GEN) which is composed of Globe University, Minnesota School of Business, Broadview University, The Institute of Production and Recording and Minnesota School of Cosmetology. Awards associate and bachelor's degrees. Setting: 7-acre urban campus. Total enrollment: 290. Faculty: 47 (9 full-time, 38 part-time). Student-undergrad faculty ratio is 10:1. Full-time: 100 students, 74% women, 26% men. Part-time: 190 students, 76% women, 24% men. 0% from out-of-state. 0.3% American Indian or Alaska Native, non-Hispanic/Latino; 3% Hispanic/Latino; 10% African American, non-Hispanic/Latino; 1% Asian, non-Hispanic/Latino; 0.3% Native Hawaiian or other Pacific Islander, non-Hispanic/Latino; 0% international. 36% 25 or older, 37% transferred in. Retention: 0% of full-time freshmen returned the following year. Academic areas with the most degrees conferred: health professions and related sciences; business/marketing. Core. Academic remediation for entering students, services for LD students, advanced placement, accelerated degree program, summer session for credit, part-time degree program, adult/continuing education programs, internships.

Entrance Requirements: Option: electronic application. Required: high school transcript, interview, High school transcript or GED, ACCUPLACER is required of all applicants unless documentation of a minimum ACT composite score of 21 or documentation of a minimum composite score of 1485 on the SAT is presented. Required for some: essay, 2 recommendations. Application deadlines: Rolling, Rolling for nonresidents. Notification: continuous, continuous for nonresidents. Transfer credits accepted: Yes.

Costs Per Year: Application fee: $50. Tuition: $15,300 full-time, $460 per credit part-time. Mandatory fees: $1548 full-time, $43 per credit part-time. Full-time tuition and fees vary according to course load, degree level, location, and program. Part-time tuition and fees vary according to course load, degree level, location, and program.

Collegiate Environment: Orientation program. Social organizations: Program specific student led organizations. Major annual events: Service Learning Projects, Applied Learning Projects, Student Appreciation Events. Campus security: 24-hour emergency response devices, late night transport-escort service. Madison East Campus Library with 1,877 books, 53,148 serials, 40 audiovisual materials, an OPAC, and a Web page. 62 computers available on campus for general student use. A campuswide network can be accessed. Students can access the following: online class registration. Staffed computer lab on campus provides training in use of computers, software, and the Internet.

■ GLOBE UNIVERSITY–MADISON WEST
1345 Deming Way
Middleton, WI 53562
Tel: (608)830-6900
E-mail: jbuenzli@globeuniversity.edu
Web Site: www.globeuniversity.edu/
Description: Proprietary, 4-year, coed. Part of Globe Education Network (GEN) which is composed of Globe University, Minnesota School of Business, Broadview University, The Institute of Production and Recording and Minnesota School of Cosmetology. Awards associate and bachelor's degrees. Setting: 4 small town campus. Total enrollment: 338. Faculty: 42 (3 full-time, 39 part-time). Student-undergrad faculty ratio is 12:1. Full-time: 98 students, 76% women, 24% men. Part-time: 240 students, 78% women, 22% men. 0% from out-of-state. 0.3% American Indian or Alaska Native, non-Hispanic/Latino; 3% Hispanic/Latino; 15% African American, non-Hispanic/Latino; 2% Asian, non-Hispanic/Latino; 0% Native Hawaiian or other Pacific Islander, non-Hispanic/Latino; 0% international. 44% 25 or older, 24% transferred in. Retention: 25% of full-time freshmen returned the following year. Academic area with the most degrees conferred: business/marketing. Core. Academic remediation for entering students, services for LD students, advanced placement, accelerated degree program, summer session for credit, part-time degree program, adult/continuing education programs, internships.
Entrance Requirements: Option: electronic application. Required: high school transcript, interview, ACCUPLACER is required of all applicants unless documentation of a minimum ACT composite score of 21 or documentation of a minimum composite score of 1485 on the SAT is presented. Required for some: essay, 2 recommendations, GED certificate in lieu of high school transcript. Application deadlines: Rolling, Rolling for nonresidents. Notification: continuous, continuous for nonresidents. Transfer credits accepted: Yes.
Costs Per Year: Application fee: $50. Tuition: $15,300 full-time, $460 per credit part-time. Mandatory fees: $1548 full-time. Full-time tuition and fees vary according to course load, degree level, location, and program. Part-time tuition varies according to course load, degree level, location, and program.
Collegiate Environment: Orientation program. Social organizations: Program specific student led organizations. Major annual events: Service Learning Projects, Applied Learning Projects, Student Appreciation Events. Campus security: 24-hour emergency response devices, late night transport-escort service. Middleton Campus Library with 1,893 books, 53,142 serials, 76 audiovisual materials, an OPAC, and a Web page. 74 computers available on campus for general student use. A campuswide network can be accessed. Students can access the following: online class registration. Staffed computer lab on campus provides training in use of computers, software, and the Internet.

■ GLOBE UNIVERSITY–WAUSAU
1480 Country Rd. XX
Rothschild, WI 54474
Tel: (715)301-1300
E-mail: apalas@globeuniversity.edu
Web Site: www.globeuniversity.edu/
Description: Proprietary, 4-year, coed. Part of Globe Education Network (GEN) which is composed of Globe University, Minnesota School of Business, Broadview University, The Institute of Production and Recording and Minnesota School of Cosmetology. Awards associate and bachelor's degrees. Setting: 5-acre small town campus. Total enrollment: 365. Faculty: 50 (8 full-time, 42 part-time). Student-undergrad faculty ratio is 11:1. Full-time: 190 students, 80% women, 20% men. Part-time: 175 students, 86% women, 14% men. 0% from out-of-state. 1% American Indian or Alaska Native, non-Hispanic/Latino; 2% Hispanic/Latino; 1% African American, non-Hispanic/Latino; 2% Asian, non-Hispanic/Latino; 0% Native Hawaiian or other Pacific Islander, non-Hispanic/Latino; 0% international. 36% 25 or older, 39% transferred in. Retention: 0% of full-time freshmen returned the following year. Core. Academic remediation for entering students, services for LD students, advanced placement, accelerated degree program, summer session for credit, part-time degree program, adult/continuing education programs, internships.
Entrance Requirements: Option: electronic application. Required: high school transcript, interview, High school transcript or GED, ACCUPLACER is

required of all applicants unless documentation of a minimum ACT composite score of 21 or documentation of a minimum composite score of 1485 on the SAT is presented. Required for some: essay, 2 recommendations. Application deadlines: Rolling, Rolling for nonresidents. Notification: continuous, continuous for nonresidents. Transfer credits accepted: Yes.
Costs Per Year: Application fee: $50. Tuition: $15,300 full-time, $460 per credit part-time. Mandatory fees: $1548 full-time, $43 per credit part-time. Full-time tuition and fees vary according to course load, degree level, location, and program. Part-time tuition and fees vary according to course load, degree level, location, and program.
Collegiate Environment: Orientation program. Social organizations: Program specific student led organizations. Major annual events: Service Learning Projects, Applied Learning Projects, Student Appreciation Events. Campus security: 24-hour emergency response devices, late night transport-escort service. Wausau Campus Library with 1,948 books, 53,138 serials, 19 audiovisual materials, an OPAC, and a Web page. 66 computers available on campus for general student use. A campuswide network can be accessed. Students can access the following: online class registration. Staffed computer lab on campus provides training in use of computers, software, and the Internet.

■ HERZING UNIVERSITY (BROOKFIELD)
555 S Executive Dr.
Brookfield, WI 53005
Tel: (262)649-1710; Free: 800-596-0724
Fax: (262)797-9090
Web Site: www.herzing.edu/brookfield
Description: Proprietary, 4-year, coed. Awards associate and bachelor's degrees.

■ HERZING UNIVERSITY (KENOSHA)
4006 Washington Rd.
Kenosha, WI 53144
Tel: (866)724-9144; Free: 800-596-0724
Fax: (262)653-1434
Web Site: www.herzing.edu/kenosha
Description: Proprietary, 4-year, coed. Awards associate and bachelor's degrees.

■ HERZING UNIVERSITY (MADISON)
5218 E Ter. Dr.
Madison, WI 53718
Tel: (608)249-6611; Free: 800-596-0724
Fax: (608)249-8593
E-mail: info@msn.herzing.edu
Web Site: www.herzing.edu/madison/
Description: Proprietary, comprehensive, coed. Part of Herzing Institutes, Inc. Awards associate, bachelor's, and master's degrees. Founded 1948. Setting: suburban campus with easy access to Madison, Milwaukee. Total enrollment: 857. Faculty: 48 (28 full-time, 20 part-time). Core. Calendar: semesters. Academic remediation for entering students, services for LD students, advanced placement, accelerated degree program, honors program, independent study, distance learning, summer session for credit, part-time degree program, adult/continuing education programs, co-op programs and internships, graduate courses open to undergrads. Study abroad program.
Entrance Requirements: Open admission. Required: high school transcript, interview. Application deadline: Rolling. Transfer credits accepted: Yes.
Costs Per Year: Application fee: $0. Tuition: $11,400 full-time, $5760 per year part-time. Full-time tuition varies according to course load, location, and program. Part-time tuition varies according to course load, location, and program.
Collegiate Environment: Orientation program. Student services: personal-psychological counseling. Campus security: 24-hour emergency response devices. Herzing University Library with 1,500 books, 30 serials, an OPAC, and a Web page. 363 computers available on campus for general student use. Computer purchase/lease plans available. A campuswide network can be accessed from off-campus. Staffed computer lab on campus provides training in use of computers, software, and the Internet.

■ HERZING UNIVERSITY ONLINE
525 N 6th St.
Milwaukee, WI 53203
Free: 866-508-0748

Web Site: www.herzingonline.edu/

Description: Proprietary, comprehensive, coed. Awards bachelor's and master's degrees.

■ ITT TECHNICAL INSTITUTE (GERMANTOWN)

W177 N9886 Rivercrest Dr.
Ste. 200
Germantown, WI 53022
Tel: (262)257-7100; Free: 877-213-8538
Web Site: www.itt-tech.edu/

Description: Proprietary, 4-year, coed. Awards associate and bachelor's degrees.

Entrance Requirements: Entrance: minimally difficult.

■ ITT TECHNICAL INSTITUTE (GREEN BAY)

470 Security Blvd.
Green Bay, WI 54313
Tel: (920)662-9000; Free: 888-884-3626
Web Site: www.itt-tech.edu/

Description: Proprietary, primarily 2-year, coed. Part of ITT Educational Services, Inc. Awards terminal associate and bachelor's degrees. Founded 2000.

Entrance Requirements: Entrance: minimally difficult.

■ ITT TECHNICAL INSTITUTE (GREENFIELD)

6300 W Layton Ave.
Greenfield, WI 53220-4612
Tel: (414)282-9494
Web Site: www.itt-tech.edu/

Description: Proprietary, primarily 2-year, coed. Part of ITT Educational Services, Inc. Awards terminal associate and bachelor's degrees. Founded 1968. Setting: suburban campus.

Entrance Requirements: Entrance: minimally difficult.

■ ITT TECHNICAL INSTITUTE (MADISON)

2450 Rimrock Rd., Ste. 100
Madison, WI 53713
Tel: (608)288-6301; Free: 877-628-5960
Web Site: www.itt-tech.edu/

Description: Proprietary, primarily 2-year, coed. Part of ITT Educational Services, Inc. Awards terminal associate and bachelor's degrees.

Entrance Requirements: Entrance: minimally difficult.

■ LAC COURTE OREILLES OJIBWA COMMUNITY COLLEGE

13466 W Trepania Rd.
Hayward, WI 54843-2181
Tel: (715)634-4790; Free: 888-526-6221
Web Site: www.lco.edu/

Description: Federally supported, 2-year, coed. Awards certificates, transfer associate, and terminal associate degrees. Founded 1982. Setting: 2-acre rural campus. Endowment: $2.3 million. Total enrollment: 561. Faculty: 70 (15 full-time, 55 part-time). Student-undergrad faculty ratio is 15:1. 135 applied, 100% were admitted. Full-time: 341 students, 65% women, 35% men. Part-time: 220 students, 71% women, 29% men. 0% from out-of-state. 63% 25 or older, 6% transferred in. Core. Calendar: semesters. Academic remediation for entering students, services for LD students, honors program, independent study, distance learning, double major, part-time degree program, external degree program, adult/continuing education programs, internships.

Entrance Requirements: Open admission. Option: early admission. Required: high school transcript, ACT COMPASS. Entrance: noncompetitive. Application deadline: Rolling. Transfer credits accepted: Yes.

Collegiate Environment: Orientation program. Drama-theater group. Social organizations: 4 open to all. Most popular organizations: Student Association, AISES, Drama Club, Student Ambassadors. Major annual events: Welcome Feast, Thanksgiving Feast, graduation. Campus security: 24-hour emergency response devices. Lac Courte Oreilles Ojibwa Community College Library with 25,267 books, 248 microform titles, 82 serials, 4,193 audiovisual materials, an OPAC, and a Web page. 63 computers available on campus for general student use. A campuswide network can be accessed. Staffed computer lab on campus (open 24 hours a day) provides training in use of computers, software, and the Internet.

■ LAKELAND COLLEGE

PO Box 359
Sheboygan, WI 53082-0359
Tel: (920)565-1000; Free: 800-569-2166
Fax: (920)565-1206
E-mail: admissions@lakeland.edu
Web Site: www.lakeland.edu/

Description: Independent, comprehensive, coed, affiliated with United Church of Christ. Awards bachelor's and master's degrees. Founded 1862. Setting: 240-acre rural campus with easy access to Milwaukee. Endowment: $12.1 million. Educational spending for the previous fiscal year: $6767 per student. Total enrollment: 3,749. Faculty: 71 (57 full-time, 14 part-time). Student-undergrad faculty ratio is 15:1. 687 applied, 77% were admitted. 15% from top 10% of their high school class, 30% from top quarter, 70% from top half. 5 valedictorians. Full-time: 995 students, 48% women, 52% men. Part-time: 1,969 students, 61% women, 39% men. Students come from 30 states and territories, 16 other countries, 17% from out-of-state. 1% American Indian or Alaska Native, non-Hispanic/Latino; 5% Hispanic/Latino; 6% African American, non-Hispanic/Latino; 2% Asian, non-Hispanic/Latino; 0.1% Native Hawaiian or other Pacific Islander, non-Hispanic/Latino; 3% international. 15% 25 or older, 67% live on campus, 6% transferred in. Retention: 81% of full-time freshmen returned the following year. Academic areas with the most degrees conferred: business/marketing; computer and information sciences; social sciences. Core. Calendar: 4-4-1. Academic remediation for entering students, ESL program, services for LD students, advanced placement, honors program, independent study, distance learning, double major, summer session for credit, part-time degree program, adult/continuing education programs, internships, graduate courses open to undergrads. Off campus study. Study abroad program.

Entrance Requirements: Options: electronic application, deferred admission, international baccalaureate accepted. Required: essay, high school transcript, minimum 2 high school GPA, SAT or ACT. Required for some: interview. Entrance: minimally difficult. Application deadline: Rolling. Notification: continuous until 9/1. SAT Reasoning Test deadline: 8/15.

Costs Per Year: Application fee: $0. Comprehensive fee: $28,582 includes full-time tuition ($21,242) and college room and board ($7340). Full-time tuition varies according to degree level. Room and board charges vary according to board plan and housing facility. Tuition guaranteed not to increase for student's term of enrollment.

Collegiate Environment: Orientation program. Drama-theater group, choral group, student-run newspaper. Social organizations: 40 open to all; local fraternities, local sororities; 20% of eligible men and 15% of eligible women are members. Most popular organizations: Lakeland College Campus Activities Board, Student Association, Black Student Union, Mortar Board, Global Students Association. Major annual events: Homecoming, Family Weekend, Spring Fling. Student services: health clinic, personal-psychological counseling. Campus security: 24-hour emergency response devices, student patrols, late night transport-escort service, controlled dormitory access. 667 college housing spaces available; 588 were occupied in 2012-13. Freshmen guaranteed college housing. On-campus residence required through senior year. Options: coed, men-only, women-only housing available. Esch Memorial Library with 57,216 books, 36,517 microform titles, 282 serials, 2,064 audiovisual materials, an OPAC, and a Web page. Operations spending for the previous fiscal year: $287,841. 157 computers available on campus for general student use. Computer purchase/lease plans available. A campuswide network can be accessed from student residence rooms and from off campus. Students can access the following: online class registration. Staffed computer lab on campus provides training in use of computers and software.

Community Environment: The college is located 12 miles northwest of Sheboygan, Wisconsin, 60 miles north of Milwaukee and 60 miles south of Green Bay. Sheboygan has a population of 48,800 and offers students off-campus opportunities for work and recreation. Sheboygan's county airport, the bus depot, and Interstate 43 offer easy access to Lakeland.

■ LAKESHORE TECHNICAL COLLEGE

1290 N Ave.
Cleveland, WI 53015-1414
Tel: (920)693-1000; Free: 888-GO TO LTC
Fax: (920)693-1363
Web Site: www.gotoltc.com/

Description: State and locally supported, 2-year, coed. Part of Wisconsin Technical College System. Awards certificates, diplomas, transfer associate, and terminal associate degrees. Founded 1967. Setting: 160-acre rural campus with easy access to Milwaukee. Research spending for the previous fiscal year: $147,565. Total enrollment: 2,789. Faculty: 229 (99 full-time, 130 part-time). Student-undergrad faculty ratio is 14:1. 1,982 applied, 51% were admitted. Full-time: 702 students, 54% women, 46% men. Part-time: 2,087 students, 60% women, 40% men. Students come from 5 states and territories, 1% from out-of-state. 54% 25 or older. Core. Calendar: semesters. Academic remediation for entering students, ESL program, services for LD students, advanced placement, accelerated degree program, self-designed majors, independent study, distance learning, double major, summer session for credit, part-time degree program, external degree program, adult/continuing education programs, co-op programs and internships.

Entrance Requirements: Open admission. Options: electronic application, early admission, deferred admission. Recommended: SAT or ACT, ACCUPLACER/ACT ASSET. Required for some: high school transcript, interview. Entrance: noncompetitive. Application deadline: Rolling. Notification: continuous.

Collegiate Environment: Orientation program. Social organizations: 14 open to all. Most popular organizations: student government, Business Professionals of America, Police Science Club, Lakeshore Student Nurse Association, Dairy Herd Club. Major annual events: Hypnotist, Fun Flicks, Virtual Reality. Student services: health clinic, personal-psychological counseling. Campus security: 24-hour patrols. 15,749 books, 220 serials, and an OPACOperations spending for the previous fiscal year: $280,669. 720 computers available on campus for general student use. A campuswide network can be accessed. Staffed computer lab on campus.

Community Environment: See Lakeland College.

■ **LAWRENCE UNIVERSITY**
711 E Boldt Way
Appleton, WI 54911
Tel: (920)832-7000; Free: 800-227-0982
Fax: (920)832-6606
E-mail: excel@lawrence.edu
Web Site: www.lawrence.edu/
Description: Independent, 4-year, coed. Awards bachelor's degrees. Founded 1847. Setting: 84-acre small town campus. Total enrollment: 1,525. Faculty: 196 (161 full-time, 35 part-time). Student-undergrad faculty ratio is 9:1. 2,599 applied, 76% were admitted. 46% from top 10% of their high school class, 71% from top quarter, 92% from top half. Full-time: 1,473 students, 54% women, 46% men. Part-time: 52 students, 46% women, 54% men. 63% from out-of-state. 1% American Indian or Alaska Native, non-Hispanic/Latino; 4% Hispanic/Latino; 3% African American, non-Hispanic/Latino; 3% Asian, non-Hispanic/Latino; 0.1% Native Hawaiian or other Pacific Islander, non-Hispanic/Latino; 9% international. 0% 25 or older, 98% live on campus, 2% transferred in. Retention: 90% of full-time freshmen returned the following year. Academic areas with the most degrees conferred: visual and performing arts; social sciences; biological/life sciences. Core. Calendar: trimesters. Services for LD students, advanced placement, self-designed majors, independent study, double major, part-time degree program, internships. Off campus study at Associated Colleges of the Midwest, Great Lakes Colleges Association. Study abroad program.

Entrance Requirements: Options: electronic application, early admission, early decision, early action, deferred admission, international baccalaureate accepted. Required: essay, high school transcript, 1 recommendation, audition for music program. Recommended: minimum 3 high school GPA, interview. Entrance: very difficult. Application deadlines: 1/15, 11/15 for early decision, 12/1 for early action. Notification: 4/1, 12/1 for early decision, 1/30 for early action. SAT Reasoning Test deadline: 1/15. SAT Subject Test deadline: 1/15. Transfer credits accepted: Yes. Applicants placed on waiting list: 61. Wait-listed applicants offered admission: 12. Early decision applicants: 48. Early decision applicants admitted: 37.

Costs Per Year: Application fee: $40. Comprehensive fee: $48,270 includes full-time tuition ($39,732), mandatory fees ($291), and college room and board ($8247). College room only: $3858. Room and board charges vary according to board plan.

Collegiate Environment: Orientation program. Drama-theater group, choral group, student-run newspaper, radio station. Social organizations: 100 open to all; national fraternities, national sororities; 18% of eligible men and 9% of eligible women are members. Most popular organizations: Lawrence Swing Dancers, Lawrence International, Outdoor Recreation Club, Sustainable Lawrence University Gardens (SLUG), Greenfire. Major annual events: Fall Festival, Jazz Celebration Weekend, Midwest Trivia Contest. Student services: health clinic, personal-psychological counseling. Campus security: 24-hour emergency response devices and patrols, student patrols, late night

transport-escort service, controlled dormitory access, evening patrols by trained security personnel. 1,364 college housing spaces available. Freshmen guaranteed college housing. On-campus residence required through senior year. Options: coed, men-only, women-only housing available. Seeley G. Mudd Library with an OPAC and a Web page.

Community Environment: Appleton is a thriving and dynamic small city (pop. 70,217), located in the papermaking center of the country and rated among the best communities in the United States for quality of life. The city is accessible by car, bus, and plane.

■ **MADISON AREA TECHNICAL COLLEGE**
1701 Wright St.
Madison, WI 53704
Tel: (608)246-6100; Free: 800-322-6282
Fax: (608)246-6880
Web Site: madisoncollege.edu/
Description: District-supported, 2-year, coed. Part of Wisconsin Technical College System. Awards certificates, diplomas, transfer associate, and terminal associate degrees. Founded 1911. Setting: 150-acre urban campus. Research spending for the previous fiscal year: $195,238. Total enrollment: 13,479. Faculty: 1,881 (393 full-time, 1,488 part-time). 1% from top 10% of their high school class, 31% from top half. Students come from 9 states and territories. 50% 25 or older. Core. Calendar: semesters. Academic remediation for entering students, ESL program, services for LD students, summer session for credit, part-time degree program, adult/continuing education programs, co-op programs and internships. Off campus study at University of Wisconsin-Baraboo/Sauk County.

Entrance Requirements: Open admission except for data processing, technology, health occupations, quota programs. Option: early admission. Required for some: high school transcript, ACT. Entrance: noncompetitive. Application deadline: 7/1. Notification: continuous. Preference given to state residents.

Collegiate Environment: Drama-theater group, choral group, student-run newspaper. Social organizations: 45 open to all. Most popular organizations: Marketing Club, Minority Networking Groups, Data Processing Management Association, Student Nurses Association, Business Professionals of America. Major annual events: spring picnic, Celebrate Diversity Series, service-learning activities. Student services: health clinic, personal-psychological counseling, women's center. Campus security: 24-hour emergency response devices and patrols, late night transport-escort service. Truax-Information Resource Center with 66,000 books, 657 serials, an OPAC, and a Web page. Operations spending for the previous fiscal year: $921,250. 1,500 computers available on campus for general student use. Staffed computer lab on campus.

Community Environment: Home of the state capital and the University of Wisconsin, Madison is a lovely city situated between two lakes. Four campuses are in smaller cities with growing industrial bases.

■ **MADISON MEDIA INSTITUTE**
2702 Agriculture Dr.
Madison, WI 53718
Tel: (608)663-2000; Free: 800-236-4997
Fax: (608)442-0141
Web Site: www.mediainstitute.edu/
Description: Proprietary, 2-year, coed. Awards terminal associate degrees. Founded 1969. Setting: urban campus. Total enrollment: 133. Faculty: 22 (20 full-time, 2 part-time). Calendar: semesters.
Entrance Requirements: Entrance: noncompetitive. Application deadline: Rolling. Notification: continuous.

■ **MARANATHA BAPTIST BIBLE COLLEGE**
745 W Main St.
Watertown, WI 53094
Tel: (920)261-9300; Free: 800-622-2947
Fax: (920)261-9109
E-mail: admissions@mbbc.edu
Web Site: www.mbbc.edu/
Description: Independent Baptist, comprehensive, coed. Awards associate, bachelor's, and master's degrees. Founded 1968. Setting: 60-acre small town campus with easy access to Milwaukee. Endowment: $206,798. Educational spending for the previous fiscal year: $4941 per student. Total enrollment: 983. Faculty: 76 (44 full-time, 32 part-time). Student-undergrad faculty ratio is 15:1. 398 applied, 74% were admitted. Full-time: 690 students, 53% women, 47% men. Part-time: 197 students, 55% women,

45% men. Students come from 47 states and territories, 8 other countries, 82% from out-of-state. 0.1% American Indian or Alaska Native, non-Hispanic/Latino; 1% Hispanic/Latino; 0.1% African American, non-Hispanic/Latino; 1% Asian, non-Hispanic/Latino; 0% Native Hawaiian or other Pacific Islander, non-Hispanic/Latino; 0.3% international. 7% 25 or older, 71% live on campus, 4% transferred in. Retention: 67% of full-time freshmen returned the following year. Academic areas with the most degrees conferred: education; theology and religious vocations; business/marketing. Core. Calendar: semesters. Academic remediation for entering students, advanced placement, independent study, distance learning, double major, summer session for credit, part-time degree program, internships, graduate courses open to undergrads. Off campus study. Study abroad program. ROTC: Army, Air Force (c).

Entrance Requirements: Option: electronic application. Required: essay, high school transcript, 4 recommendations, SAT or ACT. Entrance: noncompetitive. Application deadline: Rolling. Notification: continuous. Preference given to Christians. SAT Reasoning Test deadline: 7/31. SAT Subject Test deadline: 7/31. Transfer credits accepted: Yes.

Costs Per Year: Application fee: $50. Comprehensive fee: $19,340 includes full-time tuition ($11,720), mandatory fees ($1140), and college room and board ($6480). Full-time tuition and fees vary according to course load. Part-time tuition: $500 per credit hour. Part-time mandatory fees: $48 per credit hour. Part-time tuition and fees vary according to course load.

Collegiate Environment: Orientation program. Drama-theater group, choral group. Major annual events: Christmas Festival of Music, Semi-Annual College Play, Commencement. Student services: health clinic, personal-psychological counseling. Campus security: student patrols, late night transport-escort service, controlled dormitory access. 650 college housing spaces available; 513 were occupied in 2012-13. Freshmen guaranteed college housing. On-campus residence required through senior year. Options: men-only, women-only housing available. Cedarholm Library and Resource Center with 105,691 books, 229 microform titles, 374 serials, 2,692 audiovisual materials, an OPAC, and a Web page. Operations spending for the previous fiscal year: $71,828. 120 computers available on campus for general student use. A campuswide network can be accessed from student residence rooms and from off campus. Students can access the following: online class registration.

■ **MARIAN UNIVERSITY**
45 S National Ave.
Fond du Lac, WI 54935-4699
Tel: (920)923-7600; Free: 800-2-MARIAN
Fax: (920)923-8755
E-mail: admission@marianuniversity.edu
Web Site: www.marianuniversity.edu/

Description: Independent Roman Catholic, comprehensive, coed. Awards bachelor's, master's, and doctoral degrees. Founded 1936. Setting: 78-acre small town campus with easy access to Milwaukee. Endowment: $7.2 million. Educational spending for the previous fiscal year: $5425 per student. Total enrollment: 2,306. Faculty: 257 (94 full-time, 163 part-time). Student-undergrad faculty ratio is 12:1. 1,031 applied, 77% were admitted. 11% from top 10% of their high school class, 33% from top quarter, 62% from top half. Full-time: 1,405 students, 71% women, 29% men. Part-time: 393 students, 72% women, 28% men. Students come from 15 states and territories, 8 other countries, 8% from out-of-state. 1% American Indian or Alaska Native, non-Hispanic/Latino; 5% Hispanic/Latino; 7% African American, non-Hispanic/Latino; 2% Asian, non-Hispanic/Latino; 0.1% Native Hawaiian or other Pacific Islander, non-Hispanic/Latino; 1% international. 32% 25 or older, 34% live on campus, 8% transferred in. Retention: 70% of full-time freshmen returned the following year. Academic areas with the most degrees conferred: health professions and related sciences; business/marketing; homeland security, law enforcement, firefighting, and protective services. Core. Calendar: semesters. Academic remediation for entering students, ESL program, services for LD students, advanced placement, accelerated degree program, self-designed majors, honors program, independent study, distance learning, double major, summer session for credit, part-time degree program, co-op programs and internships. Study abroad program. ROTC: Army.

Entrance Requirements: Options: electronic application, deferred admission. Required: high school transcript, SAT or ACT. Recommended: minimum 2 high school GPA, interview. Required for some: interview. Entrance: moderately difficult. Application deadline: Rolling. Notification: 8/15. Transfer credits accepted: Yes.

Costs Per Year: Application fee: $20. One-time mandatory fee: $100.

Comprehensive fee: $29,580 includes full-time tuition ($23,090), mandatory fees ($350), and college room and board ($6140). College room only: $3690. Full-time tuition and fees vary according to course load and program. Room and board charges vary according to board plan. Part-time tuition: $350 per credit hour. Part-time tuition varies according to course load and program.

Collegiate Environment: Orientation program. Choral group, student-run newspaper. Social organizations: 35 open to all; national fraternities, national sororities; 5% of eligible men and 5% of eligible women are members. Most popular organizations: Student Senate, Student Nurses Association, Student Education Association, Science and Math Association, Business Club. Major annual events: Big Band event, Academic Symposium, Midnight madness. Student services: health clinic, personal-psychological counseling. Campus security: 24-hour emergency response devices and patrols, student patrols, late night transport-escort service, controlled dormitory access. 498 college housing spaces available; 487 were occupied in 2012-13. Freshmen guaranteed college housing. On-campus residence required through sophomore year. Option: coed housing available. Cardinal Meyer Library with 161,589 books, 3,570 microform titles, 1,381 serials, 1,787 audiovisual materials, an OPAC, and a Web page. Operations spending for the previous fiscal year: $611,350. 500 computers available on campus for general student use. Computer purchase/lease plans available. A campuswide network can be accessed from student residence rooms and from off campus. Students can access the following: online class registration. Staffed computer lab on campus provides training in use of computers, software, and the Internet.

Community Environment: Marian College of Fond du Lac, Wisconsin (population 42,400) is located on the edge of the scenic Kettle Moraine region, the dominant glacial formation of Wisconsin. It is less than a mile from beautiful Lake Winnebago. The campus is easily reached by U.S. Highways 41, 45, and 151. There is efficient bus service from other cities and airports. Fond du Lac offers its own cultural attractions: a modern public library, churches, local community theaters, and the Civic Music Center. Students who wish to expand their cultural horizons may easily travel to the nearby cities of Green Bay, Madison, Milwaukee, or Oshkosh.

■ **MARQUETTE UNIVERSITY**
PO Box 1881
Milwaukee, WI 53201-1881
Tel: (414)288-7250; Free: 800-222-6544
E-mail: admissions@marquette.edu
Web Site: www.marquette.edu/

Description: Independent Roman Catholic (Jesuit), university, coed. Awards bachelor's, master's, and doctoral degrees and post-master's certificates. Founded 1881. Setting: 98-acre urban campus with easy access to Milwaukee. Endowment: $407 million. Research spending for the previous fiscal year: $22.4 million. Educational spending for the previous fiscal year: $9591 per student. Total enrollment: 11,749. Faculty: 1,161 (634 full-time, 527 part-time). Student-undergrad faculty ratio is 15:1. 22,900 applied, 55% were admitted. 38% from top 10% of their high school class, 67% from top quarter, 94% from top half. 8 National Merit Scholars, 29 valedictorians. Full-time: 7,969 students, 52% women, 48% men. Part-time: 324 students, 45% women, 55% men. Students come from 51 states and territories, 48 other countries, 64% from out-of-state. 0.2% American Indian or Alaska Native, non-Hispanic/Latino; 9% Hispanic/Latino; 5% African American, non-Hispanic/Latino; 5% Asian, non-Hispanic/Latino; 0.2% Native Hawaiian or other Pacific Islander, non-Hispanic/Latino; 3% international. 2% 25 or older, 54% live on campus, 2% transferred in. Retention: 88% of full-time freshmen returned the following year. Academic areas with the most degrees conferred: business/marketing; communication/journalism; biological/life sciences. Core. Calendar: semesters. ESL program, services for LD students, advanced placement, accelerated degree program, self-designed majors, honors program, independent study, distance learning, double major, summer session for credit, part-time degree program, adult/continuing education programs, co-op programs and internships, graduate courses open to undergrads. Off campus study at Milwaukee Institute of Art and Design, Les Aspin Center for Government, Washington, DC. Study abroad program. ROTC: Army, Naval, Air Force.

Entrance Requirements: Options: electronic application, deferred admission, international baccalaureate accepted. Required: essay, high school transcript, minimum 2.5 high school GPA, SAT or ACT. Recommended: minimum 3.4 high school GPA. Entrance: moderately difficult. Application deadline: 12/1. Notification: 1/31. SAT Reasoning Test deadline: 12/1. SAT Subject Test deadline: 12/1. Transfer credits accepted: Yes. Applicants placed on waiting list: 3,789. Wait-listed applicants offered admission: 505.

Costs Per Year: Application fee: $30. Comprehensive fee: $45,370 includes full-time tuition ($34,200), mandatory fees ($440), and college room and board ($10,730). College room only: $6900. Full-time tuition and fees vary according to course load and program. Room and board charges vary according to housing facility. Part-time tuition: $995 per credit. Part-time tuition varies according to program.

Collegiate Environment: Orientation program. Drama-theater group, choral group, student-run newspaper, radio station. Social organizations: 250 open to all; national fraternities, national sororities; 11% of eligible men and 14% of eligible women are members. Most popular organizations: student government, club sports, community service organizations, band/jazz/orchestra, Residence Hall Association. Major annual events: Winter Flurry, Hunger Clean-Up, Midnight Madness Basketball Kick-Off. Student services: health clinic, personal-psychological counseling. Campus security: 24-hour emergency response devices and patrols, student patrols, late night transport-escort service, 24-hour desk attendants in residence halls. 4,800 college housing spaces available; 4,375 were occupied in 2012-13. Freshmen guaranteed college housing. On-campus residence required through sophomore year. Options: coed, men-only, women-only housing available. Raynor Memorial Libraries plus 1 other with 1.7 million books, 820,669 microform titles, 39,040 serials, 19,560 audiovisual materials, an OPAC, and a Web page. Operations spending for the previous fiscal year: $19.2 million. 1,132 computers available on campus for general student use. A campuswide network can be accessed from student residence rooms and from off campus. Students can access the following: online class registration, AV Software, MATLAB. Staffed computer lab on campus provides training in use of computers, software, and the Internet.

Community Environment: Located in the heart of the city, students have access to a multitude of social, educational and cultural opportunities. Marquette's mission statement comes alive with the countless opportunities to volunteer. Whether it's tutoring elementary school students or building homes through Habitat for Humanity, Marquette students put the "community" in community service and have been nationally recognized for their efforts. The Milwaukee business district provides students with an excellent chance to network with professionals in their field, or to gain valuable experience through internships or part-time work. Theaters, concerts, and museums offer a fun and relaxing way to expand the college experience and the lakefront recreational area and downtown shopping provide students with a way to unwind after a week of classes.

■ **MID-STATE TECHNICAL COLLEGE**
500 32nd St. N
Wisconsin Rapids, WI 54494-5599
Tel: (715)422-5300
Fax: (715)422-5345
Web Site: www.mstc.edu/

Description: State and locally supported, 2-year, coed. Part of Wisconsin Technical College System. Awards certificates, diplomas, transfer associate, and terminal associate degrees. Founded 1917. Setting: 155-acre small town campus. Endowment: $1.2 million. Educational spending for the previous fiscal year: $5646 per student. Total enrollment: 10,737. Faculty: 300 (200 full-time, 100 part-time). 1,100 applied, 95% were admitted. Students come from 2 states and territories, 1% from out-of-state. 51% 25 or older. Core. Calendar: semesters. Academic remediation for entering students, ESL program, services for LD students, independent study, distance learning, double major, summer session for credit, part-time degree program, adult/continuing education programs, co-op programs and internships.

Entrance Requirements: Open admission. Options: electronic application, early admission, deferred admission. Required: high school transcript. Entrance: noncompetitive. Application deadline: Rolling. Notification: continuous.

Collegiate Environment: Student-run newspaper. Most popular organizations: Business Professionals of America, Civil Tech Club, Barber and Cosmetology Club, Society of Hosteurs, UICA. Major annual events: Tech Fest, Winter Fest. Student services: health clinic, personal-psychological counseling, women's center. Mid-State Technical College Library with 20,148 books, 910 microform titles, 539 serials, 2,685 audiovisual materials, and an OPAC. Operations spending for the previous fiscal year: $274,887. 120 computers available on campus for general student use. A campuswide network can be accessed from off-campus. Staffed computer lab on campus.

Community Environment: The college serves the area which includes Marshfield (population 19,400), Stevens Point (population 24,298), and Wisconsin Rapids (population 17,621), the county seat of Wood, near the geographical center of the state of Wisconsin.

■ **MILWAUKEE AREA TECHNICAL COLLEGE**
700 W State St.
Milwaukee, WI 53233-1443
Tel: (414)297-6600
Fax: (414)297-7990
E-mail: adamss4@matc.edu
Web Site: www.matc.edu/

Description: District-supported, 2-year, coed. Part of Wisconsin Technical College System. Awards certificates, diplomas, transfer associate, and terminal associate degrees. Founded 1912. Setting: urban campus. Total enrollment: 20,215. Faculty: 1,351 (580 full-time, 771 part-time). Student-undergrad faculty ratio is 14:1. 13,086 applied, 51% were admitted. Full-time: 7,048 students, 47% women, 53% men. Part-time: 13,167 students, 59% women, 41% men. Students come from 16 states and territories, 50 other countries, 1% from out-of-state. 55% 25 or older, 16% transferred in. Retention: 47% of full-time freshmen returned the following year. Core. Calendar: semesters. Academic remediation for entering students, ESL program, services for LD students, advanced placement, accelerated degree program, self-designed majors, freshman honors college, honors program, independent study, distance learning, double major, summer session for credit, part-time degree program, external degree program, adult/continuing education programs, co-op programs and internships. Off campus study. Study abroad program.

Entrance Requirements: Open admission for students satisfying minimum degree requirements (students not meeting these requirements are placed in pre-program curricula). Option: electronic application. Required: high school transcript, ACCUPLACER. Entrance: noncompetitive. Application deadline: Rolling. Notification: continuous until 8/20. Transfer credits accepted: Yes. Applicants placed on waiting list: 1,148. Wait-listed applicants offered admission: 701.

Collegiate Environment: Orientation program. Choral group, student-run newspaper. Social organizations: 50 open to all. Most popular organizations: Student Senate, MATC Times, Ethnic Organizations (Latino Students, Black Student Union, Native American, and Asian student groups), Black Engineers Organization, Future Hospitality Managers of America. Major annual events: Honors Induction Ceremonies (National Technical Honor Society, Phi Theta Kappa Honor Society, Lamp of Knowledge), Soul Food Dinner Grand Ball, Ethnic Festivals (Native American PowWow, Awareness Weeks for Asian, Latino, and Black students). Student services: legal services, personal-psychological counseling, women's center. Campus security: 24-hour emergency response devices and patrols, student patrols, late night transport-escort service. William F. Rasche Library plus 4 others with 90,000 books, 17,000 serials, 3,500 audiovisual materials, an OPAC, and a Web page. 3,500 computers available on campus for general student use. A campuswide network can be accessed from off-campus. Students can access the following: online class registration. Staffed computer lab on campus provides training in use of computers, software, and the Internet.

Community Environment: Located on the west shore of Lake Michigan, Milwaukee (population 640,000) is the largest city in Wisconsin with all major forms of commercial transportation available. Milwaukee is the nation's brewing center, also a major grain market and manufacturing center. Products of industry are metal, machinery, food, leather, chemicals, textiles, electrical machinery, and other items. The city is headquarters of the Lake States National Forest Region. The county has a park system and many of the units contain public golf courses, tennis courts, and other recreational facilities. Milwaukee's State Fair is held each year in August.

■ **MILWAUKEE INSTITUTE OF ART AND DESIGN**
273 E Erie St.
Milwaukee, WI 53202-6003
Tel: (414)276-7889; Free: 888-749-MIAD
Fax: (414)291-8077
E-mail: admissions@miad.edu
Web Site: www.miad.edu/

Description: Independent, 4-year, coed. Awards bachelor's degrees. Founded 1974. Setting: urban campus. Total enrollment: 681. Student-undergrad faculty ratio is 15:1. 442 applied, 71% were admitted. 33% from out-of-state. 8% 25 or older. Retention: 69% of full-time freshmen returned the following year. Core. Calendar: semesters. Academic remediation for entering students, services for LD students, advanced placement, independent study, double major, summer session for credit, adult/continuing education programs, co-op programs and internships. Off campus study at Marquette University, Association of Independent Colleges of Art and Design. Study abroad program.

Entrance Requirements: Options: electronic application, deferred admission. Required: essay, high school transcript, interview, portfolio. Recommended: minimum 2.0 high school GPA. Entrance: moderately difficult. Application deadline: Rolling.

Costs Per Year: Application fee: $25. Tuition: $28,205 full-time, $940 per credit hour part-time. Mandatory fees: $1737 full-time. Full-time tuition and fees vary according to course load and student level. Part-time tuition varies according to course load. College room only: $6651. Room charges vary according to housing facility.

Collegiate Environment: Orientation program. Drama-theater group. Student services: health clinic, personal-psychological counseling. Campus security: 24-hour emergency response devices, late night transport-escort service. 34,844 books, 24,292 serials, an OPAC, and a Web page.

■ MILWAUKEE SCHOOL OF ENGINEERING
1025 N Broadway
Milwaukee, WI 53202-3109
Tel: (414)277-7300; Free: 800-332-6763
Fax: (414)277-7475
E-mail: grennier@msoe.edu
Web Site: www.msoe.edu/

Description: Independent, comprehensive, coed. Awards bachelor's and master's degrees. Founded 1903. Setting: 15-acre urban campus. Endowment: $40.6 million. Research spending for the previous fiscal year: $5.3 million. Educational spending for the previous fiscal year: $11,545 per student. Total enrollment: 2,564. Faculty: 231 (132 full-time, 99 part-time). Student-undergrad faculty ratio is 14:1. 2,014 applied, 57% were admitted. Full-time: 2,193 students, 22% women, 78% men. Part-time: 185 students, 14% women, 86% men. Students come from 33 states and territories, 26 other countries, 31% from out-of-state. 0.5% American Indian or Alaska Native, non-Hispanic/Latino; 4% Hispanic/Latino; 2% African American, non-Hispanic/Latino; 3% Asian, non-Hispanic/Latino; 1% Native Hawaiian or other Pacific Islander, non-Hispanic/Latino; 6% international. 14% 25 or older, 37% live on campus, 8% transferred in. Retention: 81% of full-time freshmen returned the following year. Academic areas with the most degrees conferred: engineering; business/marketing; health professions and related sciences. Core. Academic remediation for entering students, ESL program, services for LD students, advanced placement, independent study, double major, summer session for credit, part-time degree program, adult/continuing education programs, internships, graduate courses open to undergrads. Study abroad program. ROTC: Army (c), Naval (c), Air Force (c).

Entrance Requirements: Options: electronic application, deferred admission. Required: high school transcript, minimum 2.5 high school GPA, SAT or ACT. Required for some: essay, interview. Entrance: moderately difficult. Application deadline: 1/1. Notification: continuous until 10/1. SAT Reasoning Test deadline: 9/1. SAT Subject Test deadline: 9/1. Transfer credits accepted: Yes.

Costs Per Year: Comprehensive fee: $42,741 includes full-time tuition ($32,880), mandatory fees ($1590), and college room and board ($8271). College room only: $5280. Full-time tuition and fees vary according to course load. Room and board charges vary according to board plan and housing facility. Part-time tuition: $570 per credit. Part-time tuition varies according to course load.

Collegiate Environment: Orientation program. Drama-theater group, choral group, student-run radio station. Social organizations: 71 open to all; national fraternities, national sororities, local fraternities, local sororities; 7% of eligible men and 8% of eligible women are members. Most popular organizations: Architectural Engineering and Construction Management Societies, Student Athletic Advisory Committee, MAGE, Student Government Association, Student Union Board. Major annual events: Welcome Week/Orientation, St. Patrick's Week, SUB-Zero Days. Student services: health clinic, personal-psychological counseling, women's center. Campus security: 24-hour emergency response devices and patrols, late night transport-escort service, controlled dormitory access. 932 college housing spaces available; 817 were occupied in 2012-13. Freshmen guaranteed college housing. On-campus residence required through sophomore year. Option: coed housing available. Walter Schroeder Library with 157,572 books, 80,654 microform titles, 2,035 serials, 2,451 audiovisual materials, an OPAC, and a Web page. Operations spending for the previous fiscal year: $614,888. 125 computers available on campus for general student use. Computer purchase/lease plans available. A computer is required for all students. A campuswide network can be accessed from student residence rooms and from off campus. Students can access the following: online class registration. Staffed computer lab on campus (open 24 hours a day) provides training in use of computers, software, and the Internet.

Community Environment: See Milwaukee Area Technical College.

■ MORAINE PARK TECHNICAL COLLEGE
235 N National Ave.
Fond du Lac, WI 54936-1940
Tel: (920)922-8611; Free: 800-472-4554
Fax: (920)924-2471
E-mail: kjarvis@morainepark.edu
Web Site: www.morainepark.edu/

Description: District-supported, 2-year, coed. Part of Wisconsin Technical College System. Awards certificates, diplomas, transfer associate, and terminal associate degrees. Founded 1967. Setting: 40-acre small town campus with easy access to Milwaukee. Educational spending for the previous fiscal year: $8503 per student. Total enrollment: 6,074. Faculty: 297 (142 full-time, 155 part-time). Student-undergrad faculty ratio is 14:1. Full-time: 1,079 students, 54% women, 46% men. Part-time: 4,995 students, 63% women, 37% men. 1% American Indian or Alaska Native, non-Hispanic/Latino; 2% Hispanic/Latino; 1% African American, non-Hispanic/Latino; 1% Asian, non-Hispanic/Latino; 0.03% Native Hawaiian or other Pacific Islander, non-Hispanic/Latino; 0% international. 70% 25 or older. Core. Calendar: semesters. Academic remediation for entering students, ESL program, services for LD students, advanced placement, accelerated degree program, self-designed majors, independent study, distance learning, double major, summer session for credit, part-time degree program, external degree program, adult/continuing education programs, internships. Study abroad program.

Entrance Requirements: Open admission. Options: electronic application, deferred admission, international baccalaureate accepted. Required: high school transcript. Placement test required for all; Criminal background ground check required for some, ACT, ACCUPLACER OR COMPASS. Required for some: interview, ACT. Entrance: noncompetitive. Application deadlines: Rolling, Rolling for nonresidents. Notification: continuous, continuous for nonresidents. Transfer credits accepted: Yes.

Costs Per Year: Application fee: $30. State resident tuition: $3688 full-time, $122.63 per credit hour part-time. Nonresident tuition: $5,442 full-time, $181 per credit hour part-time. Mandatory fees: $297 full-time, $9.85 per credit hour part-time. Full-time tuition and fees vary according to program. Part-time tuition and fees vary according to program.

Collegiate Environment: Orientation program. Social organizations: Program related clubs, Student Veterans, SAGA. Student services: personal-psychological counseling. Campus security: late night transport-escort service, Safety & Security provided between the hours of 5-10 p.m. when students are on campus and will provide late night transportation/escort. College housing not available. Moraine Park Technical College Library/Learning Resource Center with 41,021 books, 185 serials, 12,025 audiovisual materials, an OPAC, and a Web page. Operations spending for the previous fiscal year: $764,717. 1,350 computers available on campus for general student use. A campuswide network can be accessed from off-campus. Students can access the following: online class registration. Staffed computer lab on campus provides training in use of computers, software, and the Internet.

Community Environment: See Marian College of Fond du Lac.

■ MOUNT MARY COLLEGE
2900 N Menomonee River Pky.
Milwaukee, WI 53222-4597
Tel: (414)258-4810; Free: 800-321-6265
Fax: (414)256-1224
E-mail: admiss@mtmary.edu
Web Site: www.mtmary.edu/

Description: Independent Roman Catholic, comprehensive. Awards bachelor's, master's, and doctoral degrees and post-master's certificates. Founded 1913. Setting: 80-acre urban campus. Endowment: $10.7 million. Total enrollment: 1,640. Faculty: 206 (63 full-time, 143 part-time). Student-undergrad faculty ratio is 12:1. 420 applied, 49% were admitted. 21% from top 10% of their high school class, 36% from top quarter, 75% from top half. Full-time: 727 students, 99% women, 0.4% men. Part-time: 327 students, 96% women, 4% men. Students come from 6 states and territories, 18 other countries, 4% from out-of-state. 0.4% American Indian or Alaska Native, non-Hispanic/Latino; 13% Hispanic/Latino; 24% African American, non-Hispanic/Latino; 6% Asian, non-Hispanic/Latino; 0% Native Hawaiian or other Pacific Islander, non-Hispanic/Latino; 1% international. 35% 25 or older, 16% live on campus, 8% transferred in. Retention: 67% of full-time freshmen returned the following year. Academic areas with the most degrees conferred: health professions and related sciences; visual and performing arts; business/marketing. Core. Calendar: semesters. Academic remediation for entering students, services for LD students, advanced placement, accelerated degree program, self-designed majors, honors program, independent study, distance learning, double major, summer session for credit, part-time degree program, adult/continuing education programs, internships, graduate courses open to undergrads. Study abroad program. ROTC: Army (c), Naval (c).

Entrance Requirements: Options: electronic application, deferred admission, international baccalaureate accepted. Required: high school transcript, SAT or ACT. Recommended: minimum 2.5 high school GPA. Required for some: essay, 1 recommendation, interview. Entrance: moderately difficult. Application deadline: Rolling. Notification: continuous. SAT Reasoning Test deadline: 8/15. SAT Subject Test deadline: 8/15. Transfer credits accepted: Yes.

Costs Per Year: Application fee: $0. Comprehensive fee: $32,836 includes full-time tuition ($24,598), mandatory fees ($500), and college room and board ($7738). Full-time tuition and fees vary according to program. Room and board charges vary according to board plan. Part-time tuition: $746 per credit. Part-time mandatory fees: $310 per year. Part-time tuition and fees vary according to course load and program.

Collegiate Environment: Orientation program. Choral group, student-run newspaper. Social organizations: 41 open to all. Most popular organizations: Department-affiliated clubs, Campus Ministry, International Club, student government, Caroline Hall Council. Major annual events: Christmas on the Mount, Gospel Extravaganza, Spring Formal. Student services: personal-psychological counseling. Campus security: 24-hour patrols, late night transport-escort service, controlled dormitory access. 193 college housing spaces available; 135 were occupied in 2012-13. No special consideration for freshman housing applicants. Option: women-only housing available. The Patrick and Beatrice Haggerty Library with 869,710 books, 2,130 microform titles, 33,204 serials, 17,260 audiovisual materials, an OPAC, and a Web page. Operations spending for the previous fiscal year: $415,011. 210 computers available on campus for general student use. A campuswide network can be accessed from student residence rooms and from off campus. Students can access the following: online class registration. Staffed computer lab on campus provides training in use of computers, software, and the Internet.

Community Environment: Mount Mary is one of 5 private colleges in Milwaukee. The campus is located on the northwest side of the city, about 15 minutes from the downtown area. It is within walking distance of a shopping mall and restaurants. The city of Milwaukee boasts a major symphony, well-respected dance companies, a beautiful lakefront art museum, and a fine natural history museum. Three professional sports divide the Milwaukee seasons. It is also the ideal site in which to explore various career options.

■ **NICOLET AREA TECHNICAL COLLEGE**
Box 518
Rhinelander, WI 54501-0518
Tel: (715)365-4410; Free: 800-544-3039
Fax: (715)365-4445
E-mail: inquire@nicoletcollege.edu
Web Site: www.nicoletcollege.edu/

Description: State and locally supported, 2-year, coed. Part of Wisconsin Technical College System. Awards certificates, diplomas, transfer associate, and terminal associate degrees. Founded 1968. Setting: 280-acre rural campus. Total enrollment: 1,600. Faculty: 100. Student-undergrad faculty ratio is 16:1. Students come from 8 states and territories, 4 other countries, 1% from out-of-state. 64% 25 or older. Core. Calendar: semesters. Academic remediation for entering students, ESL program, services for LD students, advanced placement, independent study, distance learning, double major, summer session for credit, part-time degree program, adult/continuing education programs, co-op programs and internships. Study abroad program.

Entrance Requirements: Open admission. Options: electronic application, early admission. Required: high school transcript, ACCUPLACER Testing or ACT. Recommended: ACT. Entrance: noncompetitive. Application deadline: Rolling. Notification: continuous. Preference given to district residents. Transfer credits accepted: Yes.

Collegiate Environment: Orientation program. Drama-theater group, student-run newspaper. Student services: personal-psychological counseling. Campus security: 24-hour emergency response devices, student patrols. Richard Brown Library with 38,369 books, 598 serials, an OPAC, and a Web page. 100 computers available on campus for general student

use. A campuswide network can be accessed from off-campus. Students can access the following: online class registration. Staffed computer lab on campus provides training in use of computers and software.

Community Environment: The county seat for Oneida County, Rhinelander (population 7,889) is a summer and winter resort, located in the most concentrated lake area of the Middle West. Rhinelander has one of the largest paper mills under one roof in America. All commercial transportation is available. Parks and many lakes and trout streams and rivers provide facilities for all water sports and fishing. The Logging Museum is a reproduction of a logging camp with living quarters. Also on display is a narrow gauge engine built in 1879.

■ **NORTHCENTRAL TECHNICAL COLLEGE**
1000 W Campus Dr.
Wausau, WI 54401-1899
Tel: (715)675-3331
Fax: (715)675-9776
Web Site: www.ntc.edu/

Description: District-supported, 2-year, coed. Part of Wisconsin Technical College System. Awards certificates, diplomas, transfer associate, and terminal associate degrees. Founded 1912. Setting: 96-acre rural campus. Total enrollment: 4,764. Student-undergrad faculty ratio is 23:1. Full-time: 2,012 students, 52% women, 48% men. Part-time: 2,752 students, 65% women, 35% men. 1% American Indian or Alaska Native, non-Hispanic/Latino; 1% Hispanic/Latino; 1% African American, non-Hispanic/Latino; 5% Asian, non-Hispanic/Latino; 0.1% Native Hawaiian or other Pacific Islander, non-Hispanic/Latino; 0% international. 49% 25 or older. Retention: 60% of full-time freshmen returned the following year. Calendar: semesters. Academic remediation for entering students, ESL program, services for LD students, advanced placement, self-designed majors, independent study, distance learning, double major, summer session for credit, part-time degree program, adult/continuing education programs, internships.

Entrance Requirements: Open admission except for Associate Degree Nursing, Dental Hygiene, and Radiography programs. Options: electronic application, early admission, deferred admission. Required: high school transcript. Required for some: interview. Entrance: noncompetitive. Application deadline: Rolling. Notification: continuous. Preference given to district residents.

Collegiate Environment: Student-run newspaper. Student services: health clinic, personal-psychological counseling, women's center. Campus security: 24-hour emergency response devices, student patrols, late night transport-escort service. Northcentral Technical College, Wausau Campus Library plus 1 other with 30,000 books, 400 serials, an OPAC, and a Web page.

Community Environment: Wausau (population 37,292) is one of the major industrial centers in the state. Over 70 highly diversified industries are located here, producing over 40 different products. The area is one of the nation's leading producers of cheddar cheese, and it is a major center of dairy farming in both the state and nation and a leading exporter of ginseng. The community offers many cultural and recreational programs plus an excellent public school system. The school works closely with the branch campus of the University of Wisconsin to maximize use of facilities and programs and to eliminate duplication.

■ **NORTHEAST WISCONSIN TECHNICAL COLLEGE**
2740 W Mason St.
Green Bay, WI 54307-9042
Tel: (920)498-5400; Free: 888-385-6982
Web Site: www.nwtc.edu/

Description: State and locally supported, 2-year, coed. Part of Wisconsin Technical College System. Awards certificates, diplomas, and terminal associate degrees. Founded 1913. Setting: 192-acre suburban campus. Total enrollment: 8,105. 47% 25 or older. Core. Calendar: semesters. Academic remediation for entering students, ESL program, services for LD students, advanced placement, accelerated degree program, self-designed majors, distance learning, summer session for credit, part-time degree program, adult/continuing education programs.

Entrance Requirements: Option: early admission. Required for some: high school transcript. Entrance: minimally difficult. Application deadline: Rolling. Preference given to state residents.

Collegiate Environment: Student services: health clinic, personal-psychological counseling. Campus security: 24-hour emergency response devices, late night transport-escort service. 22,250 books and 450 serials.

Community Environment: Green Bay, population 101,200 and the oldest permanent settlement in Wisconsin, is in an important harbor for the Great

Lakes-St. Lawrence Seaway System. Industries in the area include shipping, cheese producing, paper, and jobbers wholesale and distribution. Points of interest are the Bay Beach Park, Heritage Hill Park, Neville Public Museum, Cotton House, Fort Howard Hospital Museum, Lambeau Stadium, National Railroad Museum, Tank Cottage, and the Green Bay Packer Hall of Fame.

■ NORTHLAND COLLEGE

1411 Ellis Ave.
Ashland, WI 54806-3925
Tel: (715)682-1699; Free: 800-753-1040
Fax: (715)682-1258
E-mail: admit@northland.edu
Web Site: www.northland.edu/

Description: Independent, 4-year, coed, affiliated with United Church of Christ. Awards bachelor's degrees. Founded 1892. Setting: 130-acre small town campus. Endowment: $18.1 million. Total enrollment: 600. Faculty: 61 (48 full-time, 13 part-time). Student-undergrad faculty ratio is 11:1. 946 applied, 66% were admitted. 20% from top 10% of their high school class, 34% from top quarter, 76% from top half. Full-time: 567 students, 54% women, 46% men. Part-time: 23 students, 74% women, 26% men. Students come from 32 states and territories, 6 other countries, 51% from out-of-state. 2% American Indian or Alaska Native, non-Hispanic/Latino; 5% Hispanic/Latino; 1% African American, non-Hispanic/Latino; 1% Asian, non-Hispanic/Latino; 0.2% Native Hawaiian or other Pacific Islander, non-Hispanic/Latino; 2% international. 7% 25 or older, 78% live on campus, 7% transferred in. Retention: 78% of full-time freshmen returned the following year. Academic areas with the most degrees conferred: natural resources/environmental science; biological/life sciences; physical sciences. Core. Calendar: 4-4-1. Services for LD students, advanced placement, self-designed majors, honors program, independent study, double major, summer session for credit, part-time degree program, co-op programs and internships. Off campus study at Eco League (includes the following institutions: Northland College, Alaska Pacific University, College of the Atlantic, Green Mountain College, Prescott College). Study abroad program.

Entrance Requirements: Options: electronic application, deferred admission, international baccalaureate accepted. Required: high school transcript, SAT or ACT. Recommended: minimum 2 high school GPA. Entrance: moderately difficult. Application deadlines: Rolling, Rolling for nonresidents. Notification: continuous, continuous for nonresidents. SAT Reasoning Test deadline: 5/1. SAT Subject Test deadline: 5/1. Transfer credits accepted: Yes.

Costs Per Year: Application fee: $0. Comprehensive fee: $37,500 includes full-time tuition ($29,000), mandatory fees ($990), and college room and board ($7510). College room only: $3220. Full-time tuition and fees vary according to course load. Room and board charges vary according to board plan and housing facility. Part-time tuition: $600 per credit hour. Part-time tuition varies according to course load.

Collegiate Environment: Orientation program. Drama-theater group, choral group, student-run newspaper, radio station. Most popular organizations: Northland Volunteer Program, Northland College Student Association, Native American Student Association, Environmental Council, N Club. Major annual events: Job and Internship Fair, Snow Fest, Everybody Party. Student services: health clinic, personal-psychological counseling. Campus security: 24-hour emergency response devices and patrols, late night transport-escort service, controlled dormitory access. 548 college housing spaces available; 443 were occupied in 2012-13. Freshmen guaranteed college housing. On-campus residence required through sophomore year. Options: coed, women-only housing available. Dexter Library with 75,000 books, 91,300 microform titles, 201 serials, 1,440 audiovisual materials, an OPAC, and a Web page. Operations spending for the previous fiscal year: $294,439. 125 computers available on campus for general student use. Computer purchase/lease plans available. A campuswide network can be accessed from student residence rooms and from off campus. Students can access the following: online class registration. Staffed computer lab on campus provides training in use of software and the Internet.

Community Environment: Ashland (population 8,306) is located on Lake Superior near the Chequamegon National Forest.

■ NORTHLAND INTERNATIONAL UNIVERSITY

W10085 Pke. Plains Rd.
Dunbar, WI 54119
Tel: (715)324-6900
Web Site: www.ni.edu/

Description: Independent religious, comprehensive, coed. Calendar: semesters.

■ RASMUSSEN COLLEGE APPLETON

3500 E Destination Dr.
Appleton, WI 54915
Tel: (920)750-5900; Free: 888-549-6755
E-mail: susan.hammerstrom@rasmussen.edu
Web Site: www.rasmussen.edu/

Description: Proprietary, 4-year, coed. Part of Rasmussen College System. Awards associate and bachelor's degrees. Setting: suburban campus. Total enrollment: 328. Student-undergrad faculty ratio is 22:1. 87% 25 or older. Core. Academic remediation for entering students, accelerated degree program, distance learning, double major, summer session for credit, part-time degree program, adult/continuing education programs, internships.

Entrance Requirements: Options: electronic application, early admission, deferred admission. Required: high school transcript, minimum 2 high school GPA, Internal Exam. Required for some: interview. Entrance: minimally difficult. Application deadline: Rolling. Transfer credits accepted: Yes.

Costs Per Year: Tuition: $12,600 full-time. Mandatory fees: $1800 full-time. Full-time tuition and fees vary according to course level, course load, degree level, location, and program.

Collegiate Environment: Orientation program. College housing not available. Rasmussen College Library - Appleton with 1,645 books, 21 serials, 9 audiovisual materials, an OPAC, and a Web page. 76 computers available on campus for general student use. A campuswide network can be accessed from off-campus.

■ RASMUSSEN COLLEGE GREEN BAY

940 S Taylor St.
Ste. 100
Green Bay, WI 54303
Tel: (920)593-8400; Free: 888-549-6755
E-mail: susan.hammerstrom@rasmussen.edu
Web Site: www.rasmussen.edu/

Description: Proprietary, primarily 2-year, coed. Part of Rasmussen College System. Awards certificates, diplomas, transfer associate, terminal associate, and bachelor's degrees. Setting: suburban campus. Total enrollment: 582. Student-undergrad faculty ratio is 22:1. 91% 25 or older. Core. Academic remediation for entering students, accelerated degree program, distance learning, double major, summer session for credit, part-time degree program, adult/continuing education programs, internships.

Entrance Requirements: Options: electronic application, early admission, deferred admission. Required: high school transcript, minimum 2 high school GPA, Internal Exam. Required for some: interview. Entrance: minimally difficult. Application deadline: Rolling. Transfer credits accepted: Yes.

Costs Per Year: Tuition: $12,600 full-time. Mandatory fees: $1800 full-time. Full-time tuition and fees vary according to course level, course load, degree level, location, and program.

Collegiate Environment: Orientation program. College housing not available. Rasmussen College Library - Green Bay with 2,097 books, 15 serials, 138 audiovisual materials, an OPAC, and a Web page. 137 computers available on campus for general student use. A campuswide network can be accessed from off-campus.

■ RASMUSSEN COLLEGE WAUSAU

1101 Westwood Dr.
Wausau, WI 54401
Tel: (715)841-8000; Free: 888-549-6755
E-mail: susan.hammerstrom@rasmussen.edu
Web Site: www.rasmussen.edu/

Description: Proprietary, 4-year, coed. Part of Rasmussen College System. Awards associate and bachelor's degrees. Setting: suburban campus. Total enrollment: 580. Student-undergrad faculty ratio is 22:1. 88% 25 or older. Core. Academic remediation for entering students, accelerated degree program, distance learning, double major, summer session for credit, part-time degree program, adult/continuing education programs, internships.

Entrance Requirements: Options: electronic application, early admission, deferred admission. Required: high school transcript, minimum 2 high school GPA, Internal Exam. Required for some: interview. Entrance: minimally difficult. Application deadline: Rolling. Transfer credits accepted: Yes.

Costs Per Year: Tuition: $12,600 full-time. Mandatory fees: $1800 full-time. Full-time tuition and fees vary according to course level, course load, degree level, location, and program.

Collegiate Environment: Orientation program. College housing not available. Rasmussen College Library - Wausau with 2,559 books, 14 serials, 95 audiovisual materials, an OPAC, and a Web page. 74 computers available on campus for general student use. A campuswide network can be accessed from off-campus.

■ **RIPON COLLEGE**
300 Seward St.
Ripon, WI 54971
Tel: (920)748-8115; Free: 800-947-4766
Fax: (920)748-7243
E-mail: adminfo@ripon.edu
Web Site: www.ripon.edu/

Description: Independent, 4-year, coed. Awards bachelor's degrees. Founded 1851. Setting: 250-acre small town campus with easy access to Milwaukee. Endowment: $6.2 million. Educational spending for the previous fiscal year: $11,317 per student. Total enrollment: 931. Faculty: 104 (69 full-time, 35 part-time). Student-undergrad faculty ratio is 11:1. 1,046 applied, 78% were admitted. 26% from top 10% of their high school class, 50% from top quarter, 82% from top half. Full-time: 921 students, 53% women, 47% men. Part-time: 10 students, 40% women, 60% men. Students come from 31 states and territories, 12 other countries, 25% from out-of-state. 1% American Indian or Alaska Native, non-Hispanic/Latino; 5% Hispanic/Latino; 2% African American, non-Hispanic/Latino; 1% Asian, non-Hispanic/Latino; 0% Native Hawaiian or other Pacific Islander, non-Hispanic/Latino; 3% international. 2% 25 or older, 86% live on campus, 2% transferred in. Retention: 86% of full-time freshmen returned the following year. Academic areas with the most degrees conferred: social sciences; parks and recreation; history. Core. Calendar: semesters. Services for LD students, advanced placement, accelerated degree program, self-designed majors, double major, part-time degree program, internships. Off campus study at American University, Newberry Library, Oak Ridge National Laboratory, University of Chicago, Associated Colleges of the Midwest Wilderness Field Station. Study abroad program. ROTC: Army.
Entrance Requirements: Options: electronic application, deferred admission, international baccalaureate accepted. Required: essay, high school transcript, minimum 2 high school GPA, 1 recommendation, SAT or ACT. Recommended: interview. Required for some: interview. Entrance: moderately difficult. Application deadline: Rolling. Notification: continuous. Transfer credits accepted: Yes.
Costs Per Year: Application fee: $30. Comprehensive fee: $40,417 includes full-time tuition ($31,327), mandatory fees ($275), and college room and board ($8815). College room only: $4665.
Collegiate Environment: Orientation program. Drama-theater group, choral group, student-run newspaper, radio station. Social organizations: 45 open to all; national fraternities, national sororities, local fraternities, local sororities; 26% of eligible men and 24% of eligible women are members. Most popular organizations: Environmental Group, Student Senate, Community Service Coalition, SMAC (Student Media and Activities Committee). Major annual events: Springfest, Winterfest, Frisbee Golf Tournament. Student services: health clinic, personal-psychological counseling. Campus security: 24-hour emergency response devices and patrols, student patrols, late night transport-escort service, controlled dormitory access. 1,056 college housing spaces available; 791 were occupied in 2012-13. Freshmen guaranteed college housing. On-campus residence required through senior year. Options: coed, men-only, women-only housing available. Lane Library with 173,259 books, 9,182 microform titles, 257 serials, 495 audiovisual materials, an OPAC, and a Web page. Operations spending for the previous fiscal year: $466,403. 150 computers available on campus for general student use. A campuswide network can be accessed from student residence rooms and from off campus. Staffed computer lab on campus provides training in use of computers, software, and the Internet.
Community Environment: Students who select Ripon seek a small-town community and enjoy the recreational opportunities of Green Lake. In east central Wisconsin, the town is a one and one-half hour drive to Madison and Milwaukee, and 3 hours from Chicago. Various community groups encourage student participation in service-oriented activities.

■ **ST. NORBERT COLLEGE**
100 Grant St.
De Pere, WI 54115-2099
Tel: (920)337-3181; Free: 800-236-4878
Fax: (920)403-4088
E-mail: admit@snc.edu
Web Site: www.snc.edu/
Description: Independent Roman Catholic, comprehensive, coed. Awards

bachelor's and master's degrees. Founded 1898. Setting: 93-acre suburban campus. Endowment: $73 million. Research spending for the previous fiscal year: $378,058. Educational spending for the previous fiscal year: $7889 per student. Total enrollment: 2,287. Faculty: 201 (139 full-time, 62 part-time). Student-undergrad faculty ratio is 14:1. 2,377 applied, 80% were admitted. 25% from top 10% of their high school class, 58% from top quarter, 85% from top half. 2 class presidents, 20 valedictorians. Full-time: 2,171 students, 58% women, 42% men. Part-time: 58 students, 60% women, 40% men. Students come from 34 states and territories, 32 other countries, 25% from out-of-state. 1% American Indian or Alaska Native, non-Hispanic/Latino; 2% Hispanic/Latino; 1% African American, non-Hispanic/Latino; 1% Asian, non-Hispanic/Latino; 0.05% Native Hawaiian or other Pacific Islander, non-Hispanic/Latino; 4% international. 1% 25 or older, 75% live on campus, 2% transferred in. Retention: 84% of full-time freshmen returned the following year. Academic areas with the most degrees conferred: business/marketing; education; social sciences; communication/journalism. Core. Calendar: semesters. Academic remediation for entering students, ESL program, services for LD students, advanced placement, self-designed majors, honors program, independent study, distance learning, double major, summer session for credit, part-time degree program, internships. Off campus study at Higher Education Consortium for Urban Affairs, American University. Study abroad program. ROTC: Army.
Entrance Requirements: Options: electronic application, deferred admission, international baccalaureate accepted. Required: high school transcript, 1 recommendation, SAT or ACT. Recommended: essay. Required for some: interview. Entrance: moderately difficult. Application deadlines: Rolling, Rolling for nonresidents. Notification: continuous, continuous for nonresidents. Preference given to children of alumni, siblings of current or former students, dependents of employees. SAT Reasoning Test deadline: 7/1. SAT Subject Test deadline: 7/1. Transfer credits accepted: Yes. Applicants placed on waiting list: 30. Wait-listed applicants offered admission: 13.
Costs Per Year: Application fee: $25. Comprehensive fee: $38,488 includes full-time tuition ($30,165), mandatory fees ($510), and college room and board ($7813). College room only: $4170. Full-time tuition and fees vary according to course load. Room and board charges vary according to board plan, housing facility, and student level. Part-time tuition: $943 per credit. Part-time tuition varies according to course load.
Collegiate Environment: Orientation program. Drama-theater group, choral group, student-run newspaper, radio station. Social organizations: 71 open to all; national fraternities, national sororities; 8% of eligible men and 10% of eligible women are members. Most popular organizations: Wisconsin Student Education Association, Pre-Health Sciences Club, Knight Theatre, Ballroom Club, Circle K. Major annual events: Opening Campus Picnic/Convocation, E2K Homecoming, SNC Day. Student services: health clinic, personal-psychological counseling, women's center. Campus security: 24-hour emergency response devices and patrols, student patrols, late night transport-escort service, controlled dormitory access, crime prevention programs. 1,670 college housing spaces available; 1,661 were occupied in 2012-13. Freshmen guaranteed college housing. On-campus residence required through senior year. Options: coed, women-only housing available. Miriam B. and James J. Mulva Library with 235,487 books, 16,014 microform titles, 78,002 serials, 1,293 audiovisual materials, an OPAC, and a Web page. Operations spending for the previous fiscal year: $1.1 million. 247 computers available on campus for general student use. Computer purchase/lease plans available. A campuswide network can be accessed from student residence rooms and from off campus. Students can access the following: online class registration. Staffed computer lab on campus provides training in use of computers, software, and the Internet.

■ **SILVER LAKE COLLEGE OF THE HOLY FAMILY**
2406 S Alverno Rd.
Manitowoc, WI 54220-9319
Tel: (920)684-6691; Free: 800-236-4752
Fax: (920)684-7082
E-mail: admslc@silver.sl.edu
Web Site: www.sl.edu/
Description: Independent Roman Catholic, comprehensive, coed. Awards associate, bachelor's, and master's degrees. Founded 1869. Setting: 30-acre rural campus with easy access to Milwaukee. Endowment: $5.2 million. Educational spending for the previous fiscal year: $15,117 per student. Total enrollment: 720. Faculty: 109 (35 full-time, 74 part-time). Student-undergrad faculty ratio is 7:1. 116 applied, 72% were admitted. 7% from top 10% of their high school class, 17% from top quarter, 57% from top half. Full-time: 194 students, 69% women, 31% men. Part-time: 288 students, 70% women,

30% men. Students come from 6 states and territories, 4 other countries, 4% from out-of-state. 54% 25 or older, 18% live on campus, 14% transferred in. Retention: 63% of full-time freshmen returned the following year. Academic areas with the most degrees conferred: business/marketing; education; psychology. Core. Calendar: semesters. Academic remediation for entering students, services for LD students, advanced placement, accelerated degree program, self-designed majors, independent study, distance learning, double major, summer session for credit, part-time degree program, adult/continuing education programs, internships, graduate courses open to undergrads.

Entrance Requirements: Options: electronic application, deferred admission. Required: high school transcript, minimum 2 high school GPA, SAT or ACT. Required for some: interview. Entrance: minimally difficult. Application deadline: 8/1. Notification: continuous. SAT Reasoning Test deadline: 8/1. Transfer credits accepted: Yes.

Collegiate Environment: Orientation program. Choral group. Social organizations: 16 open to all. Most popular organizations: Campus Ministry projects, Education-related clubs, Student Forum (Student government), Optimist Club, Tri Beta (Biology). Major annual events: Homecoming, Awards Banquet, Pancake Breakfast. Student services: health clinic, personal-psychological counseling. Campus security: 24-hour emergency response devices, student patrols, late night transport-escort service, controlled dormitory access. The Erma M. and Theodore M. Zigmunt Library with 62,418 books, 2,154 microform titles, 259 serials, 11,005 audiovisual materials, and an OPAC. Operations spending for the previous fiscal year: $168,522. 88 computers available on campus for general student use. A campuswide network can be accessed. Students can access the following: online class registration. Staffed computer lab on campus provides training in use of computers, software, and the Internet.

Community Environment: The communities of Manitowoc and Two Rivers were founded in 1838 and are located on the shore of Lake Michigan with convenient access to major Wisconsin cities. This industrial and tourism-based community has 37 churches, 3 modern hospitals, museums, and numerous parks and recreation areas.

■ SOUTHWEST WISCONSIN TECHNICAL COLLEGE

1800 Bronson Blvd.
Fennimore, WI 53809-9778
Tel: (608)822-3262; Free: 800-362-3322
Fax: (608)822-6019
E-mail: student-services@swtc.edu
Web Site: www.swtc.edu/

Description: State and locally supported, 2-year, coed. Part of Wisconsin Technical College System. Awards certificates, diplomas, and terminal associate degrees. Founded 1967. Setting: 53-acre rural campus. Total enrollment: 3,409. Faculty: 112 (94 full-time, 18 part-time). Student-undergrad faculty ratio is 18:1. 500 applied, 100% were admitted. Full-time: 852 students, 49% women, 51% men. Part-time: 2,557 students, 58% women, 42% men. Students come from 5 states and territories, 0% from out-of-state. 40% 25 or older, 3% live on campus, 1% transferred in. Retention: 71% of full-time freshmen returned the following year. Core. Calendar: semesters. Academic remediation for entering students, ESL program, services for LD students, advanced placement, self-designed majors, independent study, distance learning, double major, summer session for credit, part-time degree program, internships. Off campus study at Madison Area Technical College (clinical laboratory technician, dental hygienist, radiography); Northeast Wisconsin Technical College (criminal justice-corrections); Lakeshore Technical College (pharmacy technician); Western Technical College (respiratory therapist).

Entrance Requirements: Open admission except for nursing program. Options: electronic application, early admission. Required: high school transcript, interview. Required for some: TABE and the HESI (nursing students only). Entrance: noncompetitive. Application deadlines: Rolling, Rolling for nonresidents. Notification: continuous, continuous for nonresidents. Preference given to district residents. Transfer credits accepted: Yes.

Collegiate Environment: Orientation program. Social organizations: 3 open to all. Most popular organizations: Student Senate, Student Ambassadors, Phi Theta Kappa. Major annual events: Spring and Fall annual picnics on campus, variety shows, comedians, open-mic, bean bag tournament, intramural basketball/volleyball, motivational speakers. Student services: personal-psychological counseling. Campus security: 24-hour emergency response devices. Southwest Technical College Library with 28,000 books, 400 serials, 5,600 audiovisual materials, an OPAC, and a Web page. 630 computers available on campus for general student use. A campuswide network can be accessed from off-campus. Students can access the follow-

ing: online class registration. Staffed computer lab on campus provides training in use of computers, software, and the Internet.

■ STRAYER UNIVERSITY - MILWAUKEE CAMPUS

9000 W Chester St.
Ste. 300
Milwaukee, WI 53214
Tel: (414)203-7800
Fax: (414)456-0246
Web Site: www.strayer.edu/campus/milwaukee
Description: Proprietary, comprehensive, coed. Awards associate, bachelor's, and master's degrees.

■ UNIVERSITY OF PHOENIX–MADISON CAMPUS

2310 Crossroads Dr., Ste. 3000
Madison, WI 53718-2416
Tel: (608)240-4701; Free: 866-766-0766
Web Site: www.phoenix.edu/
Description: Proprietary, comprehensive, coed. Awards bachelor's, master's, and doctoral degrees.

■ UNIVERSITY OF WISCONSIN–BARABOO/SAUK COUNTY

1006 Connie Rd.
Baraboo, WI 53913-1015
Tel: (608)356-8351
Fax: (608)356-4074
E-mail: booinfo@uwc.edu
Web Site: www.baraboo.uwc.edu/

Description: State-supported, 2-year, coed. Part of University of Wisconsin System. Awards certificates, transfer associate, and terminal associate degrees. Founded 1968. Setting: 68-acre small town campus. Total enrollment: 553. Faculty: 42 (15 full-time, 27 part-time). Student-undergrad faculty ratio is 13:1. 6% from top 10% of their high school class, 24% from top quarter, 60% from top half. Students come from 2 states and territories, 3 other countries, 1% from out-of-state. 16% 25 or older. Core. Calendar: semesters. Academic remediation for entering students, services for LD students, advanced placement, self-designed majors, honors program, independent study, distance learning, summer session for credit, part-time degree program, external degree program, internships. Off campus study at other units of the University of Wisconsin Colleges, four-year campuses of the University of Wisconsin and University of Wisconsin Extension, also UW Colleges distance learning, University of Plymouth Colleges, England. Study abroad program.

Entrance Requirements: Options: electronic application, early admission, deferred admission. Required: high school transcript, SAT or ACT. Recommended: ACT. Required for some: interview. Entrance: moderately difficult. Application deadlines: Rolling, Rolling for nonresidents. Notification: continuous until 8/31, continuous until 8/31 for nonresidents. Preference given to racial minorities.

Collegiate Environment: Orientation program. Drama-theater group, choral group, student-run newspaper. Social organizations: 10 open to all. Most popular organizations: Student Government Association, chorus and band, Dance Team, Gaming Club, Business Club. Major annual events: Boo Bash, Welcome Picnic, Packer parties/bonfires. Student services: personal-psychological counseling. T. N. Savides Library with 45,000 books, 52 microform titles, 300 serials, and an OPAC. Operations spending for the previous fiscal year: $120,000. 50 computers available on campus for general student use. A campuswide network can be accessed from off-campus. Students can access the following: online class registration, financial aid application. Staffed computer lab on campus.

■ UNIVERSITY OF WISCONSIN–BARRON COUNTY

1800 College Dr.
Rice Lake, WI 54868-2497
Tel: (715)234-8176
Web Site: www.barron.uwc.edu/

Description: State-supported, 2-year, coed. Part of University of Wisconsin System. Awards transfer associate degrees. Founded 1966. Setting: 142-acre small town campus. Core. Calendar: semesters. Academic remediation for entering students, services for LD students, advanced placement, independent study, distance learning, summer session for credit, part-time degree program, adult/continuing education programs, internships. Off campus study at other units of the University of Wisconsin Colleges, four-year campuses of the University of Wisconsin. Study abroad program.

Entrance Requirements: Options: electronic application, deferred admission. Required: high school transcript, ACT. Required for some: essay, 1 recommendation. Entrance: minimally difficult. Application deadline: 9/15. Notification: continuous.

Collegiate Environment: Orientation program.

■ **UNIVERSITY OF WISCONSIN–EAU CLAIRE**

PO Box 4004

Eau Claire, WI 54702-4004

Tel: (715)836-2637

Fax: (715)836-2380

E-mail: admissions@uwec.edu

Web Site: www.uwec.edu/

Description: State-supported, comprehensive, coed. Part of University of Wisconsin System. Awards associate, bachelor's, master's, and doctoral degrees and post-master's certificates. Founded 1916. Setting: 337-acre small town campus with easy access to Minneapolis-St. Paul. Endowment: $44 million. Research spending for the previous fiscal year: $1.3 million. Educational spending for the previous fiscal year: $5860 per student. Total enrollment: 11,046. Faculty: 583 (432 full-time, 151 part-time). Student-undergrad faculty ratio is 21:1. 6,625 applied, 76% were admitted. 20% from top 10% of their high school class, 34% from top quarter, 96% from top half. 4 National Merit Scholars, 63 valedictorians. Full-time: 9,605 students, 58% women, 42% men. Part-time: 894 students, 64% women, 36% men. Students come from 37 states and territories, 39 other countries, 23% from out-of-state. 0.4% American Indian or Alaska Native, non-Hispanic/Latino; 2% Hispanic/Latino; 1% African American, non-Hispanic/Latino; 3% Asian, non-Hispanic/Latino; 0.04% Native Hawaiian or other Pacific Islander, non-Hispanic/Latino; 2% international. 8% 25 or older, 38% live on campus, 6% transferred in. Retention: 83% of full-time freshmen returned the following year. Academic areas with the most degrees conferred: business/marketing; health professions and related sciences; education. Core. Calendar: semesters. Academic remediation for entering students, ESL program, services for LD students, advanced placement, accelerated degree program, self-designed majors, honors program, independent study, distance learning, double major, summer session for credit, part-time degree program, external degree program, adult/continuing education programs, co-op programs and internships, graduate courses open to undergrads. Off campus study at National Student Exchange. Study abroad program. ROTC: Army.

Entrance Requirements: Options: electronic application, early admission, international baccalaureate accepted. Required: high school transcript, SAT or ACT. Recommended: essay. Entrance: moderately difficult. Application deadline: Rolling. Notification: continuous. SAT Reasoning Test deadline: 2/1. Transfer credits accepted: Yes. Applicants placed on waiting list: 0. Wait-listed applicants offered admission: 0.

Costs Per Year: Application fee: $44. State resident tuition: $7361 full-time, $307 per credit part-time. Nonresident tuition: $14,934 full-time, $622 per credit part-time. Mandatory fees: $1330 full-time, $55 per credit part-time, $3 per term part-time. Full-time tuition and fees vary according to reciprocity agreements. Part-time tuition and fees vary according to reciprocity agreements. College room and board: $6300. College room only: $3192. Room and board charges vary according to board plan and housing facility.

Collegiate Environment: Orientation program. Drama-theater group, choral group, marching band, student-run newspaper, radio station. Social organizations: 250 open to all; national fraternities, national sororities; 1% of eligible men and 1% of eligible women are members. Most popular organizations: American Marketing Association, Beta Upsilon Sigma, Blue Gold Marching Band, Singing Statesmen, Navigators. Major annual events: Blugold Organizations Bash (BOB), Homecoming, Winter Carnival. Student services: legal services, health clinic, personal-psychological counseling, women's center. Campus security: 24-hour emergency response devices and patrols, student patrols, late night transport-escort service, controlled dormitory access. College housing designed to accommodate 3,924 students; 4,019 undergraduates lived in college housing during 2012-13. Freshmen guaranteed college housing. On-campus residence required through sophomore year. Options: coed, men-only, women-only housing available. William D. McIntyre Library plus 1 other with 1.2 million books, 529,378 microform titles, 54,943 serials, 12,152 audiovisual materials, an OPAC, and a Web page. Operations spending for the previous fiscal year: $3.1 million. 900 computers available on campus for general student use. A campuswide network can be accessed from student residence rooms and from off campus. Students can access the following: online class registration, course management system, library reference staff online chat, ability to check where there are open seats in the general access computer labs,

laptop check out pool. Staffed computer lab on campus provides training in use of computers, software, and the Internet.

Community Environment: Eau Claire is a cultural, commercial, educational, and medical center in west-central Wisconsin. The city, which is located at the confluence of the Eau Claire and Chippewa Rivers, is served by air and bus lines. Community facilities and services include numerous hotels, motels, hospitals, churches, restaurants, shopping areas, a public library and YMCA, as well as numerous civic organizations and clubs. The city and the surrounding area abound in colorful, natural beauty and offers numerous year-round recreational activities. Local lakes and parks provide opportunities to enjoy aquatic sports, golf, skiing, skating, tennis, baseball, and many other sports.

■ **UNIVERSITY OF WISCONSIN–FOND DU LAC**

400 University Dr.

Fond du Lac, WI 54935

Tel: (920)929-1100

E-mail: tom.martin@uwc.edu

Web Site: www.fdl.uwc.edu/

Description: State-supported, 2-year, coed. Part of University of Wisconsin System. Awards transfer associate degrees. Founded 1968. Setting: 182-acre small town campus with easy access to Milwaukee. Total enrollment: 779. Faculty: 37 (20 full-time, 17 part-time). Student-undergrad faculty ratio is 19:1. 381 applied, 85% were admitted. 5% from top 10% of their high school class, 15% from top quarter, 48% from top half. Full-time: 506 students, 52% women, 48% men. Part-time: 273 students, 52% women, 48% men. Students come from 3 states and territories, 1% from out-of-state. 18% 25 or older, 4% transferred in. Retention: 58% of full-time freshmen returned the following year. Core. Calendar: semesters. Academic remediation for entering students, services for LD students, advanced placement, accelerated degree program, independent study, distance learning, summer session for credit, part-time degree program, adult/continuing education programs, co-op programs. Off campus study at other units of the University of Wisconsin Colleges, four-year campuses of the University of Wisconsin. Study abroad program.

Entrance Requirements: Option: electronic application. Required: high school transcript, SAT or ACT. Entrance: minimally difficult. Application deadlines: Rolling, Rolling for nonresidents. Transfer credits accepted: Yes.

Collegiate Environment: Orientation program. Drama-theater group, choral group, student-run newspaper. Social organizations: 8 open to all. Most popular organizations: student government, Campus Ambassadors, Multicultural Club, chorus, band. Student services: personal-psychological counseling. Campus security: 24-hour emergency response devices. 41,891 books and 160 serials 65 computers available on campus for general student use. A campuswide network can be accessed. Students can access the following: online class registration. Staffed computer lab on campus provides training in use of computers.

■ **UNIVERSITY OF WISCONSIN–FOX VALLEY**

1478 Midway Rd.

Menasha, WI 54952

Tel: (920)832-2600

Fax: (920)832-2674

E-mail: foxinfo@uwc.edu

Web Site: www.uwfox.uwc.edu/

Description: State-supported, 2-year, coed. Part of University of Wisconsin System. Awards certificates, transfer associate, and terminal associate degrees. Founded 1933. Setting: 33-acre urban campus. Total enrollment: 1,797. Faculty: 91 (31 full-time, 60 part-time). Student-undergrad faculty ratio is 20:1. Full-time: 1,037 students, 52% women, 48% men. Part-time: 760 students, 52% women, 48% men. Students come from 3 states and territories, 4 other countries, 1% from out-of-state. 25% 25 or older. Core. Calendar: semesters. Academic remediation for entering students, services for LD students, advanced placement, accelerated degree program, honors program, independent study, distance learning, summer session for credit, part-time degree program, adult/continuing education programs, co-op programs and internships. Off campus study at other units of the University of Wisconsin Colleges and four-year campuses of the University of Wisconsin. Study abroad program.

Entrance Requirements: Required: essay, high school transcript, ACT.

Costs Per Year: State resident tuition: $5017 full-time. Nonresident tuition: $12,001 full-time. Mandatory fees: $172 full-time. Full-time tuition and fees vary according to course load and reciprocity agreements.

Collegiate Environment: Orientation program. Drama-theater group, choral

group, student-run newspaper, radio station. Social organizations: 30 open to all. Most popular organizations: Business Club, Education Club, Earth Science Club, Computer Science Club, Political Science Club. Major annual events: Honors Convocation and Commencement, Campus Picnic, Scholar Series. Student services: personal-psychological counseling. Campus security: 24-hour emergency response devices, late night transport-escort service. College housing not available. UW Fox Library with 30,000 books, 230 serials, an OPAC, and a Web page. 150 computers available on campus for general student use. Computer purchase/lease plans available. A campuswide network can be accessed from off-campus. Students can access the following: online class registration.

■ UNIVERSITY OF WISCONSIN–GREEN BAY

2420 Nicolet Dr.
Green Bay, WI 54311-7001
Tel: (920)465-2000
Fax: (920)465-2032
E-mail: uwgb@uwgb.edu
Web Site: www.uwgb.edu/

Description: State-supported, comprehensive, coed. Part of University of Wisconsin System. Awards associate, bachelor's, and master's degrees. Founded 1968. Setting: 700-acre suburban campus with easy access to Milwaukee. Endowment: $18.4 million. Research spending for the previous fiscal year: $1.6 million. Educational spending for the previous fiscal year: $5810 per student. Total enrollment: 6,790. Faculty: 335 (187 full-time, 148 part-time). Student-undergrad faculty ratio is 23:1. 3,298 applied, 64% were admitted. Full-time: 4,616 students, 63% women, 37% men. Part-time: 1,995 students, 70% women, 30% men. Students come from 39 states and territories, 28 other countries, 7% from out-of-state. 1% American Indian or Alaska Native, non-Hispanic/Latino; 3% Hispanic/Latino; 1% African American, non-Hispanic/Latino; 3% Asian, non-Hispanic/Latino; 0.05% Native Hawaiian or other Pacific Islander, non-Hispanic/Latino; 1% international. 28% 25 or older, 33% live on campus, 13% transferred in. Retention: 74% of full-time freshmen returned the following year. Academic areas with the most degrees conferred: business/marketing; interdisciplinary studies; liberal arts/general studies. Core. Calendar: semesters. Academic remediation for entering students, services for LD students, advanced placement, self-designed majors, independent study, distance learning, double major, summer session for credit, part-time degree program, external degree program, adult/continuing education programs, internships, graduate courses open to undergrads. Off campus study at National Student Exchange; Collaborative Nursing Program (BSN@Home); Northeast Wisconsin Engineering Program (Milwaukee). Study abroad program. ROTC: Army (c).

Entrance Requirements: Options: electronic application, deferred admission, international baccalaureate accepted. Required: essay, high school transcript, SAT or ACT. Required for some: interview. Entrance: moderately difficult. Application deadlines: Rolling, Rolling for nonresidents. Notification: continuous, continuous for nonresidents. Transfer credits accepted: Yes. Applicants placed on waiting list: 63. Wait-listed applicants offered admission: 32.

Costs Per Year: Application fee: $44. One-time mandatory fee: $200. State resident tuition: $6298 full-time, $262 per credit hour part-time. Nonresident tuition: $13,871 full-time, $578 per credit hour part-time. Mandatory fees: $1350 full-time, $57 per credit hour part-time. Full-time tuition and fees vary according to course load and reciprocity agreements. Part-time tuition and fees vary according to reciprocity agreements. College room and board: $7076. College room only: $4032. Room and board charges vary according to board plan and housing facility.

Collegiate Environment: Orientation program. Drama-theater group, choral group, student-run newspaper, radio station. Social organizations: 80 open to all; local fraternities, local sororities; 1% of eligible men and 1% of eligible women are members. Most popular organizations: Good Times, Psychology and Human Development Club, Student Ambassadors, Residence Hall Apartment Association, Student Government Association. Major annual events: Welcome Week, Frost Fest, Senior Celebration. Student services: health clinic, personal-psychological counseling. Campus security: 24-hour emergency response devices and patrols, late night transport-escort service, controlled dormitory access. 2,049 college housing spaces available; 2,000 were occupied in 2012-13. Freshmen given priority for college housing. Option: coed housing available. Cofrin Library with 360,795 books, 1.4 million microform titles, 4,452 serials, 48,563 audiovisual materials, an OPAC, and a Web page. Operations spending for the previous fiscal year: $1.4 million. 550 computers available on campus for general student use. Computer purchase/lease plans available. A campuswide network can be accessed

from student residence rooms and from off campus. Students can access the following: online class registration, online degree progress, online financial records and bill paying. Staffed computer lab on campus provides training in use of computers, software, and the Internet.

Community Environment: Green Bay, a trading and transportation center in Northeastern Wisconsin, is a city of approximately 100,000 inhabitants located in Wisconsin's third largest population area. The city has an outstanding regional museum, an excellent public library system and many parks. A community symphony orchestra, community chorus and several theater groups provide cultural enrichment and added opportunities for participation and performance by qualified students. Nearby resort areas provide a variety of recreational opportunities and summer jobs for students. The university is easy to reach by air, bus or interstate highway.

■ UNIVERSITY OF WISCONSIN–LA CROSSE

1725 State St.
La Crosse, WI 54601-3742
Tel: (608)785-8000
Fax: (608)785-6695
E-mail: admissions@uwlax.edu
Web Site: www.uwlax.edu/

Description: State-supported, comprehensive, coed. Part of University of Wisconsin System. Awards associate, bachelor's, master's, and doctoral degrees. Founded 1909. Setting: 121-acre suburban campus. Endowment: $16.1 million. Research spending for the previous fiscal year: $3.5 million. Educational spending for the previous fiscal year: $5818 per student. Total enrollment: 10,227. Faculty: 572 (457 full-time, 115 part-time). Student-undergrad faculty ratio is 20:1. 6,908 applied, 71% were admitted. 26% from top 10% of their high school class, 77% from top quarter, 98% from top half. Full-time: 8,958 students, 58% women, 42% men. Part-time: 483 students, 54% women, 46% men. Students come from 33 states and territories, 29 other countries, 16% from out-of-state. 0.3% American Indian or Alaska Native, non-Hispanic/Latino; 3% Hispanic/Latino; 1% African American, non-Hispanic/Latino; 2% Asian, non-Hispanic/Latino; 0.1% Native Hawaiian or other Pacific Islander, non-Hispanic/Latino; 2% international. 5% 25 or older, 37% live on campus, 5% transferred in. Retention: 86% of full-time freshmen returned the following year. Academic areas with the most degrees conferred: business/marketing; biological/life sciences; health professions and related sciences. Core. Calendar: semesters. Academic remediation for entering students, ESL program, services for LD students, advanced placement, independent study, distance learning, double major, summer session for credit, part-time degree program, adult/continuing education programs, co-op programs and internships, graduate courses open to undergrads. Off campus study at Viterbo College; National Student Exchange. Study abroad program. ROTC: Army.

Entrance Requirements: Options: electronic application, international baccalaureate accepted. Required: essay, high school transcript, SAT or ACT. Required for some: interview. Entrance: moderately difficult. Application deadlines: Rolling, Rolling for nonresidents. Notification: continuous, continuous for nonresidents. Transfer credits accepted: Yes.

Costs Per Year: Application fee: $44. State resident tuition: $8754 full-time. Nonresident tuition: $16,327 full-time. Full-time tuition varies according to program and reciprocity agreements. College room and board: $6000. College room only: $3500. Room and board charges vary according to board plan and housing facility.

Collegiate Environment: Orientation program. Drama-theater group, choral group, marching band, student-run newspaper, radio station. Social organizations: 181 open to all; national fraternities, national sororities; 1% of eligible men and 1% of eligible women are members. Most popular organizations: Sports and Activities Club, Residential Hall Council, religious/spiritual organizations, Human Diversity Organizations, departmental/professional. Major annual events: Family, Friends and Alumni Weekend, spring concert, Turkey Trot. Student services: legal services, health clinic, personal-psychological counseling, women's center. Campus security: 24-hour emergency response devices and patrols, late night transport-escort service, controlled dormitory access. College housing designed to accommodate 3,180 students; 3,343 undergraduates lived in college housing during 2012-13. Freshmen given priority for college housing. On-campus residence required in freshman year. Option: coed housing available. Murphy Library with 500,370 books, 581,624 microform titles, 10,697 serials, 14,372 audiovisual materials, an OPAC, and a Web page. Operations spending for the previous fiscal year: $3.1 million. 200 computers available on campus for general student use. A campuswide network can be accessed from student residence rooms and from off campus. Students can access the following:

online class registration. Staffed computer lab on campus provides training in use of computers, software, and the Internet.

Community Environment: Founded in 1842 as an Indian trading post, La Crosse is situated on the east bank of the Mississippi River in southern Wisconsin. It is approximately midway between Minneapolis-St. Paul and Chicago. Noted for its exceptional natural beauty and outstanding recreational opportunities, the city is the industrial, commercial and medical center of Wisconsin's famous "Coulee Country." The population is approximately 50,000. All commercial transportation is convenient.

■ UNIVERSITY OF WISCONSIN–MADISON

500 Lincoln Dr.
Madison, WI 53706-1380
Tel: (608)262-1234
Fax: (608)262-1429
E-mail: onwisconsin@admissions.wisc.edu
Web Site: www.wisc.edu/

Description: State-supported, university, coed. Part of University of Wisconsin System. Awards bachelor's, master's, and doctoral degrees and post-master's certificates. Founded 1848. Setting: 936-acre urban campus with easy access to Milwaukee. Endowment: $1.8 billion. Research spending for the previous fiscal year: $838.9 million. Total enrollment: 42,820. Faculty: 2,925 (2,384 full-time, 541 part-time). Student-undergrad faculty ratio is 17:1. 29,034 applied, 55% were admitted. 56% from top 10% of their high school class, 94% from top quarter, 100% from top half. Full-time: 28,188 students, 52% women, 48% men. Part-time: 2,675 students, 50% women, 50% men. Students come from 52 states and territories, 130 other countries, 34% from out-of-state. 0.2% American Indian or Alaska Native, non-Hispanic/Latino; 4% Hispanic/Latino; 2% African American, non-Hispanic/Latino; 5% Asian, non-Hispanic/Latino; 0.1% Native Hawaiian or other Pacific Islander, non-Hispanic/Latino; 7% international. 4% 25 or older, 25% live on campus, 4% transferred in. Retention: 95% of full-time freshmen returned the following year. Academic areas with the most degrees conferred: social sciences; biological/life sciences; business/marketing. Core. Calendar: semesters. ESL program, services for LD students, advanced placement, accelerated degree program, self-designed majors, honors program, independent study, distance learning, double major, summer session for credit, part-time degree program, adult/continuing education programs, co-op programs and internships, graduate courses open to undergrads. Study abroad program. ROTC: Army, Naval, Air Force.

Entrance Requirements: Options: electronic application, deferred admission, international baccalaureate accepted. Required: essay, high school transcript, SAT or ACT. Recommended: 2 recommendations. Entrance: very difficult. Application deadline: 2/1. Notification: continuous. SAT Reasoning Test deadline: 2/1. SAT Subject Test deadline: 2/1. Transfer credits accepted: Yes.

Costs Per Year: Application fee: $44. State resident tuition: $9,273 full-time, $386.39 per credit hour part-time. Nonresident tuition: $25,523 full-time, $1,063.46 per credit hour part-time. Mandatory fees: $1,111 full-time, $49.05 per credit hour part-time. Full-time tuition and fees vary according to program and reciprocity agreements. Part-time tuition and fees vary according to course load, program, and reciprocity agreements. College room and board: $8080. Room and board charges vary according to board plan and housing facility.

Collegiate Environment: Orientation program. Drama-theater group, choral group, marching band, student-run newspaper, radio station. Social organizations: 873 open to all; national fraternities, national sororities, local fraternities, local sororities; 9% of eligible men and 8% of eligible women are members. Student services: health clinic, personal-psychological counseling, women's center. Campus security: 24-hour emergency response devices and patrols, late night transport-escort service, controlled dormitory access. 7,411 college housing spaces available; all were occupied in 2012-13. Freshmen given priority for college housing. Options: coed, men-only, women-only housing available. Memorial Library plus 40 others with an OPAC and a Web page. 1,000 computers available on campus for general student use. A campuswide network can be accessed from student residence rooms and from off campus. Students can access the following: online class registration. Staffed computer lab on campus provides training in use of computers, software, and the Internet.

Community Environment: Founded in 1836, the city was named for James Madison, the fourth President of the United States, and is the capital of Wisconsin. Madison is the center of one of the richest dairy regions in America and has over 200 industries. The city is also important as a medical center with its 12 hospitals and its manufacturing of precision surgical instru-

ments. Recreational facilities include 10 golf courses, 3 of which are public, tennis courts, and a number of beaches for water sports. Fishing boats are for hire. Points of interest are the Henry Vilas Park Zoo, Nevin Fish Hatchery, U.S. Forest Products Laboratory, State Historical Society Museum, and the Wisconsin State Capitol which is one of the most impressive in the United States.

■ UNIVERSITY OF WISCONSIN–MANITOWOC

705 Viebahn St.
Manitowoc, WI 54220-6699
Tel: (920)683-4700
Fax: (920)683-4776
E-mail: christopher.lewis@uwc.edu
Web Site: www.manitowoc.uwc.edu/

Description: State-supported, 2-year, coed. Part of University of Wisconsin System. Awards certificates, transfer associate, and terminal associate degrees. Founded 1935. Setting: 50-acre small town campus with easy access to Milwaukee. Educational spending for the previous fiscal year: $4991 per student. Total enrollment: 596. Faculty: 40 (22 full-time, 18 part-time). Student-undergrad faculty ratio is 24:1. 458 applied, 100% were admitted. 2% from top 10% of their high school class, 24% from top quarter, 46% from top half. Full-time: 596 students, 49% women, 51% men. 0% from out-of-state. 27% 25 or older, 5% transferred in. Core. Calendar: semesters. Academic remediation for entering students, services for LD students, advanced placement, self-designed majors, distance learning, adult/continuing education programs, co-op programs and internships. Off campus study at other units of the University of Wisconsin Colleges, four-year campuses of the University of Wisconsin. Study abroad program.

Entrance Requirements: Options: electronic application, early admission, deferred admission, international baccalaureate accepted. Required: high school transcript, minimum 1.0 high school GPA, SAT or ACT. Required for some: essay, interview. Entrance: minimally difficult. Application deadline: 9/1. Notification: continuous until 9/1.

Collegiate Environment: Orientation program. Drama-theater group, choral group, student-run newspaper. Social organizations: 4 open to all. Most popular organizations: Business Club, Student Senate, Environmental Club, Phi Theta Kappa, Extreme Outdoors Club. Major annual events: Campus Life Nights (Every Wednesday Night), Fall Kick Off, End of the Year Party. Student services: personal-psychological counseling. 25,750 books, 150 serials, and an OPAC Operations spending for the previous fiscal year: $126,743. 65 computers available on campus for general student use. Computer purchase/lease plans available. A campuswide network can be accessed from off-campus. Students can access the following: online class registration. Staffed computer lab on campus.

■ UNIVERSITY OF WISCONSIN–MARATHON COUNTY

518 S Seventh Ave.
Wausau, WI 54401-5396
Tel: (715)261-6100; Free: 888-367-8962
Fax: (715)261-6333
Web Site: www.uwmc.uwc.edu/

Description: State-supported, 2-year, coed. Part of University of Wisconsin System. Awards transfer associate degrees. Founded 1933. Setting: 7-acre small town campus. Core. Calendar: semesters. Academic remediation for entering students, advanced placement, self-designed majors, honors program, summer session for credit, part-time degree program, adult/continuing education programs. Off campus study at other units of the University of Wisconsin Colleges, four-year campuses of the University of Wisconsin. Study abroad program. ROTC: Army (c).

Entrance Requirements: Options: electronic application, early admission, deferred admission. Required: ACT. Recommended: minimum 2.0 high school GPA. Required for some: interview. Entrance: minimally difficult.

Collegiate Environment: Orientation program. Campus security: 24-hour emergency response devices, controlled dormitory access.

■ UNIVERSITY OF WISCONSIN–MARINETTE

750 W Bay Shore
Marinette, WI 54143-4299
Tel: (715)735-4300
E-mail: cynthia.bailey@uwc.edu
Web Site: www.marinette.uwc.edu/

Description: State-supported, 2-year, coed. Part of University of Wisconsin System. Awards transfer associate degrees. Founded 1965. Setting: 36-acre small town campus. Total enrollment: 462. Faculty: 31 (18 full-time, 13 part-time). Student-undergrad faculty ratio is 15:1. 30% 25 or older. Core. Calendar: semesters. Academic remediation for entering students, ESL program, services for LD students, advanced placement, independent study, distance learning, summer session for credit, part-time degree program, adult/continuing education programs, co-op programs and internships. Off campus study at other units of the University of Wisconsin Colleges, four-year campuses of the University of Wisconsin.

Entrance Requirements: Open admission. Option: electronic application. Required: high school transcript. Recommended: SAT or ACT. Entrance: noncompetitive. Application deadline: Rolling. Notification: continuous.

Collegiate Environment: Orientation program. Drama-theater group, choral group, student-run newspaper. Social organizations: 5 open to all. Most popular organizations: Student Senate, Writers Club/Literature Club, Phi Theta Kappa, Student Ambassadors. Major annual events: Spring Banquet, End of Year Party, Commencement. Student services: personal-psychological counseling. Main library plus 1 other with 23,000 books and 135 serials. 48 computers available on campus for general student use. A campuswide network can be accessed from off-campus. Students can access the following: online class registration. Staffed computer lab on campus provides training in use of computers, software, and the Internet.

■ **UNIVERSITY OF WISCONSIN–MARSHFIELD/WOOD COUNTY**
2000 W 5th St.
Marshfield, WI 54449
Tel: (715)389-6500
Web Site: marshfield.uwc.edu/

Description: State-supported, 2-year, coed. Part of University of Wisconsin System. Awards transfer associate and terminal associate degrees. Founded 1964. Setting: 71-acre small town campus. Endowment: $500,000. Total enrollment: 643. Faculty: 36 (13 full-time, 23 part-time). Student-undergrad faculty ratio is 17:1. 322 applied, 93% were admitted. 8% from top 10% of their high school class, 17% from top quarter, 55% from top half. 2 National Merit Scholars, 1 class president, 10 student government officers. Students come from 2 states and territories, 1 other country, 1% from out-of-state. 25% 25 or older. Retention: 99% of full-time freshmen returned the following year. Core. Calendar: semesters. Academic remediation for entering students, services for LD students, advanced placement, accelerated degree program, independent study, distance learning, summer session for credit, part-time degree program, external degree program, adult/continuing education programs. Off campus study at other units of the University of Wisconsin Colleges, four-year campuses of the University of Wisconsin. Study abroad program. ROTC: Army (c).

Entrance Requirements: Options: electronic application, early admission, deferred admission. Required: high school transcript, SAT or ACT. Required for some: essay, interview. Entrance: moderately difficult. Application deadline: Rolling.

Collegiate Environment: Orientation program. Drama-theater group, choral group, student-run newspaper. Social organizations: 10 open to all. Most popular organizations: Student Nurses Association, student newspaper, literary magazine, Student Education Association, Inter-Varsity Christian Fellowship. Major annual events: Fall Picnic, campus plays, Spring Picnic. Campus security: 24-hour patrols, patrols by city police. Learning Resource Center with 35,000 books, 185 serials, an OPAC, and a Web page. Operations spending for the previous fiscal year: $80,151. 60 computers available on campus for general student use. A campuswide network can be accessed. Staffed computer lab on campus.

■ **UNIVERSITY OF WISCONSIN–MILWAUKEE**
PO Box 413
Milwaukee, WI 53201-0413
Tel: (414)229-1122
Fax: (414)229-6940
E-mail: uwmlook@uwm.edu
Web Site: www.uwm.edu/

Description: State-supported, university, coed. Part of University of Wisconsin System. Awards bachelor's, master's, and doctoral degrees and post-master's certificates. Founded 1956. Setting: 104-acre urban campus. Research spending for the previous fiscal year: $59.6 million. Educational spending for the previous fiscal year: $7925 per student. Total enrollment: 29,114. Faculty: 1,626 (1,073 full-time, 553 part-time). Student-undergrad faculty ratio is 20:1. 10,667 applied, 71% were admitted. 10% from top 10% of their high school class, 29% from top quarter, 68% from top half. Full-time: 19,721 students, 50% women, 50% men. Part-time: 4,454 students, 55% women, 45% men. Students come from 49 states and territories, 52 other countries, 6% from out-of-state. 0.5% American Indian or Alaska Native, non-Hispanic/Latino; 7% Hispanic/Latino; 8% African American, non-Hispanic/Latino; 6% Asian, non-Hispanic/Latino; 0.1% Native Hawaiian or other Pacific Islander, non-Hispanic/Latino; 2% international. 21% 25 or older, 16% live on campus, 7% transferred in. Retention: 69% of full-time freshmen returned the following year. Academic areas with the most degrees conferred: business/marketing; health professions and related sciences; education. Core. Calendar: semesters. Academic remediation for entering students, ESL program, services for LD students, advanced placement, accelerated degree program, self-designed majors, honors program, independent study, distance learning, double major, summer session for credit, part-time degree program, adult/continuing education programs, co-op programs and internships, graduate courses open to undergrads. Off campus study at University of Wisconsin-Parkside, University of Wisconsin-Washington County, Medical College of Wisconsin, Marquette University. Study abroad program. ROTC: Army (c), Naval (c), Air Force (c).

Entrance Requirements: Options: electronic application, deferred admission, international baccalaureate accepted. Required: high school transcript, SAT or ACT. Recommended: essay. Required for some: Students whose native language is not English and who were not educated in an entirely English-speaking country will likely need to submit results from the Test of English as a Foreign Language (TOEFL). Entrance: moderately difficult. Application deadline: 7/16. Notification: continuous. SAT Reasoning Test deadline: 7/1. Transfer credits accepted: Yes.

Costs Per Year: Application fee: $44. State resident tuition: $8091 full-time, $337.13 per credit part-time. Nonresident tuition: $17,819 full-time, $742.18 per credit part-time. Mandatory fees: $1096 full-time. Full-time tuition and fees vary according to course load, degree level, location, program, and reciprocity agreements. Part-time tuition varies according to course load, degree level, location, program, and reciprocity agreements. College room and board: $7945. College room only: $4983. Room and board charges vary according to board plan, housing facility, and location.

Collegiate Environment: Orientation program. Drama-theater group, choral group, student-run newspaper. Social organizations: 313 open to all; national fraternities, national sororities, local fraternities, local sororities. Major annual events: Fall Welcome, PantherFest. Student services: legal services, health clinic, personal-psychological counseling, women's center. Campus security: 24-hour emergency response devices and patrols, student patrols, late night transport-escort service, controlled dormitory access. 4,283 college housing spaces available; 3,541 were occupied in 2012-13. Freshmen given priority for college housing. On-campus residence required in freshman year. Option: coed housing available. Golda Meir Library with 2.3 million books, 1.8 million microform titles, 73,211 serials, 206,497 audiovisual materials, an OPAC, and a Web page. Operations spending for the previous fiscal year: $6.9 million. 532 computers available on campus for general student use. Computer purchase/lease plans available. A campuswide network can be accessed from student residence rooms and from off campus. Students can access the following: online class registration. Staffed computer lab on campus (open 24 hours a day) provides training in use of computers, software, and the Internet.

Community Environment: Located on the west shore of Lake Michigan, Milwaukee (population 578,800) is the largest city in Wisconsin. All major forms of commercial transportation are available. Milwaukee is the nation's brewing center, as well as a major grain market and manufacturing center. Products of industry are metal, machinery, food, leather, chemicals, textiles, electrical machinery, and other items. The city is the headquarters of the Lake States National Forest Region. The county has a park system and many of the units contain public golf courses, tennis courts, and other recreational facilities. Wisconsin's State Fair is held each year in August.

■ **UNIVERSITY OF WISCONSIN–OSHKOSH**
800 Algoma Blvd.
Oshkosh, WI 54901
Tel: (920)424-1234
Fax: (920)424-1098
E-mail: oshadmuw@uwosh.edu
Web Site: www.uwosh.edu/

Description: State-supported, comprehensive, coed. Part of University of Wisconsin System. Awards associate, bachelor's, and master's degrees. Founded 1871. Setting: 192-acre suburban campus with easy access to Milwaukee. Total enrollment: 12,669. Faculty: 608 (413 full-time, 195 part-time). Student-undergrad faculty ratio is 21:1. 4,901 applied, 85% were admitted. 10% from top 10% of their high school class, 35% from top quarter, 85% from top half. Full-time: 9,242 students, 58% women, 42% men.

Students come from 30 states and territories, 32 other countries, 3% from out-of-state. 16% 25 or older, 34% live on campus, 11% transferred in. Retention: 76% of full-time freshmen returned the following year. Academic areas with the most degrees conferred: business/marketing; education; health professions and related sciences. Core. Calendar: semesters. Academic remediation for entering students, ESL program, services for LD students, advanced placement, accelerated degree program, self-designed majors, honors program, independent study, distance learning, double major, summer session for credit, part-time degree program, adult/continuing education programs, co-op programs and internships, graduate courses open to undergrads. Study abroad program. ROTC: Army.

Entrance Requirements: Options: electronic application, deferred admission, international baccalaureate accepted. Required: high school transcript, SAT or ACT, ACT required for state residents. Recommended: essay. Entrance: moderately difficult. Application deadline: Rolling. Notification: continuous.

Collegiate Environment: Orientation program. Drama-theater group, choral group, student-run newspaper, radio station. Social organizations: 175 open to all; national fraternities, national sororities; 3% of eligible men and 3% of eligible women are members. Most popular organizations: USRH, Model UN, Pi Sigma Epsilon, Human Services Organization. Major annual events: Homecoming, Winter Carnival, Taste of UW Oshkosh. Student services: legal services, health clinic, personal-psychological counseling, women's center. Campus security: 24-hour emergency response devices and patrols, student patrols, late night transport-escort service, controlled dormitory access. Forrest R. Polk Library with 446,774 books, 1.3 million microform titles, 5,219 serials, an OPAC, and a Web page. 475 computers available on campus for general student use. A campuswide network can be accessed from student residence rooms and from off campus. Students can access the following: online class registration. Staffed computer lab on campus (open 24 hours a day).

Community Environment: A city of 60,000, Oshkosh is situated between Lake Winnebago and Lake Butte des Morts. The Fox River runs through the city with parks and marinas dotting its shores. At historic Wittman Field, the Experimental Aircraft Association's annual international convention is the world's largest.

■ **UNIVERSITY OF WISCONSIN–PARKSIDE**
900 Wood Rd., Box 2000
Kenosha, WI 53141-2000
Tel: (262)595-2345
Fax: (262)595-2630
E-mail: possehl@uwp.edu
Web Site: www.uwp.edu/
Description: State-supported, comprehensive, coed. Part of University of Wisconsin System. Awards bachelor's and master's degrees. Founded 1968. Setting: 700-acre suburban campus with easy access to Chicago, Milwaukee. Endowment: $2 million. Research spending for the previous fiscal year: $510,825. Educational spending for the previous fiscal year: $5304 per student. Total enrollment: 4,769. Faculty: 259 (181 full-time, 78 part-time). Student-undergrad faculty ratio is 18:1. 1,883 applied, 57% were admitted. 9% from top 10% of their high school class, 32% from top quarter, 66% from top half. Full-time: 3,252 students, 50% women, 50% men. Part-time: 1,349 students, 56% women, 44% men. 11% from out-of-state. 0.2% American Indian or Alaska Native, non-Hispanic/Latino; 10% Hispanic/Latino; 10% African American, non-Hispanic/Latino; 2% Asian, non-Hispanic/Latino; 0.1% Native Hawaiian or other Pacific Islander, non-Hispanic/Latino; 2% international. 24% 25 or older, 16% live on campus, 12% transferred in. Retention: 62% of full-time freshmen returned the following year. Academic areas with the most degrees conferred: business/marketing; homeland security, law enforcement, firefighting, and protective services; social sciences. Core. Calendar: semesters. Academic remediation for entering students, services for LD students, advanced placement, honors program, independent study, distance learning, double major, summer session for credit, part-time degree program, external degree program, internships, graduate courses open to undergrads. Off campus study at Carthage College. Study abroad program. ROTC: Army (c).
Entrance Requirements: Options: electronic application, international baccalaureate accepted. Required: high school transcript, minimum of 17 high school units distribution. Required for some: SAT or ACT. Entrance: moderately difficult. Application deadline: 8/1. Notification: continuous.
Costs Per Year: Application fee: $44. State resident tuition: $6298 full-time, $262 per credit part-time. Nonresident tuition: $13,871 full-time, $578 per

credit part-time. Mandatory fees: $989 full-time. College room and board: $7082. College room only: $4152. Room and board charges vary according to board plan.
Collegiate Environment: Orientation program. Drama-theater group, choral group, student-run newspaper, radio station. Social organizations: 71 open to all; national fraternities, national sororities, local fraternities, local sororities; 1% of eligible men and 1% of eligible women are members. Most popular organizations: Black Student Union, Parkside Asian Organization, Parkside Activities Board, Latinos Unidos, Men's Rugby Club. Major annual events: Fall Fest, Worldfest Week, ice cream social. Student services: health clinic, personal-psychological counseling, women's center. Campus security: 24-hour emergency response devices and patrols, late night transport-escort service, controlled dormitory access. 1,030 college housing spaces available. No special consideration for freshman housing applicants. On-campus residence required through sophomore year. Option: coed housing available. UWP Library with 400,799 books, 979,004 serials, 23,718 audiovisual materials, an OPAC, and a Web page. Operations spending for the previous fiscal year: $1.7 million. 84 computers available on campus for general student use. A campuswide network can be accessed from student residence rooms and from off campus. Students can access the following: online class registration. Staffed computer lab on campus provides training in use of computers, software, and the Internet.
Community Environment: See Gateway Technical College.

■ **UNIVERSITY OF WISCONSIN–PLATTEVILLE**
1 University Plz.
Platteville, WI 53818-3099
Tel: (608)342-1491; Free: 800-362-5515
E-mail: rulea@uwplatt.edu
Web Site: www.uwplatt.edu/
Description: State-supported, comprehensive, coed. Part of University of Wisconsin System. Awards associate, bachelor's, and master's degrees. Founded 1866. Setting: 820-acre small town campus. Total enrollment: 8,442. Faculty: 417 (240 full-time, 177 part-time). Student-undergrad faculty ratio is 25:1. 10% from top 10% of their high school class, 31% from top quarter, 72% from top half. Full-time: 7,025 students, 35% women, 65% men. Part-time: 623 students, 32% women, 68% men. 23% from out-of-state. 1% American Indian or Alaska Native, non-Hispanic/Latino; 2% Hispanic/Latino; 2% African American, non-Hispanic/Latino; 1% Asian, non-Hispanic/Latino; 0.1% Native Hawaiian or other Pacific Islander, non-Hispanic/Latino; 1% international. 10% 25 or older, 43% live on campus, 6% transferred in. Retention: 77% of full-time freshmen returned the following year. Academic areas with the most degrees conferred: engineering; business/marketing; homeland security, law enforcement, firefighting, and protective services. Core. Calendar: semesters. Academic remediation for entering students, services for LD students, advanced placement, self-designed majors, honors program, independent study, distance learning, double major, summer session for credit, part-time degree program, external degree program, adult/continuing education programs, co-op programs and internships, graduate courses open to undergrads. Off campus study. Study abroad program. ROTC: Army (c).
Entrance Requirements: Required: high school transcript, SAT or ACT. Recommended: essay, ACT.
Costs Per Year: State resident tuition: $6298 full-time, $262.43 per credit hour part-time. Nonresident tuition: $15,036 full-time, $577.97 per credit hour part-time. Mandatory fees: $1165 full-time. College room and board: $6464. College room only: $3520. Room and board charges vary according to board plan and housing facility.
Collegiate Environment: Orientation program. Drama-theater group, choral group, marching band, student-run newspaper, radio station. Social organizations: 201 open to all; national fraternities, national sororities, local fraternities, local sororities. Most popular organizations: Criminal Justice Association, Platteville Gaming Association, Dodgeball, American Society of Mechanical Engineers, Outdoor Adventure Club. Major annual events: Welcome Back Concert, Homecoming Parade, Distinguished Lecturer. Student services: health clinic, personal-psychological counseling, women's center. Campus security: 24-hour emergency response devices and patrols, student patrols, late night transport-escort service. Freshmen guaranteed college housing. On-campus residence required through sophomore year. Options: coed, men-only, women-only housing available. Karrmann Library plus 1 other with 3,117 books, 322,884 microform titles, 538 serials, 9,901 audiovisual materials, an OPAC, and a Web page.
Community Environment: Located in the heart of Wisconsin's dairyland and lead and zinc mining district, Platteville (population 9,850) was settled in

1827. Scheduled air transportation is available from Dubuque, Iowa, 20 miles away. Community facilities include a hospital, library, churches, mining museum, other historical sites, and various civic and service organizations. Recreational activities are golf, hunting, fishing, swimming, tennis, bowling, and horseback riding.

■ UNIVERSITY OF WISCONSIN–RICHLAND

1200 Hwy. 14 W
Richland Center, WI 53581
Tel: (608)647-6186
Fax: (608)647-6225
E-mail: john.poole@uwc.edu
Web Site: richland.uwc.edu/

Description: State-supported, 2-year, coed. Part of University of Wisconsin System. Awards transfer associate degrees. Founded 1967. Setting: 135-acre rural campus. Total enrollment: 519. Faculty: 31 (13 full-time, 18 part-time). Student-undergrad faculty ratio is 17:1. 4% from top 10% of their high school class, 16% from top quarter, 36% from top half. Full-time: 291 students, 51% women, 49% men. Part-time: 228 students, 58% women, 42% men. 0.4% American Indian or Alaska Native, non-Hispanic/Latino; 1% Hispanic/Latino; 4% African American, non-Hispanic/Latino; 1% Asian, non-Hispanic/Latino. 16% 25 or older. Retention: 58% of full-time freshmen returned the following year. Calendar: semesters. Academic remediation for entering students, services for LD students, advanced placement, independent study, distance learning, summer session for credit, part-time degree program, external degree program, adult/continuing education programs. Off campus study at four-year campuses of the University of Wisconsin, other units of the University of Wisconsin Colleges. Study abroad program.

Entrance Requirements: Option: electronic application. Required: high school transcript, SAT or ACT. Recommended: ACT. Required for some: interview. Entrance: moderately difficult. Application deadline: Rolling. Notification: continuous until 9/1.

Costs Per Year: Application fee: $44. State resident tuition: $5272 full-time, $198 per credit part-time. Nonresident tuition: $12,255 full-time, $489 per credit part-time. Mandatory fees: $439 full-time. Full-time tuition and fees vary according to reciprocity agreements. Part-time tuition varies according to reciprocity agreements. College room only: $3500.

Collegiate Environment: Orientation program. Drama-theater group, choral group. Social organizations: 15 open to all. Most popular organizations: Student Senate, International Club, Campus Ambassadors, Educators of the Future, Gamers Club. Major annual events: Burlap Olympic Games, Roadrunner Road Rallye, Bedrock Café. Student services: personal-psychological counseling. 120 college housing spaces available. Option: coed housing available. Miller Memorial Library with 40,000 books, 200 serials, an OPAC, and a Web page. 50 computers available on campus for general student use. A campuswide network can be accessed. Students can access the following: online class registration. Staffed computer lab on campus provides training in use of computers and software.

■ UNIVERSITY OF WISCONSIN–RIVER FALLS

410 S Third St.
River Falls, WI 54022
Tel: (715)425-3911
Fax: (715)425-0678
E-mail: admit@uwrf.edu
Web Site: www.uwrf.edu/

Description: State-supported, comprehensive, coed. Part of University of Wisconsin System. Awards bachelor's and master's degrees and post-master's certificates. Founded 1874. Setting: 225-acre suburban campus with easy access to Minneapolis-St. Paul. Endowment: $12.2 million. Research spending for the previous fiscal year: $329,475. Educational spending for the previous fiscal year: $6022 per student. Total enrollment: 6,455. Faculty: 365 (283 full-time, 82 part-time). Student-undergrad faculty ratio is 19:1. 3,008 applied, 75% were admitted. 12% from top 10% of their high school class, 38% from top quarter, 74% from top half. 20 valedictorians. Full-time: 5,487 students, 60% women, 40% men. Part-time: 574 students, 63% women, 37% men. Students come from 29 states and territories, 18 other countries, 51% from out-of-state. 0.3% American Indian or Alaska Native, non-Hispanic/Latino; 2% Hispanic/Latino; 1% African American, non-Hispanic/Latino; 2% Asian, non-Hispanic/Latino; 0.1% Native Hawaiian or other Pacific Islander, non-Hispanic/Latino; 1% international. 10% 25 or older, 34% live on campus, 8% transferred in. Retention: 68% of full-time freshmen returned the following year. Academic areas with the most

degrees conferred: agriculture; education; business/marketing. Core. Calendar: semesters. Academic remediation for entering students, ESL program, services for LD students, advanced placement, honors program, independent study, distance learning, double major, summer session for credit, part-time degree program, external degree program, adult/continuing education programs, internships, graduate courses open to undergrads. Off campus study at National Student Exchange. Study abroad program. ROTC: Army.

Entrance Requirements: Options: electronic application, deferred admission, international baccalaureate accepted. Required: essay, high school transcript, SAT or ACT. Recommended: Rank in upper 40% of high school class, ACT. Entrance: moderately difficult. Application deadline: Rolling. Notification: continuous. SAT Reasoning Test deadline: 8/1. Transfer credits accepted: Yes.

Costs Per Year: Application fee: $44. State resident tuition: $6428 full-time, $262.43 per credit part-time. Nonresident tuition: $14,001 full-time, $577.97 per credit part-time. Mandatory fees: $1272 full-time. Full-time tuition and fees vary according to course load, degree level, and reciprocity agreements. Part-time tuition varies according to course load, degree level, and reciprocity agreements. College room and board: $6902. Room and board charges vary according to board plan and housing facility.

Collegiate Environment: Orientation program. Drama-theater group, choral group, student-run newspaper, radio station. Social organizations: 152 open to all; national fraternities, national sororities; 16% of eligible men and 24% of eligible women are members. Most popular organizations: Intervarsity Christian Fellowship, Swing Dance Club, Gender and Sexuality Alliance, Dairy Club, Asian American Student Association. Major annual events: Homecoming, Unity in the Community, UWRF Rodeo. Student services: health clinic, personal-psychological counseling. Campus security: 24-hour emergency response devices and patrols, student patrols, late night transport-escort service, controlled dormitory access. 2,730 college housing spaces available; 2,257 were occupied in 2012-13. Freshmen guaranteed college housing. On-campus residence required through sophomore year. Options: coed, women-only housing available. Chalmer Davee Library plus 1 other with 403,537 books, 250,383 microform titles, 19,056 audiovisual materials, an OPAC, and a Web page. Operations spending for the previous fiscal year: $1.8 million. 700 computers available on campus for general student use. Computer purchase/lease plans available. A campuswide network can be accessed from student residence rooms and from off campus. Students can access the following: online class registration. Staffed computer lab on campus (open 24 hours a day) provides training in use of computers, software, and the Internet.

Community Environment: Location is an important asset to the learning environment of the university. At UW-River Falls, students are exposed to the quiet charm of a friendly community nestled in the scenic St. Croix River Valley. Balanced against that setting is the opportunity and excitement of the metropolitan area of the Twin Cities of Minneapolis and St. Paul, located 20 minutes away. This unique region offers access to internationally renowned theater and cultural resources, major league sports, and an industrial and business complex that provides opportunities for internships and cooperative education experiences as well as employment.

■ UNIVERSITY OF WISCONSIN–ROCK COUNTY

2909 Kellogg Ave.
Janesville, WI 53546-5699
Tel: (608)758-6565; Free: 888-INFO-UWC
Fax: (608)758-6564
Web Site: rock.uwc.edu/

Description: State-supported, 2-year, coed. Part of University of Wisconsin System. Awards certificates and transfer associate degrees. Founded 1966. Setting: 50-acre suburban campus with easy access to Milwaukee. Core. Calendar: semesters. Academic remediation for entering students, services for LD students, advanced placement, distance learning, summer session for credit, part-time degree program, adult/continuing education programs. Off campus study at other units of the University of Wisconsin Colleges, four-year campuses of the University of Wisconsin.

Entrance Requirements: Options: electronic application, deferred admission. Required: high school transcript, ACT. Entrance: minimally difficult. Application deadline: Rolling. Notification: continuous.

Costs Per Year: Application fee: $44. State resident tuition: $5,098 full-time, $212.43 per credit part-time. Nonresident tuition: $12,082 full-time, $0 per credit. Full-time tuition varies according to reciprocity agreements. Part-time tuition varies according to reciprocity agreements.

Collegiate Environment: Orientation program. University of Wisconsin-Rock County Library with an OPAC and a Web page.

■ UNIVERSITY OF WISCONSIN–SHEBOYGAN

One University Dr.
Sheboygan, WI 53081-4789
Tel: (920)459-6600
Fax: (920)459-6602
Web Site: www.sheboygan.uwc.edu/

Description: State-supported, 2-year, coed. Part of University of Wisconsin System. Awards transfer associate degrees. Founded 1933. Setting: 75-acre small town campus with easy access to Milwaukee. Core. Calendar: semesters. Academic remediation for entering students, ESL program, services for LD students, advanced placement, independent study, distance learning, summer session for credit, part-time degree program, adult/continuing education programs. Off campus study at other units of the University of Wisconsin Colleges, four-year campuses of the University of Wisconsin.

Entrance Requirements: Open admission. Option: electronic application. Required: high school transcript. Required for some: interview. Entrance: noncompetitive. Application deadline: Rolling.

Collegiate Environment: Orientation program. Social organizations: coed fraternity. Campus security: 24-hour patrols by city police.

■ UNIVERSITY OF WISCONSIN–STEVENS POINT

2100 Main St.
Stevens Point, WI 54481-3897
Tel: (715)346-0123
Fax: (715)346-2561
E-mail: tcrumley@uwsp.edu
Web Site: www.uwsp.edu/

Description: State-supported, comprehensive, coed. Part of University of Wisconsin System. Awards associate, bachelor's, master's, and doctoral degrees. Founded 1894. Setting: 400-acre small town campus. Endowment: $13.9 million. Research spending for the previous fiscal year: $3.1 million. Educational spending for the previous fiscal year: $6020 per student. Total enrollment: 9,677. Faculty: 481 (413 full-time, 68 part-time). Student-undergrad faculty ratio is 20:1. 4,915 applied, 75% were admitted. 16% from top 10% of their high school class, 47% from top quarter, 89% from top half. Full-time: 8,644 students, 52% women, 48% men. Part-time: 652 students, 56% women, 44% men. Students come from 36 states and territories, 29 other countries, 9% from out-of-state. 0.5% American Indian or Alaska Native, non-Hispanic/Latino; 2% Hispanic/Latino; 1% African American, non-Hispanic/Latino; 2% Asian, non-Hispanic/Latino; 0% Native Hawaiian or other Pacific Islander, non-Hispanic/Latino; 2% international. 11% 25 or older, 38% live on campus, 8% transferred in. Retention: 82% of full-time freshmen returned the following year. Academic areas with the most degrees conferred: natural resources/environmental science; education; social sciences. Core. Calendar: semesters. Academic remediation for entering students, ESL program, services for LD students, advanced placement, accelerated degree program, self-designed majors, independent study, distance learning, double major, summer session for credit, part-time degree program, co-op programs and internships, graduate courses open to undergrads. Off campus study at University of Wisconsin campuses at Oshkosh, Eau Claire, Fond du Lac, Marinette, Marshfield, and Marathon. Study abroad program. ROTC: Army.

Entrance Requirements: Options: electronic application, deferred admission. Required: high school transcript, SAT or ACT. Recommended: essay, 3 recommendations. Entrance: moderately difficult. Application deadline: Rolling. Notification: continuous. Transfer credits accepted: Yes. Applicants placed on waiting list: 470. Wait-listed applicants offered admission: 98.

Costs Per Year: Application fee: $44. State resident tuition: $6298 full-time. Nonresident tuition: $13,871 full-time. Mandatory fees: $1207 full-time. Full-time tuition and fees vary according to course load, program, and reciprocity agreements. College room and board: $6538. College room only: $3788. Room and board charges vary according to board plan and housing facility.

Collegiate Environment: Orientation program. Drama-theater group, choral group, student-run newspaper, radio station. Social organizations: 203 open to all; national fraternities, national sororities, local fraternities, local sororities; 1% of eligible men and 1% of eligible women are members. Most popular organizations: The Wildlife Society, Student Impact, WWSP 90-FM radio station, Gender and Sexuality Alliance, Student Wisconsin Education Association. Major annual events: World's Largest Trivia Contest, International Club Dinner, Involvement Fair. Student services: health clinic, personal-psychological counseling, women's center. Campus security: 24-hour emergency response devices and patrols, student patrols, late night transport-escort service, controlled dormitory access. College housing

designed to accommodate 3,414 students; 3,425 undergraduates lived in college housing during 2012-13. Freshmen given priority for college housing. On-campus residence required through sophomore year. Options: coed, men-only, women-only housing available. Learning Resources Center plus 1 other with 810,123 books, 50,349 microform titles, 44,876 serials, 25,357 audiovisual materials, an OPAC, and a Web page. Operations spending for the previous fiscal year: $2.4 million. 1,233 computers available on campus for general student use. A campuswide network can be accessed from student residence rooms and from off campus. Students can access the following: online class registration. Staffed computer lab on campus provides training in use of computers, software, and the Internet.

Community Environment: Stevens Point is located in the very center of the state on the Wisconsin River. It lies midway between Milwaukee and Minneapolis and is approximately 250 miles from Chicago. Air service is available through the Central Wisconsin Airport. Stevens Point is a city of about 25,000 and is the "Gateway to Wisconsin's Vacationland." A wide range of cultural and year-around recreational opportunities are available. The area is known for insurance, agribusiness, paper production, finance, and light industry.

■ UNIVERSITY OF WISCONSIN–STOUT

Menomonie, WI 54751
Tel: (715)232-1122; Free: 800-HI-STOUT
Fax: (715)232-1667
E-mail: admissions@uwstout.edu
Web Site: www.uwstout.edu/

Description: State-supported, comprehensive, coed. Part of University of Wisconsin System. Awards bachelor's and master's degrees and post-master's certificates. Founded 1891. Setting: 120-acre small town campus with easy access to Minneapolis-St. Paul. Total enrollment: 9,247. Faculty: 472 (402 full-time, 70 part-time). Student-undergrad faculty ratio is 19:1. 3,388 applied, 80% were admitted. 8% from top 10% of their high school class, 26% from top quarter, 68% from top half. Full-time: 6,873 students, 49% women, 51% men. Part-time: 1,397 students, 45% women, 55% men. 32% from out-of-state. 3% American Indian or Alaska Native, non-Hispanic/Latino; 1% Hispanic/Latino; 1% African American, non-Hispanic/Latino; 0.1% Asian, non-Hispanic/Latino; 89% Native Hawaiian or other Pacific Islander, non-Hispanic/Latino; 2% international. 16% 25 or older, 40% live on campus, 9% transferred in. Retention: 70% of full-time freshmen returned the following year. Academic areas with the most degrees conferred: business/marketing; education; visual and performing arts. Core. Calendar: 4-1-4. Services for LD students, accelerated degree program, honors program, independent study, distance learning, double major, summer session for credit, part-time degree program, external degree program, adult/continuing education programs, co-op programs and internships, graduate courses open to undergrads. Off campus study at BS in Engineering Technology - Northcentral Technical College; BS in Early Childhood Education - Lac Courte Oreilles Community College; BS in Manufacturing Engineering - Northwest Technical College; BS in Info. and Comm. Technologies - WI Technical College System; BS in Sustainable Mgmt - UW-River Falls, UW-Parkside, UW-Superior, UW Extension; BS in Management - Sheboygan. Study abroad program. ROTC: Army, Air Force (c).

Entrance Requirements: Option: electronic application. Required: high school transcript, SAT or ACT. Recommended: minimum 2.5 high school GPA. Required for some: minimum 2.75 high school GPA. Entrance: moderately difficult. Application deadlines: Rolling, Rolling for nonresidents. Notification: continuous, continuous for nonresidents. SAT Reasoning Test deadline: 9/1. Transfer credits accepted: Yes.

Costs Per Year: Application fee: $44. State resident tuition: $7014 full-time. $234 per credit hour part-time. Nonresident tuition: $14,760 full-time, $492 per credit hour part-time. Mandatory fees: $1930 full-time. Full-time tuition and fees vary according to degree level and reciprocity agreements. Part-time tuition varies according to degree level and reciprocity agreements. College room and board: $6054. College room only: $3600. Room and board charges vary according to board plan and housing facility.

Collegiate Environment: Orientation program. Drama-theater group, choral group, marching band, student-run newspaper, radio station. Social organizations: national fraternities, national sororities, local fraternities, local sororities. Student services: legal services, health clinic, personal-psychological counseling. Campus security: 24-hour emergency response devices and patrols, student patrols, controlled dormitory access. Freshmen guaranteed college housing. On-campus residence required through sophomore year. Option: coed housing available. Library Learning Center with an OPAC and a Web page.

Community Environment: Menomonie, population 15,200, is located on the Red Cedar River and Lake Menomin, and is accessible by all commercial transportation.

■ **UNIVERSITY OF WISCONSIN–SUPERIOR**
Belknap and Catlin
Superior, WI 54880-4500
Tel: (715)394-8101
Fax: (715)394-8407
E-mail: admissions@uwsuper.edu
Web Site: www.uwsuper.edu/

Description: State-supported, comprehensive, coed. Part of University of Wisconsin System. Awards associate, bachelor's, and master's degrees and post-master's certificates. Founded 1893. Setting: 230-acre suburban campus. Endowment: $2.2 million. Total enrollment: 2,700. Faculty: 219 (136 full-time, 83 part-time). Student-undergrad faculty ratio is 14:1. 1,001 applied, 76% were admitted. 12% from top 10% of their high school class, 28% from top quarter, 71% from top half. 5 valedictorians. Full-time: 2,024 students, 55% women, 45% men. Part-time: 526 students, 67% women, 33% men. Students come from 33 states and territories, 37 other countries, 46% from out-of-state. 2% American Indian or Alaska Native, non-Hispanic/Latino; 2% Hispanic/Latino; 2% African American, non-Hispanic/Latino; 1% Asian, non-Hispanic/Latino; 0.2% Native Hawaiian or other Pacific Islander, non-Hispanic/Latino; 6% international. 30% 25 or older, 28% live on campus, 12% transferred in. Retention: 72% of full-time freshmen returned the following year. Academic areas with the most degrees conferred: business/marketing; education; communication/journalism. Core. Calendar: semesters. Academic remediation for entering students, ESL program, services for LD students, advanced placement, self-designed majors, freshman honors college, independent study, distance learning, double major, summer session for credit, part-time degree program, external degree program, adult/continuing education programs, co-op programs and internships, graduate courses open to undergrads. Off campus study at College of St. Scholastica, Northland College, University of Minnesota, Duluth. Study abroad program. ROTC: Air Force (c).
Entrance Requirements: Options: electronic application, early admission, deferred admission. Required: high school transcript, SAT or ACT. Recommended: interview. Required for some: essay, 1 recommendation. Entrance: moderately difficult. Application deadline: Rolling. Notification: continuous, continuous for nonresidents. SAT Reasoning Test deadline: 8/15. SAT Subject Test deadline: 8/15.
Costs Per Year: Application fee: $44. State resident tuition: $6535 full-time, $472 per credit hour part-time. Nonresident tuition: $14,108 full-time, $776 per credit hour part-time. Mandatory fees: $1369 full-time. Full-time tuition and fees vary according to course load and reciprocity agreements. Part-time tuition varies according to course load and reciprocity agreements. College room and board: $5992. College room only: $3232. Room and board charges vary according to board plan, housing facility, and student level.
Collegiate Environment: Orientation program. Drama-theater group, choral group, student-run newspaper, radio station. Social organizations: 63 open to all; national sororities. Most popular organizations: Student Senate, Student Activities Board, Residence Hall Association, Inter-Varsity Christian Fellowship, World Student Association. Major annual events: Cultural Night, Hockey Games, Winterfest. Student services: health clinic, personal-psychological counseling, women's center. Campus security: 24-hour emergency response devices and patrols, student patrols, late night transport-escort service, controlled dormitory access. 820 college housing spaces available; 714 were occupied in 2012-13. Freshmen guaranteed college housing. On-campus residence required through sophomore year. Options: coed, women-only housing available. Jim Dan Hill Library with an OPAC and a Web page. 343 computers available on campus for general student use. Computer purchase/lease plans available. A campuswide network can be accessed from student residence rooms and from off campus. Students can access the following: online class registration. Staffed computer lab on campus (open 24 hours a day) provides training in use of computers, software, and the Internet.
Community Environment: Superior is Wisconsin's leading port of entry and is located at the head of Lake Superior at the northwest corner of the state. The largest iron ore dock, grain elevator and briquette plant in the world are here at Superior. The area is a leading summer and winter recreation resort. Along with neighbor city Duluth, MN, the area offers a wide range of music, theater, shopping, and recreational opportunities.

■ **UNIVERSITY OF WISCONSIN–WASHINGTON COUNTY**
400 University Dr.
West Bend, WI 53095-3699
Tel: (262)335-5200
Fax: (262)335-5257
E-mail: dan.cibrario@uwc.edu
Web Site: www.washington.uwc.edu/

Description: State-supported, 2-year, coed. Part of University of Wisconsin System. Awards transfer associate degrees. Founded 1968. Setting: 87-acre small town campus with easy access to Milwaukee. Educational spending for the previous fiscal year: $11,190 per student. Total enrollment: 951. Faculty: 52 (29 full-time, 23 part-time). Student-undergrad faculty ratio is 21:1. 708 applied, 67% were admitted. 3% from top 10% of their high school class, 15% from top quarter, 51% from top half. Full-time: 663 students, 53% women, 47% men. Part-time: 288 students, 63% women, 37% men. Students come from 2 states and territories, 2 other countries, 1% from out-of-state. 16% 25 or older, 7% transferred in. Retention: 63% of full-time freshmen returned the following year. Core. Calendar: semesters. Academic remediation for entering students, services for LD students, advanced placement, honors program, independent study, distance learning, double major, summer session for credit, part-time degree program. Off campus study at other units of the University of Wisconsin Colleges, four-year campuses of the University of Wisconsin.
Entrance Requirements: Options: electronic application, deferred admission. Required: high school transcript. Recommended: ACT. Required for some: essay, interview. Entrance: noncompetitive. Application deadline: Rolling.
Collegiate Environment: Orientation program. Drama-theater group, choral group, student-run newspaper. Social organizations: 6 open to all. Most popular organizations: Student Government Association, Business Club, Phi Theta Kappa, Writers' Guild, Student Impact. Major annual events: Summer Send-Off Picnic, United Way Fund Drive, Convocation/Commencement. Student services: personal-psychological counseling. University of Wisconsin-Washington County Library with 46,429 books, 22 microform titles, 247 serials, an OPAC, and a Web page. 78 computers available on campus for general student use. A campuswide network can be accessed from off-campus. Staffed computer lab on campus.

■ **UNIVERSITY OF WISCONSIN–WAUKESHA**
1500 N University Dr.
Waukesha, WI 53188-2799
Tel: (414)521-5200
Fax: (414)521-5491
E-mail: deborah.kusick@uwc.edu
Web Site: www.waukesha.uwc.edu/

Description: State-supported, 2-year, coed. Part of University of Wisconsin System. Awards transfer associate degrees. Founded 1966. Setting: 86-acre suburban campus with easy access to Milwaukee. Total enrollment: 2,115. Faculty: 93 (56 full-time, 37 part-time). Student-undergrad faculty ratio is 21:1. 706 applied, 94% were admitted. 1% from top 10% of their high school class, 8% from top quarter, 15% from top half. Full-time: 891 students, 46% women, 54% men. Part-time: 1,223 students, 46% women, 54% men. Students come from 6 states and territories, 1 other country, 1% from out-of-state. 0.2% American Indian or Alaska Native, non-Hispanic/Latino; 3% Hispanic/Latino; 4% African American, non-Hispanic/Latino; 2% Asian, non-Hispanic/Latino; 0.4% international. 28% 25 or older, 8% transferred in. Core. Calendar: semesters. Academic remediation for entering students, services for LD students, advanced placement, accelerated degree program, honors program, distance learning, summer session for credit, part-time degree program, internships. Off campus study at other units of the University of Wisconsin Colleges and 4-year campuses of the University of Wisconsin. Study abroad program.
Entrance Requirements: Options: electronic application, early admission, deferred admission. Required: high school transcript, SAT or ACT. Recommended: essay, admission interview may be recommended. Required for some: interview. Entrance: minimally difficult. Application deadline: Rolling. Notification: continuous. SAT Reasoning Test deadline: 8/22. SAT Subject Test deadline: 8/22. Transfer credits accepted: Yes.
Costs Per Year: Application fee: $44. State resident tuition: $5088 full-time, $215 per hour part-time. Nonresident tuition: $12,072 full-time, $506 per hour part-time. Mandatory fees: $394 full-time. Full-time tuition and fees vary according to course load and reciprocity agreements. Part-time tuition varies according to course load and reciprocity agreements.
Collegiate Environment: Orientation program. Drama-theater group, choral

group, student-run newspaper. Social organizations: 41 open to all. Most popular organizations: student government, Student Activities Committee, Campus Crusade, Phi Theta Kappa, Circle K. Major annual events: Fall Fest, Spring Carnival, Honors and Degree Ceremony. Student services: personal-psychological counseling. Campus security: late night transport-escort service, part-time patrols by trained security personnel. College housing not available. University of Wisconsin-Waukesha Library plus 1 other with 61,000 books, 300 serials, 5,382 audiovisual materials, and a Web page. 90 computers available on campus for general student use. Computer purchase/lease plans available. A campuswide network can be accessed. Students can access the following: online class registration. Staffed computer lab on campus provides training in use of computers, software, and the Internet.

■ UNIVERSITY OF WISCONSIN–WHITEWATER

800 W Main St.
Whitewater, WI 53190-1790
Tel: (262)472-1234
Fax: (262)472-1515
E-mail: uwwadmit@uww.edu
Web Site: www.uww.edu/

Description: State-supported, comprehensive, coed. Part of University of Wisconsin System. Awards associate, bachelor's, and master's degrees. Founded 1868. Setting: 385-acre small town campus with easy access to Milwaukee. Endowment: $13 million. Research spending for the previous fiscal year: $631,323. Educational spending for the previous fiscal year: $4058 per student. Total enrollment: 11,629. Faculty: 529 (409 full-time, 120 part-time). Student-undergrad faculty ratio is 23:1. 6,309 applied, 71% were admitted. 9% from top 10% of their high school class, 31% from top quarter, 77% from top half. Full-time: 9,535 students, 50% women, 50% men. Part-time: 679 students, 47% women, 53% men. Students come from 32 states and territories, 37 other countries, 9% from out-of-state. 0.2% American Indian or Alaska Native, non-Hispanic/Latino; 4% Hispanic/Latino; 5% African American, non-Hispanic/Latino; 1% Asian, non-Hispanic/Latino; 0.1% Native Hawaiian or other Pacific Islander, non-Hispanic/Latino; 1% international. 9% 25 or older, 7% transferred in. Retention: 79% of full-time freshmen returned the following year. Academic areas with the most degrees conferred: business/marketing; education; social sciences. Core. Calendar: semesters. Academic remediation for entering students, ESL program, services for LD students, advanced placement, accelerated degree program, self-designed majors, honors program, independent study, distance learning, double major, summer session for credit, part-time degree program, external degree program, adult/continuing education programs, co-op programs and internships, graduate courses open to undergrads. Study abroad program. ROTC: Army, Air Force.

Entrance Requirements: Options: electronic application, deferred admission, international baccalaureate accepted. Required: high school transcript. Recommended: SAT or ACT. Required for some: ACT. Entrance: moderately difficult. Application deadline: Rolling. Notification: 9/15.

Costs Per Year: Application fee: $44. State resident tuition: $6,519 full-time, $271.62 per credit hour part-time. Nonresident tuition: $14,092 full-time, $587.16 per credit hour part-time. Mandatory fees: $1009 full-time. Full-time tuition and fees vary according to degree level and reciprocity agreements. College room and board: $5736. Room and board charges vary according to board plan.

Collegiate Environment: Drama-theater group, choral group, marching band, student-run newspaper, radio station. Social organizations: 125 open to all; national fraternities, national sororities, local fraternities, local sororities; 4% of eligible men and 3% of eligible women are members. Most popular organizations: Finance Association, American Marketing Association, Black Student Union, Golden Key Honor Society, Wisconsin Education Association. Major annual events: Homecoming Week, Student Open Education Fair, Career Fair. Student services: legal services, health clinic, personal-psychological counseling, women's center. Campus security: 24-hour emergency response devices, late night transport-escort service, controlled dormitory access. Andersen Library with 663,349 books, 1.2 million microform titles, 7,087 serials, 12,134 audiovisual materials, an OPAC, and a Web page. Operations spending for the previous fiscal year: $2.3 million.

Community Environment: UW-Whitewater is located in a city of 12,000 near the scenic beauty of the Southern Kettle Moraine State Forest. It is a one-hour drive from Madison and Milwaukee, and a two-hour drive from Chicago. The area around Whitewater offers lakes, recreation, cross country

skiing, backpacking, hiking, and other forms of outdoor activity. The campus is within walking distance of 2 shopping areas and a city park is adjacent to the campus.

■ VITERBO UNIVERSITY

900 Viterbo Dr.
La Crosse, WI 54601-4797
Tel: (608)796-3000; Free: 800-VITERBO
Fax: (608)796-3050
E-mail: admission@viterbo.edu
Web Site: www.viterbo.edu/

Description: Independent Roman Catholic, comprehensive, coed. Awards associate, bachelor's, and master's degrees and post-master's certificates. Founded 1890. Setting: 72-acre suburban campus. Total enrollment: 2,830. Faculty: 415 (118 full-time, 297 part-time). Student-undergrad faculty ratio is 12:1. 1,655 applied, 69% were admitted. 17% from top 10% of their high school class, 45% from top quarter, 84% from top half. Full-time: 1,569 students, 72% women, 28% men. Part-time: 536 students, 77% women, 23% men. 23% from out-of-state. 1% American Indian or Alaska Native, non-Hispanic/Latino; 2% Hispanic/Latino; 2% African American, non-Hispanic/Latino; 2% Asian, non-Hispanic/Latino; 0% Native Hawaiian or other Pacific Islander, non-Hispanic/Latino; 1% international. 32% 25 or older, 33% live on campus, 14% transferred in. Retention: 76% of full-time freshmen returned the following year. Academic areas with the most degrees conferred: health professions and related sciences; business/marketing; visual and performing arts. Core. Calendar: semesters. ESL program, accelerated degree program, self-designed majors, honors program, independent study, distance learning, double major, part-time degree program, adult/continuing education programs, internships. Study abroad program. ROTC: Army (c).

Entrance Requirements: Options: electronic application, deferred admission, international baccalaureate accepted. Required: high school transcript, minimum 2 high school GPA, SAT or ACT. Required for some: essay, interview, audition for theater and music, portfolio for art. Entrance: moderately difficult. Application deadline: 8/15. Notification: continuous. Transfer credits accepted: Yes.

Costs Per Year: Application fee: $25. Comprehensive fee: $30,070 includes full-time tuition ($22,080), mandatory fees ($590), and college room and board ($7400). College room only: $3310. Full-time tuition and fees vary according to program. Room and board charges vary according to board plan and housing facility.

Collegiate Environment: Orientation program. Drama-theater group, choral group, student-run newspaper. Social organizations: 32 open to all. Most popular organizations: Student Activities Board (SAB), Viterbo Student nurses Association (VSNA), Education Club, Colleges Against Cancer (CAL), Residence Hall Council (RHC). Major annual events: Courtyard Carni, Welcome back Bash, Viterbo Days (Family Day). Student services: health clinic, personal-psychological counseling. Campus security: 24-hour emergency response devices, late night transport-escort service, controlled dormitory access, security officers on campus 5:00 pm to 7:00 am, lighted pathways, emergency evacuation plan, self-defense education programs. 90 undergraduates lived in college housing during 2012-13. Freshmen guaranteed college housing. On-campus residence required through sophomore year. Options: coed, men-only, women-only housing available. Todd Wehr Memorial Library with 92,300 books, 307 microform titles, 229 serials, 5,110 audiovisual materials, an OPAC, and a Web page.

■ WAUKESHA COUNTY TECHNICAL COLLEGE

800 Main St.
Pewaukee, WI 53072-4601
Tel: (262)691-5566
Fax: (262)691-5693
E-mail: kkazda@wctc.edu
Web Site: www.wctc.edu/

Description: State and locally supported, 2-year, coed. Part of Wisconsin Technical College System. Awards certificates, diplomas, and terminal associate degrees. Founded 1923. Setting: 137-acre suburban campus with easy access to Milwaukee. Total enrollment: 10,286. Faculty: 857 (188 full-time, 669 part-time). Student-undergrad faculty ratio is 20:1. Full-time: 2,081 students, 41% women, 59% men. Part-time: 8,205 students, 47% women, 53% men. 1% American Indian or Alaska Native, non-Hispanic/Latino; 7% Hispanic/Latino; 8% African American, non-Hispanic/Latino; 2% Asian, non-Hispanic/Latino; 0.2% Native Hawaiian or other Pacific Islander, non-Hispanic/Latino; 0% international. 51% 25 or older. Calendar: semesters. Academic remediation for entering students, ESL program, services for LD students, advanced placement, self-designed majors, distance learning, summer session for credit, part-time degree program, adult/continuing education programs, co-op programs.

Entrance Requirements: Open admission. Option: electronic application. Required: high school transcript. Required for some: interview. Entrance: noncompetitive. Application deadline: Rolling.

Collegiate Environment: Orientation program. Campus security: patrols by police officers 8 am to 10 pm. College housing not available.

■ **WESTERN TECHNICAL COLLEGE**
304 6th St. N
La Crosse, WI 54602-0908
Tel: (608)785-9200; Free: 800-322-9982
Fax: (608)785-9205
E-mail: mildes@wwtc.edu
Web Site: www.westerntc.edu/

Description: District-supported, 2-year, coed. Part of Wisconsin Technical College System. Awards certificates, diplomas, transfer associate, and terminal associate degrees. Founded 1911. Setting: 10-acre urban campus. Research spending for the previous fiscal year: $227,769. Educational spending for the previous fiscal year: $9793 per student. Total enrollment: 4,765. Faculty: 888 (203 full-time, 685 part-time). Student-undergrad faculty ratio is 7:1. 3,443 applied, 35% were admitted. Students come from 4 states and territories, 7% from out-of-state. 16% 25 or older, 2% live on campus. Core. Calendar: semesters. Academic remediation for entering students, ESL program, services for LD students, advanced placement, accelerated degree program, self-designed majors, distance learning, summer session for credit, part-time degree program, external degree program, adult/continuing education programs, co-op programs and internships. Off campus study.

Entrance Requirements: Open admission except for health occupations programs. Options: electronic application, early admission. Required: high school transcript. Recommended: interview, ACT. Required for some: ACT ASSET. Entrance: noncompetitive. Application deadline: Rolling.

Costs Per Year: Application fee: $30. One-time mandatory fee: $30. State resident tuition: $3507 full-time, $116.90 per credit part-time. Nonresident tuition: $5,260 full-time, $175.35 per credit part-time. Mandatory fees: $274 full-time, $8.30 per credit part-time. Full-time tuition and fees vary according to class time, course level, course load, degree level, program, and reciprocity agreements. Part-time tuition and fees vary according to class time, course level, course load, degree level, program, and reciprocity agreements. College room and board: $5300. College room only: $3700. Room and board charges vary according to board plan.

Collegiate Environment: Orientation program. Student-run newspaper. Social organizations: 28 open to all. Most popular organizations: Wisconsin Marketing Management Association (WMMA), Air Conditioning, Refrigeration Organization (ACRO), Multicultural Club, Business Professionals of America (BPA), Advertising Club. Major annual event: Orientation. Student services: personal-psychological counseling. Campus security: 24-hour emergency response devices and patrols, student patrols, late night transport-escort service, controlled dormitory access. Western Wisconsin Technical College Library plus 1 other with 31,243 books, 397 microform titles, 313 serials, 3,750 audiovisual materials, and an OPAC. Operations spending for the previous fiscal year: $303,682. 800 computers available on campus for general student use. A campuswide network can be accessed from student residence rooms and from off campus. Students can access the following: online class registration. Staffed computer lab on campus.

Community Environment: See University of Wisconsin - La Crosse.

■ **WISCONSIN INDIANHEAD TECHNICAL COLLEGE**
505 Pine Ridge Dr.
Shell Lake, WI 54871
Tel: (715)468-2815; Free: 800-243-9482
Fax: (715)468-2819
E-mail: Steve.Bitzer@witc.edu
Web Site: www.witc.edu/

Description: District-supported, 2-year, coed. Part of Wisconsin Technical College System. Awards certificates, diplomas, and terminal associate

degrees. Founded 1912. Setting: 118-acre urban campus. System endowment: $2.9 million. Educational spending for the previous fiscal year: $10,262 per student. Total enrollment: 3,596. Faculty: 740 (170 full-time, 570 part-time). Student-undergrad faculty ratio is 10:1. Full-time: 1,577 students, 51% women, 49% men. Part-time: 1,959 students, 72% women, 28% men. Students come from 4 states and territories, 1% from out-of-state. 2% American Indian or Alaska Native, non-Hispanic/Latino; 0.5% Hispanic/Latino; 1% African American, non-Hispanic/Latino; 0.4% Asian, non-Hispanic/Latino; 0.03% Native Hawaiian or other Pacific Islander, non-Hispanic/Latino; 0% international. 54% 25 or older. Retention: 70% of full-time freshmen returned the following year. Calendar: semesters.

Entrance Requirements: Option: electronic application. Application deadline: Rolling.

Costs Per Year: Application fee: $30. State resident tuition: $3808 full-time, $126.93 per credit part-time. Nonresident tuition: $5610 full-time, $187.30 per credit part-time. Mandatory fees: $126.96 per credit part-time. Full-time tuition varies according to course load, location, program, and reciprocity agreements. Part-time tuition and fees vary according to course load, location, program, and reciprocity agreements.

Collegiate Environment: Orientation program. Student services: health clinic. College housing not available.

■ **WISCONSIN LUTHERAN COLLEGE**
8800 W Bluemound Rd.
Milwaukee, WI 53226-9942
Tel: (414)443-8800
Fax: (414)443-8514
E-mail: meg.wieselmann@wlc.edu
Web Site: www.wlc.edu/

Description: Independent, 4-year, coed, affiliated with Wisconsin Evangelical Lutheran Synod. Awards bachelor's degrees. Founded 1973. Setting: 48-acre suburban campus. Endowment: $24.4 million. Research spending for the previous fiscal year: $41,282. Educational spending for the previous fiscal year: $11,985 per student. Total enrollment: 753. Faculty: 96 (60 full-time, 36 part-time). Student-undergrad faculty ratio is 10:1. 646 applied, 76% were admitted. 18% from top 10% of their high school class, 43% from top quarter, 77% from top half. 9 valedictorians. Full-time: 698 students, 56% women, 44% men. Part-time: 55 students, 47% women, 53% men. Students come from 27 states and territories, 9 other countries, 23% from out-of-state. 2% 25 or older, 79% live on campus, 2% transferred in. Retention: 76% of full-time freshmen returned the following year. Academic areas with the most degrees conferred: communication/journalism; psychology; visual and performing arts. Core. Calendar: semesters. ESL program, services for LD students, advanced placement, self-designed majors, independent study, double major, summer session for credit, part-time degree program, internships. Study abroad program. ROTC: Army (c), Naval (c), Air Force (c).

Entrance Requirements: Options: electronic application, deferred admission. Required: high school transcript, minimum 2.7 high school GPA, SAT or ACT, minimum ACT score of 21. Recommended: 1 recommendation. Required for some: interview. Entrance: moderately difficult. Notification: continuous.

Costs Per Year: Application fee: $20. Comprehensive fee: $32,150 includes full-time tuition ($23,470), mandatory fees ($150), and college room and board ($8530). College room only: $4600. Full-time tuition and fees vary according to degree level and program. Room and board charges vary according to board plan, housing facility, and student level. Part-time tuition: $680 per credit. Part-time tuition varies according to degree level and program.

Collegiate Environment: Orientation program. Drama-theater group, choral group, student-run newspaper. Student services: health clinic, personal-psychological counseling. Campus security: 24-hour emergency response devices and patrols, late night transport-escort service, controlled dormitory access, closed-circuit TV monitors. Marvin M. Schwan Library with 78,107 books, 9,211 microform titles, 310 serials, 4,730 audiovisual materials, an OPAC, and a Web page. Operations spending for the previous fiscal year: $474,845. 100 computers available on campus for general student use. A campuswide network can be accessed from student residence rooms and from off campus. Students can access the following: online class registration. Staffed computer lab on campus provides training in use of computers, software, and the Internet.

■ CASPER COLLEGE

125 College Dr.
Casper, WY 82601-4699
Tel: (307)268-2110; Free: 800-442-2963
Fax: (307)268-2682
E-mail: kfoltz@caspercollege.edu
Web Site: www.caspercollege.edu/

Description: State and locally supported, 2-year, coed. Awards certificates, transfer associate, and terminal associate degrees. Founded 1945. Setting: 200-acre small town campus. Total enrollment: 4,207. Faculty: 260 (148 full-time, 112 part-time). Student-undergrad faculty ratio is 15:1. 945 applied, 100% were admitted. Full-time: 1,935 students, 56% women, 44% men. Part-time: 2,272 students, 57% women, 43% men. Students come from 37 states and territories, 17 other countries, 10% from out-of-state. 1% American Indian or Alaska Native, non-Hispanic/Latino; 5% Hispanic/Latino; 2% African American, non-Hispanic/Latino; 1% Asian, non-Hispanic/Latino; 0.3% Native Hawaiian or other Pacific Islander, non-Hispanic/Latino; 1% international. 36% 25 or older, 10% live on campus, 5% transferred in. Retention: 61% of full-time freshmen returned the following year. Core. Calendar: semesters. Academic remediation for entering students, ESL program, services for LD students, advanced placement, accelerated degree program, honors program, independent study, distance learning, summer session for credit, part-time degree program, co-op programs and internships. Off campus study at University of Wyoming-Casper Campus, University of North Dakota.

Entrance Requirements: Open admission. Options: electronic application, early admission, international baccalaureate accepted. Required: high school transcript. Entrance: noncompetitive. Application deadline: 8/15. Notification: continuous until 8/15. Transfer credits accepted: Yes.

Costs Per Year: Application fee: $0. State resident tuition: $1800 full-time, $75 per credit hour part-time. Nonresident tuition: $5400 full-time, $225 per credit hour part-time. Mandatory fees: $432 full-time, $18 per credit hour part-time. College room and board: $5530. Room and board charges vary according to board plan and housing facility.

Collegiate Environment: Orientation program. Drama-theater group, choral group, student-run newspaper. Most popular organizations: Student Senate, Student Activities Board, Agriculture Club, Theater Club, Phi Theta Kappa. Student services: health clinic, personal-psychological counseling. Campus security: 24-hour patrols, late night transport-escort service. 450 college housing spaces available; 425 were occupied in 2012-13. No special consideration for freshman housing applicants. Option: coed housing available. Goodstein Foundation Library with 128,000 books, 385 serials, an OPAC, and a Web page. 150 computers available on campus for general student use. A campuswide network can be accessed from student residence rooms and from off campus. Students can access the following: online class registration. Staffed computer lab on campus provides training in use of computers, software, and the Internet.

Community Environment: Rich in oil and uranium, Casper is Wyoming's leading industrial city. Cattle and sheep ranches in the surrounding area provide the basis for the city's wool and livestock markets. Situated at the foot of Casper Mountain in the approximate geographic center of Wyoming, the climate is invigorating with 300 days of sunshine each year. The community has 70 churches, a hospital, library, symphony orchestra, theatre group, a mall, 11 theatres and a community concert series. Local recreation includes tennis, golf, trap shooting, a multipurpose event center, swimming pools, bowling alleys, excellent fishing and hunting, city and mountain parks,

archery and rifle ranges, and a ski area. Several rodeos are held here each year, as well as skiing and mountain climbing events.

■ CENTRAL WYOMING COLLEGE

2660 Peck Ave.
Riverton, WY 82501-2273
Tel: (307)855-2000; Free: 800-735-8418
Fax: (307)855-2092
E-mail: admit@cwc.edu
Web Site: www.cwc.edu/

Description: State and locally supported, 2-year, coed. Part of Wyoming Community College Commission. Awards certificates, diplomas, transfer associate, and terminal associate degrees. Founded 1966. Setting: 200-acre small town campus. Endowment: $13.8 million. Research spending for the previous fiscal year: $67,282. Educational spending for the previous fiscal year: $5718 per student. Total enrollment: 2,164. Faculty: 152 (49 full-time, 103 part-time). Student-undergrad faculty ratio is 16:1. 478 applied, 100% were admitted. 10% from top 10% of their high school class, 25% from top quarter, 54% from top half. Full-time: 838 students, 55% women, 45% men. Part-time: 1,326 students, 59% women, 41% men. Students come from 45 states and territories, 7 other countries, 14% from out-of-state. 11% American Indian or Alaska Native, non-Hispanic/Latino; 7% Hispanic/Latino; 1% African American, non-Hispanic/Latino; 1% Asian, non-Hispanic/Latino; 0.3% Native Hawaiian or other Pacific Islander, non-Hispanic/Latino; 0.4% international. 40% 25 or older, 8% live on campus, 5% transferred in. Retention: 52% of full-time freshmen returned the following year. Core. Calendar: semesters. Academic remediation for entering students, ESL program, services for LD students, advanced placement, honors program, independent study, distance learning, double major, summer session for credit, part-time degree program, adult/continuing education programs, co-op programs. Off campus study.

Entrance Requirements: Open admission except for nursing program. Options: electronic application, early admission, deferred admission. Recommended: high school transcript. Entrance: noncompetitive. Application deadlines: Rolling, Rolling for nonresidents. Transfer credits accepted: Yes.

Costs Per Year: Application fee: $0. State resident tuition: $1896 full-time, $79 per credit part-time. Nonresident tuition: $5688 full-time, $237 per credit part-time. Mandatory fees: $672 full-time, $28 per credit part-time. Full-time tuition and fees vary according to course load, program, and reciprocity agreements. Part-time tuition and fees vary according to course load, program, and reciprocity agreements. College room and board: $4607. College room only: $2297. Room and board charges vary according to board plan and housing facility.

Collegiate Environment: Orientation program. Drama-theater group, choral group, student-run radio station. Social organizations: 16 open to all. Most popular organizations: Multi-Cultural Club, La Vida Nueva Club, Fellowship of College Christians, Quality Leaders, Science Club. Major annual events: Convocation, theater and music productions, Final Feed. Student services: personal-psychological counseling. Campus security: 24-hour emergency response devices, late night transport-escort service, controlled dormitory access. 225 college housing spaces available; 182 were occupied in 2012-13. No special consideration for freshman housing applicants. Option: coed housing available. Central Wyoming College Library with 54,974 books, 33,781 microform titles, 2,940 serials, 1,450 audiovisual materials, an OPAC, and a Web page. Operations spending for the previous fiscal year: $236,723. 450 computers available on campus for general student use.

Computer purchase/lease plans available. A campuswide network can be accessed from off-campus. Students can access the following: online class registration. Staffed computer lab on campus provides training in use of computers, software, and the Internet.

Community Environment: Located in the lower Wind River Basin, Riverton (population 9,430) is the center of a large farming, lumbering and livestock producing region. The area has a stimulating climate with a summer average temperature of 66 degrees and a winter average of 35 degrees. There are less than 10 inches of rainfall annually. The community is accessed by bus and air lines. There are 25 churches, a modern library, 2 hospitals, 3 clinics, and good shopping available. Local recreation facilities include an Olympic-size swimming pool, and provide for golf, baseball, bowling, hunting, fishing, boating, water skiing, snow skiing, rock hunting, and hiking. An Antique Museum, the Wind River Indian Reservation, and many national and state parks are of interest. Part-time employment is available for students.

■ **EASTERN WYOMING COLLEGE**
3200 W C St.
Torrington, WY 82240-1699
Tel: (307)532-8200; Free: 866-327-8996
Fax: (307)532-8222
E-mail: rex.cogdill@ewc.wy.edu
Web Site: www.ewc.wy.edu/

Description: State and locally supported, 2-year, coed. Part of Wyoming Community College Commission. Awards certificates, diplomas, transfer associate, and terminal associate degrees. Founded 1948. Setting: 40-acre rural campus. Total enrollment: 1,628. Faculty: 100 (47 full-time, 53 part-time). Student-undergrad faculty ratio is 14:1. Full-time: 674 students, 57% women, 43% men. Part-time: 954 students, 61% women, 39% men. 2% American Indian or Alaska Native, non-Hispanic/Latino; 7% Hispanic/Latino; 1% African American, non-Hispanic/Latino; 1% Asian, non-Hispanic/Latino; 0.3% Native Hawaiian or other Pacific Islander, non-Hispanic/Latino; 0.2% international. Calendar: semesters. Academic remediation for entering students, ESL program, services for LD students, advanced placement, accelerated degree program, self-designed majors, honors program, independent study, distance learning, summer session for credit, part-time degree program, adult/continuing education programs, co-op programs and internships.

Entrance Requirements: Open admission. Options: electronic application, early admission. Recommended: high school transcript. Entrance: noncompetitive. Application deadline: Rolling. Preference given to state residents.

Costs Per Year: Application fee: $0. Area resident tuition: $1800 full-time, $75 per credit hour part-time. State resident tuition: $1800 full-time, $75 per credit hour part-time. Nonresident tuition: $5400 full-time, $225 per credit hour part-time. Mandatory fees: $576 full-time, $24 per credit hour part-time. Full-time tuition and fees vary according to location. Part-time tuition and fees vary according to location. College room and board: $4880. College room only: $2630. Room and board charges vary according to housing facility.

Collegiate Environment: Orientation program. Drama-theater group, choral group, student-run newspaper. Social organizations: 24 open to all. Most popular organizations: Criminal Justice Club, Veterinary Technology Club, Student Senate, Music Club, Rodeo Club. Major annual events: school dances, Night of Elegance (dinner/formal dance), fall Welcome Back picnic. Student services: personal-psychological counseling. Campus security: 24-hour emergency response devices, controlled dormitory access. 160 college housing spaces available. Options: coed, men-only, women-only housing available. Eastern Wyoming College Library with an OPAC and a Web page. 75 computers available on campus for general student use. A campuswide network can be accessed. Staffed computer lab on campus.

Community Environment: Torrington is located in the southeastern part of the state, and is a small western town in a rural environment. The climate is invigorating, but relatively mild.

■ **LARAMIE COUNTY COMMUNITY COLLEGE**
1400 E College Dr.
Cheyenne, WY 82007-3299
Tel: (307)778-5222; Free: 800-522-2993
Fax: (307)778-1399
E-mail: learnmore@lccc.wy.edu
Web Site: www.lccc.wy.edu/

Description: District-supported, 2-year, coed. Part of Wyoming Community College Commission. Awards certificates, transfer associate, and terminal

associate degrees. Founded 1968. Setting: 271-acre small town campus. Endowment: $15.6 million. Educational spending for the previous fiscal year: $4181 per student. Total enrollment: 5,115. Faculty: 359 (115 full-time, 244 part-time). Student-undergrad faculty ratio is 16:1. 1,582 applied, 100% were admitted. Full-time: 2,088 students, 57% women, 43% men. Part-time: 3,027 students, 57% women, 43% men. Students come from 40 states and territories, 7 other countries, 12% from out-of-state. 1% American Indian or Alaska Native, non-Hispanic/Latino; 10% Hispanic/Latino; 3% African American, non-Hispanic/Latino; 1% Asian, non-Hispanic/Latino; 0.3% Native Hawaiian or other Pacific Islander, non-Hispanic/Latino; 1% international. 42% 25 or older, 4% live on campus, 5% transferred in. Retention: 58% of full-time freshmen returned the following year. Core. Calendar: semesters. Academic remediation for entering students, ESL program, services for LD students, advanced placement, honors program, independent study, distance learning, double major, summer session for credit, part-time degree program, adult/continuing education programs, co-op programs and internships. Off campus study at Albany County Campus, Eastern Laramie County Campus, FE Warren Air Force Base. ROTC: Army (c), Air Force (c).

Entrance Requirements: Open admission except for dental hygiene, diagnostic medical sonography, emergency services - paramedic, equine studies, nursing, physical therapist assistant, radiography, surgical technology, and wind energy programs. Options: electronic application, deferred admission, international baccalaureate accepted. Required for some: high school transcript, interview. Entrance: noncompetitive. Application deadlines: Rolling, Rolling for nonresidents. Notification: continuous, continuous for nonresidents. Transfer credits accepted: Yes.

Costs Per Year: Application fee: $0. State resident tuition: $1896 full-time, $79 per credit part-time. Nonresident tuition: $5688 full-time, $237 per credit part-time. Mandatory fees: $840 full-time. Part-time tuition varies according to course load. College room and board: $7594. College room only: $4648. Room and board charges vary according to housing facility.

Collegiate Environment: Orientation program. Drama-theater group, choral group, student-run newspaper. Social organizations: 35 open to all. Major annual events: Orientation, Fall All-Campus Barbeque, Homecoming Week. Student services: personal-psychological counseling. Campus security: 24-hour emergency response devices and patrols, late night transport-escort service, controlled dormitory access. 276 college housing spaces available; 245 were occupied in 2012-13. No special consideration for freshman housing applicants. Option: coed housing available. Ludden Library plus 1 other with 56,351 books, 458 microform titles, 188 serials, 5,594 audiovisual materials, an OPAC, and a Web page. Operations spending for the previous fiscal year: $134,930. 1,090 computers available on campus for general student use. A campuswide network can be accessed from off-campus. Students can access the following: online class registration. Staffed computer lab on campus provides training in use of computers, software, and the Internet.

Community Environment: Founded in 1867, Cheyenne is the capital of Wyoming. It is located on a rolling plain at the foothills of the Rocky Mountains and has a population of 55,700. The town keeps the spirit of the"Wild West" with its well-known annual Cheyenne Frontier Days celebration held in July. The State Capitol, State Museum, and Cheyenne Art Center are features of the city.

■ **NORTHWEST COLLEGE**
231 W 6th St.
Powell, WY 82435-1898
Tel: (307)754-6000; Free: 800-560-4692
Fax: (307)754-6700
E-mail: west.hernandez@northwestcollege.edu
Web Site: www.northwestcollege.edu/

Description: State and locally supported, 2-year, coed. Part of Wyoming Community College System. Awards certificates, transfer associate, and terminal associate degrees. Founded 1946. Setting: 124-acre rural campus. Endowment: $8.3 million. Educational spending for the previous fiscal year: $2529 per student. Total enrollment: 2,047. Faculty: 194 (80 full-time, 114 part-time). Student-undergrad faculty ratio is 13:1. Full-time: 1,201 students, 56% women, 44% men. Part-time: 846 students, 67% women, 33% men. Students come from 38 states and territories, 28 other countries, 21% from out-of-state. 2% American Indian or Alaska Native, non-Hispanic/Latino; 7% Hispanic/Latino; 1% African American, non-Hispanic/Latino; 1% Asian, non-Hispanic/Latino; 0.2% Native Hawaiian or other Pacific Islander, non-Hispanic/Latino; 3% international. 27% 25 or older. Retention: 59% of full-time freshmen returned the following year. Core. Calendar: semesters. Academic remediation for entering students, ESL program, services for LD students, advanced placement, independent study, distance learning, double major, summer session for credit, part-time degree program, external degree program, adult/continuing education programs, co-op programs and internships. Off campus study at WYCLASS (Wyoming Course Locator and Support Services) consortium: institutions involved include University of Wyoming, Casper College, Central Wyoming College, Eastern Wyoming College, Laramie County Community College, Northwest College, Northern Wyoming Community College District (Sheridan and Gillette Colleges), and Western Wyoming Community College. Study abroad program.

Entrance Requirements: Open admission Nursing programs and the Equine Riding and Training program have additional admission requirements and deadlines. Option: electronic application. Required: high school transcript. Recommended: minimum 2 high school GPA, SAT or ACT, ACT COMPASS. Required for some: minimum 2 high school GPA. Entrance: noncompetitive. Application deadlines: Rolling, Rolling for nonresidents. Notification: continuous, continuous for nonresidents. Transfer credits accepted: Yes.

Costs Per Year: Application fee: $0. State resident tuition: $1800 full-time, $75 per credit hour part-time. Nonresident tuition: $5400 full-time, $225 per credit hour part-time. Mandatory fees: $637 full-time, $21 per credit hour part-time. Full-time tuition and fees vary according to course load, location, and program. Part-time tuition and fees vary according to course load, location, and program. College room and board: $4650. College room only: $2070. Room and board charges vary according to board plan and housing facility.

Collegiate Environment: Orientation program. Drama-theater group, choral group, student-run newspaper, radio station. Social organizations: Phi Theta Kappa (Honor Society). Student services: health clinic, personal-psychological counseling. Campus security: 24-hour emergency response devices and patrols, late night transport-escort service, controlled dormitory access. 794 college housing spaces available. Freshmen guaranteed college housing. On-campus residence required in freshman year. Options: coed, women-only housing available. John Taggart Hinckley Library with 47,375 books, 17,124 microform titles, 59,654 serials, 28,531 audiovisual materials, an OPAC, and a Web page. Operations spending for the previous fiscal year: $589,897. 500 computers available on campus for general student use. A campuswide network can be accessed from student residence rooms and from off campus. Students can access the following: online class registration. Staffed computer lab on campus provides training in use of computers, software, and the Internet.

■ SHERIDAN COLLEGE

3059 Coffeen Ave.
Sheridan, WY 82801-1500
Tel: (307)674-6446; Free: 800-913-9139
Fax: (307)674-7205
E-mail: madams@sheridan.edu
Web Site: www.sheridan.edu/

Description: State and locally supported, 2-year, coed. Part of Wyoming Community College Commission. Awards certificates, transfer associate, and terminal associate degrees. Founded 1948. Setting: 124-acre small town campus. System endowment: $22.6 million. Educational spending for the previous fiscal year: $8064 per student. Total enrollment: 4,236. Faculty: 197 (100 full-time, 97 part-time). Student-undergrad faculty ratio is 18:1. Full-time: 1,463 students, 57% women, 43% men. Part-time: 2,773 students, 45% women, 55% men. Students come from 41 states and territories, 7 other countries, 22% from out-of-state. 1% American Indian or Alaska Native, non-Hispanic/Latino; 6% Hispanic/Latino; 1% African American, non-Hispanic/Latino; 1% Asian, non-Hispanic/Latino; 0.1% Native Hawaiian or other Pacific Islander, non-Hispanic/Latino; 0.5% international. 34% 25 or older, 11% live on campus, 2% transferred in. Core. Calendar: semesters. Academic remediation for entering students, ESL program, services for LD students, advanced placement, accelerated degree program, independent study, distance learning, double major, summer session for credit, part-time degree program, co-op programs and internships. Off campus study.

Entrance Requirements: Open admission except for dental hygiene, nursing programs, massage therapy. Options: electronic application, early admission, deferred admission. Recommended: high school transcript. Required for some: high school transcript. Entrance: noncompetitive. Application deadlines: Rolling, Rolling for nonresidents. Notification: continuous, continuous for nonresidents. Transfer credits accepted: Yes.

Costs Per Year: Application fee: $0. State resident tuition: $2678 full-time, $79 per credit part-time. Nonresident tuition: $6470 full-time, $237 per credit part-time. Mandatory fees: $896 full-time, $28 per hour part-time. Full-time

tuition and fees vary according to course load and location. Part-time tuition and fees vary according to location. College room and board: $6050. Room and board charges vary according to board plan, housing facility, and location.

Collegiate Environment: Orientation program. Drama-theater group, choral group. Social organizations: 22 open to all. Most popular organizations: National Society of Leadership and Success, Student Senate, Baptist Collegiate Ministries, Nursing Club, Dental Hygiene Club. Major annual events: Festival of Cultures, Welcome Back Dance, Casino Night. Student services: personal-psychological counseling. Campus security: 24-hour emergency response devices, student patrols, controlled dormitory access, night patrols by certified officers. 497 college housing spaces available; 458 were occupied in 2012-13. No special consideration for freshman housing applicants. Option: coed housing available. Griffith Memorial Library plus 1 other with 47,882 books, 98 serials, 4,816 audiovisual materials, an OPAC, and a Web page. Operations spending for the previous fiscal year: $568,981. 749 computers available on campus for general student use. A campuswide network can be accessed from student residence rooms and from off campus. Students can access the following: online class registration. Staffed computer lab on campus provides training in use of computers, software, and the Internet.

Community Environment: The town of Sheridan is located in northeastern Wyoming at the foot of the scenic Big Horn Mountains. The Big Horns rise to 13,165 feet above Sheridan's 3,745-foot elevation and provide year-round opportunities for outdoor recreation from wilderness hiking to rock climbing, skiing, camping, hunting and fishing. With a population of about 16,000, Sheridan retains an atmosphere of small-town friendliness while offering its citizens many fine services. The YMCA, Sheridan Recreation District, and other organizations provide activities for all ages. The community also supports a number of high-quality programs for the visual and performing arts.

■ UNIVERSITY OF PHOENIX–CHEYENNE CAMPUS

6900 Yellowstone Rd.
Cheyenne, WY 82009
Tel: (307)632-3059; Free: 866-766-0766
Web Site: www.phoenix.edu/
Description: Proprietary, comprehensive, coed. Awards associate, bachelor's, and master's degrees.

■ UNIVERSITY OF WYOMING

1000 E University Ave.
Laramie, WY 82070
Tel: (307)766-1121; Free: 800-342-5996
Fax: (307)766-2271
E-mail: admissions@uwyo.edu
Web Site: www.uwyo.edu/
Description: State-supported, university, coed. Awards bachelor's, master's, and doctoral degrees and post-master's certificates. Founded 1886. Setting: 785-acre small town campus. System endowment: $358.5 million. Research spending for the previous fiscal year: $78.7 million. Educational spending for the previous fiscal year: $12,178 per student. Total enrollment: 12,903. Faculty: 837 (766 full-time, 71 part-time). Student-undergrad faculty ratio is 14:1. 4,181 applied, 96% were admitted. 22% from top 10% of their high school class, 52% from top quarter, 83% from top half. Full-time: 8,311 students, 49% women, 51% men. Part-time: 1,883 students, 66% women, 34% men. Students come from 50 states and territories, 69 other countries, 30% from out-of-state. 1% American Indian or Alaska Native, non-Hispanic/Latino; 5% Hispanic/Latino; 1% African American, non-Hispanic/Latino; 1% Asian, non-Hispanic/Latino; 0.2% Native Hawaiian or other Pacific Islander, non-Hispanic/Latino; 4% international. 23% 25 or older, 23% live on campus, 11% transferred in. Retention: 76% of full-time freshmen returned the following year. Academic areas with the most degrees conferred: education; business/marketing; health professions and related sciences. Core. Calendar: semesters. Services for LD students, advanced placement, accelerated degree program, self-designed majors, honors program, independent study, distance learning, double major, summer session for credit, part-time degree program, external degree program, internships, graduate courses open to undergrads. Off campus study at National Student Exchange. Study abroad program. ROTC: Army, Air Force.

Entrance Requirements: Options: electronic application, deferred admission, international baccalaureate accepted. Required: high school transcript, minimum 3 high school GPA, pre-college curriculum; minimum ACT composite of 21 or SAT of 980, SAT or ACT. Entrance: moderately difficult.

Application deadlines: 8/10, 8/10 for nonresidents. Notification: continuous, continuous for nonresidents. SAT Reasoning Test deadline: 8/10. Transfer credits accepted: Yes.

Costs Per Year: Application fee: $40. One-time mandatory fee: $40. State resident tuition: $3180 full-time, $106 per credit hour part-time. Nonresident tuition: $12,330 full-time, $411 per credit hour part-time. Mandatory fees: $1098 full-time, $262 per term part-time. Full-time tuition and fees vary according to course load, location, and reciprocity agreements. Part-time tuition and fees vary according to course load, location, and reciprocity agreements. College room and board: $9084. College room only: $3901. Room and board charges vary according to board plan and housing facility.

Collegiate Environment: Orientation program. Drama-theater group, choral group, marching band, student-run newspaper. Social organizations: 244 open to all; national fraternities, national sororities; 5% of eligible men and 4% of eligible women are members. Major annual events: Homecoming, Campus Resource Fair and Club Day, Relay for Life. Student services: legal services, health clinic, personal-psychological counseling, women's center. Campus security: 24-hour emergency response devices and patrols, student patrols, late night transport-escort service, controlled dormitory access, 24-hour front desk coverage at campus housing and at campus police. 2,620 college housing spaces available; 2,344 were occupied in 2012-13. Freshmen guaranteed college housing. On-campus residence required in freshman year. Options: coed, men-only, women-only housing available. William Robertson Coe Library plus 5 others with 3.9 million books, 2.9 million microform titles, 103,083 serials, 15,925 audiovisual materials, an OPAC, and a Web page. Operations spending for the previous fiscal year: $14.3 million. 1,536 computers available on campus for general student use. Computer purchase/lease plans available. A campuswide network can be accessed from student residence rooms and from off campus. Students can access the following: online class registration. Staffed computer lab on campus (open 24 hours a day) provides training in use of computers, software, and the Internet.

Community Environment: Named for Jacques LaRamie, an early trapper for the American Fur Company, Laramie was established in 1868. Today, the community is known as the "Gem City of the Plains." The mean annual temperature is 42 degrees. The city is accessible by air and bus lines. There are 24 churches in the area, representing 20 different religious denominations, a full-service hospital, library, and civic and fraternal organizations serving the community. Local recreation includes 2 movie theaters, bowling, golf, hunting, fishing, and nearby Snowy Range ski area. An annual rodeo and jubilee are held in July.

■ **WESTERN WYOMING COMMUNITY COLLEGE**
PO Box 428
Rock Springs, WY 82902-0428
Tel: (307)382-1600; Free: 800-226-1181
Fax: (307)382-1636
E-mail: admissions@wwcc.wy.edu
Web Site: www.wwcc.wy.edu/
Description: State and locally supported, 2-year, coed. Awards certificates, diplomas, transfer associate, and terminal associate degrees. Founded 1959. Setting: 342-acre small town campus. Endowment: $9.3 million.

Educational spending for the previous fiscal year: $2228 per student. Total enrollment: 4,120. Faculty: 218 (71 full-time, 147 part-time). Student-undergrad faculty ratio is 18:1. Full-time: 1,242 students, 56% women, 44% men. Part-time: 2,878 students, 44% women, 56% men. 11% live on campus. Core. Calendar: semesters. Academic remediation for entering students, ESL program, services for LD students, advanced placement, honors program, independent study, distance learning, double major, summer session for credit, part-time degree program, adult/continuing education programs, co-op programs and internships.

Entrance Requirements: Open admission except for nursing program. Options: electronic application, early admission, deferred admission. Required: high school transcript. Entrance: noncompetitive. Application deadline: Rolling.

Collegiate Environment: Orientation program. Drama-theater group, choral group, marching band, student-run newspaper, radio station. Social organizations: 15 open to all. Most popular organizations: Phi Theta Kappa, Students Without Borders (international club), Residence Hall Association, Associated Student Government, LDSSA. Major annual events: International Night, Kick-off Day, ASG Awards Event. Student services: personal-psychological counseling. Campus security: 24-hour emergency response devices and patrols, late night transport-escort service, controlled dormitory access, patrols by trained security personnel from 4 pm to 8 am, 24-hour patrols on weekends and holidays. Hay Library with 146,229 books, 31,224 microform titles, 14,072 serials, 4,467 audiovisual materials, an OPAC, and a Web page. Operations spending for the previous fiscal year: $380,243. 350 computers available on campus for general student use. A campuswide network can be accessed from student residence rooms and from off campus. Students can access the following: online class registration. Staffed computer lab on campus.

Community Environment: This is a rural area with a cold, dry climate. Airlines, the railroad, bus lines, and Routes 30, 1-80, and 191 make the city accessible. There are a public library, churches of major denominations, a hospital, a mental health clinic and major civic and fraternal organizations are active in the community. The city has adequate shopping facilities. Local recreation includes theatres, a drive-in, bowling, hunting, fishing, and hiking. Nearby attractions include Yellowstone and Grand Teton National Parks, Flaming Gorge National Recreation Area, the Wind River Mountains and the Bridger Wilderness. A county fair is held annually. Some part-time work is available.

■ **WYOTECH LARAMIE**
4373 N Third St.
Laramie, WY 82072-9519
Tel: (307)742-3776; Free: 888-577-7559
Web Site: www.wyotech.edu/
Description: Proprietary, 2-year, coed. Awards diplomas and terminal associate degrees. Founded 1966. Setting: rural campus. Total enrollment: 1,352. Student-undergrad faculty ratio is 13:1. 92% from out-of-state. 13% 25 or older. Retention: 87% of full-time freshmen returned the following year. Calendar: 9-month program.

Entrance Requirements: Open admission. Required: high school transcript. Entrance: noncompetitive. Application deadline: Rolling.

American Samoa

■ AMERICAN SAMOA COMMUNITY COLLEGE
PO Box 2609
Pago Pago, AS 96799-2609
Tel: (684)699-9155
Fax: (684)699-6259
E-mail: admissions@amsamoa.edu
Web Site: www.amsamoa.edu/
Description: Territory-supported, 2-year, coed. Awards certificates, transfer associate, and terminal associate degrees. Founded 1969. Setting: 20-acre rural campus. Total enrollment: 1,767. 20% 25 or older. Core. Calendar: semesters. Academic remediation for entering students, summer session for credit, part-time degree program, adult/continuing education programs. Off campus study at University of Hawaii.
Entrance Requirements: Open admission. Option: deferred admission. Entrance: noncompetitive. Application deadline: 8/1.
Collegiate Environment: Student-run newspaper. 18,000 books and 50 serials.

Guam

■ GUAM COMMUNITY COLLEGE
PO Box 23069 Guam Main Facility
Barrigada, GU 96921-3069
Tel: (671)735-4422
Fax: (671)734-5238
E-mail: patrick.clymer@guamcc.edu
Web Site: www.guamcc.net/
Description: Territory-supported, 2-year, coed. Awards certificates, diplomas, and terminal associate degrees. Founded 1977. Setting: 22-acre suburban campus. Total enrollment: 2,111. Student-undergrad faculty ratio is 15:1. 0% from out-of-territory. 44% 25 or older. Core. Calendar: semesters. Academic remediation for entering students, ESL program, services for LD students, honors program, independent study, double major, summer session for credit, part-time degree program, adult/continuing education programs, co-op programs and internships. Off campus study at University of Guam. ROTC: Army (c).
Entrance Requirements: Open admission. Option: early admission. Required: high school transcript. Entrance: noncompetitive. Application deadline: Rolling. Notification: continuous.
Collegiate Environment: Student services: health clinic, personal-psychological counseling. Campus security: 12-hour patrols by trained security personnel.

■ PACIFIC ISLANDS UNIVERSITY
172 Kinney's Rd.
Mangilao, GU 96913
Tel: (671)734-1812
Fax: (671)734-1813
E-mail: guamcampus@pibc.edu
Web Site: www.piu.edu/
Description: Independent interdenominational, 4-year, coed. Awards associate and bachelor's degrees. Founded 1976. Total enrollment: 188.

Faculty: 22 (12 full-time, 10 part-time). Student-undergrad faculty ratio is 7:1. Full-time: 132 students, 58% women, 42% men. Part-time: 56 students, 54% women, 46% men. 0% from out-of-territory. Calendar: semesters.
Entrance Requirements: Required: essay, high school transcript, 2 recommendations, interview. Application deadline: 8/25.

■ UNIVERSITY OF GUAM
303 J.U. Torres Dr.
UOG Station
Mangilao, GU 96923
Tel: (671)735-2350
Fax: (671)734-6005
E-mail: admitme@uguam.uog.edu
Web Site: www.uog.edu/
Description: Territory-supported, comprehensive, coed. Awards associate, bachelor's, and master's degrees. Founded 1952. Setting: 100-acre suburban campus. Endowment: $16.4 million. Research spending for the previous fiscal year: $11.3 million. Educational spending for the previous fiscal year: $5394 per student. Total enrollment: 3,702. Faculty: 258 (182 full-time, 76 part-time). Student-undergrad faculty ratio is 13:1. 725 applied, 94% were admitted. 21% from top 10% of their high school class, 42% from top quarter, 68% from top half. Full-time: 2,551 students, 59% women, 41% men. Part-time: 860 students, 59% women, 41% men. Students come from 36 states and territories, 24 other countries, 1% from out-of-territory. 0.1% American Indian or Alaska Native, non-Hispanic/Latino; 1% Hispanic/Latino; 0.3% African American, non-Hispanic/Latino; 41% Asian, non-Hispanic/Latino; 51% Native Hawaiian or other Pacific Islander, non-Hispanic/Latino; 1% international. 18% 25 or older, 5% live on campus, 4% transferred in. Retention: 76% of full-time freshmen returned the following year. Academic areas with the most degrees conferred: business/marketing; education; homeland security, law enforcement, firefighting, and protective services. Core. Calendar: semesters. Academic remediation for entering students, ESL program, services for LD students, advanced placement, accelerated degree program, honors program, independent study, distance learning, double major, summer session for credit, part-time degree program, co-op programs and internships, graduate courses open to undergrads. Off campus study at member of the National Student Exchange program. Study abroad program. ROTC: Army.
Entrance Requirements: Open admission. Options: electronic application, deferred admission, international baccalaureate accepted. Required: high school transcript. Entrance: noncompetitive. Application deadlines: 6/1, 6/1 for nonresidents. Notification: continuous. Transfer credits accepted: Yes.
Costs Per Year: Application fee: $49. Territory resident tuition: $4560 full-time, $190 per credit part-time. Nonresident tuition: $13,560 full-time, $565 per credit part-time. Mandatory fees: $538 full-time, $269 per term part-time. Part-time tuition and fees vary according to course load. College room only: $1880. Room charges vary according to housing facility.
Collegiate Environment: Orientation program. Drama-theater group, choral group, student-run newspaper. Social organizations: 40 open to all. Most popular organizations: American Marketing Association, Student Nurses Association of Guam, Social Work Student Alliance, GO CNMI, Association of Early Childhood Education International. Major annual events: Charter Day, Annual Student Organization Membership Drive, campus theater productions. Student services: health clinic, personal-psychological counseling. Campus security: 24-hour emergency response devices and patrols, late night transport-escort service. 182 college housing spaces available; 124

were occupied in 2012-13. Option: coed housing available. University of Guam Robert F. Kennedy Memorial Library with 315,478 books, 28,845 serials, 5,289 audiovisual materials, an OPAC, and a Web page. Operations spending for the previous fiscal year: $1.9 million. 545 computers available on campus for general student use. A campuswide network can be accessed from student residence rooms and from off campus. Students can access the following: online class registration, wireless internet access. Staffed computer lab on campus provides training in use of software and the Internet.

Northern Mariana Islands

■ NORTHERN MARIANAS COLLEGE
Box 501250
Saipan, MP 96950-1250
Tel: (670)234-3690
Fax: (670)234-0759
E-mail: leilanib@nmcnet.edu
Web Site: www.nmcnet.edu/
Description: Territory-supported, primarily 2-year, coed. Awards certificates, diplomas, transfer associate, terminal associate, and bachelor's degrees. Founded 1981. Setting: 14-acre rural campus. Total enrollment: 1,299. Faculty: 99 (49 full-time, 50 part-time). Full-time: 783 students, 67% women, 33% men. Part-time: 516 students, 61% women, 39% men. Students come from 4 states and territories, 9 other countries. 40% 25 or older. Core. Calendar: semesters. Academic remediation for entering students, ESL program, services for LD students, distance learning, summer session for credit, part-time degree program, adult/continuing education programs, co-op programs and internships.
Entrance Requirements: Open admission. Options: early admission, deferred admission. Required: high school transcript. Entrance: noncompetitive. Application deadline: Rolling.
Collegiate Environment: Orientation program. Drama-theater group. Most popular organizations: Northern Marinas Academy, Korean Association, Micronesian Club, Learning Skills. Major annual events: Charter Day, International Night, Haunted House. Student services: personal-psychological counseling. Campus security: patrols by trained security personnel. Olympia T. Borja Library plus 1 other with 39,672 books, 37,336 microform titles, 465 serials, 1,928 audiovisual materials, an OPAC, and a Web page. 56 computers available on campus for general student use. A campuswide network can be accessed from off-campus. Staffed computer lab on campus.

Puerto Rico

■ AMERICAN UNIVERSITY OF PUERTO RICO
PO Box 2037
Bayamón, PR 00960-2037
Tel: (787)620-2040
Fax: (787)785-7377
E-mail: kllanos@aupr.edu
Web Site: www.aupr.edu/
Description: Independent, comprehensive, coed. Awards associate, bachelor's, and master's degrees. Founded 1963. Setting: 21-acre urban campus with easy access to San Juan. Research spending for the previous fiscal year: $90,715. Educational spending for the previous fiscal year: $1646 per student. Total enrollment: 2,468. Faculty: 162 (41 full-time, 121 part-time). 325 applied, 83% were admitted. 3% from top 10% of their high school class, 15% from top quarter, 25% from top half. Full-time: 2,123 students, 53% women, 47% men. Part-time: 201 students, 66% women, 34% men. 0% from out-of-commonwealth. 100% Hispanic/Latino. Retention: 80% of full-time freshmen returned the following year. Calendar: semesters. ESL program, services for LD students, advanced placement, freshman honors college, honors program, independent study, distance learning, double major, summer session for credit, part-time degree program, adult/continuing education programs, co-op programs and internships. ROTC: Army (c).
Entrance Requirements: Open admission. Options: electronic application, deferred admission. Required: high school transcript. Recommended: SAT, SAT and SAT Subject Tests or ACT, SAT Subject Tests. Entrance: noncompetitive. Notification: continuous. Transfer credits accepted: Yes.
Costs Per Year: Application fee: $25. Tuition: $4272 full-time, $178 per

credit hour part-time. Mandatory fees: $1075 full-time. Full-time tuition and fees vary according to class time and course load. Part-time tuition and fees vary according to class time and course load.
Collegiate Environment: Drama-theater group. Most popular organizations: Business Student Association, Information Systems Student Association, Accounting Student Association, Library Club, Office Systems Student Association. Major annual events: NCAA Tournaments, Manual Arts Fair. Student services: health clinic. Campus security: 24-hour patrols. College housing not available. Loida Figueroa Meacado with 100,000 books, 231 serials, and 2,091 audiovisual materials. Operations spending for the previous fiscal year: $666,872. 359 computers available on campus for general student use. A campuswide network can be accessed. Students can access the following: 8 Wifi access points. Staffed computer lab on campus provides training in use of computers, software, and the Internet.

■ ATLANTIC UNIVERSITY COLLEGE
PO Box 3918
Guaynabo, PR 00970
Tel: (787)720-1022
Fax: (787)720-1092
E-mail: admisiones@atlanticcollege.edu
Web Site: www.atlanticu.edu/
Description: Independent, comprehensive, coed. Awards associate, bachelor's, and master's degrees. Total enrollment: 1,236. 11% 25 or older. Calendar: semesters. Part-time degree program, internships.
Entrance Requirements: Open admission. Required: high school transcript. Required for some: interview. Notification: continuous.
Collegiate Environment: Orientation program. Resources Center with 8,663 books, 85 serials, and 412 audiovisual materials.

■ BAYAMÓN CENTRAL UNIVERSITY
PO Box 1725
Bayamón, PR 00960-1725
Tel: (787)786-3030
E-mail: chernandez@ucb.edu.pr
Web Site: www.ucb.edu.pr/
Description: Independent Roman Catholic, comprehensive, coed. Awards associate, bachelor's, and master's degrees. Founded 1970. Setting: 55-acre suburban campus with easy access to San Juan. Endowment: $1.4 million. Educational spending for the previous fiscal year: $1267 per student. Total enrollment: 1,202. Faculty: 153 (39 full-time, 114 part-time). 1,068 applied, 38% were admitted. Full-time: 857 students, 67% women, 33% men. Part-time: 81 students, 67% women, 33% men. 43% 25 or older. Academic areas with the most degrees conferred: business/marketing; education; health professions and related sciences. Core. Calendar: semesters for undergraduate programs, trimesters for graduate programs. Academic remediation for entering students, ESL program, services for LD students, advanced placement, accelerated degree program, self-designed majors, honors program, independent study, summer session for credit, part-time degree program, adult/continuing education programs, internships. ROTC: Army (c), Air Force (c).
Entrance Requirements: Option: international baccalaureate accepted. Required: high school transcript, medical history, College Examination Entrance Board Test. Recommended: minimum 2 high school GPA. Required for some: interview. Entrance: moderately difficult. Transfer credits accepted: Yes.
Costs Per Year: Application fee: $25. Tuition: $7490 full-time, $165 per credit part-time. Mandatory fees: $710 full-time, $165 per credit part-time, $350. Full-time tuition and fees vary according to course level, degree level, and program. Part-time tuition and fees vary according to course level, degree level, and program.
Collegiate Environment: Orientation program. Choral group, student-run newspaper. Student services: legal services, health clinic, personal-psychological counseling. Campus security: 24-hour patrols. BCU Library plus 1 other with 51,011 books, 336 microform titles, 3,027 serials, 900 audiovisual materials, and an OPAC.

■ CARIBBEAN UNIVERSITY
Box 493
Bayamón, PR 00960-0493
Tel: (787)780-0070
Fax: (787)785-0101
Web Site: www.caribbean.edu/
Description: Independent, comprehensive, coed. Awards associate,

bachelor's, and master's degrees. Founded 1969. Setting: 16-acre urban campus with easy access to San Juan. Endowment: $321,559. Research spending for the previous fiscal year: $22.4 million. Educational spending for the previous fiscal year: $1302 per student. Total enrollment: 5,846. Faculty: 424 (77 full-time, 347 part-time). Student-undergrad faculty ratio is 20:1. 987 applied, 80% were admitted. Full-time: 3,572 students, 60% women, 40% men. Part-time: 1,173 students, 56% women, 44% men. Students come from 4 states and territories, 0% from out-of-commonwealth. 100% Hispanic/Latino. Academic areas with the most degrees conferred: health professions and related sciences; business/marketing; engineering. Core. Calendar: trimesters. Academic remediation for entering students, ESL program, services for LD students, accelerated degree program, summer session for credit, part-time degree program, adult/continuing education programs. ROTC: Army (c).

Entrance Requirements: Open admission except for post-associate degree programs. Options: deferred admission, international baccalaureate accepted. Required: high school transcript. Required for some: 1 recommendation, interview, Only for the engineering applicants, we request test for verbal and math attitude offer by the College Board. Entrance: minimally difficult. Application deadline: Rolling. Transfer credits accepted: Yes.

Costs Per Year: Application fee: $30. Comprehensive fee: $13,465 includes full-time tuition ($4080), mandatory fees ($385), and college room and board ($9000). College room only: $5000. Full-time tuition and fees vary according to program. Part-time tuition: $170 per credit hour. Part-time mandatory fees: $225 per term. Part-time tuition and fees vary according to program.

Collegiate Environment: Drama-theater group, choral group. Social organizations: 12 open to all; Student Professional Association; 5% of eligible men and 6% of eligible women are members. Most popular organizations: Engineering Student Association, Nursing, Social Work, Speech Therapy, Physical Education. Major annual events: Jobs Fairs, Health Fairs, Athletic Tournament. Student services: health clinic, personal-psychological counseling. Campus security: 24-hour patrols. Biblioteca Virgilio Davila, Recinto de Bayamon with 133,345 books, 153 serials, 1,193 audiovisual materials, an OPAC, and a Web page. Operations spending for the previous fiscal year: $939,962.

■ **CARLOS ALBIZU UNIVERSITY**
151 Tanca St.
San Juan, PR 00901
Tel: (787)725-6500
Fax: (787)721-7187
E-mail: crodriguez@albizu.edu
Web Site: www.albizu.edu/

Description: Independent, university, coed. Awards bachelor's, master's, and doctoral degrees. Founded 1966. Setting: urban campus. Endowment: $732,270. Research spending for the previous fiscal year: $419,213. Total enrollment: 930. Faculty: 21 (2 full-time, 19 part-time). Student-undergrad faculty ratio is 8:1. 40 applied, 88% were admitted. Full-time: 84 students, 92% women, 8% men. Part-time: 78 students, 81% women, 19% men. 1% from out-of-commonwealth. 0% American Indian or Alaska Native, non-Hispanic/Latino; 62% Hispanic/Latino; 0% African American, non-Hispanic/Latino; 0% Asian, non-Hispanic/Latino; 0% Native Hawaiian or other Pacific Islander, non-Hispanic/Latino; 0% international. 38% 25 or older, 65% transferred in. Academic areas with the most degrees conferred: health professions and related sciences; psychology. Core. Calendar: semesters. Independent study, part-time degree program, co-op programs.

Entrance Requirements: Options: early admission, deferred admission, international baccalaureate accepted. Required: minimum 2 high school GPA, 1 recommendation, CEEB or SAT. Required for some: health certificate, Good Conduct Crete, official university transcript. Entrance: noncompetitive. Application deadline: 7/16. Notification: continuous. Transfer credits accepted: Yes.

Costs Per Year: Application fee: $0. Tuition: $5940 full-time, $165 per credit part-time. Mandatory fees: $979 full-time, $333 per term part-time.

Collegiate Environment: Orientation program. Social organizations: 3 open to all. Most popular organizations: Student Council, Community Services, Gender and Sexual Diversity Organization. Major annual events: Student's Welcome Activity, Christmas Activity, seminars with external resources. Campus security: 24-hour emergency response devices, late night transport-escort service, security cameras. College housing not available. Carlos Albizu Miranda plus 1 other with 22,307 books, 255 serials, 1,611 audiovisual materials, an OPAC, and a Web page. Operations spending for the previous fiscal year: $220,223. 55 computers available on campus for

general student use. A campuswide network can be accessed. Staffed computer lab on campus provides training in use of computers, software, and the Internet.

■ **THE CENTER OF CINEMATOGRAPHY, ARTS AND TELEVISION**
51 Dr. Veve St., Degetau St. Corner
Bayamon, PR 00960
Tel: (787)779-2500
Web Site: ccatmiami.com/
Description: Proprietary, 2-year, coed.

■ **CENTRO DE ESTUDIOS MULTIDISCIPLINARIOS**
Calle 13 No.1206
Ext. San Agustin
Rio Piedras, PR 00926
Tel: (787)765-4210; Free: 877-779-CDEM
Web Site: www.cempr.edu/

■ **COLEGIO UNIVERSITARIO DE SAN JUAN**
180 Jose R Oliver St.
Tres Monjitas Industrial Park
San Juan, PR 00918
Tel: (787)250-7111
Fax: (787)250-7395
Web Site: www.cunisanjuan.edu/

Description: City-supported, 4-year, coed. Awards associate and bachelor's degrees. Founded 1971. Setting: 5-acre urban campus. Total enrollment: 1,785. Student-undergrad faculty ratio is 16:1. 548 applied, 100% were admitted. 0% from out-of-commonwealth. 48% 25 or older. Retention: 48% of full-time freshmen returned the following year. Calendar: semesters. Academic remediation for entering students, ESL program, services for LD students, independent study, summer session for credit, part-time degree program, co-op programs and internships. Off campus study at Inter American University of Puerto Rico.

Entrance Requirements: Required: high school transcript, minimum 2.0 high school GPA, medical history. Required for some: interview, SAT. Entrance: noncompetitive. Notification: continuous.

Collegiate Environment: Orientation program. Campus security: 24-hour patrols. Access to Information Center with an OPAC and a Web page.

■ **COLUMBIA CENTRO UNIVERSITARIO (CAGUAS)**
PO Box 8517
Caguas, PR 00726
Tel: (787)743-4041
Fax: (787)744-7931
E-mail: xsanchez@columbianco.edu
Web Site: www.columbiaco.edu/

Description: Proprietary, comprehensive, coed. Awards associate, bachelor's, and master's degrees. Founded 1966. Setting: 6-acre urban campus with easy access to San Juan. Educational spending for the previous fiscal year: $1746 per student. Total enrollment: 1,744. Faculty: 127 (23 full-time, 104 part-time). Student-undergrad faculty ratio is 25:1. 740 applied, 73% were admitted. Full-time: 668 students, 67% women, 33% men. Part-time: 948 students, 71% women, 29% men. 0% from out-of-commonwealth. 0% 25 or older. Retention: 57% of full-time freshmen returned the following year. Academic areas with the most degrees conferred: health professions and related sciences; business/marketing. Core. Calendar: semesters. Accelerated degree program, part-time degree program.

Entrance Requirements: Option: electronic application. Required: high school transcript. Required for some: essay, minimum 2 high school GPA, 3 recommendations, interview. Entrance: noncompetitive. Application deadline: Rolling. Notification: continuous. Transfer credits accepted: Yes.

Costs Per Year: Application fee: $50. Tuition: $9435 full-time, $1575 per semester hour part-time. Mandatory fees: $262 per credit hour part-time. Full-time tuition varies according to class time, degree level, and program. Part-time tuition and fees vary according to class time, degree level, and program.

Collegiate Environment: Student services: personal-psychological counseling. Campus security: 24-hour patrols. College housing not available. Efrain Sola Bezares Library with 165 serials, an OPAC, and a Web page. Operations spending for the previous fiscal year: $154,827. 136 computers available on campus for general student use. A campuswide network can be accessed from off-campus. Students can access the following: online class registration. Staffed computer lab on campus.

■ COLUMBIA CENTRO UNIVERSITARIO (YAUCO)

Calle Betances No.3
Box 3062
Yauco, PR 00698
Tel: (787)856-0945
Fax: (787)267-2335
E-mail: cipabon@columbiaco.edu
Web Site: www.columbiaco.edu/

Description: Proprietary, 4-year, coed. Administratively affiliated with Columbia Centro Universitario, Recinto Caguas. Awards associate and bachelor's degrees. Founded 1976. Setting: urban campus. Educational spending for the previous fiscal year: $1937 per student. Total enrollment: 363. Faculty: 39 (9 full-time, 30 part-time). Student-undergrad faculty ratio is 13:1. Full-time: 181 students, 77% women, 23% men. Part-time: 182 students, 77% women, 23% men. 0% from out-of-commonwealth. 100% Hispanic/Latino. 30% 25 or older. Retention: 0% of full-time freshmen returned the following year. Academic area with the most degrees conferred: health professions and related sciences. Core. Calendar: trimesters. Independent study, distance learning, part-time degree program, co-op programs.

Entrance Requirements: Open admission. Option: electronic application. Required: high school transcript, minimum 2 high school GPA. Required for some: interview. Entrance: minimally difficult. Application deadline: Rolling. Notification: continuous. Transfer credits accepted: Yes.

Costs Per Year: Application fee: $50. Tuition: $9435 full-time, $1575 per semester hour part-time. Mandatory fees: $100 full-time. Full-time tuition and fees vary according to course load and program. Part-time tuition and fees vary according to course load and program.

Collegiate Environment: Orientation program. Social organizations: 2 open to all. Most popular organizations: Nursing Group, Librarian Group. Major annual events: Columbia Night, Columbia Fest. Student services: personal-psychological counseling. Campus security: 24-hour patrols. College housing not available. Centro de Informacion y Recursos Integrados Recinto de Yauco with 6,061 books, 684 serials, 166 audiovisual materials, an OPAC, and a Web page. Operations spending for the previous fiscal year: $103,218. 14 computers available on campus for general student use. from off-campusStaffed computer lab on campus provides training in use of computers, software, and the Internet.

■ CONSERVATORIO DE MUSICA

951 Ave. Ponce de León
Esquina F. D. Roosevelt
San Juan, PR 00907
Tel: (787)751-0160
E-mail: ihernandez@cmpr.gobierno.pr
Web Site: www.cmpr.edu/

Description: Public, comprehensive, coed. Awards bachelor's and master's degrees. Setting: 4-acre urban campus with easy access to Old San Juan. Endowment: $901,073. Total enrollment: 463. Faculty: 91 (50 full-time, 41 part-time). Student-undergrad faculty ratio is 7:1. 141 applied, 58% were admitted. Full-time: 300 students, 30% women, 70% men. Part-time: 121 students, 30% women, 70% men. Students come from 4 states and territories, 7 other countries, 1% from out-of-commonwealth. 91% Hispanic/Latino; 9% international. 19% 25 or older, 8% transferred in. Retention: 70% of full-time freshmen returned the following year. Academic areas with the most degrees conferred: visual and performing arts; education. Core. Academic remediation for entering students, ESL program, advanced placement, honors program, summer session for credit, part-time degree program, co-op programs. Off campus study at Sacred Heart University Consortium on curses in business.

Entrance Requirements: Option: international baccalaureate accepted. Required: high school transcript, minimum 2 high school GPA, instrument audition; ear training test. Recommended: interview. Required for some: essay, minimum 2.5 high school GPA. Entrance: moderately difficult. Application deadlines: 12/15, 12/15 for nonresidents. Notification: 3/1, 3/1 for nonresidents. Transfer credits accepted: Yes.

Costs Per Year: Application fee: $75. Commonwealth resident tuition: $1920 full-time, $80 per credit part-time. Nonresident tuition: $1920 full-time, $80 per credit part-time. Mandatory fees: $850 full-time, $425 per term part-time. Full-time tuition and fees vary according to course load and degree level. Part-time tuition and fees vary according to course load and degree level. College room and board: $10,000. College room only: $4600.

Collegiate Environment: Orientation program. Choral group. Campus security: 24-hour patrols. Biblioteca Amaury Veray plus 1 other with 39,995 books, 10 microform titles, 87 serials, 8,443 audiovisual materials, and an OPAC. Operations spending for the previous fiscal year: $317,055. 43 computers available on campus for general student use. A campuswide network can be accessed from off-campus. Students can access the following: online class registration. Staffed computer lab on campus provides training in use of computers, software, and the Internet.

■ CONSERVATORY OF MUSIC OF PUERTO RICO

350 Rafael Lamar St. at FDR Ave.
San Juan, PR 00918
Tel: (787)751-0160
E-mail: admisiones@cmpr.edu
Web Site: www.cmpr.edu/

Description: Commonwealth-supported, comprehensive, coed. Awards bachelor's and master's degrees. Founded 1959. Setting: 6-acre urban campus. Total enrollment: 386. 110 applied. 19% 25 or older. Calendar: semesters. Academic remediation for entering students, advanced placement, summer session for credit, part-time degree program, co-op programs. Off campus study at Sacred Heart University. ROTC: Army (c).

Entrance Requirements: Option: early admission. Required: high school transcript, minimum 2.0 high school GPA, interview, audition, music and theory examinations, SAT, SAT Subject Tests. Required for some: essay, minimum 2.5 high school GPA. Entrance: moderately difficult. Application deadline: 3/6.

Collegiate Environment: Student services: health clinic, personal-psychological counseling. Campus security: 24-hour patrols. Anaurg Veray Music Library plus 1 other with 24,865 books, 19 microform titles, 75 serials, 4,910 audiovisual materials, and an OPAC.

■ EDP UNIVERSITY OF PUERTO RICO

560 Ave. Ponce de Leon
Hato Rey, PR 00918
Tel: (787)765-3560
E-mail: ecartagena@edpuniversity.edu
Web Site: www.edpuniversity.edu/

Description: Proprietary, comprehensive, coed. Awards associate, bachelor's, and master's degrees. Founded 1968. Setting: 1-acre urban campus with easy access to San Juan. Research spending for the previous fiscal year: $264,740. Educational spending for the previous fiscal year: $1900 per student. Total enrollment: 1,198. Faculty: 93 (28 full-time, 65 part-time). Student-undergrad faculty ratio is 15:1. 211 applied, 66% were admitted. Full-time: 724 students, 65% women, 35% men. Part-time: 417 students, 66% women, 34% men. Students come from 5 states and territories, 11% from out-of-commonwealth. 62% 25 or older, 18% transferred in. Retention: 89% of full-time freshmen returned the following year. Academic areas with the most degrees conferred: business/marketing; computer and information sciences; communication technologies. Core. Calendar: semesters. Academic remediation for entering students, ESL program, services for LD students, advanced placement, accelerated degree program, independent study, distance learning, summer session for credit, part-time degree program, adult/continuing education programs, co-op programs and internships, graduate courses open to undergrads.

Entrance Requirements: Open admission. Options: electronic application, early admission, early decision, early action, deferred admission, international baccalaureate accepted. Required: high school transcript, minimum 1.6 high school GPA, placement test or College Board test, vaccination certificate, social security number, College Entrance Examination Board (CEEB) Test, Institutional Admission Exam. Recommended: minimum 2 high school GPA. Required for some: essay, minimum 2.5 high school GPA, 7 recommendations, interview, placement test or College Board test, vaccination certificate, social security number. Entrance: minimally difficult. Application deadlines: Rolling, Rolling for nonresidents. Transfer credits accepted: Yes. Applicants placed on waiting list: 30. Wait-listed applicants offered admission: 13. Early decision applicants: 244. Early decision applicants admitted: 157. Early action applicants: 244. Early action applicants admitted: 157.

Costs Per Year: Application fee: $15. Tuition: $5400 full-time, $170 per credit hour part-time. Mandatory fees: $840 full-time, $170 per credit hour part-time, $420. Full-time tuition and fees vary according to course load and program. Part-time tuition and fees vary according to course load and program.

Collegiate Environment: Social organizations: 5 open to all; 40% of eligible men and 80% of eligible women are members. Most popular organizations: Student Council, Graduate Student Association, JCI San Juan, Dance

Group. Major annual events: I Put My Hands Up Against Violence, Arts Exhibits, Honor Roll. Student services: personal-psychological counseling. Campus security: 24-hour emergency response devices, student patrols, late night transport-escort service, security and emergency telephones in working hours. College housing not available. Centro de Recursos para la Informacion with 13,695 books, 144 serials, 1,003 audiovisual materials, and an OPAC. Operations spending for the previous fiscal year: $295,483. 239 computers available on campus for general student use. A campuswide network can be accessed. Students can access the following: online class registration. Staffed computer lab on campus provides training in use of computers, software, and the Internet.

■ **EDP UNIVERSITY OF PUERTO RICO–SAN SEBASTIAN**

Ave. Betances No.49
San Sebastian, PR 00685
Tel: (787)896-2137
Fax: (787)896-0066
E-mail: pcordero@edpcollege.edu
Web Site: www.edpuniversity.edu/

Description: Proprietary, 4-year, coed. Awards associate and bachelor's degrees. Founded 1976. Setting: rural campus. Research spending for the previous fiscal year: $290,526. Educational spending for the previous fiscal year: $1261 per student. Total enrollment: 881. Faculty: 82 (19 full-time, 63 part-time). Student-undergrad faculty ratio is 17:1. 67 applied, 94% were admitted. Full-time: 605 students, 61% women, 39% men. Part-time: 276 students, 67% women, 33% men. Retention: 44% of full-time freshmen returned the following year. Academic areas with the most degrees conferred: health professions and related sciences; business/marketing; computer and information sciences. Core. Calendar: semesters. Academic remediation for entering students, ESL program, services for LD students, advanced placement, accelerated degree program, independent study, distance learning, summer session for credit, part-time degree program, adult/continuing education programs, co-op programs and internships.

Entrance Requirements: Open admission. Required: high school transcript, minimum 2 high school GPA, College Board or institutional entrance test. Required for some: minimum 2.5 high school GPA, interview. Entrance: minimally difficult. Application deadlines: Rolling, Rolling for nonresidents. Transfer credits accepted: Yes.

Costs Per Year: Application fee: $15. Tuition: $5400 full-time, $156 per credit hour part-time. Mandatory fees: $720 full-time, $156 per credit hour part-time, $360 per term part-time. Full-time tuition and fees vary according to course load and program. Part-time tuition and fees vary according to course load and program.

Collegiate Environment: Drama-theater group. Major annual events: Honor Wall, Student's Associations Iniciation. Student services: personal-psychological counseling. Juan S. Robles with 11,444 books, 78 serials, 1,112 audiovisual materials, an OPAC, and a Web page. Operations spending for the previous fiscal year: $363,153. 125 computers available on campus for general student use. A campuswide network can be accessed. Students can access the following: online class registration. Staffed computer lab on campus provides training in use of computers, software, and the Internet.

■ **ESCUELA DE ARTES PLASTICAS DE PUERTO RICO**

PO Box 9021112
San Juan, PR 00902-1112
Tel: (787)725-8120
E-mail: nmelendez@eap.edu
Web Site: www.eap.edu/

Description: Commonwealth-supported, 4-year, coed. Administratively affiliated with Puerto Rican Institute of Culture. Awards bachelor's degrees. Founded 1966. Setting: urban campus. Endowment: $1.3 million. Research spending for the previous fiscal year: $49,538. Educational spending for the previous fiscal year: $3302 per student. Total enrollment: 527. Faculty: 60 (16 full-time, 44 part-time). Student-undergrad faculty ratio is 13:1. 119 applied, 72% were admitted. Full-time: 324 students, 61% women, 39% men. Part-time: 203 students, 55% women, 45% men. Students come from 1 other country, 0% from out-of-commonwealth. 99% Hispanic/Latino; 0.2% international. 23% 25 or older, 8% transferred in. Retention: 86% of full-time freshmen returned the following year. Academic areas with the most degrees conferred: visual and performing arts; education. Core. Calendar: 3 semesters each calendar year; participant in Year Round Pell. Services for LD students, advanced placement, accelerated degree program, part-time degree program, adult/continuing education programs, internships. Off campus study.

Entrance Requirements: Option: international baccalaureate accepted. Required: essay, high school transcript, minimum 2 high school GPA, interview, The applicants must approve an evaluation regarding artistic skills through a portfolio or seminar and complete the security seminar. Recommended: 1 recommendation, SAT. Entrance: moderately difficult. Application deadlines: 7/2, 6/10 for nonresidents. Notification: 7/30, 7/30 for nonresidents. Transfer credits accepted: Yes.

Collegiate Environment: Orientation program. Social organizations: 2 open to all. Most popular organizations: student government, Literary magazine. Major annual events: Students' expositions, Health Fair, Music ensembles. Student services: personal-psychological counseling. Campus security: 24-hour emergency response devices and patrols, security cameras and institutional police of privacy. Francisco Oller Library with 31,915 books, 29,774 microform titles, 75 serials, 8,832 audiovisual materials, and an OPAC. Operations spending for the previous fiscal year: $161,584. 120 computers available on campus for general student use. Students can access the following: library online catalog, wireless access. Staffed computer lab on campus provides training in use of computers, software, and the Internet.

■ **HUERTAS JUNIOR COLLEGE**

PO Box 8429
Caguas, PR 00726
Tel: (787)743-2156
E-mail: huertas@huertas.org
Web Site: www.huertas.edu/

Description: Proprietary, 2-year, coed. Awards certificates and terminal associate degrees. Founded 1945. Setting: 4-acre urban campus with easy access to San Juan. Total enrollment: 1,843. Core. Calendar: trimesters. Academic remediation for entering students, ESL program, part-time degree program, internships.

Entrance Requirements: Open admission. Option: deferred admission. Required for some: minimum 2.0 high school GPA. Application deadline: Rolling. Notification: continuous.

Collegiate Environment: Choral group. Student services: health clinic. Campus security: 24-hour patrols. Learning Resources Center with 5,524 books and 1,144 serials.

■ **HUMACAO COMMUNITY COLLEGE**

PO Box 9139
Humacao, PR 00792
Tel: (787)852-1430
Fax: (787)850-1760
Web Site: www.hccpr.edu/

Description: Independent, 2-year, coed. Awards certificates, diplomas, and terminal associate degrees. Total enrollment: 758. 34% 25 or older. Calendar: trimesters. Academic remediation for entering students, ESL program, services for LD students, internships.

Entrance Requirements: Open admission. Option: early admission. Required: high school transcript. Entrance: noncompetitive. Notification: continuous.

Collegiate Environment: Student services: personal-psychological counseling. Campus security: 24-hour emergency response devices and patrols.

■ **INSTITUTO COMERCIAL DE PUERTO RICO JUNIOR COLLEGE**

558 Munoz Rivera Ave.
San Juan, PR 00919-0304
Tel: (787)753-6000
Fax: (787)763-7249
Web Site: www.icprjc.edu/

Description: Proprietary, 2-year, coed. Awards certificates, diplomas, and terminal associate degrees. Founded 1946. Setting: 1-acre urban campus. Total enrollment: 602. Faculty: 89 (34 full-time, 55 part-time). Student-undergrad faculty ratio is 17:1. 1% from out-of-commonwealth. Core. Calendar: trimesters. ESL program, independent study, double major, part-time degree program, adult/continuing education programs. ROTC: Army (c).

Entrance Requirements: Option: early admission. Required: high school transcript, interview, proficiency in Spanish. Entrance: minimally difficult. Notification: continuous.

Collegiate Environment: Student services: personal-psychological counseling. Campus security: 24-hour emergency response devices. Pedro Negron Library plus 1 other with 40,858 books, 173 serials, and 320 audiovisual materials. Operations spending for the previous fiscal year: $176,910. 76 computers available on campus for general student use. Staffed computer lab on campus.

■ INTER AMERICAN UNIVERSITY OF PUERTO RICO, AGUADILLA CAMPUS

Call Box 20000
Aguadilla, PR 00605
Tel: (787)891-0925
Web Site: www.aguadilla.inter.edu/

Description: Independent, comprehensive, coed. Part of Inter American University of Puerto Rico. Awards associate, bachelor's, and master's degrees. Founded 1957. Setting: 50-acre small town campus. Endowment: $151.5 million. Educational spending for the previous fiscal year: $2250 per student. Total enrollment: 4,626. Faculty: 264 (80 full-time, 184 part-time). Student-undergrad faculty ratio is 29:1. 1,266 applied, 67% were admitted. Full-time: 3,612 students, 54% women, 46% men. Part-time: 715 students, 53% women, 47% men. Students come from 28 states and territories, 2% from out-of-commonwealth. 99% Hispanic/Latino; 0.02% Asian, non-Hispanic/Latino. 25% 25 or older, 3% transferred in. Retention: 55% of full-time freshmen returned the following year. Academic areas with the most degrees conferred: business/marketing; education; public administration and social services. Core. Calendar: semesters. Academic remediation for entering students, services for LD students, advanced placement, honors program, independent study, distance learning, double major, summer session for credit, part-time degree program, external degree program, adult/continuing education programs, co-op programs and internships. ROTC: Army, Air Force.

Entrance Requirements: Options: electronic application, international baccalaureate accepted. Required: high school transcript, minimum 2 high school GPA, SAT or ACT, PAA. Entrance: moderately difficult. Application deadline: Rolling. Transfer credits accepted: Yes.

Costs Per Year: Application fee: $0. Tuition: $5100 full-time. Mandatory fees: $514 full-time.

Collegiate Environment: Orientation program. Drama-theater group, choral group, student-run newspaper. Social organizations: 23 open to all. Most popular organizations: Criminal Justice Association, Social Workers Association, Nursing Association, Microbiot Science Association, Hotel and Management Association. Major annual events: Peace March, Open House, Christmas Concert. Student services: health clinic, personal-psychological counseling, women's center. Campus security: 24-hour emergency response devices and patrols. College housing not available. Manuel Mendez Ballester Information Access Center with 61,452 books, 2,662 microform titles, 215 serials, 11,576 audiovisual materials, an OPAC, and a Web page. Operations spending for the previous fiscal year: $177,451. 716 computers available on campus for general student use. A campuswide network can be accessed from off-campus. Students can access the following: online class registration. Staffed computer lab on campus provides training in use of computers, software, and the Internet.

■ INTER AMERICAN UNIVERSITY OF PUERTO RICO, ARECIBO CAMPUS

PO Box 4050
Arecibo, PR 00614-4050
Tel: (787)878-5475
Fax: (787)880-1624
E-mail: pmontalvo@arecibo.inter.edu
Web Site: www.arecibo.inter.edu/

Description: Independent, comprehensive, coed. Part of Inter American University of Puerto Rico. Awards associate, bachelor's, and master's degrees. Founded 1957. Setting: 20-acre urban campus with easy access to San Juan. Total enrollment: 4,878. Faculty: 298 (88 full-time, 210 part-time). Student-undergrad faculty ratio is 24:1. 2,511 applied. Full-time: 3,789 students, 60% women, 40% men. Part-time: 758 students, 63% women, 37% men. Students come from 3 states and territories. 27% 25 or older, 4% transferred in. Retention: 74% of full-time freshmen returned the following year. Academic areas with the most degrees conferred: education; business/marketing; public administration and social services. Core. Calendar: semesters. Academic remediation for entering students, services for LD students, advanced placement, honors program, independent study, distance learning, summer session for credit, part-time degree program, external degree program, adult/continuing education programs, internships, graduate courses open to undergrads. Off campus study. Study abroad program. ROTC: Army (c).

Entrance Requirements: Options: electronic application, early admission, deferred admission. Required: high school transcript, minimum 2 high school GPA, PAA, CEEB. Recommended: minimum 3 high school GPA. Required for some: interview. Entrance: moderately difficult. Application deadline: Rolling. Transfer credits accepted: Yes.

Collegiate Environment: Orientation program. Drama-theater group. Social organizations: 18 open to all; local fraternities, local sororities; 30% of eligible men and 70% of eligible women are members. Most popular organizations: Circulo Futuros Trabajadores Sociales, Asociacion Estudiantes Justicia Criminal, Asociacion Futuros Maestros, Compania Teatro Ciclorama. Major annual events: Festival de la Voz, Festival de Teatro Internacional. Student services: health clinic, personal-psychological counseling. Campus security: 24-hour emergency response devices and patrols. Information Access Center Rene Marquez with 73,642 books, 640 serials, 29,267 audiovisual materials, an OPAC, and a Web page. 461 computers available on campus for general student use. A campuswide network can be accessed from off-campus. Students can access the following: online class registration. Staffed computer lab on campus provides training in use of computers, software, and the Internet.

■ INTER AMERICAN UNIVERSITY OF PUERTO RICO, BARRANQUITAS CAMPUS

PO Box 517
Barranquitas, PR 00794
Tel: (787)857-3600
Fax: (787)857-2284
E-mail: acartagena@br.inter.edu
Web Site: www.br.inter.edu/

Description: Independent, comprehensive, coed. Part of Inter American University of Puerto Rico. Awards associate, bachelor's, and master's degrees. Founded 1957. Setting: small town campus with easy access to San Juan. Educational spending for the previous fiscal year: $4100 per student. Total enrollment: 2,418. Faculty: 135 (41 full-time, 94 part-time). Student-undergrad faculty ratio is 29:1. 306 applied, 73% were admitted. 0% from out-of-commonwealth. Retention: 65% of full-time freshmen returned the following year. Core. Calendar: semesters. Academic remediation for entering students, ESL program, advanced placement, summer session for credit, part-time degree program, adult/continuing education programs. ROTC: Army (c).

Entrance Requirements: Option: deferred admission. Required: high school transcript, interview, CEEB. Required for some: SAT or ACT. Entrance: moderately difficult. Application deadline: 5/15.

Collegiate Environment: Orientation program. Drama-theater group. Most popular organization: Alumni Student Chapter. Major annual events: Relief for Life Cancer Association (Relevo por la Vida), Puerto Rico Heart Association (Caminata del Corazon). Campus security: 24-hour patrols. Luis Munoz Marin Center of Information Access plus 1 other with 32,863 books, 224 serials, and 1,280 audiovisual materials. Operations spending for the previous fiscal year: $135,778. 464 computers available on campus for general student use. Computer purchase/lease plans available. A campuswide network can be accessed. Students can access the following: online class registration. Staffed computer lab on campus (open 24 hours a day) provides training in use of computers, software, and the Internet.

■ INTER AMERICAN UNIVERSITY OF PUERTO RICO, BAYAMÓN CAMPUS

500 Rd. 830
Bayamón, PR 00957
Tel: (787)279-1912
Fax: (787)279-2205
E-mail: calicea@bayamon.inter.edu
Web Site: www.bc.inter.edu/

Description: Independent, comprehensive, coed. Part of Inter American University of Puerto Rico. Awards associate, bachelor's, and master's degrees. Founded 1912. Setting: 51-acre urban campus with easy access to San Juan. System endowment: $151.5 million. Research spending for the previous fiscal year: $915,168. Educational spending for the previous fiscal year: $2899 per student. Total enrollment: 4,915. Faculty: 329 (101 full-time, 228 part-time). Student-undergrad faculty ratio is 24:1. 2,463 applied, 36% were admitted. Full-time: 4,129 students, 46% women, 54% men. Part-time: 653 students, 41% women, 59% men. 0% from out-of-commonwealth. 94% Hispanic/Latino; 0.04% African American, non-Hispanic/Latino. 17% 25 or older, 3% transferred in. Retention: 68% of full-time freshmen returned the following year. Academic areas with the most degrees conferred: business/

marketing; health professions and related sciences; engineering. Core. Calendar: semesters. Services for LD students, advanced placement, accelerated degree program, honors program, independent study, distance learning, summer session for credit, part-time degree program, external degree program, adult/continuing education programs, co-op programs and internships. ROTC: Army (c).

Entrance Requirements: Option: electronic application. Required: high school transcript, minimum 2 high school GPA, 2.5 GPA for engineering programs, CEEB. Required for some: SAT. Application deadline: 7/30. Notification: continuous. Transfer credits accepted: Yes.

Costs Per Year: Application fee: $0. Tuition: $5100 full-time, $260 per semester hour part-time. Mandatory fees: $520 full-time. Full-time tuition and fees vary according to course load and program. Part-time tuition varies according to course load and program.

Collegiate Environment: Orientation program. Choral group, student-run newspaper. Social organizations: 18 open to all. Most popular organizations: Asociacion de Estudiantes de Administracion de Empresas, Estudiantes Unidos por la Ciencia, Asociacion Estudiantes de Aviacion, Consejo de Estudiante, Asociacion Estudiantes de Ingenieria. Student services: health clinic, personal-psychological counseling. Campus security: 24-hour patrols. 148 college housing spaces available; 128 were occupied in 2012-13. Centro de Acceso a la Informacion plus 1 other with 162,069 books, 1,623 microform titles, 335 serials, 2,750 audiovisual materials, an OPAC, and a Web page. Operations spending for the previous fiscal year: $80,634. 610 computers available on campus for general student use. Computer purchase/lease plans available. A campuswide network can be accessed from student residence rooms and from off campus. Students can access the following: online class registration. Staffed computer lab on campus.

■ INTER AMERICAN UNIVERSITY OF PUERTO RICO, FAJARDO CAMPUS
Call Box 70003
Fajardo, PR 00738-7003
Tel: (787)863-2390
E-mail: ghisita.garcia@fajardo.inter.edu
Web Site: www.fajardo.inter.edu/

Description: Independent, 4-year, coed. Part of Inter American University of Puerto Rico. Awards associate, bachelor's, and master's degrees. Founded 1965. Setting: 11-acre small town campus with easy access to San Juan. Total enrollment: 2,199. Faculty: 120 (39 full-time, 81 part-time). Student-undergrad faculty ratio is 11:1. 909 applied, 51% were admitted. Full-time: 764 students, 44% women, 56% men. Part-time: 544 students, 74% women, 26% men. Students come from 3 states and territories. 21% 25 or older. Retention: 67% of full-time freshmen returned the following year. Academic areas with the most degrees conferred: education; health professions and related sciences; computer and information sciences; social sciences. Core. Calendar: semesters. Academic remediation for entering students, ESL program, services for LD students, advanced placement, honors program, independent study, distance learning, summer session for credit, part-time degree program, external degree program, adult/continuing education programs, co-op programs and internships. Off campus study at other units of the Inter American University of Puerto Rico. ROTC: Army (c).

Entrance Requirements: Options: electronic application, early admission, deferred admission. Required: high school transcript, College Board. Required for some: interview. Entrance: moderately difficult. Application deadline: 5/15.

Costs Per Year: Application fee: $0. Tuition: $4080 full-time, $170 per credit part-time. Mandatory fees: $258 full-time. Full-time tuition and fees vary according to degree level. Part-time tuition varies according to degree level.

Collegiate Environment: Orientation program. Drama-theater group. Social organizations: 22 open to all; Noti Inter Fajardo (news through website). Most popular organizations: Future Teachers Association, Criminal Justice Student Association, Honor Program Association, Computer Science Association, Social Work Association. Major annual events: Graduation Services, Student Welcome Back, Achievement Night. Student services: personal-psychological counseling. Campus security: 24-hour patrols. College housing not available. Antonio S. Belaval Library plus 1 other with 39,951 books, 686 serials, 1,390 audiovisual materials, and a Web page. 280 computers available on campus for general student use. A campuswide network can be accessed from off-campus. Students can access the following: online class registration. Staffed computer lab on campus provides training in use of computers.

■ INTER AMERICAN UNIVERSITY OF PUERTO RICO, GUAYAMA CAMPUS
Call Box 10004
Guayama, PR 00785
Tel: (787)864-2222
E-mail: lferrer@inter.edu
Web Site: www.guayama.inter.edu/

Description: Independent, comprehensive, coed. Part of Inter American University of Puerto Rico. Awards associate, bachelor's, and master's degrees. Founded 1958. Setting: 50-acre small town campus. Endowment: $782,124. Educational spending for the previous fiscal year: $2498 per student. Total enrollment: 2,358. Faculty: 203 (45 full-time, 158 part-time). Student-undergrad faculty ratio is 23:1. 575 applied, 62% were admitted. Full-time: 1,902 students, 66% women, 34% men. Part-time: 383 students, 67% women, 33% men. 100% Hispanic/Latino. 30% 25 or older. Retention: 61% of full-time freshmen returned the following year. Academic areas with the most degrees conferred: business/marketing; education; health professions and related sciences. Core. Calendar: semesters. Academic remediation for entering students, ESL program, honors program, independent study, distance learning, summer session for credit, part-time degree program, external degree program, adult/continuing education programs. Off campus study at other units of the Inter American University of Puerto Rico. ROTC: Army (c).

Entrance Requirements: Options: electronic application, international baccalaureate accepted. Required: high school transcript, minimum 2 high school GPA, SAT, PAA. Required for some: essay, interview. Entrance: moderately difficult. Application deadline: 8/1. Transfer credits accepted: Yes.

Costs Per Year: Application fee: $0. Tuition: $4080 full-time. Mandatory fees: $482 full-time.

Collegiate Environment: Orientation program. Drama-theater group. Social organizations: 15 open to all. Most popular organizations: Criminal Justice, Honor's Program, Human Resources, Natural Sciences, Health Sciences. Major annual events: Interuniversity Athletes League Competition, Christmas Welcome, Christmas Concert. Student services: health clinic. Campus security: 24-hour emergency response devices. Information Access Center with an OPAC. Operations spending for the previous fiscal year: $58,124. 288 computers available on campus for general student use. A campuswide network can be accessed from off-campus. Students can access the following: online class registration. Staffed computer lab on campus provides training in use of computers, software, and the Internet.

■ INTER AMERICAN UNIVERSITY OF PUERTO RICO, METROPOLITAN CAMPUS
PO Box 191293
San Juan, PR 00919-1293
Tel: (787)250-1912
E-mail: jbetancourt@metro.inter.edu
Web Site: metro.inter.edu/

Description: Independent, comprehensive, coed. Part of Inter American University of Puerto Rico. Awards associate, bachelor's, master's, and doctoral degrees. Founded 1960. Setting: urban campus. Endowment: $7.5 million. Research spending for the previous fiscal year: $2872. Educational spending for the previous fiscal year: $3186 per student. Total enrollment: 10,093. Faculty: 599 (217 full-time, 382 part-time). 4,379 applied, 27% were admitted. Full-time: 5,652 students, 55% women, 45% men. Part-time: 1,309 students, 52% women, 48% men. 40% 25 or older. Core. Calendar: semesters. ESL program, services for LD students, accelerated degree program, honors program, independent study, distance learning, summer session for credit, part-time degree program, external degree program, adult/continuing education programs, co-op programs and internships, graduate courses open to undergrads. Study abroad program. ROTC: Army (c), Naval (c), Air Force (c).

Entrance Requirements: Options: electronic application, international baccalaureate accepted. Required: high school transcript, CEEB. Required for some: SAT. Entrance: moderately difficult. Application deadlines: 5/15, 5/15 for nonresidents. Transfer credits accepted: Yes.

Collegiate Environment: Orientation program. Drama-theater group, choral group, student-run newspaper. Most popular organizations: Intercultural Student Association, Club Rotaract, Biological Science, Abriendo Camino, Alpha Phi Omega. Major annual events: Intercollegiate - Justas LAI, Employment Fair, open house. Student services: health clinic, personal-psychological counseling. Campus security: 24-hour emergency response devices and patrols, video security system. Centro de Acceso a la Informacion plus 1 other with 171,173 books, 639,554 microform titles,

41,660 serials, 6,684 audiovisual materials, an OPAC, and a Web page. Operations spending for the previous fiscal year: $240,524. 625 computers available on campus for general student use. A campuswide network can be accessed from student residence rooms and from off campus. Students can access the following: online class registration. Staffed computer lab on campus provides training in use of computers, software, and the Internet.

■ INTER AMERICAN UNIVERSITY OF PUERTO RICO, PONCE CAMPUS

104 Industrial Park Turpò Rd. 1
Mercedita, PR 00715-1602
Tel: (787)284-1912
E-mail: fidiaz@ponce.inter.edu
Web Site: www.ponce.inter.edu/
Description: Independent, comprehensive, coed. Part of Inter American University of Puerto Rico. Awards associate, bachelor's, and master's degrees. Founded 1962. Setting: 50-acre urban campus with easy access to San Juan. Endowment: $151.5 million. Educational spending for the previous fiscal year: $2350 per student. Total enrollment: 5,983. Faculty: 294 (96 full-time, 198 part-time). Student-undergrad faculty ratio is 31:1. 2,464 applied, 40% were admitted. Full-time: 4,697 students, 59% women, 41% men. Part-time: 878 students, 64% women, 36% men. Students come from 39 states and territories, 3 other countries, 9% from out-of-commonwealth. 0.1% American Indian or Alaska Native, non-Hispanic/Latino; 98% Hispanic/Latino; 0.04% African American, non-Hispanic/Latino; 0.02% Asian, non-Hispanic/Latino. 30% 25 or older, 2% transferred in. Retention: 71% of full-time freshmen returned the following year. Academic areas with the most degrees conferred: business/marketing; homeland security, law enforcement, firefighting, and protective services; health professions and related sciences. Core. Calendar: semesters. Academic remediation for entering students, ESL program, services for LD students, honors program, independent study, distance learning, summer session for credit, part-time degree program, adult/continuing education programs, co-op programs and internships. Off campus study at other units of the Inter American University of Puerto Rico. Study abroad program.
Entrance Requirements: Option: deferred admission. Required: high school transcript, minimum 2 high school GPA, CEEB. Required for some: SAT. Entrance: moderately difficult. Application deadline: 5/15.
Costs Per Year: Application fee: $0. Tuition: $4080 full-time, $170 per credit part-time. Mandatory fees: $426 per semester hour part-time. Full-time tuition varies according to course load and program. Part-time tuition and fees vary according to course load and program.
Collegiate Environment: Orientation program. Drama-theater group, choral group, marching band. Social organizations: 27 open to all; 39% of eligible men and 61% of eligible women are members. Most popular organizations: Association of Future Teachers of Special Education, Accounting Students Association, Hotel Management Association, Office Systems Administration Association, Criminal Justice Association. Major annual events: Welcoming of New Students, Students Athletes. Student services: health clinic, personal-psychological counseling. Campus security: 24-hour emergency response devices and patrols. College housing not available. Centro de Acceso a la Informacion plus 1 other with 59,847 books, 221 serials, 3,071 audiovisual materials, an OPAC, and a Web page. Operations spending for the previous fiscal year: $137,478. 467 computers available on campus for general student use. A campuswide network can be accessed from off-campus. Students can access the following: online class registration. Staffed computer lab on campus provides training in use of computers and the Internet.

■ INTER AMERICAN UNIVERSITY OF PUERTO RICO, SAN GERMÁN CAMPUS

PO Box 5100
San Germán, PR 00683-5008
Tel: (787)264-1912
Fax: (787)892-6350
E-mail: milcama@sg.inter.edu
Web Site: www.sg.inter.edu/
Description: Independent, university, coed. Part of Inter American University of Puerto Rico. Awards associate, bachelor's, master's, and doctoral degrees. Founded 1912. Setting: 260-acre small town campus with easy access to Ponce, Aguadilla, Mayaguez. System endowment: $151.5 million. Research spending for the previous fiscal year: $24,397. Educational spending for the previous fiscal year: $3269 per student. Total enrollment: 5,355. Faculty: 316 (119 full-time, 197 part-time). Student-undergrad faculty

ratio is 26:1. 1,268 applied, 84% were admitted. Full-time: 3,744 students, 56% women, 44% men. Part-time: 528 students, 54% women, 46% men. Students come from 11 states and territories, 3 other countries, 0.4% from out-of-commonwealth. 0.02% American Indian or Alaska Native, non-Hispanic/Latino; 99% Hispanic/Latino; 0.02% African American, non-Hispanic/Latino. 14% 25 or older, 10% live on campus, 2% transferred in. Retention: 70% of full-time freshmen returned the following year. Academic areas with the most degrees conferred: business/marketing; education; biological/life sciences. Core. Calendar: semesters. Academic remediation for entering students, ESL program, services for LD students, advanced placement, accelerated degree program, honors program, independent study, distance learning, double major, summer session for credit, part-time degree program, external degree program, adult/continuing education programs, co-op programs and internships, graduate courses open to undergrads. Off campus study at other units of the Inter American University of Puerto Rico. ROTC: Army (c), Naval (c), Air Force (c).
Entrance Requirements: Options: electronic application, early admission, international baccalaureate accepted. Required: high school transcript, medical history, vaccination, CEEB. Recommended: essay, minimum 2 high school GPA. Required for some: 1 recommendation, interview, SAT or ACT. Entrance: moderately difficult. Application deadline: 5/15. Notification: continuous. SAT Reasoning Test deadline: 5/5. Transfer credits accepted: Yes.
Costs Per Year: Application fee: $0. Comprehensive fee: $8320 includes full-time tuition ($5100), mandatory fees ($520), and college room and board ($2700). College room only: $1200. Room and board charges vary according to board plan and housing facility. Part-time tuition: $170 per credit. Part-time mandatory fees: $170 per credit, $213 per term.
Collegiate Environment: Orientation program. Drama-theater group, choral group, student-run newspaper. Social organizations: 30 open to all. Most popular organizations: Asociacion de Pre-Medica-Caduceus, Futuros Maestros, Asociacion de Estudiantes De Psicologia (AEPSI), Asociacion de Estudiantes de Contabilidad, Asociacion de Estudiantes del Programa de Honor. Major annual events: End of Semester Dance, Freshmen Dance, Athletic Inter-University Match. Student services: personal-psychological counseling. Campus security: 24-hour emergency response devices and patrols. 442 college housing spaces available; 342 were occupied in 2012-13. No special consideration for freshman housing applicants. Options: men-only, women-only housing available. Juan Cancio Ortiz Library with 124,522 books, 571,242 microform titles, 2,300 serials, 154 audiovisual materials, an OPAC, and a Web page. Operations spending for the previous fiscal year: $87,179. 930 computers available on campus for general student use. A campuswide network can be accessed from student residence rooms. Students can access the following: online class registration. Staffed computer lab on campus provides training in use of computers, software, and the Internet.

■ NATIONAL UNIVERSITY COLLEGE (BAYAMÓN)

National College Plz. Bldg.
Bayamón, PR 00960
Tel: (787)780-5134; Free: 800-780-5134
Fax: (787)740-7360
E-mail: infobayamon@nuc.edu
Web Site: www.nuc.edu/
Description: Private, 4-year, coed. Awards associate and bachelor's degrees. Total enrollment: 2,703. Student-undergrad faculty ratio is 34:1. 950 applied, 91% were admitted. 0% from out-of-commonwealth. 37% 25 or older. Retention: 56% of full-time freshmen returned the following year.
Entrance Requirements: Required: high school transcript, certificate of immunization, SAT. Entrance: moderately difficult. Application deadline: Rolling.

■ NATIONAL UNIVERSITY COLLEGE (PONCE)

PO Box 801243
Ponce, PR 00716
Tel: (787)840-4474
Web Site: www.nuc.edu/
Description: Proprietary, comprehensive, coed.

■ NATIONAL UNIVERSITY COLLEGE (RIO GRANDE)

Carretera No.3 Km. 22.1
Bo. Ciénaga Baja
Rio Grande, PR 00745
Tel: (787)888-8286; Free: 800-981-0812
Fax: (787)888-8280

Web Site: www.nuc.edu/
Description: Proprietary, comprehensive, coed.

■ **POLYTECHNIC UNIVERSITY OF PUERTO RICO**
377 Ponce de Leon Ave.
Hato Rey, PR 00919
Tel: (787)754-8000
E-mail: tcardona@pupr.edu
Web Site: www.pupr.edu/
Description: Independent, comprehensive, coed. Awards bachelor's and master's degrees. Founded 1966. Setting: 10-acre urban campus with easy access to San Juan. Endowment: $10.7 million. Research spending for the previous fiscal year: $1 million. Total enrollment: 4,743. Faculty: 248 (149 full-time, 99 part-time). Student-undergrad faculty ratio is 19:1. 737 applied, 95% were admitted. Full-time: 1,918 students, 19% women, 81% men. Part-time: 2,113 students, 22% women, 78% men. Students come from 2 states and territories, 12 other countries. 100% Hispanic/Latino. 25% 25 or older. Retention: 73% of full-time freshmen returned the following year. Academic areas with the most degrees conferred: engineering; architecture; business/marketing. Core. Calendar: trimesters. Academic remediation for entering students, ESL program, self-designed majors, independent study, distance learning, summer session for credit, part-time degree program. ROTC: Army (c).
Entrance Requirements: Options: electronic application, early admission, deferred admission. Required: high school transcript. Required for some: SAT. Entrance: minimally difficult. Application deadline: 8/15. SAT Reasoning Test deadline: 8/15. SAT Subject Test deadline: 8/15. Transfer credits accepted: Yes.
Costs Per Year: Application fee: $30. Tuition: $6768 full-time, $188 per credit part-time. Mandatory fees: $780 full-time, $260 per term part-time. Full-time tuition and fees vary according to course level, course load, degree level, and program. Part-time tuition and fees vary according to course level, course load, degree level, and program.
Collegiate Environment: Choral group. Social organizations: 22 open to all; local fraternities. Most popular organizations: ASCE (American Society of Civil Engineering), PRWEA (Puerto Rico Water and Environment Association), ACI (American Concrete Institute), SAE PUPR AERO DESIGN TEAM, SHPE (Society of Hispanic Professional Engineers). Major annual events: Welcome Activity, Christmas Activity, Open House. Student services: personal-psychological counseling. Campus security: 24-hour patrols. College housing not available. Biblioteca de la Unidersidad Politecnica de Puerto Rico plus 1 other with 117,706 books, 984 microform titles, 18,643 serials, 3,536 audiovisual materials, an OPAC, and a Web page. Operations spending for the previous fiscal year: $777,182. 375 computers available on campus for general student use. A campuswide network can be accessed from off-campus. Students can access the following: online class registration. Staffed computer lab on campus.

■ **PONTIFICAL CATHOLIC UNIVERSITY OF PUERTO RICO**
2250 Las Americas Ave., Ste. 564
Ponce, PR 00717-0777
Tel: (787)841-2000; Free: 800-961-7696
Fax: (787)840-4295
E-mail: admissions@email.pucpr.edu
Web Site: www.pucpr.edu/
Description: Independent Roman Catholic, university, coed. Awards associate, bachelor's, master's, and doctoral degrees (branch locations in Arecibo, Guayana, Mayaguez). Founded 1948. Setting: 120-acre urban campus with easy access to San Juan. Total enrollment: 7,682. Faculty: 385 (191 full-time, 194 part-time). Student-undergrad faculty ratio is 23:1. 1,798 applied, 83% were admitted. Full-time: 4,857 students, 62% women, 38% men. Part-time: 514 students, 65% women, 35% men. 0% from out-of-commonwealth. 13% 25 or older, 4% transferred in. Retention: 76% of full-time freshmen returned the following year. Core. Calendar: semesters. Academic remediation for entering students, ESL program, services for LD students, advanced placement, honors program, independent study, double major, summer session for credit, part-time degree program, adult/continuing education programs, co-op programs, graduate courses open to undergrads. Off campus study at Polytechnic University of Puerto Rico. ROTC: Army (c), Air Force (c).
Entrance Requirements: Options: early admission, deferred admission. Required: high school transcript, minimum 2.5 high school GPA, College Entrance Examination Board (CEEB) Aptitude Test for Admission, Achieve-

ment Test for placement. Required for some: essay, minimum 3 high school GPA, 1 recommendation, interview, SAT. Entrance: moderately difficult. Notification: continuous.
Collegiate Environment: Orientation program. Drama-theater group, choral group, student-run newspaper, radio station. Social organizations: 50 open to all; national fraternities, national sororities, local fraternities, local sororities; 1% of eligible men and 1% of eligible women are members. Most popular organizations: Accounting Students Club, Foreign Students Club, Christ Heralds. Major annual events: Peace Day, Educational Professional Development Convention, Puerto Rican Heritage Week. Student services: health clinic, personal-psychological counseling. Campus security: 24-hour emergency response devices and patrols. Encarnacion Valdes Library plus 1 other with an OPAC and a Web page. 419 computers available on campus for general student use. A campuswide network can be accessed from off-campus. Staffed computer lab on campus provides training in use of software and the Internet.
Community Environment: Ponce is a metropolitan area. Mercedita Airport furnishes transportation to Mayaguez and San Juan. Bus transportation is available to all parts of the island. Community facilities include a public library, museums, churches of major denominations, hospitals, excellent shopping facilities and a number of the major civic, fraternal and service organizations. Part-time employment opportunities are limited. Carnival celebrations and Fiesta Patronales are special annual events.

■ **RAMÍREZ COLLEGE OF BUSINESS AND TECHNOLOGY**
Ave. Ponce de Leon No.70
San Juan, PR 00918
Tel: (787)763-3120
E-mail: ramirezcollege@prtc.net
Web Site: www.galeon.com/ramirezcollege/
Description: Proprietary, 2-year, coed. Awards diplomas, transfer associate, and terminal associate degrees. Founded 1922. Setting: suburban campus. Total enrollment: 460. 42% 25 or older. Calendar: trimesters. Academic remediation for entering students, adult/continuing education programs.
Entrance Requirements: Open admission. Required: minimum 2.0 high school GPA, interview. Required for some: high school transcript. Entrance: noncompetitive. Application deadline: Rolling.
Collegiate Environment: Student services: health clinic, personal-psychological counseling. Campus security: private security service. Main library plus 1 other with 9,000 books, 12 serials, and 30 audiovisual materials.

■ **UNIVERSIDAD ADVENTISTA DE LAS ANTILLAS**
PO Box 118
Mayagüez, PR 00681-0118
Tel: (787)834-9595
Fax: (787)834-9597
E-mail: admissions@uaa.edu
Web Site: www.uaa.edu/
Description: Independent Seventh-day Adventist, comprehensive, coed. Awards associate, bachelor's, and master's degrees. Founded 1957. Setting: 284-acre rural campus. Endowment: $134,104. Educational spending for the previous fiscal year: $3894 per student. Total enrollment: 1,322. Faculty: 95 (44 full-time, 51 part-time). Student-undergrad faculty ratio is 18:1. 630 applied, 87% were admitted. Full-time: 1,142 students, 59% women, 41% men. Part-time: 99 students, 59% women, 41% men. Students come from 54 states and territories, 27 other countries, 13% from out-of-commonwealth. 0% American Indian or Alaska Native, non-Hispanic/Latino; 95% Hispanic/Latino; 2% African American, non-Hispanic/Latino; 0.2% Asian, non-Hispanic/Latino; 0% Native Hawaiian or other Pacific Islander, non-Hispanic/Latino; 2% international. 22% 25 or older, 5% live on campus, 8% transferred in. Retention: 68% of full-time freshmen returned the following year. Academic areas with the most degrees conferred: health professions and related sciences; business/marketing; theology and religious vocations. Core. Calendar: semesters. Academic remediation for entering students, ESL program, services for LD students, advanced placement, double major, summer session for credit, part-time degree program, co-op programs and internships.
Entrance Requirements: Options: electronic application, early admission. Required: high school transcript, minimum 2 high school GPA, 1 recommendation. Recommended: SAT or ACT, CEEB. Required for some: essay, interview. Entrance: minimally difficult. Application deadline: 7/15. Transfer credits accepted: Yes.
Costs Per Year: Application fee: $20. One-time mandatory fee: $20.

Comprehensive fee: $8450 includes full-time tuition ($4950), mandatory fees ($600), and college room and board ($2900). College room only: $1100. Full-time tuition and fees vary according to course load and program. Room and board charges vary according to board plan and housing facility. Part-time tuition: $165 per credit hour. Part-time mandatory fees: $235 per term. Part-time tuition and fees vary according to course load and program.

Collegiate Environment: Orientation program. Choral group, student-run newspaper. Social organizations: 14 open to all; Student Council, Departmental Organization; 90% of eligible men and 90% of eligible women are members. Most popular organizations: Score Group, Gymnastic Club, Student Council, Green Movement, 3AM. Major annual events: Talent Shows, Olympic Games, Week of Prayer. Student services: health clinic, personal-psychological counseling. Campus security: 24-hour emergency response devices and patrols, student patrols, controlled dormitory access. 350 college housing spaces available; 325 were occupied in 2012-13. Freshmen given priority for college housing. On-campus residence required in freshman year. Options: men-only, women-only housing available. Dennis Soto Library plus 1 other with 67,345 books, 105 serials, an OPAC, and a Web page. Operations spending for the previous fiscal year: $439,002. 50 computers available on campus for general student use. A campuswide network can be accessed from student residence rooms and from off campus. Students can access the following: online class registration. Staffed computer lab on campus provides training in use of computers, software, and the Internet.

■ UNIVERSIDAD CENTRAL DEL CARIBE

PO Box 60-327
Bayamón, PR 00960-6032
Tel: (787)798-3001
Web Site: www.uccaribe.edu/

Description: Independent, comprehensive, coed. Awards associate, bachelor's, master's, and doctoral degrees. Founded 1976. Total enrollment: 485. Student-undergrad faculty ratio is 22:1. 43 applied. 0% from out-of-commonwealth. 29% 25 or older. Retention: 95% of full-time freshmen returned the following year. Calendar: semesters.

■ UNIVERSIDAD DEL ESTE

PO Box 2010
Carolina, PR 00984
Tel: (787)257-7373
Fax: (787)257-7373
E-mail: ue_csantiago@suagm.edu
Web Site: www.suagm.edu/une/

Description: Independent, comprehensive, coed. Part of Ana G. Mendez University System. Awards associate, bachelor's, and master's degrees. Founded 1949. Setting: small town campus with easy access to San Juan. Total enrollment: 13,317. 8,091 applied, 45% were admitted. Retention: 70% of full-time freshmen returned the following year. Calendar: semesters. Summer session for credit, part-time degree program, external degree program, adult/continuing education programs.

Entrance Requirements: Option: deferred admission. Entrance: noncompetitive.

Collegiate Environment: Campus security: 24-hour patrols.

Community Environment: See University of Puerto Rico - Rio Piedras Campus.

■ UNIVERSIDAD METROPOLITANA

Apartado 21150
San Juan, PR 00928-1150
Tel: (787)766-1717; Free: 800-747-8362
Fax: (787)759-7663
E-mail: um_frivera@suagm1.suagm.edu
Web Site: www.suagm.edu/umet/

Description: Independent, comprehensive, coed. Part of Ana G. Mendez University System. Awards associate, bachelor's, and master's degrees. Founded 1980. Setting: small town campus. Total enrollment: 12,622. Faculty: 903 (107 full-time, 796 part-time). 7,582 applied, 53% were admitted. 26% 25 or older. Retention: 72% of full-time freshmen returned the following year. Academic areas with the most degrees conferred: business/marketing; education; public administration and social services. Core. Calendar: semesters. Academic remediation for entering students, advanced placement, freshman honors college, honors program, summer session for credit, part-time degree program, adult/continuing education programs, co-op programs. Off campus study.

Entrance Requirements: Options: electronic application, early admission, international baccalaureate accepted. Required: high school transcript. Required for some: interview. Entrance: moderately difficult. Application deadline: 7/30.

Collegiate Environment: Orientation program. Drama-theater group, choral group. Social organizations: national fraternities. Campus security: 24-hour patrols. 50 computers available on campus for general student use. A campuswide network can be accessed from off-campus. Students can access the following: online class registration.

■ UNIVERSIDAD PENTECOSTAL MIZPA

Bo Caimito Rd. 199
Apartado 20966
San Juan, PR 00928-0966
Tel: (787)720-4476
Fax: (787)720-2012
Web Site: www.mizpa.edu/

Description: Independent, 4-year, coed, affiliated with Pentecostal Church. Awards associate and bachelor's degrees. Founded 1937. Total enrollment: 275. Student-undergrad faculty ratio is 13:1. 0% from out-of-commonwealth. 89% 25 or older. Retention: 67% of full-time freshmen returned the following year. Academic area with the most degrees conferred: theology and religious vocations. Calendar: semesters.

Entrance Requirements: Open admission.

■ UNIVERSIDAD TEOLÓGICA DEL CARIBE

PO Box 901
Saint Just, PR 00978-0901
Tel: (787)761-0640
E-mail: promocion@utcpr.edu
Web Site: www.utcpr.edu/

Description: Independent Pentecostal, 4-year, coed. Awards bachelor's degrees. Founded 1956. Setting: 4-acre suburban campus with easy access to San Juan. Endowment: $1 million. Educational spending for the previous fiscal year: $7992 per student. Total enrollment: 172. Faculty: 24 (7 full-time, 17 part-time). Student-undergrad faculty ratio is 7:1. Full-time: 96 students, 39% women, 61% men. Part-time: 76 students, 33% women, 67% men. Students come from 5 other countries, 1% from out-of-commonwealth. 100% Hispanic/Latino. 84% 25 or older. 0% live on campus, 9% transferred in. Retention: 73% of full-time freshmen returned the following year. Academic area with the most degrees conferred: theology and religious vocations. Core. Calendar: semesters. Services for LD students, honors program, independent study, summer session for credit, part-time degree program, internships. Off campus study.

Entrance Requirements: Open admission. Option: early admission. Required: 3 recommendations, interview, Medical Certificate, Certificate of Immunization, 1 photo 2x2 and Bible Content Exam. Required for some: high school transcript. Transfer credits accepted: Yes.

Costs Per Year: Application fee: $25. One-time mandatory fee: $13. Comprehensive fee: $6848 includes full-time tuition ($3784), mandatory fees ($664), and college room and board ($2400). College room only: $1200. Full-time tuition and fees vary according to course load. Room and board charges vary according to board plan. Part-time tuition: $18 per credit. Part-time mandatory fees: $130 per credit, $3004 per term. Part-time tuition and fees vary according to course load.

Collegiate Environment: Orientation program. Social organizations: 4 open to all; local fraternities; 3% of eligible men and 4% of eligible women are members. Most popular organizations: Student Council, Missionary Evangelistic Association, Ministerial Association, FESI. Major annual events: Revival Campaign, Open House, Opening Workship. Student services: personal-psychological counseling. Campus security: Private Security Personnel during Special Time. 12 college housing spaces available; 5 were occupied in 2012-13. No special consideration for freshman housing applicants. Option: coed housing available. Juan L. Lugo plus 1 other with 16,229 books, 1,620 microform titles, 84 serials, 300 audiovisual materials, and an OPAC. Operations spending for the previous fiscal year: $39,902. 8 computers available on campus for general student use. Students can access the following: online class registration.

■ UNIVERSIDAD DEL TURABO

PO Box 3030
Gurabo, PR 00778-3030
Tel: (787)743-7979
E-mail: ut_vgonzalez@suagm.edu

Web Site: www.suagm.edu/ut/

Description: Independent, university, coed. Part of Ana G. Mendez University System. Awards associate, bachelor's, master's, and doctoral degrees and post-master's certificates. Founded 1972. Setting: 140-acre urban campus with easy access to San Juan. Total enrollment: 17,040. Faculty: 1,317 (201 full-time, 1,116 part-time). Student-undergrad faculty ratio is 30:1. 10,474 applied, 43% were admitted. Full-time: 10,972 students, 59% women, 41% men. Part-time: 3,361 students, 62% women, 38% men. 35% 25 or older. Retention: 73% of full-time freshmen returned the following year. Academic areas with the most degrees conferred: business/marketing; social sciences; education. Calendar: semesters. Advanced placement, accelerated degree program, honors program, independent study, distance learning, double major, summer session for credit, part-time degree program, internships. Off campus study at Jackson State University, University of California, Berkeley, Rensselaer Polytechnic Institute, Georgia Institute of Technology, University of New Mexico, New Mexico State University. ROTC: Army (c), Air Force (c).

Entrance Requirements: Option: electronic application. Required: high school transcript. Recommended: SAT. Entrance: minimally difficult. Application deadline: Rolling. Notification: continuous. Transfer credits accepted: Yes.

Costs Per Year: Application fee: $15. Comprehensive fee: $28,112 includes full-time tuition ($19,512) and college room and board ($8600). Full-time tuition varies according to course level, course load, and program.

Collegiate Environment: Orientation program. Student-run newspaper, radio station. Student services: health clinic, personal-psychological counseling. Campus security: 24-hour patrols.

■ UNIVERSITY OF PHOENIX–PUERTO RICO CAMPUS

B7 Tabonuco St., Ste. 700 Santander Twr.
Guaynabo, PR 00968
Tel: (787)731-5400; Free: 866-766-0766
Fax: (787)731-1510
Web Site: www.phoenix.edu/

Description: Proprietary, comprehensive, coed. Awards bachelor's and master's degrees (courses conducted at 121 campuses and learning centers in 25 states). Founded 1995. Setting: urban campus. Total enrollment: 2,815. Faculty: 228 (22 full-time, 206 part-time). 73 applied, 100% were admitted. Full-time: 1,117 students, 55% women, 45% men. 0% from out-of-commonwealth. 89% 25 or older. Academic area with the most degrees conferred: business/marketing. Core. Calendar: continuous. Services for LD students, advanced placement, accelerated degree program, independent study, distance learning, external degree program, adult/continuing education programs, graduate courses open to undergrads.

Entrance Requirements: Open admission. Options: electronic application, deferred admission. Required: 1 recommendation. Required for some: high school transcript. Entrance: noncompetitive. Application deadline: Rolling.

Collegiate Environment: Campus security: late night transport-escort service. University Library plus 1 other with 16,781 serials, an OPAC, and a Web page. Operations spending for the previous fiscal year: $6.8 million.

■ UNIVERSITY OF PUERTO RICO, AGUADILLA UNIVERSITY COLLEGE

PO Box 6150
Aguadilla, PR 00604
Tel: (787)890-2681
Web Site: www.uprag.edu/

Description: Commonwealth-supported, 4-year, coed. Part of University of Puerto Rico System. Awards associate and bachelor's degrees. Founded 1972. Setting: 32-acre suburban campus. Total enrollment: 3,076. 901 applied, 89% were admitted. Core. Calendar: semesters. Academic remediation for entering students, ESL program, advanced placement, honors program, summer session for credit, part-time degree program, adult/continuing education programs. ROTC: Army.

Entrance Requirements: Options: early admission, deferred admission. Required: high school transcript, SAT, SAT Subject Tests, PAA. Entrance: moderately difficult. Notification: continuous.

Collegiate Environment: Orientation program. Choral group. Social organizations: local fraternities. Campus security: 24-hour patrols. 31,420 books and 242 serials.

■ UNIVERSITY OF PUERTO RICO AT ARECIBO

PO Box 4010
Arecibo, PR 00613

Tel: (787)878-2830
E-mail: dbarrios@upra.edu
Web Site: www.upra.edu/

Description: Commonwealth-supported, 4-year, coed. Part of University of Puerto Rico System. Awards associate and bachelor's degrees. Founded 1967. Setting: 44-acre urban campus with easy access to San Juan. Total enrollment: 4,352. 2,588 applied, 47% were admitted. Core. Calendar: semesters. Academic remediation for entering students, ESL program, services for LD students, advanced placement, honors program, distance learning, summer session for credit, adult/continuing education programs. ROTC: Army.

Entrance Requirements: Required: high school transcript, SAT Subject Tests, PAA or SAT, CEEB. Entrance: very difficult.

Collegiate Environment: Orientation program. Drama-theater group, choral group, marching band. Social organizations: local fraternities, local sororities. Student services: health clinic, personal-psychological counseling. Campus security: 24-hour emergency response devices and patrols. General Library with 65,000 books and 3,660 serials.

■ UNIVERSITY OF PUERTO RICO AT BAYAMÓN

Industrial Minillas 170 Carr 174
Bayamón, PR 00959
Tel: (787)786-2885
E-mail: carmen.montes@upr.edu
Web Site: www.uprb.edu/

Description: Commonwealth-supported, 4-year, coed. Part of University of Puerto Rico System. Awards associate and bachelor's degrees. Founded 1971. Setting: 78-acre urban campus with easy access to San Juan. Research spending for the previous fiscal year: $89,000. Educational spending for the previous fiscal year: $4776 per student. Total enrollment: 5,051. Faculty: 261 (197 full-time, 64 part-time). Student-undergrad faculty ratio is 21:1. 5,147 applied, 28% were admitted. Full-time: 4,406 students, 51% women, 49% men. Part-time: 645 students, 52% women, 48% men. 1% from out-of-commonwealth. 100% Hispanic/Latino. 10% 25 or older, 11% transferred in. Retention: 82% of full-time freshmen returned the following year. Academic areas with the most degrees conferred: business/marketing; education; biological/life sciences. Core. Calendar: semesters. Academic remediation for entering students, services for LD students, advanced placement, honors program, independent study, summer session for credit, part-time degree program, adult/continuing education programs, co-op programs and internships. ROTC: Army, Air Force (c).

Entrance Requirements: Option: electronic application. Required: high school transcript, College Board. Entrance: very difficult. Application deadline: 12/15. Notification: 5/1. Transfer credits accepted: Yes.

Costs Per Year: Application fee: $25. Commonwealth resident tuition: $1870 full-time, $55 per credit part-time. Nonresident tuition: $3910 full-time, $115 per credit part-time. Mandatory fees: $342 full-time. Full-time tuition and fees vary according to class time, course load, program, and student level. Part-time tuition varies according to class time, course load, program, and student level. Tuition guaranteed not to increase for student's term of enrollment.

Collegiate Environment: Orientation program. Drama-theater group, choral group. Social organizations: 5 open to all. Most popular organizations: American Marketing Association, Collegiate International Secretaries, Electronic Association, Materials Management Association, Society for Human Resources Management. Major annual events: Basketball Tournament El Chicharion, Ceremony of the Insiquia letra, Interuniversities Track and Field event. Student services: health clinic, personal-psychological counseling. Campus security: 24-hour patrols. Centro Recursos para el Aprendizaje with 65,000 books, 3,357 microform titles, 280 serials, 3,995 audiovisual materials, an OPAC, and a Web page. Operations spending for the previous fiscal year: $1.2 million. 760 computers available on campus for general student use. A campuswide network can be accessed from off-campus. Students can access the following: online class registration. Staffed computer lab on campus provides training in use of computers, software, and the Internet.

■ UNIVERSITY OF PUERTO RICO AT CAROLINA

PO Box 4800
Carolina, PR 00984-4800
Tel: (787)257-0000
Web Site: uprc.edu/

Description: Commonwealth-supported, 4-year, coed. Part of University of Puerto Rico System. Awards associate and bachelor's degrees. Founded

1974. Setting: 60-acre urban campus with easy access to San Juan. Total enrollment: 4,321. Student-undergrad faculty ratio is 22:1. 1,759 applied, 76% were admitted. 0% from out-of-commonwealth. 9% 25 or older. Core. Academic remediation for entering students, ESL program, services for LD students, part-time degree program, adult/continuing education programs. ROTC: Army (c), Air Force (c).

Entrance Requirements: Required: high school transcript, SAT, ACT, SAT Subject Tests, CEEB Test. Entrance: moderately difficult. Notification: continuous.

Collegiate Environment: Orientation program. Drama-theater group, choral group, marching band. Student services: health clinic, personal-psychological counseling. Learning Resource Center, Prof. Jose Paulino Fernandez-Miranda with an OPAC and a Web page. 20 computers available on campus for general student use.

■ **UNIVERSITY OF PUERTO RICO, CAYEY UNIVERSITY COLLEGE**
205 Ave. Antonio R. Barcelo
Cayey, PR 00736
Tel: (787)738-2161
E-mail: wilfredo.lopez3@upr.edu
Web Site: www.cayey.upr.edu/

Description: Commonwealth-supported, 4-year, coed. Part of University of Puerto Rico System. Awards associate and bachelor's degrees. Founded 1967. Setting: 177-acre urban campus with easy access to San Juan. Total enrollment: 3,830. Faculty: 164. Student-undergrad faculty ratio is 21:1. 2,471 applied, 78% were admitted. Full-time: 3,458 students, 71% women, 29% men. Part-time: 372 students, 73% women, 27% men. 0.01% from out-of-commonwealth. 0.1% 25 or older, 2% transferred in. Retention: 89% of full-time freshmen returned the following year. Academic areas with the most degrees conferred: education; business/marketing; interdisciplinary studies. Core. Calendar: semesters. Academic remediation for entering students, advanced placement, accelerated degree program, honors program, summer session for credit, part-time degree program. Off campus study at University of Puerto Rico at Mayaguez; University of Puerto Rico School of Medicine. Study abroad program. ROTC: Army.

Entrance Requirements: Options: early admission, early decision. Required: high school transcript, CEEB. Required for some: SAT. Entrance: moderately difficult. Notification: continuous.

Collegiate Environment: Orientation program. Drama-theater group, choral group, marching band. Social organizations: 32 open to all; national fraternities, national sororities, local fraternities; 1% of eligible men and 1% of eligible women are members. Most popular organizations: Asociacion de Estudiantes de Psicologia Psy-Chi, Sociedad Honoraria de Biologia - Tri Beta, Asociacion Cristiana Universitaria-CONFRA, Asociacion de Estudiantes del Programa de Estudios de Honor, GAIA. Major annual event: Student Day. Student services: health clinic, personal-psychological counseling, women's center. Campus security: 24-hour emergency response devices and patrols, late night transport-escort service. Victor M. Pons Library with 109,776 books, 53 microform titles, 2,013 serials, 2,286 audiovisual materials, an OPAC, and a Web page. 1,000 computers available on campus for general student use. A campuswide network can be accessed. Students can access the following: online class registration. Staffed computer lab on campus provides training in use of computers, software, and the Internet.

■ **UNIVERSITY OF PUERTO RICO AT HUMACAO**
HUC Station 100, Rd. 908
Humacao, PR 00791
Tel: (787)850-0000
Fax: (787)852-4638
E-mail: elizabeth.gerena@upr.edu
Web Site: www.uprh.edu/

Description: Commonwealth-supported, 4-year, coed. Part of University of Puerto Rico System. Awards associate and bachelor's degrees. Founded 1962. Setting: 62-acre suburban campus with easy access to San Juan. Research spending for the previous fiscal year: $2.6 million. Educational spending for the previous fiscal year: $8565 per student. Total enrollment: 3,774. Faculty: 257 (219 full-time, 38 part-time). Student-undergrad faculty ratio is 16:1. 1,913 applied, 40% were admitted. Full-time: 3,473 students, 66% women, 34% men. Part-time: 301 students, 70% women, 30% men. 1% from out-of-commonwealth. 86% Hispanic/Latino; 0.2% African American, non-Hispanic/Latino; 0.1% Asian, non-Hispanic/Latino; 0.1% international. 8% 25 or older, 0.2% transferred in. Retention: 81% of full-time freshmen returned the following year. Academic areas with the most degrees

conferred: business/marketing; biological/life sciences; education. Core. Calendar: semesters. Academic remediation for entering students, ESL program, services for LD students, advanced placement, honors program, summer session for credit, part-time degree program, internships.

Entrance Requirements: Option: deferred admission. Required: high school transcript, Pruebas de Evaluacion y Admision Universitaria (PEAU). Required for some: interview, SAT or ACT, SAT Subject Tests. Entrance: moderately difficult. Application deadline: 1/31. Notification: 4/15. SAT Reasoning Test deadline: 2/15. SAT Subject Test deadline: 2/15. Transfer credits accepted: Yes.

Costs Per Year: Application fee: $20. Commonwealth resident tuition: $1870 full-time, $55 per credit hour part-time. Nonresident tuition: $3892 full-time, $114.46 per credit hour part-time. Mandatory fees: $1142 full-time. Full-time tuition and fees vary according to class time, course load, and student level. Part-time tuition varies according to class time, course load, and student level. College room and board: $8280. College room only: $3000. Tuition guaranteed not to increase for student's term of enrollment.

Collegiate Environment: Orientation program. Drama-theater group, choral group, marching band, student-run radio station. Social organizations: 33 open to all; national fraternities, national sororities. Most popular organizations: Recreational Organization, Accounting Students Association, Management Students Association, Microbiology Students Association, Human Resources Students Association. Major annual events: Student Day, Shakespeare Festival, Puerto Rican Culture Week. Student services: personal-psychological counseling, women's center. Campus security: 24-hour patrols, 24-hour gate security. Aguedo Mojica Marrero with 75,518 books, 14 microform titles, 57,383 serials, an OPAC, and a Web page. 1,000 computers available on campus for general student use. A campuswide network can be accessed from off-campus. Students can access the following: online class registration. Staffed computer lab on campus.

■ **UNIVERSITY OF PUERTO RICO, MAYAGÜEZ CAMPUS**
PO Box 9000
Mayagüez, PR 00681-9000
Tel: (787)832-4040
E-mail: smarty@uprm.edu
Web Site: www.uprm.edu/

Description: Commonwealth-supported, university, coed. Part of University of Puerto Rico System. Awards bachelor's, master's, and doctoral degrees. Founded 1911. Setting: 315-acre urban campus. Total enrollment: 13,852. Student-undergrad faculty ratio is 16:1. 3,275 applied, 77% were admitted. 0% from out-of-commonwealth. 5% 25 or older. Core. Calendar: semesters. Advanced placement, honors program, distance learning, summer session for credit, part-time degree program, adult/continuing education programs, co-op programs and internships, graduate courses open to undergrads. Off campus study at State University of New York College at Oswego, National Student Exchange. Study abroad program. ROTC: Army, Air Force.

Entrance Requirements: Option: early action. Required: high school transcript, SAT Subject Tests, PEAU, CEEB Test. Entrance: moderately difficult.

Collegiate Environment: Orientation program. Drama-theater group, choral group, marching band, student-run newspaper. Social organizations: national fraternities, national sororities, local fraternities, local sororities. Student services: health clinic, personal-psychological counseling. Campus security: 24-hour emergency response devices and patrols. General Library plus 1 other with an OPAC.

■ **UNIVERSITY OF PUERTO RICO, MEDICAL SCIENCES CAMPUS**
PO Box 365067
San Juan, PR 00936-5067
Tel: (787)758-2525
Fax: (787)754-0474
E-mail: margarita.rivera4@upr.edu
Web Site: www.rcm.upr.edu/

Description: Commonwealth-supported, university, coed. Part of University of Puerto Rico System. Awards associate, bachelor's, master's, and doctoral degrees (bachelor's degree is upper-level). Founded 1950. Setting: 11-acre urban campus. Total enrollment: 2,381. 28% 25 or older. Calendar: semesters. Academic remediation for entering students, summer session for credit. Off campus study at University of Puerto Rico, Rio Piedras.

Entrance Requirements: Entrance: moderately difficult. Preference given to commonwealth residents.

Collegiate Environment: Orientation program. Campus security: 24-hour emergency response devices. Medical Sciences Library with an OPAC and a Web page.

Community Environment: San Juan juxtaposes the old and the new: Old San Juan and the moss-covered El Morro castle are contrasted with high-rise office buildings. Founded in 1521, San Juan is a metropolitan city with a mild climate. Museums (e.g. colonial architecture, rare books Puerto Rican art), outdoor sports (swimming, surfing, baseball, fishing, cock fighting), hospitals and excellent shopping are available to everyone. Special San Juan events include drama festivals, native carnivals, the International Theatrical Festival and the Casals Festival.

■ UNIVERSITY OF PUERTO RICO AT PONCE

PO Box 7186
Ponce, PR 00732-7186
Tel: (787)844-8181
Fax: (787)844-8679
E-mail: avelazquez@uprp.edu
Web Site: upr-ponce.upr.edu/

Description: Commonwealth-supported, 4-year, coed. Part of University of Puerto Rico System. Awards associate and bachelor's degrees. Founded 1970. Setting: 86-acre urban campus with easy access to San Juan. Research spending for the previous fiscal year: $180,424. Educational spending for the previous fiscal year: $5171 per student. Total enrollment: 3,089. Faculty: 193 (143 full-time, 50 part-time). Student-undergrad faculty ratio is 16:1. 1,205 applied, 82% were admitted. Full-time: 2,900 students, 58% women, 42% men. Part-time: 189 students, 67% women, 33% men. 100% Hispanic/Latino. 5% 25 or older, 12% transferred in. Retention: 81% of full-time freshmen returned the following year. Academic areas with the most degrees conferred: business/marketing; psychology; biological/life sciences. Core. Calendar: semesters. Academic remediation for entering students, ESL program, advanced placement, accelerated degree program, freshman honors college, honors program, summer session for credit, part-time degree program, internships. ROTC: Army.

Entrance Requirements: Option: early admission. Required: high school transcript, SAT and SAT Subject Tests or ACT. Entrance: moderately difficult. Application deadline: 11/15. Notification: 3/4.

Costs Per Year: Application fee: $20. Commonwealth resident tuition: $1870 full-time. Nonresident tuition: $3824 full-time. Mandatory fees: $949 full-time. Full-time tuition and fees vary according to student level. College room and board: $8280. Tuition guaranteed not to increase for student's term of enrollment.

Collegiate Environment: Orientation program. Drama-theater group, choral group. Student services: health clinic. Campus security: 24-hour patrols. Adelina Coppin with 125,056 books, 23 microform titles, 487 serials, 14,513 audiovisual materials, and an OPAC. Operations spending for the previous fiscal year: $1.4 million. 81 computers available on campus for general student use. A campuswide network can be accessed. Students can access the following: online class registration. Staffed computer lab on campus provides training in use of computers, software, and the Internet.

■ UNIVERSITY OF PUERTO RICO, RÍO PIEDRAS

PO Box 23300
San Juan, PR 00931-3300
Tel: (787)764-0000
Web Site: www.uprrp.edu/

Description: Commonwealth-supported, university, coed. Part of University of Puerto Rico System. Awards bachelor's, master's, and doctoral degrees and post-master's certificates. Founded 1903. Setting: 281-acre urban campus. Research spending for the previous fiscal year: $17.1 million. Total enrollment: 18,966. Faculty: 1,084 (749 full-time, 335 part-time). Student-undergrad faculty ratio is 16:1. 8,290 applied, 36% were admitted. Students come from 34 other countries, 0.3% from out-of-commonwealth. 7% 25 or older. Retention: 91% of full-time freshmen returned the following year. Academic areas with the most degrees conferred: business/marketing; education; social sciences. Core. Calendar: semesters. Academic remediation for entering students, services for LD students, advanced placement, self-designed majors, honors program, double major, summer session for credit, part-time degree program, adult/continuing education programs, co-op programs and internships, graduate courses open to undergrads. Study abroad program. ROTC: Army, Air Force.

Entrance Requirements: Option: electronic application. Required: high school transcript, SAT, Aptitude Test in mathematics and verbal reasoning and the Academic Achievement Test in English, mathematics and Spanish offered by the College Entrance Examination Board (CEEB). Required for some: interview. Entrance: very difficult. Application deadline: 12/15.

Collegiate Environment: Orientation program. Drama-theater group, choral

group, student-run radio station. Social organizations: national fraternities, national sororities, local fraternities, local sororities. Student services: legal services, health clinic, personal-psychological counseling. Campus security: 24-hour emergency response devices, late night transport-escort service. Jose M. Lazaro Library plus 10 others with 1.8 million books, 1.7 million microform titles, 5,599 serials, 5,599 audiovisual materials, and an OPAC. 170 computers available on campus for general student use. A campuswide network can be accessed from student residence rooms. Students can access the following: online class registration. Staffed computer lab on campus.

■ UNIVERSITY OF PUERTO RICO AT UTUADO

PO Box 2500
Utuado, PR 00641-2500
Tel: (787)894-2828
Web Site: www.uprutuado.edu/

Description: Commonwealth-supported, 4-year, coed. Part of University of Puerto Rico System. Awards associate and bachelor's degrees. Founded 1979. Setting: 180-acre small town campus with easy access to San Juan. Total enrollment: 1,623. Faculty: 107 (74 full-time, 33 part-time). Student-undergrad faculty ratio is 18:1. 1,854 applied, 45% were admitted. Full-time: 1,448 students, 56% women, 44% men. Part-time: 175 students, 64% women, 36% men. 8% 25 or older, 0.2% transferred in. Retention: 59% of full-time freshmen returned the following year. Academic areas with the most degrees conferred: education; business/marketing. Core. Calendar: semesters. Academic remediation for entering students, services for LD students, honors program, summer session for credit, co-op programs.

Entrance Requirements: Options: electronic application, early admission, deferred admission. Required: SAT Subject Tests, CEEB required. Entrance: moderately difficult. Application deadline: Rolling.

Collegiate Environment: Orientation program. Drama-theater group, choral group. Social organizations: national fraternities, national sororities, local fraternities, local sororities. Major annual events: Festival Tierra Adentro, Baile de Bienvenida a Estudiants, Festival de la Voz. Student services: health clinic, personal-psychological counseling. Campus security: 24-hour emergency response devices and patrols.

■ UNIVERSITY OF THE SACRED HEART

PO Box 12383
San Juan, PR 00914-0383
Tel: (787)728-1515
Web Site: www.sagrado.edu/

Description: Independent Roman Catholic, comprehensive, coed. Awards associate, bachelor's, and master's degrees. Founded 1935. Setting: 33-acre urban campus. Endowment: $18.5 million. Total enrollment: 5,666. Faculty: 367 (122 full-time, 245 part-time). Student-undergrad faculty ratio is 20:1. 5,261 applied, 35% were admitted. Full-time: 3,765 students, 62% women, 38% men. Part-time: 870 students, 59% women, 41% men. 2% from out-of-commonwealth. 20% 25 or older, 8% transferred in. Retention: 75% of full-time freshmen returned the following year. Academic areas with the most degrees conferred: communication/journalism; business/marketing; psychology. Core. Calendar: semesters. Academic remediation for entering students, services for LD students, advanced placement, accelerated degree program, honors program, summer session for credit, part-time degree program, co-op programs and internships.

Entrance Requirements: Option: early admission. Required: high school transcript, minimum 2.5 high school GPA, 1 recommendation. Entrance: moderately difficult. Application deadline: 6/30.

Collegiate Environment: Orientation program. Drama-theater group, choral group, student-run newspaper. Most popular organizations: La Red (personal development center), Student Council, Judo Club, Athletic Association. Major annual events: Welcome Party, Inter-University Athletic Competition. Student services: health clinic, personal-psychological counseling. Campus security: 24-hour patrols. 500 computers available on campus for general student use. A campuswide network can be accessed from off-campus. Students can access the following: online class registration. Staffed computer lab on campus.

United States Virgin Islands

■ UNIVERSITY OF THE VIRGIN ISLANDS

2 John Brewers Bay
Saint Thomas, VI 00802-9990

Tel: (340)776-9200
E-mail: xallen@uvi.edu
Web Site: www.uvi.edu/

Description: Territory-supported, comprehensive, coed. Awards associate, bachelor's, and master's degrees and post-master's certificates. Founded 1962. Setting: 518-acre small town campus. System endowment: $26.4 million. Research spending for the previous fiscal year: $17.7 million. Total enrollment: 2,423. Faculty: 254 (108 full-time, 146 part-time). Student-undergrad faculty ratio is 12:1. 704 applied, 96% were admitted. 7% from top 10% of their high school class, 14% from top quarter, 24% from top half. 6 valedictorians. Full-time: 1,421 students, 68% women, 32% men. Part-time: 819 students, 73% women, 27% men. Students come from 28 states and territories, 16 other countries, 3% from out-of-territory. 0.05% American Indian or Alaska Native, non-Hispanic/Latino; 6% Hispanic/Latino; 78% African American, non-Hispanic/Latino; 0.3% Asian, non-Hispanic/Latino; 0% Native Hawaiian or other Pacific Islander, non-Hispanic/Latino; 6% international. 28% 25 or older, 14% live on campus, 4% transferred in. Retention: 70% of full-time freshmen returned the following year. Academic areas with the most degrees conferred: business/marketing; education; psychology. Core. Calendar: semesters. Academic remediation for entering students, services for LD students, advanced placement, honors program, independent study, distance learning, double major, summer session for credit, part-time degree program, external degree program, adult/continuing education programs, internships, graduate courses open to undergrads. Off campus study at National Student Exchange. Study abroad program. ROTC: Army.

Entrance Requirements: Options: electronic application, early admission, deferred admission. Required: SAT or ACT. Recommended: high school transcript, minimum 2 high school GPA. Entrance: minimally difficult. Application deadline: 4/30. Notification: continuous. SAT Reasoning Test deadline: 8/1. SAT Subject Test deadline: 8/1. Transfer credits accepted: Yes.

Costs Per Year: Application fee: $25. Territory resident tuition: $3990 full-time. Nonresident tuition: $11,970 full-time. Mandatory fees: $604 full-time. Full-time tuition and fees vary according to reciprocity agreements. College room and board: $9900. College room only: $4120. Room and board charges vary according to board plan and housing facility.

Collegiate Environment: Orientation program. Drama-theater group, choral group, student-run newspaper, radio station. Social organizations: 33 open to all; national sororities. Most popular organizations: The Squad, Predators, Golden Key Honor Society, National Student Exchange Club, St. Kitts and Nevis. Major annual events: Welcome Kontiki Boat Ride, Afternoon on the Green, Miss University of the Virgin Islands. Student services: health clinic, personal-psychological counseling. Campus security: 24-hour patrols. 366 college housing spaces available; 343 were occupied in 2012-13. No special consideration for freshman housing applicants. Options: coed, men-only, women-only housing available. Ralph M. Paiewonsky Library with 104,062 books, 370 serials, 1,351 audiovisual materials, an OPAC, and a Web page. 500 computers available on campus for general student use. A campuswide network can be accessed from student residence rooms. Students can access the following: online class registration.

■ ALBERTA BIBLE COLLEGE

635 Northmount Dr., NW
Calgary, AB, Canada T2K 3J6
Tel: (403)282-2994; Free: 877-542-9492
Fax: (403)282-3084
E-mail: admissions@abccampus.ca
Web Site: www.abccampus.ca/
Description: Independent Christian, 4-year, coed. Awards bachelor's degrees.
Costs Per Year: Tuition and fee charges are reported in Canadian dollars. Tuition: $5850 full-time, $585 per course part-time. Mandatory fees: $360 full-time, $95 per credit part-time. Full-time tuition and fees vary according to course load and program. Part-time tuition and fees vary according to course load and program.

■ ALBERTA COLLEGE OF ART & DESIGN

1407 14 Ave. NW
Calgary, AB, Canada T2N 4R3
Tel: (403)284-7600; Free: 800-251-8290
E-mail: admissions@acad.ca
Web Site: www.acad.ca/
Description: Province-supported, 4-year, coed. Awards bachelor's degrees. Founded 1926. Setting: 1-acre urban campus. Endowment: $5.1 million. Educational spending for the previous fiscal year: $7681 per student. Total enrollment: 1,155. Faculty: 135 (46 full-time, 89 part-time). Student-undergrad faculty ratio is 15:1. 365 applied, 64% were admitted. Full-time: 1,042 students, 72% women, 28% men. Part-time: 113 students, 72% women, 28% men. Students come from 9 provinces and territories, 22 other countries, 11% from out-of-province. 5% international. 23% 25 or older, 9% live on campus, 3% transferred in. Retention: 64% of full-time freshmen returned the following year. Academic area with the most degrees conferred: visual and performing arts. Core. Calendar: semesters. Academic remediation for entering students, services for LD students, advanced placement, independent study, summer session for credit, part-time degree program, adult/continuing education programs, internships. Study abroad program.
Entrance Requirements: Options: electronic application, early decision, international baccalaureate accepted. Required: essay, high school transcript, minimum 2 high school GPA, portfolio of artwork. Entrance: moderately difficult. Application deadlines: 2/1, 2/1 for nonresidents. Notification: 3/15, 3/15 for nonresidents. Transfer credits accepted: Yes.
Costs Per Year: Application fee: $85 Canadian dollars. Tuition, fee, and room only charges are reported in Canadian dollars. Province resident tuition: $4435 full-time, $147 per credit part-time. Canadian resident tuition: $466 per credit part-time. Mandatory fees: $831 full-time, $196 per term part-time. Full-time tuition and fees vary according to course load, program, and student level. Part-time tuition and fees vary according to course load, program, and student level. College room only: $5904. Room charges vary according to housing facility. International student tuition: $13,996 full-time.
Collegiate Environment: Orientation program. Social organizations: 12 open to all. Most popular organizations: The Rendez-Vous Collective, Conceptual Arts Club, Arts Mob, Anime and Gaming Club, ACAD Glass. Major annual events: Show and Sale, Artawearness, Graduating Exhibition. Student services: health clinic, personal-psychological counseling. Campus security: 24-hour emergency response devices and patrols, late night transport-escort service, controlled dormitory access. No special consider-

ation for freshman housing applicants. Option: coed housing available. Luke Lindoe Library with 110,826 books, 980 microform titles, 101 serials, 1,278 audiovisual materials, an OPAC, and a Web page. Operations spending for the previous fiscal year: $483,295. 103 computers available on campus for general student use. A campuswide network can be accessed. Students can access the following: online class registration. Staffed computer lab on campus.

■ AMBROSE UNIVERSITY COLLEGE

630, 833 4th Ave., SW
Calgary, AB, Canada T2P 3T5
Tel: (403)410-2000; Free: 800-461-1222
E-mail: enrolment@ambrose.edu
Web Site: www.ambrose.edu/
Description: Independent, comprehensive, coed, affiliated with The Christian and Missionary Alliance. Awards bachelor's and master's degrees (graduate and professional degrees are offered by Canadian Theological Seminary). Founded 1941. Setting: 16-acre urban campus. Student-undergrad faculty ratio is 15:1. Core. Calendar: semesters. Academic remediation for entering students, ESL program, services for LD students, advanced placement, accelerated degree program, honors program, independent study, distance learning, double major, summer session for credit, part-time degree program, external degree program, adult/continuing education programs, co-op programs and internships. Off campus study at University of Regina. Study abroad program.
Entrance Requirements: Open admission. Options: electronic application, early admission, deferred admission, international baccalaureate accepted. Required: essay, high school transcript, 2 recommendations. Recommended: medical history. Required for some: interview. Entrance: noncompetitive. Application deadline: Rolling. Notification: continuous until 9/1.
Costs Per Year: Application fee: $50 Canadian dollars. Tuition, fee, and room and board charges are reported in Canadian dollars. Comprehensive fee: $12,914 includes full-time tuition ($9090), mandatory fees ($850), and college room and board ($2974). College room only: $1549. Full-time tuition and fees vary according to course load, degree level, and program. Room and board charges vary according to board plan and housing facility. Part-time tuition: $303 per credit hour. Part-time mandatory fees: $28.25 per credit hour. Part-time tuition and fees vary according to course load, degree level, and program.
Collegiate Environment: Orientation program. Drama-theater group, choral group, student-run newspaper. Student services: health clinic, personal-psychological counseling, women's center. Campus security: 24-hour emergency response devices, controlled dormitory access. Archibald Foundation Library with 65,000 books, 546 serials, and an OPAC.

■ ATHABASCA UNIVERSITY

1 University Dr.
Athabasca, AB, Canada T9S 3A3
Tel: (780)675-6100; Free: 800-788-9041
Fax: (780)675-6437
Web Site: www.athabascau.ca/
Description: Province-supported, comprehensive, coed. Awards bachelor's, master's, and doctoral degrees and post-master's certificates (offers only external degree programs). Founded 1970. Setting: 480-acre small town

campus. Endowment: $1 million. Research spending for the previous fiscal year: $1.7 million. Educational spending for the previous fiscal year: $5780 per student. Total enrollment: 38,862. Faculty: 384. Part-time: 35,071 students, 68% women, 32% men. Students come from 33 provinces and territories, 87 other countries, 63% from out-of-province. 54% 25 or older. Core. Calendar: continuous. Academic remediation for entering students, ESL program, services for LD students, advanced placement, accelerated degree program, self-designed majors, independent study, distance learning, double major, summer session for credit, part-time degree program, external degree program, adult/continuing education programs, graduate courses open to undergrads. Off campus study. Study abroad program.
Entrance Requirements: Open admission. Options: electronic application, international baccalaureate accepted. Entrance: noncompetitive. Application deadline: Rolling. Notification: continuous. Transfer credits accepted: Yes.
Collegiate Environment: Student-run newspaper. Campus security: 24-hour emergency response devices. College housing not available. Athabasca University Library with 178,808 books, 1,000 microform titles, 32,619 serials, 17,628 audiovisual materials, an OPAC, and a Web page. Operations spending for the previous fiscal year: $1.3 million. 28 computers available on campus for general student use. Computer purchase/lease plans available. A campuswide network can be accessed from off-campus. Students can access the following: online class registration. Staffed computer lab on campus.
Community Environment: The central campus is located in a small rural town (population 2,415) in the northern section of the province. Learning Centers are located in larger urban centres.

■ **CONCORDIA UNIVERSITY COLLEGE OF ALBERTA**
7128 Ada Blvd., NW
Edmonton, AB, Canada T5B 4E4
Tel: (780)479-8481; Free: 866-479-5200
Fax: (780)474-1933
E-mail: admits@concordia.ab.ca
Web Site: www.concordia.ab.ca/
Description: Independent Lutheran, comprehensive, coed. Awards bachelor's and master's degrees. Founded 1921. Setting: 15-acre urban campus. Total enrollment: 1,579. Faculty: 153 (59 full-time, 94 part-time). Student-undergrad faculty ratio is 18:1. 1,163 applied, 65% were admitted. Students come from 11 provinces and territories, 26 other countries. 3% live on campus. Academic areas with the most degrees conferred: psychology; education; business/marketing. Core. Calendar: semesters. Services for LD students, advanced placement, honors program, independent study, double major, summer session for credit, part-time degree program, external degree program, internships. Study abroad program.
Entrance Requirements: Open admission for non-degree Open Studies students. Options: electronic application, early admission, international baccalaureate accepted. Required: high school transcript, minimum 2 high school GPA. Required for some: essay, 2 recommendations, interview. Entrance: moderately difficult. Application deadlines: 6/30, 5/1 for nonresidents. Notification: 9/5, 8/15 for nonresidents.
Collegiate Environment: Orientation program. Drama-theater group, choral group, student-run newspaper. Social organizations: 15 open to all. Most popular organizations: concert choir, Concordia Business Association, Science Club, Education Undergraduate Society, Psychology Students' Association. Major annual events: Orientation, Oktoberfest, Valentine Social and Christmas formal. Student services: personal-psychological counseling. Campus security: 24-hour patrols, late night transport-escort service. Arnold Guebert Memorial Library plus 1 other with 89,380 books, 27 microform titles, 8,565 serials, an OPAC, and a Web page. 250 computers available on campus for general student use. A campuswide network can be accessed from student residence rooms and from off campus. Staffed computer lab on campus.

■ **THE KING'S UNIVERSITY COLLEGE**
9125 50th St.
Edmonton, AB, Canada T6B 2H3
Tel: (780)465-3500; Free: 800-661-8582
Fax: (780)465-3534
E-mail: admissions@kingsu.ca
Web Site: www.kingsu.ca/
Description: Independent interdenominational, 4-year, coed. Awards bachelor's degrees. Founded 1979. Setting: 20-acre suburban campus. Endowment: $1.9 million. Research spending for the previous fiscal year: $372,727. Educational spending for the previous fiscal year: $8534 per

student. Total enrollment: 663. Faculty: 111 (50 full-time, 61 part-time). Student-undergrad faculty ratio is 9:1. 348 applied, 73% were admitted. Full-time: 555 students, 55% women, 45% men. Part-time: 32 students, 66% women, 34% men. Students come from 5 provinces and territories, 16 other countries, 14% from out-of-province. 15% 25 or older, 31% live on campus, 20% transferred in. Retention: 66% of full-time freshmen returned the following year. Academic areas with the most degrees conferred: education; psychology; social sciences. Core. Calendar: Canadian standard year. ESL program, services for LD students, advanced placement, independent study, double major, summer session for credit, part-time degree program, adult/continuing education programs, internships. Off campus study. Study abroad program.
Entrance Requirements: Options: electronic application, international baccalaureate accepted. Required: high school transcript, minimum 2 high school GPA, 1 recommendation. Required for some: essay, interview. Entrance: moderately difficult. Application deadline: Rolling. Notification: 8/15. Transfer credits accepted: Yes. Applicants placed on waiting list: 0. Wait-listed applicants offered admission: 0.
Costs Per Year: Application fee: $70 Canadian dollars. Tuition, fee, and room and board charges are reported in Canadian dollars. Comprehensive fee: $17,135 includes full-time tuition ($10,540), mandatory fees ($625), and college room and board ($5970). College room only: $3200. Full-time tuition and fees vary according to course load. Room and board charges vary according to board plan and housing facility. Part-time tuition: $340 per credit. Part-time mandatory fees: $156.25 per term. Part-time tuition and fees vary according to course load.
Collegiate Environment: Orientation program. Drama-theater group, choral group, student-run newspaper. Social organizations: 21 open to all. Most popular organizations: Micah Action and Awareness, The King's Players (drama club), Chamber and Concert Choirs, King's Science Society, The King's Commerce Association. Major annual events: Students' Association Barbecue, Students' Association Dance. Student services: personal-psychological counseling. Campus security: 24-hour emergency response devices, student patrols, controlled dormitory access. 260 college housing spaces available; 203 were occupied in 2012-13. Freshmen given priority for college housing. Options: coed, women-only housing available. Simona Maaskant with 115,115 books, 296 microform titles, 245 serials, 5,078 audiovisual materials, an OPAC, and a Web page. Operations spending for the previous fiscal year: $666,412. 70 computers available on campus for general student use. A campuswide network can be accessed from student residence rooms. Students can access the following: online class registration. Staffed computer lab on campus provides training in use of computers, software, and the Internet.

■ **MOUNT ROYAL UNIVERSITY**
4825 Mount Royal Gate SW
Calgary, AB, Canada T3E 6K6
Tel: (403)440-6111; Free: 877-440-5001
Fax: (403)440-5938
Web Site: www.mtroyal.ca/
Description: Province-supported, 4-year, coed. Awards bachelor's degrees. Founded 1911.
Entrance Requirements: Required: high school transcript.

■ **PRAIRIE BIBLE INSTITUTE**
330 Sixth Ave. N
Three Hills, AB, Canada T0M 2N0
Tel: (403)443-5511; Free: 800-661-2425
Fax: (403)443-5540
E-mail: admissions@prairie.edu
Web Site: www.prairie.edu/
Description: Independent interdenominational, 4-year, coed. Awards associate and bachelor's degrees. Founded 1922. Setting: 130-acre small town campus with easy access to Calgary. Core. Calendar: semesters. ESL program, advanced placement, accelerated degree program, part-time degree program, adult/continuing education programs, internships. Study abroad program.
Entrance Requirements: Option: electronic application. Required: essay, high school transcript, 2 recommendations. Recommended: minimum 2.0 high school GPA. Required for some: minimum 3.0 high school GPA. Entrance: minimally difficult. Application deadline: 8/15.
Collegiate Environment: Orientation program. Drama-theater group, choral group, student-run newspaper, radio station. Student services: health clinic, personal-psychological counseling. Campus security: 24-hour emergency

response devices and patrols, late night transport-escort service, controlled dormitory access. T. S. Rendall Library with 60,745 books and 458 serials. 30 computers available on campus for general student use. Staffed computer lab on campus.

■ **ROCKY MOUNTAIN COLLEGE**
4039 Brentwood Rd., NW
Calgary, AB, Canada T2L 1L1
Tel: (403)284-5100; Free: 877-YOUnRMC
E-mail: enrolment@rockymountaincollege.ca
Web Site: www.rockymountaincollege.ca/

Description: Independent, 4-year, coed, affiliated with Missionary Church. Awards bachelor's degrees. Founded 1992. Setting: 1-acre urban campus with easy access to Calgary, Alberta, Canada. Endowment: $343,200. Educational spending for the previous fiscal year: $2330 per student. Core. Calendar: semesters. Academic remediation for entering students, advanced placement, distance learning, double major, summer session for credit, part-time degree program, adult/continuing education programs, internships.

Entrance Requirements: Options: electronic application, deferred admission, international baccalaureate accepted. Required: essay, high school transcript, 2 recommendations. Required for some: interview. Entrance: noncompetitive. Application deadline: Rolling. Transfer credits accepted: Yes.

Costs Per Year: Application fee: $50 Canadian dollars. Tuition and fee charges are reported in Canadian dollars. Tuition: $310 per credit part-time.

Collegiate Environment: Orientation program. Drama-theater group, choral group. Student services: personal-psychological counseling. Campus security: 24-hour emergency response devices. Main library plus 1 other with 42,000 books, 135 serials, 225 audiovisual materials, and a Web page. Operations spending for the previous fiscal year: $101,240. 12 computers available on campus for general student use. A campuswide network can be accessed from student residence rooms and from off campus. Students can access the following: online class registration. Staffed computer lab on campus provides training in use of computers, software, and the Internet.

■ **SOUTHERN ALBERTA INSTITUTE OF TECHNOLOGY**
1301 16th Ave. NW
Calgary, AB, Canada T2M 0L4
Tel: (403)284-8110; Free: 877-284-SAIT
Fax: (403)284-7112
Web Site: www.sait.ca/

Description: Province-supported, primarily 2-year, coed. Awards certificates, diplomas, terminal associate, and bachelor's degrees. Founded 1916. Setting: 96-acre urban campus. Total enrollment: 7,672. Faculty: 962. Full-time: 6,954 students, 42% women, 58% men. Part-time: 718 students, 45% women, 55% men. Calendar: trimesters. Services for LD students, independent study, distance learning, co-op programs and internships. Off campus study.

Entrance Requirements: Options: electronic application, early admission, early decision. Required: high school transcript. Required for some: essay, interview. Application deadlines: Rolling, Rolling for nonresidents. Transfer credits accepted: Yes.

Collegiate Environment: Orientation program. Drama-theater group, student-run newspaper, radio station. Social organizations: 17 open to all. Most popular organizations: SAIT Petroleum Society, Business Student's Association, Global Passport, Environmental Technology Students Organization, Civil Engineering Technology Concrete Toboggan. Major annual events: Orientation, Welcome Week, Graduation. Student services: health clinic, personal-psychological counseling. Campus security: 24-hour emergency response devices and patrols, late night transport-escort service. SAIT Library with 135,000 books, 100 serials, an OPAC, and a Web page.

■ **UNIVERSITY OF ALBERTA**
Edmonton, AB, Canada T6G 2E1
Tel: (780)492-3111
Fax: (780)492-7172
E-mail: registrar@ualberta.ca
Web Site: www.ualberta.ca/

Description: Province-supported, university, coed. Awards bachelor's, master's, and doctoral degrees. Founded 1906. Setting: 1,200-acre urban campus. Endowment: $767.2 million. Total enrollment: 38,290. Student-undergrad faculty ratio is 20:1. Students come from 13 provinces and territories, 110 other countries, 9% from out-of province. Calendar: Canadian standard year. Academic remediation for entering students, ESL program,

services for LD students, advanced placement, accelerated degree program, self-designed majors, honors program, independent study, distance learning, double major, summer session for credit, part-time degree program, external degree program, adult/continuing education programs, co-op programs and internships, graduate courses open to undergrads. Off campus study. Study abroad program.

Entrance Requirements: Options: electronic application, early admission, early decision, early action, international baccalaureate accepted. Recommended: minimum 2 high school GPA, SAT, ACT, SAT or ACT, SAT and SAT Subject Tests or ACT, SAT Subject Tests. Required for some: essay, high school transcript, interview, portfolios/auditions. Entrance: moderately difficult. Application deadline: 5/1. Notification: continuous until 9/1. Preference given to province residents for some programs, aboriginal students. SAT Reasoning Test deadline: 8/1. SAT Subject Test deadline: 8/1. Transfer credits accepted: Yes.

Collegiate Environment: Orientation program. Drama-theater group, choral group, student-run newspaper, radio station. Social organizations: 400 open to all; national fraternities, national sororities, local fraternities, local sororities. Major annual events: Week of Welcome, Anti-Freeze (January week of welcome). Student services: legal services, health clinic, personal-psychological counseling, women's center. Campus security: 24-hour emergency response devices and patrols, student patrols, late night transport-escort service, controlled dormitory access. Rutherford Library plus 13 others with 9.7 million books, an OPAC, and a Web page. Operations spending for the previous fiscal year: $42 million. 721 computers available on campus for general student use. Computer purchase/lease plans available. A campuswide network can be accessed from student residence rooms and from off campus. Students can access the following: online class registration. Staffed computer lab on campus.

Community Environment: Edmonton is the provincial capital and largest city of Alberta, with a population of 666,100. It takes its name from Fort Edmonton, an early trading post of the Hudson Bay Company. The city, the center of an important farming region, is also an oil and gas exploration and manufacturing center. Major industries include pipeline construction, chemical plants, meat packing, construction, oilfield construction and servicing, and food processing. The city was the first to establish a municipal airport and has long been the Gateway to the North. It is easily accessible by air, rail, bus and car. It is also home to the Alberta Research Council and Edmonton Research Park.

■ **UNIVERSITY OF CALGARY**
2500 University Dr., NW
Calgary, AB, Canada T2N 1N4
Tel: (403)220-5110
Fax: (403)289-1253
E-mail: vandam@ucalgary.ca
Web Site: www.ucalgary.ca/

Description: Province-supported, university, coed. Awards bachelor's, master's, and doctoral degrees and post-master's certificates. Founded 1945. Setting: 213-hectare urban campus. Endowment: $426 million. Total enrollment: 28,069. Faculty: 2,707 (1,731 full-time, 976 part-time). Student-undergrad faculty ratio is 13:1. 6,928 applied, 58% were admitted. Students come from 12 provinces and territories, 94 other countries, 17% from out-of province. 18% 25 or older. Retention: 83% of full-time freshmen returned the following year. Academic areas with the most degrees conferred: social sciences; health professions and related sciences; business/marketing. Calendar: semesters. ESL program, services for LD students, advanced placement, honors program, distance learning, double major, summer session for credit, part-time degree program, adult/continuing education programs, co-op programs and internships, graduate courses open to undergrads. Study abroad program.

Entrance Requirements: Options: electronic application, early admission, international baccalaureate accepted. Required: high school transcript. Required for some: SAT, SAT Subject Tests. Entrance: moderately difficult. Application deadline: 4/1. Notification: continuous.

Collegiate Environment: Orientation program. Drama-theater group, choral group, student-run newspaper, radio station. Social organizations: 150 open to all; national fraternities, national sororities. Most popular organizations: Muslim Students' Association, Snowboard Club, Ski Club, Video Game Club, Student Dance Club. Major annual events: Welcome Week (Orientation U of C 101), Bermuda Shorts Day (last day of classes), Club Week. Student services: legal services, health clinic, personal-psychological counseling, women's center. Campus security: 24-hour emergency response devices and patrols, late night transport-escort service, controlled dormitory access.

MacKimmie Library plus 5 others with 3.3 million books, 3.6 million microform titles, 37,285 serials, 306,141 audiovisual materials, an OPAC, and a Web page. 800 computers available on campus for general student use. Computer purchase/lease plans available. A campuswide network can be accessed from student residence rooms and from off campus. Students can access the following: online class registration. Staffed computer lab on campus (open 24 hours a day) provides training in use of computers, software, and the Internet.

Community Environment: Situated centrally in western Canada, Calgary is located at the convergence of the Bow and Elbow Rivers, As Canada's energy capital and western Canada's business capital, Calgary is home to the second largest concentration of corporate head offices in the country. Within an hour's drive are the Rocky Mountains, Kananaskis Valley and Banff National Park where hiking, skiing, canoeing, mountain climbing, and mountain biking can be enjoyed. Calgary is home to more than 820,000 people, which makes it Canada's fifth largest city. Cultural activities abound with a philharmonic orchestra, as well as theater and dance companies, museums, art galleries, libraries, and a planetarium.

■ **UNIVERSITY OF LETHBRIDGE**
4401 University Dr.
Lethbridge, AB, Canada T1K 3M4
Tel: (403)329-2111
E-mail: inquiries@uleth.ca
Web Site: www.uleth.ca/
Description: Province-supported, university, coed. Awards bachelor's, master's, and doctoral degrees and post-master's certificates. Founded 1967. Setting: 576-acre urban campus. Endowment: $37.5 million. Research spending for the previous fiscal year: $15.1 million. Educational spending for the previous fiscal year: $8376 per student. Total enrollment: 8,359. Faculty: 645 (569 full-time, 76 part-time). Student-undergrad faculty ratio is 12:1. 2,483 applied, 52% were admitted. Students come from 21 provinces and territories, 65 other countries, 11% from out-of-province. 24% 25 or older, 10% live on campus. Retention: 76% of full-time freshmen returned the following year. Academic areas with the most degrees conferred: business/marketing; education; health professions and related sciences. Core. Calendar: semesters. Academic remediation for entering students, ESL program, services for LD students, accelerated degree program, self-designed majors, independent study, distance learning, double major, summer session for credit, part-time degree program, co-op programs and internships, graduate courses open to undergrads. Off campus study at Southern Alberta Institute of Technology. Study abroad program.
Entrance Requirements: Options: electronic application, deferred admission, international baccalaureate accepted. Required: high school transcript, minimum 2 high school GPA. Required for some: minimum 3 high school GPA, interview. Entrance: moderately difficult. Application deadline: 6/1. Notification: continuous. Transfer credits accepted: Yes.
Costs Per Year: Application fee: $75 Canadian dollars. Tuition, fee, and room and board charges are reported in Canadian dollars. Province resident tuition: $4925 full-time, $492.50 per course part-time. Canadian resident tuition: $4925 full-time, $492.50 per course part-time. Mandatory fees: $692 full-time, $117.94 per term part-time. Full-time tuition and fees vary according to course load. Part-time tuition and fees vary according to course load. College room and board: $7932. College room only: $4608. Room and board charges vary according to board plan and housing facility. International student tuition: $11,150 full-time.
Collegiate Environment: Orientation program. Drama-theater group, choral

group, student-run newspaper, radio station. Social organizations: 81 open to all; national fraternities, local fraternities, local sororities. Most popular organizations: Management Students Society, Inter-Varsity Christian Fellowship, Organization of Residence Students, Agricultural Students Society, Education Undergraduate Society. Major annual events: Fresh Fest, Imaginus, Student Union Cabarets. Student services: health clinic, personal-psychological counseling, women's center. Campus security: 24-hour emergency response devices and patrols, student patrols, late night transport-escort service, controlled dormitory access, video camera monitored entrances, hallways. The University of Lethbridge Library with 602,148 books, 894,215 microform titles, 6,533 serials, 10,661 audiovisual materials, an OPAC, and a Web page. Operations spending for the previous fiscal year: $5.8 million. 613 computers available on campus for general student use. Computer purchase/lease plans available. A campuswide network can be accessed from student residence rooms and from off campus. Students can access the following: online class registration. Staffed computer lab on campus provides training in use of computers, software, and the Internet.
Community Environment: The centre of a prosperous farming and ranching area, Lethbridge is characterized by its many green areas and parks, and its abundant cultural and recreational facilities. It is located in southern Alberta, approximately 145 kilometres (90 miles) east of the Canadian Rockies and 95 kilometres (60 miles) north of the United States border.

■ **VANGUARD COLLEGE**
11617 106 Ave., NW
Edmonton, AB, Canada T5H 0S1
Tel: (780)452-0808
Fax: (780)452-5803
E-mail: admissions@vanguardcollege.com
Web Site: www.vanguardcollege.com/
Description: Independent, 4-year, coed, affiliated with Pentecostal Assemblies of Canada. Administratively affiliated with Pentecostal Assemblies of Canada (PAOC). Awards bachelor's degrees. Founded 1946. Setting: 4-acre urban campus. Student-undergrad faculty ratio is 11:1. 6% live on campus. Core. Calendar: semesters. Services for LD students, advanced placement, accelerated degree program, independent study, distance learning, double major, summer session for credit, part-time degree program, internships. Off campus study.
Entrance Requirements: Options: electronic application, early decision. Required: essay, high school transcript, 2 recommendations. Application deadlines: 8/19, 4/15 for early decision. Transfer credits accepted: Yes.
Costs Per Year: Application fee: $75. Tuition: $6435 full-time, $195 per credit hour part-time. Mandatory fees: $1000 full-time, $12 per credit hour part-time, $55 per term part-time. Full-time tuition and fees vary according to course load and program. Part-time tuition and fees vary according to course load and program. College room only: $3600. Room charges vary according to housing facility.
Collegiate Environment: Orientation program. Choral group. Major annual events: All School Retreat, Soccer Championship, Christmas Banquet. 12 college housing spaces available; all were occupied in 2012-13. Freshmen given priority for college housing. Options: men-only, women-only housing available. Vanguard College Library: Schalm Memorial Collection with 55,000 books, 282,055 serials, 1,350 audiovisual materials, and an OPAC. 8 computers available on campus for general student use. Computer purchase/lease plans available. A campuswide network can be accessed. Students can access the following: online class registration. Staffed computer lab on campus.

■ BRITISH COLUMBIA INSTITUTE OF TECHNOLOGY

3700 Willingdon Ave.
Burnaby, BC, Canada V5G 3H2
Tel: (604)434-5734; Free: 866-434-1610
Fax: (604)278-5363
Web Site: www.bcit.ca/

Description: Province-supported, 4-year, coed. Awards associate and bachelor's degrees. Founded 1964. Setting: 103-acre urban campus with easy access to Vancouver. Total enrollment: 22,507. Faculty: 1,359 (735 full-time, 624 part-time). 7,721 applied, 44% were admitted.

Entrance Requirements: Option: electronic application. Required: high school transcript. Required for some: essay, 2 recommendations, interview. Entrance: moderately difficult.

Collegiate Environment: Student-run newspaper, radio station. Student services: health clinic, personal-psychological counseling, women's center. Campus security: 24-hour emergency response devices and patrols, student patrols, late night transport-escort service. British Columbia Institute of Technology Library plus 1 other with 169,404 books, 39,295 microform titles, 1,080 serials, 4,627 audiovisual materials, an OPAC, and a Web page. Operations spending for the previous fiscal year: $2.9 million.

■ COLUMBIA BIBLE COLLEGE

2940 Clearbrook Rd.
Abbotsford, BC, Canada V2T 2Z8
Tel: (604)853-3358; Free: 800-283-0881
Fax: (604)853-3063
E-mail: candice.green@columbiabc.edu
Web Site: www.columbiabc.edu/

Description: Independent Mennonite Brethren, 4-year, coed. Awards bachelor's degrees. Founded 1936. Setting: 9-acre urban campus with easy access to Vancouver. Endowment: $758,680. Educational spending for the previous fiscal year: $4738 per student. Total enrollment: 416. Faculty: 37 (12 full-time, 25 part-time). Student-undergrad faculty ratio is 18:1. 294 applied, 75% were admitted. Students come from 8 provinces and territories, 5 other countries, 19% from out-of-province. 18% 25 or older, 35% live on campus. Retention: 75% of full-time freshmen returned the following year. Academic area with the most degrees conferred: theology and religious vocations. Core. Calendar: semesters. Academic remediation for entering students, services for LD students, advanced placement, independent study, distance learning, part-time degree program, internships. Off campus study. Study abroad program.

Entrance Requirements: Open admission for mature students, age 21 or older without a high school diploma. Options: electronic application, early admission, early decision, deferred admission, international baccalaureate accepted. Required: essay, high school transcript, minimum 2 high school GPA, 2 recommendations, must be Christian. Entrance: noncompetitive. Application deadlines: 8/15, 8/15 for nonresidents, 5/1 for early decision. Notification: continuous, continuous for nonresidents. Transfer credits accepted: Yes. Early decision applicants: 196. Early decision applicants admitted: 108.

Costs Per Year: Application fee: $50 Canadian dollars. Tuition, fee, and room and board charges are reported in Canadian dollars. Comprehensive fee: $14,480 includes full-time tuition ($9270) and college room and board ($5210). Full-time tuition varies according to course load. Room and board charges vary according to board plan. Part-time tuition: $309 per credit. Part-time tuition varies according to course load.

Collegiate Environment: Orientation program. Choral group. Student services: personal-psychological counseling. Campus security: late night transport-escort service, controlled dormitory access, night watchman 11 pm to 6 am. 200 college housing spaces available; 144 were occupied in 2012-13. Freshmen given priority for college housing. On-campus residence required through sophomore year. Options: men-only, women-only housing available. Columbia Resource Center with 51,154 books, 2,426 microform titles, 5,972 serials, 4,236 audiovisual materials, an OPAC, and a Web page. 30 computers available on campus for general student use. A campuswide network can be accessed from student residence rooms and from off campus. Staffed computer lab on campus provides training in use of the Internet.

■ EMILY CARR UNIVERSITY OF ART + DESIGN

1399 Johnston St.
Vancouver, BC, Canada V6H 3R9
Tel: (604)844-3800; Free: 800-832-7788
Fax: (604)844-3801
E-mail: admissions@ecuad.ca
Web Site: www.ecuad.ca/

Description: Province-supported, comprehensive, coed. Awards bachelor's and master's degrees. Founded 1925. Setting: urban campus. Total enrollment: 1,584. Faculty: 220 (56 full-time, 164 part-time). Student-undergrad faculty ratio is 18:1. Retention: 87% of full-time freshmen returned the following year. Core. Services for LD students, advanced placement, part-time degree program, co-op programs. Study abroad program.

Entrance Requirements: Options: electronic application, international baccalaureate accepted. Required: essay, high school transcript, minimum 2.5 high school GPA, portfolio and questionnaire. Entrance: moderately difficult. Application deadline: 1/15. Notification: 3/1. Transfer credits accepted: Yes.

Costs Per Year: Application fee: $40 Canadian dollars. Tuition and fee charges are reported in Canadian dollars. Province resident tuition: $3642 full-time, $121.40 per credit part-time. Mandatory fees: $232 full-time. Full-time tuition and fees vary according to course load. Part-time tuition varies according to course load. International student tuition: $12,500 full-time.

Collegiate Environment: Orientation program. Student-run newspaper. Student services: personal-psychological counseling. Campus security: 24-hour emergency response devices and patrols. 25,000 books, 200 serials, 3,100 audiovisual materials, an OPAC, and a Web page.

■ OKANAGAN COLLEGE

1000 KLO Rd.
Kelowna, BC, Canada V1Y 4X8
Tel: (250)762-5445; Free: 877-755-2266
E-mail: pgcampo@okanagan.bc.ca
Web Site: www.okanagan.bc.ca/

Description: Province-supported, 4-year, coed. Part of Ministry of Advanced Education, Industry Training Authority. Awards associate and bachelor's degrees. Founded 2005. Setting: 13-acre urban campus. Total enrollment: 3,363. Faculty: 241 (173 full-time, 68 part-time). Student-undergrad faculty ratio is 14:1. Full-time: 2,122 students, 54% women, 46% men. Part-time: 1,241 students, 59% women, 41% men. Students come from 10 provinces and territories, 46 other countries, 4% from out-of-province. 24% 25 or older, 2% transferred in. Retention: 57% of full-time freshmen returned the following year. Academic areas with the most degrees conferred: business/

marketing; computer and information sciences. Academic remediation for entering students, ESL program, services for LD students, advanced placement, honors program, distance learning, summer session for credit, part-time degree program, external degree program, adult/continuing education programs, co-op programs and internships. Off campus study at BC Campus. Study abroad program.

Entrance Requirements: Required for some: essay, high school transcript, minimum 2 high school GPA, interview.

Costs Per Year: Tuition and fee charges are reported in Canadian dollars. Province resident tuition: $3,140 full-time, $100.92 per credit part-time. Canadian resident tuition: $3,140 full-time, $100.92 per credit part-time. Mandatory fees: $714 full-time, $9.20 per credit part-time, $94.25 per term part-time. Full-time tuition and fees vary according to course level, course load, location, and program. Part-time tuition and fees vary according to course level, course load, location, and program. International student tuition: $11,000 full-time.

Collegiate Environment: Orientation program. Choral group, student-run newspaper. Major annual events: Student Orientation, Graduation, Student Association Christmas Lunch. Student services: personal-psychological counseling. Campus security: 24-hour emergency response devices and patrols, late night transport-escort service, controlled dormitory access. 143 college housing spaces available; 140 were occupied in 2012-13. No special consideration for freshman housing applicants. Option: coed housing available. Okanagan College Library with 139,393 books, 64,800 serials, 11,211 audiovisual materials, an OPAC, and a Web page. 1,050 computers available on campus for general student use. A campuswide network can be accessed. Students can access the following: online class registration. Staffed computer lab on campus provides training in use of computers, software, and the Internet.

■ **ROYAL ROADS UNIVERSITY**
2005 Sooke Rd.
Victoria, BC, Canada V9B 5Y2
Tel: (250)391-2511; Free: 800-788-8028
Fax: (250)391-2522
E-mail: learn.more@royalroads.ca
Web Site: www.royalroads.ca/

Description: Province-supported, upper-level, coed. Awards bachelor's, master's, and doctoral degrees. Founded 1996. Setting: 565-acre suburban campus. Total enrollment: 3,120. Faculty: (50 full-time). Calendar: continuous. Accelerated degree program, distance learning, summer session for credit, adult/continuing education programs. Study abroad program.

Collegiate Environment: Campus security: 24-hour emergency response devices and patrols, late night transport-escort service. Coronel Memorial Library with 117,326 books, 39,667 serials, 861 audiovisual materials, an OPAC, and a Web page.

■ **SIMON FRASER UNIVERSITY**
8888 University Dr.
Burnaby, BC, Canada V5A 1S6
Tel: (604)291-3111
Fax: (604)291-4969
E-mail: undergraduate-admissions@sfu.ca
Web Site: www.sfu.ca/

Description: Province-supported, university, coed. Awards bachelor's, master's, and doctoral degrees and post-master's certificates. Founded 1965. Setting: suburban campus with easy access to Vancouver. Endowment: $176.9 million. Educational spending for the previous fiscal year: $8386 per student. Total enrollment: 29,718. Faculty: 948 (938 full-time, 10 part-time). Student-undergrad faculty ratio is 23:1. 14,618 applied, 52% were admitted. Full-time: 13,352 students, 55% women, 45% men. Part-time: 13,771 students, 53% women, 47% men. Students come from 11 provinces and territories, 84 other countries, 9% from out-of province. 12% 25 or older, 9% live on campus, 5% transferred in. Retention: 88% of full-time freshmen returned the following year. Academic areas with the most degrees conferred: social sciences; business/marketing; education. Core. Calendar: trimesters. Academic remediation for entering students, ESL program, services for LD students, advanced placement, honors program, independent study, distance learning, double major, summer session for credit, part-time degree program, adult/continuing education programs, co-op programs and internships, graduate courses open to undergrads. Off campus study. Study abroad program.

Entrance Requirements: Options: electronic application, early admission, deferred admission, international baccalaureate accepted. Required: high

school transcript, minimum 3 high school GPA. Required for some: essay, interview, SAT or ACT. Entrance: moderately difficult. Application deadline: 4/30. Notification: continuous until 6/30. SAT Reasoning Test deadline: 4/15. Transfer credits accepted: Yes.

Collegiate Environment: Orientation program. Drama-theater group, student-run newspaper, radio station. Social organizations: 147 open to all. Most popular organizations: The Peak Newspaper, orientation leaders, Crisis line, Women's Centre, Simon Fraser Public Interest Research Group. Major annual events: Convocation, Clubs' Day, Terry Fox Run. Student services: health clinic, personal-psychological counseling, women's center. Campus security: 24-hour emergency response devices and patrols, student patrols, late night transport-escort service, controlled dormitory access, safe-walk stations, 24-hour safe study area. 1,800 college housing spaces available; 1,400 were occupied in 2012-13. Freshmen given priority for college housing. Options: coed, women-only housing available. Bennett Library plus 2 others with 1.4 million books, 951,764 microform titles, 55,273 serials, 257,042 audiovisual materials, an OPAC, and a Web page. Operations spending for the previous fiscal year: $15 million. 900 computers available on campus for general student use. A campuswide network can be accessed from student residence rooms and from off campus. Students can access the following: online class registration. Staffed computer lab on campus.

Community Environment: The 1,200 acre campus is situated atop Burnaby Mountain, making Simon Fraser a striking campus with spectacular views of the coastal mountains and the cities of the Lower Mainland. The outstanding architecture has won many awards. Services on campus include day care centres, Health Services (including physicians, a psychiatrist, nurses and physiotherapists), Athletic and Recreational Services (two full gymnasia, swimming and diving pools, tennis, squash and racquetball courts, sauna, and weight rooms), a campus radio station, printshop, legal advice clinic, ecumenical chaplaincy, women's centre, bookstores and student Pub. Simon Fraser University is wheelchair accessible.

■ **SUMMIT PACIFIC COLLEGE**
Box 1700
Abbotsford, BC, Canada V2S 7E7
Tel: (604)853-7491; Free: 800-976-8388
Fax: (604)853-8951
E-mail: registrar@summitpacific.ca
Web Site: www.summitpacific.ca/

Description: Independent, 4-year, coed, affiliated with Pentecostal Assemblies of Canada. Awards bachelor's degrees. Founded 1941. Setting: 101-acre suburban campus with easy access to Vancouver. Core. Calendar: semesters. Academic remediation for entering students, summer session for credit, part-time degree program, internships. Off campus study at Fraser Valley College, Trinity Western University.

Entrance Requirements: Option: deferred admission. Required: essay, high school transcript, 3 recommendations. Required for some: interview. Entrance: moderately difficult. Application deadline: Rolling.

Collegiate Environment: Drama-theater group, choral group. Student services: personal-psychological counseling. Campus security: student patrols, campus gate locked after 11 pm. Lorne Hudson Philip Memorial Library with 35,409 books and 132 serials.

■ **THOMPSON RIVERS UNIVERSITY**
900 McGill Rd.
Kamloops, BC, Canada V2C 0C8
Tel: (250)828-5000
Fax: (250)828-5086
E-mail: jkeller@tru.ca
Web Site: www.tru.ca/

Description: Province-supported, comprehensive, coed. Part of Ministry of Advanced Education, Province of British Columbia. Awards associate, bachelor's, and master's degrees. Founded 1970. Setting: 100-acre small town campus. Endowment: $16.1 million. Research spending for the previous fiscal year: $4.1 million. Educational spending for the previous fiscal year: $7515 per student. Total enrollment: 7,649. Faculty: 457. 2,986 applied, 82% were admitted. Students come from 11 provinces and territories, 78 other countries, 9% from out-of province. 27% 25 or older, 14% live on campus. Retention: 71% of full-time freshmen returned the following year. Calendar: semesters. Academic remediation for entering students, ESL program, services for LD students, advanced placement, accelerated degree program, honors program, independent study, distance learning, double major, summer session for credit, part-time degree program, external degree program, adult/continuing education programs, co-op programs and internships. Off campus study. Study abroad program.

Entrance Requirements: Open admission For First Year University: Arts, Science, Business, Tourism. Options: electronic application, early admission, early decision, deferred admission, international baccalaureate accepted. Required: high school transcript. Required for some: essay, interview. Application deadlines: 4/30, 4/30 for nonresidents, 3/1 for early decision plan 1, 3/1 for early decision plan 2. Notification: continuous until 4/30, continuous until 4/30 for nonresidents, 3/1 for early decision plan 1, 3/1 for early decision plan 2. Transfer credits accepted: Yes. Early decision applicants: 82. Early decision applicants admitted: 82.

Costs Per Year: Application fee: $25.50 Canadian dollars. Tuition, fee, and room only charges are reported in Canadian dollars. Province resident tuition: $3755 full-time, $125.18 per credit part-time. Canadian resident tuition: $3755 full-time, $125.18 per credit part-time. Mandatory fees: $635 full-time, $21.19 per credit part-time. College room only: $6240. Room charges vary according to housing facility. International student tuition: $13,800 full-time.

Collegiate Environment: Orientation program. Drama-theater group, choral group, student-run newspaper, radio station. Social organizations: national fraternities, national sororities. Major annual events: Welcome Back BBQ, Orientation, Open House and Career Day. Student services: health clinic, personal-psychological counseling. Campus security: 24-hour emergency response devices and patrols, student patrols, late night transport-escort service, controlled dormitory access. 1,100 college housing spaces available; all were occupied in 2012-13. Option: coed housing available. Thompson Rivers University Library plus 2 others with 285,426 books, 1,817 microform titles, 9,585 serials, 11,246 audiovisual materials, an OPAC, and a Web page. Operations spending for the previous fiscal year: $2.4 million. 1,200 computers available on campus for general student use. Computer purchase/lease plans available. A campuswide network can be accessed from student residence rooms and from off campus. Students can access the following: online class registration, Learning Management systems including Moodle and Blackboard, Network drive space (250mb), Wireless access, Remote access to their network drive, student elections, Online payments, financial forms/info, updating personal contact information. Staffed computer lab on campus provides training in use of computers, software, and the Internet.

■ **TRINITY WESTERN UNIVERSITY**
7600 Glover Rd.
Langley, BC, Canada V2Y 1Y1
Tel: (604)888-7511; Free: 888-468-6898
Fax: (604)513-2061
Web Site: www.twu.ca/

Description: Independent, comprehensive, coed, affiliated with Evangelical Free Church of America. Awards bachelor's and master's degrees. Founded 1962. Setting: 100-acre suburban campus with easy access to Vancouver. Total enrollment: 4,396. Core. Calendar: semesters. ESL program, advanced placement, honors program, independent study, distance learning, double major, summer session for credit, part-time degree program, adult/continuing education programs, co-op programs and internships. Off campus study. Study abroad program.

Entrance Requirements: Options: electronic application, deferred admission, international baccalaureate accepted. Required: essay, high school transcript. Required for some: interview. Entrance: moderately difficult. Application deadline: 6/15. Notification: continuous.

Collegiate Environment: Orientation program. Drama-theater group, choral group, student-run newspaper. Student services: health clinic, personal-psychological counseling. Freshmen given priority for college housing. On-campus residence required through sophomore year.

Community Environment: Trinity Western is set on a wooded 100-acre campus, adjacent to the Trans Canada Highway No. 1, between Langley and Fort Langley. Students enjoy the solitude of a rural environment and have easy access to the beautiful urban center of Vancouver, just 45 minutes away. Public transportation is available off University Lane.

■ **THE UNIVERSITY OF BRITISH COLUMBIA**
2075 Wesbrook Mall
Vancouver, BC, Canada V6T 1Z1
Tel: (604)822-2211
Fax: (604)822-3599
E-mail: registrar.admissions@ubc.ca
Web Site: www.ubc.ca/

Description: Province-supported, university, coed. Awards bachelor's, master's, and doctoral degrees. Founded 1915. Setting: 1,000-acre urban campus with easy access to Vancouver. Endowment: $958.1 million. Total enrollment: 49,097. Faculty: 2,779 (2,722 full-time, 57 part-time). Student-undergrad faculty ratio is 15:1. 33,731 applied, 46% were admitted. Full-time: 23,221 students, 53% women, 47% men. Part-time: 10,176 students, 56% women, 44% men. Students come from 39 provinces and territories, 150 other countries. 25% live on campus, 6% transferred in. Retention: 92% of full-time freshmen returned the following year. Calendar: Canadian standard year. Academic remediation for entering students, ESL program, services for LD students, advanced placement, self-designed majors, freshman honors college, honors program, distance learning, double major, summer session for credit, part-time degree program, adult/continuing education programs, co-op programs and internships. Off campus study. Study abroad program.

Entrance Requirements: Options: electronic application, deferred admission, international baccalaureate accepted. Required: essay, high school transcript, minimum 2.6 high school GPA, English Language Admission Standard. Required for some: SAT or ACT plus Writing required of applicants following US curriculum. Entrance: very difficult. Application deadlines: 1/31, 1/31 for nonresidents. Notification: continuous, continuous for nonresidents. Transfer credits accepted: Yes.

Costs Per Year: Application fee: $102 Canadian dollars. Tuition, fee, and room and board charges are reported in Canadian dollars. Province resident tuition: $4795 full-time. Canadian resident tuition: $4795 full-time. Mandatory fees: $721 full-time. Full-time tuition and fees vary according to course load. College room and board: $8018. Room and board charges vary according to board plan, housing facility, and location. International student tuition: $23,300 full-time.

Collegiate Environment: Orientation program. Drama-theater group, choral group, student-run newspaper, radio station. Social organizations: 280 open to all; national fraternities, national sororities, local fraternities, local sororities; 3% of eligible men and 2% of eligible women are members. Most popular organizations: Ski and Board Club, Dance Club, AIESEC (international leadership organization), UBC Film Society, Varsity Outdoors Club. Major annual events: Storm the Wall, Day of the Longboat Racing. Student services: legal services, health clinic, personal-psychological counseling, women's center. Campus security: 24-hour emergency response devices and patrols, student patrols, late night transport-escort service, 24-hour desk attendants in residence halls. 8,000 college housing spaces available; all were occupied in 2012-13. Freshmen given priority for college housing. Options: coed, men-only, women-only housing available. UBC Library plus 9 others with 6.4 million books, 5.3 million microform titles, 875,000 serials, 883,000 audiovisual materials, an OPAC, and a Web page.

■ **THE UNIVERSITY OF BRITISH COLUMBIA–OKANAGAN**
3333 University Way
Kelowna, BC, Canada V1V 1V7
Tel: (250)807-8521
Fax: (250)807-8522
Web Site: www.ubc.ca/okanagan/welcome.html

Description: Province-supported, university, coed. Part of Okanagan campus is an integral part of the University of British Columbia, which comprises two campuses and two additional sites. Awards bachelor's, master's, and doctoral degrees. Founded 2005. Setting: 500-acre urban campus with easy access to Kelowna. Endowment: $952.7 million. Research spending for the previous fiscal year: $550 million. Total enrollment: 8,320. Faculty: 416 (369 full-time, 47 part-time). Student-undergrad faculty ratio is 15:1. 5,387 applied, 50% were admitted. Full-time: 5,824 students, 54% women, 46% men. Part-time: 1,683 students, 57% women, 43% men. Students come from 16 provinces and territories, 76 other countries. 40% live on campus. Retention: 76% of full-time freshmen returned the following year. Academic remediation for entering students, ESL program, services for LD students, advanced placement, self-designed majors, freshman honors college, honors program, distance learning, double major, summer session for credit, part-time degree program, co-op programs and internships. Off campus study. Study abroad program.

Entrance Requirements: Options: electronic application, deferred admission, international baccalaureate accepted. Required: essay, high school transcript, minimum 2.6 high school GPA. Required for some: SAT or ACT. Entrance: moderately difficult. Application deadlines: 1/31, 1/31 for nonresidents. Notification: continuous, continuous for nonresidents. SAT Reasoning Test deadline: 3/15. Transfer credits accepted: Yes.

Costs Per Year: Application fee: $102 Canadian dollars. Tuition, fee, and room and board charges are reported in Canadian dollars. Province resident tuition: $4794 full-time. Canadian resident tuition: $4794 full-time. Mandatory fees: $665 full-time. Full-time tuition and fees vary according to course load. College room and board: $8641. Room and board charges vary according to board plan and housing facility. International student tuition: $23,300 full-time.

Collegiate Environment: Orientation program. Drama-theater group, choral group, student-run newspaper, radio station. Social organizations: 50 open to all; national fraternities, national sororities. Most popular organizations: Save the World, Student Leadership, UBCSUO Mountain Riders Ski and Snowboard Club, Model United Nations, UBCSUO Asian Students' Association. Major annual event: Feed the Valley. Student services: legal services, health clinic, personal-psychological counseling, women's center. Campus security: 24-hour emergency response devices and patrols, controlled dormitory access, 24-hour desk attendants in residence halls. 2,500 college housing spaces available; all were occupied in 2012-13. Freshmen guaranteed college housing. Options: coed, men-only, women-only housing available. UBC Library with 6.4 million books, 5.3 million microform titles, 875,000 serials, 883,000 audiovisual materials, an OPAC, and a Web page. Operations spending for the previous fiscal year: $34 million.

■ **UNIVERSITY OF THE FRASER VALLEY**
33844 King Rd.
Abbotsford, BC, Canada V2S 7M8
Tel: (604)504-7441
Fax: (604)855-7614
E-mail: reginfo@ucfv.ca
Web Site: www.ufv.ca/
Description: Province-supported, comprehensive, coed. Awards associate, bachelor's, and master's degrees. Founded 1974. Setting: urban campus with easy access to Vancouver. Calendar: semesters. Academic remediation for entering students, ESL program, services for LD students, advanced placement, independent study, distance learning, double major, summer session for credit, part-time degree program, adult/continuing education programs, co-op programs and internships.
Entrance Requirements: Open admission for general studies programs. Options: electronic application, deferred admission, international baccalaureate accepted. Required for some: essay, high school transcript, 2 recommendations, interview, minimum GPA of 2.0 to 2.67 for specific undergraduate programs. Application deadline: 1/31. Notification: continuous until 9/1.
Collegiate Environment: Orientation program. Drama-theater group, student-run newspaper. Major annual event: Welcome Barbecue. Student services: personal-psychological counseling. Campus security: late night transport-escort service. Peter Jones Library plus 3 others with an OPAC and a Web page.

■ **UNIVERSITY OF NORTHERN BRITISH COLUMBIA**
3333 University Way
Prince George, BC, Canada V2N 4Z9
Tel: (250)960-5555
Fax: (250)960-5791
E-mail: registrar-info@unbc.ca
Web Site: www.unbc.ca/
Description: Province-supported, university, coed. Awards bachelor's, master's, and doctoral degrees. Founded 1994. Setting: 1,344-acre suburban campus. Total enrollment: 4,177. Faculty: 382 (178 full-time, 204 part-time). Student-undergrad faculty ratio is 10:1. 1,348 applied, 76% were admitted. Students come from 43 other countries. 42% 25 or older, 16% live on campus. Retention: 73% of full-time freshmen returned the following year. Academic areas with the most degrees conferred: business/marketing; natural resources/environmental science; health professions and related sciences. Core. Calendar: semesters. Services for LD students, advanced placement, self-designed majors, honors program, independent study, distance learning, double major, summer session for credit, part-time degree program, internships, graduate courses open to undergrads. Study abroad program.
Entrance Requirements: Options: early admission, early decision, international baccalaureate accepted. Required: high school transcript, minimum 2.0 high school GPA. Required for some: essay. Entrance: noncompetitive. Application deadline: 3/1.
Collegiate Environment: Orientation program. Student-run newspaper, radio station. Student services: health clinic, personal-psychological counseling, women's center. Campus security: 24-hour emergency response devices and patrols, late night transport-escort service, controlled dormitory

access. Geoffrey Weller Library with 310,433 books, 416,241 microform titles, 19,570 serials, 4,731 audiovisual materials, an OPAC, and a Web page. 300 computers available on campus for general student use. A campuswide network can be accessed from student residence rooms and from off campus. Students can access the following: online class registration, terminal services file space, personal Web space, e-mail, UNIX servers Webet. Staffed computer lab on campus.

■ **UNIVERSITY OF VICTORIA**
PO Box 1700 STN CSC
Victoria, BC, Canada V8W 2Y2
Tel: (250)721-7211
Fax: (250)721-6225
E-mail: admit@uvic.ca
Web Site: www.uvic.ca/
Description: Province-supported, university, coed. Awards bachelor's, master's, and doctoral degrees. Founded 1963. Setting: 380-acre suburban campus with easy access to Vancouver. Research spending for the previous fiscal year: $59 million. Total enrollment: 19,479. Faculty: 760 (721 full-time, 39 part-time). Student-undergrad faculty ratio is 27:1. 7,721 applied, 75% were admitted. Full-time: 10,716 students, 56% women, 44% men. Part-time: 5,866 students, 56% women, 44% men. Students come from 13 provinces and territories, 92 other countries, 13% from out-of-province. 22% 25 or older, 9% transferred in. Core. Calendar: Canadian standard year. Academic remediation for entering students, ESL program, services for LD students, advanced placement, self-designed majors, honors program, independent study, distance learning, double major, summer session for credit, part-time degree program, external degree program, adult/continuing education programs, co-op programs and internships, graduate courses open to undergrads. Off campus study at Canadian University Student Exchange Consortium. Study abroad program.
Entrance Requirements: Options: electronic application, early admission, early action, deferred admission, international baccalaureate accepted. Required: high school transcript, minimum 2.5 high school GPA. Required for some: essay, minimum 3.0 high school GPA, interview, audition, portfolio. Entrance: moderately difficult. Application deadlines: 4/30, 2/28 for early action. Notification: continuous, 5/1 for early action.
Collegiate Environment: Orientation program. Drama-theater group, choral group, student-run newspaper, radio station. Major annual events: President's Welcome Barbecue, Alumni Homecoming Weekend, Week of Welcome. Student services: legal services, health clinic, personal-psychological counseling, women's center. Campus security: 24-hour emergency response devices and patrols, student patrols, late night transport-escort service. McPherson Library plus 4 others with 1.8 million books, 2.5 million microform titles, 14,000 serials, an OPAC, and a Web page. Operations spending for the previous fiscal year: $13 million. 400 computers available on campus for general student use. A campuswide network can be accessed from student residence rooms and from off campus. Students can access the following: online class registration. Staffed computer lab on campus provides training in use of computers, software, and the Internet.
Community Environment: The university is located in the suburban Gordon Head area of Greater Victoria. It is a 10-minute drive from downtown Victoria and is easily accessible by car, bus, and bicycle. Victoria, the capital of British Columbia, boasts magnificent legislative buildings and a downtown which has been developed to retain its turn-of-the-century architecture and historic landmarks. The city is a thriving center of artistic activity, offering the exceptional Royal British Columbia Museum, several art galleries, a symphony orchestra, an opera company and several professional theatre companies. Greater Victoria has a population of 270,000. The regional economy is based on government, tourism, the University, and growing service, high technology, and clean manufacturing sectors.

■ **VANCOUVER ISLAND UNIVERSITY**
900 Fifth St.
Nanaimo, BC, Canada V9R 5S5
Tel: (250)753-3245
Web Site: www.viu.ca/
Description: Province-supported, comprehensive, coed. Awards associate, bachelor's, and master's degrees. Founded 1969. Setting: 110-acre campus. Calendar: semesters.
Community Environment: Nanaimo is situated on Vancouver Island, across the Strait of Georgia from the city of Vancouver. The island is the largest on the Pacific Coast, both in North and South America. Nanaimo is

the second largest community (95,000) on the island, being outranked by Victoria (250,000), the provincial capital located at the southern tip of the island. There are many excellent recreational facilities in the nearby mountains, forests, and lakes. Attractions include the Bastion, and the Centennial-Polk Theatre Museum. There is direct and frequent ferry service to Vancouver as well as rail, bus, and road connections to Victoria.

Manitoba

■ BOOTH UNIVERSITY COLLEGE

447 Webb Pl.
Winnipeg, MB, Canada R3B 2P2
Tel: (204)947-6701; Free: 877-942-6684
Fax: (204)942-3856
E-mail: cburt@boothcollege.ca
Web Site: www.boothuc.ca/
Description: Independent, 4-year, coed, affiliated with Salvation Army. Awards bachelor's degrees. Founded 1982. Setting: urban campus. Total enrollment: 322. Faculty: 28 (9 full-time, 19 part-time). Student-undergrad faculty ratio is 9:1. 89 applied, 71% were admitted. Students come from 14 other countries. 50% 25 or older, 10% live on campus. Retention: 98% of full-time freshmen returned the following year. Core. Calendar: semesters. Academic remediation for entering students, services for LD students, accelerated degree program, honors program, independent study, distance learning, double major, summer session for credit, part-time degree program, external degree program, adult/continuing education programs, internships. Off campus study at University of Manitoba, University of Winnipeg, Concord College. Study abroad program.
Entrance Requirements: Options: electronic application, international baccalaureate accepted. Recommended: essay, interview. Required for some: high school transcript. Application deadline: 7/31.
Collegiate Environment: Orientation program. Drama-theater group, student-run newspaper. Most popular organizations: Theatre Group, Crop Nights (scrapbooking), volleyball (women), Book Club. Major annual events: Christmas Banquet, The Well (chapel), Family Fun Night. Student services: personal-psychological counseling. Campus security: 24-hour emergency response devices, late night transport-escort service. John Fairbank Memorial Library plus 1 other with 53,000 books, 100 audiovisual materials, and an OPAC. 15 computers available on campus for general student use. A campuswide network can be accessed from student residence rooms.

■ BRANDON UNIVERSITY

270 18th St.
Brandon, MB, Canada R7A 6A9
Tel: (204)728-9520
E-mail: kerr@brandonu.ca
Web Site: www.brandonu.ca/
Description: Province-supported, comprehensive, coed. Awards bachelor's and master's degrees. Founded 1899. Setting: 30-acre small town campus. Endowment: $24 million. Research spending for the previous fiscal year: $944,580. Total enrollment: 3,524. Faculty: 228 (215 full-time, 13 part-time). Student-undergrad faculty ratio is 11:1. 2,157 applied, 70% were admitted. Students come from 28 other countries, 18% from out-of-province. 36% 25 or older, 9% live on campus. Retention: 71% of full-time freshmen returned the following year. Core. Calendar: Canadian standard year. Academic remediation for entering students, ESL program, services for LD students, accelerated degree program, self-designed majors, honors program, distance learning, double major, summer session for credit, part-time degree program, graduate courses open to undergrads. Off campus study. Study abroad program.
Entrance Requirements: Open admission. Options: electronic application, deferred admission. Required: high school transcript. Required for some: criminal and child abuse registry checks. Entrance: noncompetitive. Application deadline: Rolling. Notification: continuous until 9/30.
Collegiate Environment: Orientation program. Drama-theater group, choral

group, student-run newspaper, radio station. Social organizations: 25 open to all. Most popular organizations: Psychology Club, zoology club, Inter-Varsity Christian Fellowship, International Students Club, Business Administration Club. Major annual events: Shinerama, Orientation, Multicultural Week. Student services: personal-psychological counseling. Campus security: 24-hour emergency response devices, controlled dormitory access, night residence hall security personnel. John E. Robbins Library with 238,816 books, 615,548 microform titles, 1,699 serials, 12,233 audiovisual materials, an OPAC, and a Web page. Operations spending for the previous fiscal year: $636,522. 160 computers available on campus for general student use. A campuswide network can be accessed from student residence rooms. Staffed computer lab on campus.
Community Environment: Brandon, a city of 40,000, is located in the heart of the prairie land of Manitoba, on the Assiniboine River. The Manitoba Provincial Exhibition is held in Brandon every year. There are excellent recreational facilities in the nearby area, including camping, hunting, winter sports and fishing. Brandon is easily accessible by rail, road and air.

■ CANADIAN MENNONITE UNIVERSITY

500 Shaftesbury Blvd.
Winnipeg, MB, Canada R3P 2N2
Tel: (204)487-3300; Free: 877-231-4570
Fax: (204)487-3858
E-mail: cu@cmu.ca
Web Site: www.cmu.ca/
Description: Independent Mennonite, comprehensive, coed. Awards bachelor's and master's degrees. Founded 1943. Setting: 44-acre urban campus. Educational spending for the previous fiscal year: $4650 per student. Total enrollment: 455. Faculty: 30 (23 full-time, 7 part-time). Student-undergrad faculty ratio is 15:1. 280 applied, 95% were admitted. Full-time: 349 students, 57% women, 43% men. Part-time: 83 students, 64% women, 36% men. Students come from 7 provinces and territories, 6 other countries, 30% from out-of-province. 5% 25 or older, 45% live on campus. Retention: 65% of full-time freshmen returned the following year. Academic areas with the most degrees conferred: liberal arts/general studies; interdisciplinary studies; psychology. Core. Calendar: semesters. Academic remediation for entering students, services for LD students, independent study, double major, part-time degree program, adult/continuing education programs, internships, graduate courses open to undergrads. Off campus study at University of Winnipeg. Study abroad program.
Entrance Requirements: Options: electronic application, deferred admission. Required: high school transcript, minimum 2.0 high school GPA. Required for some: essay. Entrance: moderately difficult. Application deadline: 8/28. Notification: continuous until 9/1.
Collegiate Environment: Orientation program. Drama-theater group, choral group, student-run newspaper. Social organizations: 10 open to all. Most popular organizations: Oratorio Choir, Fellowship Groups, Christian Emphasis Committee, Peace and Social Concerns, Witness and Service Committee. Major annual events: Opening Week, Community Festival Series, Winter Retreat. Student services: personal-psychological counseling. Campus security: student patrols, late night transport-escort service, controlled dormitory access, combination door locks to sections of the campus. Canadian Mennonite University Library with 85,000 books, 125 serials, and an OPAC. Operations spending for the previous fiscal year: $361,513. 40 computers available on campus for general student use. A

The College Blue Book, 41st Edition

1221

campuswide network can be accessed from student residence rooms and from off campus. Staffed computer lab on campus.

■ COLLÈGE UNIVERSITAIRE DE SAINT-BONIFACE

200 Ave. de la Cathèdrale
Saint-Boniface, MB, Canada R2H 0H7
Tel: (204)233-0210
Fax: (204)237-3240
Web Site: www.ustboniface.mb.ca/
Description: Independent Roman Catholic, comprehensive, coed. Awards bachelor's and master's degrees. Founded 1871.

■ PROVIDENCE UNIVERSITY COLLEGE & THEOLOGICAL SEMINARY

10 College Crescent
Otterburne, MB, Canada R0A 1G0
Tel: (204)433-7488; Free: 800-668-7768
E-mail: info@prov.ca
Web Site: www.providenceuc.ca/
Description: Independent interdenominational, comprehensive, coed. Awards bachelor's, master's, and doctoral degrees. Founded 1925. Setting: 100-acre rural campus with easy access to Winnipeg. Endowment: $829,151. Educational spending for the previous fiscal year: $4933 per student. Total enrollment: 470. Faculty: 50 (18 full-time, 32 part-time). Student-undergrad faculty ratio is 19:1. 121 applied, 100% were admitted. Students come from 13 provinces and territories, 18 other countries, 30% from out-of-province. 65% live on campus. Retention: 79% of full-time freshmen returned the following year. Core. Calendar: semesters. Academic remediation for entering students, ESL program, accelerated degree program, freshman honors college, independent study, distance learning, double major, part-time degree program, internships.
Entrance Requirements: Open admission. Options: deferred admission, international baccalaureate accepted. Required: essay, high school transcript, 2 recommendations. Required for some: interview. Entrance: noncompetitive. Application deadlines: Rolling, Rolling for nonresidents. Transfer credits accepted: Yes.
Costs Per Year: Application fee: $50. Comprehensive fee: $12,542 includes full-time tuition ($6750), mandatory fees ($832), and college room and board ($4960). College room only: $1400. Room and board charges vary according to board plan and housing facility. Part-time tuition: $225 per credit hour. Part-time mandatory fees: $27.75 per credit hour. International student tuition: $7290 full-time.
Collegiate Environment: Orientation program. Drama-theater group, choral group, student-run newspaper. Social organizations: 25 open to all. Most popular organizations: Student Council, Social Concerns, Theatre, Music Touring Groups, Residence Care Groups. Major annual events: Christmas Banquet, Theatre Production, Missio Dei (Social Concerns Event). Student services: personal-psychological counseling. Campus security: student patrols, controlled dormitory access. 280 college housing spaces available; 220 were occupied in 2012-13. Freshmen guaranteed college housing. On-campus residence required in freshman year. Options: men-only, women-only housing available. William Falk Library with 71,407 books, 7,946 microform titles, 13,459 serials, 2,377 audiovisual materials, and an OPAC. Operations spending for the previous fiscal year: $224,187. 40 computers available on campus for general student use. Computer purchase/lease plans available. A campuswide network can be accessed from student residence rooms and from off campus. Students can access the following: online class registration. Staffed computer lab on campus provides training in use of software.

■ STEINBACH BIBLE COLLEGE

50 PTH 12N
Steinbach, MB, Canada R5G 1T4
Tel: (204)326-6451; Free: 800-230-8478
E-mail: info@sbcollege.ca
Web Site: www.sbcollege.ca/

■ UNIVERSITY OF MANITOBA

Winnipeg, MB, Canada R3T 2N2
Tel: (204)474-8880
Web Site: www.umanitoba.ca/
Description: Province-supported, university, coed. Awards bachelor's, master's, and doctoral degrees and post-master's certificates. Founded 1877. Setting: 685-acre suburban campus. Total enrollment: 27,751. Faculty:

2,385. Academic areas with the most degrees conferred: liberal arts/general studies; health professions and related sciences; education. Core. Calendar: 8-month academic year plus 6-week summer session. Academic remediation for entering students, ESL program, services for LD students, advanced placement, accelerated degree program, self-designed majors, honors program, independent study, distance learning, double major, summer session for credit, part-time degree program, external degree program, adult/continuing education programs, co-op programs and internships. Off campus study at University of Winnipeg, Red River Community College. Study abroad program.
Entrance Requirements: Options: electronic application, early admission, international baccalaureate accepted. Required: high school transcript. Entrance: moderately difficult.
Costs Per Year: Application fee: $65 Canadian dollars. Fee and room and board charges are reported in Canadian dollars.
Collegiate Environment: Orientation program. Drama-theater group, choral group, student-run newspaper, radio station. Social organizations: national fraternities, national sororities, local fraternities, local sororities. Student services: health clinic, personal-psychological counseling, women's center. Campus security: 24-hour emergency response devices, student patrols, late night transport-escort service. Elizabeth Dafoe Library plus 19 others with 2 million books, 1.5 million microform titles, 47,299 serials, an OPAC, and a Web page.
Community Environment: Winnipeg, despite its small size population, 652,350, and winter chill (zero to 30 degrees below Fahrenheit), offers students an extraordinary range of activities: opera, ballet, symphony orchestra, theatre, major league football and hockey, cosmopolitan restaurants, the only stone and fur trade fort still intact (Lower Fort Garry), and the 8,000-acre Oak Hammock Marsh wildlife preserve.

■ THE UNIVERSITY OF WINNIPEG

515 Portage Ave.
Winnipeg, MB, Canada R3B 2E9
Tel: (204)786-7811
E-mail: admissions@uwinnipeg.ca
Web Site: www.uwinnipeg.ca/
Description: Province-supported, comprehensive, coed. Awards bachelor's and master's degrees. Founded 1967. Setting: 8-acre urban campus. Endowment: $16.8 million. Research spending for the previous fiscal year: $2.4 million. Educational spending for the previous fiscal year: $3471 per student. Total enrollment: 9,006. Faculty: 321 (270 full-time, 51 part-time). Student-undergrad faculty ratio is 35:1. 4,203 applied, 75% were admitted. Full-time: 6,231 students, 64% women, 36% men. Part-time: 2,775 students, 61% women, 39% men. Students come from 7 provinces and territories, 32 other countries. 27% 25 or older, 3% live on campus, 3% transferred in. Retention: 60% of full-time freshmen returned the following year. Core. Calendar: Canadian standard year. Academic remediation for entering students, ESL program, services for LD students, advanced placement, accelerated degree program, self-designed majors, honors program, summer session for credit, part-time degree program, adult/continuing education programs, co-op programs and internships. Off campus study at Red River Community College. Study abroad program.
Entrance Requirements: Options: early admission, deferred admission. Required: minimum 2.0 high school GPA. Required for some: high school transcript, interview. Entrance: moderately difficult. Application deadlines: 8/9, 7/15 for nonresidents. Notification: continuous, continuous for nonresidents.
Collegiate Environment: Drama-theater group, choral group, student-run newspaper, radio station. Social organizations: 60 open to all; national fraternities, local fraternities; 25% of eligible men and 25% of eligible women are members. Most popular organizations: Woman's Centre, LGBT (Lesbian Gay Bisexual Transgender), radio station, International Resource Centre, Aboriginal Student Centre. Major annual event: Day of Action. Student services: health clinic, personal-psychological counseling, women's center. Campus security: 24-hour emergency response devices and patrols, student patrols, video controlled external access. 442,614 books, 1,840 serials, an OPAC, and a Web pageOperations spending for the previous fiscal year: $3.5 million. 175 computers available on campus for general student use. Computer purchase/lease plans available. A campuswide network can be accessed from off-campus. Staffed computer lab on campus provides training in use of computers, software, and the Internet.
Community Environment: Winnipeg is the largest city (550,000) in Manitoba, its provincial capital, and the center of its cultural, political and social life. The city has the Winnipeg Art Gallery, Centennial Center with the Manitoba Museum of Man and Nature, Concert Hall and Theatre Center and

many other cultural facilities and organizations, such as the Winnipeg Symphony and the Royal Winnipeg Ballet. Nearby Lake Winnipeg (which is larger than Lake Ontario) provides excellent recreation facilities. The city is the major east-west railroad junction and is accessible by all means of transportation. Industries include agriculture, meat packing and livestock, and manufacturing.

New Brunswick

■ CRANDALL UNIVERSITY

Box 6004
Moncton, NB, Canada E1C 9L7
Tel: (506)858-8970; Free: 888-YOU-N-ABU
Fax: (506)858-9694
E-mail: Laura.lutes@crandallu.ca
Web Site: www.crandallu.ca/

Description: Independent Baptist, 4-year, coed. Administratively affiliated with The Council of Christian Colleges and Universities. Awards bachelor's degrees and post-master's certificates. Founded 1949. Setting: 220-acre urban campus. Total enrollment: 719. Faculty: 60. Student-undergrad faculty ratio is 17:1. 207 applied, 89% were admitted. Full-time: 648 students, 68% women, 32% men. Part-time: 71 students, 54% women, 46% men. Students come from 11 provinces and territories, 3 other countries, 15% from out-of-province. 41% 25 or older, 22% live on campus, 4% transferred in. Retention: 71% of full-time freshmen returned the following year. Academic areas with the most degrees conferred: education; psychology; business/marketing. Core. Calendar: semesters. ESL program, advanced placement, accelerated degree program, honors program, double major, summer session for credit, part-time degree program, adult/continuing education programs, co-op programs and internships. Off campus study.

Entrance Requirements: Options: electronic application, early admission, early decision, deferred admission, international baccalaureate accepted. Required: high school transcript, minimum 2.67 high school GPA, 3 recommendations. Required for some: essay, interview. Entrance: minimally difficult. Application deadlines: Rolling, 11/30 for early decision. Notification: 9/15, 12/31 for early decision.

Costs Per Year: Application fee: $35 Canadian dollars. Tuition, fee, and room and board charges are reported in Canadian dollars. Comprehensive fee: $14,296 includes full-time tuition ($7395), mandatory fees ($775), and college room and board ($6126). College room only: $2686. Room and board charges vary according to board plan and housing facility. Part-time tuition: $775 per course.

Collegiate Environment: Orientation program. Drama-theater group, choral group, student-run newspaper. Social organizations: 6 open to all. Most popular organizations: Student Association, Business Society, intramurals, debate team, International Student Association. Major annual events: Christmas Banquet, Orientation week activities, Fall Foliage Day. Campus security: 24-hour emergency response devices, student patrols, controlled dormitory access. George A. Rawlyk Library with an OPAC.

■ KINGSWOOD UNIVERSITY

26 Western St.
Sussex, NB, Canada E4E 5L2
Tel: (506)432-4400; Free: 888-432-4422
Fax: (506)432-4425
E-mail: vails@kingswood.edu
Web Site: www.kingswood.edu/

Description: Independent, 4-year, coed, affiliated with Wesleyan Church. Awards associate and bachelor's degrees. Founded 1945. Setting: 57-acre small town campus. Endowment: $298,761. Educational spending for the previous fiscal year: $4137 per student. Total enrollment: 212. Faculty: 29 (9 full-time, 20 part-time). Student-undergrad faculty ratio is 17:1. 171 applied,

42% were admitted. Full-time: 193 students, 52% women, 48% men. Part-time: 19 students, 63% women, 37% men. Students come from 5 provinces and territories, 5 other countries, 50% from out-of-province. 11% 25 or older, 76% live on campus, 4% transferred in. Retention: 71% of full-time freshmen returned the following year. Academic area with the most degrees conferred: theology and religious vocations. Core. Calendar: semesters. Academic remediation for entering students, advanced placement, double major, summer session for credit, part-time degree program, internships.

Entrance Requirements: Options: electronic application, early admission, international baccalaureate accepted. Required: essay, high school transcript, 2 recommendations. Recommended: interview. Required for some: SAT or ACT. Entrance: moderately difficult. Application deadline: Rolling. Transfer credits accepted: Yes.

Costs Per Year: Application fee: $20 Canadian dollars. Tuition, fee, and room and board charges are reported in Canadian dollars. Comprehensive fee: $15,750 includes full-time tuition ($9450), mandatory fees ($600), and college room and board ($5700). College room only: $2450. Full-time tuition and fees vary according to degree level. Room and board charges vary according to board plan and housing facility. Part-time tuition: $315 per credit hour. Part-time tuition varies according to degree level.

Collegiate Environment: Orientation program. Drama-theater group, choral group. Social organizations: 8 open to all. Most popular organizations: Outreach Association, Athletic Association, Student Global Impact, Social Committee, Chorale. Major annual events: INCITE Missions Emphasis, Encounter, IGNITE. Student services: personal-psychological counseling. Campus security: student patrols, controlled dormitory access. 203 college housing spaces available; 161 were occupied in 2012-13. Freshmen guaranteed college housing. On-campus residence required through junior year. Options: men-only, women-only housing available. The Earle and Marion Trouten Library with 39,305 books, 472 microform titles, 4,864 serials, an OPAC, and a Web page. Operations spending for the previous fiscal year: $102,461. 20 computers available on campus for general student use. A campuswide network can be accessed from student residence rooms and from off campus. Staffed computer lab on campus provides training in use of computers, software, and the Internet.

■ MOUNT ALLISON UNIVERSITY

65 York St.
Sackville, NB, Canada E4L 1E4
Tel: (506)364-2269
Fax: (506)364-2272
E-mail: admissions@mta.ca
Web Site: www.mta.ca/

Description: Province-supported, comprehensive, coed. Awards bachelor's and master's degrees. Founded 1839. Setting: 50-acre small town campus. Endowment: $65 million. Educational spending for the previous fiscal year: $11,975 per student. Total enrollment: 2,688. Faculty: 187 (132 full-time, 55 part-time). Student-undergrad faculty ratio is 16:1. 2,110 applied, 74% were admitted. 64% from top 10% of their high school class, 87% from top quarter, 96% from top half. Full-time: 2,569 students, 60% women, 40% men. Part-time: 106 students, 59% women, 41% men. Students come from 22 provinces and territories, 45 other countries, 60% from out-of-province. 5% 25 or older, 50% live on campus, 4% transferred in. Retention: 80% of full-time freshmen returned the following year. Academic areas with the most degrees conferred: social sciences; business/marketing; psychology. Core. Calendar: Canadian standard year. Academic remediation for entering students, services for LD students, advanced placement, self-designed majors, honors program, independent study, distance learning, double major, summer session for credit, part-time degree program, adult/continuing education programs, internships. Off campus study at Moncton Campus, Miramichi Campus. Study abroad program.

Entrance Requirements: Options: electronic application, deferred admission, international baccalaureate accepted. Required: high school transcript, minimum 2.5 high school GPA. Recommended: 2 recommendations. Required for some: essay, interview. Entrance: moderately difficult. Application deadline: Rolling. Notification: continuous. Transfer credits accepted: Yes.

Collegiate Environment: Orientation program. Drama-theater group, choral group, student-run newspaper, radio station. Social organizations: 102 open to all. Most popular organizations: Commerce Society, Windsor Theatre, President's Leadership Development Certificate, Leadership Mount Allison, Garnet and Gold Society. Major annual events: Homecoming, Winter Carnival, Orientation. Student services: health clinic, personal-psychological counseling. Campus security: 24-hour emergency response devices, late night transport-escort service. 1,112 college housing spaces available; all were occupied in 2012-13. Freshmen guaranteed college housing. Options: coed, women-only housing available. Ralph Pickard Bell Library plus 3 others with 400,000 books, 1,700 serials, an OPAC, and a Web page. Operations spending for the previous fiscal year: $1.8 million. 100 computers available on campus for general student use. A campuswide network can be accessed from student residence rooms and from off campus. Students can access the following: online class registration, online student account/ Websis. Staffed computer lab on campus (open 24 hours a day).

■ ST. THOMAS UNIVERSITY

51 Dineen Dr.
Fredericton, NB, Canada E3B 5G3
Tel: (506)452-0640
Fax: (506)450-9615
E-mail: admissions@stu.ca
Web Site: www.stu.ca/

Description: Independent Roman Catholic, 4-year, coed. Awards bachelor's degrees. Founded 1910. Setting: 16-acre small town campus. Endowment: $26.6 million. Research spending for the previous fiscal year: $646,380. Educational spending for the previous fiscal year: $6863 per student. Total enrollment: 2,489. Faculty: 180 (106 full-time, 74 part-time). Student-undergrad faculty ratio is 19:1. 1,265 applied, 87% were admitted. Full-time: 2,182 students, 67% women, 33% men. Part-time: 150 students, 61% women, 39% men. Students come from 9 provinces and territories, 36 other countries, 21% from out-of-province. 4% international. 9% 25 or older, 30% live on campus, 5% transferred in. Retention: 70% of full-time freshmen returned the following year. Academic areas with the most degrees conferred: social sciences; psychology; English. Core. Calendar: semesters. Academic remediation for entering students, ESL program, services for LD students, advanced placement, accelerated degree program, self-designed majors, honors program, independent study, double major, summer session for credit, part-time degree program, internships. Off campus study at Miramichi At-Home Programme, a consortium of St. Thomas and the University of New Brunswick. Study abroad program.

Entrance Requirements: Options: electronic application, early action, international baccalaureate accepted. Required: high school transcript, minimum 3 high school GPA. Recommended: SAT. Required for some: essay, interview. Entrance: moderately difficult. Application deadlines: 8/31, 12/7 for early action. Notification: continuous. Transfer credits accepted: Yes.

Costs Per Year: Application fee: $35 Canadian dollars. Tuition, fee, and room and board charges are reported in Canadian dollars. Comprehensive fee: $13,096 includes full-time tuition ($4945), mandatory fees ($371), and college room and board ($7780). Full-time tuition and fees vary according to course load, degree level, and program. Room and board charges vary according to board plan, housing facility, and location. Part-time tuition: $549 per course. Part-time mandatory fees: $31 per course. Part-time tuition and fees vary according to course load. International student tuition: $12,855 full-time.

Collegiate Environment: Orientation program. Drama-theater group, choral group, student-run newspaper, radio station. Social organizations: 25 open to all. Most popular organizations: Theatre St. Thomas, St. Thomas Student Union, Criminology Society, Model UN, International Students' Association. Major annual events: Welcome Week, Multicultural Fair, Winter Formal. Student services: health clinic, personal-psychological counseling, women's center. Campus security: 24-hour emergency response devices and patrols,

student patrols, late night transport-escort service, controlled dormitory access. 830 college housing spaces available; 711 were occupied in 2012-13. Freshmen guaranteed college housing. Options: coed, women-only housing available. Harriet Irving Library plus 2 others with 1.7 million books, 3.2 million microform titles, 39,498 serials, 6,687 audiovisual materials, an OPAC, and a Web page. Operations spending for the previous fiscal year: $1.5 million. 94 computers available on campus for general student use. A campuswide network can be accessed from student residence rooms and from off campus. Students can access the following: online class registration, Moodle. Staffed computer lab on campus provides training in use of computers, software, and the Internet.

Community Environment: New Brunswick's capital city has a population of about 81,000. The university's hillside campus overlooks the downtown and the Saint John River Valley. Fredericton is home to the historic Legislative Assembly, a thriving artistic community, a professional theater troupe, one of Atlantic Canada's more impressive art galleries, tree-lined city streets and scores of elegant Victorian mansions. The city's per capita income is among the highest in the country.

■ UNIVERSITÉ DE MONCTON

Moncton, NB, Canada E1A 3E9
Tel: (506)858-4000
Fax: (506)858-4544
E-mail: gallanrm@umoncton.ca
Web Site: www.umoncton.ca/

Description: Province-supported, comprehensive, coed. Awards bachelor's, master's, and doctoral degrees (doctoral degree in French studies only). Founded 1963. Setting: 400-acre urban campus. Endowment: $19.8 million. Research spending for the previous fiscal year: $5 million. Total enrollment: 6,002. Faculty: 487 (374 full-time, 113 part-time). Student-undergrad faculty ratio is 12:1. 2,046 applied, 86% were admitted. Students come from 10 provinces and territories, 41 other countries, 11% from out-of-province. 7% 25 or older, 15% live on campus. Retention: 83% of full-time freshmen returned the following year. Calendar: semesters. Academic remediation for entering students, ESL program, services for LD students, accelerated degree program, self-designed majors, honors program, distance learning, double major, summer session for credit, part-time degree program, external degree program, adult/continuing education programs, co-op programs and internships, graduate courses open to undergrads. Off campus study at other French colleges and universities in Canada. Study abroad program.

Entrance Requirements: Options: deferred admission, international baccalaureate accepted. Required: high school transcript, French examination. Required for some: essay, minimum 2.0 high school GPA, 1 recommendation, interview. Entrance: moderately difficult. Application deadlines: 6/1, 2/1 for nonresidents. Notification: continuous until 9/1, continuous until 8/15 for nonresidents.

Collegiate Environment: Orientation program. Drama-theater group, choral group, student-run newspaper, radio station. Social organizations: 50 open to all. Most popular organizations: Amnesty International, student radio station, business clubs, Improvisational League, WSC. Major annual events: Homecoming, International Evening, Career Exposition. Student services: health clinic, personal-psychological counseling. Campus security: 24-hour emergency response devices and patrols, controlled dormitory access, student security attendants in residences 8 pm to 2 am. Bibliotheque Champlain plus 2 others with 789,046 books, 588,927 microform titles, 2,059 serials, 28,818 audiovisual materials, an OPAC, and a Web page. Operations spending for the previous fiscal year: $3.6 million. 900 computers available on campus for general student use. A campuswide network can be accessed from student residence rooms and from off campus. Staffed computer lab on campus.

■ UNIVERSITY OF NEW BRUNSWICK FREDERICTON

PO Box 4400
Fredericton, NB, Canada E3B 5A3
Tel: (506)453-4666
Fax: (506)453-5016
E-mail: admissions@unb.ca
Web Site: www.unb.ca/

Description: Province-supported, university, coed. Part of Province of NB. Awards bachelor's, master's, and doctoral degrees. Founded 1785. Setting: 7,100-acre urban campus. Endowment: $173.6 million. Research spending for the previous fiscal year: $56.9 million. Educational spending for the previous fiscal year: $11,944 per student. Total enrollment: 10,789. Faculty: 1,002 (595 full-time, 407 part-time). Student-undergrad faculty ratio is 11:1. 3,695 applied, 79% were admitted. 20% live on campus. Core. Calendar: Canadian standard year. ESL program, services for LD students, advanced placement, accelerated degree program, self-designed majors, honors program, independent study, distance learning, double major, summer session for credit, part-time degree program, external degree program, adult/continuing education programs, co-op programs and internships, graduate courses open to undergrads. Off campus study at University of Maine, Universite Laval, all forestry colleges in Canada, Saint Thomas University. Study abroad program.

Entrance Requirements: Options: electronic application, early admission, deferred admission, international baccalaureate accepted. Required: high school transcript. Required for some: essay, 1 recommendation, interview, SAT. Entrance: moderately difficult. Application deadline: 3/31. Notification: continuous until 8/31.

Collegiate Environment: Orientation program. Drama-theater group, choral group, student-run newspaper, radio station. Social organizations: 95 open to all. Major annual events: Orientation Week, Graduation Ceremony. Student services: legal services, health clinic, personal-psychological counseling, women's center. Campus security: 24-hour emergency response devices and patrols, student patrols, late night transport-escort service, controlled dormitory access. 1,300 college housing spaces available; 1,200 were occupied in 2012-13. Freshmen guaranteed college housing. Options: coed, men-only, women-only housing available. Harriet Irving Library plus 4 others with 1.3 million books, 3.2 million microform titles, 47,249 serials, 6,831 audiovisual materials, an OPAC, and a Web page. Operations spending for the previous fiscal year: $10.2 million. 1,400 computers available on campus for general student use. A campuswide network can be accessed from student residence rooms and from off campus. Students can access the following: online class registration. Staffed computer lab on campus provides training in use of computers, software, and the Internet.

Community Environment: Fredericton, the capital of New Brunswick, has a population of 81,000. The city is located in the Saint John River Valley, about 55 miles from the city of Saint John. Major employers in Fredericton are service industries, university and government.

■ UNIVERSITY OF NEW BRUNSWICK SAINT JOHN
PO Box 5050
Saint John, NB, Canada E2L 4L5
Tel: (506)648-5500
Web Site: www.unb.ca/

Description: Province-supported, comprehensive, coed. Awards bachelor's, master's, and doctoral degrees. Founded 1964. Setting: 250-acre urban campus. 5% live on campus. Core. Calendar: Canadian standard year. Academic remediation for entering students, ESL program, services for LD students, advanced placement, accelerated degree program, self-designed majors, honors program, independent study, distance learning, double major, summer session for credit, part-time degree program, adult/continuing education programs, co-op programs and internships. Off campus study at University of Maine. Study abroad program.

Entrance Requirements: Options: electronic application, early admission, deferred admission, international baccalaureate accepted. Required: high school transcript, SAT. Entrance: moderately difficult. Application deadlines: Rolling, 3/31 for nonresidents. Notification: continuous until 8/31, continuous for nonresidents.

Collegiate Environment: Orientation program. Drama-theater group, choral group, student-run newspaper, radio station. Social organizations: 20 open to all. Most popular organizations: Business Administration Society, OPTAMUS, International Student Association, Chinese Cultural Association, Muslim Student Association. Major annual events: Orientation Week, Winter Carnival. Student services: personal-psychological counseling, women's center. Campus security: 24-hour emergency response devices and patrols, student patrols, late night transport-escort service, controlled dormitory access. 230 college housing spaces available. Option: coed housing available. Hans W. Klohn Commons with 155,500 books, 700 serials, an OPAC, and a Web page. 100 computers available on campus for general student use. A campuswide network can be accessed from student residence rooms and from off campus. Students can access the following: online class registration. Staffed computer lab on campus.

Nova Scotia

■ ACADIA UNIVERSITY
Wolfville, NS, Canada B4P 2R6
Tel: (902)542-2201; Free: 877-585-1121

Fax: (902)585-1081
E-mail: admissions@acadiau.ca
Web Site: www.acadiau.ca/

Description: Province-supported, comprehensive, coed. Awards bachelor's and master's degrees. Founded 1838. Setting: 250-acre small town campus. Total enrollment: 3,959. Faculty: 243. Student-undergrad faculty ratio is 15:1. 3,759 applied, 34% were admitted. Full-time: 3,320 students, 58% women, 42% men. Part-time: 138 students, 49% women, 51% men. Students come from 13 provinces and territories, 51 other countries, 46% from out-of-province. 6% 25 or older, 45% live on campus, 6% transferred in. Retention: 79% of full-time freshmen returned the following year. Academic areas with the most degrees conferred: business/marketing; education; parks and recreation. Core. Calendar: Canadian standard year. Academic remediation for entering students, ESL program, advanced placement, honors program, distance learning, double major, summer session for credit, part-time degree program, co-op programs and internships. Off campus study at East Carolina University, Franklin College of Indiana, Bridgewater State College, New England/Nova Scotia Exchange Program. Study abroad program.

Entrance Requirements: Options: electronic application, deferred admission, international baccalaureate accepted. Required: high school transcript, minimum 2.5 high school GPA. Required for some: essay, 1 recommendation, interview. Entrance: moderately difficult. Application deadlines: 7/1, 7/1 for nonresidents. Notification: continuous, continuous for nonresidents. Transfer credits accepted: Yes.

Costs Per Year: Application fee: $25 Canadian dollars. Tuition, fee, and room and board charges are reported in Canadian dollars. Province resident tuition: $6590 full-time, $816.70 per course part-time. Canadian resident tuition: $7612 full-time, $918.90 per course part-time. Mandatory fees: $249 full-time, $10 per course part-time. Full-time tuition and fees vary according to course level, course load, degree level, and program. Part-time tuition and fees vary according to course level, course load, degree level, and program. College room and board: $8866. College room only: $4935. Room and board charges vary according to board plan and housing facility. International student tuition: $14,808 full-time.

Collegiate Environment: Orientation program. Drama-theater group, choral group, student-run newspaper, radio station. Social organizations: 53 open to all. Most popular organizations: Dance Acadia, Power Cheerleading, Water Watch Canada, LINC, Biology. Major annual events: Winter Carnival, Orientation Week, Convocation. Student services: legal services, health clinic, personal-psychological counseling, women's center. Campus security: 24-hour emergency response devices and patrols, student patrols, late night transport-escort service, controlled dormitory access, video surveillance, emergency response, emergency notification, emergency management planning. 1,630 college housing spaces available; 1,580 were occupied in 2012-13. Freshmen guaranteed college housing. Options: coed, women-only housing available. Vaughan Memorial Library with 1.4 million books, 439,562 microform titles, 23,100 serials, 13,513 audiovisual materials, an OPAC, and a Web page.

Community Environment: Acadia University is located in the Annapolis Valley town of Wolfville, 100 kilometers northwest of Halifax. The main buildings are on a high terraced slope, facing the broad diked meadows of the Evangeline Country and the Minas Basin, the body of water in the northeastern part of the Bay of Fundy. Wolfville is a beautiful, residential town of 3,000 people, with four churches and good elementary and secondary schools.

■ CAPE BRETON UNIVERSITY
Box 5300
1250 Grand Lake Rd.
Sydney, NS, Canada B1P 6L2
Tel: (902)539-5300; Free: 888-959-9995
Fax: (902)562-0119
E-mail: brendan_macdonald@cbu.ca
Web Site: www.cbu.ca/

Description: Province-supported, comprehensive, coed. Awards bachelor's and master's degrees. Founded 1974. Setting: urban campus. Total enrollment: 2,782. Faculty: 129. 24% live on campus. Retention: 74% of full-time freshmen returned the following year. Calendar: semesters.

Entrance Requirements: Options: early admission, deferred admission, international baccalaureate accepted. Required: high school transcript. Required for some: essay, 3 recommendations, interview. Entrance: moderately difficult. Application deadline: 8/1. Notification: continuous. Transfer credits accepted: Yes.

Collegiate Environment: Campus security: 24-hour emergency response devices and patrols, student patrols, late night transport-escort service, controlled dormitory access. Cape Breton University Library with 222,754 books, 22,034 microform titles, and 38,210 serials.

Community Environment: Sydney, part of the Regional Municipality of Cape Breton, is on Cape Breton Island, which is at the northeast end of Nova Scotia. The island is connected to the mainland by a causeway. Sydney is an industrial city with a self-contained steel plant. It is also a port city. There are numerous historical sites and recreational facilities. A major restoration project being undertaken on Cape Breton Island is at the Fortress of Louisbourg National Historic Park.

■ **DALHOUSIE UNIVERSITY**

Halifax, NS, Canada B3H 4R2

Tel: (902)494-2211

Fax: (902)494-1630

E-mail: admissions@dal.ca

Web Site: www.dal.ca/

Description: Province-supported, university, coed. Awards bachelor's, master's, and doctoral degrees. Founded 1818. Setting: 80-acre urban campus. Total enrollment: 18,268. Student-undergrad faculty ratio is 14:1. 15,702 applied, 60% were admitted. Students come from 13 provinces and territories, 97 other countries. 17% 25 or older. Calendar: semesters. Academic remediation for entering students, ESL program, services for LD students, advanced placement, accelerated degree program, honors program, distance learning, double major, summer session for credit, part-time degree program, co-op programs and internships. Off campus study at Saint Mary's University, Mount Saint Vincent University, Nova Scotia Agricultural College. Study abroad program.

Entrance Requirements: Options: electronic application, early admission, deferred admission, international baccalaureate accepted. Required: high school transcript, minimum 3 high school GPA, SAT or ACT. Required for some: essay, 1 recommendation, interview. Entrance: moderately difficult. Application deadline: 6/1. Notification: continuous. SAT Reasoning Test deadline: 6/1. Transfer credits accepted: Yes.

Costs Per Year: Application fee: $65 Canadian dollars. Tuition, fee, and room and board charges are reported in Canadian dollars. Province resident tuition: $7100 full-time. Canadian resident tuition: $7100 full-time. Full-time tuition varies according to course load, degree level, and program. College room and board: $8900. Room and board charges vary according to board plan, housing facility, and location. International student tuition: $15,090 full-time.

Collegiate Environment: Orientation program. Drama-theater group, choral group, student-run newspaper, radio station. Social organizations: 250 open to all; national fraternities, national sororities, local fraternities, local sororities. Most popular organizations: International Students Association, Arts Society, Science Society, Commerce Society, Dalhousie Outdoors Club. Major annual events: Frosh Week, Winter Carnival, Charity Ball. Student services: legal services, health clinic, personal-psychological counseling, women's center. Campus security: 24-hour emergency response devices and patrols, student patrols, late night transport-escort service, controlled dormitory access. 2,676 college housing spaces available. Freshmen given priority for college housing. Options: coed, women-only housing available. The Killam Library plus 3 others with 164 serials, an OPAC, and a Web page. 710 computers available on campus for general student use. Computer purchase/lease plans available. A campuswide network can be accessed from student residence rooms and from off campus. Students can access the following: online class registration. Staffed computer lab on campus provides training in use of computers, software, and the Internet.

■ **MOUNT SAINT VINCENT UNIVERSITY**

166 Bedford Hwy.

Halifax, NS, Canada B3M 2J6

Tel: (902)457-6788; Free: 877-733-6788

Fax: (902)457-6455

E-mail: admissions@msvu.ca

Web Site: www.msvu.ca/

Description: Province-supported, comprehensive, coed. Awards bachelor's, master's, and doctoral degrees. Founded 1873. Setting: 40-acre suburban campus. Endowment: $19.5 million. Research spending for the previous fiscal year: $3.1 million. Educational spending for the previous fiscal year: $7490 per student. Total enrollment: 2,946. Faculty: 376 (149 full-time, 227 part-time). Student-undergrad faculty ratio is 13:1. 584 applied, 60% were admitted. Students come from 13 provinces and territories, 40 other countries, 10% from out-of-province. 33% 25 or older. Retention: 79% of

full-time freshmen returned the following year. Academic areas with the most degrees conferred: education; business/marketing; communication/journalism. Calendar: Canadian standard year. Honors program, independent study, distance learning, double major, summer session for credit, part-time degree program, external degree program, adult/continuing education programs, co-op programs and internships, graduate courses open to undergrads. Off campus study at Metro Halifax Universities Consortium, Acadia University. Study abroad program.

Entrance Requirements: Options: electronic application, deferred admission, international baccalaureate accepted. Required: high school transcript, minimum 2.0 high school GPA. Required for some: essay, minimum 3.0 high school GPA, 2 recommendations, interview. Entrance: moderately difficult. Application deadlines: 3/15, 5/30 for nonresidents. Notification: 9/1, 1/6 for nonresidents.

Collegiate Environment: Orientation program. Choral group, student-run newspaper. Social organizations: 18 open to all. Most popular organizations: Business Society, Residence Society, Science Society, History Society. Major annual events: Frosh Week, Awards Banquet, Shinerama. Student services: health clinic, personal-psychological counseling, women's center. Campus security: 24-hour emergency response devices and patrols, late night transport-escort service, controlled dormitory access. E. Margaret Fulton Communications Centre Library plus 3 others with 356,763 books, 568,440 microform titles, 3,570 serials, an OPAC, and a Web page. Operations spending for the previous fiscal year: $1.7 million.

Community Environment: Mount Saint Vincent University is situated in Halifax, the capital of Nova Scotia. Overlooking the Bedford Basin, it offers scenic walkways and recreational facilities. Public transport and a good highway provide easy access both to the International Airport and to downtown Halifax, which offers cultural and intellectual opportunities, shopping, parks and entertainment.

■ **NSCAD UNIVERSITY**

5163 Duke St.

Halifax, NS, Canada B3J 3J6

Tel: (902)422-7381; Free: 888-444-5989

Fax: (902)425-2420

E-mail: admissions@nscad.ca

Web Site: www.nscad.ca/

Description: Province-supported, comprehensive, coed. Awards bachelor's and master's degrees. Founded 1887. Setting: 1-acre urban campus. Endowment: $1.1 million. Total enrollment: 1,021. Faculty: 114 (46 full-time, 68 part-time). Student-undergrad faculty ratio is 9:1. 306 applied, 75% were admitted. Students come from 11 provinces and territories, 17 other countries. 35% 25 or older, 10% live on campus. Academic area with the most degrees conferred: visual and performing arts. Core. Calendar: semesters. Services for LD students, self-designed majors, honors program, independent study, double major, summer session for credit, part-time degree program, external degree program, co-op programs and internships. Off campus study at AICAD Mobility Program, Independent Exchanges, 4 members of Canadian Art Colleges, New England/Nova Scotia Student Exchange (70+ institutions in total). Study abroad program.

Entrance Requirements: Options: deferred admission, international baccalaureate accepted. Required: essay, high school transcript, portfolio. Recommended: minimum 3.0 high school GPA. Required for some: 2 recommendations, interview. Entrance: moderately difficult. Application deadline: 5/15. Notification: 6/30.

Collegiate Environment: Orientation program. Student services: personal-psychological counseling. Campus security: 24-hour emergency response devices, evening patrols by trained security personnel. Nova Scotia College of Art and Design Library with 32,000 books, 100 microform titles, 235 serials, and an OPAC. Operations spending for the previous fiscal year: $492,225. 60 computers available on campus for general student use. Students can access the following: online class registration. Staffed computer lab on campus provides training in use of computers and software.

Community Environment: The College is located in Halifax, the capital city of Nova Scotia, with a metropolitan population of 300,000. Halifax is the largest city in the Atlantic region. It is the home of a number of cultural institutions including the Atlantic Symphony Orchestra, the Neptune Theatre and the Nova Scotia Museum. In addition, there are a number of active art galleries, most notably the Art Gallery of Nova Scotia and the galleries connected with the city's three universities. The Arts Center at Dalhousie University provides, during the fall and winter months, a constant round of music concerts, plays, and other performances.

■ ST. FRANCIS XAVIER UNIVERSITY

Box 5000
Antigonish, NS, Canada B2G 2W5
Tel: (902)863-3300; Free: 877-867-STFX
Fax: (902)867-2329
E-mail: mbarry@stfx.ca
Web Site: www.stfx.ca/

Description: Independent Roman Catholic, comprehensive, coed. Awards bachelor's and master's degrees. Founded 1853. Setting: 100-acre small town campus. Endowment: $67.4 million. Research spending for the previous fiscal year: $7.8 million. Educational spending for the previous fiscal year: $8277 per student. Total enrollment: 4,797. Faculty: 318 (251 full-time, 67 part-time). Student-undergrad faculty ratio is 12:1. 2,851 applied, 65% were admitted. Full-time: 2,209 students, 59% women, 41% men. Part-time: 2,046 students, 66% women, 34% men. Students come from 13 provinces and territories, 37 other countries, 43% from out-of province. 11% 25 or older, 45% live on campus, 5% transferred in. Retention: 90% of full-time freshmen returned the following year. Academic areas with the most degrees conferred: biological/life sciences; visual and performing arts; computer and information sciences; education; engineering; English; foreign languages and literature; health professions and related sciences; history; interdisciplinary studies; liberal arts/general studies; mathematics and statistics; natural resources/environmental science; physical sciences; psychology; science technologies; social sciences; business/marketing. Calendar: Canadian standard year. Academic remediation for entering students, ESL program, services for LD students, advanced placement, accelerated degree program, self-designed majors, honors program, independent study, distance learning, double major, summer session for credit, part-time degree program, adult/continuing education programs, co-op programs and internships. Off campus study at 18 colleges and universities in the New England states, St. Thomas Aquinas College. Study abroad program.

Entrance Requirements: Options: electronic application, early admission, early decision, deferred admission, international baccalaureate accepted. Required: essay, high school transcript, 2 recommendations. Recommended: SAT or ACT, SAT Subject Tests. Required for some: SAT or ACT. Entrance: moderately difficult. Application deadlines: Rolling, 1/31 for early decision. Notification: continuous until 8/15. SAT Reasoning Test deadline: 8/15. SAT Subject Test deadline: 8/15. Transfer credits accepted: Yes. Early decision applicants: 1,282. Early decision applicants admitted: 857.

Collegiate Environment: Orientation program. Drama-theater group, choral group, student-run newspaper, radio station. Social organizations: 95 open to all. Most popular organizations: X-Project, Blue Crew, orientation committee, X-Debate, ACE (Advancing Canadian Entrepreneurship). Major annual events: Christmas Ball, Winter Carnival, X-Ring Ceremony. Student services: health clinic, personal-psychological counseling, women's center. Campus security: 24-hour emergency response devices and patrols, student patrols, late night transport-escort service, controlled dormitory access. Angus L. Macdonald Library plus 1 other with 320,317 books, 312,367 microform titles, 24,293 serials, 19,971 audiovisual materials, an OPAC, and a Web page. Operations spending for the previous fiscal year: $3.2 million. 500 computers available on campus for general student use. A campuswide network can be accessed from student residence rooms and from off campus. Students can access the following: online class registration, online financial account, personal network storage, personal Web publishing, WirelessSynch iPods, Smartphones. Staffed computer lab on campus provides training in use of computers, software, and the Internet.

Community Environment: Pretty in its rural setting, Antigonish lies 140 miles from Halifax and each July hosts the Highland Games, a kind of Olympics of the Clans.

■ SAINT MARY'S UNIVERSITY

Halifax, NS, Canada B3H 3C3
Tel: (902)420-5400
Fax: (902)496-8100
E-mail: greg.ferguson@smu.ca
Web Site: www.smu.ca/

Description: Province-supported, comprehensive, coed. Awards bachelor's and master's degrees. Founded 1802. Setting: 30-acre urban campus. Calendar: semesters. Academic remediation for entering students, ESL program, services for LD students, accelerated degree program, self-designed majors, honors program, independent study, distance learning, double major, summer session for credit, part-time degree program, adult/continuing education programs, co-op programs and internships. Off campus study. Study abroad program.

Entrance Requirements: Options: early action, international baccalaureate accepted. Required: high school transcript, minimum 2.0 high school GPA. Required for some: interview. Entrance: moderately difficult. Application deadlines: 7/1, 1/1 for early action. Notification: continuous, 4/1 for early action.

Collegiate Environment: Orientation program. Drama-theater group, student-run newspaper. Student services: health clinic, personal-psychological counseling. Campus security: 24-hour emergency response devices and patrols, student patrols, late night transport-escort service, controlled dormitory access, electronic surveillance of labs and key areas. Patrick Power Library with 366,267 books, 594,793 microform titles, 1,700 serials, an OPAC, and a Web page.

■ UNIVERSITÉ SAINTE-ANNE

Church Point, NS, Canada B0W 1M0
Tel: (902)769-2114
Fax: (902)769-2930
E-mail: admission@usainteanne.ca
Web Site: www.usainteanne.ca/

Description: Province-supported, comprehensive, coed. Awards bachelor's and master's degrees. Founded 1890. Setting: 115-acre rural campus. Endowment: $1.4 million. Research spending for the previous fiscal year: $60,000. Educational spending for the previous fiscal year: $3125 per student. Total enrollment: 518. Faculty: 41 (33 full-time, 8 part-time). Full-time: 413 students, 70% women, 30% men. Part-time: 85 students, 80% women, 20% men. Students come from 9 provinces and territories, 4 other countries, 12% from out-of-province. 22% 25 or older, 60% live on campus. Academic areas with the most degrees conferred: education; business/marketing; science technologies; liberal arts/general studies; biological/life sciences. Core. Calendar: semesters. Academic remediation for entering students, ESL program, services for LD students, distance learning, double major, part-time degree program, adult/continuing education programs, co-op programs. Off campus study. Study abroad program.

Entrance Requirements: Required: high school transcript. Required for some: essay, 3 recommendations.

Collegiate Environment: Drama-theater group. Most popular organizations: Student Organization, Amnesty International, Club de Plein Air, Education Committee, Commerce Committee. Major annual events: Winter Carnival, Expo Commerce, Evening at the Theatre. Student services: health clinic, personal-psychological counseling. Campus security: student patrols, late night transport-escort service, 14-hour patrols by trained security personnel. Option: coed housing available. Louis R. Comeau Library with 85,000 books, 340 serials, and an OPAC. Operations spending for the previous fiscal year: $185,000. 30 computers available on campus for general student use. A campuswide network can be accessed from student residence rooms and from off campus. Students can access the following: online class registration. Staffed computer lab on campus (open 24 hours a day).

■ UNIVERSITY OF KING'S COLLEGE

6350 Coburg Rd.
Halifax, NS, Canada B3H 2A1
Tel: (902)422-1271
Fax: (902)423-3357
E-mail: admissions@ukings.ns.ca
Web Site: www.ukings.ca/

Description: Province-supported, 4-year, coed. Administratively affiliated with Dalhousie University. Awards bachelor's degrees. Founded 1789. Setting: 4-acre urban campus. Endowment: $28,540. Research spending for the previous fiscal year: $83,000. Educational spending for the previous fiscal year: $8690 per student. Total enrollment: 1,164. Faculty: 53 (51 full-time, 2 part-time). Student-undergrad faculty ratio is 21:1. 1,071 applied, 78% were admitted. 55% from top 10% of their high school class, 90% from top quarter, 99% from top half. Full-time: 1,134 students, 59% women, 41% men. Part-time: 30 students, 47% women, 53% men. Students come from 12 provinces and territories, 8 other countries, 61% from out-of province. 3% 25 or older, 23% live on campus, 4% transferred in. Retention: 80% of full-time freshmen returned the following year. Academic areas with the most degrees conferred: liberal arts/general studies; communication/journalism. Core. Calendar: Canadian standard year. Services for LD students, advanced placement, accelerated degree program, self-designed majors, honors program, independent study, double major, summer session for credit, part-time degree program, co-op programs and internships. Off campus study at Mount Saint Vincent University, Saint Mary's University, Nova Scotia College of Art and Design. Study abroad program.

Entrance Requirements: Options: electronic application, early admission, early decision, deferred admission, international baccalaureate accepted. Required: high school transcript, minimum 3 high school GPA. Required for some: essay, writing sample, SAT. Entrance: moderately difficult. Application deadline: 3/1. Notification: 4/15. Transfer credits accepted: Yes.

Collegiate Environment: Drama-theater group, choral group, student-run newspaper, radio station. Social organizations: 28 open to all. Most popular organizations: King's Theatrical Society, student newspaper, King's College Dance Collective, St. Andrew's Missionary Society, King's Independent Film-Makers Society. Major annual events: Frosh Week, College Christmas, Young Alexandra Society Annual Ball. Student services: legal services, health clinic, personal-psychological counseling, women's center. Campus security: student patrols, late night transport-escort service, controlled dormitory access. University of King's College Library with 80,000 books, 612 microform titles, 201 serials, and an OPAC. Operations spending for the previous fiscal year: $655,000. 18 computers available on campus for general student use. Computer purchase/lease plans available. A campuswide network can be accessed from student residence rooms and from off campus. Students can access the following: online class registration. Staffed computer lab on campus provides training in use of computers and the Internet.

Prince Edward Island

■ UNIVERSITY OF PRINCE EDWARD ISLAND

550 University Ave.
Charlottetown, PE, Canada C1A 4P3
Tel: (902)566-0439
Fax: (902)566-0795
E-mail: dmccardle@upei.ca
Web Site: www.upei.ca/

Description: Province-supported, comprehensive, coed. Awards bachelor's, master's, and doctoral degrees. Founded 1834. Setting: 130-acre small town campus. Endowment: $18.6 million. Research spending for the previous fis-

cal year: $14.8 million. Educational spending for the previous fiscal year: $23,058 per student. Total enrollment: 4,200. Faculty: 430 (240 full-time, 190 part-time). Student-undergrad faculty ratio is 12:1. 1,414 applied, 61% were admitted. Students come from 12 provinces and territories, 39 other countries, 17% from out-of-province. 19% 25 or older, 14% live on campus. Retention: 77% of full-time freshmen returned the following year. Calendar: Canadian standard year. ESL program, services for LD students, advanced placement, accelerated degree program, honors program, distance learning, double major, summer session for credit, part-time degree program, co-op programs and internships. Study abroad program.

Entrance Requirements: Options: electronic application, early admission, international baccalaureate accepted. Required: high school transcript, minimum 2.5 high school GPA. Recommended: SAT or ACT. Entrance: moderately difficult. Application deadline: 8/1. Notification: continuous until 8/31.

Collegiate Environment: Orientation program. Drama-theater group, choral group, student-run newspaper. Social organizations: 20 open to all. Most popular organizations: Business Society, Biology Club, Music Society, intramurals, Theatre Society. Student services: health clinic, personal-psychological counseling, women's center. Campus security: 24-hour emergency response devices and patrols, late night transport-escort service, controlled dormitory access, late night residence hall security personnel. Robertson Library with 402,808 books, 325,349 microform titles, 26,196 serials, 7,686 audiovisual materials, an OPAC, and a Web page. Operations spending for the previous fiscal year: $3 million. 240 computers available on campus for general student use. A campuswide network can be accessed from student residence rooms and from off campus. Students can access the following: online class registration, email forwarding, course management system presence for each course registered.

Community Environment: Charlottetown is the provincial capital and the largest community, approximately 30,000, on the island. It has an excellent harbor and is the center of the cultural and commercial activities of the island. Scenic attractions include Province House, St. Dunstan's Basilica, St. Peter's Anglican Cathedral, the Confederation Center and Government house.

■ **MEMORIAL UNIVERSITY OF NEWFOUNDLAND**
Elizabeth Ave.
Saint John's, NL, Canada A1C 5S7
Tel: (709)864-8000
Fax: (709)864-4569
E-mail: sturecru@morgan.ucs.mun.ca
Web Site: www.mun.ca/

Description: Province-supported, university, coed. Administratively affiliated with Marine Institute, Sir Wilfred Grenfell College, WRSON, CNS. Awards bachelor's, master's, and doctoral degrees. Founded 1925. Setting: 250-acre urban campus. Endowment: $60 million. Research spending for the previous fiscal year: $65 million. Total enrollment: 17,378. Faculty: 1,269 (1,233 full-time, 36 part-time). Student-undergrad faculty ratio is 12:1. Students come from 25 provinces and territories, 104 other countries, 19% from out-of province. 16% 25 or older, 10% live on campus. Retention: 81% of full-time freshmen returned the following year. Calendar: trimesters. Academic remediation for entering students, ESL program, services for LD students, advanced placement, accelerated degree program, honors program, distance learning, double major, summer session for credit, part-time degree program, adult/continuing education programs, co-op programs and internships, graduate courses open to undergrads. Off campus study at University of New Brunswick, University of New Mexico. Study abroad program.

Entrance Requirements: Options: electronic application, early admission, early decision, deferred admission, international baccalaureate accepted. Required: high school transcript. Required for some: essay, 2 recommendations, interview, audition, portfolio. Entrance: moderately difficult. Application deadlines: Rolling, 3/1 for nonresidents. Transfer credits accepted: Yes.

Collegiate Environment: Orientation program. Drama-theater group, choral group, student-run newspaper, radio station. Social organizations: 72 open to all. Most popular organizations: International Student Center, Students Older Than Average, Memorial's Organization for the Disabled, Biology Society, Student Parents at MUN. Major annual events: Winter Carnival, National University Week, Orientation. Student services: legal services, health clinic, personal-psychological counseling, women's center. Campus security: 24-hour emergency response devices and patrols, student patrols, late night transport-escort service. Queen Elizabeth II Library plus 4 others with 1.9 million books, 2.9 million microform titles, 17,170 serials, 32,160 audiovisual materials, an OPAC, and a Web page. Operations spending for the previous fiscal year: $15.3 million. 875 computers available on campus for general student use. A campuswide network can be accessed from student residence rooms and from off campus. Students can access the following: online class registration. Staffed computer lab on campus provides training in use of computers, software, and the Internet.

■ BROCK UNIVERSITY

500 Glenridge Ave.
Saint Catharines, ON, Canada L2S 3A1
Tel: (905)688-5550
Fax: (905)988-5488
E-mail: admissns@brocku.ca
Web Site: www.brocku.ca/

Description: Province-supported, university, coed. Awards bachelor's, master's, and doctoral degrees. Founded 1964. Setting: 540-acre urban campus with easy access to Toronto, ON and Buffalo, NY. Total enrollment: 17,877. Faculty: 578 (all full-time). Student-undergrad faculty ratio is 30:1. 19,885 applied. Students come from 70 other countries. 14% live on campus. Retention: 86% of full-time freshmen returned the following year. Core. Calendar: Canadian standard year. Academic remediation for entering students, ESL program, services for LD students, advanced placement, accelerated degree program, self-designed majors, honors program, double major, summer session for credit, part-time degree program, adult/continuing education programs, co-op programs and internships, graduate courses open to undergrads. Study abroad program.

Entrance Requirements: Options: electronic application, international baccalaureate accepted. Required: high school transcript, SAT or ACT. Recommended: minimum 3 high school GPA. Required for some: essay, interview, audition for Dramatic Arts and Music programs, profile questionnaire for Concurrent Education programs. Transfer credits accepted: Yes.

Collegiate Environment: Orientation program. Drama-theater group, choral group, student-run newspaper, radio station. Social organizations: 50 open to all. Most popular organizations: International Students Association, Brock University Student Association, Business Administration Association, Brock Christian Fellowship, Ace Brock. Major annual events: Orientation Week, Frost Week. Student services: health clinic, personal-psychological counseling, women's center. Campus security: 24-hour emergency response devices and patrols, student patrols, late night transport-escort service, controlled dormitory access. 2,389 college housing spaces available; all were occupied in 2012-13. Freshmen guaranteed college housing. Option: coed housing available. James A. Gibson Library plus 1 other with 769,873 books, 666,851 microform titles, 27,251 audiovisual materials, an OPAC, and a Web page. 429 computers available on campus for general student use. Computer purchase/lease plans available. A campuswide network can be accessed from student residence rooms. Students can access the following: online class registration. Staffed computer lab on campus provides training in use of computers, software, and the Internet.

■ CARLETON UNIVERSITY

1125 Colonel By Dr.
Ottawa, ON, Canada K1S 5B6
Tel: (613)520-7400
Fax: (613)520-7455
E-mail: liaison@admissions.carleton.ca
Web Site: www.carleton.ca/

Description: Province-supported, university, coed. Awards bachelor's, master's, and doctoral degrees. Founded 1942. Setting: 152-acre urban campus. Endowment: $135.2 million. Research spending for the previous fiscal year: $53.2 million. Educational spending for the previous fiscal year: $5157 per student. Total enrollment: 23,683. Faculty: 791 (783 full-time, 8 part-time). Student-undergrad faculty ratio is 26:1. 15,934 applied, 73% were admitted. Full-time: 16,509 students, 51% women, 49% men. Part-time: 4,237 students, 46% women, 54% men. Students come from 13 provinces and territories, 155 other countries, 8% from out-of province. 12% 25 or older, 15% live on campus, 4% transferred in. Retention: 87% of full-time freshmen returned the following year. Calendar: Canadian standard year. Academic remediation for entering students, ESL program, services for LD students, advanced placement, accelerated degree program, self-designed majors, honors program, independent study, distance learning, double major, summer session for credit, part-time degree program, adult/continuing education programs, co-op programs and internships, graduate courses open to undergrads. Off campus study at University of Ottawa, Algonquin College. Study abroad program.

Entrance Requirements: Options: electronic application, deferred admission, international baccalaureate accepted. Required: high school transcript, minimum 3.0 high school GPA. Recommended: SAT. Required for some: essay, minimum 3.4 high school GPA, interview, SAT and SAT Subject Tests or ACT. Entrance: moderately difficult. Application deadlines: 6/1, 4/1 for nonresidents. Notification: continuous, continuous for nonresidents.

Collegiate Environment: Orientation program. Drama-theater group, choral group, student-run newspaper, radio station. Social organizations: 100 open to all. Major annual events: Orientation, Prep Week, Charity Ball. Student services: health clinic, personal-psychological counseling, women's center. Campus security: 24-hour emergency response devices and patrols, student patrols, late night transport-escort service, controlled dormitory access. MacOdrum Library with 1.9 million books, 1.4 million microform titles, 15,824 serials, 2,661 audiovisual materials, an OPAC, and a Web page. Operations spending for the previous fiscal year: $12.4 million. 550 computers available on campus for general student use. Computer purchase/lease plans available. A campuswide network can be accessed from student residence rooms and from off campus. Students can access the following: online class registration. Staffed computer lab on campus.

Community Environment: As the site of the Parliament Buildings, the National Arts Center, and many of Canada's finest museums, Ottawa is a vibrant political and cultural center that provides Carleton's students with many unique opportunities. With its impressive network of trails, pathways, and waterways, Ottawa is an ideal location for jogging, skiing, and cycling enthusiasts. Outdoor recreation extends year-round, for Carleton is located beside the historic Rideau Canal, which in the winter becomes the world's longest skating rink, and the site of Ottawa's annual winter carnival.

■ CENTENNIAL COLLEGE

PO Box 631, Station 'A'
Scarborough, ON, Canada M1K 5E9
Tel: (416)698-4192
Fax: (416)694-9263
E-mail: success@centennialcollege.ca
Web Site: www.centennialcollege.ca/

Description: Province-supported, 4-year, coed. Part of Ontario College Application System. Awards bachelor's degrees. Setting: urban campus with easy access to Greater Toronto Area. ESL program, services for LD students, distance learning, co-op programs. Study abroad program.

Entrance Requirements: Option: electronic application. Required: high school transcript.

Collegiate Environment: Orientation program. Student services: personal-psychological counseling. Campus security: 24-hour emergency response devices and patrols. Freshmen given priority for college housing.

■ **COLLÈGE DOMINICAIN DE PHILOSOPHIE ET DE THÉOLOGIE**

96, Ave. Empress

Ottawa, ON, Canada K1R 7G3

Tel: (613)233-5696

E-mail: registraire@collegedominicain.ca

Web Site: www.collegedominicain.ca/

Description: Independent Roman Catholic, university, coed. Administratively affiliated with Institut de Pastorale. Awards bachelor's, master's, and doctoral degrees. Founded 1909. Setting: urban campus. Endowment: $7.9 million. Educational spending for the previous fiscal year: $4092 per student. Total enrollment: 216. Faculty: 50 (22 full-time, 28 part-time). Student-undergrad faculty ratio is 3:1. 57 applied, 100% were admitted. Full-time: 57 students, 37% women, 63% men. Part-time: 93 students, 74% women, 26% men. Students come from 2 provinces and territories, 6 other countries, 0% from out-of-province. 79% 25 or older, 16% live on campus, 0% transferred in. Retention: 73% of full-time freshmen returned the following year. Academic area with the most degrees conferred: theology and religious vocations. Core. Calendar: semesters. Accelerated degree program, summer session for credit, part-time degree program, graduate courses open to undergrads. Off campus study at the University of Ottawa (Faculty of Arts of the University of Ottawa), and the faculties of Philosophy and Theology of the College dominicain de philosophie et de theologie.

Entrance Requirements: Option: deferred admission. Required: high school transcript. Required for some: essay, interview. Entrance: noncompetitive. Application deadlines: 6/1, 3/1 for nonresidents. Transfer credits accepted: Yes.

Collegiate Environment: Choral group. Social organizations: 2 open to all; local fraternities; 5% of eligible men and 5% of eligible women are members. Most popular organizations: Association Etudiant College Dominicain, choral group. Major annual events: Annual Barbecue, Elections of the student association staff, student's conference. Campus security: late night transport-escort service, controlled dormitory access. Bibliotheque du College Dominicain with 125,000 books, 500 serials, and an OPAC. Operations spending for the previous fiscal year: $105,761. 4 computers available on campus for general student use. Staffed computer lab on campus provides training in use of computers and the Internet.

■ **EMMANUEL BIBLE COLLEGE**

100 Fergus Ave.

Kitchener, ON, Canada N2A 2H2

Tel: (519)894-8900

Fax: (519)894-9430

E-mail: smahon@ebcollege.on.ca

Web Site: www.emmanuelbiblecollege.ca/

Description: Independent, 4-year, coed, affiliated with Missionary Church. Awards bachelor's degrees. Founded 1940. Setting: 12-acre urban campus with easy access to Toronto. Total enrollment: 209. Core. Calendar: semesters. Academic remediation for entering students, accelerated degree program, summer session for credit, part-time degree program, internships.

Entrance Requirements: Option: deferred admission. Required: essay, high school transcript, 3 recommendations, interview, Christian testimony. Entrance: moderately difficult. Application deadline: Rolling.

Collegiate Environment: Orientation program. 19,250 books and 200 serials.

■ **HERITAGE BAPTIST COLLEGE AND HERITAGE THEOLOGICAL SEMINARY**

175 Holiday Inn Dr.

Cambridge, ON, Canada N3C 3T2

Tel: (519)651-2869; Free: 800-465-1961

E-mail: mwalther@heritagecollege.net

Web Site: www.heritage-theo.edu/

Description: Independent Baptist, comprehensive, coed. Awards associate, bachelor's, and master's degrees. Founded 1993. Setting: 7-acre urban campus with easy access to Toronto. Endowment: $1.1 million. Educational spending for the previous fiscal year: $4498 per student. Total enrollment: 274. Faculty: 36 (8 full-time, 28 part-time). Student-undergrad faculty ratio is 11:1. 24 applied, 100% were admitted. Full-time: 154 students, 40% women, 60% men. Part-time: 37 students, 32% women, 68% men. Students come from 6 provinces and territories, 3 other countries, 4% from out-of-province. 26% 25 or older, 3% transferred in. Retention: 79% of full-time freshmen returned the following year. Academic areas with the most degrees conferred: theology and religious vocations; education. Calendar: Canadian standard year. Advanced placement, independent study, distance learning,

double major, summer session for credit, part-time degree program, internships, graduate courses open to undergrads. Off campus study.

Entrance Requirements: Open admission. Options: deferred admission, international baccalaureate accepted. Required: essay, high school transcript. Required for some: audition. Entrance: noncompetitive. Application deadline: 9/1. Notification: continuous. Transfer credits accepted: Yes.

Collegiate Environment: Orientation program. Choral group, student-run newspaper. Major annual events: Missions Conference, Christmas and Graduation Banquets, Orientation. Student services: personal-psychological counseling. Campus security: controlled dormitory access. Heritage Library with 47,243 books, 254 microform titles, 118 serials, 2,239 audiovisual materials, and an OPAC. Operations spending for the previous fiscal year: $122,364. 6 computers available on campus for general student use. A campuswide network can be accessed from student residence rooms.

■ **LAKEHEAD UNIVERSITY**

955 Oliver Rd.

Thunder Bay, ON, Canada P7B 5E1

Tel: (807)343-8110; Free: 800-465-3959

Fax: (807)343-8156

E-mail: admissions@lakeheadu.ca

Web Site: www.lakeheadu.ca/

Description: Province-supported, comprehensive, coed. Awards bachelor's, master's, and doctoral degrees. Founded 1965. Setting: 345-acre suburban campus. Endowment: $37 million. Research spending for the previous fiscal year: $22.4 million. Total enrollment: 8,680. Faculty: (319 full-time). 8,277 applied, 84% were admitted. Full-time: 6,364 students, 58% women, 42% men. Part-time: 1,611 students, 64% women, 36% men. Students come from 13 provinces and territories, 28 other countries. 20% live on campus. Retention: 88% of full-time freshmen returned the following year. Academic areas with the most degrees conferred: education; health professions and related sciences; engineering. Core. Calendar: Canadian standard year. ESL program, services for LD students, advanced placement, accelerated degree program, honors program, independent study, distance learning, double major, summer session for credit, part-time degree program, external degree program, co-op programs and internships, graduate courses open to undergrads. Off campus study. Study abroad program.

Entrance Requirements: Options: electronic application, early admission, deferred admission, international baccalaureate accepted. Required: portfolio for visual arts program, audition for music program, portfolio for media studies, SAT or ACT. Recommended: minimum 3 high school GPA. Required for some: essay, high school transcript. Entrance: moderately difficult. Application deadlines: 9/12, 9/9 for nonresidents. Notification: continuous, continuous for nonresidents. SAT Reasoning Test deadline: 8/13. SAT Subject Test deadline: 8/13. Transfer credits accepted: Yes.

Collegiate Environment: Orientation program. Choral group, student-run newspaper, radio station. Social organizations: cultural groups. Most popular organizations: Outdoor Recreation Students Association, Engineering Students Society, Business Association, Educational Students Association, Native Students Association. Major annual events: Orientation, Winter Carnival. Student services: health clinic, personal-psychological counseling, women's center. Campus security: 24-hour emergency response devices and patrols, student patrols, late night transport-escort service, controlled dormitory access. Chancellor Norman M. Paterson Library plus 1 other with 715,276 books, 946,333 microform titles, 44,533 serials, 2,797 audiovisual materials, an OPAC, and a Web page. Operations spending for the previous fiscal year: $4.6 million. 594 computers available on campus for general student use. A campuswide network can be accessed from student residence rooms and from off campus. Students can access the following: online class registration. Staffed computer lab on campus (open 24 hours a day) provides training in use of computers, software, and the Internet.

■ **LAKEHEAD UNIVERSITY–ORILLIA**

500 University Ave.

Orillia, ON, Canada L3V 0B9

Tel: (705)330-4008

Web Site: orillia.lakeheadu.ca/

Description: Public, comprehensive, coed. Awards bachelor's and master's degrees.

■ **LAURENTIAN UNIVERSITY**

935 Ramsey Lake Rd.

Sudbury, ON, Canada P3E 2C6

Tel: (705)675-1151; Free: 800-263-4188

Fax: (705)675-4840

E-mail: admissions@laurentian.ca

Web Site: www.laurentian.ca/

Description: Province-supported, comprehensive, coed. Awards bachelor's, master's, and doctoral degrees. Founded 1960. Setting: 700-acre suburban campus. Total enrollment: 9,246. Students come from 46 other countries. Core. Calendar: Canadian standard year. Academic remediation for entering students, ESL program, services for LD students, accelerated degree program, honors program, distance learning, summer session for credit, part-time degree program, external degree program, adult/continuing education programs, co-op programs and internships. Off campus study. Study abroad program.

Entrance Requirements: Options: electronic application, early admission. Required: high school transcript. Required for some: essay, 2 recommendations, interview. Application deadline: 4/1.

Collegiate Environment: Orientation program. Drama-theater group, student-run newspaper, radio station. Most popular organizations: Students General Association, Association des Etudiantes/Etudiants francophones, Association of Mature and Part-time Students, Graduate Students Association. Student services: health clinic, personal-psychological counseling, women's center. Campus security: 24-hour emergency response devices and patrols, late night transport-escort service, controlled dormitory access. J. N. Desmarais Library plus 3 others with an OPAC and a Web page. 450 computers available on campus for general student use. Computer purchase/lease plans available. A campuswide network can be accessed from student residence rooms and from off campus. Students can access the following: online class registration. Staffed computer lab on campus provides training in use of computers, software, and the Internet.

Community Environment: Sudbury is the largest city (population 155,268) in Northern Ontario. Thunder Bay is 300 miles to the West. Sudbury is 100 miles east of Sault Ste. Marie. The campus is on 750 acres of scenic countryside, surrounded by three lakes, just a 10-minute drive from the downtown area.

■ **MASTER'S COLLEGE AND SEMINARY**

780 Argyle St.

Peterborough, ON, Canada K9H 5T2

Tel: (705)749-0725; Free: 800-295-6368

Fax: (705)749-0417

E-mail: flora.anthony@mcs.edu

Web Site: www.mcs.edu/

Description: Independent Pentecostal, 4-year, coed. Awards bachelor's degrees. Founded 1939. Setting: suburban campus with easy access to Toronto. Endowment: $718,092. Total enrollment: 294. Faculty: 31 (5 full-time, 26 part-time). Student-undergrad faculty ratio is 8:1. 137 applied, 94% were admitted. Students come from 7 provinces and territories, 2 other countries, 12% from out-of-province. 65% live on campus. Retention: 81% of full-time freshmen returned the following year. Academic area with the most degrees conferred: theology and religious vocations. Core. Calendar: semesters. Academic remediation for entering students, services for LD students, independent study, distance learning, summer session for credit, part-time degree program, internships. Off campus study.

Entrance Requirements: Option: deferred admission. Required: essay, high school transcript, 3 recommendations, Christian commitment. Recommended: minimum 2 high school GPA. Required for some: interview. Entrance: noncompetitive. Application deadline: 8/31. Transfer credits accepted: Yes.

Costs Per Year: Application fee: $75 Canadian dollars. Tuition, fee, and room and board charges are reported in Canadian dollars. Comprehensive fee: $12,672 includes full-time tuition ($6358), mandatory fees ($714), and college room and board ($5600).

Collegiate Environment: Orientation program. Major annual events: Fall Retreat, Winter Retreat, Christmas Social. Campus security: 24-hour emergency response devices, student patrols, controlled dormitory access. 129 college housing spaces available; 125 were occupied in 2012-13. Freshmen guaranteed college housing. On-campus residence required in freshman year. Options: men-only, women-only housing available. Master's College & Seminary Library with 45,826 books, 150 microform titles, 1,689 serials, 2,583 audiovisual materials, and an OPAC. 6 computers available on campus for general student use. A campuswide network can be accessed from student residence rooms and from off campus. Students can access the following: online class registration.

■ **MCMASTER UNIVERSITY**

1280 Main St. W

Hamilton, ON, Canada L8S 4M2

Tel: (905)525-9140

Fax: (905)527-1105

E-mail: admitmac@mcmaster.ca

Web Site: www.mcmaster.ca/

Description: Province-supported, university, coed. Awards bachelor's, master's, and doctoral degrees. Founded 1887. Setting: 300-acre suburban campus with easy access to Toronto. Total enrollment: 25,809. Faculty: 894 (all full-time). Student-undergrad faculty ratio is 25:1. 30,589 applied, 68% were admitted. Students come from 12 provinces and territories, 79 other countries. 20% live on campus. Retention: 88% of full-time freshmen returned the following year. Academic areas with the most degrees conferred: social sciences; health professions and related sciences; liberal arts/general studies. Calendar: Canadian standard year. Academic remediation for entering students, ESL program, services for LD students, advanced placement, accelerated degree program, honors program, independent study, double major, summer session for credit, part-time degree program, adult/continuing education programs, co-op programs and internships, graduate courses open to undergrads. Off campus study. Study abroad program.

Entrance Requirements: Options: electronic application, deferred admission, international baccalaureate accepted. Required: high school transcript, SAT or ACT. Required for some: essay, interview. Entrance: very difficult. Application deadlines: 6/1, 5/1 for nonresidents. Notification: 5/28.

Collegiate Environment: Orientation program. Drama-theater group, choral group, student-run newspaper, radio station. Social organizations: 120 open to all. Most popular organizations: Inter-Varsity Christian Fellowship, African-Caribbean Student Association, Chinese Students' Association, AIESEC (international leadership organization), Southeast Asian-American Society. Major annual events: Homecoming, Frosh Week, Alumni Weekend. Student services: legal services, health clinic, personal-psychological counseling, women's center. Campus security: 24-hour emergency response devices and patrols, student patrols, late night transport-escort service, controlled dormitory access. Mills Memorial Library plus 4 others with 1.7 million books, 1.6 million microform titles, 57,487 serials, 31,190 audiovisual materials, an OPAC, and a Web page. 400 computers available on campus for general student use. A campuswide network can be accessed from student residence rooms and from off campus. Students can access the following: online class registration. Staffed computer lab on campus provides training in use of computers, software, and the Internet.

Community Environment: Hamilton is the western point of the "Golden Triangle," Ontario's economic heartland. A major Great Lakes seaport, Hamilton's care for its past and present is reflected in the restored 36-room Regency Villa Dundurn Castle, and the 1,200-acre Coote's Paradise wildlife sanctuary.

■ **NER ISRAEL YESHIVA COLLEGE OF TORONTO**

8950 Bathurst St.

Thornhill, ON, Canada L4J 8A7

Tel: (905)731-1224

Description: Independent Jewish, comprehensive, men only. Awards bachelor's and master's degrees. Founded 1959. Setting: 14-acre campus. 50% from top half of their high school class, 100% from top half. Students come from 3 provinces and territories, 2 other countries. 80% 25 or older. Calendar: Canadian standard year. Summer session for credit.

Entrance Requirements: Required: high school transcript, 2 recommendations, interview. Entrance: very difficult. Application deadline: 8/15.

Collegiate Environment: Student services: personal-psychological counseling. 3,000 books.

■ **NIPISSING UNIVERSITY**

100 College Dr., Box 5002

North Bay, ON, Canada P1B 8L7

Tel: (705)474-3461

Fax: (705)474-1947

E-mail: liaison@nipissingu.ca

Web Site: www.nipissingu.ca/

Description: Province-supported, comprehensive, coed. Part of Ontario Ministry of Training, Colleges and Universities. Awards bachelor's, master's, and doctoral degrees. Founded 1992. Setting: 290-hectare urban campus. Total enrollment: 3,700. Core. Calendar: semesters. Academic remediation for entering students, services for LD students, advanced placement, accelerated degree program, honors program, independent study, distance learning, double major, summer session for credit, part-time degree program. Off campus study at Muskoka Campus, Wilfrid Laurier University. Study abroad program.

Entrance Requirements: Options: electronic application, early admission, early decision, international baccalaureate accepted. Required: high school transcript, SAT and SAT Subject Tests or ACT. Required for some: essay. Entrance: moderately difficult.

Collegiate Environment: Orientation program. Drama-theater group. Major annual events: Frosh Week, Shinerama. Student services: health clinic, personal-psychological counseling, women's center. Campus security: 24-hour emergency response devices and patrols, student patrols, late night transport-escort service, controlled dormitory access. Education Centre Library with 715,494 books, 19,115 serials, an OPAC, and a Web page.

■ **QUEEN'S UNIVERSITY AT KINGSTON**
Kingston, ON, Canada K7L 3N6
Tel: (613)533-2000
Fax: (613)533-6300
E-mail: admission@queensu.ca
Web Site: www.queensu.ca/

Description: Province-supported, university, coed. Awards bachelor's, master's, and doctoral degrees. Founded 1841. Setting: 160-acre urban campus. Endowment: $601.9 million. Research spending for the previous fiscal year: $180.4 million. Educational spending for the previous fiscal year: $9689 per student. Total enrollment: 24,343. Faculty: 1,525 (1,087 full-time, 438 part-time). Student-undergrad faculty ratio is 15:1. 23,019 applied. Full-time: 15,536 students, 59% women, 41% men. Part-time: 3,297 students, 73% women, 27% men. Students come from 46 provinces and territories, 84 other countries, 20% from out-of-province. 3% 25 or older, 32% live on campus, 1% transferred in. Retention: 96% of full-time freshmen returned the following year. Academic areas with the most degrees conferred: education; engineering; biological/life sciences. Calendar: Canadian standard year. ESL program, services for LD students, advanced placement, accelerated degree program, self-designed majors, honors program, distance learning, double major, summer session for credit, part-time degree program, adult/continuing education programs, co-op programs and internships. Study abroad program.

Entrance Requirements: Options: deferred admission, international baccalaureate accepted. Required: essay, high school transcript, minimum 2.7 high school GPA, SAT or ACT. Required for some: 1 recommendation. Entrance: most difficult. Application deadline: 2/1. Notification: 5/28. SAT Reasoning Test deadline: 4/30. Transfer credits accepted: Yes.

Collegiate Environment: Orientation program. Drama-theater group, choral group, marching band, student-run newspaper, radio station. Social organizations: 270 open to all. Most popular organizations: Arts and Sciences Undergraduate Society, Alma Mater Society, Engineering Society, Commerce Society, dance club. Major annual event: Orientation Week. Student services: legal services, health clinic, personal-psychological counseling, women's center. Campus security: 24-hour emergency response devices and patrols, student patrols, late night transport-escort service, controlled dormitory access. Joseph S. Stauffer Library plus 4 others with 3.5 million books, 3.7 million microform titles, 16,109 serials, an OPAC, and a Web page. Operations spending for the previous fiscal year: $19.6 million. 455 computers available on campus for general student use. Computer purchase/lease plans available. A campuswide network can be accessed from student residence rooms and from off campus. Students can access the following: online class registration. Staffed computer lab on campus provides training in use of computers, software, and the Internet.

■ **REDEEMER UNIVERSITY COLLEGE**
777 Garner Rd. E
Ancaster, ON, Canada L9K 1J4
Tel: (905)648-2131; Free: 800-263-6467
Fax: (905)648-2134
E-mail: recruitment@redeemer.ca
Web Site: www.redeemer.ca/

Description: Independent interdenominational, 4-year, coed. Awards bachelor's degrees. Founded 1980. Setting: 86-acre small town campus with easy access to Toronto. Endowment: $3.1 million. Research spending for the previous fiscal year: $293,580. Educational spending for the previous fiscal year: $6409 per student. Total enrollment: 918. Faculty: 89 (53 full-time, 36 part-time). Student-undergrad faculty ratio is 13:1. 389 applied, 81% were admitted. Students come from 8 provinces and territories, 6 other countries.

48% live on campus. Retention: 72% of full-time freshmen returned the following year. Academic areas with the most degrees conferred: English; history; business/marketing. Core. Calendar: semesters. Academic remediation for entering students, services for LD students, honors program, independent study, double major, summer session for credit, part-time degree program, co-op programs and internships. Off campus study at University of Guelph, Ridgetown College, Redeemer in France. Study abroad program.

Entrance Requirements: Options: electronic application, deferred admission, international baccalaureate accepted. Required: essay, high school transcript, minimum 2 high school GPA, 2 recommendations, personal reference. Required for some: interview, SAT or ACT. Entrance: moderately difficult. Application deadline: 5/31. Notification: continuous. Preference given to Christians. Transfer credits accepted: Yes.

Costs Per Year: Application fee: $40 Canadian dollars. Tuition, fee, and room and board charges are reported in Canadian dollars. Comprehensive fee: $21,232 includes full-time tuition ($14,290), mandatory fees ($510), and college room and board ($6432). Full-time tuition and fees vary according to course load and program. Room and board charges vary according to board plan and housing facility. Part-time tuition: $1428 per course. Part-time mandatory fees: $35 per course. Part-time tuition and fees vary according to course load and program.

Collegiate Environment: Orientation program. Drama-theater group, choral group, student-run newspaper. Social organizations: 28 open to all. Most popular organizations: Church in the Box, Mission trips, Social Justice Club, Concert Choir, intramurals. Major annual events: Angels and Mortals, Mainstage Productions, Midnight Breakfast. Student services: health clinic, personal-psychological counseling. Campus security: 24-hour emergency response devices, student patrols, late night transport-escort service, controlled dormitory access, path lighting. Peter Turkstra Library with 117,404 books, 350 serials, an OPAC, and a Web page. Operations spending for the previous fiscal year: $453,980. 35 computers available on campus for general student use. A campuswide network can be accessed from student residence rooms and from off campus. Staffed computer lab on campus.

Community Environment: Redeemer University College is located just inside the southwestern corner of the town of Ancaster (population 16,542), Ontario, which is adjacent to Hamilton (population 490,268), on its southwest side. It is readily accessible by road or air transportation. The nearest international airport is at Toronto, 50 miles to the northeast. Ancaster is mainly a residential community for the large Hamilton industrial base, mainly the steel industry and related secondary industries. Hamilton is well provided with modern cultural and sport facilities.

■ **ROYAL MILITARY COLLEGE OF CANADA**
PO Box 17000, Station Forces
Kingston, ON, Canada K7K 7B4
Tel: (613)541-6000
Fax: (613)542-3565
E-mail: liaison@rmc.ca
Web Site: www.rmc.ca/

Description: Federally supported, comprehensive, coed. Part of Council of Ontario Universities. Awards bachelor's, master's, and doctoral degrees. Founded 1876. Setting: 90-acre urban campus. Total enrollment: 6,500. Faculty: 149. 1,500 applied, 40% were admitted. Students come from 13 provinces and territories, 60% from out-of-province. 15% 25 or older, 90% live on campus. Retention: 90% of full-time freshmen returned the following year. Core. Calendar: Canadian standard year. ESL program, honors program, distance learning, part-time degree program. Off campus study.

Entrance Requirements: Open admission for part-time students. Options: electronic application, early decision, international baccalaureate accepted. Required: high school transcript, interview, medical, aptitude and physical fitness testing. Entrance: most difficult. Application deadline: 1/15. Notification: 5/15. Transfer credits accepted: Yes. Early decision applicants: 50. Early decision applicants admitted: 10.

Collegiate Environment: Drama-theater group, choral group, marching band, student-run newspaper. Social organizations: 30 open to all. Most popular organization: band. Major annual events: Ex-Cadet Weekend, Christmas Ball, Graduation Weekend. Student services: legal services, health clinic, personal-psychological counseling. Campus security: 24-hour emergency response devices and patrols, controlled dormitory access. Massey Library plus 1 other with 300,000 books, 18,000 microform titles, 1,100 serials, 2,510 audiovisual materials, an OPAC, and a Web page. 200 computers available on campus for general student use. A campuswide network can be accessed from student residence rooms and from off campus. Students can access the following: online class registration. Staffed computer lab on campus.

Community Environment: Kingston is situated at the confluence of Lake Ontario and the St. Lawrence River. Since 1673, when it was established as a trading post called Fort Frontenac, it has been of Canadian commercial and geographic importance. Kingston's interest in preserving its historical flavor is exemplified in the restoration of Fort Henry, the key defense of the Kingston Naval Dockyard. Kingston is a very much a university town that enjoys the presence of RMC, Queen's and St. Lawrence Colleges.

■ **RYERSON UNIVERSITY**
350 Victoria St.
Toronto, ON, Canada M5B 2K3
Tel: (416)979-5000
E-mail: inquire@ryerson.ca
Web Site: www.ryerson.ca/
Description: Province-supported, comprehensive, coed. Awards bachelor's and master's degrees. Founded 1948. Setting: 20-acre urban campus. Total enrollment: 25,181. Faculty: 955 (744 full-time, 211 part-time). 3% live on campus. Retention: 90% of full-time freshmen returned the following year. Academic areas with the most degrees conferred: business/marketing; health professions and related sciences; engineering. Calendar: Canadian standard year or semesters depending on program. Academic remediation for entering students, ESL program, services for LD students, advanced placement, honors program, distance learning, summer session for credit, part-time degree program, adult/continuing education programs, co-op programs and internships. Off campus study. Study abroad program.
Entrance Requirements: Options: electronic application, international baccalaureate accepted. Required: high school transcript. Required for some: essay, interview, portfolio, audition, entrance examination. Entrance: moderately difficult. Application deadline: 2/1. Notification: continuous.
Collegiate Environment: Orientation program. Drama-theater group, choral group, student-run newspaper, radio station. Social organizations: 55 open to all. Major annual events: Island Picnic, Winter Carnival, Cultural Caravan. Student services: health clinic, personal-psychological counseling, women's center. Campus security: 24-hour emergency response devices and patrols, late night transport-escort service, controlled dormitory access, staffed access control is in place 24 hours a day, with ID checks of all persons attempting to enter. Ryerson Library with 487,361 books, 842,860 microform titles, 28,075 serials, 18,136 audiovisual materials, an OPAC, and a Web page. 1,400 computers available on campus for general student use. Computer purchase/lease plans available. A campuswide network can be accessed from student residence rooms and from off campus. Staffed computer lab on campus.

■ **SAINT PAUL UNIVERSITY**
223 Main St.
Ottawa, ON, Canada K1S 1C4
Tel: (613)236-1393; Free: 800-637-6859
Fax: (613)782-3033
E-mail: admission@ustpaul.ca
Web Site: www.ustpaul.ca/
Description: Province-supported, university, coed. Administratively affiliated with University of Ottawa. Awards bachelor's, master's, and doctoral degrees. Founded 1848. Setting: 4-acre urban campus. Student-undergrad faculty ratio is 12:1. Calendar: Canadian standard year. Summer session for credit, part-time degree program, graduate courses open to undergrads.
Entrance Requirements: Options: deferred admission, international baccalaureate accepted. Required: high school transcript. Recommended: SAT. Entrance: moderately difficult.

■ **TRENT UNIVERSITY**
1600 W Bank Dr.
Peterborough, ON, Canada K9J 7B8
Tel: (705)748-1011
Fax: (705)748-1629
E-mail: admissions@trentu.ca
Web Site: www.trentu.ca/
Description: Province-supported, university, coed. Awards bachelor's, master's, and doctoral degrees. Founded 1963. Setting: 1,400-acre suburban campus with easy access to Toronto. Total enrollment: 8,050. Faculty: 500 (300 full-time, 200 part-time). Student-undergrad faculty ratio is 18:1. 9,300 applied, 18% were admitted. Full-time: 6,409 students, 65%

women, 35% men. Part-time: 1,165 students, 63% women, 37% men. Students come from 12 provinces and territories, 78 other countries, 2% from out-of-province. 11% 25 or older, 17% live on campus, 7% transferred in. Retention: 84% of full-time freshmen returned the following year. Calendar: Canadian standard year. Academic remediation for entering students, ESL program, services for LD students, advanced placement, accelerated degree program, self-designed majors, honors program, independent study, distance learning, double major, summer session for credit, part-time degree program, co-op programs and internships. Off campus study at Sir Sandford Fleming College. Study abroad program.
Entrance Requirements: Options: electronic application, deferred admission, international baccalaureate accepted. Required: high school transcript, minimum 2.8 high school GPA. Required for some: essay, interview. Entrance: moderately difficult. Application deadline: 6/1. Notification: continuous. Transfer credits accepted: Yes.
Costs Per Year: Application fee: $135 Canadian dollars. Tuition, fee, and room and board charges are reported in Canadian dollars. Province resident tuition: $5693 full-time, $1139 per course part-time. Canadian resident tuition: $3209 per course part-time. Mandatory fees: $1389 full-time, $110 per credit part-time. Full-time tuition and fees vary according to location, program, and student level. Part-time tuition and fees vary according to course load, location, program, and student level. College room and board: $10,300. Room and board charges vary according to board plan, housing facility, and location. International student tuition: $16,045 full-time.
Collegiate Environment: Orientation program. Drama-theater group, choral group, student-run newspaper, radio station. Social organizations: 77 open to all. Most popular organizations: Trent Radio, Trent International Program, Trent Central Student Association, Arthur (student newspaper), Excalibur (yearbook). Major annual event: Head of Trent (Homecoming). Student services: health clinic, personal-psychological counseling, women's center. Campus security: 24-hour emergency response devices and patrols, student patrols, late night transport-escort service, controlled dormitory access. 1,181 college housing spaces available; all were occupied in 2012-13. Freshmen given priority for college housing. Options: coed, women-only housing available. Thomas J. Bata Library plus 1 other with an OPAC.
Community Environment: The university is situated on the banks of the Otonabee River, three miles north of Peterborough, Ontario. Two other colleges are located in residential areas of downtown Peterborough, one of Ontario's oldest and loveliest cities.

■ **TYNDALE UNIVERSITY COLLEGE & SEMINARY**
25 Ballyconnor Ct.
Toronto, ON, Canada M2M 4B3
Tel: (416)226-6380
Fax: (416)226-4210
E-mail: admissions@tydale.ca
Web Site: www.tyndale.ca/
Description: Independent interdenominational, comprehensive, coed. Awards bachelor's, master's, and doctoral degrees. Founded 1894. Setting: 10-acre urban campus. Endowment: $2 million. Educational spending for the previous fiscal year: $1678 per student. Total enrollment: 1,142. Faculty: (54 full-time). Student-undergrad faculty ratio is 23:1. 368 applied, 53% were admitted. Full-time: 348 students, 47% women, 53% men. Part-time: 131 students, 50% women, 50% men. Students come from 7 provinces and territories, 12 other countries. 20% 25 or older, 30% live on campus. Retention: 49% of full-time freshmen returned the following year. Core. Calendar: semesters. Academic remediation for entering students, accelerated degree program, honors program, summer session for credit, part-time degree program, adult/continuing education programs. Off campus study at Seneca College.
Entrance Requirements: Options: deferred admission, international baccalaureate accepted. Required: essay, high school transcript, 2 recommendations, all post-secondary transcripts. Required for some: interview. Entrance: moderately difficult. Application deadline: 8/15. Notification: 9/19.
Collegiate Environment: Orientation program. Drama-theater group, choral group, student-run newspaper. Social organizations: 5 open to all. Most popular organizations: choir, student government, Urban Ministry Team, Steadfast drama team. Major annual events: Global Ministries Conference, Experience OBC, intramural floor hockey. Student services: personal-psychological counseling. Campus security: student patrols, late night transport-escort service, controlled dormitory access. J. William Horsey Library with 65,013 books, 1 microform title, 410 serials, and an OPAC. Operations spending for the previous fiscal year: $440,000. 30 computers available on campus for general student use. A campuswide network can be

accessed. Students can access the following: online class registration. Staffed computer lab on campus provides training in use of computers, software, and the Internet.

■ UNIVERSITY OF GUELPH

Guelph, ON, Canada N1G 2W1
Tel: (519)824-4120
E-mail: jhogan@registrar.uoguelph.ca
Web Site: www.uoguelph.ca/

Description: Province-supported, university, coed. Awards associate, bachelor's, master's, and doctoral degrees. Founded 1964. Setting: 1,017-acre urban campus with easy access to Toronto. Total enrollment: 22,400. Faculty: (860 full-time). Student-undergrad faculty ratio is 22:1. 22,584 applied, 64% were admitted. Students come from 100 other countries. 28% live on campus. Retention: 92% of full-time freshmen returned the following year. Core. Calendar: trimesters. Academic remediation for entering students, ESL program, services for LD students, advanced placement, accelerated degree program, self-designed majors, freshman honors college, honors program, independent study, distance learning, double major, summer session for credit, part-time degree program, co-op programs and internships, graduate courses open to undergrads. Off campus study. Study abroad program.

Entrance Requirements: Options: electronic application, early admission, deferred admission, international baccalaureate accepted. Required: high school transcript, minimum 3 high school GPA, SAT or ACT. Required for some: essay. Entrance: moderately difficult. Application deadline: 3/1. Notification: continuous. SAT Reasoning Test deadline: 3/1. SAT Subject Test deadline: 3/1. Transfer credits accepted: Yes.

Costs Per Year: Application fee: $135 Canadian dollars. Tuition, fee, and room and board charges are reported in Canadian dollars. Province resident tuition: $5692 full-time, $1137 per credit part-time. Mandatory fees: $1180 full-time, $480 per credit part-time. Full-time tuition and fees vary according to course level, degree level, location, program, and reciprocity agreements. Part-time tuition and fees vary according to course level, course load, degree level, location, program, and reciprocity agreements. College room and board: $9764. College room only: $5364. Room and board charges vary according to board plan, housing facility, and location. International student tuition: $17,430 full-time. Tuition guaranteed not to increase for student's term of enrollment.

Collegiate Environment: Orientation program. Drama-theater group, choral group, student-run newspaper, radio station. Social organizations: 150 open to all. Most popular organizations: Guelph Gryphon Athletics, Habitat for Humanity, Curtain Call Productions, West Indian Students Association, OXFAM-Guelph Chapter. Major annual events: Homecoming, College Royal Weekend, Trick or Eat. Student services: legal services, health clinic, personal-psychological counseling, women's center. Campus security: 24-hour emergency response devices and patrols, student patrols, late night transport-escort service, controlled dormitory access, video camera surveillance in parking lots, alarms in women's locker room. 5,000 college housing spaces available; all were occupied in 2012-13. Freshmen guaranteed college housing. Options: coed, women-only housing available. University of Guelph Library with an OPAC and a Web page. 1,500 computers available on campus for general student use. A campuswide network can be accessed from student residence rooms and from off campus. Students can access the following: online class registration. Staffed computer lab on campus (open 24 hours a day) provides training in use of computers and software.

Community Environment: Blending the sophistication of city life with the beautiful scenery of the countryside in the heart of southwestern Ontario, the city of Guelph is a lively, multicultural community of 100,000. Just a short walk from campus, students can enjoy sidewalk cafes, specialty boutiques and craft shops, and a wide variety of restaurants. An hour's drive west of Toronto, Guelph is easily accessible by bus or train. It is the home of the Guelph Spring Festival (May-June), the Guelph Jazz Festival (September), and the Hillside Folk Festival (July), as well as the site of the Guelph Center for the Performing Arts.

■ UNIVERSITY OF OTTAWA

550 Cumberland St.
Ottawa, ON, Canada K1N 6N5
Tel: (613)562-5700
E-mail: cpharand@uottawa.ca
Web Site: www.uottawa.ca/

Description: Province-supported, university, coed. Administratively affiliated with Saint-Paul University (Ottawa, Ontario). Awards bachelor's, master's, and doctoral degrees. Founded 1848. Setting: 43-hectare urban campus with easy access to Ottawa-Gatineau. Endowment: $183.9 million. Research spending for the previous fiscal year: $300.9 million. Educational spending for the previous fiscal year: $11,281 per student. Total enrollment: 42,027. Faculty: 2,239 (1,272 full-time, 967 part-time). Student-undergrad faculty ratio is 25:1. 41,600 applied, 58% were admitted. Students come from 13 provinces and territories, 134 other countries, 21% from out-of province. 18% 25 or older, 9% live on campus. Retention: 86% of full-time freshmen returned the following year. Academic areas with the most degrees conferred: education; social sciences; health professions and related sciences. Calendar: semesters. Academic remediation for entering students, ESL program, services for LD students, advanced placement, honors program, distance learning, double major, summer session for credit, part-time degree program, co-op programs and internships. Off campus study at Carleton University, Saint Paul University, Canadian Universities Student Exchange Consortium, Algonquin College, La Cite collegiale. Study abroad program.

Entrance Requirements: Options: electronic application, early admission, deferred admission, international baccalaureate accepted. Required: high school transcript, minimum 3 high school GPA. Required for some: interview, SAT or ACT required for American citizens. Entrance: moderately difficult. Application deadline: 6/1. Notification: continuous until 8/30. Transfer credits accepted: Yes.

Costs Per Year: Application fee: $167 Canadian dollars. Tuition, fee, and room and board charges are reported in Canadian dollars. One-time mandatory fee: $360. Province resident tuition: $5665 full-time, $224.54 per credit part-time. Canadian resident tuition: $714.95 per credit part-time. Mandatory fees: $640 full-time, $119.64 per term part-time. Full-time tuition and fees vary according to course load, degree level, program, and student level. Part-time tuition and fees vary according to course load, degree level, program, and student level. College room and board: $6722. College room only: $4622. Room and board charges vary according to board plan and housing facility. International student tuition: $18,446 full-time.

Collegiate Environment: Orientation program. Drama-theater group, choral group, student-run newspaper, radio station. Social organizations: national fraternities, national sororities, local fraternities, local sororities; 1% of eligible men and 1% of eligible women are members. Most popular organizations: Student Federation of the University of Ottawa, Graduate Students Association. Major annual events: 101 Week - Welcome Week, International Week, Snow Festival. Student services: legal services, health clinic, personal-psychological counseling, women's center. Campus security: 24-hour emergency response devices and patrols, student patrols, late night transport-escort service, controlled dormitory access. 2,881 college housing spaces available; 2,849 were occupied in 2012-13. Freshmen guaranteed college housing. Option: coed housing available. Morisset Library plus 7 others with 3.8 million books, 1.9 million microform titles, 90,710 serials, 38,601 audiovisual materials, an OPAC, and a Web page. Operations spending for the previous fiscal year: $25.2 million. 1,540 computers available on campus for general student use. A campuswide network can be accessed from student residence rooms and from off campus. Students can access the following: online class registration, wireless connection available on campus. Staffed computer lab on campus (open 24 hours a day) provides training in use of computers, software, and the Internet.

Community Environment: Ottawa, the capital of Canada, is a modern, cosmopolitan city with a population of 774,000. This unique setting is renowned for its museums, its national festivities, and its year-round outdoor activities in a breathtaking and readily accessible natural environment. During the academic year, students can get acquainted with monuments, museums, art galleries, restaurants, theaters, and concert halls located downtown. Nature buffs will be thrilled with the multitude of green spaces and the extensive network of cycling paths. Come winter, the paths turn into cross-country ski trails and the Rideau Canal, alongside the campus, becomes the world's longest skating rink.

■ UNIVERSITY OF TORONTO

Toronto, ON, Canada M5S 1A1
Tel: (416)978-2011
E-mail: admissions.help@utoronto.ca
Web Site: www.utoronto.ca/uoft.html

Description: Province-supported, university, coed. Awards bachelor's, master's, and doctoral degrees. Founded 1827. Setting: 714-hectare urban campus. Endowment: $1.5 billion. Research spending for the previous fiscal year: $912.5 million. Total enrollment: 80,663. Faculty: 3,135 (2,791 full-time, 344 part-time). Student-undergrad faculty ratio is 24:1. 70,906 applied, 67% were admitted. Full-time: 58,064 students, 56% women, 44% men. Part-time: 6,898 students, 50% women, 50% men. Students come from 12 provinces and territories, 162 other countries, 6% from out-of province. 27% 25 or older, 15% live on campus, 1% transferred in. Retention: 91% of full-time freshmen returned the following year. Calendar: Canadian standard year. ESL program, services for LD students, double major, summer session for credit, part-time degree program, adult/continuing education programs, co-op programs, graduate courses open to undergrads. Off campus study at Sheridan Community College. Study abroad program.

Entrance Requirements: Option: deferred admission. Required: high school transcript, SAT and SAT Subject Tests or ACT. Required for some: interview. Entrance: very difficult. Application deadline: 3/1. Notification: continuous. Preference given to province residents for pharmacy program; Canadian residents for dentistry, physical and occupational therapy, rehabilitation medicine programs.

Costs Per Year: Application fee: $135. Province resident tuition: $5865 full-time. Canadian resident tuition: $5865 full-time. Mandatory fees: $1400 full-time. Full-time tuition and fees vary according to course level, course load, and program. International student tuition: $32,865 full-time.

Collegiate Environment: Orientation program. Drama-theater group, choral group, student-run newspaper, radio station. Social organizations: national fraternities, national sororities, local sororities. Student services: legal services, health clinic, personal-psychological counseling, women's center. Campus security: 24-hour emergency response devices and patrols, student patrols, late night transport-escort service. 8,858 college housing spaces available; all were occupied in 2012-13. Freshmen guaranteed college housing. Options: coed, women-only housing available. Robarts Library plus 42 others with 14.5 million books, 5.5 million microform titles, 97,753 serials, 257,627 audiovisual materials, an OPAC, and a Web page. Operations spending for the previous fiscal year: $75 million. 2,000 computers available on campus for general student use. A campuswide network can be accessed from student residence rooms and from off campus. Students can access the following: online class registration. Staffed computer lab on campus.

Community Environment: Toronto is the financial and industrial capital of Canada as well as Provincial capital of Ontario. It is often compared to New York and, in fact, was known as "York" (after the Duke of York) until 1834. The name "Toronto" was selected and is taken from an Indian word which means "meeting place" and it has become the meeting place or crossroads for nearly all Canadian activities. Cultural attractions abound and include the Art Gallery of Ontario, the Ontario Science Center, the Marine Museum of Upper Canada, Royal Ontario Museum and the Hummingbird Centre (which is home to the National Ballet of Canada, the Canadian Opera Company and scene of numerous plays). Toronto is one of two Canadian cities with baseball teams in the major leagues but more important to Canadians, it is the home of the Hockey Hall of Fame and of the Maple Leafs. The city also has many other sport and recreation facilities including the Skydome, a domed stadium. The city is one of the great inland ports of North America and is easily accessible by air, rail, bus and road. It has one of the best subway systems in the world and an excellent public bus system.

■ **UNIVERSITY OF WATERLOO**
200 University Ave. W
Waterloo, ON, Canada N2L 3G1
Tel: (519)888-4567
Fax: (519)746-2882
E-mail: registrar@uwaterloo.ca
Web Site: www.uwaterloo.ca/

Description: Province-supported, university, coed. Awards bachelor's, master's, and doctoral degrees. Founded 1957. Setting: 1,000-acre suburban campus with easy access to Toronto. Total enrollment: 32,598. Faculty: (1,093 full-time). Student-undergrad faculty ratio is 30:1. 43,347 applied, 53% were admitted. Students come from 115 other countries. 23% live on campus. Retention: 90% of full-time freshmen returned the following year. Calendar: trimesters. Academic remediation for entering students, ESL program, services for LD students, advanced placement, accelerated degree program, self-designed majors, honors program, independent study, distance learning, double major, summer session for credit, part-time degree program, co-op programs and internships, graduate courses open to undergrads. Off campus study at Wilfrid Laurier University, Brock University, Queen's University at Kingston, University of Guelph, McMaster University, Conestoga College, Mohawk College, Canadian University Exchange Consortium, members of Regional Academic Mobility Program, members of The Group of Ten Exchange Program. Study abroad program.

Entrance Requirements: Options: electronic application, early admission, deferred admission, international baccalaureate accepted. Required: high

school transcript. Required for some: essay, minimum 3 high school GPA, interview, SAT or ACT, SAT Subject Tests. Entrance: moderately difficult. Application deadline: 3/28. Notification: 5/24.

Collegiate Environment: Orientation program. Drama-theater group, choral group, marching band, student-run newspaper, radio station. Social organizations: 160 open to all; national fraternities, national sororities; 1% of eligible men and 1% of eligible women are members. Major annual events: Oktoberfest, Canada Day, Homecoming. Student services: legal services, health clinic, personal-psychological counseling, women's center. Campus security: 24-hour emergency response devices and patrols, student patrols, late night transport-escort service. 5,750 college housing spaces available. Freshmen guaranteed college housing. Options: coed, men-only, women-only housing available. Dana Porter Library plus 6 others with 1.7 million microform titles, 41,118 serials, 990 audiovisual materials, an OPAC, and a Web page. 6,000 computers available on campus for general student use. Computer purchase/lease plans available. A campuswide network can be accessed from student residence rooms and from off campus. Students can access the following: online class registration. Staffed computer lab on campus.

Community Environment: The University of Waterloo is located near Toronto in the heart of southern Ontario, Canada's most populous and highly developed province. The University's home community of Kitchener-Waterloo, population 276,900, is ethnically one of the most diverse in Canada. Residents enjoy a high standard of living, safe and clean neighborhoods, and may cultural and recreational attractions, as well as natural parks and protected wilderness areas.

■ **THE UNIVERSITY OF WESTERN ONTARIO**
London, ON, Canada N6A 5B8
Tel: (519)661-2111
E-mail: reg-admissions@uwo.ca
Web Site: www.uwo.ca/

Description: Province-supported, university, coed. Administratively affiliated with Brescia University College, Huron University College, King's University College. Awards bachelor's, master's, and doctoral degrees. Founded 1878. Setting: 499-hectare suburban campus. Research spending for the previous fiscal year: $208.7 million. Total enrollment: 37,205. Faculty: 1,408 (all full-time). Student-undergrad faculty ratio is 20:1. 33,270 applied, 52% were admitted. Students come from 13 countries and territories, 100 other countries, 6% from out-of-province. 3% 25 or older, 21% live on campus. Retention: 94% of full-time freshmen returned the following year. Academic areas with the most degrees conferred: social sciences; health professions and related sciences; education. Core. Calendar: Canadian standard year. Academic remediation for entering students, ESL program, services for LD students, advanced placement, accelerated degree program, self-designed majors, honors program, independent study, distance learning, double major, summer session for credit, part-time degree program, adult/continuing education programs; co-op programs and internships, graduate courses open to undergrads. Off campus study. Study abroad program.

Entrance Requirements: Options: electronic application, deferred admission, international baccalaureate accepted. Required: high school transcript, minimum 3.5 high school GPA, SAT or ACT. Entrance: very difficult. Application deadlines: 6/1, 5/15 for nonresidents. Notification: continuous, continuous for nonresidents. Transfer credits accepted: Yes.

Costs Per Year: Application fee: $130. Province resident tuition: $5801 full-time, $1160 per course part-time. Canadian resident tuition: $3912 per course part-time. Full-time tuition varies according to program and student level. Part-time tuition varies according to course load, location, program, and student level. College room and board: $10,540. College room only: $5940. Room and board charges vary according to board plan, housing facility, and location. International student tuition: $19,562 full-time.

Collegiate Environment: Orientation program. Drama-theater group, choral group, marching band, student-run newspaper, radio station. Social organizations: 185 open to all; national fraternities, national sororities. Most popular organizations: Western Investment Club, Pre-Medical Society, Purple Spur Society, Canadian Asian International Students' Association (CAISA), Pre-Law Society. Major annual events: Orientation Week, Homecoming, Career Week. Student services: legal services, health clinic, personal-psychological counseling. Campus security: 24-hour emergency response devices and patrols, student patrols, late night transport-escort service, controlled dormitory access, Campus Community Police, SERT: Student Emergency Response Team, Western Foot Patrol. 5,677 college housing spaces available; all were occupied in 2012-13. Freshmen guaranteed college housing. Option: coed housing available. The University of Western Ontario Libraries plus 7 others with 4.7 million books, 4.2 million microform titles, 108,417 serials, 81,542 audiovisual materials, an OPAC, and a Web page. 414 computers available on campus for general student use. Computer purchase/lease plans available. A campuswide network can be accessed from student residence rooms and from off campus. Students can access the following: online class registration. Staffed computer lab on campus provides training in use of computers, software, and the Internet.

Community Environment: The university is located on 155 hectares of land along the banks of the Thames River in London, Ontario, a thriving city of 331,000 people and is only 200 kilometers west of Toronto.

■ **UNIVERSITY OF WINDSOR**
401 Sunset Ave.
Windsor, ON, Canada N9B 3P4
Tel: (519)253-3000
Fax: (519)973-7050
E-mail: registrar@uwindsor.ca
Web Site: www.uwindsor.ca/

Description: Province-supported, university, coed. Awards bachelor's, master's, and doctoral degrees. Founded 1857. Setting: 125-acre urban campus with easy access to Detroit, Michigan, USA. Endowment: $56 million. Research spending for the previous fiscal year: $25.3 million. Educational spending for the previous fiscal year: $6218 per student. Total enrollment: 15,999. Faculty: 871 (524 full-time, 347 part-time). Student-undergrad faculty ratio is 21:1. 12,180 applied, 78% were admitted. Full-time: 10,560 students, 56% women, 44% men. Part-time: 3,060 students, 50% women, 50% men. Students come from 16 provinces and territories, 91 other countries. 26% 25 or older, 13% live on campus, 5% transferred in. Retention: 82% of full-time freshmen returned the following year. Core. Calendar: semesters. Academic remediation for entering students, services for LD students, advanced placement, accelerated degree program, self-designed majors, honors program, distance learning, double major, summer session for credit, part-time degree program, external degree program, adult/continuing education programs, co-op programs and internships, graduate courses open to undergrads. Off campus study at Wayne State University, University of Akron, University of Massachusetts, Amherst. Study abroad program.

Entrance Requirements: Options: electronic application, early admission, international baccalaureate accepted. Required: high school transcript, minimum 3 high school GPA. Required for some: essay, minimum 3.3 high school GPA, 1 recommendation, interview, SAT or ACT, SAT and SAT Subject Tests or ACT, SAT Subject Tests. Entrance: moderately difficult. Application deadlines: Rolling, 7/1 for nonresidents. Notification: continuous until 8/30.

Costs Per Year: Application fee: $60 Canadian dollars. Tuition and fee charges are reported in Canadian dollars. Province resident tuition: $5,558 full-time, $859.83 per course part-time. Mandatory fees: $591 full-time. Full-time tuition and fees vary according to course load, degree level, location, and program. Part-time tuition varies according to course load, degree level, location, and program.

Collegiate Environment: Orientation program. Drama-theater group, choral group, student-run newspaper, radio station. Social organizations: 100 open to all; national fraternities, national sororities. Most popular organizations: University of Windsor Student Alliance, Environmental Awareness Association, Social Science Society, Commerce Society, Science Society. Major annual events: Health Fair, Job Fair, Windsor Welcome Week. Student services: legal services, health clinic, personal-psychological counseling, women's center. Campus security: 24-hour emergency response devices and patrols, student patrols, late night transport-escort service, controlled dormitory access. 1,600 college housing spaces available; 1,300 were occupied in 2012-13. Freshmen guaranteed college housing. Options: coed, men-only, women-only housing available. Leddy Library plus 2 others with 8 million books, 1.7 million microform titles, 83,605 serials, 13,724 audiovisual materials, an OPAC, and a Web page. Operations spending for the previous fiscal year: $12.8 million. 1,225 computers available on campus for general student use. A campuswide network can be accessed from student residence rooms and from off campus. Students can access the following: online class registration, online transcripts, degree audits, grades, bursaries, grants, online applications for graduation. Staffed computer lab on campus provides training in use of computers, software, and the Internet.

Community Environment: The city of Windsor lies across the Detroit River from Detroit, Michigan, and its cultural, entertainment, athletic attractions. Yet by itself Windsor is an attraction as the hub of Canada's automotive industry, the City of Roses, the site of a three-story Art Gallery displaying Canadian painting and sculpture from the eighteenth century on, home of the Windsor Symphony, and host of the International Freedom Festival.

■ **WILFRID LAURIER UNIVERSITY**
75 University Ave. W
Waterloo, ON, Canada N2L 3C5
Tel: (519)884-1970
Fax: (519)884-8826
E-mail: admissions@wlu.ca
Web Site: www.wlu.ca/

Description: Province-supported, comprehensive, coed. Awards bachelor's, master's, and doctoral degrees. Founded 1911. Setting: 40-acre urban campus with easy access to Toronto. Total enrollment: 17,382. Faculty: (516 full-time). Student-undergrad faculty ratio is 25:1. 24,597 applied, 70% were admitted. Full-time: 13,954 students, 59% women, 41% men. Part-time: 1,942 students, 52% women, 48% men. Students come from 57 other countries. 5% 25 or older, 25% live on campus. Retention: 89% of full-time freshmen returned the following year. Calendar: semesters Canadian standard year. Academic remediation for entering students, ESL program, services for LD students, advanced placement, accelerated degree program, honors program, distance learning, double major, summer session for credit, part-time degree program, adult/continuing education programs, co-op programs and internships. Off campus study at University of Waterloo and Colleges of Applied Arts and Technology throughout Ontario. Study abroad program.

Entrance Requirements: Options: electronic application, early admission, early decision, deferred admission, international baccalaureate accepted. Required: high school transcript. Required for some: essay, interview, audition for music programs, SAT or ACT. Entrance: minimally difficult. Application deadlines: 5/1, 5/1 for nonresidents. Notification: continuous until 5/25, continuous for nonresidents. Transfer credits accepted: Yes.

Collegiate Environment: Orientation program. Drama-theater group, student-run newspaper, radio station. Social organizations: 120 open to all; national fraternities, national sororities, local fraternities, local sororities. Most popular organizations: Habitat for Humanity of WLU, Laurier Musical Theatre, East Meets West, Laurier SOS, Laurier Ski and Snowboarding Club. Major annual events: First-Year Students' Orientation, Year End Celebration, Homecoming. Student services: legal services, health clinic, personal-psychological counseling, women's center. Campus security: 24-hour emergency response devices and patrols, student patrols, late night transport-escort service, controlled dormitory access. Wilfrid Laurier University Library plus 1 other with 821,924 microform titles, 14,671 serials, 24,246 audiovisual materials, an OPAC, and a Web page. 383 computers available on campus for general student use. A campuswide network can be accessed from student residence rooms and from off campus. Students can access the following: online class registration. Staffed computer lab on campus.

■ **YORK UNIVERSITY**
4700 Keele St.
Toronto, ON, Canada M3J 1P3
Tel: (416)736-2100
Fax: (416)736-5741
E-mail: intlenq@yorku.ca
Web Site: www.yorku.ca/

Description: Province-supported, university, coed. Awards bachelor's, master's, and doctoral degrees and post-master's certificates. Founded 1959. Setting: 457-acre urban campus. Endowment: $245 million. Total enrollment: 54,507. Faculty: 2,498 (1,465 full-time, 1,033 part-time). Student-undergrad faculty ratio is 19:1. 41,408 applied. Students come from 11 provinces and territories, 167 other countries, 1% from out-of-province. 20% 25 or older. Core. Calendar: semesters. Academic remediation for entering students, ESL program, services for LD students, advanced placement, accelerated degree program, self-designed majors, honors program, independent study, distance learning, double major, summer session for credit, part-time degree program, adult/continuing education programs, internships. Off campus study at Centennial College, Humber College, Seneca College, Sheridan College, Georgian College, Durham College. Study abroad program.

Entrance Requirements: Options: electronic application, deferred admission, international baccalaureate accepted. Required: high school transcript, minimum 3 high school GPA, audition for fine arts, supplemental application for business, SAT or ACT. Required for some: essay, interview. Entrance:

moderately difficult. Application deadline: 2/1. Preference given to students with identified learning disabilities, extenuating circumstances. Transfer credits accepted: Yes.

Costs Per Year: Application fee: $210. Province resident tuition: $6,523 full-time. Canadian resident tuition: $6,523 full-time. Full-time tuition varies according to course load, degree level, and program. College room and board: $7784. College room only: $4784. Room and board charges vary according to board plan and housing facility. International student tuition: $17,934 full-time.

Collegiate Environment: Orientation program. Drama-theater group, choral group, student-run newspaper, radio station. Social organizations: 290 open to all. Most popular organizations: college student councils, York Federation of Students, Jewish Student Association, First Nations and Aboriginal Student Association, International and Exchange Students Club. Major annual events: Homecoming, Orientation Week, Multicultural Week. Student services: legal services, health clinic, personal-psychological counseling, women's center. Campus security: 24-hour emergency response devices and patrols, student patrols, late night transport-escort service, controlled dormitory access. 4,000 college housing spaces available. Freshmen guaranteed college housing. Options: coed, men-only, women-only housing available. Scott Library plus 5 others with 6.5 million books, 4 million microform titles, 540,000 serials, an OPAC, and a Web page. Operations spending for the previous fiscal year: $18.4 million. 1,900 computers available on campus for general student use. A campuswide network can be accessed from student residence rooms and from off campus. Students can access the following: online class registration, online student account. Staffed computer lab on campus provides training in use of computers, software, and the Internet.

■ BISHOP'S UNIVERSITY

2600 College St.
Sherbrooke, QC, Canada J1M 0C8
Tel: (819)822-9600; Free: 877-822-8200
Fax: (819)822-9661
E-mail: recruitment@ubishops.ca
Web Site: www.ubishops.ca/

Description: Province-supported, comprehensive, coed. Part of Association of Universities and Colleges of Canada (AUCC). Awards bachelor's and master's degrees. Founded 1843. Setting: 500-acre small town campus. Student-undergrad faculty ratio is 15:1. Students come from 20 provinces and territories, 40 other countries. Calendar: semesters most students study from September to late April. Spring semester is May-June. Honors program, double major, part-time degree program, adult/continuing education programs. Study abroad program.

Entrance Requirements: Options: electronic application, early admission, deferred admission, international baccalaureate accepted. Required: high school transcript, minimum 3 high school GPA, birth certificate, copy of student visa, SAT or ACT. Recommended: essay. Required for some: essay. Entrance: moderately difficult. Application deadline: 3/1. Notification: continuous. SAT Reasoning Test deadline: 3/1. Transfer credits accepted: Yes.

Collegiate Environment: Orientation program. Campus security: 24-hour emergency response devices and patrols, student patrols, late night transport-escort service, controlled dormitory access. John Bassett Memorial Library plus 1 other with 18,408 serials, an OPAC, and a Web page. 650 computers available on campus for general student use. A campuswide network can be accessed from student residence rooms and from off campus. Students can access the following: online class registration, Web course management systems, individualized Web access. Staffed computer lab on campus provides training in use of computers, software, and the Internet.

■ CONCORDIA UNIVERSITY

1455 de Maisonneuve Blvd. W
Montréal, QC, Canada H3G 1M8
Tel: (514)848-2424
Fax: (514)848-2621
E-mail: ijkrau@alcor.concordia.ca
Web Site: www.concordia.ca/

Description: Province-supported, university, coed. Part of Quebec University Network. Awards bachelor's, master's, and doctoral degrees. Founded 1974. Setting: 52-acre urban campus with easy access to Montreal. Endowment: $77.5 million. Total enrollment: 36,198. Faculty: 1,565 (924 full-time, 641 part-time). Student-undergrad faculty ratio is 25:1. 15,347 applied, 67% were admitted. Full-time: 20,107 students, 53% women, 47% men. Part-time: 10,339 students, 51% women, 49% men. Students come from 13 provinces and territories, 147 other countries, 10% from out-of-province. 18% 25 or older, 2% live on campus. Retention: 84% of full-time freshmen returned the following year. Academic areas with the most degrees conferred: business/marketing; social sciences; visual and performing arts. Calendar: semesters. Academic remediation for entering students, ESL program, services for LD students, advanced placement, accelerated degree program, self-designed majors, honors program, independent study, distance learning, double major, summer session for credit, part-time degree program, adult/continuing education programs, co-op programs and internships, graduate courses open to undergrads. Off campus study at Through

an agreement administered by the Conference des recteurs et des principaux des universites du Quebec (CREPUQ), students may register for courses at other Quebec universities under certain conditions. Study abroad program.

Entrance Requirements: Options: electronic application, deferred admission, international baccalaureate accepted. Required: high school transcript, minimum 2.5 high school GPA. Required for some: essay, minimum 2.9 high school GPA, 2 recommendations, interview, portfolio/auditions for Performing and Visual Arts, Communications and Journalism require interview/essay/portfolio. Entrance: moderately difficult. Application deadlines: 3/1, 3/1 for nonresidents. Notification: continuous. Transfer credits accepted: Yes.

Costs Per Year: Application fee: $100 Canadian dollars. Tuition, fee, and room and board charges are reported in Canadian dollars. Province resident tuition: $2,422 full-time, $80.73 per credit part-time. Canadian resident tuition: $6,112 full-time, $205.18 per credit part-time. Mandatory fees: $1,410 full-time, $46.85 per credit part-time. Full-time tuition and fees vary according to course load. Part-time tuition and fees vary according to course load. College room and board: $7262. Room and board charges vary according to board plan, housing facility, and location. International student tuition: $16,513 full-time.

Collegiate Environment: Orientation program. Drama-theater group, choral group, student-run newspaper, radio station. Social organizations: 197 open to all; national fraternities, national sororities. Most popular organizations: undergraduate student union, departmental clubs, religious clubs, ethnic clubs, social action groups. Major annual events: Orientation (Fall and Winter), Lecture/film series. Student services: health clinic, personal-psychological counseling, women's center. Campus security: 24-hour emergency response devices and patrols, student patrols, late night transport-escort service, controlled dormitory access. 543 college housing spaces available; all were occupied in 2012-13. Freshmen given priority for college housing. Options: coed, men-only, women-only housing available. Webster Library plus 1 other with 2.3 million books, 1.3 million microform titles, 72,587 serials, 61,936 audiovisual materials, an OPAC, and a Web page. 350 computers available on campus for general student use. A campuswide network can be accessed from student residence rooms and from off campus. Students can access the following: online class registration, specialized software applications. Staffed computer lab on campus provides training in use of computers, software, and the Internet.

■ ÉCOLE POLYTECHNIQUE DE MONTRÉAL

CP 6079, Succursale Centre-Ville
Montréal, QC, Canada H3C 3A7
Tel: (514)340-4943
Web Site: www.polymtl.ca/

Description: Province-supported, university, coed. Awards bachelor's and doctoral degrees. Founded 1873. Calendar: trimesters.

■ HEC MONTREAL

3000, chemin de la Côte-Sainte-Catherine
Montréal, QC, Canada H3T 2A7
Tel: (514)340-6000
Fax: (514)340-5640
E-mail: admission.info@hec.ca
Web Site: www.hec.ca/

Description: Province-supported, comprehensive, coed. Part of Universite de Montreal. Awards bachelor's, master's, and doctoral degrees. Founded 1910. Setting: 9-acre urban campus. Total enrollment: 12,917. Faculty: 669 (280 full-time, 389 part-time). Student-undergrad faculty ratio is 21:1. 3,045 applied, 57% were admitted. Full-time: 4,865 students, 49% women, 51% men. Part-time: 4,716 students, 51% women, 49% men. Students come from 4 provinces and territories, 37 other countries, 0.3% from out-of province. 56% 25 or older, 0% transferred in. Retention: 91% of full-time freshmen returned the following year. Academic area with the most degrees conferred: business/marketing. Core. Calendar: trimesters. Academic remediation for entering students, ESL program, self-designed majors, honors program, independent study, summer session for credit, adult/continuing education programs. Off campus study at all universities in Quebec. Study abroad program.

Entrance Requirements: Options: electronic application, deferred admission. Required: high school transcript. Required for some: cote de rendement collegial. Entrance: moderately difficult. Application deadlines: 3/1, 2/1 for nonresidents. Notification: continuous, continuous for nonresidents.

Costs Per Year: Application fee: $82 Canadian dollars. Tuition, fee, and room and board charges are reported in Canadian dollars. Province resident tuition: $2,422 full-time, $80.73 per credit part-time. Canadian resident tuition: $6,155 full-time, $205.18 per credit part-time. Mandatory fees: $1,110 full-time, $32.53 per credit part-time, $71.88 per term part-time. Full-time tuition and fees vary according to program. Part-time tuition and fees vary according to program. College room and board: $3640. Room and board charges vary according to board plan and housing facility. International student tuition: $17,566 full-time.

Collegiate Environment: Choral group, student-run newspaper, radio station. Social organizations: 31 open to all. Most popular organizations: AEMBA (MBA Students' Association), AEMD (MSc and PhD Students' Association), AEDES (Post-Bachelor's Certificate Students' Association), AEHEC (BBA Students' Association), AEPC (Certificate Students' Association). Major annual events: Graduation Party, Income Tax Clinic, Commerce Games. Student services: health clinic, personal-psychological counseling. Campus security: 24-hour emergency response devices and patrols. Myriam et J.-Robert Ouimet Library plus 1 other with 567,238 books, 17,201 microform titles, 80,019 serials, 3,162 audiovisual materials, an OPAC, and a Web page. 211 computers available on campus for general student use. Computer purchase/lease plans available. A computer is required for all students. A campuswide network can be accessed. Students can access the following: online class registration, Complete Learning Management System, corporate calendar and web sites for all the resources available for classes. Staffed computer lab on campus (open 24 hours a day) provides training in use of computers, software, and the Internet.

■ MCGILL UNIVERSITY
845 Sherbrooke St. W
Montréal, QC, Canada H3A 2T5
Tel: (514)398-4455
Fax: (514)398-4193
E-mail: admissions@mcgill.ca
Web Site: www.mcgill.ca/

Description: Province-supported, university, coed. Awards bachelor's, master's, and doctoral degrees. Founded 1821. Setting: 80-acre urban campus. Endowment: $901.8 million. Research spending for the previous fiscal year: $432.9 million. Total enrollment: 31,664. Faculty: 2,556 (1,689 full-time, 867 part-time). Student-undergrad faculty ratio is 16:1. 21,242 applied, 54% were admitted. Full-time: 18,722 students, 59% women, 41% men. Part-time: 3,801 students, 60% women, 40% men. Students come from 13 provinces and territories, 118 other countries, 37% from out-of province. 11% 25 or older, 12% live on campus, 3% transferred in. Retention: 93% of full-time freshmen returned the following year. Academic areas with the most degrees conferred: social sciences; business/marketing; biological/life sciences. Calendar: semesters. ESL program, services for LD students, advanced placement, accelerated degree program, honors program, independent study, distance learning, double major, summer session for credit, part-time degree program, adult/continuing education programs, co-op programs and internships, graduate courses open to undergrads. Off campus study at Canex, CREPUQ, CUSAP, Universitas 21. Study abroad program.

Entrance Requirements: Options: electronic application, deferred admission, international baccalaureate accepted. Required: high school transcript, minimum 3.3 high school GPA. Required for some: interview, audition for

music program, portfolio for architecture program, SAT and SAT Subject Tests or ACT. Entrance: very difficult. Application deadline: 1/15. Notification: 1/30.

Collegiate Environment: Orientation program. Drama-theater group, choral group, student-run newspaper, radio station. Social organizations: 250 open to all. Most popular organizations: Muslim Students Association, Hillel McGill, Midnight Kitchen, MISN (McGill International Students Association), Queer McGill. Major annual events: Frosh Program, Activities Night (September and January), Open Air Pub Lite. Student services: legal services, health clinic, personal-psychological counseling. Campus security: 24-hour emergency response devices and patrols, student patrols, late night transport-escort service, controlled dormitory access. McLennan Library plus 13 others with 4.2 million books, 1.8 million microform titles, 49,433 serials, 84,828 audiovisual materials, an OPAC, and a Web page. Operations spending for the previous fiscal year: $29.8 million. 3,730 computers available on campus for general student use. A campuswide network can be accessed from student residence rooms and from off campus. Students can access the following: online class registration. Staffed computer lab on campus (open 24 hours a day) provides training in use of computers, software, and the Internet.

■ TÉLÉ-UNIVERSITÉ
455, rue de l'Église
C.P. 4800, succ. Terminus
Québec, QC, Canada G1K 9H5
Tel: (418)657-2262
Fax: (418)657-2094
Web Site: www.teluq.uquebec.ca/

Description: Province-supported, comprehensive, coed. Part of Universite du Quebec. Awards bachelor's and master's degrees (offers only distance learning degree programs). Founded 1972. Faculty: 36 (all full-time). 2,649 applied, 100% were admitted. Core. Calendar: trimesters. Services for LD students, accelerated degree program, summer session for credit, part-time degree program, adult/continuing education programs, internships. Off campus study at other units of the Universite du Quebec, other universities in the province of Quebec.

Entrance Requirements: Open admission. Required: Diploma of Collegiate Studies (and transcript) or equivalent. Entrance: noncompetitive. Application deadline: Rolling.

Collegiate Environment: 12,567 books and 277 serials.

■ UNIVERSITÉ LAVAL
C.P. 2208, succursale Terminus
Québec, QC, Canada G1K 7P4
Tel: (418)656-3333; Free: 877-785-2825
Fax: (418)656-2809
E-mail: info@dap.ulaval.ca
Web Site: www.ulaval.ca/

Description: Independent, university, coed. Awards associate, bachelor's, master's, and doctoral degrees. Founded 1852. Setting: 465-acre urban campus with easy access to Quebec City. Endowment: $436 million. Research spending for the previous fiscal year: $96.2 million. Educational spending for the previous fiscal year: $15,653 per student. Total enrollment: 37,896. Faculty: 1,456 (1,380 full-time, 76 part-time). Student-undergrad faculty ratio is 7:1. 12,953 applied, 63% were admitted. Students come from 109 other countries, 4% from out-of-province. 24% 25 or older, 7% live on campus. Retention: 94% of full-time freshmen returned the following year. Core. Calendar: trimesters. Academic remediation for entering students, ESL program, services for LD students, accelerated degree program, self-designed majors, honors program, distance learning, summer session for credit, part-time degree program, adult/continuing education programs, co-op programs and internships. Off campus study. Study abroad program.

Entrance Requirements: Options: electronic application, international baccalaureate accepted. Required: high school transcript, general knowledge of French language. Required for some: essay, interview. Entrance: minimally difficult. Application deadlines: 3/1, 3/1 for nonresidents. Notification: 5/15.

Collegiate Environment: Drama-theater group, choral group, student-run newspaper, radio station. Social organizations: 88 open to all; national fraternities. Most popular organizations: Drama Club, Improvisation Ligue, Creation Litteraire, Chorale de L'universite Laval, Amnistie Internationale. Major annual events: Rendez-vous Laval, Carrefour de L'Emploi, Student Festival. Student services: health clinic, personal-psychological counseling. Campus security: 24-hour emergency response devices and patrols, student patrols, late night transport-escort service, controlled dormitory access, video cameras in most buildings, underground walkways. Bibliotheque Generale plus 1 other with 3 million books, 55,507 microform titles, 13,928 serials, an OPAC, and a Web page. Operations spending for the previous fiscal year: $8.9 million. 2,200 computers available on campus for general student use. Computer purchase/lease plans available. A campuswide network can be accessed from student residence rooms and from off campus. Students can access the following: online class registration. Staffed computer lab on campus.

■ UNIVERSITÉ DE MONTRÉAL
CP 6128, Succursale Centre-ville
Montréal, QC, Canada H3C 3J7
Tel: (514)343-6111
Fax: (514)343-5788
E-mail: pierre.chenard@umontreal.ca
Web Site: www.umontreal.ca/
Description: Independent, university, coed. Administratively affiliated with L'Ecole Polytechnique de Montreal, HEC Montreal. Awards bachelor's, master's, and doctoral degrees. Founded 1920. Setting: 150-acre urban campus. Endowment: $837 million. Educational spending for the previous fiscal year: $14,061 per student. Total enrollment: 55,539. Retention: 82% of full-time freshmen returned the following year. Core. Calendar: trimesters. ESL program, services for LD students, accelerated degree program, honors program, independent study, distance learning, summer session for credit, part-time degree program, adult/continuing education programs, co-op programs and internships. Off campus study at Quebec Interuniversity Exchange.
Entrance Requirements: Required: Diploma of Collegiate Studies (and transcript) or equivalent. Required for some: interview. Entrance: moderately difficult. Application deadline: 3/1. Notification: 5/15.
Collegiate Environment: Drama-theater group, choral group, student-run newspaper, radio station. Social organizations: 50 open to all. Most popular organization: Federation des Associations Etudiantes du Campus. Major annual events: Winter Carnival, Multicultural Week, Inter-University Photograph Exhibition. Student services: legal services, health clinic, personal-psychological counseling. Campus security: 24-hour emergency response devices and patrols, student patrols, late night transport-escort service, controlled dormitory access, cameras, alarm systems, crime prevention programs. Bibliotheque des lettres et sciences humaines plus 18 others with 4 million books, 1.7 million microform titles, 18,330 serials, an OPAC, and a Web page. 1,500 computers available on campus for general student use. A campuswide network can be accessed from student residence rooms and from off campus. Students can access the following: online class registration. Staffed computer lab on campus.

■ UNIVERSITÉ DU QUÉBEC EN ABITIBI-TÉMISCAMINGUE
445 Blvd. de l'Université
Rouyn-Noranda, QC, Canada J9X 5E4
Tel: (819)762-0971
Fax: (819)797-4727
E-mail: micheline.chevalier@uqat.uquebec.ca
Web Site: www.uqat.ca/
Description: Province-supported, comprehensive, coed. Part of Universite du Quebec. Awards bachelor's and master's degrees. Founded 1983. Setting: 5-acre small town campus. Total enrollment: 755. Faculty: 159 (71 full-time, 88 part-time). Students come from 8 other countries. Core. Calendar: trimesters. Services for LD students, accelerated degree program, summer session for credit, part-time degree program, adult/continuing education programs, internships. Off campus study at other units of the Universite du Quebec, other universities in the province of Quebec.
Entrance Requirements: Open admission except for some quota programs. Required: Diploma of Collegiate Studies (and transcript) or equivalent. Required for some: interview. Entrance: noncompetitive. Application deadline: Rolling. Notification: 5/15.
Collegiate Environment: Student-run newspaper. Student services: health clinic, personal-psychological counseling. Campus security: 24-hour patrols. 135,882 books, 302 serials, an OPAC, and a Web page 85 computers available on campus for general student use. A campuswide network can be accessed from off-campus. Staffed computer lab on campus.

■ UNIVERSITÉ DU QUÉBEC À CHICOUTIMI
555, Blvd. de L'Université
Chicoutimi, QC, Canada G7H 2B1
Tel: (418)545-5011

Fax: (418)545-5012
E-mail: czoccast@uqac.uquebec.ca
Web Site: www.uqac.ca/
Description: Province-supported, university, coed. Part of Universite du Quebec. Awards bachelor's, master's, and doctoral degrees. Founded 1969. Setting: 100-acre urban campus. Faculty: 394 (221 full-time, 173 part-time). Core. Calendar: trimesters. Services for LD students, accelerated degree program, summer session for credit, part-time degree program, adult/continuing education programs. Off campus study at other units of the Universite du Quebec, other universities in the province of Quebec.
Entrance Requirements: Open admission except for some quota programs. Required: Diploma of Collegiate Studies (and transcript) or equivalent. Required for some: interview. Entrance: noncompetitive. Application deadline: 3/1. Notification: 5/15.
Collegiate Environment: Student-run newspaper. Student services: health clinic, personal-psychological counseling. Campus security: 24-hour emergency response devices and patrols. 689,214 books and 5,092 serials.

■ UNIVERSITÉ DU QUÉBEC, ÉCOLE DE TECHNOLOGIE SUPÉRIEURE
1100, rue Notre Dame Ouest
Montréal, QC, Canada H3C 1K3
Tel: (514)396-8800
Fax: (514)289-8950
E-mail: admission@ets.mtl.ca
Web Site: www.etsmtl.ca/
Description: Province-supported, comprehensive, coed. Part of Universite du Quebec. Awards bachelor's and master's degrees. Founded 1974. Setting: urban campus. Total enrollment: 4,262. Faculty: 281 (119 full-time, 162 part-time). 1,541 applied, 88% were admitted. Full-time: 2,763 students, 8% women, 92% men. Part-time: 1,091 students, 16% women, 84% men. Core. Calendar: trimesters. Services for LD students, accelerated degree program, summer session for credit, part-time degree program, adult/continuing education programs, co-op programs. Off campus study at other units of the Universite du Quebec, other universities in the province of Quebec.
Entrance Requirements: Open admission. Required: Diploma of Collegiate Studies (and transcript) or equivalent. Entrance: noncompetitive. Application deadline: 3/1. Notification: 5/15.
Collegiate Environment: Student-run newspaper, radio station. Student services: health clinic, personal-psychological counseling. 44,195 books, 630 serials, an OPAC, and a Web page.

■ UNIVERSITÉ DU QUÉBEC À MONTRÉAL
CP 8888, Succursale Centre-ville
Montréal, QC, Canada H3C 3P8
Tel: (514)987-3000
Fax: (514)987-7728
E-mail: admission@uqam.ca
Web Site: www.uqam.ca/
Description: Province-supported, university, coed. Part of Universite du Quebec. Awards bachelor's, master's, and doctoral degrees. Founded 1969. Setting: 286-acre urban campus. Faculty: 3,004 (993 full-time, 2,011 part-time). 42,208 applied. Students come from 10 provinces and territories, 102 other countries. Core. Calendar: trimesters. Services for LD students, accelerated degree program, summer session for credit, part-time degree program, adult/continuing education programs, internships. Off campus study at other units of the Universite du Quebec, other universities in the province of Quebec.
Entrance Requirements: Open admission except for some quota programs. Required: Diploma of Collegiate Studies (and transcript) or equivalent. Required for some: essay, interview. Entrance: noncompetitive. Application deadline: 3/1. Notification: 5/15.
Collegiate Environment: Drama-theater group, choral group, student-run newspaper. Social organizations: 40 open to all. Most popular organizations: Centre D'Ecoute et de Reference Halt-Ami, Groupe de Recherche d'Interet, Public du Quebec a l'UQAM, Club Marketing Uqam, Association des Etudiants Africainses de l'UQAM. Major annual event: Salon Etudiant de la Rentre. Student services: legal services, health clinic, personal-psychological counseling. Campus security: 24-hour emergency response devices and patrols, late night transport-escort service. Bibliotheque Centrale plus 15 others with 2.3 million books, 10,819 serials, an OPAC, and a Web page. 889 computers available on campus for general student use. A campuswide network can be accessed from off-campus. Staffed computer lab on campus.

■ UNIVERSITÉ DU QUÉBEC EN OUTAOUAIS

Case Postale 1250, Succursale Hull
Gatineau, QC, Canada J8X 3X7
Tel: (819)595-3900; Free: 800-567-1283
E-mail: registraire@uqo.ca
Web Site: www.uqo.ca/

Description: Province-supported, university, coed. Part of Universite du Quebec. Awards bachelor's, master's, and doctoral degrees and post-master's certificates. Founded 1981. Setting: small town campus with easy access to Ottawa. Total enrollment: 6,386. Students come from 34 other countries. Core. Calendar: trimesters. Services for LD students, accelerated degree program, independent study, summer session for credit, part-time degree program, adult/continuing education programs, co-op programs and internships. Off campus study at other units of the Universite du Quebec, other universities in the province of Quebec. Study abroad program.

Entrance Requirements: Open admission except for some quota programs. Options: electronic application, international baccalaureate accepted. Required: high school transcript, birth certificate. Required for some: essay, 3 recommendations, interview. Entrance: noncompetitive.

Collegiate Environment: Student-run newspaper, radio station. Most popular organizations: AGE (Association Generale des Etudiants), AIESEC (Association Internationale des Etudiants en Sciences Economiques et Commerciales, AEME (Association for Events Management Education), REMAA (Regroupement des Etudiants du Monde de l'Administration des Affaires. Major annual events: Salon Etudiant, Jeux du Commerce. Student services: personal-psychological counseling. Campus security: 24-hour emergency response devices and patrols. No special consideration for freshman housing applicants. Option: coed housing available. Bibliotheque UQO plus 1 other with 230,910 books, 25,908 microform titles, 12,351 serials, an OPAC, and a Web page. 500 computers available on campus for general student use. A campuswide network can be accessed from student residence rooms. Students can access the following: online class registration, pay tuition fees online. Staffed computer lab on campus.

■ UNIVERSITÉ DU QUÉBEC À RIMOUSKI

300, Allee des Ursulines, CP 3300
Rimouski, QC, Canada G5L 3A1
Tel: (418)723-1986
Fax: (418)724-1525
E-mail: philippe_horth@uqar.uquebec.ca
Web Site: www.uqar.ca/

Description: Province-supported, comprehensive, coed. Part of Universite du Quebec. Awards bachelor's and master's degrees. Founded 1973. Setting: small town campus. Faculty: 324 (168 full-time, 156 part-time). 2,278 applied, 99% were admitted. Core. Calendar: trimesters. Services for LD students, accelerated degree program, summer session for credit, part-time degree program, adult/continuing education programs, internships. Off campus study at other units of the Universite du Quebec, other universities in the province of Quebec.

Entrance Requirements: Open admission except for some quota programs. Required: high school transcript, Diploma of Collegiate Studies or equivalent. Required for some: interview. Entrance: noncompetitive. Application deadline: 3/1. Notification: 5/15.

Collegiate Environment: Student-run newspaper, radio station. Student services: legal services, health clinic, personal-psychological counseling. Campus security: 24-hour emergency response devices and patrols, security cameras. 263,142 books and 3,951 serials.

■ UNIVERSITÉ DU QUÉBEC À TROIS-RIVIÈRES

3351 Blvd. des Forges, Case post 500
Trois-Rivières, QC, Canada G9A 5H7
Tel: (819)376-5011; Free: 800-365-0922
Fax: (819)376-5210
E-mail: registraire@uqtr.ca
Web Site: www.uqtr.ca/

Description: Province-supported, university, coed. Part of Universite du Quebec. Awards bachelor's, master's, and doctoral degrees. Founded 1969. Setting: urban campus with easy access to Montreal. Endowment: $3.3 million. Research spending for the previous fiscal year: $579,866. Total enrollment: 9,618. Faculty: 730 (317 full-time, 413 part-time). Students come from 33 other countries. Core. Calendar: trimesters. Services for LD students, accelerated degree program, summer session for credit, part-time degree program, adult/continuing education programs. Off campus study at other units of the Universite du Quebec, other universities in the province of Quebec.

Entrance Requirements: Open admission except for some quota programs. Required: Diploma of Collegiate Studies (and transcript) or equivalent. Required for some: interview. Entrance: noncompetitive. Application deadline: 3/1. Notification: 6/1.

Collegiate Environment: Drama-theater group, choral group, student-run newspaper, radio station. Student services: health clinic, personal-psychological counseling. Campus security: 24-hour emergency response devices and patrols, late night transport-escort service, controlled dormitory access. Main library plus 1 other with 464,338 books, an OPAC, and a Web page. Operations spending for the previous fiscal year: $2.2 million. 200 computers available on campus for general student use. A campuswide network can be accessed from student residence rooms and from off campus. Staffed computer lab on campus.

■ UNIVERSITÉ DE SHERBROOKE

Sherbrooke, QC, Canada J1K 2R1
Tel: (819)821-8000
Fax: (819)821-7966
Web Site: www.usherbrooke.ca/

Description: Independent, university, coed. Awards bachelor's, master's, and doctoral degrees. Founded 1954. Setting: 800-acre urban campus with easy access to Montreal. Total enrollment: 24,339. Faculty: 3,073 (1,082 full-time, 1,991 part-time). 17,302 applied, 56% were admitted. Full-time: 10,842 students, 56% women, 44% men. Part-time: 3,141 students, 54% women, 46% men. Students come from 3 provinces and territories, 30 other countries, 1% from out-of-province. 26% 25 or older, 0% transferred in. Calendar: Canadian standard year. ESL program, services for LD students, accelerated degree program, self-designed majors, summer session for credit, part-time degree program, adult/continuing education programs, co-op programs and internships, graduate courses open to undergrads. Off campus study at Consortium of Quebec Universities (CREPUQ). Study abroad program.

Entrance Requirements: Options: electronic application, early admission. Required: high school transcript. Required for some: interview. Entrance: moderately difficult. Application deadline: 3/1. Notification: continuous until 5/15. Preference given to province residents.

Costs Per Year: Application fee: $70 Canadian dollars. Tuition, fee, and room only charges are reported in Canadian dollars. Province resident tuition: $2168 full-time, $72.26 per credit part-time. Canadian resident tuition: $5858 full-time, $195.27 per credit part-time. Mandatory fees: $542 full-time, $12.50 per credit part-time, $72.41 per term part-time. Full-time tuition and fees vary according to course load and location. Part-time tuition and fees vary according to course load and location. College room only: $3360. International student tuition: $16,260 full-time.

Collegiate Environment: Drama-theater group, student-run newspaper, radio station. Social organizations: 20 open to all. Major annual events: Homecoming, Winter Carnival. Student services: legal services, health clinic, personal-psychological counseling. Campus security: 24-hour emergency response devices and patrols. 1,000 undergraduates lived in college housing during 2012-13. No special consideration for freshman housing applicants. Option: coed housing available. Bibliotheque Roger-Maltais plus 5 others with 1.2 million books, 43,478 serials, 22,042 audiovisual materials, an OPAC, and a Web page. 300 computers available on campus for general student use. A campuswide network can be accessed from student residence rooms and from off campus. Students can access the following: online class registration. Staffed computer lab on campus provides training in use of computers, software, and the Internet.

■ BRIERCREST COLLEGE

510 College Dr.
Caronport, SK, Canada S0H 0S0
Tel: (306)756-3200; Free: 800-667-5199
Fax: (306)756-5500
E-mail: admissions@briercrest.ca
Web Site: www.briercrest.ca/

Description: Independent interdenominational, 4-year, coed. Part of Briercrest College and Seminary. Awards associate and bachelor's degrees. Founded 1935. Setting: 300-acre rural campus. Endowment: $1.4 million. Educational spending for the previous fiscal year: $7477 per student. 416 applied, 57% were admitted. Full-time: 141 students, 45% women, 55% men. Part-time: 11 students, 36% women, 64% men. Students come from 4 provinces and territories, 3 other countries, 0.1% from out-of-province. 10% 25 or older, 15% live on campus, 25% transferred in. Retention: 42% of full-time freshmen returned the following year. Academic areas with the most degrees conferred: theology and religious vocations; liberal arts/general studies; business/marketing. Core. Calendar: semesters. Academic remediation for entering students, independent study, distance learning, double major, summer session for credit, part-time degree program, external degree program, adult/continuing education programs, internships. Off campus study. Study abroad program.

Entrance Requirements: Open admission. Options: electronic application, deferred admission, international baccalaureate accepted. Required: essay, high school transcript, 1 recommendation, statement of faith. Required for some: interview, SAT or ACT. Entrance: noncompetitive. Application deadline: 8/15. Notification: continuous until 9/1. Transfer credits accepted: Yes.

Costs Per Year: Application fee: $50 Canadian dollars. Tuition, fee, and room and board charges are reported in Canadian dollars. Comprehensive fee: $14,064 includes full-time tuition ($8310), mandatory fees ($150), and college room and board ($5604). College room only: $3488. Full-time tuition and fees vary according to course load. Room and board charges vary according to board plan, housing facility, and location. Part-time tuition: $277 per credit. Part-time mandatory fees: $277 per term. Part-time tuition and fees vary according to course load.

Collegiate Environment: Orientation program. Drama-theater group, choral group. Major annual events: Youth Quake, Christmas Celebration, Commencement. Student services: legal services, health clinic, personal-psychological counseling. Campus security: 24-hour patrols, controlled dormitory access. 675 college housing spaces available; 446 were occupied in 2012-13. Freshmen guaranteed college housing. On-campus residence required through junior year. Options: men-only, women-only housing available. Archibald Library with 87,991 books, 509 microform titles, 14,233 serials, 5,962 audiovisual materials, an OPAC, and a Web page. Operations spending for the previous fiscal year: $230,579. 21 computers available on campus for general student use. A campuswide network can be accessed from student residence rooms and from off campus. Students can access the following: online class registration. Staffed computer lab on campus.

■ ESTON COLLEGE

730 1st St. E
Box 579
Eston, SK, Canada S0L 1A0
Tel: (306)962-3621; Free: 888-440-3424
Fax: (306)962-3810

E-mail: admissions@estoncollege.ca
Web Site: www.estoncollege.ca/

Description: Independent, 4-year, coed, affiliated with Apostolic Church of Pentecost. Awards bachelor's degrees.

■ HORIZON COLLEGE & SEMINARY

1303 Jackson Ave.
Saskatoon, SK, Canada S7H 2M9
Tel: (306)374-6655; Free: 877-374-6655
Fax: (306)373-6968
E-mail: admissions@horizon.edu
Web Site: www.horizon.edu/

Description: Independent, 4-year, coed, affiliated with Pentecostal Assemblies of Canada. Administratively affiliated with University of Saskatchewan. Awards bachelor's degrees. Founded 1930. Setting: 5-acre urban campus. Total enrollment: 61. Faculty: 12 (1 full-time, 11 part-time). Student-undergrad faculty ratio is 11:1. 13 applied, 100% were admitted. Full-time: 51 students, 47% women, 53% men. Part-time: 10 students, 50% women, 50% men. Students come from 5 provinces and territories, 55% from out-of-province. 26% 25 or older, 3% transferred in. Retention: 100% of full-time freshmen returned the following year. Core. Calendar: semesters. Academic remediation for entering students, self-designed majors, independent study, distance learning, part-time degree program, internships. Study abroad program.

Entrance Requirements: Options: electronic application, deferred admission, international baccalaureate accepted. Required: essay, high school transcript, 3 recommendations. Required for some: interview. Entrance: noncompetitive. Application deadline: 9/15. Transfer credits accepted: Yes.

Collegiate Environment: Orientation program. Choral group. Major annual events: Christmas Banquet, Graduation Exercises, Graduation Banquet. Student services: personal-psychological counseling. Campus security: 24-hour emergency response devices, late night transport-escort service, controlled dormitory access. 30 computers available on campus for general student use. A campuswide network can be accessed from student residence rooms and from off campus. Staffed computer lab on campus.

■ UNIVERSITY OF REGINA

3737 Wascana Pky.
Regina, SK, Canada S4S 0A2
Tel: (306)585-4111; Free: 800-664-4756
Fax: (306)585-5203
E-mail: admissions@uregina.ca
Web Site: www.uregina.ca/

Description: Province-supported, university, coed. Awards bachelor's, master's, and doctoral degrees. Founded 1974. Setting: 76-hectare urban campus. Endowment: $29.1 million. Research spending for the previous fiscal year: $19 million. Total enrollment: 13,115. Faculty: 484 (all full-time). Student-undergrad faculty ratio is 23:1. 3,842 applied, 66% were admitted. Full-time: 9,361 students, 61% women, 39% men. Part-time: 2,165 students, 69% women, 31% men. Students come from 13 provinces and territories, 88 other countries, 14% from out-of-province. 23% 25 or older, 10% live on campus, 4% transferred in. Retention: 81% of full-time freshmen returned the following year. Academic areas with the most degrees conferred: education; business/marketing; homeland security, law enforcement, firefighting, and protective services. Calendar: semesters. Academic remediation for entering students, ESL program, services for LD students, advanced place-ment, self-designed majors, honors program, independent study, distance learning, double major, summer session for credit, part-time degree program, adult/continuing education programs, co-op programs and intern-ships. Off campus study at Athol Murray College of Notre Dame, Chinook School Division, Gabriel Dumont Institute of Native Studies and Applied Research, Briercrest College, Carlton Trail Regional College, Cumberland Regional College, Great Plains College, Lakeland College, Northlands Col-lege, North West Regional College, Parkland Regional College, Prairie West Regional College, Southeast Regional College, SIAST Campuses, Saskatchewan Indian Institute of Technologies, Dumont Technical Institute, Yukon College YNTEP, NTEP, Prairie South School Div. Study abroad program.

Entrance Requirements: Options: electronic application, early admission, early action, deferred admission, international baccalaureate accepted. Required: high school transcript, minimum 2.3 high school GPA. Required for some: essay, 2 recommendations, interview, portfolio, audition, some programs require a higher than 2.3 minimum GPA for admission, SAT or ACT, SAT Subject Tests. Entrance: minimally difficult. Application deadlines: 8/1, 3/15 for early action. Preference given to Provincial residents in some programs; Aboriginal students in some programs. SAT Reasoning Test deadline: 8/1. SAT Subject Test deadline: 8/1. Transfer credits accepted: Yes. Early action applicants: 2,754. Early action applicants admitted: 1,663.

Costs Per Year: Application fee: $100 Canadian dollars. Tuition, fee, and room and board charges are reported in Canadian dollars. Province resident tuition: $5,756 full-time, $164 per credit hour part-time. Canadian resident tuition: $164 per credit hour part-time. Mandatory fees: $351 full-time, $94.60 per term part-time. Full-time tuition and fees vary according to course load and program. Part-time tuition and fees vary according to course load and program. College room and board: $8835. College room only: $6160. Room and board charges vary according to board plan and housing facility. International student tuition: $20,076.75 full-time.

Collegiate Environment: Orientation program. Drama-theater group, choral group, student-run newspaper. Social organizations: 54 open to all. Major annual events: May Convocation, October Convocation, Welcome Week. Student services: health clinic, personal-psychological counseling, women's center. Campus security: 24-hour emergency response devices and patrols, late night transport-escort service, controlled dormitory access, crime prevention assistance, CCTV, card access and some alarm monitoring. 1,208 college housing spaces available; all were occupied in 2012-13. Freshmen guaranteed college housing. Dr. John Archer Library plus 3 others with 1.2 million books, 1.2 million microform titles, 43,246 serials, 17,467 audiovisual materials, an OPAC, and a Web page. Operations spending for the previous fiscal year: $10.6 million. 312 computers available on campus

for general student use. A campuswide network can be accessed from student residence rooms. Students can access the following: online class registration. Staffed computer lab on campus provides training in use of computers and software.

Community Environment: Regina, population 178,225 is the capital city of Saskatchewan. Serving as a business and industrial center of the mainly agricultural province, Regina offers a wide range of cultural activities.

■ UNIVERSITY OF SASKATCHEWAN

105 Administration Pl.
Saskatoon, SK, Canada S7N 5A2
Tel: (306)966-4343
Fax: (306)966-7026
E-mail: admissions@usask.ca
Web Site: www.usask.ca/

Description: Province-supported, university, coed. Awards bachelor's, master's, and doctoral degrees. Founded 1907. Setting: 1,865-acre urban campus. Total enrollment: 20,515. Faculty: (1,119 full-time). Academic areas with the most degrees conferred: business/marketing; education; engineer-ing. Calendar: Canadian standard year. ESL program, services for LD students, advanced placement, accelerated degree program, honors program, independent study, distance learning, double major, summer ses-sion for credit, part-time degree program, co-op programs and internships. Off campus study at Regional Colleges, SIAST Campuses. Study abroad program.

Entrance Requirements: Options: electronic application, early admission, international baccalaureate accepted. Required: high school transcript. Recommended: scores sometimes used for home-educated students. Required for some: essay, interview. Application deadline: 5/1. Notification: continuous. Transfer credits accepted: Yes.

Collegiate Environment: Orientation program. Drama-theater group, choral group, student-run newspaper. Student services: legal services, health clinic, personal-psychological counseling, women's center. Campus security: 24-hour emergency response devices and patrols, student patrols, late night transport-escort service, controlled dormitory access. University of Saskatchewan Main (Murray) Library plus 7 others with 2.5 million books, 3.1 million microform titles, 47,055 serials, an OPAC, and a Web page.

Community Environment: Saskatoon (population 196,800), on the banks of the South Saskatchewan River, is known as the City of Bridges with its riverfront and many parks. It is the home of the Western Development Museum featuring Boomtown 1910, museums of Ukrainian arts and culture, the Mendel Art Gallery (Canadian, European, and Eskimo art), the Forestry Farm Park, and Saskatchewan Place (local and international sports, entertainment, and cultural events.).